BOOKS
IN PRINT
1986-1987

This edition of BOOKS IN PRINT was
prepared by the R. R. Bowker Company's Database
Publishing Group in collaboration with the
Publication Systems Department.

Peter Simon, Vice President, Database Publishing Group
Ernest Lee, Executive Editor, Bibliographies
Rebecca Olmo and Brian Phair, Senior Editors
Albert Simmonds, Senior Associate Editor, Quality Control
Basmattie Gravesande and John Thompson, Associate Editors
Frank Accurso, Patricia Cahill, Domonique Fernandez,
Yvonne Holness, Malcolm MacDermott, Angella Morgan,
Hyacinth Myers, Myriam Nunez, Beverly Palacio, Joan Russell,
Suzann Satmary, Joseph Schneider, George Tibbetts,
Joseph Tondi and Frances Walsh, Assistant Editors.

Names & Numbers:
Brenda Sutton-McElroy, Managing Editor
Keith Schiffman, Senior Editor
Rynita Anderson, Xavier Anderson and
Vincent Fiorillo, Assistant Editors.

Michael Gold, Director, Systems Development
Jack Murphy, Computer Operations Manager.

Published by R. R. Bowker Division of Reed Publishing USA
245 West Seventeenth Street, New York, N.Y. 10011
Copyright © 1986 by Reed Publishing USA, a division of Reed Holdings, Inc.

BOOKS
IN PRINT
1986-1987

Volume 7
Publishers

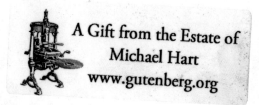
R.R.BOWKER COMPANY
New York

CONTENTS

KEY TO ABBREVIATIONS INDEX

The *Key to Abbreviations Index* is arranged alphabetically by the publishers' and distributors' name abbreviations used in Books in Print. The full form of the company's name and the ISBN prefix(es) are then given. Standard Address Number(s) (SAN); business affiliation; editorial address(es); telephone number(s); toll-free telephone number(s); ordering/distribution address(es); telephone number(s); and imprint(s) with their name abbreviation(s).

Abingdon *(Abingdon; 0-687),* Div. of United Methodist Publishing Hse., 201 Eighth Ave., S., Nashville, TN 37202 (SAN 201-0054). Tel 615-749-6301; Toll-free: 800-251-3320; 1015 Visco Dr., Nashville, TN 37210 (SAN 699-9956). *Imprints:* Apex Books (Apex); Festival Books (Festival).
Apex Books *See* **Abingdon Press**

A A A C E, *(American Assn. for Adult & Continuing Education; 0-88379),* 1201 16th St., NW, Suite 301, Washington, DC 20036 (SAN 201-2278) Tel 202-822-7866.
A A Coolidge
See Celestial Gems
A A Curran, *(Curran, Alfred A.; 0-9617186),* 119 Sefton Dr., New Britain, CT 06053 (SAN 663-2637) Tel 203-827-8023.
A A Grapevine, *(A.A. Grapevine, Inc.; 0-933685),* 468 Park Ave., S., New York, NY 10016 (SAN 692-5162) Tel 212-686-1100; Orders to: P.O. Box 1980, Grand Central Sta., New York, NY 10163 (SAN 662-7773).
A A McKenzie, *(McKenzie, Alexander A.; 0-9613211),* P.O. Box 38, Eaton Center, NH 03832 (SAN 295-6470) Tel 603-447-3385.
A A Novak, *(Novak, Anita A.; 0-9614803),* 222 E. Chestnut St., No. 2D, Chicago, IL 60611 (SAN 692-7734) Tel 312-664-7712.
A A Spohler, *(Spohler, Albert A.; 0-9606580),* P.O. Box 2322, Palos Verdes, CA 90274 (SAN 207-1983); 5417 Littlebow Rd., Palos Verdes, CA 90274 (SAN 207-1991).
A Adler Inst, *(Adler, Alfred, Institute of Chicago, Inc.; 0-918560),* 618 S. Michigan Ave., Chicago, IL 60605 (SAN 201-1956) Tel 312-294-7100.
A-albionic Res, *(A-albionic Research),* P.O. Box 20273, Ferndale, MI 48220 (SAN 210-6973) Tel 313-398-2896.
A & B Pubs
See Bask Indus
A & C Black, *(Black, A. & C., Pubs., Ltd.; 0-7136; 0-7137),* 35 Bedford Row, London WC1R 4JH, .
†A & M Bks, *(A & M Books; 0-937150),* P.O. Box 24112, Richmond, VA 23224 (SAN 214-3348) Tel 804-232-3904; *CIP.*
A & R Pub, *(A&R Publishing Co.; 0-943354),* 21B Maplewood Dr., Whiting, NJ 08759 (SAN 240-575X) Tel 201-350-8845.
†A & S Pr, *(A & S Pr.; 0-935930),* P.O. Box 3277, Chico, CA 95926 (SAN 214-4697) Tel 916-343-1493; *CIP.*
A & W Limited, *(A & W Limited Editions; 0-9615816),* 1650 E. 18th St., Suite G, Tucson, AZ 85719 (SAN 696-8899).
A Andersen, *(Andersen, Arthur, & Co.),* 69 W. Washington St., Chicago, IL 60602 (SAN 226-8817) Tel 312-580-0069.
A Arm Assoc, *(Armstrong, Alan, & Assocs.; 0-946291),* 5827 Columbia Pike, Suite 501, Falls Church, VA 22041 (SAN 679-1913).
A Atkins Pub, *(Atkins, A., Publishing Co.; 0-9617122),* 612 W. Illinois St., Oblong, IL 62449 (SAN 662-6866) Tel 618-592-4288.

A B Fuller, *(Fuller, Aletha B.; 0-9616085),* 742 Sandefer St., Abilene, TX 79601 (SAN 698-1178).
A B Hutchinson, *(Hutchinson, Ann B.; 0-9615825),* 5842 S. Sheridan, Littleton, CO 80123 (SAN 696-8414) Tel 303-795-0764.
A B M A C, *(American Bureau for Medical Advancement in China),* 2 E. 103rd St., New York, NY 10029 (SAN 266-6332) Tel 212-860-1990.
A C Hood Pub, *(Hood, Alan C., Pub.; 0-911469),* RR 3, Box 12, Putney, VT 05346 (SAN 270-8221) Tel 802-387-4309; Dist. by: Countryman Pr., P.O. Box 175, Woodstock, VT 05091 (SAN 206-4901) Tel 802-457-1049.
A C Libro Blackbird, *(Blackbird Pr. Pubns.; 0-940538),* 613 Howard Ave., Pitman, NJ 08071 (SAN 218-5334) Tel 609-589-6963; Dist. by: Joanne Nobes Hoey, 33 E. Centennial Dr., Medford, NJ 08055 (SAN 238-7921) Tel 609-983-5120.
A C Prichard, *(Prichard, Arthur C.; 0-9612788),* 214 Pleasant St., Mannington, WV 26583 (SAN 289-8063) Tel 304-986-1521.
A C S Pubns Inc, *(ACS Pubns., Inc.; 0-917086; 0-935127),* P.O. Box 16430, San Diego, CA 92116-0430 (SAN 208-5380) Tel 619-297-9203; Toll free: 800-826-1085; Toll free: 800-525-1786 (in California).
A Cartwright
See N P Cartwright
A Cohen, *(Cohen, Alan; 0-910367),* P.O. Box 1036, New Brunswick, NJ 08903 (SAN 239-4227) Tel 201-699-1744; Dist. by: Coleman Graphics, 99 Milbar Blvd., Farmingdale, NY 11735 (SAN 238-1508) Tel 516-293-0383; Dist. by: New Leaf Distributing, 1020 White St. SW, Atlanta, GA 30310 (SAN 169-1449) Tel 404-755-2665; Dist. by: DeVorss & Co., P.O. Box 550, 1046 Princeton Dr., Marina del Rey, CA 90294 (SAN 168-9886).
A Corral, *(Corral, Apache, Publishing Co.; 0-9616932),* 3048 Champion, No. 2, Oakland, CA 94602 (SAN 661-8332) Tel 415-261-5592.
†A D Bragdon, *(Bragdon, Allen D., Pubs., Inc.; 0-916410),* Brownstone Library, Munchie Bks., 153 W. 82nd St., New York, NY 10024 (SAN 208-5623) Tel 212-787-6886; Dist. by: Kampmann & Co., 9 E. 40th St., New York, NY 10016 (SAN 202-5191) Tel 212-685-2928; Dist. by: Dodd, Mead & Co., 79 Madison Ave., New York, NY 10016 (SAN 201-3339) Tel 212-685-6464; *CIP.*

†A Deepak Pub, *(Deepak, A., Publishing; 0-937194),* Div. of Science & Technology Corp., P.O. Box 7390, 101 Research Dr., Hampton, VA 23666 (SAN 240-1606) Tel 804-865-0332; *CIP.*
A Doughty, *(Doughty, Al; 0-9617246),* Rte. 1, Pinckneyville, IL 62274 (SAN 663-5601) Tel 618-357-9839.
A E Mize, *(Mize, An E.; 0-9617087),* 2151 Old Oakland Rd., No. 287, San Jose, CA 95131 (SAN 662-5894) Tel 408-263-3706.
A E Myers, *(Myers, Albert E.; 0-9602156),* 5341 Windsor Rd., Harrisburg, PA 17112 (SAN 213-1234).
A E P, *(American Enterprise Pubns.; 0-9612198),* Box 6690, R.D. 6, Mercer, PA 16137 (SAN 202-4454) Tel 412-748-3726. Do not confuse with American Enterprise Institute for Public Policy Research, Washington, DC.
A Earle, *(Earle, Arthur; 0-9600788),* 10922 Nandina Ct., Philadelphia, PA 19116 (SAN 207-4648) Tel 215-676-9762.
A Edmunds, *(Edmunds, Adeline; 0-9605846),* 421 N. Sixth Ave., Sturgeon Bay, WI 54235 (SAN 216-3756) Tel 414-743-9433.
A F Joy, *(Joy, A. F.),* 64 Gardenia Ct., Orange City, FL 32763 (SAN 695-4863) Tel 904-775-2067; Orders to: Saturscent Pubns., Box 358, South Wellfleet, MA 02663 (SAN 662-3484) Tel 617-349-2921.
A F Markus, *(Markus, A. F.),* 758 NE St. Lucie Blvd., Jensen Beach, FL 33457 (SAN 687-6439) Tel 305-334-7099.
A Fields Bks
See Dutton
A Finkelstein, *(Finkelstein, Adrian; 0-87418),* 855 E. Palatine Rd., Palatine, IL 60067 (SAN 693-4285); Dist. by: Coleman Publishing Co., 99 Milbar Blvd., Farmingdale, NY 11735 (SAN 238-1508) Tel 516-293-0383.
A Fishelis, *(Fishelis, Avraham, Pub.; 0-9605560),* 577 Grand St., New York, NY 10002 (SAN 240-0006) Tel 212-260-1760.
A Fraulo, *(Fraulo, Anne; 0-9616577),* 488 Main St., East Haven, CT 06512 (SAN 661-2296) Tel 203-469-0220.
A Fried Assocs, *(Fried, Al, Assocs.; 0-87445),* 271 North Ave., New Rochelle, NY 10801 (SAN 201-8659)
A Frommer
See Frommer-Pasmantier
A G Aharonian, *(Aharonian, Aharon G.; 0-9613300),* P.O. Box 67, Shrewsbury, MA 01545 (SAN 654-1569) Tel 617-791-3261.
A G Becker
See Scholl

1

Symbols/Abbreviations

A G Peterson, *(Peterson, Arthur G.; 0-9605664),* P.O. Box 252, DeBary, FL 32713 (SAN 214-0780) Tel 305-668-6587.

A G Small Pubns, *(Small, A. G., Pubns.; 0-915457),* P.O. Box 6222, San Rafael, CA 94903 (SAN 291-4409) Tel 415-479-6625.

A G Sweetser, *(Sweetser, Albert G.; 0-9605500),* 17 Broadleaf Dr., Clifton Park, NY 12065 (SAN 206-1864) Tel 518-371-7674.

A Garner Pub, *(Garner, Alan, Publishing Group; 0-939515),* 100 Via Estrada, Suite P, Laguna Hills, CA 92653 (SAN 663-3560) Tel 714-770-8323.

A Gauquier, *(Gauquier, Anthony V. & Beverly; 0-9609574),* 335 Spring St., Rockland, MA 02370 (SAN 260-1915) Tel 617-878-4133; Orders to: P.O. Box 1215, Plymouth, MA 02360 (SAN 650-0293).

A Glaser, *(Glaser, Anton; 0-9600324),* 1237 Whitney Rd., Southampton, PA 18966 (SAN 201-1999).

A Gonshorowski
See Ad-dee Pubs Inc

A Guthrie, *(Guthrie, Al; 0-9606526),* P.O. Box 443, Carmichael, CA 95608 (SAN 209-4436) Tel 916-483-6543.

A H Clark, *(Clark, Arthur H., Co.; 0-87062),* P.O. Box 230, Glendale, CA 91209 (SAN 201-2006) Tel 213-254-1600.

A Hardy & Assocs, *(Hardy, Arthur, & Associates; 0-930892),* P.O. Box 8058, New Orleans, LA 70182 (SAN 210-9913) Tel 504-282-2326.

A Harvey, *(Harvey, Arnold, Assocs.; 0-913014),* P.O. Box 89, Commack, NY 11725 (SAN 204-028X) Tel 516-543-2738.

A Henderson, *(Henderson, Albert; 0-917237),* 2423 Noble Sta., Bridgeport, CT 06608 (SAN 655-8607) Tel 203-367-1555.

A Hyde, *(Hyde, Arnout; 0-9604590),* 418 Lehigh Terrace, Charleston, WV 25302 (SAN 219-9750).

A I Root, *(Root, A. I., Co.; 0-936028),* Box 706, Medina, OH 44258 (SAN 205-230X) Tel 216-725-6677.

A J Donovan, *(Donovan, Anthony J.; 0-9617258),* 35 W. 82nd St., Apt. 3A, New York, NY 10024 (SAN 663-5393) Tel 212-724-7400.

A J Garvin, *(Garvin, A. J., & Assocs.; 0-9607252),* 720 E. Ann St., Ann Arbor, MI 48104 (SAN 281-7357) Tel 313-662-2734; Orders to: P.O. Box 7525, Ann Arbor, MI 48107 (SAN 281-7365).

A J Mooney, *(Mooney, Alfred J.; 0-9616946),* 2111 Evanston, Wichita, KS 67219 (SAN 661-7581) Tel 316-744-3358.

A J Nelson, *(Nelson, Alice Jean; 0-9614497),* 1233 Panama Dr., Sarasota, FL 33580 (SAN 689-3716) Tel 813-953-3656.

A J Pub, *(A. J. Publishing Co.; 0-914190),* P.O. Box 3012, Duluth, MN 55803 (SAN 201-1840) Tel 218-727-3998.

A J Sterling, *(Sterling, A. James, Jr., Architect Photographer; 0-9607042),* 2500 N. Lakeview Ave., Chicago, IL 60614 (SAN 241-5828) Tel 312-528-6648.

A Jacobsen, *(Jacobsen, Anita; 0-9604456),* 2896 Harbinger Lane, Dallas, TX 75252 (SAN 214-2473) Tel 214-323-0890.

A James Bks
See Alicejamesbooks

A Jones, *(Jones, Anson, Press; 0-912432),* P.O. Box 65, Salado, TX 76571 (SAN 201-2014) Tel 817-947-5414.

A K L M Pubns, *(AKLM Publications; 0-9612430),* 42 Lake St., Wakefield, MA 01880 (SAN 289-0771) Tel 617-245-2914.

A Karam, *(Karam, Anwar; 0-9613780),* 12000 Fondren No. 11, Houston, TX 77035 (SAN 678-9587) Tel 713-728-1317.

A Keech
See Skies Call

A Keim, *(Keim, Abe; 0-9608214),* P.O. Box 18, Mt. Hope, OH 44660 (SAN 240-3161).

A Kelner, *(Kelner, A., & Assocs.; 0-939812),* 1201 First Ave., Salt Lake City, UT 84103 (SAN 213-2249) Tel 801-359-5387.

A Korpalski, *(Korpalski, Adam),* Ferry Bridge Rd., Washington, CT 06793 (SAN 211-1977) Tel 203-868-2503.

A L Dabney, *(Dabney, A. L.),* 10441 Goodyear Dr., Dallas, TX 75229 (SAN 212-4092).

A L Ingles, *(Ingles, Andrew Lewis, & Roberta Ingles Steele; 0-9617146),* P.O. Box 3485 FSS, Radford, VA 24143 (SAN 677-1408) Tel 703-639-6383.

A L Katz Pub, *(Katz, Aaron L., Publishing Co.; 0-9615654),* 21098 Bank Mill Rd., Saratoga, CA 95070 (SAN 696-2548) Tel 408-741-1008; P.O. Box 719, Saratoga, CA 95071 (SAN 696-9658).

A L Kerth, *(Kerth, A. L.; 0-9601188),* Jericho Run, Buckland Valley Farms, Washington Crossing, PA 18977 (SAN 207-3773) Tel 215-493-6683.

A L Morse, *(Morse, Albert L.; 0-918320),* 320 Miller Ave., Mill Valley, CA 94941 (SAN 209-4614) Tel 415-332-3571.

A L White
See Arthurian Pr

A L Woods, *(Woods, Alfred L.; 0-9811160),* 1525 E. 53rd St., Suite 621, Chicago, IL 60615 (SAN 283-0485) Tel 312-955-1486.

A M Best, *(Best, A. M., Co.; 0-89408),* Ambest Rd., Oldwick, NJ 08858 (SAN 201-7407) Tel 201-439-2200.

A M Coppage, *(Coppage, A. Maxim),* 2225 Hillsborough Ct. No. 3, Concord, CA 94520 (SAN 238-0536).

A M Grannis, *(Grannis, Alberta M.; 0-9613774),* 790 NE 97th St., Miami Shores, FL 33138 (SAN 678-9579) Tel 305-759-0584.

A M Huntington Art, *(Huntington, Archer M., Art Gallery; 0-935213),* Univ. of Texas at Austin, 23rd & San Jacinto, Austin, TX 78712-1205 (SAN 695-7730) Tel 512-471-7324.

A M Johnston, *(Johnston, A. M., Publishing Co.; 0-9612116),* 118 Herron Dr., Knoxville, TN 37919 (SAN 289-3843) Tel 615-588-2206.

A M Newman, *(Newman, Albert M., Enterprises),* P.O. Box 88196, Honolulu, HI 96830-8196 (SAN 209-0864) Tel 808-923-4489.

A M Rymer
See Rymer Bks

A M Shipley, *(Shipley, Alice M.; 0-9610918),* 217 W. Roma Ave., Phoenix, AZ 85013 (SAN 265-1076) Tel 602-265-5894.

A M Watkins
See Building Inst

A M Zimmerman
See A M Zimmermann

A M Zimmermann, *(Zimmermann, A. M., & Co.; 0-912125),* 2210 Jackson St., Suite 404, San Francisco, CA 94115 (SAN 238-0897) Tel 415-929-7577; Dist. by: Publishers Group West, 5855 Beaudry St., Emeryville, CA 94608 (SAN 202-8522) Tel 415-658-3453; Dist. by: Bookpeople, 2929 Fifth St., Berkeley, CA 94710 (SAN 168-9517) Tel 415-549-3030.

A Marshall Collection, *(Marshall, Alice, Collection; 0-9616387),* 211 N. 17th St., Camp Hill, PA 17011 (SAN 658-9073) Tel 717-737-5672.

A Meriwether
See Meriwether Pub

A N Andrews, *(Andrews, Anotol N.; 0-9616592),* 6033 Dauphin Ave., Los Angeles, CA 90034 (SAN 659-4883) Tel 213-935-4058.

A N C Ent, *(ANC Enterprises; 0-9606134),* 15050 Camden Ave., San Jose, CA 95124 (SAN 223-209X) Tel 408-377-1121; 1901 Bascom Ave., No. 327, Campbell, CA 95008 (SAN 223-2103).

A N Johns, *(Johns, Agnes N.; 0-9612148),* P.O. Box 02026, Portland, OR 97202 (SAN 289-5846) Tel 503-238-4474.

A N Palmer, *(Palmer, A. N., Co., The; 0-914268; 0-913941),* 1720 W. Irving Park Rd., Schaumburg, IL 60193 (SAN 202-1374) Tel 312-894-4300; Toll free: 800-323-9563.

A Norman, *(Norman, Albert),* Three Alpine Dr., Northfield, VT 05663 (SAN 295-1053).

A Okolo, *(Okolo, Anthony; 0-9616272),* 1100 Grand Concourse, No. 5E, Bronx, NY 10456 (SAN 658-6015) Tel 212-538-1263; P.O. Box 50, Bronx, NY 10462-0050 (SAN 658-6023).

A P M Pr, *(A.P.M. Pr.; 0-937612),* 502 E. 17th St., Brooklyn, NY 11226 (SAN 214-3356).

A Paolino, *(Paolino, Adele; 0-9611448),* 50 Bedford Ave., Breezy Point, NY 11697 (SAN 277-6995) Tel 718-634-5552.

A Prichard CA, *(Pritchard, Anita; 0-9612560),* 915B Biloxi Dr., Norman, OK 73071 (SAN 289-3819) Tel 405-360-8115.

A Quartuccio, *(Quartuccio, Anthony; 0-9606934),* 4819 Kingdale Dr., San Jose, CA 95124 (SAN 239-5460).

A R Allenson, *(Allenson, Alec R., Inc.; 0-8401),* P.O. Box 447, Geneva, AL 36340 (SAN 162-4903).

A R C Pub, *(ARC Publishing Co.; 0-917187),* P.O. Box 1138, Glendale, CA 91209 (SAN 655-8704) Tel 818-244-0113; Dist. by: DeVorss & Co., P.O. Box 550, 1046 Princeton Dr., Marina del Rey, CA 90294 (SAN 168-9886).

A R Collings, *(Collings, Adam Randolph, Inc.; 0-933692),* 1829 S. Janette Ln., P.O. Box 8658, Anaheim, CA 92802 (SAN 220-4851) Tel 714-969-0415.

†A-R Eds, *(A-R Editions, Inc.; 0-89579),* 315 W. Gorham St., Madison, WI 53703 (SAN 289-7067) Tel 608-251-2114; *CIP.*

A R Harding Pub, *(Harding, A. R., Publishing Co.; 0-936622),* 2878 E. Main St., Columbus, OH 43209 (SAN 206-4936) Tel 614-231-9585.

A R Klinski
See Paranoid Pubns

†A R Liss, *(Liss, Alan R., Inc.; 0-8451),* 150 Fifth Ave., New York, NY 10011 (SAN 207-7558) Tel 212-741-2515; *CIP.*

A R Pragare
See Pine Mntn

A Raw One Shot *Imprint of* Raw Bks & Graph

A Roberts, *(Roberts, A.),* 714 Andover Ln., Albany, GA 31705 (SAN 239-4839).

A Robinson, *(Robinson, Alma),* 196 Dover Rd., Warrenton, VA 22186 (SAN 211-6308).

†A S Barnes, *(Barnes, A. S., & Co., Inc.; 0-498),* Subs. of Oak Tree Pubns., Inc., 9601 Aero Dr., San Diego, CA 92123 (SAN 201-2030) Tel 619-560-5163; *CIP.*

A S Fields, *(Fields, A. S.; 0-939307),* 4654 Hwy 6, N., Houston, TX 77084 (SAN 663-1495) Tel 713-859-2580.

A Santilli, *(Santilli, Al, Jr.; 0-9604394),* P.O. Box 2492, Dept.-5M, La Habra, CA 90631 (SAN 213-585X).

A Schiller, *(Schiller, Alexandra),* 911 E. 420 S., Provo, UT 85601 (SAN 696-7264) Tel 801-375-2938.

†A Scott Pub Co, *(Scott, Amanda, Publishing Co.; 0-916525),* 6117 Squirrelwood Lane, Cincinnati, OH 45247 (SAN 295-5261) Tel 513-741-7272; *CIP.*

A Smith Co *Imprint of* Michie Co

A Stella, *(Stella, Albert A. M.),* 220 Exchange St., Susquehanna, PA 18847 (SAN 212-1417); Orders to: Deinotation-7 Press, P.O. Box 204, Susquehanna, PA 18847 (SAN 212-1425); Dist. by: Brodart, 500 Arch St., Williamsport, PA 17705 (SAN 203-6711) Tel 717-326-2461.

A Syman Pubns, *(Syman, A., Pubns.; 0-941704),* P.O. Box 8245, Scottsdale, AZ 85252 (SAN 239-541X) Tel 602-990-1890; Dist. by: Publishers Group West, 5855 Beaudry St., Emeryville, CA 94608 (SAN 202-8522); Dist. by: Many Feathers SW Books and Maps, 5738 N. Central Ave., Phoenix, AZ 85012 (SAN 158-8877).

A System Pubns, *(A System Pubns.; 0-935739),* P.O. Box 8681, Trenton, NJ 08650 (SAN 696-1894) Tel 609-588-9022.

A T R Pubns, *(ATR Pubns.; 0-938955),* 3320 Mount Vista Dr., San Jose, CA 95127 (SAN 663-5040) Tel 408-251-5093.

A T Weinberg, *(Weinberg, Alyce T.; 0-9604552),* Box 16, Braddock Heights, MD 21714 (SAN 215-1928).

A Thomas Pub, *(A Thomas Publishing Co.; 0-937329; 0-9613884),* 19827 W. 12 Mile Rd., Suite 354, Southfield, MI 48076 (SAN 200-2795) Tel 313-559-4846; Toll free: 800-331-6871; Dist. by: Reca International Corp., 150 Haven, P.O. Box 951, Port Washington, NY 11050 (SAN 200-6332). Acquired titles published by Patricia E. Hutt.

A to Z Bk Serv, *(A to Z Bk. Serv.; 0-9614716),* P.O. Box 610813, North Miami, FL 33261 (SAN 692-946X)

A Torres, *(Torres, Angel; 0-9614110),* 6111 Dennison St., Los Angeles, CA 90022 (SAN 685-3021) Tel 213-722-1133.

A W Anderson, *(Anderson, Arthur W.; 0-9614420),* 175 Fisher St., Needham, MA 02192 (SAN 689-0989) Tel 617-449-0556; Orders to: The Windsor Press, P.O. Box 87, Wellesley Hills, MA 02181 (SAN 662-7722) Tel 617-235-0265.

A W Swenson, *(Swenson, Albert W.; 0-9616131),* 4582 Madison Ave., Trumbull, CT 06611 (SAN 699-9492) Tel 203-261-5966.

A Wade
See E Diemar

†**ABC,** *(American Book Co.; 0-278),* Div. of International Thomson Educational Publishing, Inc., 135 W. 50th St., New York, NY 10020 (SAN 201-534X) Tel 212-265-8700; Orders to: 7625 Empire Dr., Florence, KY 41042 (SAN 201-5358) Tel 800-354-9815; *CIP.*

†**ABC-Clio,** *(ABC-Clio Information Services; 0-87436; 1-85109; 0-903450),* Riviera Campus, 2040 Alameda Padre Serra, P.O. Box 4397, Santa Barbara, CA 93140-4397 (SAN 301-5467) Tel 805-963-4221; Toll free: 800-422-2546; *CIP.*

ABC Enterprises, *(A B C Enterprises; 0-9608126),* 2521-F N. Grand Ave., Santa Ana, CA 92701 (SAN 240-0790) Tel 714-835-7389.

ABC Pr Silicon, *(ABC Pr. of Silicon Valley; 0-912957),* 320 Encinal Ave., Menlo Park, CA 94025 (SAN 282-7220) Tel 415-329-0256; Dist. by: William Kaufmann, Inc., 95 First St., Los Altos, CA 94022 (SAN 202-9383) Tel 415-948-5810.

ABC's Air, *(A B C's of Air Travel, The; 0-931921),* 3532 Willow Ct., Memphis, TN 38118 (SAN 686-0575) Tel 901-363-2672.

Abdo Daughters, *(Abdo & Daughters; 0-939179),* P.O. Box 36036, Minneapolis, MN 55435 (SAN 662-9164); 6537 Cecilia Cir., Edina, MN 55435 (SAN 662-9172) Tel 612-944-5522; Dist. by: Children Pr., 1224 W. Van Buren St., Chicago, IL 60607 (SAN 201-9264) Tel 312-666-4200; Dist. by: Rockbottom Bks., 1224 W. Van Buren St., Chicago, IL 60607 (SAN 200-769X).

Abegg Grillot Ent, *(Abegg Grillot Enterprises; 0-9614131),* P.O. Box 72486, Roselle, IL 60172 (SAN 686-5062) Tel 312-980-6367.

Abigail Pub, *(Abigail Publishing Co.; 0-9616650),* 9956 84th St., N., Seminole, FL 33543 (SAN 659-6673) Tel 813-393-8185.

Abilene Christ U, *(Abigail Christian Univ. Pr.; 0-915547; 0-89112),* Div. of Abilene Christian University, 1634 Campus Ct., Abilene, TX 79601 (SAN 207-1681) Tel 915-674-2720; Toll free: 800-527-0575; Toll free: 800-592-1404 (TX). *Imprints:* Bibl Res Pr (Biblical Research Press).

†**Abingdon,** *(Abingdon Pr.; 0-687),* Div. of United Methodist Publishing Hse., 201 Eighth Ave., S., Nashville, TN 37202 (SAN 201-0054) Tel 615-749-6290; Toll free: 800-251-3320; 1015 Visco Dr., Nashville, TN 37210 (SAN 699-9956); *CIP. Imprints:* Apex (Apex Books); Festival (Festival Books).

Abingdon Pub, *(Abingdon Publishing Co, Inc.; 0-937910),* 6315 Kingston Pike, Suite 1107, Knoxville, TN 37919 (SAN 659-4824) Tel 615-584-5445. Do not confuse with Abingdon Pr., Nashville, TN.

ABK Pubns, *(ABK Pubns.; 0-9601420),* P.O. Box 962, Hanover, NH 03755 (SAN 212-6346).

†**Ablex Pub,** *(Ablex Publishing Corp.; 0-89391),* 355 Chestnut St., Norwood, NJ 07648 (SAN 209-3332) Tel 201-767-8450; *CIP.*

ABM Pub, *(ABM Publishing Co.; 0-9614774),* 5420 Coast Rd., Santa Cruz, CA 95060 (SAN 659-2635) Tel 408-427-3621.

Abmor Pub, *(Abmor Publishing; 0-915359),* P.O. Box 547, Aberdeen, MD 21001 (SAN 291-0594) Tel 301-272-0692.

Abner Schram Ltd, *(Abner Schram Ltd.; 0-8390),* 36 Park St., Montclair, NJ 07042 (SAN 685-3129) Tel 201-744-7755; c/o Biblio Distribution Ctr., 81 Adams Dr., Totowa, NJ 07512 (SAN 680-0025) Tel 201-256-8600. *Imprints:* Allanheld & Schram (Allanheld & Schram).

About Faces Pub, *(About Faces Publishing Co., Inc.; 0-931977),* 913 Collins Dr., West Chester, PA 19380 (SAN 686-1164) Tel 215-692-9911.

About Time MA, *(About Time Publishing Co., The; 0-913683),* Affil. of Friends of Freedom, P.O. Box 836, Northampton, MA 01061 (SAN 286-1186) Tel 413-545-2145; P.O. Box 1060, Amherst, MA 01004 (SAN 662-2070) Tel 413-545-2148; Orders to: P.O. Box 160, Hadley, MA 01035 (SAN 200-7304) Tel 413-586-5487; Dist. by: Richard Rawe, P.O. Box 443, Soap Lake, WA 98851 (SAN 290-7054) Tel 509-246-1559; Dist. by: Love Ministries, Inc., P.O. Box 69, Worthville, KY 41098 (SAN 662-2089).

Abracadabra Pr, *(Abracadabra Pr.; 0-934542),* P.O. Box 334, Balboa Island, CA 92662 (SAN 238-0099) Tel 714-675-0966.

Abracadata, *(Abracadata Ltd.; 0-939377),* P.O. Box 2352, Eugene, OR 97402 (SAN 662-9547); 2055 W. 25th, Eugene, OR 97405 (SAN 662-9555) Tel 503-342-3030.

†**Abrams,** *(Abrams, Harry N., Inc.; 0-8109),* Subs. of Times Mirror Co., 100 Fifth Ave., New York, NY 10011 (SAN 200-2434) Tel 212-206-7715; Toll free: 800-345-1359; Orders to: Wayne Public Warehouse, 150 Parish Dr., Wayne, NJ 07470 (SAN 699-9964); *CIP.*

Abraxas, *(Abraxas Press, Inc.; 0-932868),* 2518 Gregory St., Madison, WI 53711 (SAN 207-7744) Tel 608-238-0175; Dist. by: Bookslinger, 213 E. Fourth St., Saint Paul, MN 55101 (SAN 169-4154) Tel 612-221-0429.

Abraxas Pub WA, *(Abraxas Publishing; 0-939768),* 10245 Main St., Suite 1-3, Bellevue, WA 98004 (SAN 216-8731) Tel 206-455-8608; Orders to: P.O. Box 312, Kirkland, WA 98038-0312 (SAN 662-7099) Tel 206-455-8608.

Abt Assoc
See Abt Bks

†**Abt Bks,** *(Abt Bks.; 0-89011),* Subs. of Abt Assocs., Inc., 55 Wheeler St., Cambridge, MA 02138 (SAN 207-9402) Tel 617-492-7100; *CIP.*

Abundant Li Comm, *(Abundant Life Communications; 0-936471),* 106 Lamarck Dr., Ft. Washington, MD 20744 (SAN 698-1291) Tel 301-839-6777; P.O. Box 55487, Ft. Washington, MD 20744 (SAN 698-2603).

Abundant Life Pubns, *(Abundant Life Pubns.; 0-931867),* Subs. of Perry Gaspard Ministries, P.O. Box 336, Lake Charles, LA 70602 (SAN 686-0532) Tel 318-478-1112.

Abyss, *(Abyss Pubns.; 0-911856),* P.O. Box C, Somerville, MA 02143 (SAN 201-1859) Tel 617-666-1804.

AC Projects, *(AC Projects, Inc.; 0-931150),* Rte. 4, Box 137, Franklin, TN 37064 (SAN 211-5875) Tel 615-646-3757.

AC Pubns, *(AC Pubns.; 0-935496),* P.O. Box 238, Homer, NY 13077 (SAN 213-4462) Tel 607-749-4040.

Acad Assoc, *(Academic Assoc.; 0-918260),* P.O. Box 628, Van Nuys, CA 91408 (SAN 210-1556) Tel 818-988-2479.

Acad Bk Club, *(Academic Book Club),* N. 5411 Post St., Spokane, WA 99208 (SAN 213-6058) Tel 509-325-1435.

Acad Bks Pubs
See IBS Intl

Acad Comm, *(Academic Communication Assocs.; 0-930951),* 3917 Marvin St., P.O. Box 6044, Oceanside, CA 92056 (SAN 678-8726) Tel 619-758-9593.

Acad Dentistry Handicap, *(Academy of Dentistry for the Handicapped),* 211 E. Chicago, Suite 2133, Chicago, IL 60611 (SAN 224-2966) Tel 312-440-2660.

Acad Educ Dev, *(Academy for Educational Development, Inc.; 0-89492),* 680 Fifth Ave., New York, NY 10019 (SAN 210-0185) Tel 212-397-0040; 1414-22nd St., NW, Washington, DC 20037 (SAN 215-0379).

Acad Ent, *(Academy Enterprises of New Orleans; 0-912541),* P.O. Box 73354, Metairie, LA 70033 (SAN 282-7387).

Acad Genl Dentistry, *(Academy of General Dentistry),* 211 E. Chicago Ave., Suite 1200, Chicago, IL 60611-2670 (SAN 224-2974) Tel 312-440-4300.

†**Acad Guild,** *(Academic Guild Publishers; 0-938550; 0-938552),* 28 Hurlbut St., Cambridge, MA 02138 (SAN 216-7085) Tel 617-491-1837; Orders to: P.O. Box 397B, Cambridge, MA 02238 (SAN 688-4075) Tel 617-491-1837; *CIP.*

Acad Info Serv, *(Academic Information Service, Inc.; 0-916018),* P.O. Box 6296, Washington, DC 20015 (SAN 222-4755).

Acad Motion Pic, *(Academy of Motion Picture Arts & Sciences; 0-942102),* 8949 Wilshire Blvd., Beverly Hills, CA 90211-1972 (SAN 210-5845) Tel 213-278-8990.

Acad Nat Sci Phila, *(Academy of Natural Sciences Philadelphia; 0-8024; 0-910006),* Scientific Pubns., 19th & The Pkwy., Philadelphia, PA 19103 (SAN 204-7497) Tel 215-299-1050.

Acad New Church, *(Academy of the New Church; 0-910557),* P.O. Box 278, Bryn Athyn, PA 19009 (SAN 266-0512) Tel 215-947-4200.

Acad of Mgmt, *(Academy of Management; 0-915350),* Dept. of Management, College of Business Administration, Wichita State Univ., Wichita, KS 67208 (SAN 207-3463) Tel 601-325-3928; Orders to: Dennis F. Ray, The Academy of Management College of Business, Mississippi State University, Mississippi State, MS 39762 (SAN 207-3471).

Acad Poli Sci, *(Academy of Political Science),* 2852 Broadway, New York, NY 10025 (SAN 227-1745) Tel 212-866-6752.

†**Acad Pr,** *(Academic Pr., Inc.; 0-12),* Subs. of Harcourt Brace Jovanovich, Inc., Orlando, FL 32887 (SAN 206-8990) Tel 305-345-4143; Toll free: 800-321-5068; *CIP.*

Acad Prison Arts, *(Academy of Prison Arts, The; 0-939406),* P.O. Box 99901, Pittsburgh, PA 15233 (SAN 216-5651) Tel 412-761-1955; Dist. by: Motheroot, P.O. Box 8306, Pittsburgh, PA 15218-0306 (SAN 216-4205) Tel 412-731-4453.

Acad Prof Art, *(Academy of Professional Art Conservation & Science; 0-911877),* 165 W. Napa St., P.O. Box 192, Sonoma, CA 95476 (SAN 263-9076) Tel 707-938-3801.

Acad Pub Amer, *(Academic Publishers of America; 0-911337),* 6458 Lake Shore Dr., San Diego, CA 92119 (SAN 266-0245) Tel 619-698-0066.

Acad Pubns
See Summer Inst Ling

Acad Therapy, *(Academic Therapy Pubns.; 0-87879),* 20 Commercial Blvd., Novato, CA 94947 (SAN 201-2111) Tel 415-883-3314. *Imprints:* High Noon Books (High Noon Books).

Academia, *(Academia Pr.; 0-911880),* P.O. Box 125, Oshkosh, WI 54901 (SAN 201-2146) Tel 414-235-8362.

†**Academic Enter,** *(Academic Enterprises; 0-931399),* P.O. Box 666-A, Pullman, WA 99163-0666 (SAN 682-1804) Tel 509-334-4826; *CIP.*

Academic Intl, *(Academic International; 0-87569),* P.O. Box 1111, Gulf Breeze, FL 32561 (SAN 201-212X).

Academic Pr, *(Academic Pr./Vilencia Productions; 0-939155),* P.O. Box 946, Bellflower, CA 90706 (SAN 662-9229); 6208 Ibbetson Ave., Lakewood, CA 90713 (SAN 662-9237) Tel 213-920-7205.

Academic Pubns, *(Academic Pubns.; 0-937647),* P.O. Box 478, Notre Dame, IN 46556 (SAN 659-2678) Tel 219-239-5423; Hagger Hall, Notre Dame, IN 46556 (SAN 659-2686).

Academic World
See Acaworld

Academie Pr, *(Academie Press Inc.; 0-933136),* 1250 Sixth Ave, San Diego, CA 92112 (SAN 223-680X) Tel 714-459-1743.

Academy Bks, *(Academy Bks.; 0-914960),* P.O. Box 757, Rutland, VT 05701 (SAN 208-4325) Tel 802-773-9194; Dist. by: Charles E. Tuttle Co., Inc, P.O. Box 410, 28 S. Main St., Rutland, VT 05701-0410 (SAN 213-2621) Tel 802-773-8930.

Academy Chi Ltd
See Academy Chi Pubs

†**Academy Chi Pubs,** *(Academy Chicago Pubs.; 0-915864; 0-89733),* 425 N. Michigan Ave., Chicago, IL 60611 (SAN 213-2001) Tel 312-644-1723; *CIP.*

Academy Hill, *(Academy Hill Pr.; 0-932312),* RD Two, P.O. Box 357, Red Hook, NY 12571 (SAN 211-4607) Tel 914-758-0402.

Academy Pr-Campell
See Academy Santa Clara

Academy Pr-Santa
See Academy Santa Clara

Academy Prof Inform, *(Academy Professional Information Services, Inc.; 0-934205),* 116 W. 32nd St., 8th Flr., New York, NY 10001 (SAN 693-0085) Tel 212-736-6688.

Academy Pubns, *(Academy Pubns.; 0-931560),* P.O. Box 5224, Sherman Oaks, CA 91413 (SAN 212-1778) Tel 818-788-6662; Dist. by: Bookpeople, 2929 Fifth St., Berkeley, CA 94710 (SAN 168-9517) Tel 415-549-3030.

Symbols/Abbreviations

5

Activity Resources, (*Activity Resources Co., Inc.; 0-918932*), P.O. Box 4875, 20655 Hathaway Ave., Hayward, CA 94541 (SAN 209-0201) Tel 415-782-1300.

Actor Train Res, (*Actor Training & Research Institute Pr.; 0-9616087*), 451 W. Melrose, No. 404, Chicago, IL 60657 (SAN 698-0767); Dist. by: Baker & Taylor (Midwest Div.), 501 Gladiola Ave., Momence, IL 60954 (SAN 169-2100); Dist. by: Blackwell N. America, 1001 Fries Mill Rd., Blackwell, NJ 08012 (SAN 169-4596) Tel 609-629-0700; Dist. by: The Book House, 208 W. Chicago St., Jonesville, MI 49250-0125 (SAN 169-3859) Tel 517-849-2117.

Acupinch, (*Acupinch Outreach Ctr.; 0-9607456*), 2989 McCully Dr., NE, Atlanta, GA 30345 (SAN 238-2113) Tel 404-939-1678.

Ad Council, (*Advertising Council, Inc.*), 825 Third Ave., New York, NY 10022 (SAN 224-6082) Tel 212-758-0400; 1730 Rhode Island Ave. NW, Washington, DC 20036 (SAN 668-9515) Tel 202-331-9153; 1717 N. Highland Ave., Los Angeles, CA 90028 (SAN 668-9523) Tel 213-462-0988.

Ad-dee Pubs Inc, (*Ad-Dee Publishers, Inc.; 0-9600982*), P.O. Box 5426-B, Eugene, OR 97405 (SAN 208-6638) Tel 503-343-5868.

Ad Digest
  See Info Digest

†Ad-Lib, (*Ad-Lib Pubs.; 0-912411*), P.O. Box 1102, Fairfield, IA 52556 (SAN 265-170X) Tel 515-472-6617; Toll free: 800-624-5893; 51 N. Fifth St., Fairfield, IA 52556 (SAN 663-3005); *CIP.*

Ad Planners, (*Advertising Planners, Inc.; 0-937769*), 31050 Wallace Ave., Aptos, CA 95003 (SAN 659-2708) Tel 408-688-0768.

Ad Verbum, (*Ad Verbum Corp.; 0-939203*), 438 Hill Rd., Box 569, West Acton, MA 01720 (SAN 662-6157) Tel 617-263-5113.

Adam Pub Co, (*Adam Publishing Co.; 0-9614209*), Subs. of Adam Art Assocs., 537 Brobst St., Shillington, PA 19607 (SAN 686-9378) Tel 215-775-2739.

Adama Pubs Inc, (*Adama Pubs., Inc.; 0-915361*), 306 W. 38th St., New York, NY 10018 (SAN 291-0640) Tel 212-594-5770; Toll free: 800-672-6672; Dist. by: Franklin Watts, Inc., 387 Park Ave., S., New York, NY 10016 (SAN 200-7002) Tel 212-594-5770.

Adamant Pr, (*Adamant Pr.; 0-912362*), Div. of Precision Paper,Inc., P.O. Box Seven, Adamant, VT 05640 (SAN 201-2235).

Adamas Pub
  See Adamas Pubs

Adamas Pubs, (*Adamas Pubs.; 0-9607892*), P.O. Box 5504, Washington, DC 20016 (SAN 238-1362) Tel 301-656-0008.

Adamiak-Rare
  See Chicago Law Bk

Adams Bannister Cox, (*Adams, Bannister, Cox Pubs.; 0-937431*), 460 Riverside Dr., Suite 52, New York, NY 10027 (SAN 658-9707) Tel 212-749-6709.

†Adams County, (*Adams County Historical Society; 0-934858*), P.O. Box 102, Hastings, NE 68901-0102 (SAN 209-1917) Tel 402-463-5838; *CIP.*

Adams Inc MA, (*Adams, Bob, Inc.; 0-937860*), 840 Summer St., Boston, MA 02127 (SAN 215-2886) Tel 617-268-9570.

Adams Minn, (*Adams Press; 0-914828*), 59 Seymour Ave., SE, Minneapolis, MN 55414 (SAN 201-1867) Tel 612-378-9076; Orders to: Lerner Publications Co., 241 First Ave. N., Minneapolis, MN 55401 (SAN 201-0828).

Adams Pub Co, (*Adams Publishing Co.; 0-9615868*), P.O. Box 356, Eastsound, WA 98245 (SAN 696-6799) Tel 206-376-5256 (SAN 698-2085).

ADAPTS, (*ADAPTS (Alcohol & Drug Abuse Prevention & Training Services); 0-9606016*), 932 W. Franklin St., Richmond, VA 23220 (SAN 216-9452) Tel 804-358-0408.

Adar Pubns, (*Adar Pubs.; 0-916169*), 8434 Main St., Interlaken, NY 14847 (SAN 294-8842) Tel 607-532-4404.

Adastra Pr, (*Adastra Pr.; 0-938566*), 101 Strong St., Easthampton, MA 01027 (SAN 207-7752).

ADC NY
  See ADC Pubns

ADC Pubns, (*ADC Pubns.; 0-937414*), 488 Madison Ave., New York, NY 10022 (SAN 691-4128); Dist. by: Robert Silver Assocs., 307 E. 37th St., New York, NY 10016 (SAN 241-5801) Tel 212-686-5630.

ADCO Enterp, (*ADCO Enterprises; 0-9608870*), 465 Van Duzer St., Staten Island, NY 10304 (SAN 241-0923) Tel 718-447-3280.

Add-Effect Assoc, (*Add-Effect Assocs., Inc.; 0-940896*), P.O. Box 401, 1093 Radnor Rd., Wayne, PA 19087 (SAN 219-0761) Tel 215-688-6489.

Addison Gallery, (*Addison Gallery of American Art*), Phillips Academy, Andover, MA 01810 (SAN 206-8583).

Addison Hse, (*Addison House; 0-89169*), Subs. of American Showcase, Inc., 724 Fifth Ave., Tenth Floor, New York, NY 10019 (SAN 210-5543) Tel 212-245-0981.

Addor, (*Addor Assocs., Inc.*), P.O. Box 2128, Westport, CT 06880 (SAN 200-5948) Tel 203-226-9791; 115 Roseville Rd., Westport, CT 06880 (SAN 658-2982).

Addresso'set, (*Addresso'set Pubns.; 0-916944*), P.O. Box 3009, Vallejo, CA 94590 (SAN 208-5127) Tel 707-644-6358.

Addressoset
  See Addresso'set

ADEC, (*A-dec, Inc.; 0-9615713*), 2601 Crestview Dr., Newberg, OR 97132 (SAN 695-9423) Tel 503-538-9471; P.O. Box 111, Newberg, OR 97132 (SAN 696-5164).

Adelantre, (*Adelantre; 0-917288*), 4594 Bedford Ave., Brooklyn, NY 11235 (SAN 208-2268).

Adelphi Pr, (*Adelphi Pr.; 0-9610796*), P.O. Box 867, Hyattsville, MD 20783 (SAN 265-0541) Tel 301-622-9158.

Adelphi Pr PA, (*Adelphi Pr.; 0-9615832*), 1533 Garfield Ave., Wyomissing, PA 19610 (SAN 697-0001) Tel 215-373-3510.

Adelphi Univ, (*Adelphi Univ. Press; 0-88461*), S. Ave., Garden City, NY 11530 (SAN 201-6826) Tel 516-663-1120.

Adenine Pr, (*Adenine Pr., Inc.; 0-940030*), 11A Fullerton Ave., Schenectady, NY 12304 (SAN 281-241X) Tel 518-372-0006; Orders to: P.O. Box 355, Guilderland, NY 12084 (SAN 281-2428).

†Adinkra Pr, (*Adinkra Press; 0-9611900*), 431 Coffield Ave., Napa, CA 94558 (SAN 286-0279) Tel 707-224-3300; *CIP.*

Adiron Conserv, (*Adirondack Conservancy Committee/The Adirondack Council; 0-9613403*), P.O. Box 188, Elizabethtown, NY 12932 (SAN 656-9595) Tel 518-873-2610; Dist. by: Adirondack Mountain Club, Inc., 174 Glen St., Glens Falls, NY 12801 (SAN 204-7691) Tel 518-793-7737.

Adiron Mus
  See Adirondack Mus

Adirondack Mus, (*Adirondack Museum, The; 0-910020*), Rte. 28 N., Blue Mountain Lake, NY 12812 (SAN 201-7105) Tel 518-352-7311; P.O. Box 99, Blue Mountain Lake, NY 12812 (SAN 699-9972).

Adirondack S P, (*Adirondack Sports Pubns.; 0-9616439*), Rte. 86, Wilmington, NY 12997 (SAN 658-9715) Tel 518-946-2605.

Adirondack Yes, (*Adirondack Yesteryears, Incorporated; 0-9601158*), 246 Lake St., Saranac Lake, NY 12983 (SAN 209-4126) Tel 518-891-3206 Tel 518-891-3206.

Adizes Inst Inc, (*Adizes Institute, Inc., The; 0-89074*), 2001 Wilshire Blvd., Santa Monica, CA 90403 (SAN 265-3729) Tel 213-453-5593.

†ADK Mtn Club, (*Adirondack Mountain Club, Inc.; 0-935272*), 174 Glen St., Glens Falls, NY 12801 (SAN 204-7691) Tel 518-793-7737; *CIP.*

ADL, (*Anti-Defamation League of B'nai B'rith; 0-88464*), 823 United Nations Plaza, New York, NY 10017 (SAN 204-7616) Tel 212-490-2525; Dist. by: Hippocrene Bks., Inc., 171 Madison Ave., New York, NY 10016 (SAN 213-2060).

Adlen Bks, (*Adlen Bks.; 0-9615371*), 3303 Kerckhoff Ave., Fresno, CA 93702 (SAN 696-6322) Tel 209-264-5421.

Adler
  See Adlers Foreign Bks

Adler & Adler, (*Adler & Adler Pubs., Inc.; 0-917561*), 4550 Montgomery Ave., Suite 705, Bethesda, MD 20814 (SAN 656-5298) Tel 301-654-4271; Dist. by: Harper & Row Pubs., Inc., Keystone Industrial Pk., Scranton, PA 18512 (SAN 200-688X).

Adler Pub Co, (*Adler Publishing Co.; 0-913623*), Panorama Plaza, Box 25333, Rochester, NY 14625 (SAN 285-6808) Tel 716-377-5804; Dist. by: Writers & Bks., 740 University Ave., Rochester, NY 14607 (SAN 156-9678) Tel 716-473-2590. Do not confuse with Adler's Foreign Bks., Inc., New York, NY. *Imprints:* Nightsun Bks (Nightsun Books).

Adlerian Coun
  See Sunrise Pr

Adlers Foreign Bks, (*Adler's Foreign Bks., Inc.; 0-8417*), 915 Foster St., Evanston, IL 60201 (SAN 201-2251) Tel 312-866-6329; Toll free: 800-235-3771. Do not confuse with Adler Publishing Co., Rochester, NY.

ADM Co, (*A.D.M. Co., Inc.; 0-937974*), P.O. Box 10462, Phoenix, AZ 85016 (SAN 220-0260) Tel 602-279-2070.

Adm Nimitz Foun, (*Admiral Nimitz Foundation; 0-934841*), P.O. Box 777, Fredericksburg, TX 78624 (SAN 201-1883); 340 E. Main, Fredericksburg, TX 78624 (SAN 661-9312) Tel 512-997-4379.

Admark, (*Admark, Inc.*), 200 Lakeside Dr., Horsham, PA 19044 (SAN 699-7996) Tel 215-443-9892.

†Admates CA, (*Admates; 0-935236*), P.O. Box 210, Venice, CA 90294-0210 (SAN 215-689X) Tel 213-392-4911; *CIP.*

Admin Mgmt, (*Administrative Management Society; 0-916875*), International Headquarters, 2360 Maryland Rd., Willow Grove, PA 19090 (SAN 224-8530) Tel 215-659-4300.

Admin Mgmt Soc
  See Admin Mgmt

Admin Res
  See ARA

Admont Corp, (*Admont Corp.; 0-939421*), P.O. Box 3148, Staunton, VA 24401-6259; 198 Kalorama St., Suite B, Staunton, VA 24401 Tel 703-886-4777.

Adner Prods, (*Adner Productions; 0-941454*), 2497 New Park Ave., Melville, NY 11747 (SAN 238-9037).

Adonis Pr, (*Adonis Press; 0-932776*), Hawthorne Valley, Ghentdale, NY 12075 (SAN 218-463X); Orders to: Christy Barnes, R.D., Hillsdale, NY 12529 (SAN 661-9320) Tel 518-325-7182.

Adonis Studio, (*Adonis Studio; 0-914827*), P.O. Box 6626, Cleveland, OH 44101 (SAN 289-0461) Tel 216-526-5713.

Adonis Studios
  See Adonis Studio

Adrienne Pubns Inc, (*Adrienne Pubns., Inc.; 0-9610534*), 123 Cheshire Rd., Bethany, CT 06525 (SAN 263-9092) Tel 203-393-2323.

Adrift Edns, (*Adrift Editions; 0-916351*), 239 E. Fifth St., No. 4D, New York, NY 10003 (SAN 295-1029).

ADS Pr, (*ADS Pr.*), P.O. Box 2192, Winter Haven, FL 33883 (SAN 263-9017) Tel 813-299-1901.

Adult Dev Learn, (*Adult Development and Learning; 0-9613245*), 40 McDivitt Dr., Manchester, CT 06040 (SAN 295-5156) Tel 203-643-0468.

Adult Ed
  See A A A C E

Adv Accept, (*Advanced Acceptance*), P.O. Box 3692, Quincy, IL 62301 (SAN 217-2216).

Adv Bk Prog *Imprint of* **Benjamin-Cummings**

Adv Group, (*Advance Group, The; 0-9613500*), 400 N. Noble, Chicago, IL 60622 (SAN 657-2472) Tel 312-942-8538; Orders to: Advance Screen Printing Institute, 1401 W. Hubbard, Chicago, IL 60622 (SAN 662-7633).

Adv Prof Dev, (*Advanced Professional Development, Inc.; 0-912907*), 5519 Carpenter Ave., North Hollywood, CA 91607 (SAN 282-9576) Tel 818-506-7765.

Adv Prof Seminars, (*Advanced Professional Seminars, Inc.; 0-9604532*), 7033 Ramsgate Place, Suite "A", Los Angeles, CA 90045 (SAN 220-0279); Orders to: P.O. Box 45791, Los Angeles, CA 90045 (SAN 220-0287) Tel 213-776-0113.

†**Afro Res Inc,** *(Afro Resources Inc.; 0-915549),* P.O. Box 192, Temple Hills, MD 20748 (SAN 291-0659) Tel 301-894-3855; *CIP.*

AFTAC Ent, *(AFTAC Enterprises; 0-938029),* P.O. Box 34000, San Antonio, TX 78265 (SAN 659-6630) Tel 512-651-9000; Rte. 3, Box 1242, San Antonio, TX 78218 (SAN 659-6649).

Aftermath, *(Aftermath; 0-936579),* P.O. Box 420374, Sacramento, CA 95842 (SAN 698-0864) Tel 916-331-0600; 7005 Buskirk Dr., Sacramento, CA 95842 (SAN 698-0872).

Afton Oaks, *(Afton Oaks Typesetting & Publishing Co.; 0-912217),* Box 2098, Corpus Christi, TX 78403 (SAN 265-0576) Tel 512-881-8207.

AFUA Ent, *(AFUA Enterprises, Inc.; 0-918088),* P.O. Box 9026, General Lafayette Sta., Jersey City, NJ 07304 (SAN 210-1599) Tel 201-451-0599.

AG Access Pub, *(AG Access Publishing Corp.; 0-932857),* P.O. Box 2008, Davis, CA 95617 (SAN 688-9123) Tel 916-756-7177; 2655 Portage Bay Ave., Davis, CA 95616 (SAN 658-2729).

Ag & Nat Res, *(Agriculture & Natural Resources, Univ. of California; 0-931876),* 6701 San Pablo Ave., Oakland, CA 94608-1239 (SAN 211-4771) Tel 415-642-2431.

AG Pr, *(AG Pr.),* 16th & Yuma, P.O. Box 1009, Manhattan, KS 66502 (SAN 204-7632) Tel 913-539-7558.

Ag Sci Pubns
See Ag & Nat Res

Agadir Pr, *(Agadir Pr.; 0-913627),* P.O. Box 2015, Corvallis, OR 97339 (SAN 286-0309) Tel 503-929-5918; 424 S. 17th St., Philomath, OR 97370 (SAN 286-0317).

Agapao, *(Agapao Unlimited, Inc.; 0-937305),* Div. of ABC Institute for Better Living, Inc., 228 Bidwell Ave., Jersey City, NJ 07305 (SAN 658-7690) Tel 201-434-8098; Dist. by: Terrell's Bindery, 3620 Buena Vista, Nashville, TN 37218 (SAN 200-6324) Tel 615-242-1051.

Agape IL, *(Agape; 0-916642),* Div. of Hope Publishing Co., 380 S. Main Place, Carol Stream, IL 60188 (SAN 217-2224); Toll free: 800-323-1049.

Agape Pr, *(Agape Pr.; 0-915459),* Div. of KINGCommunications, 1900 Tribune Tower, 409 13th St., Oakland, CA 94612 (SAN 291-0675) Tel 415-763-5208.

Agascha Prods
See El-Shabazz Pr

†**Agathon,** *(Agathon Pr. Inc.; 0-87586),* 111 Eighth Ave., New York, NY 10011 (SAN 201-2367) Tel 212-741-3087; *CIP.*

Agee Pub, *(Agee Pubs., Inc.; 0-935265),* P.O. Box 526, Athens, GA 30603 (SAN 695-7498) Tel 404-548-5269; 425 N. Lumpkin St., Athens, GA 30603 (SAN 696-7035).

Ageless Bks, *(Ageless Bks.; 0-918482),* P.O. Box 6300, Beverly Hills, CA 90212 (SAN 210-0215) Tel 213-933-6338.

Agency Instr Tech, *(Agency for Instructional Technology; 0-9603244),* P.O. Box A, Bloomington, IN 47402 (SAN 225-7564) Tel 812-339-2203; Toll free: 800-457-4509; 1111 W. 17th St., Bloomington, IN 47401 (SAN 668-954X).

Agency Instr TV
See Agency Instr Tech

Agency Pr, *(Agency Pr.; 0-910887),* Div. of Agency Services, P.O. Box 1602, Greenville, SC 29602 (SAN 266-1446) Tel 803-242-5400.

Aging Alcoholism, *(Aging/Alcoholism Information Committee; 0-9612426),* 173 Windsor Dr., Daly City, CA 94015 (SAN 289-0984) Tel 415-986-4510.

Aglow Pubns, *(Aglow Pubns.; 0-930756; 0-932305),* Div. of Women's Aglow Fellowship International, P.O. Box I, Lynnwood, WA 98046-1557 (SAN 211-8297) Tel 206-775-7282.

Agnes Press, *(Agnes Pr., The; 0-936033),* 3739 Cottontail Ln., Utica, MI 48087 (SAN 696-995X) Tel 313-731-3239.

Agnew Tech-Tran, *(Agnew Tech-Tran, Inc.; 0-9606636),* P.O. Box 789, Woodland Hills, CA 91365 (SAN 212-7202) Tel 818-340-5147.

Agni Review, *(Agni Review),* P.O. Box 660, Amherst, MA 01004 (SAN 219-4600).

Agni Yoga Soc, *(Agni Yoga Society, Inc.; 0-933574),* 319 W. 107th St., New York, NY 10025-2799 (SAN 201-7121) Tel 212-864-7752.

Agri-Fence, *(Agri-Fence),* P.O. Box 521, Rough & Ready, CA 96975 (SAN 263-2519) Tel 916-273-5492.

Agri Pub Co, *(Agricutural Publishing Co.; 0-914669),* P.O. Box 1572, Eugene, OR 97440 (SAN 287-783X) Tel 503-345-4312.

Agribookstore, *(Agribookstore/Winrock),* Affil. of Winrock International, Rosslyn Plaza, 1611 N. Kent St., Suite 600, Arlington, VA 22209 (SAN 200-6693) Tel 703-525-9455.

AgriData, *(AgriData Resources, Inc.; 0-910939),* 330 E. Kilbourn Ave., Milwaukee, WI 53202 (SAN 209-6706) Tel 414-278-7676; Toll free: 800-558-9044.

Agrinde Bks
See Agrinde Pubns

†**Agrinde Pubns,** *(Agrinde Pubns., Ltd.; 0-9601068),* 220 Church St., New York, NY 10013 (SAN 281-2452) Tel 212-227-1005; Toll free: 800-251-4000; Dist. by: Dodd, Mead & Co., 79 Madison Ave., New York, NY 10016 (SAN 201-3339) Tel 212-685-6464; *CIP.*

Agronomy Pubns, *(Agronomy Pubns.; 0-9616847),* P.O. Box 83, River Falls, WI 54022 (SAN 661-1494) Tel 715-425-2353.

AGS Soft
See Astrolabe SW

AGT Pub, *(AGT Publishing Inc.; 0-933521),* 230 Park Ave., New York, NY 10169 (SAN 691-845X) Tel 212-687-8155.

Agtwo Pr, *(AG2 Pr.; 0-9606552),* 6234 N. Central Ave., Phoenix, AZ 85012 (SAN 222-9897) Tel 602-265-9407.

Ahio Pub Co, *(Ahio Publishing Co.; 0-914347),* 4313 W. 43rd St., Tulsa, OK 74107 (SAN 289-582X) Tel 918-446-9278.

AHM Pub
See Harlan Davidson

†**AHPI,** *(American Hospital Publishing, Inc.; 0-939450; 1-55648),* Subs. of American Hospital Assn., 211 E. Chicago Ave., Chicago, IL 60611 (SAN 216-5872) Tel 312-440-6800; Toll free: 800-242-2626; Orders to: AHA Services, Inc., P.O. Box 99376, 4444 W. Ferdinande, Chicago, IL 60624 (SAN 661-9363) Tel 312-280-6020; *CIP.*

Ahsahta Pr, *(Ahsahta Pr.; 0-916272),* Dept. of English, Boise State Univ., Boise, ID 83725 (SAN 207-9461) Tel 208-385-1246; Orders to: Univ. Bookstore, Boise State Univ., Boise, ID 83725 (SAN 207-947X) Tel 208-385-1276.

AIA San Antonio, *(American Institute of Architects, San Antonio Chapter; 0-9616842),* 720 6PM S. Tower, San Antonio, TX 78216 (SAN 662-5673) Tel 512-349-9971.

†**AIAA,** *(American Institute of Aeronautics & Astronautics; 0-915928),* 1633 Broadway, New York, NY 10019 (SAN 204-529X) Tel 212-581-4300; *CIP.*

AIAS, *(American Institute of Adlerian Studies, The; 0-918287),* 600 N. McClurg Ct., Suite 2502A, Chicago, IL 60611 (SAN 657-2502) Tel 312-337-5066.

Aid-U Pub, *(Aid-U Publishing Co.; 0-940370),* P.O. Box 47226, Oak Park, MI 48237 (SAN 217-149X) Tel 313-569-8288.

Aids Learning
See Activities Learning

AIGA Pubns, *(Aiga Pubns.; 0-943980),* P.O. Box 148, Laie, HI 96762 (SAN 241-094X) Tel 808-293-5277.

Aikido Fed, *(Aikido Federation of California),* P.O. Box 10962, Costa Mesa, CA 92627 (SAN 263-9122).

AIMS, *(AIMS; 0-915357),* 2701 Fondren Dr., Dallas, TX 75206 (SAN 291-0527) Tel 214-691-6451. Do not confuse with AIMS International Bks., Cincinnati, OH.

Air Age, *(Air Age, Inc.; 0-911295),* 632 Danbury Rd., Wilton, CT 06897 (SAN 266-1667) Tel 203-834-2900.

Air Diffusion, *(Air Diffusion Council),* 230 N. Michigan Ave., Suite 1200, Chicago, IL 60601 (SAN 229-4362) Tel 312-372-9800.

Air Mvmt & Cont, *(Air Movement & Control Assn., Inc.),* 30 W. University Dr., Arlington Heights, IL 60004 (SAN 224-618X) Tel 312-394-0150.

Air-Plus Ent, *(Air-Plus Enterprises; 0-940726),* P.O. Box 367, Glassboro, NJ 08028 (SAN 219-7545) Tel 609-881-0724; Dist. by: Quality Books, 400 Anthony Trail, Northbrook, IL 60062 (SAN 668-9558).

Air Pollution Control Assoc, *(Air Pollution Control Assn.),* Box 2861, Pittsburgh, PA 15230 (SAN 225-1701) Tel 412-232-3444.

Air Sci Co, *(Air Science Co.; 0-903608),* P.O. Box 143, Corning, NY 14830 (SAN 210-7791) Tel 607-962-5591.

AIR Systems, *(American Institutes for Research, Systems Division; 0-89785),* 41 North Rd., Bedford, MA 01730 (SAN 215-9368) Tel 617-275-0800.

Air Taxi Chart & Rent, *(Air Taxi Charter & Rental Directory of North America Inc.; 0-9603908),* Box 3000, Oak Park, IL 60303 (SAN 213-9049) Tel 217-546-1491.

Airborne Pr, *(Airborne Pr.; 0-934145),* 3055 Clay St., San Francisco, CA 94115 (SAN 693-3076) Tel 415-921-5617.

Aircraft Chart & Rent
See Air Taxi Chart & Rent

AIRE, *(Alternatives in Religious Education, Inc.; 0-86705),* 3945 S. Oneida St., Denver, CO 80237 (SAN 216-6534) Tel 303-363-7779.

Airman Universal, *(Airman Universal Pubns.; 0-941978),* P.O. Box 310027, Atlanta, GA 30331 (SAN 239-5118).

Airmont, *(Airmont Publishing Co., Inc.; 0-8049),* 401 Lafayette St., New York, NY 10003 (SAN 206-8710).

Airport Bk Pr, *(Airport Bk. Pr.; 0-935866),* 11205 Farmland Dr., Rockville, MD 20852 (SAN 213-7178) Tel 301-881-4996.

Airsho Pubs, *(Airsho Pubs.; 0-9601506),* 349 Homeland S. Way, 1B, Baltimore, MD 21212 (SAN 201-6974) Tel 301-323-3314.

Airshow Pubs
See Airsho Pubs

Airth Pubns, *(Airth Pubns.; 0-9616720),* Birdwood, 1015-1/2 Lovers Ln., Ocean Springs, MS 39564 (SAN 659-6770) Tel 601-875-6028.

Aish Yosef Pub, *(Yosef, Aish, Pubs.; 0-942694),* 2 W. 46th St., Rm. 402, New York, NY 10036 (SAN 239-9598) Tel 212-921-0544.

AISI, *(Advanced International Studies Institute, in association with the Univ. of Miami; 0-933074),* P.O. Box 1705, Fort Wayne, IN 46885 (SAN 201-8675) Tel 219-447-9927.

AISP
See Assn Info Sys

AJ Pub Co, *(A.J. Publishing Co.; 0-9612332),* 4200 Peachway, Boulder, CO 80301 (SAN 289-095X) Tel 303-444-7748.

AJAY Ent, *(AJAY Enterprises; 0-939440),* P.O. Box 2018, Mosby Branch, Falls Church, VA 22042-0018 (SAN 211-1209) Tel 703-573-8220.

AJFP, *(American Journal of Forensic Psychiatry; 0-935645),* Div. of American College of Forensic Psychiatry, 26701 Quail Creek, No. 295, Laguna Hills, CA 92656 (SAN 696-0774) Tel 714-831-0236.

AK Enterprises, *(AK Enterprises; 0-9614814),* 13540 Venus Way, Anchorage, AK 99515-3919 (SAN 692-9184) Tel 907-345-4948.

Akiba Pr, *(Akiba Pr.; 0-934764),* Box 13086, Oakland, CA 94661 (SAN 212-0666) Tel 415-339-1283.

Akili Bks of Amer, *(Akili Books of America; 0-9607296),* P.O. Box 1291, South Gate, CA 90280 (SAN 239-1481) Tel 213-635-7191.

Aksunai Pr, *(Aksunai Pr.; 0-930939),* P.O. Box 326B, Wakefield, MA 01880 (SAN 684-2593).

†**Al-Anon,** *(Al-Anon Family Group Headquarters; 0-910034),* 1372 Broadway, 7th flr., New York, NY 10018-6106 (SAN 201-2391) Tel 212-302-7240; P.O. Box 862 Midtown Station, New York, NY 10018-0862 (SAN 662-7110); *CIP.*

AL Cattlemen, *(Alabama Cattlemen's Assn.; 0-9616023),* P.O. Box 1746, Montgomery, AL 36197 (SAN 698-1720) Tel 205-265-1867; 600 Adams Ave., Montgomery, AL 36197 (SAN 698-1739).

AL-DEL, *(AL-DEL Hobbies, Inc.; 0-933360),* 528 SE 6th St., College Place, WA 99324 (SAN 212-4718) Tel 503-378-7909.

Al Fresco, *(Al Fresco Enterprise; 0-9612596),* Postal Drawer 11530, Pueblo, CO 81001 (SAN 211-5832) Tel 303-545-9524.

AL Law Inst, *(Alabama Law Institute),* P.O. Box 1425 Law Ctr., Rm. 326, University, AL 35486 (SAN 290-683X).

Al Lindner's Outdoors, *(Lindner's, Al, Outdoors, Inc.; 0-9605254),* P.O. Box 999, Brainerd, MN 56401 (SAN 215-8965) Tel 612-374-5581 Tel 612-341-7259.

Al Rainey Pubns, *(Rainey, Al, Pubns.; 0-932971),* 1015 N. El Centro Ave., Los Angeles, CA 90038 (SAN 690-0488) Tel 213-463-7876.

AL Revenue, *(Alabama Department of Revenue),* Administrative Bldg., Montgomery, AL 36130 (SAN 266-1934).

Aladdin *Imprint of* **Atheneum**

Aladdin Bks *Imprint of* **Macmillan**

Aladdin Pr, *(Aladdin Pr.; 0-916607),* 318 Harvard St., Suite 10, Brookline, MA 02146 (SAN 296-4422); Dist. by: Redwing Bk. Co., 44 Linden St., Brookline, MA 02146 (SAN 163-3597) Tel 617-738-4664.

Alamo Pr, *(Alamo Press; 0-9605140),* 104 Garydale Court, Alamo, CA 94507 (SAN 216-2164).

Alan I Press, *(Alan I. Pr.; 0-938827),* 99-555 Honohina St., Aiea, HI 96701 (SAN 661-6984) Tel 808-488-4674.

Alandale Pr, *(Alandale Pr.; 0-937748),* R.D. 5, Ballston Rd., Amsterdam, NY 12010 (SAN 216-0978) Tel 518-842-5189.

Alaska Angler, *(Alaska Angler Publications; 0-916771),* P.O. Box 82222, Fairbanks, AK 99708 (SAN 654-1453) Tel 907-455-6691; Orders to: P.O. Box 83550, Fairbanks, AK 99708 (SAN 693-9929) Tel 907-456-8212; Dist. by: Alaska News Agency, 325 W. Potter Dr., Anchorage, AK 99502 (SAN 168-9274) Tel 907-563-3251. *Imprints:* Alaska Hunter Pubns (Alaska Hunter Publications).

Alaska Fieldbks, *(Alaska Fieldbooks Co., Ltd.; 0-918745),* P.O. Box 1044, Anchorage, AK 99510 (SAN 657-5676) Tel 907-274-5742.

Alaska Heritage, *(Alaska Heritage Enterprises, Inc.; 0-930571),* 7404 Sand Lake Rd., Anchorage, AK 99502 (SAN 677-2196) Tel 907-243-4120; Dist. by: Pacific Pipeline, Inc., 19215 66th Ave. S., Kent, WA 98032 (SAN 208-2128).

Alaska Hist, *(Alaska Historical Commission; 0-943712),* Div. of State of Alaska, Dept. of Education, Old City Hall, 524 W. Fourth Ave., Suite 207, Anchorage, AK 99501 (SAN 240-9933) Tel 907-274-6222; Dist. by: Alaska Pacific Univ., 4101 University Dr., Anchorage, AK 99508 (SAN 215-2908).

Alaska Hunter Pubns *Imprint of* **Alaska Angler**

Alaska Labor, *(Alaska Department of Labor/Research & Analysis),* P.O. Box 25501, Juneau, AK 99802-5501 (SAN 266-2035) Tel 907-465-4500.

Alaska Legis, *(Alaska State Legislature; 0-935511),* State Capitol Bldg, Juneau, AK 99811 (SAN 266-2108).

Alaska Native, *(Alaska Native Language Ctr.; 0-933769; 1-55500),* Univ. of Alaska, P.O. Box 111, Fairbanks, AK 99775-0120 (SAN 692-9796) Tel 907-474-6577.

Alaska Natural, *(Alaska Natural History Assn.; 0-9602876),* 2525 Gambell St., Anchorage, AK 99503 (SAN 223-5269) Tel 907-274-8440.

†**Alaska Northwest,** *(Alaska Northwest Publishing Co.; 0-88240),* 130 Second Ave., S., Edmonds, WA 98020 (SAN 201-2383) Tel 206-774-4111; *CIP.*

Alaska Pacific, *(Alaska Pacific Univ. Pr.; 0-935094),* A.P.U., 4101 University Dr., Anchorage, AK 99508 (SAN 215-2908) Tel 907-564-8291.

Alaska St Coun, *(Alaska State Council on the Arts; 0-910615),* 619 Warehouse Ave., Suite 220, Anchorage, AK 99501 (SAN 260-1591) Tel 907-279-1558.

Alaska Travel, *(Alaska Travel Pubns., Inc.; 0-914164),* P.O. Box 4-2031, Anchorage, AK 99509 (SAN 201-1913) Tel 907-272-2869.

Alaskabks, *(Alaskabooks),* P.O. Box 1494, Juneau, AK 99802 (SAN 201-6990) Tel 907-586-3067.

ALB Assocs, *(ALB Assocs.; 0-913405),* 1420 Centre Avenue, Suite 1106, Washington Plaza, Pittsburgh, PA 15219 (SAN 285-8096) Tel 412-566-2525.

†**Alba,** *(Alba Hse.; 0-8189),* Div. of the Society of St. Paul, 2187 Victory Blvd., Staten Island, NY 10314 (SAN 201-2405) Tel 718-761-0047; *CIP.*

Albacore Pr, *(Albacore Pr.; 0-9601716),* P.O. Box 355, Eastsound, WA 98245 (SAN 223-4181).

Albanian Cath Info, *(Albanian Catholic Information Ctr.; 0-9614744),* P.O. Box 1217, Santa Clara, CA 95053 (SAN 692-7319) Tel 415-387-2020.

Albany County, *(Albany County Historical Assn.; 0-89062),* 9 Ten Broeck Pl., Albany, NY 12210 (SAN 219-7553); Dist. by: Publishing Ctr. for Cultural Resources, 625 Broadway, New York, NY 10012 (SAN 274-9025) Tel 212-260-2010.

Albany Hist & Art, *(Albany Institute of History & Art),* 125 Washington Ave., Albany, NY 12210 (SAN 204-7764) Tel 518-463-4478.

Albany Pub Lib, *(Albany Public Library; 0-9605090),* 161 Washington Ave., Albany, NY 12210 (SAN 215-8361).

Albatross, *(Albatross; 0-932759),* P.O. Box 333, Urbana, IL 61801 (SAN 688-5403) Tel 217-367-1598.

Albert Hse Pub, *(Albert Hse. Publishing; 0-913553),* 30 Ayles Rd., Hyde Park, MA 02136 (SAN 285-2071) Tel 617-361-4398.

Albert Schweitzer, *(Schweitzer, Albert, Fellowship),* 866 United Nations Plaza, New York, NY 10017 (SAN 225-3968) Tel 212-725-1760.

Albin
See **J R Albin**

Albion Albums, *(Albion Albums; 0-9604100),* P.O. Box 301, Albion, CA 95410 (SAN 216-2172).

Albion Am Bks, *(Albion-American Bks.),* P.O. Box 217, Elfrida, AZ 85610 (SAN 215-7225).

Albion NC, *(Albion; 0-932530),* Dept. of History, Appalachian State Univ., Boone, NC 28608 (SAN 212-2626) Tel 704-262-6004.

Albion PA, *(Albion Pr.; 0-930953),* P.O. Box 445, Exton, PA 19341 (SAN 678-8734) Tel 215-431-3362.

Albion Pr, *(Albion Pr.; 0-9606846),* 582 Stratford Ave., St. Louis, MO 63130 (SAN 217-3220) Tel 314-863-9285; Dist. by: Baker & Taylor Co., Midwest Div., 501 Gladiola Ave., Momence, IL 60954 (SAN 169-2100); Dist. by: The Distributors, 702 S. Michigan, South Bend, IN 46618 (SAN 169-2488) Tel 219-232-8500; Dist. by: Book Dynamics, 836 Broadway, New York, NY 10003 (SAN 169-5649) Tel 212-254-7798; Dist. by: Koen Book Distributors, Inc., 514 N. Read Ave., Cinnaminson, NJ 08077 (SAN 169-4642) Tel 609-786-1111; Dist. by: Paperback Supply, Inc., 4121 Forest Park Ave., St. Louis, MO 63108 (SAN 169-4324) Tel 314-652-1000.

Albion Review Pr, *(Albion Review Pr.; 0-9613841),* Albion College, Albion, MI 49224 (SAN 681-9591) Tel 517-629-5511.

Albright, *(Albright Pr.; 0-918301),* 12240 Blythen Way, Oakland, CA 94619 (SAN 657-2480); Dist. by: Bookpeople, 2929 Fifth St., Berkeley, CA 94710 (SAN 168-9537) Tel 415-549-3030.

Albright & Co, *(Albright & Co.; 0-932919),* P.O. Box 2011, Huntsville, AL 35804 (SAN 688-9174) Tel 205-539-3288.

Alchemist-Light, *(Alchemist/Light Publishing; 0-9600650),* P.O. Box 881444, San Francisco, CA 94188 (SAN 201-7164) Tel 415-345-7021.

Alchemy Bks, *(Alchemy Bks.; 0-931290),* 717 Market, Suite 514, San Francisco, CA 94103 (SAN 211-304X) Tel 415-777-2197.

Alchemy Comms, *(Alchemy Communications Group, Ltd.; 0-934323),* Subs. of Alchemy II, Inc., 9207 Eton Ave., Chatsworth, CA 91311 (SAN 693-5990) Tel 818-700-8300; Dist. by: Worlds of Wonder, Inc., 4209 Technology Dr., Fremont, CA 94538 (SAN 699-993X) Tel 415-659-4300.

Alcohol Comm, *(Alcoholism Trust Committee; 0-912399),* P.O. Box 1877, Carlsbad, CA 92008 (SAN 265-1718) Tel 619-729-2572.

Alcohol Con Serv, *(Alcoholism Consultation Service; 0-930427),* 1504 NW Blvd., Suite H, Spokane, WA 99205 (SAN 670-9931) Tel 509-326-2301.

Alcom Inc, *(Alcom, Inc.; 0-936129),* 1005 NE 72nd St., Seattle, WA 98115 (SAN 696-9860) Tel 206-527-8999.

Alcott Pr WA, *(Alcott Pr., The; 0-9616180),* W. 1114 Spofford Ave., Spokane, WA 99205 (SAN 699-8526) Tel 509-326-3373; P.O. Box 857, Spokane, WA 99210 (SAN 699-8534).

Alcove Pub Co OR, *(Alcove Publishing Co.; 0-937473),* P.O. Box 362, West Linn, OR 97068 (SAN 658-9766) Tel 503-655-5564; 6385 Barclay St., West Linn, OR 97068 (SAN 658-9774).

Alcyone Pubns, *(Alcyone Pubns.; 0-916669),* Triphammer Mall, P.O. Box 4764, Ithaca, NY 14852 (SAN 656-8785).

Alden Electronics, *(Alden Electronics & IRE Co., Inc.; 0-9607004),* Washington St., Westboro, MA 01581 (SAN 237-9287) Tel 617-366-8851.

Aldine Pub
See **De Gruyter Aldine**

Aldredg-Blair, *(Aldredg-Blair Inc.; 0-942446),* P.O. Box 7195, Dallas, TX 75209 (SAN 238-1389) Tel 214-521-6724.

Aldridge Group, *(Aldridge Group, The; 0-9612834),* 2148 Seminole, Detroit, MI 48214 (SAN 289-9647) Tel 313-876-0086.

Alef Bet Comns, *(Alef Bet Communications; 0-9616488),* 14809 Bremer Rd., New Haven, IN 46774 (SAN 659-2740) Tel 219-749-0182.

Alegra Hse Pubs, *(Alegra Hse. Pubs.; 0-933879),* Affil. of Kaya Books, P.O. Box 1443-B, Warren, OH 44482 (SAN 692-7858) Tel 216-372-2951.

Alek Pub, *(Alek Publishing Co.; 0-9613963),* 223 Tenafly Rd., Englewood, NJ 07631 (SAN 682-2843) Tel 201-569-4174.

Alemany Pr, *(Alemany Pr., Inc.; 0-88084),* Div. of Janus Bk. Pubs., Inc., 2501 Industrial Pkwy. W., Hayward, CA 94545 (SAN 240-1312) Tel 415-887-7070; Toll free: 800-227-2375.

Alembic Mktg, *(Alembic Marketing Partners; 0-9616368),* 538 Camino del Monte Sol, Santa Fe, NM 87501 (SAN 658-9804) Tel 505-984-2766.

†**Alembic Pr,** *(Alembic Pr.; 0-934184),* 1424 Stanley Rd., Plainfield, IN 46168 (SAN 281-2479) Tel 317-839-8312; *CIP.*

Alert Pubs, *(Alert Pubs.; 0-938033),* P.O. Drawer 2459, Hemet, CA 92343 (SAN 659-6819) Tel 714-929-2062; 261 W. Susan Ln., Hemet, CA 92343 (SAN 659-6827).

Aletheia Bks *Imprint of* **U Pubns Amer**

Aletheia Pubs, *(Aletheia Pubs., Inc.; 0-86717),* Div. of Alpha Omega Pub., P.O. Box 1437, Tempe, AZ 85281 (SAN 216-7824) Tel 602-438-2702.

Alethes, *(Alethes; 0-930254),* P.O. Box 5842, Carmel, CA 93921 (SAN 202-3598).

Aleutian, *(Aleutian Pribilof Islands Assn., Inc. (AANG ANGAGIN); 0-9609308),* 1689 C St., Anchorage, AK 99501 (SAN 260-0102) Tel 907-276-2700.

Alexander & Alexander, *(Alexander & Alexander Pubs.; 0-939353),* 1012 Fair Oaks, Suite 392, South Pasadena, CA 91030 (SAN 662-6912) Tel 818-799-0839.

Alexander Comms, *(Alexander Communications; 0-942454),* 212 W. Superior, Chicago, IL 60610 (SAN 238-1494) Tel 312-944-5115.

Alexander Graham, *(Bell, Alexander Graham, Assn. for the Deaf; 0-88200),* 3417 Volta Pl., NW, Washington, DC 20007 (SAN 203-6924) Tel 202-337-5220.

Alexander Pub, *(Alexander Publishing; 0-939067),* 14536 Roscoe Blvd., Suite 105, Panorama City, CA 91402 (SAN 662-9415) Tel 818-891-9831.

Alexandria Assn, *(Alexandria Assn., The; 0-9616541),* P.O. Box 178, City Hall, Alexandria, VA 22313 (SAN 659-4085) Tel 703-838-4554; Orders to: Lyceum Museum Shop, 201 S. Washington St., Alexandria, VA 22314 (SAN 662-7862) Tel 703-548-1812.

†**Alexandrian Pr,** *(Alexandrian Pr.; 0-916485),* Div. of Computer Curriculum Corporation, 1070 Avastradero Rd., Palo Alto, CA 94303 (SAN 295-5423) Tel 415-494-8450; Toll free: 800-227-8324; Dist. by: Baker & Taylor Co., Western Div., 380 Edison Way, Reno, NV 89564 (SAN 169-4464); Dist. by: Publishers Group West, 5855 Beaudry St., Emeryville, CA 94608 (SAN 202-8522); Dist. by: Bookpeople, 2929 Fifth St., Berkeley, CA 94710 (SAN 168-9517); Dist. by: Ingram Industries, 347 Reedwood Dr., Nashville, TN 37217 (SAN 169-7978); *CIP.*

Alexandrian WA, *(Alexandrian Pr.; 0-916411),* Subs. of Holmes Publishing Group, P.O. Box 623, Edmonds, WA 98020 (SAN 656-9080) Tel 206-771-2701.

ALF-CHB, *(American Life Foundations-Century House Books; 0-87282),* Old Irelandville, P.O. Box 306, Watkins Glen, NY 14891 (SAN 201-9736) Tel 607-535-4004.

Alfa Sierra, *(Alfa Sierra Pubns.; 0-9604728),* P.O. Box 9636, San Diego, CA 92109 (SAN 216-0137) Tel 619-276-6291.

Alfred, *(Alfred & Alfred Co.),* 5260 Figueroa St., Suite 114, Los Angeles, CA 90037 (SAN 206-9636).

Alfred Bay, *(Bay, Alfred; 0-9615634),* 2390 El Camino Real, No. 1, Palo Alto, CA 94306 (SAN 696-0723) Tel 415-494-1374.

Alfred Pub, *(Alfred Publishing Co., Inc.; 0-88284),* 15335 Morrison St., Sherman Oaks, CA 91413 (SAN 201-243X) Tel 818-995-8811; Toll free: 800-821-6083.

Alger Cnty Hist Soc, *(Alger County Historical Society; 0-9617008),* 203 W. Onota St., Munising, MI 49862 (SAN 662-9067) Tel 906-387-2607.

†**Algol Pr,** *(Algol Pr.; 0-916186),* P.O. Box 4175, New York, NY 10163 (SAN 207-9445) Tel 718-643-9011; *CIP.*

†**Algonquin Bks,** *(Algonquin Bks. of Chapel Hill; 0-912697),* P.O. Box 2225, Chapel Hill, NC 27515 (SAN 282-7506); 501 W. Franklin St., Suite 104, Chapel Hill, NC 27514 (SAN 662-2011) Tel 919-967-0108; Dist. by: Taylor Publishing Co., 1550 Mockingbird Ln., P.O. Box 597, Dallas, TX 75221 (SAN 202-7631) Tel 214-637-2800; *CIP.*

†**Algonquin Enter,** *(Algonquin Enterprises; 0-931979),* P.O. Box 1410, Muskegon, MI 49443 (SAN 686-1148) Tel 616-780-3815; *CIP.*

Algorithmics, *(Algorithmics, Inc.; 0-917448),* 44 W. 62nd St., New York, NY 10023 (SAN 201-2448) Tel 212-246-2366.

Algorithmics Pr
  See Algorithmics

ALI-ABA
  See Am Law Inst

Alicejamesbooks, *(Alicejamesbooks; 0-914086),* Div. of Alice James Poetry Cooperative, Inc., 138 Mt. Auburn St., Cambridge, MA 02138 (SAN 201-1158) Tel 617-354-1408.

Alida Macor, *(Macor, Alida, & Sew On; 0-9610632),* P.O. Box 71, Martinsville, NJ 08836 (SAN 264-1925) Tel 201-722-5676.

Alimar Pub, *(Alimar Publishing Co.; 0-9616034),* 8920 Wilshire Blvd., No. 316, Beverly Hills, CA 90211 (SAN 698-0449) Tel 213-271-3113.

Alin Found Pr, *(Alin Foundation Press; 0-9606924),* 2107 Dwight Way, Berkeley, CA 94704 (SAN 212-0682) Tel 415-845-4907.

Alinda Pr, *(Alinda Pr.; 0-933076),* Box 553, Eureka, CA 95502 (SAN 212-4734) Tel 707-443-2510.

Alised, *(Alised Enterprises; 0-913377),* 7808 Maryknoll Ave., Bethesda, MD 20817 (SAN 209-522X) Tel 301-320-3306.

Alistair Pr, *(Alistair Pr.; 0-9616489),* 374 Shadow Rd., Greenwood, IN 46142 (SAN 659-2767) Tel 317-888-6581.

Alive Assocs, *(Alive Assocs.; 0-915467),* 2516 Swift Run St., Vienna, VA 22180 (SAN 291-0683) Tel 703-573-4608.

Alive Films, *(Alive Films, Inc.; 0-937113),* 1414 Seabright Dr., Beverly Hills, CA 90210 (SAN 658-5469) Tel 213-275-5711.

Alive Polarity, *(Alive Polarity Pubns.; 0-941732),* 28779 Via Las Flores, Murrieta, CA 92362 (SAN 239-149X) Tel 714-677-7451.

Alive Pubns, *(Alive Pubns. Ltd.; 0-935572),* 11 Park Place, New York, NY 10007 (SAN 281-2495) Tel 212-962-0316.

Alivening Pubns, *(Alivening Pubns.; 0-9616707),* P.O. Box 1368, Land O Lakes, FL 33539 (SAN 659-6835) Tel 813-996-3659; 315 Geneva Rd., Land O Lakes, FL 33539 (SAN 659-6843).

Allabout Bks, *(Allabout Bks.; 0-930003),* P.O. Box 14155, Fremont, CA 94539 (SAN 669-7143) Tel 415-657-3613.

Allan Kelly, *(Kelly, Allan O.),* P.O. Box 1065, Carlsbad, CA 92008 (SAN 693-7810).

Allan-Michaels, *(Allan-Michaels Corp., The; 1-55621),* 120036 Ackler Sta., Nashville, TN 37212 (SAN 659-6851) Tel 615-791-2880.

†**Allanheld,** *(Allanheld, Osmun & Co. Pubs., Inc.; 0-916672; 0-86598),* Div. of Littlefield, Adams & Co., 81 Adams Dr., Totowa, NJ 07512 (SAN 211-724X) Tel 201-256-8600; *CIP.*

Allanheld & Schram *Imprint of* **Abner Schram Ltd**

Allanheld & Schram *Imprint of* **Rowman**

Allans, *(Allan's; 0-88100),* P.O. Box 4806, Inglewood, CA 90309 (SAN 265-3753).

Allbooks, *(Allbooks; 0-9616527),* 4341 Majestic Ln., Fairfax, VA 22033 (SAN 659-4093) Tel 703-968-7396.

†**Allegany Mtn Pr,** *(Allegany Mountain Pr.; 0-931588),* 111 N. Tenth St., Olean, NY 14760 (SAN 211-5034) Tel 716-372-0935; *CIP.*

Allegheny, *(Allegheny Pr.; 0-910042),* P.O. Box 220, Elgin, PA 16413 (SAN 201-2456) Tel 814-664-8504.

Allegheny Co Bar, *(Allegheny County Bar Assn.),* 620 Second Ave., Pittsburgh, PA 15219 (SAN 227-1893).

Allegheny Pubns, *(Allegheny Pubns.; 0-938037),* 2161 Woodsdale Rd., Salem, OH 44460 (SAN 659-686X) Tel 216-337-6403.

Allegro Pub, *(Allegro Publishing Co.; 0-9601042),* P.O. Box 39892, Los Angeles, CA 90039 (SAN 201-2464) Tel 213-665-6783.

Alleluia Pr, *(Alleluia Pr.; 0-911726),* P.O. Box 103, Allendale, NJ 07401 (SAN 202-3601) Tel 201-327-3513; 672 Franklin Turnpike, Allendale, NJ 07401 (SAN 202-361X).

Allen Group, *(Allen Group Inc., The; 0-943402),* 145 E. Center St., Provo, UT 84061 (SAN 240-5792) Tel 801-373-8000.

Allen Lane, *(Allen Lane),* Dist. by: Viking Penguin, Inc., 40 W. 23rd St., New York, NY 10010 (SAN 200-2442) Tel 212-337-5200.

Allen Mem Art
  See Ober Coll Allen

Allen Pr, *(Allen Pr., Inc.; 0-935868),* P.O. Box 368, Lawrence, KS 66044 (SAN 213-7186).

Allen Pub, *(Allen Publishing; 0-9614419),* P.O. Box 2129, New York, NY 10185 (SAN 689-1012) Tel 718-522-2858.

†**Allen Unwin,** *(Allen & Unwin, Inc.; 0-04; 0-86861),* Div. of Allen & Unwin, Ltd., 8 Winchester Pl., Winchester, MA 01890 (SAN 210-3362) Tel 617-729-0830; Toll free: 800-547-8889; *CIP.*

Allenby Pr, *(Allenby Pr.; 0-9615419),* 701 S. First Ave., Suite 272, Arcadia, CA 91006 (SAN 695-7544) Tel 818-446-6700.

Allenson
  See A R Allenson

Allenson-Breckinridge
  See A R Allenson

Allergan Humphrey, *(Allergan Humphrey, Inc.; 0-939425),* Div. of Smithkline Bechman, 3081 Teagarden St., San Leandro, CA 94577 (SAN 663-351X) Tel 415-895-9110.

†**Allerton Pr,** *(Allerton Press, Inc.; 0-89864),* 150 Fifth Ave., New York, NY 10011 (SAN 239-4049); *CIP.*

Allgau Bks, *(Allgau Bks.; 0-936887),* 2945 Lincoln Way, San Francisco, CA 94122 (SAN 658-3504) Tel 415-681-3471.

Allgood Bks, *(Allgood Books),* P.O. Box 1329, Jackson, MS 39205 (SAN 208-1318) Tel 601-355-5419.

Alliance Arts, *(Alliance for the Arts; 0-912443),* 330 W. 42nd St., New York, NY 10036 (SAN 211-8939) Tel 212-947-6340; Dist. by: Publishing Center for Cultural Resources, 625 Broadway, New York, NY 10012 (SAN 274-9025) Tel 212-260-2010.

Alliance Coll, *(Alliance College),* Cambridge Springs, PA 16403 (SAN 216-0862).

Alliance Plus, *(Alliance Plus; 0-9617034),* 22151 Bianco, Laguna Hills, CA 92653 (SAN 662-846X) Tel 714-581-4235.

Alliance Pubs, *(Alliance Pubs.),* Div. of Southern Program Alliance, P.O. Box 25004, Fort Lauderdale, FL 33320 (SAN 213-3768) Tel 305-722-5361.

Alliance Save ener, *(Alliance to Save Energy),* 1925 K St., NW, No. 206, Washington, DC 20006 (SAN 266-2426) Tel 202-857-0666.

Alliance Schl Health, *(Alliance for School Health; 0-9616270),* P.O. Box 2041, Fair Oaks, CA 95628-2041 (SAN 658-5434) Tel 916-487-5560; 1748 Park Pl. Dr., Carmichael, CA 95608 (SAN 658-5442).

Allied Artists America, *(Allied Artists of America, Inc),* 15 Gramercy Park S., New York, NY 10003 (SAN 225-2732) Tel 516-437-4369.

Allied Ent, *(Allied Enterprises; 0-9605082),* P.O. Box 8050, Chicago, IL 60680 (SAN 238-9045).

Allied Res Soc, *(Allied Research Society, Inc.; 0-912984),* 11057 New River Circle, Rancho Cordova, CA 95670 (SAN 201-2480) Tel 916-635-7728.

Allin Ent, *(Allin Enterprises; 0-936181),* P.O. Box 284, Orono, ME 04473 (SAN 696-9968) Tel 207-866-2579; 7 Mayo St., Orono, ME 04473 (SAN 696-9976).

Allison Ent, *(Allison Enterprises; 0-918324),* P.O. Box 200, Franklin, NJ 07416 (SAN 210-024X) Tel 201-827-5104.

Allison Pubs, *(Allison Pubs.; 0-9607936),* 1 La Playa, Box 733, Cochise, AZ 85606 (SAN 207-2009) Tel 602-384-2047.

Allnut Pub
  See Allnutt Pub

Allnutt Pub, *(Allnutt Publishing; 0-934374),* P.O. Box 879, Evergreen, CO 80439 (SAN 221-962X) Tel 303-670-3390.

Allowance, *(Allowance, Inc.; 0-9604228),* 1516 Bonnie Brae, Denton, TX 76201 (SAN 214-2805).

†**Ally Pr,** *(Ally Pr.; 0-915408),* 524 Orleans St., St. Paul, MN 55107 (SAN 207-7116); *CIP.*

†**Allyn,** *(Allyn & Bacon, Inc.; 0-205),* Div. of Simon & Schuster, 7 Wells Ave., Newton, MA 02159 (SAN 201-2510) Tel 617-964-5530; Toll free: 800-526-4799; Orders to: College Div., 1 Pond Rd., Rockleigh, NJ 07647 (SAN 201-2529); *CIP.*

ALM Assocs, *(ALM Assocs., Inc.),* 3264 Cove Rd., Jupiter, FL 33458 (SAN 287-2897).

Alma Hist Soc, *(Alma Historical Society; 0-9604684),* P.O. Box 87, Alma, WI 54610 (SAN 216-0986).

Alma Smith, *(Smith, Alma A.; 0-9614863),* 554 Anna May Dr., Cincinnati, OH 45244 (SAN 693-2320) Tel 513-528-1840.

Almaas Pubns, *(Almaas Pubns.; 0-936713),* 5975 Park Ave., Richmond, CA 94805 (SAN 699-8771) Tel 415-652-1243; P.O. Box 10114, Berkeley, CA 94709 (SAN 699-878X); Dist. by: Bookpeople, 2929 Fifth St., Berkeley, CA 94710 (SAN 168-9517) Tel 415-549-3030. Imprints: Diamond Bks (Diamond Books).(Diamond Bks.).

ALMACA, *(Association of Labor-Management Administrators & Consultants on Alcoholism),* 1800 N. Kent St., Suite 907, Arlington, VA 22209 (SAN 689-6383) Tel 703-522-6272.

Almanac Pr, *(Almanac-Pr.; 0-935090),* P.O. Box 480264, Los Angeles, CA 90048 (SAN 213-4551).

†**Almar,** *(Almar Pr.; 0-930256),* 4105 Marietta Dr., Binghamton, NY 13903 (SAN 210-5713) Tel 607-722-0265; *CIP.*

Almin, *(Almin Pr.; 0-9615631),* P.O. Box 363, Willingboro, NJ 08046 (SAN 696-0065) Tel 609-871-0422; 24 Needlepoint Ln., Willingboro, NJ 08046 (SAN 696-5180).

Almo Pubns, *(Almo Pubns.; 0-89705),* 1358 N. La Brea, Hollywood, CA 90028 (SAN 211-6995); Dist. by: Columbia Pictures Pubns., 15800 NW 48th Ave., Miami, FL 33014 (SAN 203-042X) Tel 305-620-1500.

Alms Hse Pr, *(Alms Hse. Pr.; 0-939689),* 23 Grotke Rd., Spring Valley, NY 10977 (SAN 663-5776) Tel 914-735-9548.

Aloha Pr, *(Aloha Press; 0-943758),* P.O. Box 26214, Honolulu, HI 96825 (SAN 238-0382) Tel 808-395-7369.

†**Aloray,** *(Aloray Inc.; 0-913690),* 215 Greenwich Ave., Goshen, NY 10924 (SAN 201-1190) Tel 516-595-2235; *CIP.*

Alpenglow Pr, *(Alpenglow Pr.; 0-935997),* P.O. Box 1841, Santa Maria, CA 93456 (SAN 696-6748) Tel 805-928-4904.

Alpenrose Pr, *(Alpenrose Pr.; 0-9603624),* Box 499, Silverthorne, CO 80498 (SAN 222-2612) Tel 303-468-6273.

Alpenstock, *(Alpenstock Publishing; 0-9614521),* P.O. Box 1759, Santa Ana, CA 92702 (SAN 691-7380) Tel 714-750-7621.

Alperin
See Junius Inc

Alpert, *(Alpert, Burt; 0-9600642),* 877 26th Ave., San Francisco, CA 94121 (SAN 201-1204).

Alpha and Omega, *(Alpha Omega; 0-941734),* 1026 E. Garden Ave., Coeur d'Alene, ID 83814 (SAN 239-1503) Tel 208-664-2954.

Alpha Beto Music, *(Alpha-Beto Music; 0-9616528),* 152 Sabine, Portland, TX 78374 (SAN 659-4107) Tel 512-643-6309.

Alpha Centauri, *(Alpha Centauri Pubs.; 0-940332),* P.O. Box 1011, Highland, NY 12528 (SAN 220-3162) Tel 914-691-7014.

Alpha Chi, *(Alpha Chi, National College Honor Scholarship Society),* Sta. A, Box 773, Searcy, AR 72143 (SAN 224-5086) Tel 501-268-3121.

Alpha Gamma, *(Alpha Gamma Arts; 0-941716),* 2625 Kiowa Ct., P.O. Box 4671, Walnut Creek, CA 94596 (SAN 281-2517) Tel 415-935-7409; Dist. by: China Bks., & Periodicals, Inc., 2929 24th St., San Francisco, CA 94110 (SAN 145-0557) Tel 415-282-2994.

Alpha Iota, *(Alpha Iota of Pi Lambda Theta, Pubns.; 0-914522),* 2260 N. Orange Grove Ave., Pomona, CA 91767 (SAN 206-3204) Tel 714-626-5065.

Alpha Media, *(Alpha Media Publishing; 0-918539),* 113 Fescue Ln., Roseburg, OR 97470 (SAN 657-5684) Tel 503-672-3280.

Alpha Omega Pub, *(Alpha Omega Pub.; 0-937059),* 5500 Boca Raton, Suite 427, Fort Worth, TX 76112 (SAN 658-5396) Tel 817-654-2082; P.O. Box 8383, Fort Worth, TX 76124-1383 (SAN 658-540X).

Alpha Pr, *(Alpha Press; 0-914620),* 3574 Clinton St., Gardenville, NY 14224 (SAN 201-1212) Tel 716-674-6183.

Alpha Pub Co, *(Alpha Publishing Co.; 0-933771),* Div. of Special Edition Inc., 3497 E. Livingston Ave., Columbus, OH 43227 (SAN 692-8048) Tel 614-231-4088.

Alpha Pub MN, *(Alpha Pubs.; 0-9615632),* Box 6328, Minneapolis, MN 55406-0328 (SAN 696-0618) Tel 612-721-7856; Dist. by: Spring Arbor Distributors, 10885 Textile Rd., Belleville, MI 48111 (SAN 158-9016) Tel 313-481-0900; Dist. by: Successful Living, Inc., 9905 Hamilton Rd., Eden Prarie, MN 55344 (SAN 213-0939) Tel 612-944-2511.

Alpha Pub Trust, *(Alpha Publishing Trust; 0-931753),* 897 Washington St., P.O. Box 82, Newtonville, MA 02160 (SAN 683-6135) Tel 617-864-9859; 96 Prescott St., Cambridge, MA 02138 (SAN 683-6143).

Alpha Pubns, *(Alpha Pubns., Inc.; 0-912404),* 1079 De Kalb Pike, Blue Bell, PA 19422 (SAN 201-2537) Tel 215-277-6342.

Alpha Pubns OH, *(Alpha Pubns.; 0-939427),* 1818 Wilbur Rd., Medina, OH 44256 (SAN 663-401X) Tel 216-239-1881. Do not confuse with Alpha Pubns. in Blue Bell, PA or in Winona Lake, IN.

Alpha Zeta, *(Fraternity of Alpha Zeta, The),* P.O. Box 595, Lafayette, IN 47902 (SAN 224-1315) Tel 317-742-2538.

Alphabet MA, *(Alphabet Pr.; 0-940032),* 60 N. Main St., Natick, MA 01760 (SAN 217-1449) Tel 617-655-9696; Toll free: 800-462-1252.

Alphabet Pr, *(Alphabet Pr.; 0-9602690),* P.O. Box 6180, Boston, MA 02209 (SAN 213-2753) Tel 617-323-7942. Do not confuse with Alphabet MA of Natick, MA.

Alphabet Quincy
See Alphabet MA

Alpine Bk. Co.
See Art Bks Intl

Alpine Ent
See A-albionic Res

Alpine Guild, *(Alpine Guild; 0-931712),* P.O. Box 183, Oak Park, IL 60303 (SAN 281-255X) Tel 312-386-3507.

†**Alpine Pubns,** *(Alpine Pubns.; 0-931866),* 214 19th St., SE, Loveland, CO 80537 (SAN 211-478X) Tel 303-667-2017; *CIP.* *Imprints:* Blue Rib Books (Blue Ribbon Books).(Blue Ribbon Bks.).

Alpine-Tahoe, *(Alpine-Tahoe Pr.; 0-9604574),* Box 1484, Tahoe City, CA 95730 (SAN 211-2108) Tel 916-583-3273.

Alpine WY, *(Alpine Pr.; 0-9615114),* P.O. Box 1930, Mills, WY 82644 (SAN 697-2454).

Alson Pub, *(Alson Publishing Co.; 0-916943),* 931 Santiago St., Santa Ana, CA 92701 (SAN 655-5500) Tel 714-730-5102.

Alston
See Hist Dimensions

Alt Currents, *(Alternating Currents; 0-937435),* P.O. Box 2121, Jamestown, NC 27282 (SAN 658-9820) Tel 919-379-5233; 4613 McKnight Mill Rd., Greensboro, NC 27405 (SAN 658-9839).

Alt Source
See Alter Source

Alta Gaia Bks, *(Alta Gaia Books; 0-933432),* P.O. Box 541, Millerton, NY 12546 (SAN 222-6642).

Alta House, *(Alta Hse.; 0-9616970),* P.O. Box 147, Port Townsend, WA 98368 (SAN 661-7115); 2208 Waltnut St., Port Townsend, WA 98368 (SAN 661-7123) Tel 206-385-4303.

Alta Napa, *(Alta Napa Pr.; 0-931926),* 1969 Mora Ave., Calistoga, CA 94515 (SAN 216-3276) Tel 707-942-4444.

Alta Pub Co, *(Alta Publishing Co., Inc.; 0-914855),* 6113 Robinwood Rd., Bethesda, MD 20817 (SAN 289-0488) Tel 301-320-5184; Orders to: P.O. Box 42107, Washington, DC 20015-0707 (SAN 669-3512).

Alta Vista Bks, *(Alta Vista Bks.; 0-936761),* 550 W. Vista Way, Suite 109, Vista, CA 92083 (SAN 699-8879) Tel 619-758-4584; P.O. Box 1728, Vista, CA 92083 (SAN 699-8887).

Altacom, *(Altacom, Inc.; 0-918391),* 608 Pendleton St., P.O. Box 19070, Alexandria, VA 22314 (SAN 657-3193) Tel 703-683-1442.

Altai Pub, *(Altai Publishers; 0-9609710),* P.O. Box 1972, Flagstaff, AZ 86002 (SAN 263-0281) Tel 602-779-0491.

Altair Pr, *(Altair Pr.; 0-934768),* 0-934768), P.O. Box 1286, Boulder, CO 80306 (SAN 209-1585) Tel 303-494-6405.

Altair Pub Co, *(Altair Publishing Co.; 0-9604976),* 508 S. Can-Dota, Mt. Prospect, IL 60056 (SAN 215-935X) Tel 312-255-8029.

Altair Pub UT, *(Altair Publishing Co.; 0-938117),* P.O. Box 20024, West Valley City, UT 84120 (SAN 659-6983); 3585 Cochise, West Valley City, UT 84120 (SAN 659-6991) Tel 801-967-3308.

Altara Group, *(Altara Group, The; 0-9607106),* 7 Charles Ct., P.O. Box 24, North Haven, CT 06473 (SAN 238-9363) Tel 203-239-9400.

Altarinda Bks, *(Altarinda Books; 0-9607896),* 13 Estates Dr., Orinda, CA 94563 (SAN 238-1397) Tel 415-254-3830.

Alter Abortion, *(Alternatives to Abortion, Inc.; 0-9615457),* P.O. Box 15271, Pittsburgh, PA 15237 (SAN 695-7471) Tel 412-731-2420.

Alter Currents, *(Alternating Currents Pr.; 0-9617221),* Box 525, Capitola, CA 95010 (SAN 663-4184); 644 Stewart St., Boulder Creek, CA (SAN 663-4192) Tel 408-338-4169.

Alter Parent, *(Alternative Parenting Pubns.; 0-935893),* 1298 W. Shady Mill Rd., Corona, CA 91720 (SAN 696-673X) Tel 714-736-8702; P.O. Box 2619, Corona, CA 91718 (SAN 696-7086).

Alter Source, *(Alternate Source, The; 0-915363),* 704 N. Pennsylvania Ave., Lansing, MI 48906 (SAN 265-6833) Tel 517-482-8270; Toll free: 800-253-3200 ext 700.

Altern Eighties, *(Alternatives for the Eighties; 0-9617089),* 122 Stanley Hall, Columbia, MO 65202 (SAN 662-636X) Tel 314-882-6439. Do not confuse with Alternatives of Ellenwood, GA.

Altern World, *(Alternative World Foundation, Inc.; 0-938035),* AWF-1, Goshen, IN 46526 (SAN 659-7033) Tel 219-534-3402; 803 N. Main, Goshen, IN 46526 (SAN 659-7041).

Alternate Energy, *(Alternate Energy Publishing Co.; 0-930086),* P.O. Box 26507, Albuquerque, NM 87125 (SAN 210-6981) Tel 505-873-2084.

†**Alternative Mus,** *(Alternative Museum; 0-932075),* 17 White St., New York, NY 10013 (SAN 686-2616) Tel 212-226-2158; *CIP.*

Alternatives, *(Alternatives; 0-914966),* P.O. Box 429, 5263 Bouldercrest Rd., Ellenwood, GA 30049 (SAN 206-8915) Tel 404-961-0102.

Alternatives A
See Alter Abortion

Alternatives MO
See Altern Eighties

Alternatives Vio, *(Alternatives To Violence of the Cleveland Friends Meeting Commitee),* 10916 Magnolia Dr., Cleveland, OH 44106 (SAN 693-0204).

Altitude, *(Altitude Publishing Co.; 0-917441),* 7866 S. Windermere Cir., Littleton, CO 80120 (SAN 657-0593) Tel 303-388-4989.

Altro Health Rehab, *(Altro Health & Rehabilitation Service; 0-937607),* 40 E. 30th St., New York, NY 10016 (SAN 658-988X) Tel 212-684-0600.

Alumnae
See Coun Career Plan

Alumni Assn, *(Baruch, Bernard M., College Alumni Assn., Inc.; 0-9606858),* 17 Lexington Ave., College Box 280, New York, NY 10010 (SAN 217-2275).

Alumni Assn US, *(Alumni Assn. of the US Army War College; 0-9613301),* Alumni Assn., USAWC, Box 462 USAWC, Carlisle Barracks, PA 17013-5050 (SAN 654-1968) Tel 717-243-0884.

Alyson Pubns, *(Alyson Pubns., Inc.; 0-932870; 1-55583),* 40 Plympton St., Boston, MA 02118 (SAN 213-6546) Tel 617-542-5679.

Am Acad Advert, *(American Academy of Advertising; 0-931030),* Brigham Young Univ., Graduate Schl. of Management, Provo, UT 84602 (SAN 236-073X) Tel 801-378-2080.

Am Acad Gnatho, *(American Academy of Gnathologic Orthopedics),* 211 E. Chicago Ave., No. 915, Chicago, IL 60611 (SAN 227-7646) Tel 312-642-5834.

Am Acad Inst Arts, *(American Academy & Institute of Arts & Letters; 0-915974),* 633 W. 155th St., New York, NY 10032 (SAN 204-7888) Tel 212-368-5900.

Am Acad Osteopathy, *(American Academy of Osteopathy; 0-940668),* P.O. Box 750, Newark, OH 43055 (SAN 218-5296) Tel 614-349-8701.

Am Acad Otolary, *(American Academy of Otolaryngic Allergy),* 1101 Vermont Ave. NW, Suite 302, Washington, DC 20005 (SAN 228-2348) Tel 202-682-0546.

AM Acad Pediat, *(American Academy of Pediatrics; 0-910761),* 141 Northwest Point Rd., Elk Grove Village, IL 60007 (SAN 265-3540) Tel 312-228-5005.

Am Acad Pol Soc Sci, *(American Academy of Political & Social Science; 0-87761),* 3937 Chestnut St., Philadelphia, PA 19104 (SAN 201-1239) Tel 215-386-4594; Dist. by: Sage Pubns., Inc., 275 S. Beverly Dr., Beverly Hills, CA 90212 (SAN 204-7217) Tel 213-274-8003.

Am Acad Rome, *(American Academy in Rome),* 41 E. 65th St., New York, NY 10021 (SAN 225-3801) Tel 212-535-4250.

Am Acad Surg
See Amer Acad Ortho Surg

Am Accounting, *(American Accounting Assn.),* 5717 Bessie Dr., Sarasota, FL 33583 (SAN 204-790X) Tel 813-921-7747.

Am Air Mail, *(American Air Mail Society; 0-939429),* 102 Arbor Rd. Cinnaminson, NJ 08077-3859 (SAN 225-5847) Tel 609-829-6792.

Am Allergy Assn, *(American Allergy Association),* P.O. Box 7273, Menlo Park, CA 94026 (SAN 224-2621) Tel 415-322-1663.

Am Animal Hosp Assoc, *(American Animal Hospital Assn.; 0-9616498),* 1746 Cole Blvd., Golden, CO 80401 (SAN 224-4799) Tel 303-279-2500.

Am Anthro Assn, *(American Anthropological Assn.; 0-913167),* Pubns. Dept., 1703 New Hampshire Ave., NW, Washington, DC 20009 (SAN 202-4284) Tel 202-232-8800.

11

Am Antiquarian, *(American Antiquarian Society; 0-912296),* 185 Salisbury St., Worcester, MA 01609 (SAN 206-474X) Tel 617-752-5813; Dist. by: Univ. Pr. of Virginia, P.O. Box 3608, University Sta., Charlottesville, VA 22903 (SAN 202-5361) Tel 804-924-3468.

Am-Arab Affairs, *(American Arab Affairs Council; 0-943182),* 1730 M St. NW, Suite 512, Washington, DC 20036 (SAN 240-5814) Tel 202-296-6767.

Am Arbitration, *(American Arbitration Assn.),* 140 W. 51st St., New York, NY 10020 (SAN 225-0802) Tel 212-484-4000.

Am Archives Pubs, *(American Archives Pubs.; 0-938039),* 208 Ember Glow Cir., College Station, TX 77840 (SAN 659-7092) Tel 409-268-0725.

Am Art Therapy, *(American Art Therapy Assn.),* 1980 Isaac Newton Sq. S., Reston, VA 22090 (SAN 688-7686) Tel 703-370-3223.

Am Assembly, *(American Assembly),* Columbia University, New York, NY 10027-6598 (SAN 209-6471).

†**Am Assn Blood,** *(American Assn. of Blood Banks; 0-914404; 0-915355),* 1117 N. 19th St., Suite 600, Arlington, VA 22209 (SAN 201-1573) Tel 703-528-8200; *CIP.*

Am Assn Botanical Gdns, *(American Assn. of Botanical Gardens & Arboreta, Inc.; 0-934843),* P.O. Box 206, Swarthmore, PA 19081 (SAN 225-1493) Tel 215-328-9145.

Am Assn Cereal Chem, *(American Assn. of Cereal Chemists; 0-913250),* 3340 Pilot Knob Rd., St. Paul, MN 55121 (SAN 204-7934) Tel 612-454-7250.

Am Assn Chinese Stud, *(American Assn. for Chinese Studies; 0-9606594),* Asian Studies Program, Ohio State Univ., Columbus, OH 43210 (SAN 219-757X) Tel 614-422-6681.

†**Am Assn Clinical Chem,** *(American Assn. for Clinical Chemistry; 0-915274),* 1725 K St., NW, Suite 1010, Washington, DC 20006 (SAN 214-2813); *CIP.*

Am Assn Coll Pharm
See AACP Bethesda

†**Am Assn Coll Registrars,** *(American Assn. of Collegiate Registrars & Officers; 0-910054),* 1 Dupont Cir., NW, Suite 330, Washington, DC 20036 (SAN 225-7394) Tel 202-293-9161; *CIP.*

Am Assn Comm Jr Coll, *(American Assn. of Community & Junior Colleges; 0-87117),* 1 Dupont Cir. NW, Suite 410, Washington, DC 20036 (SAN 293-2253) Tel 202-293-7050; Dist. by: AACJC Pubn. Sales, 80 S. Early St., Alexandria, VA 22304 (SAN 293-2261) Tel 703-823-6966.

Am Assn Conn
See Am Assn Comm Jr Coll

Am Assn Cost Engineers, *(American Assn. of Cost Engineers),* 308 Monongahela Bldg., Morgantown, WV 26505 (SAN 214-0942) Tel 304-296-8444.

Am Assn Coun Dev, *(American Assn. for Counseling & Development; 0-911547; 1-55620),* 5999 Stevenson Ave., Alexandria, VA 22304 (SAN 291-9141) Tel 703-823-9800.

Am Assn Diabetes Ed, *(American Assn. of Diabetes Educators),* 500 N. Michigan Ave., Suite 1400, Chicago, IL 60611 (SAN 224-3091) Tel 312-661-1700.

Am Assn Equip Lessors, *(American Assn. of Equipment Lessors; 0-912413),* 1300 N. 17th St., No. 1010, Arlington, VA 22209 (SAN 224-9359) Tel 703-527-8655.

Am Assn Gifted Children, *(American Association for Gifted Children),* 15 Gramercy Park, New York, NY 10016 (SAN 225-798X) Tel 212-473-4266.

Am Assn Homes, *(American Assn. of Homes for the Aging; 0-943774),* 1129 20th St. NW, Suite 400, Washington, DC 20036 (SAN 260-3918) Tel 202-296-5960.

Am Assn Intl Comm Jurists, *(American Assn. for the International Commission of Jurists, Inc.; 0-916265),* 777 United Nations Plaza, New York, NY 10017 (SAN 235-6473) Tel 212-972-0883.

Am Assn Law Libs, *(American Assn. of Law Libraries),* 53 W. Jackson Blvd., Chicago, IL 60604 (SAN 680-005X) Tel 312-939-4764.

†**Am Assn Mental,** *(American Assn. on Mental Deficiency; 0-940898),* 1719 Kalorama Rd., Washington, DC 20009 (SAN 206-961X) Tel 202-387-1968; Toll free: 800-424-3688; *CIP.*

†**Am Assn Mus,** *(American Assn. of Museums; 0-931201),* 1055 Thomas Jefferson St., NW, Washington, DC 20007 (SAN 233-5255) Tel 202-338-5300; *CIP.*

Am Assn Retire, *(American Assn. of Retired Persons),* 1909 K St., NW, Washington, DC 20049 (SAN 260-3985) Tel 202-872-4700; P.O. Box 19269-K, Washington, DC 20036 (SAN 668-9663); Orders to: AARP Pubns., Scott-Foresman & Co., 400 S. Edward St., Mt. Prospect, IL 60056 (SAN 697-595X).

Am Assn Sch Admin, *(American Assn. of Schl. Administrators; 0-87652),* 1801 N. Moore St., Arlington, VA 22209 (SAN 202-3628) Tel 703-528-0700.

Am Assn Strat, *(American Assn. of Stratigraphic Palynologists Foundation; 0-931871),* C.O. Mobil Research - DRL, P.O. Box 819047, Dallas, TX 75381-9047 (SAN 686-0524) Tel 214-851-8481.

Am Assn Text, *(American Assn. of Textile Chemists and Colorists; 0-9613350),* 1 Davis Dr., P.O. Box 12215, Research Triangle Park, NC 27709 (SAN 655-8747) Tel 919-549-8141.

Am Assn U, *(American Assn. of University Women; 0-9611476),* 2401 Virginia Ave., NW, Washington, DC 20037 (SAN 291-8617) Tel 202-785-7700; Toll free: 800-424-9717.

Am Assn U Women, *(American Assn. of Univ. Women, Corpus Christi Branch; 0-9615283),* Div. of American Assn. of University Women, P.O. Box 8151, Corpus Christi, TX 78412 (SAN 694-5449) Tel 512-853-4573.

Am Assn Univ Women, *(American Association of University Women Educational Foundation),* 2401 Virginia Ave., NW, Washington, DC 20037 (SAN 225-8854) Tel 202-785-7763.

Am Assn Voc Materials, *(American Assn. for Vocational Instructional Materials; 0-89606; 0-914452),* 120 Engineering, Athens, GA 30602 (SAN 225-8811) Tel 404-542-2586.

Am Assoc Med, *(American Assn. for Medical Transcription; 0-935229),* 3460 OakdaleRd., Suite F, Modesto, CA 95355 (SAN 696-0715) Tel 209-576-0883; Toll free: 800-982-2182; P.O. Box 6187, Modesto, CA 95355 (SAN 696-5202).

Am Assoc Z Pk, *(American Assn. of Zoological Parks & Aquariums),* Oglebay Pk., Wheeling, WV 26003 (SAN 684-5363) Tel 304-242-2160.

Am Astron Soc
See Am Astronaut

Am Astronaut, *(American Astronautical Society; 0-87703),* P.O. Box 28130, San Diego, CA 92128 (SAN 661-9339) Tel 619-746-4005; Orders to: Univelt, Inc., P.O. Box 28130, San Diego, CA 92128 (SAN 201-2561) Tel 619-746-4005.

Am Atheist, *(American Atheist Pr.; 0-911826; 0-910309),* P.O. Box 2117, Austin, TX 78768-2117 (SAN 206-7188) Tel 512-458-1244. *Imprints:* Gustav Broukal (Broukal, Gustav, Press).(Broukal, Gustav, Pr.).

Am Bando Assn, *(American Bando Assn.; 0-9608394),* Catonsville Community College, Catonsville, MD 21228 (SAN 240-5830) Tel 301-788-6149.

Am Bankers, *(American Bankers Assn.; 0-89982),* 1120 Connecticut Ave., NW, Washington, DC 20036 (SAN 208-4554) Tel 202-467-6660.

Am Baptist, *(American Baptist Historical Society; 0-910056),* 1106 S. Goodman St., Rochester, NY 14620 (SAN 201-257X) Tel 716-473-1740.

Am Bar Foun, *(American Bar Foundation; 0-910058; 0-910059),* Subs. of American Bar Assn., 750 N. Lake Shore Dr., Chicago, IL 60611 (SAN 201-2588) Tel 312-998-6400; Dist. by: Little, Brown & Co., 34 Beacon St., Boston, MA 02108 (SAN 200-2205).

Am Bartenders, *(American Bartenders' Assn., Inc.; 0-916689),* P.O. Box 11447, Bradenton, FL 34282 (SAN 653-7383) Tel 813-756-5265.

Am Bd Med Spec, *(American Board of Medical Specialties; 0-934277),* 1 American Plaza, No. 805, Evanston, IL 60201-4889 (SAN 228-0477) Tel 312-491-9091; Dist. by: Login Brothers Bk. Co., 1450 W. Randolph St., Chicago, IL 60607 (SAN 169-183X) Tel 312-733-6424.

Am Bed & Breakfast, *(American Bed & Breakfast Assn.; 0-934473),* Div. of Hearth & Home Enterprises, P.O. Box 23294, Washington, DC 20026 (SAN 693-8647) Tel 703-237-9777; Dist. by: National Press, Inc., 7508 Wisconsin Ave., Bethesda, MD 20814 (SAN 293-8839) Tel 301-657-1616.

Am Bible, *(American Bible Society; 0-8267),* Member of United Bible Societies, 1865 Broadway, New York, NY 10023 (SAN 203-5189) Tel 212-581-7400; Orders to: P.O. Box 5656, Grand Central Sta., New York, NY 10163 (SAN 662-7129) Tel 212-581-7400.

Am Biog Ctr, *(American Biographical Ctr.; 0-9601168),* P.O. Box 473, Williamsburg, VA 23187 (SAN 210-0266) Tel 804-725-2234.

Am Biog Inst, *(American Biographical Institute; 0-934544),* 5126 Bur Oak Cir., Raleigh, NC 27612 (SAN 213-0092) Tel 919-781-8710; P.O. Box 31226, Raleigh, NC 27622 (SAN 696-5067).

†**Am Biog Serv,** *(American Biography Service Inc.; 0-932051),* 14722 Newport C 184, Tustin, CA 92680 (SAN 686-2640) Tel 714-832-4382; *CIP.*

Am Bk Prices
See Bancroft Parkman

Am Blade Bk Serv, *(American Blade Book Service; 0-911881),* 2835 Hickory Valley Rd., P.O. Box 22007, Chattanooga, TN 37422 (SAN 265-3559) Tel 615-894-0339.

†**Am Blood Comm,** *(American Blood Commission; 0-935498),* 1117 N. 19th St., Suite 501, Arlington, VA 22209 (SAN 213-7194) Tel 703-522-8414; *CIP.*

Am Bottled Water
See Intl Bottled Water

Am Brahman Breeders, *(American Brahman Breeders Association),* 1313 La Concha Lane, Houston, TX 77054 (SAN 224-9901) Tel 713-794-4444.

Am Buddhist Shim Do, *(American Buddhist Shim Gum Do Assn., Inc.; 0-9614427),* 203 Chestnut Hill Ave., Brighton, MA 02135 (SAN 690-050X) Tel 617-787-1506.

Am Bur Eco Res, *(American Bureau of Economic Research; 0-930462),* P.O. Box 7999, Tyler, TX 75711 (SAN 222-5069) Tel 214-593-7447.

Am Bur Metal, *(American Bureau of Metal Statistics; 0-910064),* 400 Plaza Dr., Harmon Meadow, P.O. Box 1405, Secaucus, NJ 07094-0405 (SAN 201-1581) Tel 201-863-6900.

Am Busn Comm Assn
See Assn Busn Comm

Am Busn Consult, *(American Business Consultants, Inc.; 0-937152),* 1540 Nuthatch Lane, Sunnyvale, CA 94087-4999 (SAN 214-3399) Tel 408-732-8931.

†**Am Camping,** *(American Camping Assn.; 0-87603),* Bradford Woods 5000 State Rd. 67, N., Martinsville, IN 46151-7902 (SAN 201-2596) Tel 317-342-8456; *CIP.*

Am Canadian, *(American-Canadian Pubs., Inc.; 0-913844),* Box 4575, Santa Fe, NM 87502 (SAN 201-260X) Tel 505-471-7863.

†**Am Canal & Transport,** *(American Canal & Transportation Ctr.; 0-933788),* 809 Rathton Rd., York, PA 17403 Tel 717-843-4035. Do not confuse with American Canal Society, same address. ACS is a non-profit, educational organization. American Canal & Transportation Ctr. is a publishing firm; *CIP.*

Am Cancer Colo, *(American Cancer Society, Colorado Div., Inc.),* 2255 S. Oneida St., Denver, CO 80224 (SAN 217-300X).

Am Cancer Forest Hills, *(American Cancer Society, New York Div., Inc.),* 111-15 Queens Blvd., Forest Hills, NY 11375 (SAN 217-2763).

Am Cancer Iowa, *(American Cancer Society, Iowa Div., Inc.),* Box 980, Mason City, IA 50401 (SAN 217-2771).

Am Cancer Mass, *(American Cancer Society, Massachusetts Div., Inc.),* 247 Commonwealth Ave., Boston, MA 02116 (SAN 217-278X).

Am Cancer MD, *(American Cancer Society, Maryland Div., Inc.),* 200 E. Joppa Rd., Towson, MD 21204 (SAN 217-2860).

Am Cancer Mich, *(American Cancer Society, Michigan Div., Inc.),* 1205 E. Saginaw St., Lansing, MI 48906 (SAN 217-2852).

Symbols/Abbreviations

Am Fed Arts, *(American Federation of Arts; 0-917418),* 41 E. 65th St., New York, NY 10021 (SAN 201-2669) Tel 212-988-7700.

Am Fed Astrologers, *(American Federation of Astrologers; 0-86690),* Box 22040, Tempe, AZ 85282 (SAN 225-1396) Tel 602-838-1751.

Am Fed Info Process
See AFIPS Pr

Am Feed Industry, *(American Feed Industry Assn.),* 1701 N. Ft. Myer Dr., Arlington, VA 22209 (SAN 224-7283) Tel 703-524-0810.

Am Feed Mfrs
See Am Feed Industry

AM-FEM Co, *(Am-Fem Co.; 0-9607232),* P.O. Box 93, Cooper Sta., New York, NY 10276 (SAN 239-152X).

Am First Day, *(American First Day Cover Society),* 16S31 Abbey Dr., Mitchellville, MD 20716 (SAN 225-5855).

Am Fish FL, *(American Fisheries Society, Florida Chapter; 0-9616676),* Univ. of Florida, Bldg. 803, Gainesville, FL 32611 (SAN 659-7130) Tel 904-392-5870.

Am Fish Tackle, *(American Fishing Tackle Manufacturers Assn.; 0-933986),* 2625 Clearbrook Dr., Arlington Heights, IL 60005 (SAN 224-6287) Tel 312-364-4666.

Am Fisheries Soc, *(American Fisheries Society; 0-913235),* P.O. Box 1150, Columbia, MD 21044 (SAN 284-964X) Tel 301-596-3458; 5410 Grosvenor Ln., Suite 110, Bethesda, MD 20814 (SAN 284-9658) Tel 301-897-8616.

Am Forestry, *(American Forestry Assn.; 0-935050),* Bk. Editorial Dept., 1319 18th St., NW, Washington, DC 20036 (SAN 204-8175) Tel 202-467-5810.

†Am Foun Blind, *(American Foundation for the Blind; 0-89128),* 15 W. 16th St., New York, NY 10011 (SAN 201-2677) Tel 212-620-2150; CIP.

Am Foundrymen, *(American Foundrymen's Society; 0-87433),* Golf & Wolf Rds., Des Plaines, IL 60016 (SAN 224-0424) Tel 312-824-0181.

Am Fr Serv Comm, *(American Friends Service Committee; 0-910082),* 1501 Cherry St., Philadelphia, PA 19102 (SAN 201-2685) Tel 215-241-7000.

Am Fuchsia, *(American Fuchsia Society; 0-9613167),* Hall of Flowers, Ninth Ave. & Lincoln Way, San Francisco, CA 94122 (SAN 294-8931) Tel 707-442-3994.

Am Gas Assn, *(American Gas Assn.; 0-87257),* 1515 Wilson Blvd., Arlington, VA 22209 (SAN 224-7623) Tel 703-841-8400.

†Am Geographical, *(American Geographical Society),* 156 Fifth Ave., New York, NY 10010 (SAN 225-1906) Tel 212-242-0214; CIP.

†Am Geol, *(American Geological Institute; 0-913312),* 4220 King St., Alexandria, VA 22302 (SAN 202-4543) Tel 703-379-2480; Toll free: 800-336-4764; CIP.

†Am Geophysical, *(American Geophysical Union; 0-87590),* 2000 Florida Ave. NW, Washington, DC 20009 (SAN 202-4489) Tel 202-462-6903; Toll free: 800-424-2488; CIP.

Am Guidance, *(American Guidance Service, Inc.; 0-913476; 0-88671),* Publishers' Bldg., Circle Pines, MN 55014 (SAN 201-694X) Tel 612-786-4343; Toll free: 800-328-2560.

Am Hasbourgh, *(American Hasbourgh Dynasty Co.; 0-936037),* P.O. Box 2203, Long Island City, NY 11102 (SAN 696-9925) Tel 718-626-0389; 4-33 27th Ave., Astoria, NY 11102 (SAN 696-9933).

Am Health Care Assn, *(American Health Care Assn.),* 1200 15th St., NW, Washington, DC 20005 (SAN 224-3865) Tel 202-833-2050.

Am Health Consults, *(American Health Consultants, Inc.; 0-9603332),* Subs. of Medical Economics Inc., 67 Peachtree Park Dr., NE, Atlanta, GA 30309 (SAN 222-2655) Tel 404-351-4523; Toll free: 800-559-1032.

Am Heart, *(American Heart Assn., Inc.; 0-87493),* 7320 Greenville Ave., Dallas, TX 75231 (SAN 202-4551) Tel 214-706-1464; Dist. by: American Heart Association, Distribution Center, 2005 Hightower, Garland, TX 75401 (SAN 662-7137) Tel 214-278-1346; Dist. by: American Heart Association, Materials Resource Center, 4808 Eastover Cir., Mesquite, TX 75149 (SAN 662-7145).

Am Heat Ref & Air Eng, *(American Society of Heating, Refrigerating & Air Conditioning Engineers, Inc.; 0-910110),* 1791 Tullie Cir. NE, Atlanta, GA 30329 (SAN 223-9809) Tel 404-636-8400.

†Am Heritage, *(American Heritage, Inc.; 0-8281),* 60 Fifth Ave., New York, NY 10020 (SAN 206-9032) Tel 212-399-8900; Dist. by: Houghton Mifflin Co., 1 Beacon St., Boston, MA 02108 (SAN 200-2388) Tel 617-725-5000; CIP.

Am Hist Assn, *(American Historical Assn.; 0-87229),* 400 A St., SE, Washington, DC 20003 (SAN 201-159X) Tel 202-544-2422.

Am Hist Pr, *(American History Pr.; 0-89002),* Div. of Northwoods Pr., P.O. Box 123, S. Thomaston, ME 04858 (SAN 217-0876).

Am Hist Res, *(American History Research Associates; 0-910086),* P.O. Box 140, Brookeville, MD 20833 (SAN 206-717X) Tel 301-774-3573.

Am Hist Soc Ger, *(American Historical Society of Germans from Russia; 0-914222),* 631 D St., Lincoln, NE 68502 (SAN 204-7543) Tel 402-474-3363.

†Am Home Eco, *(American Home Economics Assn.; 0-8461),* 2010 Massachusetts Ave., NW, Washington, DC 20036 (SAN 266-9277) Tel 202-862-8344; CIP.

Am Horse Coun, *(American Horse Council),* 1700 K St. NW, Suite 300, Washington, DC 20006 (SAN 225-025X) Tel 202-296-4031.

†Am Hospital, *(American Hospital Assn.; 0-87258),* 840 N. Lake Shore Dr., Chicago, IL 60611 (SAN 295-2955) Tel 312-280-6000; Toll free: 800-242-2626 (Orders); CIP.

Am Hot Dip, *(American Hot Dip Galvanizers Assn.),* Suite 700 1101 Connecticut Ave., NW, Washington, DC 20036-4303 (SAN 224-6805) Tel 202-857-1119.

Am Hotel & Motel Assn, *(American Hotel & Motel Assn.; 0-86612),* 888 Seventh Ave., New York, NY 10019 (SAN 224-7917) Tel 212-265-4506.

†Am Humane Assn, *(American Humane Assn.; 0-930915),* P.O. Box 1266, Denver, CO 80201 (SAN 227-2156) Tel 303-695-0811; CIP.

Am Hungarian Foun, *(American Hungarian Foundation),* 177 Somerset St., New Brunswick, NJ 08903 (SAN 211-2086) Tel 201-846-5777.

Am Impress Bk Co, *(American Impressions Book Co.; 0-942550),* 417 Cleveland Ave., Plainfield, NJ 07060 (SAN 238-7654) Tel 201-757-2600.

Am Ind Law DC
See Occasional Papers
Am Ind Mus
See Mus Am Ind

†Am Indian Arch, *(American Indian Archaeological Institute; 0-936322),* P.O. Box 260, Washington, CT 06793 (SAN 221-2536) Tel 203-868-0518; CIP.

Am Indian Pubs, *(American Indian Pubs., Inc.; 0-937862),* 177 F Riverside Dr., Newport Beach, CA 92663 (SAN 216-3284).

Am Indus Hygiene, *(American Industrial Hygiene Assn.; 0-932627),* 475 Wolf Ledges Pkwy., Akron, OH 44311-1087 (SAN 224-3970) Tel 216-762-7294.

Am Inheritance Pr, *(American Inheritance Pr.; 0-932037),* 2314 Arctic Ave., Atlantic City, NJ 08401 (SAN 686-0729) Tel 609-344-0383.

Am Ins NY, *(American Insurance Assn.),* 85 John St., New York, NY 10038 (SAN 266-9900) Tel 212-433-4400.

Am Inst Arch, *(American Institute of Architects; 0-913962),* 1735 New York Ave., NW, Washington, DC 20006 (SAN 277-9536) Tel 202-626-7474; Orders to: AIA Service Corp., 44 Industrial Pk. Dr., Box 753, Waldorf, MD 20601 (SAN 661-9371).

Am Inst Arch Res, *(American Institute for Archaeological Research, Inc.; 0-937923),* 220 Main St., Salem, NH 03079 (SAN 659-4867) Tel 617-267-6906.

Am Inst Baking, *(American Institute of Baking),* 1213 Bakers Way, Manhattan, KS 66502 (SAN 224-6449) Tel 913-537-4750.

Am Inst Char Ed, *(American Institute for Character Education; 0-913413),* 342 W. Woodlawn, San Antonio, TX 78212 (SAN 236-154X) Tel 512-734-5091; Orders to: P.O. Box 12617, San Antonio, TX 78212 (SAN 680-0114).

†Am Inst Chem Eng, *(American Institute of Chemical Engineers; 0-8169),* 345 E. 47th St., New York, NY 10017 (SAN 204-7551) Tel 212-705-7657; CIP.

Am Inst Cons Eng
See Am Consul Eng

Am Inst Conser Hist, *(American Institute for Conservation of Historical & Artistic Works),* 3545 Williamsburg Lane, NW, Washington, DC 20008 (SAN 225-4972) Tel 202-364-1036.

Am Inst Cooperation, *(American Institute of Cooperation; 0-938868),* 1800 Massachusetts Ave., NW, Suite 508, Washington, DC 20036 (SAN 204-5281) Tel 202-296-6825.

Am Inst CPA, *(American Institute of Certified Public Accountants; 0-87051),* 1211 Ave. of the Americas, New York, NY 10036 (SAN 202-4578) Tel 212-575-6200.

Am Inst Disc, *(American Institute of Discussion; 0-910092),* P.O. Box 103, Oklahoma City, OK 73101 (SAN 202-4586) Tel 405-235-9681.

Am Inst Econ Res, *(American Institute for Economic Research; 0-913610),* Division St., Great Barrington, MA 01230 (SAN 225-6509) Tel 413-528-1216.

Am Inst Food Distr, *(American Institute of Food Distribution, Inc.),* 28-12 Broadway, Fair Lawn, NJ 07410 (SAN 224-7372) Tel 201-791-5570.

Am Inst Hist Pharm, *(American Institute of the History of Pharmacy; 0-931292),* 425 N. Charter St., Pharmacy Bldg., Madison, WI 53706 (SAN 204-5257) Tel 608-262-5378.

Am Inst Indus Eng
See Inst Indus Eng

†Am Inst Islamic, *(American Institute of Islamic Studies; 0-933017),* P.O. Box 10398, Denver, CO 80210 (SAN 266-9811) Tel 303-936-0108; CIP.

Am Inst Ital Stud, *(American Institute of Italian Studies; 0-916322),* Villa Walsh, Morristown, NJ 07960 (SAN 220-2298) Tel 201-538-2886; Dist. by: Kraus Reprint & Periodicals, Rte. 100, Millwood, NY 10546 (SAN 201-0542) Tel 914-762-2200.

Am Inst Maint, *(American Institute of Maintenance; 0-9609052),* 1120 E. Chevy Chase Dr., P.O. Box 2068, Glendale, CA 91205 (SAN 260-3179) Tel 818-244-1176.

Am Inst Marxist, *(American Institute for Marxist Studies; 0-89977),* 85 E. Fourth St., New York, NY 10013 (SAN 202-4594) Tel 212-689-4530.

Am Inst Mining
See Soc Mining Eng

Am Inst Mining Metal, *(American Institute of Mining, Metallurgical, & Petroleum Engineers; 0-89520),* 345 E. 47th St., New York, NY 10017 (SAN 688-9921) Tel 212-705-7695.

Am Inst Parliamentarians, *(American Institute of Parliamentarians; 0-942736),* 124 W. Washington Blvd., Suite 144, Ft. Wayne, IN 46802 (SAN 225-3690) Tel 219-422-3680.

Am Inst Pharmacy
See Am Inst Hist Pharm

Am Inst Physics, *(American Institute of Physics; 0-88318),* 335 E. 45th St., New York, NY 10017 (SAN 201-162X) Tel 212-661-9404; Toll free: 800-247-7497. Publisher of scholarly journals, books and databases in physics and related sciences in hardcopy, 16mm and 35mm microfilm, reel and cartridge, and microfiche. North American distributor of journals from the Institute of Physics (UK), Annals of the Israel Physical Society, Physics Briefs from the Fachinformationszentrum (West Germany), and Physica Scripta (Royal Swedish Academy of Sciences).

14

Am Inst Property, *(American Institute for Property & Liability Underwriters, Inc.; 0-89463),* 720 Providence Rd., Malvern, PA 19355 (SAN 210-1629) Tel 215-644-2100.

Am Inst Psych, *(American Institute for Psychological Research, The; 0-89920),* 614 Indian School Rd. NW, Albuquerque, NM 87102 (SAN 212-9302) Tel 505-843-7749.

†Am Inst Real Estate Appraisers, *(American Institute of Real Estate Appraisers; 0-911780),* Affil. of National Assn. of Realtors, 430 N. Michigan Ave., Chicago, IL 60611 (SAN 206-7153) Tel 312-329-8533; Dist. by: Regnery Gateway, Inc., 940-950 N. Shore Dr., Lake Bluff, IL (SAN 210-5578); CIP.

Am Inst Res, *(American Institutes for Research; 0-89785),* P.O. Box 1113, Palo Alto, CA 94302 (SAN 202-442X).

Am Inst Steel Construct, *(American Institute of Steel Construction, Inc.),* 400 N. Michigan Ave., Chicago, IL 60611 (SAN 224-6872) Tel 312-670-2400.

Am Inst Taxidermy, *(American Institute of Taxidermy, Inc.; 0-9616088),* 3232 McCormick Dr., Janesville, WI 53545 (SAN 698-0775) Tel 608-755-5160.

Am Inst Timber, *(American Institute of Timber Construction),* 333 W. Hampden Ave., Englewood, CO 80110 (SAN 230-287X) Tel 303-761-3212.

Am Inst Ultrasound, *(American Institute of Ultrasound in Medicine),* 4405 East-West Hwy., Bethesda, MD 20814 (SAN 224-4756) Tel 301-656-6117.

Am Inst Writing Res, *(American Institute for Writing Research, Corp.; 0-917944),* P.O. Box 1364, Grand Central Sta., New York, NY 10163 (SAN 210-0290) Tel 718-266-2897.

Am Intl Action, *(American Council for Voluntary International Action; 0-932140),* 200 Park Ave. S., New York, NY 10003 (SAN 225-9508) Tel 212-777-8210.
Imprints: Inneraction (Inneraction).

Am Intl Dev, *(American International Development Studies, Inc.; 0-9616279),* P.O. Box 490249, Miami, FL 33149 (SAN 658-5345) Tel 305-444-5678.

Am Iris, *(American Iris Society; 0-9601242),* 7414 E. 60th St., Tulsa, OK 74145 (SAN 210-3826) Tel 918-627-0706; Orders to: Rte. 3, Box 270, Vinita, OK 74301 (SAN 210-3834) Tel 918-782-3133.

Am Iron & Steel, *(American Iron & Steel Institute),* 1000 16th St. NW, Washington, DC 20036 (SAN 224-8719) Tel 202-452-7100.

Am Italian, *(American Italian Historical Assn., Inc.; 0-934675),* 209 Flagg Pl., Staten Island, NY 10304 (SAN 210-8828) Tel 718-454-9326.

Am Ivy Soc, *(American Ivy Society, The; 0-937233),* P.O. Box 520, West Carrollton, OH 45449-0520 (SAN 225-5685) Tel 513-434-7069.

Am Jewish Comm, *(American Jewish Committee; 0-87495),* 165 E. 56 St., New York, NY 10022 (SAN 675-0079) Tel 212-751-4000.

Am Jewish Comm
See Am Jewish Holo

Am Jewish Hist Soc, *(American Jewish Historical Society; 0-911934),* Two Thornton Rd., Waltham, MA 02154 (SAN 202-4608) Tel 617-891-8110.

Am Jewish Holo, *(American Jewish Commission on the Holocaust; 0-9613537),* Ralph Bunche, Graduate Institute School Cuny, 33 W. 42nd St., New York, NY 10036 (SAN 669-7178) Tel 212-790-4222.

Am Journal Nurse, *(American Journal of Nursing Co., Educational Services Div.; 0-937126),* 555 W. 57th St., New York, NY 10019 (SAN 202-4616) Tel 212-582-8820.

†Am Judicature, *(American Judicature Society; 0-938870),* 25 E. Washington, Suite 1600, Chicago, IL 60602 (SAN 201-7202) Tel 312-558-6900; CIP.

Am Land Dev
See ARRDA

Am Lang Acad, *(American Language Academy; 0-934270),* Regents/ALA., 2 Park Ave., New York, NY 10016 (SAN 281-2665); Toll free: 800-822-8202.

Am Law Enforce Off, *(American Law Enforcement Officers Assn.; 0-936320),* 1100 125th St. NE, North Miami, FL 33161 (SAN 225-1175).

Am Law Inst, *(American Law Institute; 0-8318),* 4025 Chestnut St., Philadelphia, PA 19104 (SAN 204-756X) Tel 215-243-1600; Toll free: 800-CLE-NEWS.

Am Law Pub, *(Am-Law Publishing Corp.; 0-9606682),* 205 Lexington Ave., New York, NY 10016 (SAN 219-7049) Tel 212-696-8900.

AM Legacy Pr. *Imprint of* **Crown**

Am Legislative, *(American Legislative Exchange Council; 0-89483),* 214 Massachusetts Ave., NE, Washington, DC 20002 (SAN 210-0274) Tel 202-547-4646.

Am Leprosy Mission, *(American Leprosy Missions, Inc.),* One Broadway, Elmwood Park, NJ 07407 (SAN 224-3474) Tel 201-794-8650.

Am Lib Pub Co, *(American Library Publishing Co., Inc.; 0-934598),* 275 Central Park W., New York, NY 10024 (SAN 201-9868) Tel 212-362-1442.

Am Liberty, *(American Liberty Pubns.; 0-917209),* 1912 Waltzer Rd., Santa Rosa, CA 95401 (SAN 656-0385) Tel 707-544-3141.

Am Liberty Pub
See Jackson Assocs

Am Liberty Pub *Imprint of* **Jackson Assocs**

†Am Life Foun, *(American Life Foundation & Study Institute; 0-89257),* P.O. Box 349, Watkins Glen, NY 14891 (SAN 201-1646) Tel 607-535-4737; CIP.

Am Lit Trans, *(American Literary Translators Assn.),* P.O. Box 830688, Richardson, TX 75083-0688 (SAN 260-3497) Tel 214-690-2093.

Am Logistics Assn, *(American Logistics Assn.; 0-915959),* 1133 15th St. NW, Suite 500, Washington, DC 20005 (SAN 225-1027) Tel 202-466-2520.

Am Lubrication Engs, *(American Society of Lubrication Engineers),* 838 Busse Hwy., Park Ridge, IL 60068 (SAN 225-2031) Tel 312-825-5536.

Am Lung Assn, *(American Lung Assn.; 0-915116),* 1740 Broadway, New York, NY 10019 (SAN 211-3503).

Am Malacologists, *(American Malacologists, Inc.; 0-915826),* Box 2255, Melbourne, FL 32902-2255 (SAN 207-6403) Tel 305-725-2260.

Am Manage Rev, *(American Management Reviews; 0-9613385),* P.O. Box 45500, Phoenix, AZ 85064 (SAN 657-0623) Tel 602-252-7622.

†Am Map, *(American Map Corp.; 0-8416),* Subs. of Langenscheidt Pubs,Inc., 46-35 54th Rd., Maspeth, NY 11378 (SAN 202-4624) Tel 718-784-0055; CIP.

Am Marine Corp, *(American Marine Corp.; 0-9615134),* 1 Burlington Woods Dr., Suite 302, Burlington, MA 01803 (SAN 694-2504) Tel 617-273-1326.

Am Martial Arts Pub, *(American Martial Arts Publishing; 0-932981),* P.O. Box 4097, Greenville, NC 27836 (SAN 686-113X) Tel 919-758-2055.

†Am Math, *(American Mathematical Society; 0-8218),* P.O. Box 6248, Providence, RI 02940 (SAN 201-1654) Tel 401-272-9500; Toll free: 800-556-7774; Orders to: P.O. Box 1571, Annex Sta., Providence, RI 02901-1571 (SAN 201-1662); CIP.

Am Med Assts, *(American Assn. of Medical Assistants; 0-942732),* 20 N. Wacker Dr., Suite 1575, Chicago, IL 60606 (SAN 224-3520) Tel 312-899-1500.

Am Med Pub, *(American Medical Publishing Assn.; 0-911411),* c/o Louis Reines, 1560 Broadway, New York, NY 10036 (SAN 691-4136) Tel 212-819-5400.

Am Med Record Assn, *(American Medical Record Assn.),* P.O. Box 97349, Chicago, IL 60690 (SAN 224-4489) Tel 312-787-2672.

Am Media, *(American Media; 0-912986),* P.O. Box 4646, Westlake Village, CA 91359 (SAN 202-4632) Tel 805-496-1649.

Am Mental Health Found, *(American Mental Health Foundation),* 2 E. 86th St., New York, NY 10028 (SAN 228-0531).

Am Metal Mkt
See AMM

Am Meteorite, *(American Meteorite Laboratory; 0-910096),* P.O. Box 2098, Denver, CO 80201 (SAN 202-4659) Tel 303-428-1371.

Am Metric, *(American Metric Journal; 0-917240),* P.O. Box 847, Tarzana, CA 91356 (SAN 209-4134) Tel 805-484-5787.

Am Mgmt
See AMACOM

Am Mideast, *(American Mideast Research; 0-9604562),* 3315 Sacramento St., Suite 511, San Francisco, CA 94118 (SAN 215-0506) Tel 415-346-9222.

†Am Mktg, *(American Marketing Assn.; 0-87757),* 250 S. Wacker Dr., No. 200, Chicago, IL 60606 (SAN 202-4667) Tel 312-648-0536; CIP.

Am Mosquito, *(American Mosquito Control Assn.),* P.O. Box 5416, Lake Charles, LA 70606 (SAN 224-3652) Tel 318-474-4736.

Am Mus Natl Hist, *(American Museum of Natural History; 0-913424),* Central Park W. at 79th St., New York, NY 10024 (SAN 208-2160) Tel 212-873-1498.

Am Music Ctr, *(American Music Ctr., Inc.; 0-916052),* 250 W. 54th St., New York, NY 10019 (SAN 225-3518).

Am Mutuality, *(American Mutuality Foundation; 0-938844),* 9428 S. Western Ave., Los Angeles, CA 90047 (SAN 216-0153).

Am Nat Hygiene, *(American Natural Hygiene Society; 0-914532),* 12816 Race Track Rd., Tampa, FL 33625 (SAN 224-3660).

Am Natl, *(American National Metric Council; 0-916148),* 1010 Vermont Ave., NW, Suite 320-21, Washington, DC 20005-4960 (SAN 207-9380) Tel 202-628-5757.

Am-Nepal Ed, *(American-Nepal Education Foundation),* 2790 Cape Meares Lp., Tillamook, OR 97141 (SAN 236-5049) Tel 503-842-4024.

Am New Church Sunday, *(American New Church Sunday School Assn.; 0-917426),* 48 Highland St., Sharon, MA 02067 (SAN 208-9432) Tel 617-784-5041; Dist. by: Swedenborg Library, 79 Newbury St., Boston, MA 02116 (SAN 208-9440).

Am Nonsmokers Rights, *(American Nonsmokers' Rights Foundation; 0-9616473),* 2054 University Ave., Suite 500, Berkeley, CA 94704 (SAN 659-2821) Tel 415-841-3032.

†Am Nuclear Soc, *(American Nuclear Society),* 555 N. Kensington Ave., La Grange Park, IL 60525 (SAN 207-5172) Tel 312-352-6611; CIP.

Am Numismatic, *(American Numismatic Society; 0-89722),* Broadway at 155th St., New York, NY 10032 (SAN 201-7067) Tel 212-234-3130.

Am Nurserymen, *(American Assn. of Nurserymen),* 1250 Eye St., NW, Suite 500, Washington, DC 20005 (SAN 225-0462) Tel 202-789-2900.

†Am Occup Therapy, *(American Occupational Therapy Assn., Inc.; 0-910317),* P.O. Box 1725, Rockville, MD 20850-4375 (SAN 224-4705); 1383 Piccard Dr., Rockville, MD 20850-4375 (SAN 662-7153) Tel 301-948-9626; CIP.

Am Oil Chemists, *(American Oil Chemists Society; 0-935315),* 508 S. Sixth St., Champaign, IL 61820 (SAN 225-1558) Tel 217-359-2344.

Am Orient Soc, *(American Oriental Society; 0-940490),* 329 Sterling Memorial Library, Yale Sta., New Haven, CT 06520 (SAN 211-3082) Tel 203-436-1040.

Am Ornithologists, *(American Ornithologists Union; 0-943610),* National Museum of Natural History, Washington, DC 20560 (SAN 225-2252) Tel 202-381-5286.

Am Parapsy Res
See AAP Calif

Am Passage Mktg, *(American Passage Mktg. Corp.; 0-937649),* 500 Third Ave. W., Seattle, WA 98119 (SAN 659-2848) Tel 206-282-8111.

Am Patent Law, *(American Patent Law Assn.),* 2001 Jefferson Davis Hwy., Rm. 203, Arlington, VA 22202 (SAN 227-3586).

†Am Petroleum, *(American Petroleum Institute Pubns.; 0-89364),* 1220 L St. NW, Washington, DC 20005 (SAN 204-5141) Tel 202-682-8375; CIP.

Am Phar & Ex, *(American Society for Pharmacology & Experimental Therapeutics; 0-9609094),* 9650 Rockville Pike, Bethesda, MD 20014 (SAN 267-3223) Tel 301-530-7060.

†Am Pharm Assn, *(American Pharmaceutical Assn.; 0-917330),* 2215 Constitution Ave., NW, Washington, DC 20037 (SAN 202-4446) Tel 202-628-4410; CIP.

Symbols/Abbreviations

Am Philatelic
See Am Philatelic Society

Am Philatelic Society, (American Philatelic Society; 0-933580), P.O. Box 8000, State College, PA 16803 (SAN 225-5863) Tel 814-237-3803; 100 Oakwood Ave., State College, PA 16803 (SAN 668-9876).

Am Philos, (American Philosophical Society; 0-87169), 104 S. Fifth St., Philadelphia, PA 19106 (SAN 206-9016) Tel 215-627-0706; Orders to: P.O. Box 40227-5227, Philadelphia, PA 19106 (SAN 661-9398).

Am Phys Therapy Assn, (American Physical Therapy Assn.; 0-912452), 1111 N. Fairfax St., Alexandria, VA 22314 (SAN 202-4683) Tel 202-466-2070.

†**Am Physiological,** (American Physiological Society), 9650 Rockville Pike, Bethesda, MD 20814 (SAN 225-2341) Tel 301-530-7070; CIP.

Am Phytopathol Soc, (American Phytopathological Society; 0-89054), 3340 Pilot Knob Rd., St. Paul, MN 55121 (SAN 212-0704) Tel 612-454-7250; Toll free: 800-328-7560.

Am Pine Barrens, (American Pine Barrens Pub. Co.; 0-937438), P.O. Box 22820, 1400 Washington Ave., Albany, NY 12222 (SAN 215-1278).

Am Plan Assn, (American Planning Assn.), 1776 Massachusetts Ave., NW, Washington, DC 20036 (SAN 267-176X) Tel 202-872-0611; Orders to: Planners Bkstore, 1313 E. 60th St., Chicago, IL 60637 (SAN 650-003X) Tel 312-947-2115.

Am Plant Life, (American Plant Life Society; 0-930653), P.O. Box 985, National City, CA 92050 (SAN 225-1507) Tel 619-477-0295.

AM-PM Pub Co, (AM/PM Publishing Co.; 0-933875), 2376 Union St., San Francisco, CA 94123 (SAN 692-7866) Tel 415-621-8100.

Am Poetry & Lit, (American Poetry & Literature Pr.; 0-933486), P.O. Box 2013, Upper Darby, PA 19082 (SAN 212-6397) Tel 215-352-5438.

Am Political, (American Political Science Assn.; 0-915654), 1527 New Hampshire Ave., NW, Washington, DC 20036 (SAN 207-3382) Tel 202-483-2512.

Am Political Collect, (American Political Items Collectors), P.O. Box 340339, San Antonio, TX 78234 (SAN 225-5308) Tel 512-655-5213.

Am Polygraph, (American Polygraph Assn.), P.O. Box 1061, Severna Park, MD 21146 (SAN 225-1205); Toll free: 800-272-8037; P.O. Box 794, Severna Park, MD 21146 (SAN 693-479X); Orders to: American Polygraph Assn. Pubns., P.O. Box 1061, Severna Park, MD 21146 (SAN 661-9401) Tel 301-647-0936.

Am Pomological, (American Pomological Society), 103 Tyson Bldg., University Park, PA 16802 (SAN 225-0195); Dist. by: Michigan State Univ. Pr., 1405 S. Harrison Rd., 25 Manly Miles Bldg., East Lansing, MI 48824 (SAN 202-6295) Tel 517-355-9543.

Am Poultry Soc, (American Poultry Historical Society), Dept. of Poultry Science, 1675 Observatory Dr., Madison, WI 53706-1284 (SAN 267-1891).

Am Powder Metal, (American Powder Metallurgy Institute), 105 College Rd. E., Princeton, NJ 08540 (SAN 211-0652).

Am Power Boat, (American Power Boat Association), 17640 E. Nine Mile Rd., P.O. Box 377, East Detroit, MI 48021 (SAN 224-5442) Tel 313-773-9700.

Am Prepaid, (American Prepaid Legal Services Institute; 0-913955), 750 N. Lake Shore Dr., Chicago, IL 60611 (SAN 241-1709) Tel 312-988-5752.

Am Pro Educ, (American Professional Education, Inc.; 0-938401), P.O. Box 705, Hackensack, NJ 07602 (SAN 659-7165) Tel 201-489-4900; 552 Summit Ave., Hackensack, NJ 07601 (SAN 659-7173).

Am Prod & Inventory, (American Production & Inventory Control Society, Inc.; 0-935406), 500 W. Annandale Rd., Falls Church, VA 22046-4274 (SAN 213-7208) Tel 703-237-8344.

Am Prudential, (American Prudential Enterprises; 0-9608346), P.O. Box 4506, Salisbury, NC 28144 (SAN 238-9053) Tel 704-637-4407.

†**Am Psychiatric,** (American Psychiatric Pr., Inc.; 0-89042; 0-88048), Subs. of American Psychiatric Assn., 1400 K St., NW, Washington, DC 20005 (SAN 293-2288) Tel 202-682-6262; Toll free: 800-368-5777. Publishing arm of the American Psychiatric Assn; CIP.

Am Psychoanalytic, (American Psychoanalytic Association), 309 E. 49 St., New York, NY 10017 (SAN 224-4381) Tel 212-752-0450.

Am Psychol, (American Psychological Assn.; 0-912704), 1200 17th St., NW, Washington, DC 20036 (SAN 202-4705) Tel 202-955-7600; Orders to: P.O. Box 2710, Hyattsville, MD 20784 (SAN 685-3137) Tel 703-247-7705.

Am Pub, (American Pub.; 0-916036), P.O. Box 102, Oxford, IN 47971 (SAN 207-7019).

Am Pub Co WI
See Diversified Ind

†**Am Pub Health,** (American Public Health Assn. Pubns.; 0-87553), 1015 15th St., NW, Washington, DC 20005 (SAN 202-4713) Tel 202-789-5660; CIP.

Am Pub Today, (American Publishing Today, Inc.; 0-911975), P.O. Box 31059, Sarasota, FL 33582 (SAN 264-6501) Tel 813-377-2048.

Am Pub Welfare, (American Public Welfare Assn.; 0-910106), 1125 15th St., NW, Washington, DC 20005 (SAN 202-4721) Tel 202-293-7550.

Am Public Works, (American Public Works Assn.; 0-917084), 1313 E. 60th St., Chicago, IL 60637 (SAN 208-130X) Tel 312-667-2200.

Am Qtr Horse, (American Quarter Horse Assn.), P.O. Box 200, Amarillo, TX 79168 (SAN 225-0306) Tel 806-376-4811.

Am Quality, (American Quality Bks.; 0-936956), 1775 SE Columbia Dr., No. 238, Richland, WA 99352 (SAN 214-2821) Tel 509-783-7976.

Am Quaternary Assn, (American Quaternary Assn.), Illinois State Museum, Springfield, IL 62706 (SAN 225-2198) Tel 313-764-1473.

Am Quilt, (American Quilt Study Group; 0-9606590), 105 Molino Ave., Mill Valley, CA 94941 (SAN 219-6867) Tel 415-388-1382.

Am Rabbit Breeders, (American Rabbit Breeders Association, Inc.), 1925 S. Main, Bloomington, IL 61701 (SAN 225-056X) Tel 309-827-6623.

Am Radio, (American Radio Relay League, Inc.; 0-87259), 225 Main St., Newington, CT 06111 (SAN 202-473X) Tel 203-666-1541.

Am Record, (American Record Collectors Exchange; 0-914652), P.O. Box 1377, F.D.R. Sta., New York, NY 10022 (SAN 201-1689) Tel 212-688-8426.

Am Reg Pro Entomologists, (American Registry of Professional Entomologists), 4603 Calvert Rd., P.O. Box AJ, College Park, MD 20740 (SAN 225-1698) Tel 301-864-1336.

Am Register
See Thomas Intl Pub

Am Rent Assn, (American Rental Assn.; 0-916487), 1900 19th St., Moline, IL 61265 (SAN 231-3987) Tel 309-764-2475.

†**Am Repr-Rivercity Pr,** (American Reprint Co./Rivercity Pr.; 0-89190), Dist. by: Amereon Ltd., P.O. Box 1200, Mattituck, NY 11952 (SAN 201-2413) Tel 516-298-5100; CIP.

†**Am Reprints,** (American Reprints Co.; 0-915706), 2200 Eldridge Ave., P.O. Box 6011, Bellingham, WA 98227 (SAN 207-5008) Tel 206-647-0107. Do not confuse us with American Reprint Co./Rivercity Pr., Mattituck, NY; CIP.

Am Resources, (American Resources Group, Ltd.; 0-913415), 127 N. Washington St., Carbondale, IL 62901 (SAN 285-8134) Tel 618-529-2741.

Am River Conser Coun, (American Rivers Conservation Council), 322 4th St., NE, Washington, DC 20002 (SAN 223-8829) Tel 202-547-6900.

Am Romanian, (American Romanian Academy of Arts & Sciences; 0-912131), 4310 Finley Ave., No. 6, Los Angeles, CA 90027 (SAN 211-2116) Tel 213-666-8379.

Am Scandinavian, (American-Scandinavian Foundation; 0-89067), 127 E. 73rd St., New York, NY 10021 (SAN 201-7075) Tel 212-879-9779; Orders to: Heritage Resource Ctr., P.O. Box 26305, Minneapolis, MN 55426 (SAN 201-7083).

Am Sch Astrol, (American School of Astrology), 21 Mellon Ave., West Orange, NJ 07052 (SAN 211-2868) Tel 201-731-2255.

†**Am Sch Athens,** (American School of Classical Studies at Athens; 0-87661), c/o Institute for Advanced Study, Princeton, NJ 08543-0631 (SAN 201-1697) Tel 609-734-8387; CIP.

†**Am Sch Health,** (American School Health Assn.; 0-917160), 1521 S. Water St., Kent, OH 44240 (SAN 208-5240) Tel 216-678-1601; P.O. Box 708, Kent, OH 44240 (SAN 662-7161); CIP.

†**Am Sch Orient Res,** (American Schls. of Oriental Research; 0-89757), P.O. Box HM, Duke Sta., Durham, NC 27706 (SAN 239-4057) Tel 219-269-2011; Dist. by: Eisenbrauns, P.O. Box 275, Winona Lake, IN 46590-0278 (SAN 213-4365) Tel 219-269-2011; CIP.

Am Sciences Pr, (American Sciences Pr., Inc.; 0-935950), 20 Cross Rd., Syracuse, NY 13224-2144 (SAN 213-8883).

Am Short Line, (American Short Line Railroad Assn.), 2000 Massachusetts Ave., NW, Washington, DC 20036 (SAN 267-2790) Tel 202-785-2250.

Am Showcase, (American Showcase, Inc.; 0-931144), 724 Fifth Ave., New York, NY 10019 (SAN 281-2681) Tel 212-245-0981; Dist. by: Watson Guptill Pubns., 1515 Broadway, New York, NY 10036 (SAN 282-5384).

Am Soc Abdominal Surg, (American Society of Abdominal Surgery), 675 Main St., Melrose, MA 02176 (SAN 224-2575) Tel 617-655-6102.

Am Soc Ad Anesthesia Dentistry, (American Society for Advancement of Anesthesia in Dentistry), 475 White Plains Rd., Eastchester, NY 10707 (SAN 225-4964) Tel 914-961-8136.

Am Soc Ag Eng, (American Society of Agricultural Engineers; 0-916150), 2950 Niles Rd., St. Joseph, MI 49085 (SAN 223-6087) Tel 616-429-0300.

†**Am Soc Agron,** (American Society of Agronomy; 0-89118), 677 S. Segoe Rd., Madison, WI 53711 (SAN 204-5060) Tel 608-273-8080; CIP.

Am Soc Appraisers, (American Society of Appraisers; 0-937828), P.O. Box 17265, Washington, DC 20041 (SAN 206-2194) Tel 703-620-3838.

Am Soc Assn Execs, (American Society of Assn. Executives; 0-88034), 1575 Eye St. NW, Washington, DC 20005 (SAN 224-8182) Tel 202-626-2723.

Am Soc Cine
See ASC Holding

†**Am Soc Civil Eng,** (American Society of Civil Engineers; 0-87262), 345 E. 47th St., New York, NY 10017 (SAN 204-7594) Tel 212-705-7538; Toll free: 800-548-2723; CIP.

†**Am Soc Clinical,** (American Society of Clinical Pathologists Pr.; 0-89189), Div. of American Society of Clinical Pathologists, Educational Products Div., 2100 W. Harrison St., Chicago, IL 60612 (SAN 207-9429) Tel 312-738-1336; Toll free: 800-621-4142 (Orders); Dist. by: Appleton-Century-Crofts, 25 Van Zant St., East Norwalk, CT 06855 (SAN 209-1488); CIP.

Am Soc Consult Phar, (American Society of Consultant Pharmacists; 0-934322), 2300 Ninth St., S., Arlington, VA 22204 (SAN 223-7350).

Am Soc Divorced Men
See Am Soc Separated

Am Soc Ed & Rel, (American Society for Education & Religion, Inc.; 0-942978), 29 Beaver Oak Ct., Baltimore, MD 21236 (SAN 240-334X) Tel 301-256-1349.

Am Soc Eng Ed, (American Society for Engineering Education; 0-87823), 11 Dupont Cir., Suite 200, Washington, DC 20036 (SAN 225-7831) Tel 202-293-7080.

Am Soc Hosp Pharm, (American Society of Hospital Pharmacists; 0-930530), 4630 Montgomery Ave., Bethesda, MD 20814 (SAN 204-5052) Tel 301-657-3000.

Symbols/Abbreviations

Amarta Pr, *(Amarta Pr.; 0-935100),* P.O. Box 202, West Franklin, NH 03235 (SAN 213-2761) Tel 603-934-2420.

Amaryllis Pr, *(Amaryllis Pr.; 0-89275; 0-943276),* 212 W. 79 St., New York, NY 10024 (SAN 201-4300) Tel 212-496-6460.

Amata Graphics, *(Amata Graphics; 0-931224),* P.O. Box 12313, Portland, OR 97212 (SAN 211-2094) Tel 503-231-8540.

Amateur Hockey Assn, *(Amateur Hockey Assn. of the U. S.),* 2997 Broadmoor Valley Rd., Colorado Springs, CO 80906 (SAN 224-5698) Tel 303-576-4900.

Amateur Radio, *(AROY, Inc.; 0-9615633),* P.O. Box 257, Malden, MO 63863 (SAN 696-0561) Tel 314-276-5476; 1012 E. Almar St., Malden, MO 63863 (SAN 696-5199).

Amaya Pub, *(Amaya Publishing Co.; 0-916949),* P.O. Box 227, Shiloh, NJ 08353 (SAN 655-5543) Tel 609-455-6637.

Amazing Even, *(Amazing Events Unlimited; 0-936237),* 459 Hamilton St., Suite 105, Palo Alto, CA 94301 (SAN 696-9380) Tel 415-327-3236.

AMB Pr, *(AMB Pr., Inc.; 0-913171),* P.O. Box 459, Riverside, PA 17868 (SAN 282-9460) Tel 717-286-5466.

Ambassador
See Gard & Co

Ambassador Pr, *(Ambassador Pr., Inc.; 0-935019),* P.O. Box 216, Edgemont, PA 19028-0216 (SAN 694-3977) Tel 215-356-1893; Orders to: Warehouse, 947 Plumsock Rd., Edgemont, PA 19028-0216 (SAN 696-0340).

Amber Co Pr, *(Amber Co. Pr.; 0-934965),* 2324 Prince St., Berkeley, CA 94705 (SAN 695-1112) Tel 415-549-2587.

Amber Pub, *(Amber Publishing Corp.; 0-916788),* 82 W. University, Alfred, NY 14802 (SAN 208-5178) Tel 212-736-2288.

Amberly Pubns, *(Amberly Pubns.; 0-9612334),* P.O. Box 4153, Chapel Hill, NC 27515-4153 (SAN 289-1018) Tel 919-493-6050.

Ambleside, *(Ambleside Publishers, Inc.; 0-913011),* 2122 E. Concorda Dr., Tempe, AZ 85282 (SAN 283-2887) Tel 602-967-3457.

AMDG Pr *Imprint of* Sugden

Amdulaine Pubns, *(Amdulaine Pubns., Inc.; 0-9615780),* 5800 One Perkins Pl. Dr., Suite 8A, Baton Rouge, LA 70808 (SAN 696-6691) Tel 504-769-0010.

Ameco, *(Ameco Publishing Corp.; 0-912146),* 220 E. Jericho Tpke., Mineola, NY 11501 (SAN 202-4799) Tel 516-741-5030.

Amelia, *(Amelia; 0-936545),* 329 E St., Bakersfield, CA 93304 (SAN 697-9920) Tel 805-323-4064.

Amen Pub, *(Amen Publishing Co.; 0-941204),* Box 3612, Arcadia, CA 91006 (SAN 217-3239) Tel 818-355-9336.

Amer Acad Advert SC
See Am Acad Advert

Amer Acad Ortho Surg, *(American Academy of Orthopaedic Surgeons; 0-89203),* 222 S. Prospect Ave., Park Ridge, IL 60068 (SAN 228-2097) Tel 312-823-7186.

Amer Artificial, *(American Assn. for Artificial Intelligence; 0-86576),* 445 Burgess Dr., Menlo Park, CA 94025 (SAN 679-1905) Tel 415-328-3123; Dist. by: Morgan Kaufman, Inc., 95 First St., Los Altos, CA 94022 (SAN 662-7668) Tel 415-941-4960.

Amer Bar Assn, *(American Bar Assn.; 0-89707),* 750 N. Lake Shore Dr., Chicago, IL 60611 (SAN 211-4798) Tel 312-988-5000; 1800 M St., NW, Washington, DC 20036 (SAN 668-968X) Tel 202-331-2200. *Imprints:* ABA Admin Law (Section of Administrative Law); ABA Antitrust (Section of Antitrust Law); ABA Bar Activities (Section of Bar Activities); ABA Bar Servs (Division of Bar Services); ABA Corp

Banking (Section of Corporation Banking & Business Law); ABA Crim Just (Section of Criminal Justice); ABA Econ Law (Section of Economics of Law Practice); ABA Endowment (American Bar Endowment); ABA Genl Prac (Section of General Practice); ABA Indiv Rts (Section of Individual Rights & Responsibilities); ABA Ins Neg (Section of Insurance Negligence & Compensation Law); ABA Intl Law (Section of International Law); ABA Jrnl (American Bar Association Journal); ABA Judicial Admin (Judicial Administration Division); ABA Labor (Section of Labor Relations Law); ABA Legal Ed (Section of Legal Education and Admissions to the Bar); ABA Litigation (Section of Litigation); ABA LSD (Law Student Division); ABA Natl Res (Section of Natural Resources Law); ABA Patent (Section of Patent, Trademark, & Copyright Law); ABA Prof Stds (Department of Professional Standards).(Dept. of Professional Standards); ABA Pub Contract (Section of Public Contract Law); ABA Pub Utility (Section of Public Utility Law); ABA Real Prop (Section of Real Property Probate & Trust Law); ABA Retirement (American Bar Retirement Association).(American Bar Retirement Assn.); ABA Sci Tech (Section of Science & Technology); ABA Tax (Section of Taxation); ABA Tort (Section of Tort & Insurance Practice Law); ABA Urban (Section of Urban, State, & Local Government Law). ABA Assist (Standing Committee on Legal Assistance for Military Personnel); ABA Environ (Special Committee on Environmental Law); ABA Title (Standing Committee on Lawyers Title Guaranty Funds); ABA Unauth (Standing Committee on Unauthorized Practice of Law); ABA Young Lawyers (Young Lawyers Section).

Amer Cancer Soc OR, *(American Cancer Society, Oregon Division; 0-9617128),* 0330 SW Curry St., Portland, OR 97201 (SAN 662-6750) Tel 503-295-6422.

Amer Christian Hist Inst, *(American Christian History Institute; 0-9616201),* 1093 Beechwood St., Camarillo, CA 93010 (SAN 658-3482).

Amer Classical, *(American Classical League, The; 0-939507),* Miami University, Oxford, OH 45056 (SAN 225-8358) Tel 513-529-3991.

Amer College, *(American College, The; 0-943590),* 270 Bryn Mawr Ave., Bryn Mawr, PA 19010 (SAN 240-5822) Tel 215-896-4544.

Amer Com E W Accord, *(American Committee on East-West Accord),* 109 11th St., SE, Washington, DC 20003 (SAN 235-7801) Tel 202-546-1700.

Amer Correct Officers, *(American Assn. of Correctional Officers),* 1474 Willow Ave., Des Plaines, IL 60016 (SAN 224-036X) Tel 312-751-6068.

Amer Due Process, *(Americans For Due Process, Inc.; 0-9617222),* P.O. Box 85, Woodhaven, NY 11421 (SAN 663-3862); 304 Bayville Rd., Locust Valley, NY 11560 (SAN 663-3870) Tel 516-671-7975.

Amer Econ Dev Council, *(American Economic Development Council; 0-9616567),* 4849 N. Scott St., Suite 10, Schiller Park, IL 60176 (SAN 225-8129) Tel 312-671-5646.

Amer Health Nutri, *(American Health & Nutrition, Inc.; 0-914851),* 262 Larkspur Plaza Dr., Larkspur, CA 94939 (SAN 289-0496) Tel 415-924-5702; Dist. by: New Leaf Distributing, The, 1020 White St. SW, Atlanta, GA 30310 (SAN 169-1449) Tel 404-755-2665.

Amer Hist Found, *(American Historical Foundation, The; 0-933489),* P.O. Box 6622, Richmond, VA 23230 (SAN 692-7386) Tel 804-353-1812.

Amer Immigration, *(American Immigration Control Foundation; 0-936247),* P.O. Box 525, Monterey, VA 24465 (SAN 697-3205) Tel 703-468-2022; 3 Water St., Monterey, VA 24465 (SAN 697-3213).

Amer Inst Bank, *(American Institute of Banking; 0-935183),* Affil. of ABA, 550 Kearny St., Suite 310, San Francisco, CA 94108 (SAN 696-9003) Tel 415-392-5286.

Amer Inst Chem, *(American Institute of Chemists, Inc.; 0-939293),* 7315 Wisconsin Ave., Bethesda, MD 20814 (SAN 232-6280) Tel 301-652-2447.

Amer Inst Mgnt, *(American Institute of Management; 0-935517),* 33 Market St., No. 46, Poughkeepsie, NY 12601 (SAN 696-074X) Tel 914-471-3240.

Amer Inst Small Bus, *(American Institute of Small Business; 0-939069),* 7515 Wayzata Blvd., Suite 201, Minneapolis, MN 55426 (SAN 662-9407) Tel 612-545-7001; Toll free: 800-328-2906.

Amer Motor, *(American Motor Logs; 0-936207),* 2099 LaCrosse Ave., St. Paul, MN 55119 (SAN 696-933X) Tel 612-735-1410.

Amer Oral Health Inst Pr, *(American Oral Health Institute Pr.; 0-936837),* P.O. Box 151528, Columbus, OH 43215-8528 (SAN 658-3296) Tel 614-447-0038; 3746 Granden Rd., Columbus, OH 43214 (SAN 658-330X).

Amer Orff, *(American Orff-Schulwerk Assn.),* 332 Gerard Ave., Elkins Park, PA 19117 (SAN 260-3519) Tel 215-635-2622; Orders to: P.O. Box 391089, Cleveland, OH 44139-1089 (SAN 661-938X).

Amer Pictures, *(American Pictures Foundation),* P.O. Box 2123, New York, NY 10009 (SAN 659-1957) Tel 212-614-0438.

Amer Practice Build, *(American Practice Builders; 0-939111),* 6725 Papermill Dr., Knoxville, TN 37919 Tel 615-584-0500.

Amer Scientific, *(American Scientific Corp.; 0-9617163),* 3250 Holly Way, Chula Vista, CA 92010 (SAN 662-9466) Tel 619-426-1280.

Amer Sec Bill, *(Americans for Second Bill of Rights; 0-936527),* P.O. Box 550, Sour Lake, TX 77659 (SAN 658-8239).

Amer Studies, *(American Studies Publishing Co.; 0-942738),* 19496 Sandcastle Ln., Huntington Beach, CA 92648 (SAN 240-1851) Tel 714-960-2117.

Amereon Ltd, *(Amereon, Ltd.; 0-88411; 0-89190; 0-8488),* P.O. Box 1200, Mattituck, NY 11952 (SAN 201-2413) Tel 516-298-5100.

American Ad Pr, *(American Advisory Pr., Inc.; 0-937387),* P.O. Box 57, Clearwater, FL 33517-0057 (SAN 658-991X) Tel 813-446-6840.

American Ap Tech, *(American Applied Technologies; 0-937425),* Div. of Erde International (U.S.A.), P.O. Box 25007, Phoenix, AZ 85002 (SAN 658-9952) Tel 602-285-1661; 3600 N. Sixth Ave., No. 16, Phoenix, AZ 85013 (SAN 658-9960).

American Demo, *(American Demographics; 0-936889),* P.O. Box 68, Ithaca, NY 14851 (SAN 658-4594) Tel 607-273-6343; 127 W. State St., Ithaca, NY 14851 (SAN 658-4608).

American Ent Pubns
See A E P

American Hispanist, *(American Hispanist, Inc.; 0-89217),* P.O. Box 64, Clear Creek, IN 47426 (SAN 209-3944).

American Hist, *(American Historic Homes; 0-9615481),* P.O. Box 336, Dana Point, CA 92629 (SAN 696-0731) Tel 714-496-7050.

American Imagery, *(American Imagery Institute; 0-9616350),* P.O. Box 13453, Milwaukee, WI 53213 (SAN 659-0039) Tel 414-781-4045; 4375 Meadow View E., Brookfield, WI 53005 (SAN 659-0047).

American Mueller, *(American V. Mueller; 0-937433),* 7280 N. Caldwell Ave., Chicago, IL 60648 (SAN 659-0063) Tel 312-774-6800.

American Music, *(American Music Conference; 0-918196),* 150 E. Huron St., Chicago, IL 60611 (SAN 209-3952) Tel 312-266-8670.

American Numismatic, *(American Numismatic Assn.; 0-89637),* 818 N. Cascade Ave., P.O. Box 2366, Colorado Springs, CO 80901-2366 (SAN 211-3481) Tel 303-632-2646; Toll free: 800-367-9723.

American Pr, *(American Pr.; 0-89641),* 520 Commonwealth Ave., Boston, MA 02215-2605 (SAN 210-7007) Tel 617-247-0022.

American Res, *(American Research Council; 0-8282),* Box 183, Rye, NY 10580 (SAN 658-6325).

American Scientist, *(American Scientist),* c/o Sigma Xi the Scientific Research Society, 345 Whitney Ave., New Haven, CT 06511 (SAN 275-357X).

†**American Studies Pr,** *(American Studies Pr., Inc.; 0-934996),* 13511 Palmwood Ln., Tampa, FL 33624 (SAN 213-2788) Tel 813-974-2857; *CIP.*

Americana *Imprint of* **Crown**

Americana Bks, *(Americana Books; 0-917902),* P.O. Box 481, Pinellas Park, FL 33565 (SAN 210-0282).

Americana Pr, *(Americana Pr.; 0-9616144),* 3516 Albemarle St., NW, Washington, DC 20008 (SAN 658-7550) Tel 202-362-8538.

Americana Pubns, *(Americana Pubns.; 0-935407),* 1121 Marion St., Manteca, CA 95336 (SAN 696-0790) Tel 209-823-7526; P.O. Box 1528, Manteca, CA 95336 (SAN 696-5210).

Americana Rev, *(Americana Review; 0-914166),* 10 Socha Ln., Scotia, NY 12302 (SAN 206-3220) Tel 518-399-6482.

Americanist, *(Americanist Pr.; 0-910120),* 1525 Shenkel Rd., Pottstown, PA 19464 (SAN 205-6003) Tel 215-323-5289.

Americans Energy Ind, *(Americans For Energy Independence; 0-934458),* 1629 K St. NW, Suite 302, Washington, DC 20006 (SAN 212-999X) Tel 202-466-2105.

Americas Found
See Spirit Am Day

Americas Watch *Imprint of* **Fund Free Expression**

Amerimark Inc, *(Amerimark, Inc.; 1-55537),* 740 N. Blue Pkwy., Suite 312, Midland Bank Bldg., Lee's Summit, MO 64063 (SAN 696-0839) Tel 816-525-5227.

Ames Pub Co, *(Ames Publishing Co.; 0-9615263),* 21172 Aspen Ave., Castro Valley, CA 94546 (SAN 695-1945) Tel 415-537-3250.

Amethyst, *(Amethyst; 0-912865),* 2800 Woodley Rd., N.W., No. 423, Washington, DC 20008 (SAN 265-377X) Tel 202-797-9707.

AMG Pubs, *(AMG Pubs.; 0-89957),* 6815 Shallowford Rd., Chattanooga, TN 37421 (SAN 211-3074).

Amhara Corp, *(Amhara Corp.; 0-917450),* 6990 S. 1700 E., Salt Lake City, UT 84121 (SAN 208-063X).

Amherst Coll
See Mead Art Mus

Amherst Coll Pr, *(Amherst College Pr.; 0-943184),* Amherst College, Amherst, MA 01002 (SAN 201-7008) Tel 413-542-2299.

Amherst Media, *(Amherst Media; 0-936262),* 418 Homecrest Dr., Amherst, NY 14226 (SAN 214-0950).

Amherst Podium, *(Amherst Podium Pr.; 0-9615133),* P.O. Box 64, Amherst, NY 14226 (SAN 694-2490).

Amherst Pr, *(Amherst Pr.),* P.O. Box 296, Amherst, WI 54406 (SAN 213-9820) Tel 715-824-5890.

AMI Pr, *(AMI International Pr.; 0-911988),* Mountain View Rd., Washington, NJ 07822 (SAN 213-6791) Tel 201-689-1700.

Amicus Pr, *(Amicus Pr.; 0-914861),* 4201 Underwood Rd., Baltimore, MD 21218 (SAN 289-0518) Tel 301-889-5056.

Amideast, *(Amideast; 0-913957),* 1100 17th St. NW, Suite 300, Washington, DC 20036 (SAN 286-7184) Tel 202-785-0022.

AMIGOS Biblio, *(AMIGOS Bibliographic Council; 0-938288),* 11300 N. Central Expressway, Suite 321, Dallas, TX 75243 (SAN 219-7596) Tel 214-750-6130.

Amis Pub, *(Ami's Publishing; 0-935131),* 13221 Valleyheart Dr., Sherman Oaks, CA 91423 (SAN 695-1953) Tel 818-784-6756; Orders to: P.O. Box 4306-P, North Hollywood, CA 91607 (SAN 662-345X).

Amish Men Pub, *(Amish Mennonite Pubns.; 0-935409),* 8117 Magnet Rd., Minerva, OH 44657 (SAN 696-0901) Tel 216-895-4721.

Amistad Brands, *(Amisted Brands, Inc.; 0-9610432),* 22 Division Ave., NE, Washington, DC 20019 (SAN 263-9165); Dist. by: Somba Bookstore, Capital Plaza, 3155 Main St., Hartford, CT 01614 (SAN 200-5441).

Amity Bks MO, *(Amity Books; 0-934864),* 1702 Magnolia, Liberty, MO 64048 (SAN 213-7216).

Amity Found, *(Amity Foundation; 0-9612716),* P.O. Box 11048, Eugene, OR 97440 (SAN 289-7210) Tel 503-683-5927.

Amity Hallmark, *(Amity Hallmark, Ltd.),* 40-09 149th Place, Flushing, NY 11354 (SAN 210-766X).

Amity Hous Inc, *(Amity House, Inc.; 0-916349),* 106 Newport Bridge Rd., Warwick, NY 10990 (SAN 295-1037) Tel 914-258-4078.

Amity Pub Co, *(Amity Publishing Co.; 0-934011),* P.O. Box 933, Allston, MA 02134 (SAN 692-7653) Tel 617-628-6816; Dist. by: Inland Book Co., 22 Hemingway Ave., P.O. Box 261, East Haven, CT 06512 (SAN 200-4151) Tel 203-467-4257.

Amity Pubns, *(Amity Publications; 0-943814),* 78688 Sears Rd., Cottage Grove, OR 97424 (SAN 285-6794).

AMJ Graffica, *(AMJ Graffica, Inc.; 0-935575),* P.O. Box 16552, St. Louis Park, MN 55416-0552 (SAN 696-4761) Tel 612-922-0746.

AMM, *(American Metal Market/Metalworking News; 0-910094),* Dist. by: Fairchild Pubns., Inc., 7 E. 12th St., New York, NY 10003 (SAN 201-470X) Tel 212-741-4280.

Ammie Enter, *(Ammie Enterprises; 0-932825),* P.O. Box 2132, Vista, CA 92083 (SAN 691-3008) Tel 619-758-4561.

Amnesty Intl USA, *(Amnesty International of the USA, Inc.; 0-939994),* Div. of Amnesty International, 304 W. 58th St., New York, NY 10024 (SAN 225-6266) Tel 212-582-4440; Toll free: 800-251-4000.

Amo Sino Bks, *(Amo-Sino Bks.; 0-9615160),* P.O. Box 10013, Newark, NJ 07101 (SAN 694-3861) Tel 201-787-6600.

AMOA, *(Amusement & Music Operators Assn.),* 111 E. Wacker Dr., Chicago, IL 60601 (SAN 230-0923) Tel 312-644-6610.

†**Amon Carter,** *(Amon Carter Museum of Western Art; 0-88360),* P.O. Box 2365, Fort Worth, TX 76113 (SAN 204-7608) Tel 817-738-1933; Dist. by: Univ. of Texas Pr., P.O. Box 7819, Austin, TX 78713 (SAN 212-9876) Tel 512-471-7233; *CIP.*

Amonics, *(Amonics; 0-918166),* 2530 Cypress Ave., Norman, OK 73069 (SAN 209-3707) Tel 405-321-8076.

AMORC, *(AMORC; 0-912057),* Div. of Supreme Grand Lodge of AMORC, Inc., Rosicrucian Order, Park Naglee, San Jose, CA 95191 (SAN 211-3864) Tel 408-287-9171.

Amory & Pugh, *(Amory & Pugh; 0-9607492),* 79 Raymond St., Cambridge, MA 02140 (SAN 238-0056).

Amoskeag Pr, *(Amoskeag Pr., Inc.),* P.O. Box 666, Hooksett, NH 03106 (SAN 208-2721) Tel 603-622-6626.

AMP
See NAVA Intl Comm

AMP Educ Servs, *(AMP Educational Services; 0-937429),* 18 Edstone Dr., Staten Island, NY 10301 (SAN 659-0004) Tel 718-390-1119.

AMPC *Imprint of* **Unipub**

Ampersand Pub, *(Ampersand Publishing; 0-9607234),* 3609 Mukilteo Blvd., Everett, WA 98203 (SAN 239-1546) Tel 206-353-7593.

Ampersand RI, *(Ampersand Pr.; 0-9604740; 0-935331),* Roger Williams College Creative Writing Program, Bristol, RI 02809 (SAN 216-2202) Tel 401-253-1040.

Amphibian Pubns, *(Amphibian Pubns.),* Three Bell St., Providence, RI 02909 (SAN 240-0812).

AMR Educ Sys, *(AMR Educational Systems; 1-55536),* 4825-C 140th Ave., N., Clearwater, FL 33520 (SAN 695-9458) Tel 813-539-6555.

AMR Pub Co, *(AMR Publishing Co.; 0-913698; 0-913599; 0-939971),* P.O. Box 3007, Arlington, WA 98223 (SAN 281-272X) Tel 206-659-6434; 3816 168th Pl., NE, Arlington, WA 98223.

Amrita Found, *(Amrita Foundation, Inc.; 0-937134),* P.O. Box 8080, Dallas, TX 75205 (SAN 284-9666) Tel 214-521-1072.

AMS *Imprint of* **Natural Hist**

AMS Kansas, *(AMS Publishing; 0-936869),* 31st & Louisiana, Lawrence, KS 66046 (SAN 699-8992) Tel 913-843-1199; P.O. Box 1, Rte. 6, Lawrence, KS 66046 (SAN 699-900X).

†**AMS Pr,** *(AMS Pr., Inc.; 0-404),* 56 E. 13th St., New York, NY 10003 (SAN 201-1743) Tel 212-777-4700; *CIP.*

AMSA *Imprint of* **Natural Hist**

Amsco Music *Imprint of* **Music Sales**

AMSCO Sch, *(AMSCO School Pubns., Inc.; 0-87720),* 315 Hudson St., New York, NY 10013 (SAN 201-1751) Tel 212-675-7000.

AMTF, *(Ascended Master Teaching Foundation; 0-939051),* 1439 Timber Hills Rd., Mount Shasta, CA 96067 (SAN 662-8680) Tel 916-926-4913.

Amulefi, *(Amulefi Publishing Co.; 0-936360),* 11 E. Utica St., Buffalo, NY 14209 (SAN 214-0969).

Amusement Pk Bks, *(Amusement Park Bks., Inc.; 0-935408),* 20925 Mastick Rd., Fairview Park, OH 44126 (SAN 222-7673) Tel 216-331-6429.

Amward Pubns, *(Amward Pubns., Inc.; 0-939676),* 824 National Press Bldg., Washington, DC 20045 (SAN 216-7131) Tel 202-628-6710.

Amys, *(Amy's; 0-9614581),* P.O. Box 1718, Fort Myers, FL 33902 (SAN 691-7585) Tel 813-334-6048; Dist. by: Spring Arbor Distributors, 10885 Textile Rd., Belleville, MI 48111 (SAN 158-9016) Tel 313-481-0900.

AN Inc, *(AN, Inc.; 0-9605316),* P.O. Box 81369, Corpus Christi, TX 78412 (SAN 214-0888).

An Inch Prods, *(An Inch at a Time Productions; 0-9613655),* P.O. Box 8133, Des Moines, IA 50306 (SAN 670-7556) Tel 515-274-1630.

†**ANA,** *(American Nurses Assn.),* 2420 Pershing Rd., Kansas City, MO 64108 (SAN 204-5176) Tel 816-474-5720; Toll free: 800-368-5643; *CIP.*

Ana-Doug Pub, *(Ana-Doug Publishing; 0-916946),* 424 W. Commonwealth, Fullerton, CA 92632 (SAN 208-4821) Tel 714-738-1655.

ANA Pleasanton, *(ANA of Pleasanton; 0-930673),* P.O. Box 5091, Pleasanton, CA 94566 (SAN 677-0584) Tel 415-658-3110.

Anacker Pub
See Ref Guide Bks

†**Anaheim Pub Co,** *(Anaheim Publishing Company, a Division of Wadsworth, Incorporated; 0-88236),* Subs. of International Thomson Organization, Inc., 10 Davis Dr., Belmont, CA 94002 (SAN 202-4802); Toll free: 800-831-6996; Orders to: Wadsworth, Inc., 7625 Empire Dr., Florence, KY 41042 (SAN 663-2858) Tel 606-525-2230; *CIP.*

Anais Nin Found, *(Anais Nin Foundation, The; 0-9611238),* P.O. Box 276, Becket, MA 01223 (SAN 283-068X) Tel 413-623-5170; Orders to: 2335 Hidalgo Ave., Los Angeles, CA 90039 (SAN 658-2338).

Anais Pr, *(Anais Pr.; 0-9608858),* P.O. Box 9635, Denver, CO 80209 (SAN 240-9976) Tel 303-778-0524.

Anal Psych SF
See Analyt Psych SF

Analog Devices, *(Analog Devices, Inc.; 0-916550),* 2 Technology Way, Norwood, MA 02062 (SAN 210-3389) Tel 617-461-3294; Orders to: P.O. Box 796, Norwood, MA 02062 (SAN 210-3397) Tel 617-461-3392.

Analysis, *(Analysis Pr.; 0-911894),* Subs. of Merrill Analysis, Inc., Box 228, Chappaqua, NY 10514 (SAN 210-9549) Tel 914-238-3641.

Analyt Psych SF, *(Analytical Psychology Club of San Francisco, Inc., The; 0-9611232),* 2411 Octavia St., San Francisco, CA 94109 (SAN 283-2461) Tel 415-524-9433; Orders to: Ivon der Hude, 615 Beloit Ave., Kensington, CA 94708 (SAN 662-751X) Tel 415-524-9433.

Analytech, *(Analytech Management Consulting; 0-9610932),* 15 Russell Rd., Alexandria, VA 22301 (SAN 265-1734) Tel 703-836-7830.

Analytic Invest, *(Analytic Investment Management, Inc.; 0-9606348),* 2222 Martin St., No. 230, Irvine, CA 92715 (SAN 210-8844) Tel 714-833-0294.

†**Analytic Pr,** *(Analytic Pr., The; 0-88163),* 365 Broadway, Suite 102, Hillsdale, NJ 07642 (SAN 267-5455) Tel 201-666-4110; Dist. by: Lawrence Erlbaum Associates, Inc., 365 Broadway, Hillsdale, NJ 07642 (SAN 213-960X) Tel 201-666-4110; *CIP.*

Analytic Psych, *(Analytical Psychology Club of Los Angeles; 0-9600936),* 10349 W. Pico Blvd., Los Angeles, CA 90064 (SAN 223-663X) Tel 213-556-1193; Orders to: C.J. Jung Institute, 10349 W. Pico Blvd., Los Angeles, CA 90064 (SAN 200-464X).

19

Analytical Psych, (Analytical Psychology Club of New York, Inc., The), 28 E. 39th St., New York, NY 10016 (SAN 267-5463) Tel 212-697-7877.

Analytichem, (Analytichem International, Inc.; 0-9616096), 24201 Frampton Ave., Harbor City, CA 90710 (SAN 698-1186) Tel 213-539-6490.

Ananda, (Ananda Pubns.; 0-916124), 14618 Tyler Foote Rd., Nevada City, CA 95959 (SAN 201-1778) Tel 916-292-3482.

Ananda Marga, (Ananda Marga Pubns.; 0-88476), 854 Pearl St., Denver, CO 80203 (SAN 206-3239) Tel 303-832-6465.

Ananse Pr, (Ananse Pr.; 0-9605670), P.O. Box 22565, Seattle, WA 98122 (SAN 216-3292) Tel 206-325-8205.

Anapauo Farm, (Anapauo Farm, Inc.; 0-9616899), Star Rte., P.O. Box 1BC, Lakemont, GA 30552 (SAN 661-4922) Tel 404-782-6442.

Anatomical Chart, (Anatomical Chart Co.; 0-9603730), 7124 N. Clark St., Chicago, IL 60626 (SAN 223-5315).

Ancestral Hist, (Ancestral Historian Society; 0-939774), Postal Unit 529, Evans, GA 30809 (SAN 216-8774) Tel 404-863-2863.

Ancestry, (Ancestry Inc.; 0-916489), 350 S. 400 East, Suite 110, Salt Lake City, UT 84111 (SAN 687-6528) Tel 801-531-1790; Toll free: 800-531-1790 (Orders only); Orders to: P.O. Box 476, Salt Lake City, UT 84110 (SAN 662-7706).

Anch Imprint of **Doubleday**

Anchor & Acorn, (Anchor & Acorn Pr.; 0-936931), 15 Kent St., Petaluma, CA 94952 (SAN 658-6872) Tel 707-762-0510.

Anchor & Dolphin, (Anchor & Dolphin Publishing Co., The; 0-9615944), 435 N. Seventh St., Allentown, PA 18102 (SAN 696-9852) Tel 215-821-7913.

Anchor Comm, (Anchor Communications; 0-935633), Div. of Imagination Unlimited, 110 Quince Ave., Highland Springs, VA 23075 (SAN 696-0944) Tel 804-737-4498; P.O. Box 70, Highland Springs, VA 23075 (SAN 696-5229).

Anchor Found, (Anchor Foundation, Inc., The; 0-913460; 0-937091), Dist. by: Pathfinder Press, 410 West St., New York, NY 10014 (SAN 202-5906) Tel 212-741-0690.

Anchor Pr Imprint of **Doubleday**

Anchorage, (Anchorage Pr.; 0-87602), P.O. Box 8067, New Orleans, LA 70182 (SAN 203-4727) Tel 504-283-8868.

Ancient City Pr, (Ancient City Pr.; 0-941270), P.O. Box 5401, Santa Fe, NM 87502 (SAN 164-5552) Tel 505-982-8195.

ANCLA Prods, (ANCLA Productions; 0-9612202), 7903 Randy Rd., Rockford, IL 61103 (SAN 289-1042) Tel 815-633-3840.

And Bks, (And Bks.; 0-89708), 702 S. Michigan, Suite 836, South Bend, IN 46618 (SAN 213-9502) Tel 219-232-3134; Dist. by: The Distributors, 702 S. Michigan, South Bend, IN 46618 (SAN 169-2488) Tel 219-232-8500.

†**And-Or Pr,** (And/Or Pr., Inc.; 0-915904), P.O. Box 2246, Berkeley, CA 94702 (SAN 206-9458) Tel 415-548-2124; CIP.

And-or Pr
See **And-Or Pr**

Andante Pub, (Andante Pubs.; 0-940038), 1812 E. 32nd St., Brooklyn, NY 11234 (SAN 220-1992) Tel 718-336-9490.

Andent Inc, (Andent, Inc.; 0-914555), 1000 North Ave., Waukegan, IL 60085 (SAN 291-8560) Tel 312-223-5077.

Anderson
See **Stretching Inc**

Anderson & Daughters, (Anderson & Daughters; 0-9615338), P.O. Box 2008, Beverly Hills, CA 90213 (SAN 695-1120) Tel 213-456-9696.

Anderson Comm
See **Armedia Con**

Anderson Gal, (Anderson Gallery; 0-935519), Div. of Virginia Commonwealth Univ., 907 1/2 W. Franklin St., Richmond, VA 23284 (SAN 277-982X) Tel 804-257-1522.

Anderson Hse Mus, (Anderson House Museum of the Society of the Cincinnati), 2118 Massachusetts Ave., NW, Washington, DC 20008 (SAN 277-9838) Tel 202-785-0540.

Anderson Kramer, (Anderson Kramer Associates, Inc.; 0-910136), Affil. of Siancy Kramer Books, Inc., 1722 H St., NW, Washington, DC 20006 (SAN 203-4735) Tel 202-298-8015.

†**Anderson MI,** (Anderson Pubns.; 0-9610088), Box 423, Davison, MI 48423 (SAN 267-5633) Tel 313-653-0984; CIP.

Anderson Negotiations, (Anderson Negotiations/Communications; 0-938515), 1295 Monterey Blvd., San Francisco, CA 94127 (SAN 661-1176) Tel 415-834-6610.

†**Anderson Pub Co,** (Anderson Publishing Co.; 0-87084), P.O. Box 1576, Cincinnati, OH 45201 (SAN 208-2799); Toll free: 800-543-0883; 646 Main St., Cincinnati, OH 45202 (SAN 661-9436) Tel 513-421-4393; CIP.

Anderson Publ, (Anderson Publishing; 0-9602128), P.O. Box 1751, Naples, FL 33939 (SAN 209-5238) Tel 813-262-5592.

Anderson R, (Anderson, Robert D., Publishing Co.; 0-942028), P.O. Box 22324, Sacramento, CA 95822 (SAN 238-4434) Tel 916-369-0223; Toll free: 800-222-3030; 9323 Tech Center Dr., Suite 1700, Sacramento, CA 95826 (SAN 661-9428).

Anderson World, (Anderson World, Inc.; 0-89037), 1400 Stierlin Rd., Mountain View, CA 94043 (SAN 281-2754) Tel 415-965-8777; Toll free: 800-257-5755; Orders to: P.O. Box 366, Mountain View, CA 94042 (SAN 281-2762).

Andersons Pubns, (Anderson's Pubns.; 0-931353), P.O. Box 11338, Santa Rosa, CA 95406 (SAN 693-7829) Tel 707-575-1280.

Andesign, (Andesign; 0-9615556), 3925 Edenborn Ave., Metairie, LA 70002 (SAN 696-4826) Tel 504-455-1210.

Andor Pub, (Andor Publishing Co., Inc.; 0-89319), P.O. Box 19, Wilton, CT 06897-0019 (SAN 208-5267). Out of business.

Andover MA
See **Town of Andover MA**

†**Andover Pr,** (Andover Press; 0-939014), 516 W. 34th St., New York, NY 10001 (SAN 216-1001); CIP.

Andre Deutsch, (Deutsch, Andre; 0-233), c/o E. P. Dutton, 2 Park Ave., New York, NY 10016 (SAN 201-0070) Tel 212-725-1818; Orders to: New American Library, P.O. Box 120, Bergenfield, NJ 07261 (SAN 661-9444) Tel 201-387-0600.

Andre's & Co, (Andre's & Co.; 0-936264), 289 Varick St., Jersey City, NJ 07302 (SAN 214-0977).

†**Andrew Mtn Pr,** (Andrew Mountain Pr.; 0-9603840; 0-916897), 81 Allendale Rd., Hartford, CT 06114 (SAN 213-7232) Tel 203-549-6723; P.O. Box 14353, Hartford, CT 06114 (SAN 658-0130); CIP.

Andrews & McMeel
See **Andrews McMeel Parker**

†**Andrews McMeel Parker,** (Andrews, McMeel & Parker; 0-8362), Subs. of Universal Press Syndicate, 4900 Main St., Kansas City, MO 64112 (SAN 202-540X) Tel 816-932-6700; Toll free: 800-826-4216; CIP. Imprints: Search (Search Books).

Andrews Univ Pr, (Andrews Univ. Pr.; 0-943872), Berrien Springs, MI 49104 (SAN 241-0958) Tel 616-471-3392.

Andrion Bks, (Andrion Bks.; 0-933773; 0-9606826), 230 Park Ave., Suite 1624, New York, NY 10169 (SAN 692-770X) Tel 212-986-5842.

Andromeda, (Andromeda Pr.; 0-9602996), 111 E. Platt, Maquoketa, IA 52060 (SAN 213-0017).

Andujar Comn Tech, (Andujar Communication Technologies, Inc.; 0-938086), 7720A Herschel Ave., P.O. Box 2622, La Jolla, CA 92037 (SAN 663-5326).

Anechron Three Pr Imprint of **First Intl Pub**

Anemone Edns, (Anemone Editions, Ltd.; 0-9604818), P.O. Box 6056, Carmel, CA 93921 (SAN 216-0161).

Angel City, (Angel City Books; 0-9605416), 8033 Sunset Blvd., No. 366, Hollywood, CA 90046 (SAN 216-0951).

Angel Pr, (Angel Pr. Pubs.; 0-912216), 561 Tyler St., Monterey, CA 93940 (SAN 205-3330) Tel 408-372-1658.

Angel Pubns, (Angel Press Publications; 0-9612324), P.O. Box 1431, Travis AFB, CA 94535 (SAN 289-1085) Tel 707-447-3374; Orders to: Angel Press, P.O. Box 1072, Mt Angel, OR 97362 (SAN 688-4164) Tel 503-845-2569.

Angelica Pr, (Angelica Pr., The; 0-9617261), 142 W. 24th St., 12th flr., New York, NY 10011 (SAN 663-5709) Tel 212-255-5155.

Angels Easter, (Angels of Easter Seal; 0-9613501), 4177 Fairway Dr., Canfield, OH 44406 (SAN 657-8306) Tel 216-533-6353; 299 Edwards St., Youngstown, OH 44502 (SAN 662-2402) Tel 216-743-1168.

Angers Pub, (Angers Publishing Corp.; 0-939524), Box H.H., Lafayette, LA 70502 (SAN 216-6542) Tel 318-981-0859.

Angriff Pr, (Angriff Pr.; 0-913022), P.O. Box 2726, Hollywood, CA 90078 (SAN 203-4743) Tel 213-386-9826.

Angst World, (Angst World Library; 0-914580), 1160 Forest Creek Rd., Selma, OR 97538 (SAN 201-1786).

Angus Cupar, (Angus Cupar Publishers; 0-9612524), 117 Hunt Dr., Princeton, NJ 08540 (SAN 287-7848) Tel 609-924-3358.

Angus Downs, (Downs, Angus, Ltd.; 0-910053), 4101 Lake Ridge Dr., Holland, MI 49423 (SAN 241-2950) Tel 616-399-1813.

Anhinga Pr, (Anhinga Pr.; 0-938078), Apalachee Poetry Ctr., P.O. Box 10423, Tallahassee, FL 32302 (SAN 216-0943).

Anima Bks Imprint of **Anima Pubns**
Anima Books
See **Anima Pubns**

†**Anima Pubns,** (Anima Pubns.; 0-89012), Div. of Conococheague Associates, Inc., 1053 Wilson Ave., Chambersburg, PA 17201 (SAN 281-2770) Tel 717-263-8303; CIP. Imprints: Anima Bks (Anima Books).

Animal Cracker, (Animal Cracker Pr.), R 6, Box 329, Bemidji, MN 56601 (SAN 210-9123).

Animal Owners, (Animal Owners Motivation Programs; 0-9604576), P.O. Box 16,, Frankfort, IL 60423 (SAN 215-1294) Tel 815-469-2284.

Animal Prot Inst, (Animal Protection Institute of America), P.O. Box 22505, 5894 S. Land Park Dr., Sacramento, CA 95822 (SAN 225-8951) Tel 916-422-1921.

Animal Stories, (Animal Stories; 0-9616202), 16783 Beach Blvd., Huntington Beach, CA 92647 (SAN 692-7327) Tel 213-322-5495.

Animal Welfare, (Animal Welfare Institute), P.O. Box 3650, Washington, DC 20007 (SAN 201-7156) Tel 202-337-2333.

Anirt Pr, (Anirt Pr.; 0-9605878), 15707 Eastwood Ave., Lawndale, CA 90260 (SAN 216-6550) Tel 213-678-9753.

Anma Libri, (Anma Libri; 0-915838), P.O. Box 876, Saratoga, CA 95071 (SAN 212-5889) Tel 415-851-3375.

Ann Arbor Bk, (Ann Arbor Bk. Co.; 0-932364), P.O. Box 8064, Ann Arbor, MI 48107 (SAN 212-0712).

Ann Arbor FL, (Ann Arbor Pubs.; 0-89039), P.O. Box 7249, Naples, FL 33940 (SAN 213-8271) Tel 813-775-3528.

Anna Olswanger, (Olswanger, Anna; 0-9614598), 177 N. Highland, No. 909, Memphis, TN 38111 (SAN 691-7593) Tel 901-327-4341.

Anna Pub, (Anna Publishing, Inc.; 0-89305), P.O. Box 218, Eight S. Bluford Ave., Ocoee, FL 32761 (SAN 281-2789) Tel 305-656-6998.

Annand Ent, (Annand Enterprises, Inc.), Ball Hill Rd., Milford, NH 03055 (SAN 240-9666).

Annandale-Intl, (Annandale-International; 0-9602562), Box 384, Bronx, NY 10472 (SAN 212-8470) Tel 212-292-8067.

†**Annual Reviews,** (Annual Reviews, Inc.; 0-8243), P.O. Box 10139, Palo Alto, CA 94303-0897 (SAN 201-1816) Tel 415-493-4400; Toll free: 800-523-8635; P.O Box 1039, Palo Alto, CA 94303-0897 (SAN 658-0149); CIP.

Annuals Pub Co, (Annuals Publishing Co.; 0-912417), 10 E. 23rd St., New York, NY 10010 (SAN 265-1742) Tel 212-475-1620; Dist. by: Robert Silver Assocs., 307 E. 37th St., New York, NY 10016 (SAN 241-5801) Tel 212-686-5630.

Another Chicago Pr, (Another Chicago Pr.; 0-9614644), P.O. Box 11223, Chicago, IL 60611 (SAN 691-8468) Tel 312-248-7665.

Symbols/Abbreviations

†**Appalach Consortium,** *(Appalachian Consortium Pr.; 0-913239),* Div. of Appalachian Consortium, Inc., Appalachian State Univ., University Hall, Boone, NC 28608 (SAN 285-8150) Tel 704-262-2064; *CIP.*

†**Appalach Mtn,** *(Appalachian Mountain Club Bks.; 0-910146),* 5 Joy St., Boston, MA 02108 (SAN 203-4808) Tel 617-523-0636; *CIP.*

Appalachian Background
See Appalach Bkground

Appalachian Bks, *(Appalachian Bks.; 0-912660),* P.O. Box 249, Oakton, VA 22124 (SAN 204-5524) Tel 703-281-2464.

Appalachian Consort Pr
See Appalach Consortium

†**Appel,** *(Appel, Paul P., Pub.; 0-911858),* 216 Washington St., Mt. Vernon, NY 10553 (SAN 202-3253) Tel 914-667-7365; *CIP.*

Appl Concepts, *(Applied Concepts; 0-930011),* 5430 S. 12th Ave., Suite C, Tucson, AZ 85706 (SAN 669-7186) Tel 602-294-1188.

Applause Pub, *(Applause Pubs.),* P.O. Box 441, Naples, FL 33939-0441 (SAN 692-3941).

Applause Pubns, *(Applause Pubns.; 0-932352),* 2234 S. Shady Hills Dr., Diamond Bar, CA 91765 (SAN 211-8807).

Applause Theater Bk Pubs, *(Applause Theater Bk. Pubs.; 0-936839),* 211 W. 71st St., New York, NY 10023 (SAN 658-3245) Tel 212-595-4735; Dist. by: Harper & Row, Keystone Industrial Pk., Scranton, PA 18512 (SAN 215-3742).

Apple
See Apple Comp

Apple Bks
See Apple Pie Bks

Apple Comp, *(Apple Computer, Inc.; 0-9609780),* 20525 Mariani Ave., Mail Stop 23-AX, Cupertino, CA 95014 (SAN 267-6044) Tel 408-996-1010.

Apple-Gems, *(Apple-Gems; 0-9602122),* P.O. Box 16292, San Francisco, CA 94116 (SAN 212-4769) Tel 415-587-9752.

Apple Hut, *(Apple Hut Publishing Co.; 0-931148),* 1047 Park Hill Dr., P.O. Box 2704, Escondido, CA 92025 (SAN 211-2159) Tel 619-741-3565. Out of business.

Apple Paperbacks *Imprint of* **Scholastic Inc**

Apple Pie Bks, *(Apple Pie Bks.; 0-934207),* 2740 Greenwich No. 416, San Francisco, CA 94123 (SAN 693-1243) Tel 415-921-4471. Do not confuse with Apple Pie Publishing, of Englewood, CO.

Apple Pie Pub Co, *(Apple Pie Publishing Co.; 0-911149),* 7521 E. Costilla Ave., Englewood, CO 80112 (SAN 267-6052) Tel 303-770-1784.

Apple Pr, *(Apple Pr.; 0-9602238),* 5536 SE Harlow, Milwaukie, OR 97222 (SAN 212-8489) Tel 503-659-2475.

Apple Pr Pub, *(Apple Pr. Publishing; 0-9615833),* 6975 SW Sandburg Rd., Portland, OR 97223 (SAN 697-2713) Tel 503-684-3398.

Apple Pub Co, *(Apple Publishing Co.; 0-9604134),* Box 624 Grand Central Station, New York, NY 10163 (SAN 215-0549).

Apple Pub Wisc, *(Apple Publishing Co.; 0-937891),* Subs. of Educational Assessment Service, Inc., W. 6050 Apple Rd., Watertown, WI 53094 (SAN 659-4123) Tel 414-261-1118.

†**Apple Tree,** *(Apple Tree Pr., Inc.; 0-913082),* P.O. Box 1012, Flint, MI 48501 (SAN 206-7366) Tel 313-234-5451; *CIP.*

Apple Tree Ln, *(Apple Tree Lane; 0-9601602),* 801 La Honda Rd., Woodside, CA 94062 (SAN 211-7177).

Apple Wood, *(Apple-Wood Bks.; 0-918222),* Box 2870, Cambridge, MA 02139 (SAN 210-3419) Tel 617-350-0311; Dist. by: Arbor House Publishing Co., 235 E. 45th St., New York, NY 10017 (SAN 201-1522) Tel 212-599-3131.

Applegate Comp Ent, *(Applegate Computer Enterprises),* 470 Slagle Creek, Grants Pass, OR 97527 (SAN 285-6840).

Appleseeds, *(Appleseeds; 0-9608944),* 4508 W. Ponds View Dr., Littleton, CO 80123 (SAN 240-9674).

Appleton
See Appleton & Lange

†**Appleton & Lange,** *(Appleton & Lange; 0-8385),* Subs. of Simon & Schuster, A Gulf & Western Co., 25 Van Zant St., East Norwalk, CT 06855 (SAN 209-1488) Tel 203-838-4400; Toll free: 800-826-2618; Drawer L, Los Altos, CA 94022 (SAN 663-2866); Orders to: Appleton & Lange, 25 Van Zant St., East Norwalk, CT 06855 (SAN 209-1488) Dist. by: Prentice-Hall, Inc., Englewood Cliffs, NJ 07632 (SAN 200-2175) Tel 201-592-2000; *CIP.*

Appleton-Century-Crofts *Imprint of* **P-H**

Appleton Davies, *(Appleton Davies, Inc.; 0-941022),* 32 S. Raymond Ave., Suite 10, Pasadena, CA 91105 (SAN 217-3255) Tel 818-792-3046.

Appletree Pr, *(Appletree Pr.; 0-9611956),* 5903 Highland Pass, Austin, TX 78731 (SAN 286-7354) Tel 512-459-0606.

Applewhite, *(Applewhite, Karen Miller; 0-9603472),* 5942 E. Sage Dr., Scottsdale, AZ 85253 (SAN 213-6074) Tel 602-941-4753.

Appleyard Agency, *(Appleyard, John, Agency, Inc.),* Box 1902, Pensacola, FL 32589 (SAN 211-2167) Tel 904-432-8396.

†**Applezaba,** *(Applezaba Pr.; 0-930090),* P.O. Box 4134, Long Beach, CA 90804 (SAN 210-7023) Tel 213-591-0015; *CIP.*

Application Eng Corp, *(Application Engineering Corp.; 0-910447),* 850 Pratt Blvd.,, Elk Grove Village, IL 60007 (SAN 260-0145) Tel 312-593-5000.

Applied Arts, *(Applied Arts Pubs.; 0-911410),* Div. of Sowers Printing Co., Box 479, Lebanon, PA 17042 (SAN 204-4838) Tel 717-272-9442.

Applied Innovations, *(Applied Innovations; 0-938831),* 2515 39th Ave., SW, Seattle, WA 98116 (SAN 661-7018) Tel 206-937-1626.

Applied Press, *(Applied Pressure Techniques, Wm. J. Bales; 0-9600560),* P.O. Box 12248, Phoenix, AZ 85002 (SAN 205-1532).

Applied Pub, *(Applied Publishing Ltd.; 0-915834),* P.O. Box 261, Wilmette, IL 60091 (SAN 207-608X).

Applied Pub MN, *(Applied Publishing; 0-935679),* Div. of Applied Software, Inc., 3402 Columbus Ave., S., Suite 225, Minneapolis, MN 55407 (SAN 696-0979) Tel 612-822-1998.

Applied Sci Pubns, *(Applied Science Publications, Inc.; 0-915061),* P.O. Box 5399 Grand Central Station, New York, NY 10163 (SAN 670-7165) Tel 212-756-6440.

Applied Sys Inst, *(Applied Systems Institute, Inc.; 0-935731),* 1910 K St., NW, Suite 600, Washington, DC 20006 (SAN 696-1037) Tel 202-785-0920.

Applied Therapeutics, *(Applied Therapeutics, Inc.; 0-915486),* P.O. Box 1903, Spokane, WA 99210 (SAN 212-2057) Tel 509-534-5713.

Apprentices, *(Apprentices of Perception Pr.; 0-9608792),* P.O. Box 3084, Berkeley, CA 94703 (SAN 240-9984). Moved, left no forwarding address.

Appropriate Techn Proj, *(Appropriate Technology Project, Volunteers in Asia, Inc.; 0-917704; 0-8048),* P.O. Box 4543 (Rm 5, Clubhouse, Old Union, Stanford Univ.), Stanford, CA 94305 (SAN 210-9638) Tel 415-497-3228.

April Enterp, *(April Enterprises, Inc.; 0-9608772),* 14136 Janna Way, Sylmar, CA 91342 (SAN 238-2385) Tel 818-367-1666.

April Hill, *(April Hill Pubs.; 0-917780),* 79 Elm St., Springfield, VT 05156 (SAN 213-6554) Tel 802-885-3151.

April Pub, *(April Publishing; 0-939122),* P.O. Box 480000, Los Angeles, CA 90048 (SAN 238-0048).

APSA, *(APSA),* P.O. Box 5503, Washington, DC 20016 (SAN 212-4009).

Apt Bks, *(Apt Bks, Inc. A; 0-86590),* 141 E. 44th St., Suite 511, New York, NY 10017 (SAN 215-7209) Tel 212-697-0887.

Aptitude Inventory, *(Aptitude Inventory Measurement Service; 0-9602710),* 2506 McKinney Ave., Suite B, Dallas, TX 75201 (SAN 215-6202).

Aptos Pub, *(Aptos Publishing Co.; 0-938187),* P.O. Box 2278, Aptos, CA 95001 (SAN 659-7246); 106 San Benito Ave., Aptos, CA 95003 (SAN 659-7254) Tel 408-688-0280.

Aqua Educ, *(Aquarian Educational Group; 0-911794),* P.O. Box 267, Sedona, AZ 86336 (SAN 203-4816) Tel 602-282-2655.

Aqua Explorers, *(Aqua Explorers, Inc.; 0-9616167),* 22 Maiden Ln., Lynbrook, NY 11563 (SAN 699-9050) Tel 516-596-0482.

Aquarelle Pr, *(Aquarelle Pr.; 0-9616679),* P.O. Box 3676, Baton Rouge, LA 70808 (SAN 659-7270); 5036 Hyacinth Ave., Baton Rouge, LA 70808 (SAN 659-7289) Tel 504-926-4220; Dist. by: F & W Pubns., Inc., 9933 Alliance Rd., Cincinnati, OH 45242 (SAN 287-0274) Tel 513-984-0717.

Aquari Corp, *(Aquari Corp.; 0-916204),* P.O. Box 2008, Rose City, MI 48654 (SAN 207-9917) Tel 517-685-2086.

Aquarian Bk Pubs, *(Aquarian Book Pubs.; 0-9605126),* 7011 Hammond Ave., Dallas, TX 75223 (SAN 216-096X) Tel 214-328-5144.

Aquarian League, *(Aquarian League, The; 0-931607),* P.O. Box 537, Louisville, KY 40201 (SAN 683-6747).

Aquarian Pr
See Bonnie Prudden

Aquarian Res, *(Aquarian Research Foundation; 0-916726),* 5620 Morton St., Philadelphia, PA 19144 (SAN 208-5305) Tel 215-849-3237; Dist. by: Bookpeople, 2929 Fifth St., Berkeley, CA 94710 (SAN 168-9517) Tel 415-549-3030.

Aquarius, *(Aquarius Enterprises; 0-941200),* 53 Central Ave. 15, Wailuku, Maui, HI 96793 (SAN 203-4824) Tel 808-244-7347.

AQUARIUS, *(AQUARIUS Enterprises; 0-922051),* 801 Harbor Dr., Suite A, Forked River, NJ 08731 (SAN 286-4304) Tel 609-693-0513.

Aquarius Rising Pr, *(Aquarius Rising Pr.; 0-933883),* 2035 S. State, P.O. Box 16438, Chicago, IL 60616 (SAN 692-6622) Tel 312-337-1607.

Aquatic Adv Pubns, *(Aquatic Adventure Pubns.; 0-9616150),* P.O. Box 60494, Palo Alto, CA 94306 (SAN 699-8712) Tel 415-856-2363.

Aquatic Spec, *(Aquatic Specialists; 0-912867),* 3405 E. Redbud Dr., Knoxville, TN 37920 (SAN 282-972X).

Aquilevie, *(Aquilevie; 0-9616035),* P.O. Box 231, Hopkins Park, IL 60944 (SAN 698-0406) Tel 815-944-5416; R.R. 4, Box 499, St. Anne, IL 60964 (SAN 698-2441).

Aquin Pub, *(Aquin Publishing Co.; 0-915352),* 4412 Laurelgrove Ave., Studio City, CA 91604 (SAN 203-4085) Tel 213-508-7169.

AR Commemorative, *(Arkansas Commemorative Commission, Trapnall Hall; 0-9606278),* 300 W. Markham, Little Rock, AR 72201 (SAN 223-2111) Tel 501-371-1749.

AR Legis Digest, *(Arkansas Legislative Digest, Inc.; 0-935765),* 500 E. Markham, No. 219, Little Rock, AR 72201 (SAN 695-8362) Tel 501-376-2843.

AR Symphony Orch, *(Arkansas Symphony Orchestra Society Guild; 0-9615625),* P.O. Box 7328, Little Rock, AR 72217 (SAN 696-1150) Tel 501-666-1761.

ARA, *(Administrative Research Associates; 0-910022),* Irvine Town Ctr., Box 4211, Irvine, CA 92716 (SAN 201-1891) Tel 714-499-3939.

Arab Petro Res, *(Arab Petroleum Research Inst.; 0-913177),* P.O. Box 535, Shelburne, VT 05482 (SAN 282-9584) Tel 802-985-3851.

Arachnes Muse, *(Arachne's Muse Foundation, The; 0-9611940),* 57 Christopher St., New York, NY 10014 (SAN 286-0244) Tel 212-874-5300.

Aragorn Bks, *(Aragorn Bks., Inc.; 0-913862),* 14698 Nordhoff St., Panorama City, CA 91402 (SAN 203-4832) Tel 213-894-3104.

Arana Press, *(Arana Pr., Inc.; 0-9617108),* P.O. Box 14238, St. Paul, MN 55114 (SAN 662-698X) Tel 612-646-7445.

†**Ararat Pr,** *(Ararat Pr.; 0-933706),* Div. of Armenian General Benevolent Union, 585 Saddle River Rd., Saddle Brook, NJ 07662 (SAN 212-8268) Tel 201-797-7600; *CIP.*

ARAS Pub, *(ARAS Publishing; 0-9612164),* 1380 156th St., NE, No. 2060, Bellevue, WA 98007 (SAN 289-1131) Tel 206-643-2757.

†**Arbit,** *(Arbit Bks., Inc.; 0-930038),* 8050 N. Pt. Washington Rd., Milwaukee, WI 53217 (SAN 210-4695) Tel 414-352-4404; Toll free: 800-558-6908; *CIP.*

Arbogast Pub, *(Arbogast Publishing Co.; 1-55598),* P.O. Box 56, Hannawa Falls, NY 13647 (SAN 659-008X) Tel 315-265-8317; Outer Grove St., Hannawa Falls, NY 13647 (SAN 659-0098).

Arbolyn Pubns, *(Arbolyn Pubns.; 0-937909),* P.O. Box 2412, Columbia, SC 29202 (SAN 659-4131) Tel 803-794-3215; 1708 Holly Hill Dr., West Columbia, SC 29169 (SAN 659-414X).

Arbor Hse, *(Arbor Hse. Pub. Co.; 0-87795),* Div. of Hearst Corp., 235 E. 45th St., New York, NY 10017 (SAN 201-1522) Tel 212-599-3131.

Arbor Pubns, *(Arbor Pubns.; 0-9602556),* P.O. Box 8185, Ann Arbor, MI 48107 (SAN 212-8276) Tel 313-668-6673.

Arc Bks
See Arco

ARC Pr, *(ARC Press; 0-9600884),* 254 W. 71 St., New York, NY 10023-3710 (SAN 263-9033).

Arc Pr AR, *(Arc Pr.; 0-938041),* P.O. Box 88, Cane Hill, AR 72717 (SAN 659-7297); Cold Springs Rd., Cane Hill, AR 72717 (SAN 659-7300) Tel 501-824-3821.

Arcade Pubs, *(Arcade Pubs.; 0-933885),* Box 5365, Berkeley, CA 94705 (SAN 692-767X) Tel 415-848-8656.

Arcadia Corp, *(Arcadia Corp.; 0-9614745),* P.O. Box 534, Franklin, NH 03235 (SAN 692-9206) Tel 603-934-6186.

Arcadia Pr, *(Arcadia Pr.; 0-938186),* 37 Washington Square West, Apt. 4C, New York, NY 10011 (SAN 215-6210) Tel 212-477-5331.

Arcadia Pubns, *(Arcadia Pubns.; 0-938829),* 6030 W. Coldspring Rd., Greenfield, WI 53220 (SAN 661-7026) Tel 414-327-5258.

Arcana Pub, *(Arcana Publishing; 0-910261),* Div. of Lotus Light Publications, P.O. Box Two, Wilmot, WI 53192 (SAN 241-3604) Tel 414-862-2395.

Arcane Bks
See Arcane Pubns

Arcane Order, *(Arcane Order Studio of Contemplation),* 2904 Rosemary Ln., Falls Church, VA 22042 (SAN 225-4743) Tel 703-536-8863.

Arcane Pubns, *(Arcane Pubns.; 0-912240),* Box 36, York Harbor, ME 03911 (SAN 203-4840).

Arcas Pr, *(Arcas Pr.; 0-9615753),* P.O. Box 90984, San Diego, CA 92109 (SAN 696-110X) Tel 619-488-2666.

Arch Ed Lake End
See Prince St Ed

Arch Lic Seminar, *(Architectural License Seminars, Inc.; 0-937705),* P.O. Box 64188, Los Angeles, CA 90064 (SAN 659-2937) Tel 213-208-7112; 924 Westwood Blvd., Suite 840, Los Angeles, CA 90024 (SAN 659-2945).

Arch News Inc, *(Archaeological News, Inc.; 0-943254),* Florida State Univ., Dept. of Classics, Tallahassee, FL 32306 (SAN 240-3374) Tel 904-644-3033.

Arch Pubns, *(Architectural Pubns.; 0-9608208),* 103 MacDougal St., New York, NY 10012 (SAN 240-3382) Tel 212-477-6385.

Archaeological Inst, *(Archaeological Institute of America; 0-9605042),* 15 Park Row, Suite 1732, New York, NY 10038 (SAN 232-542X); P.O. Box 1901, Kenmore Sta., Boston, MA 02215 (SAN 693-952X).

Archangel Pub, *(Archangel Publishing; 0-932661),* 310 W. Washington, Parisette, IL 61944 (SAN 687-7664) Tel 217-463-7895.

†**Archdiocesan,** *(Archdiocesan Historical Commission; 0-9613644),* Div. of Archdiocese of Portland in Oregon, 5000 N. Williamette Blvd., Portland, OR 97203-5798 (SAN 670-7882) Tel 503-283-7111; 2838 E. Burnside, Portland, OR 97207-0351 (SAN 200-5417) Tel 503-234-5334; Dist. by: Pacific Northwest Books, P.O. Box 314, Medford, OR 97501 (SAN 200-5263); *CIP.*

†**Archer Edns,** *(Archer Editions Pr.; 0-89097),* 318 Fry Branch Rd., Lynnville, TN 38472 (SAN 207-7124) Tel 615-527-3643; *CIP.*

Archibald Pub, *(Archibald Publishing; 0-937819),* P.O. Box 6573, Minneapolis, MN 55406. (SAN 659-4158) Tel 612-724-6431; 3336 35th Ave. S., Minneapolis, MN 55406 (SAN 659-4166).

†**Archinform,** *(Archinform; 0-937254),* P.O. Box 27732, Los Angeles, CA 90027 (SAN 212-3320) Tel 213-662-0216; *CIP.*

†**Architectural,** *(Architectural Bk. Publishing Co., Inc.; 0-8038),* 268 Dogwood Ln., Stamford, CT 06903 Tel 203-322-1460; Dist. by: Kampmann & Co., 9 E. 40th St., New York, NY 10016 (SAN 202-5191) Tel 212-685-2928; *CIP.*

Architectural Rec Bks *Imprint of* **McGraw**

Archival Pr, *(Archival Pr., Inc.; 0-915882),* P.O. Box 93, MIT Branch Sta., Cambridge, MA 02139 (SAN 214-283X).

†**Archival Servs,** *(Archival Services, Inc.; 0-910653),* P.O. Box 78191, Shreveport, LA 71137-8191 (SAN 270-1774) Tel 318-222-7655; P.O. Box 112, Blanchard, LA 71009 (SAN 662-0108) Tel 318-929-4707; *CIP.*

Archive CA
See Archive Corp

Archive Corp, *(Archive Corp.; 0-9608810),* 1650 Sunflower Ave., Costa Mesa, CA 92626 (SAN 693-1669) Tel 714-641-0279.

Archive Pr, *(Archive Press, The; 0-910720),* 2101 192nd Ave., S.E., Issaquah, WA 98027 (SAN 217-2259).

Archives Belmont, *(Archives of Belmont Abbey, The; 0-9614976),* Belmont Abbey, Belmont, NC 28012 (SAN 693-6016) Tel 704-825-7031.

Archives Pr, *(Archives, The; 0-918501),* 1259 El Camino Real, No. 188, Menlo Park, CA 94025 (SAN 657-3207) Tel 415-326-6997.

Archives Soc Hist, *(Archives of Social History; 0-914924),* P.O. Box 763, Stony Brook, NY 11790 (SAN 204-4889) Tel 516-751-3709.

Archon Bks *Imprint of* **Shoe String**

Archon Inst Leader Dev, *(Archon Institute for Leadership Development, Inc., The; 0-9616203),* 3700 Massachusetts Ave., No. 121, Washington, DC 20016 (SAN 658-3415) Tel 202-342-7710.

†**Archway,** *(Archway Paperbacks; 0-671),* ; Toll free: 800-223-2336; c/o Pocket Bks., 1230 Ave. of the Americas, New York, NY 10020 (SAN 202-5922) Tel 212-246-2121; *CIP.*

ARCI Assocs, *(ARCI Assocs.; 0-934045),* Spring Canyon Trail, P.O. Box 2724, Rapid City, SD 57709 (SAN 693-0107) Tel 605-341-7397.

Arcline Pubns, *(Arcline Pubns.; 0-913852),* P.O. Box 1550, Pomona, CA 91769 (SAN 203-2287) Tel 714-623-1738.

†**Arco,** *(Arco Publishing, Inc.; 0-668),* Div. of Prentice-Hall, Inc., 1 Gulf & Western Bldg., New York, NY 10023 (SAN 201-0003) Tel 212-333-5800; *CIP.* Imprints: Morgan Aviation (Morgan Aviation Books).(Morgan Aviation Bks.).

ARCS Inc, *(ARCS Inc.; 0-9615213),* 2628 E. Cannon Dr., Phoenix, AZ 85028 (SAN 695-1139) Tel 602-971-2867.

ARCsoft, *(ARCsoft Pubs.; 0-86668),* P.O. Box 132, Woodsboro, MD 21798 (SAN 216-2210) Tel 301-845-8856.

Arctinurus Co, *(Arctinurus Co., Inc.; 0-915386),* P.O. Box 275, Bellmawr, NJ 08031-0275 (SAN 276-9719) Tel 609-933-0212.

Arcturus Pubs, *(Arcturus Pubs., Inc.; 0-916877),* P.O. Box 606, Cherry Hill, NJ 08003 (SAN 653-9718) Tel 609-428-3863.

Arcus Pub, *(Arcus Publishing Co.; 0-916955),* P.O. Box 228, Sonoma, CA 95476 (SAN 655-5667) Tel 707-996-9529.

†**Arden Lib,** *(Arden Library; 0-8495),* Mill & Main Sts., Darby, PA 19023 (SAN 207-477X) Tel 215-726-5505; *CIP.*

Arden Pr, *(Arden Pr.; 0-912869),* P. O. Box 418, Denver, CO 80201 (SAN 277-6553) Tel 303-433-1448.

†**Ardis Pubs,** *(Ardis Pubs.; 0-88233; 0-87501),* 2901 Heatherway, Ann Arbor, MI 48104 (SAN 201-1492) Tel 313-971-2367; *CIP.*

Ardsley, *(Ardsley Hse. Pubs., Inc.; 0-912675),* 320 Central Park, W., New York, NY 10025 (SAN 282-7549) Tel 212-496-7040.

Ardsley Pr, *(Ardsley Pr.; 0-937253),* 110 Maple St., Suite 211, Springfield, MA 01105 (SAN 659-0128) Tel 413-737-4797.

ARE Pr, *(A.R.E. Pr.; 0-87604),* 215 67th St., Virginia Beach, VA 23451 (SAN 201-1484) Tel 804-428-3588; Toll free: 800-368-2727; P.O. Box 595, Virginia Beach, VA 23451 (SAN 692-8234).

Arena *Imprint of* **Pyramid Pubns**

Arena Lettres, *(Arena Lettres; 0-88479),* Div. of John Taylor, Inc., 8 Lincoln Pl., Waldwick, NJ 07463 (SAN 206-3247) Tel 201-445-7154.

AREPO, *(Astrosophical Research & Esoteric Publishing Oddities Corp.; 0-938359),* P.O. Box 6334, FDR Sta., New York, NY 10150 (SAN 659-736X); 618 49th St., Brooklyn, NY 11220 (SAN 659-7378) Tel 718-426-2957.

Ares, *(Ares Pubs., Inc.; 0-89005),* 7020 N. Western Ave., Chicago, IL 60645-3416 (SAN 201-743-1405.

Arete CO, *(Arete' Pr., of Colorado; 0-9614341),* P.O. Box 440477, Aurora, CO 80044 (SAN 687-8547) Tel 303-337-3113.

†**Arete Pr,** *(Arete Pr.; 0-941736),* 480 W. Sixth St., Claremont, CA 91711 (SAN 239-1570) Tel 714-624-7770; *CIP.*

Arete Pr
See Bellflower

Argee Pub, *(Argee Pub. Co.; 0-917961),* 14125 Haynes St., Van Nuys, CA 91401 (SAN 211-8815) Tel 818-994-9040.

Argent Pr, *(Argent Press; 0-915417),* 215 E. 61st St., New York, NY 10021 (SAN 291-0748) Tel 212-838-6509.

Argo *Imprint of* **Atheneum**

Argo Bks, *(Argo Books; 0-912148),* Main St., Norwich, VT 05055 (SAN 203-4867) Tel 802-649-1000.

Argonaut Pr
See Argonaut Pub

Argonaut Pub, *(Argonaut Publishing; 0-918777),* P.O. Box 50123, Santa Barbara, CA 93108 (SAN 657-3215) Tel 805-684-6977; 1050 Cindy Ln., Carpinteria, CA 93013 (SAN 657-3223); Dist. by: Harper & Row, Publishers, Inc., 1700 Montgomery St., San Francisco, CA 94111 (SAN 215-3734) Tel 415-989-9000.

Argonne Bks, *(Argonne Bks.; 0-915063),* 1083 Austin Ave. NE, Atlanta, GA 30307 (SAN 289-7245) Tel 404-872-0780.

Argos House, *(Argos Hse.; 0-9607082),* Crescent Ave., Saratoga Springs, NY 12866 (SAN 238-9428) Tel 518-584-5817.

Argos Pub Co, *(Argos Publishing Co.; 0-915509),* Subs. of Aaron E. Freeman, Inc., 1156 Sidonia Ct., Leucadia, CA 92024 (SAN 291-0764) Tel 619-436-4271.

Argosy, *(Argosy; 0-87266),* 116 E. 59th St., New York, NY 10022 (SAN 203-4875).

Argus Archives, *(Argus Archives; 0-916858),* 228 E. 49th St, New York, NY 10017 (SAN 208-4244) Tel 212-355-6140.

Argus Bks, *(Argus Bks & Graphics),* 1714 Capitol Ave., Sacramento, CA 95814 (SAN 203-4883).

Argus Comm, *(Argus Communications; 0-89505; 0-913592),* Div. of DLM, Inc., 1 DLM Park, P.O. Box 8000, Allen, TX 75002 (SAN 201-1476) Tel 214-727-3346; Toll free: 800-527-4748.

Argyle Pr, *(Argyle Press; 0-9610272),* P.O. Box 3215, Silver Spring, MD 20901 (SAN 291-0195).

ARI Pub Co, *(ARI Publishing Co.; 0-9616419),* 6 Sheraton Ln., No. 7, Norwich, CT 06360 (SAN 659-0144) Tel 203-889-3733.

Ariadne Bks *Imprint of* **Beacon Pr**

†**Ariadne Pr,** *(Ariadne Pr.; 0-918056),* 4817 Tallahassee Ave., Rockville, MD 20853 (SAN 210-1661) Tel 301-949-2514; *CIP.*

Ariana Prods, *(Ariana Productions; 0-916549),* P.O. Box 18627, Cleveland, OH 44118 (SAN 295-5350) Tel 216-283-5563.

Arica Inst Pr, *(Arica Institute Pr.; 0-916554),* 150 Fifth Ave. Suite 912, New York, NY 10011 (SAN 208-5321) Tel 212-807-9600.

Ariel Bks, *(Ariel Bks.; 0-9614304),* 820 Miramar Ave., Berkeley, CA 94707 (SAN 687-4738) Tel 415-525-2098; Dist. by: Blue Wind Pr., P.O. Box 7175, Berkeley, CA 94707 (SAN 206-7099) Tel 415-525-2098.

Ariel OH, *(Ariel Pr.; 0-89804),* Subs. of Light, 4082 Clotts Rd., Columbus, OH 43230 (SAN 219-8460) Tel 614-471-1163; Toll free: 800-336-7769; Toll free: 800-336-7768 (OH).

23

Ariel Pr CA, *(Ariel Pr.; 0-914863),* 1541 Pkwy. Loop, Suite D, P.O. Box 3723, Tustin, CA 92680 (SAN 289-0534) Tel 714-259-4800.
Ariel Pr TX
See Ariel Pr CA
Ariel Pubns, *(Ariel Pubns.; 0-917656),* 14417 SE 19th Pl., Bellevue, WA 98007 (SAN 207-5334) Tel 206-641-0518. Do not confuse with Ariel Bks., Berkeley, CA, or Ariel Pr., Tustin, CA, or Ariel Pr., Columbus, OH.
Aries CA, *(Aries Plus Pubns.; 0-9612570),* 6719 Hollywood Blvd., Hollywood, CA 90028 (SAN 289-0542).
Aries Prod, *(Aries Productions, Inc.; 0-910035),* 9633 Cinnabar Dr., Sappington, MO 63126 (SAN 241-2004) Tel 314-849-3722; P.O. Box 29396, Sappington, MO 63126 (SAN 669-0009).
†Aries Rising, *(Aries Rising Pr.; 0-917211),* 2132 Alcyona Dr., Los Angeles, CA 90068 (SAN 655-9573) Tel 818-957-8751; P.O. Box 29532, Los Angeles, CA 90029 (SAN 662-2313); *CIP.*
Arif, *(Arif; 0-913537),* 2748 Ninth St., Berkeley, CA 94710 (SAN 206-944X) Tel 415-848-5386.
Arion Pr, *(Arion Pr.; 0-910457),* 460 Bryant St., San Francisco, CA 94107 (SAN 203-1361) Tel 415-777-9651.
Arion Santa Rosa
See ACAT Pr
Aris Bks
See Aris Bks Harris
†Aris Bks Harris, *(Aris Bks./Harris Publishing Co.; 0-943186),* 1621 Fifth St., Berkeley, CA 94710 (SAN 219-7626) Tel 415-527-5171; Dist. by: Simon & Schuster, 1230 Ave. of the Americas, New York, NY 10020 (SAN 200-2450) Tel 212-245-6400; *CIP.*
Arista Corp NDE
See Arista Corp NY
Arista Corp NY, *(Arista Corp.; 0-89796; 0-914876; 0-8073),* Subs. of Hachette SA (France), 2 Park Ave., New York, NY 10016 (SAN 207-7078) Tel 212-889-2780; Toll free: 800-227-1606.
Aristan Pr, *(Aristan Pr.; 0-931407),* P.O. Box 395, Placentia, CA 92670 (SAN 686-9327).
Ariz Daily Star, *(Arizona Daily Star; 0-9607758),* Subs. of Pulitzer Pub. Co., P.O. Box 26807, 4850 S. Park Ave., Tucson, AZ 85726 (SAN 239-748X) Tel 602-573-4400; Toll free: 800-362-4890.
Ariz Hwy, *(Arizona Highways; 0-916179),* Div. of Arizona Department of Transportation, 2039 W. Lewis Ave., Phoenix, AZ 85009 (SAN 294-8974) Tel 602-258-6641.
Ark & Arbor, *(Ark & Arbor Press; 0-9606234),* Box 901, Little Compton, RI 02837 (SAN 238-907X).
Ark Comm Inst, *(Ark Communications Institute; 0-934325),* P.O. Box 1010, Bolinas, CA 94924 (SAN 693-0905) Tel 415-868-2222.
Ark Paperbks *Imprint of* Methuen Inc
†Ark St Univ, *(Arkansas State Univ.; 0-930677),* P.O. Box 1990, State University, AR 72467 (SAN 677-0002) Tel 501-972-3056; *CIP.*
Arkbridge Assn, *(Arkbridge Assn.; 0-9616312),* P.O. Box 3533, Pompano Beach, FL 33072 (SAN 699-8178) Tel 305-785-2257.
†Arkham, *(Arkham Hse. Pubs.; 0-87054),* P.O. Box 546, Sauk City, WI 53583 (SAN 206-9741) Tel 608-643-4500; *CIP.* *Imprints:* Mycroft & Moran (Mycroft & Moran).
ARL Pub, *(ARL Publishing; 0-936419),* P.O. Box 59983, Dallas, TX 75229-1983 (SAN 698-1747) Tel 214-243-7604; 10836 Grissom, Suite 104, Dallas, TX 75229 (SAN 698-1755).
Arlen Comm Inc, *(Arlen Communications, Inc.; 0-9609768),* 7315 Wisconsin Ave., Suite 600 E, Bethesda, MD 20814 (SAN 267-6451) Tel 301-656-7940.
Arlen Frank, *(Frank, Arlen W.; 0-9614531),* 3812 Croydon St., Slidell, LA 70458 (SAN 692-2589) Tel 504-643-7513.
Arlene McPhail, *(McPhail, Arlene; 0-9614596),* 1716 Bailey, Everett, WA 98203 (SAN 691-7844) Tel 206-355-6212.
Arlin J Brown, *(Brown, Arlin J.),* The Arlin J. Brown Info. Ctr., P.O. Box 251, Ft. Belvoir, VA 22060 (SAN 203-4891) Tel 703-451-8638.
†Arlington Bk, *(Arlington Bk. Co.; 0-930163),* P.O. Box 327, Arlington, VA 22210-0327 (SAN 200-786X) Tel 202-296-6750; *CIP.*

Arlington Hse *Imprint of* **Crown**
Arlotta, *(Arlotta Pr.; 0-918838),* 6340 Millbank Dr., Dayton, OH 45459 (SAN 210-3877) Tel 513-434-1518.
Arma Pr, *(Arma Press; 0-9603662),* Rte. 139, North Branford, CT 06471 (SAN 203-4093).
Armado & Moth, *(Armado & Moth; 0-9603626),* 2131 Arapahoe, Boulder, CO 80302 (SAN 213-4586) Tel 303-442-1415.
Armagh Press, *(Armagh Pr., The; 0-9617109),* 7816 Turning Creek Ct., Potomac, MD 20854 (SAN 662-6998) Tel 301-469-0393.
Arman Ent, *(Arman Enterprises, Inc.; 0-915438),* RD No. 1 Box 353A, Woodstock, CT 06281 (SAN 207-1673) Tel 203-928-5838.
Armedia Con, *(Armedia Consultants; 0-916903; 0-9607626),* Subs. of Armedia Corporating, Inc., 508 Colquitt St. Suite A, Houston, TX 77006 (SAN 656-1632) Tel 702-739-6612.
Armedia Pub
See Armedia Con
Armen Review, *(Armenian Review, Inc.; 0-935353),* P.O. Box 2629, Cambridge, MA 02238 (SAN 696-1231) Tel 617-926-4037; 80 Bigelow Ave., Watertown, MA 02172 (SAN 696-5237).
Armenian Her, *(Armenian Heritage Pr.; 0-935411),* Div. of National Assn. for Armenian Studies & Research, 175 Mt. Auburn St., Cambridge, MA 02138 (SAN 696-1193) Tel 617-876-7630.
Armenian Ref Bks, *(Armenian Reference Bks., Co.; 0-931539),* P.O. Box 7106, Glendale, CA 91205 (SAN 683-2407) Tel 818-507-1525.
Armond-Dalton, *(Armond Dalton Publishers, Inc.; 0-912503),* P.O. Box 318, Haslett, MI 48840 (SAN 656-8580) Tel 517-349-4695.
Armory Pubns, *(Armory Pubns.; 0-9604982; 0-939683),* P.O. Box 44372, Tacoma, WA 98444 (SAN 215-725X) Tel 206-531-4632.
Arms Control, *(Arms Control Assn.; 0-934766),* 11 Dupont Cir., NW, Washington, DC 20036 (SAN 224-053X) Tel 202-797-6450.
Armstrong Browning, *(Armstrong Browning Library; 0-914108),* P.O. Box 6336, Waco, TX 76706 (SAN 206-3263) Tel 817-755-3566.
Armstrong Chapel, *(Armstrong Chapel; 0-9616073),* 5125 Drake Rd., Cincinnati, OH 45243 (SAN 698-133X) Tel 513-575-2256.
Armstrong Pr, *(Armstrong Press, The; 0-915739),* Rte. Two, Box 509, Notasulga, AL 36866 (SAN 216-3314) Tel 205-257-3670.
Armstrong Pub, *(Armstrong Publishing Co.; 0-915936),* Div. of Croesus Co. Inc., 5514 Wilshire Blvd., Los Angeles, CA 90036 (SAN 208-533X) Tel 213-937-3600.
Arnall, *(Arnall, Franklin; 0-914638),* P.O. Box 253, Claremont, CA 91711 (SAN 204-482X) Tel 714-621-2461.
Arnan Pub
See Quartus Bks
Arner Pubns, *(Arner Pubns.; 0-914124),* P.O. Drawer A, Clark Mills, NY 13321 (SAN 201-145X) Tel 315-853-8375.
Arnold & Co, *(Arnold, James, & Co.; 0-913013),* 18533 Burbank Blvd., Suite 138, Tarzana, CA 91356 (SAN 282-9630) Tel 818-888-4883.
Arnold Assocs, *(Arnold, William, Assocs., Inc.; 0-9615458),* P.O. Box 36786, Grosse Pointe, MI 48236 (SAN 695-7420) Tel 313-886-8001.
Arnold Jones, *(Jones, Arnold, & Assocs.; 0-943036),* 3400 Ben Lomand Pl. No. 123, Los Angeles, CA 90027 (SAN 240-3919) Tel 213-662-6580.
Arnold-Porter Pub, *(Arnold-Porter Publishing Co.; 0-9605048),* P.O. Box 646, Keego Harbor, MI 48033 (SAN 220-0325) Tel 313-338-4478.
ARO Pub, *(ARO Publishing Co.; 0-89868),* Box 193, 398 S. 1100 West, Provo, UT 84601 (SAN 212-6370) Tel 801-377-8218. *Imprints:* Read Res (Reading Research).
Aro Pub Co
See ARO Pub

†Aronson, *(Aronson, Jason, Inc.; 0-87668),* 230 Livingston St., Northvale, NJ 07647 (SAN 201-0127) Tel 201-767-4093; Orders to: Jason Aronson, Inc., 1205 O'Neill Hwy., Dunmore, PA 18512 (SAN 200-7746) Tel 717-342-1449; Dist. by: Haddon Craftsmen Distribution Ctr., 1205 O'Neil Hwy., Dunmore, PA 18512 (SAN 663-2874) Tel 717-342-1449. Do not confuse with J. H. Aronson, Highmount, NY; *CIP.*
Aronson Pub
See Talmud Pr
Arpel Graphic, *(Arpel Graphics, Inc.; 0-916567),* 32 E. Micheltorena, Santa Barbara, CA 93101 (SAN 297-1836) Tel 805-687-5658.
Arrants & Assoc, *(Arrants & Associate; 0-943704),* P.O. Box 6606, Bellevue, WA 98008 (SAN 238-3675) Tel 206-644-1664.
†Arrays-Continent, *(Arrays, Inc./Continental Software; 0-88688),* 6711 Valjean Ave., Van Nuys, CA 91406 (SAN 265-0398) Tel 818-994-1899; *CIP.*
ARRDA, *(American Resort & Residential Development Assn.),* 1220 L St. NW., 5th Flr., Washington, DC 20005 (SAN 225-4379) Tel 202-371-6700.
Arriaga Pubns, *(Arriaga Pubns.; 0-9606356),* P.O. Box 652, Booneville, AR 72927 (SAN 214-0985).
Arriflex, *(Arriflex Corp.; 0-936763),* 500 Rte. 303, Blauvelt, NY 10913 (SAN 699-8828) Tel 914-353-1400.
Arrigo CA, *(Arrigo, Hargreaves, Nishimura),* 10175 Bunting Ave., Fountain Valley, CA 92708 (SAN 663-4680).
Arrow P, *(Arrow Publishing; 0-9614631),* 405 W. Washington St., Suite 26, San Diego, CA 92103 (SAN 691-893X) Tel 619-296-3201.
Arrow Pub, *(Arrow Publishing Co., Inc.; 0-913450),* 1020 Turnpike St., Canton, MA 02021 (SAN 201-6753) Tel 617-828-8013.
Arroway, *(Arroway Pubs.; 0-9600284),* 242 S. Alta Vista Blvd., Los Angelas, CA 90036 (SAN 203-4913) Tel 213-875-3730.
Arrowhead Bks
See Arrowhead Pr
Arrowhead Pr, *(Arrowhead Pr.; 0-9604152),* 3005 Fulton, Berkeley, CA 94705 (SAN 214-2562) Tel 415-540-7010.
Arrowood Bks, *(Arrowood Bks., Inc.; 0-934847),* P.O. Box 2100, Corvallis, OR 97339 (SAN 694-4531) Tel 503-753-9539; Dist. by: Pacific Pipeline, Inc., 19215 66th Ave. S., Kent, WA 98032 (SAN 208-2128) Tel 206-872-5523; Dist. by: Far West Book Service, 3515 NE Hassalo, Portland, OR 97232 (SAN 107-6760) Tel 503-234-7664.
Arrowood Pr, *(Arrowood Pr.; 0-88486),* Div. of A & W Promotional Bk. Corp., 166 Fifth Ave., New York, NY 10010 (SAN 661-8758) Tel 212-691-4688. *Imprints:* Inspirational Pr (Inspirational Press).
Arrowstar Pub, *(Arrowstar Publishing; 0-935151),* 10134 University Pk. Sta., Denver, CO 80210-1034 (SAN 695-3379) Tel 303-692-6579.
Ars Ceramica, *(Ars Ceramica, Ltd.; 0-89344),* P.O. Box 7366, Ann Arbor, MI 48107 (SAN 209-343X) Tel 313-429-7864; Dist. by: Keramos, P.O. Box 7500, Ann Arbor, MI 48107 (SAN 169-3670).
Ars Edition, *(Ars Edition Inc.; 0-86724),* 70 Air Park Dr., Ronkonkoma, NY 11779 (SAN 220-2018) Tel 516-467-2300.
ARS Enterprises, *(ARS Enterprises; 0-938630),* P.O. Box 997, Mercer Island, WA 98040 (SAN 238-9088) Tel 206-236-1755.
Ars Eterna, *(Ars Eterna Pr.; 0-9602170),* 7627 Glen Prairie, Houston, TX 77061 (SAN 212-4785).
ARS Pub, *(Ars Publishing Co.; 0-941616),* 6 W. Main St., Suite 1, Stockton, CA 95202 (SAN 239-1422) Tel 209-465-8243.
Arsenal Pr, *(Arsenal Pr.; 0-9609022),* Box 12244, Atlanta, GA 30355 (SAN 241-2012) Tel 404-261-7696.
Art *Imprint of* **B&N Imports**
Art Adventure, *(Art Adventures Press; 0-918326),* 1286 Grizzly Peak, Berkeley, CA 94708 (SAN 210-0339) Tel 415-843-6197.
Art Alliance, *(Art Alliance Pr.; 0-87982),* Dist. by: Associated University Presses, 440 Forsgate Dr., Cranbury, NJ 08512 (SAN 281-2959) Tel 609-665-4770.

Art & Antique *Imprint of* **Watson-Guptill**

Art & Comm, *(Art & Communications; 0-943188),* 812 N. Edwards, Carlsbad, NM 88220 (SAN 240-5865) Tel 505-885-3295.

Art & Human Council Tulsa, *(Arts & Humanities Council of Tulsa; 0-942374),* 2210 S. Main, Tulsa, OK 74114 (SAN 238-0064).

Art & Ref, *(Art & Reference Hse.; 0-910156),* Brownsboro, TX 75756 (SAN 203-4921).

Art Bks Intl, *(Art Bks. International, Ltd.; 0-933516; 0-88168),* 9 E. 32nd St., Suite 9C, New York, NY 10016 (SAN 214-1809) Tel 212-213-9393. *Imprints:* PA Acad Fine Arts (Pennsylvania Academy of Fine Arts, The).

Art Dir, *(Art Direction Bk. Co.; 0-910158; 0-88108),* Div. of Advertising Trade Pubns., Inc., 10 E. 39th St., 6th Flr., New York, NY 10016 (SAN 208-4023) Tel 212-889-6500.

Art Dir Club, *(Art Directors Club of Los Angeles; 0-931963),* 1258 N. Highland Ave., Los Angeles, CA 90038 (SAN 686-0443) Tel 213-465-8707.

Art Educ, *(Art Education, Inc.; 0-912242),* 28 E. Erie St., Blauvelt, NY 10913 (SAN 203-493X) Tel 914-359-2233.

Art Farm Gal, *(Art Farm Gallery The; 0-9611726),* RFD Five, Box 85, Lexington, VA 24450 (SAN 285-3361) Tel 703-463-7961.

Art Fettig
See Growth Unltd

Art History, *(Art History Pubs.; 0-9600002),* Rte. Two, Red Wing, MN 55066 (SAN 203-4948) Tel 612-388-4046.

Art in Motion, *(Art in Motion; 0-915653),* 1092 Harlan Dr., San Jose, CA 95129 (SAN 292-3912) Tel 408-255-8843.

†**Art Inst Chi,** *(Art Institute of Chicago; 0-86559),* Michigan Ave. & Adams St., Chicago, IL 60603 (SAN 204-479X) Tel 312-443-3540; Toll free: 800-621-2736; Dist. by: Univ. of Wash. Pr., P.O. Box 50096, Seattle, WA 98105 (SAN 212-2502) Tel 206-543-8870; CIP.

Art Libs Soc, *(Art Libraries Society of North America; 0-942740),* 3900 E. Timrod St., Tucson, AZ 85711 (SAN 225-3291) Tel 602-881-8479.

Art Mus Gall
See CA St U LB Art

ART Prod, *(ART Productions; 0-938671),* P.O. Box 503, Ft. Pierre, SD 57532 (SAN 661-5007); 2004 E. Sully, Fort Pierre, SD 57501 (SAN 661-5015) Tel 605-224-1425.

Art Pub
See Oregon Pr

Art Repro Pr
See Eden Press

Art Students, *(Art Students League of New York, The; 0-937750),* 215 W. 57th St., New York, NY 10019 (SAN 278-0593) Tel 212-247-4510.

Art/Tech, *(Art/Tech, Inc.; 0-939181),* 4560 127th St., Butler, WI 53007 (SAN 662-9180) Tel 414-783-4222.

†**Art Therapy,** *(Art Therapy Pubns.; 0-9611462),* Craftsbury Common, VT 05827 (SAN 212-4017); CIP.

Arte Publico, *(Arte Publico Pr.; 0-934770),* The Americas Review, Univ. of Houston Central Campus, Houston, TX 77004 (SAN 213-4594) Tel 713-749-4768.

Artech Assocs, *(Artech Assocs.; 0-936539),* 1120 1/2 N. Kickapoo, Shawnee, OK 74801 (SAN 697-8207) Tel 405-273-0942.

†**Artech Hse,** *(Artech Hse., Inc.; 0-89006),* Subs. of Horizon Hse. Microwave, Inc., 625 Canton St., Norwood, MA 02062 (SAN 201-1441) Tel 617-769-9730; CIP.

†**Artefact Co,** *(Artefact Co., The; 0-943190),* 5537 Germantown Ave., Philadelphia, PA 19144 (SAN 240-5873) Tel 215-849-0100; CIP.

Artex Pr, *(Artex Pr.; 0-930401),* 1525 Elk St., Stevens Point, WI 54481 (SAN 670-9397) Tel 715-341-6959.

Arthritis Found, *(Arthritis Foundation; 0-912423),* 1314 Spring St., NW, Atlanta, GA 30309 (SAN 267-677X) Tel 404-872-7100.

Arthse HI Pub, *(Arthouse Hawaii Publishing; 0-935021),* 1436 Young St., Honolulu, HI 96814 (SAN 694-5457) Tel 808-942-7100; P.O. Box 61544, Honolulu, HI 96822 (SAN 699-6043).

Arthur Owned, *(Arthur Owned Publishing; 0-9602112),* 606A Adams Ave., Philadelphia, PA 19120 (SAN 212-2650).

Arthur Pub, *(Arthur Publishing; 0-934849),* P.O. Box 749, Clayton, CA 94517-0749 (SAN 694-454X) Tel 415-672-4112.

Arthur Pubns, *(Arthur Pubns., Inc.; 0-932782),* P.O. Box 23101, Jacksonville, FL 32241-3101 (SAN 211-8823) Tel 904-737-8732.

Arthurian Pr, *(Arthurian Pr., The; 0-9608198),* 6 E. 45 St., Penthouse, New York City, NY 10017 (SAN 240-169X) Tel 212-286-0260.

Arti Grafiche, *(Arti Grafiche Il Torchio; 0-935194),* 123 Townsend St., Suite 450, San Francisco, CA 94107 (SAN 213-4608).

Artichoke, *(Artichoke Pr.; 0-9603916),* 3274 Parkhurst Dr., Rancho Palos Verdes, CA 90274 (SAN 213-6562).

Artichoke Pub, *(Artichoke Pubns.; 0-910163),* 7410 Baxtershire Dr., Dallas, TX 75230 (SAN 241-2020) Tel 214-233-9479.

Article One, *(Article I),* Merrill Rd., McCammon, ID 83250 (SAN 216-1028).

Artisan Sales, *(Artisan Sales; 0-934666),* P.O. Box 1497, Thousand Oaks, CA 91360 (SAN 211-8408) Tel 805-482-8076.

Artist-Dealer
See Davenport

Artistic Endeavors, *(Artistic Endeavors; 0-9604500),* 24 Emerson Place, Boston, MA 02114 (SAN 207-5733) Tel 617-227-1967.

Artists & Alchemists, *(Artists & Alchemists Pubns.; 0-915600),* 215 Bridgeway, Sausalito, CA 94965 (SAN 207-3978) Tel 415-332-0326; Dist. by: Swallow Press, 811 Junior Terrace, Chicago, IL 60613 (SAN 202-5671).

Artists Found, *(Artists Foundation, Inc., The; 0-932246),* 110 Broad St., Boston, MA 02110 (SAN 212-2073) Tel 617-482-8100.

Artmans Pr, *(Artman's Pr.; 0-9605468),* 1511 McGee Ave., Berkeley, CA 94703 (SAN 206-8923) Tel 415-527-2710.

Artra Pub, *(Artra Publishing, Inc.; 0-936725),* 628 San Dieguito Dr., Encinitas, CA 92024 (SAN 699-8666) Tel 619-436-1140; P.O. Box 575, Encinitas, CA 92024 (SAN 699-8674).

Artronix, *(Artronix Data Corp.; 0-935479),* 9 E. 96th St., New York, NY 10128 (SAN 696-1304) Tel 212-860-5479.

Arts Admin Res Inst, *(Arts Administration Research Institute; 0-915440),* 75 Spark St., Cambridge, MA 02138 (SAN 223-6222); Dist. by: Publishing Center for Cultural Resources, 625 Broadway, New York, NY 10012 (SAN 274-9025).

Arts & Arch, *(Arts & Architecture Pr.; 0-931228),* 2730 Wilshire Blvd., Suite 300, Santa Monica, CA 90403 (SAN 211-5050) Tel 213-395-0732.

Arts & Culture, *(Arts & Culture of the North; 0-9605898),* Box 1333, Gracie Square Sta., New York, NY 10028 (SAN 216-3322) Tel 212-879-9019.

Arts & Learning, *(Arts & Learning Services Foundation; 0-938541),* 4632 Vincent Ave. S., Minneapolis, MN 55410 (SAN 661-3047) Tel 612-922-8175; Dist. by: Gary E. McCuen Pubns., Inc., 411 Mallalieu Dr., Hudson, WI 54016 (SAN 691-909X) Tel 715-386-5662.

Arts Bks
See Arts Pubns

Arts Comm, *(Arts Communications; 0-918840),* 14 E. 11th St., New York, NY 10003 (SAN 210-3427).

†**Arts End,** *(Arts End Bks.; 0-933292),* P.O. Box 162, Newton, MA 02168 (SAN 213-6082) Tel 617-965-2478; CIP.

Arts Factory, *(Arts Factory, The; 0-9615873),* 23604 49th Pl., W., Mountlake Terrace, WA 98043 (SAN 696-6802) Tel 206-778-7857; P.O. Box 55547, Seattle, WA 98155 (SAN 696-9836).

Arts Pubns, *(Arts Pubns.; 0-9607458),* 80 Piedmont Ct., Larkspur, CA 94939 (SAN 238-003X) Tel 415-924-2633; Dist. by: Educational Bk. Distributor, P.O. Box 551, San Mateo, CA 94401 (SAN 158-2259).

Artus Co, *(Artus Co., The; 0-9606684),* P.O. Box 81245, Lincoln, NE 68501 (SAN 215-6687) Tel 402-477-7952.

Aruba Pub, *(Aruba Publishing Co.; 0-936251),* P.O. Box 1296, Solana Beach, CA 92075 (SAN 697-3248) Tel 619-259-9867; 1106 Second St., No. 203, Encinitas, CA 92024 (SAN 697-3256).

Arvada Hist, *(Arvada Historical Society; 0-9615540),* P.O. Box 419, Arvada, CO 80001 (SAN 696-1339) Tel 303-421-0842; 3864 Hoyt St., Wheat Ridge, CO 80033 (SAN 696-1347).

Arwyn Map, *(Arwyn Map Co.; 0-936039),* 9090 W. 74th Ave., Arvada, CO 80005 (SAN 696-9917) Tel 303-428-2864.

AS Hashim, *(Hashim, A. S.; 0-9611132),* 6407 Tuckerman Lane, Rockville, MD 20852 (SAN 282-9282) Tel 301-530-4466; Dist. by: Publisher's Marketing Group, 1104 Summit Ave., Plainview, TX 75074 (SAN 262-0995) Tel 214-423-0312.

As Is Pr
See So&So Pr

As-Shabazz Pr
See El-Shabazz Pr

As-Siddiquyah, *(As-Siddiquyah Pubs.; 0-935631),* 482 Franklin St., Buffalo, NY 14202 (SAN 696-1401) Tel 716-884-2606.

ASA, *(Attention Span Advancement Registry Service; 0-9606990),* 1940 Fifth Ave., Sacramento, CA 95818 (SAN 238-910X).

†**Asante Pubns,** *(Asante Pubns.; 0-9614210),* P.O. Box 1085, San Diego, CA 92112 (SAN 686-9599) Tel 619-448-6179; CIP.

Asbury Theological, *(Asbury Theological Seminary; 0-914368),* Wilmore, KY 40390 (SAN 208-2616).

ASC Holding, *(ASC Holding Corp.; 0-935578),* P.O. Box 2230, Hollywood, CA 90078 (SAN 287-2889) Tel 213-876-5080.

Ascend Motivational, *(Ascend Motivational Pubs.; 0-936891),* 1817 N. Hills Blvd., Suite 3004, Knoxville, TN 37917 (SAN 658-4616) Tel 615-525-5017.

Aschley Pr, *(Aschley Pr., The; 0-940900),* 2898 Kingsley Rd., Cleveland, OH 44122 (SAN 223-1735) Tel 216-752-3535.

Ascii, *(Ascii; 0-9603432; 0-939414),* P.O. Box 770222, Eagle River, AK 99577-0222 (SAN 213-6015) Tel 907-688-9485.

ASCLA, *(Assn. of Specialized Cooperative Library Agencies),* 50 E. Huron St., Chicago, IL 60611 (SAN 233-4658).

Asclepiad, *(Asclepiad Pubns., Inc.; 0-935718),* 2257 Independence, Ann Arbor, MI 48104 (SAN 213-7240).

Ascot Pr, *(Ascot Pr.; 0-9613538),* P.O. Box 1304, Hartford, CT 06143-1304 (SAN 669-7194) Tel 203-633-6911.

Ascot Pub, *(Ascot Publishing Co.; 0-936621),* 14001 Goldmark, Suite 240, Dallas, TX 75240 (SAN 698-1097) Tel 214-680-0170.

ASEI, *(Alternative Sources of Energy, Inc.; 0-917328),* 107 S. Central Ave., Milaca, MN 56353 (SAN 208-5151) Tel 612-983-6892.

Ash-Kar Pr, *(Ash-Kar Pr.; 0-9605308),* P.O. Box 14547, San Francisco, CA 94114 (SAN 213-0025) Tel 415-864-2430; Dist. by: Bookpeople, 2929 Fifth St., Berkeley, CA 94710 (SAN 168-9517) Tel 415-549-3030.

Ash Lad Pr, *(Ash Lad Pr.; 0-915492),* P.O. Box 396, Canton, NY 13617 (SAN 207-4265) Tel 315-386-8820.

Ash Pub
See Am Sports Sales

Ash Tree, *(Ash Tree; 0-9614620),* P.O. Box 64, Woodstock, NY 12498 (SAN 691-8964) Tel 914-246-8081; Dist. by: Ash Tree Publishing, P.O. Box 64, Woodstock, NY 12498 (SAN 662-7749) Tel 914-246-8081.

†**Asher-Gallant,** *(Asher-Gallant Pr.; 0-87280),* Div. of Caddylak Systems, Inc., 201 Montrose Rd., Westbury, NY 11590 (SAN 670-7947) Tel 516-333-7440; CIP.

Ashford
See Smith & Assoc

Ashford Pr CT, *(Ashford Pr.; 0-937992),* RFD 1, Box 182-A, Willimantic, CT 06226 (SAN 219-7650).

Ashiedu Pubns, *(Ashiedu Pubns.; 0-933889),* Div. of Whiz-Z-Books, P.O. Box 741151, Dallas, TX 75374 (SAN 692-7270) Tel 214-991-7148.

Ashland Poetry, *(Ashland Poetry Pr.; 0-912592),* Ashland College, Ashland, OH 44805 (SAN 203-4972) Tel 419-289-4142.

Ashlee Pub Co, *(Ashlee Publishing Co., Inc.; 0-911993),* 310 Madison Ave., New York, NY 10017 (SAN 264-7125) Tel 212-682-7681.

†**Ashley Bks,** *(Ashley Bks., Inc.; 0-87949),* 30 Main St., Pt. Washington, NY 11050 (SAN 201-1409) Tel 516-883-2221; Orders to: P.O. Box 768, Pt. Washington, NY 11050 (SAN 201-1417); *CIP.*

ASHMM, *(American Society for Hospital Materials Management),* Div. of American Hospital Assn., 840 N. Lake Shore Dr., Chicago, IL 60611 (SAN 224-3326) Tel 312-280-6137.

ASHO *Imprint of Bridge Pubns Inc*

Ashod
See Ashod Pr

†**Ashod Pr,** *(Ashod Pr.; 0-935102),* 620 E. 20th St., 11F, New York, NY 10009 (SAN 281-2894) Tel 212-475-0711; Orders to: P.O. Box 1147 Madison Sq. Sta., New York, NY 10159 (SAN 281-2908); *CIP.*

Ashton-Tate Bks
See Ashton-Tate Pub

Ashton-Tate Pub, *(Ashton-Tate Publishing Group; 0-912677),* 20101 Hamilton Ave., Torrance, CA 90502 (SAN 265-4628) Tel 213-329-8000; Toll free: 800-437-4329. Now handles all Multimate Products.

†**ASI Pubs Inc,** *(ASI Pubs., Inc.; 0-88231),* 63 W. 38th St., Suite 505, New York, NY 10018 (SAN 201-1395) Tel 212-719-2919; *CIP.*

Asia, *(Asia Publishing Hse.; 0-210),* Dist. by: Apt Bks., Inc., 141 E. 44th St., Suite 511, New York, NY 10017 (SAN 215-7209) Tel 212-697-0887.

Asia Bk Corp, *(Asia Bk. Corp. of America; 0-940500),* 94-41 218th St., Queens Village, NY 11426 (SAN 214-493X) Tel 718-740-4612.

Asia Fellows, *(Asia Fellows; 0-9617287),* 2029 National Press Bldg., Washington, DC 20045 (SAN 663-5911) Tel 703-522-5122.

Asia Resource, *(Asia Resource Ctr.; 0-9604518),* P.O. Box 15275, Washington, DC 20003 (SAN 207-7647) Tel 202-547-1114.

†**Asia Soc,** *(Asia Society, Inc.; 0-87848),* 725 Park Ave., New York, NY 10021 (SAN 281-2916) Tel 212-288-6400; Dist. by: Charles E. Tuttle, Co., P.O. Box 410, 28 S. Main St., Rutland, VT 05701-0410 (SAN 213-2621) Tel 802-773-8930; *CIP.*

Asia Soc Inc
See Asia Soc

Asia Watch *Imprint of Fund Free Expression*

Asian Am Stud, *(Asian American Studies Center, UCLA),* 3232 Campbell Hall, Univ. of California, Los Angeles, CA 90024 (SAN 210-7759) Tel 213-825-2968.

Asian Conserv Lab, *(Asian Conservation Laboratory; 0-940492),* Dist. by: Raiko Corp., P.O. Box 597, New York, NY 10003 (SAN 240-9542) Tel 212-783-2597.

Asian Human Pr, *(Asian Humanities Pr.; 0-89581; 0-87573),* 2512 Ninth St., Suite 8, Berkeley, CA 94710 (SAN 213-6503) Tel 415-485-8065; Dist. by: Great Tradition, The, 750 Adrian Way, Suite 11, San Rafael, CA 94903 (SAN 200-5743) Tel 415-492-9382.

†**Asian Music Pub,** *(Asian Music Pubns.; 0-913360),* Dist. by Theodore Front Musical Literature, Inc., 16122 Cohasset St., Van Nuys, CA 91406 (SAN 124-2601) Tel 818-994-1902; *CIP.*

ASID, *(Tennessee Amer. Soc. of Interior Designers),* P.O. Box 15391, Nashville, TN 37215 (SAN 217-2992).

Asigan Ltd, *(Asigan Limited; 0-910333),* P.O. Box 10688, Beverly Hills, CA 90213 (SAN 241-2667) Tel 213-550-1982.

ASIS *Imprint of Knowledge Indus*

Askon Pub, *(Askon Publishing Co.; 0-931609),* Subs. of Askon Corp., P.O. Box 3156, Abilene, TX 79604 (SAN 683-678X) Tel 915-672-3640; 1025 Cypress, Abilene, TX 79604 (SAN 658-2702).

ASM, *(American Society for Metals; 0-87170),* 9639 Kinsman Rd., Metals Park, OH 44073 (SAN 204-7586) Tel 216-338-5151.

†**ASME,** *(American Society of Mechanical Engineers; 0-87053),* 345 E. 47th St., New York, NY 10017 (SAN 201-1379) Tel 212-705-7722; *CIP.*

ASME Gear Res, *(ASME Gear Research Institute; 0-9617215),* P.O. Box 353, Naperville, IL 60566 (SAN 663-4125); N. Washington at East-West Tollway, Naperville, IL 60566 (SAN 663-4133) Tel 312-355-4200.

ASP
See ASP & RS

†**ASP & RS,** *(American Society for Photogrammetry and Remote Sensing; 0-937294),* 210 Little Falls St., Falls Church, VA 22046 (SAN 204-5044) Tel 703-534-6617; *CIP.*

Aspect Found, *(Aspect Foundation; 0-939073),* 39 W. 14th St., Rm. 404, New York, NY 10011 (SAN 662-913X) Tel 212-206-8463.

Aspen Art, *(Aspen Art; 0-9601120),* 401 Ctr., Evanston, WY 82930 (SAN 210-167X) Tel 307-708-9879.

Aspen Ctr Visual Arts, *(Aspen Ctr. for Visual Arts; 0-934324),* 590 N. Mill St., Aspen, CO 81611 (SAN 274-9025) Tel 303-925-8050; Dist. by: Publishing Ctr. for Cultural Resources, 625 Broadway, New York, NY 10012 (SAN 274-9025).

†**Aspen Inst Human,** *(Aspen Institute for Humanistic Studies; 0-89843; 0-915436),* P.O. Box 150, Queenstown, MD 21658 (SAN 213-0033); *CIP.*

Aspen Pr
See Rue Morgue

Aspen Prods, *(Aspen Productions; 0-913635),* 7501 Monogram Dr., Sacramento, CA 95842 (SAN 286-0384) Tel 916-344-2246.

†**Aspen Pub,** *(Aspen Pubs.; 0-912862; 0-89443; 0-87189; 0-912654),* Affil. of Wolters Samson Group, 1600 Research Blvd., Rockville, MD 20850 (SAN 203-4999) Tel 301-251-5000; Toll free: 800-638-8437; *CIP.*

Aspen Systems
See Aspen Pub

Aspen West Pub, *(Aspen West Publishing; 0-9615390),* P.O. Box 1245, Sandy, UT 84091 (SAN 694-2318) Tel 801-571-7435; Orders to: 9267 S. Tortellini Dr., Sandy, UT 84902 (SAN 699-6019).

Asphalt Inst, *(Asphalt Institute),* Asphalt Inst Bldg., College Park, MD 20740 (SAN 224-6627) Tel 301-277-4258.

ASQC Qual Pr, *(ASQC Quality Pr.; 0-87389),* Div. of American Society for Quality Control, 230 W. Wells St., Milwaukee, WI 53203 (SAN 683-5244) Tel 414-272-8575; Toll free: 800-952-6587.

ASSE, *(American Society of Safety Engineers; 0-939874),* 1800 E. Oakton Blvd., Des Plaines, IL 60018 (SAN 201-7032) Tel 312-692-4121.

Assembling Pr, *(Assembling Pr.; 0-915066),* Affil. of Rutgers University Mason Gross School of the Arts, P.O. Box 1967, Brooklyn, NY 11202 (SAN 201-1360).

Assessment Res, *(Assessment Research; 0-937987),* P.O. Box 8900-330, Salem, OR 97303-0890 (SAN 659-7319); 2335 Manzanita Dr., NE, Salem, OR 97303 (SAN 659-7327) Tel 503-390-6690.

Assistance League, *(Assistance League of Corvallis; 0-9616597),* 534 NW Fourth St., Corvallis, OR 97330 (SAN 659-4891) Tel 503-753-0408.

Assn Adv Med Instrn, *(Association for the Advancement of Medical Instrumentation; 0-910275),* 1901 N. Ft. Myer Dr., Suite 602, Arlington, VA 22209-1699 (SAN 224-3407) Tel 703-525-4890.

Assn Adv Med Instrs.
See Assn Adv Med Instrn

Assn Advance Behav Therapy, *(Association for Advancement of Behavior Therapy),* 15 W. 36th St., New York, NY 10018 (SAN 224-4357).

Assn Am Coll, *(Assn. of American Colleges; 0-911696),* 1818 R St. NW, Washington, DC 20009 (SAN 224-0572) Tel 202-387-3760.

†**Assn Am Geographers,** *(Association of American Geographers; 0-89291),* 1710 16th St., NW, Washington, DC 20009 (SAN 201-6796) Tel 202-234-1450; *CIP.*

†**Assn Am Indian,** *(Association on American Indian Affairs, Inc.),* 95 Madison Ave., New York, NY 10016 (SAN 204-4730) Tel 212-689-8720; *CIP.*

†**Assn Am Law Schls,** *(Association of American Law Schls.),* 1 Dupont Cir., NW, Suite 370, Washington, DC 20036 (SAN 225-8382) Tel 202-296-8891; *CIP.*

Assn Am St Geols
See FL Bureau Geology

Assn Arab-Amer U Grads, *(Association of Arab-American University Graduates; 0-937694),* 556 Trapelo Rd., Belmont, MA 02178 (SAN 240-0820) Tel 617-484-5483. *Imprints:* AAUG Pr (A A U G Press).

Assn Artist Gal, *(Association of Artist-Run Galleries),* 152 Wooster St., New York, NY 10012 (SAN 267-8632).

Assn Baptist Profs
See NABPR

Assn Bar NYC, *(Association of the Bar of the City of New York),* 42 W. 44th St., New York, NY 10036 (SAN 204-4706) Tel 212-382-6650.

Assn Bay Area, *(Association of Bay Area Governments),* Metrocenter, Eighth & Oak Sts., Oakland, CA 94604 (SAN 226-4374) Tel 415-464-7914; P.O. Box 2050, Oakland, CA 94604 (SAN 669-0114).

†**Assn Birth Psych,** *(Association for Birth Psychology; 0-9612182),* 444 E. 82nd St., New York, NY 10028 (SAN 289-114X) Tel 212-988-6617; *CIP.*

Assn Black Psych, *(Association of Black Psychologists),* 1118 Ninth St., NW, Washington, DC 20001 (SAN 224-0610) Tel 202-289-3663; P.O. Box 2929, Washington, DC 20013 (SAN 669-0122).

Assn Brain Tumor, *(Association for Brain Tumor Research; 0-9616451),* 6232 N Pulaski Rd., Suite 200, Chicago, IL 60646 (SAN 224-280X) Tel 312-544-4941.

Assn Busn Comm, *(Association for Business Communication, The; 0-931874),* 100 English Bldg., 608 S. Wright St., Urbana, IL 61801 (SAN 211-9382) Tel 217-333-1007.

Assn Calif Sch Admin, *(Association of California School Administrators),* Old Bayshore Hwy., Burlingame, CA 94010 (SAN 203-1310) Tel 415-692-4300.

Assn Care Child, *(Association for the Care of Children's Health),* 3615 Wisconsin Ave., NW, Washington, DC 20016 (SAN 267-8314) Tel 202-244-1801.

Assn Chemists, *(Association of Consulting Chemists & Chemical Engineers),* 50 E. 41st St., Suite 92, New York, NY 10017 (SAN 267-9000) Tel 212-684-6255.

Assn Chr Libs, *(Association of Christian Librarians),* Houghton College - Buffalo Suburban Campus, 910 Union Rd., West Seneca, NY 14224 (SAN 217-2267).

Assn Christian Pub, *(Association of Christian Pubs. & Booksellers, Inc.; 0-943258),* 3360 NW 110th St., Miami, FL 33167 (SAN 240-3390).

Assn Coll & Res Libs, *(Association of College & Research Libraries; 0-8389),* Div. of American Library Assn., 50 E. Huron St., Chicago, IL 60611 (SAN 225-3305) Tel 312-944-6780; Toll free: 800-545-2433; Toll free: 800-545-2445 (in IL); Orders to: ALA Publishing Services, 50 E. Huron St., Chicago, IL 60611 (SAN 662-717X).

Assn Coll Arts Admin, *(Association of College, University & Community Arts Administrators),* 6225 University Ave., Madison, WI 53705-1099 (SAN 225-8498) Tel 608-233-7400.

Assn Consul Mgmt Engrs
See ACME

Assn Consumer Res, *(Association for Consumer Research; 0-915552),* Graduate School of Managment, 632 TNRB, Brigham Young Univ., Provo, UT 84602 (SAN 207-3838) Tel 801-378-2080.

Assn Dept Lang, *(Association of Departments of Foreign Languages),* 10 Astor Pl., New York, NY 10003 (SAN 267-9094) Tel 212-614-6319.

†**Assn Ed Comm Tech,** *(Association for Educational Communications & Technology; 0-89240),* 1126 16th St., NW, Washington, DC 20036 (SAN 207-3277) Tel 202-466-4780; *CIP.*

Assn Ed Data
See Assn Educ Data

Assn Ed Rehab Blind, *(Association for Education & Rehabilitation of the Blind & Visually Impaired; 0-934677),* 206 N. Washington St., Suite 320, Alexandria, VA 22314 (SAN 227-6372) Tel 703-548-1884.

Assn Ed Visually Hand
See Assn Ed Rehab Blind

Assn Educ Data, *(Association for Educational Data Systems),* 1201 16th St. NW, Washington, DC 20036 (SAN 236-2074) Tel 202-822-7845.

Assn Educ Systems
See Assn Educ Data

Assn Energy Eng, *(Association of Energy Engineers),* 4025 Pleasantdale Rd., Suite 340, Atlanta, GA 30340 (SAN 225-1663) Tel 404-447-5083.

Assn Environ Eng, *(Association of Environmental Engineering Professors; 0-917567),* Univ. of Texas, Austin, Dept. of Civil Engineering, ECJ8.6, Austin, TX 78712 (SAN 236-2554).

Assn Equip Distrs, *(Associated Equipment Distributors),* 615 W. 22nd St., Oak Brook, IL 60521 (SAN 224-0548) Tel 312-574-0650.

Assn Exper Ed, *(Association for Experiential Education),* Box 249 CU, Boulder, CO 80309 (SAN 225-7742) Tel 303-492-1547.

Assn Family Living, *(Association for the Study of Family Living, The; 0-9602670),* P.O. Box 130, Brooklyn, NY 11208 (SAN 212-8772) Tel 718-647-7406.

Assn Fed Investigators, *(Association of Federal Investigators),* 810 18th St., NW, Washington, DC 20006 (SAN 225-0799).

Assn for Jewish Studies, *(Association for Jewish Studies; 0-915938),* Queens College, Dept. of History, Flushing, NY 11367 (SAN 669-0084); Dist. by: Ktav Publishing Hse., 900 Jefferson St., Box 6249, Hoboken, NJ 07030 (SAN 669-0092) Tel 201-963-9524.

Assn Former Inter, *(Assn. of Former Intelligence Officers),* 6723 Whittier Ave., Suite 303A, McLean, VA 22101 (SAN 689-6197) Tel 703-790-0320.

Assn Gen Con, *(Associated General Contractors of America),* 1957 E St. NW, Washington, DC 20006 (SAN 224-6880) Tel 203-393-2040.

Assn Gov Bds, *(Association of Governing Boards of Universities & Colleges),* 1 Dupont Cir., Suite 400, Washington, DC 20036 (SAN 267-9361) Tel 202-296-8400.

Assn Holistic, *(Association for Holistic Health; 0-915407),* P.O. Box 9532, San Diego, CA 92109 (SAN 263-9246) Tel 619-275-2694.

Assn ICC Practitioners, *(Association of Interstate Commerce Commission Practitioners),* 1112 ICC Bldg., 12th St. & Constitution Ave. NW., Suite 310, Washington, DC 20423 (SAN 224-2230) Tel 202-783-9432.

Assn Ind Camps, *(Association of Independent Camps, Inc.),* 60 Madison Ave., New York, NY 10010 (SAN 224-5531) Tel 212-679-3230.

Assn Info Image Mgmt
See Assn Inform & Image Mgmt

Assn Info Sys, *(Association of Information Systems Professionals; 0-935220; 0-928397),* 1015 N. York Rd., Willow Grove, PA 19090 (SAN 213-5191) Tel 215-657-6300.

†Assn Inform & Image Mgmt, *(Association for Information & Image Management; 0-89258),* 1100 Wayne Ave., Silver Spring, MD 20910 (SAN 202-1021) Tel 301-587-8202; *CIP.*

Assn Interp Naturalist, *(Association of Interpretive Naturalists Incorporated),* 6700 Needwood Rd., Derwood, MD 20855 (SAN 226-6644) Tel 301-948-8844.

Assn Library Serv, *(Association for Library Service to Children),* Div. of American Library Association, 50 E. Huron St., Chicago, IL 60611 (SAN 233-464X) Tel 312-944-6780; Toll free: 800-545-2433.

Assn Manage
See ACME

Assn Media Pro
See NAVA Intl Comm

Assn Muslim Sci, *(Association of Muslim Scientists & Engineers; 0-916581),* P.O. Box 38, Plainfield, IN 46168 (SAN 296-4449) Tel 317-839-8157.

Assn Natl Advertisers, *(Association of National Advertisers, Inc.),* 155 E. 44th St., New York, NY 10017 (SAN 224-6112).

Assn NC Records, *(Association for Northern California Records & Research),* P.O. Box 3024, Chico, CA 95927 (SAN 267-8063) Tel 916-895-5710.

Assn Oper Rm Nurses, *(Association of Operating Room Nurses, Inc.; 0-939583),* 10170 E. Mississippi Ave., Denver, CO 80231 (SAN 224-3814) Tel 303-755-6300.

Assn Part-Time, *(Association of Part-Time Professionals; 0-917449),* Box 3419, Alexandria, VA 22302 (SAN 689-6618) Tel 703-734-7975.

Assn Personas Mayores, *(Asociacion nacional pro personas mayores; 0-913139),* 2727 W. Sixth St., Suite 270, Los Angeles, CA 90057 (SAN 223-7768).

Assn Phys Asst Prog, *(Association of Physicians Assistant Programs),* 1117 N. 19th St., Arlington, VA 22209 (SAN 224-3539).

Assn Phys Plant Admin, *(Association of Physical Plant Administrators of Universities & Colleges; 0-913359),* 1446 Duke St, Alexandria, VA 22314-3492 (SAN 223-7776) Tel 703-684-1446.

Assn Pop Lib, *(Association for Population Family Planning International),* 105 Madison Ave., New York, NY 10016 (SAN 267-808X).

Assn Practic Infection, *(Association for Practitioners in Infection Control),* 505 E. Hawley St., Mundelein, IL 60060 (SAN 689-4585) Tel 312-949-6052.

Assn Preserv VA, *(Association for the Preservation of Virginia Antiquities, The; 0-917565),* 2300 E. Grace St., Richmond, VA 23230 (SAN 657-1247) Tel 804-359-0239.

Assn Prof Genealogists, *(Association of Professional Genealogists),* 57 WS Temple, Suite 225, Salt Lake City, UT 84101 (SAN 224-0750) Tel 801-532-3327; P.O. Box 11601, Salt Lake City, UT 84147 (SAN 669-0157); Dist. by: Genealogical Institute, 57 WS Temple, Suite 255, Salt Lake City, UT 84101 (SAN 207-1959).

Assn Public Justice, *(Association for Public Justice Education Fund; 0-936456),* 806 15th St. NW, Suite 218, Washington, DC 20005 (SAN 214-1000) Tel 202-737-2110.

Assn Recs Mgrs & Admin, *(Association of Records Managers & Administrators, Inc.; 0-933887),* 4200 Somerset Dr., Suite 215, Prairie Village, KS 66208 (SAN 224-9316) Tel 913-341-3808.

Assn Res Enlight
See ARE Pr

Assn Res Lib, *(Association of Research Libraries),* 1527 New Hampshire Ave. NW, Washington, DC 20036 (SAN 225-3321).

Assn Retarded Citizens, *(Association for Retarded Citizens of the U. S.),* 2501 Ave. J, P.O. Box 6109, Arlington, TX 76011 (SAN 224-0564) Tel 817-640-0204.

Assn Sch Busn, *(Association of Schl. Business Officials International; 0-910170),* 1760 Reston Ave., Suite 411, Reston, VA 22090 (SAN 204-5478) Tel 703-478-0405.

Assn Schl Librnship, *(International Association of School Librarianship; 0-9617248),* P.O. Box 1486, Kalamazoo, MI 49005 (SAN 665-5520) Tel 616-343-5728.

Assn Sexologists, *(Association of Sexologists, The; 0-939902),* 1523 Franklin St., San Francisco, CA 94109 (SAN 216-7867).

Assn Soil & Found Engrs, *(Association of Soil & Foundation Engineers),* 8811 Coleville Rd., Suite 225, Silver Spring, MD 20910 (SAN 224-0769) Tel 301-565-2733.

Assn Study Higher Ed, *(Association for Study of Higher Education; 0-913317),* 1 Dupont Cir., Suite 630, Washington, DC 20036 (SAN 225-803X) Tel 202-296-7597.

Assn Study Nat, *(Association for the Study of the Nationalities (USSR) & East Europe; 0-910895),* City College of New York, Russian Area Studies Program, Convent Ave. at 138th St., New York, NY 10031 (SAN 263-2470) Tel 212-690-6739.

Assn Supervision, *(Association for Supervision & Curriculum Development; 0-87120),* 125 N. West St., Alexandria, VA 22314 (SAN 201-1352) Tel 703-549-9110.

Assn Syst Coll, *(Association of Systematics Collections; 0-942924),* C/O Univ. of Kansas, Museum of Natural History, Lawrence, KS 66045 (SAN 232-5853) Tel 913-864-4867.

†Assn Syst Mgmt, *(Association for Systems Management; 0-934356),* 24587 Bagley Rd., Cleveland, OH 44138 (SAN 201-7091) Tel 216-243-6900; *CIP.*

Assn Tchr Ed, *(Association of Teacher Educators),* 1900 Association Dr., Suite ATE, Reston, VA 22091 (SAN 203-7904) Tel 703-620-3110.

Assn Tchrs Latin Amer, *(Association of Teachers of Latin American Studies; 0-938305),* 252-58 63rd Ave., Little Neck, NY 11362 (SAN 689-7428) Tel 718-428-1237.

Assn Third Wld, *(Association of Third World Studies; 0-931971),* P.O. Box 1232, Americus, GA 31709 (SAN 685-3072) Tel 912-924-8287.

Assn Trans, *(Association for Transarmament Studies; 0-9614256),* 3636 Lafayette, Omaha, NE 68131 (SAN 687-1127) Tel 402-558-2085.

Assn Trial Ed, *(Association of Trial Lawyers of America, Education Fund; 0-941916),* 1050 31st St., NW, Washington, DC 20007 (SAN 238-2156) Tel 202-965-3500; Orders to: P.O. Box 3717, Washington, DC 20007 (SAN 661-9487).

Assn Trial Lawyers, *(Association of Trial Lawyers of America; 0-933067),* 1050 31st St., NW, Washington, DC 20007 (SAN 226-4625).

Assn U Busn & Econ Res, *(Association for University Business & Economic Research),* Univ. of Alabama, Ctr. for Business & Economic Research, P.O. Box AK, University, AL 35486 (SAN 236-1299) Tel 205-348-6191.

Assn Ukrainian Writers, *(Association of Ukrainian Writers in Exile Slovo; 0-930013),* 6509 Lawnton Ave., Philadelphia, PA 19126 (SAN 669-7208) Tel 215-924-9147.

Assn Union Demo, *(Association for Union Democracy; 0-9602244),* 30 Third Ave., Brooklyn, NY 11217 (SAN 227-4337) Tel 718-855-6650.

Assoc Advert Serv
See Nunciata

Assoc Air Bal, *(Associated Air Balance Council; 0-910289),* 1518 K Street, N.W., Washington, DC 20005 (SAN 267-7113) Tel 202-737-0202.

Assoc Bk, *(Associated Booksellers; 0-87497),* Affil. of Merrimack Publishing Corp., 562 Boston Ave., Bridgeport, CT 06610 (SAN 203-5014) Tel 203-333-7268; Toll free: 800-232-2224.

Assoc Bk Pubs, *(Associated Bk. Pubs., Inc.; 0-910164),* P.O. Box 5657, Scottsdale, AZ 85261 (SAN 212-2081) Tel 602-998-5223.

Assoc Bk Pubs Guidance
See Assoc Bk Pubs

Assoc Collegiate Pr, *(Associated Collegiate Press),* Div. of National Scholastic Press Association, 620 Rarig Center, 330 21st Ave. S., Univ. of Minnesota, Minneapolis, MN 55455 (SAN 225-8323).

Assoc Coun Arts
See Am Council Arts

Assoc Creative Writers, *(Associated Creative Writers; 0-933362),* 9231 Molly Woods Ave., La Mesa, CA 92041 (SAN 212-8292) Tel 619-460-4107.

Assoc Faculty Pr, *(Associated Faculty Pr.; 0-86733; 0-87198; 0-8046),* Affil. of Kraus Reprint & Periodical, Rte. 100, Millwood, NY 10546 (SAN 217-4979) Tel 914-762-2200; Orders to: 19 W. 36th St., New York, NY 10018 (SAN 694-9495) Tel 212-307-1300. *Imprints:* Natl U (National University Publications).(National Univ. Pubns.).

Assoc Grant, *(Associated Grantmakers of Massachusetts, Inc.; 0-912427),* Suite 840, 294 Washington St., Boston, MA 02108 (SAN 265-1807) Tel 617-426-2606.

Assoc Human Res, *(Associated Human Resources; 0-9613878),* Subs. of Ingram Laboratories, Inc., 3 Meade St., Buckhannon, WV 26201 (SAN 681-9621) Tel 304-472-3261.

Assoc Integ, *(Assn. for Integrative Studies, The; 0-9615764),* Miami Univ., Schl. of Interdisciplinary Studies, 185 Peabody Hall, Oxford, OH 45056 (SAN 696-1460) Tel 513-529-6992.

Assoc Marine, *(Associated Marine; 0-9613304),* Affil. of Associated Insurance Administrators, Inc., P.O. Box 5421, San Mateo, CA 94402 (SAN 654-2131) Tel 415-349-1341.

Assoc Media Cos, *(Associated Media Cos., Ltd; 0-938731),* 4350 Via Dolce, No. 311, Marina del Rey, CA 90292 (SAN 661-7107) Tel 213-821-2011.

Assoc Mus
See Schirmer Bks
†**Assoc Official,** *(Association of Official Analytical Chemists; 0-935584),* 1111 N. 19th St., Suite 210, Arlington, VA 22209 (SAN 260-3411) Tel 703-522-3032; *CIP.*
Assoc Parents, *(Associated Parents Group of Hillsborough, Inc.; 0-9616566),* 300 El Cerito Ave., Hillsborough, CA 94010 (SAN 659-4174) Tel 415-340-1565.
†**Assoc Pr,** *(Associated Press; 0-917360),* 50 Rockefeller Plaza, New York, NY 10020 (SAN 206-7137) Tel 212-621-1500; *CIP.*
Assoc Print, *(Associated Printers),* Grafton-Grand Forks, Box 471, Grafton, ND 58237 (SAN 209-5254) Tel 701-352-0640.
Assoc Pubns, *(Associated Pubns; 0-9608806),* P.O. Box 728, Glendora, CA 91740 (SAN 238-2407).
Assoc Pubs Guidance
See Assoc Bk Pubs
†**Assoc Univ Prs,** *(Associated University Presses; 0-8453),* 440 Forsgate Dr., Cranbury, NJ 08512 (SAN 281-2959) Tel 609-655-4770; *CIP. Imprints:* Cornwall Bks (Cornwall Books).
Assoc Writing Progs, *(Associated Writing Programs; 0-936266),* c/o Old Dominion Univ., Norfolk, VA 23508 (SAN 214-0993) Tel 804-440-3840.
Association
See Am Assn Clinical Chem
Assocs James Bell, *(Associates of the James Ford Bell Library; 0-9601798),* 472 Wilson Library, Univ. of Minnesota, 309 19th Ave. S., Minneapolis, MN 55455 (SAN 209-1763) Tel 612-373-2888.
Assocs Thanatology, *(Associates in Thanatology; 0-9607928),* 115 Blue Rock Rd., South Yarmouth, MA 02664 (SAN 281-2967) Tel 617-394-6520; Dist. by: DeVorss & Co., P.O. Box 550, 1046 Princeton Dr., Marina del Rey, CA 90294 (SAN 168-9886) Tel 213-870-7487; Dist. by: Inland Bk. Co., P.O. Box 261, East Haven, CT 06512 (SAN 200-4151) Tel 203-467-4257.
Assocs Urbanus, *(Associates of Urbanus; 0-930957),* P.O. Box 457, 36200 Freedom Rd., Farmington, MI 48024 (SAN 678-8750) Tel 313-474-9110.
Assocs Youth Dev, *(Associates for Youth Dev., Inc.; 0-913951),* P.O. Box 36748, Tucson, AZ 85740 (SAN 286-7214) Tel 602-297-1056; 1935 Harran Cir., Tucson, AZ 85704 (SAN 286-7222).
Assurance Pubs, *(Assurance Pubs.; 0-932940),* 330 Clover Ln., Garland, TX 75043 (SAN 213-005X).
Astara, *(Astara, Inc.; 0-918936),* 800 W. Arrow Hwy., P.O. Box 5003, Upland, CA 91785 (SAN 207-6446) Tel 714-981-4941.
†**Aster Pub Co,** *(Aster Publishing Co.; 0-933019),* Div. of Health Management Institute, P.O. Box 10752, Merrillville, IN 46411 (SAN 689-5387) Tel 219-980-6554; Dist. by: Biofeedback & Stress Management Services, P.O. Box 95, Schererville, IN 46375 (SAN 200-5271) Tel 503-726-1200; *CIP.*
Aster Pub Corp, *(Aster Publishing Corp.; 0-943330),* 320 N. A St., Springfield, OR 97477 (SAN 240-4869).
Asthma & Allergy, *(Asthma & Allergy Foundation of America),* 1835 K St. NW, Suite P-900, Washington, DC 20006 (SAN 227-6011) Tel 202-293-2950.
†**ASTM,** *(American Society for Testing & Materials; 0-8031),* 1916 Race St., Philadelphia, PA 19103 (SAN 201-1344) Tel 215-299-5400; *CIP.*
Astonisher Pr, *(Astonisher Pr.; 0-937255),* P.O. Box 80635, Lincoln, NE 68501 (SAN 659-0152) Tel 402-474-6227; 540 W. Joel, Lincoln, NE 68521 (SAN 659-0160).
Astor-Honor, *(Astor-Honor, Inc.; 0-8392),* 48 E. 43rd St., New York, NY 10017 (SAN 203-5022).
Astro Artz, *(Astro Artz; 0-937122),* 240 S. Broadway, 5th Fl., Los Angeles, CA 90012 (SAN 215-6229) Tel 213-687-7362.
Astro Comp Serv
See A C S Pubns Inc
Astro Dynasty Pub Hse, *(Astro Dynasty Publishing Hse.; 0-914725),* 270 N. Canon Dr., No. 1021, Beverly Hills, CA 90210 (SAN 291-8307) Tel 213-274-7249.
Astro-Graphics Servs
See Astrolabe SW

Astro Pr TX, *(Astro Press; 0-9608568),* P.O. Box 820399, Dallas, TX 75382 (SAN 238-2415).
Astro Pubs, *(Astro Pubs.; 0-941272),* 1332 University Blvd. N., Jacksonville, FL 32211 (SAN 238-9096) Tel 904-743-7344.
Astroart Ent, *(Astroart Enterprises; 0-917814),* P.O. Box 503, South Houston, TX 77587 (SAN 203-5030) Tel 713-649-6601.
Astrol Wheels, *(Astrologer on Wheels, Inc.; 0-940044),* 141 E. 55th St., New York, NY 10022 (SAN 220-2034); P.O. Box 5255, F. D. R. Sta., New York, NY 10150 (SAN 220-2042).
Astrolabe
See Astrolabe SW
Astrolabe SW, *(Astrolabe; 0-87199; 0-913637),* Div. of Astro-Graphics Services, Inc., P.O. Box 28, Orleans, MA 02653 (SAN 670-7416); 45 S. Orleans Rd., Orleans, MA 02653 (SAN 662-2038) Tel 617-255-0510; Dist. by: ACS Pubns., Inc., P.O. Box 16430, San Diego, CA 92116-0430 (SAN 208-5380) Tel 619-297-9203.
Astrologers Lib *Imprint* of **Inner Tradit**
Astrologize Am, *(Astrologize America; 0-939585),* P.O. Box 884561, San Francisco, CA 94188 (SAN 663-5113); 68 Sycamore St., San Francisco, CA 94110 (SAN 663-5121) Tel 415-558-8004.
†**AstroMedia,** *(AstroMedia; 0-913135),* Div. of Kalmbach Publishing Co., 1027 N 7th St., Milwaukee, WI 53233 (SAN 282-9703) Tel 414-272-2060; Dist. by: Tide-Mark Pr., P.O. Box 813, Hartford, CT 06142 (SAN 222-1802) Tel 203-289-0363; *CIP.*
Astron Cal
See Astron Wkshp
Astron Soc Pacific, *(Astronomical Society of the Pacific; 0-937707),* 1290 24th Ave., San Francisco, CA 94122 (SAN 225-1426) Tel 415-661-8660.
Astron Wkshp, *(Astronomical Workshop; 0-934546),* Furman Univ., Greenville, SC 29613 (SAN 209-5602) Tel 803-294-2208.
Astropoint Res, *(Astropoint Research Assocs.; 0-9615454),* 5020 S. Lake Shore Dr., Chicago, IL 60615 (SAN 695-7382) Tel 312-493-3595.
Astrosonics, *(Astrosonics Research Institute; 0-939192),* 11037 1/2 Freeman Ave., Lennox, CA 90304 (SAN 220-1631) Tel 213-673-4649.
ASU Ctr Asian, *(Arizona State Univ. Ctr. for Asian Studies; 0-939252),* Tempe, AZ 85287 (SAN 220-1623) Tel 602-965-7184.
†**ASU Lat Am St,** *(Arizona State Univ., Ctr. for Latin American Studies; 0-87918),* Social Sciences Bldg., Rm. 213, Tempe, AZ 85287 (SAN 201-1336) Tel 602-965-5127; *CIP.*
Asylums Pr
See Asylums Pr-Language
Asylums Pr-Language, *(Asylum's Press/Language; 0-940220),* 464 Amsterdam Ave., New York, NY 10024 (SAN 220-3235) Tel 212-799-4475.
At Speed Pr, *(At Speed Press; 0-940046),* P.O. Box 5400, Santa Barbara, CA 93108 (SAN 220-2050) Tel 805-966-2814; Dist. by: Motorbooks International, P.O. Box 2, 729 Prospect Ave., Osceola, WI 54020 (SAN 212-3304) Tel 715-294-3345.
At-Swim, *(At-Swim Pr.; 0-939254),* c/o Facsimile Book Shop, 16 W. 55th St., New York, NY 10019 (SAN 215-3084) Tel 212-581-2672.
At The Sign, *(At The Sign Of The Cock; 0-9613491),* 2341 Brixton Rd., Columbus, OH 43221 (SAN 657-3231) Tel 614-488-3986.
Ata Bks, *(Ata Books; 0-931688),* 1928 Stuart St., Berkeley, CA 94703 (SAN 211-4801) Tel 415-841-9613.
AT&T Comns, *(American Telephone & Telegraph-Communications; 0-938963),* Div. of AT&T Co., 295 N. Maple Ave, Rm. 5237A3, Basking Ridge, NJ 07920 (SAN 661-7166) Tel 201-221-5351. Do not confuse with AT&T Co. of New York, NY.
ATAP Corp, *(A T A P Corp.; 0-942026),* 7125 Stagecoach Trail, Knoxville, TN 37919 (SAN 238-6313) Tel 615-690-3130.
Ataraxia, *(Ataraxia; 0-915109),* 5401 Hyde Park Blvd., Chicago, IL 60615 (SAN 289-7296) Tel 312-241-7694.

Atcom, *(Atcom, Inc.; 0-915260),* 2315 Broadway, New York, NY 10024 (SAN 208-4252) Tel 212-873-5900.
ATG Co Parma, *(ATG Co.; 0-9616072),* P.O. Box 29508, Parma, OH 44129 (SAN 697-8215) Tel 216-582-4134; 11691 Mapleridge Dr., North Royalton, OH 44133 (SAN 697-8223).
Atheist Assn, *(Atheist Association),* Box 2832, San Diego, CA 92112 (SAN 226-0077).
Athena Pr, *(Athena Press, Inc.; 0-9602736),* P.O. Box 776, Vienna, VA 22180 (SAN 213-0076).
Athena Pr ND, *(Athena Pr., The; 0-940730),* 602 S. Fourth St., Grand Forks, ND 58201 (SAN 219-7081) Tel 701-775-9156.
Athena Pubns, *(Athena Pubns.; 0-932950),* P.O. Box 61, West Peterborough, NH 03468 (SAN 212-7156).
†**Athenaeum Phila,** *(Athenaeum of Philadelphia; 0-916530),* 219 S. Sixth St., E. Washington Square, Philadelphia, PA 19106 (SAN 208-5402) Tel 215-925-2688; *CIP.*
†**Atheneum,** *(Atheneum Pubs.; 0-689),* Subs. of Scribner Bk. Cos., Inc., 115 Fifth Ave., New York, NY 10003 (SAN 201-0011) Tel 212-614-1300; Toll free: 800-257-5755; Dist. by: Riverside Distribution Ctr., Front & Brown Sts., Riverside, NJ 08075 (SAN 200-5018); *CIP. Imprints:* Aladdin (Aladdin Books).(Aladdin Bks.); Argo (Argo Books).(Argo Bks.); Childrens Bk (Children's Books); McElderry Bk (McElderry Book).(McElderry Bk.).
†**Athletic,** *(Athletic Pr.; 0-87095),* P.O. Box 80250, Pasadena, CA 91108 (SAN 203-5057) Tel 213-283-3446; *CIP.*
Athletic Inst, *(Athletic Institute; 0-87670),* 200 N. Castlewood Dr., North Palm Beach, FL 33408 (SAN 203-5065) Tel 305-842-3600; Dist. by: Sterling Publishing Co., 2 Park Ave., New York, NY 10016 (SAN 211-6324) Tel 212-502-7160.
Athletics Cong, *(Athletics Congress/USA, The; 0-939254),* P.O. Box 120, Indianapolis, IN 46206 (SAN 220-164X) Tel 317-638-9155.
Atkins Video, *(Atkins Video Society; 0-9616437),* P.O. Box 120355, Nashville, TN 37212 (SAN 659-0179) Tel 914-763-8177; 1013 17th Ave., S., Nashville, TN 37212 (SAN 659-0187).
Atkinson, *(Atkinson, Mary D.; 0-937436),* 10405B 46th Ave., Beltsville, MD 20705 (SAN 215-6091) Tel 301-595-5138.
Atlan Pub Corp, *(Atlantis Publishing Corp.; 0-936158),* P.O. Box 59467, Dallas, TX 75229 (SAN 223-3959).
Atlanta Pro, *(Atlanta Professional Women's Directory, Inc.; 0-935197),* 1103 N. Hill Pkwy., Atlanta, GA 30341 (SAN 695-7331) Tel 404-524-5121; Orders to: P.O. Box 28122, Atlanta, GA 30358 (SAN 662-779X).
Atlanta TakeOut, *(Atlanta TakeOut; 0-9614544),* Div. of Lifestyle Publications Inc., P.O. Box 720635, Atlanta, GA 30358 (SAN 691-7925) Tel 404-256-6455.
Atlantas Best, *(Atlanta's Best Buys; 0-9608196),* P.O. Box 11662, Atlanta, GA 30355 (SAN 240-1878) Tel 404-261-0566.
Atlantic Coast, *(Atlantic Coastal Equity Corp.; 0-935635),* 936 47th Ave., Vero Beach, FL 32960 (SAN 696-1584) Tel 305-569-4364.
Atlantic Council US, *(Atlantic Council of the United States; 0-88410),* 1616 H St. NW, Washington, DC 20006 (SAN 225-6282) Tel 202-347-9353; Dist. by: Oelgeschlager, Gunn & Hain, 131 Clarendon St., Boston, MA 02116 (SAN 213-6937) Tel 617-437-9620.
Atlantic FL, *(Atlantic Publishing Co.; 0-910627),* P.O. Box 1197, Silver Springs, FL 32688 (SAN 268-1250) Tel 904-551-0991.
Atlantic Lakeland, *(Atlantic Publishing; 0-938677),* 1034 S. Florida Ave., Lakeland, FL 33803 (SAN 661-3829) Tel 813-688-8000.
Atlantic Law, *(Atlantic Law Bk. Co.),* 445 Capitol Ave., Hartford, CT 06106 (SAN 204-4692) Tel 203-527-1313.
†**Atlantic Monthly,** *(Atlantic Monthly Pr.; 0-87113),* Div. of Atlantic Monthly Co., 8 Arlington St., Boston, MA 02116 (SAN 264-4587) Tel 617-536-9500; Toll free: 800-343-9204; Dist. by: Little, Brown & Co., 34 Beacon St., Boston, MA 02108 (SAN 200-2205) Tel 617-227-0730; *CIP.*

Symbols/Abbreviations

†**Atlantic Pub,** *(Atlantic Publishing Co.; 0-932349),* P.O. Box 18126, Jacksonville, FL 32229 (SAN 687-3618) Tel 912-638-3559; *CIP.*

Atlantic Pub Co, *(Atlantic Publishing Co.; 0-937866),* P.O. Box 67, Tabor City, NC 28463 (SAN 215-6237) Tel 919-653-3153.

Atlantic Pub FL
See Atlantic FL

Atlantic Sunrise, *(Atlantic Sunrise Publishing; 0-9614585),* Affil. of Atlantic City Diary, 165 Atlantic Ave., McKee City, NJ 08232 (SAN 691-764X) Tel 609-641-1222; Orders to: P.O. Box 574, Pleasantville, NJ 08232 (SAN 662-2895) Tel 609-641-1222.

Atlantis, *(Atlantis Editions),* 11 E. 73rd St., New York, NY 10021 (SAN 209-312X)

Atlantis Bks
See Atlantis Edns

Atlantis Edns, *(Atlantis Editions; 0-910174; 0-917183),* P.O. Box 18326, Philadelphia, PA 19120 (SAN 207-5849) Tel 408-625-6697.

Atlas Powder, *(Atlas Powder Co.; 0-9616284),* Div. of Tyler Corp., 15301 Dallas Pkwy. Colonnade, Suite 1200, Dallas, TX 75248-4692 (SAN 658-5833) Tel 717-386-4121.

Atlas Pub, *(Atlas Publishing Corp.),* 2121 S. 48th St. ,Suite 102, Scottsdale, AZ 85253 (SAN 686-2950).

†**Atma Bks,** *(Atma Bks.; 0-914557),* Box 432, Fallsburg, NY 12733 (SAN 289-1425) Tel 914-434-6707; *CIP.*

Atomic Indus Forum, *(Atomic Industrial Forum, Inc.),* 7101 Wisconsin Ave., Bethesda, MD 20814-4805 (SAN 225-221X).

Atonement Ent, *(Atonement Enterprises; 0-9616739),* P.O. Box 660460, Sacramento, CA 95866-0460 (SAN 659-7386); 616 25th St., Apt. 1, Sacramento, CA 95816 (SAN 659-7394) Tel 916-443-5540.

ATQ, *(ATQ American Transcendental Quarterly; 0-9607894),* Univ. of Rhode Island, Dept. of English, Kingston, RI 02881 (SAN 237-9325).

ATRA, *(American Training & Research Assocs., Inc.; 0-9613999),* 147 Range Rd., Windham, NH 03087 (SAN 683-5694) Tel 603-898-1280.

Atre Soft, *(Atre Software, Inc.; 0-937989),* P.O. Box 727, Rye, NY 10580 (SAN 659-7408) Tel 914-967-2037; 16 Elm Pl., Rye, NY 10580 (SAN 659-7416).

Attic Bks, *(Attic Books Ltd.; 0-915018),* Subs. of Alex G. Malloy, Inc., P.O.Box 38, S. Salem, NY 10590 (SAN 206-8931) Tel 203-438-0396.

Attic Discoveries, *(Attic Discoveries; 0-936253),* 342 E. 50th St., Suites 1A-2F, New York, NY 10022 (SAN 697-3264) Tel 212-758-0678.

Attic Pr, *(Attic Pr.; 0-87921),* Stony Point, Rte. 2, Greenwood, SC 29646 (SAN 201-1328) Tel 803-374-3013.

Attic Salt, *(Attic Salt Pr., The; 0-9615512),* Div. of Inscript, Inc., P.O. Box 8335, Mobile, AL 36689 (SAN 696-1630); 4501 Old Shell Rd., Mobile, AL 36608 (SAN 696-1649) Tel 205-343-4691.

Atticus Pr, *(Atticus Pr.; 0-912377),* 720 Heber Ave., Calexico, CA 92231 (SAN 265-1815) Tel 619-357-3721; Dist. by: Bookpeople, 2929 Fifth St., Berkeley, CA 94710 (SAN 168-9517) Tel 415-549-3030; Dist. by: Small Press Distribution, Inc., 1814 San Pablo Ave., Berkeley, CA 94702 (SAN 204-5826) Tel 415-549-3336.

ATW Pubs
See Bishop-Rogers

†**Auburn Hse,** *(Auburn Hse. Publishing Co., Inc.; 0-86569),* Affil. of Affiliated Publications, 14 Dedham, St., Boston, MA 02030 (SAN 220-0341) Tel 617-785-2220; *CIP.*

Auburn Pr, *(Auburn Pr., Inc.; 0-938205),* 9167 Chesapeake Dr., San Diego, CA 92123 (SAN 659-7424) Tel 619-560-6431.

Auburn-Wolfe, *(Auburn-Wolfe Publishing; 0-912385),* 584 Castro St., No. 351, San Francisco, CA 94114 (SAN 265-1823) Tel 415-665-2025.

Auction Index, *(Auction Index, Inc.; 0-918819),* 30 Valentine Park, West Newton, MA 02165 (SAN 682-773X).

Auction Pr, *(Auction Pr.; 0-9613483),* 96 S. Clermont, Denver, CO 80222 (SAN 657-324X) Tel 303-399-0049.

Audio-Forum *Imprint of* **J Norton Pubs**

Audio Pr, *(Audio Pr., The; 0-939643),* 930 Sherman St., Suite 101, Denver, CO 80203 (SAN 663-5717) Tel 303-839-1112.

Audio-Visual, *(Audio-Visual Designs; 0-917451),* P.O. Box 24, Earlton, NY 12058-0024 (SAN 656-8793) Tel 518-731-2054.

Audit Investment
See Audit Investments

Audit Investments, *(Audit Investments Inc.; 0-912840),* 136 Summit Ave., Montvale, NJ 07645 (SAN 201-1301) Tel 201-358-2735.

Audubon MD, *(Audubon Naturalist Society of the Central Atlantic States, Inc.; 0-939587),* 8940 Jones Mill Rd., Chevy Chase, MD 20815 (SAN 663-6195) Tel 301-652-9188.

Audubon Naturalist, *(Audubon Naturalists Society of the Central Altlantic States, Inc.),* 8940 Jones Mill Rd., Chevy Chase, MD 20815 (SAN 225-0012) Tel 301-652-9188.

Audubon Pk Pr, *(Audubon Park Pr.; 0-9616452),* P.O. Box 4327, New Orleans, LA 70178 (SAN 659-2988) Tel 504-861-2537; 6500 Magazine St., New Orleans, LA 70118 (SAN 659-2996).

Audubon Soc Portland, *(Audubon Society of Portland; 0-931686),* 5151 NW Cornell Rd., Portland, OR 97210 (SAN 211-2132).

†**Auerbach,** *(Auerbach Pubs., Inc.; 0-87769),* Subs. of Warren, Gorham & Lamont, 1 Penn Center, New York, NY 10119 (SAN 213-0084) Tel 212-760-7500; Toll free: 800-257-8162; Orders to: 210 South St., Boston, MA 02111 (SAN 662-7188); *CIP.*

Aug Col Pr, *(Augustana College Pr., The; 0-9615558),* P.O. Box 2172, Humanities Ctr., Sioux Falls, SD 57197 (SAN 696-4834) Tel 605-336-5436.

†**Augsburg,** *(Augsburg Publishing Hse.; 0-8066),* 426 S. Fifth St., P.O. Box 1209, Minneapolis, MN 55440 (SAN 169-4081) Tel 612-330-3300; Toll free: 800-328-4648; Orders to: 57 E. Main St., Columbus, OH 43215 (SAN 146-3365) Tel 604-221-7411; Orders to: 5210 N. Lamar, P.O. Box 49337, Austin, TX 78765 (SAN 661-9495) Tel 512-459-1112; Orders to: 3224 Beverly Blvd., Box 57974, Los Angeles, CA 90057 (SAN 661-9509) Tel 213-386-3722; *CIP.*

August Corp, *(August Corp.; 0-933482),* P.O. Box 582, Scottsdale, AZ 85252 (SAN 215-2940) Tel 602-949-7366.

†**August Hse,** *(August Hse.; 0-935304; 0-87483),* P.O. Box 3223, Little Rock, AR 72203-3223 (SAN 223-7288) Tel 501-663-7300; *CIP.*

August Pubns, *(August Pubns.; 0-9613902),* P.O. Box 67, San Rafael, CA 94915 (SAN 686-290X) Tel 415-454-7772.

Augusta Jr Womans, *(Augusta Junior Woman's Club, Inc.; 0-9615980),* P.O. Box 3133, Augusta, GA 30904 (SAN 698-1682) Tel 404-736-0557.

Augusta Pubs, *(Augusta Pubs.; 0-9613217),* P.O. Box 1257, Woodbridge, CA 95258 (SAN 291-8625) Tel 209-368-2496.

Augustana, *(Augustana Historical Society; 0-910184),* Augustana College Library, Rock Island, IL 61201 (SAN 206-6378) Tel 309-794-7266.

Augustana Coll, *(Augustana College Library; 0-910182),* 35th St. & Seventh Ave., Rock Island, IL 61201 (SAN 203-5073) Tel 309-794-7266.

Augustine Fellow, *(Augustine Fellowship, Sex & Love Addicts Anonymous, Fellowship-wide Services, Inc., The; 0-9615701),* P.O. Box 119, New Town Branch, Boston, MA 02258 (SAN 696-169X) Tel 617-332-1845; Orders to: P.O. Box 88, New Town Branch, Boston, MA 02258 (SAN 696-1711).

Augustinian Coll Pr, *(Augustinian College Press; 0-9612336),* 3900 Harewood Rd. NE, Washington, DC 20017 (SAN 289-1174) Tel 202-526-4580.

Aum Pubns, *(Aum Pubns.; 0-88497),* Subs. of Agni Press, P.O. Box 32433, Jamaica, NY 11431 (SAN 201-128X) Tel 718-523-3471.

Aunt Ellen's *Imprint of* **Mod Handcraft**

Aunt Louise Pub, *(Aunt Louise Publishing Co.; 0-9616662),* P.O. Box 164, Highland Park, IL 60035 (SAN 659-7432) Tel 312-433-0204; 1229 Eaton Ct., Highland Park, IL 60035 (SAN 659-7440).

Aunt Lute Bk Co, *(Aunt Lute Bk., Co.; 0-918040),* P.O. Box 2568, Iowa City, IA 52244 (SAN 210-217X) Tel 319-338-7022.

Aura Bks, *(Aura Books; 0-937736),* 7911 Willoughby Ave., Los Angeles, CA 90046 (SAN 215-7268) Tel 213-656-9373; Toll free: 800-843-6666; Dist. by: Bookpeople, 2929 Fifth St., Berkeley, CA 94710 (SAN 168-9517) Tel 415-549-3030; Dist. by: Samuel Weiser, Inc., P.O. Box 612, York Beach, ME 03910 (SAN 202-9588) Tel 207-363-4393.

Aura Pub Co, *(Aura Publishing Co.; 0-9615513),* 707 Mill St., Santa Rosa, CA 95404 (SAN 696-1878) Tel 707-527-0270. Do not confuse with Aura Publishing Co. of New Haven, CT or Aura Publishing Co. of Brooklyn, NY.

Aurea, *(Aurea Pubns.; 0-87174),* P.O. Box 176, Allenhurst, NJ 07711 (SAN 203-5081) Tel 201-531-4535.

Aurelon, *(Aurelon Tales; 0-912388),* R.F.D. No. 3, 177 Sarles St., Mt. Kisco, NY 10549 (SAN 203-509X).

Aureon Pub, *(Aureon Publishing Co.; 0-9613386),* 716 Mountain Dr., Kerrville, TX 79057 (SAN 657-0674) Tel 512-896-1650.

Aurico, *(Aurico Publishing Co.; 0-910186),* 87 Elmwood St., Somerville, MA 02144 (SAN 203-1442) Tel 617-491-4992.

Auromere, *(Auromere, Inc.; 0-89744),* 1291 Weber St., Pomona, CA 91768 (SAN 169-0043) Tel 714-629-8255; Toll free: 800-243-0138; Dist. by: Bookpeople, 2929 Fifth St., Berkeley, CA 94710 (SAN 168-9517) Tel 415-549-3030; Dist. by: Devorss & Co., Bk. Pubs. & Distributors, P.O. Box 550, 1040 Princeton Dr., Marina del Rey, CA 90294 (SAN 168-9886) Tel 213-870-7478; Dist. by: New Leaf Distributing Co., 1020 White St. SW, Atlanta, GA 30310 (SAN 169-1449) Tel 404-755-2665; Dist. by: Samuel Weiser, P.O. Box 612, York Beach, ME 03910 (SAN 202-9588) Tel 207-363-4393; Dist. by: Inland Bk. Co., P.O. Box 261, 22 Hemingway Ave., East Haven, CT 06512 (SAN 200-4151) Tel 203-467-4257; Dist. by: Distributors, 702 S. Michigan St., South Bend, IN 46618 (SAN 212-0364) Tel 219-232-8500; Dist. by: Starlite Distributors, P.O. Box 20729, Reno, NV 89515 (SAN 131-1921).

Aurora Assocs, *(Aurora Assocs., Inc.; 0-931211),* 1140 Connecticut Ave., NW Suite 1200, Washington, DC 20036 (SAN 681-9672) Tel 202-463-0950.

Aurora News Reg, *(Aurora News Register Publishing Co.; 0-8300),* 1320 K, Aurora, NE 68818 (SAN 281-2991); Dist. by: Shirley Lueth, 1409 9th St., Aurora, NE 68818 (SAN 282-5910) Tel 402-694-3988.

Aurora Press, *(Aurora Pr.; 0-943358),* 205 Third Ave., Apt 2-A, New York, NY 10003 (SAN 240-5881) Tel 212-673-1831; Dist. by: New Leaf Distributing, The, 1020 White St., SW, Atlanta, GA 30310 (SAN 169-1449) Tel 404-755-2665; Dist. by: Samuel Weiser, Inc., P.O. Box 612, York Beach, ME 03910 (SAN 202-9588) Tel 207-363-4393; Dist. by: Bookpeople, 2929 Fifth St., Berkeley, CA 94710 (SAN 168-9517) Tel 415-549-3030.

Aurora Pubns, *(Aurora Pubns.; 0-913417),* Div. of Pacific Empire Corporation, 6214 Meridian Ave., San Jose, CA 95120 (SAN 285-8207) Tel 408-997-0437 (SAN 285-8215).

†**Aurora Pubs,** *(Aurora Pubs.; 0-87695),* 118 16th Ave., S, Nashville, TN 37203 (SAN 201-1271) Tel 615-254-5842; *CIP.*

Ausonia Pr, *(Ausonia Press; 0-912429),* 100 Thorndale Dr., No. 457, San Rafael, CA 94903 (SAN 265-1831) Tel 415-931-5553.

Austin Bilingual Lang Ed, *(Austin Bilingual Language Editions; 0-940048),* P.O. Box 3864, Austin, TX 78764 (SAN 220-2069) Tel 512-441-1436.

†**Austin Hill Pr,** *(Austin Hill Pr., Inc.; 0-89690),* 2955 Renault Pl., San Diego, CA 92122 (SAN 211-8831) Tel 619-453-6486; *CIP.*

Austin Inst Pub Aff
See LBJ Sch Pub Aff

Austin Junior, *(Austin Junior Forum, Inc.; 0-9607152),* P.O. Box 26628, Austin, TX 78755-0628 (SAN 238-9436) Tel 512-474-1311.

Austin Pr, *(Austin Pr.; 0-914872),* Div. of Lone Star Pubs. Inc., P.O. Box 9774, Austin, TX 78766 (SAN 206-7870) Tel 512-453-8611.

Austin Univ Forestry, *(Austin, Stephen F., State Univ., Schl. of Forestry; 0-938361),* P.O. Box 6109, Nacogdoches, TX 75952 (SAN 659-7459) Tel 409-569-3304; North St. & E. College Ave., Nacogdoches, TX 75961 (SAN 659-7467).

Australiana, *(Australiana Pubns.; 0-909162),* 6511 Riviera Dr., Coral Gables, FL 33146 (SAN 209-3235) Tel 305-666-9404. Name formerly Dryden Pr. of Australia.

Authentic Am Art, *(Authentic American Art, Inc.; 0-9614524),* 142 Helios Ave., Metairie, LA 70130 (SAN 689-7347) Tel 504-837-0882.

Author Aid, *(Author Aid/Research Associates International; 0-911085),* Div. of Research Associates International, 340 E. 52nd St., New York, NY 10022 (SAN 263-0672) Tel 212-758-4213.

Authors Co Op
   See AC Projects

Authors Edn
   See Authors Edn MA

Authors Edn MA, *(Authors Edition, Inc.; 0-918058),* Box 803, Lenox, MA 01240 (SAN 210-1696) Tel 413-637-0666.

Authors Note, *(Author's Note; 0-938927),* P.O. Box 30117, Long Beach, CA 90853 (SAN 661-7085); 2800 Neilson Way, No.715, Santa Monica, CA 90405 (SAN 661-7093) Tel 213-399-7528.

Authors Unltd, *(Authors Unlimited; 1-55666),* 3330 Barham Blvd., Suite 204, Los Angeles, CA 90068 (SAN 662-8044) Tel 213-874-0902.

†**Auto Bk,** *(Auto Bk. Pr.; 0-910390),* P.O. Bin 711, San Marcos, CA 92069 (SAN 201-1263) Tel 619-744-3582; *CIP.*

Auto Contact Inc, *(Automotive Contact, Inc.; 1-55527),* 3075 Canal Rd., Suite 2, Terre Haute, IN 47802 (SAN 695-4995) Tel 812-232-2441.

Auto Logic Pubns, *(Auto Logic Publns., Inc.; 0-915845),* P.O. Box 9187, San Jose, CA 95157 (SAN 293-9606) Tel 408-435-1101.

Auto Pub, *(Auto Publishing; 0-938517),* P.O. Box 425, Mira Loma, CA 91752 (SAN 661-115X); 9430 Mission Blvd., Riverside, CA 92509 (SAN 661-1168) Tel 714-685-8570.

Auto Quarterly, *(Automobile Quarterly Pubns.; 0-911968),* Div. of Princeton Publishing, 221 Nassau St, Princeton, NJ 08542 (SAN 281-3017) Tel 609-924-7555; Orders to: Rte. 222 & Sharadin Rd., P.O. Box 348, Kutztown, PA 19530 (SAN 281-3025) Tel 215-683-8352.

Automated Mktg
   See Natl Res Bur

Automated TrainingSyst, *(Automated TrainingSystems),* 21250 Califast, No. 107, Woodland Hills, CA 91367 (SAN 694-3985).

Automation in Housing Mag, *(Automation in Housing; 0-9607408),* P.O. Box 120, Carpinteria, CA 93014 (SAN 239-1589) Tel 805-684-7659.

Autonomy Hse, *(Autonomy House Publications; 0-9612204),* 417 N. Main St., Monticello, IN 47960 (SAN 263-9254) Tel 219-583-8593.

Autotronic Conversions, *(Autotronic Conversions),* P.O. Box 17249, El Paso, TX 79917 (SAN 208-2241).

Autumngold Pub, *(Autumngold Publishing; 0-931253),* P.O. Box 634, Beverly Hills, CA 90213 (SAN 681-9664) Tel 818-783-2477.

Auxiliary U Pr, *(Auxiliary Univ. Pr.; 0-913034),* Box 772, Barrington, IL 60010 (SAN 202-327X) Tel 312-381-7888.

Auxosia Gold Bks, *(Auxosia/Gold Bks.; 0-935374),* P.O. Box 4275, Houston, TX 77210 (SAN 221-2846).

AV Enter Pr, *(AV Enterprises Pr.; 0-9615715),* P.O. Box 6778, Oxnard, CA 93030 (SAN 695-9520) Tel 805-984-5800; 60 W. Fiesta Green, Port Hueneme, CA 93041 (SAN 695-9539).

AV Text Corp, *(AV-Text Corporation; 0-914865),* 733 Kings Rd., Suite 140, Los Angeles, CA 90069 (SAN 289-0577) Tel 213-658-5260.

Avalon Comm, *(Avalon Communications, Inc.; 0-88041),* 1705 Broadway, Hewlett, NY 11557 (SAN 281-3033) Tel 516-599-4555; Dist. by: Doubleday & Co., Inc., 501 Franklin Ave., Garden City, NY 11530 (SAN 281-6083) Tel 516-873-4561.

Avalon Hill, *(Avalon Hill Pubs.),* 4517 Harford Rd., Baltimore, MD 21214 (SAN 204-4633) Tel 301-254-5300.

Avant-Garde, *(Avant-Garde Media, Inc.; 0-913568),* 251 W. 57th St., New York, NY 10019 (SAN 206-9563) Tel 212-581-2000. Do not confuse with Avant-Garde Publishing Corp., Novato, CA.

Avant Garde Cr
   See Avant-Garde Pub

Avant-Garde Pub, *(Avant-Garde Publishing Corp.; 0-930182; 0-87275),* 37B Commercial Blvd., Novato, CA 94947 (SAN 210-5853) Tel 415-883-8083; Toll free: 800-874-6544. Do not confuse with Avant-Garde Media, Inc., New York, NY.

Avantage Pub, *(Avantage Publishing; 0-938733),* 85 School St., Shrewsbury, MA 01545 (SAN 661-7069) Tel 617-842-2052.

Avanyu Pub, *(Avanyu Publishing, Inc.; 0-936755),* Adobe Gallery, 413 Romero NW, Albuquerque, NM 87104 (SAN 699-8550) Tel 505-243-8485; P.O. Box 27134, Albuquerque, NM 87125 (SAN 699-8569).

Avatar MO, *(Avatar; 0-936040),* P.O. Box 16703, Raytown, MO 64133 (SAN 220-2328).

Avatar NY, *(Avatar Pr.; 0-9614674),* 41-50 48th St., Sunnyside, NY 11104 (SAN 692-5138) Tel 718-937-1933.

Avatar Pr, *(Avatar Pr.; 0-914790),* P.O. Box 7727, Atlanta, GA 30357 (SAN 206-7579) Tel 404-892-8511.

Avcom Intl, *(Avcom International Inc.; 0-941024),* P.O. Box 2398, Wichita, KS 67201 (SAN 223-1743) Tel 316-262-1491.

Ave Maria, *(Ave Maria Pr.; 0-87793),* Notre Dame, IN 46556 (SAN 201-1255) Tel 219-287-2831.

Avenel *Imprint of* Outlet Bk Co

Avenue B, *(Avenue B; 0-939691),* P.O. Box 542, Bolinas, CA 94924 (SAN 663-4753); 87 Brighton Ave., Bolinas, CA 94924 (SAN 663-4761) Tel 415-868-0681; Dist. by: Small Press Distribution, Inc., 1814 San Pablo Ave., Berkeley, CA 94702 (SAN 658-179X) Tel 415-549-3336 (SAN 204-5826).

Avenue Pub, *(Avenue Publishing Co.; 0-910977),* 9417 Conant Ave., Hamtramck, MI 48212 (SAN 268-1811) Tel 313-875-6635; 9417 Conant Ave., Hamtramck, MI 48212 (SAN 699-5144).

Avery Color, *(Avery Color Studios; 0-932212),* Star Rte., Box 275, Au Train, MI 49806 (SAN 211-1470) Tel 906-892-8251.

Avery Pr Inc, *(Avery Pr., Inc.; 0-937321),* 600 Kalmia Ave., Boulder, CO 80302 (SAN 658-8042) Tel 303-443-1592. Do not confuse with Avery Pr., Atlanta, GA.

†**Avery Pub,** *(Avery Pub. Group, Inc.; 0-89529),* 350 Thorens Ave., Garden City Park, NY 11040 (SAN 210-3915) Tel 516-741-2155; *CIP.*

†**AVI,** *(AVI Publishing Co., Inc.; 0-87055),* 250 Post Rd. E., P.O. Box 831, Westport, CT 06881 (SAN 201-4017) Tel 203-226-0738; *CIP.*

Avian Pubns, *(Avian Pubns.; 0-910335),* 310 Maria Dr., Wausau, WI 54401 (SAN 241-2691) Tel 715-845-5101.

Aviat Pub, *(Aviation Pubns.; 0-87994),* P.O. Box 357, Appleton, WI 54912 (SAN 201-713X).

Aviation, *(Aviation Bk. Co.; 0-911720; 0-911721),* 1640 Victory Blvd., Glendale, CA 91201 (SAN 120-1530) Tel 818-240-1771; Toll free: 800-423-2708; Toll free: 800-542-6657 (in California). *Imprints:* Progressive Pilot Sem (Progressive Pilot Seminars).

†**Aviation,** *(Aviation Bk. Co.; 0-911720; 0-911721; 0-916413),* 1640 Victory Blvd., Glendale, CA 91201 (SAN 212-0259) Tel 818-240-1771; Toll free: 800-423-2708; *CIP. Imprints:* Pub. by Bomber (Bomber Books).(Bomber Bks.).

Aviation Lang Sch, *(Aviation Language School Inc.; 0-941046),* 4031 Woodridge Rd., Miami, FL 33133 (SAN 239-0639) Tel 305-665-9041.

Aviation Maintenance
   See Intl Aviation Pubs

Aviation Pubns, *(Aviation Pubns., Inc.; 0-917539),* P.O. Box 12848, University Sta., Gainesville, FL 32604 (SAN 656-0563) Tel 904-375-0772.

AViation Pubs *Imprint of* Ultralight Pubns

Avocet Inc., *(Avocet, Inc.; 0-9607236),* Box 7615, Menlo Park, CA 94025 (SAN 239-1597) Tel 415-321-8501.

†**Avon,** *(Avon Bks.; 0-380),* Div. of Hearst Corp., 1790 Broadway, New York, NY 10019 (SAN 201-4009) Tel 212-399-4500; Toll free: 800-247-5470; *CIP. Imprints:* Avon Lib (Avon Library); Banner (Banner Books).(Banner Bks.); Bard (Avon Bard Books).(Avon Bard Bks.); Camelot (Avon Camelot Books).(Avon Camelot Bks.); Discus (Avon Discus Books).(Avon Discus Bks.); Flare (Avon Flare Books).(Avon Flare Bks.); Snuggle & Read (Snuggle & Read).

Avon Lib *Imprint of* Avon

†**Avons Res,** *(Avons Research Pubns.; 0-913772),* P.O. Box 40, La Canada, CA 91011 (SAN 202-3644) Tel 818-790-5370; *CIP.*

Avva, *(Avva, Inc.; 0-938013),* 735 Dolores St., Stanford, CA 94305 (SAN 659-7475) Tel 415-328-0852.

Awakening Heart Pubns, *(Awakening Heart Pubns.; 0-9616529),* P.O. Box 10092, Burbank, CA 91506 (SAN 659-4182) Tel 818-353-1584; 1512 1/2 W. Alameda Ave., Burbank, CA 91506 (SAN 659-4190).

Awakening Prods, *(Awakening Productions Inc.; 0-914706),* 4132 Tuller Ave., Culver City, CA 90230 (SAN 205-6046).

Awani Pr, *(Awani Pr.; 0-915266),* P.O. Box 881, Fredericksburg, TX 78624 (SAN 206-4626) Tel 512-997-5514.

†**AWARE,** *(AWARE; 0-916831),* P.O. Box 8371, Los Angeles, CA 90008 (SAN 654-1275) Tel 213-215-1881; *CIP.*

Awareness Marketing, *(Awareness Marketing; 0-915961),* P.O. Box 11822, Costa Mesa, CA 92627 (SAN 293-9622) Tel 714-642-3401.

AWWA Res Found, *(AWWA Research Foundation; 0-915295),* 6666 W. Quincy Ave., Denver, CO 80235 (SAN 289-9655) Tel 303-794-7711; Orders to: Computer Services, 6666 W. Quincy Ave., Denver, CO 80235 (SAN 662-7560) Tel 303-794-7711.

Axcess Soft, *(Axcess Software, Inc.; 0-938929),* 6303 S. Rural Rd., Suite 9, Tempe, AZ 85283 (SAN 697-5658) Tel 602-838-3030; Toll free: 800-AXCENTS.

Axelrod Pub, *(Axelrod Publishing of Tampa Bay; 0-936417),* 1410 N. 21st St., Tampa, FL 33605 (SAN 698-1658) Tel 813-251-5269; P.O. Box 14248, Tampa, FL 33690 (SAN 698-2611).

Axiom Pr
   See Axiom Pr Pubs

Axiom Pr Pubs, *(Axiom Pr. Pubs.; 0-933800),* P.O. Box 1668, Burlingame, CA 94011-1668 (SAN 213-2354) Tel 415-441-1211; Dist. by: J. A. Majors Co. California, 11511 Tennessee Ave., Los Angeles, CA 90064 (SAN 168-9800) Tel 213-879-1607.

Axlon Inc, *(Axlon, Inc.; 0-934571),* 1287 Lawrence Station Rd., Sunnyvale, CA 94089 (SAN 694-4353) Tel 408-747-1900.

Axlon Inc SW
   See Axlon Inc

†**Ayd Medical Comm,** *(Ayd Medical Communications; 0-931858),* 1130 E. Cold Spring Lane, Baltimore, MD 21239 (SAN 222-4712); *CIP.*

Ayer Co
   See Ayer Co Pubs

†**Ayer Co Pubs,** *(Ayer Co. Pubs., Inc.; 0-88143),* 382 Main St., P.O. Box 958, Salem, NH 03079 (SAN 211-6936) Tel 603-898-1200; *CIP.*

Aylmer Pr, *(Aylmer Pr.; 0-932314),* P.O. Box 2735, Madison, WI 53701 (SAN 212-6044) Tel 608-233-2259.

Aylsworth, *(Aylsworth Publishing Co.; 0-916572),* 21 Fairview Rd., Wilbraham, MA 01095 (SAN 208-516X) Tel 413-596-9234.

Ayt Ventures Pubs, *(Ayt Ventures Pubs.; 0-937895),* 6863 E. Mary Dr., Tucson, AZ 85730 (SAN 659-4077) Tel 602-790-1989.

AZ Antique Direct, *(Arizona Antique Directory, The; 0-9615549),* 943 W. Keating, Mesa, AZ 85202 (SAN 696-4907) Tel 602-831-9493; Dist. by: Treasure Chest Publications, P.O. Box 5250, Tucson, AZ 85703 (SAN 209-3243); Dist. by: Central Arizona Distributing, 4932 W. Pasadena Ave., Glendale, AZ 85301 (SAN 200-7630).

AZ Archaeol, *(Arizona Archaeological Society; 0-939071),* P.O. Box 9665, Phoenix, AZ 85068 (SAN 662-9342); 2602 W. Bloomfield Rd., Phoenix, AZ 85029 (SAN 662-9350) Tel 602-944-6034.

AZ Game & Fish, *(Arizona Game & Fish Dept.; 0-917563),* 2222 W. Greenway Rd., Phoenix, AZ 85023 (SAN 273-9194) Tel 602-942-3000.

AZ Hist Foun, *(Arizona Historical Foundation; 0-910152),* Hayden Memorial Library, Arizona State University, Tempe, AZ 85287 (SAN 201-7040) Tel 602-966-8331.

†AZ Hist Soc, *(Arizona Historical Society; 0-910037),* 949 E. Second St., Tucson, AZ 85719 (SAN 201-6982) Tel 602-628-5774; *CIP.*

AZ Law Inst, *(Arizona Law Institute College of Law; 0-910039),* Univ. of Arizona, Tucson, AZ 85721 (SAN 227-3535) Tel 602-621-5522.

AZ St Bar, *(State Bar of Arizona; 0-88726),* 363 N. First Ave., Phoenix, AZ 85003 (SAN 227-1400) Tel 602-252-4804.

AZ Univ ARP, *(Arizona State Univ. Anthropological Research Papers; 0-936249),* Arizona State Univ., Anthropology Dept., Tempe, AZ 85287 (SAN 697-323X) Tel 602-965-7596.

Aza Khana, *(A. Aza Khana-E-Zahra; 0-933543),* 1365 Exeter St., Baldwin, NY 11510 (SAN 691-8492) Tel 516-223-7294.

Azimuth Pr, *(Azimuth Pr.; 0-913179),* P.O. Box 660, Arnold, MD 21012 (SAN 282-9754) Tel 301-757-4455. Do not confuse with Azimuth Pr., Houston, TX.

AZSU Theatre, *(Arizona State Univ., Dept. of Theatre; 0-938675),* Arizona State Univ., Dept. of Theatre, Tempe, AZ 85287 (SAN 661-3802) Tel 602-965-2661.

Aztex, *(Aztex Corp.; 0-89404),* 1126 N. Sixth Ave., P.O. Box 50046, Tucson, AZ 85703 (SAN 210-0371) Tel 602-882-4656.

Azure Coast, *(Azure Coast Publishing Co.; 0-942514),* Div. of Werner R. Hashagen Architect & Assocs., 7480 La Jolla Blvd., La Jolla, CA 92037 (SAN 238-1419) Tel 619-459-0122; Dist. by: Quality Bks., 918 Sherwood Dr., Lake Bluff, FL 60044-2204 (SAN 169-2127) Tel 312-498-4000.

Azure Zephyr, *(Azure Zephyr Pubns.; 0-9614833),* P.O. Box 1917, Lakeside, CA 92040-0979 (SAN 693-0840); 9395 Harriet Rd., No. 105, Lakeside, CA 92040 (SAN 696-7000) Tel 619-561-0690.

B A H Publishing, *(BAH Publishing Co.; 0-9617236),* P.O. Box 302, Ashville, OH 43103 (SAN 663-5431) Tel 614-983-3735; Lot 24, Lockbourne Lodge, Rte. 1, 10610 Ashville Pike, Lockbourne, OH 43137 (SAN 663-544X).

B A Scott, *(Scott, Beverly A., Pub.),* P.O. Box 114, Chandler, AZ 85224 (SAN 207-6101) Tel 602-963-5787.

B A Trice, *(Trice, Bernie A.; 0-9616006),* 19840 SW 242nd Terr., Homestead, FL 33031 (SAN 697-9696) Tel 305-245-3395.

B & B Prod, *(B & B Productions; 0-9614578),* Box 295, St. Helena, CA 94574 (SAN 692-2880) Tel 707-963-0852.

B & B Pub CA, *(B. & B. Publishing; 0-9607008),* P.O. Box 165, Saugus, CA 91350 (SAN 238-9452) Tel 805-255-3422. Do not confuse with either B&B Pub., Inc., Westminster, CO.

B & B Pubs, *(B&B Pubs.; 0-9608674),* P.O. Box 1062, Brooksville, FL 33512 (SAN 240-5903) Tel 904-796-7712. Do not confuse with B&B Pub., Saugus, CA.

B & C Pub, *(B & C Publishing; 0-937239),* 1224 SW Lakeview Dr., Sebring, FL 33870 (SAN 658-666X) Tel 813-385-8693.

B & D Pub, *(B & D Publishing; 0-9613328),* 1915 Solano St., Suite B, Corning, CA 96021 (SAN 289-5854) Tel 916-824-1410.

B & E Pub Co, *(Butterfly & The Eagle Publishing Co., The; 0-9615560),* P.O. Box 38002, Los Angeles, CA 90038 (SAN 696-480X) Tel 213-737-6143.

B & G Assoc, *(B & G Associates; 0-9604230),* 408 Larkwood Dr., Montgomery, AL 36109 (SAN 215-0565).

B & K Ent, *(B & K Enterprises, Inc.; 0-941458),* 1053 Montview Rd., Ft. Collins, CO 80521 (SAN 239-0647) Tel 303-484-4254.

B & K Fisher, *(Fisher, Bill & Kay; 0-9603004),* P.O. Box 714, Colfax, CA 95713 (SAN 659-0918) Tel 916-346-2941.

B & M Waite Pr, *(Waite, Benjamin & Martha, Press, Ltd.; 0-934528),* 1126 E. 59th St., Chicago, IL 60637 (SAN 213-3989).

B & R Samizdat, *(B & R Samizdat Express; 0-915232),* P.O. Box 161, West Roxbury, MA 02132 (SAN 207-1037) Tel 617-469-2269.

B & S Garges, *(Garges, Beverly & Sherman, Pubs.; 0-9614041),* P.O. Box 811, Michigan Center, MI 49254 (SAN 684-8109) Tel 517-764-4183; 5235 Pine Dr., Jackson, MI 49201 (SAN 693-5184).

B & W Bks, *(B & W Bks.; 0-9614996),* 445 Meadowcrest Cir., Memphis, TN 38117 (SAN 693-0980) Tel 901-682-8009.

B B Choate, *(Choate, Betty Burton; 0-9616352),* Rte. 2, Box 156, Winona, MS 38967 (SAN 659-0330) Tel 601-283-1192; Burton Dr., Winona, MS 38967 (SAN 659-0349).

B B Feinsot, *(Feinsot, Bernice B.; 0-915526),* 330 W. 28th St., Apt. 1F, New York, NY 10001 (SAN 207-351X) Tel 212-929-2918.

B-B Leather, *(B-B Leather; 0-9616569),* P.O. Box 478, Blackfoot, ID 83221 (SAN 659-7645) Tel 208-785-1731; 719 W. Pacific, Blackfoot, ID 83221 (SAN 659-7653).

B B Stabell, *(Stabell, Brenda B.; 0-9610872),* 10827 Overbrook, Houston, TX 77042 (SAN 264-407X).

B Becker, *(Becker, Beverly; 0-9602000),* P.O. Box 360, Park Ridge, IL 60068 (SAN 212-2693) Tel 312-635-0306.

B Beckham Bks
See Beckham House

B Berkel, *(Berkel, Boyce N., M.D.; 0-9603184),* 2245 McMullen Booth Rd., Clearwater, FL 33519 (SAN 213-4667).

B Blackman, *(Blackman; 0-9615074),* P.O. Box 414, Tarzana, CA 91356 (SAN 693-9481) Tel 818-708-8877.

B Boyink, *(Boyink, Betty, Publishing; 0-9612608),* 818 Sheldon Rd., Grand Haven, MI 49417 (SAN 289-0658) Tel 616-842-3304.

B Butler, *(Butler, Barbara; 0-9614105),* P.O. Box 1044, Sisters, OR 97759 (SAN 685-9755) Tel 503-382-0755.

B C Decker, *(Decker, B. C., Inc.; 0-941158; 1-55664),* P.O. Box 30246, Philadelphia, PA 19103 (SAN 663-1584); 1919 Chestnut St., Philadelphia, PA 19103 (SAN 663-1592) Tel 215-963-9456. Canadian office: 3228 S. Service Rd., Burlington, ON L7N 3H8. Tel: 416-639-6215.

B C Elrod, *(Elrod, Bruce C.; 0-9614805),* P.O. Box 363, White Rock, SC 29177 (SAN 692-7629) Tel 803-781-8690; Toll free: 800-722-8690.

B C Scribe, *(Scribe, B. C., Pubns.; 0-930548),* P.O. Box 2453, Providence, RI 02906-0453 (SAN 212-1727) Tel 401-245-6478.

B Coats, *(Bill Coats Ltd.; 0-931709),* 1406 Grandview Dr., Nashville, TN 37215 (SAN 683-6046) Tel 615-383-8536; Dist. by: Publishers Marketing Group, 1104 Summit Ave., Plainview, TX 75074 (SAN 262-0995) Tel 214-423-0312.

B Cogill, *(Cogill, Burgess; 0-9617227),* 350 University Ave., San Francisco, CA 94134 (SAN 663-3943) Tel 415-644-1571.

B Collins, *(Collins, B.; 0-9615515),* 718 N. 23rd St., Philadelphia, PA 19130 (SAN 696-3358) Tel 215-765-5708.

B Conroy, *(Conroy, Barbara),* P.O. Box 9331, Santa Fe, NM 87504 (SAN 214-2961) Tel 505-983-9217.

B Corona, *(Corona, Belva; 0-9616840),* 1629 SW 81st, Oklahoma City, OK 73159 (SAN 661-5384) Tel 405-681-9731.

B D Beale, *(Beale, B. DeRoy; 0-9602132),* 8529 Spalding Dr., Richmond, VA 23229 (SAN 223-4971) Tel 804-741-1836.

B Dolls
See Barbara Dolls

B Dolphin Pub, *(Blue Dolphin Publishing, Inc.; 0-931892),* P.O. Box 1908, Nevada City, CA 95959 (SAN 223-2480) Tel 916-265-6923; 12380 Nevada City Hwy., Grass Valley, CA 95945 (SAN 696-009X).

B Drewry, *(Drewry, Betty; 0-9615928),* 3025 Dale Dr., NE, Atlanta, GA 30305 (SAN 697-1059) Tel 404-233-6281.

B Dube, *(Dube, Brian, Inc.; 0-917643),* 25 Park Place, New York, NY 10007 (SAN 657-0704) Tel 212-619-2182.

B E Lipman
See Bell Pub

B F Burr, *(Burr, Betty Fagan; 0-911619),* 613 Bostwick, Nacogdoches, TX 75961 (SAN 263-9491) Tel 409-564-7478.

†B Farwell, *(Farwell, Brice; 0-9600484),* 330 Heidi Ct., Morgan Hill, CA 95037 (SAN 206-7129) Tel 408-778-1650; *CIP.*

B Farwell
See Butler-Farwell

†B Franklin, *(Franklin, Burt, Pub.; 0-89102),* Affil. of Lenox Hill Publishing & Distributing Corp., 235 E. 44th St., New York, NY 10017 (SAN 282-597X) Tel 212-687-5250; Toll free: 800-223-0766; *CIP.*

B Fuller Pub, *(Fuller, Ben, Publishing Co.; 0-938807),* P.O. Box 11669, Atlanta, GA 30355-1669 (SAN 661-4973); 334 Campbell Rd., Symrna, GA 30080 (SAN 661-4981) Tel 404-433-1037.

B G Heyman, *(Heyman, Barbara G.; 0-9616831),* 2530 E. 30th St., Tulsa, OK 74114 (SAN 661-3322) Tel 918-742-7100.

B Garges
See B & S Garges

B Gaunt, *(Gaunt, Bonnie; 0-9602688),* 510 Golf Ave., Jackson, MI 49203 (SAN 221-8267).

B Gill, *(Gill, Bernard),* 4204 W. Warren, Apt. 1, Detroit, MI 48210 (SAN 699-7961).

B Glassman, *(Glassman, Barbara; 0-9614443),* P.O. Box 1058, Makawao, Maui, HI 96768 (SAN 689-3619) Tel 808-572-7132.

B Gould Pubns, *(Gould, Bruce, Pubns.; 0-918706),* P.O. Box 16, Seattle, WA 98111 (SAN 210-9964).

B Greene, *(Greene, Bill; 0-934668),* Box 810, Mill Valley, CA 94942 (SAN 213-0149).

B Grimes
See B & D Pub

B H Ward Pubns, *(Ward, Baldwin H., Pubns.; 0-913482),* 1364 N. McDowell Blvd., Petaluma, CA 94952 (SAN 203-025X) Tel 707-762-0737; 11 Davis Dr., Belmont, CA 94002 (SAN 695-4529).

B Haines, *(Haines, Ben M.; 0-9600586),* Box 1111, Lawrence, KS 66044 (SAN 202-3660) Tel 816-525-2579.

B Hallum, *(Hallum, Boen; 0-9608854),* 4977 Lockbourne Rd., Columbus, OH 43207 (SAN 241-0265) Tel 614-491-3886.

B Harris, *(Harris, Barbara; 0-9601060),* P.O. Box 2992, Portland, OR 97208 (SAN 281-7691) Tel 503-223-6434.

B Hawkins Studio, *(Hawkins, Beverly, Studio & Gallery; 0-9608084),* 20104 Halloway Ave., Matoaca, VA 23803 (SAN 240-1495) Tel 804-861-9403.

B Hochberg, *(Hochberg, Bette; 0-9600990),* 333 Wilkes Circle, Santa Cruz, CA 95060 (SAN 281-7845) Tel 408-427-2127; Dist. by: Textile Artists Supplies, 3006 San Pablo Ave., Berkeley, CA 94702 (SAN 282-6461) Tel 415-548-9988.

B Howard, *(Howard, Barney; 0-935602),* 2206 Meadowlark Dr., Harrisonville, MO 64701 (SAN 214-0314) Tel 816-884-5461.

B Hubbard, *(Hubbard, Bill; 0-9616674),* P.O. Box 1246, Cooper Sta., New York, NY 10276 (SAN 661-180X) Tel 212-460-4673; 119-20 201st Pl., St. Albans, NY 11412 (SAN 661-1818).

B I Pubs, *(B.I. Pubs.; 0-933021),* P.O. Box 1606, Indianapolis, IN 46206 (SAN 689-5433) Tel 317-312-1716.

B J Edgar, *(Edgar, Betsy J.),* Rte. 4, Box 130, Lewisburg, WV 24901 (SAN 204-174X) Tel 304-645-7642.

B J Gill, *(Gill, Bernard Jamil; 0-9616510),* 5012 Ridgewood, Detroit, MI 48204 (SAN 659-4549) Tel 313-898-1074.

B J Hebrew Tchrs, *(Beth Jacob Hebrew Teachers College Inc.; 0-934390),* 1213 Elm Ave., Brooklyn, NY 11230 (SAN 222-741X).

B J Phunn
See Phunn Pubs

B J Raheb, *(Raheb, Barbara J.; 0-938759),* 4166 Ellenita Ave., Tarzana, CA 91356 (SAN 661-7379) Tel 818-344-9640.

B J Serv, *(BJ Service; 0-911535),* 152 S. Reeves Dr., Suite 105, Beverly Hills, CA 90212 (SAN 263-9270) Tel 213-276-8945.

B J Wilson, *(Wilson, Barbara Juarez; 0-9610712),* 15 Ledyard St., San Francisco, CA 94124 (SAN 264-813X) Tel 619-454-3746.

B Jensen, *(Jensen, Bernard, Pub.; 0-9608360; 0-932615),* Rte. One, Box 52, Escondido, CA 92025 (SAN 240-690X).

B Johnson Pub, *(Johnson, Blake, Pub.; 0-9615685),* 24 Oakwood Dr., N., Englewood, FL 33533 (SAN 696-303X) Tel 813-474-4708.

B Jones U
See Bob Jones Univ Pr

B Klein Pubns, *(Klein, B., Pubns.; 0-87340),* P.O. Box 8503, Coral Springs, FL 33065 (SAN 210-7554) Tel 305-752-1708.

B L Shrout, *(Shrout, Beatrice Lentz; 0-9609070),* 513 Riverside Dr., Welch, WV 24801 (SAN 241-2500) Tel 304-436-3411.

B L Winch, *(Winch, B. L., & Assocs./Jalmar Pr.; 0-935266),* 45 Hitching Post Dr., Bldg. 2, Rolling Hills Estates, CA 90274-4297 (SAN 214-1728) Tel 213-539-6430; Toll free: 800-662-9662.

B Leahy, *(Leahy, Barbara; 0-9610312),* 15 Missin Rd., Sedona, AZ 86336 (SAN 264-1720) Tel 602-282-3518.

B Loft, *(Loft, Barnell, Ltd.; 0-87965; 0-8484),* 958 Church St., Baldwin, NY 11510 (SAN 202-3679) Tel 516-868-6064.

B M Johnson, *(Johnson, Barbara Mary),* 7381 Webb Rd., Chatsworth, CA 91311 (SAN 263-2381) Tel 818-703-1594.

†B M Rosenthal Inc, *(Rosenthal, Bernard M., Inc., Booksellers; 0-9600094),* 251 Post St., San Francisco, CA 94108 (SAN 209-0465) Tel 415-982-2219; *CIP.*

B M Stewart, *(Stewart, B. M.),* 4494 Wausau Rd., Okemos, MI 48864 (SAN 202-0548) Tel 517-349-0297.

B McBogg, *(McBogg, Bruce; 0-941400),* 3405 Alcott St., Denver, CO 80211 (SAN 237-9848).

B McGaw Graphics, *(Bruce McGaw Graphics, Inc.; 0-9613932),* 230 Fifth Ave., New York, NY 10001 (SAN 683-5600) Tel 212-679-7823.

B Martin Pubs, *(Martin, Ben, Pubs.; 0-936449),* P.O. Box 4912, Shreveport, LA 71104 (SAN 697-9041) Tel 318-798-1022.

B Matthews Inc, *(Bill Matthews, Inc.; 0-9613734),* P.O. Box 26727, Lakewood, CO 80226 (SAN 677-5446) Tel 303-922-0055.

B Minkow, *(Minkow, Barry; 0-9615900),* 7040 Darby Ave. No. 207-208, Reseda, CA 91335 (SAN 696-6381) Tel 818-344-7615.

B Montgomery, *(Montgomery, Barbara; 0-9615738),* 2481 Morton St., Oak park, MI 48237 (SAN 695-8613) Tel 313-399-0824.

B Morrow Conjunctions
See Conjunctions

B Movie, *(B-Movie Publishing; 0-930959),* 743 N. Harper Ave., Los Angeles, CA 90046 (SAN 678-8769) Tel 213-651-3317.

B Nixdorf, *(Nixdorf/Bert),* 9 Randolph Drive, Mt. Holly, NJ 08060 (SAN 264-2530).

B of A, *(B of A Communications Co.; 0-911238),* P.O. Box 22252, Louisiana State Univ., Baton Rouge, LA 70893 (SAN 204-6776) Tel 504-272-6600; Pelican Office Ctr., 11628 S. Choctaw Dr., Baton Rouge, LA 70815 (SAN 200-4208); Orders to: P.O. Box 15809, Broadview Sta., Pelican Office Products Ctr., Baton Rouge, LA 70895 (SAN 669-2567). *Imprints:* Acct Pubns (Accounting Publications); Malibu Pubns (Malibu Publications); Regent House (Regent House).

B O'Hara, *(O'Hara, Betsy; 0-9604188),* 2562 26th Ave., San Francisco, CA 94116 (SAN 219-9777) Tel 415-731-1472. Not to be confused with O'Hara Publications in Burbank, CA.

B P Reynolds, *(Reynolds, Bryan P.; 0-9606448),* P.O. Box 186, Palos Park, IL 60464 (SAN 215-8027) Tel 312-257-7757.

B Palmer
See R H Palmer

B Pearson, *(Pearson, Bob, Enterprises, Inc.; 0-9608378),* Box 9901, Birmingham, AL 35220-0901 (SAN 240-4249) Tel 205-833-6944.

B R E Pub, *(B.R.E. Pubs.; 0-9611368),* Affil. of Non-Denominational Bible Prophesy Study Assn., 339 E. Laguna Dr., Tempe, AZ 85282 (SAN 265-380X) Tel 602-967-3066.

B R K Ent, *(B.R.K. Enterprises, Inc.),* 336 S. Donald Ave., Arlington Heights, IL 60004 (SAN 285-6859) Tel 312-259-8376.

B R Landes, *(Landes, Burton R.; 0-915568),* 11 College Ave., Trappe, PA 19426 (SAN 207-3625) Tel 215-489-2908.

B R Phillips, *(Phillips, Bradley Ray & Kyle Lee Helmick; 0-9613513),* Rte. 3 Box 333, Buckhannon, WV 26201 (SAN 679-2049).

B Rabin, *(Rabin, Barry; 0-9603968),* 5595 E. Seventh St., Suite 353, Long Beach, CA 90804 (SAN 658-8433) Tel 213-494-5604.

B Royal Pr, *(Ben Royal Pr.; 0-9603198),* 19 Highland Ave., Randolph, VT 05060 (SAN 222-2817).

B Rubes
See Rubes Pubns

B Rugged, *(Rugged, B.; 0-9612018),* 11 S. Adelaide Ave., Highland Park, NJ 08904 (SAN 277-6561) Tel 201-828-6098.

B Ryder, *(Ryder, Beverly; 0-9614390),* 2428 Lisa Ln., Madison, WI 53711 (SAN 688-6558) Tel 608-271-3452.

B S Beaulieu, *(Beaulieu, Beth Sea; 0-9608796),* 22 Wells Ave., Chicopee, MA 01020 (SAN 241-0001) Tel 413-598-8551.

B S Prods, *(B. S. Productions; 0-939565),* P.O. Box 4465, Sparks, NV 89432 (SAN 663-4931); 5200 Pyramid Lake Hwy., Spanish Springs, NV 89432 (SAN 663-494X) Tel 702-673-9425.

B Sales, *(Sales, Billee; 0-9605244),* 2638 NW 59th Ave., Margate, FL 33063 (SAN 215-8051).

B Schneider, *(Schneider, Bennett, Bookseller; 0-918797),* 300 Ward Parkway, Kansas City, MO 64112 (SAN 657-3266) Tel 816-531-8484.

B Segal, *(Segal, Berty, Inc.; 0-938395),* 1749 Eucalyptus St., Brea, CA 92621 (SAN 660-9759) Tel 714-529-5359.

B Sheldon, *(Sheldon, Bill, Pub.; 0-9616668),* 5478 Mary Jo Way, San Jose, CA 95124 (SAN 659-9079) Tel 408-264-2728.

B Stallard, *(Stallard, Bernard; 0-9606908),* 73 Woodsdale, Cincinnati, OH 45216 (SAN 282-3061); Orders to: Rte. 1, Box 60, Morningview, KY 41063 (SAN 662-1511) Tel 606-356-3990.

B Success Press, *(B. Success Pr.; 0-933523),* 5030 Arundel Dr., Woodland Hills, CA 91364 (SAN 691-8506) Tel 818-346-3829; Box 812, Tarzana, CA 91356 (SAN 698-2077).

B T Memorial Hospital, *(Auxiliary of Burdette Tomlin Memorial Hospital; 0-9608326),* Cape May Court House, Cape May, NJ 08210 (SAN 240-5156) Tel 609-368-5068.

B Terrell, *(Terrell, Bob),* P.O. Box 66, Asheville, NC 28802 (SAN 209-1941) Tel 704-255-8435.

B Twitchell, *(Twitchell, Bob; 0-9616798),* 207 W. Holly, Bellingham, WA 98225 (SAN 661-0366) Tel 206-676-1222.

B-TwoC, *(B2C Adventures; 0-939368),* 2 Carvel Rd., Annapolis, MD 21401 (SAN 212-2103) Tel 301-974-0642.

B-TwoFDC
See B-TwoC

B W Brace, *(Brace, Beverly W.),* 6352 St. Joseph Ave. NW, Albuquerque, NM 87120 (SAN 210-3435) Tel 505-831-5551.

B W H Pubns, *(Busche-Waugh-Henry Pubns.; 0-931511),* P.O. Box 10382, Seattle, WA 98101 (SAN 682-2878) Tel 206-382-0386.

B W Hice, *(Hice, Bethell Whitley; 0-9608046),* 1344 Fairview Ave., Bridgeport, WA 98813 (SAN 240-1509).

B Warrior, *(Warrior, Betsy; 0-9601544),* 46 Pleasant St., Cambridge, MA 02139 (SAN 210-993X)Box E-94, Earlham College, Richmond, IN 47374 (SAN 662-1813) Tel 317-962-6561.

B West, *(West, Bill; 0-911614),* 536 E. Ada Ave., Glendora, CA 91740 (SAN 202-3687) Tel 818-335-7060.

B Wikenhauser, *(Wikenhauser, Betty; 0-9613796),* 15212 Harvest Ave., Norwalk, CA 90650 (SAN 678-9609) Tel 213-868-7039.

B Wilson, *(Wilson, Bob; 0-9608192),* 1542 Big Horn Ave., Sheridan, WY 82801 (SAN 240-3021) Tel 307-674-8422.

B Wilson KY, *(Wilson, Billy; 0-9617160),* Rte. 5, Box 222, Irvine, KY 40336 (SAN 662-9520) Tel 606-723-5889. Do not confuse with B. Wilson of Sheridan, WY.

B Winkelman Prods, *(Winkleman, Babe, Productions, Inc.; 0-915405),* P.O. Box 407, 213 NW Fourth St., Brainerd, MN 56401 (SAN 291-4700) Tel 218-829-1144.

B Witt, *(Witt, Bud; 0-9604932),* P.O. Box 2527, 4212 W. Olive, Fullerton, CA 92633 (SAN 215-7160).

B Wood Assocs, *(Wood, Bob, Assocs.; 0-937863),* 6916 E. Fourth Plain Blvd., Vancouver, WA 98668 (SAN 659-6045) Tel 206-694-0628; Dist. by: Pacific Pipeline, 19215 66th Ave. S., Kent, WA 98032 (SAN 208-2128) Tel 206-872-5523; Dist. by: All Sports Book Distributors, Box 5793, Denver, CO 80217 (SAN 200-7398).

B Woodley Pr, *(Woodley, Bob, Memorial Pr., The; 0-939391),* Div. of Bob Woodley Memorial Foundation, Washburn Univ., Topeka, KS 66621 (SAN 663-1266) Tel 913-295-6448.

Babies Milk Fund, *(Babies Milk Fund Children's & Prenatal Clinics; 0-9614115),* 231 Bethesda Ave., Rm. 6109, Cincinnati, OH 45267 (SAN 686-256X) Tel 513-281-8000; Dist. by: Seven Hills Bks., 49 Central Ave., Suite 300, Cincinnati, OH 45202 (SAN 169-6629) Tel 513-381-3881.

Babka Pub, *(Babka Publishing Co.; 0-930625),* P.O. Box 1050, Dubuque, IA 52001 (SAN 204-4609); 100 Bryant, Dubuque, IA 52001 (SAN 661-9525) Tel 319-588-2073.

Babson College, *(Babson College Ctr. for Entrepreneurial Studies; 0-910897),* Babson College, Wellesley, MA 02157 (SAN 263-0737) Tel 617-239-4332.

Baby Grande Prods, *(Baby Grande Productions; 0-9614348),* 352 N. Columbus St., Galion, OH 44833 (SAN 687-7699) Tel 419-468-9672.

Bacadaa, *(Bacadaa, Ltd.; 0-9616763),* 18928 Sorrento, Detroit, MI 48235 (SAN 659-7742) Tel 313-864-1320.

Bacchus Pr, *(Bacchus Press; 0-940416),* 4225 Candleberry Ave., Seal Beach, CA 90740 (SAN 219-7669) Tel 213-430-5245; Dist. by: Publishers Group West, 5835 Beaudry Ave., Emeryville, CA 94608 (SAN 202-8522) Tel 415-658-3453; Dist. by: GBC Press, 630 S. 11th St., Las Vegas, NV 89127 (SAN 203-414X) Tel 702-382-7555.

Bacchus Wine, *(Bacchus Wine Pr.; 0-9613525),* Div. of Bacchus Press, Ltd., 1421 Jordan St., Baltimore, MD 21217 (SAN 657-5773) Tel 301-576-0762.

Back Bay, *(Back Bay Bks., Inc.; 0-939126),* P.O. Box 1396, Newport Beach, CA 92663 (SAN 216-1060) Tel 714-645-4900.

Back Door Pr, *(Back Door Pr.; 0-9605568),* 124B Fourth Ave., N., Edmonds, WA 98020 (SAN 241-3620).

Back Fork Bks, *(Back Fork Bks.),* Drawer 752, Webster Springs, WV 26288 (SAN 240-4699).

Back Roads
See Monday Bks

†Back Row Pr, *(Back Row Pr.; 0-917162),* 1803 Venus Ave., St. Paul, MN 55112 (SAN 208-5569) Tel 612-633-1685; *CIP.*

Back to Eden, *(Back To Eden Bks., Publishing Co.; 0-940676),* P.O. Box 1439, Loma Linda, CA 92354 (SAN 218-5318) Tel 714-796-9615.

†Backcountry Pubns, *(Backcountry Pubns., Inc.; 0-942440),* P.O. Box 175, Woodstock, VT 05091 (SAN 238-1427) Tel 802-457-1049; Toll free: 800-635-5009; Dist. by: Countryman Pr., P.O. Box 175, Woodstock, VT 05091 (SAN 206-4901) Tel 802-457-1049; *CIP.*

†Backeddy Bks, *(Backeddy Bks.; 0-9603566),* Box 301, Cambridge, ID 83610 (SAN 211-4615); *CIP.*

Backroads, *(Backroads; 0-933294),* Box 14, Kelly, WY 83011 (SAN 213-831X).

Backside Pr, *(Backside Pr.; 0-915855),* P.O. Box 112412, San Diego, CA 92111 (SAN 293-9630) Tel 619-291-1740.

Backspace Ink, *(Backspace Ink; 0-9616675),* 372 Second Ave., San Francisco, CA 94118 (SAN 659-7777) Tel 415-387-6892.

Backstreet, *(Backstreet Editions, Inc.; 0-943018),* Box 555, Port Jefferson, NY 11777 (SAN 240-3404) Tel 516-821-0678.

†Backwater Corp, *(Backwater Corp.; 0-913539),* 7438 SE 40th St., Mercer Island, WA 98040 (SAN 285-1520) Tel 206-232-2171; *CIP.*

Backwoods Bks, *(Backwoods Bks.; 0-938833),* P.O. Box 9, Gibbon Glade, PA 15440 (SAN 661-700X) Tel 412-329-4581.

Backwoods Pubns, *(Backwoods Pubns.; 0-911997),* Div. of Backwoods Films, 130 Watervliet Ave, Dayton, OH 45420 (SAN 263-9289) Tel 513-254-5299.

Backyard Music, *(Backyard Music; 0-9614939),* P.O. Box 9047, New Haven, CT 06532 (SAN 693-6776) Tel 203-469-5756.

Bacon St Pr, *(Bacon St. Pr.; 0-9610438),* 46 Western Ave., Sherborn, MA 01770 (SAN 238-0390).

†**Badger Bks,** *(Badger Books; 0-930478),* P.O. Box 40336, San Francisco, CA 94140 (SAN 211-0008) Tel 415-285-2708; *CIP.*

Badlands Natl Hist, *(Badlands Natural History Assn.; 0-912410),* P.O. Box 6, Interior, SD 57750 (SAN 202-3695) Tel 605-433-5361.

Bae Pub Co, *(Bae Publishing Co.; 0-9613363),* P.O. Box 225, Higley, AZ 85236 (SAN 292-3270) Tel 602-988-2182.

Baen Bks, *(Baen Bks.; 1-55594),* Div. of Baen Publishing Enterprises, 260 Fifth Ave., New York, NY 10001 (SAN 658-8417) Tel 212-532-4111; Dist. by: Simon & Schuster, Inc., 1230 Ave. of the Americas, New York, NY 10020 (SAN 200-2450) Tel 212-245-6400.

Baffico Breger, *(Baffico/Breger Video, Inc.; 0-939243),* 915 Broadway, New York, NY 10010 Tel 212-254-3900.

Baggeboda Pr, *(Baggeboda Pr.; 0-932591),* 1128 Rhode Island St., Lawrence, KS 66044 (SAN 687-505X) Tel 913-842-0490.

Baggiani-Tewell, *(Baggiani-Tewell Educational Materials, Inc.; 0-934329),* 4 Spring Hill Ct., Chevy Chase, MD 20815 (SAN 693-6024) Tel 301-656-3353.

†**Baha'i,** *(Baha'i Publishing Trust; 0-87743),* 415 Linden Ave., Wilmette, IL 60091 (SAN 213-7496) Tel 312-251-1854; Toll free: 800-323-1880; *CIP.*

Bahm, *(Bahm, Archie J.; 0-911714),* 1915 Las Lomas Rd., NE, Albuquerque, NM 87106 (SAN 212-5854) Tel 505-242-9983. *Imprints:* World (World Books).

Baikar Assn, *(Baikar Assn., Inc.; 0-936893),* 468 Mt. Auburn St., Watertown, MA 02172 (SAN 658-4748) Tel 617-924-4420.

Bailliere-Tindall *Imprint of* **Saunders**

Baines, *(Baines, Gwendolyn; 0-9614505),* 1800 Meade St., Nashville, TN 37207 (SAN 691-7429) Tel 615-262-9615.

Baja Bks, *(Baja Bks.; 0-9602838; 0-9615829),* P.O. Box 4151, Santa Barbara, CA 93140 (SAN 213-0122) Tel 805-962-4029; Dist. by: Ingram Bk. Co., P.O. Box 17266, Nashville, TN 37217 (SAN 169-7978); Dist. by: Cogan Bks., 4332 W. Artesia Ave., Fullerton, CA 92633 (SAN 168-9649); Dist. by: Publishers Group West, 5855 Beaudry St., Emeryville, CA 94608 (SAN 202-8522) Tel 415-658-3453.

Baja Enter, *(Baja Enterprises; 0-9609470),* P.O. Box 11988, Costa Mesa, CA 92627 (SAN 260-163X) Tel 714-760-7036.

Baja Pr, *(Baja Pr.; 0-910041),* 2829 Nipoma St., San Diego, CA 92106 (SAN 241-2055) Tel 619-223-1563.

Baja Trail, *(Baja Trail Pubns., Inc.; 0-914622),* P.O. Box 6088, Huntington Beach, CA 92615 (SAN 206-3301) Tel 714-847-2252.

Bakar Press, *(Bakar Pr.; 0-939295),* P.O. Box 496, Cape Neddick, ME 03902 (SAN 662-7927); Old Mountain Rd., Cape Neddick, ME 03902 (SAN 662-7935) Tel 207-646-6210.

Bakebks & Cookbks, *(Bakebooks & Cookbooks, Inc.; 0-9606686),* P.O. Box 92185, Milwaukee, WI 53202 (SAN 219-7111) Tel 414-461-9813.

Baker-Berwick, *(Baker-Berwick Pubns., Inc.; 0-938403),* 304 S. Prospect St., Kent, OH 44240 (SAN 659-7807) Tel 216-673-5162.

Baker Bk, *(Baker Bk. Hse.; 0-8010),* P.O. Box 6287, Grand Rapids, MI 49516-6287 (SAN 201-4041) Tel 616-676-9186.

Baker Gallery, *(Baker Gallery Pr.; 0-912196),* P.O. Box 1920, Lubbock, TX 79408 (SAN 202-3709) Tel 806-763-2500.

Baker Library *Imprint of* **Kelley**

Baker Pub, *(Baker Publishing; 0-913193),* 9348 Monogram Ave. Suite 120, Sepulveda, CA 91343 (SAN 282-9762) Tel 818-892-5747.

†**Baker St Prod,** *(Baker Street Production, Ltd.; 0-914867),* 502 Range St., Box 3610, Mankato, MN 56001 (SAN 289-0585) Tel 507-625-2482; *CIP.*

Baker St Pub, *(Baker Street Pub.; 0-9594025),* 402 Hemingway Dr., Bel Air, MD 21014 (SAN 687-6471).

Baker Voorhis, *(Baker, Voorhis & Co., Inc.; 0-8320),* 30 Smith Ave., Mount Kisco, NY 10549 (SAN 658-6384).

Baker's Plays, *(Baker, Walter H., Co.; 0-87440),* 100 Chauncy St., Boston, MA 02111 (SAN 202-3717) Tel 617-482-1280.

†**Bala Bks,** *(Bala Bks.; 0-89647),* 268 W. 23rd St., New York, NY 10011 (SAN 284-9747) Tel 212-929-8073; *CIP.*

Balaban Intl Sci Serv, *(Balaban International Science Services; 0-86689),* Dist. by: International Pubs. Service, P.O. Box 230, Accord, MA 02018 (SAN 654-9357) Tel 617-749-2966.

Balaban Pub, *(Balaban Publishing Co.; 0-9617121),* 163 Joralemon St., Suite 1502, Brooklyn, NY 11201 (SAN 662-4731) Tel 718-403-9743.

†**Balamp Pub,** *(Balamp Publishing; 0-913642),* 4205 Fullerton Ave., Detroit, MI 48238 (SAN 202-4330) Tel 313-491-1950; Orders to: P.O. Box 02367, North End, Detroit, MI 48202 (SAN 202-4349); *CIP.*

Balance Beam Pr, *(Balance Beam Pr., Inc.; 0-912701),* 12711 Stoneridge Rd., Dayton, MN 55327 (SAN 282-9770) Tel 612-427-3168.

Balboa Pub, *(Balboa Publishing; 0-935902),* 101 Larkspur Landing Cir., Larkspur, CA 94939 (SAN 220-035X) Tel 415-461-8884.

Balch I E S, *(Balch Institute; 0-937437),* 18 S. Seventh St., Philadelphia, PA 19106 (SAN 695-7838).

Balcom, *(Balcom Bks.; 0-9600008),* 320 Bawden St., Apt. 401, Ketchikan, AK 99901 (SAN 202-3725) Tel 907-225-2496.

Balcones Co, *(Balcones Co.; 0-9615782),* 225 Congress Ave., No. 153, Austin, TX 78711 (SAN 696-6837) Tel 512-346-8337; P.O. Box 2143, Austin, TX 78711 (SAN 698-2093).

Baldner J V, *(Baldner, Jean V.; 0-9615317),* 19203 N. 29th Ave., Phoenix, AZ 85027 (SAN 694-6526) Tel 602-582-0312.

Baldwin Manor Pr, *(Baldwin Manor Pr.; 0-9617094),* 4722 Baptist Rd., Pittsburgh, PA 15227 (SAN 662-474X) Tel 412-881-4384.

Bale Bks, *(Bale Bks.; 0-912070),* Div. of Bale Pubns., P.O. Box 2727, New Orleans, LA 70176 (SAN 201-405X); 5121 St. Charles Ave., Suite 13, New Orleans, LA 70115 (SAN 661-9533).

Bales
See Applied Press

Baliey Pubns
See Rockcom Pub

Ball State Art, *(Ball State Univ. Art Gallery; 0-915511),* Muncie, IN 47306 (SAN 278-1344) Tel 317-285-5242.

†**Ball State Univ,** *(Ball State Univ.; 0-937994),* Muncie, IN 47306 (SAN 239-4081); *CIP.*

†**Ballantine,** *(Ballantine Bks., Inc.; 0-345),* Div. of Random Hse., Inc., 201 E. 50th St., New York, NY 10022 (SAN 214-1175) Tel 212-751-2600; Toll free: 800-638-6460; Orders to: 400 Hahn Rd., Westminster, MD 21157 (SAN 214-1183); *CIP.* *Imprints:* Del Rey (Del Rey Bks.).(Del Rey Bks.).

Ballantrae Tech, *(Ballantrae Technical Bks.; 0-936333),* 9 Grandview Rd., Suite 2201, Windham, NH 03087 (SAN 697-8231) Tel 603-434-1246.

Ballena Pr, *(Ballena Pr.; 0-87919),* 823 Valparaiso Ave., Menlo Park, CA 94025 (SAN 201-4076) Tel 415-323-9261; Orders to: Ballena Press Publishers Service, P.O. Box 2510, Novato, CA 94948 (SAN 669-0181) Tel 415-883-3530.

Balletmonographs, *(Balletmonographs; 0-9604232),* 2545 Pomeroy Ct., S, San Francisco, CA 94080 (SAN 214-3054).

†**Ballinger Pub,** *(Ballinger Publishing Co.; 0-88410; 0-88730),* Subs. of Harper & Row, Inc., 54 Church St., Harvard Sq., Cambridge, MA 02138 (SAN 201-4084) Tel 617-492-0670; Toll free: 800-638-3030; *CIP.*

Ballyhoo Bks, *(Ballyhoo Bks.; 0-936335),* P.O. Box 534, Shoreham, NY 11786 (SAN 697-8487) Tel 516-929-8148; R.R. 1, Box 447C, Sylvan Dr., Wading River, NY 11792 (SAN 698-2239).

†**Balsam Pr,** *(Balsam Pr., Inc.; 0-917439),* Div. of Rutledge Bks., 122 E. 25th St., 4th Flr., New York, NY 10010 (SAN 208-4503) Tel 212-598-6976; Dist. by: Kampmann & Co., Inc., 9 E. 40th St., New York, NY 10016 (SAN 202-5191) Tel 212-685-2928; *CIP.*

Baltic Cinema, *(Baltic Cinematographic Research Centre Press, The; 0-941618),* 921 Norwood, Melrose Park, IL 60160 (SAN 239-1619) Tel 312-343-8857.

Baltimore CFSCC, *(Baltimore County Fire Service Centennial Committee; 0-9608952),* 800 York Rd., Towson, MD 21204 (SAN 241-2063) Tel 301-494-4531.

Baltimore Co Pub Lib, *(Baltimore County Public Library; 0-937076),* 320 York Rd., Towson, MD 21204 (SAN 214-3429).

†**Baltimore Mus,** *(Baltimore Museum of Art; 0-912298),* Art Museum Dr., Baltimore, MD 21218 (SAN 201-7431) Tel 301-396-6316; Orders to: The Museum Shop, Art Museum Dr., Baltimore, MD 21218 (SAN 201-744X) Tel 301-396-6338; *CIP.*

Baltimore NRHS, *(Baltimore NRHS Pubns.; 0-9601320),* 4710 Keswick Rd., Baltimore, MD 21210 (SAN 202-4365) Tel 301-467-8849; Orders to: 2107 N. Charles St., Baltimore, MD 21218 (SAN 202-4373) Tel 301-685-6161.

Baltimore Streetcar, *(Baltimore Streetcar Museum; 0-9609638),* Box 7184, Baltimore, MD 21218 (SAN 262-5857) Tel 301-484-7773.

Baltimore Veg, *(Baltimore Vegetarians; 0-931411),* P.O. Box 1463, Baltimore, MD 21203 (SAN 686-2098) Tel 301-752-8348; Dist. by: New Leaf Distributing, The, 1020 White St., SW, Atlanta, GA 30310 (SAN 169-1449) Tel 404-755-2665.

Bamberger, *(Bamberger Bks.; 0-917453),* P.O. Box 1126, Flint, MI 48501-1126 (SAN 657-0690) Tel 313-234-8069; Dist. by: Small Pr. Distribution, 1814 San Pablo Ave., Berkeley, CA 94702 (SAN 204-5826) Tel 415-549-3336; Dist. by: Inland Bk. Co., P.O. Box 261, 22 Hemingway Ave., East Haven, CT 06512 (SAN 200-4151) Tel 203-467-4257; Dist. by: Bookslinger, 213 E. Fourth St., St. Paul, MN 55101 (SAN 169-4154) Tel 612-221-0429.

Bamboo Ridge Pr, *(Bamboo Ridge Pr.; 0-910043),* P.O. Box 61781, Honolulu, HI 96822-8781 (SAN 240-8740) Tel 808-395-7098.

Bambook Pubns, *(Bambook Pubns.; 0-939567),* P.O. Box 1403, Weatherford, TX 76086-1403 (SAN 663-4648); 405 Valley Ln., Weatherford, TX 76086 (SAN 663-4656) Tel 817-594-8202.

BAN Pub Boston, *(BAN Publishing Co.; 0-938357),* 6 Rollins Pl., Boston, MA 02114 (SAN 698-178X) Tel 617-227-1332; Orders to: Bettina A. Norton, 6 Rollins Pl., Boston, MA 02114 (SAN 662-7846).

Banbury *Imprint of* **Dell**

Banbury Pub Co, *(Banbury Publishing Co.; 0-9609598),* P.O. Box 926, 302 W. Jefferson, Effingham, IL 62401 (SAN 260-1648) Tel 217-347-7555.

Bancroft Parkman, *(Bancroft Parkman, Inc.; 0-914022),* P.O. Box 236, Washington, CT 06793 (SAN 215-0581) Tel 212-737-2715.

Bancroft Pr, *(Bancroft Press; 0-914888),* 27 McNear Dr., San Rafael, CA 94901 (SAN 206-4634) Tel 415-454-7094.

Bancroft Whitney Co, *(Bancroft-Whitney Co.; 0-8321),* 301 Brannan St., San Francisco, CA 94107 (SAN 204-5389) Tel 415-986-4410.

Bandanna Bks, *(Bandanna Bks.; 0-942208),* 209 W. de la Guerra, Santa Barbara, CA 93101 (SAN 238-7956) Tel 805-962-9996.

Bandar Log, *(Bandar Log, Inc.; 0-9617036),* P.O. Box 86, Magdalena, NM 87825 (SAN 662-8222).

Bande Hse Pub, *(Bande House Publishing Co.; 0-943760),* 1142 Manhattan Ave., Manhattan Beach, CA 90266 (SAN 238-2458) Tel 213-379-6924.

B&N
See B&N Imports

B&N Bks *Imprint of* **Har-Row**
B&N Imports, *(Barnes & Noble Bks.-Imports; 0-389),* Div. of Littlefield, Adams & Co., 81 Adams Dr., Totowa, NJ 07512 (SAN 206-7803) Tel 201-256-8600. *Imprints:* Art (Art Series); FB (Focus Books).(Focus Bks.); Key (Keynote Series); SocSP (Social Science Paperbacks); SP (Science Paperbacks); U (U Books).(U Bks.); UP (University Paperbacks).(Univ. Paperbacks).
Bandon Hist, *(Bandon Historical Society; 0-932368),* P.O. Box 737, Bandon, OR 97411 (SAN 212-2677) Tel 503-347-2164.
B&T, *(Brodsky & Treadway; 0-9610914),* 10-R Oxford St., Somerville, MA 02143 (SAN 265-0924) Tel 617-666-3372.
Banjar Pubns, *(Banjar Pubns.; 0-9617181),* Box 32164, Minneapolis, MN 55432 (SAN 663-6292).
Banjo Pr
   See Tamarack Edns
Bank Admin Inst, *(Bank Administration Institute; 1-55520),* 60 Gould Ctr., Rolling Meadows, IL 60008 (SAN 204-4552) Tel 312-228-2308.
Bank Lease Pubns, *(Bank Lease Consultants Financial Pubns.; 0-933355),* Div. of Bank Lease Consultants Inc., 2950 Merced St., San Leandro, CA 94577 (SAN 691-7658) Tel 415-895-1900; 3401 W. End Ave., Suite 706, Nashville, TN 37203 (SAN 662-2909) Tel 615-383-1930.
Bank Mktg Assn, *(Bank Marketing Assn.),* 309 W. Washington St., Chicago, IL 60606 (SAN 224-8611) Tel 312-782-1442.
Bank St Pr, *(Bank Street Pr., The; 0-935505),* 24 Bank St., New York, NY 10014 (SAN 696-0634) Tel 212-255-0692.
†**Bankers,** *(Bankers Publishing Co.; 0-87267),* 210 South St., Boston, MA 02111 (SAN 201-4564) Tel 617-426-4495; *CIP.*
Bankers Pr, *(Bankers Pr., Inc.; 0-9602414),* 5810 S. Green St., Chicago, IL 60621 (SAN 213-0130).
Banks-Baldwin, *(Banks-Baldwin Law Publishing Co.; 0-8322),* University Ctr., P.O. Box 1974, Cleveland, OH 44106 (SAN 204-5370) Tel 216-721-7373; Toll free: 800-362-4500 (OH).
Banmar Inc, *(Banmar Inc.; 0-9614989),* 4239 Monroe St., Toledo, OH 43606 (SAN 693-7594) Tel 419-473-2940.
Bannack Pub Co, *(Bannack Publishing Co.; 0-916027),* 207 Iowa Dr., Golden, CO 80403 (SAN 294-6785) Tel 303-279-2207.
Banned Bks *Imprint of* **Williams Pub Co**
Banner *Imprint of* **Avon**
Banner *Imprint of* **Exposition Pr FL**
Banner Bks, *(Banner Bks., Inc.; 0-9615938),* P.O. Box 70302, Reno, NV 89570 (SAN 697-0184) Tel 702-825-6363.
Banner Books CA, *(Banner Bks.; 0-939693),* 6458 Lake Shore Dr., San Diego, CA 92119 (SAN 663-4745) Tel 619-697-4182. Do not confuse with Banner Bks. Intl., Sherman Oaks, CA.
Banner of Truth, *(Banner of Truth, The; 0-85151),* P.O. Box 621, Carlisle, PA 17013 (SAN 211-7738) Tel 717-249-5747.
†**Banner Pr AL,** *(Banner Pr., Inc.; 0-87121),* P.O. Box 20180, Birmingham, AL 35216 (SAN 204-5362) Tel 205-822-4783; *CIP.*
†**Banner Pr NY,** *(Banner Pr.; 0-916650),* P.O. Box 6469, Chicago, IL 60680 (SAN 212-0119) Tel 312-663-1843; *CIP.*
Banning Pr, *(Banning, Arthur J., Pr.; 0-938060),* 509 Foshay Tower, Minneapolis, MN 55402 (SAN 220-0368) Tel 612-788-9248.
Banquet Hse, *(Banquet Hse. Pubs.; 0-934109),* 184 Main St., Lancaster, NH 03584 (SAN 693-2800) Tel 603-788-4427.
Banster Pr, *(Banster Pr., The; 0-9604620),* P.O. Box 7326, Menlo Park, CA 94025 (SAN 218-4656) Tel 415-851-8032.
†**Bantam,** *(Bantam Bks., Inc.; 0-553),* 666 Fifth Ave., New York, NY 10019 (SAN 201-3975) Tel 212-765-6500; Toll free: 800-323-9872; Orders to: 414 E. Golf Rd., Des Plaines, IL 60016 (SAN 201-3983); *CIP.* *Imprints:* Minibooks (Minibooks); Pathfinder (Pathfinder Books).(Pathfinder Bks.); Peacock (Peacock); Skylark (Skylark); Spectra (Spectra); Starfire (Starfire); Windstone (Windstone).

†**Banyan Bks,** *(Banyan Books; 0-916224),* P.O. Box 431160, Miami, FL 33243 (SAN 208-340X) Tel 305-665-6011; *CIP.*
Banyan Tree, *(Banyan Tree Bks.; 0-9604320),* 1963 El Dorado Ave., Berkeley, CA 94707 (SAN 207-3862); Dist. by: Bookpeople, 2929 Fifth St., Berkeley, CA 94710 (SAN 168-9517) Tel 415-549-3030.
Baptist Pub Hse, *(Baptist Publishing Hse.; 0-89114),* 1319 Magnolia St., Texarkana, TX 75501-4493 (SAN 183-6544) Tel 214-793-6531.
Baptist Span
   See Casa Bautista
Bar Co, *(Bar Co.; 0-9615482),* 1900 Westlake Ave., N., Seattle, WA 98109 (SAN 696-0669) Tel 206-282-0212.
Bar Guide, *(Bar Guide Enterprises; 0-918338),* P.O. Box 4044, Terminal Annex, Los Angeles, CA 90051 (SAN 210-041X) Tel 818-883-5369.
Barah, *(Barah Publishing; 0-930292),* P.O. Box 697, San Anselmo, CA 94960 (SAN 209-3480) Tel 415-459-1165.
Baraka Bk, *(Baraka Bks.; 0-914829),* Subs. of Movement of Spiritual Inner Awareness, P.O. Box 3935, Los Angeles, CA 90051 (SAN 289-1395) Tel 213-737-4055; 3500 W. Adams Blvd., Los Angeles, CA 90018 (SAN 289-1409).
Baranski Pub Co, *(Baranski Pub. Co.; 0-941974),* P.O. Box 4527, Topeka, KS 66604 (SAN 238-0005).
Baranski Pub Corp
   See Baranski Pub Co
Bararossa Pr, *(Barbarossa Pr.; 0-9617086),* P.O. Box 4, Victor, CO 80860 (SAN 662-5908); 200 N. Third St., Victor, CO 80860 (SAN 662-7900) Tel 303-689-2714.
Barbacoa Pr, *(Barbacoa Pr.; 0-933579),* P.O. Box 32576, Kansas City, MO 64111 (SAN 692-2058) Tel 816-753-3208; Toll free: 800-255-0513; Dist. by: Ingram Industries, 347 Reedwood Dr., Nashville, TN 37217 (SAN 169-7978); Dist. by: Publishers Group West, 5855 Beaudry St., Emeryville, CA 94608 (SAN 202-8522) Tel 415-658-3453.
Barbara Dolls, *(Barbara Dolls; 0-918564),* Box 736, Bowie, MD 20715 (SAN 210-0665); 2700 Balsam Pl., Bowie, MD 20715 (SAN 210-0673) Tel 301-262-2968.
Barbara Schwartz, *(Schwartz, Barbara; 0-936627),* 3835 Sedgwick Ave., 9-B, Bronx, NY 10463 (SAN 699-6930) Tel 212-365-2611.
Barbary Coast Bks, *(Barbary Coast Bks.; 0-936041),* P.O. Box 3645, Oakland, CA 94609 (SAN 697-0060) Tel 415-653-8048; 5362 Miles Ave., Oakland, CA 94618 (SAN 697-0079).
Barbed Wire Pr, *(Barbed Wire Pr.; 0-935269),* Subs. of Western Imports, Inc., P.O. Box 2107, Stillwater, OK 74076 (SAN 695-748X) Tel 405-743-3370.
Barber Co, *(Barber Co.; 0-937125),* 2203 NW 63rd St., Seattle, WA 98107 (SAN 658-4713) Tel 206-782-2779.
†**Barber Pr,** *(Barber, Lilian, Pr.; 0-936508),* P.O. Box 232, Grand Central Sta., New York, NY 10163 (SAN 214-1817) Tel 212-874-2678; *CIP.* *Imprints:* Ethnographica (Ethnographica).
Barber W A
   See W A Barber
Barbour & Co, *(Barbour & Co., Inc.; 0-916441),* Div. of Book Bargains, Inc., 164 Mill St., Westwood, NJ 07675 (SAN 295-7094) Tel 201-664-0577; Toll free: 800-221-2648; Dist. by: Spring Arbor Distributors, 10885 Textile Rd., Belleville, MI 48111 (SAN 158-9016) Tel 313-481-0900; Dist. by: Ingram Industries, 347 Reedwood Dr., Nashville, TN 37217 (SAN 169-7978) Tel 615-361-5000; Dist. by: Baker & Taylor Cos., The, 1515 Broadway, New York, NY 10036 (SAN 169-5606) Tel 212-730-7650; Dist. by: Riverside Bk. & Bible Hse., Inc., 1500 Riverside Dr., P.O. Box 370, Iowa Falls, IA 50126 (SAN 169-2666) Tel 515-648-4269; Dist. by: Living Bks., Inc., 12155 Magnolia Ave., Bldg. 11-B, Riverside, CA 92503 (SAN 169-006X) Tel 714-354-7330; Dist. by: Cicero Bible Pr., 1901 Airport Rd., Harrison, AR 72601 (SAN 200-7231) Tel 501-741-3400.

Barclay Bridge, *(Barclay Bridge Supplies, Inc.; 0-87643),* 8 Bush Ave., Port Chester, NY 10573 (SAN 202-3768) Tel 914-937-4200.
Barclay Pr, *(Barclay Pr.; 0-913342),* P.O. Box 232, Newberg, OR 97132 (SAN 201-7520) Tel 503-538-7345.
Barclay Pubs, *(Barclay Pubs., Inc.; 0-9614429),* 203 Gary Rd., Carrboro, NC 27510 (SAN 690-0410) Tel 919-967-5350.
Bard *Imprint of* **Avon**
Bard Games, *(Bard Games/Arcanum, Inc.; 0-9610770),* P.O. Box 7729, Greenwich, CT 06836 (SAN 265-0789) Tel 203-661-4547.
Bard Hall Pr, *(Bard Hall Pr.; 0-916491),* 32 Nickerbocker at Oak, Tenafly, NJ 07670 (SAN 295-2459) Tel 201-567-7629; Dist. by: Persea Books, Inc., 225 Lafayette St., New York, NY 10012 (SAN 212-8233) Tel 212-431-5270.
Bard Pr, *(Bard Pr.; 0-934776),* 799 Greenwich St., New York, NY 10014 (SAN 214-1035) Tel 212-929-3169. Do not confuse with Avon Bard, an imprint of Avon Bks.
Bardavon Bks *Imprint of* **Valentine Pub**
Bardic, *(Bardic Echoes Pubns.; 0-915020),* P.O. Box 5339, Ft. Wayne, IN 46895 (SAN 207-0952) Tel 219-484-3718.
Barding Pub, *(Barding, L.F., Publishing; 0-9605848),* P.O. Box 06264, Ft. Myers, FL 33906 (SAN 216-5880) Tel 813-936-2774.
Bargain Hunt Ntebks, *(Bargain Hunter's Notebooks; 0-9613971),* P.O. Box 157, Old Greenwich, CT 06870 (SAN 682-2851) Tel 203-637-3320.
Bargara Pr, *(Bargara Press; 0-911087),* 1523 Fillmore St., Lynchburg, VA 24501 (SAN 268-2176) Tel 804-332-5147; Rte. 2, Box 444, Rustburg, VA 24588 (SAN 268-2184) Tel 804-332-0961.
Bark-Back, *(Bark-Back; 0-9603338),* P.O. Box 235, Glenshaw, PA 15116 (SAN 213-4624) Tel 412-364-3743.
Barking Dog, *(Barking Dog Pr.; 0-937131),* Box 253, Storm Lake, IA 50588 (SAN 658-4675) Tel 712-732-5671.
Barks Pubns, *(Barks Pubns., Inc.; 0-943876),* 400 N. Michigan Ave., Suite No. 1016, Chicago, IL 60611-4198 (SAN 241-0974) Tel 312-321-9440.
Barksdale Foun, *(Barksdale Foundation; 0-918588),* P.O. Box 187, Idyllwild, CA 92349 (SAN 210-1718) Tel 714-659-4676.
†**Barlenmir,** *(Barlenmir House, Pubs.; 0-87929),* 413 City Island Ave., New York, NY 10464 (SAN 201-4556) Tel 212-885-2120; *CIP.*
Barleycorn, *(Barleycorn Books; 0-935566),* 290 SW Tualatin Loop, West Linn, OR 97068 (SAN 213-6104) Tel 503-225-0234.
Barlina Bks, *(Barlina Bks., Inc.; 0-937525),* 7405 Colshire Dr., Suite 240, McLean, VA 22102 (SAN 659-0217) Tel 703-442-8870.
Barn Owl Bks, *(Barn Owl Books; 0-9609626),* Box 7727, Berkeley, CA 94707 (SAN 268-2214) Tel 415-848-1395.
Barnaby Bks, *(Barnaby Books; 0-940350),* 3290 Pacific Heights Rd., Honolulu, HI 96813 (SAN 217-5010) Tel 808-524-1490.
Barnard Roberts, *(Barnard, Roberts & Co., Inc.; 0-934118),* 305 Gun Rd., Baltimore, MD 21227 (SAN 213-4632) Tel 301-247-2242.
Barnegat, *(Barnegat Light Pr.; 0-937996),* P.O. Box 305, Barnegat Light, NJ 08006 (SAN 215-6253); 7 Wynnewood Dr., Cranbury, NJ 08512 (SAN 661-9541) Tel 609-395-0316. *Imprints:* Pine Barrens Pr (Pine Barrens Pr.).
Barnes-Bks, *(Barnes-Bks.; 0-917732),* Div. of MOIC, R.R. 1, Box 14340, Ft. Ann, NY 12827 (SAN 682-2622) Tel 518-793-4791; Orders to: Baker & Taylor, 501 S. Gladiolus St., Momence, IL 60954 (SAN 169-4901).
Barnes Pub, *(Barnes, John W., Publishing, Inc.; 0-914822),* P.O. Box 323, Scarsdale, NY 10583 (SAN 223-6281).
Barney Pr, *(Barney Press; 0-9607888),* 8300 Kern Canyon Rd. No. 60, Bakersfield, CA 93306 (SAN 238-1443) Tel 805-395-4433.
Barniak Pubns, *(Barniak Pubns.; 0-9613803),* 424 S. Kentucky Ave., Evansville, IN 47714 (SAN 679-3959) Tel 812-425-1272.
Barnstable, *(Barnstable Bks.; 0-918230),* 799 Broadway, Rm. 506A, New York, NY 10003 (SAN 210-1726) Tel 212-473-8681.
Barnwood Pr, *(Barnwood Pr. Cooperative, The; 0-935306),* River Hse., R.R. 2, Box 11C, Daleville, IN 47334 (SAN 223-7245).

Baron Pub Co, *(Baron Publishing Co., Inc.; 0-935843),* P.O. C-230, Scottsdale, AZ 85252 (SAN 696-0693) Tel 602-941-2418; 7777 E. Main St., Suite 161, Scottsdale, AZ 85251 (SAN 696-0707).

Baron-Scott Enterp, *(Baron/Scott Enterprises, Inc.; 0-943588),* 8804 Monard Dr., Silver Spring, MD 20910 (SAN 240-5938) Tel 301-587-2444.

Barone & Co, *(Barone & Co.; 0-89234; 0-89234),* 3530 Edmunds St. NW, Washington, DC 20007 (SAN 293-2326) Tel 202-337-0076; c/o 1984 Almanac National Journal, 1730 M St. NW, Washington, DC 20036 (SAN 293-2334) Tel 202-857-1400.

Baroness FL, *(Baroness Pubns., Ltd., Inc.; 0-938568),* 1442 Gulf-to-Bay, Clearwater, FL 33515 (SAN 238-714X).

Barr-Randol Pub, *(Barr-Randol Publishing Co.; 0-934581),* 136A N. Grand Ave., West Covina, CA 91791 (SAN 694-0714) Tel 818-339-0270.

†**Barre,** *(Barre Publishing Co.),* ; Toll free: 800-526-4264; Dist. by: Crown Publishers, Inc., 225 Park Ave., New York, NY 10003 (SAN 200-2639) Tel 212-254-1600; *CIP. Imprints:* Westover (Westover Pub Co.).

Barrett, *(Barrett & Co., Pubs.; 0-9609396),* P.O. Box 6700, Jackson, MS 39212 (SAN 240-8732) Tel 601-373-4400; P.O. Box 1182, Houston, TX 77251 (SAN 685-3161) Tel 713-641-6335.

Barrett Bk, *(Barrett Bk. Co.; 0-932684),* 1123 High Ridge Rd., Stamford, CT 06905 (SAN 211-5883).

Barrie Rd Bks, *(Barrie Road Bks.; 0-937293),* 6400 Barrie Rd., No. 611, Edina, MN 55435 (SAN 658-7771) Tel 612-929-7692.

Barrier & Kennedy, *(Barrier & Kennedy, ESL; 0-911743),* P.O. Box 58273, Raleigh, NC 27658 (SAN 276-9689) Tel 919-847-1079.

Barrington AZ, *(Barrington Pr.; 0-916229),* 4102 E. 27th St., Tucson, AZ 85711 (SAN 294-8990) Tel 602-745-0070; Dist. by: Pacific Literary Assocs., 4102 E. 27th St., Tucson, AZ 85711 (SAN 200-7770).

Barrington CA
   See Barrington AZ

Barrington Hse, *(Barrington Hse. Publishing Co.; 0-935323),* 1119 Lorne Way, Sunnyvale, CA 94087 (SAN 695-7501) Tel 408-241-8422.

Barrington IA, *(Barrington Hall Pr.; 0-942066),* Box 118, Greeley, IA 52050 (SAN 238-6429) Tel 319-925-2962.

Barrington MA, *(Barrington Pr.; 0-9616920),* P.O. Box 291, Boston Univ. Sta., Boston, MA 02215 (SAN 661-3942); 28 Lakewood Rd., Newton Highlands, MA 02161 (SAN 661-3950) Tel 617-969-9346.

Barron Enter, *(Barron Enterprises; 0-9603446),* 714 Willow Glen Rd., Santa Barbara, CA 93105 (SAN 222-2787) Tel 805-687-5873.

Barrows Co, *(Barrows Co., Inc.; 0-89069),* 116 E. 66th St., New York, NY 10021 (SAN 203-137X) Tel 212-772-1199.

Barth, *(Barth, Robert L.; 0-941150),* 14 Lucas St., Florence, KY 41042 (SAN 238-9126).

Bartholomew Bks, *(Bartholomew Bks.; 0-933123),* P.O. Box 634, Inverness, CA 94937 (SAN 689-7363) Tel 415-669-1664.

Bartleby, *(Bartleby, The, a Cape Elizabeth Journal; 0-937981),* Cape Elizabeth High Schl., Ocean House Rd., Cape Elizabeth, ME 04107 (SAN 659-4905) Tel 207-799-3309.

Bartleby Pr, *(Bartleby Pr.; 0-910155),* 11141 Georgia Ave., No. A6, Silver Spring, MD 20902 (SAN 241-2098) Tel 301-949-2443.

Barton-Jay Proj, *(Barton-Jay, David, Projects, The; 0-910409),* 175 Fifth Ave., Suite 3156, New York, NY 10010 (SAN 260-1168) Tel 212-929-4576.

Barton Pub, *(Barton Publishing Co.; 0-9616702),* P.O. Box 160786, Austin, TX 78746 (SAN 659-7939); 1406-B Rabb Rd., Austin, TX 78704 (SAN 659-7947) Tel 512-447-2871.

Basal Books, *(Basal Books; 0-916961),* Div. of Basal-Tech, Inc., 726 Lafayette Ave, Cincinnati, OH 45220 (SAN 292-3289) Tel 513-751-2723.

Basbery Pub, *(Basbery Publishing Co.; 0-912875),* 2349 Seven Pines Dr., Suite 4, St. Louis, MO 63146 (SAN 283-2941) Tel 314-434-0329.

Base Eight, *(Base 8 Publishing; 0-938207),* P.O. Box 1211, Carpinteria, CA 93013 (SAN 659-7874); 4415-A Catlin Cir., Carpinteria, CA 93013 (SAN 659-7882) Tel 805-684-1153.

Baseball Hist, *(Baseball Histories, Inc.; 0-9608534),* P.O. Box 15168, St. Louis, MO 63110 (SAN 240-5954) Tel 314-535-4215.

Basement Pr, *(Basement Pr.; 0-9611240),* P.O. Box 284, Columbus, NE 68601 (SAN 283-0825) Tel 402-564-5054.

Bash Educ Serv, *(Bash Educational Services, Inc.; 0-938408),* P.O. Box 2115, San Leandro, CA 94577 (SAN 218-4664) Tel 415-278-8275.

†**Basic,** *(Basic Bks., Inc.; 0-465),* Subs. of Harper & Row Pubs., Inc., 10 E. 53rd St., New York, NY 10022 (SAN 201-4521) Tel 212-207-7292; Toll free: 800-242-7737; *CIP.*

BASIC Bedell, *(B. A. S. I. C./Bedell Advertising Selling Improvement Corp.; 0-916014),* 2040 Alameda Padre Serra, Santa Barbara, CA 93103 (SAN 223-6648).

Basic Comp Lit, *(Basic Computer Literacy Inc.; 0-931983),* 370 N. Locust, Manteno, IL 60950 (SAN 686-0931) Tel 815-468-8178.

Basic Eng Rev, *(Basic English Revisited; 0-9605312; 0-939045),* P.O. Box J, Burlington, WI 53105 (SAN 215-2959) Tel 414-763-8258.

Basic Sci Pr, *(Basic Science Pr.; 0-917410),* 1608 Via Lazo, Palos Verdes Estates, CA 90274 (SAN 209-6498) Tel 213-375-6740.

†**Basil Blackwell,** *(Blackwell, Basil, Inc.; 0-631; 0-85520; 0-423; 0-900186; 0-904679; 0-7456; 0-233),* Subs. of Basil Blackwell, Ltd. (UK), 432 Park Ave. S., Suite 1503, New York, NY 10016 (SAN 680-5035) Tel 212-684-2890; Orders to: (Individuals' orders only), P.O. Box 1655, Hagerstown, MD 21741 (SAN 658-2656) Tel 301-824-7300; Orders to: Harper & Row Pubs., Inc. (Trade orders), Keystone Industrial Pk., Scranton, PA 18512 (SAN 215-3742); *CIP.*

Basil Blackwell *Imprint of* **Porcupine Pr**

Basil Hill Inc, *(Basil Hill, Inc.; 0-910207; 0-930299),* R.D. 1, Morris, PA 16938 (SAN 238-0625) Tel 301-622-3289.

Basin Plateau Pr, *(Basin/Plateau Pr.; 0-9617133),* P.O. Box 155, Eureka, UT 84628 (SAN 662-9563); Hatfield at Emerald Alley, Eureka, UT 84628 (SAN 662-9571) Tel 801-248-0709.

Basin Pub, *(Basin Publishing Co.),* 168 Weyford Terrace, Garden City, NY 11530 (SAN 208-4562) Tel 516-741-0668.

Basis Bks, *(Basis Bks.; 0-9614676),* P.O. Box 5254, Lake Station, IN 46405 (SAN 690-0402) Tel 219-962-3502.

†**Bask Indus,** *(Bask Industries; 0-917746),* 400 Dwight Rd., Burlingame, CA 94010 (SAN 209-1992) Tel 415-347-8396; *CIP.*

Bassett & Brush, *(Bassett & Brush; 0-9605548),* W. 4108 Francis Ave., Spokane, WA 99205 (SAN 216-3349).

Bassion Pub
   See Happy Hands Pub Co

Bataan Bk Pubs, *(Bataan Bk. Pubs., Inc.; 0-9608294),* P.O. Box 18238, Pittsburgh, PA 15236 (SAN 240-1339) Tel 412-653-3884.

Bath Maine
   See ME Maritime Mus

Bath St Pr, *(Bath Street Press; 0-937618),* 1016 Bath St., Ann Arbor, MI 48103 (SAN 215-2967) Tel 313-663-2071.

BATI, *(Biofeedback & Advanced Therapy Institute, Inc.; 0-942558),* 5979 W. Third St., Suite 205, Los Angeles, CA 90036 (SAN 239-6181) Tel 213-938-0478.

Battaglia Ent, *(Battaglia Enterprises Inc.; 0-9614063),* 3280 Turner Hill Rd., Lithonia, GA 30058 (SAN 686-0540) Tel 404-482-2603.

†**Battelle,** *(Battelle Pr.; 0-935470),* Div. of Battelle Memorial Institute, 505 King Ave., Columbus, OH 43201-2693 (SAN 213-4640) Tel 614-424-6393; Toll free: 800-526-7254; *CIP.*

Batterers Anon, *(Batterers Anonymous Press; 0-9612754),* 1269 North E St., San Bernardino, CA 92405 (SAN 289-730X) Tel 714-884-6809.

Battery Pk, *(Battery Park Book Co.; 0-89782),* Box 710, Forest Hills, NY 11375 (SAN 211-5891).

.**Battery Pr,** *(Battery Pr.; 0-89839),* P.O. Box 3107, Uptown Sta., Nashville, TN 37219 (SAN 212-5897) Tel 615-298-1401.

Bauer, *(Bauer, Rosemarie),* Rte. 1, Box 1438, Granite City, IL 62040 (SAN 217-2984).

†**Bauhan,** *(Bauhan, William L., Inc.; 0-87233),* Old County Rd., Dublin, NH 03444 (SAN 204-384X) Tel 603-563-8020; *CIP.*

Bawa Muhaiyad
   See Fellowship Pr PA

Bawden Bros, *(Bawden Bros, Inc.),* 400 S. 14th Ave., Eldridge, IA 52748 (SAN 212-0585) Tel 319-285-4800.

Baxter Group, *(Baxter Group, The; 0-938949),* P.O. Box 61672, Sunnyvale, CA 94086 (SAN 661-7247); 2966 Moorpark, No. 36, San Jose, CA 95128 (SAN 661-7255) Tel 408-248-8308.

Bay Alfred
   See Alfred Bay

Bay Area CA, *(Bay Area Explorers; 0-9615635),* P.O. Box 519, San Ramon, CA 94583 (SAN 696-0782) Tel 415-828-4957.

Bay Area Cross, *(Bay Area Cross Cultural Consultants; 0-932211),* 10344 San Pablo Ave., El Cerrito, CA 94530 (SAN 686-600X) Tel 415-526-1633.

Bay Area Pilipino, *(Bay Area Pilipino Writers; 0-9616181),* P.O. Box 5646, San Francisco, CA 94101 (SAN 658-3148) Tel 415-626-1650.

†**Bay Brewster,** *(Bay Bks., of Brewster; 0-918781),* P.O. Box L, Brewster, MA 02631 (SAN 657-3290) Tel 617-255-7591; *CIP.*

Bay Inst SF, *(Bay Institute of San Francisco; 0-937995),* 5080 Paradise Dr., Tiburon, CA 94920 (SAN 659-7890) Tel 415-435-5922.

Bay Pr, *(Bay Pr.; 0-941920),* 3710 Discovery Rd., N, Port Townsend, WA 98368 (SAN 237-9902) Tel 206-385-1270.

Bay Pubns, *(Bay Pubns.; 0-9615014),* P.O. Box 404, Panama City, FL 32401 (SAN 694-034X) Tel 904-785-7870; Dist. by: Wimmer Brothers Bks., 4210 B.F. Goodrich Blvd., Memphis, TN 38181 (SAN 209-6544) Tel 901-362-8900.

Bay Vil Womens, *(Bay Village Women's Club & Foundation; 0-9616678),* 343 Walmar Dr., Bay Village, OH 44140 (SAN 659-7904) Tel 216-871-3075.

Bayard Pubns, *(Bayard Pubns., Inc.; 0-933268),* 500 Summer St., Stamford, CT 06901 (SAN 212-4033) Tel 203-327-0800.

Bayberry NY, *(Bayberry Pr.; 0-936403),* 7 Colonial Rd., Port Washington, NY 11050 (SAN 698-164X) Tel 516-767-0633.

Bayberry Pr, *(Bayberry Pr.; 0-916326),* 21 Little Fox Ln., Westport, CT 06880 (SAN 222-562X).

Bayland Pub, *(Bayland Publishing, Inc.; 0-934010),* P.O. Box 25386, Houston, TX 77005 (SAN 214-1051) Tel 713-524-3000. *Imprints:* Houston Home-Garden Mag (Houston Home/Garden Magazine Books).

Baylin Gale, *(Baylin/Gale Productions; 0-917893),* 1905 Mariposa, Boulder, CO 80302 (SAN 697-2721) Tel 303-449-4551.

Bayliss Corbett, *(Corbett, Bayliss; 0-933152),* 762 Ave N. SE, Winter Haven, FL 33880 (SAN 212-5935) Tel 813-294-5555.

Baylor Univ Pr, *(Baylor Univ. Pr.; 0-918954),* Academic Pubns., CSB 547, Baylor Univ., Waco, TX 76798 (SAN 685-317X) Tel 817-755-3164; Orders to: Book Dept., Baylor Bk. Store, P.O. Box 6325, Waco, TX 76706 (SAN 204-4404) Tel 817-755-2161.

Bayou Chene
   See Beau Bayou

Bayou Cuisine, *(Bayou Cuisine; 0-9606490),* P.O. Box 1005, Indianola, MS 38751 (SAN 208-0613) Tel 601-887-5425.

Bayou Pr, *(Bayou Pr.; 0-9615254),* Div. of Angleton Investments, Inc., P.O. Box 1086, Angleton, TX 77515 (SAN 694-4574) Tel 409-849-4874.

Bayou Pub Co, *(Bayou Publishing Co.; 0-9602570),* 5200 Bon Air Dr., Monroe, LA 71203 (SAN 213-2850) Tel 318-343-1964.

†**Bayshore Bks,** *(Bayshore Books; 0-9602314),* Box 848, Nokomis, FL 33555 (SAN 212-7237) Tel 813-485-2564; *CIP.*

Bayside, *(Bayside Publishing Co.; 0-913794),* 1350 77th Ave. N., St. Petersburg, FL 33702 (SAN 202-3806).

Bayway Bks, (Bayway Bks.; 0-938363), P.O. Box 66436, St. Petersburg Beach, FL 33736 (SAN 659-7912); 4900 Brittany Dr. S., Suite 901, St. Petersburg, FL 33715 (SAN 659-7920) Tel 813-867-0025.

†**Baywood Pub,** (Baywood Publishing, Co., Inc.; 0-89503), 120 Marine St., P.O. Box D, Farmingdale, NY 11735 (SAN 206-9326) Tel 516-293-7130; CIP.

BBIP
See ISD

BBM Assocs
See Calif Street

BC
Imprint of Grove

BCC, (Business Communications Co., Inc.; 0-89336), P.O. Box 2070C, 9 Viaduct Rd., Stamford, CT 06906 (SAN 207-706X) Tel 203-325-2208.

BCG Ltd, (BCG Ltd.; 0-9615201), Div. of DPMS, 1209 NW Blvd., Spokane, WA 99205 (SAN 694-3578) Tel 509-328-7307.

BCM Inc
See BCM Intl Inc

BCM Intl Inc, (BMC International, Inc.; 0-86508), 237 Fairfield Ave., Upper Darby, PA 19082 (SAN 211-7762) Tel 215-352-7177.

BCS Assocs, (BCS Associates; 0-914515), P.O. Box 3614, Univ. Sta., Moscow, ID 83843 (SAN 289-5838) Tel 208-855-6692.

BCS Educ Aids, (BCS Educational Aids, Inc.; 0-938416), P.O. Box 100, Bothell, WA 98041 (SAN 239-9326) Tel 206-485-4110.

Bd Cert Safety, (Board of Certified Safety Professionals), 208 Burwash Ave., Savoy, IL 61874 (SAN 225-2422) Tel 217-359-9263.

Bd Church & Soc, (Board of Church & Society of United Methodist Church), 100 Maryland Ave. NE., Washington, DC 20002 (SAN 234-5625); Dist. by: Discipleship Resources for Church and Society, 1908 Grand Ave., P.O. Box 189, Nashville, TN 37202 (SAN 661-9932).

Bd of Pubn LCA, (Board of Pubn., LCA; 0-8006), 2900 Queen Lane, Philadelphia, PA 19129 (SAN 213-1110) Tel 215-848-6800; Toll free: 800-367-8737.

Bd of Pubns CRC
See CRC Pubns

BDR Learn Prods, (BDR Learning Products, Inc.; 0-934698), P.O. Box 3356, Annapolis, MD 21403 (SAN 212-2227) Tel 301-263-1775.

Be All Bks, (Be All Books; 0-9601848), P.O. Box 941, Sonoma, CA 95476 (SAN 212-1476).

BE Pubs, (BE Pubs.; 0-9617074), 955 Connecticut Ave., Bridgeport, CT 06607 (SAN 662-6246) Tel 203-576-1007; Toll free: 800-826-8692.

Beacham, (Beacham, Roger, Pub.; 0-911796), 4509 Balcones Dr., Austin, TX 78731 (SAN 202-3814) Tel 512-451-4572.

Beachcomber Bks, (Beachcomber Books; 0-913076), P.O. Box 197, Cortaro, AZ 85652 (SAN 202-3822) Tel 602-744-1619.

Beachcomber Pr, (Beachcomber Press; 0-9614628), Box 1313 Belgrade Rd., Oakland, ME 04963 (SAN 691-8891) Tel 207-465-7197.

Beacon
See Beacon Hill

Beacon Hill, (Beacon Hill Pr. of Kansas City; 0-8341), Subs. of Nazarene Publishing Hse., ; Dist. by: Nazarene Publishing Hse., P.O. Box 527, Kansas City, MO 64141 (SAN 202-9022) Tel 816-931-1900.

Beacon Hse, (Beacon Hse., Inc.; 0-87648), Welsh Rd. & Butler Pk., Ambler, PA 19002 (SAN 202-3830) Tel 215-643-7800.

†**Beacon Pr,** (Beacon Pr., Inc.; 0-8070), 25 Beacon St., Boston, MA 02108 (SAN 201-4483) Tel 617-742-2110; Orders to: Harper & Row Pubs., Inc., 10 E. 53rd St., New York, NY 10022 (SAN 200-2086) Tel 212-207-7099; CIP. Imprints: Ariadne Bks (Ariadne Books).

Beacon West, (Beacon West Pubns.; 0-9613168), P.O. Box 1176, Encinitas, CA 92024 (SAN 294-9008) Tel 619-753-4707.

Bead-Craft, (Bead-Craft; 0-9613503), 1549 Ashland Ave., St. Paul, MN 55104 (SAN 657-2510) Tel 612-645-1216.

Bead Society, (Bead Society, The; 0-939678), 6500 Romaine St., No.7, Los Angeles, CA 90038 (SAN 216-7166) Tel 213-467-8982; Orders to: P.O. Box 2513, Culver City, CA 90231 (SAN 661-955X) Tel 213-838-0110.

Beagle Bks NY, (Beagle Bks., Inc.; 0-8441), 101 Fifth Ave., New York, NY 10003 (SAN 658-6295) Tel 212-691-7131.

Bean Assoc
See Bean Pub

†**Bean Pub,** (Carolyn Bean Publishing, Ltd.; 0-916860), 120 Second St., San Francisco, CA 94105 (SAN 208-5445) Tel 415-957-9574; CIP.

Bean Pub Co, (Bean Publishing Co.; 0-935905), 2624 Green Oak Pl., Los Angeles, CA 90068 (SAN 696-6888) Tel 213-463-2033.

Beanie Bks, (Beanie Bks.; 0-933530), 7443 Stanford, St. Louis, MO 63130 (SAN 281-3130).

Beanstalk Prod, (Beanstalk Productions, Inc.; 0-937629), 160 Madison Ave., 6th Flr., New York, NY 10016 (SAN 659-0241) Tel 212-686-3270.

Bear, (Bear Pubns.; 0-912934), P.O. Box 16, Cambridge, NY 12816 (SAN 202-3857) Tel 518-677-2766.

Bear & Co, (Bear & Co., Inc.; 0-939680), P.O. Drawer 2860, Santa Fe, NM 87504-2860 (SAN 216-7174) Tel 505-983-5968; Toll free: 800-932-3277; Dist. by: Bookpeople, 2929 Fifth St., Berkeley, CA 94710 (SAN 168-9517) Tel 415-549-3030; Dist. by: Spring Arbor Distributors, 10885 Textile Rd., Belleville, MI 48111 (SAN 158-9016) Tel 313-481-0900; Dist. by: New Leaf Distributing, 1020 White St., SW, Atlanta, GA 30310 (SAN 169-1449) Tel 404-755-3454; Dist. by: Distributors, The, 702 S. Michigan, South Bend, IN 46618 (SAN 212-0364) Tel 404-755-3454; Dist. by: Inland Bk. Co., 22 Hemingway Ave., East Haven, CT 06512 (SAN 200-4151) Tel 203-467-4257; Dist. by: Quality Bks., 400 Anthony Trail, Northbrook, IL 60062 (SAN 169-2127).

Bear Creek Pub, (Bear Creek Publishing Co.; 0-941026), P.O. Box 254, Ouray, CO 81427 (SAN 217-3298) Tel 303-325-4700; P.O. Box 2024, Cottonwood, AZ 86326 (SAN 692-4166) Tel 602-634-9636.

Bear Crk Pubns, (Bear Creek Pubns.; 0-936005), 2507 Minor Ave. E., Seattle, WA 98102 (SAN 696-687X) Tel 206-885-0864.

Bear Flag Bks, (Bear Flag Bks.; 0-933271), 941 Populus Pl., Sunnyvale, CA 94086 (SAN 691-7941) Tel 408-739-7508.

Bear Hollow Pr, (Bear Hollow Pr.; 0-938209), Subs. of Shuttle Hill Herb Shop, Inc., 110 Salisbury Rd., Delmar, NY 12054 (SAN 659-459X) Tel 518-439-9065.

Bear Pub Co, (Bear, Clair, Publishing Co.; 0-934857), P.O. Box 13623, Kansas City, MO 64199 (SAN 694-5589) Tel 913-648-6017; Dist. by: Distributors, The, 702 S. Michigan, South Bend, IN 46618 (SAN 169-2488) Tel 219-232-8500.

Bear State, (Bear State Books), 304 High St., Santa Cruz, CA 95060 (SAN 213-6112) Tel 408-426-3272.

Bear Tribe, (Bear Tribe Publishing; 0-943404), P.O. Box 9167, Spokane, WA 99209 (SAN 207-8643) Tel 509-326-6561.

Bear Wallow Pub, (Bear Wallow Publishing Co., The; 0-936376), High Valley Foothill Rd., Union, OR 97883 (SAN 223-3916) Tel 503-562-5687.

Beardsley Pr, (Beardsley Pr., The; 0-9616445), P.O. Box 32, Sanford, FL 32772-0032 (SAN 659-0268) Tel 305-321-5283; 827 Rosalia Dr., Sanford, FL 32771 (SAN 659-0276).

Bearly Ltd, (Bearly Ltd.; 0-943456), 149 York St., Buffalo, NY 14213 (SAN 239-3549) Tel 716-883-4571.

Beatitude SF, (Beatitude; 0-9617010), 575 Columbus Ave., No. 27, San Francisco, CA 94133 (SAN 662-8966) Tel 415-986-9684. Do not confuse wity Beatitude Pr., Berkeley, CA.

Beatty, (Beatty, R. W.; 0-87948), P.O. Box 26, Arlington, VA 22210 (SAN 206-7110).

Beau Bayou, (Beau Bayou Publishing Co.; 0-935619), P.O. Box 53089, Lafayette, LA 70505 (SAN 696-0804) Tel 318-234-5991; Toll free: 800-624-0466; 227 LaRue France, Lafayette, LA 70508 (SAN 696-0812).

Beau Lac, (Beau Lac Pubs.; 0-911980), P.O. Box 248, Chuluota, FL 32766 (SAN 202-3865) Tel 305-365-3830.

Beau R D Prof Ent, (Davis, Beau Robert, Professional Enterprises, Inc.; 0-9603644), 4535 W. Sahara Ave. Suite 105, Las Vegas, NV 89102 (SAN 221-6949) Tel 818-998-3611.

Beau Rivage, (Beau Rivage Press; 0-931174), Seven E. 14th St., Suite 1112, New York, NY 10003 (SAN 211-3090) Tel 212-989-1625.

Beaufort
See Beaufort SC

†**Beaufort Bks NY,** (Beaufort Bks., Inc.; 0-8253), 9 E. 40th St., New York, NY 10016 (SAN 215-2304) Tel 212-685-8588; Toll free: 800-526-7626; Dist. by: Kampmann & Co., 9 E. 40th St., New York, NY 10016 (SAN 202-5191) Tel 212-685-2928; CIP.

Beaufort Book Co
See Beaufort SC

Beaufort County, (Beaufort County Open Land Trust, Inc.), Box 75, Beaufort, SC 29902 (SAN 217-2879).

Beaufort SC, (Beaufort Bk. Co.; 0-910206), Box 1127, Beaufort, SC 29902 (SAN 202-3873) Tel 803-524-5172. Do not confuse with Beaufort Bks., Inc., New York, NY.

Beaumont Bks, (Beaumont Bks.; 0-9616108), Affil. of Malsam Marketing, 3333 W. 55th Ave., Denver, CO 80221 (SAN 699-7155) Tel 303-433-9192.

†**Beautiful Am,** (Beautiful America Publishing Co.; 0-89802; 0-915796), 9725 SW Commerce Cir., Wilsonville, OR 97070 (SAN 211-4623) Tel 503-682-0173; CIP.

Beautiful Day, (Beautiful Day Bks.; 0-930296), 3318 Gumwood Dr., Hyattsville, MD 20783 (SAN 210-587X) Tel 301-442-3609.

Beauty Without Cruelty, (Beauty Without Cruelty), 175 W. 12th St., New York, NY 10011 (SAN 225-896X).

Beaux Arts, (Beaux Arts, Inc.; 0-9607010), c/o Lowe Art Museum, 1301 Stanford Dr., Coral Gables, FL 33146 (SAN 279-4357) Tel 305-667-9346.

†**Beaux-Arts Pr,** (Beaux-Arts Pr./BAP Bks.; 0-916965), 808 Post St., Suite 1106, San Francisco, CA 94109 (SAN 655-5713) Tel 415-474-4900; Dist. by: Bookpeople, 2929 Fifth St., Berkeley, CA 94710 (SAN 168-9517) Tel 415-549-3030; CIP.

Beaver Pubns, (Beaver Publications; 0-9611234), 15605 NW. Cornell Rd., Beaverton, OR 97006 (SAN 282-8286) Tel 503-645-8425.

Beaver Tails, (Beaver Tails & Dorsal Fins; 0-9615949), P.O. Box 615, Menominee, MI 49858 (SAN 697-3353) Tel 906-863-3820; 3301 15th St., Menominee, MI 49858 (SAN 697-3361).

Beavers, (Beavers; 0-910208), Star Rte., Box 537, Laporte, MN 56461 (SAN 202-389X) Tel 218-224-2182.

Beckham House, (Beckham Hse. Pubs., Inc.; 0-931761), 77 Ives St., Suite 49, Providence, RI 02906 (SAN 683-2237).

Beckwith, (Beckwith, Burnham Putnam; 0-9603262), 656 Lytton Ave., (C430), Palo Alto, CA 94301 (SAN 211-884X) Tel 415-324-0342.

Becoming Pr, (Becoming Pr.; 0-9616204), P.O. Box 221383, Carmel, CA 93922 (SAN 658-3172) Tel 408-625-3188.

Bed & Breakfast, (Bed & Breakfast Registry; 0-9616205), P.O. Box 8174, St. Paul, MN 55108 (SAN 658-3210) Tel 612-646-4238; 1519 Grantham, St. Paul, MN 55108 (SAN 658-3229).

Beddoe Pub, (Beddoe Publishing; 0-9606106), 430 Closter Dock Rd., Closter, NJ 07624 (SAN 220-2344).

Bedford Bks, (Bedford Bks.; 0-935199), P.O. Box 709, Bedford, TX 76021 (SAN 695-7366) Tel 817-540-0346.

Bedford Hills Pub, (Bedford Hills Publishing Co., Inc.; 0-936153), 205 Adams St., Bedford Hills, NY 10507 (SAN 697-0087) Tel 914-241-7007.

Bedford Pr, (Bedford Pr. Pubs.; 0-938491), 472 Jackson St., San Francisco, CA 94133 (SAN 659-7955) Tel 415-362-3730.

Bedford Publishers, (Bedford Publishers, Inc.; 0-911557), 779 Kirts, Troy, MI 48084 (SAN 268-2435) Tel 313-362-0369.

Bedous Press, (Bedous Press; 0-918094), P.O. Box K, Beaverton, OR 97075 (SAN 210-1742) Tel 503-649-7844.

Bedpress *Imprint of* **New Bedford**

Bedrick Blackie *Imprint of* **P Bedrick Bks**

Bee Bk Bind
See Book Binder

Bee Bk Bind Co.
See Book Binder

Bee Tree, *(Bee Tree Productions; 0-937083),* P.O. Box 9156, Asheville, NC 28815 (SAN 699-7767) Tel 704-298-2877; 298 Long Branch Rd., Swannanoa, NC 28778 (SAN 658-3032).

Beeberry Bks, *(Beeberry Books; 0-9601996),* 230 Maclane, Palo Alto, CA 94306 (SAN 216-017X) Tel 415-494-2969.

†Beech Hill, *(Beech Hill Publishing Co.; 0-933786),* Box 136, Southwest Harbor, ME 04679 (SAN 212-6419) Tel 207-244-3931; *CIP.*

Beech Hill Ent
See Beech Hill

Beech Leaf, *(Beech Leaf Press; 0-939294),* Dist. by: Kalamazoo Nature Ctr., Inc., 7000 N. Westnedge Ave., Kalamazoo, MI 49007 (SAN 268-2478) Tel 616-381-1574.

Beech Tree, *(Beech Tree Farm Publications; 0-910210),* 702 Edwards Rd. No. 121, Greenville, SC 29615 (SAN 201-4475) Tel 803-268-7888.

Beechcliff Bks, *(Beechcliff Bks.; 0-9608930),* 100 Severn Ave., Suite 605, Annapolis, MD 21403 (SAN 241-001X) Tel 301-263-3580.

Beecher Found, *(Beecher, Willard & Marguerite, Foundation; 0-942350),* 8400 Westchester, Suite 300, Dallas, TX 75225 (SAN 281-3165); c/o Today's Books, 3775 Walnut Hill Lane, Dallas, TX 75229-6139 (SAN 281-3173).

Beechtree Pr, *(Beechtree Pr.),* P.O. Box 15669, Long Beach, CA 90815 (SAN 669-6465) Tel 213-429-5210.

Beechwood, *(Beechwood Bks.; 0-912221),* P.O. Box 20484, Birmingham, AL 35216 (SAN 265-0797) Tel 205-823-2376.

Beefmasters, *(Beefmasters Breeders Universal),* 11201 Morning Court, San Antonio, TX 78213 (SAN 224-9936) Tel 512-344-3132.

Beekman Hill, *(Beekman Hill, Pr.; 0-940534),* 342 E. 51st St., Apt. 3A, New York, NY 10022 (SAN 222-9919) Tel 212-755-0218.

†Beekman Pubs, *(Beekman Publishers, Inc.; 0-8464),* P.O. Box 888, Woodstock, NY 12498 (SAN 201-4467) Tel 914-679-2300; *CIP.*

Beeline Bks, *(Beeline Bks.; 0-9611020),* P.O. Box 6121, Albany, NY 12206 (SAN 285-127X) Tel 518-434-3236; 169 Central Ave., Albany, NY 12206 (SAN 285-1288).

Beer Adv
See Bullworks

Beer Can Coll, *(Beer Can Collectors of America),* 747 Merus Ct., Fenton, MO 63026 (SAN 268-2486) Tel 314-343-6486.

Beer Flat, *(Beer Flat Music; 0-911999),* 3451 Riviera Dr., San Diego, CA 92109 (SAN 264-6021) Tel 619-272-2514.

Beersheba
See Herschel Gower

†Beginner, *(Beginner Books; 0-394),* Div. of Random House, Inc., 201 E. 50th St., New York, NY 10022 (SAN 202-3288) Tel 212-751-2600; Toll free: 800-638-6460; Orders to: 400 Hahn Rd., Westminster, MD 21157 (SAN 202-3296); *CIP.*

Beginning Pr, *(Beginning Pr.; 0-9615514),* 1000 Union, No. 202, Seattle, WA 98101 (SAN 696-0855) Tel 206-682-3622; Dist. by: Pacific Pipeline, Inc., 19215 66th Ave., S., Kent, WA 98032 (SAN 208-2128) Tel 206-872-5523.

Behav Sci Ctr Pubns, *(Behavioral Science Ctr., Inc., Pubs.; 0-938837),* Div. of Behavioral Science Ctr., Inc., 2522 Highland Ave., Cincinnati, OH 45219 (SAN 661-6895) Tel 513-221-8545.

Behavior Sci Systs, *(Behavior Science Systems, Inc.; 0-936787),* P.O. Box 1108, Minneapolis, MN 55440 (SAN 699-8976) Tel 612-929-6220; 4860 W. 39th St., No. 317, St. Louis Park, MN 55416 (SAN 699-8984).

Behavioral Mass, *(Behavioral Research Council; 0-913610),* Div. of American Institute for Economic Research, Division St., Great Barrington, MA 01230 (SAN 201-7458) Tel 413-528-1216.

Behavioral Med Pr, *(Behavioral Medicine Press; 0-9613198),* 3390 Andover, Ann Arbor, MI 48105 (SAN 295-6519).

Behavioral Pub, *(Behavioral Publishing Co.; 0-940904),* Div. of Behavioral Therapy Institute, 1736 Old Grove Rd., Pasadena, CA 91107 (SAN 217-3301) Tel 818-791-7999.

Behavioral Pubns
See Human Sci Pr

Behavioral Re
See Learning Line

Behavioral Sci, *(Behavioral Science Research Pr., Inc.; 0-935907),* 2695 Villa Creek Dr., No. 180, Dallas, TX 75234 (SAN 696-6896) Tel 214-243-8543.

Behavioral Studies, *(Behavioral Studies Press; 0-911958),* P.O. Box 5323, Beverly Hills, CA 90210 (SAN 202-3903) Tel 213-472-2662.

Behavioronics, *(Behavioronics; 0-938679),* P.O. Box 8207, Corpus Christi, TX 78412-0207 (SAN 661-3837); 1746 Star Cove Dr., Corpus Christi, TX 78412 (SAN 661-3845) Tel 512-993-8297.

Behavorial Sys Inc, *(Behavioral Systems, Inc.; 0-9610136),* Rte. 2, P.O. Box 630, Marshall, VA 22115 (SAN 268-2559) Tel 703-435-8181.

Behemoth Pub, *(Behemoth Publishing; 0-9606782),* Star Rte., Oasis, UT 84650 (SAN 217-331X) Tel 801-864-2842.

Behemoth Pub CA
See Media & Travel Pubns

†Behrman, *(Behrman Hse., Inc.; 0-87441),* 235 Watchung Ave., West Orange, NJ 07052 (SAN 201-4459) Tel 201-669-0447; Toll free: 800-221-2755; *CIP.*

Beil, *(Beil, Frederic C., Publishing Co.; 0-913720),* 321 E. 43rd St., New York, NY 10017 (SAN 240-9909) Tel 212-682-5519. Imprints: Sandstone Pr (Sandstone Press).

Beil F C
See Beil

Being Bks, *(Being Books; 0-938292),* 19834 Gresham St., Northridge, CA 91324 (SAN 215-7292) Tel 818-341-0283.

Being Pubns, *(Being Pubns),* 1530 Valley Ave. NW, Grand Rapids, MI 49504 (SAN 207-7876).

Bek Indus
See Bek Tech

BEK Pr, *(BEK Pr.; 0-9613766),* No. 1 Woodbury Hills, Woodbury, CT 06798 (SAN 656-8807) Tel 203-263-4389.

Bek Tech, *(Bek Technical Pubs., Inc.; 0-912884),* 1700 Painters Run Rd., Pittsburgh, PA 15243 (SAN 202-3911) Tel 412-221-0900.

Bel-Air, *(Bel-Air Publishing Co.),* 249 S. Camden Drive, Beverly Hills, CA 90212 (SAN 263-2454).

Bel-Del Ent, *(Bel-Del Enterprises, Ltd., The; 0-9616893),* 1016 Vista Grande Dr. NW, Albuquerque, NM 87105 (SAN 661-3217) Tel 505-836-4353; Dist. by: Tri-State Railway Historical Society, Inc., P.O. Box 2243, Clifton, NJ 07015-2243 (SAN 239-3301) Tel 201-857-2987.

Bel Esprit, *(Bel Esprit Press; 0-9607118),* 10 E. 23rd St., New York, NY 10010 (SAN 239-409X).

Belforte Assoc, *(Belforte Assocs.; 0-916389),* P.O. Box 245, Sturbridge, MA 01566 (SAN 295-9429) Tel 617-347-9324.

Belier Pr, *(Belier Pr., Inc.; 0-914646),* P.O. Box 1234 Old Chelsea Sta., New York, NY 10113 (SAN 206-4766) Tel 212-620-4276.

Believers Bkshelf, *(Believers Bookshelf; 0-941202),* Box 261, Sunbury, PA 17801 (SAN 211-7746) Tel 717-672-2134.

Believers Faith, *(Believers Faith Center; 0-912573),* 148 E. 22nd St., Costa Mesa, CA 92627 (SAN 277-657X) Tel 714-650-0447.

Bell *Imprint of* **FS&G**

Bell *Imprint of* **Outlet Bk Co**

Bell Assn Deaf
See Alexander Graham

Bell Ent, *(Bell Enterprises, Inc.; 0-918340),* P.O. Box 9054, Pine Bluff, AR 71611 (SAN 209-1895) Tel 501-247-1922.

Bell Gal
See D W Bell Gallery

†Bell Pub, *(Bell Publishing; 0-943064),* 15 Surrey Ln., East Brunswick, NJ 08816 (SAN 240-1266) Tel 201-257-7793; *CIP.*

Bell Springs Pub, *(Bell Springs Publishing; 0-917510),* P.O. Box 640, Laytonville, CA 95454 (SAN 209-3138); Bell Springs Rd., Laytonville, CA 95454 (SAN 661-9576) Tel 707-984-6746.

Bell Telephone, *(Bell Telephone Laboratories, Inc.; 0-932764),* 600 Mountain Ave., Rm. 6G-301A, Murray Hill, NJ 07974 (SAN 223-6346).

Belle Grove, *(Belle Grove, Inc.; 0-9616530),* P.O. Box 137, Middletown, VA 22645 (SAN 659-4204) Tel 703-869-2028; Rte. 11 S., Middletown, VA 22645 (SAN 659-4212).

Belle Mead Pr, *(Belle Mead, Pr.; 0-9610346),* 306 Dutchtown Rd., Belle Mead, NJ 08502 (SAN 263-9351) Tel 201-359-5683.

Belle Pubns, *(Belle Pubns.; 0-9605732),* 172 Pathway Ln., West Lafayette, IN 47906 (SAN 216-1036) Tel 317-463-6361.

Belle Trac, *(Belle Trac Corp.; 0-9615835),* 306 W. Wabash Ave., Effingham, IL 62401 (SAN 697-0125) Tel 217-347-7090.

Bellefontaine Bks, *(Bellefontaine Books; 0-932786),* P.O. Box 1554, Arroyo Grande, CA 93420 (SAN 212-5900) Tel 805-481-8357.

Belleraphon, *(Belleraphon Pr.; 0-9613906),* 20317 Farmington Rd., Bldg. D, Suite B, Livonia, MI 48152 (SAN 683-2318) Tel 313-478-7860.

†Bellerophon Bks, *(Bellerophon Bks; 0-88388),* 36 Anacapa St., Santa Barbara, CA 93101 (SAN 202-392X) Tel 805-965-7034; *CIP.*

†Belles-Lettres, *(Belles-Lettres Bks.; 0-917747),* P.O. Box 20405, Oakland, CA 94620-0405 (SAN 656-9633) Tel 415-655-9783; *CIP.*

Bellevue Art, *(Bellevue Art Museum; 0-942342),* 310 Bellevue Sq., Bellevue, WA 98004 (SAN 278-1670) Tel 206-454-3322.

†Bellevue Pr, *(Bellevue Press; 0-933466),* 60 Schubert St., Binghamton, NY 13905 (SAN 207-7884) Tel 607-729-0819; *CIP.*

Bellflower, *(Bellflower Pr.; 0-934958),* Case Western Reserve Univ., Dept. of English, Cleveland, OH 44106 (SAN 213-2346) Tel 216-368-2340.

Bellman, *(Bellman Publishing Co.; 0-87442),* P.O. Box 34937, Bethesda, MD 20817 (SAN 202-3938) Tel 301-897-0033.

Bellwether Bks *Imprint of* **EJP Pub Co**

Bellwether Pub, *(Bellwether Publishing Co.; 0-913144),* 167 E. 67th St., New York, NY 10021 (SAN 209-0880).

Belmary, *(Belmary Press; 0-910214),* 4652 E. Pinewood, Mobile, AL 36618 (SAN 202-3946) Tel 205-342-7171.

Belmont Hist Dist Comm, *(Belmont Historic District Commission),* Town Hall, Belmont, MA 02178 (SAN 292-3661).

Belnice Bks, *(Belnice Bks.; 0-941274),* Box 1325, Claremont, CA 91711 (SAN 239-4103) Tel 714-626-1167.

Beloved Bks, *(Beloved Bks.; 0-9613907),* 3103 Wells Drive, Parlin, NJ 08859 (SAN 683-2296) Tel 201-721-2435.

Belvoir Pubns, *(Belvoir Pubns., Inc.; 0-9615196),* 1111 E. Putnam Ave., Riverside, CT 06878 (SAN 694-3586) Tel 203-637-5900.

Ben-Simon, *(Ben-Simon Pubns.; 0-914539),* P.O. Box 2124, Port Angeles, WA 98362 (SAN 289-1492) Tel 604-652-6332.

Bench Mark IL, *(Bench Mark Publications; 0-9610892),* P.O. Box 755, Charleston, IL 61920 (SAN 265-0819) Tel 217-345-7581.

Bench Pr NY, *(Bench Pr.; 0-9616160),* P.O. Box 1446, Sag Harbor, NY 11963 (SAN 699-8321) Tel 516-725-4593; 200 Noyac Ave., Sag Harbor, NY 11963 (SAN 699-833X).

Bench Press Pa, *(Bench Pr., The; 0-930769),* 1355 Raintree Dr., Columbia, SC 29210 (SAN 677-6663) Tel 803-781-7232.

Benchmark Bks
See Benchmark Inc

Benchmark Inc, *(Benchmark Books, Inc.; 0-9615052),* P.O. Box 27004, Chinatown Sta., Honolulu, HI 96827 (SAN 694-0706) Tel 808-833-7563.

Benchmark Ltd, *(Benchmark Pubns., Ltd.; 0-9615467),* 1 First St., Suite N, Los Altos, CA 94022 (SAN 696-088X) Tel 415-941-3823.

Benchmark Pr, *(Benchmark Pr., Inc.; 0-936157),* 8435 Keystone Crossing, Suite 175, Indianapolis, IN 46240 (SAN 697-0095) Tel 317-253-3763.

Benchmark Pubns
See Benchmark Winnetka
Benchmark Winnetka, *(Benchmark Publications; 0-928520),* P.O. Box 154-B, Winnetka, IL 60093 (SAN 672-2547) Tel 312-446-0430.
Bender, *(Bender, Matthew, & Co., Inc.; 0-87571),* Subs. of Times Mirror Co., ; Toll free: 800-821-2232; Orders to: 235 E. 45th St., New York, NY 10017 (SAN 202-330X) Tel 212-661-5050.
Bender Pub CA, *(Bender, R. James, Publishing; 0-912138),* P.O. Box 23456, San Jose, CA 95153 (SAN 201-7296) Tel 408-225-5777.
Benedict Con Adoration, *(Benedictine Convent of Perpetual Adoration; 0-913180),* 3888 Paducah Dr., San Diego, CA 92117 (SAN 204-5346) Tel 619-274-1030.
Bengal Pr, *(Bengal Pr., Inc.; 0-935650),* P.O. Box 1128, Grand Rapids, MI 49501 (SAN 213-7259).
Bengor Pubns, *(Bengor Pubns., Inc.; 0-913799),* 3827 NE 100th, Seattle, WA 98125 (SAN 286-0473) Tel 206-622-4090.
Benin, *(Benin Press, Ltd.; 0-910216),* 5225 S. Blackstone Ave., Chicago, IL 60615 (SAN 202-3962).
Beninda, *(Beninda Books; 0-931868),* 173 SE Fifth Ave., No. 2, Delray Beach, FL 33444 (SAN 211-8874).
Benjamin Bks, *(Benjamin Bks.; 0-916967),* 7238 Munsee Ln., Indianapolis, IN 46260 (SAN 655-5756) Tel 317-253-1032.
Benjamin Co, *(Benjamin Co., Inc.; 0-87502),* 1 Westchester Plaza, Elmsford, NY 10523 (SAN 202-3970) Tel 914-592-8088.
†**Benjamin-Cummings,** *(Benjamin-Cummings Publishing Co.; 0-8053),* Subs. of Addison-Wesley Pub. Co., 2727 Sand Hill Rd., Menlo Park, CA 94025 (SAN 200-2353) Tel 415-854-6020; Orders to: South St., Reading, MA 01867 (SAN 206-7862); *CIP. Imprints:* Adv Bk Prog (Advance Book Program).
Benjamin Pr, *(Benjamin Pr.; 0-936317),* P.O. Box 112, Northampton, MA 01061 (SAN 697-3396) Tel 413-586-6272; 88 Turkey Hill Rd., Northampton, MA 01060 (SAN 697-340X) Tel 413-586-6272.
†**Benjamins North Am,** *(Benjamins, John, North America, Inc.; 90-272; 1-55619),* 1 Buttonwood Sq., No. 101, Philadelphia, PA 19130 (SAN 219-7677) Tel 215-564-6379; *CIP.*
Benmir Bks, *(Benmir Bks.; 0-917883),* 570 Vistamont Ave., Berkeley, CA 94718 (SAN 656-9641) Tel 415-527-0266.
Bennet Pub, *(Bennet, Rebecca, Pubns., Inc.; 0-910218),* 5409 18th Ave., Brooklyn, NY 11204 (SAN 206-8443) Tel 718-256-1954.
Bennett Arch & Eng, *(Bennett, Robert, Architect & Engineer; 0-9601718),* 6 Snowden Rd., Bala Cynwyd, PA 19004 (SAN 211-657X) Tel 215-667-7365.
Bennett Co
See Bennett Il
Bennett-Edwards, *(Bennett-Edwards; 0-9617271),* 337 W. 36th St., New York, NY 10018 (SAN 663-4508) Tel 212-675-5053.
Bennett Il, *(Bennett Pub. Co.),* Div. of Macmillan, Inc., 866 Third Ave., New York, NY 10022 (SAN 201-4440) Tel 309-691-4454.
Bennington Coll, *(Bennington College; 0-9614940),* Bennington College, Bennington, VT 05201 (SAN 693-675X) Tel 802-442-5401.
Benshaw Pub, *(Benshaw Pubns.; 0-9607508),* 940 Princeton Dr., Marina del Rey, CA 90291 (SAN 238-633X) Tel 213-821-7871.
Benson, *(Benson, W. S., & Co., Inc.; 0-87443),* P.O. Box 1866, Austin, TX 78767 (SAN 202-3989) Tel 512-476-5050.
Benson Co TN
See Paragon Benson
Bentley, *(Bentley, Robert, Inc.; 0-8376),* 1000 Massachusetts Ave., Cambridge, MA 02138 (SAN 213-9839) Tel 617-547-4170; Toll free: 800-423-4595.
Benton Cutter Pr, *(Benton-Cutter Pr., The; 0-9615702),* Div. of Kaminari Design, 515-A W. Lambert Rd., Brea, CA 92621 (SAN 696-091X) Tel 714-529-6399.
Bentwood Pr, *(Bentwood Pr.; 0-938839),* P.O. Box 172, Sutton, AK 99674 (SAN 661-6909) Tel 907-745-6840.
Benziger
See Glencoe

Benziger Pub Co, *(Benziger Publishing Co.; 0-02; 0-8460),* Div. of Glencoe Publishing Co., ; c/o Macmillan Publishing Co., Inc., 866 Third Ave., New York, NY 10022 (SAN 202-5574) Tel 212-935-2000.
Benziger Sis, *(Benziger Sisters Pubs.),* 466 E. Mariposa St., Altadena, CA 91001 (SAN 209-5297).
Berea College Pr, *(Berea College Pr.; 0-938211),* Berea College Box 2317, Berea, KY 40404 (SAN 659-8218) Tel 606-986-9341; Berea College, Chestnut St., Lincoln Hall, Berea, KY 40404 (SAN 659-8226); Dist. by: Gnomon Pr., P.O. Box 106, Frankfort, KY 40602-0106 (SAN 209-0104) Tel 502-223-1858.
Bereny Bear, *(Bereny Bear, Bks.; 0-914345),* 333 E. 79th St., New York, NY 10021 (SAN 289-601X) Tel 212-744-7433; Orders to: P.O. Box 1601, F.D.R. Sta., New York, NY 10150 (SAN 693-9856) Tel 212-744-7433.
Berg, *(Berg, Norman S. , Publisher, Ltd.; 0-910220),* P.O. Box 15232, Atlanta, GA 30333 (SAN 226-8086).
Berg
See Larlin Corp
Berg Am, *(Berg America Co., Ltd.; 0-9616074),* 1136 SE Third Ave., Ft. Lauderdale, FL 33316 (SAN 697-998X) Tel 305-764-3636.
Berg Pub Co, *(Berg Publishing Co.; 0-932861),* Box 359, Shakopee, MN 55379 (SAN 688-9212) Tel 612-445-4425.
Berg Pub Group
See R J Berg & Co
Bergano Bk Co, *(Bergano Bk. Co.; 0-917408),* P.O. Box 6430, Fairfield, CT 06430 (SAN 659-6118) Tel 203-254-2054.
Bergee Corp, *(Bergee Corp., A; 0-935413),* Publishers' Bldg., Circle Pines, MN 55014 (SAN 696-4893) Tel 612-786-5720.
Berger Pub, *(Berger Publishing Co., The; 0-9616397),* 52 Penn Cir. W., Pittsburgh, PA 15206 (SAN 699-8267).
†**Bergh Pub,** *(Bergh Publishing, Inc.; 0-930267),* 1049 Park Ave., New York, NY 10028 (SAN 670-8633) Tel 212-860-8599; *CIP.*
†**Bergin & Garvey,** *(Bergin & Garvey Pubs., Inc.; 0-89789),* 670 Amherst Rd., South Hadley, MA 01075 (SAN 213-6120) Tel 413-467-3113; *CIP.*
Bergling
See Gem City Coll
Bergquist Pub, *(Bergquist Publishing; 0-9615483),* 414 W. Seventh, Willmar, MN 56201 (SAN 696-0952) Tel 612-235-4516.
Bergwall, *(Bergwall Productions, Inc.; 0-943008; 0-8064),* P.O. Box 238, Garden City, NY 11530 (SAN 240-3064) Tel 516-222-1130; Toll free: 800-645-1737; 106 Charles Lindbergh Blvd., Uniondale, NY 11553 (SAN 696-9399).
Bergwall Ed Soft, *(Bergwall Educational Software, Inc.; 0-943008; 0-8064),* 106 Charles Lindbergh Blvd., Uniondale, NY 11553 (SAN 659-3879) Tel 516-222-1130; Toll free: 800-645-1737.
Berkeley Art, *(Berkeley Art Center; 0-942744),* 1275 Walnut St., Berkeley, CA 94709 (SAN 240-1916) Tel 415-644-6893.
Berkeley Elect, *(Berkeley Electronic Publishing; 0-933859),* Subs. of International Publishing & Computer Publishing, Inc., P.O. Box 3056, Berkeley, CA 94703 (SAN 692-8692) Tel 415-652-6004.
Berkeley Poets
See BPW & P
Berkeley Sci, *(Berkeley Scientific Pubns.; 0-910224),* P.O. Box 4546, Anaheim, CA 92803 (SAN 211-7231) Tel 714-497-3522.
Berkeley Slavic, *(Berkeley Slavic Specialties; 0-933884),* P.O. Box 3034, Oakland, CA 94609 (SAN 212-7245) Tel 415-658-8048.
BerkeleyMorgan, *(BerkeleyMorgan/Pubs; 0-9615186),* 1742 Riggs Pl., NW, Washington, DC 20009 (SAN 694-3357) Tel 202-797-0647.
Berkley Bks
See Berkley Pub

†**Berkley Pub,** *(Berkley Publishing Group; 0-425; 0-515),* Affil. of G.P. Putnam's Sons, 200 Madison Ave., New York, NY 10016 (SAN 201-3991) Tel 212-686-9820; Toll free: 800-223-0510; Dist. by: ICD, 250 W. 55th St., New York, NY 10019 (SAN 169-5800) Tel 212-262-7444; *CIP. Imprints:* Highland (Highland Books).(Highland Bks.); Medallion (Medallion Books).(Medallion Bks.); Windhover (Windhover).
Berkshire Hse, *(Berkshire Hse. Pubns.; 0-936399),* P.O. Box 28, Great Barrington, MA 01230 (SAN 698-1666) Tel 413-528-3156; 315 W. 102nd St., New York, NY 10025 (SAN 698-1674); Dist. by: Ingram Industries, 347 Reedwood Dr., Nashville, TN 37217 (SAN 169-7978) Tel 615-360-2819.
Berkshire Pub Co, *(Berkshire Publishing Co., Ltd.; 0-910555),* P.O. Box 27910, St. Louis, MO 63146 (SAN 260-1656).
Berkshire Soft, *(Berkshire Software Co.; 0-938213),* 72-61 113th St., Suite 5-K, Forest Hills, NY 11375 (SAN 659-8234) Tel 718-263-1221.
†**Berkshire Traveller,** *(Berkshire Traveller, Pr.; 0-912944),* Pine St., Stockbridge, MA 01262 (SAN 201-4424) Tel 413-298-3636; *CIP.*
Berle Bks, *(Berle Bks.; 0-9617296),* 2700 Neilson Way, No. 1735, Santa Monica, CA 90405 (SAN 663-4354) Tel 213-396-5111.
Berlitz *Imprint of Macmillan*
Bermont Bks, *(Bermont Bks., Inc.; 0-930686),* P.O. Box 309, Glenelg, MD 21737 (SAN 211-1705) Tel 301-531-3560.
Bermuda Bio, *(Bermuda Biological Station; 0-917642),* c/o Prof. James N. Butler, Pierce Hall, 29 Oxford St., Cambridge, MA 02138 (SAN 206-4995) Tel 617-495-2845.
Bern Porter, *(Porter, Bern; 0-911156),* 22 Salmond Rd., Belfast, ME 04915 (SAN 202-0130). Do not confuse with Porter Publishing Co., Center City, MN.
Bernardo Press, *(Bernardo Press),* Div. of Mayo & Associates, Inc., 16496 Bernardo Center Dr., San Diego, CA 92128 (SAN 679-1875) Tel 619-451-3790.
Berot Bk, *(Berot Book, Inc., The; 0-940372),* 220 E. Hillsdale St., Lansing, MI 48933 (SAN 217-1589) Tel 517-371-4647.
Berringer Pub, *(Berringer Publishing; 0-9614987),* 15335 Morrison St. No. 100, Sherman Oaks, CA 91403 (SAN 693-7608) Tel 818-990-1700.
Berry Bks, *(Berry Bks.; 0-9614746),* 1114 SE 22nd Terr., Cape Coral, FL 33904-4626 (SAN 692-9214).
Berry Good Child Bks, *(Berry Good Children's Bks.; 0-9616555),* RR 2, P.O. Box 823, Lot 342, Coconut Creek, FL 33067 (SAN 659-4220); 6800 NW 39th Ave., Coconut Creek, FL 33067 (SAN 659-4239).
Berry Hill Pr, *(Berry Hill, Pr.; 0-933863),* 7336 Berry Hill, Rancho Palos Verdes, CA 90274 (SAN 692-7041) Tel 213-377-7040.
Berry Patch, *(Berry Patch Pr.; 0-9609912),* 3350 NW Luray Terr., Portland, OR 97210 (SAN 268-2729) Tel 503-224-3350; Dist. by: Far West Bk. Service, 3515 NE Hassalo, Portland, OR 97232 (SAN 107-6760) Tel 503-234-7664; Dist. by: Pacific Pipeline, Inc., 19215 66th Ave., S., Kent, WA 98032 (SAN 208-2128).
Berry Pub, *(Berry Publishing; 0-942556),* Box 33, Hazel Crest, IL 60429 (SAN 240-0669) Tel 312-335-0347.
Bert & I Bks
See Bert & I Inc
Bert & I Inc, *(Bert & I, Inc.; 0-9607546),* 35 Mill Rd., Ipswich, MA 01938 (SAN 238-2202) Tel 617-356-0151.
Berwyn-London, *(Berwyn-London Pubs.; 0-916536),* 2401 Calumet St., Flint, MI 48503 (SAN 208-550X).
Bess Pr, *(Bess Pr., Inc.; 0-935848),* P.O. Box 22388, Honolulu, HI 96822 (SAN 239-4111); 2555 Makaulii Pl., Honolulu, HI 96816 (SAN 661-9584) Tel 808-734-7159.
Bessandy Pubns, *(Bessandy Pubns.; 0-9610936),* 49 N. Main, P.O. Box 87, Clawson, UT 84516 (SAN 265-1912) Tel 801-384-2608.
Bessemer Jr Serv Leag, *(Bessemer Junior Service League; 0-9614351),* P.O. Box 928, Bessemer, AL 35021-0928 (SAN 687-8083) Tel 205-938-7713.

Best Antiques, *(Best, Charles, Antiques; 0-914346),* 6288 S. Pontiac, Englewood, CO 80111 (SAN 202-9723) Tel 303-771-3153.

Best Bks, *(Best Bks., Inc.; 0-910228),* P.O. Box 2309, Henderson, NV 89015 (SAN 202-4012) Tel 702-565-7182.

Best Bks CA, *(Best Bks. Publishing; 0-936255),* 1993 Orchard Rd., Hollister, CA 95023 (SAN 697-3426) Tel 408-991-5493.

Best Bks Pub, *(Best Bks. Pubs.; 0-88429),* P.O. Box 1895, McAlister, OK 74502 (SAN 202-1730) Tel 918-423-7296.

Best Cookbks, *(Best Cookbooks, Inc.; 0-935687),* 2721 Church St., Zachary, LA 70791 (SAN 696-0995) Tel 504-654-6523.

Best Friends, *(Best of Friends; 0-9615950),* P.O. Box 5573, Kingwood, TX 77325 (SAN 697-3450) Tel 713-359-6733; 4006 Oak Gardens Dr., Kingwood, TX 77339 (SAN 697-3469).

Best Pub Co, *(Best Publishing, Co.; 0-941332),* P.O. Box 1978, San Pedro, CA 90732 (SAN 238-9509) Tel 213-548-4545.

Best West Pr, *(Best Western Press; 0-941192),* P.O. Box 494, Bakersfield, CA 93302 (SAN 238-9134).

Bestsell Pubns, *(Bestsell Pubns.; 0-9616807),* RFD 1, Box 662, New Seabury, MA 02649 (SAN 661-2962); 337 High Wood Way, New Seabury, MA 02649 (SAN 661-2970) Tel 617-477-1774.

Bet-Ken Prods, *(Bet-Ken Productions; 0-9603698),* 4363 Cherry Ave., San Jose, CA 95118 (SAN 213-683X) Tel 408-267-3425.

Bet Yoatz Lib Serv
See BYLS Pr

Beta Phi Mu, *(Beta Phi Mu Chapbooks; 0-910230),* School of Library and Information Science; Univ. of Pittsburgh, Pittsburgh, PA 15260 (SAN 202-4020) Tel 412-624-5234; Toll free: Univ. of Pittsburgh, Schl. of Library & Information Science.

Beth Israel, *(Beth Israel Sisterhood; 0-9613256),* 9411 Liberty Rd., Randallstown, MD 21133 (SAN 296-452X) Tel 301-922-6565.

Bethany Coll
See Bethany Coll KS

†**Bethany Coll KS,** *(Bethany College Pr-Kansas; 0-916030),* 421 N. First St., Lindsborg, KS 67456-1897 (SAN 211-8882) Tel 913-227-3311; *CIP.*

Bethany Fell
See Bethany Hse

†**Bethany Hse,** *(Bethany Hse. Pubs.; 0-87123; 1-55661),* Div. of Bethany Fellowship, Inc., 6820 Auto Club Rd., Minneapolis, MN 55438 (SAN 201-4416) Tel 612-944-2121; Toll free: 800-328-6109; *CIP.*

Bethany Pr
See CBP

Bethel Hist Soc, *(Bethel Historical Society Inc.; 0-9614153),* 15 Broad St., Bethel, ME 04217 (SAN 686-5305) Tel 207-824-2908.

Bethel Pub, *(Bethel Publishing Co.; 0-934998),* Div. of Missionary Church, Inc., 1819 S. Main St., Elkhart, IN 46516 (SAN 201-7555) Tel 219-293-8585; Toll free: 800-348-7657.

Bethel Pub OR, *(Bethel Pubns.; 0-9600096),* 4803 Kathy, Temple, TX 76502 (SAN 241-273X) Tel 503-859-8365.

Bethsheva's Concern, *(Bethsheva's Concern; 0-9610802),* P.O. Box 276, Clifton, NJ 07011-9990 (SAN 265-0878); Dist. by: Starlite Distributors, P.O. Box 20729, Reno, NV 89515 (SAN 200-7789) Tel 702-359-5676; Dist. by: New Leaf Distributing, The, 1020 White St. SW, Atlanta, GA 30310 (SAN 169-1449) Tel 404-755-2665.

BETOM Pubns, *(BETOM Pubns.; 0-9605172),* P.O. Box 1873, Appleton, WI 54913 (SAN 238-5198) Tel 414-731-2947.

Betsy Ross Pr, *(Betsy Ross Pr.; 0-934120),* P.O. Box 986, Fort Collins, CO 80522 (SAN 222-7428).

Betsy Ross Pub
See Betsy Ross Pubns

Betsy Ross Pubns, *(Ross, Betsy, Pubns.; 0-943232),* 3057 Betsy Ross Dr., Bloomfield Hills, MI 48013 (SAN 240-7612) Tel 313-646-5357.

Bette Stoler Gallery, *(Bette Stoler Gallery; 0-9614551),* 13 White St., New York, NY 10038 (SAN 691-795X) Tel 212-966-5090.

Better Am Corp
See J Blalock

Better Baby, *(Better Baby Pr., The; 0-936676),* Div. of Institutes for the Achievement of Human Potential, 8801 Stenton Ave., Philadelphia, PA 19118 (SAN 215-7314) Tel 215-233-2050.

Better Baseball, *(Better Baseball; 0-913557),* 2309 Colcord Ave., Waco, TX 76707 (SAN 285-2152); Dist. by: Publishers Marketing Group, 1104 Summit Ave., Plainview, TX 75074 (SAN 285-2160) Tel 214-423-0312.

Better Bks, *(Better Bks. Pub.),* Rte. 2, Box 2574, Vale, OR 97918 (SAN 215-7322) Tel 503-473-2133.

Better H Prog, *(Better Health Programs; 0-933161),* 2107 Van Ness Ave., Suite 408, San Francisco, CA 94109 (SAN 692-2597) Tel 415-775-5921.

Better Health, *(Better Health Pubs., Inc.; 0-932213),* 3368 Governor Dr., Suite F-224, San Diego, CA 92122 (SAN 686-6018) Tel 619-549-8897; Dist. by: Baker & Taylor Co., Eastern Div., 50 Kirby Ave., Somerville, NJ 08876 (SAN 169-4901) Tel 201-526-8000; Dist. by: Publishers Group West, 5855 Beaudry St., Emeryville, CA 94608 (SAN 202-8522) Tel 415-658-3453; Dist. by: Nutri-Books Corp., P.O. Box 5793, Denver, CO 80223 (SAN 169-054X) Tel 303-778-8383; Dist. by: Gordon's Bks., Inc., 5450 N. Valley Hwy., Denver, CO 80216 (SAN 169-0531) Tel 303-296-1830; Dist. by: Living Bks., Inc., 12155 Magnolia Ave., Bldg. 11-B, Riverside, CA 92503 (SAN 169-006X) Tel 714-354-7330; Dist. by: Spring Arbor Distributors, 10885 Textile Rd., Belleville, MI 48111 (SAN 158-9016) Tel 313-481-0900.

Better Life, *(Better Life Products; 0-9614258),* 421 N. Pleasant Hill Blvd., Des Moines, IA 50317 (SAN 687-116X) Tel 515-262-6040.

†**Betterway Pubns,** *(Betterway Pubns., Inc.; 0-932620),* White Hall, VA 22987 (SAN 215-2975) Tel 804-823-5661; *CIP. Imprints:* White Hall Bks (White Hall Books).

Bettienal, *(Bettienal Pubs.; 0-914037),* 3212 Gleneagles Dr., Silver Spring, MD 20906 (SAN 287-489X) Tel 301-598-7934.

Betty's Soup, *(Betty's Soup Shop Pr.; 0-9612914),* 847 Junipero Ave., Pacific Grove, CA 93950 (SAN 291-0780) Tel 408-375-1873.

Between Hours, *(Between Hours Press; 0-910232),* 29 E. 63rd St., New York, NY 10021 (SAN 202-4039).

Betz Pub Co Inc, *(Betz Publishing, Co., Inc.; 0-941406),* P.O. Box 34631, Bethesda, MD 20817 (SAN 238-9886) Tel 301-340-0030.

Betzold, *(Betzold, Michael; 0-9602452),* 20025 Renfrew St., Detroit, MI 48221 (SAN 211-6170) Tel 313-864-1496.

Beulah, *(Beulah Records & Publishing Co.; 0-911870),* Rte. 1, Crossville, IL 62827 (SAN 202-4047) Tel 618-966-3405.

Beverage Media, *(Beverage Media, Ltd.; 0-9602566),* 161 Sixth Ave., New York, NY 10013 (SAN 214-106X).

Beverly Found, *(Beverly Foundation, The; 0-938485),* 841 S. Fair Oaks, Pasadena, CA 91105 (SAN 659-8277) Tel 818-792-2292.

Bewick Edns, *(Bewick Editions; 0-935590),* P.O. Box 14140, Detroit, MI 48214 (SAN 213-6139) Tel 313-521-5049.

Bey-Len Cat Bks, *(Bey-Len Cat Bks.; 0-9615398),* P.O. Box 628, Maspeth, NY 11378 (SAN 696-1053).

Beyond Words Pub, *(Beyond Words Publishing Co.; 0-99610),* 112 Meleana Pl., Honolulu, HI 96817 (SAN 211-1403) Tel 808-595-8166.

Bezkorovainy, *(Bezkorovainy, Anatoly; 0-9607600),* 6801 N. Kilpatrick, Chicago, IL 60646 (SAN 218-4672) Tel 312-942-5429.

BFP *Imprint of* HarBraceJ

BGSU Dept Phil, *(Bowling Green State Univ., Dept. of Philosophy; 0-935756),* Bowling Green State Univ., Bowling Green, OH 43403 (SAN 213-2923) Tel 419-372-2117.

BGTC
See B Greene

BH & GB
See BH&G

BH Ent, *(BH Enterprises; 0-9604896),* P.O. Box 216, Midwood Sta., Brooklyn, NY 11230 (SAN 220-0562) Tel 718-336-0521.

Bhaktipada Bks, *(Bhaktipada Bks.; 0-932215),* Div. of Palace Press, Rd 1, Box 331, Moundsville,, VA 26041 (SAN 686-5763) Tel 304-845-3890.

Bhaktive Inst, *(Bhaktivedanta Institute of Religion & Culture, The; 0-936405),* 11693 N. Shore Dr., No. 11B, Reston, VA 22090 (SAN 698-1607).

†**Bhaktivedanta,** *(Bhaktivedanta Bk. Trust; 0-912776),* 3764 Watseka Ave., Los Angeles, CA 90034 (SAN 203-8560) Tel 213-559-4455; Toll free: 800-356-3000; *CIP.*

†**BH&G,** *(Better Home & Gardens Bks.; 0-696),* Div. of Meredith Corp., 1716 Locust St., Des Moines, IA 50336 (SAN 202-4055) Tel 515-284-2844; *CIP. Imprints:* Am Express (American Express Pubns.).

BHRA Fluid, *(BHRA Fluid Engineering; 0-900983),* Dist. by: Air Science Co., P.O. Box 143, Corning, NY 14830 (SAN 210-7791) Tel 607-962-5591.

Bi World Indus, *(Bi World Industries, Inc.; 0-89557),* P.O. Box 1143, 671 N. State St., Orem, UT 84057 (SAN 210-5888) Tel 801-224-5803.

Bibl Res Pr *Imprint of* Abilene Christ U

Bible Baptist, *(Bible Baptist Church),* Cross St. at Lock St., P.O. Box 1348, Nashua, NH 03061 (SAN 656-044X) Tel 603-888-4020.

Bible Light, *(Bible Light Pubns.; 0-937078),* P.O. Box 168, Jerome Ave. Sta., Bronx, NY 10468 (SAN 214-3445).

Bible Memory, *(Bible Memory Assn., Inc.; 0-89323),* P.O. Box 12000, Ringgold, LA 71068 (SAN 214-1019).

Bible Pr
See Bible Temple

Bible-Speak, *(Bible-Speak Enterprises; 0-911423),* 1940 Mount Vernon Ct., No. 4, Mountain View, CA 94040 (SAN 268-2931) Tel 415-965-9020.

Bible Study Pr, *(Bible Study, Pr.; 0-9600154),* 9017 N. 70th St., Milwaukee, WI 53223 (SAN 281-3211) Tel 414-354-3504; Dist. by: Omnibook Co., N. 57 W. 136 88 Carmen Ave., Menomonee Falls, WI 53051 (SAN 281-322X) Tel 414-781-2866. *Imprints:* Omnibook (Omnibook, Company).(Omnibook, Co.).

Bible Temple, *(Bible Temple Pubns.; 0-914936),* 7545 NE Glisan St., Portland, OR 97213 (SAN 206-1953) Tel 503-253-9020.

Bibli O'Phile Pub Co, *(Bibli O'Phile Publishing Co.; 0-942104),* 156 E. 61st St., New York, NY 10021 (SAN 238-6437) Tel 212-888-1008; Toll free: 800-255-1660; Dist. by: E. P. Dutton & Co., 2 Park Ave., New York, NY 10016 (SAN 201-0070) Tel 212-725-1818.

Biblia Candida, *(Biblia Candida; 0-9617134),* 4466 Winterville Rd., Spring Hill, FL 33526 (SAN 663-1878) Tel 904-686-3527.

Biblical Arch Soc, *(Biblical Archaeology Society; 0-9613089),* 3000 Connecticut Ave. NW., Suite 300, Washington, DC 20008 (SAN 293-9673) Tel 202-387-8888.

Biblical Res Assocs, *(Biblical Research Assocs., Inc.; 0-935106),* The College of Wooster, Wooster, OH 44691 (SAN 211-2876) Tel 216-263-2470.

Biblio Dist, *(Biblio Distribution Ctr.),* Div. of Littlefield, Adams & Co., 81 Adams Dr., Totowa, NJ 07512 (SAN 211-724X) Tel 201-256-8600. Do not confuse with Biblio Pr. in Fresh Meadows, NY.

Biblio NY, *(Biblio Pr.; 0-9602036),* P.O. Box 22, Fresh Meadows, NY 11365-0022 (SAN 217-0892) Tel 718-361-3141; 50-17 40th St., Sunnyside, NY 11104 (SAN 695-4464). Do not confuse with Biblio Distribution Centre of Totowa, NJ.

Biblio Siglo, *(Biblioteca Siglo de Oro; 0-916613),* 530 N. First St., Charlottesville, VA 22901 (SAN 208-2705) Tel 804-295-1021.

Biblio Soc Am, *(Bibliographical Society of America),* P.O. Box 397, Grand Central Sta., New York, NY 10163 (SAN 225-333X) Tel 718-638-7957; Dist. by: Univ. Pr. of Virginia, P.O. Box 3608, University Sta., Charlottesville, VA 22903 (SAN 680-019X) Tel 804-924-3468.

Bibliographic Pr, *(Bibliographic Press, The; 0-930429),* 154-61 22nd Ave., Whitestone, NY 11357 (SAN 670-9788).

Bibliophile, *(Bibliophile Legion Bks, Inc.;
0-918184),* P.O. Box 612, Silver Spring, MD
20901 (SAN 207-6322) Tel 301-490-4367.
Bibliotec Systems & Pub, *(Bibliotechnology
Systems & Publishing Co.; 0-936857),* P.O.
Box 657, Lincoln, MA 01773
(SAN 699-8690) Tel 617-259-0524; 16
Blueberry Ln., Lincoln, MA 01773
(SAN 699-8704).
Bibliotheca, *(Bibliotheca Islamica, Inc.; 0-88297),*
P.O. Box 14474, University Sta.,
Minneapolis, MN 55414 (SAN 202-4063)
Tel 612-221-9883.
Bibliotheca Persica, *(Bibliotheca Persica;
0-933273),* 450 Riverside Dr., No. 4, New
York, NY 10027 (SAN 691-7968)
Tel 212-280-4366; Dist. by: Caravan Bks.,
P.O. Box 344, Delmar, NY 12054
(SAN 206-7323) Tel 518-439-5978.
†Biblo, *(Biblo & Tannen Booksellers & Pubs.,
Inc.; 0-8196),* 321 Sandbank Rd., P.O. Box
302, Cheshire, CT 06410 (SAN 202-4071)
Tel 213-272-2308; *CIP.*
Bibulophile Pr, *(Bibulophile Pr.; 0-911153),*
P.O. Box 399, Bantam, CT 06750-0399
(SAN 268-2990) Tel 203-567-5543.
Bicent Era, *(Bicentennial Era Enterprises;
0-9605734),* P.O. Box 1148, Scappoose, OR
97056 (SAN 216-2245) Tel 503-684-3937.
Bicycle Books, *(Bicycle Bks., Inc.; 0-933201),*
1282a Seventh Ave., San Francisco, CA
94122 (SAN 692-2600) Tel 415-665-8214;
Dist. by: Kampmann & Co., Inc., 9 E. 40th
St., New York, NY 10016 (SAN 202-5191)
Tel 212-685-2928; Dist. by: Raincoast Bk.
Distributors, Ltd., 112 E. Third Ave.,
Vancouver, BC V5T 1C8, (SAN 200-6170)
Tel 604-873-6581.
Bid Pub Co, *(Bid Publishing; 0-915587),* Div. of
Beyond Interior Design, Inc., 606 Wilshire
Blvd., No. 404, Santa Monica, CA 90401
(SAN 291-0810) Tel 213-215-3400.
Bielawski, *(Bielawski, Maxwell; 0-9600014),* 320
Lakeshore Dr., Dunkirk, NY 14048
(SAN 204-5338) Tel 716-366-2241.
†Bieler, *(Bieler Pr.; 0-931460),* 212 Second St.,
N., Studio 1, 4th Flr., Minneapolis, MN
55401 (SAN 209-7087) Tel 612-339-1978;
CIP.
Big Apple Co, *(Big Apple Co.,The; 0-918853),*
195 Claremont, Suite 391, Long Beach, CA
90803 (SAN 670-0578) Tel 714-879-0452.
Big Bend, *(Big Bend Natural History Assn., Inc.;
0-912001),* Box 68, Big Bend National Park,
TX 79834 (SAN 268-3075)
Tel 915-477-2236.
Big Blue Bks, *(Big Blue Bks.; 0-916969),* 13239
Vanguard Way, Lakeside, CA 92040
(SAN 655-5772) Tel 619-443-6397.
†Big Brothers-Big Sisters, *(Big Brothers-Big
Sisters of America; 0-9613820),* 230 N. 13th
St., Philadelphia, PA 19107
(SAN 681-9648) Tel 215-567-2748; *CIP.*
Big Daddy Pr, *(Big Daddy Pr.; 0-939771),*
14033 Burbank No. 128, Van Nuys, CA
91401 (SAN 677-6221) Tel 818-994-2139.
Big Foot NY, *(Big Foot Pr.; 0-917455),* 57
Seafield Ln., Bay Shore, NY 11706
(SAN 657-0720) Tel 516-666-8512.
Big Horn Imprint of **Intl Aviation Pubs**
Big Hse Pub, *(Big House Publishing Co.;
0-937529),* P.O. Box 202, Steger, IL 60475
(SAN 659-0373) Tel 312-758-8786; 22901
Sherman Rd., Chicago Heights, IL 60411
(SAN 659-0381).
Big Island, *(Big Island Club Hawaii, Inc.;
0-9608396),* P.O. Box 344, Paauilo, HI
96776 (SAN 240-5962) Tel 808-775-7331.
Big Kids Pub, *(Big Kids Publishing, Inc.;
0-930249),* P.O. Box 10237, Rochester, NY
14610 (SAN 670-8617) Tel 716-248-1048.
Big Moose, *(Big Moose Pr.; 0-914692),* P.O.
Box 180, Big Moose, NY 13331
(SAN 206-3336) Tel 315-357-2821.
Big Morning Pr, *(Big Morning Pr.; 0-935056),*
Box 3342, Lawrence, KS 66044
(SAN 211-4100) Tel 913-843-0012.
Big Nickel, *(Big Nickel Pubns.; 0-936433),* P.O.
Box 157, Milford, NH 03055
(SAN 697-8495) Tel 617-486-8971.
Big Red Cartoon, *(Big Red Cartoon Co.;
0-9616098),* Box 27112, Ralston, NE
68127 (SAN 698-1380) Tel 402-592-4291;
8636 "S" Plaza, No. 10, Omaha, NE 68127
(SAN 698-1399); Dist. by: Nelson News,
Inc., 4651 F St., Omaha, NE 68117
(SAN 169-443X).

Big Santa Hist, *(Big Santa Anita Historical
Society; 0-9615421),* 7 N. Fifth Ave.,
Arcadia, CA 91006 (SAN 696-2955)
Tel 818-967-8008.
Big Sur Pubs, *(Big Sur Pubs.; 0-9613141),* 8300
Delongpre Ave., Los Angeles, CA 90069
(SAN 294-9415) Tel 213-654-8677.
Big Sur Women, *(Big Sur Women Pr;
0-9614678),* P.O. Box 40, Big Sur, CA
93920 (SAN 692-5073) Tel 408-667-2498.
Big Toad Pr, *(Big Toad Press; 0-940536),* 617
25th St., Sacramento, CA 95816
(SAN 209-5300) Tel 916-446-7363.
Big Valley Pub, *(Big Valley Publishing Co.;
0-9616795),* 18024 Ventura Blvd., Encino,
CA 91316 (SAN 659-8293)
Tel 818-345-0773.
Bigelow Soc, *(Bigelow Society, Inc., The;
0-9616682),* 1516 Evergreen St., Fairbanks,
AK 99709 (SAN 659-8323)
Tel 907-456-6272.
Biggs Pubs, *(Biggs Pubs.; 0-9616590),* P.O. Box
105, Newalla, OK 74857 (SAN 659-4913)
Tel 405-391-3144; 11008 Squirmy Dr.,
Newalla, OK 74857 (SAN 659-4921).
Bigoni Bks, *(Bigoni Bks.; 0-938996),* 4121 NE
Highland, Portland, OR 97211
(SAN 216-3357) Tel 503-288-0997.
Bijon, *(Bijon; 0-938391),* 9 Sumner Pl.,
Piscataway, NJ 08854 (SAN 659-8366)
Tel 201-463-1505; P.O. Box 91, Piscataway,
NJ 08854 (SAN 660-9589).
Biling Rev-Pr, *(Bilingual Review/Pr.; 0-916950),*
Hispanic Research Ctr., Arizona State Univ.,
Tempe, AZ 85287 (SAN 208-5526)
Tel 607-724-9495.
Bilingual Bks, *(Bilingual Bks., Inc.; 0-916682),*
6018 Seaview NW., Seattle, WA 98107
(SAN 220-2352) Tel 206-789-7544; Toll
free: 800-128-4078; Dist. by: Cliffs Notes
Inc., P.O. Box 80728, Lincoln, NE 68501
(SAN 200-4275) Tel 402-477-6971.
Bilingual Ed Serv, *(Bilingual Educ. Servs., Inc.;
0-86624),* 2514 S. Grand Ave., Los Angeles,
CA 90007 (SAN 218-4680)
Tel 213-749-6213.
Bilingual Pr
   See Biling Rev-Pr
Bilingue Pubns, *(Bilingue Pubns.; 0-933196),*
P.O. Drawer H, Las Cruces, NM 88004
(SAN 223-6389) Tel 505-526-1557.
BillArt, *(BillArt Pubns.; 0-9611112),* 23
Overlook Rd., Woodbridge, CT 06525
(SAN 282-8693) Tel 203-397-0338; Orders
to: P.O. Box 124, Rowayton, CT 06853
(SAN 699-5713).
Billboard Bks Imprint of **Watson-Guptill**
Billib Press, *(Billib Pr.; 0-9613767),* P.O. Box
340026, Boca Raton, FL 33434
(SAN 678-9595) Tel 305-487-1494.
†Billner & Rouse, *(Billner & Rouse, Inc.;
0-932755),* P.O. Box 20465, Hammarskjold
Ctr., New York, NY 10017
(SAN 658-5462) Tel 212-868-1121; Dist.
by: Longwood Publishing Group, Inc., 27 S.
Main St., Wolfeboro, NH 03894-2069
(SAN 209-3170) Tel 603-569-4576; *CIP.*
BILR Corp, *(BILR Corp., The; 0-937177),* P.O.
Box 22918, Denver, CO 80222
(SAN 658-4624) Tel 303-789-9974; 43
Sunset Dr., Englewood, CO 80110
(SAN 658-4632).
Binary Eng Assocs, *(Binary Engineering Assocs.,
Inc.; 0-932217),* P.O. Box 528, Holden, MA
01520 (SAN 686-6026) Tel 617-829-4361.
Binford
   See Binford-Metropolitan
Binford & Mort Pubs
   See Binford-Metropolitan
†Binford-Metropolitan, *(Binford & Mort
Publishing; Metropolitan Pr.; 0-8323),* 1202
NW 17th Ave., Portland, OR 97209
(SAN 201-4386) Tel 503-221-0866; *CIP.*
Imprints: Van Veer Nursery (Van Veer
Nursery).
Binney & Smith, *(Binney & Smith, Inc.;
0-86696),* P.O. Box 431, Easton, PA 18042
(SAN 216-5899).
Bio-Dynamic Farm, *(Bio Dynamic Farming &
Gardening Assn., Inc.; 0-938250),* P.O. Box
253, Wyoming, RI 02898 (SAN 224-9871)
Tel 401-539-2320; Richmond Townhouse
Rd., Wyoming, RI 02898 (SAN 669-0203).
Bio Energy, *(Bio Energy Council),* c/o
Volunteers in Technical Assistance, P.O Box
12438, Arlington, VA 22209-8438
(SAN 209-6145) Tel 703-276-1800.

Bio Graphics, *(Bio-Graphics Publishing;
0-935649),* 4095 Adrian St., Tucker, GA
30084 (SAN 696-1088) Tel 404-934-7855.
Bio Illustra, *(Biological Illustrations Inc.;
0-932353),* P.O. Box 15292, Gainesville, FL
32604 (SAN 687-3669) Tel 904-375-4582.
Bio Marine, *(Bio-Marine Images; 0-9617106),*
22906 Edmonds Way, No. 14, Edmonds,
WA 98020 (SAN 662-4758)
Tel 206-775-8578.
Bio-Pub, *(Bio-Publishing Co.; 0-916833),* 2200
Sunderland Rd., Winston-Salem, NC 27103
(SAN 654-3758) Tel 919-760-0944.
Biobehavioral Pr, *(Biobehavioral Pr.; 0-938176),*
9725 Louedd Ave., Houston, TX 77070
(SAN 214-4875) Tel 713-890-8575.
Biocomm, *(Biocomm; 0-938841),* P.O. Box
2151, Seal Beach, CA 90740
(SAN 661-6933); 5042 Hampton Ct.,
Westminster, CA 92683 (SAN 661-6941)
Tel 714-892-3930.
Bioenergetics Pr, *(Bioenergetics Pr.; 0-9613177),*
Subs. of Bioenergetics, Inc., 1129 Drake St.,
Madison, WI 53715 (SAN 295-6624)
Tel 608-255-4028.
Biofeed Pr, *(Biofeedback Pr.; 0-9606358),* 3428
Sacramento St., San Francisco, CA 94118
(SAN 212-8187) Tel 415-921-5455.
Biofeedback Research, *(Biofeedback Research
Institute Inc.; 0-930758),* 6399 Wilshire
Blvd., Suite 900, Los Angeles, CA 90048
(SAN 208-2225) Tel 213-933-9451.
Biograf Pubns Imprint of **Garber Comm**
Biograph Bks, *(Biograph Bks.; 0-938311),* 260
W. 35th St., Suite 607, New York, NY
10001 (SAN 659-8390) Tel 212-330-0970.
BioGuide Pr, *(BioGuide Pr.; 0-9615277),* P.O.
Box 16072, Alexandria, VA 22302
(SAN 694-4582) Tel 703-820-9045; 1225
Martha Custis Dr., Apt. 411, Alexandria, VA
22302 (SAN 699-6027).
Biohydrant, *(Biohydrant Pubns.; 0-918562),* 56
Congress St., St. Albans, VT 05478
(SAN 209-6374) Tel 802-524-6307.
Biokinesiology Institute, *(Biokinesiology
Institute; 0-937216),* P.O. Box 910,
Monticello, UT 84535 (SAN 214-3437)
Tel 801-587-2972; Orders to: The Nutrition
Place, 5432 Hwy. 227, Trail, OR 97541
(SAN 661-9592) Tel 503-878-2080.
Biomat Pub Co, *(Biomateria Publishing, Co.,
Inc.; 0-9609098),* P.O. Box 523, Stony
Brook, NY 11790 (SAN 241-2748)
Tel 516-689-9492.
Biomateria
   See Biomat Pub Co
Biomed Pubns
   See PSG Pub Co
Biomed Pubns Imprint of **PSG Pub Co**
Biomedical Eng, *(Biomedical Engineering
Society),* P.O. Box 2399, Culver City, CA
90231 (SAN 225-1477) Tel 213-206-6443.
†Biomedical Info, *(Biomedical Information
Corp.; 0-935404),* 800 Second Ave., New
York, NY 10017 (SAN 223-7172)
Tel 212-599-3400; *CIP.*
Biomedical Pr Imprint of **Elsevier**
Bionomic, *(Bionomic Publishers, Inc.; 0-912987),*
28306 Industrial Blvd. Suite M, Hayward,
CA 94545 (SAN 283-2879).
Bios Pubs, *(Bios Publishers; 0-9610636),* Box
159, Aransas Pass, TX 78336
(SAN 264-6528) Tel 512-758-2105.
BioSci Info, *(BioSciences Information Services;
0-916246),* 2100 Arch St., Philadelphia, PA
19103 (SAN 287-6809) Tel 215-587-4800.
Microfilm & microfiche editions of & indexes
to Biological Abstracts & Biological
Abstracts/RRM (Reports, Reviews,
Meetings).
BioServ Corp, *(BioService Corp.; 0-938278),*
500 S. Racine Ave., Suite 302, Chicago, IL
60607 (SAN 215-7330).
Biosis Biosciences
   See BioSci Info
Biotech Vet, *(Biotechnical Veterinary
Consultants; 0-9612756),* P.O. Box 789,
Cardiff-by-the-Sea, CA 92007
(SAN 289-7334) Tel 619-756-1344.
Birch Ballast, *(Birch Ballast Notificatory (BBN);
0-915271),* 1319 Pitkin Ave., Akron, OH
44310 (SAN 289-968X) Tel 216-929-5097.
Birch Portage, *(Birch Portage Pr.; 0-916691),*
502 Leicester Ave., Duluth, MN 55803
(SAN 654-1305) Tel 218-728-1991; Orders
to: P.O. Box 3055, Duluth, MN 55803
(SAN 654-1313).

Birch Run Pub, *(Birch Run Publishing; 0-931964),* 19 Sycamore Ln., Madison, CT 06443 (SAN 211-5921).

Birch Tree Gr
See Summy-Birchard

Birchfield Bks, *(Birchfield Bks.; 0-912871),* P.O. Box 1305, N. Conway, NH 03860 (SAN 277-6510) Tel 603-447-3086.

Bird & Bull Pr *Imprint of* **U Pr of Va**

Bird Hand Pub, *(Bird In Hand Publishing; 0-9613994),* 3620 Weston Pl., Long Beach, CA 90807 (SAN 683-2261) Tel 213-427-4393.

Bird Prof Pubns, *(Bird Professional Pubns.; 0-9616174),* 2320 Lynx Way, Boise, ID 83705 (SAN 699-8607) Tel 208-384-1600.

Bird-Sci Bks *Imprint of* **Foris Pubns**

Bird Shoal Bks, *(Bird Shoal Bks.; 0-9617135),* P.O. Box 503, Harkers Island, NC 28531 (SAN 663-1622); Pentecostal Church Rd., Harkers Island, NC 28531 (SAN 663-1630) Tel 919-728-4635.

Birds' Meadow Pub, *(Birds' Meadow Publishing Co., Inc.; 0-9606360),* 1150 N. Olson Rd., Coupeville, WA 98239-9776 (SAN 208-0710).

Birdseed, *(Birdseed; 0-933006),* 1560-C Lincoln Ave., Alameda, CA 94501 (SAN 212-3339).

†**Birkhauser,** *(Birkhauser Boston, Inc.; 0-8176),* 380 Green St., Cambridge, MA 02139 (SAN 213-2869) Tel 617-876-2333; *CIP.*

Birmingham Hist Soc, *(Birmingham Historical Society; 0-943994),* 1 Sloss Quarters, Birmingham, AL 35222-1243 (SAN 240-1347).

Birth & Parenting, *(Birth & Parenting Pubns.; 0-9615484),* Rte. 1, Box 137, Earlysville, VA 22936 (SAN 696-1134) Tel 804-973-1529.

Birth Day, *(Birth Day Publishing Co.; 0-9600958),* P.O. Box 7722, San Diego, CA 92107 (SAN 208-5542) Tel 619-296-3194.

Bisbee Pr, *(Bisbee Pr., Collective; 0-938196),* Drawer HA, Bisbee, AZ 85603 (SAN 215-8418).

Bisel Co, *(Bisel, George T., Co.),* 710 S. Washington Sq., Philadelphia, PA 19106 (SAN 201-727X) Tel 215-922-5760; Toll free: 800-247-3526 in Pennsylvania.

†**Bishop Graphics,** *(Bishop Graphics, Inc.; 0-9601748; 0-938009),* P.O. Box 5007, Westlake Village, CA 91359 (SAN 658-0181); Toll free: 800-222-5808; Dist. by: PMS Industries (mail orders), 1790 Hembree Rd., Alpharetta, GA 30201 (SAN 683-1486) Tel 404-475-1818; Orders to: 538 Sterling Center Dr., Westlake Village, CA 91359 (SAN 663-2882) Tel 818-991-2600; *CIP.*

Bishop Mus, *(Bishop Museum Pr.; 0-910240),* P.O. Box 19000-A, Honolulu, HI 96819 (SAN 202-408X) Tel 808-847-3511.

Bishop Pine, *(Bishop Pine Press; 0-9612760),* P.O. Box 128, Inverness, CA 94937 (SAN 289-7342) Tel 415-663-1744; Dist. by: Nancy Kleban, Box 486, Point Reyes Station, CA 94956 (SAN 200-4283).

Bishop Pr, *(Bishop Pr. The; 0-911329),* P.O. Box 894, Rancho Santa Fe, CA 92067 (SAN 268-3334) Tel 619-756-4667.

Bishop-Rogers, *(Bishop-Rogers Pubns.; 0-914727),* P.O. Box 85152-276, San Diego, CA 92138 (SAN 287-7813) Tel 619-278-9695.

Bismarck Mandan, *(Bismarck-Mandan Symphony League; 0-9612998),* P.O. Box 131, Bismarck, ND 58502 (SAN 293-4922) Tel 701-258-2867; 2217 Ave. E, Bismarck, ND 58501 (SAN 293-4930) Tel 701-223-6571.

Bison *Imprint of* **U of Nebr Pr**

Biting Idge, *(Biting Idge Miracle Pr.; 0-942352),* c/o Chrysalis Pubns., P.O. Box 151493, Columbus, OH 43215 (SAN 239-7153) Tel 614-221-6827.

Bits Pr, *(Bits Pr.; 0-933248),* Case Western Reserve Univ., Dept. of English, Cleveland, OH 44106 (SAN 212-5927) Tel 216-795-2810.

Bitteroot Ed
See Bitterroot Ed

Bitteroot West
See West Boston

Bitterroot Ed, *(Bitterroot Educational Resources for Women; 0-915111),* 315 S. Fourth East, Missoula, MT 59801 (SAN 289-7350) Tel 406-728-3041.

Bittersweet
See Bittersweet Pub

Bittersweet Evanston, *(Bittersweet Pr.; 0-9611962),* 819 Clinton Pl., Evanston, IL 60201 (SAN 286-7451) Tel 312-492-9472. Do not confuse with Bittersweet Publishing Co., Livermore, CA.

Bittersweet Pr
See Bittersweet Evanston

Bittersweet Pub, *(Bittersweet Publishing Co.; 0-931255),* Subs. of Bittersweet Enterprises, 5658 Oakmont Cir., Livermore, CA 94550 (SAN 681-9656) Tel 415-455-5816. Do not confuse with Bittersweet Pr., Evanston, IL.

Biviano, *(Biviano, Ronald; 0-9605476),* 909 Charles, Crete, IL 60417 (SAN 215-9880).

Biworld
See Bi World Indus

Biworld Pubs
See Bi World Indus

Bixter Bks, *(Bixter Bks.; 0-936933),* Div. of Allan M. Keene & Co., 250 E. 63rd St., New York, NY 10021 (SAN 658-6929) Tel 212-308-3698.

BIZ Pub, *(B.I.Z. Publishing; 0-9615544),* 2424 Congress Ave., Suite G, San Diego, CA 92110 (SAN 696-0480) Tel 619-295-6337.

Bizarre Butterfly, *(Bizarre Butterfly Publishing; 0-915113),* Subs. of Green Davis & Assocs., 1347 E. San Miguel, Phoenix, AZ 85014 (SAN 289-5900).

BJ Noles, *(Noles, BJ; 0-9613684),* 11859 SW Riverwood Rd., Portland, OR 97219 (SAN 671-0115) Tel 503-636-6896; Dist. by: Pacific Pipeline Inc., 19215 66th Ave. S, Kent, WA 98031 (SAN 208-2128); Dist. by: Pacific Trade Group, P.O. Box 668, Pearl City, HI 96782-0668 (SAN 169-1635).

BJA Family, *(BJA Family Pubns.; 0-9615320),* 136 Washington St., Paterson, NJ 07505 (SAN 694-6518) Tel 201-684-3119.

BJIS Pub, *(BJIS Publishing; 0-9614211),* 1000 Olive Dr., Suite 22, P.O. Box 6718, Bakersfield, CA 93386 (SAN 670-6991) Tel 805-393-7022.

†**Bk Co,** *(Book Co., The; 0-912003),* Subs. of Arrays, Inc., 11223 S. Hindry Ave., Los Angeles, CA 90045 (SAN 264-603X) Tel 213-410-3977; *CIP.*

Bk Express, *(Book Express; 0-9612322),* P.O. Box 1249, Bellflower, CA 90706 (SAN 289-1301) Tel 213-867-3723; Dist. by: Publishers Group West, 5855 Beaudry Ave., Emeryville, CA 94608 (SAN 202-8522) Tel 415-658-3453; Dist. by: Ingram Book Co., P.O. Box 17266, Nashville, TN 37217 (SAN 169-7978); Dist. by: Baker & Taylor (Western Div.), 380 Edison Way, Reno, NV 89564 (SAN 169-4464) Tel 702-786-6700; Dist. by: Gordons Books, Inc., 5450 N. Valley Hwy., Denver, CO 80216 (SAN 169-0531) Tel 303-296-1830.

Bk Habit
See C Annegan

Bk Indus Study, *(Book Industry Study Group, Inc.; 0-940016),* 160 Fifth Ave., New York, NY 10010 (SAN 216-793X) Tel 212-929-1393.

Bk Look, *(Book Look; 0-934781),* 51 Maple Ave., Warwick, NY 10990 (SAN 694-2474) Tel 914-986-1981.

Bk Page, *(Book Page; 0-910266),* 904 Silver Spur Rd., Suite 120, Rolling Hills Estate, CA 90274 (SAN 158-8869) Tel 213-373-1914.

Bk Paper Group, *(Book & Paper Group, The; 0-937685),* Univ. of Chicago Library, 1100 E. 57th St., Chicago, IL 60637 (SAN 659-3062) Tel 312-962-8705.

Bk Pubs, *(Bk. Pubs., Inc.; 0-931541),* P.O. Box 21492, Tampa, FL 33622 (SAN 682-286X) Tel 813-876-1521.

Bk Revel
See B R E Pub

Bk Serv Assocs, *(Book Service Assocs., Inc.; 0-916253),* P.O. Box 10830, Winston-Salem, NC 27108 (SAN 294-9059) Tel 919-725-7557; 612 S. Main St., Winston-Salem, NC 27101 (SAN 294-9067).

Bk Value Intl *Imprint of* **Quality Bks IL**

Bkhaus, *(Bkhaus; 0-931613),* P.O. Box 299, East Detroit, MI 48021 (SAN 683-681X); 23323 Teppert, East Detroit, MI 48021 (SAN 662-2631) Tel 313-778-5688; Dist. by: Quality Books, Inc., 918 Sherwood Dr., Lake Bluff, IL 60044-2204 (SAN 169-2127) Tel 312-295-2010; Dist. by: Publishers Group West, 5855 Beaudry St., Emeryville, CA 94608 (SAN 202-8522) Tel 415-658-3453.

Bklyn Botanic, *(Brooklyn Botanic Garden),* 1000 Washington Ave., Brooklyn, NY 11225 (SAN 203-1094) Tel 718-622-4433.

Bklyn Coll Music, *(Brooklyn College Conservatory of Music; 0-9600976),* Brooklyn College, Brooklyn, NY 11210 (SAN 208-4813) Tel 718-780-5286.

Bklyn Coll Schl Perform
See Bklyn Coll Music

Bklyn Educ, *(Brooklyn Educational & Cultural Alliance; 0-933250),* Pratt Institute, 200 Willoughby Ave., Brooklyn, NY 11205 (SAN 212-4858) Tel 718-636-3600.

†**Bklyn Mus,** *(Brooklyn Museum; 0-87273; 0-913696),* Pubns. & Marketing Services, Eastern Pkwy., Brooklyn, NY 11238 (SAN 206-3387) Tel 718-638-5000; *CIP.*

BkMaster, *(BookMasters; 0-917889),* P.O. Box 159-Z, Ashland, OH 44805 (SAN 656-9668) Tel 419-289-6051.

†**BkMk,** *(BkMk Pr., of Missouri-Kansas City; 0-933532),* UMKC, 5216 Rockhill Rd., Suite 204, Kansas City, MO 64110 (SAN 207-7914) Tel 816-276-2258; Dist. by: Baker & Taylor Co., Midwest Div., 501 Gladiola Ave., Momence, IL 60954 (SAN 169-2100) Tel 815-472-2444; Dist. by: Blackwell North America, 1001 Fries Mill Rd., Blackwood, NJ 08012 (SAN 169-4596) Tel 609-629-0700; *CIP.*

BkPr Ltd, *(Bookpress Ltd.; 0-916271),* P.O. Box KP, Williamsburg, VA 23187 (SAN 295-6721) Tel 804-229-1260.

Bks Americana, *(Bks. Americana, Inc.; 0-89689),* P.O. Box 2326, Florence, AL 35630 (SAN 212-1816) Tel 205-757-9966; Dist. by: Collector Books, 5801 Kentucky Dam Rd., Paducah, KY 42001 (SAN 213-2621) Tel 502-898-6211; Dist. by: Charles E. Tuttle Co., Inc., 28 S. Main St., Rutland, VT 05701-0410 (SAN 213-2621) Tel 802-773-8229; Dist. by: Ingram Book Co., P.O. Box 17266r, Nashville, TN 37217 (SAN 651-1163) Tel 615-361-5000.

Bks Brooks
See Bks By Brooks

Bks Business, *(Books for Business; 0-89499),* Box 5474, New York, NY 10163 (SAN 210-0436).

Bks By Brooks, *(Books by Brooks; 0-9616207),* 2946 Housley Dr., Dallas, TX 75228 (SAN 658-3288) Tel 817-898-2169.

Bks by Kellogg, *(Books by Kellogg; 0-9603972),* P.O. Box 487, Annandale, VA 22003 (SAN 214-0454) Tel 703-256-2483.

Bks Demand UMI, *(Books on Demand; 0-8357),* Div. of University Microfilms, International, 300 N. Zeeb Rd., Ann Arbor, MI 48106 (SAN 212-2464) Tel 313-761-4700; Toll free: 800-521-0600. On-demand reprints of out-of-print books reproduced by xerography and bound in paper covers (cloth covers are available for 6.00 additional. Imprint of University Microfilms International.

Bks for All Times, *(Books for All Times, Inc.; 0-939360),* P.O. Box 2, Alexandria, VA 22313 (SAN 216-2253) Tel 703-548-0457.

Bks for Profs, *(Books for Professionals; 0-935422),* 4600 Valley Hi Dr., Sacramento, CA 95823 (SAN 212-3355) Tel 916-428-5984.

Bks Intl DH-TE, *(Books International of DH-TE International, Inc.),* P.O. Box 14487, St. Louis, MO 63178 (SAN 202-4101) Tel 314-721-8787.

Bks New China *Imprint of* **Hippocrene Bks**

Bks Of A Feather, *(Books Of A Feather; 0-9613060),* P.O. Box 3095, Terminal Annex, Los Angeles, CA 90051 (SAN 293-972X) Tel 213-797-5551.

Bks of New Univ, *(Books of The New Universe; 0-9611638),* P.O. Box 982, Centereach, NY 11720 (SAN 285-1350) Tel 516-585-7261; 164 Noel Dr., Centereach, NY 11720 (SAN 285-1369).

Bks of Sci, *(Books of Science; 0-916615),* P.O. Box 462, Columbia, MD 21045 (SAN 296-4589) Tel 301-730-8391.

Bks of Truth, *(Bks. of Truth; 0-939399),* P.O. Box 2324, Bath, OH 44210 (SAN 663-1304); 1742 Orchard Dr., Akron, OH 44313 (SAN 663-1312) Tel 216-666-3852.

Bks of Value, *(Books of Value; 0-9603174),* 2458 Chislehurst Dr., Los Angeles, CA 90027 (SAN 210-5896) Tel 213-664-8981.

Bks On Bus, *(Books On Business; 0-932355),* P.O. Box 113, Buena Park, CA 90621 (SAN 687-3685) Tel 714-523-0357.

Bks on Tape, *(Books on Tape, Inc.; 0-913369),* P.O. Box 7900, Newport Beach, CA 92660 (SAN 286-8959) Tel 714-548-5525; Toll free: 800-626-3333.

†**Bks With Ideas,** *(Bks. With Ideas, Inc.; 0-917569),* 74 Arguello Cir., San Rafael, CA 94901 (SAN 657-1263) Tel 415-456-5463; *CIP.*

Bkworld Pub, *(Bookworld Publishing Co., Inc.; 1-55633),* 3165 McCrory Pl., Suite 260, Orlando, FL 32803 (SAN 663-3854) Tel 305-894-0661.

†**Black-A-Moors,** *(Black-A-Moors, Inc., The; 0-933886),* 2339 N. Fairhill St., Philadelphia, PA 19133 (SAN 223-7180) Tel 215-634-1440; *CIP.*

Black & Red, *(Black & Red; 0-934868),* P.O. Box 02374, Detroit, MI 48202 (SAN 208-5550).

Black & White, *(Black & White Publishing; 0-940050),* Subs. of Sun-Rose Assocs., Inc., 18 Cogswell Ave., Cambridge, MA 02140 (SAN 220-2077) Tel 617-576-3863.

Black Bear, *(Black Bear Pubns.; 0-932593),* 1916 Lincoln St., Croydon, PA 19020-8026 (SAN 687-5068) Tel 215-788-3543.

Black Box, *(Black Box Corp.)* Subs. of Micom Systems, Mayview Rd. at Park Dr., P.O. Box 12800, Pittsburgh, PA 15241 (SAN 277-1985) Tel 412-746-5530.

Black Buzzard, *(Black Buzzard, Pr.; 0-938872),* 4705 S. Eighth Rd., Arlington, VA 22204 (SAN 216-0196).

Black Caucus Am Black Lib
See Black Caucus Am Lib

Black Caucus Am Lib, *(Black Caucus of the American Library Assn.),* 499 Wilson Library, Univ. of Minneapolis Libraries, Minneapolis, MN 55455 (SAN 211-8890) Tel 612-373-3097.

Black Classic, *(Black Classic, Pr.; 0-933121),* P.O. Box 13414, Baltimore, MD 21203 (SAN 219-5836) Tel 301-728-4595.

Black Current, *(Black Current, Pr., The; 0-938975),* P.O. Box 1149, Haines, AK 99827 (SAN 659-8552); Second St., Haines, AK 99827 (SAN 659-8560) Tel 907-766-2146.

Black Dog Pr, *(Black Dog, Pr.; 0-933525),* P.O. Box 1213, Capitola, CA 95010 (SAN 691-8514) Tel 408-462-4162.

Black Experience, *(Black Experience Publishing Co.; 0-9611778),* P.O. Box 224244, Dallas, TX 75216 (SAN 285-2195).

Black Flag Pr, *(Black Flag Pr.; 0-937259),* 638 Main St., Woburn, MA 01801 (SAN 659-039X) Tel 617-933-5260.

Black Graphics, *(Black Graphics; 0-939569),* 3023 Woodcreek Ln., Suite 209, Houston, TX 77073 (SAN 663-4958) Tel 713-821-1576.

Black Heron Pr, *(Black Heron, Pr.; 0-930773),* P.O. Box 95676, Seattle, WA 98145 (SAN 677-623X) Tel 206-523-2637.

Black I Press, *(Black Ice, Pr.; 0-918411),* 6022 Sunnyview Rd., NE, Salem, OR 97305 (SAN 657-5781) Tel 503-363-6064; Dist. by: Bookslinger, 213 E. Fourth St., St. Paul, MN 55101 (SAN 169-4154) Tel 612-221-0429.

Black Ice, *(Black Ice Pubs.; 0-939250),* 100 Prescott St., Worcester, MA 01605 (SAN 216-0889) Tel 617-755-1525.

Black Letter, *(Black Letter Pr.; 0-912382),* 601 Bridge St., NW, Grand Rapids, MI 49504 (SAN 201-436X) Tel 616-538-2516.

Black Light Fellow, *(Black Light Fellowship; 0-933176),* P.O. Box 5369, Chicago, IL 60680 (SAN 212-3347) Tel 312-722-1441; 2859 W. Wilcox, Chicago, IL 60612 (SAN 669-0211).

Black Mntn, *(Black Mountain Bks.; 0-936310),* P.O. Box 601, State College, PA 16804 (SAN 216-3365) Tel 814-234-1967.

Black Oak, *(Black Oak, Pr.; 0-930674),* Box 4663, Univ. Pl. Sta., Lincoln, NE 68504 (SAN 212-7261).

Black Oak Bks
See Blk Oak Pub CA

Black Oak NY, *(Black Oak Pubs; 0-9608834),* Lloyd Harbor Rd., Huntington, NY 11743 (SAN 241-0044) Tel 516-421-5646.

Black Oyster, *(Black Oyster Pr.; 0-9605966),* 821 Hampshire St., San Francisco, CA 94110 (SAN 216-7182) Tel 415-285-8367.

Black Plankton, *(Black Plankton Pr.; 0-9611236),* P.O. Box 521, Fulton, CA 95439 (SAN 277-6588).

Black Pursuit, *(Black Pursuit, Inc.; 0-935979),* 1809 Hall Ave., Huntington, WV 25701 (SAN 696-6861) Tel 304-523-5392; P.O. Box 5524, Huntington, WV 25703 (SAN 698-2123).

Black Resource, *(Black Resource Guide, Inc.; 0-9608374),* 501 Oneida Place, NW, Washington, DC 20011 (SAN 240-1363) Tel 202-291-4373.

Black Rose Bks, *(Black Rose Bks.; 0-919618; 0-919619; 0-920057),* 33 E. Tupper St., Buffalo, NY 14230 (SAN 661-9606). U. S. office of Black Rose Bks. Canadian address: 3981 boul. St.-Laurent, Montreal, PQ H2W 1T7. Tel: 514-844-4076.

Black Scholar Pr, *(Black Scholar Pr.; 0-933296),* P.O. Box 2869, Oakland, CA 94609 (SAN 222-5816) Tel 415-547-6633.

†**Black Sparrow,** *(Black Sparrow Pr.; 0-87665),* 24 Tenth St., Santa Rosa, CA 95401 (SAN 201-4343) Tel 707-579-4011; *CIP.*

Black Stallion Ctry Pr, *(Black Stallion Country Press; 0-9607694),* P.O. Box 2250, Culver City, CA 90231 (SAN 237-9376).

Black Star, *(Black Star Series; 0-9607630),* 16 Clipper St., San Francisco, CA 94114 (SAN 293-2369); Dist. by: Subco., P.O. Box 10233, Eugene, OR 97440 (SAN 293-2377).

Black Star Pub, *(Black Star Publishing Co.; 0-9605426),* 450 Park Ave., S., New York, NY 10016 (SAN 204-4153) Tel 212-679-3288.

Black Stone, *(Black Stone Pr.; 0-937002),* (SAN 209-5319); Dist. by: Small Press Distribution, Inc., 1814 San Pablo Ave., Berkeley, CA 94702 (SAN 204-5826).

†**Black Swan CT,** *(Black Swan Bks., Ltd.; 0-933806),* P.O. Box 327, Redding Ridge, CT 06876 (SAN 213-4675) Tel 203-938-9548; *CIP.*

Black Swan Pr, *(Black Swan Pr./Surrealist Editions; 0-941194),* 1726 W. Jarvis Ave., Chicago, IL 60626 (SAN 211-593X).

Black T T, *(Black Think Tank; 0-915921),* 1801 Bush St., Suite 127, San Francisco, CA 94109 (SAN 293-969X) Tel 415-929-0204.

†**Black Thorn Bks,** *(Black Thorn Bks.; 0-932366),* 1 Camp St., Cambridge, MA 02140 (SAN 213-2877); *CIP.*

Black Willow, *(Black Willow Poetry; 0-910047),* 401 Independence Dr., Sunrise Towamencin Township, Harleysville, PA 19438 (SAN 240-9682) Tel 215-368-0163.

Blackberry Bks, *(Blackberry Bks.),* 26 Stonecrest Rd., Ridgefield, CT 06877 (SAN 208-4201). Do not confuse with Blackberry-Salted in the Shell, South Harpswell, ME.

Blackberry ME, *(Blackberry - Salted in the Shell; 0-942396),* P.O. Box 687, South Harpswell, ME 04079 (SAN 207-7949) Tel 207-833-6051. Do not confuse with Blackberry Bks., Ridgefield, CT.

Blackbird Pr, *(Blackbird Pr.; 0-933473),* 1812 Keyway, Dubuque, IA 52001 (SAN 692-4069) Tel 319-556-8474.

Blackman Kallick, *(Blackman, Kallick, Co. Ltd., Certified Public Accountants; 0-916181),* 300 S. Riverside Plaza, Chicago, IL 60606 (SAN 294-9024) Tel 312-207-1040.

Blackpot Enterprises, *(Blackpot Enterprises; 0-937823),* P.O. Box 1773, Zephyrhills, FL 34283-1773 (SAN 659-4247) Tel 813-788-4455; 737 Tucker Rd., Zephyrhills, FL 34248 (SAN 659-4255).

Blacksmith Corp, *(Blacksmith Corp.; 0-941540),* P.O. Box 424, Southport, CT 06490 (SAN 239-0671) Tel 203-367-4041; Toll free: 800-531-2665.

Blackstone Pub, *(Blackstone Publishing Co.; 0-9615836),* 1507 Cochise Dr., Arlington, TX 76012 (SAN 697-0117) Tel 817-274-6915.

Blackwater Pub Co, *(Blackwater Publishing Co., Inc.; 0-910341),* 530 Allison Ave., SW, Roanoke, VA 24016 (SAN 241-2756) Tel 703-362-4810.

†**Blackwell Pubns,** *(Blackwell Scientific Pubns., Inc.; 0-632; 0-86542),* Div. of Blackwell Scientific Pubns, Ltd. (UK), 667 Lytton Ave., Palo Alto, CA 94301 (SAN 673-2569) Tel 415-324-1688; Orders to: P.O. Box 50009, Palo Alto, CA 94303 (SAN 688-4245) Tel 415-965-4081. Palo Alto, CA offices of Blackwell Scientific Pubns., Inc.: publishers of earth and life science books. See Boston, MA offices of Blackwell Scientific Pubns., for books on medicine and nursing; *CIP.*

†**Blackwell Sci,** *(Blackwell Scientific Pubns., Inc.; 0-86542),* Subs. of Blackwell Scientific Publications, Ltd., 52 Beacon St., Boston, MA 02108 (SAN 215-2029) Tel 617-720-0761; Toll free: 800-325-4177; Dist. by: C. V. Mosby Co., 11830 Westline Industrial Dr., St. Louis, MO 63146 (SAN 200-2280) Tel 314-872-8370; Orders to: Research Report Ctr., 411 Fairchild Ave., Mountain View, CA 94043 (SAN 661-9614) Tel 415-965-4081. Boston, MA office of Blackwell Scientific Pubns., Inc.: publishers of medical and nursing books. See Palo Alto, CA office of Blackwell Scientific Pubns., Inc. for books on the earth and life sciences; *CIP.*

Blackwells Pr, *(Blackwells Pr.; 0-930513),* 2925B Freedom Blvd., Watsonville, CA 95076 (SAN 696-5024) Tel 408-722-4534.

Blagrove Pubns, *(Blagrove Pubns.; 0-9604466; 0-939776),* 80 Pitkin St., P.O. Box 584, Manchester, CT 06040 (SAN 215-1316) Tel 203-647-1785.

Blaine Ethridge
See Ethridge

†**Blair,** *(Blair, John F., Pub.; 0-910244; 0-89587),* 1406 Plaza Dr., Winston-Salem, NC 27103 (SAN 201-4319) Tel 919-768-1374; Toll free: 800-222-9796; *CIP.*

Blair Columbus, *(Blair of Columbus, Inc.; 0-9613709),* Div. of Country Cakes, P.O. Box 7852, Columbus, GA 31908 (SAN 677-1882) Tel 404-561-1144.

Blair McGill Co, *(Blair, McGill & Company; 0-915771),* 5101-13 S. New Hope Rd., Gastonia, NC 28054 (SAN 294-1368) Tel 704-824-2597.

Blake Print Pub, *(Blake Printing & Publishing, Inc.; 0-918303),* 2222 Beebee St., San Luis Obispo, CA 93401 (SAN 657-2618) Tel 805-543-6843; Toll free: 800-792-6946.

Blake Schools, *(Blake Schls., The; 0-933023),* 511 Kenwood Pkwy., Minneapolis, MN 55403 (SAN 689-5441) Tel 612-339-1700.

Blakely, *(Blakely, Jordan; 0-9614582),* (SAN 692-3291); Dist. by: The Pullum Corp., G3500 Flushing Rd., Suite 450, Flint, MI 48504 (SAN 200-7797) Tel 313-733-2662.

Blandin Found, *(Blandin Foundation; 0-9613861),* 100 Pokeyama Ave. N., Grand Rapids, MN 55744 (SAN 685-1932) Tel 218-326-0523.

Blankenship & Co., *(Blankenship & Co; 0-9613038),* 16418 Kleinwood, Spring, TX 77379 (SAN 293-9088) Tel 713-370-0006.

Blarney Bks, *(Blarney Books; 0-935420),* 6129 Shenandoah Dr., Sacramento, CA 95841 (SAN 213-4683).

Blarney Co, *(Blarney Co., The; 0-9616083),* 334 Old Joppa, Fallston, MD 21047 (SAN 698-1151) Tel 301-879-7967; Box 127, Bel Air, MD 21014 (SAN 698-2565).

Blazing Flowers, *(Blazing Flowers Pr.; 0-9610562),* 358 Willowdell, Mansfield, OH 44906 (SAN 263-9378) Tel 419-529-2649.

Blazon Bks, *(Blazon Bks.; 0-913017),* 1934 W. Belle Plaine, Chicago, IL 60613 (SAN 283-2860) Tel 312-975-0317; Dist. by: Bookpeople, 2929 Fifth St., Berkeley, CA 94710 (SAN 168-9517) Tel 415-549-3030; Dist. by: Inland Bk. Co., P.O. Box 261, 22 Hemingway Ave., East Haven, CT 06512 (SAN 200-4151) Tel 203-467-4257.

Bleecker St Pub, *(Bleecker Street Publishing Corp.; 0-941376),* P.O. Box 13066, 18 Koger Executive Ctr., Norfolk, VA 23506 (SAN 238-9525) Tel 804-461-1212.

Bleeker St Pub
See Bleecker St Pub

Bless Israel, *(Bless Israel Today Ministries, Inc.; 0-913961),* P.O. Box 39, New City, NY 10956 (SAN 286-7257) Tel 914-634-1255.

Blessitt Pub, *(Blessitt Publishing; 0-934461),* P.O. Box 69544, Hollywood, CA 90069 (SAN 693-7616) Tel 213-659-8683.

Blewstone Pr, *(Blewstone Pr.; 0-930961),* Div. of Allergenco, P.O. Box 8571, Wainwright Sta., San Antonio, TX 78208 (SAN 678-8777) Tel 512-822-4116.

Blind John, *(Blind John Pubns.; 0-940388),* 2740 Onyx St., Eugene, OR 97403 (SAN 217-0906).

Blip Prods, *(Blip Productions; 0-936917),* 10656 Riverview Pl., Minneapolis, MN 55433 (SAN 658-3253) Tel 612-427-1004.

Blithedale, *(Blithedale Press; 0-917637),* 321 W. Blithedale Ave., Mill Valley, CA 94941 (SAN 656-8815) Tel 415-383-2886.

Blitz Pub Co, *(Blitz Publishing Co.; 0-928404; 0-9606344),* 1600 Verona St., Middleton, WI 53562 (SAN 215-1324) Tel 608-836-7550.

Blk Fam Inst Pub, *(Black Family Institute Pubs.; 0-939205),* Box 24739, Oakland, CA 94623 (SAN 662-6130); 155 Filbert St., Oakland, CA 94607 (SAN 662-6149) Tel 415-836-3245.

Blk Oak Pub CA, *(Black Oak Publishing; 0-939392),* P.O. Box DB, Bloomington, CA 92316 (SAN 216-5597).

Blk Pumpkin Pr, *(Black Pumpkin Pr.; 0-9616206),* Main St., Dunstable, MA 01827 (SAN 658-3326) Tel 617-649-9057.

BLOC Devel, *(BLOC Development Corp.; 0-938843),* 1301 Dade Blvd., Miami Beach, FL 33139 (SAN 697-8452) Tel 305-531-5486; Toll free: 800-231-1149.

Bloch, *(Bloch Publishing, Co.; 0-8197),* 19 W. 21st St., New York, NY 10010 (SAN 214-204X) Tel 212-989-9104.

Bloch & Co OH, *(Bloch & Co.; 0-914276),* P.O. Box 18058, Cleveland, OH 44118 (SAN 201-7261) Tel 216-371-0979.

Block, *(Block Pubs.; 0-916864),* P.O. Box 1802, Palm Springs, CA 92263 (SAN 208-5577) Tel 619-327-0321.

Blondo-Campbell, *(Blondo/Campbell; 0-9616654),* 2325 Tenth Ave. E., Apt. 101, Seattle, WA 98102 (SAN 659-8595) Tel 206-323-4775.

Blood-Horse, *(Blood-Horse, Inc.; 0-936032; 0-939049),* Subs. of Thoroughbred Owners & Breeders Assn., P.O. Box 4038, Lexington, KY 40544 (SAN 203-5294) Tel 606-278-2361; Toll free: 800-354-9207.

Blood Info, *(Blood Information Service; 0-914508),* 508 Getzville Rd., Buffalo, NY 14226 (SAN 206-3344) Tel 716-832-7997.

Bloom Bks, *(Bloom Books Inc.; 0-935000),* 1020 Broad St., Newark, NJ 07102 (SAN 215-1332) Tel 201-642-1130.

Blooming, *(Blooming Prairie Warehouse; 0-9608298),* 2340 Heinz Rd., Iowa City, IA 52240 (SAN 240-3420) Tel 319-337-6448.

Bloomsberry Pr, *(Bloomsberry Pr.; 0-839),* 839 Williamson St., No. 1, Madison, WI 53703 (SAN 291-8161).

Blossom Bks, *(Blossom Bks.; 0-943280),* 9842 Hibert St., Suite 234, San Diego, CA 92131 (SAN 240-5997) Tel 619-695-8472.

Blossom Valley, *(Blossom Valley Press; 0-939894),* P.O. Box 4044, Blossom Valley Sta., Mountain View, CA 94040 (SAN 216-7905) Tel 415-941-7525.

Blue Begonia, *(Blue Begonia Press; 0-911287),* 225 S. 15th Ave., Yakima, WA 98902 (SAN 268-3652) Tel 509-452-9748.

†**Blue Bird Pub,** *(Blue Bird Publishing; 0-933025),* 1428 W. Broad, No. 202, Columbus, OH 43222 (SAN 200-5603) Tel 614-275-6275; Toll free: 800-255-2665; *CIP.*

Blue Boar Pr, *(Blue Boar Pr., The; 0-9617182),* P.O. Box 964, Manchaca, TX 78652 (SAN 663-2645); 11040 Manchaca Rd., Manchaca, TX 78652 (SAN 663-2653) Tel 512-282-3493.

Blue Book, *(Blue-Book Pubs.; 0-918698),* 64 Prospect St., White Plains, NY 10606 (SAN 210-2935) Tel 914-949-0890.

Blue Cat, *(Blue Cat; 0-936200; 0-932679),* 349 Paseo Tesoro, Walnut, CA 91789 (SAN 214-0322) Tel 714-594-3317; Dist. by: Ingram Industries, 347 Reedwood Dr., Nashville, TN 37217 (SAN 169-7978); Dist. by: Baker & Taylor Co., Eastern Div., 50 Kirby Ave., Somerville, NJ 08876 (SAN 169-4901); Dist. by: Baker & Taylor Co., Midwest Div., 501 Gladiola Ave., Momence, IL 60954 (SAN 169-2100); Dist. by: Baker & Taylor Co., Southeast Div., Mt. Olive Rd., Commerce, GA 30529 (SAN 169-1503).

Blue Cloud, *(Blue Cloud Quarterly Press; 0-9612864),* Blue Cloud Abbey, Marvin, SD 57251 (SAN 208-5585) Tel 605-432-5528.

†**Blue Cross & Shield,** *(Blue Cross & Blue Shield Assn.; 0-914818),* 840 N. Lake Shore Dr., Chicago, IL 60611 (SAN 223-629X) Tel 312-440-6182; *CIP.*

Blue Cross Assn
See Blue Cross & Shield

Blue Diamond, *(Blue Diamond Press, The; 0-930856),* 801 Tilden St., Bronx, NY 10467 (SAN 220-4142).

Blue Dragon, *(Blue Dragon Press),* 1515 Poplar Ave., Richmond Heights, CA 94805 (SAN 214-3453) Tel 415-235-0361.

Blue Engine, *(Blue Engine Express, The; 0-9611370),* 173 E. Iroquois, Pontiac, MI 48053 (SAN 283-2852) Tel 313-338-3275.

†**Blue Feather,** *(Blue Feather Press; 0-932482),* P.O. Box 5113, Santa Fe, NM 87502 (SAN 211-9293) Tel 505-983-2776; *CIP.*

Blue Flower, *(Blue Flower; 0-9603924),* Dist. by: Han Bks., 3607 Baring St., Philadelphia, PA 19104 (SAN 214-2864) Tel 215-382-1410.

Blue Giant Pr, *(Blue Giant Press; 0-940054),* 24 Concord Ave., No. 308, Cambridge, MA 02138 (SAN 220-2093) Tel 617-661-2591.

Blue Goose MA
See Castle & Cooke

Blue Harbor, *(Blue Harbor Press; 0-9605278),* P.O. Box 1028, Lomita, CA 90717-0280 (SAN 215-8442).

Blue Haven, *(Blue Haven Area Foundation, Inc.; 0-9609210),* Rte. 3, Box 629, Marble Falls, TX 78654 (SAN 241-2764) Tel 512-598-5727; Dist. by: Collection, Inc., 2101 Kansas City Rd., Olathe, KS 66061 (SAN 200-6359) Tel 913-764-5900; Dist. by: Southwest Cookbook Distributors, 1901 South Shore Dr., Bonham, TX 75418 (SAN 200-4925) Tel 214-583-8898.

Blue Heron, *(Blue Heron Pr., Inc.; 0-939198),* 1728 Herrick, NE, Grand Rapids, MI 49505 (SAN 220-0376) Tel 616-363-7810.

Blue Heron Pr
See Blue Heron WA

Blue Heron WA, *(Blue Heron Pr.; 0-935317),* P.O. Box 5182, Bellingham, WA 98227 (SAN 695-7536); 5 Harbor Mall, Bellingham, WA 98225 (SAN 662-3565) Tel 206-671-1155; Dist. by: Robert Hale & Co., 1840 130th Ave., NE, Suite 10, Bellevue, WA 98005 (SAN 200-6995) Tel 206-881-5212; Dist. by: Pacific Pipeline, Inc., 19215 66th Ave., S., Kent, WA 98032 (SAN 208-2128) Tel 206-872-5523.

Blue Horizon, *(Blue Horizon Press; 0-9607622),* 1517 Crestwood Dr., Greenville, TN 37743 (SAN 213-0254) Tel 615-639-1264.

Blue J, *(Blue J, Inc.; 0-936531),* 3808 S. Calhoun St., Fort Wayne, IN 46807 (SAN 697-8509) Tel 219-432-5776.

Blue Lagoon, *(Blue Lagoon Pubs.; 0-9605338),* 3960 Laurel Canyon, Studio City, CA 91604 (SAN 215-9899) Tel 818-761-2114.

Blue Leaf, *(Blue Leaf Editions; 0-915206),* P.O. Box 857, New London, CT 06320 (SAN 207-205X) Tel 203-445-7391.

Blue Moon Pr, *(Blue Moon, Pr., Inc.; 0-933188),* Orders to: College of Arts & Science, Spalding Hall, Lewis-Clark State College, Lewis-Clark State College, Lewiston, ID 83501 (SAN 213-0157); Dist. by: Kampmann & Co., Inc., 9 E. 40th St., New York, NY 10016 (SAN 202-5191) Tel 212-685-2928.

Blue Mouse, *(Blue Mouse Studio, The; 0-9609640),* P.O. Box 312, Union, MI 49130 (SAN 268-3725) Tel 616-641-5468.

Blue Mtn Arts
See Blue Mtn Pr CO

Blue Mtn Com, *(Blue Mountain Computer, Inc.; 0-914729),* 6818 Woodstream Circle, Seabrook, MD 20706 (SAN 289-5919).

Blue Mtn MI, *(Blue Mountain Pr.; 0-9602408),* 2005 Academy St., Kalamazoo, MI 49007 (SAN 207-7965) Tel 616-349-3924.

Blue Mtn Pr CO, *(Blue Mountain Pr., Inc.; 0-88396),* P.O. Box 4549, Boulder, CO 80306 (SAN 169-0477) Tel 303-449-0536; Toll free: 800-525-0642.

Blue Note, *(Blue-Note Press; 0-9610658),* 54 Cherrywood Lane, Erie, PA 16509 (SAN 264-7168) Tel 814-864-9759.

Blue Oak, *(Blue Oak Press; 0-912950),* P.O. Box 27, Sattley, CA 96124 (SAN 207-0383).

Blue Poppy, *(Blue Poppy Enterprises Pr.; 0-936185),* 2140 Pine St., Boulder, CO 80302 (SAN 697-0168) Tel 303-442-0796; Dist. by: Bookpeople, 2929 Fifth St., Berkeley, CA 94710 (SAN 168-9517) Tel 415-549-3030; Dist. by: Redwing Bk. Co., 44 Linden St., Brookline, MA 02146 (SAN 163-3597) Tel 617-738-4664.

Blue Raven Pub Co, *(Blue Raven Publishing Co.; 0-916029),* P.O. Box 5641, Bellevue, WA 98006 (SAN 294-6920) Tel 206-643-2203.

Blue Reed, *(Blue Reed Arts Inc.; 0-916783),* 839 Williamson St., No. 1, Madison, WI 53703 (SAN 654-2069) Tel 608-251-2206.

Blue Rib Books *Imprint of* Alpine Pubns

Blue Ribbon Bks *Imprint of* Scholastic Inc

Blue Ridge, *(Blue Ridge Press of Boone; 0-938980),* Route 2, Vilas, NC 28692 (SAN 216-3373).

Blue River, *(Blue River Publishing Co.; 0-936324),* P.O. Box 882, Sheboygan, WI 53082-0882 (SAN 215-627X).

Blue River Pubns, *(Blue River Pubns.; 0-930431),* P.O. Box 684, Anoka, MN 55303 (SAN 671-0107).

Blue Rooster Pr, *(Blue Rooster Pr.; 0-9617075),* Rte. 4, Box 540, Perry, FL 32347 (SAN 662-6289); Green Farm Rd., Perry, FL 32347 (SAN 662-6297) Tel 904-584-8589.

Blue Scarab, *(Blue Scarab Pr.; 0-937179),* 243 S. Eighth St., Pocatello, ID 83201 (SAN 658-4640) Tel 208-232-5118.

Blue Sea, *(Blue Sea Press; 0-917549),* P.O. Box 9426, Arlington, VA 22209-0426 (SAN 657-0747) Tel 703-522-8826.

Blue Sky, *(Blue Sky Marketing, Inc.; 0-911493),* P.O. Box 17003, St. Paul, MN 55117 (SAN 263-9394) Tel 612-774-2920.

Blue Star, *(Blue Star Pr.; 0-939602),* 163 Joralemon St., Suite 1144, Brooklyn, NY 11201 (SAN 216-616X) Tel 718-237-9497.

Blue Tulip Pr, *(Blue Tulip Pr.; 0-9616763),* 110 S. El Camino, Suite 113, San Mateo, CA 94401 (SAN 699-8372) Tel 415-348-4356.

Blue Unicorn, *(Blue Unicorn; 0-9608574),* 22 Avon Rd., Kensington, CA 94707 (SAN 238-0447) Tel 415-526-8439.

Blue Whale Pr, *(Blue Whale Pr.; 0-9615303),* 2980 Edgewick Rd., Glendale, CA 91206 (SAN 694-5236) Tel 213-245-5624; Dist. by: Bookpeople, 2929 Fifth St., Berkeley, CA 94710 (SAN 168-9517) Tel 415-549-3030; Dist. by: Baker & Taylor Co., Western Div., 380 Edison Way, Reno, NV 89564 (SAN 169-4464) Tel 702-786-6700; Dist. by: Pacific Pipeline, Inc., 19215 66th Ave., S., Kent, WA 98032 (SAN 208-2128) Tel 206-872-5523.

†**Blue Wind,** *(Blue Wind Press; 0-912652),* P.O. Box 7175, Berkeley, CA 94707 (SAN 206-7099) Tel 415-525-2098; *CIP.*

Bluebird Pr, *(Bluebird Pr., Inc.; 0-930169),* P.O. Box 941, Eunice, LA 70535 (SAN 670-7335) Tel 318-546-6100.

Bluebird Pr CA, *(Bluebird Press (CA); 0-934003),* P.O. Box 1000, Wildomar, CA 92395 (SAN 692-669X) Tel 714-674-4888.

Bluefish, *(Bluefish; 0-914102),* Box 1601, Southampton, NY 11968 (SAN 201-6346) Tel 516-283-8811.

Bluejay Bks, *(Bluejay Bks.; 0-312),* 1123 Broadway, Suite 306, New York, NY 10010 (SAN 293-0188) Tel 212-206-1538; Dist. by: St. Martin's Pr., 175 Fifth Ave., New York, NY 10010 (SAN 200-2132) Tel 212-674-5151. Do not confuse with Bluejay Pr., Kokomo, IN.

Bluejay Pr IN, *(Bluejay Pr.; 0-939132),* 5900 Dartmouth Ct., Kokomo, IN 46902 (SAN 216-3381) Tel 317-453-2240. Do not confuse with Bluejay Books, New York, NY.

Bluestem Prod, (*Bluestem Productions;*
0-9609064), Box 334, 2327 Lafayette Rd.,
Wayzata, MN 55391 (SAN 240-9747); Dist.
by: Bluestem & the Bookmen, Inc., 525 N.
Third St., Minneapolis, MN 55401
(SAN 169-409X) Tel 612-471-7795; Dist.
by: Badger Periodicals Distributors, Inc.,
2420 W. Fourth St., Appleton, WI 54914
(SAN 169-9024) Tel 414-731-9521; Dist.
by: Voelz Educational Services, 1528 Vista
Ave., Janesville, WI 53545 (SAN 200-4291)
Tel 608-752-0211; Dist. by: The Distributors,
702 South Michigan, South Bend, IN 46618
(SAN 169-2488) Tel 219-232-8500.

Bluetick Pub, (*Bluetick Publishing; 0-9612102*),
2014 Carroll Ave., San Francisco, CA 94124
(SAN 285-6824) Tel 415-467-2719.

Blumarts Inc, (*Blumarts, Inc.; 0-935875*), 14 W.
Tenth St., New York, NY 10011
(SAN 696-1223) Tel 212-475-0227.

Blume & Assocs, (*Blume, Augie, & Assocs.;*
0-932521), P.O. Box 190, San Anselmo, CA
94960 (SAN 687-4649) Tel 415-457-0215.

Blustein-Geary, (*Blustein/Geary Associates;*
0-9605248), 46 Glen Circle, Waltham, MA
02154 (SAN 215-8450).

Blyden Pr, (*Blyden, Edward W., Pr., Inc.;*
0-914110), P.O. Box 621, Manhattanville
Sta., New York, NY 10027
(SAN 206-4804) Tel 212-222-6000.

Blythe-Pennington, (*Blythe-Pennington, Ltd.;*
0-943778), P.O. Box 338,
Croton-on-Hudson, NY 10520
(SAN 241-0060) Tel 914-271-4905.

BM Consumer Pubns, (*BM Consumer Pubns;*
0-942662), 556 Sunnymount Ave.,
Sunnyvale, CA 94087 (SAN 239-6165)
Tel 408-737-2950.

BM Surveying
See CARBEN Survey

BMA Pr
See Bible Memory

BMB Pub Co, (*BMB Publishing Co.; 0-930924;*
0-9600164), P.O. Box 1622, Boston, MA
02105 (SAN 201-4270) Tel 617-492-5762.

BMDP Stat, (*BMDP Statistical Software;*
0-935386), 1440 Sepulveda Blvd., Los
Angeles, CA 90025 (SAN 213-8069)
Tel 213-479-7799.

BMH Bks, (*BMH Bks.; 0-88469*), Div. of
Brethren Missionary Herald, Inc., P.O. Box
544, Winona Lake, IN 46590
(SAN 201-7571) Tel 219-267-7158; Toll
free: 800-348-2756.

†**BNA,** (*BNA Bks.; 0-87179*), Div. of Bureau of
National Affairs, Inc., 2550 M St., NW, Suite
699, Washington, DC 20037
(SAN 201-4262) Tel 202-452-5742; Toll
free: 800-372-6033; Toll free: 800-3521400;
Orders to: BNA Bks. Distribution Ctr., 300
Raritan Ctr. Pkwy., CN94, Edison, NJ 08818
(SAN 661-9649) Tel 201-225-1900; Orders
to: BNA Customer Service (Reports &
Services), 9435 Key West Ave., Rockville,
MD 20850-3397 (SAN 661-9657)
Tel 301-258-1033; *CIP.*

B'nai B'rith-Hillel, (*B'nai B'rith Hillel*
Foundations; 0-9603058), 1640 Rhode
Island Ave., NW, Washington, DC 20036
(SAN 204-4080) Tel 202-857-6556.

Bnos Zion, (*Bnos Zion of Bobov, Inc.;*
0-937143), 5000 14th Ave., Brooklyn, NY
11219 (SAN 658-4659) Tel 718-438-3080.

BNR Pr, (*BNR Pr.; 0-931960*), 132 E. Second
St., Port Clinton, OH 43452
(SAN 211-5948) Tel 419-734-2422.

Bo-Tree Prods, (*Bo-Tree Productions, Inc.;*
0-933714), 1137 San Antonio Rd., Suite E,
Palo Alto, CA 94303 (SAN 216-7050)
Tel 415-967-1817.

BOA Edns, (*BOA Editions, Ltd.; 0-918526*), 92
Park Ave., Brockport, NY 14420
(SAN 281-3351) Tel 716-637-3844; Dist.
by: Bookslinger, 213 E. Fourth St., St. Paul,
MN 55101 (SAN 169-4154)
Tel 612-221-0429.

Boals Pub, (*Boals, Prudencia, Publishing Co.;*
0-9604270), R no.6, P.O. Box 89A, Ripley,
TN 38063 (SAN 214-2104).

Board Jewish Educ, (*Board of Jewish Education*
of Greater New York; 0-88384), 426 W.
58th St., New York, NY 10019
(SAN 213-0165) Tel 212-245-8200.

Board Pub Evang, (*Board for Publications of The*
Evangelical Lutheran Synod; 0-89279), 734
Marsh St., Mankato, MN 56001
(SAN 262-0030).

†**Boardman,** (*Boardman, Clark, Co., Ltd.;*
0-87632), Subs. of International Thomson
Organization, Inc., 435 Hudson St., New
York, NY 10014 (SAN 202-4136)
Tel 212-929-7500; Toll free: 800-221-9428;
CIP.

†**Boardroom,** (*Boardroom Bks.; 0-932648;*
0-88723), Div. of Boardroom Reports, Inc.,
330 W. 42nd St., New York, NY 10036
(SAN 211-5956) Tel 212-239-9000; Orders
to: P.O. Box 1026, Millburn, NJ 07041
(SAN 662-7196) Tel 201-379-4642; *CIP.*

Boardroom Repr
See Boardroom

Boardworks Pub, (*Boardworks Publishing;*
0-934863), 35 Eldridge Rd. No. 110,
Jamaica Plain, MA 02130 (SAN 694-5619)
Tel 617-522-5493; Orders to: Boardworks
Publishing, P.O. Box 1241, Jamaica Plain,
MA 02130 (SAN 200-7118); Dist. by:
Bryant Altman, 84 Beaconfield Rd.,
Brookline, MA 02146 (SAN 662-3409)
Tel 617-232-6818.

Boars Head, (*Boar's Head Press; 0-932114;*
0-9606674), P.O. Box 16413, St. Louis, MO
63125 (SAN 211-1489) Tel 314-846-2694.

Boat Own Assn US, (*Boat Owners Association*
of the United States), 880 S. Pickett St.,
Alexandria, VA 22304 (SAN 224-5450).

Boathouse Pr, (*Boathouse Pr.; 0-9614829*), P.O.
Box 58907, Philadelphia, PA 19102
(SAN 693-0123) Tel 215-333-9632.

Boatner-Norton, (*Boatner Norton Pr.;*
0-9606654), c/o The Million Year Picknick,
99 Mt. Auburn St., Cambridge, MA 02138
(SAN 219-7162) Tel 617-492-7896.

Bob Bks, (*Bob Bk. Pubns.; 0-9612104*), 6516
SW Barnes Rd., Portland, OR 97225
(SAN 685-3781) Tel 503-292-6248.

Bob Jones Univ Pr, (*Jones, Bob, Univ. Pr.;*
0-89084), Bob Jones Univ., Greenville, SC
29614 (SAN 223-7512) Tel 803-242-5100;
Toll free: 800-235-5731.

Bobbeh Meisehs, (*Bobbeh Meisehs Pr.;*
0-9616933), 137 Tremont St., Cambridge,
MA 02139 (SAN 661-7077)
Tel 617-547-2874; Dist. by: Inland Bk. Co.,
22 Hemingway St., P.O. Box 261, East
Haven, CT 06512 (SAN 200-4151)
Tel 203-467-4257; Dist. by: Bookpeople,
2929 Fifth St., Berkeley, CA 94710
(SAN 168-9517) Tel 415-549-3030.

Bobbi Ent, (*Bobbi Enterprises; 0-9603200*), Rte.
1, Box 44, Mt. Iron, MN 55768
(SAN 213-2885) Tel 218-735-8364.

†**Bobbs,** (*Bobbs-Merrill Co.; 0-672*), Subs. of
Macmillan Publishing Co., Inc., 866 Third
Ave., New York, NY 10022
(SAN 201-3959) Tel 212-702-2000; *CIP.*
Imprints: Chart (Charter Books).(Charter
Bks.); Lib (Liberal Arts Press).(Liberal Arts
Pr.).

Bobets, (*Bobets Publishing Co.; 0-9609782*),
P.O. Box 8385, Scottsdale, AZ 85251
(SAN 263-2446) Tel 602-948-2756.

Bobley, (*Bobley Publishing Corp.; 0-8324*), Subs.
of Illustrated World Encyclopedia, Inc., 311
Crossways Park Dr., Woodbury, NY 11797
(SAN 202-3334) Tel 516-364-1800.

Boca Raton Museum, (*Boca Raton Museum of*
Art; 0-936859), 801 W. Palmetto Park Rd.,
Boca Raton, FL 33432 (SAN 278-2251)
Tel 305-392-2500.

Bock Pub, (*Bock Publishing; 0-9614747*), 1777
Sheridan Ave., St. Paul, MN 55116
(SAN 692-9222) Tel 612-699-3252.

Bodhi, (*Bodhi Press; 0-914187*), P.O. Box
44914, Phoenix, AZ 85064
(SAN 287-492X) Tel 602-840-7116.

Bodima, (*Bodima; 0-88875*), Dist. by: Altarinda
Books, 13 Estates Dr., Orinda, CA 94563
(SAN 238-1397) Tel 415-254-3830.

Bodine, (*Bodine & Assocs., Inc., Pubs.;*
0-910254), The Quadrangle, Suite 132,
Village of Cross Keys, Baltimore, MD 21210
(SAN 201-4246) Tel 301-433-7491.

Body Blueprints, (*Body Blueprints; 0-9617110*),
1213 W. California Ave., Mill Valley, CA
94941 (SAN 662-7005) Tel 415-388-1155.

Body Enterprises, (*Body Enterprises; 0-941460*),
P.O. Box 80577, Lincoln, NE 68501
(SAN 239-068X) Tel 402-466-8877.

Body Sculpt, (*Body Sculpture; 0-918227*), 1419
Superior Ave., Suite 2, Newport Beach, CA
92663 (SAN 657-2545) Tel 714-760-8235;
Dist. by: PMG International, 1343 Columbia,
Suite 405, Richardson, TX 75081
(SAN 200-4763).

Bodymind Bks, (*Bodymind Bks.; 0-938405*), 450
Hillside Ave., Mill Valley, CA 94941
(SAN 659-8625) Tel 415-383-4017; Dist.
by: Bookpeople, 2929 Fifth St., Berkeley, CA
94710 (SAN 168-9517) Tel 415-549-3030.

Boehmer Pub, (*Boehmer Publishing; 0-9601728*),
134 Beechwood Rd., Braintree, MA 02184
(SAN 211-5964) Tel 617-848-0486.

Bogden & Son, (*Bogden, George A., & Sons,*
Inc.; 0-942068), P.O. Box 3, Ridgewood, NJ
07451 (SAN 237-9813) Tel 201-652-3755.

Boggaston, (*Boggaston Bk. Co., The; 0-937085*),
21 Blandin Ave., Framingham, MA 01701
(SAN 658-4802) Tel 617-620-1332.

Bohemica, (*Bohemica; 0-935504*), Columbia
Univ. Dept. of Slavic Languages, New York,
NY 10027 (SAN 223-7148).

Bohn Bland Pubs, (*Bohn & Bland Pubs., Inc.;*
0-930965), 750 Menlo Ave., Suite 250,
Menlo Park, CA 94025 (SAN 678-8793)
Tel 415-324-0622.

Boian Bks, (*Boian Bks.; 0-9604420*), 780
Riverside Dr., Apt. 5E, New York, NY
10032 (SAN 220-1305) Tel 212-234-0173.

Boise St Univ, (*Boise State Univ.; 0-88430;*
0-932129), 1910 University Dr., Boise, ID
83725 (SAN 206-7080) Tel 208-385-1182;
Orders to: BSU Bookstore, 1910 University
Dr., Boise, ID 83725 Tel 208-385-1274.

Bola Pr, (*Bola Pr.; 0-9608062*), P.O. Box 96,
Village Sta., New York, NY 10014
(SAN 295-2971).

Bola Pubns, (*Bola Pubns.; 0-943118*), 2378
Willowbrae Dr., Eagle Pass, TX 78852
(SAN 240-3439).

Bolchazy-Carducci, (*Bolchazy-Carducci Pubs.;*
0-86516), 44 Lake St., Oak Park, IL 60302
(SAN 219-7685) Tel 312-386-8360.

Bold Age Pr, (*Bold Age Pr.; 0-936841*), 10475
Bruceville Rd., Suite G, Elk Grove, CA
95624 (SAN 658-3423) Tel 916-685-3929.

Bold Blue Jay Pubns, (*Bold Blue Jay Pubns.;*
0-9608182), 229 Moonlite Dr., Circle Pines,
MN 55014 (SAN 238-0412)
Tel 612-784-7522.

Bold Prodns, (*Bold Productions; 0-938267*),
P.O. Box 328, Oviedo, FL 32765
(SAN 659-8684); 475 Carrigan Ave.,
Oviedo, FL 32765 (SAN 659-8692)
Tel 305-365-8957.

Bold Strummer Ltd, (*Bold Strummer, Ltd;*
0-933224), 1 Webb Rd., Westport, CT
06880 (SAN 213-0262) Tel 203-226-8230.

Bollenbaugh Hill, (*Bollenbaugh Hill Bks.;*
0-937653), 10910 Bollenbaugh Rd., Monroe,
WA 98272 (SAN 659-3054)
Tel 206-794-8065.

Bolton Pr, (*Bolton Pr.; 0-9616326*), 1325
Belmore Way, NE, Atlanta, GA 30338
(SAN 659-0446) Tel 404-237-1577.

Bomb Shelter Prop, (*Bomb Shelter Propaganda;*
0-938309), P.O. Box 1393, Tempe, AZ
85281 (SAN 659-7696) Tel 602-275-6473.

Bon Chance Ent, (*Bon Chance Enterprises;*
0-941922), 14547 Titus St. Suite 102,
Panorama City, CA 91412 (SAN 238-6356)
Tel 213-785-3149.

Bon Mot Pubns, (*Bon Mot Pubns.; 0-9601044*),
Rte. 15, P.O. Box 857, Pigeon Force, TN
37863 (SAN 209-3472) Tel 615-436-3919.

Bonanza Imprint of Outlet Bk Co

Bond Double-O Seven, (*James Bond 007 Fan*
Club, The; 0-9605838), P.O. Box 414,
Bronxville, NY 10708 (SAN 216-5902)
Tel 914-961-3440.

Bond Pub Co, (*Bond Publishing Co.; 0-939296*),
Div. of Progressive Artistic Communications
Enterprises, Inc., P.O. Box 1217, Landover,
MD 20785 (SAN 220-1488)
Tel 301-946-8152.

Bond Res, (*Bond Research; 0-939511*), 592
Baird St., Akron, OH 44311
(SAN 663-3528) Tel 216-773-5682.

Bondscourt Pr, (*BondsCourt Pr.; 0-914377*),
P.O. Box 23160, Ft. Lauderdale, FL 33307
(SAN 289-6044) Tel 305-772-1072.

Bone Bks, (*Bone Bks.; 0-9611174*), 45 Canyon
Wren, Sedona, AZ 86336 (SAN 277-6596)
Tel 602-282-7707; Dist. by: Missouri
Archaeological Society, P.O. Box 958,
Columbia, MO 65205 (SAN 238-8316).

Bonjour Books, (*Bonjour Bks.; 0-915785*), 6221
Carlson Dr., New Orleans, LA 70122
(SAN 293-9096) Tel 504-282-4660.

Boston Music, *(Boston Music Company, The; 0-88121),* 116 Boylston St., Boston, MA 02116 (SAN 201-7326) Tel 617-426-5100.

Boston Organ Club, *(Boston Organ Club Chapter, Organ Historical Society; 0-9610092),* P.O. Box 104, Harrisville, NH 03450 (SAN 268-4128) Tel 603-827-3055.

Boston Pub Co, *(Boston Publishing, Co.; 0-939526),* 314 Dartmouth St., Boston, MA 02116 (SAN 216-6577) Tel 617-267-8800; Dist. by: Addison-Wesley Publishing Co., 5 Jacob Way, Reading, MA 01867 (SAN 200-2000) Tel 617-944-3700; Dist. by: Time-Life Books, 777 Duke St., Rm. 204, Alexandria, VA 22314 (SAN 202-7836) Tel 703-960-5421.

†**Boston Public Lib,** *(Boston Public Library; 0-89073),* P.O. Box 286, Boston, MA 02117 (SAN 204-3971) Tel 617-536-5400; *CIP.*

Boston Risk Mgmt, *(Boston Risk Management Corp.; 0-9607398),* 70 Chestnut St., Boston, MA 02108 (SAN 239-5142) Tel 617-723-5592.

Boston St Rwy, *(Boston Street Railway Assn.; 0-938315),* P.O. Box 102, Cambridge, MA 02238-0102 (SAN 239-5150) Tel 617-749-1540; 207 South St., Hingham, MA 02043 (SAN 658-0211).

Boston U African, *(African Studies Ctr., Boston Univ.; 0-915118),* 270 Bay State Rd., Boston, MA 02215 (SAN 223-5927) Tel 617-353-7306.

Bostonian Soc, *(Bostonian Society; 0-934865),* 206 Washington St., Old State House, Boston, MA 02109 (SAN 225-2937) Tel 617-242-5610; Orders to: Bostonian Society Gift Shop, 206 Washington Street, Old State House, Boston, MA 02109 (SAN 661-9622) Tel 617-242-5619.

Botanical Soc, *(Botanical Society of America, Inc.; 0-939201),* Indiana Univ., Dept. of Biology, Bloomington, IN 47405 (SAN 224-0866) Tel 812-335-9455; Univ. of Texas, Dept. of Botany, Austin, TX 78712 (SAN 661-9630).

Botany Bks, *(Botany Bks.; 0-9611966),* 1518 Hayward Ave., Bremerton, WA 98310 (SAN 286-7494) Tel 206-377-6489.

Bottom Dog Pr, *(Bottom Dog, Pr.; 0-933087),* c/o Firelands College of Bowling Green State Univ., Huron, OH 44839 (SAN 689-5492) Tel 419-433-5560.

Bottom Line Pr, *(Bottom Line Pr.; 0-943020),* P.O. Box 31420, San Francisco, CA 94131 (SAN 240-3455) Tel 415-661-1040.

Bottom Line Soft, *(Bottom Line Software; 0-937973),* P.O. Box 10545, Eugene, OR 97440 (SAN 659-4948) Tel 503-484-0520; 474 Willamette, Suite 201, Eugene, OR 97401 (SAN 659-4956).

Boulevard, *(Boulevard Books; 0-910278),* P.O. Box 89, Topanga, CA 90290 (SAN 202-4179) Tel 213-445-1036.

Bouregy, *(Bouregy, Thomas, & Co., Inc.; 0-8034),* 401 Lafayette St., 2nd Flr., New York, NY 10003 (SAN 201-4173) Tel 212-598-0222.

Bovin, *(Bovin Publishing; 0-910280),* 68-36 108th St., Forest Hills, NY 11375 (SAN 202-4187) Tel 718-268-2292.

Bowden Pub, *(Bowden Publishing; 0-9616177),* 6252 Cedarwood Rd., Mentor, OH 44060 (SAN 699-8895) Tel 216-942-8729.

Bowdoin Coll, *(President & Trustees of Bowdoin College; 0-916606),* Bowdoin College, Getchell Hse., Brunswick, ME 04011 (SAN 695-6394) Tel 207-725-8731.

Bowens Pub Div., *(Bowen's Publishing Division; 0-942354),* P.O. Box 270, Bedford, MA 01730-0270 (SAN 239-717X) Tel 617-275-1660.

†**Bowker,** *(Bowker, R. R., Co.; 0-8352; 0-911255),* Div. of Reed Publishing USA, 205 E. 42nd St., New York, NY 10017 (SAN 214-1191) Tel 212-916-1600; Toll free: 800-521-8110 US; Toll free: 800-537-8416 Canada. On April 1, 1986, R. R. Bowker Co. became the sole supplier for all Bowker annuals & continuation books. Any orders or standing orders for these titles placed with wholesalers should be changed, & ordered directly from Bowker from the address above. BOWKER NOW OFFERS A 5 PERCENT DISCOUNT FOR ALL STANDING ORDERS. This new policy does not affect subscriptions and non-continuation titles. On or about Oct. 15, 1986, R. R. Bowker Co. will move to a new location. NEW ADDRESS: 245 W. 17TH ST., NEW YORK, NY 10011; *CIP.*

Bowling Gr Pr, *(Bowling Green Pr.; 0-9614621),* P.O. Box 582, Bowling Green, OH 43402 (SAN 691-9138) Tel 419-352-0493.

Bowling Green Univ, *(Bowling Green Univ. Popular Pr.; 0-87972),* Bowling Green State Univ., Popular Culture Ctr., Bowling Green, OH 43403 (SAN 201-4165) Tel 419-372-7865.

Bowling Prop Assn, *(Bowling Proprietors' Assn. of America),* P.O. Box 5802, Arlington, TX 76005 (SAN 268-4241) Tel 817-649-5105.

Bowman Pub Inc, *(Bowman Publishing, Inc.; 0-934969),* 743 Harvard Ave., St. Louis, MO 63130 (SAN 695-1147) Tel 314-726-0353.

Bowmar
See Bowmar-Noble

Bowmar-Noble, *(Bowmar/Noble Pubs.; 0-8372; 0-8107),* Div. of Economy Co, P.O. Box 25308, 1901 N. Walnut St., Oklahoma City, OK 73125 (SAN 201-4157) Tel 405-528-8444.

Box Four Twenty-Four, *(Box Four Twenty-Four Press; 0-9614506),* Box 424, Pacific Grove, CA 93950 (SAN 691-7364) Tel 408-649-8215.

Box Twenty One, *(Box 21, Inc.; 0-918846),* Tucson, AZ 85702 (SAN 210-394X) Tel 602-325-9602.

Boxes & Arrows, *(Boxes & Arrows; 0-939479),* P.O. Box 792, Jacksonville, FL 32201 (SAN 663-2726); 8150 Baytree Towne Cir., Jacksonville, FL 32201 (SAN 663-2734) Tel 904-642-5388.

†**Boxwood,** *(Boxwood Pr.; 0-910286; 0-940168),* 183 Ocean View Blvd., Pacific Grove, CA 93950 (SAN 201-4149) Tel 408-375-9110; *CIP.*

Boyar, *(Boyar Bks.; 0-9608464),* 2802 E. Locust St., Davenport, IA 52803 (SAN 240-6039) Tel 319-355-7246.

†**Boyce-Pubns,** *(Boyce-Pubns; 0-918823),* 1023 Oxford, Clovis, CA 93612 (SAN 669-652X) Tel 209-299-8495; *CIP.*

†**Boyd & Fraser,** *(Boyd & Fraser Publishing Co.; 0-87835; 0-87709),* Subs. of International Thomson Organization, Ltd., 20 Park Pl., Boston, MA 02116 (SAN 201-4130) Tel 617-426-2292; *CIP.*

Boyd Co, *(Boyd Co., The; 0-9616796),* P.O. Box 5280, Austin, TX 78763-5280 (SAN 659-8803); 16007 Scenic Oak Trail, Buda, TX 78610 (SAN 659-8811) Tel 512-478-7707. *Imprints:* Patch & Frazzle (Patch & Frazzle Press).

Boyd Deep Canyon, *(Univ. of California at Riverside, Boyd Deep Canyon Desert Research Ctr.; 0-942290),* Univ. of California, Riverside, Dept. of Biology, Riverside, CA 92521 (SAN 210-8852) Tel 714-787-5917.

Boyd Griffin, *(Griffin, Boyd, Inc.; 0-941726),* 425 E. 51st St., New York, NY 10022 (SAN 239-2194) Tel 212-399-4226.

Boyertown Hist, *(Boyertown Area Historical Society; 0-9616068),* 43 S. Chestnut St., Boyertown, PA 19512 (SAN 697-824X) Tel 215-369-1868.

Boykin, *(Boykin, James H.; 0-9603342),* 1260 NW 122nd St., Miami, FL 33167 (SAN 215-0603) Tel 305-681-7663.

Boyne Bks, *(Boyne Bks.; 0-9615889),* 1526 Sheffield, Jackson, MS 39211 (SAN 697-0176) Tel 601-362-7297.

Boynton & Assocs, *(Boynton & Assocs.; 0-933168),* Clifton Hse., Clifton, VA 22024 (SAN 212-9310); Dist. by: Hobby Bk. Distributors, 3150 State Line Rd., North Bend, OH 45052 (SAN 200-6669) Tel 513-353-3390.

†**Boynton Cook Pubs,** *(Boynton Cook Pubs., Inc.; 0-86709),* P.O. Box 860, 52 Upper Montclair Plaza, Upper Montclair, NJ 07043 (SAN 216-6186) Tel 201-783-3310; *CIP.*

Boys Clubs, *(Boys Clubs of America; 0-9604288),* 771 First Ave., New York, NY 10017 (SAN 204-3920) Tel 212-557-7755.

†**Boys Town Ctr,** *(Boys Town, Nebraska, Ctr., Communications & Public Service Div.; 0-938510),* Div. of Father Flanagan's Boys' Home, Boys Town, NE 68010 (SAN 215-8477) Tel 402-498-1580; *CIP.*

BPW & P, *(Berkeley Poets' Workshop & Press (BPW & P); 0-917658),* P.O. Box 459, Berkeley, CA 94701 (SAN 208-5488) Tel 415-528-2252.

Br-Three Pr, *(BR-3 Pr.; 0-9607566),* 1129 S. Seventh St., Ann Arbor, MI 48103 (SAN 238-4469) Tel 313-665-2330.

Brace-Park, *(Brace-Park Pr.; 0-942560),* P.O. Box 526, Lake Forest, IL 60045 (SAN 239-412X).

Brad Pub Co, *(Bradford Publishing Co.; 0-935355),* 360 Pine St., 6th Flr., San Francisco, CA 94104 (SAN 696-1320) Tel 415-362-0435.

†**Bradbury Pr,** *(Bradbury Pr.; 0-87888),* Affil. of Macmillan, Inc., 866 Third Ave., New York, NY 10022 (SAN 201-4114) Tel 212-702-3598; Toll free: 800-257-5755; Dist. by: Macmillan Pub. Co., Inc., Front & Brown Sts., Riverside, NJ 08370 (SAN 202-5582); *CIP.*

†**Braddock Pubns,** *(Braddock Pubns., Inc.; 0-931147),* 1001 Connecticut Ave., NW, Rm 210, Washington, DC 20036 (SAN 237-7772) Tel 202-296-3630; *CIP.*

Bradford & Wilson, *(Bradford & Wilson, Ltd.; 0-915073),* Box 7189 University Sta., Provo, UT 84602 (SAN 289-7466) Tel 801-377-4819.

Bradford Co, *(Bradford Co., The),* P.O. Box 256, Scituate, MA 02066 (SAN 263-242X) Tel 617-545-5750.

Bradford Mtn Bk, *(Bradford Mountain Bk. Enterprises, Inc.; 0-945610),* 125 E. 23rd St. No. 300, New York, NY 10010 . (SAN 289-7237) Tel 212-473-2990.

Bradford Pr MA, *(Bradford Pr.; 0-9615783),* 502 Richard Rd., Bradford, MA 01830 (SAN 696-6845) Tel 617-372-1775; P.O. Box 224, Bradford, MA 01830 (SAN 698-2107).

Bradford Pub
See Jeanene's

Bradford Pubs, *(Bradford Pubs.; 0-936935),* 2843 Ash Dr., Springfield, OH 45504 (SAN 658-3466).

Bradford Soft, *(Bradford Software; 0-935507),* 6216 E. Ensenada St., Mesa, AZ 85205 (SAN 696-4958) Tel 602-985-7455.

Bradfords VA, *(Bradford's Directory of Marketing Research Agencies & Management Consultants; 0-910290),* Div. of Denlinger's Publishers, Ltd., P.O. Box 276, Dept. B-15, Fairfax, VA 22030 (SAN 204-2754) Tel 703-830-4646.

Bradgate Cent, *(Bradgate Centennial Committee; 0-89279),* Bradgate, IA 50520 (SAN 283-9342).

Bradley Bks, *(Bradley Bks.; 0-936765),* 4310 Valli Vista Rd., Colorado Springs, CO 80915 (SAN 699-8518) Tel 303-596-5709.

Bradley Comm, *(Bradley Communications; 0-936045),* P.O. Box 299, Haverford, PA 19041 (SAN 697-0028) Tel 215-896-6146; 1 Coopertown Rd., Haverford, PA 19041 (SAN 697-0036).

Bradley-Nord, *(Bradley-Nord Sun Enterprises; 0-941278),* HC 72 Box 31,, Coldwater, KS 67029 (SAN 238-9169); 323 Pacific St., Bakersfield, CA 93305 (SAN 238-9177).

Bradley Pub, *(Bradley Publishing; 0-940716),* P.O. Box 7383, Little Rock, AR 72217 (SAN 219-6891) Tel 501-224-0692.

Bradley Pubns, *(Bradley Pubns.; 0-89748),* 80 Eighth Ave., New York, NY 10011 (SAN 696-2912) Tel 201-348-0700; Dist. by: Warner Brothers Publications, Incorporated, 265 Secaucus Rd., Secaucus, NJ 07094 (SAN 203-0586) Tel 201-348-0700.

Bradson, *(Bradson Pr.; 0-9603574),* 31200 LaBaya Dr., Suite 304, Westlake Village, CA 91362 (SAN 213-7267) Tel 818-707-0471.

Bradt Ent, *(Bradt Enterprises Pubns.; 0-9505797),* 93 Harvey St., Apt. 8, Cambridge, MA 02140 (SAN 169-328X) Tel 617-492-8776.

Brady, *(Brady, Frank; 0-9614639),* P.O. Box 4653, Annapolis, MD 21403-6653 (SAN 691-9219) Tel 301-263-8388.

†Brady Comm, *(Brady Communications Co., Inc.; 0-87618; 0-87619; 0-89303),* Subs. of Prentice-Hall, Inc., Rte. 9W, Englewood Cliffs, NJ 07632 (SAN 200-2175) Tel 201-592-2352; Toll free: 800-638-0220; Orders to: P.O. Box 500, Englewood Cliffs, NJ 07632 (SAN 215-3939) Tel 201-592-2000; *CIP.*

Brady St Pr, *(Brady Street Pr.; 0-9616168),* 1808 N. Farwell Ave., Milwaukee, WI 53202 (SAN 699-9123) Tel 414-272-1232.

Braemar OR, *(Braemar Bks.; 0-9612044),* P.O. Box 25296, Portland, OR 97225 (SAN 286-7524) Tel 503-292-4226.

Braemar Pr, *(Braemar Pr.; 0-9616791),* 130 Prospect Blvd., St. Paul, MN 55107 (SAN 659-8897) Tel 612-224-6211.

Bragdon A
See A D Bragdon

Braidwood Pub, *(Braidwood Publishing Co.; 0-9616790),* P.O. Box 232, Harwich, MA 02645 (SAN 659-8927); 740 Main St., Harwich Center, MA 02645 (SAN 659-8935) Tel 617-432-0350.

Brain Age Pubs, *(Brain Age Pubs.; 0-933125),* Subs. of Rolles Edan, Inc, P.O. Box 427, New Rochelle, NY 10802 (SAN 689-7371) Tel 914-632-9029.

Brain-Image, *(Brain-Image Power Pr.; 0-9609246),* P.O. Box 1723, Hollywood, CA 90078 (SAN 260-0218).

Brain Res, *(Brain Research Pubns.; 0-916088),* Highbridge Terrace, Fayetteville, NY 13066 (SAN 207-9666).

†Brainchild Bks, *(Brainchild Bks.; 0-9613286),* P.O. Box 837, Paia, Maui, HI 96779 (SAN 654-3383) Tel 808-572-9102; *CIP.*

Brainerd
See SUNYP Brainerd

Brancaleone Educ, *(Brancaleone Educational Co; 0-9601186),* 18 Plymouth St., Montclair, NJ 07042 (SAN 209-6218) Tel 201-746-4021.

Branch Libraries Imprint of NY Pub Lib

Branch Redd, *(Branch Redd; 0-9615784),* P.O. Box 46466, Philadelphia, PA 19160 (SAN 696-6853) Tel 215-324-1462.

Branch-Smith, *(Branch-Smith, Inc.; 0-87706),* P.O. Box 1868, Fort Worth, TX 76101 (SAN 201-7237) Tel 817-332-6377; 120 St. Louis Ave., Fort Worth, TX 76101 (SAN 201-7245).

Branchemco, *(Branchemco, Inc.; 0-9610178),* 8286 Western Way Cir., C-2, Jacksonville, FL 32216-8389 (SAN 268-442X) Tel 904-737-0984; Toll free: 800-874-5990; Toll free: 800-342-1259 (In Florida).

Brand, *(Brand, Irene B.; 0-9615285),* Rte. 1, Box 110, Southside, WV 25187 (SAN 694-5465) Tel 304-675-2977.

Brandeis-Bardin Inst, *(Brandeis-Bardin Institute Pubns., The; 0-916952),* Brandeis, CA 93064 (SAN 208-5666) Tel 213-348-7201.

Branden
See Branden Pub Co

Branden Pub Co, *(Branden Publishing Co.; 0-8283),* Box 843, Brookline Village, Boston, MA 02147 (SAN 201-4106) Tel 617-734-2045.

Brandon Hse, *(Brandon Hse., Inc.; 0-913412),* P.O. Box 240, Bronx, NY 10471 (SAN 201-4092).

Brandon-Lane-Pr, *(Four Six Zero Five Brandon Lane Press),* 4605 Brandon Ln., Beltsville, MD 20705 (SAN 692-2066) Tel 301-937-1446.

Brandt Bks, *(Brandt Bks.; 0-9616327),* 1134 Willits Dr., Corona, CA 91720 (SAN 659-0454) Tel 714-735-6167.

Brandywine, *(Brandywine Pr., Inc., The; 0-89616),* c/o E. P. Dutton, 2 Park Ave, New York, NY 10016 (SAN 201-0070).

Brandywine Conserv, *(Brandywine Conservancy; 0-940540),* P.O. Box 141, Chadds Ford, PA 19317 (SAN 214-3518) Tel 215-388-7601.

†Branford, *(Branford, Charles T., Co.; 0-8231),* P.O. Box 41, Newton Centre, MA 02159 (SAN 201-9302) Tel 617-964-2441; *CIP.*

Brant, *(Brant, Michelle; 0-9611346),* 2435 Gough St., San Francisco, CA 94123 (SAN 283-2518) Tel 415-775-3024; Dist. by: Bookpeople, 2929 Fifth St., Berkeley, CA 94710 (SAN 168-9517) Tel 415-549-3030; Dist. by: L & S Distributors, 480 9th St., San Francisco, CA 94103 (SAN 169-0213) Tel 415-861-6300.

Brason-Sargar, *(Brason-Sargar Pubns.; 0-9602534),* P.O. Box 872, Reseda, CA 91335 (SAN 281-3416) Tel 213-305-7726; Dist. by: DeVorss & Co., P.O. Box 550, 1046 Princeton Dr., Marina del Rey, CA 90294 (SAN 168-9886) Tel 213-870-7478.

†Brass Pr, *(Brass Pr.; 0-914282),* 136 Eighth Ave., N., Nashville, TN 37203-3798 (SAN 201-8608) Tel 615-254-8969; *CIP.*

Brattle, *(Brattle Pubns.; 0-918938),* 1753 Massachusetts Ave., Cambridge, MA 02140 (SAN 210-3958) Tel 617-661-7467.

Brayden, *(Brayden Bks.; 0-9610994),* 719 Post Rd. E., Westport, CT 06880 (SAN 265-1939) Tel 203-227-9667.

†Braziller, *(Braziller, George, Inc.; 0-8076),* 1 Park Ave., New York, NY 10016 (SAN 201-9310) Tel 212-889-0909; *CIP.*

Brd Pubns Christ
See CRC Pubns

Brdgwtr Pub Co, *(Bridgewater Publishing Co.; 0-911563),* P.O. Box 336, Glen Ellyn, IL 60137 (SAN 263-9459) Tel 312-469-6078.

Breachwood Pubns Imprint of Riverrun NY

Bread and Butter, *(Bread & Butter, Pr.; 0-912549),* 2582 S. Clayton, Denver, CO 80210 (SAN 223-1700) Tel 303-753-0912.

Bread for the World, *(Bread for the World),* 32 Union Sq. E., New York, NY 10003 (SAN 226-0182).

Breaking Point, *(Breaking Point, Inc.; 0-917020),* P.O. Box 328, Wharton, NJ 07885 (SAN 208-0699) Tel 201-361-7238.

Breakthrough, *(Breakthrough Pubns., Inc.; 0-914327),* Scarborough Sta. Plaza, Briarcliff, NY 10510 (SAN 287-4946) Tel 914-762-5111; Toll free: 800-824-5000; Orders to: P.O. Box 594, Millwood, NY 10546 (SAN 662-2127).

Breakthru Pub, *(Breakthru Publishing; 0-942540),* 3603 Piedmont Ave., Oakland, CA 94611 (SAN 293-2407) Tel 415-547-4724; Dist. by: Publishers Group West, 5855 Beaudry, Emeryville, CA 94608 (SAN 202-8522) Tel 415-658-3453.

Brean-Jones Pub, *(Brean-Jones Publishing Co.; 0-9615785),* 445 N. Pennsylvania, Suite 709, P.O. Box 449081, Indianapolis, IN 46202 (SAN 694-5317) Tel 317-632-1984; Dist. by: R.W. Haldeman & Assoc., 445 N. Pennsylvania, Indianapolis, IN 46202 (SAN 200-576X).

Breck School, *(Breck Schl.; 0-9617136),* 123 Ottawa Ave., N., Minneapolis, MN 55422 (SAN 663-1770) Tel 612-377-5000.

Breed Manual Pubns, *(Breed Manual Pubns.; 0-938681),* 3370 Jackson Dr., Jackson, WI 53037 (SAN 661-387X) Tel 414-677-3112.

Breezewood Pub, *(Breezewood Publishing Co.; 0-9606984),* P.O. Box 5421, Greenville, SC 29606 (SAN 691-2648) Tel 803-834-9836.

†Breitenbush Bks, *(Breitenbush Bks; 0-932576),* P.O. Box 02137, Portland, OR 97202 (SAN 219-7707) Tel 503-230-1900; *CIP.*

Breland & Farmer, *(Breland & Farmer, Designers, Inc.; 0-938007),* 631 Lakeland East Dr., Jackson, MS 39208 (SAN 661-2512) Tel 601-932-3232.

Bremer Bks, *(Bremer Bks.; 0-9615766),* 83 Proteus Ave., Groton, CT 06340 (SAN 696-1436) Tel 203-446-1540.

Brendon Hill Pub, *(Brendon Hill Publishing Co.; 0-937751),* 6116 Merced Ave., Suite 192, Oakland, CA 94611 (SAN 659-2473) Tel 415-895-7033.

Brennan Bks, *(Brennan Bks., Inc.; 0-89270),* 18660 Bonnie Ln., Brookfield, WI 53005 (SAN 208-5674) Tel 414-786-4092.

Brentwood Comm, *(Brentwood Communications Group; 0-916573; 1-55630),* 3914 Cody Rd., Columbus, GA 31907 (SAN 297-1895) Tel 404-561-1772; Toll free: 800-334-8861.

Brentwood Pub, *(Brentwood Publishing Corp.; 0-939442),* 825 S. Barrington Ave., Los Angeles, CA 90049 (SAN 216-3438).

Breslov Res Inst, *(Breslov Research Institute; 0-930213),* 3100 Brighton Third St., Brooklyn, NY 11235 (SAN 670-7890) Tel 718-777-5252.

Bret Pubns, *(B'Ret Publications; 0-933357),* 1810 Michael Faraday Dr., Suite 101, Reston, VA 22090 (SAN 691-7666) Tel 703-471-7388.

Bret Scot Pr, *(Scot, Bret, Pr.; 0-936443),* Div. of College Marketing Group, Inc., 50 Cross St., Winchester, MA 01890 (SAN 699-7597) Tel 617-729-4813.

†Brethren, *(Brethren Pr.; 0-87178),* Div. of Church of the Brethren, 1451 Dundee Ave., Elgin, IL 60120 (SAN 201-9329) Tel 312-742-5100; Toll free: 800-323-8039. Do not confuse with Brethren Publishing Co., Ashland, Ohio; *CIP.*

†Brethren Encyclopedia, *(Brethren Encyclopedia; 0-936693),* Bethany Theological Seminary, Oak Brook, IL 60521 (SAN 291-817X); Orders to: 313 Fairview Ave., Ambler, PA 19002 (SAN 685-3803); *CIP.*

Brethren Ohio, *(Brethren Publishing Co.; 0-934970),* 524 College Ave., Ashland, OH 44805 (SAN 201-730X) Tel 419-289-1708. Do not confuse with Brethren Pr., Elgin, Illinois.

†Breton Pubs, *(Breton Pubs.; 0-534),* Div. of Wadsworth Publishing Co., Inc., Statler Office Bldg., 20 Park Plaza, Boston, MA 02116 (SAN 213-4691) Tel 617-482-2344; Toll free: 800-343-2204; Toll free: 800-354-9706 (Orders); Dist. by: Wadsworth Publishing Co., Inc., 10 Davis Dr., Belmont, CA 94002 (SAN 200-2213) Tel 415-595-2350; Dist. by: Delmar Publishers, Inc., 2 Computer Dr., W., Albany, NY 11212 (SAN 206-7544); *CIP.*

Brevet Pr, *(Brevet Pr.; 0-88498),* Box 1404, Sioux Falls, SD 57101 (SAN 201-7563) Tel 605-361-6121.

Brevis Corp, *(Brevis Corp.; 0-9617125),* 3310 S. 2700 E., Salt Lake City, UT 84109 (SAN 662-6785) Tel 801-466-6677.

Brevity, *(Brevity Press; 0-917838),* P.O. Box 120622, Nashville, TN 37212 (SAN 209-3979) Tel 615-292-0211.

Brewers Pubns, *(Brewers Pubns.; 0-937381),* P.O. Box 4888, Boulder, CO 80306 (SAN 659-0462) Tel 303-441-0840; 7349 Pebble Ct., Longmont, CO 80501 (SAN 659-0470).

Brian's Hse, *(Brian's House, Inc.; 0-9606970),* Box 736, West Chester, PA 19381 (SAN 238-9185).

Brians Pub, *(Visually Handicapped Inspiration Library; 0-9608650; 0-914009; 1-55677),* 8010 Petaluma Hill Rd., Penngrove, CA 94951 (SAN 213-3679) Tel 707-795-4875.

Brians Pub
See Brians Pub

Briarcliff, *(Briarcliff Pub. Co.; 0-915754),* 8111 Timberlodge Trail, Dayton, OH 45459 (SAN 210-573X).

Briarcliff Pr, *(Briarcliff Pr.; 0-932523),* Subs. of Settel Associates Inc., 11 Wimbledon Ct., Jericho, NY 11753 (SAN 687-4703) Tel 516-681-1505.

Bric-A-Brac, *(Bric-a-Brac Bookworks),* Box 887, Forked River, NJ 08731 (SAN 282-6364) Tel 609-693-4053.

Brick Alley Books Press, *(Brick Alley Bks. Pr.; 0-933467),* 423 S. Main St., Stillwater, MN 55082 (SAN 691-8824) Tel 612-439-0266.

†Brick Hse Pub, *(Brick Hse. Publishing, Co.; 0-931790),* Subs. of Mont Chat, Inc., 3 Main St., Andover, MA 01810 (SAN 213-201X) Tel 617-475-9568; *CIP.*

Brick Inst Amer, *(Brick Institute of America),* 11490 Commercial Pk. Dr., Suite 300, Reston, VA 22091 (SAN 241-3647) Tel 703-620-0010.

Brick Row, *(Brick Row Bk. Shop),* 278 Post St., No. 303, San Francisco, CA 94108-5071 (SAN 692-3917) Tel 415-398-0414.

Bricker's Intl, *(Bricker's International Directory; 0-916404),* 425 Family Farm Rd., Woodside, CA 94062 (SAN 208-5682) Tel 415-851-3090.

Bridal Sense, *(Bridal Sense Pubns.; 0-933359),* P.O. Box 765, Framingham, MA 01701 (SAN 691-7674) Tel 617-435-3504.

Bride Guide, *(Bride Guide Enterprises; 0-939884),* 15301 Ventura Blvd., Suite 500, Sherman Oaks, CA 91403 (SAN 695-6750) Tel 213-907-0218; Dist. by: United Bk. Service, 1310 San Fernando Rd., Los Angeles, CA 90065 (SAN 168-986X); Dist. by: Cogan Bks., 4332 W. Artesia Ave., Fullerton, CA 92633 (SAN 168-9649).

Bridge Pub, (Bridge Publisnting, Inc.; 0-88270), 2500 Hamilton Blvd., South Plainfield, NJ 07080 (SAN 239-5061) Tel 201-754-0745; Toll free: 800-631-5802. *Imprints:* Haven Bks (Haven Books); Open Scroll (Open Scroll).

Bridge Pubns Inc, (Bridge Pubns. Inc.; 0-88404), 1414 N. Catalina St., Los Angeles, CA 90027 (SAN 208-3884) Tel 213-382-0382; Toll free: 800-722-1733; Toll free: 800-843-7389 (in California). *Imprints:* ASHO (ASHO Pubns.).

Bridgeberg, (Bridgeberg Books; 0-915358), 2163 Ewing, Los Angeles, CA 90039 (SAN 210-3028) Tel 213-469-9972.

Bridgehead Pr, (Bridgehead Pr.; 0-912543; 0-915271), P.O. Box 850125, New Orleans, LA 70185-0125 (SAN 265-1963); Dist. by: Adler Publishing Co., Panorama Plaza, Box 25333, Rochester, NY 14625 (SAN 285-6808) Tel 716-377-5804.

Bridges Sound, (Bridges to the Sound Publishing Corp.; 0-938316), P.O. Box 260607, Tampa, FL 33685 (SAN 215-7357).

Bridgeview, (Bridgeview Bks.; 0-9613365), 1065 Central Blvd., Hayward, CA 94542 (SAN 657-0755) Tel 415-889-6355.

Bridgewater Pubns
See Brdgwtr Pub Co

Brigadoon, (Brigadoon Pubns., Inc.; 0-938512), 52 Otis Ave., Staten Island, NY 10306 (SAN 216-0218).

†**Brigham,** (Young, Brigham, Univ. Pr.; 0-8425), P.O. Box 140, Tanner Bldg., Provo, UT 84602 (SAN 201-9337) Tel 801-378-6599; Toll free: 800-453-3235; Orders to: 205 University Press Bldg., Provo, UT 84602 (SAN 201-9345) Tel 801-378-2809; CIP.

Bright Baby, (Bright Baby, Bks.; 0-930681), 101 Star Lane, Whitethorn, CA 95489 (SAN 676-9608) Tel 707-986-7693.

Bright Bks, (Bright Books; 0-9605968), P.O. Box 428, Akron, IN 46910 (SAN 216-7204) Tel 219-893-4113.

Bright Morning, (Bright Morning Pubns.; 0-937101), P.O. Box 5338, Kailua Kona, HI 96745 (SAN 658-5809) Tel 808-325-6699.

†**Bright Mtn Bks,** (Bright Mountain Bks.; 0-914875), 138 Springside Rd., Asheville, NC 28803 (SAN 289-0674) Tel 704-684-8840; Dist. by: Bright Horizons, 138 Springside Rd., Asheville, NC 28803 (SAN 200-7193) Tel 704-684-8840; CIP.

Bright Ring, (Bright Ring Publishing; 0-935607), P.O. Box 5768-B, Bellingham, WA 98227 (SAN 696-0537) Tel 206-733-0722; Dist. by: Pacific Pipeline, Inc., 19215 66th Ave. S., Kent, WA 98032 (SAN 208-2128) Dist. by: Baker & Taylor, Eastern Div., 50 Kirby Ave., Somerville, NJ 08876 (SAN 169-4901) Tel 201-526-8000.

Brightfield Pub Co, (Brightfield Publishing Co.; 0-939777), 2531 Sawtelle Blvd., No. 38A, Los Angeles, CA 90064 Tel 213-477-6130.

Brighton House, (Brighton Hse. Pubns.; 0-9603256), 500 Bright Water Ct., Brooklyn, NY 11235 (SAN 213-6570).

Brighton Pubns, (Brighton Pubns.; 0-918420), P.O. Box 12706, New Brighton, MN 55112 (SAN 210-0452) Tel 612-636-2220.

Brighton St Pr, (Brighton Street Press, The; 0-9609642), 53 Flastaff Rd., Rochester, NY 14609 (SAN 268-4667) Tel 716-889-5564.

Brightwaters, (Brightwaters Pr., Inc.; 0-918305), 235 Park Ave. S., New York, NY 10003 (SAN 657-2626) Tel 212-777-1711.

Brillig Works, (Brillig Works Pub., Co.; 0-89681), 1322 College Ave., Boulder, CO 80302 (SAN 211-5999).

Brinkerhoff & Rippy
See Cupbd Cookbk

Bristen Pr, (Bristen Pr.; 0-936337), P.O. Box 336, New Hartford, NY 13413 (SAN 697-8517) Tel 315-724-5463; 109 Patricia Ln., Utica, NY 13501 (SAN 697-8525).

Bristol Pub Co
See Sherwood Comns

†**British Bk Ctr,** (British Book Center; 0-8277), Fairview Park, Elmsford, NY 10523 (SAN 201-9361) Tel 914-592-7700; CIP.

Brittany Hse, (Brittany Hse.; 0-9613982), 1721 Carr St., Palatka, FL 32077 (SAN 682-1812) Tel 904-325-7834.

Brittany Pr, (Brittany Press; 0-912749), P.O. Box 888311, Atlanta, GA 30356-0311 (SAN 283-9350) Tel 404-433-5711.

Brittany Pubns, (Brittany Pubns., Ltd.; 0-941394), P.O. Box 11572, Ontario Station, Chicago, IL 60611 (SAN 238-9541) Tel 312-645-1017.

Britton Inc, (Britton, Inc.; 0-9611782), 507 Main St., Hingham, MA 02043 (SAN 285-225X) Tel 617-749-9175.

Bro Life Bks
See Bro Life Inc

Bro Life Inc, (Brotherhood of Life, Inc.; 0-914732), 110 Dartmouth, SE, Albuquerque, NM 87106 (SAN 202-4233) Tel 505-255-8980.

Broadblade Pr, (Broadblade Pr.; 0-9614640), 11314 Miller Rd., Swartz Creek, MI 48473 (SAN 691-9227) Tel 313-635-3156; Dist. by: Baker & Taylor, Midwest Div., 501 Gladiola Ave., Momence, IL 60954 (SAN 169-2100).

Broadcast Info, (Broadcast Information Bureau, Inc.; 0-943174), Div. of National Video Clearinghouse, Inc., 100 Lafayette Dr., Syosset, NY 11791 (SAN 240-3463) Tel 516-496-3355.

Broadcast Inter, (Broadcast Interview Source; 0-934333), 2500 Wisconsin No. 930, Washington, DC 20007 (SAN 693-6040) Tel 202-333-4904.

Broadfoot, (Broadfoot Publishing, Co.; 0-916107), Rte. 4, Box 508C, Wilmington, NC 28405 (SAN 294-9075) Tel 919-686-4379.

†**Broadman,** (Broadman Pr.; 0-8054), Div. of Southern Baptist Convention, Sunday School Board, 127 Ninth Ave. N., Nashville, TN 37234 (SAN 201-937X) Tel 615-251-2544; Toll free: 800-251-3225; CIP.

Broadman Large Type
See Broadman

Broadsheet Pubns, (Broadsheet Pubns.; 0-941142), P.O. Box 616, McMinnville, OR 97128 (SAN 223-1751) Tel 503-472-5524.

†**Broadside,** (Broadside Press Pubns.; 0-910296), P.O. Box 04257, Detroit, MI 48204 (SAN 201-9388) Tel 313-935-8396; CIP.

Broadway Play, (Broadway Play Publishing; 0-88145), 357 W. 20th St., New York, NY 10011 (SAN 260-1699) Tel 212-627-1055; Toll free: 800-752-9782 (except NY, HI, AK).

Broadway Pr, (Broadway Pr.; 0-911747), 120 Duane St., Suite 407, New York, NY 10007 (SAN 263-9467) Tel 212-693-0570.

Brob Hse Bks, (Brob Hse. Bks.; 0-938407), P.O. Box 7829, Atlanta, GA 30309 (SAN 659-9117); 242 12th St., Atlanta, GA 30309 (SAN 659-9125) Tel 404-876-1311.

Brock Pub, (Brock Publishing Co.; 0-930534), P.O. Box 1685, Chico, CA 95927 (SAN 208-8616) Tel 714-673-6310.

Brockton Art
See Brockton Art-Fuller

Brockton Art-Fuller, (Brockton Art Museum/Fuller Memorial; 0-934358), Oak St., Brockton, MA 02401 (SAN 262-0049) Tel 617-588-6000.

†**Brodart,** (Brodart Co.; 0-87272), 500 Arch St., Williamsport, PA 17705 (SAN 203-6711) Tel 717-326-2461; Toll free: 800-233-8467; CIP.

Broken Moon, (Broken Moon Press; 0-913089), 330 Del Monte Ave., Tacoma, WA 98466 (SAN 283-2844).

Broken Whisker, (Broken Whisker Studio; 0-932220), P.O. Box 1303, Chicago, IL 60690 (SAN 209-0856) Tel 312-987-0906.

Brokering Pr, (Brokering Press; 0-942562), 11641 Palmer Rd., Bloomington, MN 55437 (SAN 239-622X) Tel 612-888-5281.

Brolet, (Brolet Pr.; 0-910298), Div. of Van Valkenburgh Nooger & Neville, Inc., 33 Gold St., New York, NY 10038 (SAN 202-425X) Tel 212-227-6280.

Bronwen Pr, (Bronwen Pr.; 0-915423), Div. of Jennifer James, Inc., 3903 E. James, Seattle, WA 98122 (SAN 291-2287) Tel 206-329-8157; Dist. by: Pacific Pipeline, 19215 66th Ave. S., Kent, WA 98032 (SAN 208-2128) Tel 206-872-5523.

Bronx Bks, (Bronx Bks.; 0-9616765), P.O. Box 100, Bronx, NY 10463 (SAN 659-9192); 98 Van Cortland Park S., Bronx, NY 10463 (SAN 659-9206) Tel 212-796-3677.

†**Bronx County,** (Bronx County Historical Society, The; 0-941980), 3309 Bainbridge Ave., Bronx, NY 10467 (SAN 238-4485) Tel 212-881-8900; CIP.

†**Bronx Mus,** (Bronx Museum of the Arts, The; 0-917535), 1040 Grand Concourse, Bronx, NY 10456 (SAN 656-0598) Tel 212-681-6000; Dist. by: Publishing Center, for Cultural Resources, Inc., 625 Broadway, New York, NY 10012 (SAN 274-9025) Tel 212-260-2010; CIP.

Brooding Heron Pr, (Brooding Heron Pr.; 0-918116), Waldron Island, WA 98297 (SAN 210-2188).

Brookfield Pub Co, (Brookfield Pub. Co.), Old Post Rd., Brookfield, VT 05036 (SAN 213-4446) Tel 802-276-3162. *Imprints:* Online Pubns Ltd (Online Publications Ltd); Pub. by Multisci Pubns Ltd (Multiscience Publications Ltd.).

†**Brookings,** (Brookings Institution; 0-8157), 1775 Massachusetts Ave., NW, Washington, DC 20036 (SAN 201-9396) Tel 202-797-6000; CIP.

†**Brookline Bks,** (Brookline Bks.; 0-914797), P.O. Box 1046, Cambridge, MA 02238 (SAN 289-0690) Tel 617-868-0360; CIP.

Brookline Book
See Brookline Bks

Brooklyn Coll Pr, (Brooklyn College, Pr.; 0-930888), 2227 Boylan Hall, Society In Change, Brooklyn, NY 11210 (SAN 281-3467); Orders to: 136 S. Broadway, Irvington-on-Hudson, NY 10533 (SAN 281-3475) Tel 914-591-9111.

Brookman Stamp, (Brookman Stamp Co.; 0-936937), Div. of Barrett & Worthen, Inc., 215 Middlesex Tpke., Burlington, MA 01803 (SAN 658-6902) Tel 617-229-6097.

†**Brooks-Cole,** (Brooks/Cole Publishing, Co.; 0-8185; 0-534), Div. of Wadsworth, Inc., 555 Abrego St., Monterey, CA 93940 (SAN 202-3369) Tel 408-373-0728; Orders to: Wadsworth, Inc., Customer Service Ctr., 7625 Empire Dr., Florence, KY 41042 (SAN 200-2213); CIP.

†**Brooks Pub Co,** (Brooks Publishing Co.; 0-932370), 2740 Fulton Ave., Suite 113, Sacramento, CA 95821 (SAN 212-8829) Tel 916-972-0633; Orders to: P.O. Box 1066, Carmichael, CA 95609 (SAN 212-8837) Tel 916-972-0633; CIP.

Broome Closet, (Broome Closet, The; 0-9608130), 34-892 Rancho Vista, Cathedral City, CA 92234 (SAN 238-8340) Tel 619-328-4694.

Brossart Pub, (Brossart Pub.; 0-9615153), 20715 Viento Valle, Escondido, CA 92025 (SAN 694-3349) Tel 619-741-3255.

Brost Heus, (Brost-Heus; 0-9616109), 384 Elizabeth St., San Francisco, CA 94114 (SAN 699-7392) Tel 415-641-8864.

Brotherhood Aum, (Brotherhood Aum; 0-939777), Div. of David Miilphen Assn., 556A W. 110th St., New York, NY 10025 (SAN 677-6213) Tel 212-663-8977.

Brotherhood Comm, (Brotherhood Commission), 1548 Poplar Ave., Memphis, TN 38104 (SAN 225-4662) Tel 901-272-2461.

Broude, (Broude Brothers Ltd., Music; 0-8450), 170 Varick St., New York, NY 10013 (SAN 281-3483) Tel 212-242-7001; Toll free: 800-225-3197; 141 White Oaks Rd., Williamstown, MA 01267 (SAN 281-3491).

Broude Intl Edns, (Broude International Editions, Inc.; 0-89371), 141 White Oaks Rd., Williamstown, MA 01267 (SAN 208-9483) Tel 413-458-8131.

Brouhaha Pub, (Brouhaha Publishing Co.; 0-9616036), 180 Richmond Ave., Buffalo, NY 14222 (SAN 697-8533) Tel 716-884-0248.

Brown Bk, (Brown Book Co.; 0-910294), P.O. Box 69-3883, Miami, FL 33269 (SAN 202-4276) Tel 305-932-0707.

Brown Cherry Pub, (Brown Cherry Pubns; 0-910515), 738 Plum Ave., Hampton, VA 23661 (SAN 260-1702) Tel 804-247-3230.

Brown Cnty Hist Soc, (Brown County Historical Society, Inc.; 0-9616808), P.O. Box 668, Nashville, IN 47448 (SAN 661-0846); State Rd. 135 N., Nashville, IN 47448 (SAN 661-0854) Tel 812-988-4297.

Brown Henniker NH
See Brown Katharine

Brown House, *(Brown Hse. Communications; 0-936895),* P.O. Box 15457, Stamford, CT 06901 (SAN 658-4772) Tel 203-834-0050; 108 Pond Rd., Wilton, CT 06897 (SAN 658-4780).

Brown Hse Gall, *(Brown Hse. Galleries Ltd.; 0-9604534),* 5717 Hammersley Rd., P.O. Box 4243, Madison, WI 53711 (SAN 215-7365).

Brown Katharine, *(Brown, Katharine; 0-9613959),* RFD No 1 Old Warner Rd., Henniker, NH 03242 (SAN 688-4318) Tel 603-428-7516; 2101 S. Pine St., Englewood, FL 33533 (SAN 693-5176) Tel 813-474-4470. Use the Second Address for Winter Only.

Brown Rabbit, *(Brown Rabbit Press; 0-933988),* No. 3 Smithdale Ct., Houston, TX 77024 (SAN 213-0246) Tel 713-465-1168.

Brown Unlimited, *(Brown Unlimited; 0-9615755),* P.O. Box 6357, Arlington, VA 22206 (SAN 696-1495) Tel 703-931-6068; 3700 N. Rosser St., Alexandria, VA 22311 (SAN 696-1509).

†**Browning Inst,** *(Browning Institute, Inc.; 0-930252),* P.O. Box 2983, Grand Central Sta., New York, NY 10163 (SAN 210-704X); Dist. by: Wedgestone Pr., P.O. Box 1757, Winfield, KS 67156 (SAN 276-5888) Tel 316-221-2779; *CIP.*

Browning Pubns, *(Browning Pubns.; 0-933718),* 4850 Gaidrew Rd., Alpharetta, GA 30201 (SAN 212-8845) Tel 404-475-3430.

Brownlee Books, *(Brownlee Books; 0-9613049),* P.O. Box 489, Hooks, TX 75561 (SAN 293-9126).

Brownlow Pub Co, *(Brownlow Publishing Co., Inc.; 0-915720),* 6309 Airport Freeway, Fort Worth, TX 76117 (SAN 207-5105) Tel 817-831-3831; Toll free: 800-433-7610.

Brown's Studio, *(Brown's Studio; 0-9604822),* 4004 Seven Springs Blvd., New Port Richey, FL 33552 (SAN 215-6288) Tel 813-376-5711.

Brownstone Bks, *(Brownstone Bks.; 0-941028),* 1711 Clifty Dr., Madison, IN 47250 (SAN 217-3387) Tel 812-273-6908.

Brownstone Pubns, *(Brownstone Pubns.; 0-9613101),* P.O. Box 8185, Rolling Meadows, IL 60008 (SAN 293-9800) Tel 312-934-0144.

Bruach HaTorah, *(B'ruach HaTorah Pubns.; 0-89655),* 7617 Reading Rd., Cincinnati, OH 45237 (SAN 284-9844) Tel 513-821-8941; P.O. Box 37366, Cincinnati, OH 45222 (SAN 284-9852).

Brubaker, *(Brubaker, E. S.; 0-9613496),* 645 N. President Ave., Lancaster, PA 17603 (SAN 209-5343) Tel 717-397-3120.

†**Bruccoli,** *(Bruccoli Clark Pubs.; 0-89723),* 2006 Summer St., Columbia, SC 29201 (SAN 209-3987) Tel 803-771-4642; *CIP.*

Bruce Pub Co
See Glencoe

Brun Pr, *(Brun Pr., Inc.; 0-932574),* 701 NE 67th St., Miami, FL 33138 (SAN 293-2423) Tel 305-756-6249.

Bruner, *(Bruner, William T.; 0-9606566),* 3848 Southern Pkwy., Louisville, KY 40214 (SAN 211-2884) Tel 502-367-7089.

†**Brunner-Mazel,** *(Brunner/Mazel, Inc.; 0-87630),* 19 Union Sq. W., New York, NY 10003 (SAN 164-9167) Tel 212-924-3344; *CIP.*

Brunswick Hist Soc, *(Brunswick Historical Society),* P.O. Box 1776, Cropseyville, NY 12052 (SAN 213-0289).

Brunswick Pub, *(Brunswick Publishing Co.; 0-931494; 1-55618),* Rte. 1, Box 1A1, Lawrenceville, VA 23868 (SAN 211-6332) Tel 804-848-3865.

Brush Hill, *(Brush Hill Pr., Inc.; 0-915087),* P.O. Box 96, Boston, MA 02137 (SAN 289-758X) Tel 617-333-0612.

Bryan-Lee Pub, *(Bryan-Lee Publishing; 0-9614494),* 581 Paseo Miramar, Pacific Palisades, CA 90272 (SAN 689-3422) Tel 213-454-9461.

Bryans *Imprint of Dell*

Bryant Library, *(Bryant Library, The; 0-9602242),* Paper Mill Rd., Roslyn, NY 11576 (SAN 223-484X) Tel 516-621-2240.

Bryce-Waterton Pubns, *(Bryce-Waterton Pubns.; 0-913339),* 6411 Mulberry Ave., Portage, IN 46368 (SAN 283-9202) Tel 219-762-5106; Dist. by: Independent Publishers Group, 1 Pleasant Ave., Port Washington, NY 11050 (SAN 287-2544) Tel 516-944-9325; Dist. by: Quality Bks., 918 Sherwood Dr., Lake Bluff, IL 60044-2204 (SAN 169-2127).

Bryn Ffyliaid, *(Bryn Ffyliaid Pubns.; 0-9611114),* 5600 Bellaire Dr., New Orleans, LA 70124 (SAN 283-2720) Tel 504-486-7036.

Brynmorgen, *(Brynmorgen Pr., Inc.; 0-9615984),* P.O. Box 405, Boylston, MA 01505 (SAN 698-1585) Tel 617-869-2624; 23 Mill Rd. Circuit, Boylston, MA 01505 (SAN 698-1593).

Brynwood Pub, *(Brynwood Publishing Co.; 0-937615),* 13567 Brynwood Ln., Ft. Myers, FL 33912 (SAN 659-0527) Tel 813-369-2117.

BS Propaganda
See Bomb Shelter Prop

BSA, *(Boy Scouts of America; 0-8395),* 1325 Walnut Hill Ln., Irving, TX 75038-3096 (SAN 284-9798) Tel 214-659-2273; Orders to: Eastern Distribution Ctr., 2109 Westinghouse Blvd., P.O. Box 7143, Charlotte, NC 28217 (SAN 284-9801) Tel 704-588-4260.

BSC Assocs
See BCS Assocs

Bubba Pr, *(Bubba Pr.; 0-9607240),* 560 Hartz Ave., Suite 406, Danville, CA 94526 (SAN 239-4138) Tel 415-820-6237.

Bubbling-Well, *(Bubbling-Well Pr.; 0-938045),* P.O. Box 961, St. Cloud, MN 56302 (SAN 659-9257); 701 Germain Mall, Rm. 201, St. Cloud, MN 56301 (SAN 659-9265) Tel 612-253-0426.

BUC Intl, *(BUC International Corp.; 0-911778),* 1314 NE. 17 Ct., Fort Lauderdale, FL 33305 (SAN 201-9426) Tel 305-565-6715; Toll free: 800-327-6929.

Buccaneer Bks, *(Buccaneer Bks.; 0-89966),* P.O. Box 168, Cutchogue, NY 11935 (SAN 209-1542).

Buccaneer CA, *(Buccaneer Bks.; 0-934765),* P.O. Box 518, Laguna Beach, CA 92652 (SAN 694-1907) Tel 714-494-4243.

Buchan Pubns, *(Buchan Pubns.; 0-915067),* P.O. Box 7218, St. Petersburg, FL 33734 (SAN 289-761X) Tel 813-526-9121.

Buchanan L, *(Buchanan, Laurie; 0-943102),* Div. of Pages to Go, 12540 Oak Knoll Rd., Suite B-11, Poway, CA 92064 (SAN 240-8236) Tel 619-748-1055.

Buck Hill, *(Buck Hill Assocs.; 0-917420),* 129 Garnet Lake Rd., Johnsburg, NY 12843 (SAN 202-4403) Tel 518-251-2743.

Buck Mntn Pr, *(Buck Mountain Pr.; 0-9616710),* P.O. Box 774407, Steamboat Springs, CO 80477 (SAN 659-9281); 3005 Trails Edge Rd., Steamboat Springs, CO 80477 (SAN 659-929X) Tel 303-879-4204.

Buck Pub, *(Buck Publishing Co.; 0-934530),* 2409 Vestavia Dr., Birmingham, AL 35216 (SAN 213-0203) Tel 205-979-2296.

Buckeye Pr, *(Buckeye Pr.; 0-9615559),* 1803 Park Dr., Columbus, GA 31906 (SAN 696-1533) Tel 404-324-3823; Toll free: 800-241-8981.

Buckingham Assoc, *(Buckingham Assocs.),* 591 Parker Hill Rd., Springfield, VT 05156 (SAN 692-3771) Tel 802-885-5052.

Buckle Pr, *(Buckle Pr.; 0-9616809),* RR 2, P.O. Box 2283, Lake George, NY 12845 (SAN 661-0862); Schermerhorn Dr., Lake George, NY 12845 (SAN 661-0870) Tel 518-668-2530.

Buckley-Little, *(Buckley-Little Bk. Catalogue Co., Inc.; 0-916667),* Canal St. Sta., P.O. Box 512, New York, NY 10013 (SAN 297-0104) Tel 212-982-9357; Dist. by: New York Zoetrope, 80 E. 11th St., Suite 516, New York, NY 10003 (SAN 209-6293) Tel 212-420-0590.

Buckley Pubns, *(Buckley Pubns., Inc.; 0-915388),* 4848 N. Clark St., Chicago, IL 60640-4711 (SAN 208-1954) Tel 312-271-0202.

Buckminster Fuller, *(Fuller, Buckminster, Institute; 0-911573),* 1743 S. La Cienega Blvd., Los Angeles, CA 90035-4601 (SAN 264-0511) Tel 213-837-7710.

Bucknell U Pr, *(Bucknell Univ. Pr.; 0-8387),* Dist. by: Associated University Presses, 440 Forsgate Dr., Cranbury, NJ 08512 (SAN 281-2959) Tel 609-655-4770.

Bucks Cnty Gen, *(Bucks County Genealogical Society; 0-9612804),* P.O. Box 1092, Doylestown, PA 18901 (SAN 289-9698) Tel 215-345-0210.

Bucks Co Hist, *(Bucks County Historical Society; 0-910302),* Pine & Ashland Sts., Doylestown, PA 18901 (SAN 203-6835) Tel 215-345-0210.

Bucyrus-Erie Co, *(Bucyrus-Erie Co.; 0-9604136),* P.O. Box 56, South Milwaukee, WI 53172 (SAN 214-1825).

Buddhist Assn US, *(Buddhist Assn. of the U.S., The; 0-915078),* Dist. by: Institute for Advanced Studies of World Religions, 2150 Center Ave., Fort Lee, NJ 07024 (SAN 265-3885).

†**Buddhist Bks,** *(Buddhist Bks. International; 0-914910),* 9701 Wilshire Blvd., Suite 850, Beverly Hills, CA 90212 (SAN 281-3548); *CIP.*

†**Buddhist Study,** *(Buddhist Study Center, The; 0-938474),* c/o Press Pacifica, P.O. Box 47, Kailua, HI 96734 (SAN 284-9860) Tel 808-538-3805; Offices of Buddhist Education, 1727 Pali Hwy., Honolulu, HI 96813 (SAN 284-9879); *CIP.*

Buddhist Text, *(Buddhist Text Translation Society; 0-917512),* Box 217, City of Ten Thousand Buddhas, Talmage, CA 95481 (SAN 281-3556) Tel 707-462-0939.

Budgate Pr, *(Budgate Press; 0-9610746),* 7421 Day Forest Rd., Empire, MI 49630 (SAN 264-7192) Tel 616-334-3387.

Budlong, *(Budlong Pr. Co.; 0-910304),* 5915 N. Northwest Hwy., Chicago, IL 60631 (SAN 202-4837).

†**Buffalo Acad,** *(Buffalo Fine Arts Academy; 0-914782),* Albright-Knox Art Gallery, 1285 Elmwood Ave., Buffalo, NY 14222 (SAN 202-4845) Tel 716-882-8700; Dist. by: Univ. of Washington Pr., P.O. Box C50096, Seattle, WA 98145 (SAN 212-2502) Tel 206-543-4050; *CIP.*

Buggy Whip, *(Buggy Whip Press; 0-9612824),* 121 Park Ave., Lexington, KY 40508 (SAN 289-5927) Tel 606-233-7176.

Builders of Adytum, *(Builders of the Adytum, Ltd.; 0-938002),* 5105 N. Figueroa St., Los Angeles, CA 90042 (SAN 202-4853) Tel 213-255-7141; Orders to: P.O. Box 42278, Dept., O, Los Angeles, CA 90042 (SAN 202-4861).

Builders Pub, *(Builders Publishing Co., The; 0-941000),* P.O. Box 2278, Salt Lake City, UT 84110 (SAN 212-8675) Tel 801-364-7396; Dist. by: New Leaf Distributing, The, 1020 White St. SW, Atlanta, GA 30310 (SAN 169-1449) Tel 404-755-2665; Dist. by: Bookpeople, 2929 Fifth St., Berkeley, CA 94710 (SAN 168-9517) Tel 415-549-3030; Dist. by: The Distributors, 702 S. Michigan, South Bend, IN 46618 (SAN 169-2488) Tel 219-232-8500; Dist. by: Devorss & Co., P.O. Box 550, 1046 Princeton Dr., Marina del Rey, CA 90294 (SAN 168-9886) Tel 213-870-7478.

Building Blocks, *(Building Blocks; 0-943452),* 3893 Brindlewood Ln., Elgin, IL 60120 (SAN 240-6063) Tel 312-742-1013.

Building Cost File, *(Building Cost File, Inc.; 0-942564),* 2906 Anthony St., Wantagh, NY 11793 (SAN 238-0293) Tel 516-785-1676.

Building Inst, *(Building Institute, The; 0-911749),* 855 Piermont Rd., Piermont, NY 10968 (SAN 263-9483) Tel 914-359-0299; Dist. by: Caroline House, Inc., 5S 250 Frontenac Rd., Naperville, IL 60540 (SAN 211-2280) Tel 312-983-6400.

Bull City, *(Bull City; 0-933974),* 3425 B. Randolph Rd., Durham, NC 27705 (SAN 222-7223).

†**Bull Pub,** *(Bull Publishing, Co.; 0-915950),* P.O. Box 208, Palo Alto, CA 94302 (SAN 208-5712) Tel 415-322-2855; Dist. by: Kampmann & Co., Inc., 9 E. 40th St., New York, NY 10016 (SAN 202-5191) Tel 212-685-2928; *CIP.*

Bullbrier Pr, *(Bullbrier Pr.; 0-9612610),* 10 Snyder Heights, Ithaca, NY 14850 (SAN 289-0704) Tel 607-273-5109.

Bulldog Club Amer, *(Bulldog Club of America, Div. III; 0-9616531),* 4345 Army St., San Francisco, CA 94131 (SAN 659-4263) Tel 415-282-9079.

Bullet Pubns, *(Bullet Pubns., Inc.; 0-9614186),* Subs. of Bullet Word Processing, P.O. Box 7657, Phoenix, AZ 85011 (SAN 686-6034) Tel 602-265-0678.

Bullock Pub Co
See Basbery Pub

Bullworks, *(Bullworks; 0-9601190),* 20 Fairway Dr., Stamford, CT 06903 (SAN 211-4097) Tel 203-968-1925.

Bumann Spec Works, *(Bumann, Richard L.; 0-9607112),* 2139 Ranch View Terrace, Olivenhain, CA 92024 (SAN 238-9568) Tel 714-753-7279.

†**Bumper Crop Pr,** *(Bumper Crop Pr.; 0-932769),* 12960 State Rte. 700, Hiram, OH 44234 (SAN 688-5497) Tel 216-569-3129; *CIP.*

Bunkhouse, *(Bunkhouse Pubs., Inc.; 0-918628),* 123 N. Sultana Ave., Ontario, CA 91764 (SAN 215-062X).

Bunneys Guides, *(Bunney's Guides; 0-9616711),* P.O. Box 75565, Northgate Sta., Seattle, WA 98125 (SAN 659-932X); 10800 Roosevelt Way, NE, Seattle, WA 98125 (SAN 659-9338) Tel 206-367-3219.

Bunting, *(Bunting & Lyon, Inc.; 0-913094),* 238 N. Main St., Wallingford, CT 06492 (SAN 202-487X) Tel 203-269-3333.

Bur Busn Prac, *(Bureau of Business Practice, Inc.; 0-87622),* Div. of Simon & Schuster, Inc. A Gulf & Western Co., 24 Rope Ferry Rd., Waterford, CT 06386 (SAN 204-3742) Tel 203-442-4365.

Bur Busn Res U Nebr, *(Univ. of Nebraska-Lincoln, Bureau of Business Research; 0-917810),* Div. of Univ. of Nebraska, Univ. of Nebraska, 200 CBA Bldg., Lincoln, NE 68588-0406 (SAN 209-262X) Tel 402-472-2334.

Bur Busn Wis, *(Univ. of Wisconsin, Graduate Schl. of Business, Bureau of Business Research; 0-866303),* 1155 Observatory Dr., Rm. 110, Commerce Bldg., Madison, WI 53706 (SAN 669-0319) Tel 608-262-1550.

Bur Econ Geology, *(Bureau of Economic Geology),* Div. of Univ. of Texas at Austin, University Sta., Box X, Austin, TX 78713 (SAN 207-432X) Tel 512-471-1534.

Bur Faculty Res Wash, *(Western Washington State College, Bureau for Faculty Research; 0-930216),* Western Washington State College, Bellingham, WA 98225 (SAN 210-6841) Tel 206-676-3234.

Bur Health Hosp, *(Bureau of Health & Hospital Careers Counseling; 0-917364),* Lincoln Hospital Medical Ctr., P.O. Box 238, Scarsdale, NY 10583 (SAN 208-5720) Tel 914-241-0610.

Bur Intl Aff, *(Bureau of International Affairs; 0-938780),* 1613 Chelsea Rd., San Marino, CA 91108 (SAN 201-9442) Tel 818-793-2841.

Bur Public Secrets, *(Bureau of Public Secrets; 0-939682),* P.O. Box 1044, Berkeley, CA 94701 (SAN 216-2261).

Bur Univ Gov SC, *(Bureau of Governmental Research & Services; 0-917069),* University of South Carolina, Gambrell Hall, Columbia, SC 29208 (SAN 655-4849) Tel 803-777-8156.

Burda Pubns, *(Burda Pubns.; 0-914926),* Rockefeller Ctr., Suite 1918, 1270 Ave. of the Americas, New York, NY 10020 (SAN 206-7595).

Burdette, *(Burdette & Co., Inc.; 0-910306),* c/o T. Thomte & Co., Inc., 661 Massachusetts Ave., Arlington, MA 02174 (SAN 202-4888) Tel 617-641-2700.

Burdick Ancestry Lib, *(Burdick Ancestry Library, The; 0-9609100),* 2317 Riverbluff Pkwy., No. 249, Sarasota, FL 33581-5032 (SAN 241-2802).

Bureau Busn Re Sch
See WSU Bur Bus Res

Bureau Busn Res U Wis
See Bur Busn Wis

†**Bureau Busn UT,** *(Univ. of Texas, Bureau of Business Research; 0-87755),* P.O. Box 7459, Austin, TX 78713-7459 (SAN 203-3232) Tel 512-471-1616; *CIP.*

Bureau Issues, *(Bureau Issues Assn.; 0-930412),* 7070 Wolftree Ln., Rockville, MD 20852 (SAN 213-0483).

Bureau Pub Admin U Tenn, *(Univ. of Tennessee, Bureau of Public Administration; 0-914079),* Div. of Univ. of Tennessee, 1001 McClung Tower, Knoxville, TN 37996-0410 (SAN 291-9192) Tel 615-974-5278.

Burger Pubns, *(Burger Pubns.; 0-914561),* Suite 210, 1515 Pacific Ave., Venice, CA 93001 (SAN 289-1549) Tel 213-392-5165.

Burgess
See Burgess MN Intl

Burgess-Intl Ideas, *(Burgess, Jack K., Inc.),* 2175 Lemoine Ave., Ft. Lee, NJ 07024 (SAN 650-017X) Tel 201-592-0739.

Burgess MN Intl, *(Burgess International Group, Inc.; 0-8087),* 7110 Ohms Ln., Edina, MN 55435 (SAN 212-6001) Tel 612-831-1344. *Imprints:* CEPCO (Continuing Education Pubn., Co.); Feffer & Simons (Feffer & Simons).

Burgundy Pr, *(Burgundy Pr.; 0-917574),* P.O. Box 313, Southampton, PA 18966 (SAN 212-1859).

Burkehaven Pr, *(Burkehaven Press; 0-914062),* Penacook Rd., Contoocook, NH 03229 (SAN 202-4896) Tel 603-746-3625.

Burke's Bk Store, *(Burke's Book Store, Inc.; 0-937130),* 634 Poplar Ave., Memphis, TN 38105 (SAN 127-3124) Tel 901-527-7484.

Burkharts, *(Burkhart's; 0-9615199),* 259 Midway Ave., P.O. Box 807, Blandon, PA 19510 (SAN 694-3594) Tel 215-926-2564.

Burlage Corp, *(Burlage Corp.; 0-9616208),* 800 Atlantic Ave., Virginia Beach, VA 23451 (SAN 658-3377) Tel 804-480-3673.

Burn Books, *(Burn, Billie, Bks.; 0-9614670),* P.O. Box 29, Daufuskie Island, SC 29915 (SAN 692-4565) Tel 803-842-6801.

Burn Hart, *(Burn, Hart & Co., Pubs.; 0-918060),* 632 Calle Yucca, Box 1772, Thousand Oaks, CA 91360 (SAN 210-1823) Tel 805-498-3985.

Burnell Co, *(Burnell Co./Publishers, Inc., The; 0-916973),* P.O. Box 304, Mankato, MN 56001 (SAN 655-587X) Tel 507-625-4302.

Burnett Micro, *(Burnett Microfiche Co.; 0-916497),* 3891 Commander Dr., Atlanta, GA 30341-0016 (SAN 295-5547) Tel 404-455-6445.

Burnetts Micro Co
See Burnett Micro

Burning Deck, *(Burning Deck; 0-930900; 0-930901),* Div. of ANTART Contemporary Art Ctr., 71 Elmgrove Ave., Providence, RI 02906 (SAN 207-7981); Dist. by: Small Pr. Distribution, Inc., 1814 San Pablo Ave., Berkeley, CA 94702 (SAN 204-5826) Tel 415-549-3336.

†**Buros Inst Mental,** *(Buros Institute of Mental Measurements; 0-910674),* Div. of Univ. of Nebraska-Lincoln, Univ. of Nebraska-Lincoln, 135 Bancroft, Lincoln, NE 68588-0348 (SAN 698-1895) Tel 402-472-6203; Orders to: Univ. of Nebraska Pr., 901 N. 17th St., Lincoln, NE 68588-0520 (SAN 662-4022) Tel 402-472-3581; *CIP.*

Burr Pubns, *(Burr Pubns., Ltd.; 0-911994),* RD 1, Rte. 33, Box 429, Hightstown, NJ 08520 (SAN 207-2068).

Burrell Ctr Inc, *(Burrell Center, Inc.; 0-9606362),* P.O. Box 1611 SSS, Springfield, MO 65805 (SAN 223-7520) Tel 417-883-5400.

†**Burrill-Ellsworth,** *(Burill-Ellsworth Assocs.; 0-935310),* 26 Birchwood Pl., Tenafly, NJ 07670 (SAN 281-3602); Orders to: Box 295, Tenafly, NJ 07670 (SAN 281-3610); *CIP.*

Burrows & Baker, *(Burrows & Baker; 0-930414),* 201 E. 21st St., New York, NY 10010 (SAN 223-2618).

Burtis Ent, *(Burtis Enterprises, Pubs.; 0-939530),* 23651 Gerrad Way, Canoga Park, CA 91307 (SAN 216-6593) Tel 818-346-8534.

Burtt Co, *(Burtt & Co.; 0-937087),* 9 Hampden St., Wellesley, MA 02181 (SAN 658-4853) Tel 617-235-7616.

Burwell Ent, *(Burwell Enterprises; 0-938519),* 5106 F.M. 1960, Suite 349, Houston, TX 77069 (SAN 674-7078) Tel 713-537-9051.

Busby Pubns, *(Busby Pubns.; 0-9610288),* APO PSC Box 5766, New York, NY 09179-5379 (SAN 263-9505).

Buscombe
See NWU Astro

Business Bks CT, *(Business Bks. International; 0-916673),* P.O. Box 1587, New Canaan, CT 06840 (SAN 297-1860) Tel 203-966-9645.

Business Plan, *(Business Plan Publishing; 0-936257),* P.O. Box 3841, St. Augustine, FL 32084 (SAN 697-3574) Tel 904-471-6779; Oceanside Condominium, No. 402, St. Augustine, FL 32084 (SAN 698-2220).

Business Pubns, *(Business Pubns., Inc.; 0-256),* Subs. of Richard D. Irwin, Inc., 1700 Alma Rd., Suite 390, Plano, TX 75075 (SAN 202-4926) Tel 214-422-4389; Dist. by: Richard D. Irwin, Inc., 1818 Ridge Rd., Homewood, IL 60430 (SAN 206-8400) Tel 312-798-6000.

Business Research, *(Business Research Services Inc.; 0-933527),* 2 E. 22nd St., Suite 308, Lombard, IL 60148 (SAN 691-8522) Tel 312-495-8787; Toll free: 800-325-8720.

Business Technology Bks
See Busn Tech Info Serv

Busn *Imprint of P-H*

Busn Comp CO, *(Business Computers),* 1315 N. Main Ave., Suite 230, Durango, CO 81301 (SAN 675-3744).

Busn Inst Furn, *(Business & Institutional Furniture Manufacturers Assn.),* 2335 Burton SE, Grand Rapids, MI 49506 (SAN 224-0890) Tel 616-243-1681.

Busn Intl Corp, *(Business International Corporation; 0-87180),* 1 Dag Hammerskjold Plaza, New York, NY 10017 (SAN 237-7896).

Busn Journals, *(Business Journals),* 22 S. Smith St., P.O. Box 5550, E. Norwalk, CT 06856 (SAN 204-2053).

Busn Journals
See Turbo Intl Pubn

Busn Legal Reports, *(Business & Legal Reports; 1-55645),* 64 Wall St., Madison, CT 06443 (SAN 661-504X) Tel 203-245-7448.

Busn Media Res, *(Business Media Resources; 0-938545),* 150 Shoreline Hwy., Bldg. B, Suite 27, Mill Valley, CA 94941 (SAN 661-2806) Tel 415-331-6021.

†**Busn News,** *(Business News Publishing Co.; 0-912524),* P.O. Box 2600, Troy, MI 48007 (SAN 201-9450) Tel 313-362-3700; *CIP.*

Busn Pro Bks, *(Business & Professional Bks., Inc.; 0-9608576),* P.O. Box 9671, San Jose, CA 95157 (SAN 238-2539) Tel 408-294-3960.

Busn Proposals
See Courier Pr FL

Busn Psych, *(Business Psychology International; 0-931918),* P.O. Box 235-6, Boston, MA 02159 (SAN 211-6014) Tel 617-332-3820.

Busn Pub TX, *(Business Publishing Co.),* 2631A Gwendolyn Ln., Austin, TX 78748 (SAN 659-5626).

Busn Pubns CA, *(Business Pubns., Inc.; 0-9610808),* 8505 Commerce Ave., San Diego, CA 92121-2610 (SAN 683-2229).

Busn Sale Inst, *(Business Sale Institute; 0-933808),* 170 Park Center Plaza, Suite 202, San Jose, CA 95113 (SAN 212-8853) Tel 408-286-4850.

Busn Tech Info Serv, *(Business/Technology Information Service; 0-930978; 0-89934),* P.O. Box 574, Orinda, CA 94563 (SAN 282-5902) Tel 415-254-2913; Orders to: Manufacturing Productivity Ctr., IIT Ctr., 10 W. 35th St., Chicago, IL 60616 (SAN 694-9606) Tel 312-567-4808.

Busn Travel *Imprint of Watts*

Busn Trend, *(Business Trend Analysts; 0-88073),* 2171 Jericho Tpke., Commack, NY 11725 (SAN 217-2313) Tel 516-462-5454.

Busy Bees, *(Busy Bees; 0-9617073),* 8041 Lake Waunatta Dr., Winter Park, FL 32792 (SAN 662-6084) Tel 305-671-6127.

Butcher Block Pr, *(Butcher Block Pr.; 0-9614367),* 2932 Benjamin, Wichita, KS 67204 (SAN 688-5527) Tel 316-838-7717.

Buten Mus, *(Buten Museum; 0-912014),* 246 N. Bowman Ave., Merion Station, PA 19066 (SAN 202-4942) Tel 215-664-6601.

Buteo, *(Buteo Bks.; 0-931130),* P.O. Box 481, Vermillion, SD 57069 (SAN 212-0054).

Butler-Farwell, *(Butler, JoNett, /Bea Farwell; 0-9614834),* 1117 Second Ave., S. Crescent Dr., Clinton, IA 52732 (SAN 693-0875) Tel 319-242-8378; Orders to: America's Best Appetizers, P.O. Box 335, Clinton, IA 52732-0335 (SAN 662-3115) Tel 319-242-8378.

Butler Pub Hse, *(Butler Publishing Hse., Inc.; 0-932315),* P.O. Box 21212, Detroit, MI 48221 (SAN 687-0384) Tel 313-891-5877.

Butte Hist Soc, *(Butte Historical Society; 0-930683)*, P.O. Box 3913, Butte, MT 59703 (SAN 676-9209) Tel 406-782-3113; Dist. by: Pacific Pipeline, Inc., 19215 66th Ave S., Kent, WA 98032 (SAN 208-2128) Tel 206-872-5523.

Buttercup Bks, *(Buttercup Bks.; 0-9614997)*, 3641 Kimworth Ln., Shingle Springs, CA 95682 (SAN 693-9503) Tel 916-677-9142.

Butterfield, *(Butterfield Pr.; 0-935767)*, 304 Federal Rd., Brookfield, CT 06804 (SAN 695-8354) Tel 203-775-0939.

Butterfield Pr, *(Butterfield Pr.; 0-932579)*, 140 Stuyvesant Dr., San Anselmo, CA 94960 (SAN 689-6472) Tel 415-485-5568.

Butterfly Bks, *(Butterfly Bks.; 0-939077)*, 4526 Queens Way, Sierra Vista, AZ 85635 (SAN 661-6925) Tel 602-458-0869.

Butterfly Pr, *(Butterfly Press; 0-918766)*, 13635 Queensbury, Houston, TX 77079 (SAN 209-7133) Tel 713-464-7570; Orders to: P.O. Box 19571, Houston, TX 77224-9571 (SAN 661-9665) Tel 713-464-7579; Dist. by: Richardsons Educators, 2014 Lou Ellen Ln., Houston, TX 77018 (SAN 200-7177) Tel 713-688-2244. Formerly Terzarima System.

Butterfly Pub, *(Butterfly Publishing, Inc.; 0-941254)*, P.O. Box 21116, Salt Lake City, UT 84121 (SAN 237-935X) Tel 801-263-3577.

Butterfly Santa Monica, *(Butterfly Publishing Co.; 0-9614637)*, 2210 Wilshire Blvd., Suite 845, Santa Monica, CA 90403 (SAN 691-9146) Tel 213-829-2002; Dist. by: Nutri-Books Corp., P.O. Box 5793, Denver, CO 80223 (SAN 169-054X) Tel 303-778-8383; Dist. by: New Leaf Distributing, The, 1020 White St., SW, Atlanta, GA 30310 (SAN 169-1449) Tel 404-755-2665; Dist. by: Baker & Taylor Co., Western Div., 380 Edison Way, Reno, NV 89564 (SAN 169-4464) Tel 702-786-6700; Dist. by: Great Tradition, The, 750 Adrian Way, Suite 111, San Rafael, CA 94903 (SAN 200-5743) Tel 415-492-9382.

Butternut & Blue, *(Butternut & Blue; 0-935523)*, 2804 Maple Ave., Baltimore, MD 21234 (SAN 696-1576) Tel 301-668-0824.

Butternut Pr, *(Butternut Press; 0-913419)*, Div. of Zullo & Van Sickle Bks., 18761 (W) N. Frederick, Gaithersburg, MD 20879 (SAN 285-8991) Tel 301-963-7878.

†**Butterworth,** *(Butterworth's (Scientific, Technical, Medical); 0-408; 0-250; 0-409; 0-407)*, Subs. of Reed International, 80 Montvale Ave., Stoneham, MA 02180 (SAN 206-3964) Tel 617-438-8464; Toll free: 800-544-1013; *CIP. Imprints:* Newnes-Butterworth (Newnes-Butterworth); Westbury Hse (Westbury House).(Westbury Hse.).

†**Butterworth Legal Pubs,** *(Butterworth U. S., Legal Pubs., Inc., New England Div.; 0-88063; 0-86673; 0-406; 0-409)*, 84 Montvale Ave., Stoneham, MA 02180-2471 (SAN 238-1451) Tel 617-438-8464; *CIP.*

†**Butterworth MN,** *(Butterworth Legal Pubs.; 0-917126; 0-86678)*, 289 E. Fifth St., St. Paul, MN 55101-1989 (SAN 205-8839) Tel 612-227-4200; *CIP.*

Butterworth of Cape Cod, *(Butterworth Co. of Cape Cod, Inc., The; 0-937338)*, 350 Main St., West Yarmouth, MA 02673 (SAN 239-524X).

Butterworth TX, *(Butterworth Legal Pubs.; 0-409)*, Div. of Reed Holdings, Inc., 1321 Rutherford Ln., Suite 180, Austin, TX 78753-6798 (SAN 654-6692) Tel 512-835-7921.

†**Butterworth WA,** *(Butterworth Legal Pubs.)*, Div. of Reed International, 15014 NE 40th St., Suite 205, Redmond, WA 98052-5325 (SAN 695-670X) Tel 206-881-3900; Orders to: 80 Montvale Ave., Stoneham, MA 02180-2471 (SAN 662-3522) Tel 617-438-8464; *CIP.*

Butterworths
See Butterworth

Button Gwin, *(Gwinnett, Button, Publishers, Inc.; 0-938386)*, 125 Scott St., P.O. Box 508, Buford, GA 30518 (SAN 264-0732).

Button Pub, *(Button Publishing; 0-915115)*, Subs. of Michael F. Ingbar Art Co., Inc., 7 E. 20th St., 4th Fl., New York, NY 10003 (SAN 289-7636).

Buttonwood Pr, *(Buttonwood Pr.; 0-934867)*, 41 Park Ave., Suite 5D, New York, NY 10016 (SAN 694-5635) Tel 212-689-4643.

Buttrill Reid, *(Buttrill & Reid; 0-9612214)*, 5515 Hooks St., Beaumont, TX 77706 (SAN 289-1522) Tel 301-320-6781; 5506 Ridgefield Rd., Bethesda, MD 20816 (SAN 289-1530).

Buxbaum, *(Buxbaum, Edwin C.; 0-9600494)*, P.O. Box 465, Wilmington, DE 19899 (SAN 201-7482) Tel 302-994-2663.

Buyer's Directory, *(Buyer's Directory; 0-936588)*, R.D. 3, Box 533, Olean, NY 14760 (SAN 214-1108) Tel 716-372-0514.

Buyout
See Kemah Pr

Buyout Pubns
See Busn Pubns CA

BW Enterprises, *(BW Enterprises Publishing Co.; 0-9616280)*, 2289 Berrydale Rd., Cantonment, FL 32533 (SAN 658-554X) Tel 904-968-6244.

By By Prods, *(By By Productions; 0-938826)*, P.O. Box 1676, Glendora, CA 91740 (SAN 216-0242).

By Hand & Foot, *(By Hand & Foot, Ltd.; 0-938670)*, Div. of Green River Tools, Inc., 5 Cotton Mill-Hill, P.O. Box 611, Brattleboro, VT 05301 (SAN 215-8493).

Byelorussian-Am, *(Byelorussian-American Association)*, 166-34 Gothic Dr, Jamaica, NY 11432 (SAN 225-4042) Tel 718-397-5341.

BYLS Pr, *(BYLS Pr.; 0-934402)*, 6247 N. Francisco Ave., Chicago, IL 60659 (SAN 212-7253) Tel 312-262-8959.

Byrd, *(Byrd, Harold E.; 0-9601972)*, P.O. Box 191278, Los Angeles, CA 90019 (SAN 212-2707) Tel 213-931-9094.

Byrd SDI, *(Byrd/S D and I/1.0 Communications; 0-9613299)*, 480-60th St., Oakland, CA 94609 (SAN 654-2344) Tel 415-548-6177; Orders to: P.O. Box 5925, Berkeley, CA 94705 (SAN 654-2352).

Byrd Systems
See Byrd SDI

Byrnam Pr, *(Byrnam Press; 0-9613268)*, 484 Lake Park Ave., Box 220, Oakland, CA 94610 (SAN 297-021X) Tel 415-658-9146.

Byron Daven Pubs, *(Byron-Davenport Pubs.; 0-930895)*, P.O. Box 34165, Bethesda, MD 20817 (SAN 679-2022) Tel 301-983-0742.

Byron Pr, *(Byron Pr.; 0-935101)*, 1840 N. Beverly Glen Blvd., Los Angeles, CA 90077 (SAN 695-0639) Tel 213-470-2817.

BYTE Bks *Imprint of* McGraw

Bytecraft, *(Bytecraft, Inc.; 0-935033)*, Div. of Future Byte, P.O. Box 1860, Casper, WY 82602-1860 (SAN 693-7950) Tel 307-235-6010.

BYU Clark Law, *(Brigham Young Univ., J. Reuben Clark Law Schl.)*, Brigham Young Univ., Provo, UT 84602 (SAN 226-4188).

BYU CSCVL, *(Center for the Study of Christian Values in Literature; 0-939555)*, Brigham Young University, Center for the Study of Christian Values in Literature, 3134 JKHB, Provo, UT 84602 (SAN 663-4257) Tel 801-378-2304.

BYU Family Commun Hist, *(Brigham Young Univ., Family & Community History Ctr.; 0-938605)*, Brigham Young Univ., 335 KMB, Provo, UT 84602 (SAN 661-3489) Tel 801-378-4386.

BYU Law Lib, *(Brigham Young Univ. Law Library)*, Brigham Young University, Provo, UT 84602 (SAN 268-4640).

Byzantine Pr, *(Byzantine Pr.; 0-913168)*, 115 N. Seventh St., Las Vegas, NV 89101 (SAN 204-3785) Tel 702-384-4200.

Byzantium Pr, *(Byzantium Pr.; 0-937439)*, 5 Mayfair Ln., Westport, CT 06880 (SAN 659-0543) Tel 203-227-5503.

C A Celorio, *(Celorio, Cesar Alberto; 0-918168)*, 28-02 Ditmars Blvd., Astoria, NY 11105 (SAN 210-1858) Tel 718-278-7890.

C A Gillespie, *(Gillespie, Charles A.; 0-9609974)*, 3 Lynwood Ave., Titusville, FL 32796 (SAN 263-1032) Tel 305-269-0643.

C A M Co, *(C.A.M Co.; 0-942752)*, P.O. Box 352, Hortonville, WI 54944 (SAN 281-3645) Tel 414-982-2856; Dist. by: The Distributors, 702 S. Michigan, South Bend, IN 46618 (SAN 169-2488) Tel 219-232-8500; Dist. by: Baker & Taylor, Midwest Div., 501 Gladiola Ave., Momence, IL 60954 (SAN 169-2100) Tel 815-472-2444.

C A Miller
See Trackaday

C A Parker Pubns, *(Parker, Clayton A., Publications; 0-9606438)*, 450 Wendell Dr., Salt Lake City, UT 84115 (SAN 218-5768) Tel 801-266-2292.

C A Smith, *(Smith, Carolyn A.; 0-9606292)*, 12901 Twisted Oak Rd., Oklahoma City, OK 73120 (SAN 214-140X) Tel 405-751-3166.

C A Wilson, *(Wilson, Charles A.; 0-9616261)*, P.O. Box 278, Story, WY 82842 (SAN 658-3806) Tel 307-683-2188.

C A Zapffe, *(Zapffe, Carl A.; 0-9601448)*, 6410 Murray Hill Rd., Baltimore, MD 21212 (SAN 221-2978).

C & A Kiser, *(C & A Kiser; 0-9611920)*, P.O. Box 154, Bessemer City, NC 28016 (SAN 286-1275) Tel 704-629-4674.

C & E Ent Pub, *(C & E Enterprises, Pubs.; 0-9610096)*, 980 West St., San Luis Obispo, CA 93401 (SAN 268-5620) Tel 805-543-8187.

C & G Ent, *(C & G Enterprises; 0-9607154)*, P.O. Box 58567, Tukwila, WA 98188 (SAN 238-9576) Tel 206-937-3378.

C & H Pub
See Cay-Bel

C & I Pubns, *(C & I Pubns.; 0-916835)*, 2101 14th Ave. SW, Largo, FL 33540 (SAN 654-2506) Tel 813-585-1164.

C and L Bks, *(C & L Books; 0-9614751)*, P.O. Box 955, Medina, OH 44258 (SAN 692-9273) Tel 216-722-3610.

C & L Pub Co, *(C&L Publishing Co.; 0-9605724)*, 2525 Wilson Blvd., Arlington, VA 22201 (SAN 216-3462).

C & R Anthony, *(C. & R. Anthony, Inc.; 0-910140)*, 300 Park Ave. S., P.O. Box 781, Madison Sq. Sta., New York, NY 10157 (SAN 203-4786) Tel 212-986-7693. Do Not Confuse with Anthony Pub Co.

C & R Loo, *(Loo, C. & R., Inc.)*, 1550 62nd St., P.O. Box 8397, Emeryville, CA 94608 (SAN 211-366X).

C & S Ent, *(C & S Enterprises; 0-9609028)*, 5169 Wheelis Dr., Memphis, TN 38117 (SAN 281-367X) Tel 901-767-7961.

C & S Michaud, *(Michaud, Carole & Susan; 0-9617264)*, 30 Plaza Rd., Garden City, NY 11530 (SAN 663-4885) Tel 516-437-8798.

C & T Pub, *(C & T Publishing; 0-914881)*, P.O. Box 1456, Lafayette, CA 94549 (SAN 289-0720) Tel 415-284-1177; Dist. by: Gutcheon Patchworks, 611 Broadway, New York, NY 10012 (SAN 200-5352) Tel 212-505-0305; Dist. by: Dicmar Trading Co., Inc., 4057 Highwood Ct., NW, Washington, DC 20007 (SAN 200-5298).

C Annegan, *(Annegan, Charles; 0-9605200)*, P.O. Box 1304, San Marcos, CA 92069 (SAN 215-8469).

C B Enterprises, *(CB Enterprises; 0-9616997)*, Div. of A. M. Communications, 9304 Mill Hollow, Dallas, TX 75243 (SAN 663-5008).

C B North, *(North, Christina Bolt; 0-9609008)*, 41-06 12th St., Long Island City, NY 11101 (SAN 239-5487) Tel 718-784-7705.

C B Pratt, *(Pratt, Collin B.; 0-9617049)*, P.O. Box 18401-7K, Las Vegas, NV 89114 (SAN 662-8877); 2600 Arville, F 14, Las Vegas, NV 89102 (SAN 662-8885) Tel 702-871-9764.

C B Pub & Dist
See Caratzas

C B Slack
See Slack Inc

C B Taylor, *(Taylor, Carl B.; 0-9605948)*, 773 Augusta, Morgantown, WV 26505 (SAN 216-6488) Tel 304-292-8190.

C B Vega, *(Vega, Carlos B., Pub.; 0-88174)*, P.O. Box 4195, West New York, NJ 07093 (SAN 287-7724) Tel 201-869-6916.

C Barton, *(Barton, Cyril; 0-9613277)*, Rte. One, Waltonville, IL 62894 (SAN 654-357X) Tel 618-279-3475.

C Bergbower, *(Bergbower, Cornelius; 0-9616653)*, Louie Ave., Bluford, IL 62814 (SAN 659-8250) Tel 618-732-6195.

C Berke, *(Berke, Carl)*, 20 Simmons Dr., Milford, MA 01757 (SAN 216-2105) Tel 617-473-8034.

C Bernard Gallery Ltd, *(Bernard, Claude, Gallery, Ltd.; 0-936827)*, 33 E. 74th St., New York, NY 10021 (SAN 699-9042) Tel 212-988-2050.

C Bissell, *(Bissell, Charles B., III; 0-9612604)*, 1911 Flintwood Dr., Richmond, VA 23233 (SAN 289-0631) Tel 804-741-6008.

C Bks, *(C Bks.; 0-941786),* Div. of Cartographic Enterprises, P.O. Box 548, Del Mar, CA 92014 (SAN 239-4154) Tel 619-755-2505; Dist. by: Publishers Group West, 5855 Beaudry St., Emeryville, CA 94608 (SAN 202-8522) Tel 415-658-3453.

C Boast & C Nyberg, *(Boast, Carol, & Cheryl Rae Nyberg; 0-9616293),* 716 W. Indiana Ave., Urbana, IL 61808 (SAN 658-4683) Tel 217-367-4583.

C Boyer, *(Boyer, Carl; 0-936124),* P.O. Box 333, Newhall, CA 91322-0333 (SAN 215-7349) Tel 805-259-3154.

C C Brown Pub, *(Brown, C. C., Publishing Co.; 0-9600378),* Box 462, Airway Heights, WA 99001 (SAN 203-6789) Tel 509-244-5807.

C C Fisher, *(Fisher, Clay C.),* 702 Tenth St., NE, Massillon, OH 44646 (SAN 202-4977).

C C Geer, *(Geer, Corinne C.; 0-9601508),* 2222 Wallington Dr., Albany, GA 31707 (SAN 211-3937).

C C M I, *(Center for Communications Management, The (CCMI)),* 76 Arch St., Ramsey, NJ 07446 (SAN 239-5185) Tel 201-825-3311.

C C Pierce, *(Pierce, Clayton C.; 0-9601564),* 325 Carol Dr., Ventura, CA 93003 (SAN 210-9336) Tel 805-653-5979.

C C Pubns, *(C.C. Pubns., Inc.; 0-88120),* P.O. Box 23699, Tigard, OR 97223 (SAN 241-0990) Tel 503-692-6880; Toll free: 800-547-4800. Do not confuse with C C Pubs, Clearwater FL.

C C Pubs, *(CC Pubs.; 0-9603766),* P.O. Box 4044, Clearwater, FL 33518 (SAN 223-5471) Tel 813-797-3321. Do not confuse with CC Pubns., Tigard OR

†C C Thomas, *(Thomas, Charles C., Pub.; 0-398),* 2600 S. First St., Springfield, IL 62794-9265 (SAN 201-9485) Tel 217-789-8980; *CIP.*

C C W Y P, *(Central Coast Women's Yellow Pages; 0-934335),* 301 S. Miller, Suite 214, Santa Maria, CA 93454 (SAN 693-6067) Tel 805-928-8563; Dist. by: Tri-County News, 1376 W. Main St., Santa Maria, CA 93454 (SAN 169-0345) Tel 805-925-6541.

C C Y P W
See C C W Y P

C C York, *(York, C. C.),* 9000 E. Jefferson Ave., Apt. 1511, Detroit, MI 48214 (SAN 264-5165) Tel 313-824-9506.

C Carr, *(Carr, Claudia),* Box 205, Ketchum, ID 83340 (SAN 696-9178).

C Coleman, *(Coleman, Candy, Enterprises; 0-943768),* 1309 Main St.,Suite 103, Dallas, TX 75202 (SAN 238-2628) Tel 214-747-0429.

C D Gibson
See Ensign Pr

C de Bussy, *(De Bussy, Carvel; 0-9602260),* 3901 Connecticut Ave., NW, Suite 208, Washington, DC 20008 (SAN 212-6516).

C Del Grullo, *(Cayo Del Grullo Press; 0-9611604),* c/o History Dept., Texas A & I Univ., Kingsville, TX 78363 (SAN 284-9313) Tel 512-595-3603.

C Drumm Bks, *(Drumm, Chris, Bks.; 0-936055),* P.O. Box 445, Polk City, IA 50226 (SAN 697-0478) Tel 515-984-6749.

C E Barbour
See Pitts Theolog

C E Heilman, *(Heilman, Carl E.; 0-9613161),* P.O. Box 213A, Rte. 8, Brant Lake, NY 12815 (SAN 294-9385) Tel 518-494-3072.

C E Jones
See Honor Pub

C E M Comp, *(C. E. M. Co.; 0-930004),* 3154 Coventry Dr., Bay City, MI 48706 (SAN 209-5378) Tel 517-686-4208.

C E NY NJ, *(Coalition for Equity of New York & New Jersey; 0-9617090),* 32 Washington Pl., Rm. 72, New York, NY 10003 (SAN 662-5851) Tel 212-598-2705.

C E Pub, *(CE Publishing; 0-912227),* P.O. Box 488, Plantsville, CT 06479 (SAN 265-0983) Tel 203-621-6811.

C E R I Pr, *(C. E. R. I. Press; 0-941822),* Subs. of Communication & Education Resources, Inc., 5513 Forrestal Ave., Alexandria, VA 22311 (SAN 239-1678) Tel 703-820-7459.

C E Stuart, *(Stuart, C. E., Gnathological Instruments; 0-9613441),* P.O. Box 1298, Ventura, CA 93001 (SAN 657-0771) Tel 805-647-1478.

C E Tuttle, *(Tuttle, Charles E., Co., Inc.; 0-8048),* P.O. Box 410, 28 S. Main St., Rutland, VT 05701-0410 (SAN 213-2621) Tel 802-773-8930.

C Elder, *(Elder, Charles & Randy, Pubs.; 0-918450),* 2115 Elliston Place, Nashville, TN 37203 (SAN 201-8292) Tel 615-327-1867.

C F Rehnborg, *(Rehnborg, C. F., Literary Foundation, The; 0-9606564),* 5600 Beach Blvd., Buena Park, CA 90622-5940 (SAN 218-5857); 7412 E. Bonita Dr., Scottsdale, AZ 85253 (SAN 693-9759).

C F S Pub Corp, *(CFS Publishing Corp.; 0-913095),* 122 E. 25th St., 4th Fl., New York, NY 10010 (SAN 282-9894); Dist. by: Kampmann & Co., 9 E. 40th St., New York, NY 10016 (SAN 202-5191) Tel 212-685-2928.

C F Sexauer, *(Sexauer, Charles F., Publishing Co.; 0-9607148),* 13909 Old Harbor Ln., No. 102, Marina del Rey, CA 90291 (SAN 239-0337) Tel 213-821-2164.

C Faber Audiotapes *Imprint of* Perseus Pr
C-Four Res, *(C-4 Resources; 0-914527),* 115 Neil St., Champaign, IL 61820 (SAN 289-1565) Tel 217-395-6242.

C Franklin Pr
See Franklin Pr WA

C G Jung Foun, *(Jung, C. G., Foundation Publications; 0-913430),* 28 E. 39th St., New York, NY 10016 (SAN 207-0391) Tel 212-697-6430.

C G Jung Frisco, *(Jung, C.G., Institute of San Francisco; 0-932630),* 2040 Gough St., San Francisco, CA 94109 (SAN 281-8493); Dist. by: Spring Pubs., P.O. Box 222069, Dallas, TX 75222 (SAN 282-6127).

C G Jung Inst, *(Jung, C.G., Institute of Los Angeles, Inc.; 0-918608),* 10349 W. Pico Blvd., Los Angeles, CA 90064 (SAN 220-6927).

C G Smith, *(Smith, Cortland Gray),* 248 Circle Dr., Plandome, NY 11030 (SAN 209-1771) Tel 516-627-5856.

C Gebhardt, *(Gebhardt, Chuck; 0-9601410),* P.O. Box 6821, San Jose, CA 95150 (SAN 211-1934).

C Gersna, *(Gersna, Charles; 0-9615747),* 130 Sixth Ave., New Eagle, PA 15067 (SAN 696-4362) Tel 412-258-9731.

C H Fairfax, *(Fairfax, C. H., Co., Inc.; 0-935132),* P.O. Box 502, Columbia, MD 21045 (SAN 221-170X).

C H Hall, *(Hall, Clarence H.; 0-9604084),* 3409 Altwater Rd., Avon Park, FL 33825 (SAN 214-3119).

C H Kerr, *(Kerr, Charles H., Publishing, Co.; 0-88286),* 1740 W. Greenleaf Ave., Chicago, IL 60626 (SAN 207-7043) Tel 312-465-7774.

C H McKee, *(McKee, Christian H.; 0-9611046),* 210 Main St., Rm. No. One, Landisville, PA 17538 (SAN 282-9290) Tel 717-898-7109.

C H Museum
See Cooper-Hewitt Museum

C H Neuffer, *(Neuffer, Claude Henry),* 4532 Meadowood Rd., Columbia, SC 29206 (SAN 207-2076) Tel 803-787-3823.

C Hallberg, *(Hallberg Publishing Corp.; 0-87319),* P.O. Box 547, Delavan, WI 53115 (SAN 205-3063) Tel 414-728-3173.

C Hinckley, *(Hinckley, Clive; 0-9602984),* 106 E. Sunset Dr., S., Redlands, CA 92373 (SAN 207-480X).

C Hsin Pr, *(Hsin, Cheng, Pr.; 0-9615378),* 6601 Telegraph Ave., Oakland, CA 94609 (SAN 695-5355) Tel 415-658-0802; Dist. by: Bookpeople, 2929 Fifth St., Berkeley, CA 94710 (SAN 168-9517) Tel 415-549-3030.

C Hughes, *(Hughes, Clarence),* P.O. Box 451, Annawan, IL 61234 (SAN 208-1229) Tel 309-935-6715.

C Hungness, *(Hungness, Carl, Publishing; 0-915088),* P.O. Box 24308, Speedway, Indianapolis, IN 46224 (SAN 207-1193) Tel 317-638-1466; Orders to: Wilma A. Steffy, P.O. Box 24308, Speedway, IN 46224 (SAN 662-0426).

C I B A Pharm
See CIBA Med

C I L Inc, *(C.I.L., Inc., Bks.; 0-9613326),* P.O. Box 27-3855, Boca Raton, FL 33427 (SAN 655-6205) Tel 305-392-3936.

C I M Systems, *(CIM Systems, Inc.),* 9451 LBJ Freeway, Dallas, TX 75243 (SAN 669-3598) Tel 214-437-5171.

C I S, *(CIS, Inc.; 0-914891),* P.O. Box 7741, Philadelphia, PA 19101 (SAN 289-0852).

C J Adams, *(Adams, Charles J. III; 0-9610008),* 14 E. 34th St., Reading, PA 19606 (SAN 266-0865) Tel 215-779-8173.

C J Bks, *(C J Books; 0-942878),* P.O. Box 922, Gig Harbor, WA 98335 (SAN 263-9548) Tel 206-851-3778; Dist. by: Pacific Pipline, Inc., 19215 66th Ave., S., Kent, WA 98032 (SAN 208-2128) Tel 206-872-5523.

C J Brown, *(Brown, Cathy J.; 0-9614796),* Dist. by: Creative Expressions, P.O. Box 456, Colchester, VT 05446 (SAN 200-5816).

†C J Frompovich, *(Frompovich, C. J., Pubns.; 0-935322),* R.D. 1, Chestnut Rd., Coopersburg, PA 18036 (SAN 213-3121) Tel 215-346-8461; *CIP.*

C J Hogrefe
See Hogrefe Intl

C J Wheeler, *(Wheeler, Carol Jean; 0-9608448),* 420 Carolwood Ln., NE, Atlanta, GA 30342 (SAN 240-5733) Tel 404-252-9157; Dist. by: Dot Gibson's Publications, P.O. Box 117, Waycross, GA 31502 (SAN 241-3760) Tel 912-285-2848; Dist. by: Southwest Cookbook Distributors, 1901 S. Shore Dr., Bonham, TX 75418 (SAN 200-4925) Tel 214-583-8898; Dist. by: Quik Cook Inc., 439 Central Ave., Rochester, NY 14605 (SAN 200-5115) Tel 716-546-7663; Dist. by: Collection, The, 2101 Kansas City Rd., Olathe, KS 66061 (SAN 689-8467) Tel 913-764-1811.

C Jordan, *(Jordan, Carol; 0-9605360),* 654 Jerome St., Davis, CA 95616 (SAN 216-0463).

C Kimball, *(Kimball, Charles, (0-9613507),* 151 Capt. Lijah Rd., Centerville, MA 02632 (SAN 657-2634) Tel 617-775-1410.

C King, *(King, C. D., Ltd.; 0-9608862),* 311 12th St., Huntington Beach, CA 92648 (SAN 241-0397) Tel 714-960-5285.

C Kinsinger, *(Kinsinger, Chris; 0-9615612),* 2205 N. Second St., Harrisburg, PA 17110 (SAN 696-2793) Tel 717-238-2218.

C Kroll, *(Kroll, Cecelia; 0-9614913),* P.O. Box 71764, Los Angeles, CA 90071-0764 (SAN 693-4544) Tel 213-481-8086.

C L Bishop, *(Bishop, Charles Lawrence; 0-9616120),* 13014 Open Hearth Way, Germantown, MD 20874 (SAN 699-7422) Tel 301-496-6411.

C L Bland, *(Bland, Charles; 0-9610804),* 154 Delamere Rd., Williamsville, NY 14221 (SAN 265-0886) Tel 716-631-3193.

C L C Press, *(CLC Pr.; 0-930779),* P.O. Box 478, San Andreas, CA 95249 (SAN 677-8437) Tel 209-369-2781.

C L Cook, *(Cook, Chester L.; 0-9604670),* P.O. Box 1511, Slidell, LA 70458 (SAN 220-1194) Tel 504-643-3254.

C L Hall Pub
See Hall Pub AL

C L Mast, *(Mast, C. L., Jr. & Associates),* 2041 Vardon Lane, Flossmoor, IL 60422 (SAN 205-8804) Tel 312-798-1817.

C L Pelton
See Fam Health Media

C L Simmons, *(Simmons, Carol Lynn; 0-9615885),* 220 Hedgewood Terr., Greer, SC 29651 (SAN 696-7485) Tel 803-244-4511.

C L Vidano Pub, *(Vidano, Carl L., Publishing Co.; 0-9616606),* P.O. Box 5446, Huntington Beach, CA 92615 (SAN 659-8102); 9601 Gleneagles Cr., Westminster, CA 92683 (SAN 659-8110) Tel 714-895-4563.

C Latin Schls, *(Charlotte Latin Schls., Inc.; 0-9615616),* P.O. Box 6143, Charlotte, NC 28207 (SAN 696-2742) Tel 704-366-7260; 9900 Providence Rd., Matthews, NC 28105 (SAN 696-5261).

C Logan, *(Logan, Carolyn; 0-9602804),* Peck Slip P.O. Box 607, New York, NY 10272 (SAN 699-8186).

C M Hall, *(Hall, C. Mitchel; 0-914574),* 3401 Bangor St., SE, Washington, DC 20020 (SAN 206-5339) Tel 202-583-3297.

C M Kent, *(Kent, Carol Miller; 0-9604886),* 929 E. 50th, Austin, TX 78751 (SAN 212-5188).

C M Ltd, *(Cox-Miller Ltd.; 0-9617244),* P.O. Box 5741, Phoenix, AZ 85010 (SAN 663-5482); 2317 W. Dahlia Dr., Phoenix, AZ 85029 (SAN 663-5490) Tel 602-997-9118.

C M Otstot, *(Otstot, Charles M.; 0-9603808),* 5124 N. 33rd St., Arlington, VA 22207 (SAN 206-9539) Tel 703-538-5446.

C M Province, *(Province, C. M.; 0-932348),* 11307 Vela Dr., San Diego, CA 92126 (SAN 211-4445) Tel 619-271-6517.

C M Pub, *(C M Publishing; 0-9607514),* 330 Eubank, El Paso, TX 79902 (SAN 237-9856) Tel 915-584-3008.

C M Pursifull, *(Pursifull, Carmen M.; 0-9607856),* 809 W. Maple, Champaign, IL 61820 (SAN 237-9880) Tel 217-359-5056.

C Mackey, *(Mackey, Cleo, Publishing; 0-9608176),* 6435 Seco Blvd., Dallas, TX 75217 (SAN 240-2467) Tel 214-391-5597.

C Marshall
See Conmar Pub

C Mendoza, *(Mendoza, Carlos R.; 0-9608420),* 613 Point Caiman Ct., Chula Vista, CA 92011 (SAN 240-7205) Tel 619-421-8848.

C N Aronson, *(Aronson, Charles N., Writer-Publisher; 0-915736),* 11520 Bixby Hill Rd., Arcade, NY 14009 (SAN 207-6144) Tel 716-496-6002.

C N Potter Bks *Imprint of* Crown

C O M A P Inc, *(COMAP , Inc.; 0-912843),* 60 Lowell St., Arlington, MA 02174 (SAN 282-9991) Tel 617-641-2600.

C O'Donnell Pub, *(O'Donnell, Chuck Publishing; 0-9613166),* 216 N. Chester, Park Ridge, IL 60068 (SAN 294-9873) Tel 312-698-4560.

C P Ela, *(Ela, Chipman P.; 0-9607464),* 1841 Massachusetts Ave., Lexington, MA 02173 (SAN 238-616X) Tel 617-861-8332; Dist. by: Arlington Bk. Co., P.O. Box 327, Arlington, VA 22210-0327 (SAN 200-786X) Tel 202-296-6750.

C P Mills, *(Mills, Charles P.),* 952 Old Huntingdon Pike, Huntingdon Valley, PA 19006 (SAN 201-8640).

C P P, *(College of Physicians of Philadelphia, The; 0-943060),* 19 S. 22nd St., Philadelphia, PA 19103 (SAN 240-4591) Tel 215-561-6050.

C P Peterson, *(Peterson, Carrol P.),* P.O. Box 244, Lewiston, MN 55952 (SAN 678-920X).

C P Pr, *(C. P. Press; 0-9600452),* 31 Woodmont Rd., Upper Montclair, NJ 07043 (SAN 202-4985).

C P Pubns TN, *(C & P Pubns.; 0-9617092),* P.O. Box 381813, Germantown, TN 38183-1813 (SAN 662-5266); 1485 Stonegate Pass, Germantown, TN 38183-1813 (SAN 662-5274) Tel 901-756-1641. Do not confuse with C P Pubns., Port Angeles, WA.

C Perry Pub, *(Perry, Charles, Pub.; 0-9615139),* 2790 Flora, Memphis, TN 38114 (SAN 694-2482) Tel 901-528-4571.

C Price, *(Price, Christine; 0-9603654),* c/o Esalen Institute, Big Sur, CA 93920 (SAN 221-7252).

C R Clar, *(Clar, Raymond C.; 0-9613635),* 1681 Parkmead Way, Sacramento, CA 95822 (SAN 678-9110); Dist. by: River Mist Distributors, 624 University Ave., Palo Alto, CA 94301 (SAN 200-7827).

C R King
See Grayking Pub

C R LaDow, *(LaDow, Charles R.; 0-9617232),* 3735 Trudy Ln., San Diego, CA 92106 (SAN 663-5784) Tel 619-222-3790.

C R Leonard & Assocs, *(Leonard, Cliff R., & Assocs.; 0-9603818),* P.O. Box 43003, Jacksonville, FL 32203 (SAN 213-9804).

C R Leonard & D Coleman
See C R Leonard & Assocs

C R Winkler Ltd, *(Winkler, Charles R., Ltd.; 0-9615613),* 7222 W. Cermak Rd., North Riverside, IL 60546 (SAN 696-3145) Tel 312-447-3800.

C Redd Ctr, *(Redd, Charles, Center for Western Studies),* 4069 Harold B. Lee Library, Brigham Young Univ., Provo, UT 84602 (SAN 287-2900) Tel 801-378-4048; Dist. by: Signature Books, 3503 4th East, Suite G4, Salt Lake City, UT 84111 (SAN 217-4391) Tel 801-531-1483.

C Rowland, *(Rowland, C., Pub.; 0-9601426),* Rte. 2, Box 131-J, Berkeley Springs, WV 25411 (SAN 210-9832) Tel 304-258-1835. Out of business.

C S Garner, *(Garner, Clifford S.; 0-9612808),* 444 Saratoga Ave., No. 29H, Santa Clara, CA 95050 (SAN 289-9868) Tel 408-249-4192; Orders to: Enterprises Store, The, 1200 N. Lake Ave., Pasadena, CA 91104 (SAN 662-2216) Tel 818-798-7893.

C Schneider, *(Schneider, Coleman; 0-9601662),* P.O. Box 762, Tenafly, NJ 07670 (SAN 211-4186) Tel 201-567-9157.

C Scientol LA, *(Church of Scientology of California),* 2723 W. Temple St., Los Angeles, CA 90026 (SAN 209-6501) Tel 213-380-0710; Dist. by: Grosset & Dunlap, Inc., 51 Madison Ave., New York, NY 10010 (SAN 205-5457) Tel 212-689-9200.

C Shore Pr, *(Shore, C., Pr.; 0-9612136),* P.O. Box 14008, Bradenton, FL 34280 (SAN 286-8733) Tel 813-792-4535.

C T Collopy, *(Collopy, C. T.; 0-9617234),* 1200 E. Elizabeth St., Ft. Collins, CO 80524 (SAN 663-477X) Tel 303-493-0112.

C T Olivo, *(Olivo, C. Thomas, Assocs.; 0-938561),* 169 Rosemont St., Albany, NY 12206 (SAN 661-4744) Tel 518-459-4653; Dist. by: Delmar Pubs., Inc., 2 Computer Dr., W, Albany, NY 12212 (SAN 206-7544) Tel 518-459-1150.

C Tuszynski, *(Tuszynski, Carole; 0-9617170),* 6 Bronze Ct., Huntington, NY 11743 (SAN 662-9512) Tel 516-427-2454.

C Two F Inc, *(C2F, Inc.; 0-9616328),* 6600 SW 111th Ct., Beaverton, OR 97005 (SAN 659-0624) Tel 503-643-9050; P.O. Box 1417, Beaverton, OR 97075 (SAN 659-0632).

C V Barnes, *(Barnes, C. Virginia),* 2 Fifth Ave.-16M, New York, NY 10011 (SAN 218-6438).

C W Cleworth, *(Cleworth, Charles W., Pub.; 0-934212),* 1736 Downing St., Denver, CO 80218 (SAN 212-7326) Tel 303-832-5000.

C White, *(White, Carter; 0-9613384),* Box 708, Hale Center, TX 79041 (SAN 657-078X) Tel 806-839-2666.

C Woodward, *(Woodward, Claire; 0-9606812),* 10806 Fairway Ct. W., Sun City, AZ 85351 (SAN 217-4618) Tel 602-974-6919.

CA Agri Lnd Pr, *(California Agricultural Lands Project; 0-912005),* Subs. of Round Valley, 227 Clayton St., San Francisco, CA 94117 (SAN 264-6056) Tel 415-751-3144.

CA Assn Older, *(California Association for Older Americans; 0-917154),* Tel 415-386-3500; Orders to: Volcano Press, 330 Ellis St., San Francisco, CA 94102 (SAN 268-5795) Tel 415-664-5600.

CA Clock, *(California Clock Co.; 0-939513),* 26131 Avenida Aeropuerto, San Juan Capistrano, CA 92675 (SAN 663-3544) Tel 714-493-4552.

CA Dreamers, *(California Dreamers, Inc.; 0-939471),* 3505 N. Kimball, Chicago, IL 60618 (SAN 663-2696) Tel 312-478-0660.

CA Ed Plan, *(California Education Plan; 0-936047),* 942 Acacia Ave., Los Altos, CA 94022 (SAN 697-0265) Tel 415-948-6412.

CA Farmer Pub, *(California Farmer Publishing Co.; 0-936815),* 731 Market St., San Francisco, CA 94103-2011 (SAN 699-8720) Tel 415-495-3340.

CA Finan Pubns *Imprint of* Calif Health

CA Folklore Soc, *(California Folklore Society, The; 0-914563),* P.O. Box 4552, Glendale, CA 91202 (SAN 289-1603) Tel 818-244-3229.

CA Guitar Archv, *(California Guitar Archives; 0-939297),* P.O. Box 7000-166, Palos Verdes Peninsula, CA 90274 (SAN 662-7943); 25126 Walnut St., Lomita, CA 90717 (SAN 662-7951) Tel 213-539-0738.

CA Inst Arts, *(California Institute of the Arts),* Placement Office, 24700 McBean Pkwy., Valencia, CA 91355 (SAN 658-8263) Tel 805-253-7871.

CA Intl Arts, *(California/International Arts Foundation; 0-917571),* 2737 Outpost Dr., Los Angeles, CA 90068 (SAN 657-128X) Tel 213-874-4107.

CA Landmark, *(California Landmark Pubns.; 0-9613382),* 1450 Koll Circle, No. 110, San Jose, CA 95112 (SAN 657-0798) Tel 408-293-7291.

CA Lib Media, *(California Library Media Consortium for Classroom Evaluation of Microcomputer Courseware),* 333 Main St., Redwood City, CA 94063 (SAN 674-8937) Tel 415-363-5471.

CA Med Pubns, *(California Medical Pubns.; 0-9615638),* 715 E. Chapman Ave., Orange, CA 92666 (SAN 695-8788) Tel 714-639-3519.

CA Rocketry, *(California Rocketry; 0-912468),* P.O. Box 1242, Claremont, CA 91711 (SAN 204-692X) Tel 714-620-1733.

CA St U LB Art, *(University Art Museum, California State University, Long Beach; 0-936270),* 1250 Bellflower Blvd., Long Beach, CA 90840 (SAN 223-3827) Tel 213-498-5761.

CA St U Religious, *(California State Univ. Fullerton, Dept. of Religious Studies; 0-9615339),* 800 N. State College Blvd., Fullerton, CA 92634 (SAN 695-1155) Tel 714-773-3722.

CA Supreme Ct, *(California Supreme Court; 0-936629),* Div. of the State of California, 350 McAllister St., Suite 3000, San Francisco, CA 94102 (SAN 699-7252) Tel 415-557-0205; Orders to: P.O. Box 1015, N. Highlands, CA 95660 (SAN 662-4049).

CA Thea-Westcoast, *(California Theatre Council/Westcoast Plays; 0-934782),* 849 S. Broadway, Suite 621, Los Angeles, CA 90014 (SAN 263-9629) Tel 213-622-6727.

Caann Verlag, *(Caann Verlag Gmbtt),* Dist. by: Associated Booksellers, 147 McKinley Ave., Bridgeport, CT 06606 (SAN 206-9717).

CAB *Imprint of* Unipub

Cabala Pr, *(Cabala Press; 0-941542),* 2421 W. Pratt Ave., Chicago, IL 60645 (SAN 239-071X) Tel 312-761-0682.

Caballero Pr, *(Caballero Press; 0-9601346),* 1936 Caballero Way, Las Vegas, NV 89109 (SAN 210-6825) Tel 702-735-3406.

Caballus Pubs
See Printed Horse

Cabashon Pub, *(Cabashon Publishing; 0-937825),* 11770 Bernardo Plaza Ct., San Diego, CA 92128 (SAN 659-428X) Tel 619-451-0377.

Cabat Studio Pubns, *(Cabat Studio Pubns.; 0-913521),* 627 N. Fourth Ave., Tucson, AZ 85705 (SAN 285-1539) Tel 602-62-6362.

Cabell Cty Med Soc, *(Cabell County Medical Society; 0-9616839),* 1340 Hal Green Blvd., Huntington, WV 25701 (SAN 661-2792) Tel 304-522-3450.

Cabell Pub, *(Cabell Publishing, Co.; 0-911753),* Box 7173, Tobe Hahn Station, Beaumont, TX 77706 (SAN 263-9564) Tel 409-898-0575.

Cabin Pub MN, *(Cabin Publishing MN; 0-933363),* P.O. Box 73, Long Lake, MN 55356 (SAN 691-6678) Tel 612-472-6434.

Cable TV Info Ctr, *(Cable Television Information Ctr., The; 0-943336),* 1500 N. Beauregard St., Suite 205, Alexandria, VA 22311 (SAN 240-6071) Tel 703-845-1700.

Caboose Pr, *(Caboose Pr.; 0-9608064),* 499 Embarcadero, Oakland, CA 94606 (SAN 240-1983) Tel 415-465-6323.

Cachalot Bks, *(Cachalot Books; 0-913023),* 4959 Hollywood Blvd., Suite 409, Hollywood, CA 90027 (SAN 283-0000) Tel 213-466-9724.

Cache Pr, *(Cache Pr.),* 801 Juniper Ave., Boulder, CO 80302 (SAN 212-0763).

Cache Valley, *(Cache Valley Newsletter Publishing Co.; 0-941462),* 1219 West Oneida, Preston, ID 83263 (SAN 239-0728) Tel 208-852-3167.

Cactus Max, *(Cactus Max Pr.; 0-932925),* Div. of Cactus Max, Inc., P.O. Box 12477, El Paso, TX 79913 (SAN 688-9263) Tel 915-584-7649.

Cad Cam, *(CAD-CAM Decisions; 0-938800),* P.O. Box 76042, Atlanta, GA 30328 (SAN 240-012X) Tel 404-255-5271.

Cad-Cam Pub, *(Cad/Cam Publishing, Inc.; 0-934869),* 841 Turquoise St., Suites D & E, San Diego, CA 92109 (SAN 694-5643) Tel 619-488-0533.

CAD Ventures Unltd, *(Computer Aided Design Ventures Unlimited; 0-937687),* P.O. Box 1816, Glendora, CA 91740 (SAN 659-3259) Tel 818-445-1359; 1344 S. Bruning Ave., Glendora, CA 91740 (SAN 659-3267).

Caddylack Pub
See Asher-Gallant

Cadillac
See A Fried Assocs

Cadmus Eds, *(Cadmus Editions; 0-932274),* P.O. Box 687, Tiburon, CA 94920 (SAN 212-887X) Tel 707-894-3048; Dist. by: The Subterranean Co., 1327 W. Second, P.O. Box 10233, Eugene, OR 97440 (SAN 169-7102) Tel 503-343-6324.

Cadmus Press, *(Cadmus Pr.; 0-930685),* 25 Waterview Dr., Port Jefferson, NY 11777 (SAN 677-1300) Tel 516-928-9896.

†Caedmon, *(Caedmon; 0-9601156; 0-89845),* Div. of Raytheon Co., 1995 Broadway, New York, NY 10023 (SAN 206-278X) Tel 212-580-3400; Toll free: 800-223-0420; *CIP.*

CAFH Found Inc, *(CAFH Foundation, Inc.; 0-9609102),* P.O. Box 4665, Berkeley, CA 94704 (SAN 281-3696) Tel 415-620-0222; 1510 White Hill Rd., Yorktown, NY 10598 (SAN 662-3530); Dist. by: Bookpeople, 2929 Fifth St., Berkeley, CA 94710 (SAN 168-9517) Tel 415-549-3030.

Cagg, *(Cagg, Richard D.; 0-9605636),* 423 W. Fourth, Cameron, MO 64429 (SAN 215-6296) Tel 816-632-2973.

Cahill Pub Co, *(Cahill Publishing Co.; 0-9610810),* P.O. Box 91053, Houston, TX 77088 (SAN 263-9572) Tel 713-447-4550.

Cain Lockhart, *(Cain-Lockhart Pr.; 0-937133),* P.O. Box 1129, Issaquah, WA 98027-1129 (SAN 658-4977); 19510 SE 51st St., Issaquah, WA 98027-1129 (SAN 658-4985) Tel 206-392-0508.

CAIS U of Miami
See AISI

Caislan Pr, *(Caislan Pr.; 0-937444),* Box 28371, San Jose, CA 95159 (SAN 295-3048) Tel 408-723-8514; Dist. by: Baker & Taylor, Eastern Div., 50 Kirby Ave., Somerville, NJ 08876 (SAN 169-4901); Dist. by: Baker & Taylor, Midwest Div., 501 Gladiola Ave., Momence, IL 60954 (SAN 169-2100); Dist. by: Blackwell N. America, 1001 Fries Mill Rd., Blackwood, NJ 08012 (SAN 169-4596) Tel 609-629-0700; Dist. by: Bk. Hse., Inc., 208 W. Chicago St., Jonesville, MI 49250-0125 (SAN 295-3099) Tel 517-849-2117.

Caissa Edit, *(Caissa Editions; 0-939433),* Div. of Dale Brandeth Bks., P.O. Box 151, Yorklyn, DE 19736 (SAN 659-1965); Box 461, White Briar Rd., Hockessin, DE 19707 (SAN 663-317X) Tel 302-239-4608.

Cajun Bayou, *(Cajun Bayou Distributors & Management, Inc.; 0-9613196),* 7110 Airline Hwy., Baton Rouge, LA 70805 (SAN 294-9105) Tel 504-356-5482.

Cajun Pubs, *(Cajun Pubs.; 0-933727),* Rte. 4, Box 88, New Iberia, LA 70560 (SAN 692-4948) Tel 318-363-6653; Toll free: 800-551-3076.

CAK Assocs Inc, *(CAK Associates; 0-911245),* P.O. Box 16042, Albuquerque, NM 87191 (SAN 268-5612) Tel 505-293-2293.

Cal Aero Pr, *(California Aero Pr.; 0-914379),* P.O. Box 1365, Carlsbad, CA 92008 (SAN 289-5943) Tel 619-729-6002.

Cal College Pr, *(California College Pr.; 0-933195),* 222 W. 24th St., National City, CA 92050 (SAN 692-2643) Tel 619-477-4800; Toll free: 800-221-7374.

Cal Cont Ed Bar, *(California Continuing Education of the Bar; 0-88124),* 2300 Shattuck Ave., Berkeley, CA 94704 (SAN 237-6105) Tel 415-642-3973.

†Cal Creative Pubns, *(California Creative, Pubns.; 0-9613962),* 14252 Culver Dr., Ste. A-159, Irvine, CA 92714 (SAN 682-2894) Tel 714-679-1855; *CIP.*

Cal Farm Bureau, *(California Farm Bureau Federation),* 1601 Exposition Blvd., Sacramento, CA 95815 (SAN 217-2976).

Cal Features, *(California Features Inc.; 0-933781),* P.O. Box 58, Beverly Hills, CA 90213 (SAN 692-6975) Tel 213-939-3200.

Cal Hist Mus
See UCLA Mus Hist

Cal Inst Intl, *(California Institute of International Studies; 0-912098),* 766 Santa Ynez, Stanford, CA 94305 (SAN 206-8532) Tel 415-322-2026.

†Cal Inst Public, *(California Institute of Public Affairs; 0-912102),* Affil. of the Claremont Colleges, P.O. Box 10, Claremont, CA 91711 (SAN 202-2087) Tel 714-624-5212; *CIP.*

Cal Journal, *(California Journal Pr.; 0-930302),* 1714 Capitol Ave., Sacramento, CA 95814 (SAN 210-1122) Tel 916-444-2840.

Cal Lath & Plaster, *(California Lathing & Plastering Contractors Assn.),* 25332 Narbonne Ave., Suite 170, Lomita, CA 90717 (SAN 224-0912) Tel 213-539-6080.

Cal Lawyers Pr, *(California Lawyer's Press, Inc.),* P.O. Box 2435, Los Angeles, CA 90051 (SAN 219-7715); Orders to: Living Books, Inc., 12155 Magnolia Ave., Bldg. 11B, Riverside, CA 92503 (SAN 219-7723).

Cal-Pendleton
See Sampson Bowers

Cal Poet, *(California Poetry Pubns.; 0-916183),* P.O. Box 12323, Santa Ava, CA 92701 (SAN 294-9113) Tel 714-646-6592.

Cal State Leg, *(California State Legislature, Joint Committee on Rules; 0-9611168),* State Capitol, Rm. 124, Sacramento, CA 95814 (SAN 289-0313) Tel 916-324-2089.

Cal State Pr, *(Press at California State Univ., Fresno, The; 0-912201),* Shaw & Maple, Fresno, CA 93740 (SAN 264-6307) Tel 209-294-3056.

Cal-Syl Pr, *(Cal-Syl Press; 0-930638),* 3960 E. 14th St., Oakland, CA 94601 (SAN 211-8424) Tel 415-534-5032.

Cal Theatre
See CA Thea-Westcoast

Calabasas Pub, *(Calabasas Publishing, Co.; 0-930025),* P.O. Box 9002, Calabasas, CA 91302-9002 (SAN 669-7429) Tel 818-888-1079.

Calaciura Pr, *(Calaciura Pr.; 0-9614464),* P.O. Box 25544, Cleveland, OH 44125 (SAN 688-6507); 12500 Oakview Blvd., Cleveland, OH 44125 (SAN 662-7714) Tel 216-921-8074; Dist. by: Quality Bks., Inc., 918 Sherwood Dr., Lake Bluff, IL 60044-2204 (SAN 169-2127) Tel 312-295-2010; Dist. by: Targeted Communications, 3644 Rolliston Rd., Cleveland, OH 44120-5137 (SAN 689-4674) Tel 216-921-8074.

Calaciura Pubns
See Calaciura Pr

Calaloux Pubns, *(Calaloux Pubns.; 0-911565),* P.O. Box 6803, Ithaca, NY 14850 (SAN 263-9599); 470 Broome St., New York, NY 10013 (SAN 263-9602) Tel 212-799-7749.

Calamus Bks, *(Calamus Bks.; 0-930762),* Box 689, Cooper Sta., New York, NY 10276 (SAN 211-7002).

Calan Enter
See McLennan Hse

Calapooia Pubns, *(Calapooia Pubns.; 0-934784),* 27006 Gap Rd., Brownsville, OR 97327 (SAN 223-7040) Tel 503-466-5208.

Calapooya Bks, *(Calapooya Bks.; 0-935004),* 136 High St., Eugene, OR 97401 (SAN 213-6147) Tel 503-344-4301.

Calcon Pr, *(Calcon Press; 0-9600740),* P.O. Box 536, Bruce, MS 38915 (SAN 201-8683).

Caldwell Pubns, *(Caldwell Pubns., Inc.; 0-932777),* P.O. Box 5332, Arlington, VA 22205 (SAN 688-475X) Tel 703-533-1567.

Caledonia Pr, *(Caledonia Pr.; 0-932282),* P.O. Box 245, Racine, WI 53401 (SAN 213-8432) Tel 414-637-6200.

Calem Pub Co, *(Calem Publishing Co.; 0-9616444),* 444 Appleton St., Holyoke, MA 01040 (SAN 659-0705) Tel 413-533-0338.

Caliban, *(Caliban Pr.; 0-936897),* 114 Westview Rd., Montclair, NJ 07043 (SAN 658-490X) Tel 201-744-4453.

†Calibre Pr, *(Calbre Pr., Inc.; 0-935878),* 666 Dundee Rd., Suite 1607, Northbrook, IL 60062 (SAN 213-9146) Tel 312-498-5680; Toll free: 800-323-0037 outside Illinois; *CIP.*

Calico Barn, *(Calico Barn; 0-9616848),* 626 Shadowwood Ln., SE, Warren, OH 44484 (SAN 661-3071) Tel 216-856-7384.

Calico Pr, *(Calico Pr.; 0-912714),* P.O. Box 758, Twentynine Palms, CA 92277 (SAN 202-4993) Tel 619-367-7661.

Calif Acad Sci, *(California Academy of Sciences Pubns.; 0-940228),* Golden Gate Park, San Francisco, CA 94118 (SAN 204-3661) Tel 415-221-5100.

Calif Books, *(California Bks.; 0-934112),* Box 9551, Stanford, CA 94305 (SAN 212-8888).

Calif Cam, *(California Cambrian Pr.; 0-911247),* P.O. Box 2331, Carlsbad, CA 92008 (SAN 268-5817) Tel 619-729-0050.

Calif Child Pubns, *(California Childrens Publication; 0-9610442),* P.O. Box 91102, Long Beach, CA 90809-1102 (SAN 285-6867).

Calif Dept CA, *(California Dept. of Consumer Affairs),* Div. of Consumer Services, 1020 N St., Room 45, Sacramento, CA 95814 (SAN 223-8853) Tel 916-445-7450.

Calif Dept Co, *(California Department of Consumer Affairs Co-op Development Program; 0-910427),* 1020 N St., Rm. 509, Sacramento, CA 95814 (SAN 262-0057) Tel 916-322-7674; Orders to: Co-op Pubns., P.O. Box 310, Sacramento, CA 95802 (SAN 661-9673).

Calif Health, *(California Health Pubs.; 0-930926),* Subs. of California Financial Pubns., Box 220, Carlsbad, CA 92008 (SAN 211-6588). *Imprints:* CA Finan Pubns (California Financial Pubns.).

Calif Hist, *(California Historical Society; 0-910312),* 2090 Jackson St., San Franciso, CA 94109 (SAN 281-3734) Tel 415-567-1848 Tel 415-567-1848.

Calif Irvine, *(California Bks.; 0-939478),* Seven Bridgewood, Irvine, CA 92714 (SAN 216-5910) Tel 714-551-2795.

†Calif Native, *(California Native Plant Society, the; 0-943460),* 909 12th St., Suite 116, Sacramento, CA 95814 (SAN 240-6098) Tel 916-447-2677; *CIP.*

Calif Photo, *(California Photo Service; 0-9615357),* 5760 Hollis St., Emeryville, CA 94608 (SAN 695-3409) Tel 415-658-9200.

Calif Pubns, *(California Pubns.; 0-917306),* P.O. Box 8014, Calabasas, CA 91302 (SAN 208-578X) Tel 213-880-4181.

Calif Span Lang Data Base
See Floricanto Pr

Calif Street, *(California Street; 0-915090),* 723 Dwight Way, Berkeley, CA 94710 (SAN 207-673X) Tel 415-549-2461.

Calif Weekly, *(California Weekly Explorer, Inc.; 0-936778),* Suite 305-4521 Campus Dr. P.O. Box 19553, Irvine, CA 92713 (SAN 217-0914) Tel 714-786-7604; Dist. by: R. C. Law Co., 579 S. State College Blvd., Fullerton, CA 92631 (SAN 200-609X) Tel 714-871-0940.

Califia Prod, *(Califia Productions; 0-938521),* 22982 La Cadena, Suite 15, Laguna Hills, CA 92653 (SAN 661-1230) Tel 714-855-4319.

Call Pub Co, *(Call Publishing Co.; 0-939589),* P.O. Box 52130, Raleigh, NC 27612 (SAN 663-6160); 2532 Boothbay Ct., Raleigh, NC 27612 (SAN 663-6179) Tel 919-847-0311.

†Callaghan, *(Callaghan & Co.; 0-8366),* 3201 Old Glenview Rd., Wilmette, IL 60091 (SAN 206-9393) Tel 312-256-7000; Toll free: 800-323-1336 (Orders); Toll free: 800-323-8067 (Editorial); *CIP.*

Callahan CA, *(Callahan, John D.; 0-9615767),* P.O. Box 1281, LaCanada, CA 91011 (SAN 696-1789) Tel 818-767-5362; 8601 Sunland Blvd., Suite 44, Sun Valley, CA 91352 (SAN 696-1797).

Callahans Guides, *(Callahan's Guides; 0-910967),* 20 Main St., P.O. Box 116, Essex Junction, VT 05452 (SAN 263-2411).

Callaloo Fic Poetry, *(Callaloo Fiction Series/Poetry Series; 0-912759),* Univ. of Virginia, Dept. of English, Charlottesville, VA 22903 (SAN 282-7654) Tel 804-924-7105.

Callaloo Journ
See Callaloo Fic Poetry

Callarman Hse, *(Callarman Hse.; 0-930092),* 2582 Anchor, Port Hueneme, CA 93041 (SAN 210-7066) Tel 805-985-9500.

†Callaway Edns, *(Callaway Editions; 0-935112),* 108 W. 18th St., New York, NY 10011 (SAN 213-2931) Tel 212-929-5212; *CIP.*

Calli Callul, *(Calli Callul; 0-9617223),* c/o D. Beaver, 8135 W. Floyd Ave. 9-201, Lakewood, CO 80227 (SAN 663-3927) Tel 303-987-8545.

Calligrafree, *(Calligrafree-The Calligraphy Co.; 0-942032),* P.O. Box 98, Brookville, OH 45309 (SAN 240-9496); Dist. by: Hunt Manufacturing Co., 1405 Locust St., Philadelphia, PA 19102 (SAN 678-7339) Tel 215-732-7700.

Calligraphy Donna, *(Calligraphy by Donna; 0-9604308),* 565 SE Airpark Dr., Bend, OR 97702 (SAN 216-0250) Tel 503-382-8215.

Calliope Music, *(Calliope Music; 0-9605912),* P.O. Box 1460, Ansonia Sta., New York, NY 10023 (SAN 216-6607).

Calliope Pr, *(Calliope Pr.; 0-939684),* P.O. Box 2273, N. Hollywood, CA 91602 (SAN 216-7212) Tel 818-841-5119.

Calliopes Corner, *(Calliopes Corner, 3 A.M. Pr.; 0-938219),* P.O. Box 110647, Anchorage, AK 99511-0647 (SAN 659-946X); 450 Daily, Anchorage, AK 99511 (SAN 659-9478) Tel 907-349-7170.

Callwyn, *(Callwyn Bks. U. S. A.; 0-9615639),* Div. of Simple Classics, Inc., P.O. Box 4131, Louisville, KY 40204 (SAN 696-2157) Tel 502-451-7996; 933 Baxter Ave., Louisville, KY 40204 (SAN 696-2165).

CalMedia, *(CalMedia; 0-939782),* P.O. Box 156, La Mirada, CA 90637 (SAN 216-8820) Tel 714-522-7575.

Calvary Episcopal, *(Calvary Episcopal Church),* Box 67, Cleveland, MS 38732 (SAN 217-2895).

Calvary Miss Pr, *(Calvary Missionary Pr.; 0-912375),* Div. of Calvary Missionary Fellowship, P.O. Box 13532, Tucson, AZ 85732 (SAN 265-2021) Tel 602-745-3822.

Calvary Pr, *(Calvary Pr.; 0-9604138),* 400 S. Bennett St., Southern Pines, NC 28387 (SAN 223-4505).

Calwood Pubns, *(Calwood Pubns.),* P.O. Box 284, Monsey, NY 10952 (SAN 210-9557) Tel 914-352-7760.

Calyx Bks, *(Calyx Bks.; 0-934971),* Div. of Calyx Inc., P.O. Box B, Corvallis, OR 97339 (SAN 695-1171) Dist. by: Inland Bk. Co., P.O. Box 261, 22 Hemingway Ave., East Haven, CT 06512 (SAN 204-0151) Tel 203-467-4257; Dist. by: Bookpeople, 2929 Fifth St., Berkeley, CA 94710 (SAN 168-9517) Tel 415-549-3030; Dist. by: Small Press Dist., 1814 San Pablo Ave., Berkeley, CA 94702 (SAN 204-5826) Tel 415-549-3336; Dist. by: Pacific Pipeline, 19215 66th Ave., S., Kent, WA 98032 (SAN 208-2128) Tel 206-872-5523.

Cam-Tri Prods, *(Cam-Tri Productions; 0-9606218),* 1895 Tigertail Rd., Eugene, OR 97405 (SAN 217-5045) Tel 503-344-0118.

†**Camaro Pub,** *(Camaro Publishing, Co.; 0-913290),* 90430 World Way Ctr., Los Angeles, CA 90009 (SAN 201-7865) Tel 213-837-7500; *CIP.*

Camas Pr, *(Camas Pr., The; 0-9616066),* P.O. Box 41, Camas Valley, OR 97416 (SAN 697-8541) Tel 503-445-2327; 1061 Main Camas Rd., Camas Valley, OR 97416 (SAN 697-855X).

Cambia WA, *(Cambia; 0-938221),* 4040 148th Ave., SE, Bellevue, WA 98006 (SAN 659-9508) Tel 206-643-1681.

Cambita Bks, *(Cambita Bks.; 0-9610444),* 2214 W. Appletree Rd., Milwaukee, WI 53209 (SAN 263-9637) Tel 414-351-0263; P.O. Box 09330, Milwaukee, WI 53209 (SAN 699-5187).

Cambria Records, *(Cambria Records & Publishing; 0-936930),* 2625 Colt Rd., Rancho Palos Verdes, CA 90274 (SAN 658-6937) Tel 213-427-1494; P.O. Box 374, Lomita, CA 90717 (SAN 658-6945).

Cambrian, *(Cambrian Pubns.; 0-912548),* P.O. Box 191, Little River Sta., Miami, FL 33138 (SAN 202-5019) Tel 305-751-1122.

Cambrian Pr, *(Cambrian Pr.; 0-936669),* 3681 Union Ave., San Jose, CA 95124 (SAN 699-7430) Tel 408-266-3030.

Cambric, *(Cambric Pr.; 0-918342),* 901 Rye Beach Rd., Huron, OH 44839 (SAN 210-0460) Tel 419-433-5560.

Cambridge Arch Pr, *(Cambridge Architectural Pr.; 0-937999),* 300 Franklin St., Cambridge, MA 02139 (SAN 659-9516) Tel 617-491-8386.

Cambridge Bk, *(Cambridge Bk. Co.; 0-8428),* Div. of Simon & Schuster (Gulf & Western), 888 Seventh Ave., New York, NY 10106 (SAN 169-5703) Tel 212-957-5300; Toll free: 800-221-4764.

Cambridge Sci, *(Cambridge Scientific Abstracts; 0-88387),* 5161 River Rd., Bethesda, MD 20816 (SAN 201-2995) Tel 301-951-1400.

Cambridge Strat, *(Cambridge Stratford, Ltd.; 0-935637),* 867 Hopkins Rd., Suite 101, Amherst, NY 14221 (SAN 696-2173) Tel 716-688-4927.

†**Cambridge U Pr,** *(Cambridge Univ. Pr.; 0-521),* 32 E. 57th St., New York, NY 10022 (SAN 200-206X) Tel 212-688-8888; Toll free: 800-431-1580; Orders to: 510 North Ave., New Rochelle, NY 10801 (SAN 281-3769) Tel 914-235-0300; *CIP.*

Camda, *(Camda; 0-9600434),* P.O. Box 2467, Staunton, VA 24401 (SAN 202-5027).

Camden Harbor Pr, *(Camden Harbor Pr.; 0-935853),* 13160 Mindanao Way, Suite 270, Marina del Rey, CA 90292 (SAN 696-2246) Tel 213-305-9783.

Camden Hse, *(Camden Hse., Inc.; 0-938100),* Drawer 2025, Columbia, SC 29202 (SAN 215-9376) Tel 803-788-8689; Dist. by: Camden Hse., Inc., P.O. Box 4836, Hampden Sta., Baltimore, MD 21211 (SAN 661-9681) Tel 301-338-6950.

†**Camelback Inc,** *(Camelback Records, Inc.; 0-917215),* P.O. Box 2245, Scottsdale, AZ 85252-2245 (SAN 656-1535) Tel 602-945-1101; *CIP.*

Camelot *Imprint of Avon*

Camelot Consult, *(Camelot Consultants; 0-938481),* 50 N. 21st St., Las Vegas, NV 89101 (SAN 659-9524) Tel 702-384-5262.

Camelot Pub, *(Camelot Publishing Co.; 0-89218),* P.O. Box 1357, Ormond Beach, FL 32074 (SAN 202-5035) Tel 904-672-5672.

†**Camelot Pub MN,** *(Camelot Publishing; 0-942450),* 1551 Camelot Lane NE, Fridley, MN 55432 (SAN 240-0855); *CIP.*

Cameo Pub GA, *(Cameo Publishing, Co.; 0-9614430),* Subs. of Val J. Webb Numismatics, P.O. Box 723064, Atlanta, GA 30339 (SAN 689-3430) Tel 404-952-8741.

Camerawork
See NFS Pr

Cameron & Co, *(Cameron & Co.; 0-918684),* 543 Howard St., San Francisco, CA 94105 (SAN 210-9700) Tel 415-777-5582.

Cameron Pr, *(Cameron Pr.),* P.O. Box 535, Alexandria, VA 22313 (SAN 679-2014).

Camex, *(Camex Inc.; 0-932565),* 489 Fifth Ave., New York, NY 10017 (SAN 687-4746) Tel 212-682-8400.

Camin, *(Camin; 0-9614123),* 3123 Childers St., Raleigh, NC 27612 (SAN 686-5089) Tel 919-782-4686.

Camino E E & B, *(Camino E. E. & B. Company; 0-940808),* P.O. Box 510, Camino, CA 95709 (SAN 219-841X).

Camm Pub, *(Camm Publishing Co.; 0-9608400),* P.O. Box 640358, Uleta Branch, Miami, FL 33164 (SAN 240-6101) Tel 305-949-7536.

Camp Denali, *(Camp Denali Publishing; 0-9602792),* P.O. Box 67, McKinley Park, AK 99755 (SAN 213-0297).

Camp Guideposts, *(Camping Guideposts; 0-942684),* Whiteface Woods, Cotton, MN 55724 (SAN 239-6246) Tel 218-482-3446.

Campaign World Gvt, *(Campaign for World Government),* 331 Park Ave., Suite 304, Glencoe, IL 60022 (SAN 224-0920) Tel 312-835-3685 Tel 312-835-1377.

Campana Art, *(Campana Art Co. Inc.; 0-939608),* 721 W. Wilks St., Pampa, TX 79065 (SAN 204-3572) Tel 806-665-3618.

Campanile
See SDSU Press

Campanile *Imprint of SDSU Press*

Campbell Inc, *(Campbell, Arthur, Inc.; 0-932775),* P.O. Box 2549, Portland, OR 97208 (SAN 688-4768) Tel 503-635-7894.

Campbells List, *(Campbell's List; 0-933089),* P.O. Box 428, 100 E. Ventris Ave., Maitland, FL 32751 (SAN 237-6288) Tel 305-644-8298; Toll free: 800-624-2232.

Campus, *(Campus Pubs.; 0-87506),* 713 W. Ellsworth Rd., Ann Arbor, MI 48104 (SAN 201-9558) Tel 313-663-4033.

Campus Crusade, *(Campus Crusade for Christ, International; 0-918956),* c/o Heres Life Pub., P.O. Box 1576, San Bernardino, CA 92402 (SAN 212-4254) Tel 714-886-7981.

Campus Scope, *(Campus Scope Pr.; 0-915858),* 2928 Dean Pkwy., Apt. 4D, Minneapolis, MN 55416 (SAN 216-0269).

Can Do Pubns, *(Can Do Pubns.; 0-943024),* P.O. Box 396, Shrewsbury, MA 01545 (SAN 240-3501) Tel 617-842-7322.

Can-to-Pan, *(Can-to-Pan Cookery; 0-9605536),* 143 Benson Ave., Vallejo, CA 94590 (SAN 240-9461) Tel 707-557-0578.

Canal Captains, *(Canal Captains Pr.; 0-9613675),* 103 Dogwood Ln., Berkeley Heights, NJ 07922 (SAN 670-9680) Tel 201-464-9335.

Canal Pr, *(Canal Pr.; 0-9611116),* Box 28, Canal Winchester, OH 43110 (SAN 282-8774) Tel 614-885-9757.

Canaveral, *(Ryter, A. E.),* 315 Montana Ave., No. 203, Santa Monica, CA 90403 (SAN 281-3777) Tel 213-394-0514.

Cancer Bk Hse
See Cancer Control Soc

Cancer Care, *(Cancer Care, Inc.; 0-9606494),* 1180 Sixth Ave., New York, NY 10036 (SAN 225-9087) Tel 212-221-3300.

Cancer Control Soc, *(Cancer Control Society; 0-943080),* 2043 N. Berendo St., Los Angeles, CA 90027 (SAN 216-2296) Tel 213-663-7801.

Cancer Res, *(Cancer Research, Inc.; 0-938547),* Affil. of American Assn. for Cancer Research, Temple Univ., Schl. of Medicine, 3440 N. Broad St., Philadelphia, PA 19140 (SAN 661-3284) Tel 215-221-4720.

C&G Pub, *(C & G Publishing; 0-941030),* 941 Sherwood Ave., Los Altos, CA 94022 (SAN 217-3395) Tel 415-941-4082.

Candle Bks, *(Candle Bks., Inc.; 0-9609644),* 1010 Grey Oak, San Antonio, TX 78213 (SAN 262-0065) Tel 512-342-5880.

C&M Bessie Bks *Imprint of Har-Row*

C&M Pubns, *(C&M Pubns.; 0-938934),* 6110 Hwy. 290 W., Austin, TX 78735 (SAN 216-227X).

Candy Apple Pub, *(Candy Apple Publishing Co.; 0-9616464),* P.O. Box 48421, St. Petersburg, FL 33743-8421 (SAN 659-3178) Tel 813-544-0355; 6575 Bonnie Bay Cir. N., Pinellas Park, FL 33565 (SAN 659-3186).

Cane Curiosa, *(Cane Curiosa),* 4121 Forest Park, St. Louis, MO 63108 (SAN 289-5951).

Cane Patch, *(Cane Patch, The; 0-9615765),* P.O. Box 1382, Myrtle Beach, SC 29578 (SAN 696-2270) Tel 803-448-3461; 1102 N. Oak St., Myrtle Beach, SC 29578 (SAN 696-2289).

Cane River, *(Cane River Pecan Co.; 0-9613404),* P.O. Box 161, New Iberia, LA 70560 (SAN 656-8831) Tel 318-364-2591; Orders to: 101 Taylor St., New Iberia, LA 70560 (SAN 662-233X) Tel 318-365-4136.

Caney Station Bks, *(Caney Station Bk., Inc.; 0-9613634),* Route 1, Box 1, Greenville, KY 42345 (SAN 682-2584) Tel 502-338-4880.

Canfield Pr *Imprint of Har-Row*

Canner, *(Canner, J. S., & Co.; 0-910324),* Div. of Plenum Publishing Corp., 49-65 Lansdowne St., Boston, MA 02215 (SAN 202-5094) Tel 617-437-1923. Microcards; also microfilm of Plenum journals only.

Canning Pubns, *(Canning Pubns., Inc.; 0-938516),* 925 Anza Ave., Vista, CA 92084 (SAN 215-9384) Tel 619-724-5900.

Canning Trade Inc, *(Canning Trade Inc,The; 0-930027),* 2619 Maryland Ave., Baltimore, MD 21218 (SAN 669-7437) Tel 301-467-3338.

Cannon-S & K, *(Cannon/S & K, Inc.; 0-9616991),* 1732 Glade St., Muskegon, MI 49441 (SAN 661-8359) Tel 616-722-6036.

Canoe Press, *(Canoe Pr.; 0-9613768),* 537 S. Elmwood, Oak Park, IL 60304 (SAN 678-9633) Tel 312-989-2626; Orders to: P.O. Box 1443, Oak Park, IL 60304 (SAN 685-4117) Tel 312-386-5279.

Canon Law Soc, *(Canon Law Society of America; 0-943616),* Catholic Univ., Caldwell Hall, Rm. 431, Washington, DC 20064 (SAN 237-6296) Tel 202-269-3491.

Canon Pr, *(Canon Pr.; 0-939651),* P.O. Box 213, Centerville, UT 84014-0213 (SAN 663-5830); 497 E. 400 N., Bountiful, UT 84010 (SAN 663-5849) Tel 801-295-6003.

Canon Pubns, *(Canon Publications; 0-88181),* P.O. Box 698, Talent, OR 97540 (SAN 264-7206) Tel 503-535-1490.

Canon Pubs, *(Canon Pubs., Ltd.; 0-9616591),* 29056 Histead Dr., Evergreen, CO 80439 (SAN 659-4972) Tel 303-674-0472.

Canter & Assoc, *(Canter & Assocs.; 0-9608978; 0-939007),* 1553 Euclid Ave., Santa Monica, CA 90404 (SAN 240-8716); Toll free: 800-262-4347.

Canterbury, (Canterbury Pr.; 0-933753), 2318 Eighth St., Berkeley, CA 94710 (SAN 692-6045) Tel 415-843-1860; Dist. by: Bookpeople, 2929 Fifth St., Berkeley, CA 94710 (SAN 168-9517) Tel 415-549-3030; Dist. by: Inland Bk Co., P.O. Box261, 22 Hemingway Ave., East Haven, CT 06512 (SAN 200-4151) Tel 203-467-4257.

Canterbury Pr, (Canterbury Pr.; 0-933990), 5540 Vista Del Amigo, Anaheim, CA 92807 (SAN 212-890X).

Canticle Pr, (Canticle Pr.; 0-941396), 1986 S. 2600, E., Salt Lake City, UT 84106 (SAN 238-9606) Tel 801-466-4028.

Cantine & Kilpatrick, (Cantine & Kilpatrick, Pubns.; 0-940548), P.O. Box 798, Huntington, NY 11743 (SAN 222-9927) Tel 516-271-8990.

Cantor & Co, (Cantor & Company, Inc.; 0-9608980), Suburban Station Bldg., Philadelphia, PA 19103 (SAN 237-630X).

Cantor Art Found, (Cantor, B.G., Art Foundation; 0-939912), 1 World Trade Ctr., 105th Fl., New York, NY 10048 (SAN 216-7964) Tel 212-938-5136.

Cantor Art Gallery, (College of the Holy Cross, Cantor Art Gallery; 0-9616183), 1 College St., Worcester, MA 01610 (SAN 658-3202) Tel 617-793-3356.

Canyon Pr, (Canyon Pr.; 0-936899), 162 Ruby Ave., San Carlos, CA 94070 (SAN 658-4918) Tel 415-593-5639.

Canyon Pub Co, (Canyon Publishing Co.; 0-942568), 8561 Eatough Ave., Canoga Park, CA 91304 (SAN 240-0685) Tel 818-702-0171.

Canyonlands, (Canyonlands Natural History Assn.; 0-937407), 125 W. 200 S., Moab, UT 84532 (SAN 659-0764) Tel 801-259-8161.

CAO Times, (CAO Times, Inc.), P.O. Box 75, Old Chelsea Sta., New York, NY 10113 (SAN 657-1298).

Cap & Gown, (Cap & Gown Pr., Inc.; 0-88105), Sales Office, P.O Box 58825, Houston, TX 77258 (SAN 240-611X); 4519 Woodrow Ave., Galveston, TX 77550 (SAN 661-969X) Tel 409-763-3410.

Cap K Pubns, (Cap K Pubns.; 0-9616532), 358 S. Bentley Ave., Los Angeles, CA 90049 (SAN 659-4298) Tel 213-472-9206.

Capability's, (Capability's Bks.; 0-931643), P.O. Box 114, Hwy. No. 46, Deer Park, WI 54007 (SAN 286-0759). Tel 715-269-5346.

Capablanca Imprint of Imprint Edns

Capaco, (Capaco; 0-9615837), 7825 Patriot Dr., Annandale, VA 22003 (SAN 697-0338) Tel 703-941-8558.

Cape Ann Antiques, (Cape Ann Antiques; 0-9616832), P.O. Box 3502, Peabody, MA 01960 (SAN 661-2733); 15 Mildred Rd., Danvers, MA 01923 (SAN 661-2741) Tel 617-777-3011.

Cape Ann Hist Assoc, (Cape Ann Historical Assn.; 0-938791), 27 Pleasant St., Gloucester, MA 01930 (SAN 278-3401) Tel 617-283-0455.

Cape Cod Hist Pubns, (Cape Cod Historical Pubns.; 0-9616740), P.O. Box 281, Yarmouth Port, MA 02675 (SAN 659-9532); 425 Main St., Yarmouth Port, MA 02675 (SAN 659-9540) Tel 617-362-4761.

†Cape Cod Mus Nat His, (Cape Cod Museum of Natural History; 0-916275), Brewster, MA 02631 (SAN 295-6942) Tel 617-896-3867; CIP.

†Capistrano Pr, (Capistrano Pr., Ltd.; 0-912433), 12882 Valley View, Suite 15, Garden Grove, CA 92465 (SAN 265-2064) Tel 714-891-7451; CIP.

Capital Bird
 See N Lyons Bks

Capital Futures Assocs, (Capital Futures Assocs., Ltd.; 0-939397), P.O. Box 2618, Chicago, IL 60690 (SAN 663-1320); 1605 W. Chase, Chicago, IL 60626 (SAN 663-1339) Tel 312-274-9254.

Capital Press, (Capital Pr.), Six Kennedy St., Alexandria, VA 22305 (SAN 678-9102).

Capital Pub Co, (Capital Publishing Co.; 0-9615703), P.O. Box 19655, Sacramento, CA 95819 (SAN 696-317X) Tel 916-455-0846; 84 Sandburg Dr., Sacramento, CA 95819 (SAN 696-3188).

Capital Pub Corp Imprint of Unipub

Capital Pub Corp
 See Venture Econ Inc

Capital Tech, (Capital Technology, Inc.; 0-9603460), P.O. Box 2428, Charlotte, NC 28211-8240 (SAN 213-294X).

Capitalist
 See Capitalist Pr OH

Capitalist Pr OH, (Capitalist Pr.; 0-938770), P.O. Box 2753, North Canton, OH 44720 (SAN 696-9194).

Capitol Enquiry, (Capitol Enquiry; 0-917982), P.O. Box 22246, Sacramento, CA 95822 (SAN 211-5077) Tel 916-428-3271.

Capitol Times Pub Co
 See Skyline West Pr

Capitol VA, (Capitol Pubns., Ltd., Education Research Group; 0-937925), 1101 King St., P.O. Box 1453, Alexandria, VA 22313-2053 (SAN 659-4980) Tel 703-683-4100; Toll free: 800-827-7204 (Orders only).

Capitola Bk, (Capitola Bk. Co.; 0-932319), 1475 41st Ave., Capitola, CA 95010 (SAN 687-0449) Tel 408-475-9042.

CAPP Bks, (C.A.P.P. Bks.; 0-9606824), P.O. Box 416, Williamsburg, VA 23187 (SAN 209-1984) Tel 804-253-1393.

†Capra Pr, (Capra Pr.; 0-88496; 0-912264), P.O. Box 2068, Santa Barbara, CA 93120 (SAN 201-9620) Tel 805-966-4590; CIP.

†Capricorn Bks, (Capricorn Bks.), 2 Aztec Ct., Toms River, NJ 08757 (SAN 260-0013) Tel 201-349-0725; CIP.

Capricorn Corp, (Capricorn Corp.; 0-910719), 4961 Rebel Trail NW, Atlanta, GA 30327 (SAN 262-0073) Tel 404-843-8668.

Capricornus Pr, (Capricornus Pr.; 0-9608544), P.O. Box 1023, Boulder, CO 80306 (SAN 240-6128) Tel 303-442-2663.

Caprine Pr, (Caprine Pr.; 0-914381), 1878 E. 15th St., Tulsa, OK 74104 (SAN 289-596X) Tel 918-743-4936.

Caprock Pr, (Caprock Pr.; 0-912570), 4806 17th St., Lubbock, TX 79416 (SAN 201-9639) Tel 806-795-7599.

†Capstan Pubns, (Capstan Pubns.; 0-914565), P.O. Box 306, Basin, WY 82410 (SAN 289-162X) Tel 307-568-2604; CIP. Imprints: Glenndale Bks (Glenndale Books); Timbertrails (Timbertrails).

Capstone Edns, (Capstone Editions; 0-9610662), P.O. Box 13143, Tucson, AZ 85732 (SAN 264-6552) Tel 602-745-6750.

Captain Fiddle Pubns, (Captain Fiddle Pubns.; 0-931877), 4 Elm Ct., Newmarket, NH 03857 (SAN 686-0508) Tel 603-659-2658.

Captains Lady, (Captain's Lady Collections, The; 0-9609534), 65-69 High St., Springfield, MA 01105 (SAN 260-1729) Tel 413-739-6655.

†Carabelle, (Carabelle Bks.; 0-938634), Box 1611, Shepherdstown, WV 25443 (SAN 281-3785) Tel 304-876-2723; CIP.

Carabis, (Carabis, Anne J.; 0-9605802), 25 Nelson Ave., Latham, NY 12110 (SAN 216-5600) Tel 518-783-9807.

†Caratzas, (Caratzas, Aristide D., Pub.; 0-89241), Affil. of C.B.P. Publishing & Distributing CO. Inc., 481 Main St., New Rochelle, NY 10802 (SAN 201-3134) Tel 914-632-8487; P.O. Box 210, New Rochelle, NY 10802 (SAN 658-0238); CIP.

Caratzas Bros
 See Caratzas

Caratzas Pub Co
 See Caratzas

†Caravan Bks, (Caravan Bks.; 0-88206), Subs. of Scholar's Facsimiles & Reprints, P.O. Box 344, Delmar, NY 12054 (SAN 206-7323) Tel 518-439-5978; CIP.

Caravan-Maritime, (Caravan-Maritime Bks.; 0-917368), 87-06 168th Pl., Jamaica, NY 11432 (SAN 201-8705) Tel 718-526-1380. Do not confuse with Caravan Bks.

Caravan Pr, (Caravan Pr.; 0-912159), 343 S. Broadway, Los Angeles, CA 90013 (SAN 264-7222) Tel 213-628-2563.

Caravelle NY, (Caravelle Bks., Inc.; 0-501), 207 E. 37th St., New York, NY 10016 (SAN 658-6236).

Carbarn Press, (Carbarn Press; 0-934406), P.O. Box 255, Tiburon, CA 94920 (SAN 223-7024) Tel 415-435-9073.

CARBEN Survey, (CARBEN Surveying Reprints), 1403 Woodmont Dr., Johnson City, TN 37601 (SAN 209-5327).

CARC, (Creative Arts Rehabilitation Ctr.; 0-9606876), 251 W. 51st St., New York, NY 10019 (SAN 217-3484) Tel 212-246-3113.

Carcanet, (Carcanet Pr.; 0-85635; 0-902145), Subs. of Carcanet Press, (UK), 108 E. 31st St., New York, NY 10016 (SAN 686-192X) Tel 212-686-1033; Toll free: 800-242-7737; Dist. by: Harper & Row Pubs., Inc., Keystone Industrial Pk., Scranton, PA 18512 (SAN 215-3742).

Carcosa, (Carcosa; 0-913796), P.O. Box 1064, Chapel Hill, NC 27514 (SAN 202-5124) Tel 919-929-2974.

Cardamom, (Cardamom Pr.; 0-9611118), P.O. Box D, Richmond, ME 04357 (SAN 283-2836) Tel 207-666-5645.

Carden Cherry Adv, (Carden & Cherry Advertising; 0-934319), 1220 McGavock St., Nashville, TN 37203 (SAN 693-4633) Tel 615-255-6696; Dist. by: Ballantine Bks., 201 E. 50th St., New York, NY 10022 (SAN 214-1175) Tel 212-751-2600.

Carderock Pr, (Carderock Pr.; 0-938813), P.O. Box 56, Cabin John, MD 20818 (SAN 662-5630); 8305 Fenway Rd., Bethesda, MD 20817 (SAN 662-5649) Tel 301-365-0768.

Cardi-Bel, (Cardi-Bel, Inc.; 0-938119), G.P.O. Box 2073, San Juan, PR 00936 (SAN 659-9559); Perseo & Sirio St., Urb. Altamira, San Juan, PR 00922 (SAN 659-9567) Tel 809-783-6857.

Cardiff, (Cardiff-By-The-Sea Publishing Co.; 0-9608038), 6065 Mission Gorge Rd., San Diego, CA 92120 (SAN 240-2009) Tel 619-286-6902.

Cardinal Pr, (Cardinal Pr., Inc.; 0-943594), 76 N. Yorktown, Tulsa, OK 74110 (SAN 219-1385) Tel 918-583-3651.

Cardinal Prod, (Cardinal Productions; 0-939245), 3636 Lemmon Ave., Suite 205, Dallas, TX 75219 (SAN 662-6351) Tel 214-528-5750.

Cardinal Pt, (Cardinal Point, Inc.; 0-932065), P.O. Box 596, Ellettsville, IN 47429 (SAN 685-4273) Tel 812-876-7811; Toll free: 800-628-2828.

Cardinal Pubs, (Cardinal Pubs.; 0-912930), P.O. Box 207, Davis, CA 95616 (SAN 201-9647).

Cardot Entpr Inc, (Cardot Enterprises; 0-9607516), 214 Avenida Barbera, Sonoma, CA 95476 (SAN 238-6283).

Cardoza Pub, (Cardoza Publishing; 0-9607618), P.O. Box 1404, Studio City, NY 91604 (SAN 281-3904) Tel 818-980-4471; Dist. by: Bookazine, 303 West 10th St., New York, NY 10014 (SAN 169-5665); Dist. by: Book Dynamics, 836 Broadway, New York, NY 10003 (SAN 169-5649) Tel 212-254-7798; Dist. by: Koen Distributors, 514 N. Read Ave., Cinnaminson, NJ 08077 (SAN 169-4642); Dist. by: Publishers Group West, 5855 Beaudry Street, Emeryville, CA 94608 (SAN 202-8522) Tel 415-658-3453. Imprints: Cardoza Sch Blackjk (Cardoza Schl of Blackjack); Gambling Res (Gambling Research Institute).

Cardoza Sch Blackjk Imprint of Cardoza Pub

Care Comm Inc, (Care Communications, Incorporated; 0-916499), 200 E. Ontario, Chicago, IL 60611 (SAN 295-5180) Tel 312-943-0463.

Care-Share, (Care/Share Productions; 0-9611628), P.O. Box 12245, Charleston, SC 29412 (SAN 284-9267) Tel 803-795-7234; Orders to: Gene Dillard Ministries, P.O. Box 90546, Charleston, SC 29410 (SAN 688-4156) Tel 803-747-6967.

Career Directions, (Career Directions; 0-933163), 171 Rte. 34, Holmdel, NJ 07733 (SAN 692-2783) Tel 201-946-8457.

Career Inst
 See Career Pub IL

Career Manage Consults
 See Career Mgmt Consult

Career Manage Pr, (Career Management Pr.; 0-9613630), Subs. of Career Management Ctr., 8301 State Line, No. 202, Kansas City, MO 64114 (SAN 670-8560) Tel 816-363-1500; Dist. by: Talman Co., 150 Fifth Ave., Rm. 514, New York, NY 10011 (SAN 200-5204) Tel 212-620-3182.

Career Mgmt, (Career Management Assocs.; 0-937595), 39505 Luckiamute Rd., Philomath, OR 97370 (SAN 659-0829) Tel 503-929-2254.

Career Mgmt Consult, *(Career Management Consultants; 0-9616157),* 544 NW 28th St., Corvallis, OR 97330 (SAN 699-9360) Tel 503-753-6478; P.O. Box 1802, Corvallis, OR 97330 (SAN 699-9379).

Career Plan, *(Career Planning Pubs.; 0-910595),* 7101 York Ave. S. No. 100, Edina, MN 55435 (SAN 260-0242) Tel 612-921-3379.

†**Career Pub,** *(Career Publishing, Inc.; 0-89262),* 910 N. Main St., Orange, CA 92667 (SAN 208-581X) Tel 714-771-5155; Toll free: 800-854-4014; P.O. Box 5486, Orange, CA 92613-5486 (SAN 658-0246); *CIP.*

Career Pub Corp, *(Career Publishing Corp.; 0-934829),* 505 Fifth Ave., Suite 1003, New York, NY 10017 (SAN 694-3640) Tel 212-840-7011; Toll free: 800-835-2246.

Career Pub IL, *(Career Publishing, Inc.; 0-911744),* 905 Allanson Rd., Mundelein, IL 60060 (SAN 202-5132) Tel 312-949-0011.

Career Resources, *(Career Resources Co.; 0-9616617),* Drawer 29388, Richmond, VA 23229 (SAN 659-9575); 1543-C Honey Grove Dr., Richmond, VA 23229 (SAN 659-9583) Tel 804-285-4410.

Careers Unltd, *(Careers Unlimited; 0-916275),* P.O. Box 470886, Tulsa, OK 74147 (SAN 295-6993) Tel 918-622-2811.

CareerTrack Pubns, *(CareerTrack Pubns., Inc.; 0-943066),* 1800 38th St., Boulder, CO 80301 (SAN 240-4133) Tel 303-440-7440; Toll free: 800-334-1018; Dist. by: Acropolis Bks., 2400 17th St. NW, Washington, DC 20009 (SAN 201-2227) Tel 202-387-6805.

Carefree Living, *(Carefree Living Co.; 0-938411),* 2509 E. Thousand Oaks Blvd., No. 160, Thousand Oaks, CA 91362-3249 (SAN 659-9613); 642 Camino Manzanas, Thousand Oaks, CA 91360 (SAN 659-9621) Tel 805-498-2654.

Caregiving Resc, *(Caregiving Resources; 0-939273),* 29 Oberlin St., Maplewood, NJ 07040 (SAN 662-8834) Tel 201-761-0456.

CareInst, *(CareInstitute; 0-917877),* Subs. of Comprehensive Care Corp., 660 Newport Ctr. Dr., Newport Beach, CA 92660 (SAN 657-0682) Tel 714-640-8950.

Cargo Serv Inc, *(Cargo Service Inc.; 0-9610616),* Box 466, Middletown, OH 45042 (SAN 276-959X) Tel 513-746-3993.

Carib Hse, *(Carib Hse. (USA); 0-936378),* P.O. Box 38834, Hollywood, CA 90038 (SAN 214-1124) Tel 818-890-1056.

Carib Pubns *Imprint of Casa Bautista*

Caribbean Bks, *(Caribbean Bks.; 0-931209),* 801 4th Ave, Parkersburg, IA 50665 (SAN 681-9680) Tel 319-346-2048.

Carikean Pub, *(Carikean Publishing; 0-9616741),* P.O. Box 11771, Chicago, IL 60611-0771 (SAN 659-963X); 833 W. Buena, No. 1909, Chicago, IL 60613 (SAN 659-9648) Tel 312-327-3743.

Carillon Bks, *(Carillon Bks.; 0-89310),* Div. of Catholic Digest, 2115 Summit Ave., St. Paul, MN 55105 (SAN 208-5828) Tel 612-647-5251.

Caring, *(Caring, Inc.; 0-911163),* P.O. Box 400, Milton, WA 98354 (SAN 268-6597) Tel 206-922-8194.

Carith Hse, *(Carith Hse.; 0-9616697),* 514 Warren St., Brookline, MA 02146 (SAN 659-9656); Marylake, Rte. 4, Box 1150, Little Rock, AR 72206 (SAN 659-9664) Tel 818-888-3052.

Carleton Coll, *(Carleton College; 0-9613911),* NorthField, MN 55057 (SAN 683-244X) Tel 507-663-4267.

Carleton Pr, *(Carleton Pr.; 0-9615890),* Lambs Ln., Cresskill, NJ 07626 (SAN 697-029X) Tel 201-567-3858.

Carlette Pub, *(Carlette Publishing; 0-9615423),* 2416 N. Fairview, Rochester Hills, MI 48064 (SAN 696-2297) Tel 313-456-8506.

Carlino Co, *(Carlino & Co.; 0-937827),* P.O. Box 15182, Honolulu, HI 96815 (SAN 659-4301) Tel 808-926-1752; 711 Ulili St., Honolulu, HI 96816 (SAN 659-431X).

Carlinshar, *(Carlinshar & Assoc. Applied Research Corp.; 0-934872),* 519 E. Briarcliff, Bolingbrook, IL 60439 (SAN 212-8918) Tel 312-739-7720.

Carlisle Indus, *(Carlisle Industries; 0-9600344),* 31000 Tower Rd., Visalia, CA 93291 (SAN 202-5140) Tel 209-798-1544.

Carlisle Pub, *(Carlisle Pub., Inc.; 0-910177),* P.O. Box 112, Hartsdale, NY 10530 (SAN 240-9739) Tel 914-725-0408.

Carlsbad His, *(Carlsbad Caverns Natural History Assn.; 0-916907),* 3225 National Parks Hwy, Carlsbad, NM 88220 (SAN 268-6627) Tel 505-785-2318.

Carlton, *(Carlton Pr.; 0-8062),* 11 W. 32nd St., New York, NY 10001 (SAN 201-9655) Tel 212-714-0300.

Carlton Pubns CA, *(Carlton Pubns., Inc.; 0-937348),* 10949 Fruitland Dr., Studio City, CA 91604 (SAN 215-9414).

Carlyle Assocs, *(Carlyle Assocs.; 0-935084),* 1236 Ninth St., Santa Monica, CA 90403 (SAN 213-4764) Tel 213-393-3323; P.O. Box 3391, Santa Monica, CA 90403 (SAN 658-0262); Dist. by: Wallaby Books, 1230 Ave. of the Americas, New York, NY 10020 (SAN 200-2450) Tel 212-245-6400.

Carlyle Sports, *(Carlyle Sports, Inc.; 0-9616136),* 958 Alexandria Dr., Newark, DE 19711 (SAN 699-9174) Tel 302-366-8047.

Carma, *(Carma Pr., Inc.; 0-918328),* Box 12633, St. Paul, MN 55112 (SAN 209-5351) Tel 612-631-9417.

Carmaral Pub Co
  See Catmaral Pub Co

Carmarthen Oak, *(Carmarthen Oak Pr.; 0-915117),* 1835 University Ave., No. A, Berkeley, CA 94703 (SAN 289-7768) Tel 415-848-0648.

Carmonelle Pubns, *(Carmonelle Pubns.; 0-943334),* P.O. Box 74, 304 Main St., Cameron, WI 54822 (SAN 240-5237) Tel 715-458-2684.

Carnation, *(Carnation Pr.; 0-87601),* P.O. Box 101, State College, PA 16804 (SAN 203-5103); 346 W. Hillcrest Ave., State College, PA 16803 (SAN 661-9703) Tel 814-238-3577.

Carnegie
  See Mus Art Carnegie

Carnegie Board, *(Carnegie Institute, Board of Trustees, The; 0-911239),* 4400 Forbes Ave., Pittsburgh, PA 15213 (SAN 268-6686) Tel 412-622-3377.

Carnegie Endow, *(Carnegie Endowment for International Peace; 0-87003),* 11 Dupont Cir., NW, Washington, DC 20036 (SAN 281-3955) Tel 202-797-6424.

Carnegie Ethics & Intl Affairs, *(Carnegie Council on Ethics & International Affairs; 0-87641),* 170 E. 64th St., New York, NY 10021 (SAN 203-5960) Tel 212-838-4120.

Carnegie Forum Ed Eco, *(Carnegie Forum on Education & the Economy; 0-9616685),* Affil. of Carnegie Corp. of New York, 1001 Connecticut Ave., NW, Suite 301, Washington, DC 20036 (SAN 660-9945) Tel 202-463-0747.

†**Carnegie Found,** *(Carnegie Foundation for the Advancement of Teaching),* 5 Ivy Ln., Princeton, NJ 08540 (SAN 268-6643) Tel 609-452-1780; Dist. by: Princeton Univ. Pr., 3175 Princeton Pike, Lawrenceville, NJ 08648 (SAN 202-0254) Tel 609-896-1344; *CIP.*

†**Carnegie Inst,** *(Carnegie Institution of Washington; 0-87279),* 1530 P St. NW, Washington, DC 20005 (SAN 201-9663) Tel 202-387-6411; *CIP.*

Carnegie-Mellon, *(Carnegie-Mellon Univ., Pr.; 0-915604),* P.O. Box 21, Schenley Park, Pittsburgh, PA 15216 (SAN 211-2329) Tel 412-578-2861; Dist. by: Harper & Row, 10 E. 53rd St., New York, NY 10022 (SAN 200-2086) Tel 212-207-7099.

Carnegie Pr, *(Carnegie Pr., Inc.; 0-935506),* 100 Kings Rd., Madison, NJ 07940 (SAN 223-7032).

Carnot Pr, *(Carnot Press; 0-917308),* P.O. Box 1544, Lake Oswego, OR 97034 (SAN 268-5852) Tel 503-636-6894.

Carnton Assn, *(Carnton Association, Inc.),* Rte. 2, Carton Lane, Franklin, TN 37064 (SAN 277-5794).

Carol Dunne, *(Dunne, Carol; 0-9616138),* 220 NE 51st Ct., Fort Lauderdale, FL 33334 (SAN 699-864X) Tel 305-771-5646.

Carol Mendel, *(Mendel, Carol; 0-9607696; 0-935179),* P.O. Box 6022, San Diego, CA 92106 (SAN 219-3329) Tel 619-226-1406.

Carolando, *(Carolando Pr.; 0-940542),* 6545 W. N Ave., Oak Park, IL 60302 (SAN 219-3426) Tel 312-383-6480.

Carolina Acad Pr, *(Carolina Academic Pr.; 0-89089),* P.O. Box 8795, Forest Hills Sta., Durham, NC 27707 (SAN 210-7848) Tel 919-489-7486.

†**Carolina Art,** *(Carolina Art Assn.; 0-910326),* Affil. of Gibbes Art Gallery, ; Orders to: Gibbes Gallery Shop, 135 Meeting St., Charleston, SC 29401 (SAN 203-512X) Tel 803-722-2706; *CIP.*

Carolina Banks Pub, *(Carolina Banks Publishing; 0-9617003),* 196 Ocean Blvd., Southern Shores, Kitty Hawk, NC 27949 (SAN 662-653X) Tel 919-261-2478.

Carolina Biological, *(Carolina Biological Supply Co.; 0-89278),* 2700 York Rd., Burlington, NC 27215 (SAN 208-5860) Tel 919-584-0381; Toll free: 800-334-5551.

Carolina Edns, *(Carolina Editions, Inc.; 0-914056),* P.O. Box 3169, Greenwood, SC 29646 (SAN 201-8721) Tel 803-229-3503.

Carolina Ind, *(Carolina Independent Publications, Inc.; 0-916975),* P.O. Box 2690, 2824 Hillsborough Rd., Durham, NC 27705 (SAN 655-6108) Tel 919-286-9692.

†**Carolina Pop Ctr,** *(Univ. of North Carolina at Chapel Hill, Carolina Population Ctr.; 0-89055),* Population Pubns., University Sq. 300A, Chapel Hill, NC 27514-3997 (SAN 201-7687) Tel 919-966-2152; *CIP.*

Carolina Pr, *(Carolina Pr.; 0-9616475),* 2660 Nantucket Dr., Winston-Salem, NC 27103 (SAN 659-3194) Tel 919-760-0944.

†**Carolina Wren,** *(Carolina Wren Pr., The; 0-932112),* Affil. of Durham Arts Council, 300 Barclay Rd., Chapel Hill, NC 27514 (SAN 213-0327) Tel 919-967-8666; *CIP.*

Caroline Hse, *(Caroline Hse., Inc.),* 5S 250 Frontenac Rd., Naperville, IL 60540 (SAN 211-2280) Tel 312-983-6400; Toll free: 800-245-2665.

†**Carolrhoda Bks,** *(Carolrhoda Bks., Inc.; 0-87614),* 241 First Ave., N., Minneapolis, MN 55401 (SAN 201-9671) Tel 612-332-3344; Toll free: 800-328-4929; *CIP.*

Carothers, *(Carothers Co.; 0-943026),* Box 2518, Escondido, CA 92025 (SAN 240-3536) Tel 619-741-2755.

Carousel Art, *(Carousel Art, Inc.; 0-914507),* P.O. Box 150, Green Village, NJ 07935 (SAN 290-697X) Tel 201-377-1483.

†**Carousel Pr,** *(Carousel Pr.; 0-917120),* P.O. Box 6061, Albany, CA 94706 (SAN 209-2646) Tel 415-527-5849; *CIP.*

Carousel Pub Corp, *(Carousel Publishing Corp.; 0-935474),* 27 Union St., Brighton, MA 02135 (SAN 287-7333).

Carpe Librum, *(Carpe Librum; 0-9617242),* 3277 Roswell Rd., Suite 447, Atlanta, GA 30319 (SAN 663-5512) Tel 404-458-2441.

Carpenter Ctr, *(Carpenter Ctr. for the Visual Arts & Peabody Museum),* c/o Harvard Univ. Pr., 79 Garden St., Cambridge, MA 02138 (SAN 200-2043) Tel 617-495-2480.

†**Carpenter Pr,** *(Carpenter Pr.; 0-914140),* Rte. 4, Pomeroy, OH 45769 (SAN 206-4650) Tel 614-992-7520; *CIP.*

Carpet Rug Inst, *(Carpet & Rug Institute, Inc.; 0-89275),* 310 Holiday Dr., Box 2048, Dalton, GA 30720 (SAN 268-6724) Tel 404-278-3176.

Carrera Intl, *(Carrera International, Inc.; 0-910597),* RFD 1682, Laurel Hollow, NY 11791 (SAN 263-967X) Tel 516-487-1616.

Carreta Pr, *(Carreta Pr.; 0-914199),* P.O. Box 5153, Mesa, AZ 85202 (SAN 287-5330) Tel 602-274-7480.

Carri Pub, *(Carri Publishing; 0-935771),* 1696 Morning Glory Ln., San Jose, CA 95124 (SAN 695-8389) Tel 408-723-5133.

Carriage House, *(Carriage House Pr. (NY); 0-939713),* 1 Carriage Ln., East Hampton, NY 11937 (SAN 663-6152) Tel 516-267-8773. Do not confuse with Carriage House Pr. of Brookline, MA.

Carriage Hse Pr, *(Carriage House Press; 0-9612216),* Eight Evans Rd., Brookline, MA 02146 (SAN 287-7279) Tel 617-232-1636.

Carriers Bees, *(Carrier's Beekeeping Supplies; 0-9607550),* 601 S. Baywood Ave., San Jose, CA 95128 (SAN 238-6291) Tel 408-296-6100.

Carrington Hse Ltd, *(Carrington Hse., Ltd.; 0-936695),* 1124 W. Barry Ave., Chicago, IL 60657 (SAN 699-9093) Tel 312-348-8613.

Carrol Gate Pr, *(Carrol Gate Press, The; 0-9608714),* 951 W. Liberty Dr., Wheaton, IL 60187 (SAN 238-048X) Tel 312-690-8574.

Carroll & Graf, *(Carroll & Graf Pubs.; 0-88184),* 260 Fifth Ave., New York, NY 10001 (SAN 264-6560) Tel 212-889-8772; Toll free: 800-982-8319; Dist. by: Publishers Group West, 5855 Beaudry St., Emeryville, CA 94608 (SAN 202-8522) Tel 415-658-3453.

Carroll Coll, *(Carroll College Press; 0-916120),* 100 NE Ave., Waukesha, WI 53186 (SAN 208-5879) Tel 414-547-1211.

†Carroll Pr, *(Carroll Pr.; 0-910328),* 43 Squantum St., Cranston, RI 02920 (SAN 203-6231) Tel 401-942-1587; P.O. Box 8113, Cranston, RI 02920 (SAN 658-0270); *CIP.*

Carroll St Pr, *(Carroll St., Pr.; 0-918869),* P.O. Box 70743, Sunnyvale, CA 94086 (SAN 670-073X); Dist. by: Dai Sing Distributing, P.O. Box 884, Feltor, CA 95018 (SAN 200-4879).

Carron Pubs, *(Carron, L.P., Pubs.; 0-9607241),* 205 Ridgewood Rd., Easton, PA 18042 (SAN 238-9207).

Carrousel Pubns, *(Carrousel Pubns., Inc.; 0-939826),* P.O. Box 225, Springfield, NJ 07081 (SAN 216-910X) Tel 201-379-2515.

Carrousels D, *(Carrousels & Dreams Publishing; 0-9615874),* 4664 Pasadena, Sacramento, CA 95821 (SAN 697-0354) Tel 916-485-6831.

CARS, *(Council of American Revolutionary Sites; 0-9616323),* Pennsylvania Rte. 32, Washington Crossing, PA 18977 (SAN 658-6643) Tel 215-493-4076; P.O. Box 103, Washington Crossing, PA 18977-0103 (SAN 658-6651).

Carson-Dellos, *(Carson-Dellosa Publishing Co., Inc.; 0-88724),* 207 Creek Ridge, Greensboro, NC 27406 (SAN 287-5896) Tel 919-274-1150.

†Carson Pr, *(Carson Press; 0-934360),* 733 W. Carson St., Torrance, CA 90502 (SAN 213-2958) Tel 213-328-3180; *CIP.*

Carstens Pubns, *(Carstens Pubns., Inc.; 0-911868),* P.O. Box 700, Newton, NJ 07860 (SAN 281-3971) Tel 201-383-3355; Orders to: Shipments to UPS, Purolator Etc., Fredon Springdale Rd., Fredon Township, Newton, NJ 07860-0700 (SAN 281-398X).

Carter Craft, *(Carter Craft Doll House; 0-9604404),* 5505 42nd Ave., Hyattsville, MD 20781 (SAN 203-624X) Tel 301-277-3051.

Carter Pub
See Unicorn NJ

Carter's Free & Easy Pubns, *(Carter's, Fred F., Free & Easy Publications; 0-916391),* 212 Race St., Suite 3A, Philadelphia, PA 19106 (SAN 295-7019) Tel 215-925-6766.

Cartmaral Pub Co
See Catmaral Pub Co

Cartographic Ent
See C Bks

CartoGraphics, *(CartoGraphics, Inc.; 0-937441),* 2729-E Merrilee Dr., Fairfax, VA 22031 (SAN 659-0853) Tel 703-573-9342.

Carver Pub, *(Carver Publishing, Inc.; 0-915044),* P.O. Box 6002, Hampton Institute, Hampton, VA 23668 (SAN 201-0143) Tel 804-727-5000.

Carver Pub MN
See L J McCann

Carves, *(Carves Cards),* 179 S St., Chestnut Hill, MA 02167 (SAN 209-4177) Tel 617-469-9175.

Carvin Pub, *(Carvin Publishing, Inc.; 0-9616390),* P.O. Box 850200, New Orleans, LA 70185-0200 (SAN 659-0888) Tel 504-866-4351; 57 Neron Pl., New Orleans, LA 70118 (SAN 659-0896).

Cary Arboretum
See NY Botanical

CAS, *(Competence Assurance Systems; 0-89147),* Div. of Whole Brain Corp., Harvard Sq., P.O. Box 81, Cambridge, MA 02138 (SAN 208-0001) Tel 617-661-9151.

CAS Inc, *(C.A.S., Inc.),* 2525 Murworth Dr., No. 202, Houston, TX 77054 (SAN 692-2562) Tel 713-661-0346; P.O. Box 20762, Houston, TX 77225-0762 (SAN 699-5926).

Casa Bautista, *(Casa Bautista de Publicaciones; 0-311),* Div. of Southern Baptist Convention, P.O. Box 4255, 7000 Alabama St., El Paso, TX 79914 (SAN 220-0139) Tel 915-566-9656; Dist. by: Broadman Press, 127 Ninth Ave., N., Nashville, TN 37234 (SAN 201-937X) Tel 615-251-2606. *Imprints:* Carib Pubns (Carib Publications).(Carib Pubns.); Centre De Pubns Baptistes (Centre De Publications Baptistes); Edit Mundo (Editorial Mundo Hispano).

Casa Unidad, *(Casa de Unidad; 0-9615977),* 1920 Scotten, Detroit, MI 48209 (SAN 697-2071) Tel 313-843-9598.

Cascade Photo, *(Cascade Photographics; 0-935818),* 6906 Martin Way, Olympia, WA 98506 (SAN 213-7291) Tel 206-491-5473.

Cascade Pub, *(Cascade Publishing Co., The; 0-9610664),* P.O. Box 27343, Seattle, WA 98125 (SAN 264-7249) Tel 206-668-2467.

Case Pub *Imprint of* **Lord Pub**

CASE Third Wave, *(CASE/Third Wave Publishing; 0-937951),* 80 Grand St., Jersey City, NJ 07302 (SAN 659-9389) Tel 201-333-0227.

†Case Western, *(Case Western Reserve Univ., Schl. of Law),* 11075 East Blvd., Cleveland, OH 44106 (SAN 227-0218) Tel 216-368-3280; *CIP.*

Casenotes Pub, *(Casenotes Publishing Co., Inc.; 0-87457),* P.O. Box 3946, Beverly Hills, CA 90212 (SAN 688-931X) Tel 213-475-1141; Dist. by: Law Distributors, Inc., 14415 S. Main St., Gardena, CA 90248 (SAN 212-3681) Tel 213-321-3275.

Casino, *(Casino Publishing; 0-9611120),* P.O. Box 54081, San Jose, CA 95154 (SAN 277-6626) Tel 408-365-1538.

Casino Gam Seminars, *(Casino Gaming Seminars),* P.O. Box 718, Solvang, CA 93463 (SAN 239-5304).

Casino Res, *(Casino Research Productions; 0-916619),* c/o Norby Walters Associates, 1650 Broadway-Suite 1410, New York, NY 10019 (SAN 296-4724) Tel 212-245-3939.

Caspers Wine, *(Caspers Wine Press; 0-933298),* 15222 Magnolia Blvd., Suite 107, Sherman Oaks, CA 91403 (SAN 212-1492) Tel 818-788-1481.

Cass County His, *(Cass County Historical Commission),* P.O. Box 98, Vandalia, MI 49095 (SAN 695-2283) Tel 616-445-8651.

Cassady & Calhoun, *(Cassady, Jim, & Fryar Calhoun; 0-9613650),* P.O. Box 3580, Berkeley, CA 94703 (SAN 670-7572) Tel 415-540-0800.

Cassandra Pr, *(Cassandra Pr.; 0-9615875),* P.O. Box 2044, Boulder, CO 80306 (SAN 697-0389) Tel 303-499-7651; 445 43rd St., Boulder, CO 80306 (SAN 697-0397); Dist. by: Bookpeople, 2929 Fifth St., Berkeley, CA 94710 (SAN 168-9517) Tel 415-549-3030; Dist. by: New Leaf Distributing, The, 1020 White St., SW, Atlanta, GA 30310 (SAN 169-1449) Tel 404-755-2665; Dist. by: Publishers Group West, 5855 Beaudry St., Emeryville, CA 94608 (SAN 202-8522) Tel 415-658-3453; Dist. by: Samuel Weiser, Inc., P.O. Box 612, York Beach, ME 03910 (SAN 202-9588) Tel 415-658-3453; Dist. by: Inland Bk. Co., P.O. Box 261, 22 Hemingway Ave., East Haven, CT 06512 (SAN 200-4151) Tel 203-467-4257; Dist. by: Nutri-Bks., Corp., P.O. Box 5793, Denver, CO 80223 (SAN 295-3404); Dist. by: Starlite, P.O. Box 20729, Reno, NV 89515 (SAN 131-1921) Tel 702-359-5676.

Cassell Commun Inc, *(Cassell Communications Inc.; 0-942980),* P.O. Box 9844, Fort Lauderdale, FL 33310 (SAN 240-138X) Tel 305-485-0795; Toll free: 800-351-9278; Toll free: 800-851-3392 (FL).

Cassette Concepts, *(Cassette Concepts, Inc.; 0-935525),* 28-A Lee Rd., Crozier, VA 23039 (SAN 696-2300) Tel 804-784-3978.

Cassizzi, *(Cassizzi, Vic),* P.O. Box 8788, 710 Town Mtn. Rd., Asheville, NC 28804 (SAN 217-0922) Tel 704-253-5016.

Cassone Pr, *(Cassone Press; 0-9610024),* 3028 Emerson Ave. S. Suite 3, Minneapolis, MN 55408 (SAN 268-6813) Tel 612-827-4774.

†Castalia Pub, *(Castalia Publishing Co.; 0-916154),* P.O. Box 1587, Eugene, OR 97440 (SAN 208-2403); *CIP.*

Castelli-Artspace, *(Castelli Graphics/Artspace; 0-9604140),* 4 E. 77th St., New York, NY 10021 (SAN 214-1140).

Castenholz Sons, *(Castenholz & Sons; 0-9603498),* 1055 Hartzell St., Pacific Palisades, CA 90272 (SAN 237-9449).

Castle & Cooke, *(Castle & Cooke, Inc.; 0-9611512),* 50 California St., San Francisco, CA 94111 (SAN 285-6816) Tel 415-986-3000.

Castle Bks, *(Castle Bks., Inc.; 0-916693),* Div. of Book Sales, Inc., P.O. Box 12506, Memphis, TN 38182 (SAN 204-4005); 233 Crestmere Pl., Memphis, TN 38112 (SAN 658-2575) Tel 901-276-1968.

Castle Dist, *(Castle Distributors),* 316 Estes Dr., Chapel Hlll, NC 27514 (SAN 239-3530) Tel 919-967-6439.

Castle Ent
See Castle Vent

Castle NY, *(Castle Publishing Co., Ltd.; 0-9611502),* 505 W. End Ave., New York, NY 10024 (SAN 213-0343) Tel 212-362-5209.

†Castle Pub Co, *(Castle Publishing Co.; 0-9603372),* P.O. Box 188, Portland, ME 04112 (SAN 209-2565) Tel 207-772-7851; *CIP.*

Castle Pub Connecticut
See Castle NY

Castle Pubns, *(Castle Pubns., Ltd.; 0-943178),* P.O. Box 580, Van Nuys, CA 91408 (SAN 240-3544) Tel 818-629-7823.

†Castle Vent, *(Castle Ventures; 0-930211),* 1111 Blanche St., No. 307, Pasadena, CA 91106 (SAN 670-7955) Tel 818-793-0935; *CIP.*

Castlemarsh, *(Castlemarsh Pubns.; 0-942250),* P.O. Box 30340, Savannah, GA 31410-0340 (SAN 240-8708) Tel 912-897-3455.

Castleton Pub, *(Castleton Publishing; 0-935885),* P.O. Box 2197, Corona, CA 91718 (SAN 696-2319) Tel 714-734-8587; 1997 Starfire Ave., Corona, CA 91719-2946 (SAN 696-2327).

Castro, *(Castro, Mercedes; 0-9604748),* 78-10 147th St., Apt. 3D, Flushing, NY 11367 (SAN 215-6113).

Cat-Tales Pr, *(Cat-Tales Pr.; 0-917107),* 229 St. Johns Pl., No. 2-D, Brooklyn, NY 11217 (SAN 655-6132) Tel 718-230-0724.

Catalan Communs, *(Catalan Communications; 0-87416),* 43 E. 19th St., Suite 200, New York, NY 10003 (SAN 687-7753) Tel 212-254-4996; Dist. by: Bud Plant, Inc., 12555 Loma Rica Dr., No. 10, Grass Valley, CA 95945 (SAN 268-5086) Tel 916-273-9588; Dist. by: Glenwood Distributors, 1624 Vandalia, Collinsville, IL 62234 (SAN 158-1740); Dist. by: Capital City, 2827 Perry St., Madison, WI 53713 (SAN 200-5328).

Catalyst, *(Catalyst; 0-89584),* 250 Park Ave. S., New York, NY 10003 (SAN 203-6258) Tel 212-777-8900.

Catalyst Pubns, *(Catalyst Pubns.; 0-931143),* 143 Dolores St., San Francisco, CA 94103 (SAN 658-6498) Tel 415-552-5045.

Catan, *(Catan, Omero C.; 0-9600618),* 1901 SW 87th Terr., Ft. Lauderdale, FL 33324 (SAN 203-6266).

Catering, *(Catering to You, Inc.; 0-935271),* P.O. Box 2161, Del Mar, CA 92014 (SAN 695-7390) Tel 619-295-5801.

Cath Authors, *(Catholic Authors Press; 0-910334),* 1201 S. Kirkwood Rd., Kirkwood, MO 63122 (SAN 203-6274) Tel 314-965-4801.

Cath Free Choice, *(Catholics for a Free Choice; 0-915365),* 2008 17th St. NW, Washington, DC 20009 (SAN 291-1116) Tel 202-638-1706.

†Cath Health, *(Catholic Health Assn. of the U.S.; 0-87125),* 4455 Woodson Rd., St. Louis, MO 63134-0889 (SAN 201-968X) Tel 314-427-2500; *CIP.*

Cath Hospital
See Cath Health

Cath Lib Assn, *(Catholic Library Assn.; 0-87507),* 461 W. Lancaster Ave., Haverford, PA 19041 (SAN 203-6282) Tel 215-649-5251.

Cath News Pub Co, *(Catholic News Publishing Co.; 0-910635),* 210 North Ave., New Rochelle, NY 10801 (SAN 268-7240) Tel 914-632-7771.

Cath Peace Fell, *(Catholic Peace Fellowship; 0-942252),* Affil. of Fellowship of Reconciliation, 339 Lafayette St, New York, NY 10012 (SAN 225-6932) Tel 212-673-8990.

Cath Pr Assn, *(Catholic Pr. Assn.),* 119 N. Park Ave., Rockville Centre, NY 11570 (SAN 204-3335) Tel 516-766-3400.

†**Cath U Pr,** *(Catholic Univ. of America Pr.; 0-8132),* 620 Michigan Ave., NE, Washington, DC 20064 (SAN 203-6290) Tel 202-635-5052; Orders to: P.O. Box 4852, Hampden Sta., Baltimore, MD 21211 (SAN 203-6304) Tel 301-338-6953; *CIP.*

Cathedral of Knowledge, *(Cathedral of Knowledge),* 235 NE 84th Ave., Portland, OR 97220 (SAN 211-6022) Tel 503-255-3859.

Cathedral Shop, *(Cathedral Shop, The; 0-915075),* The Cathedral of St. John the Divine 112th St. & Amsterdam Ave., New York, NY 10025 (SAN 289-7792) Tel 212-222-7448.

†**Catholic Bibl Assn,** *(Catholic Biblical Assn. of America; 0-915170),* Catholic Univ., 620 Michigan Ave. NE, Washington, DC 20064 (SAN 210-7856) Tel 202-635-5519; *CIP.*

Catholic Bk Pub, *(Catholic Bk. Publishing Co.; 0-89942),* 257 W. 17th St., New York, NY 10011 (SAN 204-3432) Tel 212-243-4515.

Catholic Bulletin Pub, *(Catholic Bulletin Publishing Co.; 0-935587),* 244 Dayton Ave., St. Paul, MN 55102 (SAN 696-2378) Tel 612-291-4444; Dist. by: Paulist Pr., 997 MacArthur Blvd., Mahwah, NJ 07430 (SAN 202-5159) Tel 201-825-7300.

Catholic Charities, *(Catholic Charities, U.S.A.; 0-938748),* 1319 F St., NW, Washington, DC 20004 (SAN 202-0890) Tel 202-639-8400.

Catmaral Pub Co, *(Catmaral Publishing Co.; 0-9611598),* 2401 Burridge Rd., Baltimore, MD 21234 (SAN 284-9283) Tel 301-661-7389.

Catnip Pr, *(Catnip Pr.; 0-9615475),* 117 Garth Rd., Apt. 2D, Scarsdale, NY 10583 (SAN 696-3161) Tel 914-472-2157.

†**Cato Inst,** *(Cato Institute; 0-932790),* 224 Second St., SE, Washington, DC 20003 (SAN 212-6095) Tel 202-546-0200; *CIP.*

Cato Pr, *(Cato Pr.; 0-916621),* 2 Bryn Mawr Ave., Suite 205, P.O. Box 205, Bryn Mawr, PA 19010 (SAN 296-4767) Tel 215-527-3939.

Catoctin Pr, *(Catoctin Press; 0-914385),* 709 E. Main St., Middletown, MD 21769 (SAN 289-6117) Tel 301-371-6293.

Cats Pajamas, *(Cat's Pajamas Press; 0-916866),* 527 Lyman Ave., Oak Park, IL 60304 (SAN 207-8015) Tel 312-386-5137.

Catskill Art, *(Catskill Art Supply; 0-9600350),* 35 Mill Hill Rd., Woodstock, NY 12498 (SAN 205-4663).

Catskill Ctr Conserv, *(Catskill Ctr. for Conservation & Development, Inc.; 0-9616712),* General Delivery, Arkville, NY 12406 (SAN 660-9953); Rte. 28, Arkville, NY 12406 (SAN 660-9961) Tel 914-586-2611.

Catspaw Inc, *(Catspaw, Inc.; 0-939793),* P.O. Box 1123, Salida, CO 81201; 9395 County Rd. 160, Salida, CO 81201 Tel 303-539-3884.

Cauce Pubs, *(Cauce, Cesar, Pubs. & Distributors; 0-86686),* 44 Fifth Ave. Box 120, Brooklyn, NY 11217 (SAN 216-5287).

Causa Intl, *(Causa International; 0-933901),* 401 Fifth Ave., New York, NY 10016 (SAN 692-7793) Tel 212-684-6122.

CAUSE, *(CAUSE; 0-933783),* 737 29th St., Boulder, CO 80303 (SAN 225-7378) Tel 303-449-4430.

Cavalier, *(Cavalier Press; 0-910338),* P.O. Box 111, Matteson, IL 60443 (SAN 203-6312).

Cavanaugh, *(Cavanaugh; 0-9614212),* 3833 Calvert St. NW, Washington, DC 20007 (SAN 687-0511) Tel 202-338-7257.

Cavco
See Cavco Pubns

Cavco Pubns, *(Cavco Pubns.; 0-932137),* 1829 E. Franklin St., Chapel Hill, NC 27514 (SAN 686-1606) Tel 919-929-0222; Orders to: Health Science Consortium, 103 Laurel Ave., Carrboro, NC 27510 (SAN 662-2690) Tel 919-942-8731.

†**Cave Bks MO,** *(Cave Bks.; 0-939748),* Subs. of Cave Research Foundation, 756 Harvard Ave., St. Louis, MO 63130 (SAN 216-7220) Tel 314-862-7646; Orders to: 901 Buford Pl., Nashville, TN 37204 (SAN 699-5195) Tel 615-269-3921; *CIP.*

Caverne Pub
See Double C Pub

CAVU Pr, *(CAVU Pr.; 0-9616265),* P.O. Box 23, Harrison, NY 10528 (SAN 658-3156).

Cawood & Assocs
See FC&A Pub

†**Caxton,** *(Caxton Printers, Ltd.; 0-87004),* P.O. Box 700, Caldwell, ID 83605 (SAN 201-9698) Tel 208-459-7421; Toll free: 800-451-8791 (Idaho only); *CIP.*

Caxton Club, *(Caxton Club; 0-940550),* 60 W. Walton St., Chicago, IL 60610 (SAN 216-3195) Tel 312-943-9090.

Cay-Bel, *(Cay-Bel Publishing Co.; 0-941216),* 45 Center St., Brewer, ME 04412 (SAN 238-9215) Tel 207-989-3820.

CAYC Learning Tree, *(CAYC Learning Tree; 0-940908),* 9998 Ferguson Rd., Dallas, TX 75228 (SAN 212-8861) Tel 214-321-6484.

Cayucos, *(Cayucos Books; 0-9600372),* P.O. Box 2113, Monterey, CA 93940 (SAN 208-5887) Tel 408-375-5289.

Cayuse Pr, *(Cayuse Pr.; 0-933529),* P.O. Box 9086, Berkeley, CA 94709 (SAN 693-8744) Tel 415-525-8515; Dist. by: Bookpeople, 2929 Fifth St., Berkeley, CA 94710 (SAN 168-9517) Tel 415-549-3030; Dist. by: The Distributors, 702 South Michigan, South Bend, IN 46618 (SAN 169-2488) Tel 219-232-8500.

CB City Intl, *(CB City International; 0-943132),* P.O. Box 31500, Phoenix, AZ 85046 (SAN 240-5199) Tel 602-996-8700.

CBEMA, *(Computer & Business Equipment Manufacturers Assn.; 0-912797),* 311 First St. NW, Suite 500, Washington, DC 20001 (SAN 269-2341) Tel 202-737-8888 Tel 202-638-4922.

CBH Pub, *(CBH Publishing, Inc.; 0-9604538),* 446 Central Ave., Northfield, IL 60093 (SAN 216-2288) Tel 312-446-6346.

CBN Univ, *(CBN Univ.; 1-55574),* Centerville Tpke., Virginia Beach, VA 23463 (SAN 699-9484) Tel 804-424-7000.

†**CBP,** *(CBP Pr.; 0-8272),* Div. of Christian Board of Publication, P.O. Box 179, St. Louis, MO 63166 (SAN 201-4408) Tel 314-371-6900; Toll free: 800-351-2665; *CIP.*

†**CBS Ed,** *(CBS Educational & Professional Publishing; 0-03),* Div. of CBS, Inc., 383 Madison Ave., New York, NY 10017 (SAN 200-2108) Tel 201-947-3306; Toll free: 800-CBS-ASK4; *CIP.*

CBSI, *(CBSI),* 3390 Peachtree Rd. NE, Suite 1148, Atlanta, GA 30326 (SAN 670-7386).

CC *Imprint of* **WSP**

CC Exchange, *(CC Exchange; 0-939078),* P.O. Box 1251, Laguna Beach, CA 92652 (SAN 239-7536) Tel 714-494-4310.

CC Studios, *(CC Studios, Inc.; 1-55592),* 389 Newton Tpke., Weston, CT 06883 (SAN 658-652X) Tel 203-226-3355.

CCC Pubns, *(CCC Pubns.; 0-918259),* 20306 Tau Pl., Chatsworth, CA 91311 (SAN 669-666X) Tel 818-407-1661. *Imprints:* Magic Publish (Magic Publishing).

CCCO, *(Central Committee for Conscientious Objectors; 0-933368),* 2208 South St., Philadelphia, PA 19146 (SAN 207-9852) Tel 215-545-4626; 1251 Second Ave., San Francisco, CA 94122 (SAN 680-0238) Tel 415-566-0500.

CCF, *(Custom Cycle Fitments; 0-940558),* 726 Madrone Ave., Sunnyvale, CA 94086 (SAN 223-7644) Tel 408-734-9426.

CCFL Bahamian, *(CCFL Bahamian Field Station; 0-935909),* 270 SW 34th St., Ft. Lauderdale, FL 33315 (SAN 696-7191) Tel 305-524-3009.

CCG *Imprint of* **Doubleday**

CCM, *(CCM Co., The; 0-914393),* 1308 E. Eighth St., Tucson, AZ 85719 (SAN 289-6192) Tel 602-622-2796.

CCPr *Imprint of* **Macmillan**

CCVI Pub, *(CCVI Publishing; 0-935579),* 120 E. 34th St., New York, NY 10016 (SAN 696-1606) Tel 212-683-1185.

CCW Pub, *(C.C.W. Publishing; 0-9613206),* P.O. Box 2069, Chapel Hill, NC 27514 (SAN 295-6861) Tel 919-967-7254.

CCW Pubns, *(CCW Pubns.; 0-9615561),* 3401 NE 11th St., Renton, WA 98056 (SAN 695-8478) Tel 206-228-8707.

CDC Pr, *(CDC Pr.; 0-935769),* 88 Bradley Rd., Woodbridge, CT 06525 (SAN 695-8338) Tel 203-387-8887.

CDI, *(Center for Defense Information),* 1500 Massachusetts Ave., Washington, DC 20005 (SAN 260-3322) Tel 202-862-0700.

CDI Inc, *(CDI, Inc.; 0-939021),* P.O. Box 11065, Birmingham, AL 35202 (SAN 662-5495); 5560 Cahaba Valley Rd., Birmingham, AL 35243 (SAN 662-5509) Tel 205-991-7315.

CDS Pub, *(CDS Publishing Co.; 0-916376),* Subs. of Man-Computer Systems, Inc., 84-13 168th St., Jamaica, NY 11432 (SAN 208-5755) Tel 718-739-4242.

CDT Pub, *(CDT Publishing Co.; 0-9616998),* 27103 E. Millpond, Capistrano Beach, CA 92624 (SAN 662-5533) Tel 714-240-8131.

CEA Bks Pr, *(CEA Bks. Pr.; 0-933588),* George Mason Univ., 129 Boyd Dr., Box 1329, Flat Rock, NC 28731 (SAN 211-8459) Tel 601-324-2340.

CEBCO, *(CEBCO Standard Publishing; 0-88320; 0-8278),* 9 Kulick Rd., Fairfield, NJ 07006 (SAN 207-1568) Tel 201-575-8153.

Cedar Creek IN, *(Cedar Creek Pubs.; 0-935316),* 2310 Sawmill Rd., Fort Wayne, IN 46825 (SAN 213-4780) Tel 219-637-3856.

Cedar Crest Bks, *(Cedar Crest Bks.; 0-910291),* P.O. Box 15, Cochituate, MA 01778 (SAN 241-2837) Tel 617-491-0683.

Cedar Data, *(Cedar Data Communications; 0-916977),* 150 Pamela Rd., Monrovia, CA 91016 (SAN 655-6140) Tel 818-244-1387.

Cedar Elm Pub, *(Cedar Elm Publishing Co.; 0-9617161),* 3312 Bellaire Pk. Ct., Fort Worth, TX 76109 (SAN 663-1517) Tel 817-927-8160.

Cedar River Pub, *(Cedar River Publishing Co.; 0-938047),* 5619 S. Augusta, Seattle, WA 98178 (SAN 660-997X) Tel 206-723-3127; Dist. by: Adams News Co., 1555 W. Galer St., Seattle, WA 98119 (SAN 169-8842) Tel 206-284-7617.

Cedars Pr, *(Cedars Pr.; 0-936326),* P.O. Box 29351, Columbus, OH 43229 (SAN 223-3835).

Cedars WI, *(Cedars Pr., The; 0-917575),* Rte. 2, Box 336, Green Lake, WI 54941 (SAN 657-1301) Tel 414-294-6754.

Cedarshouse, *(Cedarshouse Pr.; 0-912435),* 406 W. 28th St., Bryan, TX 77803 (SAN 265-2099) Tel 409-822-5615.

Cedarwinds, *(Cedarwinds Publishing Co.; 0-915297),* P.O. Box 13618, Tallahassee, FL 32317 (SAN 212-1700) Tel 904-224-9261.

Cedarwood Pr, *(Cedarwood Pr.; 0-930417),* 1115 E. Wylie St., Bloomington, IN 47401 (SAN 268-750X) Tel 812-332-3017.

CEF Press, *(Child Evangelism Fellowship Press),* Highway M, Warrenton, MO 63383 (SAN 211-7789) Tel 314-456-4321.

CEG Pr, *(CEG Pr.; 0-9614566),* P.O. Box 384, Lake Oswego, OR 97034 (SAN 691-7690) Tel 503-636-7704; Dist. by: Western States Bookservice, P.O. 855, Clackamas, OR 97015 (SAN 200-5662).

CEL Educ Resc, *(CEL Educational Resources; 0-938815),* Div. of CEL Communications, Inc., 515 Madison Ave., New York, NY 10022 (SAN 661-8391) Tel 212-421-4030.

Celcom Pr, *(Celcom Press),* 901 Boren Ave., Cabrini Medical Tower, Suite 1036, Seattle, WA 98104 (SAN 208-2411).

Celebrate Life Ent, *(Celebrate Life Enterprises; 0-9614507),* P.O. Box 95127, Seattle, WA 98145-2127 (SAN 691-7372) Tel 206-527-5406.

Celebrate One, *(Celebrate One; 0-937893),* 9422 SW 55th St., Portland, OR 97219 (SAN 659-4328) Tel 503-246-1591.

Celebrity Pr, *(Celebrity Pr., Inc.; 0-9607412),* 6656 W. Fifth St., Los Angeles, CA 90048 (SAN 239-1759) Tel 213-653-4012.

†**Celestial Arts,** *(Celestial Arts Pub. Co.; 0-912310; 0-89087),* Subs. of Ten Speed Press, P.O. Box 7327, Berkeley, CA 94707 (SAN 159-8333) Tel 415-524-1801; Toll free: 800-841-2665; *CIP.*

Celestial Gems, *(Celestial Gems; 0-914154),* 404 State St., Centralia, WA 98531 (SAN 201-1948) Tel 206-736-5083.

Celestial Gifts, *(Celestial Gifts),* Rd. 1, Box 150, Chestertown, MD 21620 (SAN 219-1431) Tel 301-778-0309.

Celestial Pr, *(Celestial Pr.; 0-910340),* 441 NE 24th St., Boca Raton, FL 33432 (SAN 203-6320) Tel 305-368-1309.

Celia Totus Enter, *(Celia Totus Enterprises Inc.; 0-931363),* P.O. Box 539, Toppenish, WA 98948 (SAN 682-5567) Tel 509-865-2480; Rte. 1, Box 1207, Toppenish, WA 98948 (SAN 662-2593).

Celilo Pubns, *(Celilo Pubns.; 0-9614529),* 6819 SW 32nd Ave., Portland, OR 97219 (SAN 689-738X) Tel 503-244-2688.

Cellar, *(Cellar Bk. Shop),* 18090 Wyoming, Detroit, MI 48221 (SAN 213-4330) Tel 313-861-1776.

†**Celo Pr,** *(Celo Pr.; 0-914064),* 1901 Hannah Branch Rd., Burnsville, NC 28714 (SAN 201-971X) Tel 704-675-4925; *CIP.*

Celt Heritage Pr, *(Celtic Heritage Pr., Inc.; 0-9614753),* 59-10 Queens Blvd., No. 9B, Woodside, NY 11377 (SAN 692-929X) Tel 718-478-8162.

Cembura, *(Cembura, Al; 0-912454),* 139 Arlington Ave., Berkeley, CA 94707 (SAN 201-9728) Tel 415-524-0478.

CeMoMedServ, *(CeMoMedServ Pubns.; 0-916109),* Div. of Central Missouri Medical Servs., 516 E. Capitol Ave. No. E, Jefferson City, MO 65101 (SAN 294-9083) Tel 314-634-2925; Dist. by: Cowley Distributing, Inc., 732 Heisinger Rd., Jefferson City, MO 65101 (SAN 169-426X) Tel 314-636-6511.

Cenotto Pubns, *(Cenotto Pubns.; 0-938121),* P.O. Box 623, Jackson, CA 95642 (SAN 660-9988); 557 Clinton Rd., Jackson, CA 95642 (SAN 660-9996) Tel 209-223-3196.

Centaur, *(Centaur Bks., Inc.; 0-87818),* 799 Broadway, New York, NY 10003 (SAN 201-7725) Tel 212-677-1720.

Centennial, *(Centennial Pr.; 0-8220),* Div. of Cliff's Notes, Inc., P.O. Box 80728, Lincoln, NE 68501 (SAN 203-6339) Tel 402-477-6971; Toll free: 800-228-4078.

Centennial Photo Serv, *(Centennial Photo Service; 0-931838),* Rte. 3, Box 1125, Grantsburg, WI 54840 (SAN 212-6443) Tel 715-689-2153; Dist. by: Watson-Guptill, 1515 Broadway, New York, NY 10036 (SAN 282-5384) Tel 212-764-7457.

Centennial Repros, *(Centennial Reproductions; 0-9606474),* 27 E. Cache la Poudre, Colorado Springs, CO 80707 (SAN 239-4162).

Center African Art, *(Center for African Art, The; 0-9614587),* 54 E. 68th St., New York, NY 10021 (SAN 691-7712) Tel 212-861-1200.

Center Archaeo, *(Southern Ill. Univ. at Carbondale, Ctr. for Arch. Investigations; 0-88104),* Carbondale, IL 62901 (SAN 240-5709) Tel 618-536-5529.

Center Bus Eco Res, *(Center for Business and Economic Research; 0-931497),* Western Illinois University, Macomb, IL 61455 (SAN 683-2180) Tel 309-298-1594.

Center City, *(Center City Financial Group; 0-937341),* 8637 Navajo Rd., San Diego, CA 92119 (SAN 659-0950) Tel 619-465-7400.

Center Communi Mini
See Ctr Comm Ministry

Center Community, *(Center for Community Economic Development),* P.O. 13065, Washington, DC 20009 (SAN 217-6742) Tel 202-659-3986.

Center Concern, *(Center of Concern; 0-934255),* 3700 13th St., NE, Washington, DC 20017 (SAN 268-8115) Tel 202-635-2757.

Center Creative Ed
See Josephson-Kluwer Legal Educ Ctrs

Center Creative Life, *(Center for Creative Life Pubns.; 0-9614588),* 415 Ave. A, E., Rm. 2, Bismarck, ND 58501 (SAN 691-7747) Tel 701-224-0102.

Center Independent, *(Center for Independent Living, Inc.; 0-942846),* Access Project, 2539 Telegraph Ave., Berkeley, CA 94704 (SAN 240-2025) Tel 415-841-4776.

Center Pr, *(Center Pr.; 0-934320),* 2045 Francisco St., Berkeley, CA 94709 (SAN 213-0351) Tel 415-526-8373.

Center Pr
See Bible Temple

Center Prof, *(Center for Professional Development; 0-9608190),* P.O. Box 1283, USU, Logan, UT 84322 (SAN 240-2033) Tel 801-750-1810.

†**Center Pubns,** *(Center Pubns.; 0-916820),* Div. of Zen Center of Los Angeles, Inc., 923 S. Normandie Ave., Los Angeles, CA 90006 (SAN 208-9386) Tel 213-387-2351; Dist. by: Bookpeople, 2929 Fifth St., Berkeley, CA 94710 (SAN 168-9517) Tel 415-549-3030; *CIP.*

Center Pubns Inc, *(Center Pubns., Inc.; 0-942452),* 2025 Zonal Ave., Los Angeles, CA 90033 (SAN 238-1478) Tel 213-224-7384.

Center Reform, *(Center for Reformation Research; 0-910345),* 6477 San Bonita Ave., St. Louis, MO 63105 (SAN 241-2845) Tel 314-727-6655.

Centerline, *(Centerline Pr.; 0-913111),* 2005 Palo Verde, Suite 325, Long Beach, CA 90815 (SAN 283-9369) Tel 213-421-0220.

Centerpoint Pr, *(Centerpoint Pr.; 0-937897),* P.O. Box 4771, Bryan, TX 77805 (SAN 659-4352) Tel 409-775-7887.

Centerstream Pub, *(Centerstream Publishing; 0-931759),* P.O. Box 5066, Fullerton, CA 92635 (SAN 683-8022) Tel 714-738-6489.

Centra Pubns, *(Centra Pubns.; 0-9617288),* 4705 Laurel St., San Diego, CA 92105 (SAN 663-6136) Tel 619-263-7942.

Central Agency, *(Central Agency For Jewish Education; 0-930029),* 4200 Biscayne Blvd., Miami, FL 33137 (SAN 669-747X) Tel 305-576-4030.

Central Am Res, *(Central America Resource Ctr.; 0-938049),* P.O. Box 2327, Austin, TX 78768 (SAN 661-0005); 600 W. 28th St., Suite 203, Austin, TX 78705 (SAN 661-0013) Tel 512-476-9841.

†**Central Conf,** *(Central Conference of American Rabbis; 0-916694),* 21 E. 40th St., New York, NY 10016 (SAN 204-3262) Tel 212-684-4990; *CIP.*

Central Electric, *(Central Electrial Railfans' Assn.; 0-915348),* P.O. Box 503, Chicago, IL 60690 (SAN 207-3110) Tel 312-346-3723.

Central FL Voters, *(Central Florida Voters Congress),* P.O. Box 1172, Orlando, FL 32802 (SAN 214-4882).

Centralia Pr, *(Centralia Press; 0-9611008),* P.O. Box 607, Floral Park, NY 11002 (SAN 283-9857) Tel 516-328-0239.

Centre De Pubns Baptistes *Imprint of Casa Bautista*

Centre Ent, *(Centre Enterprise, The; 0-932876),* Box 640506 Station "O", San Francisco, CA 94164-0506 (SAN 212-3401) Tel 415-673-1377.

Centro Invest
See CIRMA

Centurion Pr, *(Centurion Press),* Drawer 62, Los Angeles, CA 90028 (SAN 206-4839).

Centurion Pr AZ, *(Centurion Pr.; 0-935527),* 4360 N. Bear Claw Way, Tucson, AZ 85749 (SAN 696-2580) Tel 602-749-2245.

Century Bookbindery, *(Century Bookbindery; 0-89984),* P.O. Box 6471, Philadelphia, PA 19145 (SAN 209-2441) Tel 215-583-4550.

Century Comm, *(Century Communications, Inc.; 0-930264),* 5520 W. Touhy, Suite G, Skokie, IL 60077 (SAN 208-1911) Tel 312-676-4060.

Century Farms, *(Century Farms Heritage Committee; 0-9615152),* 743 17th St., SE, Owatonna, MN 55060 (SAN 694-3381) Tel 507-455-1674.

Century Hse
See ALF-CHB

Century One, *(Century One Pr.; 0-937080),* 2325 E. Platte Ave., Colorado Springs, CO 80909 (SAN 214-3534) Tel 303-471-1322.

Century Pr, *(Century Press; 0-915680),* 412 N. Hudson, Oklahoma City, OK 73102 (SAN 207-382X).

Century Pub, *(Century Publisher; 0-9614739),* Box 204, Holts Summit, MO 65043 (SAN 692-7246) Tel 314-896-4968; Dist. by: Cowley Distributing Inc., 732 Heisinger Rd., Jefferson City, MO 65101 (SAN 169-426X).

CEO Pubns, *(CEO Pubns.; 0-937415),* 2429 Rio Lindo, Healdsburg, CA 95448 (SAN 659-0594) Tel 707-431-7474; Dist. by: Publishers Group West, 5855 Beaudry St., Emeryville, CA 94608 (SAN 202-8522) Tel 415-658-3453.

CEP, *(Council on Economic Priorities; 0-87871),* 30 Irving Pl., New York, NY 10003 (SAN 204-269X) Tel 212-420-1133.

CEPA Gall, *(CEPA Gallery; 0-939784),* 700 Main St., 4th Fl., Buffalo, NY 14202 (SAN 216-8839) Tel 716-856-2717.

CEPCO *Imprint of* Burgess MN Intl

†**Cerberus,** *(Cerberus Bk. Co., The; 0-933590),* 2009 North Mckinley, Hobbsragg, NH 88240 (SAN 213-8352) Tel 505-393-5612; *CIP.*

Cerberus Assocs, *(Cerberus Assocs., Inc.; 0-936397),* 9 Willow St., Douglaston, NY 11363 (SAN 698-1577) Tel 718-224-4343.

Ceres Pr, *(Ceres Pr.; 0-9606138),* Box 87, Woodstock, NY 12498 (SAN 217-0949) Tel 914-679-8561; Dist. by: Bookpeople, 2929 Fifth St., Berkeley, CA 94710 (SAN 168-9517) Tel 415-549-3030; Dist. by: Great Tradition, The, 750 Adrian Way, Suite 111, San Rafael, CA 94903 (SAN 200-5743) Tel 415-492-9382; Dist. by: New Leaf Ditributing, The, 1020 White St., SW, Atlanta, GA 30310 (SAN 169-1449) Tel 404-755-2665; Dist. by: Nutri-Books Corp., P.O. Box 5793, Denver, CO 80223 (SAN 295-3404).

CERF Inc, *(Coastal Education & Research Foundation, Inc.; 0-938415),* P.O. Box 8068, Charlottesville, VA 22906 (SAN 661-0137); 355 W. Rio Rd., Charlottesville, VA 22901 (SAN 661-0145) Tel 305-523-6768.

Certain Ethnic, *(Certain Ethnic Publishing; 0-9615918),* c/o Malrite Creative Services, 1200 Statler Office Tower, Cleveland, OH 44115 (SAN 697-0303) Tel 216-781-3010.

Certified Feelings, *(Certified Feelings, Inc.; 0-936903),* P.O. Box 799 Times Square Sta., New York, NY 10108 (SAN 658-5663).

Cerulean Pr, *(Cerulean Pr.; 0-917458),* c/o Kent Pubns., 18301 Halsted St., Northbridge, CA 91325 (SAN 209-0597) Tel 818-349-2080.

CES, *(Continuing Education Systems, Inc.; 0-916780),* 112 S. Grant St., Hinsdale, IL 60521 (SAN 208-6107) Tel 312-654-2596.

CES Industries, *(CES Industries, Inc.; 0-86711),* 130 Central Ave., Farmingdale, NY 11735 (SAN 237-9864) Tel 516-293-1420.

Cesareans Ed, *(Cesareans/Support, Education & Concern),* 22 Forest Rd., Framingham, MA 01701 (SAN 268-5698) Tel 617-877-8266.

CFA Co, *(CFA Co.; 0-933897),* 11208 Korman Dr, Potomac, MD 20854 (SAN 692-6630) Tel 301-299-5060.

CFKR Career, *(CFKR Career Materials, Inc.; 0-934783),* P.O. Box 437, Meadow Vista, CA 95722 (SAN 694-2547) Tel 916-878-0118.

CFPR Pubns, *(CFPR Pubns.; 0-9613278),* P.O. Box 19446, Portland, OR 97219 (SAN 654-1534) Tel 503-246-6184.

Chaco Pr, *(Chaco Pr.; 0-9616019),* 5218 Donna Maria Ln., La Canada-Flintridge, CA 91011 (SAN 697-1784) Tel 818-952-0108; Orders to: Treasure Chest, P.O. Box 5250, Tucson, AZ 85703 (SAN 662-3913) Tel 602-623-9558.

†**Chadwyck-Healey,** *(Chadwyck-Healey, Inc.; 0-914146; 0-89887; 0-85964),* 1021 Prince St., Alexandria, VA 22314 (SAN 282-3306) Tel 203-683-4890; *CIP.*

Chaffey Commun Cult Ctr, *(Chaffey Communities Cultural Center; 0-9603586),* P.O. Box 772, Upland, CA 91785 (SAN 213-8360) Tel 714-982-8010.

Chain Store Pub
See Lebhar Friedman

Chal Public, *(Challenge Pubns., Inc.; 0-935415),* 7950 Deering Ave., Canoga Park, CA 91304 (SAN 696-2602) Tel 818-887-0550.

†**Chalfant Pr,** *(Chalfant Pr., Inc.; 0-912494),* P.O. Box 787, Bishop, CA 93514 (SAN 203-6347) Tel 619-873-3535; *CIP.*

Challenge Exp, *(Challenge Expedition Co.; 0-9608120),* P.O. Box 1852, Boise, ID 83701 (SAN 240-0871) Tel 208-386-9300.

†**Challenge Pr,** *(Challenge Pr.; 0-89421),* Div. of Economic Research Ctr., Inc., 1107 Lexington Ave., Dayton, OH 45407 (SAN 210-0509) Tel 513-275-8637; *CIP.*

Challenge Pub Co, *(Challenge Publishing, Co.; 0-916115),* 2750 Bellflower Blvd., Suite 210, Long Beach, CA 90815 (SAN 294-9148) Tel 213-429-5265.

CHAMAH Pubs, *(CHAMAH Pubs.; 0-938666),* 25 Broadway, Suite 1042, New York, NY 10004 (SAN 215-9430).

Chamber Comm US, *(Chamber of Commerce of the United States; 0-89834),* Special Pubns. Office, 1615 H St., NW, Washington, DC 20062 (SAN 225-6134) Tel 202-659-6111.

Chambers & Asher
See Chase Comns

Chameleon Prods, *(Chameleon Productions, Inc.; 0-9613843),* 5800 Arlington Ave., Studio 3M, Bronx, NY 10471 (SAN 681-9702) Tel 212-548-2932.

CHAMH Pubs
See CHAMAH Pubs

Champ Pr Inglewood, *(Champion Pr.; 0-936691),* Centinela Hospital, 555 E. Hardy St., Inglewood, CA 90301 (SAN 699-7228) Tel 213-673-2086. Do not confuse with Champion Pr., Scottsdale, AZ.

Champagne Pr, *(Champagne Pr.; 0-9612146),* 313 Walnuthaven Dr., West Covina, CA 91790 (SAN 290-6996) Tel 818-814-2052; P.O. Box 631, West Covina, CA 91793 (SAN 290-7003).

Champaign County, *(Champaign County Historical Archives Illinois; 0-9609646),* The Urbana Free Library, 201 S. Race St., Urbana, IL 61801 (SAN 268-8476) Tel 217-367-4057.

Champaign Pub Lib, *(Champaign Public Library & Information Ctr.; 0-9617184),* 505 S. Randolph, Champaign, IL 61820 (SAN 663-2629) Tel 217-356-7243.

Champaign Syst, *(Champaign Systems, Inc.; 0-937547),* 2518 Brett Dr., Champaign, IL 61821 (SAN 659-0977) Tel 217-359-9013.

Champion Athlete, *(Champion Athlete Publishing Co.; 0-938074),* Box 2936, Richmond, VA 23235 (SAN 215-6148) Tel 804-794-6034.

Champion Pr, *(Champion Pr.; 0-938636),* P.O. Box 1969, Scottsdale, AZ 85252 (SAN 218-4710) Tel 602-949-0786; Dist. by: Tom Hopkins International, Inc., 7531 E. Second St., Scottsdale, AZ 85252 (SAN 200-5174) Tel 602-949-0786. Do not confuse with Champion Pr. of Inglewood, CA.

Championship Bks, *(Championship Bks.; 0-89279),* 2109 N. Western, Ames, IA 50010 (SAN 656-1217) Tel 515-232-1101.

†**Champlain Coll Pr,** *(Champlain College Pr.; 0-9612704),* P.O. Box 670, Burlington, VT 05402-9990 (SAN 289-8144) Tel 802-658-0800; 163 S. Willard St., Burlington, VT 05402 (SAN 658-2451); *CIP.*

Champlin Museum, *(Champlin Museum, Pr.; 0-912173),* 4636 Fighter Aces Dr., Mesa, AZ 85205 (SAN 264-7257) Tel 602-830-4540.

Chan Shal Imi, *(Chan Shal Imi Society Press; 0-936380),* P.O. Box 1365, Stone Mountain, GA 30086 (SAN 213-2974).

†**Chandler & Sharp,** *(Chandler & Sharp Pubs., Inc.; 0-88316),* 11A Commercial Blvd., Novato, CA 94947 (SAN 205-6127) Tel 415-883-2353; *CIP.*

Chandler Inst, *(Chandler Institute; 0-918877),* P.O. Box 394, Mission, SD 57555 (SAN 669-9758) Tel 605-856-4472.

Chandler Pub
See Har-Row

Chandler-Smith, *(Chandler-Smith Publishing Hse., Inc.; 0-916787),* 132 Lowell St., Peabody, MA 01960 (SAN 654-3936) Tel 617-531-4952.

Chandler Tertius, *(Chandler, Tertius; 0-9693872),* 2500 Buena Vista, Berkeley, CA 94708 (SAN 693-9961) Tel 415-849-1850.

†**Changing Times,** *(Changing Times Education Service; 0-89247),* Div. of EMC Corp., 300 York Ave., St. Paul, MN 55101 (SAN 208-4015) Tel 612-771-1555; *CIP.*

Channels Children, *(Channels to Children; 0-9616396),* P.O. Box 25834, Colorado Springs, CO 80936 (SAN 658-9936) Tel 303-223-4317; 2625 Dunbar Ave., Ft. Collins, CO 80526 (SAN 658-9944).

Channing Bks, *(Channing Bks. & Whaleship Plans; 0-9600496),* P.O. Box 552, Marion, MA 02738 (SAN 203-6363) Tel 617-748-0087; 35 Main St., Marion, MA 02738 (SAN 658-0297).

Channings
See Channing Bks

Chans Bks
See Chans Corp

Chans Corp, *(Chan's Corp.; 0-914322),* 230 S. Garfield Ave., Monterey Park, CA 91754 (SAN 201-8764) Tel 213-572-0425.

Chanteyman, *(Chanteyman Pr.; 0-9601250),* 42 Crocus St., Woodbridge, NJ 07095 (SAN 210-4008) Tel 201-634-4123.

Chanticleer, *(Chanticleer Pr., Inc.; 0-918810),* 424 Madison Ave., New York, NY 10017 (SAN 201-5749) Tel 212-486-3900.

Chanticleer CA, *(Chanticleer; 0-9615876),* 4974 N. Fresno St., Suite 242, Fresno, CA 93726 (SAN 697-0346) Tel 209-275-9040.

Chanticleer FL, *(Chanticleer Pr.; 0-9612442),* 1428 State St., Suite 107, Sarasota, FL 33577 (SAN 289-176X) Tel 813-371-8544.

Chanticleer Pr
See Stevens Bk Pr

Chantry Pr, *(Chantry Pr.; 0-941608),* P.O. Box 144, Midland Park, NJ 07432 (SAN 239-0752) Tel 201-423-5882.

Chaosium, *(Chaosium Inc.; 0-933635),* P.O. Box 6302, Albany, CA 94706 (SAN 692-6460) Tel 415-527-7361.

Chapel *Imprint of* Dell

Chapel Hill Pr, *(Chapel Hill Pr.; 0-934001),* P.O. Box 958, Murray Hill Sta., 115 E. 34th St., New York, NY 10156 (SAN 692-6649) Tel 212-425-1153.

Chapin PTO, *(Chapin PTO; 0-9611640),* Rte. 3, Box 384, Chapin, SC 29036 (SAN 284-9348) Tel 803-345-3590.

Chapman & Bkman, *(Chapman & Bookman; 0-9613544),* 2409 NE 12th Ct., Ft. Lauderdale, FL 33304 (SAN 669-7488) Tel 305-564-1650.

Chapman Assocs, *(Chapman Assocs.; 0-937243),* 9 Farrington Pkwy., Burlington, VT 05401 (SAN 658-6740) Tel 802-862-8633.

Chapman Brook, *(Chapman, Brook & Kent; 0-930687),* Div. of Institute for Reading Research, P.O. Box 21008, Santa Barbara, CA 93121 (SAN 677-1173) Tel 805-962-0055.

Chapter & Cask, *(Chapter & Cask; 0-940056),* Div. of Collart Enterprises, P.O. Box 3604, Glyndon, MD 21071 (SAN 217-0663) Tel 301-833-7172.

†**Char-L,** *(Char-L Pub. Co.; 0-9605654),* P.O. Box 121, Niantic, IL 62551 (SAN 238-7751); *CIP.*

Character Res, *(Character Research Pr.; 0-915744),* 266 State St., Schenectady, NY 12305 (SAN 209-1240) Tel 518-370-0025.

Chariot Bks *Imprint of* Cook

Charioteer, *(Charioteer Press; 0-910350),* P.O. Box 57223, Washington, DC 20037 (SAN 203-6371) Tel 202-965-5046.

Charisma Pr, *(Charisma Pr.; 0-933402),* P.O. Box 263, Andover, MA 01810 (SAN 212-6478) Tel 617-851-7910.

Charisma Pubns, *(Charisma Pubns., Inc.; 0-937008),* P.O. Box 40321, Indianapolis, IN 46240 (SAN 214-3542) Tel 317-843-4143.

Charismatic Ren Servs, *(Charismatic Renewal Services; 0-943780),* 237 N. Michigan, South Bend, IN 46601 (SAN 268-8492) Tel 219-234-6021; Toll free: 800-348-2227.

†**Chariton Review,** *(Chariton Review Pr.; 0-933428),* Northeast Missouri State Univ., Kirksville, MO 63501 (SAN 212-4890) Tel 816-785-4499; *CIP.*

Charlemarie, *(Charlemarie Pr.; 0-937181),* 707 Watkins, Conway, AR 72032 (SAN 658-4896) Tel 501-327-2181.

†**Charles,** *(Charles Pr. Pubs.; 0-914783; 0-89303),* P.O. Box 15711, Philadelphia, PA 19103 (SAN 203-638X) Tel 215-735-3665; *CIP.*

†**Charles Pub,** *(Charles Publishing Co.; 0-912880),* 5039 Bluebell, North Hollywood, CA 91607 (SAN 201-9779) Tel 818-763-2031; *CIP.*

†**Charles River Bks,** *(Charles River Bks.; 0-89182),* 1 Thompson Sq., Boston, MA 02129 (SAN 209-2530) Tel 617-259-8857; *CIP. Imprints:* CRR (Charles River Reprints).

Charleston Pr, *(Charleston Pr.; 0-935773),* 4911 S. Sherwood Forest Blvd., Baton Rouge, LA 70816 (SAN 695-8311) Tel 504-293-9472.

Charlotte Drug, *(Charlotte Drug Education Ctr. Pubns.; 0-934337),* 1416 E. Morehead St., Charlotte, NC 28204 (SAN 693-6083) Tel 704-336-3211.

Charlton Hse, *(Charlton Hse. Publishing; 0-916697),* Div. of Charlton Industries, Ltd., P.O. Box 2474, Newport Beach, CA 92663 (SAN 654-2360) Tel 714-760-8528.

Charm City Assocs, *(Charm City Assocs.; 0-9617229),* 401 Hawthorne Rd., Baltimore, MD 21210 (SAN 663-4265) Tel 301-243-5997.

Charon Ferguson Pub
See Ferguson Comns Pubs

Charred Norton, *(Charred Norton Publishing Co.; 0-930975),* 43 Elm St., Camillus, NY 13031 (SAN 678-884X) Tel 315-672-8012.

Chart *Imprint of* Bobbs

Chartcraft
See Chartcrafters Pubs

Chartcrafters Pubs, *(Chartcrafters Pubs.; 0-930151),* P.O. Box 26136, Baltimore, MD 21210 (SAN 669-6678) Tel 301-889-2628; Dist. by: Yankee Inc., Main St., Dublin, NH 03444 (SAN 293-4434) Tel 603-563-8111.

Charter Oak Pr, *(Charter Oak Pr.; 0-87521),* P.O. Box 7783, Lancaster, PA 17604 (SAN 692-4581) Tel 717-656-4293.

Charter Pr, *(Charter Press; 0-9614681),* Subs. of James B. Warkentin, Realtor, 2429 Martindale Rd., Shelburne, VT 05482 (SAN 692-5103) Tel 802-985-3862.

†**Charters W,** *(Charters West; 0-9613913),* P.O. Box 675, Goleta, CA 93116 (SAN 682-2355); *CIP.*

ChartGuide
See ChartGuide Ltd

ChartGuide Ltd, *(ChartGuide Ltd.; 0-938206),* 300 N. Wilshire Ave., Suite 5, Anaheim, CA 92801 (SAN 215-7373) Tel 714-533-1423.

Chartmasters, *(Chartmasters; 0-917190),* P.O. Box 1264, Covington, LA 70434 (SAN 208-5917) Tel 504-892-9135.

Chartrand, *(Chartrand, Robert Lee),* 5406 Dorset Ave., Chevy Chase, MD 20815 (SAN 211-1152).

Chartwell, *(Chartwell Hse., Inc.; 0-910354),* P.O. Box 166, Bowling Green Sta., New York, NY 10004 (SAN 203-6398).

Chase Comns, *(Chase Communications, Inc.; 0-9615565),* 1776 Nancy Creek Bluff, NW, Atlanta, GA 30327 (SAN 696-2610) Tel 404-355-4142.

†**Chase Pubns,** *(Chase Pubns.; 0-914779),* 1654-33rd Ave., San Francisco, CA 94122 (SAN 297-1720) Tel 415-731-0158; Dist. by: Bookpeople, 2929 Fifth St., Berkeley, CA 94710 (SAN 168-9517) Tel 415-549-3030; Dist. by: Publishers Group West, 5855 Beaudry St., Emeryville, CA 94608 (SAN 202-8522) Tel 415-658-3453; *CIP.*

Chase Trade
See Wrld Info NY

Chasse Pubns, *(Chasse Pubns.; 0-913930),* 8760 Grand, Beulah, CO 81023 (SAN 203-6401) Tel 303-485-3136; P.O. Box 38, Beulah, CO 81023 (SAN 699-5209).

Chateau Pub, *(Chateau Publishing, Inc.; 0-88435),* P.O. Box 20432, Herndon Sta., Orlando, FL 32814 (SAN 201-7814) Tel 305-898-1641.

Chateau Thierry, *(Chateau Thierry Pr.; 0-935046),* 1668 W. Olive Ave., Chicago, IL 60660 (SAN 281-4056) Tel 312-262-2234.

†**Chatham Bkseller,** *(Chatham Bookseller; 0-911860),* 8 Green Village Rd., Madison, NJ 07940 (SAN 203-641X) Tel 201-822-1361; *CIP.*

Chatham Comm Inc, *(Chatham Communicators, Inc.; 0-910347),* 3857 N. High St., P.O. Box 14091, Columbus, OH 43214 (SAN 241-2861) Tel 614-268-8989.

Chatham His Soc, *(Chatham Historical Society Inc.; 0-9615051),* Box 381, Chatham, MA 02633 (SAN 693-8795) Tel 617-945-9812; Dist. by Pabnassus Imprint, 21 Camal Rd., Box 335, Orleans, MA 02653 (SAN 200-5158).

†**Chatham Hse Pubs,** *(Chatham Hse., Pubs., Inc.; 0-934540),* Box 1, Chatham, NJ 07928 (SAN 213-036X) Tel 201-635-2059; Orders to: Chatham Hse. Distributors, 540 Barnum Ave., Bridgeport, CT 06608 (SAN 281-4080) Tel 203-366-1900; *CIP.*

†**Chatham Pr,** *(Chatham Pr.; 0-85699),* P.O. Box A, Old Greenwich, CT 06870 (SAN 201-9795) Tel 203-531-7880; Dist. by: Devin-Adair Pubs., Inc., 6 N. Water St., Greenwich, CT 06830 (SAN 213-750X) Tel 203-531-7755; *CIP.*

Chatham Pub CA, *(Chatham Pub. Co.; 0-89685),* P.O. Box 283, Burlingame, CA 94010 (SAN 210-4016) Tel 415-348-0331.

Chatham River Pr *Imprint of* Outlet Bk Co

†**Chatham Sq,** *(Chatham Square Press, Inc.; 0-89456),* 401 Broadway, 23rd Fl., New York, NY 10013 (SAN 210-1874) Tel 212-226-3368; *CIP.*

Chathman His Soc
See Chatham His Soc

Chatsworth, *(Chatsworth Pr.; 0-917181),* Subs. of Woodland Media, Inc., 21540 Prairie St., Chatsworth, CA 91311 (SAN 696-9186) Tel 818-341-3156; Toll free: 800-262-7367; Dist. by: Media Products, 21540 Prairie, Suite C, Chatsworth, CA 91311 (SAN 200-6960) Tel 818-341-3156; Dist. by: Publishers Group West, 5855 Beaudry St., Emeryville, CA 94608 (SAN 202-8522) Tel 415-658-3453.

Chattanooga Christ, *(Chattanooga Christian Schl.; 0-9615039),* 3354 Broad St., Chattanooga, TN 37409 (SAN 656-0415) Tel 615-266-3296.

Chatterbox Voice Lrn Syst, *(Chatterbox Voice Learning Systems; 0-939557),* 29 Elk Ridge Ln., Boulder, CO 80302 (SAN 661-888X) Tel 303-444-4654; Toll free: 800-531-5314.

Chatterton Pr, *(Chatterton Pr.; 0-930574),* 2471 Berthbrook Dr., Cincinnati, OH 45231 (SAN 211-4631).

Chauncy Pr, *(Chauncy Pr., The; 0-918517),* Div. of M & M Pubns. & Sails, Ltd., Turtle Pond Rd., Saranac Lake, NY 12983 (SAN 657-6842) Tel 518-891-1650.

Chaves Hist, *(Chaves County Historical Society; 0-9615310),* 200 N. Lea Ave., Roswell, NM 88201 (SAN 694-5988) Tel 505-622-8333.

CHB-ALF
See ALF-CHB

CHB Goodyear Comm, *(Childrens Hospital of Buffalo, Josephine Goodyear Committee; 0-9616699),* 219 Bryant St., Buffalo, NY 14222 (SAN 661-227X) Tel 716-634-7778.

CHC Pub, *(Colon Health Ctr. Publishing Co.; 0-9616184),* 105 Locust, Larkspur, CA 94939 (SAN 658-3261) Tel 415-924-6106; P.O. Box 1013, Larkspur, CA 94939 (SAN 658-327X); Dist. by: Nutri-books Corp., P.O. Box 5793, Denver, CO 80223 (SAN 169-054X) Tel 303-778-8383; Dist. by: Bookpeople, 2929 Fifth St., Berkeley, CA 94710 (SAN 168-9517) Tel 415-548-3030.

CHCUS Inc
See Chinese Cult Serv

Cheap St, *(Cheap St.; 0-941826),* Rte. 2, Box 293, New Castle, VA 24127 (SAN 239-1783) Tel 703-864-6288.

Checkmark *Imprint of* **Facts on File**

Chedney, *(Chedney Pr.; 0-910358),* P.O. Box 1148, Auburn, ME 04210 (SAN 203-6428).

Cheeruppet, *(Cheeruppet World, Inc.; 0-914201),* 2264 Calle Iglesia, Mesa, AZ 85202 (SAN 287-6000); Orders to: 2405 E. Southern Ave., Sta., Tempe, AZ 85282 (SAN 287-6019) Tel 602-831-6088.

Cheese Pr, *(Cheese Pr., The; 0-9607404),* P.O. Box 85, Main St., Ashfield, MA 01330 (SAN 239-1791) Tel 413-628-3808.

Cheetah Pub, *(Cheetah Publishing Co.; 0-936241),* 275 N. Forest Lake Dr., Altamonte Springs, FL 32714 (SAN 697-0443) Tel 305-862-2951.

Cheever Pub, *(Cheever Publishing, Inc.; 0-915708),* P.O. Box 700, Bloomington, IL 61702 (SAN 207-9410) Tel 309-378-2961.

Chefs Pub Co, *(Chefs Publishing, Co.; 0-933903),* P.O. Box 541202, Houston, TX 77254-1202 (SAN 692-7556) Tel 713-664-0884.

Chelonia Pr, *(Chelonia Pr.; 0-938947),* 1850 Union St., Suite 196, San Francisco, CA 94123 (SAN 661-8367) Tel 415-665-0621.

Chelsea Green Pub, *(Chelsea Green Publishing Co.; 0-930031),* P.O. Box 283, Chelsea, VT 05038 (SAN 669-7631) Tel 802-685-3108; 1 Court St., Chelsea, VT 05038 (SAN 658-2583).

†**Chelsea Hse,** *(Chelsea Hse. Pubs.; 0-87754; 1-55546),* Div. of Chelsea Hse. Educational Communications, Inc., 5014 West Chester Pike, Edgemont, PA 19028 (SAN 206-7609) Tel 215-353-3625; Toll free: 800-523-0458; *CIP.*

Chelsea-Lee Bks, *(Chelsea-Lee Bks.; 0-913974),* P.O. Box 66273, Los Angeles, CA 90066 (SAN 201-9817) Tel 213-616-0391.

†**Chelsea Pub,** *(Chelsea Pub. Co.; 0-8284),* 15 E. 26 St., New York, NY 10010 (SAN 201-9825) Tel 212-889-8095; *CIP.*

Cheltenham Pr, *(Cheltenham Pr.; 0-9615838),* Box 591046, San Francisco, CA 94159-1046 (SAN 697-0311) Tel 415-552-2994; 1673 Oak St., San Francisco, CA 94117 (SAN 697-032X).

Chem Educ, *(Journal of Chemical Education; 0-910362),* 238 Kent Rd., Springfield, PA 19064 (SAN 203-6436); Orders to: 20th & North Hampton Sts., Easton, PA 18042 (SAN 662-0590) Tel 215-250-7264.

Chem Eng *Imprint of* **McGraw**

Chem Info Sys
See C I S

Chem-Orbital, *(Chem-Orbital; 0-930376),* P.O. Box 134, Park Forest, IL 60466 (SAN 213-3466) Tel 312-755-2080.

†**Chem Pub,** *(Chemical Publishing Co., Inc.; 0-8206),* 80 Eighth Ave., New York, NY 10011 (SAN 203-6444) Tel 212-255-1950; *CIP.*

Chen Chi Studio, *(Chen Chi Studio; 0-9604652),* 15 Gramercy Park, New York, NY 10003 (SAN 215-1359).

Chen Fu, *(Chen Fu Tien),* P.O. Box 1854, Norwalk, CA 90650 (SAN 287-2870).

Cheng & Tsui, *(Cheng & Tsui Co.; 0-917056; 0-88727),* 25-31 West St., Boston, MA 02111 (SAN 169-3387) Tel 617-426-6074.

Chenonta, *(Chenonta, Inc.; 0-938845),* P.O. Box 3727, West Sedona, AZ 86340 (SAN 661-695X).

Cherniak-Damele, *(Cherniak/Damele Publishing Co.; 0-911093),* P.O. Box 19077, Oakland, CA 94619 (SAN 268-8670) Tel 415-533-1598; Dist. by: Informedia, 103 Godwin Ave., Midland Park, NJ 07432 (SAN 268-8689) Tel 201-447-2569.

†**Cherokee,** *(Cherokee Publishing Co.; 0-87787),* P.O. Box 1523, Marietta, GA 30061 (SAN 650-0404) Tel 404-424-6210; *CIP.*

Cherokee Pubns, *(Cherokee Pubns.; 0-935741),* P.O. Box 256, Cherokee, NC 28719 (SAN 696-2785) Tel 704-488-2988.

Cherry County Cent, *(Cherry County Centennial Committee; 0-9614508),* Box 284, Valentine, NE 69201 (SAN 691-7275) Tel 402-376-1477.

†**Cherry Lane,** *(Cherry Lane Bks.; 0-89524),* Div. of Cherry Lane Music Co., Inc., 110 Midland Ave., Port Chester, NY 10573 (SAN 219-0788) Tel 914-937-8601; Toll free: 800-354-4004; P.O. Box 430, Port Chester, NY 10573; *CIP.*

Cherry Lane Bks
See Cherry Lane

†**Cherry Valley,** *(Cherry Valley Editions; 0-916156),* P.O. Box 303, Cherry Valley, NY 13320 (SAN 208-1482) Tel 607-264-3707; Orders to: Beach & Co., Pubs., P.O. Box 303, Cherry Valley, NY 13320 (SAN 200-6847); *CIP.*

Cherryable, *(Cherryable Brothers; 0-930689),* 130 Seventh St., Suite 448, Garden City, NY 11530 (SAN 677-1106) Tel 516-486-5090.

Cherubim, *(Cherubim; 0-938574),* P.O. Box 75, Ft. Tilden, NY 11695 (SAN 215-8523).

Ches & OH Hist, *(Chesapeake & Ohio Historical Society, Inc.; 0-939487),* P.O. Box 417, Alderson, WV 24910 (SAN 225-3798) Tel 804-445-5252.

Chesapeake Bay Pr, *(Chesapeake Bay Pr.; 0-938225),* Div. of WJBM Assocs., Inc., P.O. Box 951, Rockville, MD 20851 (SAN 661-003X); 2214 McAuliffe Dr., Rockville, MD 20851 (SAN 661-0048) Tel 301-424-9677.

Chesbro, *(Chesbro Pr.; 0-938006),* 230 Longview Ave., Morgan Hill, CA 95037 (SAN 220-0392) Tel 408-779-5930; P.O. Box 126, Morgan Hill, CA 95037 (SAN 658-0300).

Cheshire, *(Cesire Bks.; 0-917352),* 514 Bryant St., Palo Alto, CA 94301 (SAN 208-5925) Tel 415-321-2449; Dist. by: Bookpeople, 2929 Fifth St., Berkeley, CA 94710 (SAN 168-9517) Tel 415-549-3030.

Chess Ent Inc, *(Chess Enterprises, Inc.; 0-931462),* 107 Crosstree Rd., Coraopolis, PA 15108 (SAN 277-5808) Tel 412-262-2138.

Chess Info Res Ctr, *(Chess Information & Research Ctr.; 0-9617207),* P.O. Box 534, Gracie Sta., New York, NY 10028 (SAN 663-2793); 512 E. 83rd St., Apt. 3D, New York, NY 10028 (SAN 663-2807) Tel 212-754-8706.

Chess Pub, *(Chess Pubns.; 0-935273),* 6007 Beech Ave., Bethesda, MD 20817 (SAN 695-7404) Tel 301-243-5943; Dist. by: Betty Cox Assocs., 232 E. University Pkwy., Baltimore, MD 21218 (SAN 200-7819).

Chester Hse Pubs, *(Chester Hse. Pubs.; 0-935763),* P.O. Box 1469, Grand Central Station, New York, NY 10163 (SAN 696-284X) Tel 914-478-4256; 160-01 77th Ave., Flushing, NY 11366 (SAN 696-2858) Tel 718-591-8579.

Chestnut Hill Pr, *(Chestnut Hill Pr.; 0-9608132),* 5320 Groveland Rd., Geneseo, NY 14454 (SAN 238-0498) Tel 716-243-3616.

Chestnut Hill Sr Servs
See CHSSC Phila

Cheswick Pr, *(Cheswick Pr.; 0-9616686),* 8106 Three Chopt Rd., Richmond, VA 23229 (SAN 661-0056) Tel 804-288-7795.

Cheval Bks, *(Cheval Bks.; 0-910368),* P.O. Box 2783, Hollywood, CA 90028 (SAN 208-306X) Tel 213-657-7311.

Cheyenne Cor, *(Cheyenne Corral; 0-9609648),* 7101 Tumbleweed Dr., Cheyenne, WY 82009 (SAN 281-4099).

Chi Ctr Afro-Am Stud, *(Chicago Center for Afro-American Studies & Research, Inc.; 0-937954),* P.O. Box 7610, Chicago, IL 60680 (SAN 215-9449).

Chi Horticult, *(Chicago Horticultural Society; 0-939914),* P.O. Box 400, Glencoe, IL 60022 (SAN 216-7980) Tel 312-835-5440.

Chi Ofc Fine Arts, *(Chicago Office of Fine Arts, Dept. of Cultural Affairs; 0-938903),* Cultural Ctr., 78 Washington St., Chicago, IL 60608 (SAN 661-8340) Tel 312-744-8927.

Chicago Arch, *(Chicago Architectural Club, The; 0-9614052),* 4 W. Burton Place, Chicago, IL 60610 (SAN 684-9113) Tel 312-266-1783.

Chicago Bd Trade, *(Chicago Board of Trade; 0-917456),* 141 W. Jackson, Chicago, IL 60604 (SAN 203-6460) Tel 312-435-7210.

Chicago Contemp Photo
See Columbia College Chi

†**Chicago Hist,** *(Chicago Historical Society; 0-913820),* Clark St. at North Ave., Chicago, IL 60614 (SAN 203-6479) Tel 312-642-4600; Toll free: 800-621-2736; *CIP.*

Chicago Inst
See Art Inst Chi

Chicago Law Bk, *(Chicago Law Bk. Rare; 0-9610650),* 4814 S. Pulaski Rd., Chicago, IL 60632 (SAN 264-648X) Tel 312-376-1713.

Chicago Ling, *(Chicago Linguistic Society; 0-914203),* c/o Univ. of Chicago, Classics 314A, 1050 E. 59th St., Chicago, IL 60637 (SAN 287-6027) Tel 312-962-8529.

Chicago Map, *(Chicago Map Society, The; 0-916789),* 60 W. Walton, Chicago, IL 60610 (SAN 654-200X) Tel 312-943-9090.

Chicago Original Paperback *Imprint of* **U of Chicago Pr**

Chicago Psych, *(Chicago Institute for Psychoanalysis; 0-918568),* 180 N. Michigan Ave., Chicago, IL 60601 (SAN 210-1432) Tel 312-726-6300.

Chicago Publishing, *(Chicago Publishing Co.; 0-9603264),* P.O. Box 635, Chicago, IL 60690 (SAN 209-5394) Tel 312-528-1523.

Chicago Rep, *(Chicago Reporter; The; 0-9615553),* Div. of Community Renewal Society, 18 S. Michigan Ave., Chicago, IL 60603 (SAN 696-4842) Tel 312-236-4830.

†**Chicago Review,** *(Chicago Review Pr., Inc.; 0-914090; 1-55652),* 814 N. Franklin St., Chicago, IL 60610 (SAN 213-5744) Tel 312-337-0747; *CIP.* Imprints: Landmarks Comm Village Oak Pk (Landmarks Commission Village of Oak Park).

Chicago Talent Sourcebook
See Alexander Comms

Chicago Trib, *(Chicago Tribune Books Today),* 435 N. Michigan Ave., Chicago, IL 60611 (SAN 204-2959) Tel 312-222-3232.

Chicago Visual Lib *Imprint of* **U of Chicago Pr**

Chicago Zoo, *(Chicago Zoological Society; 0-913934),* 3300 Golf Rd., Brookfield, IL 60513 (SAN 663-4672).

Chick Pubns, *(Chick Pubns.; 0-937958),* P.O. Box 662, Chino, CA 91710 (SAN 211-7770) Tel 714-987-0771.

Chickasaw Bayou, *(Chickasaw Bayou Press; 0-9606372),* 103 Trace Harbor Rd., Madison, MS 39110 (SAN 217-1651) Tel 601-856-7062.

†**Chicot Pr,** *(Chicot Pr., The; 0-913845),* P.O. Box 21988, Baton Rouge, LA 70893 (SAN 286-7389) Tel 813-933-7098; Orders to: 13014 N. Dale Mabry, Suite 249, Tampa, FL 33618 (SAN 662-2100) Tel 813-933-7098; *CIP.*

Chiefton Pub, *(Chiefton Publishing, Inc.; 0-9615945),* Div. of Chiefton Enterprises, Inc., 5125 Blake Rd., Edina, MN 55436 (SAN 697-046X) Tel 612-935-0564.

Child & Family Ent, *(Child & Family Enterprises, Inc.; 0-935202),* 7 Leonard Pl., Albany, NY 12202 (SAN 213-8379) Tel 518-449-5735.

Child & Waters Inc, *(Child & Waters Incorporated; 0-9611200),* 516 Fifth Ave., New York, NY 10036 (SAN 283-2569) Tel 212-840-1935.

Child Bk Coun, *(Children's Bk. Council, Inc., The; 0-933633),* 67 Irving Pl., New York, NY 10003 (SAN 225-2929) Tel 212-254-2666.

Child Care, *(Child Care Information Exchange; 0-942702),* P.O. Box 2890, Redmond, WA 98073 (SAN 240-3072) Tel 206-882-1066.

Child Care Admin, *(Child Care Administrative Services; 0-937261),* 11742 W. Pico Blvd., Suite 202, Los Angeles, CA 90064 (SAN 659-025X) Tel 213-477-2177.

Child Council SF, *(Children's Council of San Francisco; 0-937711),* 3896 24th St., San Francisco, CA 94114 (SAN 659-3240) Tel 415-647-0778.

Child Focus Co, *(Child Focus Co.; 0-933892),* P.O. Box 1885, Fallbrook, CA 92028 (SAN 207-5199) Tel 619-723-8542.

Child Health Assn, *(Child Health Assn. of Sewickley, Inc.; 0-9607634),* 1108 Ohio River Blvd., Sewickley, PA 15143 (SAN 240-088X) Tel 412-741-3221.

Child Hospice VA, *(Children's Hospice Intl.; 0-932321),* 501 Slaters Ln., Suite 207, Alexandria, VA 22314 (SAN 687-0570) Tel 703-549-1811.

Child Mus, *(Children's Museum of Indianapolis; 0-9608982),* 30th & Meridian, Indianapolis, IN 46208 (SAN 268-9057).

Child Safe, *(Child Safe Products, Inc., Publishing Div.; 0-917461),* 449 N. University Dr., Plantation, FL 33324 (SAN 657-0836); Toll free: 800-334-0090.

Child Savers, *(Child-Savers, Inc.; 0-936049),* 30 W. 61st St., Suite 27c, New York, NY 10023 (SAN 697-0230) Tel 212-247-6580.

Child Trends, *(Child Trends Inc.; 0-932359),* 1990 M St. NW, Washington, DC 20036 (SAN 687-3707) Tel 202-223-6288.

Child Ventures, *(Children's Ventures; 0-9615985),* P.O. Box 3000, Grants Pass, OR 97526 (SAN 698-1569) Tel 503-479-2929; Dist. by: Pacific Pipeline, Inc., 19215 66th Ave, S., Kent, WA 98032 (SAN 208-2128) Tel 206-872-5523.

†**Child Welfare,** *(Child Welfare League of America, Inc.; 0-87868),* 440 First St., NW, Washington, DC 20001 (SAN 201-9876) Tel 202-638-2952; *CIP.*

Childbirth Graphics, *(Childbirth Graphics, Ltd.; 0-943114),* 1210 Culver Rd., Rochester, NY 14609 (SAN 240-3587) Tel 716-482-7940.

Children, *(Children of Mary; 0-933731),* P.O. Box 40, Pearblossom, CA 93553 (SAN 692-6053) Tel 805-944-1132.

Children First, *(Children First Press; 0-9603696),* Box 8008, Ann Arbor, MI 48107 (SAN 212-4904) Tel 313-668-8056.

Children Learn Ctr, *(Children's Learning Center, Inc.; 0-917206),* 4660 E. 62nd St., Indianapolis, IN 46220 (SAN 208-5933) Tel 317-251-6241.

†**Childrens,** *(Childrens Pr.; 0-516),* Div. of Regensteiner Publishing Enterprises, Inc., 1224 W. Van Buren St., Chicago, IL 60607 (SAN 201-9264) Tel 312-666-4200; Toll free: 800-621-1115; *CIP. Imprints:* Elk Grove Bks (Elk Grove Books); Golden Gate (Golden Gate); Sextant (Sextant).

Childrens Art, *(Children's Art Foundation, Inc.; 0-89409),* Box 83, Santa Cruz, CA 95063 (SAN 210-0533) Tel 408-426-5557.

Childrens Bk *Imprint of Atheneum*

Childrens Bk Co, *(Childrens Bk. Co., Inc.; 0-89813),* Div. of Creative Education, Inc., P.O. Box 227, Mankato, MN 56001 (SAN 204-5532) Tel 507-625-2490. Out of business.

Childrens Book Pr, *(Children's Book Press/Imprenta de Libros Infantiles; 0-89239),* 1461 9th Ave., San Francisco, CA 94122 (SAN 210-7864) Tel 415-664-8500.

†**Childrens Ctr,** *(Children's Ctr. Pubns. of California; 0-915861),* Creativity Ctr. S., P.O. Box 885, Bonita, CA 92002 (SAN 293-9878) Tel 619-479-0602; *CIP.*

Children's Defense, *(Children's Defense Fund; 0-938008),* 122 C St., NW, Washington, DC 20001 (SAN 216-1133) Tel 202-628-8787; Toll free: 800-424-9602.

Childrens Hosp, *(Children's Hospital of San Francisco, Pubn. Dept.; 0-931421),* P.O. Box 3805, San Francisco, CA 94119 (SAN 683-5422); 3700 California St., OPR-110, San Francisco, CA 94119 (SAN 658-2699) Tel 415-387-8700.

Childrens Hosp VA
See Child Hospice VA

Childrens Lit
See CHLA Pubns

Children's Memorial, *(Children's Memorial Hospital, The; 0-9607400),* 2300 Children's Plaza, Chicago, IL 60614 (SAN 239-4189).

Children's Mus, *(Children's Museum of Oak Ridge; 0-9606832),* P.O. Box 3066, Oak Ridge, TN 37830 (SAN 219-7227) Tel 615-482-1075.

Childrens Mus Denver, *(Children's Museum of Denver,Inc.; 0-933027),* 2121 Cresent Dr., Denver, CO 80211 (SAN 689-5514) Tel 303-433-7444.

Childrens Theatre, *(Children's Theatre Assn. of America; 0-940528),* Div. of American Theatre Assn., 1010 Wisconsin Ave., NW, Washington, DC 20007 (SAN 239-3581) Tel 202-342-7530.

Childrens Yellow, *(Children's Yellow Pages; 0-9613059),* P.O. Box 48636, Los Angeles, CA 90048 (SAN 293-9916); 542 S. Lorraine Blvd., Los Angeles, CA 90020 (SAN 293-9924) Tel 213-930-1733; Dist. by: Publishers Group West, 5855 Beaudry St., Emeryville, CA 94608 (SAN 202-8522) Tel 415-658-3453.

Childs Play, *(Childs Play; 0-931749),* 12423 Fleet Ct., Sterling Heights, MI 48077 (SAN 683-5120) Tel 313-939-9245.

Childs Pub
See Pack Pub

†**Childs World,** *(Child's World, Inc., The; 0-89565; 0-913778),* 980 N. McLean Blvd., Elgin, IL 60121 (SAN 211-0032) Tel 312-741-7591; P.O. Box 989, Elgin, IL 60121 (SAN 661-9738); Dist. by: Children's Pr., 1224 W. Van Buren St., Chicago, IL 60607 (SAN 201-9264) Tel 312-666-4200; *CIP.*

Childwrite, *(Childwrite, Inc.; 0-943194),* 26409 Timberlane Dr., SE, Kent, WA 98042 (SAN 240-527X) Tel 206-631-8972.

Chilmark Hse, *(Chilmark House; 0-937532),* 4224 38th St. NW, Washington, DC 20016 (SAN 215-9457) Tel 202-363-4222.

Chiltern Yoga, *(Chiltern Yoga Foundation; 0-9612762),* 1029 Hyde St., Suite 6, San Francisco, CA 94109 (SAN 289-8284) Tel 415-776-1158.

†**Chilton,** *(Chilton Bk. Co.; 0-8019),* Subs. of ABC Publishing, Chilton Way, Radnor, PA 19089 (SAN 658-0319) Tel 215-964-4000; Orders to: Schl., Library Services, Chilton Way, Radnor, PA 19089 (SAN 202-1552) Tel 215-964-4729; Dist. by: Hobby Bk. Distributors, 3150 State Line Rd., (SAN 200-6669); *CIP.*

Chilton Corp, *(Chilton Corp.; 0-9616037),* 12606 Greenville, Dallas, TX 75243 (SAN 698-0384) Tel 214-699-6320.

†**China Bks,** *(China Bks. & Periodicals, Inc.; 0-8351),* 2929 24th St., San Francisco, CA 94110 (SAN 145-0557) Tel 415-282-2994; *CIP.*

China Hse Arts, *(China House of Arts; 0-9609104),* 1100 Madison Ave., New York, NY 10028 (SAN 241-287X) Tel 212-794-9652.

China Phone, *(China Phone Book Co., Ltd., The),* P.O. Box 2385-N, Menlo Park, CA 94025 (SAN 268-9146).

China Res, *(China Research; 0-9605190),* 1500 NW 103rd Lane, Coral Springs, FL 33065 (SAN 223-1654) Tel 305-752-6274.

China West, *(China West Bks.; 0-941340),* P.O. Box 2804, San Francisco, CA 94126 (SAN 238-9231) Tel 415-755-3715.

Chinese Acad Prof Soc, *(Chinese Academic & Professional Society of Mid-America; 0-9616137),* 6711 Innsbruck Ct., Naperville, IL 60532 (SAN 699-8577) Tel 312-996-4860.

Chinese Art App, *(Chinese Art Appraisers Assn.; 0-930940),* Box 734, 633 Post St., San Francisco, CA 94109 (SAN 211-495X) Tel 415-673-6023.

Chinese Cult Serv, *(Chinese Culture Service, Inc.; 0-937256),* P.O. Box 444, Oak Park, IL 60303 (SAN 215-2401) Tel 312-848-2210.

Chinese Hist CA, *(Chinese Historical Society of Southern California, Inc.; 0-930377),* 1648 Redcliff St., Los Angeles, CA 90026 (SAN 670-7580) Tel 213-828-6911.

Chinese Lib, *(Chinese-American Librarians Assn.; 0-930691),* c/o Ohio University Library, Athens, OH 45701 (SAN 677-0991) Tel 614-594-5228.

Chinkapin, *(Chinkapin Press, Inc.; 0-938874),* P.O. Box 10565, Eugene, OR 97401 (SAN 220-2360).

Chinoperl, *(Conference for Chinese Oral & Performing Literature),* 140 Uris Hall, Cornell Univ., Ithaca, NY 14853 (SAN 269-2570) Tel 607-255-6222.

Chips, *(Chip's Bookshop, Inc.; 0-912378),* Box 639, Cooper Sta., New York, NY 10003 (SAN 203-6517) Tel 212-362-9336.

Chiron Pr, *(Chiron Pr., Inc.; 0-913462),* 24 W. 96th St., New York, NY 10025 (SAN 202-1560) Tel 212-662-5486; Orders to: Chiron Pr., Inc., Publishers Storage & Shipping Co., 231 Industrial Pk., Fitchburg, MA 01420 (SAN 202-1579) Tel 617-491-1727.

Chiron Pub Co, *(Chiron Publishing, Co.; 0-915053),* P.O. Box 575, Bethel Park, PA 15102 (SAN 289-8330) Tel 412-831-2929.

Chiron Pubns, *(Chiron Publications; 0-933029),* 400 Linden Ave., Wilmette, IL 60091 (SAN 689-1659) Tel 312-256-7551; Dist. by: Open Court Publishing Co., P.O. box 599, Peru, IL 61354 (SAN 202-5876) Tel 815-223-2520.

Chiropractic, *(Who's Who in Chiropractic International Publishing Co.; 0-918336),* P.O. Box 2615, Littleton, CO 80161 (SAN 209-9209) Tel 303-798-5128.

†**Chiropractic Pub,** *(Chiropractic Publishing Services; 0-914893),* 2017 S. Ventura, Tempe, AZ 85282 (SAN 289-0879) Tel 602-277-6293; *CIP.*

Chisos Mount, *(Chisos Mountain Pr.; 0-9614040),* P.O. Box 6268, Pasadena, TX 77506 (SAN 684-7293) Tel 713-943-3203.

Chisum Pub, *(Chisum Publishing, Inc.; 0-937689),* 1000 E. 14th St., Suite 388, Plano, TX 75074 (SAN 659-0284) Tel 214-423-2120; 1541 Ave. K, Plano, TX 75074 (SAN 659-0292) Tel 214-422-7066.

Chiuzac Ltd, *(Chiuzac, Ltd.),* 630 First Ave., New York, NY 10016 (SAN 699-7775).

Chiwaukee Pub Co, *(Chiwaukee Publishing Co.; 0-9613129),* 11745 First Ave., Kenosha, WI 53140 (SAN 294-703X) Tel 414-694-9532.

CHLA Pubns, *(Childrens Literature Assn. Pubns.; 0-937263),* Purdue Univ., 210 Education, West Lafayette, IN 47907 (SAN 225-297X) Tel 317-494-2355.

Chlorine Inst, *(Chlorine Institute; 0-940230),* 70 W. 40th St., New York, NY 10018 (SAN 204-2983) Tel 212-819-1677.

†**Chockstone Pr,** *(Chockstone Pr.; 0-9609452; 0-934641),* 526 Franklin St., Denver, CO 80218 (SAN 276-6809) Tel 303-377-1970; *CIP.*

Chogie Pubs, *(Chogie Pubs.; 0-9610818),* 123 Virginia Rd., Oak Ridge, TN 37830 (SAN 285-1199) Tel 615-482-7320; Orders to: Rte. 5, Box 286A, Paris, TN 38242 (SAN 285-1202) Tel 901-642-9752.

†**Choice,** *(CHOICE; 0-930659),* 125 S. Ninth St., Suite 603, Philadelphia, PA 19107 (SAN 260-3969) Tel 215-592-0550; *CIP.*

Choice Pub CA, *(Choice Publishing Co.; 0-9615891),* P.O. Box 3568, Santa Monica, CA 90403-3568 (SAN 696-2998) Tel 213-394-2313.

Choice Pubns, *(Choice Pubns.; 0-934685),* 1335 Rosewood, Ferndale, MI 48220 (SAN 694-3438) Tel 313-399-0711.

Chopping Board Inc, *(Chopping Board, Inc.; 0-915747),* P.O. Box 2549, Gainesville, FL 32602 (SAN 292-3319).

Choral Resource, *(Choral Resource Seminars; 0-9616618),* P.O. Box 15068, San Francisco, CA 94115 (SAN 661-0064); 1332 Dolores, No. 2, San Francisco, CA 94110 (SAN 661-0072) Tel 415-648-6854.

Chou-Chou, *(Chou-Chou Pr.; 0-9606140),* P.O. Box 152, Shoreham, NY 11786 (SAN 220-2379).

Chowder Pr, *(Chowder Pr.; 0-9614546),* 13 Schuyler Dr., Saratoga Springs, NY 12866 (SAN 691-7984) Tel 518-587-2808.

Chr Acad Success, *(Christian Academy of Success; 0-941280),* 5428 W. Barbara Ave., Glendale, AZ 85302 (SAN 238-924X).

Chr Bk Club *Imprint of* **Noontide**

Chr Bksellers, *(Christian Booksellers Assn.),* 2620 Venetucci Blvd., P.O. Box 200, Colorado Springs, CO 80901 (SAN 216-3519) Tel 303-576-7880.

Chr Classics, *(Christian Classics, Inc.; 0-87061),* P.O. Box 30, Westminster, MD 21157 (SAN 203-6525) Tel 301-848-3065.

Chr Coll Pr *Imprint of* **Christendom Pubns**

Chr Concil Serv, *(Christian Conciliation Service),* P.O. Box 2069, Oak Park, IL 60303 (SAN 277-6634).

Chr Educ Res Inst, *(Christian Education Research Institute; 0-943708),* Box 888-747, Atlanta, GA 30356 (SAN 238-0501) Tel 404-972-3888.

Chr Intl Pubs, *(Christian International Pubs.; 0-939868),* Rt. 2 Box 351, Point Washington, FL 32454 (SAN 281-4102).

Chr Lib Pr, *(Christian's Library Pr., Inc.; 0-934874),* P.O. Box 2226, Grand Rapids, MI 49501 (SAN 222-7061).

Chr Light
See Christian Light

Chr Lit, *(Christian Literature Crusade, Inc.; 0-87508),* P.O. Box 1449, Fort Washington, PA 19034-8449 (SAN 169-7358) Tel 215-542-1240.

Chr Marriage, *(Christian Marriage Enrichment; 0-938786),* 1913 E. 17th St., Suite 118, Santa Ana, CA 92701 (SAN 216-1141) Tel 714-542-3506.

Chr Overeaters Bks
See Brians Pub

Chr Pubns, *(Christian Pubns., Inc.; 0-87509),* 3825 Hartzdale Dr., Camp Hill, PA 17011-8870 (SAN 202-1617) Tel 717-761-7044; Toll free: 800-932-0382.

Chr Restor Assn, *(Christian Restoration Assn.; 0-9614213),* 5664 Cheviot Rd., Cincinnati, OH 45247 (SAN 687-0635) Tel 513-385-0461.

Chr Stud Ctr, *(Christian Studies Center; 0-939200),* P.O. Box 11110, Memphis, TN 38111 (SAN 220-0406) Tel 901-458-0738.

†**Chr Today,** *(Christianity Today, Inc.; 0-917463),* 465 Gundersen Dr., Carol Stream, IL 60188 (SAN 656-884X) Tel 312-260-6200; *CIP.*

Chr Univ Pr *Imprint of* **Eerdmans**

Chris Mass, *(Christopher Publishing Hse. (Massachusetts); 0-8158),* 106 Longwater Dr., Norwell, MA 02061 (SAN 202-1625) Tel 617-878-9336.

Chris Pub UT, *(Christopher Publishing; 0-936863),* P.O. Box 412, Springville, UT 84663 (SAN 200-2787) Tel 801-489-4254; Dist. by: Bookpeople, 2929 Fifth St., Berkeley, CA 94710 (SAN 168-9517); Dist. by: The Distributors, 702 S. Michigan Ave., South Bend, IN 46618 (SAN 169-2488) Tel 219-232-8500; Dist. by: New Leaf Distributing, Co., 1020 White Street SW, Atlanta, GA 30310 (SAN 169-1449) Tel 404-755-2665; Dist. by: Nutri-Books Corporation, P.O. Box 5793, Denver, CO 80223 (SAN 169-054X) Tel 303-778-8383 (SAN 169-8834); Dist. by: Pacific Pipeline, Inc., 19215 66th Ave. South, Kent, WA 98032 (SAN 169-2127) Tel 206-872-5523. *Imprints:* Littlegreen (Littlegreen).

Chrisolith Bks, *(Chrisolith Books; 0-916085),* Box 9437, New Haven, CT 06534 (SAN 294-7099) Tel 203-789-7347.

Christ Coll Coal, *(Christian College Coalition),* 1776 Massachusetts Ave. NW, No. 700, Washington, DC 20036 (SAN 268-9499) Tel 202-293-6177.

Christ Episcopal
See Pass the Plate

Christ Found, *(Christ Foundation, The; 0-910315),* P.O. Box 10, Port Angeles, WA 98362 (SAN 241-4872) Tel 206-452-5249.

Christ Nations, *(Christ for the Nations, Inc.; 0-89985),* P.O. Box 769000, Dallas, TX 75376-9000 (SAN 211-7800) Tel 214-376-1711.

Christ Serv Ctrs, *(Christian Service Ctrs., Inc.; 0-936801),* 5300 Ulmerton Rd., Clearwater, FL 33520 (SAN 699-8798) Tel 813-535-4532.

Christ United Meth Ch, *(Christ United Methodist Church; 0-9616507),* 4488 Poplar Ave., Memphis, TN 38117 (SAN 659-4379) Tel 901-682-8299.

Christendom Educ
See Christendom Pubns

Christendom Pubns, *(Christendom Pubns.; 0-931888),* Rte. 3, Box 87, Front Royal, VA 22630 (SAN 214-2570) Tel 703-636-2908. *Imprints:* Chr Coll Pr (Christendom College Press); Crossroads (Crossroads Books).

Christian Bks, *(Christian Bks. Pub. Hse.; 0-940232),* P.O. Box 959, Gardiner, ME 04345 (SAN 201-8942); Toll free: 800-228-2665.

Christian Fellow Pubs, *(Christian Fellowship Pubs., Inc.; 0-935008),* 11515 Allecingie Pkwy., Richmond, VA 23235 (SAN 207-4885) Tel 804-794-5333.

Christian Freedom, *(Christian Freedom Press, Inc.),* 518 Lincoln Ave., West Chicago, IL 60185 (SAN 289-7059).

Christian Heritage *Imprint of* **Holmes Pub**

Christian Horizons
See Jean Thomas

Christian Lib
See Barbour & Co

Christian Light, *(Christian Light Pubns., Inc.; 0-87813),* P.O. Box 1126, Harrisonburg, VA 22801 (SAN 206-7315) Tel 703-434-0768.

Christian Mini, *(Christian Ministries Pubns.; 0-911567),* 173 Woodland Ave., Lexington, KY 40502 (SAN 264-2115) Tel 606-254-6003.

Christian Pub, *(Christian Publishing Services, Inc.; 0-88144),* Subs. of Harrison House Pubs., P.O. Box 55388, Tulsa, OK 74155 (SAN 260-0285) Tel 918-584-5535; Toll free: 800-826-5992.

†**Christian Res Pr,** *(Christian Research, Pr., The; 0-915923),* P.O. Box 2013, Des Moines, IA 50310 (SAN 293-4868) Tel 515-255-8854; 3825 Kingman, Des Moines, IA 50311 (SAN 293-4876); *CIP.*

Christian Rest
See Chr Restor Assn

Christianica, *(Christianica Ctr.; 0-911346),* 6 N. Michigan Ave., Chicago, IL 60602 (SAN 204-739X) Tel 312-782-4230.

Christlife Pubs, *(Christlife Pubs.; 0-939079),* 1909 Willowbend, Deer Park, TX 77536 (SAN 662-9199) Tel 713-476-9916.

Christmas Star, *(Christmas Star Church; 0-9613670),* P.O. Box 3921, St. Augustine, FL 32085 (SAN 676-2085).

Christopher Res, *(Christopher Resources, Inc.; 0-9610034),* 34 N. White St., P.O. Box E, Frankfort, IL 60423 (SAN 268-9707) Tel 312-655-4923.

†**Christophers Bks,** *(Christopher's Bks.; 0-87922),* 390 62nd St., Oakland, CA 94618 (SAN 212-5870) Tel 415-428-1120; *CIP.*

Christophers NY
See Chrstphrs NY

Christophers Travel
See Travel Discover

Christs Mission, *(Christ's Mission; 0-935120),* P.O. Box 203, Prospect Heights, IL 60070 (SAN 211-7819) Tel 312-870-3800.

Christward, *(Christward Ministry; 0-910378),* 20560 Questhaven Rd., Escondido, CA 92025 (SAN 202-1633) Tel 619-744-1500.

Chromatic Comm, *(Chromatic Communications Enterprises, Inc.; 0-912673),* P.O. Box 3249, Walnut Creek, CA 94598 (SAN 277-6642) Tel 415-945-1602.

Chrome Yellow, *(Chrome Yellow Private Pr./Nords Studio; 0-935656),* 125 Central Ave., Crescent City, FL 32012 (SAN 200-7614) Tel 904-698-2430; Dist. by: Educational Trade Publishing, 124 Central Ave., Crescent City, FL 32012 (SAN 200-7606).

Chron Guide, *(Chronicle Guidance Pubns., Inc.; 0-912578; 1-55631),* P.O. Box 1190, Moravia, NY 13118-1190 (SAN 202-1641) Tel 315-497-0330.

†**Chronicle Bks,** *(Chronicle Bks.; 0-87701),* Div. of Chronicle Publishing Co., 1 Hallidie Plaza, Suite 806, San Francisco, CA 94102 (SAN 202-165X) Tel 415-777-7240; Toll free: 800-652-1657; *CIP.*

Chrstn Pub Palm Springs, *(Christian Pub CA; 0-939501),* P.O. Box 828, Palm Springs, CA 92263 (SAN 663-4095); 2250 Alhambra Dr., Palm Springs, CA 92262 (SAN 663-4109) Tel 619-327-1866.

Chrstphrs NY, *(Christophers, The; 0-939055),* 12 E. 48th St., New York, NY 10017 (SAN 226-6679) Tel 212-759-4050.

Chrysalis, *(Chrysalis Publishing, Ltd.; 0-940402),* P.O. Box 10690, Phoenix, AZ 85064 (SAN 218-4729) Tel 602-944-8804.

Chrysler Mus
See Chrysler Museum

Chrysler Museum, *(Chrysler Museum, The; 0-940744),* Olney Rd., & Mowbray Arch, Norfolk, VA 23510 (SAN 284-4885) Tel 804-622-1211.

Chrysopylon, *(Chrysopylon Pubs.; 0-9615640),* 1832 Lexington, San Mateo, CA 94402 (SAN 696-7116) Tel 415-574-2028; P.O. Box 3113, San Mateo, CA 94403 (SAN 698-2131).

CHSSC Phila, *(Chestnut Hill Senior Services Ctr.; 0-9616330),* 8434 Germantown Ave., Philadelphia, PA 19118 (SAN 659-0225) Tel 215-248-0180.

Chthon Pr, *(Chthon Pr.),* 77 Mark Vincent Dr., Westford, MA 01886 (SAN 208-2438).

Chulainn Press, *(Chulainn Press, Inc.; 0-917600),* 1040 Butterfield Rd., P.O. Box 770, San Anselmo, CA 94960 (SAN 209-3286).

Church Bytes, *(Church Bytes, Inc.; 0-9615086),* 201 W. Laflin, Waukesha, WI 53186 (SAN 694-3411) Tel 414-542-0905.

Church Cross, *(Church of the Cross; 0-9601178),* 4068 S. Willow Way, Denver, CO 80237 (SAN 210-055X) Tel 303-770-2272.

Church God, *(Church of God, Dept. of General Education; 0-937443),* Keith & 25th St., Cleveland, TN 37311 (SAN 659-1949) Tel 615-472-3361.

Church History, *(Church History Research & Archives; 0-935122),* 220 Graystone Dr., Gallatin, TN 37066 (SAN 211-7827) Tel 615-452-7027.

†**Church Lib,** *(Church Library Council; 0-9603060),* 5406 Quintana St., Riverdale, MD 20737 (SAN 210-5322) Tel 301-864-9308; *CIP.*

Church Man Pub, *(Church of Man Publishing Co.; 0-936435),* 6112 N. Mesa No., 210, El Paso, TX 79912 (SAN 697-8568) Tel 915-533-5777.

Church of Light, *(Church of Light; 0-87887),* Box 76862, Sanford Sta., Los Angeles, CA 90076 (SAN 209-150X) Tel 818-352-9335.

Church of Scient CA
See C Scientol CA

Church of Scient Info, *(Church of Scientology Information Service-Pubns.; 0-915598),* c/o Bridge Pubns., Inc., 4833 Fountain Ave., Los Angeles, CA 90029 (SAN 268-9774).

Church Open Door, *(Church of the Open Door; 0-935729),* 701 W. Sierra Madre Ave., Glendora, CA 91740 (SAN 693-9465) Tel 818-914-4646.

Church Scient NY, *(Church of Scientology of New York, The),* 227 W. 46th St., New York, NY 10036 (SAN 211-786X).

Church St. Leo, *(Church of St. Leo the Great Press; 0-9607014),* 227 S. Exeter St., Baltimore, MD 21202 (SAN 238-9630) Tel 301-727-8600.

Churches Alive, *(Churches Alive, International; 0-934396),* P.O. Box 3800, San Bernardino, CA 92413 (SAN 213-2982) Tel 714-886-5361.

†**Churchill,** *(Churchill Livingstone, Inc.; 0-443),* Subs. of Longman Holdings, Inc., 1560 Broadway, New York, NY 10036 (SAN 281-501X) Tel 212-819-5400; Dist. by: J.A. Majors Co., 3770A Zip Industrial Blvd., Atlanta, GA 30354 (SAN 169-1406) Tel 404-768-4956; Dist. by: Brown & Connolly, Inc., 2 Keith Way, Hingham, MA 02043 (SAN 169-3298) Tel 617-749-8570; Dist. by: Login Brothers Bk. Co., 1450 W. Randolph St., Chicago, IL 60607 (SAN 169-183X); Dist. by: J.A. Majors Co., P.O. Box 819074, Dallas, TX 75061-9074 (SAN 169-8117); Dist. by: J.A. Majors Co., 1806 Southgate Blvd., Houston, TX 77030 (SAN 169-8281); *CIP.*

Churchill Pr, *(Churchill Pr.; 0-932223),* 2948 Dothan Ln., Dallas, TX 75229 (SAN 686-6069) Tel 214-247-5390.

Churchilliana, *(Churchilliana Co.; 0-917684),* 4629 Sunset Dr., Sacramento, CA 95822 (SAN 211-2248) Tel 916-448-8053.

Chute Corp, *(Chute, Phillip B., Corporation; 0-930981),* 3585 Main St., Riverside, CA 92501 (SAN 678-8866) Tel 714-686-6970.

CIBA Med, *(CIBA Medical Education Div.; 0-914168),* Div. of CIBA-Geigy Corp., 14 Henderson Dr., West Caldwell, NJ 07006 (SAN 207-2084); Toll free: 800-631-1181 (Orders) 800-631-1162 (Editorial); Orders to: P.O. Box 18060, Newark, NJ 07101 (SAN 207-2092).

Cibbarelli & Assocs
See Pacific Info

CIBC, *(Council on Interracial Bks. for Children, Inc.; 0-930040),* 1841 Broadway, Rm. 500, New York, NY 10023 (SAN 210-7155) Tel 212-757-5339.

†Cider Mill, *(Cider Mill Pr.; 0-910380),* P.O. Box 211, Stratford, CT 06497 (SAN 201-7792) Tel 203-378-4066; *CIP.*

Ciga Pr, *(Ciga Pr.; 0-942574),* Box 654, Fallbrook, CA 92028 (SAN 239-6289) Tel 619-728-9308.

Cimarron Pr, *(Cimarron Pr., Inc.; 0-9609106),* 1721 S. Tyler, Amarillo, TX 79105 (SAN 241-2888) Tel 806-372-2364.

CIMI, *(Chemical Information Management, Inc.),* P.O. Box 2740, Cherry Hill, NJ 08034 (SAN 212-9345) Tel 609-795-6767.

Cin Post, *(Cincinnati Post, The; 0-933002),* Div. of Scripps Howard, 125 E. Court St., Cincinnati, OH 45202 (SAN 224-4703) Tel 513-352-2787.

Cincinnati Schl, *(Cincinnati Schl. of Hypnosis, The; 0-936139),* 5827 Happy Hollow Rd., Suite 101, Cincinnati, OH 45150 (SAN 697-0206) Tel 513-831-3600.

Cinco Puntos, *(Cinco Puntos Pr.; 0-938317),* 2709 Louisville, El Paso, TX 79930 (SAN 661-0080) Tel 915-566-9072.

Cinebooks, *(CineBooks, Inc.; 0-933997),* 6135 N. Sheridan Rd., Chicago, IL 60660 (SAN 692-8838) Tel 312-274-2617; Dist. by: R. R. Bowker Co. (selected titles), 205 E. 42nd St., New York, NY 10017 (SAN 214-1191) Tel 212-916-1600.

CIPRA, *(CIPRA Advertising; 0-9613520),* 314 E. Curling Dr., Boise, ID 83702 (SAN 657-6761) Tel 208-344-7770.

Circa Pr Portland, *(Circa Pr.; 0-936339),* 11015 SW Collina, Portland, OR 97219 (SAN 697-8258) Tel 503-636-7241.

Circinatum Pr, *(Circinatum Pr.; 0-931594),* Box 99309, Tacoma, WA 98499 (SAN 211-5522) Tel 206-588-2503.

Circle-A Pubs, *(Circle-A Pubs.; 0-9614415),* 8608 E. Hubbell, Scottsdale, AZ 85257 (SAN 691-2869) Tel 602-947-8233.

Circle Fine Art, *(Circle Fine Art Corp.; 0-932240),* 875 N. Michigan Ave., Suite 3160, Chicago, IL 60611 (SAN 216-1168) Tel 312-943-0664.

Circular Ltd, *(Circular Ltd.; 0-916067),* One Public Square, Cleveland, OH 44113 (SAN 294-7153) Tel 216-241-2600.

Circulo Cult Panam, *(Circulo de cultura panamericano; 0-917370),* 16 Malvern Place, Verona, NJ 07044 (SAN 226-6687) Tel 201-239-3125.

CIRI-BETH, *(Ciri-Beth; 0-9609834),* P.O. Box 1331, Tacoma, WA 98401 (SAN 268-9936) Tel 206-627-0434.

CIRMA, *(Centro de Investigaciones Regionales de Mesoamerica; 0-910443),* Affil. of Plumsock Mesoamerican Studies, P.O. Box 38, S. Woodstock, VT 05071 (SAN 260-0269) Tel 802-457-1199.

CIS Comm, *(CIS Communications, Inc.; 0-935063),* 674 Eighth St., P.O. Box 26, Lakewood, NJ 08701 (SAN 694-5953) Tel 201-367-7858.

CIS Inc, *(CIS, Inc.; 0-9615562),* 5415 The Estates Dr., Oakland, CA 94618 (SAN 696-4788) Tel 415-547-7655.

CISP, *(Council for Intercultural Studies & Programs; 0-939288),* 777 United Nations Plaza, Suite 9H, New York, NY 10017 (SAN 220-2417).

†Cistercian Pubns, *(Cistercian Pubns., Inc.; 0-87907),* WMU Sta., Kalamazoo, MI 49008 (SAN 202-1668) Tel 616-383-4985; *CIP.*

CITA NY, *(Court Interpreters & Translators Assn., Inc.; 0-939733),* Peck Slip Sta., P.O. Box 406, New York, NY 10172 (SAN 663-6128) Tel 718-965-0217.

†Citadel Pr, *(Citadel Pr.; 0-8065),* Subs. of Lyle Stuart, Inc., 120 Enterprise Ave., Secaucus, NJ 07094 (SAN 202-1676) Tel 201-866-4199; Toll free: 800-572-6657; *CIP.*

Citation *Imprint of* **Scholastic Inc**

CITE, *(Center for International Training & Education; 0-938960),* 777 United Nations Plaza, Suite 9-A, New York, NY 10017 (SAN 217-0957).

CITE Pr, *(Cite Press; 0-9611122),* P.O. Box, Huntington Station, NY 11746 (SAN 282-8812) Tel 516-673-8187.

Citizen Involve, *(Citizen Involvement Training Project; 0-934210),* c/o Univ. of Massachusetts, 225 Schl. of Education, Amherst, MA 01003 (SAN 203-3089) Tel 413-545-2038.

Citizen Pub, *(Citizen Publishing; 0-9615867),* Box 44, Chapel Hill, NC 27514 (SAN 696-3021) Tel 919-942-2194.

Citizens Defense, *(Citizens in Defense of Civil Liberties; 0-9608328),* Suite 918, 343 S. Dearborn St., Chicago, IL 60604 (SAN 240-5288) Tel 312-939-2492.

Citizens Energy, *(Citizens' Energy Project; 0-89988),* 1110 Sixth St. NW, No. 300, Washington, DC 20001-3687 (SAN 213-4799) Tel 202-289-4999.

Citizens Forum Gov, *(Citizens Forum on Self-Government, National Municipal League),* 55 W. 44th St., New York, NY 10036 (SAN 225-073X) Tel 212-730-7930.

†City Baltimore, *(City of Baltimore, Dept. of Legislative Reference; 0-916623),* City Archives & Records Management Office , 211 E. Pleasant St., Rm. 201, Baltimore, MD 21202 (SAN 296-4791) Tel 301-396-4861; *CIP.*

City Bank-Rockford, *(City National Bank & Trust Co. of Rockford; 0-9602150),* Box 1628, 1100 Broadway, Rockford, IL 61110 (SAN 212-4920).

City Coll Physics, *(City College of New York, Physics; 0-9611452),* Convent Ave. at 138th St., New York, NY 10031 (SAN 283-1074) Tel 212-690-6923.

City Coll Wk, *(City College Workshop Ctr.; 0-918374),* Convent Ave. & 136th St., N. Academic Ctr. 4th Flr. Rm.200, New York, NY 10031 (SAN 209-9233) Tel 212-690-4162.

City Desk, *(City Desk Inc. The; 0-9614280),* 1346 Connecticut Ave. NW, Washington, DC 20036 (SAN 687-4398) Tel 202-775-8587.

City Edina, *(City of Edina; 0-9605054),* 4801 W. 50th St., Edina, MN 55424 (SAN 219-774X) Tel 612-927-8861.

City Hope, *(City of Hope; 0-940876),* 1500 E. Duarte Rd., Duarte, CA 91010 (SAN 209-1267) Tel 818-359-8111.

City Hope Natl Med
See City Hope

City in Print-Bibl Proj, *(City in Print Bibliography; 0-918010; 0-88874),* P.O. Box 40157, Tucson, AZ 85717 (SAN 209-231X) Tel 602-795-9719; Dist. by: ICU Publisher, P.O. Box 40157, Tucson, AZ 85717 (SAN 219-368X).

†City Lights, *(City Lights Bks.; 0-87286),* 261 Columbus Ave., San Francisco, CA 94133 (SAN 202-1684) Tel 415-362-8193; Dist. by: Subterranean Co., 1327 W. Second, P.O. Box 10233, Eugene, OR 97440 (SAN 169-7102) Tel 503-343-6324; *CIP.*

City Miner Bks, *(City Miner Bks.; 0-933944),* P.O. Box 176, Berkeley, CA 94701 (SAN 222-7010) Tel 415-841-1511; Dist. by: Bookpeople, 2929 Fifth St., Berkeley, CA 94710 (SAN 168-9517); Dist. by: Publishers Group West, 5855 Beaudry St., Emeryville, CA 94608 (SAN 202-8522) Tel 415-658-3453.

City of Cleveland, *(City of Cleveland; 0-9615479),* Bolivar County Library, 104 Leflore Ave., Cleveland, MS 38732 (SAN 696-3099) Tel 601-843-2774.

City of Cocoa Beach, *(City of Cocoa Beach, Florida; 0-9616571),* P.O. Box 280, Cocoa Beach, FL 32923 (SAN 661-0099); 2 S. Orlando Ave., Cocoa Beach, FL 32931 (SAN 661-0102) Tel 305-783-4911.

Cityhill Pub, *(Cityhill Publishing; 0-939159),* Div. of Christian Fellowship of Columbia, 4600 Christian Fellowship Rd., Columbia, MO 65203 (SAN 662-9393) Tel 314-445-8561.

Civic Data, *(Civic-Data Corp.; 0-937628),* 523 Superior Ave., Newport Beach, CA 92663 (SAN 204-3351) Tel 714-646-1623; Orders to: Southern California Business Directory, 523 Superior Ave., Newport Beach, CA 92663 (SAN 661-9754) Tel 714-646-1623.

Civic Educ Assn
See Schl Admin Bkst

Civil War, *(Civil War Round Table of New York; 0-910382),* 168 Weyford Terr., Garden City, NY 11530 (SAN 202-3490).

Civilized Pubns, *(Civilized Pubns.; 0-933405),* 2019 S. Seventh St., Philadelphia, PA 19148 (SAN 691-4829) Tel 215-467-0744; Dist. by: New Leaf Distributing, The, 1020 White St., SW, Atlanta, GA 30310 (SAN 169-1449) Tel 404-755-2665.

Civitas, *(CIVITAS, Inc.; 0-9610016),* 60 E. 42nd St., Suite 411, New York, NY 10165 (SAN 268-5647) Tel 212-752-4530.

CK Wildlife Res, *(Kleberg, Caesar, Wildlife Research Institute; 0-912229),* Subs. of Texas A & M Univ., Texas A & I Univ., College of Agriculture, Campus Box 218, Kingsville, TX 78363 (SAN 265-1041) Tel 512-595-3922.

CKE Pubns, *(CKE Pubns.; 0-935133),* Div. of Carolyn Kyle Enterprises, 2030 N. Milroy St., Olympia, WA 98502 (SAN 695-197X) Tel 206-943-4323.

CL Pubns Inc, *(CL Pubns., Inc.; 0-9615697),* 131 Townsend St., San Francisco, CA 94107 (SAN 696-1673) Tel 415-957-9353.

Claitors, *(Claitors Publishing Div.; 0-87511),* 3165 S. Acadian at Interstate 10, Box 239, Baton Rouge, LA 70821 (SAN 206-8346).

Clancys Kitchen, *(John Clancy's Kitchen Workshop),* 324 W. 19th St., New York, NY 10011 (SAN 213-5264) Tel 212-243-0958; Orders to: Johnson Press, 49 Sheridan Ave., Albany, NY 12210 (SAN 213-5272).

Clar Call Bks, *(Clarion Call Bks.; 0-935993),* Subs. of Clarion Call Music, 102 Bluebonnet Tr., Keene, TX 76059 (SAN 696-7140) Tel 817-645-8785; P.O. Box 45, Keene, TX 76059 (SAN 698-214X).

Clare Co, *(Clare Co.; 0-918848),* 8001 Lockwood Ave., Skokie, IL 60077 (SAN 210-4040).

Claremont, *(Claremont Research & Pubns., Inc.; 0-912439),* 160 Claremont Ave., New York, NY 10027 (SAN 265-2196) Tel 212-662-0707.

Claremont CA, *(Claremont Pr.; 0-941358),* 2819 Arizona, Suite D, Santa Monica, CA 90404-1527 (SAN 240-8694) Tel 213-828-2868; Orders to: Box 3434, Will Rogers Sta., Santa Monica, CA 90403 (SAN 661-9762).

Claremont Grad, *(Claremont Graduate School, Ctr. for Developmental Studies in Education; 0-941742),* Harper Hall 200, Claremont, CA 91711 (SAN 239-1813) Tel 714-621-8075.

Claremont House, *(Claremont Hse.; 0-913680),* 231 E. San Fernando St., No. 1, San Jose, CA 95112 (SAN 203-6606) Tel 408-293-8650.

Claremont Inst, *(Claremont Institute for the Study of Statesmanship and Political Philosophy, The; 0-930783),* 4650 Arrow Hwy., Suite D-6, Montclair, CA 91763-1223 (SAN 657-6191) Tel 714-621-6825.

Claremount Pr, *(Claremount Press),* Box 177, Cooper Sta., New York, NY 10003 (SAN 219-466X).

Clarence Bass, *(Bass, Clarence, Ripped Enterprises; 0-9609714),* 528 Chama NE, Albuquerque, NM 87108 (SAN 268-229X) Tel 505-266-5858.

Claretian Pubns, *(Claretian Pubns.; 0-89570),* 221 W. Madison St., Chicago, IL 60606 (SAN 207-5598) Tel 312-236-7782.

Clarion Class *Imprint of* **Zondervan**

Clarions Call Pub, *(Clarion's Call Publishing; 0-9617176),* 225 Cory Ave., Prescott, AZ 86301 (SAN 663-1703) Tel 602-778-2090.

Clarity Pr, *(Clarity Pr.; 0-932863),* 3277 Roswell Rd., NE, Suite 469, Atlanta, GA 30305 (SAN 688-9530) Tel 404-662-6806.

†Clarity Pub, *(Clarity Publishing; 0-915488),* 75 Champlain St., Albany, NY 12204 (SAN 211-5093) Tel 518-465-4591; *CIP.*

Clark Art Inst
See S & F Clark Art

Clark County Hist Soc, *(Clark County Historical Society),* 300 W. Main St., Springfield, OH 45504 (SAN 204-3378) Tel 513-324-0657.

Clark Inc, *(Clark Publishing, Inc.; 0-913821),* P.O. Box 11003, Tacoma, WA 98411 (SAN 286-0481) Tel 206-472-4469; Orders to: P.O. Box 5603, Tacoma, WA 98405 (SAN 286-049X).

Clark Pub, *(Clark Publishing Co.; 0-931054),* Dist. by: The Caxton Printers, Ltd., P.O. Box 700, Caldwell, ID 83605 (SAN 201-9698) Tel 208-459-7421.

Clark Pub KY, *(Clark Publishing; 0-939053),* P.O. Box 435, Henderson, KY 42420 (SAN 662-9296); 3020 Zion Rd., Henderson, KY 42420 (SAN 662-930X) Tel 502-827-8995.

Clark Pubs
See Dean Clark

†**Clark U Pr,** *(Clark Univ. Pr.; 0-914206),* 950 Main St., Worcester, MA 01610 (SAN 205-6135) Tel 617-793-7206; *CIP.*

Clarke His, *(Clarke Historical Library; 0-916699),* Div. of Central Michigan Univ., Central Michigan Univ., Pk. 408, Mt. Pleasant, MI 48859 (SAN 218-6799) Tel 517-774-3352.

Clarke Memorial, *(Clarke Memorial Museum, Inc.; 0-9615641),* 240 E St., Eureka, CA 95501 (SAN 278-4505) Tel 707-443-1947.

Clarksburg-Harrison, *(Clarksburg-Harrison Bicentennial Committee; 0-9615566),* 404 W. Pike St., Clarksburg, WV 26301 (SAN 696-4877) Tel 304-624-6512.

Clarus Music, *(Clarus Music, Ltd.; 0-86704),* 340 Bellevue Ave., Yonkers, NY 10703 (SAN 216-6615) Tel 914-591-7715.

Class Media Prod, *(Class Media Productions; 0-942098),* P.O. Box 26465, Los Angeles, CA 90026 (SAN 237-9961) Tel 213-665-2970; Dist. by: Publishers Group West, 58 Beaudry St., Emeryville, CA 94608 (SAN 202-8522) Tel 415-658-3453.

Classic *Imprint of* Exposition Pr FL

Classic CA, *(Classic Pubs.; 0-9609762),* P.O. Box 49454, Los Angeles, CA 90049 (SAN 264-326X) Tel 213-476-6869.

Classic Car, *(Classic Car Club of America),* P.O. Box 443, Madison, NJ 07940 (SAN 225-5057).

Classic Cons, *(Classic Consultants Pr.; 0-935499),* Div. of Classic Consultants, Ltd., 3402 E. Libby, Phoenix, AZ 85032 (SAN 696-4966) Tel 602-992-7441.

Classic Fire, *(Classic Fire Pictures; 0-938229),* P.O. Box 240382, Memphis, TN 38124 (SAN 661-0110); 4503 Charleswood, Memphis, TN 38117 (SAN 661-0129) Tel 901-767-9367.

Classic Furn Kits, *(Classic Furniture Kits),* 343 Lantana St., Camarillo, CA 93010 (SAN 203-6614).

Classic Hse, *(Classic House; 0-931954),* P.O. Box 87564, San Diego, CA 92138-7564 (SAN 211-5816); 3409 Waco St., Suite 1, San Diego, CA 92117 (SAN 660-9457) Tel 619-275-3112.

Classic Nonfic, *(Classic Nonfiction Library; 0-9606540),* Woodward, PA 16882 (SAN 203-6622).

Classic Press *Imprint of* Gold Bk

Classic Pub, *(Classic Publishers/Louisville; 0-937222),* Prospect, KY 40059 (SAN 215-0662) Tel 502-228-4446.

Classic Theatre Child, *(Classic Theatre for Children; 0-938735),* 146 York St., New Haven, CT 06511 (SAN 661-5031) Tel 203-624-7636.

Classical Folia, *(Classical Folia),* College of the Holy Cross, Worcester, MA 01610 (SAN 207-5369).

Classics Comp, *(Classics on Computer; 0-938523),* 5435 Columbus Ave., Van Nuys, CA 91411 (SAN 661-1222) Tel 818-785-7340.

Classics Unltd, *(Classics Unlimited, Inc.; 0-936660),* 2121 Arlington Ave., Caldwell, ID 83605 (SAN 214-1868).

Clatworthy, *(Clatworthy Colorvues; 0-918290),* 111 1/2 Riverview, Santa Cruz, CA 95062 (SAN 209-5424) Tel 408-426-6401.

Claud Crawford, *(Crawford, Claud C.; 0-933697),* 4627 Martin Mill Pike, Knoxville, TN 37920 (SAN 692-5200) Tel 615-573-7248.

Claussen Bks, *(Claussen Books; 0-9603266),* 434 Arballo Dr., San Francisco, CA 94132 (SAN 211-9412) Tel 415-585-0716.

Clautice Pubs, *(E. W. Clautice, Pubs.; 0-9614359),* 231 Lynbrok Dr. N., York, PA 17402 (SAN 688-4776) Tel 717-755-6809.

Clawson, *(Clawson Printing Co.),* 107 W. Second, Frankfort, KS 66427 (SAN 215-1367).

Clay-Jon Pubs, *(Clay-Jon Publishers; 0-913103),* P.O. Box 59221, Birmingham, AL 35259-9221 (SAN 283-0310) Tel 205-951-3681; 5140 Crowley Dr., Birmingham, AL 35259-9221 (SAN 699-5721).

†**Claymont Comm,** *(Claymont Communications; 0-934254),* Box 112, Charles Town, WV 25414 (SAN 211-7010) Tel 304-725-1523; *CIP.*

Clayton Pub Hse, *(Clayton Publishing House, Inc.; 0-915644),* 3438 Russell Blvd., Suite 203, St. Louis, MO 63104 (SAN 158-6807) Tel 314-772-5757; Dist. by: People Lovers Bks, 27 N. Gore, Webster Groves, MO 63117 (SAN 200-6138).

CLCB Pr, *(CLCB Pr.),* Div. of CLCBI International Inc. of Scotland, P.O. Box 99, Newell, NC 28126 (SAN 211-2892).

CLE Pubns
See FL Bar Legal Ed

Cleaning Cons, *(Cleaning Consultant Services, Inc.; 0-9601054),* 1512 Western Ave., Seattle, WA 98101 (SAN 208-2179) Tel 206-682-9748.

Cleaning Consul
See Cleaning Cons

Clear Creek, *(Clear Creek Pubs., Inc.; 0-9609318),* P.O. Box 8008, Boulder, CO 80306 (SAN 260-1753) Tel 303-449-1278.

Clear Fork Pub, *(Clear Fork Publishing),* P.O. Box 569, Tomball, TX 77375 (SAN 698-1879).

Clear Fork Ranch, *(Clear Fork Ranch, Inc.; 0-9616868),* 4800 Bryant Irvin Ct., Ft. Worth, TX 76109-4103 (SAN 661-1575) Tel 817-737-3703.

Clear Marks, *(Marks, Clear; 0-9602388),* 2408 McKinley, Berkeley, CA 94703 (SAN 212-5285).

Clear View Pubns, *(Clear View Pubns.; 0-941156),* P.O. Box 3008, Fox Valley Mall, Aurora, IL 60505 (SAN 237-9929).

Clearview Pr, *(Clearview Press; 0-9606976),* 1927 N Hudson Ave., Chicago, IL 60614 (SAN 238-9258).

Clearwater, *(Clearwater Junior Woman's Club; 0-9615642),* P.O. Box 4061, Clearwater, FL 33518 (SAN 696-3102) Tel 813-725-2802; 105 Woodburn Ct., Safety Harbor, FL 33572 (SAN 696-3110).

†**Clearwater Pub,** *(Clearwater Publishing Co., Inc.; 0-8287; 0-88354),* 1995 Broadway, New York, NY 10023 (SAN 201-8969) Tel 212-873-2100. Primarily microfilm & microfiche, but also books, audiocassettes & videocassettes on American Indian studies, art, & architechture, history, Judaica, Latin American studies, law & peace studies, material culture. Microform distributor for ACRPP, Alpha COM GmbH, Bibliotheque Nationale, CREDOC, Emmett Microforms, France Expansion, Hachette Microeditions, Inter Documentation Co. (IDC), Irish Microforms, The Irish Times, MFO Mikrofilm Gmbh, Microform Academic Publishers, Micropress GmbH, Mindata Ltd., Georg Olms Verlag, Studio Harcourt, World Microfilms Pubns., Yushudo Booksellers; *CIP.*

Cleckley-Thigpen, *(Cleckley-Thigpen Psychiatric Associates, The),* P.O. Box 2619, Augusta, GA 30904 (SAN 238-051X) Tel 404-724-7492.

Cleis Pr, *(Cleis Pr.; 0-939416),* P.O. Box 8933, Pittsburgh, PA 15221 (SAN 284-9968) Tel 412-731-3863; P.O. Box 14684, San Francisco, CA 94114 (SAN 284-9976); Dist. by: Bookpeople, 2929 Fifth St., Berkeley, CA 94710 (SAN 168-9517) Tel 415-549-3030; Dist. by: Baker & Taylor, Eastern Div., 50 Kirby Ave., Somerville, NJ 08876 (SAN 169-4901); Dist. by: Inland Bk. Co., 22 Hemingway St., East Haven, CT 06512 (SAN 200-4151) Tel 203-467-4257.

Clementine, *(Clementine Press; 0-943880),* 2342 SW Thorton, Des Moines, IA 50321 (SAN 241-1024) Tel 515-285-0588.

Clene Pubns, *(Clene Publications),* 620 Michigan Ave. NE, Washington, DC 20064 (SAN 277-6650). Out of business.

Clergy & Laity, *(Clergy And Laity Concerned Chicago; 0-931879),* 17 N State No. 904, Chicago, IL 60602 (SAN 686-0494) Tel 312-899-1800.

Cleveland Cliffs, *(Cleveland-Cliffs; 0-9607174),* 1460 Union Congress Bldg., Cleveland, OH 44115 (SAN 239-0760) Tel 216-241-2356.

Cleveland Clinic
See Clvlnd Clinic Found

Cleveland Daycare
See M Pellegrini

Cleveland Landmarks, *(Cleveland Landmarks, Pr., Inc.; 0-936760),* 4601 E. Pleasant Valley Rd., Cleveland, OH 44131 (SAN 214-2929).

Cleveland St Univ Poetry Ctr, *(Cleveland State Univ. Poetry Ctr.; 0-914946),* Cleveland State Univ., Cleveland, OH 44115 (SAN 209-2816) Tel 216-687-3986; Dist. by: Nacscorp, Inc., 528 E. Lorain St., Oberlin, OH 44074 (SAN 169-6823) Tel 216-775-1561.

Cleveland St Univ Poetry Ser
See Cleveland St Univ Poetry Ctr

Cleydale Engineering, *(Cleydale Engineering; 0-937303),* Rte. 1, Box 217-B, Blacksburg, VA 24060 (SAN 658-7739) Tel 708-775-4915.

Click Inc, *(Click!, Inc.; 0-937187),* 7398 Washington Ave., S., Eden Prairie, MN 55344 (SAN 658-697X) Tel 612-944-8977.

Click's Cookbooks, *(Click's Cookbooks; 0-9612920),* 2714 NE 95th St., Seattle, WA 98115 (SAN 292-3300).

Cliffhanger Pr *Imprint of* Ed-it Prods

Cliffs, *(Cliff's Notes, Inc.; 0-8220),* 1701 P St., Lincoln, NE 68501 (SAN 202-1706) Tel 402-477-6971; Toll free: 800-228-4078.

CLIMB, *(C.L.I.M.B.(Creative Learning is More Beautiful); 0-914191),* Nine Heritage Dr., Freehold, NJ 07728 (SAN 287-511X) Tel 201-431-2264.

Clin Soc Assn, *(Clinical Sociology Assn.; 0-942756),* c/o General Hall, Inc., 5 Talon Way, Dix Hills, NY 11746 (SAN 692-8315) Tel 516-243-0155.

Cline-Sigmon, *(Cline-Sigmon Pubs.; 0-914760),* P.O. Box 367-T, Hickory, NC 28601 (SAN 205-6151) Tel 704-322-5090.

Clinical Hearing Consults, *(Clinical Hearing Consultants; 0-9614656),* 8100 E. Indian School Rd., P.O. Box 398, Scottsdale, AZ 85252 (SAN 692-2031) Tel 602-941-1200.

Clinical Psych, *(Clinical Psychology Publishing Co., Inc. (CPPC); 0-88422),* 4 Conant Square, Brandon, VT 05733 (SAN 201-7679) Tel 802-247-6871.

Clinitemp, *(Clinitemp, Inc.; 0-937450),* P.O. Box 40273, Indianapolis, IN 46240 (SAN 215-1375) Tel 317-872-4155.

Clipboard, *(Clipboard Pubns.; 0-9606084),* 606 Pine St., Coulee Dam, WA 99116 (SAN 216-8006) Tel 509-633-1546.

Cliveden Pr, *(Cliveden Pr., The; 0-941694),* Suite COMM. 2, 1133 13th St., NW, Washington, DC 20005 (SAN 277-6669) Tel 202-789-0231.

Cloak Dagger, *(Cloak & Dagger Pubns.; 0-937617),* 825 25th St., Ogden, UT 84401 (SAN 659-1302) Tel 801-394-4162.

Clodele, *(Clodele Enterprises, Inc.; 0-930416),* 2004 Vaugine Ave., Pine Bluff, AR 71601 (SAN 209-5432) Tel 501-534-8804.

Clone Records, *(Clone Records, Inc.; 0-9606292),* 44 Maple Rd., Rocky Point, NY 11778 (SAN 219-7766).

Close Up Foun, *(Close Up Foundation; 0-932765),* 1235 Jefferson Davis Hwy., Arlington, VA 22202 (SAN 679-1980) Tel 703-892-5400; Toll free: 800-336-5479; Dist. by: Social Studies Schl. Services, 10000 Culver Blvd., Box 802, Culver City, CA 90232 (SAN 168-9592) Tel 213-839-2436; Dist. by: Close Up Foundation, 1235 Jefferson Davis Hwy., Arlington, VA 22202 (SAN 679-1980) Tel 703-892-5400.

Closing Gap, *(Closing the Gap, Inc.; 0-932719),* P.O. Box 68, Henderson, MN 56044 (SAN 669-5833) Tel 612-248-3294.

Closson Pr, *(Closson Pr.; 0-933227),* 1935 Sampson Dr., Apollo, PA 15613-9238 (SAN 297-1712) Tel 412-337-4482.

Clothespin Fever Pr, *(Clothespin Fever Pr.; 0-9616572),* 5529 N. Figueroa, Los Angeles, CA 90042 (SAN 699-8119) Tel 213-257-4968.

Clothing Mfrs, *(Clothing Manufacturers Assn. of the U. S. A.),* 1290 Ave. of the Americas, New York, NY 10104 (SAN 224-6198) Tel 212-757-6664.

Cloud Ent
See Star-Gate

Cloud Marauder, *(Cloud Marauder Pr.),* Dist. by: SBD: Small Press Distribution, 1814 San Pablo Ave., Berkeley n, CA 94702 (SAN 204-5826) Tel 415-549-3336.

Cloud Pr, *(Cloud Marauder Pr.; 0-935713),* 1422 Bonita Ave., Berkeley, CA 94709 (SAN 696-3226) Tel 415-526-1969.

Cloud Ridge Pr, *(Cloud Ridge Pr.; 0-9615617),* P.O. Box 926, Boulder, CO 80306-0926 (SAN 696-3242) Tel 303-442-6163; Sugarloaf Star Rte., Boulder, CO 80302 (SAN 696-3250).

Cloud Ten, *(Cloud 10 Creations Inc.; 0-910349),* P.O. Box 99, Cazenovia, NY 13035 (SAN 241-2896) Tel 315-655-9517.

Cloudburst Press Bk *Imprint of Hartley & Marks*

Cloudcap, *(Cloudcap; 0-938567),* Div. of Alpenbooks, P.O. Box 27344, Seattle, WA 98125 (SAN 661-2598); 11309 Durland Pl. NE, Seattle, WA 98125 (SAN 661-2601) Tel 206-365-9192.

Cloudcrest, *(Cloudcrest; 0-9612340),* Box 333, Nashville, IN 47448 (SAN 263-9726).

Clover Intl, *(Clover International; 0-911249),* P.O. Box 928, Adelphi, MD 20783-0928 (SAN 269-0373) Tel 301-431-6617.

CLP Pubs
See Master Bks

Clvlnd Clinic Found, *(Cleveland Clinic Foundation; 0-9615424),* 9500 Euclid Ave., Cleveland, OH 44106 (SAN 696-3196) Tel 216-444-2662.

Clyde Pr, *(Clyde Pr., The; 0-933190),* 373 Lincoln Pkwy, Buffalo, NY 14216 (SAN 213-8395) Tel 716-875-4713.

Clymer Pubns, *(Clymer Pubns.; 0-89287),* P.O. Box 4520, Arleta, CA 91333-4520 (SAN 204-3416) Tel 818-767-7660; 12860 Muscatine St., Arleta, CA 91333 (SAN 658-0327).

Cmdrs-Rusty's, *(CMDRS-Rusty's Maps; 0-943714),* P.O. Box 5, Arvada, CO 80001-0005 (SAN 241-0087) Tel 303-421-8833.

Cmnty Arts, *(Community Arts, Inc.; 0-9617165),* 15 Douglass St., San Francisco, CA 94114 (SAN 662-9474) Tel 415-771-7020.

Cmnwlth Pr Worcester, *(Commonwealth Press; 0-914274),* 44 Portland St., Worcester, MA 01608 (SAN 204-3076) Tel 617-755-4391.

Cmnwlth Sci, *(Commonwealth Scientific Corp.; 0-930787),* 500 Pendleton St., Alexandria, VA 22314 (SAN 677-6094) Tel 303-221-5026.

CMPS NYC, *(Center for Modern Psychoanalytic Studies; 0-916850),* 16 W. Tenth St., New York, NY 10011 (SAN 208-7537) Tel 212-260-7050.

CMS Pub, *(CMS Publishing, Inc.; 0-932311),* Subs. of Communication Management Services, 3570 N. Rice St., St. Paul, MN 55112 (SAN 687-0414) Tel 612-484-5893.

CN *Imprint of* **Har-Row**

Cntnt Pubs SF, *(Continent Pubs.; 0-9616169),* 110 Pacific Ave., Suite 218, San Francisco, CA 94111 (SAN 699-7783).

Cntr Arab Islamic Studies
See Amana Bks

Cntr Gallery Buck Univ, *(Center Gallery of Bucknell University; 0-916279),* Bucknell Univ., Center Gallery, Lewisburg, PA 17837 (SAN 295-706X) Tel 717-524-3792.

CO Legal Pub, *(Colorado Legal Publishing Co., Inc.; 0-936381),* 1360 S. Clarkson St., Suite 300, Denver, CO 80210 (SAN 697-3337) Tel 303-778-6811.

CO Mtn Club Found, *(Colorado Mountain Club Foundation, The; 0-9617023),* 2530 W. Alameda, Denver, CO 80219 (SAN 662-6513) Tel 303-355-9620.

†**CO RR Mus,** *(Colorado Railroad Museum; 0-918654),* P.O. Box 10, Golden, CO 80402 (SAN 201-7830) Tel 303-279-4591; CIP.

CO Springs Fine Arts, *(Colorado Springs Fine Arts Ctr.; 0-916537),* 30 W. Dale St., Colorado Springs, CO 80903 (SAN 240-9372) Tel 303-634-5581. *Imprints:* Taylor Museum (Taylor Museum of the Colorado Springs Fine Arts Ctr.).

Coach Hse, *(Coach Hse. Pr., Inc.; 0-88020),* P.O. Box 458, Morton Grove, IL 60053 (SAN 201-7709) Tel 312-967-1777.

Coal Info Net, *(Coal Information Network of Kentucky),* Ashland Community College, 1400 College Dr., Ashland, KY 41101 (SAN 679-1999).

Coalition Ind Coll, *(Coalition of Independent College-University Students),* 1 Dupont Cir., NE, Washington, DC 20036 (SAN 225-7815) Tel 202-659-1747.

Coalition NE Govn, *(Coalition of Northeastern Governors Policy Research Ctr.; 0-914193),* 400 N. Capitol St. NW, Suite 382, Washington, DC 20001 (SAN 287-7317).

Coalition Women-Relig, *(Coalition on Women & Religion; 0-9603042),* 4759 15th Ave. NE, Seattle, WA 98105 (SAN 210-7880) Tel 206-525-1213.

Coalson-Kuhn, *(Coalson-Kuhn Publishing Co.; 0-915551),* P.O. Box 913, Denton, TX 76201 (SAN 291-1183) Tel 817-387-4006.

Coast Aire, *(Coast Aire Pubns.; 0-9606874),* 2823 N. Yucca St., Chandler, AZ 85224 (SAN 217-3433) Tel 602-899-6151.

Coast Pubns NY, *(Coast to Coast Pubns., Inc.; 0-915816),* 679A Hempstead Turnpike, Franklin Square, NY 11010 (SAN 223-3053) Tel 516-485-4234.

Coast to Coast, *(Coast to Coast, Bks.; 0-9602664),* 2934 NE 16th Ave., Portland, OR 97212 (SAN 212-7334) Tel 503-282-5891.

Coastal Plains, *(Coastal Plains Publishing Co.; 0-9607300),* P.O. Box 1101, Danville, VA 24541 (SAN 239-183X) Tel 919-299-7581.

Coastal Pr FL, *(Coastal Pr.; 0-9615728),* P.O. Box 5343, Sarasota, FL 33579 (SAN 695-2887) Tel 813-922-6960; 4014 Red Rock Ln., Sarasota, FL 33581 (SAN 696-0375).

Coastar Pub
See NewTEK Indust

Coastlight Pr, *(Coastlight Pr.; 0-9606288),* 210 A California Ave., Palo Alto, CA 94306 (SAN 223-2146) Tel 415-325-9088; Dist. by: Bookpeople, 2929 Fifth Ave., Berkeley, CA 94710 (SAN 168-9517) Tel 415-549-3030.

Coastline Assoc, *(Coastline Assoc.; 0-9615425),* 3111 Camino del Rio N., Suite 407, San Diego, CA 92123 (SAN 695-7374) Tel 619-563-0304.

Coastline Pub Co, *(Coastline Publishing, Co.; 0-932927),* P.O. Box 223062, Carmel, CA 92922 (SAN 692-9508) Tel 408-625-9388; Dist. by: Bookpeople, 2929 Fifth St., Berkeley, CA 94710 (SAN 168-9517) Tel 415-549-3030; Dist. by: Inland Book Co., 22 Hemingway Ave., P.O. Box 261, East Haven, CT 06512 (SAN 200-4151) Tel 203-467-4257; Dist. by: Baker & Taylor Co., Eastern Div., 50 Kirby Ave., Somerville, NJ 08876 (SAN 169-4901) Tel 201-526-8000.

COB Assocs, *(COB Assocs., Inc.; 0-938409),* P.O. Box 21416, Philadelphia, PA 19126 (SAN 661-0153); 6501 N. Gratz St., Philadelphia, PA 19126 (SAN 661-0161) Tel 215-548-6684.

Cobb Group, *(Cobb Group, Inc., The; 0-936767),* 301 N. Hurstbourne Ln., Suite 115, Louisville, KY 40222 (SAN 699-8860) Tel 502-425-7756.

Cobble Mickle Bks, *(Cobble & Mickle Bks.),* P.O. Box 3521, San Diego, CA 92103-0160 (SAN 659-395X) Tel 619-291-4235; 4285 Maryland St., San Diego, CA 92103 (SAN 659-3968); Dist. by: Quality Bks., Inc., 918 Sherwood Dr., Lake Bluff, IL 60044-2204 (SAN 169-2127).

Cobblesmith, *(Cobblesmith; 0-89166),* Box 191, RFD 1, Freeport, ME 04032 (SAN 210-346X) Tel 207-865-6495.

Cobblestone Pub, *(Cobblestone Publishing, Inc.; 0-9607638),* 20 Grove Street, Peterborough, NH 03458 (SAN 237-9937).

Cobra Co, *(Cobra Co., The; 0-933907),* 8842 SW 72 St., Apt. J-258, Miami, FL 33173 (SAN 692-7459) Tel 305-596-2887.

Cobra Pr, *(Cobra Press; 0-9600384),* 15381 Chelsea Dr., San Jose, CA 95124 (SAN 203-6657) Tel 408-559-4899.

Coburn, *(Coburn, Warren; 0-9614044),* 516 N. 11th St. Apt. D, Las Vegas, NV 89101 (SAN 684-7846).

COC, *(Chamber of Commerce),* P.O. Box 51, Philadelphia, MS 39350 (SAN 217-2968).

Cochran Pub, *(Cochran Publishing Co.; 0-936259),* Suburban Rte., Box 193, Rapid City, SD 57701 (SAN 697-3582) Tel 605-232-7242.

Cochrun, *(Cochrun, Inc.; 0-9601050),* 11933 72nd Ave., N., Seminole, FL 33542 (SAN 209-0627) Tel 813-398-5939.

Cocinero Pr, *(Cocinero Press; 0-9606366),* Box 11583, Phoenix, AZ 85061 (SAN 219-7774).

Cockpit Mgmt Trng, *(Cockpit Management Training, Inc.; 0-938051),* P.O. Box 205, Piedmont, OK 73078 (SAN 661-017X); 1209 Blugil Dr., NE, Piedmont, OK 73078 (SAN 661-0188) Tel 405-373-1357.

Cocoa Beach W, *(Cocoa Beach Woman's Club; 0-9615567),* 215 Beachwood Blvd., Melbourne Beach, FL 32951 (SAN 696-3285) Tel 305-724-6952.

Cocono
See Kokono

Coda Pr, *(Coda Pr., Inc.; 0-930956),* 700 W. Badger Rd., Suite 101, Madison, WI 53713 (SAN 211-4968). Moved, left no forwarding address.

CoDe North, *(CoDe North, Inc.; 0-9614942),* 622 Keel Ave., Rear, Memphis, TN 38107 (SAN 693-661X) Tel 901-527-7704.

Coelacanth, *(Coelacanth Pubns.; 0-918239),* 55 Bluecoat, Irvine, CA 92720 (SAN 657-5846) Tel 714-544-0914.

Coffee Break, *(Coffee Break Press; 0-933992),* P.O. Box 103, Burley, WA 98322 (SAN 212-341X) Tel 206-857-4329.

†**Coffee Hse,** *(Coffee Hse. Pr./Toothpaste Pr.; 0-915124; 0-918273),* P.O. Box 10870, Minneapolis, MN 55440 (SAN 206-3883) Tel 612-338-0125; Dist. by: Consortium Bk. Sales & Distribution, 213 E. Fourth St., St. Paul, MN 55101 (SAN 200-6049) Tel 612-221-9035; CIP. *Imprints:* Hot Choco (Hot Chocolate Books); Morning Coffee (Morning Coffee Chapbooks).

Coffeetable, *(Coffeetable Pubns.; 0-938252),* P.O. Box 884, Bay Minette, AL 36507 (SAN 215-739X) Tel 205-937-6432.

Coffin, *(Coffin, George; 0-939452),* 257 Trapelo Rd., Waltham, MA 02154 (SAN 202-1714) Tel 617-893-0057.

Cogan Prod, *(Cogan Productions; 0-939025),* 555 W. Illinois Ave., Aurora, IL 60506 (SAN 662-6491) Tel 312-896-6555.

Cohasco, *(Cohasco, Inc.; 0-940746),* Div. of Snyder Graphics, P.O. Drawer 821, Yonkers, NY 10702 (SAN 219-7243) Tel 914-476-8500.

Cohen Pub, *(Cohen Publisher; 0-9614943),* 1855 Sanford St., Philadelphia, PA 19116 (SAN 693-6555) Tel 215-698-7726.

Coin & Curr, *(Coin & Currency Institute, Inc.; 0-87184),* P.O. Box 1057, Clifton, NJ 07014 (SAN 203-5650) Tel 201-471-1441.

Coit & Assocs, *(Coit & Assocs.; 0-936475),* P.O. Box 296, South Laguna, CA 92677 (SAN 698-1283) Tel 714-499-5848.

Coker Bks
See Coker Pub

Coker Pub, *(Coker Publishing, Hse.; 0-933012),* 135 Gran-de Ct., Fayetteville, GA 30214 (SAN 284-9984) Tel 404-461-3386.

Colbben Pub, *(Colbben Publishing Co.; 0-938123),* 8455 W. 38th Ave., Wheat Ridge, CO 80033 (SAN 661-0196) Tel 303-431-7552.

Colburn & Tegg, *(Colburn & Tegg; 0-9600594),* 19709 Hollis Ave., Hollis, NY 11412 (SAN 209-1003) Tel 718-468-3278.

Colby College, *(Colby College; 0-910394),* College Editor's Office, Waterville, ME 04901 (SAN 203-5669) Tel 207-872-3000.

Cold Dreams Ent, *(Cold Dreams Enterprises; 0-937549),* P.O. Box 6022, Denver, CO 80206 (SAN 659-1213) Tel 303-973-0593; 8007 Culebra Peak, Littleton, CO 80127 (SAN 659-1221).

†**Cold Spring Harbor,** *(Cold Spring Harbor Laboratory; 0-87969),* P.O. Box 100, Cold Spring Harbor, NY 11724 (SAN 203-6185) Tel 516-367-8351; Toll free: 800-843-4388; CIP.

Colden Method, *(Colden United Methodist Women; 0-9615568),* P.O. Box 177, Colden, NY 14033 (SAN 696-3331) Tel 716-941-3197; 8476 Blanchard Rd., Colden, NY 14033 (SAN 696-334X).

Cole Hse Inc, *(Cole Hse., Inc.; 0-936297),* P.O. Box 19526, Alexandria, VA 22320-0526 (SAN 697-3302); 702 Prince St., Alexandria, VA 22314 (SAN 697-3310) Tel 703-548-3347.

Cole-Outreach, *(Cole, David M./Outreach Books),* P.O. Box 425, Corona, CA 91718 (SAN 214-2589).

Coleman Pub, *(Coleman Publishing, Inc.; 0-942494; 0-87418),* 99 Milbar Blvd., Farmingdale, NY 11735 (SAN 238-1508) Tel 516-293-0383; Toll free: 800-227-3489.

Coles Cumber, *(Coles-Cumberland Pr., International Inc.; 0-930893),* P.O. Box 9925, Phoenix, AZ 85068 (SAN 679-1964) Tel 602-943-2643.

Colgate U Pr, *(Colgate Univ. Pr.; 0-912568),* 304 Lawrence Hall, Hamilton, NY 13346 (SAN 204-3181) Tel 315-824-1000.

Colgin Pub, *(Colgin Publishing; 0-9604582),* Box 301, Manlius, NY 13104 (SAN 240-0898) Tel 315-682-6081.

Colin-Pr, *(Colin-Pr.; 0-9613844),* 128 Dean St., Brooklyn, NY 11201 (SAN 681-9710) Tel 718-852-7270; Dist. by: Baker & Taylor Co., Midwest Div., 501 Gladiola Ave., Momence, IL 60954 (SAN 169-2100) Tel 815-472-2444; Dist. by: The Distributors, 702 S. Michigan, South Bend, IN 46618 (SAN 169-2488) Tel 219-232-8500.

Coll Acceptance, *(College Acceptance; 0-9615165),* 2 Clover Ln., Randolph, NJ 07869 (SAN 694-3624) Tel 201-895-3390.

Coll Admin Pubns, *(College Administration Pubns., Inc.; 0-912557),* Box 8492, Asheville, NC 28814 (SAN 240-8155) Tel 704-252-0883.

Coll Am Pathol, *(College of American Pathologists; 0-930304),* 7400 N. Skokie Blvd., Skokie, IL 60077 (SAN 224-4160) Tel 312-677-3500.

Coll & U Personnel, *(College & Univ. Personnel Assn.; 0-910402),* 11 Dupont Cir., Suite 120, Washington, DC (SAN 236-5170).

Coll & U Pr
See New Coll U Pr

Coll Atlantic, *(College of the Atlantic; 0-9601024),* 105 Eden St., Bar Harbor, ME 04609 (SAN 208-7235) Tel 207-288-5015.

Coll Comm Health, *(College of Community Health Sciences),* P.O. Box 6291, University, AL 35486 (SAN 287-2684); Dist. by: Univ. of Alabama Pr., P.O. Box 2877, University, AL 35486 (SAN 287-2692).

Coll Ent Exam
See College Bd

Coll Kids Cook, *(College Kids Cookbooks; 0-912848),* 624 N. Bailey Ave., Fort Worth, TX 76107 (SAN 201-761X) Tel 817-626-4083.

†**Coll Placement,** *(College Placement Council, Inc.; 0-913936),* 62 Highland Ave., Bethlehem, PA 18017 (SAN 201-7822) Tel 215-868-1421; CIP.

Coll Store, *(College Store; 0-910408),* Middlebury College, 5 Hillcrest Rd., Middlebury, VT 05753 (SAN 203-5693) Tel 802-388-3711.

Coll Survival, *(College Survival, Inc.; 0-942456),* 2650 Jackson Blvd., Rapid City, SD 57702 (SAN 238-1516); Toll free: 800-528-8323 Tel 605-341-3901.

Coll Wooster, *(College of Wooster, Office of Pubns.; 0-9604658),* Wooster, OH 44691 (SAN 203-5707) Tel 216-263-2000.

Collaborare Pub, *(Collaborare Publishing; 0-931881),* 354 Front, Upper Sandusky, OH 43351 (SAN 686-0486) Tel 419-294-3207; Dist. by: Gallopade: Carole Marsh Bks., General Delivery, Bath, NC 27808 (SAN 213-8441) Tel 919-923-4291.

Collaborative Learn, *(Collaborative Learning Systems; 0-910817),* P.O. Box 37043, Tucson, AZ 85740 (SAN 269-0721) Tel 602-626-1019.

Collage Inc, *(Collage, Inc.; 0-938728),* Subs. of Whitehall Co., 1200 S. Willis Ave., Wheeling, IL 60090 (SAN 205-5244) Tel 312-541-9290.

Collamore Educational
See Heath

Colleagues Pr Inc, *(Colleagues Pr., Inc.; 0-937191),* Box 4007, East Lansing, MI 48823 (SAN 658-487X) Tel 517-337-1054; 311 Kensington Rd., East Lansing, MI 48823 (SAN 658-4888).

Colleasius Pr, *(Colleasius Press; 0-941036),* P.O. Box 514, Goffstown, NH 03045 (SAN 212-1522) Tel 603-529-2222.

Collector Bks, *(Collector Bks.; 0-89145),* Div. of Schroeder Publishing Co., Inc., 5801 Kentucky Dam Rd., Paducah, KY 42001 (SAN 157-5368) Tel 502-898-6211; Toll free: 800-626-5420; P.O. Box 3009, Paducah, KY 42001 (SAN 200-7479).

Collectors, *(Collectors Club, Inc.; 0-912574),* 22 E. 35th St., New York, NY 10016-3806 (SAN 202-1722) Tel 212-683-0559.

Collectors Choice, *(Collector's Choice; 0-9602742),* c/o French-Bray Inc., P.O. Box 698, Glen Burnie, MD 21061 (SAN 204-2479) Tel 301-768-6000.

Collectors Club IL, *(Collector's Club of Chicago, Inc.; 0-916675),* 1029 N. Dearborn, Chicago, IL 60610 (SAN 297-0325) Tel 312-441-7790.

Colleen Ent, *(Colleen Enterprises, Inc.; 0-9616698),* P.O. Box 23417, Honolulu, HI 96822 (SAN 661-020X); 1030D Awawamalu St., Honolulu, HI 96821 (SAN 661-0218) Tel 808-946-1226.

College Bd, *(College Board, The; 0-87447),* 888 Seventh Ave., New York, NY 10106 (SAN 203-4667) Tel 212-582-6210; Orders to: College Board Pubns., P.O. Box 886, New York, NY 10101 (SAN 203-5685).

College Choice, *(College Choice Pubns.; 0-935275),* 55 Wedgewood Rd., West Newton, MA 02165 (SAN 695-7439) Tel 617-965-4828.

College Div Imprint of Watts

College Engineering KS, *(Kansas State Univ., College of Engineering; 0-9609342),* Durland Hall, Manhattan, KS 66506 (SAN 260-213X) Tel 913-532-5590.

†**College-Hill,** *(College-Hill Pr., Inc.; 0-316),* Subs. of Little, Brown & Co., 4284 41st St., San Diego, CA 92105 (SAN 220-0414) Tel 619-563-8899; Toll free: 800-854-2541; Orders to: Little, Brown & Co., 200 West St., Waltham, MA 02254 (SAN 661-9789) Tel 617-890-0250; CIP.

College Pr Pub, *(College Pr. Publishing Co., Inc.; 0-89900),* Box 1132, 205 N. Main, Joplin, MO 64802 (SAN 211-9951) Tel 417-623-6280; Toll free: 800-641-7148.

College Readings, *(College Readings, Inc.; 0-916580),* P.O. Box 168, Clifton, VA 22024 (SAN 206-8354).

College Skills, *(College Skills Ctr.; 0-89026),* 320 W. 29th St., Baltimore, MD 21211 (SAN 206-3433) Tel 301-235-1700; Toll free: 800-638-1010; 2936 Remington Ave., Baltimore, MD 21211 (SAN 661-9797) Tel 301-235-1722.

Collegiate Pub
See Best Bks Pub

Collegiate Visitors, *(Collegiate Visitors Guides; 0-9600260),* 170 Bridge Rd., Hillsborough, CA 94010 (SAN 203-5723).

†**Collegium Bk Pubs,** *(Collegium Bk. Pub., Inc.; 0-89669),* 525 Executive Blvd., Elmsford, NY 10523 (SAN 214-2341); CIP.

Collier Imprint of Macmillan

Colman Pubs, *(Colman Pubs.; 0-9602456),* 1147 Elmwood, Stockton, CA 95204 (SAN 212-4939) Tel 209-464-9503.

Colo Assoc, *(Colorado Associated Univ. Pr., Univ. of Colorado; 0-87081),* 1344 Grandview Ave., Univ. of Colorado, Boulder, CO 80309 (SAN 202-1749) Tel 303-492-7191; P.O. Box 480, Univ. of Colorado, Boulder, CO 80309 (SAN 658-0343).

Colo Big Game, *(Colorado Big Game Trophy Records, Inc.; 0-9611376),* 2707 Holiday Lane, Colorado Springs, CO 80909 (SAN 283-9385) Tel 703-590-3638.

Colo Classics, *(Colorado Classics; 0-9607198),* Rt. One, P.O. Box 434, Calhoun, LA 71225 (SAN 239-0779) Tel 318-396-1457.

Colo Coll Music, *(Colorado College Music Pr.; 0-933894),* Colorado Springs, CO 80903 (SAN 213-6600) Tel 303-473-2233.

Colo Creat Supply, *(Colorado Creative Supply, Inc.; 0-911613),* 2900 Cherryridge Rd., Englewood, CO 80110 (SAN 263-9734) Tel 303-761-1798.

Colo Holistic, *(Colorado Holistic Health Network; 0-912539),* P.O. Box 61297, Denver, CO 80206 (SAN 265-2218) Tel 303-399-1840.

Colo Leisure, *(Colorado Leisure Sports; 0-9613458),* Box 1953, Estes Park, CO 80517 (SAN 669-6686) Tel 303-586-6846.

Colo River Pr, *(Colorado River Pr.; 0-931302),* P.O. Box 7547, Austin, TX 78713 (SAN 211-1179) Tel 512-452-0989.

†**Colo Sch Mines,** *(Colorado Schl. of Mines; 0-918062),* Pubns. Dept. Sales, Golden, CO 80401 (SAN 201-7962) Tel 303-273-3607; Toll free: 800-446-9488; CIP.

Colo Sch Mining
See Colo Sch Mines

†**Cologne Pr,** *(Cologne Pr.; 0-9602310),* P.O. Box 682, Cologne, NJ 08213 (SAN 214-2937) Tel 609-965-5163; CIP.

Colonial Pr AL, *(Colonial Pr.; 0-938991),* 1237 Stevens Rd, SE, Bessemer, AL 35023 (SAN 662-6599) Tel 205-428-8327. Do not confuse with Colonial Pr. of Cedar Knolls, NJ.

Colonial Pub, *(Colonial Publishing, Inc.; 0-939435),* 65 Oakway Rd., Timonium, MD 21093 (SAN 663-4079) Tel 301-666-3380.

Colonial Soc MA Imprint of U Pr of Va

Colony Pub, *(Colony Publishing, Ltd.; 0-934651),* Div. of Eastern Marketing, 8000 Franklin Farms Dr., Richmond, VA 23288 (SAN 694-0749) Tel 804-288-2884; Dist. by: Talman Co., 150 Fifth Ave., Rm. 514, New York, NY 10011 (SAN 200-5204) Tel 212-620-3182.

Colophon, *(Colophon Book Shop, The),* P.O. Box E, Epping, NH 03042 (SAN 213-8409) Tel 603-679-8006.

Colophone Pub, *(Colophone Publishing; 0-937873),* 217 Sampson St., Clinton, NC 28328 (SAN 659-4581) Tel 919-592-2170.

Color Center, *(Color Center U. S. A., Inc.; 0-9615447),* 610 E. 250 N., Centerville, UT 84014 (SAN 695-7463) Tel 801-298-0621.

Color Coded Charting, *(Color Coded Charting & Filing Systems; 0-9605902),* 7759 California Ave., Riverside, CA 92504 (SAN 211-1888) Tel 714-688-0800.

Color Market, *(Color Market, Inc., The; 0-940014),* 3177 MacArthur Blvd., Northbrook, IL 60062 (SAN 216-8049) Tel 312-564-3770.

Color Pr, *(Color Charisma Pr.; 0-916359),* 3127 Presidential Dr., Atlanta, GA 30340 (SAN 295-7213) Tel 404-458-3580; Dist. by: PMG International, 1343 Columbia, No. 405, Richardson, TX 75081 (SAN 200-4763).

Colorado Expr, *(Colorado Express, The; 0-939396),* 18214 Capitol Hill Sta., Denver, CO 80218 (SAN 216-5929) Tel 303-320-6976.

Colourpicture, *(Colourpicture Pubs., Inc.; 0-938440),* 76 Atherton St., Boston, MA 02130 (SAN 216-2318); Dist. by: Smith Novelty Co., 460 Ninth St., San Francisco, CA 94103 (SAN 216-2326) Tel 415-861-4900.

Coltharp Pub, *(Coltharp Publishing Co.),* P.O. Box 7461, Amarillo, TX 79109 (SAN 240-1398).

Colton Bk, *(Colton Bk. Imports),* 908 Southgate Ave., Daly City, CA 94015 (SAN 204-7136).

Colton Found, *(Colton, Ann Ree, Foundation; 0-917189),* 336 W. Colorado St., P.O. Box 2057, Glendale, CA 91209 (SAN 655-8798) Tel 818-244-0113; Dist. by: DeVorss & Co., P.O. Box 550, 1046 Princeton Dr., Marina del Rey, CA 90294 (SAN 168-9886).

†**Coltrane & Beach,** *(Coltrane & Beach Bk.; 0-913425),* Box 6249, Westlake Village, CA 91359 (SAN 285-9025) Tel 213-889-4052; Dist. by: Kampmann & Co., Nine E. 40th St., New York, NY 10016 (SAN 202-5191) Tel 212-685-2928; CIP.

Colum Pr MD, *(Columbia Pr.; 0-936051),* 7304 Silent Bird Ct., Columbia, MD 21045 (SAN 697-0257) Tel 202-387-4398.

Columba Pub, *(Columba Publishing Co.; 0-938655),* Div. of V. C. Kistler & Assocs., 2661 W. Market St., Fairlawn, OH 44313 (SAN 661-132X) Tel 216-836-2805.

Columbia Bks, *(Columbia Bks. Inc., Pubs.; 0-910416),* 1350 New York Ave., NW, Suite 207, Washington, DC 20005 (SAN 202-1757) Tel 202-737-3777.

Columbia Bookkeeping
See Columbia Busn Sys

Columbia Busn Sys, *(Columbia Business Systems Inc.; 0-9604828),* 21 George St., Lowell, MA 01852 (SAN 215-8531) Tel 617-453-0154.

Columbia College Chi, *(Columbia College Chicago; 0-932026),* c/o Columbia College, 600 S. Michigan Ave., Chicago, IL 60605 (SAN 204-3041) Tel 312-663-1600.

†Columbia County Hist Soc., *(Columbia County Historical Society; 0-88023),* P.O. Box 197, Orangeville, PA 17859 (SAN 217-345X) Tel 717-683-6011; CIP.

Columbia Enter, *(Columbia Enterprise; 0-937343),* 20 Jules Dr., Albany, NY 12205 (SAN 699-8097) Tel 518-438-2069; Orders to: Bookhouse, Inc., 208 W. Chicago St., Jonesville, MI 49250-0125 (SAN 662-4073) Tel 517-849-2117.

Columbia Hse Pub, *(Columbia Hse. Publishing Corp.; 0-942200),* P.O. Box 1711, Clemson, SC 29633 (SAN 237-9422).

Columbia Lang Serv, *(Columbia Language Services; 0-9604126),* P.O. Box 28365, Washington, DC 20038 (SAN 213-9936) Tel 301-587-4979.

Columbia Law, *(Columbia University School of Law),* 435 W 116th St, New York, NY 10027 (SAN 237-6601).

Columbia Pictures, *(Columbia Pictures Pubns.; 0-913650),* 15800 NW 48th Ave., Miami, FL 33014 (SAN 203-042X) Tel 305-620-1500; Toll free: 800-327-7643 (outside FL).

†Columbia Pub, *(Columbia Publishing Co., Inc.; 0-914366),* Drawer AA, Frenchtown, NJ 08825 (SAN 201-8977) Tel 201-996-2141; Dist. by: Vanguard Press, Inc., 424 Madison Ave., New York, NY 10017 (SAN 202-9316) Tel 212-753-3906; CIP.

Columbia Scholastic, *(Columbia Scholastic Pr. Assn.; 0-916084),* Div. of Columbia University, Box 11, Central Mailroom, Columbia Univ., New York, NY 10027 (SAN 127-9750) Tel 212-280-3311.

Columbia U Ctr Soc Sci, *(Columbia Univ., Center for the Social Sciences; 0-938436),* 420 W. 118th St., 814 I.A.B., New York, NY 10027 (SAN 215-7403) Tel 212-280-3621. Do Not Confuse with Columbia Univ. Pr., Columbia Schl of Social Work, or Teachers College.

Columbia U E Asian Inst, *(Columbia Univ., East Asian Institute; 0-913418),* 420 W. 118th St., New York, NY 10027 (SAN 204-1790) Tel 212-280-2591.

Columbia U GPPPA, *(Columbia Univ., Graduate Program in Public Policy & Administration; 0-910955),* 400 W. 119th St., Apt. 10J, New York, NY 10027 (SAN 269-1183).

Columbia U Libs, *(Columbia Univ. Libraries; 0-9607862),* 535 W. 114th St., New York, NY 10027 (SAN 211-1896) Tel 212-280-2231.

Columbia U Oral Hist Res, *(Columbia Univ., Oral History Research Office; 0-9602492),* Box 20, Butler Library, New York, NY 10027 (SAN 223-4742) Tel 212-280-2273.

†Columbia U Pr, *(Columbia Univ. Pr.; 0-231),* 562 W. 113th St., New York, NY 10025 (SAN 212-2472) Tel 212-316-7100; Orders to: 136 S. Broadway, Irvington-on-Hudson, NY 10533 (SAN 212-2480) Tel 914-591-9111; CIP. Imprints: King's Crown Paperbacks (King's Crown Paperbacks).

Columbia U Res
See CU Ctr Career Res

Columbine *Imprint of Fawcett*

Columbine Pr, *(Columbine Press; 0-9609108),* Box 845, Aspen, CO 81612 (SAN 241-483X) Tel 303-925-6025.

Columbine Pubns, *(Columbine Pubns.; 0-9613830),* Subs. of Jacquelyn Peake Assocs., 1013 Mirrormere Cir., Ft. Collins, CO 80526 (SAN 681-9745) Tel 303-493-6755.

Columbus Mus Art, *(Columbus Museum of Art; 0-918881),* 480 E. Broad St., Columbus, OH 43215 (SAN 278-5102).

Columbus Single, *(Columbus Single Scene; 0-935913),* 55 Caren Ave. Suite 202, Worthington, OH 43085 (SAN 696-7248) Tel 614-436-2076.

Columbus Youth Hostels, *(Columbus Council of American Youth Hostels; 0-9616175),* P.O. Box 23111, Columbus, OH 43223 (SAN 699-8658); 629 Dennison, Columbus, OH 43215 (SAN 658-3059) Tel 406-721-1776.

Columella Pr, *(Columella Pr.; 0-9605972),* 5040 N. 15th Ave. No. 408, Phoenix, AZ 85015 (SAN 216-7247) Tel 602-254-5015.

Colutron Research, *(Colutron Research Corporation; 0-933407),* 5420 Arapahoe Ave., Boulder, CO 80303 (SAN 691-4888) Tel 303-443-5211.

Colwell
See Colwell Syst

Colwell Syst, *(Colwell Systems, Inc.; 0-940012),* Subs. of Deluxe Check Printer, Inc., 201 Kenyon Rd., Champaign, IL 61820 (SAN 208-1431) Tel 217-351-5400; Toll free: 800-248-7000; Toll free: 800-233-7777.

Colwyn-Tangno, *(Colwyn-Tangno),* 96 Old River Rd., Wilkes Barre, PA 18702 (SAN 215-7411).

COMAL Users, *(COMAL Users Group, USA, Ltd.; 0-928411),* 6041 Monona Dr., Madison, WI 53716 (SAN 669-5256) Tel 608-222-4432.

Coman Assocs, *(Coman Assocs.),* P.O. Box 9602, Tulsa, OK 74157 (SAN 698-1887).

Combustion Eng, *(Combustion Engineering Power Systems Group; 0-9605974),* 1000 Prospect Hill Rd., Dept. 7015-1921, Windsor, CT 06095 (SAN 216-7255) Tel 203-285-2344.

Comedy Ctr, *(Comedy Ctr., The),* Div. of Assocs. International, 700 Orange St., Wilmington, DE 19801 (SAN 276-9751) Tel 302-656-2209; Toll free: 800-441-7098.

Comedy Writ, *(Comedy Writings & Co.; 0-9609224),* 2034 Grace Ave., Los Angeles, CA 90068 (SAN 240-9771).

Comenius World, *(Comenius World Council; 0-916824),* 247 South St., Hartford, CT 06114 (SAN 208-6050) Tel 203-524-5741.

Comet Pr, *(Comet Pr.; 0-939517),* 1259 El Camino Real, Suite 251, Menlo Park, CA 94025 (SAN 663-3595) Tel 408-294-1948.

Comet Pub, *(Comet Publishing Co., The; 0-9616742),* Box 6507, Napa, CA 94581 (SAN 661-0250); 2400 Silverado Trail, St. Helena, CA 94574 (SAN 661-0269) Tel 707-963-2559.

Comicana, *(Comicana, Inc., Book Div.; 0-940420),* Div. of Comicana, Inc., RFD 2, Box 242, Hickory Kingdom Rd., Bedford, NY 10506 (SAN 219-7782) Tel 914-939-3035; Dist. by: Henry Holt & Co., 521 Fifth Ave., 6th Flr., New York, NY 10175 (SAN 200-6472) Tel 212-599-7600.

Comico Comic Co, *(Comico The Comic Co.; 0-938965),* 1547 DeKalb St., Norristown, PA 19401 (SAN 661-6836) Tel 215-277-4305.

Comm Abol Prison, *(Committee to Abolish Prison Slavery; 0-910007),* P.O. Box 3207, Washington, DC 20010 (SAN 241-3280) Tel 202-797-7721.

Comm Adv Public Interest, *(Commission for the Advancement of Public Interest Organizations; 0-9602744),* 1875 Connecticut Ave., NW, No. 1010, Washington, DC 20009 (SAN 213-0408).

Comm & Family, *(Univ. of Chicago, Community & Family Study Ctr.; 0-89836),* 1411 E. 60th St., Chicago, IL 60637 (SAN 276-4164) Tel 312-753-2974.

Comm & Learning, *(Communication & Learning Innovators Ltd.; 0-932361),* 4906 Painters St., New Orleans, LA 70122 (SAN 687-3723) Tel 504-282-1174.

Comm Architects, *(Communication Architects; 0-935597),* P.O. Box 300, Lynnwood, WA 98046-0300 (SAN 696-3544) Tel 206-774-4461.

Comm Arts, *(Communicative Arts Group; 0-941874),* Div. of Beautiful You, Inc., 1343 Columbia Suite 405, Richardson, TX 75081 (SAN 239-1848) Tel 214-690-1200.

Comm Builders, *(Community Builders; 0-9604422),* Canterbury, Shaker Rd., NH 03224 (SAN 215-3009) Tel 603-783-4743.

Comm Channels, *(Communication Channels, Inc.; 0-915962; 0-916164),* 6255 Barfield Rd., Atlanta, GA 30328 (SAN 203-8641) Tel 404-256-1490; Toll free: 800-241-9834.

Comm Chi Hist & Arch, *(Commission on Chicago Historical & Architectural Landmarks; 0-934076),* 320 N. Clark, Chicago, IL 60610 (SAN 213-7313); Dist. by: Chicago Review Pr., 820 N. Franklin, Chicago, IL 60610 (SAN 213-5744) Tel 312-337-0747.

Comm Collaborators, *(Community Collaborators; 0-930388),* P.O. Box 5429, Charlottesville, VA 22905 (SAN 213-3008) Tel 804-977-1126.

Comm Con Ev, *(Community for Conscious Evolution, The; 0-9607066),* 171 Jackson St., Newton, MA 02159 (SAN 238-9657) Tel 617-964-7448.

Comm Consultants, *(Communication Consultants International; 0-938320),* P.O. Box 1212, San Diego, CA 92112 (SAN 215-742X).

Comm Coun Great NY, *(Community Council of Greater New York; 0-86671),* 275 Seventh Ave. 12th Fl., New York, NY 10001 (SAN 203-0047) Tel 212-741-8844.

Comm Creat, *(Communication Creativity; 0-918880),* P.O. Box 213, Saguache, CO 81149 (SAN 210-3478) Tel 303-589-8223.

Comm Creat Non-Violence, *(Community for Creative Non-Violence; 0-9611972),* 1345 Euclid St., NW, Washington, DC 20009 (SAN 277-6677) Tel 202-332-4332.

†Comm Econ Dev, *(Committee for Economic Development; 0-87186),* 477 Madison Ave., New York, NY 10022 (SAN 202-1765) Tel 212-688-2063; CIP.

Comm Europe Comm, *(Commission of the European Communities),* 2100 M St. NW, Suite 707, Washington, DC 20037 (SAN 680-0297) Tel 202-862-9500.

Comm Foun DC, *(Community Foundation of Greater Washington Inc.; 0-933409),* 3221 M St. NW, Washington, DC 20007 (SAN 686-1873) Tel 202-338-8993.

Comm Inst Coop, *(Committee on Institutional Cooperation),* 302 E. John St., Suite 1705, Champaign, IL 61820 (SAN 269-1744).

Comm Intervention, *(Community Intervention, Inc.; 0-9613416),* 529 S. Seventh St., Suite 570, Minneapolis, MN 55415 (SAN 656-9706) Tel 612-332-6537.

Comm Lib, *(Communications Library; 0-934339),* Div. of Communications Institute, Lockbox 5891, San Francisco, CA 94101-5891 (SAN 693-6091) Tel 415-626-5050.

Comm Materials, *(Communication Materials Center; 0-940912),* 110 Rices Mill Rd., Wyncote, PA 19095 (SAN 207-9356) Tel 215-884-0928.

Comm Media, *(Communications Media Ctr.; 0-941888),* New York Law Schl., 57 Worth St., New York, NY 10013 (SAN 238-227X) Tel 212-966-2053.

Comm Natl Security, *(Committee for National Security, The; 0-937115),* 1601 Connecticut Ave., NW, Washington, DC 20009 (SAN 658-4934) Tel 202-745-2450.

Comm Networks, *(Communication Networks, Inc.; 0-935419),* 102 W. Leigh St., Richmond, VA 23220 (SAN 696-3587) Tel 804-225-7868; Toll free: 800-882-4800.

Comm Nuclear Respon, *(Committee for Nuclear Responsibility, Inc.; 0-932682),* Main P.O. Box 11207, San Francisco, CA 94101 (SAN 212-1530) Tel 415-776-8299.

Comm Peace, *(Commission to Study the Organization of Peace),* 866 United Nations Plaza, New York, NY 10017 (SAN 203-5324).

Comm Pr, *(Communitarian Press; 0-932225),* Rt. 1, Box 159, Kyle, TX 78640 (SAN 686-6077) Tel 512-398-7513.

†Comm Pr CA, *(Communication Pr.; 0-918850),* Box 22541, Sunset St., San Francisco, CA 94122 (SAN 210-4067) Tel 415-383-1914; CIP.

†Comm Pr Inc, *(Communications Pr., Inc.; 0-89461),* 1735 DeSales St., NW, Washington, DC 20036 (SAN 210-3486) Tel 202-639-8822; CIP.

Comm Present Danger, *(Committee on the Present Danger),* 905 16th St., NW, Washington, DC 20006 (SAN 224-0971) Tel 202-628-2409.

†Comm Res, *(Communications Research; 0-9611910),* 12267 Natural Bridge Rd., Bridgeton, MO 63044 (SAN 286-0813) Tel 314-739-1742; CIP.

Comm Res OH, *(Communication Resources; 0-930921),* 1425 W. Maple St. P.O. Box 2625, North Canton, OH 44720 (SAN 686-1830) Tel 216-499-1950.

Comm Research Assocs, *(Communication Research Assocs., Inc.; 0-9615952),* 7100 Baltimore Blvd., Suite 500, College Park, MD 20740 (SAN 697-3418) Tel 301-927-3998.

Comm Restore Const, *(Committee to Restore the Constitution, Inc.),* P.O. Box 986, Fort Collins, CO 80522 (SAN 225-6398).

Comm Rights Rumania, *(Committee for Human Rights in Rumania; 0-9605258),* P.O. Box J, Gracie Sta., New York, NY 10028 (SAN 225-6606) Tel 212-289-5488.

Comm Sci Investigation, *(Committee for Scientific Investigation of Claims of Paranormal),* 3151 Bailey Ave., Buffalo, NY 14215 (SAN 285-0001); P.O. Box 229, Central Park Sta., Buffalo, NY 14215 (SAN 285-001X) Tel 716-834-3223.

Comm Serv
See Comm Serv OH

Comm Serv OH, *(Community Service, Inc.; 0-910420),* 114 E. Whiteman, Yellow Springs, OH 45387 (SAN 203-5758) Tel 513-767-2161; P.O. Box 243, Yellow Springs, OH 45387 (SAN 669-0483).

Comm Serv Soc NY, *(Community Service Society of New York; 0-88156),* Office of Information 105 E. 22nd St., New York, NY 10010 (SAN 204-3149) Tel 212-254-8900.

Comm Single Adopt, *(Committee for Single Adoptive Parents),* P.O. Box 15084, Chevy Chase, MD 20815 (SAN 225-8862).

Comm Skills, *(Communication Skills/Press; 0-911703),* 926 Coachella Ave., Sunnyvale, CA 94086 (SAN 263-9742) Tel 408-738-2434.

Comm Strat Inc, *(Communication Strategies, Inc.; 0-930353),* P.O. Box 14773, Albuquerque, NM 87191 (SAN 670-7599) Tel 505-293-9159.

Comm Stud
See Comn Studies

Comm Support Solidarity, *(Committee in Support of Solidarity, Inc.; 0-935417),* 275 Seventh Ave., 25th Flr., New York, NY 10001 (SAN 696-3463) Tel 212-989-0909.

Comm Tech, *(Communications Technology, Inc.; 0-918232),* Main St., Greenville, NH 03048 (SAN 159-8198) Tel 603-878-1441.

Comm Trends Inc, *(Communications Trends, Inc.; 0-88709),* 2 East Ave., Larchmont, NY 10538 (SAN 285-9092) Tel 914-833-0600.

Comm Unltd, *(Communicatons Unlimited),* 11032 Pinyon Dr., Northglenn, CO 80234 (SAN 209-5459).

Comm Unltd CA, *(Communication Unltd. (CA); 0-910167),* P.O. Box 1001, Carpinteria, CA 93013 (SAN 682-2568).

Comm Voluntary Serv & Action, *(Commission on Voluntary Service & Action),* 475 Riverside Dr., Rm. 1126, New York, NY 10115 (SAN 210-7899) Tel 212-870-2801.

†Comm Wholistic Growth, *(Community Wholistic Growth Center Inc; 0-918833),* 10 W. Lockwood, Webster Groves, St Louis, MO 63119 (SAN 682-2363); *CIP.*

Command Comp, *(Command Computer Corp.),* 36 Columbia Terr., Weehawken, NJ 07087 (SAN 694-2970) Tel 201-865-8500.

Command Prods, *(Command Productions; 0-933132),* Box 26348, San Francisco, CA 94126 (SAN 223-3150).

Comment Pr, *(Commentary Pr.; 0-914675),* P.O. Box 43532, Atlanta, GA 30336 (SAN 289-7040) Tel 404-949-4947.

Commerce, *(Commerce Clearing Hse., Inc.; 0-8080),* 4025 W. Peterson Ave., Chicago, IL 60646 (SAN 202-3504) Tel 312-583-8500.

Commercial Law, *(Commercial Law League of America),* 222 W. Adams St., Chicago, IL 60606 (SAN 225-0845) Tel 312-236-4942.

Committee IL, *(Committee, The; 0-937352),* 2901 S. King Dr., No. 515, Chicago, IL 60616 (SAN 217-0965) Tel 312-567-9522.

Commodity Ctr, *(Commodity Ctr. Corp.; 0-9615644),* 600 S. Dearborn, No. 1911, Chicago, IL 60605 (SAN 696-3528) Tel 312-663-1368.

Commodity Res, *(Commodity Research Bureau, Inc.; 0-910418),* Subs. of Knight-Ridder Business Information Service, 75 Montgomery St., Jersey City, NJ 07302 (SAN 204-3092) Tel 201-451-7500.

Common Cause, *(Common Cause; 0-914389),* 2030 M St. NW, Washington, DC 20036 (SAN 219-7790) Tel 202-833-1200.

Common Hap, *(Common-Sense Happiness; 0-9615786),* 4470 SW Hall Blvd., Suite 294, Beaverton, OR 97005 (SAN 696-7124) Tel 503-620-8691.

Common Knowledge, *(Common Knowledge Press; 0-943004),* Subs. of Commonweal, P.O. Box 316, Bolinas, CA 94924 (SAN 240-3080) Tel 415-868-0970.

Common Sen Pubns, *(Common Sense Pubns.; 0-916979),* P.O. Box 130275, Tyler, TX 75713 (SAN 655-6213) Tel 214-561-0110.

Common Sense, *(Common Sense Press, Inc.; 0-917572),* P.O. Box 417, Corona del Mar, CA 92625 (SAN 209-424X).

Common Women, *(Common Women Collective; 0-9601122),* c/o Women's Center, 46 Pleasant St., Cambridge, MA 02139 (SAN 210-1890) Tel 617-354-8807.

Commonground Pr, *(Commonground Pr.; 0-9610348),* 546 Albany Post Rd., New Paltz, NY 12561 (SAN 211-1187).

Commonweal Env
See Commonweal PA

Commonweal PA, *(Commonwealth of Pennsylvania, Dept. of General Services, Bureau of Pubns. & Paperwork Management; 0-8182),* P.O. Box 1365, Harrisburg, PA 17105 (SAN 658-8858) Tel 717-787-3978. *Imprints:* Enviro Resources (Commonwealth of Pennsylvania, Dept. of Environmental Resources, Bureau of Topographic & Geologic Survey).

Commonwealth Pr, *(Commonwealth Pr., Inc.; 0-89227),* 415 First St., Radford, VA 24141 (SAN 281-515X) Tel 703-639-2475.

Commonwealth Sci
See Cmnwlth Sci

Commonweth Pr
See Cmnwlth Pr Worcester

Commonwlth Pub, *(Commonwealth Publishing Co., Inc.; 0-943882),* 3657 Thousand Oaks Blvd., Westlake Village, CA 91362 (SAN 241-1032) Tel 805-496-6642.

CommTek Pub, *(CommTek Publishing Co.; 0-934543),* Div. of Commtek, Inc., P.O. Box 53, Boise, ID 83707 (SAN 693-8671) Tel 208-322-2800.

CommTex Pub
See CommTek Pub

Commun Design-MLM, *(Communications by Design/MLM; 0-9615477),* 1354 Hancock St., Quincy, MA 02169 (SAN 696-3625) Tel 617-770-4341.

Commun Service, *(Community Service Pubns.; 0-9615812),* 2104 Park Ave., Minneapolis, MN 55401 (SAN 696-7094) Tel 612-871-3333.

Communacad, *(Communications Academy, The),* P.O. Box 541, Wilton, CT 06897 (SAN 241-3671) Tel 203-762-9538.

Communication Arts *Imprint of* **Hastings**

†Communication Skill, *(Communication Skill Builders; 0-88450),* 3130 N. Dodge Blvd., P.O. Box 42050, Tucson, AZ 85733 (SAN 201-7768) Tel 602-323-7500; *CIP.*

†Communicom, *(Communicom Publishing Co.; 0-932617),* 548 NE 43rd Ave., Portland, OR 97213 (SAN 680-4438) Tel 503-239-5141; *CIP.*

Communigraphics, *(Communigraphics of Oconomowoc, Inc.; 0-9615001),* 225 W. Wisconsin Ave., Oconomowoc, WI 53066 (SAN 694-0250) Tel 414-567-8904; Dist. by: The Distributors, 702 S. Michigan, South Bend, IN 46618 (SAN 169-2488) Tel 219-232-8500.

†Community Law, *(Community Law Reports, Inc.; 0-89035),* 8771 Elm Ave., Orangevale, CA 95662 (SAN 206-3441) Tel 916-988-7576; *CIP.*

†Community Pub, *(Community Publishing Co.),* 103 Lewis St., Perth Amboy, NJ 08861 (SAN 201-8993); *CIP.*

Comn Studies, *(Communication Studies; 0-931814),* 6145 Anita St., Dallas, TX 75214-2612 (SAN 211-5530) Tel 214-823-1981.

Comns Monitor Pr *Imprint of* **First Intl Pub**

Comp *Imprint of* **Viking**

Comp Awareness, *(Computer Awareness; 0-934531),* 43612 Greenview Dr., Mt. Clemens, MI 48043 (SAN 693-7896) Tel 313-468-8585.

Comp Compatible
See CCM

Comp Entrepreneur, *(Computer Entrepreneur Publishing Co., The),* P.O. Box 456, Grand Central Station, New York, NY 10163 (SAN 677-8941).

Comp Graphics, *(Composers' Graphics; 0-931553),* 5702 N. Ave., Carmichael, CA 95608 (SAN 682-1847) Tel 916-489-7889.

Comp Info Ltd, *(Computer Information Ltd.; 0-9614906),* P.O. Box 60369, San Diego, CA 92106-8369 (SAN 693-4692) Tel 619-266-9141; Toll free: 800-528-3665.

Comp Info Sci, *(Comprehensive Information Sciences, Inc.; 0-936477),* P.O. Box 622, Huntington, NY 11743 (SAN 698-1135) Tel 516-423-7528.

Comp Law Rep, *(Computer Law Reporter),* 1519 Connecticut Ave., NW Suite 200, Washington, DC 20036 (SAN 692-8765).

Comp Options, *(Computer Options; 0-9614937),* 198 Amherst Ave., Berkeley, CA 94708 (SAN 693-5311) Tel 415-525-5033.

Comp Pr, *(Competency Pr.; 0-9602800),* P.O.. Box 95, White Plains, NY 10605 (SAN 223-5579).

Comp Res, *(Computer Research Corp.; 0-939559),* 500 West End Ave., Suite 11E, New York, NY 10024 (SAN 663-429X) Tel 212-580-2633.

†Compact Bks, *(Compact Bks.; 0-936320),* 2500 Hollywood Blvd., Hollywood, FL 33020 (SAN 215-0670) Tel 305-925-5242; Dist. by: Interbook, Inc., 14895 E. 14th St., Suite 370, San Leandro, CA 94577 (SAN 662-3034) Tel 415-352-9221; *CIP.*

Compact Pubns
See Compact Bks

Comparable Worth, *(Comparable Worth Project; 0-9615953),* 488 41st St., No. 5, Oakland, CA 94609 (SAN 697-3434) Tel 415-658-1808.

Comparahatch, *(Comparahatch Ltd., Inc.; 0-914521),* RD 1, Box 102, Tannersville, PA 18372 (SAN 289-6184) Tel 717-629-2962.

Compass Bk Pub, *(Compass Bk. Pubs.; 0-937507),* Box 9996, Phoenix, AZ 85068 (SAN 659-1310) Tel 602-944-8526.

Compass Pubns NY, *(Compass Pubns.; 0-9606282),* 115 E. 87th St., Box 12-F, New York, NY 10128 (SAN 220-3286) Tel 212-289-2368.

Compass Va, *(Compass Pubns., Inc.; 0-910422),* 1117 N. 19th St., Arlington, VA 22209 (SAN 203-5774) Tel 703-524-3136.

†CompCare, *(CompCare Pubns.; 0-89638),* Div. of Comprehensive Care Corp., 2415 Annapolis Ln., Minneapolis, MN 55441 (SAN 211-464X) Tel 612-559-4800; Toll free: 800-328-3330; *CIP.*

Competent Assocs
See Comptex Assocs Inc

Comprehen Health Educ, *(Comprehensive Health Education Foundation; 0-935529),* 20832 Pacific Hwy., S., Seattle, WA 98188 (SAN 696-3668) Tel 206-824-2907.

COMPress, *(COMPress; 0-933694; 0-88720),* Div. of Wadsworth, Inc., P.O. Box 102, Wentworth, NH 03282 (SAN 284-9887); Toll free: 800-221-0419 Tel 603-764-5831.

Compress Gas, *(Compressed Gas Association),* 1235 Jefferson Davis Highway, Arlington, VA 22202 (SAN 260-3136) Tel 703-979-0900.

CompTech, *(CompTech Pubs., Inc.; 0-935397),* 663 S. Bernardo Ave., Suite 173, Sunnyvale, CA 94087-1020 (SAN 696-3684) Tel 408-736-8082; 125-73 Connemara Way, Sunnyvale, CA 94087-3226 (SAN 696-3692) Tel 408-736-8082; Dist. by: George L. Oliver Co., P.O. Box 1842, Fremont, CA 94538-0184 (SAN 200-6111) Tel 415-651-6720; Dist. by: George L. Oliver Co., 44834 S. Grimmer Blvd., Fremont, CA 94538 (SAN 200-612X).

Comptex Assocs Inc, *(Comptex Associates, Inc.; 0-911849),* P.O. Box 6745, Washington, DC 20020 (SAN 265-3710).

Compton Pr, *(Compton Pr.; 0-9607302),* P.O. Box 871, Cathedral Sta., New York, NY 10025 (SAN 239-1856) Tel 212-749-5377.

Compu-Sul, *(Compu-Sultants; 0-9610734),* 940 Wild Forest Dr., Gaithersburg, MD 20879 (SAN 264-6609) Tel 301-977-3511.

Compu-Tech Pub, *(Compu-Tech Publishing, Inc.; 0-917531),* 615 South St., Garden City, NY 11530 (SAN 669-6708) Tel 516-222-1637.

†**Confluence Pr,** *(Confluence Pr., Inc.; 0-917652),* Spalding Hall, Lewis-Clark Campus, Lewiston, ID 83501 (SAN 209-5467) Tel 208-746-2341; Dist. by: Kampmann & Co., 9 E. 40th St., New York, NY 10016 (SAN 202-5191) Tel 212-685-2928; *CIP.*

†**Cong Shaarai,** *(Congregation Shaarai Shomayim),* 508 N. Duke St., Lancaster, PA 17602 (SAN 215-7438) Tel 717-397-5575; *CIP.*

Congdon & Lattes
See Congdon & Weed

†**Congdon & Weed,** *(Congdon & Weed; 0-86553),* 298 Fifth Ave., 7th Flr., New York, NY 10001 (SAN 214-3585) Tel 212-736-4883; Toll free: 800-221-7945; Dist. by: Contemporary Bks., 180 N. Michigan Ave., Chicago, IL 60601 (SAN 202-5493) Tel 312-782-9181; *CIP.*

Congeros Pubns, *(Congeros Pubns.; 0-918628),* Affil. of Stump's Printing, P.O. Box 1387, Ontario, CA 91762 (SAN 213-733X).

†**Congr Quarterly,** *(Congressional Quarterly, Inc.; 0-87187),* 1414 22nd St., NW, Washington, DC 20037 (SAN 202-1803) Tel 202-887-8500; *CIP.*

Congr Sons Israel, *(Congregation Sons of Israel; 0-9603994),* 116 Grandview Ave., Chambersburg, PA 17201 (SAN 239-5215).

Congr Staff, *(Congressional Staff Directory, Ltd.; 0-87289),* P.O. Box 62, Mount Vernon, VA 22121 (SAN 203-5820) Tel 703-765-3400.

Congress Sq, *(Congress Square Pr.; 0-9611320),* P.O. Box 4060, Portland, ME 04101 (SAN 283-2763) Tel 207-772-0181.

Conifer Pub
See Corey-Stevens Bks

Conjunctions, *(Conjunctions; 0-941964),* 33 W. Ninth St., New York, NY 10011 (SAN 239-5169) Tel 212-477-1136.

Conmar Pub, *(Conmar Publishing, Co.; 0-9613784),* P.O. Box 641, Citrus Heights, CA 95610 (SAN 678-9617) Tel 916-962-2028; Dist. by: Wellman Publishing, P.O. Box 484, Folsom, CA 95630 (SAN 683-7441) Tel 916-985-7064.

Conn Fireside, *(Connecticut Fireside Pr.),* P.O. Box 5293, Hamden, CT 06518 (SAN 207-8090) Tel 203-248-1023.

Conn Hist Com, *(Connecticut Historical Commission; 0-918676),* 59 S. Prospect St., Hartford, CT 06106 (SAN 223-3223).

Conn Hist Soc, *(Connecticut Historical Society Pr., The; 0-940748),* 1 Elizabeth St., Hartford, CT 06105 (SAN 204-2843) Tel 203-236-5621.

Conn Hospice, *(Connecticut Hospice, Inc., The; 0-936479),* 61 Burban Dr., Branford, CT 06405 (SAN 698-1070) Tel 203-481-6231.

Conn Yankee, *(Connecticut Yankee Publishers, Inc.; 0-915129),* 17 Blue Mountain Rd., Norwalk, CT 06851 (SAN 289-9035) Tel 203-847-6512.

Connecting Link, *(Connecting Link, The; 0-9608678),* P.O. Box 716, Stone Mountain, GA 30086-0716 (SAN 238-2636) Tel 404-979-8013.

Connections CA, *(Connections; 0-911719),* 5009 San Joaquin Dr., San Diego, CA 92109 (SAN 263-9815) Tel 619-272-6565.

Connell & Connell, *(Connell & Connell, Inc.; 0-9616573),* 39 Desoto Cir., Texarkana, TX 75503 (SAN 661-0374) Tel 214-793-7845.

Conner & Sanderson, *(Conner & Sanderson Publications; 0-9606904),* Dist. by: Coleman Publishing Inc., 99 Milbar Blvd., Farmingdale, NY 11735 (SAN 238-1508) Tel 516-293-0383.

Connoisseur, *(Connoisseur Enterprises; 0-912605),* 12540 SE Linwood, Apt. 26, Milwaukie, OR 97222 (SAN 277-6685) Tel 503-655-2070.

Connolly Sec Commonw, *(Connolly Secretary of the Commonwealth; 0-9613915),* State House Rm. 340, Boston, MA 02133 (SAN 683-1796) Tel 617-727-9121.

Conococheague Assoc
See Anima Pubns

Conquest
See R W Bolz

Conquest Corp MI, *(Conquest Corp.; 0-936682),* 32724 Friartuck, Birmingham, MI 48010 (SAN 219-9734) Tel 313-646-1344.

Conscience & Military Tax, *(Conscience & Military Tax Campaign-U. S.; 0-9616313),* Affil. of National War Tax Resistance Co-ordinating Commitee and Mobilization For Survival, 4534 1/2 University Way, Seattle, WA 98105 (SAN 658-6503) Tel 206-547-0952.

Conscientious Obj
See CCCO

Conserv Pr, *(Conservation Press),* Australian Government Trade Commission, 636 Fifth Ave., New York, NY 10111 (SAN 238-0528).

†**Conservation Foun,** *(Conservation Foundation; 0-89164),* 1255 23rd St., NW, Washington, DC 20037 (SAN 207-6640) Tel 202-293-4800; *CIP.*

ConSol, *(ConSol Network, Inc.; 0-917893),* 1905 Mariposa St., Boulder, CO 80302 (SAN 656-9714) Tel 303-449-4551; Dist. by: Baker & Taylor., Midwest Div., 501 Gladiola Ave., Momence, IL 60954 (SAN 169-2100).

Consol Athletic Comm, *(Consolidated Athletic Commission),* 851 N Leavitt St, Chicago, IL 60622 (SAN 224-5388).

†**Consol Cap Comm Grp,** *(Consolidated Capital Communications Group, Inc. (CCCG); 0-930032),* 2000 Powell St., Emeryville, CA 94608 (SAN 283-9407); *CIP.*

Consort Pac Arts *Imprint of* **UH Pr**

Consortium Soft, *(Consortium Soft; 0-939519),* 504 East Walnut, Nevada, MO 64772 (SAN 663-3625) Tel 417-667-9489.

Constant Soc, *(Constant Society; 0-931894),* P. O. Box 45513, Seattle, WA 98105 (SAN 211-4976) Tel 206-525-5947.

Constellation Pr, *(Constellation Pr., Inc.; 0-9616620),* Box 1271, Manhattan Beach, CA 90266 (SAN 661-0404); 1817 Agnes Rd., Manhattan Beach, CA 90266 (SAN 661-0412) Tel 213-545-2284.

Constitutional Rights Found, *(Constitutional Rights Foundation),* 601 S. Kingsley Dr., Los Angeles, CA 90005 (SAN 225-6401) Tel 213-487-5590.

Constr Ind Pr, *(Construction Industry Pr.; 0-9605442),* Affil. of WPL Assocs., Inc., 1105-F Spring St., Silver Spring, MD 20910 (SAN 238-7549) Tel 301-589-4884.

Constr Prod Manuf, *(Construction Products Manufacturers Council),* 1600 Wilson Blvd., Suite 1005, Arlington, VA 22209 (SAN 224-1013) Tel 703-522-0613.

Construct Bkstore, *(Construction Bookstore, Inc.; 0-935715),* P.O. Box 2959, Gainseville, FL 32602-2959 (SAN 696-3935) Tel 904-378-9784; 1830 NE Second St., Gainesville, FL 32609 (SAN 696-3943).

Construct Educ, *(Constructive Educational Concepts, Inc.; 0-934734),* 213 Duncaster Rd., Box 667, Bloomfield, CT 06002 (SAN 215-7446).

Construct Pubns, *(Construction Pubns.; 0-912324),* 4552 E. Palomino Rd., Phoenix, AZ 85018 (SAN 201-7970) Tel 602-840-3947.

Construct Trade, *(Construction Trade Pubns.; 0-9616849),* 24611 Tabuenca, Mission Viejo, CA 92692 (SAN 661-308X) Tel 714-770-6334.

Constructive Action, *(Constructive Action, Inc.; 0-911956),* P.O. Box 4006, Whittier, CA 90607 (SAN 203-5839) Tel 213-947-5707.

Consult Serv NW, *(Consultant Services Northwest, Inc.; 0-9617216),* 839 NE 96th St., Seattle, WA 98115 (SAN 663-4249) Tel 206-524-1950.

Consultants *Imprint of* **Plenum Pub**

Consultants News, *(Consultants News; 0-916654),* Subs. of Kennedy & Kennedy, Inc., Templeton Rd., Fitzwilliam, NH 03447 (SAN 206-4871) Tel 603-585-2200.

†**Consulting Psychol,** *(Consulting Psychologists Pr., Inc.; 0-89106),* 577 College Ave., Palo Alto, CA 94306 (SAN 201-7849) Tel 415-857-1444; *CIP.*

Consumer Aware, *(Consumer Awareness Learning Laboratory; 0-910599),* RD 3, Box 237, Fort Elfsborg Rd., Salem, NJ 08079 (SAN 260-1761) Tel 609-935-6264.

Consumer Comm Ltd, *(Consumer Communications, Ltd.; 0-940060),* P.O. Box 35429, Station D, Albuquerque, NM 87176 (SAN 217-0671) Tel 505-881-0313.

Consumer Energy Coun, *(Consumer Energy Council of America),* 2000 L St. NW, Suite 320, Washington, DC 20036 (SAN 224-103X) Tel 202-659-0404.

Consumer Info Pubns, *(Consumer Information Pubns.; 0-940062),* 2245 Curlew Rd., Palm Harbor, FL 33563 (SAN 220-2395) Tel 813-784-7795.

Consumer Pub, *(Consumer Publishing Co.; 0-9600270),* New & Friendship Rds., Vincentown, NJ 08088 (SAN 206-927X).

Consumer Pubn, *(Consumer Publications; 0-914087),* P.O. Box 465, Kings Park, NY 11754 (SAN 283-9431) Tel 516-979-9183.

Consumer Reports, *(Consumer Reports Bks.; 0-89043),* Div. of Consumers Union of US, Inc., 110 E. 42nd St., No. 1301, New York, NY 10017 (SAN 224-1048) Tel 212-682-9280.

Consumers Advisory, *(Consumer's Advisory, Pr.; 0-9606340),* P.O. Box 77107, Greensboro, NC 27407 (SAN 219-0818).

Consumers Checkbk, *(Consumers Checkbk.),* 806 15th St. NW 925, Washington, DC 20005 (SAN 678-9137).

Consumers Union, *(Consumers Union of U. S., Inc.; 0-89043),* Div. of Comsumer Reports Bks., 256 Washington St., Mt. Vernon, NY 10553 (SAN 269-3518) Tel 914-667-9400; Orders to: Consumer Reports Bks., 540 Barnum Ave., Bridgeport, CT 06608 (SAN 661-9800).

Consumertronics, *(Consumertronics Co.; 0-934274),* 2011 Crescent Dr., Alamogordo, NM 88310 (SAN 212-7369); P.O. Drawer 537, Alamogordo, NM 88310 (SAN 658-036X) (SAN 661-9819).

Cont Hist Soc, *(Continental Historical Society; 0-9609900),* 3145 Geary Blvd., No. 126, San Francisco, CA 94118 (SAN 269-3607) Tel 415-751-1253.

Contact Edit, *(Contact Editions; 0-937645),* P.O. Box 603, Northampton, MA 01061 (SAN 659-1450) Tel 413-586-1181; 30 N. Maple St., Florence, MA 01060 (SAN 659-1469).

Contact Two, *(Contact/II Pubns; 0-936556),* P.O. Box 451, Bowling Green, New York, NY 10004 (SAN 200-4151) Tel 212-674-0911; Dist. by: Small Press Distribution, Inc., 1814 San Pablo Ave., Berkeley, CA 94702 (SAN 204-5826) Tel 415-549-3336; Dist. by: NY New Papers, 611 Broadway, New York, NY 10012 (SAN 200-8130) Tel 212-777-6157; Dist. by: Ingram Industries, 347 Reedwood Dr., Nashville, TN 37217 (SAN 169-7978) Tel 615-793-5000.

Contemp Arts, *(Contemporary Arts Ctr., The; 0-917562),* 115 E. Fifth St., Cincinnati, OH 45202 (SAN 210-5551) Tel 513-721-0390.

†**Contemp Bks,** *(Contemporary Bks., Inc.; 0-8092),* 180 N. Michigan Ave., Chicago, IL 60601 (SAN 202-5493) Tel 312-782-9181. Formerly: Henry Regnery Co; *CIP.* Imprints: Gate (Gateway Editions); GrDeb (Great Debate Series); Logos (Logos Books).(Logos Bks.).

Contemp Image, *(Contemporary Image Advertising, Ltd.; 0-9616743),* 300 S. Washington Ave., Suite 380 J, Lansing, MI 48933 (SAN 661-0463) Tel 517-484-4922.

Contemp Issues, *(Contemporary Issues Clearinghouse; 0-914677),* 1410 S. Second St., Pocatello, ID 83201 (SAN 289-7024).

Contemp Lit Pr, *(Contemporary Literature Pr.; 0-930266),* P.O. Box 26462, San Francisco, CA 94126 (SAN 201-9027).

Contemp Pub Co of Raleigh, *(Contemporary Publishing, Co. of Raleigh; 0-89892),* 508 St. Mary's St., Raleigh, NC 27605 (SAN 213-0424) Tel 919-821-4566.

Contemp Pub O
See Contemp Pub Co of Raleigh

Contemp Res, *(Comptemporary Research Assocs., Inc.; 0-935061),* P.O. Box 7240, Dallas, TX 75209 (SAN 694-5937) Tel 214-690-5882; 1218 Glen Cove, Richardson, TX 75080 (SAN 694-5945).

Contemplative Bks, *(Contemplative Bks.; 0-939419),* P.O. Box 8065, Columbus, GA 31908 (SAN 663-1819); 3400 St. Mary's Rd., Columbus, GA 31906 (SAN 663-1827) Tel 404-689-1892.

†**Contemporary Arts,** *(Contemporary Arts Pr.; 0-931818),* Div. of La Mamelle, Inc., P.O. Box 3123, Rincon Annex, San Francisco, CA 94119 (SAN 213-3016); *CIP.*

Contemporary Lit
See Contemp Lit Pr

†**Context Pubns,** *(Context Pubns.; 0-932654),* P.O. Box 2909, Rohnert Park, CA 94928-6506 (SAN 212-8977) Tel 707-584-4423; Dist. by: Bookpeople, 2929 Fifth St., Berkeley, CA 94710 (SAN 168-9517) Tel 415-549-3030; *CIP.*

Continent Assn Funeral, *(Continental Association of Funeral & Memorial Societies, Inc.),* 2001 S St. NW, Suite 530, Washington, DC 20009 (SAN 202-6201) Tel 202-745-0634.

Continent Divide, *(Continental Divide Trail Society; 0-934326),* P.O. Box 30002, Bethesda, MD 20814 (SAN 213-0432) Tel 301-493-4080.

Continent Edns, *(Continental Editions; 0-916868),* 2300 Indian Hills Dr., 3-231, Sioux City, IA 51104 (SAN 208-192X) Tel 712-239-5954.

Continent Herit, *(Continental Heritage Pr.; 0-932986),* 6 E. Fifth, Suite 410, Tulsa, OK 74103 (SAN 212-0348) Tel 918-582-5100.

Continent Media, *(Continental Media Co.; 0-912349),* P.O. Box 31256, Hartford, CT 06103 (SAN 265-1114) Tel 203-247-0300.

Continent Pubs CA
See Cntnt Pubs SF

Continental CA, *(Continental Pubns. Ltd.; 0-916096),* P.O. Box 1729, Carlsbad, CA 92008 (SAN 208-6093) Tel 619-434-7017.

Continental Servs, *(Continental Services, Ltd.; 0-9616277),* 301 W 53rd. St., Apt. 6C, New York, NY 10019 (SAN 658-5604) Tel 212-333-7348.

Continuing Ed *Imprint of* **Wadsworth Pub**

Continuing Ed Pubns, *(Continuing Education Pubns.; 0-930253),* Subs. of Portland State University, 1633 SW Pk., Portland, OR 97207 (SAN 670-8552) Tel 503-229-4846.

Continuing SAGA, *(Continuing SAGA Pr.),* P.O. Box 194, San Anselmo, CA 94960 (SAN 215-7454) Tel 415-454-4411.

Continuity Pr, *(Continuity Press, The; 0-939408),* P. O. Box 677, Gualala, CA 95445 (SAN 216-5724) Tel 707-884-3766.

†**Continuum,** *(Continuum Pub. Co.; 0-8264),* 370 Lexington Ave., New York, NY 10017 (SAN 213-8220) Tel 212-532-3650 (SAN 201-002X); Dist. by: Harper & Row, Keystone Industrial Pk., Scranton, PA 18512 (SAN 215-3742); *CIP.*

Contract Data, *(Contract Data Pubs.; 0-939260),* P.O. Box 366, Alta Loma, CA 91701 (SAN 220-1666) Tel 714-987-6850.

Control Data
See Control Patents

Control Eng, *(Control Engineering Technical Publishing; 0-914331),* Subs. of Dun & Bradstreet Corp., 1301 S. Grove Ave., Barrington, IL 60010 (SAN 287-587X) Tel 312-381-1840.

Control Patents, *(Control Data Patents & Trademarks Dept.; 0-918852),* 1225 Conneticut Ave.,N.W. Suit 202, Washington, DC 20036 (SAN 204-2525) Tel 202-296-4523.

Convex Indus, *(Convex Industries, Inc.; 0-913920),* 4720 Cheyenne, Boulder, CO 80303 (SAN 203-5871) Tel 303-494-4176.

Conveyor Equip Mfrs, *(Conveyor Equipment Manufacturers Assn.),* 152 Rollins Ave., Suite 208, Rockville, MD 20852 (SAN 224-8492) Tel 301-984-9080.

Conway Data, *(Conway Data, Inc.; 0-910436),* 40 Technology Park, Norcross, GA 30092 (SAN 203-1183) Tel 404-446-6996.

Conway Hse, *(Conway House; 0-914402),* P.O. Box 424, Bellaire, MI 49615 (SAN 203-6207).

Conway Pubns
See Conway Data

Conway Twitty, *(Twitty, Conway, Enterprises; 0-9616438),* 1 Music Village Blvd., Hendersonville, TN 37075 (SAN 659-1477) Tel 615-822-3210.

Cook, *(Cook, David C., Publishing Co.; 0-89191; 0-912692; 1-55513),* 850 N. Grove Ave., Elgin, IL 60120 (SAN 206-0981) Tel 312-741-2400; Toll free: 800-323-7543.
Imprints: Chariot Bks (Chariot Books).

Cook MO, *(Cook, Fred B.; 0-9614001),* 2433 E. Edgewood, Springfield, MO 65804 (SAN 683-5724) Tel 417-881-5055.

Cookbks Unltd, *(Cookbooks Unlimited; 0-932443),* 1 Wind Poppy Ct., The Woodlands, TX 77381 (SAN 687-083X) Tel 713-363-2661.

Cookbook Fact, *(Cookbook Factory, The; 0-910983),* P.O. Box 11515, Eugene, OR 97440 (SAN 262-012X) Tel 503-344-7759.

Cookbook Pubs, *(Cookbook Pubs.; 0-934474),* Lenexa, KS 66215 (SAN 213-2427) Tel 501-741-7340; Dist. by: Southern Star, Inc., P.O. Box 968, Harrison, AR 72601 (SAN 213-2435).

Cooke City, *(Cooke City Store; 0-9608876),* Box 1097, Cooke City, MT 59020 (SAN 241-1040) Tel 406-838-2234.

Cookie Pr
See Electric Bank

Coole
See M Akers

Coolidge Pr, *(Coolidge Pr.; 0-9615343),* Div. of Chattanooga Printing & Engraving Co., 110 Somerville Ave., Chattanooga, TN 37405 (SAN 695-121X) Tel 615-484-8788.

Cooling Spring, *(Cooling Spring Pr., The; 0-935883),* Div. of Challenge Hse., 405 Jefferson St., Saluda, SC 29138 (SAN 696-3412) Tel 704-669-2782 (SAN 696-3420) Tel 803-445-2351.

†**Coop Ext Serv Univ Nebraska,** *(Universiy of Nebraska, Cooperative Extension Service; 0-9613015),* Div. of University of Nebraska, 202 Natural Resources Hall, Lincoln, NE 68583-0819 (SAN 294-2909) Tel 402-472-6822; *CIP.*

Coop Food Dists Am
See Nat Grocers Assn

Coop League USA
See NCBA

Coop Power, *(Cooperative Power, Inc.),* Subs. of Cooperation Corporation, R. R. 1, Box 24A, Springfield, IL 62707 (SAN 210-7473) Tel 217-523-8663.

Cooper
See Frosty Peak Bks

Cooper *Imprint of* **Shoe String**

Cooper & Cooper Pub, *(Cooper & Cooper Pub.; 0-931429),* P.O. Box 1516, Palo Alto, CA 94302 (SAN 683-2121) Tel 415-327-6472.

†**Cooper-Hewitt Museum,** *(Cooper-Hewitt Museum; 0-910503),* Affil. of Smithsonian Institution, 2 E. 91st St., New York, NY 10128 (SAN 260-0366) Tel 212-860-6868; *CIP.*

Cooper Hse Pub, *(Cooper Hse. Publishing Co.; 0-939121),* P.O. Box 44021, Shreveport, LA 71134 (SAN 662-4766); 160 Prospect, Shreveport, LA 71104 (SAN 662-4774) Tel 318-424-8036.

Cooper-Morgan, *(Cooper-Morgan, Inc.; 0-9614801),* 6649 E. Roswell Rd., Ste. 659, Atlanta, GA 30328 (SAN 692-6665) Tel 404-636-7508.

†**Cooper Sq,** *(Cooper Sq. Pubs., Inc.; 0-8154),* Div. of Littlefield, Adams & Co., 81 Adams Dr., Totowa, NJ 07512 (SAN 281-5621) Tel 201-256-8600; *CIP.*

Coord Coun Lit Mags, *(Coordinating Council of Literary Magazines; 0-942332),* 666 Broadway, 11th flr., New York, NY 10012 (SAN 225-3410) Tel 212-614-6551; Dist. by: Moyer Bell Ltd., Colonial Hill, RFD 1, Mt. Kisco, NY 10549 (SAN 669-6961) Tel 914-666-0084.

Cop-A-Form, *(Cop-A-Form, Inc.; 0-914567),* P.O. Box 02227, 443 Crestview Rd., Columbus, OH 43202 (SAN 289-1875) Tel 614-261-9917.

Copesthetic, *(Copesthetic),* 2032 Belmont Rd. NW, No. 612, Washington, DC 20009 (SAN 295-0103) Tel 202-667-0470.

Copley & Assocs
See Defense & Foreign Aff

†**Copley Bks,** *(Copley Bks.; 0-913938),* Subs. of The Copley Press, Inc., P.O. Box 957, La Jolla, CA 92038 (SAN 202-1846); 7776 Ivanhoe Ave., La Jolla, CA 92037 (SAN 662-720X) Tel 619-454-1842; *CIP.*

Copouts Ink, *(Copouts Ink; 0-938417),* P.O. Box 6223, Anaheim, CA 92806 (SAN 661-051X); 1733 Chelsea, Anaheim, CA 92805 (SAN 661-0528)
Tel 714-776-2718.

†**Copper Beech,** *(Copper Beech Pr.; 0-914278),* Box 1852, Brown Univ., Providence, RI 02912 (SAN 212-8063); *CIP.*

†**Copper Canyon,** *(Copper Canyon Pr.; 0-914742; 1-55659),* P.O. Box 271, Port Townsend, WA 98368 (SAN 206-488X) Tel 206-385-4925; Dist. by: Consortium Bk. Sales & Distribution, 213 E. Fourth St., St. Paul, MN 55101 (SAN 200-6049) Tel 612-221-9035; *CIP.*

Copper Devel Assn, *(Copper Development Assn.),* Greenwich Office Pk. 2, Box 1840, Greenwich, CT 06836-1840 (SAN 230-9793) Tel 203-625-8210.

Copper Orchid, *(Copper Orchid Publishing Co., The; 0-9608522),* 1966 Westbrook Dr., Jackson, MI 49201 (SAN 240-6195) Tel 517-750-4625.

Copperfield Pr, *(Copperfield Pr.; 0-933857),* P.O. Box 15025, Austin, TX 78761 (SAN 692-7351) Tel 512-837-2931.

Copperfield Pr NY
See Copprfld NYC

Copple Hse, *(Copple Hse. Bks.; 0-932298),* Roads' End, Lakemont, GA 30552 (SAN 658-0378) Tel 404-782-2134 (SAN 281-5648).

Copprfld NYC, *(Copperfield Pr., The; 0-9617037),* 80-85 Dumfries Pl., Jamaica, NY 11432 (SAN 662-5843) Tel 718-969-1797. Do not confuse with Copperfield Pr., Austin, TX.

Copy Concepts, *(Copy & Concepts, Ltd.; 0-937983),* 22 Grove St., New York, NY 10014 (SAN 659-4999) Tel 212-243-8065.

Copy Fast, *(Copy Fast Printing; 0-9612032),* 246 King St., Pottstown, PA 19464 (SAN 286-7710) Tel 215-326-7456.

Copy Fast Ctr, *(Copy Fast Printing Ctr., Inc.; 0-930579),* 505 Worcester Rd., Rt. 9, Framingham, MA 01702 (SAN 678-4445) Tel 617-875-0621.

Copy-Write, *(Copy-Write Artograph Co.; 0-912392),* Div. of E. Wynn Vogel Co., 1865 77th St., Brooklyn, NY 11214-1233 (SAN 203-588X) Tel 718-331-1045.

Copyright Info, *(Copyright Information Services; 0-914143),* P.O. Box 1460, Friday Harbor, WA 98250 (SAN 287-6388) Tel 206-378-5128.

Coraco, *(Coraco; 0-917628),* 1017 S. Arlington Ave., Los Angeles, CA 90019 (SAN 203-5898) Tel 213-737-1066.

Coral Gables Pub, *(Coral Gables Publishing Co., Inc.; 0-938993),* 8065 SW 107th Ave., Miami, FL 33173 (SAN 662-5320) Tel 305-279-9049.

Coral Reef
See Laura Bks

Corban Prods, *(Corban Productions; 0-9608710),* P.O. Box 215, Worthington, OH 43089 (SAN 238-0544) Tel 614-889-0102.

Corbett, *(Corbett, H. Roger, Jr.),* 8100 Cardiff St., Lorton, VA 22079 (SAN 211-1160) Tel 703-550-7317.

†**Corcoran,** *(Corcoran Gallery of Art; 0-88675),* 17th St. & New York Ave. NW, Washington, DC 20006 (SAN 204-2797) Tel 202-638-3211; *CIP.*

Cordovan Pr, *(Cordovan Pr.; 0-89123),* 5314 Bingle Rd. P.O. Box 920973, Houston, TX 77292 (SAN 204-2789) Tel 713-688-8811.

Cordus Pr, *(Cordus Press; 0-935118),* P.O. Box 587, North Amherst, MA 01059 (SAN 208-3108) Tel 413-549-6888.

CORE, *(Congress of Racial Equality; 0-917354),* 1916-38 Park Ave., New York, NY 10037 (SAN 204-2886) Tel 212-694-9300.

Coren Assocs, *(Coren Assocs.; 0-9611642),* P.O. Box 58, Mamaroneck, NY 10543 (SAN 284-947X) Tel 914-698-9113.

Corey & Co, *(Corey & Co. Designers; 0-9615538),* 249 Newbury St., Boston, MA 02116 (SAN 696-4028) Tel 617-266-1850.

Corey-Stevens Bks, *(Corey/Stevens Bks.; 0-942666),* 7958 SW Barbur Blvd., Portland, OR 97219 (SAN 240-2106) Tel 503-246-7418.

†**Coriander Pr,** *(Coriander Pr.; 0-912837),* 361 Scenic Dr., Ashland, OR 97520 (SAN 283-0051) Tel 503-488-1016; P.O. Box 337, Ashland, OR 97520 (SAN 658-232X); *CIP.*

Corinth Bks, *(Corinth Bks.; 0-87091),* 4008 EW Hwy., Chevy Chase, MD 20815 (SAN 281-5656) Tel 301-652-1016; Orders to: Bookslinger, 213 E. Fourth St., St. Paul, MN 55101 (SAN 169-4154) Tel 612-221-0429.

Corinth Hse, *(Corinth Hse. Pubs.; 0-938280),* 2238 E. Vermont Ave., Anaheim, CA 92806 (SAN 214-3607) Tel 714-635-6930.

Corinth Pub, *(Corinthian Pubns.; 0-935915),* 2518 E. Ocean View Ave., Norfolk, VA 23518 (SAN 696-7256) Tel 804-587-2671; P.O. Box 8279, Norfolk, VA 23503 (SAN 698-2166).

Corinthian, *(Corinthian Pr., The; 0-86551),* Div. of EDR Corp., 3592 Lee Rd., Shaker Heights, OH 44120 (SAN 216-1214) Tel 216-751-7300.

Corita Comm, *(Corita Communications; 0-933016),* 1301 N. Kenter Ave., Los Angeles, CA 90049 (SAN 212-2723).

Corja Bks, *(Corja Bks.; 0-916887),* 2726 Blenheim Ave., Redwood City, CA 94063 (SAN 655-9565) Tel 415-365-8939.

Cormorant Bks, *(Cormorant Bks.; 0-936261),* 405 E. 300 S., Lehi, UT 84043 (SAN 697-3442) Tel 801-968-3232.

Cornell China-Japan Pgm, *(Cornell Univ. China-Japan Program, East Asia Papers; 0-939657),* 140 Uris Hall, Cornell Univ., Ithaca, NY 14853 (SAN 219-3604) Tel 607-255-6222.

Cornell Daily, *(Cornell Daily Sun, Inc., The; 0-938304),* 109 E. State St., Ithaca, NY 14850 (SAN 239-8370) Tel 607-273-3606.

Cornell Des, *(Cornell Design Publishers; 0-914397),* P.O. Box 278, East Hanover, NJ 07936 (SAN 289-6281) Tel 201-884-0330.

Cornell Manu, *(Cornell Univ. Libraries, Dept. of Manuscripts & Univ. Archives; 0-935995),* 101 Olin Library, Ithaca, NY 14853-5301 (SAN 696-7159) Tel 607-255-3530.

†Cornell Maritime, *(Cornell Maritime Pr., Inc.; 0-87033),* P.O. Box 456, Centreville, MD 21617 (SAN 203-5901) Tel 301-758-1075; Toll free: 800-638-7641; *CIP.*

Cornell Mod Indo, *(Cornell Modern Indonesia Project; 0-87763),* Affil. of Cornell University, 102 West Ave., Ithaca, NY 14850 (SAN 203-591X) Tel 607-255-4359.

Cornell Ornithology, *(Cornell Laboratory of Ornithology; 0-938027),* Cornell Univ., 159 Sapsucker Woods Rd., Ithaca, NY 14850 Tel 607-255-5056; Dist. by: Houghton Mifflin Co., 1 Beacon St., Boston, MA 02108 (SAN 200-2388) Tel 617-725-5000.

Cornell SE Asia, *(Cornell Univ., Southeast Asia Program; 0-87727),* 120 Uris Hall, Ithaca, NY 14853 (SAN 206-6416) Tel 607-256-2378.

Cornell U Dept, *(Cornell Univ., Dept. of Agronomy; 0-932865),* 1008 Bradfield Hall, Ithaca, NY 14853 (SAN 688-9158) Tel 607-255-1736; Orders to: International Soils/Dept. of Agronomy, Cornell Univ., 1014 Bradford Hall, Ithaca, NY 14853 (SAN 662-2828).

†Cornell U Pr, *(Cornell Univ. Pr.; 0-8014),* 124 Roberts Pl., P.O. Box 250, Ithaca, NY 14851 (SAN 202-1862) Tel 607-257-7000; Orders to: 714 Cascadilla St., Ithaca, NY 14851 (SAN 281-5680) Tel 607-277-2211; *CIP.*

Cornell U Sch Hotel, *(Cornell Univ., Schl. of Hotel Administration; 0-937056),* 327 Statler Hall, Ithaca, NY 14853 (SAN 204-2746) Tel 607-255-5093.

Cornell Widow, *(Cornell Widow, Inc.; 0-9605870),* 104 Willard Straight Hall, Cornell University, Ithaca, NY 14853 (SAN 216-356X).

Corner Hse, *(Corner Hse. Pubs.; 0-87928),* 1321 Green River Rd., Williamstown, MA 01267 (SAN 203-5936) Tel 413-458-8561.

CornerBrook Pr, *(CornerBrook Pr.; 0-913523),* Box 106, Lansing, NY 14882 (SAN 285-1563) Tel 607-533-4056; 178 N. Lansing School Rd., RD 1, Groton, NY 13073 (SAN 285-1571) Tel 607-255-3182.

†Cornerstone, *(Cornerstone Library, Inc.; 0-346),* Div. of Simon & Schuster, Inc., ; Toll free: 800-223-2336; Orders to: Simon & Schuster, Inc., 1230 Ave. of the Americas, New York, NY 10020 (SAN 200-2450) Tel 212-245-6400; *CIP.*

Cornerstone Pr, *(Cornerstone Pr.; 0-918476),* P.O. Box 28048, St. Louis, MO 63119 (SAN 210-0584) Tel 314-296-9662.

Cornhusker Pr, *(Cornhusker Pr.; 0-933909),* Subs. of Dutton-Lainson Co., P.O. Box 729, Hastings, NE 68901 (SAN 682-2819); 426 W. Second St., Hastings, NE 68901 (SAN 692-6363) Tel 402-463-6702.

Cornick, *(Cornick Concepts, Inc.; 0-9615516),* 437 Midsummer Ct., West Palm Beach, FL 33411 (SAN 696-4036) Tel 305-798-3550.

Corning, *(Corning Museum of Glass; 0-87290),* 1 Museum Way, Corning, NY 14830-2253 (SAN 202-1897) Tel 607-937-5371; Dist. by: Associated University Presses, 440 Forsgate Dr., Cranbury, NJ 08512 (SAN 281-2959) Tel 609-655-4770.

Corning Pub Co, *(Corning Publishing Co.; 0-9614945),* 171 Ontario Ave., Holyoke, MA 01040 (SAN 693-6512) Tel 413-536-1947.

Cornrows & Co, *(Cornrows & Co.; 0-939183),* 5401 14th St. NW, Washington, DC 20011 (SAN 662-8303) Tel 202-723-1827.

Cornucop Pub, *(Carolina Cornucopia Educational Publishing Company; 0-935911),* 5610 Laurel Crest Dr., Durham, NC 27712 (SAN 696-7213) Tel 919-471-1873; Dist. by: Nancy Robert's Collection, 3600 Chevington Rd., Charlotte, NC 28211 (SAN 200-5786).

Cornucopia Pubns, *(Cornucopia Pubns.; 0-914207),* 2515 E. Thomas Rd., Suite 16, Phoenix, AZ 85016 (SAN 287-6396) Tel 602-279-1122.

Cornwall Bks *Imprint of Assoc Univ Prs*

Corona Pub, *(Corona Publishing, Co.; 0-931722),* 1037 S. Alamo, San Antonio, TX 78210 (SAN 211-8491) Tel 512-227-1771.

Coronado Pr, *(Coronado Pr., Inc.; 0-87291),* P.O. Box 3232, Lawrence, KS 66044 (SAN 201-7776) Tel 913-843-5988.

Coronet Bks, *(Coronet Bks.; 0-89563),* 311 Bainbridge St., Philadelphia, PA 19147 (SAN 210-6043) Tel 215-925-2762.

Corp Cmnt Col TV, *(Corporation for Community College Television; 0-9617111),* 5400 Orange Ave., Suite 109, Cypress, CA 90630 (SAN 662-7013) Tel 714-828-5770.

Corp Ent Dev, *(Corporation for Enterprise Development, The; 0-9605804),* 1725 K St., NW, Suite 1401, Washington, DC 20006 (SAN 216-5619) Tel 202-293-7963.

Corp Organ Pro, *(Corporate Organizing Project; 0-931987),* Subs. of Ctr. for Urban Education, 611 Vanderbilt St., Brooklyn, NY 11218 (SAN 683-2458) Tel 718-871-5356.

Corporate Comm Studies, *(Corporate Communication Studies, Inc.; 0-915683),* P.O. Box 9538, Daytona Beach, FL 32020 (SAN 292-4528) Tel 904-673-3848.

Corporate Support Systs, *(Corporate Support Systems; 0-936879),* 615 W. Kirby Ave., Champaign, IL 61820 (SAN 658-3237) Tel 217-398-2077.

Corporate West Inc, *(Corporate West, Inc.; 0-9613119),* 2602 N. 20th Ave., Phoenix, AZ 85009 (SAN 294-7285) Tel 602-253-0514.

CorpTech, *(Corporate Technology Information Services, Inc.; 0-936507),* 2 Laurel Ave., Wellesley Hills, MA 02181 (SAN 697-8576) Tel 617-235-5330 (SAN 697-8584).

Corpus Christi Area, *(Corpus Christi Area Garden Council, Inc.),* P.O. Box 6165, Corpus Christi, TX 78411 (SAN 663-088X).

†Correlan Pubns, *(Correlan Pubns.; 0-913842),* P.O. Box 337, Watsonville, CA 95077 (SAN 202-0386) Tel 408-728-1766; *CIP.*

Corridor Pub, *(Corridor Publishing Co.; 0-936053),* P.O. Box 1008, Crawfordsville, IN 47933 (SAN 697-0249) Tel 317-362-1509.

Corroboree Pr, *(Corroboree Pr.; 0-911169),* 2729 Bloomington Ave. S., Minneapolis, MN 55407 (SAN 269-3925) Tel 612-724-1355.

Corsi, *(Corsi, Petro; 0-9615871),* 4404 Sherman Oaks Ave., Sherman Oaks, CA 91403 (SAN 696-6187) Tel 213-553-9761.

Cortland Pub, *(Cortland Publishing, Inc.; 0-914825),* 5775 Wayzata Blvd., Rm. 700, Minneapolis, MN 55416 (SAN 289-0941) Tel 612-544-1375.

Corvallis Software, *(Corvallis Software, Inc.; 0-942358),* P.O. Box 1412, Corvallis, OR 97339 (SAN 237-9406) Tel 503-754-9245.

Corwin Pubs, *(Corwin Pubs., Inc.; 0-938569),* 826 San Francisco, San Francisco, CA 94126 (SAN 661-2571); 123 Corwin St., Suite C, San Francisco, CA 94114 (SAN 661-258X) Tel 415-621-4346.

Cos Cob Pr, *(Cos Cob Pr.; 0-915639),* 82 Valleywood Rd, Cos Cob, CT 06807 (SAN 292-4676) Tel 203-661-7918.

Cos Sci Orange, *(Cosmic Science Pub.; 0-9615973),* 12932 Malma Dr., Santa Ana, CA 92705 (SAN 696-785X) Tel 714-771-0448. Do not confuse with Cosmic Science Pub. of Louisville, KY.

COSMEP, *(COSMEP (The International Assn. of Independent Pubs.); 0-9611378),* P.O. Box 703, San Francisco, CA 94101 (SAN 209-7222) Tel 415-922-9490.

Cosmic Comm, *(Cosmic Communication Co.; 0-912038),* 100 Elm Ct., Decorah, IA 52101 (SAN 201-9043) Tel 319-382-8350.

Cosmic Hse NM, *(Cosmic Hse.; 0-932492),* P.O. Box 10515, Alameda, NM 87184 (SAN 211-9331) Tel 505-897-2240.

Cosmoenergetics Pubns, *(Cosmoenergetics Pubns.; 0-938954),* P.O. Box 86353, San Diego, CA 92138 (SAN 239-8184) Tel 619-295-1664; Dist. by: New Leaf, 1020 White St, SW, Atlanta, GA 30310 (SAN 169-1449) Tel 404-755-3454.

†Cosmos Humanists, *(Cosmos Of Humanists Pr.; 0-913429),* P.O. Box 11143, San Francisco, CA 94101 (SAN 285-8827) Tel 415-337-1787; *CIP.*

Cosmotic Concerns, *(Cosmotic Concerns; 0-938104),* c/o Jacef Relations, P.O. Box 621, Langley, WA 98260-0621 (SAN 238-0552) Tel 206-221-2617.

Cosray Res, *(Cosray Research Institute; 0-9606374),* 2505 S. Fourth East, P.O. Box 151045, Salt Lake City, UT 84115 (SAN 216-3578).

Costa, *(Costa),* 23 Old Field Pl., Red Bank, NJ 07701 (SAN 263-9858).

Costano, *(Costano Bks.; 0-930268),* P.O. Box 355, Petaluma, CA 94953 (SAN 210-3508) Tel 707-762-4848.

Costello and Witty, *(DJC, Inc., A Witty Enterprise; 0-9609894),* 16222 Monterey Ln., No. 114, Huntington Beach, CA 92649-2236 (SAN 269-5596).

Cott Ind Phoenix, *(Cottage Industry, Inc.; 0-9615721),* 5112 N. 40th St., Phoenix, AZ 85018 (SAN 696-4052) Tel 602-951-8989.

Cottage, *(Cottage Craft; 0-935203),* P.O. Box 505, Mableton, GA 30059 (SAN 695-7315) Tel 404-426-4004.

Cottage Bks, *(Cottage Bks.; 0-911253),* P.O. Box 2071, Silver Spring, MD 20902 (SAN 285-0044) Tel 301-649-5433; Dist. by: LIDCO, 2849 Georgia Ave., NW, Washington, DC 20001 (SAN 282-6011) Tel 202-328-0191; Dist. by: Acropolis Books Ltd., 2400 17th St., NW, Washington, DC 20009 (SAN 201-2227) Tel 202-387-6805.

Cottage Indus, *(Cottage Industries; 0-938348),* Box 244, Cobalt, CT 06414 (SAN 215-7462) Tel 203-342-2599.

Cottage Indust
See Cott Ind Phoenix

Cottage Pr, *(Cottage Pr., Inc.; 0-918343),* P.O. Box 1265, Englewood Cliffs, NJ 07632 (SAN 657-3339) Tel 201-894-1011.

Cottage Pub Co, *(Cottage Publishing Co.; 0-915479),* 566 Wyckoff Ave., Wyckoff, NJ 07481 (SAN 291-1299) Tel 201-891-8295; Orders to: P.O. Box 21, Ridgefield, CT 06877 (SAN 291-1302).

Cotton Lane, *(Cotton Lane Pr.; 0-9604810),* Cotton Ln. at 18 Eighth St., Augusta, GA 30901 (SAN 281-5699) Tel 404-722-0232.

Cottontail Pubns, *(Cottontail Pubns.; 0-942124),* R.R. 1, Box 198, Bennington, IN 47011 (SAN 238-6526) Tel 812-427-3914.

Cottonwood Bks, *(Cottonwood Bks.; 0-935775),* 1216 Lillie Cir., Salt Lake City, UT 84121 (SAN 696-4079) Tel 801-262-4586.

†Cottonwood Pubns, *(Cottonwood Pubns.; 0-918887),* 1091 Morning St., Worthington, OH 43085 (SAN 669-9820); Orders to: P.O. Box 264, Worthington, OH 43085 (SAN 662-2429) Tel 614-885-8132; *CIP.*

Cougar Bks, *(Cougar Bks.; 0-917982),* P.O. Box 22246, Sacramento, CA 95822 (SAN 209-4266) Tel 916-428-3271.

Coulee Pr, *(Coulee Pr.; 0-9611456),* Box 1744, La Crosse, WI 54602-1744 (SAN 283-1171) Tel 608-788-6253.

Couleur Inc Assoc, *(Couleur, Inc. & Assocs.; 0-9613208),* 27830 Ten Oaks Ctr., Conroe, TX 77302 (SAN 295-7272) Tel 713-363-3116.

Coun Adv & Supp Ed, *(Council for Advancement & Support of Education; 0-89964),* 11 Dupont Cir., Suite 400, Washington, DC 20036 (SAN 225-8641) Tel 202-328-5900; Orders to: CASE Pubns. Order Dept., 80 S. Early St., Alexandria, VA 22304 (SAN 202-4500) Tel 703-823-6966.

Coun Agri Sci, *(Council for Agricultural Science & Technology),* P.O. Box 1550, Iowa State Univ. Sta., Ames, IA 50010-1550 (SAN 225-7416) Tel 515-292-2125.

Coun Am Affairs
See Coun Soc Econ

Coun Basic Educ, *(Council for Basic Education; 0-931989),* 725 15th St., NW, Washington, DC 20005 (SAN 269-4093) Tel 202-347-4171.

Coun Biology Eds, *(Council of Biology Editors; 0-914340),* 9650 Rockville Pike, Bethesda, MD 20814 (SAN 207-0693) Tel 301-530-7036.

Coun Career Plan, *(Council for Career Planning, Inc.; 0-916340),* P.O. Box 2466, New York, NY 10168-2466 (SAN 201-2545) Tel 212-687-9490.

Coun Europe Direct, *(Council of Europe, Directorate of Legal Affairs),* Dist. by: Manhattan Publishing Co., 225 Lafayette St., New York, NY 10012 (SAN 213-442X).

†**Coun Foreign,** *(Council on Foreign Relations; 0-87609),* 58 E. 68th St., New York, NY 10021 (SAN 201-7784) Tel 212-734-0400; Orders to: 540 Barnum Ave., Bridgeport, CT 06608 (SAN 661-9835) Tel 203-334-8500; *CIP.*

Coun Found, *(Council on Foundations, Inc.; 0-913892),* 1828 L St., NW, Suite 1200, Washington, DC 20036 (SAN 210-3524) Tel 202-466-6512; Orders to: P.O. Box 0002, Washington, DC 20055 (SAN 661-9843).

Coun Hemispheric Aff, *(Council on Hemispheric Affairs; 0-937551),* 1612 20th St., NW, Washington, DC 20009 (SAN 235-7674) Tel 202-745-7000.

Coun Indep Colleges, *(Council of Independent Colleges; 0-937012),* 1 Dupont Cir., NW, Suite 320, Washington, DC 20036 (SAN 690-0291) Tel 202-466-7230.

Coun India Ed, *(Council for Indian Education; 0-89992),* 517 Rimrock Rd., Billings, MT 59102 (SAN 202-2117) Tel 406-252-1800; Orders to: Box 31215, Billings, MT 59107 (SAN 689-836X) Tel 406-252-1800.

†**Coun Inter-Am,** *(Council for Inter-American Security; 0-943624),* 122 C St., NW, Suite 330, Washington, DC 20001 (SAN 238-2660) Tel 202-543-6622; *CIP.*

Coun Inter Ed, *(Council for Inter-American Security, Educational Institute; 0-910637),* 122 C St., NW, Suite 330, Washington, DC 20001 (SAN 269-4174) Tel 202-543-6622.

Coun Intl Urb
See Intl Ctr Academy

Coun Jewish Feds, *(Council of Jewish Federations & Welfare Funds, Inc.),* 575 Lexington Ave., New York, NY 10022 (SAN 225-9532).

Coun Logistics Mgt, *(Council of Logistics Management),* 2803 Butterfield Rd., Oak Brook, IL 60521 (SAN 224-7100) Tel 312-574-0985.

Coun NY Law, *(Council of New York Law Associates; 0-910639),* 99 Hudson St., New York, NY 10013 (SAN 237-6997).

Coun Oak Bks, *(Council Oak Bks., Ltd.; 0-933031),* 1428 S. St. Louis, Tulsa, OK 74120 (SAN 689-5522) Tel 918-587-6454; Toll free: 800-526-7626; Dist. by: Kampmann & Co., 9 E. 40th St., New York, NY 10016 (SAN 202-5191).

Coun on Municipal, *(Council on Municipal Performance; 0-916450),* 30 Irving Pl., New York, NY 10003 (SAN 208-6166) Tel 212-420-5950; Dist. by: John Wiley & Sons, Inc., 605 Third Ave., New York, NY 10158 (SAN 200-2272) Tel 212-850-6418.

Coun Plan Lib
See CPL Biblios

†**Coun Plan Librarians,** *(Council of Planning Librarians; 0-86602),* 1313 E. 60th St., Chicago, IL 60637-2897 (SAN 225-3364) Tel 312-947-2007; *CIP.*

Coun Postsecondary Accredit, *(Council on Postsecondary Accreditation),* 1 Dupont Cir., Suite 305, Washington, DC 20036 (SAN 225-736X) Tel 202-452-1433.

Coun Rel & Intl
See Carnegie Ethics & Intl Affairs

Coun Rel & Law, *(Council on Religion and Law),* P.O. Box 30, Cambridge, MA 02140 (SAN 237-5842).

Coun Soc Econ, *(Council for Social & Economic Studies, Inc.; 0-930690),* 1133 13th St., NW, Suite COMM. 2, Washington, DC 20005 (SAN 210-1130) Tel 202-789-0231.

Coun Soc Studies
See Nat Coun Soc Studies

†**Coun Soc Wk Ed,** *(Council on Social Work Education; 0-87293),* P.O. Box 43469, Columbia Heights Sta., Washington, DC 20009 (SAN 225-8714); *CIP.*

Coun State Govts, *(Council of State Governments; 0-87292),* Iron Works Pike, P.O. Box 11910, Lexington, KY 40578 (SAN 225-1264) Tel 606-252-2291.

Coun State Plan
See CSPA

Coun Tall Bldg, *(Council on Tall Buildings & Urban Habitat; 0-939493),* Bldg. 13, Lehigh University, Bethlehem, PA 18015 (SAN 663-4168) Tel 215-861-3515.

Council Public TV, *(Council for Public Television, Channel 6, Inc.; 0-9616209),* 1261 Glenarm Pl., Denver, CO 80227 (SAN 658-3318) Tel 303-892-6666.

Counsel & Consult, *(Counseling & Consulting Services (CCS) Publications; 0-910819),* 4020 Moorpark Ave., Suite 204, San Jose, CA 95117 (SAN 262-0146) Tel 408-246-1128.

Counsel & Stress, *(Counseling & Stress Research Center; 0-912561),* 21 Montauk Ave, New London, CT 06320 (SAN 283-9466) Tel 203-447-9935.

Counseling Res, *(Counseling Research Institute; 0-935205),* 8000 W. 14th Ave., Suite 1 & 2, Lakewood, CO 80215 (SAN 695-1066) Tel 303-237-9159; Dist. by: Institue for Rational Living, Inc., 45 E. 65th St., New York, NY 10021 (SAN 218-7833) Tel 212-535-0822.

†**Counter-Prop Pr,** *(Counter-Propaganda Pr., The; 0-943468),* P.O. Box 365, Park Forest, IL 60466 (SAN 240-6217) Tel 312-534-8679; *CIP.*

Country Bazaar, *(Country Bazaar Publishing & Distributing; 0-936744),* Honey, Inc. Bldg., Rte. 2, Box 190, Berryville, AR 72616 (SAN 215-1669) Tel 501-423-3131.

Country Cooking, *(Country Cooking; 0-940750),* P.O. Box 1563, Woodbridge, VA 22193 (SAN 223-128X) Tel 703-670-9093.

Country Dance & Song, *(Country Dance & Song Society of America; 0-917024),* 505 Eighth Ave., Suite 2500, New York, NY 10018-6505 (SAN 208-1423) Tel 212-594-8833.

Country Garden, *(Country Garden Pr.; 0-9611974),* 4412 McCulloch St., Duluth, MN 55804 (SAN 220-2425) Tel 218-525-3294.

Country Hse, *(Country Hse., The; 0-940554),* 15 Thomas Ave., Topsham, ME 04086 (SAN 216-3586) Tel 207-729-8941.

Country Journ
See Historical Times

Country Music Found, *(Country Music Foundation Pr.; 0-915608),* 4 Music Sq. E., Nashville, TN 37203 (SAN 207-5121) Tel 615-256-1639.

Country Pr Mohawk, *(Country Pr.; 0-9616225),* Ward Rd., Mohawk, NY 13407 (SAN 663-0855).

Country Pr NY, *(Country Press, The; 0-913174),* Rte. One, P.O. Box 7652, Henderson, NY 13650 (SAN 203-5995) Tel 315-938-5481.

Country Pub, *(Country Pub.; 0-935777),* P.O. Box 12153, Tallahassee, FL 32308 (SAN 696-4087) Tel 904-878-2837; 324 Louvinia Ct., Tallahassee, FL 32308 (SAN 696-5377).

Country Pub Inc, *(Country Pubs., Inc., The; 0-9610772; 0-939685),* P.O. Box 432, Middleburg, VA 22117 (SAN 265-1130) Tel 703-687-6306.

Country Rd, *(Country Road Press; 0-939596),* 414 W. Jonquil Rd., Santa Ana, CA 92706 (SAN 216-6194) Tel 714-836-0458.

Country Squire, *(Country Squire, The; 0-9609228),* 11 Lake St., Granville, MA 01034 (SAN 241-4864) Tel 413-357-8525.

†**Countryman,** *(Countryman Pr., Inc.; 0-914378; 0-88150),* Box 175, Woodstock, VT 05091 (SAN 206-4901) Tel 802-457-1049; Toll free: 800-635-5009 (orders only); *CIP.*
Imprints: Foul Play (Foul Play Press).

Countryside Bks, *(Countryside Bks.; 0-88453),* Northwood Plaza Sta., Clearwater, FL 33519-0360 (SAN 201-7954) Tel 813-796-7337.

Countryside Studio, *(Countryside Studio, Inc.; 0-9605428),* P.O. Box 88, Hwy. 25 W., Cottontown, TN 37048 (SAN 216-1222).

County Rd
See Country Rd

County Super Assn CA, *(County Super Assn., of California),* 1100 K St., Suite 101, Sacramento, CA 95814 (SAN 680-0300) Tel 916-441-4011.

Couple to Couple, *(Couple to Couple League, The; 0-9601036),* P.O. Box 111184, Cincinnati, OH 45211 (SAN 208-1490) Tel 513-661-7612; 3621 Glenmore Ave., Cincinnati, OH 45211 (SAN 669-0564).

Courier Pr, *(Courier Press; 0-917310),* C/O First American National Bank, Trust Dept., First American Center, Nashville, TN 37237 (SAN 208-4139) Tel 615-748-2341.

Courier Pr FL, *(Courier Press; 0-934602),* 428 NE 82nd St., Suite 1, Miami, FL 33138 (SAN 212-9949).

Courseware, *(Courseware, Inc.; 0-89805),* 10075 Carroll Canyon Rd., San Diego, CA 92131 (SAN 212-4955) Tel 619-578-1700.

Court Scribe, *(Court Scribe, The; 0-9601572),* 2201 Friendly St., Eugene, OR 97405 (SAN 210-8879) Tel 503-343-7562.

Courtroom Comp, *(Courtroom Compendiums; 0-910355),* 22106 Clarendon, P.O. Box 705, Woodland Hills, CA 91365 (SAN 260-0374) Tel 818-884-9039.

Couturier Pr, *(Couturier Pr.; 0-934875),* Div. of Dori's Bears, 10636 Main St., Suite 498, Bellevue, WA 98004 (SAN 694-4620) Tel 206-746-3385.

Cove Pub Co
See R H Barnes

†**Cove View,** *(Cove View Pr.; 0-931896),* P.O. Box 3234, Ashland, OR 97520 (SAN 220-0422); *CIP.*

Covenant, *(Covenant Pr.; 0-910452),* 3200 W. Foster Ave., Chicago, IL 60625 (SAN 203-6029) Tel 312-478-4676; Toll free: 800-621-1290.

Coventry *Imprint of Fawcett*

Coventry Hse, *(Coventry Hse.; 0-933761),* 490 E. Walnut Ave., Pasadena, CA 91101 (SAN 692-7688) Tel 818-304-6804.

Cover Pub, *(Cover Publishing Co.; 0-912912),* P.O. Box 1092, Tampa, FL 33601 (SAN 203-6037) Tel 813-237-0266.

Cow Puddle, *(Cow Puddle Pr.; 0-9600672),* Sunset Trading Post, Sunset, TX 76270 (SAN 206-5282) Tel 817-872-2027.

Cowan, *(Cowan, Robert G.; 0-910456),* 1650 Redcliff St., Los Angeles, CA 90026 (SAN 203-6045) Tel 213-664-7401.

Coward *Imprint of Putnam Pub Group*

Cowboy Poet, *(Cowboy Poet Pub Co.; 0-9614907),* 4475 Memphis St., Dallas, TX 75207 (SAN 693-5346) Tel 214-631-5770.

Cowley Pubns, *(Cowley Pubns.; 0-936384),* Div. of Society of St. John the Evangelist, 980 Memorial Dr., Cambridge, MA 02138 (SAN 213-9987) Tel 617-876-3507.

Cox, *(Cox, Harold E.; 0-911940),* 80 Virginia Terrace, Forty Fort, PA 18704 (SAN 202-1943) Tel 717-287-7647.

Cox Pubns, *(Cox Pubns.; 0-912665),* P.O. Box 958, El Cerrito, CA 94530 (SAN 282-7573) Tel 415-527-2552.

Coyne & Chenoweth, *(Coyne & Chenoweth; 0-941038),* P.O. Box 81905, Pittsburgh, PA 15217 (SAN 217-3476) Tel 412-321-4528.

Coyote, *(Coyote Bks.; 0-940556),* P.O. Box 629, Brunswick, ME 04011 (SAN 212-6060).

Coyote Bks MN, *(Coyote Bks.; 0-9616901),* 3953 Alabama Ave., S., St. Louis Park, MN 55416 (SAN 661-4930) Tel 612-925-9244. Do not confuse with Coyote Bks., in Brunswick, ME.

Coyote Cowboy
See R Stockman & Coyote

Coyote Love, *(Coyote Love Pr.; 0-913341),* 87 State St., No. 2, Portland, ME 04101 (SAN 283-040X) Tel 207-774-8451; Dist. by: Small Press Distribution, 1814 San Pablo Ave., Berkeley, CA 94702 (SAN 204-5826) Tel 415-549-3336.

Coyote Press, *(Coyote Pr.; 1-55567),* P.O. Box 3377, Salinas, CA 93912 (SAN 699-6752) Tel 408-422-4912 (SAN 699-6760).

Coyote Prod, *(Coyote Productions; 0-936147),*
P.O. Box 167, Auburn, ME 04210
(SAN 697-0214) Tel 207-934-2588; 25
Cookman Ave., Old Orchard Beach, ME
04064 (SAN 697-0222).

†**CPI Pub,** *(CPI Publishing, Inc.; 0-675),* 145 E.
49th St., New York, NY 10017
(SAN 218-6896) Tel 212-753-3800; Dist.
by: Modern Curriculum Pr., 13900 Prospect
Rd., Cleveland, OH 44136 (SAN 206-6572);
CIP.

†**CPL Biblios,** *(CPL Bibliographies),* 1313 E.
60th St., Merriam Ctr., Chicago, IL
60637-2897 (SAN 210-3516)
Tel 312-947-2007; *CIP.*

Cptn Stanislaus, *(Captain Stanislaus Mlotkowski
Memorial Brigade Society; 0-9600814),* 247
Philadelphia Pike, Wilmington, DE 19809
(SAN 207-124X).

CR Pub, *(CR Publishing, Inc.; 0-938467),* 805
E. State Ave., Terra Alta, WV 26764
(SAN 659-9397) Tel 304-789-2464.

CRA Readers Serv, *(CRA Readers Service;
0-9616505),* RD 1, P.O. Box 278, Claysville,
PA 15323 (SAN 659-4271)
Tel 412-948-3588.

Crabtree, *(Crabtree Publishing; 0-937070),* P.O.
Box 3451, Federal Way, WA 98063
(SAN 214-3615) Tel 206-927-3777.

Cracker Bks Pub, *(Cracker Bks. Publishing, Inc.;
0-932827),* P.O. Box 214, Winter Beach, FL
32971 (SAN 688-6205) Tel 305-231-4871.

Craftree, *(Craftree; 1-55564),* Div. of McCall's
(A.B.C.) Needlework & Crafts Magazines,
825 Seventh Ave., New York, NY 10019
(SAN 699-7082) Tel 212-887-8462; Dist.
by: Gaylenot Publishing, 740 Monroe Way,
Placentia, CA 92670 (SAN 200-5972).

†**Craftsman,** *(Craftsman Bk. Co.; 0-910460;
0-934041),* 6058 Corte del Cedro, Box 6500,
Carlsbad, CA 92008 (SAN 159-7000)
Tel 619-438-7828; *CIP.*

Craftways, *(Craftways Pubns.; 0-9607224),* 1465
Fourth St., Berkeley, CA 94710
(SAN 239-0809) Tel 415-527-4561.

†**Cragmont Pubns,** *(Cragmont Pubns.; 0-89666),*
1308 E. 38th St., Oakland, CA 94602
(SAN 211-4860) Tel 413-530-8436; *CIP.*

Craig
See Lollipop LA

Craig Inc, *(Craig Inc.; 0-9614816),* P.O. Box
05383, Detroit, MI 48205 (SAN 693-0131)
Tel 313-526-3204.

Craig Pub Hse, *(Craig Publishing Hse.;
0-9615135),* 100 S. Kanawha St.,
Buckhannon, WV 26201 (SAN 694-2512)
Tel 304-472-5543.

Craig Pubns, *(Craig Publications; 0-9613396),*
P.O. Box 4382, San Clemente, CA 92672
(SAN 676-9071).

Crain Bks, *(Crain Bks.; 0-87251),* Div. of Crain
Communications, Inc., 740 Rush St.,
Chicago, IL 60611 (SAN 207-1967)
Tel 312-649-5250; Toll free: 800-621-6877.

Cram Cassettes, *(Cram Cassettes; 1-55651),*
P.O. Box 1275, South Bend, IN 46624
(SAN 661-8316); 2118 Renfrew Ct., South
Bend, IN 46614 (SAN 661-8324)
Tel 219-291-2645.

Crambruck, *(Crambruck Pr.; 0-87699),* 381 Park
Ave. S., New York, NY 10016
(SAN 204-2622) Tel 212-532-0871.

Cramer Bkstore, *(Cramer Bk. Store; 0-913118),*
Box 7235, Kansas City, MO 64113
(SAN 203-607X).

Crampton Assoc, *(Crampton Assocs., Inc.;
0-9610142),* Box 1214, Homewood, IL
60430 (SAN 269-5049) Tel 312-798-3710.

Cranberry Knoll, *(Cranberry Knoll Pubs.;
0-9614737),* Subs. of Mary Webber, Inc.,
P.O. Box 293, Yarmouth, ME 04096
(SAN 692-7149) Tel 207-846-4954.

Cranberry Pr, *(Cranberry Pr., The; 0-9615645),*
276 East St., Pittsford, NY 14534
(SAN 696-4117) Tel 716-318-1928.

Cranbrook, *(Cranbrook Institute of Science;
0-87737),* 500 Lone Pine Rd., P.O. Box 801,
Bloomfield Hills, MI 48013
(SAN 203-6088) Tel 313-645-3255.

Cranbrook Pub, *(Cranbrook Publishing;
0-9604690),* 2302 Windemere, Flint, MI
48503 (SAN 215-7470).

Crane Pub Co, *(Crane Publishing Co.; 0-89075),*
Div. of MLP, 1301 Hamilton Ave., Box
3713, Trenton, NJ 08629 (SAN 207-1053)
Tel 609-586-6400.

Crane Pubns CA, *(Crane Pubns. (CA);
0-915561),* Box 90155, San Diego, CA
92109 (SAN 292-3297) Tel 619-273-7018.

†**Crane Russak & Co,** *(Crane, Russak & Co.,
Inc.; 0-8448),* Affil. of Taylor & Francis,
Ltd. (London), 3 E. 44th St., New York, NY
10017 (SAN 202-1978) Tel 212-867-1490;
CIP.

Crane-Russak Co
See Crane Russak & Co

Cranky Nell Bk *Imprint of* **Kane-Miller Bk**

Crawford Aviation, *(Crawford Aviation;
0-9603934),* P.O. Box 1262, Torrance, CA
90505 (SAN 213-4810); Dist. by: Aviation
Bk. Co., 1640 Victory Blvd., Glendale, CA
91201 (SAN 212-0259) Tel 818-240-1771.

Crawford Pr
See Econo-Clad Bks-Crawford Pr

Crazy Horse, *(Crazy Horse Memorial
Foundation),* Crazy Horse, Black Hills, SD
57730 (SAN 233-4089) Tel 605-673-4681.

Crazy Sam, *(Crazy Sam Enterprises),* 8301
Ambassador Rd, Dallas, TX 75247
(SAN 678-9056).

CRB Res, *(CRB Research; 0-939780),* P.O. Box
56, Commack, NY 11725 (SAN 216-8812)
Tel 516-543-7486.

†**CRC Pr,** *(CRC Pr., Inc.; 0-87819; 0-8493),*
2000 Corporate Blvd., Boca Raton, FL 33431
(SAN 202-1994) Tel 305-994-0555; Toll
free: 800-272-7737; *CIP.*

†**CRC Pubns,** *(CRC Pubns.; 0-933140;
0-930265),* 2850 Kalamazoo Ave. SE, Grand
Rapids, MI 49560 (SAN 212-727X)
Tel 616-246-0752; *CIP.*

†**CRCS Pubns NV,** *(CRCS Pubns.; 0-916360),*
P.O. Box 20850, Reno, NV 89515
(SAN 200-626X) Tel 702-358-2850. Do
Not Confuse with CRC Pr, Florida; *CIP.*

CRCS Pubns WA
See CRCS Pubns NV

CRD *Imprint of* Unipub

CRDWLP, *(Center for Research &
Documentation on World Language
Problems; 0-934973),* 777 United Nations
Plaza, New York, NY 10017
(SAN 695-118X) Tel 212-687-7041.

Creat Arts Dev, *(Creative Arts Development;
0-912801),* P.O. Box 1240, Soquel, CA
95073 (SAN 277-6693) Tel 408-475-2396.

Creat Black Bk, *(Creative Black Bk., Inc.;
0-916906),* 401 Park Ave. S., New York,
NY 10016 (SAN 207-9496)
Tel 212-684-4255.

Creat Conc Children, *(Creative Concepts for
Children; 0-938231),* 1214 Ensenada Ave.,
Orlando, FL 32825 (SAN 661-0587)
Tel 305-273-6259.

Creat Concepts MO, *(Creative Concepts In
Communications Ltd.; 0-9614433),* 1250 W.
63rd St., Kansas City, MO 64113
(SAN 689-3457) Tel 816-523-9207.

Creat Concern, *(Creative Concern Pubns.;
0-917117),* 3208 E. Mayaguana Ln.,
Lantana, FL 33462 (SAN 655-6221)
Tel 305-433-5735.

Creat Educ Found, *(Creative Education
Foundation, Inc.; 0-930222),* 437 Franklin
St., Buffalo, NY 14202 (SAN 685-3218)
Tel 716-884-2774; c/o State Univ. College at
Buffalo, 437 Franklin St., Buffalo, NY 14202
(SAN 210-7163) Tel 716-884-2774.

Creat Gospel Prod, *(Creative Gospel
Productions, Incorporated; 0-931965),* 23381
L'Enfant Plaza, SW, Washington, DC 20026
(SAN 686-0753) Tel 202-563-6319.

Creat Gospel Prod A Wright
See Creat Gospel Prod

Creat Media, *(Creative Media Works; 0-89411),*
692 Elkader St., Ashland, OR 97520
(SAN 209-3561) Tel 503-482-0088.

Creat Prog Inc, *(Creative Programming, Inc.;
0-912079),* 28990 W. Pacific Coast Hwy.,
Suite 109, Malibu, CA 90265
(SAN 264-7303); Toll free: 800-323-6354.

Creat Pubns
See Creat Pubns B P C M

Creat Pubns B P C M, *(Creative Pubns B P C
M; 0-914569),* 1431 St. James Pkwy.,
Concord, CA 94521 (SAN 289-1921)
Tel 415-687-6401.

Creat Res NC, *(Creative Resources, Inc.;
0-937306),* 3548 Round Oak Rd., Charlotte,
NC 28210 (SAN 200-2779)
Tel 704-554-8357.

Creat Res OH, *(Creative Resources; 0-910601),*
683 Riddle Rd., Cincinnati, OH 45220
(SAN 260-1788) Tel 513-559-1481.

Creat Resource, *(Creative Resource Systems,
Inc.; 0-938772),* P.O. Box 890, 116 Railroad
St., Winterville, NC 28590 (SAN 238-7301)
Tel 919-756-9658.

Creat Teach Pr, *(Creative Teaching Pr., Inc.;
0-916119),* 15598 Producer Ln., Huntington
Beach, CA 92649 (SAN 294-9180)
Tel 714-892-5523; Toll free: 800-732-1548.

Creat Ventures IN, *(Creative Ventures, Inc.;
0-942034),* P.O. Box 2286, West Lafayette,
IN 47906 (SAN 239-5231).

Create Learn, *(Creative Learning Assn.;
0-88193),* R.R. 4, Box 330, Charleston, IL
61920 (SAN 669-4101) Tel 217-345-1010.

Creation Hse, *(Creation Hse.; 0-88419),* 396 E.
St. Charles Rd., Wheaton, IL 60188
(SAN 202-2001) Tel 312-653-1472.

Creation Res
See Creation Research

Creation Research, *(Creation Research Society
Bks.; 0-940384),* Div. of Creation Research
Society, 5093 Williamsport Dr., Norcross,
GA 30092 (SAN 216-2873)
Tel 404-449-4758.

Creation Sci Fellowship, *(Creation Science
Fellowship, Inc.; 0-9617068),* 362 Ashland
Ave., Pittsburgh, PA 15228
(SAN 662-8559) Tel 412-341-4908.

Creations Unltd, *(Creations Unlimited;
0-938900),* P.O. Box 2591, Farmington
Hills, MI 48018 (SAN 216-1109).

Creative Alter Pr, *(Creative Alternatives Pr.;
0-932041),* P.O. Box 50142, Jacksonville
Beach, FL 32240 (SAN 685-3013)
Tel 904-249-7721.

Creative Amer Pub, *(Creative Publishing Corp.
of America; 0-9608340),* 633 Jefferson
Heights Ave., Jefferson, LA 70121
(SAN 239-5320) Tel 504-733-1275.

†**Creative Arts Bk,** *(Creative Arts Bk. Co.;
0-88739; 0-916870),* 833 Bancroft Way,
Berkeley, CA 94710 (SAN 208-4880)
Tel 415-848-4777; *CIP.*

Creative AV, *(Creative AV Things, Inc.;
0-937927),* P.O. Box 582, Glen Rock, NJ
07452 (SAN 659-3941).

†**Creative Bks,** *(Creative Books/Creative
Services; 0-914606),* P.O. Box 5162, Carmel,
CA 93921 (SAN 203-6215)
Tel 408-624-7573; Dist. by: Peanut Butter
Publishing, 911 Western Ave., Suite 401,
Maritime Bldg., Seattle, WA 98104
(SAN 212-7881); *CIP.*

Creative Catalyst, *(Creative Catalyst; 1-55663),*
6023 Majestic Ave., Oakland, CA 94605
Tel 415-562-8617; Dist. by: Bookpeople,
2929 Fifth St., Berkeley, CA 94710
(SAN 168-9517) Tel 415-549-3030; Dist.
by: Alchemy Bks., 717 Market St., Suite 514,
San Francisco, CA 94101 (SAN 211-304X)
Tel 415-777-2197.

Creative Center Ed
See Josephson-Kluwer Legal Educ Ctrs

Creative Comm, *(Creative Communications;
0-939116),* 529 Dayton St., Edmonds, WA
98020 (SAN 239-684X) Tel 206-775-5877.

†**Creative Comp,** *(Creative Computing;
0-916688; 0-87194),* 1 Park Ave., New
York, NY 10016 (SAN 281-5737)
Tel 212-503-5315; Toll free: 800-631-8112;
39 E. Hanover Ave., Morris Plains, NJ
07950 (SAN 281-5745) Tel 201-540-0445;
CIP.

Creative Concepts, *(Creative Concepts, Inc.;
0-9614356),* 3400 First St., N., Suite 203, St.
Cloud, MN 56301 (SAN 687-7443)
Tel 612-252-1220.

Creative Cuisine, *(Creative Cuisine Inc.;
0-9614122),* P.O. Box 518, Naples, FL
33939 (SAN 686-5100) Tel 813-263-7121.

Creative Curriculum, *(Creative Curriculum),*
4302 Rolla Lane, Madison, WI 53711
(SAN 240-8678).

Creative Develop Pr, *(Creative Developmental
Pr.; 0-9615723),* 2431 Petaluma Ave., Long
Beach, CA 90815 (SAN 696-4125)
Tel 213-596-0026; P.O. Box 33, Long Beach,
CA 90801 (SAN 696-7051).

Creative Ed, *(Creative Education, Inc.; 0-87191;
0-88682),* 123 S. Broad St., P.O. Box 227,
Mankato, MN 56001 (SAN 202-201X)
Tel 507-388-6273.

Creative Editions
See Cougar Bks

Creative Foods, *(Creative Foods, Ltd.;
0-9615708),* 1700 Vine St., West Des
Moines, IA 50265 (SAN 696-4133)
Tel 515-223-4888.

Creative Forum, *(Creative Forum Publishing; 0-936411),* 4900 SW Centralwood Ave., Lake Oswego, OR 97034 (SAN 698-1550) Tel 503-639-9210.

†**Creative Homeowner,** *(Creative Homeowner Pr.; 0-932944),* Div. of Federal Marketing Corp., 24 Park Way, Upper Saddle River, NJ 07458 (SAN 213-6627) Tel 201-934-7100; Toll free: 800-631-7795; *CIP.*

Creative Images, *(Creative Images Ltd.; 0-941378),* 12000 Windflower Place, Oklahoma City, OK 73120 (SAN 238-9266) Tel 405-755-0099.

Creative Infomatics, *(Creative Infomatics, Inc.; 0-917634),* P.O. Box 1607, Durant, OK 74702-1607 (SAN 211-5557) Tel 405-924-0643.

Creative Intl, *(Creative Ventures International; 0-9615787),* 3341 Hidden Acres Dr., Atlanta, GA 30340 (SAN 696-7132) Tel 404-496-0988.

Creative Learning, *(Creative Learning Pr., Inc.; 0-936386),* P.O. Box 320, Mansfield Center, CT 06250 (SAN 214-2368) Tel 203-281-4036.

Creative Lit, *(Creative Literature; 0-9609110),* 1521 E. Flower St., Phoenix, AZ 85014 (SAN 281-5753) Tel 602-274-4151.

Creative Options, *(Creative Options Publishing Co.; 0-938106),* Div. of Laing Communications, Inc., 110-110th NE, Suite 309, Bellevue, WA 98004 (SAN 240-0901) Tel 206-451-9331.

Creative Part, *(Creative Partners; 0-9615930),* P.O. Box 84, Little Neck, NY 11363 (SAN 697-0419) Tel 516-482-5309; 254-09 West End Dr., Great Neck, NY 11363 (SAN 697-0427).

Creative Pubns UT
See Creatv Pubns UT

Creative Res, *(Creative Research Systems; 0-918577),* 1649 Del Oro, Petaluma, CA 94952 (SAN 284-6071) Tel 707-765-1001.

Creative Res & Educ, *(Creative Research & Educational Systems for Today; 0-935770),* 168-02 Jewel Ave., Flushing, NY 11365 (SAN 213-9170).

†**Creative Roots,** *(Creative Roots, Inc.; 0-940508),* P.O. Box 401, Planetarium Sta., New York, NY 10024 (SAN 218-4737) Tel 212-799-2294; *CIP.*

Creative Sales, *(Creative Sales Corp.; 0-933162),* 762 W. Algonquin Rd., Arlington Heights, IL 60005 (SAN 212-3436).

Creative Serv, *(Creative Services, Inc.; 0-939975),* P.O. Box 6008, High Point, NC 27262 (SAN 694-2385) Tel 919-889-3010; 502 Blake Ave., High Point, NC 27262.

Creative Storytime, *(Creative Storytime Pr.; 0-934876),* P.O. Box 572, Minneapolis, MN 55440 (SAN 211-6634) Tel 612-926-9740.

Creative Tchr
See World Rec Pubns

†**Creative Texas,** *(Creative Publishing, Co.; 0-932702),* P.O. Box 9292, College Station, TX 77840 (SAN 209-3499) Tel 409-775-6047; *CIP.*

†**Creative Therapeutics,** *(Creative Therapeutics; 0-933812),* 155 County Rd., Cresskill, NJ 07626-0317 (SAN 212-6508) Tel 201-567-7295; *CIP.*

†**Creative Vent,** *(Creative Ventures; 0-917166),* 1709 Dickenson, Olympia, WA 98502 (SAN 208-6190) Tel 206-754-4019; Orders to: 1721 Conger NW, Olympia, WA 98502 (SAN 208-6204) Tel 206-352-2755; *CIP.*

Creative Walking, *(Creative Walking, Inc.; 0-939041),* 175 Elkton Rd., Newark, DE 19711 (SAN 662-6521) Tel 302-368-2222.

Creative Words Pubns, *(Creative with Words Pubns.; 0-936945),* P.O. Box 223226, Carmel, CA 93922 (SAN 658-6961) Tel 408-625-3542.

Creativity Unltd Pr, *(Creativity Unlimited Pr.; 0-912559),* 30819 Casilina, Rancho Palos Verdes, CA 90274 (SAN 282-7646) Tel 213-377-7908.

Creatures at Large, *(Creatures at Large; 0-940064),* 1082 Grand Teton Dr., Pacifica, CA 94044 (SAN 281-577X) Tel 415-359-4341; P.O. Box 687, Pacifica, CA 94044 (SAN 281-5788).

Creatv Pubns UT, *(Creative Pubns.; 0-9616992),* 370 E. 230th S., Orem, UT 84058 (SAN 661-6852) Tel 801-224-0724; P.O. Box 1104, Orem, UT 84058 (SAN 661-6860). Do not confuse with Creative Pubns., Oak Lawn, CA, Quincy, MA, Concord, CA.

Credence Pub Hse, *(Credence Publishing Hse.; 0-9606226),* P.O. Box 6125, Olympia, WA 98502 (SAN 217-5126) Tel 206-866-4648.

Credit Res Found
See Credit Res NYS

Credit Res NYS, *(Credit Research Foundation, Inc.; 0-939050),* 3000 Marcus Ave., Lake Success, NY 11042 (SAN 204-2606) Tel 516-488-1166.

Credit Union Execs, *(Credit Union Executives Society),* 6320 Monona Dr., Madison, WI 53716 (SAN 224-697X).

Creek Hse, *(Creek House; 0-9600490),* P.O. Box 793, Ojai, CA 93023 (SAN 203-6126) Tel 805-646-3200.

Creighton Pub, *(Creighton Publishing; 0-9617139),* P.O. Box 1509, Port Aransas, TX 78373 (SAN 663-3447); 405 Ruthie Ln., Port Aransas, TX 78373 (SAN 663-3455) Tel 512-749-5550.

Cremona Found, *(Cremona Foundation, Inc., The; 0-936325),* Cremona Farm, Mechanicsville, MD 20659 (SAN 697-3477) Tel 301-884-3140.

Crerar Lib
See Nat Transl Ctr

Crescendo *Imprint of* **Taplinger**

†**Crescent Bks,** *(Crescent Bks.; 0-9614251),* Box 10000, New Orleans, LA 70181 (SAN 687-0864) Tel 504-626-4168; *CIP.*

Crescent Heart, *(Crescent Heart Publishing; 0-9609916),* 150 Cerro Crest Dr., Novato, CA 94947 (SAN 262-4664) Tel 415-897-6763.

Cresheim Pubns
See Swansea Pr

Creso, *(Creso, Irene; 0-9613916),* Irene Creso Herbarium, William O. Rieke Science Ctr., Pacific Lutheran University, Tacoma, WA 98447 (SAN 683-1915) Tel 206-535-7571.

Cresset Pubs, *(Cresset Pubs.; 0-936082),* 519 E. Tabor Rd., Philadelphia, PA 19120 (SAN 215-9473).

Cresswell Ent, *(Cresswell Enterprises; 0-930943),* 335 E. 11th St., Casper, WY 82601 (SAN 693-0417).

Crest *Imprint of* **Fawcett**

Crest Challenge, *(Crest Challenge Books; 0-913776),* 42 Dart St., Loma Linda, CA 92354 (SAN 203-6142) Tel 714-796-1536; Orders to: P.O. Box 993, Loma Linda, CA 92354 (SAN 203-6150).

Crest Pr Inc, *(Crest Pr., Inc.; 0-9615359),* 5 Crestway, Silver City, NM 88061 (SAN 695-2275) Tel 505-538-2324; Dist. by: Many Feathers SW Bks. & Maps Distributor, 5738 N. Central, Phoenix, AZ 85012 (SAN 158-8877).

Crest Sftware, *(Crest Software; 0-930615),* 2132 Crestview Dr., Durango, CO 81301 (SAN 676-262X) Tel 303-247-9518.

Crestline, *(Crestline Publishing Co.; 0-912612),* 1251 N. Jefferson Ave., Sarasota, FL 33577 (SAN 202-2044) Tel 813-955-8080.

†**Crestwood Hse,** *(Crestwood Hse., Inc.; 0-89686; 0-913940),* P.O. Box 3427, Mankato, MN 56002 (SAN 206-3492) Tel 507-388-1616; Toll free: 800-535-4393; *CIP.*

CRG Pr, *(CRG Pr.; 0-939686),* 1000 16th St., NW, Suite 400, Washington, DC 20036 (SAN 216-7239) Tel 202-223-2400.

CRI, *(Communications Research Institute),* 25 Central Park West, New York, NY 10023 (SAN 211-9420) Tel 212-752-5566.

CRI-Comm Res, *(CRI/Communication Research, Inc.; 0-934547),* 4156 Danvers Ct., S6, Grand Rapids, MI 49508 (SAN 693-8663) Tel 616-949-6743.

CRI NH, *(Computer Resources, Inc.; 0-938193),* Barrington Mall, Barrington, NH 03820 (SAN 661-0285) Tel 603-664-5811.

CRI Pubns, *(CRI Pubns.; 0-935689),* Div. of CrossRoads of Ames, Ltd., P.O. Box 565, Ames, IA 50010 (SAN 696-172X) Tel 515-292-7700.

CRIC Prod, *(CRIC Productions, Inc.; 0-935357),* Box 1214, Kingshill, St. Croix, VI 00850 (SAN 696-4141) Tel 809-778-2043.

Cricket Pubns, *(Cricket Pubns.; 0-912883),* P.O. Box 8771, Toledo, OH 43623 (SAN 283-0116) Tel 419-535-8739.

Cricket Software, *(Cricket Software; 0-936727),* 3508 Market St., Phildelphia, PA 19104 (SAN 699-9298) Tel 215-387-7955.

Cricketfield Pr, *(Cricketfield Pr.; 0-9614281),* 39 Megunticook St., Camden, ME 04843 (SAN 687-4401) Tel 207-236-3083.

Crim Jus Dept, *(Criminal Justice Department; 0-942754),* Loyola Univ. of Chicago, 820 N. Michigan Ave., Chicago, IL 60611 (SAN 679-1956).

Crime & Soc Justice, *(Crime & Social Justice; 0-935206),* P.O. Box 40601, San Francisco, CA 94140 (SAN 213-2133) Tel 415-550-1703.

Criminal Jus Ctr, *(Criminal Justice Ctr., Office of Pubns.; 0-935530),* Sam Houston State Univ., Huntsville, TX 77341 (SAN 217-2348) Tel 409-294-1692.

Crises Res Pr, *(Crises Research Pr.; 0-86627),* 301 W. 45th St., New York, NY 10036 (SAN 238-9274).

†**Crisp Pubns,** *(Crisp Pubns., Inc.; 0-931961),* 95 First St., Los Altos, CA 94022 (SAN 686-0400) Tel 415-949-4888; *CIP.*

Crispo Gallery, *(Crispo, Andrew, Gallery, Inc.; 0-937014),* 41 E. 57th St., New York, NY 10022 (SAN 214-297X).

Criterion Mus, *(Criterion Music Corp.; 0-910468),* 6124 Selma Ave., Hollywood, CA 90028 (SAN 203-6177) Tel 213-469-2296; Dist. by: Joe Goldfeder Music Enterprises, P.O. Box 660, Lynbrook, NY 11563 (SAN 203-6177).

Criterion Pr, *(Criterion Press; 0-9609428),* P.O. Box 1014, Torrance, CA 90505 (SAN 260-0382) Tel 213-326-3503.

Criterion Pubns, *(Criterion Pubns.; 0-937969),* 209 N. Beckley, De Sotoer, TX 75115 (SAN 659-5006) Tel 214-223-9348; Orders to: P.O. Box 214749, Dallas, TX 75221-4749 (SAN 662-426X).

Critical Book, *(Critical Thinking Bk. Co.; 0-935475),* 110 Sarah Dr., Mill Valley, CA 94941 (SAN 696-415X) Tel 405-383-8805.

Critical Mass, *(Critical Mass Energy Project of Public Citizen),* 215 Pennsylvania Ave., SE, Washington, DC 20003 (SAN 225-6878) Tel 202-546-4996.

Critics Choice Paper, *(Critics Choice Paperbacks; 0-931773; 1-55547),* 31 E. 28th St., New York, NY 10016 (SAN 684-7412) Tel 212-685-1550; Dist. by: Kable News Co., 777 Third Ave., New York, NY 10017 (SAN 169-5835); Dist. by: World Wide Media Services, Inc., 386 Park Ave. S., New York, NY 10016 (SAN 165-1684).

Critique Pub, *(Critique Publishing; 0-911485),* P.O. Box 11451, Santa Rosa, CA 95406 (SAN 692-6738).

Crittenden
See Crittenden Pub

Crittenden Pub, *(Crittenden Publishing, Inc.; 0-913153),* P.O. Box 1150, 85 Galli, Novato, CA 94948 (SAN 283-2771) Tel 415-883-8771; Toll free: 800-421-3483. Imprints: Union Square Bks (Union Square Books).

Crockett Pub Co, *(Crockett Publishing Co.; 0-915131),* 1319 Fremont Dr., Twin Falls, ID 83301 (SAN 289-9094) Tel 208-733-6531; Dist. by: Perry Enterprises, 2666 N. 650 E., Provo, UT 84601 (SAN 689-2485) Tel 801-375-9529.

Crofton Pub, *(Crofton Publishing Corp.; 0-89020),* 21 Wilson Ave., Belmont, MA 02178 (SAN 206-7560) Tel 617-489-2149.

†**Croissant & Co,** *(Croissant & Co.; 0-912348),* P.O. Box 282, Athens, OH 45701 (SAN 204-255X) Tel 614-593-3008; *CIP.*

Cromwel, *(Cromwel Press; 0-916298),* P.O. Box 335, Santa Margarita, CA 93453 (SAN 210-3540) Tel 805-543-1581.

Cromwell-Smith, *(Cromwell-Smith Services; 0-933086),* 60 Montego Ct., No. 26MB, Coronado, CA 92118 (SAN 213-2443) Tel 619-435-1928; Orders to: P.O. Box 1714, La Jolla, CA 92038 (SAN 661-9851) Tel 619-935-1928.

Croner, *(Croner Pubns.; 0-87514),* 211-03 Jamaica Ave., Queens Village, NY 11428 (SAN 203-8706) Tel 718-464-0866.

Cronk
See Shepard J

Crop Dust Pr, *(Crop Dust Pr.; 0-9616621),* Rte. 5, Box 75, Warrenton, VA 22186 (SAN 661-0617) Tel 703-642-6255.

Crop Res Proj
See NC Path Intl Dev

Symbols/Abbreviations

Crop Sci Soc Am, *(Crop Science Society of America),* 677 S. Segoe Rd., Madison, WI 53711 (SAN 213-8247) Tel 608-273-8080.

Crosby County, *(Crosby County Pioneer Memorial; 0-9606940),* P.O. Box 386, Crosbyton, TX 79322 (SAN 220-116X) Tel 806-675-2331.

Crosley, *(Crosley, Inc.; 0-9603268),* 1515 Kitchen, Jonesboro, AR 72401 (SAN 212-8985) Tel 501-935-3928.

Cross Bks, *(Cross Books; 0-9601672),* 50 MacArthur Dr., North Providence, RI 02911 (SAN 211-5239) Tel 401-231-0874.

Cross Country, *(Cross Country Pr.; 0-916696),* P.O. Box 492, Ridgefield, CT 06877 (SAN 208-3094) Tel 203-431-8225.

†**Cross Cult,** *(Cross-Cultural Communications; 0-89304),* 239 Wynsum Ave., Merrick, NY 11566 (SAN 208-6212) Tel 516-868-5635; CIP.

Cross Cult Pr, *(Cross Cultural Pr.; 0-930693),* 1166 S. 42nd St., Springfield, OR 97478 (SAN 677-0754) Tel 503-746-7401.

Cross Harp, *(Cross Harp Pr.; 0-930948),* 530 Ranch Rd., Visalia, CA 93291 (SAN 223-1050) Tel 209-733-1679 Tel 213-851-7438.

Cross Info, *(Cross Information Co.; 0-923426),* 1881 Ninth St., Suite 311, Boulder, CO 80302-5151 (SAN 286-3898) Tel 303-444-7799.

Cross Press
See Cross Cult Pr

Crossbar Ent, *(Crossbar Enterprises; 0-9604994),* 9522 Stevebrook Rd., Fairfax, VA 22032 (SAN 215-6326) Tel 703-978-0288.

Crossbow Bks, *(CrossBow Bks.; 0-915973),* P.O. Box 857, Easton, PA 18042 (SAN 293-941X) Tel 201-859-3512.

Crosscurrents, *(Crosscurrents),* 2200 Glastonbury Rd., Westlake Village, CA 91361 (SAN 659-6401).

Crosscut Saw, *(Crosscut Saw Pr.; 0-931020),* Tel 415-843-7869; Orders to: Bookpeople, 2929 Fifth St., Berkeley, CA 94710 (SAN 168-9517).

†**Crossing Pr,** *(Crossing Pr., The; 0-89594; 0-912278),* Box 640, Trumansburg, NY 14886 (SAN 202-2060) Tel 607-387-6217; CIP.

Crossroad Bks Public, *(Crossroads Books with the Public Library of Cincinnati & Hamilton County; 0-9611380),* 485 Wood Ave., Cincinnati, OH 45220 (SAN 283-9490).

†**Crossroad NY,** *(Crossroad Pub. Co.; 0-8245),* 370 Lexington Ave., New York, NY 10017 (SAN 287-0118) Tel 212-532-3650; Dist. by: Harper & Row Pubs., Inc., Keystone Industrial Pk., Scranton, PA 08075 (SAN 215-3742); CIP.

Crossroads Imprint of African Studies Assn
Crossroads Imprint of Christendom Pubns
Crossroads Comm, *(Crossroads Communications; 0-916445),* P.O. Box 7, Carpentersville, IL 60110 (SAN 295-1258) Tel 312-587-1658.

Crossway Bks Imprint of Good News
Crow Canyon, *(Crow Canyon Press; 0-937760),* 2050 Ridgewood Road, Alamo, CA 94507 (SAN 215-6334).

Crowell Jr Bks, *(Crowell, Thomas Y., Junior Bks.; 0-690),* Div. of Harper Junior Bks. Group, 10 E. 53rd St., New York, NY 10022 (SAN 200-2086) Tel 212-207-7000; Toll free: 800-638-3030; 1700 Montgomery St., San Francisco, CA 94111 (SAN 215-3734) Tel 415-989-9000; Orders to: Keystone Industrial Pk., Scranton, PA 18512 (SAN 215-3742).

†**Crown,** *(Crown Pubs., Inc.; 0-517),* 225 Park Ave., S, New York, NY 10003 (SAN 200-2639) Tel 212-254-1600; Toll free: 800-526-4264; CIP. Imprints: Americana (Americana); Arlington Hse (Arlington House).(Arlington Hse.); AM Legacy Pr. (American Legacy Press); C N Potter Bks (Potter, Clarkson N., Books).(Potter, Clarkson N., Bks.); Harmony (Harmony Books).(Harmony Bks.); Julian Pr. (Julian Press); Knapp Pr. (Knapp Press); Michelman Books (Michelman, Herbert, Books).(Michelman, Herbert, Bks.); Outdoor Life (Outdoor Life Books).(Outdoor Life Bks.); Prince Paper (Prince Paperback).

Crown Ark Pubns, *(Crown Ark Pubns.; 0-943762),* P.O. Box 23941, Webster Groves, MO 63119 (SAN 238-2679).

Crown Min, *(Crown Ministries International; 0-935779),* P.O. Box 49, Euclid, MN 56722 (SAN 696-7108) Tel 218-745-5826.

CRPS, *(Center for Research on Population & Security; 0-937307),* 322 Azalea Dr., Chapel Hill, NC 27514 (SAN 658-7712) Tel 919-933-7491; P.O. Box 13067, Research Triangle Park, NC 27709 (SAN 658-7720).

CRR Imprint of Charles River Bks
CRS Con
See CRS Pr

CRS Pr, *(CRS Consultants Pr.; 0-911127),* P.O. Box 490175, Key Biscayne, FL 33149 (SAN 268-5663) Tel 305-361-9573.

Cruikshank, *(Cruikshank, Eleanor P.; 0-9605284),* 194 San Carlos Ave., Sausalito, CA 94965 (SAN 215-7489).

Cruising, *(Cruising Chef; 0-931297),* 421 Gerona Ave., Coral Gables, FL 33146 (SAN 683-2474) Tel 305-665-8376.

Crumb Elbow Pub, *(Crumb Elbow Publishing),* P.O. Box 294, Rhododendron, OR 97049 (SAN 679-128X) Tel 503-622-4798.

Crusade Pubs, *(Crusade Pubns),* 11326 Ranchito St., El Monte, CA 91732 (SAN 203-8595). Religious Publications Only.

Cruzada Span Pubns, *(Cruzada Spanish Pubns.; 0-933648),* P.O. Box 650909, Miami, FL 33165 (SAN 214-2376).

Cryptologia, *(Cryptologia; 0-9610560),* Div. of Rose-Hulman Institute of Technology, 5500 Wabash Ave., Terre Haute, IN 47803 (SAN 263-9920) Tel 812-877-1511.

Crystal Butterfly, *(Crystal Butterfly Prints & Pr.; 0-938233),* P.O. Box 672, Oak Lawn, IL 60454-0672 (SAN 661-0625); 8420 S. Knox, Chicago, IL 60652 (SAN 661-0633) Tel 312-767-3881.

Crystal Co, *(Crystal Co., The; 0-9614094),* P.O. Box 348, Sunol, CA 94586 (SAN 656-0407) Tel 415-862-2332; Dist. by: Samuel Weiser, P.O. Box 612, York Beach, ME 03910 (SAN 202-9588) Tel 207-363-4393; Dist. by: Starlite Dist., P.O. Box 20729, Reno, NV 89515 (SAN 131-1921); Dist. by: New Leaf Dist., 1020 White St. SW, Atlanta, GA 30310 (SAN 169-1449) Tel 404-755-2665; Dist. by: Bookpeople, 2929 Fifth St., Berkeley, CA 94710 (SAN 168-9517) Tel 415-549-3030; Dist. by: Brotherhood of Life, 110 Dartmouth SE, Albuquerque, NM 87106 (SAN 202-4233) Tel 505-255-8980.

Crystal Cove, *(Crystal Cove Pr.; 0-9616787),* 4011 Calle Abril, San Clemente, CA 92672 (SAN 661-0668) Tel 714-496-0830.

Crystal Intl Pub, *(Crystal International Publishing Co.; 0-9616622),* 2622 Woodlake, No. 1, Wyoming, MI 49509 (SAN 661-0714) Tel 616-530-9615.

Crystal MI, *(Crystal Pr.; 0-930402),* 1909 Proctor St., Flint, MI 48504 (SAN 220-522X) Tel 313-239-8281.

Crystal Pr, *(Crystal Pr., Ltd.; 0-938108),* P.O. Box 215, Crystal Bay, NV 89402 (SAN 239-5282).

Crystal Pubns, *(Crystal Pubns.; 0-9610820),* 827 Arlington Ave., Berkeley, CA 94707 (SAN 265-2269) Tel 415-526-8736.

Crystal Pubs, *(Crystal Pubs.; 0-934687),* 140 Garfield Ave., Colonia, NJ 07067 (SAN 694-1443) Tel 201-382-1315.

Crystal Rainbow, *(Crystal Rainbow Publishing Co.; 0-938125),* 3712 Fort Hill Dr., Alexandria, VA 22310 (SAN 661-0684) Tel 703-960-3859.

CS Pubns, *(CS Pubns.; 0-934206),* 1791 Primrose Dr., El Cajon, CA 92020 (SAN 213-0459).

CSA Pr, *(CSA Pr.; 0-87707),* Lake Ravun Rd., Lakemont, GA 30552 (SAN 207-7329) Tel 404-782-4723; P.O. Box 7, Lakemont, GA 30552 (SAN 658-0408). Imprints: Tarnhelm (Tarnhelm Press).(Tarnhelm Pr.).

CSA Pubn, *(CSA Pubns.; 0-933199),* Subs. of the State Univ. of New York at Binghamton, SUNY-Binghamton, Ctr. for Education & Social Research, Binghamton, NY 13901 (SAN 692-2619) Tel 607-777-2116.

CSI Campbell, *(Cultural Studies Institute; 0-9606058),* 999 W. Hamilton Ave., Suite 104, Campell, CA 95008 (SAN 216-8863) Tel 408-370-2267; Dist. by Professional Pubns., P.O. Box 199, San Carlos, CA 94070 (SAN 264-6315) Tel 415-595-8437.

CSI Pr, *(Casino Schools Pr. (CSI Pr.); 0-913421),* 1923 Bacharach Blvd., Atlantic City, NJ 08401 (SAN 285-9017) Tel 609-345-0303.

†**CSI Studies,** *(Georgetown Univ., Ctr. for Strategic & International Studies; 0-89206),* 1800 K St. NW, Suite 400, Washington, DC 20006 (SAN 281-4021) Tel 202-775-3119; CIP.

†**CSLA,** *(Church & Synagogue Library Assn.; 0-915324),* P.O. Box 1130, Bryn Mawr, PA 19010 (SAN 210-7872) Tel 215-853-2870; CIP.

†**CSPA,** *(Council of State Policy & Planning Agencies; 0-934842),* Affil. of National Governor's Association, 400 N. Capitol St. NW, Suite 291, Washington, DC 20001 (SAN 213-3032) Tel 202-624-5386; CIP.

CSPP-Fresno Pubns, *(CSPP-Fresno Pubns.; 0-931309),* 1350 M St., Fresno, CA 93721 (SAN 685-2572) Tel 209-486-8420.

CSS of Ohio, *(C.S.S. of Ohio; 0-89536; 1-55673),* 628 S. Main St., Lima, OH 45804 (SAN 207-0707) Tel 419-227-1818; Toll free: 800-537-1030.

CSS Pub
See CSS of Ohio

†**CSS Pubns,** *(CSS Pubns.; 0-942170),* P.O. Box 23, Iowa Falls, IA 50126 (SAN 238-0471); CIP.

CSSEAS
See Ctr S&SE Asian

CST Enterprises
See Chenonta

CST Jewish-Christian, *(College of St. Thomas, Ctr. for Jewish-Christian Learning; 0-9616619),* P.O. Box 5010, St. Paul, MN 55105 (SAN 661-0234); 2115 Summit Ave., St. Paul, MN 55105 (SAN 661-0242) Tel 612-647-5715.

CSU Art Gallery, *(California State Univ., Fullerton, Visual Arts Ctr.; 0-935314),* 800 N. State College Blvd., Fullerton, CA 92634 (SAN 223-7059).

CSU Ctr Busn Econ, *(California State Univ. at Chico, Center for Business & Economic Research; 0-9602894),* Chico, CA 95929 (SAN 215-9481).

CSU Fresno Pr
See Cal State Pr

CSU Fullerton, *(California State Univ. at Fullerton Foundation),* Fullerton, CA 92634 (SAN 215-1952); Dist. by: Hackett Publishing Co., Inc., P.O. Box 55573, 4047 N. Pennsylvania St., Indianapolis, IN 46205 (SAN 201-6044) Tel 317-283-8187.

CSU Oral Hist
See CSUF Oral Hist

CSU Sacto Lib, *(California State Univ., Sacramento Library; 0-938847),* 2000 Jed Smith Dr., Sacramento, CA 95819 (SAN 661-6976) Tel 916-278-6201.

CSUDH, *(California State Univ., Dominguez Hills Educational Resources Center),* 800 E. Victoria, Dominguez Hills, CA 90747 (SAN 211-4887).

CSUF Oral Hist, *(California State Univ. Fullerton, Oral History Program; 0-930046),* Fullerton, CA 92634 (SAN 210-3982) Tel 714-773-3580.

CSUN, *(California State Univ., Northridge Library; 0-937048),* 18111 Nordhoff St., Northridge, CA 91330 (SAN 203-8722) Tel 818-885-2271.

CSUN Disabled, *(California State Univ. at Northridge, Office of Disabled Student Services; 0-937475),* 18111 Nordhoff St., Northridge, CA 91330 (SAN 659-0020) Tel 818-885-2869.

CT Academy Imprint of Shoe String
CT Farm Bureau Assn, *(Connecticut Farm Bureau Assn., Inc.; 0-9615485),* 101 Reserve Rd., Hartford, CT 06114 (SAN 696-3870) Tel 203-237-9774.

CT Law Trib, *(Connecticut Law Tribune; 0-910051),* 179 Allyn St., Hartford, CT 06103-1418 (SAN 237-675X).

CT River Water, *(Connecticut River Watershed Council, Inc.; 0-9616371),* 125 Combs Rd., Easthampton, MA 01027 (SAN 659-1426) Tel 413-584-0057.

CTB McGraw Hill Imprint of McGraw
CTPI-NVP
See CareerTrack Pubns

Ctr Action Endangered, *(Center for Action on Endangered Species),* 175 W Main St, Ayer, MA 01432 (SAN 231-844X).

†**Ctr Adv Psychic Res,** *(Center for Advanced Psychic Research & Development, The; 0-9611788),* P.O. Box 1000, Cutchogue, NY 11935 (SAN 285-2284) Tel 516-727-4270; CIP.

Ctr Afro Stud Ohio, *(Ohio Univ. Ctr. for Afro-American Studies; 0-911393),* Ohio Univ., Athens, OH 45701 (SAN 274-2586) Tel 614-594-5477.

Ctr Agri & Rural Dev, *(Center for Agricultural & Rural Development; 0-936911),* Iowa State Univ., 578 Heady Hall, Ames, IA 50010 (SAN 658-3121) Tel 515-294-1183.

†Ctr Amer Arche, *(Center for American Archeology Pr.; 0-942118),* Kampsville Archeological Ctr., Kampsville, IL 62053 (SAN 237-9457) Tel 618-653-4532; Orders to: P.O. Box 366, Kampsville, IL 62053 (SAN 694-9517) Tel 618-653-4316; *CIP.*

Ctr Analysis Public Issues, *(Center for Analysis of Public Issues; 0-943136),* 16 Vandeventer Ave., Princeton, NJ 08540 (SAN 209-3227) Tel 609-924-9750.

Ctr Appl Ling, *(Center for Applied Linguistics; 0-87281),* 1118 22nd St., NW, Washington, DC 20037 (SAN 281-3998) Tel 202-429-9292; Dist. by: Harcourt Brace Jovanovich, International Div., Orlando, FL 32887 (SAN 200-2299) Tel 305-345-3800.

†Ctr Appl Res, *(Center for Applied Research in Education, The; 0-87628),* Subs. of Prentice-Hall, Englewood Cliffs, NJ 07632 (SAN 206-6424) Tel 201-592-2494; Orders to: P.O. Box 430, West Nyack, NY 10995 (SAN 206-6432) Tel 201-767-5030; *CIP.*

†Ctr Applications Psych, *(Center for Applications of Psychological Type, Inc.; 0-935652),* 2720 NW Sixth St., Gainesville, FL 32609 (SAN 213-9162) Tel 904-375-0160; *CIP.*

Ctr Art Living, *(Center for the Art of Living; 0-9602552),* Subs. of Training Systems, P.O. Box 788, Evanston, IL 60204 (SAN 212-8926) Tel 312-864-8664.

Ctr Bio-Gerontology, *(Center for Bio-Gerontology, The; 0-937777),* 8760 Sunset Blvd., Los Angeles, CA 90069 (SAN 659-3208) Tel 213-652-5731.

Ctr Black Stud
See Ctr Black Studies
Ctr Black Studies, *(Center for Black Studies; 0-939242),* Wayne State University, Detroit, MI 48202 (SAN 216-5171) Tel 313-577-2321.

Ctr Black Success, *(Center for Black Success, The; 0-9616936),* 250 W. 54th St., Suite 811, New York, NY 10019 (SAN 661-8375) Tel 212-541-7600.

Ctr Bus Devel
See U ID Ctr Busn
Ctr Bus Devel & Res
See U ID Ctr Busn
Ctr Busn Info, *(Center for Business Information; 0-936936),* P.O. Box 2404, Meriden, CT 06450 (SAN 214-2902) Tel 203-481-0888.

Ctr Calif Public
See Cal Inst Public
†Ctr Canal Hist, *(Center for Canal History & Technology; 0-930973),* P.O. Box 877, Easton, PA 18044-0877 (SAN 678-8831) Tel 215-250-6700; *CIP.*

Ctr Comm Ministry, *(Center For Communications Ministry; 0-9606188),* 1962 S. Shenandoah, Los Angeles, CA 90034 (SAN 220-293X) Tel 213-559-2944.

Ctr Comp Assisted, *(Center for Computer Assisted Research in the Humanities; 0-936943),* 525 Middlefield Rd., Suite 120, Menlo Park, CA 94025 (SAN 658-6708) Tel 415-322-7050.

Ctr Comp Law, *(Center for Computer/Law; 0-935200),* P.O. Box 3549, Manhattan Beach, CA 90266 (SAN 223-7008).

Ctr Conflict Resol, *(Center for Conflict Resolution; 0-941492),* 731 State St., Madison, WI 53703 (SAN 239-0736) Tel 608-255-0479.

Ctr Conn Stud
See Ctr CT Studies
Ctr Consumer Aff
See UWIM CCA
Ctr Cont Poetry, *(Center for Contemporary Poetry; 0-917540),* Div. of Murphy Library, University of Wisconsin at La Crosse, Murphy Library, Univ. of Wisconsin at La Crosse, La Crosse, WI 54601 (SAN 201-906X) Tel 608-785-8511.

Ctr Creat Leader, *(Center for Creative Leadership; 0-912879),* Affil. of Smith Richardson Foundation, P.O. Box P-1, 5000 Laurinda Dr., Greensboro, NC 27402-1660 (SAN 282-9924) Tel 919-288-7210.

Ctr CT Studies, *(Center for Connecticut Studies),* Eastern Connecticut State Univ., Willimantic, CT 06226 (SAN 212-4874) Tel 203-456-2231.

Ctr Econ Analysis
See CEA Bks Pr
Ctr Econ Conversion, *(Center for Economic Conversion; 0-930471),* 222c View St., Mountain View, CA 94041 (SAN 670-8951) Tel 415-968-8798.

Ctr Ed Alternatives, *(Center for Educational Alternatives; 0-943346),* 908 Ridgecrest Circle, Anaheim, CA 92807 (SAN 240-5245) Tel 714-974-6476.

Ctr Educ Policy Mgmt, *(Univ. of Oregon, Ctr. for Educational Policy & Management; 0-936276),* College of Education, Eugene, OR 97403 (SAN 211-223X) Tel 503-686-5077.

Ctr Educ Res, *(Center for Education & Research in Free Enterprise; 0-86599),* Texas A&M Univ., College Station, TX 77843 (SAN 215-0646).

Ctr Env Des Res, *(Ball State Univ., Ctr. for Environmental Design, Research & Service; 0-912431),* College of Architecture and Planning /AB104, Muncie, IN 47306-1099 (SAN 265-1890) Tel 317-285-5859.

Ctr Env Educ, *(Center for Environmental Education; 0-9615294),* 624 Ninth St., NW, Washington, DC 20001 (SAN 694-566X) Tel 202-737-3600.

Ctr for African, *(Center For African Studies; 0-932219),* P.O. Box 689, New York, NY 10030 (SAN 686-6042) Tel 212-678-7184.

†Ctr for Arts Info, *(Center for Arts Information; 0-935654),* Subs. of Clearinghouse for Arts Information, Inc., 625 Broadway, New York, NY 10012 (SAN 282-7034) Tel 212-677-7548; *CIP.*

Ctr for Holo, *(Center for Holocaust Studies, Documentation & Research; 0-9609970),* 1610 Ave. J, Brooklyn, NY 11230 (SAN 268-7755) Tel 718-338-6494.

Ctr for NE & North African Stud
See UM Ctr NENAS
Ctr Futures Ed, *(Center for Futures Education, Inc.; 0-915513),* P.O. Box 489, Cedar Falls, IA 50613 (SAN 291-1132) Tel 319-277-7529.

Ctr Health Info, *(Center for Health Information; 0-932567),* P.O. Box 4636, Foster City, CA 94404 (SAN 687-4754) Tel 415-345-6669.

Ctr Hist Am Needle, *(Center for the History of American Needlework; 0-934074),* P.O. Box 359, Valencia, PA 16059 (SAN 225-3003) Tel 412-586-5325.

Ctr Info Sharing, *(Center for Information Sharing; 0-939532),* 77 N. Washington St., Boston, MA 02114 (SAN 216-3489) Tel 617-742-3222.

Ctr Innovation, *(Center for Innovation in Education; 0-9614646),* 19225 Vineyard Ln., Saratoga, CA 95070 (SAN 691-8530) Tel 408-867-6873.

Ctr Intl Ed U of MA, *(Univ. of Massachusetts, Ctr. for International Education; 0-932288),* Div. of School of Ed., 285 Hills Hse., S., Amherst, MA 01003 (SAN 212-9329) Tel 413-545-0465.

Ctr Intl Policy, *(Center for International Policy),* Subs. of Fund for Peace, 236 Massachusetts Ave., NE, Washington, DC 20002 (SAN 225-6592) Tel 202-544-4666.

†Ctr Intl Stud Duke, *(Duke Univ., Ctr. for International Studies; 0-916994),* 2122 Campus Dr., Durham, NC 27706 (SAN 213-5795); *CIP.*

Ctr Judaic-Christ Studies, *(Center for Judaic-Christian Studies; 0-918873),* P.O. Box 202707, Austin, TX 78720 (SAN 669-9979) Tel 512-343-3101.

Ctr Juris Stud, *(Center for Jurisdictional Studies; 0-9614259),* 323 E. William St., Suite 205, Ann Arbor, MI 48104 (SAN 687-1208) Tel 313-582-4782.

Ctr Korean U HI at Manoa, *(Center for Korean Studies, Univ. of Hawaii at Manoa; 0-917536),* 1881 East-West Rd., Honolulu, HI 96822 (SAN 208-0044) Tel 808-949-1833.

Ctr Land Grant, *(Center for Land Grant Studies, The; 0-9605202),* 136 Grant Ave., Santa Fe, NM 87501 (SAN 216-3497).

Ctr Latin Am Univ
See U Wis-Mil Ctr Latin Am

Ctr Law & Ed, *(Center for Law & Education, Incorporated; 0-912585),* 14 Appian Way, 6th Flr., Cambridge, MA 02138 (SAN 237-6431) Tel 617-495-4666.

Ctr Law Related, *(Center for Law-Related Education; 0-937709),* 4400 Cathedral Oaks Rd., Santa Barbara, CA 93160 (SAN 659-3216) Tel 805-964-4711.

†Ctr Leadership, *(Center for Leadership Studies; 0-931619),* Div. of Leadership Studies, Inc., 230 W. Third Ave., Escondido, CA 92025 (SAN 683-7131) Tel 619-741-6595; Dist. by: University Assocs., Inc., 8517 Production Ave., San Diego, CA 92121 (SAN 203-333X) Tel 619-578-5900; *CIP.*

Ctr Marital Sexual, *(Center for Marital & Sexual Studies; 0-9600626),* 5251 Los Altos Plaza, Long Beach, CA 90815 (SAN 203-8587) Tel 213-597-4425.

Ctr Mex Studies, *(Center for U. S.-Mexican Studies; 0-935391),* Univ. of California, San Diego, CA 92093 (SAN 696-2483) Tel 619-452-4503; 10111 N. Torrey Pines Rd., La Jolla, CA 92037 (SAN 696-2491).

†Ctr Migration, *(Center for Migration Studies; 0-913256; 0-934733),* 209 Flagg Pl., Staten Island, NY 10304 (SAN 281-4013) Tel 718-351-8800; *CIP.*

Ctr Mod Psych Stud
See CMPS NYC
†Ctr Multiple Birth, *(Center for the Study of Multiple Birth; 0-932254),* 333 E. Superior St., Suite 476, Chicago, IL 60611 (SAN 274-1997) Tel 312-266-9093; *CIP.*

Ctr Natl Pol Rev, *(Center for National Policy Review),* 1025 Vermont Ave., NW, Suite 360, Washington, DC 20005 (SAN 237-6350) Tel 202-783-5640.

Ctr Natl Security, *(Center for National Security Studies; 0-86566),* 122 Maryland Ave. NE, Washington, DC 20002 (SAN 215-2991) Tel 202-544-1681.

Ctr Neo Hellenic, *(Center for Neo-Hellenic Studies; 0-932242),* 1010 W. 22nd St., Austin, TX 78705 (SAN 211-8467) Tel 512-477-5526.

†Ctr Occupational Hazards, *(Center for Occupational Hazards; 0-918875),* 5 Beekman St., New York, NY 10038 (SAN 669-9936) Tel 212-227-6220; *CIP.*

Ctr Peace Stud, *(Georgetown Univ., Center for Peace Studies; 0-912239),* 410 Maguire Bldg., Georgetown Univ., Washington, DC 20057 (SAN 265-1394) Tel 202-625-4240.

Ctr Philos & Pub Policy, *(Center for Philosophy & Public Policy),* Div. of University of Maryland, Univ. of Maryland, Woods Hall, Rm. 0123, College Park, MD 20742 (SAN 225-7009) Tel 301-454-4103.

Ctr Polish, *(Center for Polish Studies & Culture; 0-9615564),* Div. of Orchard Lake Schls., Orchard Lake Schls., 3355 Indian Trail, Orchard Lake, MI 48033 (SAN 696-2440) Tel 313-682-1885.

Ctr Politics, *(Center for Responsive Politics; 0-939715),* 2001 O St. NW, Washington, DC 20036 (SAN 663-6144) Tel 202-857-0044.

Ctr Productive Public
See Natl Ctr Public Prod
†Ctr Prof Adv, *(Center for Professional Advancement; 0-86563),* 197 Rt. 18, P.O. Box H, E. Brunswick, NJ 08816 (SAN 214-185X) Tel 201-249-1400; *CIP.*

Ctr Pub, *(Center for Public Advocacy Research, Inc.; 0-943138),* 12 W. 37th St., New York, NY 10018 (SAN 240-5253) Tel 212-736-7440.

Ctr Renew Resources, *(Center for Renewable Resources; 0-937446),* 1001 Connecticut Ave., NW, Suite 638, Washington, DC 20036 (SAN 223-9876) Tel 202-466-6880.

Ctr Res Ambulatory, *(Center for Research in Ambulatory Health Care Administration; 0-933948),* Affil. of Medical Group Management Association, 1355 S. Colorado Blvd., Suite 900, Denver, CO 80222 (SAN 230-9459) Tel 303-753-1111.

Ctr Res & Dev, *(Center for Occupational Research & Development; 1-55502),* 601C Lake Air Dr., Waco, TX 76710 (SAN 694-2121) Tel 817-772-8756.

Ctr Res Lib, *(Ctr. for Research Libraries, The; 0-932486),* 6050 S. Kenwood Ave., Chicago, IL 60637 (SAN 225-3348) Tel 312-955-4545.

Ctr Res Soc Chg, (Center for Research in Social Change; 0-89937), Emory Univ., Fred Roberts Crawford Witness to the Holocaust Project, Atlanta, GA 30322 (SAN 211-5247) Tel 404-727-7525; Dist. by: Witness to the Holocaust Project, Emory University, Atlanta, GA 30322 (SAN 264-5025) Tel 404-727-7525.

Ctr Research Lib
See Ctr Res Lib

Ctr Respon Govern
See CRG Pr

Ctr Respon Psych, (Center for Responsive Psychology; 1-55524), Brooklyn College, CUNY, Brooklyn, NY 11210 (SAN 225-7165) Tel 718-780-5960.

Ctr Responsive Law, (Center for Study of Responsive Law; 0-936758), P.O. Box 19367, Washington, DC 20036 (SAN 281-403X) Tel 202-387-8030.

Ctr Sacred Healing, (Center for Sacred Healing Arts Publishing Co.; 0-936901), 1329 W. 37th Dr., Los Angeles, CA 90007 (SAN 658-5558) Tel 213-733-1272.

Ctr S&SE Asian, (Univ. of Michigan, Ctr. for South & Southeast Asian Studies; 0-89148), 130 Lane Hall, Ann Arbor, MI 48109 (SAN 206-491X) Tel 313-764-0352.

Ctr Sci Public, (Center for Science in the Public Interest; 0-89329), 1501 16th St. NW, Washington, DC 20036 (SAN 207-6543) Tel 202-332-9110.

Ctr Sci Study, (Center for the Scientific Study of Religion; 0-913348), 5757 University Ave., Chicago, IL 60637 (SAN 203-8749) Tel 312-752-5757.

Ctr Self Suff, (Center for Self-Sufficiency Publishing; 0-910811), Box 7234, Houston, TX 77248 (SAN 698-1828).

Ctr Sexual Comm, (Ctr. for Sexual Communication), 195 Claremont, Suite 374, Long Beach, CA 90803 (SAN 687-6595).

†Ctr South Folklore, (Center for Southern Folklore; 0-89267), 1216 Peabody Ave., P.O. Box 40105, Memphis, TN 38104 (SAN 209-2247) Tel 901-726-4205; CIP.

Ctr Study Aging, (Center for the Study of Aging, Inc.; 0-937829), 706 Madison Ave., Albany, NY 12208 (SAN 659-4344) Tel 518-465-6927.

Ctr Study Elephants, (Center for the Study of Elephants, The; 0-942074), P.O. Box 4444, Carson, CA 90749 (SAN 239-5177).

Ctr Study Language, (Center for the Study of Language & Information; 0-937073), Stanford Univ., Ventura Hall, Stanford, CA 94305 (SAN 658-5582) Tel 415-723-1712; Dist. by: Univ. of Chicago Pr., 5801 Ellis Ave., 3rd Flr., Chicago, IL 60637 (SAN 202-5280) Tel 312-962-7723.

Ctr Study Presidency, (Center for the Study of the Presidency; 0-938204), 208 E. 75 St., New York, NY 10021 (SAN 225-6339) Tel 212-249-1200.

Ctr Study Serv, (Center for the Study of Services; 0-9611432), 806 15th St. NW, Suite 925, Washington, DC 20005 (SAN 287-2862) Tel 202-347-9612.

Ctr Sutton Movement, (Center For Sutton Movement Writing, Incorporated, The; 0-914336), P.O. Box 7344, Newport Beach, CA 92658-7344 (SAN 203-154X) Tel 714-644-8342.

Ctr Tech Environ, (Center for Technology, Environment, & Development; 0-939436), Clark Univ., 950 Main St., Worcester, MA 01610 (SAN 216-5708).

Ctr Thanatology, (Center for Thanatology Research & Education, Inc.; 0-930194), 391 Atlantic Ave., Brooklyn, NY 11217-1701 (SAN 210-7414) Tel 718-858-3026; Orders to: P.O. Box 989, Brooklyn, NY 11202-1202 (SAN 215-0425).

†Ctr Thomistic, (Univ. of St. Thomas, Ctr. for Thomistic Studies; 0-9605456), University of Notre Dame, Notre Dame, IN 46544 (SAN 662-1732) Tel 219-239-6346; Dist. by: Univ. of Notre Dame Pr., P.O. Box L, Notre Dame, IN 46556 (SAN 203-3178) Tel 219-239-6346; Dist. by: Harper & Row, 1 Baker Dr., Conklin, NY 13748 (SAN 200-688X) Tel 607-775-4142; CIP.

Ctr Trad Orthodox, (Center for Traditionalist Orthodox Studies; 0-911165), P.O. Box 398, Etna, CA 96027 (SAN 287-0029) Tel 916-467-3228; c/o St. Gregory Palamas Monastery, P.O. Box 398, Etna, CA 96027 (SAN 287-0037).

Ctr Trans Acct Fin, (Center for Transnational Accounting & Financial Research; 0-913795), Univ. of Connecticut, U-41A, Storrs, CT 06268 (SAN 291-9273).

†Ctr Urban Pol Res, (Center for Urban Policy Research; 0-88285), Rutgers Univ., Kilmer Campus, Bldg. 4051, New Brunswick, NJ 08903 (SAN 206-6297) Tel 201-932-3133; CIP.

Ctr Western Studies, (Center for Western Studies; 0-931170), Augustana College, Box 727, Sioux Falls, SD 57197 (SAN 211-4844) Tel 605-336-4007.

Ctr Women's Studies, (Center for Women's Studies & Services; 0-9600856), 2467 E St., San Diego, CA 92102 (SAN 225-7297) Tel 619-233-8984.

CTS-GWU, (George Washington Univ., Ctr. for Telecommunications Studies; 0-932768), 2130 H St., NW, Rm. W1, Washington, DC 20052 (SAN 212-4491) Tel 202-676-6455.

CU Ctr Career Res, (Columbia Univ., Ctr. for Career Research & Human Resource Management), 314 Uris Hall, Graduate School of Business Administration, New York, NY 10027 (SAN 289-6141) Tel 212-280-5570.

CU Law Natl
See Ctr Natl Pol Rev

CUB, (Concerned United Birthparents, Inc.), 595 Central Ave., Dover, NH 03820 (SAN 241-3736) Tel 603-749-3744.

Cube Pubns, (Cube Pubns., Inc.; 0-911603), 1 Buena Vista Rd., Pt. Jefferson, NY 11777 (SAN 263-9939) Tel 516-331-4990; P.O. Box 665, Pt. Jefferson, NY 11777 (SAN 696-5083).

Cuckoo Bird Pr
See Andrion Bks

Cuisinart Cooking, (Cuisinart Cooking Club; 0-936662), 15 Valley Dr., Greenwich, CT 06830 (SAN 214-2287) Tel 203-622-4689; P.O. Box 2150, Greenwich, CT 06836-2150 (SAN 658-0416).

Cuisine Con
See Cuisine Prods

Cuisine Prods, (Cuisine Productions; 0-910327), P.O. Box 795217, Dallas, TX 75379 (SAN 241-4902) Tel 214-386-6708.

Cuissential, (Cuissential Arts; 0-9615136), P.O. Box 22337, Sacramento, CA 95822 (SAN 694-2520) Tel 916-421-1957.

Culinary Arts, (Culinary Arts, Ltd.; 0-914667), 8050 SW 85th St., Portland, OR 97223 (SAN 289-1972) Tel 503-639-4549.

Cullins, (Cullins & Cullins; 0-9608386), P.O. Box 241, Sloughhouse, CA 95683 (SAN 240-530X) Tel 916-687-6745.

Cultural Assist
See Alliance Bks

Cultural Res, (Cultural Resource; 0-918421), 120 Tuscarora Dr., Hillsborough, NC 27278 (SAN 657-5854) Tel 919-732-7116.

Cultural Serv, (Cultural Services, Inc.; 0-913169), P.O. Box 30435, Bethesda, MD 20814 (SAN 283-0469) Tel 301-654-2092; Dist. by: Oryx Pr., 2214 N. Central, Phoenix, AZ 85004 (SAN 692-8420).

Cultural Stud Inst
See CSI Campbell

Culver Pubns, (Culver Pubns.; 0-9615155), P.O. Box 3103, Kingston, NY 12401 (SAN 693-126X) Tel 914-331-6215.

Cum Index Nursing, (Cumulative Index to Nursing & Allied Health Literature; 0-910478), Div. of Glendale Adventist Medical Ctr., Box 871, Glendale, CA 91209 (SAN 217-2356) Tel 818-240-2819.

Cumberland Pr, (Cumberland Pr.; 0-87027), 136 Main St., Freeport, ME 04032 (SAN 203-2090) Tel 207-865-6045.

Cummings
See Benjamin-Cummings

Cunningham Pr, (Cunningham Press), 3063 W. Main, Alhambra, CA 91801 (SAN 203-8773) Tel 818-283-8838; Dist. by: Theosophy Co., 245 W. 33rd St., Los Angeles, CA 90007 (SAN 295-3560) Tel 213-748-7244.

Cunningham Pub Co, (Cunningham Publishing Co.; 0-911659), 701 Washington, Box 1345, Buffalo, NY 14205 (SAN 263-9947) Tel 519-587-5143.

Cupbd Cookbk, (Cupboard Cookbook, The; 0-9613676), Box 444, Salem, IL 62881 (SAN 238-0455) Tel 618-548-3049.

Cupbdr Cookbk
See Cupbd Cookbk

†Curbstone, (Curbstone Pr.; 0-915306), 321 Jackson St., Willimantic, CT 06226 (SAN 209-4282) Tel 203-423-9190; Dist. by: Talman Co., 150 Fifth Ave., Rm. 514, New York, NY 10011 (SAN 200-5204) Tel 212-620-3182; CIP.

Curbstone Pub NY TX
See Curbstone Pub TX

Curbstone Pub TX, (Curbstone Publishing; 0-931604), P.O. Box 7445 Univ. Sta., Austin, TX 78712 (SAN 281-5796) Tel 512-263-3237.

CURE, (Council for Unified Research & Education), 617 W. 113th St., New York, NY 10025 (SAN 233-0091) Tel 212-666-4766.

Curl, (Curl; 0-9614282), Edgemont, SD 57735 (SAN 687-441X) Tel 307-325-6545.

Current Digest, (Current Digest of the Soviet Press, The; 0-913601), Affil. of American Assn. for the Advancement of Slavic Studies & American Council of Learned Societies, 1480 W. Lane Ave., Columbus, OH 43221 (SAN 282-7069) Tel 614-422-4234.

†Current Issues, (Current Issues Pubns.; 0-936012), 2214 Stuart St., Berkeley, CA 94705 (SAN 213-9189) Tel 415-549-1451; CIP.

Current Lit Pubns, (Current Literature Pubns., Inc.; 0-914899), 1513 E. St., Bellingham, WA 98225 (SAN 289-0976) Tel 206-734-9233.

Current Nine Pub, (Current Nine Publishing; 0-9615413), 4167 S. Four Mile Run Dr., No. 203, Arlington, VA 22204 (SAN 695-4979) Tel 703-920-9587; P.O. Box 6089, Arlington, VA 22206 (SAN 695-4987).

Curriculum Info Ctr, (Curriculum Information Ctr., Inc.; 0-914608; 0-89770), Ketchum Pl., P.O. Box 510, Westport, CT 06880 (SAN 206-3506) Tel 203-226-8941. Purchased by Market Data Retrieval in 1979.

Currier-Davis, (Currier Davis Publishing; 0-930507), P.O. Box 58, Winter Park, FL 32790-0058 (SAN 670-963X) Tel 305-788-8677; 1180 Spring Ctr., S. Blvd., Suite 120, Altamonte Springs, FL 32714 (SAN 670-9648).

Curriers Fine Art, (Currier's Fine Art Appraisals & Publishing; 0-935277), P.O. Box 2098-A, Brockton, MA 02402 (SAN 695-751X) Tel 617-588-4509; 22 Martland Ave., Brockton, MA 02401 (SAN 696-9518) Tel 617-588-4509.

Curry County, (Curry County Historical Society; 0-932368), 920 S. Ellensburg, Gold Beach, OR 97444 (SAN 215-7500) Tel 503-247-2165.

Curson Hse, (Curson House, Inc. Publishers; 0-913694), 250 S. 18th St. Chestnut St., Philadelphia, PA 19103 (SAN 203-8781) Tel 215-732-7111.

†Curtin & London, (Curtin & London, Inc.; 0-930764), P.O. Box 363, Marblehead, MA 01945 (SAN 212-0151) Tel 617-631-0762; Orders to: (Computer & business titles), P.O. Box 363, Marblehead, MA 01945 (SAN 212-0151); Orders to: Focal Pr. (Photography titles), 80 Montvale Ave., Stoneham, MA 02180 (SAN 220-0066) Tel 617-438-8464; Dist. by: Van Nostrand Reinhold, 115 Fifth Ave., New York, NY 10003 (SAN 202-5183) Tel 212-254-3232; CIP.

Curtis Instruments, (Curtis Instruments, Inc.; 0-939488), 200 Kisco Ave., Mt. Kisco, NY 10549 (SAN 216-3616) Tel 914-666-2971.

Curtis Lieberman, (Curtis-Lieberman Bks.; 0-930985), Box 186, Woodstock, VT 05091 (SAN 678-9285) Tel 802-457-2877.

Curtis Media, (Curtis Media Corp.; 0-88107), 9954 Brockbank Dr., Dallas, TX 75220 (SAN 240-7310).

Curtis Pub Co, (Curtis Publishing Co., The; 0-89387), Div. of Saturday Evening Post, 1100 Waterway Blvd., Indianapolis, IN 46206 (SAN 216-3624) Tel 317-634-1100.

Curtis Wood Pubs, (Wood, Curtis, Pubns.; 0-9614875), 4416 Eaton's Creek Rd., Nashville, TN 37218 (SAN 693-2312) Tel 615-876-1729.

Cushman Pubs, (Cushman Pubs.; 0-9607084), 7720 Brandeis Way, Springfield, VA 22153 (SAN 238-9681) Tel 703-243-4960.

Custer, (Custer, Marquis, Pubns.; 0-9600274), 1021 S. Lee Ave., Lodi, CA 95240 (SAN 206-9261) Tel 209-368-0502.

D Grossman Pr, *(Grossman, David, Press; 0-910563),* 212 E. 47th St., Apt. 33a, New York, NY 10017 (SAN 260-1958) Tel 212-486-9598.

D H Shubin, *(Shubin, Daniel H.),* 5865 Crown Dr., Mira Loma, CA 91752 (SAN 659-4026).

D Hannon, *(Hannon, Douglas; 0-937866),* Rte. 2, Box 991, Odessa, FL 33556 (SAN 215-7705); Dist. by: Great Outdoors Publishing Co., St. Petersburg, FL 33714 (SAN 201-6273); Dist. by: Atlantic Publishing Company, P.O. Box 67, Tabor City, NC 28463 (SAN 215-6237) Tel 919-653-3153.

D Hooper, *(Hooper, Doug; 0-9604702),* P.O. Box 792, Danville, CA 94526 (SAN 217-2402).

D Hyk Pub Co, *(Hyk, Doyle, Publishing Co.; 0-9615817),* P.O. Box 1021, Rochester, MI 48308-1021 (SAN 696-8430) Tel 313-375-0645.

D I Fine, *(Fine, Donald I.; 0-917657; 1-55611),* 128 E. 36th St., New York, NY 10016 (SAN 656-9749) Tel 212-696-1838; Orders to: Haddon Craftsmen, Inc., 1205K O'Neill Hwy., Dunmore, PA 18512 (SAN 662-7625) Tel 717-348-9292.

D Ives, *(Ives, Dorthea S.; 0-9616225),* R.D. 1, Dolgeville, NY 13329 (SAN 697-1628).

D J Bolton, *(Bolton, D. Joyce; 0-9602368),* 700 Paseo De Peralta, Santa Fe, NM 87501 (SAN 211-2922) Tel 505-982-4953.

D J Cantor
See Cantor & Co

D J Content, *(Content, Derek J., Rare Bks., Inc.; 0-935681),* Crow Hill, Houlton, ME 04730 (SAN 696-3986) Tel 207-532-7794.

D J Davenport, *(Davenport, Donald Jordan; 0-9606640),* 17700 Northland Pk. Ct., Southfield, MI 48075 (SAN 219-7278) Tel 313-443-9000.

D J Fortunato
See Fortunato Bks

D J Gingery, *(Gingery, David J.; 0-9604330),* 2045 Boonville, Springfield, MO 65803 (SAN 214-3771) Tel 417-866-7770.

D J P Geer, *(Geer, D.J.P.; 0-9613061),* 10731 Sinclair Ave., Dallas, TX 75218 (SAN 294-8095) Tel 214-327-4938.

D J Perkins, *(Perkins, Dorothy J.; 0-9604742),* Box 194, Moylan, PA 19065 (SAN 215-6970).

D Jenkins, *(Jenkins, Doris; 0-9606578),* 1201 Lincoln Mall, No. 611, Lincoln, NE 68508 (SAN 208-2624) Tel 402-477-2779.

D K Blenderman, *(Blenderman, Doretta K.; 0-9615637),* 9972 Duffy, Temple City, CA 91780 (SAN 696-1185) Tel 818-286-4757.

D K Dolphin, *(Dolphin, Deon K.; 0-9613157),* 2130 Hwy 101 D12, Greenbrae, CA 94904 (SAN 294-9229) Tel 415-461-7916.

D K Gleason, *(Gleason, David King; 0-9612038),* 1766 Nicholson Dr., Baton Rouge, LA 70802 (SAN 286-7869) Tel 504-383-8989.

D Keasbey, *(Keasbey, Doramay; 0-9611136),* 5031 Alta Vista Rd., Bethesda, MD 20814 (SAN 283-9512) Tel 301-530-5031.

D Knox, *(Knox, Daryl K.; 0-9605790),* 3533 Queensway Dr., Brownsville, TX 78521 (SAN 216-4035) Tel 512-544-2428.

D Kushner Ltd, *(Kushner, Daniel, , Ltd.; 0-9615694),* 2441 W. Sharon Ave., Phoenix, AZ 85029 (SAN 696-2203) Tel 602-263-8411; P.O. Box 26243, Phoenix, AZ 85068 (SAN 696-5598).

D L Barber Ventures, *(Barber, D. L., Ventures; 0-938895),* 13351 Benton St., Garden Grove, CA 92643 (SAN 662-6637) Tel 213-425-3460; P.O. Box 2248, Garden Grove, CA 92642-2248 (SAN 663-3242) Tel 714-530-6716.

D L Hamilton
See Intl Computer

D L Howard, *(Howard, Daniel L.; 0-936144),* P.O. Box 41432, Los Angeles, CA 90041 (SAN 213-9316) Tcl 213-258-2121.

D L Jensen, *(Jensen, Deana L.; 0-9615793),* Rte. 3, Box 97, Idaho Falls, ID 83401 (SAN 696-8678) Tel 208-357-3914.

D L Mathews, *(Mathews, Diane L.; 0-917247),* P.O. Box 134, Salisbury Center, NY 13454 (SAN 656-1187) Tel 315-429-3409.

D L Moss Pubns, *(Moss, David L., Publications; 0-914509),* 7986 Daggett St., San Diego, CA 92111 (SAN 289-6575) Tel 619-571-0506.

D L Price, *(Price, David L.; 0-9604482),* 1954 Old Hickory Blvd., Brentwood, TN 37027 (SAN 215-3351) Tel 615-373-0946.

D L Shyh Yuan, *(Lee, Shyh-Yuan David; 0-9611810),* P.O. Box 795759, Dallas, TX 75379 (SAN 285-3329) Tel 214-733-0015.

D L Smith, *(Smith, Dean Lance, P.E.; 0-918699),* P.O. Box 31245, Houston, TX 77231-1245 (SAN 294-4804) Tel 713-721-5499.

D L Taylor, *(Taylor, Dorothy Loring; 0-9610640),* R. R. 2, Box 152, Virginia, IL 62691 (SAN 265-3567) Tel 217-458-2506.

D Landman
See Dennis-Landman

D Lekas, *(Lekas, Danny; 0-930759),* 10 Jamaicaway, Apt 18, Boston, MA 02130 (SAN 679-193X) Tel 617-738-0736.

D Lem Assocs, *(Lem, Dean, Associates, Inc.; 0-914218),* 1526 Pontius Ave., Suite C, Los Angeles, CA 90025 (SAN 201-5005) Tel 213-478-0092; Orders to: P.O. Box 25920, Los Angeles, CA 90025 (SAN 201-5013).

D Luebbers, *(Luebbers, David J.; 0-9607406),* 78 S. Jackson, Denver, CO 80209 (SAN 209-5777) Tel 303-388-8534.

D M Abbott, *(Abbott, Delila M.; 0-9607336),* 4775 Bon Air St., Salt Lake City, UT 84117 (SAN 239-1449) Tel 801-277-2733; Dist. by: Zion's Book Store, 254 S. Main St., Salt Lake City, UT 84101 (SAN 239-1457) Tel 801-328-2586; Dist. by: Deseret Book Store, 44 ES. Temple, Salt Lake City, UT 84111 (SAN 200-4097) Tel 801-328-8191; Dist. by: Country Furniture, Old Gardner Mill, 1050 W. 7800 S., West Jordan, UT 84084 (SAN 200-4100) Tel 801-566-2842.

D M Chase, *(Chase, Don M.; 0-918634),* 8569 Lawrence Lane, Sebastopol, CA 95472 (SAN 209-4215) Tel 707-823-7670.

D M Grant, *(Grant, Donald M., Publisher, Inc; 0-937986),* West Kingston, RI 02892 (SAN 281-7535) Tel 401-783-3266; Dist. by: Pacific Comics, Inc., 4887 Ronson Ct., Suite E, San Diego, CA 95945 (SAN 169-0124); Dist. by: Bud Plant Inc., 13393 Grass Valley Dr., Suite 7, P.O. Box 1886, Grass Valley, CA 95945 (SAN 268-5086); Dist. by: F & S.F. Book Co., P.O. Box 415, Staten Island, NY 10302 (SAN 169-6270).

D M Kennedy Ctr Brigham, *(Kennedy, David M., International Ctr., Brigham Young Univ.; 0-912575),* 280 HRCB, Provo, UT 84602 (SAN 283-2895) Tel 801-378-6528.

D M Moore, *(Moore, Diane M.; 0-9604030),* P.O. Box 1073, New Iberia, LA 70560 (SAN 214-0608) Tel 318-364-6730.

D M Wagner, *(Wagner, D. M., Enterprises; 0-937053),* P.O. Box 559, Alva, OK 73717 (SAN 658-6716) Tel 405-327-1883; 318 College Ave., Alva, OK 73717 (SAN 658-6724).

D M Whiteside, *(Whiteside, Dora M., Pub.; 0-938353),* 501 Juniper Dr., Prescott, AZ 86301 (SAN 659-9133) Tel 602-445-7245; Dist. by: Magee Bk. Store, 118 N. Montezuma St., Prescott, AZ 86301 (SAN 200-6588).

D McCalden
See Truth Missions

D McMillan, *(McMillan, Dennis; 0-9609986; 0-939767),* 1995 Calais Dr., No. 3, Miami Beach, FL 33141 (SAN 272-1686) Tel 305-861-9164.

D McPhail, *(McPhail, David),* 242 Trinity Ave., Berkeley, CA 94708 (SAN 207-6586).

D March, *(March, David; 0-9615493),* 200 W. 54th St., New York, NY 10019 (SAN 696-3765) Tel 212-581-9150.

D Maurer, *(Maurer, Diane, Hand-Marbled Papers; 0-9616863),* RD 1, P.O. Box 11, Centre Hall, PA 16828 (SAN 661-1699); Brush Valley Rd., Centre Hall, PA 16828 (SAN 661-1702) Tel 814-364-9618.

D Moriarty, *(Moriarty, Dan, Associates; 0-933968),* 1410 Second Ave., Newport, MN 55055 (SAN 211-6448) Tel 612-459-1857.

D Mysiewicz, *(Mysiewicz, Deborah, Pubs., Inc.; 0-936451),* Box 1210, Port Angeles, WA 98362 (SAN 697-9165) Tel 206-928-3176.

D N McLean, *(McLean, Dabney N.; 0-9614934),* 12274 1st St., W., No. A4, Treasure Island, FL 33706 (SAN 693-3823).

D O A C, *(Diocese of Armenian Church; 0-934728),* 630 Second Ave., New York, NY 10016 (SAN 216-0625).

D-OR Pr, *(D'OR Pr.; 0-935045),* 200 N. Pickett St., No. 1113, Alexandria, VA 22304 (SAN 694-4671) Tel 703-751-7140.

D P Enter, *(D.P. Enterprises; 0-935208),* P.O. Box 23241, Phoenix, AZ 85063 (SAN 213-4837).

D P Filbrun, *(Filbrun, Daniel P.; 0-9614439),* 12859 Euphemia-Castine Rd., West Manchester, OH 45382 (SAN 689-3465) Tel 513-678-4074.

D Pagen
See Black Mntn

D Ponicsan, *(Ponicsan, Darryl),* P.O. Box 1596, Ojai, CA 93023 (SAN 206-8192) Tel 805-646-4215.

D Powell, *(Powell, Dan),* 2515 Olive St., Cedar Falls, IA 50613 (SAN 695-8435).

D-Q Univ Pr, *(D-Q University Pr.; 0-935279),* P.O. Box 409, Davis, CA 95617 (SAN 695-7250) Tel 916-758-0470.

D Quixote Pub, *(Don Quixote Publishing Co., Inc.; 0-943078),* P.O. Box 9442, Amarillo, TX 79105 (SAN 240-3676).

D R Bell, *(Bell, D. Rayford, Bishop; 0-9604820; 0-938195),* 1225 McDaniel Ave., Evanston, IL 60202 (SAN 215-8388) Tel 618-869-1907.

D R Benbow, *(Benbow, D. R.; 0-931611),* 441 Clairmont Ave., Apt. 1014, Decatur, GA 30030 (SAN 206-7293) Tel 404-378-7028.

D R Kronour, *(Kronour, David R., Publishing Co.; 0-9616118),* 3939 N. Diamond Mill Rd., Dayton, OH 45426 (SAN 699-718X) Tel 513-837-4260.

D R Pub, *(D & R Publishing; 0-937445),* Div. of D & R Enterprises, 3141 33rd Ave. S., Minneapolis, MN 55406 (SAN 659-1558) Tel 612-729-0897.

D R Richards, *(Richards, David R.; 0-9614431),* 480 W. Ash St., Zionsville, IN 46077 (SAN 688-5802) Tel 317-929-8517.

D Rendina, *(Rendina, Dave, Publishing Co.),* 1 Lake Rd., Newfield, NJ 08344 (SAN 212-0461).

D S C Pub, *(D.S.C. Publishing; 0-910985),* Div. of D.S.C., Inc., 2 Dogwood Dr. & Hayestown Rd., P.O. Box 769, Danbury, CT 06811 (SAN 269-7696) Tel 203-748-3231.

D S Coleman, *(Coleman, Dorothy S.; 0-910396),* 4315 Van Ness St., Washington, DC 20016 (SAN 203-8811) Tel 202-966-2655.

†D S Lake Pubs, *(Lake, David S., Pubs.; 0-8224),* 19 Davis Dr., Belmont, CA 94002 (SAN 212-775X) Tel 415-592-7810; *CIP.*

D Schiedt, *(Schiedt, Duncan P.; 0-9603528),* R.R.1, Box 217A, Pittsboro, IN 46167 (SAN 211-3996) Tel 317-852-8528.

D Smith, *(Smith, Doug; 0-9602728),* P.O. Box 260, Corvallis, OR 97330 (SAN 212-8144) Tel 503-754-3434; Dist. by: Bookpeople, 2929 Fifth St., Berkeley, CA 94710 (SAN 168-9517) Tel 415-549-3030.

D Sonenschein, *(Sonenschein, David; 0-915289),* P.O. Box 15744, San Antonio, TX 78212-8944 (SAN 290-0432) Tel 512-829-0048.

D Strauss, *(Strauss, Daniel; 0-9608338),* 2870 Grand Concourse, Bronx, NY 10458 (SAN 240-4478) Tel 212-369-0500.

D W Bell Gallery, *(Brown Univ., David Winton Bell Gallery; 0-933519),* 64 College St., Providence, RI 02912 (SAN 278-2758) Tel 401-863-2421.

D W Carrey, *(Carrey, Dixeann W.; 0-931882),* 6256 NW 16th Ct., Margate, FL 33063 (SAN 212-4068) Tel 305-975-0113.

D W Hemingway, *(Hemingway, Donald W.),* 309 S. Tenth W., Salt Lake City, UT 84104 (SAN 220-2506); Dist. by: George Mc. Co. Inc., P.O. Box 15671, Salt Lake City, UT 84115 (SAN 220-2514).

D W Rano, *(Rano, Dennis W.; 0-9612510),* P.O. Box 7842, South Lake Tahoe, CA 95705 (SAN 291-798X).

D Walker Pr, *(Walker, David, Pr., Inc.; 0-912135),* P.O. Box 741, Brooklyn, NY 11207 (SAN 264-8075) Tel 718-788-2044; 670 Carroll St., Brooklyn, NY 11215 (SAN 264-8083).

†D White, *(White, David, Co.; 0-87250),* One Pleasant Ave., Port Washington, NY 11050 (SAN 201-2936) Tel 516-944-9325; *CIP.*

D Winters, *(Winters, David/Music; 0-9616283),* 103 Van Ness St., Santa Cruz, CA 95060 (SAN 277-6707) Tel 408-426-0198.

D Wood, *(Wood, Debby; 0-9607490),* Box 1737, Cape Coral, FL 33910 (SAN 239-961X) Tel 813-481-6297; 3689 Liberty Square, Fort Myers, FL 33908 (SAN 693-5060).

†**Da Capo,** *(Da Capo Pr., Inc.; 0-306),* Subs. of Plenum Publishing Corp., 233 Spring St., New York, NY 10013 (SAN 201-2944) Tel 212-620-8000; Toll free: 800-221-9369; Toll free: 800-221-9369; *CIP.*

Daan Grap, *(Daan Graphics; 0-9609788),* 906 Lincoln Blvd., Middlesex, NJ 08846 (SAN 269-5634) Tel 201-469-1887.

Dabbs, *(Dabbs, Jack A.; 0-911494),* 2806 Cherry Lane, Austin, TX 78703 (SAN 205-4248) Tel 512-472-7463.

Dabney, *(Dabney; 0-9614155),* 2000 Hawkins Lane, Eugene, OR 97405 (SAN 686-5410) Tel 503-485-5847; Orders to: Human Creative Services, 2000 Hawkins Lane, Eugene, OR 97405 (SAN 693-5192) Tel 503-485-5847.

†**DaCa Pub,** *(DaCa Publishing Co.; 0-917904),* 1636 Monaco Dr., St. Louis, MO 63122 (SAN 209-3634) Tel 314-966-5678; *CIP.*

Dace Pub, *(Dace Publishing, Inc.; 0-932045),* P.O. Box 60, Quinque, VA 22965 (SAN 686-0001) Tel 804-985-3183.

Dada Ctr, *(Dada Center Pubns.; 0-930608),* 2319 W. Dry Creek Rd., Healdsburg, CA 95448 (SAN 211-1225) Tel 707-433-1237.

†**Dadant & Sons,** *(Dadant & Sons; 0-915698),* Hamilton, IL 62341 (SAN 224-1137); *CIP.*

Dade Variety Pr, *(Dade Variety Press),* 18154 NW Second Ave., Miami, FL 33169 (SAN 206-7005).

Daedalus Act, *(Daedalus Acting Lab; 0-9615815),* 629 Park Ave., No. 2A, New York, NY 10021 (SAN 696-7302) Tel 212-249-5356; P.O. Box 667, Lenox Hill Sta., New York, NY 10021 (SAN 698-2182).

Dah A Dee, *(Dah-A-Dee, Inc.; 0-9616561),* 5644 40th Ave., SW, Seattle, WA 98136 (SAN 659-4395) Tel 206-937-5524.

Daheshist, *(Daheshist Publishing Co., The; 0-935359),* 575 Lexington Ave., New York, NY 10022 (SAN 696-298X) Tel 212-751-6700.

Dahlstrom & Co, *(Dahlstrom & Co., Inc.; 0-940712),* 76 Prospect St., Franklin, MA 02038 (SAN 239-5088) Tel 617-528-1043. *Imprints:* Study Buddy (Study Buddy Books).

Daily Planet, *(Daily Planet Almanac, Inc., The; 0-939882),* P.O. Box 1641, Boulder, CO 80306 (SAN 281-5893) Tel 303-440-0268; Dist. by: Planet Productions, P.O. Box 1641, Boulder, CO 80306 (SAN 282-5899) Tel 415-549-3030.

†**Daimax Pub Hse,** *(Daimax Publishing House),* Dist. by: Press Pacifica, Ltd., P.O. Box 47, Kailua, HI 96734 (SAN 169-1635); *CIP.*

Dairy Goat, *(Dairy Goat Journal Publishing Corp.; 0-930848),* Box 1808, Scottsdale, AZ 85252 (SAN 223-5730) Tel 602-991-4628.

Daisy Pub WA, *(Daisy Publishing, Inc.; 0-943470),* P.O. Box 67A, Mukilteo, WA 98275 (SAN 240-6233) Tel 206-347-1414.

Dajan Ent, *(Dajan Enterprises; 0-9615542),* P.O. Box 4647, Huntsville, AL 35815 (SAN 696-3064) Tel 205-881-5034; 12025 Chicamauga Trail, Huntsville, AL 35803 (SAN 696-527X).

Dakota Kids, *(Dakota Kids Co.; 0-938165),* P.O. Box 189, Sturgis, SD 57785 (SAN 200-6731); S. Blucksberg Mt. Rd., Sturgis, SD 57785 (SAN 202-9243) Tel 605-347-5668; Dist. by: North Plains Pr., P.O. Box 1830, Aberdeen, SD 57402-1830 (SAN 661-0811) Tel 605-225-5360.

Dakota Pr, *(Dakota Pr.; 0-88249),* Univ. of South Dakota, Vermillion, SD 57069 (SAN 207-7345) Tel 605-677-5281.

Dakota Special, *(Dakota Specialties; 0-935337),* P.O. Box 307, Mandan, ND 58554 (SAN 696-3080) Tel 701-663-5047; 410 E. Main St., Mandan, ND 58554 (SAN 696-5288).

Dale Bks CA, *(Dale Bks., Inc.; 0-935917),* 901 H St. Suite 307, Sacramento, CA 95814 (SAN 696-7337) Tel 916-652-0206; 9403 Whiskey Bar Rd., Loomis, CA 95650 (SAN 662-3832) Tel 916-652-0206; Orders to: Books & Things, 9403 Whiskey Bar Rd., Loomis, CA 95650 (SAN 662-7838).

†**Dalkey Arch,** *(Dalkey Archive Pr., The; 0-916583),* 1817 79th Ave., Elmwood Park, IL 60635 (SAN 296-4910) Tel 312-453-2024; Dist. by: Inland Book Co., P.O. Box 261, 22 Hemingway Ave., East Haven, CT 06512 (SAN 200-4151); Dist. by: Small Press Distribution, Inc., 1814 San Pablo Ave., Berkeley, CA 94702 (SAN 204-5826) Tel 415-549-3336; *CIP.*

Dallas A & M Moth
See Dallas A & M Mothers

Dallas A & M Mothers, *(Dallas A & M Univ. Mothers' Club; 0-9612446),* 6209 Pineview Rd., Dallas, TX 75248 (SAN 289-2014) Tel 214-980-6488; Orders to: Hullabaloo in the Kitchen, P.O. Box 796212, Dallas, TX 75379 (SAN 662-2151) Tel 214-980-6488.

Dallas Inst Pubns, *(Dallas Institute Pubns., The; 0-911005),* 2719 Routh St., Dallas, TX 75201 (SAN 274-4872) Tel 214-698-9090.

Dallas Jr Forum, *(Dallas Junior Forum; 0-9617187),* 4666 Chapel Hill Rd., Dallas, TX 75214 (SAN 663-2564) Tel 214-821-4025.

Dallas Morning, *(Belo, A. H., Corp., The Dallas Morning News; 0-914511),* Texas Almanac Div., Communications Ctr., Dallas, TX 75265 (SAN 289-5986) Tel 214-977-8261.

Dallas Mus, *(Dallas Museum of Art; 0-9609622; 0-936227),* 1717 N. Harwood, Dallas, TX 75201 (SAN 204-2436) Tel 214-922-0220; Dist. by: Univ. of Texas Pr., P.O. Box 7819, Austin, TX 78713 (SAN 652-186X) Tel 512-471-7233.

Dallas Sandt, *(Dallas Sandt Co.; 0-936263),* 3104 E. Camelback Rd., Suite 301, Phoenix, AZ 85016 (SAN 697-3515) Tel 602-224-5410.

Dallas South Memorial, *(Dallas Southern Memorial Assn., The; 0-9615569),* P.O. Box 252232, Dallas, TX 75225 (SAN 696-4885) Tel 214-694-6831.

Dalmas & Ricour, *(Dalmas & Ricour; 0-940066),* 6322 Cool Shade Dr., Fayetteville, NC 28303 (SAN 220-2433).

Dalton, *(Dalton, Pat),* 410 Lancaster Ave., Haverford, PA 19041 (SAN 215-9902).

Dalyn Pr, *(Dalyn Pr.; 0-9613200),* 820 Alhambra Blvd., Sacramento, CA 95816 (SAN 295-7302) Tel 916-446-2757.

Damar Pub, *(Damar Publishing; 0-938421),* P.O. Box 660, Lake Worth, FL 33460-0660 (SAN 661-0889); 1519 14th Ave., North Lake Worth, FL 33460 (SAN 661-0897) Tel 305-586-8623.

Damas Pub, *(Damas Publishing Co.; 0-917268),* 6515 Sunset Blvd., Suite 202, Hollywood, CA 90028 (SAN 208-4783) Tel 213-851-4653.

Damascus Hse, *(Damascus Hse.),* Dist. by: Doubleday, 501 Franklin Ave., Garden City, NY 11530 (SAN 201-3231).

Dame Pubns, *(Dame Pubns., Inc.; 0-931920),* 7800 Bissonnet, Suite 415, Houston, TX 77074 (SAN 214-3623) Tel 713-995-1000.

Damgood Bks, *(Damgood Books; 0-912659),* 5870 Green Valley Circle, apt. 333, Fox Hills, CA 90230 (SAN 277-6715) Tel 213-838-7445.

D'amico, *(D'amico, Paul M.; 0-9607270),* Main St., Livingston Manor, NY 12758 (SAN 239-4200).

Damien-Dutton Soc, *(Damien-Dutton Society for Leprosy Aid, Inc.; 0-9606330),* 616 Bedford Ave., Bellmore, NY 11710 (SAN 217-1694) Tel 516-221-5829.

Damon Pr, *(Damon Press, Inc.; 0-910641),* Box 224, Leonia, NJ 07605 (SAN 262-6144) Tel 201-944-3393.

Dan Anderson, *(Anderson, Dan; 0-9614527),* 6083 Fred Dr., Cypress, CA 90630-3905 (SAN 692-2791).

Dan River Pr, *(Dan River Pr.; 0-89754),* Div. of Conservatory of American Letters, P.O. Box 123, South Thomaston, ME 04858 (SAN 212-7377); P.O. Box 88, Thomaston, ME 04861 (SAN 661-9878) Tel 207-354-6550.

Dana Co, *(Dana, William B., Co.; 0-9614837),* 45 John St., Suite 911, New York, NY 10038 (SAN 693-0999) Tel 212-233-5200.

DaNa Pubns, *(DaNa Pubns.; 0-937103),* 1050 Austin Ave., Idaho Falls, ID 83401 (SAN 658-568X) Tel 208-524-1067.

DanBury Hse Bks, *(Danbury Hse., Bks.; 0-935207),* P.O. Box 253, Oakland, ME 04963 (SAN 669-6724) Tel 207-465-2610.

Dance Films, *(Dance Films Association, Inc.; 0-914438),* 241 E. 34th St., New York, NY 10016 (SAN 206-3522) Tel 212-686-7019.

Dance Horiz
See Princeton Bk Co

Dance Mag Inc, *(Dance Magazine, Inc.; 0-930036),* 33 W. 60th St., New York, NY 10023 (SAN 210-4091) Tel 212-245-9050; Toll free: 800-331-1750.

Dance Notation, *(Dance Notation Bureau, Inc.; 0-932582),* 33 W. 21st St., 3rd Flr., New York, NY 10010 (SAN 212-3452) Tel 212-807-7899.

Dance Theater, *(DTW Pubns./Dance Theater Workshop; 0-9617483),* 219 W. 19th St., New York, NY 10011 (SAN 283-121X) Tel 212-691-6500.

Danceway Bks, *(Danceways Books; 0-937180),* 393 West End Ave. 14F, New York, NY 10024 (SAN 219-4724) Tel 212-799-2860; Dist. by: Variety Arts, Inc., 305 Riverside Dr., Suite 4A, New York, NY 10025 (SAN 200-691X).

Dancin Bee, *(Dancin' Bee Co.; 0-933192),* 107 Maple Ave., P.O. Box 237, Ridgely, MD 21660 (SAN 213-4845).

Dancing Bear Pubns, *(Dancing Bear Pubns.; 0-931139),* P.O. Box 3013, Del Mar, CA 92014 (SAN 679-3991) Tel 619-942-2291.

†**Dandelion Hse,** *(Dandelion Hse., The; 0-89693),* Div. of Child's World, Inc., P.O. Box 989, Elgin, IL 60121 (SAN 240-8910) Tel 312-741-7591; Dist. by: Scripture Pr., 1825 College Ave., Wheaton, IL 60187 (SAN 222-9471) Tel 312-668-6000; *CIP.*

Dandelion Pr, *(Dandelion Pr.; 0-89799),* 184 Fifth Ave., New York, NY 10010 (SAN 212-0836) Tel 212-929-0090.

Dandick Co, *(Dandick Co., The; 0-917546),* P.O. Box 55, Scottsdale, AZ 85252 (SAN 223-5765).

D&S Publishing, *(D & S Publishing; 0-9615954),* P.O. Box 7343 Indian Creek Sta., Shawnee Mission, KS 66207 (SAN 697-3493) Tel 913-764-5900; 11901 Canterbury, Leawood, KS 66209 (SAN 697-3507).

D&S Pubns, *(D&S Pubns.; 0-9607090),* 6334 St. Andrews Cir., Ft. Myers, FL 33907 (SAN 238-9290).

D&S Pubs
See D & S Pub

Dandy Lion, *(Dandy Lion Pubns.; 0-931724),* P.O. Box 190, San Luis Obispo, CA 93406 (SAN 211-5565) Tel 805-543-3332.

†**Dane Bks,** *(Dane Books; 0-917655),* 15 St. Regis Circle, Salinas, CA 93905 (SAN 657-1336) Tel 415-956-5966; *CIP.*

Daneco Pubns, *(Daneco Pubns.; 0-910519),* 3451 18th Ave. S., Minneapolis, MN 55407 (SAN 260-180X) Tel 612-724-6285.

Danella Pubns, *(Danella Pubns.; 0-940562),* P.O. Box C, Sausalito, CA 94966 (SAN 218-5407) Tel 415-332-9601.

Dangary Pub, *(Dangary Publishing, Co.; 0-910484),* 205 S. Smallwood St., Baltimore, MD 21223 (SAN 204-2398) Tel 301-685-8894 Tel 202-621-5732.

Danly Prods, *(Danly Productions, Inc.; 0-9617278),* 7609 W. Industrial Dr., Forest Park, IL 60130 Tel 312-771-0200.

Danmark Enterprises, *(Danmark Enterprises, Ltd.; 0-9616596),* 1221 Minor Ave., No. 201, Seattle, WA 98101 (SAN 659-5022) Tel 206-682-1734.

Dante U Am, *(Dante Univ. of America Pr., Inc.; 0-937832),* P.O. Box 843, Brookline Village, Boston, MA 02147 (SAN 220-150X) Tel 617-734-2045.

†**Danubian,** *(Danubian Pr., Inc.; 0-87934),* Rte. 1, Box 59, Astor, FL 32002 (SAN 201-8047) Tel 904-759-2255; *CIP.*

DAR Syst, *(DAR Systems International; 0-916163; 1-55616),* P.O. Box 4925, Berkeley, CA 94704-4925 (SAN 294-7323) Tel 415-689-1312; Dist. by: Baker & Taylor, Midwest Div., 501 Gladiolus Ave., Momence, IL 60954 (SAN 169-2100) Tel 815-472-2444; Orders to: Micro Data Products (Software orders only), 537 S. Olathe Ct., Aurora, CO 80011 (SAN 662-2267) Tel 303-360-6200.

Daratech, *(Daratech, Inc.; 0-938484),* 16 Myrtle Ave., Cambridge, MA 02138 (SAN 281-5915) Tel 617-354-2339; Orders to: P.O. Box 410, Cambridge, MA 02238 (SAN 281-5923). No longer publishes software.

Darby Bks, *(Darby Bks.; 0-89987),* P.O. Box 148, Darby, PA 19023 Tel 215-583-4550.

Darby Books
See Darby Bks

DARE, *(Dare, Inc.; 0-943690),* 3628 Grant Ave., Rockford, IL 61103 (SAN 238-2695) Tel 815-877-8511.

Dare Co, *(Dare-Co.; 0-936729),* Div. of Daisy R. & E. Co., 2508 Nottingham Ave., Los Angeles, CA 90027 (SAN 699-8909) Tel 213-662-3204; P.O. Box 27164, Los Angeles, CA 90027 (SAN 699-8917).

Dargaud Pub, *(Dargaud Publishing International, Ltd.; 0-917201),* 2 Lafayette Ct., Greenwich, CT 06830 (SAN 655-8100) Tel 203-661-0707.

Darian Bks, *(Darian Books; 0-910899),* 9027 N. 52nd Ave., Glendale, AZ 85302 (SAN 269-5898) Tel 602-931-3788.

Darien Hse, *(Darien House Books; 0-88201),* c/o Images Graphiques, 37 Riverside Dr., New York, NY 10023 (SAN 210-4415) Tel 212-787-4000.

Darin Devel
See J Reynolds

†**Daring Bks,** *(Daring Bks.; 0-938936),* Div. of Daring Publishing Group, 2020 Ninth St., SW, Canton, OH 44706 (SAN 216-0293) Tel 216-454-7519; Orders to: P.O. Box 526, Canton, OH 47701 (SAN 685-3242); *CIP.*

Daring Pr
See Daring Bks

Dark Child Pr, *(Dark Child Pr.; 0-932139),* 1329 N. Garfield, Pocatello, ID 83204 (SAN 686-4279) Tel 208-233-1283; Dist. by: Inland Bk. Co., P.O. Box 261. 22 Hemingway Ave., East Haven, CT 06512 (SAN 200-4151) Tel 203-467-4257.

Dark Harvest, *(Dark Harvest Bks.; 0-913165),* P.O. Box 48134, Niles, IL 60648-0134 (SAN 283-0558) Tel 312-991-6290.

Dark Sun, *(Dark Sun Pr.; 0-937968),* c/o MFA Photography, Rochester Institute of Technology, 1 Lomb Mem. Dr., Rochester, NY 14623 (SAN 220-0430) Tel 716-475-2616.

Darrow, *(Darrow, Frank M.; 0-912636),* P.O. Box 305, Trona, CA 93562 (SAN 201-4661); 82194 7th St., Argus, CA 93562 (SAN 201-467X).

Dart Pub Co, *(Dart Publishing Co.; 0-931243),* 19344 Wyandotte St., Suite 122, Reseda, CA 91335 (SAN 681-977X) Tel 818-885-6169.

Dartnell Corp, *(Dartnell Corp.; 0-85013),* 4660 Ravenswood Ave., Chicago, IL 60640 (SAN 207-5407) Tel 312-561-4000; Toll free: 800-621-5463.

†**Darwin Pr,** *(Darwin Pr., Inc.; 0-87850),* P.O. Box 2202, Princeton, NJ 08540 (SAN 201-2987) Tel 609-737-1349; *CIP.*

Darwin Pubns, *(Darwin Pubns.; 0-933506),* Div. of Howell North-Darwin-Superior, 850 N. Hollywood Way, Burbank, CA 91505 (SAN 207-4370) Tel 818-848-0944.

Data Analysis, *(Data Analysis Group; 0-936677),* 8263 Vista Dr., La Mesa, CA 92041 (SAN 697-7588) Tel 619-464-6888.

Data & Res Tech, *(Data & Research Technology Corp.; 0-935025),* 1102 McNeilly Ave., Pittsburgh, PA 15216 (SAN 694-5503) Tel 412-563-2212.

†**Data Courier,** *(Data Courier Inc.; 0-914604),* 620 S. Fifth St., Louisville, KY 40202 (SAN 289-7016); *CIP.*

Data Courier
See Cambridge Sci

Data Dec, *(Data Decisions),* 20 Brace Rd., Cherry Hill, NJ 08034 (SAN 670-7378) Tel 609-429-7100.

Data Description, *(Data Description, Inc.; 0-935321),* P.O. Box 4555, Ithaca, NY 14852 (SAN 695-7358) Tel 607-257-1000 (SAN 696-9496).

Data Desk
See Data Description

Data Financial, *(Data Financial Press; 0-933088),* P.O. Box 668, Menlo Park, CA 94025 (SAN 212-4106); Dist. by: Caroline House, P.O. Box 801, Menlo Park, CA 94025 (SAN 212-4114) Tel 415-321-4553.

Data Hse, *(Data House Publishing Co., Inc.; 0-935922),* 5724 N. Pulaski Ave.,, Chicago, IL 60646 (SAN 214-0020) Tel 312-478-0900.

Data Process Mgmt, *(Data Processing Management Assn.),* 505 Busse Hwy., Park Ridge, IL 60068-3191 (SAN 654-1046) Tel 312-825-8124.

Data Res MN, *(Data Research, Inc.; 0-939675),* 4635 Nicols Rd., Suite 100, Eagan, MN 55122 (SAN 663-5857) Tel 612-452-8267.

Database Serv, *(Database Services; 0-939920),* 2685 Marine Way., No. 1305, Mountain View, CA 94043-1125 (SAN 216-8073) Tel 415-961-2880; Orders to: P.O. Box 50545, Suite 1305, Mountain View, CA 94043 (SAN 663-2890) Tel 415-961-2880; Dist. by: Online, Inc., 11 Tannery Ln., Weston, CT 06883 (SAN 200-822X) Tel 203-227-8466.

DataCompatable, *(DataCompatable; 0-938793),* 2423 Willowbend Dr., Richmond, TX 77469 (SAN 661-4906) Tel 713-232-4372.

Datafax Corp, *(Datafax Corp.; 0-935169),* 511 11th Ave. S., No. 54, Minneapolis, MN 55415 (SAN 695-846X).

Datalan Inc, *(Datalan, Inc.; 0-9617245),* 21054 Sherman Way, Canoga Park, CA 91303 (SAN 698-455X) Tel 818-702-9744.

†**Datametrics Syst,** *(Datametrics Systems Corp.; 0-932853),* 5270 Lyngate Ct., Burke, VA 22015 (SAN 691-2885) Tel 703-425-1006; *CIP.*

Datamost, *(Datamost, Inc.; 0-88190),* 21040 Nordhoff St., Chatsworth, CA 91311 (SAN 264-7311) Tel 818-709-1202; Toll free: 800-692-1649.

DataMyte Corp, *(DataMyte Corp.; 0-930345),* 14960 Industrial Rd., Minnetonka, MN 55345 (SAN 669-7070) Tel 612-935-7704.

Dataplan, *(Dataplan; 0-9606878),* 2450 Foothill Blvd., Calistoga, CA 94515 (SAN 217-3506) Tel 707-942-0217.

†**Datapro Res,** *(Datapro Research Corp.; 0-07),* Div. of McGraw-Hill Information Systems Co., 1805 Underwood Blvd., Delran, NJ 08075 (SAN 226-7179); *CIP.*

Dataquest, *(Dataquest Inc.),* 1290 Ridder Park Dr., San Jose, CA 95131 (SAN 201-825X) Tel 408-971-9001.

Datar Pub, *(Datar Publishing Co.; 0-931572),* 9351 Ewers Dr., Crestwood, MO 63126 (SAN 211-4135) Tel 314-843-5343; Toll free: 800-633-8378.

Datarule, *(Datarule Pub. Co., Inc.; 0-911740),* Rte. 4, Box 7, West Rd., South Salem, NY 10590 (SAN 201-2693) Tel 914-533-2263; Orders to: P.O. Box 448, New Canaan, CT 06840 (SAN 201-9886).

Datatext, *(Datatext Co.; 0-916187),* P.O. Box 2097, 540 Brook Lane, Warminster, PA 18974 (SAN 294-9202) Tel 215-674-3030.

Daughter Cult, *(Daughter Culture Pubns.; 0-935281),* 3109 Scotts Valley Dr., Suite 168, Scotts Valley, CA 95066 (SAN 695-7447) Tel 408-438-7412.

Daughters of HI, *(Daughters of Hawaii; 0-938851),* 2913 Pali Hwy., Honolulu, HI 96817 (SAN 662-5789) Tel 808-598-6291.

Daughters Utah, *(Daughters of Utah Pioneers),* 300 N. Main St., Salt Lake City, UT 84103 (SAN 240-8465) Tel 801-533-5759.

DAurora Pr, *(D'Aurora Press; 0-933022),* 190 Cascade Dr., Mill Valley, CA 94941 (SAN 212-4122).

Dav-A-Lynn Ent, *(Dav-A-Lyn Enterprise; 0-9614798),* P.O. Box 88682, Seattle, WA 98188 (SAN 692-6681) Tel 206-433-2747.

Davar Pub, *(Davar Publishing Co., Inc.; 0-937831),* P.O. Box 854, Pacific Palisades, CA 90272 (SAN 659-4409) Tel 213-459-8600; 16015 Northfield, Pacific Palisades, CA 90272 (SAN 659-4417).

Davenport, *(Davenport, May, Pubs.; 0-9603118; 0-943864),* 26313 Purissima Rd., Los Altos Hills, CA 94022 (SAN 212-467X) Tel 415-948-6499.

Davenport Pub, *(Davenport Publishing; 0-9616110),* 1302 Beachmont, Ventura, CA 93001 (SAN 696-9224) Tel 805-644-7054.

Davey, *(Davey, Daniel, & Co., Inc., Pubs.; 0-8088),* P.O. Box 6088, Hartford, CT 06106 (SAN 203-882X) Tel 203-525-4334.

Davicone Inc, *(Davicone, Inc.; 0-937089),* 1075 Lullwater Rd., NE, Atlanta, GA 30307 (SAN 658-5159) Tel 404-377-0208.

David & Charles, *(David & Charles, Inc.; 0-7153),* P.O. Box 257, North Pomfret, VT 05053 (SAN 213-8859) Tel 802-457-1911; Toll free: 800-423-4525. *Imprints:* Weddy Rail Bks (Weedy Rail Books).(Weedy Rail Bks.).

David Pub MN, *(David Publishing; 0-9616767),* Box 7, St. Bonifacius, MN 55375-0007 (SAN 661-0935); 6425 County Rd. 30, St. Bonifacius, MN 55375 (SAN 661-0943) Tel 612-472-7126.

Davida Pubns, *(Davida Pubns.; 0-9603022),* 32 Longate Rd., Clinton, CT 06413 (SAN 212-1565) Tel 203-669-0656; Dist. by: Devorss & Co., P.O. Box 550, 1046 Princeton Dr., Marina del Rey, CA 90294 (SAN 282-6151).

Davis & Co, *(Davis & Co.; 0-9614214),* P.O. Box 26318, Colorado Springs, CO 80936-6318 (SAN 687-0899) Tel 303-574-1874.

Davis Ascs PA, *(Davis Assocs.; 0-931431),* 1143 Wright Dr., Huntingdon Valley, PA 19006 (SAN 683-1729) Tel 215-947-1752.

Davis Assocs, *(Davis & Assocs., Inc.; 0-923643),* 1655 Peachtree St., NE, No. 1104, Atlanta, GA 30309 (SAN 654-8644) Tel 404-875-0793.

†**Davis Co,** *(Davis, F. A., Co.; 0-8036),* 1915 Arch St., Philadelphia, PA 19103 (SAN 295-3250) Tel 215-568-2270; Toll free: 800-523-4049; Dist. by: Brown & Connolly, Inc., 2 Keith Way, Hingham, MA 02043 (SAN 169-3298) Tel 617-749-8590; Dist. by: Login Brothers Bk. Co., Inc., 1450 W. Randolph St., Chicago, IL 60607 (SAN 169-183X) Tel 312-733-6424; Dist. by: J. A. Majors Co., P.O. Box 819074, Dallas, TX 75061-9074 (SAN 169-8117) Tel 214-247-2929; Dist. by: Login Brothers NJ, 135 New Dutch Ln., Box 2700, Fairfield, NJ 07006 (SAN 157-1427); Dist. by: Rittenhouse Bk. Distributors, Inc., 511 Feheley Dr., King of Prussia, PA 19406 (SAN 213-4443); Dist. by: J. A. Majors Co., 3770A Zip Industrial Blvd., Atlanta, GA 00354 (SAN 169-1406) Tel 404-786-4956; Dist. by: Login Brothers East, 1550 Enterprise Rd., Twinsburg, OH 44087 (SAN 156-4439); Dist. by: J. A. Majors Co., 1806 Southgate, Houston, TX 77030 (SAN 169-8281) Tel 713-526-5757; Dist. by: J. A. Majors Co., 3909 Bienville, New Orleans, LA 70119 (SAN 169-2984) Tel 504-486-5956; *CIP.*

Davis Mass, *(Davis Pubns., Inc.; 0-87192),* 50 Portland St., Worcester, MA 01608 (SAN 201-3002) Tel 617-754-7201; Dist. by: Sterling Publishing Co., Inc., 2 Park Ave., New York, NY 10016 (SAN 211-6324) Tel 212-532-7160.

Davis Math Pr, *(Davis Mathematics Pr.; 0-916327),* P.O. Box 1212, Davis, CA 95617-1212 (SAN 295-7310) Tel 916-753-3587.

Davis Pr, *(Davis, L., Pr., Inc.; 0-9607902; 0-933485),* 1125 Oxford Pl., Schenectady, NY 12308 (SAN 238-1540) Tel 518-374-5636.

Davis Pub, *(Davis Publishing Co.; 0-9615877),* 4112 Hart Rd., Richfield, OH 44286 (SAN 697-0591) Tel 216-659-4449.

Davis Pub Co, *(Davis Publishing Co., Inc.; 0-89368),* 250 Potrero St., Santa Cruz, CA 95060 (SAN 201-8152) Tel 408-423-4968; Orders to: P.O. Box 841, Santa Cruz, CA 95061 (SAN 201-8160).

Davis Pubns, *(Davis Pubns., Inc.; 0-89559),* 380 Lexington Ave., New York, NY 10017 (SAN 290-6848) Tel 212-557-9100; Dist. by: Doubleday & Co., 501 Franklin Ave., Garden City, NY 11530 (SAN 281-6075).

Davis Pubns *Imprint of Sterling*

Davison, *(Davison Publishing Co., Inc.; 0-87515),* P.O. Box 477, Ridgewood, NJ 07451 (SAN 204-2339) Tel 201-445-3135.

Davus Pub, *(Davus Publishing; 0-915317),* P.O. Box 280, Madison Square Sta., New York, NY 10159 (SAN 289-9787); 141 E. 26th St., New York, NY 10010 (SAN 650-9975) Tel 212-685-0957.

DAW Bks, *(DAW Bks.; 0-8099),* Affil. of New American Library, ; Toll free: 800-526-0275; c/o New American Library, 1633 Broadway, New York, NY 10019 (SAN 206-8079) Tel 212-397-8000.

Dawn Heron, *(Dawn Heron Pr.; 0-939790),* Subs. of Dashiell Hammett Tour, 537 Jones St., No. 9207, San Francisco, CA 94102 (SAN 216-8871) Tel 415-564-7021.

†**Dawn Horse Pr,** *(Dawn Horse Pr.; 0-913922; 0-918801),* Div. of Advaitayana Buddhist Communion, 750 Adrian Way, San Rafael, CA 94903 (SAN 201-3029) Tel 415-492-0922; Toll free: 800-521-4785; *CIP.*

Dawn Ministries, *(Dawn Ministries; 0-9605892),* 2789 Mendel Way, Sacramento, CA 95833 (SAN 216-5937).

†**Dawn Pr,** *(Dawn Press; 0-933704),* 1011 Jeffrey Rd., Wilmington, DE 19810 (SAN 221-2269); *CIP.*

Dawn Valley, *(Dawn Valley, Pr.; 0-936014),* P.O. Box 58, New Wilmington, PA 16142 (SAN 208-9734) Tel 412-946-2948.

Dawnfire, *(Dawnfire Books; 0-942058),* 2218 24th St., No. B, Santa Monica, CA 90405 (SAN 239-4332) Tel 213-450-2911; Dist. by: Bookpeople, 2929 Fifth St., Berkeley, CA 94710 Tel 415-549-3030.

†**Dawnwood Pr,** *(Dawnwood Pr.; 0-911025),* c/o Sterling Publishing Co., 2 Park Ave., Suite 2650, New York, NY 10016 (SAN 211-6324) Tel 212-532-7160; *CIP.*

Dawson & Co
See City in Print-Bibl Proj

Dawsons, *(Dawson's Bk. Shop; 0-87093),* 535 N. Larchmont Blvd., Los Angeles, CA 90004 (SAN 201-3045) Tel 213-469-2186.

Day Bk Co, *(Day Book Company; 0-9611310),* 3641 N Maple Ave., Fresno, CA 93726 (SAN 277-6723).

Day Star, *(Day Star Pubs.; 0-932994),* 1550 View Dr., San Leandro, CA 94577 (SAN 212-4130).

Day Star NV, *(Day Star; 0-939614),* P.O. Box 14052, Las Vegas, NV 89114 (SAN 216-6208) Tel 702-361-3022.

Daybreak Pr, *(Daybreak Press; 0-940916),* 646 Dale Court S., St. Paul, MN 55112 (SAN 217-2372).

Daymaker Pub, *(Daymaker Publishing Co.; 0-938601),* 1512 Berkeley St., Suite B, Santa Monica, CA 90404 (SAN 661-1397) Tel 213-453-2457.

Dayspring CA
See Larksong Dayspring

Daystar Co Carson, *(Daystar Publishing Co.; 0-933650),* 21405 Lostime Ave., Carson, CA 90745 (SAN 221-2277).

Daystar Comm, *(Daystar Communications; 0-930037),* P.O. Box 748, Millville, NJ 08332 (SAN 669-7798) Tel 609-327-1231.

DayStar Pr
See White & Spencer

Daystar Pub Co, *(Daystar Publishing Co.; 0-938962),* P.O. Box 707, Angwin, CA 94508 (SAN 281-5974) Tel 707-965-2085; Dist. by Bookpeople, 2929 Fifth St., Berkeley, CA 94710 (SAN 168-9517) Tel 415-549-3030; Dist. by: Publisher's Group West, 5855 Beaudry St., Emeryville, CA 94608 (SAN 202-8522) Tel 415-658-3453.

Dayton Art, *(Dayton Art Institute; 0-937809),* P.O. Box 941, Dayton, OH 45401 (SAN 278-6206) Tel 513-223-5277.

Dayton Hudson, *(Dayton Hudson Foundation; 0-9607450),* 777 Nicollet Mall, Minneapolis, MN 55402 (SAN 238-2326) Tel 612-370-6555.

Dayton Labs, *(Dayton Laboratories; 0-916750),* 3235 Dayton Ave., Lorain, OH 44055 (SAN 208-1946) Tel 216-246-1397.

Dayton Newspapers, *(Dayton Newspapers, Inc.; 0-938492; 0-9616347),* Div. of Cox Newspapers, Inc., Fourth & Ludlow Sts., Dayton, OH 45401 (SAN 215-8809) Tel 513-225-2184.

Dayton Phil, *(Dayton Philharmonic Women's Assn.; 0-9614169),* 125 E. First St., Dayton, OH 45402 (SAN 686-6506) Tel 513-224-3521.

Dazet Creations, *(Dazet Creations, Inc.; 0-936209),* 15775 N. Hillcrest, Suite 508, Dallas, TX 75248 (SAN 697-1083) Tel 214-380-1987.

DBA Bks, *(DBA Bks.; 0-9605276),* 323 Beacon St., Boston, MA 02116 (SAN 281-5877) Tel 617-739-2200; 358 Chestnut Hill Ave., Brookline, MA 02146 (SAN 281-5885).

DBA Monte Vista, *(DBA Monte Vista Centennial Commission; 0-943640),* P.O. Box 63, Monte Vista, CO 81144 (SAN 238-3012) Tel 303-852-2525.

DBA Pr, *(DBA Pr.; 0-914399),* P.O. Box 2932, Toledo, OH 43606 (SAN 289-629X) Tel 419-474-2140.

DBC, *(DBC; 0-9608798),* 1164 Wall Rd., Webster, NY 14580 (SAN 241-0109) Tel 716-872-0393.

DBI, *(DBI Bks., Inc.; 0-910676; 0-87349),* 4092 Commercial Ave., Northbrook, IL 60062 (SAN 202-9960) Tel 312-272-6310.

DBJ Pub, *(DBJ Publishing; 0-9616870),* 200 Moraga Way, Orinda, CA 94563 (SAN 661-1508) Tel 415-254-1290.

DC Bar Assn, *(District of Columbia Bar Assn.),* 1426 H St. NW, Rm. 840, Washington, DC 20005 (SAN 226-7314).

DC Pub Co, *(DC Publishing Co., Inc.; 0-933911),* 1686 Tustin Avenue, Suite A-163, Costa Mesa, CA 92627 (SAN 692-7785) Tel 714-645-2036.

DCA, *(Darien Community Assn., Inc.),* Orders to: Tory Hole, 274 Middlesex Rd., Darien, CT 06820 (SAN 208-4902) Tel 203-655-9050.

DCarlin Pub, *(D'Carlin Publishing; 0-939342),* 2729 Carlsbad Blvd., Carlsbad, CA 92008 (SAN 216-2369) Tel 619-729-7758.

De Graff
See J De Graff

†**De Gruyter,** *(De Gruyter, Walter, Inc.; 3-11; 0-89925),* Div. of Walter de Gruyter & Co., 200 Saw Mill River Rd., Hawthorne, NY 10532 (SAN 201-3088) Tel 914-747-0110; *CIP.*

De Gruyter Aldine, *(De Gruyter/Aldine; 0-202),* Div. of Walter De Gruyter, Inc., 200 Saw Mill River Rd., Hawthorne, NY 10532 (SAN 212-4726) Tel 914-747-0110.

De Karsan, *(De Karsan Publishing Co.; 0-9602308),* P.O. Box 28404, San Diego, CA 92128 (SAN 210-8941) Tel 619-280-3334.

De Mortmain, *(De Mortmain Bks.; 0-932501),* 2259 University Ave., Sacramento, CA 95825 (SAN 687-391X) Tel 916-481-5614.

De Novo Pr, *(De Novo Pr.; 0-912357),* Box 5106, Berkeley, CA 94705 (SAN 265-1173) Tel 415-849-9382; Dist. by: Bookpeople, 2929 Fifth St., Berkeley, CA 94710 (SAN 168-9517) Tel 415-549-3030.

De Serio, *(De Serio, Louis F.; 0-9603568),* P.O. Box 1163, Sedona, AZ 86336 (SAN 213-6163) Tel 602-282-2634.

De Vito, *(DeVito Enterprises; 0-910506),* 28 Dean St., Box 11, East Windsor, CT 06088 (SAN 203-8846) Tel 203-623-3152.

De Vorss, *(De Vorss & Co.; 0-87516),* P.O. Box 550, Marina del Rey, CA 90292 (SAN 168-9886) Tel 213-870-7478.

De Young Pr, *(De Young Pr.; 0-936128),* P.O. Box 7252, Spencer, IA 51301-7252 (SAN 212-7652).

Deacon Pr, *(Deacon Press, The; 0-940684),* 1244 Brian St., Placentia, CA 92670 (SAN 218-5415) Tel 714-524-0939.

Dead Angel, *(Dead Angel; 0-911757),* 1206 Lyndale Dr. SE, Atlanta, GA 30316 (SAN 264-0031).

Dead Reckoning, *(Dead Reckoning Pr.; 0-935733),* P.O. Box 31, Cambria, CA 93428 (SAN 696-3153) Tel 805-927-3054; 2677 Tipton St., Cambria, CA 93428 (SAN 696-5296).

Deago Ent
See Ovation Pubns

Dealers Choice, *(Dealer's Choice Bks., Inc.),* 6402 N. Nebraska Ave., Tampa, FL 33604 (SAN 687-6390); Toll free: 800-238-8288.

Dean Clark, *(Clark, Dean, Pubs.; 0-935091),* Div. of Dean Clark Communications, P.O. Box 3192, Palmer, PA 18043 (SAN 695-0647) Tel 215-253-8263.

Dean Pubns, *(Dean Pubns.; 0-939052),* 2204 El Canto Circle, Rancho Cordova, CA 95670 (SAN 217-0744).

Deanna Hse, *(House, Deanna, Specialties, Inc.; 0-9610752),* Box 492, Portage, MI 49081 (SAN 264-7508) Tel 616-327-4571.

Deanne Inc, *(Deanne II Inc.; 0-9611584),* Rte. 4, P.O. Box 82A, No. 3 Quil Run, Carthage, MO 64836 (SAN 285-6654) Tel 417-358-7814; Dist. by: Dot Gibson Pubns., 161 Knight Ave., Cir., Waycross, GA 31501 (SAN 200-4143) Tel 912-285-2848; Dist. by: Southwest Cookbook Distributors, Inc., 1901 South Shore Dr., Bonham, TX 75418 (SAN 200-4925) Tel 214-583-8898.

Dear Kids, *(Dear Kids Pubs.),* Currierville Rd., Newton, NH 03858 (SAN 206-4677) Tel 603-382-7503.

Dearen Pub, *(Dearen, Leah, Publishing; 0-938575),* P.O. Box 162, Alpine, CA 92001 (SAN 661-1036); 3330 Zumbrota Rd., Alpine, CA 92001 (SAN 661-1044) Tel 619-445-9611.

Dearhorse Pubns, *(Dearhorse Pubns.; 0-9614170),* P.O. Box 15121, Portland, OR 97215 (SAN 686-6522) Tel 503-233-1206.

Death Valley Fortyniners, *(Death Valley 49ers, Inc.; 0-936932),* c/o Chalfant Press, Box 787, Bishop, CA 93514 (SAN 203-6347) Tel 619-873-3535.

Deaver Corp, *(Deaver Corp.; 0-932665),* 155 W. 68th St., Suite 630, New York, NY 10023 (SAN 687-7923) Tel 212-799-9835.

Debron, *(Debron Enterprises; 0-911347),* P.O. Box 8242, Witchita, KS 67208 (SAN 269-6118) Tel 316-262-0695.

Debton Pubns, *(Debton Pubns., Inc.; 0-916321),* 1731 Vulcan St., El Cajon, CA 92021 (SAN 295-737X).

Decade Media, *(Decade Media Bks. Communications, Inc.; 0-910365),* 1133 Broadway, Suite 707, New York, NY 10010 (SAN 263-2152) Tel 212-929-8044.

†**Decatur Hse,** *(Decatur House Press, Ltd; 0-916276),* 2122 Decatur Place, NW, Washington, DC 20008 (SAN 208-1539) Tel 202-387-3913; *CIP.*

Decatur Jr Serv, *(Decatur Junior Service League, Inc.; 0-9614406),* P.O. Box 486, Decatur, AL 35602 (SAN 688-6221) Tel 205-350-1917.

December Pr, *(December Pr., Inc.; 0-913204),* 3093 Dato,, Highland Park, IL 60035 (SAN 203-8854) Tel 312-432-6804; Dist. by: Chicago Review Pr., 814 N. Franklin St., Chicago, IL 60610 (SAN 213-5744) Tel 312-337-0747.

December Rose, *(December Rose Publishing House; 0-9612730),* Div. of Retirement Housing Foundation, 255 S. Hill St., Suite 407, Los Angeles, CA 90012 (SAN 289-9191) Tel 213-617-7002.

Deciduous, *(Deciduous; 0-9601640),* 1456 W. 54th St., Cleveland, OH 44102 (SAN 211-4143) Tel 216-651-7725.

Decision-Making, *(Decision-Making Ctr.; 0-9616604),* 761 Wells Rd., Wethersfield, CT 06109 (SAN 661-1052) Tel 203-529-8747.

†**Decker Pr Inc,** *(Decker Pr., Inc.; 0-933724),* P.O. Box 3838, Grand Junction, CO 81502 (SAN 216-115X) Tel 303-241-6193; Toll free: 800-525-3454; *CIP.*

Deco Design Studio, *(Decorative Design Studio, Inc.; 0-941284),* Rte. 3, Box 155, Smithsburg, MD 21783 (SAN 238-9320) Tel 301-824-7592.

Deco-Pr Pub, *(Deco-Press Publishing Co.; 0-937016),* 500 E. 84th Ave., Box 29489, Denver, CO 80229 (SAN 220-2441).

Dectur Corp, *(Dectur Corp.; 0-9602228),* 2878 Forest St., Denver, CO 80207 (SAN 212-4149).

Dedeaux, *(Dedeaux Publishing, Inc.; 0-930987),* 907 Rve Dauphine St., New Orleans, LA 70116 (SAN 678-8882) Tel 504-529-3406.

Dee Pub Co, *(Dee Publishing Co.; 0-934476),* 864 S. Commercial, Salem, OR 97302 (SAN 206-4685) Tel 503-363-2410.

Deej Pub, *(DEEJ Publishing Co.; 0-9608832),* 8200 Rosewood Lane, Prairie Village, KS 66208 (SAN 241-0133) Tel 816-474-8120.

Deep River Pr, *(Deep River Press; 0-935232),* 51141/2 E. Second St., P.O. Box 3444, Long Beach, CA 90803 (SAN 213-8425) Tel 213-433-8738.

Deep Sea Pr, *(Deep Sea Pr.; 0-939591),* Collington Rd., P.O. Box 48, Kitty Hawk, NC 27949 (SAN 663-6187) Tel 919-441-4637.

Deepstar Pubns, *(Deepstar Pubns.; 0-918888),* P.O. Box 1266, Crestine, CA 92325 (SAN 210-4121) Tel 714-338-4440.

Deer Creek Pr, *(Deer Creek Pr.; 0-9613596),* Div. of California School of Design, 516 Olive St, Sausalito, CA 94965 (SAN 669-6732) Tel 415-332-1990.

Deer Crossing, *(Deer Crossing Press; 0-932792),* Rte. 1, Box 18, Paducah, KY 42001 (SAN 212-1867).

Deer Crossing Camp
See Deer Xing Camp

Deer Xing Camp, *(Deer Crossing Camp Pr.; 0-938525),* 940 Providence Ct., Cupertino, CA 95014 (SAN 661-146X) Tel 408-996-9448.

85

Deercreek Pubs, *(Deercreek Pubs.; 0-9616768),* 197 Road 154, Carpenter, WY 82054 (SAN 661-1060) Tel 307-549-2296.

Deere & Co, *(Deere & Co. Technical Services; 0-86691),* Dept. 333, John Deere Rd., Moline, IL 61265 (SAN 216-3659) Tel 309-752-6941; Orders to: 1400 Third Ave., Moline, IL 61265 (SAN 661-9894) Tel 309-757-5903.

Deermouse, *(Deermouse Press; 0-9600596),* 4 Berkeley Place, Cambridge, MA 02138 (SAN 201-8039) Tel 617-876-0836.

Dees Delights, *(Dee's Delights, Inc.; 0-938685),* Div. of Hobby Bk. Distributors, 3150 State Line Rd., North Bend, OH 45052 (SAN 661-3969) Tel 513-353-3390.

Defenders Pubns, *(Defenders Pubns.; 0-910643),* P.O. Box 11134, Las Vegas, NV 89111 (SAN 269-6207) Tel 702-451-5773.

Defense & Foreign Aff, *(Defense & Foreign Affairs Publications Ltd.; 0-9605932),* 1777 T St. NW, Washington, DC 20009 (SAN 216-3551) Tel 202-223-4934.

Defensive Tips, *(Defensive Tips; 0-933531),* P.O. Box 6033, Concord, CA 94524-1033 (SAN 679-1700) Tel 415-689-0159.

Definition, *(Definition Pr.; 0-910492),* Subs. of Eli Siegel-Martha Baird Foundation, 141 Greene St., New York, NY 10012 (SAN 201-310X) Tel 212-777-4490.

Dehack, *(Dehack Effort),* P.O. Box 922, Campbell, CA 95009 (SAN 208-1512) Tel 408-265-8799.

Deinotation Seven, *(Deinotation-7 Press; 0-9602044),* P.O. Box 204, Susquehanna, PA 18847-0204 (SAN 223-4661); 220 Exchange Pl., Susquehanna, PA 18847 (SAN 658-0424); Orders to: Brodart Books, 500 Arch St., Williamsport, PA 17705 (SAN 669-0637).

Dekalb, *(Dekalb Historical Society; 0-9615459),* Old Courthouse on the Square, Decatur, GA 30030 (SAN 695-734X) Tel 404-373-1088.

†**Dekker,** *(Dekker, Marcel, Inc.; 0-8247),* 270 Madison Ave., New York, NY 10016 (SAN 201-3118) Tel 212-696-9000; Toll free: 800-228-1160; *CIP.*

Dekotek Inc
 See Bowker

Del Casa Educ, *(Del Casa Educational Productions; 0-910183),* 175 Fifth Ave., New York, NY 10010 (SAN 238-132X) Tel 212-677-2200.

Del Mar Pr, *(Del Mar Press; 0-9611124),* P.O. Box 2508, Del Mar, CA 92014 (SAN 283-2682) Tel 619-481-1808.

Del Rey *Imprint of* **Ballantine**

Del Sol Editores, *(Del Sol Editores; 0-9616267),* 53 Stephen Hopkins Ct., University Heights, Providence, RI 02904 (SAN 658-3547) Tel 401-272-3566.

Del Valley, *(Delaware Valley Poets; 0-937158),* P.O. Box 6203, Lawrenceville, NJ 08648 (SAN 215-1391) Tel 609-737-0222.

†**Delacorte,** *(Delacorte Pr.; 0-87459),* 1 Dag Hammarskjold Plaza, New York, NY 10017 (SAN 201-0097) Tel 212-605-3000; Toll free: 800-221-4676; *CIP.* Imprints: E Friede (Friede, Eleanor); Sey Lawr (Lawrence, Seymour).

Delafield Pr, *(Delafield Press; 0-916872),* P.O. Box 335, Suttons Bay, MI 49682 (SAN 208-3817) Tel 616-271-3826.

Delair
 See World Bible

Delamar Duverus
 See Duverus Pub

Delapeake Pub Co, *(Delapeake Publishing, Co.; 0-911293),* P.O. Box 1148, Wilmington, DE 19899 (SAN 269-6274) Tel 302-571-6979.

Delapr Inc, *(Delapress, Inc.; 0-87571),* Rte. 1, Hwy. 304, Delaplaine, AR 72425 (SAN 692-896X) Tel 501-249-3392.

Delbridge Pub Co, *(Delbridge Publishing, Co.; 0-88232),* P.O. Box 2989, Stanford, CA 94305-0028 (SAN 207-2122) Tel 408-446-3131.

Delcon, *(Delcon Corp.; 0-934856),* P.O. Box 323, Harlan St. Rte., Eddyville, OR 97343 (SAN 213-4853).

DeLethein Pr, *(DeLethein Pr., The),* Dept. BP, 4605 Holborn Ave., Annandale, VA 22003 (SAN 287-2846).

DeLeuw-Cather Co, *(De Leuw, Cather & Co.),* 600 Fifth Street, NW, Washington, DC 20001 (SAN 283-1813).

Delford Pr, *(Delford Pr.; 0-931726),* P.O. Box 27, Oradell, NJ 07649 (SAN 209-7311) Tel 201-262-0647.

Delgren Bks, *(Delgren Bks.; 0-943472),* 3000 N. Romero Rd., No. A29, Tuscon, AZ 85705 (SAN 240-4702) Tel 602-887-8730; Toll free: 800-528-4923.

Delilah Bks, *(Delilah Bks.; 0-933328),* 118 E. 25th St., New York, NY 10010 (SAN 238-9339); Toll free: 800-847-5515; Dist. by: Putnam Publishing Group, 200 Madison Ave., New York, NY 10016 (SAN 202-5531).

Delilah Comm, *(Delilah Communications, Ltd.; 0-933368; 0-88715),* 118 E. 25th St., New York, NY 10010 (SAN 212-4157) Tel 212-477-2100; Dist. by: Dell Publishing Co., 1 Dag Hammarskjold Plaza, 245 E. 47th St., New York, NY 10017 (SAN 201-0097).

†**Dell,** *(Dell Publishing Co., Inc.; 0-440),* Subs. of Doubleday & Co., Inc., 1 Dag Hammarskjold Plaza, 245 E. 47th St., New York, NY 10017 (SAN 201-0097) Tel 212-605-3000; Toll free: 800-932-0070; *CIP.* Imprints: Banbury (Banbury); Bryans (Bryans); Chapel (Chapel Books).(Chapel Bks.); Dell Trade Pbks (Dell Trade Paperbacks); Delta (Delta Books).(Delta Bks.); Emerald (Emerald); LE (Laurel Editions); LFL (Laurel Leaf Library); MB (Mayflower Books).(Mayflower Bks.); Standish (Standish); YB (Yearling Books).(Yearling Bks.).

Dell Trade Pbks *Imprint of* **Dell**

†**Dellen Pub,** *(Dellen Publishing Co.; 0-89517),* Subs. of Macmillan Publishing Co., 3600 Pruneridge Ave., Santa Clara, CA 95051 (SAN 219-0834) Tel 408-246-4215; *CIP.*

†**Delmar,** *(Delmar Pubs., Inc.; 0-8273),* Div. of International Thomson Educational Pub., Inc., 2 Computer Dr. W., Albany, NY 12212 (SAN 206-7544) Tel 518-459-1150; Toll free: 800-833-3350; P.O. Box 15-015, Albany, NY 12212 (SAN 658-0440); *CIP.*

Delmar Co, *(Delmar Co., The; 0-912081),* Div. of Republic Corp., P.O. Box 220025, 9601 Monroe Rd., Charlotte, NC 28222 (SAN 264-732X) Tel 704-847-9801; Toll free: 800-438-1504.

Delmar Pub, *(Del Mar Publishing; 0-935361),* 389 Rainer Dr., Salinas, CA 93906 (SAN 696-320X) Tel 408-449-3260.

DeLong & Assocs, *(DeLong & Assocs.; 0-9603414),* P.O. Box 1732, Annapolis, MD 21404 (SAN 213-215X) Tel 301-263-5592.

deLorenzo diSalvo, *(deLorenzo & diSalvo Inc.; 0-933709),* 2130 Jackson St., No. 306, San Francisco, CA 94115 (SAN 692-5219) Tel 415-346-2519.

DeLorme Pub, *(Delorme Publishing Co.; 0-89933),* P.O. Box 298, Freeport, ME 04032 (SAN 220-1208) Tel 207-865-4171; Toll free: 800-227-1656.

Delphi Pr WA, *(Delphi Pr.; 0-939202),* 1750 K St., NW, Suite 1110, Washington, DC 20006 (SAN 220-1674) Tel 202-466-7951.

Delphi Res, *(Delphi Research Center; 0-916987),* P.O. Box 428, Lincoln, MA 01773 (SAN 655-6248) Tel 617-259-0527.

Delta *Imprint of* **Dell**

Delta G Pr, *(Delta Group Pr.; 0-913787),* 245 Ponderosa Way, Evergreen, CO 80439 (SAN 286-0902) Tel 303-674-9850.

Delta Pi Epsilon, *(Delta Pi Epsilon, Inc.; 0-9603064),* National Office, Gustavus Adolphus College, St. Peter, MN 56082 (SAN 223-565X) Tel 507-931-4184.

Delta Queen, *(Delta Queen Steamboat Co., The; 0-937331),* 30 Robin St. Wharf, New Orleans, LA 70130 (SAN 658-8085) Tel 504-586-0631.

Delta Sales, *(Delta Sales; 0-931626),* 399 Southgate Ave., Daly City, CA 94015 (SAN 212-2510).

Delta Systems, *(Delta Systems Co., Inc.; 0-937354),* 570 Rock Road Dr., Unit H, Dundee, IL 60118 (SAN 220-0457) Tel 312-551-9595.

Deltiologists Am, *(Deltiologists of America; 0-913782),* 10 Felton Ave., Ridley Park, PA 19078 (SAN 225-607X) Tel 215-521-1092.

Demarais Studio, *(Demarais Studio Press, Inc.; 0-9607462),* 64 Lawn Park Ave., Trenton, NJ 08648 (SAN 238-6224) Tel 609-833-1737.

†**Dembner Bks,** *(Dembner Bks.; 0-934878),* Div. of Red Dembner Enterprises Corp., 80 Eighth Ave., New York, NY 10011 (SAN 211-5573) Tel 212-924-2525; Dist. by: W. W. Norton & Co., Inc., 500 Fifth Ave., New York, NY 10110 (SAN 202-5795) Tel 212-354-5500; *CIP.*

Demecon, *(Demecon Pubs.; 0-943700),* P.O. Box 13759, Reading, PA 19612 (SAN 212-8314) Tel 215-929-8336.

Demeter *Imprint of* **Times Bks**

DemoNet, *(DemoNet, Inc.; 0-933337),* 7310 C Adams, Paramount, CA 90723 (SAN 107-9476) Tel 213-408-1966.

DeMos Music, *(DeMos Music Pubns.; 0-940026),* P.O. Box 14125, Houston, TX 77221 (SAN 217-0698) Tel 713-433-5235.

Den Hamwood, *(Denhamwood, Inc.; 0-931544),* 16944 Ventura Blvd., Encino, CA 91316 (SAN 223-3665) Tel 818-783-2758.

Den Rey Pubns, *(Den Rey Pubns.; 0-9617113),* Rte 3, St. Agusta, St. Cloud, MN 56301 (SAN 662-8036) Tel 612-255-0480.

Denali Press, *(Denali Pr., The; 0-938737),* P.O. Box 1535, Juneau, AK 99802 (SAN 661-8278); 1950 Glacier Hwy., Juneau, AK 99802 (SAN 661-8286) Tel 907-586-6014.

Denco Intl, *(Denco International),* P.O. Box 1052, Deerfield Beach, FL 33441-1052 (SAN 213-6171) Tel 305-822-6666.

Dendle & Schraibman, *(Dendle & Schraibman; 0-9608168),* 272 S. Hanover, Lexington, KY 40502 (SAN 240-4729).

Dendrobium Bks, *(Dendrobium Bks.; 0-936831),* 387 Ivy St., San Francisco, CA 94102 (SAN 699-8542) Tel 415-558-8444.

Denison, *(Denison, T. S., & Co., Inc.; 0-513),* 9601 Newton Ave. S., Minneapolis, MN 55431 (SAN 201-3142) Tel 612-888-1460; Toll free: 800-328-3831. Do Not Confuse with Dennison Pubns.

Dennis & Co Inc
 See W S Hein

Dennis-Landman, *(Dennis-Landman Pubs.; 0-930422),* 1150 18th St., Santa Monica, CA 90403 (SAN 210-9352) Tel 213-453-4643.

Dennison, *(Dennison Pubns.),* Dist. by: Borden Publishing Co., 1855 W. Main St., Alhambra, CA 91801 (SAN 201-419X) Tel 818-283-5031.

Denoyer, *(Denoyer-Geppert Co.; 0-87453),* 5235 N. Ravenswood Ave., Chicago, IL 60640 (SAN 204-2215) Tel 312-561-9200; Toll free: 800-323-1887.

Denson Pr, *(Denson Pr.; 0-9614188),* P.O. Box 29165, San Francisco, CA 94129 (SAN 686-6530); 1200 Gough St., Suite 5D, San Francisco, CA 94109 (SAN 662-2720) Tel 415-441-1804.

Dent-Info
 See Dental-Info

Dental Folk, *(Dental Folklore, Bks. of K.C.; 0-930989),* Div. of Dental Folklore, 7612 W. 95th St., Apt. A, Overland Park, KS 66212 (SAN 678-8890) Tel 913-341-0855; Orders to: Dental Folklore of K.C., P.O. Box 25642, Overland Park, KS 66225 (SAN 688-4261).

Dental-Info, *(Dental-Info; 0-9607518),* 2509 N. Campbell, No. 9, Tucson, AZ 85719 (SAN 239-4340).

Dentan Pr, *(Dentan Press; 0-9610080),* 1404 Buchanan St.,P.O. Box 1745, Novato, CA 94948 (SAN 269-6738) Tel 415-897-1483.

Denton Senior Ctr, *(Denton Senior Center; 0-9606146),* c/o Department Of Parks And Recreation, 215 E. Mckinney, Denton, TX 76201 (SAN 218-4745).

Denver Art Mus, *(Denver Art Museum; 0-914738),* Pubns. Dept. 100 W. 14th Ave. Pkwy., Denver, CO 80204 (SAN 206-3530) Tel 303-575-5582; Dist. by: Museum Shop, 100 W. 14th Ave., Denver, CO 80204 (SAN 200-4704) Tel 303-575-2253; Dist. by: Univ. of Washington Pr., P.O. Box C-50096, Seattle, WA 98145 (SAN 212-2502).

Denver Ctr Performing Arts, *(Denver Ctr. for Performing Arts, The; 0-936947),* 1245 Champa St., Denver, CO 80204 (SAN 658-6732) Tel 303-893-4000.

Denver Mus Natl Hist, *(Denver Museum of Natural History; 0-916278),* City Park, Denver, CO 80205 (SAN 204-2193) Tel 303-370-6302.

Denver Public, *(Denver Public Library; 0-942214),* 3840 York St., Denver, CO 80205 (SAN 208-1504) Tel 303-571-2367.

DePauw Univ, (*DePauw Univ.; 0-936631*), Office of Pubns., Charter Hse., Greencastle, IN 46135 (SAN 699-6973) Tel 317-658-4629.

Depot Pr, (*Depot Pr.; 0-910151*), P.O. Box 60072, Nashville, TN 37206 (SAN 240-1401) Tel 615-226-1890.

Dept Anthro U Minn, (*Univ. of Minnesota, Dept. of Anthropology; 0-911599*), 215 Ford Hall, 224 Church St. SE, Minneapolis, MN 55455 (SAN 264-4576) Tel 612-373-4614.

Dept Consumer Aff CA *See* Calif Dept CA

Dept Hist Org, (*American Univ., Dept. of History, Organization of Historical Studies*), American Univ., Massachusetts & Nebraska Aves., NW, Washington, DC 20016 (SAN 283-2666).

Dept Intl Health, (*Johns Hopkins Univ., Dept. of International Health; 0-912888*), 615 N. Wolfe St., Baltimore, MD 21205 (SAN 202-3520).

Dept Mech E CA, (*Stanford Univ., Dept. of Mechanical Engineering; 0-9607348*), Stanford Univ., Stanford, CA 94305 (SAN 265-9778).

Der Angriff *See* Griffin Bks

Derby Pub, (*Derby Publishing Co.; 0-940424*), P.O. Box 221474, Charlotte, NC 28222 (SAN 217-1716) Tel 704-366-7029.

Derek Prince, (*Prince, Derek, Ministries Pubns.; 0-934920*), P.O. Box 300, Fort Lauderdale, FL 33302 (SAN 211-822X) Tel 305-763-5202.

Dermody, (*Dermody, Gail R. & Eugene M.*), P.O. Box 324, Lakewood, CA 90714 (SAN 212-0860).

Derry Lit, (*Derry Literary Guild; 0-9612586*), P.O. Box U, Hershey, PA 17033 (SAN 289-1034); Orders to: One of A Kind, Hershey's Chocolate World, Box 800, Hershey, PA 17033 (SAN 692-8439) Tel 717-534-5439.

DeRu's Fine Art, (*DeRu's Fine Art Bks.; 0-939370*), Div. of DeRu's Fine Art Gallery, 9100 E. Artesia Blvd., Bellflower, CA 90706 (SAN 216-3667) Tel 213-920-1312.

†Deseret Bk, (*Deseret Bk. Co.; 0-87747; 0-87579*), Div. of Deseret Management Corp., P.O. Box 30178, Salt Lake City, UT 84130 (SAN 201-3185) Tel 801-534-1515; Toll free: 800-453-3876; *CIP.*

Deseret News, (*Deseret News Publishing Company; 0-910901*), 30 E. First S. St., P.O. Box 1257, Salt Lake City, UT 84110 (SAN 269-6835) Tel 801-237-2137.

Desert Arthritis, (*Desert Arthritis Medical Clinic; 0-930703*), 13630 Mountain View Dr., Desert Hot Springs, CA 92240 (SAN 677-1947) Tel 619-329-6422.

Desert Bio Pubns, (*Desert Biological Publications; 0-9614003*), P.O. Box 291, Dona Ana, NM 88032 (SAN 686-1784).

Desert Botanical, (*Desert Botanical Garden; 0-9605656*), 1201 N. Galvin Parkway, Phoenix, AZ 85008 (SAN 212-9000) Tel 602-941-1225.

Desert First, (*Desert First Works, Inc.; 0-916556*), 3870 N. Vine Ave., Tucson, AZ 85719 (SAN 208-6263) Tel 602-326-1041.

Desert Light, (*Desert Light Pub.; 0-942128*), Lorraine Wood, Phoenix, AZ 85283 (SAN 238-6550) Tel 602-840-2217.

Desert Min, (*Desert Ministries, Inc.; 0-914733*), P.O. Box 13235, Pittsburgh, PA 15243 (SAN 657-6036) Tel 412-854-3311.

Desert Pr, (*Desert Pr., The; 0-937764*), Box K, Bouse, AZ 85325 (SAN 215-6342).

Desert Tortoise Coun, (*Desert Tortoise Council*), 5319 Cerritos Ave., Long Beach, CA 90805 (SAN 225-0039) Tel 213-422-6172.

Desert Wind Pub, (*Desert Wind Publishing Co.; 0-9615217*), Div. of Signature Galleries, 7534 First St., Scottsdale, AZ 85251 (SAN 695-1295) Tel 602-946-0270.

Design Ent SF, (*Design Enterprises of San Francisco; 0-932538*), P.O. Box 14695, San Francisco, CA 94114 (SAN 211-6359) Tel 415-282-8813.

Design Meth, (*Design Methods Group, The; 0-910821*), P.O. Box 5, San Luis Obispo, CA 93406 (SAN 269-6886) Tel 805-546-1321.

Design Pubns, (*Design Publications, Inc.; 0-934341*), 330 W. 42nd St., New York, NY 10036 (SAN 693-6113) Tel 212-695-4955.

Design Schools, (*Design Schools, The; 0-9607016*), 101 Park Ave., New York, NY 10178 (SAN 238-969X) Tel 212-972-1505.

Designed Impacts, (*Designed Impacts; 0-930791*), 910 Woodmont Blvd., H-6, Nashville, TN 37204 (SAN 677-8488) Tel 615-269-5580.

Designer Bks, (*Designer Bks.; 0-9616966*), P.O. Box 18181, Garden City, GA 31418-0181 (SAN 661-8251); 618 Hwy. 80, Garden City, GA 31408 (SAN 661-826X) Tel 912-772-5183.

Designs Three, (*Designs III Pubs.; 0-9609254*), 515 W. Commonwealth Ave., Fullerton, CA 92632 (SAN 209-2336) Tel 714-871-9100.

Desperation Pr, (*Desperation Pr.; 0-9609112*), Los Alamos Technical Equipment Co., P.O. Box 659, Los Alamos, NM 87544 (SAN 241-4929) Tel 505-662-4815.

Desserco Pub, (*Desserco Publishing; 0-916698*), P.O. Box 2433, Culver City, CA 90230 (SAN 208-3914) Tel 213-827-4600.

Destiny, (*Destiny Pubs.; 0-910500*), 43 Grove St., Merrimac, MA 01860 (SAN 203-8889) Tel 617-346-9311.

Destiny Bks *Imprint of* Inner Tradit

Det Inst Arts *See* Detroit Inst Arts

Determined Prods, (*Determined Productions, Inc.; 0-915696*), 315 Pacific Ave. at Battery, P.O. Box 2150, San Francisco, CA 94126 (SAN 212-7385) Tel 415-433-0660.

Detroit Black, (*Detroit Black Writers' Guild; 0-9613078*), 5601 W. Warren, Detroit, MI 48210 (SAN 294-7315) Tel 313-898-7629.

Detroit Guide, (*Detroit Guide; 0-9600448*), 15365 Glastonbury, Detroit, MI 48223 (SAN 218-4567).

†Detroit Inst Arts, (*Detroit Institute of Arts; 0-89558*), 5200 Woodward Ave., Detroit, MI 48202 (SAN 204-2150) Tel 313-833-7960; *CIP.*

Detroit Symphony, (*Detroit Symphony League; 0-9611348*), 5567 Westwood Ln., Birmingham, MI 48010 (SAN 282-8847) Tel 313-851-3485.

Deus *Imprint of* Paulist Pr

Dev Markets, (*Developing Markets, Inc.; 0-936949*), 40 High St., Hamilton, OH 45011 (SAN 658-6996) Tel 513-896-1539.

Devco Pr, (*Devco Pr.; 0-9611790*), P.O. Box 842, Golden, CO 80402 (SAN 285-2330) Tel 303-278-0736.

Devel Self Rel, (*Development through Self-Reliance, Inc.; 0-936731*), 9527 Good Lion Rd., Columbia, MD 21045 (SAN 699-9077) Tel 301-596-0794; Box 281, Columbia, MD 21045 (SAN 699-9085) Tel 301-964-1647.

Develop Read Dist, (*Developmental Reading Distributors; 0-910504*), P.O. Box 1451, Cape Coral, FL 33910 (SAN 201-8187).

Develop Res, (*Development of Research & Human Services; 0-9609114*), Div. of Development of Research & Human Services, P.O. Box 1865, Albuquerque, NM 87103 (SAN 241-4937); 5501 Kettle, NW, Albuquerque, NM 87120 (SAN 661-9908) Tel 505-898-3739.

Developmental Arts, (*Developmental Arts; 0-9605372*), P.O. Box 389, Arlington, MA 02174 (SAN 215-8566).

Devida Pubns, (*Devida Pubns.; 0-9607498*), Six Darby Rd., E. Brunswick, NJ 08816 (SAN 238-7964)P.O. Box 761, Princeton, NJ 08550 (SAN 238-7972) Tel 201-257-7257.

†Devil Mountain Bks, (*Devil Mountain Bks.; 0-915685*), P.O. Box 4115, Walnut Creek, CA 94596 (SAN 292-4803) Tel 415-939-3415; *CIP.*

†Devin, (*Devin-Adair Pubs., Inc.; 0-8159*), 6 N. Water St., Greenwich, CT 06830 (SAN 213-750X) Tel 203-531-7755; *CIP.*

†Devon Pr, (*Devon Pr., Inc.; 0-934160*), 820 Miramar, Berkeley, CA 94707 (SAN 212-8500) Tel 415-525-2098; *CIP.*

Devon Pub, (*Devon Publishing Co., Inc., The; 0-941402*), 2700 Virginia Ave., NW, Washington, DC 20037 (SAN 238-9703) Tel 202-337-5197.

Devonshire Pub, (*Devonshire Publishing Co., The; 0-918897*), P.O. Box 7066, Chicago, IL 60680 (SAN 669-9987); 11 N. Batavia Rd., Batavia, IL 60510-1722 (SAN 662-2437) Tel 312-242-3846; Dist. by: New Leaf Distributing, 1020 White St, SW, Atlanta, GA 30310 (SAN 169-1449) Tel 404-755-2665; Dist. by: Baker & Taylor (Southeast Div.), Mt. Olive Rd., Commerce, GA 30529 (SAN 169-1503); Dist. by: Baker & Taylor (Midwest Div.), 501 Gladiola Ave, Momence, IL 60954 (SAN 169-2100).

DeVore & Sons, (*DeVore & Sons, Inc.; 1-55665*), P.O. Box 118, Wichita, KS 67201; Toll free: 800-835-1051; 1199 E. Central, Wichita, KS 67214; Dist. by: Riverside Bk. & Bible Hse., P.O. Box 370, Iowa Falls, IA 50126 (SAN 169-2666) Tel 515-648-4269.

Dewey Pubns, (*Dewey Pubns., Inc.; 0-9615053*), 353 N. Edison St., Arlington, VA 22203 (SAN 694-1451) Tel 703-522-4761; Orders to: 1717 K St., NW, Suite 1102, Washington, DC 20006 (SAN 662-3328).

DeWitt & Sheppard, (*DeWitt & Sheppard Pubs.; 0-932365*), P.O. Box 5603, Tacoma, WA 98405 (SAN 687-3758) Tel 206-272-7588.

†DeWitt Hist, (*DeWitt Historical Society; 0-942690*), Clinton House, 116 N. Cayuga, Ithaca, NY 14850 (SAN 264-004X); *CIP.*

Deya Brashears, (*Brashears, Deya; 0-9614717*), 1 Corte Del Rey, Orinda, CA 94563 (SAN 692-641X) Tel 415-376-3516; Dist. by: Gryphon House, Inc., 3706 Otis Street, P.O. Box 275, Mt. Rainier, MD 20712 (SAN 169-3190) Tel 301-779-6200.

DFM Assoc, (*DFM Assocs.; 0-9616372*), 10 Chrysler, Irvine, CA 92718 (SAN 239-8508) Tel 714-859-8700.

†Dghtrs St Paul, (*Daughters of St. Paul; 0-8198*), 50 St. Paul's Ave., Boston, MA 02130 (SAN 203-8900) Tel 617-522-8911; *CIP.*

DGL InfoWrite, (*DGL InfoWrite; 0-9614944*), 3010 Vassar Dr., Boulder, CO 80303 (SAN 693-6520) Tel 303-499-1749.

Dharma Drum Pubns, (*Dharma Drum Pubns.; 0-9609854*), 90-31 Corona Ave., Elmhurst, NY 11373 (SAN 269-6967) Tel 718-592-6593.

†Dharma Pub, (*Dharma Publishing; 0-913546; 0-89800*), 2425 Hillside Ave., Berkeley, CA 94704 (SAN 201-2723) Tel 415-548-5407; *CIP.*

Di-Tri Bks, (*Di-Tri Bks.; 0-9603374*), 261 Waubesa St., Madison, WI 53704 (SAN 209-1712).

Dia Press, (*Dia Pr.; 0-9615517*), P.O. Box 71326, Reno, NV 89570 (SAN 696-3269) Tel 702-827-6753.

Diabetes Ctr MN, (*Diabetes Ctr., Inc.; 0-937721*), Div. of Park Nicollet Medical Foundation, 13911 Ridgedale Dr., Minnetonka, MN 55343 (SAN 659-252X) Tel 612-541-0239.

†Diablo, (*Diablo Pr.; 0-87297*), P.O. Box 7042, Berkeley, CA 94707 (SAN 201-3223) Tel 415-524-9624; *CIP.*

Diablo Bks, (*Diablo Bks.; 0-9607520*), 1317 Cayonwood Ct., No. 1, Walnut Creek, CA 94595 (SAN 238-6232) Tel 415-939-8644.

Diablo West Pr, (*Diablo Western Pr.; 0-932438*), P.O. Box 5364, Walnut Creek, CA 94596 (SAN 211-9471).

Dial *Imprint of* Doubleday
Dial *See* Doubleday

†Dial Bks Young, (*Dial Bks. for Young Readers*), Div. of E. P. Dutton, 2 Park Ave., New York, NY 10016 (SAN 264-0058) Tel 212-725-1818; Toll free: 800-526-0275; Orders to: New American Library, P.O. Box 120, Bergenfield, NJ 07261 (SAN 200-6758) Tel 201-387-0600; *CIP.* Imprints: Hillside Bks (Hillside Books).(Hillside Bks.).

Dialectics Workshop, (*Dialectics Workshop; 0-939275*), 53 Hickory Hill Rd., Tappan, NY 10983 (SAN 662-8869) Tel 914-359-2283.

†Dialog, (*Dialog Pr.; 0-914153*), Subs. of Feature Group, Inc., Dept. 856, P.O. Box 59072, Chicago, IL 60659 (SAN 669-3474); *CIP.*

†Dialogue Hse, (*Dialogue Hse. Library; 0-87941*), 80 E. 11th St., New York, NY 10003 (SAN 201-8195) Tel 212-673-5880; Toll free: 800-221-5844; *CIP.*

†**Dialogue Pr Man World,** *(Dialogue Pr. of Man & World, The; 0-932540),* 246 Sparks Bldg., University Park, PA 16802 (SAN 211-9447) Tel 814-865-6397; *CIP.*

Diamond Bks *Imprint of Almaas Pubns*

Diamond Communications, *(Diamond Communications, Inc.; 0-912083),* P.O. Box 88, South Bend, IN 46624 (SAN 264-7346) Tel 219-287-5008.

Diamond Farm Bk, *(Diamond Farm Bk. Pubs.; 0-9506932),* Div. of Diamond Enterprises, P.O. Box 537, Alexandria Bay, NY 13607 (SAN 674-9054) Tel 613-475-1771.

Diamond Heights, *(Diamond Heights Publishing Co.,; 0-936182),* 25 Grand View Ave., San Francisco, CA 94114 (SAN 215-3017) Tel 415-821-9133.

Diamond Pr PA, *(Diamond Pr.; 0-9615843),* Regency Woods G-5, Doylestown, PA 18901 (SAN 696-7329) Tel 215-345-6094.

Diamond Pub
See Triple Play Pubns

Diamond Pubs, *(Diamond Pubs.; 0-936519),* Div. of Landmark International, 23818 Twin Pines Ln., Diamond Bar, CA 91765 (SAN 216-0307) Tel 714-595-4977.

Dianas Bimonthly, *(Diana's Bimonthly Pr.; 0-933442),* 23 N. Fair St., Warwick, RI 02888 (SAN 207-8147) Tel 401-274-5417.

Diane Bks, *(Diane Bks. Publishing, Inc.; 0-88264),* 2807 Oregon Ct., No. E, Torrance, CA 90503 (SAN 201-2731) Tel 213-320-2591; P.O. Box 2948, Torrance, CA 90509 (SAN 661-9916); Orders to: Diane Books, P.O. Box 2948, Torrance, CA 90509 (SAN 693-4862) Tel 213-533-5872.

Diantha Chris
See D C Rau

Dickay Pub, *(Dickay Publishing; 0-9611068),* P.O. Box 664, Buckeye Lake, OH 43008 (SAN 282-8596) Tel 614-928-4566.

Dickenson Pr, *(Dickenson Pr.; 0-9615487),* 1012 Chesapeake Ct., Huntington, WV 25701 (SAN 696-3307) Tel 304-525-9561.

Dickerson Pr, *(Dickerson Pr.; 0-9615621),* 2215 Lincolnwood Dr., Evanston, IL 60201 (SAN 696-3323) Tel 312-869-0132.

Dict Soc NA, *(Dictionary Society of North America),* Indiana State Univ., Dept. of Instructional Services, Terre Haute, IN 47809 (SAN 233-4755) Tel 812-237-2330.

Diction Bks, *(Diction Bks.; 0-9609198),* 1313 Fifth St., SE, Suite 223, Minneapolis, MN 55414 (SAN 241-4945) Tel 612-379-3888.

Dicul Pub, *(Dicul Publishing; 0-938784),* P.O. Box 091111, Columbus, OH 43209-7111 (SAN 216-0315) Tel 614-231-4670; Dist. by: DeVorss & Co., Inc., P.O. Box 550, 1046 Princeton Dr., Marina del Rey, CA 90294 (SAN 168-9886) Tel 213-870-7478; Dist. by: PEP Distributors, 2070 Rosewood Ln., Lima, OH 45806 (SAN 200-4194); Dist. by: Toastmaster International, 2200 N. Grand Ave., Santa Ana, CA 92711 (SAN 206-1112) Tel 714-542-6793.

Didactic Syst, *(Didactic Systems Inc.; 0-89401),* P.O. Box 457, Cranford, NJ 07016 (SAN 209-1739) Tel 212-789-2194.

Diemer-Smith, *(Diemer, Smith Publishing Co., Inc.; 0-941138),* 3377 Solano Ave., Suite 322, Napa, CA 94558 (SAN 238-874X) Tel 707-224-0813.

Diesel Engine, *(Diesel Engine Manufacturers Assn.),* 712 Lakewood Ctr., N., 14600 Detroit Ave., Cleveland, OH 44107 (SAN 224-7232).

Diesel Pubns
See Busn Journals

Diet Teach Progs, *(Diet Teaching Programs, Inc., The; 0-941040),* P.O. Box 1832, Sun City, AZ 85372 (SAN 217-3522) Tel 602-977-6677.

Dietz, *(Dietz Pr.; 0-87517),* 109 E. Cary, Richmond, VA 23219 (SAN 201-3258) Tel 804-648-0195.

Diffendal & Johnson, *(Diffendal & Johnson; 0-9614260),* 614 Eighth St., NE, Washington, DC 20002 (SAN 687-1224) Tel 202-546-4103; Orders to: P.O. Box 76985, Washington, DC 20013 (SAN 662-2739).

Different Drum, *(Different Drummer Press; 0-9609580),* 306 Eighth St., Des Moines, IA 50309 (SAN 262-6217) Tel 515-243-8105.

Digit Concept, *(Digital Concept Systems, Inc.; 0-936327),* 4826 Bucknell, Suite 201, San Antonio, TX 78249 (SAN 697-354X) Tel 512-692-1201.

Digital Equip, *(Digital Equipment Corp.; 1-55558),* 12 Crosby Dr., Bedford, MA 01730 (SAN 677-8968).

†**Digital Pr,** *(Digital Pr./Digital Equipment Corp.; 0-932376; 1-55558),* 12 Crosby Dr., Bedford, MA 01730 (SAN 212-2529) Tel 617-276-1536; Toll free: 800-343-8322; Orders to: 12-A Esquire Rd., North Billerica, MA 01862 (SAN 212-2537); *CIP.*

Dignatus Co, *(Dignatus Co.; 0-9605820),* P.O. Box 2254, Mission Viejo, CA 92690 (SAN 216-5732) Tel 714-493-0710.

Dignity Inc, *(Dignity, Inc.; 0-940680),* 1500 Massachusetts Ave., NW, No. 11, Washington, DC 20005 (SAN 223-7431) Tel 202-861-0017.

Dildo Pr
See Mho & Mho

Dilettante, *(Dilettante Pr., Inc.; 0-935421),* 1826 St. Claude Ave., New Orleans, LA 70116 (SAN 696-3366) Tel 504-943-3822.

†**Dilithium Pr,** *(Dilithium Pr.; 0-918398; 0-88056; 0-930206),* P.O. Box 606, Beaverton, OR 97075 (SAN 210-0649) Tel 503-243-3313; Toll free: 800-547-1842; *CIP.*

Dillingham Pr, *(Dillingham Pr.; 0-9616071),* Box 2601, Santa Fe, NM 87501 (SAN 697-8592) Tel 505-983-3447.

†**Dillon,** *(Dillon Pr., Inc.; 0-87518),* 242 Portland Ave., S., Minneapolis, MN 55415 (SAN 201-3266) Tel 612-333-2691; Toll free: 800-328-8322; *CIP. Imprints:* Gemstone Bks (Gemstone Books).

Dillon-Donnelly, *(Dillon-Donnelly; 0-933508),* 7058 Lindell Blvd., St. Louis, MO 63130 (SAN 208-4589) Tel 314-862-6239.

Dillon-Liederbach, *(Dillon/Liederbach, Inc.; 0-913228),* 4953 Stonington Rd., Winston-Salem, NC 27103 (SAN 201-3274) Tel 919-768-7014.

Dillon-Tyler Pubs, *(Dillon-Tyler Pubs.; 0-916280),* 1041 W. Salvador Ave., Napa, CA 94558 (SAN 208-1075) Tel 707-224-2525.

Dilman Pr, *(Dilman Pr.; 0-9615301),* 773 Cole, No. 8, San Francisco, CA 94117 (SAN 464-4639) Tel 415-386-6072; Dist. by: Bookpeople, 2929 Fifth St., Berkeley, CA 94710 (SAN 168-9517) Tel 415-549-3030.

Dimedia, *(Dimedia, Inc.; 0-89300),* 162 Washington St., Newark, NJ 07102 (SAN 240-057X); Dist. by: Publishers Group West, 5855 Beaudry St., Emeryville, CA 94608 (SAN 202-8522) Tel 415-658-3453.

Dimedinha Inc, *(Dimedinha, Inc.; 0-9616453),* P.O. Box 71566, Madison Heights, MI 48071-0566 (SAN 658-8387) Tel 313-368-3983.

Dimen Graphics Intl, *(Dimensional Graphics International, Ltd.; 0-941444),* 1154 Fort St. Mau, Suite 308, Honolulu, HI 96813 (SAN 238-9711) Tel 808-521-2000.

Dimension Bks, *(Dimension Bks.; 0-87193),* P.O. Box 811, Denville, NJ 07834 (SAN 211-7916) Tel 201-627-4334.

Dimension Four Unltd, *(Dimension Four Unlimited; 0-937805),* 6821 Convoy Ct., Suite B, San Diego, CA 92111 (SAN 659-3372) Tel 619-541-1170.

Dimension Pr, *(Dimension Pr., The; 0-911173),* 4205 Far West Blvd., Austin, TX 78755 (SAN 269-7114) Tel. 512-345-0622; P.O. Box 26673, Austin, TX 78755 (SAN 658-0459).

Dimensionist Pr, *(Dimensionist Press; 0-9602374),* 5931 Stanton Ave., Highland, CA 92346 (SAN 212-2545) Tel 714-946-9687.

Dimes Group
See US Info Moscow

Dimond Pubs, *(Dimond Pubs.; 0-937610),* 3431 Fruitvale Ave., Oakland, CA 94602 (SAN 215-1405).

Dinograph SW, *(Dinograph Southwest, Inc.; 0-932680),* P.O. Box 1600, Alamogordo, NM 88310 (SAN 212-1573).

†**Dinosaur,** *(Dinosaur Pr., The; 0-9605458),* 86 Leverett Rd., Amherst, MA 01002 (SAN 213-618X) Tel 413-549-0404; *CIP.*

Dionex Corp, *(Dionex Corp.; 0-9617173),* P.O. Box 3603, Sunnyvale, CA 94088 (SAN 663-1347); 1228 Titan Way, Sunnyvale, CA 94088 (SAN 663-1355) Tel 408-737-0700.

Dioscorides Pr, *(Dioscorides Pr., Inc.; 0-931146),* 9999 SW Wilshire, Suite 124, Portland, OR 97225 (SAN 659-3917) Tel 503-292-0745.

Diotima Bks, *(Diotima Bks.; 0-935772),* Box H, Glen Carbon, IL 62034 (SAN 214-3631).

DiPaul, *(DiPaul, H. Bert; 0-9605418),* 1066 Brennan Dr., Warminster, PA 18974 (SAN 216-0323).

Diplomatic Fla
See Diplomatic IN

†**Diplomatic IN,** *(Diplomatic Pr.; 0-910512),* Indiana Univ., Goodbody Hall 344, Bloomington, IN 47405 (SAN 201-3290) Tel 812-335-1605; *CIP.*

Direct Intl, *(Direct International, Inc.; 0-9616409),* 150 E. 74th St., New York, NY 10021 (SAN 659-1574) Tel 212-861-4188.

Direct Mail Market, *(Direct Mail Marketing Assn., Inc.; 0-933641),* 6 E. 43rd St., New York, NY 10017 (SAN 224-862X) Tel 212-689-4977.

Direct Market, *(Direct Market Designs; 0-9609790),* P.O. Box 142, Island Lake, IL 60042 (SAN 293-2466) Tel 312-526-5141; Dist. by: Publishers Group West, 5855 Beaudry St., Emeryville, CA 94608 (SAN 202-8522) Tel 415-658-3453.

Direct Mktng Assn
See Direct Mail Market

Directed Media, *(Directed Media Inc.; 0-939688),* P.O. Box 3005, Wenatchee, WA 98801 (SAN 216-7263) Tel 509-662-7693.

Direction Dynamics, *(Direction Dynamics; 0-933583),* 309 Honeycutt Dr., Wilmington, NC 28403 (SAN 692-2082) Tel 919-799-6544.

Directions
See Easi-Bild

Directions Pr, *(Directions Pr.; 0-940564),* 523 Gainsborough, No. 101, Thousand Oaks, CA 91360 (SAN 215-6350).

Directories, *(Directories; 0-9607992),* 436 E. 88th St., New York, NY 10128 (SAN 238-5635) Tel 212-722-8460.

Directories Pub, *(Directories Publishing Co., Inc.; 0-937020),* P.O. Box 1824, Clemson, SC 29633-1824 (SAN 203-8919) Tel 803-646-7840; Toll free: 800-222-4531.

Directory Creat Servs DC, *(Directory of Washington Creative Services; 0-938053),* 1506 19th St., NW, Washington, DC 20036 (SAN 661-1087) Tel 202-462-6110; Dist. by: Ross Bk. Service, 3718 Seminary Rd., Alexandria, VA 22304 (SAN 200-6634).

Directory Systems Inc, *(Directory Systems, Inc.; 0-942036),* 51 Bank St., Stamford, CT 06901 (SAN 238-6240) Tel 203-348-6319.

Disa Press Inc, *(Disa Pr., Inc.; 0-913255),* P.O. Box 9284, Wilmington, DE 19809 (SAN 285-8681) Tel 302-475-4509.

Discipleship Res, *(Discipleship Resources; 0-88177),* Subs. of Board of Discipleship of the United Methodist Church, P.O. Box 840, 1908 Grand Ave., Nashville, TN 37202 (SAN 264-0074) Tel 615-327-2700; Orders to: P.O. Box 189, Nashville, TN 37202 (SAN 661-9932).

Discount America, *(Discount America Guide; 0-942528),* 51 E. 42 St., Rm, 417, New York, NY 10017 (SAN 239-6343) Tel 212-687-0810.

Discov Pubns
See Jim Rohn Prod

Discoveries, *(Discoveries Publishing Co.; 0-934000),* P.O. Box 424, Glastonbury, CT 06033 (SAN 212-7393).

Discovery Bks, *(Discovery Bks.; 0-913976),* Star Route, Mountain View, Owls Heads, NY 12969 (SAN 206-9512) Tel 518-483-0079.

Discovery Calif, *(Discovery Pr.; 0-9617131),* P.O. Box 3461, Mission Viejo, CA 92690 (SAN 662-8052); 3459 Via Verde, No. B, Capistrano Beach, CA 92624 (SAN 662-8060) Tel 714-496-3503. Do not confuse with Discovery Pr., Portland, OR.

Discovery Pr, *(Discovery Pr.; 0-9614261),* P.O. Box 12241, Portland, OR 97212 (SAN 687-1240) Tel 503-282-9372.

Discovery Stuff, *(Discovery Stuff; 0-930484),* 5328 W. 67th St., Shawnee Mission, KS 66208 (SAN 211-0636).

Discovery Toys, *(Discovery Toys; 0-939979),* P.O. Box 232008, Pleasant Hill, CA 94523; 400 Ellinwood Way, Suite 300, Pleasant Hill, CA 94523 Tel 415-680-8697.

Discus *Imprint of Avon*

Disharmony Bks *Imprint of Moonstone*

Displays Sch, *(Displays for Schools, Inc.; 0-9600962),* P.O. Box 163, Gainesville, FL 32602 (SAN 157-9711) Tel 904-373-2030.

Dissemination & Assessment, *(Dissemination & Assessment Ctr. for Bilingual Education; 0-89417),* 7703 N. Lamar, Austin, TX 78752 (SAN 209-3073) Tel 512-458-9131.

Distant Pr, *(Distant Thunder Pr.; 0-9614525),* 301 Racine Rd., Madison, WI 53705 (SAN 650-0218) Tel 608-231-3625.

Distant Thunder, *(Distant Thunder Pr.; 0-9614360),* 906 Pine St., Seattle, WA 98101 (SAN 688-4792) Tel 206-622-0996.

distributors, *(Distributors, The; 0-942520),* 702 S. Michigan, South Bend, IN 46618 (SAN 169-2488) Tel 219-232-8500; Toll free: 800-348-5200.

DITO Pub, *(DITO Publishing; 0-937929),* 15051 N. 20th St., Phoenix, AZ 85022 (SAN 659-5014) Tel 602-867-4587.

Divers Pubns, *(Diversified Pubns.; 0-939593),* P.O. Box 548, Colorado City, CO 81019 (SAN 663-6209); 3041 Lunar Dr., Colorado City, CO 81019 (SAN 663-6217) Tel 303-676-3090.

Diversified Ind, *(Diversified Industries; 0-89534),* Div. of Dicom Corp, 2841 Index Rd., Madison, WI 53713 (SAN 210-301X) Tel 608-271-6544.

Diversified Pub Co, *(Diversified Pub. Co; 0-942306),* 5301-44, Lubbock, TX 79414 (SAN 239-8494).

Diversity Okla, *(Diversity Pr.; 0-936715),* 1000 SE Adams, Idabel, OK 74745 (SAN 699-9131) Tel 405-286-3148. Do not confuse with Diversity Pr., Chicago, IL.

Diversity Pr, *(Diversity Pr.; 0-941906),* 2738 N. Racine St., Chicago, IL 60614 (SAN 239-197X) Tel 312-472-5662.

Divesports Pub, *(Divesports Publishing; 0-9611522),* P.O. Box 1397, Austin, TX 78767-1397 (SAN 285-2462) Tel 512-443-5883.

Divine Love Pub, *(Divine Love Publishing Co.; 0-9617038),* P.O. Box 1844, Soquel, CA 95073 (SAN 662-8230); 4631 Soquel Dr., Soquel, CA 95073 (SAN 662-8249) Tel 408-462-6282.

Divine Sci Fed, *(Divine Science Federation International),* 1819 E. 14th Ave., Denver, CO 80218 (SAN 204-1103) Tel 303-322-7730.

Diving Safety, *(Diving Safety Digest; 0-9614638),* P.O. Box 2735, Menlo Park, CA 94026 (SAN 691-9200) Tel 415-322-6984.

Divisions, *(Divisions; 0-934276),* P.O. Box 18647, Cleveland Heights, OH 44118 (SAN 223-579X).

Divorce Res, *(Divorce Research Ctr.),* P.O. Box 18-1515, Coronado, CA 92118 (SAN 287-5373).

Divry, *(Divry, D. C., Inc.; 0-910516),* 148 W. 24th St., New York, NY 10011 (SAN 201-3320) Tel 212-255-2153.

Dixon Enter, *(Dixon Enterprises; 0-9614394),* P.O. Box 1231, Oak Ridge, TN 37831 (SAN 688-668X) Tel 615-482-6721; Dist. by: Baker & Taylor, Eastern Div., 50 Kirby Ave., Somerville, NJ 08876 (SAN 169-4901).

DIY Bks, *(D.I.Y. Bks., Inc.; 0-9604036),* P.O. Box 2055, Hollywood, CA 90028 (SAN 239-4219).

DJA Writ Circle, *(D.J.A.'s Writing Circle; 0-9608924),* 2900 Country Club Rd., Jacksonville, NC 28540 (SAN 241-0117) Tel 919-346-8976.

DJS Ent, *(D. J. S. Enterprises; 0-933634),* 1027 E. College St., Iowa City, IA 52240-5545 (SAN 692-0640) Tel 319-338-0148; Orders to: 31244 Palos Verdes Dr. W., Suite 229, Rancho Palos Verdes, CA 90274 (SAN 692-0659) Tel 213-377-5017.

DJs Guides, *(DJ's Guides; 0-9615919),* Div. of Eicurean Delight, 138 SE 53rd, Portland, OR 97215 (SAN 697-0540) Tel 503-232-1324; P.O. Box 06472, Portland, OR 97206 (SAN 697-0559).

DK Halcyon, *(DK Halcyon Group; 0-939550),* Div. of Thom Doran & Partners, Inc., 2640 Lance Dr., Dayton, OH 45409 (SAN 216-678X) Tel 513-293-9211.

DL Inc, *(DL, Inc.; 0-937075),* P.O. Box 17356, Tucson, AZ 85731 (SAN 658-5698) Tel 602-291-7412; 9450 Paseo Tierra Verde, Tucson, AZ 85731 (SAN 658-5701).

Dlaw Pubns, *(Dlaw Pubns.; 0-9614350),* 5243 Tacoma Way, Tacoma, WA 98409 (SAN 687-7931) Tel 206-475-9200; Orders to: 1614 S. 74th St., Tacoma, WA 98408 (SAN 662-2798).

DLM CPA, *(DLM/CPA; 0-935730),* P.O. Box 70125, Sunnyvale, CA 94086 (SAN 223-1662).

DM Pub, *(D.M. Publishing Co.; 0-938419),* P.O. Box 5064, Sioux City, IA 51102 (SAN 661-0730); 901 N. St. Mary's, Sioux City, IA 51102 (SAN 661-0749) Tel 712-258-3133.

DMC Pubns, *(DMC Pubns.; 0-9616810),* 45 Fairlawn Ave., Black Rock, CT 06605 (SAN 661-0900) Tel 203-368-1742.

DMR Pubns, *(D.M.R. Pubns., Inc.; 0-89552),* 1020 N. Broadway, Suite 111, Milwaukee, WI 53202 (SAN 205-325X) Tel 414-272-9977.

DMS Publishing Co, *(DMS Publishing Co.; 0-914731),* 28311 S. Ridge Haven Ct., Rancho Palos Verdes, CA 90274 (SAN 291-8188) Tel 213-541-9441; Orders to: Holy Shroud Shrine, c/o Marcia Mascia, Corpus Christi Church, 136 S. Regent St., Port Chester, NY 10573 (SAN 662-2232) Tel 914-939-2553.

DMSO News Serv, *(Aphra Behn Pr.; 0-940530),* 9513 SW Barbur Blvd., Suite 103, Portland, OR 97219 (SAN 223-7571) Tel 503-646-0471.

DMSO News Serv
See DMSO News Serv

Dnomro Pubns, *(Dnomro Pubns.; 0-913565),* 40 Fairmont Ave., Waltham, MA 02154 (SAN 201-274X) Tel 617-893-5631.

DNR Pr, *(D.N.R. Pr.; 0-9604682),* 441 Hillsmont Pl., El Cajon, CA 92020 (SAN 216-7107) Tel 619-442-4647.

Do It Now, *(Do It Now Foundation; 0-89230),* P.O. Box 21126, Phoenix, AZ 85036 (SAN 225-9265) Tel 602-257-0797; 2050 E. University, No. 7, Phoenix, AZ 85034 (SAN 669-0661).

Do It Now Foun
See Do It Now

Do-It Pub Group, *(Do-It Publishing Group; 0-936265),* 211 Franklin St., Alexandria, VA 22314 (SAN 697-3280) Tel 703-549-5192.

†**Do It Yourself Legal Pubs,** *(Do-It-Yourself Legal Pubs.; 0-932704),* 150 Fifth Ave., New York, NY 10011 (SAN 214-1876) Tel 212-242-2840; CIP.

Do It Yourself Pubs
See Do It Yourself Legal Pubs

Doane Pub, *(Doane Publishing; 0-932250),* 11701 Borman Dr., St. Louis, MO 63146 (SAN 207-2149) Tel 314-569-2700.

Doane-Western
See Doane Pub

Dobry Enter, *(Dobry Enterprise; 0-9615218),* 2152 Poplar Ridge Rd., Pasadena, MD 21122 (SAN 695-1309) Tel 301-437-0297.

Doc Bk Pubs, *(Documentary Bk. Pubs. Corp.; 0-935503),* 11661 SE First, Suite 201, Bellevue, WA 98005 (SAN 696-4818) Tel 206-462-7400.

Doc Reprocessors, *(Document Reprocessors Pubns.; 0-9616850),* 41 Sutter St., Suite 1120, San Francisco, CA 94104 (SAN 661-3101) Tel 415-362-1298.

Doctors Pr, *(Doctors' Ophthalmic Pr.; 0-9617262),* 401 China Basin St., San Francisco, CA 94107 (SAN 663-5687) Tel 415-777-2020.

Doctrine Christ, *(Doctrine of Christ Pubns.; 0-940068),* 2215 Bourbon St., Beaumont, TX 77705 (SAN 220-2131).

Documan, *(Documan Pr., Ltd.; 0-932076),* 3201 Lorraine Ave., Kalamazoo, MI 49008 (SAN 281-6032) Tel 616-344-0805; Orders to: Box 387, Kalamazoo, MI 49005 (SAN 281-6040).

Documentary Pubns, *(Documentary Pubns.; 0-89712),* 106 Kenan St., Chapel Hill, NC 27514 (SAN 211-559X) Tel 919-929-1833.

Documentary Res, *(Documentary Research Inc.; 0-931627),* 96 Rumsey Rd., Buffalo, NY 14209 (SAN 683-7298) Tel 716-885-9777.

DODC, *(Directory of Directors Co., Inc.; 0-936612),* P.O. Box 462, Southport, CT 06490 (SAN 204-2037) Tel 203-255-8525.

†**Dodd,** *(Dodd, Mead & Co.; 0-396; 0-89696),* 79 Madison Ave., New York, NY 10016 (SAN 201-3339) Tel 212-685-6464; Toll free: 800-251-4000; Orders to: P.O. Box 141000, Nashville, TN 37214 (SAN 287-0177); CIP.

Dodd-Blair Assocs, *(Dodd-Blair & Assocs.; 0-930205),* P.O. Box 644, Rangeley, ME 04970 (SAN 670-7874) Tel 207-864-5195.

DOE, *(U. S. Dept. of Energy; 0-87079),* DOE Office of Scientific & Technical Information, Oak Ridge, TN 37831 (SAN 210-7996) Tel 615-576-1541; Dist. by: National Technical Information Service (NTIS), U. S. Dept. of Commerce, 5285 Port Royal Rd., Springfield, VA 22161 (SAN 205-7263) Tel 703-487-4838.

Dog Ear, *(Dog Ear Pr., The; 0-937966),* P.O. Box 143, South Harpswell, ME 04079 (SAN 216-3675) Tel 207-729-7791.

Dog Eared Pubns, *(Dog-Eared Pubns.; 0-941042),* P.O. Box 814, Corvallis, OR 97339 (SAN 281-6059) Tel 503-753-4274; Dist. by: Pacific Pipeline, Inc., 19215 66th Ave., S, Kent, WA 98032 (SAN 208-2128) Tel 206-872-5523.

Dog Master, *(Dog-Master Systems),* Div. of Environmental Research Labs, 1020 K-9 Way, P.O. Box 250, Agoura Hills, CA 91301 (SAN 209-181X); Toll free: 800-824-7888.

Dog River, *(Dog River Publishing; 0-932509),* P.O. Box 1922, Douglasville, GA 30133-1922 (SAN 687-4428) Tel 404-942-5090.

Dogwood Pr, *(Dogwood Pr., Inc.; 0-9614978),* P.O. Box 2023, Stone Mountain, GA 30086 (SAN 693-6121) Tel 404-296-1073.

DOK Pubs, *(DOK Pubs., Inc.; 0-914634),* Div. of United Educational Services, Inc., Box 605,, East Aurora, NY 14052 (SAN 201-3347) Tel 716-652-9131; Toll free: 800-458-7900.

Dole Pub, *(Dole Pub.; 0-9614216),* 1503 Franklin Ave., Redlands, CA 92373 (SAN 687-0953) Tel 714-793-9768.

Dolice Graphics, *(Dolice Graphics; 0-935901),* 3 W. 19th St., New York, NY 10011 (SAN 696-7280) Tel 212-206-0770.

Doll Collect Am, *(Doll Collectors of America, Inc.; 0-9603210),* Dist. by: Patry/Edgar, 11 Charlemont Rd., Medford, MA 02155 (SAN 282-695X).

†**Doll Works,** *(Doll Works, The; 0-940070),* P.O. Box 91910, Santa Barbara, CA 93190 (SAN 220-214X) Tel 805-966-6692; CIP.

Dollar's Info Bks, *(Dollar's Info Bks.; 0-915453),* 1500 Pecan Pl. Dr., Plaquemine, LA 70764 (SAN 291-2279) Tel 504-687-6516.

Dolly Ridge
See Menasha Ridge

Dolores Pr, *(Dolores Pr.; 0-934117),* 69 Rensselaer Dr., Commack, NY 11725 (SAN 693-2916) Tel 516-499-4281.

Dolores SF, *(Mission Dolores; 0-912748),* 16th & Dolores Sts., San Francisco, CA 94103 (SAN 696-6349).

Dolp *Imprint of* **Doubleday**

Doma, *(Doma Pr./SPI; 0-917816),* Affil. of Spritual Pathways Institute, P.O. Box 564, Lisle, IL 60532 (SAN 210-0681) Tel 312-969-0734.

Dome Pr
See Dome Pubns

Dome Pubns, *(Dome Pubns.; 0-88267),* 1169 Logan Ave., Elgin, IL 60120 (SAN 203-8927) Tel 312-697-4814.

Domesday Bks, *(Domesday Bks.; 0-912195),* P.O. Box 734, Peter Stuyvesant Sta., New York, NY 10009 (SAN 264-6102) Tel 212-254-1004.

Dominica Inst, *(Dominica Institute, The; 0-935959),* 2516 Christie Pl., Owensboro, KY 42301 (SAN 697-2357) Tel 809-449-3346.

Dominion Pr, *(Dominion Pr.; 0-912132),* Div. of The Invisible Ministry, P.O. Box 37, San Marcos, CA 92069-0025 (SAN 203-8935) Tel 619-746-9430.

Dominion Pub, *(Dominion Publishing; 0-913431),* P.O. Box 1293, Parker, CO 80134 (SAN 285-8711) Tel 303-841-2215.

Dominus Vobiscum Pub, *(Dominus Vobiscum Publishing, Inc.; 0-9617076),* P.O. Box 62, Stuart St. P.O., Back Bay Annex, Boston, MA 02117 (SAN 662-622X); 257 Commonwealth Ave., Suite 03, Boston, MA 02116 (SAN 662-6238) Tel 617-262-4400.

Domjan Studio, *(Domjan Studio; 0-933652),* West Lake Rd., Tuxedo Park, NY 10987 (SAN 293-2512) Tel 914-351-4596.

Domus Bks
See Quality Bks IL

Domus Bks *Imprint of* **Quality Bks IL**

Don Bosco Multimedia, *(Don Bosco Multimedia; 0-89944),* Div. of Salesian Society, Inc., 457 North Ave., Box T, New Rochelle, NY 10802 (SAN 213-2613) Tel 914-576-0122. *Imprints:* D Bosco Pubns (Don Bosco Publications); Patron (Patron Books); Salesiana (Salesiana Publishers).

Don Cregier, *(Cregier, Don M.; 0-9614536),* 301 S. 15th St., Murray, KY 42071 (SAN 692-2848); Dist. by: Lorrah & Hitchcock Publishers Inc., 301 S. 15th St., Murray, KY 42071 (SAN 220-7915).

Don Surincik, *(Surincik, Don; 0-9613231),* P.O. Box 127, Andrews Rd. RD 2, Edinburg, PA 16116 (SAN 295-1614).

Donahoe Pubs, *(Donahoe, Edward D., Pubs.; 0-938400),* P.O. Box 22011, Louisville, KY 40222 (SAN 217-0973) Tel 502-423-9638.

Donald Franklin, *(Franklin, Donald; 0-914714),* 7852 Ducor Ave., Canoga Park, CA 91304 (SAN 201-2758) Tel 818-883-4247.

Dong Nam P & C, *(Dong Nam P & C Inc.; 0-914524),* 2946 N. Lincoln Ave., Chicago, IL 60657 (SAN 206-3557) Tel 312-549-4660.

Donnan Pubns, *(Donnan Publications; 0-931299),* P.O. Box 773, Martinez, CA 94553 (SAN 685-1975) Tel 415-229-3581.

Donnell Pub Co, *(Donnell Publishing Co.; 0-9613091),* P.O. Box 5055, Willowick, OH 44094 (SAN 294-734X) Tel 216-944-0318.

Donnelly, *(Donnelly, Mary Louise; 0-939142),* P.O. Box 306, Burke, VA 22015 (SAN 214-0039) Tel 703-250-4967.

†**Donning Co,** *(Donning Co. Pubs.; 0-915442; 0-89865),* Subs. of Walsworth Publishing Co., 5659 Virginia Beach Blvd., Norfolk, VA 23502 (SAN 211-6316) Tel 804-461-8090; Toll free: 800-446-8752; 801 S. Missouri Ave., Marceline, MO 64658 (SAN 661-9940); *CIP. Imprints:* Starblaze (Starblaze); Unilaw (Unilaw).

Donoghue Organ Inc, *(Donoghue Organization, Inc., The; 0-913755),* Box 540, 360 Woodland St., Holliston, MA 01746 (SAN 285-2365).

Doolco Inc, *(Doolco, Inc.; 0-914626),* 11252 Goodnight Ln., Suite 600, Dallas, TX 75229 (SAN 205-6178) Tel 214-241-2326.

Dooryard, *(Dooryard Pr.; 0-937160),* P.O. Box 221, Story, WY 82842 (SAN 216-1230) Tel 307-683-2937.

Dorchester Pub Co, *(Dorchester Publishing Co., Inc.; 0-8439),* 6 E. 39th St., Suite 900, New York, NY 10016 (SAN 264-0090) Tel 212-725-8811; Dist. by: Kable News Co., 777 Third Ave., New York, NY 10017 (SAN 169-5835).

Dorchester Savings
See First Am Bank

Dordt Coll Pr, *(Dordt College Pr.; 0-932914),* 498 Fourth Ave., NE, Sioux Center, IA 51250 (SAN 221-2110) Tel 712-722-6420.

Doris Pubns, *(Doris Pubns.; 0-933865),* P.O. Box 1576, Louisville, KY 40201 (SAN 692-7033) Tel 502-774-3297.

†**Dorison Hse,** *(Dorison Hse. Pubs., Inc.; 0-916752),* 31 St. James Ave., Boston, MA 02116 (SAN 208-3140) Tel 617-426-1715; *CIP.*

Dorje Ling, *(Dorje Ling Pubs.; 0-915880),* P.O. Box 287, Lagunitas, CA 94938 (SAN 208-2144) Tel 415-488-9017.

Dorland Pub Co, *(Dorland, Wayne E., Publishing Co.; 0-9603250),* Box 264, Mendham, NJ 07945 (SAN 213-2451) Tel 201-543-2694.

Dorleac-MacLeish, *(Dorleac-MacLeish; 0-916329),* 5100 Longfellow St., Los Angeles, CA 90042 (SAN 295-7442) Tel 213-255-6730.

Dormac, *(Dormac, Inc.; 0-86575),* P.O. Box 1699, Beaverton, OR 97075 (SAN 209-3502) Tel 503-641-3128; Toll free: 800-547-8032.

Dormant Brain Res, *(Dormant Brain Research & Development Laboratory; 0-938967),* Laughing Coyote Mountain, Box 10, Black Hawk, CO 80422 (SAN 219-7820).

Dormition Pubns, *(Dormition Skete Pubns.; 0-935889),* 29060 County Rd. 185, Buena Vista, CO 81211 (SAN 696-3439) Tel 303-395-6395.

Dorrance, *(Dorrance & Co.; 0-8059),* 828 Lancaster Ave., Bryn Mawr, PA 19010 (SAN 201-3363) Tel 215-527-7880.

Dorset Hse Pub Co, *(Dorset Hse. Publishing Co., Inc.; 0-932633),* 353 W. 12th St., New York, NY 10014 (SAN 687-794X) Tel 212-620-4053; Toll free: 800-342-6657.

Dorset Pr, *(Dorset Pr.; 0-88029),* Subs. of Marboro Bks.; c/o Marboro Bks., 105 Fifth Ave., New York, NY 10003 (SAN 287-6663) Tel 212-924-8395.

Dorset Pub Co, *(Dorset Publishing Co., Inc.; 0-533),* P.O. Box 907, Boulder City, NV 89005 (SAN 689-0555) Tel 702-294-1048.

Dorsey, *(Dorsey Pr., The; 0-256),* Div. of Richard D. Irwin, Inc., 224 S. Michigan Ave., Chicago, IL 60604 (SAN 203-8943) Tel 312-322-8400; Toll free: 800-323-4560; Orders to: Richard D. Irwin, Inc., 1818 Ridge Rd., Homewood, IL 60430 (SAN 661-9959) Tel 312-798-6000.

Dorward Photo, *(Dorward, D. M., Photography; 0-9615729),* Box 1620, Ketchum, ID 83340 (SAN 696-3455) Tel 208-788-2376; 301 Canyon East Fork Rd., Ketchum, ID 83340 (SAN 696-9690).

Dos Pasos Ed, *(Dos Pasos Editores, Inc.; 0-9615403),* P.O. Box 261 UTEP, El Paso, TX 79968 (SAN 696-351X) Tel 915-584-2475.

Dos Tejedoras, *(Dos Tejedoras Fiber Arts Pubns.; 0-932394),* 3036 N. Snelling Ave., St. Paul, MN 55113 (SAN 213-4861) Tel 612-646-7445.

Dots Pubns, *(Dots Pubns.; 0-9605204),* 625 Mahoney Ave., Oakview, CA 93022 (SAN 215-7535) Tel 805-649-3126; Orders to: P.O. Box 563, Ventura, CA 93002 (SAN 661-9967).

Double A, *(Double A Pubns.; 0-9615550),* 18000 Pacific Hwy. S., No. 1105, Seattle, WA 98188 (SAN 696-3617) Tel 206-243-9115.

Double C Inc
See Double C Pub

Double C Pub, *(Double C Publishing; 0-943288; 0-937844),* 1401-G E. Fourth St., Long Beach, CA 90802 (SAN 240-6292) Tel 213-432-0882.

Double Crown, *(Double Crown; 0-935010),* 51995 Hernley Road, Aguanga, CA 92302 (SAN 212-0372) Tel 714-763-5174.

Double Det *Imprint of* **Godine**

Double E Pubs, *(Double E Pubs.; 0-936195),* 277 NE Conifer, No. 12, Corvallis, OR 97330 (SAN 697-1091) Tel 503-753-7085.

Double Eagle, *(Double Eagle Bk. Co.; 0-935781),* 160 Eileen Ln., Orcutt, CA 93455 (SAN 696-7299) Tel 805-937-0241; P.O. Box 2262, Orcutt, CA 93455 (SAN 698-2174).

Double Elephant, *(Double Elephant Press),* Dist. by: Ten Speed Press, P.O. Box 7123, Berkeley, CA 94707 (SAN 202-7674) Tel 415-845-8414.

Double H Pubns, *(Double H Pubns.; 0-9615469),* 2879 E. Valley View, Holladay, UT 84117 (SAN 696-3641) Tel 801-277-1997.

Double Helix, *(Double Helix Press; 0-930578),* 1300 Tigertail Rd., Los Angeles, CA 90049 (SAN 211-0083) Tel 213-472-6452; Toll free: 800-631-3577; Dist. by: International Universities Press, Inc., 59 Boston Post Rd., P.O. Box 1524, Madison, CT 06443-1524 (SAN 202-7186); Dist. by: Penguin Books, 40 W. 23rd St., New York, NY 10010 (SAN 202-5914) Tel 212-807-7300.

Double Lee, *(Double Lee Productions; 0-9607540),* 401 First Ave., New York, NY 10010 (SAN 239-5339).

Double M Pr, *(Double M Pr.; 0-916634),* 16455 Tuba St., Sepulveda, CA 91343 (SAN 213-9510) Tel 818-360-3166.

Double M Pub, *(Double M Publishing Co.; 0-913379),* Rte. 1, Nadia Dr., Joliet, IL 60436 (SAN 285-872X) Tel 815-741-0576; Dist. by: Baker & Taylor Co., Midwest Div., 501 Gladiola Ave., Momence, IL 60954 (SAN 169-2100) Tel 815-472-2444.

Double Page, *(Double Page, Inc.; 0-935711),* c/o AVI Group, 1211 Sixth Ave., 14th Flr., New York, NY 10036 (SAN 696-3676) Tel 212-575-0707P.O. Box 939, Radio City Sta., New York, NY 10101 (SAN 696-5326); Dist. by: Como Sales, Inc., 799 Broadway, New York, NY 10003 (SAN 202-8549).

Double Talk, *(Double Talk; 0-9615839),* P.O. Box 412, Amelia, OH 45102 (SAN 697-0575) Tel 513-753-7117.

Double Trouble Day *Imprint of* **White Hse**

†**Doubleday,** *(Doubleday & Co., Inc.; 0-385),* 245 Park Ave., New York, NY 10017 (SAN 201-0089) Tel 212-953-4561; Toll free: 800-645-6156 (Orders); Toll free: 800-457-7605 (Sales Service); Orders to: 501 Franklin Ave., Garden City, NY 11530 (SAN 281-6083) Tel 516-873-4561; *CIP. Imprints:* Anch (Anchor Books); Anchor Pr (Anchor Press); CCG (College Course Guides); Dial (Dial Press).(Dial Pr.); Dolp (Dolphin Books); Echo (Echo Books); Galilee (Galilee); Image Bks (Image Books); Made (Made Simple Books); NLB (Lyons, Nick, Books); Quantum Pr (Quantum Press); Virago (Virago); Waymark (Waymark Books).(Waymark Bks.); Windfall (Windfall); Zenith (Zenith Books); Zephyr (Zephyr); Zephyr-BFYR (Zephyr-BFYR).

DoubLeo Pubns, *(DoubLeo Pubns.; 0-936560),* 227 E. 11th St., New York, NY 10003 (SAN 214-0047) Tel 212-473-2739.

Doug Butler, *(Butler, Doug; 0-916992),* P.O. Box 370, Maryville, MO 64468 (SAN 206-3999) Tel 816-582-3202.

Douglas Cty Planning, *(Douglas County Planning Dept.; 0-9616574),* Courthouse Annex No. 2, 205 SE Jackson St., Roseburg, OR 97470 (SAN 661-1109) Tel 503-440-4289.

Douglass Pubs, *(Douglass Pubs., Inc.; 0-935392),* P.O. Box 3270, Alexandria, VA 22302 (SAN 211-7037) Tel 703-998-6948.

Dove *Imprint of* **Macmillan**

Dove Ecclesiastical, *(Dove Ecclesiastical Ministries; 0-9611978),* 25974 S. River Rd., Mount Clemons, MI 48045 (SAN 286-7753) Tel 313-468-7038.

Dove Pubns, *(Dove Pubns.; 0-917123),* P.O. Box 33, Cass City, MI 48726 (SAN 655-8119) Tel 517-872-4581.

Dove Sys, *(Dove Systems),* 1199 4th St., Los Osos, CA 93402 (SAN 683-2482).

Dovebks, *(Dovebooks; 0-9613450),* 3740 Silver Leaf Ct., Marietta, GA 30060 (SAN 657-2553) Tel 404-436-7911; Dist. by: Writers & Books, 740 University, Rochester, NY 14609 (SAN 156-9678).

Dovehaven Pr Ltd, *(Dovehaven Pr., Ltd.),* Box HH, Jackson, WY 83001 (SAN 693-2231) Tel 307-733-8050.

†**Dover,** *(Dover Pubns., Inc.; 0-486),* 180 Varick St., New York, NY 10014; Toll free: 800-223-3130; Orders to: 31 E. Second St., Mineola, NY 11501 (SAN 201-338X) Tel 516-294-7000; *CIP.*

Dovetail, *(Dovetail Pr.; 0-935468),* 250 W. 94th St., New York, NY 10025 (SAN 209-6609) Tel 212-865-9216.

†**Dow Jones,** *(Dow Jones & Co., Inc.; 0-87128),* P.O. Box 300, Princeton, NJ 08549 (SAN 201-8055) Tel 609-452-2000. Formerly known as Dow Jones Bks; *CIP.*

†**Dow Jones-Irwin,** *(Dow Jones-Irwin, Inc.; 0-87094; 0-256; 1-55623),* Div. of Richard D. Irwin, Inc., 1818 Ridge Rd., Homewood, IL 60430 (SAN 220-0236) Tel 312-798-6000; Toll free: 800-323-4566; *CIP.*

Dowling, *(Dowling College Pr.; 0-917428),* Oakdale, NY 11769 (SAN 208-9521) Tel 516-589-6100.

Down East, *(Down East Bks.; 0-89272),* Div. of Down East Enterprise Inc., P.O. Box 679, Camden, ME 04843 (SAN 208-6301) Tel 207-594-9544; Toll free: 800-432-1670 (In ME only); Roxmont, Rte. One, Rockport, ME 04856 (SAN 658-0467).

Down Home Pr, *(Down Home Pr.; 0-937697),* P.O. Box 408, Stony Brook, NY 11790 (SAN 659-3453) Tel 516-689-3221; 2 William Penn Dr., Stony Brook, NY 11790 (SAN 659-3461).

Down the Shore Pub, *(Down the Shore Publishing; 0-9615208),* 72 Maiden Ln., Harvey Cedars, NJ 08008 (SAN 661-082X) Tel 609-494-3346; P.O. Box 353, Harvey Cedars, NJ 08008 (SAN 661-0838).

†**Down There Pr,** *(Down There Pr.; 0-9602324; 0-940208),* P.O. Box 2086, Burlingame, CA 94010 (SAN 212-3312) Tel 415-342-9867; Dist. by: Bookpeople, 2929 Fifth St., Berkeley, CA 94710 (SAN 168-9517); Dist. by: Children's Small Pr. Collection, The, 719 N. Fourth Ave., Ann Arbor, MI 48104 (SAN 200-514X); Dist. by: Distributors, The, 702 S. Michigan, South Bend, IN 46618 (SAN 169-2488) Tel 219-232-8500; Dist. by: Ingram Industries, 347 Reedwood Dr., Nashville, TN 37217 (SAN 169-7978); Dist. by: Inland Bk. Co., P.O. Box 261, 22 Hemingway Ave., East Haven, CT 06512 (SAN 200-4151) Tel 203-467-4257; Dist. by: New Leaf Distributing, The, 1020 White St., SW, Atlanta, GA (SAN 169-1449); *CIP. Imprints:* Yes Pr (Yes Press).

Down to Earth Pubns, *(Down to Earth Pubns.; 0-939301),* 873 Lincoln, St. Paul, MN 55105 (SAN 662-8079) Tel 612-222-6576.

†**Downey Place,** *(Downey Place Publishing Hse., Inc.; 0-910823),* P.O. Box 1352, El Cerrito, CA 94530-1352 (SAN 269-753X) Tel 415-529-1012; *CIP.*

Downtown Bk, *(Downtown Bk. Ctr., Inc.; 0-941010),* 245 SE First St., Suites 236-237, Miami, FL 33131 (SAN 169-1112) Tel 305-377-9941.

Downtown Poets, *(Downtown Poets Co-Op; 0-917402),* c/o Home Planet News, P.O. Box 415, Stuyvesant Sta., New York, NY 10009 (SAN 208-9653) Tel 212-625-4245.

Downtown Res, *(Downtown Research & Development Ctr.; 0-915910),* 1133 Broadway , Suite 1407, New York, NY 10010 (SAN 207-9658) Tel 212-206-7979.

Dowsing Inst, *(Dowsing Institute of America; 0-931740),* 414 Biscayne Dr., Wilmington, NC 28405 (SAN 211-643X).

Doxey, *(Doxey, W. S.),* 550 N. White, Carrollton, GA 30117 (SAN 211-8955).

Dozenal, *(Dozenal Society of America; 0-933789),* Nassau Community College, Math Dept., Garden City, NY 11530 (SAN 224-1145) Tel 516-222-7611; 6 Brancatelli, West Islip, NY 11795 (SAN 693-4870) Tel 516-669-0273.

DP Books, *(DP Bks.; 0-939299),* 7545 Katella, No. 118, Stanton, CA 90680 (SAN 662-796X) Tel 714-761-3496.

Dr Pepper, *(Dr. Pepper Co., The; 0-9607448),* P.O. Box 225086, Dallas, TX 75231 (SAN 239-1996) Tel 214-824-0331.

DRACO, *(DRACO; 0-9617189),* 410 E. Indiana St., Princeton, IN 47670 (SAN 663-2580) Tel 812-386-7142.

Draco Prod Pubns, *(Draco Productions & Pubns.; 0-936121),* 2036 Pauoa Rd., Honolulu, HI 96813 (SAN 697-0664) Tel 808-523-1752; P.O. Box 27373, Honolulu, HI 96827 (SAN 697-0672).

Dracula Pr, *(Dracula Pr.; 0-9611944),* Subs. of Dracula, Unlimited, 29 Washington Sq. W., Penthouse, New York, NY 10011 (SAN 219-4228) Tel 212-533-5018.

Dragon Ent, *(Dragon Enterprises; 0-9606382),* P.O. Box 200, Genoa, NV 89411 (SAN 215-3025) Tel 702-782-2486.

Dragon Ent CA
See Bluebird Pr CA

†**Dragon Gate,** *(Dragon Gate, Inc.; 0-937872),* 6532 Phinney Ave., N., Seattle, WA 98103 (SAN 217-099X) Tel 206-783-8387; Orders to: 508 Lincoln St., Pt. Townsend, WA 98368 (SAN 697-7073) Tel 206-385-5848; *CIP.*

Dragon Tree, *(Dragon Tree Pr., The; 0-940918),* 1310 College Ave., Suite 1102, Boulder, CO 80302 (SAN 217-3557) Tel 303-444-7926.

Dragonlord Pr, *(Dragonlord Pr.; 0-9614201),* 311 MsCalley St., Chapel Hill, NC 27514 (SAN 687-1054) Tel 919-781-8580.

Dragon's Lair, *(Dragon's Lair; 0-910987),* P.O. Box 14197, San Francisco, CA 94114-0917 (SAN 264-0104) Tel 415-921-7054.

Dragons Teeth, *(Dragons Teeth Pr.; 0-934218),* El Dorado National Forest, Georgetown, CA 95634 (SAN 201-3398).

Dragonsbreath, *(Dragonsbreath Pr., The; 0-943120),* 10595 Bay Shore Dr., Sister Bay, WI 54234 (SAN 219-3612) Tel 414-854-2742.

Dragonscales & Mane Pub, *(Dragonscales & Mane Publishing; 0-918899),* 151 Chenery St., San Francisco, CA 94131 (SAN 669-974X) Tel 415-821-6846.

Dragonwyck Pub, *(Dragonwyck Publishing, Inc.; 0-9606148),* Burrage Rd., Contoocook, NH 03229 (SAN 281-6113) Tel 603-746-5606; Orders to: P.O. Box 385, Contoocook, NH 03229 (SAN 281-6121).

Drain Enterprise, *(Drain Enterprise, The; 0-930419),* 309 First St., Drain, OR 97435 (SAN 240-902X).

Drake-Hurst Pubns, *(Drake-Hurst Pubns.; 0-9614156),* 4596 Bridlewood Terr., St. Louis, MO 63128 (SAN 686-5356) Tel 314-892-0501.

Drake's Ptg & Pub, *(Drake's Printing & Publishing; 0-912013),* 225 N. Magnolia Ave., Orlando, FL 32801 (SAN 216-1249) Tel 305-841-3491.

Drakes View Publishing, *(Drakes View Publishing; 0-939123),* P.O. Box 438, Inverness, CA 94937 (SAN 663-5016); 245 Drakes View Dr., Inverness, CA 94937 (SAN 663-5024) Tel 415-663-1730; Dist. by: Bookpeople, 2929 Fifth St., Berkeley, CA 94720 (SAN 168-9517).

†**Drama Bk,** *(Drama Bk. Pubs.; 0-910482; 0-89676),* 821 Broadway, New York, NY 10003 (SAN 213-5752) Tel 212-627-2158; *CIP.*

Drama Jazz Hse Inc, *(Drama Jazz Hse., Inc.; 0-915833),* 33 Heritage Ct., Annapolis, MD 21401 (SAN 293-924X) Tel 202-636-7050.

Dramaline Pubns, *(Dramaline Pubns.; 0-9611792),* 10470 Riverside Dr., Suite 201, Toluca Lake, CA 91602 (SAN 285-239X) Tel 818-985-9148; Dist. by: Samuel French, Inc., 45 W. 25th St., New York, NY 10010 (SAN 206-4170) Tel 212-206-8990; Dist. by: Samuel French, Inc., 7625 Sunset Blvd., Hollywood, CA 90046 (SAN 206-6855) Tel 213-876-0570.

Dramatika, *(Dramatika; 0-9604000),* 429 Hope St., Tarpon Springs, FL 33589 (SAN 207-8155).

Dramatists Play, *(Dramatists Play Service, Inc.; 0-8222),* 440 Park Ave. S., New York, NY 10016 (SAN 205-5717) Tel 212-683-8960.

Drame Pr, *(Drame Pr.; 0-9617190),* 2928 W. Washington, Phoenix, AZ 85009 (SAN 663-2599).

Draydel Pr, *(Draydel Pr.; 0-9614112),* 36 W. 56th St., New York, NY 10014 (SAN 685-3048) Tel 212-489-9874.

DRC Graphics Serv, *(DRC Graphics Service; 0-9614887),* P.O. Box 4594, Portland, OR 97208 (SAN 693-2347) Tel 503-244-5026.

Dream Garden, *(Dream Garden Pr.; 0-9604402; 0-942688),* P.O. Box 27076, Salt Lake City, UT 84127 (SAN 217-1007) Tel 801-972-0663; 1042 S. Seventh W., Salt Lake City, UT 84104 (SAN 696-5547).

Dream Res, *(Dream Research; 0-9607172),* P.O. Box 1142, Tacoma, WA 98401 (SAN 239-085X) Tel 206-565-4999; Dist. by: Pacific Pipeline, Inc., 19215 66th Ave. S., Kent, WA 98032 (SAN 208-2128) Tel 206-872-5523; Dist. by: DeVorss & Co., P.O. Box 550, 1046 Princeton Dr., Marina del Rey, CA 90294 (SAN 168-9886) Tel 203-870-7478; Dist. by: New Leaf Distributing, The, 1020 White St., SW, Atlanta, GA 30310 (SAN 169-1449) Tel 404-755-2665.

Dreaming, *(Dreaming Spring Pr., The; 0-9611336),* Div. of The Dreaming Spring Corp., 510 Woodgate Dr., Marietta, GA 30066 (SAN 283-2658) Tel 404-427-1238; Dist. by: DeVorss & Co., P.O. Box 550, 1046 Princeton Dr., Marina del Rey, CA 90294 (SAN 282-6151) Tel 203-870-7478; Dist. by: Starlite Distributors, P.O. Box 20729, Reno, NV 89515 (SAN 200-7789) Tel 702-359-5676.

Dreenan Pr, *(Dreenan Pr., Ltd.; 0-88376),* P.O. Box 385, Croton-on-Hudson, NY 10520 (SAN 201-808X) Tel 914-271-5085.

Drelwood Pubns, *(Drelwood Pubns.; 0-937766),* P.O. Box 10605, Portland, OR 97210 (SAN 215-756X); Orders to: Communication Creativity, P.O. Box 213, Saguache, CO 81149 (SAN 210-3478) Tel 303-655-2504.

DREMEL, *(Dremel; 0-9606512),* Div. of Emerson Electric Co., 4915 21st St., Racine, WI 53406 (SAN 223-1530) Tel 414-554-1390.

Drift Group, *(Drift Group, The; 0-938365),* P.O. Box 5144, Helena, MT 59604 (SAN 661-1117) Tel 406-442-2746.

Drivers License
See Drivers License Guide

Drivers License Guide, *(Drivers License Guide Co.; 0-938964),* 1492 Oddstad Dr., Redwood City, CA 94063 (SAN 215-949X); Toll free: 800-227-8827.

Drollery Pr, *(Drollery Pr.; 0-940920),* 1615 Encinal Ave., Alameda, CA 94501 (SAN 223-1808) Tel 415-521-4087; Dist. by: Publishers Group West, 5855 Beaudry St., Emeryville, CA 94608 (SAN 202-8522) Tel 415-658-3453.

Dropsie Coll, *(Dropsie College; 0-9602686; 0-935135),* 250 N. Highland, Merion, PA 19066 (SAN 223-4602); Dist. by: Eisenbrauns, P.O. Box 275, Winona Lake, IN 46590-0278 (SAN 200-7835) Tel 219-269-2011.

Dropzone Pr, *(Dropzone Pr.; 0-913257),* P.O. Box 882022, San Francisco, CA 94188 (SAN 285-6638) Tel 415-776-7164; Dist. by: Publishers Group West, 5855 Beaudry St., Emeryville, CA 94608 (SAN 202-8522) Tel 415-658-3453.

†**Drug Intell Pubns,** *(Drug Intelligence Pubns.; 0-914768),* 4720 Montgomery Ln. Suite 807, Bethesda, MD 20814 (SAN 201-2804) Tel 301-654-8736; Orders to: 1241 Broadway, Hamilton, IL 62341 (SAN 201-2812) Tel 217-847-2504; *CIP.*

Drug Intl Pubns
See Drug Intell Pubns

Drug Store Mkt, *(Drug Store Market Guide; 0-9606064),* 1739 Horton Ave., Mohegan Lake, NY 10547 (SAN 216-888X) Tel 914-528-7147.

Druid Bks, *(Druid Bks.; 0-912518),* P.O. Box 231, Ephraim, WI 54211 (SAN 210-797X).

Druid Heights, *(Druid Heights Books; 0-9606568),* 685 Camino del Canyon, Muir Woods, Mill Valley, CA 94941 (SAN 206-4693) Tel 415-388-2111.

Drum Assocs, *(Drum Associates; 0-9611024),* Affil. of John Scherer & Assocs., W. 201 Sumner, Spokane, WA 99204 (SAN 277-674X) Tel 509-747-1029.

Drumbeat Imprint of **Longman**

Dry Color Mfrs, *(Dry Color Manufacturers Assn.),* 206 N. Washington St., Suite 202, Alexandria, VA 22314 (SAN 224-683X) Tel 703-684-4044.

Dry Eye Inst, *(Dry Eye Institute; 0-9616938),* P.O. Box 98069, Lubbock, TX 79499 (SAN 661-8235); 301 York Ave., Lubbock, TX 79416 (SAN 661-8243) Tel 806-799-1862.

Dry Ridge, *(Dry Ridge Co.; 0-9613545),* 733 James Ln., Walton, KY 41094 (SAN 669-7801) Tel 606-485-6193.

†**Dryad Pr,** *(Dryad Pr.; 0-931848),* 15 Sherman Ave., Takoma Park, MD 20912 (SAN 206-197X) Tel 301-891-3729; *CIP.*

†**Dryden Pr,** *(Dryden Pr.; 0-8498),* Div. of Holt, Rinehart & Winston, Inc., 901 N. Elm, Hinsdale, IL 60521 (SAN 281-613X) Tel 312-325-2985; Toll free: 800-323-7437; 1 Salt Creek Ln., Hinsdale, IL 60521 (SAN 658-0483); Orders to: CBS College Publishing, 383 Madison Ave., New York, NY 10017 (SAN 281-6148) Tel 212-872-2219; *CIP.*

DT Pubs, *(DT Pubs.; 0-9616069),* P.O. Box 657, Princeton Junction, NJ 08550 (SAN 697-8606) Tel 609-443-4222.

DTM Intl, *(DTM International; 0-9616210),* Box 5, Lake Orion, MI 48035 (SAN 658-5078) Tel 313-693-7300; 1081 Indianwood Rd., Lake Orion, MI 48035 (SAN 658-5086).

Du Ewa, *(Du Ewa; 0-933033),* Box 6300108, Spuyten Duyvil Sta., New York, NY 10463 (SAN 690-0364) Tel 212-796-3070.

Du Ewg
See Du Ewa

Du Sable Mus, *(Du Sable Museum Press),* 740 E. 56th Place, Chicago, IL 60637 (SAN 201-8004) Tel 312-947-0600.

Du Vall Financial, *(Du Vall Pr. Financial Pubns.; 0-931232),* 920 W. Grand River, Williamston, MI 48895 (SAN 212-0380).

Dual Pubns, *(Dual Pubns., Inc.; 0-914041),* 1542 Sunflower Ct. S., Palm Springs, CA 92262 (SAN 287-6493) Tel 619-320-5330.

Duane Shinn, *(Shinn, Duane, Pubns.; 0-912732),* Box 700, Medford, OR 97501 (SAN 204-5931) Tel 503-664-2317.

Dubis Assoc, *(Dubis Assocs., Inc.; 0-942076),* 2043 W. Rock Rd., Perkasie, PA 18944 (SAN 238-4558) Tel 904-756-4937.

DuBose Pub, *(DuBose Publishing; 0-938072),* P.O. Box 924, Atlanta, GA 30301 (SAN 215-7586).

Duck Dist, *(Duck Distributing; 0-9616420),* 11103 Clear Fork, Humble, TX 77338 (SAN 659-1582) Tel 713-454-7294.

Duck Down, *(Duck Down, Pr.; 0-916918),* P.O. Box 1047, Fallon, NV 89406 (SAN 208-502X) Tel 702-423-6643.

Duck Tale Prods, *(Duck Tale Productions; 0-9610374),* P.O. Box 11159, Memphis, TN 38111 (SAN 264-0155) Tel 901-452-8944.

Duende, *(Duende Pr; 0-915008),* 6434 Raymond St, Oakland, CA 94609 (SAN 207-8163).

†**Dufour,** *(Dufour Editions, Inc.; 0-8023),* Box 449, Chester Springs, PA 19425-0449 (SAN 201-341X) Tel 215-458-5005; *CIP.*

Dugdale, *(Dugdale, Kathleen; 0-9600028),* C/O Indiana University Foundation, P.O. Box 500, Bloomington, IN 47402 (SAN 201-3428) Tel 812-335-8311.

Duggan Pubns, *(Duggan & Duggan Pubns.; 0-916989),* P.O. Box 282, New Lenox, IL 60451 (SAN 655-7899) Tel 815-485-9519.

Duir Press, *(Duir Pr.; 0-9602912),* 919 Sutter St., Apt. 9, San Francisco, CA 94109 (SAN 223-5722).

Dujarie Pr, *(Dujarie Pr.; 0-8275),* Columbia Hall, Notre Dame, IN 46556 (SAN 658-6309) Tel 219-283-7133.

†**Duke,** *(Duke Univ. Pr.; 0-8223),* Box 6697 College Sta., Durham, NC 27708 (SAN 201-3436) Tel 919-684-2173; *CIP.*

Duke Pub Co, *(Duke Publishing Co.; 0-9613727),* P.O. Box 210368, San Francisco, CA 94121 (SAN 677-5187) Tel 415-759-0118.

†**Dumbarton Oaks,** *(Dumbarton Oaks; 0-88402),* 1703 32nd St., NW, Washington, DC 20007 (SAN 293-2547) Tel 202-342-3259; Dist. by: Dumbarton Oaks Publishing Service, P.O. Box 4866, Hampden Sta., Baltimore, MD 21211 (SAN 293-2555) Tel 301-338-6954; *CIP.*

Dun, *(Dun & Bradstreet Corp.),* 299 Park Ave., New York, NY 10171 (SAN 287-0134) Tel 212-593-6800; Orders to: 99 Church St., New York, NY 10007 (SAN 287-0142).

Duna Studios, *(Duna Studios, Inc.; 0-942928),* P.O. Box 24051, Minneapolis, MN 55424 (SAN 240-1428) Tel 612-926-5201.

Dunbar Pub, *(Dunbar Publishing Co.; 0-931680),* P.O. Box 13368, Jamaica, NY 11413 (SAN 221-2048).

Duncan & Gladstone, *(Duncan & Gladstone Publishing Co.; 0-9616212),* P.O. Box 50355, Austin, TX 78763 (SAN 698-1852) Tel 512-477-1080; 1209 W. 10th St., Austin, TX 78703 (SAN 658-3008).

Duncan Gun, *(Duncan Gun Shop Inc.; 0-9613502),* 414 Second St., North Wilkesboro, NC 28659 (SAN 683-2490).

Duncan-Holmes, *(Duncan-Holmes Publishing Co.; 0-9609480),* P.O. Box 481, Syracuse, IN 46567 (SAN 269-7750).

Duncliffs Intl, *(Duncliff's International; 0-911663),* 3662 Katella Ave., Los Alamitos, CA 90720 (SAN 264-018X).

Dunconor Bks, *(Dunconor Books; 0-918820),* P.O. Box 106, Crestone, CO 81131 (SAN 208-1776).

Dundee Pub, *(Dundee Publishing; 0-935210),* P.O. Box 202, Dundee, NY 14837 (SAN 213-6848) Tel 301-432-8079.

Dunedin Youth, *(Dunedin Youth Guild Inc.; 0-9613858),* P.O. Box 1453, Dunedin, FL 34296-1453 (SAN 683-2504) Tel 813-734-0394.

Dunes, *(Dunes Enterprises; 0-9613419),* P.O. Box 601, Beverly Shores, IN 46301 (SAN 207-0146) Tel 219-872-8077.

Dunk Rock *Imprint of* **Four Quarters**

†**Dunlap Soc,** *(Dunlap Society; 0-89481),* Lake Champlain Rd., Essex, NY 12936 (SAN 281-6156) Tel 518-963-7373; Orders to: Princeton Univ. Pr., 41 Williams St., Princeton, NJ 07302 (SAN 281-6164) Tel 609-452-4879; *CIP.*

Dun's Mktg, *(Dun's Marketing Services; 0-918257),* 49 Old Bloomfield Ave., Mountain Lakes, NJ 07046 (SAN 226-5508) Tel 201-299-0181; Toll free: 800-526-0651; 3 Century Dr., Parsippany, NJ 07054 (SAN 661-9975) Tel 201-455-0900.

Dunsmuir Centennial, *(Dunsmuir Centennial Committee; 0-9614838),* P.O. Box 605, Dunsmuir, CA 96025 (SAN 693-0212) Tel 916-235-2144.

Dunstan Pr, *(Dunstan Pr.; 0-930995),* 30 Linden St., Rockland, ME 04841 (SAN 678-8920) Tel 207-596-0064.

Dunwoody Pr, *(Dunwoody Pr.; 0-931745),* Div. of MRM, Language Research Ctr., Inc., P.O. Box 1825, Silver Spring, MD 20902 (SAN 683-5309) Tel 301-946-7006.

Dunwoody Pubs, *(Dunwoody Pubs.; 0-9616895),* Mt. Vernon Rd., Dunwoody, GA 30338 (SAN 661-3403) Tel 404-425-9112.

DUO *Imprint of* **Unipub**

Duobooks, *(Duobooks, Inc.; 0-918394),* 154 W. 57th St., New York, NY 10019 (SAN 210-0703) Tel 212-757-4438; Orders to: 300 Fairfield Rd., Fairfield, NJ 07006 (SAN 210-0711).

Dupont & Disend, *(Dupont & Disend; 0-9614927),* 2137 Mt. Vernon Rd., Atlanta, GA 30338 (SAN 693-4005) Tel 404-395-7483.

†**Duquesne,** *(Duquesne Univ. Pr.; 0-8207),* 600 Forbes Ave., Pittsburgh, PA 15282 (SAN 658-0491) Tel 412-434-6610; Toll free: 800-221-3845; Dist. by: Humanities Pr. International, Inc., 171 First Ave., Atlantic Highlands, NJ 07716-1289 (SAN 201-9272) Tel 201-872-1441; *CIP.*

Duquesne Pub, *(Duquesne Publishing Co.; 0-89653),* P.O. Box 222, West Brookfield, MA 01585 (SAN 211-1233) Tel 617-867-9341.

Durand Intl, *(Durand International; 0-9604056),* P.O. Box 925, Lynwood, CA 90262 (SAN 214-1884).

Durant Pub, *(Durant Publishing Co.; 0-9606128),* 1208 Tatum Dr., Alexandria, VA 22307 (SAN 217-488X) Tel 703-765-4311.

Durbin Assoc, *(Durbin Assocs.; 0-936786),* 3711 Southwood Dr., Easton, PA 18042 (SAN 215-0697).

Durrell, *(Durrell Pubns., Inc.; 0-911764),* P.O. Box 743, Kennebunkport, ME 04046 (SAN 201-3452) Tel 207-985-3904.

Dushkin Pub, *(Dushkin Publishing Group, Inc.; 0-87967),* Sluice Dock, Guilford, CT 06437 (SAN 201-3460) Tel 203-453-4351; Toll free: 800-243-6532.

†**Dustbooks,** *(Dustbooks; 0-913218; 0-916685),* P.O. Box 100, Paradise, CA 95969 (SAN 204-1871) Tel 916-877-6110; *CIP.*

Dustin Pubns, *(Dustin Pubns.; 0-9614622),* 935 W. Mountain St., Glendale, CA 91202 (SAN 679-1840) Tel 818-242-7000.

Dutch Fork Pr, *(Dutch Fork Press; 0-9611610),* P.O. Box 21766-A, Columbia, SC 29221 (SAN 285-2640) Tel 803-772-6919.

†**Dutton,** *(Dutton, E. P.; 0-525),* 2 Park Ave., New York, NY 10016 (SAN 201-0070) Tel 212-725-1818; Toll free: 800-221-4676; *CIP.* Imprints: Elsevier-Phaidon (Elsevier-Phaidon); Gingerbread (Gingerbread House.); Hawthorn (Hawthorn Books).(Hawthorn Bks.); Pub. by Phaidon (Phaidon); Windmill (Windmill Books).(Windmill Bks.).

Duval Bibb Pub, *(Duval-Bibb Publishing Co.; 0-937713),* P.O. Box 23704, Tampa, FL 33623 (SAN 659-3119) Tel 813-870-1970; 200 N. Westshore Blvd., Tampa, FL 33609 (SAN 659-3127).

Duverus Pub, *(Duverus Publishing Corp.; 0-918700),* P.O. Box 107, Seligman, MO 65745 (SAN 209-1305) Tel 417-662-3690.

Duxbury Pr *Imprint of* **PWS Pubs**

Dvorak Intl, *(Dvorak International Federation; 0-9615788),* 11 Pearl St., Brandon, VT 05733 (SAN 696-7310) Tel 802-247-6020.

Dvorion Bks, *(Dvorion Bks.; 0-9611328),* 508 Fifth Ave., Bethlehem, PA 18018 (SAN 282-888X) Tel 215-691-6318.

Dwapara, *(Dwapara Herald Pubs., Inc.; 0-917952),* P.O. Box 429, Marble Hill, MO 63764 (SAN 209-5513) Tel 314-238-4273.

Dyco Inc, *(Dyco, Inc.; 0-937224),* 6702 E. Cactus Rd., Scottsdale, AZ 85254 (SAN 216-1257) Tel 602-948-4784.

Dynabyte Books, *(Dynabyte Bks.; 0-9610220),* 281 Morning Sun Ave., Mill Valley, CA 94941 (SAN 264-0198) Tel 415-381-9108.

Dynamic Comm, *(Dynamic Communications; 0-9613917),* 1001 Slayton Ave., Grand Haven, MI 49417 (SAN 683-2083) Tel 616-842-8466.

Dynamic Graph, *(Dynamic Graphics, Inc.; 0-939437),* 6000 N. Forest Park Dr., Peoria, IL 61614 (SAN 663-3463) Tel 309-688-8800.

Dynamic Info, *(Dynamic Information Publishing; 0-941286),* 8311 Greeley Blvd., Springfield, VA 22152 (SAN 240-091X).

Dynamic Ink Pub, *(Dynamic Ink Publishing, Co.; 0-934089),* 8900 Keystone Crossing, No. 680 Tower, Indianapolis, IN 46240 (SAN 693-0239) Tel 317-841-7884.

Dynamic Pubns, *(Dynamic Pubns., Inc.; 0-915569),* 901 Bonifant Rd., Silver Spring, MD 20904 (SAN 291-1418) Tel 301-236-6800; Toll free: 800-255-1777.

Dynamic Reflections, *(Dynamic Reflections; 0-9616971),* P.O. Box 881, East Brunswick, NJ 08816 (SAN 661-8219); 24 Colonial Dr., New Brunswick, NJ 08816 (SAN 661-8227) Tel 201-254-0415.

Dynamic Teaching, *(Dynamic Teaching Co.; 0-937899),* 2247 Palmwood Ct., Rancho Cordova, CA 95670 (SAN 659-4425) Tel 916-638-1136.

Dynamics Chr Liv, *(Dynamics of Christian Living Inc.; 0-940386),* Box 1053, Akron, OH 44309 (SAN 219-7839).

Dynamis Corp, *(Dynamis Corp.; 0-936173),* P.O. Box 1900, Ansonia Station, NY 10023 (SAN 697-0486) Tel 914-234-9217.

Dynamo
See **Dynamo Inc**

†**Dynamo Inc,** *(Dynamo, Inc.; 0-936294; 0-913659),* P.O. Box 173, Wheaton, IL 60189 (SAN 214-0675) Tel 312-665-0060; *CIP.*

Dynasty Pub, *(Dynasty Publishing; 0-936541),* 1188 Bishop St., Suite 3011, Honolulu, HI 96813 (SAN 697-8614) Tel 808-527-4995.

D'Zign Land Survey Dev, *(D'Zign Land Survey & Development; 0-9616846),* 747 Geary St., No. 203, San Francisco, CA 94109 (SAN 661-1710) Tel 415-775-2275.

E A Brown Co, *(Brown, Arthur E., Co.; 0-912579),* 1702 Oak Knoll Dr., Alexandria, MN 56308 (SAN 282-7581) Tel 612-762-8847.

E A Burtt, *(Burtt, E. A.; 0-9616132),* 227 Willard Way, Ithaca, NY 14850 (SAN 699-8429) Tel 607-273-5421.

E A Lippa, *(Lippa Ph.D., M.D., Erik A.; 0-9607980),* 1045 Stevens Dr., Fort Washington, PA 19034 (SAN 238-5481) Tel 215-628-8003.

E A Martin, *(Martin, Edward A.),* 550 North Ave., Grand Junction, CO 81501 (SAN 210-6108) Tel 303-243-1538.

E A Mittman, *(Mittman, Edward A., & Associates; 0-942940),* 311 Ruby, Balboa Island, CA 92662 (SAN 238-8200) Tel 714-673-0188.

E A Poe Soc
See **Poe Soc Baltimore**

†**E A Seemann,** *(Seemann, E. A., Publishing, Inc.; 0-912458; 0-89530),* P.O. Box K, Miami, FL 33156 (SAN 201-3495) Tel 305-233-5852; *CIP.*

E A Zimmer, *(Zimmer, Elizabeth A.; 0-9615968),* 355 E. Woodward Ave., Roger City, MI 49779 (SAN 697-3124).

E Adams, *(Adams, Earl; 0-9612748),* P.O. Box 5145, Vienna, WV 26105 (SAN 289-7172); Dist. by: Gambler's Bk. Club, 630 S. 11th St., P.O. Box 4115, Las Vegas, NV 89127 (SAN 203-414X) Tel 702-382-7555.

E & C Bks, *(E&C Bks.; 0-935126),* 20 Atwater Pl., Massapequa, NY 11758 (SAN 213-8433).

†**E & E Enterprises,** *(E&E Enterprises; 0-917954),* 1203 Pomelo Ct., Longwood, FL 32779 (SAN 208-3906) Tel 305-862-2823; *CIP.*

E & P Enter, *(E & P Enterprises; 0-9614095),* P.O. Box 2613, Lawton, OK 73502 (SAN 685-9895) Tel 512-224-4431.

E & S Brickel, *(Brickel, Estelle D. & Stephen B.; 0-9609844),* c/o Brickel Associates, Inc., 515 Madison Ave., New York, NY 10022 (SAN 284-9836).

E Arnold, *(Arnold, Edward, Pubs., Ltd.; 0-7131),* 3 E. Read St., Baltimore, MD 21202 (SAN 263-9203) Tel 301-539-1529; Toll free: 800-638-7511; York County Industrial Pk., Connolly Rd., Emigsville, PA 17318 (SAN 200-6367).

E B Enterprise, *(E & B Enterprise; 0-9616364),* Rte. 2, Box 128-B, Hempstead, TX 77445 (SAN 659-1590) Tel 409-826-6303.

E B Grandin, *(Grandin, E. B., Bk. Co., Inc.; 0-910523),* 148 N. 100 W., Provo, UT 84601 (SAN 260-1931) Tel 801-224-6706.

E Torres & Sons, *(Torres, Eliseo, & Sons; 0-88303)*, Box 2, Eastchester, NY 10709 (SAN 207-0235).

E Urquhart, *(Urquhart, Edward F.; 0-9611618)*, Box 75092, Northgate Sta., Seattle, WA 98125 (SAN 284-902X) Tel 206-523-3200.

E V Salitore, *(Salitore, Edward V., & Evelyn D.)*, P.O. Box 500, Temecula, CA 92390 (SAN 201-2847) Tel 714-676-6355.

E V White, *(White, Eugene V.; 0-9602034)*, 1 W. Main St., Berryville, VA 22611-0286 (SAN 212-5838) Tel 703-955-2280.

E W Beitzel
   See E W Beitzell

E W Beitzell, *(Beitzell, Edwin W.; 0-9604502)*, P.O. Box 107, Abell, MD 20606 (SAN 204-4374) Tel 301-769-3279; Dist. by: St. Mary's County Historical Society, P.O. Box 212, Leonardtown, MD 20650 (SAN 200-545X) Tel 301-475-2467.

E W Bragg, *(Bragg, Emma White, Ph. D.; 0-9611930)*, 707 Ringgold Dr., Nashville, TN 37207 (SAN 286-0732) Tel 615-227-8923.

E W Center HI
   See EW Ctr HI

E-W Cultural Ctr, *(East-West Cultural Ctr.; 0-930736)*, 2865 W. Ninth St., Los Angeles, CA 90006 (SAN 211-0121) Tel 213-480-8325.

E W Jameson Jr, *(Jameson, E. W., Jr.; 0-9606576)*, 13 Oakside, Davis, CA 95616 (SAN 207-5148) Tel 916-758-5704.

E-W Pub Co, *(East/West Publishing Co.; 0-934788)*, 838 Grant Ave., Suite 302, San Francisco, CA 94108 (SAN 215-8574) Tel 415-781-3194.

E W Russell, *(Russell, E. W., Publications; 0-918467)*, 2305 Bunker Ave., El Monte, CA 91732 (SAN 657-6125) Tel 818-579-7031.

E Washington, *(Washington, Eliza; 0-939354)*, 614 Wilshire Ave., Waterloo, IA 50701 (SAN 216-4957) Tel 319-234-1460.

E Wegeleben, *(Wegeleben, Eilene, Enterprises; 0-9616861)*, P.O. Box 58154, Renton, WA 98058 (SAN 661-6054) Tel 206-255-7755.

E Windsor, *(East Windsor Historical Society, Inc.; 0-910506)*, P.O. Box 232, East Windsor, CT 06088 (SAN 218-7116).

E Wolfe Pubns, *(Wolfe, Ernest, Pubns.; 0-9603660)*, 1655 Sawtelle Blvd., Los Angeles, CA 90025 (SAN 213-6481) Tel 213-478-2960.

E Y Anderson, *(Anderson, Elizabeth Y.; 0-9614002)*, 8302 Stevens Rd., Thurmont, MD 21788 (SAN 694-5333).

E-Z Learning, *(E-Z Learning Methods; 0-931924)*, P.O. Box 2582, Pomona, CA 91766 (SAN 212-3495) Tel 714-622-6835.

EA Enas, *(Enas, Enas A.; 0-9616232)*, 1935 Green Trails Dr., Lisle, IL 60532 (SAN 658-5752) Tel 312-961-0279.

EA Lippa
   See E A Lippa

Eades Pub, *(Eades Publishing Co.; 0-9615892)*, 126 Lummi, LaConner, WA 98257 (SAN 697-0915) Tel 206-466-3472.

EAF NH, *(Environmental Action Foundation, Inc)*, Church Hill, Harrisville, NH 03450 (SAN 232-7635).

Eagle Bank Pr, *(Eagle Bank Pr.; 0-937501)*, Div. of Greentree Pictures, Jan Del, Box 63030, Bronx, NY 10463-9992 (SAN 659-1663) Tel 212-796-5792; 4705 Henry Hudson Pkwy., No. 2K, Riverdale, NY 10471 (SAN 659-1671).

Eagle Bks, *(Eagle Bks.; 0-910971)*, 1900 W. B St., Joplin, MO 64801 (SAN 263-2160).

Eagle Comm, *(Eagle Communications; 0-9605462)*, 340 W. Main St., Missoula, MT 59806 (SAN 216-1303).

Eagle Foun, *(Eagle Foundation, The)*, Box 155, Apple River, IL 61001 (SAN 225-1736) Tel 815-594-2259; 300 E. Hickory, Apple River, IL 61001 (SAN 669-070X).

Eagle Peak Pub, *(Eagle Peak Publishing Co.; 0-9611102)*, 15703 Vista Vicente Dr., Ramona, CA 92065 (SAN 282-8634) Tel 619-789-4177.

Eagle Pr CA, *(Eagle Pr.; 0-9615068)*, 3315 Sacramento St., No 427, San Francisco, CA 94115 (SAN 693-9414) Tel 415-591-6815.

Eagle Pub, *(Eagle Publishing Co.; 0-941624)*, 7283 Kolb Pl., Dublin, CA 94568 (SAN 239-2011) Tel 415-828-1350.

Eagle Valley
   See Eagle Foun

Eaglenest Pub, *(Eaglenest Publishing Co.; 0-9616392)*, 2120 Crestmoor Rd., Suite 398, Nashville, TN 37215 (SAN 659-171X) Tel 615-385-0101.

Eagles Five, *(Eagles 5, The; 0-9616745)*, 45-057 Waikalualoko Loop, Kaneohe, HI 96744 (SAN 661-2202) Tel 808-263-5182.

†Eagles View, *(Eagles View Publishing; 0-943604)*, Subs. of Eagle Feather Trading Post, Inc., 706 W. Riverdale Rd., Ogden, UT 84405 (SAN 240-6330) Tel 801-393-3991; CIP.

†Eakin Pubns, *(Eakin Pubns., Inc.; 0-89015)*, P.O. Box 23066, Austin, TX 78735 (SAN 207-3633) Tel 512-288-1771; CIP.

†Eakins, *(Eakins Pr. Foundation; 0-87130)*, 5 W. 73rd St., New York, NY 10023 (SAN 201-3541) Tel 212-496-2255; CIP.

Ear-Lit Imprint of Pierce Ellis Ent

Ear Say, *(Ear Say Bks.; 0-9613871)*, 29-06210 St., Bayside, NY 11360 (SAN 656-8874); Dist. by: Ear-Say, Main P.O. Box 299, Purchase, NY 10577 (SAN 685-1886) Tel 914-342-0234.

Eardley Pubns, *(Eardley Pubns.; 0-937630)*, P.O. Box 281, Rochelle Park, NJ 07662 (SAN 215-6377) Tel 201-791-5014.

Earendil Pr, *(Earendil Pr.; 0-914577)*, 1958 Manzanita, Oakland, CA 94611 (SAN 289-2235) Tel 415-339-1352.

Earhart Pr, *(Earhart Pr.; 0-937061)*, 424 Hilldale, Ann Arbor, MI 48105 (SAN 658-5744) Tel 313-665-9261.

Earl Ent, *(Earl Enterprises; 0-9602504)*, P.O. Box 1254, 7400 Cutting Blvd., El Cerrito, CA 94530 (SAN 223-4645).

Earle Herbarium
   See Desert Botanical

†Early Am Indus, *(Early American Industries Assn., Inc.; 0-943196)*, P.O. Box 2128, Empire State Plaza, Albany, NY 12220-0128 (SAN 669-0718) Tel 518-439-2215; CIP.

Early Educators, *(Early Educators Pr.; 0-9604390)*, P.O. Box 1177, Lake Alfred, FL 33850 (SAN 216-2407) Tel 813-956-1569; Dist. by: Gryphon Hse., Inc., 3706 Otis St., P.O.Box 275, Mt. Rainier, MD 20712 (SAN 169-3190) Tel 301-779-6200.

Early Learn Assoc, *(Early Learning Assocs., Inc.; 0-933373)*, 25118 35th Ave., S, Kent, WA 98032 (SAN 691-6732) Tel 206-839-3156.

Early Stages, *(Early Stages Press, Inc.; 0-915786)*, P.O. Box 31463, San Francisco, CA 94131 (SAN 209-0155).

Early Winters, *(Early Winters Press; 0-941984)*, 110 Prefontaine S., Seattle, WA 98104 (SAN 238-0110).

Earnest Pubns, *(Earnest Pubns.; 0-9616789)*, P.O. Box 1302, Chicago Heights, IL 60411 (SAN 661-2210); 161 Kathleen Ln., Chicago Heights, IL 60411 (SAN 661-2229) Tel 312-756-7739.

Earpacker Pr, *(Earpacker Press; 0-9611304)*, P.O. Box 5029, Philadelphia, PA 19111 (SAN 277-6766).

Earth Basics, *(Earth Basics Pr.; 0-910361)*, P.O. Box 1021, Milpitas, CA 95035 (SAN 260-0463) Tel 408-945-9134.

Earth First, *(Earth First!; 0-933285)*, P.O. Box 5871, Tucson, AZ 85703 (SAN 692-3585) Tel 602-744-0623.

Earth Heart, *(Earth Heart; 0-934747)*, 30 Manana Way, Point Reyes Station, CA 94956 (SAN 694-1966) Tel 415-663-8010; P.O. Box 1027, Point Reyes Station, CA 94956 (SAN 658-2818); Dist. by: Bookpeople, 2929 Fifth St., Berkeley, CA 94710 (SAN 168-9517) Tel 415-549-3030.

Earth Sci Assocs, *(Earth Science Assocs.; 0-9616753)*, 6321 Cate Rd., Powell, TN 37849 (SAN 661-2245) Tel 615-947-9698.

Earth Science
   See R M Pearl Bks

Earth-Song, *(Earth-Song Pr.; 0-9605170)*, 202 Hartnell Pl., Sacramento, CA 95825 (SAN 220-0473) Tel 916-927-6863.

Earth Space, *(Earth-Space Innovations)*, P.O. Box 43, Van Etten, NY 14889 (SAN 241-3779).

†Earth View, *(Earth View, Inc; 0-932898)*, 6514 18th Ave., NE, Seattle, WA 98115 (SAN 213-0491) Tel 206-527-3168; CIP.

Earthlight, *(Earthlight Pubs.; 0-935128)*, 5539 Jackson, Kansas City, MO 64130 (SAN 213-3059).

Earthquake Eng, *(Earthquake Engineering Research Ctr.; 0-943198)*, 6431 Fairmount Ave., Suite 7, El Cerrito, CA 94530 (SAN 224-117X) Tel 415-848-0972.

Earthquake Ready, *(Earthquake Ready Now; 0-9615360)*, P.O. Box 7360, Santa Cruz, CA 95061 (SAN 695-2631) Tel 408-458-1966.

Earthstewards Pubns, *(Earthstewards Publications)*, Box 873, Monte Rio, CA 95462 (SAN 240-1436).

†Earthview Press, *(Earthview Pr.; 0-930705)*, 1818 Samos Cir., Lafayette, CO 80026 (SAN 677-2072) Tel 303-666-8130; Orders to: P.O. Box 11036, Boulder, CO 80301 (SAN 662-2526); CIP.

Earthwise Pubns, *(Earthwise Pubns.; 0-933494)*, P.O. Box 680-536, Miami, FL 33168 (SAN 223-7407) Tel 305-688-8558.

Earthwise Pubs
   See Earthwise Pubns

EarthZ, *(EarthZ; 0-9614271)*, 1575 S. Lincoln St., Kent, OH 44240 (SAN 687-1593) Tel 216-678-6108.

Easi-Bild, *(Easi-Bild Directions Simplified, Inc.; 0-87733)*, 529 N. State Rd., P.O. Box 215, Briarcliff Manor, NY 10510 (SAN 201-3304) Tel 914-941-6600.

East Brother, *(East Brother Light Station, Inc.; 0-9614254)*, 117 Park Place, Point Richmond, CA 94801 (SAN 686-6751).

East Dennis, *(East Dennis Publishing Co.; 0-87299)*, P.O. Box 555, East Dennis, MA 02641 (SAN 210-8011) Tel 617-385-2000.

East Eagle, *(East Eagle Press; 0-9605738)*, P.O. Box 812, Huron, SD 57350 (SAN 216-3705) Tel 605-352-5875.

East Eur Quarterly, *(East European Quarterly; 0-914710; 0-88033)*, Univ. of Colorado, Boulder, CO 80302 (SAN 661-9983); Dist. by: Columbia Univ. Pr., 136 S. Braodway, Irvington-on-Hudson, NY 10533 (SAN 212-2472) Tel 914-591-9111.

East Linden Pr, *(East Linden Pr.; 0-9614902)*, 905 Linden Ave., Boulder, CO 80302 (SAN 693-3262) Tel 303-444-0879.

East Oregonian, *(East Oregonian; 0-934880)*, P.O. Box 1089, Pendleton, OR 97801 (SAN 201-2863) Tel 503-276-2211.

East Ridge Pr, *(East Ridge Press; 0-914896)*, 126 Ridge Rd., Hankins, NY 12741 (SAN 201-2871) Tel 914-887-5161; Dist. by: Ridge Book Service, 161 Ridge Rd., Hankins, NY 12741 (SAN 282-6453).

East River Pub CO, *(East River Publishing Co.; 0-915789)*, P.O. Box 654, Crested Butte, CO 81224 (SAN 293-9274) Tel 303-349-7400.

East Rock Pr, *(East Rock Pr., Ltd.; 0-9615543)*, 150 Edgehill Rd., New Haven, CT 06511 (SAN 696-3471) Tel 203-776-7825.

East School Pr, *(Eastern School Press; 0-912181)*, P.O. Box 684, Talent, OR 97540 (SAN 264-7362) Tel 503-535-1490.

East Wash Univ, *(Eastern Washington Univ. Press; 0-910055)*, Eastern Washington Univ., Cheney, WA 99004 (SAN 241-2977) Tel 509-359-2201.

East West Cult, *(East West Culture Exchange; 0-9601274)*, 5204 N. Leicester Dr., Muncie, IN 47304 (SAN 210-3559) Tel 317-289-3123.

East West Health, *(East West Health Bks.; 0-936184)*, Div. of East West Journal, Inc., 17 Station St., Box 1200, Brookline, MA 02147 (SAN 221-1939) Tel 617-232-1000.

East West Journ
   See East West Health

East West Pr, *(East West Pr.; 0-9606090)*, P.O. Box 4204, Minneapolis, MN 55414 (SAN 216-809X) Tel 612-379-2049.

East-West Pub, *(East-West Publishing, Co.; 0-931955)*, 988 Roslyn, Grosse Pointe, MI 48236 (SAN 686-0362) Tel 313-885-7308; 2413 S. Broadway, Santa Ana, CA 92707 (SAN 662-7692) Tel 714-549-1498.

†East Woods, *(East Woods Pr./Fast & McMillan Pubs.; 0-914788; 0-88742)*, 429 East Blvd., Charlotte, NC 28203 (SAN 212-0127) Tel 704-334-0897; Toll free: 800-438-1242; CIP.

Easter Rehabilitation Inc, *(Easter Seal Rehabilitation Center of Eastern Fairfield County, Inc.; 0-9613209),* Affil. of National Easter Seal Society, 226 Mill Hill Ave., Bridgeport, CT 06610 (SAN 295-7639) Tel 203-366-7551; Dist. by: Dot Gibson Pubns., P.O. Box 117, Waycross, GA 31502 (SAN 200-4143) Tel 912-285-2848; Dist. by: Collection, Inc., The, 2101 Kansas City Rd., Olathe, KS 66061 (SAN 200-6359) Tel 913-764-1811; Dist. by: Baker & Taylor Co., Eastern Div., 50 Kirby Ave., Somerville, NJ 08876 (SAN 169-4901) Tel 201-526-8000.

†**Eastern Acorn,** *(Eastern Acorn Press; 0-915992),* Div. of Eastern National Park & Monument Assn., 339 Walnut St., Philadelphia, PA 19106 (SAN 219-9793) Tel 215-597-7129; *CIP.*

Eastern Bks
See Colony Pub

Eastern CT St Coll Fdn, *(Eastern Connecticut State College Foundation; 0-915884),* P.O. Box 431, Willimantic, CT 06226 (SAN 207-4834) Tel 203-456-2231.

Eastern Mount, *(Eastern Mountain Sports),* 11312 Vose Farm Rd., Peterborough, NH 03458 (SAN 213-3067) Tel 603-924-9571; Dist. by: Appalachian Mountain Club, 5 Joy St., Boston, MA 02108 (SAN 203-4808) Tel 617-523-0636.

Eastern Natl Park
See Eastern Acorn

Eastern Orthodox, *(Eastern Orthodox Bks.; 0-89981),* P.O. Box 302, Willits, CA 95490 (SAN 201-355X).

Eastern Pr, *(Eastern Pr.; 0-939758),* 426 E Sixth St., Bloomington, IN 47402 (SAN 216-3713) Tel 812-336-5865; Orders to: P.O. Box 881, Bloomington, IN 47401 (SAN 661-9991).

†**Eastern Wash,** *(Eastern Washington State Historical Society; 0-910524),* W. 2316 First Ave., Spokane, WA 99204 (SAN 203-8293) Tel 506-456-3931; *CIP.*

Eastham Edns, *(Eastham Editions; 0-915102),* P.O. Box 10, Prospect, NY 13435 (SAN 207-1258) Tel 315-896-6388.

Eastland, *(Eastland Pr.; 0-939616),* P.O. Box 12689, Seattle, WA 98111 (SAN 216-6216) Tel 206-283-7085.

Eastman Kodak, *(Eastman Kodak Co.; 0-87985),* 343 State St., Bldg. 16, 2nd Flr., Dept. 373, Rochester, NY 14650 (SAN 201-3568) Tel 716-724-4254; Toll free: 800-242-7737.

†**Eastman Sch Music,** *(Eastman School of Music Press; 0-9603186),* 26 Gibbs St., Rochester, NY 14604 (SAN 222-3260); *CIP.*

Eastview, *(Eastview Editions, Inc.; 0-89860),* P.O. Box 783, Westfield, NJ 07091 (SAN 169-4952) Tel 201-964-9485.

Eastwest Ctr *Imprint of* **UH Pr**

Eastwood Orem, *(Eastwood Publishing Co.; 0-9617053),* 130 S. Eastwood Dr., Orem, UT 84058 (SAN 662-958X) Tel 801-224-8423. Do not confuse with Eastwood Pub. Co., Denver, CO.

Eastwood Pub Co, *(Eastwood Publishing Co.; 0-9612692),* 2901 Blake St., Denver, CO 80205 (SAN 291-8323) Tel 303-296-1905.

Eastwood Pub UT
See Eastwood Orem

Easy Banana Prods, *(Easy Banana Productions; 0-9613879),* 2000 Gough St., San Francisco, CA 94109 (SAN 681-9788) Tel 415-776-0868.

Easy Read Pub, *(Easy Read Publishing Corp.; 0-937199),* 1522 N. Dixie, West Palm Beach, FL 33401 (SAN 658-7038) Tel 305-588-1612.

Easy St Pubns, *(Easy Street Pubns.; 0-916009),* 12351 Osborne St., No. 13, Pacoima, CA 91331 (SAN 293-9266) Tel 213-899-6770.

Eaton Pub, *(Eaton Publishing; 0-9610904),* P.O. Box 729, Tinley Park, IL 60477 (SAN 265-1319) Tel 312-479-2345.

Eatongude Pr, *(Eatongude Pr.; 0-9614721),* 227 W. 13th St., 4th Fl., New York, NY 10011 (SAN 692-5227) Tel 212-691-9384.

Ebaesay, *(Ebaesay-Namreplican (EBN) Pubns.; 0-9608212),* 210 W. Lemon Ave. No. 22, Monrovia, CA 91016 (SAN 240-3692) Tel 818-358-1763.

Ebe, *(Ebe, John),* 445 Grand St., Brooklyn, NY 11211 (SAN 238-8758) Tel 718-388-7074.

Ebenezer Ctr, *(Ebenezer Ctr. for Aging & Human Development; 0-938846),* Subs. of Ebenezer Society, 2500 Park Ave., Minneapolis, MN 55404 (SAN 240-0162) Tel 612-879-1457.

Eberly Pr, *(Eberly Press; 0-932296),* 430 N. Harrison, East Lansing, MI 48823 (SAN 214-0055) Tel 517-351-7299.

†**EBHA Pr,** *(EBHA Press; 0-935662),* Div. of Economic and Business History Assocs., 5919 Cullen Dr., Lincoln, NE 68506-1433 (SAN 213-6201) Tel 402-488-0684; *CIP.*

Ebonics, *(Ebonics Publishers Internationale; 0-910363),* P.O. Box 36518, Atlanta, GA 30032 (SAN 240-9038) Tel 404-696-6357.

Ebony Pub
See Carver Pub

EBSCO Ind, *(EBSCO Industries, Inc.; 0-913956),* P.O. Box 1943, Birmingham, AL 35201 (SAN 201-3584) Tel 205-991-6600; Toll free: 800-633-6088.

ECA Assoc, *(ECA Assocs.; 0-938818),* P.O. Box 15004, Great Bridge Sta., Chesapeake, VA 23320 (SAN 215-9503) Tel 804-547-5542; P.O. Box 20186, Cathedral Finance Sta., New York, NY 10025 (SAN 215-9511) Tel 212-866-8694.

Eccles Pr, *(Eccles Pr.; 0-9616812),* Newmark's Yacht Ctr., Berth 204, Wilmington, CA 90744 (SAN 658-8247) Tel 213-835-3760.

Ecclesia *Imprint of* **William Carey Lib**

†**Ecco Pr,** *(Ecco Pr.; 0-88001),* 18 W. 30th St., New York, NY 10001 (SAN 202-5795) Tel 212-685-8240; Toll free: 800-223-2584; Dist. by: W. W. Norton & Co., Inc., 500 Fifth Ave, New York, NY 10110 (SAN 202-5795) Tel 212-354-5500; *CIP.*

Echo *Imprint of* **Doubleday**

†**Echo Pub Co,** *(Echo Publishing Co.; 0-916121),* 8865 Laura Ln., Beaumont, TX 77707 (SAN 294-9237) Tel 409-866-0997; *CIP.*

Echo Pubns, *(Echo Pubns., Inc.; 0-940562),* P.O. Box 6548, New Orleans, LA 70174 (SAN 297-1690) Tel 504-348-4050.

Echo Pubs, *(Echo Publishers; 0-912852),* P.O. Box 7130, West Menlo Park, CA 94026 (SAN 201-3592) Tel 415-524-1575; Dist. by: B.Dalton Bookseller, P.O. Box 317, Minneapolis, MN 55440 (SAN 662-7218); Dist. by: SCHOENHOFS foreign books, P.O. Box 182, Cambridge, MA 02138 (SAN 662-7226).

Echo Stage Co, *(Echo Stage Co., Ltd.; 0-9607886),* 250 W. 16th St., Suite 1A, New York, NY 10011 (SAN 239-5347) Tel 212-243-6865.

Echoes & Shadows, *(Echoes and Shadows; 0-942130),* P.O. Box 241, Elm Grove, WI 53122 (SAN 238-0129).

†**Echolight Corp,** *(Echolight Corp., The; 0-931547),* 151 Kentucky Ave., SE, Washington, DC 20003 (SAN 682-1685) Tel 202-546-1220; *CIP.*

Eclectic Pr, *(Eclectic Pr.; 0-9605920),* P.O. Box 984, Ansonia Sta., New York, NY 10023 (SAN 216-6682) Tel 212-874-2867. Publishes poetry exclusively.

Eclectical, *(Eclectical Publishing Co., Inc.; 0-912447),* P.O. Box 7326, New Orleans, LA 70186 (SAN 265-346X) Tel 504-246-5413.

Eclipse Bks, *(Eclipse Bks.; 0-913035),* Div. of Eclipse Enterprises, Inc., P.O. Box 199, Guerneville, CA 95446 (SAN 283-0566).

Eco Images, *(Eco Images; 0-938423),* Box 61413, Virginia Beach, VA 23462 (SAN 661-230X); 4302 Blackwater Rd., Virginia Beach, VA 23451 (SAN 661-2318) Tel 804-421-3929.

Ecofunding, *(Ecofunding Pr.; 0-936529),* 100 E. 85th St., New York, NY 10028 (SAN 697-8274) Tel 212-472-1214.

Econ Info Syst
See Trinet

†**Econ Inst,** *(Economics Institute; 0-88036),* 1030 13th St., Boulder, CO 80302 (SAN 239-0493) Tel 303-492-8419; *CIP.*

Econ Res Ctr, *(Economics Research Center),* 1600 Campus Rd., Occidental College, Los Angeles, CA 90041 (SAN 203-8307).

Econo-Clad Bks-Crawford Pr, *(Crawford Press; 0-88103; 0-8085),* Div. of American Companies, Inc., Box 1777, Topeka, KS 66601 (SAN 240-365X) Tel 913-233-4252; Toll free: 800-255-3502.

Econo Comm, *(Econo Communications; 0-913525),* 412 Edsam Ave., Pitman, NJ 08071 (SAN 285-158X); Dist. by: Baker & Taylor, Eastern Div., 50 Kirby Ave., Somerville, NJ 08876 (SAN 169-4901); Dist. by: Scholarly Bk. Ctr., 3828 Hawthorn Ct., Waukegan, IL 60087 (SAN 169-2259).

Economic Pr
See Economics Pr

Economics Pr, *(Economics Pr., Inc.; 0-910187),* 12 Daniel Rd., Fairfield, NJ 07006 (SAN 204-1774) Tel 201-227-1224; Toll free: 800-526-2554; Toll free: 800-526-1128 (NJ).

Ecotope, *(Ecotope, Inc.; 0-934478),* 2812 E. Madison, Seattle, WA 98112 (SAN 221-1955) Tel 206-322-3753.

ECR Assocs, *(ECR Associates; 0-9600352),* 4832 Park Rd Suite 125, Charlotte, NC 28209 (SAN 201-9752) Tel 704-372-3227.

ECRI, *(ECRI),* 5200 Butler Pike, Plymouth Meeting, PA 19462 (SAN 224-1234) Tel 215-825-6000.

ECS Inc, *(Episcopal Churchwoman of All Saints, Inc.; 0-9606880),* 100 Rex Dr., River Ridge, LA 70123 (SAN 217-3581) Tel 504-737-1416; Orders to: La Bonne Cuisine, P.O. Box 23065, New Orleans, LA 70183 (SAN 662-0795); Dist. by: Publishers Group West, 5855 Beaudry St., Emeryville, CA 94608 (SAN 202-8522) Tel 415-658-3453; Dist. by: Collection, Inc., The, 2101 Kansas City Rd., Olathe, KS 66061 (SAN 200-6359) Tel 913-764-1811.

Ecumenical Phila, *(Ecumenical Pr.; 0-931214),* Temple Univ., 511 Humanities Bldg., Philadelphia, PA 19122 (SAN 222-8211); Dist. by: Hippocrene Bks., 171 Madison Ave., New York, NY 10016 (SAN 213-2060) Tel 718-454-2366.

ED *Imprint of* **Unipub**

Ed Acad, *(Educator's Academy; 0-9607160),* P.O. Box 75, Dayton, OH 45402 (SAN 238-9738) Tel 513-274-1662.

Ed Activities, *(Educational Activities, Inc.; 0-914296; 0-89525),* 1937 Grand Ave., Baldwin, NY 11510 (SAN 207-4400) Tel 516-223-4666; Toll free: 800-645-3739; Orders to: P.O. Box 392, Freeport, NY 11520.

Ed & Training, *(Education & Training Consultants Co.; 0-87657),* Box 2085, Sedona, AZ 86336-2085 (SAN 201-3665) Tel 602-282-3009.

Ed Assocs, *(Education Assocs.; 0-918772),* P.O. Box 8021, Athens, GA 30603 (SAN 210-4180) Tel 404-542-4244.

Ed Assocs KY, *(Education Assocs., Inc.; 0-940428; 1-55549),* 45 Fountain Pl., P.O. Box Y, Frankfort, KY 40602 (SAN 223-0674).

Ed Bk Pubs OK, *(Educational Book Pubs.; 0-932188),* P.O. Box 1219, Guthrie, OK 73044 (SAN 215-8582).

Ed Buryn Photo-Pub
See Ed Buryn Pub

Ed Buryn Pub, *(Buryn, Ed, Pub.; 0-916804),* Box 31123, San Francisco, CA 94131 (SAN 211-3880) Tel 415-824-8938; Dist. by: Bookpeople, 2929 Fifth St., Berkeley, CA 94710 (SAN 168-9517) Tel 415-549-3030; Dist. by: Pacific Pipeline, Inc., 19215 66th Ave., S., Kent, WA 98032 (SAN 208-2128) Tel 206-872-5523; Dist. by: The Distributors, 702 S. Michigan, South Bend, IN 46618 (SAN 169-2488) Tel 219-232-8500; Dist. by: Book Dynamics, 836 Broadway, New York, NY 10003 (SAN 169-5649) Tel 212-254-7798.

Ed Buryn Publ
See Ed Buryn Pub

Ed Comm States, *(Education Commission of the States),* 1860 Lincoln St., Suite 300, Denver, CO 80295 (SAN 224-120X).

Ed Comms Inc
See Educ Comm

Ed Data Res, *(Educational Data Resources; 0-9616851),* P.O. Box 23069, Washington, DC 20026-3069 (SAN 661-3454); 236 33rd St., NE, Washington, DC 20019 (SAN 661-3462) Tel 202-399-6253.

Ed Design Inc, *(Educational Design, Inc.; 0-87694),* 47 W. 13th St., New York, NY 10011 (SAN 204-1588) Tel 212-255-7900; Toll free: 800-221-9372.

Ed Dev Assn, *(Educational Development Association),* P.O. Box 181, Hazel Crest, IL 60429 (SAN 205-6143).

Ed Devel Corp, *(Educational Development Corp.; 0-913332; 0-89403),* 10302 E. 55th Pl., Tulsa, OK 74146 (SAN 204-1626) Tel 918-622-4522; Toll free: 800-331-4418.

Ed Direct, *(Educational Directories Inc.; 0-910536),* P.O. Box 199, Mt. Prospect, IL 60056 (SAN 201-3614) Tel 312-392-1811.

Ed El Gato Tuerto, *(Ediciones El Gato Tuerto; 0-932367),* P.O. Box 210277, San Francisco, CA 94121 (SAN 687-3774); 205 16th Ave., Apt. 6, San Francisco, CA 94118 (SAN 662-2755) Tel 415-752-0473.

†Ed Facilities, *(Educational Facilities Laboratories; 0-88481),* c/o Academy for Educational Development, 680 Fifth Ave., New York, NY 10019 (SAN 210-0185) Tel 212-397-0040; Dist. by: Publishing Center for Cultural Resources, 625 Broadway, New York, NY 10012 (SAN 274-9025) Tel 212-260-2010; *CIP.*

Ed Factors, *(Educational Factors, Inc.; 0-936864),* 1462 Jenvey Ave., P.O. Box 6389, San Jose, CA 95150 (SAN 221-9204).

Ed Francaises, *(Editions Francaises de Louisiana/Louisiana French Editions, Inc.; 0-935085),* P.O. Box 1344, Jennings, LA 70546 (SAN 695-0779) Tel 318-824-7380; 302 E. Nezpique St., Jennings, LA 70546 (SAN 695-0787).

Ed Freedom, *(Education Freedom Foundation),* 20 Parkland, St. Louis, MO 63122 (SAN 225-7955) Tel 314-966-3485.

Ed Graphics Pr, *(Educational Graphics Pr.; 0-916123),* P.O. Box 180476, Austin, TX 78718 (SAN 294-9245) Tel 512-251-9620.

Ed-it Prods, *(Ed-it Productions),* P.O. Box 29527, Oakland, CA 94604-9527 (SAN 669-0408) Tel 415-763-3510; Dist. by: Strawberry Hill Pr., 2594 15th Ave., San Francisco, CA 94127 (SAN 238-8103) Tel 415-664-8112. *Imprints:* Cliffhanger Pr (Cliffhanger Press).

Ed-Lynne Jones, *(Jones, Edward-Lynne, & Assocs.; 0-9602458),* 5517 17th Ave., NE, Seattle, WA 98105 (SAN 263-2195) Tel 206-524-9604.

Ed Media Corp, *(Educational Media Corp.; 0-932796),* P.O. Box 21311, Minneapolis, MN 55421 (SAN 212-4203) Tel 612-636-5098.

Ed Methods *Imprint of* **Longman Finan**

Ed Ministries, *(Educational Ministries, Inc.; 0-940754),* 2861-C Saturn St., Brea, CA 92621 (SAN 219-7316) Tel 714-961-0622; Toll free: 800-221-0910.

Ed News Serv, *(Education News Service; 0-936423),* P.O. Box 1789, Carmichael, CA 95609 (SAN 693-6237) Tel 916-483-6159.

Ed Pr, *(Education Pr., The; 0-915481),* P.O. Box 19532, Greensboro, NC 27419 (SAN 291-1442) Tel 919-292-5903.

Ed Prog, *(Educators Progress Service, Inc.; 0-87708),* 214 Center St., Randolph, WI 53956 (SAN 201-3649) Tel 414-326-3126.

Ed Progress Corp
See Ed Devel Corp

Ed Pubns, *(Educational Pubns.; 0-942930),* P.O. Box 41870, Tuscon, AZ 85717 (SAN 240-3706) Tel 602-791-9690.

Ed Research, *(Educational Research Service),* 1800 N. Kent St., Arlington, VA 22209 (SAN 203-7912) Tel 703-243-2100.

Ed Skills Dallas, *(Educational Skills; 0-9604058),* 9636 Hollow Way, Dallas, TX 75220 (SAN 221-6086).

Ed Solutions, *(Educational Solutions, Inc.; 0-87825),* 95 University Pl., New York, NY 10003-4555 (SAN 205-6186) Tel 212-674-2988.

Ed Sys Pub, *(Education System Pub.; 0-915676; 0-916011),* Terminal Annex, Box 54579, Los Angeles, CA 90054 (SAN 207-4028).

Ed Tamm, *(Tamm, Edward; 0-9616793),* P.O. Box 498, North Amherst, MA 01059 (SAN 661-048X); 83 Spring St., North Amherst, MA 01059 (SAN 661-0498) Tel 413-253-5070.

Ed Tecnicos
See French & Eur

Ed-U Pr, *(Ed-U Pr., Inc.; 0-934978),* P.O. Box 583, Fayetteville, NY 13066 (SAN 221-1866) Tel 315-637-9524.

Ed Venture CA, *(Ed-Venture Films/Bks.; 0-935873),* 1122 Calada St., Los Angeles, CA 90023 (SAN 696-3498) Tel 213-261-1885; Orders to: P.O. Box 23214, Los Angeles, CA 90023-0214 (SAN 696-530X).

Edasi, *(Edasi; 0-9614148),* P.O. Box 286, Lenox Hill Sta., New York, NY 10021 (SAN 686-4295); 221 E. 70th St., New York, NY 10021 (SAN 663-3102).

EDC, *(EDC Publishing; 0-88110),* Div. of Educational Development Corp., 10302 E. 55th Pl., Tulsa, OK 74146 (SAN 226-2134) Tel 918-622-4522; Toll free: 800-331-4418; P.O. Box 470663, Tulsa, OK 74147 (SAN 658-0505); P.O. Box 702253, Tulsa, OK 74170 (SAN 658-0513). *Imprints:* Usborne-Hayes (Usborne-Hayes).

EdCom, *(EdCom-Jean Wiley Huyler Communications; 0-941554),* 922 N. Pearl A-27, Tacoma, WA 98406 (SAN 264-021X) Tel 206-759-1579.

Edelson, *(Edelson, Mary Beth; 0-9604650),* 110 Mercer St., New York, NY 10012 (SAN 215-7594) Tel 212-226-0832.

Edelweiss Pr, *(Edelweiss Pr.; 0-9600874),* 124 Front St., Massapequa Park, NY 11762 (SAN 208-0419) Tel 516-799-1150.

Eden Co
See A Cohen

Eden Games, *(Eden Games, Inc.; 0-937655),* P.O. Box 148, Clackamas, OR 97015 (SAN 659-3518) Tel 503-656-9215.

Eden Hill Pr, *(Eden Hill Pr.; 0-9614355),* P.O. Box 337, Cruz Bay, St. John, VI 00830 (SAN 687-7435) Tel 809-776-6573.

Eden Hill Pub *Imprint of* **Signature Bks**

Eden Med Res
See Eden Pr

Eden Pr, *(Eden Pr.; 0-920792; 0-88831),* Dist. by: Univ. of Toronto Pr., 33 E. Tupper St., Buffalo, NY 14203 (SAN 214-2651) Tel 716-852-0342.

Eden Press, *(Eden Pr./Art Reproductions; 0-939373),* P.O. Box 745, Corona del Mar, CA 92625 (SAN 687-6455) Tel 714-675-1201.

Eden Project Pubs, *(Eden Project, Pubs.; 0-939385),* P.O. Box 1348, Mt. Shasta, CA 96067 (SAN 663-3889); 111 McLoud Ave., No. 2, Mt. Shasta, CA 96067 (SAN 663-3897) Tel 916-926-4322; Dist. by: Bookpeople, 2929 Fifth St., Berkeley, CA 94710 (SAN 168-9517).

Edenite, *(Edenite Society, Inc.; 0-938520),* Rte. 526, Imlaystown, NJ 08526 (SAN 239-9040) Tel 609-259-7517.

Eden's Work, *(Eden's Work; 0-937226),* RFD 1, Box 540A, Franklin, ME 04634 (SAN 219-998X) Tel 207-565-3533.

Edenwood Hse, *(Edenwood Hse.),* P.O. Box 607, Garner, NC 27529 (SAN 263-2179) Tel 919-772-0107.

Eder Pub, *(Eder Publishing; 0-9614252),* 178 Commonwealth Ave., Boston, MA 02116 (SAN 687-1070) Tel 617-262-5367.

Edgemoor, *(Edgemoor Publishing Co.; 0-88204),* 721 Durham Dr., Houston, TX 77007 (SAN 201-3681) Tel 713-861-3451; Orders to: P.O. Box 13612, Houston, TX 77019 (SAN 201-369X).

Edgepress, *(Edgepr.; 0-918528),* P.O. Box 69, Point Reyes, CA 94956 (SAN 209-6625) Tel 415-663-1511.

Edgerton, *(Edgerton, William H.; 0-9601172),* Box 88, Darien, CT 06820 (SAN 210-0738) Tel 203-655-9510.

Edgewater, *(Edgewater Bk. Distributors; 0-937424),* P.O. Box 40238, Cleveland, OH 44140 (SAN 215-3033) Tel 216-835-3108.

Edgewood, *(Edgewood Pr.; 0-9602472),* 2865 East Rock Rd., Clare, MI 48617 (SAN 212-6559).

Edgewood Pubs, *(Edgewood Pubs.; 0-9616151),* 234 Park St., New Haven, CT 06511 (SAN 699-9190) Tel 203-865-0661.

Edgeworth Pub, *(Edgeworth Publishing Co., Ltd.; 0-939191),* 226-10 137th Ave., Laurelton, NY 11413 (SAN 662-9040) Tel 718-978-1782.

Edging Ahead Pr, *(Edging Ahead Pr.; 0-9615488),* P.O. Box 19071, San Diego, CA 92119 (SAN 696-3536) Tel 619-448-2206.

Edicion Kerigma, *(Ediciones Kerigma; 0-938127),* P.O. Box 557428, Miami, FL 33255 (SAN 661-2377); 4467 SW 75th Ave., Miami, FL 33155 (SAN 661-2385) Tel 305-261-5200.

Ediciones, *(Ediciones Universal; 0-89729),* 3090 SW Eighth St., Miami, FL 33135 (SAN 207-2203) Tel 305-642-3355; P. O. Box 450353, Shenandoah Sta., Miami, FL 33145 (SAN 658-0548).

Ediciones Arauco, *(Ediciones Arauco),* P.O. Box 5855, Collegeville, MN 56321 (SAN 659-1973) Tel 612-363-2748.

Ediciones El
See Ed El Gato Tuerto

Ediciones Huracan, *(Ediciones Huracan, Inc.; 0-940238),* Avenida Gonzalez 1002, Rio Piedras, PR 00925 (SAN 217-5134) Tel 809-763-7407.

Ediciones Norte, *(Ediciones Del Norte; 0-910061),* P.O. Box A130, Hanover, NH 03755 (SAN 241-2993) Tel 603-795-2433; 13 Dartmouth College Hwy., Lyme, NH 03768 (SAN 658-053X).

Ediciones Viento y Marea, *(Ediciones Contra Viento y Marea; 0-931852),* Box M-228, Hoboken, NJ 07030 (SAN 222-8157).

Edins Hispamerica, *(Ediciones Hispamerica; 0-935318),* 5 Pueblo Ct., Gaithersburg, MD 20878 (SAN 213-9200) Tel 301-948-3494.

Edis Anderson, *(Anderson, Edis J.; 0-9616097),* P.O. Box 160, RR 3, Geneseo, IL 61254 (SAN 698-1208) Tel 309-944-6682; 2050 N. 900 E. Rural, Geneseo, IL 61254 (SAN 698-1216).

Edison Elec
See Edison Electric

†Edison Electric, *(Edison Electric Institute; 0-931032),* 1828 L St., Suite 709, Washington, DC 20036 (SAN 224-7119) Tel 202-828-7551; *CIP.*

†Edison Inst, *(Edison Institute, The; 0-933728),* 20900 Oakwood Blvd., Dearborn, MI 48121 (SAN 216-4841); *CIP. Imprints:* Ford Mus (Henry Ford Museum Press).

Edit Arcos, *(Editorial Arcos, Inc.; 0-937509),* P.O. Box 652253, Miami, FL 33265-2253 (SAN 659-1744) Tel 305-223-2344; 10850 W. Flagler St., Apt. D-103, Miami, FL 33174 (SAN 659-1752).

Edit Asol, *(Editorial Asol),* Box 21942, Univ. of Puerto Rico, Rio Piedras, PR 00931 (SAN 238-8766).

Edit Betania, *(Editorial Betania; 0-88113),* Div. of Bethany Fellowship, Inc., 5541 NW 82nd Ave., Miami, FL 33166 (SAN 240-6349) Tel 305-592-5121.

Edit Caribe, *(Editorial Caribe; 0-89922),* 3934 SW Eighth St., Suite 303, Miami, FL 33134 (SAN 215-1421) Tel 305-445-0564; Toll free: 800-222-5342; 4243 NW 37 Ct., Miami, FL 33134 (SAN 658-0556).

Edit Centro Pedagogico, *(Editorial Centro Pedagogico, Inc.; 0-934541),* Calle Luna No. 72, Box 310, Ponce, PR 00733 (SAN 693-790X) Tel 809-843-0686; 1144 E. Third St., Brooklyn, NY 11230 (SAN 693-7918).

Edit Concepts, *(Editorial Concepts, Inc.; 0-939193),* 7116 SW 47th St., Miami, FL 33155 (SAN 662-8958) Tel 305-661-6588; Dist. by: Spanish Periodical & Bk. Sales, 10100 NW 25th St., Miami, FL 35127 (SAN 200-7576); Dist. by: Agencia de Publicaciones de Puerto Rico, GPO Box 4903, San Juan, PR 00936 (SAN 169-9296); Dist. by: Southeast Periodicals, P.O. Box 340008, Coral Gables, FL 33134 (SAN 238-6909) Tel 305-856-5011.

Edit Consult, *(Editorial Consultants, Inc.; 0-917636),* 1728 Union St., San Francisco, CA 94123 (SAN 212-6567) Tel 415-474-5010.

Edit Experts, *(Editorial Experts, Inc.; 0-935012),* 85 S. Bragg St., Suite 400, Alexandria, VA 22312-2731 (SAN 216-3748) Tel 703-642-3040.

Edit Mensaje, *(Editorial Mensaje; 0-86515),* 125 Queen St., Staten Island, NY 10314 (SAN 214-0063) Tel 718-761-0556.

Edit Mundo *Imprint of* **Casa Bautista**

Edit Orphee, *(Éditions Orphee, Inc.; 0-936186),* P.O. Box 21291, Columbus, OH 43221 (SAN 221-1890).

Edit Res Serv, *(Editorial Research Service; 0-933592),* P.O. Box 411832, Kansas City, MO 64141 (SAN 212-7407) Tel 913-829-0609.

Edit Review, *(Editorial Review; 0-916447),* 1009 Placer St., Butte, MT 59701 (SAN 295-1231) Tel 406-782-2546.

Edit Roche, *(Editorial Roche; 0-939081),* P.O. Box 3583, Haio Rey, PR 00919 (SAN 662-9083); Urb. Del Carmen 2, No. 19, Juana Diaz, PR 00665 (SAN 662-9091) Tel 809-837-2468.

Edit Services
See Image Industry

Editions Ltd, *(Editions, Ltd.; 0-9607938),* 1123 Kapahulu Ave., Honolulu, HI 96816-5811 (SAN 691-9510) Tel 808-735-7644.

Editorial AI, *(Editorial AI; 0-930795),* 2200 Hendon, St. Paul, MN 55108 (SAN 677-8267) Tel 612-644-5937.

Editorial D O, *(Editorial Doble Omega; 0-88696),* P.O. Box 650712, Miami, FL 33165 (SAN 283-0590) Tel 305-554-4865; 13895 SW 22nd St., Miami, FL 33175 (SAN 283-0604).

Editorial Justa, *(Editorial Justa Pubns. Inc.; 0-915808),* 2831 Seventh St., Berkeley, CA 94710 (SAN 208-1962) Tel 415-848-3628; Orders to: P.O. Box 2131-C, Berkeley, CA 94702 (SAN 208-1970).

Editors, *(Editors & Engineers, Ltd.; 0-672),* Dist. by: Bobbs-Merrill Co., Inc., 866 Third Ave., New York lis, NY 10022 (SAN 201-3959) Tel 212-402-7809.

EDITS Pubs, *(EDITS Pubs.),* P.O. Box 7234, San Diego, CA 92107 (SAN 208-4600) Tel 619-488-1666.

†Edlo Bks, *(Edlo Books; 0-9613007),* P.O. Box 259, RD 1, Marlton, NJ 08053 (SAN 292-482X) Tel 609-424-1305; *CIP.*

EDM Digest, *(E D M Digest Co.; 0-9614302),* 31505 Grand River, Suite 1, Farmington, MI 48024 (SAN 687-4762) Tel 313-474-3489.

Edmund Miller, *(Miller, Edmund; 0-9600486),* 61-07 Woodside Ave., Apt. 5J, Woodside, NY 11377 (SAN 203-8374) Tel 718-424-0480.

Edna Nation, *(Nation, Edna; 0-9614669),* 61 Mediation Way, Florissant, MO 63031 (SAN 692-4700) Tel 314-921-0349.

Edns Alba, *(Ediciones Alba; 0-9600714),* Encarnacion 1573, Caparra Heights, San Juan, PR 00920 (SAN 206-3581) Tel 809-781-5984.

Edns Delta *Imprint of* **Unipub**

Edns Des Deux Mondes, *(Editions des Deux Mondes; 0-939586),* P.O. Box 56, Newark, DE 19711 (SAN 216-373X) Tel 302-398-2834.

EDRA, *(Environmental Design Research Assn.; 0-939922),* L'Enfant Plaza Sta., P.O. Box 23129, Washington, DC 20026 (SAN 216-8103) Tel 301-657-2651.

Eds Pub Co, *(Ed's Publishing, Co.; 0-9612822),* 9366 Greenwell Springs Rd., Baton Rouge, LA 70814 (SAN 289-9809) Tel 504-925-0991.

Edu Read Serv
See Troll Assocs

Edu Strategies, *(Educational Strategies; 0-9615789),* 223 W. Walnut St., Oneida, NY 13421 (SAN 696-7361) Tel 315-363-1716; P.O. Box 598, Oneida, NY 13421 (SAN 698-2190).

Edu-Tech
See EduTech

Educ & Trainin, *(Education & Training Consultants, Inc.; 0-937196),* Subs. of Education & Training Dev. Consultants-"Multi-Ethnic Bks. & Games", P.O. Box 1691, Ann Arbor, MI 48106 (SAN 282-3780); 1402 Astor Dr., Ann Arbor, MI 48104 (SAN 662-1562) Tel 313-668-0572.

Educ Awareness, *(Educators United for Global Awareness; 0-9613232),* c/o Jackson State Univ., History Dept., Jackson, MS 39217 (SAN 295-768X).

Educ Comm, *(Educational Communications, Inc.; 0-915130; 0-930315),* 721 N. McKinley Rd., Lake Forest, IL 60045 (SAN 201-6540) Tel 312-295-6650.

Educ Comp Syst, *(Educational Computer Systems, Inc.; 0-935919),* 17 Peacock Farm Rd., Lexington, MA 02173 (SAN 696-7396) Tel 617-863-8037.

Educ Des Edit Cons, *(Education Design/Editorial Consultants; 0-9613138),* P.O. Box 31975, Aurora, CO 80041 (SAN 294-7722) Tel 303-442-5156.

Educ Dev Ctr, *(Education Development Ctr., Inc.; 0-89292),* Orders to: EDC Publishing Ctr., 55 Chapel St., Newton, MA 02160 (SAN 207-821X) Tel 617-969-7100.

Educ Development, *(Educational Development; 0-914763),* 200 W. Bullard Ave., Suite E-1, Clovis, CA 93612 (SAN 677-4733) Tel 209-299-4131.

Educ Direction, *(Educational Direction, Inc.; 0-940432),* 150 N. Miller Rd., Bldg. 200, Akron, OH 44313 (SAN 217-1724).

Educ Editions, *(Educational Editions; 0-933092),* MS-293, P.O. Box 420240, Houston, TX 77243 (SAN 212-6575) Tel 713-467-2241.

†Educ Equity Con, *(Educational Equity Concepts, Inc.; 0-931629),* 114 E. 32nd St., Suite 306, New York, NY 10016 (SAN 212-725-1803; Dist. by: Gryphon Hse., 3706 Otis St., P.O. Box 275, Mount Rainier, MD 20712 (SAN 169-3190) Tel 301-779-6200; *CIP.*

Educ Found, *(Education Foundation, Inc.; 0-914498),* P.O. Box 1187, Charleston, WV 25324 (SAN 204-1685) Tel 304-342-0855.

Educ Found for Nucl Sci, *(Educational Foundation for Nuclear Science, Inc.; 0-941682),* 5801 S. Kenwood Ave., Chicago, IL 60637 (SAN 679-9876) Tel 312-363-5225; Dist. by: Univ. of Chicago Pr., 5801 Ellis Ave., 3rd Flr. S., Chicago, IL 60637 (SAN 202-5280) Tel 312-962-7693.

Educ Guide, *(Education Guide; 0-914880),* P.O. Box 421, Randolph, MA 02368 (SAN 201-4580) Tel 617-961-2217.

Educ Insights, *(Educational Insights, Inc.; 0-88679),* 150 W. Carob St., Compton, CA 90220 (SAN 283-8745) Tel 213-637-2131.

†Educ Inst Am Hotel, *(American Hotel & Motel Assn., Educational Institute; 0-86612),* 1407 S. Harrison Rd., East Lansing, MI 48823 (SAN 215-8590) Tel 517-353-5500; Warehouse, 2113 N. High St., Lansing, MI 48906 (SAN 669-0726); *CIP.*

Educ Leadership, *(Educational Leadership & Counseling Dept.; 0-911467),* Eastern Michigan Univ., Office of Community Educational Research, 34F Boone Hall, Ypsilanti, MI 48197 (SAN 264-0228).

Educ Lrn Syst, *(Eucational Learning Systems, Inc.; 0-939303),* P.O. Box 225, Tulsa, OK 74101 (SAN 663-1738); 2407 E. 17th Pl., Tulsa, OK 74101 (SAN 663-1746) Tel 918-743-9494.

Educ Materials, *(Educational Materials Co.; 0-937117),* R.R. 2, Box 89, River Rd., South Windham, ME 04082 (SAN 658-5175).

Educ Medical, *(Educational Medical Pubs.; 0-930728),* 18 Kling St., West Orange, NJ 07052 (SAN 211-1268).

Educ Patterns
See Learning Well

Educ Plan Serv, *(Educational Planning Services Corp.; 0-9609720),* P.O. Box 182, Newton Highlands, MA 02161 (SAN 263-2187) Tel 617-235-8101.

Educ Pr Assn, *(Educational Press Assn. of America; 0-89972),* Glassboro State College, Glassboro, NJ 08028 (SAN 204-1634) Tel 609-863-7349.

Educ Pr CA, *(Education Pr., The; 0-9601706),* Box 2358, Huntington Beach, CA 92647 (SAN 213-1323).

Educ Pr FL, *(Educational Pr.; 0-9616075),* P.O. Box 21147, Sarasota, FL 33583 (SAN 697-9963) Tel 813-922-5051.

Educ Prog Dev, *(Educational Program Development Associates, Inc.),* 2103 Crestmoor Rd., Nashville, TN 37215 (SAN 240-9895) Tel 615-269-5755.

Educ Pubns, *(Educators' Pubns., Inc.; 0-935423),* 1585 Rosecrans St., San Diego, CA 92106 (SAN 696-4974) Tel 619-224-1955.

Educ Res Consortium, *(Education Resource Consortium Inc.; 0-931263),* 190 E. Sweetbriar Dr., Claremont, CA 91711 (SAN 681-9796) Tel 714-621-6261.

Educ Res MA, *(Education Research Assocs.; 0-913636),* P.O. Box 767, Amherst, MA 01004 (SAN 215-3068) Tel 413-253-3582. *Imprints:* ERA Pr (E R A Press).(ERA Press).

Educ Serv, *(Educational Service, Inc.; 0-89273),* P.O. Box 219, Stevensville, MI 49127 (SAN 206-9423) Tel 616-429-1451; Toll free: 800-253-0763; 5060 St., Joe Rd., Stevensville, MI 49127 (SAN 658-0564).

Educ Serv Pr, *(Educational Services Pr.; 0-914911),* 99 Bank St., Suite 2F, New York, NY 10014 (SAN 289-1212); Dist. by: Children's Small Pr. Collection, 719 N. Fourth Ave., Ann Arbor, MI 48104 (SAN 200-514X); Dist. by: Blackwell North America, 1001 Fries Mill Rd., Blackwood, NJ 08012 (SAN 169-4596) Tel 609-629-0700; Dist. by: Baker & Taylor Co., Eastern Div., 50 Kirby Ave., Somerville, NJ 08876 (SAN 169-4901) Tel 201-526-8000; Dist. by: Baker & Taylor Co., Midwest Div., 501 Gladiola Ave., Momence, IL 60954 (SAN 169-2100); Dist. by: Baker & Taylor Co., Southeast Div., Mt. Olive Rd., Commerce, GA 30529 (SAN 169-1503); Dist. by: Baker & Taylor Co., Western Div., 380 Edison Way, Reno, NV (SAN 169-4464).

Educ Serv Pub, *(Educational Service Publications; 0-9608250),* Box 205, Boones Mill, VA 24065 (SAN 240-3714) Tel 703-334-2269.

Educ Strategies, *(Educational Strategies, Inc.; 0-938809),* Div. of Antenna Products International Sales Corp., 1815 Monetary Ln., Carrollton, TX 75006 (SAN 661-499X) Tel 214-241-6610. Do not confuse with Educational Strategies Oneida, NY.

†Educ Stud Pr, *(Educational Studies Pr.; 0-934328),* Northern Illinois Univ., L.E.P.S. Dept., 325 Graham Hall, DeKalb, IL 60115 (SAN 213-3083) Tel 815-753-1499; Orders to: ISURF, Inc., Iowa State Univ., 350 Beardshear Hall, Ames, IA 50011 (SAN 662-0000) Tel 515-294-4740; *CIP.*

Educ Studies
See Commonground Pr

Educ Sys Pub
See Ed Sys Pub

Educ Tech IL, *(Educational Technology; 1-55639),* Subs. of Prescription Learning, P.O. Box 2372, Springfield, IL 62705 (SAN 659-8609) Tel 217-786-2500.

†Educ Tech Pubns, *(Educational Technology Pubns, Inc.; 0-87778),* 720 Palisade Ave., Englewood Cliffs, NJ 07632 (SAN 201-3738) Tel 201-871-4007; *CIP.*

Educ Testing Serv, *(Educational Testing Service; 0-88685),* Rosedale Rd., Princeton, NJ 08541-6000 (SAN 238-034X) Tel 609-921-9000.

Educ Today
See D S Lake Pubs

EduCALC Pubns, *(EduCALC Pubns; 0-936356),* 27953 Cabot Rd,, South Laguna, CA 92677 (SAN 281-6229) Tel 714-831-2631; Dist. by: Publishers Group West, 5855 Beaudry St., Emeryville, CA 94608 (SAN 202-8522) Tel 415-658-3453.

Educalc Pubns
See EduCALC Pubns

Educated Eye, *(Educated Eye Pr., The; 0-9615607),* 2030 Park Newport, Newport Beach, CA 92660 (SAN 696-4923) Tel 714-759-0966; P.O. Box 9601, Newport Beach, CA 92660 (SAN 696-5474).

Education Serv, *(Education Services; 0-936394),* P.O. Box 5281, Atlanta, GA 30307 (SAN 221-1920).

Educational Assocs, *(Educational Associates),* P.O. Box 35221, Phoenix, AZ 85069 (SAN 670-686X) Tel 602-869-9223.

Educator Bks, *(Educator Bks., Inc.; 0-912092),* Drawer 32, San Angelo, TX 76901 (SAN 203-8382) Tel 915-653-0152.

Educator Pubns, *(Educator Pubns.; 0-913558),* 1110 S. Pomona Ave., Fullerton, CA 92632 (SAN 201-3746) Tel 714-871-2950; P.O. Box 333, Fullerton, CA 92632 (SAN 201-3754).

EDUCOM, *(EDUCOM),* P.O. Box 364, Rosedale & Carter Rds., Princeton, NJ 08540 (SAN 223-0321) Tel 609-734-1915.

†Educomp Pubns, *(Educomp Pubns.; 0-9612226),* 14242 Wyeth Ave., Irvine, CA 92714 (SAN 287-7384) Tel 714-551-4073; *CIP.*

Eduplay, *(Eduplay; 0-935609),* Div. of EPI Corp., 9707 Shelbyville Rd./Hold Box No. 60, Louisville, KY 40223 (SAN 696-3552) Tel 502-895-3547; Dist. by: Gelber Marketing, Inc., 200 Fifth Ave., New York, NY 10010 (SAN 200-5727).

Edutech, *(EduTech Press; 0-9610102),* 22158 Ramona, Apple Valley, CA 92307 (SAN 269-865X) Tel 619-247-7633.

EduTech, *(EduTech, Inc.; 0-938082; 0-923809),* 303 Lamartine St., Jamaica Plain, MA 02130 (SAN 293-1184) Tel 617-524-1774.

EduTech Courseware, *(EduTech Courseware; 0-938581),* 7801 E. Bush Lake Rd., Suite 350, Minneapolis, MN 55331 (SAN 661-1133) Tel 612-831-0445.

Edutrends, *(Edutrends, Inc.; 0-935987),* 6949 Park Dr. E., Kew Gardens, NY 11367 (SAN 696-7353) Tel 718-793-5262; Dist. by: Deltak Inc., East/West Technological Ctr., 1751 W. Diehl Rd., Naperville, IL 60566 (SAN 294-281X) Tel 312-369-3000.

Edw Rucker Ent, *(Rucker, Edward W., Enterprises; 0-9614352),* P.O. Box 25674, Oklahoma City, OK 73125 (SAN 687-8350) Tel 405-478-3299.

Edw Rucker Pubn
See Edw Rucker Ent

Edward Pr, *(Edward Pr.; 0-9606020),* 62 Brighton St., Rochester, NY 14607 (SAN 216-8898) Tel 716-271-4272.

Edwards & Manley, *(Edwards, Carol L., & Kathleen E. B. Manley, Pubs.; 0-9615687),* California State Univ., Long Beach, Dept. of Comparative Literature, Long Beach, CA 90840 (SAN 696-3609).

Edwards Bros, *(Edwards Brothers, Inc.; 0-910546),* 2500 S. State St., P.O. Box 1007, Ann Arbor, MI 48106 (SAN 206-9814) Tel 313-769-1000.

Edward's CA, *(Edward's Publishing Co., Inc.; 0-935531),* 14115 Chadron Ave., P.O. Box 1668, Hawthorne, CA 90251-1668 (SAN 695-1015) Tel 213-644-5643.

Edwards Pub Co, *(Edwards Publishing Co.; 0-911935),* P.O. Box 42218, Tacoma, WA 98442 (SAN 264-0236).

EE Ford, *(Ford, Edward E., Publishing; 0-9616716),* 10209 N. 56th St., Scottsdale, AZ 85253 (SAN 659-4964) Tel 602-991-4860.

EEBART, *(EEBART; 0-9614991),* Box 127, Leaf River, IL 61047 (SAN 693-7632) Tel 815-738-2237.

EEBRAT
See EEBART

EEPC Pub, *(EEPC Publishing Co.; 0-937699),* 653 E. 118, Cleveland, OH 44108 (SAN 659-3496) Tel 216-451-5242.

†Eerdmans, *(Eerdmans, William B., Publishing Co.; 0-8028),* 255 Jefferson Ave., SE, Grand Rapids, MI 49503 (SAN 220-0058) Tel 616-459-4591; Toll free: 800-253-7521; *CIP. Imprints:* Chr Univ Pr (Christian University Press).(Christian Univ. Pr.).

Effect Learn Sys, *(Effective Learning Systems, Inc.; 0-913261),* P.O. Box 85, Moraga, CA 94556 (SAN 283-0620) Tel 415-376-6162.

Effect Learning GA, *(Effective Learning Pubns.; 0-933594),* 218 Valley Rd., Statesboro, GA 30458 (SAN 213-487X).

Effect Mgmt, *(Effective Management Resources Corp.; 0-939740),* 2229 Nyon Ave., Anaheim, CA 92806 (SAN 216-3764).

Effect Pub, *(Effect Publishing, Inc.; 0-911971),* 501 Fifth Ave., Suite 1612, New York, NY 10017 (SAN 264-665X) Tel 212-557-1321.

Effective Learn, *(Effective Learning, Inc.; 0-915474),* 7 N. MacQuesten Pkwy., P.O. Box 2212, Mount Vernon, NY 10550 (SAN 208-4791) Tel 914-664-7944; 25 N. MacQuesten Pkwy., Mount Vernon, NY 10550 (SAN 658-0572).

Effectiveness Train, *(Effectiveness Training Associates; 0-918460),* 321 River St., Manistee, MI 49660 (SAN 209-553X) Tel 616-723-8422.

EFLA, *(Educational Film Library Assn.; 0-87520),* 45 John St., Suite 301, New York, NY 10038 (SAN 201-8233) Tel 212-227-5599.

EFQ Pubns, *(EFQ Pubns.; 0-937265),* P.O. Box 4958, San Francisco, CA 94101 (SAN 659-1620).

EG Bkslr Pubs, *(EG Booksellers & Pubs.; 0-938979),* 99 Sanchez St., San Francisco, CA 94114 (SAN 661-6828) Tel 415-863-5864; Dist. by: Small Pr. Distribution, 1814 San Pablo Ave., Berkeley, CA 94702 (SAN 204-5826) Tel 415-549-3336.

Eggplant Pr, *(Eggplant Pr.; 0-935060),* c/o Cloud Woman/Chocolate Waters, 415 W. 44th St., No. 7, New York, NY 10036 (SAN 211-6030) Tel 212-581-6820.

Eggs Pr, *(Eggs Pr.; 0-9602914),* 3038 41st Ave., S., Minneapolis, MN 55406 (SAN 213-6228).

EGM Ent, *(EGM Enterprises; 0-9604586),* 1223 S. 155th St., Omaha, NE 68144 (SAN 215-1448) Tel 402-333-3698.

Ego Bks, *(Ego Bks.; 0-933540),* 6011 Meadowbrook Ln., Lincoln, NE 68510 (SAN 212-159X) Tel 402-489-6982.

Egret Pub Co, *(Egret Publishing Co., The; 0-9615730),* 369 Eighth St., Eureka, CA 95501 (SAN 696-3706) Tel 707-445-5475; P.O. Box 991, Eureka, CA 95501 (SAN 696-9704).

Egret Pubns, *(Egret Pubns.; 0-938425),* 594 Broadway, New York, NY 10012 (SAN 661-2393) Tel 212-226-1330.

Egyptian Museum
See AMORC

Ehde Pub Co, *(Ehde Publishing Co.; 0-936188),* Sontag, MS 39665 (SAN 214-0071).

Ehling Clifton Bks, *(Ehling Clifton Bks.),* 2401 Clifton Ave., Cincinnati, OH 45219 (SAN 240-1444).

EHM Pub, *(EHM Publishing; 0-9609828),* Box 3173, Tallahassee, FL 32315 (SAN 262-0170) Tel 904-539-9767.

EHUD, *(EHUD International Language Foundation),* 1755 Trinity Ave., No. 79, Walnut Creek, CA 94596 (SAN 281-6172) Tel 415-937-4841; Orders to: Box 2082, Dollar Ranch Sta., Walnut Creek, CA 94595 (SAN 281-6180) Tel 415-937-4841.

EIC Intell, *(EIC/Intelligence, Inc.; 0-89947),* 48 W. 38th St., New York, NY 10018 (SAN 211-1276) Tel 212-944-8500; Toll free: 800-223-6275.

Eidolon Pr, *(Eidolon Pr.; 0-9609044),* P.O. Box 8204, Pensacola, FL 32505 (SAN 241-3787).

Eighth Mount Pr, *(Eighth Mountain Pr.; 0-933377),* 624 SE 29th Ave., Portland, OR 97214 (SAN 691-6767) Tel 503-233-3936; Dist. by: Bookpeople, 2929 Fifth St., Berkeley, CA 94710 (SAN 168-9517) Tel 415-549-3030; Dist. by: Inland Bk. Co, P.O. Box 261, 22 Hemingway Ave., East Haven, CT 06512 (SAN 200-4151) Tel 203-467-4257.

Eighties Pr, *(Eighties Pr.; 0-87390),* 308 First St., Moose Lake, MN 55767 (SAN 204-5869); Dist. by: Ally Press, 524 Orleans St., St. Paul, MN 55107 (SAN 207-7116).

Eileens Enter, *(Eileen's Enterprises; 0-934807),* 420 E. Patterson, Dunkirk, OH 45836 (SAN 694-3497) Tel 419-759-3081.

Eisenberg Ed, *(Eisenberg Educational Enterprises; 0-930080),* Belevedere Towers 108, 1190 W. Northern Pkwy., Baltimore, MD 21210 (SAN 210-5942) Tel 301-435-8351.

Eisenberg Inc, *(Eisenberg, Jerome M.; 0-934749),* 153 E. 57th St., New York, NY 10022 (SAN 694-1974) Tel 212-355-2034; Orders to: Royal-Athena Galleries, 153 E. 57th St., New York, NY 10022 (SAN 694-1974).

Eisenbrauns, *(Eisenbrauns; 0-931464),* P.O. Box 275, Winona Lake, IN 46590-0278 (SAN 200-7835) Tel 219-269-2011.

Eisenhower Lib, *(Eisenhower, Dwight D., Library; 0-9605728),* Abilene, KS 67410 (SAN 217-1015) Tel 913-263-4751.

Eiteljorg Pubns, *(Eiteljorg, Harrison, Pubns.; 0-9607596),* 4567 Cold Spring Rd., Indianapolis, IN 46208 (SAN 239-4359); Dist. by: Independent Publishers Group, 1 Pleasant Ave., Port Washington, NY 11050 (SAN 287-5294).

Either-or Pr, *(Either-or Pr.; 0-910931),* 122 North St., Pittsfield, MA 01201 (SAN 262-0189).

EJP Pub Co, *(EJP Publishing Co.; 0-934883),* P.O. Box 44268, Tucson, AZ 85733 (SAN 694-4426); 4420 E. Speedway, Suite 202, Tucson, AZ 85719 (SAN 662-3387) Tel 602-628-7678. *Imprints:* Bellwether Bks (Bellwether Books); Gecko Pr (Gecko Press).

EK Pub Co, *(EK Publishing Co.; 0-937833),* 535 NE Adams, Chehalis, WA 98532 (SAN 659-4433) Tel 206-748-0545.

Ekay Music, *(Ekay Music, Inc.; 0-943748),* 223 Katonah Ave., Katonah, NY 10536 (SAN 241-0680) Tel 914-232-8108; Orders to: Songbooks Unlimited, 352 Evelyn St., Paramus, NJ 07652 (SAN 662-1430) Tel 201-967-9495.

EKB Bks, *(EKB Bks.; 0-9616714),* P.O. Box 608291, Chicago, IL 60626 (SAN 661-2075); 7613 N. Paulina, Chicago, IL 60626 (SAN 661-2083) Tel 312-973-4317.

Eko Pubns, *(Eko Pubns.),* P.O. Box 5492, Philadelphia, PA 19143 (SAN 201-4599).

EKS Pub Co, *(EKS Publishing, Co.; 0-939144),* 5336 College Ave., Oakland, CA 94618 (SAN 216-1281) Tel 415-653-5183.

El Camino, *(El Camino Pubs.; 0-942060),* 4010 Calle Real, Suite 4, Santa Barbara, CA 93110 (SAN 238-6151) Tel 805-682-9340.

El Cariso
See Life Understanding

El Moro, *(El Moro Pubns.; 0-9602484),* P.O. Box 965, Morro Bay, CA 93442 (SAN 211-5255) Tel 805-772-3514.

El Renacimiento, *(El Renacimiento),* 1132 N. Washington Ave., Lansing, MI 48906 (SAN 219-2667) Tel 517-485-4389.

El-Shabazz Pr, *(El-Hajj Malik El-Shabazz Pr.; 0-913358),* P.O. Box 1115, Washington, DC 20013 (SAN 201-2340).

El-Shabazz Pr
See El-Shabazz Pr

El Siglo Pr
See El Siglo Pubs

El Siglo Pubs, *(El Siglo Pubs.; 0-9614985),* 2730 W. Los Reales, Tucson, AZ 85706 (SAN 693-224X) Tel 602-327-0506 Tel 602-578-2778.

Elan NW Pubs, *(Elan Northwest Pubs.; 0-9603272),* P.O. Box 5442, Eugene, OR 97405 (SAN 206-4707) Tel 503-485-3462.

Elan Pubs
See Elan NW Pubs

Elar Pub Co, *(Elar Publishing Co.,Inc.; 0-914130),* 1120 Old Country Rd., Plainview, NY 11803 (SAN 215-952X) Tel 516-433-6530.

Eldan Pr, *(Eldan Pr.; 0-9615128),* 1259 El Camino, No. 288, Menlo Park, CA 94025 (SAN 694-1982) Tel 415-322-8777; Dist. by: Publishers Group West, 5855 Beaudry St., Emeryville, CA 94608 (SAN 202-8522) Tel 415-658-3453.

Elder, *(Elder Care),* P.O. Box 212, Chittenango, NY 13037 (SAN 655-184X) Tel 315-687-9764.

Eldridge Pub, *(Eldridge Publishing Co.; 0-912963),* P. O. Drawer 216, Franklin, OH 45005 (SAN 204-1553) Tel 513-746-6531.

Elec Consumers Res, *(Electricity Consumers Resource Council),* 1828 L St., Suite 403, Washington, DC 20036 (SAN 209-8846).

Elec Ind Assn, *(Electronic Industries Assn.),* 2001 Eye St., NW, Washington, DC 20006 (SAN 230-0702) Tel 202-457-4900.

Elect Bkshelf, *(Electronic Bookshelf, Inc., The; 0-935325),* R.R. No. 9, Box 64, Frankfort, IN 46041 (SAN 695-765X) Tel 317-324-2182.

Electret Sci, *(Electret Scientific Co.; 0-917406),* P.O. Box 4132, Morgantown, WV 26505 (SAN 206-4715) Tel 304-594-1639.

Electric Bank, *(Electric Bank, The; 0-938236),* 4225 University, Des Moines, IA 50311 (SAN 209-7214) Tel 515-255-3552.

Electric Pr, *(Electric Pr.; 0-916919),* 3455 E. Lamona Ave., Fresno, CA 93703 (SAN 297-1658) Tel 209-264-6215.

Electro Horiz, *(Electro-Horizons Pubns.; 0-939527),* 114 Lincoln Rd. E., Plainview, NY 11803 (SAN 663-3757) Tel 516-938-1159.

Electro-Optical, *(Electro-Optical Research Co.; 0-936581),* Suite 422, 2029 Century Park E., Los Angeles, CA 90067 (SAN 207-2211) Tel 213-277-7422.

Electrodata, *(Electrodata, Inc.; 0-943890),* P.O. Box 206, Glen Echo, MD 20812 (SAN 241-1083) Tel 202-338-0669.

Electron Course, *(Electronic Courseware Systems, Inc.; 0-942132; 1-55603),* 1210 Lancaster Dr., Champaign, IL 61821 (SAN 238-6577) Tel 217-359-7099.

Electron Optics Pub Grp, *(Electron Optics Publishing Group; 0-9612934),* Subs. of Philips Electronic Instruments, Inc., 85 McKee Dr., Mahwah, NJ 07430 (SAN 292-4854) Tel 802-785-3042.

Electronic Flea, *(Electronic Flea Market),* 2020 Girard Ave. S., Minneapolis, MN 55405 (SAN 206-4529).

Electronic Trend, *(Electronic Trend Publications; 0-914405),* 10080 N. Wolfe Rd., Suite 372, Cupertino, CA 95014 (SAN 287-7457) Tel 408-996-7416.

Elegant Stew, *(Elegant Stew Pr.; 0-9612618),* General Delivery, Boston, MA 02205-9999 (SAN 289-1220).

ELEMENT Pubs, *(ELEMENT Pubs., Inc.; 0-939393),* 708 Greenwich St., New York, NY 10014 (SAN 663-1363) Tel 212-929-8275.

Elenchus Ent, *(Elenchus Enterprises, Inc.; 0-936953),* 87 Van Buren St., Woodbridge, NJ 07095 (SAN 658-7046) Tel 201-634-5140.

Eleutherian Mills-Hagley
See Hagley Museum

Elevation Pr, *(Elevation Pr.; 0-932624),* 1031 24th St., Greeley, CO 80631 (SAN 212-1875) Tel 303-352-2979.

Eleventh Hour, *(11th Hour Gospel; 0-9608662),* Box 190, Prosser, WA 99350 (SAN 240-6365) Tel 509-786-4230.

Elghund Pub, *(Elghund Publishing Co.; 0-9612112),* P.O. Box 158, Simpsonville, MD 21150 (SAN 289-0380) Tel 301-997-9490.

Eli Mail, *(Eli Mail-Order, Inc.; 0-9602230),* P.O. Box 81, Brooklyn, NY 11208 (SAN 212-3509).

Elijah-John, *(Elijah-John Pubns.; 0-9614311),* 103 Russell, Apt. 6, Saline, MI 48176 (SAN 687-5106) Tel 313-429-5717.

Eliopoulos, *(Eliopoulos, Nicholas C, Publishing; 0-9605396),* P.O. Box 65, Oak Park, IL 60303 (SAN 220-0856); 5711 W. School St., Chicago, IL 60634 (SAN 662-0027) Tel 312-725-1960.

Elisabetta Denti, *(Denti, Elisabetta; 0-9614723),* 7545 Bradburn, No. 403, Westminister, CO 80030 (SAN 692-5235) Tel 403-429-2213.

†Elite, *(Elite Publishing Corp.; 0-918367),* 11-03 46th Ave., Long Island City, NY 11101 (SAN 657-338X) Tel 718-937-4606; *CIP.*

Elite Pub Co, *(Elite Publishing Co., Inc.; 0-935589),* 2346 S. Lynhurst Dr., Indianapolis, IN 46241 (SAN 696-3773) Tel 317-244-5665.

†Elizabeth Pr, *(Elizabeth Pr.),* 103 Van Etten Blvd., New Rochelle, NY 10804 (SAN 201-3789); *CIP.*

Elizabeth St Pr, *(Elizabeth St. Pr.; 0-910323),* 240 Elizabeth St., New York, NY 10012 (SAN 241-5003) Tel 212-758-7400.

Elk Grove Bks *Imprint of* **Childrens**

Elk Grove Vill, *(Elk Grove Village Public Library; 0-9605940),* 1 Morrison Blvd., Elk Grove Village, IL 60007 (SAN 216-6224) Tel 312-439-0447.

Ell Ell Diversified, *(Ell Ell Diversified, Inc.; 0-937428),* P.O. Box 1702, Santa Rosa, CA 95402 (SAN 215-3076) Tel 707-542-8663.

Eller
See Brethren

Ellingsworth, *(Ellingsworth Press; 0-9605698),* 20 E. Main St., Rm. 338, Waterbury, CT 06702 (SAN 211-1519).

Elliots Bks, *(Elliot's Bks.; 0-911830),* P.O. Box 6, Northford, CT 06472 (SAN 204-1529) Tel 203-484-2184.

Elliott & Hammett, *(Elliott, Carroll, & Ellen Gale Hammett; 0-9615630),* R.F.D. 3, St. Mary's, WV 26170 (SAN 696-3803) Tel 304-665-2254.

Elliott Graph, *(Elliott Graphics, Inc.; 0-9614793),* 1133 Broadway, New York, NY 10010 (SAN 692-9818).

Ellis & Stewart Pub, *(Ellis & Stewart Pubs.; 0-942532),* 270 N. Canon Dr., Suite 103, Beverly Hills, CA 90210 (SAN 239-6386) Tel 213-276-5424.

Ellis Pr, *(Ellis Pr., The; 0-933180),* P.O. Box 1443, Peoria, IL 61655 (SAN 214-008X).

Ellison Ent, *(Ellison Enterprises; 0-930580),* 3466 N. Miami Ave., Miami, FL 33127 (SAN 211-0091) Tel 305-576-6600.

Elm Hollow Inc Pub, *(Elm Hollow Inc. Pubs.; 0-916553),* S.R. Box 21A2 , Elm Hollow Rd., Livingston Manor, NY 12758 (SAN 295-2602) Tel 914-439-5400.

Elm Pr, *(Elm Pr.; 0-9613420),* 12859 Via Latina, Del Mar, CA 92014 (SAN 656-9781) Tel 619-452-8692.

Elm Pubns, *(Elm Pubns.; 0-911175),* P.O. Box 23192, Knoxville, TN 37933-1192 (SAN 269-8986) Tel 615-966-5703.

Elm Pubs
See Elm Pubns

Elmer
See Greenspires

Elmer Edwards, *(Edwards, Elmer Eugene; 0-9604834),* P.O. Box 584, Miami, FL 33161 (SAN 215-143X).

Elmwood Park Pub, *(Elmwood Park Publishing, Co.; 0-933181),* P.O. Box 35132, Elmwood Park, IL 60635-0132 (SAN 691-7178) Tel 312-453-5023.

Elmwood Pub Co, *(Elmwood Publishing Co., The; 0-931396),* 1509 Norman Ave., San Jose, CA 95125 (SAN 211-6650) Tel 408-267-2498.

Elon College Alum Assoc, *(Elon College Alumni Assn.; 0-9605976),* P.O. Box 2116, Elon College, NC 27244 (SAN 216-7298) Tel 919-584-2380.

Elpenor, *(Elpenor Bks.; 0-931972),* Box 3152, Merchandise Mart Plaza, Chicago, IL 60654 (SAN 222-8076).

Elra Pr, *(Elra Press; 0-933200),* 140 University Ave., Box 30, Palo Alto, CA 94301 (SAN 222-8009).

ELRAMCO Enter, *(Elramco Enterprises, Inc.; 0-930355),* 1533 Central Ave., Albany, NY 12205 (SAN 670-7629) Tel 518-458-9095.

Elsa II Pub, *(Elsa II Pubs.; 0-939595),* 788 G. Laurel Walk, Goleta, CA 93117 (SAN 663-6225) Tel 805-687-6707.

Elsah Landing, *(Elsah Landing Restaurant, The; 0-9606150),* 10041 Conway Rd., St. Louis, MO 63124 (SAN 285-0095) Tel 314-993-4843; Orders to: Elsah Landing Restaurant Cookbook, P.O. Box 98, Elsah, IL 62028 (SAN 285-0117).

Elsevier, *(Elsevier Science Publishing Co., Inc.; 0-444; 0-7204),* Subs. of Elsevier NDU NV, 52 Vanderbilt Ave., New York, NY 10017 (SAN 200-2051) Tel 212-370-5520; *CIP.* *Imprints:* Biomedical Pr (Elsevier North-Holland Biomedical Press).(Elsevier North-Holland Biomedical Pr.); Excerpta Medica (Excerpta-Medica); North Holland (North-Holland); Thomond Pr (Thomond Press).(Thomond Pr.)

Elsevier-Phaidon *Imprint of* **Dutton**

Elsevier Sci
See Elsevier

Elysian Pr, *(Elysian Pr.; 0-941692),* P.O. Box 94, Cold Spring Harbor, NY 11724 (SAN 239-2844) Tel 212-831-0596.

Elysium, *(Elysium Growth Pr.; 1-55599),* 700 Robinson Rd., Topanga, CA 90290 (SAN 210-5950) Tel 213-455-1000; 5436 Fernwood Ave., Los Angeles, CA 90027 (SAN 688-3915) Tel 213-455-7121.

EMC, *(EMC Publishing; 0-88436; 0-912022; 0-8219),* Div. of EMC Corp., 300 York Ave., St. Paul, MN 55101 (SAN 201-3800) Tel 612-771-1555; Toll free: 800-328-1452.

EMC Controls, *(EMC Controls, Inc.; 0-9609256),* P.O. Box 242, Cockeysville, MD 21030 (SAN 260-0455) Tel 301-667-8162.

Emami Coalson
See Emami-Coulson

Emami-Coulson, *(Emami, Mary Lou & Suzanne Coulson; 0-9602316),* 1691 Dickinson Dr., Wheaton, IL 60187 (SAN 213-9197).

Embassy Imp, *(Embassy Imprint, Inc.; 0-930527),* Bridge Rd., Haddam, CT 06438 (SAN 682-7896) Tel 203-345-2574.

Embee Pr, *(Embee Pr.; 0-89816),* 82 Pine Grove, Kingston, NY 12401 (SAN 212-1603).

Embroidery, *(Embroidery Themes Co.; 0-9614004),* RD. 3, Lebanon, NJ 08833 (SAN 693-4013).

Embroidy Bk
See C Schneider

Emerald *Imprint of* **Dell**

Emerald CA, *(Emerald Publishing Co.; 0-935675),* P.O. Box 2813, El Segundo, CA 90245-1913 (SAN 696-3862) Tel 213-322-8049.

Emerald City, *(Emerald City Pr.; 0-932531),* P.O. Box 21066, Little Rock, AR 72212 (SAN 687-4673) Tel 501-224-3897.

Emerald Forest, *(Emerald Forest Music; 0-9613159),* P.O. Box 161034, San Diego, CA 92116 (SAN 294-9261) Tel 619-298-5530.

Emerald Hse, *(Emerald House; 0-936958),* P.O. Box 1769, Sandpoint, ID 83864 (SAN 214-3682) Tel 208-263-1071; Dist. by: DeVorss & Co., P.O. Box 550, 1046 Princeton Dr., Marina del Rey, CA 90294 (SAN 168-9886); Dist. by: Angel Book Distribution Center, 561 Tyler St., Monterey, CA 93940 (SAN 200-5042); Dist. by: New Pathways, 103 Goldencrest Ave., Waltham, MA 02154 (SAN 200-5050).

Emerald NV, *(Emerald Publishing; 0-9615757),* P.O. Box 11830, Reno, NV 89510 (SAN 696-3846) Tel 415-658-6470.

Emerald People, *(Emerald People Productions; 0-938055),* P.O. Box 58996, 2 Penn Ctr., Philadelphia, PA 19102 (SAN 661-2407); 352 Keswick Ave., Glenside, PA 19038 (SAN 661-2415) Tel 215-886-8243.

Emerald Pub, *(Emerald Valley Publishing Co.; 0-933094),* P.O. Box 70288, Eugene, OR 97401 (SAN 222-8025) Tel 503-485-8796.

Emerald Pub MI, *(Emerald Publishing; 0-9617095),* P.O. Box 906, Sterling Heights, MI 48311 (SAN 662-4790); 42275 Malbeck Dr., Sterling Heights, MI 48310 (SAN 662-4804) Tel 313-739-9497. Do not confuse with other companies with the same name in El Segundo, CA, Reno, NV.

Emerg Med Tech Pr *Imprint of* **First Intl Pub**

Emerg Nurses IL, *(Emergency Department Nurses Association; 0-935890),* 666 N. Lakeshore Dr., Chicago, IL 60511 (SAN 269-9036) Tel 312-649-0297.

Emerg Service Products & Prod, *(Emergency Service Products & Productions; 0-9606144),* P.O. Box 1513, Orange, CA 92668 (SAN 217-5142) Tel 714-830-1754.

†Emergence, *(Emergence Pubns.; 0-89465),* P.O. Box 1394, Hillsboro, OR 97123 (SAN 210-6299) Tel 503-648-2758; *CIP.*

Emergency Care
See ECRI

Emergency Dept
See Emerg Nurses IL

Emerging Island, *(Emerging Island Cultures Pr.; 0-931003),* 612 Second Ave., San Francisco, CA 94118 (SAN 678-8963) Tel 415-752-6347.

Emeritus Inc, *(Emeritus Inc., Pub.; 0-943694),* 15 Jade Lane, Cherry Hill, NJ 08002 (SAN 238-2768) Tel 609-667-4278.

Emerson, *(Emerson Bks., Inc.; 0-87523),* 121 N. Hampton Dr., White Plains, NY 10603 (SAN 201-3819) Tel 914-739-3506; Madelyn Ave., Vrplanck, NY 10596 (SAN 658-0580).

Eminent Pubns, *(Eminent Pubns. Enterprises; 0-936955),* P.O. Box 1026, Jeffersonville, IN 47131 (SAN 658-6589) Tel 812-282-8338.

Emissaries Divine, *(Emissaries of Divine Light; 0-932869),* 5569 N. County Rd., Loveland, CO 80537 (SAN 688-9875) Tel 303-667-4675.

Emissary Pubns, *(Emissary Pubns.; 0-941380),* P.O. Box 642, S. Pasadena, CA 91030 (SAN 238-9746) Tel 818-794-3400.

Emmanuel Christian, *(Emmanuel Christian Ministries; 0-9615955),* 1050 Barberry Rd., Yorktown Heights, NY 10598 (SAN 697-3299) Tel 914-245-5635.

Emmett, *(Emmett Pub. Co.; 0-934682),* 2861 Burnham Blvd., Minneapolis, MN 55416 (SAN 210-556X).

Emmons-Fairfied Pub, *(Emmons-Fairfied Publishing Co.; 0-9607956),* 18674 Fairfield, Detroit, MI 48221 (SAN 240-0707) Tel 313-284-0180.

Emory Pub Co, *(Emory Publishing Co.; 0-934681),* P.O. Box 55022, Birmingham, AL 35255 (SAN 694-2008) Tel 205-979-0971.

Emotions Anony Intl, *(Emotions Anonymous International; 0-9607356),* P.O. Box 4245, St. Paul, MN 55104 (SAN 239-5495) Tel 612-647-9712; 1595 Selby Ave., St. Paul, MN 55104 (SAN 669-0734).

Empak Enter, *(Empak Enterprises, Inc.; 0-9616156),* 520 N. Michigan Ave., Chicago, IL 60611 (SAN 699-9182) Tel 312-642-3434.

Empey Ent, *(Empey Enterprises; 0-9613084),* 810 Alexander St., Greenville, MI 48838 (SAN 293-9290) Tel 616-754-7036.

Empire Bks, *(Empire Books; 0-88015),* 527 Madison Ave., New York, NY 10022 (SAN 219-7324) Tel 212-752-6451; Toll free: 800-242-7737; Orders to: Harper & Row Pubs., In.., Keystone Industrial Park, Scranton, PA 18512 (SAN 215-3742).

Empire Games Pr, *(Empire Games Pr.; 0-913037),* Div. of Empire Games, Inc., P.O. Box 5462, Arlington, TX 76011 (SAN 283-0663) Tel 817-261-3666; 700 E. Abram, Arlington, TX 76010 (SAN 283-0671).

Empire Pub Co, *(Empire Publishing Co., The; 0-9616213),* 25 Bryant Ave., Milton, MA 02186 (SAN 658-5205) Tel 617-696-8592.

Employee, *(Employee Relocation Council; 0-912614),* 1720 N. St., NW, Washington, DC 20036 (SAN 201-3827) Tel 202-857-0857.

†**Employee Benefit,** *(Employee Benefit Research Institute; 0-86643),* 2121 K St., NW, Suite 860, Washington, DC 20037-2121 (SAN 216-2423) Tel 202-659-0670; Toll free: 800-354-5425; Orders to: P.O. Box 753, Waldorf, MD 20601 (SAN 662-0035) Tel 301-843-1020; CIP.

Emporia State, *(Emporia State Univ. Pr.),* 1200 Commercial St., Emporia, KS 66801 (SAN 207-9771) Tel 316-343-1200.

Emprise Pubns, *(Emprise Pubns.; 0-938129),* P.O. Box 456, Cayucos, CA 93430 (SAN 661-2423); 3499 Studio Dr., Cayucos, CA 93430 (SAN 661-2431) Tel 408-422-0415.

Empyrean Pubns, *(Empyrean Pubns.; 0-935283),* P.O. Box 49, Portland, CT 06480 (SAN 696-6772) Tel 203-928-2301; 21 Highland Ave., Portland, CT 06480 (SAN 696-6780).

EMT Inc, *(EMT Inc.; 0-916363),* 2026 Beechwood, Wilmatte, IL 60091 (SAN 295-7604) Tel 312-943-1900.

En Passant Poet, *(En Passant Poetry Press; 0-9605098),* 4612 Sylvanus Dr., Wilmington, DE 19803 (SAN 212-4211) Tel 302-774-4571.

†**ENAAQ Pubns,** *(ENAAQ Pubns.; 0-915867),* P.O. Box 1375, Chicago, IL 60690 (SAN 293-9339) Tel 312-643-4247; 5226 S. Ingleside, Chicago, IL 60615 (SAN 293-9347); CIP.

Enabling Syst, *(Enabling Systems, Inc.; 0-917688),* P.O. Box 2813, Honolulu, HI 96803 (SAN 207-2440) Tel 808-545-2646.

Enabling Tech Inc, *(Enabling Technologies, Inc.; 0-936299),* 600 S. Dearborn, Suite 1304, Chicago, IL 60605 (SAN 697-3329) Tel 312-427-0386; Dist. by: Ashton-Tate Bks., 8901 S. La Cienega Blvd., Inglewood, CA 90301 (SAN 265-4628).

Enchiridion, *(Enchiridion International; 0-916649),* Box 2589, Cullowhee, NC 28723 (SAN 296-5054).

Encino Pr, *(Encino Press; 0-88426),* 510 Baylor St., Austin, TX 78703 (SAN 201-3843) Tel 512-476-6821.

Encode Comp Serv, *(Encode Computer Services; 0-939439),* P.O. Box 5070, Kingwood, TX 77325 (SAN 663-348X); 2218 Running Spring, Kingwood, TX 77339 (SAN 663-3498) Tel 713-358-6687.

Enctr *Imprint of* **Times Bks**

Ency Brit Ed, *(Encyclopaedia Britannica Educational Corp.; 0-87827; 0-8347),* Affil. of Encyclopaedia Britannica, Inc., 425 N. Michigan Ave., Chicago, IL 60611 (SAN 201-3851) Tel 312-321-6800; Toll free: 800-554-9862.

Ency Brit Inc, *(Encyclopaedia Britannica, Inc.; 0-85229),* 310 S. Michigan Ave., Chicago, IL 60604 (SAN 204-1464) Tel 312-347-7000; Toll free: 800-554-9862.

End Age Ministries, *(End of the Age Ministries; 0-936131),* P.O. Box 3321, Littleton, CO 80161 (SAN 697-0974) Tel 303-797-1000; 1508 W. Briarwood Ave., Littleton, CO 80120 (SAN 697-0982).

End is Here Pubns, *(End is Here Pubns., The; 0-9607640),* 1522 Micheltorena , No. 4, Los Angeles, CA 90026 (SAN 663-5350).

End-Times Mini, *(End-Time Ministries; 0-9615220),* P.O. Box 55127, Tulsa, OK 74155 (SAN 695-1503) Tel 918-258-4767.

End Violence, *(End Violence Against the Next Generation, Inc.; 0-932141),* 977 Keeler Ave., Berkeley, CA 94708-1498 (SAN 225-9184) Tel 415-527-0454.

Endeavor Pub, *(Endeavor Publishing Co.; 0-942172),* 30064 Annapolis Cir., Inkster, MI 48141 (SAN 204-1448); Dist. by: Baker & Taylor Co., Midwest Div., 501 Gladiola Ave., Momence, IL 60954 (SAN 169-2100) Tel 815-472-2444; Dist. by: Baker & Taylor Co., Eastern Div., 50 Kirby Ave., Somerville, NJ 08876 (SAN 169-4901) Tel 201-526-8000.

Endless Rhymes, *(Endless Rhymes & Lines; 0-9615717),* 3714 Russell Ave. N., Minneapolis, MN 55412 (SAN 696-3889) Tel 612-521-8243.

Endowment Res Human Bio, *(Endowment for Research in Human Biology, The; 0-938321),* 250 Longwood Ave.,c/o Center for Biochemical & Biophysical Science & Medical, Boston, MA 02115 (SAN 661-244X) Tel 617-732-1367.

Endurance, *(Endurance Press; 0-910552),* 5695 Lumley St., Detroit, MI 48210 (SAN 203-8412) Tel 313-843-0310.

Energize, *(Energize Bks.; 0-940576),* Div. of Energize Assocs., 5450 Wissahickon Ave., Lobby A, Philadelphia, PA 19144 (SAN 218-5458) Tel 215-438-8342.

Energon Co, *(Energon Company; 0-9601552),* P. O. Box 1352, Laramie, WY 82070 (SAN 693-5443) Tel 307-742-3458.

Energy Blacksouth, *(Energy Blacksouth Press),* Box 441, Howard University, Washington, DC 20059 (SAN 208-1393); 2805 Southmore, Houston, TX 77004 (SAN 208-1407). Out of business.

Energy Educ, *(Energy Education Pubs.),* 1151 Conlon SE, Grand Rapids, MI 49506 (SAN 211-0105) Tel 616-949-3666.

Energy Forum, *(Energy Forum, Inc.; 0-917882),* P.O. Box 840, Lanham, MD 20706 (SAN 241-3795) Tel 301-927-5090; Dist. by: Maryland Historical Press, 9205 Tuckerman St., Lanham, MD 20706 (SAN 202-6147) Tel 301-577-2436.

Energy Self Suff, *(Energy Self-Sufficiency; 0-9608402),* P.O. Box 1410, Paso Robles, CA 93447 (SAN 240-639X) Tel 805-238-0437.

Energy Textbks, *(Energy Textbooks International, Inc.; 0-910649),* 2809 NW Expressway, Suite 540, Oklahoma City, OK 73112 (SAN 262-0200) Tel 405-842-6676; Dist. by: Penwell Books, 1421 S. Sheridan, Tulsa, OK 74112 (SAN 282-1559) Tel 918-835-3161; Dist. by: Kraftbilt Products, 7659 E. 46th Pl., Tulsa, OK 74145 (SAN 662-7234) Tel 918-628-1260.

Enetai Pr, *(Enetai Pr.; 0-9615811),* 105 S. Main St., Seattle, WA 98104 (SAN 696-7345) Tel 206-624-2540; Dist. by: Pacific Pipeline, 19215 66th Ave. S., Kent, WA 98032 (SAN 208-2128) Tel 206-872-5523.

Eng Cocker Spaniel, *(English Cocker Spaniel Club of America, Inc.; 0-9613761),* P.O. Box 223, Sunderland, MA 01375 (SAN 225-5588) Tel 413-665-3567.

Eng Communi Inc, *(Englander Communications Inc.; 0-9613139),* 1111 E. Putnam Ave., Riverside, CT 06878 (SAN 294-7765) Tel 203-637-5900.

Eng Comp Tut, *(English I Computer Tutorials, Inc.; 0-915869),* 1617 N. Troy St., Chicago, IL 60647 (SAN 293-9363) Tel 312-489-1588.

Eng Educ Serv, *(English Educational Services International, Inc.; 0-936808),* 139 Massachusetts Ave., Boston, MA 02115 (SAN 215-160X) Tel 617-267-8063.

Eng Found, *(Engineering Foundation; 0-939204),* 345 E. 47th St., New York, NY 10017 (SAN 216-3772).

Eng Index Inc
See **Eng Info**

Eng Info, *(Engineering Information, Inc.; 0-911820; 0-87394),* 345 E. 47th St., New York, NY 10017 (SAN 203-8420) Tel 212-705-7615.

Eng Joint Coun
See **AAES**

Eng Language, *(English Language Services; 0-87789; 0-89285; 0-89318),* Div. of Washington Educational Research Associates, Inc., 5761 Buckingham Pkwy., Culver City, CA 90230 (SAN 281-6326) Tel 213-642-099414350 NW Science Park Dr., Portland, OR 97229 (SAN 281-6334).

Eng Pr
See **Engineering**

Eng Pubns, *(Engineering Pubns.; 0-9605004),* P.O. Box 302, Blacksburg, VA 24060 (SAN 220-0481).

Engdahl Typo, *(Engdahl Typography; 0-939489),* 829 St. Helena Ave., Santa Rosa, CA 95404 (SAN 663-3935) Tel 707-544-4532; Dist. by: Clamshell Press, 160 California Ave., Santa Rosa, CA 95404 (SAN 219-1512).

Engelmeier, *(Engelmeier, Philip A.; 0-9605002),* 909 Geary-517, San Francisco, CA 94109 (SAN 215-6415).

†**Engineering,** *(Engineering Pr., Inc.; 0-910554),* P.O. Box 1, San Jose, CA 95103-0001 (SAN 201-3878) Tel 408-258-4503; CIP.

Engineers Pr, *(Engineer's Pr.; 0-930644),* P.O. Box 1651, Coral Gables, FL 33134 (SAN 201-5668) Tel 305-856-0031.

Engler Pub, *(Engler Publishing; 0-9615003),* 6117 Linden Rd., Woodbury, MN 55125 (SAN 693-9430) Tel 612-735-7192.

English Fact, *(English Factory, The; 0-911349),* 2202 N. Mitchel St., Phoenix, AZ 85006 (SAN 269-9257) Tel 602-258-7747.

English Lang
See **Eng Language**

Eno River Pr, *(Eno River Press, Inc.; 0-88024),* P.O. Box 4900, Duke Sta., Durham, NC 27706 (SAN 217-3573) Tel 919-929-0078.

Enoch Pratt, *(Enoch Pratt Free Library; 0-910556),* 400 Cathedral St., Baltimore, MD 21201-4484 (SAN 201-3916) Tel 301-396-5494.

Enquiry Pr, *(Enquiry Press; 0-941494),* 799 Broadway, Suite 325, New York, NY 10003 (SAN 239-0876) Tel 212-982-2406.

ENR Word, *(ENR Wordsmiths; 0-911511),* P.O. Box 160081, Miami, FL 33116 (SAN 264-2468) Tel 305-596-4523.

Enrich, *(Enrich; 0-933358; 0-86582),* Subs. of Ohaus Scale Corp., 2325 Paragon Dr., San Jose, CA 95131 (SAN 213-2168) Tel 408-263-7111; Toll free: 800-ENRICH-1.

Enrich Enter, *(Enrichment Enterprises; 0-9609612),* 1424 Hacienda Pl., Pomona, CA 91768 (SAN 264-0260) Tel 714-622-4887.

Enrich-Ohaus
See **Enrich**

Enrichment
See **Enrich Enter**

Ensign Pr, *(Ensign Pr.; 0-9608996),* P.O. Box 638, Camden, ME 04843 (SAN 240-866X) Tel 207-236-6545.

Ensign Pub, *(Ensign Publishing Co.; 0-910558),* P.O. Box 298, Riverton, UT 84065 (SAN 686-287X).

†**Enslow Pubs,** *(Enslow Pubs., Inc.; 0-89490),* Bloy St. & Ramsey Ave., Box 777, Hillside, NJ 07205 (SAN 213-7518) Tel 201-964-4116; CIP.

Ensminger, *(Ensminger Publishing Co.; 0-941218),* 648 W. Sierra Ave., P.O. Box 429, Clovis, CA 93612 (SAN 239-4375).

Ent Emmanuel, *(Enterprises for Emmanuel; 0-9616332),* P.O. Box 2450, Elkhart, IN 46515 (SAN 659-1647) Tel 219-262-3440; 53038 Faith Ave., Elkhart, IN 46514 (SAN 659-1655).

Entelek, *(Entelek, Inc.; 0-87567),* Ward-Whidden Hse., The Hill, P.O. Box 1303, Portsmouth, NH 03801 (SAN 201-3924) Tel 603-436-0439.

†**Enter Achieve,** *(Enterprise Achievement Associates; 0-930305),* Hudson, OH 44236 (SAN 686-2837); CIP.

Enter Yellow, *(Entertainment Yellow Pages; 0-916909),* 6000 Sunset Blvd. No. 209, Hollywood, CA 90028 (SAN 655-8836) Tel 213-857-8326.

Enteracom Inc, *(Enteracom, Inc.; 0-936509),* 5070 Parkside Ave., Suite 1420, Philadelphia, PA 19131 (SAN 697-8282) Tel 215-877-9409.

Enterpress, *(Enterpress Partners; 0-939355),* P.O. Box 7097, Redlands, CA 92374 (SAN 662-6815); 1322 San Pablo, Redlands, CA 92373 (SAN 662-6823) Tel 714-798-1155.

Enterprise Bks UT, *(Enterprise Bks.; 0-936957),* 123 Westminster Ave., Salt Lake City, UT 84115 (SAN 658-6570) Tel 801-485-1585.

Enterprise Calif, *(Enterprise Pubns.; 0-918558),* P.O. Box 4001, Downey, CA 90241 (SAN 207-222X).

Enterprise Del, *(Enterprise Publishing, Inc.; 0-913804),* 725 Market St., Wilmington, DE 19801 (SAN 201-3932) Tel 302-654-0110.

Enterprise Educ, *(Enterprise for Education, Inc.;*
0-934653; 0-928609), 1320-A Santa Monica
Mall, Suite 205, Santa Monica, CA 90401
(SAN 694-0730) Tel 213-394-9864.

Enterprise IL, *(Enterprise Pubns.),* 20 N.
Wacker Dr., Chicago, IL 60606
(SAN 204-1421) Tel 312-332-3571.

Enterprise Pr, *(Enterprise Pr.; 0-9604726),* Box
108, Bath, MI 48808 (SAN 214-2406)
Tel 517-339-9564.

Enterprise Pub, *(Enterprise Publishing Assn.;*
0-939542), Box 29, W. Second St.,
Coudersport, PA 16915 (SAN 216-6704)
Tel 814-274-8044.

Enterprise Pubns *Imprint of* **Newspaper Ent**

Entertainment Factory, *(Entertainment Factory,*
The; 0-936086), P.O. Box 407, Cave Creek,
AZ 85331 (SAN 214-0098)
Tel 602-488-2510.

Entheos, *(Entheos Communications; 0-939750),*
Div. of Entheos Mountain Agriculture, P.O.
Box 370, Seabeck, WA 98380-0370
(SAN 216-3209) Tel 206-830-4758.
Imprints: Wild Skies Pr (Wild Skies Press).

Entity Pub Co, *(Entity Publishing Co.; 0-89913),*
1314 Larmor Ave., Rowland Heights, CA
91748 (SAN 213-3091) Tel 714-598-1755.

Entomography, *(Entomography Pubns.;*
0-9608404), 1722 J St., Suite 19,
Sacramento, CA 95814 (SAN 240-6403)
Tel 916-444-9133.

Entomol Soc, *(Entomological Society of*
America; 0-938522), 4603 Calvert Rd.,
College Park, MD 20740 (SAN 201-3940)
Tel 301-864-1334; P.O. Box 4104,
Hyattsville, MD 20781 (SAN 669-0769).

†Entomological Repr, *(Entomological Reprint*
Specialists; 0-911836), P.O. Box 77224,
Dockweiler Sta., Los Angeles, CA 90007
(SAN 201-4602) Tel 213-227-1285; *CIP.*

Entre Group, *(Entrepreneur Group; 0-936133),*
2311 Pontius St., Los Angeles, CA 90064
(SAN 697-0885) Tel 619-457-3260.

Entre Prods, *(Entrepreneurs Productions;*
0-911665), 5 White St., New York, NY
10013 (SAN 264-0279) Tel 212-966-6464.

Entreprenuer Pr
See Showcase Fairfield

Entropy Ltd, *(Entropy, Ltd.; 0-938876),* S.
Great Rd., Lincoln, MA 01773
(SAN 215-6423) Tel 617-259-8901.

Entry Pub, *(Entry Publishing, Inc.; 0-941342),*
27 W. 96th St., New York, NY 10025
(SAN 238-9754) Tel 212-662-9703.

†Entwhistle Bks, *(Entwhistle Bks.; 0-9601428;*
0-934558), P.O. Box 611, Glen Ellen, CA
95442 (SAN 211-0113) Tel 707-996-3901;
CIP.

Entwood Pub, *(Entwood Publishing, Inc.;*
0-9605978), P.O. Box 268, Wausau, WI
54402-0268 (SAN 216-7301)
Tel 715-842-7250; Dist. by: Caroline Hse.,
Inc., 5S 250 Frontenac Rd., Naperville, IL
60540 (SAN 211-2280) Tel 312-983-6400.

Envir Studies Coun, *(Environmental Studies*
Council, Inc.; 0-916629), 2900 NE Indian
River Dr., Jensen Beach, FL 33457
(SAN 296-5127) Tel 305-334-1262.

Enviro Pr, *(Enviro Press; 0-937976),* c/o Aware
Inc., 621 Mainstream Dr., Nashville, TN
37228 (SAN 220-049X) Tel 615-255-2288;
Dist. by: Butterworth Publishers, 80
Montvale Ave., Stoneham, MA 02180
(SAN 200-500X) Tel 617-438-8464.

Enviro Resources *Imprint of* **Commonweal PA**

Environ Design, *(Environmental Design &*
Research Ctr.; 0-915250), 261 Port Royal
Ave., Foster City, CA 94404
(SAN 285-0125).

Environ Info
See EIC Intell

†Environ Law Inst, *(Environmental Law*
Institute; 0-911937), 1616 P. St., NW Suite
200, Washington, DC 20036
(SAN 225-0853) Tel 202-328-5150; *CIP.*

Environ Pr, *(Environmental Pr.; 0-936960),*
1201 Dusky Thrush, Austin, TX 78746
(SAN 214-3003) Tel 512-327-5479.

Environ Pubns, *(Environmental Pubns.*
Associates, Ltd; 0-9606694), 17 Jefryn Blvd.
W., Deer Park, NY 11729 (SAN 209-5564)
Tel 516-667-8896.

Environ Res Inst, *(Environmental Research*
Institute of Michigan; 0-9603590), P.O. Box
8618, Ann Arbor, MI 48107
(SAN 213-2176).

Environ Stud
See Envir Studies Coun

Envision Comm, *(Envision Communications;*
0-9605942), 10 Thurlow Terr., Albany, NY
12203 (SAN 216-6232) Tel 518-462-1135.

Envo Pub Co, *(ENVO Publishing Co. Inc.;*
0-932871), P.O. Box 415, Bethlehem, PA
18016 (SAN 688-9913) Tel 215-691-1339.

Envoy Press, *(Envoy Pr., Inc.; 0-938719),* 141
E. 44th St., Suite 511, New York, NY 10017
(SAN 661-5023) Tel 212-696-0887.

EO Pr, *(EO Pr.; 0-935830),* RR 1, Box 353-A
Minuet Ln., Kingston, NY 12401
(SAN 221-1858) Tel 914-336-8797.

Epic Pub Inc, *(Epic Publishing, Inc.; 0-9616122),*
Country Green Shopette, 3055 E. Hwy. 50,
Canon City, CO 81212 (SAN 699-6884)
Tel 303-275-0555.

Epic Pubns, *(Epic Pubns., Inc.; 0-914244),* 4420
Westover Dr., Orchard Lake, MI 48033
(SAN 203-8439) Tel 313-626-6217.

EPICA, *(Ecumenical Program for Interamerican*
Communication & Action; 0-918346), 1470
Irving St. NW, Washington, DC 20010
(SAN 207-8244) Tel 202-332-0292.

Epicurean, *(Epicurean Traveler Pr.),* 229-A
Upper Terr., San Francisco, CA 94117
(SAN 281-6741) Tel 415-731-0475.

Epidemiology, *(Epidemiology Resources Inc.;*
0-917227), P.O. Box 57, Chestnut Hill, MA
02167 (SAN 656-0342) Tel 617-734-9100.

EPIGEM, *(EPIGEM; 0-916705),* 5914 Pulaski
Ave., Philadelphia, PA 19144
(SAN 654-1445) Tel 215-849-4510.

Epimetheus Pr, *(Epimetheus Pr., Inc.; 0-88008),*
P.O. Box 565, Gracie Sq. Sta., New York,
NY 10028 (SAN 285-0133)
Tel 212-879-0553; P.O. Box 4508, Sunrise
Sta., Ft. Lauderdale, FL 33338
(SAN 285-0141) Tel 305-522-4496; P.O.
Box 361, Blackwood, NJ 08012
(SAN 658-0599).

Epiphany Pr, *(Epiphany Press; 0-916700),* P.O.
Box 14606, San Francisco, CA 94114
(SAN 206-5037) Tel 415-431-1917.

Episcopal Ctr, *(Episcopal Ctr. for Evangelism;*
0-918903), P.O. Box 920, Live Oak, FL
32060 (SAN 208-1598).

Epistemics, *(Epistemics Institute Pr.; 0-930371),*
Subs. of Institute for Applied Epistemics,
8620 Wilshire Blvd., Suite 104, Beverly Hills,
CA 90211 (SAN 670-7637)
Tel 213-659-4541; Orders to: P.O. Box
18672, Los Angeles, CA 90007
(SAN 662-247X) Tel 213-389-0307.

Epistemology Pubs, *(Epistemology Publishers;*
0-931889), P.O. Box 564, Mableton, GA
30059 (SAN 686-0338) Tel 404-944-0917.

†EPM Pubns, *(EPM Pubns.; 0-914440;*
0-939009), 1003 Turkey Run Rd., McLean,
VA 22101 (SAN 206-7498)
Tel 703-442-7810; Orders to: P.O. Box 490,
McLean, VA 22101 (SAN 206-7501); *CIP.*

Epoch Pr, *(Epoch Pr.; 0-9614068),* P.O. Box
3047, San Rafael, CA 94912
(SAN 693-9996) Tel 415-332-0685.

Epsilon Pi Tau, *(Epsilon Pi Tau),* Technology
Building, Bowling Green State University,
Bowling Green, OH 43403 (SAN 224-5140)
Tel 419-372-2425.

Epsilon Pr
See Potshot Pr

Epstein M C, *(Epstein, Max C.; 0-9612046),* 1
Montgomery Pl., Brooklyn, NY 11215
(SAN 286-7796) Tel 718-783-1605.

Equal Employ, *(Equal Employment Advisory*
Council; 0-937856), 1015 Fifteenth St. NW,
Suite 1220, Washington, DC 20005
(SAN 220-0511).

Equal Just Con, *(Equal Justice Consultants &*
Educational Products; 0-930413), P.O. Box
5582, Eugene, OR 97405 (SAN 682-0492)
Tel 503-343-6761.

Equality Pr, *(Equality Pr.; 0-938795),* 42
Ranchita Way, Chico, CA 95928
(SAN 661-4914) Tel 916-895-5249.

Equanimity, *(Equanimity Pr.; 0-941362),* P.O.
Box 839, Bolinas, CA 94924
(SAN 238-9762); Dist. by: Bookpeople, 2929
Fifth St., Berkeley, CA 94710
(SAN 168-9517) Tel 415-549-3030
(SAN 662-0051).

Equipment Guide
See Dataquest

Equity, *(Equity Pr.; 0-931769),* P.O. Box 3841,
Tallahassee, FL 32315-3841
(SAN 684-8877) Tel 904-385-5497.

†Equity Inst, *(Equity Institute The; 0-932469),*
P.O. Box 30245, Bethesda, MD 20814
(SAN 687-4215) Tel 301-654-2904; *CIP.*

Equity Policy, *(Equity Policy Center (EPOC);*
0-941696), 4818 Drummond Ave., Chevy
Chase, MD 20815 (SAN 239-4235)
Tel 301-656-4475.

Equity Pub NH, *(Equity Publishing Corp.;*
0-87454), Main St., Orford, NH 03777
(SAN 204-1383) Tel 603-351-4374.

ERA-CCR, *(ERA/CCR Corp.; 0-913935),* P.O.
Box 650, Nyack, NY 10960
(SAN 217-5622) Tel 914-358-6806; Toll
free: 800-845-8402.

Era Davidson, *(Era Press; 0-9605270),* Box 548,
Davidson, NC 28036 (SAN 215-8612).

ERA Pr *Imprint of* **Educ Res MA**

Erde Intl, *(Erde International; 0-911973),* P.O.
Box 25007, Phoenix, AZ 85002
(SAN 264-701X) Tel 602-285-1661.

ERGO Business Bks, *(Ergo Business Bks.;*
0-941046), 1401 Pasadena Ave., Fillmore,
CA 93015 (SAN 217-359X)
Tel 805-495-3237.

ERIC Clear, *(ERIC Clearinghouse on*
Information Resources; 0-937597), Syracuse
Univ., Schl. of Education, Huntington Hall,
Syracuse, NY 13244-2340 (SAN 672-8189)
Tel 315-423-3640; Orders to: Syracuse Univ.,
030 Huntington Hall, Syracuse, NY
13244-2340 (SAN 662-250X).

Eric's Pr, *(Edges Design Co.-Eric's Pr.;*
0-911985), Box 1680, Tahoe City, CA
95730 (SAN 264-6668) Tel 408-663-0633.

Ericson, *(Ericson; 0-9605868),* 215 Foster Dr.,
Des Moines, IA 50312 (SAN 220-1682)
Tel 515-255-0798.

Ericson Bks, *(Ericson Bks.; 0-911317),* 1614
Redbud St., Nacogdoches, TX 75961
(SAN 263-0923) Tel 409-564-3625.

Erie Art Mus, *(Erie Art Museum; 0-9616623),*
411 State St., Erie, PA 16501
(SAN 661-2458) Tel 814-459-5477.

Erie St Pr, *(Erie Street Pr., The; 0-942582),* 221
S. Clinton Ave., Oak Park, IL 60302
(SAN 285-015X) Tel 312-848-5716.

†Eriksson, *(Eriksson, Paul S., Pub.; 0-8397),* 208
Battell Bldg., Middlebury, VT 05753
(SAN 201-6702) Tel 802-388-7303; Dist.
by: Independent Publishers Group, 1 Pleasant
Ave., Pt. Washington, NY 11050
(SAN 287-2544) Tel 516-944-9325; *CIP.*

Erin Hills, *(Erin Hills Pubs.; 0-9600754),* 1390
Fairway Dr., San Luis Obispo, CA 93401
(SAN 206-4537) Tel 805-543-3050.

Eros Pub, *(Eros Publishing, Co.; 0-911571),*
P.O. Box 355, Parkchester Sta., Bronx, NY
10462 (SAN 264-0317) Tel 212-828-5569.

Erskine, *(Erskine, Kathryn A.; 0-9605058),* Box
398, Hurricane, WV 25526
(SAN 215-9538).

Erskine Pr, *(Erskine Pr.; 0-914353),* P.O. Box
21622, Concord, CA 94518
(SAN 289-6214) Tel 415-687-8313.

ERUHG, *(External Representation of the*
Ukrainian Helsinki Group; 0-86725), P.O.
Box 770, Cooper Sta., New York, NY 10003
(SAN 217-0701) Tel 212-564-4334.

Ervin Pub Co, *(Ervin, W & S, Publishing Co.;*
0-915447), 739 Indian Hill Dr., Port
Orange, FL 32019 (SAN 291-1531).

Erwin Marvin M, *(Erwin/Marvin M.; 0-914598),*
661 Mar Vista Dr., Los Osos, CA 93402
(SAN 670-6959) Tel 805-528-0783.

Escape Ventures, *(Escape Ventures Inc.;*
0-930039), P.O. Box 4330, Virginia Beach,
VA 23454 (SAN 669-7844)
Tel 804-481-1026.

Escortguide, *(Escortguide: The People*
Connection To New Mexico; 0-9607818),
535 Cordova Rd., Suite 125, Santa Fe, NM
87501 (SAN 238-1583) Tel 505-988-7099.

ESE Calif, *(ESE California; 0-912076),* 509 N.
Harbor Blvd., La Habra, CA 90631
(SAN 201-4629) Tel 213-691-0737.

Esmond Julie Pub, *(Esmond Julie Publishing;*
0-9616333), 7787 Carraway Ct., Maineville,
OH 45039 (SAN 659-1701)
Tel 513-398-8395.

ESP, *(ESP, Inc.; 0-8209),* P.O. Drawer 5037,
1201 E. Johnson Ave., Jonesboro, AR 72401
(SAN 241-497X); Toll free: 800-643-0280.

ESP Corp, *(ESP Corp.; 0-9601610),* 195
Cortlandt St., Belleville, NJ 07109
(SAN 211-4194).

Esperance Enter, *(Esperance Enterprises, Inc.;*
0-930757), Box 218, 14625 Watt Rd.,
Novelty, OH 44072 (SAN 679-1654)
Tel 216-338-1625.

Esperanto League North Am, *(Esperanto League for North America, Inc.; 0-939785),* P.O. Box 1129, El Cerrito, CA 94530 (SAN 201-8241) Tel 415-653-0998; 5712 Hollis St., Emeryville, CA 94608 (SAN 669-0785).

Esperanto Soc, *(Esperanto Society of Chicago; 0-9615986),* P.O. Box 1698, Chicago, IL 60690 (SAN 698-1534) Tel 312-549-0057.

ESPress, *(ESPress; 0-917200),* P.O. Box 8606, Washington, DC 20011 (SAN 206-748X) Tel 202-723-4578.

Esprit, *(Esprit; 0-9614437),* 900 Minnesota St., San Francisco, CA 94107 (SAN 689-352X) Tel 415-648-6900.

†**Esquire,** *(Esquire, Inc.; 0-695),* Div. of Follett Corp., 1010 W. Washington Blvd., Chicago, IL 60607 (SAN 200-2035); *CIP.*

Essai Seay Pubns, *(Essai Seay Publishing Co.; 0-9607958),* P.O. Box 55, East St. Louis, IL 62202 (SAN 240-0715) Tel 618-271-5323.

Essays in Lit W Ill U, *(Essays in Literature; 0-934312),* Dept. of English, Western Illinois Univ., Macomb, IL 61455 (SAN 212-6583) Tel 309-298-2212.

Essence Pubns, *(Essence Pubns; 0-940756),* 168 Woodbridge Ave., Highland Park, NJ 08904 (SAN 211-4909) Tel 201-572-3120.

Essex County Brd
See Essex Cty Bd Sup

Essex County MA, *(Essex County History),* P.O. Box 418, West Newbury, MA 01985 (SAN 209-3731) Tel 617-465-5397. Out of business.

Essex Cty Bd Sup, *(Essex County Board of Supervisors),* P.O. Box 1079, Tappahannock, VA 22560 (SAN 669-6740).

Essex Inst, *(Essex Institute; 0-88389),* 132 Essex St., Salem, MA 01970 (SAN 203-8447) Tel 617-744-3390.

Essex Pr, *(Essex Press; 0-930381),* Rte. 1, P.O. Box 77C, Erwin, TN 37650 (SAN 670-7645) Tel 615-743-7685.

Essex Pub Ltd, *(Essex Publishing, Ltd.; 0-912889),* P.O. Box 317, Ada, MI 49301 (SAN 283-2585) Tel 616-459-0031.

Essex Pubns, *(Essex Pubns; 0-930332),* Portsmouth, NH 03824 (SAN 694-3144) Tel 603-436-7974.

Estacado Bks, *(Estacado Books),* P.O. Box 4516, Lubbock, TX 79409 (SAN 207-6756) Tel 806-799-1986.

Esther McBride, *(McBride, Esther; 0-9613017),* 1460 Bramble Ct., Rio Rancho, NM 87124 (SAN 293-8928) Tel 505-892-6277.

Estonian Wrld, *(Estonian World Council Inc.; 0-932595),* 2206 Chilham Rd., Baltimore, MD 21209 (SAN 687-5114) Tel 301-542-1735.

Estrela Pr, *(Estrela Press; 0-943632),* 2318 2nd Ave., Box 23, Seattle, WA 98121 (SAN 238-2792) Tel 206-322-5402.

Estrilda Dist, *(Estrilda Distributors Inc.),* 1005 W. Hill St., Champaign, IL 61821 (SAN 677-4806) Tel 217-398-6975.

Estuarine Res, *(Estuarine Research Federation; 0-9608990),* Belle Baruch Institute, Univ. of South Carolina, Columbia, SC 29208 (SAN 241-3027) Tel 803-777-3916.

ETC Assocs, *(ETC Assocs.; 0-910565),* 507 Rider Rd., Clayville, NY 13322 (SAN 269-9796) Tel 315-839-5184.

†**ETC Pubns,** *(ETC Pubns.; 0-88280),* 700 E. Vereda del Sur, Palm Springs, CA 92262 (SAN 201-4637) Tel 619-325-5352; Orders to: Order Dept., Box ETC, Palm Springs, CA 92263-1608 (SAN 201-4645); *CIP.*

Eterna Pr, *(Eterna Pr.; 0-934670),* P.O. Box 1344, Oak Brook, IL 60521 (SAN 221-1807).

Eternal Ent, *(Eternal Enterprises; 0-917578),* P.O. Box 60913, Sacramento, CA 95860 (SAN 206-4383). Name Formerly L P Price.

Etheridge Minist, *(Etheridge, G. & M., Ministries, Inc.; 0-937417),* P.O. Box 564, Sikeston, MO 63801 (SAN 658-8581) Tel 314-471-9344; 415 Louise Ave., Sikeston, MO 63801 (SAN 658-859X).

Ethical Enterprises, *(Ethical Enterprises; 0-9614810),* 6083 Charlesworth St., Dearborn Heights, MI 48127 (SAN 692-9311) Tel 313-278-7074.

†**Ethics & Public Policy,** *(Ethics & Public Policy Ctr., Inc.; 0-89633),* 1030 15th St., NW, Suite 300, Washington, DC 20005 (SAN 216-132X) Tel 202-682-1200; *CIP.*

Ethics Res Ctr, *(Ethics Resource Ctr., Inc.; 0-916152),* 1025 Connecticut Ave., NW, Suite 1003, Washington, DC 20036 (SAN 201-6893) Tel 202-223-3411.

Ethiopian Ent, *(Ethiopian Cookbook Enterprise; 0-9616345),* 3800 Powell Ln., No. 404, Falls Church, VA 22041 (SAN 658-7747) Tel 703-823-0988.

Ethnographic Arts Pubns, *(Ethnographic Arts Pubns.; 0-9611006),* 1040 Erica Rd., Mill Valley, CA 94941 (SAN 282-8650) Tel 415-383-2998.

Ethnographica *Imprint of* **Barber Pr**

†**Ethridge,** *(Ethridge, Blaine, Bks.; 0-87917),* 15 E. Kirby, No. 510, Detroit, MI 48202 (SAN 201-4327) Tel 313-872-3160; *CIP.*

ETS
See Educ Testing Serv

Ettinger, *(Ettinger, L. J.; 0-9614840),* 16170 Rhyolite Cir., Reno, NV 89511 (SAN 693-1049) Tel 702-851-3061; Orders to: 3949 Knobhill Dr., Sherman Oaks, CA 91423 (SAN 699-5950) Tel 818-789-7724.

Eubanks Intl Pubns, *(Eubanks International Pubns., Inc.; 0-9616214),* P.O. Box 3634, Silver Spring, MD 20901 (SAN 658-523X) Tel 301-496-4768; 1131 University Blvd., W., Silver Spring, MD 20902 (SAN 658-5248).

Eucalyptus Pr, *(Eucalyptus Pr.; 0-9611980),* P.O. Box 7073, Kansas City, MO 64113 (SAN 287-7430).

Euclid NW Pubns, *(Euclid Northwest Pubns.; 0-9615088),* 4227 Crestview St., Wenatchee, WA 98801 (SAN 694-1478) Tel 509-662-8131; Orders to: 4145 80th Ave., SE, Mercer Island, WA 98040 (SAN 662-3336).

Euclid Pr, *(Euclid Pr.; 0-936583),* 900 Euclid Ave., Apt. 205, Santa Monica, CA 90403 (SAN 698-0805) Tel 213-394-2868.

Euclid Pub, *(Euclid Publishing Co., The; 0-935490),* Dist. by: Bond & Bacon Assocs., P.O. Box 121, Cathedral Sta., New York, NY 10025 (SAN 211-6057).

Eupsychian, *(Eupsychian Pr., The; 0-939344),* 950 Roadrunner Rd., Austin, TX 78746 (SAN 216-5627) Tel 512-327-2214; Orders to: P.O. Box 3090, Austin, TX 78764-3090 (SAN 662-006X).

EUR *Imprint of* **Unipub**

Eur-Am Music, *(European American Music; 0-913574),* P.O. Box 850, Valley Forge, PA 19482 (SAN 201-7393) Tel 215-648-0506.

Eurail Guide, *(Eurail Guide Annual; 0-912442),* 27540 Pacific Coast Hwy., Malibu, CA 90265 (SAN 207-9704) Tel 213-457-7286.

Euramerica Pr, *(Euramerica Pr.; 0-916876),* 381 N. Main St., Pittston, PA 18640 (SAN 208-1563) Tel 717-693-4678.

Eurasia Pr NJ
See Eurasia Pr NY

Eurasia Pr NY, *(Eurasia Pr.; 0-932030),* 168 State St., Teaneck, NJ 07666-3516 (SAN 222-7886) Tel 212-564-4099; Toll free: 800-242-7737; 302 Fifth Ave., New York, NY 48202 (SAN 658-0602); 21 Market St., Paterson, NJ 07509 (SAN 658-0610).

†**Eureka Pubns,** *(Eureka Pubns.; 0-942848),* Box 372, Mantua, NJ 08051 (SAN 240-2165) Tel 609-468-4145; *CIP.*

Eureka-Vonpali
See Von Palisaden Pubns

Euro-Dutch Pub, *(Euro-Dutch, Pubs.),* P.O. Box 1070, Buffalo, NY 14221-1070 (SAN 265-3826).

Eurofit Pub, *(Eurofit Publishing Co.; 0-938821),* 70 E. Ridgewood Ave., Ridgewood, NJ 07450 (SAN 661-8200) Tel 201-652-2012.

Eurolingua, *(Eurolingua; 0-931922),* P.O. Box 101, Bloomington, IN 47402-0101 (SAN 222-7894).

Europa, *(Europa; 0-905118),* c/o Unipub, Customer Service Dept., P.O. Box 1222, Ann Arbor, MI 48106 (SAN 202-5264).

Europa AZ, *(Europa Co.; 0-937215),* 5645 W. Camelback Rd., Phoenix, AZ 85031 (SAN 658-7011) Tel 602-846-0124.

Eustace CSB, *(Eustace, Herbert W., C.S.B.),* P.O. Box 7328, Berkeley, CA 94707 (SAN 276-9743) Tel 415-524-0846.

Euterpe Pr, *(Euterpe Pr.; 0-9616315),* 45 Buckingham Dr., Billerica, MA 01821 (SAN 658-7054) Tel 617-667-6377.

Eva Hruska, *(Hruska, Eva J. Cummings; 0-9614616),* Rte. 2, Schuyler, NE 68661 (SAN 691-6805) Tel 402-352-3645.

Eval Dissemination
See Natl Dissem Ctr

Evanel, *(Evanel Assocs.; 0-918948),* Box 42, Northfield, OH 44067 (SAN 209-4347) Tel 216-467-1750.

Evang & Ref, *(Evangelical & Reformed Historical Society; 0-910564),* 555 W. James St., Lancaster, PA 17603 (SAN 281-6849).

Evang Assn, *(Evangelist Assn.; 0-9603014),* P.O. Box 368014, Chicago, IL 60636 (SAN 217-2380).

Evang Sisterhood Mary, *(Evangelical Sisterhood of Mary),* 9849 N. 40th St., Phoenix, AZ 85028 (SAN 211-8335) Tel 602-996-4040.

Evang Tchr, *(Evangelical Teacher Training Assn.; 0-910566),* 110 Bridge St., P.O. Box 327, Wheaton, IL 60189 (SAN 203-8471) Tel 312-668-6400.

Evangel Indiana, *(Evangel Pr., (IN); 0-916035),* Div. of Brethren in Christ Church, 301 N. Elm, Nappanee, IN 46550-0189 (SAN 211-7940) Tel 219-773-3164.

Evangel Pr & Drama Serv, *(Evangeline Pr. & Dramatists Service, Inc.; 0-935425),* 1071 Sunny Dell Ln., Sunny Dell Acres, Hueytown, AL 35023 (SAN 696-4982) Tel 205-426-1034.

Evangel Pubns, *(Evangel Pubns; 0-935515),* P.O. Box 11007, Huntsville, AL 35814 (SAN 696-4931) Tel 205-533-0498; 1119 Retlaw St., Huntsville, AL 35816 (SAN 696-494X).

Evangelical Lit, *(Evangelical Literature League, The; 0-939125),* P.O. Box 6219, Grand Rapids, MI 49516-6219 (SAN 662-4812); 941 Wealthy, SE, Grand Rapids, MI 49516-6219 (SAN 662-4820) Tel 616-454-3196.

Evans
See M Evans

Evans FL, *(Evans Pubns; 0-932715),* Subs. of Eva-Tone, Inc., 4801 Ulmerton Rd., Clearwater, FL 33520 (SAN 687-7419) Tel 813-577-7000.

Evans Pub, *(Evans Publishing Co.; 0-9614583),* P.O. Box 26126, Denver, CO 80226 (SAN 692-7084).

Evans Pub Hse, *(Evans Publishing Hse.; 0-934889),* P.O. Box 1042, Boca Raton, FL 33429 (SAN 694-4442).

Evans Pubns, *(Evans Pubns.; 0-934188),* P.O. Box 520, Perkins, OK 74059 (SAN 212-9019) Tel 405-547-2411.

Ever *Imprint of* **Grove**

EverBC *Imprint of* **Grove**

Everest Hse
See Dodd

†**Everett-Edwards,** *(Everett/Edwards, Inc.; 0-912112),* P.O. Box 1060, DeLand, FL 32720 (SAN 201-4653) Tel 904-734-7458; *CIP.*

Everett Pr *Imprint of* **Street Pr**

Evergreen, *(Evergreen Pr., Inc.; 0-914510),* P.O. Box 4971, Walnut Creek, CA 94596 (SAN 206-3638) Tel 415-935-3700; 3380 Vincent Rd., Pleasant Hill, CA 94523 (SAN 658-0629).

Evergreen Calif, *(Evergreen Publishing Co.; 0-939083),* 136 S. Atlantic Blvd., Monterey Park, CA 91754 (SAN 662-9113) Tel 818-281-3622; Dist. by: East Wind Bks. & Art, 1435 Stockton St., San Francisco, CA 94133 (SAN 200-7584). Do not confuse with Evergreen Pub., North Andover, MA, or Evergreen Pub., Seattle, WA.

Evergreen Christmas
See Evergreen Christmas

Evergreen Co, *(Evergreen Publishing Co.; 0-9611960),* 1665 Nome St., Aurora, CO 80010 (SAN 286-7427) Tel 303-366-0879.

Evergreen Comm, *(Evergreen Communications, Inc.; 0-943782),* 301 W. Washington, Bloomington, IL 61701 (SAN 241-192X) Tel 309-829-9411. *Imprints:* Pantagraph Bks (Pantagraph Books).

Evergreen Dist, *(Evergreen Book Distributors; 0-903729),* 6513 Lankershim Blvd., Suite 37, N. Hollywood, CA 91606 (SAN 223-1522) Tel 818-986-9689.

Evergreen Ed, *(Evergreen Educational Services; 0-9616769),* P.O. Box 3863, Pinedale, CA 93650 (SAN 661-2482); 622 E. Tenaya, Fresno, CA 93710 (SAN 661-2490) Tel 209-439-6040.

Evergreen Ent, *(Evergreen Enterprises; 0-933183),* P.O. Box 763, Laurel, MD 20707-0763 (SAN 691-7186) Tel 301-953-1861.

Evergreen Pacific, *(Evergreen Pacific; 0-9609036),* 4535 Union Bay Place NE, Seattle, WA 98105 (SAN 240-9119).

Evergreen Paddleways, *(Evergreen Paddleways; 0-916166),* 1416 21st St., Two Rivers, WI 54241 (SAN 205-6208) Tel 414-794-8485.

Evergreen Pr, *(Evergreen Pr.; 0-913056),* P.O. Box 306, Avalon, CA 90704 (SAN 206-9415) Tel 213-510-1700.

Evergreen Prods, *(Evergreen Productions; 0-9613919),* 3300 16th St., NW, No. 714, Washington, DC 20010 (SAN 682-5249) Tel 202-483-4392.

Evergreen Pub WA, *(Evergreen Publishing Co.; 0-937627),* 901 Lenora, Seattle, WA 98121 (SAN 659-1728) Tel 206-624-8400.

Everlast Pr, *(Everlast Pr.; 0-9607262),* 365 Maple St., W. Hempstead, NY 11552 (SAN 239-0884) Tel 516-483-8581.

Everson Mus, *(Everson Museum of Art; 0-914407),* 401 Harrison St., Syracuse, NY 13202 (SAN 278-7458) Tel 315-474-6064.

Everybodys Pr, *(Everybody's Press),* Fame Ave.,, Hanover, PA 17331 (SAN 237-949X) Tel 717-632-3535.

Everyday Ser, *(Everyday Series; 0-915517),* 13 Riverview Terrace, Rensselaer, NY 12144 (SAN 291-154X) Tel 518-449-8737.

EVKAR Pub, *(EVKAR Publishing; 0-9616965),* 842 Eastfield Rd., Westbury, NY 11590 (SAN 661-8197) Tel 516-334-4101.

Evolutionary Pr
See Mindbody

Evolving Pubns, *(Evolving Pubns.; 0-912389),* 2531 Sawtelle Blvd., No. 42, Los Angeles, CA 90064 (SAN 265-2390) Tel 213-390-5993.

†**EW Ctr HI,** *(East-West Ctr.; 0-86638),* 1777 East-West Rd., Honolulu, HI 96848 (SAN 210-802X) Tel 808-944-7391; *CIP.*

EW Eng, *(EW Engineering, Inc.; 0-931728),* P.O. Box 28, Dunn Loring, VA 22027 (SAN 212-3487).

Ewing Pubns, *(Ewing Pubns.),* 114 Main St., Kingston, NJ 08528 (SAN 212-9388).

Ex Libris ID, *(Ex Libris; 0-9605212),* Box 225, Sun Valley, ID 83353 (SAN 215-7608) Tel 208-622-8174.

Ex Libris PA, *(Ex Libris; 0-9617141),* Logan Square East, Apt. 2305, Philadelphia, PA 19103 (SAN 682-2800) Tel 215-563-1800.

Ex Libris Sun
See Ex Libris ID

Exanimo Pr, *(Exanimo Pr.; 0-89316),* P.O. Box 18, 23520 Hwy. 12, Segundo, CO 81070 (SAN 209-0910).

Excel, *(Excel, Inc.; 0-9608992),* 200 W. Station St., Barrington, IL 60010 (SAN 237-9503) Tel 312-382-7272.

Excel Fitness, *(Excel Fitness, Pubs.; 0-916915),* P.O. Box 19257, Seattle, WA 98119 (SAN 656-0350) Tel 206-282-7476; Dist. by: Pacific Pipeline, 19215 66th Ave. S., Kent, WA 98032 (SAN 208-2128) Tel 206-872-5523.

Excel Pr, *(Excel Pr.; 0-9609582),* 459 59th St., Brooklyn, NY 11220 (SAN 262-0227) Tel 718-492-4789.

Excelsior Music Pub Co, *(Excelsior Music Publishing Co.; 0-935016),* 35-19 215th Pl., Bayside, NY 11361 (SAN 221-1742); Dist. by: STBS, 50 W. 23rd St., New York, NY 10010 (SAN 200-6162) Tel 212-206-8795.

Excelsior Pub, *(Excelsior Publishing; 0-9614096),* P.O. Box 141, Houston, DE 19954 (SAN 685-9879) Tel 302-422-3980.

Exceptional Parent
See Excptnl Parent

Exceptional Pr Inc, *(Exceptional Press, Inc.; 0-914420),* P.O. Box 344, San Juan Capistrano, CA 92675 (SAN 206-3646) Tel 714-493-8405.

Exceptional Res, *(Exceptional Resources Inc.; 0-935594),* P.O. Box 9221, Austin, TX 78766 (SAN 221-1750); Dist. by: Pro-ED, 5341 Industrial Oaks Blvd., Austin, TX 78735 (SAN 222-1349) Tel 512-892-3142.

Excerpta Medica *Imprint of* Elsevier

Excerpta Princeton, *(Excerpta Medica-Princeton),* 3131 Princeton Pike, Lawrenceville, NJ 08648 (SAN 209-5041).

Excogitations, *(Excogitations; 0-939597),* P.O. Box 6260, Pasadena, TX 77506 (SAN 663-6241); 226 E. Oak, Deer Park, TX 77536 (SAN 663-625X) Tel 713-476-1767.

Excptnl Parent, *(Exceptional Parent Pr., The; 0-930958),* 605 Commonwealth Ave., Boston, MA 02215 (SAN 211-5611) Tel 617-536-8961.

Exec Chauffeuring, *(Executive Chauffeuring Schl.; 0-9616215),* 3115 Fujita St., Torrance, CA 90505 (SAN 658-4799) Tel 213-534-3535.

Exec Ed Pr, *(Executive Education Press; 0-9606022),* Div. of Executive Education, Inc., P.O. Box 160, Camden, ME 04843 (SAN 216-8928) Tel 207-236-6782.

Exec Ent
See Exec Ent Inc

†**Exec Ent Inc,** *(Executive Enterprises, Inc.; 0-917386; 0-88057),* 22 W. 21st St., New York, NY 10010 (SAN 208-953X); Toll free: 800-645-7880; *CIP.*

Exec Grapevine, *(Executive Grapevine, Inc.),* Affil. of Executive Grapevine (London), 575 Madison Ave., Suite 1006, New York, NY 10022 (SAN 659-493X) Tel 212-605-0414.

†**Exec Reports,** *(Executive Reports Corp.; 0-13),* Subs. of Prentice-Hall, Inc., 190 Sylvan Ave., Englewood Cliffs, NJ 07632 (SAN 204-1294) Tel 201-592-2075; Orders to: Dept. 200-B, Englewood Cliffs, NJ 07632 (SAN 204-1308) Tel 201-767-5059; *CIP.*

Exec Sal, *(Executive Salary Research Co.; 0-912716),* 1685 Sunrise Dr., Lima, OH 45805 (SAN 201-8268) Tel 419-991-3936; Orders to: P.O. Box 832, Lima, OH 45802 (SAN 201-8276).

Exec Speaker Co, *(Executive Speaker Co., The; 0-930255),* P.O. Box 292437, Dayton, OH 45429 (SAN 670-8528) Tel 513-294-8493.

Exec Stand, *(Executive Standards, Inc.; 0-917818),* 811 East St., New Britain, CT 06051 (SAN 210-0797) Tel 203-224-3357.

Exec Systems, *(Executive Systems, Inc.; 0-937867),* 15300 Ventura Blvd., Suite 305, Sherman Oaks, CA 91403 (SAN 659-445X) Tel 818-990-3457.

Exec West, *(Executives West Publishing Co.; 0-939148),* 4250 E. Camelback, Suite 180K, Phoenix, AZ 85018 (SAN 219-9742).

Execucom Sys Corp, *(Execucom Systems Corp.; 0-911941),* 9442 Capital of Texas Hwy. N., Austin, TX 78759-6311 (SAN 264-0325) Tel 512-346-4980.

Executive Comm, *(Executive Communications; 0-917168),* 919 Third Ave., New York, NY 10022 (SAN 208-3043) Tel 212-421-3713.

Executive Ent, *(Executive Enterprises),* 5811 La Jolla Corona Dr., La Jolla, CA 92037 (SAN 209-1259) Tel 619-459-4901. Do Not Confuse with Executive Enterprises Pubns. in NY.

Executive Pub, *(Executive Publishing (MO); 0-943338),* Box 3155, Springfield, MO 65804 (SAN 240-6438) Tel 417-883-0950.

Exelrod Pr, *(Exelrod Press; 0-917388),* P.O. Box 2303, Pleasant Hill, CA 94523 (SAN 208-1555) Tel 415-934-3357.

Exeter Pub, *(Exeter Publishing Co.; 0-937193),* 3752 Motor Ave., Los Angeles, CA 90034 (SAN 699-8259) Tel 213-305-1762.

Exhibit Pr, *(Exhibit Press; 0-9607908),* N.E. Box 44844, Los Olivos Station, AZ 02130 (SAN 238-0315) Tel 413-528-4894.

Exhorters, *(Exhorters, Inc., The; 0-9609260),* P.O. Box 492, Vienna, VA 22180 (SAN 241-3825) Tel 703-698-6880.

Exile Pr, *(Exile Pr.; 0-933515),* P.O. Box 1768, Novato, CA 94948 (SAN 297-1747) Tel 415-883-2132.

†**Existential Bks,** *(Existential Books; 0-89231),* 1816 Stevens Ave. S., Suite 25, Minneapolis, MN 55403 (SAN 208-1547) Tel 612-871-7275; *CIP.*

Exodus Intl N Am, *(Exodus International North America; 0-931593),* P.O. Box 2121, San Rafael, CA 94912 (SAN 682-5214) Tel 415-454-0960.

Exodus Trust
See Specific Pr

Exp *Imprint of* Viking

Expansion Pr, *(Expansion Pr.; 0-9616099),* 852 Rosedale Ave., SE, Atlanta, GA 30312 (SAN 698-1224) Tel 404-622-7072.

Expedited, *(Expedited Publishing Co.; 0-9603122),* Div. of Parent Rights, Inc., P.O. Box 67, Scarborough, NY 10510 (SAN 213-490X).

Experiment Pr, *(Experiment Pr., The; 0-936141),* Div. of Experiment in International Living, Kipling Rd., Brattleboro, VT 05301 (SAN 696-7388) Tel 802-257-7751.

EXPIM Co, *(Expim Co.; 0-9611794),* P.O. Box 23084, Washington, DC 20026 (SAN 285-2446) Tel 202-426-8350; 7237 Hillmead Ct., Springfield, VA 22150 (SAN 285-2454).

Exploration Pr, *(Exploration Pr.; 0-913552),* Div. of Chicago Theological Seminary, Chicago Theological Seminary, 5757 S. University Ave., Chicago, IL 60637 (SAN 203-851X) Tel 312-752-5757.

Explorations Inst, *(Explorations Institute; 0-918600),* P.O. Box 1254, Berkeley, CA 94701 (SAN 210-8968).

Explorations Pr
See Explr Pr MA

Explorer Bks, *(Explorer Books; 0-9605938),* 601 LeGrand, Route 6, Panama City Beach, FL 32407 (SAN 216-6240) Tel 904-234-1378.

Explr Pr MA, *(Explorations Pr.; 0-941830),* P.O. Box 907, Greenfield, MA 01302 (SAN 239-2054).

Exponent, *(Exponent Ltd.; 0-935722),* Box 481, Bedford Hills, NY 10507 (SAN 214-3038).

Exposition
See Exposition Pr FL

Exposition Pr FL, *(Exposition Pr. of Florida, Inc.; 0-682),* 1701 Blount Rd., Suite C, Pompano Beach, FL 33069 (SAN 207-0642) Tel 305-979-3200. *Imprints:* Banner (Banner); Classic (Classic); Lochinvar (Lochinvar); OEG Found (O.E.G. Foundation); Testament (Testament); University (University).

ExPress, *(ExPress Publishing; 0-932956),* P.O. Box 1639, El Cerrito, CA 94530-4639 (SAN 208-6433) Tel 415-236-5496; Dist. by: Bookpeople, 2929 Fifth St., Berkeley, CA 94710 (SAN 168-9517) Tel 415-549-3030; Dist. by: Distributors, The, 702 S. Michigan, South Bend, IN 46618 (SAN 169-2488) Tel 219-232-8500; Dist. by: Cogan Bks., 4332 W. Artesia Ave., Fullerton, CA 92633 (SAN 168-9649) Tel 714-523-0309; Dist. by: Law Distributors, 14415 S. Main St., Gardena, CA (SAN 212-3681).

ExPressAll, *(ExPressAll; 0-936190),* 260 Dean Rd., Brookline, MA 02146 (SAN 207-5903) Tel 617-734-3508.

Expression, *(Expression Co.),* P.O. Box 153, Londonderry, NH 03053 (SAN 203-8536) Tel 603-432-5232.

Expressive Images Studio, *(Expressive Images Studio; 0-915701),* 1215 Kuehnle St., Ann Arbor, MI 48103 (SAN 292-4919) Tel 313-665-7804.

Expro Pr, *(Expro Pr.; 0-936391),* Boston College, 519 B McGuinn Hall, Chestnut Hill, MA 02167 (SAN 697-3345) Tel 617-552-4198; Dist. by: Talman Co., 150 Fifth Ave., Rm. 514, New York, NY 10011 (SAN 200-5204) Tel 212-620-3182.

Extension Div, *(Extension Division, Univ., of Missouri; 0-933842),* Argricultural Editor's Office, 1-98 Agriculture Building, Univ. of Missouri, Columbia, MO 65211 (SAN 679-1638); Orders to: Extension Pubns., Univ. of Missouri, 222 S. Fifth St., Columbia, MO 65211 (SAN 688-427X) Tel 314-882-7216.

Extequer, *(Extequer Pr.; 0-935892),* P.O. Box 60193, Pasadena, CA 91106 (SAN 281-6873) Tel 818-797-3627.

Exxon Human Resources, *(Exxon Corp., Human Resources; 0-938933),* 1251 Ave. of the Americas, New York, NY 10020 (SAN 661-8170) Tel 212-333-1921.

Eyecontact, *(Eyecontact; 0-938112),* 465 Lexington Ave., New York, NY 10017 (SAN 281-692X) Tel 212-683-1641; Dist. by: Golden Lee, 1000 Dean St., Brooklyn, NY 11238 (SAN 169-5126) Tel 212-857-6333; Dist. by: Publishers Group West, 5855 Beaudry St., Emeryville, CA 94608 (SAN 202-8522) Tel 415-658-3453.

EZ Cookin, *(EZ Cookin' Bk. Co.; 0-937545),* 9925 Currant Ave., Fountain Valley, CA 92708 (SAN 240-9364).

F A Bowen, *(Bowen, F. A., Reports, Inc.; 0-9602830),* P.O. Box 213, Janesville, WI 53547 (SAN 212-8810) Tel 608-752-6333.

F A Countway, *(Countway, Francis A., Library of Medicine),* 10 Shattuck St., Boston, MA 02115 (SAN 206-4057).

Symbols/Abbreviations

F A Everest, *(Everest, F. Alton; 0-9608352),* 6275 South Rounhill Dr., Whittier, CA 90601 (SAN 662-0078) Tel 213-698-8831; Dist. by: Mix Pubns., Inc., 2608 Ninth St., Berkeley, CA 94710 (SAN 693-9562) Tel 415-843-7901.

F A Perry
See G B H Pub

F Adams
See AMR Pub Co

F Amato Pubns, *(Amato, Frank, Pubns.; 0-936608),* P.O. Box 02112, Portland, OR 97202 (SAN 214-3372) Tel 503-653-8108.

F & F Pub, *(F & F Publishing Co.; 0-9616875),* 50 Shady Glen Rd., Memphis, TN 38119 (SAN 661-3748) Tel 901-685-9915.

F & R Corser, *(Corser, Frank Rose; 0-9608636),* 215 Baseline, San Dimas, CA 91773 (SAN 263-984X).

F B Foster Pubns, *(Foster, Fred B., Pubns.; 0-9613762),* 5670 Stockton Blvd., No. 21, Sacramento, CA 95824 (SAN 682-269X) Tel 916-383-8579.

F B Johnson, *(Johnson, Forrest Bryant; 0-9600510),* 485 Mckellar, Suite 1, Las Vegas, NV 89119 (SAN 205-5694) Tel 702-735-1730.

F Babineaux, *(Babineaux, Floyd; 0-9616648),* P.O. Box 3468, Irving, TX 75061 (SAN 659-7718) Tel 214-438-3000.

F Cass Co
See Biblio Dist

F D M Distrib
See FDM Distributor

F D Ramey, *(Ramey, Fredric D.; 0-910889),* 126 W. 119th St., New York, NY 10026 (SAN 274-9734).

F D Roosevelt Phil Soc
See FDR Philatelic Soc

F E B Pr, *(F E B Press; 0-9610144),* P.O. Box 2431, Ann Arbor, MI 48106 (SAN 270-0662) Tel 313-973-2282.

F E Peters, *(Peters, Ferguson E., Co.; 0-918214),* P.O. Box 3527, Vero Beach, FL 32964 (SAN 210-2579) Tel 305-231-6285.

F Eckhardt Assocs, *(Eckhardt, Fred, Associates; 0-9606302),* P.O. Box 546, Portland, OR 97207 (SAN 211-2930) Tel 503-289-7596.

F Elmo
See Action Life Pubns

F Evans-Kimbrell, *(Evans-Kimbrell, Frances; 0-9616264),* Star Rte., Box 102, Allardt, TN 38504 (SAN 658-3539) Tel 615-879-5299.

F F Fournies
See F Fournies

F Fergeson, *(Fergeson, F., Productions; 0-935510),* Mount Zion, IL 62526 (SAN 214-3704) Tel 217-869-5608.

F Fournies, *(Fournies, F., & Associates, Inc.; 0-917472),* 129 Edgewood Dr., Bridgewater, NJ 08807 (SAN 205-5708) Tel 201-526-2442.

F H Balenseifer, *(Balensiefer, F. H.; 0-9617228),* 8337 Orchard St., Alta Loma, CA 91701 (SAN 663-4273) Tel 714-987-4991.

F H Breise, *(Breise, Frederic H.; 0-938576),* 5750 Severin Dr., La Mesa, CA 92041 (SAN 215-8485).

F Harris, *(Harris, Frank; 0-9610458),* 2129 Rose St., Berkeley, CA 94709 (SAN 264-0848) Tel 415-548-8709.

F I Comm, *(F. I. Communications; 0-89533),* 45 Alhambra, Portola Valley, CA 94025 (SAN 201-8489) Tel 415-851-0254; Orders to: P.O. Box 3121, Stanford, CA 94305-0036 (SAN 201-8497).

F J Adams, *(Adams, Florence J.; 0-9617276),* 504 E. Knotts Ave., Grafton, WV 26354 (SAN 663-4699); Dist. by: McClain Printing Co., 212 Main St., Parsons, WV 26287 (SAN 203-9478) Tel 304-478-2881.

F K Fruth, *(Fruth, Florence Knight),* 64 St. Andrews Dr., Beaver Falls, PA 15010 (SAN 211-156X) Tel 412-846-5282.

F Klein Pubns, *(Klein, F., Pubns.; 0-913051),* 515 Magdalena, Los Altos, CA 94022 (SAN 283-1287).

F L Beddow, *(Beddow, F. Lorlene; 0-9615982),* 1437 SW 37th St., No. 2, Pendleton, OR 97801 (SAN 698-1623) Tel 503-276-2610; Dist. by: Pacific Northwest Bks., P.O. Box 314, Medford, OR 97501 (SAN 200-5263) Tel 503-664-4442.

F L Colon, *(Colon, Fernando L., Jr.; 0-9615643),* 232 Seventh St., Jersey City, NJ 07302 (SAN 696-3374) Tel 201-656-0782.

F L Gonzalez, *(Gonzalez, Fernando L.; 0-9601090),* P.O. Box 1812, Flushing, NY 11352 (SAN 210-0924).

F L McKibbin
See Franje CA

F M Atlas, *(FM Atlas Publishing Co.; 0-917170),* P.O. Box 24, Adolph, MN 55701 (SAN 207-6764) Tel 218-879-7676.

F M Bruington, *(Bruington, F. M.; 0-9616838),* 1201 Eighth Ave. W., Lot M-4, Palmetto, FL 33561 (SAN 661-2822) Tel 813-729-3704.

F M Crawford, *(Crawford, F. Marion, Memorial Society),* Saracinesca House 3610 Meadowbrook Ave., Nashville, TN 37205 (SAN 225-2821) Tel 615-292-9695.

F M McCarty, *(McCarty, F. M., Co.; 0-911990),* 4527 Clawson Rd., Austin, TX 78745 (SAN 205-5716) Tel 512-447-6201.

F M Re, *(Re, Frank M.),* 68 Palm Club, Pompano Beach, FL 33062 (SAN 208-0818) Tel 305-946-1234.

F M Roberts, *(Roberts, F. M., Enterprises; 0-912746),* P.O. Box 608, Dana Point, CA 92629-0608 (SAN 201-4688) Tel 714-493-1977.

F M Swan, *(Swan, Frances M.; 0-9602126),* 11533 Old St. Charles Rd., Bridgeton, MO 63044 (SAN 212-3835).

F M Wood, *(Wood, Fern Morrow; 0-9606922),* Rte. 2, Cherryvale, KS 67335 (SAN 217-460X).

F Magazine, *(F Magazine, Inc.; 0-936959),* 1405 W. Belle Plaine, Chicago, IL 60613 (SAN 658-6511) Tel 312-929-8044.

F Merriwell, *(Merriwell, Frank, Inc.; 0-8373),* Subs. of National Learning Corp., 212 Michael Dr., Syosset, NY 11791 (SAN 209-259X) Tel 516-921-8888; Toll free: 800-645-6337.

F Morrow, *(Morrow, Felix, Pub; 0-9615659),* 13 Welwyn Rd., Great Neck, NY 11021 (SAN 696-1029) Tel 516-482-1044; Orders to: The Talman Company, Distributor, 150 Fifth Ave., Rm. 514B, New York, NY 10011 (SAN 662-3654) Tel 212-620-3182.

F Murat, *(Murat, Felix, Co.; 0-9600356),* 2132 NW 11th Ave., Miami, FL 33127 (SAN 205-5724).

F O Braynard, *(Braynard, Frank O.; 0-9606204),* 98 Du Bois Ave., Sea Cliff, NY 11579 (SAN 223-2138) Tel 516-676-0733.

F O Copley, *(Copley, Frank O.; 0-9615724),* 1291 Forest Ave., Rogers City, MI 49779 (SAN 696-4001) Tel 517-734-4381; Box 216, Rogers City, MI 49779 (SAN 696-5369).

F Pilbat, *(Pilbat, Frank; 0-9614411),* 41-07 Bowne St., Flushing, NY 11355 (SAN 688-6035) Tel 718-445-0368.

F Preston, *(Preston, France; 0-939222),* 1800 S. Robertson Blvd., Suite 281, Los Angeles, CA 90035 (SAN 216-5090).

F R Dougherty, *(Dougherty, F. Robert; 0-936267),* 4809 Horseshoe Pike, Downingtown, PA 19335 (SAN 698-1542) Tel 215-269-1146.

F R Walker, *(Walker, Frank R., Co.; 0-911592),* 5030 N. Harlem Ave., Chicago, IL 60656 (SAN 206-4022) Tel 312-867-7070; Toll free: 800-631-7795.

F Roberts Crawford
See Ctr Res Soc Chg

F S Hyde, *(Hyde, Floy S.; 0-9600528),* Box 100, Owls Head, NY 12969 (SAN 205-5732).

F Sherman, *(Sherman, Faith; 0-9607286),* 159 S. Lakewood Rd., Tygh Valley, OR 97063 (SAN 239-3107) Tel 503-544-3392.

F Sypher, *(Sypher, Francis),* 220 E. 50th St., New York, NY 10022 (SAN 215-0492).

F T Allum, *(Allum, Fred T.; 0-9613349),* 1104 Larke Ave., Rogers City, MI 49779 (SAN 655-8739) Tel 517-734-4517.

F T Smith, *(Smith, Fred T.; 0-9611210),* P.O. Box 120, Lathrup Village, MI 48076 (SAN 224-8731) Tel 313-258-5411; Dist. by: Merle Distributing Co., 27222 Plymouth Rd., Detroit, MI 48239 (SAN 169-3778) Tel 313-937-8400.

F T Yoon, *(Yoon, F. T., Co.; 0-931168),* P.O. Box 470, Pebble Beach, CA 93953 (SAN 212-873X) Tel 408-646-9499.

F-Twenty-Two, *(F/22 Pr.; 0-933596),* P.O. Box 141, Leonia, NJ 07605 (SAN 671-6830) Tel 201-568-6250.

F V Kosikowski, *(Kosikowski, F. V., & Assocs.; 0-9602322),* P.O. Box 139, Brooktondale, NY 14817 (SAN 211-6693) Tel 607-272-7779.

F W Readel, *(Readel, Fred W.; 0-9616822),* 2970 N. Victoria, St. Paul, MN 55113 (SAN 661-1214) Tel 612-484-1408.

FA Mus LI, *(Fine Arts Museum of Long Island, The; 0-933535),* 295 Fulton Ave., New York, NY 11550 (SAN 691-8581) Tel 516-481-5700.

†**Faber & Faber,** *(Faber & Faber, Inc.; 0-571; 0-905209),* 50 Cross St., Winchester, MA 01890 (SAN 218-7256) Tel 617-721-1427; Dist. by: Harper & Row Pubs., Inc., Keystone Industrial Pk., Scranton, PA 18512 (SAN 215-3742); CIP.

Fablewaves, *(Fablewaves Pr.; 0-937578),* P.O. Box 7874, Van Nuys, CA 91409 (SAN 215-0719) Tel 213-372-2983.

Fabrication Pr, *(Fabrication Pr.; 0-9616233),* 3446 Garfield Ave. S., Minneapolis, MN 55408 (SAN 658-5841) Tel 612-870-3574; 3446 Garfield Ave. S. No. 1, Minneapolis, MN 55408 (SAN 662-4138) Tel 612-825-3898.

Facets Multimed, *(Facets Multimedia, Inc.; 0-9615518),* 1517 W. Fullerton Ave., Chicago, IL 60614 (SAN 696-4176) Tel 312-281-9075.

Facing Hist, *(Facing History & Ourselves National Foundation, Inc.; 0-9615841),* 25 Kennard Rd., Brookline, MA 02146 (SAN 697-0710) Tel 617-232-1595; Dist. by: Reading Matters, Inc., 64 Walnut St., Brookline, MA 02146 (SAN 200-5891).

FACM Pub Co, *(FACM Publishing Co., Inc.),* The JBI Bldg., Box 521, Mahwah, NJ 07430 (SAN 693-1030) Tel 201-529-3883.

Facsimile Bk, *(Facsimile Bk. Shop, Inc.),* 16 W. 55th St., New York, NY 10019 (SAN 215-3084).

Fact Pub, *(Fact Publishing; 0-9613171),* 1310 N. Benton Way, Los Angeles, CA 90026 (SAN 294-927X) Tel 213-413-5524.

Factor Pub, *(Factor Publishing Co.; 0-935629),* P.O. Box 815, Eastsound, WA 98245 (SAN 696-4184) Tel 206-276-2808.

Factory Mutual, *(Factory Mutual System),* 1151 Boston-Providence Tpke., P.O. Box 688, Norwood, MA 02062 (SAN 224-8115) Tel 617-762-4300.

Facts FL, *(Facts; 0-910991),* 727 Granada Dr.,, Boca Raton, FL 33432 (SAN 263-2209).

†**Facts on File,** *(Facts on File, Inc.; 0-87196; 0-8160),* Subs. of Commerce Clearing Hse., 460 Park Ave. S., New York, NY 10016 (SAN 201-4696) Tel 212-683-2244; Toll free: 800-322-8755; CIP. Imprints: Checkmark (Checkmark).

Faculty Pub C A, *(Faculty Publishing; 0-915141),* 1421 Tulane Dr., Davis, CA 95616 (SAN 289-923X) Tel 916-756-3195.

Fade In, *(Fade in Pubs.; 0-936748),* 312 S. 6th, Bozeman, MT 59715 (SAN 215-0727).

Fads Fashions, *(Fads & Fashions Co.; 0-9616534),* P.O. Box 9221, Forestville, CT 06010 (SAN 659-4468) Tel 203-582-9415; 15 Evergreen St., Forestville, CT 06010 (SAN 659-4476).

Fag Rag, *(Fag Rag Bks.; 0-915480),* P.O. Box 331, Kenmore Sta., Boston, MA 02215 (SAN 207-3498).

Fahnestock, *(Fahnestock Studios; 0-936057),* 70 E. Clinton Ave., Tenafly, NJ 07670 (SAN 697-0680) Tel 201-568-2141.

Fainshaw Pr, *(Fainshaw Pr.; 0-943290),* Subs. of B. R. Smith & Assocs., Inc., Box 961, Westmoreland, NH 03467 (SAN 240-6454) Tel 603-585-6654; Dist. by: Great Tradition, The, 750 Adrian Way, Suite 111, San Rafael, CA 94903 (SAN 200-5743) Tel 415-492-9382.

Fair Haven Pr, *(Fair Haven Pr.; 0-932227),* P.O. Box 2152, Meriden, CT 06450 (SAN 686-6093) Tel 203-634-8098.

Fairborn Observ, *(Fairborn Observatory),* 1357 N. 91st Pl., Mesa, AZ 85207 (SAN 270-0255) Tel 602-986-2828.

Fairchild, *(Fairchild Bks.; 0-87005),* Div. of Fairchild Pubns., 7 E. 12th St., New York, NY 10003 (SAN 201-470X) Tel 212-741-4280.

Fairfax County, *(Fairfax County; 0-9601630),* 4100 Chain Bridge Rd., Fairfax, VA 22030 (SAN 212-632X).

Fairfield, *(Fairfield Press, Inc.; 0-913158),* 128 E. 62nd St., New York, NY 10021 (SAN 206-4049) Tel 212-838-7424.

Fairfield Hse, *(Fairfield House; 0-9602048),* 3 Fairfield Dr., Baltimore, MD 21228 (SAN 209-374X) Tel 301-747-6590.

Fairleigh Dickinson, *(Fairleigh Dickinson Univ. Pr.; 0-8386),* Dist. by: Associated University Presses, 440 Forsgate Dr., Cranbury, NJ 08512 (SAN 281-2959) Tel 609-655-4770.

FairMail Serv, *(FairMail Service, Inc.; 0-9601262),* 417 Cleveland Ave., Plainfield, NJ 07060 (SAN 210-4210) Tel 201-754-7770.

Fairmont Pr, *(Fairmont Pr., Inc., The; 0-88173; 0-915586),* 700 Indian Trail, Lilburn, GA 30247 (SAN 207-5946) Tel 404-925-9388; Orders to: Prentice-Hall, P.O. Box 500, Englewood Cliffs, NJ 07632 (SAN 663-2904) Tel 201-592-2000.

Fairway Hse, *(Fairway House; 0-9603180),* P.O. Box 6344, Bakersfield, CA 93386 (SAN 213-6856); Dist. by: James A. Glynn, 2 Monte Vista Dr., Bakersfield, CA 93305 (SAN 200-7355).

Fairweather Pr OR, *(Fairweather Pr. OR; 0-9614005),* 1718 SW Myrtle St., Portland, OR 97201 (SAN 208-2128) Tel 503-223-4707; Dist. by: Far West Book Service, 3515 NE Hassalo, Portland, OR 97232 (SAN 282-6429) Tel 503-234-7664; Dist. by: Pacific Pipeline Inc., 19215 66th Ave. S., Kent, WA 98032 (SAN 208-2128) Tel 206-872-5523.

Fairy Pubns, *(Fairy Publications; 0-9611088),* P.O. Box 450, Laguna Beach, CA 92652 (SAN 282-8669) Tel 714-661-7533; Dist. by: Cogan Books, 4332 W. Artesia Ave., Fullerton, CA 92633 (SAN 168-9649); Dist. by: Distributors The, 702 S. Michigan, South Bend, IN 46618 (SAN 212-0364) Tel 219-232-8500.

Faith & Life, *(Faith & Life Pr.; 0-87303),* 718 Main St., Newton, KS 67114-0347 (SAN 201-4726) Tel 316-283-5100; Box 347, Newton, KS 67114-0347 (SAN 658-0637).

Faith Messenger, *(Faith Messenger Pubns.; 0-938544),* P.O. Box 1041, Upland, CA 91785 (SAN 281-7020) Tel 714-946-3134.

Faith Print, *(Faith Printing Co.; 0-939241),* Rte. 2, Hwy. 290, Taylors, SC 29687 (SAN 694-5341) Tel 803-895-3822.

Faith Pub Hse, *(Faith Publishing Hse.),* P.O. Box 518, Guthrie, OK 73044 (SAN 204-1243) Tel 405-282-1479; 920 W. Mansur, Guthrie, OK 73044 (SAN 658-0645).

FaithAmerica, *(FaithAmerica Foundation; 0-942770),* Suite 216, 4130 N. 70th St., Scottsdale, AZ 85251 (SAN 240-1452).

Falcon Bks *Imprint of* **Gibbs M Smith**

Falcon Co, *(Falcon Co.; 0-935921),* 3675 Syracuse Ave., San Diego, CA 92122 (SAN 696-7442) Tel 619-453-8965; P.O. Box 22569, San Diego, CA 92122 (SAN 698-2204).

Falcon Ent, *(Falcon Enterprises; 0-9613551),* P.O.Box 210094, Anchorage, AK 99521 (SAN 669-7984) Tel 907-337-2646.

Falcon Head Pr, *(Falcon Head Press, Ltd.; 0-914802),* P.O. Box 913, Golden, CO 80401 (SAN 206-4065).

Falcon Hill Pr, *(Falcon Hill Pr.; 0-936332),* Box 1431, Sparks, NV 89432-1431 (SAN 221-1718) Tel 702-786-2134.

Falcon Pr Az, *(Falcon Pr.; 0-941404),* 3660 N. Third St., Phoenix, AZ 85012 (SAN 262-0243) Tel 602-246-3546; Dist. by: Inland Bk. Co., P.O. Box 261, 22 Hemingway Ave., East Haven, CT 06512 (SAN 200-4151) Tel 203-467-4257; Dist. by: Samuel Weiser, Inc., P.O. Box 612, York Beach, ME 03910 (SAN 202-9588) Tel 207-363-4393; Dist. by: Baker & Taylor Co., Western Div., 380 Edison Way, Reno, NV 89564 (SAN 169-4464) Tel 702-786-6700; Dist. by: Bookpeople, 2929 Fifth St., Berkeley, CA 94710 (SAN 168-9517); Dist. by: Great Tradition, The, 750 Adrian Way, Suite 111, San Rafael, CA 94903 (SAN 200-5743) Tel 415-492-9382; Dist. by: Nascorp, Inc., 528 E. Lorain St., Oberlin, OH 44074 (SAN 169-6823) Tel 216-775-8048.

Falcon Pr MT, *(Falcon Pr. Publishing Co., Inc.; 0-934318; 0-937959),* P.O. Box 731, Helena, MT 59624 (SAN 221-1726) Tel 406-442-6597; 27 Neill Ave., Helena, MT 59624 (SAN 658-0653); Orders to: P.O. Box 279, Billings, MT 59103 (SAN 281-7047).

Falcon Printing
See Falcon Pub Venice

Falcon Pub, *(Falcon Publishing; 0-932542),* P.O. Box 688, Ben Lomond, CA 95005 (SAN 213-0513) Tel 408-336-2906.

Falcon Pub Venice, *(Falcon Publishing; 0-942764),* 2000 Strongs, Venice, CA 92091 (SAN 212-8322) Tel 213-399-4791.

Falk, *(Falk; 0-9614108),* 3470 Rolling View Ct., White Bear Lake, MN 55110 (SAN 685-2998) Tel 612-770-1922.

Falk-Leeds Intl
See Photo Arts Ctr

Falkynor Bks, *(G-Jo Institute/Falkynor Bks., The; 0-916878),* 4950 SW 70th Ave., Davie, FL 33314 (SAN 208-645X) Tel 305-791-1562; Dist. by: The Great Tradition, 750 Adrian Way, Suite 111, San Rafael, CA 94903 (SAN 200-5743) Tel 415-492-9382; Dist. by: Samuel Weiser, P.O. Box 612, York Beach, ME 03910 (SAN 202-9588) Tel 207-363-4393; Dist. by: The Distributors, 702 S. Michigan, South Bend, IN 46618 (SAN 169-2488) Tel 219-232-8500.

Fallen Angel, *(Fallen Angel Pr.; 0-931598),* 17606 Muirland, Detroit, MI 48221 (SAN 211-8963) Tel 313-864-0982.

Fallen Leaf, *(Fallen Leaf Pr.; 0-914913),* P.O. Box 10034, Berkeley, CA 94709 (SAN 289-1255) Tel 415-848-7805.

Falling Wall, *(Falling Wall Pr.; 0-905046),* Dist. by: Flatiron Bk. Distributors, Inc., 1170 Broadway, Suite 807, New York, NY 10001 (SAN 240-9917) Tel 212-206-1118.

Falling Water, *(Falling Water Pr.; 0-932229),* P.O. Box 4554, Ann Arbor, MI 48106 (SAN 686-5771) Tel 313-761-7605.

Falls Tar, *(Falls of the Tar Pubns.; 0-938828),* P.O. Box 4194, Rocky Mount, NC 27801 (SAN 240-0189) Tel 919-442-7423.

Falmer Pr *Imprint of* **Taylor & Francis**

Falmouth Hist Com, *(Falmouth Historical Commission; 0-9616647),* 59 Town Hall Sq., Falmouth Town Hall, Falmouth, MA 02540 (SAN 659-5618) Tel 617-548-5800.

Falsoft, *(Falsoft, Inc.; 0-932471),* P.O. Box 385, Prospect, KY 40059 (SAN 687-4223); 9509 U.S. Hwy. 42, Prospect, KY 40059 (SAN 662-2771).

Falztar Bks, *(Falztar Bks.; 0-9616465),* P.O. Box 4462, Wichita, KS 67204 (SAN 659-2201).

Fam Ctr Pr
See Mailman Family

Fam Health Intl, *(Family Health International; 0-939704),* Triangle Dr., Research Triangle Park, NC 27709 (SAN 216-7409) Tel 919-549-0517.

Fam Health Media, *(Family Health Media; 0-931470),* 201 S. Lloyd, Suite 230 Physician's Plaza, Aberdeen, SD 57401 (SAN 211-965X) Tel 605-229-5990.

Fam Hist & Gen, *(Family History & Genealogy Ctr.; 0-912017),* 1300 E. 109th St., Kansas City, MO 64131 (SAN 264-6145) Tel 816-942-5497.

Fam Skills, *(Family Skills, Inc.; 0-934275),* 1 Galleria Tower No. 1940, 13355 Noel Rd., Dallas, TX 75240 (SAN 693-2576) Tel 214-458-2867; Toll free: 800-543-7545; Dist. by: Kampmann & Co., Inc., 9 E. 40th St., New York, NY 10016 (SAN 202-5191) Tel 212-685-2928.

Family Album, *(Family Album, ABAA, The; 0-934630),* RD 1, Box 42, Glen Rock, PA 17327 (SAN 212-5021).

Family Care Assocs, *(Family Care Assocs.; 0-935467),* 201 Barclay Cir., Cheltenham, PA 19012 (SAN 696-4222) Tel 215-635-3553; Orders to: P.O. Box 37, Cheltenham, PA 19012 (SAN 662-3743).

Family Circle Bks, *(Family Circle Bks.; 0-933585),* Subs. of Family Circle, Inc., 488 Madison Ave., New York, NY 10022 (SAN 692-2120) Tel 212-593-8419; Toll free: 800-247-2904; Orders to: P.O. Box 10814, Des Moines, IA 50381 (SAN 662-2976).

Family Friends, *(Family Friends Pubns.; 0-9609324),* R.R. 1, Box 43A, Oelh, IA 52223 (SAN 240-849X) Tel 319-927-2377.

Family God, *(Family of God, The; 0-932873),* P.O. Box 19571, Las Vegas, NV 89132 (SAN 688-993X) Tel 702-731-4750.

Family Health, *(Family & Health Improvement Society; 0-9606024),* P.O. Box 952, Cambridge, OH 43725 (SAN 211-3562) Tel 614-432-3007.

Family Herit, *(Family Heritage Publishing Co.; 0-9615453),* 8275 Louisiana St., Merrillville, IN 46410 (SAN 695-7692) Tel 219-924-4124; Dist. by: Pratik Pubn., P.O. Box 11133, Merrillville, IN 46411 (SAN 200-7878).

Family Hist TX, *(Family Histories; 0-9616624),* 2320 Country Green Ln., Arlington, TX 76011 (SAN 661-2032) Tel 817-277-3281.

Family History, *(Family History Foundation; 0-943162),* P.O. Drawer 4464, Bryan, TX 77805-4464 (SAN 240-3749) Tel 409-775-0809.

Family Man
See Family God

Family Pr, *(Family Press; 0-9600666),* P. O. Box 16005, St. Paul, MN 55116 (SAN 205-5740) Tel 612-699-9108.

Family Process, *(Family Process Pr.; 0-9615519),* Div. of Family Process, Inc., 149 E. 78th St., New York, NY 10021 (SAN 696-4249) Tel 212-861-6059; Dist. by: W. W. Norton & Co., 500 Fifth Ave., New York, NY 10110 (SAN 202-5795) Tel 212-354-5500.

Family Pub CA, *(Family Publishing Co., The; 0-937770),* P.O. Box 462, Bodega Bay, CA 94923 (SAN 215-3092) Tel 707-875-3373.

Family Pubns, *(Family Pubns.; 0-931128),* P.O. Box 398, Maitland, FL 32751 (SAN 211-3147) Tel 305-894-7060.

†**Family Relat,** *(Family Relations Foundation; 0-9614218),* P.O. Box 462, Sebastopol, CA 95472 (SAN 687-1097) Tel 707-823-0876; Dist. by: Bookpeople, 2929 Fifth St., Berkeley, CA 94710 (SAN 168-9517) Tel 415-549-3030; *CIP.*

Family Relations, *(Family Relations Learning Ctr.; 0-9607250),* 450 Ord Dr., Boulder, CO 80303 (SAN 239-4243) Tel 303-499-1171.

Family Res, *(Family Resource, Inc., The; 0-914915),* 4901 W. Lovers Ln., Dallas, TX 75209 (SAN 289-128X) Tel 214-350-6621.

†**Family Serv,** *(Family Service America; 0-87304),* 44 E. 23rd St., New York, NY 10010 (SAN 206-4073) Tel 212-674-6100; *CIP.*

Family Therapy
See Mehetabel & Co

Family Tree Pony Farm, *(Family Tree Pony Farm, Pubns. Div.; 0-940074),* 2690 SE Lund Ave., Port Orchard, WA 98366 (SAN 220-2174) Tel 206-895-2116.

Family Visions, *(Family Visions, Inc.; 0-934835),* 1400 Homer Rd., Winona, MN 55987 (SAN 694-3845) Tel 507-452-8966; P.O. Box 30067, Winona, MN 55987 (SAN 658-2834).

Family World Pub Hse, *(Family World Publishing House, Inc.; 0-934176),* 3951 Providence Rd., New Town Square, PA 19073 (SAN 213-0521) Tel 215-353-3555.

Family YMCA Stanislaus
See Swimfants

Famous Last Wds, *(Famous Last Words; 0-916331),* 4815 Fairfax Ave., Oakland, CA 94601-4811 (SAN 654-7273) Tel 415-534-8468.

Famous Pr Pub, *(Famous Pr. Publishing; 0-942010),* P.O. Box 1673, Mansfield, OH 44901 (SAN 238-2377) Tel 419-522-4735; 200 N. Diamond St., Mansfield, OH 44901 (SAN 658-0661).

Fan Pub Co, *(Fan Publishing Co.; 0-932179),* P.O. Box 20306, Raleigh, NC 27619 (SAN 686-5364) Tel 919-846-0607.

F&J Mazzulla, *(Mazzulla, Fred & Jo),* 2060 Dunes Cir., Reno, NV 89509 (SAN 205-8723).

F&S Pr, *(F&S Pr.; 0-86621),* Div. of Frost & Sullivan, 106 Fulton St., New York, NY 10038 (SAN 220-0538) Tel 212-233-1080. Out of business.

Fanferon Pr, *(Fanferon Pr.; 0-9614841),* P.O. Box 5804, Bellingham, WA 98227 (SAN 693-1057) Tel 206-671-5808.

Fannin County, (Fannin County Historical Commission; 0-9609602), P.O. Box 338, Bonham, TX 75418 (SAN 260-1842) Tel 214-583-2832.

Fant-Freeman-Madson, (Fant, Freeman, Madson; 0-87518), 209 Shady Oak Rd., Hopkins, MN 55343 (SAN 223-0682); Dist. by: Alver R. Freeman, 8315 Dupont Ave., Minneapolis, MN 55420 (SAN 223-0690).

Fantaco, (Fantaco Pubns.; 0-938782), Affil. of Fantaco Enterprises, Inc., 21 Central Ave., Albany, NY 12210-1391 (SAN 662-0086) Tel 518-463-1400; Orders to: Fantaco Enterprises, Inc., 21 Central Ave., Albany, NY 12210 (SAN 270-0379).

Fantasy Fact, (Fantasy Factory, Inc.; 0-939717), 10344 Cheviot Dr., Los Angeles, CA 90064 (SAN 663-6276) Tel 213-559-7426.

Fantasy Pub Co, (Fantasy Publishing Co., Inc.), c/o Borden Publishing Co., 1855 W. Main St., Alhambra, CA 91801 (SAN 201-419X) Tel 213-337-7947.

FAO Imprint of **Unipub**

FAR & MS
See FARMS

Far Eastern Pubns, (Yale Univ., Far Eastern Pubns; 0-88710), 340 Edwards St., New Haven, CT 06520 (SAN 219-0710) Tel 203-436-1075.

Far Eastern Res, (Far Eastern Research & Pubns. Center; 0-912580), P.O. Box 151, Prince Georges, MD 20748 (SAN 205-5759).

Far West Edns, (Far West Editions; 0-914480), P.O. Box 549, San Francisco, CA 94101 (SAN 207-0456) Tel 415-587-4951.

Far West Lab, (Far West Laboratory for Educational Research & Development; 0-914409), 1855 Folsom St., San Francisco, CA 94103 (SAN 289-6222) Tel 415-565-3139.

Far West Pr
See Far West Edns

Far Western Phil, (Far Western Philosophy of Education Society; 0-931702), Arizona State Univ., College of Education, Hiram Bradford Farmer Education Bldg., Rm. 412, Tempe, AZ 85281 (SAN 210-8062) Tel 602-965-3674.

Faraday, (Faraday Press; 0-939762), P.O. Box 4098, Mountain View, CA 94040 (SAN 216-731X).

Farago Pubns, (Farago Pubns.; 0-935363), Div. of Vita Juice, 6510 W. Sixth St., Los Angeles, CA 90048 (SAN 696-4192) Tel 213-655-8310.

Farm & Ranch, (Farm & Ranch Vacations, Inc.; 0-913214), 36 E. 57th St., New York, NY 10022 (SAN 201-4734) Tel 212-355-6334.

†**Farm Journal,** (Farm Journal, Inc.; 0-89795), 230 W. Washington Sq., Philadelphia, PA 19105 (SAN 212-0887) Tel 215-829-4755; Toll free: 800-237-1212; CIP.

Farmer Ent, (Farmer, Wesley M., Enterprises,Inc.; 0-937772), P.O. Box 1323, Santee, CA 92071 (SAN 215-6431) Tel 619-448-8697.

Farmington Cookbook, (Farmington Cookbook, The; 0-9602646), 3033 Bardstown Rd., Louisville, KY 40205 (SAN 218-4486).

FARMS, (FARMS; 0-934893), P.O. Box 7113, Univ. Sta., Provo, UT 84602 (SAN 694-4469) Tel 801-378-3295.

Farmworker Justice, (Farmworker Justice Fund, Inc.; 0-9616026), 2001 S St., NW, No. 312, Washington, DC 20009 (SAN 659-4492) Tel 202-462-8192.

Farnum Films, (Farnum Films; 0-915790), Executive House, 225 E. 46th St., New York, NY 10017 (SAN 206-1988) Tel 212-371-8679; Orders to: P.O. Box 1094, New York, NY 10017 (SAN 206-1996).

Farr Pubs, (Farr Pubs.; 0-9614476), P.O. Box 175, Gainesville, VA 22065 (SAN 689-3538) Tel 703-347-5785.

Farragut Pub, (Farragut Publishing Co.; 0-918535), 810 18th St. NW, Washington, DC 20006 (SAN 657-6168) Tel 202-347-5415; Dist. by: Baker & Taylor Co., Eastern Div., 50 Kirby Ave., Somerville, NJ 08876 (SAN 169-4901) Tel 201-526-8000; Dist. by: Inland Bk. Co., P.O. Box 261, 22 Hemingway Ave., East Haven, CT 06512 (SAN 200-4151) Tel 203-467-4257.

Farrah Upland, (Farrah, Upland, Westmoreland & Granger; 0-943568), Rte. 2, Box 384, Pittsboro, NC 27312 (SAN 240-6470) Tel 919-542-4052.

Farris Pub, (Farris Publishing; 0-9616391), 2401 Repsdorph, No. 1711, Seabrook, TX 77586 (SAN 658-8530) Tel 713-532-1448.

FAS Pubs, (FAS Pubs.), P.O. Box 5453, Madison, WI 53705 (SAN 201-4750) Tel 608-274-1733.

Fashion Imprints, (Fashion Imprints Assocs.; 0-9602860), Box 3523, Merchandise Mart, Chicago, IL 60654 (SAN 213-0548) Tel 312-821-5922.

Fast & McMillan
See East Woods

Fat Control, (Fat Control Inc.; 0-918275), P.O. Box 10117, Towson, MD 21204 (SAN 682-2711).

Fat Wars Ent, (Fat Wars Enterprises; 0-9614219), 9842 Hibert St. Suite 264, San Diego, CA 92131 (SAN 687-1100) Tel 619-695-8771.

Father Tree Pr, (Father Tree Pr.; 0-936861), Div. of WARP Graphics, Inc., 2 Reno Rd., Poughkeepsie, NY 12603 (SAN 699-9204) Tel 914-462-0588; Dist. by: Bud Plant, Inc., 12555 Loma Rica Dr., No. 10, Grass Valley, CA 95945 (SAN 268-5086) Tel 916-273-9588.

Fathom Eight, (Fathom Eight; 0-910651), P.O. Box 80505, San Marino, CA 91108-8505 (SAN 270-0611) Tel 818-289-5088.

Fathom Pr, (Fathom Pr.; 0-936849), P.O. Box 191, Eastport, NY 11941 (SAN 658-358X) Tel 516-878-9825; 11 Beverly Ln., East Moriches, NY 11940 (SAN 658-3598).

Fathom Pub, (Fathom Publishing Company; 0-9607358), Box 821, Cordova, AK 99574 (SAN 239-7684) Tel 907-424-7770.

Faubus, (Faubus, Orval E.), 114 E. 2nd St., Little Rock, AR 72203 (SAN 220-1526); c/o Pioneer Pr., P.O. Box 191, Little Rock, AR 72201 (SAN 220-1518) Tel 501-374-0271.

Faulkner Bks, (Faulkner Bks.; 0-916631), 870 Seventh Ave., Suite 31E, New York, NY 10019 (SAN 296-6921) Tel 212-541-7459.

†**Fault Pubns,** (Fault Pubns.; 0-930646), 33513 6th St., Union City, CA 94587 (SAN 207-8252) Tel 415-487-1383; CIP.

Faust Pub Co, (Faust Publishing Co.; 0-917905), 7523 Maple St., New Orleans, LA 70118 (SAN 656-9846) Tel 504-866-4916.

†**Fawcett,** (Fawcett Bk. Group; 0-449), 201 E. 50th St., New York, NY 10022 (SAN 201-4572) Tel 212-751-2600; Toll free: 800-638-6460; CIP. Imprints: Columbine (Columbine); Coventry (Coventry); Crest (Crest Books).(Crest Bks.); GM (Gold Medal Books).(Gold Medal Bks.); Juniper (Juniper); Prem (Premier Books).(Premier Bks.).

Fawcett World
See Fawcett

Fax Collect, (Fax Collector's Editions, Inc.; 0-913960), P.O. Box 851, Mercer Island, WA 98040 (SAN 208-6468) Tel 206-232-8484; Dist. by: Starmont House, Inc., P.O. Box 851, Mercer Island, WA 98040 (SAN 208-8703) Tel 206-232-8484; Dist. by: F & SF Bk., Co., P.O. Box 415, Staten Island, NY 10302 (SAN 169-6262) Tel 718-201-3526.

Fax Pub Co, (Fax Publishing Co.; 0-9614842), Subs. of Kadmos Corp., 1119 Vermont, P.O. Box 808, Quincy, IL 62306 (SAN 693-1081) Tel 217-224-5105.

†**Faxon,** (Faxon Co., The; 0-87305), 15 SW Park, Westwood, MA 02090 (SAN 159-8619) Tel 617-329-3350; Toll free: 800-225-6055; CIP.

Fay-West Her, (Fay-West Heritage Pubns.; 0-9609326), 247 Ironshire South, Laurel, MD 20707 (SAN 260-1850) Tel 301-725-1908.

Fayova Pubns, (Fayova Publications; 0-932970), 3052 Bayberry Ct., E., Carmel, IN 46032 (SAN 277-6790).

FB Imprint of **B&N Imports**

FBF Pubns, (FBF Pubns.; 0-9616026), P.O. Box 3296, San Bernardino, CA 92413 (SAN 698-1518) Tel 714-864-0865; 5695 McKinley Ave., San Bernardino, CA 92413 (SAN 698-1526) Tel 714-820-2280.

FCA Bks
See Foun Commun Artists

FC&A Pub, (FC&A Publishing; 0-915099), 103 Clover Green, Peachtree City, GA 30269 (SAN 289-7946) Tel 404-487-6307.

FDC Pub, (F.D.C. Publishing Co.; 0-89794), P.O. Box 206, Stewartsville, NJ 08886 (SAN 212-2758).

FDM Distributor, (F.D.M. Distributor; 0-9615720), 7807 Hohman Ave., Munster, IN 46321 (SAN 696-4168) Tel 219-836-8107.

FDP Assocs, (FDP Assocs.; 0-937209), 461 Park Ave., S., New York, NY 10016 (SAN 658-7194) Tel 212-213-8730.

FDR Philatelic Soc, (Franklin D. Roosevelt Philatelic Society; 0-9612272), 154 Laguna Ct., St. Augustine Shores, FL 32086 (SAN 225-591X) Tel 904-797-3513.

FDS Gourmet, (FDS Gourmet Enterprises; 0-9616834), 4136 Indiana Ave., Kenner, LA 70065 (SAN 661-2563) Tel 504-468-1834.

FDW Arts, (FDW Arts; 0-9608354), 1394 Old Quincy Lane, Reston, VA 22094 (SAN 240-6446) Tel 703-437-4818.

Fear Free, (Fear Free Foundation; 0-939637), P.O. Box 16119, North Hollywood, CA 91615 (SAN 663-575X); 900 E. Palmar, No. 10, Glendale, CA 91205 (SAN 663-5768) Tel 818-760-1113.

Feather & Good, (Feather & Good; 0-9607642), Box 141, Radnor, PA 19087 (SAN 239-8532).

Feather Pr, (Feather Press; 0-9607960), Box 1225, Dumas, TX 79029 (SAN 240-0723) Tel 806-935-4348.

Features NW, (Features Northwest; 0-931435), 5132 126th Pl., NE, Marysville, WA 98270 (SAN 683-2059) Tel 206-659-7559; Dist. by: Creative Communications, 529 Dayton St., Edmonds, WA 98020 (SAN 239-684X) Tel 206-775-5877.

Fed Am Health Systs, (Federation of American Health Systems), 1405 N. Pierce, Suite 311, Little Rock, AR 72207 (SAN 224-3334) Tel 501-661-9555.

Fed Am Hosp
See Fed Am Health Systs

Fed Aviation, (Federal Aviation Exams Co.; 0-938706), Box 718, Solvang, CA 93463 (SAN 215-8620).

Fed Aviation Pub, (Federal Aviation Publishing, Inc.; 0-939357), Four Embarcadero Center, Suite 5040, San Francisco, CA 94111 (SAN 662-6807) Tel 415-571-5458. Do not confuse with Federal Aviation Exams, in Solvang, CA.

Fed Bu Invest, (Federal Bureau of Investigation, Laboratory Div.; 0-932115), U. S. Dept. of Justice, Washington, DC 20535 (SAN 686-4740) Tel 703-640-6131.

Fed Doc Retrieval, (Federal Document Retrieval Inc.; 0-932929), 514 C St. NE, Washington, DC 20002 (SAN 689-1632) Tel 202-638-0520; Toll free: 800-368-1009.

Fed Employ & Guidance, (Federation Employment & Guidance Service; 0-934186), 510 Sixth Ave., 4th Flr., New York, NY 10011 (SAN 213-0556) Tel 212-741-7150.

Fed Employment Bul, (Federal Employment Bulletin; 0-933791), P.O. Box 11715, Washington, DC 20008 (SAN 692-8722) Tel 202-667-3050.

Fed Employees, (Federal Employees News Digest, Inc.; 0-910582), P.O. Box 7528, Falls Church, VA 22046 (SAN 204-1170) Tel 703-533-3031.

Fed Fly Fishers, (Federation of Fly Fishers; 0-9614193), P.O. Box 1088, West Yellowstone, MT 59758 (SAN 686-8002) Tel 406-646-9541.

Fed Jewish Mens Clubs, (Federation of Jewish Men's Clubs; 0-935665), 475 Riverside Dr., Suite 244, New York, NY 10115 (SAN 273-4230) Tel 212-749-8100.

Fed Judicial Ctr, (U. S. Federal Judicial Ctr.), 1520 H St., NW, Washington, DC 20005 (SAN 226-2541).

Fed Legal Pubn, (Federal Legal Pubns., Inc.; 0-87945), 157 Chambers St., New York, NY 10007 (SAN 201-4769) Tel 212-243-5775.

Fed Pubns Inc, (Federal Pubns., Inc.), 1120 20th St., NW, Washington, DC 20036 (SAN 237-7071) Tel 202-337-7000.

Fed Res Bank MN
See FRB Minneapolis

Fed Soc Coat Tech, (Federation of Societies for Coatings Technology; 0-934010), 1315 Walnut St., Suite 832, Philadelphia, PA 19107 (SAN 212-9035) Tel 215-545-1506.

FEDAPT, *(FEDAPT; 0-9602942),* 165 W. 46th St., Suite 310, New York, NY 10036 (SAN 224-1307) Tel 212-869-9690.

Feder, *(Feder, Michal E.; 0-9615449),* 706 Hydra Ln., Foster City, CA 94404 (SAN 695-7781) Tel 415-345-0809.

Feder Pub, *(Feder, Jay, Pub.; 0-9616084),* 910 16th St., Rm. 335, Denver, CO 80202 (SAN 698-1127) Tel 303-534-0251.

Federal Bar, *(Federal Bar Assn.),* 1815 H St., NW, Washington, DC 20006 (SAN 223-7784) Tel 202-638-0252.

Federlin, *(Federlin, Tom; 0-9603136),* 47 Cardinal Ct., Saratoga Springs, NY 12866 (SAN 213-4934) Tel 518-587-3704.

Feedback Thea Bks, *(Feedback Theatrebooks; 0-937657),* Div. of Feedback Services, P.O. Box 606, Nashville, IN 47448 (SAN 659-221X); Anandale Estates, Nashville, IN 47448 (SAN 659-2228).

FEELGREAT, *(FEELGREAT; 0-942106),* 1370 Windsor Rd., Teaneck, NJ 07666 (SAN 239-5363) Tel 201-833-0068.

Feeling Good Assocs, *(Feeling Good Assocs.; 0-9615412),* Div. of Barry Blum, M.D., Inc., 507 Palma Way, Mill Valley, CA 94941 (SAN 695-5002) Tel 415-383-5439.

Feezor Betty Bks, *(Feezor, Betty, Bks.; 0-915605),* 6217 Glenridge Rd., Charlotte, NC 28211 (SAN 292-501X) Tel 704-366-4147.

Feffer & Simons *Imprint of* **Burgess MN Intl**

Feist Pubns, *(Feist Pubns.),* 2827 Seventh St., Berkeley, CA 94710 (SAN 204-1138) Tel 415-841-5771.

Feldheim, *(Feldheim, Philipp, Inc.; 0-87306),* 200 Airport Executive Pk., Spring Valley, NY 10977 (SAN 164-9671) Tel 914-356-2282.

Feldman, *(Feldman, Mildred L. B.; 0-9606700),* 1424 S. Alameda Dr., Baton Rouge, LA 70815 (SAN 209-1135) Tel 504-925-9666.

†**Feldman Fine Arts,** *(Feldman, Ronald, Fine Arts, Inc.; 0-914661),* 31 Mercer St., New York, NY 10013 (SAN 289-2421) Tel 212-226-3232; *CIP.*

Felicity, *(Felicity Pr.; 0-9603846),* Box 14382, University Sta., Gainesville, FL 32604 (SAN 215-0743) Tel 904-475-2963.

Felicity Pr ME, *(Felicity Pr.; 0-931265),* P.O. Box 2066, Augusta, ME 04330 (SAN 681-9826) Tel 207-622-0815.

†**Fell,** *(Fell, Frederick, Pubs., Inc.; 0-8119),* 2500 Hollywood Blvd., Suite 302, Hollywood, FL 33020 (SAN 208-2365) Tel 305-925-5242; Toll free: 800-526-7626; Dist. by: Pubs. Distribution Ctr., 25 Branca Rd., East Rutherford, NJ 07073 (SAN 200-5018) Tel 201-939-6064; *CIP. Imprints:* Pegasus Rex (Pegasus Rex).

Fellendorf Assocs Inc, *(Fellendorf Assocs., Inc.; 0-9613033),* 1300 Ruppert Rd., Silver Spring, MD 20903 (SAN 295-3781) Tel 301-593-1636.

Fellows Cont Art, *(Fellows of Contemporary Art; 0-911291),* 333 S. Hope St. 48th Fl., Los Angeles, CA 90071 (SAN 270-1219) Tel 213-620-1780; Orders to: Art Catalogues, 625 N. Almont Dr., Los Angeles, CA 90069 (SAN 662-0094) Tel 213-274-0160.

Fellowship
See Fellowship of Recon

Fellowship Crown, *(Fellowship of the Crown),* P.O. Box 3743, Carmel, CA 93921 (SAN 206-4103) Tel 408-624-5600.

Fellowship of Recon, *(Fellowship of Reconciliation; 0-911810),* Box 271, Nyack, NY 10960 (SAN 210-7279) Tel 914-358-4601; 523 N. Broadway, Nyack, NY 10960 (SAN 669-0815).

Fellowship Pr PA, *(Fellowship Pr.; 0-914390; 0-87728),* 5820 Overbrook Ave., Philadelphia, PA 19131 (SAN 201-6117) Tel 215-879-8604.

Fels & Firn, *(Fels & Firn Pr.; 0-918704),* 2940 Seventh St., Berkeley, CA 94710 (SAN 293-2628) Tel 415-457-4361; Dist. by: The Distributors, 702 S. Michigan St., South Bend, IN 46618 (SAN 293-2636).

Felsun Pr, *(Felsun Pr.; 0-940928),* 1800 Old Meadow Rd., Suite 305, McLean, VA 22102 (SAN 217-3611) Tel 703-356-7799.

Fem Writers Guild, *(Feminist Writers Guild-Milwaukee Chapter; 0-9606982),* c/o The Womens Coalition, 2211 E. Kenwood Blvd., Milwaukee, WI 53211 (SAN 238-0595).

Feminist Comm, *(Feminist Committee Pr., The; 0-9603330),* 1957 Westminster Way, NE, Atlanta, GA 30307 (SAN 211-1292)

†**Feminist Pr,** *(Feminist Pr. at the City Univ. of New York, The; 0-912670; 0-935312),* 311 E. 94th St., New York, NY 10128 (SAN 213-6813) Tel 212-360-5790; Dist. by: Harper & Row, Pubs., Inc., Keystone Industrial Pk., Scranton, PA 18512 (SAN 215-3742); *CIP.*

Fen Winnie, *(Fen Winnie Ink; 0-9614438),* P.O. Box 13658, San Luis Obispo, CA 93406 (SAN 689-1586) Tel 805-927-3979.

Fenimore Bk, *(Fenimore Bk. Store),* Affil. of New York State Historical Assn., P.O. Box 800 Lake Rd., Cooperstown, NY 13326 (SAN 285-0176) Tel 607-547-2533.

Fenn Gall Pub
See Fenn Pub Co

Fenn Pub Co, *(Fenn Publishing Co.; 0-937634),* 1075 Paseo de Peralta, Santa Fe, NM 87501 (SAN 215-2436) Tel 505-982-4631.

Fennwyn Pr, *(Fennwyn Pr.),* 920 E., St. Patrick, Rapid City, SD 57701 (SAN 207-1177); Dist. by: Honor Books, P.O. Box 641, Rapid City, SD 57709 (SAN 208-0877) Tel 605-348-9734.

Fenton Assocs, *(Fenton Assocs.; 0-915345),* 3235 Columbia Pike, Westmont Shopping Ctr., Arlington, VA 22204 (SAN 289-9817) Tel 703-892-1232.

Fenton Valley Pr, *(Fenton Valley Pr.; 0-9615149),* 657 Chaffeeville Rd., Storrs, CT 06268 (SAN 694-3683) Tel 203-429-0710; Dist. by: DeVorss & Co., P.O. Box 550, 1046 Princeton Dr., Marina del Rey, CA 90294 (SAN 169-9886); Dist. by: Inland Bk. Co., P.O. Box 261, 22 Hemingway Ave., East Haven, CT 06512 (SAN 200-4151) Tel 203-467-4257; Dist. by: New Leaf Distributing Co., 1020 White St. SW, Atlanta, GA 30310 (SAN 169-1449) Tel 404-755-2665; Dist. by: Baker & Taylor, Eastern Div., 50 Kirby Ave., Somerville, NJ 08876 (SAN 169-4901).

FER Pub Co, *(FER Publishing Co.; 0-9614380),* 13 Vine St., Manchester, MA 01944 (SAN 688-4822) Tel 617-526-1529; Dist. by: Globe Pequot Pr., Old Chester Rd., Chester, CT 06412 (SAN 201-9892) Tel 203-526-9571.

†**Ferguson,** *(Ferguson, J. G., Publishing Co.; 0-89434),* 111 E. Wacker Dr., Suite 500, Chicago, IL 60601 (SAN 207-1363) Tel 312-861-0666; *CIP.*

Ferguson Comns Pubs, *(Ferguson Communications Publishers; 0-917231),* 1540 E. Moore Rd., Hillsdale, MI 49242 (SAN 656-0326) Tel 517-437-7205.

Ferguson-Florissant, *(Ferguson-Florissant School District/Early Education; 0-939418),* 1005 Waterford Dr., Florissant, MO 63033 (SAN 216-5740) Tel 314-831-8809.

FERM, *(Food Equipment Repair & Maintenance),* 462 Hillside, Rochester, NY 14610 (SAN 682-2681) Tel 716-244-5869.

Fermata, *(Fermata Pr.; 0-939792),* 40 Harriett Rd., Gloucester, MA 01930 (SAN 216-8936) Tel 617-283-5849.

Ferment Pr, *(Ferment Pr.; 0-9605318),* P.O. Box 2195, San Leandro, CA 94577 (SAN 293-2644) Tel 415-895-2739; Dist. by: Bookpeople, 2929 Fifth St., Berkeley, CA 94710 (SAN 168-9517) Tel 415-549-3030; Orders to: The Distributors, 702 S. Michigan, South Bend, IN 46618 (SAN 293-2660) Tel 219-232-8500.

Fern Pubns, *(Fern Pubns.; 0-9614097),* Subs. of Mueller Assocs., 2117 S. High St., Bloomington, IN 47401 (SAN 685-3080) Tel 812-339-0347.

Fern Ridge Pr, *(Fern Ridge Pr.; 0-9615332),* 1927 McLean Blvd., Eugene, OR 97405 (SAN 695-0868) Tel 503-485-8243.

†**Ferndale Hse,** *(Ferndale Hse.; 0-931637),* P.O. Box 1029, Ferndale Hse., CA 95536 (SAN 683-7735) Tel 707-786-9332; Dist. by: Spring Arbor Distributors, 10885 Textile Rd., Belleville, MI 48111 (SAN 158-9016) Tel 313-481-0900; *CIP.*

Ferndock Pub, *(Ferndock Publishing; 0-9616321),* P.O. Box 86, Rte. 1, Dennison, MN 55018 (SAN 658-7224) Tel 507-778-3357.

Fernglen Pr, *(Fernglen Pr.; 0-9612630),* 473 Sixth St., Lake Oswego, OR 97034 (SAN 289-2790) Tel 503-635-4719.

Ferrari Pubn
See Ferrari Pubns

Ferrari Pubns, *(Ferrari Pubns./Places of Interest; 0-942586),* P.O. Box 35575, Phoenix, AZ 85069 (SAN 239-6424) Tel 602-863-2408.

Ferri, *(Ferri, Roger C., & Assocs.; 0-9605928),* 261 W. 22nd St., New York, NY 10011 (SAN 216-6712) Tel 212-929-8192.

Ferris St Coll, *(Ferris State College; 0-9615299),* Schl. of Graphic Arts Dept., Big Rapids, MI 49307 (SAN 694-4655) Tel 616-796-0461.

†**Fertig,** *(Fertig, Howard, Inc.; 0-86527),* 80 E. 11th St., New York, NY 10003 (SAN 201-4777) Tel 212-982-7922; *CIP.*

FES Ltd, *(F.E.S., Ltd., Publishing; 0-937063),* P.O. Box 70, Bayside, NY 11361 (SAN 658-6066) Tel 718-423-6662.

Festival *Imprint of* **Abingdon**

†**Festival Pubns,** *(Festival Pubns.; 0-930828),* P.O. Box 10180, Glendale, CA 91209 (SAN 211-1527) Tel 818-887-0034; *CIP.*

Fevertree Pr, *(Fevertree Pr.; 0-911027),* Rte. 3, Box 216, Camilla, GA 31730 (SAN 270-1405) Tel 518-398-7764.

Fgn Lang Young Child, *(Foreign Language for Young Children; 0-937531),* 21 Lake Ave., Newton Centre, MA 02159 (SAN 658-8522) Tel 617-332-2427; Dist. by: Long Play, Inc., 2611 E. Franklin Ave., Minneapolis, MN 55406 (SAN 200-6375).

Fiasco Prod, *(Fiasco Productions; 0-935735),* 7062 14th Ave., NW, Seattle, WA 98117 (SAN 696-4230) Tel 206-789-4935.

Fibar Designs, *(Fibar Designs; 0-932086),* The Fannings, P.O. Box 2634, Menlo Park, CA 94026 (SAN 211-6847).

Fiberarts
See Lark Bks

FICOA, *(Film Instruction Co. of America; 0-931974),* 2901 S. Wentworth Ave., Milwaukee, WI 53207 (SAN 206-2003).

†**Fiction Coll,** *(Fiction Collective, Inc.; 0-914590; 0-932511),* Brooklyn College, c/o English Dept., Brooklyn, NY 11210 (SAN 201-4785) Tel 718-780-5547; Dist. by: Sun & Moon Pr., 6363 Wilshire Blvd., Suite 115, Los Angeles, CA 90048 (SAN 216-3063) Tel 213-653-6711; *CIP.*

Fiction Intl, *(Fiction International; 0-931362),* St. Lawrence Univ., Canton, NY 13617 (SAN 221-1548) Tel 315-379-5961.

Fictioneer Bks, *(Fictioneer Books, Ltd; 0-934882),* Box B.I.P., Screamer Mountain, Clayton, GA 30525 (SAN 213-3113) Tel 404-782-3318.

Fiddleback, *(Fiddleback, Inc.; 0-939027),* 2861 Glen Oaks Dr., Salt Lake City, UT 84109 (SAN 662-6505) Tel 801-486-0454.

Fideler, *(Fideler Co.; 0-88296),* 203 Logan St., SW, Grand Rapids, MI 49503 (SAN 201-4793) Tel 616-456-8577.

Fidelio Pr, *(Fidelio Pr.; 0-912681),* 504 Second SE., Apt. 4, Washington, DC 20003 (SAN 283-2577) Tel 202-544-8321.

Fidelity Assoc, *(Fidelity Assocs., Inc.; 0-9615570),* P.O. Box 3766, Gastonia, NC 28053 (SAN 696-4257) Tel 704-864-3766; 2936 Rousseau Ct., Gastonia, NC 28054 (SAN 696-5385).

Fidelity Hse, *(Fidelity Hse.; 0-942254),* 42 Wenonah Ave., Rockaway, NJ 07866 (SAN 682-255X).

Fidelity Pub, *(Fidelity Publishing Corp. of America, The; 0-942496),* 2021 Business Ctr. Dr., Suite 107, Irvine, CA 92715 (SAN 238-1591) Tel 714-752-5544; Toll free: 800-826-3830 (CA only).

Field & Wood Med, *(Field & Wood, Inc., Medical Pubs.; 0-938607),* 1405 Locust St., 11th Flr., Philadelphia, PA 19102 (SAN 661-3519) Tel 215-828-4010.

Field Ent
See World Bk

Field Mus, *(Field Museum of Natural History; 0-914868),* Roosevelt Rd. at Lake Shore Dr., Chicago, IL 60605-2496 (SAN 211-3554) Tel 312-922-9410.

Field Oberlin
See Oberlin Coll Pr

Field Pubns, *(Field Publications; 0-8374),* Div. of Field Corp., 245 Long Hill Rd., Middletown, CT 06457 (SAN 207-060X) Tel 203-638-2400; Toll free: 800-852-5000; Orders to: 1250 Fairwood Ave., Columbus, OH 43216 (SAN 207-0618) Tel 614-253-0892. Acquired in 1985 by the Field Corp.

Field Translat
See Oberlin Coll Pr
Field Translat Ser *Imprint of* **Oberlin Coll Pr**
Fielding
See Fielding Travel Bks
Fielding Travel Bks, *(Fielding Travel Bks.),* c/o William Morrow & Co., Inc., 105 Madison Ave., New York, NY 10016 (SAN 201-4823) Tel 212-889-3050; Orders to: William Morrow & Co., Order Dept., 6 Henderson Dr., West Caldwell, NJ 07006 (SAN 202-5779).
Fields, *(Fields, Virginia B.; 0-9614510),* 150 W. Forest, Slidell, LA 70458 (SAN 691-7410) Tel 504-643-4284.
Fieldston Co, *(Fieldston Co., Inc.; 0-9613656),* 1133 15th St., NW, Suite 1000, Washington, DC 20005 (SAN 670-7653) Tel 202-775-0240.
Fiery Water, *(Fiery Water Pr.; 0-9613401),* 1202 Loma Dr., No. 129, Ojai, CA 93023 (SAN 656-9854) Tel 805-646-1671; Dist. by: DeVorss & Co., P.O. Box 550, 1046 Princeton Dr., Marina del Rey, CA 90294 (SAN 168-9886) Tel 213-870-7478; Dist. by: Valley Lights Pubns., P.O. Box 1537, Ojai, CA 93023 (SAN 219-8320) Tel 805-646-9888.
Fiesta City, *(Fiesta City Pubs.; 0-940076),* P.O. Box 5861, Santa Barbara, CA 93150-5861 (SAN 217-071X) Tel 805-969-2891.
Fiesta Pub, *(Fiesta Publishing Corp.; 0-88473),* 6360 NE Fourth Ct., Miami, FL 33138 (SAN 201-8470) Tel 305-751-1181.
Fifth Ave Brides, *(Fifth Avenue Brides, Inc.; 0-9615882),* Affil. of Bridal Guide, Ltd., P.O. Box 2091, La Crosse, WI 54601 (SAN 697-0729); 2820 Leonard St., La Crosse, WI 54602-2091 (SAN 697-0737) Tel 608-782-8580; Dist. by: Clergy Bk. Services, 12855 W. Silver Spring Dr., Butler, WI 53007 (SAN 169-9032) Tel 414-781-1234; Dist. by: Howard Gardiner, Inc., 1743 Dallas Trade Mart, Dallas, TX 75207 (SAN 200-6944) Tel 214-748-3387; Dist. by: Primarily Paper, Inc., Orange UMAGA, Rm. 304, Minnetonka, MN 55343 (SAN 200-6952) Tel 612-462-3229.
Fifth Estate, *(Fifth Estate, Inc., The; 0-937217),* 1008 Dougals Ave., Providence, RI 02904 (SAN 658-7240) Tel 401-861-0361; P.O. Box 3172, Providence, RI 02906 (SAN 658-7259).
Fifth Wave Pr, *(Fifth Wave Pr.; 0-911761),* P.O. Box 9355, San Rafael, CA 94912 (SAN 264-0368) Tel 415-457-2019.
Fig Leaf, *(Fig Leaf Creations; 0-918774),* 1706 Olive Ave., Santa Barbara, CA 93101 (SAN 210-4245) Tel 805-962-4987.
Fig Leaf Pr, *(Fig Leaf Pr.; 0-912235),* 5791 E. Shields Ave., Fresno, CA 93727 (SAN 264-0376) Tel 209-292-4222.
FIG Ltd, *(F. I. G. Ltd.; 0-9601452),* P.O. Box 23, Northbrook, IL 60062 (SAN 211-8971).
Figures, *(Figures, The; 0-935724),* 27 1/2 Rosseter St., Great Barrington, MA 01230 (SAN 209-2468) Tel 413-528-2552; Dist. by: Small Pr. Distribution, 1814 San Pablo Ave., Berkeley, CA 94702 (SAN 204-5826) Tel 415-549-3336.
Filas Des Unltd, *(Fila's Designs Unlimited, Inc.; 0-9610588),* 1013 Big Baer Dr., Glen Burnie, MD 21061 (SAN 264-7338) Tel 301-761-1471.
Filkon Pub, *(Filkon Publishing, Ltd.; 0-936807),* 21 W. 46th St., 2nd Flr., New York, NY 10036 (SAN 699-9433) Tel 212-719-4237.
Fill the Gap, *(Fill the Gap Pubns.; 0-89858),* P.O. Box 30760, Lafayette, LA 70503 (SAN 211-9978) Tel 318-984-2004.
Film Classics, *(Film Classic Exchange; 0-9610916),* P.O. Box 77568 Dockweiler Stn., Los Angeles, CA 90007 (SAN 265-1351) Tel 213-731-3854.
Film Communicators, *(Film Communicators; 0-9606702),* 11136 Weddington St., N. Hollywood, CA 91601 (SAN 219-7359) Tel 818-766-3747; Toll free: 800-423-2400.
Filmquest Bks, *(Filmquest Bks.; 0-9610670),* 857 Partridge Ave., No. 1, Menlo Park, CA 94025 (SAN 264-7397).
Filsinger & Co, *(Filsinger & Co., Ltd.; 0-916754),* 288 W. 12 St., New York, NY 10014 (SAN 208-3574) Tel 212-243-7421.
Filson Club, *(Filson Club, Inc.; 0-9601072),* 1310 S. Third St., Louisville, KY 40208-2306 (SAN 205-5791) Tel 502-635-5083.

Filter, *(Filter Pr.; 0-910584; 0-86541),* P.O. Box 5, Palmer Lake, CO 80133 (SAN 201-484X) Tel 303-481-2523.
Fin Learn Syst
See LFSI Minnesota
Fin Mktg Assocs, *(Financial Marketing Assoc.; 0-9616902),* 1011 E. Main St., Richmond, VA 23219 (SAN 661-4965) Tel 804-643-6069.
Final Call Found, *(Final Call Foundation, Inc.; 0-938483),* 4503 Seventh St., Lubbock, TX 79416 (SAN 661-3136) Tel 806-793-7234.
Finan Acct, *(Financial Accounting Standards Board; 0-910065),* High Ridge PK., P.O. Box 3821, Stamford, CT 06905-0831 (SAN 241-3051) Tel 203-329-8401.
Finan Analysts, *(Financial Analysts Federation, the),* 1633 Broadway, 14th Floor, New York, NY 10019 (SAN 224-7305) Tel 212-957-2866.
Finan Data Corp, *(Financial Data Corp.; 0-940758),* 1313 Fifth St. SE, Suite 124, Minneapolis, MN 55414 (SAN 219-7367) Tel 612-379-3866.
Finan Exec, *(Financial Executives Research Foundation; 0-910586),* 10 Madison Ave., Morristown, NJ 07960 (SAN 206-4111) Tel 201-898-4600; P.O. Box 1938, Morristown, NJ 07960 (SAN 660-9295).
Finan Freedom, *(Financial Freedom Pubs.; 0-942360),* 9260 E. Colonville Rd., Clare, MI 48617 (SAN 281-7101) Tel 517-386-7729; Dist. by: Financial Freedom Consultants, P.O. Box 268, Clare, MI 48617 (SAN 281-711X) Tel 517-386-7720.
Finan Guide Bks, *(Financial Guide Bks.; 0-916407),* 12610 Bentree Rd., Minneapolis, MN 55343 (SAN 295-8031) Tel 612-544-8482.
Finan Mgmt Assn, *(Financial Management Association),* College of Business Administration, University of South Florida, Tampa, FL 33620 (SAN 236-2775) Tel 813-974-2084.
Finan Mgrs Soc, *(Financial Managers Society for Savings Institutions, Inc.),* 111 E. Wacker Dr., Suite 2221, Chicago, IL 60601 (SAN 230-6174) Tel 312-938-2576.
Finan Press, *(Financial Pr., The; 0-9615066),* 2555 Kennedy Blvd., Jersey City, NJ 07304 (SAN 693-9325) Tel 201-434-6110.
Finan Pub, *(Financial Publishing Co.; 0-87600),* 82 Brookline Ave., Boston, MA 02215 (SAN 205-5805) Tel 617-262-4040.
Finan Strategies
See Quissett Corp
Financial, *(Financial Partners Publishing; 0-9607644),* 4929 S. 121st St., Omaha, NE 68137 (SAN 679-1530) Tel 402-895-0346.
Financial Aid, *(Financial Aid Assistance Service; 0-9610018),* P.O. Box 1497, Springfield, OR 97477 (SAN 270-1561) Tel 503-726-2205.
Financial Guidance, *(Financial Guidance Ctr., Inc.; 0-938323),* 147 Main St., Maynard, MA 01754 (SAN 661-3187) Tel 617-897-6470.
Financial Pr, *(Financial Pr., Inc.),* 4975 SW 82nd St., Miami, FL 33143 (SAN 206-4545).
Finch Bks, *(Finch Bks.; 0-9616491),* 340 Birch St., Titusville, FL 32780 (SAN 659-2236) Tel 305-268-5420.
FIND-SVP, *(FIND-SVP Information Clearing Hse.; 0-931634),* 500 Fifth Ave., New York, NY 10110 (SAN 212-6680) Tel 212-354-2424; Toll free: 800-346-3787.
Fine Arts Mus, *(Fine Arts Museums of San Francisco, The; 0-88401),* M. H. De Young Memorial Museum, Golden Gate Pk., San Francisco, CA 94118 (SAN 206-524X) Tel 415-221-4811; Orders to: Museum Society Bookshops, M. H. De Young Memorial Museum, Golden Gate Pk., Sna Francisco, CA 94118 Tel 415-750-3642.
Fine Arts Muse LI
See FA Mus LI
Fine Arts Soc, *(Fine Arts Society; 0-932192),* 50459 N. Portage Rd., South Bend, IN 46628 (SAN 211-3902) Tel 219-272-9290; Orders to: 2314 W. Sixth St., Mishawaka, IN 46544 (SAN 211-3910) Tel 219-255-8606.
Fine Edge, *(Fine Edge Productions; 0-938665),* Rte. 2, Box 303, Bishop, CA 93514 (SAN 661-3225); 303 Valley View Rd., Bishop, CA 93514 (SAN 661-3233) Tel 619-387-2412.

Fine Line
See Fineline
Fine Line Prodns, *(Fine Line Productions; 0-936413),* 3181-A Mission St., San Francisco, CA 94110 (SAN 698-150X) Tel 415-282-5502; Dist. by: Bookpeople, 2929 Fifth St., Berkeley, CA 94710 (SAN 168-9517) Tel 415-549-3030; Dist. by: New Leaf Distributing, The, 1020 White St., SW, Atlanta, GA 30310 (SAN 169-1449) Tel 404-755-2665.
Fine Print, *(Fine Print; 0-9607290),* P.O. Box 3394, San Francisco, CA 94119 (SAN 239-2070) Tel 415-776-1530.
Fine Tools, *(Fine Tools, Inc.; 0-936059),* 2028 Backus Ave., Danbury, CT 06810 (SAN 697-0699) Tel 203-797-0183.
Fine View Pr, *(Fine View Pr.; 0-9615571),* 474 Fineview, Kalamazoo, MI 49007 (SAN 696-4273) Tel 616-342-6048.
Fineline, *(Fineline Co.; 0-913917; 0-917520),* 23501 Carlow Rd., Torraine, CA 90505 (SAN 286-8997) Tel 213-378-1904.
Fineline Pubns
See Cosmic Hse NM
Finesse Pr, *(Finesse Pr.; 0-938981),* 2068 Via Las Cumbres, No. 7, San Diego, CA 92111 (SAN 661-6798) Tel 619-569-7728.
Finestkind Bks, *(Finestkind Bks.; 0-938849),* Div. of Connecticut Cane & Reed Co., 205 Hartford Rd., Manchester, CT 06040 (SAN 662-5576) Tel 203-646-6586.
Fineview Pr
See Fine View Pr
Finn Hill, *(Finn Hill Arts; 0-917270),* P.O. Box 542, Silverton, CO 81433 (SAN 208-5054) Tel 303-387-5729.
Finney Co, *(Finney Co.; 0-912486),* 3350 Gorham Ave., Minneapolis, MN 55426 (SAN 206-412X) Tel 612-929-6165.
Finnish Am Lit, *(Finnish American Literary Heritage Foundation; 0-943478),* P.O. Box 1838, Portland, OR 97207 (SAN 240-6497) Tel 503-229-3064.
FinnRoots, *(FinnRoots, Inc.; 0-940034),* 40 E.49th St. No. 1602, New York, NY 10017 (SAN 220-2190) Tel 212-832-8989.
Fins Pubns, *(Fins Pubns.; 0-9615221),* Box 13005, Roseville, MN 55113 (SAN 695-1511) Tel 612-483-8187; Dist. by: Bookman, Inc., 519 N. Third St., Minneapolis, MN 55401 (SAN 282-7352) Tel 612-341-3333.
Fiore Ent, *(Fiore Enterprises; 0-9616687),* P.O. Box 2164, River Grove, IL 60171 (SAN 661-3411); 2119 78th Ave., Elmwood Park, IL 60635 (SAN 661-342X) Tel 312-453-8964.
Fire & Light Bks, *(Fire & Light Bks.; 0-911327),* P.O. Box 688, Madison, WI 53701 (SAN 270-1677).
Fire Call Pr *Imprint of* **First Intl Pub**
Fire Eng, *(Fire Engineering Bk. Service; 0-912212),* Div. of Technical Publishing Co., A Dun & Bradstreet Co., 875 Third Ave., New York, NY 10022 (SAN 281-7128) Tel 212-605-9515; Orders to: Fire Engineering Bk. Service, 1301 S. Grove Ave., Barrington, IL 60010 (SAN 281-7136) Tel 312-381-1840.
Fire Engine Bk
See Fire Eng
Fire Lake, *(Fire in the Lake; 0-9615693),* 1875 Oak St., No. 2, San Francisco, CA 94117 (SAN 696-429X) Tel 415-626-1708.
Fire Police Direct Pr *Imprint of* **First Intl Pub**
Fire Pr, *(Fire Pr., The; 0-912607),* P.O. Box 327, Metuchen, NJ 08840 (SAN 283-2593) Tel 201-964-8476.
Firebird Pr, *(Firebird Pr.; 0-912019),* P.O. Box 69, Dunlap, IL 61525 (SAN 265-3834).
Firebrand Bks, *(Firebrand Bks.; 0-932379),* 141 The Commons, Ithaca, NY 14850 (SAN 687-3855) Tel 607-272-0000.
FireBuilders, *(FireBuilders, The; 0-9601794),* RR1, Box 620, Stetson Rd., Brooklyn, CT 06234 (SAN 210-5977) Tel 203-774-4824.
Firelands Hist, *(Firelands Historical Society; 0-932535),* 4 Case Ave, Norwalk, OH 44857 (SAN 687-469X) Tel 419-668-6038; 45 N. Pleasant St., Norwalk, OH 44857 (SAN 693-5214) Tel 419-668-8031; Dist. by: Baker & Taylor Co., Eastern Div., 50 Kirby Ave, Somerville, NJ 08876 (SAN 169-4901).

†**Fireside Bks,** *(Fireside Bks.; 0-87527),* Div. of Warren H. Green, Inc., 8356 Olive Blvd., St. Louis, MO 63132 (SAN 201-8500) Tel 314-991-1335; Toll free: 800-223-2336; *CIP.*

Fireside Pr, *(Fireside Pr.),* Box 5293, Hamden, CT 06518 (SAN 209-7400) Tel 203-248-1023.

Firestein Bks, *(Firestein Bks.; 0-9602498),* P.O. Box 370643, El Paso, TX 79937-0643 (SAN 212-940X) Tel 915-594-2966.

Firestone, *(Firestone, W. D., Press; 0-934562),* 1313 S. Jefferson Ave., Springfield, MO 65807 (SAN 213-2478) Tel 417-866-5141.

Fireweed, *(Fireweed Pr.; 0-912683),* P.O. Box 6011, Falls Church, VA 22046 (SAN 277-6839) Tel 703-560-0810.

Fireweed Pr AK, *(Fireweed Pr.; 0-914221),* P.O. Box 83970, Fairbanks, AK 99708 (SAN 287-4911) Tel 907-479-2398.

Firey, *(Firey, Walter; 0-9603066),* 1307 Wilshire Blvd., Austin, TX 78722 (SAN 209-5572) Tel 512-454-2418.

Firm Foun Pub *(Firm Foundation Publishing Hse.; 0-88027),* P.O. Box 17200, Pensacola, FL 32522 (SAN 201-4858) Tel 904-433-4258.

First Am Bank, *(First American Bank for Savings),* 154 East St., Dorchester, MA 02122 (SAN 207-5164) Tel 617-288-9491.

First Amend, *(First Amendment Press),* P.O. Box 7334, Stanford, CA 94305 (SAN 215-7616) Tel 415-851-3391.

First Bapt AL, *(First Baptist Church AL; 0-9616158),* P.O. Box 400, Jacksonville, AL 36265 (SAN 699-9557) Tel 205-435-7263; 231 E. Seventh St., Jacksonville, AL 36265 (SAN 699-9565).

First Baptist, *(First Baptist Church of Steinhatchee),* P.O. Box 113, Steinhatchee, FL 32359 (SAN 240-1754) Tel 904-498-3242.

First Choice, *(First Choice; 0-9606704),* P.O. Box 1680, Ramona, CA 92065 (SAN 219-7375) Tel 619-789-8878.

First Church, *(First Church of Christ Scientist; 0-87952),* 1 Norway St., Boston, MA 02115 (SAN 206-6467) Tel 617-262-2300.

First Commonwealth, *(First Commonwealth Pr.; 0-912709),* 1300 NE 157th St., North Miami Beach, FL 33162 (SAN 283-0280) Tel 305-949-7797.

First East, *(First East Coast Theatre and Publishing Co., Inc.; 0-910829),* P.O. Box A244, Village Sta., New York, NY 10014 (SAN 270-1812) Tel 718-296-1979.

First Encounter, *(First Encounter Pr., The; 0-912609),* P.O. Box 946, N. Eastham, Cape Cod, MA 02651 (SAN 282-7697) Tel 617-255-3389.

First Impressions, *(First Impressions Publishing Co.; 0-934794),* P.O. Box 9073, Madison, WI 53715 (SAN 213-0572) Tel 608-238-6254.

First Intl Pub, *(First International Publishing Corp.; 1-55632),* P.O. Box 20279, Seattle, WA 98102-1279 (SAN 659-6126); 2803 Eighth Ave., Seattle, WA 98119 (SAN 659-6134) Tel 206-282-1438. *Imprints:* Anechron Three Pr (Anechron Three Press); Comns Monitor Pr (Communications Monitor Press); Emerg Med Tech Pr (Emergency Medical Technology Press); Fire Call Pr (Fire Call Press, The); Fire Police Direct Pr (Fire & Police Directory Press, The); Small Busn Success Pr (Small Business Success Press); United Galactic Pub (United Galactic Publishing Foundation Press).

First Love Min, *(First Love Ministries; 0-9614947),* P.O. Box 317, Linden, NJ 07036 (SAN 693-6482) Tel 201-862-7172.

First Mntn Foun, *(First Mountain Foundation, The; 0-916834),* Montclair State College, Upper Montclair, NJ 07042 (SAN 281-7144) Tel 201-893-4277; Orders to: P.O. Box 196, Montclair, NJ 07042 (SAN 281-7152).

First Ozark Pr, *(First Ozark Pr., The; 0-911559),* P.O. Box 1137, Harrison, AR 72601 (SAN 217-734X).

First Parish Concord, *(First Parish in Concord),* 20 Lexington Rd., Concord, MA 01742 (SAN 658-8220) Tel 617-369-9602; Orders to: Eric P. Smith, 35 Academy Ln., Concord, MA 01742 (SAN 662-4170).

First Person, *(First Person; 0-916452),* Box 604, Palisades, NY 10964 (SAN 208-0508) Tel 914-359-7340; Dist. by: Small Pr. Distribution, Inc., 1814 San Pablo Ave., Berkeley, CA 94702 (SAN 204-5826) Tel 415-549-3336.

First Pubns, *(First Pubns., Inc.; 0-912891),* P.O. Box 1832, Evanston, IL 60204 (SAN 283-2607) Tel 312-869-7210.

First Stage, *(First Stage Arts Project; 0-939695),* 1800 S. Robertson Blvd., Suite 322, Los Angeles, CA 90035 (SAN 663-4729) Tel 213-836-6398; 4913 Indian Wood Rd., No. 507, Culver City, CA 90230 (SAN 663-4737).

First Step Ent, *(First Step Enterprises; 0-9614220),* P.O. Box 87265, San Diego, CA 92138-7265 (SAN 686-8010) Tel 619-224-0578.

Firsthand, *(Firsthand Press; 0-939620),* 137 Sixth St., Juneau, AK 99801 (SAN 295-3307) Tel 907-568-1411; Orders to: 137 Sixth St., Juneau, AK 99801 (SAN 295-3315) Tel 907-568-1411.

Firth, *(Firth, Robert H.; 0-9605060),* Cable Cellarbook., 20351 Lake Erie Dr., Walnut, CA 91789 (SAN 293-2679); Dist. by: The Cellar Book Shop., 18090 Wyoming, Detroit, MI 48221 (SAN 213-4330) Tel 313-861-1776.

Fiscal Policy, *(Fiscal Policy Council; 0-940494),* 100 E. 17th St., Riviera Beach, FL 33404 (SAN 217-1740) Tel 305-863-9701.

Fischer Inc NY, *(Fischer, Carl, Inc.; 0-8258),* 62 Cooper Sq., New York, NY 10003 (SAN 215-1979).

Fischer Pub, *(Fischer Publishing; 0-915421),* P.O. Box 116, 7851 Herbert Rd., Canfield, OH 44406 (SAN 291-1574) Tel 216-533-4446.

Fisher Bks, *(Fisher Bks.; 1-55561),* 3499 N. Campbell Ave., No. 909, Tucson, AZ 85719 (SAN 698-1410) Tel 602-325-5263.

Fisher-Bradley, *(Fisher-Bradley, Inc.; 0-934751),* 77 Bralan Ct., Gaithersburg, MD 20877 (SAN 694-1745) Tel 301-840-9755.

Fisher Co, *(W.A. Fisher Co.; 0-933287),* 123 Chestnut St., Virginia, MN 55792 (SAN 692-3518) Tel 218-741-9544.

Fisher Hse Pubns, *(Fisher Hse. Pubns.; 0-938325),* P.O. Box 863, Merrifield, VA 22116 (SAN 661-3241); 3366 Woodburn Rd., No. 21, Annandale, VA 22003 (SAN 661-325X) Tel 703-849-9654.

†**Fisher Inst,** *(Fisher Institute, The; 0-933028),* 6350 LBJ Freeway, Suite 183E, Dallas, TX 75240 (SAN 213-4942); *CIP.*

Fisher Pubns, *(Fisher Pubns.; 0-911303),* 748 Springdale Rd., Statesville, NC 28677 (SAN 270-1871) Tel 704-873-3776.

Fishergate, *(Fishergate Publishing Co., Inc.; 0-942720),* 2521 Riva Rd., Annapolis, MD 21401 (SAN 240-2181) Tel 301-841-6646.

Fisheries Comm, *(Fisheries Communications, Inc.; 0-9608932),* Box 37, Dept B, Stonington, ME 04681 (SAN 241-0184) Tel 207-367-2396.

Fishing with Jack Pubns, *(Fishing with Jack Pubns.; 0-9616975),* 1 Marvel Ct., San Francisco, CA 94121 (SAN 661-8146) Tel 415-221-1592.

Fishner Bks, *(Fishner Bks.; 0-9606848),* P.O. Box 445, Vienna, VA 22180 (SAN 217-3638) Tel 703-281-4255.

Fisons Corp, *(Fisons Corp.; 0-914132),* 2 Preston Ct., Bedford, MA 01730 (SAN 220-5459) Tel 617-275-1000.

Fitchburg Pr, *(Fitchburg Pr., Inc.; 0-9617191),* 2805 Florann Dr., Madison, WI 53711 (SAN 663-5865) Tel 608-273-3266.

Fitness, *(Fitness Pubns.; 0-918278),* P.O. Box 1786, Poughkeepsie, NY 12601 (SAN 209-3995) Tel 914-463-1626.

Fitness Alt Pr, *(Fitness Alternatives Pr.; 0-943364),* Box 761, Evergreen, CO 80439 (SAN 240-1096).

Fitness Ctr Info, *(Fitness Ctr. Information Network, The; 0-935783),* P.O. Box 906, Greenfield, MA 01302 (SAN 699-8089) Tel 413-773-8769.

Fitzg Unicorn, *(Fitzgerald Unicorn; 0-9604564),* 808 Charlotte, Fredericksburg, VA 22401 (SAN 214-2643) Tel 703-371-3253.

FitzGerald & Assocs, *(FitzGerald, Jerry, & Associates; 0-932410),* 506 Barkentine Ln., Redwood City, CA 94065 (SAN 214-0128) Tel 415-591-5676.

Fitzgerald & Co, *(Fitzgerald, Vincent, & Co.; 0-935581),* 11 E. 78th St., New York, NY 10021 (SAN 695-9261) Tel 212-249-1971.

FitzSimons, *(FitzSimons, H.T., Co., Inc.; 0-912222),* 357 W. Erie St., Chicago, IL 60610 (SAN 206-4200) Tel 312-944-1841.

Five Arms Corp
See Weber Systems

Five Assocs
See Mus Graphics

Five Hundred Seven Parachute, *(517 Parachute Combat Team Assn.; 0-9616015),* 6600 Josie Ln., Hudson, FL 33567 (SAN 697-3272) Tel 813-863-2995.

Five M Pubs, *(5 M Pubs.; 0-9614306),* P.O. Box 6641, New Orleans, LA 70174 (SAN 687-4983) Tel 504-391-9412.

Five Starr Prods, *(Five Starr Productions; 0-9606026),* 1610 Christine, Wichita Falls, TX 76302 (SAN 216-8944) Tel 301-838-8059.

Five Windmills, *(Five Windmills Pub. Co.; 0-9609600),* P.O. Box 5841, Scottsdale, AZ 85261 (SAN 260-1877) Tel 602-998-0713.

†**Fjord Pr,** *(Fjord Pr.; 0-940242),* P.O. Box 16501, Seattle, WA 98116 (SAN 220-3332) Tel 206-625-9363; Dist. by: Academy Chicago Pubs., 425 N. Michigan Ave., Chicago, IL 60611 (SAN 213-2001) Tel 312-644-1723; *CIP.*

FL Bar Legal Ed, *(Florida Bar Continuing Legal Education Pubns., The; 0-910373),* 600 Apalachee Pkwy., Tallahassee, FL 32301-8226 (SAN 260-0579) Tel 904-222-5286; Toll free: 800-874-0005.

FL Bureau Geology, *(Association of American State Geologists),* Dept. of Natural Resources, Geological Survey, P.O. Box 30028, Lansing, MI 48909 (SAN 224-0580) Tel 517-373-8014.

FL Ctr Public, *(Florida Ctr. for Public Management; 0-932143),* Florida State Univ., Tallahassee, FL 32306-4025 (SAN 686-4287) Tel 904-644-6460.

FL Mail Pr, *(Florida Mail Pr.; 0-937759),* P.O. Box 6, Old Town, FL 32680 (SAN 659-2244) Tel 904-542-7904; 400 Madison Ave., Old Town, FL 32680 (SAN 659-2252).

FL Sea Grant Coll, *(Florida Sea Grant College Program; 0-912747),* Univ. of Florida, G.O. 22, McCarty Hall, Gainesville, FL 32611 (SAN 282-7719) Tel 904-392-1771.

FL Sinkhole Res, *(Florida Sinkhole Research Institute; 0-937971),* Univ. of Central Florida, Orlando, FL 32765 (SAN 659-5030) Tel 305-275-2043.

FL St U-Inst Soc Re, *(Florida State Univ., Institute for Social Research),* Tallahassee, FL 32306 (SAN 204-1081) Tel 904-599-2525.

Fla Med Entom, *(Florida Medical Entomology Laboratory; 0-9615224),* 200 Ninth St. SE, Vero Beach, FL 32962 (SAN 694-6453) Tel 305-562-5435.

Fla Rare Coin, *(Florida Rare Coin Galleries; 0-9614824),* P.O. Box 13193, Tallahassee, FL 32317 (SAN 693-0026) Tel 904-878-5779.

Flame Intl, *(Flame International Inc.; 0-933184),* P.O. Box 305, Quantico, VA 22134 (SAN 215-3114).

Flaming Arrow Pubns, *(Flaming Arrow Pubns.; 0-930043),* R.F.D, Walpole, NH 03608 (SAN 669-8123) Tel 603-756-4152.

Flaming Hooker Pr, *(Flaming Hooker Pr.; 0-9615223),* Div. of Markin Medical Research, 1236 Ginger Crescent, Virginia Beach, VA 23456 (SAN 695-152X) Tel 804-427-0220; P.O. Box 9106, Virginia Beach, VA 23450 (SAN 662-3441).

Flamingo Pr CA, *(Flamingo Pr.; 0-938905),* 2304 Altisma Way, No. 208, Carlsbad, CA 92008 (SAN 661-812X) Tel 619-438-3011. Do not confuse with Flamingo Pr., New York, NY.

Flare *Imprint of Avon*

Flashmaps Pubns, *(Flashmaps Pubns., Inc.; 0-942226),* P.O. Box 13, Chappaqua, NY 10514 (SAN 239-8540) Tel 914-238-5116.

Flat Five Pr, *(Flat Five Pr.; 0-935285),* 3214A Golden City Blvd., Roanoke, VA 24014 (SAN 696-4214) Tel 703-345-2151.

Flat Glass Mktg, *(Flat Glass Marketing Assn.),* 3310 Harrison, Topeka, KS 66611 (SAN 224-7720) Tel 913-226-7013.

†**Flatiron Book Dist,** *(Flatiron Bk. Distributors),* 1170 Broadway, New York, NY 10001 (SAN 663-2998); *CIP.*

Flayderman, *(Flayderman, N., & Co., Inc.; 0-910598),* Squash Hollow Rd., New Milford, CT 06776 (SAN 205-5813) Tel 203-354-5567.

†**Fleet,** *(Fleet Pr. Corp.; 0-8303),* Subs. of Fleet Academic Editions, Inc., 160 Fifth Ave., New York, NY 10010 (SAN 201-4874) Tel 212-243-6100; *CIP.*

Fleet St Corp, *(Fleet Street Corp.; 0-9611314),* 656 Quince Orchard Rd., Gaithersburg, MD 20878 (SAN 282-9053) Tel 301-977-3900.

Fleming Pub, *(Fleming Publishing; 0-937835),* 414 Glover Ave., Enterprise, AL 36330 (SAN 659-4506) Tel 205-393-3062.

Fleur-Di-Lee, *(Fleur-Di-Lee; 0-911579),* 5969 Donna, Tarzana, CA 91356 (SAN 264-0422).

Fleury Found, *(Fleury Foundation Inc.; 0-933537),* P.O. Box 19352, Orlando, FL 32814 (SAN 691-859X) Tel 305-422-4999.

Flex-A-bility, *(Flex-A-bility Inc.; 0-932931),* P.O. Box 7252, 890 S. Long, Freeport, NY 11520 (SAN 690-0348) Tel 516-223-7965.

Flight Safety, *(Flight Safety Foundation, Inc.; 0-912768),* 5510 Columbia Pike, Arlington, VA 22204 (SAN 205-5821) Tel 703-820-2777.

Flightshops, *(National Flightshops; 0-939158),* St. Petersburg-Clearwater Airport, Clearwater, FL 33520 (SAN 240-9127).

Flint Hills, *(Flint Hills Book Co.),* 1735 Fairview, Manhattan, KS 66502 (SAN 208-1806).

Flint Inst Arts, *(Flint Institute of Arts; 0-939896),* 1120 E. Kearsley St., Flint, MI 48503 (SAN 216-812X) Tel 313-234-1695.

FlipTrack, *(FlipTrack Learning Systems; 0-917792),* Div. of Mosaic Media, Inc., 999 Main St., Suite 200, Glen Ellyn, IL 60137 (SAN 286-9136) Tel 312-790-1117; Toll free: 800-222-3547.

Floating Island, *(Floating Island Pubns.; 0-912449),* P.O. Box 516, Point Reyes Station, CA 94956 (SAN 212-9043) Tel 415-669-1612.

†**Flora & Fauna,** *(Flora & Fauna Pubns.; 0-916846),* Div. E. J. Brill Publishing Co., 4300 NW 23rd Ave., Suite 100, Gainesville, FL 32606 (SAN 220-2468) Tel 904-371-9858; *CIP.*

Floral Pub, *(Floral Publishing; 0-938057),* P.O. Box 55282, Madison, WI 53705 (SAN 661-1842); 717 Eugenia Ave., Madison, WI 53705 (SAN 661-1850) Tel 603-238-5626.

Floraprint USA, *(Henry, John, Company),* Div. of American Printers & Lithographers, 5800 W. Grand River Ave., Lansing, MI 48901 (SAN 216-7069) Tel 312-966-6500; Dist. by: International Specialized Bk., Servs., Inc., 5602 NE Hassalo St., Portland ove, OR 97213-3640 (SAN 169-7129) Tel 503-287-3093.

Floraprint USA See Floraprint USA

Flores De Papel, *(Flores De Papel Inc.; 0-915475),* 12 Robyn Lane, Greenleaf Golf & Racquet Club, Haines City, FL 33844 (SAN 291-1582) Tel 813-422-8113.

Florham, *(Florham Park Press, Inc.; 0-912598),* 12 Leslie Ave., P.O. Box 303, Florham Park, NJ 07932 (SAN 206-4219) Tel 201-377-3670.

Floricanto Pr, *(Floricanto Pr.; 0-915745),* Div. of Hispanex, 604 William St., Oakland, CA 94612 (SAN 293-9169) Tel 415-893-8702.

Florida Classics, *(Florida Classics Library; 0-912451),* P.O. Drawer 1657, Pt. Salerno, FL 33492-1657 (SAN 265-2404) Tel 305-546-9380.

Florida Flair Bks, *(Florida Flair Bks.; 0-9613236),* 8955 SW 93rd Ct., Miami, FL 33176 (SAN 295-4192) Tel 305-274-5734.

Florida State U Found See Florida State U Inst

Florida State U Inst, *(Florida State Univ. Institute of Science & Public Affairs; 0-9606708),* 361 Bellamy Bldg, Florida State Univ., Tallahassee, FL 32306 (SAN 219-7405).

Florida Sun-Gator, *(Florida Sun-Gator Publishing Co.),* P.O. Box 365, Oviedo, FL 32765 (SAN 209-3030) Tel 305-671-3633.

Florida Trend, *(Florida Trend Bk. Division; 0-88251),* Div. of Florida Trend, Inc., P.O. Box 611, St. Petersburg, FL 33731 (SAN 202-8018) Tel 813-821-5800.

Florida Women, *(Florida Women's Yellow Pages Directory; 0-935785),* P.O. Box 1523, Clearwater, FL 33517 (SAN 695-8133) Tel 813-443-1300; Dist. by: Surf & Sand, P.O. Box 1312, Largo, FL 33540 (SAN 200-7886).

Flourtown Pub, *(Flourtown Publishing Co.; 0-9603376),* P.O. Box 148, Flourtown, PA 19031 (SAN 207-6381).

Flower & Garden Imprint of **Mod Handcraft**

Flower Pr, *(Flower Press; 0-942256),* 10332 Shaver Rd., Kalamazoo, MI 49002 (SAN 217-7358) Tel 616-327-0108.

†**Flume Pr,** *(Flume Press; 0-9613984),* 644 Citrus Ave., Chico, CA 95926 (SAN 682-1898) Tel 916-342-1583; *CIP.*

Fly Tyer See Saco River Pub

Flying Bks, *(Flying Bks.; 0-911139),* 3850 Coronation Rd., Eagan, MN 55122 (SAN 270-2185) Tel 612-454-2493.

Flying Buttress See NBM

Flying Diamond Bks, *(Flying Diamond Bks.; 0-918532),* Rte. 2, Box 612, Hettinger, ND 58639 (SAN 209-5580) Tel 701-567-2646.

Flying Ent, *(Flying Enterprises, Inc; 0-912470),* Box 7000, Dallas, TX 75209 (SAN 201-4882) Tel 214-358-3456.

Flying Fingers, *(Flying Fingers; 0-9612448),* P.O. Box 5455, Santa Monica, CA 90405 (SAN 289-2456) Tel 213-396-5648.

Flying Fox Pr, *(Flying Fox Pr., The; 0-9617225),* 4700 Jamestown Rd., Bethesda, MD 20816 (SAN 663-3692) Tel 301-229-8160.

Flying Pencil, *(Flying Pencil Pubns.; 0-916473),* P.O. Box 19062, Portland, OR 97219 (SAN 295-1398) Tel 503-245-2314.

Flying Pubns See Flying Pencil

Flying Yankee, *(Flying Yankee Enterprises; 0-9615574),* 13 Nutting Rd., Groton, MA 01450 (SAN 696-4311) Tel 617-448-5339; P.O. Box 595, Littleton, MA 01460 (SAN 696-5393).

Flyway Pub, *(Flyway Publishing Co., Inc.; 0-9616657),* 137 Veto St., Chenoa, IL 61726 (SAN 661-3500) Tel 815-945-7862.

FMA Bus, *(FMA Business Bks.; 0-930566),* 3928 Iowa St., San Diego, CA 92104 (SAN 221-1483) Tel 619-563-0599.

FMI Pub, *(FMI Publishing; 0-9606164),* P.O. Box 26464, Tempe, AZ 85282 (SAN 217-5576).

FMME Imprint of **Unipub**

FMME-COA Imprint of **Unipub**

FNB Imprint of **Unipub**

Focal Point Pr, *(Focal Point Pr.),* 321 City Island Ave., City Island, NY 10464 (SAN 663-1894) Tel 212-885-1403.

†**Focal Pr,** *(Focal Pr.; 0-240; 0-480),* Div. of Butterworth Publishers, 80 Montvale Ave., Stoneham, MA 02180 (SAN 220-0066) Tel 617-438-8464; *CIP.*

Focus Pub, *(Focus Pub. Co.; 0-938442),* 29175 Oak Point Dr., Farmington Hills, MI 48018 (SAN 281-7160) Tel 313-553-0298; Dist. by: Distributor, The, 702 S. Michigan, South Bend, IN 46618 (SAN 169-2488) Tel 219-232-8500.

Focus Pubns, *(Focus Pubns. (DC); 0-930197),* 4520 East-West Hwy., No. 600, Bethesda, MD 20814 (SAN 670-8005) Tel 301-656-0091.

Focus Pubns MO, *(Focus Pubns.; 0-911921),* P.O. Box 15853, St. Louis, MO 63114 (SAN 264-0449) Tel 314-426-7011.

Focus Quality, *(Focus Quality Games Corp.; 0-915236),* P.O. Box 114, Blythebourne Sta., Brooklyn, NY 11219 (SAN 207-1266).

Fog Pubns, *(Fog Pubns.; 0-9616535),* 413 Pennsylvania NE, Albuquerque, NM 87108 (SAN 659-4484) Tel 505-255-3096.

Fogg Art See Harvard Art Mus

Fogg Art Mus See Harvard Art Mus

Foggy Bottom Pubns, *(Foggy Bottom Pubns.; 0-934891),* Box 57150 West End Sta., Washington, DC 20037 (SAN 694-4450) Tel 202-337-4352.

Foghorn Pr, *(Foghorn Pr.; 0-935701),* 2687 45th Ave., San Francisco, CA 94116 (SAN 696-4346) Tel 415-564-4918; Orders to: 2022 Taraval, No. 9523, San Francisco, CA 94116 (SAN 662-782X) Tel 415-564-4918; Dist. by: Bookpeople, 2929 Fifth St., Berkeley, CA 94710 (SAN 168-9517); Dist. by: Publishers Group West, 5855 Beaudry St., Emeryville, CA 94608 (SAN 202-8522) Tel 415-658-3453.

†**Folcroft,** *(Folcroft Library Editions; 0-8414; 0-88305; 0-8482),* P.O. Box 182, Folcroft, PA 19032 (SAN 206-8362) Tel 215-583-4550; *CIP.*

Foldabook Pub, *(Foldabook Publishing Co.; 0-89726),* 111 N. Fuller Ave., Los Angeles, CA 90036 (SAN 217-2399) Tel 213-933-3009.

Folder Edns, *(Folder Editions; 0-913152),* 103-26 68th Rd., Apt. A 47, Forest Hills, NY 11375 (SAN 206-6475) Tel 718-275-3839.

Folger Bks, *(Folger Bks.; 0-918016),* Dist. by: Associated University Presses, 440 Forsgate Dr., Cranbury, NJ 08512 (SAN 281-2959) Tel 609-655-4770.

Folio, *(Folio Publishing Corp.; 0-918110),* Subs. of Hanson Publishing Group, P.O. Box 4949, Stamford, CT 06907-0949 (SAN 210-2021); 6 River Bend, Stamford, CT 06907-0949 (SAN 658-0718) Tel 203-358-9900.

Folio Press See Folio Pubs

Folio Pubs, *(Folio Pubs.; 0-9613702),* Box 1807, Sta. B, Vanderbilt Univ., Nashville, TN 37235 (SAN 677-167X) Tel 615-322-2828.

Folk Art, *(Folk Art Studios; 0-930310),* 608 E. First St., Tustin, CA 92680 (SAN 207-5601) Tel 714-731-3355.

Folk-Legacy, *(Folk-Legacy Records, Inc.),* Sharon Mountain Rd., Sharon, CT 06069 (SAN 207-3390) Tel 203-364-5661.

Folk-Life, *(Folk-Life Books; 0-914917),* P.O. Box 128, Princeton, LA 71067 (SAN 289-1336) Tel 318-949-3915; Rte. 4, Box 299, Haughton, LA 71037 (SAN 289-1344).

Folk Press, *(Folk Pr., The; 0-938603),* Kapiolani Community College, Office of Community Services, 4303 Diamond Head Rd., Honolulu, HI 96816 (SAN 661-356X) Tel 808-735-8256.

Folkestone, *(Folkestone Pr.; 0-910600),* P.O. Box 3142, St. Louis, MO 63130 (SAN 206-4227) Tel 314-725-2767.

Folkloric Studies, *(Folkloric Studies T.G.B. Pr.; 0-9615745),* P.O. Box 7484, Menlo Park, CA 94026 (SAN 696-4354) Tel 415-854-3184.

Folklorica Pr, *(Folklorica Pr., Inc.; 0-939544),* 70 Greenwich Ave., Suite 377, New York, NY 10011 (SAN 216-6720) Tel 212-929-1921.

Folks Pubns, *(Folks Pubns.; 0-941628),* P.O. Box 1121, N. Highland, CA 95660 (SAN 239-2089) Tel 916-331-2106.

Folksay Pr, *(Folksay Pr.; 0-916454),* 67131 Mills Rd., R.R. 3, St. Clairsville, OH 43950 (SAN 208-6514) Tel 614-695-3348; Dist. by: Bookpeople, 2929 Fifth St., Berkeley, CA 94710 (SAN 168-9517) Tel 415-549-3030.

Folkstone Pr, *(Folkstone Press, The),* P.O. Box 3142, St. Louis, MO 63130 (SAN 285-6778); Dist. by: Paperback Supply, 4121 Forest Park Blvd., St. Louis, MO 63108 (SAN 285-6786).

Follett See Esquire

Fontana See J M Fontana

Fontana Pap Imprint of **Watts**

Fontastic, *(Fontastic; 0-9603596),* 157 Judd St., Madison, WI 53714 (SAN 222-3368) Tel 608-249-8701.

Food & Energy Coun, *(Food & Energy Council),* 409 Vandiver W., Suite 202, Columbia, MO 65202 (SAN 225-1884) Tel 314-875-7155.

Food for Thought, *(Food for Thought Pubns.),* P.O. Box 331, Amherst, MA 01004 (SAN 209-4363) Tel 413-253-5432.

Food Lrn Ctr, *(Food Learning Ctr.; 0-931149),* 6518 Fremont Ave. N., Seattle, WA 98103 (SAN 679-4173) Tel 206-783-9679.

†**Food Marketing,** *(Food Marketing Institute; 0-939813),* 1750 K St., NW, Washington, DC 20006 (SAN 224-7429) Tel 202-452-8444; *CIP.*

Symbols/Abbreviations

Food Processors, *(Food Processors Institute, The; 0-937774),* 1401 New York Ave. NW, Suite 400, Washington, DC 20005 (SAN 215-3122) Tel 202-393-0890.

†**Food Res,** *(Food Research & Action Ctr.; 0-934220),* 1319 F St., NW, Washington, DC 20004 (SAN 215-9937) Tel 202-393-5060; *CIP.*

Food Res Action
See Food Res

Food Thought Pr, *(Food for Thought Pr.; 0-9616876),* 1712 Markham Ave. NE, Tacoma, WA 98422 (SAN 661-3675) Tel 206-952-2142.

Food Trends, *(Food Trends; 0-9615572),* 7953 First Ave. S., St. Petersburg, FL 33707 (SAN 696-4389) Tel 813-345-1166.

Foodwork, *(Foodwork, Inc.; 0-9615573),* 1658 Cowling Ave., Louisville, KY 40205 (SAN 696-4486) Tel 502-459-0249.

Fool Court, *(Fool Court Pr., The; 0-910305),* P.O. Box 25824, Charlotte, NC 28212 (SAN 240-8503) Tel 704-537-7375.

Football Hobbies, *(Football Hobbies, Pubs.; 0-912122),* 4216 McConnell, El Paso, TX 79904 (SAN 204-1057) Tel 915-565-7354.

Foothills, *(Foothills Pr.; 0-936061),* P.O. Box 5194, Orange, CA 92613-5194 (SAN 697-0702) Tel 714-491-1372.

Foothills Art
See Riverstone Foothills

Footprint Pub, *(Footprint Publishing Co.; 0-9613548),* P.O. Box 1542, Lima Linda, CA 92354 (SAN 677-4873) Tel 714-883-4114.

Footsteps, *(Footsteps Press; 0-934796),* 1327 E. Bender, Hobbs, NM 88240 (SAN 213-666X).

Footwear Indus, *(Footwear Industries of America),* 3700 Market St., Philadelphia, PA 19104 (SAN 679-3665) Tel 215-222-1484; Orders to: P.O. Box 6930, Falls Church, VA 22046 (SAN 662-2577).

†**For Policy Res,** *(Foreign Policy Research Institute; 0-910191),* 3508 Market St., Suite 350, Philadelphia, PA 19104 (SAN 218-7280) Tel 215-382-0685; *CIP.*

For Us Pubns, *(For Us Pubns.; 0-915383),* P.O. Box 33147 Farragut Sta., Washington, DC 20033 (SAN 291-1604) Tel 202-462-1465.

Foran Pubn, *(Foran Pubn.; 0-912941),* P.O. Box 356, Elsie, MI 48831 (SAN 283-2615); Dist. by: Publishers Marketing Group, 1104 Summit Ave., Plainview, TX 75074 (SAN 262-0995) Tel 214-423-0312.

Forbes
See G F Forbes

Forbes Inc, *(Forbes, Inc.; 0-935705),* 60 Fifth Ave., New York, NY 10011 (SAN 696-4494) Tel 212-206-5548.

Force Pub, *(Force Pub. Co.; 0-942362),* P.O. Box 4037, Salinas, CA 93912 (SAN 239-8559) Tel 408-663-0537.

Ford Assocs, *(Ford Associates; 0-88017),* 824 E. Seventh St., Auburn, IN 46706 (SAN 207-6508) Tel 219-925-3378.

Ford-Brown, *(Ford-Brown & Co., Pubs.; 0-918644),* P.O. Box 600574, Houston, TX 77260 (SAN 209-6048) Tel 713-526-8699.

†**Ford Found,** *(Ford Foundation; 0-916584),* 320 E. 43rd St., New York, NY 10017 (SAN 222-9730) Tel 212-573-5000; Orders to: Box 559, Naugatuck, CT 06770 (SAN 685-3277) Tel 203-729-3100; *CIP.*

Ford Mus *Imprint of* **Edison Inst**

Fordham, *(Fordham Univ. Pr.; 0-8232),* University Box L, Bronx, NY 10458 (SAN 201-6516) Tel 212-579-2319.

Fordham Pub, *(Fordham Equipment & Publishing Co.; 0-913308),* 3308 Edson Ave., Bronx, NY 10469 (SAN 207-2254) Tel 212-379-7300.

Fords Travel, *(Fords Travel Guides; 0-916486),* Box 505, 22151 Clarendon St., Woodland Hills, CA 91365 (SAN 212-9418) Tel 818-347-1677.

Forecast PAP, *(Forecast Public Artspace Productions; 0-9613083),* 2955 Bloomington Ave. S., Minneapolis, MN 55407 (SAN 294-0248) Tel 612-721-4394.

Forecaster Pub, *(Forecaster Publishing Co., Inc.; 0-911353),* 19623 Ventura Blvd., Tarzana, CA 91356 (SAN 218-7272) Tel 818-345-4421.

Foreign Policy, *(Foreign Policy Assn.; 0-87124),* 205 Lexington Ave., New York, NY 10016 (SAN 212-9426) Tel 212-481-8450.

Foreign Trade, *(Foreign Trade Association of Southern California),* World Trade Center, 350 S. Figueroa St., Suite 226, Los Angeles, CA 90017 (SAN 224-1293) Tel 213-627-0634.

Foreman Co, *(Foreman Co., Pubs., The; 0-936009),* 302 S. Plumer, Tucson, AZ 85719 (SAN 696-7469) Tel 602-623-5012.

Foremost Pubs, *(Foremost Pubs., Inc.; 0-940078),* W. Main Rd., Little Compton, RI 02837 (SAN 220-2204) Tel 401-635-2900.

†**Forest Hill,** *(Forest Hill Pr.; 0-9605472),* 3974 Forest Hill Ave., Oakland, CA 94602 (SAN 215-9945); *CIP.*

Forest Hist Soc, *(Forest History Society, Inc.; 0-89030),* 701 Vickers Ave., Durham, NC 27701 (SAN 201-6524) Tel 919-682-9319; Dist. by: Duke Univ. Pr., 6697 College Sta., Durham, NC 27708 (SAN 201-3436) Tel 919-684-2173.

Forest Ind Comm, *(Forest Industries Committee on Timber Valuation & Taxation; 0-914272),* 1250 Connecticut Ave., Suite 800, Washington, DC 20036 (SAN 204-1049) Tel 202-223-2314; Dist. by: International Specialized Book Services Inc., 5602 NE Hassalo St., Portland, OR 97213-3640 (SAN 169-7129) Tel 503-287-3093.

Forest Peace, *(Forest of Peace Bks., Inc.; 0-939516),* Rte. One, Box 247, Easton, KS 66020 (SAN 216-6739) Tel 913-773-8255.

Forest Pr, *(Forest Pr.; 0-910608),* Div. of Lake Placid Educ. Foundation, 85 Watervliet Ave., Albany, NY 12206 (SAN 210-8070) Tel 518-489-8549.

Forest Prod, *(Forest Products Research Society; 0-935018),* 2801 Marshall Ct., Madison, WI 53705 (SAN 211-4216) Tel 608-231-1361.

Forest Pub, *(Forest Publishing; 0-9605118),* Div. of National Speakers Bureau, 222 Wisconsin, Suite 201, Lake Forest, IL 60045 (SAN 215-7624) Tel 312-295-1122; Toll free: 800-323-9442.

Forest Res Syst, *(Forest Resources Systems Institute; 0-9615391),* 201 N. Pine St., Suite 24, Florence, AL 35630 (SAN 695-3433) Tel 205-767-0250.

Foreverly, *(Foreverly Music; 0-9614221),* P.O. Box 3933, Seattle, WA 98124 (SAN 686-7146) Tel 206-783-1798.

Foris Pubns, *(Foris Pubns., USA; 0-938198),* Orders to: Box C-50, Cinnaminson, NJ 08077 (SAN 220-1151) Tel 609-829-6830. *Imprints:* Bird-Sci Bks (Bird-Sci Books).

Forman Pub, *(Forman Publishing Inc.),* 11661 San Vicente Blvd., Suite 206, Los Angeles, CA 90049 (SAN 692-980X) Tel 213-820-8672.

Formatcen, *(Formatcen; 0-8259),* Cultural Education Ctr., Albany, NY 12230 (SAN 658-6279) Tel 518-474-5801.

Formur Intl, *(Formur International; 0-89378),* 4200 Laclede Ave., St. Louis, MO 63108 (SAN 207-5768).

Forrest Bryant
See F B Johnson

Forsan Bks, *(Forsan Books; 0-9612298),* 865 Karen Dr., Chico, CA 95926 (SAN 289-2286) Tel 916-343-7361.

Forsyth Gall, *(Forsyth Gallery; 0-9601560),* P.O. Box 525, Cooper Sta., New York, NY 10003 (SAN 211-6677) Tel 212-925-6697.

Forsyth Lib Travel, *(Forsyth Travel Library, Inc.; 0-931212),* P.O. Box 105, Coarsegold, CA 93614 (SAN 210-6051) Tel 209-683-5883.

Forsythe & Cromwell, *(Forsythe & Cromwell; 0-940390),* P.O. Box 271, Andover, NJ 07821 (SAN 217-3646) Tel 201-625-1989.

Fort Frederica, *(Fort Frederica Assn., Inc.; 0-930803),* Rte. 9, Box 286-C, St. Simons Island, GA 31522 (SAN 677-6299) Tel 912-638-3639.

Forth Interest, *(Forth Interest Group; 0-935533),* 1330 S. Bascom Ave., No. D, San Jose, CA 95155 (SAN 696-4508) Tel 408-277-0667; P.O. Box 8231, San Jose, CA 95155 (SAN 696-544X).

Forth Pub, *(Forth Publishing, Inc.; 0-9615575),* 301 E. Grand Ave., San Francisco, CA 94080 (SAN 696-4516) Tel 415-583-0786.

†**Fortress,** *(Fortress Pr.; 0-8006),* 2900 Queen Ln., Philadelphia, PA 19129 (SAN 220-0074); Toll free: 800-367-8737; *CIP.*

Fortuna, *(Fortuna Book Sales; 0-910610),* 8035 Fairlane Ave., Brooksville, FL 33512 (SAN 206-4278).

Fortunato Bks, *(Fortunato Bks.; 0-9612494),* 7 Halko Dr., Cedar Knolls, NJ 07927 (SAN 213-0599) Tel 201-540-8852.

Fortune Soft, *(Fortune Software, Co.; 0-939277),* 70 Sierra Rd., Boston, MA 02136 (SAN 662-8192) Tel 617-361-0900.

Forum Death Educ, *(Forum for Death Education & Counseling; 0-9607394),* Millikin Univ., Decatur, IL 62522 (SAN 237-952X).

Forum for Death Educ
See Forum Death Educ

†**Forum Pr IL,** *(Forum Pr., Inc.; 0-88273),* Subs. of Harlan Davidson Inc., 3110 N. Arlington Heights Rd., Arlington Heights, IL 60004 (SAN 201-2375) Tel 312-253-9720; *CIP.* *Imprints:* Marston (Marston Press); Piraeus (Piraeus Publishers).

Forum Press Inc
See New Forums

Forum Quorum, *(Forum Quorum; 0-9606778),* Div. of Forum School Foundation, P.O. Box 43, Waldwick, NJ 07463 (SAN 219-7413) Tel 201-444-0499; Orders to: The Collection, P.O. Box 1220, Olathe, KS 66061-1220 (SAN 662-0116).

Forum Script, *(Forum for Scriptural Christianity, Inc.; 0-917851),* P.O. Box 165, Wilmore, KY 40390 (SAN 225-4638) Tel 606-858-4661; Dist. by: Cokesbury, 201 Eighth Ave. S., Nashville, TN 37203 (SAN 200-6863).

Forward Movement, *(Forward Movement Pubns.; 0-88028),* 412 Sycamore St., Cincinnati, OH 45202-4195 (SAN 208-3841) Tel 513-721-6659; Toll free: 800-543-1813.

Forward Pr, *(Forward Press, The; 0-941262),* 30 S. First Ave., Suite 301, Arcadia, CA 91006 (SAN 239-426X) Tel 818-445-7204.

Forza Pr, *(Forza Pr.; 0-9614045),* 521 Entrada Way, Menlo Park, CA 94025 (SAN 684-8028) Tel 415-322-9108.

Foster Parents, *(Foster Parents Plan International, Inc.; 0-918397),* P.O. Box 804, East Greenwich, RI 02818 (SAN 657-341X) Tel 401-826-2500.

Fotonovel, *(Fotonovel Pubns.; 0-89752),* 8831 Sunset Blvd., PH-W, Los Angeles, CA 90069 (SAN 213-2486) Tel 213-659-8888; Dist. by: The Independent News Co., 75 Rockefeller Plaza, New York, NY 10019 (SAN 208-6158).

Foul Play *Imprint of* **Countryman**

Foun Adv Man, *(Foundation for the Advancement of Man; 0-939794),* P.O. Box 2876, Escondido, CA 92025 (SAN 218-4761).

Foun Am Comm, *(Foundation for American Communications; 0-910755),* 3383 Barham Blvd., Los Angeles, CA 90068 (SAN 270-2746) Tel 213-851-7372.

Foun Bks, *(Foundation Bks.; 0-934988),* P.O. Box 29229, Lincoln, NE 68529 (SAN 201-6567) Tel 402-466-4988.

Foun Chr Self Govt
See Mayflower Inst

Foun Christ Serv, *(Foundation for Christian Services Inc.),* P.O. Box 1555, Altamonte Springs, FL 32715 (SAN 264-0457) Tel 305-830-7424.

Foun Church New Birth
See New Age Min Spiritualist

Foun Commun Artists, *(Foundation for the Community of Artists; 0-933032),* 280 Broadway, Suite 412, New York, NY 10017 (SAN 225-2678) Tel 212-227-3770.

Foun Econ Ed, *(Foundation for Economic Education, Inc.; 0-910614),* 30 S. Broadway, Irvington-on-Hudson, NY 10533 (SAN 311-3515) Tel 914-591-7230.

Foun Ext Am Theatre
See FEDAPT

Foun Hist Rest, *(Foundation for Historic Restoration in Pendleton Area; 0-912462),* P.O. Box 444, Pendleton, SC 29670 (SAN 206-4286) Tel 803-654-3283.

Foun Human GA, *(Foundation for Human Understanding),* Box 5712, Athens, GA 30604 (SAN 214-3720).

Foun Human Under, *(Foundation of Human Understanding, The; 0-933900),* P.O. Box 811, 111 NE Evelyn St., Grants Pass, OR 97526-9997 (SAN 213-9545) Tel 503-479-0549; 8780 Venice Blvd., P.O. Box 34036, Los Angeles, CA 90034 (SAN 680-0327) Tel 213-559-3711.

Foun Int Design, (Foundation for Interior Design Education Research; 0-931007), 322 Eighth Ave., Suite 1501, New York, NY 10001 (SAN 225-8145) Tel 212-929-8366.

Foun Miracles, (Foundation for "A Course In Miracles"; 0-933291), P.O. Box 783, Crompond, NY 10517 (SAN 692-2902) Tel 914-528-0101.

Foun Mot Dent, (Foundation for Motivation in Dentistry; 0-913740), Schooleys Mountain, NJ 07840 (SAN 201-6583).

Foun Natl Prog, (Foundation for National Progress; 0-938806), Housing Information Ctr., 4020 Blue Bonnet Blvd., Houston, TX 77025 (SAN 215-9554).

Foun Phil Creat, (Foundation for Philosophy of Creativity, Inc.), North Texas State Univ., Dept. of Philosophy, Denton, TX 76203 (SAN 283-183X); Orders to: University Pr. of America, 4720 Boston Way, Lanham, MD 20706 (SAN 200-2256) Tel 301-459-3366.

Foun Pr
See Foun Pubns

Foun Pubns, (Foundation Pubns., Inc.; 0-910618), P.O. Box 6439, Anaheim, CA 92806 (SAN 206-4294) Tel 714-630-6450.

Found Am Christ, (Foundation for American Christian Education; 0-912498), 2946 25th Ave., San Francisco, CA 94132 (SAN 205-5856) Tel 415-661-1775.

Found Am Res Mgmt, (Foundation for American Resource Management; 0-8223), Dist. by: Duke Univ. Pr., 6697 College Sta., Durham, NC 27708 (SAN 201-3436) Tel 919-684-2173.

Found Amelio, (Foundation for Ameliorology; 0-935923), 6609 Hwy. 93, Golden, CO 80403 (SAN 696-7450) Tel 303-278-3215.

Found Audit Res *Imprint of* **Inst Inter Aud**

†Found Class Reprints, (Foundation for Classical Reprints, The; 0-89901), 607 McKnight St. NW, Albuquerque, NM 87102 (SAN 212-9051) Tel 505-843-7749; CIP.

Found Inner Peace, (Foundation for Inner Peace; 0-9606388), P.O. Box 635, Tiburon, CA 94920 (SAN 212-422X) Tel 415-435-2255.

Found Life Act, (Foundation for Life Action; 1-55531), 902 S. Burnside Ave., Los Angeles, CA 90036 (SAN 696-4532) Tel 213-933-5591; Toll free: 800-367-2246; Toll free: 800-732-5489 (In California); Orders to: P.O. Box 36456, Los Angeles, CA 90036 (SAN 662-3751).

Found Pos Jud, (Foundation for Positive Thought Judaism; 0-935683), P.O. Box 5512, New York, NY 10185 (SAN 696-4281) Tel 212-686-2904.

Found PSP, (Foundation for the Peoples of the South Pacific), 2-12 W. Park Ave., Long Beach, NY 11561 (SAN 237-1626) Tel 516-432-3563; P.O. Box 727, Long Beach, NY 11561 (SAN 658-0726) Tel 516-432-3563.

Found Pub, (Foundation Publishing; 0-932032), P.O. Box 3243, Burlington, VT 05401 (SAN 211-6189) Tel 802-862-7386.

Foundation Bks, (Foundation Bks.; 0-932477), 151 Tremont St., P. H., Boston, MA 02111 (SAN 687-1291) Tel 617-423-4958; Dist. by: Baker & Taylor Co., Eastern Div., 151 Treamont St., Boston, MA 02111 (SAN 169-4901); Dist. by: Baker & Taylor Co., Western Div., 380 Edison Way, Reno, NV 89564 (SAN 169-4464) Tel 702-786-6700; Dist. by: Baker & Taylor Co., Midwest Div., 501 Gladiola Ave., Momence, IL 60954 (SAN 169-2100); Dist. by: Baker & Taylor Co., Southeast Div, Mt. Olive Rd., Commerce, GA 30529 (SAN 169-1503).

Foundation Ctr, (Foundation Ctr., The; 0-87954), 79 Fifth Ave., New York, NY 10003 (SAN 207-5687) Tel 212-620-4230; Toll free: 800-424-9836.

Foundation Hse, (Foundation Hse. Pubns., Inc.; 0-935427), Div. of Emissary Foundation International, Inc., 4817 N. Country Rd. 29, Loveland, CO 80537 (SAN 696-5512) Tel 303-669-2166.

†Foundation Pr, (Foundation Pr., Inc.; 0-88277), 170 Old Country Road, Mineola, NY 11501 (SAN 281-7225) Tel 516-248-5580; CIP.

Fountain Hse East, (Fountain Hse. East; 0-914736), Box 99298, Jeffersontown, KY 40299 (SAN 206-6262) Tel 502-267-5414.

Fountain Pr, (Fountain Press, Inc.; 0-89350), Dist. by: Inspirational Marketing Inc., Box 301, Indianola, IA 50125 (SAN 208-6557).

Fountain Publications Oregon, (Fountain Pubns.; 0-911376), 3728 NW Thurman St., Portland, OR 97210 (SAN 205-5880) Tel 503-223-2232.

Fountain Valley Pub, (Fountain Valley Pubblishing Co.; 0-933039), 16533 Sequoia St., Fountain Valley, CA 92708 (SAN 689-7509) Tel 714-839-1351.

Fountainhead, (Fountainhead Pubs., Inc.; 0-935497), 155 E. 55th St., Suite 8C, New York, NY 10022 (SAN 206-4324) Tel 212-421-1556.

Four Circles Pr, (Four Circles Pr.; 0-938739), 556-H102 Main St., N., Roosevelt Island, New York, NY 10044 (SAN 661-8111) Tel 212-759-5174.

Four D Pub Co, (Four D Publishing Co.; 0-9610006), Box 381, Princeton, IL 61356 (SAN 270-3092).

Four Mile Hist Pk, (Four Mile Historic Park, Inc.; 0-9617039), 715 S. Forest St., Denver, CO 80222 (SAN 662-8257) Tel 303-399-1859.

Four Peaks Ent, (Four Peaks Enterprises, Inc.; 0-9616872), P.O. Box 17569, Fountain Hills, AZ 85268 (SAN 661-1524); 16705 E. Fairfax Dr., Fountain Hills, AZ 85268 (SAN 661-1532) Tel 602-837-9693.

Four Quarters, (Four Quarters Publishing Co.; 0-931500), 1200 Boston Post Rd., Guilford, CT 06437 (SAN 213-8123). *Imprints:* Dunk Rock (Dunk Rock Books).

Four S Pubns, (Four Seasons Pubns.; 0-9615987), P.O. Box 125, Newark, DE 19715-0125 (SAN 698-1488) Tel 302-834-7522.

Four Seas Bk, (Four Seasons Book Pubs.; 0-9605400), 220 Piney Point Landing, P.O. Box 576, Grasonville, MD 21638 (SAN 215-8639) Tel 301-827-7350.

†Four Seasons Foun, (Four Seasons Foundation; 0-87704), P.O. Box 31190, San Francisco, CA 94131 (SAN 201-6591) Tel 415-824-5774; Dist. by: Subterranean Co., 1327 W. Second, P.O. Box 10233, Eugene, OR 97440 (SAN 169-7102) Tel 503-343-6324; CIP.

Four Sons, (Four Sons Pr.; 0-918503), 1545 E. Roberts Ave., Fresno, CA 93710 (SAN 657-3428) Tel 209-439-1677.

Four Trees Pubns, (Four Trees Pubns.; 0-936329), P.O. Box 31220, San Francisco, CA 94131 (SAN 697-337X) Tel 415-641-4035; 1484 Dolores St., San Francisco, CA 94110 (SAN 697-3388); Dist. by: Bookpeople, 2929 Fifth St., Berkeley, CA 94710 (SAN 168-9517) Tel 415-549-3030.

Four Ways West, (Four Ways West Pubns.; 0-9616874), P.O. Box 1734, La Mirada, CA 90637-1734 (SAN 661-3195); 14618 Valley View, La Mirada, CA 90638 (SAN 661-3209) Tel 714-521-4259.

Four Zoas Night Ltd, (Four Zoas Night House, Ltd.; 0-939622), P.O. Box 111, Ashuelot Village, NH 03441 (SAN 216-6267) Tel 603-239-6830.

Foursquare Pr, (Foursquare Press; 0-930616), 648 Ransom Rd., Lancaster, NY 14086 (SAN 211-8998) Tel 716-681-2586.

†Fourth NA Am Fur, (Fourth North American Fur Trade Conference; 0-9613451), 240 Summit Ave., St. Paul, MN 55102 (SAN 657-2537) Tel 612-296-9393; CIP.

Fourth World, (Fourth World; 0-9613920), 110 West Geneva Drive, Tempe, AZ 85282 (SAN 669-6767) Tel 602-966-0039.

Fowler & Wells, (Fowler & Wells, Publisher; 0-937776), 2175 Hudson Terrace, No. 6P, Fort Lee, NJ 07024 (SAN 277-6804) Tel 201-592-8717; Dist. by: Inland Book Co., P.O. Box 261, Hemingway Ave., East Haven, CT 06512 (SAN 200-4151) Tel 203-467-4257.

Fowler Music, (Fowler Music Enterprises; 0-943894), 808 S. Alkire St., Lakewood, CO 80228 (SAN 241-113X) Tel 303-986-7309.

Fox Assocs, (Fox Assocs./Fox Theatre; 0-9615933), 527 N. Brand, St. Louis, MO 63103 (SAN 697-0745) Tel 314-534-1678; Dist. by: Paperback Supply, 4121 Forest Park Blvd., St. Louis, MO 63108 (SAN 169-4324).

Fox Head, (D Fox Head Press; 0-910521), 28 Vandeventer Ave., Princeton, NJ 08540 (SAN 260-1893) Tel 609-924-9316.

†Fox Hills Pr, (Fox Hills Pr., The; 0-914932), 2676 Cunningham Hole Rd., Annapolis, MD 21401 (SAN 211-139X) Tel 301-266-6626; CIP.

Fox Hills Press
See Fox Hills Pr

Fox Hollow, (Fox Hollow Fibres; 0-9608074), 560 Milford Rd., Earlysville, VA 22936 (SAN 240-0928) Tel 804-973-9621.

Fox Reading Res, (Fox Reading Research Co.; 0-938131), P.O. Box 1059, Coeur D'Alene, ID 83814 (SAN 213-0602) Tel 208-772-4524.

Fox River, (Fox River Publishing Co.; 0-939398), Box 54, Princeton, WI 54968 (SAN 216-3802).

Fox Thoughts, (Fox Thoughts Pubns.; 0-912403), 2640 East Twelfth Ave., Department 571, Denver, CO 80206 (SAN 265-4040) Tel 303-736-8238; Dist. by: DeVorss & Co., P.O. Box 550, 1046 Princeton Dr., Marina del Rey, CA 90294 (SAN 168-9886) Tel 203-870-7478.

Foxhall Pr, (Foxhall Press; 0-9611128), P.O. Box 9629, Washington, DC 20016 (SAN 282-9061) Tel 202-362-5870.

Foxhound Ent, (Foxhound Enterprises; 0-940502), 25 Tazewell St., Fredericksburg, VA 22405 (SAN 223-1034) Tel 703-371-7498; Dist. by: M. E. Repass, Box 68, Louisa, KY 41230 (SAN 223-1042).

Foxmoor, (Foxmoor Pr.; 0-938604), Rte. 6, P.O. Box 28, Tahlequah, OK 74464 (SAN 215-8647).

Foxy Owl Pubns, (Foxy Owl Pubns.; 0-9613246), 515 Dalton St., Emmaus, PA 18049 (SAN 295-2866) Tel 215-965-3405.

Fragments Valentine
See J Hoffman

Fragments West, (Fragments West/Valentine Pr., The; 0-9611890), 3908 E. Fourth St., Long Beach, CA 90814 (SAN 286-1933) Tel 213-438-3424.

Fragonard Pr, (Fragonard Pr.; 0-930807), Aspen Hill, P.O. Box 6365, Silver Spring, MD 20906 (SAN 677-6280) Tel 302-651-5005.

Framo Pub, (Framo Publishing; 0-936398), 561 W. Diversey Pkwy., Chicago, IL 60614 (SAN 214-0160) Tel 312-477-1485.

Franas Pr, (Franas Press; 0-9600482), 1116 Ocean Ave., Mantoloking, NJ 08738 (SAN 205-5899).

Franciscagraphics, (Franciscagraphics; 0-933925), P.O. Box 28322, Atlanta, GA 30358 (SAN 693-0298) Tel 404-252-1962.

†Franciscan Herald, (Franciscan Herald Pr.; 0-8199), 1434 W. 51st St., Chicago, IL 60609 (SAN 201-6621) Tel 312-254-4462; CIP.

Franciscan Inst, (Franciscan Institute Pubns.), Drawer F, St. Bonaventure Univ., St. Bonaventure, NY 14778 (SAN 201-8543) Tel 716-375-2105.

Franje CA, (Franje; 0-9601078), 1175 Barbara Dr., Vista, CA 92084 (SAN 205-5902) Tel 619-726-7129.

Frank Nance Co, (Nance, Frank, Co.; 0-9615739), 2700 Pierce Ave., El Paso, TX 79930 (SAN 695-8567) Tel 915-565-6450.

Frank Pubns, (Frank Pubns.; 0-942952), 60 E. 42nd St., Suite 757, New York, NY 10017 (SAN 240-4737) Tel 212-687-3383.

Franklin & Marshall, (Franklin & Marshall College; 0-910626), P.O. Box 3003, Lancaster, PA 17604-3003 (SAN 226-3408) Tel 717-291-3981.

Franklin Beedle, (Franklin, Beedle & Assocs.), 4521 Campus Dr., Suite 327, Irvine, CA 92715 (SAN 661-3179) Tel 714-552-4155.

Franklin Bryn Mawr, (Franklin Pubns.; 0-916503), Box 1338, Bryn Mawr, PA 19010 (SAN 295-4141) Tel 215-525-1225.

Franklin-Hill Pr, (Franklin-Hill Pr.; 0-937447), 6250 El Cajon Blvd., No. 805, San Diego, CA 92115 (SAN 658-8514) Tel 619-698-5333.

†Franklin Inst Pr, (Franklin Institute Pr., The; 0-89168), Div. of Lawrence Erlbaum Assocs., Inc., 365 Broadway, Hillsdale, NJ 07642 (SAN 209-5599) Tel 201-666-4110; CIP.

Franklin Pierce Col
See Man NE

Franklin Pr WA, (Franklin, Charles, Pr., The; 0-932091; 0-9603516), 7821 175th St., SW, Edmonds, WA 98020 (SAN 692-9001) Tel 206-774-6979; Toll free: 800-99B-00KS.

Franklin Pub
See Franklin Bryn Mawr
Frantasy Wkshp, *(Frantasy Workshop;
0-9612696),* 1400 W. Cross St., Lakewood,
NJ 08701 (SAN 289-193X)
Tel 201-363-3988.
Franzak & Foster, *(Franzak & Foster Co.;
0-942588),* 4012 Bridge Ave., Cleveland,
OH 44113 (SAN 240-0731)
Tel 216-961-4134.
Frary Family, *(Frary Family Assn.; 0-9616030),*
Harmony Rd., No. 162, Northwood, NH
03261 (SAN 698-1461) Tel 603-942-8520.
Fraser Co CT
See Fraser Inc
Fraser Inc, *(Fraser, Inc.; 0-930045),* P.O. Box
1507, Madison, CT 06443 (SAN 295-0464);
38 Academy St., Madison, CT 06443
(SAN 658-2540) Tel 203-245-3279; Dist.
by: Williamson Publishing Co., P.O. Box 185,
Charlotte, VT 05445 (SAN 285-3884)
Tel 802-425-2102.
Fraser Prods Co, *(Fraser Products Co.;
0-933379),* 10730 Wheatland Ave., Sunland,
CA 91040 (SAN 691-6775)
Tel 818-767-3334; Dist. by: Baker & Taylor
Co., Eastern Div., 50 Kirby Ave., Somerville,
NJ 08876 (SAN 169-4901)
Tel 201-526-8000.
†**Fraser Pub Co**, *(Fraser Publishing Co.;
0-87034),* Div. of Fraser Management
Assocs., Inc., 309 S. Willard St., Burlington,
VT 05401 (SAN 213-9529)
Tel 802-658-0322; Orders to: Box 494,
Burlington, VT 05402 (SAN 213-9537);
CIP.
Fraunces Tavern, *(Fraunces Tavern Museum;
0-9616415),* 54 Pearl St., New York, NY
10004 (SAN 669-6783) Tel 212-425-1778.
Frazier-Long, *(Frazier-Long Inc.; 0-9614192),*
288 Craig Dr., Lawrenceville, GA 30245
(SAN 686-6549) Tel 404-962-6345.
FRB Minneapolis, *(Federal Reserve Bank of
Minneapolis; 0-915484),* Research Dept.,
250 Marquette Ave., Minneapolis, MN
55480 (SAN 281-7063) Tel 612-340-2355;
Orders to: Office of Public Information, 250
Marquette Ave., Minneapolis, MN 55480
(SAN 281-7071) Tel 612-340-2443.
Fred Pr, *(Fred Pr.; 0-937393),* 59 Suydam St.,
New Brunswick, NJ 08901 (SAN 658-8573)
Tel 201-878-7976; Orders to: 1178 Castleton
Rd., Cleveland Heights, OH 44121
(SAN 662-4189).
Fred Robot Factory, *(Fred's Robot Factory Pr.;
0-936733),* P.O. Box 474, San Manuel, AZ
85631 (SAN 699-9611) Tel 602-896-2721;
Redington Rd., San Manuel, AZ 85631
(SAN 699-962X).
Fredericks Pub, *(Fredericks Publishing Co.;
0-939690),* P.O. Box 97, Mertztown, PA
19539 (SAN 216-7328) Tel 215-682-7784.
Fredonia, *(Fredonia; 0-940204),* 29169 W.
Heathercliff, Suite 9490, Malibu, CA 90265
(SAN 217-104X).
Free-Bass, *(Free-Bass Pr.; 0-8256),* Box 563,
Eugene, OR 97440 (SAN 217-1058)
Tel 503-345-1795; Dist. by: Music Sales
Corp., 5 Bellvale Rd., P.O. Box 572, Chester,
NY 10918 (SAN 209-0988)
Tel 914-469-2271.
Free Begin Pr, *(Free Beginning Press; 0-930707),*
41 Beryl St, Roslindale, MA 02131
(SAN 677-2145) Tel 617-323-2561.
Free Church Pubns, *(Free Church Pubns.;
0-911802),* Div. of Evangelical Free Church
of America, 1515 E. 66th St., Minneapolis,
MN 55423 (SAN 206-4146)
Tel 612-866-3343.
Free Congr Res, *(Free Congress Research &
Education Foundation; 0-942522),* 721
Second St., NE, Washington, DC 20002
(SAN 238-1605) Tel 202-546-3004.
Free Ener Pr, *(Free Energy Pr.; 0-931009),*
313A Noyac Rd., Sag Harbor, NY 11963
(SAN 678-9668) Tel 516-725-1211.
Free Ent Inst, *(Free Enterprise Institute;
0-940434),* Subs. of Amway Corp., 7575 E.
Fulton Rd., Ada, MI 49355
(SAN 217-1767) Tel 616-676-7946.
Free Ent System, *(Free Enterprises Services,
Inc.; 0-943636),* 2120 Beneva Rd., Sarasota,
FL 33582 (SAN 238-2849)
Tel 813-924-4211.
Free Enter Pr, *(Free Enterprise Pr., The;
0-939571),* 12500 NE Tenth Pl., Bellevue,
WA 98005 (SAN 663-5342)
Tel 206-455-5038.

Free Life *Imprint of* **Universe**
Free Market, *(Free Market Books; 0-930902),*
P.O. Box 186, Irvington, NY 10533
(SAN 209-1143) Tel 914-591-7769.
Free Market Ins, *(Free Market Institute;
0-935429),* 9707 S. Gesner, No. 114,
Houston, TX 77071 (SAN 696-4303)
Tel 713-995-8228.
†**Free Pr**, *(Free Pr.; 0-02),* Div. of Macmillan
Publishing Co., Inc., 866 Third Ave., New
York, NY 10022 (SAN 201-6656)
Tel 212-702-2004; Toll free: 800-257-5755;
Dist. by: Macmillan Co., Front & Brown Sts.,
Riverside, NJ 08370 (SAN 202-5582)
Tel 609-461-6500; *CIP.*
†**Free Spirit Pub Co**, *(Free Spirit Publishing Co.;
0-915793),* 123 N. Third St., Suite 716,
Minneapolis, MN 55401 (SAN 293-9584)
Tel 612-338-2068; *CIP.*
Free State Constitution, *(Free State
Constitutionists Media Publishing Co.;
0-934005),* 640 Aldershot Rd., Baltimore,
MD 21229 (SAN 692-7726)
Tel 301-747-5025.
Freedeeds Bks *Imprint of* **Garber Comm**
Freedman, *(Freedman Gallery of Art; 0-941972),*
Albright College, Reading, PA 19603
(SAN 278-856X) Tel 215-921-2381.
†**Freedom Bks**, *(Freedom Bks.; 0-930374),* P.O.
Box 5303, Hamden, CT 06518
(SAN 210-9255) Tel 203-281-6791; *CIP.*
Freedom Hse, *(Freedom Hse.; 0-932088),* 48 E.
21st St., New York, NY 10010
(SAN 211-7339) Tel 212-473-9691.
Freedom Intl, *(Freedom Pr. International, Ltd.;
0-917639),* 1601 Northwest Expwy.,
Oklahoma City, OK 73118
(SAN 656-920X).
Freedom Ltd, *(Freedom Press, Ltd.; 0-915031),*
1601 Northwest Expressway, Oklahoma City,
OK 73118 (SAN 289-9256).
Freedom Pr, *(Freedom Pr.; 0-941630),* P.O. Box
5503, Scottsdale, AZ 85261
(SAN 239-2100) Tel 607-991-5414.
Freedom Pubns, *(Freedom, Pubns.; 0-915721),*
Div. of Sedona Institute, 2408 Arizona
Biltmore Circle, No. 115, Phoenix, AZ 85016
(SAN 293-9614) Tel 602-956-8766.
Freedom Pubs, *(Freedom Pubs.; 0-935787),*
3960 S. Denker, Los Angeles, CA 90062
(SAN 696-432X) Tel 213-666-8093.
Freedom Rel Found, *(Freedom from Religion
Foundation),* P.O. Box 750, Madison, WI
53701 (SAN 276-9484) Tel 608-256-8900.
Freedom Sem Pr
See Freedom Univ-FSP
Freedom Tree, *(Freedom Tree, Inc.; 0-938969),*
P.O. Box 2406, Cheyenne, WY 82003
(SAN 661-7131); 2232 Del Range Blvd.,
Suite 205, Cheyenne, WY 82003
(SAN 661-714X) Tel 307-635-0369.
Freedom Univ-FSP, *(Freedom
University/Freedom Seminary Press),* 5927
Windhover Dr., Orlando, FL 32819
(SAN 209-505X) Tel 305-351-0898.
Freedoms Found Vall, *(Freedoms Foundation At
Valley Forge, Los Angeles County Chapter;
0-9612726),* 17040 Rancho St., Encino, CA
91316 (SAN 289-9264) Tel 818-784-6626.
Freehand
See Menses
Freelance Comm, *(Freelance Communications;
0-935309),* P.O. Box 1895, Upland, CA
91785 (SAN 695-7773) Tel 714-982-3199.
Freelance Pubns, *(Freelance Pubns. Ltd;
0-9602050),* P.O. Box 1385, Meredith, NH
03253 (SAN 213-0734) Tel 603-279-8661.
Freeland Pr, *(Freeland Pr.; 0-9615893),* P.O.
Box 26044, Santa Ana, CA 92799
(SAN 697-0850); 2727 S. Croddy Way, No.
J, Santa Ana, CA 92704 Tel 714-979-5737.
Freeland Pubns, *(Freeland Pubns.; 0-936868),*
P.O. Box 18941, Philadelphia, PA 19119
(SAN 215-3130).
Freelandia, *(Freelandia Institute; 0-914674),* Star
Rte., Cassville, MO 65625 (SAN 205-6216).
Freeman C
See Freeman Cooper
Freeman Cooper, *(Freeman, Cooper & Co.;
0-87735),* 1736 Stockton St., San Francisco,
CA 94133 (SAN 201-6672)
Tel 415-362-6171.
Freeman Farms, *(Freeman Farms Pr.;
0-9617300),* 4306 Freeman Rd., Orchard
Park, NY 14127 (SAN 663-463X).
Freeman Inst
See Natl Ctr Constitutional

Freeman Sr
See H P Freeman CA
Freeperson, *(Freeperson Pr.; 0-918236),* Div. of
TH-EC, Inc., 455 Ridge Rd., Novato, CA
94947 (SAN 209-438X) Tel 415-897-0336.
Freeport Hist, *(Freeport Historical Society;
0-9613259),* 45 Main St., Freeport, ME
04032 (SAN 296-5844); P.O. Box 358,
Freeport, ME 04032 (SAN 699-5772).
†**Freer**, *(Freer Gallery of Art, Smithsonian
Institution; 0-934686),* 12th & Jefferson Dr.,
SW, Washington, DC 20560
(SAN 201-856X) Tel 202-357-2102; *CIP.*
Freestone Pub Co, *(Freestone Publishing Co.;
0-913512),* Box 398, Monroe, UT 84754
(SAN 206-4154) Tel 801-527-3738; Dist.
by: Bookpeople, 2929 Fifth St., Berkeley, CA
94710 (SAN 168-9517) Tel 415-549-3030.
Freidus Gallery, *(Freidus, Robert, Gallery),* 158
Lafayette St., New York, NY 10013
(SAN 223-2065) Tel 212-925-0113.
Freline, *(Freline, Inc.; 0-913853),* P.O. Box 889,
32 East Ave., Hagerstown, MD 21740
(SAN 286-7508) Tel 301-797-9689.
Fremar Pr, *(Fremar Press, The; 0-9612348),* 160
Ravenswood Court, Vacaville, CA 95688
(SAN 290-7011) Tel 707-448-2870.
French, *(French, Samuel, Inc.; 0-573),* 45 W.
25th St., New York, NY 10010
(SAN 206-4170) Tel 212-206-8990; 7625
Sunset Blvd., Hollywood, CA 90046
(SAN 200-6855) Tel 213-876-0570.
French & Eur, *(French & European Pubns., Inc.;
0-8288),* 115 Fifth Ave., New York, NY
10003 (SAN 206-8109) Tel 212-673-7400.
French Bks Print, *(French Bks. in Print),* P.O.
Box 1445, Long Island City, NY 11101
(SAN 659-2007).
French Forum, *(French Forum Pubs., Inc.;
0-917058),* P.O. Box 5108, Lexington, KY
40505 (SAN 208-4996) Tel 606-299-9530.
French Inst, *(French Institute-Alliance Francaise;
0-933444),* 22 E. 60th St., New York, NY
10022-1077 (SAN 204-207X)
Tel 212-355-6100.
French Lit
See Summa Pubns
†**Freneau**, *(Freneau, Philip, Press; 0-912480),* 18
Valentine St., Box 116, Monmouth Beach,
NJ 07750 (SAN 201-6680)
Tel 201-222-6458; *CIP.*
Fresh Pr, *(Fresh Press; 0-9601398),* 3712
Ortega Ct., Palo Alto, CA 94303
(SAN 210-6000) Tel 415-493-3596.
FreshCut, *(FreshCut Pr.; 0-9605550),* 133 Clara
Ave., Ukiah, CA 95482 (SAN 215-8655)
Tel 707-462-6482; 410 Clara Ave., Ukiah,
CA 95482 (SAN 215-8663).
Freshet Pr, *(Freshet Press, Inc.; 0-88395),* 90
Hamilton Rd., Rockville Centre, NY 11570
(SAN 205-5929) Tel 516-766-3011.
Freshwater, *(Freshwater Pr., Inc.; 0-912514),*
1701 E. 12th St., Suite 3KW, Cleveland, OH
44114-3201 (SAN 201-6699)
Tel 216-241-0373.
Freund Pub Co
See Camino E E & B
†**Freundlich**, *(Freundlich Bks.; 0-88191),* Div. of
Lawrence Freundlich Pubns., Inc., 212 Fifth
Ave., Suite 1305, New York, NY 10010
(SAN 264-7419) Tel 212-532-9666; Dist.
by: Kampmann & Co., Inc., 9 E. 40th St.,
New York, NY 10016 (SAN 202-5191)
Tel 212-685-2928; *CIP.*
Frick Art Mus, *(Frick Art Museum),* 7227
Reynolds St., Pittsburgh, PA 15208
(SAN 278-8624) Tel 412-371-7766.
Friede Pubns, *(Friede Pubns.; 0-9608588),* 2339
Venezia Dr., Davison, MI 48423
(SAN 238-2865) Tel 313-658-1955.
†**Friedman**, *(Friedman, Ira J.; 0-87198),* Div. of
Associated Faculty Pr., Inc., Rte. 100,
Millwood, NY 10546 (SAN 217-4979)
Tel 914-767-2200; *CIP.*
Friend Freedom, *(Friends of Freedom Pubs.;
0-915854),* P.O. Box 6124, Waco, TX 76706
(SAN 207-3757) Tel 817-662-4643.
Friend Pr, *(Friendship Pr.; 0-377),* Subs. of
National Council of the Churches of Christ
USA, 475 Riverside Dr., Rm. 772, New
York, NY 10027 (SAN 201-5773)
Tel 212-870-2495; Orders to: Friendship Pr.
Distribution, P.O. Box 37844, Cincinnati,
OH 45237 (SAN 201-5781)
Tel 513-761-2100.

Friendly City, *(Friendly City Publishing Co.; 0-938212),* 318 Cedar Springs Road, Athens, TN 37303 (SAN 215-6458) Tel 615-745-2960.

†**Friendly Oregon,** *(Friendly Press; 0-938070),* 2744 Friendly St., Eugene, OR 97405 (SAN 215-8671); *CIP.*

Friendly Pr Inc
See Creat Black Bk

†**Friendly Pr NY,** *(Friendly Pr., Inc.; 0-914919),* 401 Park Ave. S, New York, NY 10016 (SAN 207-9496) Tel 212-684-4255; *CIP.*

Friendly Pubns
See Creat Black Bk

Friendly VA, *(Friendly Press (VA), The; 0-916127),* P.O. Box 1215, McLean, VA 22101 (SAN 294-930X) Tel 703-790-0428.

Friends Arcadia, *(Friends of Arcadia Public Library),* 20 W. Duarte Rd., Arcadia, CA 91006 (SAN 216-3829) Tel 818-446-0351.

Friends CCBC, *(Friends of the C.C.B.C., Inc; 0-931641),* P.O. Box 5288, Madison, WI 53704-0288 (SAN 683-7638) Tel 608-251-7051.

Friends City Park, *(Friends of City Park; 0-9610062),* City Park Administration Bldg., New Orleans, LA 70119 (SAN 262-8643) Tel 504-561-8989.

Friends Earth
See Friends of Earth

Friends Elmer
See FER Pub Co

Friends Fla St, *(Friends of Florida State Univ. Library),* Florida State Univ., Tallahassee, FL 32306 (SAN 205-5937).

Friends Fols Lib, *(Friends of the Folsom Library; 0-9610718),* Rensselaer Polytechnic Institute, Troy, NY 12181 (SAN 264-7427) Tel 518-270-6706.

Friends Genl Conf, *(Friends General Conference),* 1520-B Race St., Philadelphia, PA 19102 (SAN 225-4484).

Friends Governors, *(Friends of the Governor's Mansion; 0-9615894),* P.O. Box 13022, Austin, TX 78711 (SAN 697-077X); 200 E. Sixth St., Suite 201, Austin, TX 78701 (SAN 697-0788) Tel 512-474-9960; Dist. by: Univ. Texas Press, P.O. Box 7819, Austin, TX 78712 (SAN 212-9876) Tel 512-471-4032.

Friends Hist Assn, *(Friends Historical Assn.; 0-9609122),* Haverford College Library, Quaker Collection, Haverford, PA 19041 (SAN 225-4492) Tel 215-896-1161.

Friends Israel
See Frnds Israel

Friends Israel-Spearhead Pr, *(Friends of Israel-Spearhead Press, The),* P.O. Box 123, West Collingswood, NJ 08107 (SAN 212-5056) Tel 215-922-3030.

Friends Lib KSU, *(Friends of the Libraries of Kansas State Univ.; 0-9616658),* Kansas State Univ., Farrell Library, Manhattan, KS 66506 (SAN 661-1826) Tel 913-532-5693.

Friends Long Island, *(Friends for Long Island's Heritage; 0-911357),* 1864 Muttontown Rd., Syosset, NY 11791 (SAN 270-3564) Tel 516-364-1050; Dist. by: Publishing Center for Cultural Resources, 625 Broadway, New York, NY 10012 (SAN 274-9025) Tel 212-260-2010.

Friends Mineralogy, *(Friends of Mineralogy; 0-9614396),* 1590 Olive Barber Rd., Coos Bay, OR 97420 (SAN 688-6833) Tel 503-267-2193; Orders to: Mineralogical Record, The, P.O. Box 1656, Carson City, NV 98702 (SAN 662-281X) Tel 702-882-2598.

Friends Minn Music, *(Friends of Minnesota Music, Inc.; 0-9614761),* Firehouse Sta. Box 13405, Minneapolis, MN 55414 (SAN 692-9370) Tel 612-874-1491.

Friends Mus Inc, *(Friends of the Museum, Inc.; 0-913965),* 800 W. Wells St., Milwaukee, WI 53233 (SAN 286-7532) Tel 414-278-2787; Orders to: The Muses-Cookbook Milwaukee Public Museum, 800 W. Wells St., Milwaukee, WI 53233 (SAN 286-7540) Tel 414-278-2710.

Friends Nature, *(Friends of Nature, Inc.; 0-910636),* Brookville, ME 04617 (SAN 205-5945). Canadian address: Chester, NS B0J 1J0.

Friends of Comm Lib, *(Friends of the Commerce Public Library; 0-9615374),* P.O. Box 308, Commerce, TX 75428 (SAN 695-538X) Tel 214-886-6858.

Friends of Earth, *(Friends of the Earth, Inc.; 0-913890),* 1045 Sansome, San Francisco, CA 94111 (SAN 201-579X) Tel 415-433-7373.

†**Friends of Pol Mus,** *(Friends of Polish Music at USC; 0-916545),* 3428 wrightview Dr., Studio City, CA 91604 Tel 213-877-1906; c/o Univ. of Southern California, Schl. of Music, University Park, Los Angeles, CA 90089-0851 (SAN 295-2815) Tel 213-743-6935; *CIP.*

Friends Ohio St U Lib, *(Friends of the Ohio State Univ. Libraries; 0-88215),* Rm. 112, Main Lib., 1858 Neil Ave. Mall, Columbus, OH 43210 (SAN 202-814X) Tel 614-422-3387.

Friends Osterhout, *(Friends of the Osterhout Free Library; 0-9616411),* 71 S. Franklin St., Wilkes-Barre, PA 18701 (SAN 658-8549) Tel 717-823-0156.

Friends Peace Comm
See Nonviol & Children

Friends Photography, *(Friends of Photography, The; 0-933286),* P.O. Box 500, Sunset Ctr., Carmel, CA 93921 (SAN 212-5064) Tel 408-624-6330.

Friends Pr, *(Friends' Pr.; 0-9615090),* P.O. Box 1006, Weston, CT 06883 (SAN 694-3691) Tel 203-227-6643; Dist. by: DeVorss Distributors, P.O. Box 550, 1046 Princeton Dr., Marina del Rey, CA 90294 (SAN 168-9886) Tel 203-870-7478; Dist. by: Bookpeople, 2929 Fifth St., Berkeley, CA 94710 (SAN 168-9517) Tel 415-549-3030; Dist. by: Starlite Distributors, P.O. Box 20729, Reno, NV 89515 (SAN 200-7789); Dist. by: Inland Book Company, 22 Hemingway Ave., East Haven, CT 06512 (SAN 200-4151) Tel 203-467-4257; Dist. by: New Leaf Distributing, 1020 White St., SW, Atlanta, GA 30310 (SAN 169-1449) Tel 404-755-2665.

Friends Refugees, *(Friends of Refugees of Eastern Europe; 0-86639),* 1383 President St., Brooklyn, NY 11213 (SAN 215-9953) Tel 718-467-0860; Orders to: SVET Publishers, Inc., 455 Albany Ave., Brooklyn, NY 11213 (SAN 693-9589) Tel 718-774-0065.

Friends Sch Balt, *(Friends Schl. of Baltimore, Inc.; 0-9610826),* 5114 N. Charles St., Baltimore, MD 21210 (SAN 265-2447) Tel 301-435-2800. In cooperation with Museum & Library of Maryland History-The Maryland Historical Society.

Friends Symphony Pubns, *(Friends of The Symphony Pubns.; 0-9617142),* P.O. Box 1603, Muskegan, MI 49443 (SAN 663-2491); 800 First St., Muskegan, MI 49443 (SAN 663-2505) Tel 616-780-2496.

Friends Towson Lib, *(Friends of the Towson Library, Inc.; 0-9602326),* 320 York Rd., Towson, MD 21204 (SAN 293-2695); c/o Baltimore County Public Library, Board of Library Trustees for Baltimore County, 320 York Road,, Towson, MD 21204 (SAN 293-2709).

Friends Truth, *(Friends of Truth; 0-930682),* 1509 Bruce Rd., Oreland, PA 19075 (SAN 211-0423) Tel 215-576-1450.

Friends Tucson, *(Friends of the Tucson Public Library; 0-9608370),* 110 E. Pennington St., Tuscon, AZ 85701 (SAN 662-0140) Tel 602-791-4391; c/o Tuscon Writes Project, Tuscon Public Library, Box 27470, Tuscon, AZ 85726 (SAN 240-3765).

Friends Tuscon Lib
See Friends Tucson

Friends U Rochester Imprint of U Pr of Va

†**Friends United,** *(Friends United Pr.; 0-913408),* 101 Quaker Hill Dr., Richmond, IN 47374 (SAN 201-5803) Tel 317-962-7573; *CIP.*

Friends Univ Toledo, *(Friends of the Univ. of Toledo Library; 0-918160),* Univ. of Toledo Library, 2801 W. Bancroft St., Toledo, OH 43606 (SAN 208-1792) Tel 419-537-2326.

Friends World Teach, *(Friends of World Teaching; 0-9601550),* P.O. Box 1049, San Diego, CA 92112 (SAN 212-906X) Tel 619-274-5282.

Friis-Pioneer Pr, *(Friis-Pioneer Press; 0-943480),* 1611 S. Minnie St., Santa Ana, CA 92707 (SAN 202-1498) Tel 714-835-3456.

Frisch H, *(Frisch, Howard; 0-910638),* P.O. Box 128, Village Sta., New York, NY 10014 (SAN 220-5610) Tel 212-243-6188.

Frnds Israel, *(Friends of Israel Gospel Ministry, Inc., The; 0-915540),* 475 White Horse Pike, P.O. Box 908, Bellmawr, NJ 08031 (SAN 225-445X) Tel 609-853-5590.

Frog Hair, *(Frog Hair Pr.; 0-9616031),* 16 Devonshire Blvd., San Carlos, CA 94070 (SAN 698-1453) Tel 415-592-5728.

†**Frog in Well,** *(Frog in the Well; 0-9603628),* 25A Buena Vista Terr., San Francisco, CA 94117 (SAN 207-8295) Tel 415-431-2113; *CIP.*

From Here, *(From Here Pr.; 0-89120),* P.O. Box 219, Fanwood, NJ 07023 (SAN 209-746X) Tel 201-889-7886. Imprints: Old Plate (Old Plate Press).

From Me, *(From Me to You; 0-9608590),* 811 Sioux Ave., Box 38, Mapleton, IA 51034 (SAN 238-2873) Tel 712-882-1517.

†**Fromm Intl Pub,** *(Fromm International Publishing Co.; 0-88064),* 560 Lexington Ave., New York, NY 10022 (SAN 239-7269) Tel 212-308-4010; Dist. by: Kampmann & Co., Inc., 9 E. 40th St., New York, NY 10016 (SAN 202-5191) Tel 212-685-2928; *CIP.*

Frommer-Pasmantier, *(Frommer-Pasmantier Pubs.; 0-671),* Div. of Simon & Schuster, One Gulf & Western Plaza, New York, NY 10023 (SAN 205-2725) Tel 212-333-4101.

Front Row, *(Front Row Experience; 0-915256),* 540 Discovery Bay Blvd., Byron, CA 94514 (SAN 207-1274) Tel 415-634-5710.

Frontal Lobe, *(Frontal Lobe; 0-931400),* 836 Starlite Lane, Los Altos, CA 94022 (SAN 211-9013).

Frontier Coop Herbs, *(Frontier Cooperative Herbs; 0-9616218),* Box 299, Norway, IA 52318 (SAN 658-6058) Tel 319-227-7991; Dist. by: International Distributors, RFD, Baker Hill Rd., Bradford, NH 03221 (SAN 200-6340); Dist. by: New Leaf Distributing, 1020 White St, SW, Atlanta, GA 30310 (SAN 169-1449).

Frontier Heritage, *(Frontier Heritage Pr.),* 1108 Davis St., Suite 109, Evanston, IL 60201 (SAN 659-199X).

Frontier Pr, *(Frontier Pr., The; 0-932237),* 15 Quintana Dr., Galveston, TX 77551 (SAN 686-578X) Tel 409-740-0138.

Frontier Pr Co, *(Frontier Pr. Co.; 0-912168),* P.O. Box 1098, Columbus, OH 43216 (SAN 205-5953) Tel 614-864-3737. Imprints: Lincoln Lib (Lincoln Library).

Frontier Press Calif, *(Frontier Press),* P.O. Box 5023, Santa Rosa, CA 95402 (SAN 206-653X) Tel 707-544-5174.

Frontier Pubns, *(Frontier Pubns.; 0-9614948),* 124 Ivy, Nampa, ID 83651 (SAN 693-6458) Tel 208-466-7439.

Frontline, *(Frontline Pubns.; 0-910657),* P.O. Box 1104, El Toro, CA 92630 (SAN 260-1907) Tel 714-837-6258.

Frontline Pub, *(Frontline Publishing; 0-935789),* 203 Brimbal Ave., Beverly, MA 01915 (SAN 696-4338) Tel 617-927-2535; P.O. Box 327, Beverly, MA 01915 (SAN 696-5407).

Frost & Sullivan, *(Frost & Sullivan, Inc.; 0-86621),* 106 Fulton St., New York, NY 10038 (SAN 215-8698) Tel 212-233-1080; Toll free: 800-242-7737.

Frost Art, *(Frost Art Distributors; 0-9604802),* 781 S. Kohler St., Los Angeles, CA 90021 (SAN 220-0546) Tel 213-626-3830.

Frosty Peak Bks, *(Frosty Peak Bks.; 0-9607116),* P.O. Box 4073, Malibu, CA 90265 (SAN 281-5591) Tel 213-457-2832; Orders to: P.O. Box 80584, Fairbanks, AK 99708 (SAN 699-5233) Tel 907-479-8411; Dist. by: Wilderness Pr., 2440 Bancroft Way, Berkeley, CA 94704-1676 (SAN 203-2139) Tel 415-843-8080.

Fruition Pubns, *(Fruition Pubns., Inc.; 0-939926),* Box 103, Blawenburg, NJ 08504 (SAN 216-8146) Tel 609-466-3196.

Fruitlands Mus, *(Fruitlands Museums, Inc.; 0-941632),* 102 Prospect Hill Rd., Harvard, MA 01451 (SAN 239-2119) Tel 617-456-3924.

†**FS&G,** *(Farrar, Straus & Giroux, Inc.; 0-374),* 19 Union Sq., W., New York, NY 10003 (SAN 206-782X) Tel 212-741-6900; Toll free: 800-242-7737; *CIP.* Imprints: Bell (Bell Bks.).(Bell Bks.); FS&G Pap (FS&G Paperbacks); Page (L. C. Page Co.); Sunburst (Sunburst Books).(Sunburst Bks.); Vision (Vision Books).(Vision Bks.).

FS&G Pap *Imprint of* **FS&G**

FSSSN Collo & Sympo, *(FSSSN Colloquia & Symposia at the Univ. of Wisconsin),* FSSSN, Univ. of Wisconsin, P.O. Box 285, Brookfield, WI 53005 (SAN 682-2738).

FSU Geology, *(Florida State University, Geology Dept.; 0-938426),* Tallahassee, FL 32306 (SAN 239-9350) Tel 904-644-3208.

FTI, *(Facing Tile Institute),* Box 8880, Canton, OH 44711 (SAN 270-0239).

FUJI *Imprint of* **Unipub**

Fulcrum Inc, *(Fulcrum, Inc.; 1-55591),* 350 Indiana St., Suite 510, Golden, CO 80401 (SAN 200-2825) Tel 303-277-2623; Toll free: 800-992-2908.

Full Count Pr OK, *(Full Count Press; 0-936908),* 223 N. Broadway, Edmond, OK 73034 (SAN 215-1456).

†Full Court NY, *(Full Court Press, Inc.; 0-916190),* 138-140 Watts St., New York, NY 10013 (SAN 211-9021) Tel 212-966-1831; *CIP.*

Full Court VA, *(Full Court Pr., Inc.; 0-913767),* Box 5177, Roanoke, VA 24012 (SAN 285-2527) Tel 703-345-5440.

Full Gospel, *(Full Gospel Business Men's Fellowship International; 0-86595),* P.O. Box 5050, 3150 Bear St., Costa Mesa, CA 92626 (SAN 220-2476) Tel 714-754-1400.

Fuller Golden Gal, *(Fuller Golden Gallery; 0-9607452),* 228 Grant Ave., San Francisco, CA 94108 (SAN 239-7749) Tel 415-982-6177.

Fuller Pub, *(Fuller Publishing Co.; 0-9605850),* 1060 Cragmont, Berkeley, CA 94708 (SAN 216-5953) Tel 415-527-4412.

Fuller Theol Soc, *(Fuller Theological Seminary; 0-9602638),* 84 N. Los Robles, Pasadena, CA 91101 (SAN 221-8259).

Fulness Hse, *(Fulness Hse., Inc.; 0-937778),* P.O. Box 79350, Ft. Worth, TX 76179 (SAN 215-9961).

Fulton Coun Art, *(Fulton County Arts Council; 0-9606650),* 501 William-Oliver Bldg., 32 Peachtree St., NW, Atlanta, GA 30303 (SAN 223-1328) Tel 404-577-7378.

Fun Bk Enter, *(Fun Bk. Enterprises; 0-937511),* P.O. Box 50397, Atlanta, GA 30302-0397 (SAN 658-8492) Tel 404-987-2178; 1980 Overton Trail, Stone Mountain, GA 30088 (SAN 658-8506).

Fun Co Inc
See Havin Fun Inc

Fun Foreign Lang, *(Fun in a Foreign Language; 0-9615956),* 3115 E. Mulberry Dr., Phoenix, AZ 85016 (SAN 697-3485) Tel 602-954-7075.

Fun Life, *(Fun Life Enterprises),* P.O. Box 3481, Oak Brook, IL 60521 (SAN 657-8624).

Fun Pub
See Fun Pub AZ

Fun Pub AZ, *(Fun Publishing Co.; 0-918858),* P.O. Box 2049, Scottsdale, AZ 85252 (SAN 210-4261) Tel 602-946-2093. Do not confuse with Fun Publishing Co., Cincinnati, OH.

Fun Pub OH, *(Fun Publishing Co.; 0-938293),* 5860 Miami Rd., Cincinnati, OH 45243 (SAN 661-1761) Tel 513-272-3672. Do not confuse with Fun Publishing Co., Scottsdale, AZ.

Fun Reading, *(Fun Reading Co.; 0-9608466),* 2409 Glenwood Rd., Brooklyn, NY 11210 (SAN 240-6055) Tel 718-453-5582.

Function Ind Pr, *(Function Industries Pr.; 0-930257),* P.O. Box 9915, Seattle, WA 98109 (SAN 670-8498) Tel 206-284-3489.

Fund Free Expression, *(Fund for Free Expression; 0-938579),* 36 W. 44th St., New York, NY 10036 (SAN 661-2555) Tel 212-840-9460. *Imprints:* Americas Watch (Americas Watch); Asia Watch (Asia Watch); Helsinki Watch (Helsinki Watch).

Fund Raisers Inc, *(Fund Raisers, Inc.; 0-916555),* 524 S. First Ave., Arcadia, CA 91006 (SAN 295-2904) Tel 818-445-0802.

Fund Raising, *(Fund-Raising Institute; 0-930807),* Box 365, Ambler, PA 19002 (SAN 677-6302) Tel 215-628-8729.

Fundation, *(Fundation, The; 0-930451),* 1404 Briarwood Rd. NE, Atlanta, GA 30319 (SAN 670-946X) Tel 404-321-1376.

Fundingsland, *(Fundingsland Productions; 0-932099),* 1825-15 1/2 St., SW, Minot, ND 58701 (SAN 686-5127) Tel 701-839-5159.

†Funk & W, *(Funk & Wagnalls Co.; 0-308),* C/O Harper & Row Pubs., 10 E. 53rd St., New York, NY 10022 (SAN 211-6944); Toll free: 800-242-7737; Dist. by: Harper & Row Pubs, Keystone Industrial Park, Scranton, PA 18512 (SAN 215-3742); *CIP.* *Imprints:* FW-J (Funk & Wagnalls Juvenile Books); FW-T (Funk & Wagnalls Trade Books).

Funky-Punky-Chic, *(Funky, Punky & Chic; 0-940762),* P.O. Box 601, Cooper Sta., New York, NY 10276 (SAN 219-7448) Tel 212-533-1772.

Funn Music, *(Funn Music; 0-9611130),* P.O. Box 5067, Garden Grove, CA 92645 (SAN 282-9142) Tel 714-895-3770.

FunPrax, *(FunPrax Associates; 0-9609972),* 711 Skinner Building, Seattle, WA 98101 (SAN 270-4005).

Fur-Fish-Game
See A R Harding Pub

Fur Line Pr, *(Fur Line Press; 0-912662),* Dist. by: ManRoot Press, Box 982, South San Francisco, CA 94080 (SAN 201-5811).

Furman U Bkstr, *(Furman Univ. Bookstore),* Greenville, SC 29613 (SAN 101-0670) Tel 803-294-2164.

Furst Pubns, *(Furst Pubns.; 0-931612),* 111 Kings Hwy. S., Westport, CT 06880 (SAN 211-4666).

Furuta, *(Furuta/Associates; 0-916129),* P.O. Box 399, Fallbrook, CA 92028 (SAN 294-9318) Tel 619-723-8678.

Fusion Energy Found, *(Fusion Energy Foundation; 0-938460),* 1010 16th St., NW,, Washington, DC 20036 (SAN 237-9538) Tel 703-689-2490; Box 17149, Washington, DC 20041-0149 (SAN 692-8307).

Fusion Groups, *(Fusion Groups, Inc.; 0-912778),* Indian Brook Rd., Garrison, NY 10524 (SAN 205-5988). Name Formerly Sonja.

Futura Pub, *(Futura Publishing Co., Inc.; 0-87993),* P.O. Box 330, Mt. Kisco, NY 10549 (SAN 201-582X) Tel 914-666-3505; 295 Main St., Mt. Kisco, NY 10549 (SAN 658-0750) Tel 914-666-3505.

Future Arts, *(Future Arts, Inc.; 0-943122),* Rt 2, Box 691, Baileys Harbor, WI 54202 (SAN 240-3781).

Future Direct, *(Future Directions, Inc.; 0-914413),* 9620 Chesapeake Dr., Suite 200, San Diego, CA 92123 (SAN 289-6249) Tel 619-698-5140.

Future Gen, *(Future Generations; 0-935791),* 2936 Macomb St. NW, Washington, DC 20008 (SAN 696-4370) Tel 202-364-4363.

Future Heal
See Prof Bks Future Health

Future Health
See Prof Bks Future Health

Future Home, *(Future Homemakers of America),* 1910 Association Dr., Reston, VA 22091 (SAN 236-3135) Tel 703-476-4900.

Future Pr, *(Future Pr.; 0-918406),* P.O. Box 73, Canal St. Sta., New York, NY 10013 (SAN 210-0886).

Future Pub FL, *(Future Publishing Co.),* P.O. Box 1207, Oviedo, FL 32765 (SAN 223-081X).

Future Schls Inc, *(Future Schools, Inc.; 0-936219),* R.D. 2, Box 260, Hopewell Junction, NY 12533 (SAN 697-0958) Tel 914-897-5688; Dist. by: School Computers Systems, Inc., Jeanne Dr., Putnam Valley, NY 10579 (SAN 200-5905) Tel 914-528-2456.

Future Sci Res, *(Future Science Research Publishing Co.; 0-941292),* P.O. Box 06392, Portland, OR 97206 (SAN 239-4278) Tel 503-235-1971.

Future Shop, *(Future Shop; 0-930490),* P.O. Box 3262, Santa Barbara, CA 93130 (SAN 211-2396) Tel 805-682-5460.

Future Syst, *(Future Systems, Inc.; 0-938907),* P.O. Box 26, Falls Church, VA 22046 (SAN 661-8081); 2209 N. Quintana, Arlington, VA 22205 (SAN 661-809X) Tel 703-241-1799.

FuturePace, *(FuturePace Inc.; 0-932573),* P.O. Box 1173, San Rafael, CA 94915 (SAN 687-4770) Tel 415-485-1200; Dist. by: Publishers Group West, 5855 Beaudry St., Emeryville, CA 94608 (SAN 202-8522) Tel 415-658-3453; Dist. by: Bookpeople, 2929 Fifth St., Berkeley, CA 94710 (SAN 168-9517) Tel 415-549-3030.

Futures Group, *(Futures Group, The; 0-9605196),* 76 Eastern Blvd., Glastonbury, CT 06033-1264 (SAN 215-8701) Tel 203-633-3501.

Futures Pub, *(Futures Publishing Group; 0-936624),* Div. of LJR Communications, Inc., 5513 Twin Knolls, Suite 213, Columbia, MD 21045 (SAN 215-2541) Tel 301-730-5365. *Imprints:* Mngd Acct Reprts (Managed Account Reports).

Futures Unlimited Inc., *(Futures Unlimited, Inc.; 0-940082),* 5200 W. 73rd St., Minneapolis, MN 55435 (SAN 220-2220) Tel 612-835-7729.

Futuro Ohio, *(Futuro Co., The; 0-9617392),* Div. of The Jung Corp., 5801 Mariemont Ave., Cincinnati, OH 45227 (SAN 663-6101) Tel 513-271-3400.

FVN Corp, *(FVN Corp.; 0-915687),* 1660 Dyerville Loop Rd., Redcrest, CA 95569 (SAN 292-496X) Tel 707-946-2206.

FW-J *Imprint of* **Funk & W**

FW-T *Imprint of* **Funk & W**

G A Eversaul
See Health Res Las Vegas

G A Rogers, *(Rogers, Gay Ann),* Box 181, Claremont, CA 91711 (SAN 287-301X).

G A Tanner Ctr
See Woolf UT Sys

G A Voland, *(Voland, Gerard A.; 0-9615603),* 522 Callet St., Palmdale, CA 93550 (SAN 696-2556) Tel 805-947-2781.

G Alexander, *(George, Alexander; 0-930923),* 79 Washington St., Hempstead, NY 11550 (SAN 683-2563).

G & G Pub Co, *(G & G Publishing Co.; 0-9610028),* P.O. Box 49231, Atlanta, GA 30359 (SAN 262-8708) Tel 404-992-1198.

G & H Bks, *(G & H Bks.; 0-9616717),* 2515 E. Thomas Rd., Suite 16, Phoenix, AZ 85016 (SAN 661-3780) Tel 602-955-3812.

G B H Pub, *(G B H Publishing),* 825 32nd Ave., Santa Cruz, CA 95062 (SAN 270-4153) Tel 408-462-4916.

G B Pr, *(G.B. Pr.; 0-9615406),* 49 Wilbur St., Weatherly, PA 18255 (SAN 695-5010) Tel 717-427-8398.

G Barker Bks, *(Barker, Gray, Books; 0-911306),* Box D, Jane Lew, WV 26378 (SAN 204-7292) Tel 304-269-2719.

G Beale Pr, *(Beale, Guthrie, Pr.; 0-937781),* 7508 42nd Ave., NE, Seattle, WA 98115 (SAN 659-2279) Tel 206-525-6596.

G Black, *(Black, Gloria; 0-9616466),* 2039 NE 98th St., Seattle, WA 98115 (SAN 659-3038) Tel 206-524-6636.

G Bowen Comm, *(Bowen, Glen, Communications; 0-910173),* 2415 Villa Creek, Kingwood, TX 77339 (SAN 241-2772) Tel 713-359-3039.

G Breese, *(Breese, Gerald),* Princeton Univ., Princeton, NJ 08540 (SAN 206-1007).

G Brummel Pub, *(Brummel Publishing Company; 0-9613041),* P.O. Box 198, Richmond Hill, NY 11419 (SAN 295-3765) Tel 718-835-1155; 116-10 103rd Ave., Richmond Hill, NY 11419 (SAN 295-3773).

G Brune, *(Brune, Gunnar; 0-9604766),* 2014 Royal Club Ct., Arlington, TX 76017 (SAN 215-0611) Tel 817-465-3171.

G C Dickey, *(Dickey, Grover C.),* 200 Gill Dr., Midwest City, OK 73110 (SAN 208-3612).

G C E Pubns, *(GCE Pubns.; 0-915668),* P.O. Box 539, Los Alamitos, CA 90720 (SAN 207-6772) Tel 213-493-4421.

G C Jaye, *(Jaye, Gail C.),* 4 Chalet Dr., Bay Minette, AL 36507 (SAN 217-2941).

G D Jackson
See Jackson Assocs

G Davis, *(Davis, Grant, Co., Inc.; 0-934786),* P.O. Box 692, Lewisville, TX 75067 (SAN 213-2141).

G Drasnar, *(Drasnar, George, Productions; 0-936951),* 706-A S. Pacific Coast Hwy., Redondo Beach, CA 90277 (SAN 658-7003) Tel 213-316-9065.

G E C, *(G.E.C. Publishing Firm; 0-9613391),* 1613 Chelsea Rd., Suite 160, San Marino, CA 91108 (SAN 657-0895) Tel 818-445-6329.

G E Company FL, *(General Electric Co.; 0-9617205),* P.O. Box 861, Gainesville, FL 32602-0861 (SAN 692-5154) Tel 904-462-3911.

G E Gifford Memorial, *(Gifford, George E., Memorial Committee),* Calvert School, Rising Sun, MD 21911 (SAN 281-739X); Orders to: Frances M. Hubis, 24 Hubis Lane, Rising Sun, MD 21911 (SAN 281-7403) Tel 301-658-6479.

G E McCuen Pubns, *(McCuen, Gary E., Pubns., Inc.; 0-86596),* 411 Mallalieu Dr., Hudson, WI 54016 (SAN 691-909X)

G E Moir, *(Moir, George E.; 0-9616974),* 1341 Holbrook St., Wenatchee, WA 98801 (SAN 661-7603) Tel 509-662-6004.

G E R P A, *(G.E.R.P.A. Pubns.; 0-9613352),* 1404 Union St., Schenectady, NY 12308 (SAN 655-8763) Tel 518-346-6127.

G E Radke, *(Radke, George E.; 0-9607994),* 41 Harvard Rd., Havertown, PA 19083 (SAN 238-8308) Tel 215-446-0786.

G E Siepierski, *(Siepierski, Gerald E.; 0-9611278),* 20257 Ecorse Rd., Taylor, MI 48180 (SAN 283-1643) Tel 313-382-4816.

G E Smith, *(Smith, Gary E.; 0-9613113),* P.O. Box 463, Azusa, CA 91702-0463 (SAN 294-0876) Tel 818-969-2492.

G F Edwards, *(Edwards, G. F.; 0-932318),* Box 1461, Lawton, OK 73502 (SAN 212-1719) Tel 405-248-6870.

G F Forbes, *(Forbes, George F.; 0-910604),* 22085 Alamogordo Rd., Saugus, CA 91350 (SAN 281-7209) Tel 805-254-0734.

G F Ritchie, *(Ritchie, George F.; 0-9604392),* 1840 Clay St., No. 203, San Francisco, CA 94109 (SAN 212-6834) Tel 415-441-7126.

G F Stickley Co, *(Stickley, George F., Co.; 0-89313),* 210 W. Washington Sq., Philadelphia, PA 19106 (SAN 209-0783) Tel 215-922-7126.

G Flynn, *(Flynn, George),* 145 W. Twelfth St., New York, NY 10011 (SAN 211-3929) Tel 212-929-6257.

G Foreman, *(Foreman, Gloria, Publishing Co.; 0-915198),* P.O. Box 405, Oklahoma City, OK 73101 (SAN 203-4263) Tel 918-723-5925.

G Funston, *(Funston, Gwendolen; 0-9615862),* 3781 Lodge Ln., Trenton, MI 48183 (SAN 694-535X) Tel 313-676-9456.

G Gajda, *(Gajda, George J.; 0-9608018),* P.O. Box 1846, Santa Monica, CA 90406 (SAN 209-4398).

G Gannett, *(Gannett Bks.; 0-930096),* Subs. of Guy Gannett Publishing Co., P.O. Box 1460B, Portland, ME 04101 (SAN 210-7295) Tel 207-775-5811; Toll free: 800-442-6036.

G Gessert, *(Gessert, George; 0-9615895),* 1230 W. Broadway, Eugene, OR 97402 (SAN 697-1032) Tel 503-343-2920.

G Gorin, *(George, Gorin; 0-9613974),* 11 Fifth Ave., New York, NY 10003 (SAN 682-2401) Tel 212-260-5422.

G Graham, *(Graham, Gordon, & Co.; 0-9616353),* P.O. Box 608, Fall City, WA 98024 (SAN 658-9464) Tel 206-282-9840; 5815 Preston Hwy., Fall City, WA 98024 (SAN 658-9472).

G H Alsterda, *(Alsterda, Grayce Harper; 0-9617035),* 915 W. White Gate Dr., Mt. Prospect, IL 60056 (SAN 662-8214) Tel 312-394-0023.

G H Hayes, *(Hayes, Gordon; 0-9605880),* 3626 Meyler St., San Pedro, CA 90731 (SAN 216-6798) Tel 213-833-7066.

G H Irwin & Co, *(Irwin, G. H., & Co.; 0-936243),* P.O. Box 945, Enumclaw, WA 98022 (SAN 696-9364) Tel 206-927-4029; 41115 SE 236th, Enumclaw, WA 98022 (SAN 696-9372).

G H laBarre, *(LaBarre, George H., Galleries, Inc.; 0-941538),* P.O. Box 746, Hollis, NH 03049 (SAN 239-1066) Tel 603-882-2411.

G Handwerk, *(Handwerk, Gordon, Pubs.; 0-940524),* P.O. Box 685, Madison, NJ 07940 (SAN 217-1791) Tel 201-377-1644.

G Hein, *(Hein, G.; 0-9614649),* 141 N. 11th St., Lehighton, PA 18235 (SAN 691-862X) Tel 215-377-3595.

G Hill, *(Hill, Grace; 0-9604506),* 3 Haskins Rd., Hanover, NH 03755 (SAN 213-0785) Tel 603-643-4059.

G I Krumwiede, *(Krumwiede, Grace I.),* 3713 S. George Mason Dr., No. 608W, Falls Church, VA 22041 (SAN 213-0998) Tel 703-998-0251.

G J Abraham, *(Abraham, George J.; 0-9617177),* 23 Monroe Ave., Geneva, NY 14456 (SAN 663-1657) Tel 315-789-6126.

G J Ent, *(G.J. Enterprises; 0-9612912),* 446 Old Stonebrook Rd., Acton, MA 01718 (SAN 291-1612) Tel 617-568-1401.

G J Mauer, *(Mauer, George J.; 0-9616803),* 351 Brassie Dr., Longwood, FL 32750 (SAN 661-289X) Tel 305-834-5842.

†G K Hall, *(Hall, G. K., & Co.; 0-8161),* Div. of Macmillian Publishing Co., 70 Lincoln St., Boston, MA 02111 (SAN 206-8427); Toll free: 800-343-2806; *CIP. Imprints:* Hall Library (Hall Library Catalogs); Hall Medical (Hall, G. K., Medical Pubs.); Hall Reference (Hall Reference Books).(Hall Reference Bks.); Large Print Bks (Large Print Books).(Large Print Bks.); Pub. by Biblio Guides (Bibliographic Guides); Univ Bks (University Books).(Univ. Bks.).

G K Pr, *(G K Press; 0-910067),* 415 Sheffield Rd., Cherry Hill, NJ 08034 (SAN 241-3078) Tel 609-877-9115.

G K Westgard, *(Westgard, Gilbert, K. II; 0-916061),* 1001 SW Fifth Ct., Boynton Beach, FL 33435 (SAN 240-5032).

G Kici, *(Kici, Gasper),* P.O. Box 1855, Washington, DC 20013 (SAN 203-4115) Tel 703-560-6467.

G Kurian, *(Kurian, George, Reference Bks.; 0-914746),* P.O. Box 519, Baldwin Place, NY 10505 (SAN 203-1981) Tel 914-962-3287.

G L Holmgren Pubs, *(Holmgren, Gary L., Pubs.; 0-932999),* P.O. Box 8205, Dallas, TX 75205 (SAN 689-108X) Tel 214-891-8153.

G L Lowe, *(Lowe, Grayson L.),* 401 E. 32nd St., Chicago, IL 60616 (SAN 217-1155).

G L Tucker, *(Tucker, Grayson L.; 0-9610706),* 2310 Tyler Ln., Louisville, KY 40205 (SAN 264-8024) Tel 502-458-2234.

G Lakes Bks
See Great Lakes Bks

G LedBetter, *(LedBetter, Gwenda; 0-9617007),* 18 Woodcrest Rd., Ashville, NC 28804 (SAN 662-5525) Tel 704-254-3133.

G Leeman, *(Leeman, Gertrude; 0-9613628),* 7612 1/2 Eads Ave., La Jolla, CA 92037 (SAN 670-8471) Tel 619-454-4415; Dist. by: James Elko, 3590 Bayside Ln., San Diego, CA 92109 (SAN 200-7185) Tel 619-488-8471.

G Lutheran Foun, *(Grace Lutheran Foundation of Boulder Colorado, Inc.; 0-9606516),* 1001 13th St., Boulder, CO 80302 (SAN 217-1783) Tel 303-442-1883.

G M Parker, *(Parker, Gertrude M.; 0-89279),* Southview, Apt. 4, Stanhope, IA 50246 (SAN 286-3480).

G McBride, *(McBride, Gisela; 0-9613270),* 1443 Court St., Allentown, PA 18101 (SAN 297-0252) Tel 215-776-1824.

G Mancini, *(Mancini, Genevieve),* 176 Moffit Blvd., Islip, NY 11751 (SAN 213-1145) Tel 516-277-9547.

G Markim, *(Markim, Greg, Pubs.; 0-938251),* P.O. Box 183, Appleton, WI 54912 (SAN 661-3659); 1916 N. Drew St., Appleton, WI 54912 (SAN 661-3667) Tel 414-734-9678.

G North, *(North, Gloria; 0-931758),* 15 Estelle Ave., Larkspur, CA 94939 (SAN 211-5115).

G O Kamp, *(Kamp, Gayle O.; 0-9613163),* 7741 Lola Court, Indianapolis, IN 46219 (SAN 294-9687) Tel 317-357-6128.

G Oberling, *(Oberling, Grace; 0-9616924),* 6732 Berneil Dr., Paradise Valley, AZ 85253 (SAN 661-485X) Tel 602-951-4310; Orders to: LUVType, 7707 N. 27th Ave., Phoenix, AZ 85051 (SAN 661-4868).

G Ohsawa, *(Ohsawa, George, Macrobiotic Foundation; 0-918860),* 1511 Robinson St., Oroville, CA 95965 (SAN 207-7663) Tel 916-533-7702.

G P Courseware
See GP Courseware

G P Ed Serv, *(Plossl, George, Educational Services, Inc.; 0-926219),* 1850 Parkway Pl., Suite 335, Marietta, GA 30067 (SAN 294-457X) Tel 404-423-7620.

G P Jones, *(Jones, Gladys Powelson; 0-9612628),* 1507 E. Fox Farm Rd., Cheyenne, WY 82007 (SAN 287-7422) Tel 307-632-7568.

G P Perkins, *(Perkins, George P.; 0-9613144),* Box 910, South Lake Tahoe, CA 95705 (SAN 294-9512) Tel 916-544-2100. Summer: 916-565-3260.

G P Raintree
See Raintree Pubs

G R Cockle, *(Cockle, George R., Assocs.; 0-916160),* P.O. Box 1224, Downtown Sta., Omaha, NE 68101 (SAN 211-3104).

G R Schoepfer, *(Schoepfer, G. R.; 0-931436),* 786 Hudson Pkwy., Whiting, NJ 08759 (SAN 211-1659) Tel 201-849-0689.

G Ritner, *(Ritner, George),* 411 Broadway, Suite 203, San Diego, CA 92101 (SAN 211-268X).

G Ronald Pub, *(Ronald, George, Pub., Ltd.; 0-85398),* P.O. Box 447, St. Louis, MO 63166 (SAN 679-1859).

G Rose Pr, *(Rose, Gena, Pr.; 0-9604178),* 2424 Franklin, Denver, CO 80205 (SAN 215-0751).

G S E Pubns
See G C E Pubns

G S Pubs, *(GS Pubs.; 0-9606338),* P.O. Box 6213, Laguna Niguel, CA 92677 (SAN 282-5619) Tel 714-951-9009; Orders to: 26355 Palomita Cir., Mission Viejo, CA 92691 (SAN 282-5627) Tel 714-951-9009.

G S Swenson
See Swenson Pub

G Schnatz Pubns, *(Schnatz, G, Pubns.; 0-9614145),* 192 Woodside Ave., Lodi, NJ 07644 (SAN 686-2276) Tel 201-471-2624.

G Seibels, *(Seibels, Gren; 0-9613056),* 2400 Heyward St., Columbia, SC 24205 (SAN 294-1287) Tel 803-799-1838; Dist. by: Morris Aviation Ltd., P.O. Box 718, Statesboro, GA 30458 (SAN 652-0286) Tel 912-489-8161.

G Sroda, *(Sroda, George; 0-9604486),* P.O. Box 97, Amherst Junction, WI 54407 (SAN 210-8607) Tel 715-824-3868.

G Stempien, *(Stempien, G., Publishing Co.; 0-930472),* 1213 Edgehill Ave., Joliet, IL 60432 (SAN 210-9840) Tel 815-722-4216.

G T Forrers *Imprint of* **Haynes Pubns**

G T M Co, *(GTM, Inc.; 0-9615112),* P.O. Box 776, Arnold, MD 21012 (SAN 693-8221) Tel 301-757-7082.

G T M Inc
See G T M Co

G T Yeamans, *(Yeamans, George Thomas; 0-9601006),* 4507 W. Burton Dr., Muncie, IN 47304 (SAN 208-9351) Tel 317-288-4345; Orders to: Ball State Bookstore, Muncie, IN 47306 (SAN 209-1623) Tel 317-285-8080.

G Tartt, *(Tartt, Gene; 0-934746),* The Vineyard Almanac, P.O. Box 2641, Saratoga, CA 95070 (SAN 220-2778) Tel 408-867-1614.

G Throwkoff, *(Throwkoff, G.; 0-942004),* 223 Arballo Dr., San Francisco, CA 94132 (SAN 238-4841) Tel 415-585-9996.

G Twesten, *(Twesten, Gary, Publisher; 0-9602428),* Fox Run, Millstadt, IL 62260 (SAN 209-1402) Tel 618-233-5070.

G Van Wariebey, *(Van Wariebey, Glean; 0-916829),* 2 E. River St., Susquehanna, PA 18847 (SAN 699-8283).

G Vanderstoel, *(Vanderstoel, Graeme),* P.O. Box 599, El Cerrito, CA 94530 (SAN 263-239X) Tel 415-527-2882.

G W Ferguson
See B Franklin

G W May, *(May, George W.; 0-9605566),* Rte. 1 Box 117, Metropolis, IL 62960 (SAN 216-0471) Tel 618-524-4029.

G W Noble, *(Noble, Gilbert W.; 0-911036),* P.O. Box 931, Winter Park, FL 32789 (SAN 206-4472) Tel 305-647-2431.

G Whitefield Pub, *(Whitefield, George, Publishing Co.; 0-9614323),* P.O. Box 243, Gladstone, OR 97027 (SAN 687-5343) Tel 503-653-2249.

G Whittell Mem, *(Whittell, George, Memorial Pr.; 0-910781),* 3722 S. Ave., Youngstown, OH 44502 (SAN 260-2776) Tel 216-783-0645.

G Wolf, *(Wolf, George; 0-9616503),* 2323 Delanoy Ave., Bronx, NY 10469 (SAN 659-3577) Tel 212-519-0256.

GA Ag Commodity
See GA Peanut Comm

GA Assn Hist, *(Georgia Assn. of Historians; 0-939346),* Kennesaw College, History Dept., Marietta, GA 30061 (SAN 216-5643) Tel 404-429-2945.

GA Dept Archives, *(Georgia Department of Archives & History),* 330 Capitol Ave., Atlanta, GA 30334 (SAN 218-7426) Tel 404-656-2358.

Symbols/Abbreviations

Symbols/Abbreviations

Gard & Co, *(Gard & Co.; 0-9603316),* P.O. Box 34579, NW Sta., Omaha, NE 68134 (SAN 209-0198) Tel 402-493-1352.

Garden Bks, *(Garden Bks.),* P.O. Box 3446, Oakland, CA 94609 (SAN 656-822X).

Garden City, *(Garden City Historical Society; 0-9604654),* Box 179, Garden City, NY 11530 (SAN 215-1472).

Garden Club Lex, *(Garden Club of Lexington Inc., The; 0-9614443),* P.O. Box 22091, Lexington, KY 40522 (SAN 689-3597) Tel 606-266-3438.

Garden Club Sav, *(Garden Club of Savannah; 0-9613370),* P.O. Box 8806, Savannah, GA 31412 (SAN 657-1417).

Garden GA, *(Garden Club of Georgia, Inc., The; 0-9612486),* 325 Lumpkin St., Athens, GA 30605 (SAN 289-2510) Tel 912-234-4106.

Garden Way Pub *Imprint of* **Storey Comm Inc**

Gardens Inc
See Natl Gardening Assn

Gardner Farkas Pr, *(Gardner-Farkas Pr., Inc.; 0-9613874),* 1701 River Run, River Plaza Office Tower, Suite 603, Fort Worth, TX 76107 (SAN 681-9850); Orders to: P.O. Box 33229, Fort Worth, TX 76162 (SAN 662-2585) Tel 817-870-2113.

Gardner Mus
See I S Gardner Mus

Gardner-O'Brien, *(Gardner-O'Brien Fine Arts Research, Inc.; 0-9616580),* 17 Cortes St., Boston, MA 02116 (SAN 661-2326) Tel 617-329-9107.

†Gardner Pr, *(Gardner Pr., Inc.; 0-89876),* 19 Union Sq., W., New York, NY 10003 (SAN 214-1906) Tel 212-924-8293; *CIP.*

Gardner Pub, *(Gardner Publishing, Inc.; 0-9617183),* 150 Marine St., City Island, NY 10464 (SAN 663-2661) Tel 212-885-1036.

Gardnor Hse, *(Gardnor House; 0-943602),* P.O. Box 1928, Spring, TX 77383 (SAN 240-6578).

Garfield Pubns, *(Garfield Pubns.; 0-9609856),* 6095 Ripley Ln., Paradise, CA 95969 (SAN 270-4382) Tel 916-872-4184.

†Garland Pub, *(Garland Publishing, Inc.; 0-8240),* 136 Madison Ave., New York, NY 10016 (SAN 201-5897) Tel 212-686-7492; *CIP.*

Garmer Pr Inc, *(Garmer Pr., Inc.; 0-9612960),* 7800 Sandy Cove Dr., New Orleans, LA 70128 (SAN 292-5117) Tel 504-246-4023; Dist. by: Forest Sales & Distributors, 2616 Spain St., New Orleans, LA 70117 (SAN 157-5511) Tel 504-947-2106.

Garnet Pr, *(Garnet Pr.; 0-938133),* P.O. Box 1094, North Falmouth, MA 02556 (SAN 661-2172); 35 Deep Pond Dr., East Falmouth, MA 02536 (SAN 661-2180) Tel 617-540-8639.

Garnet Pub, *(Garnet Pub. Co.; 0-917475),* P.O. Box 14713, Spokane, WA 99214 (SAN 656-0660) Tel 509-926-4176.

Garnet Pub CA, *(Garnet Publishing Co.; 0-935793),* 1177 Cielo Cir., Rohnert Park, CA 94928 (SAN 696-9275) Tel 707-792-2294.

†Garrard, *(Garrard Pub. Co.; 0-8116),* 29 Goldsborough St., Easton, MD 21601 (SAN 201-5900); Orders to: 1607 N. Market St., Champaign, IL 61820 (SAN 201-5919) Tel 217-352-7685; *CIP.*

Garrett & String, *(Garrett & Stringer, Inc.; 0-9615791),* P.O. Box 330677, Coconut Grove Sta., Miami, FL 33233 (SAN 696-9259) Tel 305-447-1019; 3126 Center St., Coconut Grove, FL 33133 (SAN 696-9267).

Garrett Corp, *(Garrett Corp., The; 0-9617029),* DIv. of Allied-Signal, Inc., 18200 Coastline Dr., Malibu, CA 90265 (SAN 662-8788) Tel 213-454-1041.

Garrett Pk, *(Garrett Park Pr.; 0-912048),* P.O. Box 190 E, Garrett Park, MD 20896 (SAN 201-5927) Tel 301-946-2553.

Garrett Pub, *(Garrett Publishing Co.; 0-939085),* 13117 Balboa Blvd., Granada Hills, CA 91344 (SAN 662-9288) Tel 818-360-5052.

Garric Pr, *(Garric Pr.; 0-9609922),* P.O. Box 517, Glen Ellen, CA 95442 (SAN 270-4404) Tel 707-938-3625.

Garson Associates, *(Garson Assocs.; 0-9614591),* 172 Babylon Tpke., Merrick, NY 11566 (SAN 691-7763) Tel 516-868-9833.

Gartner Group, *(Gartner Group, Inc.; 0-9614408),* 72 Cummings Point Rd., Stamford, CT 06904 (SAN 688-2579) Tel 203-964-0096.

Garvin A J
See A J Garvin

Gary Guthrie, *(Guthrie, Gary; 0-9612980),* 977 Myra Ave., Chula Vista, CA 92011 (SAN 292-515X) Tel 619-427-8098.

Gaslight, *(Gaslight Pubns.; 0-934468),* 112 E. Second St., Bloomington, IN 47401 (SAN 213-5019) Tel 812-332-5169. *Imprints:* McGuffin Bks (McGuffin Books).

Gasogene Pr, *(Gasogene Pr.; 0-938501),* P.O. Box 1041, Dubuque, IA 52001 (SAN 661-2717) Tel 612-546-4671; 1325 Jersey Ave. S., 308, St. Louis Park, MN 55426 (SAN 663-3218).

Gate *Imprint of* **Contemp Bks**

Gateway Arts, *(Gateway Arts; 0-935327),* P.O. Box 3267, Oakland, CA 94609 (SAN 695-7668) Tel 415-655-5240.

Gateway Bks, *(Gateway Bks.; 0-933469),* 66 Cleary Ct., Suite 1405, San Francisco, CA 94109 (SAN 691-8808) Tel 415-929-7134; Dist. by: Strawberry Hill Pr., 2594 15th Ave., San Francisco, 94127 (SAN 238-8103) Tel 415-664-8112; Dist. by: Publishers Group West, 5855 Beaudry St., Emeryville, CA 94608 (SAN 202-8522) Tel 415-658-3453; Dist. by: Ingram Bk. Co., 347 Reedwood Dr., Nashville, TN 37217 (SAN 169-7978); Dist. by: Book Dynamics, Inc., 836 Broadway, New York, NY 10003 (SAN 169-5649) Tel 212-254-7798.

Gateway Ed Ltd
See Regnery Bks

Gateway Editions *Imprint of* **Regnery Bks**

†Gateway MO, *(Gateway Publishing, Inc.; 0-9616128),* 1177 N. Warson Rd., St. Louis, MO 63132 (SAN 699-6809) Tel 314-997-7462. Do not confuse with Gateway Publishing, 4121 Forest Park Blvd., St. Louis, MO; *CIP.*

Gateway Pr, *(Gateway Pr.; 0-936533),* P.O. Box 5180, Mill Valley, CA 94942 (SAN 697-8622) Tel 415-332-1428; Dist. by: Publishers Group West, 5855 Beaudry St., Emeryville, CA 94608 (SAN 202-8522) Tel 415-658-3453; Dist. by: Bookpeople, 2929 Fifth St., Berkeley, CA 94710 (SAN 168-9517) Tel 415-549-3030.

Gateway Pr
See Hughes Enter

Gateway Pr TX, *(Gateway Pr.; 0-9613155),* P.O. Box 6867, Tyler, TX 75701 (SAN 294-8052) Tel 214-561-3479.

Gateway Prod, *(Gateway Productions, Inc.; 0-936769),* 3011 Magazine St., New Orleans, LA 70115 (SAN 699-9808) Tel 504-891-2600.

Gateway Pubns, *(Gateway Pubns.; 0-937661),* 1106 Greenbanks Dr., Mt. Pleasant, MI 48858 (SAN 659-235X) Tel 517-772-1432; Dist. by: Baha'i Distribution Service, 415 Linden Ave., Wilmette, IL 60091 (SAN 200-643X); Dist. by: Kalimat Pr., 10889 Wilshire Blvd., Suite 700, Los Angeles, CA 90024 (SAN 213-7666).

GATT *Imprint of* **Unipub**

Gauntlet Bks, *(Gauntlet Books),* 144 King St., Franklin, MA 02038 (SAN 201-5935) Tel 617-528-4414.

Gaus, *(Gaus, Theo, Ltd.; 0-912444),* P.O. Box 1168, Brooklyn, NY 11202 (SAN 203-4174) Tel 718-625-4651.

Gavea-Brown, *(Gavea-Brown Pubns.; 0-943722),* Box O, Brown Univ., Providence, RI 02912 (SAN 240-4788).

Gavelston Arts, *(Galveston Arts; 0-9616139),* P.O. Box 1105, Galveston, TX 77553 (SAN 699-9670) Tel 409-763-7173; 2020 Post Office, Galveston, TX 77553 (SAN 699-9689).

†Gay Pr NY, *(Gay Presses of New York; 0-9604724),* P.O. Box 294, New York, NY 10014 (SAN 215-210X) Tel 212-255-4713; *CIP.*

†Gay Sunshine, *(Gay Sunshine Pr.; 0-917342),* Box 40397, San Francisco, CA 94140 (SAN 208-0915) Tel 415-824-3184; Dist. by: Bookpeople, 2929 Fifth St., Berkeley, CA 94710 (SAN 168-9517); Dist. by: Inland Bk. Co., P.O. Box 261, 22 Hemingway Ave., East Haven, CT 06512 (SAN 200-4151) Tel 203-467-4257; *CIP.*

Gaylord's Guides, *(Gaylord's Guides, Ltd.; 0-936907),* 204 W. 20th St., New York, NY 10011 (SAN 658-3334).

Gazebo Pubns, *(Gazebo Pubns.; 0-914161),* P.O. Box 368, Milton, IN 47357-0368 (SAN 287-4989).

Gazelle Pubns, *(Gazelle Pubns.; 0-930192),* 5580 Stanley Dr., Auburn, CA 95603 (SAN 209-5610) Tel 916-878-1223.

Gazette Intl, *(Gazette International Networking Institute; 0-931301),* 4502 Maryland Ave., St. Louis, MO 63108 (SAN 683-2539) Tel 314-361-0475.

Gazette Pr, *(Gazette Press, Inc.; 0-933390),* 225 Hunter Ave., North Tarrytown, NY 10591 (SAN 203-4182) Tel 914-631-8866.

Gazette Print, *(Gazette Printing),* 1114 Broadway, Wheaton, MN 56296 (SAN 679-1514).

GB Publishing
See O'Connor Hse-Pubs

GBC Pub, *(GBC Publishing; 0-9606228),* 947 Garfield Ave., Oak Park, IL 60304 (SAN 217-5207) Tel 312-848-1995.

†GBIP, *(Genealogical Bks. in Print; 0-89157),* 6818 Lois Dr., Springfield, VA 22150 (SAN 220-2484) Tel 703-971-5877; *CIP.*

GBM Bks, *(GBM Books; 0-912695),* Div. of God's Broadcaster Ministries, Inc., P.O. Box 4895, 4850 Whisett Ave., North Hollywood, CA 91607 (SAN 277-6820) Tel 818-763-0942.

GBS CA, *(GBS Pubns.; 0-913855),* 1969 Benecia Ave., Los Angeles, CA 90025 (SAN 287-7473) Tel 213-552-1440.

GBS Pubs, *(GBS Pubs.; 0-939928),* Div. of Gordon's Booksellers, 8 E. Baltimore St., Baltimore, MD 21202 (SAN 216-8154).

GCNHA, *(Grand Canyon Natural History Assn.; 0-938216),* P.O. Box 399, Grand Canyon, AZ 86023 (SAN 215-7675).

GCT Pub, *(GCT Publishing Co., Inc.; 0-937659),* P.O. Box 6448, Mobile, AL 36660 (SAN 659-2325) Tel 205-478-4700; 350 Weinacker Ave., Mobile, AL 36660 (SAN 659-2333).

GDA Pubns, *(G. D. A. Pubns.; 0-938640),* P.O. Box 30119, Lafayette, LA 70503 (SAN 215-2452).

GDE Pubns OH, *(GDE Pubns.; 0-940934),* Div. of Glen Eley Enterprises, P.O. Box 304, Lima, OH 45802 (SAN 222-9749).

GE-PS Cancer, *(GE-PS Cancer Memorial; 0-9601644),* 519 Austin Ave., Park Ridge, IL 60068 (SAN 215-7659) Tel 312-823-5425.

GE Tech Marketing
See Genium Pub

GE Tech Prom & Train, *(General Electric Co., Technical Promotion & Training Services; 0-932078),* 1 River Rd., Bldg. 22, Rm. 232, Box MK, Schenectady, NY 12345 (SAN 206-9911).

GE Train & Ed
See GE Tech Prom & Train

Geal T Pubns Inc
See Thomas Geale

Geankoplis, *(Geankoplis, Christie J.; 0-9603070),* 101 W. 35th St., Minneapolis, MN 55408 (SAN 209-5629) Tel 612-625-1586; Dist. by: Ohio State Univ. Bookstores, 1315 Kinnear Rd., Columbus, OH 43212 (SAN 209-5637) Tel 614-422-2991.

Gearhart-Edwards, *(Gearhart-Edwards Press),* 2917 N. Summit Ave., Milwaukee, WI 53211 (SAN 214-0217).

Geary L Baese, *(Baese, Geary L.; 0-9615510),* 610 W. Mountain Ave., Ft. Collins, CO 80521 (SAN 696-0588) Tel 303-221-5802.

Gebbie Pr, *(Gebbie Pr.),* P.O. Box 1000, New Paltz, NY 12561 (SAN 226-5443) Tel 914-255-7560.

GEC Research, *(GEC Research Pr.; 0-939525),* Div. of GEC Research, Box 3053, Santa Barbara, CA 93130 (SAN 658-8182) Tel 805-687-5480.

Gecko Pr *Imprint of* **EJP Pub Co**

GED Inst, *(GED Institute; 0-937128),* G St. NW, Waterville, WA 98858 (SAN 276-945X).

Gee Tee Bee, *(Gee Tee Bee; 0-917232),* 11901 Sunset Blvd., No. 102, Los Angeles, CA 90049 (SAN 206-9652) Tel 213-476-2622.

Gehry Pr, *(Gehry Pr.; 0-935020),* 1319 Pine St., Iowa City, IA 52240 (SAN 213-0629).

Geistenblumen
See R J Diefendorf

Symbols/Abbreviations

Gekko Press, *(Gekko Pr.; 0-9616903),* 10745 Molony Rd., Culver City, CA 90230 (SAN 661-5147) Tel 213-824-4507.

Gem City Coll, *(Gem City College Pr.; 0-910222),* 700 State St., P.O. Box 179, Quincy, IL 62306 (SAN 202-4004) Tel 217-222-0391.

GEM McCuen Pubns
See G E McCuen Pubns

Gem O Lite, *(Gem-O-Lite Plastics Co.; 0-911888),* P.O. Box 985, N. Hollywood, CA 91603 (SAN 203-4204) Tel 213-877-3491.

Gem Pr, *(Gem Press; 0-9613554),* 731 Preston Ave, Lewiston, ID 83501 (SAN 669-8255) Tel 208-743-7422.

Gem Pubns, *(Gem Pubns.; 0-941832),* P.O. Box 2499, Melbourne, FL 32902 (SAN 239-2143) Tel 305-727-3034.

Gemaia Pr, *(Gemaia Press; 0-9602232),* 209 Wilcox Lane, Sequim, WA 98382 (SAN 212-4238).

Gemak Pub, *(Gemak Publishing; 0-9608742),* 3084 S. Gavilan, Las Vegas, NV 89122 (SAN 262-0278) Tel 702-458-1770.

Gembooks, *(Gembooks; 0-910652),* 3677 San Gabriel Pkwy., Pico Rivera, CA 90660 (SAN 201-5943).

Gemfield Assn, *(Gemfield Assn., Inc.; 0-9614845),* P.O. Box 610092, North Miami, FL 33161-0092 (SAN 693-1154) Tel 305-893-6223.

Gemini Music *Imprint of* **Pilgrim NY**

Gemini Pr, *(Gemini Press; 0-9601690),* 625 Pennsylvania Ave., Oakmont, PA 15139 (SAN 211-4933) Tel 412-828-3315.

Gemini Pub Co, *(Gemini Publishing Co.; 0-937164),* 11543 Gullwood Dr., Houston, TX 77089 (SAN 215-2460) Tel 713-484-2424.

Gemini Pub NY, *(Gemini Publications; 0-9613030),* 177-31 Edgerton Rd., Jamaica, NY 11432 (SAN 293-9711) Tel 718-380-1787; Dist. by: American Networking Resources, 177-31 Edgerton Rd., Jamaica Estates, NY 11432 (SAN 662-7579) Tel 718-380-1787.

Gemini Pubns TX, *(Gemini Pubns.; 0-938427),* P.O. Box 60328, San Angelo, TX 76906 (SAN 661-2903); 3206 Grandview Dr., San Angelo, TX 76904 (SAN 661-2911) Tel 915-944-7262. Do not confuse with Gemini Pubns., St. Lukes, MO, New York, NY.

Gemini Smith, *(Gemini Smith, Inc.; 0-935022),* 5858 Desert View Dr., La Jolla, CA 92037 (SAN 212-6125) Tel 619-454-4321.

Gemmeg Pr, *(Gemmeg Pr.; 0-9608076),* P.O. Box 322, Parkville Sta., Brooklyn, NY 11204 (SAN 240-4796) Tel 718-259-5379.

Gemological, *(Gemological Institute of America; 0-87311),* 1660 Stewart St., Santa Monica, CA 90404 (SAN 203-4212) Tel 213-829-2991.

Gems N Gold Pub, *(Gems 'n' Gold Publishing Co.; 0-9614846),* P.O. Box 6577, Marietta, GA 30065-6577 (SAN 693-0263).

Gemstone Bks *Imprint of* **Dillon**

Gen Aviation Pr, *(General Aviation Press),* P.O. Box 110918, Carrollton, TX 75011 (SAN 212-9078) Tel 214-446-2502; Dist. by: Airways Supply, P.O. Box 810469, Dallas, TX 75381 (SAN 200-5182) Tel 213-240-1771.

Gen Comm Arch, *(General Commission on Archives & History),* 36 Madison Ave., P.O. Box 127, Madison, NJ 07940 (SAN 240-9410) Tel 201-822-2787.

Gen Comm Co, *(General Communications Co. of America; 0-914761),* 720 W. 8th St., Los Angeles, CA 90017 (SAN 655-4504).

Gen Hall, *(General Hall, Inc.; 0-930390),* 5 Talon Way, Dix Hills, NY 11746 (SAN 211-1306) Tel 516-243-0155.

GEN Pubns, *(GEN Pubns.; 0-914225),* P.O. Box 291189, Los Angeles, CA 90029 (SAN 287-5012) Tel 213-413-3264.

Gen Syst Sci, *(General Systems Science Corp.; 0-938235),* 2611 Terrace View, Arcata, CA 95521 (SAN 661-4299) Tel 707-839-2861.

Gen Tech Serv, *(General Technical Services, Inc.; 0-914780),* 1200 Lincoln Rd., Prospect Park, PA 19076 (SAN 201-5951) Tel 215-522-1500.

Gen Welfare
See Psychogenic Disease

Gen Welfare Pubns, *(General Welfare Publications; 0-87312),* Box 19098, Sacramento, CA 95819 (SAN 240-4753) Tel 916-677-1610.

Genaway, *(Genaway & Assocs., Inc.; 0-943970),* 530 W. Regency Circle, P.O. Box 477, Canfield, OH 44406 (SAN 241-3833). Trade name: Business Technical Information Service.

Gene Press, *(Gene Pr.; 0-939087),* 18 Donald Pl., Elizabeth, NJ 07208 (SAN 662-9121) Tel 201-353-1655.

Genealog Assn SW, *(Genealogical Assn. of Southwestern Michigan, Dept. C),* P.O. Box 573, St. Joseph, MI 49085 (SAN 223-0364) Tel 616-429-7914.

Genealog Inst, *(Genealogical Institute; 0-940764),* P.O. Box 22045, Salt Lake City, UT 84122 (SAN 662-0175) Tel 801-532-3327; Dist. by: Family History World, P.O. Box 22045, Salt Lake City, UT 84122 (SAN 282-6402).

†Genealog Pub, *(Genealogical Publishing Co., Inc.; 0-8063),* 1001 N. Calvert St., Baltimore, MD 21202 (SAN 206-8370) Tel 301-837-8271; *CIP.*

Genealog Sources, *(Genealogical Sources, Unlimited; 0-913857),* 407 Regent Ct., Knoxville, TN 37923 (SAN 286-7583) Tel 615-690-7831.

Genealogic Ent, *(Genealogical Enterprises; 0-9616020),* 1140 Windsong Ln., Siesta Key, Sarasota, FL 34242 (SAN 698-147X) Tel 813-349-8001.

General Board, *(General Board of Church and Society of the United Methodist Church; 0-9613222),* 100 Maryland Ave. NE, Washington, DC 20002 (SAN 295-1266) Tel 202-488-5631.

General Comns, *(General Communications, Inc.; 0-939185),* 100 Garfield St., Denver, CO 80206 (SAN 662-8338) Tel 303-322-6400.

General Educ, *(General Education Pubns.; 0-914504),* 99 S. Van Ness Ave., San Francisco, CA 94103 (SAN 209-2182) Tel 415-621-5410.

General Means, *(General Means, Inc.; 0-9608852),* P.O. Box 3546, City of Industry, CA 91744 (SAN 241-0222) Tel 818-336-7763.

General Philatelic *Imprint of* **General Trade**

General Trade, *(General Trade Corp.; 0-88219),* P.O. Box 402, Loveland, CO 80539 (SAN 209-3812) Tel 303-667-1133. *Imprints:* General Philatelic (General Philatelic Corporation).

Generations Pub, *(Generations Publishing Co.; 0-9606392),* 901 Post Oak Ln., Charleston, IL 61920 (SAN 222-9978) Tel 217-258-2568.

Genesee Ctry Mus Pr, *(Genesee Country Museum Pr.; 0-931535),* Flint Hill Rd., Mumford, NY 14511 (SAN 682-2940) Tel 716-538-6822.

Genesis Inc, *(Genesis, Inc.; 0-9615457),* P.O. Box 42403, Pittsburgh, PA 15203 (SAN 696-3978) Tel 412-761-5505.

Genesis Pr, *(Genesis Pr.; 0-9615923),* P.O. Box 66929, Baton Rouge, LA 70896 (SAN 697-0753) Tel 504-769-9627 (SAN 206-8346).

Genesis Project, *(Genesis Project, The; 0-86702),* P.O. Box 37282, Washington, DC 20013 (SAN 216-6747) Tel 703-998-0800.

Genesis Pubns, *(Genesis Pubns., Inc.; 0-904351),* 1613 Spear St. Tower, 1 Market Plaza, San Francisco, CA 94105 (SAN 239-4286). Do not confuse with Genesis Pubns., Standardsville, VA or Genesis Pubns., Inc., Tucson, AZ.

Genesis Pubns AZ
See Gnsis Pubns Tucson

Genesis Pubs Inc, *(Genesis Pubs.; 0-913331),* 8825 Roswell Rd., No. 161, Atlanta, GA 30338-1140 (SAN 283-0914); Dist. by: Llewellyn Pubns., P.O. Box 64383, St. Paul, MN 55101 (SAN 281-9155) Tel 612-291-1970.

Genesis Two, *(Genesis II; 0-9615649),* 99 Bishop Allen Dr., Cambridge, MA 02139 (SAN 696-3994) Tel 617-576-1801.

Geneva Divinity
See Geneva Ministr

Geneva Hist Soc Mus, *(Geneva Historical Society & Museum, The; 0-9613821),* 543 S. Main St., Geneva, NY 14456 (SAN 278-9078) Tel 315-789-5151.

Geneva Ministr, *(Geneva Ministries; 0-939404),* 708 Hamvassy Rd., Tyler, TX 75701 (SAN 216-5759) Tel 214-592-0620.

†Geneva Pr, *(Geneva Pr., The; 0-664),* 925 Chestnut St., Philadelphia, PA 19107 (SAN 215-076X) Tel 215-928-2700; Toll free: 800-523-1631; *CIP.*

Geneva Pr TX
See Geneva Ministr

†Genitron Press, *(Genitron Pr.; 0-915781),* P.O. Box 31391, Seattle, WA 98103 (SAN 293-9746) Tel 206-382-1711; *CIP.*

Genium Pub, *(Genium Publishing Corp.; 0-931690),* 1145 Catalyn St., Schenectady, NY 12303 (SAN 213-5027) Tel 518-377-8855.

Genius Pub, *(Genius Publishing; 0-935925),* 1450 S. Rexford Dr., Los Angeles, CA 90035 (SAN 697-094X) Tel 213-553-8009.

Genl Edu Media, *(General Edu-Media, Inc.; 0-939531),* P.O. Box 1549, Troy, MI 48099 (SAN 663-432X); 4349 Greensboro, Troy, MI 48099 (SAN 663-4338) Tel 313-524-2317.

Genny Smith Bks, *(Genny Smith Bks.; 0-931378),* 1304 Pitman Ave., Palo Alto, CA 94301 (SAN 211-3570) Tel 415-321-7247; Dist. by: William Kaufmann Inc., 95 First St., Los Altos, CA 94022 (SAN 202-9383) Tel 415-948-5810.

†Genotype, *(Genotype; 0-936618),* 15042 Montebello Rd., Cupertino, CA 95014 (SAN 214-3089); *CIP.*

Genova Inc, *(Genova, Inc.; 0-9616509),* 7034 E. Court St., Davison, MI 48423-0309 (SAN 659-4514); Toll free: 800-521-7488; P.O. Box 309, Davison, MI 48423 (SAN 659-4522).

Genre Comms, *(Genre Communications; 0-9610948),* 5697 Xenon Court, Arvada, CO 80002 (SAN 265-2463) Tel 303-425-4214.

Gentle Touch, *(Gentle Touch Pr.; 0-9610894),* P.O. Box 12305, Boulder, CO 80303 (SAN 265-1386) Tel 303-449-7499.

Gentle Wind, *(A Gentle Wind; 0-939065),* P.O. Box 3103, Albany, NY 12203; 186 Partridge St., Albany, NY 12203 Tel 518-482-9023.

Gentle World, *(Gentle World, Inc.; 0-9614248),* P.O. Box 1418, Umatilla, FL 32784 (SAN 686-7448) Tel 904-669-2822; Dist. by: New Leaf, 1020 White St., SW, Atlanta, GA 30310 (SAN 169-1449) Tel 404-755-2665; Dist. by: Nutri-Books Corp., P.O. Box 5793, Denver, CO 80223 (SAN 169-054X) Tel 303-778-8383.

Gentrace Assocs, *(Gentrace Assocs., Inc.; 0-936065),* 2810 Babe Ruth Dr., San Jose, CA 95132 (SAN 697-080X) Tel 408-923-7885.

Genun Pubs, *(Genun Pubs.; 0-912811),* Div. of Genealogy Unlimited Inc., 789 S. Buffalo Grove Rd., Buffalo Grove, IL 60089 (SAN 282-7700) Tel 312-541-3175.

Geo Space, *(Geo-Space Research Foundation; 0-936961),* 4120 Rio Bravo, No. 104, El Paso, TX 79902 (SAN 658-649X) Tel 915-532-1136.

Geo Speleo Pubns, *(Geo Speleo Pubns.; 0-9613107),* P.O. Box 52, East Texas, PA 18046 (SAN 294-0124) Tel 215-683-4367.

Geo U Kennedy Inst, *(Georgetown Univ., Kennedy Institute of Ethics; 0-9614448),* Georgetown Univ., Washington, DC 20057 (SAN 689-3775) Tel 202-625-8709.

Geo U Sch For Serv, *(Georgetown Univ., Schl. of Foreign Service; 0-934742),* Georgetown Univ., Institute for the Study of Diplomacy, Washington, DC 20057 (SAN 221-1580) Tel 202-625-3784. *Imprints:* Inst Study Diplomacy (Institute for the Study of Diplomacy); Sch For Serv (School of Foreign Service).

GeoApp Pub Co, *(GeoApp Publishing Co.; 0-9615842),* Appalachian State Univ., Geography Dept., Boone, NC 28608 (SAN 697-0966) Tel 704-262-3001.

Geographics, *(Geographics; 0-930722),* Box 133, Easton, CT 06612 (SAN 211-1810).

Geol Soc, *(Geological Society of America, Inc.; 0-8137),* P.O. Box 9140, 3300 Penrose Pl., Boulder, CO 80301 (SAN 201-5978).

Geologic Pubns, *(Geologic Pubns),* Div. of Geology & Earth Resources, Department of Natural Resources, Olympia, WA 98504 (SAN 240-0936).

Geophysical Inst, *(Geophysical Institute; 0-915360),* Univ. of Alaska, 611 C. T. Elvey Bldg., Fairbanks, AK 99701 (SAN 216-2482) Tel 907-474-7798.

Geopolymer Inst, *(Geopolymer Institute, The),* 16863 Lenore, Detroit, MI 48219 (SAN 663-3048) Tel 313-592-0216; Dist. by: US Distribution Ctr., 13119 Glenfield, Detroit, MI 48213 (SAN 289-145X).

Geoprint, *(Geoprint, Inc.; 0-9616454),* 11431 W. River Hills Dr., Burnsville, MN 55337 (SAN 659-2368) Tel 612-890-0110; Dist. by: Bookmen, 525 N. 3rd St., Minneapolis, MN 55401 (SAN 169-409X); Dist. by: Pacific Trade Group, P.O. Box 668, Pearl City, HI 96782-0668 (SAN 169-1635).

George Sand, *(Sand, George, , Books; 0-942498),* 9011 Melrose Ave., Los Angeles, CA 90069 (SAN 239-6084) Tel 213-858-1648.

Georgetown Herit, *(Georgetown Heritage Society; 0-936149),* P.O. Box 467, Georgetown, TX 78627 (SAN 697-0990) Tel 512-863-1980; 109 E. Eighth St., Georgetown, TX 78626 (SAN 697-1008).

Georgetown Pr, *(Georgetown Pr.; 0-914558),* 483 Francisco St., San Francisco, CA 94133 (SAN 206-7463) Tel 415-397-4753.

†**Georgetown U Pr,** *(Georgetown Univ. Pr.; 0-87840),* Intercultural Ctr., Rm. 111, Washington, DC 20057 (SAN 203-4247) Tel 202-625-8041; *CIP.*

Georgian Intl, *(Georgian International, Ltd., Inc.; 0-9611392),* P.O. Box 24346, Fort Lauderdale, FL 33307 (SAN 285-3035); 2725 Center Ave., Fort Lauderdale, FL 33308 (SAN 662-2054) Tel 305-564-1011.

†**Georgian Pr,** *(Georgian Pr. Co., The; 0-9603408),* 2620 SW Georgian Pl., Portland, OR 97201 (SAN 213-9766) Tel 503-223-9899; Dist. by: Pacific Pipeline, Inc., 19215 66th Ave., S., Kent, WA 98032 (SAN 208-2128) Tel 206-872-5523; *CIP.*

Geosci Info, *(Geoscience Information Society; 0-934485),* c/o American Geological Institute, 4220 King St., Alexandria, VA 22302 (SAN 266-8467).

Geoscience Analytical, *(Geoscience Analytical; 0-941054),* Chemistry UCLA, Los Angeles, CA 90024 (SAN 217-3670) Tel 213-825-7675.

Geotech Engineer Prog, *(Colorado State Univ., Geotechnical Engineering Program; 0-910069),* Dept. of Civil Engineering, Ft. Collins, CO 80523 (SAN 241-3272) Tel 303-491-6081.

Geothermal, *(Geothermal Resources Council; 0-934412),* P.O. Box 1350, Davis, CA 95617-1350 (SAN 213-0637); 111 G St., Suite 28, Davis, CA 95616 (SAN 669-0874) Tel 916-758-2360.

Geothermal World, *(Geothermal World Publishers),* 5762 Firebird Court, Mission Oaks, Camarillo, CA 93010 (SAN 226-2061) Tel 805-482-6288.

Geraventure, *(Geraventure Corp.; 0-938524),* P.O. Box 2131, Melbourne, FL 32902-2131 (SAN 216-0331).

Gerecor, *(Gerecor, Ltd.; 0-935613),* 232 Madison Ave., New York, NY 10016 (SAN 696-401X) Tel 212-725-2350.

Geri-Rehab, *(Geri-Rehab, Inc.; 0-941930),* Box 170, Hibbler Rd., Lebanon, NJ 08833 (SAN 239-4383) Tel 201-735-8918.

Geriatric Educ, *(Geriatric Educational Consultants; 0-937663),* 43 Middleton Ln., Willingboro, NJ 08046 (SAN 659-2376) Tel 609-877-5972.

Gerisch Pub Co, *(Gerisch Publishing Co.; 0-934201),* 1217 David Whitney Bldg., Detroit, MI 48226 (SAN 693-028X) Tel 313-962-3969.

Germainbooks, *(Germainbooks; 0-914142),* 91 St. Germain Ave., San Francisco, CA 94114 (SAN 201-5986) Tel 415-731-8155.

German Am Chamber, *(German American Chamber of Commerce, Inc.; 0-86640),* 666 Fifth Ave., New York, NY 10103 (SAN 216-3845).

Gernshack *Imprint of* **TAB Bks**

Geron-X, *(Geron-X, Inc.; 0-87672),* P.O. Box 1108, Los Altos, CA 94023-1108 (SAN 201-5994) Tel 415-941-1692.

Geronima, *(Geronima Pr.; 0-943164),* 2216 Cliff Dr., Santa Barbara, CA 93109 (SAN 240-7191) Tel 805-966-7563.

Gerontological Soc, *(Gerontological Society of America),* 1411 K St. NW, Suite 300, Washington, DC 20005 (SAN 224-2591) Tel 202-393-1411.

Gerosota Pub, *(Gerosota Pubns.; 0-9609126),* 3530 Pine Valley Dr., Sarasota, FL 33579-4335 (SAN 241-5046) Tel 813-924-3251.

Gestalt Journal, *(Gestalt Journal; 0-939266),* P.O. Box 990, Highland, NY 12528 (SAN 216-5317) Tel 914-691-7192.

Getal, *(Getal Inc.; 0-916131),* P.O. Box 25242, Portland, OR 97225 (SAN 294-9326) Tel 503-292-3201.

Getwell Church, *(Getwell Church of Christ; 0-9615751),* 1511 Getwell Rd., Memphis, TN 38111 (SAN 696-4397) Tel 901-743-0464.

†**GFI Assocs,** *(GFI Assocs.; 0-915309),* Div. of The Republic Group, 5801 Lee Hwy., Arlington, VA 22207 (SAN 289-985X) Tel 703-533-8555; P.O. Box 408, Middleburg, VA 22117 (SAN 662-2208) Tel 703-327-4866; Dist. by: Frederick Fell Pubs., 2500 Hollywood Blvd., Suite 302, Hollywood, FL 33020 (SAN 208-2365) Tel 305-925-5242; Dist. by: Kampmann & Co., 9 E. 40th St., New York, NY 10016 (SAN 202-5191) Tel 212-685-2928; *CIP.*

GGL Educ Press, *(GGL Educational Pr.; 0-915751),* 2555 E. Chapman, Suite 606, Fullerton, CA 92631 (SAN 293-9665) Tel 714-525-1256.

GHA Pubns, *(G.H.A. Pubns.; 0-9614441),* 603 Fifth Ave., Juniata, Altoona, PA 16601 (SAN 689-0695) Tel 814-942-9855.

GHC, *(GHC Business Bks.; 0-9609046),* Div. of GHC Sales, 4214 N. Post Rd., Omaha, NE 68112 (SAN 241-3183) Tel 402-453-1769; P.O. Box 299, Fort Calhoun, NE 68023 (SAN 662-0264).

Ghirardelli Choc, *(Ghirardelli Chocolate Co.; 0-9610218),* 1111 139th Ave., San Leandro, CA 94578 (SAN 270-5028) Tel 415-483-6970.

Ghosh A, *(Ghosh, A.; 0-9611614),* 5720 W. Little York, Suite 216, Houston, TX 77091 (SAN 285-2780) Tel 713-445-5526.

Ghost Dance, *(Ghost Dance Pr.; 0-939520),* ATL EBH MSU, East Lansing, MI 48824 (SAN 207-8317) Tel 517-351-5977.

Ghost Pony Pr, *(Ghost Pony Pr.; 0-941160),* 2518 Gregory St., Madison, WI 53711 (SAN 237-9546) Tel 608-238-0175; Dist. by: Small Pr. Distribution, Inc., 1816 San Pablo Ave., Berkeley, CA 94702 (SAN 204-5826) Tel 415-549-3336.

Ghost Town, *(Ghost Town Pubns.; 0-933818),* P.O. Drawer 5998, Carmel, CA 93921 (SAN 209-4401) Tel 408-373-2885.

GIA Pubns, *(G.I.A. Pubns., Inc.),* 7404 S. Mason Ave., Chicago, IL 60638 (SAN 205-3217) Tel 312-496-3800.

Giant Poplar Pr, *(Giant Poplar Pr.; 0-9616536),* 452 Sylva Hwy., Franklin, NC 28734 (SAN 659-4530) Tel 704-369-6486.

Gibbelin's Gazatte, *(Gibbelins Gazatte Pubns./Silver EEL Pr., The; 0-9610452),* 3217-G Whisper Lake, Winter Park, FL 32792 (SAN 264-0589) Tel 305-657-2236.

†**Gibbs M Smith,** *(Smith, Gibbs M., Inc.; 0-87905),* P.O. Box 667, Layton, UT 84041 (SAN 201-9906) Tel 801-554-9800; Toll free: 800-421-8714; *CIP. Imprints:* Falcon Bks (Falcon Books); Peregrine Smith (Peregrine Smith Books).

Gibbs Pub NH
See Gibbs Pub OH

Gibbs Pub OH, *(Gibbs Publishing Co.; 0-932027),* P.O. Box 2345, Toledo, OH 43603 (SAN 212-2138) Tel 419-592-4581.

Gibraltar, *(Gibraltar Pr.; 0-9606284),* P.O. Box 121425, Nashville, TN 37212 (SAN 216-3853); 171 Fuller St., Brookline, MA 02146 (SAN 216-3861).

Gibson, *(Gibson, C. R., Co.; 0-8378),* 32 Knight St., Norwalk, CT 06856 (SAN 201-5765) Tel 203-847-4543; Toll free: 800-243-6004; Dist. by: C.R. Gibson, Distribution Ctr., Beacon Falls, CT 06403 (SAN 281-7462).

Gibson Hiller, *(Gibson-Hiller Co.; 0-918892),* P.O. Box 22, Dayton, OH 45406 (SAN 210-427X) Tel 513-277-2427.

Gick, *(Gick Publishing Co.; 0-918170),* 9 Studebaker Dr., Irvine, CA 92714 (SAN 209-6641) Tel 714-581-5830.

Giddings Studio Pub, *(Giddings Studio Publishing; 0-9615226),* 2700 Wakonda Dr., Ft. Collins, CO 80521 (SAN 695-1406) Tel 303-484-5028; Dist. by: Vet Text, Colorado State Univ., Veterinary Teaching Hospital, Fort Collins, CO 80523 (SAN 200-7150) Tel 303-491-7101.

Gielow, *(Gielow, Fred C.; 0-9603938),* 110 Crestview Ct., Cary, NC 27511 (SAN 215-0778) Tel 914-254-0639.

Giffard Pubns, *(Giffard Pubns.; 0-937411),* 11011 SW 117th Ave., Miami, FL 33176 (SAN 658-8697) Tel 305-596-3460.

Gifford F L, *(Gifford, Frederick L; 0-9613464),* 52 W. Main St., Clifton Springs, NY 14432 (SAN 692-9826).

Gift Pubns, *(Gift Pubns.; 0-86595),* 3150 Bear St., Costa Mesa, CA 92626 (SAN 216-387X).

Gifted Child Prog, *(Gifted Child Program),* P.O. Box 2503, Berkeley, CA 94702 (SAN 670-7033).

Gifted Educ Pr, *(Gifted Education Pr.),* 10201 Yuma Ct., Manassas, VA 22110 (SAN 694-132X) Tel 703-369-5017; P.O. Box 1586, Manassas, VA 22110 (SAN 658-280X).

Gilbert Res, *(Gilbert Research; 0-937975),* Div. of Don Gilbert Industries, Inc., P.O. Box 2188, Jonesboro, AR 72402 (SAN 659-5049) Tel 501-932-6070; 5611 Krueger Dr., Jonesboro, AR 72402 (SAN 659-5057).

Gilchem Corp, *(Gilchem Corp.; 0-917122),* Woodlawn Rd., Suite 112, Bldg. 3, Woodlawn Green, Box 11291, Charlotte, NC 28209 (SAN 208-659X) Tel 704-523-2889.

Gilfer, *(Gilfer Assocs., Inc.; 0-914542),* P.O. Box 239, Park Ridge, NJ 07656 (SAN 208-3981) Tel 201-391-7887.

Gilgal Pubns, *(Gilgal Pubns.; 0-916895),* P.O. Box 3386, Sunriver, OR 97707 (SAN 655-8801) Tel 503-593-8639.

Gilgamesh Pr IL, *(Gilgamesh Pr. Ltd.; 0-936684),* 1059 W. Ardmore Ave., Chicago, IL 60660 (SAN 219-9882) Tel 312-334-0327.

Gilgamesh Pub, *(Gilgamesh Publishing Co.; 0-914246),* 6050 Blvd. East, West New York, NJ 07093 (SAN 203-6916).

Giligia, *(Giligia Pr.; 0-87791),* P.O. Box 126, East Chatham, NY 12002 (SAN 203-4255) Tel 518-312-3793.

Gillespie Co, *(Gillespie & Co.; 0-9616404),* P.O. Box 2376, Daly City, CA 94017 (SAN 658-8735) Tel 415-755-5123.

Gilmar Pr, *(Gilmar Enterprises; 0-936402),* P.O. Box 597, Newcastle, CA 95658 (SAN 214-2430).

Gilmore City, *(Gilmore City Centennial Committee; 0-89279),* c/o Mrs. Eugene Dunn, Box 393, Gilmore City, IA 50541 (SAN 655-1750).

Gim-Ho, *(Gim-Ho Enterprises; 0-9615006),* 5781 Calaveras Cir., La Palma, CA 90623 (SAN 692-3038) Tel 714-531-4108.

Gimbaling Gourmet, *(Gimbaling Gourmet Pr.; 0-9617263),* P.O. Box 4264, Annapolis, MD 21403 (SAN 663-5644); 11C President Point Dr., Annapolis, MD 21403 (SAN 663-5652) Tel 301-267-8511.

Ginger Jolley, *(Jolley, Ginger; 0-9616228),* P.O. Box 156, Rim Forest, CA 92378 (SAN 658-5523) Tel 714-337-4991; 26375 Apache Trail, Rim Forest, CA 92378 (SAN 658-5531).

Gingerbread *Imprint of* **Dutton**

Giniger, *(Giniger, K. S., Co., Inc.; 0-934025),* 1133 Broadway, Suite 1301, New York, NY 10010 (SAN 201-8381) Tel 212-645-5150; Orders to: Regnery Gateway Distributors, 940-950- North Shore Dr., Lake Bluff, IL 60044 (SAN 662-0183) Tel 312-295-8088.

Ginkgo Hut, *(Ginkgo Hut; 0-936620),* 13 Augusta Dr., Lincroft, NJ 07738 (SAN 215-3157) Tel 201-530-9572.

Ginn Custom
See Ginn Pr

Ginn Pr, *(Ginn Pr.; 0-536),* Div. of Ginn & Co., 191 Spring St., Lexington, MA 02173 (SAN 214-0225) Tel 617-863-2700; Toll free: 800-848-9500.

Ginseng Pr, *(Ginseng Pr.; 0-932800),* 74 Poplar Grove Rd., Franklin, NC 28734 (SAN 211-4224) Tel 704-369-9735.

Ginseng Res Inst, *(Ginseng Research Institute; 0-9613800),* P.O. Box 42, Roxbury, NY 12474 (SAN 679-419X) Tel 607-326-7888.

Giordano-Webb, (Giordano-Webb Pubns.; 0-935795), P.O. Box 1668, Bakersfield, CA 93302 (SAN 697-1377) Tel 805-325-9431; 1930 Truxtun Ave., Bakersfield, CA 93301 (SAN 697-1385).

Giorgi, (Giorgi; 0-9614222), 4168 Woodland St., Santa Maria, CA 93455 (SAN 686-807X) Tel 805-937-3518.

Giorno Poetry, (Giorno Poetry Systems), 222 Bowery, New York, NY 10012 (SAN 207-8325) Tel 212-925-6372.

Giovanni's Tour, (Giovanni's Tours, Inc.; 0-9612528), P.O. Box 24, Agoura, CA 91301 (SAN 297-1763).

Girl Scouts USA, (Girl Scouts of the USA; 0-88441), 830 Third Ave., New York, NY 10022 (SAN 203-4611) Tel 212-940-7500.

Girls Clubs Amer
See Advocacy Pr

Girs Pr, (Girs Press), Streeter Hill Rd., West Chesterfield, NH 03466 (SAN 206-202X) Tel 603-256-8484; Orders to: P.O. Box 91, West Chesterfield, NH 03466 (SAN 206-2038).

Girtman Pr, (Girtman Pr.; 0-9616220), 1900 Hollyoaks Lake Rd., E, Jacksonville, FL 32211 (SAN 658-5388) Tel 904-641-9751.

†Gita-Nagari, (Gita-Nagari Pr.; 0-911233), 10310 Oaklyn Rd., Potomac, MD 20854 (SAN 262-8759) Tel 301-983-3386; CIP.

GLA Pr
See Yellow Rose Pr

†Glacier Nat Hist Assn, (Glacier Natural History Assn., Inc.; 0-916792), Glacier National Park, West Glacier, MT 59936 (SAN 208-6603) Tel 406-888-5441; CIP.

Glanville, (Glanville Pubs., Inc.; 0-87802), Div. of Ocean Group, 75 Main St., Dobbs Ferry, NY 10522 (SAN 201-6478) Tel 914-693-1733.

Glass Art, (Glass Art Pubns.; 0-9608356), P.O. Box 2244, Van Nuys, CA 91404 (SAN 240-6594) Tel 818-769-6410.

Glass Pub Co, (Glass Publishing Co.; 0-9614759), 8711 Village Dr., Suite 112, San Antonio, TX 78217 (SAN 676-5947) Tel 512-653-9555.

Glass Tempering, (Glass Tempering Assn.), 3310 Harrison St., Topeka, KS 66611 (SAN 224-7739).

Glass Works, (Glass Works Press; 0-934280), P.O. Box 81782, San Diego, CA 92138 (SAN 207-2297) Tel 619-563-8165.

Glassbooks Mo, (Glassbooks; 0-913074), Rte. 1, Box 357a, Ozark, MO 65721 (SAN 237-9554).

Glassman Pub
See B Glassman

Glastonbury Pr, (Glastonbury Pr.; 0-932145), 12816 E. Rose Dr., Whittier, CA 90601 (SAN 686-4309) Tel 213-698-4243; Dist. by: Publishers Group West, 5855 Beaudry St., Emeryville, CA 94608 (SAN 202-8522) Tel 415-658-3453; Dist. by: Quality Books, Inc., 918 Sherwood Dr., Lake Bluff, IL 60044-2204 (SAN 169-2704) Tel 312-498-4000.

Glen-Bartlett, (Glen-Bartlett Publishing Co.; 0-9602802), 105 W. Main St., Westboro, MA 01581 (SAN 213-0645) Tel 617-366-7669.

Glen Hse, (Glen Hse. Communications; 0-918269), Subs. of Stanley Chase Productions, Inc., 1937 S. Beverly Glen Blvd., Los Angeles, CA 90025 (SAN 657-257X) Tel 213-475-4236.

Glen-L Marine, (Glen-L Marine Design), 9152 Rosecrans, Bellflower, CA 90706 (SAN 203-428X) Tel 213-630-6258.

Glen Pr, (Glen Pr.; 0-9603518), 2247 Glen Ave., Berkeley, CA 94709 (SAN 215-7667).

Glencoe, (Glencoe Publishing Co.; 0-02), Affil. of Macmillan Publishing Co., 17337 Ventura Blvd., Encino, CA 91316 (SAN 201-6451) Tel 818-990-3080; Toll free: 800-257-5755.

Glendale Advent Med
See Cum Index Nursing

Glendessary
See Boyd & Fraser

Glenhurst Pubns, (Glenhurst Pubns., Inc.; 0-914227), Central Community Ctr., 6300 Walker St., St. Louis Park, MN 55416 (SAN 295-365X) Tel 612-925-3632.

Glenmary Res Ctr, (Glenmary Research Ctr.; 0-914422), 750 Piedmont Ave., NE, Atlanta, GA 30308 (SAN 201-6443) Tel 404-876-6518.

Glenn Educ Med, (Glenn Educational Medical Services, Inc.; 0-937449), P.O. Box 690028, Houston, TX 77269-0028 (SAN 658-876X) Tel 713-586-9056; 176 Old Bridge Lake, Houston, TX 77069 (SAN 658-8778).

Glenn-Ryan Pub, (Glenn-Ryan Publishing; 0-936963), 1729 Bette, Mesquite, TX 75149 (SAN 658-6538) Tel 214-222-8409.

Glenn Vargas, (Vargas, Glenn; 0-917646), 85-159 Ave. 66, Thermal, CA 92274 (SAN 203-4301) Tel 619-397-4264.

Glenndale Bks Imprint of Capstan Pubns

Glennon Pub, (Glennon Publishing Co.; 0-918523), 636 23rd St., Manhattan Beach, CA 90266 (SAN 657-3452) Tel 213-545-4349.

Glenson Pub, (Glenson Publishing; 0-934884), P.O. Box 298, Sterling Heights, MI 48077 (SAN 214-378X).

GLGLC Music, (GLGLC Music; 0-9607558; 0-932303), Subs. of La Costa Music Consultants, P.O. Box 147, Cardiff by the Sea, CA 92007 (SAN 238-6194) Tel 619-436-7219.

Glide
See Volcano Pr

Global Acad Pubs, (Global Academic Pubs.; 1-55633), Div. of Eden Cross, 234 Fifth Ave., New York, NY 10001 (SAN 661-3276); Dist. by: Inland Bk. Co., P.O. Box 261, 22 Hemingway Ave., East Haven, CT 06512 (SAN 200-4151) Tel 203-467-4257.

Global Bks, (Global Bks.; 0-9617235), P.O. Box 2025, Gaithersburg, MD 20879 (SAN 663-5539); 10747 Wayridge Dr., Gaithersburg, MD 20879 (SAN 663-5547) Tel 301-869-1888.

Global Church
See Overseas Crusade

Global Comm, (Global Communications; 0-938294), 316 Fifth Ave., New York, NY 10001 (SAN 216-3896) Tel 212-685-4080; Orders to: Box 753, New Brunswick, NJ 08903 (SAN 662-0191).

Global Eng, (Global Engineering Documents; 0-912702), Div. of Information Handling Services, 2625 Hickory St., P.O. Box 2504, Santa Ana, CA 92707 (SAN 205-2873) Tel 714-540-9870; Toll free: 800-854-7179.

Global Games, (Global Games, Inc.; 0-9616154), E. 8112 Sprague Ave., Spokane, WA 99212 (SAN 699-8496) Tel 509-927-0555.

Global Man, (Global Management, Inc.; 0-935871), P.O. Box 975, Mathews, VA 23109 (SAN 696-4400) Tel 804-725-7795; R.D. Box 107A, Mathews County, Newpoint, VA 23125 (SAN 696-9712).

Global Perspectives, (Global Perspectives in Education), 218 E. 18th St., New York, NY 10003 (SAN 236-364X) Tel 212-674-4167.

Global Pr CO, (Global Pr., The; 0-911285), 1510 York St., Suite 204, Denver, CO 80206 (SAN 263-1059) Tel 303-393-7647.

Global Pubns CA, (Global Pubns.; 0-9604752), P.O. Box 2112, Palm Springs, CA 92263 (SAN 215-2207) Tel 619-323-4204.

Global Pubns WI
See Global Pubns CA

Global Risk, (Global Risk Assessments, Inc.; 0-914325), 3638 University Ave., Suite 215, Riverside, CA 92501 (SAN 287-4806) Tel 714-788-0672.

Global Studies Ctr, (Global Studies Ctr., The; 0-937585), 1611 N. Kent St., Suite 600, Arlington, VA 22209 (SAN 658-8794) Tel 703-841-0048.

Globe Pequot, (Globe Pequot Pr.; 0-87106), Subs. of Boston Globe, Old Chester Rd., Chester, CT 06412 (SAN 201-9892) Tel 203-526-9572; Toll free: 800-243-0495 Orders only; P.O. Box Q, Chester, CT 06412 (SAN 658-0769) Tel 203-526-9572; Toll free: 800-962-0973 (CT only).

Globe Pr, (Globe Pr., The; 0-910321), 18803 N. Park Blvd., Cleveland, OH 44122 (SAN 241-5062).

Globe Pr Bks, (Globe Pr. Bks.; 0-936385), P.O. Box 2045, Madison Sq. Sta., New York, NY 10159 (SAN 697-3523) Tel 212-807-7540.

Globe Three, (Globe Three, Inc.; 0-934647), P.O. Box 265, Middletown, OH 45042 (SAN 694-0293) Tel 513-422-4155.

Globus Pubs, (Globus Pubs.; 0-88669), P.O. Box 27086, San Francisco, CA 94127 (SAN 265-1416); 332 Balboa St., San Francisco, CA 94118 (SAN 265-1424) Tel 415-668-4723. deceased.

Gloria Pubs, (Gloria Pubs.; 0-9604080), 2489 East Lake Rd., Livonia, NY 14487 (SAN 221-6132).

Glorycliff Pub, (Glorycliff Publishing Co.; 0-938571), 4325 Hwy. 91 N., Dillon, MT 59725 (SAN 661-6224) Tel 406-683-5219.

†Gloucester Art, (Gloucester Art Pr.; 0-930582; 0-86650), P.O. Box 4526, Albuquerque, NM 87196 (SAN 205-2865); 607 McKnight St., NW, Albuquerque, NM 87102 (SAN 662-0205) Tel 505-843-7749; CIP.

Gloucester Cres, (Gloucester Crescent; 0-931151), 961 Pheasant Run Dr., Spring Valley, OH 45370 (SAN 670-6681) Tel 513-885-4764.

Gloucester Pr Imprint of Watts

Glover Pubns, (Glover Pubns.; 0-9602328), P.O. Box 21745, Seattle, WA 98111 (SAN 221-8275).

Gloy Enter, (Gloy Enterprises; 0-9616051), 4336 Market, Suite 504, Riverside, CA 92501 (SAN 698-0716) Tel 714-683-2850.

Gluten Co, (Gluten Co., Inc., The; 0-935596), 509 E. 2100 N., Box 482, Provo, UT 84604 (SAN 213-0653) Tel 801-377-6390.

Glyndwr Resc, (Glyndwr Resources; 0-937505), 43779 Valley Rd., Decatur, MI 49045 (SAN 658-8832) Tel 616-423-8639.

Glynn Pubns, (Glynn Pubns.; 0-9616342), P.O. Box 38, Donaldson, IN 46513 (SAN 658-781X) Tel 219-936-3385; 20893 Ninth Rd., Plymouth, IN 46563 (SAN 658-7828).

Glyphic Pr, (Glyphic Pr.; 0-935962), 665 Killarney Dr., Morgantown, WV 26505 (SAN 213-9235) Tel 304-599-3659.

GM Imprint of Fawcett

GMG Pub
See Galison

GMI Pubns Inc, (GMI Pubns., Inc.; 0-937408), P.O. Box 16824, Jacksonville, FL 32216 (SAN 215-2479) Tel 904-359-2427.

GNK Pr, (GNK Pr.; 0-9609266), Div. of Good Natured Kitchen, 453 Half Hollow Rd., Dix Hills, NY 11746 (SAN 260-0587) Tel 516-271-9565.

Gnomon Pr, (Gnomon Pr.; 0-917788), P.O. Box 106, Frankfort, KY 40602-0106 (SAN 209-0104) Tel 502-223-1858.

Gnosis Pubns, (Gnosis Pubns.; 0-940988), 1440 Tyler Ave., San Diego, CA 92103 (SAN 223-7709) Tel 619-296-1628.

Gnsis Pubns Tucson, (Genesis Pubns., Inc.; 0-936633), 2509 N. Campbell, No. 287, Tuscon, AZ 85719 (SAN 699-7260) Tel 602-795-8751. Do not confuse with Genesis Pubns., Inc. of San Francisco, CA, or Genesis Pubns., Inc. of Standardsville, VA.

GNU, (GNU Publishing; 0-915914), P.O. Box 6820, San Francisco, CA 94101 (SAN 203-5367).

Goal Ent, (Goal Enterprises & Associates; 0-9612350), 6354 N. 11th, Fresno, CA 93710 (SAN 297-1755).

Goat Rock, (Goat Rock Pubns.; 0-9610240), P.O. Box 21, Jenner, CA 95450 (SAN 264-0600) Tel 707-865-2762.

God Unltd-U of Healing
See U of Healing

†Godine, (Godine, David R., Pub., Inc.; 0-87923), 300 Massachusetts Ave., Horticultural Hall, Boston, MA 02115 (SAN 213-4381) Tel 617-536-0761; Dist. by: Harper & Row Pubs., Inc., Keystone Industrial Pk., Scranton, PA 18512 (SAN 215-3742); CIP. Imprints: Double Det (Double Detectives); Godine Storytellers (Godine Storytellers); Nonpareil Bks (Nonpareil Books).(Nonpareil Bks.).

Godine Storytellers Imprint of Godine

Godiva Pub, (Godiva Publishing; 0-938018), P.O. Box 42305, Portland, OR 97242 (SAN 214-3097) Tel 503-233-1228.

Gods Universe, (Gods of the Universe; 0-9607228), P.O. Box 1543, Highland, IN 46322 (SAN 239-0957) Tel 219-924-8200.

Goehringer & Sons, (Goehringer & Sons Associates; 0-9601704), Box 9626, Pittsburgh, PA 15226 (SAN 211-562X) Tel 412-531-9549; 2194 Pauline Ave., Pittsburgh, PA 15216 (SAN 211-5638).

Goethe Pubs, (Goethe, Meredyth, Pubs. Ltd.; 0-9606714), 3200 Lenox Rd., NE, E411, Atlanta, GA 30324 (SAN 223-7636) Tel 404-237-3735. deceased.

Gold Bk, (Gold Book, Publications; 0-915493), P.O. Box 2361, Redding, CA 96099 (SAN 291-171X). *Imprints:* Classic Press (Classic Press).

Gold Circle, (Gold Circle Productions; 0-943986), 10783 Eagle Cir., Nevada City, CA 95959 (SAN 241-3841) Tel 916-265-9218.

Gold Crest, (Gold Crest Publishing; 0-941790), 834 Tyvola Rd., Suite 110, Charlotte, NC 28210 (SAN 239-4294) Tel 704-523-2118.

Gold Door Inc, (Golden Door, Inc.; 0-9610790), P.O. Box 1567, Escondido, CA 92025 (SAN 265-1203) Tel 619-295-5791; 3085 Reynard Way, San Diego, CA 92103 (SAN 265-1211). *Imprints:* Len Forman Pub Co (Len Forman Publishing Co., Inc.).

Gold Hill, (Gold Hill Publishing Co., Inc.; 0-940936), Drawer F, Virginia City, NV 89440 (SAN 217-3697) Tel 702-847-0222.

Gold Horse, (Gold Horse Publishing, Inc.; 0-912823), 1981 Moreland Pkwy., Annapolis, MD 21401 (SAN 285-3957) Tel 301-269-0680.

Gold-Kane Ent, (Gold/Kane Enterprises; 0-9604430), 1580 Garfield St., Denver, CO 80206 (SAN 220-0554) Tel 303-333-9659.

Gold Key Succ, (Golden Keys Success Seminar, Inc.), P.O. Box 9358, Salt Lake City, UT 84109 (SAN 240-852X).

Gold Penny, (Gold Penny Press, The; 0-87786), Box 2177, Canoga Park, CA 91306 (SAN 281-7470) Tel 213-368-1417; Orders to: Associated Booksellers, 147 McKinley Ave., Bridgeport, CT 06606 (SAN 281-7489) Tel 203-366-5494.

†Gold Quill Pubs CA, (Golden Quill Pubs., Inc.; 0-933904), P.O. Box 1278-R, Colton, CA 92324 (SAN 213-0726) Tel 714-783-0119; *CIP.*

Gold R
See Prelude Press

Gold Robes Pr, (Golden Robes Pr.; 0-9616140), P.O. Box 632, Siletz, OR 97380 (SAN 699-9743) Tel 503-444-2778; 5137 Logsden Rd., Siletz, OR 97380 (SAN 699-9751).

Gold Run Pubs, (Gold Run Pubs.; 0-9615975), 4234 Pueblo St., Carmichael, CA 95608 (SAN 697-3558) Tel 916-481-5733.

Gold Rush, (Gold Rush Sourdough Co., Inc.; 0-912936), 122 E. Grand Ave., S. San Francisco, CA 94080 (SAN 203-4336) Tel 415-871-0340.

Gold Star Pr, (Gold Star Pr.; 0-915153), P.O. Box 433, New London, NC 28127 (SAN 289-9337) Tel 704-983-2287.

Gold Star Pubns, (Gold Star Pubns.; 0-941508), P.O. Box 1451, Sioux Falls, SD 57101 (SAN 239-0965) Tel 605-332-4582.

Gold Stein Pr, (Gold Stein Pr.; 0-938237), P.O. Box 12280, Santa Ana, CA 91712-2280 (SAN 661-4272); 1600 Galaxy Dr., Newport Beach, CA 92660 (SAN 661-4280) Tel 714-631-4053.

Golden Adler, (Golden Adler Bks.; 0-9616094), P.O. Box 641, Issaquah, WA 98027-0641 (SAN 698-1089) Tel 206-392-1823.

Golden Aires, (Golden Aires, Inc.; 0-9607910), 615 W. Deer St., Glenrock, WY 82637 (SAN 239-6513) Tel 307-634-3391.

Golden Aloha, (Golden Aloha; 0-9614202), 3450 Meadowbrook Dr., Napa, CA 94558 (SAN 686-7170) Tel 707-255-7042; Dist. by Gedare Enterprises, Inc., 3450 Meadowbrook Dr., Napa, CA 94558 (SAN 200-5433) Tel 707-255-7042.

Golden Argosy, (Golden Argosy Publishing Co.; 0-9615618), 112 E. Burnett, Stayton, OR 97383 (SAN 696-4419) Tel 503-769-6088.

Golden Bear Pub, (Golden Bear Publishing, Inc.; 0-938295), Div. of Golden Bear, Inc., P.O. Box 573, Westport, CT 06881 (SAN 661-1745) Tel 203-226-6022; 56 Hermit Ln., Westport, CT 06881 (SAN 661-1753) Tel 203-226-0892.

Golden Bell, (Golden Bell Press; 0-87315), 2403 Champa St., Denver, CO 80205 (SAN 203-4344) Tel 303-572-1777.

Golden-Kane Coast, (Golden Coast Publishing Co.; 0-932958), 22 Waite Dr., Savannah, GA 31406 (SAN 212-355X).

Golden Dragon Pub, (Golden Dragon Pubs, Inc.; 0-910295), P.O. Box 1529, Princeton, NJ 08540 (SAN 241-5070) Tel 609-896-1332.

Golden Gambit, (Golden Gambit Bks.; 0-918862), 76 Weaton Dr., Attleboro, MA 02703 (SAN 210-1181).

Golden Gate *Imprint* of **Childrens**

Golden Gate Law, (Golden Gate Univ. Press; 0-943844), 536 Mission St., San Francisco, CA 94105 (SAN 241-0249) Tel 415-442-7204.

Golden Gate Prod, (Golden Gate Productions/KQED, Inc.; 0-912333), 500 Eighth St., San Francisco, CA 94103 (SAN 265-1246) Tel 415-553-2221.

Golden Gate SF, (Golden Gate Pr.; 0-9616288), 2022 Taraval, No. 2185, San Francisco, CA 94116 (SAN 658-6074) Tel 415-586-3388.

Golden Glow, (Golden Glow Publishing; 0-933072), 9240 Limekiln Rd., Sturgeon Bay, WI 54235 (SAN 212-3568) Tel 414-824-5774. Do not confuse with Golden Glow Pr., Aptos, CA.

Golden Glow Pr, (Golden Glow Pr.; 0-931355), P.O. Box 1689, Aptos, CA 95001 (SAN 688-2633) Tel 408-425-3208. Do not confuse with Golden Glow Publishing, Sturgeon Bay, WI.

Golden Hands Pr, (Golden Hands Pr.; 0-9616422), 29505 Sugarspring Rd., Farmington Hills, MI 48018 (SAN 658-8859) Tel 313-626-4093.

Golden Hill, (Golden Hill Books; 0-9605364), P.O. Box 5598, Helena, MT 59604 (SAN 216-1354) Tel 406-443-0678.

Golden Hind Pr, (Golden Hind Pr.; 0-931267), 3 Church Cir., Suite 206, Annapolis, MD 21401 (SAN 681-9869) Tel 301-263-7330.

Golden Hinde Pub, (Golden Hinde Publishing; 0-936717), 760 Market St., No. 1036, San Francisco, CA 94102 (SAN 699-847X) Tel 415-956-5966.

Golden Hl Pr NY, (Golden Hill Pr.; 0-9614876), Box 122, Spencertown, NY 12165 (SAN 693-031X) Tel 518-392-2358. Do not confuse with Golden Pr of Racine, WI.

Golden Horseshoe, (Golden Horseshoe; 0-9617096), P.O. Drawer O, Emory, VA 24327 (SAN 662-4839) Tel 703-944-3529.

Golden Key, (Golden Key Pubns.; 0-9602166), P.O. Box 1463, Mesa, AZ 85201-0270 (SAN 212-3576) Tel 602-834-7000; Dist. by: DeVorss & Co., P.O. Box 550, Marina del Rey, CA 90291 (SAN 662-7250) Tel 213-870-7478.

†Golden-Lee Bk, (Golden-Lee Bk.; 0-912331), Div. of Golden-Lee Book Distributors, Inc., 1000 Dean St., Brooklyn, NY 11238 (SAN 265-1254) Tel 718-857-6333; Toll free: 800-221-0960; *CIP.*

Golden Light, (Golden Light Press; 0-940086), 4956 Sable Pine Circle C-1, West Palm Beach, FL 33409 (SAN 217-0728).

Golden Mean, (Golden Mean Pubs., The; 0-937698), 271 Beach St., Ashland, OR 97520 (SAN 216-2490) Tel 503-482-9771.

Golden Owl Pub, (Golden Owl Pubs.; 0-9601258), 182 Chestnut Rd., Lexington Park, MD 20653 (SAN 210-4288) Tel 301-863-9253.

Golden Palm Pr, (Golden Palm Pr.; 0-937319), Div. of Educational Services Unltd., P.O. Box 3822, Santa Ana, CA 92703 (SAN 658-7836) Tel 714-834-9225; 2525 N. Park Blvd., Santa Ana, CA 92706 (SAN 658-7844).

Golden Phoenix, (Golden Phoenix Pr.; 0-910727), 1300 LaPlaya No. 1, San Francisco, CA 94122 (SAN 262-6772) Tel 415-681-1563.

Golden Poplar Pr, (Golden Poplar Pr.; 0-918907), Box 792, East Lansing, MI 48823 (SAN 670-1043) Tel 517-351-6751.

Golden Pr *Imprint* of **Western Pub**

Golden Pubns, (Golden Publications; 0-918783), 21393 Back Alley Rd., Bend, OR 97702 (SAN 657-3460) Tel 503-382-1622.

Golden Puffer, (Golden Puffer Press; 0-9607022), 3150 W. Tucana, Tucson, AZ 85745 (SAN 238-8774) Tel 602-743-7827.

Golden Quill, (Golden Quill Pr., The; 0-8233), Subs. of Audio Amateur Pubns., Avery Rd., Francestown, NH 03043 (SAN 201-6419) Tel 603-547-6622.

Golden Rainbow, (Golden Rainbow Press), P.O. Box 106, Houston, TX 77001 (SAN 212-6605).

Golden Sceptre, (Golden Sceptre Publishing; 0-9615117), 1442A Walnut St., Suite 61, Berkeley, CA 94706 (SAN 694-1532) Tel 415-525-1481; Dist. by: Bookpeople, 2929 Fifth St., Berkeley, CA 94710 (SAN 168-9517); Dist. by: New Leaf Distributing, 1020 White St., SW, Atlanta, GA 30310 (SAN 169-1449) Tel 404-755-2665.

Golden Seal, (Golden Seal Research Headquarters; 0-912368), P.O. Box 27821, Hollywood, CA 90027 (SAN 201-8365).

Golden St Dance Teach Assn, (Golden State Dance Teachers Assn.; 0-932980), Affil. of Alterra Publishing, 10804 Woodruff Ave., Downey, CA 90241-3910 (SAN 212-6613) Tel 213-869-8949.

Golden State Indus, (Golden State Industries Corp.), 5042 E. Third St., Los Angeles, CA 90022 (SAN 211-9536).

Golden West Hist, (Golden West Historical Pubns.; 0-930960), P.O. Box 1906, Ventura, CA 93002-1906 (SAN 212-6621).

†Golden West Pub, (Golden West Pubs.; 0-914846), 4113 N. Longview, Phoenix, AZ 85014 (SAN 207-5652) Tel 602-265-4392; *CIP.*

†Goldenleaf Pub Co, (Goldenleaf Pub; 0-930047), P.O. Box 405, Valley Center, CA 92082 (SAN 669-8344) Tel 619-749-0023; *CIP.*

Goldermood Rainbow, (Goldermood Rainbow; 0-916402), 331 W. Bonneville St., Pasco, WA 99301 (SAN 207-835X) Tel 509-547-5525.

Goldfield Pub, (Goldfield Publishing), 8400 Melrose Ave., Los Angeles, CA 90069 (SAN 241-385X).

Goldfield Pubns
See Goldfield San Diego

Goldfield San Diego, (Goldfield Pubns., Inc.; 0-936341), 1501 Goldfield St., San Diego, CA 92122 (SAN 697-8630) Tel 619-276-5035.

Goldstein MN, (Goldstein Gallery, Univ. of Minnesota; 0-939719), 1985 Buford St., 240 McNeal Hall, St. Paul, MN 55108 (SAN 663-6268) Tel 612-624-3292.

Goldstein Soft, (Goldstein Software, Inc.; 0-939933), 12520 Prosperity Dr., Suite 340, Silver Spring, MD 20904 (SAN 661-8782) Tel 301-622-9020.

†Golem, (Golem Pr.; 0-911762), P.O. Box 1342, Boulder, CO 80306 (SAN 203-4379) Tel 303-444-0841; *CIP.*

Golembe Assocs, (Golembe Assocs., Inc.; 0-9608840), 1025 Thomas Jefferson St. NW, Suite 301, Washington, DC 20007 (SAN 238-8235) Tel 202-337-5550.

Golf Assoc, (Golf Assocs.; 0-9607140), P.O. Box 2244, Menlo Park, CA 94025 (SAN 238-9835) Tel 415-854-4621.

Golf Digest, (Golf Digest/Tennis, Inc.; 0-914178), Subs. of New York Times, 5520 Park Ave., Box 395, Trumbull, CT 06611-0395 (SAN 212-7431) Tel 203-373-7119; P.O. Box 0395, Trumbull, CT 06611-0395 (SAN 699-5276); Dist. by: Simon & Schuster, 1230 Ave. of the Americas, New York, NY 10020 (SAN 200-2450) Tel 212-245-6400.

Golf Digest Bks
See Golf Digest

Golf Sports Pub, (Golf Sports Publishing; 0-930049), P.O. Box 3687, Lacey, WA 98503 (SAN 669-8387) Tel 206-491-8067.

Goliards Pr, (Goliards Press), 3515 18th St., Bellingham, WA 98225 (SAN 206-9903).

Golle & Holmes
See LFSI Minnesota

Gollehon Pr, (Gollehon Pr., Inc.; 0-914839), 3105 Madison Ave. SE, Grand Rapids, MI 49508 (SAN 289-2170) Tel 616-247-8231; Toll free: 800-262-4947.

Gollehon Pub Co
See Gollehon Pr

GoLo Press, (GoLo Pr.; 0-9614983), Div. of Golo Enterprises, P.O. Box 1500, Shepherdstown, WV 25443 (SAN 693-756X) Tel 304-876-3254.

Gondolier, (Gondolier Pr.; 0-935824), P.O. Box QQQ, Southampton, NY 11968 (SAN 214-0233).

Gondwana Bks, (Gondwana Books; 0-931926), Div. of Alta Napa Pr., 1969 Mora Ave., Calistoga, CA 94515 (SAN 212-0208) Tel 707-942-4444.

Gong Ent, *(Gong Enterprise Incorporated; 0-916713),* P.O. Box 1753, Bristol, VA 24203 (SAN 654-5122) Tel 703-466-4672.

Gong Prods, *(Gong Productions),* 3525 Diamond Ave., Suite 309, Oakland, CA 94602 (SAN 289-1581).

Gonzaga U Pr, *(Gonzaga Univ. Press),* Spokane, WA 99202 (SAN 206-4480).

Good Apple, *(Good Apple, Inc.; 0-916456; 0-86653),* P.O. Box 299, Carthage, IL 62321 (SAN 208-6646) Tel 217-357-3981; Toll free: 800-435-7234.

†**Good Bks PA,** *(Good Bks.; 0-934672),* Subs. of Good Enterprises, Ltd., Main St., Intercourse, PA 17534 (SAN 693-9597) Tel 717-768-7171; Toll free: 800-762-7171; *CIP.*

Good Food Bks, *(Good Food Books; 0-932398),* 17 Colonial Terrace, Maplewood, NJ 07040 (SAN 212-8535) Tel 201-762-0841.

Good Friends *Imprint* of Ideals

†**Good Gay,** *(Good Gay Poets),* P.O. Box 277, Astor Sta., Boston, MA 02123 (SAN 207-3536) Tel 617-661-7534; *CIP.*

Good Hope GA, *(Good Hope Press; 0-9608596),* 75 Silverwood Rd., NE, Atlanta, GA 30342 (SAN 240-6608) Tel 404-255-7416.

Good Hope Pub, *(Good Hope Publishing Co., The; 0-9608562),* 16541 Warwick, Detroit, MI 48219 (SAN 240-6616) Tel 313-532-2531.

Good Ideas, *(Good Ideas Co.; 0-9603940),* Box 296, Berea, OH 44017 (SAN 212-5072) Tel 216-234-5411.

Good Life, *(Good Life Pr.; 0-89074),* Div. of Charing Cross Publishing Co., 658 S. Bonnie Brae St., Los Angeles, CA 90057 (SAN 206-4944) Tel 213-483-5832.

Good Life Resources, *(Goodlife Resources, Inc.),* 5764 Mill St., Erie, PA 16509 (SAN 241-3868) Tel 814-868-3349.

Good Life VA, *(Good Life Publishers; 0-917374),* 14200 Nash Rd., Chesterfield, VA 23832 (SAN 208-6654) Tel 804-794-4954.

Good Money News
  See Good Money Pubns

Good Money Pubns, *(Good Money Pubns., Inc.; 0-933609),* Box 363, Worcester, VT 05682 (SAN 692-459X) Tel 802-223-3911; Toll free: 800-535-3551.

Good News, *(Good News Pubs.; 0-89107),* 9825 W. Roosevelt Rd., Westchester, IL 60153 (SAN 211-7991) Tel 312-345-7474; Toll free: 800-323-3890 Sales only. *Imprints:* Crossway Bks (Crossway Books).

Good News KY, *(Good News: A Forum For Scriptual Christianity, Inc.),* 308 E. Main St., Wilmore, KY 40390 (SAN 657-1441) Tel 606-858-4661.

Good Old Spot Pr, *(Good Old Spot Pr.; 0-9616718),* 10727 20th Ave. NE, Seattle, WA 98125 (SAN 661-3764) Tel 206-363-2685; Dist. by: Pacific Pipeline, Inc., 19215 66th Ave. S, Kent, WA 98032 (SAN 208-2128) Tel 206-872-5523.

Good Sign, *(Good Sign Pubns.; 0-937730),* 457 Ruthven Ave., Palo Alto, CA 94301 (SAN 215-6482).

Good Soldier Pubns, *(Good Soldier Pubns.; 0-9616499),* 4817 Crestwood, Waco, TX 76710 (SAN 659-2384) Tel 817-772-5630.

Goodale Pub, *(Goodale Publishing; 0-9609662),* 1903 Kenwood Pkwy., Minneapolis, MN 55405 (SAN 262-0294) Tel 612-377-5783.

Goode-Steely Assocs, *(Goode/Steely Associates; 0-9612620),* 31473 Rudolph Rd., Cottage Grove, OR 97424 (SAN 289-2162) Tel 503-942-7361.

Goodfellow, *(Goodfellow Catalog Pr., Inc.; 0-936016),* P.O. Box 4520, Berkeley, CA 94704 (SAN 206-4499) Tel 415-845-2062. *Imprints:* Pub. by Liplop (Liplop Press).

†**Goodheart,** *(Goodheart-Willcox Co.; 0-87006),* 123 W. Taft Dr., South Holland, IL 60473 (SAN 203-4387) Tel 312-333-7200; Toll free: 800-323-0440; *CIP.*

Goodlife Pubs, *(Goodlife Pubs.; 0-938593),* 323 Franklin Bldg., Suite 804/J-55, Chicago, IL 60606-7095 (SAN 661-1559); 50 Broome St., Brooklyn, NY 11222 (SAN 661-1567) Tel 718-384-7015.

Goodmaster Bks, *(Goodmaster Bks.; 0-937235),* 1490 Rte. 23, Wayne, NJ 07470 (SAN 658-6481) Tel 201-284-1963.

Goodrich Pr, *(Goodrich Press; 0-9612734),* P.O. Box 2265, Ann Arbor, MI 48106 (SAN 289-9345) Tel 313-665-6597.

Goose Pond Pr, *(Goose Pond Pr.; 0-910835),* 11600 Southwest Freeway, Suite 179, Houston, TX 77031 (SAN 270-5419) Tel 617-259-9842.

Gopher, *(Gopher Graphics; 0-936511),* RD 2, Box 323, Greene, NY 13778 (SAN 697-8649) Tel 607-656-4531.

†**Gorak Bks,** *(Gorak Bks.; 0-918803),* P.O. Box 5411, Pasadena, CA 91107 (SAN 669-6856) Tel 818-795-5520; *CIP.*

Goranson Pr, *(Goranson Press),* 7624 W. Raschen, Chicago, IL 60656 (SAN 207-2300).

†**Gordian,** *(Gordian Pr., Inc.; 0-87752),* P.O. Box 304, Staten Island, NY 10304 (SAN 201-6389) Tel 718-273-4700; *CIP.*

Gordon
  See Gordon & Breach

†**Gordon & Breach,** *(Gordon & Breach Science Pubs., Inc.; 0-677),* P.O. Box 786 Cooper Sta., New York, NY 10276 (SAN 201-6370) Tel 212-206-8900; *CIP.*

Gordon-Cremonesi, *(Gordon-Cremonesi Book),* 115 Fifth Ave., New York, NY 10003 (SAN 694-9541) Tel 212-486-2700.

†**Gordon Pr,** *(Gordon Pr. Pubs.; 0-87968; 0-8490),* P.O. Box 459, Bowling Green Sta., New York, NY 10004 (SAN 201-6362); *CIP.*

Gordon Soules Econ, *(Soules, Gordon, Economic Marketing Research; 0-919574),* 507 Third Ave., Suite 1240, Seattle, WA 98104 (SAN 208-2845).

Gordons & Weinberg, *(Gordons & T. Weinberg; 0-9603484),* P.O. Box 3101, Princeville, HI 96722 (SAN 213-571X) Tel 808-826-6380.

Gordonstown, *(Gordonstown Press; 0-9603942),* Box U, Dillon, CO 80435 (SAN 214-3100).

Gordy Pr, *(Gordy Press; 0-936472),* 330 Pine Ridge Rd., Jackson, MS 39206 (SAN 216-1362) Tel 601-362-6518.

Gorsuch Scarisbrick, *(Gorsuch Scarisbrick, Pubs.; 0-89787),* 8233 Via Paseo del Norte, Suite E400, Scottsdale, AZ 85258 (SAN 220-5920) Tel 602-991-7881.

Gos Inc, *(Gos Inc.; 0-942258),* P.O. Box 3912, Missoula, MT 59806 (SAN 237-9562).

Goshen Coll, *(Goshen College; 0-913859),* 1700 S. Main St., Goshen, IN 46526 (SAN 287-7260) Tel 219-533-3161.

Goshindo Martial, *(Goshindo Martial Arts; 0-9613678),* 11 Sterling Ave., Tappan, NY 10983 (SAN 670-9427) Tel 914-359-7023.

†**Gospel Advocate,** *(Gospel Advocate Co., Inc.; 0-89225),* P.O. Box 150, Nashville, TN 37202 (SAN 205-2792); Toll free: 800-251-8446; 1006 Elm Hill Pike, Nashville, TN 37210 (SAN 662-0213); Toll free: 800-242-8006 in Tennesee; Dist. by: Christian Communications, P.O. Box 150, Nashville, TN 37202 (SAN 200-7207); *CIP.*

Gospel Place, *(Gospel Place, The),* P.O. Box 110304, Nashville, TN 37211 (SAN 277-6847) Tel 615-377-3910.

†**Gospel Pub,** *(Gospel Publishing Hse.; 0-88243),* Div. of General Council of the Assemblies of God, 1445 Boonville Ave., Springfield, MO 65802 (SAN 206-8826) Tel 417-862-2781; Toll free: 800-641-4310; Toll free: 800-492-7625 in Missouri; *CIP.*

Gospel Pubns FL
  See GMI Pubns Inc

Gospel Themes Pr, *(Gospel Themes Pr.; 0-938855),* 710 S. 140th, Seattle, WA 93168 (SAN 662-5797) Tel 206-243-8591.

Gospic Realty, *(Gospic Realty Corp.; 0-943898),* 63 Little Clove Rd., Staten Island, NY 10301 (SAN 241-1172) Tel 718-981-6361.

Goss, *(Goss & Co., Pubs.; 0-912010),* 396 Redwood Dr., Pasadena, CA 91105 (SAN 203-4409) Tel 213-257-1773.

Gotham, *(Gotham Book Mart; 0-910664),* 41 W. 47th St., New York, NY 10036 (SAN 203-4417) Tel 212-719-4448.

Gothic, *(Gothic Bookshop; 0-917585),* P.O. Box LM, Durham, NC 27706 (SAN 656-8866) Tel 919-684-3986.

Gottlieb & Allen, *(Gottlieb & Allen; 0-930768),* 200 E. 27th St., New York, NY 10016 (SAN 211-4232).

Gottlieb's Bakery, *(Gottlieb's Bakery),* 1601 Bull St., Savannah, GA 31401 (SAN 655-8372); Dist. by: Wimmer Brothers, 4120 B.F. Goodrich Blvd., Memphis, TN 38181 (SAN 209-6544) Tel 901-362-8900.

Gotuit Ent, *(Gotuit Enterprises; 0-931490),* 13342 El Dorado Dr., No. 191-A., P.O. Box 2568, Seal Beach, CA 90740 (SAN 211-3597) Tel 213-430-5198.

Gould, *(Gould Pubns.; 0-87526),* 199/300 State St., Binghamton, NY 13901 (SAN 201-6354) Tel 607-724-3000.

Gourmet Guides, *(Gourmet Guides; 0-937024),* 1767 Stockton St., San Francisco, CA 94133 (SAN 214-3798).

Gourmet Pubns, *(Gourmet Publications; 0-9611388),* 1401 W. Calle Kino, Tucson, AZ 85704 (SAN 283-9024) Tel 602-297-1281.

Gov Data Pubns, *(Government Data Pubns.),* 1120 Connecticut Ave., NW, Washington, DC 20036 (SAN 207-3439).

Gov Insts, *(Government Institutes, Inc.; 0-86587),* 966 Hungerford Dr., Suite 24, Rockville, MD 20850 (SAN 214-3801).

†**Gov Printing Office,** *(U. S. Government Printing Office),* USGPO Stop SSMR, Washington, DC 20401 (SAN 206-152X) Tel 202-783-3238; Orders to: Superintendent of Documents, Washington, DC 20402-9325 (SAN 658-0785) Tel 202-783-3238; *CIP.*

Gov Prod News, *(Government Product News; 0-9611182),* 1111 Chester Ave., Cleveland, OH 44114 (SAN 277-6855) Tel 216-696-7000.

†**Gov Res Pubns,** *(Government Research Pubns.; 0-931684),* Box 122, Newton Center, MA 02159 (SAN 211-4674); *CIP.*

Govt Res Serv, *(Government Research Service; 0-9615227),* 701 Jackson, Rm. 304, Topeka, KS 66603 (SAN 695-1430) Tel 913-232-7720.

Gowan, *(Gowan, J. C.; 0-9606822),* 1426 Southwind, Westlake Village, CA 91361 (SAN 202-0343) Tel 818-991-0342.

†**Gower Pub Co,** *(Gower Publishing Co.; 0-566),* Div. of Gower Publishing Co., Ltd. (UK), Old Post Rd., Brookfield, VT 05036 (SAN 262-0308) Tel 802-276-3162; *CIP.*

Gower Pub Ltd
  See Gower Pub Co

GP Courseware, *(GP Courseware; 0-87683),* Subs. of General Physics Corp., 10650 Hickory Ridge Rd., Columbia, MD 21044 (SAN 294-0264) Tel 301-964-6032; Toll free: 800-638-3838.

GPO
  See Gov Printing Office

Gr Arts Ctr Pub, *(Graphic Arts Ctr. Publishing Co.; 0-912856; 0-932575),* P.O. Box 10306, Portland, OR 97210 (SAN 201-6338) Tel 503-226-2402; Toll free: 800-452-3032.

GRA, *(Governmental Research Assn., Inc.; 0-931684),* 24 Province St., Boston, MA 02108 (SAN 205-275X) Tel 617-720-1000.

Grace Dangberg, *(Dangberg, Grace, Foundation, Inc., The; 0-913205),* P.O. Box 9621, University Sta., Reno, NV 89507-0621 (SAN 283-0493) Tel 702-883-2017.

†**Grace Pub Co,** *(Grace Publishing Co.),* P.O. Box 23385, Tampa, FL 33622 (SAN 211-8017) Tel 813-884-8003; *CIP.*

Grace Pub House, *(Grace Publishing House; 0-9605576),* 10505 Cole Rd., Whittier, CA 90604 (SAN 238-3543) Tel 213-944-7372.

Grace Pubns, *(Grace Pubns.; 0-911925),* P.O. Box 1383, San Marcos, CA 92069 (SAN 264-0635) Tel 619-722-4161.

Grace World Outreach, *(Grace World Outreach Ctr.; 0-933643),* 2695 Creve Coeur Mill Rd., Maryland Heights, MO 63043 (SAN 692-6495) Tel 314-291-6647.

Gracelaine, *(Gracelaine Pubns.; 0-932984),* 3001 Ashley Ave., Montgomery, AL 36109 (SAN 212-2804).

Graceway, *(Graceway Publishing Co., Inc.; 0-932126),* P.O. Box 159, Sta."C", Flushing, NY 11367 (SAN 212-0976) Tel 718-261-0759.

Gracie Ent, *(Gracie Enterprises, Inc.; 0-9606398),* P.O. Box 506, Chula Vista, CA 92012 (SAN 226-7934) Tel 619-421-8055.

Grad Mgmt Admin, *(Graduate Management Admission Council; 0-943846),* 11601 Wilshire Blvd., Los Angeles, CA 90025-1748 (SAN 218-7469); Dist. by: Educational Testing Service, P.O. Box 966, Princeton, NJ 08541 (SAN 238-034X) Tel 609-921-9000.

Grad Program
  See Columbia U GPPPA

Grad Sch Bus NY, *(Columbia Univ., Graduate Schl. of Business; 0-9612584),* 801 Uris Hall, New York, NY 10027 (SAN 204-305X) Tel 212-280-3423.

Grad School, *(Graduate School Pr.; 0-87771),* U.S. Dept. of Agriculture, South Bldg., Rm. 1404, Washington, DC 20250 (SAN 203-4425) Tel 202-447-7123; Orders to: 600 Maryland Ave., SW, Rm. 142, Washington, DC 20024 (SAN 662-0221) Tel 202-382-8635.

Grade Finders, *(Grade Finders, Inc.),* 642 Lancaster Ave., Berwyn, PA 19312 (SAN 208-2322) Tel 215-644-4159; Orders to: P.O. Box 444, Bala-Cynwyd, PA 19004 (SAN 208-2330).

Graduate Group, *(Graduate Group, The; 0-938609),* Div. of Whitman Assocs., 86 Norwood Rd., West Hartford, CT 06117 (SAN 661-5902) Tel 203-232-3100.

Graeff, *(Graeff, Roderich W., Dr.-Ing.; 0-9604570),* 607 Church, Ann Arbor, MI 48104 (SAN 215-2126) Tel 313-769-6588.

Graeme Pub, *(Graeme Publishing Corp.; 0-937587),* P.O. Box 549, Wilbraham, MA 01095 (SAN 658-8893) Tel 413-596-3176.

Graffeo's Hostess, *(Graffeo's Hostess Helper, Inc.; 0-9616869),* 705 S. Guegnon, Abbeville, LA 70510 (SAN 661-1311) Tel 318-893-3897.

Graham & Trotman, *(Graham & Trotman, Inc.; 0-86010),* Subs. of Graham & Trotman Ltd., 13 Park Ave., Gaithersburg, MD 20877 (SAN 699-5284) Tel 301-670-1767.

Graham Conley, *(Graham Conley Pr.; 0-912087),* Box 2968, New Haven, CT 06515 (SAN 264-746X) Tel 203-389-0183.

Graham Pubns, *(Graham Pubns., Inc.; 0-936167),* Winsted Ctr., Rte. 59 N., Joliet, IL 60435 (SAN 697-0923) Tel 815-436-8988.

†Gramercy Bks, *(Gramercy Books Press, Inc.; 0-935134),* 354 George St, New Brunswick, NJ 08901 (SAN 213-845X); *CIP.*

Grammar, *(Grammar Simplified; 0-9616040),* 4010 N. Brandywine Dr., No. 318, Peoria, IL 61614 (SAN 698-0260) Tel 309-685-7025.

Grammatical Sci, *(Grammatical Sciences),* 1236 Jackson St., Santa Clara, CA 95050 (SAN 203-4433).

Grand Bks Inc, *(Grand Bks., Inc.; 0-930809),* P.O. Box 7, Middleton, MA 48856 (SAN 677-6361) Tel 517-875-4249.

Grand River, *(Grand River Pr.; 0-936343),* P.O. Box 1342, East Lansing, MI 48823 (SAN 697-8657) Tel 517-351-3641; 144 Highland Ave., East Lansing, MI 48823 (SAN 698-2255).

Grand Strand, *(Grand Strand Humane Society; 0-9616904),* 6300 N. Ocean Blvd., Myrtle Beach, SC 29577 (SAN 698-0686) Tel 803-449-5206.

Granger Bk
See Roth Pub Inc

Granite Hill, *(Granite Hill Corp.),* RFD No. 1, P.O. Box 210, Hallowell, ME 04347 (SAN 287-1718).

Granite Pr, *(Granite Pr.; 0-9614886),* P.O. Box 7, Penobscot, ME 04476 (SAN 693-2428) Tel 207-326-9322; Dist. by: Bookslinger, 213 E. Fourth St., St. Paul, MN 55101 (SAN 169-4154); Dist. by: Bookpeople, 2929 Fifth St., Berkeley, CA 94710 (SAN 168-9517); Dist. by: Inland Bk. Co., P.O. Box 261, 22 Hemingway Ave., East Haven, CT 06512 (SAN 200-4151).

Granite Pubns
See Bluefish

Granite Pubs, *(Granite Pubs.; 0-935669),* 2717 B Houma Blvd., Metairie, LA 70006 (SAN 696-4435) Tel 504-455-3380.

Grant Corner Inn, *(Grant Corner Inn; 0-9616719),* 122 Grant Ave., Santa Fe, NM 87501 (SAN 661-373X) Tel 505-983-6678.

Grant Dahlstrom, *(Dahlstrom, Grant, /Castle Press),* 516 N. Fair Oaks Ave., Pasadena, CA 91103 (SAN 206-7455).

Granville Pubns, *(Granville Pubns.; 0-931349),* 10960 Wilshire, Suite 826, Los Angeles, CA 90024 (SAN 682-5796) Tel 213-477-3924.

†Grapetree Prods, *(Grapetree Productions, Inc.; 0-941374),* Box 10cn, 600 Grapetree Dr., Key Biscayne, FL 33149 (SAN 239-3638) Tel 305-361-2060; *CIP.*

Grapevine Inc, *(Grapevine, Inc.; 0-937931),* P.O. Box 706, Ooltewah, TN 37363 (SAN 659-5065) Tel 615-238-5586; 9515 Lee Way, Suite E, Ooltewah, TN 37363 (SAN 659-5073).

Grapevine Pubns, *(Grapevine Pubns., Inc.; 0-931011),* P.O. Box 118, Corvallis, OR 97339 (SAN 678-9714) Tel 503-754-0583.

Graph Arts Res RIT
See Tech & Ed Ctr Graph Arts RIT

Graph Arts Trade, *(Graphic Arts Trade Journals; 0-910762),* 399 Conklin St., Suite 306, P.O. Box 81, Farmingdale, NY 11735 (SAN 206-8281) Tel 516-694-4842.

Graph Comm Assn, *(Graphic Communications Assn.; 0-933505),* 1730 N. Lynn St., Suite 604, Arlington, VA 22209 (SAN 224-7798).

Graph Comm Computer
See Graph Comm Assn

Graphic Artists, *(Graphic Artists Guild; 0-932102),* c/o Robert Silver Associates, 307 E. 37th St., New York, NY 10016 (SAN 295-334X).

Graphic Arts Tech Found, *(Graphic Arts Technical Foundation),* 4615 Forbes Ave., Pittsburgh, PA 15213 (SAN 224-778X) Tel 412-621-6941.

Graphic Comm, *(Graphic Communications, Inc.; 0-924247),* 200 Fifth Ave., Waltham, MA 02254 (SAN 284-8880) Tel 617-890-8778.

Graphic Comm Ctr, *(Graphic Communications Ctr.; 0-89667),* P.O. Box 357, Appleton, WI 54912 (SAN 201-632X).

Graphic Crafts, *(Graphic Crafts, Inc.; 0-9605024),* P.O. Box 327, 300 Beaver Valley Pike, Willow Street, PA 17584 (SAN 209-3294) Tel 717-464-2733.

Graphic Dimensions, *(Graphic Dimensions; 0-930904),* 8 Frederick Rd., Pittsford, NY 14534 (SAN 213-067X) Tel 716-381-3428.

Graphic Ent, *(Graphic Enterprises, Inc.; 0-914921),* Div. of North Texas Printing Company, 316 E. Abram St., Arlington, TX 76010 (SAN 289-2189) Tel 817-277-9442.

Graphic Enter NC, *(Graphic Enterprises of the Carolinas; 0-936135),* P.O. Box 18251, Greensboro, NC 27419 (SAN 697-0648) Tel 919-855-6880; 402 Edwardia Dr., Greensboro, NC 27419 (SAN 697-0656).

Graphic Image, *(Graphic Image Pubns.; 0-912457),* P.O. Box 1740, La Jolla, CA 92038 (SAN 265-4059) Tel 619-755-6558.

Graphic Impress, *(Graphic Impressions; 0-914628),* 1939 W. 32nd Ave., Denver, CO 80211 (SAN 201-6311) Tel 303-458-7475.

Graphic Learning, *(Graphic Learning Corp.; 0-943068; 0-87746),* Subs. of Graphic Learning of Canada, 855 Broadway, Boulder, CO 80302 (SAN 240-3803) Tel 303-492-8197; P.O. Box 13829, Tallahassee, FL 32317 (SAN 650-0315) Tel 904-878-8284.

Graphic Pr, *(Graphic Press; 0-89284),* Div. of Carl Nelson Associates, P.O. Box 13056, Washington, DC 20009 (SAN 208-6662) Tel 202-232-2927.

Graphic Pr CT
See Graphics Pr

Graphic Pr LA, *(Graphic Pr., Inc.; 0-936183),* 3719 Magazine St., New Orleans, LA 70115 (SAN 697-1016) Tel 504-891-6377.

Graphic Pub, *(Graphic Publishing Co., Inc.; 0-89279),* 204 N. Second Ave., W., Lake Mills, IA 50450 (SAN 202-4306) Tel 515-592-2000.

Graphic World, *(Graphic World),* Harding St., Minneapolis, MN 55413 (SAN 663-0863).

Graphics Calif, *(Graphics Press; 0-937536),* 3010 Santa Monica Blvd. Suite 406, Santa Monica, CA 90404 (SAN 215-2487) Tel 213-393-9029.

Graphics Comm, *(Graphics-Communication Associates),* P.O. Drawer 10549, Tallahassee, FL 32302 (SAN 240-9356).

Graphics Mktg Syst, *(Graphics Marketing Systems, Inc.; 0-934093),* P.O. Box 260686, Tampa, FL 33685 (SAN 693-0344) Tel 813-968-1475.

Graphics Pr, *(Graphics Pr.; 0-9613921),* P.O. Box 430, Cheshire, CT 06410 (SAN 670-7289) Tel 203-272-9187.

Graphie Intl, *(Graphie International Inc.; 0-916189),* 349 Paseo Tesoro, Walnut, CA 91789 (SAN 294-9342) Tel 714-981-1072.

Graphitti Designs, *(Graphitti Designs; 0-936211),* 515 W. Valencia Dr., Unit E, Fullerton, CA 92632 (SAN 697-1105) Tel 714-738-5480.

Grass Hooper Pr, *(Grass Hooper Press; 0-933038),* 4030 Connecticut St., St. Louis, MO 63116 (SAN 221-1157) Tel 314-772-8164; Dist. by: Paperback Supply, 4121 Forest Park Ave., St. Louis, MO 63108 (SAN 169-4324) Tel 314-652-1000.

Grass Roots Montana, *(Grass Roots Publishing; 0-9616221),* P.O. Drawer 789, Red Lodge, MT 59068 (SAN 658-5418) Tel 406-446-1687; 1500 S. Broadway, Red Lodge, MT 59068 (SAN 658-5426).

Grass Roots Productions, *(Grass Roots Productions; 0-9614589),* 444 W. 54th St., New York, NY 10019 (SAN 691-7771) Tel 212-957-8386.

Grass Roots Pub
See Grass Roots Montana

Grassdale
See Grassdale Pubs

Grassdale Pubs, *(Grassdale Pubs., Inc.; 0-939798),* 1002 Lincoln Green, Norman, OK 73072 (SAN 216-8960) Tel 405-329-7071; Orders to: P.O. Box 53158, Oklahoma City, CA 73152 (SAN 662-023X) Tel 405-525-9458.

Grasshopper Pubns, *(Grasshopper Pubns.; 0-937139),* 604 E. Third, Hennessey, OK 73742 (SAN 658-5302) Tel 405-853-6689.

Grassroots Ed Serv, *(Grassroots Educational Service; 0-933426),* 102 1/2 Broadway, Glendale, CA 91205 (SAN 212-5099) Tel 818-240-1683.

Grastorf & Lang, *(Grastorf, Lang & Co., Inc.; 0-933408),* 142 W. 24th St., New York, NY 10011 (SAN 215-0786) Tel 212-255-5693.

Gravel-Kellogg, *(Gravel-Kellogg Publishing Co.; 0-9608684),* 235 W. 20th St., Fremont, NE 68025 (SAN 238-292X) Tel 402-727-4859.

Gravesend Pr, *(Gravesend Press; 0-9608508),* 4392 Bussey Rd., Syracuse, NY 13215 (SAN 240-6632).

Gravity Pub, *(Gravity Publishing; 0-936067),* 6324 Heather Ridge, Oakland, CA 94611 (SAN 696-9240) Tel 415-339-3774; Dist. by: Publishers Group West, 5855 Beaudry St., Emeryville, CA 94608 (SAN 202-8522) Tel 415-658-3453; Dist. by: Quality Bks., 918 Sherwood Dr., Lake Bluff, IL 60044-2204 (SAN 169-2127); Dist. by: Bookpeople, 2929 Fifth St., Berkeley, CA 94710 (SAN 663-3145) Tel 415-549-3030.

Gravity Research, *(Gravity Research Pubns.; 0-913001),* 1237 Camino Del Mar, Suite C-131, Del Mar, CA 92014 (SAN 283-0981).

Gray Assoc, *(Gray & Associates; 0-937636),* P.O. Box 961, Madison, WI 53701 (SAN 215-2118) Tel 608-274-7458.

†Gray Beard, *(Gray Beard Publishing; 0-933686),* 107 W. John St., Seattle, WA 98119 (SAN 212-8543); *CIP.*

Gray Data, *(Gray Data; 0-924256),* 3071 Palmer Sq., Chicago, IL 60647 (SAN 653-4201) Tel 312-278-8080.

Gray Falcon Pr, *(Gray Falcon Pr.; 0-935335),* P.O. Box 3, Martinsville, NJ 08836 (SAN 696-4443) Tel 201-685-2063; 901 Brown Rd., Bridgewater, NJ 08807 (SAN 696-5423).

Gray Moose, *(Gray Moose Press, The; 0-9608078),* 19 Elmwood Ave., Rye, NY 10580 (SAN 239-4308) Tel 914-967-0665.

Gray Pubns CA, *(Gray Pubns.),* 31300 Via Colinas, No. 102, Westlake Village, CA 91362 (SAN 663-5369).

Gray Pubns WV, *(Gray Pubns.; 0-934805),* Box 460, Franklin, WV 26807 (SAN 694-3721) Tel 304-358-2791.

Grayking Pub, *(Grayking Publishing; 0-9610786),* 124 Webster Rd., Spencerport, NY 14559 (SAN 265-1580) Tel 716-352-5152.

Graylock, *(Graylock Press; 0-910670),* 428 E. Preston St., Baltimore, MD 21202 (SAN 203-445X) Tel 301-528-4105.

Grays Sporting
See GSJ Press

†Graywolf, *(Graywolf Pr.; 0-915308; 1-55597),* P.O. Box 75006, St. Paul, MN 55175 (SAN 207-1665) Tel 612-222-8342; 370 Selby Ave., No. 203, St. Paul, MN 55102 (SAN 658-0793); Dist. by: Consortium Bk. Sales & Distribution, 213 E. Fourth St., St. Paul, MN 55101 (SAN 200-6049) Tel 612-221-9035; *CIP.*

GRDA Pubns, *(GRDA Pubns.; 0-9614808),* Div. of Goldberg Research & Development Assocs. Corp., 110 Tiburon Blvd., Mill Valley, CA 94941 (SAN 692-9524) Tel 415-388-6080.

GrDeb *Imprint of Contemp Bks*

Grdinic, *(Grdinic, Eva; 0-9604176),* 6661 Vista del Mar Dr., Playa del Rey, CA 93001 (SAN 214-2449).

Great Advent Pub, *(Great Adventure Publishing, Inc.; 0-936069),* 921 Douglas Ave., Altamonte Springs, FL 32714 (SAN 697-0893) Tel 305-862-4101.

†Great Am Bks, *(Great American Books; 0-936790),* 256 S. Robertson Blvd., Beverly Hills, CA 90211 (SAN 215-1499); *CIP.*

Great Am Gift, *(Great American Gift Co., The; 1-55569),* 33 Portman Rd., New Rochelle, NY 10801 (SAN 699-7198) Tel 914-576-7660.

Great & Sm Pubs, *(Great & Small Pubs.; 0-930907),* Subs. of Great & Small Enterprise, P.O. Box 13115, Houston, TX 77219 (SAN 679-6818) Tel 713-961-5134.

Great Basin, *(Great Basin Pr.; 0-930830),* Box 11162, Reno, NV 89510 (SAN 211-1144) Tel 702-826-7729.

Great Bear Pr, *(Great Bear Pr., The; 0-938559),* P.O. Box 5164, Eugene, OR 97405 (SAN 661-6232); 2437 Miami Ln., Eugene, OR 97403 (SAN 661-6240) Tel 503-485-3683.

Great Comm Pubns, *(Great Commission Pubns.; 0-934688),* 7401 Old York Rd., Philadelphia, PA 19126 (SAN 215-1502) Tel 215-635-6510.

Great Eastern
See Shambhala Pubns

Great Eastern *Imprint of Shambhala Pubns*

Great Elm, *(Great Elm Pr.; 0-9613465),* RD 2, P.O. Box 37, Rexville, NY 14877 (SAN 657-2588) Tel 607-225-4592.

Great Game Pro, *(Great Game Products; 0-935307),* 8804 Chalon Dr., Bethesda, MD 20817 (SAN 695-7765) Tel 301-365-3297; Toll free: 800-426-3748.

Great Lakes Bks, *(Great Lakes Bks.; 0-9606400),* P.O. Box 164, Brighton, MI 48116 (SAN 222-9994) Tel 313-227-7471.

Great Lakes Pr
See Grt Lks Pr

Great Northwest, *(Great Northwest Publishing Co., Inc.; 0-937708),* P.O. Box 103902, Anchorage, AK 99510 (SAN 219-9890).

Great Oak Pr VA, *(Great Oak Press of Virginia; 0-9608234),* Box 6541, Falls Church, VA 22046 (SAN 240-3129) Tel 703-560-6347.

†Great Ocean, *(Great Ocean Pubs.; 0-915556),* 1823 N. Lincoln St., Arlington, VA 22207 (SAN 207-527X) Tel 703-525-0909; *CIP.*

†Great Outdoors, *(Great Outdoors Publishing Co.; 0-8200),* 4747 28th St., N., St. Petersburg, FL 33714 (SAN 201-6273) Tel 813-525-6609; Toll free: 800-433-5560 (Florida only); *CIP.*

Great Plains, *(Great Plains National Instructional Television Library; 0-9614949),* Box 80669, Lincoln, NE 68501 (SAN 213-0696); Toll free: 800-228-4630.

Great Plains Emporium
See Grt Plains Emporium

Great Plains Soft, *(Great Plains Software; 0-924261),* 1701 SW 38th St., Fargo, ND 58103 (SAN 264-8830) Tel 701-281-0550; Toll free: 800-345-3276.

Great Pyramid, *(Great Pyramid Press; 0-9605822),* P.O. Box 2745, Augusta, GA 30904 (SAN 220-1704) Tel 404-736-3514.

Great Raven Pr, *(Great Raven Press),* Box 858, Lewiston, ME 04240 (SAN 211-9595).

Great Traditions, *(Great Traditions),* P.O. Box 3680, Clearlake, CA 95422 (SAN 679-1301). *Imprints:* Wisdom Pubns (Wisdom Publications).(Wisdom Pubns.).

Great Wash Re, *(Greater Washington Research Ctr.; 0-935535),* 1717 Massachusetts Ave., NW, Suite 403, Washington, DC 20036 (SAN 696-4451) Tel 202-387-0900.

†Great Wine Grapes, *(Great Wine Grapes),* 157 24th Ave., San Francisco, CA 94121 (SAN 211-5271); Dist. by: Wine Appreciation Guild Ltd., 155 Connecticut St., San Francisco, CA 94107 (SAN 201-9515) Tel 415-864-1202; *CIP.*

Greater Alton Jr League, *(Junior League of Greater Alton; 0-9615898),* P.O. Box 27, Alton, IL 62002 (SAN 696-8759) Tel 618-462-4897; 78 Fairmont Addition, Alton, IL 62002 (SAN 699-6469).

Greater Gold, *(Greater Golden Hill Poetry Express, The; 0-9611842),* 4604 Niagara Ave., San Diego, CA 92107 (SAN 286-195X) Tel 619-224-5951.

Greater Portland, *(Greater Portland Landmarks, Inc.; 0-9600612; 0-939761),* 165 State St., Portland, ME 04101 (SAN 203-4484) Tel 207-774-5561.

Greater PWYP, *(Greater Philadelphia Women's Yellow Pages, The; 0-9611844),* P.O. Box 42397, Philadelphia, PA 19101 (SAN 286-1968) Tel 215-235-4042.

Greater Works, *(Greater Works Outreach; 0-9616324),* 301 College Pk. Dr., Monroeville, PA 15146 (SAN 658-778X) Tel 412-327-6500.

Greatest Graphics, *(Greatest Graphics, Inc.; 0-936120),* 1904 B East Meadowmere, Springfield, MO 65804 (SAN 213-7410); Orders to: P.O. Box 4467gs, Springfield, MO 65804 (SAN 213-7429) Tel 417-862-6500.

Greatland Graphics, *(Greatland Graphics/Puffin Pr.; 0-936425),* Box 100333, Anchorage, AK 99510 (SAN 698-1763) Tel 907-271-5555; 450 Atlantis, Anchorage, AK 99518 (SAN 698-1771).

†Green, *(Green, Warren H., Inc.; 0-87527),* 8356 Olive Blvd., St. Louis, MO 63132 (SAN 201-4939) Tel 314-991-1335; *CIP.*

Green Acres Schl, *(Green Acres School; 0-9608998),* 11701 Danville Dr., Rockville, MD 20852 (SAN 206-2046) Tel 301-881-4100.

Green Apple, *(Green Apple Pr.; 0-933381),* P.O. Box 1908, North Myrtle Beach, SC 29582 (SAN 691-6791) Tel 803-249-5402.

Green Ball Pr, *(Green Ball Press, The; 0-9610950),* P.O. Box 29771, Elkins Park, PA 19117 (SAN 287-7368) Tel 215-379-6449.

Green Block, *(Green Block Publishing; 0-9609748),* Rte. 2, Carthage, TN 37030 (SAN 263-1520).

Green Bough Pr, *(Green Bough Pr.; 0-9615007),* 3156 W. Laurelhurst Dr., NE, Seattle, WA 98105 (SAN 693-9333) Tel 206-523-0022.

Green Briar Pr, *(Green Briar Pr.; 0-9614511),* 6612 Green Briar Rd., Middleton, WI 53562 (SAN 691-7291) Tel 608-831-3530.

Green Creek Pub Co, *(Green Creek Publishing Co.; 0-930051),* 2251 Van Antwerp Rd., Schenectady, NY 12309 (SAN 669-831X) Tel 518-372-7156.

Green Crown Pr, *(Green Crown Pr.; 0-9613804),* P.O. Box 15445, 7035 Laurel Canyon, North Hollywood, CA 91615-5445 (SAN 679-4084).

Green Dolphin, *(Green Dolphin Bookshop; 0-911904),* 1300 SW Washington St., Portland, OR 97205 (SAN 205-3268) Tel 503-224-3060.

Green Eagle Pr, *(Green Eagle Press; 0-914018),* 241 W. 97th St., New York, NY 10025 (SAN 203-4492) Tel 212-663-2167.

Green Fields Bks, *(Green Fields Bks.; 0-937715),* P.O. Box 8228, Washington, DC 20024 (SAN 659-2287) Tel 202-863-1564; 240 M St., SW, Washington, DC 20024 (SAN 659-2295).

†Green Hill, *(Green Hill Pubs.; 0-916054; 0-89803; 0-915463),* 722 Columbus St., Ottawa, IL 61350 (SAN 281-7578) Tel 815-434-7905; Dist. by: Kampmann & Co., 9 E. 40th St., New York, NY 10016 (SAN 202-5191) Tel 212-685-2928; *CIP.* *Imprints:* Pegma Bks (Pegma Books).(Pegma Bks.); Pub. by Jameson Bks (Jameson Books).

Green Hut, *(Green Hut Pr.; 0-916678),* 1015 Jardin St. E., Appleton, WI 54911 (SAN 208-2888) Tel 414-734-9728.

Green Key Pr, *(Green Key Pr.; 0-910783),* P.O. Box 3801, Seminole, FL 33542 (SAN 264-0708).

Green Leaf CA, *(Green Leaf Pr.; 0-938462),* P.O. Box 6880, Alhambra, CA 91802 (SAN 239-3646) Tel 818-281-6809; 20 W. Commonwealth Ave., Alhambra, CA 91801 (SAN 239-3654).

Green Meadow Bks, *(Green Meadow Bks.; 0-9614817),* Weld Rd. Offices, Phillips, ME 04966 (SAN 693-0441) Tel 207-639-3814.

Green Mountain, *(Green Mountain Micro; 0-916015),* Bathory Rd., Roxbury, VT 05669 (SAN 294-0140) Tel 802-485-6112.

Green Mtn Club, *(Green Mountain Club, The),* P.O. Box 889, 43 State St., Montpelier, VT 05602 (SAN 695-5436).

†Green Oak Pr, *(Green Oak Pr.; 0-931600),* 9339 Spicer Rd., Brighton, MI 48116 (SAN 211-9544) Tel 313-449-4802; *CIP.*

Green Oak Township, *(Green Oak Township Historical Society; 0-936792),* P.O. Box 84, Brighton, MI 48116 (SAN 218-477X).

Green Pub Inc, *(Green, Wayne, Ent.; 0-88006),* Subs. of International Data Group, Rte. 202, N., Peterborough, NH 03458 (SAN 219-7855) Tel 603-525-4201.

Green Pubns, *(Green, Bill, Pubns.; 0-9616095),* 1210c Quarry Rd., Marion, IN 46259 (SAN 698-0996) Tel 317-664-2941.

Green Riv Forge
See Pomme le Terre

Green River, *(Green River Press, Inc.; 0-940580),* Saginaw Valley State College, University Center, MI 48710 (SAN 207-5881) Tel 517-790-4376.

Green St Pr, *(Green Street Pr., The; 0-9614285),* P.O. Box 1957, Cambridge, MA 02238 (SAN 687-4460) Tel 617-628-0539.

Green Tiger Pr, *(Green Tiger Pr., The; 0-88138; 0-915676),* 1061 India St., San Diego, CA 92101 (SAN 219-4775) Tel 619-238-1001. *Imprints:* Star & Elephant Bks (Star & Elephant Books).

Green Val World, *(Green Valley World, Inc.; 0-913444),* 41 S. Ocean Ave., Cayucos, CA 93430 (SAN 663-0758) Tel 805-995-1378.

Green Valley, *(Green Valley Film and Art Center; 0-9614313),* 300 Maple St., Burlington, VT 05401 (SAN 687-5149) Tel 802-862-4929; Dist. by: Countryman Press, P.O. Box 175, Woodstock, VT 05091 (SAN 206-4901) Tel 802-457-1049.

Green Valley Pr, *(Green Valley Pr.; 0-932047),* P.O. Box 816, Williamson, WV 25661 (SAN 683-2601) Tel 304-235-5561.

Greenbeck, *(Greenbeck; 0-9613079),* 849 S. Mountain Ave., Ontario, CA 91762 (SAN 294-8133) Tel 714-988-9513.

Greenbecks
See Greenbeck

†Greenberg Pub Co, *(Greenberg Publishing Co.; 0-89778),* 7543 Main St., Sykesville, MD 21784 (SAN 211-9552) Tel 301-795-7447; *CIP.*

Greenbriar Bks, *(Greenbriar Books; 0-932970),* 5906 Hodgman Dr., Cleveland, OH 44130 (SAN 264-0716).

Greencastle Pr, *(Greencastle Pr., The; 0-934347),* 5 Hanna Court, Greencastle, IN 46135 (SAN 693-6105) Tel 317-653-4770.

Greencrest, *(Greencrest Pr., Inc.; 0-939800),* P.O. Box 7745, Winston-Salem, NC 27109 (SAN 216-8979) Tel 919-722-6463.

†Greene, *(Greene, Stephen, Pr.; 0-8289; 0-86616),* Div. of Viking Penguin, Inc., 15 Muzzey St., Lexington, MA 02173 (SAN 201-6222) Tel 617-861-0170; Dist. by: Viking Penguin, Inc., 40 W. 23rd St., New York, NY 10010 (SAN 200-2442) Tel 212-337-5200; *CIP.*

Greene & Assocs, *(Greene, R. M., & Assocs.; 0-934487),* 14291 Prospect Ave., Tustin, CA 92680 (SAN 693-8892) Tel 714-731-7419.

Greene Coun Home Ext Assn, *(Greene County Homemakers Extension Assn.; 0-9613043),* P.O. Box 56, Wrights, IL 62098 (SAN 293-9827) Tel 217-368-2162.

Greene Pub, *(Greene Publishing; 0-9613371),* P.O. Box 22715, Knoxville, TN 37933-0715 (SAN 657-1433) Tel 615-574-1532.

Greene Pubns, *(Greene Pubns.; 0-9608892),* 1412 Glendale Blvd., Los Angeles, CA 90026 (SAN 241-1180) Tel 213-413-2150.

Greenes Pub, *(Greene's Publishing Co., Inc.; 0-917233),* P.O. Box 69249, Los Angeles, CA 90069 (SAN 655-8577) Tel 818-985-2877; Dist. by: Publishers Group West, 5855 Beaudry St., Emeryville, CA 94608 (SAN 202-8522) Tel 415-658-3453.

Greenfield Bks, *(Greenfield Bks.; 0-9615576),* P.O. Box 4682, Greenwich, CT 06836 (SAN 696-446X) Tel 203-625-5045; 27 Indian Field Rd., Greenwich, CT 06830 (SAN 696-5431).

Greenfield Bks *Imprint of* **Pierian**
Greenfield Pr, *(Greenfield Press; 0-9611846),*
P.O. Box 176, Southport, CT 06490
(SAN 286-1798) Tel 203-268-4878.
Greenfield Pubns, *(Greenfield Pubns.;*
0-9606666), 8720 E. Forrest Dr., Scottsdale,
AZ 85257 (SAN 223-7717)
Tel 602-994-1452.
Greenfld Rev Pr, *(Greenfield Review Pr.;*
0-912678), R.D.1, Box 80, Greenfield Ctr.,
NY 12833 (SAN 203-4506)
Tel 518-584-1728.
†**Greenhaven,** *(Greenhaven Pr.; 0-912616;*
0-89908), 577 Shoreview Park Rd., St. Paul,
MN 55126 (SAN 201-6214)
Tel 612-482-1582; Toll free: 800-231-5163;
CIP.
Greenhigh, *(Greenhigh Pubs.; 0-9615770),* Rte.
9, Box 390-A, Tyler, TX 75706
(SAN 696-4478) Tel 214-597-0757.
Greenhouse Pub, *(Greenhouse Publishing Co.;*
0-9616844), P.O. Box 525, Marshall, VA
22115 (SAN 661-1729) Tel 703-364-1959.
Greenhse Pr, *(Greenhouse Pr.; 0-9615912),*
1239 Sunset Ave., Clinton, NC 28328
(SAN 697-0907) Tel 919-592-3725.
Greenlawn Pr, *(Greenlawn Pr.; 0-937779),* Div.
of LaSalle Co., 107 S. Greenlawn Ave.,
South Bend, IN 46617 (SAN 659-2309);
Dist. by: CRS/Communication Ctr., 107 N.
Michigan, South Bend, IN 46606
(SAN 200-6421).
Greenleaf Co, *(Greenleaf Co.; 0-940582),* P.O.
Box 11393, Chicago, IL 60611
(SAN 223-0011) Tel 312-288-2205.
Greenlf Bks, *(Greenleaf Bks.; 0-934676),*
Canton, ME 04221 (SAN 203-4514).
Greenlf Pubns, *(Greenleaf Pubns.; 0-9608812),*
P.O. Box 50357, Pasadena, CA 91105
(SAN 238-2938).
Greenlight Pr, *(Greenlight Press; 0-930864),*
P.O. Box 360, 1230 Grant Ave., San
Francisco, CA 94133 (SAN 211-6669).
Greenpeace-Ctr Invest Re, *(Greenpeace/Center*
for Investigative Reporting; 0-9607166), 54
Mint St., 4th Floor, San Francisco, CA
94103 (SAN 239-0973) Tel 415-543-1200.
Greenprint Pr
See Neahtawanta Pr
Greens Creek, *(Green's Creek Press; 0-9609406),*
Rte. 5, Dublin, TX 76446 (SAN 262-0316).
Greensboro Symphony, *(Greensboro Symphony*
Guild; 0-9617247), 3607 Sagamore Dr.,
Greensboro, NC 27410 (SAN 663-5563)
Tel 919-668-2072.
Greenspires, *(Greenspires Bks.; 0-9601028),* 2
Chestnut St., Andover, MA 01810
(SAN 208-1571) Tel 617-475-1020.
Greenspring, *(Greenspring Pubns.; 0-915351),* 3
Barstad Court, Lutherville, MD 21093
(SAN 289-9914) Tel 301-828-9316; Dist.
by: Liberty Publishing Co., Inc., P.O. Box
298, Cockeysville, MD 21030
(SAN 211-030X) Tel 301-667-6680.
†**Greenswamp,** *(Greenswamp Pubns.; 0-917431),*
4216 Blackwater Rd., Virginia Beach, VA
23457 (SAN 656-1438) Tel 804-421-3397;
CIP.
Greensward Pr, *(Greensward Pr.; 0-930165),*
P.O. Box 640472, San Francisco, CA 94109
(SAN 670-7149) Tel 213-663-7801; Dist.
by: Nutri Books, P.O. Box 5793, Denver, CO
80223 (SAN 169-054X) Tel 303-778-8383;
Dist. by: Bookpeople, 2929 Fifth St.,
Berkeley, CA 94710 (SAN 168-9517)
Tel 415-549-3030.
GreenTower Pr, *(GreenTower Pr.; 0-9616467),*
Northwest Missouri State Univ., 113 Colden
Hall, Maryville, MO 64468
(SAN 659-2317) Tel 816-562-1559.
Greenvale, *(Greenvale Press; 0-911876),* P.O.
Box 242, Kopperl, TX 76652
(SAN 203-4522) Tel 817-772-8576.
Greenview Pubns, *(Greenview Pubns.;*
0-9606994), Box 7051, Chicago, IL 60680
(SAN 238-8782).
Greenville County Med, *(Greenville County*
Medical Society Aux.; 0-9613679), 2407
Augusta St., Greenville, SC 29605
(SAN 685-4354) Tel 803-233-3205.
Greenville SC Jr League, *(Junior League of*
Greenville, Inc.; 0-9608172), P.O. Box 8703,
Sta. A, Greenville, SC 29604
(SAN 240-236X) Tel 803-288-1991.
Greenw Pr Ltd, *(Greenwich Pr., Ltd.; 0-86713),*
30 Lindeman Dr., Trumbull, CT 06611
(SAN 216-8170) Tel 203-371-6568; Toll
free: 800-243-4246.

Greenwich CT
See Greenw Pr Ltd
Greenwich Des, *(Greenwich Design; 0-9603892),*
Box 611, Hopkins, MN 55343
(SAN 210-7333) Tel 612-935-2574; 910
1/2 Excelsior Ave. W., Hopkins, MN 55343
(SAN 210-7341).
Greenwich Hse *Imprint of* **Outlet Bk Co**
Greenwich Hse-Chatham River Pr *Imprint of*
Outlet Bk Co
†**Greenwillow,** *(Greenwillow Bks.; 0-688),* Div.
of William Morrow & Co., Inc., 105 Madison
Ave., New York, NY 10016
(SAN 202-5760) Tel 212-889-3050; Toll
free: 800-631-1199; Orders to: William
Morrow & Co., Inc., Wilmor Warehouse, 6
Henderson Dr., West Caldwell, NJ 07006
(SAN 202-5779); *CIP.*
†**Greenwood,** *(Greenwood Pr.; 0-8371; 0-313;*
0-89930), Div. of Congressional Information
Services, Inc., 88 Post Rd., W., Westport, CT
06881 (SAN 213-2028) Tel 203-226-3571;
P.O. Box 5007, Westport, CT 06881
(SAN 696-5555); *CIP. Imprints:* Quorum
Bks (Quorum Books).(Quorum Bks.).
Greenwood Hse, *(Greenwood Hse.; 0-9601982),*
1655 Flatbush Ave., Apt. B1902, Brooklyn,
NY 11210 (SAN 212-3584)
Tel 718-253-9299.
Greeting Card Assn, *(Greeting Card Assn.;*
0-938369), 1350 New York Ave., NW, Suite
615, Washington, DC 20005
(SAN 661-275X) Tel 202-393-1778.
Greetings Pub Co, *(Greetings Publishing Co.;*
0-9611848), P.O. Box 107, Asbury Park, NJ
07712 (SAN 286-1844) Tel 201-222-4667.
Gregg-Hamilton, *(Gregg-Hamilton; 0-934800),*
410 S. Meridian, Aberdeen, MS 39730
(SAN 211-9560) Tel 601-369-8120.
Gregg Inc, *(Gregg, Inc.; 0-9615229),* 693 Maple,
Plymouth, MI 48170 (SAN 694-3780)
Tel 313-455-0606.
Gregg Intl, *(Gregg International; 0-576),* Old
Post Rd., Brookfield, VT 05036
(SAN 695-2046) Tel 802-276-3162.
Gregory Pub, *(Gregory Publishing Co.;*
0-911541), 806 N. Maple St., Itasca, IL
60143 (SAN 211-5646).
Gregory Pubns, *(Gregory Pubns.; 0-917224),*
Gateway Sta., Box 440950, Aurora, CO
80044 (SAN 208-6689).
Grenadier Bks, *(Grenadier Bks, Inc.; 0-935691),*
7001 Ulmerton Rd., Suite 4205, Largo, FL
33541 (SAN 696-4524) Tel 813-535-2674;
P.O. Box 17327, Airport Sta., Clearwater, FL
33520 (SAN 696-5458).
Grendhal Poetry Review, *(Grendhal Poetry*
Review Pr., The; 0-938781), 116 Tamarack
St., Vandenberg AFB, Lompoc, CA 93437
(SAN 661-5457) Tel 805-734-1987.
Grenridge Pub, *(Grenridge Publishing;*
0-943410), P.O. Box 4587, Greenville, SC
29608 (SAN 240-6659) Tel 803-294-2207.
†**Greta Bear,** *(Greta Bear Enterprises; 0-931452),*
P.O. Box 9525, Berkeley, CA 94709
(SAN 209-6420); Dist. by: Bookpeople, 2929
Fifth St., Berkeley, CA 94610
(SAN 168-9517); *CIP.*
Grey Art Gallery Study Ctr, *(Grey Art Gallery*
& Study Ctr., New York Univ.; 0-934349),
33 Washington Pl., New York, NY 10003
(SAN 279-8697) Tel 212-598-7603.
Grey Bk, *(Grey Book; 0-912021),* P.O. Box
1237, Flagstaff, AZ 86002 (SAN 264-617X)
Tel 602-774-2923.
†**Grey Fox,** *(Grey Fox Pr.; 0-912516),* Box
31190, San Francisco, CA 94131
(SAN 201-6176); Dist. by: Subterranean Co.,
1327 W. Second, P.O. Box 10233, Eugene,
OR 97440 (SAN 169-7102)
Tel 503-343-6324; *CIP.*
Grey Gull Pubns, *(Grey Gull Publications;*
0-9614592), P.O. Box 69, Damariscotta, ME
04543 (SAN 691-778X) Tel 207-563-1625.
Grey Home Pr, *(Grey Home Pr.),* 8 Court Rd.,
Westford, MA 01886 (SAN 683-2636).
†**Grey Hse Pub,** *(Grey Hse., Publishing, Inc.;*
0-939300), Colonial Bank Bldg., Sharon, CT
06069 (SAN 216-390X) Tel 203-364-0533;
CIP.
Grey Smith-Group
See G S Pubs
Grey Towers Pr, *(Grey Towers Pr.; 0-938549),*
P.O. Box 188, Milford, PA 18337
(SAN 661-6259); Grey Towers, Milford, PA
18337 (SAN 661-6267) Tel 717-296-6401.

Greycliff Pub, *(Greycliff Publishing Co.),* P.O.
Box 1273, Helena, MT 59624
(SAN 663-0804) Tel 406-443-4171.
Greyfalcon Hse, *(Greyfalcon House; 0-914870),*
496 Hudson St., Suite 443, New York, NY
10014 (SAN 207-0723) Tel 212-777-9042.
Greystone Pr, *(Greystone Pr.; 0-9615376),* 306
Mecherle, Apt. 7, Bloomington, IL 61701
(SAN 695-5339) Tel 309-438-2528.
Greystone Pubs, *(Greystone Pubs.; 0-9614761),*
46 Monument Ave., Harrisonburg, VA 22801
(SAN 692-9060) Tel 703-434-2019.
GRF Ltd
See Pomme le Terre
Grgtwn U Law Ctr, *(Georgetown Univ. Law*
Ctr.), 600 New Jersey Ave., NW,
Washington, DC 20001 (SAN 663-6314)
Tel 202-624-8230.
Grieco, *(Grieco; 0-931843),* P.O. Box 1262, San
Juan Capistrano, CA 92693
(SAN 686-0273) Tel 714-498-1536.
Griefworks Pub Co, *(Griefworks Publishing*
Company; 0-932667), 1119 Sylvania Ave.,
Toledo, OH 43612 (SAN 687-7974)
Tel 419-478-2100.
Griesinger Films, *(Griesinger Films; 0-9616762),*
Rte. 2, P.O. Box 1986, French Creek, WV
26218 (SAN 661-3918) Tel 304-924-5035.
Griffin Bks, *(Griffin Bks.; 0-9604770),* 743 11th
Ave., Huntington, WV 25701
(SAN 215-8558).
Griffin Herit, *(Griffin Heritage Assn., The),*
RFD 2, Box 49, Ochlocknee, GA 31773
(SAN 694-5376).
Griffon Hse, *(Griffon Hse. Pubns./Bagehot*
Council; 0-918680), P.O. Box 81,
Whitestone, NY 11357 (SAN 211-6685)
Tel 718-767-8380.
Griggs Print, *(Griggs Printing & Publishing;*
0-918292), Box 1351, 426 First St., Havre,
MT 59501 (SAN 209-441X)
Tel 406-265-7431.
Grindle Pr, *(Grindle Pr.; 0-937065),* Div. of
Avalon Corp., 8340 E. Raintree Dr., Suite
B2, Scottsdale, AZ 85260 (SAN 658-6104)
Tel 602-483-3901.
Grinnell Coll, *(Grinnell College; 0-9607182),*
Grinnell, IA 50112 (SAN 216-3918).
Grinnen-Barrett Pub Co, *(Grinnen-Barrett*
Publishing Co.; 0-9613063), 36 Winchester
St., No. 8, Brookline, MA 02146
(SAN 294-8184) Tel 617-232-1993.
Grinning, *(Grinning Idiot Press; 0-88100),* P.O.
Box 1577, Brooklyn, NY 11202
(SAN 283-2674).
Gris Gris Pr, *(Gris Gris Pr.; 0-9614138),* 2431
S. Acadian, No. 590, Baton Rouge, LA
70808 (SAN 686-5135) Tel 504-927-5437.
Grist Mill, *(Grist Mill; 0-917820),* Energy
Conservation Services, 90 Depot Rd., Eliot,
ME 03903 (SAN 207-4710)
Tel 207-439-3873.
Gritz La Ritz, *(Gritz La Ritz; 0-939679),* P.O.
Box 42619, Portland, OR 97242
(SAN 663-4850); 3212 SE 9th St., No. 8,
Portland, OR 97202 (SAN 663-4869)
Tel 503-232-6800; Dist. by: Far West Book
Services, 3515 NE Hassalo, Portland, OR
97232 (SAN 107-6760) Tel 503-234-7664.
Grolier Ed Corp
See Grolier Inc
Grolier Inc, *(Grolier, Inc.; 0-7172),* Sherman
Tpke., Danbury, CT 06816 (SAN 205-3195)
Tel 203-797-3500.
Groome Ctr, *(Groome Center; 0-916964),* 5225
Loughboro Rd., NW., Washington, DC
20016 (SAN 208-6697) Tel 202-362-7644.
Grooming, *(Grooming Made E-Z; 0-9615460),*
8306 Wilshire Blvd., Suite 840, Beverly Hills,
CA 90211 (SAN 695-7641)
Tel 213-938-5400.
Gros Ventre Treaty, *(Gros Ventre Treaty*
Committee), Ft. Belknap Agency, Harlem,
MT 59526 (SAN 210-900X).
Gross Ent, *(Gross Enterprises; 0-913854),* 1705
The Strand, Manhattan Beach, CA 90266
(SAN 203-4573) Tel 213-545-5410.
Gross Johnson, *(Gross & Johnson Publishing*
Co.; 0-935351), 989 Woodbourne Dr., Suite
500, Atlanta, GA 30310 (SAN 696-4540)
Tel 404-977-5350.
Grosvenor Soc, *(Grosvenor Society, The (Friends*
of the Buffalo & Erie County Public Library);
0-9615896), Lafayette Sq., Buffalo, NY
14203 (SAN 697-1040) Tel 716-856-7525.

Grosvenor Sq, (Grosvenor Square Assocs, USA; 0-9611472), P.O. Box 153, Wilkinsonville, MA 01590 (SAN 283-1341) Tel 714-458-1869.

Grosvenor USA, (Grosvenor U. S. A.; 0-901269), Subs. of Grosvenor Bks., London, UK, P.O. Box 8647, Richmond, VA 23226 (SAN 663-1606) Tel 703-288-7624; Dist. by: M & B Fulfillment, 540 Barnum Ave., Bridgeport, CT 06610 (SAN 282-6062) Tel 203-366-1900.

Grounder Pub, (Grounder Publishing; 0-930271), P.O. Box 42399, Houston, TX 77242-2399 (SAN 670-8447) Tel 713-784-8739.

Group Bks, (Group Bks.; 0-936664; 0-931529), P.O. Box 481, Loveland, CO 80539 (SAN 214-4689); 2890 N. Monroe, Loveland, CO 80539 (SAN 662-1376) Tel 303-669-3836.

Group Four Pub
See Group Four Pubns

Group Four Pubns, (Group Four Pubns., Inc.; 0-934125), 1307 N. 45th St., Seattle, WA 98103 (SAN 693-2630) Tel 206-526-8577.

Group Health Assoc of Amer, (Group Health Assn. of America; 0-936164), 1129 20th St., NW, Washington, DC 20036 (SAN 270-627X).

Groupwork Today, (Groupwork Today Inc.; 0-916068), P.O. Box 258, South Plainfield, NJ 07080 (SAN 208-0370) Tel 201-755-4803.

†**Grove,** (Grove Pr.; 0-8021; 0-394), 920 Broadway, New York, NY 10010 (SAN 201-4890) Tel 212-529-3600; Toll free: 800-638-6460; CIP. Imprints: BC (Black Cat Books).(Black Cat Bks.); Ever (Evergreen Books).(Evergreen Bks.); EverBC (Evergreen-Black Cat Books).(Evergreen-Black Cat Bks.); Zebra (Zebra Books).(Zebra Bks.).

Grove Educ Tech, (Grove Educational Technologies; 0-936735), P.O. Box 405, Lake Grove, NY 11755 (SAN 699-9840) Tel 516-588-5948; 27 Hy Pl., Lake Grove, NY 11755 (SAN 699-9859).

Grove Farm Home, (Grove Farm Homestead & Waioli Mission Hse.; 0-9617174), P.O. Box 1631, Lihue, Kauai, HI 96766 (SAN 663-1282) Tel 808-245-3202.

†**Groves Dict Music,** (Groves Dictionaries of Music, Inc.; 0-943818), Div. of Peninsula Publishers Ltd., 15 E. 26th St., New York, NY 10010 (SAN 211-9579) Tel 212-481-1332; Toll free: 800-221-2123; CIP. Imprints: Pub. by Stockton Pr (Stockton Press).

Growing Pains Pr, (Growing Pains Press; 0-941834), 90 Club Rd., Riverside, CT 06878 (SAN 239-2208) Tel 203-637-9771.

Growing Together, (Growing Together Press; 0-9604118), P.O. Box 2983, Stanford, CA 94305 (SAN 215-7683).

Growth Assoc, (Growth Assocs.; 0-918834), P.O. Box 18429, Rochester, NY 14618-0429 (SAN 210-430X) Tel 716-244-1225.

Growth Assocs Inc, (Growth Associates, Inc.; 0-915469), P.O. Box 38705, Germantown, TN 38183-0705 (SAN 291-1825) Tel 901-754-6678; 7698 Blackberry Ridge Cove, Germantown, TN 38138 (SAN 291-1833).

Growth Bks
See Growth Pub

Growth Pub, (Growth Publishing; 0-931225), P.O. Box 661, Herndon, VA 22070 (SAN 682-9112) Tel 703-471-1160.

Growth Resources, (Growth Resources, Inc.; 0-936965), 22322 Pineapple Walk, Boca Raton, FL 33433 (SAN 658-6546) Tel 305-394-5915.

Growth Unltd, (Growth Unlimited, Inc.; 0-9601334; 0-916927), 31 East Ave., S., Battle Creek, MI 49017 (SAN 210-8976) Tel 616-965-2229.

GRQ Inc, (GRQ, Inc.), 19 E. Central Ave., Paoli, PA 19301 (SAN 663-4621) Tel 215-251-9525.

Grt Lks Pr, (Great Lakes Pr., Inc.; 0-9614760), 4662 Vanatta Rd., Okemos, MI 48864 (SAN 692-9745) Tel 517-349-3302.

Grt Plains Emporium, (Great Plains Emporium; 0-9616365), P.O. Box 416, Schaller, IA 51053 (SAN 658-9448) Tel 712-275-4542; 303 Berwick, Schaller, IA 51053 (SAN 658-9456).

†**Grune,** (Grune & Stratton, Inc.; 0-8089), Subs. of Harcourt Brace Jovanovich Inc., ; Toll free: 800-321-5068; c/o Promotion Dept., Orlando, FL 32887-0018 (SAN 206-8990) Tel 305-345-4212; CIP.

Gruter Inst, (Gruter Institute for Law & Behavioral Research), 158 Goya Rd., Portola Valley, CA 94025 (SAN 200-5859) Tel 415-854-2034.

Grynberg Pub, (Grynberg Publishing Corp.; 0-935537), 5000 S. Quebec, Suite 500, Denver, CO 80237 (SAN 696-4559) Tel 303-850-7497.

Gryphon Bks, (Gryphon Bks.; 0-936071), P.O. Box 209, Brooklyn, NY 11228 (SAN 697-0834); 1148 73rd St., Brooklyn, NY 11228 (SAN 697-0842) Tel 718-745-1811.

Gryphon Hse, (Gryphon Hse., Inc.; 0-87659), 3706 Otis St., P.O. Box 275, Mount Rainier, MD 20712 (SAN 169-3190) Tel 301-779-6200; Toll free: 800-638-0928.

Gryphon West Pubs, (Gryphon West Pubs.; 0-943482), P.O. Box 12096, Seattle, WA 98102 (SAN 240-4818).

GS
See Girl Scouts USA

G's Frankly Speaking, (Gerry's Frankly Speaking; 0-9612578), P.O. Box 2225, Salem, OR 97308 (SAN 289-2138) Tel 503-585-8411; 475 Cottage, Salem, OR 97301 (SAN 289-2146).

GSJ Press, (GSJ Pr.; 0-9609842), Div. of Gray Endeavors, Inc., 205 Willow St., South Hamilton, MA 01982 (SAN 270-577X) Tel 617-468-4486.

GSMNH, (Great Smoky Mountains Natural History Assn.; 0-937207), Rte. 2, Gatlinburg, TN 37738 (SAN 658-7267) Tel 615-436-7318.

GU Clin Soc
See Clin Soc Assn

GU-Sch Summer & Cont Ed, (Georgetown Univ., School for Summer & Continuing Education; 0-939998), Washington, DC 20057 (SAN 216-8162).

Guadalupe River Pr, (Guadalupe River Press), c/o Trinity University Bookstore, 715 Stadium Rd., San Antonio, TX 78284 (SAN 238-0617).

Guappones Pubs, (Guappone's Pubs.; 0-9615230), R.D. 1, Box 10, McClellandtown, PA 15458 (SAN 209-4428) Tel 412-737-5172.

Guarionex Pr, (Guarionex Pr., Ltd.; 0-935966), 201 W. 77th St., New York, NY 10024 (SAN 216-1370) Tel 212-724-5259; Dist. by: Bookpeople, 2929 Fifth St., Berkeley, CA 94710 (SAN 168-9517) Tel 415-549-3030.

Guastella Pubns, (Guastella Pubns.; 0-9607230), P.O. Box 6082, Tallahassee, FL 32301 (SAN 239-0981).

Guffey Bks, (Guffey Books, Inc.), 6634 S. Broadway, Littleton, CO 80120 (SAN 203-462X) Tel 303-798-6406.

Guggenheim, (Guggenheim Research Assn.; 0-910377), 444 SW Birdsdale Dr., Gresham, OR 97030 (SAN 262-0324); Dist. by: Salem Press of Oregon, 1021 Oregon National Bldg., 610 SW Adler, Gresham, OR 97205 (SAN 262-0332).

Guggenrobin Pubs, (Guggenrobin Pubs.; 0-936967), 30-08 Broadway, Astoria, NY 11106 (SAN 658-7798) Tel 718-956-4476; P.O. Box 156, Astoria, NY 11106 (SAN 658-7801).

Guidance Ent, (Guidance Enterprises; 0-930199), P.O. Box 4500, Prescott, AZ 86302 (SAN 670-7920) Tel 602-776-0277.

Guide Pr WI, (Guide Pr.; 0-9615699), 50 Whitcomb Cir., No. 5, Madison, WI 53705 (SAN 696-4567) Tel 608-273-2914; P.O. Box 173, Verona, WI 53593 (SAN 696-5466).

Guide-Pro Assocs, (Guide-Pro Assocs.; 0-9615947), P.O. Box 402, Massapequa Park, NY 11762 (SAN 697-1113) Tel 516-798-9481; 21 Ave. Louise, Massapequa Park, NY 11762 (SAN 697-1121).

Guide to Reprints, (Guide to Reprints, Inc.; 0-918086), P.O. Box 249, Kent, CT 06757 (SAN 210-2080) Tel 203-927-4588.

Guide to Rich, (Guide to Richmond; 0-9607442), P.O. Box 242, Midlothian, VA 23113 (SAN 239-2216) Tel 804-794-8068.

Guideline Pub, (Guideline Publishing Co.; 0-917474), 336 S. Occidental Blvd., Los Angeles, CA 90057 (SAN 203-4638) Tel 213-382-4500.

Guidelines Pr, (Guidelines Press; 0-932570), 1307 S. Killian Dr., Lake Park, FL 33403 (SAN 212-0984) Tel 305-842-9411.

Guidepost Pubs & Dists, (Guidepost Pubs. & Distributors, Inc.; 0-936217), P.O. Box 93112, Cleveland, OH 44101 (SAN 697-1067) Tel 216-268-1356; 1 Public Sq., Suite 802, Cleveland, OH 44113-2101 (SAN 697-1075); Dist. by: Circular, Ltd., 1 Public Sq., Suite 802, Cleveland, OH 44113-2101 (SAN 294-7153) Tel 216-241-2600.

Guides Multinatl Busn, (Guides to Multinational Business, Inc.; 0-931000), P.O. Box 92, Harvard Sq., Cambridge, MA 02138 (SAN 212-2561).

Guifford-Hill, (Guifford-Hill Publishing Co.), Rte. 8, Box 264, London, KY 40741 (SAN 211-5123).

†**Guignol Bks,** (Guignol Bks.; 0-941062), P.O. Box 247, Rhinebeck, NY 12572 (SAN 281-7594) Tel 914-876-2141; CIP.

Guild Bks, (Guild Books, Catholic Polls, Inc.; 0-912080), 86 Riverside Dr., New York, NY 10024 (SAN 203-4646) Tel 212-799-2600.

Guild Hall, (Guild Hall Museum; 0-933793), 158 Main St., East Hampton, NY 11937 (SAN 278-9698) Tel 516-324-0806.

Guild Pr, (Guild Pr.; 0-940248), P.O. Box 22583, Robbinsdale, MN 55422 (SAN 220-3340) Tel 612-566-1842.

†**Guild Psy,** (Guild for Psychological Studies Publishing Hse.; 0-917479), 2230 Divisadero St., San Francisco, CA 94115 (SAN 656-0687) Tel 415-788-3035; CIP.

Guildhall Pubs, (Guildhall Pubs., Ltd.; 0-940518), P.O. Box 325, Peoria, IL 61651 (SAN 219-838X); 231 Oak Ct, Peoria, IL 61614 (SAN 662-0256) Tel 309-688-5985.

†**Guilford Pr,** (Guilford Pr., The; 0-89862), Div. of Guilford Pubns. Inc., 200 Park Ave., S., New York, NY 10003 (SAN 212-9442) Tel 212-674-1900; Toll free: 800-221-3966; CIP.

Guinea Hollow, (Guinea Hollow Press/Films; 0-916344), P.O. Box 59, Stanhope, NJ 07874 (SAN 281-7624); Orders to: 190 Waverly Place, New York, NY 10014 (SAN 281-7616) Tel 212-924-4586.

Guitar & Song, (Guitar & Song Publications; 0-932327), 1015 Highland Ave., Dayton, OH 45410 (SAN 686-8088) Tel 513-252-0424.

Guitar Editions, (Guitar Editions, Inc.; 0-939721), P.O. Box 2042, Charlottesville, VA 22902 (SAN 663-592X); 1116 E. Market St., Charlottesville, VA 22901 (SAN 663-5938) Tel 804-296-0105.

Guitar Found Amer, (Guitar Foundation of America; 0-9616877), P.O. Box 1090A, Garden Grove, CA 92642 (SAN 661-6631) Tel 415-326-3809; 604 Tennyson Ave., Palo Alto, CA 94301 (SAN 661-664X).

Gulf Coast Ed, (Gulf Coast Educators Press), 4430 Piedmont Rd., Pensacola, FL 32503 (SAN 262-0340).

†**Gulf Coast Lab,** (Gulf Coast Research Laboratory; 0-917235), E. Beach, Ocean Springs, MS 39564 (SAN 655-8593) Tel 601-875-2244; CIP.

Gulf Coast Pub, (Gulf Coast Publishing Co.; 0-939127), P.O. Box 66940, St. Petersburg, FL 33736 (SAN 662-4847); 7645 Sun Island Dr., St. Petersburg, FL 33707 (SAN 662-4855) Tel 813-360-1495.

†**Gulf Pub,** (Gulf Publishing Co.; 0-87201; 0-88415), P.O. Box 2608, Houston, TX 77252 (SAN 201-6125) Tel 713-529-4301; CIP. Imprints: Hutchins Hse (Hutchins House).(Hutchins Hse.); Lone Star Bks (Lone Star Books).(Lone Star Bks.).

Gulfport Hist, (Gulfport Historical Society; 0-9615746), 3134 Beach Blvd., Saint Petersburg, FL 33707 (SAN 696-4575) Tel 813-321-7095.

Gull Bks, (Gull Bks.; 0-940584), Box 273A, Prattsville, NY 12468 (SAN 281-7632) Tel 518-299-3171.

Gumbs & Thomas, (Gumbs & Thomas Pubs.; 0-936073), 2067 Broadway, Suite 41, New York, NY 10023 (SAN 697-0877) Tel 212-870-0969.

Gun Hill, *(Gun Hill Publishing Co.; 0-9600228),* P.O. Box 539, Yazoo City, MS 39194 (SAN 203-4654) Tel 601-746-3196.

Gun Ownrs Fund, *(Gun Owners Foundation; 0-9613968),* 5881 Leesburg Pike, Suite 204, Falls Church, VA 22041 (SAN 682-2959) Tel 703-931-5033.

Gun Room, *(Gun Room Pr.; 0-88227),* 127 Raritan Ave., Highland Park, NJ 08904 (SAN 201-8357) Tel 201-545-4344.

Gunderson, *(Gundersen, Dr. Richard O.; 0-9608080),* 350 W. 66th St., Yuma, AZ 85364 (SAN 240-2270) Tel 602-726-9229.

Gunnerman Pr, *(Gunnerman Pr.; 0-936075),* P.O. Box 4292, Auburn Hills, MI 48057 (SAN 695-541X); 6444 Malvern, Troy, MI 48098 (SAN 696-9461) Tel 313-879-2779.

Gunther Pubs, *(Gunther Pubs.; 0-916191),* P.O. Box 75932, Washington, DC 20013 (SAN 294-9350) Tel 202-722-5111.

Guptill, *(Guptill Music; 0-916715),* P.O. Box 521, Orange, CA 92666 (SAN 653-8657) Tel 714-538-2667; 1419 Joana Dr., Santa Ana, CA 92701 (SAN 653-8665).

Gurze Bks, *(Gurze Bks.; 0-936077),* P.O. Box 20066, Santa Barbara, CA 93120 (SAN 697-0818) Tel 805-687-7922; 1727 Mountain Ave., Santa Barbara, CA 93101 (SAN 697-0826) Tel 805-682-0956.

Gustafson Horse
See GHC

Gustav Broukal *Imprint of Am Atheist*

Gusto Pr, *(Gusto Press; 0-933906),* P.O. Box 1009, 2960 Philip Ave., Bronx, NY 10465 (SAN 212-9450) Tel 212-931-8964.

Gut Level Pub, *(Gut-Level Publishing; 0-9616814),* 296 Bonefish Ct., Aptos, CA 95003 (SAN 661-0986) Tel 408-688-6547.

†**Gutenberg,** *(Gutenberg Press, The; 0-9603872),* P.O. Box 26345, San Francisco, CA 94126 (SAN 213-9278) Tel 415-548-3776; *CIP.*

Guthrie Gary
See Gary Guthrie

Guthrie Pub, *(Guthrie Publishing Co.; 0-941064),* P.O. Box 152, Dalbo, MN 55017 (SAN 217-3751) Tel 612-689-4350.

Gutman Lib, *(Harvard University, Gutman Library; 0-943484),* Educational Technology Ctr., Appian Way, Cambridge, MA 02138 (SAN 658-0807) Tel 617-495-4225.

Gwendolyn Pr, *(Gwendolyn Pr.; 0-937503),* 107 Gwendolyn Dr., Vidalia, GA 30474 (SAN 658-9480) Tel 912-537-0195.

Gwenthie Pub
See Gwethine Pub Co

Gwethine Pub Co, *(Gwethine Publishing Co.; 0-9605288),* 201 N. Wells St., Chicago, IL 60606 (SAN 220-0007) Tel 312-372-8105.

Gwinnett Hist, *(Gwinnett Historical Society; 0-914923),* P.O. Box 261, Lawrenceville, GA 30246 (SAN 289-2197) Tel 404-962-1450.

GWP
See Natl Lit Guild

GWU Law, *(George Washington Univ. Law Schl.),* 720 20th St., NW, Washington, DC 20006 (SAN 227-3004).

GWU Natl Law, *(George Washington Univ. National Law Ctr., Government Contracts Program; 0-935165),* Academic Ctr., Rm. T412, 801 22nd St. NW, Washington, DC 20052 (SAN 227-3012) Tel 202-676-6815; Toll free: 800-446-2221.

Gypsum Assn, *(Gypsum Assn.),* 1603 Orrington Ave., Suite 1210, Evanston, IL 60201 (SAN 224-8808) Tel 312-491-1744.

Gypsy Lore Soc, *(Gypsy Lore Society, North American Chapter),* Affil. of Gypsy Lore Society, 2104 Dexter Ave., No. 203, Silver Spring, MD 20902 (SAN 241-3876) Tel 301-681-3123.

H Allen Enterprises
See Howard Allen

H & B Hess Co, *(H & B Hess Co.; 0-916507),* P.O. Box 12653, Jackson, MS 39211 (SAN 295-4184) Tel 601-956-0717.

H & D Pr, *(H & D Pr.; 0-9614223),* P.O. Box 1284, Staten Island, NY 10314 (SAN 686-7189) Tel 718-447-5647.

H & E Van Pelt, *(Van Pelt, Harold & Erica; 0-9616785),* 752 Seward St., Los Angeles, CA 90038 (SAN 659-3712) Tel 213-462-6604.

H & H Pub, *(H&H Pub. Co., Inc.; 0-943202),* 2165 Sunnydale Blvd., Suite N, Clearwater, FL 33575 (SAN 240-5350) Tel 813-442-7760.

H & H Pubns CA, *(H & H Pubns.; 0-910197),* 1524 Hudson St., Redwood City, CA 94061 (SAN 241-5364) Tel 415-364-3402.

H-&-H Pubs, *(H & H Pubs.),* P.O. Box 555, Hope Mills, NC 28348 (SAN 670-6940) Tel 919-425-2241.

H & S Pub Co, *(H & S Publishing Co.; 0-9609268),* P.O. Box 304, Allenhurst, NJ 07711 (SAN 260-0641) Tel 201-775-3251.

H Ashby Bks, *(Ashby, Helena, Bks.; 0-9614781),* Box 187, Roachdale, IN 46172 (SAN 692-9230) Tel 317-522-1309.

H Askenasy, *(Askenasy, Hans; 0-9613497),* P.O. Box 4197, Laguna Beach, CA 92652 (SAN 657-3479) Tel 714-896-7251.

H B A
See Heirloom Bks

H B Davis, *(Davis, H.B., Co.; 0-942016),* 480 Canal Street, New York, NY 10013 (SAN 239-5223).

H B Reid, *(Reid, Hugh B.; 0-911244),* 2500 S. State St., Ann Arbor, MI 48104 (SAN 694-3195); Dist. by: Reid Publishing, 1255 Buckingham, Grosse Pointe, MI 48230 (SAN 238-566X) Tel 313-882-0532.

H C Billings, *(Billings, Harold C., Jr.; 0-9613642),* 35 Woolson Ave., Springfield, VT 05156 (SAN 670-8021) Tel 802-885-4764.

H C Lanks, *(Lanks, Herbert),* Inter-American Features, Jenkintown, PA 19046 (SAN 265-3869).

H C Lund, *(Lund, Harry C.; 0-9614818),* 1440 Wayne St., Traverse City, MI 49684 (SAN 693-0662).

H C Maxwell, *(Maxwell, Harvey C.; 0-9600068),* P.O. Box 824, Laguna Beach, CA 92652 (SAN 217-2518) Tel 714-494-2606.

H C Molinoff, *(Molinoff, Henry C.; 0-9616983),* 234 Edgewood Ave., Smithtown, NY 11787 (SAN 661-759X) Tel 516-277-9708; Dist. by: New Era Pr., P.O. Box 29, Farmingdale, NY 11735 (SAN 264-2441) Tel 516-277-9708.

H C Sun, *(Sun, H. C.),* 114 South Fox Road, Sterling, VA 22170 (SAN 210-1386) Tel 703-430-7040.

H D Burrows, *(Burrows, Hal D., /Inner Press; 0-916886),* 429 E. 98th St., No. 1, Inglewood, CA 90301 (SAN 211-0180) Tel 213-671-5959.

H D Saunders, *(Saunders, H. Duane; 0-9616461),* 9840 Purgatory Rd., Eden Prairie, MN 55344 (SAN 659-3046) Tel 612-944-1656.

H E Bixler, *(Bixler, Herbert E.; 0-9610066),* 13 South Hill Rd., Jaffrey Center, NH 03454 (SAN 268-3415) Tel 603-532-6918.

H E Blanck, *(Blanck, Helen E.; 0-9603700),* 1228 108th Ave., NE., Minneapolis, MN 55434 (SAN 208-0702) Tel 612-757-5374.

H E Crissey, *(Crissey, Harrington E., Jr.; 0-9608878),* 1806 Benton St., No. 1, Philadelphia, PA 19152 (SAN 241-1059) Tel 215-745-8503.

H E Ferguson, *(Ferguson, Howard E.; 0-9611180),* 22445 Lorain Rd., Fairview Park, OH 44126 (SAN 277-6863) Tel 216-734-3233.

H E Howard, *(H. E. Howard, Inc.; 0-930919),* P.O. Box 4161, Lynchburg, VA 24502 (SAN 679-680X) Tel 804-846-1146.

H E Reid, *(Reid, Hazel E.; 0-9601892),* P.O. Box 317, Manhattanville, New York, NY 10027 (SAN 211-0148) Tel 212-490-0077.

H E Seals, *(Seals, Howard E.; 0-9600232),* 3831 S. Michigan Ave., Rear Bldg., Chicago, IL 60653 (SAN 203-4697) Tel 312-285-3256.

H E Wheeler, *(Wheeler, Harris E., Pub.; 0-9616830),* Box 245, Bradford, NH 03221 (SAN 661-163X); Water St., Bradford, NH 02331 (SAN 661-1648).

H Estes, *(Estes, Hiawatha, & Assocs.; 0-911008),* P.O. Box 404-RR, Northridge, CA 91328 (SAN 206-8389) Tel 818-885-6588.

H F Snow, *(Snow, Helen F.; 0-911392),* 148 Mungertown Rd., Madison, CT 06443 (SAN 206-3131) Tel 203-245-9714.

H G Carson Ent, *(Carson, H. Glenn, Enterprises, Ltd.; 0-941620),* Drawer 71, Deming, NM 88031 (SAN 239-1716) Tel 505-546-6100.

H G Cushing, *(Cushing, Helen Grant; 0-9603588),* 339 E. 58th St., New York, NY 10022 (SAN 213-9995) Tel 212-355-6048; Orders to: G. H. Cushing, 16237 Gledhill St., Sepulveda, CA 91343 (SAN 214-0004).

H G Gordon, *(Gordon, Harry G.; 0-9612184),* 711 Coleridge Dr., Greensboro, NC 27410 (SAN 287-2935) Tel 919-279-6400.

H Glackin
See Goshindo Martial

H Gray, *(Gray, Herbi; 0-9608406),* P.O. Box 2343, Olympia, WA 98507 (SAN 240-6640) Tel 206-491-4138.

H Gregory, *(Gregory, Howard, Associates; 0-9607086),* 640 The Village No. 209, Redondo Beach, CA 90277 (SAN 206-4502) Tel 213-379-7190.

H H Towne, *(Towne, Holly H.; 0-9613947),* Rte. 7, P.O. Box 378, Sevierville, TN 37862 (SAN 686-2713).

H H Wolfe, *(Wolfe, Howard H.; 0-9600850),* 12405 Davis Blvd., SE, Fort Myers, FL 33905 (SAN 206-0167) Tel 813-694-1825.

H Hayashi, *(Hayashi, Hiroshi; 0-9616815),* 112 Allston St., Allston, MA 02134 (SAN 661-0994) Tel 617-354-0365.

H Holt & Co, *(Holt, Henry, & Co.; 0-8050),* 521 Fifth Ave., New York, NY 10175 (SAN 200-6472) Tel 212-599-7600. Former trade-book arm of Holt, Rinehart & Winston. Acquired in 1985 by Verlagsgruppe Georg von Holtzbrinck, from CBS. *Imprints:* North South Bks (North-South Books).

H I Hays, *(Hays, Helen Ireland; 0-9611798),* 108 S. William St., Johnstown, NY 12095 (SAN 285-2675) Tel 212-757-1176.

H Isaacs, *(Isaacs, Harold; 0-9601406),* P.O. Box 237, Plains, GA 31780 (SAN 663-2947); Dist. by: Peanut Brigade, P.O. Box 237, Plains, GA 31780 (SAN 210-976X) Tel 912-924-8287.

H J Cichy, *(Cichy, Helen J.; 0-9601852),* Brandon, MN 56315 (SAN 211-190X).

H J Dhillon, *(Dhillon, Harinder J.; 0-9617188),* 2907 Bristol Channel Ct., Pasadena, MD 21122 (SAN 663-2572) Tel 301-437-7978; Dist. by: U. S. Government Printing Office, Stop SSMR, Washington, DC 20401 (SAN 206-152X) Tel 202-783-3238.

H J Kramer Inc, *(Kramer, H. J., Inc.; 0-915811),* P.O. Box 1082, Tiburon, CA 94920 (SAN 294-0833); Orders to: 1474 West Ave. No. 43, Los Angeles, CA 90065 (SAN 662-2259); Dist. by: Publishers Group West, 5855 Beaudry St., Emeryville, CA 94608 (SAN 202-8522); Dist. by: Bookpeople, 2929 Fifth St., Berkeley, CA 94710 (SAN 168-9517).

H J Schneider
See World Wide OR

H J Williams, *(Williams, H. J.; 0-9616843),* P.O. Box 203, Sausalito, CA 94966 (SAN 661-101X); 191 Santa Rosa Ave., Sausalito, CA 94965 (SAN 661-1028) Tel 415-332-8635; Dist. by: Publishers Group West, 5855 Beaudry St., Emeryville, CA 94608 (SAN 202-8522) Tel 415-658-3453.

H John & Co
See Henry John & Co

H Jones, *(Jones, Harry; 0-9601980),* P.O. Box 10054, Austin, TX 78766-1054 (SAN 212-615X) Tel 512-451-2644.

H Jones Pub, *(Jones, Hank, Publishing Co.; 0-9613888),* P.O. Box 8341, Universal City, CA 91608 (SAN 682-2983) Tel 818-766-3567.

H K Goodkind, *(Goodkind, Herbert K., Estate of; 0-9600498),* 151 Fenimore Rd., Apt. 63B, Mamaroneck, NY 10543 (SAN 203-4700) Tel 914-698-7854.

H Kahn, *(Kahn, Hannah; 0-9602340),* 3301 NE Fifth Ave., Suite 318, Miami, FL 33137 (SAN 208-1342) Tel 305-576-1499.

H Keith Burns, *(Burns, H. Keith, Publishing; 0-943842),* 6026 Mesa Ave., Los Angeles, CA 90042 (SAN 241-0079) Tel 213-256-5436.

H Keller Natl Ctr, *(Keller, Helen, National Ctr. for Deaf-Blind Youths & Adults; 0-9615138),* 111 Middle Neck Rd., Sands Point, NY 11050 (SAN 277-7150) Tel 516-944-8900.

H L Levin, *(Levin, Hugh Lauter, Assocs.; 0-88363),* 236 W. 26th St., Suite 5 NE, New York, NY 10001 (SAN 201-6109) Tel 212-242-1405; Dist. by: Macmillan Publishing Company, Front & Brown Sts., Riverside, NJ 08370 (SAN 650-0412).

H L Markow, *(Markow, Herbert L.; 0-934108),* P.O. Box 011451, Miami, FL 33101 (SAN 281-9759) Tel 305-858-0200; Dist. by: William W Gaunt & Sons, Inc., 3011 Gulf Dr., Holmes Beach, FL 33510-2199 (SAN 202-9413) Tel 813-778-5211.

H L Murvin, *(Murvin, H. L., Publisher; 0-9608498),* 500 Vernon St., Oakland, CA 94610 (SAN 240-7264) Tel 415-658-7517.

H L Shenson, *(Shenson, Howard L., Inc.; 0-910549),* 20121 Ventura Blvd., No. 245, Woodland Hills, CA 91354 (SAN 260-1346) Tel 818-703-1415.

H L Willis, *(Willis, Harold L.; 0-912311),* 623 Vine St., Wisconsin Dells, WI 53965 (SAN 277-6871).

H Lalvani, *(Lalvani, Haresh),* P.O. Box 1538, New York, NY 10116 (SAN 211-3228).

H Lamb, *(Lamb, Howard; 0-9609150),* P.O. Box 796, Mill Valley, CA 94942 (SAN 241-3906) Tel 415-388-1163.

H Lavin Assocs Inc
See Lavin Assocs

H Leonard Pub Corp, *(Leonard, Hal, Publishing Corp.; 0-9607350; 0-88188),* 8112 W. Bluemound Rd., P.O. Box 13819, Milwaukee, WI 53213 (SAN 239-250X) Tel 414-774-3630; Toll free: 800-558-4774.

H Linder, *(Linder, Herbert; 0-917396),* 55 Park Ave., New York, NY 10016 (SAN 206-8605) Tel 212-685-2571.

H M Cardamone, *(Cardamone, Helen M., Pub.; 0-9608330),* 2108 Genesee St., Utica, NY 13502 (SAN 240-5229) Tel 315-735-0363.

H M Gousha, *(Gousha, H. M., Co., The; 0-88098),* 2001 The Alameda, San Jose, CA 95150 (SAN 281-7519) Tel 408-296-1060; Orders to: Dept. TM, P.O. Box 6227, San Jose, CA 95150 (SAN 281-7527).

H M Rogers, *(Rogers, Helga M.; 0-9602294),* 4975 59th Ave., S., St. Petersburg, FL 33715 (SAN 207-0316) Tel 813-864-3292.

H M Shelton
See Willow Pub

H M Ward Lab, *(Ward, H. M., Memorial Laboratory, Inc.; 0-9615506),* P.O. Box 207, Valley Home, CA 95384 (SAN 696-2939) Tel 209-847-2509; Lab Building, 13906 Valley Home Rd., Oakdale, CA 95801 (SAN 696-2947).

H Mark-Corbett, *(Mark-Corbett, Harry; 0-9608152),* 34 Janet Dr., North Haven, CT 06473 (SAN 240-1487).

H Miller Res, *(Miller, Herman, Research Corp.; 0-936658),* Subs. of Herman Miller, Inc., 3971 S. Research Park Dr., Ann Arbor, MI 48104 (SAN 221-3842) Tel 313-994-0200.

H Ouimette, *(Ouimette, Helen; 0-9617116),* 1706 Pitcher St., Neillsville, WI 54456 (SAN 662-7048) Tel 715-743-3422.

H P Bks
See HP Bks

H P Freeman CA, *(Freeman, H. P., Writer-Pub.; 0-9609920),* 1125 Monroe St., Red Bluff, CA 96080 (SAN 270-3408) Tel 916-527-1679; P.O. Box 93, Red Bluff, CA 96080 (SAN 658-0742).

H Peck Bks, *(Peck, Herbert Books; 0-9617153),* 174-4550 N. Flowing Wells Rd., Tucson, AZ 85705 (SAN 663-3676) Tel 602-887-9734.

H R Gale, *(Gale, Hoyt Rodney),* 669 Sturtevant Dr., Sierra Madre, CA 91024 (SAN 212-8209) Tel 818-355-2988.

H R Lurie, *(Lurie, Hannah Ross; 0-9600728),* Carlene Apts., B102, 2500 Belmont Ave., Philadelphia, PA 19131 (SAN 201-6079) Tel 215-472-3510.

H R M Comm Inc, *(HRM Communications, Inc.; 0-9611254),* 201 E. 77th St., New York, NY 10021 (SAN 282-8723) Tel 212-734-4958.

H R Niemi, *(Niemi, Helena Ruth; 0-9607800),* P.O. Box 155, Oakridge, OR 97463 (SAN 240-0537) Tel 503-782-3165.

H R O'Donnell Guild, *(O'Donnell, Hugh Roe, Guild, The; 0-9617208),* ST. Paul's Church, c/o Father Gerald McCarthy, Tappen, ND 58487 (SAN 663-2785) Tel 701-845-0432; Dist. by: Irish Books & Media, 683 Osceola Ave., St. Paul, MN 55105 (SAN 215-1987) Tel 612-647-5678.

H R Schwab, *(Schwab, Henry R., /Doberman Bks.; 0-939681),* 290 York St., New Haven, CT 06511 (SAN 663-4842) Tel 203-777-8954; Dist. by: Inland Book Co., P.O. Box 261, 22 Hemingway Ave., East Haven, CT 06512 (SAN 200-4151) Tel 203-467-4257.

H Ranieri, *(Ranieri, Helene),* 2760 Devonshire Place, NW, Washington, DC 20008 (SAN 212-8128).

H Reichner, *(Reichner, Herbert; 0-9601520),* Shaker Hill, Enfield, NH 03748 (SAN 205-2210) Tel 603-632-7725.

H S Dakin, *(Dakin, H. S., Co.; 0-930420),* 3101 Washington St., San Francisco, CA 94115 (SAN 210-5934).

H S S W I, *(Huron Shores Summer Writing Institute; 0-939345),* 445 N. Fourth St., Rogers City, MI 49779 (SAN 662-4871) Tel 517-734-3310.

H S Wake, *(Wake, Harry S.; 0-9607048),* 4171 Stettler Way, San Diego, CA 92122 (SAN 293-4302) Tel 619-455-1370; Dist. by: Metropolitan Music Co., Mountain Rd., Stowe, VT 05672 (SAN 293-4310); Dist. by: International Violin Co., 4026 W. Belvedere Ave., Baltimore, MD 21215 (SAN 293-4329); Dist. by: International Luthier Supply, Inc., P.O. Box 15444, Tulsa, OK 74112 (SAN 293-4337); Dist. by: Vitali Import Co., P.O. Box 249, Maywood, CA 90270 (SAN 293-4345); Dist. by: Howard Core & Co., Rte. No. 1 "The Cedars", Munford, AL 36268 (SAN 293-4353); Dist. by: Buck Musical Instruments Products, 40 Sand Rd., New Britain, PA 18901 (SAN 293-4361); Dist. by: Luthier's Mercantile, 412 Moore Lane, Healdsburg, CA 95448 (SAN 293-437X); Dist. by: Elderly Instruments, 1100 N. Washington, Lansing, MI 48906 (SAN 293-4388).

H S Worth, *(Worth, H. S., Co.; 0-939248),* P.O. Box 601, Oakridge, OR 97463 (SAN 220-1615) Tel 503-782-2703; Dist. by: Louise Loehr, 163 W. Main St., Kutztown, PA 19530 (SAN 200-8300).

H Spriggle, *(Spriggle, Howard; 0-938686),* Box 550, Ocean View, DE 19970 (SAN 211-271X) Tel 302-539-2816.

H T Hallowell, *(Hallowell, H. Thomas),* 916 The Benson East, Jenkintown, PA 19046 (SAN 695-6351) Tel 215-572-3030.

H T Taylor, *(Taylor, Henry T.; 0-938956),* P.O. Box 111, Eggertville, NY 14226 (SAN 264-5149).

H Three, *(H3 Enterprises; 0-943578),* 7 Victoria Vale, Monterey, CA 93940 (SAN 240-8317) Tel 408-372-4054.

H U Fish, *(Fish, Harriet; 0-9612344),* P.O. Box 135, Carlsborg, WA 98324 (SAN 287-1726) Tel 206-452-9195.

H-U Public, *(H/U Pubns.; 0-917292),* 1121 S. Redwood Rd., P.O. Box 27042, Salt Lake City, UT 84127-0042 (SAN 208-6816) Tel 801-973-4620.

H V Meredith, *(Meredith, H. V.; 0-9603120),* Orders to: The State Printing Company, P.O. Box 1388, Columbia, SC 29202 (SAN 204-6334) Tel 803-799-9550.

H Vogt, *(Vogt, Helen; 0-9602542),* 121 Blaine Ave., Brownsville, PA 15417 (SAN 212-579X) Tel 412-785-3804.

H W Bks, *(Whitney, Harvey, Bks.; 0-9606488),* P.O. Box 42696, Cincinnati, OH 45242 (SAN 217-2143) Tel 513-793-3555.

H W H Meyer, *(Meyer, Herbert W. H.; 0-9616723),* 184 N. Burnet Dr., Baytown, TX 77520 (SAN 661-3861) Tel 713-424-5266.

H W Hall, *(Hall, H. W.; 0-935064),* 3608 Meadow Oaks Lane, Bryan, TX 77802 (SAN 208-4678) Tel 409-845-2316.

H W Jasper, *(Jasper, Hazel Wright; 0-9608106),* 6615 Mt. Vista Rd., Kingsville, MD 21087 (SAN 238-8618) Tel 301-592-5363.

H W Reynolds
See H W Jasper

H Webb, *(Webb, Helen; 0-9615859),* Rte. 1, Box 635, South Point, OH 45680 (SAN 698-1836).

H Williams, *(Williams, Howard D.; 0-9615684),* 60 Broad St., Hamilton, NY 13346 (SAN 695-8176) Tel 315-824-0974.

H Winston Inc, *(Winston, Harry, Inc.; 0-87311),* 718 Fifth Ave., New York, NY 10019 (SAN 695-1058) Tel 212-245-2000; Toll free: 800-223-2305.

H. H. Wait
See N S Wait

Haas, *(Haas, Frederick C.; 0-9601180),* Rte. 2 Box 78A, Blackstone, VA 23824 (SAN 210-0932) Tel 804-292-4726.

Haas Ent NH, *(Haas Enterprises; 0-9605552),* 7 N. Main, Box 218, Ashland, NH 03217 (SAN 216-034X) Tel 603-968-7177.

Haase-Mumm Pub Co, *(Haase-Mumm Publishing Co., Inc.; 0-940114),* 100 E. Ohio St., Rm. B20, Chicago, IL 60611 (SAN 220-2867) Tel 312-951-5267; Dist. by: Amart Bk. & Catalog Dist. Co., Inc., 100 E. Ohio St., Rm. B20, Chicago, IL 60611 (SAN 276-9778).

Habel, *(Habel, Robert E.; 0-9600444),* 1529 Ellis Hollow Rd., Ithaca, NY 14850 (SAN 203-4719) Tel 607-272-3199.

Haberman Pr, *(Haberman Pr.; 0-9617000),* P.O. Box 71, Merrick, NY 11566 (SAN 662-5355); 67-15 Parsons Blvd., No. 6H, Flushing, NY 11365 (SAN 662-5363) Tel 718-591-0916.

Hach, *(Hach, Phila; 0-9606192),* 1601 Madison St., Clarksville, TN 37040 (SAN 217-0736) Tel 615-647-4084.

Hacker, *(Hacker Art Bks.; 0-87817),* 54 W. 57th St., New York, NY 10019 (SAN 201-6052) Tel 212-757-1450.

†**Hackett Pub,** *(Hackett Publishing Co., Inc.; 0-915144; 0-915145; 0-87220),* P.O. Box 44937, Indianapolis, IN 46204 (SAN 201-6044) Tel 317-635-9250; *CIP.*

Hadady Corp
See Key Bks Pr

Haddad's Fine Arts, *(Haddad's Fine Arts, Inc.; 0-88445),* P.O. Box 3016 C, Anaheim, CA 92803 (SAN 206-5312) Tel 714-996-2100; 3855 E. Mira Loma Ave., Anaheim, CA 92803 (SAN 206-5320).

Hadronic Pr Inc, *(Hadronic Pr., Inc.; 0-911767),* Nonantum, MA 02195 (SAN 264-0740) Tel 617-864-9859.

Haer Inst, *(Haer Institute for Electro Physiological Research; 0-940090),* P.O. Box 337 4 Industrial Pkwy, Brunswick, ME 04011 (SAN 220-2255).

Haffenreffer Mus Anthro, *(Haffenreffer Museum of Anthropology; 0-912089),* Brown University, Mt. Hope Grant, Bristol, RI 02809 (SAN 278-9817) Tel 401-253-8388.

†**Hafner,** *(Hafner Pr.; 0-02),* Div. of Macmillan Publishing Co., Inc., 866 Third Ave., New York, NY 10022 (SAN 201-6001) Tel 212-702-2000; Toll free: 800-257-5755; Dist. by: Collier-Macmillan Distribution Ctr., Front & Brown Sts., Riverside, NJ 08075 (SAN 202-5582); *CIP.*

Hage Pubns, *(Hage Pubns.; 0-933619),* P.O. Box 21, Somerville, NJ 08876 (SAN 692-4654) Tel 201-722-2933.

Hagglund
See HEH Med Pubns

Hagin Evangelistic
See Hagin Ministries

Hagin Ministries, *(Hagin, Kenneth, Ministries, Inc.; 0-89276),* P.O. Box 50126, Tulsa, OK 74150-0126 (SAN 208-2578) Tel 918-258-1588.

Hagley Museum, *(Hagley Museum & Library; 0-914650),* P.O. Box 3630, Wilmington, DE 19807 (SAN 204-1545) Tel 302-658-2400.

Hagley Vol Ckbk, *(Hagley Volunteers Cookbook Committee; 0-9610990),* Hagley Museum & Library, P.O. Box 3 630, Greenville, DE 19807 (SAN 265-2501) Tel 302-658-2400.

Hagstrom Co
See Hagstrom Map

Hagstrom Map, *(Hagstrom Map Co., Inc.; 0-910684),* Subs. of American Map Corp., 46-35 54th Rd., Maspeth, NY 11378 (SAN 203-543X) Tel 718-784-0055.

Hague Pr, *(Hague Pr., The; 0-936851),* 965 Norview Ave., Norfolk, VA 23513 (SAN 658-3393) Tel 804-853-4661; P.O. Box 385, Norfolk, VA 23501 (SAN 658-3407).

Hailstone, *(Hailstone; 0-9616979),* 2601 NW Expwy., No. 1210W, Oklahoma City, OK 73112 (SAN 661-8022) Tel 405-842-0131.

Haimo, *(Haimo, Oscar),* 252 E. 61st St., New York, NY 10021 (SAN 202-2664) Tel 212-838-6627.

Haimowoods, *(Haimowoods Press; 0-917790),* 1101 Forest Ave., Evanston, IL 60202 (SAN 210-296X) Tel 312-864-7209.

Hake, *(Hake's Americana & Collectibles; 0-918708),* P.O. Box 1444, York, PA 17405 (SAN 210-3575) Tel 717-843-3731.

Haker Books, *(Haker Books; 0-9609964),* 2707 First Ave. N., Great Falls, MT 59401 (SAN 262-0359) Tel 406-454-1487.

Hakims Pubs, *(Hakim's Pubs.),* 210 S. 52nd St., Philadelphia, PA 19139 (SAN 207-2327).

Hal Herman Promo, *(Herman, Hal, Promotions; 0-9613201),* Rte. 19, P.O. Box 1152, Tallahassee, FL 32308 (SAN 295-8260) Tel 904-893-4343.

Hal Z Bennett, *(Bennett, Hal Z.),* 124 Ardmore Rd., Kensington, CA 94707 (SAN 212-6052).

Halbur, *(Halbur Publishing; 0-9603520),* P.O. Box 11354, Santa Rosa, CA 95406 (SAN 212-9469) Tel 707-544-7537.

Halcyon *Imprint of* **Natl Book**

Halcyon Bk, *(Halcyon Bk. Concern/The Temple of the People; 0-933797),* P.O. Box 7095, Halcyon, CA 93420 (SAN 692-8773) Tel 805-489-2822; Dist. by: DeVorss & Co., P.O. Box 550, 1046 Princeton Dr., Marina del Rey, CA 90294-0550 (SAN 168-9886); Dist. by: The Philosophical Research Society, 3910 Los Feliz Blvd., Los Angeles, CA 90027 (SAN 205-3829); Dist. by: Starlite Distributors, P.O. Box 20729, Reno, NV 89515 (SAN 200-7789) Tel 702-359-5676.

Halcyon Hse, *(Halcyon House, Publishers, Inc.; 0-911311),* P.O. Box 9547, Kansas City, MO 64133 (SAN 270-6555) Tel 816-737-0064.

Halcyon Ithaca, *(Halcyon Press of Ithaca; 0-9604006),* 111 Halcyon Hill Rd., Ithaca, NY 14850 (SAN 215-1510) Tel 607-257-1864.

Haldor Co, *(Haldor Co.; 0-9614517),* P.O. Box 12354, Las Vegas, NV 89112 (SAN 689-6006) Tel 702-458-1723.

Hale and Hawthorne, *(Hale and Hawthorne Publishers; 0-931647),* P.O. Box 1394, Williamsburg, VA 23187-1394 (SAN 683-7336).

Halevy Finan Pubns, *(Halevy Financial Pubns.; 0-935651),* 13431 Pepperdine Cir., Westminster, CA 92683 (SAN 695-958X) Tel 714-891-9084.

Half Court, *(Half Court Press; 0-911179),* 1122 18th St. No. 201, Santa Monica, CA 90403 (SAN 270-6563) Tel 213-453-5029.

Half Court Pr, *(Half Court Pr.; 0-937619),* 16475 Dallas Pkwy., Suite 650, Dallas, TX 75248 (SAN 658-9510) Tel 214-248-3902.

Half Halt Press, *(Half Halt Pr.; 0-939481),* P.O. Box 3512, Gaithersburg, MD 20878 (SAN 663-270X); 125 Lamont Ln., Gaithersburg, MD 20878 (SAN 663-2718) Tel 301-948-2187.

Halfcourt Pr, *(Halfcourt Pr.; 0-914585),* 3299 N. Fourth Ave., Wausau, WI 54401 (SAN 287-7481) Tel 715-675-3710; Orders to: P.O. Box 137, Iola, WI 54945 (SAN 662-2143).

Halgo Inc, *(Halgo, Inc.; 0-9613805),* 2732 Maryland Ave., Baltimore, MD 21218 (SAN 679-4157) Tel 301-467-8186 (SAN 699-5861); Orders to: P.O. Box 4866, Hampden Sta., Baltimore, MD 21211 (SAN 202-7348).

Haljan Pubns, *(Haljan Pubns.; 0-910907),* P.O. Box 291, 136 S. Main St., LaMoille, IL 61330 (SAN 270-6571) Tel 815-638-2152.

Hall Fame Mgt, *(Hall of Fame Management, Inc.; 0-9612238),* P.O. Box 396, New York, NY 10185 (SAN 287-7392) Tel 212-534-4102.

Hall J, *(Hall, Joseph S; 0-910738),* 1654 N. Cherokee Ave., Hollywood, CA 90028 (SAN 204-0646) Tel 213-464-4164.

Hall Library *Imprint of* **G K Hall**

Hall Medical *Imprint of* **G K Hall**

Hall Pr, *(Hall Pr.; 0-932218),* P.O. Box 5375, San Bernardino, CA 92412 (SAN 211-7061) Tel 714-887-3466.

Hall Pub
See **Hall Pub AL**

Hall Pub AL, *(Hall Publishing Co.; 0-931859),* 919 Greenboro Ave. Central Sq. 104, Tuscaloosa, AL 35401 (SAN 686-0265).

Hall Reference *Imprint of* **G K Hall**

Hall Reunion, *(Hall Reunion, The; 0-9617071),* 5720 Nella Blvd., NW, Canton, OH 44720 (SAN 662-8915) Tel 813-446-0206.

Halldin Pub, *(Halldin, A. G., Publishing Co.; 0-935648),* P.O. Box 667, Indiana, PA 15701 (SAN 208-208X) Tel 412-463-8450.

Halleys Comet, *(Halley's Comet; 0-937451),* P.O. Box 706, Andover, NY 14806 (SAN 658-9529); 10 Barney St., Andover, NY 14806 (SAN 658-9537) Tel 607-478-8868.

Hallmark, *(Hallmark Card, Inc.; 0-87529),* 25th & McGee Sts., Kansas City, MO 64108 (SAN 202-2672) Tel 816-274-5111.

Halls of Ivy, *(Halls of Ivy Press; 0-912256),* 3445 Leora Ave., Simi Valley, CA 93063 (SAN 204-0204) Tel 805-527-0525.

Hallwalls Inc, *(Hallwalls, Inc.; 0-936739),* 700 Main St., Buffalo, NY 14202 (SAN 699-9026) Tel 716-854-5828.

Halpern & Simon Publishing, *(Halpern & Simon; 0-942898),* Div. of AaronCorp, P.O. Box 9399, Coral Springs, FL 33075 (SAN 240-3137); 3255 NW 94th Ave., Coral Springs, FL 33075 (SAN 662-0272); Orders to: P.O. Box 697, New York, NY 10272 (SAN 662-0280) Tel 718-712-5258.

†Halsted Pr, *(Halsted Pr.; 0-470),* Div. of John Wiley & Sons, Inc., 605 Third Ave., New York, NY 10158 (SAN 202-2680) Tel 212-850-6465; Toll free: 800-526-5368; *CIP.*

HALT
See **HALT DC**

HALT DC, *(HALT, Inc.; 0-910073),* 201 Massachusetts Ave., NE, Suite 319, Washington, DC 20002 (SAN 223-7873) Tel 202-546-4258.

Halty Ferguson, *(Halty Ferguson; 0-912604),* 376 Harvard St., Cambridge, MA 02138 (SAN 202-2699) Tel 617-868-6190.

Halyburton, *(Halyburton Pr.; 0-916717),* P.O. Box 2973, Ann Arbor, MI 48106 (SAN 653-7480) Tel 313-662-0060; 931 Hockey Ln., Ann Arbor, MI 48103 (SAN 653-7499).

Hamaker-Weaver, *(Hamaker-Weaver Pubs.; 0-941550),* Rt. 1, Box 158, Seymour, MO 65746 (SAN 239-2224) Tel 417-935-2116.

HamanD Pub, *(HamanD Publishing Co.),* 525 B St., Suite 342, San Diego, CA 92101 (SAN 208-1172) Tel 619-234-8393.

Hamaya USA, *(Hamaya U.S.A., Inc.; 0-9615266),* 929 E. Second St., Suite 108, Los Angeles, CA 90012 (SAN 694-647X) Tel 213-626-1017.

Hamba Bks, *(Hamba Books; 0-9606152),* 1901 Creekwood Dr., Conway, AR 72032 (SAN 217-5223) Tel 501-329-6147.

Hamber
See **BH Ent**

Hambledon Press, *(Hambledon Pr., The; 0-907628),* 309 Greenbrier Ave., Ronceverte, WV 24970 (SAN 677-4946) Tel 304-645-1058.

Hamburg Pr, *(Hamburg Pr., The; 0-916587),* P.O. Box 171, Augusta, GA 30903 (SAN 296-693X) Tel 404-724-0364.

Hamilton Hse, *(Hamilton Hse.; 0-917908),* 936 N. Fifth, Philadelphia, PA 19123 (SAN 209-3308) Tel 215-923-9161.

Hamilton Inst, *(Hamilton, Alexander, Institute, Inc.; 0-86604),* 1633 Broadway, New York, NY 10019 (SAN 205-311X); Orders to: 1501 Broadway, New York, NY 10036 (SAN 689-8319) Tel 212-397-3580.

Hamiltons, *(Hamilton's; 0-9608598),* P.O. Box 932, Bedford, VA 24523 (SAN 264-0759) Tel 703-586-5592.

Hamiltons Pub, *(Hamilton's Publishing; 0-939129),* 390 Oak Ave., Suite D, Carlsbad, CA 92008 (SAN 662-8583) Tel 619-434-6911. Do not confuse with Hamilton's in Bedford, VA.

Hamlet Hse, *(Hamlet House; 0-913861),* P.O. Box 791044, New Orleans, LA 70179-1044 (SAN 286-7699) Tel 504-482-4903; 631 N. Carrollton Ave., New Orleans, LA 70119 (SAN 286-7702).

Hamline Law, *(Hamline Univ. Schl. of Law, Advanced Legal Education; 0-88055),* 1536 Hewitt Ave., St. Paul, MN 55104 (SAN 293-9851) Tel 612-641-2122.

Hamma, *(Hamma Library of Trinity Lutheran Seminary),* 2199 E. Main St., Columbus, OH 43209 (SAN 677-1602).

Hammer Gal, *(Hammer Galleries; 0-9611570),* Subs. of Knoedler Art Galleries, 33 W. 57th St., New York, NY 10019 (SAN 283-1414) Tel 212-644-6373.

Hammer Mntn Bk, *(Hammer Mountain Bk. Halls; 0-9616659),* 841 Union St., Schenectady, NY 12308 (SAN 661-3497) Tel 518-393-5266.

Hammer Pub
See **Hammer Gal**

Hammond-Harwood, *(Hammond-Harwood House Assn., Inc.; 0-910688),* Orders to: Maryland's Way, Hammond Harwood House, 19 Maryland Ave., Annapolis, MD 21401 (SAN 204-0220) Tel 301-267-6891.

†Hammond Inc, *(Hammond Inc.; 0-8437),* 515 Valley St., Maplewood, NJ 07040 (SAN 202-2702) Tel 201-763-6000; Toll free: 800-526-4953; *CIP.*

Hammond Pubns, *(Hammond Pubns.; 0-937979),* P.O. Box 8212, Wichita, KS 67208 (SAN 659-5081) Tel 316-683-3077; 6622 Aberdeen, Wichita, KS 67208 (SAN 659-509X).

Hammond Records, *(Hammond Records; 0-942874),* P.O. Box 3431, Thousand Oaks, CA 91360 (SAN 239-5517) Tel 805-495-1143; 874 Chelterham Cir., Thousand Oaks, CA 91360 (SAN 658-0815).

Hamoroh Pr, *(Hamoroh Pr.; 0-9604754),* P.O. Box 48862, Los Angeles, CA 90048 (SAN 215-6512).

Hampol Pub Co, *(Hampol Publishing Co.; 0-9609330),* Box 36, 47 Harvard Ave., Boston, MA 02134 (SAN 260-1990) Tel 617-232-2430; Orders to: 1284 Beacon St., Brookline, MA 02146 (SAN 662-0299).

Hampshire Pacific, *(Hampshire Pacific Pr.; 0-939930),* 3043 SW Hampshire St., Portland, OR 97201 (SAN 216-8189).

Hampshire Pr, *(Hampshire Pr., The),* 900 Main St., Wilmington, MA 01887 (SAN 296-127X); Dist. by: Henrietta Howard-Moineau, P.O. Box 235, West Boylston, MA 01505 (SAN 296-1288).

Hampton-Brown, *(Hampton-Brown Co.; 0-917837),* 200 Clock Tower Pl., Suite 201-A, Carmel, CA 93923 (SAN 657-145X) Tel 408-625-3666.

Hampton Court Pub, *(Hampton Court Pubs.; 0-910569),* Wixon Pond Rd., Mahopac, NY 10541 (SAN 264-0767) Tel 914-628-6155; Orders to: P.O. Box 655, Mahopac, NY 10541 (SAN 662-0302) Tel 914-628-6155.

Hampton Mae, *(Hampton Mae Institute; 0-9616511),* 4104 Lynn Ave., Tampa, FL 33603 (SAN 659-4611) Tel 813-238-2221.

Hampton Pr MI, *(Hampton Pr.; 0-938352),* P.O. Box 805, Rochester, MI 48063 (SAN 216-0358) Tel 313-852-0980.

Hampton Pub Co, *(Hampton Publishing Co.; 0-934895),* 927 Cybus Way, Southampton, PA 18966 (SAN 694-4485) Tel 215-357-4531.

Hampton Univ Muse, *(Hampton Univ., Univ. Museum; 0-9616982),* Hampton, VA 23668 (SAN 279-0009) Tel 804-727-5308.

Han Bks
See **Blue Flower**

Hancock BC
See **Hancock House**

†Hancock House, *(Hancock Hse. Pubs.; 0-88839),* 1431 Harrison Ave., Blaine, WA 98230 (SAN 240-8546) Tel 604-538-1114; Dist. by: Big Country Books, Inc., 1431 Harrison Ave., Blaine, WA 98230 (SAN 200-7215) Tel 604-538-1114; *CIP.*

Hancraft, *(Hancraft Studios; 0-941248),* P.O. Box 578, Claremont, CA 91711 (SAN 219-9556) Tel 714-621-7046.

Hand Pr, *(Hand Pr.; 0-9605620),* 12015 Coyne St., Los Angeles, CA 90049 (SAN 218-4788) Tel 213-472-9691; Dist. by: Aperture, Millerton, NY 12546 (SAN 201-1832).

Hand Tools Inst, *(Hand Tools Institute; 0-9609220),* 25 N. Broadway, Tarrytown, NY 10591 (SAN 224-7852).

Hands off, *(Hands Off; 0-9609596),* P.O. Box 68, Tacoma, WA 98401 (SAN 260-2016) Tel 206-752-2525.

Hands-On Pub Co, *(Hands-On Publishing Co.; 0-934789),* 1539 Lexington Ave., New York, NY 10029 (SAN 694-2075) Tel 212-876-9252.

Hands on Pubns, *(Hands on Pubns.; 0-931178),* 451 Silvera Ave., Long Beach, CA 90803 (SAN 213-9286) Tel 213-596-4738.

Handy *Imprint of* **HarBraceJ**

Handy Bk Co, *(Handy Bk. Co.; 0-934049),* 2509 S. Padre Island Dr. P.O. Box 721203, Corpus Christi, TX 78472-1203 (SAN 693-0484) Tel 512-851-2240; Dist. by: Baker & Taylor, Eastern Div., 50 Kirby Ave., Somerville, NJ 08876 (SAN 169-4901) Tel 201-526-8000.

Haney Bks, *(Haney Bks.; 0-9609552),* P.O. Box 552, Salem, IL 62881 (SAN 283-9059) Tel 618-548-1276.

Hang Gliding, *(Hang Gliding Pr.; 0-938282),* Box 22552, San Diego, CA 92122 (SAN 215-6520) Tel 619-452-1768.

†**Hanging Loose,** *(Hanging Loose Pr.; 0-914610),* 231 Wyckoff St., Brooklyn, NY 11217 (SAN 206-4960) Tel 718-643-9559; Dist. by: Inland Book Co., P.O. Box 261, 22 Hemingway Ave., East Haven, CT 06512 (SAN 200-4151) Tel 203-467-4257; Dist. by: Bookslinger, 213 E. Fourth St., St. Paul, MN 55101 (SAN 169-4154) Tel 612-221-0429; Dist. by: Small Press Dist., Inc., 1814 San Pablo Ave., Berkeley, CA 94702 (SAN 204-5826) Tel 415-549-3336; *CIP.*

Hanley & Belfus, *(Hanley & Belfus Inc.; 0-932883),* 210 S. 13th St., Philadelphia, PA 19107 (SAN 689-0032) Tel 215-546-7293.

Hanna-Barbera Prod, *(Hanna-Barbera Productions, Inc.; 0-936817),* 3400 Cahuenga Blvd., Los Angeles, CA 90068-1376 (SAN 699-8615) Tel 213-721-1414; Dist. by: Worldvision Enterprises, 660 Madison Ave., New York, NY 10021 (SAN 200-6235).

Hanover Pub KY, *(Hanover Publishing Co.; 0-936021),* P.O. Box 591, Ashland, KY 41105 (SAN 696-7957) Tel 606-329-0077; 1505 Carter Ave., Ashland, KY 41105 (SAN 696-7965).

Hansa Pub, *(Hansa Publishing; 0-933593),* 2124 Kittredge St., No. 76, Berkeley, CA 94704 (SAN 692-2147) Tel 415-528-6377; Dist. by: Bookpeople, 2929 Fifth St., Berkeley, CA 94710 (SAN 168-9517) Tel 415-549-3030.

Hansen Ed Mus, *(Hansen, Charles, Educational Music & Bks., Inc.; 0-8494),* 1860 West Ave., Miami Beach, FL 33139 (SAN 205-0609) Tel 305-673-4612; Dist. by: Hansen Hse., 1860 West Ave., Miami Beach, FL 33139 (SAN 200-7908) Tel 305-532-5461. *Imprints:* Maestro Pubn (Maestro Publication); Musica Ninos (Musica para Ninos); Shattinger (Shattinger International).

Hansen Pub MI, *(Hansen Publishing Co.; 0-930098),* P.O. Box 1723, East Lansing, MI 48823 (SAN 210-735X) Tel 517-332-5946; Dist. by: Holley International Co., 63 Kercheval, Suite 204A, Grosse Pointe Farms, MI 48236 (SAN 241-5178) Tel 313-882-0405.

Hansen Pubns
See Hansen Ed Mus

Hansen Reshanov, *(Hansen-Reshanov Consultants, Inc.; 0-937553),* P.O. Box 27541, Golden Valley, MN 55402 (SAN 658-9545) Tel 612-544-1211; 8009 40th Ave., N., New Hope, MN 55427 (SAN 658-9553).

Hansi, *(Hansi Ministries, Inc.; 0-932878),* P.O. Box 3009, Fallbrook, CA 92028-0945 (SAN 213-5086) Tel 619-728-7847.

Hanson, *(Hanson, Margaret B.; 0-9605834),* Mayoworth Rte., Kaycee, WY 82639 (SAN 216-4884) Tel 307-738-2215.

Hanuman Bks, *(Hanuman Bks.; 0-937815),* P.O. Box 1070, Old Chelsea Sta., New York, NY 10113 (SAN 659-462X) Tel 212-645-1840; 222 W. 23rd St., Suite 807, New York, NY 10011 (SAN 659-4638).

Hanuman Foun, *(Hanuman Foundation; 0-9614444),* Div. of Prison-Ashram Project, Rte. 1, Box 201-N, Durham, NC 27705 (SAN 689-3635) Tel 919-942-2138.

Hapi Pr, *(Hapi Pr.; 0-913244),* 512 SW Maplecrest Dr., Portland, OR 97219 (SAN 699-5292) Tel 503-246-9632.

Happibook Pr, *(Happibook Pr.; 0-937395),* P.O. Box 218, Montgomery, NY 12549-0218 (SAN 658-9561) Tel 914-457-9328; E. Kaisertown Rd., Montgomery, NY 12549 (SAN 658-957X).

Happiness Pr, *(Happiness Pr.; 0-916508),* 14351 Wycliff, Postal Drawer DD, Magalia, CA 95954 (SAN 208-6719) Tel 916-873-0294; Orders to: P.O. Box B-DD, Magalia, CA 95954 (SAN 662-0329).

Happiness Unltd, *(Happiness Unlimited Pubns.; 0-939372),* 4317 Tillman Dr., Virginia Beach, VA 23452 (SAN 220-1550) Tel 804-498-1552; Toll free: 800-525-5018, Ext 552.

Happy Eye
See Grassroots Ed Serv

Happy Hands
See Happy Hands Pub Co

Happy Hands Pub Co, *(Happy Hands Publishing Co.; 0-941468),* 3750 S. University Dr., Suite 201, Fort Worth, TX 76109 (SAN 264-0775) Tel 817-932-9081.

Happy Health, *(Happy Health Pubs.; 0-9606402),* 13048 Delmonte Dr. 42-D, Seal Beach, CA 90740 (SAN 206-4979) Tel 213-431-0069.

Happy History, *(Happy History, Inc.; 0-918430),* P.O. Box 2160, Boca Raton, FL 33432 (SAN 210-0940) Tel 305-483-8093.

Happy Thoughts & Rainbow, *(Happy Thoughts & Rainbow Co., The; 0-9608686),* Rte. 2, P.O. Box 419, Aurora, MN 55705 (SAN 238-2954) Tel 218-229-3451.

Happy Val Whittier, *(Happy Valley Pubs.; 0-936805),* 12413 Cullman Ave., Whittier, CA 90604 (SAN 699-8763) Tel 213-943-5660.

Happy Valley Apple, *(Happy Valley Apple; 0-913768),* Dist. by: Bookpeople, 2929 Fifth St., Berkeley, CA 94710 (SAN 168-9517) Tel 415-549-3030.

Happy Valley Pubs
See Happy Val Whittier

†**Har-Row,** *(Harper & Row Pubs., Inc.; 0-06),* 10 E. 53rd St., New York, NY 10022 (SAN 200-2086) Tel 212-207-7099; Toll free: 800-242-7737; 1700 Montgomery St., San Francisco, CA 94111 (SAN 215-3734) Tel 415-989-9000; Dist. by: Harper & Row Pubs. Inc., Keystone Industrial Pk., Scranton, PA 18512 (SAN 215-3742); *CIP.* Imprints: B&N Bks (Barnes & Noble Books); C&M Bessie Bks (Cornelia & Michael Bessie Books); Canfield Pr (Canfield Press).(Canfield Pr.); CN (Colophon Books).(Colophon Bks.); Harper Medical (Lippincott, J. B., /Harper & Row Medical Division).(Lippincott, J. B., /Harper & Row Medical Div.); HarpC (Harper's College Division); HarpR (Harper Religious Books).(Harper Religious Bks.); HarpT (Harper Trade Books).(Harper Trade Bks.); HarCrest (Harper Crest); HW (Harrow Books Paperback Department).(Harrow Bks. Paperback Dept.); Icon Edns (Icon Editions); IntlDept (International Department).(International Dept.); Open U (Open University).(Open Univ.); Perennial Fiction Lib (Perennial Fiction Library); Perennial Mystery Library (Perennial Mystery Library); PL (Perennial Library); SchDept (School Department).(School Dept.); Torch (Torchbooks); Torch Lib (Torchbooks Library Binding).

Haralson Pub Co, *(Haralson Publishing Co.; 0-934534),* P.O. Box 20366, Atlanta, GA 30325 (SAN 221-1076) Tel 404-872-6471.

Harben Pub, *(Harben Publishing Company; 0-9608158),* P.O. Box 1055, Safety Harbor, FL 33572 (SAN 238-8375).

Harbin Comm, *(Harbin Communications Group Inc.; 0-932539),* 7420 FDR Sta., New York, NY 10150 (SAN 687-4789) Tel 212-319-9085.

Harbinger
See New Harbinger

Harbinger FL, *(Harbinger Publishing; 0-939441),* 2413 NW 40th Circle, Boca Raton, FL 33431 (SAN 663-3536); Dist. by: Banyan Bks., P.O. Box 431160, Miami, FL 33143 (SAN 208-340X).

Harbinger Group, *(Harbinger Group, Inc.; 0-935963),* Div. of Xerox Corp., 17 North Ave., Norwalk, CT 06851 (SAN 696-8007) Tel 203-849-5000.

Harbinger Med Pr NC, *(Harbinger Medical Pr.; 0-9612242),* P.O. Box 17201, Winston-Salem, NC 27116 (SAN 291-834X).

Harbinger Pubns, *(Harbinger Pubns.; 0-933611),* 23815 Pine Lake Dr., P.O. Box 164, Sugar Pine, CA 95346 (SAN 692-4603) Tel 209-586-5740.

†**Harbor Hill Bks,** *(Harbor Hill Bks., Inc.; 0-916346; 0-915585),* P.O. Box 407, Harrison, NY 10528 (SAN 201-9159) Tel 914-698-3495; *CIP.*

Harbor Hse MI, *(Harbor Hse. Pubs.; 0-937360),* Subs. of Seaway Review, Inc., 221 Water St., Boyne City, MI 49712 (SAN 200-5751) Tel 616-582-2814.

Harbor Pr, *(Harbor Pr.; 0-936197),* P.O. Box 1656, Gig Harbor, WA 98335 (SAN 696-8953); 1602 Lucille Pkwy., NW, Gig Harbor, WA 98335 (SAN 696-8961) Tel 206-851-9598.

†**Harbor Pub,** *(Harbor Publishing Co.; 0-937638),* 80 N. Moore St., Suite 4J, New York, NY 10013 (SAN 656-8882) Tel 212-349-1818; *CIP.*

Harboridge Pr, *(Harboridge Press),* 455 E. Ridge St., Marquette, MI 49855 (SAN 201-9167).

Harbottle Pr, *(Harbottle Pr.; 0-9615145),* 3601 Allen Pkwy., No. 97, Houston, TX 77019 (SAN 694-2059) Tel 713-529-7079.

†**HarBraceJ,** *(Harcourt Brace Jovanovich, Inc.; 0-15),* 1250 Sixth Ave., San Diego, CA 92101 (SAN 200-2736) Tel 619-699-6335; Toll free: 800-543-1918; Harcourt Brace Jovanovich Bldg., Orlando, FL 32887 (SAN 200-2299); *CIP. Imprints:* BFP (B F P (Books for Professionals)).(BFP (Bks. for Professionals)); Handy (Handy Books); Harv (Harvest Books); Hbgr (Harbinger Books); HC (Harcourt Brace Jovanovich, Inc., College Dept.); HJ (HarBraceJ Juvenile Books).(HarBraceJ Juvenile Bks.); HPL (Harbrace Paperback Library); Law & Business (Law & Business, Inc.); Psych Corp (Psychological Corporation).(Psychological Corp.); VoyB (Voyager Books).(Voyager Bks.).

Harcourt
See HarBraceJ

HarCrest *Imprint of* **Har-Row**

†**Hard Pr,** *(Hard Pr.; 0-938878),* 340 E. 11th St., New York, NY 10003 (SAN 219-1849); *CIP.*

Hard Soft Pr, *(Hard/Soft Pr.; 0-938611),* Div. of Hard/Soft, Inc., P.O. Box 1277, Riverdale, NY 10471 (SAN 661-5759) Tel 212-543-9313.

Hardin, *(Hardin, Albert N., Jr.; 0-9601778),* 5414 Lexington Ave., Pennsauken, NJ 08109 (SAN 210-9026) Tel 609-662-2221.

Hardin Pub Co, *(Hardin Publishing Co.; 0-916255),* P.O. Box 269, Avera, GA 30803 (SAN 294-9369) Tel 404-598-2312.

Hardin-Simmons, *(Hardin-Simmons Univ. Pr.; 0-910075),* Box 896, HSU, Abilene, TX 79698 (SAN 241-3205) Tel 915-677-7281.

Hardscrabble Bks, *(Hardscrabble Bks.; 0-915056),* Rte. 2, Box 285, Berrien Springs, MI 49103 (SAN 207-0960) Tel 616-473-5570.

Hardscrabble Hse Pubns, *(Hardscrabble House Publications; 0-9613995),* 60 Franklin St, Malone, NY 12953 (SAN 682-5095) Tel 518-483-5595.

Hardwd Ply, *(Hardwood Plywood Manufacturers Assn),* Box 2789, 1825 Michael Faraday Dr., Reston, VA 22090 (SAN 224-7569) Tel 703-435-2900.

Hardy Hse, *(Hardy House Publishing Co.; 0-917844),* A Hardy-Roberts Enterprise, P.O. Box 705, South Laguna Beach, CA 92677 (SAN 210-0959) Tel 714-497-2670.

Hardywill Grp, *(Hardywill Group, Inc.; 0-916797),* 2108 Lafayette Tower E., Detroit, MI 48207 (SAN 654-3480) Tel 313-259-0504; Dist. by: The Distributors, 702 S. Michigan, South Bend, IN 46618 (SAN 169-2488) Tel 219-232-8500; Dist. by: Ludington News Co., 1600 E. Grand Blvd., Detroit, MI 48207 (SAN 169-3972) Tel 313-925-7600.

Hargreaves
See Ross-Hargreaves

Hari Kari
See HK Pub Co

Harian, *(Harian Bks.; 0-87036),* 1 Vernon Ave., Floral Park, NY 11001 (SAN 202-2729).

Harian Creative, *(Harian Creative Pr.-Bks.; 0-911906),* Subs. of Harian Creative Assocs., 47 Hyde Blvd., Ballston Spa, NY 12020 (SAN 204-0255) Tel 518-885-7397.

Harker Van Pelt, *(Harker & Van Pelt Hse.; 0-930639),* 65 Larchwood Ave., West Long Branch, NJ 07764 (SAN 676-3014) Tel 201-222-3608; 145 E. 49th St., New York, NY 10017 (SAN 676-3022).

†**Harlan Davidson,** *(Davidson, Harlan, Inc.; 0-88295),* 3110 N. Arlington Heights Rd., Arlington Heights, IL 60004 (SAN 201-2375) Tel 312-253-9720; *CIP.*

Harlequin Bks, *(Harlequin Bks.; 0-373),* Dist. by: Simon & Schuster, Inc., 1230 Ave. of the Americas, New York, NY 10020 (SAN 200-2450) Tel 212-245-6400.

Harley Smith Invest, *(Smith, Harley, Investments, Inc.; 0-916350),* 740 West Willow, Stockton, CA 95203 (SAN 208-1679) Tel 209-943-1650.

131

Harlin Jacque, (Harlin Jacque Pubns.; 0-940938), 89 Surrey Ln., Hempstead, NY 11550 (SAN 281-7659) Tel 516-489-8564; Orders to: 71 N. Franklin St., Suite 207, Hempstead, NY 11550 (SAN 281-7667) Tel 516-489-0120.

Harlo Pr, (Harlo Pr.; 0-8187), 50 Victor Ave., Detroit, MI 48203 (SAN 202-2745) Tel 313-883-3600.

Harlo Printing
See Harlo Pr

Harmon-Meek Gal, (Harmon-Meek Gallery; 0-911431), 1258 Third St., S., Naples, FL 33940 (SAN 264-0791) Tel 813-261-2637.

Harmonious Pr, (Harmonious Circle Pr.; 0-9610544), 15 Ozone Ave., Apt. 2, Venice, CA 90291 (SAN 264-0813).

Harmony Imprint of Crown

Harmony & Co
See Buccaneer Bks

Harmony Hse Pub LO, (Harmony Hse. Pubs.-Louisville; 0-916509), 1008 Kent Rd., Goshen, KY 40026 (SAN 295-4257) Tel 502-228-4446; Orders to: P.O. Box 90, Prospect, KY 40059 (SAN 662-2275) Tel 502-228-2010.

Harmony Inst Pr, (Harmony Institute Pr.; 0-938687), P.O. Box 210, Tollhouse, CA 93667 (SAN 661-5538); 28974 Harmony Ranch Rd., Tollhouse, CA 93667 (SAN 661-5546) Tel 209-855-3643.

Harmony Mark, (Harmony Mark, Inc.; 0-9616761), 604 N. Burghley Ave., Ventnor, NJ 08406 (SAN 661-3756) Tel 609-822-0287.

Harmony Pr, (Harmony Pr., Inc.; 0-941600), P.O. Box 122, North Granby, CT 06060 (SAN 238-8790) Tel 203-653-2722.

Harmony Pub
See Georgian Intl

Harmony Raine, (Harmony Raine & Co.; 0-89967), Div. of Buccaneer Books, Inc., Box 133, Greenport, NY 11944 (SAN 262-0367) Tel 516-734-5650.

Harmony Soc, (Harmony Society Pr.; 0-937640), Clark Univ., Worcester, MA 01610 (SAN 215-6539) Tel 617-793-7351.

Harmsen, (Harmsen Publishing Co.; 0-9601322), 1331 E. Alameda Ave., Denver, CO 80209 (SAN 213-0742).

Harp & Lion, (Harp & Lion Pr.; 0-936345), 197 Main St., Annapolis, MD 21401 (SAN 697-8673) Tel 301-267-7094.

Harp & Thistle, (Harp & Thistle, Ltd. of Warner Robins Georgia), P.O. Drawer BO, Agana, GU 96910 (SAN 270-6792).

Harp N Harmonica, (Harp 'N Harmonica Music Publishing Co.; 0-936601), 2160 Monterey, B1, Hermosa Beach, CA 90254 (SAN 698-0562) Tel 213-372-8727; Orders to: P.O. Box 671, Hermosa Beach, CA 90254.

Harp Pr, (Harp Press; 0-9610456), 822 Magdeline Dr., Madison, WI 53704 (SAN 264-0821) Tel 608-249-3458.

HarpC Imprint of Har-Row

Harper
See Har-Row

Harper Assocs, (Harper & Assocs., Inc.; 0-9612352), 2221 Acacia Dr., Wilmington, NC 28403 (SAN 289-5471) Tel 919-762-4962.

Harper Coloron, (Harper Coloron; 0-9616278), 604 State St., Bldg. 6, Box 48, Kings L., Brewster, MA 02631 (SAN 658-621X) Tel 617-896-5613.

Harper Medical Imprint of Har-Row

Harper Sq Pr, (Harper Square Press; 0-933908), Artcrest Products Co., Inc., c/o Artcrest Products Co., Inc., 500 E. Cermak Rd., Chicago, IL 60616 (SAN 212-9086) Tel 312-733-7117.

Harpers Ferry Pr, (Harpers Ferry Pr.; 0-9616354), Div. of Harpers Ferry Enterprises, Inc., P.O. Box 304, Harpers Ferry, WV 25425 (SAN 658-9588) Tel 304-535-2593; Rte. 3, Box 120, Harpers Ferry, WV 25425 (SAN 658-9596).

HarpJ (Harper & Row Junior Bks.; 0-06), Div. of Harper Junior Bks. Group, 10 E. 53rd St., New York, NY 10022 (SAN 200-2086) Tel 212-207-7000; Orders to: Keystone Industrial Pk., Scranton, PA 18512 (SAN 215-3742). Imprints: Trophy (Trophy).

HarpR Imprint of Har-Row

Harpswell Pr, (Harpswell Pr.; 0-88448), 132 Water St., Gardiner, ME 04345 (SAN 208-1199) Tel 207-582-1899.

HarpT Imprint of Har-Row

Harrane Pub, (Harrane Publishing Co.; 0-931897), P.O. Box 1855, Kailua, HI 96734 (SAN 686-0257) Tel 808-261-0050.

Harriet's Kitchen, (Harriet's Kitchen; 0-938592), P.O. Box 424, Forest Hills, NY 11375 (SAN 216-2520).

†**Harrington Pk,** (Harrington Park Pr., Inc.; 0-918393), Subs. of Haworth Pr., 28 E. 22nd St., New York, NY 10010-6194 (SAN 657-3487) Tel 212-228-2800; Orders to: Kim LaBarre, 75 Griswold St., Binghamton, NY 13904 (SAN 211-0156) Tel 607-722-7068; Dist. by: The Haworth Pr., Inc., 28 E. 22 St., New York, NY 10010-6194 (SAN 662-2372) Tel 212-228-2800; CIP.

Harris Academy, (Harris Learning Academy; 0-911181), 2402 S. Newberry Ct., Denver, CO 80222 (SAN 264-0856); Dist. by: Publishers Group West, 5855 Beaudry St., Emeryville, CA 94608 (SAN 202-8522) Tel 415-658-3453.

Harris & Co, (Harris, H. E., & Co., Inc.; 0-937458), Lafayette West Industrial Pk., P.O. Box 7087, Portsmouth, NH 03801 (SAN 202-1137) Tel 603-433-0400; Orders to: P.O. Box 7086, Portsmouth, NH 03801 (SAN 662-0337).

Harris Pub, (Harris Publishing Company; 0-916512), 2057-2 E. Aurora Rd., Twinsburg, OH 44087 (SAN 208-3280) Tel 216-425-9000; Toll free: 800-321-9136.

Harrison Co GA, (Harrison Co.; 0-910694), 3110 Crossing Park, Norcross, GA 30071 (SAN 205-0536) Tel 404-447-9150; Toll free: 800-241-3561; Toll free: 800-282-9867 (In Georgia).

†**Harrison Hse,** (Harrison Hse., Inc.; 0-89274), P.O. Box 35035, Tulsa, OK 74153 (SAN 208-676X) Tel 918-582-2126; Toll free: 800-331-3647; CIP.

Harrison Pubns, (Harrison Pubns.; 0-916089), P.O. Box 252, Williamstown, MA 01267 (SAN 294-8230) Tel 413-689-3230.

Harrow & Heston, (Harrow & Heston; 0-911577), Stuyvesant Plaza, P.O. Box 3934, Albany, NY 12203 (SAN 264-0872) Tel 518-442-5223.

†**Harrowood Bks,** (Harrowood Books; 0-915180), 3943 N. Providence Rd., Newtown Square, PA 19073 (SAN 207-1622) Tel 215-353-5585; CIP.

Harry Gillig, (Gillig, Harry; 0-9600848), 2624 NE 26th Ave., Fort Lauderdale, FL 33306 (SAN 207-3242) Tel 305-564-8432.

Harsand Pr, (Harsand Pr.; 0-9612310), N. 8565 Holseth Rd., Holmen, WI 54636 (SAN 287-7309) Tel 608-526-3848; Dist. by: Publishers Group West, 5855 Beaudry St., Emeryville, CA 94608 (SAN 202-8522) Tel 415-658-3453; Dist. by: Hardsand Distributing, P.O. Box 515, Holmen, WI 54636 (SAN 200-7223) Tel 608-526-3848.

Hart Bro Pub, (Hart Brothers Publishing; 0-910077), P.O. Box 205, Williston, VT 05495 (SAN 240-8562) Tel 802-879-4670.

Hart Eden Pr, (Hart-Eden Pr.; 0-937497), 6114 LaSalle, Suite 283, Oakland, CA 94611 (SAN 658-9626) Tel 415-339-1753.

Hart Graphics, (Hart Graphics; 0-9605422), P.O. Box 968, Austin, TX 78767 (SAN 217-1074).

Hart Pubns, (Hart Pubns., Inc.; 0-912553), 1900 Grant St., Suite 400, P.O. Box 1917, Denver, CO 80201 (SAN 282-7883) Tel 303-837-1917.

†**Hartley & Marks,** (Hartley & Marks, Inc.; 0-88179), P.O. Box 147, Point Roberts, WA 98281 (SAN 264-0880) Tel 206-945-2017; Dist. by: Kampmann & Co., 9 E. 40th St., New York, NY 10016 (SAN 202-5191) Tel 212-685-2928; CIP. Imprints: Cloudburst Press Bk (A Cloudburst Press Book).

Hartley Ent, (Hartley Enterprises), P.O. Box 701, Rancho Mirage, CA 92270 (SAN 209-3278).

Hartley Hse, (Hartley House; 0-937518), P.O. Box 1352, Hartford, CT 06143 (SAN 220-0570) Tel 203-525-2376.

Hartline Pub
See Zephyr Pr AZ

†**Hartmore,** (Hartmore Hse.; 0-87677), Subs. of Media Judaica, Inc., 304 E. 49th St., New York, NY 10017 (SAN 293-2717) Tel 212-319-6666; Orders to: Media Judaica, Inc., 1363 Fairfield Ave., Bridgeport, CT 06605 (SAN 207-0022) Tel 203-384-2284; CIP.

Hartnell Pubns, (Hartnell Pubns.; 0-9605754), 195 Hartnell Place, Sacramento, CA 95825 (SAN 219-7863) Tel 916-925-6064.

Hartnett Marian Pr, (Hartnett, Marian, Pr.; 0-9613008), 5 W. Alexandria Ave., Alexandria, VA 22301 (SAN 292-5281) Tel 703-683-4972.

Harts Spring Wks, (Hart's Spring Works; 0-943096), P.O. Box 330178, San Francisco, CA 94133 (SAN 240-3846) Tel 415-982-8043.

Hartt Pub Indiana, (Hartt Publishing of Indiana; 0-9614495), P.O. Box 5078, Fort Wayne, IN 46895 (SAN 682-2703) Tel 219-484-4473.

Harv Imprint of HarBraceJ

†**Harvard Art Mus,** (Harvard Univ. Fogg Art Museum; 0-916724), 32 Quincy St., Cambridge, MA 02138 (SAN 270-6865) Tel 617-495-2397; CIP.

Harvard Busn, (Harvard Business Schl. Pr.; 0-87584), Harvard Business Schl., Gallatin E117, Boston, MA 02163 (SAN 202-277X) Tel 617-495-6700; Dist. by: Harper & Row Pubs., Inc., Keystone Industrial Pk., Scranton, PA 18512 (SAN 215-3742).

Harvard CMES, (Harvard Univ., Ctr. for Middle Eastern Studies; 0-932885), 1737 Cambridge St., Cambridge, MA 02138 (SAN 688-9409) Tel 617-495-4051.

†**Harvard Common Pr,** (Harvard Common Pr.; 0-916782; 0-87645), 535 Albany St., Boston, MA 02118 (SAN 208-6778) Tel 617-423-5803; Dist. by: Kampmann & Co., 9 E. 40th St., New York, NY 10016 (SAN 202-5191) Tel 212-685-2928; CIP.

†**Harvard E Asian,** (Harvard Univ., Council on East Asian Studies), Dist. by: Harvard Univ. Pr., 79 Garden St., Cambridge, MA 02138 (SAN 200-2043) Tel 617-495-2600; CIP.

Harvard Educ Rev, (Harvard Educational Review; 0-916690), 13 Appian Way, Cambridge, MA 02138 (SAN 208-3426) Tel 617-495-3432.

Harvard Eng
See Bermuda Bio

†**Harvard Law Intl Tax,** (Harvard Law School, International Tax Program; 0-915506), Harvard Law School, Cambridge, MA 02138 (SAN 207-3803) Tel 617-495-4407; CIP.

Harvard U Ctr Jewish, (Harvard Univ. Ctr. for Jewish Studies), Dist. by: Harvard Univ. Pr., 79 Garden St., Cambridge, MA 02138 (SAN 200-2043) Tel 617-495-2600.

Harvard U Grad Schl Design
See Harvard U GSD

Harvard U GSD, (Harvard Univ. Graduate Schl. of Design; 0-935617), Div. of Harvard Univ., 48 Quincy St., Cambridge, MA 02138 (SAN 695-9210) Tel 617-495-4004.

Harvard U Har Law, (Harvard Univ., Harvard Law Schl. Library, Pubns. Dept.; 0-88086), Langdell Hall, Cambridge, MA 02138 (SAN 218-7558) Tel 617-495-3170.

Harvard U Intl Aff, (Harvard Univ. Ctr. for International Affairs; 0-87674), Coolidge Hall-International Studies, 1737 Cambridge St., Cambridge, MA 02138 (SAN 204-0271) Tel 617-495-2137.

†**Harvard U Pr,** (Harvard Univ. Pr.; 0-674), 79 Garden St., Cambridge, MA 02138 (SAN 200-2043) Tel 617-495-2600; CIP.

†**Harvard U Romance Lang & Lit,** (Harvard Univ., Dept. of Romance Languages & Literatures; 0-940940), 201 Boylston Hall, Cambridge, MA 02138 (SAN 217-3786) Tel 617-495-2546; c/o French Forum, Inc., P.O. Box 5108, Lexington, KY 40505 (SAN 208-4996) Tel 606-299-9530; CIP.

Harvard U St Local
See St Local Inter

Harvard U Studies
See Harvard CMES

Harvard Ukrainian, (Harvard Ukrainian Research Institute; 0-916458), 1583 Massachusetts Ave., Cambridge, MA 02138 (SAN 208-967X) Tel 617-495-3692.

Harvest Age, (Harvest Age Ministries; 0-9616405), 803 Ebenezer Rd., Kannapolis, NC 28081 (SAN 658-9650) Tel 704-938-7250.

Harvest Hse, (Harvest Hse. Pubs., Inc.; 0-89081), 1075 Arrowsmith, Eugene, OR 97402 (SAN 207-4745) Tel 503-343-0123; Toll free: 800-547-8979.

Harvest IL, (Harvest Pubns.; 0-935797), Div. of Baptist General Conference, 2002 S. Arlington Heights Rd., Arlington Heights, IL 60005 (SAN 696-8023) Tel 312-228-0200.

Harvest Moon, (Harvest Moon Books; 0-9602886), P.O. Box 172, Riverside, CA 92502 (SAN 213-0750) Tel 714-682-4907.

Harvest NJ, (Harvest House Press; 0-89523), Eden West, 30 Nassau St., Princeton, NJ 08540 (SAN 212-7768) Tel 609-924-8715.

Harvest Pr, (Harvest Press; 0-917332), 480 Nelson Road, Santa Cruz, CA 95066 (SAN 208-6794) Tel 408-335-5015.

Harvest Pubns, (Harvest Pubns.; 0-939074), Box 2466, Hollywood, CA 90078 (SAN 209-2964) Tel 213-469-0786.

Harvestman, (Harvestman & Associates), P.O. Box 271, Menlo Park, CA 94026 (SAN 212-1662) Tel 415-326-6997.

Harvey Assoc
See A Harvey

Harvey J M, (Harvey, James M.; 0-933799), 825 N-Lamb Blvd., Las Vegas, NV 89110 (SAN 692-8943) Tel 702-452-1217.

Harvey Womans Club, (Harvey Woman's Club; 0-961654), P.O. Box 1058, Palestine, TX 75801 (SAN 285-306X) Tel 214-723-7342; Dist. by: Southwest Cookbook Distributors Inc., 1901 South Shore Dr., Bonham, TX 75418 (SAN 200-4925) Tel 214-583-8898; Dist. by: The Collection, P.O. Box 15624, Kansas City, MO 64106 (SAN 689-8440).

Harvey Yorke, (Yorke, Harvey; 0-9607598), 495 Rowland Blvd., Novato, CA 94947 (SAN 200-2612) Tel 415-897-4050; P.O. Box 252, Novato, CA 94948 (SAN 237-9767).

Harwal Pub Co Imprint of **Wiley**

†Harwood Academic, (Harwood Academic Pubs.; 3-7186), P.O. Box 786, Cooper Sta., New York, NY 10276 (SAN 213-9294) Tel 212-206-8900; CIP.

Hascom Pubs, (Hascom Pubs.; 0-935927), P.O. Box 1396, Provo, UT 84603 (SAN 696-804X) Tel 801-375-0790.

Haskala Pr, (Haskala Pr.; 0-9613846), 640 Orange Ave., Los Altos, CA 94022 (SAN 681-9885) Tel 415-948-4648.

Haskell, (Haskell Booksellers, Inc.; 0-8383), P.O. Box Y20, Blythebourne Sta., Brooklyn, NY 11219 (SAN 202-2818) Tel 718-435-7878.

Haskett Spec, (Haskett Specialties; 0-9609724), 26 E. Harrison St., Mooresville, IN 46158 (SAN 270-6946) Tel 317-831-1668.

†Hastings, (Hastings Hse. Pubs.; 0-8038), Div. of Gallen Fund, Inc., 260 Fifth Ave., New York, NY 10001 (SAN 213-9561) Tel 212-889-9624; Toll free: 800-52607626; Dist. by: Kampmann & Co, Inc., 9 E. 40 St., New York, NY 10016 (SAN 202-5191) Tel 212-685-2928; CIP. Imprints: Communication Arts (Communication Arts Books); Visual Communication (Visual Communication Books).

Hastings Bks, (Hastings Bks.; 0-940846), 116 N. Wayne Ave., Wayne, PA 19087 (SAN 205-048X).

†Hastings Ctr, (Hastings Center; 0-916558), 360 Broadway, Hastings-on-Hudson, NY 10706 (SAN 208-6980) Tel 914-478-0500; CIP.

Hastings Ctr Inst Soc
See Hastings Ctr

Hastings Pr, (Hastings Pr.; 0-935799), 693 Columbus Ave., New York, NY 10025 (SAN 696-4664) Tel 518-465-5222; Box 20108, New York, NY 10025 (SAN 699-6337).

Hat Stevens, (Stevens, Hat, Pub.; 0-9605690), 5718 Dorsett Dr., Madison, WI 53711 (SAN 239-698X) Tel 608-271-2683.

Hat Tree Studio, (Hat Tree Studio), 2713 W. 96th Pl., Evergreen Park, IL 60642 (SAN 663-0782).

Hatch's Dist, (Hatch's Distributors; 0-939723), Subs. of Hatch's Card Shops, Inc., 15677 E. 17th Ave., Aurora, CO 80011 (SAN 663-5946) Tel 303-341-7240.

Hatfield, (Hatfield, Glen; 0-9600216), P.O. Box 329, Kankakee, IL 60901 (SAN 204-0298) Tel 815-939-1818.

Hatfield Hse, (Hatfield Hse. Bks.; 0-931015), 783 Concord, Richmond, KY 40475 (SAN 678-9757) Tel 606-369-3919.

Hatfield Hse Pub, (Hatfield Hse., Publishing Co.; 0-9617030), P.O. Box 24175, San Jose, CA 95124 (SAN 662-8664); 1655 York St., San Jose, CA 95124 (SAN 662-8672) Tel 408-266-2615.

Hathaway Hse, (Hathaway Hse., Inc.; 0-912241), 601 Memorial Pkwy., Rochester, MN 55902 (SAN 265-1270) Tel 507-288-8483.

Hathor House Bks, (Hathor Hse. Bks.; 0-934482), 138 N. Third St., Douglas, WY 82633 (SAN 221-1033) Tel 307-358-2166.

Hattori Corp, (Hattori Corp. of America; 0-936971), 555 W. 57th St., New York, NY 10019 (SAN 658-7852) Tel 212-977-7755.

Haunted Bk Shop, (Haunted Bookshop, The; 0-940882), 214 St. Francis St., Mobile, AL 36602 (SAN 223-1344) Tel 205-432-6606.

Hausladen Pub, (Hausladen Publishing; 0-9617130), 820 6th Ave. NW, Apt. 5, New Brighton, MN 55112 (SAN 662-6947) Tel 612-639-1130.

Havasupai Council, (Havasupai Tribal Coucil; 0-9614648), P.O. Box 10, Supai, AZ 86435 (SAN 691-8603) Tel 602-448-2731.

Havemeyer Bks, (Havemeyer Books; 0-911397), 12 Havemeyer Place, Greenwich, CT 06830 (SAN 270-6962) Tel 203-661-3823.

Haven Bks Imprint of **Bridge Pub**

Haven Corp, (Haven Corp.; 0-911361), 802 Madison, Evanston, IL 60202 (SAN 275-9977) Tel 312-869-3434.

Haven Pubns, (Haven Pubns.; 0-930586), G.P.O. Box 2046, New York, NY 10001 (SAN 220-6293) Tel 212-219-0672.

Haverford, (Haverford Hse.; 0-910702), 347 E. Conestoga Rd., P.O. Box 408, Wayne, PA 19087 (SAN 204-0301) Tel 215-688-5191.

Havertown Bks, (Havertown Books), P.O. Box 711, Havertown, PA 19083 (SAN 208-4384).

Havin Fun Inc, (Havin' Fun, Inc.; 0-937513), P.O. Box 70468, Eugene, OR 97401-0124 (SAN 658-8476) Tel 503-726-5327; 650 Harlow Rd., No. 123, Springfield, OR 97477 (SAN 658-8484).

Hawaii CTE, (Hawaii Council of Teachers of English; 0-9616581), Windward Community College, 45-720 Keaahala Rd., Kaneohe, HI 96744 (SAN 661-2369) Tel 808-235-7424.

Hawaiian Serv, (Hawaiian Service, Inc.; 0-930492), P.O. Box 2835, Honolulu, HI 96803 (SAN 205-0463) Tel 808-841-0134.

Hawaiian Sugar, (Hawaiian Sugar Planters Assn.), 99-193 Aiea Heights Dr., Aiea, HI 96701 (SAN 270-7012) Tel 808-487-5561; P.O. Box 1057, Aiea, HI 96701 (SAN 669-0939).

Hawk Hands Pr, (Hawk Hands Pr.; 0-9615827), 2661 California St., No. 4, San Francisco, CA 94115 (SAN 696-8066) Tel 415-446-7125.

Hawk-Island, (Hawk-Island Associates; 0-937342), 2630 N. 8th St., Sheboygan, WI 53081 (SAN 215-0794).

Hawk Migration Assn, (Hawk Migration Assn. of North America; 0-938239), 254 Arlington St., Medford, MA 02155 (SAN 661-4264) Tel 617-895-6924.

Hawkes Pub Inc, (Hawkes Publishing Inc.; 0-89036), Box 15711, Salt Lake City, UT 84115 (SAN 205-6232) Tel 801-262-5555.

Hawkins Pub, (Hawkins Publishing; 0-9612770), 310 Tahiti Way, No. 108, Marina del Rey, CA 90291 (SAN 289-9426) Tel 213-821-2971.

Hawkland Pr, (Hawkland Pr., Ltd.; 0-918431), P.O. Box 15599, 5822 Taylor, Davenport, IA 52806 (SAN 657-6184) Tel 319-386-3815.

Hawkline Bks, (Hawkline Books; 0-9609860), 520 Military Way, Palo Alto, CA 94306 (SAN 270-7020) Tel 415-493-4387.

Hawks Inn Hist Soc, (Hawks Inn Historical Society Inc.; 0-9613121), P.O. Box 104, Delafield, WI 53018 (SAN 294-8265); 500 Mill Rd., Delafield, WI 53018 (SAN 294-8273) Tel 414-646-8540.

Hawkshead Bk, (Hawkshead Bk. Distribution Co.), P.O. Box 294, Old Westbury, NY 11568 (SAN 212-8217) Tel 516-333-6325.

Hawley, (Hawley Pubns.; 0-910704), 8200 Gould Ave., Hollywood, CA 90046 (SAN 204-0328) Tel 213-654-1573.

†Haworth Pr, (Haworth Pr., Inc., The; 0-917724; 0-86656), 28 E. 22nd St., New York, NY 10010-6194 (SAN 211-0156) Tel 212-228-2800; CIP.

Hawthorn Imprint of **Dutton**

Hawthorne Co, (Hawthorne Publishing Co.; 0-9617238), Div. of Vantage Companies, 2777 Stemmons Freeway, Suite 2000, Dallas, TX 75207 (SAN 663-5695) Tel 214-631-0600.

Hay House, (Hay Hse.; 0-937611), 1242 Berkeley St., Santa Monica, CA 90404 (SAN 658-9618) Tel 213-828-3666.

†Hayden, (Hayden Bk. Co.; 0-8104), Div. of Hayden Publishing Co, 10 Mulholland Dr., Hasbrouck Heights, NJ 07604 (SAN 200-2094) Tel 201-393-6300; Toll free: 800-631-0856; CIP. Imprints: Rider (Rider, John F.); Spartan (Spartan Books, Incorporated).(Spartan Bks., Inc.).

Hayden Enter, (Hayden Enterprises; 0-9613969), 2999 Twin Oaks Place, Salem, OR 97304 (SAN 682-241X).

Hayden Hse
See Pub Service

Hayes, (Hayes Publishing Co., Inc.; 0-910728), 6304 Hamilton Ave., Cincinnati, OH 45224 (SAN 277-6154) Tel 513-681-7559.

Hayes Bk Co
See T I Hayes Pub Co

Hayes Owners Workshop Manuals Imprint of **Haynes Pubns**

Hayes Pub, (Hayes Publishing, Ltd.; 0-88625), 219 N. Milwaukee St., Milwaukee, WI 53202 (SAN 696-4591).

Hayfield Pub, (Hayfield Publishing Co.; 0-913856), Box 11, Hayfield, MN 55940 (SAN 204-0336) Tel 507-477-2511.

Haymark, (Haymark Pubns.; 0-933910), P.O. Box 243, Fredericksburg, VA 22401 (SAN 213-2508) Tel 703-373-1144.

Haymart Bks, (Haymart Books; 0-9613826), RR 1, Box 8, Giltner, NE 68841 (SAN 681-9966) Tel 402-849-2288.

†Haynes Pubns, (Haynes Pubns., Inc.; 0-85696), P.O. Box 456, 859 Lawrence Dr., Newbury Park, CA 91320 (SAN 212-1611) Tel 805-498-6703; Dist. by: Interbook, 14895 E. 14th St., Suite 370, San Leandro, CA 94577 (SAN 692-7564) Tel 415-352-9221; CIP. Imprints: G T Forrers (Forrers, G. T., & Co., Ltd.); Hayes Owners Workshop Manuals (Haynes Owners Workshop Manuals).

Hays Humane Soc, (Hays Humane Society; 0-9616537), P.O. Box 311, Hays, KS 67601 (SAN 659-4646) Tel 913-625-7685; 3504 Hillcrest Dr., Hays, KS 67601 (SAN 659-4654).

Hays Rolfes, (Hays, Rolfes & Assocs.; 0-9602448), P.O. Box 11465, Memphis, TN 38111 (SAN 212-6656) Tel 901-682-8128; Dist. by: The Collection, Inc., P.O. Box 1220, 2101 Kansas City Rd., Olathe, KS 66061 (SAN 200-6359) Tel 913-764-5900.

Hayward Area Hist, (Hayward Area Historical Society; 0-936427), 22701 Main St., Hayward, CA 94541 (SAN 697-869X) Tel 415-581-0223.

†Haywire Pr, (Haywire Press), 44 S. Mountain Rd., New City, NY 10956 (SAN 210-8100) Tel 914-634-5214; CIP.

Haywood Pr, (Haywood Pr.; 0-9609892), Box 176, Brooklyn, NY 11205-0176 (SAN 270-7055) Tel 718-891-6460.

Hazard Mgmt, (Hazard Management Co., Inc.; 0-935623), P.O. Box 468, Cazenovia, NY 13035 (SAN 695-9431) Tel 315-655-3486; 3957 Rippleton Rd., Cazenovia, NY 13035 (SAN 695-944X).

Hazardous Mat Control, (Hazardous Materials Control Research Institute), 9300 Columbia Blvd., Silver Spring, MD 20910 (SAN 276-9433) Tel 301-587-9390.

Hazelden, (Hazelden Foundation; 0-89486), Box 176, Center City, MN 55012 (SAN 209-4010) Tel 612-257-4010; Toll free: 800-328-9000.

Hazlett Print, (Hazlett Printing & Publishing, Inc.; 0-940588), Div. of Valkyrie-Hazlett Printing, Inc., 2135 First Ave., S., St. Petersburg, FL 33712 (SAN 264-0902) Tel 813-822-6069.

HBC, (H. B. C.; 0-9601276), Box 626, Lansing, IL 60438 (SAN 210-4318) Tel 312-474-7999.

Hbgr Imprint of **HarBraceJ**

HC Imprint of **HarBraceJ**

HCC Enter, (HCC Enterprises; 0-9614847), 2501 Greenwood Ave., Sacramento, CA 95821 (SAN 693-1197) Tel 916-488-8409.

HCP Res, *(HCP Research; 0-941210),* 20655
Sunrise Dr., Cupertino, CA 95014
(SAN 217-376X) Tel 408-446-1565.

HCP Systems, *(HCP Systems, Inc.; 0-930945),*
11905 Whistler Ct., Potomac, MD 20854
(SAN 692-8226) Tel 301-340-9794.

HDL Pubs, *(HDL Publishing Co.; 0-937359),*
Div. of HDL Communications, 599
Adamsdale Rd., North Attleboro, MA 02760
(SAN 659-0403).

Headlands Pr, *(Headlands Pr., Inc.; 0-915500),*
P.O. Box 862, Tiburon, CA 94920
(SAN 207-3234) Tel 415-435-0770.

Headwaters Pr, *(Headwaters Press; 0-932428),*
3734 131st Ave. N., Suite 7, Clearwater, FL
33520 (SAN 211-9609).

Headway Pubns, *(Headway Pubns.; 0-89537),*
1700 Port Manleigh Circle, Newport Beach,
CA 92660 (SAN 210-4342)
Tel 714-644-9126.

Heahstan Pr, *(Heahstan Press, The; 0-9604244),*
P.O. Box 954, Denton, TX 76202
(SAN 214-3127).

Heal, *(Heal; 0-9614132),* P.O. Box 385, Pratt,
WV 25162 (SAN 686-5143)
Tel 304-442-4759.

Heal Tao Bks, *(Healing Tao Bks.; 0-935621),* 2
Creskill Pl., Huntington, NY 11743
(SAN 695-9318) Tel 516-549-9452; Dist.
by: The Talman Co., 150 Fifth Ave., Rm.
514, New York, NY 10011
(SAN 200-5204) Tel 212-620-3182.

Heald Pubns, *(Heald Pubns.; 0-9613127),* 420
Rutgers Ave., Swarthmore, PA 19081
(SAN 294-8281) Tel 215-447-7255. Out of
business.

Healing Tao Pr
See Heal Tao Bks

Health Act Pr, *(Health Action Press; 0-913571),*
Subs. of Center for Health Action, 6439
Taggart Rd., Delaware, OH 43015
(SAN 285-2691) Tel 614-548-5340.

Health Activ, *(Wellness and Health Activation
Networks),* P.O. Box 923, Vienna, VA
22180 (SAN 224-3237) Tel 703-281-3830.

†Health Admin Pr, *(Health Administration Pr.;
0-914904; 0-910701),* Div. of Foundation of
the American College of Healthcare
Executives, 1021 E. Huron St., Ann Arbor,
MI 48104-9990 (SAN 207-0464)
Tel 313-764-1380; *CIP.*

Health Alert Pr, *(Health Alert Pr.; 0-936571),*
P.O. Box 2060, Cambridge, MA 02238
(SAN 698-0732) Tel 617-497-4190
(SAN 698-0740).

Health Care
See Healthcare Pr

Health Comm, *(Health Communications, Inc.;
0-932194),* 1721 Blount Rd., Suite 1,
Pompano Beach, FL 33069
(SAN 212-100X); Toll free: 800-857-9100.

Health Ed Aids, *(Health Education Aids;
0-89829),* 8 S. Lakeview Dr., Goddard, KS
67052 (SAN 220-6323) Tel 316-794-2216.

Health Ed & Life Exp Res, *(Health Education &
Life Expansion Research; 0-9607142),* Box
70027, Los Angeles, CA 90309
(SAN 238-9878) Tel 213-738-9940.

Health Ed Pubns, *(Health Educator Publications
Inc.; 0-932887),* 525 Lincoln St., Rockville,
MD 20850 (SAN 689-0059)
Tel 301-424-1363.

Health Ed Train, *(Health Education Training
and Administration Consortium, Inc., The;
0-911067),* 1764 Bising Ave., No. 4, North
College Hill, OH 45239 (SAN 270-711X)
Tel 513-931-9227.

Health Explo, *(Health Explosion, The;
0-9613424),* P.O. Box 2375, Owensboro, KY
42302 (SAN 656-8890) Tel 502-684-4439.

Health Info Lib, *(Health Information Library;
0-911931),* Krames Communications, 312
90th St., Daly City, CA 94015
(SAN 264-2816) Tel 415-994-8800.

Health Med Amer, *(Health Media of America;
0-937325),* 11300 Sorrento Valley Rd., No.
250, San Diego, CA 92121 (SAN 658-8069)
Tel 619-453-3887.

Health PAC, *(Health Policy Advisory Center),*
17 Murray St, New York, NY 10007
(SAN 224-3288) Tel 212-267-8890.

Health Phys Soc, *(Health Physics Society,
Columbia Chapter; 0-9613108),* P.O. Box
564, Richland, WA 99352 (SAN 294-0183)
Tel 509-376-8085.

Health Plus, *(Health Plus, Pubs.; 0-932090),*
P.O. Box 22001, Phoenix, AZ 85028
(SAN 211-4984) Tel 602-992-0589; Dist.
by: Contemporary Bks., 180 N. Michigan
Ave., Chicago, IL 60601 (SAN 202-5493)
Tel 312-782-9181.

Health Prof Ed
See Betz Pub Co Inc

Health Prom Group, *(Health Promotion Group,
Inc., The; 0-935105),* P.O. Box 59687,
Homewood, AL 35259 (SAN 695-1449)
Tel 205-934-6020.

Health Pub Co, *(Health Publishing Co.;
0-917591),* P.O. Box 1922, Chula Vista, CA
92012 (SAN 657-1468) Tel 706-612-1941.

Health Res Las Vegas, *(Health Research;
0-9601978),* Box 19420, Las Vegas, NV
89132 (SAN 212-2553) Tel 702-733-8476.

Health Sci, *(Health Science; 0-87790),* Div. of
Live Food Products, Inc., Box 7, Santa
Barbara, CA 93102 (SAN 208-1016)
Tel 805-968-1028.

Health Sci Comm, *(Health Sciences
Communications),* 6105 Lindell Blvd.,
St. Louis, MO 63112 (SAN 224-2915)
Tel 314-725-4722.

Healthcare Fin Mgmt Assn, *(Healthcare
Financial Management Assn.; 0-930228),*
1900 Spring Rd., Suite 500, Oak Brook, IL
60521 (SAN 207-5911) Tel 312-655-4600.

Healthcare Pr, *(Healthcare Pr.; 0-9613775),*
P.O. Box 4488, Rollingbay, WA 98061
(SAN 678-9749) Tel 206-842-5243.

HealthProInk, *(HealthProInk Publishing;
0-933803),* Div. of Spelman Productions,
Inc., P.O. Box 3333, Farmington Hills, MI
48018 (SAN 692-8803); Toll free:
800-802-4966 in Michigan; 26941
Pebblestone Rd., Southfield, MI 48034
(SAN 662-3050) Tel 313-355-3686.

Healthtalk, *(Healthtalk; 0-936439),* 1888
Century Pk. E., Suite 405, Los Angeles, CA
90067 (SAN 697-8711) Tel 213-556-0603.

Healthwise, *(Healthwise, Inc.; 0-9612690),* P.O.
Box 1989, Boise, ID 83701 (SAN 289-2367)
Tel 208-345-1161; 904 W. Fort St., Boise,
ID 83702 (SAN 289-2375).

Healthworks, *(Healthworks, Inc.; 0-938480),*
30131 Town Ctr. Dr., Suite 135, Laguna
Niguel, CA 92677-2034 (SAN 215-7721)
Tel 714-495-8550.

Hearn Assocs, *(Hearn Assocs.; 0-9615450),*
1270 Covington Rd., Los Altos, CA 94022
(SAN 695-7676) Tel 415-968-4713.

Hearne Bks, *(Hearne-Books U.S.A.; 0-918760),*
22 River St., Braintree, MA 02184
(SAN 210-4350) Tel 617-843-5702.

HearSay Pr, *(HearSay Pr.; 0-938613),* P.O. Box
42265, Portland, OR 97242
(SAN 661-5805); 2916 SE 21st Ave.,
Portland, OR 97202 (SAN 661-5813)
Tel 503-233-2637.

Hearst Bks, *(Hearst Bks.; 0-910992; 0-87851;
0-910990; 0-688),* Div. of William Morrow
& Co., Inc., 105 Madison Ave., New York,
NY 10016 (SAN 202-2842)
Tel 212-889-3050.

Heart Am Pr, *(Heart of America Pr.; 0-913902),*
10101 Blue Ridge Blvd., Kansas City, MO
64134 (SAN 204-0379) Tel 816-761-0080.

Heart Ctry TN Pubns, *(Heart Country
Tennessee Pubns.; 0-9616334),* Rte. 1, Box
196-B, Big Sandy, TN 38221
(SAN 658-960X) Tel 901-584-2038.

Heart of the Lakes, *(Heart of the Lakes
Publishing; 0-932334),* 2989 Lodi Rd.,
Interlaken, NY 14847-0299
(SAN 213-0769) Tel 607-532-4997.

Heartbeat
See Brancaleone Educ

Heartfire Mktg, *(Heartfire Marketing;
0-935211),* Box 2004, Grants Pass, OR
97526 (SAN 695-7722).

Hearth Pub, *(Hearthstone Pubns.; 0-943098),*
145 Quinn St., Naugatuck, CT 06770
(SAN 240-3864) Tel 203-734-5398.

Hearthstone, *(Hearthstone Press; 0-937308),*
708 Inglewood Dr., Broderick, CA 95605
(SAN 209-4460) Tel 916-372-0250.

Hearthstone CO, *(Hearthstone, Inc.; 0-9616308),*
506 N. Cascade, Colorado Springs, CO
80903 (SAN 658-7283) Tel 303-473-4413.

Heartland Image, *(Heartland Image; 0-915945),*
P.O. Box 69, Big Fork, MT 59911
(SAN 294-0302) Tel 406-837-5587; 162
Lake Hills Dr., Big Fork, MT 59911
(SAN 294-0310).

HeartLight Pubns, *(HeartLight Pubns.;
0-9615911),* 193 W. Mariposa St., Altadena,
CA 91001 (SAN 696-8120)
Tel 818-791-1597.

Hearts & Crafts, *(Hearts & Crafts; 0-9617072),*
5585 E. Pacific Coast Hwy, No. 132, Long
Beach, CA 90804 (SAN 662-9105)
Tel 213-498-3506.

Heartspring Unltd, *(Heartspring Unlimited;
0-9615606),* P.O. Box 10385, Glendale, CA
91209 (SAN 695-9725) Tel 818-507-8800;
321 W. Milford St., Suite 8, Glendale, CA
91203 (SAN 695-9733).

Heartstart, *(Heartstart Pubns.; 0-912825),* 2392
Nancy Pl., St. Paul, MN 55113
(SAN 282-7913) Tel 612-484-3443.

Heartwind Pubns, *(Heartwind Pubns.; 0-916193),*
P.O. Box 4833, Shreveport, LA 71104
(SAN 294-9377) Tel 318-222-4697.

†Heartwork Pr, *(Heartwork Press; 0-935598),*
220 Redwood Hwy., Mill Valley, CA 94941
(SAN 214-025X); *CIP.*

†Heath, *(Heath, D. C., Co.; 0-669; 0-278;
0-88408),* 125 Spring St., Lexington, MA
02173 (SAN 213-7526) Tel 617-862-6650;
Toll free: 800-428-8071; Orders to: D. C.
Heath & Co. Distribution Ctr., 2700 Richardt
Ave., Indianapolis, IN 46219
(SAN 202-2885) Tel 317-359-5585; *CIP.*
Imprints: Sterling Swift (Swift, Sterling).

Heather Foun, *(Heather Foundation; 0-9600300),*
P.O. Box 48, San Pedro, CA 90733
(SAN 204-0387) Tel 213-831-6269.

Heather Pub Co, *(Heather Publishing Co.;
0-9613620),* P.O. Box 77347, Oklahoma
City, OK 73177 (SAN 682-8922)
Tel 405-751-2922.

Heatherdown Pr, *(Heatherdown Press;
0-9610038),* 3450 Brantford Rd., Toledo,
OH 43606 (SAN 270-7284)
Tel 419-877-0073.

†Heathkit-Zenith Ed, *(Heathkit/Zenith
Educational System; 0-87119),* Div. of
Zenith Electronics Corp., P.O. Box 1288,
Benton Harbor, MI 49022 (SAN 296-6476)
Tel 616-982-3641; *CIP.*

Heavenow Prod, *(Heavenow Productions;
0-9616770),* 7800 185th Pl., SW, Edmonds,
WA 98020 (SAN 661-339X)
Tel 206-775-8365.

Hebraeus Pr, *(Hebraeus Press; 0-910511),* Box
32 HBLL Brigham Young Univ., Provo, UT
84603 (SAN 260-0692) Tel 801-347-8839.

†Hebrew Pub, *(Hebrew Publishing Co.; 0-88482),*
100 Water St., Brooklyn, NY 11202-0875
(SAN 201-5404) Tel 718-858-6928; *CIP.*

†Hebrew Union Coll Pr, *(Hebrew Union College
Press; 0-87820),* Clifton Ave., Cincinnati,
OH 45220 (SAN 220-6358)
Tel 513-221-1875; Dist. by: Ktav Publishing
Hse., Inc., 900 Jefferson St., Hoboken, NJ
07030 (SAN 658-1056) Tel 201-963-9524;
CIP.

Hedgehog Pr, *(Hedgehog Press; 0-943486),*
3041 Lopez, Pebble Beach, CA 93953
(SAN 240-6705) Tel 408-649-3415.

Hedman Steno, *(Hedman Stenotype; 0-939056),*
1158 W. Armitage Ave., Chicago, IL 60614
(SAN 239-7579) Tel 312-871-6500.

Heedays, *(Heeday's Pubns.; 0-917822),* 94-12
Kipaa Pl., Waipahu, HI 96797
(SAN 209-5653).

Heene Enter, *(Heene Enterprises; 0-9616054),*
3420 Ediwhar St., San Diego, CA 92123
(SAN 698-0651) Tel 619-268-8090.

Heffron Ent, *(Heffron, Dan, Enterprises;
0-9605104),* P.O. Box 9019, Cleveland, OH
44137 (SAN 216-0366).

Hegeler Inst, *(Hegeler Institute, The; 0-914417),*
The Monist, School of Philosophy, University
of Southern California, Los Angeles, CA
90089 (SAN 289-6346) Tel 815-223-1231;
Orders to: The Monist, P.O. Box 600, La
Salle, IL 61301 (SAN 662-7552)
Tel 815-223-1231.

HEH Med Pubns, *(HEH Medical Pubns.;
0-9614173),* 2227 W. Lindsey, Suite 1401,
Norman, OK 73069 (SAN 686-6557)
Tel 405-329-4457.

Heian Intl, *(Heian International Publishing, Inc.;
0-89346),* P.O. Box 1013, Union City, CA
94587 (SAN 213-2036) Tel 415-471-8440.

†Heidelberg Graph, *(Heidelberg Graphics;
0-918606),* P.O. Box 3606, Chico, CA 95927
(SAN 211-5654) Tel 916-342-6582; Orders
to: 1116 Wendy Way, Chico, CA
95926-1511 (SAN 662-0345); *CIP.*

Heidenreich, *(Heidenreich House; 0-9600428),* 5012 Oak Point Way, Fair Oaks, CA 95628 (SAN 204-0395) Tel 916-961-3297.

Heimburger Hse Pub, *(Heimburger House Publishing Co.; 0-911581),* 310 Lathrop Ave., River Forest, IL 60305 (SAN 264-0929) Tel 312-366-1973.

†**Heineman,** *(Heineman, James H., Inc., Pub.; 0-87008),* 475 Park Ave., New York, NY 10022 (SAN 204-0409) Tel 212-688-2028; CIP.

†**Heinemann Ed,** *(Heinemann Educational Bks., Inc.; 0-435),* 70 Court St., Portsmouth, NH 03801 (SAN 210-5829) Tel 603-431-7894; CIP.

Heinemann Educational
See Heinemann Ed

Heinle & Heinle, *(Heinle & Heinle Pubs., Inc.; 0-8384),* 20 Park Plaza, Boston, MA 02116 (SAN 216-0730) Tel 617-451-1940; Toll free: 800-225-3782.

Heinman, *(Heinman, W. S., Imported Bks.; 0-88431),* 225 W. 57th St., Rm. 404, New York, NY 10019 (SAN 121-6201) Tel 212-757-7628; P.O. Box 926, New York, NY 10023 (SAN 660-935X).

Heirloom Bks, *(Heirloom Bks.; 0-914925),* 3039 McClellan, Detroit, MI 48214 (SAN 289-2332) Tel 313-331-7244; Box 15472, Detroit, MI 48215 (SAN 669-3555).

Heirloom Pr, *(Heirloom Pr.; 0-9615377),* 3430 Georgia Ave. N., Minneapolis, MN 55427 (SAN 695-5347) Tel 612-536-0564; Orders to: P.O. Box 28168, Minneapolis, MN 55428 (SAN 662-3492).

Heirloom Pub, *(Heirloom Publishing; 0-938015),* P.O. Box 183, Mills, WY 82644 (SAN 661-2334); 4340 Hideaway Ln., Mills, WY 82644 (SAN 661-2342) Tel 307-235-3561.

Heirloom Pubns, *(Heirloom Pubns. Ltd.; 0-9609488),* P.O. Box 667, Cedar Rapids, IA 52406 (SAN 270-7403) Tel 319-366-4690.

Heirs Intl, *(Heirs International; 0-915970),* 444 Lombard St., No. 6, San Francisco, CA 94133 (SAN 207-8414) Tel 415-956-8752.

Helander, *(Helander, Joel E.; 0-935600),* 36 Norton Ave., Guilford, CT 06437 (SAN 213-7445) Tel 203-453-6626.

Heldon Pr, *(Heldon Pr.; 0-933169),* 9146 Arrington Ave., Downey, CA 90240 (SAN 692-3127) Tel 213-869-5741.

Heldref Pubns, *(Heldref Pubns.; 0-916882),* Div. of The Helen Dwight Reid Educational Foundation, 4000 Albemarle St., NW, Washington, DC 20016 (SAN 208-0788) Tel 202-362-6445.

Helen Pub, *(Helen Publishing Co.; 0-9617192),* 25 Lake St., Apt. 5A, White Plains, NY 10603 (SAN 663-2823) Tel 914-682-0555.

Helene Obolensky Ent, *(Obolensky, Helene, Enterprises, Inc.; 0-9609736),* P.O. Box 87, 909 Third Ave., New York, NY 10150 (SAN 274-2381) Tel 212-838-4722.

Heli World Pr, *(Heli-World Pr.; 0-939177),* 3229 Sunset Way, Bellingham, WA 98226 (SAN 662-9156) Tel 206-758-7396.

Helikon NY, *(Helikon Press; 0-914496),* 120 W. 71st St., New York, NY 10023 (SAN 201-9175) Tel 212-873-6884.

Helix Bks *Imprint of* **Rowman**

Helix Hse *(Helix House Pubs.; 0-930866),* 9231 Molly Woods Ave., La Mesa, CA 92041 (SAN 211-3171). Out of business.

Helix Pr, *(Helix Pr.; 0-914587),* 4410 Hickey, Corpus Christi, TX 78413 (SAN 289-2669) Tel 512-852-8834.

Helix Pr VA, *(Helix Pr.; 0-935653),* Div. of RGS, Inc., P.O. Box 5144, Springfield, VA 22150 (SAN 695-9393); 7606 Chancellor Way, Springfield, VA 22153 (SAN 695-9407) Tel 703-455-7614.

hell box, *(hell box, the; 0-9614593),* 4022 Greenhill Pl., Austin, TX 78759 (SAN 691-7798) Tel 512-345-0776.

Hellcoal Pr, *(Hellcoal Press; 0-916912),* P.O. Box 4, S. A. O. , Brown Univ., Providence, RI 02912 (SAN 208-6808) Tel 401-863-2341.

Hellenes, *(Hellenes-English Biblical Foundation; 0-910710),* P.O. Box 10412, Jackson, MS 39209 (SAN 204-0433).

†**Hellenic Coll Pr,** *(Hellenic College Press; 0-917653),* Div. of Holy Cross Orthodox Press, 50 Goddard Ave., Brookline, MA 02146 (SAN 213-6694) Tel 617-731-3500; CIP.

Hello Reader *Imprint of* **Scholastic Inc**

Helmers Howard Pub, *(Helmers & Howard, Pubs., Inc.; 0-939443),* 1221 E. Madison St., Colorado Springs, CO 80907 (SAN 663-3552) Tel 303-520-1559.

Helotes Area, *(Helotes Area Volunteers Fire Dept. Inc.; 0-9612736),* P.O. Box 186, Helotes, TX 78023 (SAN 289-9434) Tel 512-695-3254.

HELP Bks, *(H.E.L.P Bks., Inc.; 0-918500),* 1201 E. Calle Elena, Tucson, AZ 85718 (SAN 209-665X) Tel 602-297-6452.

Helpful Beginnings, *(Helpful Beginnings; 0-938783),* P.O. Box 1684, Clovis, CA 93613-1684 (SAN 661-5465); 1502 Celeste, Clovis, CA 93612 (SAN 661-5473) Tel 209-299-1876.

HelpLine, *(HelpLine; 0-930053),* 200 Ross St, Pittsburgh, PA 15219 (SAN 669-8522) Tel 412-255-1140.

Helsinki Watch *Imprint of* **Fund Free Expression**

HEMA Pub, *(HEMA Publishing; 0-938805),* P.O. Box 23977, Rochester, NY 14623 (SAN 661-5120); 56 Wildbriar Rd., Rochester, NY 14623 (SAN 661-5139) Tel 716-334-7697.

HEMECO, *(Harrison Education Motivation Enterprises; 0-9611440),* 21863 Brill Rd., Riverside, CA 92508 (SAN 212-744X) Tel 714-653-4779.

Heming W Studies, *(Hemingway Western Studies Research Ctr.; 0-932129),* Boise State Univ., 1910 University Dr., Boise, ID 83725 Tel 208-385-1572.

Hemisphere Hse, *(Hemisphere House Books; 0-930770),* P.O. Box 1934, Corpus Christi, TX 78403 (SAN 211-0717).

Hemisphere NY
See H-U Public

†**Hemisphere Pub,** *(Hemisphere Publishing Corp.; 0-89116),* 79 Madison Ave., Suite 1110, New York, NY 10016 (SAN 207-4001) Tel 212-725-1999; Toll free: 800-242-7737 (Ordering); CIP.

Hemisphere Pub NY
See Hemisphere Pub

Hemlock CA
See Hemlock Soc

Hemlock Soc, *(Hemlock Society; 0-9606030),* P.O. Box 66218, Los Angeles, CA 90066 (SAN 293-275X) Tel 213-391-1871; Dist. by: Grove Pr., 196 W. Houston St., New York, NY 10014 (SAN 201-4890) Tel 212-242-4900.

Hemming, *(Hemming, H. & G.; 0-9614224),* 14812 N. Cameo Dr., Sun City, AZ 85351 (SAN 686-8096) Tel 602-977-9488.

Hemmings, *(Hemmings Motor News; 0-917808),* Box 256, Bennington, VT 05201 (SAN 210-3060) Tel 802-442-3101.

Hemphill, *(Hemphill Publishing Co.; 0-914696),* 1400 Wathen Ave., Austin, TX 78703 (SAN 204-0441) Tel 512-476-9422.

Hempstead House, *(Hempstead House; 0-940094),* 1019 Jerome St., Houston, TX 77009 (SAN 220-2271) Tel 713-864-6130.

Henart Bks, *(Henart Bks.; 0-938059),* 4711 NW 24th Ct., Lauderdale Lakes, FL 33313 (SAN 661-1885) Tel 305-485-4286; Dist. by: Banyan Bks., P.O. Box 431160, Miami, FL 33243 (SAN 208-340X) Tel 305-665-6011.

Henceforth, *(Henceforth Pubns.; 0-913437; 0-913439),* c/o Berkshire Christian College, Lenox, MA 01240 (SAN 285-1628) Tel 413-637-1451.

Henchanted Bks, *(Henchanted Bks.; 0-9615756),* P.O. Box H, Calpella, CA 95418 (SAN 696-4468) Tel 707-485-7551.

Henderikse, *(Henderikse; 0-932455),* 110 Christopher St., New York, NY 10014 (SAN 686-8118) Tel 212-242-7513.

Hendershot, *(Hendershot Bibliography; 0-911832),* 4114 Ridgewood Dr., Bay City, MI 48706-2499 (SAN 204-045X) Tel 517-684-3148.

†**Hendrick-Long,** *(Hendrick-Long Publishing Co.; 0-937460),* 4811 W. Lovers Ln., Dallas, TX 75209 (SAN 281-7748) Tel 214-358-4677; P.O. Box 25123, Dallas, TX 75225 (SAN 281-7756); CIP.

Hendricks-Ferguson, *(Hendricks-Ferguson; 0-9615468),* 3521 Heyward St., Columbia, SC 29205 (SAN 695-9334) Tel 803-254-3875.

Hendricks House, *(Hendricks Hse., Inc.; 0-87532),* Main St., Putney, VT 05346 (SAN 206-9830) Tel 802-387-4185.

Hendricks Pub, *(Hendricks Publishing; 0-943764),* P.O. Box 724026, Atlanta, GA 30339 (SAN 264-0945).

Henke M A, *(Henke, Mary Alice; 0-9611032),* Box 327, Enders, NE 69027 (SAN 282-8782) Tel 308-882-4004.

Hennepin Hall, *(Hennepin Hall Pubns.; 0-912243),* P.O. Box 84, Rockford, IL 61105 (SAN 265-1289) Tel 815-877-5345.

†**Hennessey,** *(Hennessey & Ingalls, Inc.; 0-912158),* 1254 Third St. Mall, Santa Monica, CA 90401 (SAN 293-2776) Tel 213-458-9074; Dist. by: Hennessy, 8325 Campion Dr., Los Angeles, CA 90045 (SAN 293-2784) Tel 213-458-9074; CIP.

Henry Art, *(Henry Art Gallery; 0-935558),* DE-15, Univ. of Washington, Seattle, WA 98195 (SAN 213-6708) Tel 206-543-2280.

Henry Fischer, *(Fischer, Henry G.),* R.R. 1, Box 389, Sherman, CT 06784 (SAN 692-3135); Dist. by: Metropolitan Museum of Art, Book Sales Dept., 82nd St. & Fifth Ave., New York, NY 10028 (SAN 202-6279) Tel 212-879-5500.

Henry John & Co, *(Henry John & Co.; 0-937028),* P.O. Box 10235, Dillingham, AK 99576 (SAN 214-3909) Tel 907-842-5458.

Heptangle, *(Heptangle Books; 0-935214),* P.O. Box 283, Berkeley Heights, NJ 07922 (SAN 210-6329) Tel 201-647-4449.

Her Pub Co, *(Her Publishing Co., Inc.; 0-930676),* P.O. Box 1168, Oakwood Shopping Ctr., Gretna, LA 70053 (SAN 211-0164).

Herald Bks, *(Herald Bks.; 0-910714),* P.O. Box 17, Pelham, NY 10803 (SAN 202-2893) Tel 914-576-1121.

Herald Hse, *(Herald Hse.; 0-8309),* P.O. Box HH, Independence, MO 64055 (SAN 202-2907) Tel 816-252-5010; Toll free: 800-821-7550.

Herald NC, *(Herald Books),* Kings at Canterbury, Kings Mountain, NC 28086 (SAN 656-8904).

†**Herald Pr,** *(Herald Pr.; 0-8361),* Div. of Mennonite Publishing Hse., Inc., 616 Walnut Ave., Scottdale, PA 15683 (SAN 202-2915) Tel 412-887-8500; Toll free: 800-245-7894; CIP.

†**Heraldic Pub,** *(Heraldic Publishing Co., Inc.; 0-910716),* 305 West End Ave., New York, NY 10023 (SAN 204-0476) Tel 212-874-1511; CIP.

Herb Farm Pr, *(Herb Farm Pr.; 0-9614650),* Rte. 123A, New Ipswich, NH 03071 (SAN 691-8638) Tel 603-878-1151.

Herb Society, *(Herb Society of America, Inc.),* 2 Independence Ct., Concord, MA 01742 (SAN 232-6078) Tel 617-371-1486.

Herbal Perception, *(Herbal Perception, The; 0-943638),* Box 143, Mt. Clemens, MI 48043 (SAN 238-2997) Tel 313-949-7932.

Herbal Res Pub, *(Herbal Research Publishing; 0-937643),* 25 Leonard Rd., Lexington, MA 02173 (SAN 658-8565) Tel 617-862-0171.

†**Heres Life,** *(Here's Life Pubs., Inc.; 0-89840),* P.O. Box 1576, San Bernardino, CA 92402 (SAN 212-4254) Tel 714-886-7981; CIP.

Heresy Pr, *(Heresy Press; 0-9603276),* 713 Paul St., Newport News, VA 23605 (SAN 213-2516).

Herit Pub CA, *(Heritage Publishing Co.; 0-936011),* 1056 McClellan Way, Stockton, CA 95207 (SAN 696-8147) Tel 209-951-2238. Do Not Confuse With Heritage Publishing Co., Matthews, NC.

Herit Pub NC, *(Heritage Publishing Co.; 0-936013),* 207 Kimrod Ln., Matthews, NC 28105 (SAN 696-818X) Tel 704-867-8729. Do Not Confuse With Heritage Publishing Co., Stockton, CA.

Herit Pubs Servs, *(Heritage Pubs. Services; 0-939379),* 2000 S. Dairy Ashford, Suite 685, Houston, TX 77077 (SAN 662-9539) Tel 713-589-7080.

Heritage, *(Heritage Publishing Co.; 0-9613922),* 202 Lexington Pl., Uniontown, PA 15401 (SAN 682-5087) Tel 412-439-0560.

Heritage Acad, *(Heritage Academy; 0-9612048),* P.O. Box 9251, Columbus, MS 39701 (SAN 286-7907) Tel 601-327-4004.

Heritage Arts, *(Heritage Arts; 0-911029),* 1807 Prairie Ave., Downers Grove, IL 60515 (SAN 270-7543) Tel 312-964-1194.

Heritage Assocs, *(Heritage Assocs., Inc.; 0-910467),* P.O. Box 6291, Albuquerque, NM 87197 (SAN 260-0706); 2217 Lead SE, Albuquerque, NM 87106 (SAN 662-0353) Tel 505-268-0155.

Heritage Bk, *(Heritage Bks., Inc.; 0-917890; 1-55613),* 3602 Maureen Ln., Bowie, MD 20715 (SAN 209-3367) Tel 301-464-1159.

Heritage Books, *(Heritage Books),* 5176 E. Country Club Rd., Salina, KS 67401 (SAN 212-0410) Tel 913-827-7861.

Heritage Computer, *(Heritage Computer Corp.; 0-935433),* Div. of Heritage Mutual Insurance Co., 2800 S. Taylor Dr., Sheboygan, WI 53081 (SAN 696-1924) Tel 414-457-1422.

Heritage Found, *(Heritage Foundation; 0-89195),* 214 Massachusetts Ave., NE, Washington, DC 20002 (SAN 209-3758) Tel 202-546-4400.

Heritage Kansas
See Heritage Books

Heritage Map Co, *(National Heritage Map Co.; 0-934827),* 20121 Ventura Blvd., Suite 125, Woodland Hills, CA 91364 (SAN 694-2296) Tel 818-347-8151.

Heritage Margaretville, *(Heritage Pubns.; 0-937213),* P.O. Box 642, Main St., Margaretville, NY 12455 (SAN 658-7291) Tel 914-586-3810.

Heritage N Pr, *(Heritage North Press; 0-913905),* 3809 Barbara Dr., Anchorage, AK 99517 (SAN 286-8679).

Heritage PA, *(Heritage Trails; 0-936441),* P.O. Box 307, Turbotville, PA 17772 (SAN 697-8746) Tel 717-649-5846; 82 Main St., Turbotville, PA 17772 (SAN 697-8754).

Heritage Pac, *(Heritage Press of Pacific; 0-9609132),* 1279-203 Ala Kapuna St., Honolulu, HI 96819 (SAN 264-0961) Tel 808-839-1238.

†**Heritage Pr,** *(Heritage Press; 0-935428),* P.O. Box 18625, Baltimore, MD 21216 (SAN 221-2684) Tel 301-383-8521; *CIP.*

Heritage Printers
See McNally & Loftin

Heritage Pubns, *(Heritage Pubns.; 0-9612868),* P.O. Box 76072, Birmingham, AL 35253 (SAN 291-1876); 400 Office Pk. Dr., Suite 111, Birmingham, AL 35223 (SAN 291-1884) Tel 205-871-4233; Dist. by: Dot Gibson Pubns., P.O. Box 117, Waycross, GA 31502 (SAN 200-4143); Dist. by: The Collection, Inc., P.O. Box 1220, Olathe, KS 66061 (SAN 658-277X) Tel 913-764-5900.

Heritage Pubns NY
See Heritage Margaretville

Heritage Pubs Servs
See Herit Pubs Servs

Heritage Rec, *(Heritage Recording; 0-9602888),* P.O. Box 13232, St. Paul, MN 55113 (SAN 211-1942) Tel 612-780-4058.

Heritage Res Hse, *(Heritage Research Hse., Inc.; 0-912617),* Box 64003, Virginia Beach, VA 23464 (SAN 282-7956) Tel 804-467-4777.

Heritage Tech Serv, *(Heritage Technical Services; 0-914769),* P.O. Box 5635, Kent, WA 98031 (SAN 291-8374).

Heritage Trails, *(Heritage Trails Pr.; 0-910083),* 94 Santa Maria Dr., Novato, CA 94947 (SAN 240-8589) Tel 415-897-5679.

Heritage Trails
See Heritage PA

Hermagoras Pr, *(Hermagoras Pr.; 0-9611800),* P.O. Box 1555, Davis, CA 95617 (SAN 285-2802); Dist. by: Univ. of California, Davis, UCD Bookstore, Davis, CA 95616 (SAN 200-4267) Tel 916-752-1984.

Herman Miller, *(Miller, Herman, Inc.; 0-925614; 0-87911),* 8500 Byron Rd., Zeeland, MI 49464 (SAN 296-2357) Tel 616-531-8860.

Hermes Hse, *(Hermes Hse. Pr.; 0-9605008),* 39 Adare Pl., Northampton, MA 01060 (SAN 220-0589) Tel 413-584-8402; Dist. by: Associated Booksellers, 562 Boston Ave., Bridgeport, CT 06610 (SAN 203-5014) Tel 203-333-7268; Dist. by: The Distributors, 702 S. Michigan, South Bend, IN 46618 (SAN 169-2488) Tel 219-232-8500.

Hermes Hse Imprint of **Shambhala Pubns**

Hermes Pub Co, *(Hermes Publishing Company; 0-930421),* P.O. Box 100819, Fort Lauderdale, FL 33310-0819 (SAN 682-0506) Tel 305-735-3141.

Hermetician Pr, *(Hermetician Pr.; 0-935895),* P.O. Box 611381, North Miami, FL 33261-1381 (SAN 696-8198) Tel 305-891-7312; 1048 NE 128 St. No. 5, North Miami, FL 33161 (SAN 696-8201); Dist. by: New Leaf Distributing, 1020 White St. SW, Atlanta, GA 30310 (SAN 169-1449) Tel 404-755-2665; Dist. by: Starlite, P.O. Box 20729, Reno, NV 89515 (SAN 685-9593) Tel 702-359-5676; Dist. by: Astro Computing Services, P.O. Box 16430, San Diego, CA 92116 (SAN 200-8149) Tel 619-297-9209.

Hermit Pr FL, *(Hermit Pr.; 0-939017),* P.O. Box 933, Marianna, FL 32446 (SAN 662-5452); 121 S. Madison St., Marianna, FL 32446 (SAN 662-5460) Tel 904-482-2300. Do not confuse with Hermit Press in Terre Haute, IN.

†**Hermitage,** *(Hermitage; 0-938920),* P.O. Box 410, Tenafly, NJ 07670 (SAN 239-4413) Tel 201-894-8247; *CIP.*

†**Hermon,** *(Sepher-Hermon Pr., Inc.; 0-87203),* 1265 46th St., Brooklyn, NY 11219 (SAN 169-5959) Tel 718-972-9010; *CIP.*

Hermosa, *(Hermosa Pubs.; 0-913478),* P.O. Box 8172, Albuquerque, NM 87198 (SAN 203-0012) Tel 505-262-0440.

Hero Books, *(Hero Bks.; 0-915979),* 8316 Arlington Blvd., Fairfax, VA 22031 (SAN 294-0345) Tel 703-560-6427.

Hero Games, *(Hero Games; 0-917481; 0-915795),* Affil. of Iron Crown Enterprises, Inc., P.O. Box 1605, Charlottesville, VA 22902 (SAN 656-0695) Tel 804-295-3917; Toll free: 800-325-0479; Orders to: Iron Crown Enterprises, Inc., P.O. Box 1605, Charlottesville, VA 22902 (SAN 663-3064).

Hero Pub
See Hero Books

Heroic Pub Inc, *(Heroic Publishing, Inc.; 0-936079),* P.O. Box 13735, Milwaukee, WI 53213 (SAN 696-8228) Tel 414-547-2671; 1402 Josephine, Waukesha, WI 53186 (SAN 696-8236).

Heroica Bks, *(Heroica Bks.; 0-935539),* Box 12718, Northgate Sta., San Rafael, CA 94913 (SAN 696-1940) Tel 415-897-6067; Dist. by: Baker & Taylor Co., Western Div., 380 Edison Way, Reno, NV 89564 (SAN 169-4464) Tel 702-786-6700; Dist. by: Blackwell North America, 1001 Fries Mill Rd., Blackwood, NJ 08012 (SAN 169-4596) Tel 609-629-0700; Dist. by: Blackwell North America, 6024 SW Jean Rd., Bldg. G, Lake Oswego, OR 97034 (SAN 169-7048) Tel 503-684-1140; Dist. by: Key Bk. Service, 425 Asylum St., Bridgeport, CT 06610 (SAN 169-0671) Tel 203-334-2165. Imprints: Modern Studies Group (Modern Studies Group).

Heron Bks, *(Heron Bks.; 0-89739),* P.O. Box 1230, McMinnville, OR 97128 (SAN 678-4917).

Heron Hse, *(Heron House Pubs.; 0-916920),* 9610 Manitou Beach Dr., NE, Bainbridge Island, WA 98110 (SAN 208-4767) Tel 206-842-3768.

Heron Pr, *(Heron Press, The; 0-931246),* 36 Bromfield St., Boston, MA 02108 (SAN 206-5002) Tel 617-482-3615.

Heron Pr CA, *(Heron Pr.; 0-935999),* P.O. Box 31539, San Francisco, CA 94131 (SAN 696-8260) Tel 415-695-0323; Dist. by: Publishers Group West, 5855 Beaudry St., Emeryville, CA 94608 (SAN 202-8522) Tel 415-658-3453; Dist. by: Ingram Bk. Co., P.O. Box 17266, Nashville, TN 37217 (SAN 169-7978) Tel 615-361-5000.

Herpetological Search, *(Herpetological Search Service & Exchange),* 117 E. Santa Barbara Rd., Lindenhurst, NY 11757 (SAN 287-7406).

Herring Design, *(Herring Design Press; 0-917001),* 1216 Hawthorne, Houston, TX 77006 (SAN 655-6426) Tel 713-526-1250; Dist. by: Publishers Marketing Group, 1104 Summit Ave., Plainview, TX 75074 (SAN 262-0995).

Herring Pr, *(Herring Pr.),* 1216 Hawthorne, Houston, TX 77006 (SAN 696-1983) Tel 713-526-1250.

Herschel Gower, *(Gower, Herschel; 0-9613156),* 1006 Estes Rd., Nashville, TN 37215 (SAN 294-9334) Tel 615-269-0669; Dist. by: Austin Periodical Services, 499 Merritt Ave., Nashville, TN 37203 (SAN 169-5576).

Hershel Shanks Pubs, *(Shanks, Hershel, Pub.; 0-9607092),* 3111 Rittenhouse St. NW, Washington, DC 20015 (SAN 237-9570) Tel 202-244-9011.

Hershey, *(Hershey, Virginia Sharpe; 0-9605320),* 5325 Wikiup Bridgeway, Santa Rosa, CA 95404 (SAN 216-2024).

Hershey Foods, *(Hershey Foods Corporation; 0-943296),* 14 E. Chocolate Ave., Hershey, PA 17033 (SAN 240-6713) Tel 717-534-4912.

Hertzberg-New Meth
See Perma Bound

Herzl Pr, *(Herzl Pr.; 0-930832),* Subs. of World Zionist Organization, 515 Park Ave., New York, NY 10022 (SAN 201-5374) Tel 212-752-0600.

Hesher Publ, *(Hesher Publishing; 0-914013),* P.O. Box 402, Grand Island, NY 14072 (SAN 286-7745) Tel 716-773-1327.

†**Hesperian Found,** *(Hesperian Foundation, The; 0-942364),* P.O. Box 1692, Palo Alto, CA 94302 (SAN 239-8567) Tel 415-325-9017; *CIP.*

Heuristicus, *(Heuristicus Publishing Co.; 0-934016),* 401 Tolbert St., Brea, CA 92621 (SAN 212-8551).

Hevenly World
See L A Wholistic

Hewlett-Packard, *(Hewlett-Packard Co.; 0-9612030),* 3410 Central Expwy., Santa Clara, CA 95051 (SAN 285-1253) Tel 408-749-9500; Toll free: 800-367-4772; 3003 Scott Blvd., Santa Clara, CA 95050 (SAN 285-1261) Tel 408-988-7000.

Heyday Bks, *(Heyday Bks.; 0-930588),* P.O. Box 9145, Berkeley, CA 94709 (SAN 207-2351) Tel 415-549-3564.

Heyeck Pr, *(Heyeck Pr., The; 0-940592),* 25 Patrol Ct., Woodside, CA 94062 (SAN 217-7692) Tel 415-851-7491.

Heywood Pubs, *(Heywood Pubs.; 0-9614314),* 4523 Lonsdale Blvd., Northfield, MN 55057 (SAN 687-5157) Tel 507-645-6453.

HHH Horticultural, *(HHH Horticultural),* 68 Brooktree Rd., Hightstown, NJ 08520 (SAN 213-1951).

HI Auditor, *(Hawaii Office of the Auditor),* State Capitol, Honolulu, HI 96813 (SAN 227-2733).

Hi Barbaree Pr, *(Hi Barbaree Pr.; 0-9614477),* 17 Golf View Dr., Hingham, MA 02043 (SAN 689-3651) Tel 617-749-5467.

Hi Country Pubs, *(Hi-Country Pubs.; 0-938354),* P.O. Box 2362, Littleton, CO 80161 (SAN 216-0374).

HI Legis Ref, *(Hawaii Legislative Reference Bureau),* State Capitol, Honolulu, HI 96813 (SAN 227-2741).

HI Pr Cold Spring, *(HI Pr. of Cold Spring, Inc.; 0-9615988),* Box 361, Cold Spring, NY 10516 (SAN 697-8894) Tel 914-265-3098.

Hi Tech Pub, *(Hi-Tech Publishing House, Inc.; 0-912619),* P.O. Box 19656, Atlanta, GA 30325 (SAN 282-8006).

Hi-Time Pub, *(Hi-Time Publishing Corp.; 0-937997),* P.O. Box 13337, Milwaukee, WI 53213 (SAN 661-2520); Toll free: 800-558-2292; 12040-F W. Feerick St., Wauwatosa, WI 53222 (SAN 661-2539) Tel 414-466-2420.

Hi Willow, *(Hi Willow Research & Publishing; 0-931510),* Box 1801, Fayetteville, AR 72702 (SAN 211-3945) Tel 501-751-9096.

Hiawatha Bondurant, *(Hiawatha Bk. Co.),* 7567 NE 102nd Ave., Bondurant, IA 50035 (SAN 162-8348) Tel 515-967-4025.

Hiawatha Pr, *(Hiawatha Pr; 0-930276),* 3505 St. Paul Ave., Minneapolis, MN 55416 (SAN 211-1799).

Hickman Systems, *(Hickman Systems; 0-915689),* 4 Woodland Ln., Kirksville, MO 63501 (SAN 292-5311) Tel 816-665-1836.

Himalayan Pubs, (Himalayan Pubs.; 0-89389), Div. of Himalayan International Institute of Yoga Science & Philosophy, RR 1, Box 405, Honesdale, PA 18431 (SAN 207-5067) Tel 717-253-3022.

Hines Legal Dir, (Hine's Legal Directory Incorporated; 0-910911), 443 Duane St, P.O. Box 71, Glen Ellyn, IL 60138 (SAN 226-4331) Tel 312-469-3983.

Hinman-Synder, (Hinman-Snyder Productions; 0-9613472), 1881 Louden Heights, Charleston, WV 25314 (SAN 657-2707) Tel 304-346-0609.

Hinsdale Pr, (Hinsdale Pr.; 0-931375), 526 Third Ave., San Francisco, CA 94118 (SAN 682-594X) Tel 415-752-8748.

Hinshaw Mus, (Hinshaw Music, Inc.; 0-937276), P.O. Box 470, Chapel Hill, NC 27514 (SAN 693-4072) Tel 919-933-1691.

†Hippocrene Bks, (Hippocrene Bks., Inc.; 0-87052; 0-88254), 171 Madison Ave., New York, NY 10016 (SAN 213-2060) Tel 212-685-4371; CIP. Imprints: Bks New China (Books New China).(Bks. New China); NW Illus (Northwest Illustrated).

Hippogriff Pubns, (Hippogriff Pubns.; 0-936973), 111 E. Fifth, Bonham, TX 75418 (SAN 658-7860) Tel 214-583-3218.

Hired Hand, (Hired Hand Press; 0-9602256), P.O. Box 426, Dover, MA 02030 (SAN 212-4262) Tel 617-325-8155.

Hirsch A J, (Hirsch, A. Jay; 0-9610920), 1711 Dana Place, Fullerton, CA 92631 (SAN 285-662X) Tel 714-871-5512.

HIS Imprint of **HR&W**

Hispanic Bk Dist, (Hispanic Bk. Distributors & Pubs., Inc.; 0-938243), 1870 W. Prince Rd., Suite 8, Tucson, AZ 85705 (SAN 661-423X) Tel 602-887-8879.

Hispanic Inst, (Hispanic Institute in the United States), 612 W 116th St, New York, NY 10027 (SAN 225-3100).

Hispanic Policy Dev Proj, (Hispanic Policy Development Project; 0-918911), 1001 Connecticut Ave., Suite 310, Washington, DC 20036 (SAN 670-0861) Tel 202-822-8414.

Hispanic Seminary, (Hispanic Seminary of Medieval Studies; 0-942260), 3734 Ross St., Madison, WI 53705 (SAN 207-9836).

†Hispanic Soc, (Hispanic Society of America; 0-87535), 613 W. 155th St., New York, NY 10032 (SAN 204-0573) Tel 212-926-2234; CIP.

Hist Assn FL, (Historical Assn. of Southern Florida; 0-935761), 101 W. Flagler St., Miami, FL 33130 (SAN 696-4737) Tel 305-375-1492.

Hist Aviation, (Historical Aviation Album; 0-911852), P.O. Box 33, Temple City, CA 91780 (SAN 213-5108) Tel 818-286-7655.

Hist Balt Soc, (Historic Baltimore Society, Inc.; 0-942460), 4 Willow Brook Ct., Randallstown, MD 21133 (SAN 285-0257) Tel 301-922-3649; Dist. by: LMC, P.O. Box 355, Linthicum Heights, MD 21090-0355 (SAN 200-7169) Tel 301-766-1211.

Hist Bus Inc, (History Business Inc. The; 0-9614203), 1421 Peachtree St. NE, Unit 410, Atlanta, GA 30309 (SAN 686-8126) Tel 404-875-0603.

Hist Cher
See Hist Cherry Hill

Hist Cherry Hill, (Historic Cherry Hill; 0-943366), 523 1/2 S. Pearl St., Albany, NY 12202 (SAN 240-6721) Tel 518-434-4791.

Hist Comm S Baptist, (Historical Commission of the Southern Baptist Convention; 0-939804), 901 Commerce St., Suite 400, Nashville, TN 37203-3620 (SAN 216-7352) Tel 615-244-0344.

Hist Denver, (Historic Denver Inc.; 0-914248), 1701 Wynkoop, Suite 200, Denver, CO 80202 (SAN 220-651X).

Hist Dimensions, (Historical Dimensions Pr.; 0-9614733), P.O. Box 12042, Washington, DC 20005 (SAN 692-7580).

Hist Fl Keys, (Historic Florida Keys Preservation Board; 0-943528), 500 Whitehead, Monroe County Courthouse, Key West, FL 33040 (SAN 240-6748) Tel 305-294-7511.

Hist Heart Assn Inc, (Historic Heartland Assn., Inc.; 0-910623), P.O. Box 1, Brainerd, MN 56401 (SAN 260-2024) Tel 218-963-2218; 6410 Murray Hill Rd., Baltimore, MD 21212 (SAN 699-5306) Tel 301-377-7294.

Hist Heart Assoc Inc
See Hist Heart Assn Inc

Hist Jefferson Found, (Historic Jefferson Foundation; 0-935077), Drawer 2049, Marshall, TX 75671 (SAN 695-0914) Tel 214-938-4332; Orders to: P.O. Box 1088, Hughes Springs, TX 75656 (SAN 662-3425) Tel 214-639-2012.

Hist Kansas City, (Historic Kansas City Foundation; 0-913504), 20 W. Ninth St., Kansas City, MO 64105 (SAN 239-4421) Tel 816-471-3391.

Hist Key West
See Hist Fl Keys

Hist Natchez, (Historic Natchez Foundation, The; 0-936549), P.O. Box 1761, Natchez, MS 39120 (SAN 697-9874) Tel 601-442-2500; 107 N. Commerce St., Natchez, MS 39120 (SAN 697-9882).

Hist Pubns, (Historic Pubns. of Fredericksburg; 0-9608408), 300 Princess Anne St., Fredericksburg, VA 22401 (SAN 240-673X) Tel 703-371-0585.

Hist Res Reposit, (Historical Research Repository, Inc.; 0-935319), 19805 Greenfield No. 26, Detroit, MI 48235 (SAN 695-7803) Tel 313-899-2500.

Hist Saranac, (Historic Saranac Lake; 0-9615159), P.O. Box 1030, Saranac Lake, NY 12983 (SAN 694-387X) Tel 518-891-0971.

Hist Sci Soc, (History of Science Society, Inc.; 0-934235), 215 S. 34th St./D6, Philadelphia, PA 19104 (SAN 225-1930) Tel 215-898-8575; Toll free: 800-341-1522.

Hist Soc Baldwin Pk, (Historical Society of Baldwin Park, The; 0-9607306), 13009 Amar Rd., P.O. Box 1, Baldwin Park, CA 91706 (SAN 239-2267) Tel 818-337-3285.

Hist Soc Carroll, (Historical Society of Carroll County; 0-9614125), 210 E. Main St., Westminster, MD 21157 (SAN 686-4724) Tel 301-848-6494.

Hist Soc Rockland Cty
See Rockland County Hist

Hist Soc Seattle, (Historical Society of Seattle & King County; 0-939806), 2700 24th Ave. E., Seattle, WA 98112 (SAN 216-7360) Tel 206-324-1125.

Hist Soc West Pa, (Historical Society of Western Pennsylvania; 0-936340), 4338 Bigelow Blvd., Pittsburgh, PA 15213 (SAN 214-0276) Tel 412-681-5537.

Hist Soc Wisconsin
See State Hist Soc Wis

Hist Tales, (Historical Tales Ink; 0-938404), 7344 Rich St., Reynoldsburg, OH 43068 (SAN 215-7748).

Historic Frankfort, (Historic Frankfort, Inc.; 0-9615489), P.O. Box 775, Frankfort, KY 40602 (SAN 696-205X) Tel 502-223-0870.

Historic New Orleans, (Historic New Orleans Collection, The; 0-917860), 533 Royal St., New Orleans, LA 70130 (SAN 281-7829) Tel 504-523-4662.

Historic Photos, (Historic Photos; 0-933206), 3460 St. Helena Hwy. N., St. Helena, CA 94574 (SAN 212-6672) Tel 707-963-3117.

Historic Pres Bourbon, (Historic Preservation Assn. of Bourbon County, Inc.; 0-9601568), 502 S. National Ave., Fort Scott, KS 66701 (SAN 211-528X) Tel 316-223-3300.

Historic Preserv Durham
See HPS Durham

Historic Sav, (Historic Savannah Foundation, Inc.; 0-9610106), P.O. Box 1983, Savannah, GA 31402 (SAN 270-7802) Tel 912-233-7787.

Historic Seattle, (Historic Seattle Preservation & Development Authority; 0-9616090), 207 1/2 First Ave S., Seattle, WA 98104 (SAN 698-0791) Tel 206-622-6952.

Historical Pubns, (Historical Pubns.; 0-9616470), 13 Oxford Dr., Lompoc, CA 93436 (SAN 658-8670) Tel 805-736-4160.

Historical Soc
See Hist Soc Baldwin Pk

Historical Soc MI, (Historical Society of Michigan; 0-9614344), 2117 Washtenaw Ave., Ann Arbor, MI 48104 (SAN 687-8008) Tel 313-769-1829.

Historical Times, (Historical Times Inc.; 0-918678), 2245 Kohn Rd., Box 8200, Harrisburg, PA 17105 (SAN 685-320X) Tel 717-657-9555.

Hit Ent, (Hit Enterprises; 0-935938), 2945 Leticia Dr., Hacienda Heights, CA 91745 (SAN 213-7453).

HIT pubns, (HIT Pubns.; 0-910993), P.O. Box 11198, Costa Mesa, CA 92627 (SAN 270-6482) Tel 714-722-7458.

†Hive Pub, (Hive Publishing Co.; 0-87960), P.O. Box 1004, Easton, PA 18042 (SAN 202-2958) Tel 215-258-6663; CIP.

HJ Imprint of **HarBraceJ**

HK Pub Co, (HK Publishing Co.; 0-913809), P.O. Box 610053, Houston, TX 77208 (SAN 283-9598) Tel 713-827-1651.

Hlth Challenge, (Health Challenge Pr.; 0-935929), 7601 Calle Sin Envidia, No. 14, Tucson, AZ 85718 (SAN 696-8074) Tel 602-742-4594.

Hlth Homeopathy, (Health & Homeopathy Publishing, Inc.; 0-9616800), 515 S. Tenth St., Unit J, Philadelphia, PA 19147 (SAN 661-3314) Tel 215-592-0854.

Hlth Psy Pubns, (Health Psychology Pubns.; 0-9617145), 710 11th Ave., Suite 106, Greeley, CO 80631 (SAN 663-3366) Tel 303-587-2543.

†HM, (Houghton Mifflin Co.; 0-395; 0-87466), 1 Beacon St., Boston, MA 02108 (SAN 200-2388) Tel 617-725-5000; Toll free: 800-225-3362; Orders to: Wayside Rd., Burlington, MA 01803 (SAN 215-3793) Tel 617-272-1500; CIP. Imprints: HoughtonT (Houghton Trade Books).(Houghton Trade Bks.); Piper (Piper Books).(Piper Bks.); RivEd (Riverside Editions); RivLit (Riverside Literature Series); RivSL (Riverside Studies in Literature); RRS (Riverside Reading Series); Sandpiper (Sandpiper Paperbacks); SenEd (Sentry Editions).

HM Soft-Ref Div, (Houghton Mifflin Software, Reference Div.; 0-395), 1 Beacon St., Boston, MA 02108 (SAN 654-9438) Tel 617-725-5000.

HMB Pubns, (HMB Pubns.; 0-937086), 7406 Monroe Ave., Hammond, IN 46324 (SAN 214-3836) Tel 219-932-1798; Dist. by: The Distributors, 702 S. Michigan, South Bend, IN 46618 (SAN 169-2488) Tel 219-232-8500.

HMJ Ltd, (Holtvluwer, Meyers, & John, Ltd.; 0-938431), 1322 Edna, SE, Grand Rapids, MI 49507 (SAN 661-2938) Tel 616-243-0538.

Hmong United, (Hmong United Assn. of Pennsylvania, Inc.; 0-917003), 3944 Baring St., Phildelphia, PA 19104 (SAN 655-7279) Tel 215-387-3308.

Hoard & Sons Co, (Hoard, W. D., & Sons Co.; 0-932147), 28 Milwaukee Ave., W., Ft. Atkinson, WI 53538 (SAN 686-4341) Tel 414-563-5551.

Hobar Pubns, (Hobar Publications; 0-913163; 0-939381), Div. of Hobar Enterprises, Inc., 1234 Tiller Lane, St. Paul, MN 55112 (SAN 283-1120) Tel 612-633-3170.

Hobart & Wm Smith, (Hobart & William Smith Colleges Press; 0-934888), Hobart & William Smith Colleges, Geneva, NY 14456 (SAN 213-3202) Tel 315-789-5500.

Hobbit Hse, (Hobbit House Press; 0-9604300), 5920 Dimmway, Richmond, CA 94805 (SAN 214-3852).

Hobby Horse, (Hobby Horse Publishing; 0-935138), 10091 Hobby Horse Lane, Box 54, Mentor, OH 44060 (SAN 213-5132) Tel 216-255-3434.

Hobby Hse, (Hobby Hse. Pr.; 0-87588), 900 Frederick St., Cumberland, MD 21502 (SAN 204-059X) Tel 301-759-3770.

Hobby Pub Serv, (Hobby Publishing Service; 0-917922), 1318 Seventh St., NW, Albuquerque, NM 87102 (SAN 207-6330) Tel 505-242-9465.

Hoffman Enter, (Hoffman Enterprises; 0-942662), P.O. Box 2091, Manteca, CA 95336 (SAN 241-5380) Tel 209-239-5576.

Hoffman Res, (Hoffman Research Services; 0-910203), P.O. Box 342, Rillton, PA 15678 (SAN 240-8597).

Hofmann, (Hofmann, Margret; 0-9600166), 2706 Nottingham Lane, Austin, TX 78704 (SAN 204-0603) Tel 512-444-8877.

Symbols/Abbreviations

Homeward Pr, *(Homeward Pr.; 0-938392),* P.O. Box 2307, Berkeley, CA 94702 (SAN 220-2522).

Homosexual Info, *(Homosexual Information Center, Inc.),* Affil. of The Tangent Group, 6758 Hollywood Blvd., No. 208, Hollywood, CA 90028 (SAN 210-8127) Tel 213-464-8431.

Hondale, *(Hondale, Inc.; 0-942462),* 553 Auburndale Ave., Akron, OH 44313 (SAN 238-1664) Tel 216-867-9701.

Honduras Info, *(Honduras Information Service; 0-937538),* 501 Fifth Ave., Suite 1611, New York, NY 10017 (SAN 213-084X) Tel 212-490-0766.

Honey Hill, *(Honey Hill Publishing Co.; 0-937642),* 1022 Bonham Terrace, Austin, TX 78704 (SAN 220-0600) Tel 512-442-4177.

Honeycomb Pr, *(Honeycomb Press; 0-9612244),* 6633 N. 8th St., Philadelphia, PA 19126 (SAN 287-7295) Tel 215-548-8453.

Honnold Lib
See Lib Claremont Coll

Honolulu H, *(Honolulu He'e; 0-9612452),* 2543 Saul Place, Honolulu, HI 96816 (SAN 289-2707) Tel 808-737-2024.

Honolulu Japanese, *(Honolulu Japanese Chamber of Commerce),* 2454 S. Beretania St., Honolulu, HI 96826 (SAN 225-6215).

Honor Bks, *(Honor Books; 0-931446),* P.O. Box 641, Rapid City, SD 57709 (SAN 208-0877).

Honor Pub, *(Honor Publishing Co.),* P.O. Box 932, Greenwood, MS 38930 (SAN 693-0913); 802 W. President, Greenwood, MS 38930 (SAN 662-3123) Tel 601-453-1584.

Honor Soc P K P, *(Honor Society of Phi Kappa Phi; 0-9614651),* P.O. Box 16000 Louisiana State Univ., Baton Rouge, LA 70893 (SAN 283-9776) Tel 504-388-4917.

Hoofnagle Graph, *(Hoofnagle Graphics; 0-9616468),* 513 E. 25th Ave., No. 3, Anchorage, AK 99503 (SAN 659-2449) Tel 907-261-0061.

Hooper Pub Co, *(Hooper Publishing Inc.; 0-9613648),* P.O. Box 875, Lovington, NM 88260 (SAN 670-767X) Tel 505-396-3741.

†**Hoover Inst Pr,** *(Hoover Institution Pr.; 0-8179),* Affil. of Hoover Institution, Stanford Univ., Stanford, CA 94305-2323 (SAN 202-3024) Tel 415-723-3373; Dist. by: East-West Export Bks., Univ. Pr. of Hawaii, 2840 Kolowalu St., Honolulu, HI 96822 (SAN 200-738X) Tel 808-948-8255; CIP.

Hoover Lib, *(Hoover, Herbert, Presidential Library & Assn., Inc.; 0-938469),* P.O. Box 696, West Branch, IA 52358 (SAN 224-229X); Parkside Dr., West Branch, IA 52358 (SAN 658-0858) Tel 619-643-5327.

Hope Ent Fla, *(Hope Enterprises of Jacksonville, Florida, Inc.; 0-932650),* Box 8401, Jacksonville, FL 32211 (SAN 211-5298).

Hope Farm, *(Hope Farm Press & Bookshop; 0-910746),* Strong Rd., Cornwallville, NY 12418 (SAN 204-0697) Tel 518-239-4745.

Hope Pr, *(Hope Pr.; 0-9615878),* P.O. Box 40611, Washington, DC 20016-0611 (SAN 696-835X) Tel 202-337-4507; 3923 Georgetown Ct., NW, Washington, DC 20007 (SAN 696-8368).

Hope Pub, *(Hope Publishing Co.; 0-916642),* 380 S. Main Pl., Carol Stream, IL 60188 (SAN 208-3361) Tel 312-665-3200; Toll free: 800-323-1049.

Hope Pub Hse, *(Hope Publishing Hse.; 0-932727),* Subs. of S. Calif. Ecumenical Council, P.O. Box 60008, Pasadena, CA 91106 (SAN 688-4849) Tel 818-792-2121.

Hopewood Pr, *(Hopewood Press; 0-936286),* P.O. Box 27541, Minneapolis, MN 55427 (SAN 215-0816).

Hopkins, *(Hopkins Syndicate, Inc.; 0-910748),* Hopkins Bldg., Mellott, IN 47958 (SAN 204-0700) Tel 317-295-2253.

Hor Bks MI, *(Horizon Bks.; 0-915937),* 224 E. Front, Traverse City, MI 49684 (SAN 294-0388) Tel 616-946-7290.

Horatio Pub Co, *(Horatio Publishing Co.; 0-915879),* Jamestown Star Rte., Boulder, CO 80302 (SAN 294-037X) Tel 303-449-1360.

†**Horizon,** *(Horizon Pr.; 0-8180),* P.O. Box 402, New York, NY 10108 (SAN 202-3040) Tel 212-757-4420; CIP.

Horizon Bks CA, *(Horizon Bks.; 0-938840),* P.O. Box 3083, Fremont, CA 94539 (SAN 216-0390) Tel 415-657-6439.

Horizon Comms, *(Horizon Communications Pubs./Distributors; 0-913945),* 2710 San Diego, SE, Albuquerque, NM 87106 (SAN 286-7761) Tel 505-266-3431.

Horizon Trust, *(Horizon Trust Co.; 0-9616335),* 1200 N. Federal Hwy., Suite 413, Boca Raton, FL 33432 (SAN 658-8689) Tel 305-394-4441.

Horizon Utah, *(Horizon Pubs. & Distributors, Inc.; 0-88290),* P.O. Box 490, 50 S. 500 West, Bountiful, UT 84010 (SAN 159-4885) Tel 801-295-9451; Toll free: 800-453-0812.

†**Horn Bk,** *(Horn Bk., Inc.; 0-87675),* 31 St. James Ave., Park Sq. Bldg., Boston, MA 02116 (SAN 202-3059) Tel 617-482-5198; Toll free: 800-325-1170; CIP.

Horn Moon Ent, *(Horn of the Moon Enterprises; 0-9614070),* RRI, Box 5100, Montpelier, VT 05602 (SAN 686-0222) Tel 802-229-4220.

Hornbeam Pr, *(Hornbeam Press, Inc.; 0-917496),* 6520 Courtwood Dr., Columbia, SC 29206 (SAN 209-0325) Tel 803-782-7667.

Horse & Bird, *(Horse & Bird Press, The; 0-9602214),* Pfieffer Ridge, RC1 Box 4726, Big Sur, CA 93920 (SAN 281-7888) Tel 408-667-2433; Dist. by: The Distributors, 702 S. Michigan, South Bend, IN 46618 (SAN 169-2488) Tel 219-232-8500; Dist. by: Bookpeople, 2929 Fifth St., Berkeley, CA 94710 (SAN 168-9517) Tel 415-549-3030; Dist. by: The New Leaf Distributing, 1020 White St., SW, Atlanta, GA 30310 (SAN 169-1449) Tel 404-755-2665; Dist. by: Starlite Distributors, P.O. Box 20729, Reno, NV 89515 (SAN 131-1921).

Horsebreeder
See Printed Horse

Horsesense Inc, *(Horsesense, Inc.; 0-9613034),* 4760 Thatchwood Dr., Manlius, NY 13104 (SAN 294-0108) Tel 315-637-6689.

Horsethief Pubns, *(Horsethief Pubns.; 0-9613777),* 334 W. Hyman, Aspen, CO 81611 (SAN 678-9730) Tel 303-925-3220.

Hort Gettys Hill Mem, *(Hill, Hortense Gettys, Memorial Fund; 0-9613799),* Box 2153, Rockford, IL 61130 (SAN 682-2614).

Horticult FL, *(Horticultural Books, Inc.; 0-9600046),* P.O. Box 107, Stuart, FL 33495 (SAN 204-0735) Tel 305-287-1091.

Horticult Pubns, *(Horticultural Pubns.; 0-938378),* 3906 NW 31st Place, Gainesville, FL 32606 (SAN 216-1389) Tel 904-392-1753.

Horticult Research, *(Horticultural Research Institute, Inc.; 0-935336),* Affil. of American Assn. Nurserymen, 1250 I St. NW, Suite 500, Washington, DC 20005 (SAN 213-3210) Tel 202-789-2900.

Horticultural
See Horticult FL

Horvath Sculpture, *(Horvath Sculpture & Graphics, Inc.; 0-9616359),* 1121 Cosper Pl., Rockford, IL 61107 (SAN 658-8700) Tel 815-965-0120; Dist. by: Alan L. Horvath Memorial Pubns., 68 Marco Ln., Centerville, OH 45459 (SAN 663-3161) Tel 513-434-8573.

Hosp Compensation, *(Hospital Compensation Service),* Subs. of John R. Zabka Assocs., Inc., P.O. Box 321, Hawthorne, NJ 07507 (SAN 217-1090); 155 Watchung Dr., Hawthorne, NY 07507 (SAN 662-0396).

Hosp Council S Cal, *(Hospital Council of Southern California; 0-939089),* 6255 Sunset Blvd., Suite 817, Los Angeles, CA 90028 (SAN 662-9016) Tel 213-469-7311.

Hosp Practice
See HP Pub Co

Hosp Pubns, *(Hospitality Publications Inc.; 0-932235),* P.O. Box 448, Okemos, MI 48864 (SAN 686-5801) Tel 517-676-4030.

†**Hosp Res & Educ,** *(Hospital Research & Educational Trust; 0-87914),* Affil. of American Hospital Assn., 840 N. Lake Shore Dr., Chicago, IL 60611 (SAN 206-9121) Tel 312-280-6620; Toll free: 800-AHA-2626; Orders to: AHA Services, Inc., 4444 W. Ferdinand, Chicago, IL 60626 (SAN 662-040X); CIP.

Hospital Finan
See Healthcare Fin Mgmt Assn

Host Assoc, *(Host, Jim, & Associates, Inc.; 0-934554),* 120 Kentucky Ave., Suite A-1, Lexington, KY 40502 (SAN 216-1400).

Hot Choco Imprint of **Coffee Hse**

Hot House Pr, *(Hot Hse. Pr.; 0-9616939),* 411 W. Drew St., Houston, TX 77006 (SAN 661-8006) Tel 713-528-6288.

Hot off Pr, *(Hot off the Pr.; 0-9605904; 0-933491),* 7212 S. Seven Oaks, Canby, OR 97013 (SAN 216-3977) Tel 503-266-8306.

Hot Water Pubs, *(Hot Water Publishing Co.; 0-941904),* P.O. Box 773783, Eagle River, AK 99577 (SAN 239-2283) Tel 907-694-8644.

Hotchkiss House, *(Hotchkiss House, Inc.; 0-912220),* 14 Shelter Creek Ln., Fairport, NY 14450 (SAN 159-5415).

Hotel Sales Mgmt Assn, *(Hotel Sales and Marketing Association),* 1400 K St., Suite 810, Washington, DC 20005 (SAN 224-7925) Tel 202-789-0089.

Hothem Hse, *(Hothem Hse.; 0-9617041),* P.O. Box 458, Lancaster, OH 43130 (SAN 662-8591); 1650 Northwood Dr., Lancaster, OH 43130 (SAN 662-8605) Tel 614-653-9030.

Hotline Multi-Ent, *(Hotline Multi-Enterprises; 0-935864),* 2709 Georgetown Rd., Mechanicsville, VA 23111 (SAN 214-3860) Tel 804-746-4450.

HoughtonT Imprint of **HM**

Hour Press, *(Hour Pr.; 0-939131),* P.O. Box 12743, Northgate Sta., San Rafael, CA 94913-2743 (SAN 662-4863) Tel 415-883-1539.

Hour Pub, *(Hour Publishing; 0-931343),* 24 Westminster, Venice, CA 90291 (SAN 681-8323) Tel 213-399-3901.

Hourglass Pub, *(Hourglass Publishing; 0-932479),* P.O. Box 924, Salida, CO 81201 (SAN 687-4258) Tel 303-539-2058.

Housatonuc, *(Housatonuc Bookshop; 0-910756),* Main St., Salisbury, CT 06068 (SAN 201-5447) Tel 203-435-2100.

House of Print, *(House of Print),* 322 Benzel Ave., Madelia, MN 56062 (SAN 211-0687) Tel 507-642-3298.

Housesmith's, *(Housesmith's Press; 0-918238),* P.O. Box 157, Kittery Point, ME 03905 (SAN 210-2102) Tel 207-439-0638.

Housing Connect, *(Housing Connection, The; 0-9609586),* P.O. Box 5536, Arlington, VA 22205 (SAN 262-0405) Tel 703-243-6805.

Houston C, *(Houston, Charles S.; 0-9612246),* 77 Ledge Rd., Burlington, VT 05401 (SAN 220-2727) Tel 802-863-6441.

Houston Home-Garden Mag Imprint of **Bayland Pub**

Houston Law Review, *(Houston Law Review; 0-913797),* 3801 Cullen Blvd., Houston, TX 77004 (SAN 226-5427) Tel 713-374-2616.

Houston Pub, *(Houston Publishing; 0-9616818),* 760 Rosewood Dr., Reno, NV 89509 (SAN 661-1192) Tel 702-826-6326.

Hover, *(Hover Co., The; 0-934414),* 14713 La Mesa Dr., La Mirada, CA 90638 (SAN 213-747X) Tel 714-521-3046.

Hovnanian, *(Hovnanian, Ralph R.; 0-9607774),* 2128 Prospect Ave., Evanston, IL 60201 (SAN 241-5399).

How-To Bks, *(How-To Bks.; 0-9615231),* Box 8234, Northfield, IL 60093 (SAN 695-1708) Tel 312-446-1607.

How-to Pr, *(How-to Press; 0-938356),* P.O. Box 483, Arlington, TX 76010 (SAN 215-7764).

Howard Allen, *(Howard, Allen, Enterprises, Inc.; 0-914576),* P.O. Box 76, Cape Canaveral, FL 32920 (SAN 203-4662).

Howard & Assocs, *(Howard & Assocs.; 0-935801),* P.O. Box 263, Fortuna, CA 95540 (SAN 696-8384) Tel 707-725-2987; 1727 Main St., Suite C, Fortuna, CA 95540 (SAN 696-8392).

Howard Doyle, *(Doyle, Howard A., Publishing Co.; 0-87299),* P.O. Box 555, East Dennis, MA 02641 (SAN 204-0751) Tel 617-385-2000.

Howard Gantzer, *(Gantzer, Howard J.; 0-9614532),* 1111 Archwood Dr., Olympia, WA 98502 (SAN 692-3143) Tel 206-754-4890.

Howard Pub, *(Howard Publishing; 0-9614225),* 121 N. Fir St., Suite C, Ventura, CA 93001 (SAN 686-7618) Tel 805-648-2092.

†**Howard U Pr,** *(Howard Univ. Pr.; 0-88258),* 2900 Van Ness St. NW, Washington, DC 20008 (SAN 202-3067) Tel 202-686-6696; CIP.

Howarth Pr, *(Howarth Pr., Inc., The; 0-939533),* P.O. Box 2608, Falls Church, VA 22042-0608 (SAN 663-4362); 7306 Brad St., Falls Church, VA 22042 (SAN 663-4370) Tel 703-573-8521.

†**Howe Brothers,** *(Howe Brothers; 0-935704),* Box 6394, Salt Lake City, UT 84106 (SAN 222-0318) Tel 801-485-7409; 1127 Wilmington Ave., Salt Lake City, UT 84106 (SAN 658-2214); *CIP.*

Howe St Pr, *(Howe Street Press, The; 0-9609666),* 212 E. Howe St., Seattle, WA 98102 (SAN 270-8507).

†**Howell Bk,** *(Howell Bk. Hse., Inc.; 0-87605),* Helmsley Bldg., 230 Park Ave., New York, NY 10169 (SAN 202-3075) Tel 212-986-4488; *CIP.*

Howell North, *(Howell-North Bks., Inc.; 0-8310),* Div. of Howell North-Darwin-Superior, 850 N. Hollywood Way, Burbank, CA 91505 (SAN 202-3083) Tel 818-848-0944.

Howell Pr, *(Howell Pr.; 0-936975),* Subs. of Max Communications, 611 W. Main St., Louisville, KY 40202 (SAN 658-7879) Tel 508-589-7603.

Howell Pr VA, *(Howell Pr., Inc.; 0-9616878),* 2000 Holiday Dr., Charlottesville, VA 22901 (SAN 661-6607) Tel 804-977-4006. Do not confuse with Howell Pr., Louisville, KY.

HOWever, *(HOW(ever); 0-933539),* 554 Jersey St., San Francisco, CA 94114 (SAN 691-8646) Tel 415-282-8873; Dist. by: Small Press Distribution, 1784 Shattuck Ave., Berkeley, CA 94702 (SAN 204-5826) Tel 415-549-3336; Dist. by: Inland Bk. Co., P.O. Box 261, 22 Hemingway Ave., East Haven, CT 06512 (SAN 200-4151) Tel 203-467-4257.

Hoyle Bks, *(Hoyle Bks.; 0-937351),* HBU 27, Petrolia, CA 95558 (SAN 658-8719) Tel 415-525-0421.

HP Bks, *(HP Bks.; 0-912656; 0-89586),* Subs. of Knight-Ridder Newspapers, Inc., P.O. Box 5367, Tucson, AZ 85703 (SAN 201-6087) Tel 602-888-2150; Toll free: 800-528-4923.

HP Pub Co, *(HP Publishing Co., Inc.; 0-913800),* 575 Lexington Ave., New York, NY 10022 (SAN 207-1738) Tel 212-421-7320.

HPL *Imprint of* **HarBraceJ**

HPS Durham, *(Historic Preservation Society of Durham; 0-9615577),* 120 Morris St., Durham, NC 27701 (SAN 696-2076); Duke Univ., 341 Perkins, Durham, NC 27706 (SAN 696-2084) Tel 919-684-5637.

HR Assocs, *(HR Assocs.; 0-9616423),* 6520 Misty Creek Dr., Citrus Heights, CA 95610 (SAN 658-9499) Tel 916-722-9398; P.O. Box 95866-0876, Sacramento, CA 95866 (SAN 658-9502).

HRAFP, *(Human Relations Area Files Pr., Inc.; 0-87536),* Affil. of Yale Univ., P.O. Box 2015, Yale Sta., New Haven, CT 06520 (SAN 200-4348); 755 Prospect St., New Haven, CT 06520 (SAN 669-0971) Tel 203-777-2334.

†**HR&W,** *(Holt, Rinehart & Winston, Inc.; 0-03),* Div. of CBS College Publishing, 383 Madison Ave., New York, NY 10017 (SAN 200-2108) Tel 212-750-1330; *CIP.* *Imprints:* HoltC (Holt College Department).(Holt College Dept.); HoltE (Holt Elementary Books).(Holt Elementary Bks.); HIS (Holt Information Systems); Owl Bks (Owl Books).(Owl Bks.).

HR&WRS *See* **Saunders**

HRH Systems, *(HRH Systems, Inc.; 0-936737),* P.O. Box 4496, Silver Spring, MD 20904 (SAN 699-8801) Tel 301-384-7159; 12918 Allerton Ln., Silver Spring, MD 20904 (SAN 699-881X) Tel 301-384-7159.

HS *Imprint of* **Oxford U Pr**

HSA Pubns, *(HSA Pubns.; 0-910621),* 4 W. 43rd St., New York, NY 10036 (SAN 270-6490) Tel 212-977-0050.

Hse Better Sales, *(House of Better Sales; 0-9617290),* P.O. Box 2163, Ocala, FL 32678-2163 (SAN 663-5954); 818 SW Fort King St., Ocala, FL 32674 (SAN 663-5962).

Hse by the Sea, *(House by the Sea Publishing Co.),* 8610 Highway 101, Waldport, OR 97394 (SAN 212-9477).

Hse of Affirmation *See* **Affirmation**

Hse of Charles, *(House of Charles; 0-9605344),* 4833 NE 238th Ave., Vancouver, WA 98662 (SAN 215-8728) Tel 206-892-1589.

Hse of Collectibles, *(House of Collectibles, Inc.; 0-87637),* 1904 Premier Row, Orlando, FL 32809 (SAN 202-3113) Tel 305-857-9095; Toll free: 800-327-1384.

Hse of Haig, *(House of Haig; 0-9615331),* 19 Sea Meadow Dr., Tuckerton, NJ 08087 (SAN 695-0922) Tel 609-296-8257; Orders to: House of Haig, P.O. Box 1068, Tuckerton, NJ 08087 (SAN 662-3433).

Hse of Peace, *(House of Peace; 0-936269),* P.O. Box 153, Yonkers, NY 10703 (SAN 697-8762) Tel 914-963-3197; 10 Flagg St., Yonkers, NY 10703 (SAN 698-2263).

Hse of Starr, *(House of Starr, Inc.; 0-938857),* 120 Kenmore Ave., Council Bluffs, IA 51501 (SAN 661-7042) Tel 712-328-8329.

Hse of Tomorrow, *(House of Tomorrow Publishing Co.; 0-913609),* P.O. Box 931, Weaverville, CA 96093 (SAN 285-287X) Tel 916-623-6525.

Hse of York, *(House of York; 0-916660),* P.O. Box 311, Aromas, CA 95004 (SAN 208-2357) Tel 408-726-2025.

Hse ov Day Vid, *(House ov Day Vid; 0-912672),* 978 Amherst St., Apt. 6, Buffalo, NY 14216 (SAN 204-0778) Tel 716-873-8856.

Hse UKE Pubns, *(House of UKE Pubns., Inc.; 0-937749),* 1610 N. Argyle Ave., Suite 109, Hollywood, CA 90078 (SAN 659-2457) Tel 213-462-7918.

Hsiang *See* **Amo Sino Bks**

HTC Pub, *(HTC Publishing Co. (Hot Tub Cooks); 0-9605582),* 10636 Main St., Suite 284, Bellevue, WA 98004 (SAN 239-8230) Tel 206-453-5569.

†**HTH Pubs,** *(HTH Pubs.; 0-916658),* P.O. Box 550, Coupeville, WA 98239 (SAN 208-1148) Tel 206-678-4447; *CIP.*

Hubbard Sci, *(Hubbard Scientific; 0-8331),* Div. of Spectrum Industries, P.O. Box 104, 1946 Raymond Dr., Northbrook, IL 60062 (SAN 202-3121) Tel 312-272-7810; Toll free: 800-323-8368.

Huber-Copeland Pub, *(Huber/Copeland Publishing; 0-934293),* P.O. Box 665, Mattoon, IL 61938 (SAN 693-2657) Tel 317-872-4472.

HUC Pr *Imprint of* **Ktav**

Huddleston-Brown Pubs, *(Huddleston-Brown Pubs., Inc.; 0-934355),* 18 Lewis Ln., Port Washington, NY 11050 (SAN 693-6148) Tel 516-944-3593.

Hudson Clearwater, *(Hudson River Sloop Clearwater),* 112 Market St., Poughkeepsie, NY 12601 (SAN 225-316X) Tel 914-454-7673.

†**Hudson Hills,** *(Hudson Hills Pr., Inc.; 0-933920),* 230 Fifth Ave., Suite 1308, New York, NY 10001-7704 (SAN 213-0815) Tel 212-889-3090; Dist. by: Rizzoli International Pubns., Inc., 597 Fifth Ave., New York, NY 10017 (SAN 207-7000) Tel 212-223-0100; *CIP.*

Hudson Inst, *(Hudson Institute),* Quaker Ridge Rd, Croton-on-Hudson, NY 10520 (SAN 225-7122) Tel 914-762-0700.

Hudson-Mohawk, *(Hudson-Mohawk Association of Colleges & Universities),* 91 Fiddlers Lane, Latham, NY 12110 (SAN 241-5402) Tel 518-785-3219.

Hudson Rev, *(Hudson Review, The),* 684 Park Ave., New York, NY 10021 (SAN 209-2859) Tel 212-650-0020.

Huebner Foun Insur, *(Huebner, S. S., Foundation for Insurance Education; 0-918930),* 3641 Locust Walk CE, Philadelphia, PA 19104 (SAN 211-6405) Tel 215-898-5644; Dist. by: Richard D. Irwin, Inc., 1818 Ridge Rd., Homewood, IL 60430 (SAN 206-8400) Tel 312-798-6000.

†**Huenefeld Co,** *(Huenefeld Co., Inc.; 0-931932),* P.O. Box U, Bedford, MA 01730 (SAN 211-5662) Tel 617-861-9650; *CIP.*

Huffman Pr, *(Huffman Press),* 805 N. Royal St., Alexandria, VA 22314 (SAN 208-0826) Tel 703-683-1695.

Huggy Bears, *(Huggy Bears Inc.; 0-9614134),* 28230 Orchard Lake Rd., Farmington Hills, MI 48018 (SAN 686-516X) Tel 313-626-8850.

Hugh Formhals, *(Formhals, Hugh),* 542 Mullen Rd., NW, Albuquerque, NM 87107 (SAN 681-8285) Tel 505-344-8313.

Hughes Enter, *(Hughes Enterprises; 0-9608106),* 1001 N. Calvert St., Baltimore, MD 21202 (SAN 205-3047) Tel 301-837-8271.

Hughes Pr, *(Hughes Press; 0-912560),* 500 23rd St. NW, Box B203, Washington, DC 20037 (SAN 210-9360) Tel 202-293-2686.

Hughes Pub, *(Hughes Publishing Co.; 0-9604772),* 453 De Soto Dr., El Paso, TX 79912 (SAN 217-7781) Tel 915-584-0276.

Hughes Pub Co, *(Hughes Publishing Co.; 0-9616112),* 640 Church St., San Francisco, CA 94114 (SAN 699-7104) Tel 415-626-4653.

Hughley Pubns, *(Hughley Pubns.; 0-9605150),* P.O. Box 261, Springfield Gardens, NY 11413 (SAN 215-8078) Tel 718-712-5892.

Huguenot Hist, *(Huguenot Historical Society),* P.O. Box 339, New Paltz, NY 12561 (SAN 234-4211) Tel 914-255-1660; 18 Brodhead Ave., New Paltz, NY 12561 (SAN 669-0955).

Huguley Co, *(Huguley, John, Co., Inc.; 0-9605064),* 269 King St., Charleston, SC 29401 (SAN 215-8736) Tel 803-577-2721.

Hugworks, *(Hugworks; 0-936835),* 29161 Grove, Livonia, MI 48154 (SAN 699-8585) Tel 313-522-2092.

Huh Pubns, *(Huh Pubns.; 0-938642),* P.O. Box 30782, Santa Barbara, CA 93105 (SAN 222-9765).

Hui-Hanai-Queen, *(Hui-Hanai, Queen Lilioukalani Childrens Center),* Dist. by: Press Pacifica, P.O. Box 47, Kailua, HI 96734 (SAN 169-1635).

Hull, *(Hull, Harry H.; 0-9606118),* 1710 Del Webb Blvd., Sun City Center, FL 33570 (SAN 281-7942) Tel 813-634-4967; c/o Albert E. Deeds Associates, 318 Martin Bldg,119 Federal St., Pittsburgh, PA 15212 (SAN 281-7950) Tel 412-323-1616.

Hulogos'i Inc, *(Hulogos'i Communications, Inc.; 0-938493),* P.O. Box 1188, Eugene, OR 97440 (SAN 661-4132); 454 Willamette St., Eugene, OR 97401 (SAN 661-4140) Tel 503-343-0606.

Human Behavior, *(Human Behavior Research Group, Inc.; 0-939552),* P.O. Box 17122, Irvine, CA 92713 (SAN 216-6801) Tel 714-786-6946.

Human Conserv Pr, *(Human Conservancy Press; 0-9612052),* 838 Grant St., Denver, CO 80203 (SAN 283-9164) Tel 303-830-2714.

Human Dev Educ Lab, *(Human Development & Educational Laboratories, Inc.; 0-939309),* P.O. Box 27247, Orlando, FL 32867-7274 (SAN 663-1509); Dist. by: Stackpole Bks., Cameron & Kelker Sts., Harrisburg, PA 17105 (SAN 202-5396) Tel 717-234-5041.

Human Dev Pr, *(Human Development Press; 0-938024),* 10701 Lomas NE, 210, Albuquerque, NM 87112 (SAN 215-6555) Tel 505-292-0370.

Human Dev Train *See* **Palomares & Assoc**

Human Eco Res *See* **Keats Pub**

Human Equat, *(Human Equations, Inc.; 0-915159),* World Trade Center, Suite 544, Baltimore, MD 21202 (SAN 289-9477) Tel 301-539-0344.

Human Futures, *(Human Futures; 0-932385),* P.O. Box 893, Hermosa Beach, CA 90254-0893 (SAN 687-3871).

Human Growth Dev, *(Human Growth & Development Assocs.; 0-9616626),* 1675 Fillmore St., Denver, CO 80206 (SAN 661-1796) Tel 303-320-0991.

Human Issues *See* **ISHI PA**

†**Human Kinetics,** *(Human Kinetics Pubs.; 0-931250; 0-87322),* P.O. Box 5076, Champaign, IL 61820 (SAN 211-7088); 1607 N. Market St., Champaign, IL 61820 (SAN 658-0866) Tel 217-351-5076; *CIP.* *Imprints:* Life Enhancement (Life Enhancement Publications).

Human Miracles *See* **Big Sur Pubs**

Human Netwrks, *(Human Networks Inc.; 0-933933),* 3517 Terhune, Ann Arbor, MI 48104 (SAN 693-0506) Tel 313-971-8342; Dist. by: Askit Co., 3517 Terhune, Ann Arbor, MI 48104 (SAN 200-7037) Tel 313-971-1034.

Human Policy Pr, *(Human Policy Press; 0-937540),* Div. of Center on Human Policy, Division of Special Education, Syracuse Univ., P.O. Box 127, Syracuse, NY 13210 (SAN 213-8476) Tel 315-423-3851.

Human Potential, (Human Potential Pubns.; 0-939268), 17330 Warrington Dr., Detroit, MI 48221 (SAN 215-0832) Tel 313-341-0492.

Human Res Comm, (Human Resource Communications Group; 0-9609088), 2355 E. Stadium Blvd., Ann Arbor, MI 48104 (SAN 264-102X) Tel 313-994-9285.

Human Res Ctr, (Human Resources Center), Iuwillts Rd, Albertson, NY 11507 (SAN 227-0323).

Human Res Dev Pr, (Human Resource Development Pr.; 0-914234; 0-87425), 22 Amherst Rd., Amherst, MA 01002 (SAN 201-9213) Tel 413-253-3488; Toll free: 800-822-2801.

Human Res Inst, (Human Resources Institute), Tempe Wick Rd., Morristown, NJ 07960 (SAN 681-8234).

Human Resources, (Human Resources Research Organization, Robotics Ctr.), 300 N. Washington St., Alexandria, VA 22314 (SAN 207-3692) Tel 703-549-3611.

Human Rights, (Human Rights Internet; 0-939338), 1338 G St. SE, Washington, DC 20003 (SAN 216-5325) Tel 202-543-9200.

†Human Sci Pr, (Human Sciences Pr., Inc.; 0-87705; 0-89885), 72 Fifth Ave., New York, NY 10011 (SAN 200-2159) Tel 212-243-6000; Dist. by: Independent Pubs. Group, 1 Pleasant Ave., Port Washington, NY 11050 (SAN 287-2544); CIP.

Human Serv Pr, (Human Services Pr.; 0-9610834), 200 E. 24th, New York, NY 10010 (SAN 277-688X) Tel 212-679-2750.

†Humana, (Humana Pr., The; 0-89603), P.O. Box 2148, Clifton, NJ 07015 (SAN 212-3606) Tel 201-773-4389; Crescent Manor, Clifton, NJ 07015 (SAN 658-0874); CIP.

Humane Soc, (Humane Society of the United States), 2100 L St. NW, Washington, DC 20037 (SAN 225-8986).

Humanetics Educ Serv See Madison Ave Pub

†Humanics Ltd, (Humanics, Ltd.; 0-89334), P.O. Box 7447, Atlanta, GA 30309 (SAN 208-3833) Tel 404-874-2176; Toll free: 800-874-8844; 1389 Peachtree St. NE, Suite 370, Atlanta, GA 30309 (SAN 658-0882); CIP.

Humanist Pr, (Humanist Pr.; 0-931779), 7 Harwood Dr., P.O. Box 146, Amherst, NY 14226-0146 (SAN 684-8702) Tel 716-839-5080.

Humanitarian, (Humanitarian Publishing Co.; 0-916285), RD 3, Clymer Rd., Quakertown, PA 18951 (SAN 295-8422) Tel 215-536-1900; Dist. by: Philosophical Pub. Co. & Humanitarian Soc., P.O. Box 220, Quakertown, PA 18951 (SAN 295-8430) Tel 215-536-5168.

†Humanities, (Humanities Pr., International, Inc.; 0-391), 171 First Ave., Atlantic Highlands, NJ 07716-1289 (SAN 201-9272) Tel 201-872-1441; Toll free: 800-221-3845 (orders); CIP.

Humanities Arts Pr, (Humanities & Arts Pr.; 0-9616835), 1 Washington Sq., English Dept., San Jose, CA 95192 (SAN 661-602X); 1761 Edgewood Rd., Redwood, CA 94062 (SAN 662-4332) Tel 415-367-1466.

Humbird Ent, (Humbird Enterprise; 0-914128), P.O. Box 1197, San Francisco, CA 94101 (SAN 206-9148) Tel 415-861-2333.

Humble Hills, (Humble Hills Books; 0-935858), P.O. Box 7, Kalamazoo, MI 49004 (SAN 209-8466) Tel 616-343-2211.

Humble Pub Co, (Humble Publishing Co.; 0-9611756), 33 Ivy Trail , NE, Atlanta, GA 30342 (SAN 285-2950) Tel 404-261-3243.

Hummbird Pr, (Hummbird Pr.; 0-915161), 3521 Trevis Way, Carmel, CA 93923 (SAN 289-9485) Tel 408-624-0401; Dist. by: L-S Distributors, 480 Ninth St., San Francisco, CA 94103 (SAN 169-0213) Tel 415-861-6300.

Hummingbird, (Hummingbird Pr.; 0-912998), 2400 Hannett, NE, Albuquerque, NM 87106 (SAN 204-0794) Tel 505-268-6277.

Humphreys Acad, (Humphreys Academy Patrons; 0-9610058). P.O. Box 717, Belzoni, MS 39038 (SAN 262-9070) Tel 601-247-1572.

Huna Res Assocs See Huna Res Inc

Huna Res Inc, (Huna Research Inc.; 0-910764), 126 Camellia Dr., Cape Girardeau, MO 63701 (SAN 201-548X) Tel 314-334-3478; Dist. by: The Great Tradition, 750 Adrian Way, Suite 111, San Rafael, CA 94903 (SAN 200-5743) Tel 415-492-9382.

Hundred Pound Pr, (Hundred Pound Pr., The; 0-939483), 4422 Whitsett Ave., No. 12A, Studio City, CA 91604 (SAN 663-2742) Tel 818-505-0472.

Hungarian Alumni, (Hungarian Alumni Assn.; 0-910539), P.O. Box 174, New Brunswick, NJ 08903 (SAN 260-0722) Tel 201-249-7921; Dist. by: Puski Corvin, 251 E. 82 St., New York, NY 10028 (SAN 200-7924) Tel 212-879-8893.

Hungarian Cultural, (Hungarian Cultural Foun¹ation; 0-914648), P.O. Box 364, Stone Mountain, GA 30086 (SAN 205-6240) Tel 404-377-2600.

Hungarian Rev, (American Hungarian Review; 0-911862), 5410 Kerth Rd., St. Louis, MO 63128 (SAN 204-0816) Tel 314-487-7566.

Hunt Assocs Consult, (Hunt & Assocs., Consulting Engineers; 0-934617), 140 Mayhew Way, Suite 401, Pleasant Hill, CA 94523 (SAN 693-935X) Tel 415-935-3650.

Hunt Inst Botanical, (Hunt Institute for Botanical Documentation; 0-913196), Carnegie-Mellon Univ., Pittsburgh, PA 15213 (SAN 206-9156) Tel 412-268-2434.

Hunter Ariz, (Hunter Publishing Co.; 0-918126), P.O. Box 9533, Phoenix, AZ 85068 (SAN 209-2980) Tel 602-944-1022.

Hunter Art, (Hunter Museum of Art; 0-9615080), 10 Bluff View, Chattanooga, TN 37403 (SAN 279-1455) Tel 615-267-0968.

Hunter Bks, (Hunter Books; 0-917726), 201 McClellan St., Kingwood, TX 77339-2815 (SAN 209-2611) Tel 713-358-7575; Toll free: 800-231-3024.

Hunter Hse, (Hunter Hse., Inc.; 0-89793), Box 1302, Claremont, CA 91711 (SAN 281-7969) Tel 714-624-2277; c/o Publisher's Services, Box 2510, Novato, CA 94948 (SAN 281-7977) Tel 415-883-3530; Dist. by: Bookpeople, 2929 Fifth St., Berkeley, CA 94710 (SAN 169-2488) Tel 415-549-3030; Dist. by: Publishers Group West, 5855 Beaudry St., Emeryville, CA 94608 (SAN 202-8522) Tel 415-658-3453; Dist. by: Distributors, The, 702 S. Michigan, South Bend, IN 46618 (SAN 212-0364) Tel 219-232-8500; Dist. by: New Leaf Distributors, The, 1020 White St., SW, Atlanta, GA 30310 (SAN 169-1449) Tel 404-658-3453; Dist. by: Quality Bks., Inc., 918 Sherwood Dr., Lake Bluff, IL 60044-2204 (SAN 169-2127) Tel 312-498-4000; Dist. by: Devorss & Co., P.O. Box 550, Marina del Rey, CA 90294 (SAN 168-9886) Tel 213-870-7478; Dist. by: Inland Bk. Co., P.O. Box 261, 22 Hemingway Ave., East Haven, CT 06512 (SAN 200-4151) Tel 203-467-4257; Dist. by: Great Tradition, The, 750 Adrian Way, Suite 111, San Rafael, CA 94903 (SAN 200-5743) Tel 415-492-9382.

Hunter Ministries See Hunter Bks

Hunter NC See Hunter Textbks

Hunter Pub NC, (Hunter Publishing Co.; 0-9615429), 2505 Empire Dr., Winston-Salem, NC 27103 (SAN 696-4583) Tel 919-765-0070.

Hunter Pub NY, (Hunter Publishing, Inc.; 0-935161; 1-55650), 300 Raritan Ctr. Pkwy., CN 94, Edison, NJ 08818 (SAN 695-3425); 155 Riverside Dr., New York, NY 10024 (SAN 663-3137) Tel 212-595-8933.

Hunter Pubns, (Hunter Pubns.; 0-931019), P.O. Box 14220, 2760-R S. Havana, Aurora, CO 80014 (SAN 678-9781) Tel 303-699-8870.

Hunter Textbks, (Hunter Textbooks, Inc.; 0-88725), 823 Reynolds Dr., Winston-Salem, NC 27104 (SAN 209-567X) Tel 919-725-0608.

Hunterdon County Bd, (Hunterdon County Board of Agriculture; 0-9606584), R.D. 6, Box 48, Flemington, NJ 08822 (SAN 223-7695) Tel 201-236-2022.

Hunterdon Hse, (Hunterdon Hse.; 0-912606), 38 Swan St., Lambertville, NJ 08530 (SAN 204-0824) Tel 609-397-2523.

Huntington Hse Inc, (Huntington Hse., Inc.; 0-910311), P.O. Box 53788, Lafayette, LA 70505 (SAN 241-5208); Toll free: 800-572-8213.

Huntington Lib, (Huntington Library Pubns.; 0-87328), 1151 Oxford Rd., San Marino, CA 91108 (SAN 202-313X) Tel 818-405-2172.

Huntleigh, (Huntleigh House; 0-918354), P.O. Drawer 20602, Oklahoma City, OK 73156 (SAN 209-4487) Tel 405-751-8444.

Hurd Comm, (Hurd Communications; 0-931021), P.O. Box 1183, Glendale, AZ 85311 (SAN 678-979X) Tel 602-846-5853.

Hurland-Swenson, (Hurland-Swenson Pubs.; 0-9614667), P.O. Box 283, Venice, CA 90291 (SAN 692-4778) Tel 213-827-5162; Orders to: 648 Woodlawn Ave., Venice, CA 90291 (SAN 662-2992).

Hurricane Co, (Hurricane Co., The; 0-933272), P.O. Box 426, Jacksonville, NC 28540 (SAN 212-7466).

Husher & Welch, (Husher & Welch; 0-9603944), 50 Nahant Rd., Nahant, MA 01908 (SAN 215-6563).

Husky Bks AK, (Husky Bks. of Alaska; 0-938061), 6130 E. 12th Ave., No. C-3, Anchorage, AK 99504 (SAN 661-1834) Tel 907-337-4393.

Huston, (Huston, Harvey; 0-9600048), 860 Mount Pleasant St., Winnetka, IL 60093 (SAN 204-0840) Tel 312-446-1594.

Hutar, (Hutar Growth Management Institute; 0-918896), 1701 E. Lake Ave. Suite 270, Glenview, IL 60025 (SAN 210-4385).

Hutchins Hse Imprint of Gulf Pub

Hutson Assoc, (Hutson, Martha, Associates; 0-9606126), P.O. Box 185, Orefield, PA 18069 (SAN 215-7772) Tel 215-799-2597.

HW Imprint of Har-Row

HWH Creative Prod, (HWH Creative Productions, Inc.; 0-936969), 87-53 167th St., Jamaica, NY 11432 (SAN 658-7887) Tel 718-297-2208.

Hwong Pub, (Hwong Publishing Co.; 0-89260), 5525 E. 7th St., Suite C, Long Beach, CA 90804 (SAN 208-2306) Tel 213-597-7743.

Hy-Teck Prods, (Hy-Teck Productions; 0-916511), 822 N. Ninth Ave., Wausau, WI 54401 (SAN 295-5695) Tel 715-848-2681.

Hyacinth Pr, (Hyacinth Pr.; 0-932283), P.O. Box 15477, Santa Fe, NM 87506-0477 (SAN 696-0286).

Hyacinth Pub See Hyacinth Pr

Hybar Bks, (Hybar Books; 0-9614345), P.O. Box 1247, College Park, MD 20740 (SAN 687-8024) Tel 301-982-2923.

Hybrid Pub, (Hybrid Publishing; 0-9616539), P.O. Box 10725, Erie, PA 16510-0725 (SAN 659-4670) Tel 814-454-7833; 1520 Prospect Ave., Erie, PA 16514-0725 (SAN 659-4689).

Hyde Col See Hyde Collect

Hyde Collect, (Hyde Collection, The; 0-9606718), 161 Warren St., Glens Falls, NY 12801 (SAN 219-6638) Tel 518-792-1761.

Hyde Park Pr, (Hyde Park Press; 0-9608454), 2302 Ellis, Boise, ID 83702 (SAN 240-4834).

Hyde Sch, (Hyde School, The; 0-9607904), 616 High St., Bath, ME 04530 (SAN 238-1672).

Hydraulic Inst, (Hydraulic Institute), 712 Lakewood Ctr. N., 14600 Detroit Ave., Cleveland, OH 44107 (SAN 224-7984) Tel 216-226-7700.

Hydronics Inst, (Hydronics Institute), 35 Russo Pl., Berkeley Heights, NJ 07922 (SAN 224-7887) Tel 201-464-8200.

Hymnary Pr, (Hymnary Press, The; 0-942466), P.O. Box 5782, Missoula, MT 59806-5782 (SAN 239-6564) Tel 406-721-4943.

HyperDynamics, (HyperDynamics), P.O. Box 392, Santa Fe, NM 87501 (SAN 208-290X) Tel 505-988-2416.

Hyperion Conn, *(Hyperion Pr., Inc.; 0-88355; 0-8305),* 47 Riverside Ave., Westport, CT 06880 (SAN 202-3148) Tel 203-226-1091; P.O. Box 591, Westport, CT 06880 (SAN 658-0890).

Hypnos Pr, *(Hypnos Press; 0-939628),* 3000 Connecticut Ave. NW, Suite 308, Washington, DC 20008 (SAN 216-6283) Tel 202-462-0221.

Hypoglycemia Foun, *(Adrenal Metabolic Research Society Society of Hypoglycemia Foundation),* 153 Pawling Ave., Troy, NY 12180 (SAN 266-0946) Tel 518-272-7154.

Hyst'ry Myst'ry, *(Hyst'ry Myst'ry Hse.; 0-937884),* One Brush Ct., Garnerville, NY 10923 (SAN 218-4796) Tel 914-947-3141; Dist. by: Associated Booksellers, 562 Boston Ave., Bridgeport, CT 06610 (SAN 203-5014) Tel 203-333-7268.

i a d Pub
See I A D Pubns

I A D Pubns, *(I A D Pubns.; 0-912827),* P.O. Box 504, Brisbane, CA 94005 (SAN 283-362X) Tel 415-467-1700.

I & I Sports, *(I & I Sports Supply Co.; 0-934489),* 3840 Crenshaw Blvd., Suite 108, Los Angeles, CA 90008 (SAN 693-8906) Tel 213-732-7212.

I & O Pub, *(I & O Publishing Co.; 0-911752),* P.O. Box 906, Boulder City, NV 89005 (SAN 202-3156).

I B C A, *(International Bk. Ctr. of Atlanta),* 2576 Acorn Ave., NE, Atlanta, GA 30305 (SAN 678-9064) Tel 404-261-7437.

I B C Pubns, *(IBC Pubns.; 0-931090),* Illinois Benedictine College, Lisle, IL 60532 (SAN 265-3877) Tel 312-960-1500.

I B P C Inc, *(International Business & Publishing Consultants; 0-88115),* P.O. Box 11225, San Francisco, CA 94101 (SAN 239-5541) Tel 415-751-6876.

I C Y Pub, *(I C Y Publishing Co.; 0-9613721),* 4904 Old Court Rd., Randallstown, MD 21133 (SAN 687-6331).

I Can See, *(I Can See Clearly Now; 0-9609532),* P.O. Box 784, Coupeville, WA 98239 (SAN 260-2059) Tel 206-678-4606.

I Chalmers, *(Chalmers, Irena, Cookbooks, Inc.; 0-941034),* 23 E. 92nd St., New York, NY 10128 (SAN 217-3425) Tel 212-289-3105; Toll free: 800-334-8128; Orders to: P.O. Box 988, Denton, NC 27239 (SAN 661-972X).

I D I C P, *(Inka Dinka Ink Childrens Pr.; 0-939700),* Div. of HeBo, Inc., 4741 Guerley Rd., Cincinnati, OH 45238 (SAN 293-2814) Tel 513-471-0825; Dist. by: Baker & Taylor, Midwest Div., 501 Gladiola Ave., Momence, IL 60954 (SAN 169-2100) Tel 201-722-8000; Dist. by: Baker & Taylor, Southwest Div., Mt. Olive Rd., Commerce, GA 30529 (SAN 169-1503) Tel 404-335-5000; Dist. by: Baker & Taylor, Eastern Div., 50 Kirby Ave., Somerville, NJ 08876 (SAN 169-4901); Dist. by: Inka Dinka Ink Wizard Productions, 4741 Guerley Rd., Cincinnati, OH 45238 (SAN 293-2814) Tel 513-471-0825.

I Dare You, *(I Dare You Committee; 0-9602416),* P.O. Box 1606, St. Louis, MO 63188 (SAN 210-9034) Tel 314-982-3210.

I E C, *(I E C; 0-9611802),* 402 S. High St., Selinsgrove, PA 17870 (SAN 286-1097) Tel 717-374-2616.

I E Clark, *(Clark, I. E., Inc.; 0-88680),* St. Johns Rd., Schulenburg, TX 78956 (SAN 282-7433) Tel 409-743-3232; Orders to: P.O. Box 246, Schulenburg, TX 78956 (SAN 662-2003).

I Fischer, *(Fischer, Inge; 0-9610238),* 1616 Kewalo St., No. 507, Honolulu, HI 96822 (SAN 264-0406) Tel 808-531-5764.

I G Group, *(I. G. Group, The; 0-9614951),* P.O. Box 7006, Wilton, CT 06897 (SAN 693-7578) Tel 203-762-7952.

I J E Bk Pub, *(I.J.E. Book Publishing, Inc.; 0-87660),* Div. of I.J.E. Inc., 450 N. Park Rd., Fifth Floor, Hollywood, FL 33021 (SAN 294-040X) Tel 305-966-8520.

I J Hoffman, *(Hoffman, Irwin J., Inc.; 0-9604082),* 5734 S. Ivanhoe St., Denver, CO 80237 (SAN 214-0284).

I J Nelson, *(Nelson, Irene J.; 0-9601464),* P.O. Box 28, Tuskegee Institute, AL 36088 (SAN 211-0725).

I Klang, *(Innerer Klang; 0-911623),* 7 Sherman St., 2B, Charlestown, MA 02129 (SAN 264-1542) Tel 617-242-0689.

I Like Me Pub, *(I Like Me Publishing Co., the; 0-9608516),* P.O. Box 43287, Chicago, IL 60628 (SAN 240-6772) Tel 312-445-6497.

I M Armstrong, *(Armstrong, Irma M.; 0-9611106),* 1188 Harrison Ave., Salt Lake City, UT 84105 (SAN 283-2925) Tel 801-484-7123.

I M Tillotson, *(Tillotson, Ira M.),* P.O. Box 3019, Missoula, MT 59801 (SAN 212-9299).

I-Med Pr, *(I-Med Press, The; 0-933131),* 11823 E. Slauson Ave., No. 40, Santa Fe Springs, CA 90670 (SAN 689-7606) Tel 213-696-1161.

I N Inst
See N Isaac Inst

I N Thut World Educ Ctr, *(World Education Project; 0-918158),* Univ. of Connecticut, Schl. of Education, Box U-32, Storrs, CT 06268 (SAN 209-6358) Tel 203-486-3321.

I Newman, *(Newman, Isadore; 0-917180),* Univ. of Akron, Dept. of Educational Foundations, Akron, OH 44325 (SAN 208-7863) Tel 216-867-7519.

I Osteen, *(Osteen, Ike; 0-9602724),* 380 Kansas St., Springfield, CO 81073 (SAN 212-9248) Tel 303-523-6580.

I S C CA, *(I. S. C. Press; 0-912713),* P.O. Box 779, Fortuna, CA 95540 (SAN 283-0477) Tel 707-768-3284.

†I S Gardner Mus, *(Gardner, Isabella Stewart, Museum; 0-914660),* 2 Palace Rd., Boston, MA 02115 (SAN 201-9221) Tel 617-566-1401; CIP.

I Stephanus Pub, *(Stephanus, Isidore, Sons Publishing; 0-9615964),* P.O. Box 6772, Ithaca, NY 14851 (SAN 697-2950) Tel 607-272-0056.

I Tompkins, *(Tompkins, Iverna, Ministry; 0-9611260),* 7036 E. Thunderbird Rd., Scottsdale, AZ 85254 (SAN 283-2240) Tel 602-991-8803.

I Young, *(Young, Ione; 0-9605660),* 4107 Wildwood Rd., Austin, TX 78722 (SAN 207-6268).

IA City Women
See Aunt Lute Bk Co

IA Conf Com Arch, *(Iowa Conference Commission on Archives & History; 0-9616298),* 1019 Chestnut St., Des Moines, IA 50309 (SAN 658-5450) Tel 712-275-4247; Orders to: Rev. Lyle Johnston, Box 416, Schaller, IA 51053 (SAN 662-412X) Tel 712-275-4247.

IAAEE *Imprint of* Noontide

IADB, *(Inter-American Development Bank; 0-940602),* 808 17th St. NW, Washington, DC 20577 (SAN 226-5745).

IAEA *Imprint of* Unipub

IAFWA, *(International Assn. of Fish & Wildlife Agencies; 0-932108),* 1412 16th St., NW, Washington, DC 20036 (SAN 213-5205) Tel 202-639-8200; Dist. by: World Wide Furbearer Conference, Inc. Book Distributor Center, 1111 E. Cold Spring Ln., Baltimore, MD 21212 (SAN 263-2217).

Iapetus Pr, *(Iapetus Press; 0-941602),* 2009 Tidewater Lane, Madison, MS 39110 (SAN 239-1023) Tel 601-987-5950.

IAQC Pr, *(IAQC Press; 0-916429),* Subs. of International Assn of Quality Circles, 801-B W. 8th St., Cincinnati, OH 45203 (SAN 295-8333) Tel 513-381-1959.

IASL, *(International Assn. of School Librarianship),* Box 1486, Kalamazoo, MI 49005 (SAN 233-4828); 1006 Westmorland, Kalamazoo, MI 49007 (SAN 650-0366) Tel 616-343-5728.

IAWC Mfg, *(International Association of Wiping Cloth Manufacturers),* 300 W. Washington St., Chicago, IL 60606 (SAN 230-5402) Tel 312-726-0050.

IB *Imprint of* U of Ill Pr

IBC *Imprint of* McGraw

Iberian Pub, *(Iberian Publishing Co.; 0-935931),* 548 Cedar Creek Dr., Athens, GA 30605-3408 (SAN 696-8473) Tel 404-546-6740.

Ibersoft, *(Ibersoft, Inc.; 0-935287),* P.O. Box 3455, Trenton, NJ 08619 (SAN 695-7714) Tel 609-890-1496.

Ibis Pr TX, *(Ibis Pr. of College Station, Texas; 0-935215),* P.O. Box 1434, College Station, TX 77841 (SAN 695-7749) Tel 409-696-6257.

Ibis Pub VA, *(Ibis Publishing; 0-935005),* Div. of Teleprint Publishing, Inc., 7 Elliewood Ave., Charlottesville, VA 22903 (SAN 661-6658) Tel 804-979-3420; Toll free: 800-582-0026.

IBM Armonk, *(IBM Corp., Information Systems Group, National Accounts Div.; 0-933186),* 1133 Westchester Ave., White Plains, NY 10604 (SAN 214-1914) Tel 914-765-1900.

IBMA Pubns, *(Independent Battery Manufacturers Assn.; 0-912254),* 100 Larchwood Dr., Largo, FL 33540 (SAN 206-9180) Tel 813-586-1408.

IBMS Corp
See IBMS Inc

IBMS Inc, *(IBMS Inc.; 0-933738),* P.O. Box 395, Westwood, NJ 07675 (SAN 212-9094) Tel 201-343-6855.

IBS Intl, *(I.B.S. Internacional; 0-89564),* 3144 Dove St., San Diego, CA 92103 (SAN 210-3001) Tel 619-298-5061.

IBS Press, *(IBS Pr.; 0-9616605),* 2339 28th St., Santa Monica, CA 90405 (SAN 661-2547) Tel 213-450-6485.

ICA Inc, *(Institute of Contemporary Art; 0-910663),* 955 Boylston St., Boston, MA 02115 (SAN 279-1870).

ICA Pubs, *(ICA Pubs.; 0-941472),* 303 W. Pleasantview Ave., Hackensack, NJ 07601 (SAN 239-3662) Tel 201-343-8833.

IC&P
See Coop Power

ICARE Pr, *(ICARE Pr., Inc.; 0-9609492),* 193-12 Nero Ave., Jamaica, NY 11423 (SAN 270-8809) Tel 718-465-2843.

†Icarus, *(Icarus Pr., Inc.; 0-89651),* 120 W. LaSalle St., Suite 906, South Bend, IN 46601 (SAN 211-7096) Tel 219-233-6020; Toll free: 800-242-7737; Box 1225, South Bend, IN 46601 (SAN 658-0920); Dist. by: Harper & Row, Keystone Industrial Park, Scranton, PA 18512 (SAN 215-3742); CIP.

ICBS Inc, *(International Consortium of Businesses & Services, Inc.; 0-938197),* 44 Montgomery, 5th Flr., San Francisco, CA 94104 (SAN 661-2199) Tel 415-782-3016.

ICC Pub, *(ICC Publishing Corp.),* Affil. of International Chamber of Commerce, 156 Fifth Ave., Suite 820, New York, NY 10010 (SAN 297-1984) Tel 212-206-1150.

ICED Pubns, *(Iced Pubns.),* P.O. Box 217, Essex, CT 06426 (SAN 241-5429) Tel 203-767-2726; 680 Fifth Ave., New York, NY 10019 (SAN 669-0998) Tel 212-582-3970; 127 River Rd., Essex, CT 06426 (SAN 669-1005).

ICER, *(Institute for Computer Engineering Research; 0-937227),* Div. of Access Conference Assocs., Inc., 9719 Duffer Way, Gaithersburg, MD 20879 (SAN 658-7380) Tel 301-927-9424.

ICER Pr, *(ICER Pr.; 0-914704),* P.O. Box 877, Claremont, CA 91711 (SAN 205-6267).

Ichthus Pub
See Ichthys Bks

Ichthys Bks, *(Ichthys Bks.; 0-930711),* 916 Red Mountain Dr., Glenwood Springs, CO 81601 (SAN 677-2390) Tel 303-945-7052.

ICIA
See Internatl Comms

ICJ *Imprint of* Unipub

ICJ Corp, *(I.C.J. Corp.; 0-9615943),* P.O. Box 7086, Thousand Oaks, CA 91359 (SAN 696-897X) Tel 805-496-5243; 4372 Golf Course Dr., Westlake Village, CA 91362 (SAN 696-8988).

ICM Denver, *(Institute of Court Management),* 1331 17th St., Suite 402, Denver, CO 80202 (SAN 227-0250) Tel 303-293-3063.

Icon Edns *Imprint of* Har-Row

Icon Pr, *(Icon Pr.; 0-9615471),* Box 3240, Vail, CO 81658 (SAN 696-2629) Tel 303-476-1263; 1548 Spring Hill Ln., No. 2, Vail, CO 81658 (SAN 696-2637).

ICPSR, *(Inter-University Consortium for Political & Social Research; 0-89138),* Affil. of Univ. of Michigan Institute for Social Research, P.O. Box 1248, Ann Arbor, MI 48106 (SAN 207-7450) Tel 313-763-5010.

ICR, *(Institute for Cross-Cultural Research; 0-911976),* 4000 Albermarle St., NW, Washington, DC 20016 (SAN 206-6505).

ICS Bks, *(ICS Bks., Inc.; 0-934802),* 1000 E. 80th Pl., Suite 314S, Merrillville, IN 46410 (SAN 295-3358) Tel 219-769-0585; Toll free: 800-732-3669; Dist. by: Stackpole Bks., P.O. Box 1831, Cameron & Kelker Sts., Harrisburg, PA 17105 (SAN 202-5396) Tel 717-234-5041.

†**ICS Pr,** *(ICS Pr.; 0-917616),* Div. of Institute for Contemporary Studies, 785 Market St., Suite 750, San Francisco, CA 94103 (SAN 276-9735) Tel 415-543-6412; *CIP.*

ICS Pubns, *(ICS Pubns., Institute of Carmelite Studies; 0-9600876; 0-935216),* 2131 Lincoln Rd., NE, Washington, DC 20002 (SAN 201-5285) Tel 202-832-6622.

ICSU *Imprint of Unipub*

ICSU Pr, *(ICSU Pr.; 0-930357),* P.O. Box 016129, Miami, FL 33101 (SAN 670-7688) Tel 305-547-6265.

ICTL Pubns, *(ICTL Pubns.; 0-910733),* 3889 Ashford St., San Diego, CA 92111 (SAN 262-0413) Tel 619-279-6279.

ICU Group, *(ICU Group, The; 0-936395),* P.O. Box 5027, Cortland, NY 13045 (SAN 696-9127) Tel 716-425-2519.

ICUC Pr, *(ICUC Pr.; 0-910205),* P.O. Box 1447, Springfield, VA 22151 (SAN 241-5216) Tel 703-323-8065.

Idaho First Natl Bank, *(Idaho First National Bank; 0-9600776),* c/o R. O. Beatty & Assocs., Inc., P.O. Box 763, Boise, ID 83701 (SAN 207-9909).

Idaho Mus Nat Hist, *(Idaho Museum of Natural History; 0-939696),* Campus Box 8096, Idaho State Univ., Pocatello, ID 83209 (SAN 201-5315) Tel 208-236-3168.

Idaho Press Club, *(Idaho Press Club, The; 0-9616307),* 132 W. Third St., Boise, ID 83701 (SAN 658-7348) Tel 208-733-0931; P.O. Box 2221, Boise, ID 93701 (SAN 658-7356).

Idaho Secy, *(Idaho. Secretary of State Office of the Secretary of State),* State Capitol, Rm. 203, Boise, ID 83720 (SAN 270-8965).

Idaho State Soc, *(Idaho State Historical Society; 0-931406),* 610 N. Julia Davis Dr., Boise, ID 83702-7695 (SAN 221-0827) Tel 208-334-2120.

Ide Hse, *(Ide Hse., Inc.; 0-86663),* 4631 Harvey Dr., Mesquite, TX 75150-1609 (SAN 216-146X) Tel 214-681-2552; Dist. by: Liberal Pr., P.O. Box 160361, Las Colinas, TX 75016-9998 (SAN 200-5360) Tel 817-478-8564.

Ideal World, *(Ideal World Publishing Co.; 0-915068),* P.O. Box 1237-EG, Melbourne, FL 32935 (SAN 201-923X) Tel 305-254-6003.

Ideals, *(Ideals Publishing Corp.; 0-89542; 0-8249),* Subs. of Thomas Nelson, Inc., Nelson Pl. at Elm Hill Pike, Nashville, TN 37214 (SAN 213-4403) Tel 615-889-9000; Toll free: 800-558-0740. *Imprints:* Good Friends (Good Friends).

IDEALS PA, *(Institute for the Development of Emotional Life Skills (IDEALS)),* Box 391, State College, PA 16801 (SAN 224-358X).

Ideas Inc OR, *(Ideas!, Inc.; 0-939447),* 3340 SW Stonebrook Dr., Portland, OR 97201 (SAN 663-3420) Tel 503-245-0018; Dist. by: Far West Book Service, 3515 NE Hassale, Portland, OR 97232 (SAN 107-6760).

†**Identity Inst,** *(Identity Institute, The; 0-912093),* P.O. Box 11039, Honolulu, HI 96828 (SAN 277-6898); *CIP.*

IDHHB, *(Institute for the Development of the Harmonious Human Being Publishing, Inc.; 0-89556),* P.O. Box 370, Nevada City, CA 95959 (SAN 211-3635) Tel 916-786-7313.

Idthekkethan, *(Idthekkethan Publishing Co.; 0-918347),* 58 Roble Rd., Berkeley, CA 94705 (SAN 657-3533) Tel 415-644-1128.

IDTTC
    See Poet Tree Pr

Idylwild Bks, *(Idylwild Books; 0-9613054),* P.O. Box 246, Ojai, CA 93023 (SAN 295-3870) Tel 805-646-2646; 1465 Foothill Rd., Ojai, CA 93020 (SAN 295-3889); Dist. by: Bookpeople, 2929 Fifth St., Berkeley, CA 94710 (SAN 168-9517) Tel 415-549-3030; Dist. by: The New Leaf Distributing, 1020 White St., SW, Atlanta, GA 30310 (SAN 169-1449) Tel 404-755-2665; Dist. by: Starlite Distributors, P.O. Box 20729, Reno, NV 89515 (SAN 131-1921) Tel 702-359-5676.

IEAS, *(Univ. of California, Institute of East Asian Studies; 0-912966),* Publications Office, 2223 Fulton St., 6th Flr., Berkeley, CA 94720 (SAN 203-8730) Tel 415-643-6325.

IEAS Ctr Chinese Stud
    See IEAS

IEEE
    See IEEE Comp Soc

IEEE
    See Inst Elect Eng

IEEE
    See Inst Electrical

IEEE Comp Soc, *(IEEE Computer Society Pr.; 0-8186),* Subs. of IEEE Computer Society, 1730 Massachusetts Ave., NW, Washington, DC 20036-1903 (SAN 264-620X) Tel 202-371-0101; Toll free: 800-272-6657 orders only; 10662 Los Vaqueros Cir., Los Alamitos, CA 90270 (SAN 264-6218) Tel 714-821-8380; Orders to: P.O. Box 80452, Worldway Postal Ctr., Los Angeles, CA 90080 (SAN 662-1988) Tel 714-821-8380.

If & Win Pub, *(If & Win Publishing; 0-9617025),* P.O. Box 1262, Placentia, CA 92670 (SAN 662-572X); 4711 Rapallo Plaza, Yorba Linda, CA 92686 (SAN 662-5738) Tel 714-970-8542.

IFBL Press, *(IFBL Pr.; 0-938327),* Subs. of Image Feedback Labs, 196 Conantville Rd., Willimantic, CT 06226 (SAN 661-3268) Tel 203-423-7758.

IFI-Plenum *Imprint of Plenum Pub*
IFPA *Imprint of Unipub*

Igaku-Shoin, *(Igaku-Shoin Medical Pubs.; 0-89640),* Subs. of Igaku-Shoin, Ltd. (Japan), 1140 Ave. of the Americas, New York, NY 10036 (SAN 211-5689) Tel 212-944-7540.

IGJ Pubns, *(IGJ Pubns.; 0-9617042),* P.O. Box 1852, Hoboken, NJ 07030 (SAN 662-8273); 1117 Park Ave., Hoboken, NJ 07030 (SAN 662-8281) Tel 201-653-2130.

Ignatius Pr, *(Ignatius Pr.; 0-89870),* Div. of Guadalupe Assocs., Inc., P.O. Box 18990, San Francisco, CA 94118 (SAN 214-3887) Tel 415-387-2324; Orders to: 15 Oakland Ave., Harrison, NY 10528 (SAN 289-0127) Tel 914-835-4216.

Igram Pr, *(Igram Press; 0-911119),* 2020 16th Ave. SW, Cedar Rapids, IA 52404 (SAN 263-1709) Tel 319-366-5335.

IHEMI, *(International Health Economics & Management Institute; 0-914943),* Southern Illinois Univ. at Edwardsville, Box 1101, Edwardsville, IL 62026-1101 (SAN 289-2626) Tel 618-692-2291.

IHI Pr, *(IHI Press),* International Homophilics Institute, 165 Marlborough St., Boston, MA 02116 (SAN 209-5688).

IIA, *(Insurance Institute of America, Inc.; 0-89462),* 720 Providence Rd., Malvern, PA 19355 (SAN 210-2129) Tel 215-644-2100.

IIP Assocs, *(IIP Assocs.; 0-916423),* Univ. of Utah, College of Health, Salt Lake City, UT 84112 (SAN 294-4281) Tel 801-582-3202.

IISJ, *(Institute for Independent Social Journalism; 0-917654),* 33 W. 17th St., New York, NY 10011 (SAN 201-842X) Tel 212-691-0404.

IIWPA
    See Assn Info Sys

IJA NYU, *(Institute of Judicial Administration New York University School of Law; 0-943904),* Washington Square Village, New York, NY 10012 (SAN 227-0013).

IJG Inc
    See Blue Cat

IJK Intl, *(IJK International; 0-9605146),* 25 Lyon Ave., Greenwich, CT 06830 (SAN 293-2903) Tel 203-661-0686; Orders to: P.O. Box 41, White Plains, NY 10605 (SAN 293-2911) Tel 203-661-0686.

IJP, *(Index to Jewish Periodicals; 0-939698),* P.O. Box 18570, Cleveland Heights, OH 44118 (SAN 204-8566) Tel 216-321-7296.

Ike & Dudatt Pubns, *(Ike & Dudatt Pubns.; 0-930297),* 9361 La Jolla Cir., P.O. Box 5762, Huntington Beach, CA 92646 (SAN 670-8412).

Ike&Dudatt Pubns
    See Ike & Dudatt Pubns

IL Inst Tech, *(Illinois Institute of Technology),* 10 W. 32nd St., Chicago, IL 60616 (SAN 230-8304); Dist. by: Univ. of Chicago Pr., 5801 Ellis Ave., 3rd Flr., S., Chicago, IL 60637 (SAN 202-5280) Tel 312-962-7693.

ILCI, *(International Loss Control Institute; 0-88061),* P.O. Box 345, Loganville, GA 30249 (SAN 240-9887) Tel 404-466-2208.

Ili-Cor Pubns, *(Ili-Cor Pubns.),* 1460 Webster St., No. 3, San Francisco, CA 94115 (SAN 240-1525) Tel 415-567-6568.

ILI Pr, *(I L I Press; 0-932183),* Subs. of Infinety Limited Inc., 836 Chippewa Ave., St. Paul, MN 55107 (SAN 686-5380) Tel 612-228-0105.

Ill Academy, *(Illinois Academy of Criminology; 0-933757),* 8939 W. Emerson St., Des Plaines, IL 60016 (SAN 692-7483) Tel 312-670-2775.

Ill Baptist St Assn, *(Illinois Baptist State Assn.; 0-9600896),* P.O. Box 3486, Springfield, IL 62708 (SAN 208-2608).

Ill Labor Hist Soc, *(Illinois Labor History Society; 0-916884),* 28 E. Jackson Blvd., Chicago, IL 60604 (SAN 281-8019) Tel 312-663-4107.

Ill St Hist Lib, *(Illinois State Historical Library; 0-912154),* Div. of Illinois Historic Preservation Agency, Old State Capitol, Springfield, IL 62701 (SAN 203-7963) Tel 217-782-4836.

Ill St Hist Soc, *(Illinois State Historical Society; 0-912226),* Old State Capitol, Springfield, IL 62701 (SAN 203-7971) Tel 217-782-4836.

Ill St Museum, *(Illinois State Museum Society; 0-89792),* Spring & Edwards, Springfield, IL 62706 (SAN 201-5137) Tel 217-782-7386.

Illinois Bar, *(Illinois State Bar Assn.),* Illinois Bar Ctr., 424 S. Second St., Springfield, IL 62701 (SAN 226-2207) Tel 217-525-1760.

Illinois Governor, *(Illinois Office of the Governor),* State Capitol, Springfield, IL 62706 (SAN 270-9082).

Illinois Secy
    See Illinois Secy State

Illinois Secy State, *(Illinois Secretary of State),* State Capitol, Rm. 213, Springfield, IL 62706 (SAN 270-9112).

Illinois South, *(Illinois South Project; 0-943724),* 116 1/2 W. Cherry, Herrin, IL 62948 (SAN 241-0303) Tel 618-942-6613.

Illiterati Pr, *(Illiterati Pr.; 0-937837),* 8306 Wilshire Blvd., No. 129, Beverly Hills, CA 90211 (SAN 659-4697) Tel 213-467-5232; 2142 1/2 N. Beachwood Dr., Hollywood, CA 90068 (SAN 659-4700).

Illum Eng, *(Illumination Engineering Society of North America; 0-87995),* 345 E. 47th St., New York, NY 10017 (SAN 202-3180) Tel 212-705-7913.

Illum Pr, *(Illuminations Pr.; 0-937088),* P.O. Box 126, St. Helena, CA 94574 (SAN 241-5445) Tel 707-963-9342.

Illum Way Pr
    See IWP Pub

†**Illuminati,** *(Illuminati; 0-89807),* P.O. Box 67E07, Los Angeles, CA 90067 (SAN 212-856X) (SAN 696-0189); *CIP.*

Illuminations Pr, *(Illuminations Pr.; 0-941442),* 2110 Ninth St., Apt. B, Berkeley, CA 94710 (SAN 209-8172) Tel 415-849-2102.

ILM, *(Interdependent Learning Model; 0-939632),* Fordham Univ. at Lincoln Ctr., 113 West 60th St., Rm. 1003, New York, NY 10023 (SAN 216-6305) Tel 212-841-5282.

ILO *Imprint of Unipub*

ILR Pr, *(ILR Pr.; 0-87546),* Div. of New York State Schl. of Industrial Relations, Cornell Univ., New York State Schl. of Industrial Relations, Cornell Univ., Ithaca, NY 14851-0952 (SAN 270-8825) Tel 607-255-3061.

IM-Pr, *(IM-Pr.; 0-931543),* 1412 Rosewood St., Ann Arbor, MI 48104 (SAN 682-2967) Tel 313-761-2231.

IM-Press, *(IM-Pr.; 0-915727),* 1527 Virginia St., Berkeley, CA 94703 (SAN 294-0213) Tel 415-845-8409.

Ima Boyd, *(Boyd, Ima Gene (Guthery); 0-9600502),* 370 E. Archwood Ave., Akron, OH 44301 (SAN 203-7998) Tel 216-773-1757.

Image & Idea, *(Image & Idea, Inc.; 0-934570),* Box 1991, Iowa City, IA 52240 (SAN 213-3229); Dist. by: Iowa State Univ. Press, 2121 S. State Ave., Ames, IA 50010 (SAN 202-7194).

Image Awareness, *(Image Awareness Corp.; 0-9604592),* 1271 High St., Auburn, CA 95603 (SAN 215-1545) Tel 916-823-7092.

Ind Curators, *(Independent Curators Incorporated; 0-916365),* 799 Broadway, New York, NY 10003 (SAN 295-9496) Tel 212-254-8200; Dist. by: World Wide Books, 37-39 Antwerp St., Boston, MA 02135 (SAN 287-7805) Tel 617-787-9100.

Ind Hist Soc, *(Indiana Historical Society; 0-87195),* 315 W. Ohio St., Rm. 350, Indianapolis, IN 46202 (SAN 201-5234) Tel 317-232-1878.

Ind Liquid Terms, *(Independent Liquid Terminals Assn.),* 1133 15th St., NW, Suite 204, Washington, DC 20005 (SAN 224-9367) Tel 202-659-2301.

Ind Mus Art, *(Indianapolis Museum of Art; 0-936260),* 1200 W. 38th St., Indianapolis, IN 46208 (SAN 215-6571) Tel 317-925-7034.

Ind Petrol Assn, *(Independent Petroleum Association of America),* 1101 16th St. NW, Washington, DC 20036 (SAN 224-9006) Tel 202-857-4770.

†Ind Pr MO, *(Independence Press; 0-8309),* Div. of Herald House, P.O. Box HH, 3225 S. Noland Rd., Independence, MO 64055 (SAN 202-6902) Tel 816-252-5010; Toll free: 800-821-7550; *CIP.*

Ind Pubns, *(Independent Pubns.; 0-914937),* P.O. Box 162 Park Sta., Paterson, NJ 07543 (SAN 289-2464) Tel 201-943-7299.

Ind Res Servs Irvine, *(Independent Research Services of Irvine; 0-932669),* 10 Sunfish, Irvine, CA 92714 (SAN 687-8059) Tel 714-551-0182.

Ind Sch Pr, *(Independent School Pr.; 0-88334),* 51 River St., Wellesley Hills, MA 02181 (SAN 203-8013) Tel 617-237-2591.

Ind Sector, *(Independent Sector),* 1828 L St., NW, Washington, DC 20036 (SAN 679-1670).

Ind St Univ, *(Indiana State Univ.; 0-940100),* Parsons Hall, Rm. 111, Terre Haute, IN 47809 (SAN 211-0202) Tel 812-232-6311.

Ind U African
See Ind U Afro-Amer Arts

Ind U Afro-Amer Arts, *(Indiana Univ. Afro-American Arts Institute),* 109 North Jordon Ave., Bloomington, IN 47405 (SAN 209-5696).

Ind U Busn Res, *(Indiana Univ., Bureau of Business Research; 0-87925),* Bloomington, IN 47405 (SAN 202-6880) Tel 812-335-5507.

Ind U Mus
See W H Mathers Mus

†Ind U Pr, *(Indiana Univ. Pr.; 0-253),* Tenth & Morton Sts., Bloomington, IN 47405 (SAN 202-5647) Tel 812-335-7681. Do not confuse with Indian U Pr OK; *CIP.* Imprints: MB (Midland Books).(Midland Bks.).

Ind U Res Ctr
See Res Ctr Lang Semiotic

Ind U Res Inst, *(Indiana Univ. Research Institute for Inner Asian Studies; 0-933070),* Goodbody Hall 344, Bloomington, IN 47405 (SAN 215-1553) Tel 812-335-1605.

Ind-US Inc, *(Ind-US, Inc.; 0-86578),* Box 56, East Glastonbury, CT 06025 (SAN 213-5809) Tel 203-663-0045.

Independ Sch, *(Independent School District , 535; 0-917009),* Rochester Public Schools, Edison Bldg., 615 SW 7th St., Rochester, MN 55901 (SAN 655-7376) Tel 507-285-8560.

Independence House, *(Independence Hse. Publishing Co., Inc.; 0-912551),* Div. of Independence House, Inc., 15100 Birmingham Dr., Burtonsville, MD 20866 (SAN 265-2587) Tel 301-490-0112.

Independence Pr
See Ind Pr MO

Index-Citator, *(Index/Citator System, Inc.; 0-936603),* 4400 Lindell Blvd., No. 19-F, St. Louis, MO 63108 (SAN 698-0481) Tel 314-652-6578.

Index Hse, *(Index Hse.; 0-936697),* 7206 Farmington Way, Madison, WI 53717 (SAN 699-8682) Tel 608-833-1617.

†Index Pub, *(Index Publishing; 0-914311),* Dept. R, P.O. Box 11476, Salt Lake City, UT 84147 (SAN 287-5500); *CIP.*

India Enterprises West, *(India Enterprises of the West, Inc.; 0-933047),* P.O. Box 462, Wakefield Stn., Bronx, NY 10466 (SAN 689-7614) Tel 212-519-0709.

Indian Bk Ctr, *(Indian Bk. Center, Inc.; 0-932639),* P.O. Box 2541, Edison, NJ 08818 (SAN 687-8067) Tel 201-494-8175.

Indian Crossing Bks, *(Indian Crossing Bks.; 0-9616222),* 101 Seminole, DeForest, WI 53532 (SAN 658-5485) Tel 608-846-4134.

Indian Feather, *(Indian Feather Publishing; 0-937962),* 7218 SW Oak, Portland, OR 97223 (SAN 215-9996).

Indian Hist Pr, *(Indian Historian Press, Inc.; 0-913436),* 1451 Masonic Ave., San Francisco, CA 94117 (SAN 202-6929) Tel 415-626-5235.

Indian Peaks Pub, *(Indian Peaks Publishing Co.; 0-9616582),* Salina Star Rte., Boulder, CO 80302 (SAN 661-2008) Tel 303-440-9394; 531 Canyonside Dr., Boulder, CO 80302 (SAN 661-2016).

Indian U Pr OK, *(Indian Univ. Press; 0-940392),* Div. of Bacone College, Bacone College, Muskogee, OK 74403 (SAN 217-1821) Tel 918-683-4581. Do not confuse with Ind U Pr Indiana.

Indiana Africa, *(Indiana University, African Studies Program; 0-941934),* 221 Woodburn Hall Indiana University, Bloomington, IN 47405 (SAN 238-6135) Tel 812-335-8284.

Indigenous Pubns, *(Indigenous Pubns.; 0-930740),* P.O. Box 1614, Aptos, CA 95003 (SAN 210-8801) Tel 209-529-5087.

Indigo Pr, *(Indigo Press; 0-9604060),* 5950 Fern Flat Rd., Aptos, CA 95003 (SAN 239-443X); Dist. by: Straw into Gold, 3006 San Pablo, Berkeley, CA 94702 (SAN 239-4448).

Indisota Pubs
See D E Brown

Indiv Educ Syst, *(Individualized Education Systems; 0-938911),* P.O. Box 5136, Fresno, CA 93755 (SAN 661-8405); 134 Poppy Ln., Clovis, CA 93612 (SAN 661-8413) Tel 209-299-4639.

Indiv Potentials, *(Individual Potentials Unlimited; 0-9616223),* 3540 S. 4000 W., Suite 430, West Valley City, UT 84404 (SAN 658-5493) Tel 801-968-3292.

Individual Learn, *(Individual Learning Systems, Inc.; 0-86589),* Div. of Southwest Offset, Inc., P.O. Box 225447, Dallas, TX 75265 (SAN 203-8021) Tel 214-630-0313.

Indochina Curriculum Grp, *(Indochina Curriculum Group; 0-9607794),* 11 Garden St., Cambridge, MA 02138 (SAN 217-7854) Tel 617-354-6583.

Indus Bk Pub, *(Industry Book Publishing, Inc.; 0-939554),* 1437 Tuttle Ave., Wallingford, CT 06492 (SAN 220-1720) Tel 203-269-9184.

Indus Design, *(Industrial Designers Society of America),* 1360 Beverly Rd., Suite 303, McLean, VA 22101-3671 (SAN 224-7941) Tel 703-556-0919.

Indus Dev Inst Sci, *(Industrial Development Div., Institute of Science & Technology; 0-938654),* Univ. of Michigan, 2200 Bonisteel Blvd., Ann Arbor, MI 48105 (SAN 204-8590) Tel 313-764-5260.

Indus Fabrics, *(Industrial Fabrics Assn. International; 0-935803),* 345 Cedar Bldg., Suite 450, St. Paul, MN 55101 (SAN 224-134X) Tel 612-222-2508.

Indus Health Inc, *(Industrial Health Foundation, Inc.; 0-911890),* 34 Penn Cir. W., Pittsburgh, PA 15206 (SAN 203-803X) Tel 412-363-6600.

†Indus Pr, *(Industrial Pr., Inc.; 0-8311),* 200 Madison Ave., New York, NY 10016 (SAN 202-6945) Tel 212-889-6330; Orders to: P.O. Box C-772, Brooklyn, NY 11205 (SAN 662-0434) Tel 718-852-7519; *CIP.*

Indus Rel, *(Industrial Relations Counselors, Inc.; 0-87330),* P.O. Box 1530, New York, NY 10101 (SAN 203-8048) Tel 212-541-6086; Orders to: Industrial Relations Research Assn., 7226 Social Science Bldg., Madison, WI 53706 (SAN 663-2939) Tel 608-262-2762.

Indus Relations Res, *(Univ. of Wisconsin, Industrial Relations Research Assn.; 0-913447),* 7226 Social Science Bldg., Madison, WI 53706 (SAN 224-8077) Tel 608-262-2762.

Indus Res Serv, *(Industrial Research Service, Inc.),* 26 Strafford Ave., Durham, NH 03824 (SAN 204-8612) Tel 603-868-2593.

Indus Res Unit-Wharton, *(Industrial Research Unit-The Wharton Schl.; 0-89546),* Univ. of Pennsylvania, Vance Hall/CS, 3733 Spruce St., Philadelphia, PA 19104 (SAN 206-0744) Tel 215-898-5606.

Indus Workers World, *(Industrial Workers of the World; 0-917124),* 3435 N. Sheffield, No. 202, Chicago, IL 60657 (SAN 209-1909) Tel 312-549-5045.

Industrial Marketscope
See Marketscope Bks

Indytype
See Shepard Poorman

Infax Corp, *(Infax Corp.; 0-933937),* 5205 Hampden Ln., Bethseda, MD 20814 (SAN 693-0522) Tel 301-986-8011.

Infection Control, *(Infection Control Pubns.; 0-936751),* P.O. Box 541, North Salt Lake City, UT 84054 (SAN 699-8836) Tel 801-298-0880; 421 W. 900 N., North Salt Lake City, UT 84054 (SAN 699-8844).

Infernal Artists, *(Infernal Artists Scribes Publishers),* Div. of Apollo/Athena Enterprises, Ltd., 185 Butler St., Hamden, CT 06511 (SAN 209-4495) Tel 203-787-4376; P.O. Box 4034, Hamden, CT 06514 (SAN 209-4509); Orders to: P.O. Box 4034, Hamden, CT 06514 (SAN 662-0442).

Inflation Reports, *(Inflation Reports),* P.O. Box 60148, Los Angeles, CA 90060 (SAN 291-8382) Tel 213-660-8201.

Info Aids, *(Information Aids, Inc.; 0-936474),* 1401 Windy Meadow Dr., Plano, TX 75023 (SAN 220-2557) Tel 214-422-4058.

Info All Bk, *(Info-All Book Co.; 0-9617218),* 5 Old Well Ln., Dallas, PA 18612 (SAN 663-4087) Tel 717-288-9375.

Info Alternative, *(Information Alternative; 0-936288),* P.O. Box 5571, Chicago, IL 60680 (SAN 215-8744).

Info Arts, *(Information Arts; 0-937665),* P.O. Box 1032, Carmel Valley, CA 93924 (SAN 659-2481) Tel 408-659-5135; 13 Via Contenta, No. 1, Carmel Valley, CA 93924 (SAN 659-249X).

Info Bks
See Dollar's Info Bks

Info Clearing House
See FIND-SVP

†Info Coord, *(Information Coord., Inc.; 0-911772; 0-89990),* 1435-37 Randolph St., Detroit, MI 48226 (SAN 206-7641) Tel 313-962-9720; *CIP.*

Info Digest, *(Info Digest; 0-939670),* 9302 Parkside Ave., Morton Grove, IL 60053 (SAN 216-9460) Tel 312-965-1456; Orders to: P.O. Box 165, Morton Grove, IL 60053 (SAN 662-7102).

Info Dynamics, *(Information Dynamics, Inc.; 0-935437),* 111 Claybrook Dr., Silver Spring, MD 20902 (SAN 696-2688) Tel 301-593-8650.

Info Gatekeepers, *(Information Gatekeepers, Inc.; 0-918435),* 214 Harvard St., Boston, MA 02134 (SAN 237-9597) Tel 617-232-3111.

Info Guides, *(Information Guides; 0-938329),* P.O. Box 0531, Hermosa Beach, CA 90254 (SAN 661-4337); 32 18th St., Hermosa Beach, CA 90254 (SAN 661-4345) Tel 213-374-1914.

Info Indus, *(Information Industry Assn.; 0-942774),* 555 New Jersey Ave., NW, Washington, DC 20001 (SAN 674-5415) Tel 202-639-8262.

Info Mgmt Pr, *(Information Management Press; 0-9606408),* P.O. Box 19166, Washington, DC 20036 (SAN 218-5563) Tel 202-293-5519.

Info Oregon, *(Information Pr., The; 0-911927),* P.O. Box 957, Sisters, OR 97759 (SAN 264-1127) Tel 503-549-5181.

Info Pr
See Info Oregon

Info Pr NY, *(Info Pr., Inc.; 0-9692267),* 728 Center, Lewiston, NY 14092 (SAN 271-0005) Tel 716-754-4669.

Info Prods, *(Information Products; 0-937978),* 30917 Rue de la Pierre, Rancho Palos Verdes, CA 90274 (SAN 214-0349) Tel 213-377-2880.

Info Pubns, *(Information Pubns.; 0-931845),* P.O. Box 356, Wellesley Hills, MA 02181 (SAN 686-0214) Tel 617-235-5427.

Symbols/Abbreviations

Inst Analysis, *(Institute for the Analysis, Evaluation & Design of Human Action; 0-938526),* 44 Clifford Ave., Pelham, NY 10803 (SAN 215-8752).

Inst Appl Forth, *(Institute For Applied Forth Research, The; 0-914593),* 478 Thurston Rd., Rochester, NY 14619 (SAN 295-3676) Tel 716-235-0168; Dist. by: Institute for Applied Forth Research, Inc., P.O. Box 27686, Rochester, NY 14627 (SAN 295-3692).

Inst Arab Stud, *(Institute of Arab Studies; 0-912031),* 556 Trapelo Rd., Belmont, MA 02178 (SAN 265-3583).

Inst Basic Youth, *(Institute in Basic Youth Conflicts; 0-916888),* P.O. Box 1, Oak Brook, IL 60521 (SAN 208-6972) Tel 312-323-9800.

Inst Behav, *(Institute of Behavioral Learning; 0-910265),* 4550 Wilshire Blvd., Los Angeles, CA 90010 (SAN 240-8619).

Inst Biblical, *(Institute of Biblical Studies; 0-934743),* P.O. Box 34098, San Diego, CA 92103 (SAN 694-1672) Tel 619-291-7438.

Inst Briquetting, *(Institute for Briquetting & Agglomeration),* P.O. Box 794, Erie, PA 16512 (SAN 224-8816) Tel 814-838-1133; 2615 W. Tenth St., Erie, PA 16505 (SAN 669-1064).

†Inst Busn Plan, *(Institute for Business Planning, Inc.; 0-87624),* B & P Marking, Route 9W, Englewood Cliffs, NJ 07632 (SAN 202-7003) Tel 201-542-2015; Orders to: Eleanor Brigida, Customer Service, 200 Old Tappan Rd., Old Tappan, NJ 07675 (SAN 685-3331) Tel 201-767-5059; *CIP.*

Inst Byzantine, *(Institute for Byzantine & Modern Greek Studies, Inc.; 0-914744),* 115 Gilbert Rd., Belmont, MA 02178 (SAN 201-5110) Tel 617-484-6595.

Inst Cert Trav Agts, *(Institute of Certified Travel Agents; 0-931202),* 148 Linden St., Wellesley, MA 02181 (SAN 238-7700) Tel 617-237-0280.

Inst Charter Finan Analysts, *(Institute of Chartered Financial Analysts; 0-935015),* Box 3668, Charlottesville, VA 22901 (SAN 224-7313) Tel 804-977-6600.

Inst Christ Leadership, *(Institute for Christian Leadership; 0-933939),* Div. of International Foundation, 9733 SE French Acres Dr., Portland, OR 97266 (SAN 693-0557) Tel 503-774-0111.

Inst Christian, *(ICE; 0-930464),* Affil. of American Bureau of Economic Research, P.O. Box 8000, Tyler, TX 75711 (SAN 297-1828) Tel 214-593-8919. *Imprints:* Reconstruct Pr (Reconstruction Press).

Inst Community, *(Univ. of Georgia, Institute of Community & Area Development, The; 0-911847),* Div. of UGA, 300 Old College, Athens, GA 30602 (SAN 264-4541) Tel 404-542-7103.

Inst Constructive Cap, *(Univ. of Texas at Austin, Graduate Schl. of Business, Institute for Constructive Capitalism),* Univ. of Texas at Austin, Austin, TX 78712 (SAN 211-3198).

Inst Contemp Art
See ICA Inc

Inst Contemporary
See ICS Pr

Inst Creation *Imprint of Master Bks*

Inst Cult Prog, *(Institute for Cultural Progress; 0-942776),* 1710 Connecticut Ave., NW, Washington, DC 20009 (SAN 219-8398) Tel 202-387-7305; Dist. by: Publishing Center for Cultural Resources, 625 Broadway, New York, NY 10012 (SAN 274-9025) Tel 212-260-2010.

Inst Def & Dis, *(Institute for Defense & Disarmament Studies; 0-915883),* 2001 Beacon St., Brookline, MA 02146 (SAN 289-6052).

Inst Dem Socialism, *(Institute For Democratic Socialism; 0-9613009),* 145 Tremont St., Boston, MA 02111 (SAN 293-4949) Tel 617-426-9026.

Inst Dev & Econ, *(Institutional Development & Economic Affairs Service, Inc.),* Magnolia Star Rte., Nederland, CO 80466 (SAN 225-6681) Tel 303-443-8789.

Inst Dev Indian Law, *(Institute for the Development of Indian Law),* 1104 Glydon St., SE, Vienna, VA 22180 (SAN 662-0485) Tel 703-938-7822.

Inst Dev Skills
See IDEALS PA

Inst Dowsing
See Dowsing Inst

Inst Early Am, *(Institute of Early American History & Culture; 0-910776),* P.O. Box 220, Williamsburg, VA 23187 (SAN 201-5161) Tel 804-253-5118; Toll free: 800-223-2584.

Inst Earth, *(Institute for Earth Education, The; 0-917011),* P.O. Box 288, Warrenville, IL 60555 (SAN 655-7449) Tel 312-393-3096; Dist. by: Pacific Pipeline, 19215 66th Ave. S., Kent, WA 98032 (SAN 208-2128) Tel 206-872-5523; Dist. by: Bookpeople, 2929 Fifth St., Berkeley, CA 94710 (SAN 168-9517) Tel 415-549-3030.

Inst Ecological, *(Institute for Ecological Policies; 0-937786),* 9208 Christopher St., Fairfax, VA 22031 (SAN 215-6598).

†Inst Econ Finan, *(Institute for Economic & Financial Research; 0-86654; 0-918968),* Subs. of American Classical College, 607 McKnight St., NW, Albuquerque, NM 87102 (SAN 662-0450); Dist. by: American Classical College Pr., P.O. Box 4526, Albuquerque, NM 87196 (SAN 201-2618) Tel 505-843-7749; *CIP.*

†Inst Econ Pol, *(Institute for Economic & Political World Strategic Studies; 0-930008; 0-86722),* Affil. of American Classical College, P.O. Box 4526, Sta. A, Albuquerque, NM 87106 (SAN 210-4431) Tel 505-843-7749; 607 McKnight St., Albuquerque, NM 87102 (SAN 662-0469); *CIP.*

†Inst Econmetric, *(Institute for Econometric Research; 0-917604),* 3471 N. Federal Hwy., Suite 350, Ft. Lauderdale, FL 33306 (SAN 209-2174) Tel 305-563-9000; Toll free: 800-327-6720; *CIP.*

Inst Ed Leadership
See Inst Educ Lead

Inst Ed Management, *(Institute for Educational Management; 0-934222),* Harvard Graduate School of Education, 339 Gutman Library, Six Appian Way, Cambridge, MA 02138 (SAN 213-5175) Tel 617-495-2655.

Inst Educ Lead, *(Institute for Educational Leadership; 0-937846),* 1001 Connecticut Ave. NW, Suite 310, Washington, DC 20036 (SAN 225-7823) Tel 202-676-5900.

Inst Effect Mgmt, *(Institute for Effective Management; 0-914804),* Chapman Rd., Fountainville, PA 18923 (SAN 206-4553) Tel 215-345-0265.

Inst Elect Eng, *(Institution of Electrical Engineers; 0-85296),* PPL/IEEE Service Ctr., 445 Hoes Ln., Piscataway, NJ 08854-4150 (SAN 213-0882) Tel 201-981-0060.

Inst Electrical, *(Institute of Electrical & Electronics Engineers; 0-87942),* 345 E. 47th St., New York, NY 10017 (SAN 203-8064) Tel 212-705-7900; Orders to: IEEE Service Ctr., 445 Hoes Ln., Piscataway, NJ 08854 (SAN 203-8072) Tel 201-981-1393.

Inst Energy, *(Institutes for Energy Development, Inc.; 0-89419),* 101 SW 25th St., Oklahoma City, OK 73107 (SAN 209-9322) Tel 405-232-2801.

Inst Environ
See Inst for Environ

Inst Environ Sci, *(Institute of Environmental Sciences; 0-915414),* 940 E. Northwest Hwy., Mt. Prospect, IL 60056 (SAN 209-2077) Tel 312-255-1561.

Inst Evolutionary, *(Institute for Evolutionary Research; 0-938710),* 200 Park Ave., Suite 303 East, New York, NY 10166 (SAN 215-8760) Tel 212-687-0281; Orders to: P.O. Box 7404, Charlottesville, VA 22906 (SAN 662-0477) Tel 804-979-1270; Dist. by: DeVorss & Co., 1046 Princeton Dr., P.O. Box 550, Marina del Rey, CA 90294 (SAN 168-9886) Tel 213-870-7478; Dist. by: Samuel Weiser, Inc., P.O. Box 612, York Beach, ME 03910 (SAN 202-9588) Tel 207-363-4393.

Inst Fam Res
See Ed-U Pr

Inst Finan Educ, *(Institute of Financial Education; 0-912857),* Affil. of U.S. League of Savings Institutions, 111 E. Wacker Dr., Chicago, IL 60601 (SAN 224-1382) Tel 312-644-3100; Dist. by: Caroline Hse., 2S, 250 Frontenac Rd., Naperville, IL 60540 (SAN 211-2280) Tel 312-983-6400.

Inst Food & Develop, *(Institute for Food & Development Policy; 0-935028),* 1885 Mission St., San Francisco, CA 94103 (SAN 213-327X) Tel 415-864-8555.

Inst for Environ, *(Institute for Environmental Studies),* 3400 Walnut St, Philadelphia, PA 19104 (SAN 226-5648).

Inst for Info
See Basil Hill Inc

Inst for the arts, *(Rice Univ., Institute for the Arts; 0-914412),* P.O. Box 1892, Houston, TX 77251 (SAN 218-933X) Tel 713-527-4858; Orders to: Menil Foundation, Institute for the Arts Catalogue Orders, 1427 Branard, Houston, TX 77006 (SAN 662-1260).

Inst for Urban & Regional, *(Institute for Urban & Regional Studies, Washington Univ.),* P.O. Box 1051, St. Louis, MO 63130 (SAN 212-2812).

†Inst Foreign Policy Anal, *(Institute for Foreign Policy Analysis, Inc.; 0-89549),* 675 Massachusetts Ave., Central Plaza Bldg. 10th Flr., Cambridge, MA 02139 (SAN 210-444X) Tel 617-492-2116; Dist. by: Pergamon Brassey's International Defence Pubs., Maxwell House, Fairview Pk., Elmsford, NY 10523 (SAN 200-741X) Tel 914-592-7700; *CIP.*

Inst Found Employ
See Intl Found Employ

Inst Future, *(Institute for the Future),* 2740 Sand Hill Rd., Menlo Park, CA 94025 (SAN 225-1892) Tel 415-854-6322.

Inst Gas Tech, *(Institute of Gas Technology; 0-910091),* 3424 S. State St., Chicago, IL 60616 (SAN 224-7631) Tel 312-567-3650.

Inst Gen Seman, *(Institute of General Semantics; 0-910780),* 163 Engle St., Englewood, NJ 07631 (SAN 203-8080) Tel 201-568-0551.

†Inst Gov Stud Berk, *(Univ. of California, Institute of Governmental Studies; 0-87772),* 109 Moses Hall, Berkeley, CA 94720 (SAN 202-7011) Tel 415-642-1428; Orders to: Univ. of California, Publications Office, 119 Moses Hall, Berkeley, CA 94720 (SAN 662-1686) Tel 415-642-5537; *CIP.*

Inst Hist Rev, *(Institute for Historical Review; 0-939484),* P.O. Box 1306, Torrance, CA 90505 (SAN 220-1275) Tel 213-533-8108.

Inst Hist Rev *Imprint of* **Noontide**

Inst Human Growth, *(Institute for Human Growth & Awareness, The; 0-87852),* P.O. Box 6695, San Jose, CA 95150 (SAN 202-3636) Tel 408-275-1911.

Inst Human Soc, *(Institute for Human Potential & Social Development; 0-916843),* P.O. Box 3071, Dept. L-7, Iowa City, IA 52244 (SAN 653-8762) Tel 319-354-6910; 1530 Bladenburg Rd., Box 29, Ottumwa, IA 52501 (SAN 653-8770) Tel 515-682-4305.

†Inst Humane, *(Institute for Humane Studies, Inc.; 0-89617),* P.O. Box 1149, Menlo Park, CA 94025 (SAN 214-123X) Tel 415-323-2464; 1177 University Dr., Menlo Park, CA 94025 (SAN 669-1072); Orders to: P.O. Box 2256, Wichita, KS 67201 (SAN 214-1248) Tel 316-832-5604; *CIP.*

Inst Indp Study, *(Institute for Independent Study, Inc.; 0-938247),* 1609 Westover Hills Rd., Richmond, VA 23225 (SAN 661-4221) Tel 804-231-3451.

Inst Indus Eng, *(Institute of Industrial Engineers; 0-89806),* 25 Technology Pk., Norcross, GA 30092 (SAN 213-2338) Tel 404-449-0460.

Inst Info Mgmt, *(Institute for Information Management; 0-931900),* Pruneyard Towers, 1901 S. Boscom Ave., Suite 230, Campbell, CA 95008 (SAN 209-0686) Tel 408-559-6911.

†Inst Info Stud, *(Institute for Information Studies; 0-935294),* 200 Little Falls St., Suite 104, Falls Church, VA 22046 (SAN 215-6601); *CIP.*

Inst Inter Aud, *(Institute of Internal Auditors, Inc.; 0-89413),* 249 Maitland Ave., Altamonte Springs, FL 32701 (SAN 213-4411) Tel 305-830-7600. *Imprints:* Found Audit Res (Foundation for Auditability Research & Education, Incorporated).(Foundation for Auditability Research & Education, Inc.).

Inst Intl Eco, *(Institute for International Economics; 0-88132),* 11 Dupont Cir., NW, Pubns., Dept., Washington, DC 20036 (SAN 293-2865) Tel 202-328-0583.

Inst Intl Educ, *(Institute of International Education; 0-87206),* 809 United Nations Plaza, New York, NY 10017 (SAN 202-702X) Tel 212-984-5410.

Inst Jesuit, *(Institute of Jesuit Sources, The; 0-912422),* Fusz Memorial, St. Louis Univ., 3700 W. Pine Blvd., St. Louis, MO 63108 (SAN 202-7038) Tel 314-652-5737.

Inst Labor & Indus
See U of Mich Inst Labor

Inst Labor & Mental, *(Institute for Labor & Mental Health; 0-935933),* 3137 Telegraph Ave., Oakland, CA 94609 (SAN 696-8643) Tel 415-482-0805.

Inst Lesbian, *(Institute of Lesbian Studies; 0-934903),* P.O. Box 60242, Palo Alto, CA 94306 (SAN 696-5059) Tel 415-941-3722; Dist. by: Inland Bk. Co., P.O. Box 261, 22 Hemingway Ave., East Haven, CT 06512 (SAN 200-4151) Tel 203-467-4257; Dist. by: Bookpeople, 2929 Fifth St., Berkeley, CA 94710 (SAN 168-9517) Tel 415-549-3030.

Inst Libs Inter
See Somerton Pr

Inst Local Self Re, *(Institute for Local Self-Reliance; 0-917582),* 2425 18th St., NW, Washington, DC 20009 (SAN 217-7919) Tel 202-232-4108.

Inst Logo, *(Institute of Logotherapy Pr.; 0-917867),* 2000 Dwight Way, Berkeley, CA 94794 (SAN 657-095X) Tel 415-845-2522.

Inst Math, *(Institute of Mathematical Statistics; 0-940600),* 3401 Investment Blvd., No.7, Hayward, CA 94545 (SAN 218-558X) Tel 415-783-8141.

Inst Math Philo Pr, *(Institute for Mathematical Philosophy Pr.; 0-931441),* P.O. Box 3410, Annapolis, MD 21403 (SAN 683-1931) Tel 301-267-0811.

Inst Mediaeval Mus, *(Institute of Mediaeval Music; 0-912024; 0-931902),* P.O. Box 295, Henryville, PA 18332 (SAN 658-0955) Tel 717-629-1278.

Inst Medit Affairs, *(Institute for Mediterranean Affairs),* 27 E. 62nd St, New York, NY 10028 (SAN 225-6789) Tel 212-988-1725.

Inst Meeting Con Mgmt, *(Institute for Meeting and Conference Management; 0-931273),* P.O. Box 14097, Washington, DC 20044 (SAN 681-9923) Tel 703-281-0932.

Inst Mennonite, *(Institute of Mennonite Studies; 0-936273),* 3003 Benham Ave., Elkhart, IN 46517 (SAN 697-8835) Tel 219-295-3726.

Inst Mgmt & Labor, *(Institute of Management & Labor Relations),* Industrial Relations & Human Resources Dept., P.O Box 231, Ryders Lane, Cook Campus, New Brunswick, NJ 08903 (SAN 215-8779).

Inst Mgmt Sci, *(Institute of Management Sciences, The),* 290 Westminster St., Providence, RI 02903 (SAN 224-1390) Tel 401-274-2525.

Inst Mid East & North Africa, *(Institute of Middle Eastern & North African Affairs; 0-934484),* P.O. Box 1674, Hyattsville, MD 20788 (SAN 213-8506).

Inst Mind Behavior, *(Institute of Mind & Behavior; 0-930195),* P.O. Box 522, Village Sta., New York, NY 10014 (SAN 691-9618) Tel 718-783-1471.

Inst Mod Lang, *(Institute of Modern Languages; 0-88499; 0-8325),* Div. of Voluntad Pub., Inc., 4255 W. Touhy, Lincolnwood, IL 60646 (SAN 662-0493) Tel 312-679-5500; Dist. by: National Textbook Co., 4255 W. Touhy Ave., Lincolnwood, IL 60646 (SAN 169-2208) Tel 312-679-5500.

Inst Motiv Devel, *(Institute of Motivational Development; 0-9616032; 0-939701),* 2200 S. Main St., Lombard, IL 60148 (SAN 697-8851) Tel 312-627-5000.

†Inst Palestine, *(Institute for Palestine Studies; 0-88728),* P.O. Box 25697, Georgetown Sta., Washington, DC 20007 (SAN 207-611X) Tel 202-342-3990; Toll free: 800-874-3614; Dist. by: Ubiquity Distributors, 1050 E. Fourth St., Brooklyn, NY 11230 (SAN 200-7428) Tel 718-789-3137; *CIP.*

Inst Paper Chem, *(Institute of Paper Chemistry; 0-87010),* P.O. Box 1039, Appleton, WI 54912 (SAN 203-8099) Tel 414-734-9251.

Inst Peace, *(Institute For Peace & Justice, Inc.; 0-912765),* 4144 Lindell Blvd., Suite 400, St. Louis, MO 63108 (SAN 282-7891) Tel 314-533-4445.

Inst People's Church, *(Institute for a People's Church; 0-9612114),* 1051 N. Rademacher, Detroit, MI 48209 (SAN 287-7414) Tel 313-841-5885.

Inst Pers Image, *(Institute of Personal Image Consultants),* c/o Image Industry Pubns., 10 Bay St. Landing, No. 7K, Staten Island, NY 10301-2511 (SAN 224-1412); Dist. by: Fairchild Bks., 7 E. 12th St., New York, NY 10003 (SAN 201-470X) Tel 212-741-4280.

†Inst Personality & Ability, *(Institute for Personality & Ability Testing, Inc.; 0-918296),* P.O. Box 188, Champaign, IL 61820 (SAN 209-3197) Tel 217-352-4739; *CIP.*

Inst Philosophy, *(Institute of Philosophy; 0-930583),* P.O. Box 3705, Myrtle Beach, SC 29577 (SAN 677-1351).

†Inst Policy Stud, *(Institute for Policy Studies; 0-89758),* 1901 Q St., NW, Washington, DC 20009 (SAN 212-1026) Tel 202-234-9382; *CIP.*

Inst Political Res, *(Institute of Political Research, The; 0-935543),* 104 Meays Dr., Syracuse, NY 13209 (SAN 696-2505) Tel 315-635-7045.

Inst Polynesian, *(Institute for Polynesian Studies, The; 0-939154),* Brigham Young Univ., Hawaii Campus, Laie, HI 96762 (SAN 219-1911) Tel 508-293-3667; Brigham Young Univ., Box 1829, ; Dist. by: University of Hawaii Press, 2840 Kolowalu St., Honolulu, HI 96822 (SAN 202-5353) Tel 808-948-8697.

Inst Pr, *(Institute Press; 0-931976),* 2210 Wilshire Blvd., Suite 171, Santa Monica, CA 90403 (SAN 211-321X) Tel 213-828-6541.

Inst Preserv Wealth, *(Institute for the Preservation of Wealth, The; 0-938689),* 268 Greenwood Ave., Bethel, CT 06801 (SAN 661-5708) Tel 203-748-2036; P.O. Box 60, Bethel, CT 06801 (SAN 661-5716); Dist. by: Silver & Gold Report, 268 Greenwood Ave., Bethel, CT 06801 (SAN 221-9972).

Inst Product, *(Institute for Product Safety; 0-938830),* P.O. Box 1931, Durham, NC 27702 (SAN 216-0439).

Inst Psych Inc, *(Institute of Psychorientology; 0-913343),* P.O. Box 2249, 1110 Cedar, Laredo, TX 78044-2249 (SAN 283-118X) Tel 512-722-6391.

Inst Pub GA
See ILCI

Inst Pub Mgmt, *(Institute for Public Management; 0-935807),* Div. of Peter Warner Assocs., 550 W. Jackson Blvd., Suite 365, Chicago, IL 60606 (SAN 238-8251) Tel 312-559-0515.

Inst Public Adm, *(Institute of Public Administration; 0-913824),* 55 W. 44th St., New York, NY 10036 (SAN 203-8102) Tel 212-661-2540.

Inst Qual Hum Life, *(Institute for Quality in Human Life; 0-939630),* 6335 N. Delaware Ave., Portland, OR 97217 (SAN 206-4367) Tel 503-289-6136.

Inst Rat Liv, *(Institute for Rational Living),* 1162 Beacon St., Brookline, MA 02146 (SAN 209-5068) Tel 617-739-5063.

Inst Rational-Emotive, *(Institute for Rational-Emotive Therapy; 0-917476),* 45 E. 65th St., New York, NY 10021 (SAN 210-3079) Tel 212-535-0822.

†Inst Real Estate, *(Institute of Real Estate Management; 0-912104),* Affil. of National Assn. of Realtors, 430 N. Michigan Ave., Chicago, IL 60611-4090 (SAN 202-7046) Tel 312-661-1930; 1955 Estes Ave., Elk Grove Village, IL 60007 (SAN 650-034X); *CIP.*

Inst Recreation Res, *(Institute of Recreation Research & Service, Dept. of Leisure Studies & Services; 0-943272),* University of Oregon, Rm. 133, Esslinger Hall, Eugene, OR 97403 (SAN 219-0249) Tel 503-686-3396.

Inst Res Hist, *(Institute for Research in History, The; 0-913865),* 1133 Broadway, Rm. 923, New York, NY 10010 (SAN 286-780X) Tel 212-691-7110.

Inst Res Rheumatic
See Inst Rheumatic

Inst Resp Ed
See Inst Responsive

Inst Responsive, *(Institute for Responsive Education; 0-917754),* 605 Commonwealth Ave., Boston, MA 02215 (SAN 216-1451) Tel 617-353-3309.

Inst Rheumatic, *(Institute for Research of Rheumatic Diseases),* 2025 Broadway, 19C, New York, NY 10023 (SAN 271-048X) Tel 212-595-1368; P.O. Box 955, New York, NY 10023 (SAN 692-834X).

Inst Sci Res, *(Institute of Scientific Resources; 0-913651),* P.O. Box 636, Hawthorne, CA 90251 (SAN 286-1135) Tel 213-973-6954.

Inst Self Dev
See Mindbody Inc

Inst Sino-Amer, *(Institute of Sino-American Research; 0-913973),* 108 Shady Dr., Indiana, PA 15701 (SAN 241-5453) Tel 412-463-0513.

Inst Soc Ethics
See Hastings Ctr

†Inst Soc Res, *(Institute for Social Research Univ. of Michigan; 0-87944),* P.O. Box 1248, Ann Arbor, MI 48106-1248 (SAN 210-6035) Tel 313-764-7509; *CIP.*

Inst Soc Sci, *(Institute of Social Sciences & Arts, Inc.; 0-915165),* P.O. Box 5663, Johnson City, TN 37603 (SAN 289-9507) Tel 615-282-9023.

†Inst Socioecon, *(Institute for Socioeconomic Studies; 0-915312),* Airport Rd., White Plains, NY 10604 (SAN 235-6023) Tel 914-428-7400; *CIP.*

Inst Software Eng
See Inst Info Mgmt

Inst Southern Studies, *(Institute for Southern Studies),* 604 Chapel Hill St., Durham, NC 27701 (SAN 219-192X) Tel 919-688-8167; P.O. Box 531, Durham, NC 27702 (SAN 669-1080).

Inst Space-Time
See Lib Humane Sci

Inst Study Animal, *(Institute for the Study of Animal Problems; 0-937712),* 2100 L St., NW, Washington, DC 20037 (SAN 215-2088) Tel 202-452-1148.

Inst Study Diplomacy *Imprint of* **Geo U Sch For Serv**

Inst Study Hum Aware, *(Institute for the Study of Human Awareness; 0-937067),* P.O. Box 11068, Minneapolis, MN 55411 (SAN 658-6112) Tel 612-522-1585; 3931 Sheridan Ave., N, Minneapolis, MN 55412 (SAN 658-6120).

Inst Study Man, *(Institute for the Study of Man. Inc.),* 1133 13th St., NW, Suite Comm. 2, Washington, DC 20005 (SAN 213-523X) Tel 202-789-0231.

Inst Study Psych
See Inst Rational-Emotive

Inst Subs Abuse Res, *(Institute for Substance Abuse Research; 0-935847),* Subs. of Security Consultant Services, Inc., 1717 20th St., Suite 100, Vero Beach, FL 32960 (SAN 699-7759) Tel 305-569-3121; Orders to: P.O. Box 6837, Vero Beach, FL 32961-6837 (SAN 662-4065) Tel 305-569-3121.

Inst Tech Policy, *(Institute for Technology Policy in Development; 0-9616141),* SUNY, Graduate Physics Bldg. A-134, Stony Brook, NY 11733 (SAN 699-8968) Tel 516-246-8230.

Inst Theory Test, *(Institute For Theory Testing, The; 0-937719),* P.O. Box 635, Williamsville, NY 14221 (SAN 659-2503) Tel 716-688-5981; 60 Groton Dr., Williamsville, NY 14221 (SAN 659-2511).

Inst Trad Med, *(Institute for Traditional Medicine; 0-939163),* 2442 SE Sherman, Portland, OR 97214 (SAN 662-8346) Tel 503-233-1324.

Inst Tuberculosis, *(Institution for Tuberculosis Research, Univ. of Illinois, Medical Ctr.; 0-915314),* 904 W. Adams St., Chicago, IL 60607 (SAN 207-1428) Tel 312-996-4688.

Inst Univ, *(Institute of Universal Faith; 0-916801),* P.O. Box 3732 Rd.3, Grove City, PA 16127 (SAN 654-5432) Tel 814-786-9085.

Inst Urban Des, *(Institute for Urban Design; 0-942468),* Main P.O. Box 105, Purchase, NY 10577 (SAN 264-1178) Tel 914-253-9341.

Inst Urban Studies, *(Institute of Urban Studies, The Univ. of Texas at Arlington; 0-936440),* P.O. Box 19588, Arlington, TX 76019 (SAN 207-5253) Tel 817-273-3071.

Inst Vaishnava, *(Institute for Vaishnava Studies, The; 0-936979),* 42 Francis Ave., No. 3, Cambridge, MA 02138 (SAN 658-7968) Tel 617-498-4075.

Inst World Order
See World Policy

Institute Pr
See ILCI

Instituto Desarrollo, *(Instituto Para El Desarrollo Del Derecho, Inc.; 0-914939),* Calle Antolin Nin 469, Hato Rey, PR 00918 (SAN 289-2502) Tel 809-790-7150.

†**Instru Soc,** *(Instrument Society of America; 0-87664; 1-55617),* P.O. Box 12277, 67 Alexander Dr., Research Triangle Park, NC 27709 (SAN 202-7054) Tel 919-549-8411; CIP.

Instruct Object
See IOX Asses Assocs

Instruct Res, *(Instructional Resources Inc.; 0-938026),* P.O. Box 3452, Tallahassee, FL 32315 (SAN 215-7799) Tel 904-385-2546.

Instruct Tech, *(Instructional Technologies, Inc.; 0-935115),* P.O. Box 828, Plymouth, MI 48170 (SAN 695-2666) Tel 313-565-7053.

Instructional Aides Inc
See Info Aids

Instructivision, *(Instructivision, Inc.; 0-938797),* 3 Regent St., Livingston, NJ 07039 (SAN 661-5090) Tel 201-992-9081.

Instructo *Imprint of McGraw*

Instructor Bks, *(Instructor Books),* 545 Fifth Ave., New York, NY 10017 (SAN 669-6813); Orders to: P.O. Box 6177, Duluth, MN 55806 (SAN 699-5810).

Instrumental Co, *(Instrumentalist Co.),* 200 Northfield Rd., Northfield, IL 60093 (SAN 203-7033) Tel 312-446-5000; Toll free: 800-323-5559.

Insur Indus, *(Insurance Industries Publishing Co.; 0-918767),* 17462 Parker Dr., Tustin, CA 92680 (SAN 657-355X) Tel 714-731-3389.

Insur Info, *(Insurance Information Institute; 0-932387),* 110 William St., New York, NY 10038 (SAN 271-1192).

Insurance Achiev, *(Insurance Achievement, Inc.; 0-88171),* 7330 Highland Rd., Baton Rouge, LA 70808 (SAN 264-1186); Toll free: 800-535-3042.

Inswinger, *(Inswinger, Inc.; 0-9608170),* 5580 La Jolla Blvd., Suite 418, La Jolla, CA 92037 (SAN 238-826X).

Int Test Eval, *(International Test & Evaluation Assn.),* 5641 Burke Centre Pkwy, Burke, VA 22015 (SAN 689-6898) Tel 703-425-8522.

Intecon MA, *(Intecon; 0-9617127),* Div. of International Technology Consultants, Inc., 16 Chauncy St., Apt. G, Cambridge, MA 02138 (SAN 662-6769) Tel 617-868-0722.

Integ Energy, *(Integrated Energy Systems; 0-9608358),* Div. of Edith Shedd & Assocs., Inc., Rte. 2, Box 61A1, Monroe, GA 30655 (SAN 240-6802) Tel 404-267-3534.

Integ Pr, *(Integration Pr.; 0-9609928),* c/o H. Newton Malony, 135 N. Oakland, Pasadena, CA 91101 (SAN 271-1257) Tel 818-584-5528.

†**Integral Yoga Pubns,** *(Integral Yoga Pubns.; 0-932040),* Satchidananda Ashram-Yogaville, Rte. 1, Box 172, Buckingham, VA 23921 (SAN 285-0338) Tel 804-969-4801; CIP.

Integrated Ed Assoc, *(Integrated Education Assocs.; 0-912008),* Univ. of Massachusetts, Schl. of Education, Amherst, MA 01003 (SAN 203-8129) Tel 413-545-0327.

Integrated Excel Pr, *(Integrated Excellence Pr.; 0-938383),* P.O. Box 1085, Bemidji, MN 56601 (SAN 661-4507); Rte. 2, P.O. Box 170, Becida, MN 56625 (SAN 661-4515) Tel 218-854-7300.

Integrated Pr, *(Integrated Press; 0-9610310),* 526 Comstock Dr., Tiburon, CA 94920 (SAN 263-2403) Tel 415-435-2446.

Integrity, *(Integrity Pr.; 0-918048),* 3888 Morse Rd., Columbus, OH 43219 (SAN 210-2145) Tel 614-471-2759.

Integrity Times, *(Integrity Times Pr.; 0-930131),* 118 Laidley St., San Francisco, CA 94131 (SAN 669-6864) Tel 415-647-3679; Dist. by: Bookpeople, 2929 Fifth St., Berkeley, CA 94710 (SAN 168-9517) Tel 415-549-3030.

Intel
See Intel Corp

Intel Corp, *(Intel Corp.; 0-917017; 1-55512),* 3065 Bowers Ave., SC6-60, Santa Clara, CA 95051 (SAN 277-1446) Tel 408-496-7973; Toll free: 800-548-4725.

Intel Machine, *(Intelligent Machine Co.; 0-937397),* 3813 N. 14th St., Arlington, VA 22201 (SAN 658-8727) Tel 703-528-9136.

Intent Ed Inc, *(Intentional Educations, Inc.; 0-9607970),* 341 Mt. Auburn St., Watertown, MA 02172 (SAN 239-6610) Tel 617-923-7707.

Inter-Am Safety, *(Inter-American Safety Council),* 33 Park Pl, Englewood, NJ 07631 (SAN 237-1847) Tel 201-871-0004.

Inter-Am Tropical, *(Inter-American Tropical Tuna Commission; 0-9603078),* P.O. Box 1529, La Jolla, CA 92093 (SAN 214-3143); Scripps Inst. of Oceanography, La Jolla, CA 92038 (SAN 680-0467).

†**Inter Am U Pr,** *(Inter American Univ. Pr.; 0-913480),* Call Box 5100, San German, PR 00753 (SAN 202-7062) Tel 809-892-5055; CIP.

Inter Comp Rec, *(International Computer Recovery; 0-912247),* 7708 Briarcliff Cts., Smithfield, TX 76180 (SAN 265-1505).

Inter-Crescent, *(Inter-Crescent Publishing Co., Inc.; 0-916400),* 12021 Nieta Dr., Garden Grove, CA 92640 (SAN 208-7006) Tel 714-537-1000.

Inter Design, *(Interior Design Bks.; 0-943370),* Div. of Cahners Publishing Co., 475 Park Ave. S., New York, NY 10016 (SAN 240-6810) Tel 212-686-0555; Dist. by: Van Nostrand Reinhold, Co., 115 Fifth Ave., New York, NY 10003 (SAN 202-5191) Tel 212-254-3232.

Inter-Hem Educ, *(Inter-Hemispheric Educ. Resource Ctr.; 0-911213),* P.O. Box 4506, Albuquerque, NM 87106 (SAN 275-0570) Tel 505-266-5009.

Inter-Noise
See Noise Control

Inter-Optics Pubns, *(Inter-Optics Pubns., Inc.; 0-935726),* P.O. Box 233, Ambler, PA 19002 (SAN 214-0403) Tel 215-641-0133.

Inter Print Pubs, *(Interstate Printers & Pubs., Inc.; 0-8134),* 19 N. Jackson St., Danville, IL 61832 (SAN 206-6548) Tel 217-446-0500; Toll free: 800-843-4774; P.O. Box 50, Danville, IL 61834-0050 (SAN 658-0998).

Inter Pub, *(Interdimensional Publishing; 0-932389),* Div. of Interdimensional Productions, P.O. Box 41173, Nashville, TN 37204 (SAN 687-1364) Tel 615-790-2818; Dist. by: New Leaf Book Dist. Co., 1020 White St., SW, Atlanta, GA 30310 (SAN 169-1449) Tel 415-658-3453; Dist. by: Starlite Dist., P.O. Box 20729, Reno, NV 89515 (SAN 200-7789) Tel 702-359-5676.

Inter-Religious Task, *(Inter-Religious Task Force for Social Analysis; 0-936476),* 361 Athol Ave., Oakland, CA 94606 (SAN 216-2563).

Inter Res Corp, *(Interamerican Research Corp.; 0-9614035),* 2030 N. 53rd St., Milwaukee, WI 53208 (SAN 683-8049) Tel 414-267-3389.

Inter-Sellf, *(Inter-Sellf Inc.; 0-932127),* P.O. Box 55759, Seattle, WA 98155 (SAN 686-5186) Tel 206-742-8244; Dist. by: Pacific Pipeline Inc., 19215 66th Ave. S., Kent, WA 98032 (SAN 208-2128) Tel 206-872-5523; Dist. by: Baker & Taylor, 50 Kirby Ave., Somerville, NJ 08876 (SAN 169-4901).

Inter-Ski, *(Inter-Ski Services, Inc.; 0-931636),* P.O. Box 3635, Georgetown Sta., Washington, DC 20007 (SAN 221-0622) Tel 202-342-0886.

Inter Soc Drama, *(International Society of Dramatists; 0-934131),* P.O. Box 1310, Miami, FL 33153 (SAN 693-2681) Tel 305-756-8313.

Inter-Travel Comms, *(Inter-Travel Communications Inc.; 0-933615),* P.O. Box 12765, Jackson, MS 39211 (SAN 692-4670) Tel 601-957-3642.

†**Inter-Varsity,** *(Inter-Varsity Pr.; 0-87784; 0-8308),* Div. of Inter-Varsity Christian Fellowship of the USA, P.O. Box 1400, Downers Grove, IL 60515 (SAN 202-7089) Tel 312-964-5700; Toll free: 800-843-7225; CIP.

Interaction Bk Co, *(Interaction Bk. Co.; 0-939603),* 162 Windsor Ln., New Brighton, MN 55112 (SAN 663-5970) Tel 612-631-1693.

InterActive, *(InterActive Pubns.; 0-917015),* 2811 Wilshire Blvd., Suite 590, Santa Monica, CA 90403 (SAN 655-1297) Tel 213-829-0516.

†**Interbk Inc,** *(Interbook, Inc.; 0-913456; 0-89192),* 131 Varick St., 2nd Fl., New York, NY 10013 (SAN 202-7070) Tel 212-691-7248; CIP.

Interbook, *(Interbook Inc.; 0-946609),* Subs. of Haynes Pubns., 861 Lawrence Dr., Newbury Park, CA 91320 (SAN 662-3034) Tel 805-498-6703; Orders to: 14895 E. 14th St., Suite 370, San Leandro, CA 94577 (SAN 662-3042) Tel 415-352-9221.

Interchange, *(Interchange, Inc.; 0-916966),* P.O. Box 16012, St. Louis Park, MN 55416 (SAN 207-2386) Tel 612-929-6669.

Intercoll Studies, *(Intercollegiate Studies Institute, Inc.),* 14 S. Bryn Mawr Ave., Bryn Mawr, PA 19010 (SAN 226-577X).

Intercont Press, *(Intercontinental Press; 0-933142),* P.O. Box 565, Auburn, AL 36830 (SAN 281-8167) Tel 205-887-5297; Orders to: Intercontinental Press, Box 565, Auburn, AL 36830 (SAN 281-8175) Tel 205-887-5297.

Intercontinental Pubns, *(Intercontinental Pubns.),* 25 Sylvan Rd. S., P.O. Box 5017, Westport, CT 06881 (SAN 208-9572) Tel 203-226-7463.

Intercult Network
See Intercult Pr

Intercult Pr, *(Intercultural Pr., Inc.; 0-933622),* P.O. Box 768, Yarmouth, ME 04096 (SAN 212-6699) Tel 207-846-5168.

INTEREG, *(International Regulations Publishing & Distributing Organization; 0-940394),* Dist. by: Labelmaster, 5724 N. Pulaski Rd., Chicago, IL 60646 (SAN 218-480X).

Interface Assocs, *(Inter/Face Assocs., Inc.; 0-938135),* 62 Washington St., Middletown, CT 06457 (SAN 661-177X) Tel 203-344-1046; Toll free: 800-433-1116.

Intergalactic NJ, *(Intergalactic Publishing Co.; 0-936918),* Div. of Regal Communications Corp., P.O. Box 5013, Cherry Hill, NJ 08034 (SAN 213-988X) Tel 609-665-7577.

Interhouse Pub, *(Interhouse Publishing; 0-932380),* 457 Highland, Elmhurst, IL 60126 (SAN 221-0576).

Interiors, *(Interiors by Arden; 0-934892),* 1924 Swallow Ln., Carlsbad, CA 92008 (SAN 213-2540) Tel 619-931-1295.

†**Interland Pub,** *(Interland Publishing, Inc.; 0-87989),* 799 Broadway, New York, NY 10003 (SAN 203-8145) Tel 212-673-8280; CIP.

Interlingual, *(Interlingual Institute; 0-917848),* Box 126, Canal St. Sta., New York, NY 10013 (SAN 209-9330) Tel 212-929-0264.

Intermarket, *(Intermarket Publishing Corp.; 0-937453),* 401 S. LaSalle St., No. 1100, Chicago, IL 60605 (SAN 658-8751) Tel 312-922-4300.

Intermed Eater, *(Intermediate Eater Publishing Company; 0-914687),* Box 1281, Bellevue, WA 98009 (SAN 289-1697); Dist. by: Pacific Pipeline, 19215 66th Ave. S., Kent, WA 98032 (SAN 208-2128) Tel 206-872-5523P.O. Box 3711, Seattle, WA 98124 (SAN 289-1719).

Intermedia, *(Intermedia, Inc.; 0-910788),* 434 Woodward Rd., Nassau, NY 12123 (SAN 206-6947).

Intermedia WA, *(Intermedia, Inc.; 0-937889),* 1600 Dexter Ave., N., Seattle, WA 98109 (SAN 659-4735) Tel 206-282-7262. Do not confuse with Intermedia, Nassau, NY.

Intermediate Tech, *(Intermediate Technology Development Group of North America; 0-942850),* P.O. Box 337, Croton-on-Hudson, NY 10520 (SAN 218-4303) Tel 914-271-6500.

Intermntn Arts, *(Intermountain Arts & Crafts; 0-9605840),* Rte. 2, Box 2042, Burney, CA 96013 (SAN 216-5996) Tel 916-335-4330.

Intermtn Air, *(Intermountain Air Press; 0-914680),* 171 S. Second E., Preston, ID 83263 (SAN 206-5428).

Internatl Comms, *(International Communications Industries Assn.),* 3150 Spring St., Fairfax, VA 22031 (SAN 224-6376) Tel 703-273-7200.

Interp Mktg Prods, *(Interpretive Marketing Products; 0-936023),* Div. of Gibco, Inc., 490 N. 31st St., Suite 108, Billings, MT 59101 (SAN 696-8651) Tel 406-248-3555; Orders to: P.O. Box 21697, Billings, MT 59104 (SAN 662-3891) Tel 406-248-3555.

Interpersonal Comm, *(Interpersonal Communication Programs, Inc.; 0-917340),* 715 Florida, Suite 209, Minneapolis, MN 55426 (SAN 208-7057) Tel 612-871-7388.

Interpharm, *(Interpharm Pr., Inc.; 0-935184),* P.O. Box 530, Prairie View, IL 60069 (SAN 295-3374) Tel 312-459-8480.

Interport U S A, *(Interport USA, Inc.; 0-932331),* P.O. Box 02009, Portland, OR 97202 (SAN 686-7634) Tel 503-771-6804; Toll free: 800-233-5729.

Interpretive Pubns, *(Interpretive Pubns., Inc.; 0-936478),* Box 1383, Flagstaff, AZ 86002-1383 (SAN 221-4830) Tel 602-525-1934.

Intersoc Comm Path Info, *(Intersociety Committee Pathology Information; 0-937888),* 4733 Bethesda Ave., Suite 735, Bethesda, MD 20814 (SAN 205-0072) Tel 301-656-2944.

Interspace Bks, *(Interspace Bks.; 0-930061),* 4500 Chesapeake St., NW, Washington, DC 20016 (SAN 669-8913) Tel 202-363-9082.

Interstate
See Inter Print Pubs

Interstate Info, *(Interstate Information, Inc.; 0-939451),* P.O. Box 38548, Houston, TX 77238-8548 (SAN 663-3730); 7503 Greenlawn Dr., Houston, TX 77088 (SAN 663-3749) Tel 713-847-1152.

Interstate Piano, *(Interstate Piano Co.; 0-9604092),* 4001 N. Interstate Ave., Portland, OR 97227 (SAN 214-0829) Tel 503-288-2600.

Intersystems, *(Intersystems Software, Inc.; 0-924695),* 62 Bethpage Rd., Hicksville, NY 11801 (SAN 284-298X) Tel 516-367-3776.

Intersystems Pubns, *(Intersystems Pubns; 0-914105),* 401 Victor Way, No. 3, Salinas, CA 93907 (SAN 237-9619).

Intertec Pub, *(Intertec Publishing Corp.; 0-87288),* Subs. of Macmillan, Inc., P.O. Box 12901, Overland Park, KS 66212 (SAN 670-8463) Tel 913-888-4664; Toll free: INTERTEC OLPK.

†**Intertxt AK,** *(Intertext; 0-912767),* 2633 E. 17th Ave., Anchorage, AK 99508 (SAN 282-8030); *CIP.*

†**Interurban,** *(Interurban Pr.; 0-916374; 0-87046),* P.O. Box 6444, Glendale, CA 91205 (SAN 207-9593) Tel 818-240-9130; *CIP.*

Interurbans
See Interurban

Intervale Pub Co, *(Intervale Publishing Co., Inc.; 0-932400),* Box 777, Meredith, NH 03253 (SAN 211-9633) Tel 603-284-7726.

Interweave, *(Interweave Pr., Inc.; 0-934026),* 306 N. Washington Ave., Loveland, CO 80537 (SAN 214-3151) Tel 303-669-7672; Toll free: 800-272-2193.

Interwood Pr, *(Interwood Pr.; 0-9610376),* 3562 Interwood Ave., Cincinnati, OH 45220 (SAN 264-1224) Tel 513-751-5239; Dist. by: National Art Education Assn., 1916 Association Dr., Reston, VA 22091 (SAN 203-7084) Tel 703-860-8000.

Intl Advertising Assn, *(International Advertising Assn.),* 475 Fifth Ave., New York, NY 10017 (SAN 224-6120) Tel 212-684-1583.

Intl Arabian, *(International Arabian Horse Assn.),* P.O. Box 33696, Denver, CO 80233 (SAN 224-1447) Tel 303-450-4774.

Intl Art Alliance, *(International Art Alliance, Incorporated; 0-943488),* P.O. Box 1608, Largo, FL 34294 (SAN 240-6829) Tel 813-581-7328.

Intl Arts & Sci
See M E Sharpe

†**Intl Assess,** *(International Assn. of Assessing Officers; 0-88329),* 1313 E. 60th St., Chicago, IL 60637-9990 (SAN 205-0277) Tel 312-947-2069; Orders to: Prepaid, P.O. Box 88874, Chicago, IL 60680-1874 (SAN 691-9529) Tel 312-947-2044; *CIP.*

Intl Assn Busn Comm, *(International Assn. of Business Communicators; 0-943372),* 870 Market St., Suite 940, San Francisco, CA 94102 (SAN 224-893X) Tel 415-433-3400.

†**Intl Assn Chiefs Police,** *(International Assn. of Chiefs of Police; 0-88269),* P.O. Box 6010, 13 Firstfield Rd., Gaithersburg, MD 20760 (SAN 211-5301) Tel 301-948-0922; *CIP.*

Intl Assn Energy Econ, *(International Association of Energy Economists),* 1133 15 St., NW, No. 620, Washington, DC 20005 (SAN 224-1501) Tel 202-293-5913.

Intl Assn Housing Sci, *(International Assn. for Housing Science),* P.O. Box 340254, Coral Gables, FL 33134 (SAN 271-2105) Tel 305-448-3532.

Intl Assn Hydro Energy, *(International Association for Hydrogen Energy),* Univ. of Miami, 219 McArthur Hall, Engineering Bldg., Coral Gables, FL 33146 (SAN 283-1872) Tel 305-284-4666; P.O. Box 248266, Coral Gables, FL 33124 (SAN 650-1117).

Intl Assn Milk, *(International Assn. of Milk, Food, & Environmental Sanitarians, Inc.),* P.O. Box 701, Ames, IA 50010 (SAN 224-7437) Tel 515-232-6699; Toll free: 800-525-5223.

Intl Assn Schools, *(International Assn. of Schls. of Social Work; 0-931638),* c/o Council on Social Work Education, 111 Eighth Ave., New York, NY 10011 (SAN 692-8358).

Intl Assn Trichologists, *(International Assn. of Trichologists; 0-9614548),* 37320 22nd St., Kalamazoo, MI 49009 (SAN 224-4586) Tel 616-375-4430.

Intl Assoc Phys Sci Ocean, *(International Assn. for the Physical Sciences of the Ocean),* P.O. Box 7325, San Diego, CA 92107 (SAN 224-1463) Tel 619-222-3680.

Intl Av Consult, *(International Aviation Consultants, Inc.; 0-9609000),* 301 SW 30th Court, Miami, FL 33135 (SAN 240-9798).

†**Intl Aviation Pubs,** *(International Aviation Pubs., Inc.; 0-89100),* P.O. Box 36, Riverton, WY 82501-0036 (SAN 209-3189); Toll free: 800-443-9250; 1000 College View Dr., Riverton, WY 82501 (SAN 658-0173) Tel 307-856-1582; *CIP.* Imprints: Big Horn (Big Horn Book Co.).

Intl Basement, *(International Basement Tectonics Assn.; 0-916347),* 675 S. 400 E., Salt Lake City, UT 84111 (SAN 295-835X) Tel 518-474-5819.

Intl Better Life, *(International Better Life for All Movement Pr.; 0-915935),* 3972 Dallas, Warren, MI 48091 (SAN 294-0256) Tel 313-754-8134.

Intl Bk Co IL, *(International Book Co.; 0-910790),* 332 S. Michigan Ave., Chicago, IL 60604 (SAN 205-0250) Tel 312-427-4545.

†**Intl Bk Ctr,** *(International Bk. Ctr.; 0-917062; 0-86685),* 2007 Laurel Dr., P.O. Box 295, Troy, MI 48099 (SAN 169-4014) Tel 313-879-8436; *CIP.*

Intl Bk Ctr GA
See I B C A

Intl Bk Dist, *(International Book Distributors; 0-86732),* P.O. Box 180, Murray Hill Sta., New York, NY 10016 (SAN 206-6337).

Intl Bottled Water, *(International Bottled Water Assn.),* 113 N. Henry St., Alexandria, VA 22314 (SAN 224-649X) Tel 703-683-5213.

Intl Broadcasting Serv, *(International Broadcasting Services, Ltd.; 0-914941),* 825 Cherry Ln., Penn's Park, PA 18943 (SAN 289-2553) Tel 215-598-3298; Orders to: P.O. Box 300, Penn's Park, PA 18943 (SAN 662-216X) Tel 215-794-8252.

Intl Busn Aesthetics, *(International Business Aesthetics; 0-936757),* 2082 Michelson Dr., Suite 100, Irvine, CA 92715 (SAN 699-9034) Tel 714-476-3181.

Intl Busn Educ, *(International Business Education & Research Program, Graduate School of Business Administration; 0-939322),* IBEAR/GSBA, Univ. of Southern California, Los Angeles, CA 90089-1421 (SAN 216-5562) Tel 213-743-2272.

Intl Busn Inform, *(International Business Information Group; 0-934493),* Subs. of International ICS Group, P.O. Box 4082, Irvine, CA 92716 (SAN 693-8922) Tel 714-552-8494.

Intl Chi Snuff, *(International Chinese Snuff Bottle Society; 0-9609668),* 2601 N. Charles St., Baltimore, MD 21218 (SAN 271-311X); Dist. by: Paragon Book Gallery, 2130 Broadway, New York, NY 10023 (SAN 213-1986) Tel 212-496-2378.

Intl Child Fest, *(International Children's Festival, Inc., The; 0-939029),* 322 W. 57th St., Suite 43B, New York, NY 10019 (SAN 662-8478) Tel 212-245-3463.

†**Intl Childbirth,** *(International Childbirth Education Association; 0-934024),* P.O. Box 20048, Minneapolis, MN 55420 (SAN 224-3962) Tel 612-854-8660; *CIP.*

Intl City Mgr
See Intl City Mgt

†**Intl City Mgt,** *(International City Management Association; 0-87326),* 1120 G St., NW, Washington, DC 20005 (SAN 204-9120) Tel 202-626-4600; *CIP.*

Intl Co-Op, *(International Co-Operative Publishing House; 0-89974),* P.O. Box 245, Burtonsville, MD 20866 (SAN 213-6260).

Intl Comm Christ, *(International Community of Christ; 0-936202),* Pub. Dept. Chancellery, 643 Ralston St., Reno, NV 89503 (SAN 214-0373).

Intl Comm Ctr, *(International Communication Center; 0-933236),* Univ. of Washington, School of Communications DS-40, Seattle, WA 98195 (SAN 212-3614).

†**Intl Comm Rad Meas,** *(International Commission on Radiation Units & Measurements; 0-913394),* 7910 Woodmont Ave., Suite 1016, Bethesda, MD 20814 (SAN 202-7127) Tel 301-657-2652; *CIP.*

Intl Comm Serv, *(International Commercial Service; 0-935402),* Subs. of International ICS Group, P.O. Box 4082, Irvine, CA 92716 (SAN 281-8183) Tel 714-552-8494; Dist. by: IBMI-International Commercial Services, Univ. Town Ctr., P.O. Box 4082, Irvine, CA 92716 (SAN 281-8183) Tel 714-552-8494.

Intl Communications Imprint of Watts

Intl Computer, *(International Computer Programs, Inc.; 0-88094),* 9100 Keystone Crossing, Indianapolis, IN 46240 (SAN 218-7949) Tel 317-844-7461; P.O. Box 40946, Indianapolis, IN 46240 (SAN 699-5373).

Intl Conf Bldg Off, *(International Conference of Building Officials),* 5360 S. Workman Mill Rd., Whittier, CA 90601 (SAN 225-0713) Tel 213-699-0541.

Intl Cons Credit
See Intl Credit Assn

Intl Consumer Pub, *(International Consumer Publishing Co.; 0-938859),* P.O. Box 300128, Arlington, TX 76010 (SAN 661-7174); 2305 Stillmeadow Dr., Arlington, TX 76014 (SAN 661-7182) Tel 817-468-1350.

Intl Copper, *(International Copper Research Assn.; 0-943642),* 708 Third Ave., New York, NY 10017 (SAN 230-9858) Tel 212-697-9355.

Intl Coun Comp
See Intl Council Comp

Intl Coun Shop, *(International Council of Shopping Ctrs.; 0-913598),* 665 Fifth Ave., New York, NY 10022 (SAN 206-7412) Tel 212-421-8181.

Intl Coun Trad, *(International Council for Traditional Music),* Dept of Music, Columbia Univ., New York, NY 10027 (SAN 223-8934) Tel 212-280-5439.

Intl Council Comp, *(International Council for Computers in Education; 0-924667),* Univ. of Oregon, 1787 Agate St., Eugene, OR 97403 (SAN 296-7693) Tel 503-686-4414.

Intl Counseling Svcs, *(International Association of Counseling Services),* 5999 Stevenson Ave., Third Floor, Alexandria, VA 22304 (SAN 224-148X) Tel 703-820-4710.

Intl Crane, *(International Crane Foundation),* Rt. 1, Box 230 C, Shady Lane Rd., Baraboo, WI 53913 (SAN 224-165X) Tel 608-356-9462.

Intl Credit Assn, *(International Credit Assn.),* P.O. Box 27357, St. Louis, MO 63141-1757 (SAN 224-7003) Tel 314-991-3030; 243 N. Lindbergh Blvd., St. Louis, MO 63141-1757 (SAN 699-120X).

Intl Ctr Academy, *(International Center of the Academy for State & Local Government, The),* Academy for State & Local Government, 444 N. Capitol St., NW, Suite 349, Washington, DC 20001 (SAN 224-1080) Tel 202-638-1445.

Intl Ctr Arid & Semi-Arid, *(International Center for Arid & Semi-Arid Land Studies),* Div. of Texas Tech. Univ., P.O. Box 4620, Lubbock, TX 79409 (SAN 224-1609) Tel 806-742-2218.

Intl Ctr Creat Think, *(International Center for Creative Thinking),* 56 Harrison St., New Rochelle, NY 10801 (SAN 695-5363) Tel 914-632-4492; Toll free: 800-828-8285.

Intl Ctr Environment
See ICER Pr

Intl Ctr Law, *(International Center for Law in Development),* 777 United Nations Plaza, New York, NY 10017 (SAN 221-0592).

†**Intl Ctr Photo,** *(International Ctr. of Photography; 0-933642),* 1130 Fifth Ave., New York, NY 10028 (SAN 213-3296) Tel 212-860-1777; *CIP.*

Intl Ctr Spec Studies, *(International Ctr. for Special Studies; 0-934495),* 400 Hobron Ln., Suite 3502, Honolulu, HI 96815-1209 (SAN 693-8930) Tel 808-947-6473.

Intl Currency, *(International Currency Analysis, Inc.; 0-917645),* 7239 Ave. N, Brooklyn, NY 11234 (SAN 657-0968) Tel 718-531-3685.

Intl Defense & Aid, *(International Defense & Aid Fund for Southern Africa),* P.O. Box 17, Cambridge, MA 02138 (SAN 217-796X) Tel 617-491-8343.

Intl Design *Imprint of Stemmer Hse*

Intl Develop Ins. *See Intl Development*

Intl Development, *(International Development Institute; 0-89249),* Indiana University, 201 N. Indiana, Bloomington, IN 47405 (SAN 208-7030) Tel 812-335-8596.

Intl Diabetes Ctr *See Diabetes Ctr MN*

Intl Dialogue Pr, *(International Dialogue Pr.; 0-89881; 0-931364),* P.O. Box 1257, Davis, CA 95617 (SAN 212-3827) Tel 916-758-6500.

Intl Downtown, *(International Downtown Executives Assn.; 0-910473),* 915 15th St., NW, Suite 900, Washington, DC 20005 (SAN 223-890X) Tel 202-783-4963.

Intl DXers, *(International DXers Club of San Diego),* 1826 Cypress St., San Diego, CA 92194 (SAN 241-547X) Tel 619-429-9728.

Intl Educ Dev, *(International Educational Development, Inc.; 0-939420),* P.O. Box 7066, Silver Spring, MD 20910 (SAN 216-2571).

Intl Educ Servs, *(International Education Services; 0-935439),* 1537 Franklin St., San Francisco, CA 94109 (SAN 696-270X) Tel 415-775-2400.

Intl Educ Systems, *(International Educational Systems, Inc.; 0-934806),* 5521 W. 110th St., Chicago, IL 60653 (SAN 210-6248) Tel 312-423-1717.

Intl Electrical *See Inst Electrical*

Intl Enlightenment, *(International Enlightenment; 0-9616471),* P.O. Box 583, Fort Washington, PA 19034 (SAN 658-8808) Tel 215-885-0942; 37 Red Oak Rd., Oreland, PA 19275 (SAN 658-8816).

Intl Evang, *(International Evangelism Crusade, Inc.; 0-933470),* 14617 Victory Blvd., Suite 4, Van Nuys, CA 91411 (SAN 203-8153) Tel 818-989-5942; Orders to: P.O. Box 73, Van Nuys, CA 91408 (SAN 688-3966).

Intl Exhibit Foun *See Intl Exhibitions*

Intl Exhibitions, *(International Exhibitions Foundation; 0-88397),* 1700 Pennsylvania Ave., NW, Suite 580, Washington, DC 20006 (SAN 204-0964) Tel 202-737-4740.

Intl Fanorona, *(International Fanorona Association; 0-932329),* 278-A Meeting St., Charleston, SC 29401 (SAN 686-7626) Tel 803-722-2531.

Intl Fed Ageing, *(International Federation on Ageing),* 1909 K St. NW, Washington, DC 20049 (SAN 225-8889) Tel 202-662-4927.

Intl Fed Travel, *(International Federation of Women's Travel Organizations),* 7432 Caminito Carlotta, San Diego, CA 92120 (SAN 691-5094) Tel 619-287-0893.

Intl Fertility *See Fam Health Intl*

Intl Fertilizer, *(International Fertilizer Development Ctr.; 0-88090),* P.O. Box 2040, Muscle Shoals, AL 35662 (SAN 240-1150) Tel 205-381-6600.

Intl Film, *(International Film Bureau, Inc.; 0-8354),* 332 S. Michigan Ave., Chicago, IL 60604 (SAN 207-4931) Tel 312-427-4545.

Intl Fire Prot *See Intl Fire Serv*

Intl Fire Serv, *(International Fire Service Training Association; 0-87939),* Oklahoma State Univ., Stillwater, OK 74078 (SAN 204-1111) Tel 405-624-5723; Toll free: 800-654-4055.

Intl Found Biosocial Dev, *(International Foundation for Biosocial Development & Human Health; 0-934314),* 6 Lomond Ave., Spring Valley, NY 10977 (SAN 214-0381).

Intl Found Employ, *(International Foundation of Employee Benefit Plans; 0-89154),* P.O. Box 69, 18700 W. Bluemound Rd., Brookfield, WI 53008 (SAN 317-9214) Tel 414-786-6700.

Intl Franchise *See Intl Franchise Assn*

Intl Franchise Assn, *(International Franchise Assn.; 0-936898),* 1350 New York Ave., NW, Suite 900, Washington, DC 20005-4709 (SAN 214-3747) Tel 202-628-8000.

Intl Friend, *(International Friendship; 0-935340),* P.O. Box 248, Waxhaw, NC 28173 (SAN 213-5183) Tel 704-843-2185.

Intl Game Fish, *(International Game Fish Assn.; 0-935217),* 3000 E. Las Olas Blvd., Ft. Lauderdale, FL 33316-1616 (SAN 225-1876) Tel 305-467-0161.

Intl Gen Semantics, *(International Society for General Semantics; 0-918970),* 834 Mission St., 2nd flr., San Francisco, CA 94103 (SAN 203-8161) Tel 415-543-1747; P.O. Box 2469, San Francisco, CA 94126 (SAN 669-1315).

Intl General, *(International General; 0-88477),* P.O. Box 350, New York, NY 10013 (SAN 206-5436).

Intl Guatemala, *(International Society of Guatemala Collectors),* P.O. Box 246, Troy, NY 12181 (SAN 225-5952) Tel 518-271-7629.

Intl Hse Pubns, *(International Hse. Pubns.; 0-937127),* 2711 LBJ Freeway, Suite 122, Dallas, TX 75234 (SAN 658-5477) Tel 214-241-9991.

†**Intl Human Res,** *(International Human Resources Development Corp.; 0-934634; 0-88746),* 137 Newbury St., Boston, MA 02116 (SAN 220-2549) Tel 617-536-0202; Toll free: 800-327-6756; *CIP.*

Intl Ideas *See Coronet Bks*

Intl Imports, *(International Imports; 0-943832),* 8050 Webb Ave., North Hollywood, CA 91605-1504 (SAN 209-8202) Tel 818-768-0069.

Intl Info Mgmt Con, *(International Information Management Congress),* P.O. Box 34404, Bethesda, MD 20817 (SAN 224-8786) Tel 301-983-0604.

Intl Inst Adv Stud, *(International Institute for Advanced Studies; 0-940604),* 8000 Bonhomme Ave., Suite 403, Clayton, MO 63105 (SAN 218-4818).

Intl Inst Environment, *(International Institute for Environment & Development),* 1717 Massachusetts Ave., NW, Suite 302, Washington, DC 20036 (SAN 225-1779) Tel 202-462-0900.

Intl Inst Fin Res, *(International Institute For Financial Research; 0-933001),* 1930 Allen Dr., Jefferson City, MO 65101 (SAN 689-1519) Tel 314-636-3464.

Intl Inst Garibaldian, *(International Institute of Garibaldian Studies, Inc.),* 1025 Shadowlawn Way, Sarasota, FL 34242 (SAN 238-0137) Tel 813-349-0585.

Intl Inst Nat Health, *(International Institute of Natural Health Sciences, Inc.; 0-86664),* 7422 Mountjoy Dr., Huntington Beach, CA 92648 (SAN 216-258X).

Intl Inst Rural, *(International Institute of Rural Reconstruction),* 1775 Broadway, New York, NY 10019 (SAN 225-9710).

Intl Intertrade, *(International Intertrade Index Printing Consultants, Pubs.; 0-910794),* P.O. Box 636, Federal Square, Newark, NJ 07101 (SAN 202-7143) Tel 201-686-2382.

Intl Labour Office, *(International Labour Office; 92-2),* Washington Branch, 1750 New York Ave., NW, Suite 330, Washington, DC 20006 (SAN 203-817X) Tel 202-376-2137.

Intl Law Inst, *(International Law Institute; 0-935328),* 1330 Connecticut Ave. NW, Washington, DC 20036 (SAN 224-1676) Tel 202-463-7979.

Intl Law Libs, *(International Association of Law Libraries),* P.O. Box 5709, Washington, DC 20016-1309 (SAN 226-5818).

Intl League Human, *(International League for Human Rights),* 236 E. 46th St., New York, NY 10017 (SAN 226-5850).

Intl Learn Syst, *(International Learning Systems, Inc.),* 1715 Connecticut Ave., NW, Washington, DC 20009 (SAN 209-1615) Tel 202-232-4111.

Intl Liaison, *(International Liaison, United States Coordinating Center for Lay Missioners),* Affil. of U. S. Catholic Conference, 1234 Massachusetts Ave. NW, Washington, DC 20005 (SAN 234-7407) Tel 202-638-4197; 225 S. Euclid St., St. Louis, MO 63110 (SAN 669-1226); 2451 Ridge Rd., Berkeley, CA 94709 (SAN 669-1234).

Intl Lib, *(International Library Bk. Pubs., Inc.; 0-914250),* 7315 Wisconsin Ave., Suite 229, E., Bethesda, MD 20814 (SAN 202-7151) Tel 301-961-8850.

Intl Life Mess, *(International Life Message Inc.; 0-916075),* Nine Ruth Dr., New City, NY 10956 (SAN 294-846X) Tel 914-634-8980.

Intl Life Mgmt, *(International Assocs. for Life Management, Ltd.; 0-937515),* 5 Roble Rd., Suffern, NY 10901 (SAN 658-8786) Tel 914-354-7323.

Intl Linguistics, *(International Linguistics Corp.; 0-939990),* 401 W. 89th St., Kansas City, MO 64114 (SAN 220-2573) Tel 816-941-9797.

Intl Lrn Inst, *(International Learning Institute; 0-939311),* P.O. Box 60, Petaluma, CA 94952 (SAN 663-1533); 22 Wooddale Dr., Petaluma, CA 94952 (SAN 663-1541) Tel 707-763-1460; Dist. by: Bookpeople, 2929 Fifth St., Berkeley, CA 94710 (SAN 168-9517) Tel 415-549-3030.

Intl Mahayana, *(International Mahayana Yoga Publishing Co.; 0-9615731),* 325 Harvard St., Suite 14, Brookline, MA 02146 (SAN 696-4656) Tel 617-232-5967.

Intl Map Co, *(International Map Co.; 0-937455),* 5316 Santa Teresa, El Paso, TX 79932 (SAN 658-8824) Tel 915-833-0745.

†**Intl Marine,** *(International Marine Publishing Co.; 0-87742; 0-8286),* Subs. of Diversified Communications Inc., 21 Elm St., Camden, ME 04843 (SAN 202-716X) Tel 207-236-4342; Toll free: 800-328-0059 (Trade Customers Only); *CIP.*

Intl Marriage, *(International Marriage Encounter, Inc.; 0-936098),* 955 Lake Dr., St. Paul, MN 55120 (SAN 215-6830).

Intl Melo Proj *See NC Path Intl Dev*

Intl Merc OH, *(International Merchandising Corp.; 0-9615344),* 1 Erieview Plaza, Cleveland, OH 44114 (SAN 695-1457) Tel 216-522-1200.

Intl Micro *See Intl Info Mgmt Con*

Intl Mktg, *(International Marketing Institute; 0-942286),* Univ. of New Orleans, New Orleans, LA 70148 (SAN 239-4464).

†**Intl Monetary,** *(International Monetary Fund; 0-939934),* Editorial Div., 700 19th St., NW, Rm. 12-510, Washington, DC 20431 (SAN 203-8188) Tel 202-623-7090; *CIP.*

Intl Mus Photo, *(International Museum of Photography at George Eastman Hse.; 0-935398),* 900 East Ave., Rochester, NY 14607 (SAN 205-0153) Tel 716-271-3361.

Intl Myopia, *(International Myopia Prevention Association; 0-9608476),* RD 5, Box 171, Ligonier, PA 15658 (SAN 228-1848) Tel 412-238-2101.

Intl Oil Scouts, *(International Oil Scouts Assn.),* 4818 E. Ben White Blvd., Suite 301, Austin, TX 78741-7309 (SAN 231-2204) Tel 512-448-4088.

Intl Ozone *See Pan Am Intl Ozone*

Intl Parents, *(International Parents Organization),* Subs. of Alexander Graham Bell Assn. for the Deaf, 3417 Volta Pl., NW, Washington, DC 20007 (SAN 203-6924) Tel 202-337-5220.

Intl Peace, *(International Peace Academy; 0-937722),* 777 United Nations Plaza, 4th Flr., New York, NY 10017 (SAN 225-6940) Tel 212-949-8480.

†**Intl Personnel Mgmt,** *(International Personnel Management Assn.; 0-914945),* 1617 Duke St., Alexandria, VA 22314 (SAN 203-8196) Tel 703-549-7100; *CIP.*

Intl Plan Parent, *(International Planned Parenthood Federation; 0-916683),* Western Hemisphere Region 105 Madison Ave., 7th Flr., New York, NY 10016 (SAN 271-5171) Tel 212-679-2230.

Intl Polygonics, *(International Polygonics, Ltd.;
0-930330),* P.O. Box 1563, Madison Sq.
Sta., New York, NY 10159
(SAN 211-0210) Tel 212-683-2914.

Intl Postal Mkting, *(International Postal
Marketing Corp.; 0-9606786),* 115 Main
Rd., Montville, NJ 07045 (SAN 223-1867)
Tel 201-299-1500.

Intl Prev Med, *(International Preventive
Medicine Foundation; 0-936553),* 3325 W.
New Haven Ave., Melbourne, FL 32904
(SAN 697-984X) Tel 305-723-5640.

Intl Print, *(International Print Co.),* 711 South
50th St., Philadelphia, PA 19143
(SAN 240-8627); Dist. by: Sebastian Ben
Giletto, 1127 Watkins St., Philadelphia, PA
19148 (SAN 240-8635).

Intl Print Soc, *(International Print Society;
0-915169),* P.O. Box 323, New Hope, PA
18938 (SAN 289-9523) Tel 215-862-2615.

†**Intl Prog Agricult,** *(Purdue Univ., Dept. of
International Programs in Agriculture;
0-9614109),* Purdue Univ., AGAD Bldg.,
West Lafayette, IN 47907 (SAN 685-3005)
Tel 317-494-5962; Orders to: ACS Mailing
Rm., 301 S. Second St., Lafayette, IN 47901
(SAN 662-264X) Tel 317-494-6794; *CIP.*

†**Intl Prog Controls,** *(International
Programmable Controls Inc.; 0-915425),* 35
Glenlake Parkway, Suite 445, Atlanta, GA
30328 (SAN 291-2384) Tel 404-396-5064;
CIP.

Intl Prtn Pr, *(International Partners Press;
0-932895),* Box 392, Soquel, CA 95073
(SAN 689-013X) Tel 408-475-1827.

Intl Psych Pr, *(International Psychological Press,
Inc.; 0-915662),* 1850 Hanover Dr., Suite 69,
Davis, CA 95616 (SAN 207-3722)
Tel 916-756-1347.

Intl Pub Co
See Intl Pubs Co

†**Intl Pubns Serv,** *(International Pubns. Service;
0-8002),* Div. of Taylor & Francis, Inc., 242
Cherry St., Philadelphia, PA 19106-1906
(SAN 169-5819) Tel 215-238-0939; Toll
free: 800-821-8312; *CIP.*

Intl Pubs Co, *(International Pubs. Co.; 0-7178),*
381 Park Ave. S., Suite 1301, New York,
NY 10016 (SAN 202-5655)
Tel 212-685-2864. *Imprints:* LLL (Little
Lenin Library); LML (Little Marx Library);
LNW (Little New World Paperbacks); NW
(New World Paperbacks).

Intl Radio Club Am, *(International Radio Club
of America),* P.O. Box 17088, Seattle, WA
98107 (SAN 224-2133) Tel 206-522-2521.

†**Intl Reading,** *(International Reading Assn.;
0-87207),* 800 Barksdale Rd., P.O. Box
8139, Newark, DE 19714-8139
(SAN 203-8218) Tel 302-731-1600; *CIP.*

Intl Rel Found
See Paragon Hse

Intl Res Ctr Energy, *(International Research
Center for Energy & Economic
Development; 0-918714),* Box 263, 216
Economics Bldg., Univ. of Colo., Boulder,
CO 80309-0263 (SAN 211-3643).

Intl Res Dev, *(International Resource
Development, Inc.; 0-924680),* 6 Prowitt St.,
Norwalk, CT 06855 (SAN 264-1208)
Tel 203-866-7800.

Intl Res Eval, *(International Research &
Evaluation; 0-930318),* Research Pubns.
Div., 21098 IRE Control Ctr., Eagan, MN
55121 (SAN 209-6668) Tel 612-888-9635.

Intl Research Serv, *(International Research
Service, Inc.; 0-934366),* P.O. Box 225, Blue
Bell, PA 19422 (SAN 213-1935).

Intl Review, *(International Review Service;
0-87138),* 15 Washington Pl., New York,
NY 10003 (SAN 202-3539)
Tel 212-751-0833; UN Bureau: Rm. 301,
United Nations, New York, NY 10017
(SAN 202-3547).

Intl Right Way, *(International Right of Way
Association),* 6133 Bristol Pkwy., Suite 270,
Culver City, CA 90020 (SAN 232-5004)
Tel 213-649-5323.

Intl Rodeo, *(International Pro Rodeo Assn.),*
P.O. Box 615, 106 E. McClure, Pauls Valley,
OK 73075 (SAN 224-5833)
Tel 405-238-6488; Dist. by: Rodeo News
Publishing, P.O. Box 587, Pauls Valley, OK
73075 (SAN 669-1285).

Intl Sat Users, *(International Association of
Satellite Users & Suppliers),* 6845 Elm St.,
Suite 710, P.O. Box DD, McLean, VA 22101
(SAN 224-1536) Tel 703-759-2095.

Intl Schl Psych, *(International School
Psychology Association; 0-917668),* 92 S.
Dawson Ave., Columbus, OH 43209
(SAN 209-2913) Tel 614-252-6687.

Intl Schol Bk Serv
See Intl Spec Bk

Intl School Servs, *(International Schls. Service;
0-913663),* P.O. Box 5910, 13 Roszel Rd.,
Princeton, NJ 08540 (SAN 225-8196)
Tel 609-452-0990.

Intl Sci Tech, *(International Science &
Technology Institute, Inc.; 0-936130),* 2033
M St. NW, Suite 300, Washington, DC
20036 (SAN 212-5110) Tel 202-466-7290.

Intl Servs Guild, *(International Services Guild;
0-9616129),* 845 Lone Oak Rd., St. Paul,
MN 55121 (SAN 699-7147)
Tel 612-774-5980.

Intl Soc Artifical Organs, *(International Society
for Artificial Organs; 0-936022),* 8937
Euclid Ave., Cleveland, OH 44106
(SAN 214-039X).

Intl Soc Cert Elect, *(International Society of
Certified Electronics Technicians),* 2708 W.
Berry, Ft. Worth, TX 76109
(SAN 271-5805) Tel 817-921-9101.

Intl Soc Cert Emp
See Intl Soc Emp

Intl Soc Emp, *(International Society of Certified
Employees Benefit Specialists; 0-911731),*
18700 W. Bluemound Rd., Brookfield, WI
53008 (SAN 264-1216)

Tel 414-786-8711.

Intl Soc Fire Serv, *(International Society of Fire
Service Instructors; 0-9615990),* 20 Main
St., Ashland, MA 01721 (SAN 697-8878)
Tel 617-881-5800.

Intl Spec Bk, *(International Specialized Bk.
Services; 0-89955),* 5602 NE Hassalo St.,
Portland, OR 97213-3640 (SAN 169-7129)
Tel 503-287-3093; Toll free:

800-547-7734.

Intl Sport Fish, *(International Sport Fishing
Pubns.; 0-914543),* P.O. Box 873, Captiva
Island, FL 33924 (SAN 289-2960)
Tel 813-337-8818.

Intl Sport Pubns, *(International Sport Pubns.,
Inc.; 0-913927),* 3030 S. Main, Salt Lake
City, UT 84115 (SAN 286-7826)
Tel 801-483-1777.

Intl Taekwon-Do, *(International Taekwon-Do
Assn.; 0-937314),* P.O. Box 281, Grand
Blanc, MI 48439 (SAN 214-4182)
Tel 313-655-6434.

Intl Telecommunications, *(International
Telecommunications Satellite Organization;
0-916233),* 3400 International Dr., NW,
Washington, DC 20008 (SAN 294-9431)
Tel 202-944-7034.

Intl Training, *(International Training
Consultants, Inc.; 0-9603702),* P.O. Box
35613, Richmond, VA 23235-0613
(SAN 215-1561)

Tel 804-320-2415.

Intl Transactional, *(International Transactional
Analysis Assn.; 0-89489),* 1772 Vallejo St.,
San Francisco, CA 94123

(SAN 224-4365).

Intl Typeface, *(International Typeface Corp.;
0-9608034),* 2 Hammarskjold Pl. 3rd Fl.,
New York, NY 10017 (SAN 239-6637); c/o
Robert Silver Assocs., 307 E. 37th St., New
York, NY 10016 (SAN 241-5801)
Tel 212-686-5630.

Intl Univ Foun
See Intl Univ Pr

Intl Univ MO
See Intl Univ Pr

†**Intl Univ Pr,** *(International Univ. Pr.; 0-89697),*
1301 S. Noland Rd., Independence, MO
64055 (SAN 271-6291) Tel 816-461-3633;
CIP.

†**Intl Univs Pr,** *(International Univs. Pr., Inc.;
0-8236),* 59 Boston Post Rd., P.O. Box
1524, Madison, CT 06443-1524
(SAN 202-7186) Tel 203-245-4000;
CIP.

Intl Vet Acup, *(International Veterinary
Acupuncture Society; 0-9616627),* RR. 1,
Chester Springs, PA 19425 (SAN 689-6979)
Tel 513-281-2162.

Intl Video, *(International Video Entertainment;
1-55658),* Div. of NCB Entertainment,
21800 Burbank Blvd., Woodland Hills, CA
91365 Tel 818-888-3040; Toll free:
800-423-7455.

Intl Wealth, *(International Wealth Success, Inc.;
0-914306; 0-934311),* 24 Canterbury Rd.,
Rockville Centre, NY 11570
(SAN 201-5129) Tel 516-766-5850.

Intl Woman Ctr, *(International Woman Center;
0-9614609),* P.O. Box 5293, Santa Cruz, CA
95063-5293 (SAN 691-7801).

Intl Yoga Soc
See Yoga Res Foun

IntlDept Imprint of **Har-Row**

Intraworld Trade News
See China Res

Intrepid, *(Intrepid Press),* P.O. Box 1423,
Buffalo, NY 14214 (SAN 207-8503)
Tel 716-886-7136.

Inventor Work, *(Inventors Workshop
International Education Foundation),* P.O.
Box 251, Tarzana, CA 91356
(SAN 260-3373) Tel 818-344-3375; Dist.
by: Ilma Printing & Publishing, P.O. Box
251, Tarzana, CA 91356 (SAN 260-3381)
Tel 818-344-3375.

Inventors Licensing, *(Inventors Licensing &
Marketing Agency),* P.O. Box 251, Tarzana,
CA 91356 (SAN 223-9981)
Tel 818-344-3375; 5068 Mecca Ave.,
Tarzana, CA 91356 (SAN 669-1366).

Inverted-A, *(Inverted-A, Inc.; 0-938245),* 401
Forest Hill Ln., Grand Prairie, TX 75051
(SAN 661-4213) Tel 214-264-0066.

Invest Co Inst, *(Investment Company Institute;
0-9616113),* 1600 M St. NW, Washington,
DC 20036 (SAN 224-9502)
Tel 202-293-7700.

Invest Eval, *(Investment Evaluations Corp.;
0-9603282),* 2000 Goldenvue Dr., Golden,
CO 80401 (SAN 210-9042)
Tel 303-278-3464.

Invest Info, *(Investment Information Services
Pr.; 0-930369),* Affil. of Investment
Information Services, Inc., 205 W. Wacker
Dr, Chicago, IL 60606 (SAN 678-9048)
Tel 312-750-9300; Dist. by: Caroline Hse.,
5S 250 Frontenac Rd., Naperville, IL 60540
(SAN 211-2280) Tel 312-983-6400.

Invest Psych Consult, *(Investment Psychology
Consulting; 0-935219),* 1410 E. Glenoaks
Blvd., Glendale, CA 91206 (SAN 695-7757)
Tel 818-241-8165.

Invest USA, *(Investigations U.S.A., Inc.;
0-9616336),* 373 N. University Dr., No.
C-135, Plantation, FL 33325
(SAN 658-8840) Tel 305-476-7716.

Investigations, *(Investigations Institute;
0-9607876),* 53 W. Jackson Blvd., Chicago,
IL 60604 (SAN 205-0064)
Tel 312-939-6050.

Investor Ctr, *(Investor Responsibility Research
Ctr., Inc.; 0-931035),* 1755 Massachusetts
Ave., NW, Suite 600, Washington, DC 20036
(SAN 271-6631) Tel 202-936-6500.

Investor Pubns, *(Investor Pubns.;
0-914230),* 219 Parkade, Cedar Falls, IA
50613 (SAN 201-5307) Tel 319-277-6341;
Toll free: 800-553-1789; Sales/Marketing:
250 S. Wacker Dr., Suite 950, Chicago, IL
60606 (SAN 281-8213) Tel 312-977-0999.

Investor Relations, *(Investor Relations Assocs.;
0-9614409),* 364 Lorraine, Glen Ellyn, IL
60137 (SAN 688-6019) Tel 312-858-0016.

Investor's Syst, *(Investor's Systems, Inc.;
0-915610),* P.O. Box 1422, Dayton, OH
45401 (SAN 207-3420) Tel 513-223-6870.

Investrek, *(Investrek Publishing; 0-9604914),*
419 Main St., No. 160, Huntington Beach,
CA 92648 (SAN 216-1443); Toll free:
800-334-0854, Ext 864; Dist. by: Liberty
Publishing, 50 Scott Adam Rd., Cockeysville,
MD 21030 (SAN 658-1145)
Tel 301-667-6680.

Invisible-Red Hill, *(Invisible City/Red Hill Pr.;
0-88031),* P.O. Box 2853, San Franscisco,
CA 94126 (SAN 205-6429)
Tel 415-527-1018; Dist. by: Small Press
Distribution, Inc., 1814 San Pablo Ave.,
Berkeley, CA 94702 (SAN 204-5826)
Tel 415-549-3336.

Involve Group Pr, *(Involvement Group Press;
0-9610421),* 1512 N. Nicholas St.,
Arlington, VA 22205 (SAN 264-1240)
Tel 703-241-2879.

153

IO, *(I O Publishing Co.; 0-9609334),* P.O. Box 528, Graton, CA 95444 (SAN 260-2075) Tel 707-823-6433.

IO Pubns
See North Atlantic

Ion Books, *(Ion Bks., Inc.; 0-938507),* 3387 Poplar, Suite 205, Memphis, TN 38111 (SAN 661-3330) Tel 401-323-8858.

Iona Phila, *(Iona Foundation; 0-941638),* P.O. Box 29136, Philadelphia, PA 19127 (SAN 239-2364) Tel 215-482-8372.

Iona Pr, *(Iona Press Company, The; 0-910789),* P.O. Box C-3181, Wooster, OH 44691 (SAN 271-6666) Tel 216-263-2470.

†Iota Pr, *(Iota Pr.; 0-936412),* 4302 Pickwick Circle, No. 320, Huntington Harbour, CA 92649 (SAN 214-3895) Tel 714-895-8367; *CIP.*

Iowa Nat Heritage, *(Iowa Natural Heritage Foundation; 0-943490),* 505 Fifth Ave., Des Moines, IA 50309 (SAN 240-6845) Tel 515-288-1846.

Iowa St Fair, *(Iowa State Fair; 0-930463),* State House, Des Moines, IA 50319 (SAN 670-9214).

†Iowa St U Pr, *(Iowa State Univ. Pr.; 0-8138),* 2121 S. State Ave., Ames, IA 50010 (SAN 202-7194) Tel 515-292-0140; *CIP.*

IOX Asses Assocs, *(IOX Assessment Assocs.; 0-932166),* 11411 W. Jefferson Blvd., Culver City, CA 90230 (SAN 211-1322) Tel 213-391-6295; Orders to: P.O. Box 24095, Los Angeles, CA 90024 (SAN 669-1110) Tel 213-391-5514.

IPIC
See Inter-Crescent

†IPS, *(International Pubs. Service, Inc.),* P.O. Box 230, Accord, MA 02018 (SAN 654-9357) Tel 617-749-2966; *CIP.*

Ipse Dixit Pr, *(Ipse Dixit Press, Inc.; 0-9602468),* Box 4277, St. Paul, MN 55104 (SAN 212-8098) Tel 612-690-0980.

Ipswich Pr, *(Ipswich Pr., The; 0-938864),* P.O. Box 291, Ipswich, MA 01938 (SAN 218-4826) Tel 617-426-3900.

IQ Found, *(IQ Foundation, The),* Box 303, Pearland, TX 77588-0303 (SAN 696-6314).

IR Pubns, *(IR Pubns. Ltd.; 0-931023),* 35 W. 38th St. No. 3W, New York, NY 10018 (SAN 216-2113) Tel 212-730-0518.

IR Serv, *(IR Services; 0-9616041),* Box 85508, Las Vegas, NV 89185-0508 (SAN 698-0236) Tel 702-386-0472; 1200 Chapman Dr., Las Vegas, NV 89104 (SAN 698-2417).

Iran Bks, *(Iran Bks.; 0-936347),* 8014 Old Georgetown Rd., Bethesda, MD 20814 (SAN 696-866X) Tel 301-986-0079.

IRBN Pr, *(IRBN Pr., The; 0-936925),* 360 E. 72nd St., New York, NY 10021 (SAN 658-3490) Tel 212-340-6284.

IRDIS, *(Industrial Relations & Data Information Services, Inc.; 0-9613023),* P.O. Box 226WOB, West Orange, NJ 07052 (SAN 683-5627) Tel 201-731-1554.

Irego, *(Irego; 0-911732),* P.O. Box 286, Lenox Hill Sta., 221 E. 70th St., New York, NY 10021 (SAN 215-661X).

†Ireland Educ, *(Ireland Educational Corp.; 0-89103),* 7076 S. Alton Way, Bldg. C, Englewood, CO 80112 (SAN 207-9488); *CIP.*

Iridescence, *(Iridescence; 0-938331),* P.O. Box 3556, Culver City, CA 90230 (SAN 661-3144); 5925 Canterbury Dr., No. 202, Culver City, CA 90230 (SAN 661-3152) Tel 213-370-0796.

Iris Dunn, *(Dunn, Iris; 0-9616135),* HCR 8, Box 455, Beeville, TX 78102 (SAN 699-8593) Tel 512-358-3750.

Iris IO, *(Iris I O Publishing; 0-932987),* Subs. of Strawberry Hill Pr., 316 California Ave. No.428, Reno, NV 89509 (SAN 689-0156) Tel 702-747-1638; Dist. by: Strawberry Hill Pr., 2594 15th Ave., San Francisco, CA 94127 (SAN 238-8103) Tel 415-664-8112.

Iris Pr
See Iris Pr Inc

†Iris Pr Inc, *(Iris Press, Inc.; 0-916078),* 27 Chestnut St., Binghamton, NY 13905 (SAN 219-6824) Tel 607-722-6739; *CIP.*

Iris Ten
See Iris IO

Irish Am Cult, *(Irish American Cultural Institute, The; 0-9614900),* 683 Osceola, St. Paul, MN 55105 (SAN 225-3240) Tel 612-647-5678.

Irish Bk Ctr, *(Irish Bk. Ctr.),* 245 W. 104th St., New York, NY 10025 (SAN 209-1089) Tel 212-866-0309.

Irish Bks Media, *(Irish Bks. & Media; 0-937702),* 683 Osceola Ave., St. Paul, MN 55105 (SAN 215-1987) Tel 612-647-5678.

Irish Childs Fund, *(Irish Children's Fund, Inc.; 0-9614331),* 5602 Hillcrest Rd., Downers Grove, IL 60516 (SAN 687-8075) Tel 312-968-6275; Dist. by: The Collection, Inc., P.O. Box 11465, Memphis, TN 38111 (SAN 289-9574) Tel 901-458-9830.

Irish Family Names, *(Irish Family Names Society, The; 0-9601868),* P.O. Box 2095, La Mesa, CA 92044-0600 (SAN 221-3567) Tel 619-466-8739.

Irish Genealog, *(Irish Genealogical Foundation; 0-940134),* Div. of O'Laughlin Pr., P.O. Box 7575, Kansas City, MO 64116 (SAN 218-4834) Tel 816-454-1463.

IRL Pr, *(IRL Pr.; 0-917000; 0-904147),* P.O. Box Q, McLean, VA 22101 (SAN 208-693X) Tel 703-998-2980.

Iron & Steel, *(Iron & Steel Society; 0-932897),* 410 Commonwealth Dr., Warrendale, PA 15086 (SAN 224-876X) Tel 412-776-1535.

Iron Crown Ent Inc, *(Iron Crown Enterprises, Inc.; 0-915795),* P.O. Box 1605, Charlottesville, VA 22902 (SAN 294-0272) Tel 804-295-3917; Toll free: 800-325-0479; 300 W. Main St., Charlottesville, VA 22901 (SAN 693-5109); Dist. by: Berkley Publishing Group, 200 Madison Ave., New York, NY 10016 (SAN 201-3991) Tel 212-686-9820.

Iron Horse Pr, *(Iron Horse Pr.; 0-937219),* 20954 Pacific Coast Hwy., Malibu, CA 90265 (SAN 658-7364) Tel 213-456-8713.

†Iron Mtn Pr, *(Iron Mountain Press; 0-931182),* P.O. Box D, Emory, VA 24327 (SAN 217-7994); *CIP.*

Iron Pr, *(Iron Press, The; 0-912363),* P.O. Box 176, Franklin, MI 48025 (SAN 265-1548) Tel 313-626-1075.

†Ironwood Calif, *(Ironwood Press; 0-936800),* 11251 Macmurray St., Garden Grove, CA 92641 (SAN 221-9379) Tel 714-539-9830; *CIP.*

Ironwood Scottsdale, *(Ironwood Pr. (Scottsdale); 0-932541),* P.O. Box 8464, Scottsdale, AZ 85252 (SAN 687-4800) Tel 602-947-8872.

Iroquois Bk, *(Iroquois Bk. Co.; 0-9616628),* P.O. Box 317, North Amherst, MA 01059 (SAN 661-2059); 52 Old Bay Rd., Belchertown, MA 01007 (SAN 661-2067) Tel 413-323-5589.

IRR *Imprint of* Oxford U Pr

Irresistible, *(Irresistible Books),* P.O. Box 1059, Angleton, TX 77515 (SAN 283-3816).

Irrigation, *(Irrigation Assn.; 0-935030),* 1911 N. Fort Myer Dr., Suite 1009, Arlington, VA 22209 (SAN 202-0807) Tel 703-524-1200.

†Irvington, *(Irvington Pubs.; 0-89197; 0-8290; 0-8452),* 740 Broadway, New York, NY 10003 (SAN 207-2408) Tel 212-777-4100; *CIP.*

Irvington Hist, *(Irvington Historical Society; 0-9611394),* 35 Clinton Terrace, Irvington, NJ 07111 (SAN 285-3280) Tel 201-994-4210.

Irwin, *(Irwin, Richard D., Inc.; 0-256),* Subs. of Dow Jones & Co., Inc., 1818 Ridge Rd., Homewood, IL 60430 (SAN 206-8400) Tel 312-798-6000; Toll free: 800-323-4560.

Irwinton, *(Irwinton Pubs.),* 9685 Anderson Rd., Mercersburg, PA 17236 (SAN 202-7208).

Isao Ltd, *(Isao, Ltd.; 0-9616819),* 235 W. Orangewood Ave., 4-D, Anaheim, CA 92802 (SAN 661-1206) Tel 714-750-5361.

ISC Consultants, *(ISC Consultants, Inc.; 0-935593),* 14 E. Fourth St., Suite 602, New York, NY 10012 (SAN 696-2459) Tel 212-477-8800.

ISC Pr, *(International Self-Counsel Pr.; 0-88908),* Subs. of International Self-Counsel Pr., Ltd., 1303 N. Northgate Way, Seattle, WA 98133 (SAN 240-9925) Tel 206-522-8383; Dist. by: TAB Bks., P.O. Box 40, Blue Ridge Summit, PA 17214 (SAN 202-568X) Tel 717-794-2191.

ISC Pubns, *(ISC Pubns.; 0-942916),* P.O. Box 10857, Costa Mesa, CA 92627 (SAN 240-1169).

Ischua Bks, *(Ischua Bks.; 0-9616797),* 4611 Gile Hollow Rd., Hinsdale, NY 14743 (SAN 661-3012) Tel 716-557-2518.

ISD, *(IBM Corporation - ISD),* New Circle Rd., Lexington, KY 40511 (SAN 651-4413). 3.

ISES *Imprint of* Unipub

ISHA Enterprises, *(ISHA Enterprises; 0-936981),* 4033 W. Libby St., Glendale, AZ 85308 (SAN 658-7895) Tel 602-843-8908.

Isham, *(Isham; 0-9614226),* P.O. Box 2191, Glenview, IL 60025 (SAN 686-7642) Tel 312-459-0618.

†ISHI PA, *(Institute for the Study of Human Issues; 0-89727; 0-915980),* 210 S. 13th St., Philadelphia, PA 19107 (SAN 207-6608) Tel 215-732-9729; *CIP.*

Ishiyaku Euro, *(Ishiyaku EuroAmerica, Inc.; 0-912791),* Subs. of Ishiyaku Group of Cos. (Japan), 11559 Rock Island Ct., St. Louis, MO 63043 (SAN 282-8057) Tel 314-432-1933.

ISI Pr, *(ISI Pr.; 0-89495; 0-86689; 0-946395; 0-906083),* Subs. of Institute for Scientific Info., 3501 Market St., Philadelphia, PA 19104 (SAN 209-9349) Tel 215-386-0100; Toll free: 800-523-1850.

ISIS, *(International Strategic Institute at Stanford; 0-935371),* Stanford Univ., 320 Galvez St., Stanford, CA 94305 (SAN 696-2718) Tel 415-723-9731.

Isis Pr, *(Isis Press; 0-940944),* 1516 Morton Ave., Ann Arbor, MI 48104 (SAN 223-1883) Tel 313-665-4740. Do Not Confuse with an Isis Press in San Francisco, CA.

Isis Pr CA, *(Isis Pr.; 0-931037),* 1827 Haight St., No. 95, San Francisco, CA 94117 (SAN 678-9943) Tel 415-346-1359.

Isl Pub Lummi, *(Island Publishing; 0-937391),* 3876 Centerview Rd., Lummi Island, WA 98262 (SAN 658-8867) Tel 206-758-7457.

Isl Resources, *(Island Resources Foundation),* Red Hook Ctr., P.O. Box 33, St. Thomas, VI 00802 (SAN 225-4956) Tel 809-775-3225; 1718 P St., NW, Washington, DC 80036 (SAN 650-0374) Tel 202-265-9712.

Islamic Center of Detroit, The
See Islamic Ctr

Islamic Ctr, *(Islamic Center of America, The; 0-942778),* 15571 Joy Rd., Detroit, MI 48228 (SAN 240-2335) Tel 313-582-7442.

†Islamic Found, *(Islamic Foundation; 0-932815),* 300 W. High Ridge Rd., Villa Park, IL 60181 (SAN 688-6604) Tel 312-752-4575; *CIP.*

Islamic Prods, *(Islamic Productions International; 0-934894),* 739 E. Sixth St., Tucson, AZ 85719 (SAN 203-8625) Tel 602-791-3989. *Imprints:* Renaissance Inst (Renaissance Institute); Renaissance Prods (Renaissance Productions).

Islamic Seminary, *(Islamic Seminary, The; 0-941724),* 50-11 Queens Blvd., Woodside, NY 11377 (SAN 239-2372) Tel 718-458-0924.

Island Bed & Breakfast, *(Island Bed & Breakfast Hawaii, Inc.; 0-9615970),* P.O. Box 449, Kapaa, HI 96746 (SAN 697-2926) Tel 805-822-7771; 4-1380 Kuhio Hwy., Suite 202, Kapaa, HI 96746 (SAN 697-2934) Tel 808-822-7771; Dist. by: Pacific Trade Group, P.O. Box 668, Pearl City, HI 96782-0668 (SAN 169-1635) Tel 808-671-6735; Dist. by: Pacific Pipeline, Inc., 19215 66th Ave., S., Kent, WA 98032-1171 (SAN 208-2128) Tel 206-872-5523.

†Island CA, *(Island Pr.; 0-933280),* Div. of Center for Resource Economics, Star Rte. 1, Box 38, Covelo, CA 95428 (SAN 212-5129) Tel 707-983-6432; *CIP.*

Island Canoe, *(Island Canoe Co.; 0-918439),* 3556 W. Blakely Ave. NE, Bainbridge Island, WA 98110 (SAN 657-6249) Tel 206-842-5997; Dist. by: Pacific Pipeline, 19215 66th Ave. S., Kent, WA 98032-1171 (SAN 208-2128).

Island Herit-Wrldwide Dist, *(Island Heritage/Worldwide Distributors; 0-931548),* 1819 Kahai St., Honolulu, HI 96819-3136 (SAN 211-3392) Tel 808-531-0133.

Island Pr, *(Island Pr.; 0-87208),* 175 Bahia Via, Fort Myers Beach, FL 33931 (SAN 202-7216) Tel 813-463-9482.

Island Pub, *(Island Publishing House; 0-916424),* P.O. Drawer 758, Manteo, NC 27954 (SAN 208-0362) Tel 919-473-2838.

Island Pubs WA, *(Island Pubs.; 0-9615580),* Box 201, Anacortes, WA 98221 (SAN 696-2726) Tel 206-293-5398; 477 Section Rd., Anacortes, WA 98221 (SAN 696-2734).

Symbols/Abbreviations

Island Writers, *(Island Writers Publishing Co.; 0-9604798)*, P.O. Box 953, Ocean Shores, WA 98569 (SAN 220-0619) Tel 206-289-2004; Dist. by: Pacific Trade Group, Ltd., P.O. Box 668, Pearl City, HI 96782-0668 (SAN 169-1635).

Isle of Guam, *(Isle of Guam International Publishers; 0-942780)*, P.O. Box 21119, Guam Main Facility, GU 96921 (SAN 240-2343) Tel 808-963-6317.

Isle Royale Hist, *(Isle Royale Natural History Assn., Inc.; 0-935289)*, 87 N. Ripley St., Houghton, MI 49931 (SAN 696-2513) Tel 906-482-8479.

†**Ism Pr,** *(Ism Pr., Inc.; 0-910383)*, P.O. Box 12447, San Francisco, CA 94112 (SAN 241-5496) Tel 415-333-7641; *CIP.*

ISS Found, *(ISS Foundation; 0-911277)*, 410 Commonwealth Dr., Warrendale, PA 15086 (SAN 270-8833) Tel 412-776-1583.

ISS Pubns, *(I.S.S. Pubns.; 0-915817)*, 160 Washington, SE, Suite 64-R, Albuquerque, NM 87108 (SAN 294-0175) Tel 505-255-2872.

Issue Action Pubns, *(Issue Action Pubns., Inc.; 0-913869)*, 105 Old Long Ridge Rd., Stamford, CT 06903 (SAN 286-7966) Tel 203-329-1425.

ITA
See D S Lake Pubs

ITA Pubns, *(ITA Pubns.; 0-933935)*, P.O. Box 1599, Willits, CA 95490 (SAN 693-062X) Tel 707-459-6100.

Italica Pr, *(Italica Pr.; 0-934977)*, 625 Main St., Suite 641, New York, NY 10044 (SAN 695-1805) Tel 212-935-4230.

Italimuse, *(Italimuse, Inc.; 0-910798)*, 3128 Burr St, Fairfield, CT 06430 (SAN 203-8242) Tel 203-259-5788.

ITEC, *(ITEC, Inc.; 0-943908)*, Box 464, Beaver, PA 15009 (SAN 241-1237) Tel 412-728-4318.

Ithaca Coll, *(Ithaca College; 0-9610556)*, South Hill Campus, Ithaca, NY 14850 (SAN 264-1267) Tel 607-274-3452.

†**Ithaca Hse,** *(Ithaca Hse.; 0-87886)*, P.O. Box 6484, Ithaca, NY 14851 (SAN 202-7224) Tel 607-272-4968; *CIP.*

Ithaca Pr MA, *(Ithaca Pr.; 0-915940)*, P.O. Box 853, Lowell, MA 01853 (SAN 208-709X) Tel 617-453-2177.

IUCN *Imprint of Unipub*

Ivans Pub NY, *(Ivans Publishing Co.; 0-9607476)*, 211-10 23rd Ave., Bayside, NY 11360 (SAN 238-6143) Tel 212-423-4307.

Ivers St Lloyd, *(Ivers-Saint Lloyd Pubs.; 0-938063)*, P.O. Box 11245, San Francisco, CA 94101 (SAN 661-261X); 2450 Vicente, San Francisco, CA 94116 (SAN 661-2628) Tel 415-681-5267.

Ivey Pubns, *(Ivey Pubns.; 0-9600864)*, 1845 Arkoe Dr., SE, Atlanta, GA 30316 (SAN 207-6799).

Ivory Hse, *(Ivory House; 0-9608896)*, P.O. Box 676, 121 Randolph Rd., Freehold, NJ 07728 (SAN 241-1245) Tel 201-462-1620.

Ivory Pal, *(Ivory Palaces Music Publishing Co., Inc.; 0-943644)*, 3141 Spottswood Ave., Memphis, TN 38111 (SAN 238-3020) Tel 901-323-5099.

Ivory Pub, *(Ivory Publishing; 0-9614738)*, P.O. Box 4595, Denver, CO 80204 (SAN 692-7440) Tel 303-572-8286; Dist. by: Publishers Group West, 5855 Beaudry St., Emeryville, CA 94608 (SAN 202-8522) Tel 415-658-3453; Dist. by: Bookpeople, 2929 Fifth St., Berkeley, CA 94710 (SAN 168-9517) Tel 415-549-3030; Dist. by: Samuel Weiser, Inc., P.O. Box 612, York Beach, ME 03910 (SAN 202-9588) Tel 207-363-4393.

Ivory Scroll, *(Ivory Scroll Books, Pubs.)*, P.O. Box 7526, Philadelphia, PA 19101 (SAN 205-003X).

Ivory Tower Pub, *(Ivory Tower Publishing Co., Inc.; 0-88032)*, 125 Walnut St., Watertown, MA 02172 (SAN 658-3989) Tel 617-923-1111; Toll free: 800-322-5016; Dist. by: Contemporary Bks., Inc., 180 N. Michigan Ave., Chicago, IL 60601 (SAN 202-5493) Tel 312-782-9181.

Ivy Books, *(Ivy Bks.; 0-8041)*, Div. of Ballantine Bks., Inc., 201 E. 50th St., New York, NY 10022 (SAN 661-7832) Tel 212-572-2573.

Ivy Club, *(Ivy Club, The; 0-934756)*, 43 Prospect Ave., Princeton, NJ 08540 (SAN 213-0904).

Ivy Hill, *(Ivy Hill Pr.; 0-9601542; 0-933461)*, Subs. of Mentors, Inc., 8817 Greenview Pl., Spring Valley, CA 92077 (SAN 212-5145) Tel 619-464-4235.

IVY League Pr, *(Ivy League Press, Inc; 0-918921)*, P.O. Box 15035, Arlington, VA 22215 (SAN 670-0543) Tel 202-892-1110.

Ivystone, *(Ivystone Pubns.; 0-935604)*, Box 23, Ada, MI 49301 (SAN 215-3211) Tel 616-452-8376.

IWM Intl, *(Integrity Word Ministries International, Inc.; 0-938433)*, Rte. 12, P.O. Box 91, Raleigh, NC 27610 (SAN 661-2946) Tel 919-266-3602; P.O. Box 19962, Raleigh, NC 27619 (SAN 661-2954).

IWP Pub, *(IWP Publishing; 0-914766; 0-88155)*, Div. of Eckankar, P.O. Box 27200, Minneapolis, MN 55427 (SAN 203-798X); Toll free: 800-843-6666.

J A Allen, *(Allen, J. A., & Co. Ltd.; 0-85131)*, Dist. by: Sporting Bk. Ctr., Inc., Canaan, NY 12029 (SAN 222-8734) Tel 518-794-8998.

J A Elkins Brs, *(Elkins, J. A., Brothers Publishing Co.)*, P.O. Drawer 785, Porter, TX 77365 (SAN 669-6880).

J A Ent, *(J. A. Enterprises; 0-9606722)*, 1447 11th St., Greeley, CO 80631 (SAN 219-6654) Tel 303-356-8630.

J A King
See K&K Pub Calif

J A Lohmann, *(Lohmann, Jeanne A.; 0-9607688)*, 722 Tenth Ave., San Francisco, CA 94118 (SAN 209-2204) Tel 415-387-7644.

J A Taylor, *(Taylor, J. A.; 0-9615675)*, Box 147 B Cohasset Stage, Chico, CA 95926 (SAN 696-3005) Tel 916-342-1675.

J A White, *(White, John A.; 0-9603242)*, 1200 Toyon Dr, Millbrae, CA 94030 (SAN 207-1932) Tel 415-697-1187.

J A Willard, *(Willard, John A.; 0-9612398)*, 3119 Country Club Circle, Billings, MT 59102 (SAN 289-5323) Tel 406-259-1966.

J A Winski, *(Winski, Joseph Anthony; 0-9616976)*, 13815 S. Normandie Ave., No. 48, Gardena, CA 90249 (SAN 661-8103) Tel 213-327-8000.

J Abbott, *(Abbott, Joseph Jr.; 0-9615351)*, P.O. Box 343, Woodridge, NJ 07075-0343 (SAN 695-1988) Tel 201-939-2871.

J Ackerman, *(Ackerman, Jan; 0-9616199)*, 1019 Columbia St., Hood River, OR 97031 (SAN 658-3369) Tel 503-386-5970.

J Alden, *(Alden, Jay, Pubns.; 0-914844)*, P.O. Box 1295, 546 S. Hofgaarden St., La Puente, CA 91749 (SAN 204-7780) Tel 818-968-6424.

J Alex Munro, *(Munro, J Alex; 0-9601670)*, 304 Saxon Dr., Springfield, IL 62704 (SAN 212-1174) Tel 217-787-6621.

J & A Enterprises, *(J&A Enterprises; 0-934368)*, 5522 W. Acoma Rd., Glendale, AZ 85306 (SAN 212-9116).

J & B Bks, *(J & B Bks.; 0-941186)*, 26 Marwood St., Albany, NY 12209 (SAN 285-0958) Tel 518-489-4009; Dist. by: Fulmont News Co., 182 Division St., Amsterdam, NY 12010 (SAN 200-7487).

J & B Pubs, *(J&B Pubs.; 0-943498)*, Box 2866, Taos, NM 87571 (SAN 240-6861) Tel 505-776-2355.

J & C Bks, *(J & C Bks.; 0-9616091)*, P.O. Box 1378, Scarborough, ME 04074-1378 (SAN 698-1267) Tel 207-883-4423.

J & D Peterson, *(Peterson, John C. & Doris M.; 0-9604376)*, R R 1, Box 25, Delphi, IN 46923 (SAN 216-0056) Tel 317-564-2855.

J & F Ents, *(J & F Enterprises; 0-918441)*, P.O. Box 265, Shepherdstown, WV 25443 (SAN 657-6281) Tel 304-876-3136.

J & J Baby Prod, *(Johnson & Johnson Baby Products Co.; 0-931562)*, Grandview Rd., Skillman, NJ 08558 (SAN 211-5131).

J & J Bks, *(J & J Books, Inc.; 0-914464)*, 1004 Springhill Dr., Angola, IN 46703 (SAN 202-7232) Tel 219-665-5346.

J & J Child Develop
See J & J Baby Prod

J & J Dist, *(J. & J. Distributors)*, P.O. Box 247, Raymondville, TX 78580 (SAN 213-5256) Tel 512-689-2523.

J & L Ent, *(J&L Enterprises; 0-9613425)*, 2485 Riverside Dr., Laramie, WY 82070 (SAN 656-8939) Tel 307-742-0849.

J & L Lee, *(Lee, J. & L., Co.; 0-934904)*, P.O. Box 5575, Lincoln, NE 68505 (SAN 213-8557) Tel 402-467-4416.

J & M R Reunions, *(Reunions, Joseph & Mary Ray)*, 8416 Forest Hills Blvd., Dallas, TX 75218 (SAN 203-8250) Tel 214-321-1302.

J & N Pubs, *(J & N Pubs.; 0-9616042)*, 121 Putnam Dr., Oroville, CA 95966 (SAN 697-8940) Tel 916-589-1487.

J & R Enter, *(J&R Enterprises; 0-9608550)*, P.O. Box 140264, Anchorage, AK 99514 (SAN 240-687X) Tel 907-333-4442.

J & R Pub, *(J & R Publishing Co.; 0-9616771)*, P.O. Box 1514, Greenwood, SC 29646 (SAN 661-3373); Royal Oak 22, Greenwood, SC 29648 (SAN 661-3381) Tel 803-229-0154.

J Arnold
See Arnold & Co

J Arvidson, *(Arvidson, J., Press; 0-9602098)*, P.O. Box 4022, Helena, MT 59601 (SAN 209-0848) Tel 406-442-0354.

J B Brewster, *(Brewster, Janet Bradham; 0-9616934)*, P.O. Box 269, Manning, SC 29102 (SAN 662-5606); 316 Brockington St., Manning, SC 29102 (SAN 662-5614) Tel 803-435-4016.

J B Burns, *(Burns, J. B.; 0-9602998)*, 4250 Lauderdale Ave., La Crescenta, CA 91214 (SAN 213-473X).

J B Dawson CA, *(Dawson, J. B.; 0-9615084)*, P.O. Box 50457, Phoenix, AZ 85076 (SAN 694-4337) Tel 602-893-0108.

J B Fisher, *(Fisher, John B.; 0-9612308)*, 2029 Robin Rd., Salisbury, NC 28144 (SAN 289-2251) Tel 704-637-0988.

J B Muns, *(Muns, J. B., Bks.)*, 1162 Shattuck Ave., Berkeley, CA 94707 (SAN 213-8786) Tel 415-525-2420.

J B Pal, *(Pal, J. B., & Co., Inc.; 0-916836)*, 904 W. Castlewood Terr., Chicago, IL 60640 (SAN 208-0567) Tel 312-271-0123.

J B Pr, *(J.B. Pr.; 0-9614881)*, P.O. Box 4843, Duke Sta., Durham, NC 27706 (SAN 693-1227) Tel 919-493-5221.

J-B Pub, *(J-B Publishing Co.; 0-916170)*, 430 Ivy Ave., Crete, NE 68333 (SAN 207-2424) Tel 402-826-3356.

J B Pub NC
See J B Pr

J-B Pubs
See J-B Pub

J B Simpson, *(Simpson, J. B. & Associates; 0-9603882)*, 2345 Oglesby Bridge Rd., Conyers, GA 30208 (SAN 221-6590) Tel 404-922-6256.

J B Thomas, *(Thomas, James Blake; 0-9616285)*, 2946 Mt. Hope, Okemos, MI 48864 (SAN 658-4462) Tel 517-351-3447.

J B Wilson, *(Wilson, J. B., Pr., Inc.; 0-933458)*, 1730 Columbia Dr. E., Fresno, CA 93727 (SAN 211-769X) Tel 209-251-8751.

J Bankston
See Terrenate Assocs

J Barnard, *(Barnard, Jerry, Ministries; 0-938043)*, P.O. Box 413, San Diego, CA 92112 (SAN 659-784X); 6550 Soledad Mountain Rd., La Jolla, CA 92037 (SAN 659-7858) Tel 619-275-1944.

J Barton
See Biokinesiology Institute

J Bellestri, *(Bellestri, Joseph; 0-9615777)*, 2819 Yost Blvd., Ann Arbor, MI 48104 (SAN 696-6810) Tel 313-971-2170.

J Bjoerling, *(Bjoerling, Jussi, Memorial Archive, Inc., The; 0-9608546)*, P.O. Box 2638, Indianapolis, IN 46206 (SAN 240-5989) Tel 317-635-2021.

J Blair, *(Blair, John; 0-9601880)*, P.O. Box 70043, Riverside, CA 92513 (SAN 211-8858) Tel 714-785-4975.

J Blalock, *(Blalock, Jack; 0-9605156)*, P.O. Box 8746, Pembroke Pines, FL 33084-0746 (SAN 215-8396).

J Bradshaw, *(Bradshaw, Jim; 0-9616474)*, 186 Catherine St., Lafayette, LA 70503 (SAN 659-3070) Tel 318-234-0393.

J Buchs, *(Buchs, J., Pubns.)*, 5301 Richmond, No. 24B, Houston, TX 77027 (SAN 208-256X).

J Burger, *(Burger, Joanne; 0-916188)*, 57 Blue Bonnet Court, Lake Jackson, TX 77566 (SAN 211-2191).

J C Bancroft, *(Bancroft, John C.)*, 5855 Sheridan Rd., Apt. 7D, Chicago, IL 60660 (SAN 207-6071) Tel 312-271-7747.

J C Brown, *(Brown, John Carter, Library; 0-916617)*, P.O. Box 1894, Providence, RI 02912 (SAN 203-6797) Tel 401-863-2725.

J C Buskens, *(Buskens, Joy Callaway; 0-9616351),* Rte. 1, Box 2690, Gulf Shores, AL 36542 (SAN 658-8948) Tel 205-968-7026.

J C C Wang, *(Wang, Joan Chi Chin; 0-9617295),* 4328 Muscatel, Rosemead, CA 91770 (SAN 663-4605); Dist. by: Evergreen Publishing Co., 136 S. Atlantic Blvd., Monterey Park, CA 91754-2727 (SAN 662-9113) Tel 818-281-3622.

J-C Church, *(Church, Jim & Cathy; 0-9616093),* 7230 Trenton Pl., Gilroy, CA 95020 (SAN 698-1062) Tel 408-842-9682; P.O. Box 80, Gilroy, CA 95021 (SAN 698-2549).

J C Print, *(J. C. Printing Co.),* Dawnsonville, GA 30534-0579 (SAN 211-0245) Tel 404-265-2036.

J C Smith Univ, *(Smith, Johnson C., Univ.; 0-9614603),* 100 Beatties Ford Rd., Charlotte, NC 28216 (SAN 691-8328) Tel 704-378-1019.

J C Welch, *(Welch, Julia Conway; 0-9615535),* 204 S. Florida, Caldwell, ID 83605 (SAN 695-9113) Tel 208-454-9125.

J Calvin Keene, *(Keene, J. Calvin; 0-9603084),* 134 Verna Rd., Lewisburg, PA 17837 (SAN 211-9099).

J Cole, *(Cole, Jim; 0-9601200),* 627 Kay St., Fairbanks, AK 99701 (SAN 661-9770) Tel 907-479-6107; Orders to: Ed & Janet Reynolds, 37 Lomita Dr., Mill Valley, CA 94941 (SAN 269-0713) Tel 415-388-1621.

J Cordner, *(Cordner, John; 0-9617224),* 3712 35th Ave. SW, Seattle, WA 98126 (SAN 663-365X) Tel 206-935-8403.

J Countryman Pubs, *(Countryman, J., Pubs.; 0-937347),* 4420 FM 1960 W., Suite 120, Houston, TX 77068 (SAN 659-1523) Tel 214-630-4300.

J Custis
See D Brown Bks

J D Adams, *(Evergreen; 0-939523),* P.O. Box 794, Pico Rivera, CA 90660-0794 (SAN 663-4443); 1334 E. 216th St., Carson, CA 90745 (SAN 663-4451) Tel 213-948-6436.

J D Bentz, *(Bentz, John D.; 0-9612438),* 13139 Old West Ave., San Diego, CA 92129 (SAN 289-0801) Tel 619-484-1708.

J D Bowers, *(Bowers, John D.; 0-9601360),* P.O. Box 101, Radnor, PA 19087 (SAN 208-0028) Tel 215-688-5541.

J D Craig, *(Craig, James D.; 0-9602042),* P.O. Box 42, Pebble Beach, CA 93953 (SAN 212-0356).

J D Freudy, *(Freudy, Joan D.; 0-9616440),* 24 Oakfield Ave., Freeport, NY 11520 (SAN 658-8468) Tel 516-623-6695.

J Daniel, *(Daniel, John, Pub.; 0-936784),* P.O. Box 21922, Santa Barbara, CA 93121 (SAN 215-1995) Tel 805-962-1780.

J De Graff, *(De Graff, John, ,Inc.; 0-8286),* Clinton Corners, NY 12514 (SAN 201-3061) Tel 914-266-5800; Dist. by: International Marine Publishing Co., 21 Elm St., Camden, ME 04843 (SAN 202-716X) Tel 207-236-4342.

J Delaney Pubns, *(Delaney, John, Pubns.; 0-9608514),* P.O. Box 404, Bogota, NJ 07603-0404 (SAN 240-625X) Tel 201-836-2543.

J Dick
See Res Pubns CT

J Doe Pr, *(Doe, John, Pr.; 0-9609476),* 420 13th Ave. E., Seattle, WA 98105 (SAN 263-2233) Tel 206-525-7901.

J Domjan
See Domjan Studio

J Donaghey, *(Donaghey, John, Pubns.; 0-9604298),* P.O. Box 402021, Garland, TX 75046 (SAN 214-364X) Tel 214-272-7607; Dist. by: Baker & Taylor Co., Eastern Div., 50 Kirby Ave., Somerville, NJ 08876 (SAN 169-4901) Tel 201-526-8000.

J Downey, *(Downey, Joel; 0-9601284),* 7625 Hutchinson Ave., Pittsburgh, PA 15218 (SAN 210-4156) Tel 412-371-5880.

J Duco, *(Duco, Joyce; 0-9612896),* BNA Corporate Center, Bldg. 200, Suite 207, Nashville, TN 37217 (SAN 291-140X) Tel 615-366-0455; Dist. by: DeVorss & Co., P.O. Box 550, 1046 Princeton Dr., Marina del Rey, CA 90294 (SAN 168-9886) Tel 213-870-7478; Dist. by: Spring Arbor Distributors, 10885 Textile Rd., Belleville, MI 48111 (SAN 158-9016) Tel 313-481-0900.

J Duren, *(Duren, Joyce; 0-9616196),* 328 Myers Pl., Inglewood, CA 90301 (SAN 699-9018) Tel 213-671-5271.

J E Brickley, *(Brickley, James E.; 0-9611514),* 914 N. 35th St., Renton, WA 98056 (SAN 284-9224).

J E Fry, *(Fry, Joan E.; 0-9600984),* 4025 State St., 22, Santa Barbara, CA 93110 (SAN 208-6565) Tel 805-967-8384.

J E Haigwood, *(Haigwood, John E.; 0-9614500),* P.O. Box 5001, Rome, GA 30162 (SAN 690-0100) Tel 404-234-6414.

J E Krebs, *(Krebs, John E.; 0-9607026),* 711 Santa Fe Dr., Apt. 232, Weatherford, TX 76086 (SAN 239-0027) Tel 817-594-6135.

J E Robertson, *(Robertson, James E.; 0-9600756),* 5213 Don Pio Dr., Woodland Hills, CA 91364 (SAN 202-7267) Tel 818-884-9008.

J E Seagram, *(Seagram, Joseph E., & Sons, Inc.; 0-916745),* 375 Park Ave., New York, NY 10152 (SAN 654-2077) Tel 212-572-7379.

J E Sexson, *(Sexson, Jeanne E.; 0-9613817),* 1906 Polster, Evansville, IN 47715 (SAN 682-2630).

J E Trossbach, *(Trossbach, J. E.; 0-9608936),* 2608 W. Columbine Rd., Phoenix, AZ 85029 (SAN 241-1628) Tel 602-997-2882.

J Eddowes, *(Eddowes, John; 0-9615646),* 1716 Irvin St., Vienna, VA 22180 (SAN 696-4699) Tel 703-281-5994.

J Ellerbach, *(Ellerbach, John; 0-9616813),* 878 41st St., Des Moines, IA 50312 (SAN 661-0978) Tel 515-255-5604.

J F Brown
See United West Pr

J F Fiske, *(Fiske, Jane F.; 0-9615790),* 44 Stonecleave Rd., Boxford, MA 01921 (SAN 696-7426) Tel 617-887-8787.

J F Miles, *(Miles, James F.; 0-9600480),* P.O. Box 1041, Clemson, SC 29631 (SAN 203-8978) Tel 803-654-2410.

J F Morton, *(Morton, Julia F.; 0-9610184),* 20534 SW 92nd Ct., Miami, FL 33189 (SAN 272-5185) Tel 305-284-3741.

J F Whitley, *(Whitley, Joe F., Pub.; 0-937577),* 1414 Spokane Ave., Coeur d'Alene, ID 83814 (SAN 659-1345) Tel 208-664-2329.

J F Wine, *(Wine, J. F.; 0-9604350),* 924 Woodland Ave., Winchester, VA 22601 (SAN 206-0221) Tel 703-662-5735.

J Fairhurst, *(Fairhurst, Jim),* P.O. Box 153, Dover, NH 03820 (SAN 697-1601) Tel 603-742-2715.

J Fankhauser, *(Fankhauser, Jerry; 0-9617006),* 2650 Fountainview, Suite 208, Houston, TX 77057 (SAN 662-5517) Tel 713-783-7264; Dist. by: DeVorss & Co., P.O. Box 550, 1046 Princeton Dr., Marina del Rey, CA 90294 (SAN 168-9886) Tel 213-870-7478; Dist. by: Miracle Pub. Co., 18 Charleston N., Sugar Land, TX 77478 (SAN 272-4618).

J Farrell, *(Farrell, John, Texas Slanguage Bks.; 0-939305),* 2015 Stehle Rd., Rosenberg, TX 77471 (SAN 663-172X) Tel 713-232-7841.

J Fleming, *(Fleming, Jim, Pubns.; 0-939415),* P.O. Box 1211, Vail, CO 81658 (SAN 663-2513); 1860 W. Meadow, No. 8, Vail, CO 81658 (SAN 663-2521) Tel 303-934-3237.

J Franklin, *(Franklin, J., Inc. Pub.; 0-9616736),* P.O. Box 14057, Tulsa, OK 74159 (SAN 661-4302); 4123 S. Victor Ct., Tulsa, OK 74105 (SAN 661-4310) Tel 918-747-9858.

J Freedman Liturgy, *(Freedman, Jacob, Liturgy Research Foundation),* P.O. Box 317, Forest Park Sta., Springfield, MA 01108 (SAN 207-7582).

J G Anderson
See Anderson Publ

J G Bruhn, *(Bruhn, John G.; 0-9616570),* 7521 Beluche, Galveston, TX 77551 (SAN 659-9230) Tel 409-761-3001.

J G Panozzo, *(Panozzo, Joseph Guido; 0-9615974),* 609 Dennis St., Rochelle, IL 61068 (SAN 696-8945) Tel 815-562-2571.

J G Schneider, *(Schneider, J. G.; 0-9613335),* Box 165 1402 S. Cage, Pharr, TX 78577 (SAN 655-7503) Tel 512-781-0045.

J G Stanoff, *(Stanoff, Jerrold G.),* P.O. Box 1599, Aptos, CA 95001 (SAN 213-1706) Tel 408-724-4911.

J G Stella, *(Stella, Joseph G.; 0-9600908, 0-8390),* P.O. Box 2158, Ft. Lauderdale, FL 33303 (SAN 208-8746) Tel 305-561-2487; Dist. by: Abner Schram, 36 Park St., Montclair, NJ 07042 (SAN 169-4766).

J G V Maciora, *(Maciora, Joseph G. V.; 0-9613407),* 89 Palomino Dr., Pittsfield, MA 01201 (SAN 679-1441).

J Gallo, *(Gallo, John; 0-9615648),* R.D. 2, Oneonta, NY 13820 (SAN 696-5032) Tel 607-432-3022.

J Gillen, *(Gillen, Jack, Seminars, Inc.; 0-9617143),* P.O. Box 5179, Orlando, FL 32855 (SAN 663-3285); 2822 Oranole Way, Apopka, FL 32703 (SAN 663-3293) Tel 305-299-1260.

J Gindick, *(Gindick, Jon),* 530 Ranch Rd., Visalia, CA 93291 (SAN 211-0741) Tel 209-733-1679; Orders to: 530 Ranch Rd., Visalia, CA 93291 (SAN 211-075X).

J Gould, *(Gould, Jay, Enterprises; 0-9608332),* 7840 Old Auburn Rd., Fort Wayne, IN 46825 (SAN 240-5334) Tel 219-489-4441.

J Graham, *(Graham, Josephine),* c/o Suggin Productions, 7710 Choctaw Rd., Little Rock, AR 72205 (SAN 209-8911).

J Grauer, *(Grauer, Jack; 0-930584),* 2005 S.E. 58th, Portland, OR 97215 (SAN 208-0885) Tel 503-232-5596.

J Gross, *(Gross, Joseph; 0-9616476),* 28 Parkhurst Dr., Spencerport, NY 14559 (SAN 659-2260) Tel 716-552-6766.

J H Aronson, *(Aronson, J. H.; 0-9613348),* P.O. Box 302, Highmount, NY 12441 (SAN 655-816X) Tel 914-254-5701. Do not confuse with Jason Aronson, Northvale, NJ.

J H Dobbins, *(Dobbins, Joan H.; 0-9610540),* 419 Windover Circle, Meridian, MS 39305 (SAN 264-0082) Tel 601-483-5081.

J H Flynn, *(Flynn, James H.; 0-9613258),* 1704 Drewlaine Dr., Vienna, VA 22180 (SAN 296-6891) Tel 703-938-2489.

J H Hammill, *(Hammill, J. H., III; 0-9600652),* 1081 Bollinger Canyon Rd., Moraga, CA 94556 (SAN 203-8986) Tel 415-376-0210.

J H Hargrove & Co
See La Jolla Pub CA

J H Hoffmann, *(Hoffman, J. Henry; 0-9614287),* Drawer 8170, Tamuning, GU 96911 (SAN 687-4509).

J H Mason, *(Mason, James H.; 0-9609032),* 116 N. Belmont St., Glendale, CA 91206 (SAN 240-9704).

J H Nash, *(Nash, James H.; 0-9612498),* 16740 Obispo Lane, San Diego, CA 92128 (SAN 655-7538).

J H Reed, *(Reed, James H.; 0-9601314),* 1315 Melrose, Richardson, TX 75080 (SAN 209-0031) Tel 214-826-8835.

J H Roush, *(Roush, John H., Jr.; 0-9600830),* 27 Terrace Ave., Kentfield, CA 94904 (SAN 207-1827) Tel 415-453-7130.

J H Strunk, *(Strunk, J. H.; 0-9613943),* 100 Wakefield Terr, RD 2, Box 262, Mansfield, PA 16933 (SAN 687-7508).

J H Wiggins, *(Wiggins, John H.; 0-9600346),* 1650 S. Pacific Coast Hwy., Suite 206, Redondo Beach, CA 90277 (SAN 205-5287).

J H Windsor, *(Windsor, Janna H.; 0-9600400),* 225 E. Laurel Ave., Arcadia, CA 91006 (SAN 221-5438).

J Hill Assocs, *(Hill, Joyce, Assn.; 0-914685),* 1023 South 24th St., Kingsville, TX 78363 (SAN 292-3335).

J Hoffman, *(Hoffman, Jane, Publishing),* P.O. Box 16966, Irvine, CA 92713 (SAN 219-1725).

J Hurter, *(Hurter, Jerry; 0-9615054),* 1173 Hawkstone Dr., Cincinnati, OH 45230 (SAN 694-1370) Tel 513-231-6430.

J Huston, *(Huston, John, Inc.; 0-9616260),* 514 Santa Monica, Corpus Christi, TX 78411 (SAN 658-344X) Tel 512-853-6512; P.O. Box 6372, Corpus Christi, TX 78411 (SAN 658-3458).

J Hutchins, *(Hutchins, Jerry, Photography; 0-9615989),* P.O. Box 84899, San Diego, CA 92138 (SAN 697-8789); 1536 E. Seventh St., National City, CA 92138 (SAN 697-8797) Tel 619-477-1320.

J I Baublitz, *(Baublitz, Jacinth Ivie; 0-9610316),* 3708 Westbrier Terrace, Midland, MI 48640 (SAN 263-9327) Tel 517-835-6351.

J J Augustin, *(Augustin, J. J., Inc., Pub.; 0-87439),* 123 Buckram Rd., Locust Valley, NY 11560 (SAN 204-5451) Tel 516-676-1510.

†**J P Tarcher,** *(Tarcher, Jeremy P., Inc; 0-87477),* 9110 Sunset Blvd., Suite 250, Los Angeles, CA 90069 (SAN 202-0424) Tel 213-273-3274; Toll free: 800-225-3362; Dist. by: St. Martin's Pr., 175 Fifth Ave., New York, NY 10010 (SAN 200-2132) Tel 212-674-5151; *CIP.*

J P Werner, *(Werner, J. Paul; 0-9601368),* 4643 N. Front St., Philadelphia, PA 19140 (SAN 209-6013) Tel 215-457-4081.

J Paduano, *(Paduano, Joseph; 0-9615590),* 14 Heidl Ave., West Long Branch, NJ 07764 (SAN 289-355X) Tel 201-222-7620.

J Palmer, *(Palmer, J., Pub.),* 155 W. Clark St., No. 5, Manchester, NH 03104 (SAN 206-2097) Tel 603-625-5103.

J Patelson Mus, *(Patelson, Joseph, Music House, Ltd.; 0-915282),* 160 W. 56th St., New York, NY 10019 (SAN 203-9028) Tel 212-757-5587.

J Pearse Mus Pub, *(Pearse, John, Music Publishing),* P.O. Box 295, Center Valley, PA 18034 (SAN 663-1711) Tel 215-282-3319.

J Phillips Pub
See P Friends Co Inc

J Pisapia Assocs, *(Pisapia, John, Associates; 0-917964),* 210- Kanawha Blvd., Charleston, WV 25311 (SAN 209-9845) Tel 304-345-4868.

J Pohl Assocs, *(Pohl, J., Assocs.; 0-939332),* 461 Spring Run Rd., Coraopolis, PA 15108 (SAN 220-181X) Tel 412-457-6300.

J Pomerinke
See Young Pr Idaho

J Porter Bks, *(Porter, Janice, Bks.; 0-9607670),* P.O. Box 2367, Reston, VA 22090 (SAN 240-0979).

J Prescott, *(Prescott, Joseph),* 79-31 257th St., Floral Park, NY 11004-1228 (SAN 695-9784).

J R Albin, *(Albin, James R.; 0-916210),* 431 Bridgeway, Sausalito, CA 94965 (SAN 207-4850) Tel 415-332-6438.

J R and G, *(J.R.&G. Co.; 0-9608844),* 4165 Greenwood Dr., Bethlehem, PA 18017 (SAN 241-0311) Tel 215-694-0860.

J R Assocs, *(Racila, John, Assocs.; 0-916655),* 2820 Oak Brook Rd., Oak Brook, IL 60521 (SAN 296-6905) Tel 312-655-1444.

J R Bennett, *(Bennett, James R.; 0-9617257),* Rte. 1, Box 124, McCalla, AL 35111 (SAN 663-5458) Tel 205-477-5711.

J R Berry, *(Berry, John R., Evangelical Assn.; 0-9616900),* P.O. Box 8252, Philadelphia, PA 19101 (SAN 661-4949); 5622 Florence Ave., Philadelphia, PA 19143 (SAN 661-4957) Tel 215-727-4325.

J R Brittingham, *(Brittingham, Janet R.; 0-9613351),* 2143 Harmony Lane, Jamison, PA 18929 (SAN 655-8755) Tel 215-343-6838.

J R C Pub, *(J.R.C. Publishing & Minerals; 0-916367),* 3 Roswell St., New Bedford, MA 02740 (SAN 295-852X) Tel 617-994-3403.

J R Craig, *(Craig, James R.),* 1542 S. Cody, Lakewood, CO 80226 (SAN 263-9874) Tel 303-985-0790.

J R Elliott, *(Elliott, J. R.),* 9 Country Manor, Fergus Falls, MN 56537 (SAN 283-2380) Tel 218-736-3453.

J R Enterline, *(Enterline, J.R.),* 144 W. 95th St., New York, NY 10025 (SAN 208-399X) Tel 212-865-9648.

J R Greene, *(Greene, J. R.; 0-9609404),* 33 Bearsden Rd., Athol, MA 01331 (SAN 262-6845) Tel 617-249-9376.

J R Laverty, *(Laverty, J. R.),* P.O. Box 303, Jasper, AR 72641 (SAN 688-5829).

J R Long Antiquarian, *(Long, Judith R., Antiquarian Bks.; 0-9614522),* 2710 Harvest Way, Marietta, GA 30062 (SAN 158-4944) Tel 404-977-0794.

J R Messenger, *(Messenger, J. R., Pub.; 0-914695),* P.O. Box 217, Piscataway, NJ 08854 (SAN 296-1199) Tel 201-356-0679.

J R O'Dwyer, *(O'Dwyer, J.R., Co., Inc.; 0-941424),* 271 Madison Ave., New York, NY 10016 (SAN 226-3386).

J R Pubns, *(J.R. Pubns.; 0-913952),* 170 NE 33rd St., Ft. Lauderdale, FL 33334 (SAN 202-7283) Tel 305-563-1844.

J R Simon, *(Simon, Jeffrey R., Publishing Co.; 0-916343),* P.O. Box 13390, Pittsburgh, PA 15243 (SAN 295-9801) Tel 412-279-6525.

J R Simpson, *(Simpson, Jeanne R., Gallery of Fine Art Ltd.; 0-9611558),* 2811 W. 67 Terrace, Shawnee Mission, KS 66208 (SAN 284-9127) Tel 913-831-1902.

J R Taylor, *(Taylor, James R., Pub.; 0-9616670),* 2811 Zinnia Ct., Union City, CA 94587 (SAN 659-9044) Tel 415-487-4628.

J R Weckstein, *(Weckstein, Joyce R.; 0-9600980),* 28290 Tavistock Trail, Southfield, MI 48034 (SAN 208-9173) Tel 313-353-6221.

J Ramsey
See Brainchild Bks

J Rehmel, *(Rehmel, Judy, Quilt Books; 0-913731),* P.O. Box 1002, Richmond, IN 47375 (SAN 286-116X) Tel 317-935-1127.

J Reynolds, *(Reynolds, Jane; 0-930114),* 2135 Encinitas Blvd., Encinitas, CA 92024 (SAN 210-6604) Tel 619-942-1025.

J Rothbart
See Rothbart

J Rucker, *(Rucker, John; 0-9613658),* P.O. Box 9432, Greensboro, NC 27429 (SAN 670-7696) Tel 919-621-9775. Summer address only.

J Russell, *(Russell, John),* 19 Doughty Lane, Fair Haven, NJ 07701 (SAN 262-0731) Tel 201-747-6722.

J S Auvinen, *(Auvinen, Jewell Shelly; 0-9610158),* P.O. Box 5185, Santa Cruz, CA 95063 (SAN 263-9262) Tel 408-335-3543.

J S Hanna, *(Hanna, J. S., House; 0-9607024),* Div. of Reports for Government, 183 Gifford Way, Sacramento, CA 95864 (SAN 238-986X) Tel 916-486-1670.

J Sanchez, *(Sanchez, Jacqueline; 0-910863),* 2076 Vinewood, Detroit, MI 48216 (SAN 275-2042).

†**J Simon,** *(Simon, Joseph; 0-934710),* Div. of Pangloss Press, Box 4071, Malibu, CA 90265 (SAN 213-9669); 29500 Heathercliff Rd., No. 161, Malibu, CA 90265 (SAN 662-1457) Tel 213-457-3293; *CIP.*

J Smith Soc, *(Smith, Jedediah, Society, The; 0-9612094),* c/o University of the Pacific, Stockton, CA 95211 (SAN 286-8776) Tel 209-946-2404.

J Stafford, *(Stafford, Joseph, Pub.; 0-9617123),* P.O. box 07011, Detroit, MI 48207 (SAN 662-684X); 8200 E. Jefferson, Apt. 403, Detroit, MI 48214 (SAN 662-6858) Tel 313-331-5680; Dist. by: Baker & Taylor, Eastern Div., 50 Kirby Ave., Somerville, NJ 08876 (SAN 169-4901).

J Sturge, *(Sturge, Judi),* 18 Lodge Pole Rd., Pittsford, NY 14534 (SAN 211-7622).

J Szoke Graphics, *(Szoke, John, Graphics, Inc.; 0-936598),* 164-166 Mercer St., New York, NY 10012 (SAN 222-1748).

J T Brown & Assocs, *(Brown & Assocs.; 0-938742),* 2951 N. Clark St., Chicago, IL 60657 (SAN 216-4736) Tel 312-248-3092.

J T Maltsberger, *(Maltsberger, John T.; 0-9616355),* 30 Brimmer St., Boston, MA 02108 (SAN 658-9049) Tel 617-242-5610.

J T Ordeman, *(Ordeman, John T.; 0-9610638),* St. Paul's School, Brooklandville, MD 21022 (SAN 265-3613).

J T Pub Co, *(J.T. Publishing Co.; 0-9615455),* P.O. Box 4, Manning, SC 29102 (SAN 695-7684) Tel 803-478-8407; Box 1024, Rte. 4, Manning, SC 29102 (SAN 696-0405).

J T Richards, *(Richards, John Thomas; 0-9605980),* 309 W. Ninth St., Rolla, MO 65401 (SAN 220-1917) Tel 314-364-5723; Orders to: New Frontiers Foundation, Inc., Fellowship Farm, Route 1, Oregon, WI 53575 (SAN 214-0659) Tel 608-835-3795.

J Taylor Bks, *(Taylor, Joanna, Bks.),* 2461 el Pavo Way, Rancho Cordova, CA 95670 (SAN 238-8227).

J Taylor CA, *(Taylor, James, Ltd.; 0-943950),* P.O. Box 12502, La Crescenta, CA 91214 (SAN 241-5860).

J Terrell, *(Terrell, Judy; 0-9616780),* 2405 Clublake Trail, McKinney, TX 75069 (SAN 661-0579) Tel 214-542-1530.

J Thompson Pub, *(Thompson, Joseph M., Pub.; 0-9616281),* 5154 Mountain View Dr., Boise, ID 83704 (SAN 658-5213) Tel 208-322-0672.

J Tiffany, *(Tiffany, Jennifer),* 525 S. Danby Rd., Spencer, NY 14883 (SAN 287-2943).

J V Aho
See Townsend Harbor

J V Bush, *(Bush, Joseph V., Inc.; 0-9616684),* P.O. Box 626, Bonita, CA 92002 (SAN 659-9362); 4554 Cresta Verde, Bonita, CA 92002 (SAN 659-9370) Tel 619-479-0874.

J V Hays, *(Hays, J. V., Inc.; 0-941948),* 531 W. Pennsylvania Ave., Deland, FL 32720-3338 (SAN 238-4809) Tel 904-734-8944.

J V Smith, *(Smith, John V.),* 974 Hancock Ave., Akron, OH 44314 (SAN 289-503X) Tel 216-848-3474.

J Van Impe, *(Van Impe, Jack, Ministries; 0-934803),* 800 N. Crooks, Clawson, MI 48017 (SAN 697-3620).

J W Bell, *(Bell, James W., Publisher; 0-939130),* 7611 Briarwood Dr., Little Rock, AR 72205 (SAN 216-1044); Dist. by: Publishers Distribution Service, 7509 Cantrell Rd., Little Rock, AR 72207 (SAN 282-5937).

J W Brown Pub, *(Brown, J. W., Publishing, Inc.; 0-938215),* P.O. Box 1592, Sedona, AZ 86336 (SAN 659-9214); 55 Southwest Dr., Sedona, AZ 86336 (SAN 659-9222) Tel 602-282-6715.

J W Edwards
See Edwards Bros

J W Linn, *(Linn, Jo White; 0-918470),* Box 1948, Salisbury, NC 28144 (SAN 209-9489) Tel 704-633-3575.

J W Swanson
See Wayfinder Pr

J W Walch, *(Walch, J. Weston, Pub.; 0-8251),* P.O. Box 658, Portland, ME 04104 (SAN 669-6562) Tel 207-772-2846; Toll free: 800-341-6094.

J W Warner, *(Warner, John W., Inc., Pubs.; 0-938097),* 4800 Bayview Dr., Ft. Lauderdale, FL 33308 (SAN 659-7106) Tel 305-771-6881.

J Wallis, *(Wallis, Joe; 0-9605950),* P.O. Box 2294, Washington, DC 20013 (SAN 216-4752).

J Wampler, *(Wampler, Joseph Carson; 0-935080),* Box 45, Berkeley, CA 94701 (SAN 206-1910).

J Weber Gall, *(Weber, John, Gallery; 0-9608288),* 142 Greene St., New York, NY 10012 (SAN 240-4575).

J Willert, *(Willert, James; 0-930798),* 12804 S. Graff Dr., La Mirada, CA 90638 (SAN 212-2456) Tel 213-691-5641.

J Winnen, *(Winnen, Jo; 0-9603404),* 624 S. Fancher Rd., Racine, WI 53406 (SAN 207-2416).

J Woods Pubns, *(Woods, Jo, Pubns.),* 2701 Ozark Drive, North Little Rock, AR 72116 (SAN 213-8832) Tel 501-835-0795.

J Y Cho, *(Cho, Jun Young; 0-9617185),* 1801 Edgewater Dr., Plano, TX 75075 (SAN 663-2688) Tel 214-828-8143.

J-Y Ent, *(J-Y Enterprises; 0-9609670),* 717 Ponce de Leon, Stockton, CA 95210 (SAN 271-7123) Tel 209-951-2341.

J Y Sundstrom, *(Sundstrom, Jessie Y.; 0-936281),* P.O. Box 528, Custer, SD 57730 (SAN 699-7651) Tel 605-673-4377.

J Young Bks, *(Young, Jean, Bks.),* P.O. Box 8, Woodstock, NY 12498 (SAN 670-6967).

J Zink, *(Zink, J., Inc.; 0-942490),* P.O. Box 3279, Manhattan Beach, CA 90266 (SAN 239-9601) Tel 213-545-1031.

JA Micropublishing, *(JA Micropublishing, Inc.; 0-912127),* 271 Main Street Box 218, Eastchester, NY 10707 (SAN 264-6730) Tel 914-793-2130; Toll free: 800-227-2477.

Jaap Rietman, *(Rietman, Jaap; 0-930034),* 167 Spring St., New York, NY 10012 (SAN 205-2105) Tel 212-966-7044.

JAARS Inc, *(JAARS, Inc.; 0-9615959),* Affil. of Summer Institute of Linguistics, Box 248, JAARS Rd., Waxhaw, NC 28173 (SAN 697-2896) Tel 704-843-2185.

JABA, *(JABA; 0-938583),* 9521 Business Ctr. Dr., Rancho Cucamonga, CA 91730 (SAN 661-1141) Tel 714-980-2722.

Jacar Pr, *(Jacar Pr.; 0-936481),* 223 N. Main, Wendell, NC 27591 (SAN 698-1038) Tel 919-365-4188; P.O. Box 4, Wendell, NC 27591 (SAN 698-2530).

Jacbar Pubns, *(Jacbar Pubns.; 0-9606154),* Box 103, Randolph, OH 44265 (SAN 217-1120).

Jacek, *(Jacek Publishing Co.; 0-9601084),* 38 Morris Lane, Milford, CT 06460 (SAN 209-4029).

Jack Mack, *(Jack Mack Paperbacks; 0-910391),* 612 E. Manning, Apt. 3, Reedley, CA 93654 (SAN 260-0994) Tel 209-638-3392.

Jack Scott, *(Scott, Jack; 0-9616029),* 26 Township Line Rd., Apt. C48, Elkins Park, MD 19117 (SAN 699-7600) Tel 215-379-2898.

Jack Shank, *(Shank, Jack; 0-9616123),* 3633 48th St., Meridian, MS 39305 (SAN 699-7139) Tel 601-483-1681.

†**Jackpine Pr,** *(Jackpine Press; 0-917492),* 1878 Meadowbrook Dr., Winston-Salem, NC 27104 (SAN 208-273X) Tel 919-725-8828; *CIP.*

Jackrabbit, *(Jackrabbit Books; 0-9612454),* P.O. Box 1, Minneapolis, MN 55440 (SAN 289-5072) Tel 213-941-4446.

Jacks Art Mus
See Jacksonville Art

Jackson Assocs, *(Jackson, Don, Assocs.; 0-913211),* 461 Park Ave. S., 9th Flr., New York, NY 10016 (SAN 283-1228) Tel 212-213-9566. *Imprints:* Am Liberty Pub (American Liberty Publishing).

Jackson G B, *(Jackson, G. B.),* 1030 Edgewater Ave. W., St. Paul, MN 55112 (SAN 287-2757).

Jackson Games, *(Jackson, Steve, Games, Inc.; 1-55634),* P.O. Box 18957, Austin, TX 78760 (SAN 661-3292); 2700A Metcalfe Rd., Austin, TX 78741 (SAN 661-3306) Tel 512-447-7866.

Jackson Mtn, *(Jackson Mountain Pr.; 0-918499),* P.O. Box 2652, Renton, WA 98056 (SAN 657-3576) Tel 206-255-6635; 1550 Union NE, Renton, WA 98056 (SAN 657-3584).

Jackson Pubns, *(Jackson Pubns.; 0-937457),* Hwy. 626 & Pecan, Rm. 8, Boley, OK 74829 (SAN 658-8875) Tel 918-667-3394.

Jackson St Hse
See Rainy Day Oreg

Jacksonville Art, *(Jacksonville Art Museum, Inc.; 0-916235),* 4160 Blvd. Center Dr., Jacksonville, FL 32207 (SAN 294-944X) Tel 904-398-8336.

Jacobs, *(Jacobs Publishing Co.; 0-918272),* 3334 E. Indian School Rd., Suite C, Phoenix, AZ 85018 (SAN 209-4525) Tel 602-954-6581.

Jacobs Enter
See J & J Dist

Jacobs Ladder Pubns, *(Jacobs Ladder Pubns.; 0-933647),* 5003 Cascade Ct., Culver City, CA 90230 (SAN 692-6517) Tel 213-558-1166.

Jacobs Pub, *(Jacobs Publishing Inc.; 0-9615234),* 101 E. Carmel Dr., Suite 200, Carmel, IN 46032 (SAN 692-4905) Tel 317-844-9400.

Jacobsen Prop, *(Jacobsen Properties, Inc.; 0-9613260),* P.O. Box 96, Westwego, LA 70094 (SAN 296-6026) Tel 504-348-2276.

JACP Inc, *(JACP, Inc.; 0-934609),* 414 E. Third Ave., San Mateo, CA 94401 (SAN 693-8841) Tel 415-343-9408; Orders to: P.O. Box 367, San Mateo, CA 94401 (SAN 662-3271).

Jacqueline Enter, *(Jacqueline Enterprises, Inc.; 0-932446),* 4896 South El Camino Dr., Englewood, CO 80111 (SAN 221-0487) Tel 303-779-8278.

Jadd Pub Hse, *(Jadd Publishing Hse.; 0-9616772),* P.O. Box 4, Melrose, WI 54642 (SAN 661-3349); 311 Washington St., Melrose, WI 54642 (SAN 661-3357) Tel 608-488-4971.

Jade Hse Pubns, *(Jade House Pubns.; 0-942596),* P.O. Box 419, Bryantown, MD 20617 (SAN 239-6653) Tel 301-274-3441.

Jade Mist Pr, *(Jade Mist Pr.; 0-935107),* P.O. Box 5229, Eugene, OR 97405 (SAN 695-0981) Tel 503-345-9538.

Jade Mtn, *(Jade Mountain Pr.; 0-916133),* P.O. Box 72, Mountain Lakes, NJ 07046 (SAN 294-9474) Tel 203-334-1189; 11 Hillcrest Rd., Mountain Lakes, NJ 07046 (SAN 294-9482).

Jade Pubns, *(Jade Pubns.; 0-937399),* P.O. Box 5567, Sherman Oaks, CA 91413 (SAN 658-8891); 8758 Sophia, Sepulveda, CA 91343 (SAN 658-8905) Tel 818-892-9433.

Jadestone, *(Jadestone Publishing Corp.),* 3341 West Peoria Avenue, Phoenix, AZ 85029 (SAN 264-1348).

Jadetree Pr, *(Jadetree Pr., Inc.; 0-917135),* P.O. Box 11130, Arlington, VA 22210 (SAN 655-8178) Tel 703-522-9550.

Jaeger, *(Jaeger, Julia, Mrs.),* The Tenth Muse, P.O. Box 1417, Pacifica, CA 94044 (SAN 211-2957).

Jaguar Bks, *(Jaguar Bks.; 0-937723),* P.O. Box 6360, Santa Fe, NM 87502 (SAN 659-2554) Tel 505-983-8068; 601 Canyon Rd., Santa Fe, NM 87501 (SAN 659-2562).

Jahan Bk Co, *(Jahan Bk. Co; 0-936665),* 116 Greenbank Ave., Piedmont, CA 94611 (SAN 699-7163) Tel 415-428-0933; Orders to: 116 Greenbank Ave., Piedmont, CA 94611 (SAN 662-4030) Tel 415-428-0933.

†**Jai Pr,** *(Jai Pr., Inc.; 0-89232),* P.O. Box 1678, Greenwich, CT 06836 (SAN 208-4082) Tel 203-661-7602; *CIP.*

Jaks Pub Co, *(Jaks Publishing Co.; 0-935674),* 1106 N. Washington St., Helena, MT 59601 (SAN 214-042X).

Jakubowsky, *(Jakubowsky; 0-932588),* 1565 Madison St., Oakland, CA 94612 (SAN 212-1034) Tel 415-763-4324.

Jalamap, *(Jalamap Pubns., Inc.; 0-934750; 1-55649),* 601 D St., South Charleston, WV 25303-0917 (SAN 216-1478) Tel 304-744-1353.

†**Jalmar Pr,** *(Jalmar Pr.; 0-915190),* Subs. of B. L. Winch & Assocs., 45 Hitching Post Dr., Bldg. 2, Rolling Hills Estate, CA 90274-4297 (SAN 281-8302) Tel 213-539-6430; Toll free: 800-662-9662; *CIP.*

Jama Bks, *(Jama Books; 0-934130),* 1120 Beach Dr., Flint, MI 48502 (SAN 281-8329).

Jamenair Ltd, *(Jamenair, Ltd.; 0-938667),* P.O. Box 241957, Los Angeles, CA 90024 (SAN 661-6194); 10660 Wellworth Ave., Los Angeles, CA 90024 (SAN 661-6208) Tel 213-470-8105.

James Andrews Co, *(Andrews, James, & Co., Inc., Publishing; 0-9614643),* 1942 Mt. Zion Dr., Golden, CO 80401 (SAN 691-8670) Tel 303-279-1277.

James K Polk, *(Polk, James K., Memorial Auxilary; 0-9607668),* Box 741, Columbia, TN 38401 (SAN 239-5908) Tel 615-388-2354.

James McCormick & Co, *(James, McCormick & Co., Pubs.; 0-934979),* 15127 NE 24th St. C-3, Suite 156, Redmond, WA 98052 (SAN 694-0323) Tel 206-643-7850.

James Manning, *(Manning, James, Pub.; 0-9616234),* 112 Ocean Dr., Apt. 18, Miami Beach, FL 33139 (SAN 658-585X).

James Pr Inc, *(James Pr., Inc.; 0-9617280),* 4915 11th Ave., Brooklyn, NY 11219 (SAN 663-5229) Tel 718-853-3863.

James Pub Inc, *(James Publishing, Inc.; 0-931903),* P.O. Box 27310, Santa Ana, CA 92799 (SAN 686-0192) Tel 714-556-0960.

James Pub Santa Ana, *(James Publishing, Inc.; 0-938065),* P.O. Box 27370, Santa Ana, CA 92799 (SAN 661-1869); 3520 Cadillac Ave., Suite A, Costa Mesa, CA 92626 (SAN 661-1877) Tel 714-556-0960. Do not confuse with James Pub. of East Irvine, CA.

James Pubns NY, *(James Pubns.; 0-9615267),* Box 545, Guilderland, NY 12084 (SAN 695-1783) Tel 518-462-3311.

James Reep, *(Reep, James W.; 0-9614602),* 3511 55th Ave., Hyattsville, MD 20784 (SAN 691-8255) Tel 301-927-7241.

Jameson & Peeters
See E W Jameson Jr

Jamestown Pubs, *(Jamestown Pubs., Inc.; 0-89061),* P.O. Box 9168, Providence, RI 02940 (SAN 201-5196) Tel 401-351-1915; Toll free: 800-872-7323.

†**Jamieson Pr,** *(Jamieson Pr.; 0-915607),* Div. of Family Business Management Services, P.O. Box 909, 2967 Attleboro Rd., Cleveland, OH 44120 (SAN 292-5478) Tel 216-752-7970; *CIP.*

Jamison Stn, *(Jamison Sta. Pr.),* 7115 Pembroke Dr., Reno, NV 89502 (SAN 277-691X).

JAMV Pub, *(JAMV Publishing; 0-911371),* 199 Posada del Sol, Suite 219, Novato, CA 94947 (SAN 271-7166) Tel 415-883-4958; Orders to: P.O. Box 1748, Novato, CA 94948 (SAN 662-0507).

Jan Ents
See Jan Pubns Inc

Jan Pubns Inc, *(Jan Pubns., Inc.; 0-934896),* P.O. Box 1860, Cape Coral, FL 33910 (SAN 213-2222) Tel 813-549-2093.

J&J Pubns MI, *(J&J Pubns.; 0-9605786),* Box 1424, Traverse City, MI 49684 (SAN 216-4000).

J&M Pub, *(J&M Publishing Co.; 0-930630),* 11 Matthews Ave., Riverdale, NJ 07457 (SAN 211-1411) Tel 201-838-9434.

J&W Tex-Mex, *(J&W Tex-Mex; 0-9604842),* P.O. Box 983, Arlington, VA 22216 (SAN 215-6628).

Janeric Pr, *(Janeric Press; 0-911373),* P.O. Box 477, Banner Elk, NC 28604 (SAN 271-7182) Tel 704-898-5500.

Janes Pub Eugene, *(Janes Publishing; 0-938333),* 28787 Gimpl Hill Rd., Eugene, OR 97402 (SAN 661-311X) Tel 503-343-2408.

Jane's Pub Inc, *(Jane's Publishing, Inc.; 0-86720; 0-7106),* Subs. of Jane's Publishing Co., Ltd. (England), 115 Fifth Ave., 4th Flr., New York, NY 10003 (SAN 286-357X) Tel 212-254-9097; Orders to: 20 Park Plaza, Boston, MA 02116 (SAN 226-9791) Tel 617-542-6564.

Janevar Pub, *(Janevar Publishing Co.; 0-937174),* 1303 Sunset Dr., North Manchester, IN 46962 (SAN 215-157X) Tel 219-982-8885.

JanJe Pr, *(JanJe Pr.; 0-9617148),* 4843 Snowden Ave., Lakewood, CA 90713 (SAN 663-3684) Tel 213-429-9253.

Janova Pr, *(Janova Press, Inc.; 0-917294),* 3833 Barker Rd., Cincinnati, OH 45229 (SAN 208-3671) Tel 513-861-0511.

Jansen Pub
See Forsyth Lib Travel

Jantrex & Co, *(Jantrex & Co.; 0-9615490),* Sunset Cove, Brookfield, CT 06804 (SAN 696-2807) Tel 203-775-2491.

Janus Bks, *(Janus Bk. Pubs.; 0-88102; 0-915510; 0-88084),* 2501 Industrial Pkwy. W., Hayward, CA 94545 (SAN 208-0478) Tel 415-887-7070; Toll free: 800-227-2375.

Janus Pr, *(Janus Pr.; 0-916172),* P.O. Box 1050, Rogue River, OR 97537 (SAN 207-5806) Tel 503-582-1520. Do not confuse with Janus Pr., Winter Springs, FL.

Janus Pr FL, *(Janus Pr.; 0-9616341),* P.O. Box 3633, Winter Springs, FL 32708 (SAN 658-7461) Tel 305-671-5433; 1105 Howell Creek Dr., Casselberry, FL 32708 (SAN 658-747X).

Janus Pubns, *(Janus Pubns.; 0-9613426),* Box 8705, Wichita, KS 67206 (SAN 657-0453) Tel 316-686-8320.

Japan-Am Soc, *(Japan-America Society of Washington, Inc.),* 606 18th St., NW, Washington, DC 20006 (SAN 233-4356) Tel 202-289-8290.

Japan Amer Anthlgy Com, *(Japanese American Anthology Committee; 0-9603222),* P.O. Box 5024, San Francisco, CA 94101 (SAN 222-3643).

Japan Pubns
See Japan Pubns USA

Japan Pubns USA, *(Japan Pubns. (USA), Inc.; 0-87040),* 45 Hawthorn Pl., Briarcliff Manor, NY 10510 (SAN 680-0513).

Japan Soc, *(Japan Society; 0-913304),* 333 E. 47th St., New York, NY 10017 (SAN 225-3259) Tel 212-832-1155.

Japanese Am Citizens, *(Japanese American Citizens League),* 941 E. Third St., Los Angeles, CA 90013 (SAN 225-4093) Tel 213-626-6936.

JAPOS Study Grp, *(Journalists Authors & Poets on Stamps Study Group),* 154 Laguna Ct., St. Augustine Shores, FL 32086 (SAN 225-5979) Tel 904-797-3513.

Jargon Soc, *(Jargon Society, Inc., The; 0-912330),* Highlands, NC 28741 (SAN 662-0515); Toll free: 800-243-0138; 1000 W. Fifth St., Winston-Salem, NC 28741 (SAN 662-0523); Dist. by: Inland Bk. Co., P.O. Box 261, 22 Hemingway Ave., East Haven, CT 06512 (SAN 200-4151) Tel 203-467-4257.

Jarrett, *(Jarrett, Richard Buhler; 0-9606884),* P.O. Box 6007, Suite 250, Redding, CA 96099 (SAN 217-3840).

Jasmine Pub, *(Jasmine Publishing Co.; 0-938861),* 1641 Third Ave., Suite 8BE, New York, NY 10128 (SAN 661-7328) Tel 212-348-8487.

Jason Pub, *(Jason Publishing; 0-9613180),* 170 Sisson Ave. 2-408, Hartford, CT 06105 (SAN 295-8570) Tel 203-232-6772.

Jason Pub OH, *(Jason Publishing; 0-938067),* 5763 Belmont Ave., Cincinnati, OH 45224 (SAN 661-1931) Tel 513-541-4346. Do not confuse with Jason Pub., Hartford, CT.

Jasper Assocs, *(Jasper Assocs.; 0-9613373),* P.O. Box 8971, Salt Lake City, UT 84108 (SAN 657-1476) Tel 801-277-7615.

Symbols/Abbreviations

Jasper County, *(Jasper County Abstract Co.; 0-9604474),* Kellner at Van Rensselaer St., Rensselaer, IN 47978 (SAN 215-0840).

Jawbone Pr
See Brooding Heron Pr

Jay & Assoc, *(Jay & Associates, Pubs.; 0-939422),* P.O. Box 13898, Arlington, TX 76013 (SAN 281-837X) Tel 817-273-2876; Orders to: Marketing Department, P.O. Box 19469, Arlington, TX 76019 (SAN 281-8388).

Jay Pub, *(Jay Publishing Co.; 0-930140),* P.O. Box 454, Lakewood, CA 90714 (SAN 209-4533) Tel 714-893-0326.

Jay Pubns, *(Jay Pubns.; 0-916666),* P.O. Box 1141, San Andreas, CA 95249 (SAN 208-3922) Tel 209-754-4520.

Jay Ra Prods, *(Jay Ra Productions; 0-913155),* P.O. Box 785, Mill Valley, CA 94942 (SAN 283-1260) Tel 415-381-0290.

†Jayco Pub, *(Jayco Pub. Co.; 0-9607728),* P.O. Box 1511, South Bend, IN 46634 (SAN 237-9627) Tel 219-291-2291; *CIP.*

Jayell Ent, *(Jayell Enterprises Inc.; 0-916197),* P.O. Box 2616, Dearborn, MI 48123 (SAN 294-9490) Tel 313-565-9687; Dist. by: Inland Bk. Co., P.O. Box 261, 22 Hemingway Ave., East Haven, CT 06512 (SAN 200-4151) Tel 203-467-4257.

Jaykay Pub Inc, *(Jaykay Publishing Inc.; 0-9613778),* 4930 Walnut Ave., White Bear Lake, MN 55110 (SAN 678-9951) Tel 612-372-4412; Orders to: P.O. Box 15775, Minneapolis, MN 55415 (SAN 662-2550).

†Jazz Discographies, *(Jazz Discographies Unlimited,* 337 Ellerton S., Laurel, MD 20707 (SAN 212-6710) Tel 301-776-3148; *CIP.*

Jazz Pr, *(Jazz Pr.; 0-937310),* P.O. Box 2409, Aptos, CA 95001 (SAN 215-1596).

JB & Me, *(JB & Me; 0-9616226),* P.O. Box 480311, Los Angeles, CA 90048 (SAN 658-5515) Tel 213-546-1255.

JC-DC Cartoons, *(JC/DC Cartoons Ink; 0-934574),* 5536 Fruitland Rd NE, Salem, OR 97301 (SAN 213-0963).

JCL Hse, *(JCL House; 0-9610274),* P.O. Box 1821, East Lansing, MI 48823 (SAN 264-1305) Tel 616-385-2870.

JCMC Louisiana, *(Jewish Council Millenium Covenant),* 1812 N. Hwy. 171, De Ridder, LA 70634 (SAN 663-6306).

JCP *Imprint of* Unipub

JCP Corp VA, *(JCP Corp. of Virginia; 0-938694),* P.O. Box 814, Virginia Beach, VA 23451 (SAN 220-1313) Tel 804-422-5426.

JD-J *Imprint of* John Day

JD McG Pubns, *(JD McG. Pubns.; 0-932619),* 32 W. Glendale Ave., Alexandria, VA 22301 (SAN 687-5173) Tel 703-683-3463.

JD Pub & Seminars, *(JD Publishing & Seminars; 0-937841),* 3520-B Cadillac Ave., Costa Mesa, CA 92626 (SAN 659-4743) Tel 714-751-2787.

JD Pubs, *(J. D. Pubs.; 0-9616688),* 13162 Miller Rd., Johnstown, OH 43031 (SAN 661-4388).

JD-T *Imprint of* John Day

Jean Thomas, *(Jean-Thomas, Inc.; 0-910459),* P.O. Box 5650, Lakeland, FL 33803 (SAN 260-0277) Tel 813-644-3548.

Jeanene's, *(Jeanene's Needle Arts; 0-931716),* P.O. Box 6701, Woodland Hills, CA 91365 (SAN 211-5972) Tel 818-346-7276.

Jeanies Classics, *(Jeanies Classics; 0-9609672),* 2123 Oxford St., Rockford, IL 61103 (SAN 271-7395) Tel 815-968-4544; Dist. by: Jeanies Classics Publishing, P.O. Box 4303, Rockford, IL 61110 (SAN 271-7409).

Jeannes Dreams, *(Jeanne's Dreams; 0-9604694),* P.O. Box 211, La Farge, WI 54639 (SAN 213-6872) Tel 608-625-2425.

JEB Pub, *(J. E. B. Pub. Co.; 0-940946),* Rte. 2 Box 400, Franklin, GA 30217 (SAN 281-8396); Orders to: Groover Medical Bldg., Ambulance Dr., Carrollton, GA 30117 (SAN 281-840X) Tel 404-832-6861.

Jebco Bks, *(Jebco Books Division; 0-9609494),* P.O. Box 268, Harrison, OH 45030 (SAN 262-7574) Tel 513-385-5986.

JED, *(JED; 0-9602200),* P.O. Box 7143 RC, Toledo, OH 43615 (SAN 212-3622) Tel 419-885-2932.

Jedick Ent, *(Jedick, Peter, Enterprises; 0-9605568),* 1708 Wooster Rd., Rocky River, OH 44116 (SAN 216-0455).

JEF Pr, *(JEF Pr.; 0-9616022),* 179 E. Third St., New York, NY 10009 (SAN 699-7589) Tel 212-505-5143.

Jeff Burkett, *(Burkett, Jeff; 0-9616303),* 2700 W. 44th St., Apt. 207, Minneapolis, MN 55410 (SAN 658-4543) Tel 612-922-6324.

Jefferson County Office Hist Pres Arch, *(Jefferson County Office of Historic Preservation & Archives; 0-9607612),* 100 Fiscal Court Building, Louisville, KY 40202 (SAN 237-9635).

Jefferson High, *(Jefferson High School; 0-9614227),* 1243 20th St. SW, Cedar Rapids, IA 52404 (SAN 686-7650) Tel 319-398-2231.

Jefferson Med Anest, *(Jefferson Medical College, Dept. of Anesthesiology),* Thomas Jefferson Univ., 1020 Walnut St., Philadelphia, PA 19107 (SAN 651-5975) Tel 215-928-6161.

Jefferson Natl, *(Jefferson National Expansion Historical Assn.; 0-931056),* 11 N. 4th St., St. Louis, MO 63102 (SAN 213-0912).

Jefferson Pubns, *(Jefferson Pubns., Inc.),* Monticello Bks. Div., 44 S. Old Rand Rd., Box 771, Lake Zurich, IL 60047 (SAN 207-639X) Tel 312-438-4114.

Jeffries Banknote, *(Jeffries Banknote Co.),* 1330 W. Pico Blvd., Los Angeles, CA 90015 (SAN 227-2229) Tel 213-742-8888.

Jefren Pub, *(Jefren Pub. Co.; 0-917244),* 1513 Auburn Ave., Rockville, MD 20850 (SAN 208-7138).

Jehara Pr, *(Jehara Pr.; 0-9616227),* P.O. Box 19156, Chicago, IL 60619 (SAN 658-5612) Tel 312-873-4253; 8040 Wabash Ave., Chicago, IL 60619 (SAN 658-5620) Tel 312-873-4253.

Jei-Ai Pub Co, *(Jei-Ai Publishing Company, Incorporated),* 2101 1/2 Bush St., San Francisco, CA 94115 (SAN 293-7980) Tel 415-922-4780; Dist. by: Jei-Ai International Corp., P.O. Box 10115, Beverly Hills, CA 90213 (SAN 293-7999) Tel 213-986-4644.

†Jelm Mtn, *(Jelm Mountain Pubns.; 0-936204),* c/o Green Mountain Book Co. P.O. Box 338, Markleeville, CA 96120 (SAN 216-1419) Tel 916-694-2141; *CIP.*

Jems Pub, *(Jems Publishing; 0-936174),* P.O. Box 1026, Solana Beach, CA 92075 (SAN 241-550X) Tel 619-481-1128.

Jems Pub Co
See Jems Pub

Jemta Pr, *(Jemta Press; 0-9604246),* 11313 Beech Daly Rd., Redford Township, MI 48239 (SAN 209-1372) Tel 313-937-1986.

†Jen Hse Pub Co, *(Jen Hse. Publishing Co.; 0-910841),* 119 Cherry Valley Rd., Reisterstown, MD 21136 (SAN 262-7604) Tel 301-833-8931; *CIP.*

Jende-Hagan, *(Jende-Hagan, Inc.; 0-939650),* P.O. Box 177-A, Frederick, CO 80530 (SAN 169-0574) Tel 303-833-2030; 541 Oak St., Frederick, CO 80530 (SAN 658-1404). *Imprints:* Platte n Pr (Platte 'n Press); Renaissance Hse (Renaissance House).

Jende-Hagan Bk
See Jende-Hagan

Jenfred Pr, *(Jenfred Pr.),* P.O. Box 767, Trinidad, CA 95570 (SAN 215-6644).

Jenkins, *(Jenkins Publishing Co.; 0-8363),* P.O. Box 2085, Austin, TX 78767 (SAN 202-7321) Tel 512-444-6616.

Jenna Pr, *(Jenna Pr.; 0-941752),* 37 W. Eighth St., New York, NY 10011 (SAN 293-2881) Tel 212-477-4471; R.D. 1, Box 227, Petersburg, NY 12138 (SAN 293-289X).

Jennilee-Angel, *(Jennilee-Angel Pr.; 0-930217),* P.O. Box 44, Laguna Beach, CA 92652 (SAN 670-7858) Tel 714-497-7079.

Jenning Pr
See Jennings Pr

Jennings Pr, *(Jennings Pr., Inc.; 0-931781),* 2222 Fuller Rd. Suite 801A, Ann Arbor, MI 48105 (SAN 684-8621) Tel 313-665-7410.

Jenstan, *(Jenstan; 0-9612624),* P.O. Box 674, Franklin, MI 48025 (SAN 289-2685) Tel 313-626-1768.

Jeppesen Sanderson, *(Jeppesen Sanderson; 0-88487),* Affil. of Times-Mirror Co., 55 Inverness Dr. E., Englewood, CO 80112 (SAN 201-0224) Tel 303-779-9090.

Jepson Herbarium, *(Jepson Herbarium; 0-935628),* Univ. of California, Berkeley, Botany Dept., Berkeley, CA 94720 (SAN 214-2112) Tel 415-642-2465; Dist. by: Lubrecht & Cramer, RD 1, Box 244, Rte. 42, Forestburgh Rd., Forestburgh, NY 12777 (SAN 214-1256) Tel 914-794-8539.

Jerald Brown, *(Brown, Jerald R.; 0-9614679),* 17440 Taylor Ln., Occidental, CA 95465 (SAN 692-5081) Tel 707-874-3344; Dist. by: Bookpeople, 2929 Fifth St., Berkeley, CA 94710 (SAN 168-9517) Tel 415-549-3030; Dist. by: Inland Book Co., P.O. Box 261, 22 Hemingway Ave., East Haven, CT 06512 (SAN 200-4151) Tel 203-467-4257.

Jeremy Bks, *(Jeremy Books; 0-89877),* Dist. by: Successful Living, Inc., 9905 Hamilton Road, Eden Prairie, MN 55344 (SAN 213-0939).

Jesse Bks, *(Jesse Bks.; 0-9616027),* Box 339, Huntingdon Valley, PA 19006 (SAN 697-8916) Tel 215-947-5584; 960 Hunters Turn, Huntingdon Valley, PA 19006 (SAN 698-2271).

Jest Four You Pub, *(Jest 4 You Publishing; 0-9615794),* 10164 Disney Cir., Huntington Beach, CA 92646 (SAN 696-8686) Tel 714-964-4380.

Jester Pr *Imprint of* Red Hen Pr

Jesuit Bks, *(Jesuit Books; 0-913452),* Gonzaga University, Spokane, WA 99258 (SAN 201-0232) Tel 509-328-4220.

Jesuit Hist, *(Jesuit Historical Institute),* 3441 N. Ashland Ave., Chicago, IL 60657 (SAN 662-0531) Tel 312-281-1818; Toll free: 800-621-1008; c/o Loyola Univ. Pr., 3441 N. Ashland Ave., Chicago, IL 60657 (SAN 211-6537).

Jesuits Holy Cross, *(Jesuits of Holy Cross College, Inc.; 0-9606294),* College of the Holy Cross, Worcester, MA 01610 (SAN 210-1211) Tel 617-793-3314.

Jesus-First, *(Jesus-First Pubs., Inc.; 0-9602440),* 1116-4th St., NW, Ruskin, FL 33570 (SAN 212-3630) Tel 813-645-5726.

Jetiquette, *(Jet'iquette; 0-9600786),* 510 Michigan Ave., Charlevoix, MI 49720 (SAN 202-733X) Tel 616-547-6443.

Jets, *(JETS, Inc.),* 1180 Ave. of the Americas, New York, NY 10036 (SAN 236-2570) Tel 212-705-7690; 345 E. 47th St., New York, NY 10017 (SAN 693-4919).

Jetsand Pr
See Jetsand Pubs Ltd

Jetsand Pubs Ltd, *(Jetsand Pubs., Ltd.; 0-933374),* Box 17052, West Hartford, CT 06117 (SAN 212-8349) Tel 203-658-1423.

Jewel Pr, *(Jewel Pr.; 0-937093),* Div. of Jewel Communications International, P.O. Box 1833, Fort Collins, CO 80522 (SAN 658-6139) Tel 303-226-5914; 4414 E. Harmony Rd., Fort Collins, CO 80525 (SAN 658-6147); Orders to: P.O. Box 904, Fort Collins, CO 80526 (SAN 662-4146); Orders to: 4414 E. Harmony Rd., Fort Collins, CO 80526 (SAN 662-4154).

Jewel Pub Co, *(Jewel Publishing Co.; 0-9614890),* 165 Congress Run Rd., Cincinnati, OH 45215 (SAN 693-2460) Tel 513-521-1149; Dist. by: The South Bend Distributors, 702 S. Michigan, South Bend, IN 46618 (SAN 200-7134); Dist. by: Baker & Taylor (Midwest Div.), 501 Gladiola Ave., Momence, IL 60954 (SAN 169-2100).

Jewel Pub Hse, *(Jewel Publishing Hse.; 0-9607000),* P.O. Box 146, New York, NY 10002 (SAN 241-5879).

Jewel Pubns, *(Jewel Pubns.; 0-917728),* 2417 Hazelwood Ave., Fort Wayne, IN 46805 (SAN 209-3049) Tel 219-483-6625.

Jewelers Circular, *(Jewelers' Circular-Keystone; 0-931744),* Chilton Way, Radnor, PA 19089-0140 (SAN 210-9050) Tel 215-964-4480; Orders to: Jeweler's Book Club, Chilton Way, Radnor, PA 19089-0140 (SAN 662-054X).

Jewell-Johnson, *(Jewell-Johnson & Co. Inc.; 0-930198),* 502 Benton St., Port Townsend, WA 98368 (SAN 210-9077) Tel 206-385-4342.

Jewish Bd Family, *(Jewish Board of Family & Children's Services, Library Inc.),* c/o Central Library, 120 W. 57th St., New York, NY 10019 (SAN 211-9080) Tel 212-582-9100.

Jewish Bk Council
See JWB

Jewish Com Pub, *(Jewish Combatants Pubs. House, Inc.; 0-9613219),* P.O. Box 323, Brooklyn, NY 11236 (SAN 295-8821) Tel 718-763-7551.

Jewish Comm Ctr, *(Jewish Community Center of Greater Boston; 0-9605624),* 333 Nahanton St., Newton, MA 02159 (SAN 218-4842).

Jewish Ed Soc Res, *(Jewish Educators for Social Responsibility; 0-9615897),* Div. of Educators for Social Responsibility, 90 Hanson Rd., Newton, MA 02159 (SAN 696-8708) Tel 617-738-5329.

Jewish Genealogical, *(Jewish Genealogical Society Of Illinois; 0-9613512),* 1025 Antique Ln., Northbrook, IL 60062 (SAN 657-3592) Tel 312-564-1025.

†Jewish Hist, *(Jewish Historical Society of New York, Inc.; 0-916790),* 8 W. 70th St., New York, NY 10023 (SAN 208-7146) Tel 212-873-0300; *CIP.*

Jewish Hosp Aux MO, *(Jewish Hospital Auxiliary of the Jewish Hospital of St. Louis; 0-9614764),* 216 S. Kingshighway, P.O. Box 14109, St. Louis, MO 63178 (SAN 692-9109) Tel 314-454-7130.

Jewish Mens Clubs
See Fed Jewish Mens Clubs

Jewish Mus West
See Magnes Mus

Jewish Pubn
See Jewish Pubns

†Jewish Pubns, *(Jewish Pubns. Society of America; 0-8276),* 1930 Chestnut St., Philadelphia, PA 19103 (SAN 201-0240) Tel 215-564-5925; *CIP.*

†Jewish Sem, *(Jewish Theological Seminary of America; 0-87334),* 3080 Broadway, New York, NY 10027 (SAN 204-9902) Tel 212-678-8000; Dist. by: Publishing Ctr. for Cultural Resources, 625 Broadway, New York, NY 10012 (SAN 274-9025) Tel 212-260-2010; *CIP.*

JFJ Assocs, *(JFJ Assocs.; 0-935707),* P.O. Box 56628, Washington, DC 20011 (SAN 695-6955) Tel 202-726-5248; 1302 Floral St., NW, Washington, DC 20012 (SAN 696-0391).

JFJ Pub, *(JFJ Publishing; 0-9616148),* Div. of Jews for Jesus, 60 Haight St., San Francisco, CA 94102 (SAN 699-8240); Toll free: 800-227-3190.

†JH Pr, *(JH Pr.; 0-935672),* P.O. Box 294, Village Sta., New York, NY 10014 (SAN 213-6279); *CIP.*

JHAFRP, *(Jackson Hole Alliance for Responsible Planning; 0-9617014),* P.O. Box 2728, Jackson, WY 83001 (SAN 662-9202); 260 E. Broadway, Jackson, WY 83001 (SAN 662-9210) Tel 307-733-9417.

Jim Cook, *(Cook, Jim, Pub.; 0-936941),* 494 Conejo Rd., Santa Barbara, CA 93103 (SAN 658-5051) Tel 805-962-7879.

Jim Lyons, *(Lyons, Jim; 0-9616231),* P.O. Box 608, Mountain View, CA 94042 (SAN 658-5728) Tel 415-494-0790.

Jim Rohn Prod, *(Rohn, Jim, Productions, Inc.; 0-939490),* 22951 Mill Creek Dr. Dr., No. 100, Laguna Hills, CA 92653 (SAN 216-5945) Tel 714-951-5740.

Jinro Pub, *(Jinro Publishing Co.; 0-940772),* 432 Board of Trade Bldg., 127 W. Tenth St., Kansas City, MO 64105 (SAN 219-6670) Tel 816-221-6640.

JIR, *(Journal of Irreproducible Results; 0-9605852),* P.O. Box 234, Chicago Hts, IL 60411 (SAN 282-7077) Tel 312-755-2080P.O. Box 234, Chicago Heights, IL 60411 (SAN 282-7085) Tel 312-755-2080.

JJ Pub FL, *(JJ Publishing; 0-9604610),* 1312 Arthur St., Hollywood, FL 33019 (SAN 220-0090) Tel 305-929-3559; Dist. by: Milady Publishing Corporation, 3839 White Plains, Bronx, NY 10467 (SAN 202-635X).

JKL Pubs, *(JKL Pubs.; 0-935757),* 8 Prince St., P.O. Box 1575, Rochester, NY 14603 (SAN 696-4753) Tel 716-624-4101.

JL Columbus GA, *(Junior League of Columbus, Georgia, Inc.; 0-9606300),* 1440 Second Ave., Columbus, GA 31901 (SAN 220-1569) Tel 404-327-4207.

JL Palm Beaches, *(Junior League of the Palm Beaches, The; 0-9608090),* P.O. Box 168, Palm Beach, FL 33480 (SAN 240-1177).

JL Press, *(JL Pr.; 0-939279),* Subs. of the Print Shoppe, P.O. Box 2414, Abilene, TX 79604 (SAN 662-7072); 2410 S. 14th, Abilene, TX 79605 (SAN 662-7080) Tel 915-691-0110.

Jl Pub Co
See Jei-Ai Pub Co

JLA Pubns, *(JLA Pubns.; 0-940374),* 50 Follen St., Suite 507, Cambridge, MA 02138 (SAN 223-1441) Tel 617-547-6382; Dist. by: Publishers Group West, 5855 Beaudry St., Emeryville, CA 94608 (SAN 202-8522) Tel 415-685-3453.

JLC Inc, *(Junior League of Chicago, Inc., The; 0-9611622),* 1447 N. Astor St., Chicago, IL 60610 (SAN 238-8863) Tel 312-664-4462.

JLJ Pubs, *(JLJ Pubs.; 0-937172),* 824 Shrine Rd., Springfield, OH 45504-3999 (SAN 215-322X) Tel 513-322-4454.

JM Pubns, *(JM Pubns., Inc.; 0-9615844),* P.O. Box 1408, Hendersonville, TN 37077-1408 (SAN 696-8716) Tel 615-822-0857; Walton Mall, No. 13, Hendersonville, TN 37077 (SAN 696-8724).

JMA Pr, *(JMA Pr., Inc.; 0-9614742),* 9215 Ashton Ridge, Austin, TX 78750 (SAN 692-7211) Tel 512-331-9027.

JMB Pubns, *(JMB Pubns.; 0-9606834),* 10810 Cherry Grove Ct., Louisville, KY 40299 (SAN 217-2410).

JML Ent
See Lawrence & Co Pubs

JML Enter MD, *(JML Enterprises, Inc.; 0-938464),* P.O Box 488, Bel Air, MD 21014 (SAN 238-5279) Tel 301-879-8552.

JMP Mfg, *(JMP Manufacturing Corp.; 0-9608898),* 4467 Eaton-Gettysburg Rd., Eaton, OH 45320 (SAN 264-133X) Tel 513-456-6995.

JMT Pubns, *(JMT Pubns.; 0-942782),* P.O. Box 603, Camp Hill, PA 17011 (SAN 238-8189) Tel 717-761-6513.

JNZ, *(JNZ, Inc.; 0-913871),* 729 Windward Dr., Rodeo, CA 94572 (SAN 286-7990) Tel 415-799-1446.

JO-D Bks, *(JO-D Bks.; 0-937791),* 81 Willard Terr., Stamford, CT 06903 (SAN 688-1203) Tel 203-322-0568.

Jo-Jo Pubns, *(Jo-Jo Pubns.; 0-9602266),* 208 N. Sparrow Rd., Chesapeake, VA 23325 (SAN 212-5153) Tel 804-420-8614.

Joane Pubns, *(Joane Pubns.; 0-9613925),* P.O. Box 459, Reading, MA 01867 (SAN 692-395X).

Job Data, *(Job Data Inc.; 0-918443),* 105 W. Madison, Chicago, IL 60602 (SAN 657-6303) Tel 312-348-4060.

Job Hunters Forum, *(Job Hunters Forum; 0-918350),* 132 Pinecrest Dr., Annapolis, MD 21403 (SAN 209-178X) Tel 301-268-6425.

JOB Pubns, *(JOB Pubns.; 0-9608520),* P.O. Box 1862, Hagerstown, MD 21742 (SAN 240-6004) Tel 301-791-3250.

Job Shop
See Woods Hole Pr

Jobeco Bks, *(Jobeco Bks.; 0-9607572),* P.O. Box 3323, Humble, TX 77347-3323 (SAN 237-9651) Tel 713-358-2791.

Jobhunter's Comp, *(Jobhunter's Companion; 0-9613020),* 843 St. George Ave., Roselle, NJ 07203 (SAN 294-0558) Tel 201-925-0080.

Joby Bks, *(Joby Bks.; 0-9604284),* P.O. Box 512, Fulton, CA 95439 (SAN 209-1518); Dist. by: Bookpeople, 2929 Fifth St., Berkeley, CA 94710 (SAN 168-9517) Tel 415-549-3030.

Jochum, *(Jochum, Helen Parker; 0-9606206),* 79 Huntington Rd., Garden City, NY 11530 (SAN 215-8787); Dist. by: Skills, 24 S. Prospect St., Amherst, MA 01002 (SAN 215-8795) Tel 413-253-9500.

Joe D Johnson, *(Johnson, Joe Donald; 0-915564),* P.O. Box 6692, Napa, CA 94581 (SAN 207-3366).

Joe Lane Pub, *(Lane, Joe, Publishing Co; 0-9603378),* P.O. Box 2646, Evergreen, CO 80439 (SAN 211-0784) Tel 303-674-5314.

Joe Miller Pub, *(Miller, Joe, Publishing; 0-9616542),* 5905-D Clark Rd., Suite 183, Paradise, CA 95969 (SAN 659-5227) Tel 916-877-1649.

JOED Orig, *(JOED Originals of California, Inc.; 0-916237),* P.O. Box 22439, San Diego, CA 92122-0439 (SAN 294-9520) Tel 619-453-7533.

Johannes, *(Johannes Pr.; 0-910810),* c/o Galerie St. Etienne, 24 W. 57th St., New York, NY 10019 (SAN 206-9806) Tel 212-245-6734.

Johannes Schwalm Hist, *(Johannes Schwalm Historical Assn., Inc.; 0-939016),* 800-S Westbury Pl., 4807 Old Spartanburg Rd., Taylors, SC 29687 (SAN 209-5076) Tel 216-382-5711.

Johmax Bks Inc, *(Johmax Bks., Inc.; 0-912095),* 48 Pine Brook Dr., Larchmont, NY 10538 (SAN 264-7559) Tel 914-834-0822.

John Alden Bks, *(Alden, John, Bks.; 0-9605818),* 187 Barmont Dr., P.O. Box 26668, Rochester, NY 14626 (SAN 216-5678) Tel 716-225-8534.

†John Day, *(John Day Co., Inc.; 0-381),* C/O Harper & Row Pubs., 10 E. 53rd St., New York, NY 10022 (SAN 211-6960); Toll free: 800-242-7737; Dist. by: Harper & Row Pubs., Keystone Industrial Pk., Scranton, PA 18512 (SAN 215-3742); *CIP. Imprints:* JD-J (John Day Juvenile Books); JD-T (John Day Trade Books).

†John Jay Pr, *(John Jay Pr.; 0-89444),* 444 W. 56th St., New York, NY 10019 (SAN 210-2196) Tel 212-489-3592; *CIP.*

†John Knox, *(Knox, John, Pr.; 0-8042),* Div. of Presbyterian Publishing Hse., 341 Ponce de Leon Ave., NE, Rm. 416, Atlanta, GA 30365 (SAN 201-0275) Tel 404-873-1549; Toll free: 800-334-6580; Toll free: 800-822-1917 (in GA); Orders to: P.O. Box 54658, Atlanta, GA 30308 (SAN 662-0566); *CIP.*

†John Muir, *(Muir, John, Pubns.; 0-912528),* P.O. Box 613, Santa Fe, NM 87504-0613 (SAN 203-9079) Tel 505-982-4078; Dist. by: W.W. Norton & Co., 500 Fifth Ave., New York, NY 10110 (SAN 202-5795) Tel 212-354-5500; *CIP.*

John Philipps, *(Phillipps, John; 0-9611412),* 1111 Belair Dr., Fallbrook, CA 92028 (SAN 285-6743) Tel 619-723-9126.

John Pubs
See Rae John

John Tracy Clinic, *(Tracy, John, Clinic Bulletin; 0-9606312),* 806 W. Adams Blvd., Los Angeles, CA 90007 (SAN 203-056X) Tel 213-748-5481.

John Wright-PSG
See PSG Pub Co

Johnny Alfalfa Sprout, *(Johnny Alfalfa Sprout; 0-9616229),* P.O. Box 294, Lewisburg, PA 17837 (SAN 658-5566) Tel 717-523-7878; 606 Market St., Lewisburg, PA 17837 (SAN 658-5574).

Johnny Inc
See K Diehl

Johnny Reads, *(Johnny Reads, Inc.; 0-910812),* P.O. Box 12834, St. Petersburg, FL 33733 (SAN 201-0283) Tel 813-867-7647. *Imprints:* Pub. by Ed Pubns (Educational Pubns.).

†Johns Hopkins, *(Johns Hopkins Univ. Pr.; 0-8018),* 701 W. 40th St., Suite 275, Baltimore, MD 21211 (SAN 202-7348) Tel 301-338-6956; *CIP.*

Johns Johns & Johns, *(Johns, Johns, & Johns; 0-939091),* 2160 Dowing St., No. 102, Denver, CO 80205 (SAN 662-8974) Tel 303-863-0043.

Johns Pr, *(John's Pr.; 0-9607730),* Box 3405 CRS, Rock Hill, SC 29731 (SAN 238-7948) Tel 803-366-7392.

Johnson & Simpson, *(Johnson & Simpson; 0-9615012),* 49 Bleeker St., Newark, NJ 07102 (SAN 693-9376) Tel 201-624-7788; Dist. by: Collectors Bks., P.O. Box 3009, Paducah, KY 42001 (SAN 200-7479).

Johnson Bks, *(Johnson Bks.; 0-933472; 1-55566),* Div. of Johnson Publishing Co., P.O. Box 990, Boulder, CO 80301 (SAN 201-0313) Tel 303-443-1576; 1880 S. 57th Ct., Boulder, CO 80301 (SAN 658-1013).

†Johnson Chi, *(Johnson Publishing Co., Inc.; 0-87485),* 820 S. Michigan Ave., Chicago, IL 60605 (SAN 201-0305) Tel 312-322-9248; *CIP.*

Johnson Colo
See Johnson Bks

Johnson Inst, *(Johnson Institute; 0-935908),* 510 First Ave. N., Minneapolis, MN 55403-1607 (SAN 221-4717) Tel 612-341-0435; Toll free: 800-231-5165.

Johnson NC, *(Johnson Publishing Co.; 0-930230),* P. O. Box 217, Murfreesboro, NC 27855 (SAN 201-0291).

Johnson Ref Bks, *(Johnson Reference Bks.; 0-9600906),* P.O. Box 7152, Alexandria, VA 22307 (SAN 208-7162) Tel 703-373-9150; Toll free: 800-851-BOOK; Chatham Square Pk., Johnson-Matherly Bldg. No. 403, Fredericksburg, VA 22405 (SAN 662-0574) Tel 703-373-9150.

†**Johnson Repr,** *(Johnson Reprint Corp.; 0-384),* Subs. of Harcourt, Brace, Jovanovich, Inc., 111 Fifth Ave., New York, NY 10003 (SAN 285-0362) Tel 212-614-3150; Toll free: 800-543-1918; *CIP.*

Johnston AR, *(Johnston Publishing Co.; 0-936853),* Rte. 8, Box 79A, Lincoln, AR 72744 (SAN 658-3555) Tel 501-846-3768.

Johnston Pub, *(Johnston Publishing, Inc.; 0-942934),* Box 96, Afton, MN 55001 (SAN 240-3900) Tel 612-436-7344.

Joi Prod Enter, *(Joi Production Enterprises; 0-9616294),* 9111 Third Ave., Inglewood, CA 90305 (SAN 658-5590) Tel 213-753-1222.

Joint Cen Urban
See St Local Inter

†**Joint Comm Hosp,** *(Joint Commission on Accreditation of Hospitals; 0-86688),* Dept. of Pubns., 875 N. Michigan Ave., Chicago, IL 60611 (SAN 210-8194) Tel 312-642-6061; *CIP.*

Jolean Pub Co *(Jolean Publishing Co.; 0-934284),* P.O. Box 163, Arverne, NY 11692 (SAN 212-9507).

Jolex, *(Jolex, Inc.; 0-89149),* P.O. Box 717, Southport, CT 06490 (SAN 662-0582) Tel 203-367-4041.

Jomax Pr
See Johmax Bks Inc

Jomilt Pubns, *(Jomilt Pubns.; 0-9616076),* 329 W. Mt. Airy Ave., Philadelphia, PA 19119 (SAN 697-9939) Tel 215-750-4173.

Jonathan David, *(Jonathan David Pubs., Inc.; 0-8246),* 68-22 Eliot Ave., Middle Village, NY 11379 (SAN 169-5274) Tel 718-456-8611.

Jonathan LA, *(Jonathan Publishing; 0-940718),* 3604 Pinnacle Rd., Austin, TX 78746 (SAN 219-7936) Tel 512-328-2480.

Jonathan Pubns, *(Jonathan Pubns.; 0-9603348),* 660 Prospect Ave., Hartford, CT 06105 (SAN 213-330X) Tel 203-523-7587.

†**Jones & Bartlett,** *(Jones & Bartlett Pubs., Inc.; 0-86720),* 20 Park Plaza, Boston, MA 02116 (SAN 285-0893) Tel 617-482-5243; Toll free: 800-832-0034 (Orders only); *CIP.* Imprints: Marine Sci Intl (Marine Science International).

Jones Intl, *(Jones International Ltd.; 0-935910),* 9697 E. Mineral Ave., Englewood, CO 80112 (SAN 213-8530) Tel 303-792-3111.

Jones Lib, *(Jones Library; 0-9616559),* 43 Amity St., Amherst, MA 01002 (SAN 204-9872) Tel 413-256-0246.

Jones Med, *(Jones Medical Pubns.; 0-930010),* 355 Los Cerros Dr., Greenbrae, CA 94904 (SAN 210-4466) Tel 415-461-3749.

Jones Pub, *(Jones, Stan, Publishing, Inc.; 0-939936),* 3421 E. Mercer St., Seattle, WA 98112 (SAN 216-8243).

Jordan & Co
See JCP Corp VA

Jordan Assn, *(Jordan Assn., Ltd.; 0-9610354),* P.O. Box 814, Virginia Beach, VA 23451 (SAN 264-1437).

Jordan Assoc
See Jordan Assn

Jordan Enter, *(Jordan Enterprises; 0-931597),* 512 W. 35th St., Norfolk, VA 23508 (SAN 682-5079) Tel 804-627-3336.

Jordan Pr, *(Jordan Pr.; 0-9613427),* 5 Amberson Ave., Yonkers, NY 10705 (SAN 657-047X) Tel 203-387-3799.

Jordan Pub, *(Jordan Publishing; 0-910213),* Div. of Jordan College, 155 Seven Mile Rd., Comstock Park, MI 49321 (SAN 240-9712) Tel 616-784-7595.

Jordan Valley, *(Jordan Valley Heritage Hse.; 0-939810),* 43592 Hwy. 226, Stayton, OR 97383 (SAN 216-7425) Tel 503-859-3144.

Jordan-Volpe Gall, *(Jordan-Volpe Gallery, The; 0-942410),* 457 W. Broadway, New York, NY 10012 (SAN 214-0438) Tel 212-505-5240; Dist. by: Peregrine Smith, Inc., P.O. Box 667, Layton, UT 84041 (SAN 201-9906).

Jordon Ent, *(Jordon Enterprises; 0-9612256),* 2625 Merry Oaks Trail, Winston-Salem, NC 27103 (SAN 289-5161) Tel 919-760-0194.

Jorg Pubns CA, *(Jorgensen Pubns., Inc.; 0-943340),* 20370 Town Center Ln., No. 245, Cupertino, CA 95014 (SAN 240-5393) Tel 408-252-1111.

Jorgensen Pub, *(Jorgensen Publishing Co.; 0-938128),* 350 Cambridge Ave., Suite 300, Palo Alto, CA 94306 (SAN 219-7944) Tel 415-328-9200.

Jory Pubns, *(Jory Pubns.; 0-9607732),* 12535 Sunview Dr., Creve Coeur, MO 63146 (SAN 238-0935) Tel 314-434-0066.

Joseph Nichols, *(Nichols, Joseph, Pub.; 0-912484),* 100 Center Plaza, No. 303, P.O. Box 2394, Tulsa, OK 74101 (SAN 203-901X) Tel 918-583-3390; P.O. Box 2394, Tulsa, OK 74119 (SAN 658-1021).

Joseph Pub Co, *(Joseph Publishing Co.; 0-915878),* P.O. Box 770, San Mateo, CA 94401 (SAN 207-8538) Tel 415-345-4100.

Josephson-Kluwer Legal Educ Ctrs, *(Josephson/Kluwer Legal Educational Ctrs., Inc.; 0-940366),* 10101 W. Jefferson Blvd., Culver City, CA 90232 (SAN 209-5386) Tel 213-558-3100; Toll free: 800-421-4577.

Josey Enter Inc, *(Josey Enterprises, Inc.; 0-934499),* Rte. 2, Box 235, Karnack, TX 75661 (SAN 693-8957) Tel 214-935-5358.

Joshua I Minist, *(Joshua I Ministries, Inc.; 0-939313),* 50 Coe Rd., Suite 223, Belleair, FL 33516 (SAN 663-1398) Tel 813-442-5535.

Joshua Pub Co
See Script Writers

Joslin Ctr
See Joslin Diabetes

Joslin Diabetes, *(Joslin Diabetes Foundation),* 1 Joslin Pl, Boston, MA 02215 (SAN 271-8200).

Joslyn Art, *(Joslyn Art Museum; 0-936364),* 2200 Dodge St., Omaha, NE 68102 (SAN 281-8442); Orders to: Joslyn Museum Shop, 2200 Dodge St., Omaha, NE 68102 (SAN 281-8450) Tel 402-342-3300; Orders to: Univ. of Nebraska Pr., 901 N. 17th, Lincoln, NE 68583 (SAN 669-1390).

†**Jossey Bass,** *(Jossey-Bass, Inc., Pubs.; 0-87589; 1-55542),* 433 California St., San Francisco, CA 94104 (SAN 201-033X) Tel 415-433-1740; Dist. by: Kampmann & Co., 9 E. 40th St., New York, NY 10016 (SAN 202-5191) Tel 212-685-2928; *CIP.*

Jostens, *(Jostens Pubns.; 0-88136),* P.O. Box 1903, Topeka, KS 66601 (SAN 241-5313) Tel 913-266-3300.

JostGIs, *(JostGIs),* 401 Science Park Rd., State College, PA 16804-0297 (SAN 655-7589).

Jotarian, *(Jotarian Productions; 0-943454),* 5353 Columbia Pike, No. 110, Arlington, VA 22204 (SAN 240-6918) Tel 703-845-1819; Orders to: P.O. Box 75683, Washington, DC 20013 (SAN 699-539X).

Journal Herald
See Dayton Newspapers

Journal Printing, *(Journal Printing Co.; 0-9613631),* 709 N. Davis St., Kirksville, MO 63501 (SAN 670-8838) Tel 816-665-4082; Dist. by: First United Methodist Church, 300 E. Washington St., Kirksville, MO 63501 (SAN 200-7460) Tel 816-665-7712.

Journal Span Stud, *(Journal of Spanish Studies: Twentieth Century; 0-89294),* Div. of Society of Spanish and American Studies, University of Colorado, Dept Spanish & Portuguese, Campus Box 278, Boulder, CO 80309-0278 (SAN 209-4541) Tel 303-492-7308; Orders to: Society of Spanish & Spanish-American Studies, University of Colorado, Dept. Spanish & Portuguese, Campus Box 278, Boulder, CO 80309-0278 (SAN 208-3221).

Journey Co, *(Journey Co.; 0-9616469),* 4790 Irvine Blvd., Suite 105-112, Irvine, CA 92720 (SAN 659-2589) Tel 714-731-6173.

†**Journey Pr,** *(Journey Pr.; 0-918572),* Box 9036, Berkeley, CA 94709 (SAN 281-8469) Tel 415-540-5500; Dist. by: Bookpeople, 2929 Fifth St., Berkeley, CA 94710 (SAN 168-9517) Tel 415-549-3030; *CIP.*

Journey Pubns, *(Journey Pubns.; 0-918038),* P.O. Box 423, Woodstock, NY 12498 (SAN 209-570X) Tel 914-657-8434.

JOV Pubns, *(J.O.V. Pubns.; 0-936321),* P.O. Box 399, Needham Heights, MA 02194 (SAN 272-2861) Tel 617-367-1080; 333 Boston Rd., Chelmsford, MA 01824 (SAN 697-287X).

Jove Pubns, *(Jove Pubns., Inc.; 0-515),* Div. of Berkley/Jove Pub. Group, 200 Madison Ave., New York, NY 10016 (SAN 215-8817) Tel 212-686-9820; Toll free: 800-223-0510; Dist. by: Kable News Co., Inc., 777 Third Ave., New York, NY 10017 (SAN 169-5835) Tel 212-371-5321.

Joy-Co, *(Joy-Co Pr.; 0-9605984),* 2636 Burgener Blvd., San Diego, CA 92110 (SAN 216-7433) Tel 619-276-9760.

Joy Money Pub, *(Joy of Money Publishing; 0-9616661),* 535 Ocean Ave., No. 7A, Santa Monica, CA 90402 (SAN 661-3608) Tel 213-393-3110.

Joy Pub Co, *(Joy Publishing Co.; 0-9601758),* P.O. Box 2532, Boca Raton, FL 33427 (SAN 211-0806) Tel 305-276-5879.

Joybug, *(Joybug Teaching Aids, Inc.; 0-931218),* P.O. Box 2238, 1125 E. Wayne, Salina, KS 67402-2238 (SAN 212-1050) Tel 913-825-1589; Dist. by: Publishers Group West, 5855 Beaudry St., Emeryville, CA 94608 (SAN 202-8522) Tel 415-658-3453.

Joyce Media, *(Joyce Media Inc.; 0-917002),* P.O. Box 57, Action, CA 93510 (SAN 208-7197) Tel 805-269-1169.

Joyce Motion Pict
See Joyce Media

Joydeism Pr, *(Joydeism Pr.; 0-913483),* P.O. Box 14, Point Arena, CA 95468 (SAN 285-189X).

Joyful Noise, *(Joyful Noise Productions, International; 0-936874),* 109 Minna St., Suite 153, San Francisco, CA 94105 (SAN 215-0883).

Joyful Woman, *(Joyful Woman, The; 0-912623),* Div. of Joyful Christian Ministries, P.O. Box 90028, Chatanooga, TN 37412 (SAN 282-8073).

JP Designs, *(JP Designs; 0-9616904),* P.O. Box 6175, Kent, WA 98064-6175 (SAN 661-5155); 12916 SE 245th, Kent, WA 98064-6175 (SAN 661-5163) Tel 206-631-8910.

JP Pubns CA, *(J P Pubns.; 0-910703),* 2952 Grinnel, Davis, CA 95616 (SAN 260-2083).

JP Pubns WI, *(JP Pubns.; 0-9602978),* P.O. Box 4173, Madison, WI 53711 (SAN 214-0411) Tel 608-231-2373.

JP SF, *(Johnson, Pace, Simmons & Fennell Pubs.; 0-9615268),* P.O. Box 711207, Los Angeles, CA 90071 (SAN 694-6046); 515 Flower St., Los Angeles, CA 90071 (SAN 662-3417) Tel 818-352-9258.

Jr Bd Tri-City Symph, *(Junior Board of the Tri-City Symphony Orchestra; 0-9606524),* P.O. Box 67, Davenport, IA 52805 (SAN 218-5601).

Jr Charlottesville, *(Junior League of Charlottesville, Inc., The; 0-9615013),* P.O. Box 3603, Univ. Station, Charlottesville, VA 22903 (SAN 694-0331) Tel 804-971-2937.

Jr Chatta, *(Junior League of Chattanooga, Inc.; 0-9611806),* 100 Stivers St., Chattanooga, TN 37405 (SAN 283-9628) Tel 615-265-9614.

Jr Comm Cleveland, *(Junior Committee of The Cleveland Orchestra, The; 0-9609142),* Severance Hall, Cleveland, OH 44106 (SAN 241-5321) Tel 216-231-7300.

Jr Guild Rocky Mt NC, *(Junior Guild of Rocky Mount, North Carolina, The; 0-9616940),* P.O. Box 7912, Rocky Mount, NC 27804 (SAN 661-7972); 724 Brassie Club Dr., Rocky Mount, NC 27804 (SAN 661-7980) Tel 919-977-2607.

Jr League Albany Pubns, *(Junior League of Albany Pubns.; 0-9614012),* 419 Madison Ave., Albany, NY 12210 (SAN 683-6585) Tel 518-458-8085.

Jr League Amarillo, *(Junior League of Amarillo Texas, Inc., The; 0-9604102),* P.O. Box 381, Amarillo, TX 79105 (SAN 215-0891).

Jr League Antonio, *(Junior League of San Antonio, The; 0-9610416),* 819 Augusta Street, San Antonio, TX 78215 (SAN 264-1461) Tel 512-225-1861.

Jr League Asheville, *(Junior League of Asheville Publications; 0-9608444),* P.O. Box 8723, Asheville, NC 28814 (SAN 240-6926) Tel 704-258-2098.

Jr League Austin, *(Junior League of Austin, Texas; 0-9605906),* 5416 Parkcrest, Suite 100, Austin, TX 78731 (SAN 216-6828) Tel 512-467-8982.

Symbols/Abbreviations

163

JTG Nashville, *(JTG of Nashville; 0-938971),* 1024C 18th Ave., S., Nashville, TN 37212 (SAN 661-6917) Tel 615-329-3036.

JTV Ent, *(JTV Enterprises; 0-9614253),* P.O. Box 1409, Cary, NC 27511 (SAN 686-7685) Tel 919-851-8253.

Ju I Hsiung
See Art Farm Gal

Jubilee Pr, *(Jubilee Pr., Inc.; 0-9609674),* 7906 Hillside Ave., Los Angeles, CA 90046 (SAN 262-7663) Tel 213-851-5893.

Judaea Bks
See Judaea Pub Co

Judaea Pub Co, *(Judaea Publishing Co.; 0-933447),* P.O. Box 510, Hewlett, NY 11557 (SAN 691-781X) Tel 516-374-6080; P.O. Box 370773, Miami, FL 33137 (SAN 662-2917) Tel 305-576-3852; Dist. by: Sparks & Co., 979 Summer St., Stamford, CT 06905 (SAN 200-7444) Tel 203-967-3617.

Judaica Pr, *(Judaica Pr., Inc.; 0-910818),* 521 Fifth Ave., New York, NY 10017 (SAN 204-9856) Tel 212-260-0520.

Judith Malzahn, *(Malzahn, Judith; 0-9614565),* Rt. 1, Box 35-S, Clinton, MS 39056 (SAN 691-8042) Tel 601-924-8477.

†Judson, *(Judson Pr.; 0-8170),* P.O. Box 851, Valley Forge, PA 19482-0851 (SAN 201-0348) Tel 215-768-2119; Toll free: 800-331-1053; *CIP.*

Judson Press Ga
See One Candle

Judson St Pr, *(Judson Street Pr.; 0-9617149),* 4248 Judson, Houston, TX 77005 (SAN 663-3331) Tel 713-665-5151.

Judy, *(Judy Publishing Co.; 0-87702),* Main P.O., Box 5270, Chicago, IL 60680 (SAN 202-7372) Tel 312-787-7233.

Judy Buch, *(Buch, Judy; 0-9614749),* 111 Olson Dr., Southington, CT 06489 (SAN 692-9249) Tel 203-628-4535; Dist. by: Gryphon House Inc., 3706 Otis St., P.O. Box 275, Mt. Rainier, MD 20712 (SAN 169-3190) Tel 301-779-6200.

Jugglebug, *(Jugglebug; 0-9615521),* 7506 J Olympic View Dr., Edmonds, WA 98020 (SAN 696-2882) Tel 206-542-2030.

Jukebox Coll New, *(Jukebox Collector Newsletter; 0-912789),* 2545 SE 60th Ct., Des Moines, IA 50317 (SAN 282-809X) Tel 515-265-8324.

Jukebox Press, *(Jukebox Pr.; 0-930693),* 3717 Market St., Oakland, CA 94608 (SAN 678-1969) Tel 415-652-1314.

Jules' Bks, *(Jules' Books; 0-939537),* 420 Buchanan St., San Francisco, CA 94102 (SAN 663-4427) Tel 415-864-1139.

Juliahouse Pubs, *(Juliahouse Pubs.; 0-9614228),* 1100 Poydras St., Suite 1800 Energy Ctr., New Orleans, LA 70163-1800 (SAN 686-7669) Tel 504-582-2223.

Julian
See Crown

Julian Pr. *Imprint of* **Crown**

Juliet Pr, *(Juliet Pr.; 0-914426),* P.O. Box 3476, Princeton, NJ 08540-0209 (SAN 206-5479).

Jun League Charl SC, *(Junior League of Charleston, S.C., Inc.; 0-9607854),* P.O. Box 177, Charleston, SC 29402 (SAN 218-8031) Tel 803-763-5284; Dist. by: Walker, Evans & Cogswell, 5300 Rivers Ave., North Charleston, SC 29405 (SAN 265-4121) Tel 803-747-8761.

Jun League Jackson, *(Junior League of Jacksonville Inc.; 0-9609338),* 2165 Park St., Jacksonville, FL 32204 (SAN 260-2113) Tel 904-389-5497.

Jun League Mon, *(Junior League of Monroe; 0-9602364),* P.O. Box 7138, Monroe, LA 71211-7138 (SAN 208-1822) Tel 318-322-3863.

Jun League NH, *(Junior League of Newport Harbor, Inc.; 0-9608306),* 170 Newport Center Dr., .Suite 100, Newport, CA 92660 (SAN 240-5407) Tel 714-720-7477.

Junction Pr, *(Junction Pr., The; 0-935935),* P.O. Box 295, Tippah Rd., Grand Junction, TN 38039 (SAN 696-4621) Tel 901-764-6155.

JuneRose Prod, *(JuneRose Productions; 0-9617043),* 1750 E. Ridgeway Ave., Waterloo, IA 50702 (SAN 662-829X) Tel 319-234-9995.

Jungle Garden, *(Jungle Garden Pr.; 0-941220),* 47 Oak Rd., Fairfax, CA 94930 (SAN 210-8216) Tel 415-456-4884.

Jungle Video, *(Jungle Video; 0-9602756),* 2013 Lincoln Apt. 3, Berkeley, CA 94709 (SAN 221-8038).

Junior League
See Jr League Wichita

Junior League Mobile
See Mobile Jr League Pubns

Juniper *Imprint of* **Fawcett**

Juniper
See Juniper Pr WI

Juniper Hse, *(Juniper Hse.; 0-931870),* P.O. Box 2094, Boulder, CO 80306 (SAN 212-1891) Tel 303-449-7757.

†Juniper Ledge Pub, *(Juniper Ledge Publishing Co.; 0-931545),* P.O. Box 381, Sorrento, ME 04677 (SAN 682-2991) Tel 202-638-7929; 1012 14th St., NW, Suite 1101, Washington, DC 20005 (SAN 699-587X) Tel 202-638-7929; *CIP.*

Juniper Maine, *(Juniper Pr.; 0-913977),* c/o Betts Bookstore, Bangor Mall, Stillwater Ave., Bangor, ME 04401 (SAN 212-1077) Tel 207-947-7052.

Juniper Pr WI, *(Juniper Pr.; 0-910822),* 1310 Shorewood Dr., La Crosse, WI 54601 (SAN 207-8570) Tel 608-788-0096.

Juniper Pubs, *(Juniper Pubs.; 0-9605986),* P.O. Box 11872, Lexington, KY 40511 (SAN 207-2432) Tel 606-266-4675.

Juniper Ridge, *(Juniper Ridge Pr.; 0-916289),* P.O. Box 338, Ashland, OR 97520 (SAN 295-8899) Tel 503-482-9585.

Junius Inc, *(Junius, Inc.; 0-9603932),* 842 Lombard St., Philadelphia, PA 19147 (SAN 214-0934) Tel 215-627-8298.

Junius-Vaughn, *(Junius-Vaughn Pr., The; 0-940198),* P.O. Box 85, Fairview, NJ 07022 (SAN 217-1139) Tel 201-868-7725.

Juno-West, *(Juno-Western Publishing Co.; 0-914597),* 3086 Patricia Ave., Los Angeles, CA 90064 (SAN 289-3150) Tel 213-204-4748.

Jupiter Bks, *(Jupiter Bks.; 0-935344),* 7300 Eades Ave., La Jolla, CA 92037 (SAN 213-7658).

†Jupiter Pr, *(Jupiter Pr.; 0-933104),* P.O. Box 101, Lake Bluff, IL 60044 (SAN 212-5161) Tel 312-234-3997; *CIP.*

Jupiter Prods, *(Jupiter Productions; 0-915981),* 2125 Dailey Ave., Latrobe, PA 15650 (SAN 294-0485) Tel 412-539-2824.

Jupiter Pubns, *(Jupiter Pubns.; 0-939270),* 118 W. 74th St., New York, NY 10023 (SAN 216-5341) Tel 212-873-3132.

Jury Verdict, *(Jury Verdict Research Inc.; 0-934607),* 5325-B Naiman Pkwy., Solon, OH 44139 (SAN 227-2415); Toll free: 800-321-6910.

Just Above Midtown, *(Just Above Midtown, Inc.; 0-9605830),* 503 Broadway, 5th Flr., New York, NY 10012 (SAN 211-4704) Tel 212-966-7020.

Just Another, *(Just Another Asshole; 0-913803),* Eight Spring St., 4 EF, New York, NY 10012 (SAN 286-1291) Tel 212-966-0623.

Just Clare, *(Just Clare Corporation; 0-9608092),* 1850 Union St No. 379, San Francisco, CA 94123 (SAN 240-2386) Tel 415-563-6313.

Just Fun Horse, *(Just For Fun Horse Cartoons),* P.O. Box 2656, Boca Raton, FL 33427 (SAN 682-2436).

Justice Syst Pr, *(Justice Systems Pr.; 0-937935),* 415 E. Vashon, Port Angeles, WA 98362 (SAN 659-5103) Tel 206-457-5320.

Justim Pub, *(Justim Publishing Co.; 0-938691),* P.O. Box 1217, Lafayette, CA 94549-1217 (SAN 661-5562); 3683 Boyer Cir., Lafayette, CA 94549 (SAN 661-5570) Tel 415-283-4889.

Justin Bks, *(Justin Bks.; 0-918537),* 41 Greenwich Ave., New York, NY 10014 (SAN 657-6370) Tel 212-924-1071.

Juvenescent, *(Juvenescent Research Corp.; 0-9600148),* 807 Riverside Dr., New York, NY 10032 (SAN 206-7250) Tel 212-795-8765.

JWB, *(JWB; 0-914820),* 15 E. 26th St., New York, NY 10010 (SAN 203-9060) Tel 212-532-4949.

JWB Jewish Bk Coun
See JWB

Jym Ent, *(Jym Enterprises),* P.O. Box 73, Batavia, OH 45103 (SAN 210-5373).

K A S S T, *(KASST (Ken's Automotive Savings & Safety Tips); 0-9611716),* P.O. Box 1812, 940 W. Princeton St., Ontario, CA 91762 (SAN 285-3558) Tel 714-986-8312.

K A Sposato, *(Sposato, Kenneth A.; 0-9612832),* 46 Gedney Park Dr., White Plains, NY 10605 (SAN 290-0475) Tel 914-948-4995.

K Alstad, *(Alstad, Ken, Co.; 0-9616985),* 9096 E. Bellevue, Tucson, AZ 85715 (SAN 661-7190) Tel 602-298-0175.

K & A Pubns, *(K&A Pubns.; 0-9616230),* P.O. Box 22075, San Diego, CA 92122 (SAN 658-5981) Tel 619-455-6578.

K & K Enter, *(K & K Enterprises; 0-935346),* 22311 Caminito Tecate, Laguna Hills, CA 92653 (SAN 221-4652).

K & K Pub
See K & K Pub MA

K & K Pub MA, *(K & K Publishing; 0-9614689),* 34 Glenburnie Rd., Roslindale, MA 02131 (SAN 692-6037) Tel 617-323-6171; Dist. by: Airline Careers Media, Box 9200, Boston, MA 02114 (SAN 200-6839) Tel 617-323-1607.

K & K Pubs, *(K&K Pubs.; 0-9604218),* 216 N. Batavia Ave., Batavia, IL 60510 (SAN 214-3186) Tel 312-879-6214.

K & R Pub, *(K & R Publishing; 0-9616178),* P.O. Box 672, Eureka Springs, AR 72632 (SAN 699-8739) Tel 501-253-9215.

K & S, *(Kapilla, Cleo, & Eleanor Simons; 0-9611466),* P.O. Box 4995, Ocala, FL (SAN 277-6928) Tel 904-622-4914.

†K Anzinger-Cain, *(Anzinger-Cain, Kay; 0-9603188),* 18432 Las Cumbres Rd., Los Gatos, CA 95030 (SAN 694-3128) Tel 408-354-1628; P.O. Box 434, Los Gatos, CA 95031 (SAN 213-4748) Tel 408-354-8557; *CIP.*

K Appiah Kubi, *(Kubi, K. Appiah; 0-9614573),* P.O. Box 7601, Bloomfield, CT 06002 (SAN 691-8298) Tel 203-242-8927.

K Baikie, *(Baikie, Kenneth; 0-9607790),* 4613 N. 74th Pl., Scottsdale, AZ 85251 (SAN 207-6985) Tel 602-994-4083.

K C Pubns
See KC Pubns

K C Terry, *(Terry, Keith C., Assocs.; 0-937043),* 26 Drakes Bay Dr., Corona del Mar, CA 92625 (SAN 658-7143) Tel 714-759-1421.

K Cain
See K Anzinger-Cain

K-D Enter, *(K-D Enterprises; 0-9613877),* 14111 12th Ave. SW, Seattle, WA 98166 (SAN 681-994X) Tel 206-243-2372; Orders to: P.O. Box 66594, Seattle, WA 98166 (SAN 662-7676) Tel 206-243-2372; Dist. by: C P Publications, P.O. Box 1072, Port Angeles, WA 98362 (SAN 287-5276) Tel 206-457-7550.

K Diehl, *(Diehl, Kathryn; 0-9603552),* 554 N. McDonel, Lima, OH 45801 (SAN 285-0079) Tel 419-223-7207.

K-Dimension, *(K-Dimension Pubs.; 0-917595),* P.O. Box 371289, Decatur, GA 30037 (SAN 657-1484) Tel 404-241-1565; Toll free: 800-241-4702.

K E Dunlay, *(Dunlay, Kate E.; 0-9617024),* 27 sherman Bridge Rd., Wayland, MA 01778 (SAN 662-5746) Tel 617-358-4039; Dist. by: Fiddlecase Bks., HC 63 Box 104, East Alstead, NH 03602 (SAN 200-7495).

K E Nemouneh, *(Ketab-E-Nemouneh; 0-9616820),* P.O. Box 850029, New Orleans, LA 70185-0029 (SAN 661-4787); Carrolton Ave., New Orleans, LA 70185-0029 (SAN 661-4795) Tel 504-866-4667.

K E Schon, *(Schon, Kurt E., Ltd.; 0-9603880),* 510 Saint Louis St., New Orleans, LA 70130 (SAN 214-1361) Tel 504-524-5462.

K-Four Ent, *(K Four Enterprises, Inc.; 0-939473),* 2115 New York Ave., Whiting, IN 46394 (SAN 663-2602) Tel 219-659-2323.

K G Jewell, *(Jewell, Kenneth G.; 0-9615908),* R.D. 6, Bedford, PA 15522 (SAN 696-8694) Tel 814-623-8232.

K G Johnsen, *(Johnsen, Kenneth G.; 0-9613267),* P.O. Box 161, Renton, WA 98057 (SAN 653-7359) Tel 206-859-2111.

†K G Saur, *(Saur, K. G., Inc.; 0-89664),* Subs. of K. G. Saur Verlag, 175 Fifth Ave., New York, NY 10010 (SAN 214-1264) Tel 212-982-1302; *CIP.*

K G Wilks, *(Wilks, Karl Glyn; 0-9616912),* 528 N. Main St., McGregor, TX 76657 (SAN 661-521X) Tel 817-840-4503.

K Hansen, *(Hansen, Kathryn),* 24055 Paseo del Lago W., Tower 2, No. 1057, Laguna Hills, CA 92653 (SAN 696-7981) Tel 714-830-7777; P.O. Box 2323, Laguna Hills, CA 92653 (SAN 662-3875).

K J Brown, *(Brown, Kenneth J.; 0-9613137),* 2114 McClellan St., Philadelphia, PA 19145-1911 (SAN 294-698X) Tel 215-462-7876.

K J Callahan, *(Callahan, Kathleen J.; 0-9615563),* Affil. of St. Maurice Church, 53 Burnt Hill Rd., Hebron, CT 06248 (SAN 200-8203) Tel 203-228-0873.

K J Williams Pubns, *(Williams, Ken J., Pubns.; 0-9603742),* 881 Tenth Ave., Suite 4C, New York, NY 10019 (SAN 214-4891) Tel 212-247-3374.

K K Pub Co, *(Kaye's & Knight Pub. Co.; 0-9612140),* P.O. Box 2065, 503 Broadway, Fargo, ND 58107 (SAN 287-2765) Tel 701-237-4525.

K Karmiole, *(Karmiole, Kenneth, Bookseller, Inc.; 0-931043026),* 1225 Santa Monica Mall, Santa Monica, CA 90401 (SAN 289-5188).

K L Maddalena, *(Maddalena, Kris Louis; 0-9616189),* 8130 W. Indian Schl. Rd., No. 2169, Phoenix, AZ 85033 (SAN 658-3342).

K L Vilips, *(Vilips, Kathryn L., Studios, Inc.; 0-938473),* P.O. Drawer G, Wofford Heights, CA 93285 (SAN 660-9686); 237 Split Mountain Way, Wofford Heights, CA 93285 (SAN 660-9694) Tel 619-376-3634.

K LaTour, *(LaTour, Kathy; 0-9612870),* P.O. Box 141182, Dallas, TX 75214 (SAN 291-2511) Tel 214-827-2753.

K Mirth, *(Mirth, Karlo; 0-9615737),* Box 1767, Grand Central Sta., New York, NY 10017 (SAN 226-3289); 37-60 88th St., Jackson Heights, NY 11372 (SAN 699-5446) Tel 718-458-8556.

K N Shah, *(Shah, Kirit N.; 0-9609614),* 980 Moraga Ave., Piedmont, CA 94611 (SAN 260-2628) Tel 415-653-2076.

K Osborne
See K-D Enter

K Pierce Inc, *(Pierce, Ken, Inc.; 0-912277),* Box 322, Park Forest, IL 60466 (SAN 265-0835) Tel 312-672-4457.

K Pillman, *(Pillman, K., Pubs.; 0-9608620),* 3039 SW 116th Pl., Seattle, WA 98146 (SAN 238-339X) Tel 206-244-1266.

K Q Assocs, *(K-Q Assocs., Inc.; 0-941988),* P.O. Box 2132, Cedar Rapids, IA 52406 (SAN 238-4655).

K Roberts, *(Roberts, Ken, Publishing Co.; 0-913602),* P.O. Box 151, Fitzwilliam, NH 03447 (SAN 203-0888) Tel 603-585-6612.

K S Giniger *Imprint of* **Stackpole**

K Sefer, *(Kiryat Sefer, Ltd.; 965-17),* c/o Ridgefield Pub. Co., 6925 Canby Ave., Suite 104, Reseda, CA 91335 (SAN 215-8035). Moved, left no forwarding address.

K Singh Pub, *(Singh, Kirpal, Publishing; 0-9615501),* 147-47 Jasmine Ave., Flushing, NY 11355 (SAN 696-4060) Tel 718-359-0307.

K Starosciak, *(Starosciak, Kenneth, Bookseller; 0-9613150),* 117 Wilmot, San Francisco, CA 94115 (SAN 201-0372).

K W Canipe, *(Canipe, Kenneth W.; 0-9616329),* Rte. 12, Box 474, Hickory, NC 28602 (SAN 659-0748) Tel 704-294-3322.

K W Huskey, *(Huskey, K. W., Assocs.; 0-9604840),* P.O. Box 2715, Palm Springs, CA 92263 (SAN 659-4603).

K Young, *(Young, Katherine),* 140 East 40th St., New York, NY 10016 (SAN 237-9791) Tel 212-684-0999.

Kaaikaula, *(Kaaikaula, Hale Pa'I O; 0-914599),* P.O. Box 26448, Honolulu, HI 96825-0078 (SAN 289-3207) Tel 808-373-4430.

KABEL Pubs, *(Kabel Pubs.; 0-930329),* 11225 Huntover Dr., Rockville, MD 20852 (SAN 670-8323).

Kabyn, *(Kabyn Bks.; 0-940444),* 3341 Adams Ave., San Diego, CA 92116 (SAN 217-1902) Tel 619-284-0999.

Kadon, *(Kadon, John C.; 0-917130),* 2538 N. Eight St., Sedona, AZ 86336 (SAN 208-4074) Tel 602-990-8346.

Kaff Pub Group, *(Kaff Publishing Group; 0-916557),* 318 Nutt St., Wilmington, NC 28401 (SAN 295-4508) Tel 919-343-1100.

†Kahn & Kahan, *(Kahn & Kahan Publishing Co., Inc.; 0-9604286),* 31 South St., P.O. Box 661, Morristown, NJ 07960 (SAN 214-2597); *CIP.*

Kahn Pub, *(Kahn Publishing; 0-9611134),* P.O. Box 210404, San Francisco, CA 94121-0404 (SAN 283-3654) Tel 415-751-4286; Dist. by: Bookpeople, 2929 Fifth St., Berkeley, CA 94710 (SAN 168-9517) Tel 415-549-3030; Dist. by: L-S Distributors, 480 Ninth St., San Francisco, CA 94103 (SAN 169-0213) Tel 415-861-6300; Dist. by: Publisher's Group West, 5855 Beaudry St., Emeryville, CA 94608 (SAN 202-8522) Tel 415-658-3453.

Kaihong, *(Kaihong; 0-940446),* c/o P.O. Box 1706, MPK, Los Angeles, CA 91754-1706 (SAN 218-4850).

Kairos Bks, *(Kairos Books, Inc.; 0-9608410),* P.O. Box 708, Libertyville, IL 60048 (SAN 240-6942) Tel 312-362-1898.

Kairos Inc, *(Kairos, Inc.; 0-934501),* 2213 NW Market St., Seattle, WA 98107 (SAN 693-8965) Tel 206-789-7615; P.O. Box 71280, Seattle, WA 98107 (SAN 662-328X).

Kaiser Pub Co, *(Barlow-Kaiser Publishing Co.; 0-9610166),* P.O. Box 265, Windham, NH 03087 (SAN 268-2206) Tel 802-888-4066; Dist. by: Schiffer Publishing, Ltd., 1469 Morstein Rd., West Chester, PA 19380 (SAN 208-8428) Tel 215-696-1001.

Kajfez Con, *(Kajfez Consulting; 0-930071),* P.O. Box 757, University, MS 38677 (SAN 669-9766) Tel 601-234-4287.

Kajun Pr, *(Kajun Pr.; 0-9614385),* 209 Mississippi St., San Francisco, CA 94107 (SAN 688-6469) Tel 415-863-2494.

Kalamazoo Inst Arts, *(Kalamazoo Institute of Arts; 0-933742),* 314 S. Park St., Kalamazoo, MI 49007 (SAN 221-4660) Tel 616-349-7775.

Kaleid Educ, *(Kaleidoscope in Education Co.; 0-914741),* P.O. Box 292, St Albans, WV 25177 (SAN 291-8196).

Kaleidoscope in Educ
See Kaleid Educ

Kaleidoscope Pubns, *(Kaleidoscope Pubns.; 0-938001),* 13000 Bel-Red Rd., Suite 101, Bellevue, WA 98005 (SAN 661-4183) Tel 206-451-1961.

†Kalimat, *(Kalimat Pr.; 0-933770),* 1600 Sawtelle Blvd., Suite 34, Los Angeles, CA 90025 (SAN 213-7666) Tel 213-479-5668; Toll free: 800-323-1880; *CIP.*

Kalium, *(Kalium, Inc.; 0-9610114),* 141 Mt. Horeb Rd., Warren, NJ 07060 (SAN 271-8480) Tel 201-647-6016.

Kallman, *(Kallman Publishing Co.; 0-910824),* 1614 W. University Ave., Box 14076, Gainesville, FL 32601 (SAN 203-9141) Tel 904-376-6066.

Kalmbach, *(Kalmbach Publishing Co.; 0-89024),* 1027 N. Seventh St., Milwaukee, WI 53233 (SAN 201-0399) Tel 414-272-2060; Toll free: 800-558-1544.

Kalum Pr, *(Kalum Press; 0-937788),* 596 Joey Ave., El Cajon, CA 92020 (SAN 215-6660).

Kambrina, *(Kambrina; 0-9605742),* P.O. Box 16, Depoe Bay, OR 97341 (SAN 216-2601).

Kampmann, *(Kampmann & Co., Inc.),* 9 E. 40th St., New York, NY 10016 (SAN 202-5191) Tel 212-685-2928; Toll free: 800-526-7626.

Kan J, *(Kan, Johnny, Inc.; 0-9608900),* 708 Grant Ave., San Francisco, CA 94108 (SAN 241-127X) Tel 415-982-2388.

K&K Pub Calif, *(K & K Publishing; 0-9608500),* 1161 Nogales St., Lafayette, CA 94549 (SAN 240-5431) Tel 415-934-8196.

†Kane-Miller Bk, *(Kane/Miller Bk. Pubs.; 0-916291),* P.O. Box 529, Brooklyn, NY 11231 (SAN 295-8945) Tel 718-624-5120; 310 President St., Brooklyn, NY 11231 (SAN 693-9902); Orders to: P.O. Box 12374, La Jolla, CA 92037 (SAN 685-3897) Tel 619-456-0540; *CIP. Imprints:* Cranky Nell Bk (Cranky Nell Book, A).

Kanegis, *(Kanegis, James; 0-9600226),* 3907 Madison St., Hyattsville, MD 20781 (SAN 201-0402) Tel 301-699-5064.

Kaneshiro, *(Kaneshiro, Hansel S.; 0-9600670),* 1524 N. Hoyne Ave., Chicago, IL 60622 (SAN 203-915X) Tel 312-276-8024.

Kansas Arts Com, *(Kansas Arts Commission; 0-9607978),* 700 Kansas, Suite 1004, Topeka, KS 66603 (SAN 239-9393) Tel 913-296-3335.

Kansas St Hist, *(Kansas State Historical Society; 0-87726),* Center for Historical Research, 120 W. 10th St., Topeka, KS 66612 (SAN 207-0014) Tel 913-296-4784.

Kanthaka, *(Kanthaka Press; 0-916926),* P.O. Box 696, Brookline Village, MA 02147 (SAN 206-4375) Tel 617-734-8146.

Kanyaku Imin JV, *(Kanyaku Imin J.V.; 0-9615045),* 245 Kuupua St., Kailua, HI 96734 (SAN 693-8973) Tel 808-944-5200.

†Kapitan Szabo, *(Kapitan Szabo Publishers; 0-916845),* 2120 Pennsylvania Ave. NW, Washington, DC 20037 (SAN 200-4607); *CIP.*

Kappeler Inst Pub, *(Kappeler Institute Publishing; 0-942958),* 2019 Delaware Ave., Wilmington, DE 19806 (SAN 240-1185) Tel 302-571-9570.

Kaptur Pr, *(Kaptur Pr.; 0-936987),* P.O. Box 1829, Costa Mesa, CA 92628 (SAN 658-7992) Tel 714-962-4464; 19822 Brookhurst, No. 50, Huntington Beach, CA 92646 (SAN 658-800X).

Kar Ben, *(Kar-Ben Copies, Inc.; 0-930494),* 6800 Tildenwood Ln., Rockville, MD 20852 (SAN 210-7511) Tel 301-984-8733; Toll free: 800-452-7236.

Karan Mktg, *(Karan Marketing; 0-9616852),* 1007 Fifth Ave., Suite 1100, San Diego, CA 92101 (SAN 661-6011) Tel 619-692-9400.

Karl Bern Pubs, *(Bern, Karl, Pubs.; 0-9601524),* 9939 Riviera Dr., Sun City, AZ 85351 (SAN 211-1497) Tel 602-933-0854.

Karlins Kitchen, *(Karlin's Kitchen; 0-9615941),* 1343 Sunset Ave., Santa Monica, CA 90405 (SAN 696-8406) Tel 213-399-0261.

Karma Pub, *(Karma Publishing Co.; 0-9604568),* 4404 Pennsylvania Ave., Pittsburgh, PA 15224 (SAN 238-888X).

Karoma, *(Karoma Pubs., Inc.; 0-89720),* 3400 Daleview Dr., Ann Arbor, MI 48105 (SAN 213-8131) Tel 313-665-3331.

Karp, *(Karp Publishing; 0-9612360),* 609-B Flournoy, Austin, TX 78745 (SAN 289-3908) Tel 512-479-9255.

Karpat, *(Karpat Pub.; 0-918570),* 19608 Thornridge Ave., Cleveland, OH 44135 (SAN 209-939X) Tel 216-362-0316.

Karwyn Ent, *(Karwyn Enterprises; 0-939938),* 17227 17th Ave. W., Lynnwood, WA 98036 (SAN 289-0143) Tel 206-743-0722; Dist. by: Publishers' Marketing Group, 1104 Summit Ave., No. 100-B, Plainview, TX 75074 (SAN 262-0995) Tel 214-423-0312.

†Karz-Cohl Pub, *(Karz-Cohl Pubs., Inc.; . 0-943828),* 77 Bleecker St., Apt. PH24E, New York, NY 10012 (SAN 238-3063) Tel 212-505-2546; *CIP.*

Karz Howard
See Karz Pub

†Karz Pub, *(Karz Pubs.; 0-918294),* 320 W. 105th St., New York, NY 10025 (SAN 209-9403) Tel 212-663-9059; *CIP.*

Kashong Pubns, *(Kashong Pubns.; 0-9607734),* P.O. Box 90, Bellona, NY 14415 (SAN 218-8074) Tel 315-789-9574; Dist. by: ARGS Bookstore, 6 Glen Terr., Scotia, NY 12302 (SAN 200-7967).

Katahdin, *(Katahdin Press; 0-939212),* P.O. Box 231, Campbell, CA 95009 (SAN 216-261X).

Katanya Pubns, *(Katanya Pubns.; 0-912101),* P.O. Box 5355, Takoma Park, MD 20912 (SAN 264-7575) Tel 301-589-8263.

Katchadour Pub
See Ohanian

Katonah Gal, *(Katonah Gallery; 0-915171),* 28 Bedford Rd., Katonah, NY 10536 (SAN 279-2680) Tel 914-232-9555.

Katyd Bks & Recds, *(Katydid Bks. & Records; 0-934573),* Box 395, Jerome, AZ 86331 (SAN 693-8981) Tel 602-634-8075; Orders to: Box 395, Jerome, AZ 86331 (SAN 693-8981) Tel 602-634-8075; Dist. by: Many Feathers, 5738 N. Central Ave., Phoenix, AZ 85012 (SAN 158-8877) Tel 602-266-1043.

†Katydid Bks, *(Katydid Bks.; 0-942668),* Oakland Univ., Dept. of English, Rochester, MI 48063 (SAN 238-7603) Tel 313-377-2250; Dist. by: Univ. of Washington Pr., P.O. Box 85569, Seattle, WA 98145 (SAN 212-2502) Tel 206-543-4050; *CIP.*

Kauai Museum, *(Kauai Museum Assn., Ltd.; 0-940948),* Box 248, Lihue, HI 96766 (SAN 213-1013) Tel 808-245-6931; 4428 Rice St., Lihue, HI 96766 (SAN 685-3412).

Kauf Pubs, *(Kauf Pubs.; 0-936804),* 715 38th St., West Des Moines, IA 50265 (SAN 218-4419) Tel 515-224-0338.

Kaufman AB Pubs, *(Kaufman, Alvin B., Pubs.; 0-9607736),* 22420 Philiprimm St., Woodland Hills, CA 91367 (SAN 239-5568) Tel 818-340-8945.

Kaufman Hse, *(Kaufman House Pubs.; 0-9602500),* 366 Terrace Ave., Cincinnati, OH 45220 (SAN 212-517X) Tel 513-751-6381.

Kavanagh, *(Kavanagh, Peter, Hand Press; 0-914612),* 250 E. 30th St., New York, NY 10016 (SAN 205-6291) Tel 212-686-5099.

Kawaida Pubns, *(Kawaida Pubns.; 0-943412),* 2560 West 54th St., Los Angeles, CA 90043 (SAN 219-5925).

Kay Assocs, *(Kay Assocs.; 0-9616188),* 16840 NE 19th Ave., North Miami Beach, FL 33162 (SAN 658-3571) Tel 305-949-3922.

Kay Kitchen, *(Kay's Kitchen Cookbook; 0-9613781),* P.O. Box 2124, El Dorado, AR 71731-2124 (SAN 693-9953) Tel 501-862-6651.

Kayak, *(Kayak; 0-87711),* 325 Ocean View Ave., Santa Cruz, CA 95062 (SAN 203-9168).

Kaycee Pr, *(Kaycee Pr.; 0-9614884),* 6586 Eastpointe Pines St., Palm Beach Gardens, FL 33410 (SAN 693-1960) Tel 305-626-5368.

Kaylor Christ Co, *(Kaylor, Christopher, Co.; 0-916039),* P.O. Box 737, Huntsville, AL 35804 (SAN 294-8524) Tel 205-534-6156; 706 Holmes Ave., Huntsville, AL 35801 (SAN 294-8532).

Kaypro
See Kaypro Corp

Kaypro Corp, *(Kaypro Corp.),* P.O. Box N, Del Mar, CA 92014 (SAN 692-0446) Tel 619-481-3900; Toll free: 800-4KAYPRO; 533 Stevens Ave., Solana Beach, CA 92075 (SAN 697-8355) Tel 619-481-4300.

Kazi Pubns, *(Kazi Pubns.; 0-935782; 0-933511),* 1215 W. Belmont Ave., Chicago, IL 60657 (SAN 162-3397) Tel 312-327-7598.

KC Pubns, *(KC Pubns.; 0-916122; 0-88714),* P.O. Box 14883, Las Vegas, NV 89114 (SAN 201-0364) Tel 702-731-3123; Toll free: 800-626-9673; 2901 Industrial Rd., Las Vegas, NV 89109 (SAN 658-103X).

KCE Pub, *(Kreider Consolidated Enterprises Publishing; 0-940686),* 40 Cordone Dr., San Anselmo, CA 94960 (SAN 218-5636) Tel 415-951-6160.

KCI Comns, *(KCI Communications, Inc.; 0-937583),* 1300 N. 17th St., Arlington, VA 22209 (SAN 658-8964) Tel 703-276-7100.

KDK Pubns, *(KDK Pubns.; 0-910165),* 1892 Fell St., San Francisco, CA 94117 (SAN 241-2144) Tel 415-386-9656.

Kearney, *(Kearney Publishing Co.; 0-9604688),* 2515 Peachtree Lane, Northbrook, IL 60062 (SAN 212-7512) Tel 312-559-2985.

Keats, *(Keats Publishing, Inc.; 0-87983),* Box 876, New Canaan, CT 06840 (SAN 201-0410) Tel 203-966-8721; 27 Pine St., New Canaan, CT 06840 (SAN 658-1048).

†**Keats Pub,** *(Keats Publisher; 0-941962),* 12110 Webb Chaple Rd., Suite E305, Dallas, TX 75234 (SAN 238-2474) Tel 214-620-0620; *CIP.*

Kedcograph, *(Kedcograph Co.; 0-936605),* 3037 Montrose Ave., Chicago, IL 60618 (SAN 698-0430) Tel 312-478-5836; P.O. Box 59118, Chicago, IL 60659 (SAN 698-245X).

Keeble Pr, *(Keeble Pr., The; 0-933144),* 3634 Winchell Rd., Shaker Heights, OH 44122 (SAN 214-249X) Tel 216-283-8245.

Keegan Pr, *(Keegan Pr.; 0-9607328),* 201 Sunnyslope Ave., Petaluma, CA 94952 (SAN 239-2445) Tel 707-763-0427; Dist. by: Inland Bk Co., P.O. Box 261, 22 Hemingway Ave., East Haven, CT 06512 (SAN 200-4151) Tel 203-467-4257.

Keeling Inc, *(Keeling, Inc.; 0-9616525),* 309 Washington St., W., Charleston, WV 25302 (SAN 659-4751) Tel 304-345-0448.

Keep Am Beautiful, *(Keep America Beautiful, Inc.),* 99 Park Ave., New York, NY 10016 (SAN 232-7457) Tel 212-682-4564.

Keewaydin Camp, *(Keewaydin Camp Ltd.; 0-9691378),* 4242 Brookdale St., Jackson, MS 39206 (SAN 296-1245).

Keilco Inc, *(Keilco, Inc.; 0-9615732),* 4504 Westward, Wichita Falls, TX 76308 (SAN 695-8494) Tel 817-691-5017.

Keith County Hist, *(Keith County Historical Society; 0-9614379),* P.O. Box 27, Ogallala, NE 69153 (SAN 694-0080) Tel 308-284-3544; Dist. by: Elaine Nielsen, P.O. Box 599, Ogallala, NE 69153 (SAN 200-7975).

Keithwood, *(Keithwood Publishing Co.),* 6835 Greenway Ave., Philadelphia, PA 19142 (SAN 213-9324) Tel 215-727-0883.

KEL Pubns, *(KEL Pubns.; 0-9605710),* 443 Schley Rd., Annapolis, MD 21401 (SAN 216-1508) Tel 301-268-9704.

Kelane Pub, *(Kelane Pubns.; 0-9609394),* 5640 118th Ave., SE, Bellevue, WA 98006 (SAN 281-8558) Tel 206-747-9849.

Kelby Pub, *(Kelby Publishing; 0-937555),* P.O. Box 369, Los Lunas, NM 87031 (SAN 658-9022) Tel 505-299-7719.

Keller-Burns & McGuirk, *(Keller, Burns & McGuirk Pub. Co.; 0-9602506),* c/o James P. Gould, Colony Park Bldg., 37th & Woodland, West Des Moines, IA 50265 (SAN 213-2230) Tel 515-225-3122.

Keller Intl Pub, *(Keller International Publishing Corp.; 0-937843),* 150 Great Neck Rd., Great Neck, NY 11021 (SAN 659-476X) Tel 516-829-9210.

†**Kelley,** *(Kelley, Augustus M., Pubs.; 0-678),* 1140 Broadway, Rm. 901, New York, NY 10001 (SAN 206-975X) Tel 212-685-7202; Orders to: 300 Fairfield Rd., P.O. Box 1308, Fairfield, NJ 07006 (SAN 206-9768); *CIP.* *Imprints:* Baker Library (Baker Library); Reference Bk Pubs (Reference Book Publishers).(Reference Bk. Pubs.).

Kelley Pubns, *(Kelley Pubns.; 0-9614480),* P.O. Box No.1, Seaman, OH 45679-0001 (SAN 689-3767) Tel 513-386-2375.

Kellner-McCaffery, *(Kellner/McCaffery Associates, Inc.; 0-911069),* 150 Fifth Ave., Suite 322, New York, NY 10011 (SAN 271-8782) Tel 212-741-0280; Orders to: Gary Waller, Carnegie-Mellon Univ., English Dept., Pittsburgh, PA 15213 (SAN 662-0612) Tel 412-578-2850.

Kellogg, *(Kellogg, Edward P., Jr.; 0-9603914),* 1755 Trinity Ave., No. 79, Walnut Creek, CA 94596 (SAN 213-6880) Tel 415-937-4841; Orders to: EHUD International Language Foundation, P.O. Box 2082, Dollar Ranch Sta., Walnut Creek, CA 94595 (SAN 214-2988) Tel 415-937-4841.

Kelly, *(Kelly, Thomas; 0-910832),* 23 Prospect Terrace, Montclair, NJ 07042 (SAN 206-7242) Tel 201-746-7884.

Kelly Ent, *(Kelly Enterprises; 0-9615582),* P.O. Box 247, Holt, MI 48842-0247 (SAN 696-2815) Tel 517-694-1799; 2203 Meadowlane, Holt, MI 48842-0247 (SAN 699-6302).

Kelsey Pub, *(Kelsey Publishing; 0-9605824),* 310 E. 950 S., Springville, UT 84663 (SAN 216-5775) Tel 801-489-6666.

†**Kelsey St Pr,** *(Kelsey Street Pr.; 0-932716),* P.O. Box 9235, Berkeley, CA 94709 (SAN 212-6729) Tel 415-845-2260; *CIP.*

Kelso, *(Kelso Manufacturing Co.; 0-942140),* Rte. 2, Box 499, Greenville, MS 38701 (SAN 210-1491).

Kemah Pr, *(Kemah Press; 0-9610806),* 91 Paradise Lane, Halifax, MA 02338 (SAN 265-0959) Tel 617-293-6655.

Kemetic Inst, *(Kemetic Institute; 0-939539),* 700 East Oakwood Blvd., Chicago, IL 60653 (SAN 663-4435) Tel 312-268-7500.

Kempe Nat Ctr, *(Kempe, C. Henry, National Ctr. for the Prevention & Treatment of Child Abuse & Neglect),* Div. of Univ. of Colorado Health Science Ctr., Dept. of Pediatrics, 1205 Oneida St., Denver, CO 80220 (SAN 240-9429) Tel 303-321-3963.

Kempler Inst, *(Kempler Institute; 0-9600808),* P.O. Box 1692, Costa Mesa, CA 92628 (SAN 207-6284) Tel 714-545-8942.

Ken-Bks, *(Ken-Bks.; 0-913164),* 56 Midcrest Ave., San Francisco, CA 94131 (SAN 201-0429) Tel 415-826-6550.

Ken Kra Pubs, *(Ken Kra Pubs.; 0-941522),* 1657 Thornwood Dr., Concord, CA 94521 (SAN 239-0000) Tel 415-676-9184.

Kenco Pub Co, *(Kenco Publishing Co.; 0-916041),* 1224 Catalpa Lane, Naperville, IL 60540 (SAN 294-8591) Tel 312-346-5145.

KEND Pub, *(KEND Publishing; 0-938218),* 15 Dorchester Rd., Emerson, NJ 07630 (SAN 217-2429) Tel 201-261-9281.

Kendall Bks, *(Kendall Books; 0-935678),* 1212 N.W. 12th Ave., Gainesville, FL 32601 (SAN 221-4563) Tel 904-376-4913.

Kendall-Hunt, *(Kendall/Hunt Publishing Co.; 0-8403),* Subs. of Wm. C. Brown Co., Pubs., 2460 Kerper Blvd., Dubuque, IA 52001 (SAN 203-9184) Tel 319-589-2833.

Kendall Mus
See Kendall Whaling

Kendall Whaling, *(Kendall Whaling Museum; 0-937854),* 27 Everett St., P.O. Box 297, Sharon, MA 02067 (SAN 204-9783) Tel 617-784-5642.

Kenedy, *(Kenedy, P. J., & Sons),* Subs. of Macmillan Publishing Co., 866 Third Ave., New York, NY 10022 (SAN 203-9192) Tel 212-935-2000; Orders to: Macmillan Co., Riverside, NJ 08075 (SAN 202-5582).

Kenilworth, *(Kenilworth Press; 0-9603876),* 421 W. Grant Ave., Eau Claire, WI 54701 (SAN 204-9775) Tel 715-832-2161.

Kennebec River, *(Kennebec River Pr., Inc., The; 0-933858),* 36 Old Mill Rd., Falmouth, ME 04105 (SAN 221-458X) Tel 207-781-3002; Dist. by: Harpswell Pr., 132 Water St., Gardiner, ME 04345 (SAN 208-1199) Tel 207-582-1899.

Kennedy Alan, *(Kennedy, Alan; 0-87940),* 344 E. 63rd St., New York, NY 10021 (SAN 693-3920).

Kennedy & Co, *(Kennedy, Byron, & Co.; 0-941072),* P.O. Box 10937, St. Petersburg, FL 33733 (SAN 217-3875) Tel 813-822-3738.

Kennedy Gall, *(Kennedy Galleries; 0-87920),* 40 W. 57th St., New York, NY 10019 (SAN 207-3226).

Kennedy King Col, *(Kennedy-King College; 0-938299),* 6800 S. Wentworth Ave., Chicago, IL 60621-3798 (SAN 661-1737) Tel 312-962-3707.

Kenneth Pub Co, *(Kenneth Publishing Co.; 0-913451),* Box 344, Palos Heights, IL 60463 (SAN 285-1733) Tel 312-776-4648.

Kennikat Pr
See Assoc Faculty Pr

Kensington Hist, *(Kensington Historical Pr.),* Cardinal Sta., Box 1314, Washington, DC 20064 (SAN 696-2416).

Kensington Pub, *(Kensington Publishing Co.; 0-931445),* 3537 Mt. Diablo Blvd., Lafayette, CA 94549 (SAN 687-7516) Tel 415-283-1964.

Kent & Co, *(Kent, Edward, & Co.; 0-935625),* 1129 State St., Suite 20, Santa Barbara, CA 93101 (SAN 696-4095) Tel 805-966-1551.

Kent Popular, *(Kent Popular Press; 0-933522),* P.O. Box 715, Kent, OH 44240 (SAN 213-6295).

†**Kent Pub Co,** *(Kent Publishing Co.; 0-534),* Div. of Wadsworth, Inc., 20 Park Plaza, Boston, MA 02116 (SAN 215-3491) Tel 617-542-1629; Toll free: 800-343-2204; *CIP.*

Kent Pubns, *(Kent Pubns.; 0-917458),* 18301 Halstead St., Northridge, CA 91325 (SAN 209-0597) Tel 818-349-2080.

†**Kent St U Pr,** *(Kent State Univ. Pr.; 0-87338),* Kent, OH 44242 (SAN 201-0437) Tel 216-672-7913; Toll free: 800-USA-KENT; Toll free: 800-FOR-KENT in Ohio; Orders to: 101 Franklin Hall, Kent, OH (SAN 215-3742); Dist. by: Harper & Row, Keystone Industrial Pk., Scranton, PA 18512 (SAN 215-3742); *CIP.*

Kentucky Arts, *(Kentucky Arts Council; 0-939058),* Berry Hill, Frankfort, KY 40601 (SAN 218-4869).

Kentucky Hist, *(Kentucky Historical Society; 0-916968),* Old-State-House, Box H, Frankfort, KY 40602 (SAN 204-9759) Tel 502-564-3016.

Kentucky Mining, *(Kentucky Mining Institute; 0-9615443),* 120 Graham Ave., Lexington, KY 40506 (SAN 695-7218) Tel 606-254-0367; P.O. Box 680, Lexington, KY 40586 (SAN 696-947X).

Kentucky Rifle, *(Kentucky Rifle Assn.; 0-9615925),* 601 Madison St., Alexandria, VA 22314 (SAN 696-6667) Tel 703-836-6020.

Kentwood, *(Kentwood Publications; 0-917855),* 2515 Santa Clara Ave., No. 103, P.O. Box 2787, Alameda, CA 94501 (SAN 657-100X) Tel 415-865-4415.

Kenwood Pub, *(Kenwood Publishing; 0-9612776),* 2120 Kenwood Pkwy., Minneapolis, MN 55405 (SAN 289-7423) Tel 612-374-3337.

Kenyon, *(Kenyon Pubns.; 0-934286),* 361 Pin Oak Ln., Westbury, NY 11590 (SAN 201-5072) Tel 516-333-3236; Dist. by: G. Schirmer, Inc., 7101 Westfield Ave., Pennsauken, NJ 08110 (SAN 222-9544).

Kenyon Hill, *(Kenyon Hill Pubns., Inc.; 0-917241),* Box 170, Hanover, NH 03755 (SAN 655-8666) Tel 603-795-4027.

Keoki's Pubns, *(Keoki's Pubns.),* 1229 W. Sixth St., Ontario, CA 91762 (SAN 295-012X).

Kepler Pr, *(Kepler Pr.; 0-912938),* 84 Main St., Rockport, MA 01966 (SAN 203-9745) Tel 617-546-9614.

Kepley, *(Kepley, Ray R.; 0-9604248),* Rte. 2 Box 128A, Ulysses, KS 67880 (SAN 214-3208) Tel 316-356-1568.

Kepner-Tregoe, *(Kepner-Tregoe, Inc.),* 17 Research Rd., P.O. Box 704, Princeton, NJ 08540 (SAN 264-1496).

Keramos Bks, *(Keramos Bks.; 0-935066),* Subs. of Westwood Ceramic Supply Co., P.O. Box 2305, Bassett, CA 91746 (SAN 207-5571) Tel 213-330-0631; 14400 Lomitas Ave., City of Industry, CA 91746 (SAN 207-558X).

Kern Historical, *(Kern County Historical Society; 0-943500),* P.O. Box 141, Bakersfield, CA 93302 (SAN 240-6969) Tel 805-322-4962.

Kerning Arts, *(Kerning Arts Press, The; 0-9606956),* 719 S. Elm Blvd., Champaign, IL 61820 (SAN 239-4472) Tel 217-359-2575.

Kerr Assoc, *(Kerr Assocs., Inc.; 0-937890),* 1409 Willow St., Suite 201, Minneapolis, MN 55403 (SAN 220-0635) Tel 612-871-6503.

Kesend Pub Co *See* Kesend Pub Ltd

†**Kesend Pub Ltd,** *(Kesend, Michael, Publishing, Ltd.; 0-935576),* 1025 Fifth Ave., New York, NY 10028 (SAN 213-6902) Tel 212-249-5150; *CIP.*

Kesher, *(Kesher Pr.; 0-9602394),* 1817 21st Ave., S., Nashville, TN 37212 (SAN 212-6761).

KET, *(KET; 0-910475),* Network Ctr., 600 Cooper Dr., Lexington, KY 40502 (SAN 264-147X); Toll free: 800-354-9067.

Keter Found, *(Keter Foundation; 0-933413),* P.O. Box 1312, Provo, UT 84602 (SAN 691-4993) Tel 801-378-4161.

Keturah Pr, *(Keturah Pr.; 0-942546),* 350-A Quincy St., Brooklyn, NY 11216 (SAN 240-0774) Tel 718-636-1437.

Kevco Ben Bks, *(Kevco Beneficial Bks.; 0-932297),* 146 Stenner St., Unit 7, San Luis Obispo, CA 93401 (SAN 686-6573) Tel 805-541-6140.

Key *Imprint of* B&N Imports

Key Bk Serv, *(Key Book Service, Inc.; 0-934636),* 425 Asylum St., Bridgeport, CT 06610 (SAN 169-0671) Tel 203-334-2165; Toll free: 800-243-2790.

Key Bks, *(Key Books),* Dist. by: Associated Booksellers, 147 McKinley Ave., Bridgeport, CT 06606 (SAN 203-5014).

Key Bks Pr, *(Key Bks. Pr.; 0-9611390),* Div. of Hadady Corp., P.O. Box 90490, Pasadena, CA 91109-0490 (SAN 285-290X); 61 S. Lake Ave., No. 309, Pasadena, CA 91101 (SAN 660-9511) Tel 818-793-2645.

Key Curr Proj, *(Key Curriculum Project; 0-913684),* P.O. Box 2304, Berkeley, CA 94702 (SAN 202-6538) Tel 415-548-2304; Toll free: 800-338-7638.

Key Found, *(Key Foundation; 0-911533),* 1601 Bayshore Hwy., No. 350, Burlingame, CA 94010 (SAN 293-2229) Tel 415-692-8853; Dist. by: DeVorss & Co., P.O. Box 550, Marina del Rey, CA 90291 (SAN 168-9886).

Key of David, *(Key of David Pubns.; 0-943374),* 222 N. 17th, Philadelphia, PA 19103 (SAN 239-4480) Tel 215-664-4673.

Key Pubns, *(Key Pubns.; 0-937141),* Div. of Corporate Computer Training Ctr., 812 Lyndon Ln., Suite 4, Louisville, KY 40222 (SAN 658-5655) Tel 502-725-2148.

Key West Wmns Club, *(Key West Women's Club, The; 0-9615035),* 319 Duval St., Key West, FL 33040 (SAN 693-7934) Tel 305-294-2039; Dist. by: Langley Pr., 821 Georgia St., Key West, FL 33040 (SAN 264-164X) Tel 305-294-3156.

Keymate Syst, *(Keymate Systems; 0-936379),* 9225 Mira Mesa Blvd., No. 212, San Diego, CA 92126 (SAN 697-2780) Tel 619-566-2283.

Keystone Bks *Imprint of* **Pa St U Pr**

Keystone Pubns, *(Keystone Pubns.; 0-912126),* Subs. of Wilfred American Educational Corp., 250 W. 57th St., Suite 823, New York, NY 10019 (SAN 204-9708) Tel 212-582-2254; Toll free: 800-223-0935.

KG Bks Co, *(KG Bks. Co.; 0-930425),* 5912 Schaefer Rd., Edina, MN 55436 (SAN 682-0514) Tel 612-925-5134.

KGI Pr, *(KGI Pr.; 0-936349),* 440 Cesano Ct., No. 306, Palo Alto, CA 94306 (SAN 697-8959) Tel 415-948-9262.

KGI Pub, *(KGI Publishing; 0-939231),* 7280 Blue Hill Dr., No. 14, San Jose, CA 95129 (SAN 662-5924) Tel 408-446-5574.

Khaneghah & Maktab, *(Khaneghah & Maktab of Malekdia Naseralishah; 0-917220),* P.O. Box 665, Palisades, NY 10964 (SAN 208-5046) Tel 914-359-7547.

KhaniQahi-Nimatullahi *See* KhaniQahi-Nimatullahi-Sufi

KhaniQahi-Nimatullahi-Sufi, *(KhaniQahi-Nimatullahi, Sufi Order; 0-933546),* 306 W. 11th St., New York, NY 10014 (SAN 212-3673) Tel 212-924-7739; Dist. by: Samuel Weiser, Inc., P.O. Box 612, York Beach, ME 03910 (SAN 202-9588) Tel 207-363-4393; Dist. by: The New Leaf Distributing, 1020 White St., SW, Atlanta, GA 30310 (SAN 169-1449) Tel 404-755-2665.

Khedcanron Pub, *(Khedcanron Publishing; 0-9610264),* 126 Westward Dr., Corte Madera, CA 94925 (SAN 264-150X) Tel 415-924-1944.

Khorassan Pr, *(Khorassan Pr.; 0-9617114),* P.O. Box 9197, St. Louis, MO 63117 (SAN 662-7021); 5591 Lindell, St. Louis, MO 63112 (SAN 662-703X) Tel 314-361-0808; Dist. by: Paperback Supply Co., 4121 Forest Pk. Blvd., St. Louis, MO 63108 (SAN 169-4324) Tel 314-652-1000.

Kibler Flying, *(Kibler Flying Service; 0-9613506),* P.O. Box 823, Milford, PA 18337 (SAN 657-2774) Tel 717-296-7721.

Kibo Bks, *(Kibo Bks.; 0-941266),* P.O. Box 1442, Main Post Office, Brooklyn, NY 11202 (SAN 239-5584).

Kickapoo, *(Kickapoo Pr.; 0-933180),* P.O. Box 1443, Peoria, IL 61655 (SAN 214-2503).

Kickapoo Tribal, *(Kickapoo Tribal Pr.; 0-931045),* P.O. Box 106, Powhattan, KS 66527 (SAN 678-8998) Tel 913-474-3550.

KID Broadcast, *(KID Broadcasting Corp.; 0-9607304),* P.O. Box 2008, Idaho Falls, ID 83401 (SAN 240-9569).

Kid-Love Unltd, *(Kid-Love Unlimited; 0-912249),* 2036 Galaxy Dr., Newport Beach, CA 92660 (SAN 265-1572) Tel 714-642-1179.

Kid Power Ent, *(Kid Power Enterprises; 0-935441),* P.O. Box 2367, Decatur, GA 30031-2367 (SAN 696-2971); Dist. by: DeVorss & Co, P.O. Box 550, 1046 Princeton Dr., Marina del Rey, CA 30310 (SAN 168-9886) Tel 404-755-2665; Dist. by: The New Leaf Distributing, 1020 White St., SW, Atlanta, VA (SAN 169-1449).

Kids in Distress, *(Kids In Distress, Inc.; 0-9615864),* 2627 NE Ninth Ave., Fort Lauderdale, FL 33334 (SAN 696-6020) Tel 305-942-1800.

Kids Special, *(Kids Come in Special Flavors Co.; 0-941854),* P.O. Box 292786, Kettering Sta., Kettering, OH 45429-0786 (SAN 216-2628) Tel 513-294-2797.

Kidsmart, *(Kidsmart; 0-936985),* P.O. Box 34066, Memphis, TN 38184-0066 (SAN 658-5639) Tel 901-372-7550; 3276 Hawksmoor Pl., Cordova, TN 38018 (SAN 658-5647).

Kienast *See* Artus Co

Kiewit Comput, *(Kiewit Computation Center; 0-89580),* Dartmouth College, Hanover, NH 03755 (SAN 211-027X) Tel 603-646-2643.

Kilgore, *(Kilgore; 0-9609280),* 1424 Acacia Dr., Colorado Springs, CO 80907 (SAN 260-0870) Tel 303-598-2410.

Kilgore Assocs, *(Kilgore, Jack, & Assocs.; 0-935809),* 5209 Thurman Dr., Sioux Falls, SD 57106 (SAN 696-6055) Tel 605-361-0711.

Kilkerrin House, *(Kilkerrin Hse.; 0-9611728),* 740 Puente Dr., Santa Barbara, CA 93110 (SAN 285-3647) Tel 805-967-1903.

Kilmarnock Pr, *(Kilmarnock Pr., The; 0-937982),* P.O. Box 1302, South Pasadena, CA 91030 (SAN 265-3893) Tel 818-795-2170.

Kilthau West Pubns, *(Kilthau-West Pubns.; 0-939347),* 13514 Rainbow Falls, Houston, TX 77083 (SAN 662-4901)

Kiltie, *(Kiltie, Ordean, & Co.; 0-937364),* 2445 Fairfield, A201, Ft. Wayne, IN 46807 (SAN 209-5718) Tel 219-745-9139.

Kimbell Art, *(Kimbell Art Museum; 0-912804),* 3333 Camp Bowie Blvd., P.O. Box 9440, Ft. Worth, TX 76107 (SAN 208-0516) Tel 817-332-8451; Dist. by: University of Washington Pr., P.O. Box C-50096, Seattle, WA 98145-5096 (SAN 212-2502) Tel 206-543-8870; Dist. by: Harry N. Abrams, Inc., 100 Fifth Ave., New York, NY 10011 (SAN 200-2434) Tel 212-206-7715.

Kimberly-Jones, *(Kimberly-Jones Publishing Co.; 0-941412),* 2828 S. 94th St., P.O. Box 14213, Omaha, NE 68124 (SAN 238-8898) Tel 402-393-8121; Dist. by: International Specialized Bk., Servs., Inc., 5602 NE Hassalo St., Portland, OR 97213-3640 (SAN 169-7129) Tel 503-287-3093.

Kimberly Pr, *(Kimberly Pr.; 0-9615913),* P.O. Box 632, Baldwin Place, NY 10505 (SAN 697-225X) Tel 914-628-2636.

Kimdar Bks, *(Kimdar Books; 0-939541),* P.O. Box 19542, Houston, TX 77224 (SAN 663-4389); 15455 Point NW, Blvd., No. 2101, Houston, TX 77095 (SAN 663-4397) Tel 713-550-0482.

Kincaid Pubs, *(Kincaid Pubs.; 0-9616989),* 2101 Geer Rd., Suite 105A, Turlock, CA 95380 (SAN 661-731X) Tel 209-537-2447.

Kinder Pr, *(Kinderpress; 0-931047),* 2240 135th Pl. SE, Bellevue, WA 98005 (SAN 678-9005) Tel 206-643-2695; P.O. Box 5761, Bellevue, WA 98006 (SAN 662-2534).

Kinder Read, *(Kinder Read; 0-934361),* P.O. Box 18, Ingomar, PA 15127 (SAN 693-4552); 970 Broadmeadow Dr., Pittsburgh, PA 15237 (SAN 662-3247) Tel 412-366-9761.

Kindler, *(Kindler, Leonard; 0-943502),* P.O. Box 12328, Philadelphia, PA 19119 (SAN 240-6977) Tel 215-843-4487.

Kindred Joy, *(Kindred Joy Pubns.; 0-911141),* 554 W. 4th, Coquille, OR 97423 (SAN 262-9275) Tel 503-396-4154.

Kindred Pr, *(Kindred Pr.),* Box L, Hillsboro, KS 67063 (SAN 205-8634) Tel 316-947-3151; Orders to: 616 Walnut Ave., Scottdale, PA 15683 (SAN 202-2915) Tel 412-887-8500.

King & Mary, *(King & Mary; 0-9601890),* 4709 Comita, Fort Worth, TX 76132 (SAN 211-8602) Tel 817-292-1295.

King Authors Court, *(King Authors Court Pr. at Vision Studios; 0-936888),* Box 32, Route 1, Thompson Station, TN 37179 (SAN 214-4433) Tel 615-790-3138.

King Bks, *(King Bks.; 0-9611532),* 817 S. 265th St., Kent, WA 98032 (SAN 285-368X) Tel 206-941-2992.

King Co, *(King Publishing Co.),* 4757 Distribution Dr., Tampa, FL 33605 (SAN 260-2288) Tel 813-248-3330.

King Fisher Pr, *(King Fisher Press; 0-9612972),* 5115 E. Virginia, Phoenix, AZ 85008 (SAN 292-5567) Tel 602-840-2342.

King Freedom, *(King Freedom Pubns.; 0-911435),* Box 962, Glenwood Springs, CO 81602 (SAN 271-888X) Tel 303-945-8847.

King ME, *(King, Helen B.; 0-9615366),* 11 Pierce St., Orono, ME 04473 (SAN 695-2240) Tel 207-866-3309.

King Philip Pub, *(King Philip Publishing Co.; 0-9614811),* 466 Ocean Ave., Portland, ME 04103 (SAN 692-9133) Tel 207-772-2685.

Kingdom, *(Kingdom Pr.; 0-910840),* 105 Chestnut Hill Rd., Amherst, NH 03031 (SAN 201-0461) Tel 603-673-3208.

Kingdom Bks, *(Kingdom Bks.; 0-9613181),* 18548 Arminta St., Reseda, CA 91335 (SAN 295-902X) Tel 818-342-8740.

Kingdom God, *(Kingdom of God; 0-9607702),* P.O. Box 7123, Minneapolis, MN 55407 (SAN 238-6704) Tel 612-823-1783.

Kingdom Hse, *(Kingdom Hse.; 0-9609926),* 309 W. 7th St., Fulton, MO 65251 (SAN 271-8898) Tel 314-642-2150.

Kingman Pub, *(Kingman-Block Publishing, Inc.; 0-937353),* 180 Seventh Ave., Santa Cruz, CA 95062 (SAN 658-9030) Tel 408-375-9200.

Kings Court, (King's Court Communications, Inc.; 0-89139), 590 Pearl Rd., Box 224, Brunswick, OH 44212 (SAN 207-3730) Tel 216-273-2100.
King's Crown Paperbacks Imprint of **Columbia U Pr**
Kings Farspan, (King's Farspan, Inc.; 0-932814), 1473 S. La Luna Ave., Ojai, CA 93023 (SAN 211-8084) Tel 805-646-2928; Dist. by: Spring Arbor Distributors, 10885 Textile Rd., Bellville, MI 48111 (SAN 158-9016) Tel 313-481-0900; Dist. by: Living Bks., Inc., 12155 Magnolia Ave., Bldg 11-B, Riverside, CA 92503 (SAN 662-0639) Tel 714-354-7330.
†**King's Hse Pub,** (King's Hse. Publishing Co.; 0-916333), 3000 Fairfield at Kings Hwy., Shreveport, LA 71104 (SAN 295-9046) Tel 318-222-1995; CIP.
Kings Pr
See Kings Farspan
Kingston Ellis, (Kingston Ellis Pr.; 0-914425), 1014 Freemason St., Knoxville, TN 37917 (SAN 291-820X) Tel 615-687-8467.
Kingston Korner, (Kingston Korner, Inc.; 0-9614594), 50 Sunrise St., Norwich, CT 06360 (SAN 691-7828) Tel 203-889-5619; Orders to: 6 S. 230 Cohasset Rd., Naperville, IL 60540 (SAN 662-2925) Tel 312-961-3559.
†**Kingston Pr,** (Kingston Pr., Inc., The; 0-940670), P.O. Box 1456, Princeton, NJ 08542 (SAN 226-7950) Tel 609-921-0609; CIP.
Kinko's Pub, (Kinko's Publishing Group; 1-55577), 4141 State St., Santa Barbara, CA 93110 (SAN 699-8852) Tel 805-967-0192.
Kinnickinnic Pr, (Kinnickinnic Pr.; 0-9615065), 1101 W. Division St., River Falls, WI 54022 (SAN 694-1397) Tel 715-425-6897.
Kino Pubns, (Kino Pubns.; 0-9607366), 6625 N. First Ave., Tucson, AZ 85718 (SAN 238-2547) Tel 602-297-7278.
Kinser Pub, (Kinser Publishing, Inc.; 0-9615659), Rte. 3, Box 157A, Aurora, MO 65605 (SAN 695-9482) Tel 417-574-6961.
Kinucan & Brons, (Kinucan & Brons, Pubs.; 0-9615444), 420 N. Hulen Way, Ketchum, ID 83340 (SAN 695-7234) Tel 208-263-8604; P.O. Box 765, Ketchum, ID 83340 (SAN 696-9488).
Kiowa Pr, (Kiowa Pr.; 0-9607602), P.O. Box 555, Woodburn, OR 97071 (SAN 222-9773) Tel 503-981-3017.
Kiplinger Wash Eds, (Kiplinger Washington Editors, Inc., The; 0-938721), 1729 H St., NW, Washington, DC 20006 (SAN 661-6100) Tel 202-887-6434; Dist. by: Select Magazines, Inc., 8 E. 40th St., New York, NY 10016 (SAN 200-6693).
Kiracofe & Kile
See Quilt Digest Pr
Kirban, (Kirban, Salem, Inc.; 0-912582), 2117 Kent Rd., Huntingdon Valley, PA 19006 (SAN 201-047X) Tel 215-947-4894; Dist. by: AMG Publishers, 6815 Shallowford Rd., Chattanooga, TN 37422 (SAN 211-3074) Tel 615-894-6062.
Kirin Bks & Art, (Kirin Books & Art; 0-935034), 4528 Peacock Ave., Alexandria, VA 22304 (SAN 213-5280) Tel 703-751-3141.
Kirk Pr, (Kirk Pr.), 205 W. Kent Rd., Duluth, MN 55812 (SAN 211-4275).
Kirk Pub, (Kirk Publishing; 0-911821), Div. of Kirksite Enterprises, Inc., One E. First St., No. 1400, Reno, NV 89501 (SAN 264-1518) Tel 415-826-1005.
Kisaku, (Kisaku, Inc.; 0-934625), 920 Prospect St., Honolulu, HI 96822 (SAN 285-6603) Tel 808-533-6753.
Kitchen Classics, (Kitchen Classics; 0-9615522), 539 Stonewood Dr., Stone Mountain, GA 30087 (SAN 696-2866) Tel 404-549-2593; 1220 Mason Mill Rd., Stone Mountain, GA 30087 (SAN 699-6310).
Kitchen Harvest, (Kitchen Harvest Pr.; 0-917234), 3N 681 Bittersweet Dr., St. Charles, IL 60174 (SAN 207-2467) Tel 312-584-4084.
Kitchen Sampler
See Bessemer Jr Serv Leag
Kitchen Sink, (Kitchen Sink Pr.; 0-87816), 2 Swamp Rd., Princeton, WI 54968 (SAN 212-7784) Tel 414-295-6922.
Kitchen Treas, (Kitchen Treasures; 0-9609282), 9939 103rd Ave. N., P.O. Box 541, Maple Grove, MN 55369 (SAN 260-0897) Tel 612-425-1309.

Kitchen Wisdom, (Kitchen Wisdom Publishing Co.; 0-937383), 10032 SE Linwood Ave., Portland, OR 97222 (SAN 658-9065) Tel 503-771-1402.
Kitten Pub, (Kitten Pubns.; 0-9608722), 240 Indian Hills, Corydon, IN 47112 (SAN 238-3071) Tel 812-738-8452.
Kitwardo Pubs, (Kitwardo Pubs., Inc.; 0-932641), 115 S. Third St., Apt. No. 1108, Jacksonville Beach, FL 32250 (SAN 687-8091) Tel 904-246-2071.
†**KITwo Enter,** (KI2 Enterprises; 0-9608744), P.O. Box 13322, Portland, OR 97213 (SAN 241-1261) Tel 502-256-3486; CIP.
Kiyler Creations, (Kiyler Creations; 0-936025), 25 Maxim Southard Rd., Howell, NJ 07731 (SAN 697-2284) Tel 201-364-5481; P.O. Box 372, Howell, NJ 07731 (SAN 699-6477).
Kjellberg & Sons, (Kjellberg & Sons, Inc.; 0-912868), 24W770 Geneva Rd., Wheaton, IL 60187 (SAN 201-5102) Tel 312-653-2244.
Kjos, (Kjos, Neil A., Music Co.; 0-910842; 0-8497), 4380 Jutland Dr., San Diego, CA 92117-0894 (SAN 201-0488) Tel 619-270-9800; Toll free: 800-854-1592.
Klamath Pioneer Pub, (Klamath Pioneer Publishing; 0-9605120), 132 S. Seventh St., Klamath Falls, OR 97601 (SAN 239-8443) Tel 503-882-1821.
Klassic Advert & Pub, (Klassic Advertising & Publishing Co.; 0-9615523), 7615 Glade Ave., Unit 101, Canoga Park, CA 91304 (SAN 696-2874) Tel 818-994-4145.
Klein Post Card Serv, (Klein Post Card Service; 0-915983), 16 Havard Ave., Hyde Park, MA 02136 (SAN 294-8621) Tel 617-361-6324.
Klein Pubns
See F Klein Pubns
Kleinsinger
See IJK Intl
Kline, (Kline, Charles H., & Co., Inc.; 0-917148), 330 Passaic Ave., Fairfield, NJ 07006 (SAN 202-6546) Tel 201-227-6262.
Klock & Klock, (Klock & Klock Christian Pubs.; 0-86524), 2527 Girard Ave. N., Minneapolis, MN 55411 (SAN 212-0003) Tel 612-522-2244.
Klutz Pr, (Klutz Pr.; 0-932592), P.O. Box 2992, Stanford, CA 94305 (SAN 212-7539) Tel 415-857-0888.
†**Kluwer Academic,** (Kluwer Academic Pubs.; 0-89838), Subs. of Kluwer NV, 101 Philip Dr., Assinippi Pk., Norwell, MA 02061 (SAN 211-481X) Tel 617-871-6600; Orders to: P.O. Box 358, Accord Sta., Hingham, MA 02018-0358 (SAN 662-0647); CIP.
Kluwer Boston
See Kluwer Academic
Kluwer Law Bk, (Kluwer Law Bk. Pubs., Inc.; 0-930273), Affil. of Kluwer, N.V., 36 W. 44th St., New York, NY 10036 (SAN 670-8781) Tel 212-382-2855; Toll free: 800-821-4526.
Kluwer Netherlands
See Kluwer-Nijhoff
†**Kluwer-Nijhoff,** (Kluwer-Nijhoff Publishing; 0-89838; 90-247), Div. of Kluwer Academic Pubs., 101 Philip Dr., Assinippi Pk., Norwell, MA 02061 (SAN 211-481X) Tel 617-871-6600; Orders to: P.O. Box 358, Accord Sta., Hingham, MA 02018-0358 (SAN 662-0655); CIP.
KM Assocs, (KM Assocs.; 0-930819), 4711 Overbook Rd., Bethesda, MD 20816 (SAN 677-6582) Tel 301-652-4536.
KMG Pubns OR, (KMG Pubns.; 0-938928), 290 E. Ashland Ln., Ashland, OR 97520 (SAN 215-9562) Tel 503-488-1302.
KMS Pr CO, (KMS Pr.; 0-9605564), 765 Galena, Aurora, CO 80010 (SAN 215-9570) Tel 303-366-4566.
Knapp
See EDITS Pubs
†**Knapp Pr,** (Knapp Pr., The; 0-89535), Div. of Knapp Communications Corp., 5900 Wilshire Blvd., Los Angeles, CA 90036 (SAN 210-4490) Tel 213-937-3454; Toll free: 800-526-4264; CIP.
Knapp Pr. Imprint of **Crown**
Knauff, (Knauff, Thomas; 0-9605676), Rural Delivery, Julian, PA 16844 (SAN 216-1524) Tel 814-355-1792.
Kneeling Santa, (Kneeling Santa; 0-9616286), 821 S. Bronson Ave., Los Angeles, CA 90005 (SAN 658-6155) Tel 213-933-2686.

Knees Pbk, (Knees Paperback Publishing Co.; 0-9600978), 4115 Marshall St., Dallas, TX 75210 (SAN 208-760X) Tel 214-948-3613.
Knickerbocker, (Knickerbocker Publishing Co.; 0-911635), P.O. Box 113, 10 Summit Ave., Fiskdale, MA 01518 (SAN 264-1569) Tel 617-347-2039.
Knife World, (Knife World Pubns.; 0-940362), P.O. Box 3395, Knoxville, TN 37917 (SAN 218-5628) Tel 615-523-3339.
Knight Gallery-Spirit, (Knight Gallery-Spirit Square Arts Center; 0-915427), 110 E. 7th St., Charlotte, NC 28202 (SAN 291-2414) Tel 704-372-9664.
Knight Media, (Knight Media; 0-933545), 60 Benzing Rd., Antioch, TN 37013 (SAN 691-8689) Tel 615-833-1909; Dist. by: JM Pubns., P.O. Box 837, Brentwood, TN 37027 (SAN 200-7975).
†**Knights Pr,** (Knights Pr.; 0-915175), P.O. Box 454, Pound Ridge, NY 10576 (SAN 289-744X) Tel 203-322-7381; CIP.
Knighttime Pubns, (Knighttime Pubns.; 0-942902), P.O. Box 591, Cupertino, CA 95015 (SAN 240-317X) Tel 408-996-0668; Dist. by: Bookpeople, 2929 Fifth St., Berkeley, CA 94710 (SAN 168-9517); Dist. by: Publishers Group West, 5835 Beaudry St., Emeryville, CA 94608 (SAN 202-8522) Tel 415-658-3453; Dist. by: L-S Distributors, P.O. Box 3063, 1161 Post St., San Francisco, CA 94119 (SAN 169-0213); Dist. by: Pacific Pipeline, 19215 66th Ave., S., Kent, WA 98032 (SAN 208-2128) Tel 206-872-5523; Dist. by: Quality Bks., 918 Sherwood Dr., Lake Bluff, IL 60044-2204 (SAN 169-2127); Dist. by: Baker & Taylor (Western Div.), 380 Edison Way, Reno, NV 89564 (SAN 169-4464) Tel 702-786-6700.
Knoedler, (Knoedler Publishing Inc.; 0-937608), 19 E. 70th St., New York, NY 10021 (SAN 215-2177).
†**Knollwood Pub,** (Knollwood Publishing Co.; 0-915614), P.O. Box 735, 513 Benson Ave. E., Willmar, MN 56201 (SAN 207-5504) Tel 612-235-4950; CIP.
†**Knopf,** (Knopf, Alfred A., Inc.; 0-394), Subs. of Random Hse., Inc., 201 E. 50th St., New York, NY 10022 (SAN 202-5825) Tel 212-751-2600; Toll free: 800-638-6460; Orders to: 400 Hahn Rd., Westminster, MD 21157 (SAN 202-5833); CIP. Imprints: KnopfC (Knopf College Department).(Knopf College Dept.).
KnopfC Imprint of **Knopf**
Knott Comm Co, (Knott Communications Co.; 0-911701), P.O. Box 3755, Alhambra, CA 91803 (SAN 264-1593) Tel 818-284-2949.
Know Him Pr, (Know Himm Pr.; 0-9614014), 13425 Valna Dr., Whittier, CA 90602 (SAN 683-6542) Tel 213-693-9118; Orders to: P.O. Box 4002, Whittier, CA 90607 (SAN 662-2615) Tel 213-693-7412; Dist. by: Living Bks., Inc., 12155 Magnolia AVe., Bldg 11-B, Riverside, CA 92503 (SAN 662-2623) Tel 714-354-7330.
Know How, (Know How Pubns.; 0-910846), Box 7126, Landscape Sta., Berkeley, CA 94707 (SAN 207-0359) Tel 415-526-5400. Out of business.
Know Inc, (Know, Inc.; 0-912786), P.O. Box 86031, Pittsburgh, PA 15221 (SAN 201-050X) Tel 412-241-4844.
Know Indus
See Know Unltd
Know Unltd, (Knowledge Unlimited; 0-915291), P.O. Box 52, Madison, WI 53701 (SAN 290-0017) Tel 608-271-2771; 1409 Greenway Cross, Madison, WI 53711 (SAN 290-0025).
Knowing Pr, (Knowing Pr., The; 0-936927), 400 Sycamore, McAllen, TX 78501 (SAN 658-361X) Tel 512-686-4033.
Knowledge Bank, (Knowledge Bank Pubs., Inc.; 0-939036), P.O. Box 2364, Falls Church, VA 22042 (SAN 224-1765) Tel 703-938-4095.
Knowledge Builders, (Knowledge Builders, Inc.; 0-940950), 744 E. Green Briar, Lake Forest, IL 60045 (SAN 217-3883) Tel 312-295-2099.

†**Knowledge Indus,** *(Knowledge Industry Pubns., Inc.; 0-914236; 0-86729),* Subs. of Knowledge Industry Sciences, 701 Westchester Ave., White Plains, NY 10604 (SAN 214-2082) Tel 914-328-9157; Toll free: 800-248-5474; *CIP.* Imprints: ASIS (American Society for Information Science).

Knowledge Unltd, *(Knowledge Unlimited; 0-9616043),* 1271 W. Dundee Rd., Suite 14-A, Buffalo Grove, IL 60089 (SAN 698-0201) Tel 312-358-4795.

Knowles
See Printed Edns

Knoxville News-Sentinel, *(Knoxville News-Sentinel Co., Inc.; 0-9615656),* Subs. of Scripps Howard, 208 W. Church Ave., Knoxville, TN 37901 (SAN 696-219X) Tel 615-523-3131; P.O. Box 80, Knoxville, TN 37901 (SAN 696-9615).

†**Kober Pr,** *(Kober Press, The; 0-915034),* P.O. Box 2194, San Francisco, CA 94126 (SAN 207-0758) Tel 415-362-1231; *CIP.*

Kobro Pubns, *(Kobro Pubns., Inc.; 0-9604676),* 114 East 32nd Street, New York, NY 10016 (SAN 215-6695) Tel 212-689-4611.

†**Kodansha,** *(Kodansha International USA, Ltd.; 0-87011),* Subs. of Kodansha, Ltd. (Japan), c/o Harper & Row Pubs., 10 E. 53rd St., New York, NY 10022 (SAN 201-0526) Tel 212-207-7050; Toll free: 800-242-7737; Dist. by: Harper & Row Pubs., Inc., Keystone Industrial Pk., Scranton, PA 18512 (SAN 215-3742); Orders to: Mail Order Dept., P.O. Box 1531, Hagertown, MD 21741 (SAN 662-0671); *CIP.*

†**Kodokan IA Pub,** *(Kodokan Iowa Publishing; 0-933099),* Subs. of Judomeister, 1201 Royal Dr., Cedar Falls, IA 50613 (SAN 689-5603) Tel 319-277-4707; Dist. by: U. S. Judo Assn., 19 N. Union Blvd., Colorado Springs, CO 80909 (SAN 276-3257); *CIP.*

Kokono, *(Kokono; 0-916956),* Div. of Front Row Experience, 540 Discovery Bay Blvd., Byron, CA 94514 (SAN 208-6026) Tel 415-634-5710; Dist. by: Front Row Experience, 540 Discovery Bay Blvd., Byron, CA 94514 (SAN 207-1274) Tel 415-634-5710.

Kolowalu Bk *Imprint of* **UH Pr**

Komunikey Pub, *(Komunikey Publishing Co Inc.; 0-931219),* 28990 Pacific Coast Highway 215, Malibu, CA 90265 (SAN 681-9958) Tel 213-457-1502.

†**Konglomerati,** *(Konglomerati Florida Foundation for Literature & the Book Arts, Inc.; 0-916906),* P.O. Box 5001, Gulfport, FL 33737 (SAN 207-8589) Tel 813-323-0386; *CIP.*

Koolewong, *(Koolewong, Ltd.; 0-935221),* 118 S. Elmhurst Ave., Mt. Prospect, IL 60056 (SAN 695-720X) Tel 312-253-9357.

Kopec Pubns, *(Kopec Pubns.; 0-9615034),* P.O. Box 157, Whitmore, CA 96096 (SAN 695-1724) Tel 916-472-3438.

Korakas-Roberts-Kirby, *(Korakas, Roberts & Kirby; 0-9605744),* 600 N.W. 46th St., Oklahoma City, OK 73118 (SAN 216-1532) Tel 405-524-5985.

Korea Devel Inst *Imprint of* **UH Pr**

Korea Eco Inst, *(Korea Economic Institute of America; 0-914601),* 1030 15th St. NW, Suite 662, Washington, DC 20005 (SAN 289-338X) Tel 202-376-0690.

Korean Independent, *(Korean Independent Monitor, Inc.; 0-911987),* 32 W. 32nd St., No. 501, New York, NY 10001 (SAN 264-6757) Tel 212-244-0150.

Korn, *(Korn, Alfred, Jr.; 0-917498),* 324 Coolidge Dr., Kennilworth, NJ 07033 (SAN 209-0589).

Kosciuszko, *(Kosciuszko Foundation; 0-917004),* 15 E. 65th St., New York, NY 10021 (SAN 208-7251) Tel 212-734-2130.

†**KOSMOS,** *(KOSMOS; 0-916426),* 20 Millard Road, Larkspur, CA 94939 (SAN 415-927-1145; *CIP.*

Kosovo Pub Co, *(Kosovo Publishing Co.; 0-915887),* 1404 Norma Rd., Columbus, OH 43229 (SAN 294-0531) Tel 614-885-5977; 604 S. Hanover St., Nanticoko, PA 18634 (SAN 404-351-054X).

Kovak Bks, *(Kovak Bks.; 0-9604704),* P.O. Box 1422, Bakersfield, CA 93302 (SAN 695-1031).

KP Med, *(K/P Medical Systems),* P.O. Box 8900, Stockton, CA 95208 (SAN 209-5726) Tel 209-466-6761.

Kraken Pr, *(Kraken Pr.; 0-936623),* 3035 17th Ave., S, Minneapolis, MN 55407 (SAN 699-7112) Tel 612-729-8593.

Krank Pr, *(Krank Pr.; 0-9612260),* P.O. Box 16271, St. Louis, MO 63105 (SAN 222-9781) Tel 314-997-5907.

Krantz Co, *(Krantz Co., Pubs., Inc., The; 0-913765),* 2210 N. Burling Ave., Chicago, IL 60614 (SAN 219-8541) Tel 312-472-4900; Dist. by: Facts on File, Inc., 460 Park Ave. S, New York, NY 10016 (SAN 201-4696) Tel 212-683-2244.

†**Kraus Intl,** *(Kraus International Pubns.; 0-527),* Div. of Kraus-Thomson Organization, Ltd., 1 Water St., White Plains, NY 10601 (SAN 210-7562) Tel 914-761-9600; *CIP.*

†**Kraus Repr,** *(Kraus Reprint & Periodicals (KRP); 0-527; 3-601; 3-262; 0-8115),* Rte. 100, Millwood, NY 10546 (SAN 201-0542) Tel 914-762-2200; *CIP.*

Kraus Sikes, *(Kraus Sikes, Inc.; 0-9616012),* 150 W. 25th St., New York, NY 10001 (SAN 697-2799) Tel 212-242-3730.

Krause Pubns, *(Krause Pubns., Inc.; 0-87341),* 700 E. State St., Iola, WI 54990 (SAN 202-6554) Tel 715-445-2214.

†**Kregel,** *(Kregel Pubns.; 0-8254),* Div. of Kregel, Inc., P.O. Box 2607, Grand Rapids, MI 49501-2607 (SAN 206-9792) Tel 616-451-4775; Toll free: 800-253-5465; *CIP.*

Kreysa, *(Kreysa, Francis John; 0-9611398),* 18742 Curry Powder Lane, Germantown, MD 20874 (SAN 285-3752) Tel 301-349-5001.

†**Kricket,** *(Kricket Pubns.; 0-918785),* Subs. of Britannia Realty, Inc., P.O. Box 91832, Santa Barbara, CA 93190 (SAN 657-3606) Tel 805-962-2557; *CIP.*

†**Krieger,** *(Krieger, Robert E., Publishing Co., Inc.; 0-88275; 0-89874; 0-89464),* P.O. Box 9542, Melbourne, FL 32902-9542 (SAN 202-6562) Tel 305-724-9542; *CIP.*

Kripalu Pubns, *(Kripalu Pubns.; 0-940258),* Div. of Kripalu Ctr. for Yoga & Health, Rte. 183, Box 793, Lenox, MA 01240 (SAN 217-5320) Tel 413-637-3280; Dist. by: Samuel Weiser, P.O. Box 612, York Beach, ME 03910 (SAN 202-9588) Tel 207-363-4393; Dist. by: The New Leaf Distributing, 1020 White St., SW, Atlanta, GA 30310 (SAN 169-1449) Tel 404-755-2665.

Krishna Pr, *(Krishna Press),* Div. of Gordon Press, P.O. Box 459, Bowling Green Sta., New York, NY 10004 (SAN 202-6570).

Kristana, *(Kristana Esperantista Ligo Internacia),* Dist. by: Edwin C. Harter, Jr., 47 Hardy Rd., Levittown, PA 19056 (SAN 282-633X).

Kronos Pr, *(Kronos Pr.; 0-917994),* P.O. Box 343, Wynnewood, PA 19096 (SAN 210-2226) Tel 609-445-6048.

KronOscope, *(KronOscope Press; 0-9608768),* 1241 Independence Ave., SE., Washington, DC 20003 (SAN 238-308X) Tel 202-543-1266.

KS Bar CLE, *(Kansas Bar Association),* Div. of CLE, Box 1037, Topeka, KS 66601 (SAN 237-7314) Tel 913-234-5696.

KS Historical Soc, *(Logan County Kansas Historical Society; 0-9617260),* 700 W. Third, Oakley, KS 67748 (SAN 663-4818) Tel 913-672-4776. Do not confuse with Logan County Historical Society, Inc. of Guthrie, OK.

KSU, *(Kansas State Univ.),* Orders to: Library Publications, Kansas State Univ. Library, Manhattan, KS 66506 (SAN 210-1483).

†**Ktav,** *(Ktav Publishing Hse., Inc.; 0-87068; 0-88125),* Box 6249, Hoboken, NJ 07030 (SAN 201-0018); 900 Jefferson St., Hoboken, NJ 07030 (SAN 658-1056) Tel 201-963-9524; *CIP.* Imprints: HUC Pr (Hebrew Union College Press).

KTO Pr
See Kraus Intl

Kudzu, *(Kudzu & Co.; 0-9615015),* Box 415, Walls, MS 38680 (SAN 693-823X) Tel 601-781-0267.

Kudzu-Ivy, *(Kudzu-Ivy; 0-9605142),* P.O. Box 52743, Atlanta, GA 30355 (SAN 215-9589) Tel 404-351-4827.

Kuehn Radtke, *(Kuehn Radtke Publications & Productions; 0-916639),* P.O. Box 205, Waimanalo, HI 96795 (SAN 296-6409) Tel 808-941-5421.

Kuehn-Radtke Pubns & Prod
See Kuehn Radtke

Kukla Pr, *(Kukla Press),* 855 Morse Ave., Elk Grove Village, IL 60007 (SAN 213-3318); Dist. by: Common Sense Ltd., P.O. Box 353, Des Plaines, IL 60016 (SAN 213-2990).

†**Kulchur Foun,** *(Kulchur Foundation; 0-936538),* 888 Park Ave., New York, NY 10021 (SAN 207-2475) Tel 212-988-5193; *CIP.*

†**Kumarian Pr,** *(Kumarian Pr.; 0-931816),* 630 Oakwood Ave., Suite 119, West Hartford, CT 06110 (SAN 212-5978) Tel 203-524-0214; *CIP.*

Kundalini Research, *(Kundalini Research Foundation; 0-917776),* 475 Fifth Ave., New York, NY 10017 (SAN 688-1181) Tel 212-889-3241; Dist. by: Book Dynamics, 836 Broadway, New York, NY 10003 (SAN 169-5649) Tel 212-254-7798.

Kurios Found, *(Kurios Foundation; 0-932210),* P.O. Box 946, Bryn Mawr, PA 19010 (SAN 213-1005) Tel 215-527-4635.

†**Kurios Pr,** *(Kurious Pr.; 0-916588),* P.O. Box 946, Bryn Mawr, PA 19010 (SAN 207-7159) Tel 215-527-4635; *CIP.*

Kusel, *(Kusel, George; 0-9604476),* 600 Lakevue Dr., Willow Grove, PA 19090 (SAN 215-7837).

Kutenai Pr, *(Kutenai Pr., The; 0-937459),* 515 Stephens Ave., Missoula, MT 59801 (SAN 658-9081) Tel 406-549-6383.

Kwibidi Pub, *(Kwibidi Publisher; 0-933483),* P.O. Box 6639, Greensboro, NC 27415 (SAN 691-8867) Tel 919-275-4610.

Kwik Sew, *(Kwik Sew Pattern Co., Inc.; 0-913212),* 3000 Washington Ave. N., Minneapolis, MN 55411 (SAN 209-1380) Tel 612-521-7651.

KY Ctr Energy Res, *(Kentucky Ctr. for Energy Research Laboratory; 0-86607),* Div. of Commonwealth of Kentucky, Iron Works Pike, Box 13015, Lexington, KY 40512 (SAN 239-4456) Tel 606-252-5535.

KY Derby Mus, *(Kentucky Derby Museum, The; 0-9617103),* P.O. Box 3513, Louisville, KY 40201 (SAN 662-488X); 704 Central Ave., Louisville, KY 40208 (SAN 662-4898) Tel 502-637-1111.

L A Dexter, *(Dexter, Lincoln A.; 0-9601210),* 4002 Dexter Way, Middleburg, FL 32068-8786 (SAN 207-057X) Tel 904-282-2470.

L A Dillon, *(Dillon, Lacy A.; 0-9616811),* P.O. Box 222, Ravencliff, WV 25913 (SAN 661-0927) Tel 304-294-6559.

L A Hoskins, *(Hoskins, Linus A.; 0-9613067),* 2611 Nicholson St. Apt. 2, Hyattsville, MD 20782 (SAN 294-8370) Tel 301-559-0361.

L A Meyer, *(Meyer, Leo A., Associates, Inc.; 0-88069),* 23850 Clawiter Rd., Hayward, CA 94545 (SAN 238-0951) Tel 415-785-1091.

L A Mus Foun, *(Louisiana Museum Foundation; 0-916137),* Affil. of Louisiana State Museum, P.O. Box 2458, New Orleans, LA 70176-2458 (SAN 295-0057) Tel 504-525-6552.

L A Olympic Org, *(Los Angeles Olympic Organizing Committee; 0-9614512),* 10945 La Conte, Los Angeles, CA 90024 (SAN 691-7399). Moved, left no forwarding address.

L A Senseman, *(Senseman, Lawrence A.; 0-9614413),* 1365 Pine Ave., Carlsbad, CA 92008 (SAN 688-6086) Tel 619-729-7284.

L A Wells, *(Wells, L. A., Co.; 0-9616256),* 2025 Chatsworth Blvd., San Diego, CA 92107 (SAN 658-7275) Tel 619-224-8286.

L A Wholistic, *(L A Wholistic Publishing; 0-915157),* P.O. Box 6010, Suite 421, Sherman Oaks, CA 91403 (SAN 289-9442) Tel 213-871-8054.

L A Writer, *(L. A. Writer; 0-9613661),* P.O. Box 1183, Culver City, CA 90232 (SAN 670-7726) Tel 213-837-1196.

L Amiel Pub, *(Amiel, Leon, Pub.; 0-8148),* 31 W. 46th St., New York, NY 10036 (SAN 207-0766) Tel 212-575-0010.

L & A Winokur
See Joy Pub Co

L & J Intl, *(L & J International; 0-9615269),* 3 Northwest Ct., Little Rock, AR 72212 (SAN 695-1848) Tel 501-225-5720.

L & L Pubns, *(L & L Pubs.; 0-9612778),* 19362 S. Henrici Rd., Oregon City, OR 97045 (SAN 289-7458) Tel 503-631-2480.

L & M Bks, *(L & M Books; 0-914237),* 18387 Highway 18, Apple Valley, CA 92307 (SAN 287-525X) Tel 619-242-8102.

L Arnold, (Arnold, Luis; 0-9610434), 13 Loma Vista Pl., San Rafael, CA 94901 (SAN 263-9211) Tel 415-454-5075.

L Ashworth, (Ashworth, Lee & Assoc.; 0-918409), P.O. Box 465, Beaumont, TX 77704 (SAN 657-6451) Tel 409-769-3410.

L B Cross, (Cross, Laurella B.; 0-9612806), P.O. Box 2933, Roswell, NM 88201 (SAN 289-9760) Tel 505-625-1095.

L B Dallum, (Dallum, Linda Brinkman; 0-9616937), P.O. Box 6894, Great Falls, MT 59405 (SAN 661-8294); 4051 Sixth Ave., S., Great Falls, MT 59405 (SAN 661-8308) Tel 406-452-3114.

L B Gerard, (Gerard, Leona B.; 0-9606394), 222 E. Broadway, Apt. 709, Eugene, OR 97401 (SAN 218-5482) Tel 503-345-3029.

L B J Sch Pub
See LBJ Sch Pub Aff

†L B L Pub, (L B L Publishing; 0-914947), 214 Correo Fronteriza, San Ysidro, CA 92073 (SAN 289-2804) Tel 619-970-7289; CIP.

L Benton Geneal, (Benton, Linn, Genealogical Services; 0-939509), 1117 SE 9th St., Albany, OR 97321 (SAN 663-3501) Tel 503-928-2582.

L Boone, (Boone, Lalia; 0-9612758), 519 N. Grant, Moscow, ID 83843 (SAN 289-7431) Tel 208-882-4267.

L C Bryant, (Bryant, Lawrence C.), 467 Palmetto Pkwy., NE, Orangeburg, SC 29115 (SAN 201-0550) Tel 803-536-1305.

L C Moore, (Moore, Louis C.; 0-9616361), P.O. Box 243, Carmel Valley, CA 93924 (SAN 658-9375); Professional Bldg., Village Dr., Carmel Valley, CA 93924 (SAN 658-9383) Tel 408-659-2901.

L Cohen, (Cohen, Leo; 0-9613366), P.O. Box 3402, La Jolla, CA 92038 (SAN 657-1492) Tel 619-453-4163.

L Cope Pub, (Cope, L, Publishing; 0-9617214), 134-6 W. 32nd St., Suite 602, New York, NY 10001 (SAN 663-4028); 86 Myrtle Ave., Irvington, NJ 07111 (SAN 663-4036) Tel 201-315-8667.

L Corcoran, (Corcoran, Lawrence), 7801 Sand Bay Rd., Sturgeon Bay, WI 54235 (SAN 212-6494).

L Cornelison
See Okie Doke Pr

†L D A Pubs, (LDA Pubs.; 0-935912), 42-36 209th St., Bayside, NY 11361 (SAN 221-4423) Tel 718-224-0485; CIP.

L D Butler, (Butler, Larry D.; 0-9616497), 1260 Louisiana Ave., Port Allen, LA 70767 (SAN 659-3089) Tel 504-335-3070.

L D Manning, (Manning, Lynda D., & Associates; 0-9604062), P.O. Box 872, Temple, TX 76501 (SAN 214-0551).

L Davis Inst, (Davis, Leonard, Institute of Health Economics; 0-937695), Div. of University of Pennsylvania, 3641 Locust Walk, Philadelphia, PA 19104-6218 (SAN 659-3410) Tel 215-898-4750.

L De Waters, (DeWaters, Lillian, Pubns.), Old Greenwich, CT 06870 (SAN 203-8633) Tel 203-637-0658.

L E Edwards, (Edwards, Lowell E.; 0-936024), P.O. Box 255714, Sacramento, CA 95825 (SAN 213-7348).

L E Kay, (Kay, L. E., Publishing Co.; 0-9611256), P.O. Box 333, Fogelsville, PA 18051 (SAN 283-3026); 2 Woodsbluff Run, Fogelsville, PA 18051 (SAN 283-3034) Tel 215-398-0107.

L E Truchinski, (Truchinski, L. E.; 0-913059), 1010 E. Griffith Ave., Wisconsin Rapids, WI 54494 (SAN 283-1937) Tel 715-421-2220.

L Eide, (Eide, Lucille; 0-9610668), 1122 17th St., No. 319, Sacramento, CA 95814 (SAN 264-7370) Tel 916-443-9518.

†L Erlbaum Assocs, (Erlbaum, Lawrence, Assocs., Inc.; 0-89859; 0-8058), 365 Broadway, Hillsdale, NJ 07642 (SAN 213-960X) Tel 201-666-4110; CIP.

L F Garlinghouse Co, (Garlinghouse, L. F., Co., The; 0-938708), P.O. Box 1717, Middletown, CT 06457 (SAN 238-7077) Tel 203-632-0500.

L F Greer
See Plumbing Pubns

L F Kirk, (Kirk Fleming, Leslee; 0-9613746), 4913 E. 97th Ave., Crown Point, IN 46307 (SAN 677-6736) Tel 219-769-3388.

L F Tesseneer, (Tesseneer, Laura F., Publishing Co.; 0-9613793), 18 Linden Hill Dr., Crescent Springs, KY 41017 (SAN 679-0011) Tel 606-341-2145.

L Garcia, (Garcia, Lois), 2917 Shady Ave., Pittsburgh, PA 15217 (SAN 699-8275).

L Giblin, (Giblin, Les; 0-9616416), 3790 Quail Ridge Dr., Boynton Beach, FL 33436 (SAN 658-8662) Tel 305-737-7076; Dist. by: Executive Bks., 210 W. Allen St., Mechanicsburg, PA 17055 (SAN 156-5419).

L Grace
See L P Grace

L H Smith, (Smith, Leonard H., Jr.), P.O. Box 6745, Clearwater, FL 33518 (SAN 205-9819) Tel 813-581-4444.

L Haller, (Haller, Lynda; 0-9614174), 3400 SE 15th, Edmond, OK 73034 (SAN 686-6204) Tel 405-341-0853.

L Hansen Enter, (Hansen, Ludela, Enterprises; 0-935685), P.O. Box 340, Claymont, DE 19703 (SAN 695-9547) Tel 302-475-7382; 1511 Forsythia Ave., Wilmington, DE 19810 (SAN 695-9555).

L Howard Pubns, (Howard, Leslie, Pubns.; 0-937717), 140 Duboce Ave., Suite 204, San Francisco, CA 94103 (SAN 659-2465) Tel 415-863-1238.

L I S I Pr, (LISI Pr. The; 0-914163), Subs. of Laforest International Service Inc., P.O. Box 1063, Palm Harbor, FL 34273 (SAN 287-5128) Tel 813-784-3628.

L I S Z Pubns, (L. I. S. Z. Pubns.; 0-9611428), P.O. Box 819, Boca Raton, FL 33429-0819 (SAN 285-3345) Tel 305-426-5232.

L I U Press, (Long Island Univ. Confrontation Magazine Pr.; 0-913057), C.W. Post College,English Dept., Greenvale, NY 11548 (SAN 283-1864) Tel 516-299-2391.

L Imperio, (Imperio, Leroy; 0-9609302), Rte. 1, Box 222-C, Burlington, WV 26241 (SAN 241-5224) Tel 304-636-3434.

L J Catalina, (Catalina, Lynn J.; 0-9613769), P.O. Box 20121, Albuquerque, NM 87154-0121 (SAN 679-0003); 7405 Luella Anne Dr. NE, Albuquerque, NM 87109 (SAN 662-2569) Tel 505-821-2151.

L J Fry
See J E Fry

L J Lalonde, (Lalonde, Larry; 0-9608136), 17031 N. Eleanor, Apt 95C, Mt. Clemens, MI 48044 (SAN 238-8502) Tel 313-286-8023.

L J Lejon & Assocs, (Lejon, L.J. & Associates; 0-9612812), 29100 45th Ave. S., Auburn, WA 98001 (SAN 290-005X) Tel 206-839-9982.

L J McCann, (McCann, Lester J.; 0-9616935), 305 E. Main St., Waconia, MN 55387 (SAN 662-5711) Tel 612-442-5201.

L J McGrady, (McGrady, L. J.), 5760 St. Clement Court, Toledo, OH 43613 (SAN 295-0146); Dist. by: Ye Olde Genealogie Shoppe, P.O. Box 39128, Indianapolis, IN 46239 (SAN 200-7010).

L J Pubns, (LJ Pubns.), 359 San Miguel, Newport Beach, CA 92660 (SAN 264-1623).

L Jones, (Jones, Lowell; 0-9602074), 11832 Brookmont Dr., Maryland Heights, MO 63043 (SAN 212-2847).

L Joseph, (Joseph, Lillian; 0-9616829), 3914 Victory Cir., No. 128, Billings, MT 59106 (SAN 658-8395).

L Kempfer, (Kempfer, Lester L.), P.O. Box 317, Marysville, OH 43040 (SAN 201-0569).

L King Co, (King, Lary, Co., The; 0-9611450), P.O. Box 1247, Hollywood, CA 90078 (SAN 283-1503) Tel 818-509-3841.

L L Monroe, (Monroe, Lynn Lewis; 0-9615125), 46 Pine Hill Dr., Alfred, NY 14802 (SAN 694-177X) Tel 607-587-8240.

L Lawler, (Lawler, Lucille; 0-931706), 407 Greenwich St., New York, NY 10013 (SAN 211-7363).

L M Campbell, (Campbell, Lucile M.; 0-9607114), c/o Mrs. Joe Richardson, 615 Sixth Ave. SW, Decatur, AL 35601 (SAN 238-9592) Tel 205-355-8895.

L M Haines, (Haines, Leland M.), P.O. Box 54, Wayne, MI 48184 (SAN 661-4531).

L M Licht, (Licht, Lilla M.; 0-9607184), 490 M St., SW Apt. W604, Washington, DC 20024 (SAN 239-1074) Tel 202-554-2429.

L McMaster, (McMaster, Linda, Ms), War Cycles Institute, P.O. Box 81369, Corpus Christi, TX 78412 (SAN 211-7428).

L Mahan
See Marco Polo

L Miller Pub, (Miller, Lawrence, Publishing; 0-914021), 3 Lisa Dr., Thorndale, PA 19372 (SAN 286-8296) Tel 215-384-8944.

L Newkirk Connery, (Connery, Liz Newkirk; 0-9614333), 411 Wingrave Dr., Charlotte, NC 28226 (SAN 688-1211) Tel 704-366-4747.

L O King, (King, LeRoy O., Jr.; 0-9600938), 4815 Allencrest, Dallas, TX 75244 (SAN 208-7243) Tel 214-239-1280.

L Oliver Bk, (Oliver, Lawrence, Book; 0-9606432), 815 Armada Terrace, San Diego, CA 92106 (SAN 206-7226).

L Orr, (Orr, Leonard), Orders to: Inspiration University, P.O. Box 234, Sierraville, CA 96126 (SAN 207-2505) Tel 916-994-8984.

L P Grace, (Grace, Louise P.; 0-9613652), 8338 San Leandro, Dallas, TX 75218 (SAN 679-1808) Tel 214-327-5207.

†L P Pubns, (L P Pubns.; 0-916192), Div. of The Love Project, P.O. Box 7601, San Diego, CA 92107-0601 (SAN 207-2513) Tel 619-225-0133; 4470 Orchard Ave., San Diego, CA 92107 (SAN 650-0390); CIP.

L Paquin Pub, (Paquin, Larue, Publishing; 0-9615547), Box 61, West Tremont, ME 04690 (SAN 695-9830) Tel 207-244-5132.

L Pubns, (L Pubns.; 0-917824), 34 Fransiscan Way, Kensington, CA 94707 (SAN 209-5734).

L R Balick, (Balick, Lillian R.; 0-9615834), 15 Clermont Rd., Wilmington, DE 19803 (SAN 200-5875) Tel 302-571-3540.

L R Creamer, (Creamer, Lyle R.), 8206 Mulberry St., Cypress, CA 90630 (SAN 670-719X).

L R Frank, (Frank, Leonard Roy; 0-9601376), 2300 Webster St., San Francisco, CA 94115 (SAN 212-0917) Tel 415-922-3029.

L Roth, (Roth, Lora; 0-9616242), 5965 Crestwood, West Bloomfield, MI 48033 (SAN 658-4969) Tel 313-661-4966.

L S Brown Pub, (Brown, Lewis S.,, Publisher; 0-9608542), 124 W. Pierpont St., Kingston, NY 12401 (SAN 240-6047) Tel 914-338-4352.

L S Records, (LS Records; 0-9614370), Subs. of Cristy Lane Enterprises Inc., 120 Hickory St., Madison, TN 37115 (SAN 688-5950) Tel 615-868-7171.

L S Reeks, (Reeks, Lindsay S.; 0-9616950), 2013 Westover Dr., Pleasant Hill, CA 94523 (SAN 661-7352) Tel 415-934-9416.

†L Shaw Found, (Shaw, Lloyd, Foundation Inc., The; 0-915213), 5421 Easley Rd., Golden, CO 80403 (SAN 289-8381); Orders to: Sales Div., P.O. Box 1148, Salida, CO 81201 (SAN 650-9967); CIP.

L Shogren Quilt
See Pieceful Pleasures

L Smith Assoc, (Larry Smith Associates Inc.; 0-931741), P.O. Box 2203, Los Gatos, CA 95031-2203 (SAN 686-273X) Tel 408-354-3406; Dist. by: Motorbooks Int., 729 Prospect Ave., Osceola, WI 54020 (SAN 169-9164) Tel 715-294-3345; Dist. by: Automotion, 3535 Keifer, Santa Clara, CA 95051 (SAN 200-7339) Tel 408-736-9020.

L Stanhope, (Stanhope, Lacy, Jr.; 0-9612362), 5201 E. Sunset Rd., Knoxville, TN 37914 (SAN 289-3991) Tel 615-522-0887.

L Stewart, (Stewart, Lois; 0-9609512), 3657 W. Nichols, Springfield, MO 65803 (SAN 262-088X) Tel 417-831-6140.

L Sweetman, (Sweetman, Leonard; 0-9600518), 1712 Fisherville Rd., Coatesville, PA 19320 (SAN 203-9265).

†L Tapley, (Tapley, Lance, Pub.; 0-912769), 86 Winthrop St., P.O. Box 2439, Augusta, ME 04330 (SAN 216-2539) Tel 207-622-1179; CIP.

L Tatum, (Tatum, Larry; 0-9616249), 664 S. Oak Knoll Ave., Pasadena, CA 91106 (SAN 697-3183); Dist. by: Unique Pubns., 4201 W. Vanowen Pl., Burbank, CA 91505 (SAN 214-3313) Tel 818-845-2656.

L V D'Agostino, (D'Agostino, Lena V.; 0-9601076), Davenport Center, NY 13751 (SAN 209-2085) Tel 607-278-5808.

L Victor Pr, (Leo Victor Press; 0-9606562), 2203 Brandenburg Way, King of Prussia, PA 19406 (SAN 213-3970).

L W Anderson Genealogical, (Anderson, L. W., Genealogical Library; 0-935187), 2218 17th St., P.O. Box 1647, Gulfport, MS 39502 (SAN 662-672X) Tel 601-863-3598.

L W Laframboise, (Laframboise, Leon W.; 0-9613855), P.O. Box 6565, El Paso, TX 79906 (SAN 661-4418).

L Wiley, *(Wiley, Leonard; 0-911742)*, 2927 SE 75th Ave., Portland, OR 97206 (SAN 203-9273) Tel 503-777-3645.

LA *Imprint of Oceana*

La Bonne Vie, *(La Bonne Vie, Inc.; 0-9615991)*, 234 S. Milwaukee St., Denver, CO 80209 (SAN 699-7465) Tel 303-722-5009.

La Car Pub, *(La Car Publishing Co.)*, 2109 Broadway, New York, NY 10023 (SAN 207-7272).

La Cassette Intl, *(La Cassette Gourmet International, Ltd.; 0-935443)*, 7428 E. Stetson Dr., Suite 215, Scottsdale, AZ 85251 (SAN 696-3048) Tel 602-951-2654.

†LA Co Art Mus, *(Los Angeles County Museum of Art; 0-87587)*, 5905 Wilshire Blvd., Los Angeles, CA 90036 (SAN 201-0577) Tel 213-857-6044; *CIP.*

LA Contemp Exhib, *(Los Angeles Contemporary Exhibitions; 0-937335)*, 1804 Industrial St., Los Angeles, CA 90021 (SAN 658-8123) Tel 213-624-5650.

La Cote Pubs, *(La Cote Pubs.; 0-9615322)*, 15305 La. Hwy. 16, French Settlement, LA 70733 (SAN 694-6496) Tel 504-698-6247.

La Cumbre, *(La Cumbre Publishing Co.; 0-935222)*, P.O. Box 30959, Santa Barbara, CA 93105 (SAN 221-4431) Tel 805-682-0904.

La Grange, *(La Grange Pr.; 0-931324)*, 7732 Guenivere Way, Citrus Heights, CA 95610 (SAN 211-0601) Tel 916-967-7997.

LA Hist Assn, *(Louisiana Historical Assn.)*, P.O. Box 40831, Lafayette, LA 70504 (SAN 205-2504) Tel 318-231-6029; Orders to: P.O. Box 42808, Univ. of Southwest Louisiana, Lafayette, LA 70504 (SAN 669-1536).

La Jolla Country, *(La Jolla Country Day Schl. Parents Assn.; 0-9614176)*, 9490 Genesee Ave., La Jolla, CA 92037 (SAN 686-6190) Tel 619-459-2673.

La Jolla Inst, *(La Jolla Institute; 0-943256)*, P.O. Box 1434, La Jolla, CA 92038 (SAN 240-3935) Tel 619-454-8831.

†La Jolla Mus Contemp Art, *(La Jolla Museum of Contemporary Art; 0-934418)*, 700 Prospect St., La Jolla, CA 92037 (SAN 210-8232) Tel 619-454-3541; *CIP.*

La Jolla Pub CA, *(La Jolla Publishing Co.; 0-935365)*, P.O. Box 99638, San Diego, CA 92109 (SAN 696-2769) Tel 619-483-2693.

La La Ltd, *(La-La Ltd.; 0-937991)*, P.O. Box 2060, North Babylon, NY 11703 (SAN 661-4019); 100 Grand Blvd., Wyandanch, NY 11798 (SAN 661-4027) Tel 516-491-1889.

†La Leche, *(La Leche League International, Inc.; 0-912500)*, 9616 Minneapolis Ave., P.O. Box 1209, Franklin Park, IL 60131-8209 (SAN 201-0585) Tel 312-455-7730; *CIP.*

LA Lib Architecture, *(Los Angeles Library of Architecture; 0-86558)*, P.O. Box 402, Pasadena, CA 91102-0402 (SAN 291-8021) Tel 818-792-5024; 99 S. Raymond Ave., Suite 510, Pasadena, CA 91105 (SAN 658-2478).

La Luz Pr, *(La Luz Press, The; 0-942664)*, 2401 W. 15th St., Panama City, FL 32401 (SAN 219-8525) Tel 904-763-3333.

La Mariposa, *(La Mariposa Pr.; 0-9613714)*, P.O. Box 3519, Apache Junction, AZ 85278 (SAN 676-2670) Tel 602-981-8747.

LA Municipal Art, *(Los Angeles Municipal Art Gallery Assocs.; 0-936429)*, 4804 Hollywood Blvd., Los Angeles, CA 90027 (SAN 699-7473) Tel 213-485-4581.

La-Ran Pub Co, *(LA-RAN Publishing Co.; 0-9610842)*, 187 W. End Ave., Newark, NJ 07106 (SAN 265-2641) Tel 201-373-5216.

La Siesta, *(La Siesta Pr.; 0-910856)*, P.O. Box 406, Glendale, CA 91209 (SAN 201-0607) Tel 818-244-9305.

La Stampa Calligrafica, *(La Stampa Calligrafica; 0-9606630)*, P.O. Box 209, Franklin, MI 48025 (SAN 281-8582) Tel 313-851-0796; Dist. by: Bookpeople, 2929 Fifth St., Berkeley, CA 94710 (SAN 168-9517); Dist. by: Inland Book Company, P. O. Box 261, 22 Hemingway Ave., East Haven, CT 06512 (SAN 200-4151) Tel 203-467-4257.

†La State U Pr, *(Louisiana State Univ. Pr.; 0-8071)*, Highland Rd., Baton Rouge, LA 70893 (SAN 202-6597) Tel 504-388-6666; *CIP.*

La Tienda, *(La Tienda El Quetzal; 0-913129)*, Box 246, Troy, NY 12181 (SAN 283-1295) Tel 518-271-7629.

Laal Co, *(Laal Companies; 0-910211)*, Research Group, Nine Kaufman Dr., Westwood, NJ 07675 (SAN 241-3892) Tel 201-664-6222.

LAB
See LABS

Lab Data Control, *(Laboratory Data Control; 0-9504833)*, P.O. Box 10235, Interstate Industrial Pk., Riviera Beach, FL 33404 (SAN 210-9085).

Labor Arts, *(Labor Arts Bks.; 0-9603888)*, 1064 Amherst St., Buffalo, NY 14216 (SAN 213-8158) Tel 716-873-4131.

Labor Ed & Res, *(Labor Education & Research Project; 0-914093)*, P.O. Box 20001, Detroit, MI 48220 (SAN 287-5268) Tel 313-883-5580.

Labor Guild Bost, *(Labor Guild of Boston; 0-9611038)*, 761 Harrison Ave., Boston, MA 02118 (SAN 282-9045) Tel 617-227-8884.

Labor Pol, *(Labor Policy Assn., Inc.; 0-916603)*, 1015 15th St., NW, No. 1200, Washington, DC 20005 (SAN 271-924X) Tel 202-789-8670.

Labor Relations, *(Labor Relations Press; 0-934753)*, Div. of Axon Communications, Inc., P.O. Box 579, Fort Washington, PA 19034, Highland Office Center P.O. Box 579, 1035 Camphill Rd., Fort Washington, PA 19034 (SAN 237-8329) Tel 215-628-3113.

Labrinthos
See Labyrinthos

LABS, *(Laboratory for Applied Behavioral Science; 0-943300)*, 41 Gifford Rd., Somerset, NJ 08873 (SAN 239-4499) Tel 201-545-8269.

Labyrinth Pr, *(Labyrinth Pr., Inc., The; 0-939464)*, P.O. Box 2124, Durham, NC 27702-2124 (SAN 216-6011) Tel 919-493-5051; 2814 Chapel Hill Rd., Durham, NC 27707 (SAN 281-8620).

Labyrinthos, *(Labyrinthos; 0-911437)*, 6355 Green Valley Cir., Suite 213, Culver City, CA 90230 (SAN 217-3182) Tel 213-649-2612.

†Lace Pubns, *(Lace Pubns.; 0-917597)*, P.O. Box 10037, Denver, CO 80210-0037 (SAN 657-1506) Tel 303-778-7702; *CIP.*

Lacebark Pubns, *(Lacebark Pubns.; 0-9613109)*, Rte. 5, P.O. Box 174, Stillwater, OK 74074 (SAN 210-9220) Tel 405-377-3539.

Lacis Pubns, *(Lacis Pubns.; 0-916896)*, 2982 Adeline St., Berkeley, CA 94703 (SAN 202-9901) Tel 415-843-7178.

Lacon Pubs, *(Lacon Pubs.; 0-930344)*, Rte. 1, Box 15, Harrison, ID 83833 (SAN 204-9597) Tel 208-689-3467.

Lacret Pub, *(Lacret Publishing Co.; 0-943144)*, 601 12th St., Union City, NJ 07087 (SAN 240-3927) Tel 201-866-5257.

Lacrosse Found, *(Lacrosse Foundation, Inc.; 0-9610654)*, Charles & 34th St., Baltimore, MD 21218 (SAN 285-0389) Tel 301-235-6882.

LAD Pub, *(LAD Publishing; 0-938723)*, 17625 Drayton Hall Way, San Diego, CA 92128 (SAN 661-6097) Tel 619-487-4976.

Laddin Pr, *(Laddin Press; 0-913806)*, 2 Park Ave., New York, NY 10016 (SAN 201-0615) Tel 212-532-4384.

Ladies Home, *(Ladies Home Journal Bks.; 0-935639)*, Subs. of Family Media, 3 Park Ave., New York, NY 10016 (SAN 696-1800) Tel 212-340-9605.

Ladies Philo, *(Ladies Philoptochos Society Chapter Four Hundred & Fifty One; 0-9611164)*, Nativity of Christ Church 1110 Dickson Rd., Novato, CA 94948 (SAN 283-3581) Tel 415-499-1736; P.O. Box 543, Novato, CA 94948 (SAN 283-359X).

†Lady Lake Pub, *(Lady of Lake Pub.; 0-931905)*, P.O. Box 397, Winchester, MA 01890 (SAN 686-0184) Tel 617-729-0115; *CIP.*

Lady Raspberry, *(Lady Raspberry Press; 0-9608554)*, 213 E. 49th St., New York, NY 10017 (SAN 240-6985) Tel 212-908-8100; Dist. by: Bric-A-Brac Bookwks., Box 887, Forked River, NJ 08731 (SAN 282-6364) Tel 609-693-4053.

Ladybug Pr, *(Ladybug Pr.; 0-9616662)*, 6474 Norway Rd., Dallas, TX 75230 (SAN 661-3594) Tel 214-368-4235.

Lager Pub Co, *(Lager Publishing Co.; 0-9615524)*, 10801 Central Ave., NE, Suite 186, Albuquerque, NM 87123 (SAN 696-2890) Tel 415-956-5966.

Lahontan Images, *(Lahontan Images; 0-938373)*, P.O. Box 1093, Susanville, CA 96130 (SAN 661-2687); 700-100 Wingfield Rd., Susanville, CA 96130 (SAN 661-2695) Tel 916-257-4546.

Laid Back Pubns, *(Laid-Back Pubns.; 0-9615714)*, 276 E. Shamrock, Rialto, CA 92376 (SAN 695-8826) Tel 714-875-1309.

Laissez Faire Bks
See Libertarian Rev Found

Lake, *(Lake, A. V., & Co.; 0-910860)*, P.O. Box 1595, Beverly Hills, CA 90213 (SAN 201-0623) Tel 213-271-4386.

Lake Aire, *(Lake Aire, Inc.; 0-936989)*, 129 W. Hoover Ave., Suite 10, Mesa, AZ 85202 (SAN 658-7518) Tel 602-834-0734.

Lake Champlain, *(Lake Champlain Publishing Co., The; 0-9616412)*, 176 Battery St., Burlington, VT 05401 (SAN 658-9146) Tel 802-864-7733.

Lake Erie Col Pr, *(Lake Erie College Pr.; 0-935518)*, Lake Erie College, Painesville, OH 44077 (SAN 204-9562) Tel 216-352-3361.

Lake Forest, *(Lake Forest College Holography Workshops; 0-910535)*, Lake Forest College, Lake Forest, IL 60045 (SAN 260-0900) Tel 312-234-3100.

Lake George Hist, *(Lake George Historical Assn.; 0-9613466)*, P.O. Box 472, Lake George, NY 12845 (SAN 657-2782) Tel 518-668-5044.

Lake Lure Pr, *(Lake Lure Press; 0-9610172)*, RR 31, Box 140, Terre Haute, IN 47803 (SAN 271-9444) Tel 812-877-2204.

Lake Mich Fed, *(Lake Michigan Federation)*, 8 S. Michigan Ave., Chicago, IL 60603 (SAN 225-1787) Tel 312-263-5550.

Lake Placid Climb, *(Lake Placid Climbing Schl., Inc.; 0-9615992)*, Sundog Ski & Sports 90 Main St., Lake Placid, NY 12946 (SAN 696-7744).

Lake Pr, *(Lake Pr.; 0-9608446)*, P.O. Box 7934, Paducah, KY 42001 (SAN 240-544X) Tel 502-443-8425.

Lake Pub
See D S Lake Pubs

Lake View Pr, *(Lake View Pr.; 0-941702)*, P.O. Box 578279, Chicago, IL 60657-8279 (SAN 239-2488) Tel 312-935-2694.

Lakeside Chart, *(Lakeside-Charter Books; 0-918206)*, 5466 S. Everett, Chicago, IL 60615 (SAN 210-2234) Tel 312-955-0521.

Lakeside Hist, *(Lakeside Historical Society, The; 0-9615935)*, 9705 Prospect Ave., Lakeside, CA 92040 (SAN 696-8465) Tel 619-443-1267.

Lakewood Ctr Assocs, *(Lakewood Ctr. Assocs.; 0-9617239)*, P.O. Box 274, Lake Oswego, OR 97034 (SAN 663-5881); 368 S. State St., Lake Oswego, OR 97034 (SAN 663-589X) Tel 503-636-5935; 968 Lakeshore Rd., Lake Oswego, OR 97034 (SAN 663-5903).

Lakstun Pr, *(Lakstun Pr.; 0-9603706)*, P.O. Box 6483, Rockford, IL 61125-1483 (SAN 213-6309).

LAL Pub, *(LaL Pub.; 0-910737)*, P.O. Box 1225, Denison, TX 75020 (SAN 238-0641) Tel 214-465-7311.

Lalo Pubns, *(Lalo Pubns.; 0-9616941)*, 9266-G Regents Rd., La Jolla, CA 92037 (SAN 661-7875) Tel 619-455-1394.

Lama Foun, *(Lama Foundation)*, Box 240, San Cristobal, NM 87564 (SAN 225-3178).

Lambda Christian, *(Lambda Christian Fellowship; 0-9616853)*, 14060 Astoria St., Sylmar, CA 91342 (SAN 661-6003) Tel 818-362-8014.

Lambert Bk, *(Lambert Bk. Hse., Inc.; 0-89315)*, 133 Kings Hwy., Shreveport, LA 71104 (SAN 208-7278) Tel 318-861-3140; Box 4007, Shreveport, LA 71104 (SAN 658-1064).

Lambert Gann Pub, *(Lambert-Gann Publishing Co.; 0-939093)*, P.O. Box 0, Pomeroy, WA 99347 (SAN 662-8982); Rickman Gulch Rd., Pomeroy, WA 99347 (SAN 662-8990) Tel 509-843-1094.

Lambeth, *(Lambeth, James; 0-9601678)*, 1591 Clark St., Fayetteville, AR 72701 (SAN 211-9102) Tel 501-521-1304.

†Lambeth Pr, *(Lambeth Pr.; 0-931186)*, 143 E. 37th St., New York, NY 10016 (SAN 240-0421) Tel 212-679-0163; *CIP.*

Lame Johnny, *(Lame Johnny Pr.; 0-917624)*, Star Rte. 3, Box 9A, Hermosa, SD 57744 (SAN 207-6136) Tel 605-255-4466.

Lamkin, *(Lamkin, Geraldine E.; 0-9612632),* 8144 D. Lemon Grove Way, Lemon Grove, CA 92045 (SAN 289-2855) Tel 619-698-7255; P.O. Box 1003, Lemon Grove, CA 92045 (SAN 289-2863).

Lamm-Morada, *(Lamm-Morada Publishing Co., Inc.; 0-932128),* Box 7607, Stockton, CA 95207 (SAN 212-520X) Tel 209-931-1056.

Lamont-Doherty, *(Lamont-Doherty Geological Observatory,* Columbia University, Palisades, NY 10964 (SAN 287-2609).

Lampkin Pub, *(Lampkin, J. G., Publishing; 0-9604918),* 15346 Stone Ave. N., Seattle, WA 98133 (SAN 215-6725).

Lamplighter, *(Lamplighter Press; 0-912870),* P.O. Box 258, Carlinville, IL 62626 (SAN 201-0631).

Lampus Pr, *(Lampus Pr.; 0-9609002),* P.O. Box 541, Cape May, NJ 08204 (SAN 240-8643) Tel 609-884-4906.

Lancaster Horvath Prods, *(Lancaster Horvath Productions; 0-930647),* 3756 Grand Ave., Suite 302, Oakland, CA 94610 (SAN 676-2840) Tel 415-271-0701.

Lancaster-Miller
See Asian Human Pr

Lancaster Prod
See Lancaster Horvath Prods

Lance Pubns, *(Lance Pubns.; 0-934363),* P.O. Box 61189, Seattle, WA 98121 (SAN 693-5605) Tel 206-728-2821.

Lancer, *(Lancer Militaria; 0-935856),* P.O. Box 886, Mt. Ida, AR 71957 (SAN 213-7682) Tel 501-867-2232.

Land & Land, *(Land & Land Publishing Div.; 0-935545),* 196 S. 14th St., Baton Rouge, LA 70802 (SAN 696-2386) Tel 504-344-1059; P.O. Box 1921, Baton Rouge, LA 70821 (SAN 696-964X).

Land Design, *(Land Design Publishing; 0-9605988),* P.O. Box 857, San Dimas, CA 91773 (SAN 216-745X) Tel 714-599-7452.

Land Dev Inst; *(Land Development Institute, Ltd.),* 1401 16th St, NW, Washington, DC 20036 (SAN 237-8345) Tel 202-232-2144.

Land O' Sky Aero, *(Land O' Sky Aeronautics, Inc.; 0-9616608),* P.O. Box 636, Skyland, NC 28776 (SAN 661-4108); Bishop Rd., Skyland, NC 28776 (SAN 661-4116) Tel 704-684-2092.

Land Plenty Prods, *(Land of Plenty Prods.; 0-917887),* 787-22nd Ave., San Francisco, CA 94121 (SAN 657-1514) Tel 415-387-2246.

Land Tenure
See U of Wis Land

Landau, *(Landau Book Co., Inc.; 0-910864),* P.O. Box 570, Long Beach, NY 11561 (SAN 201-064X).

Lander Moore Bks, *(Lander Moore Bks.; 0-930751),* 6202 Olympic Overlook, Austin, TX 78746 (SAN 682-790X).

Landfall Pr, *(Landfall Pr., Inc.; 0-913428),* 5171 Chapin St., Dayton, OH 45429 (SAN 202-6627) Tel 513-298-9123.

Landgrove Pr, *(Landgrove Pr.; 0-9608726),* Landgrove, VT 05148 (SAN 238-3098) Tel 802-824-5943.

Landmark Edns, *(Landmark Editions Inc.; 0-933849),* 1420 Kansas Ave., Kansas City, MO 64127 (SAN 692-6916) Tel 816-421-4919.

Landmark Ent, *(Landmark Enterprises; 0-910845),* 10324 Newton Way, Rancho Cordova, CA 95670 (SAN 157-0242) Tel 916-363-0191.

Landmark NY, *(Landmark Book Co.),* 260 Fifth Ave, New York, NY 10000 (SAN 216-4051) Tel 212-696-5430.

Landmark Pr, *(Landmark Pr.; 0-911439),* Box 13547, St. Louis, MO 63138 (SAN 271-9568) Tel 314-355-7650; 1461 Dunn Rd., St. Louis, MO 63138 (SAN 658-1072).

Landmark Studies Imprint of **Rowman**

Landmarke Lancer, *(Landmarke Lancer Publishing Co.; 0-937639),* P.O. Box 6528, Pasadena, TX 77506 (SAN 658-9170) Tel 713-472-2475; 127 E. Pasadena Freeway, Pasadena, CA 77506 (SAN 658-9189).

Landmarks Comm Village Oak Pk Imprint of **Chicago Review**

Landmarks Found, *(Landmarks Foundation of Montgomery Inc.; 0-9614653),* 310 N. Hull St., Montgomery, AL 36104 (SAN 691-8700) Tel 205-263-4355.

Landmarks Preserv Comm, *(Landmarks Preservation Commission),* 20 Vesey St., New York, NY 10007 (SAN 240-0413).

Landon Pubns, *(Landon Pubns.; 0-937355),* 1061-C S. High St., Harrisonburg, VA 22801 (SAN 658-9227) Tel 703-433-0919; Orders to: P.O. Box 12, Bridgewater, VA 22812 (SAN 662-4197).

Landown Hse, *(Landown Hse.; 0-936562),* 5816 Esrig Way, Sacramento, CA 95841 (SAN 281-8655); Orders to: P.O. Box 176, North Highlands, CA 95660 (SAN 281-8663).

Landrum & Assocs, *(Landrum & Associates; 0-915286),* P.O. Box 16003, Chattanooga, TN 37416 (SAN 203-1949) Tel 615-892-3248.

Lands End Bks, *(Lands End Bks.; 0-9603558),* Rte. 3, Box 998, Gloucester, VA 23061 (SAN 203-9281) Tel 804-693-4262.

Landsberry Pr, *(Landsberry Pr.; 0-9616788),* 709 Massachusetts Ave., NE, Washington, DC 20002 (SAN 661-3128) Tel 202-387-3826.

Landscape Architecture, *(Landscape Architecture Foundation; 0-941236),* 1733 Connecticut Ave. NW, Washington, DC 20009 (SAN 224-1781) Tel 202-223-6229.

Landy Assocs, *(Landy & Assocs.; 0-9617077),* 5311 N. Highland, Tacoma, WA 98407 (SAN 662-6211).

Lane
See Sunset-Lane

Lane Pr, *(Lane Pr.; 0-935606),* P.O. Box 7822, Stanford, CA 94305 (SAN 221-4326).

Lang Dev Serv
See Eng Educ Serv

Lang Pubns, *(Lang Pubns.; 0-942242),* 490 N. 31st St., Suite 100, Billings, MT 59101 (SAN 238-4337); Dist. by: World Bible Publishers, Iowa Falls, IA 50126 (SAN 215-2797).

Lang Serv, *(Language Service, Inc., Pubns. Div.; 0-913942),* P.O. Box 8, Hastings-on-Hudson, NY 10706 (SAN 201-0666) Tel 914-478-3558.

Lang Svcs CA, *(Language Services; 0-9607690),* 6453 Gem Lake Ave., San Diego, CA 92119 (SAN 214-3925) Tel 619-698-7999.

Langdon & Langdon, *(Langdon & Langdon; 0-938741),* P.O. Box 633, Columbia, SC 29202 (SAN 661-7867) Tel 803-649-6679.

Langdon Assoc, *(Press of the Langdon Assocs., The; 0-916704),* 41 Langdon St., Cambridge, MA 02138 (SAN 209-2379) Tel 617-864-4518.

Langdon Pubns, *(Langdon, Larry, Pubns.; 0-943726),* 34735 Perkins Creek Rd., Cottage Grove, OR 97424-9450 (SAN 241-0427).

Lange
See Appleton & Lange

Langenscheidt, *(Langenscheidt Pubs., Inc.; 0-88729; 3-468),* Subs. of Langenscheidt KG, 46-35 54th Rd., Maspeth, NY 11378 (SAN 276-9441).

Langley, *(Langley, Ray; 0-9605158),* 3664 Scorpio Dr., Sacramento, CA 95827 (SAN 215-6733).

Langley Pr, *(Langley Pr., The; 0-911607),* 821 Georgia St., Key West, FL 33040 (SAN 264-164X) Tel 305-294-3156.

Langley Pubns, *(Langley Pubns., Inc.; 0-936991),* 1350 Beverly Rd., Suite 115-324, McLean, VA 22101 (SAN 658-7496) Tel 703-532-5388; 6609 Rosecroft Pl., Falls Church, VA 22043 (SAN 658-750X).

Langtry Pubns, *(Langtry Pubns.; 0-915369),* 7838 Burnet Ave., Van Nuys, CA 91405-1051 (SAN 291-2473) Tel 818-781-9144.

Language Intl, *(Language International; 0-935655),* 21339 Velicata St., Woodland Hills, CA 91364 (SAN 696-1398); P.O. Box 26, Woodland Hills, CA 91365 (SAN 662-3662) Tel 818-716-8222.

Language Pr, *(Language Pr.; 0-912386),* P.O. Box 342, Whitewater, WI 53190 (SAN 201-0674) Tel 414-473-6055.

Lanser Pr, *(Lanser Pr.; 0-9603900),* P.O. Box 38, Plainfield, VT 05667 (SAN 214-3933).

†**Lantern,** *(Lantern Pr., Inc. Pubs.; 0-8313),* 354 Hussey Rd., Mount Vernon, NY 10552 (SAN 201-0682) Tel 914-668-9736; CIP.

Lantern Imprint of **PB**

Lapierre Bks, *(Lapierre Bks.; 0-9615846),* 49241 I-94 Service Dr., Bldg. 12, Belleville, MI 48111 (SAN 697-2209) Tel 313-699-5102.

Lapis Pr, *(Lapis Pr., The; 0-932499),* 1850 Union St., Suite 466, San Francisco, CA 94123 (SAN 687-3979) Tel 415-622-4600; Dist. by: Consortium Bk. Sales & Distribution, 213 E. Fourth St., St. Paul, MN 55101 (SAN 200-6049) Tel 612-221-9035.

Larchmont Bks
See Comm Channels

Large Print Bks Imprint of **G K Hall**

Largo Co
See CAS Inc

Laridae Pr, *(Laridae Pr.; 0-9606094),* 3012 Wesley Ave., Ocean City, NJ 08226 (SAN 216-8278) Tel 609-399-3222.

Larimi, *(Larimi Communications; 0-935224),* 246 W. 38th St., New York, NY 10018 (SAN 210-8259) Tel 212-819-9310.

Lark Bks, *(Lark Bks.; 0-937274),* 50 College St., Asheville, NC 28801 (SAN 219-9947) Tel 704-253-0468.

Lark Comms Imprint of **Van Nos Reinhold**

Larkin, *(Larkin, Larry, Pub.; 0-9605748),* 762 S. Lake Shore Dr., Lake Geneva, WI 53147 (SAN 240-0219) Tel 414-248-2569.

†**Larksdale,** *(Larksdale; 0-89896),* 1706 Seamist, No. 575, Houston, TX 77008 (SAN 220-0643) Tel 713-869-9092; CIP. Imprints: Lindahl (Lindahl); Linolean (Linolean); Post Oak Pr (Post Oak Press).

Larksong Dayspring, *(Larksong Dayspring Pubns. of California),* P.O. Box 1667, Whittier, CA 90609 (SAN 219-0826) Tel 213-943-2320.

Larkspur, *(Larkspur Pubns.; 0-939942),* P.O. Box 211, Bowmansville, NY 14026 (SAN 216-8286) Tel 716-337-2758.

†**Larlin Corp,** *(Larlin Corp.; 0-89783; 0-87797),* P.O. Box 1523, Marietta, GA 30061 (SAN 201-4432) Tel 404-424-6210; CIP.

Larren Pubs, *(Larren Pubs.; 0-9604370),* P.O. Box 594, Nevada, MO 64772 (SAN 220-0651) Tel 417-667-3706.

Larry G Brady, *(Brady, Larry G., Publishing; 0-935489),* 424 E. H St., No. 1103, Chula Vista, CA 92101 (SAN 694-5392) Tel 619-585-9184.

Larsen's Outdoor, *(Larsen's Outdoor Publishing; 0-936513),* 3360 Kilmer Dr., Lakeland, FL 33803 (SAN 697-8975) Tel 813-644-3381; Orders to: Atlantic Publishing Co., P.O. Box 67, Tabor City, NC 28463 (SAN 215-6237).

Larson Joliet, *(Larson Pubns.; 0-9613928),* P.O. Box 2573, Joliet, IL 60434 (SAN 683-6070) Tel 815-744-6273.

Larson Pub, *(Larson Publishing Co.),* P.O. Box 286, Lompoc, CA 93438 (SAN 658-8328) Tel 805-735-2095.

Larson Pubns IL
See Larson Joliet

Larson Pubns Inc, *(Larson Pubns., Inc.; 0-943914),* 4936 Rte. 414, Burdett, NY 14818 (SAN 241-130X) Tel 607-546-9342; Dist. by: Kampmann & Co., 9 E. 40th St., New York, NY 10016 (SAN 202-5191) Tel 212-685-2928; Dist. by: Samuel Weiser Inc., P.O. Box 612, York Beach, ME 03910 (SAN 202-9588) Tel 207-363-4393.

Las Campanas, *(Las Campanas Pubns.; 0-938476),* P.O. Box 357, Bernalillo, NM 87004 (SAN 239-9369) Tel 505-867-3210.

Las Palomas, *(Las Palomas De Taos; 0-911695),* P.O. Box 3400, Taos, NM 87571 (SAN 264-1682).

Lasenda, *(Lasenda Pubs.; 0-918916),* 1590 Via Chaparral, Fallbrook, CA 92028 (SAN 210-4504) Tel 619-723-1407.

Laser Inst, *(Laser Institute of America; 0-912035),* 5151 Monroe St., Suite 102 W., Toledo, OH 43623 (SAN 225-2007) Tel 419-882-8706.

LaserSet Press, *(LaserSet Pr.; 0-939315),* P.O. Box 1747, Madison, WI 53701 (SAN 663-1460); 6 Sherman Terr., Rm. 6, Madison, WI 53704 (SAN 663-1479) Tel 608-241-7881.

Last Things, *(Last Things Pr.; 0-9616435),* P.O. Box 22642, Alexandria, VA 22304 (SAN 658-9235) Tel 202-274-6867; 5340 Holmes Run, No. 212, Alexandria, VA 22304 (SAN 658-9243).

Lat Am Jewish Studies, *(Latin American Jewish Studies Assn.; 0-916921),* 2104 Georgetown Blvd., Ann Arbor, MI 48105 (SAN 670-7300).

†**Lat Am Lit Rev Pr,** *(Latin American Literary Review Pr.; 0-935480),* P.O. Box 8385, Pittsburgh, PA 15218 (SAN 215-2142) Tel 412-351-1477; CIP.

Lateiner, *(Lateiner Publishing; 0-911722),* 282 N. Washington St., Delaware, OH 43015 (SAN 201-0690) Tel 614-363-3239.

Latham Found Pr
See Latham Found Pubn

Latham Found Pubn, *(Latham Foundation Pubn.),* Latham Plaza Bldg., Clement & Schiller Sts., Alameda, CA 94501 (SAN 682-7934).

Lathrop, *(Lathrop, Norman, Enterprises; 0-910868),* P.O. Box 198, Wooster, OH 44691 (SAN 285-0419) Tel 216-262-5587.

Latin Am Ctr
See UCLA Lat Am Ctr

Latin Assoc, *(Latin, R. R., Associates, Inc.; 0-940106),* 404 E. 55th St., New York, NY 10022 (SAN 220-2832) Tel 212-758-6389.

Latitudes Pr, *(Latitudes Pr.),* Div. of Latitudes Productions, P.O. Box 613, Mansfield, TX 76063 (SAN 202-6651) Tel 512-588-0527.

Latona Pr, *(Latona Pr.; 0-932448),* Box 154, R.F.D 2, Ellsworth, ME 04605 (SAN 216-406X).

Lattice Pr, *(Lattice Pr.; 0-9616721),* P.O. Box 340, Sunset Beach, CA 90742 (SAN 661-3896); 16695 Bay View Dr., Sunset Beach, CA 90742 (SAN 661-390X) Tel 714-840-5010.

Laughing B P, *(Laughing Buddha Pr., The; 0-910913),* Sarah Lawrence College, Bronxville, NY 10708 (SAN 271-9665) Tel 914-337-0700.

Laughing Loon, *(Laughing Loon Pubns.; 0-9616337),* P.O. Box 142, Glenville, MN 56036 (SAN 658-9251) Tel 507-448-2815; 111 Seventh St., SE, Glenville, MN 56036 (SAN 658-926X).

Laughing Sams Pr, *(Laughing Sam's Press; 0-9607824),* 5243 San Feliciano Dr., Woodland Hills, CA 91364 (SAN 238-0188) Tel 818-340-4175; Orders to: P.O. Box 426, Canoga Park, CA 91305 (SAN 662-068X).

Laughing Waters, *(Laughing Waters Pr., The; 0-939634),* 1416 Euclid Ave., Boulder, CO 80302 (SAN 216-6313).

Launch Pr, *(Launch Pr.; 0-9613205),* P.O. Box 40174, San Francisco, CA 94140 (SAN 295-0154) Tel 415-943-7603; Dist. by: Bookpeople, 2929 Fifth St., Berkeley, CA 94710 (SAN 168-9517); Dist. by: Inland Bk. Co., P.O. Box 261, 22 Hemingway Ave., East Haven, CT 06512 (SAN 200-4151) Tel 203-457-4257.

Laura Bks, *(Laura Bks., Inc.; 0-86540; 0-914042),* Box 918, Davenport, FL 33837 (SAN 220-7516) Tel 813-422-9135; 104 Bay St., Davenport, FL 33837 (SAN 658-1080).

Laurel Enter, *(Laurel Entertainment, Inc.; 0-930392),* 928 Broadway, New York, NY 10010 (SAN 211-0296) Tel 212-674-3800.

Laurel Group
See Laurel Enter

Laurel Hill Pr, *(Laurel Hill Press; 0-9608688),* 107 Wildcat Creek, Chapel Hill, NC 27514 (SAN 293-2954) Tel 919-962-6945; Orders to: P.O. Box 685, Carrboro, NC 27510 (SAN 293-2962) Tel 919-962-6945; Dist. by: F.W.F. Books, P.O. Box 7125, Winter Haven, FL 33883 (SAN 293-2970) Tel 813-294-7504; c/o Nancy Barnett, .

Laurel-Howard, *(Laurel-Howard Inc.; 0-933649),* 201 E. 21st St., No. 18J, New York, NY 10010 (SAN 694-017X) Tel 212-254-0853; Orders to: P.O. Box 3716, Grand Central Sta., New York, NY 10010 (SAN 662-7781).

Laurel Intl, *(Laurel Pubns. International; 0-934139),* P.O. Box 704, Road Town, Tortola, (SAN 693-3777) Tel 809-494-3510.

Laurel Pr, *(Laurel Pr.; 0-9613978),* P.O. Box 1553, Mill Valley, CA 94942 (SAN 682-3009) Tel 415-383-0362.

Lauren Pubns, *(Lauren Pubns.; 0-933547),* P.O. Box 815216, Dallas, TX 75381 (SAN 691-8719) Tel 214-638-4977.

Lauren Rogers, *(Lauren Rogers Museum of Art; 0-935903),* P.O. Box 1180, Laurel, MS 39441 (SAN 279-3547) Tel 601-649-6374; Fifth Ave. at Seventh St., Laurel, MS 39440 (SAN 696-6918).

Lauri Inc, *(Lauri, Inc.; 0-937763),* P.O. Box F, Phillips-Avon, ME 04966 (SAN 659-2597) Tel 207-639-2000; Avon Valley Rd., Phillips-Avon, ME 04966 (SAN 659-2600).

Laurida, *(Laurida Bk. Publishing Co.; 0-934810),* P.O. Box 2061, Hollywood, CA 90028 (SAN 203-9303) Tel 213-466-1707.

Laurie Inc
See Lauri Inc

L'Avant Studios, *(L'Avant Studios; 0-914570),* P.O. Box 1711, Tallahassee, FL 32302 (SAN 205-6038) Tel 904-576-1327.

Lavin Assocs, *(Lavin Assocs.; 0-941890),* 12 Promontory Dr., Cheshire, CT 06410 (SAN 239-779X) Tel 203-272-9121.

Law & Business *Imprint of* **HarBraceJ**

Law & Cap Dynamics, *(Law & Capital Dynamics; 0-9600708),* 700 S. Flower St. Suite 2600, Los Angeles, CA 90017 (SAN 213-7690) Tel 213-629-1100.

Law & Econ U Miami, *(University of Miami, Law & Economics Center; 0-916770),* P.O. Box 248000, Coral Gables, FL 33124 (SAN 208-9017) Tel 305-284-6174.

Law & Justice, *(Law & Justice Pubs.),* P.O. Box 6111, San Diego, CA 92106 (SAN 212-8578).

Law & Psych, *(Law & Psychology Pr.; 0-9603630),* P.O. Box 9489, Marina del Rey, CA 90295 (SAN 281-871X) Tel 213-823-4460.

Law & Tech Pr, *(Law & Technology Pr.; 0-910215),* P.O. Box 3280, Manhattan Beach, CA 90266 (SAN 241-3914) Tel 213-372-1678.

Law Anthology, *(Law Anthology Annuals; 0-936607),* 18 Lewis Ln., Port Washington, NY 11050 (SAN 698-0414) Tel 516-944-3593.

†Law Arts, *(Law-Arts Pubs.; 0-88238),* 159 W. 53rd St., No. 14F, New York, NY 10019 (SAN 201-0712) Tel 212-586-6380; *CIP.*

Law Enf Ord Co, *(Law Enforcement Ordnance Co.; 0-943850),* 2460 Peachtree Rd., NW, Suite 1411, Atlanta, GA 30305 (SAN 241-0435) Tel 404-261-1260.

Law Enforce Ref, *(Law Enforcement Reference Manual; 0-916104),* P.O. Box 7333, Trenton, NJ 08628 (SAN 206-1678) Tel 609-883-1886; Orders to: 240 Mulberry St., Newark, NJ 07101 (SAN 206-1686) Tel 201-642-0075.

Law Looseleaf
See Looseleaf Law

Law Schl Admission, *(Law School Admission Council/Law School Admission Services; 0-9610958),* Box 40, Newtown, PA 18940 (SAN 265-2676) Tel 215-968-1136.

†Law Sea Inst, *(Law of the Sea Institute; 0-911189),* Univ. of Hawaii at Manoa, William S. Richardson Schl. of Law, Honolulu, HI 96822 (SAN 226-5311) Tel 808-948-6750; *CIP.*

Law Sea RI
See Law Sea Inst

Lawells Pub, *(Lawells Publishing; 0-934981),* 311 S. Gratiot Ave., Mt. Clemens, MI 48043 (SAN 694-602X) Tel 313-469-3555.

Lawhead, *(Lawhead Pr., Inc.; 0-916199),* 900 E. State St., Athens, OH 45701 (SAN 294-9776) Tel 614-593-7744.

Lawkits, *(Lawkits, Inc.; 0-937464),* 26339 Monte Verde, Carmel, CA 93923 (SAN 215-2282) Tel 408-373-3067; Dist. by: Publishers Group West, 5855 Beaudry St., Emeryville, CA 94608 (SAN 202-8522) Tel 415-658-3453.

Lawletters, *(Lawletters, Inc.; 0-914239),* 332 S. Michigan Ave., Suite 1460, Chicago, IL 60604 (SAN 287-5322) Tel 312-922-0722.

Lawpress CA, *(Lawpress; 0-915544),* P.O. Box 596, Kentfield, CA 94914 (SAN 220-7524).

Lawrence & Co Pubs, *(Lawrence & Co. Pubs.; 0-9607096),* P.O. Box 13167, Albuquerque, NM 87192 (SAN 238-9932) Tel 505-821-7103; Dist. by: Dow Jones-Irwin, Inc., 1818 Ridge Rd., Homewood, IL 60430 (SAN 662-0558) Tel 312-798-6000.

Lawrence & Wishart, *(Lawrence & Wishart Ltd.; 0-85315),* 39 Museum St., WC1A 1LQ, .

†Lawrence Hill, *(Hill, Lawrence, & Co., Inc.; 0-88208),* 520 Riverside Ave., Westport, CT 06880 (SAN 214-1221) Tel 203-226-5980; Dist. by: Independent Publishers Group, 1 Pleasant Ave., Port Washington, NY 11050 (SAN 287-2544) Tel 516-944-9325; Dist. by: Lawrence Hill & Co., Inc., 520 Riverside Ave., Westport, CT 06880 (SAN 214-1221) Tel 203-226-5980; *CIP.*

Lawrenceville Pr, *(Lawrenceville Pr., Inc.; 0-931717),* P.O. Box 6490, Lawrenceville, NJ 08648 (SAN 218-5644) Tel 609-771-6831; Dist. by: Delmar Pubs., Inc., 2 Computer Dr. W., Albany, NY 12212 (SAN 206-7544) Tel 518-459-1150.

Lawson's Psych, *(Lawson's Psychological Services; 0-9611668),* 2051 W. Brichta Dr., Tucson, AZ 85745 (SAN 285-3418) Tel 602-792-3181.

Lawton E T, *(Lawton, Elise Timmons; 0-9617193),* 4521 Joyce Blvd., Houston, TX 77084 (SAN 240-9615) Tel 713-463-0234.

Lawton Pub Co, *(Lawton Publishing Co.; 0-9613050),* 7238 S. Garland Court, Littleton, CO 80123 (SAN 294-0949) Tel 303-973-2245.

Lawton-Teague, *(Lawton-Teague Pubns.; 0-932516),* P.O. Box 12353, Oakland, CA 94604 (SAN 211-2485); Dist. by: Bookpeople, 2929 Fifth St., Berkeley, CA 94710 (SAN 168-9517).

†Lawyers & Judges, *(Lawyers & Judges Publishing Co.; 0-913875),* P.O. Box 2744, Del Mar, CA 92014-5744 (SAN 202-2354) Tel 619-481-5944; *CIP.*

Lawyers Co-Op, *(Lawyers Co-Operative Publishing Co.),* 1 Graves St., Rochester, NY 14694 (SAN 202-6678) Tel 716-546-5530; Toll free: 800-LCP-04301 Publishers Pkwy., Webster, NY 14580 (SAN 658-1099).

Lawyers Comm Intl, *(Lawyers Committee for International Human Rights; 0-934143),* 36 W. 44th St., Suite 914, New York, NY 10036 (SAN 693-3025) Tel 212-921-2160.

Lawyers Creative Arts, *(Lawyers for the Creative Arts; 0-936122),* 623 S. Wabash, Suite 300-N, Chicago, IL 60605 (SAN 213-7704); Dist. by: Chicago Review Pr., 814 N. Franklin, Chicago, IL 60610 (SAN 213-5744) Tel 312-337-0747.

Lawyers Pr, *(Lawyers Pr.; 0-937337),* 2527 Fairmount, Dallas, TX 75201 (SAN 658-814X) Tel 214-871-7636.

Lawyers Weekly, *(Lawyers Weekly Pubns., Inc.),* 30 Court Sq., Boston, MA 02108 (SAN 679-1735) Tel 617-227-6034.

Lay Counsel Inst, *(Lay Counseling Institute; 0-936709),* P.O. Box 351, Florence, MS 39073 (SAN 699-9069) Tel 601-845-2407.

Lay Leadership, *(Lay Leadership Institute, Inc.; 0-88151),* 1267 Hicks Blvd., Fairfield, OH 45014 (SAN 271-9797).

Laylah Pubns, *(Laylah Pubns.; 0-914157),* P.O. Box 3111, Newport Beach, CA 92663 (SAN 287-5403) Tel 714-645-5796; 1515 Santa Ana, Costa Mesa, CA 92627 (SAN 287-5411).

Lazuli Prod, *(Lazuli Research Foundation Inc.; 0-9600522),* P.O. Box 19291, Portland, OR 97219 (SAN 211-738X).

LB Pubns, *(LB Pubns.; 0-9616746),* 8338 San Leandro, Dallas, TX 75218 (SAN 661-2776) Tel 214-327-5207.

LBJ Sch Pub Aff, *(Johnson, Lyndon B., Schl. of Public Affairs; 0-89940),* Univ. of Texas at Austin, Drawer DY, Univ. Sta., Austin, TX 78712 (SAN 223-0410) Tel 512-471-5713.

LBS Productions, *(L B S Productions; 0-9607796),* 2389 Sherwood Rd., Columbus, OH 43209 (SAN 240-0472).

LCD, *(L.C.D. Pub.; 0-941414),* 663 Calle Miramar, Redondo Beach, CA 90277 (SAN 239-0035) Tel 213-375-6336.

Ldrshp Pubns Miami, *(Leadership Pubns., Inc.; 0-938389),* P.O. Box 651009, Miami, FL 33165 (SAN 661-3926); 16310 SW 88th Ct., Miami, FL 33157 (SAN 661-3934) Tel 305-251-6159.

LDS Pubns, *(LDS Pubns.; 0-9614734),* 2901 Wilshire Blvd., Suite 435, Santa Monica, CA 90403 (SAN 692-7637) Tel 213-828-4480.

LDT Pr, *(LDT Pr.; 0-9613565),* 4401 Larchmont, Dallas, TX 75205 (SAN 670-0012) Tel 214-526-1723.

LE *Imprint of* **Dell**

Le Chateau, *(Le Chateau De Chaillie; 0-933299),* 4549 E. Montecito, Phoenix, AZ 85018 (SAN 692-3097) Tel 602-840-6576.

Le Jacq Pub, *(Le Jacq Publishing, Inc.; 0-937716),* 53 Park Pl., New York, NY 10007 (SAN 658-4020) Tel 212-766-4300.

†Lea & Febiger, *(Lea & Febiger; 0-8121),* 600 S. Washington Sq., Philadelphia, PA 19106-4198 (SAN 201-0747) Tel 215-922-1330; Toll free: 800-433-3850; *CIP.*

Lead Indus Assn, *(Lead Industries Assn., Inc.; 0-913284),* 292 Madison Ave., New York, NY 10017 (SAN 224-8735) Tel 212-578-4750.

Leader Learn Ctr, *(Leader Learning Ctr., Inc.; 0-936919),* 546 Anderson Ave., Closter, NJ 07624 (SAN 658-313X) Tel 201-767-3272.

Leadership Dyn, *(Leadership Dynamics Inc.; 0-911777),* 119 Longs Peak Dr., P.O. Box 320, Lyons, CO 80540 (SAN 264-1704) Tel 303-823-5146.

†**Leadership Pr,** *(Leadership Pr.; 0-936626),* Box 1144, Claremont, CA 91711 (SAN 214-3941) Tel 714-624-6242; *CIP.*

Leadership Pub, *(Leadership Pub.; 0-911943),* Div. of Roets Pubns., P.O. Box 51, New Sharon, IA 50207 (SAN 264-1712); 407 W. Cherry St., New Sharon, IA 50207 (SAN 658-1102) Tel 515-637-4563; Dist. by: Creative Learning Press, P.O. Box 320, Mansfield Center, CT 06250 (SAN 214-2368) Tel 203-423-8120; Dist. by: Zephyr Press, 1650 E. 18th St., Tucson, AZ 85719 (SAN 270-6830) Tel 602-623-2032.

Leadership Pubns
See Ldrshp Pubns Miami

League Bks, *(League Bks.),* P.O. Box 91801, Cleveland, OH 44101 (SAN 209-0406).

League Food Ed, *(League for International Food Education),* 915 15th St., NW, Suite 915, Washington, DC 20005 (SAN 224-1803) Tel 202-331-1658.

League Indus Demo, *(League for Industrial Democracy),* 275 Seventh Ave., New York, NY 10001 (SAN 225-9494) Tel 212-989-8130.

League Wmn Voters MN, *(League of Women Voters of Minnesota Education Fund; 0-9613566),* Affil. of League of Women Voters of Minnesota, 555 Wabasha, Suite 212, St. Paul, MN 55102 (SAN 670-0055) Tel 612-224-5445.

League Women Voters TX, *(League of Women Voters of TX, & League of Women Voters of TX Education Fund; 0-915757),* 1212 Guadalupe, No. 107, Austin, TX 78701 (SAN 294-121X) Tel 512-472-1100.

Leaping Hart Pr, *(Leaping Hart Pr.; 0-9615115),* 3039 N. Frederick Ave., Milwaukee, WI 53211 (SAN 694-1427) Tel 414-332-1635.

Lear, *(Lear Enterprises; 0-941990),* P.O. Box 649, Woodland Hills, CA 91365 (SAN 238-6062) Tel 818-340-8800.

†**Learn Concepts OH,** *(Learning Concepts, Inc.; 0-934902),* 7601 Mentor Ave., Mentor, OH 44060 (SAN 213-411X) Tel 216-946-6437. Not affiliated with San Diego Learning Concepts; *CIP.*

Learn Deve, *(Learning Development Systems Pubns.; 0-936585),* 281 Walnut Grove Dr., Dayton, OH 45459 (SAN 698-083X) Tel 513-885-5957; Orders to: P.O. Box 177, Dayton, OH 45459 (SAN 662-3999) Tel 513-435-1113.

Learn Int, *(Learning International; 0-935268),* Subs. of the Times Mirror Co., P.O. Box 10211, 1600 Summer St., Stamford, CT 06904 (SAN 206-0086) Tel 203-965-8400.

Learn N Laugh, *(Learn-N-Laugh Bks.; 0-9616408),* P.O. Box 4976, Boise, ID 83711-4976 (SAN 658-9316) Tel 208-939-6038; 4762 Nystrom Pl., Boise, ID 83704 (SAN 658-9324).

Learn Net Res
See LERN

Learn Res Dev, *(Learning Research & Development Center, Univ. of Pittsburgh),* 3939 O'Hara St., Pittsburgh, PA 15260 (SAN 224-1811) Tel 412-624-4829.

Learn Res Intl Stud
See LRIS

Learn to Flirt, *(Learn to Flirt; 0-9616376),* 3015 N. Ocean Blvd., Suite 115A, Ft. Lauderdale, FL 33308 (SAN 658-9359) Tel 305-566-1477.

Learn Tools, *(Learning Tools Co., The; 0-938017),* 3322 McKinley St. NW, Washington, DC 20015 (SAN 692-7297) Tel 202-363-0016.

Learned Info, *(Learned Information, Inc.; 0-938734),* 143 Old Marlton Pike, Medford, NJ 08055 (SAN 215-8841).

Learned Pubns, *(Learned Pubns., Inc.; 0-912116),* 83-53 Manton St., Jamaica, NY 11435 (SAN 201-0755) Tel 718-441-8084.

Learning Concepts, *(Learning Concepts, Inc.; 0-89384),* Orders to: Learning Concepts/Univ. Associates, 8517 Production Ave., San Diego, CA 92121 (SAN 272-006X) Tel 619-578-5900.

Learning Excell, *(Learning Excellence; 0-934657),* P.O. Box 1527, Redding, CA 96099 (SAN 694-0412) Tel 916-221-0440.

†**Learning Hse,** *(Learning Hse. Pubs.; 0-9602730),* 38 South St., Roslyn Heights, NY 11577 (SAN 214-3968) Tel 516-621-5755; Dist. by: Liberty Publishing Co., 50 Scott Adam Rd., Cockeysville, MD 21030 (SAN 211-030X) Tel 301-667-6680; *CIP.*

Learning Hse Pubns, *(Learning House Pubns.; 0-915759),* P.O. Box 49520, Chicago, IL 60649 (SAN 295-3943) Tel 312-924-6080; 4728 S. Greenwood, Chicago, IL 60615 (SAN 295-3951).

Learning Inc, *(Learning, Inc.; 0-913692),* Learning Pl., Manset, ME 04656 (SAN 201-5714) Tel 207-244-5015.

Learning Line, *(Learning Line, The; 0-8449),* P.O. Box 577, Palo Alto, CA 94302 (SAN 220-018X) Tel 415-424-1400; Orders to: P.O. Box 1200, Palo Alto, CA 94302 (SAN 220-0198).

Learning Proc Ctr, *(Learning Process Ctr.; 0-931657),* 222 W. 24th St., National City, CA 92050 (SAN 683-5589); Toll free: 800-221-7374.

Learning Pubns, *(Learning Pubns., Inc.; 0-918452; 1-55691),* 5351 Gulf Dr., Holmes Beach, FL 33510 (SAN 208-1695) Tel 813-778-5524; Toll free: 800-222-1525; Orders to: P.O. Box 1326, Holmes Beach, FL 33509 (SAN 688-3990) Tel 813-778-6818.

Learning Systs Grp, *(Learning Systems, Ltd. Group; 0-924893),* P.O. Box 9046, Ft. Collins, CO 80525 (SAN 293-1303) Tel 303-493-7285.

Learning Well, *(Learning Well; 0-917109; 0-936850; 1-55596),* 200 S. Service Rd., Roslyn Heights, NY 11577 (SAN 240-7027) Tel 516-621-1540; Toll free: 800-645-6564.

Learning Well NY
See Learning Well

Learning Wks, *(Learning Works, Inc., The; 0-88160),* P.O. Box 6187, Santa Barbara, CA 93160 (SAN 272-0078) Tel 805-964-4220; Toll free: 800-235-5767.

Learntech Pubns, *(Learntech Pubns.; 0-940108),* 8808 Hidden Hill Lane, Rockville, MD 20854 (SAN 220-2840) Tel 301-499-7142.

Leaseway Trans Corp, *(Leaseway Transportation Corp; 0-9610146),* 3700 Park East Dr., Cleveland, OH 44122 (SAN 272-0086) Tel 216-464-2700.

Leaven Pr, *(Leaven Pr.; 0-934134),* 115 E. Armour Blvd., Kansas City, MO 64141 (SAN 686-7715) Tel 816-531-0538; Toll free: 800-821-7926. Out of business.

Leaves of Grass, *(Leaves of Grass Pr., Inc.; 0-915070),* Publishers Services, P.O. Box 2510, Novato, CA 94947 (SAN 207-9321) Tel 415-833-3530.

Lebanese Cuisine, *(Lebanese Cuisine; 0-9603050),* P.O. Box 66395, Portland, OR 97266 (SAN 213-103X).

†**Lebhar Friedman,** *(Lebhar-Friedman Bks.; 0-912016; 0-86730),* Subs. of Lebhar-Friedman, Inc., 425 Park Ave, New York, NY 10022 (SAN 201-9744) Tel 212-371-9400; *CIP.*

Leco Pub, *(Leco Publishing Co.; 0-934365),* P.O. Box 789, Middletown, CA 95461 (SAN 693-5575) Tel 707-987-3569.

Lectorum Corp
See Lectorum Pubns

Lectorum Pubns, *(Lectorum Pubns.),* 137 W. 14th St., New York, NY 10011 (SAN 169-586X).

Leda Pr, *(Leda Press; 0-9605486),* 911 E. Mahanoy Ave., Mahanoy City, PA 17948 (SAN 215-2622) Tel 717-773-1586.

Ledena Pub, *(Ledena Publishing; 0-9615795),* Div. of Ledena Corp., 11370 Chipmunk Dr., Boca Raton, FL 33428 (SAN 696-6004) Tel 305-487-0010 (SAN 696-9771); Orders to: P.O. Box 272887, Boca Raton, FL 33427 (SAN 662-3786).

Lederer Enterprises, *(Lederer Enterprises; 0-9608040),* P.O. Box 15750, Asheville, NC 28813 (SAN 238-0668) Tel 704-684-8094; Toll free: 800-258-7160.

†**Ledge Bks,** *(Ledge Bks.; 0-931447),* P.O. Box 19, Bernard, ME 04612 (SAN 683-1885) Tel 207-244-3464; *CIP.*

Lee Bks, *(Lee Bks.; 0-939818),* Div. of Lee S. Cole and Assocs., Inc., P.O. Box 906, Novato, CA 94948 (SAN 216-2636) Tel 415-897-3550.

Lee Enterprises, *(Lee Enterprises, Inc.; 0-910847),* 130 E. Second St., Davenport, IA 52801 (SAN 262-7892) Tel 319-383-2208; Dist. by: Iowa & Illinois News Co., 8645 Northwest Blvd, Davenport, IA 52808 (SAN 693-4935) Tel 319-391-3723.

Lee Pub CA, *(Lee Publishing; 0-939171),* 1354 Miller Pl., Los Angeles, CA 90069 (SAN 662-8575) Tel 818-845-8455. Do not confuse with Lee Enterprises in Davenport, IA.

Lee Pub Co NH, *(Lee Publishing Co.; 0-9616394),* 135-21 Amherst St., Amherst, NH 03031 (SAN 699-8062).

Lee Pubns MN, *(Lee Pubns.; 0-9615237),* P.O. Box 331, Minneapolis, MN 55440 (SAN 695-1694) Tel 612-623-9438.

Leeco, *(Leeco, Inc.; 0-941222),* 201 Benton Ave., Linthicum Heights, MD 21090 (SAN 238-0676).

LeeRosa Pubs, *(LeeRosa Pubs.; 0-935547),* 3602 Treachwig Rd., Humble, TX 77347 (SAN 696-2343) Tel 713-821-0185; P.O. Box 3729, Humble, TX 77347 (SAN 696-9623).

Leetes Isl, *(Leete's Island Bks.; 0-918172),* P.O. Box 1131, New Haven, CT 06505 (SAN 210-2285) Tel 203-481-2536; Dist. by: Independent Pubs. Group, 1 Pleasant Ave., Pt. Washington, NY 11050 (SAN 210-2293).

Leeward Pubns *Imprint of* Presidio Pr

Lefever, *(Lefever, Barbara Susan; 0-9614690),* 1760 Alpine Rd., Dover, PA 17315 (SAN 692-6002) Tel 717-292-2827.

Left Bank, *(Left Bank Bks.; 0-939306),* 92 Pike St., Box B, Seattle, WA 98101 (SAN 216-5368) Tel 206-622-0195.

Lega Bks, *(Lega Bks.),* Div. of Charing Cross Pub. Co., 658 S. Bonnie Brae St., Los Angeles, CA 90057 (SAN 212-5218) Tel 213-483-5832.

Legacy Bks, *(Legacy Bks.; 0-913714),* Box 494, Hatboro, PA 19040 (SAN 202-2389) Tel 215-675-6762; 12 Meetinghouse Rd., Hatboro, PA 19040 (SAN 658-1129).

Legacy Hse, *(Legacy Hse., Inc.; 0-9608008),* Box 786, Orofino, ID 83544 (SAN 238-0684) Tel 209-476-5632.

Legacy Pr VA, *(Legacy Pr.; 0-9617028),* 4201 University Dr., Fairfax, VA 22030 (SAN 662-6475) Tel 703-591-9333.

Legacy Publish, *(Legacy Publishing (CA); 0-9611902),* 1442A Walnut St., Suite 295, Berkeley, CA 94709 (SAN 286-1577) Tel 415-549-3517.

Legacy Pubns, *(Legacy Pubns.; 0-933101),* Subs. of Pace Communications, Inc., Rte. 4, Box 7, Burlington, NC 27215 (SAN 689-5662) Tel 919-584-6473; Orders to: P.O. Box 20630, Greensboro, NC 27420 (SAN 662-2852).

Legal Bk Co, *(Legal Bk. Co.; 0-910874),* 316 W. Second St., Los Angeles, CA 90012 (SAN 201-0798) Tel 213-626-3494.

Legal Pr Serv, *(Legal Pr. Service, Inc.; 0-931907),* 5010 N. Ridge Club Dr., Las Vegas, NV 89103 (SAN 686-0176) Tel 702-873-4542.

Legal Pubns CA, *(Legal Pubns., Inc.; 0-940194),* P.O. Box 3723, Van Nuys, CA 91407 (SAN 210-8267) Tel 818-902-1671.

Legal Res Bureau, *(Legal Research Bureau; 0-9609346),* P.O. Box 374, Kew Gardens, NY 11415 (SAN 260-2164) Tel 718-846-4544.

Legends Pr, *(Legends Pr.; 0-9608808),* 504 S. Pacific Coast Hwy., Redondo Beach, CA 90277 (SAN 238-311X) Tel 213-540-6455.

Legerete Pr, *(Legerete Pr.; 0-936993),* P.O. Drawer 1410, Daphne, AL 36526 (SAN 695-1317).

Legis Assocs, *(Legislative Assocs., Inc.; 0-934367),* 503 W. 14th St., Austin, TX 78701 (SAN 463-5621) Tel 512-477-5698.

Legis Info Pr, *(Legislative Information Group Press; 0-916481),* 6812 Belford Dr., Takoma Park, MD 20912 (SAN 295-1169).

Legislative Track, (*Legislative Tracking Service, The; 0-938585*), P.O. Box 844, Annapolis, MD 21404 (SAN 661-1184) Tel 301-269-7558.

LEHI Pub Co, (*LEHI Publishing Co.; 0-934486*), 303 Gretna Green Way, Los Angeles, CA 90049 (SAN 213-4101) Tel 213-476-6024.

Lehigh Info, (*Lehigh Informational Services; 0-913453*), P.O. Box 6055, Bethlehem, PA 18001 (SAN 285-1768) Tel 215-837-8358.

Lehigh Univ Pr, (*Lehigh Univ. Pr.; 0-934223*), Dist. by: Associated University Presses, 440 Forsgate Dr., Cranbury, NJ 08512 (SAN 281-2959) Tel 609-655-4770.

Leibowitz, (*Leibowitz, Herbert*), 205 W. 89th St., New York, NY 10024 (SAN 239-4502) Tel 212-787-3569.

Leider & Harding
See Leider-Harding

Leider-Harding, (*Leider-Harding Enterprises; 0-9607504*), 7101 York Ave. S., Minneapolis, MN 55435 (SAN 239-7803) Tel 612-921-3336.

Leigh-Newcomb
See Airborne Pr

Leihall Pubns, (*Leihall Pubns.; 0-9615337*), 4710 Huntley Dr. NE, Atlanta, GA 30342 (SAN 695-1244) Tel 404-252-6742.

Leisure Data, (*Leisure Data Inc.; 0-913979*), 1934 Basswood Drive, Kent, OH 44240 (SAN 283-9652) Tel 216-678-0936.

Leisure Net, (*Leisure-Net, Inc.; 0-9615334*), P.O. Box 2395, Livonia, MI 48151 (SAN 695-1252) Tel 313-261-6498; 33615 Wood Dr., Livonia, MI 48154 (SAN 695-1260).

†Leisure Pr, (*Leisure Pr.; 0-918438; 0-88011*), Div. of Human Kinetics Pubs., Inc., P.O. Box 5076, Champaign, IL 61820 (SAN 211-7088) Tel 217-351-5076; 1607 N. Market, Champaign, IL 61820 (SAN 662-0698) Tel 217-351-5076; *CIP.*

†Leisure Sci Sys, (*Leisure Science Systems International; 0-932057*), P.O. Box 3832, La Mesa, CA 92041 (SAN 686-2683) Tel 619-265-4451; *CIP.*

Leland Hist, (*Leland Historical Foundation; 0-9615430*), 301 E. Third, Leland, MS 38756 (SAN 696-1517) Tel 601-982-6371.

Leland Pub Co, (*Leland Publishing Co., Inc.; 0-931306*), 81 Canal St., Boston, MA 02114 (SAN 295-0162) Tel 617-227-9314.

Lemur, (*Lemur Musical Research Corp.; 0-9606888*), P.O. Box 245, Encinitas, CA 92024 (SAN 201-5706) Tel 619-942-8202.

Len Beach Pr, (*Len Beach Press*), P.O. Box 7269 R.C., Toledo, OH 43615 (SAN 213-1048).

Len Forman Pub Co Imprint of Gold Door Inc

Lenape Pub, (*Lenape Publishing, Ltd.; 0-917178*), 3 Lanark Dr., Wilmington, DE 19803 (SAN 208-7324) Tel 302-479-0251.

LenChamps Pubs, (*LenChamps Publishers; 0-917230*), 607 Fourth St., S.W., Washington, DC 20024 (SAN 208-7332) Tel 202-484-3571.

Lenhart, (*Lenhart, John N.; 0-9615380*), P.O. Box 20261, Cleveland, OH 44120 (SAN 695-4693) Tel 216-752-4731.

Lenjalin Pubns, (*Lenjalin Publications; 0-9614768*), P.O. Box 816, Bettendorf, IA 52722-0816 (SAN 692-7017) Tel 319-359-7220.

Lenox Bks, (*Lenox Bks.; 0-9605872*), P.O. Box 104, Little Falls, NJ 07424 (SAN 216-4078).

Lenox Lib Assn Imprint of SnO Pubns

Lenox Pub, (*Lenox Publishing Co.; 0-917421*), P.O. Box 7641, Atlanta, GA 30357 (SAN 656-1373) Tel 404-881-9566.

Leo Pr, (*Leo Pr.; 0-931580*), Allen Park, MI 48101 (SAN 212-4300).

Leonaitis, (*Leonaitis, Joseph Felix; 0-9601272*), 3323 S. Lowe Ave., Chicago, IL 60616 (SAN 210-4547) Tel 312-376-7524.

Leonard Assoc Pr, (*Leonard's Assocs.; 0-936692*), 2423 N. Second St., Harrisburg, PA 17110 (SAN 221-4318); Dist. by: Mankind Research Foundation, 1315 Apple Ave., Silver Spring, MD 20910 (SAN 208-4422).

Leonard Assoc Press
See Leonard Assoc Pr

Leonardo Pr, (*Leonardo Pr.; 0-914051*), P.O. Box 403, Yorktown Heights, NY 10598 (SAN 287-542X) Tel 914-962-7056.

Leone Pubns, (*Leone Pubns.; 0-942786*), 2721 Lyle Ct., Santa Clara, CA 95051 (SAN 238-8510) Tel 415-948-8077.

Leonine Pr, (*Leonine Pr.; 0-942228*), 2317 Outlook St., Kalamazoo, MI 49001 (SAN 240-0405) Tel 616-345-2740.

†L'Epervier Pr, (*L'Epervier Pr.; 0-934332*), 4522 Sunnyside N., Seattle, WA 98103 (SAN 281-8779) Tel 206-547-8306; 3635 Fremont Ave. N., Seattle, WA 98103; Dist. by: Small Press Distribution Inc., 1814 San Pablo Ave., Berkeley, CA 94712 (SAN 204-5826) Tel 415-549-5336; Dist. by: Bookslinger, 213 E. Fourth St., St. Paul, MN 55101 (SAN 169-4154) Tel 612-221-0429; *CIP.*

Lepidopterists, (*Lepidopterists' Society, Los Angeles County Museum of Natural History*), 900 Exposition Blvd, Los Angeles, CA 90007 (SAN 225-2015) Tel 213-744-3364; Orders to: C. V. Covell, Univ. of Louisville, Louisville, KY 40208 (SAN 225-2023).

Leprechaun Pr, (*Leprechaun Pr.; 0-9607368*), 808 W. End Ave., No. 408, New York, NY 10025 (SAN 240-0391) Tel 212-666-3357.

†LERN, (*Learning Resources Network; 0-914951*), Box 1448, Manhattan, KS 66502 (SAN 289-2928) Tel 913-539-5376; *CIP.*

Lerner Bks
See Lerner Pubns

Lerner Law, (*Lerner Law Bk. Co.; 0-87342*), 53 E St., NW, Washington, DC 20001 (SAN 201-081X) Tel 202-628-5785.

†Lerner Pubns, (*Lerner Pubns. Co.; 0-8225*), 241 First Ave. N., Minneapolis, MN 55401 (SAN 201-0828) Tel 612-332-3344; Toll free: 800-328-4929; *CIP.*

Les Femmes Gourmets, (*Les Femmes Gourmets; 0-9616100*), 428 Oakview Dr., Roseburg, OR 97470 (SAN 698-1240) Tel 503-440-4600.

Leslie Pr, (*Leslie Press, Inc.; 0-913816*), 161 Pittsburg, Dallas, TX 75207 (SAN 202-6708) Tel 214-748-0564.

Lesly Co, (*Lesly, Philip, Co., The; 0-9602866*), 303 E. Wacker Dr., Chicago, IL 60601 (SAN 222-2086) Tel 312-819-3590.

Lessing Soc, (*Lessing Society*), Dept. of German, M.L. 372, Univ. of Cincinnati, Cincinnati, OH 45221 (SAN 233-2094) Tel 513-475-2989; Dist. by: Wayne State Univ. Pr, 5959 Woodward Ave., Detroit, MI 48202 (SAN 202-5221) Tel 313-577-4601.

LeTourneau Pr, (*LeTourneau Pr.; 0-935899*), 8 Stonegate Dr., Longview, TX 75601 (SAN 696-611X) Tel 214-753-0231.

Leumas Pub, (*Leumas Publishing; 0-935117*), 318 W. Hawthorne Dr., P.O. Box 7474, Round Lake Beach, IL 60073 (SAN 695-1287) Tel 312-546-7267.

Levada, (*Levada Services; 0-9605014*), P.O. Box 686, 11300 Eastside Rd., Ft. Jones, CA 96032 (SAN 215-9597).

Level Four Comm, (*Level Four Communications; 0-936995*), 3 Dallas Communications Complex, Irving, TX 75039-3510 (SAN 658-3105) Tel 214-869-7620; Box 134, 6311 N. O'Connor Rd., Irving, TX 75039-3510 (SAN 658-3113).

Levenson Pr, (*Levenson Pr.; 0-914442*), P.O. Box 19606, Los Angeles, CA 90019 (SAN 202-6716).

Levi Pub, (*Levi Publishing Co., Inc.; 0-910876*), P.O. Box 730, Sumter, SC 29150 (SAN 203-9338).

†Levinson Inst, (*Levinson Institute Inc.; 0-916516*), Box 95, Cambridge, MA 02138 (SAN 208-7359) Tel 617-489-3040; *CIP.*

Levko, (*Levko, Leo; 0-9614381*), P.O. Box 208 Planetarium Sta., New York, NY 10024 (SAN 688-4725) Tel 212-877-6154.

Lew Originals, (*Lew Originals; 0-931249*), 3116 Vanowen St., Burbank, CA 91505 (SAN 681-9974) Tel 818-705-7778.

Lewis, (*Lewis, A. F. & Co., Inc.; 0-910880*), 79 Madison Ave., New York, NY 10016 (SAN 201-0844) Tel 212-679-0770.

Lewis Carroll Soc, (*Carroll, Lewis, Society of North America; 0-930326*), 617 Rockford Rd., Silver Spring, MD 20902 (SAN 213-1064).

Lewis Lee Corp, (*Lewis Lee Corp.; 0-915847*), 1855 Cowper St., Palo Alto, CA 94301 (SAN 294-0566) Tel 415-853-1220.

Lewis Pub Hse, (*Lewis Publishing Hse.; 0-937225*), P.O. Box 23348, Minneapolis, MN 55423 (SAN 658-7534) Tel 612-861-8260; 6435 Farmer Trail, R.R. 4, Box 195, Northfield, MN 55057 (SAN 658-7542).

†Lewis Pubs Inc, (*Lewis Pubs, Inc.; 0-87371*), 121 S. Main St., P.O. Box 519, Chelsea, MI 48118 (SAN 682-1715) Tel 313-475-8619; Toll free: 800-525-7894; *CIP.*

Lewis-Roth, (*Lewis & Roth Pubs.; 0-936083*), Div. of Church Reform & Revitalization, Inc., 12431 N. Mead Way, Littleton, CO 80125-9761 (SAN 696-6454) Tel 303-794-3239.

†Lewis-Sloan, (*Lewis-Sloan Publishing Co.; 0-915114*), 2546 Etiwan Ave., Charleston, SC 29407 (SAN 201-0852) Tel 803-766-4735; *CIP.*

Lex Bk Co CA, (*Lexington Book Co.; 0-9604372*), 4872 Old Cliffs Rd., San Diego, CA 92120 (SAN 214-3992) Tel 619-583-8348.

Lex Com Enterprises Inc, (*Lex-Com Enterprises, Inc; 0-914691*), 548 S. Spring St.,Suite 512, Los Angeles, CA 90013 (SAN 291-8404).

Lexicon Bks, (*Lexicon Bks.; 0-937069*), Subs. of Lexicon Music, Inc., P.O. Box 2222, Newbury Park, CA 91320 (SAN 658-618X) Tel 805-499-5881; 3543 Old Conejo Rd., Suite 105, Newbury Park, CA 91320 (SAN 658-6198).

Lexigrow Intl, (*Lexigrow International Corp.; 0-910387*), 9202 N. Meridian St., Indianapolis, IN 46206 (SAN 262-0464) Tel 317-844-5691; P.O. Box 1491, Indianapolis, IN 46206 (SAN 658-1137).

Lexik Hse, (*Lexik House Pubs.; 0-936368*), 75 Main St., P.O. Box 247, Cold Spring, NY 10516 (SAN 214-3984) Tel 914-265-2822.

†Lexikos, (*Lexikos Publishing; 0-938530*), 4079 19th Ave., San Francisco, CA 94132 (SAN 219-8517) Tel 415-584-1085; *CIP.*

†Lexington Bks, (*Lexington Bks.; 0-669*), Div. of D. C. Heath & Co., ; Toll free: 800-235-3565; Dist. by: D. C. Heath & Co., 125 Spring St., Lexington, MA 02173 (SAN 213-7526) Tel 617-862-6650; Orders to: Phyllis McGuinness, 125 Spring St., Lexington, MA 02173 (SAN 662-0701) Tel 617-860-1204; *CIP.*

Lexington Data, (*Lexington Data, Inc.; 0-914428; 0-88178*), Box 371, Ashland, MA 01721 (SAN 202-6724) Tel 617-881-2576.

Lexington-Fayette, (*Lexington-Fayette County Historic Commission; 0-912839*), 253 Market St., Lexington, KY 40508 (SAN 277-6936) Tel 606-255-8312.

Lexis Pr, (*Lexis Pr.; 0-933741*), Subs. of Diversified Academic Services, Inc., P.O. Box 4116, Chapel Hill, NC 27515 (SAN 692-5995) Tel 919-942-1711.

Leyerle Pubns, (*Leyerle Pubns.; 0-9602296*), 28 Stanley St., Mt. Morris, NY 14510 (SAN 211-5700) Tel 716-658-2193; Orders to: Box 384, Geneseo, NY 14454 (SAN 211-5719).

LFive Soc, (*L5 Society; 0-935291*), 1060 E. Elm St., Tucson, AZ 85719 (SAN 696-3633) Tel 602-622-6351.

LFL Imprint of Dell

LFL Assocs, (*LFL Assocs.; 0-9613838*), 52 Condolea Ct., Lake Oswego, OR 97034 (SAN 681-9982) Tel 503-636-1559.

LFSI Minnesota, (*Longman Financial Services Institute, Incorporated; 0-943634*), 9201 E. Bloomington Freeway, Minneapolis, MN 55420 (SAN 238-2814) Tel 612-885-2700.

LGO Pub, (*LGO Publishing; 0-936483*), 6065 Mission Gorge Rd., Suite 235, San Diego, CA 92120 (SAN 698-102X) Tel 619-485-0822.

Li Kung Shaw, (*Shaw, Li Kung, Pubs.; 0-9607806*), 2530 33rd Ave., San Francisco, CA 94116 (SAN 240-0480) Tel 415-731-0829.

LI Lib Resources, (*Long Island Library Resources Council; 0-938435*), P.O. Box 31, Bellport, NY 11713 (SAN 661-2989); 627 N. Sunrise Service Rd., Bellport, NY 11713 (SAN 661-2997) Tel 516-286-0400.

Lib Imprint of Bobbs

Lib Arts Pr, (*Liberal Arts Pr.; 0-935175*), 4800 Kelly Elliot Rd., No. 46, Arlington, TX 76017 (SAN 695-4707) Tel 817-572-7409.

Lib Bost Athe
See Boston Athenaeum

Lib Claremont Coll, *(Libraries of the Claremont Colleges; 0-937368),* 800 Dartmouth, Claremont, CA 91711 (SAN 264-1011).

Lib Co Phila, *(Library Co. of Philadelphia; 0-914076),* 1314 Locust St., Philadelphia, PA 19107 (SAN 201-4955) Tel 215-546-3181.

†Lib Congress, *(Library of Congress; 0-8444),* Washington, DC 20540 (SAN 205-6593) Tel 202-287-5093; *CIP.*

Lib Humane Sci, *(Library of Humane Science; 0-930170),* Box 8, Colchester, VT 05446 (SAN 211-5697) Tel 802-658-1238.

Lib Info Tech, *(Library & Information Technology Assn.),* Div. of American Library Assn., 50 E. Huron St., Chicago, IL 60611 (SAN 233-4887) Tel 312-944-6780.

Lib Learn Res, *(Library Learning Resources, Inc.; 0-931315),* 61 Greenbriar Dr., P.O. Box 87, Berkeley Heights, NJ 07922 (SAN 682-7977) Tel 201-499-3406.

Lib Prof Pubns *Imprint of* Shoe String

Lib Psychol Anthrop
See Psychohistory Pr

†Lib Res, *(Library Research Assocs., Inc.; 0-912526),* Subs. of Empire State Fiction, Dunderberg Rd., RD 5, Box 41, Monroe, NY 10950 (SAN 201-0887) Tel 914-783-1144; *CIP.*

Lib Sci Theism
See Lib Humane Sci

Lib Serv Inc, *(Library Services Inc.),* Box 711, Havertown, PA 19083 (SAN 210-5381).

Lib Soc Sci, *(Library of Social Science; 0-915042),* 475 Amsterdam Ave., New York, NY 10024 (SAN 207-589X) Tel 212-749-3567.

Libera, *(Libera; 0-9614831),* 930 Alta Vista Rd., Simi Valley, CA 93063 (SAN 693-0360) Tel 818-704-9854; Orders to: Box 1920, Simi Valley, CA 93062 (SAN 662-3085).

Liberal Pr, *(Liberal Pr., The; 0-934659),* P.O. Box 160361, Las Colinas, TX 75016 (SAN 200-5360); Dist. by: Publishers Assocs., P.O. Box 160361, Las Colinas, TX 75106-9998 (SAN 200-6979) Tel 817-478-8564.

Liberation Pubns, *(Liberation Pubns., Inc.; 0-917076),* P.O. Box 4371, Los Angeles, CA 90078 (SAN 208-7367) Tel 213-871-1225.

Liberian Studies, *(Liberian Studies),* Dept. of Anthropology, Univ. of Delaware, Newark, DE 19711 (SAN 207-5032).

Libertarian Bks, *(Libertarian Bks.),* P.O. Box 5474, New York, NY 10163-5474 (SAN 208-3418).

†Libertarian Press, *(Libertarian Pr.; 0-910884),* Spring Mills, PA 16875 (SAN 201-0895) Tel 319-277-7546; *CIP.*

Libertarian Rev Found, *(Libertarian Review Foundation; 0-930073),* 532 Broadway, 7th Flr., New York, NY 10012 (SAN 210-8224) Tel 212-925-8992.

Liberty Bell Pr, *(Liberty Bell Press; 0-914053),* P.O. Box 32, Florissant, MO 63033 (SAN 202-2435) Tel 314-837-5343.

Liberty Clas *Imprint of* Liberty Fund

Liberty Comm, *(Liberty Communications, Inc.; 0-933713),* 1605 Whittier Ave., Winchester, VA 22601 (SAN 692-5006) Tel 703-667-3680; Dist. by: Publishers Mktg. Group, 1104 Summit Ave., Plainview, TX 75074 (SAN 262-0995) Tel 214-423-0312.

†Liberty Fund, *(Liberty Fund, Inc.; 0-913966; 0-86597),* 7440 N. Shadeland Ave., Indianapolis, IN 46250 (SAN 202-6740) Tel 317-842-0880; *CIP. Imprints:* Liberty Clas (Liberty Classics); Liberty Pr (Liberty Press).

Liberty Hse Pr, *(Liberty Hse. Pr., Inc.; 0-937765),* 1517 14th St., W., Billings, MT 59102 (SAN 659-2619) Tel 406-245-6841.

Liberty Lobby, *(Liberty Lobby; 0-935036),* 300 Independence Ave., SE, Washington, DC 20003 (SAN 202-2524) Tel 202-546-5611.

Liberty Pr, *(Liberty Pr.; 0-936860),* Div. of Oldham & Associates, 500 W. 1200 S., Orem, UT 84057 (SAN 264-1747).

Liberty Pr *Imprint of* Liberty Fund

Liberty Press TX, *(Liberty Pr.; 0-938743),* P.O. Box 50421, Austin, TX 78763 (SAN 661-7808) Tel 512-495-9737; 1014B N. Lamar Blvd., Austin, TX 78703 (SAN 661-7816). Do not confuse with Liberty Pr., Orem, UT, Muscatine, IA, Lansing, MI.

Liberty Pub, *(Liberty Publishing Co., Inc.; 0-89709),* P.O. Box 298, P.O. Box 298, Cockeysville, MD 21030 (SAN 211-030X) Tel 301-667-6680; 50 Scott Adam Rd., Cockeysville, MD 21030 (SAN 658-1145).

Liberty Pubns FL, *(Liberty Pubns.; 0-938487),* 5677-D Fox Hollow Dr., Boca Raton, FL 33433 (SAN 661-2814) Tel 305-395-6640.

Libra, *(Libra Pubs., Inc.; 0-87212),* 4901 Morena Blvd., Suite 330, San Diego, CA 92117 (SAN 201-0909) Tel 619-581-9449.

Libra Pr, *(Libra Press),* 1842 S. Nugent, Lummi Island, WA 98262 (SAN 241-1326) Tel 206-758-2143.

Libra Press Chi, *(Libra Pr.; 0-938863),* 2610 W. Evergreen, Chicago, IL 60622 Tel 312-235-8363. Do not confuse with Libra Press, of Wataga, IL, Lummi Island, WA, Denver, CO.

Libra Pub IL, *(Libra Publishing Co.; 0-938335),* 1350 W. Elmdale Ave., Chicago, IL 60660 (SAN 661-3098) Tel 312-743-7573. Do not confuse with Libra Pub., Burlington. VT.

Library Admin, *(Library Administration & Management Assn.; 0-8389),* Div. of American Library Assn., 50 E. Huron St., Chicago, IL 60611 (SAN 233-4879) Tel 312-944-6780.

Library of America, *(Library of America, The; 0-940450),* 14 E. 60th St., New York, NY 10022 (SAN 286-9918) Tel 212-308-3360; Toll free: 800-631-3577; Dist. by: Viking-Penguin, Inc., 40 W. 23rd St., New York, NY 10010 (SAN 200-2442) Tel 212-337-5200.

Library of Armenian, *(Library of Armenian Studies; 0-910154),* 129 Robbins Rd., Watertown, MA 02172 (SAN 209-1232) Tel 617-924-8109.

Library Pr *Imprint of* Open Court

Library Reports, *(Library Reports & Research Service, Inc.(LRRS); 0-912717),* 4140 W. 80th Place, Westminster, CO 80030 (SAN 285-659X) Tel 303-429-3192.

Libro A C
See A C Libro Blackbird

Libros Latinos, *(Libros Latinos; 0-914369),* P.O. Box 1103, Redlands, CA 92373 (SAN 289-5226).

†Libs Unl, *(Libraries Unlimited, Inc.; 0-87287),* P.O. Box 263, Littleton, CO 80160 (SAN 202-6767) Tel 303-770-1220; *CIP.*

†Libty Bell Assocs, *(Liberty Bell Assocs.; 0-918940),* P.O. Box 51, Franklin Park, NJ 08823 (SAN 206-4405) Tel 201-297-3051; *CIP.*

Libty Comm Co
See Libty Comm Hse

Libty Comm Hse, *(Liberty Communications House; 0-934334),* 3331 Liberty St., St. Louis, MO 63111 (SAN 213-4128) Tel 314-351-2846.

Lichtner, *(Lichtner, Schomer; 0-941074),* 2626A N. Maryland Ave., Milwaukee, WI 53211 (SAN 223-1891) Tel 414-962-7519.

Lidiraven Bks, *(Lidiraven Bks.; 0-936162),* 14755 Ventura Blvd., Sherman Oaks, CA 91403 (SAN 213-9340) Tel 818-892-0059; Orders to: Jade Pubns., P.O. Box 5567, Sherman Oaks, CA 91413 (SAN 658-8891).

Lieba Inc, *(Lieba, Inc.; 0-941076),* 405 W. Franklin St., Baltimore, MD 21201 (SAN 217-3913) Tel 301-727-7333.

Lieber-Atherton, *(Lieber-Atherton, Inc.; 0-88311),* P.O. Box 875, 100 Water St., Brooklyn, NY 11202-0875 (SAN 202-5639) Tel 718-858-6928. *Imprints:* TPP (Teacher's Practical Press).

Liebling Pr, *(Liebling Pr.; 0-9613567),* P.O. Box 521124, Salt Lake City, UT 84152 (SAN 670-0519) Tel 801-485-1142.

Life Arts, *(Life Arts Publishing; 0-937894),* 116 Curryer S., Santa Maria, CA 93454 (SAN 220-0686).

Life Awareness, *(Life Awareness Pubns.; 0-936351),* P.O. Box 1077, Coronado, CA 92118 (SAN 697-8991); 921 Sixth Ave., San Diego, CA 92101 (SAN 698-228X).

Life Cycle Bks, *(Life Cycle Bks.; 0-919225),* P.O. Box 792, Lewiston, NY 14092-0792 (SAN 692-7173) Tel 416-690-5860.

Life Energy Media, *(Life Energy Media; 0-937725),* P.O. Box 93, Mill Valley, CA 94942 (SAN 659-2643) Tel 415-383-0332; 58 Madrone Pk. Cir., Mill Valley, CA 94941 (SAN 659-2651).

Life Enhancement *Imprint of* Human Kinetics

Life Enrich, *(Life Enrichment Pubs.; 0-938736),* Div. of Daring Publishing Group, Box 526, Canton, OH 44701 (SAN 215-9600).

Life Enrichment, *(Life Enrichment Pubns.; 0-936275),* 1222 Meredith Dr., Spring Hill, FL 33526 (SAN 699-7457) Tel 904-686-2926.

Life in Christ
See ACTA Found

Life in Hell, *(Life in Hell; 0-9615657),* 5371 Wilshire Blvd., No. 209, Los Angeles, CA 90036 (SAN 696-1541) Tel 213-935-8366; P.O. Box 36E64, Los Angeles, CA 90036 (SAN 696-9607); Dist. by: Bookpeople, 2929 Fifth St., Berkeley, CA 94710 (SAN 168-9517); Dist. by: Publishers Group West, 5855 Beaudry St., Emeryville, CA 94608 (SAN 202-8522) Tel 415-658-3453.

Life Ins Mktg Res, *(Life Insurance Marketing & Research Assn., Inc.),* P.O. Box 208, Hartford, CT 06141 (SAN 224-831X).

Life Lines, *(Life Lines; 0-932943),* Div. of Leadership Enrichment Ministries, P.O. Box 745, Rimrock, AZ 86335 (SAN 689-1624) Tel 602-567-5864.

Life Long Learn, *(Life-Long Learning Library),* P.O. Box 467633, Atlanta, GA 30346-7633 (SAN 209-0384).

Life Mgmt IL, *(Life Management Systems; 0-9606788),* 636 Church St., No. 419, Evanston, IL 60201 (SAN 223-1905) Tel 312-869-2775.

Life Office
See LOMA

Life Press, *(Life Pr.; 0-939317),* P.O. Box 17142, Portland, OR 97217 (SAN 663-1444); 7014 N. Albina Ave., Portland, OR 97217 (SAN 663-1452) Tel 503-285-3906; Dist. by: Living Love Pubns., 790 Commercial Ave., Coos Bay, OR 97420 (SAN 281-9082) Tel 503-267-4232.

Life Pubs Intl, *(Life Pubs. International; 0-8297),* 3360 NW 110th St., Miami, FL 33167 (SAN 213-5817) Tel 305-685-6334.

Life-Renewal, *(Life-Renewal, Inc.; 0-936221),* Hwy. 18 , P.O. Box 92, Garrison, MN 56450 (SAN 696-8422) Tel 612-692-4498.

Life Science, *(Life Science Institute; 0-9609802; 1-88697),* P.O. Box 1057, Ft. Pierce, FL 33454 (SAN 263-1830) Tel 305-466-1271.

Life Skills, *(Life Skills Training Assocs.; 0-9604510; 0-932723),* P.O. Box 48133, Chicago, IL 60648 (SAN 220-0694) Tel 312-986-0070.

Life Skills Pub Co, *(Life Skills Publishing Co.; 0-9615335),* P.O. Box 6043, Appleton, WI 54915 (SAN 695-1074) Tel 414-730-8488.

Life Survival Digest, *(Life Survival Digest, Inc.; 0-938811),* P.O. Box 3256, Austin, TX 76567 (SAN 661-5279); 222 Riverside Sq., Austin, TX 76567 (SAN 661-5287) Tel 512-444-1560.

Life Sustaining, *(Life Sustaining Press; 0-9608946),* 167 N. Eastman Ave., Los Angeles, CA 90063 (SAN 241-3310) Tel 213-265-4512.

Life Understanding, *(Life Understanding Foundation; 0-88234),* P.O. Box 30305,, Santa Barbara, CA 93130 (SAN 203-8390) Tel 805-682-5151.

Life Values Pr, *(Life Values Pr.; 0-915761),* 820 F Ave., Coronada, CA 92118 (SAN 293-8847) Tel 619-435-3851.

Lifeboat Pr, *(Lifeboat Pr.; 0-939563),* P.O. Box 11782, Marina Del Rey, CA 90295 (SAN 663-4303); 14010-c Marquesas Way, Marina Del Rey, CA 90295 (SAN 663-4311) Tel 213-305-1600.

Lifecareer Pr, *(Lifecareer Press),* 5350 Fairview Blvd., P.O. Box 90254, Los Angeles, CA 90009 (SAN 670-7238).

Lifecircle, *(Lifecircle Pubns.; 0-935815),* Affil. of Jonathan Miller Health, 333 Crain Ave., Kent, OH 44240 (SAN 699-6388) Tel 216-678-8582; Dist. by: New Leaf Distributing, 1020 White St. SW, Atlanta, GA 30310 (SAN 169-1449) Tel 404-755-2665; Dist. by: Awareness & Health Unlimited, 3110 N. High St., Columbus, OH 43202 (SAN 200-6537) Tel 614-262-7087.

LifeCom, *(LifeCom; 0-9615722),* 1248 N. 13th Ave., St. Cloud, MN 56301 (SAN 696-2572) Tel 612-252-9866Box 1832, St. Cloud, MN 56302 (SAN 662-3700).

Lifecraft, *(Lifecraft; 0-911505),* Box 1, Heisson, WA 98622 (SAN 264-1755).

Lifecycle Inc, *(Lifecycle, Inc.),* 6000 Bresslyn Rd., Nashville, TN 37205 (SAN 678-9072).

Lifeline, *(Lifeline),* 3500 N. Hayden Rd., No. 1705, Scottsdale, AZ 85251 (SAN 281-8817) Tel 602-941-8094; Orders to: 1421 S. Park St., Madison, WI 53715 (SAN 281-8825). Out of business.

Lifeline Pubs, *(Lifeline Pubs., Inc.; 0-930823),* P.O. Box 1045, San Pedro, CA 90733 (SAN 677-6620) Tel 213-833-8560.

Lifesigns, *(Lifesigns: Words & Images; 0-943510),* P.O. Box 663, El Cerrito, CA 94530 (SAN 240-7043) Tel 415-527-6722.

Lifestyle One, *(Lifestyle One; 0-9603016),* P.O. Box 630668, Miami, FL 33163 (SAN 213-1099). Moved, left no forwarding address.

Lifestyle Pr, *(Lifestyle Pr.; 0-9606860),* P.O. Box 3025, Bellevue, WA 98009-3025 (SAN 223-1913) Tel 206-868-9000.

Lifestyle Pubns, *(Lifestyle Pubns.; 0-937877),* 24396 Pleasant View Dr., Elkhart, IN 46517 (SAN 659-4778) Tel 219-875-8618.

Lifestyle Systems, *(Lifestyle Systems; 0-9615184),* P.O. Box 5031, Huntington Beach, CA 92615 (SAN 694-2202) Tel 714-964-3383.

†**Lifetime Learn,** *(Lifetime Learning Pubns.; 0-534),* Div. of Wadsworth Inc., 10 Davis Dr., Belmont, CA 94002 (SAN 211-7398) Tel 415-595-2350; Toll free: 800-354-9706; Dist. by: Van Nostrand Reinhold, 115 Fifth Ave., New York, NY 10003 (SAN 202-5183) Tel 212-254-3232; Orders to: VNR Order Dept., 7265 Empire Dr., Florence, KY 41042 (SAN 202-5191) Tel 606-525-6600; *CIP.*

Lifetime Pr, *(Lifetime Pr.; 0-931571),* Subs. of Royal Publishing, 137 Campbell Ave., Roanoke, VA 24011 (SAN 686-1636) Tel 703-982-1444.

Lifetime Pubns. *Imprint of Van Nos Reinhold*

Lifetouch Inc, *(Lifetouch Inc.; 0-9617259),* 400 Paramount Plaza, 7831 Glenroy Rd., Minneapolis, MN 55435 (SAN 663-480X) Tel 612-893-0500.

Light & Life, *(Light & Life Pr. (IN); 0-89367),* 999 College Ave., Winona Lake, IN 46590 (SAN 206-8419) Tel 219-267-7161; Toll free: 800-348-2513.

Light & Sound, *(Light & Sound Communications, Inc.; 1-55626),* 279 S. Beverly Dr., No. 1188, Beverly Hills, CA 90212 (SAN 661-3691) Tel 213-275-2469.

Light Bks
See DJS Ent

Light Hearted Pub Co, *(Light Hearted Publishing Co.; 0-916043),* Div. of Montgomery's Music, P.O. Box 150246, Nashville, TN 37215 (SAN 294-8648) Tel 615-776-5678.

Light Impressions, *(Light Impressions Corp.; 0-87992),* 439 Monroe Ave. P.O. Box 940, Rochester, NY 14603 (SAN 169-619X) Tel 716-271-8960; Toll free: 800-828-6216.

Light of Yoga
See Am Yoga Assn

Light Ventures, *(Light Ventures; 0-939453),* P.O. Box 820654, Houston, TX 77282-0654 (SAN 663-3765); 3103 Misty Pk., Houston, TX 77082 (SAN 663-3773) Tel 713-496-2735.

Light Work, *(Light Work Visual Studies, Inc.; 0-935445),* 316 Waverly Ave., Syracuse, NY 13210 (SAN 696-3072) Tel 315-423-2450.

Light&Life Pub Co MN, *(Light & Life Pub. Co.; 0-937032),* 3450 Irving Ave. S., Minneapolis, MN 55408 (SAN 213-8565) Tel 612-925-3888.

Lightbooks, *(Lightbooks; 0-934420),* P.O. Box 1268, Twain Harte, CA 95383 (SAN 214-400X).

†**Lighthouse Bks,** *(Lighthouse Bks.; 0-915889),* P.O. Box 700160, San Jose, CA 95170-0160 (SAN 294-0574) Tel 408-252-6361; *CIP.*

Lighthouse Enterprises, *(Lighthouse Enterprises; 0-933549),* P.O. Box 6361, Athens, GA 30604 (SAN 691-8727) Tel 404-549-4629.

Lighthouse FL, *(Lighthouse Pubns.; 0-9610648),* 1991 Linneal Beach Dr., Apopka, FL 32703 (SAN 695-1082) Tel 305-898-5498.

Lighthouse Hill Pub, *(Lighthouse Hill Publishing; 0-9608690),* 279 Edinboro Rd., Lighthouse Hill, Staten Island, NY 10306 (SAN 238-0706) Tel 718-987-7586.

Lighthouse Pr, *(Lighthouse Pr. Co., The; 0-917021),* 1308 Lewis, La Junta, CO 81050 (SAN 655-1262) Tel 303-384-8631.

Lighthouse Pr NY
See Lightyear

Lighthouse Pubns, *(Lighthouse Pubns.; 0-914055),* P.O. Box 2972, Mission Viejo, CA 92692 (SAN 287-508X) Tel 714-581-9184.

Lighthouse Trg Inst, *(Lighthouse Training Institute; 0-938475),* 702 W. Chestnut St., Bloomington, IL 61701 (SAN 661-3160) Tel 309-827-6026.

Lighthouse Writers, *(Lighthouse Writers Guild; 0-935125),* P.O. Box 51277, Pacific Grove, CA 93950 (SAN 695-1899) Tel 408-373-4998; 457 Pine St., Monterey, CA 93940 (SAN 695-1902).

Lightning Tree, *(Lightning Tree; 0-89016),* P.O. Box 1837, Santa Fe, NM 87504 (SAN 206-555X) Tel 505-983-7434.

Lighton Pubns, *(Lighton Pubns.; 0-910892),* 73223 Sunnyvale Dr., Twentynine Palms, CA 92277 (SAN 201-0917) Tel 619-367-7386.

Lightwave Inc
See Starseed Pubns

Lightway Pubns, *(Lightway Pubns., International; 0-938617),* Div. of Waldorff Corp., P.O. Box 570, Big Bar, CA 96010 (SAN 661-5740) Tel 916-623-6731.

Lightyear, *(Lightyear Pr., Inc.; 0-89968),* P.O. Box 507, Laurel, NY 11948 (SAN 213-1102); Dist. by: Buccaneer Books, Inc., P.O. Box 168, Cutchogue, NY 11935 (SAN 209-1542).

Ligonier Comm, *(Ligonier Sesquicentennial Commission; 0-9615431),* 300 S. Main St., Ligonier, IN 46767 (SAN 696-1444) Tel 219-894-3758; Dist. by: Taylor Publishing Co., 1550 Mockingbird Lnn., P.O. Box 597, Dallas, TX 75221 (SAN 202-7631) Tel 214-637-2800.

Liguori Pubns, *(Liguori Pubns.; 0-89243),* 1 Liguori Dr., Liguori, MO 63057 (SAN 202-6783) Tel 314-464-2500; Toll free: 800-325-9521 (Orders).

Lilmat Pr, *(Lilmat Pr.; 0-935401),* 3500 E. Fletcher Ave., Suite 509, Tampa, FL 33612 (SAN 696-3579) Tel 813-971-2781.

LIM Press CA, *(Lim Pr.; 0-942714),* P.O. Box 558, Belmont, CA 94002 (SAN 240-2424) Tel 415-591-9056.

Limberlost Pr, *(Limberlost Pr.; 0-931659),* P.O. Box 1563, Boise, ID 83701 (SAN 683-7212) Tel 208-344-2120.

†**Lime Rock Pr,** *(Lime Rock Press, Inc.; 0-915998),* Mount Riga Rd., Box 363, Salisbury, CT 06068 (SAN 208-2055) Tel 203-435-2236; *CIP.*

†**Limelight Edns,** *(Limelight Editions; 0-87910),* Div. of Proscenium Pubns., 118 E. 30th St., New York, NY 10016 (SAN 290-0068) Tel 212-532-5525; Toll free: 800-242-7737; *CIP.*

Limerick Pubns, *(Limerick Pubns.; 0-9612582),* P.O. Box 2104, Iowa City, IA 52244 (SAN 289-2952) Tel 319-337-3712.

Limestone Pr, *(Limestone Pr.; 0-919642),* 125 Southwood Dr., Vestal, NY 13850 (SAN 209-0120) Tel 813-548-7403.

Limited Ed, *(Limited Editions Press),* 2324 S. Highland Ave., No. 11, Las Vegas, NV 89102 (SAN 240-9623)5055 E Charleston, F110, Las Vegas, NV 89104 (SAN 669-1471) Tel 702-459-8475.

Limitless Light, *(Limitless Light Publishing Co.; 0-917913),* 8115-1 N. 35th Ave., Phoenix, AZ 85051 (SAN 657-0518).

Linch Corp
See Linch Pub

Linch Pub, *(Linch Publishing Inc.; 0-913455),* P.O. Box 75, Orlando, FL 32802 (SAN 285-1792) Tel 305-647-3025; Toll free: 800-327-7055 (national); Toll free: 800-434-0399 (FL); Orders to: 1950 Lee Rd., Suite 205, Winter Park, FL 32789 (SAN 693-9848); Dist. by: Ingram Industries, 347 Reedwood Dr., Nashville, TN 37217 (SAN 651-1163); Dist. by: Baker & Taylor Co., Eastern Div., 50 Kirby Ave., Somerville, NJ 08876 (SAN 169-4901); Dist. by: Baker & Taylor Co., Midwest Div., 501 Gladiola Ave., Momence, IL 60954 (SAN 169-2100); Dist. by: Baker & Taylor Co., Southeast Div., Mt. Olive Rd., Commerce, GA 30529 (SAN 169-1503); Dist. by: Baker & Taylor Co., Western Div., (SAN 169-4464).

Lincol Enter, *(Lincol Enterprises),* Box 10541, Eugene, OR 97440 (SAN 692-6398).

Lincoln Arc Weld, *(Lincoln, James F., Arc Welding Foundation; 0-937390),* P.O. Box 17035, Cleveland, OH 44117 (SAN 202-2443) Tel 216-481-4300.

Lincoln Coun Hist, *(Lincoln County Historical Society; 0-911443),* 545 SW 9th St., Newport, OR 97365 (SAN 293-2989) Tel 503-265-7509.

Lincoln-Herndon Pr, *(Lincoln-Herndon Pr., The; 0-942936),* 1 Old State Capitol Plaza, Suite 503, Springfield, IL 62701 (SAN 240-3188) Tel 217-522-2732; Dist. by: Baker & Taylor, Midwest Div., 501 Gladiola Ave., Momence, IL 60954 (SAN 169-2100); Dist. by: Distributors, The, 702 S. Michigan Ave., South Bend, IN 46618 (SAN 169-2488).

Lincoln Inst Land, *(Lincoln Institute of Land Policy),* 26 Trowbridge St., Cambridge, MA 02138 (SAN 209-2506) Tel 617-661-3016.

Lincoln Lib *Imprint of* **Frontier Pr Co**

Lincoln Pr MI, *(Lincoln Pr.),* 4610 Delemere Blvd., Royal Oak, MI 48073 (SAN 211-7401) Tel 313-549-1900.

Lincoln Pub, *(Lincoln Publishing; 0-918898),* 3434 Janice Way, Palo Alto, CA 94303 (SAN 209-6730) Tel 415-494-7448.

Lincoln's Leadership, *(Lincoln's Leadership Library; 0-89764),* 5902 E. Fourth Terrace, Tulsa, OK 74112 (SAN 215-675X).

Lind Grap Pubns, *(Lind Graphics Publications; 0-910389),* 192 Third Ave., Westwood, NJ 07675 (SAN 260-0951) Tel 201-666-7313.

Lindahl, *(Lindahl, Judy; 0-9603032),* 3211 NE Siskiyou, Portland, OR 97212 (SAN 210-6086) Tel 503-288-0772.

Lindahl *Imprint of* **Larksdale**

Lindberg Pub, *(Lindberg Publishing Co.; 0-9615993),* 2106 Live Oak Dr., E, Hollywood, CA 90068 (SAN 697-2837) Tel 213-856-9835.

Lindbrook Pr, *(Lindbrook Press; 0-942882),* P.O. Box 1082, 15243 la Cruz Dr., Pacific Palisades, CA 90272 (SAN 238-0692).

Lindell Pubs, *(Lindell Pubs.; 0-9604940),* P.O. Box 28, Bucks County, Springtown, PA 18081 (SAN 215-9619).

Linden Bks, *(Linden Bks.; 0-9603288),* Interlaken, NY 14847 (SAN 209-6692).

Linden Pub Fresno, *(Linden Publishing Co., Inc.; 0-941936),* 3845 N. Blackstone, Fresno, CA 93726 (SAN 238-6089) Tel 209-227-2901; Toll free: 800-345-4447.

Linden Pubs, *(Linden Pubs.; 0-89642),* 1750 N. Sycamore, Hollywood, CA 90028 (SAN 206-7218).

Linden Tree, *(Linden Tree, The; 0-937463),* 1204 W. Prospect, Cloquet, MN 55720 (SAN 658-9391) Tel 218-879-5727.

Lindenhof Pr, *(Lindenhof Press; 0-9609678),* P.O. Box 18513, Irvine, CA 92714 (SAN 262-7981) Tel 714-545-6984.

Lindisfarne Pr *Imprint of* **Inner Tradit**

Lindon Ent, *(Lindon Pubns.; 0-939820),* Box 1162, Southold, NY 11971 (SAN 216-9053) Tel 516-765-3584.

Lindsay News, *(Lindsay Newspapers, Inc.; 0-910713),* Postal Drawer 1719, Sarasota, FL 33578 (SAN 260-2172) Tel 813-746-2178.

Lindsay Pubns, *(Lindsay Pubns., Inc.; 0-917914),* P.O. Box 12, Bradley, IL 60915 (SAN 209-9462).

Lindys Golf, *(Lindy's Golf Course Guide; 0-9612636),* 5511 Dunsmore Rd., Alexandria, VA 22310 (SAN 289-2979) Tel 202-676-7197.

Line Drive, *(Line Drive Publishing),* 113 Pleasant St., Hanover, MA 02339 (SAN 663-4575) Tel 617-878-5035.

Lineal Cleworth
See Lineal Pub Co

Lineal Pub Co, *(Lineal Publishing Co.; 0-916628; 0-9612412),* 2425 E. Commercial Blvd., Ft. Lauderdale, FL 33308 (SAN 208-4848) Tel 305-776-7308; Toll free: 800-222-4253.

Linedrive MA
See Line Drive

Lingo Pubs, *(Lingo Pubs; 0-937145),* 21403 Chagrin Blvd., No. 106, Cleveland, OH 44122 (SAN 658-5760) Tel 216-991-5730.

Lingore Pr, *(Lingore Pr.; 0-9607146),* 123 Mayo St., Americus, GA 31709 (SAN 239-0051) Tel 912-924-4505; Dist. by: Charles E. Tuttle Co., Inc., P.O. Box 410, 28 S. Main St., Rutland, VT 05701-0410 (SAN 213-2621) Tel 802-773-8936.

Lingua Pr, (Lingua Pr.), P.O. Box 3416, Iowa City, IA 52244 (SAN 215-6083) Tel 319-338-9908.

Lingual Hse Pub, (Lingual House Publishing Co.; 0-940264), P.O. Box 3537, Tucson, AZ 85722 (SAN 220-3383) Tel 602-622-2366.

Linmore Pub, (Linmore Publishing Inc.; 0-916591), 409 E. South St., Barrington, IL 60010 (SAN 296-4503) Tel 312-382-7606; Orders to: P.O. Box 1545, Palatine, IL 60078 (SAN 662-2291) Tel 815-223-7499.

Linnaea, (Linnaea Graphics; 0-912467), Div. of Best Printing Co., 3218 Manor Rd., P.O. Box 1548, Austin, TX 78767 (SAN 265-2692) Tel 512-477-9733; Michael E. Arth, P.O. Box 13246, Austin, TX 78711 (SAN 688-4148).

Linnet Imprint of **Shoe String**

Linolean Imprint of **Larksdale**

Linstok Pr, (Linstok Pr., Inc.; 0-932130), 9306 Mintwood St., Silver Spring, MD 20901 (SAN 207-6195) Tel 301-585-1939.

Lint Head Pub, (Lint Head Publishing Co.; 0-9613713), Box 3625, Savannah, GA 31414 (SAN 677-1092) Tel 912-354-4933.

Lintel, (Lintel; 0-931642), P.O. Box 8609, Roanoke, VA 24014 (SAN 213-6325) Tel 703-982-2265; 100 Bleeker, Suite 17E, New York, NY 10012 (SAN 662-071X) Tel 212-674-1466.

Linwood Oregon, (Linwood Pr.; 0-9616942), 19076 S. Midhill Dr., West Linn, OR 97068 (SAN 661-7859) Tel 503-636-3772.

†Linwood Pub, (Linwood Pubs.; 0-943512), P.O. Box 70152, North Charleston, SC 29415 (SAN 240-7051) Tel 803-873-2719; CIP.

Linworth Pub, (Linworth Publishing, Inc.; 0-938865), P.O. Box 14466, Columbus, OH 43214 (SAN 662-5800); 2950 N. High St., Columbus, OH 43214 (SAN 662-5819) Tel 614-261-6584.

Lion
See Lion Bks

†Lion Bks, (Lion Bks.; 0-87460), Dist. by: Sayre Publishing, Inc., P.O. Box 1337, Scarsdale, NY 10583 (SAN 201-0925) Tel 914-725-2280; CIP.

Lion Ent, (Lion Enterprises; 0-930962), 8608 Old Dominion Ct., Indianapolis, IN 46231 (SAN 211-3678) Tel 317-243-8048.

Lion House Pr, (Lion Hse. Pr.; 0-914107), P.O. Box 791, Canby, OR 97013 (SAN 287-5101) Tel 503-263-6688.

Lion Lamb Pr, (Lion/Lamb Pr.; 0-9616424), 678 Santa Rosa Ave., Berkeley, CA 94707 (SAN 658-8557) Tel 415-528-3386; Dist. by: Bookpeople, 2929 Fifth St., Berkeley, CA 94710 (SAN 168-9517) Tel 415-549-3030; Dist. by: Inland Book Co., 22 Hemingway Ave., East Haven, CT 06512 (SAN 200-4151).

†Lion Pub, (Lion Publishing; 0-933301), 6602 El Cajon Blvd., No. B, San Diego, CA 92115 (SAN 692-3062) Tel 619-265-8777; CIP.

Lion Pubs, (Lion Pubs.; 0-936635), P.O. Box 92541, Rochester, NY 14692 (SAN 699-6841) Tel 716-385-1269; 19 Greentree, Pittsford, NY 14534 (SAN 699-685X).

Lion USA, (Lion Publishing; 0-7459), Subs. of Lion Publishing, UK, 1705 Hubbard Ave., Batavia, IL 60510 (SAN 663-611X).

Lionhart Inc Pub, (Lionhart, Inc., Pub.; 0-9617033), 440 Canoe Hill Rd., New Canaan, CT 06840 (SAN 662-8796) Tel 203-966-7255.

Lionhead Pub, (Lionhead Publishing/Roar Recording; 0-89018), 2521 E. Stratford Ct., Shorewood, Milwaukee, WI 53211 (SAN 206-5568) Tel 414-332-7474.

Lion's Head, (Lion's Head Publishing Co.), RR2 Box 92, Albion, IN 46701 (SAN 207-2564).

Lions Head Pr, (Lions Head Pr.; 0-934661), P.O. Box 5202, Klamath Falls, OR 97601 (SAN 694-0447) Tel 503-883-2101.

Liplop
See Goodfellow

Lipp Jr Bks, (Lippincott, J. B., Junior Bks.; 0-397), Div. of Harper Junior Bks. Group, 10 E. 53rd St., New York, NY 10022 (SAN 200-2086) Tel 212-207-7000; Toll free: 800-638-3030; 1700 Montgomery St., San Francisco, CA 94111 (SAN 215-3734) Tel 415-989-9000; Orders to: Keystone Industrial Pk., Scranton, PA 18512 (SAN 215-3742).

†Lippincott, (Lippincott, J. B., Co.; 0-397), Subs. of Harper & Row, Pubs., Inc., E. Washington Sq., Philadelphia, PA 19105 (SAN 201-0933) Tel 215-238-4200; Toll free: 800-523-2945; CIP. Imprints: Lippincott Medical (Lippincott Medical); Lippincott Nursing (Lippincott Nursing, Medical).

Lippincott Medical Imprint of **Lippincott**
Lippincott Nursing Imprint of **Lippincott**

LISP Co, (LISP Co., The; 0-924856), 430 Monterey Ave., Suite 4, Los Gatos, CA 95030 (SAN 697-2551) Tel 408-354-3668.

LISP Machine, (LISP Machine; 1-55530), 1000 Massachusetts Ave., Cambridge, MA 02138 (SAN 696-2904) Tel 617-876-6819.

Listen & Learn, (Listen & Learn; 0-938137), P.O. Box 2124, Reseda, CA 91335 (SAN 661-2156); 7242 Ariel Ave., Reseda, CA 91335 (SAN 661-2164) Tel 818-705-1745.

Listen USA, (Listen USA), 60 Arch St., Greenwich, CT 06830 (SAN 695-4839) Tel 203-661-0101; Dist. by: Hearst Corp., International Circulation Div., 250 W. 55th St., 12th Flr., New York, NY 10019 (SAN 169-5800).

Listeners Pr, (Listner's Pr.; 0-9616943), 75 Old Mill Rd., Rochester, NY 14618 (SAN 661-7840) Tel 716-244-8775; Dist. by: Adler Publishing Co., Panorama Plaza, Box 25333, Rochester, NY 14625 (SAN 285-6808) Tel 716-377-5804.

Lit Renewal
See Pulsante Assn News

Lit Vol Am, (Literacy Volunteers of America, Inc.; 0-930713), 5795 Widewaters Pkwy, Widewaters 1 Office Bldg., Syracuse, NY 13214 (SAN 225-3402) Tel 315-474-7039.

Litaruan Lit, (Litaruan Literature; 0-937557), 12949 W. 68th Ave., Arvada, CO 80004 (SAN 658-8603) Tel 303-431-4345.

†Literary Classics, (Literary Classics of the U. S., Inc.; 0-940450), 14 E. 60th St., New York, NY 10022 (SAN 217-1945) Tel 212-308-3360; Dist. by: Viking Penguin, Inc., 40 W. 23rd St., New York, NY 10010 (SAN 200-2442) Tel 212-337-5200; CIP.

Literary Sketches, (Literary Sketches; 0-915588), P.O. Box 711, Williamsburg, VA 23187 (SAN 205-6305) Tel 804-229-2901.

Literations, (Literations; 0-943514), P.O. Box 1845, Pittsfield, MA 01202 (SAN 240-706X) Tel 413-499-1459.

Lith Info Ctr, (Lithuanian Information Ctr.), Affil. of Lithuanian Catholic Religious Aid, 351 Highland Blvd., Brooklyn, NY 11207 (SAN 241-5542) Tel 718-647-2434.

Lith Inst Educ, (Lithuanian Institute of Education, Inc.; 0-936694), 5620 S. Claremont Ave., Chicago, IL 60636 (SAN 656-0512).

Lith Scouts, (Lithuanian Scouts Assn., Inc.; 0-9611488), 3300 W. 63rd Place, Chicago, IL 60629 (SAN 285-3485) Tel 312-476-1739.

Lithuanian Lib, (Lithuanian Library Press; 0-932042), 3001 W. 59th St., Chicago, IL 60629 (SAN 213-8166) Tel 312-778-6872.

Litlaw Found, (Litlaw Foundation, The; 0-9615761), 2339 Silver Ridge Ave., Los Angeles, CA 90026 (SAN 695-8729) Tel 213-662-6669; P.O. Box 26305, Los Angeles, CA 90026 (SAN 696-9569); Dist. by: Joe Christensen Inc., 1540 Adams St., Lincoln, NE 68521 (SAN 200-8009).

Litmus, (Litmus, Inc.; 0-915214), 350 S. Palouse, Walla Walla, WA 99362 (SAN 207-8619).

Litt Red Hen Pr, (Little Red Hen Press; 0-9612892), Rte. 2, Box 28, Mankato, MN 56001 (SAN 291-2546) Tel 507-947-3614.

†Little, (Little, Brown & Co.; 0-316), Div. of Time, Inc., 34 Beacon St., Boston, MA 02108 (SAN 200-2205) Tel 617-227-0730; Toll free: 800-343-9204; Orders to: 200 West St., Waltham, MA 02254 (SAN 281-8892); CIP. Imprints: Little Med Div (Little, Brown Medical Division).(Little, Brown Medical Div.)

Little Bayou, (Little Bayou Press; 0-9609804), 1735 First Ave. N., St. Petersburg, FL 33713 (SAN 272-085X) Tel 813-822-3278.

†Little Bks Co, (Little Bks. & Co.; 0-9604656), 5892 E. Jefferson Ave., Denver, CO 80237 (SAN 217-247X) Tel 303-758-1282; CIP.

Little Book, (Little Book Publishing Co., The; 0-9616080), 10 State St., Newburyport, MA 01950 (SAN 698-1364) Tel 617-465-9359; Dist. by: Globe Pequot Pr., Inc., Old Chester Rd., Chester, CT 06412 (SAN 698-1372).

Little Brick Hse, (Little Brick House, The; 0-9601648), 621 Saint Clair St., Vandalia, IL 62471 (SAN 209-2069) Tel 618-283-0024; Dist. by: Illinois State Historical Society, Old State Capitol, Springfield, IL 62701 (SAN 662-0728) Tel 217-782-4836.

Little Cajun
See Little Cajun Bks

Little Cajun Bks, (Little Cajun Bks.; 0-931108), Subs. of Edler Bks., 4182 Blecker Dr., Baton Rouge, LA 70809 (SAN 212-5250) Tel 504-292-8585.

Little Feat, (Little Feat; 0-940112), P.O. Box R, Mastic Beach, NY 11951 (SAN 217-0760) Tel 516-281-5661.

Little Glass, (Little Glass Shack; 0-911508), 3161 56th St., Sacramento, CA 95820 (SAN 201-0968) Tel 916-455-8197.

Little Gnome, (Little Gnome Delights; 0-9615584), Div. of Artmarx, Inc., P.O. Box 22582, Denver, CO 80222 (SAN 696-0499) Tel 303-758-7905.

Little Lady's Pr, (Little Lady's Press, Inc., The; 0-941356), P.O. Box 10, Park Ridge, IL 60068 (SAN 238-8928).

Little London, (Little London Pr.; 0-936564), 716 E. Washington, Colorado Springs, CO 80907 (SAN 214-0489) Tel 303-471-1322.

Little Med Div Imprint of **Little**

Little Nemo Pr, (Little Nemo Pr.; 0-9614451), 198 E. Seventh St., No. 12, New York, NY 10009 (SAN 689-3848) Tel 212-254-4779.

Little People, (Little People Productions; 0-910219), Kennedy Design Center, 111 S. Lincoln St., Warsaw, IN 46580 (SAN 241-3930) Tel 219-269-3823.

Little Red Hen, (Little Red Hen, Inc.; 0-933046), P.O. Box 4260, Pocatello, ID 83201 (SAN 212-7571) Tel 208-232-1847.

Little TX Pr, (Little Texas Press; 0-9613381), P.O. Box 218190, Houston, TX 77218 (SAN 670-7017) Tel 713-492-8997.

Littlebee, (Littlebee Press; 0-940674), 791 Boulevard E., Weehawken, NJ 07087 (SAN 239-4510) Tel 201-867-2595.

Littlebird, (Littlebird Pubns.; 0-937896), 126 Fifth Ave., New York, NY 10011 (SAN 215-7853).

†Littlefield, (Littlefield, Adams & Co.; 0-8226), 81 Adams Dr., Totowa, NJ 07512 (SAN 202-6791) Tel 201-256-8600; CIP.

Littlegreen
See Chris Pub UT

Littlegreen Imprint of **Chris Pub UT**

Littoral Develop, (Littoral Development Co.; 0-914770), 252 S. Van Pelt St., Philadelphia, PA 19103 (SAN 202-2427) Tel 215-546-3285.

Liturgical
See Liturgical Conf

Liturgical Conf, (Liturgical Conference, The; 0-918208), 806 Rhode Island Ave. NE., Washington, DC 20018 (SAN 205-6488) Tel 202-529-7400.

†Liturgical Pr, (Liturgical Pr.; 0-8146), Div. of Order of St. Benedict, Inc., St. John's Abbey, Collegeville, MN 56321 (SAN 202-2494) Tel 612-363-2213; CIP.

Liturgy & Art
See Monks of New Skete

LIU Univ, (Long Island Univ. Pr.; 0-913252), Univ. Plaza, Brooklyn, NY 11201 (SAN 211-688X) Tel 718-834-6064.

Liv Bibles Int'l, (Living Bibles International), 1809C Mill St., Naperville, IL 60540 (SAN 220-1461) Tel 312-369-0100.

Live Free, (Live Free, Inc.; 0-942470; 0-938326), P.O. Box 1743, Harvey, IL 60426 (SAN 209-830X); 1125 St. Lawrence Ave., Chicago, IL 60628 (SAN 662-0736) Tel 312-928-5830.

Live Oak Media, (Live Oak Media; 0-941078; 0-87499), P.O. Box 34, Ancramdale, NY 12503 (SAN 217-3921) Tel 518-329-6300; Overmountain Rd, Ancramdale, NY 12503 (SAN 669-1498).

Live-Oak Pr, (Live-Oak Press), P. O. Box 99444, San Francisco, CA 94109 (SAN 214-4026).

†Live Oak Pubns, (Live Oak Pubns.; 0-911781), 6003 N. 51st St., P.O. Box 2193, Boulder, CO 80306 (SAN 264-1798) Tel 303-530-1087; Orders to: Liberty Publishing Co., 50 Scott Adam Rd., Cockeysville, MD 21030 (SAN 211-030X) Tel 301-667-6680; CIP.

Lively Hills, (Lively Hills Publishing Corp.; 0-938194), P.O. Box 1186, St. Charles, MO 63301 (SAN 216-1559).

Lively Mind Bks, (Lively Mind Books; 0-9612746), P.O. Box 3212, Chapel Hill, NC 27514 (SAN 283-2984) Tel 919-929-2095.

Lively Pub
See Zest Pub

†Liveright, (Liveright Publishing Corp.; 0-87140), Subs. of W. W. Norton Co., Inc., 500 Fifth Ave., New York, NY 10110 (SAN 201-0976) Tel 212-354-5500; Toll free: 800-233-4830; CIP.

Livia Pr, (Livia Pr.; 0-933949), 967 Neilson St., Albany, CA 94706 (SAN 692-6770) Tel 415-526-3281.

Living Flame Pr, (Living Flame Pr.; 0-914544), P.O. Box 74, Locust Valley, NY 11560 (SAN 202-6805) Tel 516-676-4265.

Living Histori, (Living Historical Museum; 0-933960), 826 Goodrich Ave., St. Paul, MN 55105 (SAN 221-4199).

Living Legacies, (Living Legacies; 0-934371), P.O. Box 15007, San Antonio, TX 78212-8207 (SAN 693-5648) Tel 512-231-5217.

†Living Love, (Living Love Pubns.; 0-9600688; 0-915972), 700 Commercial Ave., Coos Bay, OR 97420 (SAN 281-9082) Tel 503-267-4232; Dist. by: DeVorss & Co., P.O. Box 550, Marina del Rey, CA 90291 (SAN 168-9886) Tel 213-870-7478; Dist. by: Bookpeople, 2929 Fifth St., Berkeley, CA 94710 (SAN 168-9517) Tel 415-549-3030; Dist. by: Inland Bk. Co., P.O. Box 261, East Haven, CT 06512 (SAN 200-4151) Tel 203-467-4257; Dist. by: New Leaf Distributing Co., 1020 White St., SW, Atlanta, GA 30316 (SAN 169-1449); Dist. by: Publishers Group West, 5855 Beaudry, Emeryville, CA 94608 (SAN 202-8522) Tel 415-658-3453; Dist. by: The Whole Health Bk. Co., 4735 Wunder Ave, Trevose, PA 19047 (SAN 200-6073) Tel 215-322-2880; Dist. by: The Distributors, 702 S. Michigan, South Bend, IN 46618 (SAN 169-2488) Tel 219-232-8500; Dist. by: Starlite Distributors, P.O. Box 20729, Sparks, NV 89515 (SAN 131-1921) Tel 702-359-5676; CIP.

Living Loving Learning Center, (Living Loving Learning Ctr.; 0-9613003), 1239 Barry Ave., No. 14, Los Angeles, CA 90025 (SAN 292-5753) Tel 213-473-8588.

Living Poets, (Living Poets Pr.; 0-915726), 139 Seventh Ave., Brooklyn, NY 11217 (SAN 207-3854) Tel 718-622-4900.

Living Skills, (Living Skills Pr.; 0-941510), P.O. Box 83, Sebastosol, CA 93472 (SAN 239-1082) Tel 707-823-5104; Dist. by: Institute of Living Skills, P.O. Box 1461, Fallbrook, CA 92028 (SAN 239-1090) Tel 619-728-6437.

Living Spring Pubns, (Living Spring Pubns.; 0-941598), 389 N. Los Robles, No. 2, Pasadena, CA 91101 (SAN 239-1112) Tel 818-795-2407; 790 Metro Dr., Monterey Park, CA 91754 (SAN 699-5403) Tel 818-572-9468.

Living Stone Pubs, (Living Stone Pubs.; 0-936637), 15851 Eighth, NE, Seattle, WA 98155 (SAN 699-6817); P.O. Box 55324, Seattle, WA 98155 (SAN 699-6825).

Living Way, (Living Way Ministries; 0-916847), c/o The Church on the Way, 14300 Sherman Way, Van Nuys, CA 91405-2499 (SAN 653-7820) Tel 818-786-7090.

†Livingston, (Livingston Publishing Co.; 0-87098; 0-915180), 18 Hampstead Circle, Wynnewood, PA 19096 (SAN 202-6821); Orders to: Harrowood Books, 3943 N. Providence Rd., Newtown Sq., PA 19073 (SAN 207-1622) Tel 215-353-5585; CIP.

Livingston County, (Livingston County Genealogical Society; 0-9616142), P.O. Box 922, Brighton, MI 48116 (SAN 699-8941) Tel 313-878-3680; 9040 Farley, Pinckney, MI 48169 (SAN 699-895X).

Livingston Pr, (Livingston Press; 0-915772), 30 Niantic River Rd., Waterford, CT 06385 (SAN 207-6802) Tel 203-442-3383; Orders to: Independent Pubs. Group, One Pleasant Ave., Port Washington, NY 11050 (SAN 207-6810).

LJB Found, (LJB Foundation), 933 Overlook Rd., Whitehall, PA 18052 (SAN 210-9107) Tel 215-433-7667.

LJC Bks Pr, (LJC Bks. Pr.; 0-937461), 421 Staten Ave., No. 301, Oakland, CA 94610 (SAN 658-9103) Tel 415-272-0672.

LJR Inc
See Futures Pub

LJT Asssociates
See Tracy Pub

LKA Inc, (Linju-Ryu Karate Assn., Inc.; 0-917098), Linick Bldg. 102, 7 Putter Ln., Middle Island, NY 11953-0102 (SAN 208-7375) Tel 516-924-3888.

Lkng Glass Pubns, (Looking Glass Pubns.; 0-936485), 1735 Willard St. NW, Suite 5, Washington, DC 20009 (SAN 698-0988) Tel 202-328-3555; P.O. Box 23691, l'Enfant Plaza Sta., Washington, DC 20026 (SAN 698-2522).

LL Co, (LL Co.; 0-937892), 1647 Manning Ave., Los Angeles, CA 90024 (SAN 203-0314) Tel 213-475-3664.

LLanerch Bks, (LLanerch Books), Box 711, Haverton, PA 19083 (SAN 208-4546).

Llewellyn
See Llewellyn Pubns

†Llewellyn Pubns, (Llewellyn Pubns.; 0-87542), Div. of Chester-Kent, Inc., P.O. Box 64383, St. Paul, MN 55164-0383 (SAN 201-100X) Tel 612-291-1970; Toll free: 800-843-6666; 213 E. Fourth St., St. Paul, MN 55101 (SAN 658-1161); CIP.

LLL Imprint of Intl Pubs Co

Lloyd & Lipow, (Lloyd, D. K., & M. Lipow; 0-9601504), c/o American Society for Quality Control, 230 W. Wells St., Milwaukee, WI 53203 (SAN 211-0318) Tel 414-272-8575.

Lloyd O'Ent Pubs, (LLoyd O'Enterprises/Publishers; 0-9609886), P.O. Box 6665, Woodland Hills, CA 91365 (SAN 272-0957) Tel 818-883-4058.

Lloyd Simone Pub, (Lloyd-Simone Publishing Co.; 0-938249), 32 Hillside Ave., Monsey, NY 10952 (SAN 661-3683) Tel 914-356-7273; Dist. by: Library Research Assocs., Inc., P.O. Box 41, Monroe, NY 10950 (SAN 201-0887) Tel 914-783-1144.

Lloyds London Pr, (Lloyd's of London Pr.; 0-907432), Div. of Lloyd's of London Pr. (UK), 817 Broadway, New York, NY 10003 (SAN 679-1778) Tel 212-673-4700.

Lloylds Pub, (Lloylds Publishing Co., Inc., The; 0-917113), Main St. Bldg. Drawer 544, New Milford, CT 06776 (SAN 655-7597) Tel 803-286-5555.

LLP Maritime
See Lloyds London Pr

LMI Books, (LMI Bks.; 0-9616921), 19 Eastbrook Bend, Peachtree City, GA 30269 (SAN 661-4841) Tel 803-862-4555.

LML Imprint of Intl Pubs Co
LNW Imprint of Intl Pubs Co
Locare
See Renovare Co

Lochinvar Imprint of Exposition Pr FL

Lockhart Pr, (Lockhart Pr., The; 0-911783), Box 1207, Port Townsend, WA 98368 (SAN 264-1801) Tel 206-385-6413.

Locus, (Locus, Bk. Div.; 0-943812), Div. of T-Track Security Systems, 4311 Atlantic Ave., Suite 200, Long Beach, CA 90807 (SAN 238-3128) Tel 213-426-2368.

Locust Ent, (Locust Enterprises; 0-9606730), W. 174 N. 9422, Devonwood Rd., Menomonee Falls, WI 53051 (SAN 219-6786) Tel 414-251-1415.

Locust Hill Pr, (Locust Hill Pr.; 0-933951), P.O. Box 260, West Cornwall, CT 06796 (SAN 693-0646) Tel 203-672-0060.

Lodestar Bks, (Lodestar Bks.; 0-525), Div. of E. P. Dutton, 2 Park Ave., New York, NY 10016 (SAN 212-5013) Tel 212-725-1818; Toll free: 800-526-0275; Dist. by: New American Library, P.O. Box 999, Bergenfield, NJ 07621 (SAN 206-8079) Tel 201-387-0600.

Lodima, (Lodima Press; 0-9605646), Revere, PA 18953 (SAN 216-1567) Tel 215-847-2005.

Loeffler
See Prod Hse

Loewenthal Pr, (Loewenthal Pr.; 0-914382), P.O. Box 1107, New York, NY 10009 (SAN 206-5576).

Loftin Pubs
See Tee Loftin

Log Boom, (Log Boom Brewing; 0-9604130), Box 1825, Boulder, CO 80306 (SAN 214-4034).

Logan Design, (Logan Design Group; 0-9603856), 12344 Addison St., North Hollywood, CA 91607-3610 (SAN 213-9359) Tel 818-761-2319.

Logan Enter, (Logan Enterprises Pub Co; 0-9613718), 4214 Loch Raven Blvd., Baltimore, MD 21218 (SAN 676-2905) Tel 301-433-2693.

Logan Hill, (Logan Hill Press; 0-918610), 204 Fairmount Ave., Ithaca, NY 14850 (SAN 207-5520) Tel 607-273-0707.

†Logbridge-Rhodes, (Logbridge-Rhodes, Inc.; 0-937406), P.O. Box 3254, Durango, CO 81302 (SAN 215-0905) Tel 303-259-3053; Dist. by: Inland Book Company, P.O. Box 261, Hemingway Ave., East Haven, CT 06512 (SAN 200-4151) Tel 203-467-4257; Dist. by: Small Press Distribution, 1814 San Pablo Ave., Berkeley, CA 94702 (SAN 204-5826) Tel 415-549-3336; CIP.

Logical Solns Tech, (Logical Solutions Technology, Inc.; 0-912253), 96 Shereen Pl., Suite 101, Campbell, CA 95008 (SAN 265-1602) Tel 408-374-3650.

Logical Sols
See Logical Solns Tech

Logos Imprint of Contemp Bks

Loiry-Bonner Pr
See Bonner Pr

†Loiry Pubs Hse, (Loiry Publishing Hse.; 0-9607654; 0-933703), 226 W. Pensacola St., No. 301, Tallahassee, FL 32301 (SAN 238-7883) Tel 904-681-0019; Dist. by: Baker & Taylor Co., Eastern Div., 50 Kirby Ave., Somerville, NJ 08876 (SAN 169-4901); Dist. by: Ingram Industries, 347 Reedwood Dr., Nashville, TN 37217 (SAN 169-7978); CIP.

†Loizeaux, (Loizeaux Brothers, Inc.; 0-87213), P.O. Box 277, Neptune, NJ 07754-0277 (SAN 202-6848); 1238 Corlies Ave., Neptune, NJ 07754-0277 (SAN 699-5411) Tel 201-774-8144; Toll free: 800-526-2796; CIP.

Lokman Pub Co, (Lokman Publishing Co.; 0-937105), Div. of Lenan Enterprises, P.O. Box 1731, Columbia, MO 65205 (SAN 658-6163) Tel 314-445-7007; Rte. 3, Box 436, Columbia, MO 65203 (SAN 658-6171).

Lola Library, (Lola Library Collection; 0-930825), 10348 La Canada Way, Sunland, CA 91040 (SAN 677-6108) Tel 818-352-0402.

Lollipop Bks Co
See Lollipop LA

Lollipop LA, (Lollipop Bks. Co.; 0-9615509), P.O. Box 26A41, Los Angeles, CA 90026 (SAN 696-4109) Tel 213-423-5355; P.O. Box 454, Ocean Shores, WA 98569 (SAN 662-7811).

Lollipop Power, (Lollipop Power, Inc.; 0-914996), Affil. of Cardina Wren Pr., P.O. Box 277, Carrboro, NC 27510 (SAN 206-9733) Tel 919-933-9679.

LOM Pr, (LOM Pr., Inc.;), 1 Plaza Pl., Suite 1008, St. Petersburg, FL 33701 (SAN 217-2453).

LOMA, (L O M A (Life Office Management Assn.); 0-915322; 0-939921), 5770 Powers Ferry Rd., Atlanta, GA 30327 (SAN 207-2548) Tel 404-951-1770; Orders to: Professional Bk. Distributors, 200 Hembree Pk. Dr., Roswell, GA 30076 (SAN 207-2556) Tel 404-442-8631.

Loma Linda U, (Loma Linda Univ. Medical Ctr.-Medical Library; 0-9615491), P.O. Box 2000, Loma Linda, CA 92354 (SAN 696-3927) Tel 714-824-0800.

Lomas Pub, (Lomas Publishing Co.; 0-932485), 625 Ellis St., Suite 301, Mountain View, CA 94043 (SAN 687-3987) Tel 415-965-3378.

Lomatewama, (Lomatewama, Ramson; 0-935825), 1953 Plaza Dr., Hotevilla, AZ 86030 (SAN 696-5881); P.O. Box 132, Hotevilia, AZ 86030 (SAN 699-637X).

Lomond, (Lomond Pubns., Inc.; 0-912338), P.O. Box 88, Mt. Airy, MD 21771 (SAN 206-765X) Tel 301-829-1496; Toll free: 800-443-6299.

Lond Pubns, *(Lond Pubns.),* Pomona, NY 10970 (SAN 208-127X).

London & Goldberg
See J M Goldberg

London Bkshop, *(London Bookshop Ltd.; 0-939281),* P.O. Box 10115, Ft. Dearborn Sta., Chicago, IL 60610 (SAN 662-7056); 1360 N. Lake Shore Dr., Chicago, IL 60610 (SAN 662-7064) Tel 312-642-8417.

London Hse Pr, *(London Hse. Pr.; 0-930171),* 1550 NW Highway, Park Ridge, IL 60068 (SAN 670-7262) Tel 312-298-7311.

London Pub, *(London Publishing Co.; 0-9613262),* 1725 DeSales St. NW, Suite 401, Washington, DC 20036 (SAN 296-5976) Tel 202-833-3875.

†**Londonborn Pubns,** *(Londonborn Pubns.; 0-930235),* P.O. Box 42278, San Francisco, CA 94101 (SAN 670-7297) Tel 415-485-5433; *CIP.*

Londonderry Pr, *(Londonderry Press; 0-901869),* 15 W. Mt. Vernon Pl., Baltimore, MD 21201 (SAN 295-1010) Tel 301-837-8558.

Lone Eagle Prods
See Lone Eagle Pub

†**Lone Eagle Pub,** *(Lone Eagle Publishing; 0-943728),* 9903 Santa Monica Blvd., No. 204, Beverly Hills, CA 90212 (SAN 293-3004) Tel 213-471-8066; Dist. by: Quality Bks., 918 Sherwood Dr., Lake Bluff, IL 60044-2204 (SAN 169-2127); Dist. by: Publishers Group West, 5855 Beaudry St., Emeryville, CA 94608 (SAN 202-8522) Tel 415-658-3453; *CIP.*

Lone Oak, *(Lone Oak Bks.; 0-936550),* 10101 Old Georgetown Rd., Bethesda, MD 20814-1857 (SAN 216-1540) Tel 301-656-3360; Dist. by: Book Carrier, 9121 Industrial Ct., Gaithersburg, MD 20877 (SAN 200-4046) Tel 301-258-1177; Dist. by: Publishers Group West, 5855 Beaudry St, Emeryville, CA 94608 (SAN 202-8522) Tel 415-658-3453.

Lone Star Bks *Imprint of* **Gulf Pub**

Lone Star Pr, *(Lone Star Pr.; 0-933551),* P.O. Box 165, Laconner, WA 98257 (SAN 691-8735) Tel 206-466-3377.

Lone Wolf Pub, *(Lone Wolf Publishing Hse.; 0-933303),* 555 Sutter, Suite 305, San Francisco, CA 94102 (SAN 692-3011) Tel 415-626-4386.

Lonely Planet, *(Lonely Planet Pubns.; 0-908086),* 1555D Park Ave., Emeryville, CA 94608 (SAN 659-6541).

Long Beach Isl Pr, *(Long Beach Island Press; 0-941418),* P.O. Box 151, Tempe, AZ 85281 (SAN 239-006X) Tel 602-968-1566.

Long Beach Pubns, *(Long Beach Pubns.; 0-941910),* P.O. Box 14807, Long Beach, CA 90803 (SAN 239-782X) Tel 213-439-8962.

Long Haul, *(Long Haul Pr.; 0-9602284),* P.O. Box 592, Van Brunt Sta., Brooklyn, NY 11215 (SAN 212-5986) Tel 718-965-3639; Dist. by: Inland Bk. Co., P.O. Box 261, 22 Hemingway Ave., East Haven, CT 06512 (SAN 200-4151) Tel 203-467-4257.

Long Hse, *(Long House, Inc.; 0-912806),* P.O. Box 3, New Canaan, CT 06840-2931 (SAN 201-4947) Tel 203-966-2931.

Long Range Planners, *(Long Range Planners Pr.; 0-9614410),* P.O. Box 60400, Pasadena, CA 91106 (SAN 688-6116) Tel 213-256-5823.

Long Shadow Bks *Imprint of* **PB**

Longanecker, *(Longanecker Books; 0-9601126),* P.O. Box 127, Brewster, WA 98812 (SAN 210-2323) Tel 509-689-2441.

Longfellow, *(Longfellow National Historic Site; 0-9610844),* Div. of National Park Service, 105 Brattle St., Cambridge, MA 02138 (SAN 265-2706) Tel 617-876-4491; Dist. by: National Park Service, 105 Brattle St., Cambridge, MA 02138 (SAN 200-7517) Tel 617-876-4491.

Longhorn Pr, *(Longhorn Press; 0-914208),* Box 150, Cisco, TX 76437 (SAN 206-6920) Tel 817-442-2530.

Longleaf Pubns, *(Longleaf Pubns.),* 809 Teague Dr., Tallahassee, FL 32315 (SAN 216-4094) Tel 904-385-0383.

Longman, *(Longman, Inc.; 0-582; 0-8013),* Subs. of Longman Group USA, Inc., 95 Church St., White Plains, NY 10601 (SAN 202-6856) Tel 914-993-5000. *Imprints:* Drumbeat (Drumbeat).

Longman Fin Serv Pub *Imprint of* **Longman Finan**

†**Longman Finan,** *(Longman Financial Services Publishing; 0-88462),* Subs. of Longman Group USA, Inc., 500 N. Dearborn St., Chicago, IL 60610 (SAN 201-3622) Tel 312-836-0466; *CIP. Imprints:* Ed Methods (Educational Methods); Longman Fin Serv Pub (Longman Financial Services Publishing); Real Estate Ed (Real Estate Education Company).

Longman Inc
See Longman

Longman USA
See Longman Finan

LongRiver Bks, *(LongRiver Bks.; 0-942986),* c/o Inland Bk. Co., 22 Hemingway Ave., East Haven, CT 06512 (SAN 240-3986).

Longshank Bk
See Longshanks Bk

Longshanks Bk, *(Longshanks Bk.; 0-9601000),* 30 Church St., Mystic, CT 06355 (SAN 208-7391) Tel 203-536-8656.

Longview Pub, *(Longview Publishing Co.; 0-940614),* P.O. Box 189, Longview, WA 98632 (SAN 218-5660) Tel 206-577-2504.

Longwood Cottage, *(Longwood Cottage Publishing; 0-9616338),* 101 Magnolia Oak Dr., Longwood, FL 32779 (SAN 658-8743) Tel 305-869-1689.

Longwood Pr
See Longwood Pub Group

Longwood Pub Group, *(Longwood Publishing Group, Inc. a; 0-89341),* 27 S. Main St., Wolfeboro, NH 03894-2069 (SAN 209-3170) Tel 603-569-4576; Toll free: 800-343-9444.

Longyear Res
See Marquette Cnty

Lonstein Pubns, *(Lonstein Pubns.; 0-87990),* 1 Terrace Hill, Box 351, Ellenville, NY 12428 (SAN 215-0913).

Looking Glass, *(Looking Glass Pubns.; 0-937646),* P.O. Box 3604, Quincy, IL 62305 (SAN 238-8936).

Looking Glass Pubns
See Lkng Glass Pubns

Loom Pr, *(Loom Pr.; 0-931507),* P.O. Box 1394, Lowell, MA 01853 (SAN 686-2780).

Loompanics, *(Loompanics Unlimited; 0-915179),* P.O. Box 1197, Port Townsend, WA 98368 (SAN 206-4421) Tel 206-385-5087.

Loon Pr, *(Loon Press; 0-9612638),* 10582 Barnett Valley Rd., Sebastopol, CA 95472 (SAN 289-3037) Tel 707-823-8411.

LoonBooks, *(LoonBooks; 0-910477),* P.O. Box 901, Northeast Harbor, ME 04662 (SAN 219-2098); Main St., Northeast Harbor, ME 04662 (SAN 662-0744) Tel 207-276-3693.

Looseleaf Law, *(Looseleaf Law Pubns. Corp.; 0-930137),* P.O. Box 42, Fresh Meadows Sta., Fresh Meadows, NY 11365 (SAN 686-6929) Tel 718-359-5559.

Loras Coll Pr, *(Loras College Pr.; 0-936875),* 14th & Alta Vista Sts., Dubuque, IA 52001 (SAN 699-9166) Tel 319-588-7164.

Lord Americana, *(Lord Americana & Research, Inc.; 0-914492),* 1521 Redwood Dr., West Columbia, SC 29169 (SAN 207-5261) Tel 803-794-7104.

Lord Byron Stamps, *(Lord Byron Stamps; 0-938139),* P.O. Box 4586, Portland, OR 97208 (SAN 661-2253); 808 NE 113th Ave., Portland, OR 97220 (SAN 661-2261) Tel 503-254-7093.

Lord John, *(Lord John Pr.; 0-935716),* 19073 Los Alimos St., Northridge, CA 91326 (SAN 213-6333) Tel 818-363-6621.

Lord Pub, *(Lord Publishing; 0-930204),* Div. of R.C. Ronstadt & Assoc., Inc., 46 Glen St., Dover, MA 02030 (SAN 210-5403) Tel 617-785-1575. *Imprints:* Case Pub (Case Publishing).

Lords Line, *(Lord's Line; 0-915952),* 1734 Armour Lane, Redondo Beach, CA 90278 (SAN 207-7086) Tel 213-542-5575.

Lore Pub, *(Lore Publishing; 0-911037),* P.O. Box 492, Times Square Sta., New York, NY 10036 (SAN 272-1058).

Lore Unlim, *(Lore Unlimited, Inc.; 0-941838),* 4850 Regents Park Lane, Fremont, CA 94538 (SAN 239-2534) Tel 415-657-6331.

Loren Bks, *(Loren Bks.; 0-939605),* P.O. Box 1205, Eugene, OR 97440 (SAN 659-3984); 4490 Inwood Ln., Eugene, OR 97405 (SAN 663-3196) Tel 503-343-2104.

Lorenz & Herweg, *(Lorenz & Herweg Pubs.; 0-916494),* P.O. Box 7764, Long Beach, CA 90807 (SAN 208-7405) Tel 213-422-0059. Out of business.

Lorenz Pr, *(Lorenz Press, Inc.; 0-89328),* Div. of Lorenz Industries, Subs. of International Entertainment Corp., 501 E. Third St., Dayton, OH 45401 (SAN 208-7413) Tel 513-228-6118; Dist. by: Independent Pubs. Group, 1 Pleasant Ave., Port Washington, NY 11050 (SAN 208-7421).

Lorian Pr, *(Lorian Pr.; 0-936878),* P.O. Box 663, Issaquah, WA 98027 (SAN 214-4042) Tel 206-392-3982; Dist. by: Bookpeople, 2929 Fifth St., Berkeley, CA 94710 (SAN 168-9517) Tel 415-549-3030; Dist. by: DeVorss & Co., P.O. Box 550, Marina del Rey, CA 90291 (SAN 168-9886) Tel 213-870-7478; Dist. by: Inland Bk. Co., 22 Hemingway Ave., East Haven, CT 06512 (SAN 200-4151) Tel 203-467-4257; Dist. by: Narada Distributors (Music Only), 1804 E. North St., Milwaukee, WI 53202 (SAN 200-7649).

Lorien Hse, *(Lorien Hse.; 0-934852),* P.O. Box 1112, Black Mountain, NC 28711 (SAN 209-2999) Tel 704-669-6211.

Lorrah & Hitchcock, *(Lorrah & Hitchcock Pubs., Inc.; 0-89809),* 301 S. 15th St., Murray, KY 42071 (SAN 220-7915).

Loru Co, *(Loru Co., The; 0-915710),* P.O. Box 396, North Webster, IN 46555 (SAN 220-7923).

†**Los Alamos Hist Soc,** *(Los Alamos Historical Society; 0-941232),* P.O. Box 43, Los Alamos, NM 87544 (SAN 276-9603); Dist. by: Univ. of New Mexico Pr., Journalism Bldg., Rm. 220, Albuquerque, NM 87131 (SAN 213-9588) Tel 505-277-2346; *CIP.*

Los Angeles, *(Los Angeles Children's Museum; 0-914953),* 310 N. Main St., Los Angeles, CA 90012 (SAN 289-310X) Tel 213-687-8226; Dist. by: Publishers Group West, 5855 Beaudry St., Emeryville, CA 94608 (SAN 289-3118) Tel 415-658-3453; Dist. by: Beyda & Associates, 6943 Valjean Ave., Van Nuys, CA 91406 (SAN 289-3126).

Los Angeles Mus Contemp, *(Los Angeles Museum of Contemporary Art, The; 0-914357),* 414 Boyd St., Los Angeles, CA 90013 (SAN 289-6583) Tel 213-621-2766.

Los Arboles Pub, *(Los Arboles; 0-941992),* 820 Calle de Arboles, Redondo Beach, CA 90277 (SAN 238-020X) Tel 213-375-0759; Orders to: P.O. Box 7000-54, Redondo Beach, CA 90277 (SAN 662-0752).

Los Ninos, *(Los Ninos International Adoption & Information Ctr.; 0-935366),* 1106 Randam Cir., Austin, TX 78745 (SAN 211-9129) Tel 512-443-2833.

Lost Cemetery Pr, *(Lost Cemetary Pr.; 0-9614826),* RFD Box 37, South Conway, NH 03813 (SAN 693-0034) Tel 603-447-8429.

Lost Pleiade, *(Lost Pleiade Press; 0-915270),* 4919 55th Ave. S., Seattle, WA 98118 (SAN 207-3358).

†**Lost Roads,** *(Lost Roads Pubs.; 0-918786),* P.O. Box 5848, Weybosset Hill Sta., Providence, RI 02903 (SAN 680-0564) Tel 401-941-4188; Dist. by: Small Pr. Distribution, 1814 San Pablo Ave., Berkeley, CA 94702 (SAN 204-5826) Tel 415-549-3336; Dist. by: Spring Church Bk. Co., P.O. Box 127, Spring Church, PA 15686 (SAN 212-7075); Dist. by: Bookslinger, 213 E. Fourth St., St. Paul, MN 55101 (SAN 169-4154) Tel 612-221-0429; Dist. by: Inland Bk. Co., P.O. Box 261, 22 Hemingway Ave., East Haven, CT 06512 (SAN 200-4151) Tel 203-467-4257; *CIP.*

†**Lothrop,** *(Lothrop, Lee & Shepard Bks.; 0-688),* Div. of William Morrow & Co., Inc., 105 Madison Ave., New York, NY 10016 (SAN 201-1034) Tel 212-889-3050; Toll free: 800-631-1199; Orders to: William Morrow & Co., Inc., Wilmor Warehouse, 6 Henderson Dr., West Caldwell, NJ 07006 (SAN 202-5779); *CIP.*

LOTIC, *(LOTIC Enterprises; 0-930531),* 5301-1 Dunsmuir Rd., Bakersfield, CA 93309 (SAN 679-1328) Tel 805-325-7348.

Lotsawa, (Lotsawa, Inc.; 0-932156), 140 E. 92nd St., New York, NY 10028 (SAN 213-893X) Tel 212-534-3384; Dist. by: Book Dynamics, 836 Broadway, New York, NY 10003 (SAN 169-5649) Tel 212-254-7798; Dist. by: Bookpeople, 2929 Fifth St., Berkeley, CA 94710 (SAN 168-9517); Dist. by: Devorss & Co., P.O. Box 550, 1046 Princeton Dr., Marina del Rey, CA 90294 (SAN 168-9886).

Lotus, (Lotus Pr., Inc.; 0-916418), P.O. Box 21607, Detroit, MI 48221 (SAN 213-8867) Tel 313-861-1280. Imprints: Penway Bks (Penway Books).

Lotus Light, (Lotus Light Pubns.; 0-941524), Affil. of Specialized Software, P.O. Box 2, Wilmot, WI 53192 (SAN 239-1120) Tel 414-862-2395.

Lotus Pr CA, (Lotus Pr.; 0-934373), P.O. Box 800, Lotus, CA 95651 (SAN 693-5664) Tel 916-626-1510.

Lotus Publishing, (Lotus Publishing; 0-9617249), 1609 1/2 S. Gramercy Pl., Los Angeles, CA 90019 (SAN 663-5628) Tel 213-731-1084.

Louis & Corsell, (Louis & Corsell, Inc.; 0-935339), 2049 Century Park E., Suite 1800, Los Angeles, CA 90067 (SAN 696-3056) Tel 213-277-0028.

Louis Found
See Touch Heart

Louisville & Jefferson, (Louisville & Jefferson County Heritage Corporation; 0-9603278), One Riverfront Plaza, Louisville, KY 40202 (SAN 213-3350) Tel 502-566-5000.

Louisville Mus, (Louisville Museum of History & Science), 727 W. Main St., Louisville, KY 40202 (SAN 655-7619).

Loup Valley, (Loup Valley Queen; 0-9615586), Box 278, Kimball St., Callaway, NE 68825 (SAN 695-9245) Tel 308-836-2244.

Louvin Pub, (Louvin Publishing Co.; 0-914471), 37 Crescent Rd., Poughkeepsie, NY 12601 (SAN 217-2496).

Love, (Love; 0-9608692), Box 9, Prospect Hill, NC 27314 (SAN 238-3136) Tel 919-562-3380. Do not confuse with Love Publishers of Denver, CO.

Love Agape Min, (Love Agape Ministries Press; 0-914605), Subs. of Love Ministries, Inc., P.O. Box 69, Worthville, KY 41098 (SAN 290-7054); 467 Sandalwood Dr., Lexington, KY 40505 (SAN 290-7062) Tel 502-732-6728.

Love in Bloom Pub, (Love in Bloom Publishing; 0-9616630), 23219 Collins St., Woodland Hills, CA 91367 (SAN 661-2091) Tel 818-992-8448.

Love-Jackson, (Love-Jackson Pubns; 0-9614315), P.O. Box 4504, Carmel, CA 93921 (SAN 687-5181) Tel 408-373-8309.

Love Pub Co, (Love Publishing Co.; 0-89108), 1777 S. Bellaire St., Denver, CO 80222 (SAN 205-2482) Tel 303-757-2579.

Love Pub LA, (Love Publishing; 0-939359), 225 Norcross, Bossier, LA 71111 (SAN 662-6793) Tel 318-746-7940. Do not confuse with Love Pub. Co., Denver, CO.

Love Pubns, (Love Pubns.; 0-9613731), 17075 SW Johnson, Beaverton, OR 97006 (SAN 677-4962) Tel 503-649-8763.

Love Song Mess Assn, (Love Song to The Messiah Assn., Inc.; 0-915775), 1609 N. Atlantic Blvd., Ft. Lauderdale, FL 33305 (SAN 293-8871) Tel 305-563-0697; Dist. by: Spring Arbor Distributors, 10885 Textile Rd., Belleville, MI 48111 (SAN 158-9016) Tel 313-481-0900; Dist. by: Living Books, 12155 Magnolia Ave., Bldg., 11-B, Riverside, CA 92503 (SAN 169-006X) Tel 714-354-7630.

Love St Bks Imprint of Marathon Intl Pub Co

Lovejoy Pr, (Lovejoy Press; 0-9614264), 501 E. Main Box 36, Wellington, IL 60973 (SAN 687-1429) Tel 815-984-3996.

Lovers Stinking, (Lovers of the Stinking Rose), 1621 Fifth St., Berkeley, CA 94710 (SAN 235-2273) Tel 415-527-5171.

Lovett Sch, (Lovett School, The (The Lovett Mothers Club), 4075 Paces Ferry Rd., Atlanta, GA 30327 (SAN 265-2714) Tel 404-262-3032.

Loving Pubs, (Loving Pubs.; 0-938134), 4576 Alla Rd., Los Angeles, CA 90066 (SAN 215-6768).

Low-Tech, (Lubin Press; 0-9605626), 30-73 47th St., Long Island City, NY 11103 (SAN 216-1583) Tel 718-721-0946.

Lowe Pub, (Lowe, Joseph D., Pub.; 0-9605506), 2537 Regent St., No. 302, Berkeley, CA 94704 (SAN 240-0227) Tel 415-843-6535.

Lowell Conf Ind Hist, (Lowell Conference on Industrial History, The; 0-9607478), 800 Massachusetts Ave., North Andover, MA 01845 (SAN 238-468X) Tel 617-686-0191.

Lowell Museum, (Lowell Museum Corp.; 0-942472), P.O. Box 8415, Lowell, MA 01853 (SAN 239-9423) Tel 617-459-1066.

†Lowell Pr, (Lowell Pr.; 0-913504; 0-932845), 115 E. 31st St., Box 411877, Kansas City, MO 64141 (SAN 207-0774) Tel 816-753-4545; CIP.

Lowell Pub, (Lowell Publishing Co., Inc.; 0-943730), P.O. Box 8515, Lowell, MA 01853 (SAN 241-0338).

Lowen Pub, (Lowen Publishing; 0-933051), P.O. Box 6870-12, Torrance, CA 90504 (SAN 689-7681) Tel 213-831-2770.

Lowenkamp Pub, (Lowenkamp Publishing Co.; 0-913667), P.O. Box 878, Hazelhurst, MS 39083-0878 (SAN 286-1682) Tel 601-894-2802.

Lower Cape, (Lower Cape Publishing; 0-936972), P.O. Box 901, Orleans, MA 02653 (SAN 214-4050) Tel 617-255-2244.

Lowie Mus, (Lowie, R. H., Museum of Anthropology), 103 Kroeber Hall, Univ. of California, Berkeley, Berkeley, CA 94720 (SAN 279-4381) Tel 415-642-3681.

Lowry & Volz, (Lowry & Volz, Pubs.; 0-9601740), 2165 Greenspring Dr., Timonium, MD 21093 (SAN 211-6219) Tel 301-252-7272.

Lowry Hill, (Lowry Hill; 0-9606416), 1770 Hennepin Ave., No 42, Minneapolis, MN 55403 (SAN 223-0062) Tel 612-374-1579.

Lowy Pub, (Lowy Publishing; 0-9602940), 5047 Wigton, Houston, TX 77096 (SAN 212-9132) Tel 713-723-3209.

Loyalty Mktg, (Loyalty Marketing Co., The; 0-9617002), 608 Fifth Ave., Suite 309, New York, NY 10020 (SAN 662-538X) Tel 212-794-0100.

†Loyola, (Loyola Univ. Pr.; 0-8294), 3441 N. Ashland Ave., Chicago, IL 60657 (SAN 211-6537) Tel 312-281-1818; Toll free: 800-621-1008; CIP.

Loyola LA Law, (Loyola Univ., Schl. of Law), 6363 St. Charles Ave., New Orleans, LA 70118 (SAN 226-3513).

Loyola U Crim, (Loyola Univ., Criminal Justice Dept.; 0-942854), 820 N. Michigan Ave., Chicago, IL 60611 (SAN 693-6962) Tel 312-670-2772.

Loyola U Ctr Urban, (Loyola Univ. of Chicago, Ctr. for Urban Policy; 0-911531), Div. of Loyola Univ. of Chicago, 820 N. Michigan Ave., Chicago, IL 60611 (SAN 264-1836) Tel 312-670-3112.

LRIS, (Learning Resources in International Studies; 0-936876), 777 United Nations Plaza, Suite 9A, New York, NY 10017 (SAN 281-8752) Tel 212-972-9877; Pubns. Office, Box 337, Croton-on-Hudson, NY 10520 (SAN 658-1110).

Lrn Res Network
See LERN

Lrn Technology, (Learning Technology, Inc.; 1-55641), 21 Charles St., Westport, CT 06880 (SAN 661-1281) Tel 203-227-7454.

Lrn Unltd Pr, (Learning Unlimited Pr.; 0-9617078), P.O. Box 801, Bow, WA 98232 (SAN 662-619X); 1215 Doser St., Edison, WA 98232 (SAN 662-6203) Tel 206-766-6258.

LSU Geosci Pubns, (Louisiana State Univ., Geoscience Pubns.; 0-938909), Louisiana State Univ., Dept. of Geography & Anthropology, Baton Rouge, LA 70803-4105 (SAN 661-7824) Tel 504-388-6245.

LSU Law Center, (Louisiana State University Law Center), Baton Rouge, LA 70803 (SAN 226-3521).

LSU Law Pubns, (Louisiana State Univ., Law Schl., Pubns. Institute; 0-940448), Paul M. Habert Law Ctr., Baton Rouge, LA 70803 (SAN 226-9910) Tel 504-388-8491.

LSU Paul M Hebert Law Cen Pub Inst
See LSU Law Pubns

Lubavitch Women, (Lubavitch Women's Organization; 0-930178), 770 Eastern Pkwy., Brooklyn, NY 11213 (SAN 210-6345) Tel 718-604-2785.

Lubin Pr, (Lubin Press; 0-9612396), 396 N. Cleveland, Memphis, TN 38104 (SAN 289-4114) Tel 901-278-0561.

Lubrecht & Cramer, (Lubrecht & Cramer, Ltd.; 0-934454), RD 1, Box 244 Rte. 42 Forestburgh Rd., Forestburgh, NY 12777 (SAN 214-1256) Tel 914-794-8539.

Lucas Comns, (Lucas Communications Group, Inc.; 0-9616276), 90 Dayton Ave., Passaic, NJ 07055 (SAN 658-6201) Tel 201-471-5980.

Lucas/Evans Bks, (Lucas/Evans Bks.; 0-937291), 1123 Broadway, Rm. 313, New York, NY 10010 (SAN 658-7526) Tel 212-929-2583.

Lucas Pubs CA, (Lucas Pubs.; 0-9604806), 58 Arden Way, P.O. Box 15224, Sacramento, CA 95813 (SAN 215-6776).

†Luce, (Luce, Robert B., Inc.; 0-88331), 425 Asylum St., Bridgeport, CT 06610 (SAN 201-1069) Tel 203-334-2165; Toll free: 800-243-2790; Orders to: 540 Barnum Ave., Bridgeport, CT 06608 (SAN 201-1077) Tel 203-366-1900; CIP.

Luce Pubs, (Luce Pubns.; 0-930827), 80 Wall St., Suite 614, New York, NY 10005 (SAN 677-6167) Tel 212-422-5186; P.O. Box 483, Wall St. Sta., New York, NY 10268 (SAN 692-6339) Tel 718-622-4163. Out of business.

Lucia Gallery, (Lucia Gallery; 0-9616961), 90 W. Houston St., New York, NY 10012 (SAN 661-6801) Tel 212-460-8739.

Lucian Pr, (Lucian Pr.; 0-9937297), Div. of Rouetel Systems, International, P.O. Box 490, Veradale, WA 99037 (SAN 658-8018) Tel 509-926-2763; E16304 Valleyway, Veradale, WA 99037 (SAN 658-8026).

Lucifer Inc, (Lucifer, Inc.; 0-935375), 5567 New Peachtree Rd., Atlanta, GA 30341 (SAN 696-3714) Tel 404-455-4245.

Lucis, (Lucis Publishing Co.; 0-85330), Div. of Lucis Trust, 113 University Pl., New York, NY 10003 (SAN 201-1085) Tel 212-982-8770.

Lucky Lit, (Lucky Literature; 0-9611860), P.O. Box 21043, Woodhaven, NY 11421 (SAN 286-1402) Tel 718-296-5252.

Lucky Star Imprint of Scholastic Inc

†Lucy Mary Bks, (Lucy Mary Bks.; 0-913829), P.O. Box 2381, Grand Junction, CO 81502 (SAN 286-1712) Tel 303-243-3231; CIP.

Lueth Hse Pub, (Lueth Hse. Publishing Co.; 0-937911), 1409 Ninth St., Aurora, NE 68818 (SAN 659-4808) Tel 402-694-3988.

LUISA Prods, (LUISA Productions; 0-939584), P.O. Box 6836-AB, Santa Barbara, CA 93111 (SAN 216-4108).

†Lukas & Sons, (Lukas & Sons Pubs.; 0-930994), 4179 Fairmount Ave., San Diego, CA 92105 (SAN 211-2507); CIP.

Luker Vera
See V Luker

Lumeli Pr, (Lumeli Press; 0-930592), P.O. Box 555, Gonzales, CA 93926 (SAN 211-0326).

Lumen Christi, (Lumen Christi Pr.; 0-912414), P.O. Box 13176, Houston, TX 77019 (SAN 201-1093) Tel 713-827-0181.

Lumen Inc, (Lumen, Inc.; 0-930829), 446 W. 20th St., New York, NY 10011 (SAN 219-4430) Tel 212-989-7944; Dist. by: Bookslinger, 213 E. Fourth St., Saint Paul, MN 55101 (SAN 169-4154) Tel 612-221-0429; Dist. by: Inland Bk. Co., 22 Hemingway Ave., East Haven, CT 06512 (SAN 200-4151) Tel 203-467-4257.

Lumen Series, (Lumen Series; 0-9611722), 1310 Highland Glen Rd., Westwood, MA 02090 (SAN 285-3183) Tel 617-329-9388.

Luna Bisonte, (Luna Bisonte Productions; 0-935350), 137 Leland Ave., Columbus, OH 43214 (SAN 209-8326) Tel 614-846-4126.

Luna Pubns, (Luna Pubns.; 0-930346), 655 Orchard St., Oradell, NJ 07649 (SAN 212-288X).

Lunan-Ferguson, (Lunan-Ferguson Library, Pubs.; 0-911724), 2219 Clement St., San Francisco, CA 94121 (SAN 203-4042) Tel 415-752-6100.

Lunar & Planet Inst, (Lunar & Planetary Institute; 0-942862), 3303 Nasa Rd. One, Houston, TX 77058 (SAN 238-0730) Tel 713-486-2143.

Lunchroom Pr, (Lunchroom Pr., The; 0-938136), Box 36027, Grosse Pointe, MI 48236 (SAN 215-6784).

Lundberg
See J Johnson

Lupine Pubns, (Lupine Pubns.; 0-933743), 808 Avoca, No. 9, Sheridan, WY 82801 (SAN 692-5987) Tel 307-674-8059.

LuraMedia, (LuraMedia; 0-931055), P.O. Box 261668, 10227 Autumnview Ln., San Diego, CA 92126 (SAN 678-9234) Tel 619-578-1948; 136 Roumfort Rd., C/O Marcia Broucek, Philadelphia, PA 19119 (SAN 662-2542) Tel 215-247-4085.

Luso-Brazilian Bks, (Luso-Brazilian Bks.; 0-85051), Times Plaza Sta., Box 286, Brooklyn, NY 11213 (SAN 695-4847).

Lust, (Lust, Benedict, Pubns.; 0-87904), 25 Dewart Rd., Greenwich, CT 06830 (SAN 201-1107) Tel 203-661-0980; Orders to: P.O. Box 404, New York, NY 10156 (SAN 201-1115).

†Lustrum Pr, (Lustrum Pr.; 0-912810), 714 Broadway, New York, NY 10003 (SAN 281-9562); Dist. by: Kampmann & Co., 9 E. 40th St., New York, NY 10016 (SAN 202-5183) Tel 212-685-2928; CIP.

Luth Acad, (Lutheran Academy for Scholarship; 0-913160), c/o Richard Jungkuntz, 6310 Hillcrest Dr., SW, Tacoma, WA 98499 (SAN 285-0451).

Luth Bd of Pubn
See Bd of Pubn LCA

Luth Coun IL, (Lutheran Council in the U.S.A., Div. of Campus Ministries; 0-9609438), Div. of Lutheran Council in the U.S.A., 35 E. Wacker Dr., Suite 1847, Chicago, IL 60601 (SAN 272-135X) Tel 312-332-1387.

Lutheran Church Wmn, (Lutheran Church Women), 2900 Queen Lane, Philadelphia, PA 19129 (SAN 225-4611) Tel 215-438-2200.

Lutheran Coun US, (Lutheran Council in the U.S.A.; 0-9609438), 360 Park Ave. S., New York, NY 10010 (SAN 225-462X) Tel 212-532-6350.

Lutheran Womens, (Lutheran Women's Missionary League; 0-9614955), 3558 S. Jefferson Ave., St. Louis, MO 63118 (SAN 693-7454) Tel 314-664-7000.

Lux Natura, (Lux Natura; 0-937727), 5000 Bohemian Hwy., Occidental, CA 95465 (SAN 659-2732) Tel 707-874-3147.

LWK Ent, (LWK Enterprises; 0-931733), P.O. Box 1127, Newark, DE 19715 (SAN 687-6234) Tel 302-737-3698.

LWV MN, (League of Women Voters of Minnesota; 0-939816), 555 Wabasha St., Suite 212, St. Paul, MN 55102 (SAN 216-9045) Tel 612-224-5445.

LWV NYC, (League of Women Voters of the City of New York; 0-916130), 817 Broadway, New York, NY 10003 (SAN 207-2602) Tel 212-677-5050.

†LWV NYS, (League of Women Voters of New York State; 0-938588), 817 Broadway, New York, NY 10003 (SAN 216-1591) Tel 212-677-5050; CIP.

LWV US, (League of Women Voters of the U. S.; 0-89959), 1730 M St. NW, Washington, DC 20036 (SAN 207-5288) Tel 202-429-1965.

LWVP Ed Fund
See LWVPA

†LWVPA, (League of Women Voters of Pennsylvania; 0-931370), Strawbridge & Clothier, Eighth & Market Sts., Philadelphia, PA 19105 (SAN 207-0588) Tel 215-627-7937; CIP.

LYCO Pub, (LYCO Publishing), 3636 Drummond, Houston, TX 77025 (SAN 240-9631) Tel 713-668-0194.

Lydette, (Lydette Publishing Co.; 0-910918), P.O. Box 654, Cedar Falls, IA 50613 (SAN 203-9400) Tel 319-266-7578.

LYFE Foundation, (LYFE Foundation; 0-9616418), 2131 E. Broadway Rd., Suite 19, Tempe, AZ 85282 (SAN 658-8913) Tel 602-968-1219.

†Lyle Stuart, (Stuart, Lyle, Inc.; 0-8184), Div. of Citadel, 120 Enterprise Ave., Secaucus, NJ 07094 (SAN 201-1131) Tel 201-866-0490; Toll free: 800-LS-BOOKS; CIP.

Lyman Co Herald, (Lyman County Herald), Presho, SD 57568 (SAN 693-7802).

Lymelite Group, (Lymelite Group, Inc.; 0-9615796), 105 W. 72nd St., New York, NY 10116 (SAN 696-5997) Tel 212-787-0352.

Lymlite Group
See Lymelite Group

Lyn-Bar Pub, (Lyn-Bar Publishing Group; 0-938069), 69 Lillie St., Princeton Junction, NJ 08550 (SAN 661-1923) Tel 609-799-1476.

Lyn-Von Enter, (Lyn-Von Enterprises; 0-937151), 1515 Summit St., Suite 3, Portsmouth, OH 45662 (SAN 658-5736) Tel 614-353-0650.

Lyncean Pr, (Lyncean Press; 0-9614229), 16695 NW Yorktown Dr., Beaverton, OR 97006 (SAN 686-774X) Tel 503-629-8522; Dist. by: Quality Books, 918 Sherwood Dr., Lake Bluff, IL 60044-2204 (SAN 169-2127).

Lynch Bros Ent, (Lynch Brothers Enterprises, Inc.; 0-9617150), 3224 Timmons Ln. 125, Houston, TX 77027 (SAN 663-1525) Tel 713-840-0013.

Lynch Group Pub, (Lynch Group Publishing; 0-911671), P.O. Box 18012, Cleveland, OH 44118 (SAN 264-1852).

†Lynne Rienner, (Rienner, Lynne, Pubs., Inc.; 0-931477; 1-55587), 948 North St., No. 8, Boulder, CO 80302 (SAN 683-1869) Tel 303-444-6684; CIP.

†Lynx Hse, (Lynx House Press; 0-89924), P.O. Box 800, Amherst, MA 01002 (SAN 208-2691) Tel 413-665-3604; CIP.

Lyon Prods, (Lyon Productions; 0-933953), 44 Monterey Blvd., Suite 39, San Francisco, CA 94131 (SAN 693-0670) Tel 415-469-0175.

Lyons Busn & Pro, (Lyons Business & Professional Assn.; 0-9615472), 123 Main Ave., Clinton, IA 52732 (SAN 661-5406).

Lyric Pub Co, (Lyric Publishing Co.; 0-931453), 7826 Crenshaw Blvd., Los Angeles, CA 90043 (SAN 683-1842) Tel 213-778-7600.

Lyrica, (Lyrica; 0-937129), 90 Church St., Guilford, CT 06437 (SAN 658-571X) Tel 203-453-1503.

Lytton Pub, (Lytton Publishing Co.; 0-915728), Box 1212, Sandpoint, ID 83864 (SAN 204-4257) Tel 208-263-3564.

LZB Pub, (LZB Publishing Co.; 0-9615899), 102 SE 44th, Portland, OR 97215 (SAN 696-9828) Tel 503-232-0972.

M A Bauer, (Bauer, Mary Anne, Productions; 0-9613619), 7311 SE 31st St., Portland, OR 97202 (SAN 671-0085) Tel 503-777-0373.

M A Fenton, (Fenton, Mark A.; 0-9616217), 4808 Colfax Ave. S, Minneapolis, MN 55409 (SAN 658-3644) Tel 612-822-7314.

M A Greer, (Greer/Martha A.; 0-9617179), 2710 Woodscrest Ave., Lincoln, NE 68502 (SAN 663-186X) Tel 402-435-2710.

M A Lawrence, (Lawrence, Mark A.; 0-9616610), 6323 Navarre Rd., SW, Navarre, OH 44662 (SAN 661-4035) Tel 216-837-4430.

M A Little, (Little, Mark A.; 0-9613783), 8842 N. Winding Way, Fair Oaks, CA 95628 (SAN 678-9838) Tel 916-965-0952.

M A Lynes, (Lynes, Martha A.; 0-9616631), 1 Bancroft Rd., Wellesley, MA 02181 (SAN 661-2105) Tel 617-237-2450.

M-A Pr
See Dilithium Pr

M A R, (M.A.R.; 0-9611996), 6835 27th Ave. NE, Seattle, WA 98115 (SAN 286-813X) Tel 206-525-5583.

M A Rucks, (Rucks, Meta A.; 0-9613402), Rte. 3 Box 115, S. Haven, MN 55382 (SAN 670-7203).

M A Salant, (Salant, Michael Alan; 0-9609288), 2412 19th St. NW Apt. 9, Washington, DC 20009-1552 (SAN 260-129X) Tel 202-332-2368; Orders to: P.O. Box 33421, Farragut Sta., Washington, DC 20033-0421 (SAN 200-2760).

M A Seguin, (Seguin, Mary A.; 0-9616951), 145 S. First Ave., Alpena, MI 49707 (SAN 661-7336) Tel 517-356-1481.

M Akers, (Akers, Mona J. Coole; 0-912706), 219 S. Williams St., Denver, CO 80209 (SAN 206-9075) Tel 303-722-1892.

M & A Edns, (M & A Editions; 0-913983), Rte. 5, P.O. Box 332, San Antonio, TX 78211 (SAN 286-7877) Tel 512-628-1440.

M & A Products, (Machinery & Allied Products Institute), 1200 18th St., NW., Washington, DC 20036 (SAN 205-8014).

M & B Fulfillment, (M & B Fulfillment Services), 540 Barnum Ave., Bridgeport, CT 06610 (SAN 282-6062) Tel 203-366-1900.

M & H Enter, (M & H Enterprises; 0-936997), P.O. Box 26374, Sacramento, CA 95826 (SAN 658-3180) Tel 916-366-1053; 9230 Elmgrove Ct., Sacramento, CA 95826 (SAN 658-3199).

M & L Sales, (M & L Sales), P.O. Box 467702, Atlanta, GA 30346 (SAN 693-0409) Tel 404-394-5506.

M and R Pubns, (M & R Pubns.; 0-9607424), P.O. Box 2056, Turlock, CA 95381 (SAN 239-7838) Tel 209-892-6282.

M & S Ent, (M&S Enterprises; 0-943732), Box 42978, Tucson, AZ 85733 (SAN 241-0346) Tel 602-746-7154. Out of business.

M & T Pub Inc, (M & T Publishing, Inc.; 0-934375), 501 Galveston Dr., Redwood City, CA 94063 (SAN 210-4830) Tel 415-366-3600.

M & W Inc, (Marcon & Worthington Inc.; 0-911529), P.O. Box 760, Locust Grove, VA 22508 (SAN 264-5076) Tel 703-972-2951.

M Anthony Pubns, (Michael Anthony Pubns.; 0-9615979), 11365 SW Ironwood Loop, Tigard, OR 97223 (SAN 698-1704) Tel 503-620-0872.

M Arman, (Arman, M., Pub. Inc.; 0-933078), P.O. Box 785, Ormond Beach, FL 32074 (SAN 293-230X) Tel 904-673-5576; Orders to: 28 N. Ridgewood Ave., Rio Vista, Ormond Beach, FL 32074 (SAN 293-2318).

M B Hall
See Veritat Found

M B Hinman, (Hinman, Marjory B.), P. O. Box 345, Windsor, NY 13865 (SAN 208-1237) Tel 607-655-3174.

M B Pub, (M B Publishing; 0-932543), P.O. Box 12, Hugo, OK 74743 (SAN 687-4827) Tel 405-326-2677.

M B Stone, (Stone, Michael B.; 0-9603448), 8434 55th Ave. S., Seattle, WA 98118 (SAN 213-5973).

M B Zucker, (Zucker, Marjorie B.; 0-9604260), 333 Central Park W., New York, NY 10025 (SAN 211-335X).

M Bergerie, (Bergerie, Maurine; 0-9604234), 201 Pollard Ave., New Iberia, LA 70560 (SAN 214-2848).

M Berman, (Berman, Morris, Studio, Inc.; 0-939197), 1170 Broadway, Suite 410, New York, NY 10001 (SAN 662-9008) Tel 212-213-5960.

M Bibb, (Bibb, Mary; 0-9608778), 1002 Fall Dr. NE, Grants Pass, OR 97526 (SAN 238-0420) Tel 503-474-2581.

M Biggs, (Biggs, Marge; 0-9603218), 12475 Willet, Grand Terrace, CA 92324 (SAN 213-2400).

M Boyars
See M Boyars Pubs

†M Boyars Pubs, (Boyars, Marion, Pubs., Inc.; 0-7145; 0-905223; 0-906890), 262 W. 22nd St., New York, NY 10011 (SAN 284-981X) Tel 212-807-6574; Dist. by: Kampmann & Co., Inc., 9 E. 40th St., New York, NY 10016 (SAN 201-002X) Tel 212-685-2928; CIP.

M Boyle Pub, (Boyle, Michael, Publisher; 0-911097), 155 Afleck St., Hartford, CT 06106 (SAN 268-4284) Tel 203-728-3828.

M Brinser
See Timberwood

M Buber Pr, (Buber, Martin, Press), G.P.O. Box 2009, Brooklyn, NY 11202 (SAN 212-7318).

M Burk, (Burk, Margaret; 0-937806), P.O. Box 22, Ambassador Sta., Los Angeles, CA 90070 (SAN 214-2880).

M C Clausen, (Clausen, Muriel C.; 0-9603664), 780 W. Grand Ave., Oakland, CA 94612 (SAN 213-7305).

M C H S, (Morris County Historical Society; 0-910301), P.O. Box 170 M, Morristown, NJ 07960 (SAN 241-4104) Tel 201-267-3465.

M C I Pub, (M C I Publishing; 0-911445), P.O. Box 162, Winfield, IL 60190 (SAN 272-2968) Tel 312-858-7004.

M C Michaels, (Michaels, M. C., Enterprises; 0-9616182), 1720 Elm St., Fairfield, CA 94533 (SAN 699-9786) Tel 707-422-0758.

M C Mosley, (Mosley, Marilyn C.; 0-9614850), Rt. 1 Box 862, Vashon, WA 98070 (SAN 693-0972) Tel 206-567-4751.

M-C Pubns, (M-C Pubns.; 0-9603850), 449 N. Lamer St., Burbank, CA 91506 (SAN 214-0500).

M C Ullrich, (Ullrich, Marion Chambers, Pub.; 0-9617091), 3340 Ingelow St., San Diego, CA 92106 (SAN 662-6319) Tel 619-224-1425.

M C Winchester, (Winchester, M. C., Publishing; 0-9616703), P.O. Box 817, Hermosa Beach, CA 90254 (SAN 659-9354) Tel 213-212-6580; Dist. by: Nuth Bks., P.O. Box 5793, Denver, CO 80217 (SAN 200-6596).

M Cain, *(Cain, Mike; 0-9601458)*, 192 Terra Manor Dr., Wintersville, OH 43952 (SAN 211-2221) Tel 614-264-3687.

M Calvert, *(Calvert, Mary; 0-9609914)*, Lincoln St., East Boothbay, ME 04544 (SAN 268-6120) Tel 207-633-3693.

M Cavendish Corp
See Marshall Cavendish

M Clark, *(Clark, Merrian E.; 0-910384)*, 22151 Clarendon St., P.O. Box 505, Woodland Hills, CA 91365 (SAN 203-9419) Tel 818-347-1677.

M Corrieri, *(Corrieri, Michael, Jr.; 0-9615686)*, 19 Russell St., Lockport, NY 14094 (SAN 696-4044) Tel 716-433-8897; Orders to: Corrieri Home Inspections, P.O. Box 3262, Lockport, NY 14094 (SAN 662-3735).

M D E A, *(MDEA Pr.; 0-9614629)*, 79 Knollwood Dr., Newport, VA 23602 (SAN 691-8948) Tel 804-877-1172.

M D Miller, *(Miller, M. Dolly; 0-9613120)*, P.O. Box 26610, Tempe, AZ 85282 (SAN 294-6157) Tel 602-968-6629.

M D Weiss Pub, *(Weiss, Martin D., Publishing; 0-9613048)*, Div. of Martin D. Weiss Research, Inc., 5656 Corporate Way, West Palm Beach, FL 33407 (SAN 294-2925) Tel 305-684-8100.

M Damien Pubs, *(M. Damien Pubs.; 0-930539)*, 4810 Mahalo Dr., Eugene, OR 97405 (SAN 677-0975) Tel 503-687-9055; Dist. by: Publishers Group West, 5855 Beaudry St., Emeryville, CA 94608 (SAN 202-8522) Tel 415-658-3453; Dist. by: Pacific Pipeline Inc., 19215 66th Ave. S., Kent, WA 98032 (SAN 208-2128) Tel 206-872-5523; Dist. by: Quality Bks., Inc., 918 Sherwood Dr., Lake Bluff, IL 60044-2204 (SAN 169-2127).

M Demou & Assocs, *(Demou, Morris, & Assocs.; 0-9604794)*, 2013 Big Oak Dr., Burnsville, MN 55337 (SAN 209-1798) Tel 612-890-3579.

M E Becraft, *(Becraft, Melvin E.; 0-9615981)*, 1240 Holly Ave., Rohnert Park, CA 94928 (SAN 698-1631) Tel 707-585-2095; Orders to: P.O. Box 2236, Rohnert Park, CA 94928 (SAN 662-4014).

M E Benefield Pub, *(Benefield, M.E., Publishing; 0-9607326)*, P.O. Box 395, 200 Jennifer, Jonesboro, AR 72401 (SAN 239-1635) Tel 501-972-1376.

M E Coughlin, *(Coughlin, Michael E., Pub.; 0-9602574)*, 1985 Selby Ave., St. Paul, MN 55104 (SAN 211-5220) Tel 612-646-8917.

M E Gant, *(Gant, Margaret Elizabeth; 0-9603138)*, 7500 Deer Track Dr., Raleigh, NC 27612 (SAN 212-7415) Tel 919-848-8062.

M E Gruenwald, *(Gruenwald, Myron E.; 0-9601536)*, 1260 Westhaven Dr., Oshkosh, WI 54904 (SAN 221-5144) Tel 414-235-7398.

M E Nilles, *(Nilles, Mary E.; 0-9616845)*, P.O. Box 155, Rollingstone, MN 55969 (SAN 661-129X); 300 Jay St., Brooklyn, NY 11201 (SAN 661-1303) Tel 718-643-4900.

†M E Sharpe, *(Sharpe, M. E., Inc.; 0-87332)*, 80 Business Pk. Dr., Armonk, NY 10504 (SAN 202-7100) Tel 914-273-1800; Toll free: 800-638-6460; 39 Westmoreland Ave., White Plains, NY 10603 (SAN 658-1595); *CIP.*

M E Warren, *(Warren, M. E.; 0-9606060)*, P.O. Box 1508, Annapolis, MD 21404 (SAN 216-7670).

M Elks, *(Elks, Mary; 0-9616039)*, 2 Beech Trail, Durham, NC 27705 (SAN 698-0813) Tel 919-684-6570.

†M Evans, *(Evans, M., & Co., Inc.; 0-87131)*, 216 E. 49th St., New York, NY 10017 (SAN 203-4050) Tel 212-688-2810; Toll free: 800-526-0275; Dist. by: Henry Holt and Co., 521 Fifth Ave., New York, NY 10175 (SAN 200-6472) Tel 212-599-7600; *CIP.*

M F Allen
See Acupinch

M F Davidson, *(Davidson, Mary Frances; 0-9607792)*, Rte. 3, Gatlinburg, TN 37738 (SAN 203-8668) Tel 615-436-5429.

M F Dobbins, *(Dobbins, M. F.; 0-9607176)*, 3045 Pennypack Rd., Hatboro, PA 19040 (SAN 239-0841) Tel 215-884-8057.

M F Sohn Pubns, *(Sohn, Mark F., Pubns.; 0-9616911)*, 508 Sixth St., Pikeville, KY 41501 (SAN 661-5228) Tel 606-437-6467.

M F Turner Pub, *(Turner, M. F., Publishing; 0-9616007)*, 2963 N. 52nd Pkwy., Phoenix, AZ 85031 (SAN 697-9734) Tel 602-247-5322.

M F Weber Co, *(Weber, Martin F., Co.; 0-917121)*, Subs. of Martin Instrument Co., P.O. Box 16270, Philadelphia, PA 19114 (SAN 655-7627) Tel 215-677-5600.

M G Book Graphics, *(M. G. Bookgraphics; 0-933484)*, Los Angeles, CA 90033 (SAN 281-9600). Insufficient address, no listing in Los Angeles.

M G Chambers, *(Chambers, Melvett G.; 0-9616522)*, 2231 Dawson Cir., Aurora, CO 80011 (SAN 659-4360) Tel 303-363-7429.

M G L S Pub, *(MGLS Publishing; 0-9601682)*, 700 S. First St., Marshall, MN 56258 (SAN 212-2170) Tel 507-532-3553.

M G M Bks, *(MGM Books; 0-9613282)*, P.O. Box 682, South St. Paul, MN 55075 (SAN 654-469X) Tel 612-455-1756; Dist. by: Bookslinger, 213 E. Fourth St., St. Paul, MN 55101 (SAN 169-4154) Tel 612-221-0429.

†M Glazier, *(Glazier, Michael, Inc.; 0-89453)*, 1935 W. Fourth St., Wilmington, DE 19805 (SAN 210-2056) Tel 302-654-1635; *CIP.*

M Gordon Pub, *(Gordon, Marilyn, ,Pub.; 0-9609542)*, 2153 Westchester Ave., Bronx, NY 10462 (SAN 260-1923) Tel 212-829-0830.

M Greger, *(Greger, Margaret; 0-9613680)*, 1425 Marshall, Richland, WA 99352 (SAN 670-8994).

M Grumbacher, *(Grumbacher, M., Inc.)*, Subs. of CPG International Co., 460 W. 34th St., New York, NY 10001 (SAN 205-3179) Tel 212-279-6400; Toll free: 800-346-3278; Orders to: Engelhard Dr., Cranbury, NJ 08512 (SAN 662-0248) Tel 609-655-8282.

M H Cap, *(M.H. Cap & Co.; 0-911375)*, Rte. 9, Box 327A, Bakersfield, CA 93312 (SAN 272-3972) Tel 805-589-0520.

M H Enterprises, *(M H Enterprises; 0-9611044)*, 420 W. 4th St., Hominy, OK 74035 (SAN 282-924X) Tel 918-885-2913; Dist. by: Centennial Distributors, P.O. Box 424, Deadwood, SD 57732 (SAN 200-4321).

M Hansen, *(Hansen, Mack; 0-9606672)*, 207 Hill Blvd., Petaluma, CA 94952 (SAN 219-7499) Tel 707-763-1489.

M Hardy, *(Hardy, Max, Pub.; 0-939460)*, P.O. Box 28219, Las Vegas, NV 89126-2219 (SAN 216-597X) Tel 702-368-0379.

M Hutson
See Hutson Assoc

M I P Co, *(MIP Company; 0-916201)*, P.O. Box 27484, Minneapolis, MN 55427 (SAN 295-0073) Tel 612-546-7578 Tel 612-546-7578.

M Ismail Sloan Pubs, *(Sloan, M. Ismail, Pubs.; 0-9609190)*, 917 Old Trents Ferry Rd., Lynchburg, VA 24503 (SAN 240-1592) Tel 718-230-9736; Toll free: 800-221-5724.

M J B CA
See Brant

M J D Shoaf, *(Shoaf, Mary Jo Davis; 0-9602520)*, 5140 Hackney Ln., SW, Roanoke, VA 24018 (SAN 212-6893) Tel 703-774-2667.

M J Kearney
See Kearney

M J Light, *(Light, Melvin J.)*, 2414 Grant Dr., Ann Arbor, MI 48104 (SAN 659-5588) Tel 313-971-2792.

M J Nicholson, *(Nicholson, Mary John; 0-9607574)*, P.O. Box 1351, Skokie, IL 60076 (SAN 281-9848).

M J O'Malley, *(O'Malley, Martin J.; 0-9606610)*, 222 Paulison Ave., Passaic, NJ 07055 (SAN 204-4702) Tel 201-473-4643.

M J P Barry, *(Barry, M. J. P.; 0-9617009)*, 323 W. Harvard Ave., Anchorage, AK 99501 (SAN 262-9148) Tel 907-272-0668.

M J Powers & Co, *(Powers, M. J., & Co. Pubs.; 0-913323)*, 374 Millburn Ave., Millburn, NJ 07041 (SAN 283-9660) Tel 201-467-4556.

M Jacobs, *(Jacobs, Mary; 0-9612156)*, 6000 E. Brundage No. 46, Bakersfield, CA 93307 (SAN 289-369X) Tel 805-366-0387.

M Jarchow Pubns, *(Jarchow, Michael, Publications; 0-9608204)*, P.O. Box 3238, Seal Beach, CA 90740 (SAN 238-8278); 2606 Octavia Street, San Francisco, CA 94123 (SAN 685-3390).

M Johnson, *(Johnson, Mabel, Quality Paperbacks; 0-9600838)*, P.O. Box 7, Boring, OR 97009 (SAN 206-1015) Tel 503-663-3428.

M Jones, *(Jones, Marshall, Co.; 0-8338)*, Div. of Golden Quill Pr., Francestown, NH 03043 (SAN 206-8834).

M K Cox
See Chogie Pubs

M K L Ltd, *(M.K.L., Ltd.; 0-9614421)*, 535 Fifth Ave., New York, NY 10017 (SAN 689-0210) Tel 212-490-0172; Dist. by: Hudson County News, 1305 Paterson Plank Rd., North Bergen, NJ 07047 (SAN 169-4782).

M K Look, *(Look, Margaret K.; 0-9616922)*, P.O. Box 1173, Powell, WY 82435 (SAN 661-5074); 940 Shoshone Dr., Powell, WY 82435 (SAN 661-5082) Tel 307-754-4656.

M Kellogg
See Bks by Kellogg

M Kennedy, *(Kennedy, M.)*, 310 Franklin St., No. 285, Boston, MA 02110 (SAN 239-5576).

M L Berger, *(Berger, Margaret L.; 0-9605914)*, Orders to: E. Weyhe, Inc., 794 Lexington Ave., New York, NY 10021 (SAN 699-5152) Tel 212-838-5466.

M L Burman, *(Burman, M. L.)*, Box 72, Pineland, FL 33945 (SAN 655-3834) Tel 813-283-0777.

M L Dalton Res, *(M. L. Dalton Research; 0-9613740)*, 6035 Aberdeen, Dallas, TX 75250 (SAN 677-7112) Tel 214-691-4925.

M L Emami
See Emami-Coulson

M L Henderson, *(Henderson, Mahlon Lucas; 0-9616434)*, 4533 Flower Valley Dr., Rockville, MD 20853 (SAN 659-2023).

M L Higgins, *(Higgins, Mae L.; 0-9616410)*, 1809 Oriole Ct., Severn, MD 21144 (SAN 658-8611) Tel 301-672-2896.

M L King Pr, *(King, Martin Luther, Pr.; 0-937644)*, Subs. of Martin Luther King Fellows, Inc., 132 W. 116th St., New York, NY 10026 (SAN 658-5868) Tel 212-866-0301.

M-L Pub, *(M-L Publishing Co., Ltd.; 0-915512)*, 157 Devonshire Rd., Wilmington, DE 19803 (SAN 207-1746) Tel 302-655-3883.

M L Smith, *(Smith, Malcolm L.)*, P.O. Box 6712, Washington, DC 20020 (SAN 213-1668).

M La Pice, *(La Pice, Margaret; 0-9604508)*, 210 Montcalm, San Francisco, CA 94110 (SAN 212-1093).

M Liebert, *(Liebert, Mary Ann, Inc.; 0-913113)*, 157 E. 86th St., New York, NY 10028 (SAN 283-2259) Tel 212-289-2300.

M Lilien, *(Lilien, M.; 0-9607652)*, 68-50 Burns St., Forest Hills, NY 11375 (SAN 264-1763).

M Linden NY, *(Linden, Millicent; 0-912628)*, 500 E. 74th St., New York, NY 10021 (SAN 207-0596).

M Lisa Precision, *(Monna Lisa Precision; 0-87643)*, Dist. by: Barclay Bridge Supplies, Eight Bush Ave., Port Chester, NY 10573 (SAN 202-3768) Tel 914-937-4200.

M Loke, *(Mele Loke Publishing Co.; 0-930932)*, P.O. Box 7142, Honolulu, HI 96821 (SAN 211-1330) Tel 808-734-8611; Dist. by: Pacific Trade Group, P.O. Box 668, Pearl City, HI 96782-0668 (SAN 169-1635) Tel 808-261-6954.

M Luff, *(Luff, Moe; 0-9600162)*, 12 Greene Rd., Spring Valley, NY 10977 (SAN 205-2466) Tel 914-356-4855.

M Lukman, *(Lukman, Mphahlele, Inc.; 0-9602690)*, 9110 Ave. A, Brooklyn, NY 11236 (SAN 214-1922) Tel 718-485-7009.

M Lynch, *(Lynch, Marietta & Perry, Patricia; 0-9610962)*, 240 Atlantic Rd., Gloucester, MA 01930 (SAN 265-2722) Tel 617-283-6322.

M M Bks, *(MM Bks.; 0-9612366)*, P.O. Box 29318, Crestwood, MO 63126 (SAN 289-4149).

M M Bruce, *(Bruce, Martin M., Pubs.; 0-935198)*, 50 Larchwood Rd., Box 248, Larchmont, NY 10538 (SAN 203-6819) Tel 914-834-1555.

M M Donahue-Gandy, *(Donahue-Gandy, Marlene M.; 0-9613514)*, 6228 Westbrook Dr., Citrus Heights, CA 95610 (SAN 657-6508) Tel 916-722-5611.

M M Enter, *(McAlister, Marcia, Enterprises),* P.O. Box 381704, Germantown, TN 38138 (SAN 698-1909); 1504 Wheatstone Cove, Germantown, TN 38138 (SAN 699-6523) Tel 901-755-4444; Dist. by: Wimmer Brothers Bks., 4210 BF Goodrich Blvd., Memphis, TN 38181 (SAN 209-6544) Tel 901-362-8900.

M M Erwin
See Erwin Marvin M

M M Hofmann, *(Hofmann, Margaret M.; 0-937761),* P.O. Box 446, Roanoke Rapids, NC 27870 (SAN 659-2414) Tel 919-536-2888; 35 Longstreet Rd., Weldon, NC 27890 (SAN 659-2422); Dist. by: Reprint Co., 601 Hillcrest Offices, Spartanburg, SC 29304 (SAN 203-3828).

M M Muhammad, *(Muhammad, Mustafa M., Pubns.; 0-9616801),* P.O. Box 1423, Santa Barbara, CA 93101 (SAN 661-2652); 1125 Garden Ln., Montecito, CA 93108 (SAN 661-2660) Tel 805-969-7520.

M M Pattarozzi, *(Pattarozzi, Michelle M.),* 105 Iron Bark Ct., East Peoria, IL 61611 (SAN 682-2541) Tel 309-671-2700.

M M Pub Inc, *(M&M Publishing Inc.; 0-915927),* Subs. of M & M Creative Group, 12198 Henderson Rd., Clifton, VA 22024 (SAN 294-0582) Tel 703-830-2388.

M M Strauss, *(Strauss, Mary Miller; 0-9616837),* P.O. Box 145, Accident, MD 21520 (SAN 661-4663) Tel 301-826-8183.

M M Wrede, *(Wrede, Mary M.; 0-9615969),* P.O. Box 364, Hillsboro, IN 47949 (SAN 696-8627); 203 N. Cross St., Hillsboro, IN 47949 (SAN 699-6450) Tel 317-798-3200.

M McIver, *(McIver, Mary; 0-9613864),* 1207 Michigan St., Elizabethton, TN 37643 (SAN 685-219X) Tel 615-543-4853.

M May Ent, *(May, Michael, Enterprises; 0-9612074),* P.O. Box 127, Billings, MT 59103 (SAN 286-8164) Tel 406-248-4973.

M Mermelstein, *(Mermelstein, Mel; 0-9606534),* c/o Auschwitz Study Foundation, 7422 Cedar St., P.O. Box 2232, Huntington Beach, CA 92647 (SAN 214-4158) Tel 213-848-1101.

M Milting, *(Milting, Martha; 0-9614455),* 1980 McDade, Conroe, TX 77304 (SAN 689-3902) Tel 409-756-5810.

M Moldeven, *(Moldeven, Meyer; 0-9615092),* 2106 Valleydale Lane, Encinatas, CA 92024 (SAN 694-1761) Tel 619-942-4188.

M Morishima, *(Morishima, Michael; 0-9616866),* 20707 Crawford Dr., Sunnyvale, CA 94087 (SAN 661-1605) Tel 408-732-7381.

M Murach & Assoc, *(Murach, Mike, & Assocs., Inc.; 0-911625),* 4697 W. Jacquelyn, Fresno, CA 93711 (SAN 264-2255) Tel 209-275-3335; Toll free: 800-221-5528; Toll free: 800-221-5527 (In California).

M Murdock, *(Murdock, Maureen; 0-9616379),* 121 Wavecrest Ave., Venice, CA 90291 (SAN 658-943X) Tel 213-392-3111; Dist. by: Greater Spiral, The, P.O. Box 12515, Portland, OR 12515 (SAN 200-6383).

M N I Inc
See Mike Nicholes

M N Kemnitz, *(Kemnitz, Milton N.),* 1180 Bird Rd., P.O. Box 7390, Ann Arbor, MI 48107 (SAN 211-1586) Tel 313-668-9895.

M Nesbit, *(Nesbit, Martha; 0-9617126),* 25 E. 44th St., Savannah, GA 31405 (SAN 662-6777) Tel 912-232-7052.

M Nevin, *(Nevin, Mark; 0-9613132),* 1860 Ala Moana Apt. 704, Honolulu, HI 96815 (SAN 285-6751) Tel 808-941-6088.

M Newell Co, *(Newell, M., Co. Builders, Pub.; 0-9615901),* Subs. of M. Newell Company Builders, 16731 74th NE, Bothell, WA 98011 (SAN 696-6640) Tel 206-488-2844.

M O Haroldsen, *(Haroldsen, Mark O.; 0-932444),* 1831 E. Fourth Union Blvd., Salt Lake City, UT 84121 (SAN 281-7675).

M O Merrill, *(Merrill, Madeline O.; 0-9601332),* 109 Water St., Saugus, MA 01906 (SAN 209-035X) Tel 617-233-5442.

M O P Pr, *(M.O.P. Pr.; 0-942432),* Rte. 24, Box 53C, Ft. Myers, FL 33908 (SAN 223-0860) Tel 813-466-4690.

M Osgood, *(Osgood, Merle, Productions; 0-913067),* 720 Eleventh St., Bellingham, WA 98225 (SAN 283-975X); Dist. by: Pacific Pipeline, Inc., 19215 66th Ave. S., Kent, WA 98032 (SAN 208-2128) Tel 206-872-5523.

M P Cooper
See M P Kelley

M P Davison, *(Davison, Marguerite P.; 0-9603172),* P.O. Box 263, Swarthmore, PA 19081 (SAN 212-498X) Tel 215-876-4191.

M P Kelley, *(Kelley, Mary Palmer; 0-9613313),* Garden History Assocs., P.O. Box 12606, Columbia, SC 29211 (SAN 656-8955).

M P Kelsey, *(Kelsey, Mavis P.; 0-9613308),* No. 2 Longbow Lane, Houston, TX 77024 (SAN 654-3308) Tel 713-686-3768.

M P Pubns, *(M P Publications; 0-932187),* 510 W. Chestnut St., Oxford, OH 45056 (SAN 686-5860) Tel 513-523-8621.

M Pellegrini, *(Pellegrini, Mary; 0-9612938),* 2944 Washington Blvd., Cleveland Heights, OH 44118 (SAN 292-4447) Tel 216-371-9252.

M Powley, *(Powley, Mark, Assocs., Inc.; 0-943378),* 15 Meigs Ave., Madison, CT 06443 (SAN 240-7485) Tel 203-245-8561.

M Press, *(M Pr.,The; 0-9617067),* 1623 Connecticut Ave., NW, Washington, DC 20009 (SAN 662-8699) Tel 202-232-8484.

M Q Nichols, *(Nichols, M. Q.; 0-9612516),* 1815 Texas Ave., Bridge City, TX 77611 (SAN 291-8226).

M R K, *(M-R-K Publishing; 0-9601292),* 448 Seavey Ln., Petaluma, CA 94952 (SAN 210-461X) Tel 707-763-0056.

M R Kopmeyer
See Success Found

M R Wimer, *(Wimer, Margaret R.; 0-9617069),* P.O. Box 782, Franklin, WV 26807 (SAN 662-9024) Tel 304-358-7675.

M R Winkler, *(Winkler, Marion R.; 0-9610344),* 5225 N. 20th St., Phoenix, AZ 85016 (SAN 264-4991) Tel 602-957-2922.

M Raphael, *(Raphael, Morris, Books; 0-9608866),* 1404 Bayou Side Dr., New Iberia, LA 70560 (SAN 241-0737) Tel 318-369-3220.

M Regehr, *(Regehr, Margaret; 0-9614486),* HCR 85, Box 64, Bonners Ferry, ID 83805 (SAN 689-3929) Tel 208-267-2801.

M Reinertsen
See Union Pr

M Renino, *(Renino, Marjorie C. H.; 0-9615866),* 14 Ogden Ave., White Plains, NY 10605 (SAN 696-5709) Tel 914-946-2702.

M Rogers Mus, *(Rogers, Millicent, Museum; 0-9609818),* P.O. Box A, Taos, NM 87571 (SAN 264-3588) Tel 505-758-2462.

M Rosenberg, *(Rosenberg, Marilyn R.; 0-913615),* 101 Lakeview Ave. W., Peekskill, NY 10566 (SAN 285-3728) Tel 914-737-2052.

M Russell NY, *(Russell, Martin, Publisher; 0-912209),* 61 Kincaid Dr., Yonkers, NY 10710 (SAN 265-0967) Tel 914-793-5296.

M S Johnson, *(Johnson, Merwyn S.; 0-9601590),* P.O. Box 368, Due West, SC 29639 (SAN 212-3649) Tel 803-379-8193.

M S Rosenberg, *(Rosenberg, Mary S., Inc.; 0-917324),* 17 W. 60th St., New York, NY 10023 (SAN 205-2296) Tel 212-362-4873.

M S Wright, *(Wright, Mildred S., G.R.S.; 0-917016),* 140 Briggs, Beaumont, TX 77707-2329 (SAN 208-9335) Tel 409-832-2308.

M Schalit, *(Schalit, Michael; 0-9604630),* 451 Bell Ave., Livermore, CA 94550 (SAN 213-7933) Tel 415-443-2456.

M Scheid, *(Scheid, Margaret M., Author Pub.; 0-9616115),* P.O. Box 1167, Southwest Harbor, ME 04679 (SAN 699-7201) Tel 207-244-3870.

M Serrett Howard, *(Howard, Marilyn Serrett; 0-9616125),* 5106 Pre-Emption Rd., Geneva, NY 14456 (SAN 699-7244) Tel 315-781-0031.

M Shanken Comm, *(Shanken, M., Communications, Inc.; 0-918076),* 400 E. 51st St., New York, NY 10022 (SAN 210-2773) Tel 212-751-6500; Toll free: 800-227-1617.

M Sheldon Pub, *(Sheldon, Marc, Publishing; 0-932262),* P.O. Box 272, 777 N. Loren Ave., Azusa, CA 91702 (SAN 211-9234) Tel 818-969-1866.

M Shore Assocs, *(Shore, Michael, Assocs.; 0-910243),* 24 Westfield Rd., Milford, CT 06460 (SAN 241-4554) Tel 203-877-9218.

M Sillars, *(Sillars, Mal, Weather Consultants, Inc.; 0-9616885),* P.O. Box 36733, Grosse Pointe, MI 48236 (SAN 661-6526); 316 McKinley, Grosse Pointe Farms, MI 48236 (SAN 661-6534) Tel 313-881-3244.

M Sloane, *(Sloane, Mark, & Co.; 0-938347),* P.O. Drawer 571, Coraopolis, PA 15108 (SAN 659-9443); 104 Great Oaks Dr., Coraopolis, PA 15108 (SAN 659-9451) Tel 412-269-1490; Dist. by: Tab Bks., P.O. Box 40, Blue Ridge Summit, PA 17214 (SAN 202-568X); Dist. by: David J. Gingery, 2045 Boonville, Springfield, IL 65803 (SAN 214-3771); Dist. by: Lindsay Pubns., P.O. Box 12, Bradley, IL 60915 (SAN 209-9462).

M Springer, *(Springer, Miloslay; 0-9616955),* 2955 Cortina Dr., Colorado Springs, CO 80918 (SAN 661-7719) Tel 303-599-8407.

M Stensrud, *(Stensrud, Mary; 0-9616956),* 1102 S. 41st Ave., Yakima, WA 98908 (SAN 661-776X) Tel 509-965-0459.

M Sturgeon
See Newport Beach

M Supnick, *(Supnick, Mark; 0-9611446),* 8524 NW Second St., Coral Springs, FL 33065 (SAN 283-1694) Tel 305-755-3448.

M T C Pub Co, *(MTC Publishing Co.; 0-9613068),* P.O. Box A6-158, Suite O, Laguna Niguel, CA 92677 (SAN 294-6076) Tel 714-831-0456.

M T Finnerty, *(Finnerty, Mary T.; 0-9602222),* 33 Johnson, West Roxbury, MA 02132 (SAN 212-2766); Orders to: P.O. Box 591, Astor Sta., Boston, MA 02123 (SAN 212-2774).

M T Moore, *(Moore, Milton T., Jr.; 0-9608138),* P.O. Box 140280, Dallas, TX 75214 (SAN 240-2564) Tel 214-821-0407.

M T O Shahmag, *(M.T.O. Shahmaghsoudi; 0-910735),* P.O. Box 1135, San Rafael, CA 94915 (SAN 271-6852) Tel 415-454-1555.

M T Pub
See Maynard-Thomas

M T Smith, *(Smith, Michael T.; 0-9616494),* 504 Sharon Rd., Chapel Hill, NC 27514 (SAN 659-3275) Tel 919-929-9429.

M Torosian
See MTA Financial Servs

M V Hansen, *(Hansen, Mark Victor),* P.O. Box 7665, Newport Beach, CA 92658-7665 (SAN 694-2407) Tel 714-759-9304.

M V Micka, *(Micka, Mary Virginia, & Assocs.; 0-9617046),* 1420 Randolph Ave., St. Paul, MN 55105 (SAN 662-8141) Tel 612-690-6559; Dist. by: Bookslinger, 213 E. 4th St., St. Paul, MN 55101 (SAN 169-4154) Tel 612-221-0429.

M Victor Pub, *(Mark Victor Publishing Co.; 0-9606258),* 10855 Whipple St., No. 207, N. Hollywood, CA 91602 (SAN 217-572X).

M W Hardwick, *(Hardwick, M. Warren; 0-9616067),* 1126 E. Cedar St., Angleton, TX 77515 (SAN 697-8665) Tel 409-849-6227.

M W Johnson, *(Johnson, Miriam W.; 0-9612626),* 1459 Bowman St., Clermont, FL 32711 (SAN 289-2774) Tel 904-394-2236.

M W Riley, *(Riley, Maurice W.; 0-9603150),* 512 Roosevelt Blvd., Ypsilanti, MI 48197 (SAN 213-3628).

M Ward, *(Ward, Marcia; 0-9613444),* P.O. Box 96, Johnson City, NY 13790 (SAN 657-1050) Tel 607-729-1675.

M Warren Bks
See Warren Bks

M Weaver, *(Weaver, Marilyn; 0-9615682),* 715 21th Ave. N, Estherville, IA 51334 (SAN 696-2696) Tel 712-362-7002.

M West Pubs, *(West, Mark, Pubs.),* P.O. Box 1914, Sandpoint, ID 83864 (SAN 215-711X) Tel 708-263-0969.

M Westergaard, *(Westergaard, Marjorie; 0-9609578),* 31246 Wagner, Warren, MI 48093 (SAN 260-2768) Tel 313-977-8942.

M Wetherbee, *(Wetherbee, Martha, Basket Shop; 0-9609384),* Star Rte. 35, Sanbornton, NH 03269 (SAN 260-2709) Tel 603-286-8927.

M Wiener, *(Wiener, Moshe; 0-9605406),* 854 Newburg Ave., North Woodmere, NY 11581 (SAN 215-9856).

M Wiese Film Prod, *(Wiese, Michael, Film Production; 0-941188),* P.O. Box 406, Westport, CT 06881 (SAN 237-9716) Tel 203-226-6979.

M Wyatt, *(Wyatt, Margert; 0-9616117),* 1127 St. Mary, Casper, WY 82601 (SAN 699-721X) Tel 307-237-7531.

M Y Bastian, *(Bastian, Marlene Y.; 0-9609058),* 240 SE 87th, Portland, OR 97216 (SAN 241-2101) Tel 503-252-0989.

McLennan Hse, *(McLennan Hse., Inc.; 0-918865),* 206 S. Rogers, Waxahachie, TX 75165 (SAN 669-9243) Tel 214-937-9700.

McMallec Pub, *(McMallec Publishing Co.; 0-938745),* Div. of WCW Assocs., Inc., 3609 Memorial Pkwy., SW, Huntsville, AL 35801 (SAN 661-7611); P.O. Box 4635, Huntsville, AL 35815 (SAN 661-762X) Tel 205-882-1620.

MacManiman, *(MacManiman, Inc.; 0-9611998),* P.O. Box 546, 3023 362nd SE., Fall City, WA 98024 (SAN 212-0216) Tel 206-222-5587.

†**Macmillan,** *(Macmillan Publishing Co., Inc.; 0-02),* 866 Third Ave., New York, NY 10022 (SAN 212-702-2000; Toll free: 800-257-5755; Orders to: Front & Brown Sts., Riverside, NJ 08370 (SAN 202-5582). Do not confuse with McMillan Pubns., Woodridge, IL; *CIP.* *Imprints:* Acorn (Acorn Books).(Acorn Bks.); Aladdin Bks (Aladdin Books).(Aladdin Bks.); Berlitz (Berlitz); Collier (Collier Books).(Collier Bks.); CCPr (Crowell-Collier Press).(Crowell-Collier Pr.); Dove (Dove Books).(Dove Bks.).

Macmillan Info, *(Macmillan Information; 0-02),* Div. of Macmillan Publishing Co., Inc., 866 Third Ave., New York, NY 10022 (SAN 202-599X) Tel 212-935-2000.

McMillan Pubns, *(McMillan Pubns., Inc.; 0-934228),* 3208 Halsey Dr., Woodridge, IL 60517 (SAN 213-1137) Tel 312-968-3933. Publishes railroad books only. Do not confuse with Macmillan Publishing Co., New York, NY, and Riverside NJ.

McMurry Pub, *(McMurry, Cathryn; 0-9615936),* 14845 SW Carlsbad, Beaverton, OR 97007 (SAN 696-8546) Tel 503-641-3981.

MCN Pr, *(MCN Pr.; 0-912958),* Subs. of Military Collectors' News Pr., P.O. Box 702073, Tulsa, OK 74170 (SAN 203-9915) Tel 918-743-6048; Dist. by: Baker & Taylor Co., Midwest Div., 501 S. Gladiola Ave., Momence, IL 60945 (SAN 169-2100); Dist. by: Key Bk. Service, 425 Asylum St., Bridgeport, CT 06610 (SAN 209-6404) Tel 203-334-2165; Dist. by: Baker & Taylor Co., Eastern Div., 50 Kirby Ave., Somerville, NJ 08876 (SAN 169-4901); Dist. by: Baker & Taylor Co., Southeast Div., Mt. Olive Rd., Commerce, GA 30529 (SAN 169-1503); Dist. by: Baker & Taylor Co., Western Div., 380 Edison Way, Reno, NV 89564 (SAN 169-4464) Tel 702-786-6700.

Mcnally
See McNally & Loftin

†**McNally & Loftin,** *(McNally & Loftin, Pubs.; 0-87461),* P.O. Box 1316, Santa Barbara, CA 93102 (SAN 202-5973) Tel 805-964-5117; Orders to: 5390 Overpass Rd., Santa Barbara, CA 93111 (SAN 281-9651) Tel 805-964-6469; *CIP.*

McNally NC
See McNally & Loftin

McNamara Pubns, *(McNamara Pubns., Inc.; 0-932770),* 741 Overlook St., P.O. Box 27277, Escondido, CA 92027 (SAN 212-2189) Tel 619-743-4942.

McNichols Pub, *(McNichols Publishing Co.; 0-935227),* 731 Mulberry, Winston-Salem, NC 27101 (SAN 695-7188) Tel 919-724-6399.

McNutt Pubns, *(McNutt, Randy, Pubns.; 0-940152),* P.O. Box 455, Fairfield, OH 45014 (SAN 217-0841) Tel 513-868-9910.

Macoy Pub, *(Macoy Publishing & Masonic Supply Co., Inc.; 0-910928; 0-88053),* P.O. Box 9759, Richmond, VA 23228 (SAN 202-2265) Tel 804-262-6551.

Macoy Pub & Masonic
See Macoy Pub

MCP Bks, *(MCP Bks.; 0-9603926),* 8818 Higdon Dr., Vienna, VA 22180 (SAN 214-1930).

†**McPherson & Co,** *(McPherson & Co.; 0-914232),* P.O. Box 638, New Paltz, NY 12561 (SAN 203-0624) Tel 914-255-7084; 437 Springtown Rd., New Paltz, NY 12561 (SAN 658-2001); *CIP.*

MacPherson Pub, *(MacPherson Pub. Co.; 0-9614849),* 907 Comstock Ave., Syracuse, NY 13210 (SAN 693-1065) Tel 315-475-0339.

McQueen, *(McQueen Publishing Co.; 0-917186),* P.O. Box 198, Tiskilwa, IL 61368 (SAN 203-9516).

McQueen & Son, *(McQueen & Son Publishing Co.; 0-9609354),* 6302 Van Maren Lane, Citrus Heights, CA 95621 (SAN 260-2245) Tel 916-725-3285; Orders to: Box 776, Citrus Heights, CA 95610 (SAN 662-0760) Tel 916-725-3285.

McQuerry Orchid, *(McQuerry Orchid Books; 0-913928),* 5700 W. Salerno Rd., Jacksonville, FL 32244 (SAN 203-9427) Tel 904-387-5044.

Macra-Tack Inc, *(Macra-Tack Incorporated; 0-9611536),* P.O. Box 326, Stevensville, MT 59870 (SAN 283-3248) Tel 406-777-5408.

MacRae *Imprint of* **Watts**

MacRaes Blue Bk, *(MacRae's Blue Bk., Inc.; 0-89910),* Subs. of Business Research Pubns., Inc., 817 Broadway, New York, NY 10003 (SAN 241-5569) Tel 212-673-4700; Toll free: 800-622-7237.

Macro Bks, *(Macro Books; 0-913080),* P.O. Box 26661, Tempe, AZ 85282 (SAN 207-0480) Tel 602-991-2229.

Macrobiotics Aids Rsch, *(Macrobiotics & Aids Research Project; 0-9617097),* P.O. Box 214, Wynnewood, PA 19096 (SAN 662-4928); 945 Granite St., Philadelphia, PA 19124 (SAN 662-4936) Tel 215-535-3592.

Macrobit Corp, *(Macrobit Corp.; 0-939573),* 3785 NW 82nd Ave., No. 115, Miami, FL 33166 (SAN 663-5334) Tel 305-592-5354; Dist. by: Computer Books International, 3785 NW 82nd Ave., No. 115, Miami, FL 33166 (SAN 200-8173).

Macromedia Inc, *(Macromedia Inc.; 0-9601170),* P.O. Box 1025, Lake Placid, NY 12946 (SAN 209-3790) Tel 518-523-9683.

MCS, *(MCS; 0-932150),* P.O. Box 1774, Morganton, NC 28655 (SAN 239-4529).

Macs
See MCS

MCS Pubns KY, *(MCS Pubns. (KY); 0-933811),* P.O. Box 486, Murray, KY 42071 (SAN 692-7742) Tel 502-753-7750.

MCSA Pubns
See Med Communications

McTaggart, *(McTaggart Publishing, Inc.; 0-9611864),* 201 Gore Creek Dr., Vail, CO 81657 (SAN 286-1429) Tel 303-476-1097.

MacVeigh, *(MacVeigh, Poppy E.; 0-9615594),* 335 Crestline Ave., Cincinnati, OH 45205 (SAN 695-9040) Tel 513-921-7825.

McVicker Sutcliffe
See Geronima

McVie Pub, *(McVie Publishing Co.; 0-917487),* 17608 15th Pl., W., Lynnwood, WA 98036 (SAN 656-0733) Tel 206-743-3706.

Macys Ellinwood
See Macys Mesa

Macys Mesa, *(Macys of Mesa; 0-9414691),* 8615 E. Apache Trail, No. B-39, Mesa, AZ 85207 (SAN 217-250X).

Mad Gull Pr, *(Mad Gull Pr.; 0-9610330),* 5650 Riley St., San Diego, CA 92110 (SAN 264-1933) Tel 619-291-6399.

MAD Hse, *(M.A.D. Hse.; 0-9606732),* P.O. Box 1716, Sanford, FL 32771 (SAN 219-6794) Tel 305-323-5159.

Mad River, *(Mad River Pr.; 0-916422),* 141 Carter Ln., Eureka, CA 95501 (SAN 207-530X) Tel 707-443-2947.

Made *Imprint of* **Doubleday**

Madelon Chamb, *(Chambliss, Madelon; 0-9612420),* P.O. Box 36B 81, 510 S. Sierra Bonita Ave., Los Angeles, CA 90025 (SAN 289-1743) Tel 213-935-3770.

Mader Enter, *(Mader Enterprises; 0-9615270),* 14 Briarwood Dr., Edgartown, MA 02539 (SAN 695-183X) Tel 617-627-9927.

Madhatter, *(Madhatter Pr.; 0-941082),* 3101 12th Ave., S., Minneapolis, MN 55407 (SAN 217-3964) Tel 612-722-8951.

Madis, *(Madis, Valdemar; 0-941350),* 375 Huyler St., South Hackensack, NJ 07606 (SAN 239-4545).

†**Madison Art,** *(Madison Art Ctr., Inc.; 0-913883),* 211 State St., Madison, WI 53703 (SAN 279-4683) Tel 608-257-0158; *CIP.*

Madison Ave Pub, *(Madison Avenue Publishing Co.; 0-9613697),* P.O Box 4080, Dallas, TX 75208 (SAN 681-8269).

†**Madison Cty KY Hist,** *(Madison County Historical Society; 0-9615162),* 515 W. Main St., Richmond, KY 40475 (SAN 694-3039) Tel 606-623-1250; *CIP.*

Madison Financial, *(Madison Financial Services, Inc.; 0-913885),* 12108 Suffolk Terr., Gaithersburg, MD 20878 (SAN 286-7893) Tel 301-840-2071.

Madison Park Pr, *(Madison Park Pr.; 0-942178),* 3816 E. Madison St., Seattle, WA 98112 (SAN 238-7867).

Madison Polk, *(Madison & Polk; 0-910915),* P.O. Box 8447, Asheville, NC 28814 (SAN 272-1708).

Madison Pr, *(Madison Pr., The; 0-9612962),* 2686 Mountain View Dr., S., Salem, OR 97302 (SAN 292-5761) Tel 503-363-0422.

Madison Pr TX, *(Madison Pr.; 0-938867),* 620 King's Row, Denton, TX 76201 (SAN 662-5754) Tel 817-383-2627. Do not confuse with Madison Pr., of Salem, OR, & Beltsville, MD.

Madison Pub, *(Madison Publishing, Inc.; 0-938141),* 12 Concord Dr., Madison, CT 06443 (SAN 661-2237) Tel 203-421-5258. Do not confuse with Madison Pub., New York, NY.

Madison Square, *(Madison Square Pr.; 0-942604),* 10 E. 23rd St., New York, NY 10010 (SAN 238-5384) Tel 212-505-0950; Dist. by: Robert Silver Assocs., 307 E. 37th St., New York, NY 10016 (SAN 241-5801) Tel 212-686-5630.

Madrigal Pub, *(Madrigal Publishing Co.; 0-9617098),* P.O. Box 1629, New Milford, CT 06776 (SAN 662-4979); 517 Litchfield Rd., New Milford, CT 06776 (SAN 662-4987) Tel 203-355-2694.

Madrona Pr, *(Madrona Pr., Inc.; 0-89052),* P.O. Box 3750, Austin, TX 78764 (SAN 202-6015); Toll free: 800-624-1739.

†**Madrona Pubs,** *(Madrona Pubs., Inc.; 0-914842; 0-88089),* P.O. Box 22667, Seattle, WA 98122 (SAN 212-0283); 113 Madrona Pl., E., Seattle, WA 98112 (SAN 281-9678) Tel 206-325-3973; Dist. by: Interbook, 14895 E. 14th St., Suite 370, San Leandro, CA 94577 (SAN 202-5191) Tel 415-352-9221; *CIP.*

Maedon, *(Maedon; 0-9614549),* 825 Via Formia, Punta Gorda, FL 33950 (SAN 687-7532) Tel 813-639-8075.

Maelstrom, *(Maelstrom Pr.; 0-917554),* 8 Farm Hill Rd., Cape Elizabeth, ME 04107 (SAN 207-8899).

Maestro Pubn *Imprint of* **Hansen Ed Mus**

Mafex, *(Mafex Associates, Inc.; 0-87804),* 90 Cherry St., Johnstown, PA 15902 (SAN 202-2591) Tel 814-535-3597.

Mag Indus, *(Magazines for Industry, Inc.; 0-89451),* Subs. of Harcourt Brace Jovanovich, Inc., 747 Third Ave., New York, NY 10017 (SAN 205-7921) Tel 212-838-7778.

Maga Dubh
See F Preston

Magaru Enterprises, *(Magaru Enterprises; 0-9609154),* P.O. Box 10271, Waialae Kahala Stn., Honolulu, HI 96816 (SAN 262-0472).

Mage In Nation, *(Mage-In Nation Co., Inc.; 0-9615749),* 11716 Center Rd., Mantua, OH 44255 (SAN 695-9091) Tel 216-274-2693.

Mage Pubs Inc, *(Mage Pubs., Inc.; 0-934211),* 1032-29th St. NW, Washington, DC 20007 (SAN 693-0476) Tel 202-342-1642.

Magee, *(Magee, John, Inc.; 0-910944),* 103 State St., Boston, MA 02109 (SAN 206-6556).

Magee Ent, *(Magee Enterprises; 0-938167),* 6577 Peachtree Industrial Blvd., Norcross, GA 30092-3796 (SAN 661-1958) Tel 404-446-6611.

Magee Pubns, *(Magee Pubns.; 0-937267),* P.O. Box 26507, Prescott, AZ 86312 (SAN 658-9006) Tel 602-445-7503; 118 N. Montezuma St., Prescott, AZ 86301 (SAN 658-9014).

Magi Bks, *(Magi Bks., Inc.; 0-87343),* 33 Buckingham Dr., Albany, NY 12208 (SAN 202-6023) Tel 518-482-7781.

Magian Pr, *(Magian Pr., The; 0-917023),* P.O. Box 117, Penn Laird, VA 22846 (SAN 655-2684) Tel 703-289-5596.

Magic
See Jr League Birm

Magic By Gosh, *(Magic By Gosh; 0-9615492),* 11226 Kamloops St., Lake View Terrace, CA 91342 (SAN 696-3730) Tel 818-896-9571.

Magic Cir Pr CT, (*Magic Circle Press; 0-913660*), 10 Hyde Ridge Rd., Weston, CT 06883 (SAN 202-6031) Tel 203-226-1903; Dist. by: Walker & Co., 720 Fifth Ave., New York, NY 10019 (SAN 202-5213) Tel 212-265-3632.

Magic Circle Pr
See Magic Cir Pr CT

Magic Ltd, (*Magic Limited-Lloyd E. Jones; 0-915926*), P.O. Box 3186, San Leandro, CA 94578 (SAN 208-7480) Tel 415-352-1854; 4064 39th Ave., Oakland, CA 94619 (SAN 208-7499) Tel 415-531-5490.

Magic Ocean, (*Magic Ocean Pr., The; 0-914317*), 2711 Crooks Rd., Royal Oak, MI 48073 (SAN 287-4776) Tel 313-288-3247.

Magic Publish *Imprint of* CCC Pubns

Magic Unicorn Pubns, (*Magic Unicorn Pubns.; 0-9601836*), P.O. Box 793, Yucca Valley, CA 92286-0793 (SAN 222-0636) Tel 619-365-0401.

Magical Rainbow, (*Magical Rainbow Pubns.; 0-911281*), P.O. Box 717, Ojai, CA 93023 (SAN 272-1775) Tel 805-646-6027.

Magick Circle *Imprint of* Tech Group

Magickal Childe, (*Magickal Childe Inc.; 0-939708*), 35 W. 19th St., New York, NY 10011 (SAN 216-4124) Tel 212-242-7182; Toll free: 800-843-6666.

Magister Inc, (*Magister, Inc.; 0-9612312*), P.O. Box 13646, Tallahassee, FL 32317 (SAN 289-5307) Tel 904-385-8927.

†Magna Carta Bk, (*Magna Carta Book Co.; 0-910946*), 5502 Magnolia Ave., Baltimore, MD 21215 (SAN 203-9532) Tel 301-466-8191; *CIP.*

Magna Pub Co, (*Magna Publishing Co.; 0-912150*), 607 N. Sherman Ave., Madison, WI 53704 (SAN 203-9540) Tel 608-249-2455.

MAGNA Pubs, (*MAGNA Pubs.; 0-9613929*), P.O. Box 422, Warren, OH 44482 (SAN 682-5060) Tel 216-399-5300.

Magnaflux, (*Magnaflux Corp.*), 7300 W. Lawrence Ave., Chicago, IL 60656 (SAN 205-907X) Tel 312-867-8000.

Magnaform, (*Magnaform Corp.; 0-937845*), Div. of Beylerian, Ltd., 305 E. 63rd St., 15th Flr., New York, NY 10021 (SAN 659-512X) Tel 212-755-6302.

Magnamusic
See MMB Music

Magnes Mus, (*Magnes, Judah L., Museum; 0-943376*), 2911 Russell St., Berkeley, CA 94705 (SAN 214-2511) Tel 415-849-2710.

Magnetic Inds, (*Magnetic Indexes; 0-918933*), 1626 N. Wilcox Ave. No. 403, Los Angeles, CA 90028 (SAN 669-9332) Tel 213-383-4734.

Magnetic Way, (*Magnetic Way, The; 0-938997*), Div. of Creative Edge, Inc., 2495 N. Forest Rd., Amherst, NY 14068 (SAN 662-5401) Tel 716-689-1657.

Magnoart Pubns, (*Magnoart Pubns.; 0-918935*), Subs. of Magnoart Culture Institute, P.O. Box 2150, Van Nuys, CA 91401 (SAN 670-0993) Tel 213-780-5383; Dist. by: Wholesome Life Distributing, P.O. Box 26204, Encino, CA 91426-2204 (SAN 200-7533) Tel 818-986-7629.

Magnolia Bks, (*Magnolia Bks., Inc.; 0-9612000*), 450 17th Ave., San Francisco, CA 94121 (SAN 286-8121) Tel 415-221-3519.

Magnolia CO, (*Magnolia Pubns; 0-933679*), P.O. Box 6464, Colorado Springs, CO 80934 (SAN 692-7904) Tel 303-635-9163.

Magnolia Homes, (*Magnolia Homes Tour, Inc.; 0-9616756*), P.O. Box 817, Columbus, TX 78934 (SAN 661-4191); 435 Spring St., Columbus, TX 78934 (SAN 661-4205) Tel 409-732-2301.

Magnolia Hse Pub, (*Magnolia House Publishing; 0-913145*), 2843 Thorndyke Ave. W., Seattle, WA 98199 (SAN 265-3915) Tel 206-283-0609.

Magnolia Lab, (*Magnolia Laboratory*), 701 Beach Blvd., Pascagoula, MS 39567 (SAN 206-2127) Tel 601-762-1643.

Magnolia Pr, (*Magnolia Pr.; 0-916369*), P.O. Box 3, Swainsboro, GA 30401 (SAN 295-6233) Tel 912-237-8740.

Magnolia Pr
See Magnolia St Pub

Magnolia Pubns Inc., (*Magnolia Pubns., Inc.; 0-943516*), 380 Lexington Ave., New York, NY 10168 (SAN 240-7116) Tel 212-682-2514.

Magnolia St Pub, (*Magnolia Street Pubs.; 0-9613309*), 1250 W. Victoria, Chicago, IL 60660 (SAN 653-8843) Tel 312-561-2121.

Magnum Pub, (*Magnum Publishing; 0-937917*), 5666 La Jolla Blvd., No. 316, La Jolla, CA 92037 (SAN 659-5138) Tel 619-563-0670.

Magoos Umbrella, (*Magoo's Umbrella; 0-932904*), 18581 Devon Ave., Saratoga, CA 95070 (SAN 212-2197) Tel 408-374-7646.

Magpie Pr, (*Magpie Pr.; 0-935469*), 16 Main Ave., Wallington, NJ 07057 (SAN 696-3897) Tel 201-778-2503.

Magpie Pubns, (*Magpie Pubns.; 0-936480*), P.O. Box 636, Alamo, CA 94507 (SAN 221-4091) Tel 415-838-9287.

Mah-Tov Pubns, (*Mah-Tov Pubns.; 0-917274*), 1680 45th St., Brooklyn, NY 11204 (SAN 208-7502) Tel 718-871-5337.

Mahayana, (*Mahayana Sutra & Tantra Pr.; 0-918753*), Subs. of Mahayana Sutra & Tantra Center, 216A W. Second St., Howell, NJ 07731 (SAN 657-6532) Tel 609-261-3458.

Maher Ventril Studio, (*Maher Ventriloquist Studios*), P.O. Box 420, Littleton, CO 80160 (SAN 208-1385) Tel 303-798-6830.

Mahler Pub Co, (*Mahler Publishing Co.; 0-914431*), 24 Godwin Ave., Midland Park, NJ 07432 (SAN 289-6540) Tel 201-447-1130.

Maiden Bks, (*Maiden Bks.; 0-931138*), 300 Washington St., Newark, NJ 07102 (SAN 211-2515).

Maiden Lane, (*Maiden Lane Pr.; 0-9605688*), P.O. Box 3724, Charlottesville, VA 22903 (SAN 216-2652) Tel 703-456-8323.

Mail Order, (*Mail Order U.S.A.; 0-914694*), Suite B-10, 3100 Wisconsin Ave. NW, Washington, DC 20016 (SAN 205-6321) Tel 202-686-9521; Orders to: P.O. Box 19083, Washington, DC 20036 (SAN 205-633X).

Mail Trade, (*Mail Trade Enterprises; 0-931061*), 1801 S. Cardinal Ln., New Berlin, WI 53151 (SAN 678-9269) Tel 414-782-4424.

Mailbox, (*Mailbox Club, The; 0-9603752*), 404 Eager Rd., Valdosta, GA 31602 (SAN 281-9686) Tel 912-244-6812.

†Mailman Family, (*Mailman Family Press, The; 0-914799*), 707 Westchester Ave., White Plains, NY 10604 (SAN 289-1360) Tel 914-681-4446; Dist. by: Gryphon House, Inc., P.O. Box 275, 3706 Otis St., Mt. Rainer, MD 20712 (SAN 663-303X) Tel 301-779-6200 (SAN 669-3520); *CIP.*

Maimes, (*Maimes, S. L.; 0-917246*), 42 Bellamy Rd., Dover, NH 03820 (SAN 208-1830).

Main St *Imprint of* Universe

Main St Media, (*Main Street Media; 0-938143*), P.O. Box 381, Mocksville, NC 27028 (SAN 661-4434); 184 E. Maple Ave., Mocksville, NC 27028 (SAN 661-4442) Tel 704-634-3118.

Main St Pub, (*Main Street Publishing, Inc.; 0-935399*), 2022 E. Edgewood, Shorewood, WI 53211 (SAN 696-3129) Tel 414-964-5757.

Main Stage Pubns, (*Main Stage Pubns., Inc.; 0-936447*), P.O. Box 216, Athens, OH 45701 (SAN 697-9025) Tel 614-593-7437; 52 Depot St., Athens, OH 45701 (SAN 698-2298).

†Main Street, (*Main Street Pr., The; 0-915590; 1-55562*), William Case Hse., Pittstown, NJ 08867 (SAN 207-4443) Tel 201-735-9424; *CIP.*

Main Track, (*Main Track Pubns; 0-933866*), Subs. of Mus-Art Corporation of America, 2119 Forestwood Ct., Fullerton, CA 92633-1248 (SAN 212-758X) Tel 714-441-2041.

Maine Antique, (*Maine Antique Digest, Inc.; 0-917312*), P.O. Box 645, Waldoboro, ME 04572 (SAN 208-3949) Tel 207-832-7534.

Maine Dept Marine, (*Maine Dept. of Marine Resources; 0-89737*), Fisheries Research Sta., West Boothbay Harbor, ME 04575 (SAN 211-9145).

Maine Hist, (*Maine Historical Society; 0-915592*), 485 Congress St., Portland, ME 04111 (SAN 202-2605) Tel 207-774-1822.

Maine St Bar, (*Maine State Bar Assn.*), 124 State St., P.O. Box 788, Augusta, ME 04330 (SAN 227-0412) Tel 207-622-7523.

Maine St Mus, (*Main State Museum Pubns.; 0-913764*), State Hse., Sta. 83, Augusta, ME 04333 (SAN 203-9567) Tel 207-289-2301.

Mainespring, (*Mainespring Pr.; 0-9610536*), P.O. Box 905B, Stonington, ME 04681 (SAN 209-8342) Tel 207-367-2484.

Mainstream DC, (*Mainstream, Inc.*), 1200 15th St. NW., Suite 403, Washington, DC 20005 (SAN 225-9400) Tel 202-833-1136.

Maisner & Mason, (*Maisner & Mason; 0-9611406*), 13219 H Fiji Way, Marina del Rey, CA 90292 (SAN 283-9709) Tel 213-827-3443; Dist. by: MBF Sports, Inc., 3940 Higuera St., Culver City, CA 90232-2505 (SAN 283-9717) Tel 213-204-1551.

Maitland Enter, (*Maitland Enterprises; 0-936759*), 8118 N. 28th Ave., Phoenix, AZ 85021 (SAN 699-8437) Tel 602-269-2213.

Maitland Lib, (*Maitland Public Library; 0-9614036*), 501 S. Maitland Avenue, Maitland, FL 32751 (SAN 683-7972).

Maize Pr, (*Maize Pr.; 0-939558*), Colorado College, Box 10, Colorado Springs, CO 80903 (SAN 216-6852) Tel 303-636-3249.

Majestic Bks, (*Majestic Bks.; 0-9604968*), 2338 Henderson Mill Ct., Atlanta, GA 30345 (SAN 215-6792).

Maji Bks, (*Maji Bks.; 0-9615163*), 18 Ivest Dr., East Falmouth, MA 02536 (SAN 694-3047) Tel 617-564-5242.

Major Bks, (*Major Bks.; 0-89041*), 21335 Roscoe Blvd., Canoga Park, CA 91304 (SAN 207-4117) Tel 213-999-4100; 18-39 128th St., College Point, NY 11356 (SAN 207-4117) Tel 212-939-1119; Orders to: Kable News, Inc., 777 Third Ave., New York, NY 10017 (SAN 207-4109) Tel 212-486-2828.

Majority Pr, (*Majority Pr., The; 0-912469*), P.O. Box 538, Dover, MA 02030 (SAN 265-2757) Tel 617-828-8450; Orders to: P.O. Box 476, Canton, MA 02021 (SAN 658-2257).

Majors
See S Karger

Makana, (*Makana Ka Koloe Publishing; 0-935223*), P. O. Box 55879, Seattle, WA 98155 (SAN 695-7196) Tel 706-775-6848.

Makepeace Colony, (*Makepeace Colony Press, The; 0-87741*), P.O. Box 111, Stevens Point, WI 54481 (SAN 203-9575) Tel 715-344-2636.

Makin Do Ent, (*Makin' Do Enterprises; 0-88100*), Rte. 10, Baker Pl., Lancaster, SC 29720 (SAN 277-7118) Tel 803-285-2888.

MAKO Pub, (*MAKO Publishing Co.; 0-9616963*), 35552 Grand River, Suite 151, Farmington Hills, MI 48024 (SAN 661-7751) Tel 313-477-6113; Dist. by: Ludington News Company, 1600 E. Grand Blvd., Detroit, MI 48211 (SAN 169-3751) Tel 313-925-7600.

Makor Pub, (*Makor Publishing; 0-9608310*), 4910 Della Pl., San Diego, CA 92117 (SAN 240-5458) Tel 213-273-3306.

Malaga, (*Malaga, Rose C.; 0-939642*), 334 Livingston Ave., Babylon, NY 11702 (SAN 216-6356) Tel 516-422-2405.

Malama Arts, (*Malama Arts Inc.; 0-931909*), Div. of MAI Hawaii, P.O. Box 1761, Honolulu, HI 96806 (SAN 686-0141) Tel 808-329-5828.

Malamud-Rose, (*Malamud-Rose Pubs.; 0-9610466*), 38 Stonywood Rd., Commack, NY 11725 (SAN 285-0486); P.O. Box 194, Smithtown, NY 11787 (SAN 285-0494).

Malcolm Hse, (*Malcolm Hse.*), 805 Malcolm Dr., Silver Spring, MD 20901 (SAN 209-0368) Tel 301-439-4358.

Maledicta, (*Maledicta Pr.; 0-916500*), 331 S. Greenfield Ave., Waukesha, WI 53186 (SAN 208-1083) Tel 414-542-5853.

Malhotra, (*Malhotra, S.*), 20 Acorn Park, Cambridge, MA 02140 (SAN 203-8676); Orders to: 16 Cooke Rd., Lexington, MA 02173 (SAN 203-8684).

Malibu Pub, (*Malibu Publishing, Inc.; 0-918937*), 31304 Via Colinas, Suite 110, Westlake Village, CA 91362 (SAN 669-8263) Tel 818-889-1495 (SAN 669-8271).

Malibu Pubns *Imprint of* B of A

Malki Mus Pr, (*Malki Museum Pr.; 0-939046*), Dept. of Linguistics, Univ. of California, Los Angeles, CA 90024 (SAN 281-9724) Tel 213-474-0169; Orders to: 11-795 Fields Rd., Morongo Indian Reservation, Banning, CA 92220 (SAN 281-9732) Tel 714-849-7289.

Symbols/Abbreviations

Mallinckrodt Comm, *(Mallinckrodt Communications Research; 0-931227),* 2937 Macomb St. NW, Washington, DC 20008 (SAN 682-8752) Tel 202-362-3381.

Malvaux, *(Malvaux, Ets J.),* Orders to: Dillon-Donnelly Publishing, 7058 Lindell Blvd., St. Louis, MO 63130 (SAN 208-4589) Tel 314-862-6239.

Mammoth Pr, *(Mammoth Pr.; 0-937902),* 40-B Grecian Garden Dr., 'Rochester, NY 14626 (SAN 216-4132). Moved, left no forwarding address.

Mamre Pr, *(Mamre Pr., Inc.; 0-932945),* 1301 Sherwood Dr., Oxford, AL 36203 (SAN 689-1608) Tel 205-835-1973.

Man Inst Pol Res *Imprint of* **Universe**

Man NE, *(Man in the Northeast),* Box 241, Sullivan, NH 03751 (SAN 216-3810).

†**Man Pr TN,** *(Manuscript Pr.; 0-910159),* P.O. Box 40206, Nashville, TN 37204 (SAN 240-8651) Tel 615-298-5180; *CIP.*

Man-Root, *(Man-Root),* P.O. Box 982, Boynes, S. San Francisco, CA 94080 (SAN 207-8635); P.O. Box 762, Hot Springs, CA 95416 (SAN 693-4943).

†**Mana Pub,** *(Mana Publishing Co.; 0-935038),* P.O. Box 1855, Kailua, HI 96734 (SAN 220-1453) Tel 808-261-0050; *CIP.*

Management Advisory Pubns, *(Management Advisory Pubns.; 0-940706),* P.O. Box 151, Wellesley Hills, MA 02181 (SAN 203-8692) Tel 617-235-2895.

Management Club, *(Management Club Consultants),* P.O. Box 460028, Garland, TX 75046 (SAN 260-2199) Tel 214-272-9908.

Management Ed, *(Management Education Ltd.; 0-943170),* 12326 Riverview Rd., Prince Georges, MD 20744 (SAN 238-8197).

Management Pr, *(Management Press, Inc.; 0-9607826),* P.O. Box 34965, Memphis, TN 38134 (SAN 212-1123).

Manas, *(Manas Pubns.; 0-911804),* Strathmore Gate E., 132 Manchineel Ct., Royal Palm Beach, FL 33411 (SAN 203-9605) Tel 305-793-0032.

Manas-Sys, *(Manas-Systems; 0-9610076),* Box 3106, Newport Beach, CA 92663 (SAN 272-2062) Tel 714-870-1064; 2901 Coronado Dr., Fullerton, CA 92635 (SAN 662-0787) Tel 714-870-1064; Dist. by: Consulting Psychologists Press Inc., 577 College Ave., Palo Alto, CA 94306 (SAN 689-8351) Tel 415-857-1444.

Manchaca Pub, *(Manchaca Publishing Co.),* P.O. Box 783, Manchaca, TX 78652 (SAN 239-4553).

Manchester Group, *(Manchester Group, Ltd., The; 0-9605792),* 3501 26th Pl., W., No. 422, Seattle, WA 98199 (SAN 220-1747) Tel 206-282-2057.

Manchester Pr, *(Manchester Pr.; 0-934507),* P.O. Box 5368, Playa del Rey, CA 90296 (SAN 693-8515) Tel 213-306-8052.

Manchester Pubns, *(Manchester Pubns.; 0-934663),* 6085 Venice Blvd., Suite 125, Los Angeles, CA 90034 (SAN 694-051X) Tel 213-376-1630.

Manchurch, *(Manchurch; 0-935251),* P.O. Box 4114, Albany, NY 12204 (SAN 695-5037) Tel 518-434-8727; 435 Loudon Rd., Loudonville, NY 12211 (SAN 695-5045).

Mandala
See Irvington

Mandala Bks, *(Mandala Bks.; 0-9603226),* R.F.D Box 56, Vershire, VT 05079 (SAN 669-1676). Do Not Confuse with Mandala Press in MA (Mandala) or Mandala Press in NC (Mandala Pr).

Mandala Ent, *(Mandala Enterprises; 0-915891),* P.O. Box 534, Jessup, MD 20794 (SAN 294-0604) Tel 301-342-7170.

Mandala Holistic, *(Mandala Holistic Health; 0-939410),* P.O. Box 1233, Del Mar, CA 92014 (SAN 216-5783) Tel 619-481-7751.

Mandarin, *(Mandarin Press; 0-931514),* 210 Fifth Ave., New York, NY 10010 (SAN 211-514X).

Mandate *Imprint of* **William Carey Lib**

Mandekic, *(Mandekic, A.V., Enterprise; 0-9608312),* P.O. Box 649, Wrightwood, CA 92397 (SAN 240-5466) Tel 619-249-5105.

Mandel Pubns, *(Mandel Pubns.; 0-941420),* Div. of Management Development Institute, Inc., P.O. Box 16432, San Antonio, TX 78216-1132 (SAN 239-0094) Tel 512-344-1991.

Manderino Bks, *(Manderino Bks.; 0-9601194),* P.O. Box 291669, Los Angeles, CA 90029 (SAN 209-5793) Tel 213-665-0123.

M&L Block, *(Mary & Leigh Block Gallery, Northwestern Univ.; 0-941680),* 1967 Sheridan Rd., Evanston, IL 60201 (SAN 239-1643) Tel 312-491-4000; Dist. by: University of Washington Press, P.O. Box C50096, Seattle, WA 98145 (SAN 212-2502) Tel 206-543-8810.

M&S Pr, *(M&S Pr.; 0-87730),* Box 311, Weston, MA 02193 (SAN 203-9591) Tel 617-891-5650.

Mandyn Co, *(Mandyn Co., The; 0-9617251),* P.O. Box 36847, Houston, TX 77236 (SAN 663-558X); 2211 Norfolk, Suite 700, Houston, TX 77098 (SAN 663-5598) Tel 713-527-0516.

†**Manet Guild,** *(Manet Guild; 0-9602418),* Div. of Talco Corp., Box 73, Babson Park, MA 02157 (SAN 293-3020) Tel 617-449-3792; 33 Morningside Rd., Needham, MA 02192 (SAN 293-3039); *CIP.*

Mangan Bks, *(Mangan Bks.; 0-930208),* 6245 Snowheights Ct., El Paso, TX 79912 (SAN 209-3804) Tel 915-584-1662.

Manhattan Beach, *(Manhattan Beach Music; 0-931329),* 1595 E. 46th St., Brooklyn, NY 11234-3122 (SAN 682-000X) Tel 718-338-4137.

Manhattan Ltd NC, *(Manhattan, Ltd., Pubs.; 0-932046),* P.O. Box 18865, Raleigh, NC 27619 (SAN 211-8114) Tel 919-833-2121.

Manic D Pr, *(Manic D Pr.; 0-916397),* 1853 Stockton, San Francisco, CA 94133 (SAN 670-6932).

Manic Pr
See Manic D Pr

Manifestation, *(Manifestation, Inc.; 0-932947),* 708 Eighth Ave. S., Box 991, North Myrtle Beach, SC 29582 (SAN 689-0571) Tel 803-272-8183; Dist. by: Sheriar Pr., 1414 Madison St., North Myrtle Beach, SC 29582 (SAN 203-2457).

Manion Outdoors Co, *(Manion Outdoors Co., Inc.; 0-9612936),* P.O. Box 188, Delafield, WI 53018 (SAN 292-3378) Tel 414-646-4196.

Manivelle Pr, *(Manivelle Pr.; 0-9616106),* 7964 Jowry Terr., La Jolla, CA 92037 (SAN 699-6922).

Mankind Pub, *(Mankind Publishing Co.; 0-87687),* 8060 Melrose Ave., Los Angeles, CA 90046 (SAN 208-4422) Tel 213-653-8060.

Mann Assoc, *(Mann, Al, Assocs.; 0-9614769),* 7G Knights Bridge, Poughkeepsie, NY 12603 (SAN 693-000X) Tel 914-452-4145; Toll free: 800-437-GIMP.

Mann Found, *(Mann Foundation, Inc.; 0-9608904),* 7111 Glass Slipper Way, Citrus Heights, CA 95610 (SAN 241-1334) Tel 916-725-4488.

Mannix Clinic, *(Mannix Clinic, The),* 2021 Pontius Ave., Los Angeles, CA 90025 (SAN 219-0893).

Manor Bks
See Woodhill

Manor Health, *(Manor Health Care Corp.; 0-917025),* 10720 Columbia Pike, Silver Spring, MD 20901 (SAN 655-4059); Toll free: 800-637-1400.

Manor of Grace, *(Manor of Grace; 0-9616513),* 3816 Fannin, Houston, TX 77004 (SAN 659-5154) Tel 713-523-6277.

Manor Pub Co, *(Manor Publishing Co.; 0-937312),* 2896 Haribinger Ln., Dallas, TX 75252 (SAN 217-2488).

†**Mansell,** *(Mansell; 0-7201),* 950 University Ave., Bronx, NY 10452 (SAN 209-5807) Tel 212-685-8149; Toll free: 800-367-6770; *CIP.*

Manu Technologies, *(Manufacturers Technologies, Inc.; 0-9614980),* 27 Capital Dr., West Springfield, MA 01089 (SAN 693-6342) Tel 413-733-1972.

Manufacturers, *(Manufacturers' News Inc.),* 4 E. Huron St., Chicago, IL 60611 (SAN 670-7270) Tel 312-337-1084.

Manufacturing Confectioner, *(Manufacturing Confectioner),* 175 Rock Rd., Glen Rock, NJ 07452 (SAN 205-8979) Tel 201-652-2655.

†**Manuscript Pr,** *(Manuscript Pr.; 0-936414),* Box 1762, Wayne, NJ 07470 (SAN 214-3224) Tel 201-628-1259; Dist. by: PDA Enterprises, Box 1762, Wayne, NJ 07470 (SAN 222-0989) Tel 201-628-1259; *CIP.*

Manyland, *(Manyland Bks., Inc.; 0-87141),* 84-39 90th St., Woodhaven, NY 11421 (SAN 203-963X) Tel 718-441-6768.

Manzanas Press, *(Manzanas Pr.; 0-930831),* Div. of Leona Marie Ltd., 2641 N. Arcadia, Tucson, AZ 85712 (SAN 677-7163) Tel 602-326-9040.

Manzanita Pr, *(Manzanita Pr.; 0-931644),* P.O. Box 4027, San Rafael, CA 94903 (SAN 211-0342) Tel 415-479-9636.

Map Factory, *(Map Factory, The; 0-9611538),* Box 3484, Los Angeles, CA 90078-3484 (SAN 285-3302) Tel 818-989-7890.

Map World, *(Map World Pubns.; 0-89414),* Box 2818, Dublin, CA 94568 (SAN 209-6714) Tel 415-829-2728.

Maple Hill Pr, *(Maple Hill Pr., Ltd.; 0-930545),* 174 Maple Hill Rd., Huntington, NY 11743 (SAN 677-105X) Tel 516-549-3748.

Maple Mont, *(Maplegrove & Montgrove Pr.),* 4055 N. Keystone Ave., Chicago, IL 60641 (SAN 202-2303) Tel 312-286-2655.

†**Maple Terrace,** *(Maple Terrace Enterprises, Inc.; 0-9613738),* 1217 W. Market St., Orrville, OH 44667 (SAN 679-1336) Tel 216-682-1443; *CIP.*

Maple Tree Pub Co, *(Maple Tree Publishing Co.; 0-915387),* P.O. Box 479, General P.O., New York, NY 10116 (SAN 291-266X) Tel 516-536-6280.

Maplewood, *(Maplewood Pr.; 0-914048),* P.O. Box 90, Meadville, PA 16335 (SAN 203-9648) Tel 814-336-1768.

Mar Lor Pr, *(Mar Lor Pr.; 0-943400),* 4304 Brigadoon Dr., St. Paul, MN 55126 (SAN 240-7140) Tel 612-483-1588; Dist. by: Contemporary Bks., Inc., 180 N. Michigan Ave., Chicago, IL 60601 (SAN 202-5493) Tel 312-782-9181.

Mar Vista, *(Mar Vista Publishing Co.; 0-9604064),* 11917 Westminster Pl., Los Angeles, CA 90066 (SAN 215-255X).

Maran Pub, *(Maran Publishing Co.; 0-916526),* 320 N. Eutaw St., Baltimore, MD 21201-1886 (SAN 208-7545) Tel 301-837-3634.

Maranatha Baptist, *(Maranatha Baptist Pr.; 0-937136),* Maranatha Baptist Bible College, 745 W. Main St., Watertown, WI 53094 (SAN 220-2581).

Marathon Bks *Imprint of* **Marathon Intl Pub Co**

Marathon Intl Pub Co, *(Marathon International Publishing Co.; 0-915216),* P.O. Box 33008, Louisville, KY 40232 (SAN 206-443X) Tel 812-284-4163. *Imprints:* Love St Bks (Love Street Bks).(Love Street Bks.); Marathon Bks (Marathon Books).(Marathon Bks.).

Marathon Pr CA, *(Marathon Pr.; 0-937309),* Subs. of Marathon Pr., International, 407 W. Santa Clara Ave., Santa Ana, CA 92706 (SAN 658-8034) Tel 213-484-8420; Dist. by: Paladin Pr., P.O. Box 1307, Boulder, CO 80302 (SAN 212-0305).

Marbek Pubns
See Marber Pubns

Marber Pubns, *(Marber Pubns.; 0-931239),* P.O. Box 66251, Los Angeles, CA 90066 (SAN 682-8965).

Marburger, *(Marburger Pubns.; 0-915730),* P.O. Box 422, Manhasset, NY 11030 (SAN 208-0443).

MARC
See Missions Adv Res Com Ctr

Marcat Ent, *(Marcat Enterprises; 0-9612172),* 3050 E. Fifth St., No. 9, Long Beach, CA 90814 (SAN 289-4181). Moved, left no forwarding address.

Marcella, *(Marcella Pr.; 0-938468),* P.O. Box 1185, La Quinta, CA 92253 (SAN 215-8884).

March Hare, *(March Hare Publishing; 0-918295),* 1251 Dolores St., San Francisco, CA 94110 (SAN 657-2812) Tel 415-552-6058.

†**March of Dimes,** *(National Foundation March of Dimes; 0-86525),* 1275 Mamaroneck Ave., White Plains, NY 10605 (SAN 205-7441) Tel 914-428-7100; *CIP.*

Marco & Johnson
See Paul R Johnson

Marco Polo, *(Marco Polo Pubs.; 0-932820),* 8024 Valley Dr., N. Richland Hills, TX 76180 (SAN 212-2898) Tel 817-485-8307.

Marconi
See Tele Cable

Marconi Pr, *(Marconi Press; 0-9605434),* 7710 31st NW, Seattle, WA 98117 (SAN 218-4893) Tel 206-784-8813.

Marcor Pub, *(Marcor Pub.; 0-932248),* P.O. Box 1072, Port Hueneme, CA 93041 (SAN 220-8237).

Marcourt Pr, *(Marcourt Press; 0-9608748),* 7465 Beverly Blvd., Los Angeles, CA 90036 (SAN 241-0354) Tel 213-852-2025.

Marcroft Prods, *(Marcroft Productions; 0-935849),* P.O. Box 16405, Salt Lake City, UT 84116-0405 (SAN 695-9776) Tel 801-596-3127.

Marder
See Pine Ridge

Mardi Pr, *(Mardi Pr.),* P.O. Box 4173, Arlington, VA 22204 (SAN 240-0952).

Marduk Manumit, *(Marduk Manumit; 0-940452),* Subs. of Anderson Enterprises, P.O. Box 9202, Birmingham, AL 35213 (SAN 217-1961) Tel 205-879-5383.

Marell Ent, *(Marell Enterprise; 0-9617088),* P.O. Box 21062, Columbus Cir. Sta., New York, NY 10023 (SAN 662-6378); 250 W. 57th St., Suite 1527, New York, NY 10019 (SAN 662-6386) Tel 212-532-8447.

Margaret Media, *(Margaret Media, Inc.; 0-9616377),* 421 Manasses Pl., New Orleans, LA 70119 (SAN 695-5770) Tel 504-822-9305.

Margaretdaughters, *(Margaretdaughters, Inc.; 0-931911),* P.O. Box 70, Buffalo, NY 14222 (SAN 686-0133) Tel 716-885-5850; Dist. by: Inland Bk. Co., P.O. Box 261, 22 Hemingway Ave., East Haven, CT 06512 (SAN 200-4151) Tel 203-467-4257.

Marginal Med, *(Marginal Media; 0-942788),* P.O. Box 241, Fredonia, NY 14063 (SAN 240-2475) Tel 716-679-0462.

Margoe Jane, *(Margoe Jane Pubns.; 0-9602330),* Hollywood Ave. Rt. 1 Box 115, North Bangor, NY 12966 (SAN 212-2200) Tel 518-483-2020.

Mari-Lyn, *(Mari-Lyn Publishing; 0-912719),* 71 Wyndham Ave., Providence, RI 02908 (SAN 283-0787) Tel 401-272-3606.

Maria Pr, *(Maria Pr.; 0-9610850),* P.O. Box 887, Plandome, NY 11030 (SAN 265-2765) Tel 516-869-8173.

†Mariana Books, *(Mariana Bks.; 0-913783),* 1028 E. Pontiac Way, Fresno, CA 93704 (SAN 286-1488) Tel 209-225-0942; CIP.

Marianist Com Ctr, *(Marianist Communication Center; 0-9608124),* 1223 Maryhurst Dr., St. Louis, MO 63122 (SAN 240-2483) Tel 314-965-5634.

Marianna Jr, *(Marianna Junior Woman's Club Inc.; 0-939114),* P.O. Box 6, Marianna, FL 32446 (SAN 264-1968).

Marilyn Dorf, *(Dorf, Marilyn; 0-9616211),* 4149 E St., Lincoln, NE 68510 (SAN 658-5132) Tel 402-489-3104.

Marin Pub, *(Marin Publishing Co.; 0-9607482),* P.O. Box 436, San Rafael, CA 94901 (SAN 238-4701) Tel 415-883-4219.

Marin Pubns, *(Marin Pubns.; 0-934377),* 4 Highland Ave., San Rafael, CA 94901 (SAN 693-7985) Tel 415-459-3817.

Marine Bio, *(Marine Biological Laboratory; 0-912544),* Marine Resoures Dept., Woods Hole, MA 02543 (SAN 203-9664) Tel 617-548-3705.

Marine Corps, *(Marine Corps Assn.; 0-940328),* Box 1775, M.C.B., Quantico, VA 22134 (SAN 205-8952) Tel 703-640-6161.

Marine Corps League, *(Marine Corps League),* 933 N. Kenmore St., Arlington, VA 22201 (SAN 225-106X).

Marine Educ, *(Marine Education Textbooks; 0-934114),* 124 N. Van Ave., Houma, LA 70363-5895 (SAN 215-9651) Tel 504-879-3866.

Marine Endeavors, *(Marine Endeavors Pr.; 0-935181),* 2607 Woolsey St., Berkeley, CA 94705 (SAN 695-4677) Tel 415-849-0932.

Marine Environ, *(Marine Environmental Sciences Consortium; 0-938917),* P.O. Box 369, Dauphin Island, AL 36528 (SAN 661-7727); Bienville Ave., at Fort Gaines, Dauphin Island, AL 36528 (SAN 661-7735) Tel 205-460-6331.

Marine Sci Intl *Imprint of* **Jones & Bartlett**

Marine Tech Soc, *(Marine Technology Society; 0-933957),* 2000 Florida Ave., NW., Suite 500, Washington, DC 20009 (SAN 205-8936) Tel 202-462-7557.

Mariner Pr, *(Mariner Press; 0-911920),* P.O. Box 99, Somerset, NJ 08873 (SAN 206-6904).

†Mariner Pub, *(Mariner Publishing Co., Inc.; 0-936166),* 4835 W. Cypress St., Tampa, FL 33607 (SAN 221-4059) Tel 813-879-8032; CIP.

Mariners Boston, *(Mariners Pr., Inc., The; 0-913352),* P.O. Box 540, Boston, MA 02117-0540 (SAN 203-9680). Moved, left no forwarding address.

Mariological Soc, *(Mariological Society of America),* Marian Library, Univ. of Dayton, Dayton, OH 45469-0001 (SAN 225-4255) Tel 513-229-4214.

Marion Cnty Lib, *(Marion County Library; 0-9603086),* 101 E. Court St., Marion, SC 29571 (SAN 211-2973) Tel 803-423-2244.

Mariposa Arts, *(Mariposa Arts; 0-9617172),* 5878 Abernathy Dr., Los Angeles, CA 90045 Tel 213-391-3386.

Mariposa Print Pub, *(Mariposa Printing & Publishing Inc.; 0-933553),* 922 Baca St., Santa Fe, NM 87501 (SAN 691-8743) Tel 505-988-5582.

Mariposa Pub, *(Mariposa Publishing, Co.; 0-9615709),* 2201 N. Lexington, Suite 400, St. Paul, MN 55113 (SAN 695-8877) Tel 612-488-0305.

Maris & Assocs, *(Maris & Assocs.; 0-937517),* 912 Williamsburg Dr., Charleston, IL 61920 (SAN 658-9057) Tel 217-348-0093.

Marist Inst, *(Marist Institute for Public Opinion; 0-939319),* Marist College, 82 North Rd., Poughkeepsie, NY 12601 (SAN 663-1487) Tel 914-471-3240.

Maritime Assn, *(Maritime Assn. of the Port of New York/New Jersey, The; 0-9616995),* 17 Battery Pl., New York, NY 10004 (SAN 662-6424) Tel 212-425-5704.

Maritime Pubns, *(Maritime, Pubns.; 0-916269),* P.O. Box 527, Everson, WA 98247 (SAN 295-0081) Tel 206-966-5805.

Mark-Age, *(Mark-Age Inc.; 0-912322),* P.O. Box 290368, Fort Lauderdale, FL 33329 (SAN 202-6090) Tel 305-587-5555.

Mark Excell Pub, *(Mark of Excellence Publishing Co.; 0-933415),* 4620 Northridge Dr., Los Angeles, CA 90043 (SAN 691-5019) Tel 213-294-2136.

Mark Foster Mus, *(Mark Foster Music Co.; 0-916656),* P.O. Box 4012, Champaign, IL 61820 (SAN 208-2861) Tel 217-398-2760.

Mark III Prods, *(Mark III Productions; 0-9609982),* P.O. Box 586, Yuba City, CA 95992 (SAN 272-2461) Tel 916-674-7377.

Mark Pub, *(Mark Publishing Co.; 0-9614039),* P.O. Box 40668, Portland, OR 97240 (SAN 684-7668) Tel 503-223-9634; Dist. by: Univ. of Wash. Pr., P.O. Box C50096, Seattle, WA 98145 (SAN 212-2502) Tel 206-543-8870.

Mark Ziesing, *(Ziesing, Mark; 0-9612970),* P.O. Box 806, Willimantic, CT 06226 (SAN 292-7446) Tel 203-423-5836; 768 Main St., Willimantic, CT 06226 (SAN 658-2508).

Markay Enter, *(Markay Enterprises; 0-9616055),* 2301 S. Jefferson Davis Hwy., No. 927, Arlington, VA 22202 (SAN 697-9033) Tel 703-892-6664.

Market Data Ret, *(Market Data Retrieval, Inc.; 0-89770; 0-914608),* 16 Progress Dr., Shelton, CT 06484 (SAN 681-6312) Tel 203-926-4800; Toll free: 800-624-5669. Purchased Curriculum Information Ctr. in 1979.

Market Dyn, *(Market Dynamics; 0-913761),* 27 E. 22nd St., 9th Fl., New York, NY 10010 (SAN 285-337X) Tel 212-674-6888; Toll free: 800-262-7353.

Market Ed, *(Market Ed Inc.; 0-937470),* P.O. Box 45181, Westlake, OH 44145 (SAN 215-3246) Tel 216-779-4689.

Market Intell, *(Marketing Intelligence; 0-9615978),* 10675 S. De Anza Blvd., Suite 2-108, Cupertino, CA 95014 (SAN 697-2888) Tel 408-446-3040.

Market Res Co, *(Market Intelligence Research Company; 0-916483),* 4000 Middlefield Rd., Palo Alto, CA 94303 (SAN 295-1150) Tel 415-856-8200.

Market Timing, *(Market Timing Report; 0-9611670),* P.O. Box 225, Tucson, AZ 85702 (SAN 285-2985) Tel 602-624-6364; 2755 No. C W. Anklam Rd., Tucson, AZ 85745 (SAN 285-2993).

Marketforce Pubns, *(Marketforce Pubns.; 0-934065),* 3650 Ashford Dunwoody Rd. 8-H, Atlanta, GA 30319 (SAN 693-1308).

Marketing Alliance, *(Marketing Alliance, Inc.; 0-934985),* 3323 Old Hickory Blvd., Old Hickory, TN 37138 (SAN 695-1910) Tel 615-847-2324.

Marketing Econs, *(Marketing Economics Institute, Ltd.; 0-914078),* 108 W. 39th St., New York, NY 10018 (SAN 202-6104) Tel 212-869-8260.

Marketing Effect, *(Marketing Effectiveness, Advisory Publishing Service; 0-910797),* P.O. Box 1786, Lafayette, CA 94549 (SAN 272-2550) Tel 916-525-7951.

Marketing for Profit, *(Marketing for Profit, Inc.; 0-9603370),* Box 624, St. Charles, IL 60174 (SAN 221-7457).

Marketing Intl, *(Marketing International, Inc.; 0-912257),* 940 Bender Bldg., 1120 Court Ave. NW, Washington, DC 20036 (SAN 265-1637) Tel 301-977-2905.

Marketscope Bks, *(Marketscope Bks.; 0-934061),* 119 Richard Ct., Aptos, CA 95003 (SAN 692-9095) Tel 408-688-7535.

Markewich, *(Markewich, Reese; 0-9600160),* Bacon Hill Rd., Pleasantville, NY 10570 (SAN 203-9699) Tel 212-674-2979.

Markins Enter, *(Markins Enterprises; 0-937729),* P.O. Box 6907, Portland, OR 97206 (SAN 659-3224) Tel 503-235-1036; 2039 SE 45th Ave., Portland, OR 97215 (SAN 659-3232).

Marlance Bks, *(Marlance Bks. for Cooks; 0-9613733),* 1070 Barry Ln., Cincinnati, OH 45229 (SAN 677-4903) Tel 513-281-0050.

Marlboro Pr, *(Marlboro Pr., The; 0-910395),* P.O. 157, Marlboro, VT 05344 (SAN 281-9813) Tel 802-257-0781.

Marlborough Pubns, *(Marlborough Pubns.; 0-9604594),* P.O. Box 16406, San Diego, CA 92116 (SAN 220-0104) Tel 619-280-8310.

Marlin, *(Marlin Pubns. International, Inc.; 0-930624),* P.O. Box 649, Plandomen, NY 11030 (SAN 203-9654) Tel 516-365-3788.

Marlin Pr, *(Marlin Pr.; 0-932949),* Geneva Pk., Boulder, CO 80302 (SAN 690-0062) Tel 303-443-6868.

Marling, *(Marling Assocs.; 0-912818),* Orders to: Altarinda Books, 13 Estates Dr., Orinda, CA 94563 (SAN 238-1397) Tel 415-254-3830.

Marlor Pr
See Mar Lor Pr

Marlor Prod, *(Marlor Productions; 0-9616973),* P.O. Box 156, Hicksville, NY (SAN 661-7697); 17 Eva Ln., Plainview, NY 11802 (SAN 661-7700) Tel 516-935-9419; Dist. by: Arthur L. Newman, 10355 Slater Ave., No. 105, Fountain Valley, CA 92708 (SAN 200-6723); Dist. by: Oaklawn Bks., P.O. Box 2663, Providence, RI 02907 (SAN 200-6715).

Marmac Pub, *(Marmac Publishing Co, Inc.; 0-939944),* 3423 Piedmont Rd., Suite 212, Atlanta, GA 30305 (SAN 669-1714) Tel 404-231-1153.

Marna Pr, *(Marna Pr.; 0-9617151),* P.O. Box 1154, West Bethesda, MD 20817 (SAN 663-3315); 7009 Amy Ln., Bethesda, MD 20817 (SAN 663-3323) Tel 301-229-5763.

Marnik, *(Marnik Pubs.; 0-9611760),* 17161 New Jersey, Southfield, MI 48075 (SAN 285-3396) Tel 313-557-9033.

Maron Pubns, *(Maron Pubns.; 0-941944),* 7900 Old Branch Ave., No. 106, Clinton, MD 20735 (SAN 264-1976) Tel 301-868-5700.

Marquette, *(Marquette Univ. Pr.; 0-87462),* 1324 W. Wisconsin Ave., Rm. 409, Milwaukee, WI 53233 (SAN 203-9702) Tel 414-224-1564.

Marquette Cnty, *(Marquette County Historical Soc., Inc.; 0-938746),* 213 N. Front St., Marquette, MI 49855 (SAN 205-8871) Tel 906-226-3571.

Marquis, *(Marquis Who's Who/Macmillan Directory Division; 0-8379),* Subs. of MacMillan, Inc., 200 E. Ohio St., Chicago, IL 60611 (SAN 202-6120) Tel 312-787-2008; Toll free: 800-621-9669.

Marr Pubns, *(Marr Pubns.; 0-938712),* P.O. Box 1421, New York, NY 10101 (SAN 213-1242) Tel 516-822-7744.

Marriage
See Abbey

Mars Hill Pubns, *(Mars Hill Pubns., Inc.; 0-9614230),* P.O. Box 362, Loma Linda, CA 92354 (SAN 686-7766).

Mars Pubns, *(Mars Pubns.; 0-910759),* 1211 East Altadena Dr., Altadena, CA 91001 (SAN 264-1984) Tel 818-798-8110.

Marsh Creek, *(Marsh Creek Pr.; 0-88100),* P.O. Box 432, Clayton, CA 94517 (SAN 289-5293).

Marshall & Sons
See D C Marshall

†**Marshall Cavendish,** *(Cavendish, Marshall, Corp.; 0-85685; 0-86307),* Subs. of Marshall Cavendish, Ltd., 147 W. Merrick Rd., Freeport, NY 11520 (SAN 238-437X); Toll free: 800-821-9881; P.O. Box 410, Freeport, NY 11520 (SAN 658-0289) Tel 516-546-4200; *CIP.*

Marshall Pubs, *(Marshall Pubs.; 0-9615206),* 2990 Watson St., Memphis, TN 38118 (SAN 694-2989) Tel 901-363-9738.

Marshland Pub, *(Marshland Publishing Co.; 0-941512),* P.O. Box 3241, Stony Creek, CT 06405 (SAN 239-1139).

Marshwinds Advisory, *(Marshwinds Advisory Co.; 0-9614496),* P.O. Box 563, Midway, GA 31320 (SAN 689-3953) Tel 904-386-6555.

Marston *Imprint of* **Forum Pr IL**

Martha J Stone, *(Stone, Martha Jane; 0-9617084),* 810 Cramer Ave., Lexington, KY 40502 (SAN 662-6335) Tel 606-266-5030.

Martin Consult, *(Martin Consultants, Inc.; 0-9609060),* P.O. Box 1076, Golden, CO 80402 (SAN 241-3353) Tel 303-278-0965.

Martin Creatics, *(Martin Creatics; 0-914247),* P.O. Box 626, Fairfax, CA 94930 (SAN 287-6353) Tel 415-453-8129.

Martin Genealog, *(Martin Genealogical Services; 0-9611862),* P.O. Box Drawer 2147, Warner Robins, GA 31099 (SAN 286-1771) Tel 912-923-1261.

Martin Gordon, *(Martin Gordon, Inc.; 0-931036),* 1000 Park Ave., New York, NY 10028 (SAN 211-1608) Tel 212-249-7350.

Martin-Marrero, *(Martin-Marrero Productions; 0-9613430),* P.O. Box 30081, Indianapolis, IN 46230 (SAN 657-0526) Tel 317-251-4212.

Martin Mgmt, *(Martin Management Books; 0-9615541),* Div. of Dr. Doris Martin, Management Consultant, Box 121, R.R. No. 1, Wailuku, Maui, HI 96793 (SAN 695-5789) Tel 808-244-4187.

Martin Motorsports, *(Martin Motorsports Publishing; 0-9605068),* P.O. Box 12654, Fort Wayne, IN 46864 (SAN 215-7861).

Martin Pr CA, *(Martin Pr., The; 0-941018),* 20600 Grammercy Pl., Suite 205, Torrance, CA 90501 (SAN 217-4014); Toll free: 800-421-1212. *Imprints:* P Hanson (Hanson, Paul).

Martin Press, *(Martin Pr.; 0-9617044),* P.O. Box 2109, San Anselmo, CA 94960 (SAN 662-8702); 63 Durham Rd., San Anselmo, CA 94960 (SAN 662-8710) Tel 415-454-7985. Do not confuse with Martin Pr., Los Angeles, CA, or Martin Pr., Torrance, CA.

Martin Pub, *(Martin Publishing Co.; 0-9612640),* 4924 Comanche Dr., La Mesa, CA 92041 (SAN 289-5331) Tel 619-461-3704; Dist. by: Frank Mailing Services, P.O. Box 3038, La Mesa, CA 92041 (SAN 200-4259).

Martin Pubns, *(Martin Pubns.; 0-9610182),* P.O. Box 480672, Los Angeles, CA 90048 (SAN 272-2658) Tel 213-272-4440.

Martin Res
See Qwint Systems

Martindale Pr, *(Martindale Pr., The; 0-914959),* P.O. Box F, Stanford, CA 94305 (SAN 289-3274).

Martingale, *(Martingale Manuscripts; 0-9603088),* Box 17, North Pitcher, NY 13124 (SAN 212-8020) Tel 315-653-4401.

Marty-Nagy, *(Marty-Nagy Bookworks; 0-917296),* 624 Rhode Island St., San Francisco, CA 94107 (SAN 208-757X) Tel 415-550-2613.

Marvanco, *(Marvanco Enterprises; 0-9604336),* Box 21, Peekskill, NY 10566 (SAN 214-4093).

Marvel Comics, *(Marvel Comics Group; 0-9604146; 0-87135),* 387 Park Ave. S., New York, NY 10016 (SAN 216-9088) Tel 212-696-0808.

Marvelous Muffin, *(Marvelous Muffin Co., The; 0-9613785),* 441 Apricot Ln., Mountain View, CA 94040 (SAN 678-982X).

Marvett Pub, *(Marvett, Michael E., Publishing Co.; 0-9615734),* 7804 Fourth Ave. W., Bradenton, FL 33529 (SAN 695-8516) Tel 813-792-7419.

Marwolf Pub, *(Marwolf Publishing; 0-9615847),* P.O. Box 23045, Minneapolis, MN 55423 (SAN 696-6039) Tel 612-869-4579.

Marxist Educ
See MEP Pubns

Marxist-Leninist, *(Marxist-Leninist Pubns.; 0-86714),* Orders to: P.O. Box 11972, Ontario St. Sta., Chicago, IL 60611 (SAN 295-3382).

Mary Ellen Bks., *(Mary Ellen Books; 0-9606602),* P.O. Box 7589-Rincon Annex, San Francisco, CA 94120 (SAN 210-6388).

Mary Ellen Ent, *(Mary Ellen Enterprises; 0-941298),* 6250 Excelsior Blvd., St. Louis Park, MN 55416 (SAN 212-0429) Tel 612-925-5112.

Mary Inc, *(Mary, Inc.; 0-915872),* 72 Waterman St., Providence, RI 02906 (SAN 207-5938) Tel 401-751-0566.

Mary Noble
See McQuerry Orchid

Mary Queen Apostles, *(Mary, Queen of Apostles Formation Center, Inc.; 0-935488; 0-9615381),* Box 355, Somers, CT 06071 (SAN 215-6199) Tel 203-749-4895.

Maryben Bks, *(Maryben Bks.; 0-913184),* 619 Warfield Dr., Rockville, MD 20850 (SAN 205-6313) Tel 301-762-5291.

Maryland Hist Pr, *(Maryland Historical Pr.; 0-917882),* 9205 Tuckerman St., Lanham, MD 20706 (SAN 202-6147) Tel 301-577-5308.

Maryland Locale, *(Maryland Locale, Ltd.; 0-9616584),* 8090 Main St., Ellicott City, MD 21043 (SAN 661-4043) Tel 301-461-1714.

Maryland Pub, *(Maryland Publishing Co.; 0-911071),* 10 Jack Frost Ln., Baltimore, MD 21204 (SAN 272-2690) Tel 301-823-3460.

MAS Pr, *(MAS-Press; 0-9607984),* P.O. Box 57374, Washington, DC 20037 (SAN 238-5392) Tel 202-659-9580; Dist. by: Borden Publishing Company, 1855 W. Main St., Alhambra, CA 91801 (SAN 201-419X) Tel 818-283-5031; Dist. by: Book Dynamics, Inc., 836 Broadway, New York, NY 10003 (SAN 169-5649) Tel 212-254-7798.

Mascot Pubs, *(Mascot Pubs.; 0-9615345),* P.O. Box 1476, Theodore, AL 36590 (SAN 695-1341) Tel 205-957-2277.

Masda, *(Masda Publishing Co.),* 31 Milk St., Boston, MA 02109 (SAN 202-6155).

MASEA, *(Mid-Atlantic Solar Energy Assn.; 0-9601884),* P.O. Box 541, Brattleboro, VT 05301 (SAN 220-2603).

†**Mason Clinic,** *(Mason Clinic, The; 0-9601944),* 1100 Ninth Ave., P.O. Box 900, Seattle, WA 98111 (SAN 213-8972) Tel 206-223-6985; *CIP.*

Mason Cty Hist, *(Mason County Historical Society; 0-935693),* E. 2370 Hwy. 3, Shelton, WA 98584 (SAN 696-2475) Tel 206-426-4203.

Mason Pub
See Butterworth MN

Masonic Lodge Soft, *(Masonic Lodge Software; 0-939321),* 106 Busch Hill Rd., Wetumpka, AL 36092 (SAN 663-1754) Tel 205-567-2763.

Mass Bar Assn, *(Massachusetts Bar Assn.),* 20 West St., Boston, MA 02111 (SAN 226-9473) Tel 617-542-3602.

Mass CLE, *(Massachusetts Continuing Legal Education-New England Law Institute Inc.),* 44 School St., Boston, MA 02108 (SAN 226-3033) Tel 617-720-3606.

Mass Coalition, *(Massachusetts Coalition for Occupational Safety & Health; 0-9608416),* 718 Huntington Ave., Boston, MA 02115 (SAN 240-7159) Tel 617-277-0097.

Mass Hist Soc, *(Massachusetts Historical Society; 0-934909),* 1154 Boylston St., Boston, MA 02215 (SAN 202-2133) Tel 617-536-1608; Dist. by: Northeastern Univ. Pr., P.O.Box 250, Ithaca, NY 14851 (SAN 205-3764) Tel 607-277-2211; Dist. by: University Microfilms International, 300 North Zeeb Rd., Ann Arbor, MI 48106 (SAN 212-2464) Tel 313-761-4700.

Mass Hist Work, *(Massachusetts History Workshop; 0-9615588),* 46 Pleasant St., Cambridge, MA 02139 (SAN 695-9202) Tel 617-354-8807.

Mass State, *(Massachusetts State Council Knights of Columbus; 0-9608258),* 10 Kearney Rd., Needham, MA 02194 (SAN 240-4060) Tel 617-793-2011.

Massenet Soc, *(Massenet Society American Branch; 0-9615735),* 9 Drury Ln., Fort Lee, NJ 07024 (SAN 695-8656) Tel 201-224-4526.

Massey Law, *(Massey, Alyne Queener, Law Library; 0-935449),* Vanderbilt Univ., Nashville, TN 37240 (SAN 696-4915) Tel 615-322-2726.

MassMkt Bks, *(MassMarket Bks.; 0-939211),* 872 Massachusetts Ave., Rm. 1011, Cambridge, MA 02139 (SAN 662-6114) Tel 617-864-2126.

†**Masson Pub,** *(Masson Publishing U.S.A., Inc.; 0-89352),* 211 E. 43rd St., New York, NY 10017 (SAN 211-1764); Dist. by: Year Bk. Medical Pubs., 35 E. Wacker Dr., Chicago, IL 60601 (SAN 205-5600); *CIP.*

Masspac Pub, *(Masspac Publishing Co.; 0-918020),* 48855 N. Gratiot, Mt. Clemens, MI 48045 (SAN 209-2948) Tel 313-949-9222.

Master Bks, *(Master Bk. Pubs.; 0-89051),* Subs. of Creation-Life Pubs., Inc., P.O. Box 1606, El Cajon, CA 92022 (SAN 205-6119) Tel 619-448-1121; Toll free: 800-621-0852 ext. 134. *Imprints:* Inst Creation (Institute of Creation Research).

Master Design, *(Master Designer),* 343 S. Dearborn St., Chicago, IL 60604 (SAN 205-8782) Tel 312-922-9075.

Master Link, *(Master Link Publishing Co.; 0-9615209),* P.O. Box 30520, Long Beach, CA 90853-0520 (SAN 694-2997) Tel 213-438-3185; Dist. by: Action Distributing, P.O. Box 3811, Huntington Beach, CA 92605 (SAN 200-6782) Tel 714-840-8712.

Master Mind, *(Master Mind Publishing Co.; 0-88152),* P.O. Box 1830, Warren, MI 48090 (SAN 272-2828) Tel 313-756-7050.

Master Pr, *(Master Pr.; 0-9600818),* P.O. Box 432, Dayton, OR 97114 (SAN 209-8369) Tel 503-864-2987.

Master Tchr, *(Master Teacher, Inc., The; 0-914607),* Leadership Ln., P.O. Box 1207, Manhattan, KS 66502 (SAN 289-3495) Tel 913-539-0555.

Masterco Pr, *(Masterco Press, Inc.; 0-912164),* P.O. Box 7382, Ann Arbor, MI 48107 (SAN 205-8774) Tel 313-428-8300; Toll free: 800-443-0100.

Masterpiece Pub, *(Masterpiece Publishing Co.; 0-935699),* Subs. of Masterpiece Productions Inc., 14505 NE 29th Pl., Bellevue, WA 98007 (SAN 696-2599) Tel 206-883-4483.

Masters Pubns, *(Masters Pubns.; 0-89808),* 215 Hillcrest Rd., Berkeley, CA 94705 (SAN 226-2959) Tel 415-540-0943.

MasterSon Pub, *(MasterSon Publishing; 0-9608418),* P.O. Box 3040, Peoria, IL 61614 (SAN 240-7175) Tel 309-682-9222.

Masterwork Pr, *(Masterwork Pr.; 0-912156),* P.O. Box 302, Pottersville, NJ 07979 (SAN 206-720X) Tel 201-439-3816.

Masterworks Art, *(Masterworks Art Pubns.; 0-9615194),* 932 Larson Dr., Altamonte Springs, FL 32714 (SAN 694-2288) Tel 305-682-5171.

Masterwrks Inc, *(Masterworks, Inc., Pubs.; 0-931317),* P.O. Box 1847, Friday Harbor, WA 98250 (SAN 685-2610) Tel 206-378-4816; Toll free: 800-445-1313.

Mastery Dev, *(Mastery Development; 0-937153),* 1029 W. Second St., Mesa, AZ 85201 (SAN 658-5779) Tel 602-962-0201.

Mastery Ed, *(Mastery Education Corp.; 0-935508; 0-88106),* 85 Main St., Watertown, MA 02172 (SAN 240-5474) Tel 617-926-0329; Toll free: 800-225-3214.

MD Family Pr, *(Maryland Family Pr.; 0-9614519),* 11065 Swansfield Rd., Columbus, MD 21044 (SAN 689-5700) Tel 301-730-9346.

MD Hall Records, *(Maryland Hall of Records Commission; 0-942370),* P.O. Box 828, Annapolis, MD 21404 (SAN 205-8855) Tel 301-269-3915.

†**MD Hist,** *(Maryland Historical Society; 0-938420),* 201 W. Monument St., Baltimore, MD 21201 (SAN 203-9788); *CIP.*

MD Pub Co, *(Maryland Publishing Co.; 0-9615995),* P.O. Box 19910, Baltimore, MD 21211 (SAN 699-7481) Tel 301-243-8558; 3431 Roland Ave., Baltimore, MD 21211 (SAN 699-749X).

MD Pubns, *(MD Pubns.; 0-910922),* 30 E. 60th St., New York, NY 10022 (SAN 206-7668).

MD Sea Grant Col, *(University of Maryland, Sea Grant Program; 0-943676),* H. J. Patterson, Rm. 1224, College Park, MD 20742 (SAN 238-4035) Tel 301-454-6054.

MD Token Medal Soc, *(Maryland Token & Medal Society, Inc.; 0-9616945),* P.O. Box 3273, Baltimore, MD 21228 (SAN 661-7654); 1404 Harberson Rd., Baltimore, MD 21228 (SAN 661-7662) Tel 301-744-2631.

MD Vet Med Assn, *(Maryland Veterinary Medical Assn.; 0-9615658),* Box 439, Fallston, MD 21047 (SAN 695-9563) Tel 301-879-9108.

MDK Inc, *(MDK, Inc.; 0-934580),* P.O. Box 2831, Chapel Hill, NC 27514 (SAN 213-6341) Tel 919-929-4260.

Mdwsweet Pr, *(Meadowsweet Pr.; 0-9617297),* 1067 Meadowsweet Dr., Corte Madera, CA 94925 (SAN 663-4559) Tel 415-924-1310.

Me & My Inner Self, *(Me & My Inner Self, Inc.; 0-9617045),* P.O. Box 1396, La Canada, CA 91011 (SAN 662-8176); 357 Knight Way, La Canada, CA 91011 (SAN 662-8184) Tel 818-790-4858; Dist. by: Social Studies Schl. Servs., 10000 Culver Blvd., Culver City, CA 90230 (SAN 168-9592) Tel 213-839-2436; Dist. by: Zephyr Pr., 430 S. Essex Ln., Tucson, AZ 85711 (SAN 270-6830) Tel 602-623-2022.

ME Appalach Trail, *(Maine Appalachian Trail Club, Inc.; 0-9616457),* P.O. Box 283, Augusta, ME 04330 (SAN 659-3003) Tel 207-465-3197; 85 Summer St., Oakland, ME 04963 (SAN 659-3011); Dist. by: Stephen Clark, P.O. Box 1276, Waterville, ME 04901 (SAN 200-6472).

ME Geneal Soc, *(Maine Genealogical Society; 0-9615551),* P.O. Box 221, Farmington, ME 04938 (SAN 696-2750) Tel 207-582-4940.

ME Hist Preserv, *(Maine Historic Preservation Commission; 0-935447),* 55 Capital St. Sta., No. 65, Augusta, ME 04333 (SAN 696-3315) Tel 207-289-2132; Orders to: Maine Archaeological Society, Inc., P.O. Box 982, Augusta, ME 04330 (SAN 662-3719).

ME Maritime Mus, *(Maine Maritime Museum; 0-937410),* 963 Washington St., Bath, ME 04530 (SAN 279-4780).

Me Pubns
See Minne HA HA

Mead Art Mus, *(Amherst College, Mead Art Museum; 0-914337),* Amherst, MA 01002 (SAN 277-9730) Tel 413-542-2335.

Mead Co
See Mead Pub Corp

Mead Pub Corp, *(Mead Publishing Corp.; 0-934422),* 21176 S. Alameda St., Long Beach, CA 90810 (SAN 213-1153).

Meadow Lane, *(Meadow Lane Pubns.; 0-934826),* 211 N. Citrus Ave., Unit 277, Escondido, CA 92027 (SAN 213-5361) Tel 619-747-0258.

Meadow Pr, *(Meadow Press; 0-931058),* P.O. Box 35, Port Jefferson, NY 11777 (SAN 211-917X) Tel 516-473-1370.

†**Meadowbrook,** *(Meadowbrook, Inc.; 0-915658; 0-88166),* 18318 Minnetonka Blvd., Deephaven, MN 55391 (SAN 207-3404) Tel 612-473-5400; Dist. by: Simon & Schuster, 1230 Ave. of the Americas, New York, NY 10020 (SAN 200-2450) Tel 212-698-7000; *CIP.*

Meadowbrook Pr
See Meadowbrook

Meadowlark, *(Meadowlark Pr.; 0-941126),* P.O. Box 8172, Prairie Village, KS 66208 (SAN 238-8979) Tel 913-341-9031.

Meadowlark Pubns, *(Meadowlark Pubns.; 0-9615590),* 177 Mira del Oeste, San Clemente, CA 92672 (SAN 695-9180) Tel 714-492-8226.

Meals for Millions, *(Meals for Millions/Freedom from Hunger Foundation; 0-9607124),* 815 Second Ave., Suite 1001, New York, NY 10017 (SAN 239-0108).

Means
See R S Means

Means Co Inc
See R S Means

†**Meckler Pub,** *(Meckler Publishing Corp.; 0-930466; 0-913672),* 11 Ferry Ln. W., Westport, CT 06880 (SAN 211-0334) Tel 203-226-6967; *CIP.*

Med Aesthetics, *(Medical Aesthetics; 0-937465),* Div. of Michael Elam, M.D., Inc., 2082 Michelson Dr., Suite 100, Irvine, CA 92715 (SAN 658-9138) Tel 714-752-1339.

Med Alt Press, *(Medical Alternatives Pr.; 0-935813),* 832 Havenwood Ln. S., Ft. Worth, TX 76112 (SAN 696-6101) Tel 817-457-9830.

Med/Av Pub, *(Med/Av Publishing Co.; 0-939135),* 521 Lafayette Ave., Hawthorne, NJ 07506 (SAN 662-4960) Tel 201-423-3330.

Med-Behavior, *(Medical/Behavioral Associates, Inc.; 0-936514),* 666 Park Ave. W., Mansfield, OH 44906 (SAN 214-4131).

Med Communications, *(MCSA-Medical Communications & Services Assn.; 0-917054),* 10223 NE 58th St., Kirkland, WA 98033 (SAN 203-9796) Tel 206-828-4263.

Med Computer
See Med Communications

Med Consumers, *(Medical Consumers Publishing Co.; 0-936401),* 2515 Santa Clara Ave., No. 103, Alameda, CA 94501 (SAN 699-7503) Tel 209-723-3505.

†**Med Economics,** *(Medical Economics Bks.; 0-87489),* Div. of Medical Economics Co., Inc., 680 Kinderkamack Rd., Oradell, NJ 07649-9066 (SAN 202-2613) Tel 201-262-3030; Toll free: 800-223-0581; Orders to: P.O. Box C-779, Pratt Sta., Brooklyn, NY 11205 (SAN 202-2621); *CIP.*

Med-Ed, *(Med-Ed, Inc.; 0-9609222),* P.O. Box 738, Atlanta, GA 30301 (SAN 241-4015) Tel 404-351-3253.

Med Educ, *(Medical Education Consultants; 0-937142),* Box 67159, Century City, Los Angeles, CA 90067 (SAN 209-2891) Tel 213-475-5141.

†**Med Exam,** *(Medical Examination Publishing Co., Inc.; 0-87488),* Div. of Elsevier Science Publishing Co., Inc., 52 Vanderbilt Ave., New York, NY 10017 (SAN 206-7897) Tel 212-916-1204; *CIP.*

Med Group Mgmt, *(Medical Group Management Assn.; 0-933948),* 1355 S. Colorado Blvd., Suite 900, Denver, CO 80222 (SAN 221-3982) Tel 303-753-1111.

Med Hist Pub, *(Medical History Publishing Assocs.; 0-9616748),* 1 Claremont Ct., Arlington, MA 02174 (SAN 661-2768) Tel 617-646-6762.

Med-Info Bks, *(Medical-Info Bks.; 0-916093),* P.O. Box 1A182, Lackawaxen, PA 18435 (SAN 294-6114).

Med Letter, *(Medical Letter),* 56 Harrison St., New Rochelle, NY 10801 (SAN 223-7938) Tel 914-235-0500.

Med Lib Assn, *(Medical Library Assn., Inc.; 0-912176),* 919 N. Michigan Ave., Suite 3208, Chicago, IL 60611 (SAN 203-980X) Tel 312-266-2456.

Med Manor Bks, *(Medical Manor Bks.; 0-934232),* Subs. of Manor House Pubns., Inc., 3501 Newberry Rd., Philadelphia, PA 19154 (SAN 217-2526) Tel 215-824-1476; Toll free: 800-343-8464; Dist. by: Baker & Taylor Co., Eastern Div., 50 Kirby Ave., Somerville, NJ 08876 (SAN 169-4901); Dist. by: Ingram Industries, 347 Reedowood Dr., Nashville, TN 37217 (SAN 169-7978).

Med Media Pubs, *(Medical Media Pubs.; 0-939498),* 4320 Centre Ave., Pittsburgh, PA 15213 (SAN 216-4159).

Med Prod, *(Medical Productions Inc.; 0-933745),* Subs. of Metro Publishing, 5308-C Elm, Houston, TX 77081 (SAN 692-5979) Tel 713-666-4269; P.O. Box 270776, Houston, TX 77277-0776 (SAN 692-8544).

Med Res Assocs, *(Medical Research Assocs. Pubns.; 0-930835),* P.O. Box 1247, Ballwin, MO 63022 (SAN 677-685X) Tel 314-569-7763.

Med River Pub, *(Medicine River Publishing Co.; 0-9616479),* 1425 First Ave., N., Great Falls, MT 59401 (SAN 659-3321) Tel 406-453-3593.

Med Software, *(Medical Software Co.; 0-88672),* Box 1272, 333 Main St., Center Moriches, NY 11934 (SAN 265-1661) Tel 516-878-4840. Out of business.

MEDA Pubns, *(MEDA Pubns.; 0-9610200),* 107 Elena Drive, Scotts Valley, CA 95066 (SAN 264-1887).

Medallion *Imprint of* Berkley Pub

Medallion Bks CA, *(Medallion Bks., Inc.; 1-55627),* 5455 Wilshire Blvd., Suite 1700, Los Angeles, CA 90036 (SAN 661-3705) Tel 213-933-2665.

Medallion Pr, *(Medallion Press; 0-9610620),* 906 Shadowlawn Dr., Tallahassee, FL 32312 (SAN 265-3591) Tel 904-385-6097.

Medcards, *(Medcards, Inc.; 0-9612166),* 10012 N. Dale Marby, Suite 223, Tampa, FL 33618 (SAN 289-422X) Tel 813-961-3864.

Medea Pub Co, *(Medea Publishing Co.; 0-9615432),* 4716 Old Dominion Dr., Arlington, VA 22207 (SAN 696-1061) Tel 703-527-3546.

Medi-Comp, *(Medi Comp Press; 0-9600704),* 41 Tunnel Rd., Berkeley, CA 94705 (SAN 207-2610) Tel 415-548-1188.

Medi-Ed Pr, *(Medi-Ed Pr.; 0-936741),* P.O. Box 957, East Lansing, MI 48823 (SAN 699-9530) Tel 517-627-3653; 511 Sherman Rd., Lansing, MI 48917 (SAN 699-9549).

Media Action, *(Media Action Research Center, Inc.; 0-918084),* 475 Riverside Dr., Rm. 1370, New York, NY 10115 (SAN 210-2366) Tel 212-865-6690.

Media All, *(Media Alliance, Inc.; 0-915339),* c/o WNET, 356 W. 58th St., New York, NY 10019 (SAN 290-0130) Tel 212-560-2919.

Media & Travel Pubns, *(Media & Travel Pubns.; 0-937367),* P.O. Box 8415, San Diego, CA 92102 (SAN 659-0306) Tel 619-235-6003; 1220 23rd St., No. 3, San Diego, CA 92102 (SAN 659-0314).

Media Arts, *(Media Arts Productions; 0-9614642),* 140-9D Bellamy Loop, New York, NY 10475 (SAN 691-9197) Tel 212-562-9426; Orders to: P.O. Box 48, New York, NY 10475 (SAN 662-2968).

Media Awards, *(Media Awards Handbook; 0-910744),* 621 Sheri Lane, Danville, CA 94526 (SAN 205-8707) Tel 415-837-7562.

Media Concepts, *(Media Concepts Press; 0-935608),* 331 N. Broad St., Philadelphia, PA 19107 (SAN 215-3254) Tel 215-923-2545.

Media Forum, *(Media Forum International, Ltd.; 0-912460),* P.O. Box 8, Fleetwood, Mt. Vernon, NY 10552 (SAN 204-5559) Tel 914-667-6575; R.F.D. 1, Box 107, West Danville, VT 05873 (SAN 694-9460) Tel 802-592-3444. *Imprints:* Media Forum Bks (Media Forum Books).

Media Forum Bks *Imprint of* Media Forum

Media Horizons, *(Media Horizons Inc.; 0-915616),* 50 W. 23rd St., New York, NY 10010 (SAN 211-1012) Tel 212-645-1000.

Media Inst, *(Media Institute, The; 0-937790),* 3017 M St., NW, Washington, DC 20007 (SAN 215-966X) Tel 202-298-7512.

Media Intl Promo, *(Media International Promotions, Inc.),* 114 E. 32nd St. Rm 1306, New York, NY 10016 (SAN 291-9346) Tel 212-889-7447; Orders to: P.O. Box 292 Murray Hill Sta., New York, NY 10156 (SAN 691-9596) Tel 212-889-7447.

Media Loc, *(Medical Locations & Permits; 0-935657),* 650 N. Bronson Ave., No. 106, Los Angeles, CA 90004 (SAN 696-1908) Tel 213-464-2177; Dist. by: Publishers Group West, 5855 Beaudry St., Emeryville, CA 94608 (SAN 202-8522) Tel 415-658-3453.

Media Materials, *(Media Materials, Inc.; 0-912974; 0-89539; 0-86601),* 2936 Remington Ave., Baltimore, MD 21211 (SAN 206-9989) Tel 301-235-1722.

Media Pr, *(Media Pr.; 0-917181),* Subs. of Woodland-Media, Inc., 21540 Prairie St., Suite C, Chatsworth, CA 91311 (SAN 656-1772) Tel 818-341-3156; Toll free: 800-262-7367 (Continental U. S.); Toll free: 800-272-7367 (inside CA); Dist. by: Media Products, 21540 Prairie St., Unit C., Chatsworth, CA 91311 (SAN 659-9346) Tel 818-341-3156.

Media Prods & Mktg, *(Media Productions & Marketing, Inc.; 0-939644),* 2440 "O" St., Suite 202, Lincoln, NE 68510-1125 (SAN 216-6372) Tel 402-474-2676.

Media Ref, *(Media Referral Service; 0-911125),* P.O. Box 3586, Minneapolis, MN 55403 (SAN 272-3123) Tel 612-933-2819.

Media Servs, *(Media Services; 0-9616262),* 213 Sam Bass Rd., Willow Park, TX 76086 (SAN 658-3431) Tel 817-441-8309; Orders to: Boston Music Company, 9 Airport Dr., Hopedale, MA 01747 (SAN 201-7326) Tel 617-478-4813.

Media Unltd, *(Media Unlimited Inc.; 0-930394),* P.O. Box I, Alameda, CA 94501 (SAN 210-6124); Toll free: 800-428-0902.

†**Media Ventures,** *(Media Ventures, Inc.; 0-89645),* P.O. Box 41359, Cincinnati, OH 45241 (SAN 212-114X) Tel 513-771-1220; *CIP.*

Media Weavers, *(Media Weavers; 0-936085),* P.O. Box 19755, Portland, OR 97219 (SAN 696-6446) Tel 503-244-0406.

Media West, *(Media West; 0-939216),* 527 N. Prospect Ave., Redondo Beach, CA 90277 (SAN 281-9880) Tel 213-376-7087.

Mediac Pr, *(Mediac Pr.; 0-9616446),* P.O. Box 3315, Van Nuys, CA 91407 (SAN 658-9111); 6504 Murietta Ave., Van Nuys, CA 91401 (SAN 658-912X) Tel 818-904-0515.

MediaHlth Pubns, *(MediaHealth Pubns.; 0-938669),* P.O. Box 541, St. Helena, CA 94574 (SAN 661-6178); 660 Sanitarium Rd., St. Helena, CA 94574 (SAN 661-6186) Tel 707-963-1493.

Mediamix, *(Mediamix Assocs.; 0-915893),* 3960 Laurel Canyon Blvd., Suite 340, Studio City, CA 91604 (SAN 294-0612) Tel 213-654-2603; Dist. by: Bookpeople, 2929 Fifth St., Berkeley, CA 94710 (SAN 168-9517); Dist. by: Publishers Group West, 5855 Beaudry St., Emeryville, CA 94608 (SAN 202-8522) Tel 415-658-3453.

Mediaor Co, *(Mediaor Co.; 0-942206),* Box 631, Prineville, OR 97754 (SAN 238-7859).

Mediax
See Mediax Inter Tech

Mediax Inter Tech, *(Mediax Interactive Technologies; 0-912056),* 3029 Fairfield Ave., Black Rock Office Bldg., Black Rock, CT 06605 (SAN 205-8685) Tel 203-332-5800.

Medic Pub, *(Medic Pub. Co.; 0-934230),* P.O. Box 89, Redmond, WA 98073 (SAN 210-8313) Tel 206-881-2883.

Medical Accts Serv, *(Medical Accounts Services, Inc.; 0-9612564),* 4066 Evans Ave., Rm. 6, Fort Meyer, FL 33901 (SAN 289-3304) Tel 813-939-2299.

Medical Arts, *(Medical Arts Publishing Co.; 0-913092),* P.O. Box 36600, Grosse Pointe, MI 48236 (SAN 202-2184) Tel 313-886-5160.

Medical Group
See Med Group Mgmt

Medicaldisc, *(Medicaldisc Reporter; 0-936999),* 6471 Merritt Ct., Alexandria, VA 22312 (SAN 658-7445) Tel 703-354-8155.

Medicanto, *(Medicanto, Inc.; 0-931210),* 283 Greenwich Ave., Greenwich, CT 06830 (SAN 231-2574) Tel 203-869-5732.

Medicina Bio, *(Medicina Biologica),* 4830 NE 32nd Ave., Portland, OR 97211 (SAN 659-557X).

Medieval, *(Medieval & Renaissance Society; 0-913904),* P.O. Box 13348, N. Texas State Univ., Denton, TX 76203 (SAN 202-2257) Tel 817-565-2101.

Medieval Acad, *(Medieval Academy of America; 0-910956),* 1430 Massachusetts Ave., Cambridge, MA 02138 (SAN 203-9826) Tel 617-491-1622.

†**Medieval & Renaissance NY,** *(Medieval & Renaissance Texts & Studies; 0-86698),* Univ. Ctr. at Binghamton, Binghamton, NY 13901 (SAN 216-6119) Tel 607-777-6758; *CIP.*

†**Medieval Inst,** *(Medieval Institute Pubns.; 0-918720),* Western Michigan Univ., Kalamazoo, MI 49008 (SAN 212-2928) Tel 616-383-6096; *CIP.*

Medieval Latin, *(Medieval Latin Press; 0-916760),* P.O. Box 7847, St. Matthews Sta., Louisville, KY 40207 (SAN 208-7642) Tel 502-897-1241.

Medilex Co, *(Medilex Co., The; 0-916763),* Subs. of Robert Stephan Jr. PC, 3300 N. Central Ave., Suite 1400, Phoenix, AZ 85012 (SAN 654-3340) Tel 602-241-1400.

Medina Pr, *(Medina Univ., Press International; 0-914456),* P.O. Box 614, Wilmette, IL 60091 (SAN 206-5932) Tel 312-328-7890.

MediSci Pubs, *(MediScience Pubs.; 0-938869),* P.O. Box 256, Deerfield, IL 60015 (SAN 662-5304); 2501 Riverwoods Rd., Deerfield, IL 60015 (SAN 662-5312) Tel 312-945-7071.

MedMaster, *(MedMaster, Inc.; 0-940780),* 17500 NE Ninth Ave., North Miami Beach, FL 33162 (SAN 219-7960) Tel 305-653-3480.

Medusa, *(Medusa; 0-9601714),* 4112 Emery Place, NW, Washington, DC 20016 (SAN 215-9678) Tel 202-244-1239.

Meeker Pub, *(Meeker Publishing Co.; 0-935068),* 2605 Virginia St., NE, Albuquerque, NM 87110 (SAN 205-8650) Tel 505-299-6406.

Mega Corp, *(Mega Corp.; 0-9616170),* P.O. Box 10876, Jacksonville, FL 32247 (SAN 699-9468); 4812 Cherwell Ln., Jacksonville, FL 32217 (SAN 699-9476) Tel 904-733-2051.

Megabooks, *(Megabooks, Inc.; 0-935157),* 4300 NW 23rd Ave., Suite 192, P.O. Box 1702, Gainesville, FL 32602 (SAN 695-345X) Tel 904-371-6342.

Megan Pubns, *(Megan Pubns.; 0-9616663),* 17128 S. Angeline NE, Suquamish, WA 98392 (SAN 661-3586) Tel 206-598-4474.

Megans Wld, *(Megan's World; 0-9610150),* 124 W. Wilshire, P.O. Box 3399, Fullerton, CA 92634 (SAN 272-3239) Tel 714-871-1369.

MegaSoft, *(MegaSoft; 0-939095),* P.O. Box 991, Jennings, LA 70546 (SAN 662-6068); 915 Granger St., Apt. 3, Jennings, LA 70546 (SAN 662-6076). Do not confuse with other companies with the same name in Battleground, WA, San Jose, CA.

Megden Pub, *(Megden Publishing; 0-9603676),* P.O. Box 217, Huntington Beach, CA 92648 (SAN 214-414X) Tel 714-960-2182.

Meher Baba Info, *(Meher Baba Information; 0-940700),* Box 1101, Berkeley, CA 94701 (SAN 202-618X) Tel 415-562-1101; Dist. by: Bookpeople, 2929 Fifth St., Berkeley, CA 94710 (SAN 168-9517).

Mehetabel & Co, *(Mehetabel & Co.; 0-936094),* P.O. Box 151, Tiburon, CA 94920-0151 (SAN 281-9902) Tel 415-381-0828.

Meier & Assocs, *(Meier & Associates, Inc.; 0-917489),* Subs. of Meier Associates, P.O. Box 986, 335 College Ave., Dekalb, IL 60115 (SAN 656-0741) Tel 815-758-3808.

†**Meiklejohn Civ Lib,** *(Meiklejohn Civil Liberties Institute; 0-913876),* 1715 Francisco St., Berkeley, CA 94703 (SAN 203-9834) Tel 415-848-0599; *CIP.*

Meissner Bks, *(Meissner Bks.; 0-9613755),* P.O. Box 5296, Bend, OR 97708 (SAN 687-6242); Dist. by: Pacific Pipeline, P.O. Box 3711, Seattle, WA 98124 (SAN 169-8834).

Melcher Software, *(Melcher Software; 0-935977),* 412 Hollybrook Dr., Midland, MI 48640 (SAN 696-6047) Tel 517-631-7607.

Mele Ana, *(Ana, Mele, Inc., Publishing; 0-934509),* 3960 Laurel Canyon Blvd., Suite 170, Studio City, CA 91604 (SAN 693-8523) Tel 818-509-1196.

Melior Pubns, *(Melior Pubns.; 0-9616441),* Div. of Futurepast: The History Co., P.O. Box 1905, Spokane, WA 99210 (SAN 658-9154) Tel 509-838-5242; N. 10th Post St., Suite 550, Spokane, WA 99210 (SAN 658-9162).

Melissa Data, *(Melissa Data Co.; 0-937467),* 12 Balboa Coves, Newport Beach, CA 92663 (SAN 698-9197) Tel 714-650-1000.

Melrose Bk Co, *(Melrose Bk. Co.; 0-934972),* 384 North San Vicente Blvd., Los Angeles, CA 90048 (SAN 211-7436) Tel 213-655-5177.

Melrose Hist, *(Melrose Historical Society; 0-9615451),* Trinity Church, 131 W. Emerson St., Melrose, MA 02176 (SAN 695-7242) Tel 617-665-7569.

Melrose Pub Co
See Melrose Bk Co

Melrose Pub Inc, *(Melrose Publishing Co., Inc.; 0-932735),* 9021 Melrose Ave., Suite 301, Los Angeles, CA 90069 (SAN 240-4141) Tel 213-275-3076.

Melrose Sq *Imprint of* **Holloway**

Melton-Giardini Bk, *(Melton-Giardini Bk. Co.; 0-9614901),* Rte. 2, Box 34, Hull, GA 30646 (SAN 693-3092) Tel 404-543-8795.

Membrane Pr, *(Membrane Press; 0-87924),* P.O. Box 11601, Shorewood, Milwaukee, WI 53211 (SAN 202-621X).

Memento, *(Memento Pubns., Inc.; 0-89436),* P.O. Box 58646, Dallas, TX 75258 (SAN 210-1246) Tel 817-387-9286.

Memorial Sloan-Kettering, *(Memorial Sloan-Kettering Cancer Ctr., Alumni Office; 0-911315),* 1275 York Ave., New York, NY 10021 (SAN 272-3271) Tel 212-207-3511.

Memorial Union, *(Memorial Union Corporation; 0-934068),* Emporia State Univ., 1200 Commercial St., Emporia, KS 66801 (SAN 264-2050).

Memory Bks, *(Memory Bks.),* P.O. Box 85, New York, NY 10113 (SAN 699-783X).

Memory Impact Pub, *(Memory Impact Publishing; 0-9616664),* 520 La Honda Dr., Aptos, CA 95003 (SAN 661-3578) Tel 408-688-0270.

Memphis Musicraft, *(Memphis Musicraft Publications; 0-934017),* 3149 Southern Ave., Memphis, TN 38111 (SAN 692-7696) Tel 901-452-5265.

†**Memphis St Univ,** *(Memphis State Univ. Pr.; 0-87870),* Memphis State Univ., Memphis, TN 38152 (SAN 202-6228) Tel 901-454-2752; *CIP.*

Men North, *(Men of the North; 0-939703),* P.O. Box 46706, Bedford, OH 44146 (SAN 663-513X); 4713 Dalebridge Rd., No. F-36, Warrensville Heights, OH 44128 (SAN 663-5148) Tel 216-831-2698.

†**Menasha Ridge,** *(Menasha Ridge Pr., Inc.; 0-940752; 0-89732),* P.O. Box 59257, Birmingham, AL 35259 (SAN 219-7294) Tel 205-991-0373; Dist. by: Simon & Schuster, 1230 Ave. of the Americas, New York, NY 10020 (SAN 200-2450) Tel 212-245-6400; *CIP. Imprints:* Book Arts (Book Arts).

Mendham Publ Lib, *(Mendham Public Library, Publisher; 0-931661),* 10 Hilltop Rd., Mendham, NJ 07945 (SAN 683-7824) Tel 201-543-4152.

Mendocino Found Health, *(Mendocino Foundation for Health Education, The; 0-9615167),* P.O. Box 1377, Mendocino, CA 95460 (SAN 694-308X) Tel 707-964-0425.

Menil Found, *(Menil Foundation; 0-939594),* c/o Harvard Univ. Pr., 79 Garden St., Cambridge, MA 02138 (SAN 200-2043).

Menlo Pr, *(Menlo Pr.; 0-939607),* 1259 El Camino Real, Suite 191, Menlo Park, CA 94025 (SAN 663-5989) Tel 415-854-6553.

Menorah Med, *(Menorah Medical Center Auxilary; 0-9614735),* 4949 Rockhhill Rd., Kansas City, MO 64110 (SAN 692-7114) Tel 816-276-8133.

Menorah Pub, *(Menorah Publishing Co., Inc.; 0-932232),* 15 W. 84th St., New York, NY 10024 (SAN 212-1158) Tel 212-787-2248.

Menses, *(Menses; 0-9605700),* Box 192, Croton-on-Hudson, NY 10520 (SAN 216-2466).

Ment *Imprint of* **NAL**

Menta Pubns, *(Menta Pubns.; 0-935688),* P.O. Box 7542, Shawnee Mission, KS 66207 (SAN 213-6945) Tel 913-648-2911.

Mentors, *(Mentors, Inc.; 0-9601542),* 8817 Greenview Pl., Spring Valley, CA 92077 (SAN 241-5615) Tel 714-464-4235.

Menus Pacific NW, *(Menus from the Pacific North West; 0-9615525),* P.O. Box 532, West Linn, OR 97068 (SAN 696-2920) Tel 503-657-7659.

Meola, *(Meola, Edward A.; 0-9606008),* 5806 Circle H Place, Tucson, AZ 85713 (SAN 216-4175).

Symbols/Abbreviations

†MEP Pubns, *(MEP Pubns.; 0-930656),* Div. of Marxist Educational Press, Univ. of Minnesota, Anthropology Dept., 215 Ford Hall, 224 Church St. SE, Minneapolis, MN 55455 (SAN 276-9727) Tel 612-872-9897; *CIP.*

Mer *Imprint of* **NAL**

Mercedes-Benz, *(Mercedes-Benz of North America, Inc.; 0-936573),* 1 Mercedes Dr., Montvale, NJ 07645 (SAN 698-0678) Tel 201-573-2238.

Mercer Hse, *(Mercer House Press; 0-89080),* Clover Leaf Farm, Old Rte. 9, Rfd No. 1, Biddeford, ME 04005 (SAN 207-1754) Tel 207-282-7116; Orders to: P.O. Box 681, Kennebunkport, ME 04046 (SAN 207-1762).

Mercer Isl Preschl, *(Mercer Island Preschool Assn.; 0-936353),* P.O. Box 464, Mercer Island, WA 98040 (SAN 697-905X) Tel 206-232-6855; 7500 86th Ave. SE, Mercer Island, WA 98040 (SAN 698-2301); Orders to: Pacific Pipeline, 19215 66th Ave. S., Kent, WA 98032-1171 (SAN 169-8834) Tel 206-872-5523.

Mercer Island, *(Mercer Island Piccolo Pr.; 0-9614231),* 7441 W. Mercer Way, Mercer Island, WA 98040 (SAN 686-7790) Tel 206-232-7320.

Mercer Pr, *(Mercer Pr.; 0-9615033),* P.O. Box 525, Bluefield, WV 24701 (SAN 693-8027) Tel 304-327-0379.

†Mercer Univ Pr, *(Mercer Univ. Pr.; 0-86554),* Macon, GA 31207 (SAN 220-0716) Tel 912-744-2880; *CIP.*

Merchandising, *(Merchandising Concepts Specialists; 0-943038),* 132 S. Bedford Dr. No 206, Beverly Hills, CA 90212 (SAN 240-4087) Tel 213-276-9813.

Merchants Pub Co, *(Merchants Publishing Co.; 0-89484),* 20 Mills St., Kalamazoo, MI 49001 (SAN 209-9586) Tel 616-345-1175.

†Merck, *(Merck & Co., Inc.; 0-911910),* P.O. Box 2000, Rahway, NJ 07065 (SAN 202-6236) Tel 201-574-5403; *CIP.*

Merck-Sharp-Dohme, *(Merck Sharp & Dohme International; 0-911910),* Professional Communications Dept., West Point, PA 19486 (SAN 212-1921).

Mercury Bks, *(Mercury Books; 0-910963),* P.O. Box 442, Yardley, PA 19067 (SAN 272-3492) Tel 215-482-8404.

Mercury Hse Inc, *(Mercury Hse., Inc.; 0-916515),* 300 Montgomery St., Suite 700, San Francisco, CA 94104 (SAN 295-4656) Tel 415-433-7042; P.O. Box 640, Forest Knolls, CA 94933 (SAN 662-2283); Orders to: Kampmann & Co., Inc., 9 E. 40th St., New York, NY 10016 (SAN 202-5191) Tel 212-685-2928.

Mercury Media, *(Mercury Media Inc.; 0-932487),* P.O. Box 54, Wake, VA 23176 (SAN 687-4282) Tel 804-776-7717.

†Mercury Pr, *(Mercury Press (MO); 0-912393),* P.O. Box 8884, Munger Station, Witchita, KS 67208 (SAN 264-2069); *CIP.*

Mercury Pub, *(Mercury Publishing; 0-935717),* 4115 Flora Pl., St. Louis, MO 63110 (SAN 695-9288) Tel 314-664-6722.

Mercy Ambulance, *(Mercy Ambulance & Saint Mary's Hospital; 0-9615819),* 357 Jefferson SE, Grand Rapids, MI 49503 (SAN 696-6152) Tel 616-459-8197.

Mercy & Truth, *(Mercy & Truth Pubs.; 0-9615494),* Rte 1, P.O. Box 503, Osceola, WI 54020 (SAN 696-379X) Tel 715-294-2052.

Mercy Oceans, *(Mercy Oceans Pubns.; 0-937847),* C/O Helen Johnson, 108 Graymoor Ln., Olympia Fields, IL 60461 (SAN 659-5162) Tel 312-748-4981; Dist. by: Bookpeople, 2929 Fifth St., Berkeley, CA 94710 (SAN 168-9517); Dist. by: New Leaf Distributing, The, 1020 White St., SW, Atlanta, GA 30310 (SAN 169-1449) Tel 404-755-2665.

Merdyne Pubs, *(Merdyne Pubs., Inc.; 0-934299),* 184 Fifth Ave., New York, NY 10010 (SAN 693-3793) Tel 212-255-8448.

Meredith
See BH&G

Merganzer Pr, *(Merganzer Press; 0-9602648),* 659 Northmoor Rd., Lake Forest, IL 60045 (SAN 212-7636).

Merging Media, *(Merging Media; 0-934536),* 516 Gallows Hill Rd., Cranford, NJ 07016 (SAN 206-3662) Tel 201-276-9479.

Meridan Pr OK
See Meridian Oklahoma

Meridian, *(Meridian Press; 0-9609462),* Subs. of Center for Help for Agoraphobia/Anxiety Through New Growth Experiences, 2915 Providence Rd., Charlotte, NC 28211 (SAN 260-2253) Tel 704-365-0140.

Meridian Ed, *(Meridian Editions),* 9905 Lorain Ave., Silver Spring, MD 20901 (SAN 209-5831).

Meridian Educ, *(Meridian Education Corp.; 0-936007),* 608 E. Locust St., Bloomington, IL 61701 (SAN 696-6012) Tel 309-827-5455.

Meridian Hill, *(Meridian Hill Pubns.; 0-940206),* 2435 Vance St., Lakewood, CO 80215 (SAN 220-3413) Tel 303-237-0755; Orders to: Johnson Books, 1880 S. 57th Ct., Boulder, CO 80301 (SAN 658-1013) Tel 303-443-1576.

Meridian Oklahoma, *(Meridian Pr.; 0-9615776),* P.O. Box 21567, Oklahoma City, OK 73156-1567 (SAN 696-6144) Tel 405-751-2343.

Meridian Pr OK
See Meridian Oklahoma

Meridian Pub, *(Meridian Publishing; 0-86610),* 2643 Edgewood Rd., Utica, NY 13501 (SAN 215-2568).

Meridional Pubns, *(Meridional Pubns.; 0-939710),* 7101 Winding Way, Wake Forest, NC 27587 (SAN 216-7484) Tel 919-556-2940.

Merit Bks, *(Merit Bks.; 0-915929),* Div. of Merit Media Intl., P.O. Box 3319, Laguna Hills, CA 92654 (SAN 294-0620) Tel 714-768-5777.

Merit Calif, *(Merit Pubs.; 0-910962),* P.O. Box 1344, Beverly Hills, CA 90213 (SAN 203-9869) Tel 213-474-1888.

Meriwether Pub, *(Meriwether Publishing, Ltd.; 0-916260),* Box 7710, Colorado Springs, CO 80933 (SAN 208-4716); 885 Elkton Dr., Colorado Springs, CO 80907 (SAN 658-2877) Tel 303-574-4422.

Merk, *(Merk),* 377 Merk Rd., Watsonville, CA 95076 (SAN 215-8892).

Merl Miller Assoc, *(Miller, Merl, & Assocs.; 0-933557),* 480 SW Fifth St., Lake Oswego, OR 97034 (SAN 691-876X) Tel 503-636-2023; P.O. Box 367, Lake Oswego, OR 97034 (SAN 658-2737) Tel 503-636-0552.

Merlin Engine Wks, *(Merlin Engine Works),* 548 Elm, San Bruno, CA 94066 (SAN 217-8915).

†Merlin Pr, *(Merlin Pr.; 0-930142),* P.O. Box 5602, San Jose, CA 95150 (SAN 209-584X); *CIP.*

Mermaid Bks, *(Mermaid Bks.; 0-9617196),* 2160 S. Holly, Suite 107, Denver, CO 80222 (SAN 663-2459) Tel 303-759-4294.

Merriam
See Merriam-Webster Inc

Merriam-Eddy, *(Merriam-Eddy Co., Inc.; 0-914562),* P.O. Box 25, South Waterford, ME 04081 (SAN 202-6252).

†Merriam-Webster Inc, *(Merriam-Webster, Inc.; 0-87779),* Subs. of Encyclopaedia Britannica, Inc., P.O. Box 281, Springfield, MA 01102 (SAN 202-6244) Tel 413-734-3134; Toll free: 800-828-1880; 47 Federal St., Springfield, MA 01102 (SAN 658-1226) Tel 413-734-3134; *CIP.*

Merrifield Co, *(Merrifield Co., The),* 890 Edwards Lane, Sebastopol, CA 95472 (SAN 687-7524).

Merril Pr, *(Merril Pr.; 0-936783),* 12500 NE Tenth Pl., Bellevue, WA 98005 (SAN 699-9387) Tel 206-454-7009.

Merrill, *(Merrill Publishing Co.; 0-675),* Div. of Bell & Howell Co., 1300 Alum Creek Dr., Columbus, OH 43216 (SAN 200-2116) Tel 614-890-1111; Toll free: 800-848-6205.

Merrimack, *(Merrimack Publishing Corp.; 0-87497),* Affil. of Associated Booksellers, 562 Boston Ave., Bridgeport, CT 06610 (SAN 203-5014) Tel 203-333-7268; Toll free: 800-232-2224; Dist. by: Associated Booksellers, 562 Boston Ave., Bridgeport, CT 06610 (SAN 203-5014). Do not confuse with Merrimack Publishers Circle, Salem, NH.

Merrimack Pub Cir, *(Merrimack Pubs. Circle; 0-941938),* Div. of Salem Hse., Ltd., 462 Boston St., Topsfield, MA 01983 (SAN 212-193X) Tel 617-887-2440. Do not confuse with Merrimack Publishing Corp., Bridgeport, CT.

Merrimack Vall
See Museum America

Merritt Co, *(Merritt Co.; 0-930868),* 1661 Ninth St., Santa Monica, CA 90406 (SAN 203-8110).

Merritt Pubs Texas, *(Merritt Pubs.; 0-930238),* 718 Westwood, Richardson, TX 75080 (SAN 210-6132) Tel 214-644-5765.

Merry Bears, *(Merry Bears; 0-933103),* 27122 Ayamonte, Mission Viejo, CA 92692 (SAN 689-5778) Tel 714-495-0510.

Merry Thoughts, *(Merry Thoughts; 0-88230),* 380 Adams St., Bedford Hills, NY 10507 (SAN 206-6882) Tel 914-241-0447.

Merton Hse, *(Merton Hse. Travel & Tourism Pubs., Inc.; 0-916032),* 2100 Manchester Rd., Suite 507, Wheaton, IL 60187 (SAN 207-9739) Tel 312-668-7410.

Meru Pub, *(MERU Publishing; 0-911447),* P.O. Box 1278, Captain Cook, HI 96704 (SAN 272-1538) Tel 808-328-9656; Dist. by: Bookpeople, 2929 Fifth St., Berkeley, CA 94710 (SAN 168-9517) Tel 415-549-3030; Dist. by: Publishers Group West, 5855 Beaudry St., Emeryville, CA 94608 (SAN 202-8522) Tel 415-658-3453; Dist. by: The Book Hse., 208 W. Chicago St., Jonesville, MI 49250-0125 (SAN 169-3859) Tel 517-849-2117.

Merz Prod, *(Merz Productions; 0-937001),* 24142 El Rond, Lake Forest, CA 92630 (SAN 698-1844) Tel 714-855-9455.

Mesa Pr IL, *(Mesa Press),* 5835 Kimbark Ave., Chicago, IL 60637 (SAN 215-3270) Tel 312-962-1596.

†Mesa Prods, *(Mesa Productions; 0-914963),* 714 Westmount Ave., Dallas, TX 75211 (SAN 289-534X) Tel 214-620-9355; *CIP.*

Mesa Pubns, *(Mesa Pubns.; 0-931984),* Div. of Mesa International, Inc., 6266 N. Swan Rd., Tucson, AZ 85718 (SAN 211-8629).

Mesa Verde, *(Mesa Verde Press; 0-9607220),* P.O. Box 6415, Santa Fe, NM 87502 (SAN 239-1163). Moved, left no forwarding address.

Mesa Verde Museum, *(Mesa Verde Museum Assocs. Inc.; 0-937062),* P.O. Box 38, Verde National Park, CO 81330 (SAN 295-0456).

Mesorah Pubns, *(Mesorah Pubns., Ltd.; 0-89906),* 1969 Coney Island Ave., Brooklyn, NY 11223 (SAN 213-1269) Tel 718-339-1700; Toll free: 800-Mesorah.

Messenger Comm, *(Messenger Communications; 0-939336),* 18706 25th Ave. SE, Bothell, WA 98011 (SAN 216-5392) Tel 206-481-9399.

Messing Pub, *(Messing, Simon D., Pub.; 0-9615946),* 58 Shepard's Knoll Dr., Hamden, CT 06514 (SAN 696-8171) Tel 203-397-4477.

†Messner, *(Messner, Julian; 0-671),* A Simon & Schuster Co., Div. of Gulf & Western Corp., 1230 Ave. of the Americas, New York, NY 10020 (SAN 202-6260) Tel 212-245-6400; Toll free: 800-223-2336; *CIP.*

Met Mus Art
See Metro Mus Art

META Pubns, *(META Pubns.; 0-916990),* P.O. Box 565, Cupertino, CA 95015 (SAN 208-7448) Tel 415-326-6465.

Metacom Pr, *(Metacom Press; 0-911381),* 1 Tahanto Rd., Worcester, MA 01602 (SAN 272-3581) Tel 617-757-1683.

Metagraphics, *(Metagraphics, Inc.; 0-934030),* 12381 E. Cornell Ave, Aurora, CO 80014 (SAN 679-1352).

Metal Bldg, *(Metal Building Manufacturers Assn., Inc.; 0-9615996),* 1230 Keith Bldg., Cleveland, OH 44115 (SAN 699-7538) Tel 216-241-7333.

Metal Bulletin, *(Metal Bulletin Inc.; 0-913333),* Subs. of Metal Bulletin PLC (UK), 708 Third Ave., New York, NY 10017 (SAN 283-2070) Tel 212-490-0791.

Metal Powder, *(Metal Powder Industries Federation; 0-918404),* 105 College Rd. E., Princeton, NJ 08540 (SAN 209-6250) Tel 609-452-7700.

Metal Prop Coun, *(Metal Properties Council, Inc., The),* 345 E. 47th St., New York, NY 10017 (SAN 225-2120) Tel 212-705-7693.

Metal Soc, *(Metallurgical Society, Inc., The; 0-87339),* 420 Commonwealth Dr., Warrendale, PA 15086 (SAN 680-0572) Tel 412-776-9000.

Metal Soc Am
See Metal Soc

Metamorphic Pr, *(Metamorphic Pr.; 0-9615848),* P.O. Box 1841, Santa Rosa, CA 95402 (SAN 696-6489) Tel 707-874-2606; Dist. by: Rodale Press, Incorporated, 33 E. Minor St., Emmaus, PA 18049 (SAN 200-2477) Tel 215-967-5171.

Metamorphous Pr, *(Metamorphous Pr.; 0-943920; 1-55552),* Subs. of Metamorphosis, Inc., P.O. Box 1712, Lake Oswego, OR 97034 (SAN 264-2077) Tel 503-635-6709.

Metascience, *(Metascience Foun.; 0-935436),* Box 747, Franklin, NC 28734 (SAN 213-4179) Tel 704-524-5103.

Metatron Pr, *(Metatron Press; 0-931412),* P.O. Box 10333, Milwaukee, WI 53210 (SAN 211-142X) Tel 414-444-2442.

Metcut Res Assocs, *(Metcut Research Associates, Inc.; 0-936974),* 3980 Rosslyn Dr., Cincinnati, OH 45209 (SAN 214-4166).

Meteora, *(Meteora Press; 0-9613347),* 58 Morningside Dr., Lowell, MA 01852 (SAN 656-1748) Tel 617-452-0116.

Meth U Pr
See SMU Press

Methodius Pr, *(Methodius Press; 0-9611866),* 7878 Twin Pines Lane, Sebastopol, CA 95472 (SAN 286-1437) Tel 707-823-0978.

†Methuen Inc, *(Methuen, Inc.; 0-416; 0-7100),* 29 W. 35th St., New York, NY 10001 (SAN 213-196X) Tel 212-244-3336. Do not confuse Tavistock Publications (UK), an imprint of Methuen, Inc., with Tavistock Poetry Pr., San Diego, CA. Acquired U. S. branch of Routledge & Kegan Paul, Ltd. in 1986; *CIP. Imprints:* Ark Paperbks (Ark Paperbacks).

Methuselah Bks, *(Methuselah Books; 0-937092),* Rt. 1 Spindle Rd., Ellsworth, ME 04605 (SAN 214-4174).

Metier, *(Metier; 0-936087),* P.O. Box 51204, San Jose, CA 95151 (SAN 696-642X) Tel 408-286-9992.

Metis Pr Inc, *(Metis Pr.; 0-934816),* P.O. Box 25187, Chicago, IL 60625 (SAN 213-2575).

Metric Media Bk, *(Metric Media Book Pubs.),* Div. of Abbey Books, P.O. Box 266, Somers, NY 10589 (SAN 209-147X) Tel 914-248-5522.

Metrics Pr, *(Metrics Pr.; 0-9607126),* P.O. Box 9248, Boston, MA 02114 (SAN 293-3047); Orders to: P.O. Box 9248, Boston, MA 02114 (SAN 293-3055).

Metrics Res Corp, *(Metrics Research Corp.; 0-932393),* 130 W. Wieuca Rd., Suite 208, Atlanta, GA 30342 (SAN 686-6786) Tel 404-255-1976.

Metrix Pr
See Metrics Pr

Metro Bk Co, *(Metro Book Co.; 0-915371),* 3208 Cahuenga Blvd. W., Los Angeles, CA 90068 (SAN 291-2805) Tel 818-508-0884.

Metro Bks, *(Metro Books, Inc.; 0-8411),* 3110 N. Arlington Heights Rd., Arlington Heights, IL 60004 (SAN 203-9893) Tel 312-253-9720.

Metro Ctr Educ, *(Metropolitan Ctr. for Educational Research, Development & Training; 0-935405),* 32 Washington Pl. Rm. 72, New York, NY 10003 (SAN 696-3595) Tel 212-598-7729.

Metro Deaf Senior, *(Metro Deaf Senior Citizens, Inc.; 0-9613623),* 1298 N. Pascal St., St. Paul, MN 55108 (SAN 670-8757) Tel 612-647-9565.

Metro Found, *(Metropolitan Foundation, The; 0-9615016),* 201 E. Franklin St., Richmond, VA 23219 (SAN 694-0374) Tel 804-648-1234.

Metro Futures, *(Metropolitan Futures, Inc.; 0-915218),* P.O. Box 1151, New York, NY 10017 (SAN 207-1444).

Metro Mothers Work, *(Metropolitan Mothers at Work; 0-9615017),* 6917 Arlington Rd., Suite 303, Bethesda, MD 20814 (SAN 694-0382) Tel 301-986-0725; Dist. by: Andrik Associates, P.O. Box 5029, 311 Ashby St., Alexandria, VA 22305 (SAN 221-895X).

†Metro Mus Art, *(Metropolitan Museum of Art; 0-87099),* Fifth Ave. & 82nd St., New York, NY 10028 (SAN 202-6279) Tel 212-879-5500; Dist. by: Univ. of Chicago Pr., 5801 Ellis Ave. S., 3rd Flr., Chicago, IL 60637 (SAN 202-5280) Tel 312-962-7693; *CIP.*

Metro Pub, *(Metro Publishing; 0-933745),* Box 270776, Houston, TX 77277 (SAN 694-3934) Tel 713-666-7841.

Metro Wash Lib, *(Metropolitan Washington Library Council; 0-914095),* Div. of Metropolitan Washington Council of Governments, 1875 Eye St. NW, No. 200, Washington, DC 20006 (SAN 287-6043) Tel 202-223-6800.

Metro WI, *(Metro Pubns.; 0-936537),* 1815 N. Shore Dr., Delavan, WI 53115 (SAN 697-9106) Tel 414-728-3800.

Metron Pr, *(Metron Press; 0-941862),* St. Anthony Falls Sta., Box 4202, Minneapolis, MN 55414 (SAN 220-259X).

Metron Pubns, *(Metron Pubns.; 0-940268),* P.O. Box 1213, Princeton, NJ 08542 (SAN 217-5401) Tel 609-396-7947.

Metropol Press, *(Metropol Press),* 3323 Catturagus Ave., P.O. Box 2547, Culver City, CA 90230 (SAN 292-3351).

Metrosource Pubns, *(Metrosource Pubns., Inc.; 0-9608012),* 1006 Olive St., Denver, CO 80220 (SAN 293-440X) Tel 303-321-3607; Dist. by: Gordons Books, Inc., 5450 N. Valley Hwy., Denver, CO 80216 (SAN 169-0531) Tel 303-296-1830.

Mettler Studios, *(Mettler Studios, Inc.; 0-912536),* Tucson Creative Dance Ctr., 3131 N. Cherry Ave., Tucson, AZ 85719 (SAN 206-1589) Tel 602-327-7453.

Metzger Pr, *(Metzger Press; 0-9608750),* 303 W. Glenoaks Blvd., Suite 208, Glendale, CA 91202 (SAN 241-0370) Tel 818-244-0365.

Mex Am Cult, *(Mexican American Cultural Ctr.; 0-932545),* 3019 W. French Pl., San Antonio, TX 78228 (SAN 687-4835) Tel 512-732-2156; Toll free: 800-531-6222.

Mex Am Legal, *(Mexican American Legal Defense & Educational Fund),* 28 Geary, San Francisco, CA 94108 (SAN 232-3362).

Mexican Museum, *(Mexican Museum, The; 0-905194),* Fort Mason Ctr., Bldg. D, Laguna & Marina Blvd., San Francisco, CA 94123 (SAN 238-7832) Tel 415-441-0404.

Mey-Hse Bks, *(Mey-House Books; 0-9611140),* P.O. Box 794, Stroudsburg, PA 18360 (SAN 285-6670).

Meyerbooks, *(Meyerbooks; 0-916638),* P.O. Box 427, Glenwood, IL 60425 (SAN 208-998X) Tel 312-757-4950; 235 W Main St., Glenwood, IL 60425 (SAN 658-1234) Tel 312-757-4950.

Mezquita Edit, *(Mezquita Editorial; 0-930174),* 20 W. 22nd St., Rm 1000, New York, NY 10010 (SAN 210-640X) Tel 201-865-4067.

MG *Imprint of* **Moody**

MGM Assocs, *(MGM & Assocs.; 0-9616923),* 8118 N. 38th Ave., Phoenix, AZ 85051 (SAN 661-4590) Tel 602-841-9398.

Mgmt Advisory Assoc Inc, *(Management Advisory Associates, Inc.),* P.O. Box 703, Bowling Green, OH 43402 (SAN 203-9907) Tel 419-352-7782.

Mgmt & Indus Res Pubns, *(Management & Industrial Research Pubns.; 0-933684),* P.O. Box 7133, Kansas City, MO 64113 (SAN 214-0535) Tel 816-444-6622.

Mgmt Couns, *(Management Counselors, Inc.; 0-914950),* 2029 Robin Crest Lane, Glenview, IL 60025 (SAN 207-1592) Tel 312-724-1888.

Mgmt Info Inc, *(Management Information Source, Inc.; 0-943518),* 1107 NW 14th St., Portland, OR 97209-2802 (SAN 240-7124) Tel 503-222-2399; Toll free: 800-626-8257 (orders only).

Mgmt Info Serv
See Scholarly

Mgmt Roundtable, *(Management Roundtable. Inc.; 0-932007),* 824 Boylston St., Chestnut Hill, MA 02167 (SAN 686-0974) Tel 617-232-8080.

Mgmt Sci Health, *(Management Sciences for Health; 0-913723),* c/o Learning for Life, Department BIP, 165 Allandale Rd., Boston, MA 02130 (SAN 286-1720) Tel 617-524-7799.

Mgmt Strat Group, *(Management Strategies Group, The; 0-914165),* 1342 Lost Creek Blvd., Austin, TX 78746 (SAN 287-6248) Tel 512-327-2377.

Mgmt Tele Pub, *(Management Telecommunications Publishing; 0-938303),* 1 Park Ave., New York, NY 10016 (SAN 661-3713) Tel 212-683-3899.

MGT Info, *(MGT Information Publishing; 0-9610848),* Box 3732, Arcadia, CA 91006 (SAN 265-2730) Tel 714-594-5611.

MH Pr, *(MH Press; 0-917882),* 9205 Tuckerman St., Lanham, MD 20801 (SAN 219-0907).

MHM Pub, *(MHM Publishing; 0-936833),* 6105 Tilden Ln., Rockville, MD 20852 (SAN 699-9697) Tel 301-881-7337.

†Mho & Mho, *(Mho & Mho Works; 0-917320),* 1259 El Camino Real, Suite 108, Menlo Park, CA 94025 (SAN 238-7999) Tel 415-327-6121; Orders to: Inland Bk. Co., 22 Hemingway Ave., East Haven, CT 06512 (SAN 200-4151) Tel 203-467-4257; Orders to: Bookpeople, 2929 Fifth Ave., Berkeley, CA 94710 (SAN 168-9517); Dist. by: New Leaf Distributing Co., 1020 White St. SW, Atlanta, GA 30310 (SAN 169-1449) Tel 404-755-2665; Dist. by: The Great Tradition, 750 Adrian Way, Suite 111, San Rafael, CA 94903 (SAN 200-5743) Tel 415-492-9382; *CIP.*

MI Adventure Pubns, *(M.I. Adventure Pubns.; 0-9616395),* RFD 1, Box 472, West Lebanon, ME 04027 (SAN 658-8921) Tel 207-658-9053; Old Stagecoach Rd., West Lebanon, ME 04027 (SAN 658-893X).

MI City Hist, *(Michigan City Historical Society Inc.; 0-935549),* P.O. Box 512, Michigan City, IN 46360 (SAN 696-2335) Tel 219-872-6133.

MI Dept Hist, *(Michigan Dept. of State; 0-935719),* Bureau of History, 208 N. Capitol Ave., Lansing, MI 48933 (SAN 695-9415) Tel 517-373-3703.

MI Instructor, *(MI Instructor Series; 0-937371),* 723 SW Austin Pl., Seattle, WA 98106 (SAN 658-8972) Tel 206-763-0672.

MI Middle Educ, *(Michigan Assn. of Middle Schl. Educators; 0-918449),* c/o Michigan State Univ., College of Education, Erickson 419, East Lansing, MI 48824 (SAN 657-6672) Tel 517-353-5461.

MI Municipal, *(Michigan Municipal League),* 1675 Green Rd., Box 1487, Ann Arbor, MI 48106 (SAN 226-3157) Tel 313-662-3246.

Miami Dade Environ, *(Miami-Dade Community College Environmental Ctr.; 0-936487),* 11011 SW 104 St., Miami, FL 33176 (SAN 698-0953) Tel 305-596-4113.

Miami Univ Art, *(Miami Univ. Art Museum; 0-940784),* Patterson Ave., Oxford, OH 45056 (SAN 219-6042) Tel 513-529-2232.

Mica Pub Co, *(Mica Publishing Co.; 0-931321),* P.O. Box 14931, Portland, OR 97214 (SAN 685-2637) Tel 503-230-2903.

†Micah Pubns, *(Micah Pubns.; 2-916288),* 255 Humphrey St., Marblehead, MA 01945 (SAN 209-1577) Tel 617-631-7601; *CIP.*

Micamar Pub, *(Micamar Publishing; 0-937373),* P.O. Box 56, Barneveld, WI 53507 (SAN 658-9200) Tel 608-924-2101; Rte. 1, Lakeview Rd., Barneveld, WI 53507 (SAN 658-9219).

MICATA, *(American Translators Assn., Mid-America Chapter; 0-9616557),* 323 Brush Creek Blvd., Apt. 805, Kansas City, MO 64112 (SAN 659-4816) Tel 816-561-8441.

Micelle Pr, *(Micelle Press, Inc.; 0-9608752),* P.O. Box 653, Cranford, NJ 07016 (SAN 241-0443).

Mich Nat Res, *(Michigan Natural Resources Magazine; 0-941912),* Box 30034, Lansing, MI 48909 (SAN 239-4596).

Mich Orchid Soc, *(Michigan Orchid Society; 0-9610332),* 920 Southdown Rd., Bloomfield Hills, MI 48013 (SAN 264-2093) Tel 313-644-2183; Orders to: 14800 Harrison, Livonia, MI 48154 (SAN 662-0809) Tel 313-421-0082.

Mich Romance, *(Michigan Romance Studies; 0-939730),* Dept. of Romance Languages, Univ. of Michigan, Ann Arbor, MI 48109 (SAN 216-7654) Tel 313-764-5386.

†**Mich Slavic Pubns,** *(Michigan Slavic Pubns.; 0-930042),* Dept. of Slavic Languages & Literatures, Univ. of Michigan, Ann Arbor, MI 48109-1275 (SAN 210-4636) Tel 313-763-4496; CIP.

†**Mich St U Pr,** *(Michigan State Univ. Pr.; 0-87013),* 1405 S. Harrison Rd., 25 Manly Miles Bldg., East Lansing, MI 48824 (SAN 202-6295) Tel 517-355-9543; Dist. by: Wayne State Univ. Pr., Leonard N. Simons Bldg., 5959 Woodward Ave., Detroit, MI 48202 (SAN 202-5221) Tel 313-577-4601; CIP.

Mich St Univ, *(Michigan State Univ., African Studies Ctr.; 0-939323),* 100 International Center, East Lansing, MI 48824 (SAN 663-1762) Tel 517-353-1700.

Mich United Conserv, *(Michigan United Conservation Clubs; 0-933112),* P.O. Box 30235, Lansing, MI 48909 (SAN 208-1091) Tel 517-371-1041.

Michael Paul, *(Paul, Michael; 0-9616367),* 528 S. Church St., Apt. 1N, Decatur, IL 62522 (SAN 658-9847) Tel 217-423-4802.

Michelin, *(Michelin Guides & Maps),* Div. of Michelin Tire Corp., P.O. Box 3305, Spartanburg, SC 29304-3305 (SAN 202-6309) Tel 803-599-0850; Orders to: Bibendum Rd., at New Cut Rd., Spartanburg, SC 29303 (SAN 693-9651).

Michelin Tire
See Michelin

Michelman Books *Imprint of* **Crown**

Michie-Bobbs
See Michie Co

Michie Co, *(Michie Co., The; 0-87215; 0-672; 0-87473),* Subs. of Macmillan Publishing, P.O. Box 7587, Charlottesville, VA 22906 (SAN 202-6317) Tel 804-972-7600; Toll free: 800-446-3410; 609 E. Market St., Charlottesville, VA 22901 (SAN 699-5438). Acquired law div. of Bobbs-Merrill Co. 1981. Acquired Allen Smith Co. 1985. *Imprints:* A Smith Co (Smith, Allen, Co.).

†**Michigan Mus,** *(Univ. of Michigan, Museum of Art, Alumni Memorial Hall),* 525 S. State St., Ann Arbor, MI 48109 (SAN 280-9028); CIP.

Michilander Indust, *(Michilander Industries; 0-941640),* 1100 State St., St. Joseph, MI 49085 (SAN 238-7816) Tel 616-983-4972.

Mickler Hse, *(Mickler Hse. Pubs., The; 0-913122),* P.O. Box 38, Chuluota, FL 32766 (SAN 206-6874) Tel 305-365-3636.

Micr Wrks Inc
See Micro Works

Micro Analysis, *(Micro Analysis & Design, Inc.; 0-937197),* 9132 Thunderhead Dr., Boulder, CO 80302 (SAN 658-5825) Tel 303-442-6947.

Micro Data Mgmt, *(Micro Data Management, Inc.; 0-938623),* P.O. Box 1230, Cerritos, CA 90701 (SAN 661-5724); 18944 Vickie Ave., No. 92, Cerritos, CA 90701 (SAN 661-5732) Tel 213-594-6282.

Micro db Sys, *(Micro db Systems; 0-930627),* P.O. Box 2380 3713 Lawndale Drive, Midland, MI 48640 (SAN 687-7338).

Micro Demo, *(Micro Demographics, Inc.; 0-935965),* P.O. Box 10070, Anaheim, CA 92802-8070 (SAN 696-6128) Tel 714-535-5456.

Micro Info, *(Micro Information Publishing; 0-912603),* 4730 Dakota St. SE, Prior Lake, MN 55372 (SAN 282-7867) Tel 612-447-6959; Toll free: 800-328-0196.

Micro Ink
See Computerist

Micro Magic, *(Micro Magic Cooking Co.; 0-9606096),* 145 N. 46th St., Lincoln, NE 68503 (SAN 216-8367) Tel 402-475-4536.

Micro Pro Litera Pr, *(Micro Pro Litera Pr.; 0-939477),* P.O. Box 14045, San Francisco, CA 94114 (SAN 663-3900); 109 Douglass St., No. 2, San Francisco, CA 94114 (SAN 663-3919) Tel 415-863-3037.

Micro Tech, *(Micro-Tech Index, The; 0-9617152),* 20005 Graves Run Rd., Hampstead, MD 21074 (SAN 663-3617) Tel 301-374-5810.

Micro Text Pubns, *(Micro Text Pubns., Inc.; 0-942412),* One Lincoln Plaza, Suite 27C, New York, NY 10023 (SAN 238-1753) Tel 212-877-8539.

Micro-Wave Foods, *(Micro-Wave Foods Inc.; 0-9614957),* P.O. Box 53, Malibu, CA 90265 (SAN 693-7462) Tel 213-456-5686; Dist. by: Club Products, 1100 Redmond Rd., Jacksonville, AR 72076 (SAN 200-7509) Tel 501-982-0555.

Micro Works, *(Micro Works, Inc., The),* 1942 S. El Camino Real, Encinitas, CA 92024 (SAN 277-6049) Tel 619-942-2400.

Microbim, *(Microbim; 0-914394),* 16 Tain Dr., Great Neck, NY 11021 (SAN 202-697X) Tel 516-466-2498.

Microcomputer Appns, *(Microcomputer Applications; 0-935230),* P.O. Box E, Suisun City, CA 94585 (SAN 285-0540).

Microcomscribe
See Microlit

Microconsulting NW, *(Microconsulting Northwest; 0-916241),* P.O. Box 15075, Portland, OR 97214 (SAN 294-9695) Tel 503-227-5150.

MicroDesigns, *(MicroDesigns; 0-938799),* 2954 Orlando, Oklahoma City, OK 73120 (SAN 661-5104) Tel 405-755-9806.

Microfilming Corp, *(Microfilming Corp. of America; 0-88455; 0-667),* 200 Park Ave., New York, NY 10166 (SAN 202-6325) Tel 212-972-1070. Microforms of newspapers, periodicals, books, curriculum materials, documents & archival materials for research.

Microform Rev
See Meckler Pub

Microlit, *(Microlit Pubs.; 0-931145),* 17857 Aguacate Way, San Diego, CA 92127 (SAN 687-8679) Tel 619-485-1773; Dist. by: Micro-Pace, 1510 N. Neil, Champaign, IL 61820 (SAN 200-7762) Tel 217-356-1884; Dist. by: The Distributors, 702 S. Michigan St., South Bend, IN 46618 (SAN 162-2488) Tel 219-232-8500; Dist. by: Slawson Communications, Inc., 3719 Sixth Ave., San Diego, CA 92103-4316 (SAN 200-6901) Tel 619-291-9126.

Micronesian, *(Micronesian Productions; 0-930839),* P.O. Box 6608, Tammuning, GU 96911 (SAN 677-6906).

Microphys Prog, *(Microphys Programs; 0-925534),* 1737 W. Second St., Brooklyn, NY 11223 (SAN 265-6906) Tel 718-375-5151.

Microprints, *(Microprints; 0-935193),* 2423 S. Spencer St., Seattle, WA 98108 (SAN 695-5061) Tel 206-723-3988.

Microrim, *(Microrim, Inc.; 0-916937),* 3925 159th Ave. NE, Box 97022, Redmond, WA 98073-9722 (SAN 287-7171) Tel 206-885-2000.

Microscope Pubns, *(Microscope Pubns.; 0-904962),* Div. of McCrone Research Institute, 2508 S. Michigan Ave., Chicago, IL 60616 (SAN 209-9594) Tel 312-842-7100.

MicroScope TX, *(MicroScope; 0-9607740),* P.O. Box 79762, Houston, TX 77279 (SAN 252-3386) Tel 713-468-8455.

Microsig Pr
See Microsignal

Microsignal, *(Microsignal; 0-912911; 0-927775),* P.O. Box 60312, Santa Barbara, CA 93160 (SAN 265-881X) Tel 805-964-2227.

†**Microsoft,** *(Microsoft Pr.; 0-914845),* Div. of Microsoft Corp., 16011 NE 36th Way, Box 97017, Redmond, WA 98073-9717 (SAN 264-9969) Tel 206-882-8080; Toll free: 800-223-2336; Dist. by: Harper & Row, 10 E. 53rd St., New York, NY 10022 (SAN 200-2086) Tel 212-207-7099; CIP.

Microtraining Assocs, *(Microtraining Associates, Inc.; 0-917276),* P.O. Box 641, North Amherst, MA 01059 (SAN 208-7677) Tel 413-549-2630.

MicroUse Info, *(MicroUse Information; 0-931555),* 1400 Commonwealth Ave., West Newton, MA 02165 (SAN 682-1901) Tel 617-527-3431.

Microwave, *(Microwave News; 0-9610580),* P.O. Box 1799, Grand Central Sta., New York, NY 10163 (SAN 264-2107) Tel 212-517-2802.

Microwave Cuisine, *(Microwave Cuisine; 0-932243),* 32 Harvard St., Garden City, NY 11530 (SAN 686-5887) Tel 516-437-8160.

Microwave Helps, *(Microwave Helps; 0-9602930),* P.O. Box 32223, Minneapolis, MN 55432 (SAN 212-9531) Tel 612-571-6091.

Microwave Kitch, *(Microwave Kitchen Press; 0-912471),* P.O. Box 17466, Pittsburgh, PA 15235 (SAN 265-2803) Tel 412-824-8817.

Microwave Touch, *(Microwave Touch; 0-9614205),* 942 Greenwood Dr., Greensboro, NC 27410 (SAN 686-788X) Tel 919-294-0767.

Mid-Am Coll
See Visual Resources Assn

Mid Am Pr, *(Mid-America Press; 0-9604672),* P.O. Box 21241, Columbia Heights, MN 55421 (SAN 220-0724) Tel 612-781-5166.

Mid Am Pub, *(Mid America Publishing Company; 0-89991),* 1808 Washington Ave., St. Louis, MO 63103 (SAN 220-8660) Tel 515-282-8220.

Mid-Amer Pub Hse KS, *(Mid-America Publishing Hse.; 0-939543),* 2420 NE 39th St., Topeka, KS 66617 (SAN 663-3307) Tel 913-286-1423. Do not confuse with Mid-America Pub Co of St. Louis, MO.

Mid Atl Reg Pr, *(Middle Atlantic Regional Pr. of the Apostolic Faith Churches of God; 0-9616056),* Div. of Apostolic Faith Churches of God, 1619 13th St., NW, Washington, DC 20009 (SAN 698-0635) Tel 202-265-7609; Orders to: P.O. Box 6021, Washington, DC 20005 (SAN 663-3972).

†**Mid Atlantic,** *(Middle Atlantic Pr.; 0-912608),* P.O. Box 263, Wallingford, PA 19086 (SAN 202-6341) Tel 215-565-2445; CIP.

Mid Coast Pub, *(Middle Coast Publishing; 0-934523),* P.O. Box 2522, Iowa City, IA 52244 (SAN 693-9031) Tel 319-353-3432.

Mid East Assess, *(Middle East Assessments Group; 0-937783),* 2400 Virginia Ave., NW, Suite C916, Washington, DC 20037 (SAN 659-3402) Tel 202-822-0955.

Mid East Exec Reports Ltd, *(Middle East Executive Reports, Ltd.; 0-915797),* 717 D St. NW, Suite 300, Washington, DC 20004-2807 (SAN 293-8936) Tel 202-628-6900.

Mid East Inst, *(Middle East Institute; 0-916808),* 1761 N St., NW, Washington, DC 20036 (SAN 202-2168) Tel 202-785-1141.

Mid East Pub Co, *(Mid East Publishing Co.),* P.O. Box A 3777, Chicago, IL 60690 (SAN 212-7644) Tel 312-545-0478.

Mid-Hudson Lib, *(Mid-Hudson Library System; 0-936213),* 103 Market St., Poughkeepsie, NY 12601 (SAN 696-849X) Tel 914-471-6060.

Mid-Life, *(Mid-Lifelines; 0-9609806),* 267 Firestone Dr., Walnut Creek, CA 94598 (SAN 272-4103) Tel 415-933-5481.

Mid-Peninsula Conver
See Ctr Econ Conversion

Mid-Peninsula Lib, *(Mid-Peninsula Library Cooperative; 0-933249),* 424 Stephenson Ave., Iron Mountain, MI 49801-3455 (SAN 692-3836) Tel 906-774-3005.

Mid South Sci Pubs, *(Mid-South Scientific Pubs.; 0-935974),* Box FM, Hwy. 82 E., Mississippi State Univ., Mississippi State, MS 39762 (SAN 213-7771).

Mid St Coll & Schl, *(Middle States Assn. of Colleges & Schools),* 3624 Market St., Philadelphia, PA 19104 (SAN 225-7653) Tel 215-662-5600.

MidCoast Pubns, *(Midcoast Pubns.; 0-910025),* 1982 Karlin Dr., Suite 200, St. Louis, MO 63131 (SAN 285-0613) Tel 314-966-3023; Dist. by: Quality Books Inc., 918 Sherwood Dr., Lake Bluff, IL 60044-2204 (SAN 169-2127); Orders to: Stafford Enterprises, 201 S. Central, Suite 300, St. Louis, MO 63105 (SAN 285-0648) Tel 314-863-5060; Orders to: P.O. Box 16880, St. Louis, MO 63105 (SAN 285-0656); Dist. by: Terschluse M., 727 Westbourne Dr., Suite 112, West Hollywood, CA 90069 (SAN 212-0364) Tel 213-659-9083; Dist. by: Baker & Taylor/Midwestern Division, 501 Gladiola Ave., Momence, IL 60954 (SAN 169-2100); Dist. by: Baker & Taylor/Eastern Division, 50 Kirby Ave., Somerville, NJ 08876 (SAN 169-4901); Dist. by: Baker & Taylor/Western Division, 380 Edison Way, Reno, NV 89564 (SAN 169-4464) Tel 702-786-6700.

†**Middle East Edit,** *(Middle East Editorial Assocs.; 0-918992),* 1100 17th St., NW, Suite 300, Washington, DC 20036 (SAN 210-4644) Tel 202-785-0022; CIP.

†**Middleburg Pr,** *(Middleburg Pr., The;* *0-931940),* Box 166, Orange City, IA 51041 (SAN 212-9183); *CIP.*

Middlewood Pr, *(Middlewood Pr.; 0-935961),* 5737 Middlewood Ave., Salt Lake City, UT 84118 (SAN 696-6136) Tel 801-966-8034.

Midgard Pr, *(Midgard Pr.; 0-9615948),* 4214 Midway Ave., Grants Pass, OR 97527 (SAN 696-8538) Tel 503-476-3603.

Midlothian, *(Midlothian Mirror),* Box 1140, Midlothian, TX 76065 (SAN 205-8464).

Midmarch Arts-WAN, *(Midmarch Arts/Women Artists News; 0-9602476),* Box 3304, Grand Central Sta., New York, NY 10163 (SAN 213-3393) Tel 212-666-6990.

Midnight Call, *(Midnight Call; 0-937422),* P.O. Box 4389, West Columbia, SC 29171 (SAN 211-8130).

Midnight Express, *(Midnight Express; 0-917915),* Box 26941, Austin, TX 78755 (SAN 657-0534) Tel 512-267-5535.

Midnight Oil Pr, *(Midnight Oil Pr.; 0-937269),* 266 Morris St., Stirling, NJ 07980 (SAN 658-9278) Tel 201-580-0656; Dist. by: Baker & Taylor, Eastern Div., 50 Kirby Ave., Somerville, NJ 08876 (SAN 169-4901); Dist. by: Book Dynamics, Inc., 836 Broadway, New York, NY 10003 (SAN 169-5649) Tel 212-254-7798.

Midnight Pr, *(Midnight Pr.; 0-9616400),* Box 902, Westhampton Beach, NY 11978 (SAN 658-9286) Tel 516-288-3831; 401 Montauk Hwy., Westhampton Beach, NY 11978 (SAN 658-9294).

Midnight Sun, *(Midnight Sun; 0-935292),* 223 E. 28th St., 1RE, New York, NY 10016 (SAN 213-537X).

Midway Pubs, *(Midway Pubs.; 0-938300),* 588 Charlton St., NW, Marietta, GA 30064 (SAN 217-2534) Tel 404-422-4169.

Midway Reprint *Imprint* **of U of Chicago Pr**

†**Midwest Alliance Nursing,** *(Midwest Alliance in Nursing, Inc.; 0-942146),* Indiana Univ., 1226 W. Michigan St., Rm. 108 BR, Indianapolis, IN 46223 (SAN 238-0226) Tel 313-655-6434; *CIP.*

Midwest Finan Pubns, *(Midwest Financial Pubns., Inc.; 0-933623),* Div. of The Beckley Group, Inc., P.O. Box 992, Fairfield, IA 52556 (SAN 692-4697); 607 W. Broadway, Fairfield, IA 52556 (SAN 662-7765) Tel 515-472-0333; Dist. by: Publishers Group West, 5855 Beaudry St., Emeryville, CA 94608 (SAN 202-8522) Tel 415-658-3453.

Midwest Heritage, *(Midwest Heritage Publishing Co.; 0-934582),* 108 Pearl St., Iowa City, IA 52240 (SAN 213-1161) Tel 319-351-2364.

Midwest Inst Design, *(Midwest Institute for Design Research, Inc.; 0-937169),* 616 E. Lake View Ave., Milwaukee, WI 53217 (SAN 658-5787) Tel 414-961-0769.

Midwest Media, *(Midwest Media Assocs.; 0-9616013),* P.O. Box 10684, Midwest City, OK 73140 (SAN 697-290X); 10020 NE Fourth St., Midwest City, OK 73130 (SAN 697-2918) Tel 405-677-0334.

Midwest Motor Mart, *(Midwest Motor Mart; 0-9617015),* 506 Prior Ave, N., St. Paul, MN 55104 (SAN 662-6602) Tel 612-646-8968; Dist. by: ARA Services, P.O. Box 448, Brainerd, MN 56401 (SAN 169-4049).

Midwest Old Settlers, *(Midwest Old Settlers & Threshers Assn.),* Mount Pleasant, IA 52641 (SAN 233-6480).

†**Midwest Plan Serv,** *(Midwest Plan Service; 0-89373),* Iowa State Univ., 122 Davidson Hall, Ames, IA 50011 (SAN 209-0295) Tel 515-294-4337; *CIP.*

Midwest Pol Pubns, *(Midwest Political Pubns.; 0-9612830),* Div. of Martin Hauan Agency, 2809 NW Expressway, No. 450, Oklahoma City, OK 73112 (SAN 210-9271) Tel 405-843-7351.

Midwest Pubns, *(Midwest Pubns. Co., Inc.; 0-910974; 0-89455),* P.O. Box 448, Pacific Grove, CA 93950 (SAN 207-0510) Tel 408-375-2455.

Midwest Research, *(Midwest Research; 0-915987),* 343 S. Dearborn St., Suite 1505, Chicago, IL 60604 (SAN 294-6130) Tel 312-663-5623.

Midwest Sci-Tech, *(Midwest Sci-Tech Pubs., Inc.; 0-910853),* 17385 Conant, Detroit, MI 48212 (SAN 272-4219) Tel 313-892-8110.

Midwest Taekwon-Do *See* Intl Taekwon-Do

Midwest Villages, *(Midwest Villages & Voices Pubns.; 0-935697),* 3220 Tenth Ave. S., Minneapolis, MN 55407 (SAN 696-2653) Tel 612-224-7687.

Midwestern St U Pr, *(Midwestern State Univ. Pr.; 0-915323),* 3400 Taft, Wichita Falls, TX 76308-2099 (SAN 290-0149) Tel 817-692-6611.

Midwife Pr, *(Midwife Pr.; 0-9614513),* 2749 N. Weil, Milwaukee, WI 53212 (SAN 691-7313) Tel 414-562-1927; Orders to: Midwife Press, P.O. Box 92482, Milwaukee, WI 53212 (SAN 662-2887).

Migrations Ltd, *(Migrations Ltd.; 0-9613519),* 1385 Pine St., Suite 16, San Francisco, CA 94109 (SAN 657-6699) Tel 415-771-1388; 1347 Divisadero St., Suite 217, San Francisco, CA 94117 (SAN 699-5802) Tel 415-931-6973; Orders to: Gaston's Guide, 1347 Divisadero St. Suite 217, San Francisco, CA 94117 (SAN 662-2380).

Mih, *(Mih Pubns.),* 15 Arnold Place, New Bedford, MA 02740 (SAN 207-8651) Tel 617-993-0156.

Mike Murdock, *(Murdock, Mike, Evangelistic Assn.; 0-937427),* P.O. Box 47684, Dallas, TX 75247 (SAN 658-9634) Tel 214-438-1600; 1100 E. Airport Freeway, No. 132, Irving, TX 75062 (SAN 658-9642).

Mike Nicholes, *(Mike Nicholes; 0-932149),* Subs. of Damascus Publishing Co., P.O. Box 727 655 NE Hood St., Gresham, OR 97030 (SAN 686-4244) Tel 503-666-7478.

Milady, *(Milady Publishing Corp.; 0-87350),* Div. of John Wiley & Sons, 3839 White Plains Rd., Bronx, NY 10467 (SAN 202-635X) Tel 212-881-3000; Toll free: 800-223-8055.

Milagro Co *See* Milagro Pr Inc

Milagro Pr Inc, *(Milagro Pr., Inc.; 0-9608504),* P.O. Box 1804, Santa Fe, NM 87501 (SAN 240-7221) Tel 505-988-1166.

Milbeck Pr, *(Milbeck Pr.; 0-9615752),* Div. of Lew Miller Advertising, 1614 Dundee Way, Louisville, KY 40205 (SAN 695-9881) Tel 502-458-1752.

Mile Sq Pub, *(Mile Square Pub., Inc.; 0-9616759),* P.O. Box 44185, Indianapolis, IN 46244 (SAN 661-4469); 445 N. Pennsylvania, Suite 709, Indianapolis, IN 46204 (SAN 661-4477) Tel 317-632-1984.

Miles River, *(Miles River Pr.; 0-917917),* 1009 Duke St., Alexandria, VA 22314 (SAN 657-0550) Tel 703-683-1500.

Milestext Pr, *(Milestext Pr.; 0-910525),* 884 Whitney Dr., St. Paul, MN 55124 (SAN 260-2261) Tel 612-432-2273.

Milestone MN, *(Milestone Pr.; 0-936091),* 2173 Folwell St., St. Paul, MN 55112 (SAN 696-6403) Tel 612-631-8333.

Milestone Pr, *(Milestone Pr.; 0-9615736),* 2302 40th St., Snyder, TX 79549 (SAN 695-8540) Tel 915-573-9708.

Milestones Unltd, *(Milestones, Unlimited; 0-9616833),* 24931 Woodridge Dr., Farmington Hills, MI 48018 (SAN 661-4752) Tel 313-477-2927.

Milford Hist Soc, *(Milford Historical Society; 0-9607742),* 124 E. Commerce, Milford, MI 48042 (SAN 238-7905) Tel 313-684-0845.

Milford Hse, *(Milford House; 0-87821),* Div. of Longwood Pub. Group, 51 Washington St., Dover, NH 03820 (SAN 202-6368); Toll free: 800-343-9444.

Milford Null, *(Milford Null Modem),* Phoenixville Pike & Charlestown Rd., Malvern, PA 19355 (SAN 654-598X); Toll free: 800-345-2121.

Military Aff Aero *See* MA-AH Pub

Military Coll *See* MCN Pr

Military Marketing, *(Military Marketing Services, Inc.; 0-914862),* P.O. Box 4010, Arlington, VA 22204 (SAN 207-365X) Tel 703-237-0203.

Military Opera Res, *(Military Operations Research Society, Inc.; 0-930473),* Landmark Towers, Ste 202, 101 S. Whiting St., Alexandria, VA 22304 (SAN 670-8943) Tel 703-751-7290.

Milkweed Ed, *(Milkweed Editions; 0-915943),* Subs. of Milkweed Chronicle, Journal of Poetry & Graphics, P.O. Box 24303, Minneapolis, MN 55424 (SAN 294-0663) Tel 612-332-3192; 528 Hennepin Ave., Minneapolis, MN 55403 (SAN 294-0671); Dist. by: Consortium Bk. Sales & Distribution, 213 E. Fourth St., St. Paul, MN 55101 (SAN 200-6049) Tel 612-221-9035; Dist. by: Small Press Distribution, 1814 San Pablo Ave., Berkeley, CA 94709 (SAN 204-5826) Tel 415-549-3336.

Milky Way-Kosmos *See* KOSMOS

Mill Bks, *(Mill Books),* Mill & Main St., Darby, PA 19023 (SAN 210-6140).

Mill Creek *See* Mill Creek Pubns

Mill Creek Pubns, *(Mill Creek Pubns.; 0-933251),* P.O. Box 404, Lakeside, AZ 85929 (SAN 655-7635) Tel 714-792-8643.

Mill Press, *(Millerhill Pr.; 0-9614177),* Rte. 1, Box 280, Bryan, TX 77803 (SAN 686-659X) Tel 409-823-0828.

Mill Town Graph, *(Mill Town Graphics; 0-914613),* Div. of Higgins & Ross, 281 Princeton St., North Chelmsford, MA 01863 (SAN 289-3800) Tel 617-454-4248.

Millenium Hse, *(Millenium House Pubs.; 0-916538),* Affil. of Millenium Foundation, P.O. Box 85, Agoura, CA 91301 (SAN 203-9923) Tel 213-889-3711.

Millennial Prods, *(Millennial Productions; 0-9602626),* 2455 Calle Roble, Thousand Oaks, CA 91360 (SAN 213-3407).

Miller Bks, *(Miller Books; 0-912472),* 2908 W. Valley Blvd., Alhambra, CA 91803 (SAN 203-9931) Tel 818-284-7607.

Miller Des, *(Miller's Design Studio; 0-934155),* 555 Brush St., Suite 805, Detroit, MI 48226 (SAN 692-9036) Tel 313-222-1706.

Miller Ent, *(Miller Enterprises; 0-89566),* P.O. Box 395, Boulder Creek, CA 95006 (SAN 210-6426) Tel 408-338-9633.

Miller Freeman, *(Miller Freeman Pubns., Inc.; 0-87930),* Subs. of United Newspapers, 500 Howard St., San Francisco, CA 94105 (SAN 213-6511) Tel 415-397-1881.

Miller Money Mgmt, *(Miller Money Management Inc.; 0-933203),* 304 Safety Building, Rock Island, IL 61201-8019 (SAN 692-3194) Tel 309-793-0387.

Miller OH, *(Miller Enterprises; 0-9607658),* P.O. Box 353, Athens, OH 45701 (SAN 241-5631).

Miller Pub *See* Mill Press

Miller Pub Co, *(Miller, Janus R., Publishing Co.; 0-9606160),* P.O. Box 21634, 20017 Monica Ave., Detroit, MI 48221 (SAN 217-1163).

Millers Graphics, *(Millers Graphics; 0-931831),* 1475 W. Cypress Ave., San Dimas, CA 91773 (SAN 687-6277) Tel 714-599-1431.

Millers River Pub Co, *(Millers River Publishing Co; 0-912395),* Box 159, Athol, MA 01331 (SAN 265-3605) Tel 617-249-7612; Dist. by: Inland Book Co., P.O. Box 261, 22 Hemingway Ave., East Haven, CT 06512 (SAN 200-4151) Tel 203-467-4257.

Mills Historical, *(Mills Historical Pr.; 0-931069),* 107 Woodridge, Tuscaloosa, AL 35406 (SAN 678-9315) Tel 205-752-4031.

Mills Pub Co, *(Mills Publishing Co.; 0-935356),* King Sta., P.O. Box 6158, Santa Ana, CA 92706 (SAN 272-4464) Tel 714-541-5750.

Mills Sanderson, *(Mills & Sanderson, Pubs.; 0-938179),* Affil. of Huenefeld Co., Inc., P.O. Box U, Bedford, MA 01730 (SAN 661-1982); 10 Muzzey St., Lexington, MA 02173 (SAN 661-1990) Tel 617-861-9650.

Milo Kovar, *(Kovar, Milo; 0-941208),* 2640 Greenwich, No. 403, San Francisco, CA 94123 (SAN 239-5592) Tel 415-921-1192.

Milton Bradley Co, *(Milton Bradley Co.; 0-88049),* 443 Shaker Rd., East Longmeadow, MA 01028 (SAN 238-7891) Tel 413-525-6411.

Milw Acad Med, *(Milwaukee Academy of Medicine Pr.; 0-9617070),* P.O. Box 26509, Milwaukee, WI 53226 (SAN 662-8923); 8701 Watertown Plank Rd., Milwaukee, WI 53226 (SAN 662-8931) Tel 414-464-4460.

Milwaukee Bks, *(Milwaukee Books; 0-942608),* 2147 N. 56th St., Milwaukee, WI 53208 (SAN 238-5422) Tel 414-257-3750.

Milwaukee County, *(Milwaukee County Historical Society; 0-938076),* 910 N. Third St., Milwaukee, WI 53203 (SAN 205-8383) Tel 414-273-8288.

†**Milwaukee Pub Mus,** *(Milwaukee Public Museum; 0-89326),* 800 W. Wells St., Milwaukee, WI 53233 (SAN 202-229X) Tel 414-278-2787; CIP.

Milwaukee Sentinel, *(Milwaukee Sentinel, The),* 918 N. 4th St., P.O. Box 371, Milwaukee, WI 53201 (SAN 215-2827) Tel 414-224-2120.

Mimir, *(Mimir Pubs., Inc.; 0-912084),* P.O. Box 5011, Madison, WI 53705 (SAN 202-6376) Tel 608-231-1667.

Mimosa Pubns, *(Mimosa Pubns; 0-916335),* 135 Old Suffolk Dr., Monroeville, PA 15146 (SAN 295-6969) Tel 412-856-9324.

Mina Pr, *(Mina Pr. Publishing, Inc.; 0-942610),* P.O. Box 854, Sebastopol, CA 95472 (SAN 238-5430) Tel 707-829-0854.

Mind Body
See Mindbody

Mind Comn, *(Mind Communication, Inc.; 0-938871; 1-55667),* 945 Burton SW, Grand Rapids, MI 49509 Tel 616-241-6095.

Mind-Dog, *(Mind-Dog Bks.; 0-9613432),* 64 Windell, Cambridge, MA 02138 (SAN 657-0542) Tel 617-876-1750.

Mind-Matter-Motion, *(Mind Matter Motion; 0-9608910),* P.O. Box 1091, Tiburon, CA 94920 (SAN 262-0790) Tel 415-331-6142.

Mind Prods Assocs, *(Mind Productions & Assocs.; 0-935257),* 1411 Eleanor Dr., P.O. Box 11221, Tallahassee, FL 32302 (SAN 695-5304) Tel 904-644-2491; Dist. by: New Mind Productions, P.O. Box 11221, Tallahassee, FL 32302 (SAN 200-5565).

Mindbody, *(Mindbody Pr.; 0-939508),* 1427 Milvia St., Berkeley, CA 94709 (SAN 216-4183) Tel 415-527-4980; Dist. by: Bookpeople, 2929 Fifth St., Berkeley, CA 94710 (SAN 168-9517) Tel 415-549-3030.

Mindbody Inc, *(Mindbody, Inc.),* 50 Maple Pl., Manhasset, NY 11030 (SAN 214-0365) Tel 516-365-7722.

Mindbody Pr
See Mindbody

Mindlifter Pr, *(Mindlifter Pr.; 0-931959),* P.O. Box 571, Boston, MA 02215 (SAN 686-0087) Tel 617-236-1758.

Minds Eye Illinois, *(Mind's Eye Publishing Co., The; 0-939249),* 100 Crabtree Rd., E. Dundee, IL 60118 (SAN 662-586X) Tel 312-426-9205.

Mind's Eye Inc, *(In the Mind's Eye, Inc.; 0-9616164),* 3207-C Sutton Pl., NW, Washington, DC 20016 (SAN 699-8380) Tel 202-966-3317.

Minds Eye Pub
See Minds Eye Illinois

Mineral Soc Ari, *(Mineralogical Society of Arizona; 0-910011),* P.O. Box 902, Phoenix, AZ 85001 (SAN 241-2241) Tel 602-995-0633.

Mineralogical Soc, *(Mineralogical Society of America; 0-939950),* 1625 I St., NW, Suite 414, Washington, DC 20006 (SAN 232-8739) Tel 202-775-4344.

†**Mini-World Pubns,** *(Mini-World Pubns.; 0-931323),* 9965 Quaker Ln., Maple Grove, MN 55369 (SAN 685-2645) Tel 612-424-5440; CIP.

Minibooks *Imprint of* **Bantam**

Ministering Angel, *(Ministering Angel; 0-9617005),* 6995 Applegate Dr., Helena, MT 59601 (SAN 662-5487) Tel 406-458-9339.

Ministries, *(Ministries, Inc.; 0-9607986),* P.O. Box 4038, 319 Fleming, Montgomery, AL 36105 (SAN 238-5449) Tel 205-284-5645.

Ministry Pubns, *(Ministry Pubns.; 0-938234),* P.O. Box 276, Redlands, CA 92373 (SAN 215-787X).

Minkus, *(Minkus Pubns., Inc.; 0-912236),* c/o Minkus Stamp Journal, 41 W. 25th St., New York, NY 10010 (SAN 207-6233).

Minn Geol Surv, *(Minnesota Geological Survey; 0-934938),* Div. of University of Minnesota, 2642 University Ave., St. Paul, MN 55114 (SAN 203-994X) Tel 612-373-3372.

†**Minn Hist,** *(Minnesota Historical Society Pr.; 0-87351),* 690 Cedar St., St. Paul, MN 55101 (SAN 202-6384) Tel 612-297-3243; Toll free: 800-647-7827 (In Midwest); Orders to: 1500 Mississippi St., St. Paul, MN 55101 (SAN 202-6392); CIP.

Minn Inst Phil
See De Young Pr

Minn Library, *(Minnesota Library Assn.; 0-939098),* 1315 Lowry Ave. N., North Regional Library, Minneapolis, MN 55411 (SAN 239-6947) Tel 612-521-1735.

Minn Med Alley, *(Minnesota Medical Alley Publishing Co.; 0-931833),* P.O. Box 24796, Edina, MN 55424 (SAN 686-0079) Tel 612-935-0162.

Minn Med Found, *(Minnesota Medical Foundation, Inc.; 0-940210),* Univ. of Minn, P.O. Box 73 Mayo Bldg., 420 Delaware St. SE, Minneapolis, MN 55455 (SAN 217-541X) Tel 612-373-7933.

Minn Poetry People, *(Minnesota Poetry for the People Press; 0-916079),* P.O. Box 3818, Loring Park Sta., Minneapolis, MN 55403 (SAN 294-6289) Tel 612-488-4896; 1034 N. Victoria, St. Paul, MN 55103 (SAN 294-6297).

Minn Publ Lib
See Mpls Publ Lib

Minn Publ Radio, *(Minnesota Public Radio, Inc.; 0-942110),* 45 E. Eighth St., St. Paul, MN 55101 (SAN 238-6771) Tel 612-221-1531; Dist. by: Bookmen, Inc., 525 N. Third St., Minneapolis, MN 55401 (SAN 168-9517).

Minn Scholarly, *(Minnesota Scholarly Pr., Inc.; 0-933474),* P.O. Box 224, Mankato, MN 56001 (SAN 214-2554) Tel 507-387-4964.

Minn Soc Blind
See Minn Soc Prev Blind

Minn Soc Prev Blind, *(Minnesota Society for the Prevention of Blindness & Preservation of Hearing; 0-9612370),* 1208 Pioneer Bldg., P.O. Box 1528, St. Paul, MN 55101-0528 (SAN 289-5358) Tel 612-227-8808.

Minne HA HA, *(Minne HA! HA!; 0-937706),* P.O. Box 14009, Minneapolis, MN 55414 (SAN 215-6814).

Minneapolis Coll Art, *(Minneapolis College of Art & Design, Library & Media Center; 0-9611672),* 133 E. 25th St., Minneapolis, MN 55404 (SAN 279-604X).

Minneapolis Inst Arts, *(Minneapolis Institute of Arts; 0-912964),* 2400 Third Ave., S., Minneapolis, MN 55404 (SAN 202-2567) Tel 612-870-3029.

Minneapolis Riverfront, *(Minneapolis Riverfront Development Coordination Board; 0-9604360),* 235 City Hall, Minneapolis, MN 55415 (SAN 215-0956).

†**Minneapolis Tribune,** *(Minneapolis Star & Tribune Co.; 0-932272),* 425 Portland Ave., Minneapolis, MN 55488 (SAN 220-2611) Tel 612-372-4420; Dist. by: The Bookmen, Inc., 525 N. Third St., Minneapolis, MN 55401 (SAN 169-409X); CIP.

Minnie Ha Ha
See Minne HA HA

Mino Pubns, *(Mino Pubns.; 0-931719),* 9009 Paddock Ln., Potomac, MD 20854 (SAN 683-5511) Tel 301-294-9514.

Minobras, *(Minobras Mining Services & Research; 0-942218),* P.O. Box 1620, Fallbrook, CA 92028 (SAN 215-9694) Tel 619-726-5678.

Minor Heron, *(Minor Heron Pr.; 0-9615914),* Subs. of Society of the Muse of the Southwest, P.O. Box 2615, Taos, NM 87571 (SAN 697-2020) Tel 505-758-0081.

Minority Rights, *(Minority Rights Group (New York)),* P.O. Box 4S, 35 Claremont, New York, NY 10027 (SAN 283-1902) Tel 212-864-7986.

Minotaur Pr *Imprint of* **Penthouse Pr**

Minsa, *(MINSA; 0-914833),* 1435 State St., Suite No.609, Santa Barbara, CA 93101 (SAN 289-3339) Tel 805-964-5454.

Minuscule Univ Pr, *(Minuscule University Press Inc.; 0-931805),* 66358 Buena Vista Avenue, Desert Hot Springs, CA 92240 (SAN 684-7072) Tel 619-329-8463.

Minuteware, *(Minuteware; 0-913131),* Wilde Lake Village Green, Suite 245, Columbia, MD 21045 (SAN 283-2127) Tel 301-995-1166.

MIP Pub, *(MIP (Multi Image Presentations) Publishing; 0-9617204),* 1482 E. Valley Rd., No. A141, Santa Barbara, CA 93108 (SAN 663-2815) Tel 805-969-9338.

MIR PA, *(MIR; 0-935352),* Div. of Dr. Ilija Poplasen, 845 Suismon Dr., Pittsburgh, PA 15212 (SAN 213-5825) Tel 412-322-1319; Orders to: P.O. Box 962, Pittsburgh, PA 15230 (SAN 213-5833).

MIRA, *(MIRA Academic Press; 0-917919),* P.O. Box 4334, Civic Center Branch, San Rafael, CA 94913 (SAN 656-8963) Tel 415-472-4811.

Miracle Months, *(Miracle Months, The; 0-936515),* P.O. Box 20787, Oklahoma City, OK 73156 (SAN 697-9122) Tel 405-842-7628; 1830 Coventry Ln., Oklahoma City, OK 73120 (SAN 697-9130).

Mirage Bks, *(Mirage Bks.; 0-939137),* Subs. of Dephi-Pacific, P.O. Box 1213, Agana Facilty, Agana, GU 96910 (SAN 662-6327).

Mirage Pr, *(Mirage Pr., Ltd.; 0-88358),* P.O. Box 28, Manchester, MD 21102 (SAN 202-6406) Tel 301-239-8999.

Mirco Cooking
See A Thomas Pub

Miriam Hosp, *(Miriam Hospital Women's Assn., The; 0-9608666),* Affil. of The Miriam Hospital, 164 Summit Ave., Providence, RI 02906 (SAN 240-723X) Tel 401-274-3700; Dist. by: Wimmer Brothers Books, 4210 B.F. Goodrich Blvd., Memphis, TN 38181 (SAN 209-6544) Tel 901-362-8900.

Miriam Press, *(Miriam Pr., The; 0-939409),* P.O. Box 798, Highland, NY 12528 (SAN 663-1681); 439 Upper North Rd., Highland, NY 12528 (SAN 663-169X) Tel 914-691-7271.

Mirronic Pubns
See Carrousel Pubns

Mishler & King
See King Co

Miskar Pub, *(Miskar Publishing Co.; 0-936681),* 102 Rebecca Way, Folsom, CA 95630 (SAN 699-6779) Tel 916-985-2320.

Miss Botan, *(Missouri Botanical Garden; 0-915279),* P.O. Box 299, St. Louis, MO 63166 (SAN 290-0157) Tel 314-577-5164.

Miss Jackie, *(Miss Jackie Music; 0-939514),* 10001 El Monte, Overland Park, KS 66207 (SAN 216-4191).

Missing Diag, *(Missing Diagnosis, Inc.; 0-9615758),* 2614 Highland Ave., Birmingham, AL 35205 (SAN 695-8966) Tel 205-326-0642; Orders to: P.O. Box 26508, Birmingham, AL 35226 (SAN 662-359X) Tel 205-328-6483.

Missing Diagnosis
See Missing Diag

Missing Link, *(Missing Link Products),* 210 N. Union Blvd., Colorado Springs, CO 80909 (SAN 655-1653) Tel 303-473-8909.

Mission Dolores
See Theoscience Found

Mission Pr CA, *(Mission Pr.; 0-918418),* 124 Treehaven Ct., Suite B-330, Kenwood, CA 95452 (SAN 209-9624) Tel 707-833-4683; Box 614, Kenwood, CA 95452 (SAN 658-1242).

Mission Proj Serv, *(Mission Project Service; 0-913671),* 1 Haven Plaza, Apt. 25A, New York, NY 10009 (SAN 286-1461) Tel 212-533-6286.

Mission Pub, *(Mission Publishing Co.; 0-916910),* Woodstone Oaks, Suite 609; 11865 IH Ten W., San Antonio, TX 78230 (SAN 209-1836) Tel 512-692-3552.

Missionaries Africa, *(Missionaries of Africa),* 1624 21st St. NW, Washington, DC 20009 (SAN 223-7997) Tel 202-232-5154.

Missionary Intern, *(Missionary Internship; 0-942726),* 36200 Freedom Rd., P.O. Box 457, Farmington, MI 48024 (SAN 240-253X) Tel 313-474-9110.

Missions Adv Res Com Ctr, *(Missions Advanced Research & Communication Ctr.; 0-912552),* Div. of World Vision International, 919 W. Huntington Dr., Monrovia, CA 91016 (SAN 240-0529) Tel 818-303-8811.

Mississippi Archives, *(Mississippi Dept. of Archives & History; 0-938896),* Div. of State of Mississippi, P.O. Box 571, Jackson, MS 39205 (SAN 279-618X) Tel 601-359-1424.

Mississippi De
See Mississippi Archives

Mississippi Orni, *(Mississippi Ornithological Society; 0-912265),* Box Z, Mississippi State, MS 39762 (SAN 262-0499).

Mistaire, *(Mistaire Laboratories; 0-9602490),* 152 Glen Ave., Millburn, NJ 07041 (SAN 204-2762) Tel 201-376-0915.

Mist'er Rain, *(Mist'er Rain, Inc.; 0-916970),* 8411 Pacific Hwy E., Tacoma, WA 98424 (SAN 208-7685) Tel 206-927-7333.

Misty Hill Pr, *(Misty Hill Pr.; 0-930079),* 5024 Turner Rd., Sebastopol, CA 95472 (SAN 670-0942) Tel 707-823-7437; Dist. by: Bookpeople, 2929 Fifth St., Berkeley, CA 94710 (SAN 168-9517) Tel 415-549-3030.

MIT CAES, *(Massachusetts Institute of Technology, Ctr. for Advanced Engineering Study; 0-911379),* 77 Massachusetts Ave., Rm. 9-234, Cambridge, MA 02139 (SAN 272-2771) Tel 617-253-7444.

MIT Comm Visual Arts, *(Massachusetts Institute of Technology, Committee on the Visual Arts; 0-938437),* MIT E15-109, 20 Ames St., Cambridge, MA 02139 (SAN 661-3004) Tel 617-253-4400.

MIT Outing, *(MIT Outing Club; 0-9601698),* W20-461, MIT, Cambridge, MA 02139 (SAN 210-8291) Tel 617-253-2988.

†**MIT Pr,** *(MIT Pr.; 0-262),* 28 Carleton St., Cambridge, MA 02142 (SAN 202-6414) Tel 617-253-2884; *CIP.*

Mitchell Pub, *(Mitchell Publishing, Inc.; 0-938188),* 915 River St., Santa Cruz, CA 95060 (SAN 215-7896) Tel 408-425-3851; Toll free: 800-435-2665.

Mitzi Bks, *(Mitzi Bks.; 0-940958),* Div. of Sinai-Christian Pubns., P.O. Box 160452, Mobile, AL 36616 (SAN 223-1948) Tel 404-834-4044.

MIU Neurosci Pr, *(Mahanshi International Univ., Neuroscience Pr.; 0-9616944),* Maharishi International Univ., Neuroscience Dept., Fairfield, IA 52556 (SAN 661-7794) Tel 515-472-1109.

Mizan Pr, *(Mizan Pr.; 0-933782),* P.O. Box 4065, Berkeley, CA 94704 (SAN 213-117X) Tel 415-549-1634.

MJ Pubns, *(MJ Pubns.; 0-9605144),* 6363 Lynwood Hill Rd., McLean, VA 22101 (SAN 215-790X).

MJB Bks, *(MJB Books; 0-9609680),* P.O. Box 3246, Merced, CA 95344 (SAN 272-4731) Tel 209-384-0322.

MJB Pub, *(MJB Pub.; 0-9605990),* 7209 Skyway, No. 13, Paradise, CA 95969 (SAN 216-7468). Moved, left no forwarding address.

MJH Info Servs, *(MJH Information Services; 0-939289),* 10707 Buffalo Bend, Houston, TX 77064 (SAN 662-491X) Tel 713-469-3418.

MJK Ent, *(MJK Enterprises; 0-9610996),* P.O. Box 5571, San Antonio, TX 78201 (SAN 265-2749) Tel 512-344-4348.

Mkt Bk Pubns, *(Market Bk. Pubns.; 0-9616994),* 3015 105th SE, Bellevue, WA 98004 (SAN 661-678X) Tel 206-455-5835.

Mktg Consult Intl, *(Marketing Consultants International, Inc.; 0-937195),* 100 W. Washington St., Suite 214, Hagerstown, MD 21740 (SAN 658-5817) Tel 301-791-0290.

Mktg Mgnt Inst, *(Marketing & Management Institute, Inc.; 0-9616722),* 3182 Davcliff, Portage, MT 49002 (SAN 661-3888) Tel 616-323-1531.

MLB Pub, *(MLB Pub.; 0-941794),* P.O. Box 1732, Chesapeake, VA 23320 (SAN 239-2542) Tel 804-424-5238.

MLM Pubs, *(MLM Pubs.; 0-939102),* 515 S. We-Go Trail, Suite 139, Mt. Prospect, IL 60056 (SAN 216-1613) Tel 312-392-7145.

MLP
See Crane Pub Co

MLP Ent, *(MLP Enterprises; 0-939020),* 236 E. Durham St., Philadelphia, PA 19119 (SAN 214-4077) Tel 215-248-3218; Orders to: P.O. Box 18918, Philadelphia, PA 19119 (SAN 650-0420).

MMB Music, *(MMB Music, Inc.; 0-918812),* 10370 Page Industrial Blvd., St. Louis, MO 63132 (SAN 210-4601) Tel 314-427-5660.

MMI Pr, *(Mountain Missionary Pr.; 0-912145),* Div. of Mountain Missionary Institute, Inc., Aldworth Rd., P.O. Box 279, Harrisville, NH 03450 (SAN 264-7664) Tel 603-827-3914; Toll free: 800-367-1888.

MMI Press, *(MMI Pr.; 0-936445),* 10 Pinecrest Rd., Valley Cottage, NY 10989 (SAN 697-9017) Tel 914-268-8868.

MMO Music, *(MMO Music Group Inc.; 0-935647),* 50 S. Buckout St., Irvington, NY 10533 (SAN 696-1746) Tel 914-591-5100.

MMRC, *(Multi Media Resource Ctr.; 0-903968; 0-914684),* 1525 Franklin St., San Francisco, CA 94109 (SAN 206-6017) Tel 415-673-5100.

MN Coun Found, *(Minnesota Council of Foundations; 0-9616378),* 1216 Foshay Tower, Minneapolis, MN 55402 (SAN 658-9332) Tel 612-338-1989.

MN North, *(Minnesota North Country Pr.; 0-9613489),* 3514 Cedarlane, Bemidji, MN 56601 (SAN 657-3649) Tel 218-751-1041.

MN Pubs, *(M. N. Pubs.; 0-932964),* P.O. Box 27, Bonnerdale, AR 71933 (SAN 212-291X) Tel 501-991-3815.

Mnemosyne, *(Mnemosyne Publishing Co., Inc.),* 410 Alcazar Ave., Coral Gables, FL 33134 (SAN 203-9966) Tel 305-444-8908.

Mngd Acct Reprts *Imprint of* **Futures Pub**

MNP Star, *(MNP Star Enterprises; 0-938880),* P.O. Box 1552, Cupertino, CA 95015-1552 (SAN 215-9708).

Mntn Automation, *(Mountain Automation Corp.; 0-936206),* P.O. Box 6020, Woodland Park, CO 80866 (SAN 221-4148).

Mntn Brook Pubns, *(Mountain Brook Pubns.; 0-938747),* P.O. Box 7474, Mountain Brook, AL 35253 (SAN 661-7549); 2652 Alta Glen Dr., Birmingham, AL 35243 (SAN 661-7557) Tel 205-867-6517.

Mntn Elegance, *(Mountain Elegance),* P.O. Box 8723, Asheville, NC 28814 (SAN 240-964X).

Mntn Grizzly Pubns, *(Mountain Grizzly Pubns.; 0-9616480),* 133 E. 1600 N., Orem, UT 84057 (SAN 659-2775) Tel 801-226-8741.

Mntn Hse Pub, *(Mountain House Publishing, Inc.; 0-939274),* Rte. 1 Box 433 A, Waitsfield, VT 05673 (SAN 216-4213).

Mntn Memories Bks, *(Mountain Memories Bks.; 0-938985),* 216 Sutherland Dr., South Charleston, WV 25303 (SAN 661-6771) Tel 304-744-5772.

Mntn View Pr, *(Mountain View Pr., Inc.; 0-914699),* P.O. Box 4656, Mountain View, CA 94040 (SAN 287-3141) Tel 415-961-4103.

MO Arch Soc, *(Missouri Archaeological Society; 0-943414),* P.O. Box 958, Columbia, MO 65205 (SAN 238-8316).

MO Bar Assn, *(Missouri Bar Assn.),* P.O. Box 119, Jefferson City, MO 65102 (SAN 227-0404) Tel 314-635-4128.

MO Basketball, *(Missouri Basketball; 0-9605092),* 364 Hearnes Bldg., Columbia, MO 65211 (SAN 215-7888).

MO Poli Sci, *(Missouri Political Science Assn.),* Univ. of Missouri, 118 Middlebush Hall, Columbia, MO 65201 (SAN 226-3335).

Mobile Jr League Pubns, *(Mobile Junior League Pubns.; 0-9603054),* Div. of The Junior League of Mobile, Inc., 179 Bayshore Ave., Mobile, AL 36607 (SAN 212-1069) Tel 205-479-5133.

Mobile PO, *(Mobile Post Office Society),* RFD 1, Box 91, Contoocook, NH 03229 (SAN 225-5995).

Mockingbird Bks, *(Mockingbird Bks.; 0-89176),* Box 624, St. Simons Island, GA 31522 (SAN 207-6470) Tel 912-638-7212.

Mockingbooks, *(Mockingbooks; 0-9615626),* P.O. Box 2122, La Mesa, CA 92041 (SAN 696-1096) Tel 619-461-1055.

Mod Handcraft, *(Modern Handcraft, Inc.; 0-86675),* 4251 Pennsylvania Ave., Kansas City, MO 64111 (SAN 216-1621) Tel 816-531-5730. *Imprints:* Aunt Ellen's (Aunt Ellen's); Flower & Garden (Flower & Garden); Workbasket (Workbasket); Workbench (Workbench).

Mod LibC *Imprint of* **Modern Lib**

Mod Media Inst
See Poynter Inst

Modal Logic, *(Modal Logic Corp.; 0-937003),* 341 San Fernando Dr., San Francisco, CA 94127 (SAN 658-7402) Tel 619-481-5707; P.O. Box 1382, Solana Beach, CA 92075 (SAN 658-7410).

Model A, *(Model A Ford Club of America),* 250 S. Cypress, La Habra, CA 90631 (SAN 225-5138) Tel 213-697-2712; 2222 Loma Vista, Pasadena, CA 91104 (SAN 662-0833) Tel 818-794-9841.

Model Agency, *(Model Agency Pr., The; 0-942794),* 7021 Vicky Ave., Canoga Park, CA 91307 (SAN 240-2548) Tel 818-340-7268.

Model Cities, *(Model Cities Research Institute; 0-941496),* 11126 National Blvd., Los Angeles, CA 90064 (SAN 208-1296) Tel 213-479-7394.

Modell T, *(Modell, Tod; 0-9608292),* P.O. Box 3047, San Jose, CA 95156 (SAN 240-4095) Tel 408-258-4931.

Moderation Pr, *(Moderation Pr.),* P.O. Box 741955, Dallas, TX 75374-1955 (SAN 292-336X).

Modern Bks, *(Modern Bks., & Crafts, Inc.; 0-913274),* Dist. by: Associated Booksellers, 562 Boston Ave., Bridgeport, CT 06610 (SAN 203-5014).

Modern Comm Assocs, *(Modern Communication Assocs.; 0-9613854),* P.O. Box 670085, Dallas, TX 75367-0085 (SAN 685-2157) Tel 214-239-2183; Dist. by: Book Dynamics, 836 Broadway, New York, NY 10003 (SAN 169-5649) Tel 212-254-7798; Dist. by: Distributors, The, 702 S. Michigan, South Bend, IN 46618 (SAN 169-2488) Tel 219-232-8500.

†**Modern Curr,** *(Modern Curriculum Pr.; 0-87895; 0-8136),* Div. of Esquire, Inc., 13900 Prospect Rd., Cleveland, OH 44136 (SAN 206-6572); Toll free: 800-321-3106; *CIP.*

Modern Guides, *(Modern Guides Co.; 0-940788),* P.O. Box 1340, Old San Juan, PR 00902 (SAN 219-6069) Tel 809-723-9105.

Modern Hand
See Mod Handcraft

Modern Humanities Res, *(Modern Humanities Research Association),* George Washington University, Washington, DC 20006 (SAN 225-3186) Tel 202-676-6130.

†**Modern Lang,** *(Modern Language Assn. of America; 0-87352),* 10 Astor Pl., New York, NY 10003 (SAN 202-6422) Tel 212-614-6314; *CIP.*

†**Modern Lib,** *(Modern Library, Inc.; 0-394),* 201 E. 50th St., New York, NY 10022 (SAN 204-5605) Tel 212-751-2600; Orders to: Order Dept., 400 Hahn Rd., Westminster, MD 21157 (SAN 204-5613); *CIP.* *Imprints:* Mod LibC (Modern Library College Department).

Modern Signs, *(Modern Signs Pr., Inc.; 0-916708),* 10443 Los Alamitos Blvd., Los Alamitos, CA 90720 (SAN 282-0048) Tel 213-596-6858; Orders to: P.O. Box 1181, Los Alamitos, CA 90720 (SAN 282-0056) Tel 213-493-4168.

Modern Studies Group *Imprint of* **Heroica Bks**

Modern World, *(Modern World Publishing Co.; 0-910978),* P.O. Box 65766, Los Angeles, CA 90065 (SAN 203-9982) Tel 213-221-8044.

Modern Wrds, *(Modern Words; 0-9614055),* P.O. Box 1093, Hermosa Beach, CA 90254 (SAN 684-720X) Tel 213-461-9909.

Modular Info Syst, *(Modular Information Systems; 0-939325),* 431 Ashbury St., San Francisco, CA 94117 (SAN 663-1290) Tel 415-552-8648.

Moe-Tavation, *(Moe-Tavation; 0-9615797),* 1230 Caroline, Port Angeles, WA 98362 (SAN 696-5954) Tel 206-457-5052.

Moffat Pub, *(Moffat Publishing Co., Inc.; 0-86670),* Box 236, Nutley, NJ 07110 (SAN 217-2569) Tel 201-235-9444.

Moffett, *(Moffett Publishing Co.; 0-9605650),* Rte. 3, Box 175A, Cushing, OK 74023 (SAN 215-6822).

Mogul Bk, *(Mogul Book & Film Works; 0-9610404),* P.O. Box 2773, Pittsburgh, PA 15230 (SAN 264-2131) Tel 412-461-0705.

Mohs Seaplane Co, *(Mohs Seaplane Corp.; 0-931279),* 2355 University Ave., Madison, WI 53705 (SAN 682-0026) Tel 608-233-1627.

Mohsena Memorial, *(Mohsena Memorial Trust; 0-9617273),* 40 Tar Hees Rd., Mercerville, NJ 08619 (SAN 663-5075) Tel 609-587-4414.

Moira, *(Moira Books; 0-9600204),* 1460 Heights Blvd., Winona, MN 55987 (SAN 203-9990).

Mojave Bks, *(Mojave Bks.; 0-87881),* 7118 Canby Ave., Reseda, CA 91335 (SAN 202-6430) Tel 818-342-3403.

Mole Pub Co, *(Mole Publishing Co.; 0-9604464),* Route 4, Box 618, Bonners Ferry, ID 83805 (SAN 212-8608) Tel 208-267-7349.

Mollica Stained Glass, *(Mollica Stained Glass Press; 0-9601306),* 10033 Broadway Terr., Oakland, CA 94611 (SAN 209-2220) Tel 415-655-5736.

Molly Yes, *(Molly Yes Pr.; 0-931308),* P.O. Box 292322, Ft. Lauderdale, FL 33329 (SAN 217-9075) Tel 305-474-5010.

Molokai Bk Pubs, *(Molakai Book Pubs.;
0-930081),* P.O. Box 1239, Kaunakakai, HI
96748 (SAN 670-1000) Tel 808-553-3376.

Mom & Pop Pub, *(Mom & Pop Publishing Co.;
0-937469),* 1035 Browning Dr., Tallahassee,
FL 32308 (SAN 658-9340)
Tel 904-877-1436.

†Momos, *(Momo's Pr.; 0-917672),* 45 Sheridan
St., San Francisco, CA 94103
(SAN 206-1619) Tel 415-863-3009; *CIP.*

Mona Pubns, *(Mona Pubns.; 0-937849),* Div. of
Mona & McGrath Public Relations, 8400
Normandale Lake Blvd., Suite 1220,
Bloomington, MN 55437 (SAN 659-5235)
Tel 612-831-8515.

Monad Pr
See Anchor Found

Monarch *Imprint of* **Monarch Pr**

†Monarch Pr, *(Monarch Pr.; 0-671),* Div. of
Simon & Schuster, Inc., 215 Park Ave. S.,
New York, NY 10003 (SAN 204-5621)
Tel 212-777-6300; *CIP. Imprints:* Monarch
(Monarch).

Monarch Trails Pubns, *(Monarch Trails Pubns.;
0-9616665),* P.O. Box 05272, Detroit, MI
48205 (SAN 661-3543); 12180 Flanders St.,
Detroit, MI 48205 (SAN 661-3551)
Tel 313-521-8011.

Monday Bks, *(Monday Bks.; 0-918510),* 8450
W. Dry Creek Rd., Healdsburg, CA 95448
(SAN 209-6552) Tel 707-433-3188.

Mondiello, *(Mondiello, Anthony S.; 0-939658),*
20008 N. 28th, Phoenix, AZ 85024
(SAN 218-4931).

Money Advoc, *(Money Advocate, The;
0-913725),* 4180 W. Broadway, Robbinsdale,
MN 55422 (SAN 286-1283)
Tel 612-533-3664.

Money Digest
See Zimmerman

Money Inc
See Money Advoc

Money-Maker, *(Money-Maker Publishing Co.;
0-910481),* 311 Gruenther Ave., Rockville,
MD 20851 (SAN 260-1060)
Tel 301-762-1385.

Money Mastery Pub, *(Money Mastery
Publishing; 0-9613663),* P.O. Box 336,
Piermont, NY 10968 (SAN 670-8935).

Money Methods, *(Money Making Methods;
0-9605094),* 5556 Bloch St., San Diego, CA
92122 (SAN 276-9697) Tel 619-453-6033.

Money Mkt, *(Money Market Directories, Inc.;
0-939712),* Subs. of McGraw-Hill, Inc., 300
E. Market St., Charlottesville, VA 22901
(SAN 216-7492) Tel 804-977-1450; Toll
free: 800-446-2810.

Money Pub, *(Money Publishing; 0-9616077),*
519 S. G St., Tacoma, WA 98405
(SAN 698-0880) Tel 206-627-6010.

Money Success Prog, *(Money & Success
Program; 0-9616879),* P.O. Box 39600,
Charleston, SC 29407 (SAN 661-6615); 114
Rutledge Ave., Charleston, SC 29403
(SAN 661-6623) Tel 803-723-2026.

Moneymatters, *(Moneymatters Publishing;
0-912913),* 2616 Juniper Ave. Suite 5,
Boulder, CO 80302 (SAN 283-3050)
Tel 303-449-6689.

Mongolia, *(Mongolia Society, Inc., The;
0-910980),* 321-322 Goodbody Hall, Indiana
Univ., Bloomington, IN 47405
(SAN 204-000X) Tel 812-335-4078.

†Monitor, *(Monitor Bk. Co., Inc.; 0-9600252),*
9441 Wilshire Blvd., Beverly Hills, CA 90212
(SAN 204-0018); Orders to: P.O. Box 3668,
Beverly Hills, CA 90212 (SAN 689-2426)
Tel 213-271-5558; *CIP.*

Monkey Joe Ent, *(Monkey Joe Enterprises, Inc.;
0-933208),* 3310 Lebanon Rd., Suite 104,
Hermitage, TN 37076 (SAN 212-4319).

Monkey Man, *(Monkey Man Pr.; 0-9605594),*
3895 Fredonia Dr., Los Angeles, CA 90068
(SAN 216-1648) Tel 213-876-2299.

†Monkey Sisters, *(Monkey Sisters Inc., the;
0-933606),* 22971 Via Cruz, Laguna Niguel,
CA 92677 (SAN 212-7660)
Tel 714-859-5014; *CIP.*

Monkfish Pub, *(Monkfish Publishing Corp.;
0-9615623),* 10740 Pine Bluff, Whitmore
Lake, MI 48189 (SAN 696-1207)
Tel 313-662-1353.

Monks of New Skete, *(Monks of New Skete;
0-9607924; 0-935129),* New Skete Rd.,
Cambridge, NY 12816 (SAN 240-0553)
Tel 518-677-3928.

Mono Lake Comm, *(Mono Lake Committee,
The; 0-939716),* Box 29, Lee Vining, CA
93541 (SAN 282-0064) Tel 619-647-6386;
Dist. by: Bookpeople, 2929 Fifth St.,
Berkeley, CA 94710 (SAN 168-9517)
Tel 415-549-3030; Dist. by: Publishers
Group West, 5855 Beaudry St., Emeryville,
CA 94608 (SAN 202-8522)
Tel 415-658-3453.

Monocacy, *(Monocacy Bk. Co.; 0-913186),* P.O.
Box 765, Redwood City, CA 94064
(SAN 202-6473) Tel 415-369-8934.

Monogram Aviation, *(Monogram Aviation
Pubns.; 0-914144),* 625 Edgebrook Dr.,
Boylston, MA 01505 (SAN 206-5983)
Tel 617-869-6836.

Monogram Pr, *(Monogram Pr., Inc.; 0-938107),*
12720 Hillcrest Rd., Suite 305, Dallas, TX
75230 (SAN 661-406X) Tel 214-991-9800.

†Monograph Series, *(Univ. of Denver, Graduate
Schl. of International Studies, Monograph
Series in World Affairs; 0-87940),* Univ. of
Denver, Denver, CO 80208
(SAN 205-4701) Tel 303-871-2555; *CIP.*

Monongahela Pub, *(Monongahela Publishing Co.,
Inc.),* 106 Morningside Dr., New York, NY
10027 (SAN 209-3545) Tel 212-666-5187;
Orders to: 78 B Stony Rd., Fairmont, WV
26554 (SAN 209-3553).

Monroe County Lib, *(Monroe County Library
System; 0-940696),* 3700 S. Custer Rd.,
Monroe, MI 48161 (SAN 213-5396)
Tel 313-241-5277.

Monroe Pr, *(Monroe Pr.; 0-936781),* 16107
Gledhill St., Sepulveda, CA 91343
(SAN 699-9883) Tel 818-891-6464; Dist.
by: Baker & Taylor Co., 6 Kirby Ave.,
Somerville, NJ 08876 (SAN 169-4901)
Tel 201-526-8000; Dist. by: Quality Books,
Inc., 918 Sherwood Dr., Lake Bluff, IL
60044-2204 (SAN 169-2127); Dist. by:
Bookpeople, 2929 Fifth St., Berkeley, CA
94710 (SAN 168-9517).

Monson Product, *(Monson Productions;
0-942796),* P.O. Box 5324, Madison, WI
53705 (SAN 240-2556) Tel 608-271-2016.

Monson Trading, *(Monson Trading, Ltd.;
0-937667),* 210 Main St., Suite 4, Kirkland,
WA 98033 (SAN 659-350X)
Tel 206-822-1883.

Mont Hist Soc
See MT Hist Soc

Mont Sci Pubns, *(Montgomery Scientific Pubns.;
0-935643),* 4180 Poinciana Ave., Miami, FL
33133 (SAN 696-1614) Tel 305-326-6633.

Montaigne, *(Montaigne Publishing, Inc.;
0-917430),* 99 El Toyonal, Orinda, CA
94563 (SAN 208-9602).

Montana Bankers, *(Montana Bankers Assn.;
0-9612006),* No. One N. Last Chance
Gulch, Helena, MT 59601 (SAN 286-830X)
Tel 406-443-4121.

Montana Tech, *(Montana Tech Foundation;
0-930609),* W. Park St., Butte, MT 59701
(SAN 679-1867).

Montclair State, *(Montclair State College;
0-933559),* Upper Montclair, NJ 07043
(SAN 691-8778) Tel 201-893-7215; Dist.
by: Hispamerica, 5 Pueblo Ct., Gaithersburg,
MD 20878 (SAN 213-9200).

Monte Pub, *(Monte Publishing Co.; 0-9606942),*
P.O. Box 361, Underwood, WA 98651
(SAN 238-8987) Tel 509-493-2396.

Montecito Pr, *(Montecito Pr.; 0-935377),* 100
Oceangate, Suite 1010, Long Beach, CA
90802 (SAN 696-3277) Tel 213-432-8929.

Monterey Audubon, *(Monterey Peninsula
Audubon Society; 0-9615798),* P.O. Box
5656, Carmel, CA 93921 (SAN 696-5970)
Tel 408-373-6658.

Montessori Learn
See Parent-Child Pr

Montessori Wkshps
See Ed Sys Pub

Montevista Pr, *(Montevista Pr; 0-931551),* 5041
Meridian Rd., Bellingham, WA 98226
(SAN 682-191X) Tel 206-734-4279; Dist.
by: Pacific Pipeline, 19215 66th Ave. S.,
Kent, WA 98032 (SAN 208-2128)
Tel 206-872-5523; Dist. by: Robert Hale &
Co., 1840 130th Ave. NE, Suite 10, Bellevue,
WA 98005 (SAN 200-6995)
Tel 206-881-5212; Dist. by: Baker & Taylor,
Eastern Div., 50 Kirby Ave., Somerville, NJ
08876 (SAN 169-4901).

Montezuma Micro, *(Montezuma Micro;
0-928295),* Redbird Airport, Hangar No. 8,
P.O. Box 763009, Dallas, TX 75376-3009
(SAN 657-5390); Toll free: 800-527-0347
Tel 214-339-5105; Toll free: 800-442-1310
(TX).

Montfort Pubns, *(Montfort Pubns.; 0-910984),*
Div. of Montfort Missionaries, 26 S. Saxon
Ave., Bay Shore, NY 11706
(SAN 169-5053) Tel 516-665-0726.

Montgomery Co Hist, *(Montgomery County
Historical Society; 0-9601094),* 103 W.
Montgomery Ave., Rockville, MD 20850
(SAN 210-1262) Tel 301-762-1492.

Montgomery Hist, *(Montgomery County
Historical Society; 0-9608694),* Fort
Johnson, NY 12070 (SAN 238-3179)
Tel 518-843-0300.

Montgomery Mus, *(Montgomery Museum of
Fine Arts; 0-89280),* 440 S. McDonough St.,
Montgomery, AL 36104 (SAN 208-3299)
Tel 205-832-2976.

†Monthly Rev, *(Monthly Review Pr.; 0-85345),*
Div. of Monthly Review Foundation, Inc.,
155 W. 23rd St., New York, NY 10011
(SAN 202-6481) Tel 212-691-2555; *CIP.*

Monument Pr, *(Monument Pr.; 0-930383),* P.
O. Box 160361, Las Colinas, TX 75016
(SAN 670-7742) Tel 214-948-7001; Dist.
by: Publishers Assocs., P.O. Box 160361, Las
Colinas, TX 75016-9998 (SAN 662-2488)
Tel 817-478-8564.

Monza-Fels
See Plantin Pr

†Moody, *(Moody Pr.; 0-8024),* Div. of Moody
Bible Institute, 820 N. LaSalle Dr., Chicago,
IL 60610 (SAN 202-5604)
Tel 312-973-7800; Toll free: 800-621-5111;
Toll free: 800-621-4323 (In Illinois); *CIP.
Imprints:* MCL (Moody Colportage Library);
MG (Moody Giant); MYL (Moody Youth
Library).

Moon Bks
See Greta Bear

Moon New Ferns, *(Moon of New Ferns;
0-9612784),* Rte. 9, Box 820, Tucson, AZ
85743 (SAN 289-7660); Dist. by: New
Woman Press, 2000 King Mountain Trail,
Sunny Valley, OR 97497-9799
(SAN 209-8474).

Moon Over Mntn, *(Moon Over the Mountain
Publishing Co.; 0-9602970),* 6700 W. 44th
Ave., Wheatridge, CO 80033
(SAN 213-3415) Tel 303-420-4272.

Moon Pubns CA, *(Moon Pubns.; 0-9603322;
0-918373),* P.O. Box 1696, Chico, CA 95927
(SAN 221-7406); 133 W. Lindo, Chico, CA
95927-1696 (SAN 658-1250)
Tel 916-345-5473.

Mooney, *(Mooney, Tom; 0-9601240),* 3410
Balt-Som Rd., Millersport, OH 43046
(SAN 210-1270) Tel 614-862-8159.

Moonlight Edns *Imprint of* Schocken

Moonlight FL, *(Moonlight Pr.; 0-913545),* 3407
Crystal Lake Dr., Orlando, FL 32806
(SAN 293-3063) Tel 305-857-1113.

Moonlight Pr, *(Moonlight Pr., The; 0-941818),*
611 Pawling Ave., Troy, NY 12180
(SAN 239-2607).

Moonlight Pr IL, *(Moonlight Pr.; 0-9616493),*
202 N. Brighton Pl., Arlington Heights, IL
60004 (SAN 659-3542) Tel 312-392-8438.
Do not confuse with other companies with
same name in Orlando, FL, Austin, TX,
Troy, NY, Menominie, WI.

Moonlight Press, *(Moonlight Pr.; 0-9612002),*
1402 Mathews St., Menomonie, WI 54751
(SAN 286-8334) Tel 715-235-7465. Do not
confuse with other companies with same
name in Orlando, FL, Austin, TX, Troy, NY,
Arlington Heights, IL.

Moonlight Pubns, *(Moonlight Pubns.; 0-931350),*
Box 671, La Jolla, CA 92038
(SAN 211-2566).

Moonmad Pr, *(Moonmad Pr.; 0-917918),* P.O.
Box 757, Terre Haute, IN 47808
(SAN 209-3537).

Moonowl Creat, *(Moonowl Creations; 0-932009),*
P.O. Box 488, Pagosa Springs, CO 81147
(SAN 686-0958) Tel 303-264-5655.

Moonraker, *(Moonraker Pubns.; 0-940620),*
24452B Alta Vista, Dana Point, CA 92629
(SAN 222-9862) Tel 714-661-9172.

MoonsQuilt Pr, *(Moonsquilt Pr.; 0-943216),*
16401 NE 4th Ave., N., Miami, FL 33162
(SAN 240-5512) Tel 305-947-9534.

†**Moonstone,** *(Moonstone Pr.; 0-940410),* P.O. Box 142, Beverly Hills, CA 90213 (SAN 282-017X) Tel 714-956-2246; Dist. by: Ingram Industries, 347 Reedwood Dr., Nashville, TN 37217 (SAN 169-7978); Dist. by: Last Gasp, 2180 Bryant St., San Francisco, CA 94110 (SAN 216-8294) Tel 415-824-6636; Dist. by: Quality Bks., 918 Sherwood Dr., Lake Bluff, IL 60044-2204 (SAN 203-610X); Dist. by: Baker & Taylor Co., Midwest Div., 501 Gladiola Ave., Momence, IL 60954 (SAN 169-2100); Orders to: P.O. Box 661, Anaheim, CA 92805 (SAN 662-0841); *CIP.* Imprints: Disharmony Bks (Disharmony Books).(Disharmony Bks.).

Moontree Pr, *(Moontree Pr.),* 3719 4th St., NW, Albuquerque, NM 87107 (SAN 241-5666).

Moore & Quinn, *(Moore & Quinn; 0-9614483),* Rt. No.3, Camden, NY 13316 (SAN 689-3996); Dist. by: North Country Books, 18 Irving Pl., Utica, NY 13501 (SAN 287-0231).

Moore D, *(Moore, Donna J., Pub.; 0-9605466),* P.O. Box 723, Bainbridge Island, WA 98110 (SAN 240-0243) Tel 206-842-2170.

Moore Data, *(Moore Data Management Services; 0-918451),* 1660 South Hwy 100, Minneapolis, MN 55416 (SAN 693-5508) Tel 612-588-7205.

Moore Hist, *(Moore Historical Foundation; 0-914167),* 300 E. State St., No. 506, Redlands, CA 92373 (SAN 287-6191) Tel 714-798-2403.

Moore Memorial, *(Moore Memorial Hospital Auxiliary),* P.O. Box 704, Pinehurst, NC 28374 (SAN 217-2909) Tel 919-281-3388.

Moore Pub IL, *(Moore Publishing Co., Inc. (Il); 0-935610),* P.O. Box 709, Oak Park, IL 60303 (SAN 222-643X) Tel 312-848-7401; 136 S. Wesley Ave., Oak Park, IL 60302 (SAN 669-1803).

Moore Pubns, *(Moore Pubns; 0-9602616),* 9216 220th SW, Edmonds, WA 98020 (SAN 238-4396).

Moore-Taylor-Moore
See MTM Pub Co

Moorefields Pr, *(Moorefields Pr.; 0-9615920),* Rte. 6, Box 743, Hillsborough, NC 27278 (SAN 697-2276) Tel 919-732-5941.

Moosehead Prods, *(Moosehead Products; 0-9609208),* Rte. 1-4710, Corinna, ME 04928 (SAN 241-4090) Tel 207-278-3556.

Mor-Mac, *(Mor-Mac Publishing Co.; 0-912178),* P.O. Box 985, Daytona Beach, FL 32015 (SAN 204-0042) Tel 904-255-4427.

Morales Pubns, *(Morales Pubns.; 0-934157),* 1524 Independence, No. J, Plano, TX 75075 (SAN 693-2010) Tel 214-596-1203.

Moran Andrews, *(Moran/Andrews, Inc.; 0-912286),* 211 E. Ohio St., Chicago, IL 60611 (SAN 202-6503) Tel 312-644-2793.

Moran Pub Corp, *(Moran Publishing Corp.; 0-86518),* 5425 Florida Blvd., P.O. Box 66538, Baton Rouge, LA 70896 (SAN 214-0616) Tel 504-923-2550; Dist. by: Aviation Book Co., 1640 Victory Blvd., Glendale, CA 91201 (SAN 212-0259) Tel 213-240-1771.

Moran Pub FL, *(Moran Publishing Co.),* 9125 Bachman Rd., Orlando, FL 32859 (SAN 264-2166).

Morav Music Found, *(Moravian Music Foundation Pr.; 0-941642),* Dist. by: Associated University Presses, 440 Forsgate Dr., Cranbury, NJ 08512 (SAN 281-2959) Tel 609-655-4770.

Moravian Music, *(Moravian Music Foundation; 0-8078),* 20 Cascade Ave., Winston-Salem, NC 27107 (SAN 225-3569) Tel 919-725-0651.

Mordern Schls
See Kadon

More Info, *(More Information; 0-936355),* 4717 12th Ave, S., Minneapolis, MN 55407 (SAN 697-9149) Tel 612-822-6167.

Morehouse, *(Morehouse-Barlow Co.; 0-8192),* 78 Danbury Rd., Wilton, CT 06897 (SAN 202-6511) Tel 203-762-0721.

†**Moretus Pr,** *(Moretus Pr., The; 0-89679),* P.O. Box 867, Ossining, NY 10562-0867 (SAN 211-2523) Tel 914-941-0409; *CIP.*

Morgan, *(Morgan & Morgan, Inc.; 0-87100),* Affil. of Morgan Pr., Inc., 145 Palisade St., Dobbs Ferry, NY 10522 (SAN 202-5620) Tel 914-693-0023.

Morgan Aviation Imprint of **Arco**

Morgan Kaufmann, *(Morgan Kaufmann Pubs., Inc.; 0-934613),* 95 First St., Suite 120, Los Altos, CA 94022 (SAN 693-918X) Tel 415-941-4960; Orders to: P.O. Box 50490, Palo Alto, CA 94303 (SAN 200-2272) Tel 415-965-4081.

Morgan Pr TX, *(Morgan Pr.),* P.O. Box 580355, Houston, TX 77258-0355 (SAN 659-560X). Do not confuse with Morgan Pr., Milwaukee, WI.

Morgan-Rand, *(Morgan-Rand Pubns., Inc.; 0-913061),* 2200 Sansom St., Philadelphia, PA 19103 (SAN 283-2135) Tel 215-557-8200; Toll free: 800-354-8673.

†**Morgan State,** *(Morgan State Univ.; 0-9610324),* Cold Spring Ln., Baltimore, MD 21239 (SAN 264-2182) Tel 301-444-3165; *CIP.*

Morgantown Print & Bind, *(Morgantown Printing & Binding Co.; 0-930284),* P.O. Box 850, Morgantown, WV 26505 (SAN 213-1188) Tel 304-292-3368.

Morning Coffee Imprint of **Coffee Hse**

Morning Creation
See Lifecircle

†**Morning Glory,** *(Morning Glory Pr., Inc.; 0-930934),* 6595 San Haroldo Way, Buena Park, CA 90620 (SAN 211-2558) Tel 714-828-1998; *CIP.*

Morning Star Gal, *(Morning Star Gallery; 0-9617085),* 513 Canyon Rd., Santa Fe, NM 87501 (SAN 662-5916) Tel 505-982-8187.

Morningland, *(Morningland Pubns., Inc.; 0-935146),* 2600 E. Seventh St., Long Beach, CA 90804 (SAN 213-6368) Tel 213-433-9906.

Morningstar
See Transform Inc

Morningsun Pubns, *(Morningsun Pubns.; 0-9603424),* 692 Edna Way, San Mateo, CA 94402 (SAN 211-6235) Tel 415-341-4491.

Morris-Burt Pr, *(Morris-Burt Press; 0-9600890),* 10 Gary Way, Alamo, CA 94507 (SAN 222-0857) Tel 415-837-4426.

Morris Genealog Lib, *(Morris Genealogical Library),* P.O. Box 63, Allenhurst, NJ 07711 (SAN 207-6012).

Morris Museum Art Science, *(Morris Museum of Arts & Sciences),* 6 Normandy Heights Rd., Morristown, NJ 07960 (SAN 279-6678).

Morris Pub, *(Morris Publishing Co.; 0-9606890; 0-9615396),* Subs. of Face Metier, Inc., 3 Blue Ridge Rd., Plymouth Meeting, PA 19462 (SAN 282-0234) Tel 215-828-4865; Orders to: Box 124, Plymouth Meeting, PA 19462 (SAN 282-0242) Tel 215-828-4865.

Morris Pub CA, *(Morris Publishing Co. of San Francisco; 0-9616472),* Div. of Images by Suzie, 1958 Vallejo, Suite 3, San Francisco, CA 94123 (SAN 658-9413) Tel 415-331-6021.

Morrison Peterson Pub, *(Morrison Peterson Publishing, Inc.; 0-936062),* P.O. Box 1870, Kailua, HI 96734 (SAN 238-8944) Tel 808-262-2533; Toll free: 800-528-3665.

Morrison Pub Co, *(Morrison Publishing Co.; 0-911593),* 14 Brown St., Warren, RI 02885 (SAN 264-2190).

Morrison Rav, *(Morrison, Raven-Hill Co.; 0-912189),* 9466 Hidden Valley Pl., Beverly Hills, CA 90210 (SAN 277-6952).

Morrissette, *(Morrissette; 0-9615627),* 140 Russell St., Lewiston, ME 04240 (SAN 696-1177) Tel 207-784-1618.

Morristown Hist Soc, *(Morristown Historical Society; 0-9607288),* c/o Sargent & White, Morrisville, VT 05661 (SAN 293-308X).

†**Morrow,** *(Morrow, William, & Co., Inc.; 0-688),* Subs. of Hearst Corp., 105 Madison Ave., New York, NY 10016 (SAN 202-5760) Tel 212-889-3050; Toll free: 800-631-1199; Orders to: Wilmor Warehouse, 6 Henderson Dr., West Caldwell, NJ 07006 (SAN 202-5779); *CIP.* Imprints: Quill (Quill Paperbacks); Reynal (Reynal).

Morrow Pub
See F Morrow

Morse Pr, *(Morse Pr., Inc.; 0-933350),* 3441 Thorndyke Ave. W., Seattle, WA 98119 (SAN 211-8165) Tel 206-282-9988.

Mortal Pr, *(Mortal Press; 0-9604152),* 1516 Muldoon Rd., Rockford, IL 61103-1639 (SAN 211-254X) Tel 815-654-7943.

Morten Pub, *(Morten Publishing Co., Inc.; 0-9607848),* 605 N. Bittersweet, Muncie, IN 47304 (SAN 238-1788).

Mortensen Educ Prods, *(Mortensen Educational Products, Inc.; 0-937005),* 9757 Eton Ave., Chatsworth, CA 91311 (SAN 658-7429) Tel 818-341-1031.

Mortgage Bankers, *(Mortgage Bankers Assn. of America),* 1125 15th St., NW, Washington, DC 20005 (SAN 224-8212) Tel 202-861-6500.

Mortgage Tech, *(Mortgage Techniques; 0-9615886),* 8469 Farrah Ln., Memphis, TN 38138 (SAN 696-639X) Tel 901-755-8578; Toll free: 800-468-1255; Toll free: 800-523-1307 (In Tennessee); Orders to: Mortgage Techniques, P.O. Box 17214, Memphis, TN 38127-0214 (SAN 662-3794) Tel 901-755-8728.

Morton Falls Pub, *(Morton Falls Pub. Co.; 0-934279),* Div. of Douglas Kirk's Animals of the Performing Arts, Rt. 9, Box 810S, Canyon Lake, TX 78130 (SAN 693-3149) Tel 512-899-3290.

Morton Ln Pr, *(Morton Lane Pr.; 0-938695),* P.O. Box 4264, Athens, GA 30602 (SAN 661-5686); 320 Morton Farm Ln., Athens, GA 30605 (SAN 661-5694) Tel 404-543-8786.

Morton Pub, *(Morton Publishing Co.; 0-89582),* 925 West Kenyon Ave., Unit 4, Englewood, CO 80110 (SAN 210-9174) Tel 303-761-4805.

Mosadot Pubns, *(Mosadot Pubns., Inc.; 0-913185),* 71 Broadway, New York, NY 10006 (SAN 290-6961) Tel 212-425-3466.

Mosaic Bks, *(Mosaic Bks.; 0-914255),* 3923 Partridge Ln., Baton Rouge, LA 70809 (SAN 287-5594) Tel 504-292-1029; Dist. by: New Leaf Distributors, The, 1020 White St., SW, Atlanta, GA 30310 (SAN 169-1449) Tel 404-755-2665.

Mosaic Media, *(Mosaic Media, Inc.; 0-917792),* P.O. Box 711, Glen Ellyn, IL 60137 (SAN 209-2956) Tel 312-790-1117.

Mosaic Pr, *(Mosaic Pr., the; 0-934696),* 158 Kachina Trail, No. 1, Flagstaff, AZ 86001 (SAN 213-4187).

Mosaic Pr OH, *(Mosaic Press; 0-88014),* 358 Oliver Rd., Cincinnati, OH 45215 (SAN 219-6077) Tel 513-761-5977.

Mosby, *(Mosby, C.V., Co.; 0-8016),* Subs. of The Times Mirror Co., 11830 Westline Industrial Dr., St. Louis, MO 63146 (SAN 200-2280) Tel 314-872-8370; Toll free: 800-325-4177.

Moses Pub Pubns, *(Moses Poetry Collection & Bk. Publishing Co., Inc.; 0-932324),* P.O. Box 701 Plaza, Hudson, NY 12534-0701 (SAN 219-3779) Tel 518-828-7335.

Moss Pubns VA, *(Moss Pubns.; 0-943522),* Box 729, Orange, VA 22960 (SAN 214-4220) Tel 703-672-5921.

Mossart, *(Mossart; 0-9606162),* Box 929, Weaverville, CA 96093 (SAN 217-1171) Tel 916-523-5406.

Mostly Micro, *(Mostly Microwave; 0-9614072),* c/o Janice Martin, Rt. 1, Box 78A, Gibbon, NE 68840 (SAN 686-0060) Tel 308-468-6115.

Mostly Movement, *(Mostly Movement Ltd.; 0-934848),* 58-15 211th St.,, Bayside, NY 11364 (SAN 222-6456).

Motamed Med Pub, *(Motamed Medical Pub., Inc.; 0-910161),* 7141 N. Kedzie Ave. Suite 1504, Chicago, IL 60645 (SAN 241-2276) Tel 312-761-6667.

Moth Hse, *(Moth House Pubns.; 0-936718),* 3967 S. 2200 W., Salt Lake City, UT 84119 (SAN 222-6375).

Mother Courage, *(Mother Courage Pr.; 0-941300),* 1533 Illinois St., Racine, WI 53405 (SAN 239-4618) Tel 414-634-1047.

Mother Duck Pr, *(Mother Duck Press; 0-934600),* Rte. 1, Box 25A, McNeal, AZ 85617 (SAN 213-1196).

Mother Earth, *(Mother Earth News, The; 0-938432),* P.O. Box 70, Hendersonville, NC 28791 (SAN 215-7918); Toll free: 800-438-0238.

Mothering Pubns, *(Mothering Publications, Inc.; 0-914257),* P.O. Box 8410, Santa Fe, NM 87504 (SAN 287-5616) Tel 505-984-8116.

Motheroot, *(Motheroot Pubns.; 0-934238),* P.O. Box 8306, Pittsburgh, PA 15218-0306 (SAN 216-4205) Tel 412-731-4453.

Motiv Aids, *(Motivational Aids; 0-9607372),* 524 Dickson St., Endicott, NY 13760 (SAN 239-4626) Tel 607-785-7032.

Motiv Methods, (Motivational Methods, Inc.; 0-933664), 8569 Ramblewood Dr., Coral Springs, FL 33065 (SAN 212-7687) Tel 305-753-3579.

Motiv Unltd, (Motivators Unlimited; 0-9609084), P.O. Box 35922, Tucson, AZ 85740-5922 (SAN 241-4112) Tel 602-887-9404.

Motor Cities, (Motor Cities Publishing Co.; 0-911383), 10405 Rushton Rd., South Lyon, MI 48178 (SAN 205-8146).

Motor Veh Man, (Motor Vehicle Manufacturers Assn. of the United States; 0-943350), Orders to: Comm. Dept., 300 New Ctr. Bldg., Detroit, MI 48202 (SAN 272-5312) Tel 313-872-4311.

†**Motorbooks Intl,** (Motorbooks International, Pubs. & Wholesalers, Inc. a; 0-87938), 729 Prospect Ave., Osceola, WI 54020-0002 (SAN 169-9164) Tel 715-294-3345; Toll free: 800-826-6600; Orders to: Box 2, Osceola, WI 54020 (SAN 699-5918); CIP.

Motorcycle Safety, (Motorcycle Safety Foundation), P.O. Box 5044, Costa Mesa, CA 92628 (SAN 224-9413); Rte. 1, Chadds Ford W. Complex, Chadds Ford, PA 19317 (SAN 669-182X) Tel 215-388-1555.

Motormatics, (Motormatics Pubns.; 0-930968), Div. of Motormatics, Inc., ; c/o Beach Cities Enterprises, P.O. Box 91051, Long Beach, CA 90809 (SAN 211-1349) Tel 213-434-6701.

†**Mott Media,** (Mott Media; 0-915134; 0-88062), 1000 E. Huron, Milford, MI 48042 (SAN 207-1460) Tel 313-685-8773; CIP.

Mount St Marys, (Mount St. Mary's College; 0-9606972), Emmitsburg, MD 21727 (SAN 223-1964) Tel 301-447-6122.

†**Mount Vernon Pr,** (Mount Vernon Pr.; 0-931213), 1121 112th NE, Bellevue, WA 98004 (SAN 682-0034) Tel 206-454-6982; CIP.

Mountain Calif, (Mountain; 0-9605992), Box 1408, Lower Lake, CA 95457 (SAN 216-7522).

Mountain Laurel, (Mountain Laurel Publications; 0-911687), P.O. Box 1621, Harrisburg, PA 17105 (SAN 264-2239).

Mountain Movers, (Mountain Movers Ministry; 0-9616309), Affil. of Mountain Movers Publishers, 1231 Dewey, Wauwatosa, WI 53213 (SAN 658-7453) Tel 414-257-1259.

†**Mountain Pr,** (Mountain Pr., Publishing Co., Inc.; 0-87842), P.O. Box 2399, Missoula, MT 59806 (SAN 202-8832) Tel 406-728-1900; Toll free: 800-732-3669; 2016 Strand, Missoula, MT 59801 (SAN 662-0868); CIP.

Mountain Pr CA, (Mountain Pr.; 0-9616070), 30951 Tinkerbell Ln., Shingletown, CA 96088 (SAN 697-9157) Tel 916-474-5660.

Mountain Sea, (Mountain & Sea Publishing; 0-911449), P.O. Box 126, Redondo Beach, CA 90277 (SAN 272-5371) Tel 213-379-9321.

Mountain St Tel, (Mountain States Telephone & Telegraph Co., Regulatory Matters Division; 0-9602580), 931-14th St., Rm. 1010, Denver, CO 80202 (SAN 213-120X).

Mountain View Pr
See Mntn View Pr

Mountain West, (Mountain West Publishing Co.; 0-9610968), P.O. Box 1841, Grand Junction, CO 81502 (SAN 265-2838) Tel 303-242-5035.

†**Mountaineers,** (Mountaineers Bks., The; 0-916890; 0-89886), Div. of Mountaineers, The, 306 Second Ave. W., Seattle, WA 98119 (SAN 212-8756) Tel 206-285-2665; CIP.

Mountcastle, (Mountcastle Corp., The; 0-913063), P.O. Box 1688, Redondo Beach, CA 90278 (SAN 285-6689).

Mouse Pr, (Mouse Pr.; 0-913968), 3118 17th St., Santa Monica, CA 90405 (SAN 203-1795) Tel 213-452-3259; Dist. by: Light Impressions Corp., P.O. Box 940, 439 Monroe Ave., Rochester, NY 14603 (SAN 169-619X) Tel 716-271-8960.

Mouton, (Mouton De Gruyter; 90-279), Div. of Walter De Gruyter, Inc., 200 Saw Mill River Rd., Hawthorne, NY 10532 (SAN 210-9239) Tel 914-747-0110.

Mouvement Pubns, (Mouvement Pubns.; 0-932392), 109 E. State St., Ithaca, NY 14850 (SAN 211-7460) Tel 607-272-2157.

Move Short Soc
See Ctr Sutton Movement

Moveable Feast Pr, (Moveable Feast Pr.; 0-943430), P.O. Box 5057, El Dorado Hills, CA 95630 (SAN 240-7256) Tel 916-933-2375.

Movement New Soc
See New Soc Pubs

Moving Parts, (Moving Parts Pr.; 0-939952), 419-A Maple St., Santa Cruz, CA 95060 (SAN 216-8383) Tel 408-427-2271.

Moving Picture Co, (Moving Picture Co., Inc., The; 1-55565), 2507 Thornwood Ave., Wilmette, IL 60091 (SAN 658-5795) Tel 312-256-1111.

Mowbray, (Mowbray; 0-9614233), 108 Laguna Blvd., Jacksonville Beach, FL 32250 (SAN 686-7936) Tel 904-249-4936.

Mowry Pr, (Mowry Pr.; 0-9605368), Box 405, Wayland, MA 01778 (SAN 215-9724) Tel 617-358-4555.

Moyer
See Moyer Bell Limited

Moyer Bell Limited, (Moyer Bell, Ltd.; 0-918825), Colonial Hill, RFD 1, Mt. Kisco, NY 10549 (SAN 669-6961) Tel 914-666-0084; Dist. by: Kampmann & Co., 9 E. 40th St., New York, NY 10016 (SAN 202-5191) Tel 212-685-2928.

Moyer Bell Ltd
See Moyer Bell Limited

MPI Home Video, (MPI Home Video; 1-55607), 15825 Rob Roy Dr., Oak Forest, IL 60452 (SAN 659-2953) Tel 312-687-7881.

†**Mpls Publ Lib,** (Minneapolis Public Library & Information Center; 0-9613716), 300 Nicollet Mall, Minneapolis, MN 55401 (SAN 279-6066) Tel 612-372-6606; CIP.

Mr Coach, (Mr. Coach, Inc.; 0-9607324), P.O. Box 9171, Downers Grove, IL 60515 (SAN 239-2631) Tel 312-964-3090.

Mr Cogito Pr, (Mr. Cogito Pr.; 0-932191; 0-7401205), P.O. Box 66124, Portland, OR 97266 (SAN 212-9191) Tel 503-233-8151; Pacific Univ., UC Box 627, Forest Grove, OR 97116 (SAN 662-0825) Tel 503-357-6151.

Mr Info, (Mr. Information; 0-88635), 2515 Rainier Ave. S., Seattle, WA 98144 (SAN 692-9044) Tel 604-653-9260.

Mr Padco Pubns, (Mr. Padco Pubns.; 0-9615147), 16850 Alcross St., Covina, CA 91722 (SAN 692-9052) Tel 818-966-3439; Orders to: P.O. Box 2111, Irwindale, CA 91706 (SAN 662-3069) Tel 818-966-3439.

MRDC Educ Inst, (MRDC Educational Institute; 0-9404706), P.O. Box 15127, Dallas, TX 75201 (SAN 214-4085). Moved, left no forwarding address.

MrD's Poetic Exp, (Mr. D's Poetic Experience Publishing Co.; 0-9607748), 3208 Cahuensa Blvd., West Hollywood, CA 90068 (SAN 240-1274).

Mrng Star SF, (Morning Star Pr.; 0-937937), 16 California St., Suite 205, San Francisco, CA 94111 (SAN 659-5294) Tel 415-751-0904.

MRP, (Montana Reconnaissance Project; 0-939872), P.O. Box 8507, Missoula, MT 59807 (SAN 216-9118) Tel 406-543-7357.

Ms Leroy Pr, (Ms. Leroy Pr.; 0-9616758), 3511 S. 172nd, Seattle, WA 98188 (SAN 238-9150) Tel 206-243-3687.

MS Res & Dev Ctr, (Mississippi Research & Development Center; 0-940786), Computer Service, 3825 Ridgewood Rd., Jackson, MS 39211 (SAN 202-2109) Tel 601-982-6466.

MSA Inc, (MSA, Inc.; 0-9616897), P.O. Box 2289, Provo, UT 84603 (SAN 661-6038); 342 Wymount Terr., No. 6A, Provo, UT 84604 (SAN 661-6046) Tel 801-377-0642.

MSC Inc, (Management & Systems Consultants, Inc.; 0-918356), Univ. Sta., P.O. Box 40457, Tucson, AZ 85717 (SAN 209-9500); 3900 Los Portales, Tucson, AZ 85718 (SAN 662-0779) Tel 602-299-9615.

MSS Press, (MSS Pr.; 0-938621), SUNY at Binghamton, Binghamton, NY 13901 (SAN 219-5062) Tel 607-777-2404.

MSU Comm Dev, (Michigan State Univ., Community Development Programs; 0-941872), Michigan State Univ., 43 Kellogg Ctr., East Lansing, MI 48824-1022 (SAN 202-2583) Tel 517-355-0100.

MSU-Inst Comm Devel
See MSU Comm Dev

Mt Angel Abbey, (Mount Angel Abbey Pubns.; 0-918941), Saint Benedict, OR 97373 (SAN 669-8530) Tel 503-845-3380.

Mt Coun Indian
See Coun India Ed

Mt Eden Hist, (Mt. Eden Historical Pubs.; 0-936193), 22237 Main St., Hayward, CA 94541 (SAN 696-6624) Tel 415-582-3969.

MT Hist Soc, (Montana Historical Society Pr.; 0-917298), 225 N. Roberts St., Helena, MT 59620 (SAN 208-7693) Tel 406-444-4708; Dist. by: Univ. of Washington Pr., P.O. Box C-50096, Seattle, WA 98105 (SAN 212-2502) Tel 206-543-4050.

Mt Hood Pub, (Mount Hood Publishing Co.; 0-938071), 4135 Cunningham Dr., Mount Hood, OR 97041-9726 (SAN 661-1915) Tel 503-352-7465.

MT Mag, (Montana Magazine, Inc.; 0-938314), Box 5630, Helena, MT 59604 (SAN 220-0732) Tel 406-443-2842; Toll free: 800-821-3874 (MT).

Mt Shasta Pubns, (Mount Shasta Pubns.; 0-9616478), P.O. Box 436, Mount Shasta, CA 96067 (SAN 659-2805) Tel 916-926-5653; 200 Sheldon, No. 6, Mount Shasta, CA 96067 (SAN 659-2813).

†**Mt Vernon Ladies,** (Mt. Vernon Ladies Assn. of the Union, Library; 0-931917), Museum Shop, Mount Vernon, VA 22121 (SAN 225-3976) Tel 703-780-2000; CIP.

MTA Financial Servs, (MTA Financial Services Corp.), 1010 Hunter Court, Deerfield, IL 60015 (SAN 212-6265) Tel 312-945-3649.

MTASC, (Motor Transportation Association of South Carolina; 0-9608140), P.O. Box 50166, Columbia, SC 29205 (SAN 240-2580) Tel 803-799-4306.

MTI Tele, (MTI Teleprograms Inc./A Simon & Schuster Communications Company; 0-916070), 108 Wilmot Rd., Deerfield, IL 60015 (SAN 211-0350) Tel 312-940-1260; Toll free: 800-621-2131.

MTM Pub Co, (M/T/M Publishing Co.; 0-938758), P.O. Box 245, Washougal, WA 98671 (SAN 206-1627).

Mtn Lamp Pubns, (Mountain Lamp Pubns.; 0-9615526), Rt. 6, Box 185B, Morgantown, WV 26505 (SAN 696-2963) Tel 304-292-1108.

Mtn Valley Pub, (Mountain Valley Publishing Hse.; 0-9615415), Box 25432, Prescott Valley, AZ 86312 (SAN 695-5266) Tel 602-772-8838.

Mu Alpha Theta, (Mu Alpha Theta, National High School Mathematics Club; 0-940790), 601 Elm Ave., Rm. 423, Norman, OK 73019 (SAN 204-0077) Tel 405-325-4489.

Mu Phi Ep, (Mu Phi Epsilon), 833 Laurel Ave., Highland Park, IL 60035 (SAN 224-5191) Tel 312-940-1222.

Mudra, (Mudra; 0-914726), Dist. by: Bookpeople, 2929 Fifth St., Berkeley, CA 94710 (SAN 168-9517) Tel 415-549-3030.

Muhlbut Pr, (Muhlbut Pr.; 0-88100), P.O. Box 165, Dunmor, KY 42339 (SAN 655-167X).

Mul-T-Rul, (Mul-T-Rul Pr.; 0-9606556), Div. of Mul-T-Rul Co., P.O. Box 250, Ft. Morgan, CO 80701 (SAN 223-0097) Tel 303-867-6201.

Mulberry Ave Bks, (Mulberry Avenue Bks.; 0-938036), 2609 A&M Circle, San Angelo, TX 76904 (SAN 240-0510).

Mulberry Tree, (Mulberry Tree Press, The; 0-9610684), 327 N. Loudoun St, Winchester, VA 22601 (SAN 264-7672) Tel 703-665-0683.

†**Mulch Pr,** (Mulch Press; 0-913142), 1648 Waller St., San Francisco, CA 94117 (SAN 206-5061); Dist. by: Small Press Distribution, Inc., 1814 San Pablo Ave., Berkeley, CA 94702 (SAN 204-5826) Tel 415-549-3336; CIP.

Mule Mt Pr, (Mule Mountain Pr.; 0-932645), 108 La Cholla, Bisbee, AZ 85603 (SAN 687-8245) Tel 602-432-3160.

Mulford Colebrook, (Mulford Colebrook Publishing Co.; 0-930144), Box 289, Mifflinburg, PA 17844 (SAN 210-6434) Tel 217-344-1024.

Symbols/Abbreviations

Multi Dimen, *(Multi Dimensional Communications, Inc.; 0-89507),* P.O. Box 427, Bedford Hills, NY 10507 (SAN 209-9632).

†**Multi Media CO,** *(Mosby/Multi-Media; 0-940122; 0-8016),* Div. of Mosby/Times Mirror, 11830 Westline Industrial Dr., Saint Louis, MO 63146 (SAN 220-2913) Tel 303-778-1404; Toll free: 800-325-4177; *CIP.*

Multi Media TX, *(Multi Media Arts; 0-86617),* Box 14486, Austin, TX 78761 (SAN 214-4239) Tel 512-837-5503.

Multi Spectral, *(Multi-Spectral Pr.; 0-918210),* 4948 Meadowbrook Rd., Buffalo, NY 14221 (SAN 210-2412) Tel 716-632-0921.

Multi Strategy Pubs, *(Multi-Strategy Pubs., Inc.; 0-9616896),* P.O. Box 23, Grand Central Sta., New York, NY 10163 (SAN 661-6143); 72-10 112th St., Suite 1D, Forest Hills, NY 11375 (SAN 661-6151) Tel 718-793-9417.

Multilingual, *(Multilingual Typesetting; 0-9616413),* 56 Rockland Lake Pk., Valley Cottage, NY 10989 (SAN 658-9421) Tel 914-268-3782.

Multiple Breath Music, *(Multiple Breath Music Co.; 0-939407),* 10 Leonard St., New York, NY 10013 (SAN 663-1401) Tel 212-226-6718.

Multiple Pr, *(Multiple Pr.; 0-934911),* P.O. Box 1817, New York, NY 10009 (SAN 695-0078) Tel 212-614-0710.

Multistate Tax, *(Multistate Tax Commission),* 1790 30th St., Suite 314, Boulder, CO 80301 (SAN 272-5509).

†**Multnomah,** *(Multnomah Pr.; 0-930014; 0-88070),* Div. of Multnomah Schl. of the Bible, 10209 SE Division St., Portland, OR 97266 (SAN 210-4679) Tel 503-257-0526; Toll free: 800-547-5890; *CIP.*

MUMPS, *(MUMPS Users Group; 0-918118),* 4321 Hartwick Rd., Suite 510, College Park, MD 20740 (SAN 669-1633) Tel 301-779-6555.

Muncy Manuscripts, *(Muncy Manuscripts, Inc.; 0-9617231),* P.O. Box 1561, Grapevine, TX 76051 (SAN 663-4788); 2960 Trail Lake Dr., Grapevine, TX 76051 (SAN 663-4796) Tel 817-481-7659.

Mundo Trade Intl, *(Mundo Trade International Inc.; 0-931919),* 720 N. Barbara Ave., Solana Beach, CA 92075 (SAN 686-0052) Tel 619-755-1132.

Mundus Artium, *(Mundus Artium Pr.; 0-939378),* P.O. Box 830688, Richardson, TX 75083-0688 (SAN 206-6866) Tel 214-690-2092.

Munger Africana Lib, *(California Institute of Technology, Munger Africana Library; 0-934912),* Pasadena, CA 91125 (SAN 211-1195) Tel 818-356-4469.

Munger Oil, *(Munger Oil Information Service),* 9800 S. Sepulveda Blvd., Suite 723, Los Angeles, CA 90045 (SAN 205-7867) Tel 213-776-3990.

Muni Res WA, *(Municipal Research & Services Ctr. of Washington),* 4719 Brooklyn Ave. NE, Seattle, WA 98105 (SAN 226-630X).

Municipal, *(Municipal Finance Officers Assn. of the U. S. & Canada; 0-89125),* 180 N. Michigan Ave., Suite 800, Chicago, IL 60601 (SAN 202-2540) Tel 312-977-9700.

Municipal Analysis, *(Municipal Analysis Services, Inc.; 1-55507),* P.O. Box 13453, Austin, TX 78711 (SAN 694-2148) Tel 512-327-3328.

Municipal Art Soc, *(Municipal Art Society of New York, The; 0-9606892),* 457 Madison Ave., New York, NY 10022 (SAN 217-4065) Tel 212-935-3960.

Munro Assocs, *(Munro, John A., Assocs., Inc.; 0-911553),* 16 E. 41st St., New York, NY 10017 (SAN 272-555X) Tel 212-689-8787.

Munson Bks, *(Munson Books),* 3436 Willow Dr., Mattoon, IL 61938 (SAN 209-1593) Tel 217-234-8465.

†**Munson Williams,** *(Munson-Williams-Proctor Institute; 0-915895),* 310 Genesee St., Utica, NY 13502 (SAN 272-5568) Tel 315-797-0000; *CIP.*

Muntu Bks, *(Muntu Bks.; 0-9614140),* 2439 Jefferson Ave., Apt. B, Berkeley, CA 94703 (SAN 686-2225) Tel 415-548-6476; P.O. Box 3952, Berkeley, CA 94703 (SAN 695-4553) Tel 415-548-6476; Dist. by: Bookpeople, 2929 Fifth St., Berkeley, CA 94710 (SAN 168-9517) Tel 415-549-3030.

Muratore, *(Muratore Agency, Inc.),* 766 W. Shore Rd., P.O. Box 486, Warwick, RI 02889 (SAN 205-6356) Tel 401-737-6460.

Murphy & Broad, *(Murphy & Broad Publishing Co.; 0-940792),* 425 30th St., Suite 8, P.O. Box 3208, Newport Beach, CA 92663 (SAN 219-6085) Tel 714-673-3348.

Murphy Pub Co, *(Murphy Publishing Co.),* P.O. Box 64, Timonium, MD 21093 (SAN 205-7840) Tel 301-377-5083.

Murray & Garig, *(Murray & Garig Tool Works; 0-9611896),* 220 E. Texas Ave., Baytown, TX 77520 (SAN 285-3477) Tel 713-427-5923.

Murrayhollow, *(Murrayhollow Pubs.; 0-9610242),* Murrayhollow Rd., Shushan, NY 12873 (SAN 264-2263) Tel 518-854-3305.

Murton Pr, *(Murton Pr., The; 0-9608042),* 26 Anderson Rd., Greenwich, CT 06830 (SAN 240-0960) Tel 203-869-4434.

Mus Afr Art
See Mus African Art

Mus African Art, *(Museum of African Art, Smithsonian Institution),* 316-332 A St., NE, Washington, DC 20002 (SAN 213-1250) Tel 202-287-3490.

Mus Am China Trade, *(Museum of the American China Trade; 0-937650),* Peabody Museum of Salem, East India Sq., Salem, MA 01970 (SAN 204-1030) Tel 617-745-1876.

Mus Am Ind, *(Museum of the American Indian; 0-934490),* Broadway at 155th St., New York, NY 10032 (SAN 204-0085) Tel 212-283-2420.

Mus Anthro MO, *(University of Missouri, Museum of Anthropology; 0-913134),* 104 Swallow Hall, Columbia, MO 65211 (SAN 203-0195) Tel 314-882-3764.

Mus Art Carnegie, *(Museum of Art, Carnegie Institute; 0-88039),* 4400 Forbes Ave., Pittsburgh, PA 15213 (SAN 239-1171) Tel 412-622-3228.

Mus City NY, *(Museum of the City of New York; 0-910961),* Fifth Ave. at 103rd St., New York, NY 10029 (SAN 279-7461) Tel 212-534-1672.

Mus Collaborative, *(Museums Collaborative, Inc.),* 15 Grammercy Park S., New York, NY 10003 (SAN 219-7987) Tel 212-674-0030.

Mus Comp Zoo, *(Harvard University, Museum of Comparative Zoology; 0-910999),* Harvard University, 26 Oxford St., Cambridge, MA 02138 (SAN 270-6873) Tel 617-495-2471.

Mus Fed Ink, *(Muse Federation Ink; 0-9614084),* P.O. Box 642 St. Albans Sta., Jamaica, NY 11412 (SAN 686-0044) Tel 718-723-9880.

Mus Fine Arts Boston, *(Museum of Fine Arts, Boston; 0-87846),* 465 Huntington Ave., Boston, MA 02115 (SAN 202-2230) Tel 617-267-9300.

Mus Fine Arts Gal
See Mus Fine Arts Boston

Mus Graphics, *(Museum Graphics; 0-913832),* P.O. Box 2368, Menlo Park, CA 94025 (SAN 201-8454) Tel 415-368-5531; Orders to: Little, Brown & Co., 200 West St., Waltham, MA 02154 (SAN 201-8462).

Mus Great Plains, *(Museum of the Great Plains, Pubns. Dept.; 0-911728),* 601 Ferris, P.O. Box 68, Lawton, OK 73502 (SAN 205-7794) Tel 405-353-5675.

Mus Holography, *(Museum of Holography; 0-936210),* 11 Mercer St., New York, NY 10013 (SAN 222-6324) Tel 212-925-0581.

Mus Northern Ariz, *(Museum of Northern Arizona; 0-89734),* Rte. 4, Box 720, Flagstaff, AZ 86001 (SAN 204-0093) Tel 602-774-5211.

Mus of Art RI, *(Museum of Art Rhode Island School of Design; 0-940794),* 224 Benefit St., Providence, RI 02903 (SAN 204-0107) Tel 401-331-3511; Toll free: 800-343-9444; Dist. by: Milford House, Inc., 51 Washington St., Dover, MA 03820 (SAN 202-6368).

Mus Sci & Hist, *(Museum of Science & History, The; 0-9604642),* MacArthur Park, Little Rock, AR 72202 (SAN 215-7926).

Mus Stony Brook, *(Museums at Stony Brook; 0-943924),* 1208 Rte. 25A, Stony Brook, NY 11790 (SAN 279-7623) Tel 516-751-0066; Dist. by: Univ. of Wash. Pr., P.O. Box C50096, Seattle, WA 98145 (SAN 212-2502) Tel 206-543-8870.

Mus Sys, *(Museum Systems; 0-941094),* 760 N. La Cienaga Blvd., Los Angeles, CA 90069 (SAN 204-0123) Tel 213-657-5811.

Mus W Art, *(Museum of Western Art; 0-914965),* 1727 Tremont Pl., Denver, CO 80202 (SAN 289-3355) Tel 303-292-6776; Toll free: 800-525-7047.

Muse-Ed Comp, *(Muse-Ed Co.; 0-9604434),* 14141 Margate St., Van Nuys, CA 91401 (SAN 283-3514) Tel 818-501-3854.

Museum America, *(Museum of American Textile History; 0-937474),* 800 Massachusetts Ave., North Andover, MA 01845 (SAN 205-8537) Tel 617-686-0191.

Museum Art GA, *(Museum of Arts & Sciences, Macon, Georgia; 0-916769),* 4182 Forsyth Rd., Macon, GA 31210 (SAN 653-8851) Tel 912-477-3232.

Museum Art Sciences, *(Museum of Arts & Sciences; 0-933053),* 1040 Museum Blvd., Daytona Beach, FL 32014 (SAN 279-7127) Tel 904-255-0285.

Museum Bks, *(Museum Bks., Inc.; 0-87544),* 6 W. 37th St., New York, NY 10018 (SAN 204-0131) Tel 212-563-2770.

Museum Comp Network, *(Museum Computer Network, Inc.),* 2018 Empire State Plaza Sta., Albany, NY 12220 (SAN 223-8012) Tel 518-473-1746.

Museum Mobile, *(Museum of the City of Mobile; 0-914334),* 355 Government St., Mobile, AL 36602 (SAN 213-1218) Tel 205-438-7569.

Museum Mod Art, *(Museum of Modern Art; 0-87070),* 11 W. 53rd St., New York, NY 10019 (SAN 202-5809) Tel 212-708-9733; Toll free: 800-343-9204.

†**Museum NM Pr,** *(Museum of New Mexico Pr.; 0-89013),* P.O. Box 2087, Santa Fe, NM 87503 (SAN 202-2575) Tel 505-827-6455; *CIP.*

Museum of NM Pr
See Museum NM Pr

Museum Rockies, *(Museum of The Rockies; 0-933819),* Montana State Univ., Bozeman, MT 59717-0001 (SAN 692-8870) Tel 406-994-2251.

Museums Council, *(Museums Council of New Jersey, The; 0-9616363),* Old Barracks Museum, Barrack St., Trenton, NJ 08608 (SAN 658-9669) Tel 609-396-1776.

Mushroom Cave, *(Mushroom Cave, Inc., The; 0-9601516),* P.O. Box 894, Battle Creek, MI 49016 (SAN 211-6723) Tel 616-962-3497.

Mushroom Tech, *(Mushroom Technology Corp.),* P.O. Box 2612, Naperville, IL 60565 (SAN 670-705X) Tel 312-961-3286.

Mushrooms Etc, *(Mushrooms, Etc.; 0-9606236),* 2610 Vivian St., Lakewood, CO 80215 (SAN 220-343X) Tel 303-233-6238.

Music Child Pr, *(Music for Children Pr.; 0-9616737),* 96 County St., Norwalk, CT 06851 (SAN 661-4329) Tel 203-866-3298.

Music Ed
See Music Ed Natl

Music Ed Natl, *(Music Educators National Conference; 0-940796),* 1902 Association Dr., Reston, VA 22090 (SAN 676-8733) Tel 703-860-4000.

Music Educ Pubns, *(Music Education Pubns.; 0-943988),* P.O. Box 3402, Fullerton, CA 92634 (SAN 241-5674) Tel 714-525-1397.

Music In Action, *(Music In Action; 0-939139),* P.O. Box 204, East Stroudsburg, PA 18301 (SAN 662-4944); Meadow Lake Rd., Sciota, PA 18354 (SAN 662-4952) Tel 717-992-7953.

†**Music Library Assn,** *(Music Library Assn.),* P.O. Box 487, Canton, MA 02021 (SAN 233-4909) Tel 617-828-8450; *CIP.*

Music Pr, *(Music Pr.; 0-918318),* 155 W. 68th St., New York, NY 10023 (SAN 209-0899) Tel 212-877-3175.

Music Sales, *(Music Sales Corp.; 0-8256),* 24 E. 22nd St., New York, NY 10010 (SAN 282-0277) Tel 212-254-2100; Toll free: 800-431-7187; Orders to: Music Sales Distribution Ctr., 5 Bellvale Rd., P.O. Box 572, Chester, NY 10918 (SAN 662-0876) Tel 914-469-2271. *Imprints:* Acorn (Acorn Music Press); Amsco Music (Amsco Music); Hidden Hse (Hidden House); Oak (Oak Pubns.).

Music Study, *(Music Study Services; 0-936245),* 259 S. Madison Ave., Louisville, CO 80027 (SAN 696-852X) Tel 303-666-7836; Dist. by: Publishers Group West, 5855 Beaudry St., Emeryville, CA 94608 (SAN 202-8522) Tel 415-658-3453.

Music Tchrs, *(Music Teachers National Association),* 2113 Carew Tower, Cincinnati, OH 45202 (SAN 225-8528) Tel 513-421-1420.

Music Treasure, *(Music Treasure Pubns.; 0-912028),* 620 Fort Washington Ave., 1-F, New York, NY 10040 (SAN 204-0158).

Music Works, *(Music Works; 0-9617272),* 1250 Ollie St., Stephanville, TX 76401 (SAN 663-4877) Tel 512-454-0147.

†Musica, *(Musica Publishing Co.; 0-9600964),* Box 1266, Edison, NJ 08818 (SAN 208-9696); *CIP.*

Musica Ninos *Imprint of* **Hansen Ed Mus**

Musical Alternatives, *(Musical Alternatives; 0-9616599),* 11 Spring St., Oneonta, NY 13820 (SAN 659-5146) Tel 607-432-0570.

Musical Box Soc, *(Musical Box Society International, The; 0-915000),* 1300 E. Third St., St. Paul, MN 55106 (SAN 215-9732) Tel 612-774-2590.

Musical Scope, *(Musical Scope Pubns.; 0-913000),* P.O. Box 125, Audubon Sta., New York, NY 10032 (SAN 202-8867).

Musicbiz Pub, *(Musicbiz Publishing Co.; 0-937965),* P.O. Box 97008, Bellevue, WA 98009 (SAN 659-5170) Tel 206-453-0764; 10900 NE Eighth, Suite 169, Bellevue, WA 98004 (SAN 659-5189); Dist. by: Columbia Pictures Pubns., 15800 NW 48th Ave., Miami, FL 33014 (SAN 203-042X) Tel 305-620-1500.

†Musicdata, *(Musicdata, Inc.; 0-88478),* P.O. Box 48010, Philadelphia, PA 19144-8010 (SAN 203-1566) Tel 215-842-0555; *CIP.*

Musicgraphics, *(Musicgraphics; 0-941814),* 124 Atlantic Ave., Lynbrook, NY 11563 (SAN 239-264X) Tel 516-599-5990.

Muskingum, *(Muskingum County Footprints; 0-917033),* 2740 Adamsville Rd., Zanesville, OH 43701 (SAN 655-2536) Tel 614-453-8231.

Muso Pr, *(Muso Pr.; 0-9614614),* 180 4th Ave., Apt. 12, San Francisco, CA 94118 (SAN 691-7852) Tel 415-221-5212; Orders to: P.O. Box 590232, San Francisco, CA 94159-0232 (SAN 663-3129) Tel 415-221-5212.

Mustang Pub, *(Mustang Publishing; 0-914457),* P.O. Box 9327, New Haven, CT 06533 (SAN 289-6702) Tel 203-624-5485; Dist. by: Kampmann & Co., Inc., 9 E. 40th St., New York, NY 10016 (SAN 202-5191) Tel 212-685-2928.

Mustardseed, *(Mustardseed Press; 0-917920),* Subs. of Interuniverse, 707 N. Carolina Ave., Cocoa, FL 32922 (SAN 209-9659) Tel 305-632-2769.

Muste, *(Muste, A. J., Memorial Institute; 0-9608096),* 339 Lafayette St., New York, NY 10012 (SAN 240-2599) Tel 212-533-4335.

Mutual Pr IL, *(Mutual Pr.; 0-9605628),* 664 N. Michigan, Suite 1010, Chicago, IL 60611 (SAN 216-2717) Tel 312-478-4030.

Mutual Pub HI, *(Mutual Publishing of Honolulu; 0-935180),* 2055 N. King St., Honolulu, HI 96819 (SAN 222-6359).

Mutualist Pr, *(Mutualist Press, The),* GPO Box 2009, Brooklyn, NY 11202 (SAN 213-1226).

Mutzal Me'esh Inst, *(Mutzal Me'esh Institute; 0-914787),* 2311 Ave J., Brooklyn, NY 11210 (SAN 683-4248).

MVR Bks, *(MVR Books),* 3020 E Ave., Berwyn, IL 60402 (SAN 210-4709) Tel 312-749-7697.

MWS Pubns, *(MWS Pubns; 0-939640),* 1450 Golden Gate Ave., No.204, San Francisco, CA 94115 (SAN 216-6348).

Myco Pub Hse, *(Myco Publishing House; 0-936624),* P.O. Box 1237, Arcadia, CA 91006 (SAN 214-2538) Tel 714-661-4957.

Mycological, *(Mycological Society of San Francisco, Inc.; 0-918942),* Box 11321, San Francisco, CA 94101 (SAN 210-3621) Tel 415-839-4263.

Mycotaxon Ltd, *(Mycotaxon, Ltd.; 0-930845),* P.O. Box 264, Ithaca, NY 14851 (SAN 677-6051) Tel 607-273-4357.

Mycroft & Moran *Imprint of* **Arkham**

Myers Inc, *(Myers, S. D., Inc.; 0-939320),* P.O. Box 4724, Akron, OH 44310 (SAN 216-2725); Toll free: 800-321-9580.

Mykro, *(Mykro Pub; 0-931281),* Subs. of Santa Cruz EDP Mgmt., 2506 Charlene Ln., Santa Cruz, CA 95062 (SAN 682-0042) Tel 408-475-5346; P.O. Box 2383, Los Gatos, CA 95031-2383 (SAN 692-6355).

MYL *Imprint of* **Moody**

Myleen Pr, *(Myleen Press),* 614 Lyndhurst Ave., Roseville, CA 95678 (SAN 213-9405).

Mynabird Pub, *(Mynabird Publishing; 0-917758),* 20 Shoshone Place, Portola Valley, CA 94025 (SAN 209-1550) Tel 415-851-8554.

Myriad, *(Myriad Moods; 0-911843),* 313 Joliet, San Antonio, TX 78209 (SAN 264-2271) Tel 512-824-9554.

†Myriade, *(Myriade Pr.; 0-918142),* 7 Stony Run, New Rochelle, NY 10804 (SAN 210-2439) Tel 914-235-8470; *CIP.*

Myrin Institute, *(Myrin Institute, Inc.; 0-913098),* 136 E. 64th St., New York, NY 10021 (SAN 204-0182) Tel 212-758-6475.

Myrtle Bank, *(Myrtle Bank Pr.; 0-9606978),* 408 N. Pearl St., Natchez, MS 39120 (SAN 238-8995).

Myrtle Tree Pubns, *(Myrtle Tree Pubns.; 0-9614422),* 7522 44th Pl., Seattle, WA 98136 (SAN 689-0245) Tel 206-938-1463.

Mysterious Pr, *(Mysterious Pr.; 0-89296),* Subs. of Penzler Bks., 129 W. 56th St., New York, NY 10019 (SAN 208-2152) Tel 212-765-0901; Dist. by: Farrar, Straus & Giroux, 19 Union Sq. W., New York, NY 10003 (SAN 206-782X) Tel 212-741-6900. *Imprints:* Penzler Bks (Penzler Books).

Mystic Bay Bk, *(Mystic Bay Books; 0-9608974),* Box 525, Mystic, CT 06355 (SAN 689-0539).

Mystic Jhamom, *(Mystic Jhamom Pubs.; 0-933961),* 1650 Rocky Pl., Arroyo Grande, CA 93420 (SAN 693-0689) Tel 805-922-8802; P.O. Box 904, Santa Maria, CA 93456 (SAN 694-972X).

Mystic Seaport, *(Mystic Seaport Museum, Inc.; 0-913372),* Green Manville, Mystic, CT 06355 (SAN 213-7550) Tel 203-572-0711.

Mystic Soc, *(Mystic Light Society, The; 0-910433),* P.O. Box 53134, Philadelphia, PA 19105 (SAN 260-1494) Tel 215-925-7527.

N A Orchestra, *(N. A. Orchestra; 0-9613672),* John F. Kennedy Center for the Perfoming Arts, Washington, DC 20566 (SAN 682-0530) Tel 202-785-8100.

N Allen Pub, *(Allen, Nathan, Publishing Co.; 0-943586),* 1503 Van Stone Dr., Milford, MI 48042 (SAN 240-5806) Tel 313-363-2206.

N Am Congress Latin
See NA Cong Lat Am

N Am Man-Boy, *(North American Man/Boy Love Assn.; 0-9615497),* P.O. Box 174 Midtown Sta., New York, NY 10018 (SAN 696-382X) Tel 212-807-8578; Dist. by: Glad Day Books, 43 Winter St., Boston, MA 02108 (SAN 221-282X) Tel 617-542-0144.

N Amer Hunt Club, *(North American Hunting Club, Inc.; 0-914697),* 7901 Flying Cloud Dr., No. 210, Minneapolis, MN 55435 (SAN 661-2636); P.O. Box 35557, Minneapolis, MN 55435 (SAN 661-2644).

N Amer Pubs, *(North American Pubs., Inc.; 0-9617079),* P.O. Box 1231, Bloomington, IN 47402 (SAN 662-5878); 1113 S. High St., Bloomington, IN 47401 (SAN 662-5886) Tel 812-336-5611.

N Amer Tech, *(North American Technology; 0-911261),* 174 Concord St., Peterborough, NH 03458 (SAN 274-158X) Tel 603-924-7136.

N American Archives, *(North American Archives; 0-915431),* P.O. Box 9685, N. Hollywood, CA 91609 (SAN 291-3143) Tel 818-786-6069.

N American Assn, *(North American Association of Christians in Social Work),* P.O. Box 90, Saint Davids, PA 19087 (SAN 225-994X).

N & D Pub Co, *(N & D Publishing Co.; 0-9616044),* 806 Ewing Blvd., Murfreesboro, TN 37130 (SAN 696-0596) Tel 615-898-2386.

N & N Pub
See N & N Pub Co

N & N Pub Co, *(N&N Publishing Co., Inc.; 0-9606036),* 10 Lydia Dr., Wappinger, NY 12590 (SAN 216-4221) Tel 914-297-6389; Orders to: 44 Wisner Ave., Middletown, NY 10940 (SAN 662-0884) Tel 914-342-1677.

N & N Resources, *(N & N Resources),* P.O. Box 332, Troy, ID 83871 (SAN 209-0376) Tel 208-835-2012.

N Arizona U, *(Northern Arizona Univ., Dept. of Anthropology; 0-910953),* Box 15200, Flagstaff, AZ 86011 (SAN 264-2573) Tel 602-523-3180; Dist. by: Northern Arizona Univ. Bookstore, P.O. Box 6044, Flagstaff, AZ 86011 (SAN 200-7541) Tel 602-523-4041.

N Breslau, *(Breslau, Nathan, Publishing Co.; 0-9610716),* 918 A. Savannas Point Dr., Fort Pierce, FL 33450 (SAN 264-6544) Tel 305-466-3439.

N Burleson, *(Norm Burleson, Bookseller; 0-930577),* 104 First Ave., P.O. Box 15007, Spartanburg, SC 29302 (SAN 677-587X) Tel 803-583-8845.

N C Genealogical, *(North Carolina Genealogical Society, Inc.; 0-936370),* P.O. Box 1492, Raleigh, NC 27602 (SAN 222-4003); Orders to: Reprint Co., Pubs., P.O. Box 5401, Spartanburg, SC 29304 (SAN 203-3828) Tel 803-582-0732.

N C Hinds Pub, *(Hinds, Norman C., Jr., Publishing Co.; 0-935541),* P.O. Box 456, Newburyport, MA 01950 (SAN 695-9636) Tel 617-465-2697; Dist. by: New Leaf Distributing, The, 1020 White St., SW, Atlanta, GA 30310 (SAN 169-1449) Tel 404-755-2665.

N C Wesleyan Friends Lib
See NC Wesleyan Friends Lib

N Cartographic, *(Northern Cartographic Inc.; 0-9606738),* P.O. Box 133, Burlington, VT 05402 (SAN 219-6131) Tel 802-655-4321.

N Central Sect Wildlife, *(North Central Section Wildlife Society The; 0-932547),* 300 W. First St., Bloomington, IN 47401 (SAN 687-4924) Tel 812-334-1137.

N Crime Prevent
See Natl Crime DC

N Dak Coun Arts, *(North Dakota Council On The Arts; 0-911205),* Black Bldg., Suite 606, Fargo, ND 58102 (SAN 293-311X) Tel 701-237-8959; Dist. by: Germans From Russia Heritage Society, P.O. Box 1671, Bismarck, ND 58502 (SAN 293-3128).

N Dak Inst, *(North Dakota Institute for Regional Studies; 0-911042),* State Univ. Sta., Fargo, ND 58105 (SAN 203-1574) Tel 701-237-8655.

N E Albert, *(Albert, Nancy E.; 0-9613998),* Evanston Law Ctr., P.O. Box 110, Evanston, IL 60204 (SAN 687-6633).

N Fonville, *(Fonville, Naomi; 0-9616421),* 905 Hinton Ave., Lumberton, MS 39455 (SAN 696-6578) Tel 601-796-4338.

N Foster Baptist, *(North Foster Baptist Church),* R.R. 1 Box 282 E. Killingly Rd., Foster, RI 02825 (SAN 282-0595) Tel 401-647-5805; Dist. by: Rhode Island Publications Society, 189 Wickenden St., Providence, RI 02903 (SAN 219-9696) Tel 401-272-1776.

N Geller Pub, *(Geller, Norman, Pubs.; 0-915753),* P.O. Box 1283, Lewiston, ME 04240 (SAN 293-9681) Tel 207-783-2400.

N Grey Inc, *(Nishan Grey Inc.; 0-9605652),* P.O. Box 8368, Salt Lake City, UT 84108 (SAN 238-1303) Tel 801-466-9578.

N H Gershman, *(Gershman, Norman H., Gallery, Inc.; 0-9617237),* 710 Broadway, New York, NY 10003 (SAN 663-5660) Tel 212-349-8606.

N H Ludlow, *(Ludlow, Norman H.; 0-916706),* 516 Arnett Blvd., Rochester, NY 14619 (SAN 207-5776) Tel 716-235-0951.

N Hall, *(Hall, Norman, Ministries; 0-938429),* N. 1658 Fairmont Loop, Coeur d'Alene, ID 83814 (SAN 661-292X) Tel 208-664-4576.

N Hays
See Nicolas-Hays

N Ill Anthro, *(Anthropology Museum, The; 0-917039),* Northern Illinois University, Dekalb, IL 60115 (SAN 655-4962) Tel 815-753-0246.

†N Ill U Pr, *(Northern Illinois Univ. Pr.; 0-87580),* Williston, 320A, DeKalb, IL 60115 (SAN 202-8875) Tel 815-753-1826; *CIP.*

N Isaac Inst, *(Nathan, Isaac, Institute; 0-914615),* 22711 Cass Ave., Woodland Hills, CA 91364 (SAN 289-3924) Tel 818-346-9631.

N J Rube, *(Rube, Ned J., Publisher; 0-930562),* 68 Marion Dr., New Rochelle, NY 10804 (SAN 211-0385).

N Koch, *(Koch, Nora; 0-9615583),* 12135 N. State, Otisville, MI 48463 (SAN 696-3390) Tel 313-631-4567.

N Kolko
See S G Phillips

N Kumar, *(Kumar, Navin; 0-9611400),* 24 E. 73rd St., New York, NY 10021 (SAN 285-371X) Tel 212-734-4075.

N L Endeavors, *(N. L. Endeavors; 0-936803),* 4111 Lincoln Blvd., Suite 603, Los Angeles, CA 90045 (SAN 699-9905).

N League *Imprint of* **Noontide**

†**N Lyons Bks,** *(Lyons, Nick, Bks.),* 31 W. 21st St., New York, NY 10010 (SAN 208-1881) Tel 212-620-9580; *CIP.*

N Manderino Assocs
See Manderino Bks

N Mathis, *(Mathis, Nathaniel; 0-9616389),* 1900 Bladensburg Rd., NE, Washington, DC 20002 (SAN 658-909X) Tel 202-832-3700.

N Melkonian, *(Melkonian, Norman; 0-9616320),* 207 W. Garfield, No. 5, Glendale, CA 91204 (SAN 658-7399) Tel 818-247-6809.

N Miller, *(Miller, Neil; 0-9601444),* 747 Bruce Dr., East Meadow, NY 11554 (SAN 211-0393) Tel 516-292-9569.

N Moure
See Dustin Pubns

N N Nguyen, *(Nguyen, Nam Ngoc; 0-9614634),* 104 W. 35th St., Reading, PA 19606 (SAN 694-3950).

N Nut Growers, *(Northern Nut Growers Assn.; 0-9602248),* 13 Broken Arrow Rd., Hamden, CT 06518 (SAN 206-9695) Tel 203-288-1026; 4518 Holston Hills Rd., Knoxville, TN 37914 (SAN 650-0455) Tel 615-524-0416.

N P Cartwright, *(Cartwright, Nellie Parodi; 0-9601482),* 4348 Via Frascati, Rancho Palos Verdes, CA 90274 (SAN 210-9883) Tel 213-833-7586.

N P Evans, *(Evans, Norma P.; 0-937418),* 2211 Liberty, Beaumont, TX 77701 (SAN 213-2184) Tel 409-835-7175.

N Point Hist Soc, *(North Point Historical Society; 0-9606072),* Box 557, Milwaukee, WI 53201 (SAN 216-9177) Tel 414-271-2395.

†**N Point Pr,** *(North Point Pr.; 0-86547),* 850 Talbot Ave., Berkeley, CA 94706 (SAN 220-133X) Tel 415-527-6260; Dist. by: Farrar Straus Giroux, Inc, 19 Union Sq., W., New York, NY 10003 (SAN 206-782X) Tel 212-741-6900; *CIP.*

N Powers, *(Powers, Nancy, & Co. Pubs., Inc.; 0-941684),* 241 Central Park W., New York, NY 10024 (SAN 239-281X) Tel 212-877-3262.

N S B A
See Natl Sch Boards

N S Kline Inst, *(Kline, Nathan S., Institute; 0-936934),* Information Sciences Div., Bldg. 37, Orangeburg, NY 10962 (SAN 239-6041) Tel 914-359-1050.

N S Wait, *(Wait, N. S.; 0-911588),* Box 407, Valparaiso, IN 46384 (SAN 206-6491). Formerly H. H. Wait Pub.

†**N Stonington,** *(North Stonington Pr.; 0-938538),* P.O. Box 501, Greenwich, CT 06836 (SAN 282-0633) Tel 203-622-0878; *CIP.*

N T Smith, *(Smith, Nicholas T.; 0-935164),* P.O. Box 66, Bronxville, NY 10708 (SAN 213-6457) Tel 914-793-0610.

N Terry
See Inter Comp Rec

N Texas St U Pro Devel Inst, *(North Texas State Univ., Professional Development Institute; 0-940966),* P.O. Box 13288, Denton, TX 76203 (SAN 223-1980) Tel 817-565-2483.

†**N Trails,** *(Northern Trails Pr.; 0-914269),* P.O. Box 964, Alamosa, CO 81101 (SAN 287-5918) Tel 303-274-4162; *CIP.*

N Watson
See Watson Pub Intl

NA Blackwell, *(Blackwell North America; 0-946344),* 1001 Fries Mill Rd., Blackwood, NJ 08012 (SAN 169-4596) Tel 609-629-0700; Toll free: 800-257-7341; 6024 SW. Jean Rd., Bldg. G, Lake Oswego, OR 97034 (SAN 169-7048) Tel 503-684-1140; Toll free: 800-547-6426.

†**NA Cong Lat Am,** *(North American Congress on Latin America; 0-916024),* 151 W. 19th St., 9th Fl., New York, NY 10011 (SAN 218-0022) Tel 212-989-8890; *CIP.*

Na Pali Pub, *(Na Pali Publishing Co.; 0-917132),* P.O. Box 88082, Honolulu, HI 96830-0810 (SAN 208-3876).

NA Trackless Trolley, *(North American Trackless Trolley Association, Inc.; 0-939875),* 1042 Bradstown Rd. No. 2, Louisville, KY 40204-1318 (SAN 287-6566) Tel 502-459-5261.

NA Vegetarian Soc
See North Amer Veg

NAAHE, *(National Assn. for the Advancement of Humane Education; 0-941246),* Div. of Humane Society of the U. S., P.O. Box 362, East Haddam, CT 06423 (SAN 285-0680) Tel 203-488-3923.

NAAHP Inc, *(National Assn. of Advisors for the Health Professions, Inc.; 0-911899),* P.O. Box 5017 Sta. A, Champaign, IL 61820-9017 (SAN 264-679X) Tel 217-344-6013.

NAB *Imprint of* **Noyes**

NABPR, *(National Assn. of Baptist Professors of Religion; 0-932180; 0-86554),* Mercer Univ., Macon, GA 31207 (SAN 211-2175) Tel 912-744-2880; Dist. by: Mercer University Press, Macon, GA 31207 (SAN 220-0716).

†**NACD,** *(National Assn. of Conservation Districts; 0-9614178),* 1025 Vermont Ave., NW, Suite 730, Washington, DC 20005 (SAN 272-7536); Orders to: P.O. Box 855, League City, TX 77573 (SAN 693-9678) Tel 713-332-3402; *CIP.*

†**NACM,** *(National Assn. of Credit Management; 0-934914),* 520 Eighth Ave., New York, NY 10018-6571 (SAN 205-7573) Tel 212-947-5070; *CIP.*

†**NACUBO,** *(National Assn. of College & Univ. Business Officers; 0-915164),* 1 Dupont Cir., Suite 500, Washington, DC 20036-1178 (SAN 207-1479) Tel 202-861-2534; *CIP.*

Nadeau Pub, *(Nadeau Publishing Co.; 0-9613891),* 10607 Ainsworth Ave. S., Tacoma, WA 98444 (SAN 682-3025) Tel 206-535-2259.

NAEB, *(National Assn. of Educational Broadcasters; 0-8105),* 5807 Massachusetts Ave., NW, Bethesda, MD 20816 (SAN 220-0112) Tel 301-657-8420.

NAES Alexandria, *(National Assn. of Elementary Schl. Principals; 0-939327),* 1615 Duke St., Alexandria, VA 22314 (SAN 663-155X) Tel 703-684-3345.

NAFSA Washington, *(National Assn. for Foreign Student Affairs; 0-912207),* 1860 19th St., NW, Washington, DC 20009 (SAN 272-6742) Tel 202-462-4811.

Naftaolh Pubns, *(Naftaolh Pubns.; 0-9616130),* P.O. Box 2503, Columbus, MS 39704 (SAN 699-7368) Tel 601-325-4879; 323 Rebecca Ln., Columbus, MS 39704 (SAN 699-7376).

Nags Head Art, *(Nags Head Art; 0-9616344),* P.O. Box 88, Nags Head, NC 27959 (SAN 658-8093); 7734 Virginia Dare Trail, Nags Head, NC 27959 (SAN 658-8107) Tel 919-441-7480.

NAHRO, *(National Assn. of Housing & Redevelopment Officials),* 2600 Virginia Ave., NW, Washington, DC 20037 (SAN 680-0610) Tel 202-333-2020.

NAIA Pubns, *(National Assn. of Intercollegiate Athletics),* 1221 Baltimore St., Kansas City, MO 64105 (SAN 201-9574) Tel 816-842-5050.

†**Naiad Pr,** *(Naiad Pr.; 0-930044),* P.O. Box 10543, Tallahassee, FL 32302 (SAN 206-801X) Tel 904-539-9322; *CIP.* *Imprints:* Volute Bks (Volute Books).

Naire Ent, *(Naire, Bill O., Enterprises; 0-9615799),* 1041 Adason Dr., San Leandro, CA 94578 (SAN 696-5989) Tel 415-895-1773.

†**NAIS,** *(National Assn. of Independent Schls.; 0-934338),* 18 Tremont St., Boston, MA 02108 (SAN 202-0920) Tel 617-723-6900; *CIP.*

Nakii Ent, *(Nakii, D., Enterprises; 0-9615195),* P.O. Box 7639, Albuquerque, NM 87194 (SAN 694-2946) Tel 505-344-3843; Dist. by: Publishers Marketing Group, 1104 Summit Ave., Plainview, TX 75074 (SAN 262-0995) Tel 214-423-0312.

†**NAL,** *(New American Library; 0-451; 0-452; 0-453),* 1633 Broadway, New York, NY 10019 (SAN 206-8079) Tel 212-397-8000; Orders to: P.O. Box 999, Bergenfield, NJ 07621 (SAN 206-8087) Tel 201-387-0600; *CIP. Imprints:* Ment (Mentor Books).(Mentor Bks.); Mer (Meridian Books).(Meridian Bks.); Onyx (Onyx); Plume (Plume Books).(Plume Bks.); Sgnt (Signette); Sig (Signet Books).(Signet Bks.); Sig Classics (Signet Classics).

NAL *Imprint of* **Norton**

Nalini Intl Pubs, *(Nalini International Pubns.; 0-9614416),* P.O. Box 40, Livingston, NJ 07039 (SAN 688-9050) Tel 201-325-6444.

NALP, *(National Association for Law Placement),* Tulane Law Schl., 6325 Freret St., New Orleans, LA 70118 (SAN 260-3330) Tel 504-865-5945.

NAMAC, *(NAMAC; 0-936916),* P.O. Box 963, Ingleside, TX 78362 (SAN 216-0498) Tel 512-776-2305; Dist. by: Astrology & Spiritual Ctr., 4535 Hohman Ave., Hammond, IN 46327 (SAN 159-0456) Tel 219-931-8050; Dist. by: Devorss & Co., Box 550, 1046 Princeton Dr., Marina del Rey, CA 90291 (SAN 168-9886); Dist. by: Starlite, Box 20729, Reno, NV 89515 (SAN 169-0299); Dist. by: Parapsychology Education Ctr., P.O. Box 6240, Little Rock, AR 72216 (SAN 200-4186); Dist. by: Waldenbook Co., 201 High Ridge Rd., Stamford, CT 06905 (SAN 203-1752); Dist. by: The Distributors, 702 S. Michigan, South Bend, IN 46618 (SAN 212-0364) Tel 219-232-8500; Dist. by: Macoy Publishing, Box 9759, Richmond, VA 23228 (SAN 200-4194) Tel 804-262-6551.

Namaste Pr, *(Namaste Pr.; 0-916727),* P.O. Box 4435, Albuquerque, NM 87196 (SAN 653-886X) Tel 505-268-4231.

Namaste Pubns, *(Namaste Pubns.; 0-938147),* P.O. Box 262, Marshfield, MO 65706 (SAN 661-3438); 324 Banning, Marshfield, MO 65706 (SAN 661-3446) Tel 417-468-5053.

Namuk Intl Inc, *(Namuk International, Inc.; 0-933057),* P.O. Box 4543, Silver Spring, MD 20904 (SAN 689-7738); 1011 Brantford Ave., Silver Spring, MD 20904 Tel 301-622-4744.

Nancys Notions, *(Nancy's Notions, Ltd.; 0-931071),* 1010 DeClark, P.O. Box 683, Beaver Dam, WI 53916 (SAN 678-9323) Tel 414-885-9175.

Nanny Goat, *(Nanny Goat Productions; 0-918440),* P. O. Box 845, Laguna Beach, CA 92652 (SAN 209-9675) Tel 714-494-7930.

Nantucket Hist Assn, *(Nantucket Historical Assn.; 0-9607340),* Box 1016, Nantucket, MA 02554 (SAN 239-2666) Tel 617-228-1894.

Nantucket Nautical, *(Nantucket Nautical Pubs.; 0-9604436),* 5 New Mill St., Nantucket, MA 02554 (SAN 215-8914).

NAPA, *(Network Against Psychiatric Assault),* 2054 University Ave., Rm. 406, Berkeley, CA 94704 (SAN 260-3748) Tel 415-548-2980.

Napa Landmarks, *(Napa Landmarks; 0-935360),* P.O. Box 702, Napa, CA 94558 (SAN 213-5418) Tel 707-255-1836.

NAPC, *(National Assn. of Personnel Consultants; 0-9611608),* 1432 Duke St., Alexandria, VA 22314 (SAN 285-2926) Tel 703-684-0180.

NAPCAE, *(National Assn. for Public Continuing & Adult Education; 0-912782),* 1201 16th St., NW, Washington, DC 20036 (SAN 207-0286) Tel 202-833-5486.

NAPIM, *(National Assn. of Printing Ink Manufacturers),* 47 Halstead Ave., Harrison, NY 10528 (SAN 230-4376) Tel 914-835-5650.

NAPL, *(National Association of Printers & Lithographers),* 780 Palisade Ave., Teaneck, NJ 07666 (SAN 224-8298) Tel 201-342-0700.

Napoleonic Heritage, *(Napoleonic Heritage Bks.; 0-937811),* Div. of Robert Sherower Group, Ltd., 521 Fifth Ave., 17th Flr., New York, NY 10175 (SAN 659-381X) Tel 212-355-5633.

NAPSAC, *(National Assn. of Parents & Professionals for Safe Alternatives in Childbirth, International; 0-917314; 0-934426),* P.O. Box 646, Marble Hill, MO 63764 (SAN 208-7766) Tel 314-238-2010; Dist. by: Napsac Reproductions, Rte. 1, Box 646, Marble Hill, MO 63764 (SAN 222-4607).

Napsac Reprods, *(Napsac Reproductions; 0-934426),* Rte. 1 Box 646, Marble Hill, MO 63764 (SAN 222-4607) Tel 314-238-2010.

Narc Ed, *(Narcotics Education, Inc.),* 6830 Laurel St., NW, Washington, DC 20012 (SAN 205-7727) Tel 202-722-6740.

NAREIT, *(National Assn. of Real Estate Investment Trusts),* 1101 17th St., NW, Suite 700, Washington, DC 20036 (SAN 231-3707) Tel 202-785-8717.

†**Naris Pubns,** *(Naris Pubns.; 0-916263),* P.O. Box 30805, Santa Barbara, CA 93130 (SAN 294-9741); Dist. by: John Daniel Publisher, P.O. Box 21922, Santa Barbara, CA 93121 (SAN 215-1995) Tel 805-962-1780; *CIP.*

NARUC, *(National Assn. of Regulatory Utility Commissioners),* 1102 ICC Bldg., P.O. Box 684, Washington, DC 20044 (SAN 260-339X) Tel 202-628-7324.

NASBE, *(National Assn. of State Boards of Education),* 701 N. Fairfax St., Suite 340, Alexandria, VA 22314 (SAN 236-1205) Tel 703-684-4000.

NASCO, *(North American Students of Cooperation; 0-931062),* P.O. Box 7715, Ann Arbor, MI 48107 (SAN 260-3810) Tel 313-663-0889; 530 S. State St., Rm. 4312, Ann Arbor, MI 48109 (SAN 669-2192).

Nash Group, *(Nash Group, The; 0-934569),* P.O. Box 16200-361, Mesa, AZ 85201 (SAN 693-8566) Tel 602-838-6208.

Nass, *(Nass, Sylvan & Ulla; 0-9606468),* 220 Sunnybrook Rd., Flourtown, PA 19031 (SAN 215-9740) Tel 215-836-4884.

Nassau Co Assn Mathematics Supv, *(Nassau County Assn. of Mathematics Supervisors; 0-9612940),* Forest Rd. School, Valley Stream, NY 11582 (SAN 292-5850) Tel 516-791-2220.

Nassau Pr, *(Nassau Pr.; 0-911491),* 228 Alexander St., Princeton, NJ 08540 (SAN 272-5959) Tel 609-921-1058; Toll free: 800-526-0275.

NASSTRAC, *(NASSTRAC; 0-9616271),* 1750 Pennsylvania Ave. NW, Suite 1105, Washington, DC 20006 (SAN 272-5967) Tel 202-393-5505.

Nat Assn Bond, *(National Assn. of Bond Lawyers),* Box 397, Hinsdale, IL 60521 (SAN 688-7457) Tel 312-920-0160.

Nat Assn Expo Mgrs, *(National Assn. of Exposition Managers),* 334 E. Garfield Rd., P.O. Box 377, Aurora, OH 44202 (SAN 272-801X).

Nat Assn Gift Child, *(National Assn. for Gifted Children; 0-912723),* 4175 Lovell Rd., Suite 140, Circle Pines, MN 55014 (SAN 225-8005) Tel 612-784-3475.

†**Nat Assn H Build,** *(National Assn. of Home Builders; 0-86718),* Div. of The National Assn. of Home Manufacturers, 15th & M Sts., NW, Washington, DC 20005 (SAN 207-7035); Toll free: 800-368-5242; *CIP.*

Nat Assn Insu Comm, *(National Assn. of Insurance Commissioners; 0-89382),* 1125 Grand Ave., Kansas City, MO 64106 (SAN 225-0780) Tel 816-842-3600; 67 Wall St., New York, NY 10005 (SAN 669-1927).

Nat Assn Pro Upholsterers, *(National Assn. of Professional Upholsterers),* P.O. Box 2754, High Point, NC 27261 (SAN 699-7740).

Nat Assn Sch Psych, *(National Assn. of Schl. Psychologists),* 10 Overland Dr., Stratford, CT 06497 (SAN 223-9000) Tel 203-337-4249.

Nat Assn Stock, *(National Assn. for Stock Car Auto Racing),* 1801 Speedway Blvd., Daytona Beach, FL 32015 (SAN 272-6882) Tel 904-253-0611; P.O. Box K, Daytona Beach, FL 32015 (SAN 669-1862).

Nat Assoc Concession, *(National Assn. of Concessionaires),* 35 E. Wacker Dr., Chicago, IL 60601 (SAN 224-9766) Tel 312-236-3858.

Nat Consumer Law, *(National Consumer Law Ctr., Inc.; 0-943116),* 11 Beacon St., Boston, MA 02108 (SAN 226-6520) Tel 617-523-8010.

Nat Coun Handicapped, *(National Council on the Handicapped; 0-936825),* 800 Independence Ave., SW, No. 814, Washington, DC 20591 (SAN 699-9662) Tel 202-453-3846.

Nat Coun Soc Studies, *(National Council for the Social Studies; 0-87986),* 3501 Newark St., NW, Washington, DC 20016 (SAN 202-1900) Tel 202-966-7840.

Nat Data Service, *(National Data Service for Higher Education; 0-937767),* Div. of John Minter Assocs., Inc., 2400 Central Ave., Suite B-2, Boulder, CO 80301 (SAN 659-3798) Tel 303-449-5569.

Nat Forum Ed Admin & Supervision, *(National Forum of Educational Administration & Supervision Journal; 0-934989),* 1705 Plantation Dr., Alexandria, LA 71301 (SAN 695-1864) Tel 318-442-6976.

Nat Found Infect Diseases, *(National Foundation for Infectious Diseases, The; 0-9614520),* P.O. Box 42022, Washington, DC 20015 (SAN 689-7762) Tel 301-656-0003.

Nat Grocers Assn, *(National Grocers Assn.),* 1825 Samuel Morse Dr., Reston, VA 22090 (SAN 224-7410) Tel 703-437-5300.

Nat Hist Mus, *(Natural History Museum of Los Angeles County; 0-938644),* 900 Exposition Blvd., Los Angeles, CA 90007 (SAN 238-6925) Tel 213-744-3330.

Nat Hist Pub Co, *(Natural History Publishing Co.; 0-9603144),* P.O. Box 962, La Jolla, CA 92038 (SAN 207-7515) Tel 619-459-0835.

Nat Home Planning, *(National Home Planning Service; 0-933133),* 37 Mountain Ave., Springfield, NJ 07081 (SAN 689-7754) Tel 201-376-3200.

Nat Kidney GA, *(National Kidney Foundation of Georgia, Inc.; 0-9615527),* Affil. of National Kidney Foundation, 1627 Peachtree Rd., Suite 306, Atlanta, GA 30309 (SAN 696-3447) Tel 404-872-7540.

Nat Legal Ctr Pub Interest, *(National Legal Ctr. for the Public Interest; 0-937299),* 1000 16th St., NW, Suite 301, Washington, DC 20036 (SAN 658-8115) Tel 202-296-1683.

Nat Minority, *(National Minority Campus Chronicle; 0-935483),* P.O. Box 9869, Madison, WI 53715 (SAN 695-9989) Tel 608-244-5633.

Nat Pubs CA, *(National Pubs.; 0-935551),* Div. of Krastman & Assocs., P.O. Box 8042, Van Nuys, CA 91409 (SAN 696-2238) Tel 818-705-8865; 5941 Texhoma, Encino, CA 91316 (SAN 696-5245) Tel 818-909-2016.

Nat Res Info, *(National Research and Information Center; 0-9608220),* 1614 Central St., Evanston, IL 60201 (SAN 240-4125) Tel 312-328-6545.

Nat Seafood Educ, *(National Seafood Educators; 0-9616426),* P.O. Box 60006, Richmond Beach, WA 98160 (SAN 658-9685) Tel 206-546-6410; 20103 23rd, NW, Seattle, WA 98177 (SAN 658-9693).

Nat Select, *(Natural Selection, The; 0-9610722),* 2560 Harris St., Eugene, OR 97405 (SAN 264-7680) Tel 503-485-3915.

Nat Soc of Sons, *(National Society of the Sons of the American Revolution, The; 0-9607188),* 1000 S. Fourth St., Louisville, KY 40203 (SAN 239-121X).

Nat States Rowing, *(National States Rowing Association),* 251 N. Illinois St., Suite 980, Indianapolis, IN 46204 (SAN 224-585X) Tel 317-237-2769.

Nat Therapy, *(Natural Therapy Foundation Press, The; 0-937792),* 5 Greenleaf, Irvine, CA 92714 (SAN 215-6849) Tel 714-551-0381.

Nat Transl Ctr, *(National Translations Ctr.; 0-935599),* Univ. of Chicago, John Crerar Library, 5730 S. Ellis Ave., Chicago, IL 60637 (SAN 204-2592) Tel 312-962-7060.

Nataraj Bks, *(Nataraj Bks.),* P.O. Box 5076, Springfield, VA 22150 (SAN 696-6527) Tel 703-455-4996.

Natchez Trace, *(Natchez Trace Genealogical Society; 0-933253),* P.O. Box 420, Florence, AL 35631-0420 (SAN 692-3933) Tel 205-764-4749.

Nathan Hale Inst, *(Hale, Nathan, Institute, The; 0-935067),* Affil. of The Hale Foundation, 422 First St. SE, Suite 208, Washington, DC 20003 (SAN 694-6631) Tel 202-546-2293.

National Addiction, *(National Addiction Research Foundation; 0-937119),* 3002 E. Sylvia, Tucson, AZ 85716 (SAN 658-5965) Tel 602-881-4601.

National Coun Phys
See Coun Logistics Mgt

National Law
See Natl Law

National Railway Hist Soc, *(National Railway Historical Society, Inc., Atlanta Chapter; 0-939037),* P.O. Box 13132, Atlanta, GA 30324-0132 (SAN 663-4982); 3966 US Hwy. 23, Duluth, GA 30136-4135 (SAN 663-4990) Tel 404-266-9566.

National Square Dance Directory
See Natl Sq Dance

Native Am Pub, *(Native American Pub. Co.; 0-9614958),* P.O. Box 6338, Incline Village, NV 89450 (SAN 693-725X) Tel 702-831-7726.

Native Nevadan Pubns, *(Native Nevadan Pubns.; 0-930083),* 145 W. Plumb Lane, Reno, NV 89509 (SAN 670-106X) Tel 702-329-7557.

Natl A-V Assn
See Internatl Comms

Natl Acad Gallaudet Coll, *(National Academy of Gallaudet College, The; 0-934336),* 800 Florida Ave. NE, Washington, DC 20002 (SAN 213-3423) Tel 202-651-5595.

†**Natl Acad Pr,** *(National Academy Pr.; 0-309),* Div. of National Academy of Sciences, 2101 Constitution Ave., NW, Washington, DC 20418 (SAN 202-8891) Tel 202-334-3313; *CIP.*

Natl Acad Sci
See Natl Acad Pr

Natl Academy
See Natl Academy Songwriters

Natl Academy Songwriters, *(National Academy of Songwriters; 0-916641),* P.O. Box 421411, San Francisco, CA 94142 (SAN 200-4526).

Natl Act Res MIC, *(National Action Research Military Industrial Complex),* 1501 Cherry St., Philadelphia, PA 19102 (SAN 225-6959) Tel 215-241-7175.

Natl Adoption, *(National Committee for Adoption; 0-9615820),* 326 Connecticut Ave. NW, Washington, DC 20036 (SAN 696-6160) Tel 202-463-7559.

Natl Aero, *(National Aeronautic Assn.),* 1400 Eye St., NW, Suite 550, Washington, DC 20005 (SAN 210-6167) Tel 202-898-1313.

Natl Alliance, *(National Alliance; 0-937944),* Box 3535, Washington, DC 20007 (SAN 220-0759) Tel 703-979-1886.

Natl Alumni Assn Ed Home Econ, *(National Alumni Association of the College of Education & Home Economics; 0-9602480),* Alumni Publications (Loc. No. 24), Univ. of Cincinnati, Cincinnati, OH 45221 (SAN 212-7709) Tel 513-475-4641.

Natl Archery, *(National Archery Assn. of the U. S.),* 1750 E. Boulder St., Colorado Springs, CO 80909 (SAN 224-537X) Tel 303-578-4576.

†**Natl Archives & Records,** *(National Archives & Records Administration; 0-911333),* Pubns. Div., Seventh St. & Pennsylvania Ave., Washington, DC 20408 (SAN 210-363X) Tel 202-523-5611. Official records of the federal government on microfilm; facsimiles & reproductions of important historical documents, census records from 1790 to 1910 on microfilm. Catalog of National Archives Microfilm Publications, Black Studies, Indian Studies, immigration, and genealogical records. Catalogs of Federal Population Census, 1790 to 1910. Books and guides on the preservation and use of federal records; *CIP.*

Natl Archv
See Natl Archives & Records

Natl Art Ed, *(National Art Education Assn.; 0-937652),* 1916 Association Dr., Reston, VA 22091 (SAN 203-7084) Tel 703-860-8000.

Natl Art Serv Inc
See World-Wide Tampa

Natl Asphalt Pavement, *(National Asphalt Pavement Assn.; 0-914313),* 6811 Kenilworth Ave., Riverdale, MD 20840 (SAN 225-4417).

Natl Assessment, *(National Assessment of Educational Progress; 0-89398),* Div. of Educational Testing Service, CN 6710, P.O. Box 2923, Princeton, NJ 08541-6710 (SAN 272-653X); Toll free: 800-223-0267.

Natl Assn Accts, *(National Assn. of Accountants),* 10 Paragon Dr., P.O. Box 433, Montvale, NJ 07645-0433 (SAN 207-2637) Tel 573-6268.

Natl Assn Arm, *(National Assn. for Armenian Studies & Research; 0-935411),* 175 Mt. Auburn St., Cambridge, MA 02138 (SAN 272-6645) Tel 617-876-7630.

Natl Assn Bio Tchrs, *(National Assn. of Biology Teachers, Inc.; 0-941212),* 11250 Roger Bacon Dr., Reston, VA 22090 (SAN 217-4073) Tel 703-471-1134.

Natl Assn Broadcasters, *(National Assn. of Broadcasters; 0-89324),* 1771 N St. NW, Washington, DC 20036 (SAN 224-1986) Tel 202-293-3579.

Natl Assn Child Ed, *(National Assn. for the Education of Young Children; 0-912674; 0-935989),* 1834 Connecticut Ave., NW, Washington, DC 20009-5786 (SAN 202-8905) Tel 202-232-8777; Toll free: 800-424-2460.

Natl Assn Chr Soc Wk
See N American Assn

Natl Assn Coll
See NACUBO

Natl Assn Comm Health Ctrs, *(National Assn. of Community Health Ctrs.),* 1625 I St. NW, Suite 420, Washington, DC 20006 (SAN 224-3253) Tel 202-833-9280.

Natl Assn Con Adult Ed
See NAPCAE

Natl Assn Concessionaire
See Nat Assoc Concession

Natl Assn Cons
See NACD

Natl Assn Counties, *(National Assn. of Counties; 0-911754),* 440 First St., NW, Washington, DC 20001 (SAN 205-7565) Tel 202-393-6226.

Natl Assn Deaf, *(National Assn. of the Deaf; 0-913072),* 814 Thayer Ave., Silver Spring, MD 20910 (SAN 203-7092) Tel 301-587-1788.

Natl Assn Elect Dist, *(National Assn. of Electrical Distributors),* 600 Summer St., Stamford, CT 06901 (SAN 272-7889) Tel 203-327-1290.

Natl Assn Elem Schl
See NAES Alexandria

Natl Assn Environ Profs
See Natl Environment Pros

Natl Assn Female Execs, *(National Association for Female Executives),* 160 E. 56th St., New York, NY 10022 (SAN 224-6724).

Natl Assn Foreign Students
See NAFSA Washington

Natl Assn Gifted Chill
See Nat Assn Gift Child

Natl Assn H Mfrs
See Nat Assn H Build

Natl Assn Home
See Nat Assn H Build

Natl Assn Insurance Comm
See Nat Assn Insu Comm

Natl Assn Irish Free, *(National Assn. for Irish Freedom),* 799 Broadway, Rm. 422, New York, NY 10003 (SAN 224-1951) Tel 212-254-1757.

Natl Assn Legal Secys, *(National Assn. of Legal Secretaries),* 3005 E. Skelly Dr., Suite 120, Tulsa, OK 74105 (SAN 225-0918) Tel 918-749-6423; Dist. by: West Publishing Co., P.O. Box 64526, St. Paul, MN 55164-0526 (SAN 202-9618).

Natl Assn Media, *(National Assn. for State Educational, Media Professionals (NASTEMP); 0-9614484),* Div. of Publications, 605 S. O St., Indianola, IA 50125 (SAN 677-8976) Tel 515-961-3012.

Natl Assn Mgrs
See Nat Assn Expo Mgrs

Natl Assn Oarsmen
See Nat States Rowing

Natl Assn Pool Owners, *(National Assn. of Pool Owners),* 280 Hillside Ave., Needham, MA 02194 (SAN 224-5965).

Natl Assn Preserv & Perpet Storytelling, *(National Assn. for the Preservation & Perpetuation of Storytelling),* P.O. Box 309, Slemons Hse., Fox St., Jonesboro, TN 37659 (SAN 224-1978) Tel 615-753-2171.

Natl Assn Principals, *(National Assn. of Secondary School Principals; 0-88210),* 1904 Association Dr., Reston, VA 22091 (SAN 676-8776) Tel 703-860-0200.

Natl Assn Print Ink
See NAPIM

Natl Assn Pro, *(National Assn. of Professional Baseball Leagues),* P.O. Box A, St. Petersburg, FL 33731 (SAN 272-913X) Tel 813-822-6937.

Natl Assn Psych, *(National Association of School Psychologists; 0-932955),* 14605 Granger Rd, Maple Hts, OH 44137 (SAN 688-9077) Tel 419-734-1748.

Natl Assn Real Estate, *(National Assn. of Real Estate Appraisers),* 8715 Via DeCommercio, Scottsdale, AZ 85258 (SAN 225-4395) Tel 602-948-8000.

Natl Assn Real Estate Invest
See NAREIT

Natl Assn Ret Grocers
See Nat Grocers Assn

†**Natl Assn Soc Wkrs,** *(National Assn. of Social Workers; 0-87101),* 7981 Eastern Ave., Silver Spring, MD (SAN 202-893X); Toll free: 800-638-8799; *CIP.*

Natl Assn Student, *(National Assn. of Student Councils; 0-88210),* Div. of Student Activities of the National Assn. of Secondary School Principals, 1904 Association Dr., Reston, VA 22091 (SAN 260-3888) Tel 703-860-8550.

Natl Assn Theatre Owners, *(National Assn. of Theatre Owners),* 1560 Broadway, Suite 714, New York, NY 10036 (SAN 231-0546).

Natl Assn Trade & Tech Schls
See Natl Assn Trade Tech Schl

Natl Assn Trade Tech Schl, *(National Assn. of Trade & Technical Schls.; 0-942426),* 2251 Wisconsin Ave. NW, Suite 200, Washington, DC 20007 (SAN 238-406X) Tel 202-333-1021.

Natl Assn Watch & Clock, *(National Assn. of Watch & Clock Collectors; 0-9614984),* 514 Poplar St., Columbia, PA 17512 (SAN 223-9035) Tel 717-684-5544.

Natl Assn Wholesale Dists, *(National Assn. of Wholesale Distributors),* 1725 K St., NW, Washington, DC 20006 (SAN 224-9820) Tel 202-872-0885.

Natl Assn Women, *(National Assn. for Women Deans, Administrators & Counselors; 0-943302),* 1325 18th St. NW, Suite 210, Washington, DC 20036 (SAN 202-1080) Tel 202-659-9330.

Natl Assoc Priv Sch, *(National Assn. of Private Schls. for Exceptional Children),* 2021 K St. NW, Suite 315, Washington, DC 20006 (SAN 223-8977) Tel 202-296-1800.

Natl Assoc Realtors, *(National Assn. of Realtors; 0-938785),* 430 N. Michigan Ave., Chicago, IL 60611 (SAN 224-9294) Tel 312-329-8292.

Natl Assoc Sch Psychol
See Nat Assn Sch Psych

Natl Attorneys Pubns, *(National Attorney's Pubns., Inc.; 0-936855),* 1401 Main St., Port Jefferson, NY 11777 (SAN 658-3660) Tel 516-928-0295; P.O. Box 150, East Setauket, NY 11733 (SAN 658-3679).

Natl Attys General, *(National Assn. of Attorneys General),* Hall of States, 444 N. Capitol St., Washington, DC 20001 (SAN 225-090X) Tel 202-624-5450.

†**Natl Audubon,** *(National Audubon Society; 0-930698),* 950 Third Ave., New York, NY 10022 (SAN 282-0307) Tel 212-546-9122; *CIP.*

Natl Bed, *(National Bed & Breakfast Assn.; 0-9611298),* P.O. Box 332, Norwalk, CT 06852 (SAN 282-9355); 148 E. Rocks Rd., Norwalk, CT 06851 (SAN 669-3180) Tel 203-847-6196; 147 Mc Kinley Ave., Bridgeport, CT 06606 (SAN 669-3199).

Natl Behavior, *(National Behavior Systems; 0-937654),* 805 N. Howard St., No. 232, Alexandria, VA 22304 (SAN 282-0323) Tel 703-370-2568; Dist. by: Baker & Taylor, Eastern Div., 50 Kirby Ave., Somerville, NJ 08876 (SAN 169-4901).

Natl Bellamy, *(National Bellamy Award),* Three Oaks Court, Albany, NY 12203 (SAN 208-337X); Orders to: Frank P. Di Berardino, Three Oaks Court, Albany, NY 12203 (SAN 669-2001) Tel 518-456-0964.

Natl Bestseller, *(National Bestseller Corp.; 0-931073),* 400 Federation Pl., Elgin, IL 60120 (SAN 678-9331) Tel 312-695-1122.

Natl Bio Tchrs
See Natl Assn Bio Tchrs

Natl Biomedical, *(National Biomedical Research Foundation; 0-912466),* Georgetown Univ. Medical Ctr, 3900 Reservoir Rd., NW, Washington, DC 20007 (SAN 203-7106) Tel 202-625-2121.

Natl Book, *(National Bk. Co.; 0-89420),* Div. of Educational Research Assocs., 333 SW Park Ave., Portland, OR 97205-3784 (SAN 212-4661) Tel 503-228-6345. *Imprints:* Halcyon (Halcyon House).

Natl Braille Pr, *(National Braille Pr.; 0-939173),* 88 St. Stephen St., Boston, MA 02115 (SAN 273-0952).

Natl Buffalo Assn, *(National Buffalo Assn.; 0-9601792),* 10 Main St., Ft. Pierre, SD 57532 (SAN 224-9863) Tel 605-223-2829; P.O. Box 565, Ft. Pierre, SD 57532 (SAN 699-5470) Tel 605-223-2829.

†**Natl Bur Econ Res,** *(National Bureau of Economic Research, Incorporated; 0-87014),* 1050 Massachusetts Ave., Cambridge, MA 02138 (SAN 203-7114); Toll free: 800-621-2736; Dist. by: Ballinger Publishing Co., 54 Church St., Harvard Sq., Cambridge, MA 02138 (SAN 201-4084) Tel 617-492-0670; Dist. by: Columbia Univ. Pr., 136 S. Broadway, Irvington-on-Hudson, New York, NY 10533 (SAN 212-2472) Tel 914-591-9111; Dist. by: Harvard Univ. Pr., 79 Garden St., Cambridge, MA 02138 (SAN 281-7721) Tel 617-495-2600; Dist. by: The M.I.T. Pr., 28 Carleton St., Cambridge, MA 02142 (SAN 202-6414) Tel 617-253-2884; Dist. by: Princeton Univ. Pr., 41 William St., Princeton, NJ 08540 (SAN 202-0254) Tel 609-452-4913; Dist. by: Univ. of Chicago Pr., Order Dept., 11030 S. Langley Ave., Chicago, IL 60628 (SAN 202-5299) Tel 312-568-1550; *CIP.*

Natl Bus Trader, *(National Bus Trader, Inc.; 0-933449),* Rte. 3, Box 349B, Theater Rd., Delavan, WI 53115-9566 (SAN 691-7879) Tel 414-728-2691.

Natl Busn Ed Assoc, *(National Business Education Assn.),* 1906 Association Dr., Reston, VA 22091 (SAN 225-7610).

Natl Busn Inst, *(National Business Institute; 0-925761),* P.O. Box 1626, Eau Claire, WI 54702 (SAN 286-9691) Tel 715-835-8525.

Natl Cable, *(National Cable Television Assn.; 0-940272),* 1724 Massachusetts Ave., NW, Washington, DC 20036 (SAN 215-7934) Tel 202-775-3550.

Natl Cable TV
See Natl Cable

Natl Cartoonists, *(National Cartoonists Society),* 9 Ebony Ct., Brooklyn, NY 11229 (SAN 225-2694) Tel 718-743-6510.

Natl Cath Dev, *(National Catholic Development Conference; 0-9603196),* 86 Front St., Hempstead, NY 11550 (SAN 209-0872) Tel 516-481-6000.

Natl Cath Educ, *(National Catholic Educational Assn.),* 1077 30th St. NW, Suite 100, Washington, DC 20007-3852 (SAN 676-8636) Tel 202-337-6232.

Natl Cath Off Deaf, *(National Catholic Office for the Deaf),* 814 Thayer Ave., Silver Spring, MD 20910 (SAN 225-4271) Tel 301-587-7992.

Natl Cath Pharm, *(National Catholic Pharmacists Guild of the United States),* 1012 Surrey Hills Dr., St. Louis, MO 63117 (SAN 224-4209) Tel 314-645-0085.

Natl Cath Reporter
See Sheed & Ward MO

Natl Chamber Foun, *(National Chamber Foundation; 0-89834),* 1615 H St., NW, Washington, DC 20062 (SAN 238-0757).

Natl Christian Pr, *(National Christian Pr., Inc.; 0-934916),* P.O. Box 472, Seagoville, OK 73153 (SAN 212-1182) Tel 214-287-7179; P.O. Box 1001, Jonesboro, AR 72401 (SAN 693-496X); Orders to: National Christian Press, Inc., P.O. Box 6709, Moore, Tel 405-794-8298.

Natl Citizen's Coalition, *(National Citizens Coalition for Nursing Home Reform; 0-939611),* 1424 16th St., NW, Suite L2, Washington, DC 20036 (SAN 235-5817) Tel 202-797-0657.

Natl Clearinghse Bilingual Ed, *(National Clearinghouse for Bilingual Education; 0-89763),* 1555 Wilson Blvd., Suite 605, Arlington, VA 22209 (SAN 212-839X); Toll free: 800-336-4560.

Natl Coal Ban Handguns, *(National Coalition to Ban Handguns),* 100 Maryland Ave. NE, Washington, DC 20002 (SAN 235-6317) Tel 202-544-7190.

Natl Coaltion Ban Handguns
See Natl Coal Ban Handguns

Natl Coll Chiro, *(National College of Chiropractic; 0-9615849),* 200 E. Roosevelt Rd., Lombard, IL 60148 (SAN 696-6470) Tel 312-629-2000; Dist. by: Williams & Wilkins, 428 E. Preston St., Baltimore, MD 21202 (SAN 202-5175) Tel 301-528-8521.

Natl Coll DA, *(National College of District Attorneys),* Univ. of Houston, Bates College of Law, Houston, TX 77004 (SAN 225-0934) Tel 713-749-1571.

Natl Color Graphics, *(National Color Graphics, Inc.; 0-9616045),* E. 502 Fifth Ave., Spokane, WA 99202 (SAN 698-2409); Orders to: Pacific Pipeline, Inc., 19215 66th Ave. S., Kent, WA 98031 (SAN 169-8834).

Natl Comm Clin Lab Stds, *(National Committee for Clinical Laboratory Standards),* 771 E. Lancaster Ave., Villanova, PA 19085 (SAN 224-344X) Tel 215-525-2435.

Natl Comm Repeal, *(National Committee to Repeal the Federal Reserve Act),* P.O. Box A-H, Bunker Hill, IL 62014 (SAN 273-222X) Tel 618-585-4700.

Natl Comm Res Youth, *(National Commission on Resources for Youth; 0-912041),* Subs. of Institute for Responsive Education, 605 Commonwealth Ave., Boston, MA 02215 (SAN 225-7785) Tel 617-353-3309.

Natl Comp Graphics, *(National Computer Graphics Assn.; 0-941514),* 2722 Merrilee Dr., Suite 200, Fairfax, VA 22031 (SAN 654-1755) Tel 703-698-9600.

Natl Comp Ins, *(National Council on Compensation Insurance),* 1 Penn Plaza, New York, NY 10001 (SAN 224-8360) Tel 212-560-1829.

Natl Computer, *(National Computer Dealers Association Publishing Co.; 0-933325),* 5420 Hwy 6 N., Houston, TX 77084 (SAN 691-926X) Tel 713-859-14191343 Columbia Suite 405, Richardson, TX 75081 (SAN 691-9278).

Natl Con Coopera Bank, *(National Consumer Cooperative Bank; 0-918943),* 1630 Connecticut Ave., NW, Washington, DC 20009 (SAN 669-8514) Tel 202-745-4753.

Natl Conf Appellate, *(National Conference of Appellate Court Clerks; 0-934730),* 300 Newport Ave., Williamsburg, VA 23187-8798 (SAN 213-1285) Tel 804-253-2000.

Natl Conf Soc Welfare, *(National Conference on Social Welfare; 0-933597),* 1730 M. St., NW, Suite 911, Washington, DC 20036 (SAN 225-9958) Tel 202-785-0817.

Natl Conf State Legis, *(National Conference of State Legislatures; 0-941336; 1-55516),* 1050 17th St., Suite 2100, Denver, CO 80265-2101 (SAN 225-1000) Tel 303-623-7800.

Natl Contract Mgmt, *(National Contract Management Assn.),* 6728 Old McLean Village Dr., McLean, VA 22101 (SAN 224-2755) Tel 703-442-0137.

Natl Corp Cash Mgmt, *(National Corprate Cash Management Assn.; 0-9614799),* P.O. Box 7001, Newtown, CT 06470 (SAN 692-6789) Tel 203-426-3007.

Natl Corrosion Eng, *(National Assn. of Corrosion Engineers; 0-915567),* P.O. Box 218340, Houston, TX 77218 (SAN 224-2001) Tel 713-492-0535.

†Natl Coun Aging, *(National Council on the Aging, The; 0-910883),* 600 Maryland Ave., SW, Washington, DC 20024 (SAN 675-3361) Tel 202-479-1200; *CIP.*

Natl Coun Alcoholism, *(National Council on Alcoholism),* 12 W. 21st St., New York, NY 10010 (SAN 236-7653) Tel 212-206-6770.

Natl Coun Arab, *(National Council on U.S.-Arab Relations; 0-916729),* 1625 I St. NW, Suite 625, Washington, DC 20006 (SAN 653-9025) Tel 202-293-0801.

Natl Coun Crime, *(National Council on Crime & Delinquency),* 77 Maiden Ln., 4th Flr., San Francisco, CA 94108 (SAN 236-9095) Tel 415-956-5651.

Natl Coun Econ Dev, *(National Council for Urban Economic Development),* 1730 K St. NW, Washington, DC 20006 (SAN 225-6541) Tel 202-223-4735.

Natl Coun Intl Visitors, *(National Council for International Visitors),* Meridian Hse., 1630 Crescent Pl. NW, Washington, DC 20009 (SAN 223-9094) Tel 202-332-1028; Toll free: 800-523-8101.

Natl Coun Radiation
See NCRP Pubns

Natl Coun Tchrs English
See NCTE

Natl Coun Teach, *(National Council on Teachers Retirement),* P.O. Box 1882, Austin, TX 78767 (SAN 273-348X) Tel 512-397-6401.

Natl Coun US-China, *(National Council for US-China Trade; 0-935614),* 1818 N St. NW, Suite 500, Washington, DC 20036 (SAN 222-4631) Tel 202-429-0340.

Natl Cowboy Hall of Fame, *(National Cowboy Hall of Fame & Western Heritage Ctr.; 0-932154),* 1700 NE 63rd St., Oklahoma City, OK 73111 (SAN 225-3895) Tel 405-478-2250; Dist. by: Lowell Pr., 115 E. 31st St., P.O. Box 1877, Kansas City, MO 64141 (SAN 207-0774) Tel 816-753-4545.

Natl Crime DC, *(Natl. Crime Prevention Council; 0-934513),* 733 15th St., NW, Suite 540, Washington, DC 20005 (SAN 693-8574) Tel 202-393-7141. No Relationship to the Natl. Crime Prevention Assn., also in Washington, D.C.

Natl Ctr Cit Involv
See VTNC Arlington

Natl Ctr Computer Crime, *(National Ctr. for Computer Crime Data; 0-933561),* 2700 N. Cahuenga Blvd., Los Angeles, CA 90068 (SAN 691-8956) Tel 213-850-0509.

Natl Ctr Constitutional, *(Natl. Ctr. for Constitutional Studies; 0-88080),* 3740 W. 1987 S., Salt Lake City, UT 84104 (SAN 237-7055) Tel 801-973-1776; Orders to: P.O. Box 37110, Washington, DC 20013 (SAN 693-9570).

Natl Ctr Diaconate, *(Natl. Ctr. for the • Diaconate; 0-9605798),* 14 Beacon St., Rm. 103, Boston, MA 02108 (SAN 220-1763) Tel 617-742-1460.

Natl Ctr Educ Broker, *(Natl. Ctr. for Educ. Brokering; 0-935612),* 325 Ninth St., San Francisco, CA 94103 (SAN 211-7479).

Natl Ctr Exper Sales, *(National Center for Experiential Sales Training; 0-933343),* 2122 Coronado SE, Grand Rapids, MI 49506 (SAN 692-3267) Tel 616-243-4343.

Natl Ctr Faculty, *(Natl. Ctr. for Faculty Dev.; 0-938540),* 1320 S. Dixie Hwy., No. 900A, Coral Gables, FL 33146 (SAN 216-423X). Out of business.

Natl Ctr Fin Ed, *(National Ctr. for Financial Education, Inc.; 0-935451),* 25 Van Ness Ave., Suite 5600, San Francisco, CA 94102 (SAN 693-2061) Tel 415-621-6961.

†Natl Ctr Health Stats, *(National Ctr. for Health Statistics; 0-8406),* Div. of Dept. of Health & Human Service, Federal Ctr. Bldg., Rm. 1-57, 3700 East-West Hwy., Hyattsville, MD 20782 (SAN 206-6033) Tel 301-436-8500; *CIP.*

Natl Ctr Job Mkt, *(Natl. Ctr. for Job-Market Studies; 0-935234),* P.O. Box 3651 BN, Washington, DC 20007 (SAN 213-5841) Tel 202-229-4885.

Natl Ctr Pol, *(National Ctr. for Policy Analysis; 0-943802),* 7701 N. Stemmons, Suite 717, Dallas, TX 75247 (SAN 241-0869) Tel 214-951-0306.

Natl Ctr PT, *(National Center for Paralegal Training),* 1271 Ave. of the Americas, Rm. 777, New York, NY 10020 (SAN 227-0005) Tel 212-581-6844.

Natl Ctr Public Prod, *(National Ctr. for Public Productivity; 0-942942),* 445 W. 59th St., New York, NY 10019 (SAN 210-7929) Tel 212-489-5030.

Natl Ctr Res Voc Ed, *(National Ctr. for Research in Vocational Education),* 1960 Kenny Rd., Columbus, OH 43210 (SAN 225-882X) Tel 614-486-3655.

†Natl Ctr St Courts, *(National Ctr. for State Courts; 0-89656),* 300 Newport Ave., Williamsburg, VA 23187-8798 (SAN 210-928X) Tel 804-253-2000; Toll free: 800-446-8952; *CIP.*

Natl CTV Inst, *(National Cable Television Institute; 0-88683),* P O Box 27277, Denver, CO 80227 (SAN 224-6597) Tel 303-761-8554; Orders to: 3301 W. Hampden Ave., Englewood, CO 80110 (SAN 662-0892).

Natl Dairy Coun, *(National Dairy Council; 1-55647),* 6300 N. River Rd., Rosemont, IL 60018 (SAN 224-702X) Tel 312-696-1020.

Natl Dance Assn, *(National Dance Association),* 1900 Association Dr., Reston, VA 22091 (SAN 225-3046) Tel 703-476-3436.

Natl Decision, *(Natl. Decision Systems, Inc.; 0-911871),* 539 Encinitas Blvd., Encinitas, CA 92024 (SAN 264-2336) Tel 619-942-7000.

Natl Directions, *(National Directions; 0-9615168),* 4330 N. Franklin Ave., Loveland, CO 80537 (SAN 694-3020) Tel 303-669-6719; Orders to: 500 26th St., Greeley, CO 80631 (SAN 662-3360) Tel 303-353-0662.

Natl Dissem Ctr, *(National Dissemination Ctr.; 0-89857),* 417 Rock St., Fall River, MA 02720 (SAN 699-6701) Tel 617-678-5696.

Natl Dist Atty, *(National District Attorneys Assn.),* 1033 N. Fairfax St., Suite 200, Alexandria, VA 22314 (SAN 282-0404) Tel 703-549-9222; Dist. by: National College of District Attorneys, Univ. of Houston, Bates College of Law, Houston, TX 77004 (SAN 225-0934) Tel 713-749-1571.

Natl Easter Seal, *(National Easter Seal Society; 0-933851),* 2023 W. Ogden Ave., Chicago, IL 60612 (SAN 225-9419) Tel 312-243-8400.

Natl Ed Stand, *(National Education Standards; 0-918192),* One Wilshire Bldg., Suite 1210, 624 S. Grand Ave., Los Angeles, CA 90017 (SAN 210-3141) Tel 213-623-9135.

Natl Elec Mfrs, *(National Electrical Manufacturers Assn.),* 2101 L St., NW, Washington, DC 20037 (SAN 224-716X) Tel 202-457-8400.

Natl Elec Sign, *(National Electric Sign Assn.),* 801 N. Fairfax St., Suite 205, Alexandria, VA 22314 (SAN 224-7151) Tel 703-836-4012.

Natl Employment, *(Sam Houston State Univ., Criminal Justice Ctr., National Employment Listing Service; 0-935530),* Huntsville, TX 77341 (SAN 222-6278) Tel 409-294-1692.

Natl Encyclopedia, *(National Encyclopedia Corp.; 0-938171),* 1585 Peachtree Battle Ave., NW, Atlanta, GA 30327 (SAN 661-194X) Tel 404-351-7125.

Natl Environment Pros, *(National Assn. of Environmental Professionals),* Box 9400, Washington, DC 20016 (SAN 232-7473) Tel 301-229-7171.

Natl Farm & Power, *(National Farm & Power Equipment Dealers Assn.),* 10877 Watson Rd., St Louis, MO 63127 (SAN 224-7275).

Natl Fed High Schl Assns, *(National Federation of State High School Assns.),* P.O. Box 20626, Kansas City, MO 64195 (SAN 224-540X) Tel 816-464-5400.

Natl Film Soc, *(National Film Society),* 8340 Mission Rd., Suite 106, Shawnee Mission, KS 66206 (SAN 225-3437) Tel 913-341-1919.

Natl Finan
See Lincoln Pub

Natl Fire Prot, *(National Fire Protection Assn.; 0-87765),* Batterymarch Park, Quincy, MA 02269 (SAN 202-8948) Tel 617-770-3000; Toll free: 800-344-3555.

Natl Flag Foun, *(National Flag Foundation),* Flag Plaza, Pittsburgh, PA 15219 (SAN 225-3097) Tel 412-261-1776.

Natl Fluid Power, *(National Fluid Power Assn.; 0-942220),* 3333 N. Mayfair Rd., Milwaukee, WI 53222 (SAN 224-800X) Tel 414-778-3344.

Natl Forensic, *(National Forensic Ctr.; 0-9602962),* Div. of Forensic Services Directory, Inc., 17 Temple Terr., Lawrenceville, NJ 08648 (SAN 212-7792) Tel 609-883-0550; Toll free: 800-526-5177.

Natl Found Ileitis, *(National Foundation for Ileitis & Colitis, Inc.; 0-9615495),* 444 Park Ave. S., New York, NY 10016 (SAN 224-3393) Tel 212-685-3440.

Symbols/Abbreviations

Natl Prac Inst, *(National Practice Institute),* 510 First Ave. N., Suite 205, Minneapolis, MN 55403 (SAN 217-2577); Toll free: 800-328-4444.

Natl PTA, *(National PTA; 0-88109),* 700 N. Rush St., Chicago, IL 60611 (SAN 225-8560) Tel 312-787-0977.

Natl Pub Black Hills, *(National Pubs. of the Black Hills, Inc.; 0-935920),* 137 E. Main St., Elmsford, NY 10523 (SAN 222-6227) Tel 914-592-6006; Orders to: 521 Kansas City St., Rapid City, SD 57701 (SAN 685-351X) Tel 605-394-4482.

Natl Pub IL
See Registry Pubns

Natl Radio Club, *(National Radio Club),* P.O. Box 118, Poquonock, CT 06064 (SAN 223-9221); P.O. Box 24, Cambridge, WI 53523 (SAN 669-2087).

Natl Rail Hist Soc DC
See Natl Rail Hist Soc DC Chap

†**Natl Rail Hist Soc DC Chap,** *(National Railway Historical Society, Washington D.C. Chapter; 0-933954),* P.O. Box 487, Washington, DC 20044 (SAN 212-8403); CIP.

Natl Rail Rio Grande, *(National Railway Historical Society, Rio Grande Chapter; 0-939646),* Box 3381, Grand Junction, CO 81502 (SAN 220-1771) Tel 303-242-3304.

Natl Rail Rochester, *(National Railway Historical Society, Rochester Chapter; 0-9605296),* P.O. Box 664, Rochester, NY 14602 (SAN 282-0447) Tel 716-244-6438; Orders to: P.O. Box 664, Rochester, NY 14602 (SAN 282-0455).

†**Natl Railway Hist,** *(National Railway Historical Society, Intermountain Chapter; 0-917884),* P.O. Box 5181, Terminal Annex, Denver, CO 80217 (SAN 206-1643) Tel 303-623-6747; CIP.

Natl Real Estate Inst, *(National Real Estate Institute (NREI); 0-915799),* 12860 NE 15th Place, Bellevue, WA 98005 (SAN 293-8855) Tel 206-454-5251.

Natl Recycling, *(National Association of Recycling Industries; 0-941096),* 330 Madison Ave., New York, NY 10017 (SAN 205-7603) Tel 212-867-7330.

Natl Register, *(National Register Publishing Co.; 0-87217),* Subs. of Macmillan Inc., 3004 Glenview Rd., Wilmette, IL 60091 (SAN 207-5180) Tel 312-256-6067; Toll free: 800-323-6772.

Natl Repro Corp, *(National Reproduction Corp.; 0-932335),* 433 E. Larned, Detroit, MI 48226 (SAN 686-7960) Tel 313-761-6870.

Natl Res Bur, *(National Research Bureau; 0-912610),* Div. of Automated Marketing Systems, 310 S. Michigan Ave., Suite 1150, Chicago, IL 60604 (SAN 205-7336) Tel 312-663-5580; Orders to: 424 N. Third St., Burlington, IA 52601 (SAN 205-7344) Tel 319-752-5415.

†**Natl Res Coun,** *(National Research Council; 0-309),* 2101 Constitution Ave., Washington, DC 20418 (SAN 223-923X) Tel 202-334-2000; CIP.

Natl Res Group, *(National Research Group),* P.O. Box 93, Valdosta, GA 31601 (SAN 262-0510).

Natl Res Unltd, *(Natural Resources Unlimited Inc.; 0-912475),* 3531 Roesner Dr., Markham, IL 60426 (SAN 265-2846) Tel 312-331-7964.

Natl Resources Defense Coun, *(Natural Resources Defense Council),* 122 E. 42nd St., New York, NY 10168 (SAN 273-9615).

†**Natl Restaurant Assn,** *(National Restaurant Assn.; 0-914528),* 311 First St., NW, Washington, DC 20001 (SAN 224-7496) Tel 202-638-6100; CIP.

Natl Ret Merch, *(National Retail Merchants Assn.; 0-87102),* 100 W. 31st St., New York, NY 10001 (SAN 654-178X) Tel 212-244-8780.

Natl Retail Hardware, *(National Retail Hardware Assn.; 0-9609048),* 770 N. High School Rd., Indianapolis, IN 46224 (SAN 224-7879) Tel 317-248-1261.

Natl Reunion Assn, *(National Reunion Assn.; 0-9610470),* P.O. Box 295, Nevada City, CA 95959 (SAN 264-2360) Tel 916-265-6028.

Natl Rifle Assn, *(National Rifle Assn.; 0-935998),* 1600 Rhode Island Ave. NW, Washington, DC 20036 (SAN 213-859X) Tel 202-828-6000; Dist. by: A B & C Sales, 2010 Eisenhower Ave., Alexandria, VA 22314 (SAN 282-6607) Tel 703-960-6600.

Natl Roofing Cont, *(National Roofing Contractors Assn.; 0-934809),* 8600 Bryn Mawr Ave., Chicago, IL 60631 (SAN 229-9283) Tel 312-693-0700.

Natl Rural, *(National Rural Electric Cooperative Assn.; 0-917599),* 1800 Massachusetts Ave., NW, Washington, DC 20036 (SAN 205-7328) Tel 202-857-9550; Orders to: Bermont Bks., P.O. Box 309, Glenelg, MD 21737 (SAN 211-1705).

Natl Safety Coun, *(National Safety Council; 0-87912),* 444 N. Michigan Ave., Chicago, IL 60611 (SAN 203-7157) Tel 312-527-4800.

Natl Sanit Foun, *(National Sanitation Foundation; 0-940006),* P.O. Box 1468, 3475 Plymouth Rd., Ann Arbor, MI 48106 (SAN 216-8413) Tel 313-769-8010.

Natl Sch Assn
See Natl Assn Principals

†**Natl Sch Boards,** *(National School Boards Assns.; 0-88364),* 1680 Duke St., Alexandria, VA 22314 (SAN 676-8288) Tel 703-838-6711; CIP.

Natl Sch PR, *(National School Public Relations Assn.; 0-87545),* 1501 Lee Hwy., Dept. 5, Arlington, VA 22209 (SAN 203-7165) Tel 703-528-5840.

Natl School, *(National Schl. Services; 0-932957),* 250 N. Wolf Rd., Wheeling, IL 60090 (SAN 689-9986) Tel 312-541-2768.

Natl Sci Super Assn, *(National Science Supervisors Assn.),* Affil. of National Science Teachers Assn., P.O. Box AL, Amagansett, NY 11930 (SAN 226-8132) Tel 516-267-3692.

†**Natl Sci Tchrs,** *(National Science Teachers Assn.; 0-87355),* Affil. of the American Assn. for the Advancement of Science, 1742 Connecticut Ave., NW, Washington, DC 20009 (SAN 203-7173) Tel 202-328-5800; CIP.

Natl Sen Citizens, *(National Senior Citizens Law Center; 0-932605),* 2025 M Street NW, Suite 400, Washington, DC 20036 (SAN 687-5238) Tel 202-887-5280.

Natl Sharegraphics
See Curtis Media

Natl Shorthand Rptr, *(National Shorthand Reporters Assn.; 0-933305),* 118 Park St. SE, Vienna, VA 22180 (SAN 224-9588) Tel 703-281-4677.

Natl Skeet Shoot, *(National Skeet Shooting Assn.),* Box 28188, San Antonio, TX 78228 (SAN 224-5620).

Natl Soc Prevent Blindness, *(National Society to Prevent Blindness; 0-916102),* 79 Madison Ave., New York, NY 10016 (SAN 224-2745) Tel 212-684-3505; Toll free: 800-221-3004.

Natl Soc Prof Engrs, *(National Society of Professional Engineers; 0-915409),* 2029 K St., NW, Washington, DC 20006 (SAN 225-168X) Tel 202-463-2300.

Natl Speakers, *(National Speakers Assn.),* 4747 N. Seventh St., Suite 310, Phoenix, AZ 85014 (SAN 225-3771) Tel 602-265-1001.

Natl Speleological, *(National Speleological Society, Inc.; 0-9615093),* 2813 Cave Ave., Huntsville, AL 35810 (SAN 273-8619) Tel 205-852-1300.

Natl Sq Dance, *(National Square Dance Directory; 0-9605494),* P.O. Box 54055, Jackson, MS 39208 (SAN 215-2576) Tel 601-825-6831.

Natl Standards Assn, *(National Standards Association),* 5161 River Rd., Bethesda, MD 20816 (SAN 223-9272) Tel 301-951-1389.

Natl Steeplechase, *(National Steeplechase & Hunt Assn.),* Box 308, Elmont, NY 11003 (SAN 224-5809).

Natl Stud Ed, *(National Student Educational Fund; 0-940624),* 2000 P St. NW, Suite 305, Washington, DC 20036 (SAN 218-5199) Tel 202-785-1856.

Natl Support Ctr, *(National Support Ctr. for Families of the Aging; 0-910227),* Box 245, Swarthmore, PA 19081 (SAN 241-4147) Tel 215-544-5933.

Natl Tax, *(National Tax Assn.-Tax Institute of America; 0-934729),* 21 E. State St., Columbus, OH 43215 (SAN 225-1299) Tel 614-224-8352.

Natl Tech Info, *(National Technical Information Service, U. S. Dept. of Commerce; 0-934213),* 5285 Port Royal Rd., Springfield, VA 22161 (SAN 205-7255) Tel 703-487-4838.

†**Natl Textbk,** *(National Textbook Co.; 0-8442; 0-8325),* 4255 W. Touhy Ave., Chicago, IL 60646 (SAN 169-2208) Tel 312-679-5500; Toll free: 800-854-4014; CIP. Imprints: Passport Bks (Passport Books).

Natl Tinn Fund, *(National Tinnitus Fund; 0-9612648),* P.O. Box 5081, Springfield, MO 65801 (SAN 289-3428) Tel 417-831-0436.

Natl Tool & Mach, *(National Tooling & Machining Assn.),* 9300 Livingston Rd., Ft. Washington, MD 20744 (SAN 224-232X) Tel 301-248-6200.

Natl Tool Die & Precision
See Natl Tool & Mach

Natl Tour Assn, *(National Tour Assn.; 0-910399),* P.O. Box 3071, Lexington, KY 40596 (SAN 224-974X); Toll free: 800-NTA-8886; 546 E. Main St., Lexington, KY 40508 (SAN 662-0914) Tel 606-253-1036; Toll free: 800-828-6999 (In Canada).

Natl U Imprint of Assoc Faculty Pr

Natl Underwriter, *(National Underwriter Co.; 0-87218),* 420 E. Fourth St., Cincinnati, OH 45202 (SAN 205-7247) Tel 513-721-2140; Toll free: 800-543-0874.

Natl Urban, *(National Urban League; 0-914758),* 500 E. 62nd St., New York, NY 10021 (SAN 215-2290).

Natl Video, *(National Video Clearinghouse, Inc., The; 0-935478),* 100 Lafayette Dr., Syosset, NY 11791 (SAN 213-4209) Tel 516-364-3686.

Natl Water Well, *(National Water Well Association),* 500 W Wilson Bridge Rd, Worthington, OH 43085 (SAN 231-7273) Tel 614-846-9355.

Natl Waterways, *(National Waterways Conference, Inc.; 0-934292),* 1130 17th St. N.W., No. 200, Washington, DC 20036 (SAN 203-719X) Tel 202-296-4415.

Natl Wild Turkey, *(National Wild Turkey Federation, Inc.),* 770 Augusta Rd., Edgefield, SC 29824 (SAN 225-0098) Tel 803-637-3106; Box 530, Edgefield, SC 29824 (SAN 662-0922).

†**Natl Wildlife,** *(National Wildlife Federation; 0-912186),* Div. of Books and Special Publications, 8925 Leesburg Pike, Vienna, VA 22180 (SAN 202-8980) Tel 703-790-4227; CIP.

Natl Wmns Hall Fame, *(National Women's Hall of Fame; 0-9610622),* 76 Falls St. P.O. Box 335, Seneca Falls, NY 13148 (SAN 223-9299) Tel 315-568-8060.

Natl Womens Hist, *(National Women's History Project; 0-938625),* 2321 Coddingtown Ctr., Santa Rosa, CA 95401 (SAN 661-6275) Tel 707-526-5974.

Natl Wood Carver, *(National Wood Carvers Association),* 7424 Miami Ave., Cincinnati, OH 45243 (SAN 225-5510) Tel 513-561-9051.

Natl Writ Pr, *(National Writers Pr., The; 0-88100),* Div. of National Writers Club, Subs. of Association Headquarters, Inc., 1450 S. Havana, Suite 620, Aurora, CO 80012 (SAN 240-320X) Tel 303-751-7844.

Natl Writers Club, *(National Writers Club, The),* Subs. of Association Headquarters, Inc., 1450 S. Havana, Suite 620, Aurora, CO 80012 (SAN 225-3992) Tel 303-751-7844; Dist. by: National Writers Pr., 1450 S. Havana, Suite 620, Aurora, CO 80012 (SAN 240-320X).

Natter Pub, *(Natter Publishing Co.; 0-936143),* 36 Durham Rd., White Plains, NY 10605 (SAN 696-6373) Tel 914-428-5404.

Natural Designs, *(Natural Designs; 0-9616179),* 61 Atherton Ave., Atherton, CA 94025 (SAN 699-9735) Tel 415-326-8003; Dist. by: Publishers Group West, 5855 Beaudry St., Emeryville, CA 94608 (SAN 202-8522) Tel 415-658-3453.

Natural Hist, *(Natural History Pr.)*, Dist. by: Doubleday & Co., Inc., 501 Franklin Ave., Garden City, NY 11530 (SAN 281-6083) Tel 516-873-4561. Toll free: 800-645-6156; *Imprints:* AMS (American Museum Science Books); AMSA (American Museum Sourcebooks in Anthropology).

Natural Hygiene, *(Natural Hygiene Pr.; 0-914532)*, Div. of American Natural Hygiene Society, 12816 Race Track Rd., Tampa, FL 33625 (SAN 202-4314) Tel 813-855-6607.

Natural Pr, *(Natural Pr.; 0-939956)*, Div. of Natural Enterprises, P.O. 2107, Manitowoc, WI 54220 (SAN 287-0215) Tel 414-682-0738; Dist. by: Nutri Books, P.O. Box 5793, Denver, CO 80323 (SAN 169-054X).

Natural Prod, *(Natural Products Co.; 0-9614234)*, P.O. Box 273, Vashon, WA 98070 (SAN 686-7952) Tel 206-567-4788; Dist. by: Bookpeople, 2929 Fifth St., Berkeley, CA 94710 (SAN 168-9517) Tel 415-549-3030; Dist. by: Pacific Pipeline, 19215 66th Ave. S., Kent, WA 98032 (SAN 208-2128) Tel 206-872-5523.

Natural Res Ent, *(Natural Resources Enterprises, Inc.; 0-939870)*, P.O. Box 4523, Lincoln, NE 68504 (SAN 216-9150) Tel 402-472-1519.

Natural Sci Youth, *(Natural Science for Youth Foundation; 0-916544)*, 763 Silvermine Rd., New Canaan, CT 06840 (SAN 208-2039) Tel 203-966-5643.

Natural World, *(Natural World Pr.; 0-939560)*, 607 Chiltern Rd., Hillsborough, CA 94010 (SAN 216-6879) Tel 415-344-5014.

Naturally Beaut You, *(Naturally Beautiful You; 0-9616880)*, 1226 E. St. George Ave., Linden, NJ 07036 (SAN 661-6550) Tel 201-486-9105.

Nature Bks Pubs, *(Nature Bks. Pubs.; 0-912542)*, P.O. Box 12157, Jackson, MS 39211 (SAN 203-7211) Tel 601-956-5686.

Nature Conservancy, *(Nature Conservancy, The)*, Box 338, 122 Main St., Topsham, ME 04036 (SAN 273-964X).

Nature Life, *(Nature Life; 0-918134)*, Div. of McGill-Jensen, 655 Fairview Ave. N., St. Paul, MN 55104 (SAN 209-3596) Tel 612-645-3129.

Nature Study, *(Nature Study Guild; 0-912550)*, P.O. Box 972, Berkeley, CA 94701 (SAN 203-722X).

Nature Trails, *(Nature Trails Pr.; 0-937794)*, 933 Calle Loro, Palm Springs, CA 92262 (SAN 207-3609) Tel 619-323-9420.

Naturegraph, *(Naturegraph Pubs., Inc.; 0-911010; 0-87961)*, P.O. Box 1075, Happy Camp, CA 96039 (SAN 202-8999) Tel 916-493-5353.

Naturetrek Comn, *(Naturetrek Communications; 0-9616236)*, Box 775, Corvallis, OR 97339 (SAN 658-5949) Tel 503-757-3142; 8130 Oak Ck. Dr., Corvallis, OR 97330 (SAN 658-5957).

Nauful, *(Nauful, Eli S.)*, P.O. Box 1260, Lynchburg, VA 24502 (SAN 209-6269).

NAUI, *(National Assn. of Underwater Instructors; 0-916974)*, P.O. Box 14650, Montclair, CA 91763 (SAN 208-1024) Tel 714-824-5440.

†Nautical & Aviation, *(Nautical & Aviation Publishing Co., of America, Inc.; 0-933852)*, 101 W. Read St., Suite 314, Baltimore, MD 21201 (SAN 213-3431) Tel 301-659-0220; *CIP.*

Nautical Avia
See Nautical & Aviation

Nautical Res, *(Nautical Research Guild, Inc.; 0-9603456)*, 6413 Dahlonega Rd., Bethesda, MD 20816 (SAN 221-7260).

Nautilus Bks, *(Nautilus Bks.; 0-941476)*, Div. of Nautilus Communications, Inc., 375 Fifth Ave., New York, NY 10016 (SAN 239-1228) Tel 212-685-7007.

Nautilus Comm Inc
See Nautilus Bks

Nautilus Inc, *(Nautilus Bks., Inc.; 0-935055)*, 496 LaGuardia Pl., New York, NY 10012 (SAN 694-6054) Tel 212-243-7050.

NAVA
See NAVA Intl Comm

NAVA Intl Comm, *(NAVA, The International Communications Industries Assn.)*, 3150 Spring St., Fairfax, VA 22031-2399 (SAN 225-7807) Tel 703-273-7200.

Navajo, *(Navajo Tribal Museum)*, Div. of Navajo Tribe, Box 308, Window Rock, AZ 85615 (SAN 279-8131) Tel 602-871-6673.

†Navajo Coll Pr, *(Navajo Community College Pr.; 0-912586)*, Navajo Community College, Tsaile, AZ 86556 (SAN 201-9582); *CIP.*

Navajo Curr, *(Navajo Curriculum Ctr. Pr.; 0-936008)*, Rough Rock Demonstration Schl., Star Rte. 1, Rough Rock, AZ 86503 (SAN 203-1604) Tel 602-728-3311.

Naval Fighters, *(Naval Fighters; 0-942612)*, 1754 Warfield Cir., Simi Valley, CA 93063 (SAN 238-5457) Tel 805-584-9732.

†Naval Inst Pr, *(Naval Institute Pr.; 0-87021)*, U. S. Naval Institute, Annapolis, MD 21402 (SAN 202-9006) Tel 301-268-6110; Orders to: Customer Service, U.S. Naval Institute Operations Ctr., 2062 Generals Hwy., Annapolis, MD 21401 (SAN 662-0930) Tel 301-224-3378; *CIP.*

Navarro Pubs, *(Navarro Pubs.; 0-932079)*, 1752 S. Dayton Pl., Kennewick, WA 99337 (SAN 686-2632) Tel 509-582-6720.

NavPress, *(Navpress, A Ministry of The Navigators; 0-89109)*, P.O. Box 6000, Colorado Springs, CO 80934 (SAN 211-5352) Tel 303-598-1212; Toll free: 800-525-7151.

Navy League US, *(Navy League of the United States; 0-9610724)*, 2300 Wilson Blvd., Arlington, VA 22201-3308 (SAN 264-7699) Tel 703-631-0571; Dist. by: Almanac of Seapower, The, P.O. Box 11455, Alexandria, VA 22312 (SAN 200-8033) Tel 703-354-7094.

Nazareth Group, *(Nazareth Group, Inc., The)*, Box 448, Waynesboro, PA 17265 (SAN 656-8971) Tel 717-762-9716.

Nazareth Pubns
See Yuganta Pr

NB Mktg, *(NB Marketing; 0-939417)*, 9420 Reseda Blvd., Suite 442, Northridge, CA 91324 (SAN 663-1614) Tel 818-993-9161.

NBC, *(National Business Clearinghouse; 0-941176)*, Box 327, Croton Plaza, Croton, NY 10520 (SAN 238-9010).

NBECI, *(National Business & Education Collaborative, Inc.; 0-938697)*, 97 Hulst Rd., Amherst, MA 01002 (SAN 661-5333) Tel 413-253-5096; Rte. 1, Amherst, MA 01002 (SAN 661-5341).

NBM, *(NBM; 0-918348)*, 156 E. 39th St., New York, NY 10016 (SAN 210-0835) Tel 212-661-8129; Dist. by: Publishers Group West, 5855 Beaudry St., Emeryville, CA 94608 (SAN 202-8522) Tel 415-658-3453.

NC Archives, *(North Carolina Div. of Archives & History; 0-86526)*, Historical Pubns. Section, 109 E. Jones St., Raleigh, NC 27611 (SAN 203-7246) Tel 919-733-7442.

NC Bar Found, *(North Carolina Bar Foundation)*, 1025 Wade Ave, Raleigh, NC 27605 (SAN 237-8981) Tel 919-828-0561.

NC Bk Express, *(North Country Book Express, Inc./Solstice Press; 0-932722)*, 112 W. Fourth St., P.O. Box 9223, Moscow, ID 83843 (SAN 169-1686) Tel 208-882-0888.

NC Central Pol Sci, *(North Carolina Central Univ., Dept. of Political Science)*, Durham, NC 27707 (SAN 206-1708).

NC Haiku Soc, *(North Carolina Haiku Society Pr., The; 0-9614161)*, 326 Golf Course Dr., Raleigh, NC 27610 (SAN 686-5496) Tel 919-828-5551; Orders to: P.O. Box 14247, Raleigh, NC 27620 (SAN 662-2712).

†NC Natl Hist, *(North Carolina State Museum of Natural History; 0-917134)*, Div. of N.C. Dept. of Agriculture, 102 N. Salisbury St., P.O. Box 27647, Raleigh, NC 27611 (SAN 208-788X) Tel 919-733-7450; P.O. Box 27647, Raleigh, NC 27611 (SAN 662-0973); *CIP.*

NC Path Intl Dev, *(North Carolina State Univ., Dept. of Plant Pathology; 0-931901)*, North Carolina State Univ., Dept. of Plant Pathology, Box 7616, Raleigh, NC 27695-7616 (SAN 686-0206) Tel 919-737-2721.

NC Wesleyan Friends Lib, *(North Carolina Wesleyan College, Friends of the Library; 0-933598)*, 3400 Wesleyan Blvd., Rocky Mount, NC 27801 (SAN 238-6364).

NCAC, *(National Coalition Against Censorship; 0-9611430)*, 132 W. 43rd St., New York, NY 10036 (SAN 260-373X) Tel 212-944-9899.

NCACS Boulder, *(North Central Assn. of Colleges & Schools)*, P.O. Box 18, Boulder, CO 80306 (SAN 225-7661) Tel 303-497-0261.

NCARB, *(National Council of Architectural Registration Boards; 0-9607310)*, 1735 New York Ave., NW, Suite 700, Washington, DC 20006 (SAN 240-1282) Tel 202-783-6500.

NCAT, *(National Ctr. for Appropriate Technology; 1-55579)*, Box 3838, Butte, MT 59702 (SAN 260-342X) Tel 406-494-4572.

NCBA, *(National Cooperative Business Assn.; 0-910440)*, National Cooperative Business Ctr., 1401 New York Ave., NW, Suite 1100, Washington, DC 20005 (SAN 269-3747) Tel 202-638-6222; Orders to: P.O. Box 8293, Ann Arbor, MI 48107 (SAN 661-9827) Tel 313-665-2667.

NCCB
See T R A C

NCCC
See Catholic Charities

†NCCE, *(National Committee for Citizens in Education; 0-934460)*, 10840 Little Patuxent Pkwy., Suite 301, Columbia, MD 21044 (SAN 206-1023) Tel 301-997-9300; *CIP.*

NCEMMH, *(NCEMMH; 0-936882)*, 356 Arps Hall, 1945 N. High St., Columbus, OH 43210 (SAN 262-1118) Tel 614-422-8787.

†NCHE Press, *(NCHE Pr.; 0-914617)*, Div. of National Ctr. for Health Education, 30 E. 29th St., New York, NY 10016 (SAN 289-3959) Tel 212-689-1866; *CIP.*

NCJW, *(NCJW, Inc.; 0-941840)*, 15 E. 26th St., New York, NY 10010 (SAN 239-2658) Tel 212-532-1740.

NCLS Inc, *(National Clearinghouse for Legal Services Incorporated)*, 500 N. Michigan Ave., Rm. 1940, Chicago, IL 60611 (SAN 226-2169) Tel 312-353-2566.

†NCMA, *(North Carolina Museum of Art; 0-88259)*, 2110 Blue Ridge Blvd., Raleigh, NC 27607 (SAN 202-9030) Tel 919-833-1935; *CIP.*

NCPA Washington, *(National Ctr. for Policy Alternatives; 0-89788)*, 2000 Florida Ave., NW, Washington, DC 20009 (SAN 235-8255) Tel 202-387-6030.

NCRCRD, *(North Central Regional Ctr. for Rural Development; 0-936913)*, Iowa State Univ., No. 578 Heady Hall, Ames, IA 50010 (SAN 658-3636) Tel 515-294-1184.

†NCRP Pubns, *(National Council on Radiation Protection & Measurements; 0-913392)*, 7910 Woodmont Ave., Suite 1016, Bethesda, MD 20814 (SAN 677-1254) Tel 301-657-2652; *CIP.*

†NCTE, *(National Council of Teachers of English; 0-8141)*, 1111 Kenyon Rd., Urbana, IL 61801 (SAN 202-9049) Tel 217-328-3870; *CIP.*

†NCTM, *(National Council of Teachers of Mathematics; 0-87353)*, 1906 Association Dr., Reston, VA 22091 (SAN 202-9057) Tel 703-620-9840; *CIP.*

NDCF, *(National Defense Council Foundation; 0-936277)*, 108 S. Columbus St., Suite 101, Alexandria, VA 22314 (SAN 699-7546) Tel 703-836-3443.

NE Agri Engineer, *(Northeast Regional Agricultural Engineering Service; 0-935817)*, Cornell Univ., Riley Robb Hall, Ithaca, NY 14853 (SAN 696-6543) Tel 607-255-7654.

NE Bks, *(Northeast Bks.; 0-937374)*, Div. of Cultural Society of Northeastern Pennsylvania, 401 Clark St., Clarks Green, PA 18411 (SAN 215-2665) Tel 717-586-0077.

NE Conf Teach Foreign, *(Northeast Conference on the Teaching of Foreign Languages; 0-915432)*, P.O. Box 623, Middlebury, VT 05753 (SAN 207-5113) Tel 802-388-2598.

NE History, *(New England History Pr.; 0-89725)*, Subs. of NH Publishing Co., Inc., P.O. Box 70, Somersworth, NH 03878 (SAN 264-2433).

NE Marine Advisory, *(Northeast Marine Advisory Council; 0-9616907)*, Univ. of New Hampshire, NEC Administration Bldg., Durham, NH 03824 (SAN 661-5198) Tel 603-862-3460.

NE Outdoors, *(Northeast Outdoors, Inc.; 0-936216)*, P.O. Box 2180, Waterbury, CT 06722-2180 (SAN 214-0691).

NE Poli Sci, *(Northeastern Political Science Association)*, 426 Thompson Hall, Univ. of Massachusetts, Amherst, MA 01003 (SAN 226-9279) Tel 413-545-1354.

NE Regional Ctr, (Northeast Regional Ctr. for Rural Development; 0-9609010), Pennsylvania State Univ., 104 Weaver Bldg., University Park, PA 16802 (SAN 241-3418) Tel 814-863-4656.

NE St U Arts & Letters, (Northeastern State Univ., Div. of Arts & Letters; 0-9615355), The Phoenix SH 218, Northeastern State Univ., Tahlequah, OK 74464 (SAN 695-1821) Tel 918-456-5511.

†NE U Pr, (Northeastern Univ. Pr.; 0-930350; 1-55553), 360 Huntington Ave., Huntington Plaza, Suite 272, Northeastern Univ., Boston, MA 02115 (SAN 205-3764) Tel 617-437-5480; Orders to: P.O. Box 250, Ithaca, NY 14851 (SAN 282-0668); CIP.

†NEA, (National Education Assn.; 0-8106), 1201 16th St., NW, Washington, DC 20036 (SAN 203-7262) Tel 202-822-7250; Orders to: P.O. Box 509, West Haven, CT 06516 (SAN 203-7270) Tel 203-934-2669; CIP.

Neahtawanta Pr, (Neahtawanta Pr.; 0-943806), 309 E. Front St., Traverse City, MI 49684 (SAN 239-3689) Tel 616-947-2462.

Neal Assoc, (Neal, Richard, Assocs.; 0-9605018), Box 23, Manassas, VA 22110 (SAN 215-6857).

Neal Pubns
See Neal Pubns Inc

Neal Pubns Inc, (Neal Pubns., Inc.; 0-9609006), P.O. Box 451, Perrysburg, OH 43551 (SAN 240-8198) Tel 419-874-7422.

†Neal-Schuman, (Neal-Schuman Pubs., Inc.; 0-918212; 1-55570), 23 Leonard St., New York, NY 10013 (SAN 210-2455) Tel 212-925-8650; CIP.

Near Eastern Imprint of **Holmes Pub**

†Nebraska Art, (Nebraska Art Assn.; 0-9602018), Univ. of Nebraska-Lincoln, Sheldon Memorial Art Gallery, Lincoln, NE 68588-0300 (SAN 212-1972) Tel 402-472-2461; CIP.

†Nebraska Hist, (Nebraska State Historical Society; 0-933307), 1500 R St., P.O. Box 82554, Lincoln, NE 68501 (SAN 209-4630) Tel 402-471-4747; CIP.

Nebraska Review, (Nebraska Review; 0-937796), Southeast Community College, 924 K St., Fairbury, NE 68352 (SAN 220-262X).

NEC Home
See NEC Home Elect

NEC Home Elect, (NEC Home Electronics USA, Inc.; 0-925739), Subs. of NEC America, Inc., 1255 Michael Dr., Wood Dale, IL 60191-1094 (SAN 277-1861) Tel 312-860-9500; Toll free: 800-632-7638.

Necronomicon, (Necronomicon Pr.; 0-940884), 101 Lockwood St., West Warwick, RI 02893 (SAN 210-315X) Tel 401-828-5319.

Neechee Assoc, (Neechee Associates, Inc.; 0-9602582), 6664 Paseo Dorado, Tucson, AZ 85715 (SAN 215-6865).

Needlemania, (Needlemania, Inc.), P.O. Box 123, Franklin, MI 48025 (SAN 240-9208).

Neely Pub, (Neely Publishing Co.; 0-9616947), Div. of Neely Assocs., Inc., 528 E. Boulevard, Charlotte, NC 28203 (SAN 661-7530) Tel 704-373-0051.

Neff-Kane Imprint of **Presidio Pr**

Negative Capability Pr, (Negative Capability Pr.; 0-942544), 6116 Timberly Rd. N, Mobile, AL 36609 (SAN 238-5465) Tel 205-661-9114.

Negro U Pr
See Greenwood

Neighbors Pr
See Neighbors Pub

Neighbors Pub, (Neighbors Publishing; 0-933387), P.O. Box 15071, Minneapolis, MN 55415 (SAN 691-6821) Tel 612-372-4489.

Neihardt-Smith
See Mind-Matter-Motion

Neild-Kuvet, (Neild/Kuvet Publishing Co.; 0-912945), P.O. Box 9184, Berkeley, CA 94709 (SAN 283-1015) Tel 415-527-9640.

Neiman, (Neiman, Michele; 0-9615461), 75 Juniper, Sierra Vista, AZ 85635 (SAN 695-7226) Tel 602-378-6894.

Neither-Nor Pr, (Neither/Nor Pr., The; 0-911627), P.O. Box 8043, Ann Arbor, MI 48107 (SAN 264-2417) Tel 313-434-6172.

Nel Mar Enter, (Nel-Mar Enterprises; 0-9615760), P.O. Box 1138, Wimberley, TX 78676 (SAN 695-8699) Tel 512-847-9415.

NELF Pr, (National Unity Equality Leadership Fraternity Pr.), 78 Maplevale Dr., Woodbridge, CT 06525 (SAN 203-7297) Tel 203-393-3913.

†Nelson, (Nelson, Thomas, Pubs.; 0-8407), P.O. Box 141000, Nelson Pl. at Elm Hill Pike, Nashville, TN 37214 (SAN 209-3820) Tel 615-889-9000; Toll free: 800-872-4445; Toll free: 800-821-4370 (TN); CIP.

Nelson-Atkins, (Nelson-Atkins Museum of Art, The; 0-942614), 4525 Oak St., Kansas City, MO 64111 (SAN 238-5473) Tel 816-561-4000.

Nelson B Robinson, (Robinson, Nelson B., Bookseller; 0-930352), 51 Main St., Rockport, MA 01966 (SAN 209-004X) Tel 617-546-7323.

Nelson Comm, (Nelson Communications; 0-8407), Subs. of Thomas Nelson Pubs., Nelson Pl. at Elm Hill Pike, Nashville, TN 37214 (SAN 692-0543) Tel 615-889-9000; Toll free: 800-872-4445.

Nelson G L, (Nelson, G. L., Publishing, Inc.; 0-937416), 1505 McCormick Pl., Wheaton, IL 60187 (SAN 287-2714).

Nelson Gallery-Atkins
See Nelson-Atkins

Nelson Graphics, (Nelson Graphics; 0-936881), 201 Weed St., New Canaan, CT 06840 (SAN 658-3733) Tel 203-966-8230.

†Nelson-Hall, (Nelson-Hall, Inc.; 0-911012; 0-88229; 0-8304), 111 N. Canal St., Chicago, IL 60606 (SAN 202-9065) Tel 312-930-9446; CIP.

Nembutsu Pr, (Nembutsu Pr.; 0-912624), 6257 Golden West Ave., Temple City, CA 91780 (SAN 208-0060).

Nemeth, (Nemeth, Doris I.; 0-932192), 2314 W. Sixth St., Mishawaka, IN 46544 (SAN 217-118X).

Neo-Am Church, (Original Kleptonian Neo-American Church, The), Box 97, Bethel, VT 05032 (SAN 266-0008) Tel 512-443-8464.

Neo Med Pub, (Neo-Medical Publishing; 0-9611870), Moose River Rd., RD 3, Boonville, NY 13309 (SAN 286-1356) Tel 315-942-4253.

Neo Pr, (Neo Pr.; 0-911014), P.O. Box 32, Peaks Island, ME 04108 (SAN 203-7300).

Neolog, (Neolog Publishing; 0-9613477), 422 High St., No. 17, Medford, MA 02156 (SAN 657-3673) Tel 617-391-7894.

Neptune Bks Imprint of **Tail Feather**

Neptune His Soc, (Neptune Historical Society), 25 Neptune Blvd., Neptune, NJ 07754 (SAN 676-2093).

NERAS Syst, (NERAS Systems), 425 N. Doheny Dr., Suite 8, Beverly Hills, CA 90210 (SAN 211-1616) Tel 213-278-8584. Deceased.

Neri & Assocs, (Neri & Assocs.; 0-9615528), 15720 Ventura Blvd. No. 502, Encino, CA 91436 (SAN 696-348X) Tel 818-906-0111.

Nesbit, (Nesbit, Norman L.; 0-911746), 2104 Goddard Pl., Boulder, CO 80303 (SAN 206-1651) Tel 303-494-6206.

Nesbitt Ent, (Nesbitt Enterprises), 5220 NE Roselawn, Portland, OR 97218 (SAN 219-8029) Tel 503-287-0306.

Ness Press, (Ness Pr.; 0-938749), 1650 President St., Apt. 1E, Brooklyn, NY 11213 (SAN 661-7522) Tel 718-778-0747.

Net Pr, (NET Pr.; 0-937462), 5001 Ave. N, Lubbock, TX 79412 (SAN 291-8005) Tel 806-762-8094; Toll free: 800-NEA-GROW; Toll free: 800-TXA-GROW (in TX).

Netherton, (Netherton, H. Eugene), 1035 Park Blvd., West Sacramento, CA 95691 (SAN 238-9029).

Nettleton Hse, (Nettleton House), 737 Fifth Ave., San Francisco, CA 94118 (SAN 214-4263).

Network Ani-Males & Females, (Network for Ani-Males & Females, Inc.; 0-938073), 18707 Curry Powder Ln., Germantown, MD 20874 (SAN 661-2725) Tel 301-428-3675.

Network Bks
See Network GA Pubns

Network Comm, (Network Communications, Inc.; 0-934913), Div. of Miranontes & Assocs., Inc., 9880 Via Pasar, San Diego, CA 92126 (SAN 693-2053) Tel 619-549-3333.

Network GA Pubns, (Network Bks.; 0-915281), Roundtree Bridge Rd., Sparks, GA 31647 (SAN 656-8998) Tel 912-549-7119.

Network Media, (Network Media, Inc.; 0-939455), 2812 W. Ramada Dr., Mobile, AL 36609 (SAN 663-3781) Tel 205-666-5170.

Network Project, (Network Project), Columbia Univ., 101 Earl Hall, New York, NY 10027 (SAN 206-166X) Tel 212-923-3900.

Network Pubns, (Network Pubns.; 0-941816), Div. of ETR Assocs., Inc., P.O. Box 1830, Santa Cruz, CA 95061-1830 (SAN 216-2881) Tel 408-429-9822.

Neubauer Pr, (Neubauer Pr.; 0-9617265), 268 Russell Rd., Princeton, NJ 08540 (SAN 663-4893) Tel 609-924-9629.

Neuropsych Pr, (Neuropsychology Pr.; 0-934515), 1338 E. Edison St., Tucson, AZ 85719 (SAN 693-8256) Tel 602-795-3717.

Neuse Pr, (Neuse Pr.; 0-9613763), P.O. Box 71, New Bern, NC 28560 (SAN 683-2938) Tel 919-637-4267.

NEV Multimedia Pubs, (Nev Multimedia Pubs.; 0-9606426), 19 Summit Rd, Wellesley, MA 02181 (SAN 218-5709) Tel 617-237-7493.

Nevada County Hist Society, (Nevada County Historical Society; 0-915641), P.O. Box 1300, Nevada City, CA 95959 (SAN 291-8218) Tel 916-273-2909.

Nevada Pubns, (Nevada Pubns.; 0-913814), 4135 Badger Cir., Reno, NV 89509 (SAN 203-7319) Tel 702-747-0800.

Nevertheless, (Nevertheless Pr.; 0-9612532), Box 9779, Berkeley, CA 94709 (SAN 679-1832).

Nevins Pub Co, (Nevins Publishing Co.,Inc.; 0-914359), 508-1A Auten Rd., Somerville, NJ 08876 (SAN 289-6613) Tel 201-874-5939.

New Age, (New Age Pr., Inc.; 0-87613), P.O. Box 1216, Black Mountain, NC 28711 (SAN 203-7327) Tel 704-669-6214.

New Age Action, (New Age Action Group), 910 Crescent Dr., Alexandria, VA 22302 (SAN 213-1293) Tel 703-836-4930.

New Age Bible, (New Age Bible & Philosophy Ctr.; 0-933963), 1139 Lincoln Blvd., Santa Monica, CA 90403 (SAN 693-0697) Tel 213-395-4346; Dist. by: DeVorss & Co., P.O. Box, 1046 Princeton Dr., Marina del Rey, CA 90294 (SAN 168-9886) Tel 213-870-7478.

New Age Bus Bks, (New Age Business Books; 0-911201), P.O. Box 423, Boulder City, NV 89005 (SAN 263-1687) Tel 702-293-6590.

New Age FL Pub, (New Age Pub. Co.; 0-934619), P.O. Box 011549, Miami, FL 33101 (SAN 694-0226) Tel 305-534-8437.

New-Age Foods
See Soyfoods Center

New Age Min Spiritualist, (New Age Ministries Spiritualist Church in Christ on Earth), P.O. Box 129, Lake Helen, FL 32744 (SAN 211-7967).

New Age Study Human, (New Age Study of Humanity's Purpose; 0-9615287), P.O. Box 41883, Tucson, AZ 85717 (SAN 694-4094) Tel 602-298-2222.

New Atlantis, (New Atlantis Pr.; 0-9615480), 473 Pavonia Ave., Jersey City, NJ 07306 (SAN 695-9083) Tel 201-653-8221.

New Bedford, (New Bedford Pr.; 0-931656), 5800 W. Century Blvd., Dept. 91502, Los Angeles, CA 90009 (SAN 219-9688) Tel 213-837-2961. Imprints: Bedpress (Bedpress Books).

New Begin Co, (New Beginnings Co.; 0-932489), 711 E. Walnut St. Suite 401, Pasadena, CA 91101 (SAN 687-4304) Tel 818-793-3612.

†New Benjamin, (New Benjamin Franklin Hse., The; 0-933488), 304 W. 58th St., 5th Flr., New York, NY 10019 (SAN 212-6168) Tel 212-247-7484; CIP. Imprints: Univ Edns (University Editions).

New Bks Imprint of **R J Berg & Co**

New Boundary Design, (New Boundary Design Inc.; 0-913703), 1453 Park Rd., Chanhassen, MN 55317 (SAN 286-0899) Tel 612-474-0924; Toll free: 800-328-6795.

New Breed Pr, (New Breed Pr.; 0-9617166), Div. of Light Mgmt., 10664 Bluffside Dr., Studio City, CA 91604 (SAN 662-9482) Tel 213-826-4433.

New Canaan, (New Canaan Historical Society; 0-939958), 13 Oenoke Ridge, New Canaan, CT 06840 (SAN 216-843X) Tel 203-966-1776.

New Capernaum, *(New Capernaum Works; 0-938792),* Div. of Universal Spiritual Action, 4615 NE Emerson St., Portland, OR 97218 (SAN 215-8922) Tel 503-281-1307.

†New Century, *(New Century Pubs., Inc.; 0-8329),* Div. of New Century Education Corp., 220 Old New Brunswick Rd., Piscataway, NJ 08854 (SAN 217-1201) Tel 201-981-0820; *CIP.*

New Chess, *(New In Chess),* 2423 Noble Station, Bridgeport, CT 06608 (SAN 683-2946).

New Choices, *(New Choices Pr.; 0-934297),* 610 West End Ave., New York, NY 10024 (SAN 693-3165) Tel 212-362-6808.

New City, *(New City Pr.; 0-911782),* 206 Skillman Ave., Brooklyn, NY 11211 (SAN 203-7335) Tel 718-782-2844.

New Classics Lib, *(New Classics Library, Inc.; 0-932750),* P.O. Box 1618, Gainesville, GA 30503 (SAN 212-1190) Tel 404-536-0309; Toll free: 800-336-1618.

†New Coll U Pr, *(New College & Univ. Pr., The; 0-8084),* P.O. Box 1392, Schenectady, NY 12301 (SAN 203-6223) Tel 518-346-2649; *CIP. Imprints:* Twayne (Twayne's U. S. Author Series).

New Collage, *(New Collage Press; 0-936814),* 5700 N. Tamiami Trail, Sarasota, FL 33580 (SAN 210-6159) Tel 813-355-7671; Dist. by: Faxon Co., The, 15 SW Park, Westwood, MA 02090 (SAN 159-8619) Tel 617-329-3350.

New Collectors, *(New Collectors Group; 0-9616634),* 259 S. Teller St., Apt. 311, Lakewood, CO 80226-7338 (SAN 661-213X) Tel 303-238-5805.

New College
See New Collage

New Comet, *(New Cometerra Press; 0-914701),* P.O. Box 1026, Palatine, IL 60078 (SAN 289-6982) Tel 312-397-8005.

New Comm Pr
See BDR Learn Prods

New Concepts Pub, *(New Concepts Publishing, Inc.; 0-941136),* 475 Fifth Ave., New York, NY 10017 (SAN 217-4081) Tel 212-889-3241.

New Dawn, *(New Dawn Pubns.; 0-934271),* 1605 Edith Ln., Colorado Springs, CO 80909 (SAN 693-3181) Tel 303-591-9556.

New Day Pr, *(New Day Pr.; 0-913678),* c/o Karamu Hse., 2355 E. 89th St., Cleveland, OH 44106 (SAN 279-2664).

New Day Pubns, *(New Day Pubns, Inc.; 0-9605994; 0-9612328),* P.O. Box 70161, Washington, DC 20088 (SAN 216-7530) Tel 301-439-0271; 910 Newhall St., Silver Spring, MD 20901 (SAN 293-4841).

New Dimen Studio, *(New Dimension Studio; 0-916928),* 3872 Augusta Dr., Rm. 1, Nashville, TN 37209 (SAN 208-385X) Tel 615-876-6371; Orders to: P.O. Box 90492, Nashville, TN 37209 (SAN 208-3868).

New Dimensions Educ
See Arista Corp NY

New Dir Pr, *(New Directions Press; 0-9609616),* 80 Eighth Ave., New York, NY 10011 (SAN 260-2326) Tel 212-255-0230.

New Dir Salem, *(New Directions Publishing; 0-938393),* 4743 Nighthawk Ct., NE, Salem, OR 97301 (SAN 661-3853) Tel 503-362-4415.

New Dir Young Women, *(New Directions for Young Women, Inc.; 0-9608696),* 2356 E. Hampton St., Tucson, AZ 85719 (SAN 240-7337) Tel 602-327-4022.

†New Directions, *(New Directions Publishing Corp.; 0-8112),* 80 Eighth Ave., New York, NY 10011 (SAN 202-9081) Tel 212-255-0230; Toll free: 800-223-2584; Dist. by: W. W. Norton Co., 500 Fifth Ave., New York, NY 10110 (SAN 202-5795) Tel 212-354-5500; *CIP.*

New Eng & Reg All, *(New England & Regional Allergy Proceedings; 0-936587),* Affil. of New England Society of Allergy, 95 Pitman St., Providence, RI 02906 (SAN 698-0856) Tel 401-331-2510.

New Eng GE, *(New England Gerontology Ctr.; 0-89634),* Dist. by: Systems Planning Assocs., Pub. Div.; 3 Aliber Pl., Keene, NH 03431 (SAN 287-3028) Tel 603-357-4005.

New Eng Hist, *(New England Historic Genealogical Society; 0-88082),* 101 Newbury St., Boston, MA 02116 (SAN 274-0117) Tel 617-536-5740.

New Eng Old News, *(New England Old Newspaper Index),* P.O. Box 152, Danville, ME 04223 (SAN 295-0502).

New Eng Pr VT, *(New England Pr., Inc., The; 0-933050),* P.O. Box 575, Shelburne, VT 05482 (SAN 213-6376) Tel 802-863-2520.

New Eng Pub MA, *(New England Pub. Co.; 0-914265),* 728 Hampden St., Holyoke, MA 01040 (SAN 287-5837) Tel 413-533-4231.

New Eng SF Assoc, *(New England Science Fiction Assn.; 0-915368),* Box G, MIT Branch P.O., Cambridge, MA 02139 (SAN 223-8187).

New England Geron
See New Eng GE

New England Hist
See NE History

New England Pr, *(New England Pr.; 0-931060),* 45 Tudor City, No. 1903, New York, NY 10017 (SAN 211-9196).

New Era
See New Era Pr

New Era *Imprint of* World Merch Import

New Era Pr, *(New Era Pr.; 0-937590),* P.O. Box 124, Weaverville, CA 96093 (SAN 215-8930) Tel 916-623-5966. Do no confuse with New Era Pubns., Happy Camp, CA, or New Era Pr., Of Farmington, NY.

New Era Pubns MI, *(New Era Pubns., Inc.; 0-939830),* P.O. Box 8139, Ann Arbor, MI 48107 (SAN 220-1941) Tel 313-663-1929.

New Expressions, *(New Expressions Unltd.),* 30886 Sutherland Dr., Redlands, CA 92373 (SAN 209-4053) Tel 714-794-4868.

New Fortress Pub, *(New Fortress Pubns.; 0-937799),* 2332 S. Peck Rd., Suite 268, Whittier, CA 90601 (SAN 659-3801) Tel 213-699-3443.

New Forums, *(New Forums Pr., Inc.; 0-913507),* P.O. Box 876, Stillwater, OK 74076 (SAN 285-8673) Tel 405-372-6158.

New Glide
See Volcano Pr

New Harbinger, *(New Harbinger Pubns.; 0-934986),* 2200 Adeline, Suite 305, Oakland, CA 94607 (SAN 205-0587).

New Haven Pubs, *(New Haven Pubs.; 0-918313),* Subs. of New Haven Publishers, 1703 N. Tyland Blvd., New Haven, IN 46774 (SAN 657-2928) Tel 219-749-2646.

New Hope *Imprint of* Revell

New Hope AL, *(New Hope; 0-936625),* P.O. Box 11657, Birmingham, AL 35202-1657 (SAN 699-7015) Tel 205-991-8100; 100 Missionary Ridge, Birmingham, AL 35202-1657 (SAN 699-7023).

New Hor Bk, *(New Horizons Bk. Publishing Co.; 0-932279),* P.O. Box 10904, Marina del Rey, CA 90295 (SAN 686-547X) Tel 213-827-4940.

New Hor Pubs, *(New Horizons Pubs.; 0-915325),* 737 Tenth Ave., E., Seattle, WA 98102 (SAN 290-0238) Tel 206-323-1102; Dist. by: Pacific Pipeline, Inc., 19215 66th Ave. S., Kent, WA 98032 (SAN 208-2128) Tel 206-872-5523.

†New Horizon NJ, *(New Horizon Pr. Pubs., Inc.; 0-88282),* P.O. Box 669, Far Hills, NJ 07931 (SAN 677-119X) Tel 201-234-9546; Toll free: 800-257-5755; Orders to: Charles Scribner & Sons, Front & Brown Sts., Riverside, NJ 08075 (SAN 663-3099); *CIP.*

†New Horizons, *(New Horizons Pr.; 0-914914),* P.O. Box 1758, Chico, CA 95927 (SAN 206-7927) Tel 916-895-6227; *CIP.*

New Horizons Pub, *(New Horizons Publishing; 0-9613807),* P.O. Box 23416, Santa Barbara, CA 93121 (SAN 679-4017).

New Idea Pr, *(New Idea Pr., Inc.; 0-9617099),* P.O. Box 13083, Boulder, CO 80308-3683 (SAN 662-5002); 1736 36th St., Boulder, CO 80308-3683 (SAN 662-5010) Tel 303-494-4488.

New Image, *(New Image; 0-9609168),* 310 Colima Ct., La Jolla, CA 92037 (SAN 241-4163) Tel 619-456-2122.

New Impressions, *(New Impressions; 0-9611606),* Box 558, 118 Middle St., Lancaster, NH 03584 (SAN 285-2942) Tel 603-788-4492.

New Issues, *(New Issues, Inc.; 0-9616275),* P.O. Box 11564, Milwaukee, WI 53211 (SAN 658-5922) Tel 414-962-6990; 2720 N. Frederick Ave., Suite 232, Milwaukee, WI 53211 (SAN 658-5930).

New Issues MI, *(Western Michigan Univ., New Issues Pr.; 0-932826),* Kalamazoo, MI 49008 (SAN 276-6299) Tel 616-383-1886.

New Jersey
See NJ DOE

New Jersey Vet, *(New Jersey Veterinary Medical Assn.; 0-9614059),* P.O. Box 320, Rockaway, NJ 07866 (SAN 686-0036) Tel 201-379-1100.

New Leaf, *(New Leaf Pr.; 0-89221),* P.O. Box 311, Green Forest, AR 72638 (SAN 207-9518) Tel 501-438-5288; Toll free: 800-643-9535.

New Letters MO, *(New Letters Bks.; 0-938652),* 5310 Harrison, Kansas City, MO 64110 (SAN 209-8458) Tel 816-276-1168.

New Life Faith, *(New Life Thru Faith Pubns.; 0-934285),* P.O. Box 598, Mesa, AZ 85201 (SAN 693-3173) Tel 602-898-8513.

New Life Pubns, *(New Life Pubns.; 0-935379),* 2730 Lapey, Rockford, IL 61109 (SAN 696-3234) Tel 815-397-4563.

New Life Pubs, *(New Life Pubs.; 0-9616016),* Subs. of Creative New Life Ministries, 1797 S. Monrovia, Costa Mesa, CA 92627 (SAN 697-2942) Tel 714-642-4053.

New Lifestyle, *(New Lifestyle Publishing; 0-941256),* P.O. Box 4419, Los Angeles, CA 90051 (SAN 239-4642) Tel 213-660-8201.

New London County, *(New London County Historical Society; 0-9607744),* 11 Blinman St., New London, CT 06320 (SAN 207-0049) Tel 203-443-1209.

New London Pr, *(New London Pr.; 0-89683),* Box 7458, Dallas, TX 75209 (SAN 211-4402) Tel 214-742-9037.

New Meridian Pr, *(New Meridian Pr.; 0-914882),* P.O. Box 229, Clifton Park, NY 12065 (SAN 206-5045) Tel 518-877-5845.

New Mexico Mag, *(New Mexico Magazine; 0-937206),* Bataan Memorial Building, Santa Fe, NM 87503 (SAN 677-072X).

New Mexico St Univ, *(New Mexico State Univ. - Studies in Latin American Popular Culture; 0-9608664),* Dept. of Foreign Languages, Box 3L, Las Cruces, NM 88003 (SAN 239-5428) Tel 505-646-2942.

New Mind Prod, *(New Mind Prods.; 0-933821),* P.O. Box 5185, Jersey City, NJ 07305 (SAN 200-5565) Tel 201-434-1939.

New Mississippi, *(New Mississippi, Inc.; 0-9616362),* P.O. Box 3568, Jackson, MS 39207 (SAN 658-9863) Tel 601-352-3398.

New Moon
See Humble Hills

New Moon-Humble Hills
See Humble Hills

New Mus Contemp Art, *(New Museum of Contemporary Art, The; 0-915557),* 583 Broadway, New York, NY 10012 (SAN 291-3070) Tel 212-219-1222; Dist. by: Contemporary Arts Press, P.O. Box 3123, Rincon Annex, San Francisco, CA 94119 (SAN 213-3016) Tel 415-431-7672.

New Music Times, *(New Music Times, Inc., The; 0-9606830),* P.O. Box 8573, Albany, NY 12208 (SAN 219-6115) Tel 518-438-4815.

New Nativity, *(New Nativity Pr.; 0-940128),* P.O. Box 6223, Leawood, KS 66206 (SAN 217-0779) Tel 913-341-8369.

New Nurse, *(New Nurse, Pub., The; 0-914698),* P.O. Box 803, Plattsburgh, NY 12901 (SAN 206-6041). Name Formerly Hanton.

New Option Pub
See New Options Pub

New Options Pub, *(New Options Publishing; 0-9614635),* 1939 Park Ave., Denver, CO 80218 (SAN 692-3968) Tel 303-830-7718; Dist. by: Bookpeople, 2929 Fifth St., Berkeley, CA 94710 (SAN 168-9517) Tel 415-549-3030; Dist. by: Inland Bk. Co., P.O. Box 261, 22 Hemingway Ave., East Haven, CT 06512 (SAN 200-4151) Tel 203-467-4257.

†New Orleans Mus Art, *(New Orleans Museum of Art; 0-89494),* P.O. Box 19123, New Orleans, LA 70179-0123 (SAN 209-9713) Tel 504-488-2631; Dist. by: Univ. of Wash. Pr., P.O. Box C50096, Seattle, WA 98145 (SAN 212-2502) Tel 206-543-8870; *CIP.*

New Orleans Poetry, *(New Orleans Poetry Journal Pr., The; 0-938498),* 2131 General Pershing St., New Orleans, LA 70115 (SAN 215-8949).

New Orleans Urban, *(New Orleans Urban Folklife Society; 0-9613133),* 1210 Short St., New Orleans, LA 70118 (SAN 658-2524) Tel 504-866-8940.

†New Outlook, (New Outlook Pubs. & Distributors; 0-87898), 235 W. 23rd St., New York, NY 10011 (SAN 202-9111); CIP.

New Pacific Pubns, (New Pacific Pubns., Inc.; 0-932737), 21650 Burbank Blvd., No. 103, Woodland Hills, CA 91367 (SAN 688-5659) Tel 818-884-3987.

New page Pr
See New Pages Pr

New Pages Pr, (New Pages Pr.; 0-941644), P.O. Box 438, Grand Blanc, MI 48439 (SAN 239-2682) Tel 313-743-8055.

New Paradise Bks, (New Paradise Bks.; 0-943654), Suite 206, 3000 N. Atlantic, Cocoa Beach, FL 32931 (SAN 238-0765) Tel 305-783-5651.

New Past Pr, (New Past Pr., Inc., The; 0-938627), RR 2, 2098 18th Ave., Friendship, WI 53934 (SAN 661-6283) Tel 608-339-3907.

New Pen Pub Co, (New Pen Publishing Co.; 0-9609808), P.O. Box 1690, Newark, NJ 07101 (SAN 264-2476).

New Pittsburgh, (New Pittsburgh Pubns.; 0-9608484), P.O. Box 81875, Pittsburgh, PA 15217 (SAN 240-7345) Tel 412-681-8528.

New Place Pr, (New Place Pr.; 0-9617167), P.O. Box 2902, Taunton, MA 02780 (SAN 662-9490); 50 Prospect St., Taunton, MA 02780 (SAN 662-9504) Tel 617-823-0305.

New Plays Bks, (New Plays-Bks., Inc.; 0-932720), Box 273, Rowayton, CT 06853 (SAN 220-9411).

New Poets, (New Poets Series; 0-932616), 541 Piccadilly Rd., Baltimore, MD 21204 (SAN 209-4622) Tel 301-321-2863.

New Prod Develop, (New Product Development Newsletter Co.; 0-911909), P.O. Box 1309, Point Pleasant, NJ 08742 (SAN 265-4083).

New Puritan, (New Puritan Library, Inc.; 0-932050), 91 Lytle Rd., Fletcher, NC 28732 (SAN 213-4217).

New Ray Pr, (New Ray Pr.; 0-936303), 27835 Troublesome Gulch Rd., Kittredge, CO 80457 (SAN 697-2993) Tel 303-674-0534; P.O. Box 549, Kittredge, CO 80457 (SAN 697-3000).

New Readers, (New Readers Pr.; 0-88336), Div. of Laubach Literacy International, Box 131, Syracuse, NY 13210 (SAN 202-1064) Tel 315-422-9121; Toll free: 800-448-8878. Imprints: Sundown (Sundown).

New Research, (New Research Pubns.; 0-910891), P.O. Box 231, Greenvale, NY 11548 (SAN 274-0389) Tel 516-293-1171.

New Riders Pubn, (New Riders Publishing; 0-934035), P.O. Box 4846, Thousand Oaks, CA 91360 (SAN 692-9575) Tel 818-991-5392.

New Rivers Pr, (New Rivers Pr.; 0-912284; 0-89823), 1602 Selby Ave., St. Paul, MN 55104 (SAN 202-9138) Tel 612-645-6324; Dist. by: Bookslinger, 213 E. Fourth St., Saint Paul, MN 55101 (SAN 169-4154) Tel 612-221-0429; Dist. by: Small Press Distribution, Inc., 1814 San Pablo Ave., Berkeley, CA 94702 (SAN 204-5826) Tel 415-549-3336.

New Santander, (New Santander Pr.; 0-935071), Subs. of Omni-Media, Inc., 721 W. Sprague, P.O. Box 306, Edinburg, TX 78540 (SAN 694-6534) Tel 512-383-2567.

New Schl Mus Study, (New Schl. for Music Study Pr.; 0-913277), P.O. Box 407, Princeton, NJ 08540 (SAN 285-8266) Tel 609-921-2900.

New Sci Pr, (New Science Pr.; 0-9616114), 106 Henry St., Greenwich, CT 06830 (SAN 699-7341) Tel 203-531-5312.

New Seed, (New Seed Pr.; 0-938678), P.O. Box 9488, Berkeley, CA 94709 (SAN 282-0501); Dist. by: Bookpeople, 2929 Fifth St., Berkeley, CA 94710 (SAN 168-9517); Dist. by: Childrens Small Press Collection, The, 719 N Fourth Ave., Ann Arbor, MI 48104 (SAN 200-6081); Dist. by: Inland Book Co., Inc., P.O. Box 261, 22 Hemingway Ave., E. Haven, CT 06512 (SAN 200-4151) Tel 203-467-4257.

New Sibylline, (New Sibylline Bks., Inc.; 0-9603352), Box 266, Village Sta., New York, NY 10014 (SAN 214-4271).

New Soc Pubs, (New Society Pubs.; 0-86571), Div. of New Society Education Foundation, Inc., 4722 Baltimore Ave., Philadelphia, PA 19143 (SAN 213-540X) Tel 215-726-6543.

New South Co, (New South Co., The; 0-917990), P.O. Box 24918, Los Angeles, CA 90024-0918 (SAN 209-3340) Tel 714-548-9279.

New Start Pubns, (New Start Pubns., Inc.; 0-915451), P.O. Box 139, Sterling, VA 22170 (SAN 291-3119) Tel 703-450-5983.

New Testament Christ Pr, (New Testament Christian Pr.; 0-931247), P.O. Box 1694, Media, PA 19063 (SAN 682-0050) Tel 215-544-5065.

New Tide, (New Tide MTL Pubs.; 0-88100), Box 21 Contra Station Six, 1525 Sherman St., Denver, CO 80203 (SAN 264-2492).

New Univ Pr, (New Univ. Pr.; 0-89044), 737 N. LaSalle St., Chicago, IL 60610 (SAN 680-0661) Tel 312-944-2525; Orders to: Daphnean Press, 737 N. LaSalle St., Chicago, IL 60610 (SAN 657-1344) Tel 312-944-2525.

New VA, (New Virginia Review, Inc.), 1306 E. Cary St., 2A, Richmond, VA 23219 (SAN 656-898X) Tel 804-782-1043.

New Venture, (New Venture Research Institute; 0-916735), Subs. of Berk Enterprises, Inc., 84 Slater Ave., Providence, RI 02906 (SAN 653-8983) Tel 401-438-1324.

New Victoria Pubs, (New Victora Pubs., Inc.; 0-934678), P.O. Box 27, Norwich, VT 05055 (SAN 212-1204) Tel 802-649-5297.

New View Pr
See CareerTrack Pubns

New Viewpoints
See Watts

New Vision, (New Vision Pubns.; 0-916337), 1438 Ridge Rd., Homewood, IL 60430 (SAN 295-7299) Tel 312-957-5856.

New Vision Bks
See Manchester Pubns

New Visions Pr, (New Visions Pr.; 0-934340), P.O. Box 2025, Gaithersburg, MD 20760 (SAN 212-9213) Tel 301-869-1888.

New Vista, (New Vista Pr.; 0-936544), 10 Oak Tree Dr.,, Santa Rosa, CA 95401 (SAN 293-3098).

New Vistas Pub, (New Vistas Publishing; 0-9616881), P.O. Box 44, Simi Valley, CA 93062 (SAN 661-6569); 6676 Charing St., Simi Valley, CA 93063 (SAN 661-6577) Tel 805-583-4228.

New Voices Imprint of Noontide

New Wave, (New Wave Consultants; 0-943172), P.O. Box 2203, La Jolla, CA 92038 (SAN 240-415X) Tel 619-274-2030.

New Ways Min, (New Ways Ministry; 0-935877), 4012 29th St., Mount Rainier, MD 20712 (SAN 695-877X) Tel 301-277-5674.

New Ways Work, (New Ways to Work), 149 Ninth St., San Francisco, CA 94103 (SAN 663-4664).

New West Hse, (New West Hse. Pubs., The; 0-9614974), Box 175, Bruneau, ID 83604 (SAN 693-5591) Tel 208-845-2502.

New Woman, (New Woman Pr.), 2000 King Mountain Trail, Sunny Valley, OR 97497-9799 (SAN 209-8474).

New World
See New World Press NY

†New World Bks, (New World Bks.; 0-917480), 4515 Saul Rd., Kensington, MD 20895 (SAN 208-3388); CIP.

New World Cup CA, (New World Cup Press; 0-9604636), 9061 Madison Ave., Westminster, CA 92683 (SAN 215-1634).

†New World NY, (New World Pr.; 0-917601), P.O. Box 117, East Elmhurst, NY 11369 (SAN 657-1530) Tel 718-545-6434; CIP.

New World OH, (New World Bks.; 0-9615748), 336 Ludlow Ave., Cincinnati, OH 45220 (SAN 695-913X) Tel 513-861-6100.

†New World Press NY, (New World Press; 0-911026), P.O. Box 416, New York, NY 10017 (SAN 203-736X) Tel 212-972-0460; CIP.

New World Pubns, (New World Pubns.; 0-916933), P.O. Box 244, Highlands, NJ 07732 (SAN 655-7643) Tel 201-741-6109.

New Worlds, (New Worlds Unlimited; 0-917398), 3-42 26th St., Fair Lawn, NJ 07410 (SAN 207-267X); Orders to: P.O. Box 556, Saddle Brook, NJ 07662 (SAN 207-2688).

New Writers Guild, (New Writers Guild Pr.; 0-913459), 6323 Rimpau Blvd., Los Angeles, CA 90043 (SAN 277-6960) Tel 213-293-1281.

New Year Pubns, (New Year Pubns.; 0-935341), 316 Fifth Ave., New York, NY 10001 (SAN 696-3013) Tel 212-868-3330.

New You Pub, (New You Publishing Co.; 0-917762), 609 Santa Cruz Ave., Menlo Park, CA 94025 (SAN 209-0317) Tel 415-322-9959.

Newark Beth, (Newark Beth Israel Medical Ctr.; 0-937714), 201 Lyons Ave., Newark, NJ 07112 (SAN 215-3297).

†Newark Mus, (Newark Museum Assn., The; 0-932828), 49 Washington St., P.O. Box 540, Newark, NJ 07101 (SAN 205-700X) Tel 201-396-6550; CIP.

Newaves Pub, (Newaves Publishing; 0-930946), P.O. Box 5169, Santa Monica, CA 90405 (SAN 211-3422).

Newberry, (Newberry Library; 0-911028), 60 W. Walton St., Chicago, IL 60610 (SAN 203-7378) Tel 312-943-9090; Toll free: 800-621-2736.

Newbold Ent, (Newbold Enterprises; 0-9616906), 860 Paiute Ln., Susanville, CA 96130 (SAN 661-518X) Tel 916-257-2009.

Newbold Pub, (Newbold Publishing Inc.; 0-910945), 142-20 Franklin Ave., Flushing, NY 11355 (SAN 264-2514) Tel 718-463-2862.

Newbury Bk
See Newbury Bks

Newbury Bks, (Newbury Bks.; 0-912728; 0-912729), P.O. Box 29, Topsfield, MA 01983 (SAN 203-7386) Tel 617-887-5082.

Newbury Bks Inc
See Newbury Bks

†Newbury Hse, (Newbury Hse. Pubs.; 0-88377; 0-912066), 54 Church St., Cambridge, MA 02138 (SAN 202-9146) Tel 617-492-0670; Toll free: 800-343-1240; CIP.

†Newcastle Pub, (Newcastle Publishing Co., Inc.; 0-87877), 13419 Saticoy St., North Hollywood, CA 91605 (SAN 202-9154) Tel 818-873-3191; Orders to: P.O. Box 7589, Van Nuys, CA 91409 (SAN 202-9162); CIP.

Newconcept Pr, (Newconcept Pr., Inc.; 0-931231), P.O. Box 124, Emerson, NJ 07630 (SAN 689-1705) Tel 201-666-4225.

Newhouse Pr, (Newhouse Pr.; 0-918050), 146 N. Rampart Blvd., Los Angeles, CA 90026 (SAN 209-2689) Tel 213-383-1089; Orders to: P.O. Box 76145, Los Angeles, CA 90076 (SAN 209-2697).

Newlight Bks, (Newlight Bks.; 0-9615740), 911 Elden St., Herndon, VA 22070 (SAN 695-8575) Tel 703-471-7220.

Newmark Mgmt Inst, (Newmark Management Institute; 0-932767), 18345 Ventura Blvd., Suite 314, Tarzana, CA 91356 (SAN 688-5977) Tel 818-708-1244.

Newmark Pub, (Newmark Publishing Co.; 0-938539), P.O. Box 603, South Windsor, CT 06074 (SAN 661-4760); 729 Ellington Rd., South Windsor, CT 06074 (SAN 661-4779) Tel 203-282-7265.

†Newmarket, (Newmarket Pr.; 0-937858), Div. of Newmarket Publishing Co., 3 E. 48th St., New York, NY 10017 (SAN 217-2585) Tel 212-832-3575; Toll free: 800-257-7577; Dist. by: Harper & Row, Pubs., Inc., Keystone Industrial Pk., Scranton, PA 18512 (SAN 201-002X); CIP.

Newmarket Pub, (Newmarket Publishing Co.; 0-918315), P.O. Box 1624, Hoboken, NJ 07030 (SAN 657-2944) Tel 212-473-3652.

Newnes-Butterworth Imprint of Butterworth

Newport Bch Rent, (Newport Beach Rentals/Tours Inc.; 0-933796), P.O. Box 7223, Newport Beach, CA 92660 (SAN 222-402X).

Newport Beach, (Newport Beach Pubs; 0-9602980), 4001 Westerly Pl., Suite 106, Newport Beach, CA 92660 (SAN 213-1730) Tel 714-833-0512.

Newport Mesa Sch, (Newport-Mesa Unified Schl. District; 0-9614891), 600 Irvine Ave., Newport Harbor HS Library, Newport Beach, CA 92663 (SAN 693-1901) Tel 714-760-3328.

News & Features Imprint of R J Berg & Co

News & Letters, (News & Letters Committees; 0-914441), 59 E. Van Buren St., Suite 707, Chicago, IL 60605 (SAN 217-989X) Tel 312-663-0839.

News & Observer, (News and Observer, The; 0-935400), 215 S. McDowell St., Raleigh, NC 27602 (SAN 222-6189).

News Bks Intl, *(News Bks., International Inc.; 0-89730),* 6100 N. Keystone, Indianapolis, IN 46220 (SAN 676-8350) Tel 317-259-0569.

News Media Info, *(News Media Information Service; 0-932685),* 1325 E. Franklin Ave., Pomona, CA 91766 (SAN 687-8261) Tel 714-623-2402.

News Rev Pub, *(News Review Publishing Co.; 0-9607506),* 409 S. Jackson, P.O. Box 8187, Moscow, ID 83843 (SAN 239-7854) Tel 208-882-5561.

News-Tribune, *(News-Tribune, The; 0-939348),* P.O. Box 1116, Fort Worth, TX 76101 (SAN 220-178X) Tel 817-338-1055.

NewSage Press, *(NewSage Pr.; 0-939165),* P.O. Box 41038, Pasadena, CA 91104 (SAN 662-8370); 1250 N. Wilson, Pasadena, CA 91104 (SAN 662-8389) Tel 818-791-4122.

Newsgraphics Delmar Inc, *(Newsgraphics of Delmar, Inc.),* 125 Adams St., Delmar, NY 12054 (SAN 687-7478).

Newsletter Assn, *(Newsletter Assn. of America; 0-9610222),* Colorado Bldg., 1341 G St. NW, Suite 700, Washington, DC 20005 Tel 274-0826) Tel 202-347-5220.

Newsletter Inago, *(Newsletter Inago; 0-917835),* P.O. Box 7541, Tucson, AZ 85725 (SAN 657-1549) Tel 602-294-7031.

Newspaper Agcy, *(Newspaper Agency, Inc., The; 0-9607254),* 39 Burchell Blvd., Bay Shore, NY 11706 (SAN 239-2690).

Newspaper Bk
See Dynamo Inc

Newspaper Ent, *(Newspaper Enterprise Assn., Inc.; 0-915106),* 200 Park Ave., New York, NY 10166 (SAN 212-0615) Tel 212-692-3824. *Imprints:* Enterprise Pubns (Enterprise Publications).(Enterprise Pubns.).

Newspaper Guild, *(Newspaper Guild),* 1125 15th St., NW, Suite 550, Washington, DC 20005 (SAN 223-9353) Tel 202-296-2990.

Newspaper Serv, *(Newspaper Services; 0-918488),* P.O. Box 38, Storden, MN 56174 (SAN 209-6757) Tel 507-445-3210.

Newspaper Syn, *(Newspaper Syndication Specialists; 0-9615800),* P.O. Box 19654, Irvine, CA 92720 (SAN 696-5490).

NewTEK Indust, *(NewTEK Industries; 0-930437),* Subs. of Coastar Publishing Co., P.O. Box 46116, Hollywood, CA 90046 (SAN 670-9613) Tel 213-874-6669.

Newton, *(Newton, Fred P.),* 319 E. California, Gainesville, TX 76240 (SAN 217-2593).

Newton Pub, *(Newton Publishing; 0-930721),* Box 181, Middlebury, VT 05753 (SAN 677-2730) Tel 802-655-4621.

Newtowne Pub, *(Newtowne Publishing; 0-9615705),* P.O. Box 1882, Cambridge, MA 02238 (SAN 696-2645) Tel 617-354-0539.

Next Question, *(Next Question Please; 0-938527),* Rte. 2, P.O. Box 690, Metaline Falls, WA 99153 (SAN 661-1451) Tel 509-446-3255.

Nexus Pr, *(Nexus Press; 0-932526),* Div. of Nexus Contemporary Art Ctr., 608 Ralph McGill Blvd., Atlanta, GA 30312 (SAN 213-2265) Tel 404-577-3579.

Nexus WA, *(Nexus Press (Wa) 0-936666),* P.O. Box 911, Kirkland, WA 98083 (SAN 218-4621) Tel 206-822-5240; Dist. by: Pacific Pipeline, 19215 66th Ave. S., Kent, WA 98032 (SAN 208-2128) Tel 206-872-5523.

NFAIS, *(National Federation of Abstracting & Information Services; 0-942308),* 112 S. 16th St., 12th Fl., Philadelphia, PA 19102 (SAN 203-7394) Tel 215-563-2406.

NFCLC, *(National Federation of Christian Life Communities; 0-913605),* 3721 Westminster Pl., St. Louis, MO 63108 (SAN 276-4555) Tel 314-533-3185.

NFS Pr, *(NFS Pr.; 0-917986),* 243 Grand View Ave., San Francisco, CA 94114 (SAN 210-1831) Tel 415-282-5372.

NFSAIS
See NFAIS

NFSEEP, *(National Foundation for the Study of Equal Employment Policy; 0-916559),* 1015 15th St. NW, Suite 1200, Washington, DC 20005 (SAN 295-5245) Tel 202-789-8685.

NGCSA, *(National Guild of Community Schools of the Arts, Inc.),* P.O. Box 8018, Englewood, NJ 07631 (SAN 218-4966) Tel 201-871-3337.

NH Pub Co, *(New Hampshire Publishing Co.; 0-912274; 0-89725),* P.O. Box 70, Somersworth, NH 03878 (SAN 202-9189) Tel 603-692-3727.

NHI, *(National Health Insurance),* 1740 N St NW, Washington, DC 20036 (SAN 226-6008).

NHI Press, *(NHI Pr.; 0-9617115),* P.O. Box 825, Concord, NH 03301 (SAN 662-6874); 9 Tahanto St., Concord, NH 03301 (SAN 662-6882) Tel 603-224-3420.

NIA Techniques, *(NIA Techniques, Inc.; 0-939529),* 491 Lovell Ave., Mill Valley, CA 94941 (SAN 663-379X) Tel 415-381-8506.

Niagara U Pr, *(Niagara Univ. Pr.; 0-937656),* Niagara Univ., Niagara, NY 14109 (SAN 214-2139) Tel 716-285-1212.

Nichols Music, *(Nichols' Music; 0-932447),* 7625 E. Camelback Rd., Suite 418 B, Scottsdale, AZ 85251 (SAN 686-7979) Tel 602-945-2771; Dist. by: Baker & Taylor Co., Eastern Div., 50 Kirby Ave., Somerville, NJ 08876 (SAN 169-4901).

†Nichols Pub, *(Nichols Publishing Co.; 0-89397),* P.O. Box 96, New York, NY 10024 (SAN 212-0291) Tel 212-580-8079; *CIP.*

Nick Varner, *(Varner, Nick; 0-9607536),* P.O. Box 1309, Owensboro, KY 42302 (SAN 239-569X).

†Nicolas-Hays, *(Nicolas-Hays, Inc.; 0-89254),* P.O. Box 612, York Beach, ME 03910 (SAN 662-0949) Tel 207-363-4393; Dist. by: Samuel Weiser, Inc., P.O. Box 612, York Beach, ME 03910 (SAN 202-9588) Tel 207-363-4393; *CIP.*

Nicolaysen Art Mus, *(Nicolaysen Art Museum),* 596 N. Poplar, Casper, WY 82601 (SAN 279-8808) Tel 307-235-5247; Dist. by: University of Nebraska Press, 901 N. 17th St.,318 Nebraska Hall, Lincoln, NE 68588 (SAN 202-5337).

Nienstedt VP & L Smith, *(Nienstedt, Vermadel P. & Lynn Smith, Pubs.; 0-9613010),* 2429 Rigby Dr., Columbia, SC 29204 (SAN 292-5869) Tel 803-787-2536.

Nierenberg-Zeif, *(Nierenberg & Zeif Pubs.; 0-936305),* 230 Park Ave., New York, NY 10169 (SAN 697-3027) Tel 212-986-5555.

Nieves Pr, *(Nieves Press; 0-9612008),* P.O. Box 2205, Sta. One, Kingsville, TX 78363 (SAN 286-8385) Tel 512-477-3910.

Night Horn Books, *(Night Horn Books; 0-941842),* 495 Ellis St., Box 1156, San Francisco, CA 94102 (SAN 239-2704) Tel 415-431-6198.

Night Owl Pr, *(Night Owl Press; 0-9612902),* 1758 Hewitt Ave., St. Paul, MN 55104 (SAN 291-3127) Tel 612-646-8746.

Night Owl Pub, *(Night Owl Publishing; 0-9616237),* Div. of Night Owl, Inc., P.O. Box 1776, Groton, CT 06340-0402 (SAN 658-5906); 33A Elderkin Ave., No. 2, Groton, CT 06340 (SAN 658-5914) Tel 203-445-4063.

Night Tree Pr, *(Night Tree Pr.; 0-935939),* 414 W. Thomas St., Rome, NY 13440 (SAN 661-4159) Tel 315-337-4142.

Nightbird CA, *(Nightbird Pr.; 0-9613435),* 110 Bucareli Dr., San Francisco, CA 94132 (SAN 656-9919) Tel 415-239-5262; Dist. by: Alchemy Books, 717 Market St., Suite 514, San Francisco, CA 94101 (SAN 211-304X) Tel 415-777-2197.

Nightbird Pr, *(Nightbird Pr.; 0-916023),* 208 W. 23rd St., P.O. Box 918, New York, NY 10011 (SAN 294-0744) Tel 212-255-6269.

Nighthawk Pr, *(Nighthawk Press; 0-936518),* Box 42265, Portland, OR 97242 (SAN 214-428X).

Nightingale Pr, *(Nightingale Press,The; 0-910705),* P.O. Box 6586, Gulfport, MS 39501 (SAN 260-2350) Tel 601-896-6819.

Nightingale Res, *(Nightingale Resources; 0-911389),* P.O. Box322, Cold Spring, NY 10516 (SAN 274-1016) Tel 914-265-3282.

Nightjar Pr, *(Nightjar Pr.; 0-938751),* New Mexico State Univ., Box 3E, Las Cruces, NM 88003 (SAN 661-549X) Tel 505-522-2590.

Nightmare Alley, *(Nightmare Alley Productions),* P.O. Box 10806, South Lake Tahoe, CA 95731 (SAN 207-642X).

Nightowl, *(Press of the Nightowl; 0-912960),* 320 Snapfinger Dr., Athens, GA 30605 (SAN 205-6364) Tel 404-353-7719.

Nightphlyte, *(Nightphlyte Creations; 0-9616514),* 2270 Madison Rd., Apt. 4C, Cincinnati, OH 45208 (SAN 659-526X) Tel 513-871-4160.

Nightsun Bks Imprint **of Adler Pub Co**

NIJD Colorado, *(National Institute of Judicial Dynamics),* 411 Lakewood Cir., Suite B711, Colorado Springs, CO 80910 (SAN 224-2311) Tel 303-574-2082.

Nike Pr, *(Nike Pr.; 0-9613960),* P.O. Box 9089, Fountain Valley, CA 92728 (SAN 682-305X) Tel 714-895-4689.

Nikki Pr, *(Nikki Press; 0-943148),* 6 Heath St., Eatontown, NJ 07724 (SAN 240-7361) Tel 201-222-9343.

Nikmal Pub, *(Nikmal Publishing),* 698 River St., Mattapan, MA 02126 (SAN 219-2241) Tel 617-361-2101; 698 River St., Mattapan, MA 02126 (SAN 662-0957); Orders to: 20 Park Plaza, Rm. 480, Boston, MA 02116 (SAN 200-710X) Tel 617-542-8689.

†Nilgiri Pr, *(Nilgiri Pr.; 0-915132),* P.O. Box 477, Petaluma, CA 94953 (SAN 207-6853) Tel 707-878-2369; *CIP.*

Nilles Pub, *(Nilles Publishing; 0-9613683),* 303 N. Main, Newberg, OR 97132 (SAN 687-746X).

NILS Pub, *(NILS Publishing Co.; 0-89246),* Subs. of Capital Cities/ABC, 21625 Prairie St., Chatsworth, CA 91311 (SAN 695-6246) Tel 818-998-8830; Toll free: 800-423-5910.

NIMR, *(National Institute on Mental Retardation),* Kinsmen Bldg., York Univ. Campus, 4700 Keele St., Downsview, ON M3J 1P3, (SAN 273-5733) Tel 416-661-9611.

†Nimrod Pr, *(Nimrod Pr.),* 170 Brookline Ave., Boston, MA 02215 (SAN 237-8973); *CIP.*

Nin-Ra Ent, *(Nin-Ra Enterprises; 0-933276),* 1721 La Barranca Rd., La Canada, CA 91011 (SAN 214-1957) Tel 818-790-7137.

Nina & Zelik, *(Nina & Zelik, Inc.; 0-9616558),* 4222 Ethel Ave., Suite 24, Studio City, CA 91604 (SAN 659-5278) Tel 818-981-5263.

Nine Hundred-Ten Pr, *(910 Press; 0-9606736),* P.O. Box 22361, San Francisco, CA 94122 (SAN 219-659X) Tel 415-752-6684.

Nineteenth Cent, *(Nineteenth Century Club),* 1433 Union, Memphis, TN 38104 (SAN 217-2925) Tel 901-274-4174.

Nineteenth Hole, *(Nineteenth Hole International),* 2620 Senate Dr., Lansing, MI 48912 (SAN 223-9388).

Ninja Pr, *(Ninja Pr.; 0-9614597),* 14429 Greenleaf St., Sherman Oaks, CA 91423 (SAN 691-7887) Tel 818-906-9972.

Ninth Hse Pr
See ENR Word

Ninth Sign, *(Ninth Sign Pubns.; 0-930840),* M-525, Hoboken, NJ 07030 (SAN 210-9301).

Ninth St Ctr, *(Ninth Street Ctr., Inc.; 0-932961),* 319 E. Ninth St., New York, NY 10003 (SAN 695-6777).

Niota Pr, *(Niota Pr.; 0-9614973),* 1633 Pullan Ave., Cincinnati, OH 45223 (SAN 693-5567) Tel 513-542-4645.

Nippon, *(Nippon Shuppan Hanbai U.S.A., Inc.),* 1123 Dominguez St., Unit K, Carson, CA 90746 (SAN 670-6797).

NISBCO, *(National Interreligious Service Board for Conscientious Objectors),* 800 18th St., NW, Suite 600, Washington, DC 20006 (SAN 218-8589) Tel 202-293-5962.

NISC, *(National Intelligence Study Ctr.; 0-938450),* 1800 K St. NW, Suite 1102, Washington, DC 20036 (SAN 216-0005).

Nittany Press, *(Nittany Pr.; 0-9613823),* Box 702, State College, PA 16804 (SAN 679-1824).

†Nitty Gritty, *(Nitty Gritty Productions; 0-911954),* P.O. Box 2008, Benicia, CA 94510 (SAN 202-9197) Tel 707-746-0800; *CIP.*

NIU Ctr Govmt, *(Northern Illinois Univ. Ctr. for Governmental Studies),* 143 N. Third St., DeKalb, IL 60115 (SAN 227-0439) Tel 815-753-1901.

NJ Assocs, *(New Jersey Assocs.; 0-911273),* Box 505, Montclair, NJ 07042 (SAN 285-0702) Tel 201-746-2000.

NJ DOE, *(New Jersey Dept. of Education; 0-916855),* 225 W. State St., CN 500, Trenton, NJ 08625 (SAN 654-3138) Tel 609-292-5850.

†NJ Hist Soc, *(New Jersey Historical Society; 0-911020),* 230 Broadway, Newark, NJ 07104 (SAN 205-7131) Tel 201-483-3939; *CIP.*

NJ Inst CLE, *(New Jersey Institute for Continuing Legal Education; 0-939457),* 15 Washington St., Suite 1400, Newark, NJ 07101 (SAN 226-997X) Tel 201-648-5571.

NJ Intl Inc, *(N. J. International, Inc.; 0-934088),* 77 W. Nicholai St., Hicksville, NY 11801 (SAN 220-9276) Tel 516-433-8720.

NJ Law Journal
See Law Enforce Ref

NJ Schl Bds, *(New Jersey Schl. Board Assn.; 0-912337),* P.O. Box 909, Trenton, NJ 08605 (SAN 226-1847) Tel 609-695-7600.

NJ State Mus, *(New Jersey State Museum; 0-938766),* 205 W. State St., Trenton, NJ 08625 (SAN 220-2638) Tel 609-292-6300.

NL Assoc Inc, *(Levy, Nathan, Assocs. Inc.; 0-9608240),* P.O. Box 1199, Hightstown, NJ 08520 (SAN 240-3951) Tel 201-329-6981.

NLB *Imprint of* Doubleday

NM Philatelist
See Hobby Pub Serv

NM St U Ctr Real Est, *(New Mexico State Univ., Center for Real Estate & Land Resource Research; 0-934471),* Div. of New Mexico State Univ., New Mexico State Univ., Box 3 Rea, Las Cruces, NM 88001 (SAN 693-7640) Tel 505-646-5176.

NMSEA, *(NMSEA; 0-942372),* P.O. Box 2004, Santa Fe, NM 87504 (SAN 240-0502).

†NMSU CLAS, *(New Mexico State Univ., Ctr. for Latin American Studies; 0-937793),* Campus Box 3JBR, Las Cruces, NM 88003 (SAN 659-3607) Tel 505-646-3254; 1200 University Ave., Las Cruces, NM 88003 (SAN 659-3615); *CIP.*

NNC, *(National Nutrition Consortium),* 24 Third St., NE, Suite 200, Washington, DC 20002 (SAN 260-2903) Tel 202-547-4819.

No Amer Youth, *(North American Youth Sport Institute; 0-937412),* 4985 Oak Garden Dr., Kernersville, NC 27284 (SAN 692-9435) Tel 919-784-4926.

†No Country Comm Coll, *(North Country Community College Press; 0-940280),* 20 Winona Ave., Box 89, Saranac Lake, NY 12983 (SAN 217-5479) Tel 518-891-2915; *CIP.*

No Dead Lines, *(No Dead Lines; 0-931832),* 261 Hamilton, No. 320D, Palo Alto, CA 94301 (SAN 211-6103) Tel 415-321-0842.

No Secrets Pr, *(No Secrets Pr.; 0-936779),* 1020 Bush St., No. 10, San Francisco, CA 94109 (SAN 696-3404) Tel 415-775-9979; Dist. by: The New Leaf Distributing, 1020 White St., SW, Atlanta, GA 30310 (SAN 662-3727) Tel 404-755-2665.

Noble
See Bowmar-Noble

Noble Hse, *(Noble House Publishing; 0-9603490),* 256 S. Robertson, Beverly Hills, CA 90211 (SAN 213-4225) Tel 213-659-4210.

Noblevision Inc, *(NobleVision, Inc.; 0-918525),* P.O. Box 452, Mays Landing, NJ 08330 (SAN 657-2146) Tel 609-625-3246.

Nodin Pr, *(Nodin Pr.; 0-931714),* c/o The Bookmen, Inc., 525 N. Third St., Minneapolis, MN 55401 (SAN 204-398X) Tel 612-333-6300.

Noe, *(Noe, Fay, Estate of; 0-9600208),* Orders to: Vivian Kirkwood, HCRI Box 155, Ellis Prairie, MO 65444 (SAN 662-0965) Tel 417-967-2125.

Noells Ark, *(Noell's Ark Pub.; 0-9602422),* P.O. Box 396, Tarpon Springs, FL 35589 (SAN 213-7801) Tel 813-937-8683.

Noise Control, *(Noise Control Foundation; 0-931784),* P.O. Box 2469, Arlington Branch, Poughkeepsie, NY 12603 (SAN 215-2193) Tel 914-462-6719.

Noit Amrofer, *(Noit Amrofer Publishing Co.; 0-932998),* 5706 30th Ave. NE, Seattle, WA 98105 (SAN 212-3738).

†NOK Pubs, *(NOK Pubs., Intl.; 0-88357),* 150 Fifth Ave., New York, NY 10011 (SAN 205-7522) Tel 212-675-5785; *CIP.*

Nolo Pr, *(Nolo Pr.; 0-917316; 0-87337),* 950 Parker St., Berkeley, CA 94710 (SAN 206-7935) Tel 415-549-1976.

NOLPE, *(National Organization on Legal Problems of Education),* 3601 SW 29th St., Suite 223, Topeka, KS 66614 (SAN 226-6105) Tel 913-273-3550.

Non Fiction Pubns, *(Non-Fiction Pubns. Corp.; 0-913279),* P.O. Box 129, Island Park, NY 11558 (SAN 285-9106) Tel 516-431-2933; Dist. by: Icea Bk. Center, P.O. Box 20048, Minneapolis, MN 55420 (SAN 285-9114) Tel 612-854-8660; Dist. by: The Baker & Taylor Co., Western Div., 380 Edison Way, Reno, NV 89564 (SAN 169-4464) Tel 702-786-6700; Dist. by: Baker & Taylor Co., Midwest Div., 501 Gladiola Ave., Momence, IL 60954 (SAN 169-2100); Dist. by: Baker & Taylor Co., Eastern Div., 50 Kirby Ave., Somerville, NJ 08876 (SAN 169-4901); Dist. by: Baker & Taylor CO., Southeast Div., Mt. Olive Rd., Commerce, GA 30529 (SAN 669-3369); Dist. by: Taylor-Carlisle Booksellers, 245 Seventh Ave., New York, NY 10001 (SAN 285-9564) Tel 212-255-8702.

†Non-Stop Bks, *(Non-Stop Bks.; 0-936816),* 105 Imperial Ave., Bennington, VT 05201 (SAN 214-4298); *CIP.*

Noname Pr, *(Noname Pr.; 0-9617328),* 5200 Klingle St. NW, Washington, DC 20016 (SAN 203-1639) Tel 202-244-6243.

Nonpareil Bks *Imprint of* Godine

Nonviol & Children, *(Friends Peace Committee, Nonviolence & Children Program; 0-9605062),* Div. of Philadelphia Yearly Meeting, 1515 Cherry St., Philadelphia, PA 19102 (SAN 215-868X) Tel 215-241-7239.

Nook Pubs, *(Nook Pubs., The; 0-938339),* P.O. Box 4282, Shreveport, LA 71134 (SAN 661-2830); 937 College St., Shreveport, LA 71104 (SAN 661-2849) Tel 318-222-3029.

Noon Rock, *(Noon Rock; 0-9602934),* Station Hill Rd., Barrytown, NY 12507 (SAN 213-8611) Tel 914-758-1221.

Noontide, *(Noontide Pr., The; 0-911038; 0-939482),* P.O. Box 1248, Torrance, CA 90505 (SAN 213-1307). Imprints: Chr Bk Club (Christian Book Club of America); Inst Hist Rev (Institute for Historical Review); IAAEE (I A A E E).(IAAEE); N League (Northern League); New Voices (New Voices); Samisdat (Samisdat Publishers Ltd.).(Samisdat Pubs. Ltd.); Uriel Pubns (Uriel Publications).(Uriel Pubns); Vanguard (Vanguard Books).

Norawell Pubs, *(Norawell Pubs.; 0-9602118),* 1229 Golden Gate Blvd., Cleveland, OH 44124 (SAN 212-3754).

Norbeck Res, *(Norbeck Research),* 117 Ruch St., Coplay, PA 18037 (SAN 692-7343) Tel 215-262-8779.

Norblo Co, *(Norblo Co.; 0-933509),* The Arcade, 9th Flr. No. 3, Euclid Ave., Cleveland, OH 44114 (SAN 692-3992) Tel 216-566-1414.

NORC, *(National Opinion Research Ctr.; 0-932132),* 6030 S. Ellis Ave., Chicago, IL 60637 (SAN 205-7735) Tel 312-962-1213.

Nordbook, *(Nordbook; 0-9616967),* 3644 34th Ave., S., Minneapolis, MN 55406 (SAN 661-7514) Tel 612-729-6346.

Nordic Bks, *(Nordic Bks.; 0-933748),* P.O. Box 1941, Philadelphia, PA 19105 (SAN 212-5323) Tel 215-464-4186.

Nordic Ski, *(Nordic Ski Press; 0-9610410),* Box 36, Norden, CA 95724 (SAN 239-4650).

Nordic Trans, *(Nordic Translators; 0-938500),* 1747 Holton St., St. Paul, MN 55113 (SAN 239-9199) Tel 612-645-8352.

Nordland Her Found, *(Nordland Heritage Foundation; 0-9604816),* Humanities Box 2170, Augustana College, Sioux Falls, SD 57197 (SAN 276-9662).

Norfolk Port, *(Norfolk Port & Industrial Authority; 0-9605682),* P. O. Box 249, Wayne, PA 19087 (SAN 216-2741); Dist. by: International Society for General Semantics, 834 Mission St., 2nd Flr., San Francisco, CA 94103 (SAN 203-8161) Tel 415-543-1747.

Norman & Sandra, *(Norman & Sandra; 0-936520),* 1010 Village Lane, Orient, NY 11957-0218 (SAN 220-0252) Tel 516-323-3602.

Norman Pub, *(Norman Publishing Co.; 0-9601788),* 52 Toms Point Lane, Lincoln Park, NJ 07035 (SAN 212-2944) Tel 201-696-2256.

Normandie, *(Normandie Publishing Co., The; 0-9602986),* 225 W. 86th St., Suite 805, New York, NY 10024 (SAN 213-1315) Tel 212-873-5433.

Normandy Pubns, *(Normandy Square Pubns.; 0-916399),* 1125 Grand, Suite 500, Kansas City, MO 64106 (SAN 295-7337) Tel 816-471-1060.

Normark Corp, *(Normark Corp.),* 1710 E. 78th St., Minneapolis, MN 55423 (SAN 209-3006) Tel 612-869-3293.

Norns Pub Co, *(Norns Publishing Co./Green Turtle Pubns.; 0-939960),* P.O. Box 17925, Plantation, FL 33318 (SAN 216-8456) Tel 305-474-1318; Orders to: Green Turtle Pubns., P.O. Box 17925, Plantation, FL 33318 (SAN 693-9694).

Norris Assocs Pr, *(Norris Assocs. Pr.; 0-931569),* 215 Palisades Dr., Santa Barbara, CA 93109-1943 (SAN 682-1774) Tel 805-962-7703.

Norse Pr, *(Norse Press; 0-9602692; 0-9613274),* 909 E. 35th St, Sioux Falls, SD 57105 (SAN 221-7686) Tel 605-336-6055; Toll free: 800-843-1300.

Norseman Pub, *(Norseman Publishing Co.; 0-9613202),* P.O Box 6617, Lubbock, TX 79493-6617 (SAN 295-7507) Tel 806-795-9875.

Nortex Pr
See Eakin Pubns

North Am Edit, *(North American Editions; 0-933967),* 101 Phillips Rd., Holden, MA 01520 (SAN 693-0719) Tel 617-829-2330.

North Am Fal Hunt, *(North American Falconry & Hunting Hawks; 0-912510),* P.O. Box 1484, Denver, CO 80201 (SAN 203-7440) Tel 303-797-0442.

North Am Intl, *(North American International; 0-88265),* P.O. Box 21012, Washington, DC 20009 (SAN 202-9200) Tel 202-462-1776.

North Am Mfg Co, *(North American Manufacturing Company; 0-9601596),* 4455 E. 71st St., Cleveland, OH 44105 (SAN 222-0946).

†North Am Pub Co, *(North American Publishing Co.; 0-912920),* 401 N. Broad St., Philadelphia, PA 19108 (SAN 203-1647) Tel 215-238-5300; *CIP.*

North Am Rev, *(North American Review Pr.; 0-915996),* Univ. of Iowa, Cedar Falls, IA 50614 (SAN 206-0760) Tel 319-273-2681.

North Amer Veg, *(North American Vegetarian Society; 0-9615401),* Sweet Hill Rd., P.O. Box 72, Dolgeville, NY 13329 (SAN 695-4685) Tel 518-568-7970.

†North American Inc, *(North American, Inc.; 0-930244),* P.O. Box 65, New Brunswick, NJ 08903 (SAN 210-6469) Tel 201-246-8546; *CIP.*

†North Atlantic, *(North Atlantic Bks.; 0-938190; 0-913028; 1-55643),* Div. of Society of the Study of Native Arts & Science, 2320 Blake St., Berkeley, CA 94704 (SAN 203-1655) Tel 415-540-7934; *CIP.*

North Beach Pr, *(North Beach Pr.; 0-935093),* 524 Union St., San Francisco, CA 94133 (SAN 695-0019) Tel 415-982-8432.

North Bks, *(North Bks.; 0-939495),* P.O. Box 337, Peace Dale, RI 02883 (SAN 663-4052); 39 North Road, Peace Dale, RI 02883 (SAN 663-4060) Tel 401-783-4320.

†North Castle, *(North Castle Bks., Inc.; 0-911040),* 212 Bedford Rd., Greenwich, CT 06831 (SAN 202-9219) Tel 203-869-7766; *CIP.*

North Central, *(North Central Publishing Co.; 0-935476),* Riverview Industrial Park, 274 Fillmore Ave. East, St. Paul, MN 55107 (SAN 203-7459) Tel 612-224-5455. Imprints: Soc German-Amer Studies (Society for German-American Studies).

North Central Assn Colls & Schls
See NCACS Boulder

North Coast Pubs, *(North Coast Publishing; 0-912269),* 18428 Parkland Dr., Shaker Heights, OH 44122 (SAN 265-0703) Tel 216-561-1763.

North Country, *(North Country Bks., Inc.; 0-932052),* P.O. Box 506, Sylvan Beach, NY 13157 (SAN 287-0231) Tel 315-762-5140; 18 Irving Pl., Utica, NY 13501 (SAN 287-024X) Tel 315-735-4877.

North Frontier Pr, *(North Frontier Pr.; 0-933309),* P.O. Box 11450, Chicago, IL 60611 (SAN 692-297X) Tel 312-472-8051; Dist. by: Puett Electronics, P.O. Box 28572, Dallas, TX 75228 (SAN 205-4035) Tel 214-321-0927.

North Gull Pub, *(North Gull Publishing; 0-936753),* 3 Lamson Pl., Cambridge, MA 02139 (SAN 699-9816) Tel 617-492-3148.

North-Holland
See Elsevier

North Holland *Imprint of* Elsevier

North Ill U Ctr SE Asian, *(Center for SE Asian Studies, Northern Illinois Univ.),* Dist. by: Cellar Book Shop, 18090 Wyoming, Detroit, MI 48221 (SAN 213-4330) Tel 313-861-1776.

North Lake Prod, *(North Lake Productions; 0-9601722),* 9732 Boucher Dr., Otter Lake, MI 48464 (SAN 212-1980) Tel 517-795-2250.

†North Light Bks, *(North Light Bks.; 0-89134),* Div. of F & W Pubns., Inc., 9933 Alliance Rd., Cincinnati, OH 45242 (SAN 287-0274) Tel 513-984-0717; Toll free: 800-543-4644; *CIP.*

North Light Pub
See North Light Bks

North Pacific, *(North Pacific Pubs.; 0-913138),* P.O. Box 13255, Portland, OR 97213 (SAN 203-7467) Tel 503-236-9343.

North Plains, *(North Plains Pr.; 0-87970),* Div. of Dakota North Plains Corp., P.O. Box 1830, Aberdeen, SD 57402-1830 (SAN 202-9243); 1216 S. Main St., Aberdeen, SD 57401 (SAN 660-9392) Tel 605-225-5360.

North Pub, *(North Publishing; 0-9613355),* 3030 14th Ave. West, Suite 205, Seattle, WA 98119 (SAN 656-1616) Tel 206-624-6271.

North Ridge Bks, *(North Ridge Bks.; 0-937813),* P.O. Box 13401, Akron, OH 44313-8801 (SAN 659-3828) Tel 216-864-8786; 84 Sand Run Rd., Akron, OH 44313 (SAN 659-3836).

†North River, *(North River Pr., Inc.; 0-88427),* P.O. Box 241, Croton-on-Hudson, NY 10520 (SAN 202-1048) Tel 914-941-7175; *CIP.*

North Scale Co, *(North Scale Institute Publishing Co.; 0-916299),* P.O. Box 27555, San Francisco, CA 94127 (SAN 295-7418) Tel 415-731-5819; 2440 15th Ave., San Francisco, CA 94116 (SAN 295-7426).

North South Bks *Imprint of* H Holt & Co

†North Star, *(North Star Pr.; 0-87839),* P.O. Box 451, St. Cloud, MN 56302-0451 (SAN 203-7491) Tel 612-253-1636; *CIP.*

North Valley, *(North Valley Diver Publications; 0-911615),* 585 Royal Oak Dr., Redding, CA 96001 (SAN 264-2557) Tel 916-246-2009; Orders to: P.O. Box 6007, Suite 166, Redding, CA 96099 (SAN 662-0981).

North West Bk, *(North West Bk. Arts; 0-937631),* 18215 Ballinger Way, NE, Seattle, WA 98155 (SAN 658-9928) Tel 206-365-2907.

Northcountry Pub, *(Northcountry Publishing Co.; 0-930366),* 50 S. Cretin Ave., St. Paul, MN 55105 (SAN 211-061X) Tel 612-699-3102; Orders to: 1509 Fillmore St., Alexandria, MN 56308 (SAN 662-099X) Tel 612-763-3874.

Northcross Hse, *(Northcross Hse.; 0-9617256),* Rte. 1, Box 12-A, Elliston, VA 24087 (SAN 663-5725) Tel 703-268-5005.

Northeast A S, *(Northeast Academic Services, Inc.; 0-913811),* 10 Lydia Dr., Wappingers, NY 12590 (SAN 286-1372) Tel 914-297-6389.

†Northeast Sportsmans, *(Northeast Sportsman's Pr.; 0-942990),* P.O. Box 188, Tarrytown, NY 10591 (SAN 238-8219); *CIP.*

Northeastern Pub, *(Northeastern Publishing Co., Inc.; 0-933389),* 1378 President St., Brooklyn, NY 11213 (SAN 691-683X) Tel 718-756-1708.

Northern Cal, *(Northern California Grantmakers),* 334 Kearny St., San Francisco, CA 94108 (SAN 287-2706) Tel 415-788-2982.

Northern Mich, *(Northern Michigan Univ. Pr.; 0-918616),* 607 Cohodas Administrative Ctr., Marquette, MI 49855 (SAN 205-3748) Tel 906-227-2720; Orders to: NMU Bookstore, Don H. Bottum University Ctr., Marquette, MI 49855 (SAN 205-3756) Tel 906-227-2480.

Northern Pr, *(Northern Press),* 18 Cedar St., Potsdam, NY 13676 (SAN 211-7495).

†Northland, *(Northland Pr.; 0-87358),* Div. of Justin Industries, P.O. Box N, Flagstaff, AZ 86002 (SAN 202-9251) Tel 602-774-5251; Toll free: 800-FINE-BKS; Toll free: 800-46-BOOKS (AZ); *CIP.*

Northland Pubns
See Northland Pubns WA

Northland Pubns WA, *(Northland Pubns.),* P.O. Box 12157, Seattle, WA 98102 (SAN 210-931X)

Northland WI, *(Northland Publishing Co.; 0-939834),* Rte. 4, Box 110, Menomonie, WI 54751 (SAN 216-9193) Tel 715-235-9434.

Northlands MI, *(Northlands Press; 0-918808),* 2723 Lake Lansing Rd., East Lansing, MI 48823 (SAN 210-3176) Tel 517-332-4274.

Northstar Comm Inc
See Northstar-Maschek

Northstar-Maschek, *(Northstar Maschek A.G.; 0-910667),* P.O. Box 810, Lakeville, MN 55044-0810 (SAN 274-1911) Tel 612-469-5433; Dist. by: Northstar Commemoratives, Inc., P.O. Box 803, Lakeville, MN 55044-0803 (SAN 200-6545).

Northstar Pub, *(Northstar Publishing Co.; 0-938255),* P.O. Box 9151, San Jose, CA 95157 (SAN 661-3632); 5676 McKellar Dr., San Jose, CA 95129 (SAN 661-3640) Tel 408-257-1925.

Northumberland Pr, *(Northumberland Pr.; 0-934565),* 1717 Blvd. of the Allies, Pittsburgh, PA 15219 (SAN 693-854X) Tel 412-281-6179.

Northwest Denver, *(Northwest Denver Bks.; 0-9616057),* 2800 Vrain St., Denver, CO 80212 (SAN 698-1100) Tel 303-455-9042.

Northwest Home, *(Northwest Home Designing, Inc.; 0-936909),* 10901 Bridgeport Way, SW, Tacoma, WA 98499 (SAN 658-3725) Tel 206-584-6309.

†Northwest Learn, *(Northwest Learning Associates, Inc.; 0-931836),* 5728 N. Via Umbrosa, Tucson, AZ 85715 (SAN 211-6251) Tel 602-299-8435; *CIP.*

Northwest Memorial, *(Northwestern Memorial Hospital; 0-9605996),* 215 E. Chicago Ave Rm 1206, Chicago, IL 60611 (SAN 216-7549) Tel 312-649-7432.

Northwest Panorama, *(Northwest Panorama Publishing, Inc.; 0-9613787),* Box 1858, Bozeman, MT 59715 (SAN 678-9846); Toll free: 800-547-2525.

Northwest Pub, *(Northwestern Publishing House; 0-8100),* 3624 W. North Ave., Milwaukee, WI 53208 (SAN 206-7943) Tel 414-442-1810.

Northwest Regional, *(Northwest Regional Educational Laboratory; 0-89354),* 300 SW Sixth Ave., Portland, OR 97204 (SAN 208-9998) Tel 503-248-6800.

Northwest Res, *(Northwest Resources; 0-9614579),* 1617 E. Bay Dr., Olympia, WA 98506 (SAN 664-3488) Tel 206-943-5048.

Northwestern U Pr, *(Northwestern Univ. Pr.; 0-8101),* P.O. Box 1093, Evanston, IL 60201 (SAN 202-5787); Orders to: 1735 Benson Ave., Evanston, IL 60201 (SAN 669-2222) Tel 312-491-5313. *Imprints:* Trans (Transportation Center Publications).(Transportation Ctr. Pubns.).

Northwood Campus Bkstore
See Northwood Inst Pr

Northwood Inst
See Northwood Inst Pr

†Northwood Inst Pr, *(Northwood Institute Pr.; 0-87359),* 110 W. Signet, Midland, MI 48640 (SAN 202-098X) Tel 517-631-1600; *CIP.*

Northwoods IL, *(Northwoods Country Collection; 0-936847),* 24435 W. Blvd. de John, Plainfield, IL 60544 (SAN 658-3709) Tel 815-436-9234.

†Northword, *(Northword; 0-942802),* P.O. Box 5634, Madison, WI 53705 (SAN 240-4842) Tel 608-231-2355; Dist. by: Hazel Rice, 1206 Dartmouth Rd., Madison, WI 53705 (SAN 200-6928) Tel 608-233-6543; *CIP.*

†Norton, *(Norton, W. W., & Co., Inc.; 0-393),* 500 Fifth Ave., New York, NY 10110 (SAN 202-5795) Tel 212-354-5500; Toll free: 800-223-2584; *CIP. Imprints:* Norton Lib (Norton Library); NortonC (Norton College Division).(Norton College Div.); NAL (New American Library).

†Norton Art, *(Norton, R. W., Art Gallery; 0-913060; 0-9600182),* 4747 Creswell Ave., Shreveport, LA 71106 (SAN 213-7569) Tel 318-865-4201; *CIP.*

Norton Gal Art, *(Norton Gallery & School of Art),* 1451 S. Olive Ave., West Palm Beach, FL 33401 (SAN 279-926X); Dist. by: Publishing Center for Cultural Resources, 625 Broadway, New York, NY 10012 (SAN 692-8188).

Norton Lib *Imprint of* Norton

NortonC *Imprint of* Norton

Norwalk Pr *Imprint of* O'Sullivan Woodside

Norway Bks, *(Norway Books; 0-939648),* P.O. Box 2010, Sparks, NV 89431 (SAN 216-4248).

Norwegian-Am Hist Assn, *(Norwegian-American Historical Assn.; 0-87732),* St. Olaf College, Northfield, MN 55057 (SAN 203-1086) Tel 507-663-3221.

Nor'Westing, *(Nor'Westing Inc.; 0-931923),* P.O. Box 375, Edmonds, WA 98020 (SAN 686-0028) Tel 206-776-3138.

Norwood
See Norwood Edns

†Norwood Edns, *(Norwood Editions; 0-88305; 0-8482),* P.O. Box 38, Norwood, PA 19074 (SAN 206-8613) Tel 215-583-4550; *CIP.*

Norwood-Fontbonne, *(Norwood/Fontbonne Home & School Assn.; 0-9614938),* 8891 Germantown Ave., Dept "C", Philadelphia, PA 19118 (SAN 689-0520) Tel 215-242-3199.

Nosbooks, *(Nosbooks; 0-911046),* 42 W. 88th St., New York, NY 10024 (SAN 203-7513).

Nostos Bks, *(Nostos Bks.; 0-932963),* Box 19086, Minneapolis, MN 55419 (SAN 689-1500) Tel 612-825-0387.

Nottingham Pr, *(Nottingham Press; 0-913958),* 1448 Page St., Alameda, CA 94501 (SAN 203-7521) Tel 415-522-4547.

Nourishing Thoughts, *(Nourishing Thoughts Enterprises; 0-9601198),* 1837 Beech St., Stow, OH 44224 (SAN 210-9298).

Nova, *(Nova, Inc.; 0-9612264),* 1560 Broadway, Rm. 807, New York, NY 10036 (SAN 289-5374) Tel 212-869-3050.

Nova-NYIT U Pr, *(Nova Univ. Press; 0-917736),* College Ave., Fort Lauderdale, FL 33314 (SAN 211-6111) Tel 305-475-7300.

Nova Pub IL, *(Nova Publishing Co.; 0-935755),* P.O. Box 101, Wheaton, IL 60189-0101 (SAN 695-8117) Tel 618-392-2406.

Nova U Pr
See Nova-NYIT U Pr

Novel Ideas, *(Novel Ideas, Inc.; 0-914059),* 3499 Bunker Ave., Wantagh, NY 11793 (SAN 277-6979) Tel 516-783-8833.

November Bks, *(November Books; 0-941098),* P.O. Box 6173, Santa Barbara, CA 93111 (SAN 217-409X) Tel 805-967-3185.

Nowfel, *(Nowfel Pubns.),* Dist. by: Intercontinental Enterprises Co., 69 Stewart Ave., Eastchester, NY 10707 (SAN 218-7914). Moved, left no forwarding address.

†Noyes, *(Noyes Data Corp./Noyes Pubns.; 0-8155),* Mill Rd. at Grand Ave., Park Ridge, NJ 07656 (SAN 209-2840) Tel 201-391-8484; *CIP. Imprints:* Noyes Pubns (Noyes Publications).(Noyes Pubns.); NAB (Noyes Art Books).(Noyes Art Bks.); NP (Noyes Press).(Noyes Pr.).

Noyes Pubns *Imprint of* Noyes

NP *Imprint of* Noyes

NPA, *(NPA; 0-88806),* 1606 New Hampshire Ave. NW, Washington, DC 20009 (SAN 239-538X).

NPC Pub Co, *(NPC Publishing Co.; 0-932634),* 17237 Hiawatha St., Granada Hills, CA 91344 (SAN 212-7814) Tel 213-363-8458.

NPD Corp, *(N.P.D. Corp.; 0-937230),* 939 Driver Cir., El Paso, TX 79903 (SAN 282-0676); 7701 N. Lamar Blvd., Austin, TX 78752 (SAN 282-0684) Tel 915-565-3001.

NPP Bks, *(NPP Books; 0-916182),* P.O. Box 1491, Ann Arbor, MI 48106-1491 (SAN 208-1067) Tel 313-971-7363.

NRCCLS, *(National Resource Ctr. for Consumers of Legal Services; 0-937271),* 3254 Jones Ct., NW, Washington, DC 20007 (SAN 226-1677) Tel 202-338-0714.

NS Pub Co Inc, *(North-South Publishing Co., Inc., The; 0-913897),* P.O. Box 610, Lanham, MD 20706 (SAN 286-8423) Tel 301-552-1098; 7011 Ren Lane, Lanham, MD 20706 (SAN 286-8431).

NSF, *(National Science Foundation),* 1800 G St., NW, Rm. 527, Washington, DC 20550 (SAN 233-0113) Tel 202-257-9498.

NSIEE, *(National Society for Internships & Experiential Education),* 122 St. Mary's St., Raleigh, NC 27605 (SAN 659-5251) Tel 919-834-7536.

NSLTIGT, *(National State Leadership Training Institute on Gifted & Talented),* One Wilshire Bldg., 624 S. Grand Ave., Suite 1007, Los Angeles, CA 90017-3311 (SAN 260-3837) Tel 213-489-7470; Orders to: LTI Publications, 535 E. Main St., Ventura, CA 93009 (SAN 662-0906) Tel 805-652-7345.

NSU Pr LA, *(Northwestern State Univ. of Louisiana Press; 0-917898),* P.O. Box 5305, Natchitoches, LA 71497 (SAN 209-973X) Tel 318-357-4586.

NTL Inst, *(NTL Institute; 0-9610392),* P.O. Box 9155, Rosslyn Sta., Arlington, VA 22209 (SAN 223-9485) Tel 703-527-1500; 1501 Wilson Blvd., Suite 1000, Arlington, VA 22209 (SAN 669-2249).

Nu-Diet, *(Nu-Diet Enterprises; 0-9609896),* 1739 Blue Ash Place, P.O. Box 29250, Columbus, OH 43229 (SAN 274-2101) Tel 614-846-1423.

Nuance Pr, *(Nuance Pr. Intl.; 0-917924),* 32 E. Swan St., Columbus, OH 43215 (SAN 209-9748) Tel 614-221-1032.

Nuclear Info Res, *(Nuclear Information & Resource Service; 0-9615323),* 1616 P St., NW, Suite 160, Washington, DC 20036 (SAN 695-0140) Tel 202-328-0002.

Nuclear Project, *(Nuclear Negotiation Project; 0-9613615),* Harvard Law School, Pound Hall 513, Cambridge, MA 02138 (SAN 677-0630).

Nugget Ent, *(Nugget Enterprises; 0-931461),* 43930 228th Ave. SE, P.O. Box 184, Enumclaw, WA 98022 (SAN 683-1648) Tel 206-825-3855.

Numarc Bk Corp, *(Numarc Bk. Corp.; 0-88471),* 50 Alcona Ave., Buffalo, NY 14226 (SAN 206-8702) Tel 716-834-1390.

Numard Bks, *(Numard Bks.; 0-9612266),* 6005 Midnight Pass Rd., Sarasota, FL 34242 (SAN 289-4807) Tel 813-346-1396.

Numen Chapbks, *(Numen Chapbooks; 0-939162),* 3202 Ellerslie Ave., Baltimore, MD 21218 (SAN 216-4256).

Numer Algorithms, *(Numerical Algorithms Group, Inc.; 1-85206),* 1101 31st St., Suite 100, Downers Grove, IL 60515 (SAN 679-2693) Tel 312-971-2337.

Numismatic Fine Arts, *(Numismatic Fine Arts, Inc.),* 342 N. Rodeo Dr., Beverly Hills, CA 90212 (SAN 205-9029) Tel 213-278-1535; Orders to: P.O. Box 3788, Beverly Hills, CA 90212 (SAN 205-9037).

Nunciata, *(Nunciata Publishing),* P.O. Box 570122, Houston, TX 77257 (SAN 285-6883); Dist. by: Associated Advertisers Services, .

Nunes, *(Nunes, Leslie K.; 0-9604190),* 613 Kaimalino Place, Kailua, HI 96734 (SAN 219-9769) Tel 808-254-1242.

Nur Pubns, *(Nur-I-Alam Pubns.; 0-9608440),* 2331 N. Dunn St., Bloomington, IN 47401 (SAN 663-2963) Tel 812-339-5615; Dist. by: Worldwide Evangelization Crusade, 709 Pennsylvania Ave., Fort Washington, PA 19034 (SAN 276-8577) Tel 215-646-2322.

Nurseco
See Admates CA

Nurseline Assocs, *(Nurseline Assocs., Inc.; 0-9616339),* P.O. Box 66682, Seattle, WA 98166 (SAN 658-9979) Tel 206-242-9797; 2819 SW 169th St., Seattle, WA 98166 (SAN 658-9987).

Nurtury Fam, *(Nurtury Family School, The; 0-9610612),* 374 W. Baltimore, Larkspur, CA 94939 (SAN 264-262X) Tel 415-924-9675.

Nutri-Kinetic, *(Nutri-Kinetic Dynamics Inc.; 0-938478),* 850 Kam Hwy., Pearl City, HI 96782 (SAN 216-2768).

Nutrition Ed, *(Nutrition Education Center; 0-915187),* Subs. of C.L. Gerwick & Associates, Inc., 9500 Nall Ave., Suite 304, Overland Park, KS 66207 (SAN 289-7776) Tel 913-383-3464.

Nutrition Found, *(Nutrition Foundation, Inc.; 0-935604),* Office of Education, 888 17th St., NW, Washington, DC 20017 (SAN 224-3911).

Nutshell Enterprises, *(Nutshell Enterprises, Ltd.; 0-930723),* 3327 Charles St., Fallston, MD 20147 (SAN 677-6043) Tel 301-557-7583; Dist. by: Metra, P.O. Box 7130 University Station, Provo, UT (SAN 221-3885).

Nuttall Ornith, *(Nuttall Ornithological Club),* Harvard Univ., Museum of Comparative Zoology, Cambridge, MA 02138 (SAN 232-9123) Tel 617-495-2471.

Nuttall Ornithological
See Nuttall Ornith

NV Families Proj, *(Nevada Families Project; 0-9616633),* 1916 Maryland Pkwy., Las Vegas, NV 89104-3106 (SAN 661-2121) Tel 702-878-1742.

NV League Cities, *(Nevada League of Cities),* Box 2307, Carson City, NV 89701 (SAN 226-1782).

NW *Imprint of* **Intl Pubs Co**

NW Christian Pubns, *(Northwest Christian Pubns., Inc.; 0-914271),* P.O. Box 31133, Seattle, WA 98103 (SAN 287-5926) Tel 206-523-9911.

NW Hist Cons, *(Northwest Historical Consultants; 0-9609562),* 2780 26th St., Clarkston, WA 99403 (SAN 274-1989) Tel 509-758-5773; Dist. by: Pacific Pipeline, Inc., 19215 66th Ave. S., Kent, WA 98032 (SAN 208-2128) Tel 206-872-5523; Dist. by: Servatius News Agency, 601 2nd St., Clarkson, WA 99403 (SAN 169-8737).

NW Illus *Imprint of* **Hippocrene Bks**

NW Inst Taste, *(Northwestern Institute of Unquestionable Taste),* P.O. Box 264, Bend, OR 97709 (SAN 694-5406).

NW Intl, *(North West International Trading, Inc.),* P.O. Box 11483, Eugene, OR 97440 (SAN 264-2565) Tel 503-484-7060.

NW Mutual Life, *(Northwestern Mutual Life Insurance Co.; 0-9612010),* 720 E. Wisconsin Ave., Milwaukee, WI 53202 (SAN 286-844X) Tel 414-271-1444.

NW Panorama
See Northwest Panorama

NW Perfection Pub, *(Northwest Perfection Pubs.; 0-9616757),* 911 North L St., Tacoma, WA 98403 (SAN 661-3721) Tel 206-627-6506.

NW Plan Parent, *(Planned Parenthood of Northwest New Jersey, Inc.; 0-9609366),* Affil. of Planned Parenthood Federation of America, 196 Speedwell Ave., Morristown, NJ 07960-3889 (SAN 260-2482) Tel 201-539-9580.

†**NW Review Bks,** *(Northwest Review Bks.; 0-918402),* 369 PLC, Univ. of Oregon, Eugene, OR 97403 (SAN 209-9721) Tel 503-686-3957; *CIP.*

NW Silver Pr, *(Northwest Silver Pr.; 0-9610202),* 88 Cascade Key, Bellevue, WA 98006 (SAN 264-2581) Tel 206-643-0143.

NWR Pubns, *(N W R Pubns.; 0-916972),* 104-07 102nd St., Ozone Park, NY 11417 (SAN 208-4686).

†**NWU Astro,** *(Northwestern Univ. Dept. of Astronomy; 0-939160),* Dept. of Astronomy, Evanston, IL 60201 (SAN 217-2305); *CIP.*

†**NY Acad Sci,** *(New York Academy of Sciences; 0-89072; 0-89766),* Pubns. Dept., 2 E. 63rd St., New York, NY 10021 (SAN 203-753X) Tel 212-838-0230; Toll free: 800-843-6927; *CIP.*

†**NY Botanical,** *(New York Botanical Garden; 0-89327),* Scientific Pubns. Dept., Bronx, NY 10458 (SAN 205-7085) Tel 212-220-8721; *CIP.*

†**NY Bound,** *(New York Bound; 0-9608788),* 43 W. 54th St., New York, NY 10019 (SAN 238-3195) Tel 212-245-8503; *CIP.*

NY Chamber, *(New York Chamber of Commerce and Industry; 0-9613808),* 200 Madison Ave., New York, NY 10016 (SAN 679-405X) Tel 212-561-2176; 65 Liberty St., New York, NY 10005 (SAN 692-820X).

NY Chiro Coll, *(New York Chiropractic College; 0-938470),* P.O. Box 167, Glen Head, NY 11545 (SAN 216-1680).

NY Circus Pubns, *(New York Circus Pubns., Inc.),* P.O. Box 37, Times Sq. Sta., New York, NY 10108 (SAN 661-440X).

NY Hunting
See NY Outdoor Guide

NY Ind Labor, *(New York State School of Industrial & Labor Relations, Cornell Extension; 0-9615917),* 15 E. 26th St., New York, NY 10010 (SAN 696-6586) Tel 212-340-2800.

†**NY Inst Finance,** *(New York Institute of Finance),* 70 Pine St., New York, NY 10270-0003 (SAN 239-3697) Tel 212-344-2900; *CIP.*

NY Labor News, *(New York Labor News; 0-935534),* 914 Industrial Ave., Palo Alto, CA 94303 (SAN 202-0947) Tel 415-494-1532.

NY Law Journ, *(New York Law Journal),* 111 Eighth Ave., New York, NY 10011 (SAN 287-7023) Tel 212-741-8300. Microfilm & Microfiche.

NY Law Pub, *(New York Law Publishing Co.),* 111 Eighth Ave., New York, NY 10011 (SAN 226-2800) Tel 212-741-8300.

NY Lib Assn, *(New York Library Assn.; 0-931658),* 15 Park Row, Suite 434, New York, NY 10038 (SAN 211-6758) Tel 212-227-8032.

†**NY Lit Forum,** *(New York Literary Forum; 0-931196),* 21 E. 79th St., New York, NY 10021 (SAN 212-9221); *CIP.*

†**NY Lit Pr,** *(New York Literary Press; 0-930910),* 417 W. 56th St., New York, NY 10019 (SAN 211-5379); *CIP.*

NY-NJ Trail Confer, *(New York-New Jersey Trail Conference, Inc.; 0-9603966),* 232 Madison Ave., New York, NY 10016 (SAN 213-9421).

NY Outdoor Guide, *(New York Outdoor Guide, Inc.; 0-937328),* 328 E. Main, Rm. 300, Rochester, NY 14604 (SAN 215-6873) Tel 716-325-1636.

NY Party Pub Ass, *(New York Party Directory Publishing Assocs., The; 0-933255),* 123 E. 54th St., Suite 6C, New York, NY 10022 (SAN 692-3984) Tel 212-486-0410.

NY Prod Manual, *(New York Production Manual, Inc.; 0-935744),* 611 Broadway, Suite 807, New York, NY 10012-2608 (SAN 213-6384) Tel 212-777-4002.

†**NY Pub Lib,** *(New York Public Library; 0-87104),* Publications Office, Fifth Ave. & 42nd St., New York, NY 10018 (SAN 202-926X) Tel 212-512-0203; Orders to: Publishing Ctr. for Cultural Resources, 625 Broadway, New York, NY 10012 (SAN 209-9926) Tel 212-260-2010; Orders to: New York Public Library, Branch Libraries, 455 Fifth Ave., New York, NY 10016 (SAN 695-6254) Tel 212-340-0897; *CIP.* Imprints: Branch Libraries (Branch Libraries).

NY Rev Bks, *(New York Review of Books, Inc., The; 0-940322),* 250 W. 57th St., New York, NY 10019 (SAN 220-3448) Tel 212-757-8070.

NY Sch Indus Rel
See ILR Pr

NY St Coll Ag, *(New York State College of Agriculture & Life Sciences; 0-9605314; 0-9609010),* Media Services, 1152 Comstock Hall, Cornell Univ., Ithaca, NY 14853 (SAN 282-0536) Tel 607-255-3126; Orders to: 7 Research Park, Cornell Univ., Ithaca, NY 14850 (SAN 282-0544) Tel 607-255-2080.

NY St Eng Coun, *(New York State English Council; 0-930348),* P.O. Box 2397, Liverpool, NY 13089 (SAN 211-0377) Tel 315-487-4566.

NY Times, *(New York Times),* 229 W. 43rd St., New York, NY 10036 (SAN 208-3027) Tel 212-556-7291.

NY Zoetrope, *(New York Zoetrope; 0-918432),* 80 E. 11th St., New York, NY 10003 (SAN 209-6293) Tel 212-420-0590; Toll free: 800-242-7546.

NYC Coalition
See NYCCWMH

NYC Comm Women, *(New York City Commission on the Status of Women; 0-9610688),* 52 Chambers St., Suite 207, New York, NY 10007 (SAN 240-9224) Tel 212-566-3830; Dist. by: Golden Lee, 1000 Dean St., Brooklyn, NY 11238 (SAN 282-5805) Tel 718-857-6333; Dist. by: Inland Bk. Co., P.O. Box 261, 22 Hemingway Ave., East Haven, CT 06512 (SAN 200-4151) Tel 203-467-4257.

NYC Pub Co, *(New York City Publishing Co.; 0-9614772),* 37 W. 37th St. 4th Flr., New York, NY 10018 (SAN 696-0758).

NYCCWMH, *(New York City Coalition for Women's Mental Health; 0-9616028),* 320 W. 86th St., No 2B, New York, NY 10024 (SAN 697-9203) Tel 212-787-1766.

Nyerges, *(Nyerges, Anton N.; 0-9600954),* 201 Langford Court, Richmond, KY 40475 (SAN 208-791X) Tel 606-623-7153.

†**NYGS,** *(New York Graphic Society Bks.; 0-8212),* Div. of Little, Brown & Co., 34 Beacon St., Boston, MA 02106 (SAN 202-5841) Tel 617-227-0730; Toll free: 800-343-9204; Dist. by: Little, Brown & Co., 200 W. St., Waltham, MA 02254 (SAN 281-8892); *CIP. Imprints:* Phila Maritime Mus (Philadelphia Maritime Museum).

NYGS CT, *(New York Graphic Society in Greenwich),* P.O. Box 1469, Greenwich, CT 06836 (SAN 209-2492) Tel 203-661-2400.

NYS Bar, *(New York State Bar Assn.; 0-942954),* 1 Elk St., Albany, NY 12207 (SAN 226-1952) Tel 518-463-3200.

NYS Dept Environ Conserv, *(New York State Dept. of Environmental Conservation; 0-9615433),* 50 Wolf Rd., Rm. 522, Albany, NY 12233-4753 (SAN 696-2777) Tel 518-457-8174.

NYS Ed Dept, *(New York State Education Dept.),* State Univ. of New York, State Education Bldg., Albany, NY 12234 (SAN 280-6215).

NYS Inst Glaze, *(New York State Institute For Glaze Research; 0-914267),* 511 N. Hamilton St., Painted Post, NY 14870 (SAN 287-5861) Tel 607-962-1671.

NYS Library, *(New York State Library),* CEC, ESP, Albany, NY 12230 (SAN 205-7034) Tel 418-474-5953.

NYS Museum, *(New York State Museum; 1-55557),* Univ. of the State of New York, 3140 Cultural Education Ctr., Albany, NY 12230 (SAN 205-7026) Tel 518-474-3505.

NYSCA, *(New York State Council on the Arts),* 915 Broadway, New York, NY 10010 (SAN 220-0767) Tel 212-614-2903.

†**NYU Pr,** *(New York Univ. Pr.; 0-8147),* 70 Washington Sq., S., New York, NY 10012 (SAN 658-1293) Tel 212-598-2886; Dist. by: Columbia Univ. Pr., 562 W. 113th St., New York, NY 10025 (SAN 212-2472) Tel 212-316-7100; *CIP.*

O & B Bks, *(O & B Bks., Inc.; 0-9601586),* 1215 NW Kline Pl., Corvallis, OR 97330 (SAN 210-9328) Tel 503-752-2178.

O ARS, *(O. ARS; 0-942030),* P.O. Box 179, Cambridge, MA 02238 (SAN 238-6011) Tel 603-883-3536.

O Ichazo, *(Ichazo, Oscar, Co.; 0-937201),* 874 Kumulani Dr., Kihei, HI 96753 (SAN 658-7321) Tel 212-362-5230.

O K Davis, *(Davis, O. K.; 0-9610262),* P.O. Box 1427, Ruston, LA 71270 (SAN 264-0015) Tel 318-255-3990.

O L Holmes, *(Holmes, Opal Laurel, Publisher; 0-918522),* P.O. Box 2535, Boise, ID 83701 (SAN 210-1017) Tel 208-344-4517; Dist. by: Baker & Taylor Co., Midwest Div., 501 Gladiola Ave., Momence, IL 60954 (SAN 169-2100).

O L Hope, *(Hope, Orville L.),* 425 E. Davidson Ave., Gastonia, NC 28054 (SAN 659-9605).

O M Allred, *(Allred, O. M., Pubns.; 0-936035),* 2201 Sunrise Blvd., Ft. Myers, FL 33907 (SAN 696-9941) Tel 813-939-3606.

O Millien, *(Millien, Oneal, Publishing Co.; 0-9617055),* 306 Gardenia Dr., Donaldsonville, LA 70346 (SAN 662-8397) Tel 504-473-8880.

O N Holmes, *(Holmes, Oakley N.; 0-9604026),* c/o Black Artists in America, Macgowan Enterprises, 39 Wilshire Dr., Spring Valley, NY 10977 (SAN 270-8000).

O Parker Pub, *(Parker, Oliver, Pub.; 0-937155),* Frenchman's Hill, Bar Harbor, ME 04609 (SAN 658-4756); P.O. Box 429, Bar Harbor, ME 04609 (SAN 658-4764).

O R Aylesworth, *(Aylesworth, Owen R.; 0-9609312),* 621 W. Arrellaga St., Santa Barbara, CA 93101 (SAN 260-0161) Tel 805-962-4252.

O R Miller, *(Miller, Oscar R.; 0-9600552),* P.O. Box 229, Berlin, OH 44610 (SAN 203-7556) Tel 216-893-2870.

O T O, *(OTO (Society Ordo Templi Orientis in America); 0-913735),* P.O. Box 90144, Nashville, TN 37209 (SAN 219-9610); Dist. by: Bookpeople, 2929 Fifth St., Berkeley, CA 94710 (SAN 168-9517) Tel 415-549-3030; Dist. by: The Distributors, 702 S. Michigan, South Bend, IN 46618 (SAN 169-2488) Tel 219-232-8500.

O V N Pubns, *(OVN Pubns.; 0-9610188),* P.O. Box 491432, Los Angeles, CA 90049 (SAN 274-2632) Tel 213-820-6178.

O W Frost, *(Frost, O. W.; 0-930766),* 2141 Lord Baranof Dr., Anchorage, AK 99517 (SAN 211-3163).

O W Ltd
   See Oliver Wight

Oak *Imprint of* Music Sales

Oak Grove Pubns, *(Oak Grove Pubns.; 0-9607162),* P.O. Box 521, Menlo Park, CA 94026 (SAN 239-0140) Tel 415-854-2059.

Oak Hill Bks, *(Oak Hill Bks.; 0-9616701),* P.O. Box 576, Arroyo Grande, CA 93420 (SAN 661-3020) Tel 805-773-1977; 966 Printz Rd., Arroyo Grande, CA 93420 (SAN 661-3039) Tel 805-773-4369.

Oak Hill UT, *(Oak Hill Pub.; 0-911391),* P.O. Box 520765 Brickyard Corporate Plaza, Salt Lake City, UT 84152 (SAN 274-2357) Tel 801-278-4042; 4456 Covecrest, Salt Lake City, UT 84214 (SAN 662-1007).

Oak Hse, *(Oak House, The; 0-931335),* P.O. Box 7809, Fresno, CA 93747 (SAN 682-7543).

†**Oak Knoll,** *(Oak Knoll Books; 0-938768),* 214 Delaware St., New Castle, DE 19720 (SAN 216-2776) Tel 302-328-7232; *CIP.*

Oak Lodge Pub, *(Oak Lodge Publishing; 0-9615661),* P.O. Box 68403, Oak Grove, OR 97268 (SAN 695-8680) Tel 503-654-2058; Dist. by: Western States Bk. Service, P.O. Box 855, Clackamas, OR 97015 (SAN 200-5662).

Oak Opening Pr, *(Oak Opening Pr.; 0-9613850),* P.O. Box 811, Kalamazoo, MI 49005 (SAN 682-0077) Tel 616-388-5722.

Oak Park, *(Oak Park Michigan; 0-938968),* 24443 Roanoke, Oak Park, MI 48237 (SAN 216-1427).

Oak Pr, *(Oak Pr.; 0-9615242),* 904 Broadway Ave., Wausau, WI 54401 (SAN 695-1643) Tel 715-842-7369.

†**Oak Ridge,** *(Oak Ridge Associated Univs.; 0-930780),* P.O. Box 117, Oak Ridge, TN 37831-0117 (SAN 211-3716) Tel 615-576-3365; *CIP.*

†**Oak Tree Pubns,** *(Oak Tree Pubns., Inc.; 0-916392; 0-86679),* Div. of Lakeside Industries, Inc., 9601 Aero Dr., Suite 202, San Diego, CA 92123 (SAN 211-4828) Tel 619-560-5163; *CIP.*

Oak Valley, *(Oak Valley Pr., The; 0-9609170),* 228 Virginia Ave., San Mateo, CA 94402 (SAN 241-418X) Tel 415-343-3397.

Oak Woods Media, *(Oak Woods Media, Inc.; 0-88196),* 8701 West F Ave., P.O. Box 527, Oshtemo, MI 49077-0527 (SAN 264-6285) Tel 616-375-1429.

Oakland-PR, *(Oakland-PR; 0-9614236),* Div. of Project Review Inc., P.O. Box 1214, Oakland, CA 94604-1214 (SAN 686-6883) Tel 415-839-2767; Dist. by: Bookpeople, 2929 Fifth St., Berkeley, CA 94710 (SAN 168-9517) Tel 415-549-3030.

†**Oaklawn Pr,** *(Oaklawn Press, Inc.; 0-916198),* 1318 Fair Oaks Ave., S. Pasadena, CA 91030 (SAN 208-0621) Tel 213-799-0880; *CIP.*

Oakton Hills Pubns, *(Oakton Hills Pubns.; 0-939047),* P.O. Box 557, Oakton, VA 22124 (SAN 661-681X); 2535 Oak Valley Dr., Vienna, VA 22180 (SAN 662-7870) Tel 703-255-1270.

Oakview, *(Oakview Book Press; 0-9601104),* P.O. Box 990, Adelphi, MD 20783 (SAN 210-0088) Tel 301-434-8106.

Oakwood CA Pr
   See Oakwood Pr CA

Oakwood Pr CA, *(Oakwood Pr. (CA); 0-934247),* 2168 Feliz Dr., Novata, CA 94947 (SAN 693-191X) Tel 415-892-7149.

OAS, *(Organization of American States; 0-8270),* 17th St. & Constitution Ave., NW, Washington, DC 20006 (SAN 206-8877) Tel 202-789-3533.

Oasis *Imprint of* PSI Res

Oasis Bks, *(Oasis Bks.; 0-939213),* P.O. Box 37021, Denver, CO 80237 (SAN 662-6092); 10700 E. Dartmouth, Suite NN 312, Aurora, CO 80014 (SAN 662-6106) Tel 303-368-8545. Do not confuse with Oasis Bks. of Covina, CA.

Oasis Intl, *(Oasis International Communications, Inc.; 0-938341),* P.O. Box 17510, San Diego, CA 92117 (SAN 661-2873); 5331 Mt. Alifan, San Diego, CA 92111 (SAN 661-2881) Tel 619-277-4991.

Oaxacado Pub Co, *(Oaxacado Publishing Co., The; 0-915311),* 7333 Conestoga Ct., San Diego, CA 92120 (SAN 290-0262) Tel 619-286-9149.

OBAhouse, *(OBAhouse; 0-933653),* 108 College Ave., Columbia, MO 65201 (SAN 692-6754) Tel 314-874-0368; Orders to: P.O. Box 6024, Chicago, IL 60680-6024 (SAN 699-5934).

†**Ober Coll Allen,** *(Oberlin College, Allen Memorial Art Museum; 0-942946),* Oberlin College, Main & Lorain Sts., Oberlin, OH 44074 (SAN 240-3226) Tel 216-775-8665; Dist. by: Indiana Universtiy Pr., Tenth & Morton Sts., Bloomington, IN 47405 (SAN 202-5647); *CIP.*

Ober Pub, *(Ober Publishing; 0-911785),* 9514-9 Reseda Blvd., No. 478, Northridge, CA 91324 (SAN 264-2654) Tel 818-701-6237.

Oberlin Coll
   See Oberlin Coll Pr

†**Oberlin Coll Pr,** *(Oberlin College Pr.; 0-932440),* Rice Hall, Oberlin College, Oberlin, OH 44074 (SAN 212-1883) Tel 216-775-8407; *CIP. Imprints:* Field Translat Ser (Field Translation Series).

Oberlin Con Lib, *(Oberlin College Conservatory Library; 0-9611434),* Oberlin College, Oberlin, OH 44074 (SAN 283-3042) Tel 216-775-8280.

Oberlin Pr Times, *(Oberlin Pr. of the Times),* 60 S. Pleasant St., Oberlin, OH 44074 (SAN 659-5634).

Oblate, *(Oblate Fathers),* P.O. Box 96, San Antonio, TX 78291 (SAN 209-5890) Tel 512-736-1685.

Oblong Pr, *(Oblong Pr.; 0-9616635),* 1675 Broderson, Los Osos, CA 93402 (SAN 661-2148) Tel 805-528-4942.

Oboe Bks, *(Oboe Bks.; 0-935659),* P.O. Box 0204, Oberlin, OH 44074 (SAN 695-8702) Tel 216-774-1576; Main P.O. Box 0204, Oberlin, OH 44074 (SAN 695-8710).

Obol Intl, *(Obol International; 0-916710; 0-86723),* Div. of Unigraphics, Inc., 4747 N. Spaulding, Chicago, IL 60625 (SAN 282-0692) Tel 312-267-3662.

Obranoel Pr, *(Obranoel Press),* 63 Franklin Sq., New York, NY 11010 (SAN 208-4473).

O'Brien, *(O'Brien, F. M., Bookseller),* 34 & 36 High St., Portland, ME 04101 (SAN 203-7580).

OBriens Auto Racing Pubns, *(O'Brien's Auto Racing Pubns.; 0-9616916),* 5618 Windsor Ave., Sioux City, IA 51106 (SAN 661-5392) Tel 712-274-1541.

Observational, *(Observational Research Pubns. Co.; 0-942884),* 16 Polo Cir., Colorado Springs, CO 80906 (SAN 240-2629) Tel 303-632-2434.

Occam Pr, *(Occam Press; 0-9614238),* 1070 Queensbrook Dr., San Jose, CA 95129 (SAN 686-6891) Tel 415-857-7978.

Occasional Papers, *(Occasional Papers/Reprints Series in Contemporary Asian Studies, Inc.; 0-942182),* 500 W. Baltimore St., Univ. of Maryland, School of Law, Baltimore, MD 21201 (SAN 226-2894) Tel 301-528-3870.

Occasional Prods, *(Occasional Productions; 0-933264),* 593 Vasona Avenue., Los Gatos, CA 95030 (SAN 211-6863).

Occidental, *(Occidental Press; 0-911050),* P.O. Box 1005, Washington, DC 20013 (SAN 203-7599).

Ocean Allen Pub, *(Ocean Allen Publishing; 0-917071),* 13130 Sundance Ave., San Diego, CA 92129 (SAN 655-2382) Tel 619-484-5401; Rte. 4, Box 369, Spokane, WA 99204 (SAN 691-4276) Tel 509-466-7095.

Ocean East, *(Ocean East Publishing Co.; 0-9607028),* 1655 71st Ct., Vero Beach, FL 32960 (SAN 239-0159) Tel 305-567-0960.

Ocean Pub, *(Ocean Publishing; 0-936867),* P.O. Box 1673, Key West, FL 33041 (SAN 699-9107) Tel 305-296-6001; 425 Frances St., Key West, FL 33040 (SAN 699-9115) Tel 305-296-6001.

Ocean Tree Bks, *(Ocean Tree Bks.; 0-943734),* P.O. Box 1295, Santa Fe, NM 87504 (SAN 241-0478) Tel 505-983-1412; Dist. by: Bookpeople, 2929 Fifth St., Berkeley, CA 94710 (SAN 168-9517); Dist. by: DeVorss & Co., P.O. Box 550, 1046 Princeton Dr., Marina del Rey, CA 90294 (SAN 168-9886) Tel 213-870-7478; Dist. by: New Leaf Distributors, 1020 White St., SW, Atlanta, GA 30310 (SAN 169-1449) Tel 404-755-2665.

Ocean View Pr, *(Ocean View Pr.; 0-938075),* P.O. Box 4148, Mountain View, CA 94900 (SAN 661-1893); 1645 Mercy St., Mountain View, CA 94040 (SAN 661-1907) Tel 415-965-3721.

†Oceana, *(Oceana Pubns., Inc.; 0-379),* 75 Main St., Dobbs Ferry, NY 10522 (SAN 202-5744) Tel 914-693-1733; *CIP. Imprints:* D (Docket Series); LA (Legal Almanac Series).

Oceanic Inst, *(Oceanic Institute, The; 0-9617016),* Makapuu Point, Waimanalo, HI 96705 (SAN 662-8818) Tel 808-259-7951.

Oceanic Pub Co, *(Oceanic Publishing Co.; 0-916467),* P.O. Box 156, Na'Alehu, HI 96712 (SAN 295-1517) Tel 808-929-9101.

Oceanic Soc Stamford, *(Oceanic Society),* 185 Magee Ave., Stamford, CT 06902 (SAN 225-2236) Tel 203-327-9786; Orders to: Fort Mason, Bldg. E, San Francisco, CA 94123 (SAN 669-2273).

Oceanus, *(Oceanus Institute, Inc.; 0-915189),* Learning Place, Manset, ME 04656 (SAN 289-7784) Tel 207-244-5015.

Ocelot Pr, *(Ocelot Press; 0-912434),* P.O. Box 504, Claremont, CA 91711 (SAN 203-7602) Tel 714-621-2200.

Ochlocknee, *(Ochlocknee Community Civic Club, Inc.),* Ochlocknee, GA 31773 (SAN 694-5414).

OCLC
See OCLC Online Comp

†OCLC Online Comp, *(OCLC Online Computer Library Ctr., Inc.; 0-933418; 1-55653),* 6565 Frantz Rd., Dublin, OH 43017-0702 (SAN 694-597X); *CIP.*

O'Connor Hse-Pubs, *(O'Connor Hse-Pubs., Inc.; 0-913243),* P.O. Box 64098, Virginia Beach, VA 23464 (SAN 679-1492) Tel 804-420-2551.

O'Connor Pub., *(O'Connor Publishing Co.; 0-9615466),* 587 Greenwood Ave., Glencoe, IL 60022 (SAN 695-8753) Tel 312-835-1040.

Ocorr Pr, *(Ocorr Press, The; 0-937478),* P.O. Box 64322, Los Angeles, CA 90064 (SAN 214-2147) Tel 213-839-3155.

†Ocotillo, *(Ocotillo Press; 0-918380),* 215 N. 51st St., Seattle, WA 98103 (SAN 209-4061); *CIP.*

†Octameron Assocs, *(Octameron Assocs.; 0-917760),* P.O. Box 3437, Alexandria, VA 22314 (SAN 282-0714) Tel 703-823-1882; 4805A Eisenhower Ave., Alexandria, VA 22304 (SAN 658-1307); Orders to: P.O. Box 3437, Alexandria, VA 22302 (SAN 282-0722); *CIP.*

Octavia Pr, *(Octavia Press; 0-9605882),* 2611 Octavia St., San Francisco, CA 94123 (SAN 282-0730) Tel 415-922-4127; Orders to: P.O. Box 42493, San Francisco, CA 94101 (SAN 282-0749) Tel 415-922-4127.

October, *(October House; 0-8079),* P.O. Box 454, Stonington, CT 06378 (SAN 203-7610) Tel 203-535-3725.

October Pr, *(October Press, Inc., The; 0-935440),* 105 Blue Lake Ct., Austin, TX 78734 (SAN 220-1216).

Octopus Bks, *(Octopus Bks.; 1-55580),* One Madison Ave., New York, NY 10010 (SAN 661-4582).

Oda, *(Oda, James),* 7054 Vanscoy Ave., N. Hollywood, CA 91605 (SAN 216-4264).

Oddo, *(Oddo Publishing, Inc.; 0-87783),* Storybook Acres, Box 68, Fayetteville, GA 30214 (SAN 282-0757) Tel 404-461-7627.

Odin Pr, *(Odin Pr.; 0-930500),* P.O. Box 536, New York, NY 10021 (SAN 211-3244) Tel 212-744-2538.

Odin Pub Co, *(Odin Publishing Co.; 0-9610210),* 95 Eldridge Ave., Mill Valley, CA 94941 (SAN 274-2454) Tel 415-381-1807.

Odium, *(Odium),* P.O. Box 65594, Los Angeles, CA 90065 (SAN 218-4982) Tel 213-794-1959.

ODOT, *(Oregon Dept. of Transportation; 0-9616754),* 324 Capitol St., NE, Salem, OR 97310 (SAN 661-4493) Tel 503-378-8486.

ODS Pubns, *(ODS Pubns., Inc.; 0-9602516),* 6415 N. Lemai Ave., Chicago, IL 60646 (SAN 212-842X) Tel 312-774-6550.

Odyssey Ent, *(Odyssey Enterprise, Ltd.; 0-939006),* P.O. Box 1686, Norman, OK 73070 (SAN 216-2784) Tel 405-364-9811.

Odyssey MA, *(Odyssey Pubns., Inc.; 0-933752),* 334 E. Squantum St., Quincy, MA 02171 (SAN 214-4301) Tel 617-328-9460; Orders to: P.O. Box G-148, Greenwood, MA 01880 (SAN 662-1015).

Odyssey Pr, *(Odyssey Press; 0-672; 0-8399),* Dist. by: Bobbs-Merrill Co. Inc., 4300 W. 62nd St., Indianapolis, IN 46468 (SAN 201-3959).

OECD, *(Organization for Economic Cooperation & Development),* 1750 Pennsylvania Ave., NW, Suite 1207, Washington, DC 20006 (SAN 202-1277) Tel 202-724-1857.

OEG Found *Imprint of* **Exposition Pr FL**

†Oelgeschlager, *(Oelgeschlager, Gunn & Hain, Inc.; 0-89946),* 131 Clarendon St., Boston, MA 02116 (SAN 213-6937) Tel 617-437-9620; *CIP.*

OES Pubns, *(OES Pubns.; 0-89779),* Univ. of Kentucky, College of Engineering, Lexington, KY 40506-0046 (SAN 212-1255) Tel 606-257-3343.

Of Course Inc
See Of Course Pubns

Of Course Pubns, *(Of Course Pubns., Inc.; 0-935255),* P.O. Box 70732, Houston, TX 77270-0732 (SAN 695-507X) Tel 713-863-0250; 607 W. 14th St., Houston, TX 77008 (SAN 695-5088).

Ofc Disabled
See CSUN Disabled

†Off Air Force, *(Office of Air Force History; 0-912799),* Building 5681, Bolling Air Force Base, Washington, DC 20332 (SAN 218-8821) Tel 202-767-4548; *CIP.*

Off Christian Fellowship, *(Officers Christian Fellowship),* P.O. Box 36200, Denver, CO 80236 (SAN 291-8439).

Office Fed Register, *(Office of the Federal Register),* Div. of National Archives and Records Administration, 1100 L St., NW, Rm. 8401, Washington, DC 20408 (SAN 226-5168) Tel 202-523-5240; Orders to: Superintendent of Documents, U.S. Government Printing Office, Washington, DC 20402 (SAN 691-4195) Tel 202-783-3238.

Office Pub Instruct, *(Office of Public Instruction; 0-9614692),* State Capitol, Helena, MT 59620 (SAN 670-7327).

Office Pubns, *(Office Publications, Inc.; 0-911054),* 1600 Summer St., P.O. Box 1231, Stamford, CT 06904 (SAN 203-7637) Tel 203-327-9670.

Office Res, *(Office Research Institute; 0-911056),* 1517 Sparrow St., Longwood, FL 32750 (SAN 203-7645) Tel 305-339-8527.

Official Corp, *(Official Corp., The; 0-9605074),* 240 Newport Center Drive Suite 200, Newport Beach, CA 92660 (SAN 216-2792).

Official Shit Co, *(Official Shit Co.; 0-9616172),* 105B S. Witchduck Rd., No. 225, Virginia Beach, VA 23462 (SAN 699-9875) Tel 804-467-8845.

Offset Hse, *(Offset Hse.),* South Burlington, VT 05401 (SAN 698-1496); Dist. by: Creative Expression, P.O. Box 456, Colchester, VT 05446 (SAN 200-5816).

Offshoot Pub, *(Offshoot Pubns.; 0-910013),* 1280 Goodspring Island Rd., Eugene, OR 97401 (SAN 241-3426) Tel 503-686-8266.

Ogab Pubs, *(OGAB Publishing; 0-912477),* Subs. of Midwest Pub., 49 Grandview Dr., S. Zanesville, OH 43701 (SAN 265-3109) Tel 614-453-5574; Dist. by: Mark Wieder c/o Midwest Pub. & Dist. Service, P.O. Box 239, Portage, WI 53901 (SAN 200-805X).

Ogden Shepard Pub, *(Ogden Shepard Publishing Co.; 0-937313),* 2305 Canyon Blvd., Boulder, CO 80302 (SAN 658-8166) Tel 303-444-2381.

Ogham Hse, *(Ogham House, Inc.; 0-916590),* 6 Sherri Lane, Spring Valley, NY 10977 (SAN 208-0486).

OH Arts Council, *(Ohio Arts Council; 0-913335),* 727 E. Main St., Columbus, OH 43205 (SAN 283-2232) Tel 614-466-2613.

OH Genealogical, *(Ohio Genealogical Society; 0-935057),* 419 W. Third., P.O. Box 2625, Mansfield, OH 44906 (SAN 218-8848) Tel 419-522-9077.

OH Regional Art, *(Ohio Regional Art Directory; 0-912669),* 2803 Bridge Ave., Cleveland, OH 44113 (SAN 282-7875) Tel 216-861-0347.

Ohanian, *(Ohanian; 0-9613618),* El Capitan Assocs., P.O. Box 5025, San Diego, CA 92105 (SAN 670-8625) Tel 619-283-5994; 3911 Dove St., No. 105, San Diego, CA 92103 (SAN 663-3080) Tel 619-260-0218.

†O'Hara, *(O'Hara, J. Philip, Inc., Pubs.; 0-87955),* c/o Scroll Press, Inc., 2858 Valerie Court, Merrick, NY 11566 (SAN 202-5868) Tel 516-379-4283; *CIP. Imprints:* Potato Pr (Potato Press).

Ohara Pubns, *(Ohara Pubns., Inc.; 0-89750),* 1813 Victory Pl., Burbank, CA 91504 (SAN 205-3632) Tel 818-843-4444; Toll free: 800-423-2874; P.O. Box 7728, Burbank, CA 91510 (SAN 658-1315). Do not confuse with Betsy O'Hara, San Francisco, CA.

O'Hayre Pub, *(O'Hayre Publishing Co.; 0-9613183),* 3123 O'Hayre Ct., Lakewood, CO 80215 (SAN 295-7647) Tel 303-233-7227.

†Ohio Acad Sci, *(Ohio Academy of Science, The; 0-933128),* 445 King Ave., Columbus, OH 43201 (SAN 212-3762) Tel 614-424-6045; *CIP.*

Ohio Antique Rev, *(Ohio Antique Review, Inc.; 0-9603290),* P.O. Box 538, Worthington, OH 43085 (SAN 213-344X) Tel 614-885-9757.

Ohio Bio Survey, *(Ohio Biological Survey; 0-86727),* Subs. of Ohio State University, Ohio State Univ., 980 Biological Sciences Bldg., 484 W. 12th Ave., Columbus, OH 43210 (SAN 217-0787) Tel 614-422-9645.

Ohio Hist Soc, *(Ohio Historical Society; 0-87758),* Ohio Historical Ctr., 1985 Velma Ave., Columbus, OH 43211 (SAN 202-1331) Tel 614-466-1500.

Ohio Lib Assn, *(Ohio Library Assn.; 0-911060),* 40 S. 3rd St., Suite 230, Columbus, OH 43215 (SAN 203-7653) Tel 614-221-9057.

Ohio Lib Foun
See Ohio Lib Assn

Ohio Mag, *(Ohio Magazine; 0-938040),* 40 S. Third St., Columbus, OH 43215 (SAN 215-7969).

Ohio Nat Res, *(Ohio Dept. of Natural Resources; 0-931079),* Fountain Sq., Columbus, OH 43224 (SAN 678-9366) Tel 614-265-6807.

Ohio Poetry
See Pudding Pubns

†Ohio Psych Pub, *(Ohio Psychology Publishing Co.; 0-910707),* 5 E. Long St., Suite 610, Columbus, OH 43215 (SAN 260-2385) Tel 614-224-0034; *CIP.*

†Ohio Review, *(Ohio Review, The; 0-942148),* Ohio Univ., Ellis Hall, Athens, OH 45701-2979 (SAN 239-9687) Tel 614-593-1900; *CIP.*

Ohio Savings, *(Ohio Savings Assn.),* 13109 Shaker Square, Cleveland, OH 44120 (SAN 211-0555) Tel 216-752-7000.

Ohio St U Admin Sci, *(Ohio State Univ. College of Administrative Science; 0-87776),* 220 W. 12th Ave., Columbus, OH 43210 (SAN 203-7661) Tel 614-422-2061; Orders to: O.S.U. Pr., The Ohio State Univ., 2070 Neil Ave., Columbus, OH 43210 (SAN 202-8158).

Ohio St U Lib
See Friends Ohio St U Lib

†Ohio St U Pr, *(Ohio State Univ. Pr.; 0-8142),* 1050 Carmack Rd., Columbus, OH 43210-1002 (SAN 202-8158) Tel 614-422-6930; *CIP. Imprints:* Sandstone Bks (Sandstone Books).

Ohio-Summit Pub, *(Summit Publishing Co.; 0-9609310),* 1800 Stoney Hill Dr., P.O. Box 303, Hudson, OH 44236 (SAN 241-5844) Tel 216-650-4321.

†Ohio U Pr, *(Ohio Univ. Pr.; 0-8214),* Scott Quadrangle, Rm. 223, Athens, OH 45701 (SAN 282-0773) Tel 614-594-5852; Toll free: 800-242-7737; Orders to: Harper & Row Pubs., Inc., Keystone Industrial Pk., Scranton, PA 18512 (SAN 282-0781); *CIP.*

Ohio Vet, *(Ohio Veterinary Medical Association; 0-9613273),* 1350 W. Fifth Ave., Columbus, OH 43212 (SAN 297-0449) Tel 614-486-7253.

Oil & Gas, *(Oil & Gas Consultants International, Inc.; 0-930972),* 4554 S. Harvard, Tulsa, OK 74135 (SAN 221-9484).

†**Oil Daily,** *(Oil Daily; 0-918216),* 1401 New York Ave., NW, Suite 500, Washington, DC 20005 (SAN 210-2498) Tel 202-662-0700; Toll free: 800-368-5803; *CIP.*

Ojai, *(Ojai Printing & Publishing; 0-943134),* 111 N. Blanche, Ojai, CA 93023 (SAN 240-9216).

Ojai Val News
See O V N Pubns

Ojar Pub, *(Ojar Pub.; 0-9615075),* 24 Warrenton St., Springfield, MA 01109 (SAN 694-0455) Tel 413-783-7372.

OK Bankers, *(Oklahoma Bankers Association; 0-916937),* P.O. Box 18246, Oklahoma City, OK 73154 (SAN 654-4703) Tel 405-424-5252.

OK Pub, *(OK Publishing; 0-9616615),* 8151 Mary Ellen Ave., North Hollywood, CA 91605 (SAN 661-4078) Tel 818-901-7903.

OK Wildlife Fed, *(Oklahoma Wildlife Federation; 0-937733),* 4545 N. Lincoln, Suite 171, Oklahoma City, OK 73105 (SAN 659-3844) Tel 405-524-7009.

O'Keefe Pr, *(O'Keefe Press; 0-915191),* P.O. Box 3723, Stanford, CA 94305 (SAN 289-7806); Dist. by: Shapolsky/Steimatzky, 56 E. 11th St., New York, NY 10003 (SAN 200-8068).

Okefenokee Pr, *(Okefenokee Press; 0-9601606),* Rte. 3, Box 142-C, Folkston, GA 31537 (SAN 208-3752) Tel 912-496-7401.

Okie Doke Pr, *(Okie Doke Pr.; 0-9614329),* P.O. Box 290, Snoqualmie, WA 98065 (SAN 687-7869) Tel 206-888-0504.

Okinawan Kobujutsu
See LKA Inc

Okla Bankers
See OK Bankers

Okla Mus Art, *(Oklahoma Museum of Art; 0-911919),* 7316 Nichols Rd., Oklahoma, OK 73120 (SAN 279-957X) Tel 405-840-2759.

Okla State Univ Pr, *(Oklahoma State University Press; 0-914956),* N. Monroe St., Stillwater, OK 74078 (SAN 221-9514); Dist. by: Will Rogers Memorial, P.O. Box 157, Claremore, OK 74018 (SAN 280-3003) Tel 918-341-0719.

OLAM, *(Olam Pubns; 0-916222),* 2101 N. Court Hse. Rd., Arlington, VA 22201 (SAN 207-933X) Tel 703-527-7688.

Ol'Attic Bks, *(Ol' Attic Books; 0-9611264),* RTE 1, Box 137A, Pennsboro, WV 26415 (SAN 282-9398) Tel 304-659-2212.

Old Adobe Pr, *(Old Adobe Press),* P.O. Box 115, Penngrove, CA 94251 (SAN 203-7696).

Old Army, *(Old Army Pr.; 0-88342),* P.O. Box 2243, Fort Collins, CO 80521 (SAN 202-1307) Tel 303-484-5535.

Old Betsy Bks, *(Old Betsy Bks.; 0-9616636),* 4940 Golfview Ct., Charlotte, NC 28212 (SAN 661-1788) Tel 704-545-9172.

Old Bk Shop Pubn, *(Old Bk. Shop Pubn.; 0-938673),* P.O. Box 447, Palm Beach, FL 33480 (SAN 661-4817); 1028 N. L St., Lake Worth, FL 33460 (SAN 661-4825) Tel 305-588-5129; Dist. by: FEC News Distributing Co., 2601 Mercer Ave., West Palm Beach, FL 33402 (SAN 200-6677).

Old Cookbooks
See Old Cookbooks HT Hicks

Old Cookbooks HT Hicks, *(Old Cookbooks; 0-932965),* P.O. Box 462, Haddonfield, NJ 08033 (SAN 689-9935) Tel 609-854-2844.

Old Dominion Pr, *(Old Dominion Pr.; 0-913873),* P.O. Box 10423, Alexandria, VA 22310-0423 (SAN 285-6735) Tel 703-922-8741.

Old Farm Ken, *(Old Farm Kennels),* NE 5451 Eastside Hwy., Florence, MT 59833 (SAN 285-6727) Tel 406-273-6837.

Old Fields Pubs, *(Old Fields Pubs.; 0-942434),* P.O. Box 6154, Tallahassee, FL 32301 (SAN 239-5398).

Old Golf Shop, *(Old Golf Shop, Inc.; 0-936557),* 325 W. Fifth St., Cincinnati, OH 45202 (SAN 698-1046) Tel 513-241-7789; Toll free: 800-227-8700.

Old Harbor Pr, *(Old Harbor Pr.; 0-9615529),* P.O. Box 97, Sitka, AK 99835 (SAN 695-880X) Tel 907-747-3584; Orders to: P.O. Box 97, Sitka, AK 99835 (SAN 699-6116).

Old Hickory, *(Old Hickory Pubs.; 0-9613193),* 100 Lake Vista Dr., Hendersonville, TN 37075 (SAN 295-754X) Tel 615-824-3546.

Old Hse Journ Corp, *(Old Hse. Journal Corp., The; 0-942202),* 69A Seventh Ave., Brooklyn, NY 11217 (SAN 238-6801) Tel 718-636-4515.

Old Iron Bk Co, *(Old Iron Book Company; 0-942804),* R.R. 1, Box 28-A, Atkins, IA 52206 (SAN 238-8324).

Old Japan *Imprint of Holmes Pub*

Old Main Bks, *(Old Main Bks.; 0-940166),* 74 W. Main St., Mechanicsburg, PA 17055 (SAN 238-3586); Dist. by: Berkshire Traveller Pr., Pine St., Stockbridge, MA 01262 (SAN 201-4424) Tel 413-298-3636.

Old Man Pr, *(Old Man Pr., The; 0-934435),* P.O. Box 31463, San Francisco, CA 94131 (SAN 693-5699) Tel 415-333-7785.

Old Maps, *(Old Maps; 0-911653),* P.O. Box 54, West Chesterfield, NH 03466 (SAN 264-2689) Tel 603-256-6519.

Old Master Gallery Pr, *(Old Master Gallery Press; 0-9610970),* 15438 Hawthorne Blvd., Lawndale, CA 90260 (SAN 265-3117) Tel 213-679-2525.

Old NY Bk Shop, *(Old New York Book Shop Press; 0-937036),* 1069 Juniper St., NE, Atlanta, GA 30309 (SAN 215-9403); Dist. by: Norman S. Berg, P.O. Box 15232, Atlanta, GA 30333 (SAN 226-8086).

Old Oaktree, *(Old Oaktree Motor Co.; 0-9603194),* 2012 Hyperion Ave., Los Angeles, CA 90027 (SAN 213-2273).

Old Plate *Imprint of From Here*

Old Sparta Pr, *(Old Sparta Press; 0-9608344),* P.O. Box 6363, Raleigh, NC 27628 (SAN 239-5401) Tel 919-832-1358.

Old Stone Pres Church, *(Old Stone Presbyterian Church; 0-9611706),* 200 Church St., Lewisburg, WV 24901 (SAN 285-2756).

Old Sturbridge, *(Old Sturbridge, Inc.; 0-913387),* Old Sturbridge Village, Sturbridge, MA 01566 (SAN 203-0004) Tel 617-347-3362.

Old Suffolk, *(Old Suffolk Square Pr; 0-932247),* 476 Main St., Malden, MA 02148 (SAN 686-6220) Tel 617-324-0440.

Old Theology Bk Hse, *(Old Theology Book House; 0-9612964),* P.O. Box 12232, Minneapolis, MN 55412 (SAN 293-4965).

Old Time, *(Old Time Bottle Publishing Co.; 0-911068),* 611 Lancaster Dr., NE, Salem, OR 97301 (SAN 203-7718) Tel 503-362-1446.

Old Town Pr, *(Old Town Pr.; 0-9610140),* 833 S. Main, St. Charles, MO 63301 (SAN 274-2764).

Old Ursuline
See Ursuline

Old Violin, *(Old Violin-Art Publishing; 0-918554),* Box 500, 225 S. Cooke, Helena, MT 59624 (SAN 209-9756).

Old Warren, *(Old Warren Road Press; 0-9610858),* 141 W. 17th St., 5th Fl., New York, NY 10011 (SAN 264-2697) Tel 212-242-5762; Dist. by: Book Dynamics, Inc., 836 Broadway, New York, NY 10003 (SAN 169-5649) Tel 212-254-7798.

Old West, *(Old West Publishing Co.; 0-912094),* 1228 E. Colfax Ave., Denver, CO 80218 (SAN 202-8174) Tel 303-832-7190.

Oleander Pr, *(Oleander Pr.; 0-902675; 0-900891; 0-906672),* 210 Fifth Ave., New York, NY 10010 (SAN 206-1031).

†**Olearius Edns,** *(Olearius Editions; 0-917526),* Drawer H, Kemblesville, PA 19347 (SAN 207-2696) Tel 215-255-4335; *CIP.*

Olimpo Pub Hse, *(Olimpo Publishing Hse.; 0-938873),* 101 SW 73rd Ave., Miami, FL 33135 (SAN 662-5762) Tel 305-448-8451.

Olin Ski Co, *(Olin Ski Co., Inc.; 0-9606740),* Subs. of Olin Corp., 475 Smith St., Middletown, CT 06457 (SAN 219-6158) Tel 203-632-2000.

Olio Pubs, *(Olio Publishers; 0-934381),* P.O. Box 78, Glen Echo, MD 20812-0078 (SAN 693-8043) Tel 301-229-6916.

Olive Pierce, *(Pierce, Olive; 0-9617101),* 165 Upland Rd., Cambridge, MA 02140 (SAN 662-5045) Tel 617-864-2438.

Olive Pr, *(Olive Pr., The; 0-9612150),* 17709 Sierra Trail, P.O. Box 194, Lake Hughes, CA 93532 (SAN 289-4823) Tel 805-724-1870.

†**Olive Pr Pubns,** *(Olive Pr. Pubns.; 0-933380),* P.O. Box 99, Los Olivos, CA 93441 (SAN 212-5331) Tel 805-688-2445; *CIP.*

†**Oliver-Nelson,** *(Oliver-Nelson; 0-8407),* Nelson Pl. at Elm Hill Pike, Nashville, TN 37214 (SAN 689-1470); Toll free: 800-872-4445 (Sales); Toll free: 800-821-4370 (Sales TN); *CIP.*

Oliver Wight, *(Wight, Oliver, Ltd., Pubns., Inc.; 0-939246),* Subs. of The Oliver Wright Cos., 5 Oliver Wight Dr., Essex Junction, VT 05452 (SAN 216-5198) Tel 802-878-8161; Toll free: 800-343-0625.

Olivet, *(Olivet College Press; 0-911070),* Dist. by: Bill Whitney, P.O. Box 20, Mott Academic Ctr., Olivet, MI 49076 (SAN 282-6801).

Olivia & Hill, *(Olivia & Hill Press Inc., The; 0-934034),* P.O. Box 7396, Ann Arbor, MI 48107 (SAN 212-923X) Tel 313-663-0235.

Olken Pubns, *(Olken Pubns.; 0-934818),* 2830 Kennedy St., Livermore, CA 94550 (SAN 203-7939) Tel 415-447-5177.

Oll Korrect, *(Oll Korrect Pr.),* 6553 Bellaire Ave., N. Hollywood, CA 91606 (SAN 209-8512) Tel 818-762-3375.

Ololon Pubns, *(Ololon Pubns.; 0-9607332),* P.O. Box 569, Lumberton, NC 28359 (SAN 239-2712) Tel 919-738-9396.

Olson QMD, *(Olson, David V., Q M D, Book & Insignia Exchange; 0-9609690),* 1740 Stanbridge, St. Paul, MN 55113 (SAN 282-079X) Tel 612-633-2914; Dist. by: 4540 Morningside Ave., Vadnais Heights, MN 55110 (SAN 663-2971) Tel 612-426-9768.

OLW Editions, *(OLW Editions; 0-934995),* Rte. 4, Box 9375, Barre, VT 05641 (SAN 694-6585) Tel 802-476-4618; Dist. by: Daily Bread, Richford, VT 05476 (SAN 200-5506); Dist. by: Ravengate Pr., The, P.O. Box 103, Cambridge, MA 02238 (SAN 203-090X) Tel 617-456-8181.

Olympian King Co, *(Olympian King Co.; 0-9615662),* 14184 Penrod Rd., Detroit, MI 48223 (SAN 695-8842) Tel 313-272-7956; Dist. by: Multi-Media Education, P.O. Box 35396, Detroit, MI 48235 (SAN 200-7126) Tel 313-342-1261.

Olympic Media, *(Olympic Media Information; 0-88367),* 550 First St., Hoboken, NJ 07030-6553 (SAN 202-8190) Tel 201-963-1600.

Olympics Made, *(Olympics Made Easy; 0-910935),* 54 Cottonwood Cir., Rolling Hills Estates, CA 90274 (SAN 274-2810) Tel 213-541-2842.

†**Olympus Pub Co,** *(Olympus Publishing Co.; 0-913420),* 1670 E. 13th, S., Salt Lake City, UT 84105 (SAN 202-8204) Tel 801-583-3666; *CIP.*

Omaha Print, *(Omaha Printing Company; 0-9609116),* 4700 F. Street, Omaha, NE 68117 (SAN 264-2700).

Omaha Sec Nat, *(National Council Of Jewish Women, Omaha Section; 0-912406),* 1720 S. 86 Ave., Omaha, NE 68124 (SAN 283-3484).

Oman Ent, *(Oman Enterprises; 0-917346),* P.O. Box 222357, Carmel, CA 93922 (SAN 208-7936) Tel 408-624-4386.

OMango
See Twen Fir Cent

Omb, *(Ombudsman Pr.; 0-930175),* 470 W. Highland Ave., Sierra Madre, CA 91024 (SAN 210-3184) Tel 818-355-1325.

Omdega Pr, *(Omdega Pr.; 0-9614611),* P.O. Box 1546, Provincetown, MA 02657 (SAN 691-8182) Tel 617-487-1117.

Omega CA
See Omega LA

Omega Ctr, *(Omega Center; 0-938726),* 137 W. Station St., Barrington, IL 60010 (SAN 219-8061).

Omega LA, *(Omega Books (Los Angeles); 0-9613094),* 5648 Heatherdale Dr., Los Angeles, CA 90043 (SAN 294-6386) Tel 213-293-9608.

Omega Pr NM, *(Omega Pr.; 0-930872),* Div. of Sufi Order in the West, P.O. Box 574, Lebanon Springs, NY 12114 (SAN 214-1493) Tel 518-794-8181; Dist. by: New Leaf Distributing, 1020 White St., SW, Atlanta, GA 30310 (SAN 169-1449) Tel 404-755-2665; Dist. by: Omega Pr., P.O. Box 574, Lebanon Springs, NY 12114 (SAN 214-1493) Tel 518-794-8181.

Omega Pubns OR, *(Omega Pubns.; 0-86694),* Div. of Omega Corporation, P.O. Box 4130, Medford, OR 97501 (SAN 220-1534) Tel 503-826-1030.

Omega Three Project, (Omega-Three Project, Inc.; 0-9616775), 10615-G Tierrasanta Blvd., Suite 347, San Diego, CA 92124 (SAN 661-4450) Tel 619-278-9578.

Omenana, (Omenana; 0-943324), 116 Howland St., Roxbury, MA 02121 (SAN 240-5571) Tel 617-445-0161.

OMF Bks, (OMF Bks.; 0-85363), Div. of Overseas Missionary Fellowship, 404 S. Church St., Robesonia, PA 19551 (SAN 211-8351).

Omicron Pr, (Omicron Pr.), 8475 La Jolla Scenic Dr. N., La Jolla, CA 92037 (SAN 297-1992) Tel 619-453-0133; Orders to: P.O. Box 694, La Jolla, CA 92038 (SAN 685-3927) Tel 619-453-0133.

Omkara Pr, (Omkara Press; 0-934094), 912 Beaver St., Santa Rosa, CA 95404 (SAN 212-9558) Tel 707-575-1736.

Ommation Pr, (Ommation Pr.; 0-941240), 5548 N. Sawyer Ave., Chicago, IL 60625 (SAN 216-2997) Tel 312-539-5745.

Omni Lrn Syst, (Omni Learning Systems, Inc.; 0-938257), 2508 Fifth Ave., Suite 110, Seattle, WA 98121 (SAN 661-3616) Tel 206-682-9469; 8306 N. Point Rd., Hansville, WA 98340 (SAN 661-3624) Tel 206-638-2414.

Omni Worldwide, (Omni Worldwide Corp.; 0-938259), P.O. Box 4427, Clearwater, FL 33518 (SAN 661-4353); 1100 Cleveland, Suite 900, Clearwater, FL 33515 (SAN 661-4361) Tel 813-442-1197.

Omnibook Imprint of **Bible Study Pr**

Omnibus Pr, (Omnibus Pr.; 0-939383), 339 Naymut, Menasha, WI 54952 (SAN 662-9458) Tel 414-722-4034.

Omnicom, (Omnicom, Inc.; 0-937375), 501 Church St., NE, Suite 304, Vienna, VA 22180 (SAN 659-0055) Tel 703-281-1135.

Omnimaven Bks, (Omnimaven Bks.; 0-9614514), P.O. Box 2015, Princeton, NJ 08540 (SAN 691-7305) Tel 609-737-9421.

OMS, (Office of Management Studies), Div. of Association of Research Libraries, 1527 New Hampshire Ave. NW, Washington, DC 20036 (SAN 260-3853) Tel 202-232-8656.

OMT Assn, (Ovulation Method Teachers Assn.; 0-9616481), P.O. Box 101780, Anchorage, AK 99510 (SAN 659-3852) Tel 907-277-3189; 510 L St., Anchorage, AK 99501 (SAN 659-3860).

On Our Way, (On Our Way, Inc.; 0-9614773), P.O. Box 1972, Sedona, AZ 86336 (SAN 692-9974) Tel 602-282-5427.

On the Road Pub, (On the Road Publishing; 0-9616316), 2870-1 Twin Brooks Rd., NE, Atlanta, GA 30319 (SAN 658-7488) Tel 404-261-8396.

Onager Pub, (Onager Publishing; 0-936491), 1420 Fifth St., Berkeley, CA 94710-1234 (SAN 698-1348) Tel 415-526-0383.

Onami Pubns, (Onami Publications; 0-911929), P.O. Box 25466, Rochester, NY 14625-0466 (SAN 264-2727) Tel 716-385-5718.

Onaway, (Onaway Pubns.; 0-918900), 28 Lucky Dr., San Rafael, CA 94904 (SAN 210-4768) Tel 415-924-0884.

Once Upon Stories, (Once Upon Some Stories Publishing Co.; 0-9617219), 2581 NE 31st Ave., Portland, OR 97212 (SAN 663-4206) Tel 503-282-1319.

Onchiota Bks, (Onchiota Books; 0-934820), Rte. 99, Loon Lake, NY 12968 (SAN 213-1366) Tel 518-891-3249.

Ondine Pr, (Ondine Press; 0-910795), 6318 Vesper Ave., Van Nuys, CA 91411-2378 (SAN 262-8449) Tel 818-781-4360.

One Candle, (One Candle Pr.; 0-914032), P.O. Box 888461, Atlanta, GA 30356 (SAN 658-1331) Tel 404-394-6870.

One Eight Inc, (One Eight, Inc.; 0-935081), P.O. Box 2075, Forks, WA 98331-0822 (SAN 695-0132) Tel 206-374-6500.

One-Horse Pr, (One-Horse Pr.; 0-935941), P.O. Box 15016, Springfield, MA 01115 (SAN 696-8805) Tel 413-568-4569; 1500 Main St., Springfield, MA 01115 (SAN 696-8813).

One Hund First Air, (101st Airborne Division Assn.), 2677 Willakenzie Rd., Eugene, OR 97401 (SAN 210-1297) Tel 503-345-2236.

†**One Hund One Prods,** (101 Productions; 0-912238; 0-89286), 834 Mission St., San Francisco, CA 94103 (SAN 202-8220) Tel 415-495-6040; Toll free: 800-621-0851 Ext. 300; Dist. by: Macmillan, Front & Brown Sts., Riverside, NJ 08075 (SAN 202-5582); CIP.

One Hund Thirty-Second Infantry, (132nd Infantry Assn. of World War II; 0-9615127), P.O. Box 56189, Chicago, IL 60656-0189 (SAN 694-1796); 4935 Frank Pkwy., Norridge, IL 60656 (SAN 662-3344) Tel 312-457-0453.

One Hund Twenty Creat, (120 Creative Corner; 0-912773), 4175 Lovell Rd., Box 18, Circle Pines, MN 55014 (SAN 283-1252) Tel 612-784-8375.

One Percent, (One Percent Publishing; 0-935442), 2888 Bluff St., Suite 143, Boulder, CO 80301 (SAN 216-1702).

One-Shot Antelope Hunt, (One-Shot Antelope Hunt Foundation, The; 0-9617178), 626 Fremont St., Lander, WY 82520 (SAN 663-1851) Tel 307-332-9849.

One Ten Records, (One Ten Records; 0-9605778), 110 Chambers St., New York, NY 10007 (SAN 216-5066) Tel 212-964-2296.

One-Thousand-Seven-Hundred-&-&-Eight E, (1708 East Main, Inc.; 0-9613965), 1708 E. Main St., Richmond, VA 23223 (SAN 682-319X) Tel 804-643-7829.

One Thousand Ways, (1000 Ways Pubns.; 0-940324), Heacock Literary Agency, 1523 Sixth St., Santa Monica, CA 90401 (SAN 220-3502).

One World Enter, (One World Enterprises; 0-937939), P.O. Box 13, Kenmore Sta., Boston, MA 02215 (SAN 659-5200) Tel 617-471-6254; 1018 Beacon St., Boston, MA 02215 (SAN 659-5219).

†**One World Pr,** (One World Pr.; 0-910485), 324 Webster St., Bel Air, MD 21014 (SAN 260-1117) Tel 301-838-9396; CIP.

One World Pub, (One World Publishing; 0-916301), P.O. Box 423, Notre Dame, IN 46556 (SAN 295-7590) Tel 219-272-2024.

O'Neill Pr, (O'Neill Press; 0-930970), 305 Great Neck Rd., Waterford, CT 06385 (SAN 212-1239).

Online, (Online, Inc.; 0-910965), 989 Ave. of the Americas, 15th flr., New York, NY 10018 (SAN 264-2735) Tel 212-279-8890.

Online Pubns Ltd Imprint of **Brookfield Pub Co**

Onset Pubns
See **Creat Media**

†**Ontario Rev NJ,** (Ontario Review Pr.; 0-86538), 9 Honey Brook Dr., Princeton, NJ 08540 (SAN 658-134X); Dist. by: Persea Bks., Inc., 225 Lafayette St., New York, NY 10012 (SAN 212-8233) Tel 212-431-5270; CIP.

Onward Pr, (Onward Pr.; 0-931809), 80 Terrapin Dr., P.O. Box 858, Brandon, MS 39042 (SAN 684-7277) Tel 601-825-8943.

Onyx Imprint of **NAL**

Onyx Syst Inc, (Onyx Systems, Inc.), Div. of Onyx & IMI, Inc., 25 E. Trimble Rd., San Jose, CA 95131 (SAN 277-0865) Tel 408-946-6330. Bought by Corvus Systems, Inc.

Onyx Systems
See **Onyx Syst Inc**

†**Oolp Pr,** (OOLP Out of London Pr., Inc.; 0-915570), 1 Washington Sg. Village, New York, NY 10003 (SAN 202-8263) Tel 212-598-7860; CIP.

Op Politics, (Operational Politics Inc; 0-9614073), P.O. Box 9173, Grand Junction, CO 81501 (SAN 685-9984) Tel 303-243-8949; Dist. by: Communication Creativity, P.O. Box 213, Saguache, CO 81149 (SAN 210-3478) Tel 303-589-8223.

OPB Imprint of **Oxford U Pr**

Open Bible, (Open Bible Pubs.; 0-9608160), Affil. of Open Bible Standard Churches, 2020 Bell Ave., Des Moines, IA 50315-1096 (SAN 238-8545) Tel 515-288-6761.

Open Bk Pubns, (Open Book Pubns.; 0-940170), Div. of Station Hill Pr., Inc., Station Hill Rd., Barrytown, NY 12507 (SAN 220-3006) Tel 914-758-5840.

Open Bks & Recs, (Open Books and Records-Open Records), 44 NW. 167th St., Miami, FL 33169 (SAN 682-2746) Tel 305-940-8750.

Open Books, (Open Bks.; 0-931416), 1631 Grant St., Berkeley, CA 94703 (SAN 211-7517).

Open Connections, (Open Connections, Inc.; 0-9606434), 312 Bryn Mawr Ave., Bryn Mawr, PA 19010 (SAN 216-2806) Tel 215-527-1504.

†**Open Court,** (Open Court Publishing Co.; 9-12050; 0-89688; 0-8126; 0-87548), Div. of Carus Corp., 315 5th St., Peru, IL 61354 (SAN 202-5876) Tel 815-223-2520; Toll free: 800-435-6850; Toll free: 800-892-6831; CIP. Imprints: Library Pr (Library Press).(Library Pr.).

†**Open-Door,** (Open-Door Press; 0-912162), P.O. Box 6161, Shirlington Sta., Arlington, VA 22206 (SAN 203-7742) Tel 703-379-8655; CIP.

Open Door Foun, (Open Door Foundation, The; 0-911335), P.O. Box 3703, Carmel, CA 93921 (SAN 274-2969) Tel 408-625-3307.

Open Door Inc, (Open Door, Inc., The; 0-940136), P.O. Box 855, Charlottesville, VA 22902 (SAN 217-0795) Tel 804-293-5068.

Open Door Soc, (Open Door Society of Connecticut, Inc.; 0-918416), Box 478, Hartford, CT 06101 (SAN 209-3839).

Open Hand, (Open Hand Publishing, Inc.; 0-940880), 210 Seventh St., SE, Suite A24, Washington, DC 20003 (SAN 219-6174) Tel 202-659-9250.

Open My World, (Open My World Pub; 0-941996), 1300 Lorna St., El Cajon, CA 92020 (SAN 238-602X) Tel 619-265-0980; Orders to: P.O. Box 15011, San Diego, CA 92115 (SAN 662-1023).

Open Path, (Open Path, The; 0-9602722), 703 N. 18th St., Boise, ID 83702 (SAN 215-9759) Tel 208-342-0208.

Open Places, (Open Places; 0-913398), Box 2085, Stephens College, Columbia, MO 65215 (SAN 205-356X) Tel 314-442-2211.

Open Scroll Imprint of **Bridge Pub**

Open U Imprint of **Har-Row**

Open Univ Pr Imprint of **Taylor & Francis**

Open Window, (Open Window Books Inc.; 0-917694), Box 949, Chickasha, OK 73018 (SAN 209-4657) Tel 405-224-3217.

Opera West, (Opera West Foundation; 0-9601270), 361 Dolores St., San Francisco, CA 94110 (SAN 210-4776) Tel 415-621-2112.

Operation DOME, (Operation D.O.M.E. Press; 0-931081), 980 Whitmore, No. 202, Detroit, MI 48203 (SAN 678-9374) Tel 313-864-6070.

Ophir Intl, (Ophir International; 0-9605958), 15070 Astoria St., Sylmar, CA 91342 (SAN 216-4272).

Ophthalmic, (Ophthalmic Publishing Co.), 435 N. Michigan Ave., Suite 1415, Chicago, IL 60611 (SAN 214-431X) Tel 312-787-3853.

Opinion Res, (Opinion Research Service; 0-913577), P.O. Box 70205, Louisville, KY 40270 (SAN 285-3493) Tel 502-893-2527.

Opportunities Learn, (Opportunities for Learning, Inc.; 0-86539), 20417 Nordhoff St.,Dept. 9, Chatsworth, CA 91311 (SAN 216-6895) Tel 818-341-2535.

Opportunity Knocks, (Opportunity Knocks Publishers; 0-938908), P.O. Box 785, Vienna, VA 22180 (SAN 238-4965) Tel 703-938-8237.

Optext, (Optext; 0-9611266), Div. Of Optext Design Typography, 100 E. Ohio, Chicago, IL 60611 (SAN 282-9843) Tel 312-337-2838.

Optical Data, (Optical Data Corp.; 0-939187), P.O. Box 97, Florham Park, NJ 07932 (SAN 662-8311); 66 Hanover Rd., Florham Park, NJ 07932 (SAN 662-832X) Tel 202-377-0302.

Optical Resolution, (Optical Resolution Information Ctr.; 0-9601918), Manhattan College, Riverdale, NY 10471 (SAN 212-3770).

Optical Soc, (Optical Society of America; 0-9600380), 1816 Jefferson Pl., NW, Washington, DC 20036 (SAN 203-7750) Tel 202-223-8130.

Optimum Res Inc, (Optimum Resource, Inc.; 0-911787), Station Pl., Norfolk, CT 06058 (SAN 264-2743) Tel 203-542-5553.

Ortho, *(Ortho Bks.; 0-917102; 0-89721),* Div. of Chevron Chemical Co., Subs. of Standard Oil Co. of CA, 575 Market St., Rm. 3188, San Francisco, CA 94105 (SAN 662-7293) Tel 415-894-0277; Dist. by: Chevron Chemical Co., Consumer Products Div., Ortho Information Services, 1728 Montreal Circle, Tucker, GA 30084 (SAN 218-6780) Tel 404-934-0494; Dist. by: Chevron Chemical Co., Consumer Products Div., Ortho Information Services, One Crossroads of Commerce, Suite 1000, Rolling Meadows, IL 60008 (SAN 662-7307) Tel 312-870-3430; Dist. by: Chevron Chemical Co., Consumer Products Div., Ortho Information Services, 1200 State St., Perth Amboy, NJ 08861 (SAN 662-7315) Tel 201-738-2187; Dist. by: Chevron Chemical Co., Consumer Products Div., Ortho Information Services, 3260 Blume Dr., Suite 300, Richmond, CA 94806 (SAN 662-7323) Tel 415-222-9700.

Ortho Diag, *(Ortho Diagnostic Systems, Inc.; 0-910771),* Room B-50, Raritan, NJ 08869 (SAN 260-2393) Tel 201-524-2181.

Ortho Info, *(Ortho Information Services; 0-917102; 0-89721),* Div. of Chevron Chemical Co., 575 Market St., San Francisco, CA 94105 (SAN 699-7856) Tel 415-894-0277.

Orthodox Chr, *(Orthodox Christian Educational Society; 0-938366),* 1916 W. Warner Ave., Chicago, IL 60613 (SAN 215-1642) Tel 312-549-0584.

Orton Dyslexia, *(Orton Dyslexia Society, Inc.; 0-89214),* 724 York Rd., Baltimore, MD 21204 (SAN 224-3121) Tel 301-296-0232.

Orton Soc
See Orton Dyslexia

†**Oryn Pubns Inc,** *(Oryn Pubns., Inc.; 0-916207),* P.O. Box 18225, Washington, DC 20036 (SAN 294-989X) Tel 301-441-4645; CIP.

†**Oryx Pr,** *(Oryx Pr.; 0-912700; 0-89774),* 2214 N. Central Ave., Phoenix, AZ 85004-1483 (SAN 220-0201) Tel 602-254-6156; Toll free: 800-457-6799; CIP.

Orzano Pub Co, *(Orzano Publishing Co.; 0-936668),* P.O. Box 394, Islip, NY 11751 (SAN 214-2155) Tel 516-666-1950.

Osage Pub, *(Osage Publishing; 0-9616666),* P.O. Box 151, Osage, MN 56570 (SAN 661-3527) Tel 612-573-3463.

Osborne Dr, *(Osborne; 0-915631),* 6108 Centinella St., Simi Valley, CA 93063 (SAN 292-5893) Tel 805-527-1314; Orders to: Jean Osborne, 1409 Kuehner Dr., Suite 113, Simi Valley, CA 93063 (SAN 662-2240).

Osborne Ent, *(Osborne Enterprises; 0-932117),* P.O. Box 28312, Tempe, AZ 85282 (SAN 686-4694) Tel 602-437-3461; Orders to: Jellyroll Productions, P.O. Box 24092, Tempe, AZ 85282 (SAN 663-3110) Tel 602-437-3461.

Osborne-McGraw, *(Osborne/McGraw-Hill; 0-07),* Div. of McGraw-Hill, 2600 Tenth St., Berkeley, CA 94710 (SAN 274-3450) Tel 415-548-2805; Toll free: 800-227-0900.

Osbrone Ent
See Osborne Ent

OSI Pubns, *(OSI Pubns., Ltd.; 0-918317),* Div. of On-Line Software, Ft. Lee Executive Pk., 2 Executive Dr., Ft. Lee, NJ 07024 (SAN 657-2952) Tel 201-592-5450.

†**Osprey Bks,** *(Osprey Bks.; 0-943738),* P.O. Box 965, Huntington, NY 11743 (SAN 241-0508) Tel 516-549-0143. Do not confuse with Osprey Bks., San Diego, CA; CIP.

Osprey CA, *(Osprey Bks.; 0-9614239),* 1958 Sunset Cliffs Blvd., Suite 109, San Diego, CA 92107 (SAN 686-6905) Tel 619-223-2715. Do not confuse with Osprey Bks., Huntington, NY.

Ossi Prods
See Ossi Pubns

Ossi Pubns, *(Ossi Pubns.; 0-930912),* 195 Lake Destiny Trail, Altamonte, FL 32714 (SAN 211-0415) Tel 305-862-2392 (SAN 699-5497).

Osthoff-Thalden, *(Osthoff-Thalden & Assocs.; 0-9614346),* 7 N. Taylor, St. Louis, MO 63108 (SAN 687-830X) Tel 314-367-5677.

†**O'Sullivan Woodside,** *(O'Sullivan, Woodside & Co.; 0-89019),* 2218 E. Magnolia, Phoenix, AZ 85034 (SAN 207-4052) Tel 602-244-1000; Dist. by: Caroline House Pubs., Inc., 236 Forest Park Place, Ottawa, IL 61350 (SAN 207-6705) Tel 815-434-7905; CIP. Imprints: Norwalk Pr (Norwalk Press).

Otafra, *(Otafra Pr.; 0-9605220),* P.O. Box 814, Mesilla, NM 88046 (SAN 220-1224) Tel 505-522-6757.

Other Alligator, *(Other Alligator Creek Co. The; 0-931083),* 1195 Oakhaven Dr., Roswell, GA 30075 (SAN 678-9382) Tel 404-993-8128.

Other Bks, *(Other Bks.),* 1412 Spruce St., Berkeley, CA 94709 (SAN 209-0813) Tel 415-841-6359.

Otis Art, *(Otis Art Institute of Parsons Schl of Design; 0-930209),* Div. of New School for Social Research, 2410 Wilshire Blvd., Los Angeles, CA 90057 (SAN 280-0144) Tel 213-251-0500.

Ottawa Co Hist, *(Ottawa County Historical Society),* P.O. Box 385, Port Clinton, OH 43452 (SAN 692-719X); Dist. by: Waterfront Books, 18330 Brim Rd., No. 321, Bowling Green, OH 43402 (SAN 213-0610).

Otter Nonsense, *(Otter Nonsense; 0-9616238),* P.O. Box 2843, Santa Rosa, CA 95405 (SAN 658-599X) Tel 707-539-9598; 5815 Melita Rd., Santa Rosa, CA 95405 (SAN 658-6007).

Otter Veterinary, *(Otter Veterinary Services Inc.; 0-9614459),* 22764 Desoto St., Grand Terrace, CA 92324 (SAN 689-4127) Tel 714-783-2067.

Otterden, *(Otterden Press; 0-918868),* 111 Plymouth Rd., Hillsdale, NJ 07642 (SAN 210-4792) Tel 201-664-2583.

Otto Pubs, *(Otto Pubs.; 0-9615548),* 3730 Southview Dr., Suite 423, San Diego, CA 92117 (SAN 696-3218) Tel 619-272-5391.

Ouabache, *(Ouabache Pr.; 0-9609026),* Box 2076, West Lafayette, IN 47906 (SAN 240-9240) Tel 317-463-9857.

OUP
See Planet Bks

Our Baby's, *(Our Baby's First Seven Years; 0-937970),* 5841 Maryland Ave., Chicago, IL 60637 (SAN 287-2951) Tel 312-667-5184; Dist. by: Caroline Hse., Inc., 5 S. 250 Frontenac Rd., Naperville, IL 60540 (SAN 211-2280) Tel 312-983-6400.

†**Our Child Pr,** *(Our Child Pr.; 0-9611872),* 800 Maple Glen Ln., Wayne, PA 19087 (SAN 682-272X) Tel 215-964-1837; CIP.

Our Sunday Visitor, *(Our Sunday Visitor, Publishing Div.; 0-87973),* 200 Noll Plaza, Huntington, IN 46750 (SAN 202-8344) Tel 219-356-8400; Toll free: 800-348-2440 except Indiana.

†**Out & Out,** *(Out & Out Bks.; 0-918314),* 476 Second St., Brooklyn, NY 11215 (SAN 209-4665) Tel 718-499-9227; CIP.

Out Mouths Pr, *(Out of Mouths Pr.; 0-9616776),* 1448 Oakley Dr., Baton Rouge, LA 70806 (SAN 661-4167) Tel 504-924-2510.

Out of Harm's, *(Out of Harm's Way, Inc.; 0-9616239),* P.O. Box 63, Brooklyn, NY 11230 (SAN 658-6031) Tel 718-252-1664; 1205 Glenwood Rd., Brooklyn, NY 11230 (SAN 658-604X).

Out of the Ashes, *(Out of the Ashes Pr.; 0-912874),* P.O. Box 42384, Portland, OR 97242 (SAN 202-8352).

Outbooks, *(Outbooks, Inc.; 0-89646),* 217 Kimball Ave., Golden, CO 80401 (SAN 211-0849); Orders to: Vistabooks, Inc., 217 Kimball Ave., Golden, CO 80401 (SAN 662-1031) Tel 303-279-4070.

Outdoor Assocs, *(Outdoor Assocs.; 0-9605556),* 1279 Dean St., Schenectady, NY 12309 (SAN 207-270X) Tel 518-372-4585.

Outdoor Bks, *(Outdoor Books, Nature Series, Inc.; 0-942806),* 3813 Fenchurch Rd., Baltimore, MD 21218 (SAN 238-8561) Tel 301-243-1179.

Outdoor Circle, *(Outdoor Circle, The; 0-9069082),* 200 N. Vineyard Blvd., Suite 502, Honolulu, HI 96817 (SAN 241-4228) Tel 808-521-0074.

Outdoor Comm, *(Outdoor Communications; 0-932753),* 8942 Creekford Dr., Lakeside, CA 92040 (SAN 688-6000) Tel 619-443-6648.

†**Outdoor Empire,** *(Outdoor Empire Publishing, Inc.),* 511 Eastlake Ave., P.O. Box C-19000, Seattle, WA 98109 (SAN 207-1312) Tel 206-624-3845; CIP.

Outdoor Life Imprint of Crown

Outdoor Pict, *(Outdoor Pictures; 0-911080),* P.O. Box 277, Anacortes, WA 98221 (SAN 203-7815) Tel 206-293-3200.

Outdoor Pubns, *(Outdoor Pubns.; 0-939166),* P.O. Box 355, Ithaca, NY 14851 (SAN 202-1250) Tel 607-273-0061.

Outdoor Skills, *(Outdoor Skills Bookshelf; 0-940022),* P.O. Box 13, Louisville, AL 36048 (SAN 216-8472) Tel 205-266-5062.

Outdoors Inc
See Al Lindner's Outdoors

Outer Ring Pub, *(Outer Ring Publishing; 0-936235),* 500 Promontory Dr. W., Newport Beach, CA 92660 (SAN 696-8767) Tel 818-349-0616; Dist. by: Halley's Comet Watch '86, Inc., 158 W. Boston Post Rd., Box AB, Mamaroneck, NY 10543 (SAN 200-5840).

Outer Straubville, *(Outer Straubville Pr.),* Box 470, Occidental, CA 95465 (SAN 203-7823); Dist. by: Bookpeople, 2929 Fifth St., Berkeley, CA 94710 (SAN 168-9509).

Outermost Pr, *(Outermost Pr.; 0-940282),* Box 183, St. Johnsbury Ctr., VT 05863 (SAN 217-5509) Tel 802-748-5034.

†**Outlet Bk Co,** *(Outlet Bk. Co.; 0-87000),* Affil. of Crowns Pubs., Inc., 225 Park Ave., S., New York, NY 10003 (SAN 200-2620) Tel 212-254-1600; Toll free: 800-526-4264. Promotional books of all kinds; remainders, reprints, imports, original publications; CIP. Imprints: Avenel (Avenel); Bell (Bell); Bonanza (Bonanza); Chatham River Pr (Chatham River Press); Greenwich Hse (Greenwich House); Greenwich Hse-Chatham River Pr (Greenwich House/Chatham River Press).

Outlook, *(Outlook Bk. Service, Inc.; 0-911082),* 512 E. Main St., Richmond, VA 23219 (SAN 206-684X).

Outre House, *(Outre Hse.; 0-9605404),* 1622 N. St., No. 302, Sacramento, CA 95814 (SAN 238-7093) Tel 916-442-6354.

Outreach Press, *(Outreach Press; 0-9613699),* 198 Yerba Buena Ave., San Francisco, CA 94127 (SAN 677-5969) Tel 415-661-5969.

Outside Ent, *(Outside Enterprise Pr.; 0-937232),* P.O. Box 2650, College Sta., Pullman, WA 99165 (SAN 215-0972) Tel 509-335-2691.

Ovation Pubns, *(Ovation Pubns.; 0-910723),* 750 Joranollo, Tracy, CA 95376 (SAN 269-6088) Tel 209-835-3279.

Ovations Pubns
See Ovation Pubns

Over Easy Pub, *(Over Easy Publishing; 0-913975),* 11101 N. 21st St., Tampa, FL 33612 (SAN 286-7834) Tel 813-972-3461.

Overbrook Hse, *(Overbrook Hse.; 0-910773),* P.O. Box 7688, Mountain Brook, AL 35253 (SAN 260-2407) Tel 205-879-8222.

Overcomer Pr, *(Overcomer Pr., Inc.; 0-942504),* 7300 SW Ninth Ct., P.O. Box 14363, Ft. Lauderdale, FL 33302 (SAN 238-1834) Tel 305-797-8989.

Overland Pr, *(Overland Pr., Inc.; 0-930851),* P.O. Box 7386, Shawnee Mission, KS 66207 (SAN 670-8900); 9853 Rosewood, Shawnee Mission, KS 66207 (SAN 662-2496) Tel 913-383-2068.

Overlook Hosp, *(Overlook Hospital Auxiliary; 0-9604560),* 99 Beauvoir Pl., Summit, NJ 07901 (SAN 215-0980) Tel 201-522-2004.

†**Overlook Pr,** *(Overlook Pr.; 0-87951),* 12 W. 21st St., 12th Flr., New York, NY 10010 (SAN 202-8360) Tel 212-337-5472; Toll free: 800-631-3577; Orders to: RR 1 Box 496, Woodstock, NY 12498; Dist. by: Viking-Penguin, Inc., 40 W. 23rd St., New York, NY 10010 (SAN 200-2442) Tel 212-337-5200; CIP.

Overman Pub, *(Overman, Marjorie, Publishing; 0-9614853),* 323 E. Cavenaugh St., Wallace, NC 28466 (SAN 693-1936) Tel 919-285-3375.

Overmountain Pr, *(Overmountain Pr.; 0-932807),* P.O. Box 1261, Johnson City, TN 37605 (SAN 687-6641) Tel 615-926-2691.

Symbols/Abbreviations

P J Currier, *(Currier, Philip J.; 0-9613636),* Patterson Hill Rd., Henniker, NH 03242 (SAN 693-5141) Tel 603-428-7214.

P J Diamondis, *(Diamondis, P. J.; 0-9612110),* 255 Redwood Rd., Merritt Island, FL 32952 (SAN 289-1905) Tel 305-453-6496.

P J Martinez, *(Pepper Jones Martinez, Inc.; 0-935759),* 4640 Harry Haines Blvd., Dallas, TX 75235 (SAN 695-930X) Tel 214-630-7460; Dist. by: Lone Star Schl. Bk. Depository, 4640 Harry Haines Blvd., Dallas, TX 75235 (SAN 200-5697).

P J Neuberger, *(Neuberger, Phyllis J.; 0-9610050),* 5855 Sheridan Rd., Chicago, IL 60660 (SAN 262-9607) Tel 312-334-7744; c/o Ten Plus, Inc., Thomas Graphics, Inc., 547 S. Clark St., Chicago, IL 60605 (SAN 262-9615) Tel 312-922-1301.

P J Thompson, *(Thompson, Paul J.; 0-9601288),* 2200 Prospect Ave., Rm. 437, Cleveland, OH 44115 (SAN 210-5160).

P J Willcox, *(Willcox, P. J.; 0-9608436),* P.O. Box 39, Huntington, IN 46750 (SAN 240-8066).

P Jones Pub Co
   See Proctor Jones

†P Juul Pr, *(Juul, Peter Pr., Inc.; 0-915456),* P.O. Box 40605, Tucson, AZ 85717 (SAN 207-513X) Tel 602-622-3409; *CIP.*

P K Chang, *(Chang, Paul K.; 0-9612410),* 8005 Falstaff Rd., McLean, VA 22102 (SAN 287-735X) Tel 703-356-1135.

P K Gaudet
   See Five M Pubs

P K Hampton, *(Hampton, Patricia Kay; 0-9614397),* Rte. 1, Box 98-D, Paeonian Springs, VA 22129 (SAN 688-6868) Tel 703-777-5821.

P Kornberg, *(Kornberg, Patti; 0-9609240),* 650 N. Atlantic Ave., Cocoa Beach, FL 32931 (SAN 241-5356) Tel 305-783-7079.

P Kowalkowski, *(Kowalkowski, Pat; 0-9616583),* P.O. Box 21602, Ft. Lauderdale, FL 33335 (SAN 661-3993); 1740 SW Second St., Ft. Lauderdale, FL 33335 (SAN 661-4000) Tel 305-764-8085.

P Krejcarek, *(Krejcarek, Philip),* 1439 N. 49th, Milwaukee, WI 53208 (SAN 212-2863) Tel 414-453-1263.

P L Gilbert, *(Gilbert, Pedro L.; 0-9616124),* 1668 Belle Isle Cir., NE, Atlanta, GA 30329 (SAN 699-7384) Tel 404-873-2707.

†P Lang Pubs, *(Lang, Peter, Publishing, Inc.; 0-8204),* Subs. of Verlag Peter Lang AG (Switzerland), 62 W. 45th St., New York, NY 10036-4202 (SAN 241-5534) Tel 212-302-6740; *CIP.*

P M Hatch
   See Harper Coloron

P M Letellier, *(Letellier, Phyllis M.; 0-9611138),* Shell Rte. Box 23, Greybull, WY 82426 (SAN 283-2976) Tel 307-765-2109.

P M Satterfield, *(Satterfield, Phillip Michael; 0-9616014),* 16702 Sampan Cir., Cerritos, CA 90701 (SAN 697-3132) Tel 213-865-7844; P.O. Box 447, Cypress, CA 90630 (SAN 697-3140).

P McIlvaine, *(McIlvaine, Paul, Pub.; 0-9600410),* Sky Village, 124 Scenic Lane, Hendersonville, NC 28739 (SAN 203-7890) Tel 704-692-3971.

P Maravelas, *(Maravelas, Paul),* Box 637, Watertown, MN 55388 (SAN 659-4034).

P Mosley, *(Mosley, P, & Co.; 0-917661),* 810 N. Arthur, Fresno, CA 93728 (SAN 657-1573) Tel 209-268-7512.

P N Langley
   See PNLW

P N Luvera, *(Luvera, Paul N.; 0-9612848),* 917 S. Third St., Mount Vernon, WA 98273 (SAN 290-0106) Tel 206-336-6561; Dist. by: Washington State Trial Lawyers Assn., 225 S. Washington, Seattle, WA 98125 (SAN 290-0114) Tel 206-464-1011.

P N Nielsen, *(Nielsen, Peter N., Enterprises, Ltd.; 0-9616855),* 6689 Orchard Lake Rd., West Bloomfield, MI 48033 (SAN 661-5988) Tel 313-851-5021.

P Odegard
   See Advance Planning

P P Karagan, *(Karagan, Phillip P.; 0-9612394),* 2449 Karagan Dr., Mobile, AL 36606 (SAN 289-3886) Tel 205-473-4970.

P-P Pubns, *(P/P Pubns.; 0-9608316),* 500 N. Dearborn, Suite 900, Chicago, IL 60610 (SAN 240-4850); Dist. by: Dianco, P.O. Box 39100, Chicago, IL 60639 (SAN 200-8084).

P Peters Studio, *(Peters, Paul, Studio; 0-9607030),* 2305 Park Ave., Bay City, TX 77414 (SAN 239-0183) Tel 409-245-7527.

P R Feltus, *(Feltus, Peter R.; 0-9605286),* P.O. Box 5339, Berkeley, CA 94705 (SAN 215-3106).

P R Lees-Haley
   See Rubicon

P R N Corp, *(P.R.N. Corp.; 0-910757),* 330 First St. SE, Cedar Rapids, IA 52401 (SAN 260-2415).

P R Odens, *(Odens, Peter R.; 0-9609484),* P.O. Box 222,, El Centro, CA 92244 (SAN 274-2438) Tel 619-356-1243.

P R Pub Co, *(PR Publishing Co., Inc.),* P.O. Box 600, Exeter, NH 03833 (SAN 205-3438) Tel 603-778-0514.

P R Sullivan, *(Sullivan, Phyllis R.; 0-9615470),* 401 Flinn Ave., Apt. 22, Ravenswood, WV 26164 (SAN 696-1843) Tel 304-273-3692.

P Regan, *(Regan, Pat; 0-9615826),* 120 W. Brainard, Pensacola, FL 32592 (SAN 696-5695) Tel 904-434-5374; P.O. Box 363, Pensacola, FL 32592 (SAN 696-9755).

P Robinson, *(Robinson, Peggy),* 1326 Fell St., San Francisco, CA 94117 (SAN 215-2223) Tel 415-387-9339; Dist. by: Far West Book Service, 3515 NE Hassalo, Portland, OR 97232 (SAN 282-6429) Tel 503-234-7664.

P Rosen, *(Rosen, Pauline; 0-9600214),* 658 Main St., Placerville, CA 95667 (SAN 206-8303).

P S & M Inc, *(Phelon, Sheldon & Marsar, Inc.),* 15 Industrial Ave., Fairview, NJ 07022 (SAN 205-1869) Tel 201-941-8804.

P S Price, *(Price, Polly S.; 0-9604012),* 3102 Eisenhauer B-16, San Antonio, TX 78209 (SAN 221-6639) Tel 512-824-6523.

P S Publishing, *(P. S. Ltd. Publishing; 0-912727),* P.O. Box 16-A, Newport Beach, CA 92662 (SAN 283-3093) Tel 714-675-5253.

P Sherrod, *(Sherrod, Paul),* 4410 Olsen, Amarillo, TX 79106 (SAN 212-1395).

P Skillman, *(Skillman, Penny; 0-9603396),* 149 Anderson St., San Francisco, CA 94110 (SAN 212-0488).

P Smith, *(Smith, Phoebe; 0-9602976),* 764 North Ave., Hapeville, GA 30354 (SAN 213-1676).

P Taylor, *(Taylor, Pat; 0-9611404),* 719 Gales Ave., Winston Salem, NC 27103 (SAN 283-8796) Tel 919-722-2810.

P Tungs Gourmet
   See P Tungs Intl G

P Tungs Intl G, *(Pat Tung's International Gourmet Inc.; 0-9614469),* P.O. Box 16141, Rocky River, OH 44116 (SAN 689-4690) Tel 216-356-1987.

P Walsh Pr, *(Walsh, Patrick, Pr.; 0-86700),* 2017 S. Ventura, Tempe, AZ 85282 (SAN 216-6135) Tel 602-968-1549. *Imprints:* Synergy Bks (Synergy Books).

P Wilson Mail
   See P Wilson Serv

P Wilson Pub, *(Wilson, Pierre, Publishing Co.; 0-9616033),* 3900 Martin Luther King Way, Oakland, CA 94609 (SAN 697-9408) Tel 415-653-6666.

P Wilson Serv, *(Wilson, P., Services),* 4441 McPherson Ave., St. Louis, MO 63108 (SAN 209-3847).

PA Acad Fine Arts *Imprint of* Art Bks Intl

PA Bar Inst, *(Pennsylvania Bar Institute),* P.O. Box 1027, Harrisburg, PA 17108 (SAN 226-8329).

PA Econ League, *(Pennsylvania Economy League, Eastern Div.),* 215 S. Broad St., Philadelphia, PA 19107 (SAN 226-8337).

Pa Hist & Mus, *(Pennsylvania Historical & Museum Commission; 0-911124; 0-89271),* Box 1026, Harrisburg, PA (SAN 282-1532) Tel 717-783-1991; Orders to: Pubn. Sales Program, Dept. PL. P.O. Box 11466, Harrisburg, 17108-1466 Tel 717-787-2407.

Pa Hist Soc, *(Historical Society of Pennsylvania; 0-910732),* 1300 Locust St., Philadelphia, PA 19107 (SAN 202-8441) Tel 215-732-6200.

Pa Paperbks *Imprint of* U of Pa Pr

†Pa St U Pr, *(Pennsylvania State Univ. Pr.; 0-271),* 215 Wagner Bldg., University Park, PA 16802 (SAN 213-5760) Tel 814-865-1327; *CIP.* Imprints: Keystone Bks (Keystone Books).(Keystone Bks.).

PA State Univ
   See Penn State Food

Pac-Co Pub, *(Pac-Co Publishing Co.; 0-935141),* P.O. Box 2148, Hawthorne, CA 90250 (SAN 695-2151) Tel 213-337-0326; 11509 E. 216 St., Suite 116, Lakewood, CA 90715 (SAN 695-216X).

Pac Horizons Pubns, *(Pacific Horizons Pubns.; 0-938375),* E. 300 Dana Dr., Shelton, WA 98584 (SAN 661-0358) Tel 206-426-0752.

Pac Telecomm *Imprint of* UH Pr

Pac Whale Found Pr, *(Pacific Whale Foundation Pr.; 0-938725),* P.O. Box 1038, Kihei, HI 96753 (SAN 661-6070); Azeka Pl., Suite 303, Kihei, HI 96753 (SAN 661-6089) Tel 808-879-8811.

Pace Ed Syst
   See Pace Educ Systems

Pace Educ Systems, *(Pace Educational Systems, Inc.; 0-935385),* 61 Kingsley Rd., Kendall Park, NJ 08824 (SAN 695-8915) Tel 201-297-2525.

†Pace Gallery Pubns, *(Pace Gallery; 0-938608),* 32 E. 57th St., New York, NY 10022 (SAN 220-2646); *CIP.*

PACE Grace, *(PACE Grace Lutheran School; 0-9612728),* P.O. Box 9265, Winter Haven, FL 33880 (SAN 289-7873) Tel 813-299-6905; 227 Lake Link Rd., SE, Winter Haven, FL 33880 (SAN 289-7881); Dist. by: Dot Gibson Pubns., 161 Knight Ave. Cir., Waycross, GA 31501 (SAN 289-789X); Dist. by: Collection Inc., The, 1012 Locust St., P.O. Box 15624, Kansas City, MO 64106 (SAN 698-8467).

Pace Intl Res, *(Pace International Research Inc.; 0-89209),* P.O. Box 51, Arch Cape, OR 97102 (SAN 670-7041).

Pace Pub Co, *(Pace Publishing Co.; 0-936683),* 2545 B Ridgeway Dr., National City, CA 92050 (SAN 699-7317) Tel 619-267-2236.

†Pacesetter Pub Hse OH, *(Pacesetter Pub. Hse.; 0-9603826),* Div. of Pacesetter Enterprises, Inc., P.O. Box 33430, Cleveland, OH 44133-0430 (SAN 218-4990) Tel 216-447-9130; *CIP.*

†Pachart Pub Hse, *(Pachart Publishing Hse.; 0-88126; 0-912918),* Div. of Pachart Foundation, P.O. Box 35549, Tucson, AZ 85740 (SAN 204-9139) Tel 602-297-4797; 1130 San Lucas Cir., Tucson, AZ 85704 (SAN 662-1058) Tel 602-297-6760; *CIP.*

Pacif NW Natl Pks, *(Pacific Northwest National Parks & Forests Assn.; 0-914019),* 83S. King St., Suite 212, Seattle, WA 98104 (SAN 286-8504) Tel 206-442-7958.

Pacif Pub Hawaii, *(Pacific Publishing Hse.; 0-918872),* 2430 Kirkham St., San Francisco, CA 94122 (SAN 210-3214) Tel 415-566-2988.

†Pacific-Asian, *(Pacific/Asian American Mental Health Research Ctr.; 0-934584),* 1033 W. Van Buren St., Suite 7N, Chicago, IL 60607 (SAN 214-4336) Tel 312-996-2964; *CIP.*

Pacific Bk Supply, *(Pacific Book Supply Co.; 0-911090),* 1238 N. Rose Ave., Farmersville, CA 93223 (SAN 202-1366) Tel 209-594-4155.

†Pacific Bks, *(Pacific Bks., Pubs.; 0-87015),* P.O. Box 558, Palo Alto, CA 94302-0558 (SAN 202-8468) Tel 415-856-0550; *CIP.*

Pacific Dist Mennonite, *(Pacific District Mennonite Brethren Churches, Family Commission; 0-9606436),* 4812 E. Butler, Fresno, CA 93727 (SAN 219-807X) Tel 209-251-8681.

Pacific Edns, *(Pacific Editions; 0-938226),* 350 Arballo Dr., No. 5D, San Francisco, CA 94132 (SAN 220-0813) Tel 415-334-5716.

Pacific Gallery, *(Pacific Gallery Pubs.; 0-938942),* P.O. Box 19494, Portland, OR 97219 (SAN 220-2654) Tel 503-244-2300.

Pacific Info, *(Pacific Information, Inc.; 0-913203),* 11684 Ventura Blvd., No. 295, Studio City, CA 91604 (SAN 283-0272) Tel 818-797-7654.

Pacific Inst, *(Pacific Institute; 0-9609174),* P.O. Box 33111, San Diego, CA 92103 (SAN 241-4236) Tel 619-279-9682.

Pacific Inst Pub
   See PIPPR

Pacific Intl, *(Pacific International Publishing Co.; 0-918074),* P.O. Box 850, Friday Harbor, WA 98250 (SAN 210-2528) Tel 206-378-2393.

Pacific Isle Pub, *(Pacific Isle Publishers; 0-9614775),* P.O. Box 223, Kihei, HI 96753 (SAN 692-9966) Tel 808-879-7068.

Pacific Med Pr, *(Pacific Medical Pr.;
0-9608102),* P.O. Box 590238, San
Francisco, CA 94159 (SAN 238-8332)
Tel 415-921-4868.

Pacific Mer, *(Pacific Meridian Publishing Co.;
0-911092),* 13540 Lake City Way, NE,
Seattle, WA 98125 (SAN 206-832X)
Tel 206-362-0900.

Pacific NW Labor, *(Pacific Northwest Labor
History Assn.; 0-932942),* P.O. Box 25048,
Northgate Sta., Seattle, WA 98125
(SAN 216-1710).

Pacific Pipeline, *(Pacific Pipeline, Inc.),* 19215
66th Ave. S., Kent, WA 98032
(SAN 208-2128) Tel 206-872-5523; Toll
free: 800-562-4647 (WA); P.O. Box 3711,
Seattle, WA 98124 (SAN 169-8834); Toll
free: 800-426-4727 (OR,ID,MT,NV, &
Northern CA).

Pacific Pr MO
See Pacific Santa Barbara

†**Pacific Pr Pub Assn,** *(Pacific Pr. Publishing
Assn.; 0-8163),* P.O. Box 7000, Boise, ID
83707-1000 (SAN 202-8409)
Tel 208-465-2500; Toll free: 800-447-7377;
CIP.

Pacific Pub HI, *(Pacific Publishing; 0-934997),*
Div. of Pacific Productions Inc., 1750
Kalakaua Ave., Suite 3901, Honolulu, HI
96826 (SAN 695-1996) Tel 808-946-8833;
Dist. by: Worldwide Dist., Ltd., 550 N.
Nimitz Hwy., Honolulu, HI 96817-5030
(SAN 169-1627).

Pacific Pub Hse
See Pacif Pub Hawaii

Pacific Pubs, *(Pacific Pubs.; 0-936521),* Box
272, Tiburon, CA 94920 (SAN 697-9335)
Tel 415-868-2909; 35 Brighton, Bolinas, CA
94937 (SAN 698-2328); Orders to: Pacific
Pipeline, 19215 66th Ave. S., Kent, WA
98032 (SAN 169-8834) Tel 206-872-5523.

Pacific Rad, *(Pacific Radiation Corp.; 0-916339),*
2945 Stonehill Dr., Altadena, CA 91001
(SAN 295-7698) Tel 818-798-8100.

Pacific Rim Res, *(Pacific Rim Research;
0-9613954),* P.O. Box 4538, North
Hollywood, CA 91607 (SAN 282-0986)
Tel 818-995-7042.

Pacific Santa Barbara, *(Pacific Pr. Santa
Barbara; 0-911094),* P.O. Box 219, Pierce
City, MO 65723 (SAN 202-1161)
Tel 417-476-2034.

Pacific Sci Ctr, *(Pacific Science Ctr.; 0-935051),*
200 Second Ave., N, Seattle, WA 98109
(SAN 694-5244) Tel 206-443-2001.

Pacific Scientific, *(Pacific Scientific Press, Inc.;
0-943792),* 3506 Pennsylvania Sta., Long
View, WA 98632 (SAN 241-0532)
Tel 206-425-8592.

†**Pacific Search,** *(Pacific Search Pr.; 0-914718;
0-931397),* 222 Dexter Ave. N., Seattle, WA
98109 (SAN 202-8476) Tel 206-682-5044;
Toll free: 800-858-0628; *CIP.*

Pacific Shoreline, *(Pacific Shoreline Pr.;
0-932967),* P.O. Box 217, Temple City, CA
91780 (SAN 689-9897) Tel 818-287-4767.

Pacific Sports, *(Pacific Sports Actualities;
0-910405),* Box 2443, Berkeley, CA 94702
(SAN 260-1141) Tel 415-848-5423.

Pacific Sun, *(Pacific Sun Pr.; 0-9602908),* 3785
Arroyo Sorrento Dr., San Diego, CA 92130
(SAN 214-073X) Tel 714-755-4422.

Pacific Tech, *(Pacific Technical Group, Inc.,
Publications Division; 0-913727),* 19329 Via
Crecente Ct. P.O. Box 2115, Saratoga, CA
95070 (SAN 286-102X) Tel 408-867-0666.

Pacific-West, *(Pacific Western Publishing Co.;
0-911096),* P.O. Box 604, Bakersfield, CA
93302 (SAN 220-9772).

Pacifica, *(Pacifica House, Inc., Pubs.; 0-911098),*
c/o Borden Publishing Co., 1855 W. Main
St., Alhambra, CA 91801 (SAN 201-419X).

Pacifica Lodi CA, *(Pacifica Publishing;
0-935109),* 1732 LeBec Ct., Lodi, CA 95240
(SAN 695-2135) Tel 209-369-2368.

Pacifica Pr, *(Pacifica Pr.; 0-935553),* 1149
Grand Teton Dr., Pacifica, CA 94044
(SAN 695-8958) Tel 415-355-6678.

Pack Pub, *(Pack Publishing; 0-9616304),* P.O.
Box 16163, Panama City, FL 32406
(SAN 693-8752) Tel 904-235-0794.

Package Publ, *(Package Publicity Service, Inc.;
0-911100),* 27 W. 24 St., New York, NY
10010 (SAN 206-8621) Tel 212-255-2872.

Packard, *(Packard Publishing; 0-941710),* P.O.
Box 10372, Beverly Hills, CA 90213
(SAN 239-2895) Tel 818-716-7306.

Packard Pr Fin, *(Packard Pr., Financial Pubns.
Div.; 0-936093),* 10th & Spring Garden Sts.,
Philadelphia, PA 19123 (SAN 696-8856)
Tel 215-236-2000.

Packrat Pr, *(Packrat Press Books; 0-9607554),*
P.O. Box 4904 Glenstone Sta., Springfield,
MO 65804 (SAN 211-7525)
Tel 417-865-1113.

†**Packrat WA,** *(Packrat Pr.; 0-915433),* 4366 N.
Diana Ln., Oak Harbor, WA 98277
(SAN 291-3232); *CIP.*

Pactel Pub, *(PacTel Publishing; 0-934315),* P.O.
Box 8124, Walnut Creek, CA 94596
(SAN 693-3564) Tel 415-932-6300; Orders
to: Redbook Subscription Ctr., P.O. Box
2044, Marion, OH 43305 (SAN 662-3182).

Paddlewheel, *(Paddlewheel Pr.; 0-938274),*
15100 SW 109th, Tigard, OR 97224
(SAN 215-8972) Tel 503-639-5637.

Padilla, *(Padilla, Francisco; 0-9605292),* P.O.
Box 11468, Denver, CO 80211
(SAN 216-2814) Tel 303-629-2425.

Padma, *(Padma Press; 0-917960),* P.O. Box 56,
Oatman, AZ 86433 (SAN 209-4088).

Padre Pio Pubs, *(Padre Pio Pubs.; 0-9615916),*
P.O. Box 468, Patagonia, AZ 85624
(SAN 696-8864) Tel 602-394-2018; 223
Duquesne Ave., Patagonia, AZ 85624
(SAN 696-8872).

†**Padre Prods,** *(Padre Productions; 0-914598),*
P.O. Box 1275, San Luis Obispo, CA 93406
(SAN 202-8484) Tel 805-543-5404; *CIP.*

†**Pagan Pr,** *(Pagan Pr.; 0-943742),* 26 St. Marks
Pl., New York, NY 10003 (SAN 241-0540)
Tel 212-674-3321; *CIP.*

Paganiniana Pubns, *(Paganiniana Pubns., Inc.;
0-87666),* Div. of T.F.H. Pubns., Inc., P.O.
Box 427, Neptune, NJ 07753
(SAN 209-309X) Tel 201-988-8400; Toll
free: 800-631-2188.

Page *Imprint of FS&G*

Page One, *(Page One Pubns.; 0-9607274),* P.O.
Box 2674, La Mesa, CA 92041
(SAN 239-3700) Tel 619-697-1584.

Page Pub
See Prime Pubs

Page Pub WI, *(Page Publishing Co.; 0-89769),*
Box 432, Brookfield, WI 53005
(SAN 239-3719).

Page Wand, *(Page/Wand Pr.; 0-9615663),* 2124
Kittredge St., No. 99, Berkeley, CA 94704
(SAN 695-8974) Tel 415-841-6500.

Pageant Pub Co, *(Pageant Publishing Co.;
0-914623),* P.O. Box 4455, Seattle, WA
98104 (SAN 287-296X) Tel 206-883-3202;
Orders to: Shelley Marketing Services, P.O.
Box 1288, Champlain, NY 12919-1288
(SAN 662-2119) Tel 514-678-5774.

Pages to Go, *(Pages to Go!!; 0-943102),* 2140
N. Iris Ln., Escondido, CA 92026
(SAN 240-4206) Tel 619-747-8644.

Paget Pr, *(Paget Pr.; 0-920348),* P.O. Box 3993,
Santa Barbara, CA 93130 (SAN 692-9648).

Paideia Hse, *(Paideia House, Pubs. (CA);
0-914027),* 22704 Ventura Blvd. Suite 435,
Woodland Hills, CA 91364 (SAN 286-8547)
Tel 818-888-7834.

†**Paideia MA,** *(Paideia Pubs.; 0-913993),* P.O.
Box 343, Ashfield, MA 01330
(SAN 287-7511) Tel 413-628-3838; *CIP.*

Paige Pubns, *(Paige Pubns.; 0-938699),* P.O.
Box 1384, Rancho Mirage, CA 92270
(SAN 661-535X); 2 Lincoln Pl., Rancho
Mirage, CA 92270 (SAN 661-5368)
Tel 619-328-7898.

Paine Inst
See T Paine Inst

PaineWebber Mortgage, *(PaineWebber Mortgage
Finance; 0-9603790),* P.O. Box 905,
Columbia, MD 21044 (SAN 213-8174)
Tel 301-964-8933.

Paint Box, *(Paint Box Studio, The; 0-9613287),*
145 Ashley Rd., Hopkins, MN 55343
(SAN 653-8118) Tel 612-935-2883.

Pair O Dice, *(Pair-O'-Dice Press; 0-943446),*
525 SE 16th Ave., Portland, OR 97214
(SAN 240-740X) Tel 503-236-2931.

PAJ Pubns, *(PAJ Pubns.; 0-933826; 1-55554),*
Div. of Performing Arts Journal, Inc., 325
Spring St., Suite 318, New York, NY 10013
(SAN 220-2670) Tel 212-243-3885; Dist.
by: Farrar, Straus & Giroux, Inc., 19 Union
Sq., W., New York, NY 10003
(SAN 206-782X) Tel 212-741-6900.

Pajarito Pubns, *(Pajarito Pubns.; 0-918358),*
2633 Granite NW, Albuquerque, NM 87104
(SAN 209-8555) Tel 505-242-8075.

Pakin Assocs, *(Pakin, Sandra & Associates, Inc.;
0-9608178),* 6007 N. Sheridan Rd., Chicago,
IL 60660 (SAN 240-2637)
Tel 312-271-2848.

PAL Pr, *(P.A.L. Pr.; 0-938034),* P.O. Box 487,
San Anselmo, CA 94960 (SAN 220-0791)
Tel 415-453-8547.

Pal Pub, *(Pal Publishing; 0-918104),* 10755
Bachelor Valley Rd., Witter Springs, CA
95493 (SAN 282-1001) Tel 707-275-2777;
P.O. Box 807, Northridge, CA 91328
(SAN 282-101X)95493.

Pal Pub MA, *(Pal Publishing Co.; 0-914765),*
P.O. Box 2325, Fitchburg, MA 01420
(SAN 291-8455).

Palace Mission, *(Palace Mission, Inc.;
0-9609078),* 1622 Spring Mill Rd.,
Gladwyne, PA 19035 (SAN 238-0773)
Tel 215-525-5598; Dist. by: ADFD Pubns.,
20 S. 36th St., Suite 104, Philadelphia, PA
19104 (SAN 282-6615) Tel 215-387-4857.

Paladin, *(Paladin Software Corp.; 0-912213),*
3255 Scott Blvd., Suite 7E, Santa Clara, CA
95054 (SAN 264-9837) Tel 408-970-0566.
Formerly known as VisiCorp Personal
Software, Inc.

Paladin Ent
See Paladin Pr

Paladin Hse, *(Paladin House Pubs.; 0-88252),*
P.O. Box 387, 2623 Kaneville Rd., Geneva,
IL 60134 (SAN 203-7041)
Tel 312-232-2711.

†**Paladin Pr,** *(Paladin Pr.; 0-87364),* P.O. Box
1307, Boulder, CO 80306 (SAN 212-0305);
Toll free: 800-824-7888; 2523 Broadway
Ave., Boulder, CO 80302 (SAN 662-1066)
Tel 303-443-7250; *CIP. Imprints:*
Sycamore Island (Sycamore Island
Books).(Sycamore Island Bks.).

Palasam Pub, *(Palasam Pubs.; 0-9607430),* 6808
Bowling Dr., Sacramento, CA 95823
(SAN 239-7889).

Palatine Pubns, *(Palatine Pubns., Inc.;
0-936638),* P.O. Drawer 1265, Ruston, LA
71273-1265 (SAN 214-0748).

Pale Horse, *(Pale Horse Press; 0-914720),* 433
Fair Ave., NE, New Philadelphia, OH 44663
(SAN 206-6092) Tel 216-364-3715.

Paleo Res, *(Paleontological Research Institution;
0-87710),* 1259 Trumansburg Rd., Ithaca,
NY 14850 (SAN 204-918X)
Tel 607-273-6623.

Palestine Focus, *(Palestine Focus Pubns.;
0-935177),* 1885 Mission St., San Francisco,
CA 94103-3584 (SAN 695-460X)
Tel 415-861-1552.

†**Palisades Pub,** *(Palisades Pubs.; 0-913530),*
P.O. Box 724, Pacific Palisades, CA 90272
(SAN 204-9198) Tel 213-454-0826; *CIP.*

Palladium Bks, *(Palladium Bks.; 0-916211),*
5924-26 Lonyo, Detroit, MI 48210
(SAN 294-9504) Tel 313-843-1275.

†**Palladium Pubns,** *(Palladium Pubns., Inc.),*
P.O. Box 58672, Seattle, WA 98188
(SAN 295-0197) Tel 206-251-5477; *CIP.*

Palm Bks, *(Palm Books; 0-9608036),* 25005
Foxway, Dept. 17,, Concord, CA 94518
(SAN 239-3727) Tel 415-674-8440.

Palm Pub Co, *(Palm Publishing Co.; 0-936187),*
P.O. Box 8091, Laguna Hills, CA
92654-8091 (SAN 696-8902)
Tel 714-458-5708; 25181 Woolwich, Laguna
Hills, CA 92653 (SAN 696-8910).

Palm Pubns, *(Palm Pubns.; 0-9613110),* 2654
Gough St., No. 102, San Francisco, CA
94123 (SAN 294-0760) Tel 415-928-3369.

Palm Springs Pub, *(Palm Springs Publishing;
0-914445),* 1380 Tamarisk Rd., Palm
Springs, CA 92262 (SAN 289-663X)
Tel 619-323-9968.

Palm Tree Lib, *(Palm Tree Library; 0-933266),*
P.O. Box 84268, Los Angeles, CA 90073
(SAN 212-3789).

Palm Tree Pub, *(Palm Tree Publishing, Inc.;
0-935627),* P.O. Box 292227, Ft.
Lauderdale, FL 33329 (SAN 695-9008)
Tel 305-584-0303; 4375 60th Ave., SW,
Davie, FL 33314.

Palmen Inst, *(Palmen Institute, The; 0-9617213),*
P.O. Box 671, Edmonds, WA 98020
(SAN 663-4214); 4620 200th St. SW, Suite
D, Lynnwood, WA 98036 (SAN 663-4222)
Tel 206-672-4750.

Palmer Ent, *(Palmer Enterprises; 0-912479),*
P.O. Box 966, Orangevale, CA 95662
(SAN 215-1650) Tel 916-988-8435.

Palmer Memorial, *(Palmer Memorial Episcopal Church; 0-9617291),* 6221 S. Main St., Houston, TX 77005 (SAN 663-608X) Tel 713-529-6196.
Palmer-Pletsch, *(Palmer-Pletsch Associates; 0-935278),* P.O. Box 12046, Portland, OR 97212 (SAN 209-1933) Tel 503-231-4908.
Palmer Pub CA
See Palmer Ent
Palmer Pubns WI, *(Palmer Pubns. at Amherst),* Amherst, WI 54406 (SAN 295-3609) (SAN 295-3617).
Palmetto Pr, *(Palmetto Pr., Inc.; 0-9615619),* P.O. Box 660-445, Miami Springs, FL 33266 (SAN 695-8559) Tel 305-887-7157; 88 Glendale Dr., Miami Springs, FL 33314 (SAN 696-0421).
Palmetto Pub, *(Palmetto Publishing Co.; 0-9613853),* 1318 Geiger Ave., Columbia, SC 29201 (SAN 685-2173) Tel 803-252-4867.
Palomar, *(Palomar Publishing Co.),* P.O. Box 4444, Whittier, CA 90607 (SAN 204-9201).
†**Palomar Bks,** *(Palomar Books; 0-932882),* P.O. Box 222, San Marcos, CA 92069 (SAN 212-2952) Tel 805-931-1755; CIP.
Palomares & Assoc, *(Palomares & Associates; 0-86584),* P.O. Box 1577, Spring Valley, CA 92077 (SAN 669-0963) Tel 619-698-6654.
Palomino Pr, *(Palomino Pr.; 0-9610036),* 86-07 144th St., Briarwood, NY 11435 (SAN 241-5739) Tel 718-297-5053; Dist. by: Quality Bks., 918 Sherwood Dr., Lake Bluff, IL 60044-2204 (SAN 169-2127); Dist. by: Baker & Taylor Co., 50 Kirby Ave., Somerville, NJ 08876 (SAN 169-4901).
Palos Verdes, *(Palos Verdes Bk. Co.; 0-936848),* P.O. Box 456, Lomita, CA 90717 (SAN 218-4532) Tel 904-383-8727.
Pambili Bks, *(Pambili Books; 0-917336),* 105 Gates St., San Francisco, CA 94110 (SAN 208-8010) Tel 415-821-9717.
Pamela Pubns, *(Pamela Pubns.; 0-938003),* Subs. of Pamela, Inc., 1117 Marquette Ave., Suite 1601, Minneapolis, MN 55403 (SAN 659-7491) Tel 612-339-8139.
Pan Am Intl Ozone, *(Pan American Commmitte/International Ozone; 0-918650),* 83 Oakwood Ave., Norwalk, CT 06850 (SAN 271-5082) Tel 203-847-8169.
Pan Am Nav, *(Pan American Navigation Service, Inc.; 0-87219),* P.O. Box 9046, Van Nuys, CA 91409 (SAN 202-8506) Tel 818-345-2744; Toll free: 800-423-5932.
Pan-Am Publishing Co, *(Pan-American Publishing Co.; 0-932906),* P.O. Box 1505, Las Vegas, NM 87101 (SAN 212-5366).
Pan Am Pubns, *(Pan Am Pubns.; 0-87582),* Pan Am Bldg., New York, NY 10166 (SAN 204-9228).
Pan Ishtar, *(Pan/Ishtar Unlimited; 0-941698),* P.O. Box 216, Edgewood, TX 75117 (SAN 239-2747) Tel 214-896-1700.
Pan Prods, *(Pan Productions; 0-9606100),* Box 72, Coronado, CA 92118 (SAN 216-8480) Tel 619-435-6042.
Pana Pr, *(Pana Pr.; 0-9615244),* 4559 Fran Way, Richmond, CA 94803 (SAN 695-166X) Tel 415-222-4672.
Panache Prods, *(Panache Productions; 0-9610596),* 1388 Moorpark Rd., Thousand Oaks, CA 91360 (SAN 264-2859) Tel 805-495-6608.
Pancake Pr, *(Pancake Pr.; 0-942908),* 163 Galewood Circle, San Francisco, CA 94131 (SAN 218-0448) Tel 415-665-9215.
Panda Bks Pubs, *(Panda Bks., Pubs.; 0-937541),* P.O. Box 90488, San Diego, CA 92109-0860 (SAN 658-974X) Tel 619-461-5169. *Imprints:* Silk Butterfly Pr (Silk Butterfly Press).(Silk Butterfly Pr.).
Panda Press VA, *(Panda Pr.; 0-9616700),* 4111 Watkins Trail, Annandale, VA 22003 (SAN 659-6711) Tel 703-256-2461.
Panda Programs, *(Panda Programs; 0-942476),* 1872 W. Lotus Pl., Brea, CA 92621 (SAN 219-2403).
P&D Pub, *(P & D Publishing Co.; 0-9616614),* 588 Audubon Ave. NE, Palm Bay, FL 32907 (SAN 659-7483) Tel 305-725-7243.
Pandora's Treasures, *(Pandora's Treasures; 0-9605236),* 1609 Eastover Terrace, Boise, ID 83706 (SAN 282-1036) Tel 208-342-4002.
†**Panel Pubs,** *(Panel Pubs.; 0-916592),* Affil. of Worldwide Walter Samsom Group, 14 Plaza Rd., Greenvale, NY 11548 (SAN 204-921X) Tel 516-484-0006; CIP.

Panhandle, *(Panhandle-Plains Historical Society Museum; 0-913463),* P.O. Box 967, W.T. Sta., Canyon, TX 79016 (SAN 280-0446) Tel 806-655-7191.
†**Panjandrum,** *(Panjandrum Bks..; 0-915572),* 11321 Iowa Ave., Suite 1, Los Angeles, CA 90025 (SAN 282-1257) Tel 213-477-8771; Dist. by: Baker & Taylor (Western Div.), 380 Edison Way, Reno, NV 89564 (SAN 169-4464) Tel 702-786-6700; Dist. by: Talman Co., Inc., 150 Fifth Ave., Rm. 514, New York, NY 10011 (SAN 200-5204) Tel 212-620-3182; Dist. by: Blackwell North America, 6024 SW. Jean Rd., Bldg. G, Lake Oswego, OR 97034 (SAN 656-4917) Tel 503-684-1140; Dist. by: Bookpeople, 2929 Fifth St., Berkeley, CA 94710 (SAN 168-9517); Dist. by: Shakti Distributors, Inc., 1020 White St, SW, Atlanta, GA 30310 (SAN 200-7258); Dist. by: Coutts Library Services, 736-738 Cayuga St., Lewiston, NY 14092 (SAN 169-5401); CIP.
Panjandrum Pr
See Panjandrum
Panoply Pr, *(Panoply Press, Inc.; 0-9615067),* P.O. Box 1885, Lake Oswego, OR 97034 (SAN 693-9279) Tel 503-620-7239.
Panoptic Ent, *(Panoptic Enterprises; 0-912481),* P.O. Box 1099, Woodbridge, VA 22193-0099 (SAN 265-3141) Tel 703-670-2812.
Panorama Van Nuys, *(Panorama Publishing Co.; 0-937671),* 14640 Victory Blvd., No. 210, Van Nuys, CA 91411 (SAN 659-2627) Tel 818-988-4690.
Panorama West, *(Panorama West Bks.; 0-914330),* 2002 N. Gateway Suite 102, Fresno, CA 93727 (SAN 216-0501) Tel 209-251-7801.
Panoramic Pr CA, *(Panoramic Pr.; 0-937879),* 340 Panoromic Hwy., Mill Valley, CA 94941 (SAN 695-5529) Tel 415-454-1892; Dist. by: Ancient Future, P.O. Box 264, Kentfield, CA 94914 (SAN 200-6499).
Pant Bks Young *Imprint of* **Pantheon**
Pantagraph Bks *Imprint of* **Evergreen Comm**
†**Pantheon,** *(Pantheon Bks.; 0-394),* Div. of Random Hse., Inc., 201 E. 50th St., New York, NY 10022 (SAN 202-862X) Tel 212-751-2600; Toll free: 800-638-6460; Orders to: Random Hse., Inc., 400 Hahn Rd., Westminster, MD 21157 (SAN 202-5515); CIP. *Imprints:* Pant Bks Young (Pantheon Books for Young Readers).
Pantheon Pr
See Tulane U Conf Hispanic Lit
Pants Pr, *(Pants Pr.; 0-9614241),* 4628 Drew Ave. South, Minneapolis, MN 55410 (SAN 686-693X) Tel 612-572-3998.
Papaloa Pr, *(Papaloa Pr.; 0-9615498),* 362 Selby Ln., Atherton, CA 94025 (SAN 695-5487) Tel 415-369-9994; Dist. by: Baker & Taylor, 1515 Broadway, New York, NY 10036 (SAN 169-5606) Tel 212-730-7650; Dist. by: Quality Bks., 918 Sherwood Dr., Lake Bluff, IL 60044-2204 (SAN 169-2127); Dist. by: Western States Book Service, P.O. Box 855, Clackamas, OR 97015 (SAN 200-5602); Dist. by: Pacific Pipeline, 19215 66th Ave., S., Kent, WA 98032 (SAN 208-2128) Tel 206-872-5523.
Papa's Pr, *(Papa's Pr.; 0-9601968),* P.O. Box 81555, San Diego, CA 92138-1555 (SAN 207-6292) Tel 619-582-6294.
Paper Bag, *(Paper Bag Players; 0-9606662),* 50 Riverside Dr., New York, NY 10024 (SAN 212-9566); Orders to: Walter Baker Co., 100 Chauncey St., Boston, MA 02111 (SAN 662-1074); Orders to: Eeyore Bookstore, 82nd & Madison Ave., New York, NY 10028 (SAN 662-1082).
Paper Birch Pr, *(Paper Birch Pr., Inc.; 0-9613961; 0-939687),* P.O. Box 128, Ashland, WI 54806 (SAN 682-3076) Tel 715-682-9418; Toll free: 800-336-5666; Dist. by: Bookman, 519 N. Third St., Minneapolis, MN 55401 (SAN 282-7352) Tel 612-341-3333; Dist. by: Baker & Taylor, Midwest Div., 501 Gladiola Ave., Momence, IL 60954 (SAN 169-2100); Dist. by: The Distribtuors, 702 S. Michigan, South Bend, IN 46618 (SAN 169-2488) Tel 219-232-8500.
Paper Cloud Pr, *(Paper Cloud Pr., The; 0-9615850),* P.O. Box 2178, Santa Barbara, CA 93101 (SAN 696-8929) Tel 805-969-0863; 72 Canyon View Rd., Santa Barbara, CA 93108 (SAN 696-8937).

Paper Corp Am, *(Paper Corp. of America; 0-936239),* c/o Baldwin Paper Co., 161 Sixth Ave., New York, NY 10013 (SAN 696-8775) Tel 212-255-1600.
Paper Dreams, *(Paper Dreams; 0-937149),* 1511 Forest Way, Del Mar, CA 92014 (SAN 658-4810) Tel 619-755-3289; P.O. Box 2951, Del Mar, CA 92014 (SAN 658-4829).
†**Paper Mill Pr,** *(Paper Mill Pr.; 0-9612304),* 8650 Lords Manor Way, Rohnert Park, CA 94928 (SAN 287-7546) Tel 707-795-4132; CIP.
Paper Pile, *(Paper Pile Pr. of San Anselmo; 0-915195),* P.O. Box 337, San Anselmo, CA 94960 (SAN 287-3087) Tel 415-454-5552.
Paper Tiger Pap, *(Paper Tiger Paperbacks, Inc.; 0-933334),* 1512 NW Seventh Pl., Gainesville, FL 32603 (SAN 212-5374) Tel 904-371-7771; Dist. by: Hippocrene Bks., Inc., 171 Madison Ave., New York, NY 10016 (SAN 213-2060) Tel 718-454-2366.
Paper Vision *Imprint of* **Western Tanager**
Paper Vision
See Western Tanager
Paperback Lib
See Warner Bks
Paperback Quarterly, *(Paperback Quarterly Pubns.; 0-941858),* 1710 Vincent St., Brownwood, TX 76801 (SAN 239-4669); Dist. by: Borgo Press, P.O. Box 2845, San Bernardino, CA 92406-2845 (SAN 208-9459) Tel 714-884-5813.
Paperback Video, *(Paperback Video, Inc.; 0-937621),* 448 Ignacio Blvd., Suite 254, Novato, CA 94947 (SAN 658-9790) Tel 415-382-1560.
Paperbacks Plus, *(Paperbacks Plus Pr.; 0-942186),* 108 E. Davis, Mesquite, TX 75149 (SAN 262-0545).
Papermac *Imprint of* **St Martin**
†**Paperweight Pr,** *(Paperweight Pr.; 0-933756),* 761 Chestnut St., Santa Cruz, CA 95060 (SAN 212-5390); Dist. by: Charles Tuttle Publishing Co., 49 Central Ave., Rutland, VT 05701 (SAN 169-6629) Tel 513-381-3881; CIP.
Papier-Mache Press, *(Papier-Mache Pr.; 0-918949),* 34 Malaga Place E., Manhattan Beach, CA 90266 (SAN 669-8336) Tel 213-545-3812.
Papillon Pr, *(Papillon Pr.; 0-9608826),* 1232 Vallecito Rd., Carpinteria, CA 93013 (SAN 213-1447) Tel 805-684-5038.
Papillon Pubns, *(Papillon Pubns.; 0-938750),* 101 First St., Suite 284, Los Altos, CA 94022 (SAN 238-7468) Tel 415-948-5320.
Papp Hist Pubns, *(Papp Historical Pubns.; 0-937735),* 58 Woodlawn St., Schenectady, NY 12306 (SAN 659-266X) Tel 518-387-7727.
Pappani, *(Pappani, Debra Ann; 0-9606062),* 1990 Hurst Ave., San Jose, CA 95125 (SAN 216-9207) Tel 408-264-9907.
Papyrus Pubs, *(Papyrus Pubs.; 0-943698),* P.O. Box 466, Yonkers, NY 10704 (SAN 238-079X) Tel 914-664-0840.
†**PAR Inc,** *(P.A.R., Inc.; 0-913310; 0-89702),* Subs. of Abbott Park Associates, 290 Westminster St., Providence, RI 02903-3416 (SAN 203-0209) Tel 401-331-0130; Toll free: 800-556-7277. Do not confuse with PAR, Inc., FL; CIP.
Para-Bk-Pr, *(Para-Bk-Pr.; 0-9612120),* P.O. Box 647, N. Hollywood, CA 91603 (SAN 287-7554) Tel 818-896-1630.
†**Para Pub,** *(Para Publishing; 0-915516),* P.O. Box 4232-R, Santa Barbara, CA 93140-4232 (SAN 215-8981) Tel 805-968-7277; Dist. by: Baker & Taylor, Eastern Div., 50 Kirby Ave., Somerville, NJ 08876 (SAN 169-4901); Dist. by: Bookpeople, 2929 Fifth St., Berkeley, CA 94710 (SAN 168-9517); Dist. by: Publishers Group West, 5855 Beaudry St., Emeryville, CA 94608 (SAN 202-8522) Tel 415-658-3453; CIP.
Para Res, *(Para Research, Inc.; 0-914918),* 85 Eastern Ave., P.O. Box 61, Gloucester, MA 01930 (SAN 213-4438) Tel 617-283-3438.
Parable, *(Parable),* 38 N. Austin Blvd., Oak Park, IL 60302 (SAN 283-9792) Tel 312-848-0025.
†**Parable Pr,** *(Parable Pr.; 0-917250),* 136 Gray St., Amherst, MA 01002 (SAN 208-4449) Tel 413-253-5634; CIP.

Parables, *(Parables; 0-9614960),* Subs. of Bentley Enterprises, P.O. Box 73, Ludlow, MA 01056 (SAN 693-7535) Tel 413-543-5809.

Parabolic Pr, *(Parabolic Press, Inc.; 0-915760),* P.O. Box 3032, Stanford, CA 94305 (SAN 207-5814) Tel 415-328-1084.

Paracelsus, *(Paracelsus College; 0-915939),* 3555 S. 700 E., Utah Institute of Parachemistry, Salt Lake City, UT 84106 (SAN 294-0779) Tel 801-486-6730.

Parachute Pr, *(Parachute Pr., Inc.; 0-938753),* 200 Fifth Ave., Room 461, New York, NY 10010 (SAN 661-5554) Tel 212-691-1421. Do not confuse with Parachute Pr., Tempe, AZ.

†Parachuting Res, *(Parachuting Resources; 0-933382),* MC P.O. Box 1291, Dayton, OH 45402 (SAN 212-5404) Tel 513-258-1777; *CIP.*

Paraclete Pr, *(Paraclete Pr.; 0-941478),* Div. of Creative Joys, Inc., Box 1568, Orleans, MA 02653 (SAN 282-1508) Tel 617-255-4685; Toll free: 800-451-5006.

Paradesa Edit, *(Paradesa Editions; 0-937943),* 9 Nebraska St., San Francisco, CA 94110 (SAN 659-7505) Tel 415-824-0259.

Paradigm Corp, *(Paradigm Corp.),* 2546 W. Main St., Littleton, CO 80120 (SAN 658-8271).

Paradigm ID, *(Paradigm Co., The; 0-914981),* P.O. Box 45161, Boise, ID 83711 (SAN 682-8019) Tel 208-322-4440.

Paradigm Pr, *(Paradigm Pr.; 0-937572),* 127 Greenbrae Boardwalk, Greenbrae, CA 94904 (SAN 220-0821) Tel 415-461-5457; Dist. by: Bookpeople, 2929 Fifth St., Berkeley, CA 94710 (SAN 168-9517).

†Paradigm Pubns, *(Paradigm Pubns.; 0-912111),* 44 Linden St., Brookline, MA 02146 (SAN 264-7745); Dist. by: Redwing Book Co., 44 Linden St., Brookline, MA 02146 (SAN 159-9348) Tel 617-738-4664; *CIP.*

Paradise, *(Paradise Plus; 0-9616059),* 929 SW Salmon, 112, Portland, OR 97205 (SAN 698-0848) Tel 503-228-2316; Dist. by: Pacific Pipeline, Inc., 19215 66th Ave. S., Kent, WA 98032 (SAN 208-2128) Tel 805-543-5404; Dist. by: Booklink Distributors, P.O. Box 1275, San Luis Obispo, CA 93406 (SAN 159-0782).

Paradise Hse, *(Paradise House, Inc.; 0-87358),* 10231 N. Scottsdale Rd. B-1, Scottdale, AZ 85253 (SAN 693-3580); Dist. by: Northland Press, P.O. Box N, Flagstaff, AZ 86002 (SAN 202-9251).

Paradise Pl, *(Paradise Place; 0-9616821),* 7064 Nicholas St., Omaha, NE 68132 (SAN 661-4736) Tel 402-556-6262.

Paradise Press, *(Paradise Press; 0-940806),* P.O. Box 5306, Santa Monica, CA 90405 (SAN 219-6190) Tel 213-392-4098. Do not confuse with Paradise Pr., Corte Madera, CA.

Paradise Pubns, *(Paradise Pubns.; 0-9614113),* 8110 SW Wareham Cir., Portland, OR 97223 (SAN 685-9976) Tel 503-246-1555.

Paragon Assocs
See Paragon Benson

Paragon Benson, *(Paragon Assocs./Benson Co., Inc.; 0-89477),* 365 Great Circle Road, Nashville, TN 37228 (SAN 209-9780) Tel 615-259-9111; Dist. by: Alexandria Hse., P.O. Box 23618, Alexandria, IN 46001 (SAN 209-9799).

Paragon-Dynapress, *(Paragon Pr./Dynapress; 0-942910),* P.O. Box 866, Fern Park, FL 32730 (SAN 240-3234) Tel 305-331-5550.

Paragon Group, *(Paragon Group, Inc., The; 0-9615902),* 19417 SE 425, Enumclaw, WA 98022 (SAN 696-7876) Tel 206-825-2832.

†Paragon Hse, *(Paragon Hse., Pubs.; 0-913729; 0-88702; 0-89226; 0-943852; 0-913757),* 2 Hammarskjold Plaza, New York, NY 10017 (SAN 286-1704) Tel 212-223-6433; *CIP.*

Paragon Prods, *(Paragon Productions; 0-9602184),* 817 Pearl St., Denver, CO 80203 (SAN 213-2702) Tel 303-832-7687.

Paragon Pub CA, *(Paragon Publishing; 0-914809),* P.O. Box 53, Santa Rosa, CA 95402 (SAN 289-3592) Tel 707-527-8185.

†Paragon-Reiss, *(Paragon-Reiss; 0-910199),* Div. of National Paragon Corp., 57-07 31st Ave., Woodside, NY 11377 (SAN 241-4244) Tel 718-728-5300; *CIP.*

Paragraph Pr, *(Paragraph Press; 0-915462),* 204 Circle Dr., P.O. Box 1107, Felton, CA 95018 (SAN 207-4974) Tel 408-335-4406.

Paragraphics, *(Paragraphics; 0-9616637),* 427 Third St., Brooklyn, NY 11215 (SAN 659-672X) Tel 718-965-2231.

Paragraphics Pr, *(Paragraphics Pr.; 0-939175),* Div. of Mercury Typographers, Inc., 133 Fifth Ave., Third Flr., New York, NY 10003 (SAN 662-9075) Tel 201-332-5917. Do not confuse with Paragraphics of Brooklyn, NY.

Parallax Pr, *(Parallax Pr.; 0-938077),* P.O. Box 7355, Berkeley, CA 94707 (SAN 663-4494) Tel 415-525-0101. Do not confuse with Parallax Pr., Middletown, CT.

Parallel Integ, *(Parallel Integration; 0-9617281),* P.O. Box 6001, Lincoln, NE 68506 (SAN 663-5237); 2640 Lake Condominium "D", Lincoln, NE 68502 (SAN 663-5245) Tel 402-474-2727.

Parallel Lines, *(Parallel Lines, Inc.; 0-9616882),* RD 2, P.O. Box 673, Howell, NJ 07731 (SAN 661-6585) Tel 201-370-2095.

†Paramount, *(Paramount Publishing; 0-918668),* 800 Roosevelt Rd., Suite 413, Bldg. B, Glen Ellyn, IL 60137 (SAN 212-6796) Tel 312-790-2483; *CIP.*

Paramount Bks, *(Paramount Bks.; 0-9616024),* 1200 N. Terr., Suite 229, Provo, UT 84604 (SAN 697-936X) Tel 801-375-1053.

Paramount TX, *(Paramount Publishing; 0-942376),* P.O. Box 3730, Amarillo, TX 79116-3730 (SAN 238-1028) Tel 806-355-1040.

Paranoid Pubns, *(Paranoid Pubns.; 0-9602716),* P.O. Box 614, 631/2 S. Main, Manteno, IL 60950 (SAN 212-7857) Tel 815-468-3778.

Parapsych Foun, *(Parapsychology Foundation, Inc.; 0-912328),* 228 E. 71st St., New York, NY 10021 (SAN 203-6851) Tel 212-628-1550.

Parapsych Pr, *(Parapsych Press; 0-911106),* P.O. Box 6847, College Sta., Durham, NC 27708 (SAN 204-9252) Tel 919-688-8241.

Parchment Pr, *(Parchment Press; 0-88428),* 5345 Atlanta Hwy., Montgomery, AL 36193 (SAN 202-8670) Tel 205-272-5820.

Pardo Pr, *(Pardo Press, The; 0-9609204),* 702 Polk Avenue, Lawrenceville, NJ 08648 (SAN 241-4252) Tel 609-396-7214.

Parent-Child Pr, *(Parent-Child Pr.; 0-9601016; 0-939195),* P.O. Box 767, Altoona, PA 16603 (SAN 208-4333); 4201 Second Ave., Altoona, PA 16602 (SAN 662-7331) Tel 814-946-5213.

Parent Scene, *(Parent Scene; 0-910529),* P.O. Box 2222, 1280 E. San Bernardino Ave., Redlands, CA 92373 (SAN 260-244X) Tel 714-792-2412.

Parenthesis Pr, *(Parenthesis Press; 0-9601580),* P.O. Box 114, Bridgewater College, Bridgewater, VA 22812 (SAN 202-8689) Tel 703-828-6656.

†Parenting Pr, *(Parenting Pr.; 0-9602862; 0-943990),* P.O. Box 15163, Seattle, WA 98115 (SAN 215-6938); Toll free: 800-99B-OOKS; 7744 31st Ave. NE, Seattle, WA 98115 (SAN 699-5500); *CIP.*

†Parents, *(Parents Magazine Pr.; 0-8193),* Div. of Gruner & Jahr, USA, Publishing, 685 Third Ave., New York, NY 10017 (SAN 202-8697) Tel 212-878-8700; Toll free: 800-526-0275; Dist. by: New American Library, P.O. Box 999, Bergenfield, NJ 07621 (SAN 282-6843) Tel 201-387-0600; Dist. by: E. P. Dutton, 2 Park Ave., New York, NY 10016 (SAN 201-0070) Tel 212-725-1818; *CIP.*

Parents Anon, *(Parents Anonymous),* 7120 Franklin Ave., Los Angeles, CA 90046 (SAN 217-2607) Tel 213-876-9642; Toll free: 800-421-0353.

Parents as Tchrs, *(Parents as Teachers; 0-9616691),* P.O. Box 44093, Tacoma, WA 98444 (SAN 659-817X); 701 Violet Meadow S., Tacoma, WA 98444 (SAN 659-8188) Tel 206-531-0312.

Parents Pointers, *(Parents' Pointers Pubns.; 0-9608756),* Route 1, Box 238, Lawrenceburg, TN 38464 (SAN 241-063X) Tel 615-762-2663.

Parents Pr KY, *(Parents Pr.; 0-935111),* P.O. Box 2180, Bowling Green, KY 42102-2180 (SAN 695-1422) Tel 502-843-1245; Dist. by: Baker & Taylor (Midwest Div.), 501 Gladiola Ave., Momence, IL 60954 (SAN 169-2100) Tel 815-472-2444.

Parey Sci Pubs, *(Parey, Paul, Scientific Pubs.; 3-489),* 35 W. 38th St., No. 3W, New York, NY 10018 (SAN 216-0021) Tel 212-730-0518.

Park Ave Pubns, *(Park Avenue Pubns.; 0-938149),* P.O. Box 303, Canandaigua, NY 14424 (SAN 659-8951); 132 Park Ave., Canandaigua, NY 14424 (SAN 659-896X) Tel 716-394-8632.

Park City Pr, *(Park City Press),* Div. of Sunflower Publishing, Inc., P.O. Box 25, Glenwood Landing, NY 11457 (SAN 287-2838).

Park Lane Ent, *(Park Lane Enterprises; 0-9609362),* 24 Park Ln., Minneapolis, MN 55416 (SAN 260-2458) Tel 612-922-1888.

Park Maitland, *(Park Maitland School, The; 0-9613532),* 1450 S.Onado Ave., Maitland, FL 32751 (SAN 657-369X) Tel 305-647-3038.

Park Pr Co, *(Park Pr. Co.; 0-941226),* 2612 N. Mattis Ave., Champaign, IL 61821 (SAN 239-4685).

Park Pub, *(Park Publishing, Inc.; 0-9603294),* 1999 Shepard Rd., St. Paul, MN 55116 (SAN 204-9260) Tel 612-698-1667.

Park Pubns Ltd, *(Parkside Pubns. Ltd.; 0-9617266),* 999 Third Ave., Suite 3210, Seattle, WA 98104 (SAN 663-4907) Tel 206-621-1818.

Park Row Pr, *(Park Row Pr.; 0-935749),* 1418 Park Row, San Diego, CA 92037 (SAN 695-9105) Tel 619-459-2121.

Park Row Soft
See Park Row Pr

Park View, *(Park View Press, Inc.; 0-87813),* 1066 Chicago Ave., Harrisonburg, VA 22801 (SAN 204-9279) Tel 703-434-0765.

Park West, *(Park West; 0-9610480),* P.O. Box 1502, Sausalito, CA 94966 (SAN 264-2875); Dist. by: Bookpeople, 2929 Fifth St., Berkeley, CA 94710 (SAN 168-9517); Dist. by: Distributors, The, 702 S. Michigan, South Bend, IN 46618 (SAN 212-0364) Tel 219-232-8500; Dist. by: Publishers Group West, 5855 Beaudry St., Emeryville, CA 94608 (SAN 696-0200) Tel 415-658-3453; Dist. by: Quality Books, 918 Sherwood Dr., Lake Bluff, IL 60044-2204 (SAN 169-2127).

Parker *Imprint of P-H*

Parker & Son, *(Parker & Son Pubns., Inc.; 0-911110),* Box 60001, Los Angeles, CA 90060 (SAN 202-8719) Tel 213-727-1088.

†Parker Bro, *(Parker Brothers Publishing; · 0-910313; 0-87372; 0-926088),* Div. of Parker Brothers, 50 Dunham Rd., Beverly, MA 01915 (SAN 241-4260); Toll free: 800-225-0540; *CIP.*

Parker Chiro, *(Parker Chiropractic Research Foundation, Inc.; 0-9609606),* P.O. Box 40041, Fort Worth, TX 76140 (SAN 260-2466) Tel 816-293-6444.

Parker Engine Pub, *(Parker Engineering Publishing; 0-9611048),* 1510 Eisenhower, No. 331, Boulder, CO 80303 (SAN 283-3417) Tel 303-443-1286.

Parker Pr, *(Parker Press, The; 0-939562),* 31 Marlboro St., Newburyport, MA 01950 (SAN 216-4310) Tel 617-462-3427.

Parker Pub
See C A Parker Pubns

Parker Pubns
See C A Parker Pubns

Parkhurst, *(Parkhurst Press; 0-939500),* P.O. Box 143, Laguna Beach, CA 92652 (SAN 216-4329).

Parkhurst Br, *(Parkhurst Brook Pubs.; 0-9615664),* Perrin Rd., RD 3, Potsdam, NY 13676 (SAN 695-9121) Tel 315-265-9037.

Parkrail, *(Parkrail; 0-9616240),* 1025 Oxford, Apt. L-138, Fort Collins, CO 80525 (SAN 658-4691) Tel 303-226-1233.

Parks & Nature, *(Parks & Nature Centers, Inc.; 0-9613492),* P.O. Box 1791, Athens, GA 30603 (SAN 657-3703) Tel 404-548-3811.

Parkside, *(Parkside Press; 0-941180),* 2026 Parkside Court, West Linn, OR 97068 (SAN 239-3735).

Parkside Pub Co, *(Parkside Press Publishing Co.; 0-911585),* P.O. Box 11585, Santa Ana, CA 92711 (SAN 264-2883) Tel 714-838-1888.

Parkway, *(Parkway Pr.; 0-9610176),* P.O. Box 161, Roslyn Heights, NY 11577 (SAN 695-7099).

Parkway MO
See Parkway Pr Ltd

Parkway Pr, *(Parkway Press, Inc.; 0-930408),* 3347 E. Calhoun Pkwy., Minneapolis, MN 55408 (SAN 211-0474) Tel 612-827-3347.

Symbols/Abbreviations

Parkway Pr Ltd, *(Parkway Press Ltd.;
0-938270),* Box 174, West Tisbury, MA
02575 (SAN 239-4693) Tel 617-693-4596;
Orders to: Box 8158, Shawnee Mission, KS
66208. Do not confuse with Parkway in
Minneapolis & Parkway in Roslyn Heights
NY.
Parkway Pubns, *(Parkway Pubns.; 0-9608398),*
P.O. Box 19845, 5616 W. Rita Drive, West
Allis, WI 53219 (SAN 238-0803)
Tel 414-321-5454.
Parkwest Pubns, *(Parkwest Pubns.; 0-88186),*
P.O. Caller Box A-10, Cathedral Sta., New
York, NY 10025 (SAN 264-6846)
Tel 212-222-6100. *Imprints:* Tarquin
(Tarquin).
Parliamentarians, *(Parliamentarians
International; 0-942302),* 50 Redwood Ave.,
No. 303, Redwood City, CA 94061-3002
(SAN 238-0811) Tel 415-367-1962.
Parlimentary Pub
See Parliamentarians
Parmadale, *(Parmadale Childrens Village;
0-9615123),* 6753 State Rd., Parma, OH
44134 (SAN 694-180X) Tel 216-845-7700.
Parmly Lib, *(Parmly Billings Library;
0-9613224),* 510 N. Broadway, Billings, MT
59101 (SAN 295-1347) Tel 406-657-8294.
Parnassos NY
See Pella Pub
Parnassus Imprints, *(Parnassus Imprints;
0-940160),* Box 335, Orleans, MA 02653
(SAN 217-0809) Tel 617-225-2932; 21
Canal Rd., Orleans, MA 02653
(SAN 658-1366) Tel 617-225-2932.
Parpaglion, *(Parpaglion & Co.; 0-9604252),* 413
Woodland Ave., Cherry Hill, NJ 08002
(SAN 214-4360) Tel 609-488-4494.
Parr Pub, *(Parr Publishing Co., Inc.; 0-89473),*
1200 S. Post Oak Rd., Suite 428, Houston,
TX 77056 (SAN 209-6315)
Tel 713-626-7830.
†**Parrish Art,** *(Parrish Art Museum, The;
0-943526),* 25 Jobs Ln., Southampton, NY
11968 (SAN 240-7418) Tel 516-283-2118;
CIP.
Parrott Pr, *(Parrott Pr.; 0-9616749),* 18 Otis St.,
Watertown, MA 02172 (SAN 661-0439)
Tel 617-926-9668.
Parsonage Pr, *(Parsonage Pr., The; 0-9615872),*
4620-29th Ave. S., Minneapolis, MN 55406
(SAN 696-6179) Tel 612-729-1798.
Parsons Pr, *(Parson's Pr.; 0-931085),* 140
Garden Ave., Roselle, IL 60172
(SAN 678-9390) Tel 312-529-1307.
Part-Ease, *(Part-Ease; 0-9607664),* P.O. Box
144, New Milford, NJ 07646
(SAN 238-082X).
Parthenon Pubns, *(Parthenon Pubns.),* 139
Santa Fe Ave., El Cerrito, CA 94530
(SAN 214-4379) Tel 415-527-1374.
Partisan Pr, *(Partisan Press, Inc.; 0-935150),*
P.O. Box 31387, Seattle, WA 98103
(SAN 215-6946).
Partner Pr, *(Partner Press; 0-933212),* Box 124,
Livonia, MI 48152 (SAN 212-7865)
Tel 313-651-8997; Dist. by: Gryphon House,
Inc., 3706 Otis St., Mount Rainier, MD
20712 (SAN 169-3190) Tel 301-779-6200.
†**Partners Livable,** *(Partners for Livable Places;
0-941182),* 1429 21st St., NW, Washington,
DC 20036 (SAN 200-402X)
Tel 202-887-5990; *CIP.*
Partners Pr NJ, *(Partners Pr.; 0-942676),* 301
N. Harrison St., Bldg. B, Suite 279,
Princeton, NJ 08540 (SAN 239-8656)
Tel 609-924-4438.
Partnership Foundation, *(Partnership
Foundation, the; 0-934538),* C/O Capon
Springs & Farms, Capon Springs, WV 26823
(SAN 220-9918).
Partridge Pair, *(Partridge Pair, Inc., The;
0-9606440),* P.O. Box 61, Sandy Springs, SC
29677 (SAN 218-5776) Tel 803-261-8430.
Partyline Enter, *(Partyline Enterprises;
0-9616680),* 1517 W. Lake St., Minneapolis,
MN 55403 (SAN 659-6746)
Tel 612-339-0103.
Pasadena Art, *(Pasadena Art Alliance;
0-937042),* 314 S. Mentor Ave., Pasadena,
CA 91106 (SAN 213-5434)
Tel 818-795-9276.
Pasadena Pr, *(Pasadena Pr.; 0-930227),* 267 S.
Madison, No. 204, Pasadena, CA 91106
(SAN 694-6410) Tel 818-796-3840; P.O.
Box 60184, Pasadena, CA 91106
(SAN 699-6035).

Pasadena Public Lib, *(South Pasadena Public
Library; 0-9617293),* 1100 Oxley St., South
Pasadena, CA 91030 (SAN 663-6039)
Tel 818-799-9109.
Pascal Pubs, *(Pascal Pubs.; 0-938836),* 21
Sunnyside Ave., Wellesley, MA 02181
(SAN 215-3319).
PASE, *(PASE Inc.),* P.O. Box 1299, Highland
Park, NJ 08904 (SAN 264-2808)
Tel 201-545-0100.
Pasha Pubns, *(Pasha Pubns., Inc.; 0-935453),*
1401 Wilson Blvd., No. 910, Arlington, VA
22209 (SAN 695-9148) Tel 703-528-1244;
Toll free: 800-424-2908.
Pass, *(Pass Press; 0-9601870),* 170 2nd Ave.,
2A, New York, NY 10003
(SAN 210-5411).
Pass the Plate, *(Pass the Plate, Inc.),* P.O. Box
836, New Bern, NC 28560
(SAN 217-295X).
Passages, *(Passages, Inc.; 0-9614334),* P.O. Box
1565, Fayetteville, AR 72702
(SAN 687-6625) Tel 501-442-7662.
Passepartout, *(Passepartout Travel Pub.;
0-935981),* Subs. of Three T Group, 540
University Ave., No. 120, Palo Alto, CA
94301-1954 (SAN 696-6268)
Tel 415-327-1756.
Passive Solar, *(Passive Solar Institute; 0-933490),*
1625 Curtis St., Berkeley, CA 94702
(SAN 282-1516) Tel 415-526-1549; Orders
to: Solar Usage Now, P.O. Box 306, Bascom,
OH 44809 (SAN 282-1524)
Tel 419-937-2226.
Passport Bks *Imprint of* **Natl Textbk**
Passport NY Rest, *(Passport to New York
Restaurants; 0-937413),* 967 Lexington Ave.,
Suite 115, New York, NY 10021
(SAN 658-9812) Tel 212-772-3942.
Passport Pr, *(Passport Pr.; 0-930016),* Box
1346, Champlain, NY 12919-1346
(SAN 211-7533) Tel 514-937-8155.
Past & Mat Rene Ctr, *(Pastoral & Matrimonial
Renewal Center; 0-911905),* 67 Prince St.,
Elizabeth, NJ 07208 (SAN 264-6854)
Tel 201-353-8640.
Past in Glass, *(Past in Glass; 0-9600212),* 515
Northridge Dr., Boulder City, NV 89005
(SAN 204-9317) Tel 702-293-3114.
Pastoral Pr, *(Pastoral Press; 0-9602378;
0-912405),* 225 Sheridan St. NW,
Washington, DC 20011 (SAN 272-8966).
Pastore, *(Pastore Press),* Seven Shetland Lane,
Stony Brook, NY 11790 (SAN 209-4703)
Tel 516-751-2254.
Pat G Johnson, *(Johnson, Patricia Givens;
0-9614765),* Rt. 2, Box 50, Christiansburg,
VA 24073 (SAN 692-915X)
Tel 703-382-1251; Dist. by: Jalamap
Publications, 601 "D" St., Charleston, WV
25303 (SAN 216-1478).
Pat Pub Co, *(Pat Publishing Co.; 0-9613323),*
P.O. Box 180454, Austin, TX 78718-0454
(SAN 655-766X) Tel 512-478-4987.
Patch & Frazzle *Imprint of* **Boyd Co**
Patch As Patch, *(Patch As Patch Can;
0-9601896),* P.O. Box 843, Port Washington,
NY 11050 (SAN 239-8575)
Tel 516-671-7342.
Patchwork Pubns, *(Patchwork Pubns.;
0-930628),* 2961 Industrial Rd., Las Vegas,
NV 89109 (SAN 211-3430)
Tel 702-732-4541; Toll free: 800-634-6268.
Patent Data, *(Patent Data Pubns., Inc.;
0-935714),* 901 N. President St., Wheaton,
IL 60187 (SAN 213-9448).
Patent Ed, *(Patent Educational Pubns.;
0-913995),* P.O. Box 857, Troy, OH 45373
(SAN 286-8563) Tel 513-339-3172.
Pateo Pub, *(Pateo Publishing Co.; 0-936797),*
480 Naples St., W, Chula Vista, CA 92011
(SAN 699-8402) Tel 619-420-5126.
Path Pr NY, *(Pathfinder Pr.; 0-87348),* 410
West St., New York, NY 10014
(SAN 202-5906) Tel 212-741-0690.
Path Pubns NJ, *(Pathfinder Pubns., Inc.;
0-939888),* 210 Central Ave., Madison, NJ
07940 (SAN 216-9215) Tel 201-822-2395.
Pathfinder *Imprint of* **Bantam**
Pathfinder CA, *(Pathfinder Publishing;
0-934793),* 458 Dorothy Ave., Ventura, CA
93003 (SAN 694-2571) Tel 805-642-9278.
†**Pathfinder Fund,** *(Pathfinder Fund; 0-933853),*
1330 Boylston St, Chestnut Hill, MA 02167
(SAN 225-9664) Tel 617-731-1700; *CIP.*
Pathfinder HI, *(Pathfinder Pubns.),* Hamakua
Ctr., 150 Hamakua Dr., Suite 401, Kailua, HI
96734 (SAN 696-7922) Tel 808-261-4557.

Pathfinder Pubns
See Pathfinder HI
Pathfinder Tour Con, *(Pathfinder Tour
Consultants; 0-9613819),* P.O. Box 318,
Olney, MD 20832 (SAN 686-2772).
Pathfinders, *(Pathfinders; 0-937260),* P.O. Box
11950, Reno, NV 89510 (SAN 205-9487)
Tel 714-489-0590.
Pathfinders Pubns MS, *(Pathfinder Publications
(MS); 0-9612012),* Rte. One, P.O. Box 115,
Tillatoba, MS 38961 (SAN 286-8466)
Tel 601-647-5927.
Pathfound Pubs, *(Pathfound Pubs.; 0-930725),*
910 Florin Rd., Suite 104, Sacramento, CA
95831 (SAN 677-4784) Tel 916-422-7133.
Pathway AL, *(Pathway Press; 0-912919),* Div.
of Pittenger & Associates, ; c/o Pittenger &
Associates, 5568 Surrey Ln., Birmingham,
AL 35243 (SAN 283-2399)
Tel 205-991-7075.
Pathway Bks, *(Pathway Bks.; 0-935538),* 700
Parkview Terrace, Golden Valley, MN 55416
(SAN 213-4241) Tel 612-377-1521; Dist.
by: Publishers Group West, 5855 Beaudry
Ave., Emeryville, CA 94608
(SAN 202-8522) Tel 415-658-3453; Dist.
by: Quality Books, 918 Sherwood Dr., Lake
Bluff, IL 60044-2204 (SAN 169-2127)
Tel 312-295-2010.
Pathway Pr, *(Pathway Pr.; 0-87148),* 1080
Montgomery Ave., Cleveland, TN 37311
(SAN 202-8727) Tel 615-476-4512; Toll
free: 800-251-7216.
Pathway Pubns, *(Pathway Pubns., Inc.;
0-9606442),* 1632 Seventh Ave. W.,
Birmingham, AL 35208 (SAN 218-5784)
Tel 205-785-9584.
Pathway Pubs, *(Pathway Publishers; 0-915197),*
P.O. Box 5021, Esmond, RI 02917
(SAN 289-7911) Tel 401-231-8225.
Pathwork Pr, *(Pathwork Pr.; 0-9614777),* Box
66, Phoenicia, NY 12464 (SAN 692-7009)
Tel 914-688-2211; Orders to: Stillpoint
Publishing, Box 640, Meeting House Rd.,
Walpole, NH 03608 (SAN 662-3026)
Tel 603-756-3508.
Pathwy Pr CA
See Pathwys Pr CA
Pathwys Pr CA, *(Pathways Press; 0-9605022),*
P.O. Box 60196-A, Palo Alto, CA 94306
(SAN 283-4367).
Patio Pubns, *(Patio Pubns.; 0-9696040),* 850
Woodhollow Lane, Buffalo Grove, IL 60090
(SAN 216-9223) Tel 312-259-8500.
†**Patmos Pr,** *(Patmos Pr.; 0-915762),* P.O. Box
V, Shepherdstown, WV 25443
(SAN 207-4192) Tel 304-876-2086; *CIP.*
†**Patrice Pr,** *(Patrice Pr.; 0-935284),* Box 42,
Gerald, MO 63037 (SAN 203-1019)
Tel 314-764-2801; *CIP.*
†**Patricks Pr,** *(Patrick's Pr.; 0-9609412),* P.O.
Box 5189, Columbus, GA 31906
(SAN 274-466X) Tel 404-322-1584; *CIP.*
Patriotic Pubs, *(Patriotic Publishers; 0-9608188),*
159 Woodland Ave., Verona, NJ 07044
(SAN 240-124X).
Patron *Imprint of* **Don Bosco Multimedia**
Pattern Pubns, *(Pattern Pubns.; 0-911986),* 2627
Seabrook Island Rd., Johns Island, SC 29455
(SAN 204-9333).
Patterns Ltd, *(Patterns Ltd.; 0-9609874),* P.O.
Box 1924, Redondo Beach, CA 90278
(SAN 274-4708) Tel 213-379-9417.
†**Patterson Smith,** *(Smith, Patterson, Publishing
Corp.; 0-87585),* 23 Prospect Terr.,
Montclair, NJ 07042 (SAN 202-8735)
Tel 201-744-3291 (SAN 658-1617); *CIP.*
Pattie Prop Inc, *(Pattie Properties, Inc.;
0-911789),* 1403 Springdale Rd., Zephyrhills,
FL 34248 (SAN 264-2891)
Tel 813-782-9187.
Patton Creative, *(Patton Creative Associates;
0-911003),* 21 Tulip Circle, Salinas, CA
93905 (SAN 274-4716) Tel 408-422-4192.
Patton Pac Pr, *(Patton Pacific Pr.; 0-9614074),*
P.O. Box 5888, Chula Vista, CA 92012-5888
(SAN 679-1794).
Pau Hana Pr, *(Pau Hana Press; 0-912921),*
1750 Kalakaua Ave., Suite 3-577, Honolulu,
HI 96826 (SAN 283-9245).
Paul Mann, *(Mann, Paul, Publishing Co.;
0-8184),* 1517 Rexford Pl., Las Vegas, NV
89104 (SAN 204-9341) Tel 702-385-1585.
Paul R Johnson, *(Johnson, Paul R.; 0-910097),*
P.O. Box 2972, Pomona, CA 91769
(SAN 241-3973) Tel 818-338-7245.

Symbols/Abbreviations

Peer-Southern, *(Peer-Southern Pubns.),* 1740 Broadway, New York, NY 10019 (SAN 206-3034) Tel 212-265-3910; Dist. by: The Theodore Presser Co., Presser Pl., Bryn Mawr, PA 19010 (SAN 203-5553) Tel 215-525-3636; Dist. by: Columbia Pictures Pubns., 15800 NW, 48th Ave., Miami, FL 33014 (SAN 662-1104) Tel 305-620-1500.

Peerless, *(Peerless Publishing Co.; 0-930234),* 2745 Lafitte Ave., New Orleans, LA 70119 (SAN 210-3222) Tel 504-486-6225.

Pegasus, *(Pegasus),* Affil. of Bobbs-Merrill Co., Inc., 4300 W. 62nd St., P.O. Box 7080, Indianapolis, IN 46206 (SAN 201-3959); Toll free: 800-428-3750.

Pegasus Co SC, *(Pegasus Company; 0-9602144),* Rt. 1, Rambling Path, Anderson, SC 29621 (SAN 221-7562).

Pegasus Found
See Dallas Inst Pubns

Pegasus Prose, *(Pegasus Prose; 0-9617240),* 6423 13th Ave. NW, Rochester, MN 55901 (SAN 663-5407) Tel 507-288-0779.

Pegasus Pubns, *(Pegasus Pubns.; 0-936552),* P.O. Box 1060, Pt. Reyes Station, CA 94956 (SAN 222-1101).

Pegasus Rex *Imprint of Fell*

Pegasus Rex NJ, *(Pegasus Rex Press, Inc., The; 0-937484),* 695 Bloomfield Ave., Montclair, NJ 07042 (SAN 215-2061). Moved, left no forwarding address.

Pegma Bks *Imprint of* **Green Hill**

Pegus Pr, *(Pegus Press; 0-941218),* 648 W. Sierra Ave., Box 429, Clovis, CA 93612 (SAN 241-5763) Tel 209-299-3263.

Pejepscot, *(Pejepscot Press; 0-917638),* 10 Mason St., Brunswick, ME 04011 (SAN 202-1447) Tel 207-729-3442.

†**Pelican,** *(Pelican Publishing Co., Inc.; 0-911116; 0-88289),* 1101 Monroe St., Gretna, LA 70053 (SAN 212-0623) Tel 504-368-1175; P.O. Box 189, Gretna, LA 70053 (SAN 658-1374) Tel 504-368-1175; CIP.

Pelican *Imprint of* **Penguin**

Pelican Hill
See Royal Pub Co

Pelican Pr, *(Pelican Pr.; 0-938937),* 3463 State St., Suite 342, Santa Barbara, CA 93105 (SAN 661-7506) Tel 805-569-2269.

Pelion Pr *Imprint of* **Rosen Group**

Pella Pub, *(Pella Publishing Co., Inc.; 0-918618; 0-933824),* 337 W. 36th St., New York, NY 10018 (SAN 210-6183) Tel 212-279-9586.

†**PEM Pr,** *(PEM Press),* Div. of Pathescope Educational Media, Inc., 71 Weyman Ave., P.O. Box 719, New Rochelle, NY 10802 (SAN 214-0721) Tel 914-235-0800; CIP.

Pember Lib Mus, *(Pember Library & Museum; 0-9616427),* 33 W. Main St., Granville, NY 12832 (SAN 658-9901) Tel 518-642-1515.

Pembroke CT, *(Pembroke Pr.; 0-938563),* 99 Cross Hwy., Westport, CT 06880 (SAN 661-4728) Tel 203-226-8784. Do not confuse with Pembroke Pr., New York, NY.

PEN Am Ctr, *(PEN American Ctr.; 0-934638),* 568 Broadway, New York, NY 10012 (SAN 675-4112) Tel 212-334-1660.

Pen & Booth, *(Pen & Booth; 0-9605686),* 1608 "R" St. NW, Washington, DC 20009 (SAN 213-1439).

Pen & Ink, *(Pen & Ink Pr.; 0-9607544),* c/o Banyan Books, Inc., P.O. Box 431160, Miami, FL 33143 (SAN 208-340X) Tel 305-665-6011.

Pen & Podium, *(Pen & Podium, Inc.; 0-9603982),* 40 Central Park S., New York, NY 10019 (SAN 214-0756) Tel 212-759-8454.

Pen-Art, *(Pen-Art Pubs.; 0-941242),* 402 Fairview Ave., Westwood, NJ 07675 (SAN 211-3287) Tel 201-664-8412; Dist. by: New York Poetry Forum, Inc., 3064 Albany Crescent, Apt. 54, Bronx, NY 10463 (SAN 200-8092) Tel 212-796-5948.

Pen-Dec, *(Pen-Dec Pr.; 0-915199),* 1724 Georgia St., Marysville, MI 48040 (SAN 289-792X) Tel 313-364-8024.

Pen Notes, *(Pen Notes, Inc.; 0-939564),* 134 Westside Ave., Freeport, NY 11520 (SAN 216-4337) Tel 516-868-5753.

Pena Lydia, *(Pena, Lydia; 0-9612982),* 3001 S. Federal Blvd., Denver, CO 80236 (SAN 292-594X) Tel 303-936-8441.

Pencil Pr, *(Pencil Pr.; 0-9615665),* 109 Orange St., San Rafael, CA 94901 (SAN 695-9164) Tel 415-456-7469; P.O.Box 9011, San Rafael, CA 94912 (SAN 658-2893); Dist. by: Bookpeople, 2929 Fifth St., Berkeley, CA 94710 (SAN 662-362X).

Pencraft C Jennings, *(Pencraft of Chris Jennings, The; 0-9616295),* 22 Flagg St., Cambridge, MA 02238 (SAN 658-4837) Tel 617-497-6502; P.O. Box 411, Cambridge, MA 02238 (SAN 658-4845).

Pencraft Pr, *(Pencraft Pr., Inc.; 0-936771),* P.O. Box 1789, West Palm Beach, FL 33402-1789 (SAN 699-9212); 1603 Northbridge Tower, 515 N., Flagler Dr., West Palm Beach, FL 33401 (SAN 699-9220) Tel 305-659-2060.

Pendell Pub, *(Pendell Publishing Co.; 0-87812),* 1700 James Savage Rd., P.O. Box 2066 Bip, Midland, MI 48640 (SAN 202-8786) Tel 517-496-3333.

Pendelton Lane, *(Pendelton Lane Publishing; 0-937851),* Subs. of Flint, Inc., 3676 Collin Dr., Suite 20, West Palm Beach, FL 33406 (SAN 659-5537) Tel 305-969-7708.

Pendle Hill, *(Pendle Hill Pubns.; 0-87574),* Pendle Hill, 338 Plush Mill Rd., Wallingford, PA 19086 (SAN 202-8794) Tel 215-566-4507.

Pendleton Hse, *(Pendleton Hse., Inc.; 0-934919),* Rte. 2, Butler, KY 41006 (SAN 694-423X) Tel 606-472-2721.

Pendleton Pubns, *(Pendleton Pubns.; 0-9616609),* P.O. Box 471, Franklin, WV 26807 (SAN 659-7521); Rte. 4, Smith Creek Rd., Franklin, WV 26807 (SAN 659-753X) Tel 304-358-2822.

†**Pendragon NY,** *(Pendragon Pr.; 0-918728),* Subs. of Camelot Publishing Co., Inc., R.R. 1, Box 159, Stuyvesant, NY 12173-9720 (SAN 213-1463) Tel 518-828-3008; CIP.

Pendragon Oregon, *(Pendragon Press; 0-914010),* P.O. Box 14834, Portland, OR 97214 (SAN 204-9376) Tel 503-232-0869.

Pendulum Bks, *(Pendulum Books; 0-941760),* P.O. Box 3627, 615 Garnet St., Redondo Beach, CA 90277 (SAN 239-2771) Tel 213-372-0925.

Pendulum Pr, *(Pendulum Pr., Inc.; 0-88301),* Academic Bldg., Saw Mill Rd., West Haven, CT 06516 (SAN 202-8808) Tel 203-933-2551.

Penfield, *(Penfield Pr.; 0-9603858; 0-941016),* 215 Brown St., Iowa City, IA 52240 (SAN 221-6671) Tel 319-337-9998; Toll free: 800-255-2255 Ext. 9998.

†**Penguin,** *(Penguin Bks., Inc.; 0-14),* 40 W. 23rd St., New York, NY 10010 (SAN 202-5914) Tel 212-807-7300; Toll free: 800-631-3577; CIP. Imprints: Peacock (Peacock Books).(Peacock Bks.); Pelican (Pelican Books).(Pelican Bks.); Peregrine (Peregrine Books).(Peregrine Bks.); Puffin (Puffin Books).(Puffin Bks.).

Penguin Comns, *(Penguin Communications Group; 0-938269),* P.O. Box 984, Yakima, WA 98907 (SAN 659-8307); 336 N. 23rd Ave., Yakima, WA 98907 (SAN 659-8315) Tel 509-575-8386.

Peninsula CA, *(Peninsula Publishing; 0-932146),* P.O. Box 867, Los Altos, CA 94023 (SAN 212-257X) Tel 415-948-2511.

Peninsula NY, *(Peninsula Press; 0-9609012),* Water's Edge, Fishers Island, NY 06390 (SAN 241-3485) Tel 516-788-7868.

Peninsula Pub WA
See Peninsula WA

Peninsula Pubns, *(Peninsula Pubns.; 0-914372),* 26030 New Bridge Dr., Los Altos Hills, CA 94022 (SAN 202-8816) Tel 415-948-1405.

Peninsula United *(Peninsula United Methodist Homes, Inc.),* P.O. Box 1127, Newark, DE 19715 (SAN 687-6234) Tel 302-737-3698.

Peninsula WA, *(Peninsula Publishing, Inc.; 0-918146),* P.O. Box 412, Port Angeles, WA 98362 (SAN 210-1300) Tel 206-457-7550; Dist. by: Pacific Pipeline, 19215 66th Ave. S., Kent, WA 98032 (SAN 208-2128) Tel 206-872-5523.

Peninsular Pub Co, *(Peninsular Publishing Co.; 0-9616000),* 2503 Jackson Bluff Rd., Tallahassee, FL 32314 (SAN 697-9386) Tel 904-576-4151.

Penisula TX, *(Penisula Press of Texas; 0-9614885),* P.O. Box 1742, Crystal Beach, TX 77650 (SAN 693-1871) Tel 713-729-7355; Orders to: P.O. Box 694, Houston, TX 77001 (SAN 694-0218).

Penkevill, *(Penkevill Publishing Co., The; 0-913283),* P.O. Box 212, Greenwood, FL 32443 (SAN 285-8304).

Penmaen Pr, *(Penmean Pr.; 0-915778),* R.D. 2, P.O. Box 145, Great Barrington, MA 01230 (SAN 208-1113) Tel 413-528-2749.

Penmaen Pr & Design
See Penmaen Pr

Penn Acad Art, *(Pennsylvania Academy of Fine Arts; 0-943836),* Broad & Cherry St., Philadelphia, PA 19102 (SAN 280-0748).

Penn Assoc Not, *(Pennsylvania Association of Notaries; 0-9610862),* 14 Wood St., Pittsburgh, PA 15222 (SAN 264-2921) Tel 412-281-0678.

Penn German Soc, *(Pennsylvania German Society; 0-911122),* 55 Kohler School Rd., New Oxford, PA 17350 (SAN 205-1958) Tel 717-624-4106; Orders to: P.O. Box 397, Birdsboro, PA 19508 (SAN 205-1966) Tel 215-582-1441.

Penn Pubs, *(Pennsylvania Pubs. Grunwald, Inc.),* 5049 Admiral Wright Rd., Suite 344, Virginia Beach, VA 23462 (SAN 699-7708) Tel 804-490-1132; Orders to: Pennsylvanis Pubs., 45 N. Duke St., Lancaster, PA 17602 (SAN 662-4057) Tel 717-299-4600.

Penn Science, *(Pennsylvania Academy of Science; 0-9606670),* Dept. of Biology, Lafayette College, Easton, PA 18042 (SAN 219-6220) Tel 215-250-5464.

Penn St Art, *(Pennsylvania State Univ., Museum of Art; 0-911209),* Pennsylvania State Univ., University Park, PA 16802 (SAN 213-9014) Tel 814-863-0111.

Penn St Min Econ, *(Pennsylvania State Univ., Dept. of Mineral Economics; 0-9613333),* 221 Walker Bldg., University Park, PA 16802 (SAN 655-7678) Tel 814-865-0691.

Penn St U Min
See Penn St Min Econ

Penn St Univ Dept Art Hist, *(Pennsylvania State University, Department of Art History; 0-915773),* 227 Arts Bldg., University Park, PA 16802 (SAN 293-8995) Tel 814-865-6326; Orders to: Susan S. Munshower, 221 Arts Building, University Park, PA 16802 (SAN 685-3811).

Penn State Food, *(Pennsylvania State Univ., Dept. of Food Science; 0-9616407),* 116 Borland Laboratory, University Park, PA 16802 (SAN 658-9995) Tel 814-863-2962.

Penn Stats Mus
See Univ Mus of U PA

Penn-Yale Expedit, *(Publications of the Pennsylvania-Yale Expedition to Egypt),* Yale Univ., 102 Hall of Graduate Studies, New Haven, CT 06520 (SAN 662-118X) Tel 203-436-8779; c/o Peabody Museum of Natural History, Pubns. Office, 170 Whitney Ave., P.O. Box 6666, New Haven, CT 06511 (SAN 205-177X) Tel 203-436-1131.

Penna Secy, *(Pennsylvania. Secretary of State, Dept. of State),* North Office Bldg., Rm. 302, Harrisburg, PA 17120 (SAN 274-4937).

†**Pennant Bks,** *(Pennant Books; 0-915201),* 3463 State St., Suite 238, Santa Barbara, CA 93105 (SAN 289-7938) Tel 805-683-1079; Dist. by: Quality Bks., Inc., 918 Sherman Dr., Lake Bluff, IL 60044-2204 (SAN 169-2127); Dist. by: Baker & Taylor Co., Eastern Div., 50 Kirby Ave., Somerville, NJ 08876 (SAN 169-4901); Dist. by: Baker & Taylor Co., Midwest Div., 501 Gladiola Ave., Momence, IL 60954 (SAN 169-2100); Dist. by: Baker & Taylor Co., Southest Div., Mt. Olive Rd., Commerce, GA 30529 (SAN 169-1503); Dist. by: Baker & Taylor Co., Western Div., 380 Edison Way, Reno, NV 89564 (SAN 169-4464) Tel 702-786-6700; CIP.

Pennant Pr, *(Pennant Pr.; 0-913458),* 7620 Miramar Rd., No. 4100, San Diego, CA 92126 (SAN 201-9884) Tel 619-695-1810.

Pennington, *(Pennington Trading Post; 0-911120),* c/o Eunice Pennington, Fremont, MO 63941 (SAN 204-9392).

Pennington Pub, *(Pennington Publishing; 0-936599),* 2710 North Ave., Bridgeport, CT 06604 (SAN 698-0368) Tel 203-366-4155.

Pennon Pr, *(Pennon Pr.; 0-937941),* P.O. Box 206, Carlisle, PA 17013 (SAN 659-7513) Tel 717-243-4739.

†**Penns Valley,** *(Penns Valley Pubs.; 0-931992),* 1209 S. 28th St., Harrisburg, PA 17111 (SAN 202-1455) Tel 717-232-5844; CIP.

Symbols/Abbreviations

Perinatology, (Perinatology Pr.; 0-916859),
Subs. of Promethean Press, P.O. Box 6827,
Ithaca, NY 14851 (SAN 656-0520)
Tel 607-257-3278.

Perinton Press, (Perinton Pr.; 0-931157), P.O.
Box 1105, Fairport, NY 14450
(SAN 679-3789) Tel 716-223-2319.

Peripatetic, (Peripatetic Press, The; 0-9602870),
P.O. Box 68, Grinnell, IA 50112
(SAN 213-425X) Tel 515-236-5861.

Periscope Pr, (Periscope Press; 0-914083), P.O.
Box 6926, Santa Barbara, CA 93160
(SAN 286-8652).

Perish Pr, (Perish Press; 0-934038), P.O. Box
75, Mystic, CT 06355 (SAN 212-789X)
Tel 203-536-2304.

†**Perishable Pr,** (Perishable Pr., Ltd., The), P.O.
Box 7, Mt. Horeb, WI 53572
(SAN 210-8437) Tel 608-523-4473; CIP.

Perivale Pr, (Perivale Pr.; 0-912288), 13830
Erwin St., Van Nuys, CA 91401
(SAN 201-9922) Tel 818-785-4671; Dist.
by: Small Pr. Distribution, Inc., 1814 San
Pablo Ave., Berkeley, CA 94702
(SAN 204-5826) Tel 415-549-3336; Dist.
by: Anton Mikofsky, 57 W. 84th St.,
Apt.1-C, New York, NY 10024
(SAN 219-5747).

Periwinkle, (Periwinkle Pr.; 0-9615666), 317
Ave. B, Snohomish, WA 98290
(SAN 695-9369) Tel 206-568-2508.

Periwinkle Pubns, (Periwinkle Pubns; 0-942886),
6015 SW 187th Dr., Aloha, OR 97006
(SAN 240-2653) Tel 503-642-5009.

Perkins & Assoc, (Perkins, E. Stuart, &
Associates; 0-9606444), Box 362,
Wellington, OH 44090 (SAN 219-810X).

Perkiomen, (Perkiomen Pubns. Co., Inc.;
0-9605598), P.O. Box 36, Schwenksville, PA
19473 (SAN 218-5008).

Perm Pr, (Permanent Pr., Inc.; 0-915393), 1614
Calle San Mateo, Santurce, PR 00912
(SAN 291-3267).

Perma Bound, (Perma Bound Bks.; 0-916056;
0-8479), Subs. of Hertzberg-New Method,
617 E. Vandalia Rd., Jacksonville, IL 62650
(SAN 169-2003) Tel 217-243-5451; Toll
free: 800-637-6581.

Permanent Pr, (Permanent Pr., The; 0-932966),
RD 2 Noyac Rd., Sag Harbor, NY 11963
(SAN 212-2995) Tel 516-725-1101; Toll
free: 800-221-0960.

Perna Bks
See Podiatric Educ

Perrin Inc, (Perrin, Thomas W., Inc.; 0-933825),
P.O. Box 190, 5 Glen Rd., Rutherford, NJ
07070 (SAN 200-6510) Tel 201-460-7912;
Toll free: 800-321-7912.

Perry Enterprises, (Perry Enterprises; 0-941518),
2666 N. 650 E, Provo, UT 84604
(SAN 239-0175) Tel 801-375-9529.

Perry Omega, (Perry-Omega Pub., Inc.;
0-9602586), P.O. Box 27097, Escondido,
CA 92027 (SAN 213-1420).

Perry Pub, (Perry Publishing), 1252-20th Place,
Yuma, AZ 85364 (SAN 213-2303).

†**Persea Bks,** (Persea Bks., Inc.; 0-89255), 225
Lafayette St., New York, NY 10012
(SAN 212-8233) Tel 212-431-5270; CIP.

Persepolis Pr, (Persepolis Pr.; 0-9615741), P.O.
Box 4552, Greenville, SC 29608
(SAN 695-9490) Tel 803-834-8463;
McElhaney Rd., Rte. 3, Greenville, SC
29611 (SAN 695-9504).

Perseus Pr, (Perseus Pr.; 0-918026), P.O. Box
1221, Pacific Palisades, CA 90272
(SAN 207-2726) Tel 213-208-7991. Orders
& checks for audiotapes produced by Carl
Faber should be made out in his name, not
Perseus Pr. Imprints: C Faber Audiotapes
(Faber, Carl, Audiotapes).

†**Perseverance Pr,** (Perseverance Pr.; 0-9602676),
P.O. Box 384, Menlo Park, CA 94026
(SAN 212-9272) Tel 415-323-5572; Dist.
by: Capra Pr., P.O. Box 2068, Santa Barbara,
CA 93120 (SAN 201-9620)
Tel 805-966-4590; CIP.

Persian Rug Ctr, (Persian Rug Ctr.; 0-9615592),
2121 S. Ninth St., Springfield, IL 62703
(SAN 692-9664) Tel 217-544-3418.

Persimmon NY, (Persimmon Pr.; 0-9615462),
118 Tillinghast Pl., Buffalo, NY 14216
(SAN 695-7056) Tel 716-838-3633.

Person Person Network, (Person to Person
Network; 0-937993), 7250 Auburn Blvd.,
Suite 222, Citrus Heights, CA 95610
(SAN 659-7548) Tel 916-723-1000.

Persona LA, (Persona Pr.; 0-940142), 522
Dumaine, Apt. 3, New Orleans, LA 70116
(SAN 293-3136) Tel 504-561-0221.

Persona Pr, (Persona Press; 0-931906), P.O.
Box 14022, San Francisco, CA 94114
(SAN 212-3002) Tel 415-775-6143.

Personabks, (Personabooks; 0-932456), 434-66th
St., Oakland, CA 94609 (SAN 215-1707)
Tel 415-658-2482; Dist. by: The Talman Co.,
150 Fifth Ave., Rm. 514, New York, NY
10011 (SAN 200-5204) Tel 212-620-3182.

Personal Achievement, (Personal Achievement
Institute; 0-9606744), 535 Ocean Ave., Suite
8C, P.O. Box 1542, Santa Monica, CA 90406
(SAN 219-6247) Tel 213-393-3230.

Personal Achievement Imprint of Telecom Lib

Personal Assocs, (Personal Assocs.; 0-9613749),
P.O. Box 311, Pine Beach, NJ 08741
(SAN 677-7473) Tel 201-240-4957.

Personal Christianity, (Personal Christianity;
0-938148), Box 549, Baldwin Park, CA
91706 (SAN 211-8211) Tel 818-338-7333.

Personal Dev Ctr, (Personal Development Ctr.;
0-917828), P.O. Box 251, Windham Center,
CT 06280 (SAN 209-164X)
Tel 203-423-4785.

Personal Growth, (Personal Growth Resources;
0-937477), P.O. Box 6265, Champaign, IL
61821 (SAN 659-0101) Tel 217-359-7669;
2416 Morrissey Pk., Champaign, IL 61821
(SAN 659-011X).

Personal Planning, (Personal Planning Programs,
Inc.), 7550 France Ave. S. Suite 214,
Minneapolis, MN 55435 (SAN 217-2615)
Tel 612-893-0403.

Personal Power, (Personal Power Potential;
0-9607312), 300 N. Martingale Rd., Suite
500, Schaumburg, IL 60194
(SAN 239-2798) Tel 312-426-6979.

Personal Power Pr
See Prsnl Power Pr

Personal Press, (Personal Pr.; 0-9605634), 1515
Riebl Rd., Santa Rosa, CA 95404
(SAN 219-9807) Tel 707-525-1338; Dist.
by: Inland Book Co., P.O. Box 261. 22
Hemingway Ave., East Haven, CT 06512
(SAN 200-4151) Tel 203-467-4257; Dist.
by: Bookpeople, 2929 Fifth St., Berkeley, CA
94710 (SAN 662-1120) Tel 415-549-3030.

Personal Pubns
See Tower Pr PA

Personal Resp, (Personal Responsibility;
0-9610488), 314 Eighth St. SE, Washington,
DC 20003 (SAN 264-2972)
Tel 202-546-0492.

Personal Security, (Personal Security Systems;
0-918384), P.O. Box 152, River Forest, IL
60305 (SAN 207-2793) Tel 312-336-7330.

Personal Selling, (Personal Selling Power;
0-939613), 1127 International Pkwy.,
Fredericksburg, VA 22405 (SAN 663-5059)
Tel 703-752-7000.

Personal Sys Pubns, (Personal Systems Pubns.;
0-915097), 1802 N. Carson, Suite 214-240,
Carson City, NV 89701 (SAN 289-7970)
Tel 702-883-2116.

Personal Touch, (Personal Touch, A; 0-9616317),
P.O. Box 68392, Oak Grove, OR 97268
(SAN 658-6821) Tel 503-659-8156; 15510
SE Hugh Ave., Milwaukie, OR 97267
(SAN 658-683X).

Personnel Decisions, (Personnel Decisions, Inc.;
0-938529), 821 Marquette St., Foshay
Tower, Suite 2300, Minneapolis, MN 55402
(SAN 661-1443) Tel 612-339-0927.

Perspect Indiana, (Perspectives Pr.; 0-9609504),
905 West Wildwood Ave., Fort Wayne, IN
46807 (SAN 262-5059) Tel 219-456-8411.

Perspective Chicago, (Perspective Press;
0-9603382), 629 Deming Place, Rm. 401,
Chicago, IL 60614 (SAN 208-3191)
Tel 312-871-4820.

Perspectives Pr
See Perspect Indiana

Perspicilli Pr, (Perspicilli Press; 0-936064),
1916 Oak Knoll Dr., Belmont, CA 94002
(SAN 213-8646).

Persun & Berlin, (Persun & Berlin, Pubs.;
0-936111), P.O. Box 623, Media, PA
19063-0623 (SAN 661-6682).

Perth Pub, (Perth, J. M., Publishing, Inc.;
0-9606546), P.O. Box 82, Delaplane, VA
22025 (SAN 218-5806) Tel 703-347-3620.

PES Inc WI, (Professional Education Systems,
Inc.), 3410 Sky Park Blvd., P.O. Box 1208,
Eau Claire, WI 54702; Toll free:
800-826-7155.

Pet Pro Co, (Pet Protector Co., The; 0-931573),
146-01 Jamaica Ave., Jamaica, NY 11435
(SAN 682-1928) Tel 718-523-2211.

Peter Brooks, (Brooks, Peter; 0-9617203), 221
San Bernardino Rd., Covina, CA 91722
(SAN 663-2556) Tel 818-966-1708.

Peter Glenn, (Glenn, Peter, Pubns., Inc.;
0-87314), 17 E. 48th St., New York, NY
10017 (SAN 201-9930) Tel 212-688-7940;
Toll free: 800-223-1254.

Peter Li, (Li, Peter, Inc.; 0-89837), 2451 E.
River Rd., Dayton, OH 45439
(SAN 238-7980) Tel 513-299-8777; Toll
free: 800-531-3456.

Peter Pan, (Peter Pan Industries; 0-88149), 145
Komorn St., Newark, NJ 07105
(SAN 287-7589).

Peter Pauper, (Peter Pauper Pr., Inc.; 0-88088),
202 Mamaroneck Ave., White Plains, NY
10601 (SAN 204-9449) Tel 914-681-0144;
Dist. by: Kampmann & Co., Inc., 9 E. 40th
St., New York, NY 10016 (SAN 202-5191)
Tel 212-685-2928.

Peter Smith, (Smith, Peter, Pub., Inc.; 0-8446),
6 Lexington Ave., Magnolia, MA 01930
(SAN 206-8885) Tel 617-525-3562.

Petereins Pr, (Petereins Pr., The; 0-9606102),
P.O. Box 10446, Glendale, CA 91209
(SAN 215-9007).

Peters Corp NM, (Peters Corp.; 0-935037), P.O.
Box 2524, Santa Fe, NM 87504-2524
(SAN 697-2462) Tel 505-988-8961; Toll
free: 800-621-5884.

Peters Wright, (Peters Wright Creative Dance,
Inc; 0-916645), 2695 Sacramento St., San
Francisco, CA 94115 (SAN 296-6883)
Tel 415-931-0365.

Petersburg Pr, (Petersburg Pr.; 0-902825), 380
Lafayette St., New York, NY 10003
(SAN 240-1819) Tel 212-420-0890.

Petersen Pub, (Petersen Publishing Co., Bk. Div.;
0-8227), 8490 Sunset Blvd., Los Angeles,
CA 90069 (SAN 201-9949)
Tel 213-657-5100.

Peterson Pub, (Peterson Publishing; 0-9613986),
159 McBoal, St. Paul, MN 55102
(SAN 682-1731) Tel 612-297-9630.

Peterson Pub CO, (Peterson Publishing Co.
(CO); 0-9614806), 211 S. Main St.,
Gunnison, CO 81230 (SAN 692-7831)
Tel 303-641-3910.

†**Petersons Guides,** (Peterson's Guides, Inc.;
0-87866), P.O. Box 2123, Princeton, NJ
08543-2123 (SAN 200-2167)
Tel 609-924-5338; Toll free: 800-225-0261;
CIP.

Petervin Pr, (Petervin Pr., The; 0-943932), P.O.
Box 280, Davis, CA 95617 (SAN 238-0838)
Tel 916-756-1105.

PETEX, (Petroleum Extension Service (PETEX);
0-88698), Div. of Continuing Ed., Univ. of
Texas at Austin, Balcones Research
Ctr.-2,10100 Burnet Rd., Austin, TX 78758
(SAN 208-3892).

Petit Appetit, (Petit Appetit; 0-9616883), 9215
Ensley Ln., Leawood, KS 66206
(SAN 661-6496) Tel 913-383-3610.

Petit Press, (Petit Pr.; 0-9610174), 1661 E.
Lakeshore Dr., Baton Rouge, LA 70808
(SAN 274-5321) Tel 504-383-3270; P.O.
Box 4053, Baton Rouge, LA 70821
(SAN 695-6262).

Petras Pr, (Petras Press Inc.; 0-9614568), 70
Greenwich Ave., Room 561, New York, NY
10011 (SAN 691-8204) Tel 212-267-8448;
Dist. by: Flatiron Book Distributors Inc.,
1170 Broadway, Suite 80, New York, NY
10001 (SAN 240-9917) Tel 211-206-1118.

Petras Press Imprint of Riverrun NY

Petrie Hse, (Petrie Hse. Pubns.; 0-936824),
2140 W. Olympic Blvd., Los Angeles, CA
90006 (SAN 218-4540) Tel 213-487-2666.

Petro-Media, (Petro-Media Inc.; 0-916647),
1729 Rose Rd., Tyler, TX 75701
(SAN 296-6573) Tel 214-592-8348.

Petro Mktg Ed Found, (Petroleum Marketing
Education Foundation; 0-937273), 101 N.
Alfred St., Suite 200, Alexandria, VA 22314
(SAN 224-9014) Tel 703-684-0000.

†**Petrocelli,** (Petrocelli Bks.; 0-89433), Research
Pk., 251 Wall St., Princeton, NJ 08540
(SAN 211-3848) Tel 609-924-5851; Dist.
by: TAB Bks., P.O. Box 40, Blue Ridge
Summit, PA 17214 (SAN 202-568X)
Tel 717-794-2191; CIP.

Phoenix Soc, *(Phoenix Society, The),* 11 Rust Hill Rd., Levittown, PA 19056 (SAN 225-9796) Tel 215-946-4788.
Phoenix Syst GA, *(Phoenix Systems, Inc.; 0-936019),* 3300 NE Expressway, Atlanta, GA 30341 (SAN 696-8031) Tel 404-458-6445.
Phoenix WA, *(Phoenix Publishing, Inc.; 0-919345),* P.O. Box 10, Custer, WA 98240 (SAN 695-5517) Tel 206-467-8219.
Pholiota, *(Pholiota Pr., Inc.; 0-910231),* 6421 Antrim Cir., Huntington Beach, CA 92647 (SAN 240-8783) Tel 714-898-4129.
Photo Arts Ctr, *(Photographic Arts Ctr., The; 0-940926; 0-913069),* Div. of Photograph Collectors Newsletter, Ltd., 127 E. 59th St., New York, NY 10022 (SAN 217-3603) Tel 212-838-8640.
Photo Bk Co
  See PBC Intl Inc
Photo-Go Pr, *(Photo-Go Pr.; 0-931662),* P.O. Box 522562, El Paso, TX 79952-0014 (SAN 211-7576) Tel 915-581-6218.
Photo Graphics, *(Photo/Graphics Unlimited; 0-9613638),* P.O. Box 126342, San Diego, CA 92101 (SAN 677-5063).
Photo Memorabila, *(Photographic Memorabila; 0-9604352),* P.O. Box 351, Lexington, MA 02173 (SAN 282-163X) Tel 617-646-0775.
Photo-Optical
  See SPIE
Photo Res, *(Photographic Research Pubns.; 0-934918),* P.O. Box 333, Seven Oaks, Detroit, MI 48235 (SAN 213-9456) Tel 313-493-3503.
Photo Res Ctr, *(Photographic Resource Ctr.; 0-9615801),* 1019 Commonwealth Ave., Boston, MA 02215 (SAN 696-6217) Tel 617-783-9333.
Photo Res Inst Carson Endowment, *(Photography Research Institute/Carson Endowment; 0-915827),* 21237 S. Moneta Ave., Carson, CA 90745 (SAN 293-9002) Tel 213-328-9272.
Photo Survey, *(Photo Survey; 0-9609812),* Box 9157, Akron, OH 44305 (SAN 262-5075).
Photog West Graphics, *(Photography West Graphics, Inc.; 0-9616515),* P.O. Box 7116, Carmel, CA 93921 (SAN 659-5553) Tel 408-625-1719.
Photoglass Pr, *(Photoglass Pr.; 0-9616724),* 1203 Searle Dr., Normal, IL 61761 (SAN 659-8536) Tel 309-452-3837.
Photographit, *(Photographit; 0-9605168),* 12 S. Gallatin Ave., Uniontown, PA 15401 (SAN 215-7985).
Photopia Pr, *(Photopia Press; 0-942478),* P.O. Box 1844, Corvallis, OR 97339 (SAN 238-5562) Tel 503-757-8761.
Phrygian Pr, *(Phrygian Pr.; 0-932155),* 58-09 205th St., Bayside, NY 11364 (SAN 686-4317) Tel 718-428-9368.
Phunn Pubs, *(Phunn Pubs.; 0-931762),* P.O. Box 201, Wild Rose, WI 54984 (SAN 212-128X) Tel 414-622-3251.
Physical Stud, *(Physical Studies Institute; 0-914447),* 80 Cuesta Vista Dr., Monterey, CA 93940 (SAN 287-7597) Tel 408-373-5447.
Physicians Rec, *(Physicians' Record Co.; 0-917036),* 3000 S. Ridgeland Ave., Berwyn, IL 60402 (SAN 205-3853) Tel 312-749-3111; Toll free: 800-323-9268.
Physsardt, *(Physsardt Pubs.; 0-916062),* Dist. by: Bloomington Distribution Group, P.O. Box 841, Bloomington, IN 47402 (SAN 282-6828).
Phystiklakis & Eliopoulos
  See Eliopoulos
Pi Pr, *(Pi Pr., Inc.; 0-931420),* Box 23371, Honolulu, HI 96822 (SAN 669-2400); 3169-A Alika Ave., Honolulu, HI 96817 Tel 808-595-3426.
PI Pubns, *(P.I. Pubns.; 0-935383),* 25829 Mission Blvd., No. 122, Hayward, CA 94544 (SAN 695-9571) Tel 415-889-9668.
Pi Rho, *(Pi Rho Press; 0-9607376),* 11365 Quartz Dr. 64, Auburn, CA 95603 (SAN 239-4731).
†**Pi Yee Pr,** *(Pi Yee Press; 0-935926),* 7910 Ivanhoe Ave., No. 34, La Jolla, CA 92037 (SAN 214-0799); CIP.
Piarist Father, *(Piarist Fathers, Inc.; 0-9614908),* 512 Ave. 20, S., Los Angeles, CA 90031 (SAN 693-5362) Tel 213-223-4153.

Pic Gramics Pubns, *(Pic-Gramics Pubns.; 0-937914),* 7505 Fannin, Suite 214, Houston, TX 77054-1913 (SAN 659-2090) Tel 713-797-1345.
Pic Postcard, *(Picture Postcard Productions, Inc.; 0-934813),* 110 Buchanan Dr., Sausalito, CA 94965 (SAN 694-2768) Tel 415-331-3400.
Pica Pr *Imprint of* **Universe**
Pica Spec Stud *Imprint of* **Universe**
Picayune Pr, *(Picayune Publishing, Inc; 0-937430),* 920 Frenchman St., New Orleans, LA 70116 (SAN 215-1723).
Pick Pub
  See Intl Currency
Pick Pub MI, *(Pick Pubns., Inc.; 0-936526),* 28715 Greenfield Rd., Southfield, MI 48076 (SAN 282-1648) Tel 313-443-1799; Toll free: 800-247-1559.
Pickens County Pub, *(Pickens County Publishing; 0-937229),* P.O. Box 476, Pickens, SC 29671 (SAN 658-6554) Tel 803-878-2453; 117 W. Main St., Pickens, SC 29671 (SAN 658-6562).
Pickle Pr, *(Pickle Pr.; 0-9615499),* 400 Missouri St., San Francisco, CA 94107 (SAN 695-9601) Tel 415-826-0747.
Pickleweed, *(Pickleweed Press; 0-9607890),* 212 Del Casa Dr., Mill Valley, CA 94941 (SAN 238-1885) Tel 415-388-6002.
†**Pickwick,** *(Pickwick Pubns.; 0-915138; 1-55635),* 4137 Timberlane Dr., Allison Park, PA 15101 (SAN 210-1319) Tel 412-487-2159; CIP.
Pictorial Hist, *(Pictorial Histories Publishing Co.; 0-933126),* 713 S. Third W., Missoula, MT 59801 (SAN 212-4351) Tel 406-549-8488.
Pictorial Legends, *(Pictorial Legends; 0-939031),* Subs. of Event Co., 435 Holland Ave., Los Angeles, CA 90042 (SAN 662-8486) Tel 213-254-4416; Dist. by: Publishers Group West, 5855 Beaudry St., Emeryville, CA 94608 (SAN 202-8522) Tel 415-658-3453.
Pictorial Pubs, *(Pictorial Publishers Inc.),* 8081 Zionsville Rd., Indianapolis, IN 46268 (SAN 205-1338) Tel 317-872-7220.
Picturama, *(Picturama Pubns.; 0-918506),* Box 50, 1033 Grand Ave., Arroyo Grande, CA 93420 (SAN 209-9837) Tel 805-481-0550.
†**Picture Bk Studio USA,** *(Picture Bk. Studio, USA; 0-88708; 0-907234),* 60 N. Main St., Natick, MA 01760 (SAN 293-8227) Tel 617-655-9696; Toll free: 800-462-1252; Dist. by: Alphabet Pr., 60 N. Main St., Natick, MA 01760 (SAN 217-1449) Tel 617-655-9696; CIP.
Pidcock Pr, *(Pidcock Pr.; 0-9616111),* Box 1, Gardenville, PA 18926 (SAN 699-7406) Tel 215-794-8187; 5579 Lower Mountain Rd., R.D. 2, New Hope, PA 18938 (SAN 699-7414).
Pie Light Pub, *(Pie Light Publishing; 0-9616725),* 2 Riverview Heights, Rochester, NY 14623 (SAN 659-8617) Tel 716-235-3301.
Pieceful Pleasures, *(Pieceful Pleasures; 0-933758),* 566 30th Ave., San Mateo, CA 94403 (SAN 212-7954) Tel 415-573-9243.
†**Piedmont,** *(Piedmont Press, Inc.; 0-912680),* P.O. Box 3605, Georgetown, Washington, DC 20007 (SAN 205-3861) Tel 703-549-3980; CIP.
Piedmont Pr OH, *(Piedmont Pr.; 0-9616908),* 4080 Porter Rd., Westlake, OH 44145 (SAN 661-5201) Tel 216-871-2077.
Piequet Pr, *(Piequet Pr.; 0-914275),* 196 S. Euclid Ave., Upland, CA 91786 (SAN 286-6889) Tel 714-985-5302.
Pier Pr, *(Pier Press; 0-943306),* 190 Riverdell Dr., Saunderstown, RI 02874 (SAN 240-7442) Tel 401-295-5767.
Pierce Carolyn
  See Starlight Pubns
Pierce Coll
  See Man NE
Pierce Ellis Ent, *(Pierce-Ellis Enterprises; 0-938701),* 607 S. Park View St., 4th Flr., Los Angeles, CA 90057 (SAN 661-5376) Tel 213-388-8488. *Imprints:* Ear-Lit (Ear-Literature).
Pierian, *(Pierian Pr.; 0-87650),* P.O. Box 1808, Ann Arbor, MI 48106 (SAN 204-8949) Tel 313-434-5530. *Imprints:* Greenfield Bks (Greenfield Books).
Piermont Co, *(Piermont Co.; 0-9613685),* P.O. Box 888, West Chester, PA 19381-0888 (SAN 295-799X) Tel 215-696-1218.

†**Pierpont Morgan,** *(Morgan, Pierpont, Library; 0-87598),* 29 E. 36th St., New York, NY 10016 (SAN 204-8957) Tel 212-685-0008; CIP.
Pierremont Press, *(Pierremont Pr.; 0-930883),* P.O. Box 33932, Shreveport, LA 71130 (SAN 677-8151) Tel 318-674-6240.
Pierson Pubs, *(Romaine Pierson Pubs., Inc.; 0-935466),* 80 Shore Rd., Port Washington, NY 11050 (SAN 213-3660) Tel 516-883-6350.
Pig Iron Pr, *(Pig Iron Pr.; 0-917530),* P.O. Box 237, Youngstown, OH 44501 (SAN 209-0937) Tel 216-783-1269.
Pigeon River, *(Pigeon River Country Assn., Inc.; 0-9615851),* 110 W. Fifth, Gaylord, MI 49735 (SAN 696-6225) Tel 517-732-2607; P.O. Box 122, Gaylord, MI 49735 (SAN 696-978X).
Pigeon Roost Pr, *(Pigeon Roost Press),* 739 Clematis Dr., Nashville, TN 37205 (SAN 211-8661).
Pigiron Pr
  See Pig Iron Pr
Pigs Whisker, *(Pig's Whisker Music; 0-9602874),* P.O. Box 27522, Los Angeles, CA 90027 (SAN 218-4583).
Piirisild & Treumut, *(Piirisild & Treumut Partnership; 0-9609364),* P.O. Box 2562, Van Nuys, CA 91404 (SAN 216-2857) Tel 818-765-2587.
Pika Pr, *(Pika Press; 0-935160),* P.O. Box C-9, Mammoth Lakes, CA 93546 (SAN 213-4268).
Pike & Fischer
  See Pike Fischer
Pike Fischer, *(Pike & Fischer, Inc.; 0-937275),* Subs. of Bureau of National Affairs, 4550 Montgomery Ave., Suite 433N, Bethesda, MD 20814 (SAN 659-0411) Tel 301-654-6262.
Pikestaff Pr, *(Pikestaff Press, The; 0-936044),* Div. of Pikestaff Publications, Inc., P.O. Box 127, Normal, IL 61761 (SAN 213-8654) Tel 309-452-4831.
Pilgram Hse, *(Pilgram Hse. Publishing Co.; 0-916213),* 801 Easy St., Simi Valley, CA 63065 (SAN 294-9539) Tel 805-526-0813; Dist. by: Bookpeople, 2929 Fifth St., Berkeley, CA 94710 (SAN 168-9517).
Pilgrim Bks OK, *(Pilgrim Bks.; 0-937664),* P.O. Box 2399, Norman, OK 73070 (SAN 215-6989) Tel 405-360-5658.
Pilgrim Hall
  See Pilgrim Soc
Pilgrim Hse, *(Pilgrim Hse.; 0-932131),* 1637 Westhaven Ave. NW, Salem, OR 97304 (SAN 686-2195) Tel 503-362-4030.
Pilgrim NJ, *(Pilgrim Books; 0-9610624),* 26 Georgia, Medford, NJ 08055 (SAN 265-4075) Tel 609-953-0404.
Pilgrim NY, *(Pilgrim Pr., The United Church Pr.; 0-8298),* Div. of United Church Board for Homeland Ministries, 132 W. 31st St., New York, NY 10001 (SAN 212-601X) Tel 212-239-8700; Dist. by: Publishers Distribution Ctr., 25 Branca Rd., Rutherford, NJ 07073 (SAN 200-5018) Tel 201-939-6064. *Imprints:* Gemini Music (Gemini Music Division).
†**Pilgrim Pr,** *(Pilgrim Pr., The; 0-933476),* 39 University Pl., Princeton, NJ 08540 (SAN 211-2647) Tel 609-924-9095; CIP.
Pilgrim Pr Corp NY, *(Pilgrim Press Corp.; 0-932256),* 36-01 43rd Ave., Long Island City, NY 11101 (SAN 211-9226).
Pilgrim Pubns, *(Pilgrim Pubns.),* P.O. Box 66, Pasadena, TX 77501 (SAN 206-3069) Tel 713-477-2329.
Pilgrim Soc, *(Pilgrim Society; 0-940628),* 75 Court St., Plymouth, MA 02360 (SAN 280-1221) Tel 617-746-1620.
Pilgrimage, *(Pilgrimage Press; 0-918550),* 2398 Telegraph Ave., Berkeley, CA 94704 (SAN 210-1327) Tel 415-548-2626.
Pilgrimage Inc, *(Pilgrimage, Inc.; 0-932930),* Div. of Anderson Publishing Co., Rte. 11, Box 553, Jonesboro, TN 37659 (SAN 285-0834) Tel 615-735-4887; Toll free: 800-582-7295; 646 Main St., P.O. Box 2676, Cincinnati, OH 45201 (SAN 285-0842).
Pilgrimage Pub, *(Pilgrimage Publishing, Inc.; 0-935819),* 104 Central Ave., Tarrytown, NY 10591 (SAN 696-6276) Tel 914-631-0488.

Place in the Woods, *(Place in the Woods; 0-932991),* 3900 Glenwood Ave., Golden Valley, MN 55422-5302 (SAN 689-058X) Tel 612-374-2120; Dist. by: Bacon's, Box 228B, East Chatham, NY 12060 (SAN 200-5573); Dist. by: Walnut Pr., LTO Enterprises, 6036 N. Tenth Way, Phoenix, AZ 85014 (SAN 285-113X); Dist. by: Midwest Library Service, 11443 St. Charles Rock Rd., Bridgeton, MO 63044 (SAN 169-4243); Dist. by: BookFare, 5609-2A Fishers Ln., Rockville, MD 20852 (SAN 200-5581).

Plaid Pony Pubns, *(Plaid Pony Pubns.; 0-935195),* P.O. Box 68502, Seattle, WA 98168 (SAN 695-510X) Tel 206-242-8376; 3220 S. 166th St., Seattle, WA 98188 (SAN 695-5118).

Plain View, *(Plain View Pr.; 0-911051),* 1509 Dexter, Austin, TX 78704 (SAN 264-3073) Tel 512-441-2452.

Plains Press, *(Plains Pr.; 0-918461),* Southwest State Univ., Marshall, MN 56258 (SAN 677-0185) Tel 507-537-6463.

Plamen Pub, *(Plamen Publishing Co.; 0-9602138),* P.O. Box 3088, Steinway Sta., Astoria, NY 11103 (SAN 212-3029).

Plan Par Ctrl CA, *(Planned Parenthood of Central California; 0-9610122),* 633 N. Van Ness Ave., Fresno, CA 93728 (SAN 274-6662) Tel 209-486-2411.

†**Plan Parent,** *(Planned Parenthood Federation of America, Inc.; 0-934586),* 810 Seventh Ave., New York, NY 10019 (SAN 205-1281) Tel 212-541-7800; *CIP.*

Planet Bks, *(Planet Bks.; 0-88009),* 65-42 Fresh Meadow Lane, Fresh Meadows, NY 11365 (SAN 282-5759) Tel 718-961-9240.

Planet CA, *(Planet Press; 0-931671),* 115 29th St., Newport Beach, CA 92663-3418 (SAN 686-9203) Tel 714-675-5994.

Planet Drum Books, *(Planet/Drum Foundation; 0-937102),* P.O. Box 31251, San Francisco, CA 94131 (SAN 216-437X) Tel 415-285-6556.

Planet Watch Pubns, *(Planet Watch Pubns.; 0-9617168),* P.O. Box 515. Old Chelsea Sta., New York, NY 10113 (SAN 663-1258) Tel 212-242-1958.

Planned Parent
See PP Idaho

Planned Parenthood, *(Planned Parenthood of Westchester, Inc.; 0-9614179),* 88 East Post Rd., White Plains, NY 10601 (SAN 686-6611) Tel 914-428-7876.

Planners Pr, *(Planners Pr.; 0-918286),* Div. of American Planning Association, 1313 E. 60th St., Chicago, IL 60637 (SAN 209-3928) Tel 312-955-9100.

Planning Forum, *(Planning Forum, The; 0-912841),* P.O. Box 70, Oxford, OH 45056 (SAN 230-8673) Tel 513-523-4185; 5500 College Corner Pike, Oxford, OH 45056 (SAN 669-2435).

Planning Retire, *(Planning Retirement; 0-9614180),* 8321 Westlawn Ave., Los Angeles, CA 90045 (SAN 686-6263) Tel 213-932-6225.

Plant Pr MA, *(Plant Press, The; 0-940960),* P.O. Box 133, Halifax, MA 02338 (SAN 217-4162) Tel 617-293-3163.

Plantagenet Hse, *(Plantagenet House, Inc.; 0-940812),* P.O. Box 271, Blackshear, GA 31516 (SAN 219-6271) Tel 912-449-6601.

Plantation, *(Plantation Pr.; 0-911150),* 9140 Davies Plantation Rd., Brunswick, Memphis, TN 38134 (SAN 205-1273) Tel 901-386-2015.

Plantin Pr, *(Plantin Pr.; 0-9612546),* P.O. Box 905, Minneapolis, MN 55440 (SAN 205-1265) Tel 612-566-6795.

Platen Pub Co, *(Platen Publishing Co.; 0-932607),* 14240 Bledsoe St., Sylmar, CA 91342 (SAN 687-5246) Tel 818-367-9613.

Platform Studio, *(Platform Studio; 0-942812),* 636 Beacon St., Boston, MA 02215 (SAN 240-4885).

Platinum Pen Pubs, *(Platinum Pen Publishers, Inc.; 0-912815),* P.O. Box 11127, 4810 NE Vivion Rd., Kansas City, MO 64119 (SAN 265-394X) Tel 816-741-2894.

Platonic Acad Pr, *(Platonic Academy Pr., The; 0-937011),* Box 409, Santa Cruz, CA 95061 (SAN 658-6767) Tel 408-423-7923; 129 Spring St., Santa Cruz, CA 95060 (SAN 658-6775).

†**Platt,** *(Platt & Munk Pubs.; 0-448),* Div. of Grosset & Dunlap, 200 Madison Ave., New York, NY 10010 (SAN 211-9668) Tel 212-576-8900; *CIP.*

Platte n Pr *Imprint of* **Jende-Hagan**

†**Platypus Bks,** *(Platypus Bks., Ltd.; 0-930905),* P.O. Box 492, Pittsford, NY 14534 (SAN 679-1727) Tel 716-248-8636; Dist. by: Writers & Books, 740 University Ave., Rochester, NY 14607 (SAN 156-9678) Tel 716-473-2590; *CIP.*

Play Schs, *(Play Schools Assn.; 0-936426),* 19 W. 44th St., New York, NY 10017 (SAN 202-0076) Tel 212-921-2940.

Playboy Pbks, *(Playboy Paperbacks; 0-87216; 0-86721),* Div. of P.E.I. Bks., Inc., 200 Madison Ave., New York, NY 10019 (SAN 213-2672) Tel 212-686-9820; Dist. by: ICD, 250 W. 55th St., New York, NY 10019 (SAN 270-885X) Tel 212-262-7444.

Playboy Pr Pbks
See Playboy Pbks

Player Piano
See Interstate Piano

Players Pr, *(Players Pr., Inc.; 0-941426; 0-88734),* P.O. Box 1132, Studio City, Los Angeles, CA 91604 (SAN 239-0213) Tel 818-789-4980.

Playette Corp, *(Playette Corp.; 0-940630),* 85 Longview Rd., Port Washington, NY 11050 (SAN 203-1000) Tel 516-883-7460.

†**Plays,** *(Plays, Inc.; 0-8238),* 120 Boyston St., Boston, MA 02116 (SAN 202-0084) Tel 617-423-3157; *CIP.*

Playspaces, *(Playspaces-International; 0-85953),* 31D Union Ave., Sudbury, MA 01776 (SAN 216-2121) Tel 617-443-7146.

Playwrights Pr, *(Playwrights Pr.; 0-9617282),* c/o Amherst Writers & Artists, P.O. Box 1076, Amherst, MA 01004 (SAN 663-5180) Tel 413-584-7729; c/o Amherst Writers & Artists, 77 McClellan, Amherst, MA 01002 (SAN 663-5199).

Plaza Pubs, *(Plaza Pubs.),* 2010 Empire Blvd., Webster, NY 14580 (SAN 202-1544) Tel 716-671-1533.

Pleasant Co, *(Pleasant Co.; 0-937295),* 7 N. Pinckney St., Madison, WI 53703 (SAN 658-7755) Tel 608-251-2222.

Pleasant Hill, *(Pleasant Hill Press),* 2600 Pleasant Hill Rd., Sebastopol, CA 95472 (SAN 207-1630) Tel 701-823-6583.

Pleasantry Pr, *(Pleasantry Pr., Inc.; 0-932407),* 7 N. Pinckney St., Madison, WI 53703 (SAN 686-6948) Tel 608-251-2222.

Please Pr, *(Please Pr., Ltd.; 0-938580),* Box 3036, Flint, MI 48502 (SAN 215-8000) Tel 313-239-3110.

†**Pleasure Dome,** *(Pleasure Dome Press; 0-918870),* Div. of L.I. Poetry Collective, Inc., Box 773, Huntington, NY 11743 (SAN 210-4849) Tel 516-691-2376; *CIP.*

Pleasure Trove, *(Pleasure Trove Books; 0-930400),* 2156 Merokee Dr., Merrick, NY 11566 (SAN 207-2742) Tel 516-379-2501; Dist. by: Light House Hill Pub., 279 Edinboro Rd., Staten Island, NY 10306 (SAN 238-0706) Tel 718-987-7586; Dist. by: Quality Books, 918 Sherwood Dr., Lake Bluff, IL 60044-2204 (SAN 169-2127) Tel 312-498-4000.

Pleiades Pr, *(Pleiades Press/Studio Graphics Workshop; 0-9616152),* 310 Old Main St., W., Bradenton, FL 33505 (SAN 699-9417) Tel 813-748-8638.

Pleiades Pub, *(Pleiades Publishing; 0-9613722),* P.O. Box 2133, Sandy, UT 84091 (SAN 683-2822).

Pleneurethic Intl, *(Pleneurethic International),* Earth Light Bookstore, 113 E. Main, Walla Walla, WA 99362 (SAN 209-116X) Tel 509-525-4983.

Plenum Med Bk *Imprint of* **Plenum Pub**
Plenum Pr *Imprint of* **Plenum Pub**

†**Plenum Pub,** *(Plenum Publishing Corp.; 0-306),* 233 Spring St., New York, NY 10013 (SAN 201-9248) Tel 212-620-8000; Toll free: 800-221-9369; 170 Le Grand Ave., Northvale, NJ 07647 (SAN 658-1412); *CIP. Imprints:* Consultants (Consultants Bureau); IFI-Plenum (I F I/Plenum).(IFI/Plenum); Plenum Med Bk (Plenum Medical Book Company).(Plenum Medical Bk. Co.); Plenum Pr (Plenum Press).(Plenum Pr.); Rosetta (Plenum Rosetta).

Pletsch Assocs, *(Pletsch & Associates; 0-917927),* P.O. Box 1409, Albany, GA 31702-1409 (SAN 656-9978) Tel 912-432-7705.

Plexus Pub, *(Plexus Publishing, Inc.; 0-937548),* 143 Old Marlton Pike, Medford, NJ 08055 (SAN 212-436X) Tel 609-654-6500.

PLI, *(Practising Law Institute; 0-87224),* 810 Seventh Ave., New York, NY 10019 (SAN 203-0136) Tel 212-765-5700.

Ploof Stuff, *(Ploof Stuff; 0-9611740),* 123 W. Main, Melrose, MN 56352 (SAN 285-3655).

†**Plough,** *(Plough Publishing House, The; 0-87486),* Subs. of Woodcrest Service Committee, Hutterian Brethren, Rte. 213, Rifton, NY 12471 (SAN 202-0092) Tel 914-658-3141; *CIP.*

Ploughshare Pr, *(Ploughshare Press; 0-912396),* P.O. Box 123, Sea Bright, NJ 07760 (SAN 205-6380) Tel 201-842-0336.

Ploughshares Bks, *(Ploughshares Bks.; 0-933277),* Subs. of Ploughshares Inc., 214A Waverley Ave., Watertown, MA 02172 (SAN 691-8069) Tel 617-926-9875.

Plover Pr, *(Plover Pr.; 0-917635),* P.O. Box R, Kaneohe, HI 96744 (SAN 656-9005) Tel 808-254-5725; Dist. by: Talman Co., Inc., 150 Fifth Ave., New York, NY 10011 (SAN 200-5204) Tel 212-620-3182.

Plowshare, *(Plowshare Press, Inc.; 0-87368),* P.O. Box 2252, Boston, MA 02107 (SAN 204-899X).

Plucked, *(Plucked String, Inc.; 0-9614120),* P.O. Box 11125, Arlington, VA 22210 (SAN 669-7003) Tel 301-622-1069.

Plum Apple Pub, *(Plum Apple Publishing; 0-9616794),* 1401 Tower Rd., Winnetka, IL 60093 (SAN 659-9400) Tel 312-446-2079.

Plum Grove Bks, *(Plum Grove Bks.; 0-9616856),* 314 S. Benton St., Palatine, IL 60067 (SAN 661-5961) Tel 312-358-0408.

Plum Hall, *(Plum Hall Inc.; 0-911537),* 1 Spruce Ave., Cardiff, NJ 08232 (SAN 264-3103) Tel 609-927-3770.

Plum Nelly, *(Plum Nelly Shop, Inc., The),* 1201 Hixson Pike, Chattanooga, TN 37405 (SAN 216-1745) Tel 615-266-0585.

Plum Pub, *(Plum Publishing Co.; 0-9613789),* 25115 DeSalle St., Laguna Hills, CA 92653 (SAN 678-9854) Tel 714-770-4104.

Plumbers Ink Bks, *(Plumbers Ink Books; 0-935684),* P.O. Box 233, Cerrillos, NM 87010 (SAN 213-8662).

Plumbing Pubns, *(Plumbing Pubns.; 0-9603462),* 1700 N. H St., Midland, TX 79701 (SAN 213-3148) Tel 915-683-5574; Orders to: P.O. Box 5461, Midland, TX 79701 (SAN 213-3156) Tel 915-682-3249.

Plume *Imprint of* **NAL**

Plunkett Lake Pr, *(Plunkett Lake Pr.; 0-9614696),* 551 Franklin St., Cambridge, MA 02139 (SAN 692-655X) Tel 617-576-2738.

Pluribus Pr, *(Pluribus Pr., Inc.; 0-931028),* Div. of Teach'em, Inc., 160 E. Illinois St., Chicago, IL 60611 (SAN 238-8413) Tel 312-467-0424.

Plus One Pub, *(Plus One Publishing, Inc; 0-934822),* 625 N. Mansfield Ave., Hollywood, CA 90036 (SAN 213-1404) Tel 213-936-1783.

Plus Seven Bks, *(Plus Seven Books; 0-943416),* SR Box 13, Brandy Station, VA 22714 (SAN 240-7469) Tel 703-825-9163.

Plutarch Pr *Imprint of* **Advent NY**

Plycon Pr, *(Plycon Pr.; 0-916434),* Div. of Plycon Industries, P.O. Box 220, Redondo Beach, CA 90277 (SAN 201-8829) Tel 213-379-9725; Orders to: 10612 Collett, Granada Hills, CA 91344 (SAN 693-9716) Tel 213-379-9725.

Plymouth
See Plymouth Pr

Plymouth Col, *(Plymouth Colony Research Group),* 128 Massasoit Dr., Warwick, RI 02888 (SAN 241-4376) Tel 401-781-6759.

Plymouth Pr, *(Plymouth Press; 0-935540),* Subs. of International Language Institute, P.O. Box 390205, Miami, FL 33119 (SAN 212-9612) Tel 305-538-5022.

Plymouth Pr MI
See Ross St

Plymouth Rock Found, *(Plymouth Rock Foundation; 0-942516),* 14 McKinley Cir., Marlborough, NH 03455 (SAN 239-8583) Tel 603-876-4658.

PM Ent, *(P-M Enterprises; 0-9601846),* P.O. Box 23104, Euclid, OH 44123 (SAN 210-3192) Tel 216-289-7663.

PM Inc, *(PM, Inc.; 0-9608846),* No. 106, 14545 Friar, Van Nuys, CA 91411 (SAN 241-0524) Tel 818-873-4399.

PMA, *(PMA Inc.; 0-941562),* 180 Township Line Rd., Belle Mead, NJ 08502 (SAN 264-2824) Tel 201-359-5200.

PMF Research, *(PMF Research Co.; 0-934036),* P.O. Box 424, Kenilworth, IL 60043 (SAN 212-9574).

PMI Inc, *(Photography Media Institute, Inc.; 0-936524),* P.O. Box 78, Staten Island, NY 10304 (SAN 216-1729) Tel 718-447-3280.

PMnet, *(PMnet; 0-935293),* 580 College Ave., Palo Alto, CA 94306 (SAN 695-9679) Tel 415-856-0135.

PMS Indus, *(PMS Industries; 0-931463),* Div. of Proto Systems of Atlanta, 1790 Hembree Rd., Alpharetta, GA 30201 (SAN 683-1486) Tel 404-475-1818.

PMS Self Help, *(PMS Self Help Ctr.; 0-936614),* 170 State St., Suite 222, Los Altos, CA 94022 (SAN 216-776X) Tel 415-941-1540; Dist. by: Ingram Distribution Group, Inc., 347 Reedwood Dr., Nashville, TN 37217 (SAN 169-7978); Dist. by: Bookpeople, 2929 Fifth St,, Berkeley, CA 94710 (SAN 168-9517).

PNLW, *(Pescar Nelson Langley West Publishing Group, Inc.; 0-932457),* 3817 Atlantic Ave., Suite 227, Long Beach, CA 90807 (SAN 686-7243) Tel 213-595-8559.

P'Nye Pr, *(P'Nye Press; 0-9602402),* The Printers Shop, 4047 Transport, Palo Alto, CA 94303 (SAN 212-5463) Tel 415-494-6802.

Pocahontas Pr, *(Pocahontas Pr., Inc.; 0-936015),* 2805 Wellesley Ct., Blacksburg, VA 24060 (SAN 696-6195) Tel 703-951-0467.

Pocket Pal Pub, *(Pocket Pal Publishing Co.; 0-938079),* P.O. Box 23391, Baltimore, MD 21203 (SAN 659-6916); 2101 Callow Ave., Baltimore, MD 21217 (SAN 659-6924) Tel 301-523-6113.

Pocket Pro, *(Pocket Pro; 0-9615593),* 5627 University Way, NE, Seattle, WA 98105 (SAN 695-9695) Tel 206-527-4822.

Pocket Testament, *(Pocket Testament League, Inc),* 117 Main St., Lincoln Park, NJ 07035 (SAN 225-4204) Tel 201-696-1900; P.O. Box 368, Lincoln Park, NJ 07035 (SAN 669-2443).

Pocumtuck Valley Mem, *(Pocumtuck Valley Memorial Assn.; 0-9612876),* Memorial Hall Museum, Deerfield, MA 01342 (SAN 211-2663) Tel 413-774-7476.

Podesta Fishing, *(Podesta Fishing Co., Pubs.),* 140 S. Peter Dr., Campbell, CA 95008 (SAN 211-0881) Tel 408-377-7700.

Podiatric Educ, *(Podiatric Educational Pubns.; 0-9600302),* 28 Prospect St., Waltham, MA 02154 (SAN 204-9007) Tel 617-894-1985.

Poe Soc Baltimore, *(Poe, Edgar Allan, Society of Baltimore, The; 0-9616449),* 402 E. Gittings Ave., Baltimore, MD 21212 (SAN 659-0535) Tel 301-234-4821.

Poet Papers, *(Poet Papers; 0-9600288),* P.O. Box 528, Topanga, CA 90290 (SAN 209-4770).

Poet Tree Pr, *(Poet Tree Pr., The; 0-916922),* Box 97, Antrim, NH 03440 (SAN 202-3172) Tel 603-588-2730.

Poetasumanos, *(Poetasumanos Press; 0-938254),* 949 Capp St., No. 10, San Francisco, CA 94110 (SAN 215-6997).

Poetica, *(Poetica Pr.; 0-9613534),* Div. of Denehen, Inc., 4316 Marvin Dr., Fort Wayne, IN 46806-2596 (SAN 669-7011) Tel 219-744-4798.

Poetry Eastwest, *(Poetry Eastwest; 0-912206),* P.O. Box 391, Sumter, SC 29150 (SAN 202-0106) Tel 803-773-5170.

Poets Alive Pr, *(Poets Alive Pr.; 0-936641),* P.O. Box 999, Harrisburg, NC 28075 (SAN 699-6949); 631 Louise Ave., Charlotte, NC 28204 (SAN 699-6957) Tel 704-332-5955.

†Poets & Writers, *(Poets & Writers; 0-913734),* 201 W. 54th St., New York, NY 10019 (SAN 204-8981) Tel 212-757-1766; *CIP.*

Poets Mark, *(Poet's Mark; 0-9614820),* 19311 Orleans Ave., Detroit, MI 48203 (SAN 693-0778) Tel 313-892-4536.

Poets Playwrights, *(Poets & Playwrights, Inc., The; 0-9615306),* 322 W. 52nd St., P.O. Box 136, Radio City Sta., New York, NY 10019 (SAN 694-6003) Tel 212-582-7898.

Pogment Pr, *(Pogment Pr., The; 0-938823),* 4609 Village Dr., Fairfax, VA 22030 (SAN 661-7468) Tel 703-273-2934.

Pohl Assoc
  See J Pohl Assocs

Poiletman Pub, *(Poiletman Publishing Co.; 0-937519),* 196 Sweet Wood Cir., Columbia, SC 29210 (SAN 659-0551) Tel 803-781-1417; Orders to: P.O. Box 210726, Columbia, SC 29221-0726 (SAN 662-4200).

Point *Imprint of* **Scholastic Inc**

Point Calif, *(Point Foundation/Whole Earth Review),* 27 Gate 5 Rd., Sausalito, CA 94965 (SAN 210-7139) Tel 415-332-4335; Dist. by: Random Hse., 400 Hahn Rd., Westminster, MD 21157 (SAN 202-5515).

Point Found
  See Point Calif

Point Loma Pub, *(Point Loma Pubns., Inc.; 0-913004),* P.O. Box 6507, San Diego, CA 92106 (SAN 204-9023); 3727 Charles St., San Diego, CA 92106 (SAN 662-1155) Tel 619-222-3291.

Point Park, *(Point Park College; 0-9615172),* 201 Wood St., Pittsburgh, PA 15222 (SAN 694-2881) Tel 412-392-3860.

Point Pub Co
  See New Prod Develop

Point Reyes Pr, *(Point Reyes Pr.; 0-9613145),* P.O. Box 332, Point Reyes, CA 94956 (SAN 294-6505) Tel 415-663-1612; 39 Drake's Summit, Point Reyes, CA 94956 (SAN 294-6513); Dist. by: Bookpeople, 2929 Fifth St., Berkeley, CA 94710 (SAN 168-9517) Tel 415-549-3030.

Point Two, *(Point Two Pubns.; 0-911073),* P.O. Box 725, R.C.U., New York, NY 10185 (SAN 274-6948) Tel 212-719-9045.

Pointe Pubs, *(Pointe Pubs., Inc.; 0-935897),* P.O. Box 3078, Centerline, MI 48015-0078 (SAN 696-6292) Tel 313-778-0404; 22317 Kelly Rd., East Detroit, MI 48021 (SAN 696-981X) Tel 313-445-6724; Toll free: 800-852-7409; Dist. by: Spring Arbor, 10885 Textile Rd., Belleville, MI 48111-2398 (SAN 158-9016) Tel 313-481-0900; Dist. by: Growth Publishing, 201 Davis Dr., Suite U, Sterling Industrial Pk., Sterling, VA 22170 (SAN 682-9112) Tel 703-450-6460.

Pokeberry Pubns, *(Pokeberry Publications; 0-911111),* P.O. Box 421, Luquillo, PR 00673 (SAN 274-6956).

Poko Press, *(Poko Pr.; 0-916929),* P.O. Box 14766, Columbus, OH 43214 (SAN 661-5252); 300 Oakland Pk., Columbus, OH 43214 (SAN 661-5260) Tel 614-262-3865.

Poky Nose Pr, *(Poky Nose Pr.; 0-9613576),* P.O. Box 232E, Star Rte., Albrightsville, PA 18210 (SAN 670-168X) Tel 717-646-8748.

Pol Stud Assocs
  See PS Assocs Croton

Polamerica Pr, *(Polamerica Press; 0-914310),* P.O. Box 36415, Los Angeles, CA 90036 (SAN 206-8672).

Polanie, *(Polanie Publishing Co.; 0-911154),* 643 Madison St., N.E., Minneapolis, MN 55413 (SAN 204-9031) Tel 612-379-9134.

Polar Palm, *(Polar Palm Productions, Inc.; 0-918792),* 1238 G St., Anchorage, AK 99501 (SAN 282-1702) Tel 907-279-1859; Orders to: Box 4-907, Anchorage, AK 99509-0907 (SAN 282-1710).

Polaris Pr, *(Polaris Press; 0-930504),* 16540 Camellia Terrace, Los Gatos, CA 95030 (SAN 204-904X).

Polaroid Corp, *(Polaroid Corp.; 0-9616459),* 575 Technology Sq., No. 9P, Cambridge, MA 02139 (SAN 659-2759) Tel 617-577-3096.

Polestar, *(Polestar Pubns.; 0-942044),* 620 S. Minnesota Ave., Sioux Falls, SD 57104 (SAN 239-474X) Tel 605-338-2888.

Polestar Nexus, *(Polestar Nexus Publishing, Inc.; 0-931087),* 8333 Corbin Ave., Canoga Park, CA 91306 (SAN 678-9404) Tel 818-765-7827.

Polestar Pub
  See Polestar Nexus

Police Beat Pr, *(Police Beat Press; 0-942724),* 723 N. 53rd St., Milwaukee, WI 53208 (SAN 240-1231).

Police Bkshelf, *(Police Bookshelf; 0-936279),* P.O. Box 122, Concord, NH 03301 (SAN 697-9424) Tel 603-224-6814; 72 Broadway, Concord, NH 03301 (SAN 698-2336).

Police Exec Res, *(Police Executive Research Forum),* 2300 M St. NW, Suite 910, Washington, DC 20037 (SAN 274-7014).

Police Found, *(Police Foundation),* 1001 22 ST. NW, Suite 200, Washington, DC 20037 (SAN 237-8280).

Police Pr, *(Police Press; 0-89415),* P.O. Box 2818, Dublin, CA 94568-0818 (SAN 209-9853) Tel 415-829-2728.

Police Train, *(Police Training Foundation),* 3412 Ruby St., Franklin Park, IL 60131 (SAN 262-0626) Tel 312-678-4009.

Policy Studies, *(Policy Studies Organization; 0-918592),* Univ. of Illinois at Urbana-Champaign, 361 Lincoln Hall, 702 S. Wright St., Urbana, IL 61801 (SAN 210-1343) Tel 217-359-8541.

Polish American, *(Polish American Historical Assn.; 0-940962),* 984 Milwaukee Ave., Chicago, IL 60622 (SAN 212-3037).

Polish Genealog, *(Polish Genealogical Society; 0-9602162),* 984 N. Milwaukee Ave., Chicago, IL 60622 (SAN 224-4934).

Polish Inst Art & Sci, *(Polish Institute of Arts & Sciences),* 59 E. 66th St., New York, NY 10021 (SAN 225-3747) Tel 212-988-4338.

Polish Museum Am, *(Polish Museum of America; 0-9602162),* 984 N. Milwaukee Ave., Chicago, IL 60622 (SAN 274-7103) Tel 312-384-3352.

†Political Re, *(Political Research, Inc.; 0-915140),* 16850 Dallas Pkwy., Dallas, TX 75248 (SAN 218-9097) Tel 214-931-8831; *CIP.*

Polk, *(Polk's Bluebooks of Hobbies; 0-911399),* 314 Fifth Ave., New York, NY 10001 (SAN 274-7227) Tel 212-279-9034.

Polley Pubs, *(Polley Pubs.),* 93156 Marcola Rd., Marcola, OR 97454 (SAN 677-010X).

Pollux Pr, *(Pollux Press; 0-913933),* P.O. Box 12, Victor, CO 80860 (SAN 286-8687) Tel 303-689-3000.

Polonia Bkstore & Pubs, *(Polonia Bookstore & Pubs., Co.; 0-935455),* 2886 N. Milwaukee Ave., Chicago, IL 60618 (SAN 695-9717) Tel 312-489-2554.

Poltergeist, *(Poltergeist Press; 0-9603918),* 706 S. Morain St., Kennewick, WA 99336 (SAN 213-5477) Tel 509-735-4078.

†Poltroon Pr, *(Poltroon Pr.; 0-918395),* 2315 Carleton St., Berkeley, CA 94704 (SAN 218-2475) Tel 415-845-8097; Dist. by: Anacapa Bks., 3090 Claremont Ave., Berkeley, CA 94705 (SAN 200-724X) Tel 415-654-3517; *CIP.*

Poly Concepts, *(Poly Concepts Publishing Co.; 0-915203),* 2948 N. Terrace Dr., Wichita, KS 67220 (SAN 289-8012) Tel 316-684-8297.

Poly Tone, *(Poly Tone Pr.; 0-933830),* 16027 Sunburst St., Sepulveda, CA 91343 (SAN 210-6515) Tel 818-892-0044.

Polyconomics, *(Polyconomics, Inc.; 0-938081),* 86 Maple Ave., Morristown, NJ 07960 (SAN 659-6975) Tel 201-267-4641.

Polycrystal Bk Serv, *(Polycrystal Book Service; 0-9601304),* P.O. Box 27, Western Springs, IL 60558 (SAN 212-6753) Tel 312-246-3818.

Polyglot Prods, *(Polyglot Productions; 0-917381),* 136 Brattle St., Cambridge, MA 02138 (SAN 294-1546) Tel 617-491-3541. No longer produces software.

†Polygonal Pub, *(Polygonal Publishing Hse.; 0-936428),* 210 Broad St., Washington, NJ 07882 (SAN 218-4559) Tel 201-689-3894; *CIP.*

Polymers & Plastics Tech Pub Hse, *(Polymers & Plastics Technical Publishing House; 0-942378),* 373 Bush Hill Ct., Lake Mary, FL 32746 (SAN 239-8591).

Polymus Pub, *(Polymus Publishing Co.; 0-931379),* 20734 Schoolcraft St., Canoga Park, CA 91306 (SAN 682-613X) Tel 818-887-1297.

PolyScience, *(PolyScience Corp.; 0-913106),* 7800 Merrimac Ave., Niles, IL 60648 (SAN 209-0740) Tel 312-965-0611.

Pomegranate Calif, *(Pomegranate Artbooks, Inc.; 0-917556; 0-87654),* P.O. Box 980, Corte Madera, CA 94925 (SAN 211-0857); Toll free: 800-227-1428 Tel 415-924-8141.

Pomegranate Pr, *(Pomegranate Pr., Ltd.; 0-938817),* 3236 Bennett Dr., Los Angeles, CA 90068 (SAN 661-745X) Tel 213-850-6719.

Pomme le Terre, *(Pomme le Terre; 0-939964),* P.O. Box 357, Heber City, UT 84032 (SAN 216-8499) Tel 801-583-9870; Dist. by: Green River Forge, Ltd., Box 257, Fulton, CA 95439 (SAN 200-8114).

Pomona Val Writers, *(Pomona Valley Writers Assn.; 0-939503),* P.O. Box 3428, Ontario, CA 91761 (SAN 663-396X); 1541 North Baker Ave., Ontario, CA 91764 (SAN 663-3978) Tel 714-981-8339.

Ponce Pr, *(Ponce Pr.; 0-933829),* P.O. Box 73, 1081 Alameda, Belmont, CA 94002 (SAN 692-8757) Tel 415-591-9802.

Ponchie, *(Ponchie & Co.; 0-9604418),* W.V.U., Dept of Foreign Languages, Morgantown, WV 26506 (SAN 214-4425).

Pond Woods, *(Pond Woods Pr.; 0-9604334),* P.O. Box 82, Stony Brook, NY 11790 (SAN 212-4378) Tel 516-751-3232.

Ponderosa, *(Ponderosa Pubs.; 0-913162),* Rte. 1, Box 68, Saint Ignatius, MT 59865 (SAN 204-9058) Tel 406-745-4455.

Ponderosa Pr, *(Ponderosa Pr.; 0-933393),* P.O. Box 10225, Colorado Springs, CO 80932 (SAN 691-5051) Tel 303-471-3637.

Pong, *(Pong, Ted; 0-939966),* P.O. Box 321, Freeland, WA 98249 (SAN 216-0544).

Pong Yui, *(Pong Yui),* 2976 Vincent Rd., Cuyhoga Falls, OH 44224 (SAN 692-6800).

Pontine Pr, *(Pontine Pr.),* 1153 N. Orange, Hollywood, CA 90038 (SAN 201-8845).

Pony Pr, *(Pony Pr.; 0-9616501),* 3981 Fort Jim Rd., Placerville, CA 95667 (SAN 659-283X) Tel 916-644-6853.

Pony X Pr, *(Pony X Press; 0-939428),* 915 Shorepoint Ct. E303, Alameda, CA 94501 (SAN 220-1828) Tel 415-522-4928.

Pool Pubns, *(Pool Pubns.; 0-9609588),* Box 3362, Enfield, CT 06082 (SAN 274-7332) Tel 203-745-9162.

Poopsies, *(Poopsie's, Inc.; 0-9616060),* P.O. Box 4009, Appleton, WI 54915 (SAN 698-0503) Tel 414-735-9181; 1283 Valley Fair Mall, Appleton, WI 54915 (SAN 698-0511).

Poor Richards, *(Poor Richard's Pr.; 0-917212),* Affil. of Men's Rights Assoc., 17854 Lyons, Forest Lake, MN 55025 (SAN 208-2519) Tel 612-464-7663.

Poor Souls Pr, *(Poor Souls Pr./Scaramouche Bks.; 0-916296),* P.O. Box 236, Millbrae, CA 94030 (SAN 209-679X) Tel 415-588-4163.

Poorhouse Pr, *(Poorhouse Pr.; 0-9614728),* 8333 W. McNab Rd., Tamarac, FL 33321 (SAN 692-5057) Tel 305-726-4343.

Pop Hits Pub, *(Pop Hits Publishing; 0-934019),* 3149 Southern Ave., Memphis, TN 38111 (SAN 692-7815) Tel 901-452-5265.

Pop Med Pubns, *(Popular Medical Pubns., Inc.; 0-9614618),* 3907 Pinewood Ln., Hollywood, FL 33021 (SAN 691-6856) Tel 305-989-4183.

†**Popcorn Pubs,** *(Popcorn Pubs; 0-930506),* P.O. Box 1308, Pittsfield, MA 01202 (SAN 211-044X) Tel 413-443-5601; *CIP.*

†**Pope John Ctr,** *(Pope John Center; 0-935372),* 186 Forbes Rd., Braintree, MA 02184 (SAN 282-1729) Tel 617-848-6965; *CIP.*

Popl Rev CA, *(Population Review Pubn.; 0-9609080),* 8976 Cliffridge Ave., La Jolla, CA 92037 (SAN 241-4341) Tel 619-455-6093.

Poplar Bks, *(Poplar Books; 0-915045),* P.O. Box 62, Shiloh, TN 38376 (SAN 287-2595) Tel 901-632-1289.

Poppy Pr, *(Poppy Pr.; 0-9616145),* 913 Hampton Rd., Sacramento, CA 95864 (SAN 699-9336) Tel 916-487-9507.

Popular Med Pr, *(Popular Medicine Pr.; 0-936575),* P.O. Box 12607, Toledo, OH 43606 (SAN 658-828X) Tel 419-472-8701.

Popular Med Pub
See Pop Med Pubns

Popular Pubns, *(Popular Pubns.; 0-9615362),* P.O. Box 1558, Oroville, WA 98844-1558 (SAN 694-4108).

†**Population Coun,** *(Population Council Office of Communications; 0-87834),* 1 Dag Hammarskjold Plaza, New York, NY 10017 (SAN 225-1582) Tel 212-644-1300; *CIP.*

Population Ref, *(Population Reference Bureau; 0-917136),* 777 14th St.,NW, Washington, DC 20005 (SAN 205-1230) Tel 202-639-8040.

Population Review
See Popl Rev CA

Porcella Studios, *(Porcella Studios; 0-936589),* 3619 Shoemake Ave., Modesto, CA 95351 (SAN 698-1313) Tel 209-524-1134.

Porch Swing, *(Porch Swing Press, Inc.; 0-9606550),* P.O. Box 15014, Nashville, TN 37215 (SAN 219-8118).

†**Porcupine Pr,** *(Porcupine Pr., Inc.; 0-87991),* 310 S. Juniper St., Philadelphia, PA 19107 (SAN 202-0122) Tel 215-735-0101; *CIP.* Imprints: Basil Blackwell (Basil Blackwell (England)).

Porkyspine, *(Porkyspine Press; 0-9612014),* 99 Crosman Terrace, Rochester, NY 14620 (SAN 286-8520) Tel 716-473-2949.

Porphyrion Pr, *(Porphyrion Press; 0-913884),* RR 2, Box 439, Middle Grove, NY 12850 (SAN 206-6823) Tel 518-587-9809.

Port Love Intl, *(Port Love International Publishing Co.),* P.O. Box 423, Amazonia, MO 64421 (SAN 686-2764).

Port Pr, *(Port Press; 0-9606104),* 16 Ridge Dr., Port Washington, NY 11050 (SAN 216-8502).

Portack Pr, *(Portack Pr.; 0-938163),* P.O. Box 10, Springfield, MA 01103 (SAN 659-6959); 55 State St., Springfield, MA 01103 (SAN 659-6967) Tel 413-781-6005.

Portals Pr, *(Portals Pr.; 0-916620),* P.O. Box 1048, Tuscaloosa, AL 35403 (SAN 208-8126) Tel 205-758-1874.

Porter
See Bern Porter

Porter Co PA, *(Porter Co., The; 0-936095),* Div. of Kepner-Tregoe, P.O. Box 816, Easton, PA 18044-0816 (SAN 696-8104) Tel 215-258-9948; 705 Reeder St., Easton, PA 18042 (SAN 696-8112).

Porter Pub Co, *(Porter Publishing Co.; 0-933565),* P.O. Box 134, Center City, MN 55012 (SAN 691-9006) Tel 612-257-5232. Do not confuse with Bern Porter, Belfast, ME.

Porter Sargent, *(Porter Sargent Pubs.; Inc.; 0-87558),* 11 Beacon St., Boston, MA 02108 (SAN 208-8142) Tel 617-523-1670.

Portfolio Pr, *(Portfolio Pr.; 0-942620),* RD 1, Huntington, NY 11743 (SAN 238-5554) Tel 212-989-8700.

Porthole Fla, *(Porthole Pr.; 0-932907),* P.O. Box 15, Oldsmar, FL 33557 (SAN 689-9803) Tel 813-855-4590.

†**Portland Cement,** *(Portland Cement Assn.; 0-89312),* 5420 Old Orchard Rd., 'Skokie, IL 60077-4321 (SAN 207-6004) Tel 312-966-6200; *CIP.*

Portland Litho, *(Portland Litho; 0-9615157),* 1600 Congress St., Portland, ME 04101 (SAN 659-2082).

Portland Symphony Cookbook, *(Portland Symphony Orchestra Women's Committee; 0-9601266),* 30 Myrtle St., Portland, ME 04112 (SAN 206-9881) Tel 207-773-8191.

Portner, *(Portner, Hal; 0-913149),* 67 Westhampton Rd., Northampton, MA 01060 (SAN 283-4162) Tel 413-584-1285.

Portola CA, *(Portola Pr.; 0-936559),* 470 Cervantes Rd., Portola Valley, CA 94025 (SAN 698-1003) Tel 415-851-8953; P.O. Box 620361, Woodside, CA 94062 (SAN 698-1011).

Portola Pr, *(Portola Pr.; 0-9605998),* P.O. Box 1225, Santa Barbara, CA 93102 (SAN 216-7573) Tel 805-682-7974.

Portolan, *(Portolan Press; 0-916762),* 825 Rathjen Rd., Brielle, NJ 08730 (SAN 208-8134) Tel 201-528-8264.

Portrayal, *(Portrayal Pr.; 0-938242),* P.O. Box 1913, Bloomfield, NJ 07003 (SAN 215-9066) Tel 201-743-1851.

Portriga Pubns, *(Portriga Pubns.; 0-9602274),* 823 N. Edinburg Ave., Los Angeles, CA 90046 (SAN 212-4386).

†**Portsmouth Marine Soc,** *(Portsmouth Marine Society, The; 0-915819),* P.O. Box 147, Portsmouth, NH 03801 (SAN 293-9029) Tel 603-431-5667; *CIP.*

Poseidon Imprint of **PB**

Poseidon Pubns, *(Poseidon Pubns.; 0-937378),* 1340 N. Alameda, Las Cruces, NM 88001 (SAN 215-1731).

Posey Intl, *(Posey International; 0-940348),* P.O. Box 338, Orem, UT 84057 (SAN 220-2700) Tel 801-377-5504.

Posey Pubns
See Posey Intl

Posey Pubns CA
See PS Pubns

Positive Attitude, *(Positive Attitude Pr.; 0-936383),* 3790 El Camino Real, Suite 2002, Palo Alto, CA 94306 (SAN 697-2802) Tel 415-964-7587; 1965 San Ramon, No. 4, Mountain View, CA 94043 (SAN 697-2810).

Positive Images, *(Positive Images, Inc.; 0-9615271),* 1203 Carver St., P.O. Box 483, Myrtle Beach, SC 29578-0483 (SAN 695-2682) Tel 803-448-5361.

Positive Notes, *(Positive Notes Pubns.; 0-9612786),* P.O. Box 193, Hubbard, OH 44425 (SAN 289-8071) Tel 216-568-7306.

Post Apollo Pr, *(Post-Apollo Pr., The; 0-942996),* 35 Marie St., Sausalito, CA 94965 (SAN 240-429X) Tel 415-332-1458.

Post-Era, *(Post-Era Books; 0-911160),* Box 150, 119 S. First Ave., Arcadia, CA 91006 (SAN 205-1672) Tel 818-446-5000.

Post Horn Pr, *(Post Horn Pr., Inc.; 0-935311),* 1288 Lenox Cir., NE, Atlanta, GA 30306 (SAN 695-5525) Tel 404-876-0518.

Post Oak Pr Imprint of **Larksdale**

Post Parade, *(Post Parade Pubs.; 0-943808),* 6828-3 Quebec Court, San Diego, CA 92139 (SAN 238-3411) Tel 619-470-1035.

Post-Tribune, *(Post-Tribune Publishing Co.; 0-917495),* Subs. of Knight-Rider Newspapers, Inc., 1065 Broadway, Gary, IN 46402 (SAN 656-0792) Tel 219-881-3000.

Postilion Pubns, *(Postilion Pubns.; 0-941480),* Div. of Roger Koerber Inc., 15565 Northland Dr., Suite 605W, Southfield, MI 48075 (SAN 239-1260) Tel 313-569-1411.

Postroad Pr Inc, *(Postroad Press Inc; 0-912691),* P.O. Box 1212, Roanoke, VA 24006 (SAN 283-9318); 635 Day Ave., SW Roanoke, VA 24016 (SAN 283-9326).

Posy Pubns, *(Posy Pubns.; 0-9616061),* P.O. Box 1624, Independence, MO 64055 (SAN 698-0465) Tel 816-373-2967; 3948 Sherman Dr., Independence, MO 64055 (SAN 698-0473).

Posy Pubns
See Posy Va

Posy Va, *(Posy Pubns.; 0-9603526),* 115 Shasta Ct., Charlottesville, VA 22903 (SAN 213-3490) Tel 804-293-8506.

Pot of Gold, *(Pot of Gold Pubns.; 0-9605542),* 435 10th St., Manhattan Beach, CA 90266 (SAN 216-0552).

Potala, *(Potala Corp.; 0-9611474),* 107 E. 31st St., Fourth flr., New York, NY 10016 (SAN 283-1570) Tel 212-213-5011.

Potato Pr Imprint of **O'Hara**

Potboiler Pr, *(Potboiler Pr.; 0-939329),* 521 W. Point Ave., St. Louis, MO 63130 (SAN 663-1649) Tel 314-727-6050.

Potentials Development, *(Potentials Development, Inc.; 0-932910),* 775 Main St., Suite 321, Buffalo, NY 14203 (SAN 239-5916) Tel 716-842-2658.

Potes Poets, *(Potes & Poets Pr., Inc.; 0-937013),* 181 Edgemont Ave., Elmwood, CT 06110 (SAN 658-6759) Tel 203-233-2023.

Potola Corp
See Potala

Potomac, *(Potomac Bks., Inc., Pubs.; 0-87107),* P.O. Box 40604, Palisades Sta., Washington, DC 20016 (SAN 202-0149) Tel 703-592-3225.

Potomac Appalach, *(Potomac Appalachian Trail Club; 0-915746),* 1718 N St., NW, Washington, DC 20036 (SAN 208-1121) Tel 202-638-5307.

Potomac Area, *(Potomac Area Council, American Youth Hostels Inc.; 0-9614892),* 1332 I St. NW, Suite 451, Washington, DC 20005 (SAN 693-188X) Tel 202-783-4943; 1017 K St., Second flr., Washington, DC 20001 (SAN 662-3158) Tel 202-783-4943; Orders to: PAC-AYH, P.O. Box 28607-Central Sta., Washington, DC 20038-8607 (SAN 662-3166) Tel 202-783-4943.

Potomac Ent, *(Potomac Enterprises; 0-939836),* Box 146, Fort Branch, IN 47648 (SAN 216-924X) Tel 812-753-4977; Dist. by: Sanford J. Durst, 29-28-41st Ave., Long Island City, NY 11101 (SAN 211-6987) Tel 718-706-0303.

Potomac Pr, *(Potomac Pr.; 0-917262),* P.O. Box 31086, Washington, DC 20031 (SAN 208-8150) Tel 202-582-4064.

Potomac Val Pr, *(Potomac Valley Pr.),* 1424 16th St., NW, Washington, DC 20036 (SAN 659-8161).

Symbols/Abbreviations

PRESCOB, *(PRESCOB Publishing Co.;
0-933257),* 10421 E. 44 St., Tulsa, OK
74146 (SAN 211-612X) Tel 918-664-6717.
Prescott Durrell & Co, *(Prescott/Durrell, & Co.;
0-9609506),* Box C-32000, Richmond, VA
23261-2000 (SAN 274-7855)
Tel 804-321-3467.
Prescott Pr, *(Prescott Pr., Inc.; 0-933451),* P.O.
Box 53777, Lafayette, LA 70505
(SAN 691-8247) Tel 318-235-5127.
†Prescott St Pr, *(Prescott St. Pr.; 0-915986),*
P.O. Box 40312, Portland, OR 97240-0312
(SAN 207-4729) Tel 503-254-2922; *CIP.*
Presence Inc, *(Presence Inc.; 0-937296),* P.O.
Box 1867, Easley, SC 29641
(SAN 240-8813) Tel 803-878-7239.
Preser Trust, *(Preservation Trust of Vermont;
0-9615706),* P.O. Box 1777, Windsor, VT
05089-0021 (SAN 695-9806)
Tel 802-658-6647; Windsor Hse., Main St.,
Windsor, VT 05089-0021 (SAN 695-9814).
Preserv Ink, *(Preservation Ink; 0-9605294),*
P.O. Box 92314, Milwaukee, WI 53202
(SAN 239-9962) Tel 414-272-1193.
Preserv Pub Co, *(Preservation Publishing Co.;
0-911515),* P.O. Box 567, 719 State St.,
Grinnell, IA 50112-0567 (SAN 264-3162)
Tel 515-236-5575.
Preserv Soc Newport, *(Preservation Society of
Newport County, The),* Dist. by: Rhode
Island Pubns. Society, 189 Wickenden St.,
Providence, RI 02903 (SAN 219-9696)
Tel 401-272-1776.
†Preservation Pr, *(Preservation Pr., The;
0-89133),* Div. of National Trust for Historic
Preservation, 1785 Massachusetts Ave., NW,
Washington, DC 20036 (SAN 209-3146)
Tel 202-673-4058; *CIP.*
Presidential Acct, *(Presidential Accountability
Group; 0-936486),* Box 19312, Washington,
DC 20036 (SAN 239-5924).
Presidents Assn, *(Presidents Assn.; 0-8144),*
Div. of American Management Assns., 135
W. 50th St., New York, NY 10020
(SAN 219-385X) Tel 212-903-7945.
Presidial, *(Presidial Press; 0-935978),* P.O. Box
5248, Austin, TX 78763 (SAN 209-4789)
Tel 512-472-6653.
†Presidio Pr, *(Presidio Pr.; 0-89141),* 31
Pamaron Way, Novato, CA 94947
(SAN 214-2759) Tel 415-883-1373; *CIP.*
Imprints: Leeward Pubns (Leeward
Publications, Inc.).(Leeward Pubns., Inc.);
Neff-Kane (Neff-Kane).
Press Alley, *(Press of Appletree Alley, The;
0-916375),* P.O. Box 608, 138 S. Third St.,
Lewisburg, PA 17837 (SAN 295-9747)
Tel 717-524-7064.
†Press for Peace, *(Press for Peace; 0-9614103),*
Div. of Penichet Publishing Co., 2514 S.
Grand Ave., Los Angeles, CA 90007
(SAN 685-9771) Tel 213-749-6213; *CIP.*
Press Four Fifty One, *(Press 451; 0-917796),*
2600 S.16th St., No. 729, Arlington, VA
22204 (SAN 262-0707) Tel 202-857-7764.
Press LaPlantz, *(Press De LaPlantz; 0-942002),*
899 Bayside Cutoff, Bayside, CA 95524
(SAN 282-1842) Tel 707-822-6009.
Press N Amer, *(Press North America; 0-938271),*
835 Lakechime Dr., Sunnyvale, CA 94089
(SAN 659-8285) Tel 408-734-1680.
Press on Pr, *(Press-on-Press; 0-917043),* P.O.
Box 135, La Jolla, CA 92038
(SAN 655-2870) Tel 619-454-0573.
Press on SF, *(Press on Press; 0-9616792),* P.O.
Box 640203, San Francisco, CA 94109
(SAN 661-0692); 49 Cumberland, San
Francisco, CA 94110 (SAN 661-0706)
Tel 415-285-0260. Do not confuse with Press
on Pr., La Jolla, CA.
Press Pegacycle
    See Wm Dailey Antiq
Press Plantz
    See Press LaPlantz
Press West, *(Press West; 0-914592),* 4947 E.
Tanqueray, St. Louis, MO 63129
(SAN 202-988X) Tel 314-982-2616.
Presser Le Pas, *(Presser Le Pas; 0-9616726),*
554 W. 50th St., 6th Flr., New York, NY
10019 (SAN 659-8773) Tel 212-757-1189.
Pressure, *(Pressure Vessel Handbook Publishing,
Inc.; 0-914458),* P.O. Box 35365, Tulsa, OK
74153-0365 (SAN 206-6149)
Tel 918-742-9637.
Pressure Appli, *(Pressure Applications;
0-9614857),* 1621 Tiffany Way, San Jose,
CA 95125 (SAN 693-1898)
Tel 408-280-7420.

Pressworks, *(Pressworks Publishing, Inc.;
0-939722),* P.O. Box 12606, Dallas, TX
75225 (SAN 216-7581) Tel 214-369-3113;
6140 Deloache St., Dallas, TX 75225
(SAN 658-1471).
Prestegord Pubs, *(Prestegord Pubs.; 0-912751),*
2210A Naudain St., Philadelphia, PA 19146
(SAN 282-8251) Tel 215-568-1112; Dist.
by: Koen Book Distributors, 514 N. Read
Ave., Cinnaminson, NJ 08077
(SAN 169-4642).
†Prestige Educ, *(Prestige Educational;
0-9613577),* 100-11 67 Rd., Forest Hills,
NY 11375 (SAN 670-0462); *CIP.*
Prestige Ent, *(Prestige Enterprise; 0-915455),*
P.O. Box 723, Columbia, SC 29202
(SAN 291-3763) Tel 803-798-4792; 1041C
Barmettler Place, Columbia, SC 29210
(SAN 291-3771).
Prestige Pubns, *(Prestige Pubns.; 0-911009),*
P.O. Box 2157, Princeton, NJ 08540
(SAN 274-791X); 100 Hamilton Ave.,
Princeton, NJ 08540 (SAN 662-7366)
Tel 609-921-7403.
Prestige Video, *(Prestige Video; 1-55533),* 2400
N. Sixth St., Burbank, CA 91504
(SAN 695-9822) Tel 818-843-9697; Dist.
by: Vantage Sales & Marketing Inc., 27
Bucknell Dr., Hazlet, NJ 07730
(SAN 200-5719).
Presto Bks, *(Presto Bks.; 0-943224),* 3435 NW
54th Terr., Gainesville, FL 32606
(SAN 240-4893).
Preston Corp, *(Preston, J. A., Corp.),* 60 Page
Rd., Clifton, NJ 07012 (SAN 274-7928)
Tel 201-777-2700.
Preston-Hill, *(Preston-Hill, Inc.; 0-914616),*
P.O. Box 572, Chapel Hill, NC 27514
(SAN 201-8861) Tel 919-967-7904.
Preston Pubns, *(Preston Publications, Inc.;
0-912474),* P.O. Box 48312, Niles, IL 60648
(SAN 205-3926) Tel 312-965-0566.
Preston St Pr, *(Preston Street Press; 0-939382),*
6 Preston St., Rye, NY 10580
(SAN 220-1232) Tel 914-765-2178.
Preston Tech
    See Preston Pubns
Prestressed Concrete, *(Prestressed Concrete
Institute; 0-937040),* 201 N. Wells St., Suite
1410, Chicago, IL 60606 (SAN 202-1528)
Tel 312-346-4071.
Prestwick Pub, *(Prestwick Poetry Publishing Co.;
0-9607812),* P.O. Box 90277, San Diego,
CA 92109-0780 (SAN 239-5932)
Tel 619-456-2366.
Pretest
    See McGraw-Pretest
Pretty Good TX, *(Pretty Good Publishing;
0-9130020),* P.O. Box 40, Lindale, TX
75771-0040 (SAN 663-1940).
Pretty Penny Pr, *(Pretty Penny Pr., Inc.;
0-938509),* P.O. Box 3890, Santa Monica,
CA 90403 (SAN 661-0226)
Tel 213-476-7843; Dist. by: Panjandrum
Bks., 11321 Iowa Ave., Suite 1, Los Angeles,
CA 90025 (SAN 282-1257)
Tel 213-477-8771.
Pricare, *(Pricare Inc.; 0-9613095),* 3838 E.
Phillips Circle, Littleton, CO 80122
(SAN 294-6521) Tel 303-740-8136.
Price Guide, *(Price Guide Pubs.; 0-911182),*
P.O. Box 525, Kenmore, WA 98028-0525
(SAN 205-3934) Tel 206-362-6670.
Price-Pottenger, *(Price-Pottenger Nutrition
Foundation; 0-916764),* 5871 El Cajon
Blvd., San Diego, CA 92115
(SAN 208-1849) Tel 619-583-7450.
†Price Stern, *(Price, Stern, Sloan, Pubs., Inc.;
0-8431),* 410 N. La Cienega Blvd., Los
Angeles, CA 90048 (SAN 202-0246)
Tel 213-657-6100; Toll free: 800-421-0892;
1900 Sacramento St., Los Angeles, CA
90021 (SAN 658-148X); Toll free:
800-227-8801 (In California); *CIP.*
Price Waterhouse, *(Price Waterhouse),* National
Office Distribution Dept., 1251 Ave. of the
Americas, New York, NY 10020
(SAN 237-8094).
Prickly CA, *(Prickly Pear Pr.; 0-9605794),* 150
Midcrest Way, San Francisco, CA 94131
(SAN 216-5449); Dist. by: Bookpeople, 2929
Fifth St., Berkeley, CA 94710
(SAN 169-4217); Dist. by: Inland Bk. Co.,
22 Hemingway Ave., P.O. Box 261, East
Haven, CT 06512 (SAN 691-4225)
Tel 203-467-4257.
Prickly NY
    See Prickly CA

Prickly Pear, *(Prickly Pear Pr.; 0-933384),* 2132
Edwin St., Fort Worth, TX 76110
(SAN 212-4394).
Pride in Am, *(Pride In America Co., The;
0-9614917),* 176 Warwick Dr., Pittsburgh,
PA 15241 (SAN 223-9566)
Tel 412-833-1717.
Pride Prods, *(Pride Products Co., Inc.;
0-934383),* P.O. Box 1639, Sun City, AZ
85372 (SAN 693-8051) Tel 602-972-4925.
Prima Agua Pr, *(Prima Agua Press; 0-939652),*
302 Union, Las Cruces, NM 88001
(SAN 216-6429).
Prima Materia, *(Prima Materia Bks.;
0-9615315),* P.O. Box 1399, Quoque, NY
11959 (SAN 694-650X) Tel 516-653-5627;
Dist. by: Bookpeople, 2929 Fifth St.,
Berkeley, CA 94710 (SAN 168-9517); Dist.
by: Baker & Taylor Co., Eastern Div., 50
Kirby Ave., Somerville, NJ 08876
(SAN 169-4901); Dist. by: Baker & Taylor
Co., Midwest Div., 501 Gladiola Ave,,
Momence, IL 60954 (SAN 169-2100); Dist.
by: Baker & Taylor Co., Southeast Div,, Mt.
Olive Rd., Commerce, GA 30529
(SAN 169-1503); Dist. by: Baker & Taylor
Co., Western Div., 380 Edison Way, Reno,
NV 89564 (SAN 169-4464)
Tel 702-786-6700.
Prima Pub Comm, *(Prima Publishing &
Communication; 0-914629),* Div. of Cal Co
Am, Inc., P.O. Box 1260, Rocklin, CA
95677-1260 (SAN 289-5609)
Tel 916-624-5718; Dist. by: Interbook, Inc.,
14895 E. 147th St., Suite 370, San Leandro,
CA 94577 (SAN 692-7564)
Tel 415-352-9221.
Prima Vera Pubns, *(Prima Vera Publications;
0-934385),* 2307 Oakdale Rd., Bldg. 4, Suite
3, Modesto, CA 95355 (SAN 693-806X)
Tel 209-524-4351; P.O. Box 6958, Modesto,
CA 95355 (SAN 699-5985).
Primary, *(Primary Sources; 0-911184),* P.O. Box
472, Cooper Sta., New York, NY 10003
(SAN 205-3942).
Primary Pr, *(Primary Pr.; 0-934982),* Box 105a,
Parker Ford, PA 19457 (SAN 216-1753)
Tel 215-495-7529.
Primary Progs, *(Primary Programs; 0-9612060),*
409 Crescent Gardens Dr., Pittsburgh, PA
15235 (SAN 286-8555) Tel 412-795-7487.
Primary Pub, *(Primary Pubblishing Co.;
0-9616563),* 883 S. Marengo, Pasadena, CA
91106 (SAN 659-574X) Tel 818-449-5733.
Primate Pub, *(Primate Publishing; 0-9615289),*
1710 Baker St., San Francisco, CA 94115
(SAN 694-4191) Tel 415-563-5160.
Primavera, *(Primavera; 0-916980),* Ida Noyes
Hall, Univ. of Chicago, 1212 E. 59th St.,
Chicago, IL 60637 (SAN 208-2527)
Tel 312-684-2742.
Primavera Prods, *(Primavera Productions;
0-9607990),* 1063 N. Cove, Union, OR
97883 (SAN 238-5597) Tel 503-562-5091.
Prime Natl Pub, *(Prime National Publishing Co.;
0-932834),* 470 Boston Post Rd., Weston,
MA 02193 (SAN 212-3053)
Tel 617-899-2702.
Prime Pr AZ, *(Prime Press, Ltd.; 0-911539),*
3003 W. Northern, No. 1, Phoenix, AZ
85021 (SAN 264-3197) Tel 602-995-8803;
Orders to: Prime Press, Ltd., P.O. Box
17073, Mesa, AZ 85212 (SAN 662-1163)
Tel 602-831-5823.
Prime Pubns, *(Prime Pubns., Inc.; 0-932053),*
1111 W. 22nd St., Suite 200, Minneapolis,
MN 55408 (SAN 686-2659)
Tel 612-377-9200.
Prime Pubs, *(Prime Pubs.; 0-937514),* 1460
Boulder Ave., Cresent City, CA 95531
(SAN 209-6307) Tel 707-464-1081.
Prime Time Aerobics, *(Prime Time Aerobics;
0-9610234),* 3089C Clairmont Dr., No. 130,
San Diego, CA 92117 (SAN 264-3456)
Tel 619-268-0684.
Primer Pr CA
    See Primer Pr MA
Primer Pr MA, *(Primer Pr.; 0-910617),* 12
Sherman Bridge Rd., Wayland, MA 01778
(SAN 260-2512) Tel 617-358-2660.
Primer Pubs, *(Primer Pubs.; 0-935810),* 5738 N.
Central, Phoenix, AZ 85012
(SAN 220-0864) Tel 602-266-1043; Dist.
by: Many Feathers, 5738 N. Central,
Phoenix, AZ 85012 (SAN 220-0864).
Primipara, *(Primipara; 0-9613790),* Box 371,
Oconto, WI 54153 (SAN 218-2629)
Tel 414-834-3860.

Primo Prod, *(Primo Productions; 0-936357),* 633 Battery St., Suite 910, San Francisco, CA 94111 (SAN 697-9432) Tel 415-788-7977.

Primrose Pr, *(Primrose Press),* 2131 S. Primrose Ave., Alhambra, CA 91803 (SAN 212-9620) Tel 213-283-5468.

Prince Georges County Gen Soc, *(Prince George's County Genealogical Society; 0-916805),* Box 819, Bowie, MD 20715 (SAN 218-9135).

Prince Paper *Imprint of* **Crown**

Prince Peace Pub, *(Prince of Peace Publishing Inc.; 0-933173),* 13801 Fairview Dr., Burnsville, MN 55337 (SAN 692-3305) Tel 612-435-8102.

Prince St Ed, *(Prince Street Editions; 0-943998),* 8 Prince St., New York, NY 10012 (SAN 241-2152) Tel 212-226-7086.

Princet Res Pr, *(Princeton Research Pr.; 0-936231),* P.O. Box 704, Princeton, NJ 08540 (SAN 696-8155) Tel 609-921-2806; 11 Research Rd., Princeton, NJ 08540 (SAN 696-8163).

Princeton Arch, *(Princeton Architectural Pr.; 0-910413),* 40 Witherspoon St., Princeton, NJ 08540 (SAN 260-1176) Tel 609-924-7911; Toll free: 800-334-0854.

Princeton Bk Co, *(Princeton Bk. Co.; 0-916622; 0-903102; 0-87127; 0-932582),* P.O. Box 109, Princeton, NJ 08540 (SAN 208-404X) Tel 609-737-8178; 12 W. Delaware Ave., Pennington, NJ 08534 (SAN 658-1498).

Princeton Dept Hist, *(Princeton Univ., Dept. of History; 0-938495),* 129 Dickinson Hall, Princeton, NJ 08544 (SAN 661-0471) Tel 609-452-5550.

Princeton Hightech, *(Princeton Hightech Group Inc.; 0-934603),* 73 Maplestream Rd., E. Windsor, NJ 08520 (SAN 693-921X) Tel 609-443-4114; Orders to: Order Service, P.O. Box 231, Princeton Junction, NJ 08850 (SAN 662-3298) Tel 609-443-3470.

Princeton Lib, *(Princeton Univ. Library; 0-87811),* Nassau St., Princeton, NJ 08544 (SAN 205-3950) Tel 609-452-3184.

Princeton Opinion, *(Princeton Opinion Press),* 53 Bank St., Princeton, NJ 08542 (SAN 295-3447) Tel 609-924-9600.

Princeton Pub, *(Princeton Publishing; 0-915038),* 221 Nassau St., Princeton, NJ 08540 (SAN 663-1789) Tel 609-924-7555.

Princeton Res Inst, *(Princeton Research Institute; 0-913354),* P.O. Box 363, Princeton, NJ 08540 (SAN 207-4478) Tel 609-396-0305.

Princeton Res Pr
See Princet Res Pr

Princeton Sci Pubs, *(Princeton Scientific Publishing Co., Inc.; 0-911131),* P.O. Box 2155, Princeton, NJ 08543 (SAN 274-7995) Tel 609-683-4750.

†**Princeton U Int Finan Econ,** *(Princeton Univ. International Finance Section, Dept. of Economics; 0-88165),* Princeton Univ., Dickinson Hall, Princeton, NJ 08544 (SAN 205-1109) Tel 609-452-4048. Do not confuse with Princeton Univ. Pr; *CIP.*

†**Princeton U Pr,** *(Princeton Univ. Pr.; 0-691),* 41 William St., Princeton, NJ 08540 (SAN 202-0254) Tel 609-452-4900; Orders to: Marge Weiland, 3175 Princeton Pike, Lawrenceville, NJ 08648 (SAN 662-1171) Tel 609-896-1344; *CIP.*

Principals Lib, *(Principal's Library, The; 0-9617117),* P.O. Box 1342, Massapequa, NY 11758 (SAN 662-8095); 41 Sheppard Ln., Huntington, NY 11743 (SAN 662-8109) Tel 516-326-4687.

Principia Pr, *(Principia Press; 0-911188),* 5743 Kimbark Ave., Chicago, IL 60637 (SAN 205-3888) Tel 312-643-8295.

Prindle *Imprint of* **PWS Pubs**

Prinit Pr, *(Prinit Pr.; 0-932970),* Box 65, Dublin, IN 47335 (SAN 212-680X).

Prinroad Pubs, *(Prinroad Pubs.; 0-911629),* 5717 E. Thomas Rd., Scottsdale, AZ 85251 (SAN 264-3200) Tel 602-941-5760.

Print Indus Am, *(Printing Industries of America, Inc.; 0-89740),* 1730 N. Lynn St., Arlington, VA 22209 (SAN 224-7828) Tel 703-841-8100; 1731 N. Moore St., Arlington, VA 22209 (SAN 669-2486).

Print Mail Serv, *(Printing, Mailing Services, Inc.),* 126 N. Ontario St., Toledo, OH 43624 (SAN 216-0064) Tel 419-241-4266.

Print Med Serv Ltd, *(Print Media Services, Ltd.; 0-942398),* 1310 Jarvis Ave., Elk Grove, IL 60007 (SAN 238-1109) Tel 312-981-0100; Toll free: 800-323-8899.

Print Shop
See Schar Pub Co

†**Printed Edns,** *(Printed Editions; 0-914162),* P.O. Box 27, Sta. Hill Rd., Barrytown, NY 12507 (SAN 206-5851) Tel 914-758-6488; Dist. by: Writers & Books, 740 University Ave., Rochester, NY 14607 (SAN 156-9678) Tel 716-473-2590; Dist. by: Small Pr. Distribution, 1814 San Pablo Ave., Berkeley, CA 94702 (SAN 204-5826) Tel 415-549-3336; *CIP.*

Printed Horse, *(Printed Horse, The; 0-912830),* P.O. Box 1908, Fort Collins, CO 80522 (SAN 210-4377) Tel 303-482-2286.

Printed Matter, *(Printed Matter, Inc.; 0-89439),* 7 Lispenard St., New York, NY 10013 (SAN 169-5924) Tel 212-925-0325.

Printed Matter Pub
See Turnbull & Willoughby

Printed Word, *(Printed Word Publishing),* c/o Barber, 23561 Vaughn Rd., Veneta, OR 97487 (SAN 295-3463) Tel 503-935-7701.

Printek, *(Printek; 0-938042),* 6989 Oxford St., Minneapolis, MN 55426 (SAN 215-7012).

Printwheel, *(Printwheel Pr.; 0-916401),* 2674 E. Main St., Suite C-124, Ventura, CA 93003 (SAN 295-9208) Tel 805-643-0965.

Printworld, *(Printworld, Inc.; 0-943606),* P.O. Box 785, Bala Cynwyd, PA 19004 (SAN 240-7515) Tel 215-649-5140.

Priorities, *(Priorities Inc.; 0-932043),* 1430 Massachusetts Ave., Suite 306-85, Cambridge, MA 02138 (SAN 685-298X) Tel 718-788-7214.

Priority GA, *(Priority Pr.; 0-9615772),* P.O. Box 431, Riverdale, GA 30274 (SAN 695-9865) Tel 404-478-7498; 8381 Willows Way, Riverdale, GA 30274 (SAN 695-9873).

Priority Pr, *(Priority Press; 0-913815),* P.O. Box 670152, Dallas, TX 75367-0152 (SAN 289-5447) Tel 214-368-0135.

†**Priority Pr Pubns,** *(Priority Pr. Pubns./Twentieth Century Fund; 0-87078),* Subs. of Twentieth Century Fund, Inc., 41 E. 70th St., New York, NY 10021 (SAN 205-4647) Tel 212-535-4441; *CIP.*

Priority Pubs, *(Priority Pubs., Inc.; 0-930229),* P.O. Box 1585, Bellevue, WA 98009 (SAN 682-8272).

Priory Bks, *(Priory Bks.),* 1200 Kenwood Ave., Duluth, MN 55811 (SAN 206-1309) Tel 218-723-6555. Do not confuse with Priory Pr., Chicago, IL.

Priory Pr IL, *(Priory Pr., The; 0-8296),* 1111 N Richmond St., Chicago, IL 60622 (SAN 658-6341) Tel 218-723-6582. Do not confuse with Priory Pr., Duluth, MN.

Priory Prods, *(Priory Productions; 0-936161),* 840 S. Main St., Mt. Angel, OR 97362 (SAN 696-821X) Tel 503-845-6773.

Priscillas Pubns, *(Priscilla's Pubns., & Products; 0-917119),* Subs. of Martin Instrument Co., P.O. Box 16270, Philadelphia, PA 19114 (SAN 655-7686) Tel 215-677-5600.

Prism *Imprint of* **P-H**

Prism Enter Corp, *(Prism Entertainment Corp.; 1-55668),* 1875 Century Pk., E., Suite 1010, Los Angeles, CA 90067 Tel 213-277-3270.

†**Prism Pr,** *(Prism Press; 0-938774),* 11706 Longleaf Lane, Houston, TX 77024 (SAN 216-4388) Tel 713-782-5189; *CIP.*

Prisma Bks, *(Prisma Bks., Inc.; 0-910235),* 2501 Irving Ave. S., Minneapolis, MN 55405 (SAN 241-4384) Tel 612-377-0133.
Imprints: Prisma Inst (Prisma Institute).

Prisma Inst *Imprint of* **Prisma Bks**

Prismatique, *(Prismatique Pubns; 0-9614150),* P.O. Box 1059, Daly City, CA 94015 (SAN 686-6115) Tel 415-756-1834.

Prison Ashram
See Hanuman Foun

†**Pritchett & Hull,** *(Pritchett & Hull Assocs., Inc.; 0-939838),* 3440 Oakcliff Rd., NE, Suite 110, Atlanta, GA 30340 (SAN 216-9258) Tel 404-451-0602; Toll free: 800-241-4925; *CIP.*

Privacy Journal, *(Privacy Journal; 0-930072),* Box 15300, Washington, DC 20003 (SAN 210-6531) Tel 202-547-2865.

Private Adjudication, *(Private Adjudication Ctr., Inc.; 0-933329),* Duke Univ., Schl. of Law, Durham, NC 27706 (SAN 691-9359) Tel 919-684-2253.

Private Bks, *(Private Books; 0-9606112),* 500 19th Ave., San Francisco, CA 94121 (SAN 216-8510) Tel 415-751-2338.

Private Carrier, *(Private Carrier Conference, Inc.),* 2200 Mill Rd., Alexandria, VA 22314 (SAN 217-264X).

Private Doctors, *(Private Doctors of America),* 3422 Bienville St., New Orleans, LA 70119 (SAN 224-4241) Tel 504-486-5891.

Privateer Pub Co, *(Privateer Publishing Co; 0-931339),* 512-Viewmont St., Benicia, CA 94510 (SAN 682-0123) Tel 707-745-1627.

Pro Action Pub, *(Pro-Action Publishing; 0-9615126),* Div. of Pro-Action Sports, Inc., 1717 N. Glendale Blvd., Los Angeles, CA 90026 (SAN 694-1826) Tel 213-666-7789.

Pro Canto, *(Pro Canto Pr.; 0-935751),* 37 Phelps St., Marlboro, MA 01752 (SAN 695-989X) Tel 617-481-2322; Dist. by: Support Services, 221 Milk St., Westboro, MA 01581 (SAN 200-5700).

Pro Communications, *(Professional Communications; 0-9614654),* Div. of Kirkland Investment Management, Inc., P.O. Box 7585, Phoenix, AZ 85011 (SAN 691-9014) Tel 602-274-2128; Dist. by: Baker & Taylor Co., Eastern Div., 50 Kirby Rd., Somerville, NJ 08876 (SAN 169-4901) Tel 201-526-8000.

†**Pro Ed,** *(Pro-Ed; 0-936104),* 5341 Industrial Oaks Blvd., Austin, TX 78735 (SAN 222-1349) Tel 512-892-3142; *CIP.*

Pro Edit Serv, *(Professional Editorial Service, Inc.; 0-9615276),* 62 Floyd St., Winthrop, MA 02152 (SAN 694-4086) Tel 617-846-5639.

Pro Golfers, *(Professional Golfers Assn. of America; 0-9614856),* 100 Ave. of the Champions, Palm Beach Gardens, FL 33410 (SAN 224-5655) Tel 305-626-3600.

Pro Handicap
See Prof Jones

Pro Insure Pubns, *(Professional Insurance Publications; 0-931811),* 2495 Campus Dr., Irvine, CA 92715 (SAN 685-9887) Tel 714-955-2267.

Pro Libris Pr, *(Pro Libris Press; 0-943530),* 10 Third St., Bangor, ME 04401 (SAN 240-7523) Tel 207-942-3019.

†**Pro Lingua,** *(Pro Lingua Assocs.; 0-86647),* 15 Elm St., Brattleboro, VT 05301 (SAN 216-0579) Tel 802-257-7779; *CIP.*

Pro-Motion Music, *(Pro-Motion Music; 0-939141),* 3737 NE 112th St., Portland, OR 97220 (SAN 662-5053) Tel 503-257-8185.

Pro Pacific, *(Pro Pacific, Inc.; 0-9616429),* 7117 40th St., No. 14, Tacoma, WA 98466 (SAN 659-0586) Tel 206-565-9480.

Pro Resource, *(Professional Resource Exchange, Inc.; 0-943158),* P.O. Box 15560, Sarasota, FL 34277-1560 (SAN 240-1223) Tel 813-366-7913; Toll free: 800-443-3364; Toll free: 800-366-7913.

Pro-Se Law, *(Pro-Se Law Project, Inc.; 0-937945),* P.O. Box 164, Palmerton, PA 18071 (SAN 659-7572) Tel 215-826-2000.

Pro Se Pubns, *(Pro Se Pubns.; 0-9617267),* Box 3082, Denton, TX 76202 (SAN 663-4915); 601 Jupiter St., Denton, TX 76201 (SAN 663-4923) Tel 817-387-1878.

Pro-Search, *(Pro-Search; 0-9602540),* 3256 Ridge Rd., P.O. 24, Lansing, IL 60438 (SAN 213-148X) Tel 312-895-8800.

Pro Serve Corp, *(Pro Serve Corp. of Sarasota, Inc.; 0-936177),* 1938 Ringling Blvd., Sarasota, FL 33577 (SAN 696-8279) Tel 813-366-9024; Toll free: 800-237-9222.

Pro Servs Pub, *(Professional Services Publishing),* P.O. Box 327, Redding Ridge, CT 06876 (SAN 265-9794) Tel 203-938-9548.

Pro Soft Inc
See Prof Pub Inc

Pro West, *(Pro West; 0-9606746),* 7355 Citrus Way E., Scottsdale, AZ 85253 (SAN 215-1758) Tel 602-991-3183; Dist. by: Motorbooks International, 729 Prospect Ave., Osceola, WI 54020 (SAN 212-3304) Tel 715-294-3345.

ProActive Pr, *(ProActive Pr.; 0-914158),* 64 Vian La Cumbre, Greenbrae, CA 94904 (SAN 201-8888) Tel 415-461-7854.

Probata Pr, *(Probata Pr.; 0-933109),* P.O. Box 10522, Marina del Rey, CA 90292 (SAN 689-5905) Tel 213-827-5477.

Probe
See Veritas

243

Probe Co, (Probe Company; 0-9614050), 1830 North Grand River Ave., Lansing, MI 48906 (SAN 684-8958) Tel 517-372-8440.

†**Probus Pub Co,** (Probus Publishing Co., Inc.; 0-917253), 118 N. Clinton, Chicago, IL 60606 (SAN 655-8615) Tel 312-346-7985; CIP.

Proced Aspects Intl, (Procedural Aspects of International Law Institute; 0-9615124), 910 17th St., NW, Washington, DC 20006 (SAN 694-1699) Tel 202-293-5670.

Procedures, (Procedures Unlimited, Inc) P.O. Box 66, Palos Park, IL 60464 (SAN 287-2811) Tel 312-448-8695.

†**Process Pr,** (Process Pr.; 0-9605378), 2322 Haste, No. 31, Berkeley, CA 94704 (SAN 215-9074) Tel 415-548-6510; CIP.

Procter Gamble Educ, (Procter & Gamble Educational Services; 0-938973), 1 Procter & Gamble Plaza, Cincinnati, OH 45202 (SAN 661-6844) Tel 513-983-3152.

Proctor Jones, (Proctor, Jones Publishing Co.; 0-9608860), 3401 Sacramento St., San Francisco, CA 94118 (SAN 293-3179) Tel 415-922-9222; Dist. by: Publishers Group West, 5855 Beaudry St., Emeryville, CA 94608 (SAN 202-8522) Tel 415-658-3453.

Prod Craftrs Inc, (Product Crafters Inc.; 0-931673), 646 Hwy. 18, E. Brunswick, NJ 08816 (SAN 683-7700) Tel 201-238-1470.

Prod Hse, (Production House Corp.; 0-932638), P.O. Box 8408, La Jolla, CA 92038 (SAN 201-1018) Tel 619-287-2560.

Prod Intl
See C I M Systems

Prod Press, (Productivity Pr.; 0-915299), Div. of Productivity, Inc., P.O. Box 814, Cambridge, MA 02238 (SAN 290-036X) Tel 617-497-5146.

ProDesign, (ProDesign, Inc.; 0-931141), 58 Bank St., New York, NY 10014 (SAN 659-8153) Tel 212-929-0416.

Prodigal Publishing, (Prodigal Publishing Co.; 0-9617285), 1288 Kika St., Kailua, HI 96734 (SAN 663-6071) Tel 808-262-7229; Dist. by: Pacific Trade Group, P.O. Box 668, Pearl City, HI 96782-0668 (SAN 169-1635).

Prodist Imprint of Watson Pub Intl

Produce Mktg Assn, (Produce Marketing Assn.), 700 Barksdale Plaza, Newark, DE 19711 (SAN 224-8646) Tel 302-738-7100.

Productivity Rsch, (Productivity Research International, Inc.; 0-9616778), P.O. Box 1171, Melrose, MA 02176-0018 (SAN 661-0595); 61 W. Hill Ave., Melrose, MA 02176 (SAN 661-0609) Tel 617-665-5777.

Prof & Ref Bk Div Imprint of McGraw

Prof Assocs, (Professional Assocs.; 0-931802), Box 6254, Harrisburg, PA 17112 (SAN 693-1332).

†**Prof Bk Ctr Inc,** (Professional Bk. Ctr., Inc.; 0-943226), 5600 NE Hassalo St., Portland, OR 97213 (SAN 240-5601) Tel 503-288-1255; Orders to: International Specialized Book Services, 5602 NE Hassalo St., Portland, OR 97213-3640 (SAN 169-7129) Tel 503-287-3093; CIP.

Prof Bks Future Health, (Professional Bks./Future Health, Inc.; 0-933478), P.O. Box 3494, Jackson, TN 38301 (SAN 205-3977); 681 Skyline Dr., Jackson, TN 38301 (SAN 662-7374) Tel 901-423-5100; Orders to: P.O. Box 846, Jackson, TN 38302 (SAN 695-6270).

Prof Bks Serv, (Professional Books Service; 0-9601052), Box 366, Dayton, OH 45401-0366 (SAN 165-6309) Tel 513-223-3734.

Prof Comn Inc, (Professional Communications, Inc.; 0-937211), 5799 Tall Oaks Rd., Madison, WI 53715 (SAN 658-6791) Tel 608-271-5791; P.O. Box 9036, Madison, WI 53715 (SAN 658-6805).

Prof Desk Ref, (Professional Desk References, Inc.; 0-939735), 2246 Maiden Ln., Altadena, CA 91001 (SAN 663-1924).

Prof Dev Serv, (Professional Development Services; 0-941944), 7900 Old Branch Ave. No.106, Clinton, MD 20735 (SAN 239-4758).

Prof Driver Prods, (Professional Driver Products Corp.; 0-935879), P.O. Box 1385, Palatine, IL 60078-1385 (SAN 695-9903) Tel 312-359-2662; 706 Deer Run Dr., Palatine, IL 60067 (SAN 695-9911).

Prof Educ IL
See ABA Prof Educ Pubns

Prof Engine, (Professional Engineering Registration Program; 0-932276), P.O. Box 911, San Carlos, CA 94070 (SAN 282-1915) Tel 415-593-9731; c/o Professional Pubns., Inc., P.O. Box 199, San Carlos, CA 94070 (SAN 282-1923) Tel 415-593-9119.

Prof Engr Priv Prac, (Professional Engineers in Private Practice), 2029 K St., NW, Washington, DC 20006 (SAN 689-9641) Tel 202-652-7767.

Prof Ins Agents, (Professional Insurance Agents), 400 N. Washington St., Alexandria, VA 22314 (SAN 274-8304) Tel 703-836-9340.

Prof Jones, (Professor Jones Professional Handicapping Systems; 1-55604), 1940 W. State St., Boise, ID 83702 (SAN 697-2497) Tel 208-342-6939.

Prof Photog, (Professional Photographers of America), 1090 Executive Way, Des Plaines, IL 60018 (SAN 224-9111) Tel 312-299-8161.

Prof Picture Frame, (Professional Picture Framers Assn.), 4305 Sarellen Rd., Richmond, VA 23231 (SAN 225-2708) Tel 804-226-0430.

Prof Pr Bks NYC, (Professional Pr. Bks., Inc.; 0-87873), Div. of Fairchild Books & Visuals, 7 E. 12th St., New York, NY 10003 (SAN 205-3985) Tel 212-741-6640.

Prof Press
See Prof Pr Bks NYC

Prof Press PA, (Professional Pr.; 0-9614729), Subs. of M. Systems Inc., P.O. Box 503, Spring House, PA 19477-0503 (SAN 692-6924) Tel 215-542-7008.

Prof Pub Inc, (Professional Pubns., Inc.; 0-912045; 0-932276), P.O. Box 199, San Carlos, CA 94070 (SAN 264-6315) Tel 415-593-9119.

Prof Pub Radford, (Professional Publishing Co.; 0-937419), 1301 Madison St., Radford, VA 24141 (SAN 659-0667) Tel 703-731-5310.

Prof Pubns, (Professional Pubns.; 0-9605954), Div. of Harris & Walsh Management Consultants, Inc., P.O. Box 698, c/o Harris & Walsh, New Rochelle, NY 10802-0698 (SAN 216-4396) Tel 914-576-0820.

Prof Pubns & Educ, (Professional Pubns. & Education, Inc.), 1150 Delaware St., Denver, CO 80204 (SAN 237-8299).

Prof Pubns NY, (Professional Pubns.; 0-932836), Div. of MetaData, Inc., 310 E. 44th St., New York, NY 10017 (SAN 213-3539); Orders to: P.O. Box 319, Huntington, NY 11743 (SAN 213-3547).

Prof Pubns Ohio, (Professional Pubns., Inc.; 0-934706), 1609 Northwest Blvd., Columbus, OH 43212 (SAN 203-0942) Tel 614-488-8236.

Prof Reading Serv, (Professional Reading Services Inc.; 0-9614374), P.O. Box 7281, Roanoke, VA 24019 (SAN 688-5985) Tel 703-563-0634.

Prof Real Estate, (Professional Real Estate Pubs.; 0-89764), Orders to: Lincoln's Leadership Library, 5902 E. Fourth Terrace, Suite 100, Tulsa, OK 74112 (SAN 214-4476) Tel 918-622-7737.

Prof Rehab Wkrs
See Am Deaf & Rehab

Professional Pr
See Prof Driver Prods

Professional Pub
See Prof Pub Radford

Profiles Pub, (Profiles Publishing, Inc.; 0-912733), 49 Wethersield Ave., Hartford, CT 06114 (SAN 283-1406) Tel 203-522-2528.

Profit Ideas, (Profit Ideas; 0-940398), 8361 Vickers St., Suite 304, San Diego, CA 92111 (SAN 219-8436) Tel 619-560-6922.

Profit Sharing, (Profit Sharing Research Foundation; 0-911192), 1718 Sherman Ave., Evanston, IL 60201 (SAN 205-3993) Tel 312-869-8787.

Profs Unltd, (Professionals Unlimited; 0-915039), 3951 Lantern Dr., Silver Spring, MD 20902 (SAN 289-8098) Tel 301-933-5569.

Prog Achievement Read
See PAR Inc

†**Prog Bapt Pub,** (Progressive Baptist Publishing House; 0-89191), 850 N. Grove Ave., Elgin, IL 60120 (SAN 277-7010); CIP.

Prog Cincinnati, (Program for Cincinnati, the; 0-9608200), 230 E. 9th St., Cincinnati, OH 45202 (SAN 238-8588) Tel 513-721-5522.

Prog Concepts, (Progressive Concepts, Inc.; 0-940010), 2541 Lakewood Lane, Chesapeake, VA 23321 (SAN 285-0877) Tel 804-465-0646; Dist. by: Career Management Concepts, Inc., 2541 Lakewood Lane, Chesapeake, VA 23321 (SAN 285-0877) Tel 804-465-0646.

Prog Educ, (Progressive Education; 0-935396), P.O. Box 120574, Nashville, TN 37212 (SAN 239-4766).

Prog Found, (Progressive Found.; 0-942046), 315 W. Gorham St., Madison, WI 53703 (SAN 238-5961) Tel 608-256-4146.

Prog Grocer, (Progressive Grocer; 0-911790), 1351 Washington Blvd., Stamford, CT 06902 (SAN 202-0270) Tel 203-325-3500.

Prog Pr, (Programmed Pr.; 0-916106), 2301 Baylis Ave., Elmont, NY 11003 (SAN 203-0993) Tel 516-775-0933.

†**Prog Studies,** (Programmed Studies, Inc.; 0-917194), P.O. Box 113, Stow, MA 01775 (SAN 207-7434) Tel 617-897-2130; CIP.

Progenesys Pr, (Progenesys Pr.; 0-917255), P.O. Box 2623, Christiansburg, VA 24068 (SAN 656-0318) Tel 703-382-5493.

Progenitor Soc, (Progenitor Genealogical Society, Inc.; 0-9616381), Box 16422, Salt Lake City, UT 84116 (SAN 659-1817) Tel 801-328-8128.

Progeny Pr, (Progeny Press, Inc.; 0-934168), P.O. Box 206, Villanova, PA 19085 (SAN 213-6740) Tel 215-525-5446.

Progm Ethnom, (Program in Ethnomusicology; 0-88287), UCLA Dept. of Music, Los Angeles, CA 90024 (SAN 682-8108) Tel 213-825-5947.

Program Assocs, (Program Information Assocs.; 0-935555), 7920 Makaaoa Pl., Honolulu, HI 96825 (SAN 695-8524) Tel 808-395-0197; P.O. Box 26300, Honolulu, HI 96825 (SAN 696-9550).

Program Counsel, (Program Counsel; 0-9601096), 4900 Marine Dr., Suite 811, Chicago, IL 60640 (SAN 206-3093) Tel 312-784-3636.

Programs Comm, (Programs in Communication Press; 0-937104), P.O. Box 970, Monument, CO 80132 (SAN 218-9186) Tel 303-594-4711.

Programs Educ, (Programs for Education, Inc.; 0-935493), 82 Park Ave., Flemington, NJ 08822 (SAN 695-9962).

Progresiv Pub, (Progresiv Publishr; 0-89670), 401 E. 32nd St., No. 1002, Chicago, IL 60616 (SAN 212-6818) Tel 312-225-9181.

Progressive Pilot Sem Imprint of Aviation

Progressive Pubns, (Progressive Pubns.; 0-937157), 5719 Templar Crossing, West Bloomfield, MI 48033 (SAN 658-4721) Tel 313-661-1511; P.O. Box 307, Walled Lake, MI 48088 (SAN 658-473X).

Progressive Sci Inst, (Progressive Science Institute; 0-917929), P.O. Box 5335, Berkeley, CA 94705-0335 (SAN 657-0038) Tel 415-654-1619.

Progs & Pubns, (Programs & Pubns.; 0-934382), 321 Queen St., Philadelphia, PA 19147 (SAN 213-3555) Tel 215-467-5291.

Progs on Change, (Programs on Change; 0-9606012; 0-916471), 784 Columbus Ave., Suite 1C, New York, NY 10025 (SAN 216-759X) Tel 212-222-4606.

Proguides, (Proguides; 0-9613657), 320 Lake Crest Dr., Roswell, GA 30075 (SAN 670-7769) Tel 404-993-2298; Orders to: Proguides, P.O. Box 2738, Knoxville, TN 37901 (SAN 688-4237) Tel 615-933-3348.

Project Plan, (Project Planning Associates; 0-9613322), 157 Polsin Dr., Schenectady, NY 12303 (SAN 655-7694) Tel 518-356-1528.

Project Share, (Project Share; 0-936597), P.O. Box 2309, Rockville, MD 20852 (SAN 296-502X) Tel 301-251-5170.

Projections Ent, (Projections Enterprises, Inc.; 0-9612318), Box 1032, 1100 Huener Lane, Jacksonville, OR 97530 (SAN 289-4882) Tel 503-899-7347.

Proletarian Pubs, (Proletarian Pubs; 0-89380), P.O. Box 3925, Chicago, IL 60654 (SAN 209-2158); Orders to: Vanguard Books, P.O. Box 3566, Chicago, IL 60654 (SAN 213-8212) Tel 312-342-3425.

ProLogo, *(ProLogo; 0-9616884)*, P.O. Box 147, Quincy, MA 02170 (SAN 661-650X); 14 Sachem St., Quincy, MA 02170 (SAN 661-6518) Tel 617-471-8427.

Prologue, *(Prologue Pubns.; 0-930048)*, P.O. Box 7119, Menlo Park, CA 94026 (SAN 210-1351) Tel 415-322-1663.

Prologue Pr, *(Prologue Pr.; 0-911711)*, P.O. Box 640, Menlo Park, CA 94026 (SAN 264-4037) Tel 415-321-9110.

Promark Assocs, *(Promark Asociates; 0-9607930)*, Box 222, High Falls, NY 12440 (SAN 238-5619) Tel 914-687-7230.

Promenade Pub, *(Promenade Publishing; 0-932255)*, Div. of Promenade, P.O. Box 2092, Boulder, CO 80306 (SAN 686-628X) Tel 303-440-4807; 835 39th St., Boulder, CO 80302 (SAN 697-7103) Tel 303-440-4807.

Promethean Arts, *(Promethean Arts; 0-942624)*, P.O. Box 2619, Toledo, OH 43606 (SAN 238-5627) Tel 419-536-4257.

†Prometheus Bks, *(Prometheus Bks.; 0-87975)*, 700 E. Amherst St., Buffalo, NY 14215 (SAN 202-0289) Tel 716-837-2475; Toll free: 800-421-0351; *CIP.*

Prometheus Bound, *(Prometheus Bound; 0-9616867)*, P.O. Box 9611, New Haven, CT 06535 (SAN 661-1354); 1423 Chapel St., New Haven, CT 06511 (SAN 661-1362) Tel 203-865-7443.

Prometheus Ent, *(Prometheus Enterprises; 0-9617155)*, 4320 Stevens Creek Blvd., Suite 175, San Jose, CA 95129 (SAN 663-3668) Tel 408-985-9885.

Prometheus Nemesis, *(Prometheus Nemesis Book Co., Inc.; 0-9606954)*, P.O. Box 2748, Del Mar, CA 92014 (SAN 215-7020) Tel 619-755-5980.

Promise Corp, *(Promise Corp.; 0-936982)*, P.O. Box 1534, Pawtucket, RI 02862 (SAN 214-4484).

Promise Pub CA, *(Promise Publishing, Inc.; 0-939497)*, P.O. Box 6289, Orange, CA 92613-6289 (SAN 663-4141); 876 N. Batavia St., Orange, CA 92668 (SAN 663-415X) Tel 714-751-4080.

Promised Land, *(Promised Land Publications, Inc.; 0-911712)*, Div. of Eagle Systems International, 5600 N. University Ave., Provo, UT 84601 (SAN 204-3130) Tel 801-225-2293.

Promontory Pub, *(Promontory Publishing, Inc.; 0-938703)*, P.O. Box 117213, Carrollton, TX 75011-7213 (SAN 661-5627); 1015 Ridgeview Cir., Carrollton, TX 75007 (SAN 661-5635) Tel 214-492-0886.

Promotions Ltd, *(Promotions Ltd. Publishing; 0-913679)*, 6069 Bonnie Bern Court, Burke, VA 22015 (SAN 286-178X) Tel 703-451-0884.

Promotions Unlimit, *(Promotions Unlimited; 0-914749)*, P.O. Box 10081, Lynchburg, VA 24506 (SAN 659-2074).

Proof Pr, *(Proof Press; 0-935070)*, P. O. Box 1256, Berkeley, CA 94701 (SAN 209-8687) Tel 415-521-8741.

Prophecy Pressworks *Imprint of Sufi Islamia-Prophecy*

Proprietary Assn, *(Proprietary Assn.; 0-939060)*, 1700 Pennsylvania Ave., NW, Washington, DC 20006 (SAN 209-2034) Tel 202-393-1700.

Proscenium, *(Proscenium Pr.; 0-912262)*, P.O. Box 361, Newark, DE 19711 (SAN 203-0950) Tel 215-255-4083.

ProSeminar Pr
See Psychomet Res

Prosody Pubs, *(Prosody Publishers; 0-933977)*, 96 Dickerson Ave., Newbury Park, CA 91320 (SAN 692-6797) Tel 805-499-8190.

Prosoft AZ
See J B Dawson CA

PRosoft Prod
See J B Dawson CA

Prospect Hill, *(Prospect Hill; 0-941526)*, 216 Wendover Rd., Baltimore, MD 21218 (SAN 239-3743).

Prospect Pr, *(Prospect Press; 0-937562)*, 14427 Pebble Hill Lane, Gaithersburg, MD 20878 (SAN 282-194X); Orders to: Box 3069, Gaithersburg, MD 20878 (SAN 282-1958) Tel 301-251-4746.

Prospectors Ad Serv, *(Prospector's Advertising Service; 0-9616047)*, 5785 Hermosillo, Atascadero, CA 93422 (SAN 698-0120) Tel 805-466-9759.

Prosperity & Profits, *(Prosperity & Profits Unlimited, Distribution Services)*, Box 570213, Houston, TX 77257-0213 (SAN 200-4682).

Prosveta USA, *(Prosveta, USA; 0-911857)*, P.O. Box 49614, Los Angeles, CA 90049-0614 (SAN 264-3235) Tel 213-820-7478.

Protecto Ent, *(Protecto Enterprises)*, P.O. Box 550, Barrington, IL 60010 (SAN 285-7448) Tel 312-382-5244.

Proteus, *(Proteus Press; 0-918150)*, Subs. of Proteus Design, Inc., 9217 Baltimore Blvd., College Park, MD 20740 (SAN 210-2617) Tel 301-441-2928.

Proteus Calif, *(Proteus Press, The; 0-932864)*, 250 Thunderbird Dr., Aptos, CA 95003 (SAN 212-3800).

Proteus Pub NY, *(Proteus Publishing Co., Inc.; 0-86276)*, P.O. Box 20398, Dag Hammarskjold Ctr., New York, NY 10017-0004 (SAN 215-2363).

Proton Edit Ltd, *(Proton Editora Ltd.)*, 18 E. 23rd St. Basement, New York, NY 10010 (SAN 689-1454) Tel 212-864-6249.

Proton Pub Co
See Proton Edit Ltd

Proton Pub Hse, *(Proton Publishing Hse., Inc.; 0-939019)*, 233 Valentine Ln., Yonkers, NY 10705 (SAN 662-5827).

Proven Perf, *(Proven Performances; 0-9615869)*, 3321 Ridgeway Dr., Metairie, LA 70002 (SAN 696-7434) Tel 504-835-2706; Orders to: Proven Performances, 5660 S. Lakeshore Dr., No. 506, Shreveport, LA 71119 (SAN 662-3840) Tel 318-631-6507.

Providence Journ, *(Providence Journal Co.; 0-937550)*, 75 Fountain St., Providence, RI 02902 (SAN 264-3243) Tel 401-277-7461.

Providential Pr, *(Providential Press)*, P.O. Box 218026, Houston, TX 77218 (SAN 276-9794) Tel 713-578-7837.

Province Pub
See C M Province

Provincial NC, *(Provincial Pr.; 0-936179)*, P.O. Box 2311, Chapel Hill, NC 27514 (SAN 205-1079) Tel 919-942-6412. Do not confuse with Provincial Pr., Ashland, OR.

Provincial Pr OR, *(Provincial Press (OR); 0-9614779)*, P.O. Box 3051, Ashland, OR 97520 (SAN 692-7823) Tel 503-488-2043.

Provost, *(Provost, C. Antonio)*, 4474 Sunburst Dr., Oceanside, CA 92056-3540 (SAN 239-3751).

Provost & Blaney
See Provost

Prow Bks-Franciscan, *(Prow Bks./Franciscan Marytown Pr.; 0-913382)*, 1600 W. Park Ave., Libertyville, IL 60048 (SAN 205-1060).

Proximity Tech, *(Proximity Technology, Inc.; 0-926390)*, 3511 NE 22nd Ave., Fort Lauderdale, FL 33308 (SAN 294-5827) Tel 305-566-3511.

Prsnl Power Pr, *(Personal Power Pr.; 0-9616046)*, 611 Schuring Rd., No. 3, Portage, MI 49081 (SAN 698-0155) Tel 616-327-2761.

Prudent Pubs, *(Prudent Pubs.; 0-915499)*, 1335 Madison St., NW, Washington, DC 20011 (SAN 291-3860).

Prudential Pub Co, *(Prudential Publishing Company; 0-934432)*, 7089 Crystal Blvd., Diamond Springs, CA 95619 (SAN 213-1498) Tel 916-622-8928.

†Pruett, *(Pruett Pub. Co.; 0-87108)*, 2928 Pearl St., Boulder, CO 80301 (SAN 205-4035) Tel 303-449-4919; *CIP.*

PRWCT, *(Platte River Whooping Crane Trust, Inc.; 0-938441)*, 2550 N. Diers Ave., Suite H, Grand Island, NE 68803 (SAN 661-0455) Tel 308-384-4633.

Pryor Pettengill, *(Pettengill, Pryor; 0-933462)*, Box 7074, Ann Arbor, MI 48107 (SAN 213-8697).

Prytaneum Pr, *(Prytaneum Press; 0-907152)*, P.O. Box 7161, Amarillo, TX 79114 (SAN 214-4506).

†PS Assocs Croton, *(Policy Studies Assocs.; 0-936826)*, P.O. Box 337, Croton-on-Hudson, NY 10520 (SAN 214-4417) Tel 914-271-6500; *CIP.*

PS Media Inc, *(Palm Springs Media, Inc.; 0-939271)*, P.O. Box 2740, Palm Springs, CA 92263 (SAN 662-815X); 555 Commercial Rd., Suite 13, Palm Springs, CA 92262 (SAN 662-8168) Tel 619-322-3050.

PS Pubns, *(PS Pubns.; 0-910115)*, P.O. Box 2512, Fairfield, CA 94533 (SAN 241-435X) Tel 707-864-2010.

PSE, *(Product Structuring Enterprises; 0-940964)*, P.O. Box 17723, San Diego, CA 92117 (SAN 217-4197) Tel 619-451-1427.

†PSG Pub Co, *(PSG Publishing Co., Inc.; 0-88416; 0-7236; 0-931890)*, P.O. Box 6, Littleton, MA 01460 (SAN 201-8934) Tel 617-486-8971; Toll free: 800-225-5020; 545 Great Rd., Littleton, MA 01460 (SAN 658-2230); *CIP. Imprints:* Biomed Pubns (PSG/Biomedical).

PSI Assocs MD, *(PSI & Assocs.; 0-938261)*, 2700 Maurleen Ct., Baltimore, MD 21209 (SAN 659-834X) Tel 301-653-1913.

PSI Res, *(PSI Research; 0-916378; 1-55571)*, Subs. of Publishing Services, Inc., 720 S. Hillview Dr., Milpitas, CA 95035 (SAN 218-9240) Tel 408-263-9671; Toll free: 800-228-2275; Toll free: 800-221-4089 (In California); Dist. by: Publishers Group West, 5855 Beaudry St., Emeryville, CA 94608 (SAN 202-8522) Tel 415-658-3453. *Imprints:* Oasis (Oasis Press).

PSI Rhythms, *(P.S.I. Rhythms, Inc.; 0-918882)*, P.O. Box 1838, Ormond Beach, FL 32074 (SAN 210-4806); 2085 S. Halifax, Daytona Beach, FL 32018 (SAN 210-4814).

PSR Pubns, *(PSR Pubns.; 0-931133)*, Subs. of Fisher Investments, 433 Airport Blvd. Suite 106, Burlingame, CA 94010-2095 (SAN 678-9196) Tel 415-342-4994.

Psych & Consul Assocs, *(Psychology & Consulting Assocs. Pr.; 0-930626)*, P.O. Box 1837, La Jolla, CA 92038 (SAN 211-3856) Tel 619-457-3900.

†Psych Assess, *(Psychological Assessment Resources (PAR), Incorporated; 0-911907)*, 16102 N. Florida Ave., Lutz, FL 33549 (SAN 264-6897) Tel 813-968-3003; Toll free: 800-331-8378; *CIP.*

Psych Bks, *(Psychiatric Bks.; 0-9615865)*, 13305 Cleveland Dr., Rockville, MD 20850 (SAN 696-6233) Tel 301-762-0334; Box 10578, Rockville, MD 20850 (SAN 696-9798).

Psych Corp *Imprint of* HarBraceJ

Psych Dev Pubns, *(Psychological Development Pubns.; 0-912397)*, P.O. Box 3198, Aspen, CO 81612 (SAN 265-1904) Tel 303-925-9272.

†Psych Dimensions, *(Psychological Dimensions, Inc.; 0-88437)*, 10 W. 66th St., Suite 4H, New York, NY 10023 (SAN 204-3866) Tel 212-877-2313; *CIP.*

Psych Genocide Res, *(Psychiatric Genocide Research Institute; 0-9614961)*, P.O. Box 80071, Springfield, MA 01108 (SAN 693-7527) Tel 413-788-9523.

Psych Graphic, *(Psych Graphic Pubs.; 0-932382)*, 470 Nautilus St., Suite 303, La Jolla, CA 92037 (SAN 210-6213) Tel 619-459-3484.

Psych Pr WA, *(Psychological Pr.; 0-937668)*, Box 45435, Seattle, WA 98145-0435 (SAN 215-1766) Tel 206-323-5753.

Psych Processes Inc, *(Psychological Processes, Inc.; 0-912149)*, P.O. Box 3914, San Rafael, CA 94901 (SAN 264-7788) Tel 415-883-3530.

Psych Qtly, *(Psychoanalytic Quarterly, Inc.; 0-911194)*, 175 Fifth Ave., New York, NY 10010 (SAN 205-4043).

Psychegenics, *(Psychegenics Pr.; 0-931865)*, Subs. of MCM Inc., P.O. Box 332, Gaithersburg, MD 20877 (SAN 686-0567) Tel 301-948-1122.

Psychic Bks, *(Psychic Bks.; 0-930984)*, 440 Avalon Pl., Oxnard, CA 93033 (SAN 219-2586) Tel 805-488-8670.

Psycho Dynamics Pr, *(Psycho Dynamics Pr.; 0-937605)*, 9348 Santa Monica Blvd., Beverly Hills, CA 90210 (SAN 659-0691) Tel 213-550-6250; Dist. by: DeVorss & Co., Inc., P.O. Box 550, 1046 Princeton Dr., Marina del Rey, CA 90294 (SAN 168-9886).

Psychofeedback
See Classic CA

Psychogenic Disease, *(Psychogenic Disease Publishing Co.; 0-87312)*, P.O. Box 19098, Sacramento, CA 95819 (SAN 203-4239) Tel 916-677-1610.

†Psychohistory Pr, *(Psychohistory Pr.)*, Div. of Atcom, Inc., Pubns., 2315 Broadway, New York, NY 10024 (SAN 201-8926) Tel 212-873-5900; Toll free: 800-521-7004; *CIP.*

Psychomet Res, *(Psychomet Research;
0-9604710),* 3330 NE 135th Ave., Portland,
OR 97230 (SAN 214-4492)
Tel 503-256-4705.

Psychometric, *(Psychometric Affiliates;
0-9606044),* 1620 E. Main St.,
Murfreesboro, TN 37130 (SAN 203-1205)
Tel 219-836-1661.

Psychoneurologia
See Menta Pubns

Pt Orchard Spec, *(Port Orchard Specialties;
0-9616198),* 7775 SE Blakeview Dr., Port
Orchard, WA 98366 (SAN 699-9581)
Tel 206-871-5535.

Pterodactyl Pr, *(Pterodactyl Pr., The; 0-931757),*
Main St., Cumberland, IA 50843
(SAN 684-7722) Tel 712-774-2244.

PTL Enterprises, *(P T L Enterprises; 0-912275),*
Charlotte, NC 28279 (SAN 283-3085)
Tel 704-542-6000.

PTL Fellowship
See PTL Repro

PTL Pubns, *(PTL Pubns.; 0-915420),* Box 1277,
Tustin, CA 92680 (SAN 211-8203)
Tel 714-838-7715.

PTL Repro, *(PTL Reproductions; 0-910709),*
115 S. First St., Broken Arrow, OK 74012
(SAN 260-2423) Tel 918-251-3787.

Ptolemy Brown, *(Ptolemy/The Browns Mills
Review Press; 0-911851),* P.O. Box 905,
Browns Mills, NJ 08015 (SAN 217-3123).

Ptolemy Pr, *(Ptolemy Pr., Ltd.; 0-933550),* P.O.
Box 243, Grove City, PA 16127-0243
(SAN 211-2671) Tel 412-458-5145.

PU Indust Rel, *(Princeton Univ., Industrial
Relations Section),* Firestone Bldg., P.O. Box
248, Princeton, NJ 08540 (SAN 205-1494)
Tel 609-452-4040.

PUB *Imprint of* Unipub

Pub Admin Serv, *(Public Administration Service;
0-87151),* 1313 E. 60th St., Chicago, IL
60637 (SAN 237-8183).

Pub Aff Comm
See Pub Affr Comm

Pub Aff Info, *(Public Affairs Information Service,
Inc.),* 11 W. 40th St., New York, NY 10018
(SAN 225-3372) Tel 212-736-6629.

Pub Aff LA, *(Public Affairs Research Council of
Louisiana),* Box 3118, 300 Louisiana Ave.,
Baton Rouge, LA 70821 (SAN 237-8191).

Pub Aff Pr, *(Public Affairs Pr.; 0-8183),* 419
New Jersey Ave., Washington, DC 20003
(SAN 202-1471) Tel 202-544-3024.

Pub Aff Res, *(Public Affairs Research
Communications, Inc.; 0-930331),* 3103
South St. NW, Washington, DC 20007
(SAN 670-8366) Tel 202-337-0855.

Pub Affr Comm, *(Public Affairs Committee, Inc.;
0-88291),* 381 Park Ave. S., New York, NY
10016 (SAN 205-4027) Tel 212-683-4331.

Pub Citizen Health
See Pub Citizen Inc

Pub Citizen Inc, *(Public Citizen, Inc.; 0-937188),*
2000 P St. NW, No. 605, Washington, DC
20036 (SAN 239-4774).

†Pub Ctr Cult Res, *(Publishing Ctr. for Cultural
Resources, Inc.),* 625 Broadway, New York,
NY 10012 (SAN 274-9025)
Tel 212-260-2010; CIP.

Pub Div JCS, *(Publishing Division of J C S;
0-932411),* 3998 W. Akron Rd., Akron, MI
48701 (SAN 687-4053)
Tel 517-691-5484.

Pub Domain, *(Publishing Domain Exchange;
0-9614731),* 673 Hermitage Pl., San Jose,
CA 95134 (SAN 692-5952)
Tel 408-942-0309; Dist. by: Publishers
Group West, 5855 Beaudry Ave., Emeryville,
CA 94608 (SAN 662-300X)
Tel 415-658-3453.

Pub Enterprises, *(Publishing Enterprises, Inc.;
0-941368),* P.O. Box 66344, Seattle, WA
98166 (SAN 239-0248)
Tel 206-838-2997.

Pub Horizons, *(Publishing Horizons, Inc.;
0-942280),* 2950 N. High St., P.O. Box
02190, Columbus, OH 43202
(SAN 239-7439)
Tel 614-261-6565.

Pub Mark, *(Publishers Mark, The; 0-9614636),*
255 B Bluff Ct., Barrington, IL 60010
(SAN 691-9154) Tel 312-381-6451; Dist.
by: Paperback Supply, 4121 Forest Park
Ave., St. Louis, MO 63108
(SAN 169-4324); Dist. by: Richardson's
Education, 2014 Low Ellen Ln., Houston,
TX 77018 (SAN 691-9170); Dist. by: The
Publishers Mark, P.O. Box 267, Cary, IL
60013 (SAN 694-0153); Dist. by: Baker &
Taylor, Eastern Div., 50 Kirby Ave.,
Somerville, NJ 08876
(SAN 169-4901).

Pub Mgmt Assoc, *(Public Management
Associates; 0-939968),* 2014 Siegle Dr.,
Lemon Grove, CA 92045 (SAN 216-8537)
Tel 714-575-2395.

Pub Personnel
See Intl Personnel Mgmt

Pub Sect Lab Rel, *(Public Sector Labor
Relations Conference Board; 0-913400),*
Univ. of Maryland, Division of Behavorial
and Social Sciences, College Park, MD
20742 (SAN 205-4051).

Pub Securities, *(Public Securities Assn.;
0-9605198),* 40 Broad St., 12th flr., New
York, NY 10004-2373 (SAN 216-2903)
Tel 212-809-7000.

Pub Serv Ctr, *(Publishing Services Center),* 95
First St., Los Altos, CA 94022
(SAN 662-1198) Tel 415-965-4081; Dist.
by: William Kaufmann, Inc., 95 First St., Los
Altos, CA 94022 (SAN 202-9383)
Tel 415-948-5810.

Pub Serv Inc
See PSI Res

Pub Service, *(Publishers Services; 0-937602),*
P.O. Box 2510, Novato, CA 94948
(SAN 201-3037) Tel 415-883-3530; 11A
Commercial Blvd., Novato, CA 94947
(SAN 200-7223)
Tel 415-883-3140.

Pub Tech Inc, *(Public Technology, Inc.),* 1301
Pennsylvania Ave., NW, Washington, DC
20004 (SAN 225-1256)
Tel 202-626-2400.

Pub Vaidava, *(Publisher Vaidava; 0-936302),*
1621 S. 21st St., Lincoln, NE 68502
(SAN 214-2198).

Pub Ward Inc, *(Publishing Ward, Inc., The;
0-911631),* 700 E. Drake Rd., Q-6, Fort
Collins, CO 80525 (SAN 264-3308)
Tel 303-493-7556.

Public Cit
See Pub Citizen Inc

Public Info Pr, *(Public Info. Pr., Inc.; 0-934954),*
P.O. Box 402611, Miami Beach, FL 33140
(SAN 213-1390)
Tel 305-538-5308.

Public Insights, *(Public Insights Pr.; 0-9608776),*
Box 242, Drexel Hill, PA 19026
(SAN 238-3438).

Public Int Clear, *(Public Interest Clearinghouse,
Inc.; 0-915999),* 17 Murray St., New York,
NY 10007 (SAN 294-653X)
Tel 212-349-8155.

Public Int Econ, *(Public Interest Economics
Foundation),* 1525 New Hampshire Ave.,
NW, Washington, DC 20036
(SAN 218-9232)
Tel 202-872-0313.

Public Management, *(Public Management
Institute, Institute for Fund Raising;
0-916664),* 358 Brannan St., San Francisco,
CA 94107 (SAN 208-6964)
Tel 415-896-1900.

Public Media Inc, *(Public Media, Inc.;
0-913349),* Subs. of Public Media, Inc., 5547
N. Ravenswood Ave., Chicago, IL 60640
(SAN 283-3786) Tel 312-878-2600; Toll
free: 800-323-4222.

Public Pr, *(Public Pr.; 0-9611738),* Orders to:
Mary Clark, 646 Ninth Ave., New York, NY
10036 (SAN 219-4546)
Tel 212-333-7538.

Public Relations, *(Public Relations Publishing
Co., Inc.; 0-913046),* 888 Seventh Ave.,
New York, NY 10106 (SAN 202-957X)
Tel 212-315-8250.

Public Safety, *(Public Safety Automation;
0-939257),* P.O. Box 957, Buellton, CA
93427 (SAN 662-5193); 391 Freear Dr.,
Buellton, CA 93427 (SAN 662-5207)
Tel 805-736-2155.

Public Serv Materials, *(Public Service Materials
Center; 0-914977),* 111 N. Central Ave.,
Hartsdale, NY 10530 (SAN 211-9676)
Tel 914-949-2242.

Public Serv Pubns, *(Public Service Pubns., Inc.;
0-936656),* 1523 W. Eighth St., Los Angeles,
CA 90017 (SAN 212-1328)
Tel 213-484-1088.

Public Util, *(Public Utilities Reports, Inc.;
0-910325),* 1700 N. Moore St., Suite 2100,
Rosslyn Ctr. Bldg., Arlington, VA 22209
(SAN 241-4392) Tel 703-243-7000; Toll
free: 800-368-5001.

Publicity, *(Publicity in Print; 0-915716),* 935
Thornton Way, San Jose, CA 95128
(SAN 207-2750)
Tel 408-293-3997.

Publish or Perish, *(Publish or Perish, Inc.;
0-914098),* 3701 W. Alabama, Suite
450-130, Houston, TX 77027
(SAN 202-0319) Tel 713-524-5515; P.O.
Box 27703-130, Houston, TX 77027
(SAN 660-9422).

Publishers Assocs, *(Pubs. Assocs., Inc.;
0-915911),* 3601 West Devon Ave., Suite
108, Chicago, IL 60659 (SAN 294-0957)
Tel 312-463-2030.

Publishers Consult, *(Publishers Consultants;
0-88310),* Box 1908, Ft. Collins, CO 80522
(SAN 203-2449) Tel 303-482-2286.
Formerly Shields Publishing Co.,
Inc.

Publishers Group, *(Publishers Group West),*
5855 Beaudry St., Emeryville, CA 94608
(SAN 202-8522) Tel 415-658-3453; Toll
free: 800-982-8319.

Publishers Guild, *(Publishers Guild),* P.O. Box
754, Palatine, IL 60067 (SAN 212-7180)
Tel 312-991-0255.

Publishers Media, *(Publishers Media; 0-934064),*
5507 Morella Ave., N. Hollywood, CA
91607 (SAN 213-5493).

Publishers Pr, *(Publisher's Pr.; 0-943592),* 1935
SE 59th Ave., Portland, OR 97215
(SAN 240-7558)
Tel 503-232-9293.

†Publitec, *(Publitec Editions; 0-913581),* 271-A
Lower Cliff Dr., P.O. Box 4342, Laguna
Beach, CA 92652 (SAN 285-3663)
Tel 714-497-6100; CIP.

Publitex Intl, *(Publitex International Corp.;
0-938083),* P.O. Box 6657, Lakeland, FL
33807 (SAN 659-7009); 5295 Misty Lake
Rd., Mulberry, FL 33860
(SAN 659-7017)
Tel 813-425-5035.

Publius Pr, *(Publius Pr.; 0-9614135),* 3100
Philamena St., Tucson, AZ 85730
(SAN 686-4686)
Tel 602-886-4380.

Publius Pub, *(Publius Publishing; 0-937947),*
P.O. Box 411, Pacific Palisades, CA 90272
(SAN 659-7580); 16015 Northfield, Pacific
Palisades, CA 90272 (SAN 659-7599)
Tel 714-851-9411.

Pubn Arts NJ, *(Pub. Arts; 0-942190),* 579
Goffle Road, Ridgewood, NJ 07450
(SAN 239-9717)
Tel 201-652-9393.

Pubns Arts
See Cy De Cosse

Pubns Devl Co, *(Pubns. Development Co.;
0-936431),* P.O. Box 1075, Crockett, TX
75835 (SAN 211-0490) Tel 409-544-5137;
Hwy. 287 N., Crockett, TX 75835
(SAN 699-5543).

Pubns Intl Ltd, *(Consumer Guide Bks./Pubns.
Intl., Ltd.; 0-88176),* Div. of Pubs. Intl.,
Ltd., 3841 W. Oakton St., Skokie, IL 60076
(SAN 263-9823) Tel 312-676-3470; Toll
free: 800-526-4264; Dist. by: Crown
Publishers, Inc., 225 Park Ave., S, New
York, NY 10003 (SAN 200-2639)
Tel 212-254-1600; Dist. by: Harper & Row
Publishers, Inc., 10 E. 53rd St., New York,
NY 10022 (SAN 200-2086)
Tel 212-207-7099; Dist. by: Simon &
Schuster, Inc., 1230 Ave. of the Americas,
New York, NY 10020
(SAN 200-2450)
Tel 212-245-6400.

Pubns Organization
See Bridge Pubns Inc

Pyramid Systems, *(Pyramid Systems; 0-942888),* 2800 Corona Dr., Davis, CA 95616 (SAN 240-4907) Tel 916-756-2242.

Pyramid WV, *(Pyramid Press Publishing Co.),* 1686 Marshall St., Benwood, WV 26031 (SAN 207-6683).

Python Pub
See Dimedia

Pyxidium Pr, *(Pyxidium Pr.; 0-936568),* Box 462, Old Chelsea Sta., New York, NY 10011 (SAN 214-4514) Tel 212-242-5224.

PZA Enterp, *(PZA Enterprises; 0-943304),* One Anders Tower, Box 12852, Dallas, TX 75225 (SAN 240-7396) Tel 214-696-5291.

Q Martin Public, *(Martin, Quinn, Public Relation; 0-9613492),* 425 N. Lumpkin St., Ste. 205, Athens, GA 30601 (SAN 693-4315); P.O. Box 6004, Athens, GA 30603 (SAN 693-4323); Dist. by: Baker & Taylor Co., Eastern Div., 50 Kirby Ave., Somerville, NJ 08876 (SAN 169-4901).

QBLH Pubns, *(QBLH Pubns.; 0-9603680),* Box 1166, Ramona, CA 92065 (SAN 214-1310).

QDP Inc, *(QDP Inc.; 0-9610044),* 701 Erie St., Muskegon, MI 49441 (SAN 262-9887) Tel 616-726-6229.

QED Info Sci, *(QED Information Sciences, Inc.; 0-89435),* 170 Linden St., Wellesley, MA 02181 (SAN 210-136X) Tel 617-237-5656; Toll free: 800-343-4848.

QED Press, *(Q.E.D. Pr.; 0-9615997),* 1012 Hill St., Suite 6, Ann Arbor, MI 48104 (SAN 699-752X) Tel 313-994-0371.

QSKY Pub, *(QSKY Publishing; 0-931387),* P.O. Box 3042, Springfield, IL 62708 (SAN 679-7830).

Quad Data Corp, *(Quad Corp.),* P.O. Box 2097, Tallahassee, FL 32316 (SAN 687-7486) Tel 904-539-5759.

Quadrangle
See Times Bks

Quadrant Pr, *(Quadrant Press; 0-915276),* 19 W. 44th St., New York, NY 10036 (SAN 211-5727).

Quail Prods, *(Quail Productions; 0-9610764),* Box 312, Roseland, NJ 07068 (SAN 264-6323); 37 Belmont Dr., Livingston, NJ 07039 (SAN 264-6331) Tel 201-992-5865.

Quail Ridge, *(Quail Ridge Pr., Inc.; 0-937552),* P.O. Box 123, Brandon, MS 39042 (SAN 214-2201); Dist. by: Dot Gibson Pubns., 161 Knight Ave. Cir., Waycross, GA 31501 (SAN 241-3760) Tel 912-285-2848; Dist. by: Southwest Cookbook Distributors, 1901 S. Shore Dr., Bonham, TX 75418 (SAN 200-4925) Tel 214-583-8898; Dist. by: Quail Ridge Pr., P.O. Box 123, Brandon, MS 39042 (SAN 214-2201).

Quail Run, *(Quail Run Pubns., Inc.; 0-930380),* 2705 E. Indian School Rd., Phoenix, AZ 85016 (SAN 210-9476) Tel 602-955-5953.

Quail Valley, *(Quail Valley Pubns.; 0-934249),* 19234 Vanowen St., Reseda, CA 91335 (SAN 693-1944) Tel 818-705-1157.

Quake Eng
See Earthquake Eng

Quaker, *(Quaker Pr.; 0-911200),* 3218 O St. NW, Washington, DC 20007 (SAN 204-6547) Tel 202-338-3391.

Quaker City, *(Quaker City Books; 0-917931),* Mill & Main Sts., Darby, PA 19023 (SAN 209-1178) Tel 215-583-4550.

Quality Assurance, *(Quality Assurance Institute),* 9222 Bay Point Dr., Orlando, FL 32819 (SAN 241-5798) Tel 305-876-4292.

Quality Bks IL, *(Quality Books, Inc.; 0-89196),* 918 Sherwood Dr., Lake Bluff, IL 60044-2204 (SAN 169-2127); Toll free: 800-323-4241 (Libraries Only). Warehouse open for walk-through buyers. *Imprints:* Bk Value Intl (Book Value International); Domus Bks (Domus Books).

Quality Bks OH, *(Quality Bks.; 0-9616274),* Box 264 Hilda Cir., Bloomingdale, OH 43910 (SAN 658-4349) Tel 614-264-6643.

Quality Circle, *(Quality Circle Institute; 0-937670),* 1425 Vista Way, Airport Industrial Park, P.O. Box 1503, Red Bluff, CA 96080-1335 (SAN 220-0880) Tel 916-527-6970.

Quality Comn, *(Quality Communication; 0-939143),* 337 Empire Blvd., Rochester, NY 14609 (SAN 662-9032) Tel 716-624-2772.

Quality Ed Data, *(Quality Education Data, Inc.; 0-88747),* Subs. of Peterson's Guides, 1580 Logan St., 3rd. Fl., Denver, CO 80203 (SAN 291-3941) Tel 303-572-8692; Toll free: 800-525-5811.

Quality Educ, *(Quality Educators, Ltd.),* 1236 SE Fourth Ave., Ft. Lauderdale, FL 33316 (SAN 212-9280) Tel 305-522-2249.

†Quality Groups Pub, *(Quality Groups Publishing; 0-930733),* 5850 Thille St., Suite 107, Ventura, CA 93003 (SAN 676-5688) Tel 805-642-6691; *CIP.*

Quality Hill, *(Quality Hill Books; 0-9605044),* 674 Church St., San Luis Obispo, CA 93401 (SAN 216-0595).

Quality Lib, *(Quality Library Editions),* P.O. Box 148, Darby, PA 19023 (SAN 209-1186).

Quality MO, *(Quality Books of Kansas City, Missouri; 0-9606586),* P.O. Box 8487, Kansas City, MO 64114 (SAN 219-0923) Tel 913-383-2160.

Quality Ohio, *(Quality Pubns. Inc.; 0-934040),* P.O. Box 2633, Lakewood, OH 44107 (SAN 216-2911); Orders to: Gary S. Skeens, 1483 Winchester Ave., Lakewood, OH 44107 (SAN 662-7382).

Quality Pr MI, *(Quality Pr.; 0-9616002),* 5930 Salabelle, Jackson, MI 49201 (SAN 697-9467) Tel 517-788-2060.

Quality Pubns, *(Quality Pubns.; 0-89137),* Div. of Quality Printing Co., Inc., P.O. Box 1060, Abilene, TX 79604 (SAN 203-0071) Tel 915-677-6262.

Quality Serv, *(Quality Services, Inc.; 0-9608966),* P.O. Box 2848, Gillette, WY 82716 (SAN 240-9801) Tel 307-686-2428.

Quality Soft, *(Quality Software; 0-912985),* 21610 Lassen, No. 7, Chatsworth, CA 91311 (SAN 265-7759) Tel 818-709-1721.

Quality Time, *(Quality Time Video; 0-937095),* 274 Funston Ave., San Francisco, CA 94118 (SAN 658-4705) Tel 415-386-5061.

Quam Pr, *(Quam, Martin, Press; 0-9601600),* 1515 Columbia Dr., Cedar Falls, IA 50613 (SAN 213-3571) Tel 319-266-6242; Orders to: 201 Rio St., Rio, WI 53960 (SAN 213-358X).

Quantal, *(Quantal Publishing Co.; 0-936596),* Div. of Quetzal Investing, P.O. Box 1598, Goleta, CA 93116 (SAN 215-1014) Tel 805-964-7293.

Quantum Comns, *(Quantum Communications; 0-938939),* 3301 W. Hampden Ave., Suite N, Englewood, CO 80110 (SAN 661-7441) Tel 303-781-0679. Do not confuse with Quantum Communications, Berkeley, CA, & Falls Church, VA.

Quantum Pr *Imprint of* Doubleday

Quantum Pr
See United Res Pub

Quantum Pubns, *(Quantum Publications Enterprises; 0-9611548),* P.O. Box 1039, Orange, CT 06477-7039 (SAN 285-2578) Tel 203-934-3945; 88 Canton St., W. Haven, CT 06516 (SAN 285-2586).

Quark Pub, *(Quark Publishing Co.; 0-937949),* 4709 Rockbluff Dr., Rolling Hills Estates, CA 90274 (SAN 659-7610) Tel 213-375-6431.

†Quarterdeck, *(Quarterdeck Pr.; 0-918546),* Affil. of Yoga Transformations, P.O. Box 134, Pacific Palisades, CA 90272 (SAN 209-990X) Tel 213-454-5392; Dist. by: Bookpeople, 2929 Fifth St., Berkeley, CA 94710 (SAN 168-9517) Tel 415-549-3030; *CIP.*

Quarterly Rev, *(Quarterly Review of Literature Q R L Poetry Series),* 26 Haslet Ave., Princeton, NJ 08540 (SAN 282-1982) Tel 609-921-6976; Dist. by: B. Deboer, 113 E. Centre St., Nutley, NJ 07110 (SAN 282-1990) Tel 201-667-9300.

Quarterman, *(Quarterman Pubns., Inc.; 0-88000),* P.O. Box 156, Lincoln, MA 01773 (SAN 203-3992) Tel 617-259-8047.

Quartus Bks, *(Quartus Bks.; 0-942082),* Div. of Quartus Foundation, P.O. Box 26683, Austin, TX 78755 (SAN 238-0080); Dist. by: Quartus Books, P.O. Box 26683, Austin, TX 78755 (SAN 238-0080) Tel 512-335-8346; Dist. by: New Leaf Distributing Co., 1020 White St., Sw, Atlanta, GA 30310 (SAN 169-1449) Tel 404-755-2665.

Quartz Pr, *(Quartz Press, The; 0-911455),* P.O. Box 465, Ashland, OR 97520 (SAN 274-9246) Tel 503-482-8119.

Quartzite Bks, *(Quartzite Bks.; 0-931849),* P.O. Box 1931, Mount Vernon, WA 98273 (SAN 685-4346) Tel 206-336-3345; Dist. by: Pacific Pipeline, 19215 66th Ave. S., Kent, WA 98032 (SAN 208-2128) Tel 206-872-5523.

Quasem, *(Quasem, M. Adul),* Dist. by: Habibur Rahman, 502 N. Elm St., Centralia, IL 62801 (SAN 209-5939).

Quay Assocs, *(Quay Assocs.; 0-9616062),* P.O. Box 18052, Columbus, OH 43218 (SAN 698-0929) Tel 614-261-1990; 247 E. Beck St., Columbus, OH 43206 (SAN 698-0937).

Que Corp, *(Que Corp.; 0-88022),* Div. of Macmillan, 7999 Knue Rd., Indianapolis, IN 46250 (SAN 219-6298) Tel 317-842-7162; Toll free: 800-428-5331.

Queen Anne Pr, *(Queen Anne Press, The; 0-937692),* Div. of Wye Institute, Inc., Cheston-on-Wye, Queenstown, MD 21658 (SAN 215-272X) Tel 301-827-7401; Orders to: P.O. Box 50, Queenstown, MD 21658 (SAN 215-2738).

Queen City VT
See Houston C

Queen Missions, *(Queen of the Missions Publishing Co.; 0-941428),* 1503 la Coronilla Dr., Santa Barbara, CA 93109 (SAN 239-376X).

†Queens Coll Pr, *(Queens College Pr.; 0-930146),* Editorial Services, Flushing, NY 11367 (SAN 203-1973) Tel 718-520-7599; *CIP.*

Queens Hse
See Queens Hse-Focus Serv

†Queens Hse-Focus Serv, *(Queens House/Focus Service; 0-89244),* P.O. Box 145, Dana Point, CA 92629 (SAN 208-2802) Tel 714-240-3242; *CIP.*

Queequeg, *(Queequeg Enterprises; 0-915947),* P.O. Box 277, Ludlow, VT 05149 (SAN 294-1015) Tel 802-824-6004.

Quest *Imprint of* Theos Pub Hse

Quest Edns, *(Quest Editions),* P.O. Box 67, Sharon Hill, PA 19079 (SAN 209-1194).

Quest Natl Center, *(Quest National Ctr., Inc.; 0-933419),* 6655 Sharon Woods Blvd., Columbus, OH 43229 (SAN 691-506X) Tel 614-882-6400.

Quest NW Pub, *(Quest Northwest Publishing Co.; 1-55585),* P.O. Box 240, Salkum, WA 98582 (SAN 658-4861) Tel 206-985-2999.

Quest Pr
See San Luis Quest

Quest Prods, *(Quest Products, Inc.; 0-9608002),* 11920 Cragwood Way, Potomac, MD 20854 (SAN 264-3332) Tel 301-299-7837.

Quest Pub, *(Quest Publishing Co.; 0-930844),* 1351 Titan Way, Brea, CA 92621 (SAN 211-3740) Tel 714-738-6400.

Quest Pub IL, *(Quest Publishing; 0-940286),* 2018 29th St., Rock Island, IL 61201 (SAN 217-5584) Tel 309-786-2342.

Quest Utah, *(Quest Publishing Inc.; 0-938662),* P.O. Box 27317, Salt Lake City, UT 84127-0317 (SAN 215-9775).

Questpr, *(Questpress; 0-914631),* 103 Briar Rd., Oak Ridge, TN 37830 (SAN 289-5625) Tel 615-483-1183; Orders to: The Fayette Fellowship, 101 Carriage Ln., Peachtree City, GA 30269 (SAN 662-2186) Tel 404-487-5683.

Queue Inc, *(Queue, Inc.; 0-87200; 0-87492),* 798 North Ave., Bridgeport, CT 06606 (SAN 265-3397) Tel 203-335-0908; Toll free: 800-232-2224.

Queue Pubns, *(Queue Pubns., Inc.; 0-9615691),* 24825 Shiloh Ln., Conifer, CO 80433 (SAN 695-8508) Tel 303-838-4391; P.O. Box 1010, Conifer, CO 80433 (SAN 696-9542).

Quick Am Pub, *(Quick American Publishing Co.; 0-932551),* P.O. Box 477, San Francisco, CA 94101 (SAN 687-4843) Tel 415-843-6449; Toll free: 800-428-7825.

Quicksilver Prod, *(Quicksilver Productions; 0-930356),* P.O. Box 340, Ashland, OR 97520 (SAN 211-9684) Tel 503-482-5343; 559 S Mountain Ave., Ashland, OR 97520 (SAN 658-151X).

Quietude Prod, *(Quietude Productions; 0-936775),* P.O. Box 1011, Glendale, CA 91209 (SAN 699-9344) Tel 818-578-0177; 328 W. Bellevue Dr., Pasadena, CA 91105 (SAN 699-9352).

Quigley Pub Co, *(Quigley Publishing Co. Inc.; 0-900610),* 159 W. 53rd. St., New York, NY 10019 (SAN 205-1141) Tel 212-247-3100.

Quill *Imprint of* **Morrow**

Quill and Brush Pr, *(Quill and Brush Press; 0-9610494),* 7649 Old Georgetown Rd., Bethesda Square, Bethesda, MD 20814 (SAN 264-3340) Tel 301-951-0290.

Quill & Scroll, *(Quill & Scroll Society),* School of Journalism & Mass Communication, University of Iowa, Iowa City, IA 52242 (SAN 224-5051) Tel 319-353-4475.

Quill Bks, *(Quill Bks.; 0-943536),* Box 728, Minot, ND 58701 (SAN 274-9300) Tel 701-839-7232. *Imprints:* Peotry Pubns (Poetry Publicatons).

Quill NY, *(Quill; 0-688),* Div. of william Morrow & CO., Inc., 105 Madison Ave., New York, NY 10016 (SAN 239-4790) Tel 212-889-3050; Orders to: Wilmor Warehouse, 6 Henderson Dr., West Caldwell, NJ 07006 (SAN 662-7390).

Quill Pubns GA, *(Quill Publications GA; 0-932281),* P.O. Box 8193, Columbus, GA 31908 (SAN 686-6123) Tel 404-323-9313.

Quilt Digest Pr, *(Quilt Digest Pr., The; 0-913327),* 955 14th St., San Francisco, CA 94114 (SAN 293-4531) Tel 415-431-1222; Dist. by: Publishers Group West, 5855 Beaudry St., Emeryville, CA 94608 (SAN 202-8522) Tel 415-658-3453.

Quiltwork Pubns, *(Quiltwork Pubns.; 0-914455),* 2600 Oak Valley Dr., Vienna, VA 22180 (SAN 287-7619) Tel 703-938-6175.

Quince Mill Bks, *(Quince Mill Bks; 0-914757),* 21 Quince Mill Court, Gaithersburg, MD 20878 (SAN 291-7998).

Quincunx, *(Quincunx; 0-942626),* 235 S. 15th St. 3B, Philadelphia, PA 19102 (SAN 238-5643) Tel 215-732-0593.

Quinlan C Pub
See Quinlin C Pubs

Quinlan Pr, *(Quinlan Pr.; 0-9611268; 0-933341),* Subs. of Quinlan Publishing & AC Getchell, 131 Beverly St., Boston, MA 02114 (SAN 226-4641) Tel 617-227-4870; Toll free: 800-551-2500.

Quinlan Pub
See Quinlan Pr

Quinlin C Pubs, *(Quinlin Campbell Pubs.; 0-934665),* P.O. Box 651, Boston, MA 02134 (SAN 694-0544) Tel 617-296-4306.

Quinn-Gallagher, *(Quinn-Gallagher Press; 0-935282),* 6372 Forward Ave., Pittsburgh, PA 15217 (SAN 213-3598) Tel 412-521-1863.

Quinn Pubns, *(Quinn Pubns.),* 612 Cougar Loop, NE, Albuquerque, NM 87122 (SAN 663-0847) Tel 818-358-1846; Dist. by: Eye Communications, 870 S. Myrtle Ave., Monrovia, CA 91016 (SAN 663-3250).

†**Quint Pub Co,** *(Quintessence Publishing Co., Inc.; 0-931386; 0-86715),* 870 Oak Creek Dr., Lombard, IL 60148-6405 (SAN 215-9783) Tel 312-620-4443; Toll free: 800-621-0387; *CIP.*

†**Quintessence,** *(Quintessence Pubns.; 0-918466),* 356 Bunker Hill Mine Rd., Amador City, CA 95601 (SAN 209-5947) Tel 209-267-5470; *CIP.*

Quintilone Ent, *(Quintilone Enterprises; 0-9616980),* 29 Merrimac St., Buffalo, NY 14214 (SAN 661-7433) Tel 716-836-0945.

Quinto Sol Pubns
See Tonatiuh-Quinto Sol Intl

Quissett Corp, *(Quissett Corporation; 0-938602),* P.O. Box 484, Cambridge, MA 02138 (SAN 216-2458) Tel 617-864-7970.

Quixote, *(Quixote Pr.; 0-9600306),* Div. of Anticapitalist Wordslingers Collective, 1810 Marshall, Houston, TX 77098 (SAN 202-1463) Tel 713-529-7944; Dist. by: Inland Bk. Co., 22 Hemingway Ave., East Haven, CT 06512 (SAN 200-4151) Tel 203-467-4257.

Quixsilver Pr, *(Quixsilver Pr.; 0-9615768),* Box 7635, Baltimore, MD 21207 (SAN 696-0014) Tel 301-944-0661.

Quod Pub Co, *(Quod Publishing Co.; 0-933137),* P.O. Box 3309, Ann Arbor, MI 48106 (SAN 689-7827) Tel 313-973-7386.

Quonochontaug, *(Quonochontaug Pr., The; 0-937245),* P.O. Box 2478, Waterbury, CT 06722 (SAN 658-6856) Tel 203-758-1637; 6 Southview Ave., Middlebury, CT 06762 (SAN 658-6864).

Quorum Bks *Imprint of* **Greenwood**

Quotamus Pr, *(Quotamus Press; 0-932621),* 721 S. Catalina Ave., P.O. Box 86, Redondo Beach, CA 90274 (SAN 687-5254) Tel 213-378-3446.

Quotidian, *(Quotidian, Inc.; 0-934391),* 394 Franklin Ave., Rockaway, NJ 07866 (SAN 693-8094) Tel 201-625-4788; Dist. by: Thomas W. Perrin, Inc., P.O. Box 190, 5 Glen Rd., Rutherford, NJ 07070 (SAN 200-6510) Tel 201-460-7912.

QV Pub, *(Q V Publishing, Inc.; 0-910767),* 250 E. Hartsdale Ave., Hartsdale, NY 10530 (SAN 260-2520) Tel 914-472-7060.

Qwint Systems, *(Qwint Systems, Inc.),* 625 Barclay, Lincolnshire, IL 60069 (SAN 210-8305) Tel 312-634-6700.

R A Green, *(Green, Robert Alan; 0-9600266; 0-9615281),* 214 Key Haven Rd., Key West, FL 33040 (SAN 204-6563) Tel 305-296-6736.

R A Loreto, *(Loreto, Remy A.; 0-914209),* 3459 Melody Manor Dr., Cincinnati, OH 45239 (SAN 287-640X) Tel 513-948-1300.

R A McConnell
See McConnell

R A Shea, *(Shea, Ralph A.; 0-930409),* 489 Oak St., Ridgefield, NJ 07657 (SAN 670-8374) Tel 201-945-5150.

R A Stanger, *(Stanger, Robert A., Co.; 0-943570),* 1129 Broad St., P.O. Box 7490, Shrewsbury, NJ 07701 (SAN 262-0898) Tel 201-389-3600; Toll free: 800-631-2291.

R A Wall, *(Wall, R. A. Investments, Inc.; 0-916522),* 9465 Wilshire Blvd., Suite 525, Beverly Hills, CA 90212 (SAN 208-032X).

R & D Pr, *(R & D Pr.; 0-88274),* 885 N. San Antonio Rd., Los Altos, CA 94022 (SAN 203-0896) Tel 415-948-0370.

R & D Pubns, *(R & D Pubns., Inc.; 0-938152),* Box 351, Spring Valley, NY 10977 (SAN 282-2008).

R & D Serv, *(R & D Services; 0-89511),* P.O. Box 644, Des Moines, IA 50303 (SAN 209-6765) Tel 515-288-8391.

R & E Pubs, *(R & E Pubs.; 0-88247),* P.O. Box 2008, Saratoga, CA 95070 (SAN 293-3195) Tel 408-866-6303.

R & E Res Assoc
See R & E Pubs

R & H Pubs, *(R & H Publishers; 0-935246),* Box 3587, Georgetown Sta., Washington, DC 20007 (SAN 210-5691) Tel 703-524-4226.

R & M Pub NV, *(R & M Publishing, Inc.; 0-9616779),* 4230 Fairbanks Cir., Las Vegas, NV 89103 (SAN 661-0501) Tel 702-876-9632.

R & S Rowland, *(Rowland, Ralph & Star; 0-9605746),* 4209 San Juan Dr., Fairfax, VA 22030 (SAN 209-4800) Tel 703-273-4891.

R B Allison Co *Imprint of* **Wisconsin Bks**

R B Bernstein, *(Bernstein, R. B.; 0-9613614),* P.O. Box 817, Hermosa Beach, CA 90254 (SAN 678-9080).

R B Boies, *(Boies, Robert Brice; 0-9616981),* 1300 Hibiscus, McAllen, TX 78501 (SAN 662-5622) Tel 512-682-0956.

R B Cross Co, *(Cross, Richard B., Co.),* 103 S. Howard St., P.O. Box 405, Oxford, IN 47971 (SAN 662-4359) Tel 317-385-2255.

R B Driscoll, *(Driscoll, Robert Bruce; 0-9601374),* P.O. Box 637, Oakland, CA 94604 (SAN 204-1936) Tel 415-451-4870.

R B Forster, *(Forster, Reginald Bishop, Assocs., Inc.; 0-931398),* 3287 Ramos Cir., Sacramento, CA 95827 (SAN 211-2388) Tel 916-362-3276; Toll free: 800-328-5091; 800-321-9789 in California.

R B Powell, *(Powell, Robert Blake; 0-9600680),* P.O. Box 833, Hurst, TX 76053 (SAN 203-3968) Tel 817-284-8145.

R B Pubns, *(RB Pubns.; 0-9613579),* P.O. Box 11452, Memphis, TN 38111 (SAN 669-9286) Tel 901-767-4669.

R B Shapiro
See Winterbourne Pr

R B Walker
See Martingale

R Basu, *(Basu, Romen),* Rm. DC1-1215, P.O. Box 20, New York, NY 10163-0020 (SAN 276-9670) Tel 212-249-6743.

R Bernard, *(Bernard, Ros, Pubns.; 0-935872),* 24 Minell Pl., Teaneck, NJ 07666 (SAN 281-319X) Tel 201-837-7258; Orders to: P.O. Box 2177, Teaneck, NJ 07666 (SAN 281-3203).

R Berrick, *(Berrick, R., Engineering Co., Inc.; 0-910045),* 2312 Tilbury Ave., Pittsburgh, PA 15213 (SAN 241-3639).

R Bolz
See R W Bolz

†**R C Appleman,** *(Appleman, Robert C.; 0-9607718),* 7216 57th NE, Seattle, WA 98115 (SAN 211-0520) Tel 206-525-7909; *CIP.*

R C D P M, *(Research Council on Diagnostic & Prescriptive Mathematics, Inc.; 0-940466),* Univ. of North Carolina at Wilmington, 601 S. College Rd., Wilmington, NC 28403-3297 (SAN 217-2046) Tel 919-395-3363; Orders to: Kent State Univ., 404 White Hall, Teacher Dev., Ctr., Kent, OH 44242 (SAN 662-1252) Tel 216-672-2293.

R C Emerson, *(Emerson, R. C., Co.; 0-9614755),* 540 Latimer Rd., Santa Monica, CA 90402 (SAN 692-9168) Tel 213-454-5814.

R C Law & Co, *(R.C. Law & Co., Inc.; 0-939925),* 579 S. State College Blvd., Fullerton, CA 92631 (SAN 200-609X) Tel 714-871-0940.

R C Packard, *(Packard, Rosa Covington),* 208 W. Old Mill Rd., Greenwich, CT 06830 (SAN 211-089X) Tel 203-661-8946.

R C Pr, *(R. C. Press; 0-943854),* 7140 Madison Ave. W., Golden Valley, MN 55427 (SAN 241-0613) Tel 612-537-4065.

R-c Pubns, *(R-C Publications Inc.; 0-933311),* P.O. Box 35425, Phoenix, AZ 85069 (SAN 692-6061) Tel 602-242-9276.

R C Pubns, *(R C Pubns.; 0-915734),* 6400 Goldsboro Rd., Bethesda, MD 20817 (SAN 209-1119) Tel 301-229-9040; Toll free: 800-222-2654; 355 Lexington Ave., New York, NY 10017 (SAN 662-7404) Tel 212-682-0830.

R C Pubns OR, *(R. C. Pubns.; 0-942152),* 1828 NE Stanton, Portland, OR 97212 (SAN 239-5967) Tel 503-287-1009.

R C Rapier, *(Rapier, Regina C.; 0-9600584),* 292 S. Cherokee Rd., Social Circle, GA 30279 (SAN 204-6571) Tel 404-464-2582.

R C Thomas, *(Thomas, Robert C.; 0-9616250),* 18 Monte Vista Ave., Vallejo, CA 94590 (SAN 658-7100) Tel 707-644-0680.

R C Weaver, *(Weaver, Ruth C.; 0-9607168),* RD 2 Box 218, Canonsburg, PA 15317 (SAN 239-1376) Tel 412-745-8907.

R Carson, *(Carson, Ray),* 711 E. Camden Ave., El Cajon, CA 92020 (SAN 206-8222) Tel 619-440-7647.

R Clark, *(Clark, Rosemarie; 0-9508551),* 435 City Centre Mart, Middletown, OH 45042 (SAN 682-7764).

R Collier, *(Collier, Robert, Pub., Inc.; 0-912576),* P.O. Box 3684, Indialantic, FL 32903 (SAN 204-2908) Tel 305-723-3228.

R Collings
See A R Collings

R Crown Ctr, *(Robert Crown Center, The; 0-9613700),* 21 Salt Creek Lane, Hinsdale, IL 60521 (SAN 677-4237) Tel 312-325-1773.

R Curtis Bks, *(Curtis, Ralph, Bks.; 0-88359),* P.O. Box 183, Sanibel, FL 33957 (SAN 281-5834) Tel 813-472-5490.

R Cwieka, *(Cwieka, R.; 0-915277),* 1375 Clinton Ave., Irvington, NJ 07111 (SAN 289-9779) Tel 201-375-4589.

R D Pub, *(R & D Publishing, Inc.; 0-937483),* 2251 Grand Ave., Ft. Myers, FL 33901 (SAN 659-0926) Tel 813-332-5510.

R D Reed, *(Reed, Robert D.),* 18581 McFarland Ave., Saratoga, CA 95070 (SAN 212-8632).

R D Wood, *(Wood, Richard D.; 0-9603898),* 76 Stonehenge Rd., Kingston, RI 02881 (SAN 207-5873) Tel 401-783-2135.

R D Wuraftic, *(Wuraftic, Robert D.; 0-9616959),* 330 Norwood Ave., Providence, RI 02905 (SAN 661-8154) Tel 401-941-1717.

R deLatour, *(deLatour, Ruggles, Inc.; 0-938291),* 176 E. 77th St., New York, NY 10021 (SAN 659-6754) Tel 212-861-7589.

R Dodson, *(Dodson, Rita; 0-9615511),* Rte. 5, Dodson Rd., Cartersville, GA 30120 (SAN 696-3382) Tel 404-382-0965.

R Dominguez, *(Dominguez, Richard; 0-9616928),* P.O. Box 1860, New York, NY 10185 (SAN 661-6666) Tel 212-803-3009.

R Dultz, *(Dultz, Ron, Publishing; 0-9601636),* P.O. Box 985, Reseda, CA 91335 (SAN 211-5603) Tel 818-993-7932.

R E Bauer, *(Bauer, Richard E.),* 1524 Pleasant Court, Sheldon, IA 51201 (SAN 656-0431).

R E Davis, *(Davis, Robert E.; 0-9614255),* 21 John Maddox Dr., Rome, GA 30161 (SAN 686-6980) Tel 404-234-0718.

R E F Typesetting Pub, *(R.E.F. Typesetting & Publishing, Inc.; 0-9612862),* 9400 Fairview Ave., Manassas, VA 22110 (SAN 291-3976) Tel 703-631-1115.

R E Greene, *(Greene, Robert E.; 0-9603320),* 120 U St. NW, Washington, DC 20001 (SAN 213-313X).

R E Lee, *(Lee, Ralph E.; 0-9606268),* 5698 Hollyleaf Lane, San Jose, CA 95118 (SAN 220-3367) Tel 408-266-1440; Orders to: Publishers Group West, 5855 Beaudry St., Emeryville, CA 94608 (SAN 202-8522) Tel 415-658-3453.

R E Moen, *(Moen, R. E.; 0-9614819),* 3152 S. 27th St., La Crosse, WI 54601 (SAN 693-0794) Tel 608-788-8753.

R E Todd, *(Todd, Richard E.; 0-9605324),* 8055 N. Marion Dr., Clovis, CA 93612 (SAN 215-9805).

R E Troisi, *(Troisi, Ralph E.; 0-9615474),* 15471 S. Bigrock Hoop, Mulino, OR 97042 (SAN 696-2130) Tel 503-829-5511.

R Enslow
See Enslow Pubs

R Eshelman, *(Eshelman, Ruth; 0-9617140),* 849 Coast Blvd (Casa de Manana), La Jolla, CA 92037 (SAN 663-3277) Tel 619-454-2151.

R F Brand, *(Brand, Robert F.; 0-9615727),* 1029 Lake Ln., Pennsburg, PA 18073 (SAN 696-1355) Tel 215-679-8134.

R F Hanmer, *(Hanmer, R. F.),* P.O. Box 614, Wallingford, CT 06492 (SAN 681-820X).

R F S Cecrle, *(Cecrle, Ruth Fay Straub; 0-9616159),* 3308 Vernon Ave., Brookfield, IL 60513 (SAN 699-8399) Tel 312-485-7567.

R Forte, *(Forte, Robert L.; 0-9609328),* P.O. Box 1051, Flint, MI 48501 (SAN 260-1885) Tel 313-789-0244; Dist. by: Safeguard Security Inc., P.O. Box 1051, Dept. SMP, Flint, MI 48501 (SAN 696-5091).

R Foster Publishers
See Ray-Foster

R Franklin, *(Franklin, Rasilon; 0-9616052),* 1805 N. Scottsdale, Tempe, AZ 85282 (SAN 698-0694) Tel 602-829-2403.

R Franks Ranch, *(Franks, Ray, Publishing Ranch; 0-943976),* P.O. Box 7068, Amarillo, TX 79114 (SAN 218-7329) Tel 806-355-6417.

R G Black, *(Black, Robert G., Pub.; 0-910631),* P. O. Box 587, Franklin, NC 28734 (SAN 268-3423) Tel 704-488-6920.

R G Bowen, *(Bowen, Robert Goss, Jr.; 0-9607512),* 31 Cobb Rd., Mountain Lakes, NJ 07046 (SAN 237-983X).

R G Cook, *(Cook, Ray G.; 0-9602002),* 366 Hooker Ave., Poughkeepsie, NY 12603 (SAN 223-4009).

R G Enterprises, *(R. G. Enterprises; 0-910575),* 2000 Center St., No. 1067, Berkeley, CA 94704 (SAN 274-9327).

R G Hadley, *(Hadley, R. G., Co.; 0-9600988),* 615 E. Main St., Silverton, OR 97381 (SAN 207-1282) Tel 503-873-4241.

R G Hickox, *(Hickox, Ron G.; 0-9613064),* c/o Antique Arms & Military Research, P.O. Box 360006, Tampa, FL 33673-0006 (SAN 294-8346) Tel 813-237-0764.

R G Speltz, *(Speltz, Robert G.; 0-932299),* 505 Albert Lea St., Albert Lea, MN 56007 (SAN 686-2721) Tel 507-373-2145; Orders to: Real Runabouts, The, 505 Albert Lea St., Albert Lea, MN 56007 (SAN 662-2682) Tel 507-373-2145.

R G Willie DDS, *(Willie, Ralph G., D.D.S.),* 30317 16th Ave. S., Federal Way, WA 98003 (SAN 212-7113) Tel 206-839-7270.

R G Young, *(Young, Robert G.; 0-9611010),* P.O. Box 40743, Grand Junction, CO 81504-0743 (SAN 277-7037) Tel 303-242-1707.

R Gallen & Co., *(Gallen, Richard & Co., Inc.; 0-87760),* 260 Fifth Ave., New York, NY 10001 (SAN 294-7951); Dist. by: Dell Publishing Co., Inc., One Dag Hamarskjold Plaza, 245 E. 47th St., New York, NY 10017 (SAN 201-0097) Tel 212-605-3000. Trade Paperbacks, Formerly was a Packager.

R Garfield
See Garfield Pubns

R H Barnes, *(Barnes, Robert H.; 0-930480),* P.O. Box 418, Grayland, WA 98547 (SAN 210-3532) Tel 206-267-3601.

R H Costello, *(Costello, Ralph H.; 0-9612900),* 101 Grand Ave., No. 16, Capitola, CA 95010 (SAN 291-1264) Tel 408-476-8868.

R H K Pub
See R H Kapilian

R H Kapilian, *(Kapilian, Ralph H., Pub.; 0-916311),* 30 Lake St., Brighton, MA 02135 (SAN 295-9232) Tel 617-254-3054.

R H Love Gall
See Haase-Mumm Pub Co

†R H M Pr, *(R. H. M. Pr.; 0-89058),* 172 Forest Ave., Glen Cove, NY 11542 (SAN 206-9873) Tel 516-759-2904; CIP.

R H Mont Assocs, *(Montgomery , Richard H. & Assocs.; 0-915991),* 913 Helen St., Midland, MI 48640 (SAN 294-6319) Tel 517-631-9334.

R H Palmer, *(Palmer, Birch; 0-9610168),* 1729 Grant Ave., Ogden, UT 84404 (SAN 264-2840) Tel 801-394-6864.

R H Stone, *(Stone, Robert H.; 0-9609192),* 1439 S. Kansas, Springfield, MO 65807 (SAN 264-4169).

R H Taylor, *(Taylor, Robert H., (0-9613586),* Box 46, Lumberville, PA 18933 (SAN 282-5767).

R Hart, *(Hart, Richard; 0-9602100),* P.O. Box 649, Berkeley, CA 94701-0649 (SAN 281-7705).

R Hoppin, *(Hoppin, Ruth; 0-9615957),* 15 Portola Ave., Daly City, CA 94015 (SAN 697-2985) Tel 415-992-3179.

R I Williams, *(Williams, Russell I.; 0-9613013),* 414 E. 23rd St., Cheyenne, WY 82001 (SAN 294-2941) Tel 303-634-7905.

R in R, *(R in R Ink; 0-941530),* 203 Joaquin Dr., San Ramon, CA 94583 (SAN 239-1279) Tel 415-820-8477.

R J Berg & Co, *(Berg, R. J, & Co.; 0-89730),* P.O. Box 20450, Indianapolis, IN 46220 (SAN 286-3502) Tel 317-259-0569.
Imprints: New Bks (New Books, Incorporated).(New Books, Inc.); News & Features (News & Features Press); R. J. Berg (Berg, R. J., & Company, Pubs.).

R J Brady
See Brady Comm

R J Davenport
See Davenport Pub

R J Diefendorf, *(Diefendorf, R. J.; 0-913125),* RFD 546, West Lebanon, ME 04027 (SAN 283-264X) Tel 207-658-9715.

R J Dundas Pubns, *(Dundas, Richard J., Pubns.; 0-9617093),* 31 North St. Extension, Rutland, VT 05701 (SAN 662-4782) Tel 802-775-4558; Dist. by: Queen City Brass Pubns., Box 75054, Cincinnati, OH 45275 (SAN 200-7436).

R J Fisher, *(Fisher, Raymond John; 0-9616984),* 1271 Gaylord St., Denver, CO 80206 (SAN 661-7263) Tel 303-322-4959.

R J Liederbach, *(Liederbach, Robert J., Co.; 0-934906),* 4953 Stonington Rd., Winston-Salem, NC 27103 (SAN 213-1080) Tel 919-768-7014.

R J Persson Ent, *(Persson, R. J., Enterprises, Incorporated; 0-9608486),* P.O. Box 2069, Montrose, CO 81402-2069 (SAN 240-7426) Tel 303-249-6000.

R J Walker, *(Walker, Rebecca J.; 0-9612284),* P.O.Box 5892, Austin, TX 78763 (SAN 289-5250) Tel 512-443-7950; Dist. by: Wimmer Brothers Books, BF Goodrich Blvd., Memphis, TN 38118 (SAN 209-6544) Tel 901-362-8900.

R K Ettema, *(Ettema, Ross K.),* 16420 Claire Ln., South Holland, IL 60473 (SAN 696-9936).

R K Press, *(Kiracofe, Roderick, Pr.; 0-9613708; 0-913327),* 3242 Washington, San Francisco, CA 94115 (SAN 677-5527) Tel 415-931-6003; Dist. by: Quilt Digest Pr., 955 14th St., San Francisco, CA 94114 (SAN 293-4531) Tel 415-431-1222.

R K T Pub, *(RKT Publishing; 0-931715),* 2215 Starr, Royal Oak, MI 48073 (SAN 683-5562) Tel 313-549-3199.

R K Woltz, *(Woltz, Raymond K.; 0-9613447),* 1355 Hermes Ave., Leucadia, CA 92024 (SAN 657-1115) Tel 619-753-0055.

R Kelley
See R S Kelley

R Kuppinger, *(Kuppinger, Roger; 0-9605616),* 77 Woodland Ln., Arcadia, CA 91006 (SAN 212-677X) Tel 213-355-1785; Dist. by: Publishers Group West, 5855 Beaudry St., Emeryville, CA 94608 (SAN 202-8522).

R L Bell, *(Bell, Robert L.; 0-9602450),* 669 Main St., Melrose, MA 02176 (SAN 211-8866) Tel 617-665-4998.

R L Bryan, *(Bryan, R. L.; 0-934870),* P. O. Drawer 368, Columbia, SC 29202 (SAN 203-6827).

R L Enger, *(Enger, Ronald L.; 0-9601742),* 1853 Shadowbrook Dr., Merced, CA 95340 (SAN 211-948X).

R L Evans, *(Evans, Robert L.; 0-9606698),* 2500 St. Anthony Blvd., Minneapolis, MN 55418 (SAN 208-3450) Tel 612-781-7384.

R L Hawkins, *(Hawkins, Robert L.; 0-9607764),* P.O. Box 430, Litchfield Park, AZ 86432 (SAN 212-6648) Tel 602-247-5070.

R L Merriam, *(Merriam, Robert L.; 0-918507),* Newhall Rd., Conway, MA 01341 (SAN 163-4070) Tel 413-369-4052.

R L Reeder, *(Reeder, Robert L., Pub.; 0-9616667),* 1400 S. Andrews Ave., Fort Lauderdale, FL 33316 (SAN 659-9273) Tel 305-764-8911.

R L Shep, *(Shep, R. L.; 0-914046),* P.O. Box C-20, Lopez Island, WA 98261 (SAN 215-3432).

R Leishman, *(Leishman, Robert K.; 0-9614526),* 77 W. Del Mar Blvd., Pasadena, CA 91105 (SAN 689-7665) Tel 818-792-3138.

R Little, *(Little, Ruth; 0-9600062),* 2255 34th St., Lubbock, TX 79411 (SAN 204-6598) Tel 806-744-5162; 2255 34th St., Lubbock, TX 79411 (SAN 694-3160).

R Louis Pub, *(Louis, R., Publishing; 0-9605410),* 940 Poplar Ave., Boulder, CO 80302 (SAN 238-7409) Tel 303-444-6030.

R Lynch, *(Lynch, Ruth; 0-9617250),* 840 Ocean Dr., Apt. 803, Juno Beach, FL 33408 (SAN 663-561X) Tel 305-622-7350.

R M Campbell, *(Campbell, Robert M.; 0-9613542),* P.O. Box 7906, Ann Arbor, MI 48107 (SAN 670-1752) Tel 313-482-6571.

R M D Bruce, *(Bruce, Russell, M. D.; 0-9617241),* Lattawoods, Dyersburg, TN 38024 (SAN 663-5555) Tel 901-285-7347.

R M Ostrov
See Educ Pr CA

R M Pearl Bks, *(Pearl, R. M., Bks.; 0-940566),* 16 Valley Pl., Colorado Springs, CO 80903 (SAN 206-6440) Tel 303-634-7345.

R M Presznick, *(Presznick, Rose M.; 0-912000),* RD 1, 7810 Avon Lake Rd., Lodi, OH 44254 (SAN 205-1524).

R M R Simpson, *(Simpson, Ruth M. Rasey; 0-9604048),* 286 Goundry St., North Tonawanda, NY 14120 (SAN 212-971X) Tel 716-692-1830.

R Madden, *(Madden, Robert; 0-9608256),* 5292 Rosamond Lane, Pontiac, MI 48054 (SAN 240-4028) Tel 313-681-3354.

R Maltby, *(Maltby, Ralph, Enterprises, Inc.; 0-9606792),* 4820 Jacksontown Rd., Newark, OH 43055 (SAN 217-3972) Tel 614-323-4193; Toll free: 800-848-8358; Toll free: 800-762-1831 (In Ohio).

R Manley, *(Manley, Ray, Commercial Photography, Inc.; 0-931418),* 238 S. Tucson Blvd., Tucson, AZ 85716 (SAN 208-7456) Tel 602-623-0307.

R Miller Photo
See Image Ltd

R Myles, *(Myles, Ralph, Pub., Inc.; 0-87926),* P.O. Box 1533, Colorado Springs, CO 80901 (SAN 204-6601).

R N Adlen, *(Adlen, R. N., Publishing Co.; 0-938113),* 7822 Comanche Ave., Canoga Park, CA 91306 (SAN 659-6762) Tel 818-500-9898.

R Nader, *(Nader, Ralph; 0-936486),* P.O. Box 19367, Washington, DC 20036 (SAN 282-0285) Tel 202-387-8030; Dist. by: Learning Research Project, P.O. Box 19312, Washington, DC 20036 (SAN 282-5961).

R Nahass, *(Nahass, Rick, Publishing; 0-9608422),* P.O. Box 27630, San Francisco, CA 94127 (SAN 240-7299) Tel 415-334-7191.

R Noble, *(Noble, Robert),* 5431 N. 12th St., Philadelphia, PA 19141 (SAN 277-7029) Tel 215-329-4502.

R O Beatty Assocs, *(Beatty, R. O., & Assocs.; 0-916238),* P.O. Box 763, Boise, ID 83701 (SAN 207-9909) Tel 208-343-4949.

R O Kechely, (Kechely, Raymond O.; 0-930202), P.O. Box 4514, Palm Springs, CA 92263 (SAN 210-752X) Tel 714-327-7779.

R O Roberts, (Roberts, Richard Owen, Publishers), 5N740 Dunham Rd., Wayne, IL 60184 (SAN 239-4847) Tel 312-584-8069.

R Oman Pub, (Oman, Robert, Publishing; 0-931660), 204 Fair Oaks Park, Needham, MA 02192 (SAN 211-7509).

R Oman Pubns
See R Oman Pub

R P Blakely, (Blakely, Richard P.; 0-9607110), Rte. 6, Box 163, Astoria, OR 97103 (SAN 238-9517) Tel 503-458-6849.

R P Dews, (Dews, Robert Porter; 0-940184), P.O. Box 302, Edison, GA 31746 (SAN 213-652X) Tel 912-835-2282.

R P Long, (Long, Robert P.; 0-9600064), 445 Glen Court, Cutchogue, NY 11935 (SAN 204-661X) Tel 516-734-5368; Dist. by: Prentice-Hall, Inc., P.O. Box 500, Englewood Cliffs, NJ 07632 (SAN 200-2175) Tel 201-592-2602.

R P R Inc
See R P Refsnes Inc

R P Refsnes Inc, (Refsnes, Rauscher Pierce, Inc., Public Finance; 0-9611718), One California St. No. 2630, San Francisco, CA 94111 (SAN 285-2616) Tel 415-989-2300.

R P W Pub, (R.P.W. Publishing Corp.; 0-9608450; 0-932725), Affil. of Shepard's/McGraw-Hill, P.O. Box 729, Lexington, SC 29072 (SAN 240-561X) Tel 803-359-9941; Toll free: 800-334-5971; Orders to: Shepards/McGraw-Hill, P.O. box 1235, Colorado Springs, CO 80901 (SAN 662-1317) Tel 303-475-7230.

R Patterson, (Patterson, Richard; 0-936004), 3829 William Penn Blvd., Virginia Beach, VA 23452 (SAN 213-8638).

R Paul Pub, (Paul, Reginald F., Pub.; 0-9616241), 2415 Morena Blvd., San Diego, CA 92110 (SAN 658-4993) Tel 619-276-4222.

R Picchione, (Picchione, Richard; 0-9602840), P.O. Box 5534, Reno, NV 89513 (SAN 213-1471).

R Pound-Am Trial Lawyers, (Roscoe Pound-American Trial Lawyers Assn.; 0-933067), Subs. of Association of Trial Lawyers of America, 1050 31st. St., NW, Washington, DC 20007 (SAN 689-7894) Tel 202-965-3500; Toll free: 800-424-2725.

R Q Putney, (Putney, R. Q.; 0-9616443), P.O. Box 81903, Lincoln, NE 68501-9605 (SAN 659-0861) Tel 402-475-2389; 2954 Ryons, Lincoln, NE 68502 (SAN 659-087X).

R Quackenbush, (Quackenbush, Robert, Studios; 0-9612518), 460 E. 79th St., New York, NY 10021 (SAN 656-0458) Tel 212-734-3822.

R R Sylvester
See PhD Pub

R Ramsay Gallery, (Ramsay, Roger, Gallery, Inc.; 0-9613449), 212 W. Superior, Chicago, IL 60610 (SAN 669-7038) Tel 312-337-4678.

R Reed, (Reed, R.), P.O. Box 1106, Laguna Beach, CA 92652 (SAN 207-5644).

R Rinehart Inc, (Rinehart, Roberts, Inc. Pubs.; 0-911797), P.O. Box 3161, Boulder, CO 80303 (SAN 264-3510) Tel 303-449-3221.

R S Barnes, (Barnes, Richard S., & Co. Books; 0-942448), 821 Foster St., Evanston, IL 60201 (SAN 209-2395) Tel 312-869-2272.

R S Brodkey, (Brodkey, Robert S.; 0-9616374), 1315 Kinnear Rd., Columbus, OH 43214 (SAN 659-0497) Tel 614-422-2609; Dist. by: Ohio State Univ. Bookstores, 154 N. Oval Mall, Columbus, OH 43212 (SAN 209-5637) Tel 614-422-4539.

R S Dist
See RSVP Press

R S Francis, (Francis, Reynold S.; 0-9616349), P.O. Box 8211, Minneapolis, MN 55408 (SAN 659-3925); 3319 Pleasant Ave. S., Minneapolis, MN 55408 (SAN 659-3933).

R S G Pubns Inc
See Roswell Symphony Guild

R S Granberg, (Granberg, Ronald Scott), c/o Law Distributors, 14415 S. Main St., Gardena, CA 90248 (SAN 212-3681).

R S Hart, (Hart, R. S.; 0-9604226), 6636 Washington Blvd., Box 53, Elkridge, MD 21227 (SAN 214-2465).

R S Hoehler, (Hoehler, Richard S.; 0-930590), P.O. Box 240, Conifer, CO 80433 (SAN 204-6628) Tel 303-838-4046.

R S Kelley, (Kelley, Rosemary Sue; 0-9616905), P.O. Box 505, HCR 69, School St., Friendship, ME 04547 (SAN 661-5171)

R S Mc Combe & S Haney, (McCombe, R. S. & Sharon Haney; 0-9611326), P.O. Box 644, Delta Junction, AK 99737 (SAN 282-9606) Tel 907-895-4179.

R S Means, (Means, R. S., Co.; 0-911950; 0-87629), Subs. of McCorquodale Holdings, Inc., 100 Construction Plaza, Kingston, MA 02364 (SAN 202-6163) Tel 617-747-1270.

R S Oatman, (Oatman, Russell Swinton; 0-9616593), 132 Mirick Rd., Princeton, MA 01541 (SAN 659-5197) Tel 617-464-5530.

R S Publishing, (Shaw, Rufus, Publishing; 0-936436), P.O. Box 15568, Dallas, TX 75215 (SAN 221-9948).

R S Wood, (Wood, R. S., & Co.; 0-937635), Star Rte. 81, Box 430, Liberty, ME 04949 (SAN 659-137X).

R S Wooley, (Wooley, Rebecca Smith; 0-9601654), 1250 S. Fairfield, Chicago, IL 60608 (SAN 211-4453).

R S Young, (Young, Robert Stephan; 0-9607068), 820 Second St. NW, Albuquerque, NM 87102 (SAN 241-5968) Tel 505-243-4043.

R Schalkenbach Foun
See Schalkenbach

R Seaver Bks
See Seaver Bks

R Seltzer, (Seltzer, Rozie; 0-9615365), 8535 Casa del Lago, Apt. 37F, Boca Raton, FL 33433 (SAN 695-5428).

R Severino, (Severino, Roberto; 0-937389), 4949 Quebec St., NW, Washington, DC 20016 (SAN 659-168X) Tel 202-363-5279.

R Shaeffer, (Shaeffer, R. E.; 0-9611418), 3623 SW Nevada St., Portland, OR 97219 (SAN 284-9399) Tel 503-245-1018.

R Shoemaker, (Shoemaker, Rhoda; 0-9600474), 1141 Orange Ave., Menlo Park, CA 94025 (SAN 204-6636) Tel 415-854-5768.

R Silver, (Silver, Robert, Assocs.; 0-937414), 307 E. 37th St., New York, NY 10016 (SAN 241-5801) Tel 212-686-5630.

R Smith, (Smith, Ruth; 0-9601182), Box 327, Cooper Sta., New York, NY 10003 (SAN 210-0177) Tel 212-260-4374.

R Stockman & Coyote, (Record Stockman & Coyote Cowboy Co.; 0-939343), P.O. Box 190, Brighton, CO 80601 (SAN 663-0820); 755 S. Eighth Ave., Brighton, CO 80601 Tel 303-654-1474.

R Sukenick, (Sukenick, Ronald), Box 188, Cooper Sta., New York, NY 10003 (SAN 226-4323).

R Sutherland, (Sutherland, Ruth; 0-9616133), 815 Carson Ave., Painesville, OH 44077-1114 (SAN 699-9425) Tel 216-354-9331.

R T Garcia, (Garcia, Robert T.; 0-9610352), P.O. Box 41714, Chicago, IL 60641 (SAN 264-0562) Tel 312-867-4143.

R T Gross, (Gross, Ruth T.; 0-9606946), 1815 Tigertail Ave., Miami, FL 33133 (SAN 212-0402).

R T Sherman, (Sherman, Robert T.; 0-9613031), 3516 Lawson Rd., Glenview, IL 60025 (SAN 294-1309) Tel 312-498-9826; Orders to: Robert T. Sherman, Box 444, Glenview, IL 60025 (SAN 669-3644) Tel 312-498-9826.

R Talbert, (Talbert, Robert), 260 W. 72nd St., Suite 5D, New York, NY 10023 (SAN 211-9846) Tel 212-724-9246.

R Talsorian, (Talsorian, R., Inc.; 0-937279), P.O. Box 2288, Aptos, CA 95001-2288 (SAN 658-6600) Tel 408-462-0261; 750 Bay Ave., No. 114, Capitola, CA 95010 (SAN 658-6619).

R Tanner Assocs Inc, (Tanner, Ralph, Assocs., Inc.; 0-942078), Suite 102, Great Western Bank Bldg., 122 N. Cortez St., Prescott, AZ 86301 (SAN 239-9857) Tel 602-778-4162.

R Thrift, (Thrift, Richard; 0-9604520), 108 Clarke Court, Charlottesville, VA 22903 (SAN 211-5433).

R Tirtha, (Tirtha, Ranjit), Eastern Michigan University, Dept. of Geography, Ypsilanti, MI 48197 (SAN 214-3283) Tel 313-487-0218.

R V Greeves, (Greeves, R. V., Art Gallery; 0-9616999), P.O. Box 428, Fort Washakie, WY 82514 (SAN 662-5339); 53 N. Fork Rd., Fort Washakie, WY 82514 (SAN 662-5347) Tel 307-332-3557.

R V Wood, (Wood, R. V.), 230 Payson Rd., Belmont, MA 02178 (SAN 217-4715).

R Van Trees, (Van Trees, Robert V.; 0-9616282), 804 N. Central Ave., Fairborn, OH 45324-5216 (SAN 658-5272) Tel 513-878-3588; Orders to: Robert V. Van Trees, P.O. Box 2062, Fairborn, OH 45324-8062 (SAN 662-4111).

R W Angell, (Angell, Robert W.), 11501 NE 11th Pl., Biscayne Park, FL 33161 (SAN 686-175X).

R W Bolz, (Bolz, Roger W., & Assocs.), 205 Wyntfield Dr., Lewisville, NC 27023 (SAN 654-8857) Tel 919-945-5695.

R W Elliott, (Elliott, R. W.; 0-9616575), Rte. 5, Box 1-B, Lindale, TX 75771 (SAN 661-2350) Tel 214-882-3312; Hwys. I-20 & FM 849, Lindale, TX 75771 (SAN 662-4324).

R W Enterprises, (R & W Enterprises; 0-9616382), 3011 White Oak Ln., Oak Brook, IL 60521 (SAN 659-0969) Tel 312-887-2738.

R W Goll, (Goll, Reinhold W.; 0-9606716), 1942B Mather Way, Elkins Park, PA 19117 (SAN 212-4246).

R W McQuaid, (McQuaid, Robert W.; 0-912259), 4853 Mt. Elbrus Dr., San Diego, CA 92117 (SAN 265-1653) Tel 619-279-5827.

R W Strain, (Strain, Robert W., Publishing, Inc.; 0-939727), P.O. Box 1000, Wingdale, NY 12594 (SAN 663-4540) Tel 914-832-9384.

R Walter, (Walter, Russ, Pub.; 0-939151), 22 Ashland St., Somerville, MA 02144 (SAN 662-8206) Tel 617-666-2666.

†R West, (West, Richard; 0-8492; 0-8274), Box 6404, Philadelphia, PA 19145 (SAN 206-8907); CIP.

R Wettenstein, (Wettenstein, Raphael; 0-9617252), 59 Lawrence Ave., Staten Island, NY 10310 (SAN 663-5636) Tel 718-720-8320.

R Wismer, (Wismer, Romaine; 0-9617021), 501 Sable Palm N., Ellenton, FL 33532 (SAN 662-8826) Tel 813-729-1027; Dist. by: Gulf Coast Periodicala, 1954 Whitfield Ave., Sarasota, FL 33580 (SAN 200-7568).

R Woodrow, (Woodrow, Ralph, Evangelistic Assn., Inc.; 0-916938), P.O. Box 124, Riverside, CA 92502 (SAN 206-3700) Tel 714-686-5467.

R. J. Berg Imprint of R J Berg & Co

Rabinowitz Hebrew Book, (Rabinowitz, Solomon, Hebrew Book Store, Inc.; 0-87374), 30 Canal St., New York, NY 10002 (SAN 205-1176) Tel 212-267-2406.

Raccoon Memphis, (Raccoon Bks., Inc.; 0-938507), Div. of Ion Bks., Inc., 3387 Poplar Ave., Suite 205, Memphis, TN 38111 (SAN 659-6142).

Racer's Edge Pub Co, (Racer's Edge Publishing Co.; 0-9612062), 3336 Glenmore Dr., P.O. Box 1607, Falls Church, VA 22041 (SAN 291-8579) Tel 703-578-0853.

Racquet Sports, (Racquet Sports Information Service; 0-914934), P.O. Box 1710, Easton, MD 21601 (SAN 207-0308). Out of business.

Racz Pub, (Racz Publishing Co.; 0-916546), P.O. Box 287, Oxnard, CA 93032 (SAN 208-0265) Tel 805-642-1186.

Rad Shack TX
See Radio Shack

Rada Pr, (Rada Pr.; 0-9604212), 2297 Folwell Ave., St. Paul, MN 55108 (SAN 214-4522) Tel 612-559-2306.

Radcliffe Coll, (Radcliffe College, Bunting Institute; 0-9601774), 10 Garden St., Cambridge, MA 02138 (SAN 221-3419) Tel 617-495-8212.

Radiance Assocs, (Radiance Assocs.; 0-933267), P.O. Box 86188, St. Petersburg, FL 33738 (SAN 692-4735); Dist. by: New Leaf Distributing, 1020 White St., SW, Atlanta, GA 30310 (SAN 169-1449) Tel 404-755-2665.

Radiation Med Found SW, (Radiation and Medical Research Foundation of the Southwest; 0-9614550), 1450 Eighth Ave., Fort Worth, TX 76104 (SAN 691-8077) Tel 817-923-7393.

Radicus Comm, (Radicus Communications; 0-941564), 9356 Home Circle, Des Plaines, IL 60016 (SAN 239-2917) Tel 312-299-0912.

Radio City, *(Radio City Bk. Store; 0-911202),* 324 W. 47th St., New York, NY 10036 (SAN 204-6644) Tel 212-245-5754.

Radio Free Eur, *(Radio Free Europe Radio Liberty),* 1775 Broadway, New York, NY 10019 (SAN 274-9505) Tel 212-397-5318.

Radio Pubns, *(Radio Pubns., Inc.; 0-933616),* P.O. Box 149, Wilton, CT 06897 (SAN 215-336X) Tel 603-428-7707.

Radio Resource, *(Radio Resource Co.; 0-943382),* 301 Hillcrest Dr., Fort Atkinson, WI 53538 (SAN 287-7651) Tel 414-563-5050.

Radio Shack, *(Radio Shack; 1-55508),* Div. of Tandy Corp., 1800 One Tandy Ctr., Fort Worth, TX 76102 (SAN 692-3356) Tel 817-390-3011.

Radiofile, *(Radiofile),* c/o Tagliabue, 10 West 66th St., New York, NY 10023 (SAN 204-6652).

Radiol Mgmt Comm, *(Radiological Management Communications, Ltd.; 0-938705),* 10342 Wilkins Ave., Los Angeles, CA 90024 (SAN 661-5643) Tel 213-552-9921.

RadioResource Corp
See Radio Resource

Radius Pr, *(Radius Pr.; 0-942154),* P.O. Box 1271, FDR Sta., New York, NY 10150 (SAN 239-5975) Tel 212-988-4715.

Radix Bks, *(Radix Bks., Inc.),* 11 Knickerbocker Ln., Orinda, CA 94563 (SAN 209-1364) Tel 415-254-3039.

Rae John, *(Rae John Pubs.; 0-9605226; 0-939438),* Box 660068, Sacramento, CA 95866-0068 (SAN 220-1739) Tel 916-925-0420.

Ragan Comm, *(Ragan, Lawrence, Communications, Inc.; 0-931368),* 407 S. Dearborn St., Chicago, IL 60605 (SAN 212-2243) Tel 312-922-8245.

Ragnarok
See Merging Media

Ragusan Pr, *(Ragusan Press),* 2527 San Carlos Ave., San Carlos, CA 94070 (SAN 212-0445) Tel 415-592-1190.

Rahija, *(Rahija Associates; 0-942670),* Dist. by: ACLD, 4156 Library Rd., Pittsburgh, PA 15234 (SAN 282-6674).

Raiko, *(Raiko Corp.; 0-910263),* P.O. Box 597, New York, NY 10003 (SAN 240-9542) Tel 212-783-2597.

Rail-Europe
See Rail-Europe-Baxter

Rail-Europe-Baxter, *(Rail-Europe/Baxter Guides; 0-913384),* P.O. Box 3255, Alexandria, VA 22302 (SAN 203-3933).

†Railhead Pubns, *(Railhead Pubns.; 0-912113),* P.O. Box 526, Canton, OH 44701 (SAN 264-7826) Tel 216-454-7519; *CIP.*

Railroadians, *(Railroadians of America, Inc.; 0-941652),* 18 Okner Pkwy., Livingston, NJ 07039 (SAN 239-2925) Tel 201-487-3719.

Railway Loco Hist, *(Railway & Locomotive Historical Society, Inc.; 0-9616102),* P.O. Box 112, East Boothbay, ME 04544 (SAN 698-1275) Tel 707-633-4333; Church & Main Sts., East Boothbay, ME 04544 (SAN 698-259X).

Railways, *(Railways Atlas; 0-9615046),* P.O. Box 297, Short Hills, NJ 07078 (SAN 654-5475) Tel 201-376-8976.

Raima Corp, *(Raima Corp.; 0-928469),* 12201 SE Tenth St., Bellevue, WA 98005 (SAN 669-6589) Tel 206-747-5570; Toll free: 800-843-3313.

Raimi, *(Raimi, Ralph A.; 0-9609370),* Dept. of Mathematics, University of Rochester, Rochester, NY 14627 (SAN 240-8295) Tel 716-275-4411.

Rain Belt, *(Rain Belt Pubns., Inc.; 0-938428),* 18806-40th Ave. W., Lynnwood, WA 98036 (SAN 216-180X) Tel 206-778-5449.

Rainbow, *(Piece Of The Rainbow; 0-933477),* 166 Second Ave., Brooklyn, NY 11215 (SAN 692-4018) Tel 718-807-8603.

Rainbow Assoc
See Rainbow Assocs

Rainbow Assocs, *(Rainbow Assocs.; 0-9615830),* 5026 Chesterfield Rd., Arlington, VA 22206 (SAN 696-5652) Tel 202-363-0234; P.O. Box 1928, Bailey's Crossroads, VA 22041-0928 (SAN 696-9739).

Rainbow Bks, *(Rainbow Books, Inc.; 0-89508),* 725 Dell Rd., Carlstadt, NJ 07072 (SAN 209-9918) Tel 201-935-3369.

Rainbow Books, *(Rainbow Bks.; 0-935834),* Dept. 1-H, P.O. Box 1069, Moore Haven, FL 33471 (SAN 213-5515) Tel 813-946-0293; Dist. by: Quality Bks. (Library orders only), 918 Sherwood Dr., Lake Bluff, IL 60044-2204 (SAN 169-2127).

Rainbow Child, *(Rainbow Children's Books; 0-9608784),* Box 513, 311 E. Madison, Goshen, IN 46526 (SAN 238-3470) Tel 219-533-4232.

†Rainbow Collect, *(Rainbow Collection; 0-935448),* P.O. Box 75, Akron, OH 44309 (SAN 213-7860); *CIP.*

Rainbow Disc, *(Rainbow Disc; 0-9616048),* P.O. Box 3077, Pontiac, MI 48059 (SAN 698-0104) Tel 313-338-7241; 18 N. Glenwood, Pontiac, MI 48058 (SAN 698-2395).

Rainbow Ent, *(Rainbow Enterprises),* P.O. Box 267, West Friendship, MD 21794 (SAN 239-5983).

Rainbow Heaven, *(Rainbow Heaven, Inc.; 0-938881),* P.O. Box 554, Union City, NJ 07087 (SAN 662-6645); 9 Ridgely Pl., Weehawken, NJ 07087 (SAN 662-6653) Tel 201-392-8777.

Rainbow Med Clinic, *(Rainbow Medical Clinic, Inc.; 0-914135),* P.O. Box 2986, La Jolla, CA 92038 (SAN 287-5225) Tel 619-454-0539; 626 A Arenas St., La Jolla, CA 92037 (SAN 287-5233); Dist. by: DeVorss & Co., P.O. Box 550, 1046 Princeton Dr., Marina del Rey, CA 90294 (SAN 287-5241).

Rainbow Morn, *(Rainbow Morning Music Alternatives; 0-9615696),* 2121 Fairland Rd., Silver Spring, MD 20904 (SAN 218-2963) Tel 301-384-9207.

Rainbow Morning Music Alts
See Rainbow Morn

Rainbow Nursery, *(Rainbow Publishing Co., First United Nursery Schl.; 0-9616693),* 848 W. Lake St., Oak Park, IL 60301 (SAN 659-8412) Tel 312-848-4910.

Rainbow Pr NY, *(Rainbow Press; 0-943156),* 222 Edwards Dr., Fayetteville, NY 13066 (SAN 240-4354).

Rainbow Pub Co, *(Rainbow Publishing Co.; 0-936218),* P.O. Box 397, Chesterland, OH 44026 (SAN 219-9912).

Rainbow Pubns, *(Rainbow Pubns.; 0-9613765),* 6836 Walmore Rd., Niagara Falls, NY 14304 (SAN 679-3851) Tel 716-731-3581.

Rainbow WA, *(Rainbow Pubns.; 0-940364),* 9520 N.E. 120th, A-2, Kirkland, WA 98034-8915 (SAN 217-1279) Tel 206-821-2814.

Rainey Day Or
See Rainy Day Oreg

Rainey R, *(Rainey, Ralph; 0-9615061),* Box 296, Carlyle, IL 62231 (SAN 694-1575) Tel 615-594-3559.

Rainforest Pub, *(Rainforest Publishing; 0-937017),* P.O. Box 101251, Anchorage, AK 99510 (SAN 658-7941) Tel 907-345-0190; 2420 Dennis Way, Anchorage, AK 99510 (SAN 658-795X).

Rainshadow Pubns, *(Rainshadow Pubns.; 0-9614129),* P.O. Box 1393, Gig Harbor, WA 98335 (SAN 686-5216) Tel 206-857-6274.

Raintree Pub Group
See Raintree Pubs

†Raintree Pubs, *(Raintree Pubs., Inc.; 0-8172; 0-8393; 0-940742; 0-86514),* 310 W. Wisconsin Ave., Mezzanine Level, Milwaukee, WI 53203 (SAN 207-9607) Tel 414-273-0873; Toll free: 800-558-7264; *CIP.*

Rainy Day Fl, *(Rainy Day Pr.; 0-9615290),* P.O. Box 65-3441, Miami, FL 33265-3441 (SAN 694-4183) Tel 305-821-5407.

Rainy Day Oreg, *(Rainy Day Pr.; 0-931742),* 1147 E. 26th St., Eugene, OR 97403 (SAN 211-397X) Tel 503-484-4626.

Rainy Day Pr, *(Rainy Day Press; 0-918796),* Box 471, Sausalito, CA 94965 (SAN 209-102X); Dist. by: Bookpeople, 2929 Fifth Ave., Berkeley, CA 94710 (SAN 168-9517).

Raj Anand, *(Anand, Raj K.),* 210 Lincoln St., Worcester, MA 01605 (SAN 692-6819).

Rajah, *(Rajah Pr.; 0-911204),* P.O. Box 23, Summit, NJ 07901 (SAN 204-6679).

Rajneesh Friends Intl
See Rajneesh Pubns

Rajneesh Neo-Sannyas Intl, *(Rajneesh Neo-Sannyas International Commune; 0-918963),* P.O. Box 1, Rajneeshpuram, OR 97741 (SAN 669-8786) Tel 503-489-3411; Dist. by: Rajneesh Pubns., Inc., P.O. Box 1510, Boulder, CO 80306 (SAN 240-0987) Tel 303-665-6611.

†Rajneesh Pubns, *(Rajneesh Pubns., Inc.; 0-88050),* Div. of Rajneesh Foundation International, P.O. Box 1510, Boulder, CO 80306 (SAN 240-0987) Tel 303-665-6611; *CIP.*

RAK Pub, *(RAK Publishing Co.; 0-9616948),* 4625 Hope Valley Rd., No. D, Durham, NC 27707-5615 (SAN 661-7425) Tel 919-489-8693.

Rakhamin Pubns, *(Rakhamin Pubns.; 0-9612500),* P.O. Box 3094, Oakland, CA 94609 (SAN 291-848X); Dist. by: Bookpeople, 2929 Fifth St., Berkeley, CA 94710 (SAN 168-9517); Dist. by: Inland Bk. Co., 22 Hemingway Ave., P.O. Box 261, East Haven, CT 06512 (SAN 669-3571) Tel 203-467-4257.

Rakhamin Pubns
See Rakhamin Pubns

Raleigh Little, *(Raleigh Little Theatre, Inc.; 0-9615689),* 301 Pogue St., Raleigh, NC 27607 (SAN 696-0898) Tel 919-836-7882; P.O. Box 5637, Raleigh, NC 27607 (SAN 699-623X).

Raleigh Pub, *(Raleigh Publishing Co.; 0-9615775),* P.O. Box 898, Wayzata, MN 55391 (SAN 696-5660) Tel 612-473-3027.

Ralph Studies
See Smart

Ralston-Pilot, *(Ralston-Pilot, Inc., Pubs.; 0-931116),* P.O. Box 1357, Cedar City, UT 84720 (SAN 282-2067) Tel 801-586-7395.

Ram Assoc, *(Ram Associates, Ltd.; 0-943308),* Box 2277, Poquoson, VA 23662 (SAN 240-1118) Tel 804-868-8970.

RAM Assocs WI, *(RAM Assocs.; 0-9617209),* 1319 Oakwood Ave., Menomonie, WI 54751 (SAN 663-3846) Tel 715-235-5174. Do not confuse with RAM Assoc. of Poquoson, VA.

†Ram Pub, *(Ram Publishing Co.; 0-915920),* P.O. Drawer 38649, Dallas, TX 75238 (SAN 203-0837) Tel 214-278-8439; *CIP.*

Rama Pub Co, *(Rama Publishing Co.; 0-913071),* P.O. Box 793, Carthage, MO 64836 (SAN 283-3875) Tel 417-358-1093.

RAMCO Pubns, *(RAMCO Pubns.; 0-939844),* 224 Harding Ave., Libertyville, IL 60048 (SAN 216-9282) Tel 312-362-4948.

Ramadan Pr, *(Ramadan Pr.; 0-935387),* 5001 W. 80th St., Suite 885, Bloomington, MN 55437 (SAN 695-9296) Tel 612-835-2245.

Ramakrishna, *(Ramakrishna-Vivekananda Ctr.; 0-911206),* 17 E. 94th St., New York, NY 10128 (SAN 204-6687) Tel 212-534-9445.

Ramapo Pr, *(Ramapo Pr.; 0-915071),* 363 Seventh Ave., 10th Flr., New York, NY 10001 (SAN 289-811X) Tel 212-564-1877.

Rambler Bks, *(Rambler Bks.; 0-9614963),* 1430 Park Ave., Baltimore, MD 21217 (SAN 693-4242) Tel 301-669-6694.

Rambler Pr, *(Rambler Pr.; 0-9609754),* P.O. Box 184, Weiser, ID 83672 (SAN 264-3375) Tel 503-889-9409.

Ramfre, *(Ramfre Press; 0-911208),* 1206 N. Henderson, Cape Girardeau, MO 63701 (SAN 204-6695) Tel 314-335-6582.

Ramico Pubns, *(Ramico Pubns.; 0-9607272),* P.O. Box 5218, N. Hollywood, CA 91607 (SAN 239-2933) Tel 818-998-6196.

Ramif Julian, *(Ramifications, Unlimited; 0-936789),* P.O. Box 619, Julian, CA 92036 (SAN 658-8174) Tel 619-765-2525. Do not confuse with Ramifications Publishing, Limited, Tiburon, CA.

Ramira Pub, *(Ramira Publishing; 0-9612720),* P.O. Box 1707, Aptos, CA 95001 (SAN 289-8128) Tel 408-688-6666; Dist. by: Bookpeople, 2929 Fifth Ave., Berkeley, CA 94710 (SAN 168-9517); Dist. by: New Leaf Distributing, 1020 White St, NW, Atlanta, GA 30310 (SAN 169-1449) Tel 404-755-2665.

Rampant Lion Pubs, *(Rampant Lion Pubs; 0-942872),* 8344 Melrose Ave., 23, Los Angeles, CA 90069 (SAN 240-1215); Orders to: 216 S. Fourth St., Las Vegas, NV 89101 (SAN 662-7412).

†Ramparts, *(Ramparts Pr.; 0-87867),* P.O. Box 50128, Palo Alto, CA 94303 (SAN 203-3925) Tel 415-325-7861; *CIP.*

Ramsco Pub, *(Ramsco Publishing Co.; 0-943596),* Div. of RAM Assocs., Ltd., P.O. Box N, Laurel, MD 20707 (SAN 240-7582) Tel 301-953-3699.

Ramshorn Pub, *(Ramshorn Publishing Co.; 0-9615478),* P. O. Box 263, Fremont, MI 49412 (SAN 696-0766) Tel 616-924-3325.

Rana Hse, *(Rana Hse.; 0-930172),* Box 2997, St. Louis, MO 63130 (SAN 210-542X)

Ranch House Pr, *(Ranch House Press; 0-88100),* Rte. 2, Box 296, Pagosa Springs, CO 81147 (SAN 240-1126) Tel 303-264-2647.

Rancho Bern, *(Rancho Bernardo Junior Woman's Club, Inc.; 0-9608548),* 12652 Gibraltar Dr., San Diego, CA 92128 (SAN 240-7590) Tel 619-485-0210.

Rancho Santa Ana, *(Rancho Santa Ana Botanic Garden; 0-9605808),* 1500 N. College, Claremont, CA 91711 (SAN 220-1836) Tel 714-626-3489.

Ranck, *(Ranck, Joyce H.; 0-9606006),* 1103 Fairacres Rd., Richmond, IN 47374 (SAN 216-4426) Tel 317-966-2370.

†Rand Corp, *(Rand Corp., The; 0-8330),* P.O. Box 2138, Santa Monica, CA 90406-2138 (SAN 218-9291) Tel 213-318-3766; *CIP.*

†Rand McNally, *(Rand McNally & Co.; 0-528),* P.O. Box 7600, Chicago, IL 60680 (SAN 203-3917) Tel 312-673-9100; Toll free: 800-323-4070; *CIP.*

Rand-Tofua, *(Rand Editions/Tofua Pr.; 0-914488),* P.O. Box 2610, Leucadia, CA 92024 (SAN 206-8001) Tel 619-753-2500.

Randale Resources, *(Randale Resources; 0-9616728),* 2155 Verdugo Blvd., Suite 202, Montrose, CA 91020 Tel 818-957-1487.

Randall Bk Co, *(Randall Bk., Co.; 0-934126; 1-55517),* 9500 S. 500 W., Suite 108, Sandy, UT 84070 (SAN 214-1329) Tel 801-562-5481; Toll free: 800-453-1356; Dist. by: Publishers Marketing Group, 1104 Summit Ave., Plainview, TX 75074 (SAN 262-0995) Tel 214-423-0312.

Randall Hse, *(Randall Hse. Pubns.; 0-89265),* 114 Bush Rd., P.O. Box 17306, Nashville, TN 37217 (SAN 207-5040) Tel 615-361-1221; Toll free: 800-251-5762; Toll free: 800-624-6538 (in Tennessee).

R&D Pubs, *(R&D Pubs.),* P.O. Box 1584, Los Gatos, CA 95031 (SAN 223-1689).

R&E Miles, *(Miles, R & E; 0-936810),* P.O. Box 1916, San Pedro, CA 90733 (SAN 221-3834) Tel 213-833-8856; 1252 W. 23 St., San Pedro, CA 90731 (SAN 691-9537).

Randelle Pubns, *(Randelle Pubns.; 0-910445),* 1527 First Ave., Charleston, WV 25312 (SAN 260-1222) Tel 304-344-4494.

R&M Pub Co, *(R&M Publishing Co.; 0-936026),* P.O. Box 1276, Holly Hill, SC 29059 (SAN 213-6392) Tel 804-732-4094.

Randolph Res, *(Randolph Research),* P.O. Box 146, Nebo, NC 28761 (SAN 211-092X) Tel 704-652-8150.

Random Lgths Pubns, *(Random Lengths Pubns., Inc.; 0-9614042),* P.O. Box 867, Eugene, OR 97440-0867 (SAN 684-7978) Tel 503-686-9925.

Random, *(Random Hse., Inc.; 0-394; 0-676),* Random Hse. Publicity, (11-6), 201 E. 50th St., New York, NY 10022 (SAN 202-5507) Tel 212-572-8030; Toll free: 800-638-6460; Orders to: 400 Hahn Rd., Westminster, MD 21157 (SAN 202-5515). *Imprints:* BYR (Books for Young Readers); RanC (Random House College Division); Vin (Vintage Trade Books).

Random Motion, *(Random Motion; 0-933457),* 159 Western Ave. W, No.484, Seattle, WA 98119 (SAN 691-6864) Tel 206-284-8052.

Random Sch Div, *(Random House School Div.; 0-394; 0-676),* 201 E. 50th St., New York, NY 10022 (SAN 669-2524); Orders to: 400 Hahn Rd., Westminster, MD 21157 (SAN 204-6717).

Randy Fox, *(Fox, Randy; 0-9616578),* 7001 Summerfield Dr., Indianapolis, IN 46224 (SAN 661-2288) Tel 317-298-7060.

Ranger Assocs, *(Ranger Assocs., Inc.; 0-934588),* 600 Washington Court, Guilderland, NY 12084 (SAN 213-5523) Tel 518-456-6401.

Ranney Pubns, *(Ranney Pubns.),* 5395 Industrial Dr., Unit C,, Huntington Beach, CA 92649 (SAN 211-867X) Tel 714-891-2145.

Ransom Dist Co, *(Ransom Distributing Co.),* P.O. Box 2010, Sparks, NV 89432

Ransom Hill, *(Ransom Hill Pr.; 0-9604342),* 3601 Main St., Ramona, CA 92065 (SAN 215-9104) Tel 619-789-0620.

†Ransom ID, *(Ransom Press; 0-912737),* 125 E. Third St., Moscow, ID 83843 (SAN 283-2216) Tel 208-883-1464; *CIP.*

Ransom Pr, *(Ransom Pr.; 0-931221),* P.O. Box 1456, Bernsville, MN 55337 (SAN 682-0166) Tel 612-588-8707.

RAPCOM Enter, *(RAPCOM Enterprises),* 2109 Wilkinson Pl., Alexandria, VA 22306 (SAN 689-0563).

Rape Abuse Crisis, *(Rape and Abuse Crisis Center of Fargo Moorhead; 0-914633),* P.O. Box 2984, Fargo, ND 58108 (SAN 289-5684) Tel 701-293-7273.

Rape Crisis Ctr, *(Rape Crisis Ctr.),* P.O. Box 21005, Washington, DC 20009 (SAN 225-9680).

Rapid Syst Dev, *(Rapid System Development, Inc.; 0-914751),* 211 W. 56th St., Suite 36H, New York, NY 10019-4323 Tel 212-245-8870.

Rapides Symphony, *(Rapides Symphony Guild; 0-9603758),* P.O. Box 4172, Alexandria, LA 71301-0172 (SAN 293-3691) Tel 318-442-9707; Dist. by: Dot Gibson Publications, 161 Knight Ave. Circle, Waycross, GA 31501 (SAN 293-3705) Tel 912-285-2848; Dist. by: Express Publishing Co., 305 Decatur St., New Orleans, LA 70130 (SAN 293-3713) Tel 504-524-6963; Dist. by: South Louisiana News Agency, 102 Industrial Dr. Crowley-Rayne Industrial Park, Rayne, LA 70578 (SAN 169-2917); Dist. by: The Collection, 2101 Kansas City Rd., Olathe, KS 66061 (SAN 293-373X) Tel 913-764-1811; Dist. by: Wimmer Brothers Books, 4210 BF Goodrich Blvd., Memphis, TN 38118 (SAN 293-3748) Tel 901-362-8900; Dist. by: Forest Sales & Distributing Co., 2616 Spain St., New Orleans, LA 70117 (SAN 293-3756) Tel 504-947-2106; Dist. by: Bayou News Agency, P.O. Box 15639, Baton Rouge, LA 70815 (SAN 169-2895) Tel 504-275-5670; Dist. by: Red River News, 950 Frontage Rd., Monroe, LA (SAN 159-9321).

Rapids Christian, *(Rapids Christian Press, Inc.; 0-915374),* P.O. Box 487, 810 4th Ave. N., Wisconsin Rapids, WI 54494 (SAN 205-0986) Tel 715-423-4670.

Rapollo Bks, *(Rapollo Books; 0-9603670),* 1362 Banyan Dr., Fallbrook, CA 92028 (SAN 213-6066); Dist. by: Caroline Hse. Pubs., 2 Ellis Pl., Ossining, NY 10562 (SAN 211-2299).

Rapple Prod, *(Rapple Prod Production; 0-932784),* Subs. of Ding A Ling Press, 2039 Civic Ctr. Dr., Suite 320, North Las Vegas, NV 89030 (SAN 212-1484) Tel 702-649-1018.

Rapport Unltd Pubns, *(Rapport Unlimited Pubns.; 0-9616729),* 3 Maple Grove St., Battle Creek, MI 49017 (SAN 659-8730) Tel 616-964-1389.

Raquette Pr, *(Raquette Press; 0-916136),* Box 1, Star Route, Canton, NY 13617 (SAN 207-6187) Tel 315-386-8354.

Rare Pub, *(Rare Publishing; 0-939024),* 23352 Erwin St., Woodland Hills, CA 91367 (SAN 238-1311) Tel 805-526-7616.

Raspberry Rec, *(Raspberry Recordings; 0-934721),* Div. of Raconteur Records, P.O. Box 11247 Dr., Capitol Sta., Columbia, SC 29211 (SAN 694-1605) Tel 803-254-9120.

Rassela Pr *See Rasselas Pr*

Rasselas Pr, *(Rasselas Press; 0-9609180),* 13505 Lucca Dr., Pacific Palisades, CA 90272 (SAN 241-4422) Tel 213-937-6250.

Rateavers, *(Rateavers; 0-9600698; 0-915966),* 9049 Covina St., San Diego, CA 92126 (SAN 205-6402) Tel 619-566-8994.

Rather Pr, *(Rather Press),* 3200 Guido St., Oakland, CA 94602 (SAN 293-3772) Tel 415-531-2938; Dist. by: The Printers' Shop, 4047 Transport, Palo Alto, CA 94303 (SAN 293-3780) Tel 415-494-6802.

Rational Isl, *(Rational Island Pubs.; 0-911214; 0-913937),* P.O. Box 2081, Main Office Sta., Seattle, WA 98111 (SAN 204-6725); 719 Second Ave. N., Seattle, WA 98109 (SAN 662-1201) Tel 206-284-0311.

Rauch Assocs, *(Rauch Assocs., Inc.; 0-932157),* P.O. Box 6802, Bridgewater, NJ 08807 (SAN 686-4325) Tel 201-231-9548.

Rave Reviews, *(Rave Reviews Publications; 0-9611224),* Div. of Junior League of North Little Rock, P.O. Box 15753, N. Little Rock, AR 72231 (SAN 283-3069) Tel 501-372-1436.

†Raven, *(Raven Pr., Pubs.; 0-89004; 0-88167),* Subs. of Wolters Samson Group, 1140 Ave. of the Americas, New York, NY 10036 (SAN 203-3909) Tel 212-575-0335; *CIP.*

Raven Pub Co *See Leda Pr*

Raven Rocks Pr, *(Raven Rocks Pr.; 0-9615779),* Rte. 1, Beallsville, OH 43716 (SAN 696-5679) Tel 614-926-1481.

Ravenel Bks, *(Ravenel Books; 0-916427),* P.O. Box 3318, Alexandria, VA 22302 (SAN 295-4958) Tel 703-751-5256.

†Ravengate Pr, *(Ravengate Press; 0-911218),* P.O. Box 103, Cambridge, MA 02238 (SAN 203-090X) Tel 617-456-8181; *CIP.*

Raving Fest, *(Raving Festival Assn. Women's Board; 0-9615803),* 22 W. Monroe St., Chicago, IL 60603 (SAN 696-5687) Tel 312-782-9696.

Raw Bks & Graph, *(Raw Bks. & Graphics; 0-915043),* 27 Greene St., New York, NY 10013 (SAN 289-8136) Tel 212-226-0146. *Imprints:* A Raw One Shot (A Raw One Shot).

†Rawson Assocs, *(Rawson Assocs.; 0-89256),* Div. of Scribner Bk. Co., Inc, 115 Fifth Ave., New York, NY 10003 (SAN 209-3154) Tel 212-614-1300; Toll free: 800-257-5755; Dist. by: The Scribner Bk. Co., Inc., Front & Brown Sts., Riverside, NJ 08075 (SAN 209-3162); *CIP.*

Rawson Wade *See Rawson Assocs*

Ray-Foster, *(Ray/Foster, Publishers; 0-9612346),* 3756 Decade St., Las Vegas, NV 89121 (SAN 289-2294) Tel 702-454-0199; Orders to: P.O. Box 12807, E Las Vegas, NV 89112 (SAN 669-3547) Tel 702-454-0199.

Ray Hinkle, *(Hinkle, Ray, Pubs.; 0-9616373),* 123 W. McKinley, Blackwell, OK 74631 (SAN 658-8646) Tel 405-363-3831; P.O. Box 572, Blackwell, OK 74631 (SAN 658-8654).

Ray Riling, *(Riling, Ray, Arms Bks. Co.; 0-9603096),* P.O. Box 18925, 6844 Gorsten St., Philadelphia, PA 19119 (SAN 205-2385) Tel 215-438-2456.

Rayburn Pr, *(Rayburn Pr., The; 0-9615942),* 644 Montclair Dr., Lexington, KY 40502 (SAN 696-8139) Tel 606-266-8590.

Raycol Prods, *(Raycol Products; 0-9605176),* 5346 E. 9th St., Tucson, AZ 85711 (SAN 215-8019) Tel 602-745-1033.

Rayes Eclec, *(Raye's Eclectic Craft Yarns, Inc.; 0-9601282),* P.O. Box 2356, 8240 Parkway Drive, Suite 105, La Mesa, CA 92041 (SAN 210-3672) Tel 619-460-0721.

Rayid Pubns, *(Rayid Model Pubns.; 0-917197),* 3905 NE 38th, Portland, OR 97212 (SAN 655-8720) Tel 503-288-3617.

Rayline, *(Rayline Company),* 1413 Edinger, Santa Ana, CA 92705 (SAN 210-6566).

Raymark Pub, *(RayMark Publishing, Inc.; 0-9617275),* P.O. Box 0286, College Grove Sta., San Diego, CA 92115 (SAN 663-5253); 6970 Central Ave., Lemon Grove, CA 92045 (SAN 663-5261) Tel 619-589-4024.

Raymond Nicholas *See Apostrophe Pr*

Raymonds Quiet Pr, *(Raymond's Quiet Pr.; 0-943228),* 6336 Leslie NE, Albuquerque, NM 87109 (SAN 240-7604) Tel 505-821-3627.

Raymont Pubs *See Randall Bk Co*

Raynor Pr, *(Raynor Pr., The; 0-9615069),* 1 Raynor Rd., West Orange, NJ 07052 (SAN 693-9236) Tel 201-731-5925.

Rays Energy, *(Rays Energy Consultants; 0-936561),* 701 S. MacArthur Blvd., Springfield, IL 62704 (SAN 698-0961) Tel 217-544-2434.

Ray's Energy *See Rays Energy*

RB Pubns CA, *(RB Pubns.; 0-9616727),* 240 Tamal Vista Blvd., Corte Madera, CA 94925 (SAN 659-8765) Tel 415-924-6820.

RBH Pub, *(R. B. H. Publishing Enterprises;
0-939842),* Div. of Advertising Unlimited
Ltd., 4528 W. Charleston Blvd., Las Vegas,
NV 89102 (SAN 282-2024)
Tel 702-878-8534; Orders to: 4263 Powell
Ave, Las Vegas, NV 89121
(SAN 293-3802) Tel 702-878-8534.

RBMU Intl, *(RBMU International),* 8102
Elberon Ave., Philadelphia, PA 19111
(SAN 225-4689) Tel 215-745-0680.

RBR, *(RBR (Religious Bks. for Russia);
0-934927),* P.O. Box 631, Lenox Hill Sta.,
New York, NY 10021 (SAN 695-0167)
Tel 914-478-2151; Dist. by: MCA Pr., 575
Scarsdale Rd., Crestwood, NY 10707
(SAN 200-5514).

RCA Dist Spec Prods, *(RCA Distributor &
Special Products; 0-913970),* Deptford, NJ
08096 (SAN 208-1210).

RCA Solid State, *(RCA Solid State Div.;
0-913972),* P.O. Box 3200, Somerville, NJ
08876 (SAN 205-115X).

RC&J
See Reed & Cannon

RCM Pubns, *(RCM Pubns.; 0-938154),* P.O.
Box 33565, San Diego, CA 92103
(SAN 215-2584).

†RCP Pubns, *(RCP Pubns.; 0-89851),* P.O. Box
3486, Merchandise Mart, Chicago, IL 60654
(SAN 212-4408) Tel 312-663-5920; *CIP.*

RCS Assocs, *(RCS Assocs., Inc.; 0-930293),*
1603 Danbury Dr., Claremont, CA 91711
(SAN 292-7195) Tel 714-624-1801.

RCS Co, *(RCS Co.; 0-938153),* 9445 Bay
Colony, 2N, Des Plaines, IL 60016
(SAN 659-8986) Tel 312-824-4181.

†RD Assn, *(Reader's Digest Assn., Inc.;
0-89577),* 750 Third Ave., New York, NY
10017-2797 (SAN 240-9720)
Tel 212-850-7007; Toll free: 800-431-1726;
Orders to: Customer Service, Pleasantville,
NY 10570 (SAN 282-2091)
Tel 914-769-7000; Dist. by: Random House,
Inc., 400 Hahn Rd., Westminster, MD 21157
(SAN 202-5515). Publisher. Not a true
association; *CIP.*

RDC Ctr Intl Stud, *(Rural Development
Committee, Ctr. for International Studies;
0-86731),* 170 Uris Hall, Ithaca, NY 14853
(SAN 217-510X) Tel 607-256-6370.

RDC Pubs, *(RDC Pubs.; 0-9600576),* 4741
School St., Yorba Linda, CA 92686
(SAN 207-0154) Tel 714-777-3376.

RDIC Pubns, *(Rudolf Dreikurs Institute of
Colorado Pubns.; 0-933450),* P.O. Box 3118,
Boulder, CO 80307 (SAN 213-5566)
Tel 303-499-4500.

RE *Imprint of* **WSP**

Re-Entry, *(Re-Entry From Military Service To
Civilian Employment; 0-9605826),* P.O. Box
13535, Portland, OR 97213
(SAN 216-5821) Tel 503-285-6560.

Re-Geniusing, *(Re-Geniusing Project, The;
0-941386),* 1432 Spruce St., Berkeley, CA
94709 (SAN 239-0272) Tel 415-841-4903.

RE Pubns, *(RE Pubns.; 0-9615272),* 246
Campbell St., Harrisonburg, VA 22801
(SAN 695-2747) Tel 703-433-0382.

Re Search Media
See Re Search Pubns

Re Search Pubns, *(Re/Search Pubns.; 0-940642),*
20 Romolo, No. B, San Francisco, CA 94133
(SAN 218-5849) Tel 415-362-1465; Dist.
by: The Subterranean Company, 1327 W.
Second St., Eugene, OR 97402
(SAN 662-7420) Tel 503-343-6324P.O. Box
10233, Eugene, OR 97440 (SAN 662-7439).

Read A Bol, *(Read-A-Bol Group, The;
0-938155),* 301 Village Run E., Encinitas,
CA 92024 (SAN 659-8994)
Tel 619-753-0663.

Read Bks Pubs, *(Read Bks. Pubs.; 0-937869),*
P.O. Box 776, South Lancaster, MA 01561
(SAN 659-5758); 64 Albright Rd., Sterling,
MA 01564 (SAN 659-5766)
Tel 617-422-6303.

Read Me Pub, *(Read Me Publishing Co.;
0-9602842),* 514 Anneslie Rd., Baltimore,
MD 21212 (SAN 222-2248).

Read Pub Group, *(Read Publishing Group;
0-9614299),* Div. of Roland Read Assocs.,
811 S. Broadway, Baltimore, MD 21231
(SAN 687-4851) Tel 301-522-4000.

Read Res *Imprint of* **ARO Pub**

†Readers Digest Pr, *(Reader's Digest Pr.;
0-88349),* 200 Park Ave., New York, NY
10166 (SAN 203-3887); Dist. by:
McGraw-Hill Bk. Co., 1221 Ave. of the
Americas, New York, NY 10020
(SAN 293-3802) Tel 212-512-2000; Dist.
by: Random Hse. Inc., 201 E. 50th St., New
York, NY 10022 (SAN 293-3810)
Tel 212-872-8036; *CIP.*

Readers Intl, *(Readers International; 0-930523),*
Subscription Service Dept., P.O. Box 959,
Columbia, LA 71418 (SAN 677-5403)
Tel 318-649-7288; Dist. by: Persea Books,
225 Lafayette St., New York, NY 10012
(SAN 212-8233) Tel 212-431-5270.

†Readex Bks, *(Readex Bks.; 0-918414),* 58 Pine
St., New Canaan, CT 06840
(SAN 209-9926) Tel 203-966-5906.
Conventional reference works in reduced size
(compact editions), research & reference
collections in microprint (opaque), microfiche
& reel microfilm; *CIP.*

Readex Microprint
See Readex Bks

Reading Fun, *(Reading Fun; 0-9616296),* 9210
Westwind Ct., Dallas, TX 75231
(SAN 658-5000) Tel 214-340-2064.

Reading Gems, *(Reading Gems; 0-915988),* P.O.
Box 806, Madison, WI 53701
(SAN 207-6934).

Reading Hse, *(Reading Hse., The; 0-9604388),*
Box 2975, Seal Beach, CA 90740
(SAN 282-2105) Tel 213-598-2289; Orders
to: Box 2748, Mission Viejo, CA 92692
(SAN 168-9886) Tel 714-770-1511; Dist.
by: DeVorss & Co., P.O. Box 550, 1046
Princeton Dr, Marina Del Rey, CA 90294
(SAN 662-121X).

Reading Matters, *(Reading Matters; 0-9614780),*
P.O. Box 300309, Denver, CO 80203
(SAN 692-6827) Tel 303-388-4211; Dist.
by: Quality Bks., Inc., 918 Sherwood DR.,
Lake Bluff, IL 60044-2204 (SAN 169-2127);
Dist. by: Bookpeople, 2929 Fifth St.,
Berkeley, CA 94710 (SAN 168-9517).

Reading Reform Found, *(Reading Reform
Foundation),* 7054 E. Indian School Rd.,
Scottsdale, AZ 85251 (SAN 225-8668).

Reading Tutor
See Gifted Educ Pr

Readon Pub, *(Readon Publishing; 0-9604638),*
5016 Barranca Lora, Pensacola, FL 32514
(SAN 215-2843) Tel 904-477-1882.

†Ready Ref Pr, *(Ready Reference Press;
0-916270),* P.O. Box 5249, Santa Monica,
CA 90405 (SAN 218-9305); *CIP.*

Real Comet, *(Real Comet Pr., The; 0-941104),*
Div. of Such A Deal Corp., 500 E. Pike St.,
Seattle, WA 98112-3618 (SAN 217-4227)
Tel 206-328-1801; Dist. by: Publishers
Group West, 5855 Beaudry St., Emeryville,
CA 94608 (SAN 202-8522).

Real Comp & Int, *(Real Computers &
Intelligence; 0-934190),* P.O. Box 74, Santa
Clara, CA 95050 (SAN 212-9639).

Real Est Futures, *(Real Estate Futures;
0-9600488),* P.O. Box 2580, Vail, CO 81658
(SAN 203-4123) Tel 303-949-4858.

Real Est Sol, *(Real Estate Solutions, Inc.;
0-917935),* 2609 Klingle Rd., NW,
Washington, DC 20008 (SAN 657-0100)
Tel 202-362-9854.

Real Estate Ed *Imprint of* **Longman Finan**

Real Estate Invest, *(Real Estate Investment
Assocs.; 0-9616730),* 2715 Elizabeth, Zion,
IL 60099 (SAN 659-8706)
Tel 312-872-2681.

Real Estate Pub, *(Real Estate Publishing Co.;
0-914256),* P.O. Box 41177, Sacramento,
CA 95841 (SAN 202-9782)
Tel 916-677-3864.

Real Food, *(Real Food; 0-9611550),* P.O. Box
721, Colfax, CA 95713 (SAN 284-9496)
Tel 916-346-2450.

†Real People, *(Real People Pr.; 0-911226),* P.O.
Box F, Moab, UT 84532 (SAN 203-3879)
Tel 801-259-7578; *CIP.*

Realities, *(Realities Library; 0-916982),* 2745
Monterey Rd., No. 76, San Jose, CA 95111
(SAN 208-0761).

Reality Bks, *(Reality Bks., Ltd.; 0-9616930),*
P.O. Box 824, Lansdale, PA 19446
(SAN 661-5295); 41950 Main St.,
Sellersville, PA 18960 (SAN 661-5309)
Tel 215-257-1940.

Reality Pr
See Diversity Okla

Reality Prods, *(Reality Productions; 0-9608622),*
9978 Holder St., Buena Park, CA 90620
(SAN 238-3497) Tel 714-828-2199.

Realm Bks, *(Realm Books, Ltd.; 0-941654),*
P.O. Box 2831, Phoenix, AZ 85002
(SAN 239-2941).

RealSoft NC, *(RealSoft, Inc.; 0-939259),* P.O.
Drawer 160, Atlantic Beach, NC 28512
(SAN 662-5215) Tel 919-726-2865. Do not
confuse with Realsoft, Inc., of Ft. Myers, FL.

†Realtors Natl, *(Realtors National Marketing
Institute; 0-913652),* 430 N. Michigan Ave.,
Suite 500, Chicago, IL 60611-4092
(SAN 202-0963) Tel 312-670-3780; Toll
free: 800-621-7035; *CIP.*

Reavco Pub, *(Reavco Publishing; 0-935695),*
7646 Hayvenhurst Ave., Van Nuys, CA
91406 (SAN 696-0863) Tel 818-780-3939.

Rebel Mont Tem, *(Rebel Montgomery Temple;
0-89279),* 302 W. Main No. 3 SE, Kasson,
MN 55944 (SAN 265-3680).

Rebel Pub, *(Rebel Publishing Co., Inc.;
0-9605666),* Rte. 5 Box 347-M, Texarkana,
TX 75501 (SAN 239-4804)
Tel 214-832-4726.

Rebound Pubns, *(Rebound Pubns.; 0-9615024),*
Box 21866, Waco, TX 76750
(SAN 694-0560) Tel 314-546-2773.

Recess Press, *(Recess Pr.; 0-9616784),* P.O. Box
310, Dixon, CA 95620 (SAN 660-9716);
353 E. B St., Dixon, CA 95620
(SAN 660-9724) Tel 916-678-4664.

Rechs Pubns, *(Rechs Pubns.; 0-937568),* 8157
Madison Ave., South Gate, CA 90280
(SAN 215-2274).

Recipes Life, *(Recipes for Life, Inc.; 0-9614347),*
P.O. Box 4718, Lafayette, LA 70502
(SAN 679-1646) Tel 318-234-1295.

Recipes Unltd, *(Recipes Unlimited, Inc.;
0-918620),* P.O. Box 1271, Burnsville, MN
55337 (SAN 209-0058) Tel 612-890-6655.

Recog Tech, *(Recognition Technologies Users
Assn.; 0-943072),* P.O. Box 2016, Colburn
House, Manchester Center, VT 05255
(SAN 240-4362) Tel 802-362-4151.

Recon Pubns, *(Recon Pubns.; 0-916894),* P.O.
Box 14602, Philadelphia, PA 19134
(SAN 207-8880).

Reconstruct Pr *Imprint of* **Inst Christian**

Reconstructionist Pr, *(Reconstructionist Pr.;
0-935457),* Div. of Federation of
Reconstructionist Congregations & Havurot,
270 W. 89th St., New York, NY 10024
(SAN 695-8745) Tel 212-496-2960; Dist.
by: Hebrew Publishing Co., 100 Water St.,
Brooklyn, NY 11201 (SAN 200-6774).

Record-Rama, *(Record-Rama (Sound Archives);
0-910925),* 4981 McKnight Rd., Pittsburgh,
PA 15237 (SAN 264-3391)
Tel 412-367-7330.

Record Research, *(Record Research, Inc.;
0-89820),* P.O. Box 200, Menomonee Falls,
WI 53051 (SAN 212-9655)
Tel 414-251-5408.

Recovery Pubns, *(Recovery Pubns.; 0-9613185),*
Box 7631, Amarillo, TX 79114-7631
(SAN 295-9372) Tel 806-372-5865.

Recreat Consult, *(Recreation Consultants;
0-9614086),* P.O. Box 842, Seattle, WA
98111 (SAN 686-0788) Tel 206-329-7894.

Recreat Pub, *(Recreation Pub.; 0-932413),* P.O.
Box 168, Wakefield, RI 02880
(SAN 686-6824) Tel 401-789-3041.

Recro Products, *(Recro Products Corp.;
0-911275),* 565 Fifth Ave., Suite 702, New
York, NY 10017 (SAN 274-9904)
Tel 212-687-1228.

Rector Pr, *(Rector Pr., Ltd.; 0-934393),* P.O.
Box 301, Leverett, MA 01054-9740
(SAN 693-8108) Tel 413-548-9253; 511
Long Plain Rd., Leverett, MA 01054-9740
(SAN 658-2788).

Rector Pub, *(Rector, L. T., Publishing;
0-9606170),* 310 E. 25th St., Minneapolis,
MN 55404 (SAN 223-0704).

Red Alder, *(Red Alder Books; 0-914906),* P.O.
Box 2992, Santa Cruz, CA 95063
(SAN 206-6181) Tel 408-426-7082.

Red Cedar, *(Red Cedar Press; 0-937190),*
English Dept., Michigan State Univ., East
Lansing, MI 48824 (SAN 211-6812)
Tel 517-351-4313; Dist. by: Stone Press,
1790 Grand River, Okemos, MI 48864
(SAN 207-902X).

Red Dembner
See Dembner Bks

†**Regal,** *(Regal Bks.; 0-8307),* Div. of Gospel Light Pubns., 2300 Knoll Dr., Ventura, CA 93003 (SAN 203-3852) Tel 805-644-6869; Toll free: 800-235-3415 (outside CA); Box 3875, Ventura, CA 93006 (SAN 658-1528); CIP.

Regal Am Mktg, *(Regal American Marketing Corp.; 0-940814),* 1901 Walnut Plaza, Carrollton, TX 75006 (SAN 216-4442) Tel 214-242-7541.

Regal Rebel Rouser, *(Regal Rebel Rouser Creations; 0-9616909),* 47 Eldora Dr.., Mountain View, CA 94041 (SAN 661-5244) Tel 415-967-8022.

Regenbogen-Verlag, *(Regenbogen-Verlag; 0-940816),* Box 6214, Silver Spring, MD 20906 (SAN 216-0072) Tel 301-933-8521.

Regency *Imprint of* **Scholarly**

Regency Bks, *(Regency Bks.; 0-910019),* Div. of Investment & Tax Pubns., Inc., P.O. Box 27368, Tempe, AZ 85282 (SAN 696-2424) Tel 602-967-6923; 1600 W. Broadway, Suite 385, Tempe, AZ 85282 (SAN 697-712X); Dist. by: Kampmann & Co., 9 E. 40th St., New York, NY 10016 (SAN 202-5191) Tel 212-685-2928.

Regency Pr, *(Regency Press; 0-933324),* 32 Ridge Dr., Port Washington, NY 11050 (SAN 211-8688) Tel 516-935-1143.

Regent Graphic Serv, *(Regent Graphic Services; 0-912710),* P.O. Box 8372, Swissvale, PA 15218 (SAN 204-6768) Tel 412-371-7128.

Regent House
  See B of A

Regent House *Imprint of* **B of A**

Regent St Bks, *(Regent Street Books; 0-916147),* 2747 Regent St., Berkeley, CA 94705 (SAN 294-9717) Tel 415-548-8459.

Regents Pr KS
  See U Pr of KS

Regents Pub, *(Regents Publishing Co., Inc.; 0-88345),* Subs. of Hachette, 2 Park Ave., New York, NY 10016 (SAN 203-3844) Tel 212-889-2780; Toll free: 800-822-8202 (outside NY).

Reggie the Retiree, *(Reggie The Retiree Co.; 0-9609960),* 6946 Myerlee Country Club Blvd., Fort Myers, FL 33907 (SAN 262-9925) Tel 207-646-2767.

†**Regina Bks,** *(Regina Bks.; 0-941690),* P.O. Box 280, Claremont, CA 91711 (SAN 239-2968) Tel 714-624-8466; CIP.

†**Regional,** *(Regional Publishing Co.; 0-8063),* Affil. of Genealogical Publishing Co., 1001 N. Calvert St., Baltimore, MD 21202 (SAN 206-8842) Tel 301-837-8271; CIP.

Regional Inst Social Welfare, *(Regional Institute of Social Welfare Research, Inc.),* P.O. Box 152, Athens, GA 30603 (SAN 225-9966) Tel 404-542-7614.

†**Regional Plan Assn,** *(Regional Plan Assn.),* 1040 Ave. of the Americas, New York, NY 10011 (SAN 225-1159) Tel 212-398-1140; CIP.

Regional Sci Res Inst, *(Regional Science Research Institute),* P.O. Box 833, Amherst, MA 01004 (SAN 239-3794) Tel 413-256-8525.

Regional Study, *(Purdue Univ. Calumet, Regional Studies Institute, The; 0-943766),* Purdue Univ., Hammond, IN 46323 (SAN 238-3454) Tel 219-838-7275.

†**Regional Young,** *(Regional Young Adult Project; 0-9606198),* 330 Elis St., Rm. 518, San Francisco, CA 94102 (SAN 220-3049) Tel 415-771-8375; CIP.

Regions Beyond
  See RBMU Intl

Register Pr, *(Register Press; 0-911242),* Yarmouth Port, MA 02675 (SAN 205-2237) Tel 617-362-2111.

Registry Pubns, *(Registry Pubns., Ltd.; 0-940640),* 425 Huehl Rd., No. 6B,, Northbrook, IL 60062 (SAN 204-2932) Tel 312-498-4010.

Regmar Pub, *(Regmar Publishing Co., Inc.; 0-914338),* P.O. Box 11358, Memphis, TN 38111 (SAN 203-2015) Tel 901-323-7442.

Regnery
  See Contemp Bks

†**Regnery Bks,** *(Regnery Bks.; 0-89526),* Div. of Regnery Gateway, Inc., 700 E St., SE, Washington, DC 20003 (SAN 210-5578); Dist. by: Independent Pubs. Group, 1 Pleasant Ave., Port Washington, NY 11050 (SAN 287-2544); CIP. Imprints: Gateway Editions (Gateway Editions).

Regnery-Gateway
  See Regnery Bks

Regnier, *(Regnier, Susan L.; 0-9606266),* 5011 Turtle Lane W., Shoreview, MN 55112 (SAN 220-3480) Tel 612-483-0390.

Regs Ent, *(Regs Enterprises; 0-9614859),* 14659 Dexter Ct., Dale City, VA 22193 (SAN 693-2029) Tel 703-670-4415.

Rehab Intl, *(Rehabilitation International; 0-9605554),* 25 E. 21st St., New York, NY 10106 (SAN 216-0080) Tel 212-420-1500.

Rehab Pubns, *(Rehab Publications; 0-9614877),* P.O. Box 22606, San Francisco, CA 94122 (SAN 693-0549).

Rehi Bks, *(Rehi Bks.; 0-938273),* 734 McGill Dr., Rochester, MI 48063 (SAN 659-8331) Tel 313-370-0629.

REI
  See Religion & ethics

Reid Ent, *(Ace Reid Enterprises; 0-917207),* P.O. Box 868, Kerrville, TX 78028 (SAN 656-089X) Tel 512-257-7446.

Reidel Pub
  See Kluwer Academic

Reiff Pr, *(Reiff Press; 0-911246),* 120 S. Eighth St., Apt 3, Indiana, PA 15701 (SAN 207-3552) Tel 412-349-3347.

Reignbow, *(Reignbow; 0-942334),* P.O. Box 26174, Phoenix, AZ 85068 (SAN 239-8605).

Reilly & Lee
  See Contemp Bks

Reiman Assocs, *(Reiman Assocs.; 0-89821),* 5400 S. 60th St., Greendale, WI 53129 (SAN 208-4368) Tel 414-423-0100; Orders to: Country Store, P.O. Box 572, Milwaukee, WI 53201 (SAN 208-4376).

Reinecke Assocs, *(Reinecke Assocs.; 0-9617064),* P.O. Box 3112, West Chester, PA 19380 (SAN 662-8524); 940 Harmony Hill Rd., West Chester, PA 19380 (SAN 662-8532) Tel 215-269-1288.

Reiner, *(Reiner Pubns.; 0-87377),* Box 25, Sterling, VA 22170 (SAN 204-6784) Tel 703-430-2813.

Reinforced Res, *(Reinforced Concrete Research Council),* 5420 Old Orchard Rd., Skokie, IL 60077 (SAN 669-2575) Tel 312-966-6200; Orders to: American Society of Civil Engineers, 345 E. 47th St., New York, NY 10017 (SAN 662-1236).

Reinforcement Lrn, *(Reinforcement Learning, Inc.; 0-937901),* P.O. Box 563, Upper Saddle River, NJ 07458 (SAN 659-5804); 87 Dimmig Rd., Upper Saddle River, NJ 07458 (SAN 659-5812) Tel 201-825-2244.

Reinhold
  See Van Nos Reinhold

Reis Network, *(Reis Network; 0-9616384),* 4111 Lincoln Blvd., No. 634, Marina del Rey, CA 90292 (SAN 659-1094) Tel 213-395-4078; 1636 Palm Ct., Santa Monica, CA 90401 (SAN 659-1108).

Reisner Pub, *(Reisner Publishing; 0-9611680),* 20 Los Altos Square, Los Altos, CA 94022 (SAN 284-9542) Tel 415-948-6427.

Reiss Pub
  See Natl Paragon

Rejected Works, *(Rejected Works Publishing Hse., Ltd.; 0-932493),* N600 Wolf Lodge Creek Rd., Coeur d'Alene, ID 83814 (SAN 687-4312).

Rekalb Pr, *(Rekalb Press; 0-9604614),* 6203 Jane Lane, Columbus, GA 31909 (SAN 282-2415) Tel 404-561-3497.

Rel Psych, *(Rel-Psych, Inc.; 0-9611682),* 201 Husson Ave., Apt. T1, Bangor, ME 04401 (SAN 285-1415) Tel 207-945-5997.

Relation Family Comns, *(Relationship & Family Communications; 0-937905),* 1120 Conneticut Ave., NW, 940 Bender Bldg., Washington, DC 20036 (SAN 659-5669) Tel 202-526-5505; Orders to: Rafcom Books, P.O. Box 1554, Washington, DC 20013-1554 (SAN 662-4308) Tel 202-526-5505.

Relevant Pub, *(Relevant Pubns., Ltd.; 0-9606750),* 14241 Mango Dr., Del Mar, CA 92014 (SAN 202-974X) Tel 619-755-7522.

Reliance Health, *(Reliance Health Systems; 0-9615436),* 10341 N. Scottsdale Rd., Scottsdale, AZ 85254 (SAN 696-0820) Tel 602-948-9533.

Reliance Pub, *(Reliance Publishing Co.; 0-937740),* 380 Steinwehr Ave., Gettysburg, PA 17325 (SAN 220-0910) Tel 717-334-1103.

Reliant Pub, *(Reliant Publishing; 0-9613987),* P.O. Box 17456, Portland, OR 97217 (SAN 682-1944) Tel 503-281-3586.

Religion & ethics, *(Religion & Ethics Institute; 0-914384),* P.O. Box 664, Evanston, IL 60204 (SAN 202-9731) Tel 312-328-4049.

Religious Activ, *(Religious Activities Press),* 413 S. Main St., Goodlettsville, TN 37072 (SAN 212-7911) Tel 615-859-5519.

†**Religious Educ,** *(Religious Education Pr., Inc.; 0-89135),* 1531 Wellington Rd., Birmingham, AL 35209 (SAN 207-3951) Tel 205-879-4040; CIP. Imprints: REP Bks (REP Books).

Religious Soc Friends, *(Philadelphia Yearly Meeting, Religious Society of Friends, Book Services; 0-941308),* 1515 Cherry St., Philadelphia, PA 19102 (SAN 239-3778).

Relmo Pubs, *(Relmo Pubs.; 0-9613940),* P.O. Box 1606, Apache Junction, AZ 85220 (SAN 686-1725).

Relocation Realty, *(Relocation/Realty Consultants, Inc.; 0-939361),* 607 W. 58th Terr., Kansas City, KS 64113 (SAN 662-6920) Tel 816-444-4646.

Remcon Pub, *(Remcon Publishing, Inc.; 0-937183),* 800 W. Deleon St., Tampa, FL 33606 (SAN 658-4950) Tel 813-253-0176.

Rember Pub, *(Rember Publishing; 0-939101),* 7786 S. Elizabeth Ct., Littleton, CO 80122 (SAN 662-6017) Tel 303-770-1548.

Rembrandt Pr, *(Rembrandt Pr.; 0-9617169),* 9601 Wilshire Blvd., Suite 728, Beverly Hills, CA 90210 (SAN 663-141X) Tel 213-271-9171.

Rememberbooks, *(Rememberbooks; 0-935231),* P.O. Box 2501, Virginia Beach, VA 23450 (SAN 695-7161).

Remembrance Pr, *(Remembrance Pr., The; 0-9617210),* Div. of Rosemary House, Inc., 120 S. Market St., Mechanicsburg, PA 17055 (SAN 663-2777) Tel 717-697-5111.

Remi Bks, *(Remi Bks.; 0-943362),* 205 E. 78th St., New York, NY 10021 (SAN 240-9267) Tel 212-570-6265; Dist. by: Kampmann & Co., 9 E. 40th St., New York, NY 10016 (SAN 663-298X) Tel 212-685-2928.

Renaissance Art Writ Assn, *(Renaissance Artists & Writers Asssociation; 0-9611360),* Subs. of Ananda Marga Pubns., 854 Pearl St., Denver, CO 80203 (SAN 282-9975) Tel 303-832-6465.

Renaissance Bks, *(Renaissance Books; 0-932476),* 834 N. Plankinton Ave., Milwaukee, WI 53203 (SAN 211-9722) Tel 414-271-6850.

Renaissance Hse *Imprint of* **Jende-Hagan**

Renaissance Inst *Imprint of* **Islamic Prods**

Renaissance OH, *(Renaissance Pubns.; 0-936645),* 4782 Brodribb Ct., Box D, Columbus, OH 43220 (SAN 699-7295) Tel 614-459-9279.

Renaissance Pr
  See Renn Pr NOLA

Renaissance Prods *Imprint of* **Islamic Prods**

†**Renaissance Pubs,** *(Renaissance Pubs.; 0-916560),* 2485 NE 214th St., Miami, FL 33180 (SAN 207-5091) Tel 305-931-3392; CIP.

Renaissance Soc Am, *(Renaissance Society of America; 0-9602696),* 1161 Amsterdam Ave., New York, NY 11027 (SAN 209-4835) Tel 212-280-2318.

Rendezvous Pubns, *(Rendezvous Pubns.; 0-938447),* 701 Northview Dr., Jupiter, FL 33458 (SAN 660-9929) Tel 305-744-6149; P.O. Box 4269, Jupiter, FL 33469-4269 (SAN 660-9937).

Renfrew Group, *(Renfrew Group, The; 0-935601),* 985 High St., Bath, ME 04530 (SAN 696-0928) Tel 207-443-6070; Orders to: The Renfrew Group, P.O. Box 617, Freeport, ME 04032 (SAN 662-3646) Tel 207-443-1587.

Renfro Studios, *(Renfro, Nancy, Studios; 0-931044),* 1117 W. Ninth St., Austin, TX 78703 (SAN 211-9730) Tel 512-472-2140.

Renn Pr NOLA, *(Renaissance Pr., Inc.; 0-9616289),* P.O. Box 30808, New Orleans, LA 70190 (SAN 658-4357) Tel 504-899-8801; 805 Marengo, New Orleans, LA 70190 (SAN 658-4365).

Renouf
  See Brookfield Pub Co

Renovare Co, *(Renovare Company; 0-913986),* 8033 Sunset Blvd., No. 31, Los Angeles, CA 90046 (SAN 202-246X) Tel 213-656-4420; Dist. by: Historical Films, P.O. Box 46505, Los Angeles, CA 90046 (SAN 200-7274) Tel 213-656-4420.

REP Bks *Imprint of* **Religious Educ**

Rep Natl Com, *(Republican National Committee),* 310 First St. SE, Washington, DC 20003 (SAN 235-8875) Tel 202-863-8700.

REP Pubs, *(R.E.P. Pubs.; 0-9604876),* 12703 Red Fox Court, Maryland Hgts., MO 63043 (SAN 239-3786).

†**Report,** *(Report Store; 0-916313),* Div. of Ergosyst Assocs., Inc., 910 Massachusetts St., Suite 503, Lawrence, KS 66044 (SAN 130-1314) Tel 913-842-7348; *CIP.*

†**Reprint,** *(Reprint Co.; 0-87152),* P.O. Box 5401, 601 Hillcrest Offices, Spartanburg, SC 29304 (SAN 203-3828) Tel 803-582-0732; *CIP.*

Republican Co, *(Republican Co.; 0-9615852),* 1860 Main St., Springfield, MA 01101 (SAN 696-771X) Tel 413-788-1212.

Res Adv Serv, *(Research Advisory Services, Pubns., Inc.; 0-931602),* P.O. Box 8151, 286 N. McCarrons Blvd., St. Paul, MN 55113 (SAN 211-3759).

Res & Educ, *(Research & Education Assn.; 0-87891),* 505 Eighth Ave., New York, NY 10018 (SAN 204-6814) Tel 212-695-9487.

Res & Serv Inst, *(Research & Service Institute, Inc.; 0-942660),* Two Maryland Farms, Suite 233, Brentwood, TN 37027 (SAN 238-5678) Tel 615-377-3217; Orders to: Harry Randles, Peabody College, Box 514, Nashville, TN 37203 (SAN 662-1244) Tel 615-322-8000.

Res Appl Inc, *(Resource Applications Inc.; 0-932491),* 720 Light St., P.O. Box 6397, Baltimore, MD 21230-3895 (SAN 687-4061) Tel 301-962-0250; Toll free: 800-826-1877.

Res Assocs, *(Research Assocs., Inc.; 0-943938),* 425 W. Broadway, Suite D, North Little Rock, AR 72114 (SAN 241-144X).

Res Bks, *(Restauration Bks.; 0-934263),* 150 S. Glenoaks, No. 9176, Burbank, CA 91510 (SAN 693-2770) Tel 818-841-6479.

Res Cosmobiol
See J Reynolds

†**Res Ctr Kabbalah,** *(Research Centre of Kabbalah; 0-943688),* 200 Park Ave., Suite 303 E., New York, NY 10017 (SAN 210-9484) Tel 212-986-2515; Orders to: 83-15 124th Pl., Kew Gardens, NY 11415 (SAN 662-7447) Tel 718-805-9122; *CIP.*

Res Ctr Lang Semiotic, *(Research Ctr. for Language & Semiotic Studies; 0-87750),* Dist. by: Humanities Pr. International, Inc., 171 First Ave., Atlantic Highlands, NJ 07716 (SAN 201-9272) Tel 201-872-1441.

Res Ent Pubs, *(Research Enterprises, Pubs.; 0-915025),* P.O. Box 7569, Washington, DC 20044 (SAN 289-825X); 4701 Kenmore Ave., Suite 905, Alexandria, VA 22304 (SAN 289-8268) Tel 703-370-4044.

Res Inst Am, *(Research Institute of America),* 589 Fifth Ave., New York, NY 10017 (SAN 227-0064) Tel 212-755-8900.

Res Inst Man Rep, *(Research Institute Management Reports, Inc.),* 589 Fifth Avenue, New York, NY 10017 (SAN 265-4091).

Res Inst Stud, *(Research Institute for Studies in Education; 0-943206),* The Quadrangle, Iowa State University, Ames, IA 50011 (SAN 240-9275) Tel 515-294-7009.

Res Materials, *(Research Materials Corp.; 0-934631),* Box 243, College Park, MD 20740 (SAN 693-9228) Tel 301-552-2622.

Res Plan Inst, *(Research Planning Institute, Inc.; 0-931531),* 925 Gervais St., Columbia, SC 29201 (SAN 682-3092) Tel 803-256-7322.

†**Res Press,** *(Research Pr. Co.; 0-87822),* 2612 N. Mattis Ave., Champaign, IL 61821 (SAN 282-2482) Tel 217-352-3273; Orders to: Box 3177, Champaign, IL 61821 (SAN 282-2490). Do not confuse with Research Pr., Prairie Village, KS. Do not confuse with Resolute Pr., Edison, NJ; *CIP.*

Res Publs, *(Research Pubs.; 0-911252),* 108 S. Patton, Arlington Heights, IL 60005 (SAN 206-6645) Tel 312-255-1961.

Res Pubns AZ, *(Research Pubns.; 0-914981),* 11855 N. 19th Ave., Phoenix, AZ 85029 (SAN 289-3894) Tel 602-252-4477; Toll free: 800-528-0559.

Res Pubns Conn
See Res Pubns CT

†**Res Pubns CT,** *(Research Pubns., Inc.; 0-89235),* Subs. of International Thomson Organization, Inc., 12 Lunar Dr., Drawer AB, Woodbridge, CT 06525 (SAN 238-2717) Tel 203-397-2600; Toll free: 800-732-2477; J. Dick Publishing, 801 Green Bay Rd., Lake Bluff, IL 60044 (SAN 661-9924) Tel 312-234-1220; *CIP.*

Res Pubns NC, *(Research Pubns., Inc.; 0-935233),* 92 Fairway Dr., Asheville, NC 28815 (SAN 695-5479) Tel 704-298-8291; P.O. Box 9267, Asheville, NC 28815 (SAN 699-606X).

Res Pubns VA
See Res Pubns CT

Res Serv Unltd, *(Research Services Unlimited; 0-912177),* P.O. Box 562, Toms River, NJ 08754 (SAN 265-4105) Tel 201-349-2799; Dist. by: Gamblers Book Club, 630 S. 11th St., P.O. Box 4115, Las Vegas, NV 89127 (SAN 200-7282) Tel 702-382-7555; Dist. by: Casino Distributors, P.O. Box 849, Pleasantville, NJ 08232 (SAN 200-7290) Tel 609-646-4165.

Rescan Assocs Inc, *(Rescan Assocs., Inc.; 0-937737),* 401 Boyden Ave., Maplewood, NJ 07040 (SAN 659-2856) Tel 201-763-7534.

Research Council
See R C D P M

Research Lang, *(Language Research Educational Series; 0-9609446),* P.O. Box 29512, Washington, DC 20017 (SAN 260-0927) Tel 202-635-7907.

Research Pub, *(Research Publishing; 0-933833),* 2113 S St. NW, Washington, DC 20008 (SAN 692-8730) Tel 202-234-7069.

Research Pubns, *(Research Pubs.; 0-9600478),* P.O. Box 801, Glen Rock, NJ 07452 (SAN 204-6830).

Resolute Pr, *(Resolute Press; 0-9604382),* 13 Regent Ct., Edison, NJ 08817 (SAN 216-0099) Tel 201-287-0640. Do not confuse with Research Pr. Co., Champaign, IL.

Resource Ctr
See Inter-Hem Educ

Resource Direct, *(Resource Directories; 0-937521),* 3103 Executive Pkwy., Suite 212, Toledo, OH 43606 (SAN 659-1183) Tel 419-536-5353.

Resource Pub Grp, *(Resource Publishing Group, Inc.; 0-915619),* P.O. Box 390, Arlington, VA 22210 (SAN 293-4981) Tel 703-524-0815; 1401 Wilson Blvd., Ste. 101, Arlington, VA 22209 (SAN 293-499X).

Resource Pubns, *(Resource Pubns., Inc.; 0-89390),* 160 E. Virginia St., No. 290, San Jose, CA 95112 (SAN 209-3081) Tel 408-286-8505; Toll free: 800-228-2028.

Resource Texas, *(Resource Pr.; 0-9609182),* P.O. Box 774, 433 Belle Grove, Richardson, TX 75080 (SAN 241-4457) Tel 214-458-1466.

Resource UT, *(Resource Publications, Inc. (Utah); 0-936348),* P.O. Box 1515, Provo, UT 84603 (SAN 221-9883) Tel 801-756-6360.

Resources, *(Resources; 0-933342),* P.O. Box 1067 Harvard Square, Cambridge, MA 02238 (SAN 209-0457).

Resources Children, *(Resources for Children in Hospitals; 0-9608150),* P.O. Box 10, Belmont, MA 02178 (SAN 240-2734) Tel 617-492-6220.

†**Resources Future,** *(Resources for the Future, Inc.; 0-915707),* 1616 P St., NW, Rm. 532, Washington, DC 20036 (SAN 213-1544) Tel 202-328-5086; Dist. by: Resources for the Future Customer Services, P.O. Box 4852, Hampden Sta., Baltimore, MD 21211 (SAN 200-5166) Tel 301-338-6953; *CIP.*

Respons Logic, *(Responsive Logic; 0-928459),* 156 Donald St., Oregon City, OR 97045 (SAN 669-5108) Tel 503-655-4980.

Responsible Action
See Intl Dialogue Pr

Responsive Syst, *(Responsive Systems Assocs., Inc.; 0-9616483),* P.O. Box 846, Clinton, OK 73601 (SAN 695-1023) Tel 518-439-3838; 90-100 N. 31st St., Clinton, OK 73601 (SAN 658-2869).

Rest Recipes, *(Restaurant Recipes; 0-9613112),* P.O. Box 4618, San Luis Obispo, CA 93403 (SAN 294-0868) Tel 805-528-3142.

†**Reston,** *(Reston Publishing Co., Inc.; 0-87909; 0-8359),* A Prentice-Hall Co., Englewood Cliffs, NJ 07632 (SAN 699-556X) Tel 201-592-2427; Orders to: P.O. Box 500, Englewood Cliffs, NJ 07632 (SAN 215-3939) Tel 201-767-5049; *CIP.* *Imprints:* Reward Edn (Reward Edition).

Restoration Re, *(Restoration Research; 0-942284),* P.O. Box 547, Bountiful, UT 84010 (SAN 238-1133) Tel 801-298-4058.

Results Ent, *(Results Enterprises; 0-934713),* 2600 NE 21st. St., Fort Lauderdale, FL 33305 (SAN 694-1621) Tel 305-566-7739.

Resurge Pr, *(Resurge Pr.),* 910 Madison, Suite 805, Memphis, TN 38103 (SAN 661-4612) Tel 901-529-0874.

Resurgens Pubns, *(Resurgens Pubns., Inc.; 0-89583),* P.O. Box 49321, Atlanta, GA 30329 (SAN 211-0539) Tel 404-834-1343.

Retail Group
See Nature Life

Retail Report, *(Retail Reporting Bureau; 0-934590),* 101 Fifth Ave., New York, NY 10003 (SAN 213-1552) Tel 212-255-9595; Toll free: 800-251-4545.

Retirement Res, *(Retirement Research; 0-9602938),* Box 401, Appleton, WI 54912 (SAN 204-6849) Tel 414-734-6610.

Retriever, *(Retriever Bks.; 0-9604628),* 250 W. 87th St., New York, NY 10024 (SAN 213-5531) Tel 212-874-5579.

Reunion Pr, *(Reunion Pr.; 0-935616),* P.O. Box 1738, Twain Harte, CA 95383 (SAN 657-7148) Tel 209-928-4800.

Reunion Pub Hse, *(Reunion Publishing Hse.; 0-938173),* 140 Mayhew Way, Suite 700, Pleasant Hill, CA 94523 (SAN 659-7211) Tel 415-938-7444.

Rev Exist Psych, *(Review of Existential Psychology & Psychiatry; 0-914857),* P.O. Box 23220, Seattle, WA 98102 (SAN 289-3940) Tel 206-328-2024.

Rev Pubns, *(Rev Pubns),* P.O. Box 4787-B, Santa Barbara, CA 93103 (SAN 239-6025) Tel 805-964-0458.

Reveal Pubns, *(Reveal Pubns.; 0-9602536),* 2208 Woodlawn St., Kannapolis, NC 28081 (SAN 212-6826) Tel 704-932-3476.

Revelation, *(Revelation 2/24),* P.O. Box 7700, Pasadena, TX 77508 (SAN 692-221X).

Revelation Hse, *(Revelation Hse. Pubs., Inc.; 0-9604852),* P.O. Box 73175, Metairie, LA 70033 (SAN 217-1295).

Revelation Pr, *(Revelation Press; 0-913681),* P.O. Box 80141, Baton Rouge, LA 70898-0141 (SAN 286-1828) Tel 504-766-7746; 353 Stanford Ave., Baton Rouge, LA 70808 (SAN 286-1836).

†**Revell,** *(Revell, Fleming H., Co.; 0-8007),* Subs. of Zondervan Corp., 184 Central Ave., Old Tappan, NJ 07675 (SAN 203-3801) Tel 201-768-8060; Toll free: 800-631-1970; *CIP. Imprints:* New Hope (New Hope Books); Power Bks (Power Books); Spire Bks (Spire Books).

Reverchon Pr, *(Reverchon Press; 0-9601902),* 3520 Routh St., Dallas, TX 75219 (SAN 212-9671) Tel 214-528-6540.

Reverend Clarke
See T C Edwards NJ

†**Review & Herald,** *(Review & Herald Pub. Assn.; 0-8280),* 55 W. Oak Ridge Dr., Hagerstown, MD 21740 (SAN 203-3798) Tel 301-791-7000; Toll free: 800-582-5600; *CIP.*

Reviewer, *(Reviewer, The; 0-9606796),* 2197 Berkeley, Salt Lake City, UT 84109 (SAN 207-2815) Tel 801-487-4274.

Revisionary
See Stony Brook Pr

†**Revisionist Pr,** *(Revisionist Pr.; 0-87700),* P.O. Box 2009, Brooklyn, NY 11202 (SAN 203-378X); *CIP.*

Revival Press, *(Revival Pr., Inc.; 0-938612),* P.O. Box 130, Bedford, TX 76021 (SAN 240-8228) Tel 817-283-2873.

Revival Teach, *(Revival Teaching; 0-9616360),* 21 County Rd., Chatham, IL 62629 (SAN 659-1205) Tel 217-483-4109.

Revolutionary Pubns
See Rev Pubns
Reward *Imprint of* **P-H**
Reward Edn *Imprint of* **Reston**
Reward Systs Servs, *(Reward Systems Services, Inc.; 0-938115),* 245 E. 63rd St., New York, NY 10021 (SAN 659-6932) Tel 212-832-0590.
†**Reymont,** *(Reymont Associates; 0-918734),* 6556 Sweet Maple Lane, Boca Raton, FL 33433 (SAN 204-6857) Tel 305-483-4343; *CIP.*
Reynal *Imprint of* **Morrow**
Reynard Hse, *(Reynard House; 0-932998),* 5706 30th NE, Seattle, WA 98105 (SAN 216-2954).
Reynolds Morse, *(Reynolds Morse Foundation; 0-934236),* 10395 Stafford Rd., Chagrin Falls, OH 44022 (SAN 282-2520); Dist. by: J.D.S. Bks., P.O. Box 67, MCS, Dayton, OH 45402 (SAN 282-5864).
Reynolds Pub, *(Reynolds Publishing Co.; 0-938343),* P.O. Box 51, White Oak, TX 75693 (SAN 659-9427); 304 Mockingbird St., White Oak, TX 75693 (SAN 659-9435) Tel 214-758-8114.
RF Prod, *(RF Productions; 0-936523),* Box 310, Langley, OK 74350 (SAN 697-9491) Tel 918-782-3029.
RFF Assocs, *(RFF Assocs.; 0-9611414),* 808 Francis Pl., St. Louis, MO 63105 (SAN 283-4324) Tel 314-863-0625.
RFTS Prod, *(RFTS Productions; 0-939401),* 739 Falls Ave., Box 414, Cuyahoga Falls, OH 44222 Tel 216-928-3606.
RG Pub
See Packard
RGK Pubns, *(RGK Pubns.; 0-9616383),* 10560 NE Madison St., Blaine, MN 55434 (SAN 659-1116) Tel 612-786-1462.
RGM Pubns, *(RGM Pubns.; 0-942436),* H-28 Miriam St., Key West, FL 33040 (SAN 238-1931) Tel 305-294-5710; Dist. by: Publishers Group West, 5855 Beaudry St., Emeryville, CA 94608 (SAN 202-8522) Tel 415-658-3453; Dist. by: Comics Unlimited, 6833 Amboy Rd., Staten Island, NY 10309 (SAN 200-7029) Tel 212-948-2223.
Rhapis Gardens, *(Rhapis Gardens; 0-9612130),* P.O. Box 287, Hwy. 181, Gregory, TX 78359 (SAN 286-8628) Tel 512-643-2061.
Rhema Inc Pub, *(Rhema, Inc. Pubs.; 0-935945),* 1220 Three Mile Rd., Grosse Point Park, MI 48230 (SAN 696-7531) Tel 313-881-3299.
Rheumatoid, *(Rheumatoid Disease Foundation, The; 0-9615437),* Rte. 4, Box 137, Franklin, TN 37064 (SAN 696-0677) Tel 615-646-1030.
Rhino Books, *(Rhino Books; 0-930589),* 1201 Olympic Blvd., Santa Monica, CA 90404 (SAN 677-5454) Tel 213-450-6323.
Rhinos Pr, *(Rhino's Press, The; 0-937382),* P.O. Box 3520, Laguna Hills, CA 92654 (SAN 214-4565) Tel 714-997-3217.
RHM & Assocs, *(RHM & Assocs.; 0-9616949),* 10839 S. Houston, Jenks, OK 74037 (SAN 661-7417) Tel 918-495-6006.
Rho-Delta Pr, *(Rho-Delta Press; 0-913770),* P.O. Box 69540, Los Angeles, CA 90069 (SAN 204-6881) Tel 213-657-1925.
Rhodes Geo Lib, *(Rhodes Geographic Library, Inc.; 0-933768),* 3225 Rum Row, Naples, FL 33940 (SAN 212-792X) Tel 813-262-6713.
Rhombus Pub, *(Rhombus Publishing Co.; 0-936455),* P.O. Box 806, Corrales, NM 87048 (SAN 698-0287); Lot 4, Rincon de Corrales, Corrales, NM 87048 (SAN 698-2425) Tel 505-897-3700.
RHOPAR Corp, *(R.H.O.P.A.R. Corp., The; 0-937015),* 3 Malaga Cove Plaza, No. 844, Palos Verdes Estates, CA 90274 (SAN 658-7917) Tel 213-377-0647.
RHS Ent, *(RHS Enterprises; 0-914503),* 11368 Matinicus Ct., Cypress, CA 90630 (SAN 289-6699) Tel 714-892-9012.
Rhythmic Aerobex
See Prime Time Aerobics
RI Bicent Found *Imprint of* **RI Pubns Soc**
RI Bicentennial
See RI Pubns Soc
RI Coll Alumni, *(Rhode Island College Alumni Assn.; 0-9616171),* 600 Mt. Pleasant Ave., Providence, RI 02908 (SAN 699-9247) Tel 401-456-8086.

RI Genealogical, *(Rhode Island Genealogical Society; 0-9604144),* 128 Massasoit Dr., Warwick, RI 02888 (SAN 216-4450) Tel 401-781-6759.
RI Hist Preserv, *(Rhode Island Historical Preservation Commission; 0-939261),* 150 Benefit St., Providence, RI 02903 (SAN 662-5223) Tel 401-277-2678.
RI Hist Soc, *(Rhode Island Historical Society; 0-932840),* 110 Benevolent St., Providence, RI 02906 (SAN 203-0829) Tel 401-331-8575.
RI Mayflower, *(Rhode Island Mayflower Society; 0-930272),* 128 Massasoit Dr., Warwick, RI 02888 (SAN 209-4843) Tel 401-781-6759.
RI Pubns Soc, *(Rhode Island Pubns. Society; 0-917012),* 189 Wickenden St., Providence, RI 02903 (SAN 219-9696) Tel 401-272-1776. *Imprints:* RI Bicent Found (Rhode Island Bicentennial Foundation).
RI Spec Olym, *(Rhode Island Special Olympics; 0-9615853),* 1 Commerce Way, Suite 200, Johnston, RI 02919 (SAN 696-7574) Tel 401-421-6037.
Ribe, *(Ribe; 0-9616049),* P.O. Box 1256, Cambridge, MA 02238 (SAN 698-0082) Tel 617-576-3923; 13A Ware St., No. 8, Cambridge, MA 02138 (SAN 698-2387).
Ricci, *(Ricci, Joan; 0-9614699),* 2535 NW 41st. St., Boca Raton, FL 33434 (SAN 692-6088) Tel 305-994-4853; Toll free: 800-523-6504 (U. S.); Toll free: 800-331-1262 (FL); Dist. by: Baker & Taylor, Eastern Div., 50 Kirby Ave., Somerville, NJ 08876 (SAN 169-4901).
Rice Inst, *(Rice, A. K., Institute; 0-9615099),* P.O. Box 39102, Washington, DC 20016 (SAN 694-2024) Tel 202-857-8447.
†**Rice Univ,** *(Rice Univ. Pr.; 0-89263; 0-911216),* Rice Univ. P.O. Box 1892, Houston, TX 77251 (SAN 204-689X) Tel 713-527-6035; Dist. by: Texas A & M Univ. Pr., Drawer C, College Station, TX 77843 (SAN 207-5237) Tel 409-845-1436; *CIP.*
Rich & Snyder, *(Richardson & Snyder; 0-943940),* 25 Broad St., New York, NY 10004 (SAN 241-1458) Tel 212-344-1200; Toll free: 800-526-0275; Dist. by: New American Library, P.O. Box 999, Bergenfield, NJ 07621 (SAN 200-6758) Tel 201-387-0600.
Rich Concepts
See Sensitive Man
Rich Pub, *(Rich Publishing, Inc.),* P.O. Box 555, Temecula, CA 92390 (SAN 206-9660) Tel 714-676-5712.
Rich Pub Co, *(Rich Publishing Co.; 0-9607256),* Subs. of Dobson & Assocs., Inc., 10611 Creektree, Houston, TX 77070 (SAN 239-300X) Tel 713-469-9165.
Rich SC, *(Rich Pub.; 0-9607832),* P.O. Box 1185, Clemson, SC 29633 (SAN 207-5857) Tel 803-654-2507.
Richard Jorgensen, *(Jorgensen, Richard H; 0-914306),* 302 West Redwood, Marshall, MN 56258 (SAN 693-7772).
Richards Co, *(Richards, Peter, Co., The),* 3 Parkview Plaza, Morristown, NJ 07960 (SAN 239-4820).
Richards Hse, *(Richards Hse.-FACTS; 0-930702),* P.O. Box 208, Wellesley Hills, MA 02181 (SAN 211-0547) Tel 617-235-1142.
Richards Pub, *(Richards Publishing Co.; 0-88323),* P.O. Box 66, Phoenix, NY 13135 (SAN 203-0861) Tel 315-695-7261.
Richards Pub OK, *(Richards Publishing; 0-9616017),* 4338 E. 67th St., Tulsa, OK 74136 (SAN 699-7554) Tel 918-493-7353.
Richardson & Steirman, *(Richardson & Steirman; 0-931933),* 246 Fifth Ave., New York, NY 10001 (SAN 685-9852) Tel 212-213-1203.
Richardsons Marine, *(Richardsons' Marine Publishing, Inc.; 0-932647),* P.O. Box 23, Streamwood, IL 60103 (SAN 687-8342) Tel 312-741-4239.
†**Richboro Pr,** *(Richboro Press; 0-89713),* Box 1, Richboro, PA 18954 (SAN 214-1353) Tel 215-355-6084; *CIP.*
Richcraft Eng, *(Richcraft Engineering Ltd.; 0-940972),* Drawer 1065, No. 1 Wahmeda Industrial Park, Chautauqua, NY 14722 (SAN 219-0931) Tel 716-753-2654.

Richelieu Court, *(Richelieu Court Pubns., Inc.; 0-911519),* P.O. Box 388 Aspen Heights, Slingerlands, NY 12159 (SAN 264-3480) Tel 518-439-7942.
Richman Pub, *(Richman Publishing; 0-941846),* Div. of Richman Communications, P.O. Box 11307, Salt Lake City, UT 84147 (SAN 239-3018) Tel 801-964-0378.
Richmond Cty Hist Soc, *(Richmond County Historical Society; 0-937044),* Reese Library, Augusta College, 2500 Walton Way, Augusta, GA 30910 (SAN 662-7455) Tel 404-737-1745.
Richmond Hse, *(Richmond Hse.; 0-939505),* 573 North Mountain Ave., Suite 263, Upland, CA 91786 (SAN 663-4001) Tel 714-945-3112.
Richwood Pr, *(Richwood Pr.; 0-9613310),* 107 Konnarock Cir., Greenville, SC 29611 (SAN 653-8835) Tel 803-246-6690.
†**Richwood Pub,** *(Richwood Pub. Co.; 0-915172),* P.O. Box 381, Scarsdale, NY 10583 (SAN 207-3250) Tel 914-723-1286; *CIP.*
RICO Law, *(RICO Law Reporter),* 1519 Connecticut Ave., NW, Washington, DC 20036 (SAN 663-0812) Tel 202-462-5755.
Ricsher Pub Ltd, *(Rischer Publishing, Ltd.; 0-931347),* Subs. of Ricsher Enterprises, Inc., P.O. Box 34828, Bethesda, MD 20817 (SAN 682-6237) Tel 301-469-6481.
Ricwalt Pub Co, *(Ricwalt Publishing Co.; 0-933054),* C-3 Bldg., Rm. 110, Fishermen's Terminal, Seattle, WA 98119 (SAN 213-1587) Tel 206-282-7545.
RID Pubns, *(Registry of Intrepreters for the Deaf, Inc.; 0-9602220; 0-916883),* 814 Thayer Ave., Silver Spring, MD 20910 (SAN 216-1796) Tel 301-588-2406.
Rider *Imprint of* **Hayden**
Ridge Row, *(Ridge Row Pr.; 0-940866),* Univ. of Scranton, Dept. of Theology & Religious Studies, Scranton, PA 18510 (SAN 688-4067) Tel 717-961-7449; Dist. by: Montrose Publishing Co., 10-20 S. Main St., Montrose, PA 18801 (SAN 200-6898) Tel 717-278-1141.
Ridge Soaring, *(Ridge Soaring, Inc.),* R.D., Julian, PA 16844 (SAN 695-2569) Tel 814-355-1792.
Ridge Times Pr, *(Ridge Times Pr., The; 0-934203),* Box 90, 1020 1/2 Main St., Mendocino, CA 95460 (SAN 693-0565) Tel 707-937-1188.
Ridgefield Bicen Com, *(Ridgefield Bicentennial Commission; 0-9601114),* 400 Main St., Ridgefield, CT 06877 (SAN 209-9985) Tel 203-438-7218.
Ridgeline Pr, *(Ridgeline Pr.; 0-918967),* 1136 Orchard Rd., Lafayette, CA 94549 (SAN 669-9685) Tel 415-283-5836.
Ridgeview, *(Ridgeview Publishing Co.; 0-917930),* Box 686, Atascadero, CA 93423 (SAN 209-9993) Tel 805-466-7252.
Ridgeview Jr High Pr, *(Ridgeview Junior High Press; 0-936920),* 9424 Highlander Court, Walkersville, MD 21793 (SAN 214-4573).
Ridgeway Bks, *(Ridgeway Books),* P.O. Box 6431, Philadelphia, PA 19145 (SAN 207-7485).
Ridgeway Pr, *(Ridgeway Pr.; 0-943230),* 12032 Montecito Rd., Los Alamitos, CA 90720 (SAN 240-4915) Tel 213-596-8851.
Rieker Communications, *(Rieker Communications; 0-941656),* 48 Groveland Terr., Suite 410, Minneapolis, MN 55403 (SAN 239-3026) Tel 612-377-4770.
Rienner Pubs
See Lynne Rienner
RIF Mktg, *(RIF Marketing; 0-9606000),* 912 Five Points Rd., P.O. Box 3055, Virginia Beach, VA 23454 (SAN 216-7611) Tel 804-857-0512.
RIFD
See RID Pubns
Rigelle Pubns, *(Rigelle Pubns.; 0-9614389),* P.O. Box 1055, Cortez, CO 81321 (SAN 688-6485) Tel 303-565-7157.
Riggers Bible, *(Riggers Bible; 0-9600992),* P.O. Box 3302, Glenstone Sta., Springfield, MO 65804 (SAN 207-2823) Tel 417-869-9236.
Riggs, *(Riggs, Karen B.),* Rte. 12, Box 1559, Mechanicsville, VA 23111 (SAN 275-0899) Tel 804-779-3557.
Right Brain Pub, *(Right Brain Publishing; 0-935295),* 7812 NW Hampton Rd., Kansas City, MO 64152 (SAN 695-9350) Tel 816-587-8687.

Right Time
See About Time MA

Right to Life, (Right to Life League of Southern California; 0-9613809), 1616 W. Ninth St., Suite 220, Los Angeles, CA 90015 (SAN 219-8142) Tel 213-380-8750.

Rigsbee K, (Rigsbee, Ken; 0-9615296), 3402 Water Locust Dr., Sugar Land, TX 77479 (SAN 694-4310) Tel 713-980-1755; Dist. by: Cuerno Largo Pubns., 3402 Water Locust Dr., Sugar Land, TX`77479 (SAN 200-5476).

RIM
See Stevens & Shea

Rima Pr, (Rima Pr.; 0-9613941), 1420 Mound St., Alameda, CA 94501 (SAN 689-1713).

Rinehart
See HR&W

Ringa Pr, (Ringa Press; 0-88100), 6833 W. Grand Avenue, Chicago, IL 60635 (SAN 264-3529).

Ringling Mus Art, (Ringling, John & Mabel, Museum of Art Foundation; 0-916758), 5401 Bayshore Rd., Sarasota, FL 33578 (SAN 208-7154) Tel 813-355-5101.

†Rio Grande, (Rio Grande Pr., Inc., The; 0-87380), P.O. Box 33, Glorieta, NM 87535 (SAN 203-3763) Tel 505-757-6275; La Casa Escuela, Glorieta, NM (SAN 662-7463); CIP.

Rip off, (Rip Off Pr., Inc.; 0-89620), P.O. Box 14158, San Francisco, CA 94114 (SAN 207-7671) Tel 415-469-5800.

Risale i Nur Inst, (Risale i Nur Institute of America; 0-933552), 2506 Shattuck Ave., Berkeley, CA 94704 (SAN 212-6192) Tel 415-845-4355.

Rising Pub, (Rising Publishing; 0-917047), P.O. Box 72478, Los Angeles, CA 90002 (SAN 655-3060) Tel 213-677-5599.

Rising Star, (Rising Star Press; 0-933670), 557 Wellington Ave., San Carlos, CA 94070 (SAN 213-3636) Tel 415-592-2459.

Risk Analysis, (Risk Analysis & Research Corp.; 0-932056), P.O. Drawer DPFC, Monterey, CA 93942 (SAN 211-6464).

Risk Ent, (Risk Enterprises), 1133 Curtis, Laramie, WY 82070 (SAN 213-1560).

Risk Insurance Mgmt
See Risk Management

Risk Management, (Risk Management Society Publishing, Inc.; 0-937802), 205 E. 42nd St., New York, NY 10017 (SAN 215-8043) Tel 212-286-9292.

Risk Mgmt Pr, (Risk Management Pr.; 0-9614860), P.O. Box 670, Inverness, CA 94937 (SAN 693-2045) Tel 415-669-1501.

Risk Mgmt Soc
See Risk Management

RIT Graph Arts Res
See Tech & Ed Ctr Graph Arts RIT

Rite Bks Pub, (Rite Bks. Publishing; 0-9614423), P.O. Box 3439, Warren, OH 44485 (SAN 689-027X) Tel 216-399-4949.

Ritger Sports
See Tech Ed Pub

Rittenhouse, (Rittenhouse Bk. Distributors; 0-87381), 511 Feheley Dr., King of Prussia, PA 19406 (SAN 213-4454) Tel 215-277-1414; Toll free: 800-345-6425.

Riva, (Riva Press; 0-9613194), 8408 Paseo Del Ocaso, La Jolla, CA 92037 (SAN 295-8996) Tel 619-454-8529.

Rival Pubs, (Rival Pubs.; 0-9607100), P.O. Box 5628, Everett, WA 98206 (SAN 239-0302) Tel 206-334-3965.

RivEd Imprint of HM

River Basin, (River Basin Publishing Co.; 0-936106), P.O. Box 75573, St. Paul, MN 55175 (SAN 213-7887) Tel 612-291-0980; Dist. by: The Distributors, 702 S. Michigan, South Bend, IN 46618 (SAN 169-2488) Tel 219-232-8500; Dist. by: Baker & Taylor, Eastern Div., 50 Kirby Ave., Somerville, NJ 08876 (SAN 662-1279).

River Bend, (River Bend Publishing; 0-9605162), 1222 Vista Court, No. 2, Muscatine, IA 52761 (SAN 215-9112).

River Bend Club, (River Bend Club, Inc.; 0-9615100), P.O. Box 23021, Ft. Lauderdale, FL 33307 (SAN 694-2636) Tel 305-391-9162.

River City MO, (River City Pubs., Ltd.; 0-933150), P.O. Box 28665, St. Louis, MO 63141 (SAN 222-982X) Tel 314-724-7160.

River Falls, (River Falls Univ. Press), 113 E. Hathorn, River Falls, WI 54022 (SAN 203-6983) Tel 715-425-3100.

River Forest C C, (River Forest Community Center; 0-9606314), 414 Jackson, River Forest, IL 60305 (SAN 239-8613) Tel 312-771-6159.

River Hse, (River House; 0-940644), 2213 Pennington Bend, Nashville, TN 37214 (SAN 216-2962) Tel 615-889-2968.

River Pr, (River Press; 0-915535), P.O. Box 2006, Florissant, MO 63032 (SAN 291-4042) Tel 618-345-4731; 11 Kimberly Ct., Collinsville, IL 62034 (SAN 291-4050).

River Road Pr, (River Road Pr.), P.O. Box 1130, Conway, AR 72032 (SAN 695-5452).

River Valley Pub, (River Valley Publishing; 0-9615070), P.O. Box 99752, Jeffersontown, KY 40299 (SAN 692-722X).

River W Bks, (River West Bks.; 0-9607192), 663 S. 11th St., Coos Bay, OR 97420 (SAN 239-1287) Tel 503-269-1363.

Riverdale Co, (Riverdale Co., Inc., The; 0-913215), 5506 Kenilworth Ave., No. 102, Riverdale, MD 20737 (SAN 283-3905) Tel 301-864-2029.

Riverdale Systs, (Riverdale Systems Design, Inc.; 0-939545), 3333 Henry Hudson Pkwy., Riverdale, NY 10463 (SAN 697-4309) Tel 212-549-1692; Toll free: 800-622-4070.

Riverrun NY, (Riverrun Pr.; 0-7145; 0-86676), Affil. of John Calder Pubs. (London, UK), 1170 Broadway, Rm. 807, New York, NY 10001 (SAN 240-9917) Tel 212-889-6850; Dist. by: Kampmann & Co., Inc., 9 E. 40th St., New York, NY 10016 (SAN 202-5191) Tel 212-685-2928. Imprints: Breachwood Pubns (Breachwood Publications); Original Music (Original Music); Petras Press (Petras Press).

Riverrun Piermont, (Riverrun Pr.; 0-936415), 500 Piermont Ave., Piermont, NY 10968 (SAN 699-7511) Tel 914-359-2629.

RiversEdge Pr, (RiversEdge Press; 0-938884), P.O. Box 1547, Edinburg, TX 78539 (SAN 239-8931) Tel 512-381-3335.

Riverside Bks, (Riverside Bks.; 0-938777), 24 Riverside Dr., New York, NY 10023 (SAN 661-6399) Tel 212-874-1817.

Riverside Mus Pr, (Riverside Museum Pr.; 0-935661), 3720 Orange St., Riverside, CA 92501 (SAN 280-2740) Tel 714-787-7273.

Riverstone, (Riverstone Pr.; 0-9601130), P.O. Box 148006, Chicago, IL 60614 (SAN 210-2641).

Riverstone Foothills, (Riverstone Press of the Foothills Art Center; 0-936600), 809 15th St., Golden, CO 80401 (SAN 214-0144).

Riverstone Pr, (Riverstone Pr.; 0-9617206), 795 River Heights Dr., Meridian, ID 83642 (SAN 663-2548) Tel 208-888-6290. Do not confuse with Riverstone Press of Portland, OR, and Chicago, IL.

RivLit Imprint of HM

RivSL Imprint of HM

†Rizzoli Intl, (Rizzoli International Pubns., Inc.; 0-8478), 597 Fifth Ave., New York, NY 10017 (SAN 207-7000) Tel 212-223-0100; Toll free: 800-433-1238; CIP.

RJ Assocs, (R/J Associates; 0-9602090), 564 Tyler Ave., Livermore, CA 94550 (SAN 212-1352) Tel 415-443-7140.

RJ Pubns
See Mustang Pub

RJR Pr
See Utopian Universe

RK Edns, (RK Editions; 0-932360), P.O. Box 73, Canal St. Sta., New York, NY 10013 (SAN 211-447X).

RKM Pub Co, (RKM Publishing Co.; 0-87500), Div. of RKM Enterprises, Inc., P.O. Box 23042, Euclid, OH 44123 (SAN 689-4321) Tel 216-261-2610; Dist. by: Starlite Distributors, 395 Freeport Blvd., No. 10, Sparks, NV 89431 (SAN 131-1921) Tel 702-359-5676; Dist. by: New Leaf Distributing Co., 1020 White St., SW, Atlanta, GA 30310 (SAN 169-1449) Tel 404-755-2665.

RKO Homevideo, (RKO Homevideo; 1-55545), Div. of RKO Pictures, 1900 Ave. of the Stars, Los Angeles, CA 90067 (SAN 696-575X) Tel 818-906-1722.

RMI, (RMI Corp.; 0-910117), 341 Broadway, Cambridge, MA 02139 (SAN 240-835X).

RMK Pub, (RMK Publishing; 0-938879), Div. of R. Martin Krol & Assocs., Ltd., 2025 Fox's Lair Trail, Norfolk, VA 23518 (SAN 661-7395) Tel 804-853-6358.

RMP Finan Consul, (RMP Financial Consultants; 0-931664), 10 Petit Bayou Lane, New Orleans, LA 70129 (SAN 211-9692) Tel 504-241-1171.

RND Pub, (RND Publishing; 0-9615416), 721 Fairway Dr., Broderick, CA 95605 (SAN 695-5711) Tel 916-371-3779; P.O. Box 781, West Sacramento, CA 95691 (SAN 695-572X).

Ro-Lyn Ind, (Ro-Lyn Industries; 0-9615141), P.O. Box 162931, Sacramento, CA 95816-2931 (SAN 694-2598).

Ro-Mar, (Ro-Mar Publishing Co.; 0-9609566), 11325 Valley Oak Dr., Oakdale, CA 95361 (SAN 275-102X).

Road Runner Pr, (Road-Runner Pr.; 0-9615668), 2294 Baskerville Ave., Bishop, CA 93514 (SAN 696-0871) Tel 619-872-1706.

Road St Pr, (Road Street Press, The; 0-9609536), P.O. Box 9605, Washington, DC 20016 (SAN 275-1062); Dist. by: Mary Mitchell, 2810 R St. NW, Washington, DC 20007 (SAN 200-4100) Tel 202-333-2401.

Roadrunner Pubns, (Roadrunner Pubns., Inc.; 0-914635), P.O. Box 13548, Austin, TX 78711 (SAN 289-5749) Tel 512-454-5391. Out of Business.

Roadrunner Tech, (Roadrunner-Technical Pubns., Inc.; 0-89741), Div. of Desert Laboratories, Inc., 3136 E. Columbia St., Tucson, AZ 85714 (SAN 204-2169) Tel 602-294-3431.

Roan Horse, (Roan Horse Pr.; 0-933234), 2509 N. Campbell Ave., Suite 277, Tucson, AZ 85719 (SAN 215-9120).

Roanoke Isld
See Storie McOwen

Rob Briggs, (Briggs, Roberts, Assocs.; 0-9609850; 0-931191), Box 9, Mill Valley, CA 94942 (SAN 268-4632) Tel 415-461-7051; Dist. by: Publishers Services, 11A Commercial Blvd., Novato, CA 94947 (SAN 200-7223) Tel 415-883-3140.

Rob Lynn Pub, (Lynn, Robinson, Pub.; 0-9611994), 100 Walnut Pl., Brookline, MA 02146 (SAN 286-8075) Tel 617-277-3562.

Robbies Creations, (Robbie's Creations, Inc.; 0-9616639), P.O. Box 7997, Berkeley, CA 94707 (SAN 659-6878); 935 Filmore St., Albany, CA 94706 (SAN 659-6886) Tel 415-524-1607.

Roberta Pr, (Roberta Pr.; 0-9615742), 6311 Sanford St., Houston, TX 77096 (SAN 696-0987) Tel 713-771-6053.

Roberts Assocs
See S Roberts & Assocs

Roberts CA, (Roberts Publishing; 0-9616192), 5048 J Pkwy., Sacramento, CA 95823 (SAN 699-9263) Tel 916-421-8332.

Roberts Ent, (Roberts Enterprises; 0-9604184), 7350 N. Montero Dr., No. 1406, Tucson, AZ 85741 (SAN 214-4603) Tel 602-247-7467.

Roberts M, (Roberts, Mervin F.; 0-9615047), 1 Duck River Ln., Old Lyme, CT 06371 (SAN 693-8590) Tel 203-434-5178.

Roberts Pub, (Roberts Publishing Corp.; 0-936492), 45 John St., New York, NY 10038 (SAN 203-0772) Tel 212-233-3768.

Robertson, (Robertson, Donald W.), 3811 Marquette Pl., No. 2 G, San Diego, CA 92106 (SAN 211-0911) Tel 619-225-8060.

Robertson Pr, (Robertson Pr.; 0-9614317), 27 Wexford Rd., Delmar, NY 12054 (SAN 687-5262) Tel 518-439-3681.

Robin & Russ, (Robin & Russ Handweavers), 533 N. Adams St., McMinnville, OR 97128 (SAN 207-284X) Tel 503-472-5760.

Robinson & Robinson, (Robinson & Robinson, Ltd.; 0-932587), 5829 Wynkoop Rd., Lockport, NY 14094 (SAN 687-5009) Tel 716-434-7338.

Robinson Assocs, (Robinson & Assocs.; 0-9615804), 746 N. Eucalyptus 18, Inglewood, CA 90302 (SAN 696-253X); P.O. Box 4245, Inglewood, CA 90302 (SAN 699-6299).

Robinson Bks, (Robinson, Ruth E., Bks.; 0-9603556), Rte. 7, Box 162A, Morgantown, WV 26505 (SAN 213-4322) Tel 304-594-3140.

Robinson News, (Robinson Newspapers), 207 SW 150th St., Burien, WA 98166 (SAN 263-2268) Tel 206-242-0100.

Robinson Pr, (Robinson Press, Inc.; 0-913730), 1137 Riverside Dr., Fort Collins, CO 80524 (SAN 205-2369) Tel 303-482-5393.

Robinson Pub, (Robinson Publishing Co. Inc.), P.O. Box 48119, Seattle, WA 98148 (SAN 283-4316).

Robinson Typos, (Robinson Typographics; 0-918837), 1614 S. Clementine St., Anaheim, CA 92802 (SAN 679-1271) Tel 714-533-2610.

Roblin Enterprises, (Roblin Enterprises Inc.; 0-934968), 23 Rosedale Rd., Yonkers, NY 10710 (SAN 264-3561) Tel 914-337-4576.

Robot Inst Am, (Robotic Industries Assn.; 0-933747), P.O. Box 3724, Ann Arbor, MI 48106 (SAN 275-1119) Tel 313-994-6088.

Robotics Age, (Robotics Age Inc.; 0-916863), 174 Concord St., Peterborough, NH 03458 (SAN 296-1709) Tel 603-924-7136.

†Robotics Pr, (Robotics Pr.; 0-89661), 8285 SW Nimbus, Suite 151, Beaverton, OR 97005 (SAN 282-2563) Tel 503-646-2713; Toll free: 800-457-1842; Orders to: P.O. Box 606, Beaverton, OR 97075 (SAN 282-2571); CIP.

Robt Morris Assocs, (Morris, Robert, Assocs.; 0-936742), 1616 Philadelphia National Bank Bldg., Philadelphia, PA 19107 (SAN 224-6473).

Roca Pub, (Roca Publishing, Inc.; 0-88025), P.O. Box 176, Saint Davids, PA 19087 (SAN 217-4243) Tel 215-337-0576.

Rochester Folk Art, (Rochester Folk Art Guild), Rte. 1, Box 10, Middlesex, NY 14507 (SAN 210-9492) Tel 716-554-3539.

Rochester Philharmonic, (Rochester Philharmonic League; 0-9612176), 108 E. Ave., Rochester, NY 14604 (SAN 289-4912) Tel 716-454-2620.

Rocin, (Rocin Pr.; 0-9608304), Div. of Rocin Laboratories, Inc., 8 E. 62 St., New York, NY 10021 (SAN 240-9550) Tel 212-355-0109.

Rock Found, (Rock Foundation; 0-937691), 222 Central Pk. S., New York, NY 10019 (SAN 659-1248) Tel 212-757-9110.

Rock Harbor, (Rock Harbor Press; 0-932260), P.O. Box 1206, Hyannis, MA 02601 (SAN 214-199X).

Rock Tech Pubns, (Rock Tech Pubns.; 0-914283), 171 W. Putnam Ferry Rd., Woodstock, GA 30188 (SAN 287-5357) Tel 404-926-1311.

Rockabilia Pr, (Rockabilia Pr.; 0-9616805), 107 N. Arbor, Savannah, MO 64485 (SAN 661-0277) Tel 816-232-1567.

Rockcom Pub, (Rockcom Publishing; 0-933246), 225 South Blvd., Nyack, NY 10960 (SAN 211-7223) Tel 914-358-3631.

†Rockdale Ridge, (Rockdale Ridge Pr.; 0-9602338), 8501 Ridge Rd., Cincinnati, OH 45236 (SAN 212-4459) Tel 513-891-9900; CIP.

†Rockefeller, (Rockefeller Univ. Pr.; 0-87470), 1230 York Ave., New York, NY 10021 (SAN 203-3747) Tel 212-570-8571; Box 291, New York, NY 10021 (SAN 658-1536) Tel 212-570-8572; Orders to: Rockefeller Press, P.O. Box 5483, Church St., Sta., New York, NY 10249 (SAN 662-1295); CIP.

Rocket Pub Co, (Rocket Publishing Co.), P.O. Box 412, Normangee, TX 77871 (SAN 204-5699) Tel 713-828-4265.

Rockets
See CA Rocketry

Rockfall Pr, (Rockfall Press; 0-9601502), Cider Mill Rd., Rockfall, CT 06481 (SAN 212-1638).

Rockford Lea, (Junior League of Rockford, Inc.; 0-9613563), 4118 Pinecrest Rd., Rockford, IL 61107 (SAN 669-9596) Tel 815-399-4518.

Rockin Enter, (Rockin Enterprises, Inc.; 0-9616081), 1503 W. Greenleaf Ave., Chicago, IL 60626 (SAN 698-0759) Tel 312-761-4893.

Rocking Chair Pr, (Rocking Chair Press, Inc.; 0-913562), 2109 Queenswood Dr., Tallahassee, FL 32303 (SAN 204-6938) Tel 904-562-1207.

Rocking Horse, (Rocking Horse Pr.; 0-932306), 32 Ellise Rd., Storrs, CT 06268 (SAN 212-4467) Tel 203-429-1474.

†Rockland County Hist, (Historical Society of Rockland County, The; 0-911183), 20 Zukor Rd., New City, NY 10956 (SAN 211-4488) Tel 914-634-9629; CIP.

Rockland Research
See N S Kline Inst

Rockcom Pub
See Rockcom Pub

Rockport Art Assn, (Rockport Art Assn., Inc.; 0-9616560), P.O. Box 987, Rockport, TX 78382 (SAN 659-5820) Tel 512-729-5519.

†Rockport Pubns, (Rockport Pubns.; 0-936220), P.O. Box 2787, Newport Beach, CA 92663 (SAN 214-462X) Tel 714-646-9481; CIP.

Rockport Pubs, (Rockport Pubs.; 0-935603), 5 Smith St., Rockport, MA 09166 (SAN 696-236X) Tel 617-546-9590; P.O. Box 396, Rockport, MA 01966 (SAN 696-9631); Dist. by: Robert Silver Assocs., 307 E. 37th St., New York, NY 10016 (SAN 241-5801) Tel 212-686-5630.

Rockway Hse, (Rockway Hse. Publishing Co., Inc.; 0-932285), 130 W. Main St., P.O. Box 1, Little Chute, WI 54301 (SAN 686-6131) Tel 414-788-4310.

Rockwell Museum, (Rockwell, Norman, Museum at Stockbridge; 0-9615273), P.O. Box 308, Stockbridge, MA 01262 (SAN 695-2712) Tel 413-298-3869.

Rocky Mount CO, (Rocky Mountain Books, Inc.; 0-914459), 928 13th St. Suite Two, Greeley, CO 80631 (SAN 289-6729) Tel 303-353-9481.

Rocky Mtn Arms
See Best Antiques

Rocky Mtn Bks, (Rocky Mountain Books; 0-9605648), P.O. Box 10663, Denver, CO 80210 (SAN 215-7047).

Rocky Mtn Nature Assn, (Rocky Mountain Nature Assn.; 0-930487), Rocky Mountain National Park, Estes Park, CO 80517 (SAN 670-9036) Tel 303-586-2371.

Rocky Mtn Res, (Rocky Mountain Research Center; 0-915207), P.O. Box 4694, Missoula, MT 59806 (SAN 289-8276) Tel 406-549-6330.

Rocky Mtn Writer, (Rocky Mountain Writers Guild Pubns.; 0-915091), 837 15th St., Boulder, CO 80302 (SAN 240-9658) Tel 303-444-4100.

Rocky Point Pr, (Rocky Point Pr.; 0-930093), P.O. Box 4814, North Hollywood, CA 91607 (SAN 670-1736) Tel 818-761-3386.

Rocky Top Pubns, (Rocky Top Pubns.; 0-937317), P.O. Box 33, Stamford, NY 12167 (SAN 658-7763) Tel 607-652-2567.

RoCoCo, (RoCoCo; 0-938275), 204 Main St., Ellsworth, ME 04605 (SAN 659-8242) Tel 207-667-9353.

Rod & Staff, (Rod & Staff Pubs., Inc.), Hwy. 172, Crockett, KY 41413 (SAN 206-7633) Tel 606-522-4348.

Rod L Evans, (Evans, Rod L.; 0-9616533), RR 1, P.O. Box 33B, Conde, SD 57434 (SAN 659-4441) Tel 605-382-5963.

Rod Law, (Law, Rod; 0-9601730), P.O. Box 24025, Los Angeles, CA 90024 (SAN 222-0555).

Rodale Inst, (Rodale Institute; 0-935641), 222 Main St., Emmaus, PA 18049 (SAN 695-9466) Tel 215-967-5171.

†Rodale Pr Inc, (Rodale Pr., Inc.; 0-87857), 33 E. Minor St., Emmaus, PA 18049 (SAN 200-2477) Tel 215-967-5171; Toll free: 800-527-1800; CIP.

Rodeo Studio, (Rodeo Studio; 0-9614570), P.O. Box 1016, Pine Bluffs, WY 82082 (SAN 691-8271) Tel 307-245-3884.

Rodney, (Rodney Pubns., Inc.; 0-913830), 349 E. 49th St., New York, NY 10017 (SAN 204-6954) Tel 212-421-5444.

RoDonn Pub, (RoDonn Publishing Co.; 0-932058), P.O. Box 6976, Colorado Springs, CO 80904 (SAN 692-1116) Tel 303-632-4832.

Roehrs, (Roehrs Co.; 0-911266), P.O. Box 125, 136 Park Ave., East Rutherford, NJ 07073 (SAN 204-6962); 24 High St., East Rutherford, NJ 07073 (SAN 662-1309) Tel 201-933-0090.

Roerick Music, (Roerick Music Co.; 0-9612684), 4046 Davana Rd., Sherman Oaks, CA 91423 (SAN 239-8621) Tel 818-783-2496.

Rogers Hist Mus, (Rogers Historical Museum; 0-9616640), 322 S. Second St., Rogers, AR 72756 (SAN 659-6894) Tel 501-636-0162.

Rogers Hse Mus, (Rogers Hse. Museum Gallery; 0-9600686), 102 E. Main So., Ellsworth, KS 67439 (SAN 204-6989) Tel 913-472-3255.

Rogue Wave Pub, (Rogue Wave Publishing Co.; 0-938005), P.O. Box 7921, Berkeley, CA 94707 (SAN 659-7629) Tel 415-763-1264; 1732 Sixth Ave., No. 12, Oakland, CA 94606 (SAN 659-7637).

Rohrich Corp, (Rohrich Corporation; 0-9611500), 903 Tallmadge Ave., Akron, OH 44310-3592 (SAN 226-8965).

Role Train Assocs, (Role Training Associates of California), 6304 Marina Pacifica Dr. S., Long Beach, CA 90803 (SAN 208-0931) Tel 213-493-3400.

Rolfs Gall, (Rolf's Gallery; 0-910579), P.O. Box 9, Montevideo, MN 56265 (SAN 260-2571) Tel 612-269-8409.

Rolling Block, (Rolling Block Press; 0-940028), P.O. Box 5357, Buena Park, CA 90622 (SAN 217-0817).

Rolling Hills Pr, (Rolling Hills Pr.; 0-943978), 40 Pilgrim Park, San Rafael, CA 94903 (SAN 282-2601) Tel 415-499-8135.

Rolling Hse, (Rolling Hse. Pubns.; 0-934169), 174 Santa Clara Ave., Oakland, CA 94610 (SAN 693-3629) Tel 415-654-5920; Orders to: Rolling House Pubns., P.O. Box 3865, Berkeley, CA 94703 (SAN 662-3190); Orders to: Shirley Fontoura, 1625 Woolsey St., Suite 7, Berkeley, CA 94703 (SAN 662-3204) Tel 415-548-4228.

Rolling Meadows, (Rolling Meadows Library; 0-9602782), 3110 Martin Lane, Rolling Meadows, IL 60008 (SAN 213-7895) Tel 312-259-6050.

Rollins Coll, (Rollins College, George D. & Harriet W. Cornell Fine Arts Ctr.; 0-9615828), 601 Holt Ave., Winter Park, FL 32789-4496 (SAN 280-3054) Tel 305-646-2526.

Roman Catholic Arch, (Roman Catholic Archbishop of Boston; 0-9614384), 2121 Commonwealth Ave., Brighton, MA 02135 (SAN 688-6078) Tel 617-254-0100.

Roman Enter, (Roman Enterprises; 0-9606642), 16548 Linch Path, Lakeville, MN 55044 (SAN 217-426X) Tel 612-435-5024.

Roman Inc, (Roman, Inc.; 0-937739), 4850 N. Harlem, Harwood Heights, IL 60656-3581 (SAN 659-2899) Tel 312-867-6660.

†Romance, (Romance Monographs, Inc.), P.O. Box 7553, University, MS 38677 (SAN 209-4878) Tel 601-234-0001; CIP.

Romanian Hist, (Romanian Historical Studies; 0-937019), 1029 Euclid Ave., Miami Beach, FL 33139 (SAN 658-4942) Tel 305-534-0120.

Romantic Tidings, (Romantic Tidings Bks.; 0-935235), Rte. 2, Box 142, Watson, IL 62473 (SAN 695-7129) Tel 217-536-6848.

Romantic Times, (Romantic Times, Inc.; 0-940338), 163 Joralemon St., Brooklyn Heights, NY 11201 (SAN 218-5032).

ROMARC Inc, (ROMARC, Inc.; 0-940522), 3738 14 Mile Rd., Stockton, CA 95209 (SAN 219-8150).

Romney Pr, (Romney Press; 0-9604640), 308 Fourth Ave., Iowa City, IA 52240 (SAN 215-7055); Dist. by: Eble Music Co., P.O. Box 2570, Iowa City, IA 52244 (SAN 282-6275).

Ron Denzer, (Denzer, Ron, Publishing; 0-9616331), 2540 Roy Ave., Crescent City, CA 95531 (SAN 659-1566) Tel 707-464-3278.

Ronald Pr
See Wiley

Roncorp, (Roncorp, Inc.; 0-939103), P.O. Box 724, Cherry Hill, NJ 08003 (SAN 662-5991); 506 Morris Dr., Cherry Hill, NJ 08003 (SAN 662-6009) Tel 609-428-3492.

Rondy Pubns, (Rondy Pubns.; 0-9616638), 6704 Cheyenne Trail, Edina, MN 55435 (SAN 659-6800) Tel 612-941-2292.

Ronin Pub, *(Ronin Publishing, Inc.; 0-914171),* Affil. of And/Or Press, Inc., P.O. Box 1035, Main P.O., Berkeley, CA 94701 (SAN 287-5365) Tel 415-540-6278; Dist. by: Baker & Taylor Co., Midwest Div., 501 Gladiola Ave., Momence, IL 60954 (SAN 169-2100); Dist. by: Baker & Taylor Co., Southeast Div., Mt. Olive Rd., Commerce, GA 30529 (SAN 169-1503); Dist. by: Baker & Taylor Co., Eastern Div., 50 Kirby Ave., Somerville, NJ 08876 (SAN 169-4901); Dist. by: Baker & Taylor Co., Western Div., 380 Edison Way, Reno, NV 89564 (SAN 169-4464) Tel 702-786-6700; Dist. by: Ingram Book Company, 347 Reedwood Dr., Nashville, TN 37217 (SAN 651-1163); Dist. by: Publishers Group West, 5855 Beaudry St., Emeryville, CA 94608 (SAN 202-8522) Tel 415-658-3453; Dist. by: Pacific Pipeline, Inc., 19215 66th Ave., S., Kent, WA 98032 (SAN 208-2128) Tel 206-872-5523.

Ronini Ind
See Ronin Pub

Roof Books
See Segue NYC

Rookfield
See Peacehaven

Room to Write, *(Room to Write; 0-938449),* 7851 Lori Dr., Huntington Beach, CA 92648 (SAN 660-9902) Tel 714-841-5315.

Rooney Pubns, *(Rooney Pubns.; 0-9604600),* P.O. Box 44146, Panorama City, CA 91412 (SAN 215-1790) Tel 213-894-2585.

Roosevelt U, *(Roosevelt Univ.),* 430 S. Michigan Ave., Chicago, IL 60605 (SAN 210-3265) Tel 312-341-3808.

Roots Intl, *(Roots International; 0-932019),* 3239 N. 58th St., Milwaukee, WI 53216 (SAN 686-0869) Tel 414-871-7421.

Roper Ctr User, *(Roper Center/International Survey Library Association),* University of Connecticut, Box U-164, Storrs, CT 06268 (SAN 287-2617) Tel 203-486-4440; P.O. Box 440, Storrs, CT 06268-0440 (SAN 680-103X).

Rorge Pub Co, *(Rorge Publishing Co.; 0-914920),* 824 Laramie Ave., Alliance, NE 69301 (SAN 202-9715).

Rosallen Pubns, *(Rosallen Pubns; 0-9607486),* P.O. Box 927, North Hollywood, CA 91603 (SAN 239-605X) Tel 818-766-6045.

Rosario Prod, *(Rosario Productions; 0-9614970),* P.O. Box 563, Eastsound, WA 98245 (SAN 693-4234) Tel 206-376-4787.

Rose Deeprose, *(Rose Deeprose Press; 0-937738),* 1661 Oak St., San Francisco, CA 94117 (SAN 215-3408) Tel 415-552-0991; Dist. by: Subterranean Co., P.O. Box 10233, 1327 W. 2nd, Eugene, OR 97440 (SAN 169-7102) Tel 503-343-6324.

Rose Hill, *(Rose Hill Press; 0-917264),* 12368 Old Pen Mar Rd., Waynesboro, PA 17268 (SAN 208-8312) Tel 717-762-7072.

Rose Petal Creat CA, *(Rose Petal Creations of California; 0-9613996),* 2033 Norris Dr. W., Fresno, CA 93703 (SAN 682-4811) Tel 209-266-1671.

Rose Pr, *(Rose Press),* 1442A Walnut, No. 373, Berkeley, CA 94709 (SAN 240-8767).

Rose Pr NJ, *(Rose Pr.; 0-9616603),* 39 Hamilton Ave., Hasbrouck Heights, NJ 07604 (SAN 659-7661) Tel 201-288-5184.

Rose Pr OR, *(Rose Pr.; 0-9615248),* 6531 SE Ivon St., Portland, OR 97206 (SAN 695-1627) Tel 503-777-1337; Dist. by: Pacific Pipeline, Inc., 19215 66th Ave. S., Kent, WA 98032 (SAN 208-2128) Tel 206-872-5523; Dist. by: Far West Bk. Serv., 3515 NE Hassal, Portland, OR 97232 (SAN 107-6760) Tel 503-234-7664.

Rose Pub, *(Rose Publishing Co., Inc.; 0-914546),* 301 Louisiana, Little Rock, AR 72201 (SAN 203-3739) Tel 501-372-1666.

Rose Pub Co CA, *(Rose Publishing Co.; 0-9603356),* 124 Anderson St., San Francisco, CA 94110 (SAN 207-3188) Tel 415-285-7403; Dist. by: Bookpeople, 2929 Fifth St., Berkeley, CA 94710 (SAN 168-9517).

†**Rose Pub MI,** *(Rose Publishing Co.; 0-937320),* 4676 Morningside Dr., SE, Grand Rapids, MI 49508 (SAN 211-8378) Tel 616-698-8282; *CIP.*

Rose Pubns, *(Rose Pubns.),* 3828 Ben Lomond Ct., Toledo, OH 43607 (SAN 209-5963).

Rose Pubns AZ, *(Rose Publications; 0-914817),* P.O. Box 35033, Tucson, AZ 85740 (SAN 289-3975) Tel 602-297-3606.

Rose Sharon Pr, *(Rose of Sharon Press, Inc.; 0-932502),* G.P.O. Box 2432, New York, NY 10116 (SAN 212-3207) Tel 914-736-2521.

Rose Star, *(Rose Star Creations; 0-936719),* 177 Webster St., Monterey, CA 93946 (SAN 699-8453) Tel 408-646-1288; Box 361, Monterey, CA 93946 (SAN 699-8461).

Rose Strandtmann, *(Rose-Strandtmann Joint Venture; 0-9617102),* 3403 Canyon Rd., Lubbock, TX 79403 (SAN 662-5061) Tel 806-742-2276.

Rosecott Pub, *(Rosecott Publishing; 0-9615940),* 3140 Ave. A, Suite 19, Riviera Beach, FL 33404 (SAN 696-690X) Tel 305-842-7170; Orders to: P.O. Box 9876, Riviera Beach, FL 33404 (SAN 662-3824) Tel 305-842-7170.

Rosegarden Pr, *(Rosegarden Press; 0-9610340),* Box 49084, Austin, TX 78765 (SAN 264-3596) Tel 512-453-7919.

Rosejoy Pubns, *(Rosejoy Pubns.; 0-933453),* P.O. Box 668, Kalamazoo, MI 49005-0668 (SAN 691-828X) Tel 616-344-4016; Orders to: Spring Arbor Distributors, 10885 Textile Rd., Belleville, MI 48111-2398 (SAN 693-5222) Tel 313-483-8462.

Rosemary Hse, *(Rosemary House Press; 0-9613275),* Durrell's Bridge Rd., Kennebunk, ME 04043 (SAN 656-0393) Tel 207-985-4878; Orders to: G. Robert Butler, 109 Main St., Saco, ME 04072 (SAN 662-2321) Tel 207-284-6781.

†**Rosen Group,** *(Rosen Pub. Group; 0-8239),* 29 E. 21st St., New York, NY 10010 (SAN 203-3720) Tel 212-777-3017; *CIP.* Imprints: Pelion Pr (Pelion Press).(Pelion Pr.).

Rosen Pr
See Rosen Group

Rosenbach Found
See Rosenbach Mus & Lib

Rosenbach Mus & Lib, *(Rosenbach Museum & Library, The; 0-939084),* 2010 De Lancey Pl., Philadelphia, PA 19103 (SAN 211-9749) Tel 215-732-1600.

Rosenbaum, *(Rosenbaum, Arthur; 0-9615408),* 17 E. Thompson Ave., Springfield, PA 19064 (SAN 695-5134) Tel 215-544-3206.

Rosenthal Assocs, *(Rosenthal, Daniel, & Assocs., Inc.; 0-9615814),* 251 Lafayette Cir., Suite 310, Lafayette, CA 94549 (SAN 696-5814) Tel 415-283-7051; Orders to: Daniel Rosenthal & Assocs., 268 Greenwood Ave., Bethel, CT 06801 (SAN 662-376X) Tel 203-748-2036.

Roserich Ltd, *(Roserich Designs, Ltd.; 0-913289),* P.O. Box 1030, Carpinteria, CA 93013 (SAN 285-8401) Tel 805-684-6977.

Rosetta *Imprint of* **Plenum Pub**

Rosey-Royce, *(Rosey-Royce Publishing Co.; 0-934138),* 436 W. Ostrander Ave., Syracuse, NY 13205 (SAN 217-2666).

Rosholt Hse, *(Rosholt Hse.; 0-910417),* Box 104, Rosholt, WI 54473 (SAN 260-1249) Tel 715-677-4722.

Ross, *(Ross & Haines Old Books Co.; 0-87018),* 167 N. Snelling Ave., St. Paul, MN 55104 (SAN 204-7004) Tel 612-647-1471.

Ross-Back Roads, *(Ross/Back Rds. Pr.; 0-931272),* P.O. Box 4340, Berkeley, CA 94704 (SAN 211-2000).

†**Ross Bks,** *(Ross Bks.; 0-89496),* P.O. Box 4340, Berkeley, CA 94704 (SAN 209-5912) Tel 415-841-2474; *CIP.*

Ross Ent, *(Ross Enterprises; 0-9613186),* P.O. Box 491308, Los Angeles, CA 90049 (SAN 295-9089) Tel 213-826-7512.

†**Ross-Erikson,** *(Ross-Erikson, Inc.; 0-915520),* 223 Via Sevilla, Santa Barbara, CA 93105 (SAN 208-0494) Tel 805-965-5367; *CIP.*

Ross-Hargreaves, *(Ross-Hargreaves; 0-910690),* Div. of L & M Equipment Co., Inc., P.O. Box 11897, Lahaina, HI 96761 (SAN 204-0247) Tel 808-667-9097.

Ross Pub Co, *(Ross Publishing Co.; 0-9615202),* Rte. 3, 188A-1 Forrester Rd., Slippery Rock, PA 16057 (SAN 694-2903)

Ross St, *(Ross Street Pr.; 0-9615463),* 1310 Ross St., Plymouth, MI 48170 (SAN 695-7137) Tel 313-453-2394.

Ross Valley, *(Ross Valley Book Co., Inc., The; 0-937106),* 1407 Solano Ave., Albany, CA 94706 (SAN 216-4868) Tel 415-526-6400.

†**Rossel Bks,** *(Rossel Bks.; 0-940646),* Div. of Seymour Rossel Co., Inc., 15512 Golden Creek, Dallas, TX 75248 (SAN 213-6414) Tel 214-458-1004; *CIP.*

Rossi Pubns, *(Rossi Pubns.; 0-935618),* P.O. Box 2001, Beverly Hills, CA 90213 (SAN 213-6414) Tel 213-556-0337.

Rostrum Bks, *(Rostrum Books),* P.O. Box 1191, Miami, FL 33101 (SAN 205-227X) Tel 305-573-5900.

Roswell Hist, *(Roswell Historical Society, Inc.; 0-9615854),* 227 S. Atlanta St., Roswell, GA 30075 (SAN 696-7566) Tel 404-922-1665.

Roswell Mus, *(Roswell Museum & Art Ctr.; 0-914983),* 100 W.11th St., Roswell, NM 88201 (SAN 280-3143) Tel 505-622-4700.

Roswell Symphony Guild, *(Roswell Symphony Guild Pubns.; 0-9612466),* P.O. Box 3078, Roswell, NM 88201 (SAN 291-8501).

Rosycross Pr, *(Rosycross Pr.; 0-9070196),* Div. of The Spiritual School of the Golden Rosycross--The Lectorium Rosicrucianum, 709 A St., C-21, Bakersfield, CA 93304-1917 (SAN 659-2104) Tel 805-328-0707; Orders to: P.O. Box 9246, Bakersfield, CA 93389-9246 (SAN 662-4235) Tel 805-327-2827.

Rosywick Pr, *(Rosywick Press; 0-9608712),* 175 W. 12th St., New York, NY 10011 (SAN 238-356X).

Rotary Club, *(Rotary Club of Marquette, Michigan; 0-9609764),* c/o Marquette Area Chamber of Commerce, 501 S. Front Street, Marquette, MI 49855 (SAN 264-3618); Dist. by: Marquette County Historical Society, 213 N. Front St., Marquette, MI 49855 (SAN 205-8871) Tel 906-226-3571.

Rotary Intl, *(Rotary International; 0-915062),* 1600 Ridge Ave., Evanston, IL 60201 (SAN 207-9585) Tel 312-328-0100.

Roth Pub, *(Roth Publishing; 0-87957),* 125 Mineola Ave., Roslyn Hts., NY 11577 (SAN 203-0810) Tel 516-621-7242.

†**Roth Pub Inc,** *(Roth Publishing; 0-89609; 0-8486),* 11 Middle Neck Rd., Great Neck, NY 11021 (SAN 210-9735) Tel 516-466-3676; Toll free: 800-327-0295 (For orders). Acquired Granger Bks., and Core Collection; *CIP.*

Rothbart, *(Rothbart, Janet; 0-9612952),* 2605 S. Seventh St., Minneapolis, MN 55407 (SAN 291-4077) Tel 612-370-0516; P.O. Box 9722, Minneapolis, MN 55440 (SAN 695-6300).

†**Rothman,** *(Rothman, Fred B., & Co.; 0-8377),* 10368 W. Centennial Rd., Littleton, CO 80127 (SAN 159-9437) Tel 303-979-5657; Toll free: 800-457-1986. Acquired Rothman Reprints; *CIP.*

Rothman Repr
See Rothman

Rotunda Bks, *(Rotunda Bks.; 0-9613164),* P.O. Box 1475, Cambridge, MA 02238 (SAN 294-9784) Tel 617-354-2932.

Rotz, *(Rotz, Anna Overcash; 0-9605108),* Box 266, 12182 Main St., Fort Loudon, PA 17224 (SAN 215-9139).

Rough Notes, *(Rough Notes Co., Inc., The; 0-942326),* 1200 N. Meridial St., P.O. Box 564, Indianapolis, IN 46206 (SAN 203-5588) Tel 317-634-1541.

Rough Rock Demonst, *(Rough Rock Demonstration School Board, Inc.),* Star Rte. 1, Rough Rock, AZ 86503 (SAN 686-1644).

Round Oak, *(Round Oak Co.; 0-9616910),* P.O. Box 54, Wayne, MI 48184 (SAN 661-5236) Tel 313-595-1126.

Round River Pub, *(Round River Publishing Co.; 0-933437),* P.O. Box 3324, Madison, WI 53704 (SAN 691-5116) Tel 608-241-4289.

Roundtable Pr, *(Roundtable Pr.; 0-934512),* 4 Linden Sq., Wellesley, MA 02181-4709 (SAN 282-2628) Tel 617-235-5320. Do not confuse with Roundtable Pub., Santa Monica, CA.

Roundtable Pub, *(Roundtable Publishing; 0-9605662; 0-915677),* 933 W. Pico Blvd., Santa Monica, CA 90405 (SAN 237-9260) Tel 213-450-9777. Do not confuse with Roundtable Pub., Wellesley, MA.

Rountree Pub NC, *(Rountree Publishing; 0-934073),* P.O. Box 87, Stokes, NC 27884 (SAN 693-7780) Tel 919-746-2524.

Rouse & Co
See PaineWebber Mortgage

Roush Bks, *(Roush Bks.; 0-934044),* P.O. Box 4203, Valley Village, North Hollywood, CA 91607 (SAN 219-2705).

Routledge & Kegan
See Methuen Inc

Rovan Prod Co, *(Rovan Productions Co.; 0-9615500),* 14878 Lipson Ave., Visalia, CA 93291 (SAN 695-9253) Tel 209-798-1028.

Rovern Pr, *(Rovern Pr.; 0-943150),* 185 Birch St., Willimantic, CT 06226 (SAN 240-7620) Tel 203-423-6387.

Rovi, *(Rovi Pubs., Inc.; 0-911282),* P.O. Box 259, Belvedere, CA 94920 (SAN 204-7020) Tel 415-435-3174.

Roving Pr Pub, *(Roving Pr. Pubns.; 0-910449),* Rte. 5, Box 310, Livingston, TX 77351 (SAN 260-1257) Tel 409-327-8873.

Rowan Tree, *(Rowan Tree Pr., Ltd.; 0-937672),* 124 Chestnut St., Boston, MA 02108 (SAN 214-4638) Tel 617-523-7627; Dist. by: Bookslinger, 213 E. Fourth St., St. Paul, MN 55101 (SAN 169-4154) Tel 612-221-0429; Dist. by: Small Pr. Distribution, 1814 San Pablo Ave., Berkeley, CA 94702 (SAN 204-5826) Tel 415-549-3336; Dist. by: Bookpeople, 2929 Fifth St., Berkeley, CA 94710 (SAN 168-9517); Dist. by: Inland Bk. Co., P.O. Box 261, 22 Hemingway Ave., East Haven, CT 06512 (SAN 200-4151) Tel 203-467-4257.

Rowillan Pub, *(Rowillan Publishing Co.; 0-935237),* 890 W. 20th Ave, Box 2824, Oshkosh, WI 54903 (SAN 695-7110) Tel 414-233-4917.

†**Rowman,** *(Rowman & Littlefield, Pubs.; 0-87471; 0-8476),* Div. of Littlefield, Adams, & Co., 81 Adams Dr., Totowa, NJ 07512 (SAN 203-3704) Tel 201-256-8600; CIP. Imprints: Allanheld & Schram (Allanheld & Schram); Helix Bks (Helix Books); Landmark Studies (Landmark Studies); Rowman & Allanheld (Rowman & Allanheld).

Rowman & Allanheld *Imprint of* **Rowman**

Roxbury Data, *(Roxbury Data Interface; 0-89902),* Box 1100, Verdi, NV 89439 (SAN 212-8659) Tel 702-345-7374.

Roxbury Pub Co, *(Roxbury Publishing Co.; 0-935732),* P.O. Box 491044, Los Angeles, CA 90049 (SAN 213-6422) Tel 213-458-3493.

Roy Freed, *(Freed, Roy N.; 0-9601030),* 50 Winchester St. No. 103, Brookline, MA 02146 (SAN 201-8594) Tel 617-277-6211.

Royal *Imprint of* **Pyramid Pubns**

Royal CBS, *(Royal C. B. S. Publishing; 0-934344),* 18825 Hicrest Rd., P.O. Box 1120, Glendora, CA 91740 (SAN 692-2465).

Royal Court, *(Royal Court Reports, Pubs.; 0-941354),* 3720 NE 28 Ter., Ocala, FL 32670 (SAN 219-8177) Tel 904-351-1855.

Royal Hse, *(Royal Hse. Publishing Co.; 0-930440),* Div. of Recipes-of-the-Month Club, 9465 Wilshire Blvd., Suite 410, Beverly Hills, CA 90212 (SAN 210-9190) Tel 213-550-7170; Toll free: 800-222-3360; P.O. Box 5027, Beverly Hills, CA 90210 (SAN 215-7071).

Royal Lit, *(Royal Literary Publications; 0-918329),* P.O. Box 6794, Laguna Niguel, CA 92677 (SAN 657-3002) Tel 714-495-5049.

Royal Pr, *(Royal Pr.; 0-9616641),* 221 Westminster Rd., Rochester, NY 14607 (SAN 659-6908) Tel 716-473-4816.

Royal Pub
See Lifetime Pr

Royal Pub Co, *(Royal Publishing Co., Inc.),* P.O. Box 2241, Palm Beach, FL 33480 (SAN 226-8299) Tel 305-588-9773.

Royal Pub Co
See Royal Hse

Royal Sceptre
See Golden Sceptre

Royale LA, *(Royale Publishing Co.; 0-9614929),* 444 Fairway Dr., New Orleans, LA 70124 (SAN 693-3610) Tel 504-486-4414.

Royale Pubs, *(Royale Pubs.; 0-9601378),* 9119 Blair River Circle, Fountain Valley, CA 92708 (SAN 211-9757) Tel 714-963-4419.

Royall Pr, *(Royall Pr.; 0-914735),* P.O. Box 9022, San Rafael, CA 94912 (SAN 291-7890) Tel 415-885-1484.

Royalty Pub, *(Royalty Publishing Co.; 0-910487),* P.O. Box 2016, Manassas, VA 22110 (SAN 260-1265) Tel 703-368-9878; Dist. by: Spring Arbor Distributors, 10885 Textile Rd., Belleville, MI 48111 (SAN 158-9016) Tel 313-481-0900; Dist. by: Whitaker House, Pittsburgh & Colfax Sts., Springdale, PA 15144 (SAN 203-2104) Tel 412-274-4440.

RPI Kroll
See RPI Pubns

RPI Pubns, *(R P I Pubns., Inc.; 0-943424),* 521 Fifth Ave., New York, NY 10175 (SAN 240-7566) Tel 212-986-7510.

RPI Schl Arch, *(Rensselaer Polytechnic Institute, Schl. of Architecture; 0-937919),* Rensselaer Polytechnic Institute, Troy, NY 12180-3590 (SAN 659-5332) Tel 518-266-6862.

RRCP, *(Reconstructionist Rabbinical College Pr.; 0-938945),* Church Rd., & Greenwood Ave., Wyncote, PA 19095 (SAN 661-7360) Tel 215-576-0800.

RRN Bks, *(RRN Bks.; 0-9611416),* Div. of Rural Radio Network, Inc., P.O. Box 415, New Palestine, IN 46163 (SAN 283-9849) Tel 317-861-4394.

RRP Pub, *(R.R.P. Pubs.; 0-9607034),* 12 W. 17th St., New York, NY 10011 (SAN 239-0264) Tel 212-924-4127.

RRS *Imprint of* **HM**

RS Pub Co, *(RS Publishing Co.; 0-9614293),* P.O. Box 129, Portland, OR 97207 (SAN 687-4568) Tel 503-223-0123.

RSC Pubs, *(RSC Pubs.; 0-915074),* Div. of Research Services Corp., 3863 SW Loop 820, Suite 100, P.O. Drawer 16489, Ft. Worth, TX 76133-2076 (SAN 238-8294) Tel 817-292-4272.

RSG Pub, *(RSG Publishing; 0-9614858),* P.O. Box 441, Sidney, NY 13838 (SAN 693-0573) Tel 607-563-9000; RD. 3, Box 146A, Bainbridge, NY 13733 (SAN 662-3093) Tel 607-563-9000; Orders to: P.O. Box 441, Sidney, NY 13838-0441 (SAN 662-3107) Tel 607-563-9000.

RSVP Press, *(RSVP Pr.; 0-930865),* P.O. Box 394, Society Hill, SC 29593 (SAN 657-6346).

RTI, *(Relationship Training Institute; 0-935559),* 2036 Pauoa Rd., Honolulu, HI 96813 (SAN 696-0650) Tel 808-523-1752; P.O. Box 27373, Honolulu, HI 96827 (SAN 696-9585).

RtwouSk Inc, *(R2uSK, Inc.; 0-9616894),* P.O. Box 2504, University, AL 35486 (SAN 661-5910); 165 N. 22nd St., Tuscaloosa, AL 35406 (SAN 661-5929) Tel 205-348-1526.

Rubber Division, *(American Chemical Society, Inc., Rubber Div.; 0-912415),* Univ. of Akron, Akron, OH 44325 (SAN 265-1726).

Ruben Pub, *(Ruben Publishing; 0-917434),* P.O. Box 414, Avon, CT 06001 (SAN 208-9645) Tel 203-673-0740.

Rubes Pubns, *(Rubes Pubns.; 0-943384; 0-941364),* 14447 Titus St., Panorama City, CA 91402 (SAN 240-7647) Tel 818-782-0800; Dist. by: Alfred Publishing Co., Inc., 15335 Morrison St., Sherman Oaks, CA 91413 (SAN 201-243X) Tel 818-995-8811.

Rubicon, *(Rubicon; 0-938124),* 5 Old Chimney Rd., Huntsville, AL 35801 (SAN 215-658X) Tel 205-534-6844.

Rubicon Bks, *(Rubicon Bks.; 0-913791),* P.O. Box 37103, Phoenix, AZ 85069 (SAN 286-1895) Tel 602-978-0546.

Rubio-Boitel, *(Rubio-Boitel, Fr. Fernando),* Our Lady of Belen Church,10th and Church Sts., Belen, NM 87002 (SAN 212-5528) Tel 505-865-4455.

Ruborge Pubs
See PVC Co

Rucker & Rylander, *(Rucker, Ellie, & Carole Rylander; 0-9615692),* 166 E. Riverside, Austin, TX 78704 (SAN 696-0472) Tel 512-445-3695.

Rudolph Johnson, *(Johnson, Rudolph, Training & Development, Inc.; 0-937221),* 1004 State St., Bowling Green, KY 42101 (SAN 658-7437) Tel 502-781-1915.

Rudra Pr, *(Rudra Pr.; 0-915801),* P.O. Box 1973, Cambridge, MA 02238 (SAN 294-1260) Tel 617-576-3394.

Rue Morgue, *(Rue Morgue Pr.; 0-915230),* P.O. Box 4119, Boulder, CO 80306 (SAN 207-737X) Tel 303-443-8346.

†**Ruffled Feathers,** *(Ruffled Feathers Publishing Co.; 0-9603582),* 2725 Juniper St.,, Boulder, CO 80302-2464 (SAN 213-7917); CIP.

Rufio Ent, *(Rufio Enterprises; 0-9612658),* 7 E. 14th St., New York, NY 10003 (SAN 289-3983) Tel 212-929-7498.

Rugging Rm, *(Rugging Room, The; 0-9611554),* Ten Sawmill Dr., Westford, MA 01886 (SAN 284-9372) Tel 617-692-8600.

Ruggles Pub, *(Ruggles Publishing Co.; 0-915909),* 960 Pomelo Ave., Sarasota, FL 33577 (SAN 294-0841) Tel 813-951-0493.

Rules Serv Co, *(Rules Service Co.),* 7658 Standish Pl., Suite 106, Rockville, MD 20855 (SAN 227-0455) Tel 301-424-9402.

Rulorca, *(Rulorca Press; 0-917613),* P.O. Box 235, Half Moon Bay, CA 94019-0235 (SAN 657-1603) Tel 415-726-4214.

Rumar Ent, *(Rumar Enterprises; 0-913907),* 18700 Sherman Way No. 203, Reseda, CA 91335 (SAN 286-8717) Tel 818-609-1987.

Rumbleseat, *(Rumbleseat Pr., Inc.; 0-913444),* Affil. of Green Valley World, Inc., 41 S. Ocean Blvd., Cayucos, CA 93430 (SAN 205-6437) Tel 805-995-1378.

Runaway Pubns, *(Runaway Pubns.; 0-943662),* P.O. Box 1172, Ashland, OR 97520-0040 (SAN 238-3608) Tel 503-482-2578.

Runner's Log, *(Runner's Log; 0-933872),* 10-50 Jackson Ave., Long Island City, NY 11101 (SAN 216-2970).

†**Running Pr,** *(Running Pr. Bk. Pubs.; 0-89471),* 125 S. 22nd St., Philadelphia, PA 19103 (SAN 204-5702) Tel 215-567-5080; Toll free: 800-428-1111; CIP.

Runyon Pub, *(Runyon Publishing Co.; 0-936699),* Div. of Runyon Institute, Inc., 15 Alden Ave., Warrensburg, NY 12885 (SAN 699-9301) Tel 518-623-3930.

Rural America, *(Rural America),* 1312 18th St. NW, Washington, DC 20036 (SAN 225-946X) Tel 202-659-2800.

Rural Educ, *(Rural Education Assn.),* Colorado State Univ., 300 Education Bldg., Ft. Collins, CO 80523 (SAN 207-3269) Tel 303-491-7022.

Rural Life, *(Rural Life),* Rte. 1, Box 183-C, Whitewater, WI 53190 (SAN 206-6769).

†**Rush Assoc,** *(Rush, James E., Assoc., Inc.; 0-912803),* 2223 Carriage Rd., Powell, OH 43065-9703 (SAN 200-2744); CIP.

Rush-Presby-St Lukes, *(Rush-Presbyterian-St. Luke's Medical Center, Dept. of Preventive Medicine; 0-941516),* 1743 W. Harrison St., Tenth Floor, Chicago, IL 60612 (SAN 219-094X).

Rushlight Club, *(Rushlight Club; 0-917422),* Old Academy Library, 150 Main St., Wethersfield, CT 06109 (SAN 207-4958) Tel 203-529-7656.

Russel & King, *(Russel & King; 0-9615280),* P.O. Box 18227, Cleveland Heights, OH 44118 (SAN 694-4051) Tel 216-932-0817.

Russell, *(Russell & Russell Pubs.; 0-8462),* Div. of Atheneum Pubs., 115 Fifth Ave., New York, NY 10003 (SAN 282-2644) Tel 212-614-1315; Orders to: Scribner Book Co., Front & Brown Sts., Burlington County, Riverside, NJ 08075 (SAN 201-002X).

Russell Pr, *(Russell Pr.; 0-918377),* P.O. Box 67, Sharon Hill, PA 19079 (SAN 657-3762) Tel 215-583-4550.

Russell Pubns, *(Russell Pubns.; 0-933558),* P.O. Box 2461, Tampa, FL 33601 (SAN 210-5764) Tel 813-879-8580. Do Not Confuse with Russell & Russell in NY (Russell).

Russell Sage, *(Russell Sage Foundation; 0-87154),* 112 E. 64th St., New York, NY 10021 (SAN 203-3674) Tel 212-750-6000; Toll free: 800-242-7737; Orders to: Basic Bks., Inc., 10 E. 53rd St., New York, NY 10022 (SAN 201-4521).

Russian Hill, *(Russian Hill Hse. Bks.; 0-9608968),* P.O. Box 157, San Francisco, CA 94101 (SAN 282-2709) Tel 415-931-7249; Dist. by: Publishers Group West, 5855 Beaudry St., Emeryville, CA 94608 (SAN 202-8522) Tel 415-658-3453; Dist. by: Bookpeople, 2929 Flfth St., Berkeley, CA 94710 (SAN 168-9517); Dist. by: L-S, 480 Ninth St., San Francisco, CA 94103 (SAN 169-0213) Tel 415-771-0330.

Russian Numis, *(Russian Numismatic Society; 0-912671),* P.O. Box 3013, Alexandria, VA 22302 (SAN 277-7053) Tel 703-920-2043.

Russian Orthodox Ch, *(Russian Orthodox Church of The Nativity of Christ; 0-9617062),* 251 E. Front St., Erie, PA 16507 (SAN 662-9423) Tel 814-454-8618.

Russian Rev, *(Russian Review; 0-918444),* 1737 Cambridge St., Cambridge, MA 02138 (SAN 210-0002) Tel 617-495-4007.

†Russian River, *(Russian River Writers' Guild; 0-930489),* 378 Grand Ave., Suite 304, Oakland, CA 94610 (SAN 670-8978) Tel 415-444-6063; *CIP.*

Russica Bk Art
  See Russica Pubs

Russica Pubs, *(Russica Pubs.; 0-89830),* c/o Russica Book & Art Co., 799 Broadway, New York, NY 10003 (SAN 212-310X).

Rustler Print & Pub, *(Rustler Printing & Publishing; 0-930535),* 2420 Shevidan Ave, Cody, WY 82414 (SAN 682-8647).

Rutgers Ctr Alcohol, *(Rutgers Ctr. of Alcohol Studies Pubns.; 0-911290),* Smithers Hall, Rutgers Univ., New Brunswick, NJ 08903 (SAN 203-3658) Tel 201-932-3510; Orders to: Rutgers Ctr. of Alcohol Studies, Business Office, P.O. Box 969, Piscataway, NJ 08854 (SAN 203-3666) Tel 201-932-2190.

Rutgers PR Studies, *(Rutgers Univ., Puerto Rican Studies; 0-9615805),* Rutgers Univ., Newark College of Arts & Sciences, Newark, NJ 07102 (SAN 696-6284) Tel 201-648-5538.

†Rutgers U Pr, *(Rutgers Univ. Pr.; 0-8135),* 109 Church St., New Brunswick, NJ 08901 (SAN 203-364X) Tel 201-932-7764; Orders to: R.U.P. Distribution Ctr., P.O. Box 4869, Baltimore, MD 21211 (SAN 662-1325) Tel 303-338-6974; *CIP.*

Rutgers U SICLS, *(Rutgers Univ., Schl. of Information, Communication & Library Studies),* 4 Huntington St., New Brunswick, NJ 08903 (SAN 205-9738) Tel 201-932-7362.

Rutgers U SLIS
  See Rutgers U SICLS

Rutgers U SLS
  See Rutgers U SICLS

Rutledge Bks
  See Sammis Pub

†Rutledge Hill Pr, *(Rutledge Hill Pr.; 0-934395),* P.O. Box 140483, Nashville, TN 37214 (SAN 693-8116) Tel 615-292-7322; *CIP.*

Rutledge Pr *Imprint of* **Smith Pubs**

Ruwanga Trad, *(Ruwanga Trading; 0-9615102),* P.O. Box 1027, Puunene, HI 96784 (SAN 694-2776) Tel 808-572-8115; Dist. by: Pacific Trade Group, P.O. Box 668, Pearl City, HI 96782-0668 (SAN 169-1635) Tel 808-261-6594.

RV Indus Assn, *(Recreation Vehicle Industry Assn.),* P.O. Box 2999, 1896 Preston White Dr., Reston, VA 22090 (SAN 231-3928) Tel 703-620-6003.

RVer Annie, *(RVer Annie & Co.; 0-9613607),* 150 E. 93 St., New York, NY 10128 (SAN 670-7009) Tel 212-831-4159; Orders to: RVer Annie, Wolcott, VT 05680 (SAN 662-2461) Tel 802-888-2880.

RWS Bks, *(RWS Books; 0-939400),* 4296 Mulholland St., Salt Lake City, UT 84124 (SAN 220-1593) Tel 801-272-7835.

RWU Parachuting Pubns, *(RWU Parachuting Pubns.),* 1656 Beechwood Ave., Fullerton, CA 92635 (SAN 209-1879) Tel 714-990-0369.

RWunderground
  See RWU Parachuting Pubns

Ryan Co, *(Ryan Co.; 0-914202),* 2188 Latimer Lane, Los Angeles, CA 90024 (SAN 202-9707) Tel 213-474-4175.

Ryan Research, *(Ryan Research Intl.; 0-942158),* 1593 Filbert Ave., Chico, CA 95926 (SAN 239-9776) Tel 916-343-2373.

Rydal, *(Rydal Pr., The; 0-911292),* Div. of Great Southwest Bks., The, 960 Camino Santander, Santa Fe, NM 87501 (SAN 204-7098) Tel 505-983-1680.

Ryder Geo, *(Ryder Geosystems; 0-941784),* 6061 South Willow Dr., Suite 330, Englewood, CO 80111 (SAN 239-3042) Tel 303-740-8824; Toll free: 800-LANDSAT.

Ryder Pr, *(Ryder Press; 0-916816),* 3307 Chadbourne Rd., Shaker Heights, OH 44120 (SAN 208-8339) Tel 216-921-7975.

Ryder Pub Co, *(Ryder Publishing Co.; 0-935973),* 1914 N. Little Rib Cir., Wausau, WI 54401 (SAN 696-5822) Tel 715-675-6568.

Rye Hist Soc, *(Rye Historical Society; 0-9615327),* 1 Purchase St., Rye, NY 10580 (SAN 695-0663) Tel 914-967-7588.

Rymer Bks, *(Rymer Bks.; 0-9600792; 0-934723),* P.O. Box 104, Tollhouse, CA 93667 (SAN 207-1010) Tel 209-298-0761; 22249 E. Tollhouse, Clovis, CA 93612 (SAN 699-5586).

Rynd Comm, *(Rynd Communications; 0-932500),* 99 Painters Mill Rd., Owings Mills, MD 21117 (SAN 699-766X) Tel 301-363-6400; Toll free: 800-446-2221.

Ryukyu Philatelic, *(Ryukyu Philatelic Specialist Society, Ltd.),* P.O. Box 15368, Plantation, FL 33318-5368 (SAN 225-6037).

S-A Design Bks, *(S-A Design Books),* 515 W. Lambert, Bldg. E, Brea, CA 92621-3991 (SAN 670-736X).

S A Shopen, *(Shopen, Sylvia Ames),* Norwich, VT 05055 (SAN 212-7024).

S A Ward, *(Ward, S. Alexander; 0-939189),* 2801 NE 183rd St., No. 1416, North Miami Beach, FL 33160 (SAN 662-5282) Tel 305-935-5583.

S Akhtar, *(Akhtar, Salman; 0-9615818),* 1015 Chestnut St. 2nd Flr., Philadelphia, PA 19107 (SAN 696-6705) Tel 215-928-8420.

S & F Clark Art, *(Clark, Sterling & Francine, Art Institute; 0-931102),* P.O. Box 8, Williamstown, MA 01267 (SAN 222-8491).

S & S Pr TX
  See TX S & S Pr

S & S Pubs Inc, *(S & S Publishing, Inc.; 0-9614426),* P.O. Box 998, Greenville, NC 27834 (SAN 689-0822) Tel 919-758-4093.

S Andacht, *(Andacht, Sandra, Pub.; 0-9607616),* P.O. Box 94, Little Neck, NY 11363 (SAN 238-6402) Tel 718-229-6593.

S Aronson
  See Talmud Pr

S B Bove, *(Bove, Susan Barber; 0-9611720),* 3344 Rte. 89, Seneca Falls, NY 13148 (SAN 284-9151) Tel 315-549-7152.

S B Newman, *(Newman, S. B., Printing Co.; 0-942268),* 104 Commerce Ave., Knoxville, TN 37902 (SAN 238-8081).

S Balassanian, *(Balassanian, Sonia; 0-9608388),* 81 Murray St., New York, NY 10007 (SAN 240-5172) Tel 212-732-3598.

S Betzina, *(Betzina, Sandra; 0-9615614),* 95 Fifth Ave., San Francisco, CA 94118 (SAN 696-1010) Tel 415-221-7736; Dist. by: Bookpeople, 2929 Fifth St., Berkeley, CA 94710 (SAN 168-9517) Tel 415-549-3030.

S Breeland, *(Breeland, Samuel; 0-9615422),* 7842 Playa del Rey Cir., Jacksonville, FL 32216 (SAN 696-141X) Tel 904-731-3754.

S Butte Pr, *(Spencer Butte Pr.; 0-9609420),* 84889 Harry Taylor Rd., Eugene, OR 97405 (SAN 262-916X) Tel 503-345-3962.

S C Blaffer Found, *(Blaffer, Sarah Campbell, Foundation; 0-9615615),* 2001 Kirby Dr., Suite 913, Houston, TX 77019 (SAN 696-1142) Tel 713-528-5279.

S C M A R
  See SCMAR

S C Toof, *(S.C. Toof & Co.),* P.O. Box 14607, Memphis, TN 38114 (SAN 289-5498).

S CA Committee, *(Southern California Committee for the Olympic Games; 0-9606628),* 515 Lillian Way, Los Angeles, CA 90004 (SAN 219-6387) Tel 213-465-1669; John C. Argue, 801 S. Flower St., Los Angeles, CA 90017-4699 (SAN 685-3609) Tel 213-622-3100.

S Campbell, *(Campbell, Sandy M.; 0-917366),* 230 Central Park S., New York, NY 10019 (SAN 204-7128) Tel 212-582-6286.

S Carmel, *(Carmel, Simon J.; 0-9600886),* 10500 Rockville Pike, Apt. 1028, Rockville, MD 20852 (SAN 209-536X).

S Carver
  See Carves

S Cudinach
  See Piarist Father

S D Beckman, *(Beckman, Steven D.; 0-9609434),* 621 Palm Ave., Lodi, CA 95240 (SAN 284-9755) Tel 209-369-3903.

S Davis Pub, *(Davis, Steve, Publishing; 0-911061),* P.O. Box 190831, Dallas, TX 75219 (SAN 262-8422) Tel 214-821-8821.

S Deal Assoc, *(Deal, S., Associates; 0-930006),* 1629 Guizot St., San Diego, CA 92107 (SAN 210-4105) Tel 619-226-1731.

S Duyvil, *(Spuyten Duyvil),* 817 West End Ave., No. 4-A, New York, NY 10025 (SAN 237-9481) Tel 212-666-3648.

S E Mattox, *(Mattox, S. E., Corp.; 0-918070),* P.O. Box 431, San Pedro, CA 90733 (SAN 209-6722) Tel 213-832-0306.

S E Ward, *(S. E. Ward; 0-9613595),* 45-180-39, Mahalani Place, Kaneohe, HI 96744 (SAN 677-1475) Tel 808-247-3874.

S Eller, *(Eller, Sylvia; 0-9617012),* 727 E. Orange Grove, No. G, Pasadena, CA 91104 (SAN 662-8656) Tel 818-791-3258.

S F Kelley, *(Kelley, Sarah F., Pub.; 0-9615960),* 567 Whispering Hills Dr., Nashville, TN 37211 (SAN 697-2772) Tel 615-833-4219.

S F Knapp, *(Knapp, Susan F.; 0-9610610),* P.O. Box 140, Sewickley, PA 15143 (SAN 264-1550) Tel 412-935-0503.

S F Learnard, *(Learnard, Stephen F., The Awareness Techniques Ctr.; 0-934258),* P.O. Box 338, 15 Queens Ln., Stow, MA 01775 (SAN 212-8640) Tel 617-562-2154.

S F Love, *(Love, Stephen F.; 0-9613239),* P.O. Box 1069, Lake Oswego, OR 97034 (SAN 295-5083) Tel 503-635-7239.

S F Temmer, *(Temmer, Stephen F., Publishing Co.; 0-9617200),* 767 Greenwich St., New York, NY 10014-2111 (SAN 663-3986) Tel 212-741-7418.

S F Vanni, *(Vanni, S. F.; 0-913298),* 30 W. 12th St., New York, NY 10011 (SAN 220-0031) Tel 212-675-6336.

S Ford & Assoc, *(Ford, Sondra, & Assoc.; 0-913043),* 478 Hamilton Ave., No.173, Campbell, CA 95008 (SAN 283-0809) Tel 408-446-1351.

S Foster Fin, *(Foster, Steven, Financial Pubns.; 0-930567),* 6520 Selma Ave., Suite 332, Los Angeles, CA 90028 (SAN 695-6017).

S Fox, *(Fox, Sanford; 0-9603854),* 41-41 Christine Court, Fairlawn, NJ 07410 (SAN 214-0152).

†S G Phillips, *(Phillips, S. G., Inc.; 0-87599),* P.O. Box 83, Chatham, NY 12037 (SAN 293-3152) Tel 518-392-3068; c/o M & B Fulfillment Service, Inc., 540 Barnum Ave., Bridgeport, CT 06608 (SAN 293-3160) Tel 203-366-1900; *CIP.*

S G Phillips
  See S G Phillips

S Ganek, *(Ganek, Selene; 0-9616186),* 758 Strawberry Hill Dr., Glencoe, IL 60022 (SAN 658-3385) Tel 312-835-0830; Dist. by: Baker & Taylor (Midwest Div.), 501 Gladiola Ave., Momence, IL 60954 (SAN 169-2100).

S Gibbons, *(Gibbons, Stanley, Inc.; 0-85259),* 124 Charlotte Ave., Hicksville, NY 11801 (SAN 213-3784) Tel 516-935-9490.

S Gilbert, *(Gilbert, Skeet; 0-9600548),* Fuquay-Varina, NC 27526 (SAN 204-7144) Tel 919-552-4623.

S H Nelson, *(Nelson, Scott H.; 0-9616436),* 270 Spanglers Mill Rd., New Cumberland, PA 17070 (SAN 658-9855) Tel 717-774-6019.

S H Park, *(Park, S. H.; 0-9604440),* P.O. Box 7474, Trenton, NJ 08628 (SAN 215-1685) Tel 609-883-3551.

S H Stone, *(Stone, Sarah Howard, Inc.; 0-937773),* Rte. 2, Box 315, Old Selma Rd., Montgomery, AL 36108 (SAN 659-3445) Tel 205-262-7154.

S Heisler, *(Heisler, Suzanne; 0-9617054),* P.O. Box 212, Menlo Park, CA 94025 (SAN 662-9318); 800 Roble Ave., Menlo Park, CA 94025 (SAN 662-9326) Tel 415-323-2716.

S Ho, *(Ho, Steve; 0-9609018),* 4295 Okemos Rd., P.O. Box 99, Okemos, MI 48864 (SAN 241-5372) Tel 517-349-0795.

S Holmes Enter, *(Holmes, Stacey, Enterprises; 0-910681),* 6520 Selma Ave., Box 556, Hollywood, CA 90028 (SAN 264-0996).

S Houston Corrections, *(Houston, Sam, State Univ., Institute on Contemporary Corrections & the Behavioral Sciences),* Huntsville, TX 77340 (SAN 226-3726).

S Houston Employ, *(Houston, Sam, State Univ., National Employment Listing Service),* Texas Criminal Justice Ctr., Huntsville, TX 77340 (SAN 226-3688).

S Hurt, *(Hurt, Sam; 0-9611660),* 1209 Newning Ave., Austin, TX 78704 (SAN 285-3213) Tel 512-473-2296; Dist. by: AAR/Tantalus Inc., 1600 Rio Grande, Suite 203, Austin, TX 78701 (SAN 281-2371) Tel 512-476-3225.

†S Ill U Pr, *(Southern Illinois Univ. Pr.; 0-8093),* P.O. Box 3697, Carbondale, IL 62901-3697 (SAN 203-3623) Tel 618-453-2281; *CIP.*

S J Brooks, *(Brooks, Stanley J., Co.; 0-941806),* 1416 Westwood Blvd. Suite 201, Los Angeles, CA 90024 (SAN 213-7275) Tel 213-470-2849.

S J Durst, *(Durst, Sanford J.; 0-915262; 0-942666),* 29-28 41st Ave., Long Island City, NY 11101 (SAN 211-6987) Tel 718-706-0303.

S J F Co, *(SJF Co; 0-9614185),* 1471 Treasure Ln., Santa Ana, CA 92705 (SAN 676-9411) Tel 714-669-8034.

S J Shrubsole, *(Shrubsole, S. J., Corp.; 0-9616646),* 104 E. 57th St., New York, NY 10022 (SAN 659-770X) Tel 212-753-8920.

S Jersey Dining, *(South Jersey Dining Guide; 0-9612852),* 300 Grace Ave., Mays Landing, NJ 08330 (SAN 290-0491) Tel 609-625-7433.

S Judd Pubs, *(Spencer Judd, Pubs.; 0-911805),* Six University Ave., Sewanee, TN 37375 (SAN 264-4045) Tel 615-598-5353.

S K Abbey, *(Abbey, Stella K.),* 2840 80th St., NE, Bellevue, WA 98004 (SAN 204-7152).

S K Freshman, *(Freshman, Samuel K.; 0-9600708),* 700 S. Flower St., Suite 2600, Los Angeles, CA 90017 (SAN 206-5266) Tel 213-629-1100.

S K Shim Pub, *(Shim, Sang Kyu, Publisher; 0-942062),* 17625 W. 7 Mile, Detroit, MI 48235 (SAN 238-5929).

S K Thomas, *(Thomas, Susan K.; 0-9613660),* P.O. Box 58202, Renton, WA 98057 (SAN 670-7777) Tel 206-235-0899.

S Karger, *(Karger, S., AG; 3-8055),* 79 Fifth Ave., New York, NY 10003 (SAN 281-8531) Tel 212-924-9222.

S L Miller, *(Miller, Sandra Lake; 0-9609448),* 69 River Dr., Ormond Beach, FL 32075-2851 (SAN 262-8236) Tel 904-441-8987.

S Locke, *(Locke, Sue Hennigan; 0-9615585),* Box 206, Marthaville, LA 71450 (SAN 695-9067) Tel 318-472-6808.

S M Derrick, *(Derrick, Sara M.; 0-89279),* 1323 Johnson St., Sandusky, OH 44870 (SAN 283-9881).

S M P F Inc, *(Scientific Medical Pubns. of France),* 16 E. 34th St., 7th Flr., New York, NY 10016 (SAN 689-8998) Tel 212-683-4441.

S M S Pub, *(SMS Publishing Corp.; 0-914985),* P.O. Box 2276, Glenview, IL 60025 (SAN 289-4025) Tel 312-724-1427.

S M S U, *(Southwest Missouri State Univ., Dept. of English; 0-913785),* 901 S. National, Springfield, MO 65804 (SAN 286-1992) Tel 417-836-5107.

S Meth U Pr
See SMU Press

S Meyer Assocs, *(Meyer, Sandy, & Assocs.; 0-9613431),* P.O. Box 13652, Roanoke, VA 24036 (SAN 657-0143) Tel 703-344-7903; 400 S. Beverly Dr., Suite 214, Beverly Hills, CA 90212 (SAN 662-2348); Dist. by: Bookpeople, 2929 Fifth St., Berkeley, CA 94710 (SAN 168-9517) Tel 415-549-3030.

S N F Fin, *(SNF Financial; 0-9614300),* P.O. Box 82275, San Diego, CA 92138 (SAN 687-486X) Tel 619-295-2490.

S O L E Pubns, *(S.O.L.E. Pubns.; 0-9608626),* P.O. Box 2063, Beaverton, OR 97075 (SAN 238-3624).

S O S, *(SOS),* Box 7100, Warwick, RI 02887 (SAN 655-1424) Tel 401-739-1269.

S O S Books, *(Sultan of Swat/S.O.S. Books; 0-911809),* 1821 Kalorama Rd., NW, Washington, DC 20009 (SAN 264-4193) Tel 202-638-1956.

S O S Pubns, *(Save on Shopping),* P.O. Box 10482, Jacksonville, FL 32207 (SAN 204-7160) Tel 904-733-8877; Dist. by: Random House, 201 E. 50th St., New York, NY 10022 (SAN 202-554X) Tel 212-872-8036.

S O S Pubs, *(S.O.S. Pubs.; 0-930867),* 21777 Ventura Blvd., Suite 210, Woodland Hills, CA 91364 (SAN 677-8097) Tel 818-704-0145.

S Ohio Genealog, *(Southern Ohio Genealogical Society; 0-941000),* P.O. Box 414, Hillsboro, OH 45133 (SAN 219-6395) Tel 513-393-2452.

S Owen Pub, *(Owen, Stephen, Pub.; 0-9614830),* 5520 20th Ave., Meridian, MS 39301 (SAN 693-059X) Tel 601-483-7643; Dist. by: Southeastern Printing Co., 215 22nd Ave., Meridian, MS 39301 (SAN 200-5484).

S P Levine, *(Levine, Samuel P.; 0-9602906),* 42367 Cosmic Dr., Temecula, CA 92309 (SAN 213-1056) Tel 714-676-3976.

S P Richards, *(Richards, S. P.; 0-9608224),* Box 501, New Providence, NJ 07974 (SAN 240-1193).

S P Sill Pub, *(Sill, Stephen P., Publishing Co.; 0-9615806),* P.O. Box 1334, San Andreas, CA 95249 (SAN 696-589X) Tel 802-885-3671; Dist. by: Bible & Bk. Room, 100 River St., Springfield, VT 05156 (SAN 200-593X).

S R Abbott Mini, *(Abbott, Stanley R.; 0-915545),* Div. of Word International, P.O. Box 54975, Tulsa, OK 74155 (SAN 291-0586) Tel 918-455-2111.

†S R Guggenheim, *(Guggenheim, Solomon R., Museum; 0-89207),* 1071 Fifth Ave., New York, NY 10128 (SAN 205-3152) Tel 212-360-3573; *CIP.*

S R Herrold, *(Herrold, Stephen & Rebecca),* 1530 Montalban Dr., San Jose, CA 95120 (SAN 676-3502).

S R S Co, *(SRS Co.; 0-9610766),* No. 160, 2554 Lincoln Blvd., Marina del Rey, CA 90291 (SAN 264-634X) Tel 213-397-2600; Dist. by: Hal Leonard Pub. Corp., 8112 W. Bluemound Rd., Milwaukee, WI 53212 (SAN 239-250X) Tel 414-774-3630.

S Ramsey, *(Ramsey, Sylvia),* 6614 Whitewing, Corpus Christi, TX 78413 (SAN 696-2262).

S Regional Ed, *(Southern Regional Education Board),* 1340 Spring St. NW, Atlanta, GA 30309 (SAN 206-1783) Tel 404-875-9211.

S Res Inst, *(Southern Research Institute; 0-940824),* 2000 Ninth Ave., S., Birmingham, AL 35255 (SAN 206-1791) Tel 205-323-6592.

S Roberts & Assocs, *(Roberts, Sam, & Assocs.; 0-9615473),* 12243 Shorewood Dr., SW, Seattle, WA 98146 (SAN 696-2211) Tel 206-243-1234.

S Rusch, *(Rusch, Shari; 0-9615922),* 15421 61st Pl. NE, Bothell, WA 98011 (SAN 696-7582) Tel 206-488-7842; P.O. Box 82627, Kenmore, WA 98028 (SAN 699-6434).

S S Howe, *(Howe, Shirley Swift; 0-9616538),* 39617 CR 669, Decatur, MI 49045 (SAN 659-4662).

S S Hykes, *(Hykes, Susan S.; 0-9608894),* P.O. Box 713, Kilauea, HI 96754 (SAN 241-1202) Tel 808-828-1619.

S S J Pubns, *(S S J Publications; 0-914465),* P.O. Box 3165 Arlington Sta., Poughkeepsie, NY 12603 (SAN 289-6753) Tel 914-433-3652.

S S Juka, *(Juka, S. S.; 0-9613601),* 110 Terrace View Ave., New York, NY 10463 (SAN 670-7394); Dist. by: Baker & Taylor, 1515 Broadway, New York, NY 10036 (SAN 169-5606) Tel 212-730-7650.

S S Ross
See Sidney Scott Ross

S S S Pub Co, *(Smith, Smith & Smith Publishing Co.; 0-913626),* 17515 SW Blue Heron Rd., Lake Oswego, OR 97034 (SAN 203-3607) Tel 503-636-2979.

S Salem News, *(South Salem News; 0-9610326),* 5330 Commercial SE, Salem, OR 97306 (SAN 264-4002) Tel 503-363-1539.

S Shanelle, *(Shanelle, Sally; 0-9616642),* 3636 Camino del Rio N., Suite 110, San Diego, CA 92108 (SAN 659-6797) Tel 619-282-8864; Dist. by: Publishers West, 4535 30th St., No. 212, San Diego, CA 92116 (SAN 200-674X).

S Singh, *(Singh, Swayam; 0-935380),* 2311 Meadow Croft Dr., Lansing, MI 48912 (SAN 213-5914).

S Sobredo Tech Serv, *(Sobredo, Sergio, Technical Services; 0-9616888),* 11507 SW 34th Ln., Miami, FL 33165 (SAN 661-6410) Tel 305-221-1271.

S Soza Enters, *(Soza, Shari, Enterprises; 0-931711),* 349 N. Oregon St., P.O. Box 81, Yreka, CA 96097 (SAN 682-627X) Tel 916-842-2367.

S Stafford, *(Stafford, Shirley; 0-9607580),* 4231 Casa De Machado, La Mesa, CA 92041 (SAN 239-9806).

S Stein Prods, *(Stein, Shifra, Productions/Stein Pr.; 0-9609752),* 3733 Pennsylvania; P.O. Box 5862, Kansas City, MO 64111 (SAN 263-2284).

S Taylor & Friends, *(Taylor, Sally, & Friends; 0-9604904; 0-934101),* 1442 Willard St., San Francisco, CA 94117 (SAN 216-1990) Tel 415-824-1563; Dist. by: Bookpeople, 2929 Fifth St., Berkeley, CA 94710 (SAN 168-9517) Tel 415-549-3030; Dist. by: Publishers Group West, 5855 Beaudry St., Emeryville, CA 94608 (SAN 202-8522) Tel 415-658-3453; Dist. by: The Wine Appreciation Guild, 1377 Ninth Ave., San Francisco, CA 94107 (SAN 282-5546).

S Tract Advert, *(Tract, Sam, Advertising; 0-930579),* 505 Worcester Rd., Framingham, MA 01701 (SAN 694-5368).

S Troyanovich, *(Troyanovich, Steve),* Dist. by: Spring Church Book Co., P.O. Box 127, Spring Church, PA 15686 (SAN 212-7075).

S Van Vliet, *(Van Vliet, Sherrie),* E.C.S. P.O. Box 7000-37, Palos Verdes, CA 90274 (SAN 697-0141).

S Volin, *(Volin, Stan; 0-9600922),* 19 Steven St., Plainview, NY 11803 (SAN 207-7469) Tel 516-681-6040; Orders to: Box 571-B, Hicksville, NY 11802 (SAN 207-7477).

S W Ivosevic, *(Ivosevic, Stanley W.; 0-9611352),* 449 Wright St., Suite 2, Denver, CO 80228 (SAN 283-2267) Tel 303-988-6050.

S Wright, *(Wright, Stuart, Pub./Palaemon Pr., Ltd.; 0-913773),* P.O. Box 7527, Reynolda Sta., Winston-Salem, NC 27109 (SAN 293-4582); 2100 Faculty Dr., Winston-Salem, NC 27106 (SAN 293-4590) Tel 919-725-5985; Dist. by: Small Press Distribution, Inc., 1814 San Pablo Ave., Berkeley, CA 94702 (SAN 204-5826) Tel 415-549-3336.

S Y C Ho
See S Ho

S Yates, *(Yates, Samuel; 0-9608652),* 157 Capri-D, Kings Point, Delray Beach, FL 33445 (SAN 238-4213) Tel 305-499-0323.

S Yonay, *(Yonay, Shahar; 0-9616783),* 126 Dover St., Brooklyn, NY 11235 (SAN 661-0544) Tel 718-615-0027.

SAA Pub, *(SAA Publishing; 0-937922),* P.O. Box 117, Northport, MI 49670 (SAN 240-9194).

Sabayt Pubns, *(Sabayt Pubns.; 0-9616649),* 5441 S. Kenwood Ave., Chicago, IL 60615 (SAN 659-6940) Tel 312-667-2227.

Sabbagh Manage, *(Sabbagh Management Corp.; 0-912369),* 3310 45th St., NW, Washington, DC 20016 (SAN 265-0991) Tel 202-966-2651.

Sabbot-Natural Hist Bks, *(Sabbot, Rudolph William, Natural History Bks.),* 5239 Tendilla Ave., Woodland Hills, CA 91364 (SAN 213-2583) Tel 818-346-7164.

Sabio Pub, *(Sabio Publishing Co.; 0-9617050),* P.O. Box 9296, Santa Fe, NM 87501 (SAN 662-6408); 38 Vuelta Sabio, La Tierra, Santa Fe, NM 87501 (SAN 662-6416) Tel 505-988-4300.

Sachem Pr, *(Sachem Pr.; 0-937584),* P.O. Box 9, Old Chatham, NY 12136 (SAN 215-6075) Tel 518-794-8327.

Saco River Pub, *(Saco River Publishing Co.; 0-9607522),* P.O. Box 685, North Conway, NH 03860 (SAN 238-6178) Tel 603-356-5091.

Sacred Dance Guild, *(Sacred Dance Guild),* Pacific Schl. of Religion, 1798 Scenic Ave., Berkeley, CA 94709 (SAN 225-3054); Dist. by: Sharing Co., P.O. Box 2224, Austin, TX 78768-2224 (SAN 211-0563) Tel 512-452-4366.

Sacred Heart Convent, *(Sacred Heart Convent of Houston, Texas; 0-9617020),* 6501 Almeda Rd., Houston, TX 77021 (SAN 662-6564) Tel 713-747-3310.

Sacred Music Pr, *(Sacred Music Press, The; 0-937021),* 501 E. Third St., Dayton, OH 45401 (SAN 692-7475) Tel 513-228-6118.

Sacrum Pr, *(Sacrum Pr.; 0-937543),* P.O. Box 3044, W. Durham Sta., Durham, NC 27705 (SAN 659-1329) Tel 919-684-3325; 8 Chancery Pl., Durham, NC 27707 (SAN 659-1337).

Saddle River Day, *(Saddle River Day School Parents Guild; 0-9612374),* 147 Chestnut Ridge Rd., Saddle River, NJ 07458 (SAN 289-551X) Tel 201-327-4050.

Saddle Sore, *(Saddle Sore Pubns.; 0-9612660),* 2381 S. 2000 W., Syracuse, UT 84041 (SAN 289-405X) Tel 801-825-9303.

Saddlebag Bks, *(Saddlebag Bks.; 0-936457),* 210 S. Fourth St., Basin, WY 82410 (SAN 698-0295) Tel 307-568-3800; Box 48, Basin, WY 82410 (SAN 698-2433).

Sadlier, *(Sadlier, William H., Inc.; 0-8215),* 11 Park Place, New York, NY 10007 (SAN 204-0948) Tel 212-227-2120; Toll free: 800-221-5175.

Sadtler Res, *(Sadtler Research Laboratories, Inc.; 0-8456),* 3316 Spring Garden St., Philadelphia, PA 19104 (SAN 203-0063) Tel 215-382-7800.

SAE
See Soc Auto Engineers

Saeta, *(Saeta Ediciones; 0-917049),* 7642 SW 96th Ct., Miami, FL 33173 (SAN 655-2226) Tel 305-596-4097; Orders to: Saeta Ediciones, P.O. Box 440156, Miami, FL 33144-0156 (SAN 662-2305) Tel 305-596-4097.

Safari Mus Pr
See Safari Museum Pr

Safari Museum Pr, *(Safari Museum Pr.),* 16 S. Grant Ave., Chanute, KS 66720 (SAN 218-9364) Tel 314-431-2730.

Safe Harbor Pr, *(Safe Harbor Press; 0-913221),* West Ave. J, P.O. Box 4345, Lancaster, CA 93534 (SAN 283-9040).

Safety Now, *(Safety Now Co., Inc.; 0-917066),* P.O. Box 567, Jenkintown, PA 19046 (SAN 208-8355) Tel 215-884-0210.

SAG Pubns, *(SAG Pubns.; 0-9616105),* 662 Granville Dr., Winter Park, FL 32789 (SAN 698-1194) Tel 305-647-4292; P.O. Box 2186, Winter Park, FL 32790 (SAN 698-2581).

Sag Rising, *(Sagittarius Rising; 0-933620),* P.O. Box 252, Arlington, MA 02174 (SAN 282-2741) Tel 617-646-2692.

Sagamore, *(Sagamore Institute; 0-913393),* Sagamore Rd., Raquette Lake, NY 13436 (SAN 285-8444) Tel 315-354-5311.

Sagamore Bks
See Gibbs M Smith

Sagamore Bks MI, *(Sagamore Bks., Inc.),* P.O. Box 195, Grand Rapids, MI 49588 (SAN 699-8038) Tel 616-455-8530.

†Sagapr, *(Sagapress, Inc.; 0-89831),* Rte. 100, Millwood, NY 10546 (SAN 295-9100) Tel 914-762-2200; Dist. by: Kraus Reprint, Route 100, Millwood, NY 10546 (SAN 217-4979) Tel 914-762-2200; *CIP.*

†Sage, *(Sage Pubns., Inc.; 0-8039),* 275 S. Beverly Dr., Beverly Hills, CA 90212 (SAN 204-7217) Tel 213-274-8003; *CIP.*

Sage Oregon, *(Sage Publishing Co., Inc.; 0-937485),* 9510 Butte Falls Hwy., Eagle Point, OR 97524 (SAN 659-1353) Tel 503-772-9973; P.O. Box 2349, White City, OR 97503 (SAN 659-1361).

Sage Pr, *(Sage Pr.; 0-9615725),* 1450 E. Peoria Ave., Phoenix, AZ 85020 (SAN 696-1487) Tel 602-943-9875.

Sagebrush Pr, *(Sagebrush Pr.; 0-930704),* P.O. Box 87, Morongo Valley, CA 92256 (SAN 211-4496).

Saguaro, *(Saguaro Publishing; 0-9608864),* 1302 E. Becker Lane, Phoenix, AZ 85020 (SAN 241-0761).

Saguaro Pr, *(Saguaro Pr.; 0-935561),* 9270 E. Mission Ln., Suite 101, Scottsdale, AZ 85258 (SAN 696-1851) Tel 602-998-0824.

Sai Systems, *(Sai Systems; 0-930869),* 4000 Albermarle St., Suite 310, Washington, DC 20016 (SAN 677-8054) Tel 202-363-1903.

Saifer, *(Saifer, Albert, Pub.; 0-87556),* P.O. Box 239 W.O.B., West Orange, NJ 07052 (SAN 204-7225).

Saiga, *(Saiga Publishing Co., Ltd.; 0-86230),* 51 Washington St., Dover, NH 03820 (SAN 656-8777); Dist. by: Longwood Publishing Group, 21 Washington St., Dover, NH 03820 (SAN 209-3170).

†Sail Bks, *(Sail Bks., Inc.; 0-914814),* 34 Commercial Wharf, Boston, MA 02110 (SAN 207-0820); *CIP.*

Sail Sale Pub, *(Sail Sales Publishing; 0-943798),* P.O. Box 1028, Aptos, CA 95001 (SAN 241-077X) Tel 408-662-2456.

Sakura-Dragon Corp, *(Sakura/Dragon Corp.; 0-86568),* c/o Unique Publications, 4201 Vanowen Pl., Burbank, CA 91505 (SAN 214-3313) Tel 818-845-2656.

Sakura Press, *(Sakura Pr.; 0-936845),* 36787 Sakura Ln., Pleasant Hill, OR 97455 (SAN 658-3350) Tel 503-747-5817.

Sal Magundi Ent, *(Sal Magundi Enterprises; 0-9609024),* 12960 SW Carmel St., Portland, OR 97224 (SAN 241-2470) Tel 503-684-3972; Dist. by: Douglas County Museum, P.O. Box 1559, Roseburg, OR 97470 (SAN 200-819X)

SALALM, *(Seminar on the Acquisition of Latin American Library Materials; 0-917617),* Univ. of Wisconsin Madison, Memorial Library, Madison, WI 53706 (SAN 657-1638) Tel 608-262-3240.

Salamander Pr, *(Salamander Press; 0-912708),* P.O. Box 153, Carmel, CA 93921 (SAN 204-7233).

†Salem Pr, *(Salem Pr., Inc.; 0-89356),* P.O. Box 1097, Englewood Cliffs, NJ 07632 (SAN 208-838X) Tel 201-871-3700; Toll free: 800-221-1592; *CIP.*

Salem Pub, *(Salem Publishing Co.; 0-939475),* P.O. Box 25448, Winston Salem, NC 27114 (SAN 663-2467); 514 S. Stratford Rd., Winston Salem, NC 27103 (SAN 663-2475) Tel 919-724-2778.

Sales Execs Club, *(Sales Executives Club of New York, The),* 114 E. 32nd St., Suite 1301, New York, NY 10016 (SAN 224-9472) Tel 212-683-9755.

Sales Success, *(Sales Success Press; 0-9613319),* 425 Vista Flora Suite 777, Newport Beach, CA 92660 (SAN 656-1721) Tel 714-542-7777; Toll free: 800-772-1172.

Salesiana *Imprint of Don Bosco Multimedia*

Salesmans, *(Salesman's Guide, Inc.; 0-87228),* 1140 Broadway, New York, NY 10001 (SAN 203-3593) Tel 212-684-2985; Toll free: 800-223-1797.

Sallyforth, *(Sallyforth, Inc.; 0-939413),* 2611 Garden Rd., Monterey, CA 93940 Tel 408-375-4474.

Salome Pubns
See Ommation Pr

Salt Resc, *(Salt Resources, Inc.; 0-9616562),* 427 Lynn Ave., Winston-Salem, NC 27104 (SAN 659-5839) Tel 919-725-1750.

Salt Warrior Pr, *(Salt Warrior Pr.; 0-9611028; 0-931857),* 3800 S. Tamiami Trail, Sarasota, FL 33579 (SAN 289-5536) Tel 813-951-0473.

Salt-Works Pr, *(Salt-Works Pr.; 0-938535),* RFD 1, P.O. Box 141, Grenada, MS 38901 (SAN 209-7672); Rte. 404, Hardin Rd., Grenada, MS 38901 (SAN 660-9430); Dist. by: Small Pr. Distribution, 1814 San Pablo Ave., Berkeley, CA 94702 (SAN 204-5826) Tel 415-549-3336.

Saltillo Pr, *(Saltillo Press; 0-913473),* 607 Gregory, El Paso, TX 79902 (SAN 285-1865) Tel 915-532-3564.

Salv Army Suppl South, *(Salvation Army Supplies, Southern; 0-86544),* 1424 NE Expressway, Atlanta, GA 30329 (SAN 211-9765) Tel 404-321-7870.

Salvation Army, *(Salvation Army; 0-89216),* 120 W. 14th St., New York, NY 10011 (SAN 237-2649) Tel 212-337-7435; Orders to: 145 W. 15th St., New York, NY 10011 (SAN 662-1341).

Salvation Suppl
See Salv Army Suppl South

Salyer, *(Salyer Publishing Co.; 0-911298),* 3111 19th St., NW, Oklahoma City, OK 73107 (SAN 204-725X).

Samara Pubns, *(Samara Pubns.; 0-935513),* 15505 SE Arista Dr., Milwaukie, OR 97267 (SAN 695-8923) Tel 503-659-1067; Dist. by: Western States Bk. Service, P.O. Box 855, Clackamas, OR 97015 (SAN 200-5662).

†SamHar Pr, *(SamHar Pr.; 0-85157),* Div. of Story House Corp., Bindery Ln., Charlotteville, NY 12036 (SAN 203-3585) Tel 607-397-8725; *CIP.*

Samisdat, *(Samisdat),* Box 129, Richford, VT 05476 (SAN 207-8929) Tel 514-263-4439.

Samisdat *Imprint of Noontide*

Samizdat, *(Samizdat; 0-9613814),* 700 New Hampshire Ave., NW, Suite 701, Washington, DC 20027 (SAN 682-0298).

†Sammis Pub, *(Sammis Publishing; 0-87469),* 122 E. 25th St., New York, NY 10010 (SAN 208-4503) Tel 212-598-6976; Dist. by: M.A.G.I.C., Inc., 1950 Craig Rd., St. Louis, MO 63146 (SAN 202-5191); Dist. by: Kampmann & Co., 9 E. 40th St., New York, NY 10016 (SAN 200-2639) Tel 212-685-2928; Dist. by: Crown Publishers, 225 Park Ave., S., New York, NY 10003 (SAN 662-1333) Tel 212-254-1600; *CIP.*

Sampson Bowers, *(Bowers, Sampson; 0-916448),* P.O. Box 731, Carmel Valley, CA 93924 (SAN 208-4058).

Sams, *(Sams, Howard W., & Co.; 0-672),* Div. of Macmillan, Inc., 4300 W. 62nd St., Indianapolis, IN 46268 (SAN 203-3577) Tel 317-298-5400; Toll free: 800-428-3602.

Samson Pubs
See Samson Pubs

Samson Pubs, *(Samson Pubs.; 0-935985),* Div. of Light Pubns., 1437 40th St., Brooklyn, NY 11218 (SAN 695-5533) Tel 718-871-7265; P.O.Box 719, Midwood Sta., Brooklyn, NY 11230 (SAN 699-6078) Tel 718-435-1434.

Samuel P Co, *(Powell, Samuel, Pub. Co.; 0-910021),* 2201 I St., Sacramento, CA 95816 (SAN 219-2756) Tel 916-443-1161.

San Anselmo Pub, *(San Anselmo Publishing Co.; 0-943264),* P.O. Box 2299, Norman, OK 73070 (SAN 240-5644) Tel 405-275-2415.

San Antonio Art, *(San Antonio Art Institute; 0-9614862),* 6000 N. New Braunfels, P.O. Box 6092, San Antonio, TX 78209 (SAN 693-2819) Tel 512-824-0531.

San Antonio Jr Forum, *(San Antonio Junior Forum Pubns.; 0-9616917),* 418 W. French, San Antonio, TX 78212 (SAN 661-5414) Tel 512-735-8345; P.O. Box 16372, San Antonio, TX 78216 (SAN 661-5422).

San Die Cooking, *(San Diego's Cooking; 0-9617211),* P.O. Box 86244, San Diego, CA 92138 (SAN 663-2750); 219 Chesterfield Dr. Ste. A, Cardiff, CA 92007 (SAN 663-2769) Tel 619-753-6069.

San Diego Art Ctr, *(San Diego Art Ctr.; 0-939003),* P.O. Box 126458, San Diego, CA 92112 (SAN 662-5428) Tel 619-232-5722.

San Diego Hist, *(San Diego Historical Society; 0-918740),* P.O. Box 81825, San Diego, CA 92138 (SAN 210-5438) Tel 619-297-3258.

San Diego Pub Co, *(San Diego Publishing Co.; 0-912495),* P.O. Box 9222, San Diego, CA 92109-0060 (SAN 265-1971) Tel 619-295-9190.

San Diego Soc Nat Hist, *(San Diego Society of Natural History; 0-918969),* P.O. Box 1390, San Diego, CA 92112 (SAN 669-9618) Tel 619-232-3821.

San Diego St Univ Pr
See SDSU Press

†San Fran MOMA, *(San Francisco Museum of Modern Art; 0-928471),* 401 Van Ness Ave., San Francisco, CA 94102-4582 (SAN 218-9445) Tel 415-863-8800; *CIP.*

San Francisciana, *(San Francisciana; 0-934715),* P.O. Box 590955, San Francisco, CA 94159 (SAN 694-1613) Tel 916-363-3547.

San Francisco Pr, *(San Francisco Press, Inc.; 0-911302),* Box 6800, San Francisco, CA 94101-6800 (SAN 207-4990) Tel 415-524-1000.

San Jacinto, *(San Jacinto Publishing Co.; 0-911982),* P.O. Box. 66254, Houston, TX 77006 (SAN 694-3209) Tel 713-845-1436; c/o Texas A&M Univ. Pr., Drawer "C", College Station, TX 77843 (SAN 207-5237) Tel 409-845-1436.

San Jose Face, *(San Jose Face; 0-932161),* 475 S. 12th St., San Jose, CA 95112 (SAN 686-4678).

San Jose His Mus Assn, *(San Jose Historical Museum Assn.; 0-914139),* 635 Phelan Ave., San Jose, CA 95112 (SAN 287-5470) Tel 408-287-2290.

San Juan County, *(San Juan County Bk. Co.; 0-9608000),* P.O. Box 1, Silverton, CO 81433 (SAN 238-5775) Tel 303-387-5477.

†San Luis Quest, *(San Luis Quest Pr.; 0-935320),* Box 998, San Luis Obispo, CA 93406 (SAN 213-4306) Tel 805-543-8500; *CIP.*

San Marcos, *(San Marcos Pr.; 0-88235),* 4705 Marquette NE, Albuquerque, NM 87108 (SAN 206-3751) Tel 505-266-4412. Out of business.

San Marcos Bk, *(San Marco Bookstore; 0-935259),* 1971 San Marco Blvd., Jacksonville, FL 32207 (SAN 693-3734) Tel 904-396-7597; Dist. by: Morningside Bookshop, P.O. Box 1087, Dayton, OH 45401 (SAN 202-2206) Tel 513-461-6738.

San Pedro Hist, *(San Pedro Bay Historical Society; 0-9611556),* P.O. Box 1568, San Pedro, CA 90733 (SAN 285-1377) Tel 213-548-3208; 1159 Amar St., San Pedro, CA 90732 (SAN 285-1385) Tel 213-833-2872.

Sanatana, *(Sanatana Publishing Society; 0-933116),* 503 Pope St., Menlo Park, CA 94025 (SAN 212-7946) Tel 415-326-4232.

Sanchin Pub, *(Sanchin Publishing Co.; 0-934999),* 7210 Shawnee Way, Colorado Springs, CO 80915 (SAN 695-6033) Tel 303-596-7552.

Sanctuary Pr, *(Sanctuary Pr.; 0-935971),* P.O. Box 90159, San Jose, CA 95112 (SAN 696-5830) Tel 408-287-8210; 85 S. 12th St., San Jose, CA 95112 (SAN 699-6353).

Sand Dollar, *(Sand Dollar Press),* Landscape Station, P. O. Box 7400, Berkeley, CA 94707 (SAN 203-2686) Tel 415-527-1931.

Sand Pond, *(Sand Pond Pubs.; 0-915209),* P.O. Box 405, Shady Ln., Hancock, NH 03449 (SAN 203-0713) Tel 603-525-6615.

S&A Pubns
See S&A Pubns Inc
S&A Pubns Inc, *(S & A Pubns.; 0-9600768),* P.O. Box 2660, Sta. "A", Champaign, IL 61820 (SAN 204-7101) Tel 217-359-4222.

Sandbar, *(Sandbar Willow Pr.; 0-9615711),* 123 Sewall Ave., 1E, Brookline, MA 02146 (SAN 695-8419) Tel 617-739-2890; P.O. Box 883, Brookline, MA 02146 (SAN 696-9534).

Sandbird Pub, *(Sandbird Publishing Group, The; 0-9615111),* P.O. Box 1257, Shalimar, FL 32579 (SAN 694-1540) Tel 904-862-3746.

Sandcrab, *(Sandcrab Press; 0-9609870),* P.O. Box 1479, Corpus Cristi, TX 78403 (SAN 264-3685) Tel 512-852-5359; Dist. by: Publishers' Marketing Group, 1104 Summit Ave., Plainview, TX 75074 (SAN 262-0995) Tel 214-423-0312.

S&F Clark Art
See S & F Clark Art
Sandhills Pr, *(Sandhills Pr., Inc.; 0-911015),* 219 S. 19th St., Ord, NE 68862 (SAN 275-2050).

S&J Books, *(S & J Bks.; 0-9609608),* 387 Ocean Pkwy., Brooklyn, NY 11218 (SAN 260-2598) Tel 718-941-1833.

S&K Assocs, *(Stein & Kolber Assocs.; 0-936565),* 633 Edison Dr., East Windsor, NJ 08520 (SAN 697-7561) Tel 609-443-4513.

†**Sandlapper Pub Co,** *(Sandlapper Publishing Co., Inc.; 0-87844),* P.O. Box 1932, Orangeburg, SC 29116 (SAN 203-2678) Tel 803-531-1658; *CIP.*

Sandness, *(Sandness, Robert C.; 0-9614076),* 321 Beaumont, Las Vegas, NV 89106 (SAN 685-9712) Tel 702-382-3796.

Sandollar Pr, *(Sandollar Press),* P.O. Box 4157, Santa Barbara, CA 93140-4157 (SAN 202-9952) Tel 805-963-7077.

Sandpiper *Imprint of* HM
Sandpiper CA, *(Sandpiper Press; 0-940356),* P.O.Box 128, Solana Beach, CA 92075 (SAN 217-5657) Tel 619-481-5259.

Sandpiper MI, *(Sandpiper Pr.; 0-9614518),* 22023 Trombly, St. Clair Shores, MI 48080 (SAN 689-5921) Tel 313-773-3427.

Sandpiper OR, *(Sandpiper Pr.; 0-9603748),* P.O. Box 286, Brookings, OR 97415 (SAN 213-5582) Tel 503-469-5588.

Sandrock & Foster, *(Sandrock & Foster),* Memorial Foundation, Box 841, Winona, MN 55987 (SAN 210-9514) Tel 507-452-1859.

Sandscape Pr, *(Sandscape Pr.; 0-936721),* 1647 Willow Pass Rd., Suite 300, Concord, CA 94520 (SAN 699-8445) Tel 415-682-5327.

Sandspur Pr, *(Sandspur Pr.; 0-932837),* P.O. Box 6011, Gulf Breeze, FL 32561 (SAN 688-606X) Tel 904-932-4725.

Sandstone Bks *Imprint of* Ohio St U Pr
Sandstone Pr *Imprint of* Beil
Sangamon Pub Aff, *(Sangamon State Univ., Office of Public Affairs Communication; 0-938943),* Sangamon State Univ., Springfield, IL 62708 (SAN 661-7344) Tel 217-786-6502.

Sangamon St U, *(Sangamon State Univ.),* Shepherd Rd., Springfield, IL 62708 (SAN 226-2215) Tel 217-786-6600.

Sanguinaria, *(Sanguinaria Publishing; 0-9605210),* 85 Ferris St., Bridgeport, CT 06605 (SAN 215-806X) Tel 203-576-9168.

Sangwyne, *(Sangwyne; 0-938387),* 4548 Commonwealth, Detroit, MI 48208 (SAN 659-8781) Tel 313-832-5490.

Sankaty Head, *(Sankaty Head Press; 0-9606626),* Box 18, Siasconset, MA 02564 (SAN 223-114X).

Sansper, *(Sansper; 0-916865),* 134 Broadway, Costa Mesa, CA 92627 (SAN 654-5297) Tel 714-631-7273.

Sant Bani Ash, *(Sant Bani Ashram, Inc.; 0-89142),* Franklin, NH 03235 (SAN 209-5114) Tel 603-934-2948.

Santa Barb Botanic, *(Santa Barbara Botanic Garden; 0-916436),* 1212 Mission Canyon Rd., Santa Barbara, CA 93105 (SAN 208-8398) Tel 805-682-4726.

Santa Barb Life Ed, *(Santa Barbara Pro Life Education; 0-9609902),* P.O. Box 30815, Santa Barbara, CA 93130 (SAN 262-9992).

Santa Barb Mus Art, *(Santa Barbara Museum of Art; 0-89951),* 1130 State St., Santa Barbara, CA 93101 (SAN 130-8165) Tel 805-963-4364; Dist. by: Univ. of Wash. Pr., P.O. Box C50096, Seattle, WA 98145 (SAN 212-2502) Tel 206-543-8870.

†**Santa Barb Pr,** *(Santa Barbara Pr.; 0-915643),* 1129 State St., Suite H, Santa Barbara, CA 93101 (SAN 292-6431) Tel 805-966-2060; Dist. by: Publishers Group West, 5855 Beaudry St., Emeryville, CA 94608 (SAN 202-8522) Tel 415-658-3453; *CIP.*

Santa Barb Pro
See Santa Barb Life Ed
Santa Barbara Pr
See Santa Barb Pr
Santa Catalina, *(Santa Catalina Publishing; 0-9612300),* Santa Catalina Schl., Mark Thomas Dr., Monterey, CA 93940 (SAN 289-5552) Tel 408-649-1432.

Santa Fe Botanical, *(Santa Fe Botanical Research & Education Project; 0-9616460),* P.O. Box 9459, Santa Fe, NM 87504-9459 (SAN 659-2961) Tel 505-988-4723; 825 Calle Mejia, Apt. 134, Santa Fe, NM 87504 (SAN 659-297X).

Santa Fe Comm Sch, *(Santa Fe Community School),* P.O. Box 87504-2241, Santa Fe, NM 87504 (SAN 211-5743) Tel 505-471-6928.

Santa Fe E Gallery, *(Santa Fe East Gallery Pubns.; 0-86534),* 200 Old Santa Fe Trail, Santa Fe, NM 87501 (SAN 239-3824) Tel 505-988-3103.

Santa Fe Photo, *(Santa Fe Ctr. For Photography; 0-9615298),* 104 W. San Francisco St., Santa Fe, NM 87501 (SAN 694-4663) Tel 505-988-4363.

Santa Monica Pub, *(Santa Monica Publishing Co.; 0-917640),* 414 Camino de las Animas, Santa Fe, NM 87501 (SAN 209-3855) Tel 505-983-4138.

†**Santarasa Pubns,** *(Santarasa Pubns.; 0-935548),* P.O. Box 825, Manford, OK 74044 (SAN 213-7925); *CIP.*

Santiago Pr, *(Santiago Press, Inc.; 0-940470),* 3616 Hyde Park, Midland, TX 79703 (SAN 219-0958).

Santiam Bks, *(Santiam Books; 0-9609936),* 744 Mader Ave. SE, Salem, OR 97302 (SAN 263-0001) Tel 503-362-7471.

Santillana, *(Santillana Publishing Co.; 0-88272),* 257 Union St., Northvale, NJ 07647 (SAN 205-1133) Tel 201-767-6961; Toll free: 800-526-0107.

Santo Tomas Pr, *(Santo Tomas Pr., The; 0-930541),* P.O. Box 8, Sahuarita, AZ 85629 (SAN 687-6285).

Santos Santos Pubns, *(Santos-Santos Pubns.; 0-9616484),* 4815 E. River Rd., Tucson, AZ 85718 (SAN 659-3399) Tel 602-577-2078.

Saphrograph, *(Saphrograph Corp.; 0-87557),* 4910 Ft. Hamilton Pkwy., Brooklyn, NY 11219 (SAN 204-7276) Tel 718-331-1233.

Sara Pubns, *(Sara Publications; 0-9613096),* 603 SE Third St., Cochran, GA 31014 (SAN 294-6572) Tel 912-934-4794.

Sarasota Opera, *(Sarasota Opera Society, The; 0-9605844),* Subs. of Sarasota Opera Association, Inc., 4573 Northlake Dr., Sarasota, FL 33582 (SAN 216-3012) Tel 813-371-2408; 61 N. Pineapple St., Sarasota, FL 33582 (SAN 650-0579).

Sarasota Sci, *(Sarasota Scientific Pr.; 0-9614464),* P.O. Box 25604, Sarasota, FL 34277 (SAN 689-433X) Tel 813-922-0604.

Sarasvati, *(Sarasvati; 0-9615026),* P.O. Box 306, Brookline, MA 02146 (SAN 694-0595) Tel 617-734-2939.

Sarcastic, *(Sarcastic Toys; 0-916437),* Div. of Massen's Fabrics, P.O. Box 2448, Yountville, CA 94599 (SAN 295-9143) Tel 707-253-1100.

Sargent
See Porter Sargent
Sarmen Bk Co, *(Sarmen Book Co.; 0-9610394),* 87 Eileen St., Yarmouth Port, MA 02675 (SAN 283-2550) Tel 617-362-3518.

Sarmen Bks
See Sarmen Bk Co
SarSan Pub, *(SarSan Pub Co; 0-940336),* Box 984, Brawley, CA 92227 (SAN 217-5665) Tel 714-344-9593.

Sarsaparilla, *(Sarsaparilla; 0-930281),* 62 W. Huron, Chicago, IL 60610 (SAN 676-9810).

Saru, *(Saru; 0-935086),* P.O. Box 1067, Sedona, AZ 86336 (SAN 687-6293).

SAS Inst, *(SAS Institute, Inc.; 0-917382; 1-55544),* Box 8000, SAS Cir., Cary, NC 27511 (SAN 208-8347) Tel 919-467-8000.

Sasco, *(Sasco Associates; 0-912980),* P.O. Box 335, Southport, CT 06490 (SAN 204-7284).

Sasquatch Pub, *(Sasquatch Publishing Co.; 0-912365),* 1931 Second Ave., Seattle, WA 98101 (SAN 289-0208) Tel 206-441-5555; Dist. by: Pacific Pipeline, 19215 66th Ave. S., Kent, WA 98032 (SAN 208-2128) Tel 206-872-5523.

Sassafras MS, *(Sassafras Pr., The; 0-9609692),* C/O Mijo Lithographing Co., Inc., P.O. Box 1104, Yazoo City, MS 39194 (SAN 662-135X) Tel 601-746-4693; c/o Mijo Lithographing Co., Inc., P.O. Box 1104, Yazoo City, MS 39194 (SAN 282-275X) Tel 601-746-4693.

Sassafras Pr, *(Sassafras Pr.; 0-930528),* P.O. Box 1366, Evanston, IL 60204 (SAN 214-4662) Tel 312-670-5000.

Sassy Sayings, *(Sassy Sayings Co.; 0-9615347),* P.O. Box 1851, North Little Rock, AR 72115 (SAN 695-1481) Tel 501-753-4971; 4019 Mellene, North Little Rock, AR 72118 (SAN 695-149X); Dist. by: PMG International, 1343 Columbia, No. 405, Richardson, TX 75081 (SAN 200-4739).

Sassy Sayin's
See Sassy Sayings
Sat Eve Post
See Curtis Pub Co
Satchells Pub, *(Satchell's Publishing; 0-931841),* 3124 Fifth Ave., Richmond, VA 23222 (SAN 685-9704) Tel 804-329-2130; Orders to: Adam Pr., 30 W. Washington St., Chicago, IL 60602 (SAN 662-2658) Tel 312-676-3426.

Satellite, *(Satellite World; 0-910419),* P.O. Box 74874, Los Angeles, CA 90004 (SAN 260-1303) Tel 213-669-1984.

Satellite Cont, *(Satellite Continuing Education Inc.; 0-9609184),* 706 Second Ave., Charles City, IA 50616 (SAN 241-4503) Tel 515-228-5558.

Satori Pr, *(Satori Pr.; 0-9617268),* 904 Silver Spur Rd., No. 324, Rolling Hills Estates, CA 90274 (SAN 663-5377); 2668 Via Olivera P. V., Rolling Hills Estates, CA 90274 (SAN 663-5385) Tel 213-377-7810.

Satori Pubns, *(Satori Pubns.; 0-931937),* P.O. Box 1019, San Rafael, CA 94915-1019 (SAN 685-9690) Tel 415-955-6317.

Satori Resources, *(Satori Resources; 0-937277),* 732 Hamlin Way, San Leandro, CA 94578 (SAN 659-140X) Tel 415-895-8614; Dist. by: New Leaf Distributing, The, 1020 White St., SW, Atlanta, GA 30310 (SAN 169-1449); Dist. by: Bookpeople, 2929 Fifth St., Berkeley, CA 94710 (SAN 168-9517).

†**Saturday Pr,** *(Saturday Pr., Inc.; 0-938158),* P.O. Box 884, Upper Montclair, NJ 07043 (SAN 207-5792) Tel 201-256-1731; *CIP.*

Saturscent Pubns, *(Saturscent Pubns.; 0-934703),* Box 358, South Wellfleet, MA 02663 (SAN 694-2687) Tel 617-349-2921.

Saucerian
See G Barker Bks
†**Saugus Hist,** *(Saugus Historical Society; 0-936363),* 59 Water St., Saugus, MA 01906 (SAN 698-0317) Tel 617-242-5680; *CIP.*

Sauk, *(Sauk Valley),* Irish Hills, Brooklyn, MI 49230 (SAN 209-5122) Tel 517-467-2061.

Sauna Soc, *(Sauna Society of America),* 1001 Connecticut Ave., Washington, DC 20036 (SAN 224-6333) Tel 202-331-1365; Dist. by: Commercial Assocs., Inc., 1001 Connecticut Ave., Washington, DC 20036 (SAN 224-6341) Tel 202-331-1363.

†Saunders, *(Saunders, W. B., Co.; 0-7216),* Subs. of Columbia Broadcasting System, W. Washington Sq., Philadelphia, PA 19105 (SAN 203-266X) Tel 215-574-4808; *CIP. Imprints:* Bailliere-Tindall (Bailliere-Tindall).

Saurian Pr, *(Saurian Press; 0-936830),* New Mexico Tech, Socorro, NM 87801 (SAN 215-1065) Tel 505-835-5445.

Sauvie Island, *(Sauvie Island Press; 0-9606752),* 14745 NW Gillihan Rd., Portland, OR 97231 (SAN 219-6344) Tel 503-621-3357.

Savadove Prod, *(Savadove Productions, Inc.; 0-938707),* 7420 Franklin Ave., Los Angeles, CA 90046 (SAN 661-5651) Tel 213-851-8400.

Savage
See Hughley Pubns

Savannah Jr Aux, *(Savannah Junior Auxiliary, The; 0-939114),* P.O. Box 434, Savannah, TN 38372 (SAN 262-0758).

Savoyard *Imprint of* **Wayne St U Pr**

Sawan Kirpal Pubns, *(Sawan Kirpal Pubns.; 0-918224),* 115 S. "O" St., Lake Worth, FL 33460 (SAN 211-0571) Tel 804-633-5789; Orders to: Rte. 1, Box 24, Bowling Green, VA 22427 (SAN 211-058X).

Say When Pr, *(Say When Pr.; 0-9615174),* P.O. Box 942, Greenbelt, MD 20770 (SAN 694-2873) Tel 301-474-0352.

Saybrook Pr, *(Saybrook Pr.; 0-917941),* 146 Elm St., P.O. Box 629, Old Saybrook, CT 06475 (SAN 657-0186) Tel 203-388-5737.

Saybrook Pub Co, *(Saybrook Publishing Co., Inc.; 0-933071),* 4223 Cole Ave., Suite 4, Dallas, TX 75205 (SAN 689-7924) Tel 214-521-2375; Dist. by: W. W. Norton Co., 500 Fifth Ave., New York, NY 10110 (SAN 202-5795) Tel 212-354-5500.

Saylor, *(Saylor, Lee, Inc.; 0-931708),* 1855 Olympic Blvd., Walnut Creek, CA 94596 (SAN 211-5751).

SBA Coven, *(Coven, Susan B. Anthony; 0-937081),* P.O. Box 11363, Oakland, CA 94611 (SAN 658-4551) Tel 415-444-7724; 2927 Harrison St., Oakland, CA 94611 (SAN 658-456X).

SBD
See Small Pr Dist

SBS Pub, *(SBS Publishing, Inc.; 0-89961),* 50 Railroad Ave., Closter, NJ 07624 (SAN 213-3695) Tel 201-767-9450; Toll free: 800-631-2564.

SC Bar CLE, *(South Carolina Bar Continuing Legal Education Committee; 0-943856),* P.O. Box 11039, Columbia, SC 29211 (SAN 226-4137) Tel 803-799-6653.

SC Sea Grant, *(South Carolina Sea Grant Consortium; 0-933005),* 287 Meeting St., Charleston, SC 29401 (SAN 689-1535) Tel 803-727-2078.

Scala Books, *(Scala Bks.; 0-935748),* 1035 Fifth Ave., New York, NY 10028 (SAN 282-2784) Tel 212-737-0242; Toll free: 800-242-7737; Orders to: Harper & Row Pubs., Inc., Keystone Industrial Pk., Scranton, PA 18512 (SAN 215-3742).

Scale Mfrs, *(Scale Manufacturers Association),* 152 Rollins Ave., Suite 208, Rockville, MD 20852 (SAN 224-9812) Tel 301-984-9080.

Scand Philatelic, *(Scandinavian Philatelic Foundation; 0-936493),* 292 Green Moor Pl., Thousand Oaks, CA 91359 (SAN 698-0783) Tel 805-496-9993; Box 6716, Thousand Oaks, CA 91359 (SAN 698-2514).

Scandia Pubs, *(Scandia Pubs.; 0-937242),* 5921 Niwot Rd., Longmont, CO 80501 (SAN 282-2806) Tel 303-530-0824.

Scanner Master, *(Scanner Master Publishing Co.; 0-939430),* 13 Pond St., Natick, MA 01760 (SAN 216-583X) Tel 617-653-4016.

Scanning Electron, *(Scanning Electron Microscopy, Inc.; 0-931288),* P.O. Box 66507, AMF O'Hare, Chicago, IL 60666 (SAN 213-5868) Tel 312-529-6677.

Scarab Pr, *(Scarab Press; 0-912962),* 63 Bates Blvd., Orinda, CA 94563 (SAN 204-7306).

†Scarecrow, *(Scarecrow Pr., Inc.; 0-8108),* Subs. of Grolier Educational Corp., 52 Liberty St., Box 4167, Metuchen, NJ 08840 (SAN 203-2651) Tel 201-548-8600; *CIP.*

Scarf Pr, *(Scarf Press; 0-934386),* 58 E. 83rd St., New York, NY 10028 (SAN 212-9698) Tel 212-744-3901.

SCB Photos, *(SCB Photographics; 0-940468),* P.O. Box 491114, Brentwood, CA 94513 (SAN 223-1581) Tel 213-826-8341.

Scenographic, *(Scenographic Media; 0-913868),* Box 2122, Norwalk, CT 06851 (SAN 205-1443).

Scepter Pubs, *(Scepter Pubs.; 0-933932),* 481 Main St., New Rochelle, NY 10801 (SAN 207-2858) Tel 914-636-3377.

Sceptre Pub, *(Sceptre Publishing Co.; 0-9615855),* 12584 Cresta Ct., San Diego, CA 92128 (SAN 696-7558) Tel 619-485-9355; Orders to: Sceptre Pub. Co., P.O. Box 28531, San Diego, CA 92128 (SAN 662-3867) Tel 619-485-9355.

Sch Aid, *(School Aid Co.; 0-87385),* 911 Colfax Dr., P.O. Box 123, Danville, IL 61832 (SAN 158-3719); Toll free: 800-447-2665.

Sch Arch Interior Des, *(School of Architecture & Interior Design; 0-939592),* Univ. of Cincinnati, Cincinnati, OH 45221 (SAN 216-650X) Tel 513-475-6485.

Sch For Serv *Imprint of* **Geo U Sch For Serv**

Sch Home CourseWare, *(School & Home CourseWare, Inc.; 0-918123),* 301 W. Mesa, Fresno, CA 93704 (SAN 650-9169) Tel 209-431-8300.

Sch Journal WVU, *(West Virginia Univ., Perley Isaac Reed Schl. of Journalism; 0-930362),* West Virginia Univ., 112 Martin Hall, Morgantown, WV 26506-6010 (SAN 219-4104) Tel 304-293-3505.

Sch Lib Sci, *(School of Library and Information Management Emporia State Univ.),* 1200 Commercial, Emporia, KS 66801 (SAN 209-598X) Tel 316-343-1200.

Sch Proj Club, *(School Projectionist Club of America; 0-911328),* P.O. Box 44, State College, PA 16801 (SAN 204-7322).

Sch Sci Math, *(School Science & Mathematics Assn., Inc.; 0-912047),* Bowling Green State Univ., 126 Life Science Bldg., Bowling Green, OH 43403-0256 (SAN 275-228X) Tel 419-372-7393.

Sch Zone Pub Co, *(School Zone Publishing Co.; 0-938256; 0-88743),* 1819 Industrial Dr., P.O. Box 703, Grand Haven, MI 49417 (SAN 289-8314) Tel 616-846-5030; Toll free: 800-253-0564.

Schaefer Studios, *(Schaefer Studios; 0-9614928),* Shorewood Dr., Madison Lake, MN 56063 (SAN 693-3645) Tel 507-243-3300.

Schaffer Pubns, *(Schaffer, Frank, Pubns., Inc.; 0-86734),* 19771 Magellan Dr., Torrance, CA 90502 (SAN 217-5827) Tel 213-532-5420.

Schafler Ent, *(Schafler Enterprises; 0-9603154),* 257 Ricardo Rd., Mill Valley, CA 94941 (SAN 212-5536) Tel 415-383-0830.

Schalaco Pub, *(Schalaco Publishing Co.; 0-9608560),* 5123 E. McDonald Dr., Paradise Valley, AZ 85253 (SAN 240-768X) Tel 602-279-2885.

Schalkenbach, *(Schalkenbach, Robert, Foundation; 0-911312),* 5 E. 44th St., New York, NY 10017 (SAN 206-1317) Tel 212-986-8684.

Schar Pub Co, *(Schar Publishing Co.; 0-9611830),* 2541 W. Ainslie St., Chicago, IL 60625 (SAN 240-8279) Tel 312-784-2186; Dist. by: K. V. Schar, 2541 W. Ainslie St., Chicago, IL 60625 (SAN 240-8287).

Scharf & Sil Publishers, *(Scharf & Silverman Pubs., Ltd.; 0-916523),* 50 E. 42nd St., Suite 1007, New York, NY 10017 (SAN 295-4966) Tel 212-697-4026.

Scharff Assocs, *(Scharff Assocs.; 0-937558),* R.D. 1, Box 276, New Ringgold, PA 17960 (SAN 697-1822) Tel 717-943-2216.

†Schaumburg Pubns, *(Schaumburg Pubns., Inc.; 0-935690),* 1432 S. Mohawk, Roselle, IL 60172 (SAN 214-221X); *CIP.*

SchDept *Imprint of* **Har-Row**

Schenkman
See Schenkman Bks Inc

†Schenkman Bks Inc, *(Schenkman Bks., Inc.; 0-87073; 0-87047),* 190 Concord Ave., Cambridge, MA 02138 (SAN 203-2643) Tel 617-492-4952; Orders to: P.O. Box 1570, Cambridge, MA 02138 (SAN 662-1368); *CIP.*

Schiffer, *(Schiffer Publishing, Ltd.; 0-916838; 0-88740),* 1469 Morstein Rd., West Chester, PA 19380 (SAN 208-8428) Tel 215-696-1001.

Schiffli Lace, *(Schiffli Lace & Embroidery Manufacturers Assn., Inc.),* 512 23rd St., Union City, NJ 07087 (SAN 224-6228) Tel 201-863-7300.

Schildge Pub, *(Schildge Publishing Co.; 0-9615595),* R.D. 2, Box 336, Plattsburgh, NY 12901 (SAN 696-1770) Tel 518-561-4752.

†Schirmer Bks, *(Schirmer Bks.; 0-911320),* Div. of Macmillan Publishing Co., Inc., 866 Third Ave., New York, NY 10022 (SAN 222-9544); Toll free: 800-257-5755; *CIP.*

Schl Admin Bkst, *(School Administrators' Bookstore; 0-939136),* P.O. Box 1767, Tustin, CA 92681 (SAN 239-6823) Tel 714-720-0773.

Schl St Pr, *(School Street Pr.; 0-939105),* P.O. Box 558, Hastings-on-Hudson, NY 10706 (SAN 662-5975); 28 School St., Hastings-on-Hudson, NY 10706 (SAN 662-5983) Tel 914-478-4490.

Schmul Pub Co, *(Schmul Publishing Co. Inc.; 0-88019),* P.O. Box 4068, Salem, OH 44460 (SAN 211-8246).

Schneeberger, *(Schneeberger, Tilly, & Assoc.),* P.O. Box 623, 578 El Sol St., Ojai, CA 93023 (SAN 213-3709) Tel 805-646-0208.

Schneider, *(Schneider, Le Roy; 0-9614482),* 27515 Baretta Dr., Bonita Springs, FL 33923 (SAN 212-6214) Tel 813-992-0531.

Schneider Ent
See Schneider

Schneider Pubs, *(Schneider, R., Pubs.; 0-936984),* 312 Linwood Ave., Stevens Point, WI 54481 (SAN 217-1317) Tel 715-341-0020.

Schnell Pub, *(Schnell Publishing Co., Inc.; 0-9606454),* 100 Church St., New York, NY 10007-2694 (SAN 205-1435) Tel 212-732-9820.

†Schocken, *(Schocken Bks., Inc.; 0-8052),* 62 Cooper Sq., New York, NY 10003 (SAN 213-7585) Tel 212-475-4900; *CIP. Imprints:* Moonlight Edns (Moonlight Editions).

Schoenhof, *(Schoenhof's Foreign Books, Inc.; 0-87774),* Subs. of Editions Gallimard, 76A Mount Auburn St., Cambridge, MA 02138 (SAN 212-0062) Tel 617-547-8855.

Schofield Pub, *(Schofield Publishing Co.; 0-9608720),* 29928 Lilac Rd., Valley Ctr., CA 92082 (SAN 238-3659) Tel 714-749-1325.

†Schol Am Res, *(School of American Research Pr.; 0-933452),* P.O. Box 2188, Santa Fe, NM 87504 (SAN 212-6222) Tel 505-984-0741; *CIP.*

Schol Bk Serv
See Scholastic Inc

†Schol Facsimiles, *(Scholars' Facsimiles & Reprints; 0-8201),* P.O. Box 344, Delmar, NY 12054 (SAN 203-2627) Tel 518-439-5978; *CIP.*

Schol Test, *(Scholastic Testing Service, Inc.; 0-936224),* 480 Meyer Rd., P.O. Box 1056, Bensenville, IL 60106-8056 (SAN 200-2183) Tel 312-766-7150.

Schola Pr TX, *(Schola Press; 0-931016),* P.O. Box 294, Lorena, TX 76655 (SAN 216-4469) Tel 817-857-3566.

†Scholarly, *(Scholarly Pr., Inc.; 0-403),* P.O. Box 160, St. Clair Shores, MI 48080 (SAN 209-0473); *CIP. Imprints:* Regency (Regency Press).(Regency Pr.).

Scholarly Pubns, *(Scholarly Pubns.; 0-88065; 1-55528),* 7310 El Cresta Dr., Houston, TX 77083 (SAN 650-0587) Tel 713-879-8319.

†Scholarly Res Inc, *(Scholarly Resources, Inc.; 0-8420),* 104 Greenhill Ave., Wilmington, DE 19805 (SAN 203-2619) Tel 302-654-7713; Toll free: 800-772-8937. Source materials on 35mm microfilm, monographs, reference books & microfiche. Subjects: ethnic studies, genealogy, history, law, military studies & political science. Government documents, journals, manuscript collections & newspapers; *CIP.*

†Scholars Bk, *(Scholars Book Co.; 0-914348),* 4431 Mt. Vernon, Houston, TX 77006-5889 (SAN 205-1419) Tel 713-528-4395; *CIP.*

Scholars Bks, *(Scholars Bks.; 0-938659),* P.O. Box 160361, Irving, TX 75016 (SAN 661-1346) Tel 214-686-5332.

Scholars Portable, (Scholars Portable Pubns.; 0-9604778), 1459 Southfield Rd., Evansville, IN 47715 (SAN 211-3465) Tel 812-476-6697.

†**Scholars Pr GA,** (Scholars Pr.; 0-89130; 1-55540), P.O. Box 1608, Decatur, GA 30031-1608 (SAN 293-3896) Tel 404-636-4757; Dist. by: Johns Hopkins Univ. Pr., P.O. Box 4869, Hampden Sta., Baltimore, MD 21211 (SAN 202-7348) Tel 301-338-6946; CIP.

Scholars Pr Ltd, (Scholars' Press, Ltd.; 0-914044), P.O. Box 7231, Roanoke, VA 24019 (SAN 203-2600).

Scholars Ref Lib, (Scholar's Reference Library), P.O. Box 148, Darby, PA 19023 (SAN 205-1400).

Scholars Studies, (Scholars Studies Press; 0-89177), 109 E. Ninth St., New York, NY 10003 (SAN 208-3795) Tel 212-674-5296.

Scholastic Hardcover Imprint of Scholastic Inc

Scholastic Inc, (Scholastic, Inc.; 0-590), 730 Broadway, New York, NY 10003 (SAN 202-5442) Tel 212-505-3000; Toll free: 800-392-2179; Orders to: P.O. Box 7502, 2931 E. McCarty St., Jefferson City, MO 65102 (SAN 202-5450). Imprints: Apple Paperbacks (Apple Paperbacks); Blue Ribbon Bks (Blue Ribbon Books); Citation (Citation Press); Hello Reader (Hello Reader); Lucky Star (Lucky Star); Point (Point); Scholastic Hardcover (Scholastic Hardcover); Seesaw Bks (Seesaw Books); Starline (Starline); Sunfire (Sunfire); Vagabond (Vagabond); Wildfire (Wildfire Press); Windswept Bks (Windswept Books); Wishing Star Bks (Wishing Star Books).

†**Scholasticus,** (Scholasticus Pub.; 0-9606754), P.O. Box 2727, Springfield, VA 22152 (SAN 211-450X); CIP.

Scholium Intl, (Scholium International, Inc.; 0-87936), 265 Great Neck Rd., Great Neck, NY 11021 (SAN 169-5282) Tel 516-466-5181.

Scholl, (Scholl Communications, Inc.; 0-912519), P.O. Box 560, Deerfield, IL 60015 (SAN 265-296X) Tel 312-945-1891.

†**School Age,** (School Age Notes; 0-917505), P.O. Box 120674, Nashville, TN 37212 (SAN 656-1004) Tel 615-292-4957; CIP.

School Living, (School of Living Adult Education; 0-87663; 0-87983), RD 7, Box 388, York, PA 17402 (SAN 275-2271) Tel 717-755-2666.

Schoolhouse Pr, (Schoolhouse Pr.; 0-9615669), 46 Mountain View Dr., Peterborough, NH 03458-1325 (SAN 696-1312) Tel 603-924-7849. Do not confuse with either of two other companies with the same name: Schoolhouse Pr., Pittsville, WI, or Independence, OH.

Schoolhouse Pr
See Schoolhouse WI

Schoolhouse WI, (Schoolhouse Pr.; 0-942018), 6899 Cary Bluff, Pittsville, WI 54466 (SAN 239-8044) Tel 715-884-2799. Do not confuse with either of two other companies with the same name: Schoolhouse Pr., Peterborough, NH, or Independence, OH.

Schpitfeir, (Schpitfeir Publishing; 0-9607330), Subs. of Schpitfeir Enterprises, P.O. Box 4253, Seattle, WA 98104-0253 (SAN 293-387X) Tel 206-622-7222; Dist. by: Cogan Bks., 4332 W. Artesia Ave., Fullerton, CA 92633 (SAN 168-9649); Dist. by: The Distributors, 702 S. Michigan, South Bend, IN 46618 (SAN 212-0364) Tel 219-232-8500; Dist. by: Pacific Pipeline, 19215 66th Ave. S., Kent, WA 98032 (SAN 208-2128) Tel 206-872-5523; Dist. by: C & M Pubns., 6110 Highway 290, West Austin, TX 78735 (SAN 216-227X) Tel 512-892-5234; Dist. by: EZ Cookin Book' Co., 9925 Currant Ave., Fountain Valley, CA 92708 (SAN 240-9364) Tel 714-968-9102; Dist. by: Quality Bks., 918 Sherwood Dr., Lake Bluff, IL 60044-2204 (SAN 169-2127).

Schrello Market, (Schrello Direct Marketing; 0-935823), 555 E. Ocean Blvd., Long Beach, CA 90801 (SAN 696-5849) Tel 213-437-2230; P.O. Box 1610, Long Beach, CA 90801 (SAN 699-6361).

Schroder Music, (Schroder Music Co.; 0-915620), 1450-6th St., Berkeley, CA 94710 (SAN 207-3935) Tel 415-524-5804; Dist. by: The Childrens Small Pr. Collection, 719 N. Fourth Ave., Ann Arbor, MI 48104 (SAN 200-514X).

†**Schroeder Prints,** (Schroeder Prints, Inc.; 0-931766), Green Shed, 33 W. St., Annapolis, MD 21401 (SAN 211-6472) Tel 301-269-1812; CIP.

Schroeppel, (Schroeppel, Tom; 0-9603718), 4705 Bay View Ave., Tampa, FL 33611 (SAN 213-7941).

Schubert, (Schubert Club, The; 0-912373), 302 Landmark Center, St. Paul, MN 55102 (SAN 265-1998) Tel 612-292-3267.

Schuchman, (Schuchman-Falk; 0-9615049), 4135 Washburn Ave. N., Minneapolis, MN 55412 (SAN 693-8620) Tel 612-521-4328.

Schueler Comm, (Schueler Communications; 0-9614965), 208 N. Townsend St., Syracuse, NY 13203 (SAN 693-7500) Tel 315-472-6948.

Schulak & Assoc, (Schulak, Bernard, & Assoc. Architects, Pub.; 0-9602186), 6889 W. Maple Rd., West Bloomfield, MI 48033 (SAN 212-2278).

Schumacher Pubns, (Schumacher Pubns.; 0-917378), 28 Holly Ln., Zenith Terr., Proctor, MN 55810 (SAN 208-8436) Tel 218-624-7728.

Schwenkfelder Lib, (Schwenkfelder Library; 0-935980), 1 Seminary St., Pennsburg, PA 18073 (SAN 213-795X) Tel 215-679-3103.

†**Sci Am Bks,** (Scientific American Bks.), 41 Madison Ave., New York, NY 10010 (SAN 291-9311) Tel 212-532-7660; Orders to: 44 19 W. 1980 S., Salt Lake City, UT 84104 (SAN 291-932X); CIP.

Sci Am Ilus Lib
See Scientific Am Inc

Sci & Behavior, (Science & Behavior Bks., Inc.; 0-8314), P.O. Box 60519, Palo Alto, CA 94306 (SAN 204-7349) Tel 415-326-6465.

Sci & Tech Pr, (Science & Technology Pr.; 0-912291), P.O. Box 614, Latham, NY 12110 (SAN 203-2597) Tel 518-785-8517.

†**Sci Assoc Intl,** (Science Associates/International, Inc.; 0-87837), 1841 Broadway, New York, NY 10023 (SAN 204-7357) Tel 212-265-4995; CIP.

Sci Bks Intl
See Jones & Bartlett

Sci Citizens, (Science for Citizens Ctr.; 0-931123), Western Michigan Univ., Kalamazoo, MI 49008 (SAN 655-1335).

Sci Comm Intl, (Scientific Communication International; 0-936097), 745 High, Pullman, WA 99163 (SAN 696-7523) Tel 509-335-4300.

Sci Ent, (Science Enterprises, Inc.; 0-930116), Box 88443, Indianapolis, IN 46208 (SAN 210-6639) Tel 317-259-1054.

Sci Fict & Fant Prodns, (Science Fiction & Fantasy Productions, Inc.; 0-931683), 21111 Mapleridge, Southfield, MI 48075-5704 (SAN 683-759X) Tel 313-355-9827.

Sci Hist Imprint of Watson Pub Intl

Sci Manpower, (Scientific Manpower Commission), 1500 Massachusetts Ave., NW, Suite 831, Washington, DC 20005 (SAN 225-2058) Tel 202-223-6995.

Sci Med Pr, (Science-Med Pr.; 0-9617051), 617 Grant, No. 4, Santa Monica, CA 90405 (SAN 662-8850) Tel 213-396-5136.

Sci Museum, (Science Museum of Minnesota; 0-911338), 30 E. Tenth St., St. Paul, MN 55101 (SAN 204-7365) Tel 612-221-9488.

Sci Newsletters, (Scientific Newsletter Enterprises, Inc.; 0-930914), P.O. Box 3205, Mission Viejo, CA 92690-1205 (SAN 212-2294) Tel 714-240-3579.

Sci of Mind, (Science of Mind Pubns.; 0-917849), Div. of United Church of Religoius Science, P.O. Box 75127, Los Angeles, CA 90075 (SAN 203-2570) Tel 213-388-2181; Dist. by: Devorss & Co., P.O. Box 550, 1046 Princeton Dr., Marina del Rey, CA 90294 (SAN 168-9886); Dist. by: New Leaf Distributors, The, 1020 White St., SW, Altanta, GA 30310 (SAN 169-1449) Tel 404-755-2665.

Sci Peace Builders, (Scientific Peace Builders Foundation), P.O. Box 3037, Santa Monica, CA 90403 (SAN 204-7373) Tel 213-394-4111.

Sci People, (Science for the People; 0-9607314), 897 Main St., Cambridge, MA 02139 (SAN 218-3544) Tel 617-547-0370.

†**Sci Pr,** (Science Pr.; 0-89500), 8 Brookstone Dr., Princeton, NJ 08540 (SAN 210-0053) Tel 609-921-3405; CIP.

Sci Res Assoc Coll, (Science Research Assocs., Inc., College Div.), Subs. of IBM, 155 N. Wacker Dr., Chicago, IL 60606-1780 (SAN 215-207X) Tel 312-984-7000.

Sci Res Ctr
See Sci People

Sci Soft Prods, (Scientific Software Products, Inc.; 0-918127), 5720 W. 71st St., Indianapolis, IN 46278 (SAN 296-7065) Tel 317-293-9270.

†**Sci Tech Inc,** (Science Tech, Inc.; 0-910239), 701 Ridge St., Madison, WI 53705 (SAN 241-4511) Tel 608-238-8664; CIP.

Sci-Tech Pubns, (Sci-Tech Pubns.; 0-914469), P.O. Box 5201, San Jose, CA 95150 (SAN 289-7113) Tel 408-266-5706.

Sci Therapeutics Info, (Scientific Therapeutics Information; 0-936871), 2050 Center Ave., Suite 200, Fort Lee, NJ 07024 (SAN 699-931X) Tel 201-461-4969.

Sci-Thru-Media, (Science-Thru-Media, Inc.; 0-918473), 303 Fifth Ave., Suite 803, New York, NY 10016 (SAN 657-7156) Tel 212-684-5366.

†**Sci Ware,** (Scientific Software, Inc.; 0-89498), P.O. Box 536, Mooresville, IN 46158 (SAN 209-9691) Tel 317-831-6296; CIP.

SCIDATA Imprint of PennWell Bks

Science Identity, (Science of Identity Foundation; 0-88187), P.O. Box 27450, Honolulu, HI 96827 (SAN 264-6900) Tel 808-488-4798.

Science Man Pr, (Science Man Pr.; 0-936046), Div. of TSM Marketing, Inc., 4738 N. Harlem Ave., Harwood Heights, IL 60656 (SAN 213-7968).

Science Software, (Science Software Systems, Inc.; 0-937292), 11899 W. Pico Blvd., West Los Angeles, CA 90064 (SAN 240-155X) Tel 213-477-8541.

Scienspot, (Scienspot Pubns.; 0-937926), 39 Brunswick Ave., Troy, NY 12180 (SAN 216-1850).

Scientific Am Inc, (Scientific American, Inc.; 0-89454), Subs. of W. H. Freeman & Co., 415 Madison Ave., New York, NY 10017 (SAN 210-2676) Tel 212-754-0476.

Scientific Pr, (Scientific Pr., The; 0-89426; 0-928763), 540 University Ave., Palo Alto, CA 94301 (SAN 687-8520) Tel 415-322-5221.

Scion Info Servs, (Scion Information Services; 0-936495), 332 S. Division, No. 4, Ann Arbor, MI 48104 (SAN 698-0708) Tel 313-761-4842; P.O. Box 13, Ann Arbor, MI 48107 (SAN 698-2506).

Scion Pub
See Scion Info Servs

SCMAR, (South Carolina Magazine of Ancestral Research; 0-913363), P.O. Box 21766, Columbia, SC 29221 (SAN 285-8525) Tel 803-772-6919.

SCOAL Pr, (SCOAL Press; 0-933556), 53 Pondview Circle, Brockton, MA 02401 (SAN 213-3717) Tel 617-587-4275.

Scolar, (Scolar Pr.; 0-85967), 2430 Bancroft Way, Berkeley, CA 94704 (SAN 679-1719).

Scop & Gleeman, (Scop & Gleeman; 0-9616986), RR 4, P.O. Box 400, Putnam Valley, NY 10579 (SAN 661-7298) Tel 914-528-7385; Bell Hollow Rd., Putnam Valley, NY 10579 (SAN 661-7301).

†**SCOP Pubns,** (SCOP Pubns., Inc.), P.O. Box 376, College Park, MD 20740 (SAN 211-2035); CIP.

Scorpio Pr, (Scorpio Pr., The; 0-938727), Div. of Peralta Shipping Corp., 50 Broadway, New York, NY 10004 (SAN 661-6135) Tel 212-509-2835.

Scorpio Pubns, (Scorpio Pubns.; 0-936099), 2 E. Butler Ave., Chalfont, PA 18914 (SAN 696-7515) Tel 215-822-3987.

Scorpion Pr, (Scorpion Pr.; 0-9609290), 20125 S.W. TV Hwy. 21, Aloha, OR 97006 (SAN 240-8759).

ScotPr, (Scotpress; 0-912951), Div. of Unicorn Ltd., P.O. Box 778, Morgantown, WV 26505 (SAN 283-3670) Tel 304-599-1877.

Scott & Assocs, *(Scott, M. L., & Associates, Pubs.; 0-9602726),* P.O. Box 816, Ithaca, NY 14850 (SAN 669-2621) Tel 607-387-9560; Dist. by: R. J. Young, P.O. Box 816, Ithaca, NY 14850 (SAN 669-263X) Tel 607-387-9560.

Scott & Daughters, *(Scott & Daughters Publishing, Inc.; 0-911113),* 940 N. Highland Ave., Los Angeles, CA 90038 (SAN 275-2395) Tel 213-856-0008; Toll free: 800-547-2688.

Scott Craft Pubs, *(Scott & Craft Pubs.; 0-9614538),* P.O. Box 1312, Kingsport, TN 37662 (SAN 692-3364) Tel 615-247-7535; Orders to: Albury Press, P.O. Box 55388, Tulsa, OK 74155 (SAN 662-2984).

†Scott F, *(Scott, Foresman & Co.; 0-673),* Subs. of SFN Co., 1900 E. Lake Ave., Glenview, IL 60025 (SAN 200-2140) Tel 312-729-3000; *CIP.*

Scott Pub Co, *(Scott Publishing Co.; 0-89487),* Subs. of Amos Pr., Inc., P.O. Box 828, Sidney, OH 45365 (SAN 205-9770) Tel 513-498-0802; Toll free: 800-848-4406; 911 Vandemark Rd., Sidney, OH 45365 (SAN 658-1579).

Scott Pubns CA
See A & S Pr

†Scott Pubns MI, *(Scott Pubns.),* 30595 W. Eight Mile Rd., Livonia, MI 48152 (SAN 240-8872) Tel 313-477-6650; Toll free: 800-458-8237; *CIP.*

Scott-Wesley, *(Scott-Wesley Publishing; 0-936137),* 20155 Keswick St., Suite 210, Canoga Park, CA 91306 (SAN 697-1644); P.O. Box 2253, Canoga Park, CA 91306 (SAN 697-1652).

Scottwall Assocs, *(Scottwall Assocs.; 0-9612790),* 95 Scott St., San Francisco, CA 94117 (SAN 289-8322) Tel 415-861-1956.

Scout Creek Pr, *(Scout Creek Pr.; 0-930219),* P.O. Box 3, 3467 Chippewa Court, West Linn, OR 97068 (SAN 670-8404) Tel 503-635-1333; Orders to: Pacific Northwest Books, Inc., P.O. Box 314, Medford, OR 97501 (SAN 660-9546).

†SCP, *(Saunders College Publishing; 0-03),* Div. of CBS College Publishing, 383 Madison Ave., New York, NY 10017 (SAN 282-2768) Tel 212-872-2244; Orders to: CBS College Publishing, 383 Madison Ave., New York, NY 10017 (SAN 282-2776) Tel 212-750-1330; *CIP.*

Scream Pr, *(Scream Pr.; 0-910489),* P.O. Box 8531, Santa Cruz, CA 95061 (SAN 260-132X) Tel 408-425-0233.

Screaming Suicide, *(Screaming Suicide Pr.; 0-936365),* 140 E. Magnolia, San Antonio, TX 78212 (SAN 698-0325) Tel 512-737-2137.

Scribblers, *(Scribblers Inc.; 0-943386),* 411 N. Akard, Suite 810, Dallas, TX 75201 (SAN 240-7698) Tel 214-954-0189.

Scribe Write, *(Scribe Write; 0-939909),* P.O. Box 9263, Missoula, MT 59807 (SAN 661-454X).

†Scribner, *(Scribner's, Charles, Sons; 0-684),* Div. of Macmillan Publishing Co., 115 Fifth Ave., New York, NY 10003 (SAN 200-2191) Tel 212-614-1300; Toll free: 800-257-5755; Orders to: Order Dept., Front & Brown Sts., Riverside, NJ 08075 (SAN 282-6550); *CIP.*

†Scrimshaw, *(Scrimshaw Pr.; 0-87155),* P.O. Box 10, Centerville, MA 02632 (SAN 206-9253); *CIP.*

Scrip Pr
See Victor Bks

Scripps Inst Ocean, *(Scripps Institution of Oceanography, Univ of California, San Diego; 0-9603078),* A007, La Jolla, CA 92093 (SAN 213-1625).

Scripps Ranch Pubns, *(Scripps Ranch Pubns.; 0-9614489),* 10743 Brookview Ln., San Diego, CA 92131 (SAN 689-4542) Tel 619-271-9749.

Script Writers, *(ScriptWriters-Filmmakers Publishing Co.; 0-910665),* 8033 Sunset Blvd., Suite 306, West Hollywood, CA 90046 (SAN 262-7639) Tel 213-650-0600 Tel 714-892-2562.

†Scripta, *(Scripta Humanistica; 0-916379),* 1383 Kersey Lane, Potomac, MD 20854 (SAN 295-8562) Tel 301-340-1095; *CIP.*

Scriptorium, *(Scriptorium, The),* c/o The Gryphon Bookshop, 216 W. 89 St., New York, NY 10024 (SAN 293-3918) Tel 212-362-0706.

Scriptorium Pr, *(Scriptorium Pr., The; 0-931485),* 71 S. Main St., Alfred, NY 14802 (SAN 683-1354) Tel 607-587-9371.

Scripture U Pub, *(Scripture Union Publishing; 0-913585),* 1716 Spruce St., Philadelphia, PA 19103 (SAN 285-3817) Tel 215-732-2079.

†Scroll Pr, *(Scroll Pr., Inc.; 0-87592),* 2858 Valerie Ct., Merrick, NY 11566 (SAN 206-796X) Tel 516-379-4283; *CIP.*

Sculpt-Nouveau, *(Sculpt-Nouveau; 0-9603744),* 21 Redwood Dr., San Rafael, CA 94901 (SAN 213-9634).

SD Peace Officers, *(South Dakota Peace Officers Assn.; 0-9608456),* 3102 Pine Tree Trail, Sturgis, SD 57785 (SAN 240-5695) Tel 605-677-5242.

SDH Co, *(SDH Co.; 0-9613866),* P.O. Box 923, Spokane, WA 99210 (SAN 685-2211) Tel 509-838-2265.

†SDSU Press, *(San Diego State Univ., Pr.; 0-916304),* 5189 College Ave., San Diego, CA 92182 (SAN 202-0637) Tel 619-265-6220; *CIP. Imprints:* Campanile (Campanile Press).

SDSU Univ Art, *(San Diego State Univ., University Art Gallery; 0-937097),* 5402 College Ave., San Diego, CA 92182-0214 (SAN 280-3941) Tel 619-265-4941.

SDWA
See Soc Descend Wash Army

SE Asia Res Ctr
See Asia Resource

Sea Chall, *(Sea Challengers; 0-930118),* 4 Sommerset Rise, Skyline Forest, Monterey, CA 93940 (SAN 210-5446) Tel 408-373-6306; Dist. by: Padre Productions, P.O. Box 1275, San Luis Ospispo, CA 93406 (SAN 202-8484) Tel 805-543-5404; Dist. by: Chartguide Ltd., Anaheim, CA 92801 (SAN 215-7373) Tel 714-533-1423; Dist. by: Harrowood Bks., 3943 N. Providence Rd., Newton Square, PA 19073 (SAN 207-1622) Tel 215-353-5585.

Sea Fog Pr, *(Sea Fog Pr., Inc.; 0-917507),* P.O. Box 210056, San Francisco, CA 94121-0056 (SAN 656-1012) Tel 415-221-8527.

Sea Hist Pr, *(Sea History Pr.; 0-930248),* Div. of National Maritime Historical Society, 132 Maple St., Croton-on-Hudson, NY 10520 (SAN 210-6647) Tel 914-271-2177.

†Sea Horse, *(Sea Horse Pr., Ltd., The; 0-933322),* 307 W. 11th St., New York, NY 10014 (SAN 212-4505) Tel 212-691-9066; *CIP.*

Sea Lion Pub, *(Sea Lion Publishing Co.; 0-9616266),* 2853 N. Griggs, St. Paul, MN 55113 (SAN 658-3741) Tel 612-484-1659.

Sea-Mount Pub Co, *(Sea-Mount Publishing Co.; 0-915539),* 1545 N.E. 104 St., Miami, FL 33138 (SAN 291-4212) Tel 305-754-1027.

Sea Shore Pubn, *(Sea Shore Pubns.; 0-9611342),* 211 S. Sea Shore Ave., Long Beach, MS 39560 (SAN 283-3107) Tel 312-864-4573.

Sea Sports Pubns, *(Sea Sports Pubns.; 0-9616399),* P.O. Box 647, Belden Sta., Norwalk, CT 06850 (SAN 659-1485) Tel 203-866-5376; 10 Buckingham Pl., Norwalk, CT 06851 (SAN 659-1493).

Sea Studios, *(Sea Studios; 0-9616824),* 886 Cannery Row, Monterey, CA 93940 (SAN 661-1257) Tel 408-649-5152; Dist. by: Publishers Group West, 5855 Beaudry St., Emeryville, CA 94608 (SAN 202-8522) Tel 415-658-3453.

Sea Urchin, *(Sea Urchin Pr.; 0-9605208),* P.O. Box 10503, Oakland, CA 94610 (SAN 215-8086).

Sea-Wind Pr, *(Sea-Wind Pr.; 0-9607436),* P.O. Box 222964, Carmel, CA 93922 (SAN 239-8036) Tel 408-372-8386.

Seabird, *(Seabird Imprint; 0-933499),* Subs. of Stagecoach Road Press, 4838 Rivervale Dr., Soquel, CA 95073 (SAN 691-8859) Tel 408-475-6445; Orders to: P.O. Box 1087, Soquel, CA 95073 (SAN 694-0129) Tel 408-475-6445.

Seabird Pub, *(Seabird Publishing; 0-938105),* P.O. Box 624, Broken Arrow, OK 74013 (SAN 659-767X); 1605 N. Hickory Ct., Broken Arrow, OK 74013 (SAN 659-7688) Tel 918-258-6209.

Seablom, *(Seablom Design; 0-918800),* 2106 2nd Ave. N.,, Seattle, WA 98109 (SAN 210-4962) Tel 206-285-2308.

Seabright, *(Seabright; 0-9613824),* Rte. 1, Box 135, Nags Head, NC 27959 (SAN 679-9973) Tel 703-434-8553; Dist. by: Storie /McOwen Publishers, P.O. Box 308, Manteo, NC 27954 (SAN 265-0940).

Seacliffe, *(Seacliffe, Ltd.; 0-911017),* 6338 Otis, Detroit, MI 48210 (SAN 263-0028) Tel 313-895-7158.

Seacoast Poets, *(Seacoast Poets; 0-936367),* P.O. Box 8638, La Jolla, CA 92038 (SAN 698-0015) Tel 619-753-5784.

Seagull Pub Co, *(Seagull Publishing Co.; 0-9612698),* 2915 Stanford Ave., Suite 7, Marina del Rey, CA 90291 (SAN 295-0235).

Seahawk Pr, *(Seahawk Pr.; 0-913008),* 6840 SW 92nd St., Miami, FL 33156 (SAN 204-7411) Tel 305-667-4051.

Seahorse Pr, *(Seahorse Pr., The; 0-938787),* 350 Ward Ave., Suite 106, Honolulu, HI 96814 (SAN 661-5481) Tel 808-988-7517; Dist. by: Pacific Trade Group, P.O. Box 668, Pearl City, HI 96782-0668 (SAN 169-1635).

SeaHorse Pr
See Sea Horse

SEAI Inst
See SEAI Tech Pubns

SEAI Tech Pubns, *(SEAI Technical Pubns.; 0-89671),* P.O. Box 590, Madison, GA 30650 (SAN 212-6915).

Seajay, *(Seajay Pubns.; 0-9609014),* P.O. Box 2176, Dearborn, MI 48123 (SAN 241-2489) Tel 313-274-9731.

Seajay Pr, *(Seajay Pr, The; 0-935239),* P.O. Box 5174, Columbia, SC 29250 (SAN 695-7080) Tel 803-256-9489.

†Seal Pr, *(Seal Pr.; 0-930364),* 500 E. Pike St., Seattle, WA 98122 (SAN 210-9522) Tel 206-329-7106; *CIP.*

Seal Pr Feminist, *(Seal Pr.-Feminist; 0-931188),* 500 E. Pike, Seattle, WA 98122 (SAN 215-3416) Tel 206-329-7160; Dist. by: Bookpeople, 2929 Fifth St., Berkeley, CA 94710 (SAN 168-9517) Tel 415-549-3030; Dist. by: Inland Bk. Co., P.O. Box 261, 22 Hemingway Ave., East Haven, CT 06512 (SAN 200-4151) Tel 203-467-4257; Dist. by: Pacific Pipeline, Inc., 19215 66th Ave., S., Kent, WA 98032 (SAN 208-2128) Tel 206-872-5523; Dist. by: Bookslinger, 213 E. Fourth St., St. Paul, MN 55101 (SAN 169-4154) Tel 612-221-0429; Orders to: Consortium Bk. Sales & Distribution, Inc., 213 E. Fourth St., St. Paul, MN 55101 (SAN 200-6049) Tel 612-221-9035.

Seal Pr WA
See Seal Pr Feminist

Seamount Pubns, *(Seamount Pubns.; 0-9614294),* P.O. Box 362, Pacific Palisades, CA 90272 (SAN 687-4576) Tel 213-454-8061.

Seaport Poets & Writers, *(Seaport Poets & Writers Pr.; 0-942856),* 94 Fulton St. 4th Flr., New York, NY 10038 (SAN 240-1568).

Search, *(Search; 0-930871),* 106 Sterling Ave., Mt. Sterling, KY 40353 (SAN 677-8038) Tel 606-498-0661.

Search Imprint of Andrews McMeel Parker

Search & Rescue, *(Search & Rescue Magazine; 0-9603392),* P.O. Box 641, Lompoc, CA 93438 (SAN 204-5745) Tel 805-733-3986.

Search CA, *(Search The (CA); 0-9613723),* 5634 Caminito Isla, La Jolla, CA 92037 (SAN 682-2487).

SEARCH Grp, *(Search Group, Inc.),* 925 Secret River Dr., Suite H, Sacramento, CA 95831 (SAN 225-9257) Tel 916-392-2550; Dist. by: National Criminal Ref. Serv., Box 6000, Rockville, MD 20850 (SAN 200-7320).

Search-One, *(Search-One Productions; 0-9616694),* P.O. Box 98, McKenzie, TN 38201-0098 (SAN 659-8455); Bethel College, East Hall, Rm. 39, Box 117C, McKenzie, TN 38201-0098 (SAN 659-8463) Tel 901-352-9935.

Search Public, *(Search Pubns.; 0-910715),* 2000 Old Stage Rd., Florissant, CO 80816 (SAN 262-0766) Tel 303-748-3341.

SEARCH Tech Servs, *(SEARCH Technical Services; 0-932975),* HCR 11-Box 17, Davenport, WA 99122 (SAN 689-0873) Tel 509-725-6666.

Searchers Pubns, *(Searchers Pubns.),* 4314 Island Crest Way, Mercer Island, WA 98040 (SAN 212-5579).

Seas Pubns, *(Seas Pubns.; 0-937677),* P.O. Box 8804, Atlanta, GA 30306-0804 (SAN 659-3097).

Seascape Enters, *(Seascape Enterprises; 0-931595),* P.O. Box 176, Colonial Heights, VA 23834 (SAN 682-4765) Tel 804-520-3628.

Seattle Air, *(Seattle Airplane Pr.; 0-917196),* 6727 Glen Echo Ln., Tacoma, WA 98499 (SAN 209-0775) Tel 206-584-7307.

†Seattle Art, *(Seattle Art Museum; 0-932216),* 14th E. & E. Prospect, Seattle, WA 98112 (SAN 205-9762) Tel 206-443-4673; Dist. by: Univ. of Washington Pr., Seattle, WA 98105 (SAN 212-2502) Tel 206-543-4050; CIP.

Seattle Audubon Soc, *(Seattle Audubon Society; 0-914516),* 619 Joshua Green Bldg., 1425 Fourth Ave., Seattle, WA 98101 (SAN 203-2562) Tel 206-622-6695; Dist. by: Pacific Search Pr., 222 Dexter Ave. N., Seattle, WA 98109 (SAN 202-8476) Tel 206-682-5044.

Seattle Bk, *(Seattle Bk. Co.; 0-915112),* P.O. Box 9254, Seattle, WA 98109 (SAN 207-1835) Tel 206-285-1226. *Imprints:* Slick (Slick Books).

Seattle Child Pub, *(Seattle's Child Publishing; 0-9614626),* P.O. Box 22578, Seattle, WA 98122 (SAN 691-8999) Tel 206-322-2594; Dist. by: Pacific Pipeline, Inc., 19215-66th Ave. S., Kent, WA 98032 (SAN 694-0137) Tel 206-872-5523.

Seattle Mus Art
   See Seattle Art

Seattle Mus WA
   See Seattle Art

Seattle Pub Co, *(Seattle Publishing Co., Inc.),* RR One Box 1035, Johnson, VT 05656 (SAN 212-8667) Tel 802-635-7440.

Seaver Bks, *(Seaver Bks.; 0-394),* 333 Central Park W., New York, NY 10025 (SAN 214-4719) Tel 212-866-9278; Orders to: Grove Pr., Inc., 196 W. Houston St., New York, NY 10014 (SAN 201-4890) Tel 212-242-4900; Dist. by: Arbor Hse. Publishing Co., 235 E. 45th St., New York, NY 10017 (SAN 201-1522) Tel 212-599-3131.

Seaview *Imprint of* **Putnam Pub Group**

Seaview Pr, *(Seaview Press; 0-9606048),* P.O. Box 32, El Cerrito, CA 94530 (SAN 216-4477) Tel 415-525-5495.

Seaweeds & Cons *Imprint of* **UH Pr**

Seawinds Pr, *(Seawinds Pr.; 0-9616375),* P.O. Box 5469, Macon, GA 31208 (SAN 658-9308) Tel 912-743-1016.

Sebago Pub, *(Sebago Publishing; 0-9614880),* Div. of Sebago Inc., 800 Heinz St., Berkeley, CA 94701 (SAN 693-1146) Tel 415-658-3326.

Sebastian LI, *(Sebastian Publishing Co.; 0-9616731),* P.O. Box 471, Port Jefferson Station, NY 11776 (SAN 659-865X); Dark Hollow Rd., Port Jefferson, NY 11777 (SAN 659-8668) Tel 516-928-6745.

Sebastian Pub Co, *(Sebastian Publishing Co.; 0-913347),* 1109 Royal Ln., San Carlos, CA 94070 (SAN 287-4466) Tel 415-598-0310; Dist. by: Pacific Pipeline, Inc., 19215 66th Ave., S., Kent, WA 98032 (SAN 287-4466) Tel 206-872-5523; Dist. by: Sebastian Publishing Co., 1109 Royal Ln., San Carlos, CA 94070 (SAN 287-4466) Tel 415-598-0310; Dist. by: Baker & Taylor, Western Div., 380 Edison Way, Reno, NV 89564 (SAN 169-4464) Tel 702-786-6700.

SEBT, *(Shrine of the Eternal Breath of Tao, The; 0-937604),* 117 Stonehaven Way, Los Angeles, CA 90049 (SAN 217-2704).

Sec Thoughts OR, *(Second Thoughts Press; 0-9607036),* P.O. Box 10741, Eugene, OR 97440 (SAN 239-3832) Tel 503-344-3491.

Second Amend, *(Second Amendment Foundation; 0-911475),* 12500 NE Tenth Pl., Bellevue, WA 98005 (SAN 275-2654) Tel 206-454-7012.

Second Chance, *(Second Chance Pr.; 0-933256),* RD2, Noyac Rd., Sag Harbor, NY 11963 (SAN 213-1633) Tel 516-725-1101; Toll free: 800-221-0960; Dist. by: Golden Lee Bk. Dstb., 1000 Dean St., Brooklyn, NY 11238 (SAN 169-5126) Tel 718-857-6333.

Second City Soft, *(Second City Software; 0-937023),* P.O. Box 442, Mount Prospect, IL 60056 (SAN 697-533X) Tel 312-577-7680.

Second Coming, *(Second Coming Pr.; 0-915016),* P.O. Box 31249, San Francisco, CA 94131 (SAN 206-376X) Tel 415-647-3679.

Second Hand, *(Second Hand, The; 0-9605858),* P.O. Box 204, Plymouth, WI 53073 (SAN 220-1879) Tel 414-893-5226.

Second Lang, *(Second Language Pubns.),* P.O. Box 1700, Blaine, WA 98230 (SAN 206-3778).

Second Soc Foun, *(Second Society Foundation),* 333 N. Michigan Ave., Suite 707, Chicago, IL 60601 (SAN 203-204X).

Second T Pub, *(Second Thoughts Publishing; 0-913587),* 153 Halsted, Chicago Heights, IL 60411 (SAN 285-3825) Tel 312-756-7500.

Second Thoughts, *(Second Thoughts; 0-9601286),* 88 W. Schiller, Suite 704, Chicago, IL 60610 (SAN 210-4970) Tel 312-337-6044.

Secret Garden, *(Secret Garden; 0-939263),* 1713 Grove, Berkeley, CA 94709 (SAN 662-5231) Tel 415-540-5454.

Secret Library, *(Secret Library, The; 0-917115),* 2757 State St., San Diego, CA 92103 (SAN 655-7767) Tel 619-542-0902; Dist. by: DeVorss & Co., P.O. Box 550, 1046 Princeton Dr., Marina del Rey, CA 90294 (SAN 168-9886).

Secretarial Pubns, *(Secretarial Pubns.; 0-943544),* P.O. Box 672, Santa Barbara, CA 93102 (SAN 238-3667) Tel 805-682-5706.

Securities Industry, *(Securities Industry Assn.),* 120 Broadway, New York, NY 10271 (SAN 227-0862) Tel 212-608-1500.

Security Dupont, *(Security Dupont Pr.; 0-9611422),* 617 Sibley Tower Building, Rochester, NY 14604 (SAN 284-9275) Tel 716-494-1466; Orders to: 10 Gates St., Bergen, NY 14416 (SAN 662-2046) Tel 716-404-1466.

Security Let, *(Security Letter, Inc.; 0-9609820),* 166 E. 96th St., New York, NY 10128 (SAN 262-1134); Dist. by: Butterworths, 80 Montvale Ave, Stoneham, MA 02180 (SAN 206-3964).

Security Pr, *(Security Press, Inc.; 0-939568),* Box 854, McLean, VA 22101 (SAN 216-6933) Tel 703-734-1326.

Security Seminars, *(Security Seminars Pr.; 0-936101),* 1204 SE 28th Ave., Ocala, FL 32671 (SAN 696-7507) Tel 904-694-6185; Orders to: Security Seminars Press, P.O. Box 70162, Ocala, FL 32670 (SAN 662-3859) Tel 904-694-6185.

Security World
   See Butterworth

See Do Pr, *(See-Do Press; 0-9607836),* P.O. Box 815, Lower Lake, CA 95457 (SAN 238-1974) Tel 707-994-5204.

SEE Pub Co, *(S.E.E. Publishing Co.; 0-937147),* 1556 Halford Ave., Suite 288, Santa Clara, CA 95051 (SAN 658-5035) Tel 408-248-8244; 1201 Sycamore Terr., Suite 40, Sunnyvale, CA 94086 (SAN 658-5043); Dist. by: Bookpeople, 2929 Fifth St., Berkeley, CA 94710 (SAN 168-9517).

See-Saw Pr, *(See-Saw Pr.; 0-9614144),* 744 Newark-Pompton Turnpike, Pompton Plains, NJ 07444 (SAN 686-2268) Tel 201-835-4647.

See Sharp Pr, *(See Sharp Pr.; 0-9613289),* P.O. Box 6118, San Francisco, CA 94101 (SAN 653-8134) Tel 415-647-2710.

Seed Center, *(Seed Ctr.; 0-916108),* Box 1700, Redway, CA 95560 (SAN 203-2554) Tel 707-923-2524.

Seed Life Pubns, *(Seed of Life Pubns.; 0-930875),* P.O. Box 33961, Phoenix, AZ 85067 (SAN 677-7945) Tel 602-842-9102.

Seed Saver Pubns, *(Seed Saver Pubns.; 0-9613977),* Box 70, Decorah, IA 52101 (SAN 682-3114) Tel 319-382-3949.

Seek-It Pubns, *(Seek-It Pubns.; 0-930706),* P.O. Box 1074, Birmingham, MI 48012 (SAN 215-3424) Tel 313-642-9262.

Seeker Pr, *(Seeker Press; 0-917615),* 1020 Carol Dr., Los Angeles, CA 90069 (SAN 657-162X) Tel 213-858-1182.

Seer Ox, *(Seer Ox; 0-916064),* 807 Prospect Ave. No. 107, South Pasadena, CA 91030 (SAN 207-8945).

Seesaw Bks *Imprint of* **Scholastic Inc**

Seesaw Music, *(Seesaw Music Corp.; 0-937205),* 2067 Broadway, New York, NY 10023 (SAN 658-6899) Tel 212-874-1200.

Segue NYC, *(Segue; 0-937804),* 300 Bowery, New York, NY 10012 (SAN 699-8003).

SEIA
   See SEINAM

Seibert Assocs, *(Seibert Assocs.; 0-939461),* 3455 Spring Hill Dr., Janesville, WI 53545 (SAN 663-3374) Tel 608-755-0300.

Seiler-Doar, *(Seiler-Doar Bks., Inc.; 0-916001),* 3449 Ramona, Palo Alto, CA 94306 (SAN 294-6580) Tel 415-857-0280.

SEINAM, *(Solar Energy Institute of North America),* 1110 Sixth St., NW, Washington, DC 20001 (SAN 211-3015).

Seismograph Pubs, *(Seismograph Pubns.; 0-932977),* P.O. Box 882664, San Francisco, CA 94188 (SAN 689-9781) Tel 415-621-4450; Dist. by: The Subterranean Co., P.O. Box 10233, 1327 W. Second St., Eugene, OR 97440 (SAN 169-7102) Tel 503-343-6324.

Sekan Pubns, *(Sekan Pubns. Co.; 0-931365),* 2210 S. Main St., Fort Scott, KS 66701 (SAN 686-9173).

Sekoni Pubs, *(Sekoni Pubs.; 0-9606958),* P.O. Box 15007, Durham, NC 27704 (SAN 217-4367) Tel 919-688-5983.

Selbstverlag, *(Selbstverlag Pr.; 0-911706),* P.O. Drawer 606, Bloomington, IN 47402-0606 (SAN 204-5761) Tel 812-334-2166.

Select Bks, *(Select Bks.; 0-910458),* Rte. 2, Box 109, Willow Springs, MO 65793 (SAN 202-0602) Tel 417-934-6775.

Selective, *(Selective Pubs.; 0-912584),* P.O. Box 1140, Clearwater, FL 33517 (SAN 204-577X) Tel 813-442-5440.

Selena Pr, *(Selena Pr.; 0-938451),* P.O. Box 7082, Fargo, ND 58103 (SAN 660-9880); 1010 Southwood Dr., Fargo, ND 58103 (SAN 660-9899) Tel 701-235-2890.

Selene Bks, *(Selene Bks.; 0-9609866),* P.O. Box 136, Kew Gardens, NY 11415 (SAN 275-276X) Tel 718-847-5184.

Self Counsel Pr
   See ISC Pr

Self Help Dist, *(Self-Help Distributors, Inc.; 0-937487),* 725 W. 18th St., No. 2, Merced, CA 95340 (SAN 659-1515) Tel 209-722-7559; Dist. by: Carlton Pr., 11 W. 32nd St., New York, NY 10001 (SAN 201-9655).

Self-Motiv Careers, *(Self-Motivated Careers; 0-381),* 3589 Hermitage Plantation, Duluth, GA 30136 (SAN 220-2743).

Self OH
   See E Rothenberg

Self-Prog Control, *(Self-Programmed Control Pr.; 0-9601926),* P.O. Box 49939, Los Angeles, CA 90049 (SAN 212-2308) Tel 213-826-1959.

Self Realization, *(Self Realization Fellowship; 0-87612),* 3880 San Rafael Ave., Los Angeles, CA 90065 (SAN 204-5788) Tel 213-225-2471.

Self Reliance, *(Self Reliance Foundation; 0-941580),* P.O. Box 1, Las Trampas, NM 87576 (SAN 239-3085) Tel 505-689-2250.

Self Rich Bks, *(Self Rich Bks.; 0-914365),* 36 Midland Dr., Tolland, CT 06084 (SAN 289-6788) Tel 203-872-3419.

Self-Sufficiency, *(Self-Sufficiency Assn.; 0-9616968),* 1912 Avenida Estudiante, San Pedro, CA 90732 (SAN 661-7387) Tel 213-519-0097; Dist. by: Nutri-Books Corp., 790 W. Tennessee Ave., Denver, CO 80223 (SAN 169-054X) Tel 303-778-8383; Dist. by: Periodical Services, Inc., P.O. Box 367, Stockton, NJ 08559 (SAN 200-6707).

Self Therapy
   See Wingbow Pr

Sellars
   See Natl Ctr Exper Sales

Sellens, *(Sellens; 0-9612068),* 134 Clark St., Augusta, KS 67010 (SAN 212-3843) Tel 316-775-5540.

Sellers Pubns, *(Sellers Pubns; 0-9608122),* Crane Brook Rd., Alstead, NH 03602 (SAN 238-8383).

Seluzicki Fine Bks, *(Seluzicki, Charles, Fine Books; 0-931356),* 3733 NE 24th Ave., Portland, OR 97212 (SAN 211-9773).

Seluzicki Poetry
   See Seluzicki Fine Bks

Sem Pub Hse, *(Seminal Publishing Hse.),* P.O. Box 213, Northampton, MA 01060 (SAN 209-2018).

Semiconductor, *(Semiconductor Services; 0-9613880),* 1145 Glenn Ave., Suite 213, San Jose, CA 95125 (SAN 692-7572).

Seminary Co-Op, *(Seminary Co-Operative Bookstore, Inc.; 0-912182),* 5757 S. University Ave., Chicago, IL 60637 (SAN 204-5818) Tel 312-752-4381.

Seminary Pr, *(Seminary Pr.; 0-912832),* P.O. Box 2218, Univ. Sta., Enid, OK 73702 (SAN 203-2546) Tel 405-237-4433.

Seminole Pub Co, *(Seminole Publishing Co.; 0-9612302),* P.O. Box 3315, High Mar Sta., Boulder, CO 80307 (SAN 287-752X) Tel 303-492-7907.

Senda Nueva, *(Senda Nueva De Ediciones, Inc.; 0-918454),* 640 W. 231st St., Apt. 3-B, Mail Box 139, Bronx, NY 10463 (SAN 210-0061) Tel 212-548-5288; Orders to: P.O. Box 488, Montclair, NJ 07042 (SAN 662-1392).

Seneca Bks, *(Seneca Bks., Inc.; 0-89092),* Rte. 6, Box 81-B, Morgantown, WV 26505 (SAN 213-4322) Tel 304-594-1324.

Seneca Pk Pub, *(Seneca Park Publishing; 0-9616447),* P.O. Box 315, Lynn Haven, FL 32444 (SAN 659-1604) Tel 904-265-2314; 303 Florida Ave., Lynn Haven, FL 32444 (SAN 659-1612).

Seneca Pr MD, *(Seneca Pr.; 0-9605908),* 503 Bonifant St., Silver Spring, MD 20910 (SAN 216-6941) Tel 301-588-2688.

SenEd *Imprint of* **HM**

Senior Pubns, *(Senior Pubns.; 0-931685),* 20 South Broadway, Yonkers, NY 10701 (SAN 683-7573) Tel 914-423-0112.

Seniority Mag
See Schueler Comm

Senkers Whim Ent, *(Senkers' Whim Enterprises; 0-9610506),* P.O. Box 797, Devon, PA 19333 (SAN 264-3820) Tel 215-293-1044.

Sense Pubns Inc, *(Sense Pubns., Inc.; 0-932673),* 7910 W. Blvd. Dr., Alexandria, VA 22308 (SAN 687-8369) Tel 703-768-6892.

Sensible Sol, *(Sensible Solutions, Inc.),* 14 E. 75th St., New York, NY 10016 (SAN 661-4574).

Sensitive Man, *(Sensitive Man Project, The; 0-938582),* 33 Oakwood Dr., Fairfield, CT 06430 (SAN 685-3560) Tel 203-368-2316.

Senterfitt
See Pathfinders

Senterprises, *(Senterprises Pubns., Inc.; 0-9613189),* 3610 Avenue Q, Suite 221, Lubbock, TX 79412 (SAN 295-8783) Tel 806-744-2844.

Sentinel Pub, *(Sentinel Publishing Co.; 0-931097),* 4845 50th St., Lubbock, TX 79414 (SAN 678-9447) Tel 806-792-3801; Toll free: 800-858-4602.

Sentry, *(Sentry Books, Inc.; 0-913194),* 10781 White Oak Ave., Granada Hills, CA 91344 (SAN 205-9460) Tel 213-368-2012; Dist. by: Aviation Book Co., 1640 Victory Blvd., Glendale, CA 91201 (SAN 212-0259) Tel 213-240-1771.

Separate Real, *(Separate Reality, Inc.; 0-932163),* P.O. Box 398057, Miami Beach, FL 33139 (SAN 686-5224) Tel 305-531-4835.

SEPM, *(Society of Economic Paleontologists & Mineralogists; 0-918985),* P.O. Box 4756, Tulsa, OK 74159 (SAN 260-3462) Tel 918-743-9765.

September Pr, *(September Pr., Inc.; 0-937159),* P.O. Box 584, Jamestown, RI 02835 (SAN 658-506X) Tel 401-423-0455.

Sequatchie, *(Sequatchie County Board of Education; 0-930739),* P.O. Box 488, Dunlap, TN 37327 (SAN 677-5349) Tel 615-949-3617.

Sequoia Aud Soc, *(Sequoia Audubon Society Inc.; 0-9614301),* 720 El Camino Real Suite 403, Belmont, CA 94002 (SAN 687-4878) Tel 415-593-7368.

Sequoia NYC, *(Sequoia Pr., Inc.; 0-939033),* 150 Fifth Ave., New York, NY 10011 (SAN 662-8494) Tel 212-362-5230.

SERA Presents, *(SERA Presents; 0-938883),* 4226 Longbranch Ct., Atlanta, GA 30319 (SAN 662-6661) Tel 404-455-0389.

Seraphim Pr, *(Seraphim Pr.; 0-942632),* Suite 263, 7439 La Palma Ave., Buena Park, CA 90620 (SAN 238-5791) Tel 714-527-4475.

SERC NAHRO, *(Southeastern Regional Council of the National Assn. of Housing & Redevelopment Officials; 0-939647),* 201 Granby Mall, P.O. Box 968, Norfolk, VA 23501 (SAN 663-5474) Tel 804-623-1111.

Sercolab, *(Sercolab; 0-918332),* 244 Sesuit Neck Rd., Box 957, East Dennis, MA 02641 (SAN 209-5165).

Serconia Pr, *(Serconia Pr.; 0-934933),* P.O. Box 1786, Seattle, WA 98111 (SAN 695-006X) Tel 206-633-2375.

Serenade-Saga *Imprint of* **Zondervan**

Serendip Illinois, *(Serendipity; 0-9616864),* P.O. Box 293, Kenilworth, IL 60043 (SAN 661-1613); 1418 10th St., Wilmette, IL 60091 (SAN 661-1621) Tel 312-256-3185.

Serendipity Pr
See Price Stern

†Serenity Hse, *(Serenity Hse. Publishing; 0-914789),* P.O. Box 462, Port Washington, NY 11050 (SAN 670-6983); *CIP.*

Sergio Pub, *(Sergio Publishing, Inc.; 0-936003),* 132 W. 24th St., Suite 747, New York, NY 10011 (SAN 696-5857) Tel 305-858-1591.

Serif Pr, *(Serif Pr., Inc.; 0-914125),* 1331 H. St. NW, Suite 110 LL, Washington, DC 20005 (SAN 287-5519) Tel 202-737-4650.

Serina, *(Serina Pr.; 0-911952),* 70 Kennedy St., Alexandria, VA 22305 (SAN 204-5834) Tel 703-548-4080.

Serpent Pub Co
See Artex Pr

Serrell-Simons, *(Serrell & Simons, Pubs.; 0-943104),* P.O. Box 64, Winnebago, WI 54985 (SAN 240-4400) Tel 414-231-1939; Dist. by: Baker & Taylor, Southeast Div., Mt. Oliver Rd., Commerce, GA 30599 (SAN 169-1503); Dist. by: Baker & Taylor, Midwest Div., 501 S. Gladiola Ave., Momence, IL 60954 (SAN 169-2100); Dist. by: Baker & Taylor, Western Div., 380 Edison Way, Reno, NV 89564 (SAN 169-4464) Tel 702-786-6700; Dist. by: Baker & Taylor, Eastern Div., 50 Kirby Ave., Somerville, NJ 08876 (SAN 169-4901); Dist. by: The Distributors, 702 S. Michigan, South Bend, IN 46618 (SAN 212-0364) Tel 219-232-8500; Dist. by: Wisconsin Authors & Pubs. Alliance, 34 S. Pontiac Dr., Janesville, WI 53545 (SAN 200-6057); Dist. by: Conkey's Bk. Store, 226 E. College Ave., Appleton, WI 54911 (SAN 200-6294) Tel 414-739-1223.

†Servant, *(Servant Pubns.; 0-89283),* 840 Airport Blvd., Ann Arbor, MI 48107 (SAN 208-9238) Tel 313-761-8505; Orders to: Customer Service Dept., Box 8617, Ann Arbor, MI 48107 (SAN 208-9246) Tel 313-761-8505; Dist. by: Spring Arbor, 10885 Textile Rd., Belleville, MI 48111 (SAN 662-1406) Tel 313-481-0900; Dist. by: East Coast Christian Dist., P.O. Box 4200, 35 Readington Rd., Somerville, NJ 08876 (SAN 662-1414). Formerly Named Word of Life; *CIP.*

Service League, *(Service League of Natchitoches, Inc.; 0-9607674),* P.O. Box 2206, Natchitoches, LA 71457 (SAN 226-7993) Tel 318-352-6723.

Service Press NE, *(Service Pr.; 0-9617063),* 1021 N. Main St., Box 606, Henderson, NE 68371 (SAN 662-9431); 1524 Coventry Ln., No. 12, Grand Island, NE 68801 (SAN 662-944X) Tel 308-384-6386. Do not confuse with Service Pr., of Haslett, MI.

Service Pub, *(Service Publishing Co.; 0-913104),* Park Lane Bldg., 2025 I St. NW, Suite 722, Washington, DC 20006 (SAN 204-5842) Tel 202-872-6007.

Servnet Corp, *(Servnet Corp.; 0-933073),* 4886 54th St., San Diego, CA 92115 (SAN 689-7959) Tel 619-265-8328.

SES Development, *(SES Development Corporation; 0-943982),* Dist. by: The Book Carrier, Inc., 9121 Industrial Court, Gaithersburg, MD 20877 (SAN 200-4046) Tel 301-258-1177.

SES Johnson Div, *(Signal Environmental Systems, Inc., Johnson Division; 0-9616456),* 1950 Old Highway 8, New Brighton, MN 55112 (SAN 659-2570) Tel 612-636-3900.

Sesnon Art Gall, *(Sesnon, Mary P., Art Gallery; 0-939982),* College V, Univ. of California, Santa Cruz, CA 95064 (SAN 216-8669) Tel 408-429-2314.

Sessions, *(Sessions Pubs.; 0-911366),* 48 Nassau Dr., New Hyde Park, NY 11040 (SAN 204-5850) Tel 516-747-3144.

†Seton Med Ctr, *(Seton Medical Ctr.; 0-9616516),* Div. of Mission Services Corp., 1900 Sullivan Ave., Daly City, CA 94015 (SAN 659-5847) Tel 415-991-6733; *CIP.*

Seton Pr, *(Seton Pr., The; 0-934397),* Box 1476, Tacoma, WA 98402 (SAN 693-8124) Tel 206-564-6062.

Settles Bks, *(Settles Books),* Box 1121, Aurora, IL 60507 (SAN 240-1576).

†Seven Arts, *(Seven Arts Press, Inc.; 0-911370),* 6253 Hollywood Blvd., No. 1100, Hollywood, CA 90028 (SAN 203-2538) Tel 213-469-1095; *CIP.*

Seven Hills Bks, *(Seven Hills Bks.; 0-911403),* Div. of Books for the Decorative Arts, Inc., 49 Central Ave., Suite 300, Cincinnatti, OH 45202 (SAN 169-6629) Tel 513-381-3881.

†Seven Locks Pr, *(Seven Locks Pr.; 0-932020),* 5125 MacArthur Blvd., NW, Washington, DC 20016 (SAN 211-9781) Tel 202-362-4714; P.O. Box 27, Cabin John, MD 20818 (SAN 658-1587); *CIP.*

Seven-M Pub Co, *(7-M Publishing Co.; 0-916527),* P.O. Box 136, Chriesman, TX 77838 (SAN 295-5482) Tel 409-567-7266.

Seven Oaks, *(Seven Oaks Press; 0-932508),* 405 S. 7th St., St. Charles, IL 60174 (SAN 212-1735) Tel 312-584-0187.

Seven Palms, *(Seven Palms Pr.; 0-912593),* Box 3371, Tucson, AZ 85722 (SAN 283-3115) Tel 602-621-3791.

†Seven Seas, *(Seven Seas Pr., Inc.; 0-915160),* 2 Dean Ave., Newport, RI 02840 (SAN 206-8737) Tel 401-849-9610; Toll free: 800-723-7323; Dist. by: Simon & Schuster, 1230 Ave. of Americas, New York, NY 10020 (SAN 200-2450) Tel 212-245-6400; *CIP.*

Seven Seasons Serv Co, *(Seven Seasons Service Co.; 0-9610868),* 8187 Westmore Rd., San Diego, CA 92126 (SAN 283-9105).

Seven Seven Search, *(Seven Seven Search Pubns.; 0-934726),* P.O. Box 252, Solana Beach, CA 92075 (SAN 213-5892) Tel 714-436-4843.

Seven Shadows, *(Seven Shadows Pr.; 0-916225),* P.O. Box 1118, Shaker Heights, OH 44120 (SAN 294-9989) Tel 216-283-5578.

Seven Springs, *(Seven Springs Center; 0-943006),* RD 3, Oregon Rd., Mount Kisco, NY 10549 (SAN 240-3269) Tel 914-241-1880.

Seven Suns, *(Seven Suns Pubns.; 0-931783),* P.O. Box 773, Rte. 1, Castle Estate, Fairfield, IA 52556 (SAN 684-846X) Tel 515-472-8613; Dist. by: New Leaf Distributing, The, 1020 White St., SW, Atlanta, GA 30310 (SAN 169-1449) Tel 404-755-2665.

†Seven Woods Pr, *(Seven Woods Press; 0-913282),* P.O. Box 32 Village Sta., New York, NY 10014 (SAN 203-2503); *CIP.*

Seven Worlds Pr, *(Seven Worlds Pr.; 0-936497),* 7312 Badgett Rd., Knoxville, TN 37919 (SAN 698-066X) Tel 615-522-3548.

Seventh Son Pr, *(Seventh Son Pr.; 0-933837),* P.O. Box 13224, Baltimore, MD 21203 (SAN 692-6851) Tel 301-276-3073.

Seventh Trumpet, *(Seventh Trumpet Publishing Company; 0-9610268),* P.O. Box 18, Schiller Park, IL 60176 (SAN 264-3847).

Seventies Pr
See Eighties Pr

Sevier County Cookbk, *(Sevier County Cookbook Committee; 0-9614182),* P.O. Box 66, Lockesburg, AR 71846 (SAN 686-6298) Tel 501-289-3401.

Seville Pub, *(Seville Publishing Co.; 0-930990),* 6740 Kester Ave., Second Floor, Van Nuys, CA 91405 (SAN 222-9323) Tel 818-501-5200.

Sew-Fit, *(Sew/Fit Pub. Co.; 0-933956),* 23 Calendar Ct., No. 207, La Grange, IL 60525 (SAN 212-1387) Tel 312-579-3222; Orders to: Sew-Fit Publishing Co., P.O. Box 565, La Grange, IL 60525 (SAN 212-1387) Tel 312-579-3222.

Sew Wonderful
See Arrants & Assoc

Sewing Knits, *(Sewing Knits Inc.; 0-9605860),* 634 W. Huntington Dr., No.12, Arcadia, CA 91006 (SAN 216-6089) Tel 818-435-8069.

Sewing Machine Man, *(Sewing Machine Man; 0-9614713),* RD 1, Box 430, Glen Rock, PA 17327 (SAN 692-6576) Tel 717-235-1215.

Sewing Sampler, *(Sewing Sampler Productions; 0-937659),* P.O. Box 39, Springfield, MN 56087 (SAN 659-3135) Tel 507-723-6547; 502 N. Van Buren, Springfield, MN 56087 (SAN 659-3143).

Sextant *Imprint of* **Childrens**

Sey Lawr *Imprint of* **Delacorte**

Seybold, *(Seybold Pubns., Inc.; 0-918514),* Box 644, Media, PA 19063 (SAN 210-007X) Tel 215-565-2480.

†SF Arts & Letters, *(San Francisco Arts & Letters Foundation; 0-914024),* P.O. Box 640394, San Francisco, CA 94164 (SAN 202-8751) Tel 415-771-3431; *CIP. Imprints:* Peace & Pieces (Peace & Pieces Books).

SF Bay Guardian, *(San Francisco Bay Guardian; 0-913192),* 2700 19th St., San Francisco, CA 94110 (SAN 215-2746) Tel 415-824-7660.

SF Center Vis Stud, *(San Francisco Ctr. for Visual Studies; 0-930976),* 49 Rivoli St., San Francisco, CA 94117 (SAN 209-5106) Tel 415-664-4699.

SF Dance Coalition, *(San Francisco Bay Area Dance Coalition; 0-9616244),* Ft. Mason Ctr., Bldg. C, San Francisco, CA 94123 (SAN 658-3601) Tel 415-673-8172.

SF Design, *(SF Design, Inc. /Owlswood Productions; 0-915942),* 287 Harborway South, S. San Francisco, CA 94080 (SAN 207-7264) Tel 415-583-8050.

SF Hist Records, *(San Francisco Historic Records; 0-911792),* 1204 Nimitz Dr., Colma, CA 94014 (SAN 204-5885) Tel 415-755-2204.

SF Inst Auto Ecol
See Rose Pub Co CA

SF Mime, *(San Francisco Mime Troupe, Inc.; 0-9606902),* 855 Treat, San Francisco, CA 94110 (SAN 217-4316) Tel 415-285-1717.

SF Stud Ctr
See SF Study Ctr

SF Study Ctr, *(San Francisco Study Ctr.; 0-936434),* P.O. Box 5646, San Francisco, CA 94101 (SAN 214-4654) Tel 415-626-1650.

SF Yesterday, *(San Francisco Yesterday),* P.O. Box 4343, San Rafael, CA 94903 (SAN 209-4886) Tel 415-479-1550.

SF Zoological, *(San Francisco Zoological Society; 0-933155),* Sloat Blvd. at the Pacific Ocean, San Francisco, CA 94132 (SAN 689-8513) Tel 415-661-2023.

SFO Pr, *(SFO Pr.; 0-937741),* 55 New Montgomery St., San Francisco, CA 94105 (SAN 659-2929) Tel 415-543-6234.

SFP Designs, *(SFP Designs, Inc.; 0-936361),* 369 Redwood Ave., Corte Madera, CA 94925 (SAN 699-7562) Tel 415-331-8828.

Sgnt *Imprint of* **NAL**

Sgovio, *(Sgovio; 0-9614127),* 24 Villa Ave., Buffalo, NY 14216 (SAN 686-466X) Tel 716-873-4383.

SH Press, *(SH Pr.; 0-938157),* Div. of Sports Hotline, Inc., 2872 Heathercrest Dr., Yorktown Heights, NY 10528 (SAN 659-7157) Tel 914-835-0900.

Shacor Inc
See Ekay Music

Shadduck-Sullivan, *(Shadduck & Sullivan; 0-935975),* 3508 45th Ave. S., Minneapolis, MN 55406-2927 (SAN 696-5865) Toll 612-729-1292.

Shade Tree, *(Shade Tree Books; 0-930742),* P.O. Box 2268, Huntington Beach, CA 92647 (SAN 211-0954) Tel 714-846-3869.

Shades Blue Pubns, *(Shades of Blue Pubns.; 0-9616669),* 286 S. Batavia, Apt. 9, Orange, CA 92666 (SAN 659-9060) Tel 714-997-2328.

Shades Mother Nat, *(Shades of Mother Nature; 0-9614021),* 206 Buckingham Dr., Glen Burnie, MD 21061 (SAN 683-6283) Tel 301-768-0648.

Shadow Pr, *(Shadow Pr., U.S.A.; 0-937724),* P.O. Box 8803, Minneapolis, MN 55408 (SAN 218-3617) Tel 612-822-3488; Dist. by: Midwest Distributors, P.O. Box 4642, Kansas City, MO 64109 (SAN 219-5038).

Shadowood Pubns, *(Shadowood Pubns.; 0-937025),* 7134 Fifth Ave., N, St. Petersburg, FL 33710 (SAN 658-7097) Tel 813-384-4723.

Shadrach, *(Shadrach Productions; 0-9613356),* P.O. Box 712, Moorestown, NJ 08057 (SAN 656-1330) Tel 609-234-5892.

Shadwold, *(Shadwold Press; 0-9603024),* P.O. Box 706, Kennebunkport, ME 04046 (SAN 212-5587) Tel 207-967-4400.

Shady Side Pen, *(Shady Side Peninsula Assn. Inc.; 0-9614295),* P.O. Box 114, Shady Side, MD 20764 (SAN 687-4584) Tel 301-867-7028.

Shadyside, *(Shadyside Press),* 320 Brooks Ave., Venice, CA 90291 (SAN 265-9808); Dist. by: Bookpeople, 2929 Fifth St., Berkeley, CA 94710 (SAN 168-9517); Dist. by: The Distributors, 702 S. Michigan, South Bend, IN 46618 (SAN 695-6920) Tel 219-232-8500.

Shadyside Presby, *(Shadyside Presbyterian Church, The; 0-9615554),* 5121 Westminster Pl., Pittsburgh, PA 15232 (SAN 696-0502) Tel 412-456-3123.

Shafer Bks, *(Shafer Bks., Inc.; 0-931687),* 139 Grand St., P.O. Box 40, Croton-On-Hudson, NY 10520 (SAN 695-6939) Tel 914-271-6919.

Shain F, *(Shain, Fayga; 0-9614920),* P.O. Box 7 Rte. 524, Adelphia, NJ 07710 (SAN 693-4307) Tel 201-431-4107.

Shaker Her Soc, *(Shaker Heritage Society; 0-89062),* Albany Shaker Rd., Albany, NY 12211 (SAN 289-0410) Tel 518-456-7890.

Shaker Mus, *(Shaker Museum Foundation Inc.; 0-937942),* Shaker Museum Rd., Old Chatham, NY 12136 (SAN 206-7684) Tel 518-794-9100.

Shaker Pr ME, *(Shaker Pr., The; 0-915836),* Sabbathday Lake, Poland Spring, ME 04274 (SAN 214-1388) Tel 207-926-4597.

Shaker Prairie, *(Shaker Prairie Publication),* R.R. One, Oaktown, IN 47561 (SAN 209-5173) Tel 812-745-3153.

Shaker Savings
See Ohio Savings

Shakti Pr, *(Shakti Pr.; 0-933211),* 2929 Fifth St., Berkeley, CA 94710 (SAN 682-8655) Tel 415-843-7869; Dist. by: Bookpeople, 2929 Fifth St., Berkeley, CA 94710 (SAN 168-9517) Tel 415-549-3030.

Shale Bks, *(Shale Bks; 0-930237),* P.O. Box 7000-477, Redondo Beach, CA 90277 (SAN 676-973X).

Shalit Liter, *(Shalit Literary Service),* 38 Sherman Place, Morristown, NJ 07960 (SAN 297-195X) Tel 201-538-6118.

Shallway Foun, *(Shallway Foundation; 0-934392),* 125 S. Fourth St., Connellsville, PA 15425 (SAN 213-1641).

Shalom, *(Shalom, P., Pubns., Inc.; 0-87559),* 5409 18th Ave., Brooklyn, NY 11204 (SAN 204-5893).

Shamal Bks, *(Shamal Books, Inc.; 0-917886),* G.P.O. Box 16, New York, NY 10116 (SAN 209-3618) Tel 212-622-4426.

†Shaman Bks, *(Shaman Books; 0-9611274),* 1033 W. Loyola Ave., No. 1007, Chicago, IL 60626 (SAN 283-1627) Tel 312-262-4888; *CIP.*

Shamar Bk, *(Shamar Book, A; 0-9607058),* 9215 N. Concho Lane, Phoenix, AZ 85028 (SAN 239-3840).

Shambala Pubns, *(Shambala Pubns.; 0-9614632),* 1049 Cresewood, E. Lansing, MI 48823 (SAN 691-8875) Tel 517-332-1623.

†Shambhala Pubns, *(Shambhala Pubns., Inc.; 0-87773; 0-394),* 314 Dartmouth St., Boston, MA 02116 (SAN 203-2481); Toll free: 800-638-6460 Tel 617-424-0030; Dist. by: Random Hse., Inc., 400 Hahn Rd., Westminster, MD 21157 (SAN 202-5515); *CIP. Imprints:* Great Eastern (Great Eastern Books); Hermes Hse (Hermes House).

Shameless Hussy, *(Shameless Hussy Pr.; 0-915288),* Box 3092, Berkeley, CA 94703 (SAN 282-3071) Tel 415-547-1062; Dist. by: Bookpeople, 2929 Fifth St., Berkeley, CA 94710 (SAN 168-9517) Tel 415-549-3030; Dist. by: Bookslinger, 213 E. Fourth St., St. Paul, MN 55101 (SAN 169-4154) Tel 612-221-0429; Dist. by: The Distributors, 702 S. Michigan, South Bend, IN 46618 (SAN 212-0364) Tel 219-232-8500; Dist. by: Inland Book Company, P.O. Box 261, 22 Hemingway Ave., East Haven, CT 06512 (SAN 200-4151) Tel 203-467-4257.

Shamro Creative Prod, *(Shamro Creative Productions; 0-939711),* 9560 Black Mountain Rd., San Diego, CA 90404 (SAN 663-6047) Tel 619-695-0099.

Shamrock Pr, *(Shamrock Press & Publishing Co.; 0-910583),* P.O. Box 7256, Alexandria, VA 22307 (SAN 260-2636) Tel 703-683-3114.

Shamrock Pubns, *(Shamrock Pubns.; 0-9608142),* 406 Rising Hill Dr., Fairborn, OH 45324 (SAN 240-1584).

Shane Pub, *(Shane Publishing; 0-86632),* P.O. Box 1615, Baltimore, MD 21203 (SAN 656-9021).

Shaney Advertising
See Willow Run Pub

Shano Pubs, *(Shano Pubs.; 0-914778),* Affil. of Grace Nash Publications, P.O. Box 1753-N, Scottsdale, AZ 85252 (SAN 692-2392) Tel 602-945-8821.

†Shanty Pr, *(Shanty Pr.; 0-916403),* 3236 Dupont S., Minneapolis, MN 55408 (SAN 295-5113) Tel 612-822-2375; *CIP.*

Shapian-Morrell, *(Shapian/Morrell Productions; 0-9610992),* 9110 Sunset Blvd., No. 240, Los Angeles, CA 90069 (SAN 265-2056) Tel 213-276-1005.

Shapiro, *(Shapiro, Leonard; 0-9607318),* 1567 N. Prospect Ave.- Apt. 416, Milwaukee, WI 53202 (SAN 239-3093) Tel 414-272-8683.

Shapolsky Bks *Imprint of* **Shapolsky Steimatzky**

Shapolsky Steimatzky, *(Shapolsky/Steimatzky; 0-933503),* 56 E. 11th St., New York, NY 10003 (SAN 200-8068) Tel 212-505-2505. *Imprints:* Shapolsky Bks (Shapolsky Bks.).

Share Pub Co, *(Share Publishing Co.; 0-933344),* P.O. Box 3453, Annapolis, MD 21403 (SAN 212-5595).

Shared Care, *(Shared Care; 0-9608702),* 6102 N. 14th St., Phoenix, AZ 85014 (SAN 238-3683) Tel 602-279-2619.

Sharing Co, *(Sharing Co., The; 0-941500),* P.O. Box 2224, Austin, TX 78768-2224 (SAN 211-0563) Tel 512-452-4366.

Sharon Hill, *(Sharon Hill Books; 0-932062),* P.O. Box 67, Sharon Hill, PA 19079 (SAN 210-5632).

Sharon Pubns, *(Sharon Pubns., Inc.; 0-89531),* Subs. of Edrei Communications Corp., 1086 Teaneck Rd., Teaneck, NJ 07666 (SAN 210-0989) Tel 201-833-1133; Orders to: New American Library, 1633 Broadway, New York, NY 10019 (SAN 206-8079) Tel 212-397-8126.

Sharon Pubns NYC, *(Sharon Pubns.; 0-915697),* 270 West End Ave., New York, NY 10023 (SAN 292-6601) Tel 212-362-3141.

†Sharp & Dunn, *(Sharp & Dunningan; 0-918495),* P.O. Box 660, Forest Ranch, CA 95942 (SAN 657-3029) Tel 916-891-6602; Dist. by: Baker & Taylor, Eastern Div., 50 Kirby Ave., Somerville, NJ 08876 (SAN 169-4901); Dist. by: Ingram Book Company, 347 Reedwood Dr., Nashville, TN 37217 (SAN 651-1163); Dist. by: Quality Books, 918 Sherwood Dr., Lake Bluff, IL 60044-2204 (SAN 169-2127); *CIP.*

Sharratt & Co, *(Sharratt & Company; 0-912295),* 3713 E. Easter Circle N., Littleton, CO 80122 (SAN 277-7061) Tel 303-773-3967.

Shasta Abbey, *(Shasta Abbey Pr.; 0-930066),* P.O. Box 199, Mt. Shasta, CA 96067 (SAN 210-6655) Tel 916-926-4208; Dist. by: Bookpeople, 2929 Fifth St., Berkeley, CA 94710 (SAN 168-9517).

Shasta FL, *(Shasta Pubns.; 0-9615596),* 201 N. Federal Hwy., Suite 215, Deerfield Beach, FL 33441 (SAN 696-1665) Tel 305-426-8503.

Shasta Pubns, *(Shasta Pubns.; 0-9608202),* 1062 Tahoe Terr., Cincinnati, OH 45238 (SAN 240-2793) Tel 513-451-2774.

Shasta Pubns
See Shasta FL

Shattinger *Imprint of* **Hansen Ed Mus**

ShaunTar Ent, *(ShaunTar Enterprises; 0-910241),* P.O. Box 11784, Santa Rosa, CA 95406 (SAN 241-4546) Tel 707-544-1478; Dist. by: The Distributors, 702 S. Michigan, South Bend, IN 46618 (SAN 169-2488) Tel 219-232-8500.

Shaunter Ent
See ShaunTar Ent

Shaw Pub, *(Shaw Pubs., Inc.; 0-9615773),* Box 63, Marissa, IL 62257 (SAN 696-5873) Tel 618-295-2241.

†Shaw Pubs, *(Shaw, Harold, Pubs.; 0-87788),* P.O. Box 567, 388 Gundersen Dr., Wheaton, IL 60189 (SAN 203-2473) Tel 312-665-6700; Toll free: 800-SHAW-PUB; *CIP.*

†Shawme Ent, *(Shawme Enterprises; 0-914151),* 36 Rte. 6A, R.F.D. 1, Sandwich, MA 02563 (SAN 287-556X) Tel 617-888-2519; *CIP.*

Shawnee County Hist, *(Shawnee County Historical Society; 0-916934),* 1205 W. 29th St., Rm. 430, Topeka, KS 66611 (SAN 282-3136) Tel 913-267-0309; P.O. Box 56, Topeka, KS 66601 (SAN 282-3144).

Shawnee Pr, *(Shawnee Press, Inc.; 0-9603394),* Waring Dr., Delaware Water Gap, PA 18327 (SAN 202-084X) Tel 717-476-0550.

Shawnee Print, *(Shawnee Printing Co.; 0-9604662; 0-939371),* P.O. Box 426, Shawnee, OK 74801 (SAN 662-7978); Toll free: 800-654-4166; 132 S. Union, Shawnee, OK 74801 (SAN 662-7986) Tel 405-275-4750.

Shayna Ltd, *(Shayna Ltd.; 0-9604208),* 100 Andrew St., Newton, MA 02161 (SAN 214-4727) Tel 617-244-1870.

Shaynew Pr, *(Shaynew Pr.; 0-936705),* 2029 Stockton St., San Francisco, CA 94133 (SAN 699-945X) Tel 415-391-9295; Orders to: P.O. Box 11719, San Francisco, CA 94101 (SAN 662-7854).

†Shearer Pub, *(Shearer Publishing; 0-940672),* 406 Post Oak Rd., Fredericksburg, TX 78624 (SAN 218-5989) Tel 512-997-6529; *CIP.*

Shearwater, *(Shearwater Press; 0-938050),* Box 417, Wellfleet, MA 02667 (SAN 216-1923).

Sheba Rev, *(Sheba Review, Inc.; 0-9610626),* P.O. Box 1623, Jefferson City, MO 65102 (SAN 264-6927) Tel 314-893-5834; Dist. by: Paperback Supply, 4121 Forest Park Blvd., St. Louis, MO 63108 (SAN 169-4324); Dist. by: Cowley Distributing, Inc., 732 Heisinger Rd., Jefferson City, MO 65101 (SAN 169-426X) Tel 314-636-6511.

Shedd Aquarium, *(Shedd Aquarium Society; 0-9611074),* 1200 S. Lake Shore Dr., Chicago, IL 60605 (SAN 283-4359).

Sheed & Ward, *(Sheed & Ward, Ltd.; 0-7220),* 2 Creechurch Ln., London EC3A 5AQ, .

Sheed & Ward
See Sheed & Ward MO

Sheed & Ward MO, *(Sheed & Ward; 0-934134; 1-55612),* Div. of National Catholic Reporter Publishing Co., Inc., P.O. Box 414292, Kansas City, MO 64141-0281 (SAN 207-7396); Toll free: 800-821-7926; 115 E. Armour Blvd., Kansas City, MO 61414-0281 (SAN 658-1269) Tel 816-531-0538; Toll free: 800-821-7296.

Sheehan Indust, *(Sheehan Industries; 0-9617018),* P.O. Box 801, Lake Stevens, WA 98258 (SAN 662-8621); 11918 24th PL., NE, Lake Stevens, WA 98258 (SAN 662-863X) Tel 206-377-3466.

†Sheep Meadow, *(Sheep Meadow Pr., The; 0-935296),* 5247 Independence Ave., Riverdale-on-Hudson, NY 10471 (SAN 669-2648) Tel 212-549-3321; Dist. by: Persea Bks., Inc., 225 Lafayette St., New York, NY 10012 (SAN 293-3926) Tel 212-431-5270; *CIP.*

Sheephead Bks, *(Sheephead Books; 0-9604644),* P.O. Box 562, Vidalia, GA 30474 (SAN 215-8094) Tel 912-537-2852.

Sheer Pr, *(Sheer Press; 0-9601254),* P.O. Box 4071, Walnut Creek, CA 94596 (SAN 210-4997) Tel 415-932-1144; 3601 Valley Vista Rd., Walnut Creek, CA 94598 (SAN 210-5004).

Sheets & Assocs, *(Sheets & Associates; 0-9613266),* P.O. Box 1853, Salt Lake City, UT 84110 (SAN 297-1933); 324 S. State St., No. 500, 84110 (SAN 297-1941).

Sheffield Bks, *(Sheffield Bks.; 0-934831),* P.O. Box 578099, Chicago, IL 60657 (SAN 694-292X) Tel 312-935-3689.

Sheffield Wisc, *(Sheffield Publishing Co.; 0-917974; 0-88133),* Subs. of Waveland Pr., Prospect Heights, IL, P.O. Box 359, Salem, WI 53168 (SAN 658-4519); 9009 Antioch Rd., Salem, WI 53168 (SAN 658-4527) Tel 414-843-2281.

Shelburne, *(Shelburne Museum, Inc.; 0-939384),* Shelburne, VT 05482 (SAN 205-941X) Tel 802-985-3346.

Shelburne Pub, *(Shelburne Publishing Co.; 0-930873),* P.O. Box 6162, Shawnee Mission, KS 66206 (SAN 677-7996) Tel 816-333-9700.

Shelcor Pub, *(Shelcor Publishing, Inc.; 0-937107),* 4634 Van Nuys Blvd., Sherman Oaks, CA 91403 (SAN 658-4411) Tel 818-789-5700.

Shell Cab, *(Shell Cabinet; 0-913792),* P.O. Box 29, Falls Church, VA 22046 (SAN 122-8455) Tel 703-256-0707.

Shell House, *(Shell Hse., Inc.; 0-9615700),* P.O. Box 1027, Lake Junaluska, NC 28745 (SAN 696-1215) Tel 704-456-3960; 71 Lakeshore Dr., Lake Junaluska, NC 28745 (SAN 696-9593).

Shellback Pr, *(Shellback Pr.; 0-931099),* P.O. Box 2442, Ventnor, NJ 08406 (SAN 678-9455) Tel 609-823-4549.

Shelley Bks, *(Shelley Bks.; 0-9615188),* P.O. Box 17184, NorthHills, Raleigh, NC 27619 (SAN 694-2660) Tel 919-782-1254.

Shellie Pr, *(Shellie Press; 0-9607038),* 420 Wisteria Rd., Venice, FL 33595 (SAN 239-3859).

†Shelter Pubns, *(Shelter Pubns., Inc.; 0-936070),* P.O. Box 279, Bolinas, CA 94924 (SAN 212-4521) Tel 415-868-0280; Dist. by: Random Hse., 400 Hahn Rd., Westminster, MD 21157 (SAN 202-5515); Dist. by: HP Books, P.O. Box 5367, Tucson, AZ 85703 (SAN 201-6087) Tel 602-888-2150; *CIP.*

Shelton, *(Shelton Pubns.; 0-918742),* P.O. Box 391, Sausalito, CA 94966 (SAN 210-4733) Tel 415-332-1165; Dist. by: Publishers Group West, 5855 Beaudry St., Emeryville, CA 94608 (SAN 202-8522) Tel 415-444-3570; Dist. by: Bookpeople, 2929 Fifth St., Berkeley, CA 94710 (SAN 168-9517) Tel 415-549-3030; Dist. by: Cal-West Periodicals, 2400 Filbert St., Oakland, CA 94607 (SAN 168-9983); Dist. by: Milligan News Co., Inc., 150 N. Autumn, San Jose, CA 95110 (SAN 169-0272) Tel 408-298-3322; Dist. by: L-S Distributors, 480 Ninth St., San Francisco, CA 94103 (SAN 169-0213) Tel 415-861-6300.

Shemco, *(Shemco; 0-937057),* Div. of Shemco Copr., The, 729 Washington Rd., Pittsburgh, PA 15228 (SAN 658-3520) Tel 412-341-1223.

Shenandoah Hist, *(Shenandoah History; 0-917968),* P.O. Box 98, Edinburg, VA 22824 (SAN 210-0118) Tel 703-459-4598.

Shenandoah Nat Assn, *(Shenandoah Natural History Assn., Inc.; 0-931606),* Shenandoah National Park, Rte. 4, Box 292, Luray, VA 22835 (SAN 222-9250) Tel 703-999-2243.

Shengold, *(Shengold Pubs., Inc.; 0-88400),* 23 W. 45th St., New York, NY 10036 (SAN 203-2465) Tel 212-944-2555.

Sheorue Pr, *(Shoerue Pr.; 0-9616292),* P.O. Box 3221, Santa Barbara, CA 93110 (SAN 658-442X) Tel 805-964-5841; 4025 State St., No. 35, Santa Barbara, CA 93110 (SAN 658-4438).

Shepard J, *(Shepard, Joyce),* 13 Sixpence Way, Coronado, CA 92118 (SAN 219-3167).

Shepard Poorman, *(Shepard Poorman Communications Corp.; 0-9607968),* P.O. Box 68110, Indianapolis, IN 46268 (SAN 238-0463) Tel 317-293-1500.

†Shepards-McGraw, *(Shepard's/McGraw-Hill; 0-07),* Div. of McGraw-Hill Bk. Co., 402 N. Cascade Ave., Colorado Springs, CO 80901 (SAN 205-9886) Tel 303-633-5521; Toll free: 800-525-2474; P.O. Box 1235, Colorado Springs, CO 80901 (SAN 658-1609); *CIP.*

Shepherd-Moore Ed Foun, *(Shepherd-Moore, Marie, Educational Foundation; 0-9603948),* 692 E. 40th St., Brooklyn, NY 11210 (SAN 221-6582).

Shepherd News Trust, *(Shepherd News Trust; 0-933663),* 174 Pierce St., W. Boylston, MA 01583 (SAN 692-5383) Tel 617-835-6663.

Shepherd Pubs VA, *(Shepherd Pubs.; 0-9607308),* 118 Pinepoint Rd., Williamsburg, VA 23185 (SAN 240-1622) Tel 804-229-0661.

Sher Music, *(Sher Music Co.; 0-9614701),* P.O. Box 40742, San Francisco, CA 94140 (SAN 692-610X) Tel 415-552-3172.

†Sheriar Pr, *(Sheriar Pr., Inc.; 0-913078),* 1414 Madison St., S., North Myrtle Beach, SC 29582 (SAN 203-2457) Tel 803-272-5333; *CIP.*

†Sheridan, *(Sheridan Hse., Inc.; 0-911378),* 145 Palisade St., Dobbs Ferry, NY 10522 (SAN 204-5915) Tel 914-693-2410; *CIP.*

Sheridan Med Bks, *(Sheridan Medical Bks.; 0-911378),* Div. of Sheridan Hse., Inc., 145 Palisade St., Dobbs Ferry, NY 10522 (SAN 204-5915).

Sheridan Pubns
See Sheridan Square Pubns

†Sheridan Square Pubns, *(Sheridan Square Pubns., Inc.),* P.O. Box 677, New York, NY 10013 (SAN 678-903X) Tel 212-254-1061; *CIP.*

Sherlock, *(Sherlock; 0-9616268),* 2627 Buckeye, Newport Beach, CA 92669 (SAN 658-3717) Tel 714-760-3636.

Sherlocks Book, *(Sherlock's Bookshop; 0-934935),* 492 S. First Ave., Des Plaines, IL 60016 (SAN 694-4167) Tel 312-297-8288.

Sherman, *(Sherman, Harvey),* 4011 Garden Ave., Los Angeles, CA 90039 (SAN 210-3680).

Sherman Keene
See SKE Pub

Sherman Pr, *(Sherman Pr.; 0-9614031),* 14755 Ventura Bl. 1-626, Sherman Oaks, CA 91403 (SAN 686-2756).

Sherokee, *(Ilse, Sherokee, & Associates; 0-9609456),* Div. of Wintergreen Press, 4105 Oak St., Long Lake, MN 55356 (SAN 260-0749) Tel 612-476-1303.

Sherry Urie, *(Urie, Sherry; 0-9603324),* RFD No. 3, Box 63, Barton, VT 05822 (SAN 211-4526).

†Sherway Pub, *(Sherway Publishing Co.; 0-912641),* P.O. Box 3096, Chatsworth, CA 91313-3096 (SAN 282-7905) Tel 818-700-9049; *CIP.*

Sherwood Co, *(Sherwood Co., The; 0-933056),* P.O. Box 21645, Denver, CO 80221 (SAN 212-8136) Tel 303-422-7900.

Sherwood Comns, *(Sherwood Communications; 0-914877),* P.O. Box 535, Southampton, PA 18966 (SAN 289-0682) Tel 215-357-9065.

Sherwood Pr, *(Sherwood Pr.; 0-9613290),* 17 High St., Woodbury, NJ 08096 (SAN 653-8355) Tel 609-848-8231.

Shetal Ent, *(Shetal Enterprises; 0-932888),* 1787-B. W. Touhy, Chicago, IL 60626 (SAN 213-9553) Tel 312-262-1133.

SHHH, *(Self Help for Hard of Hearing People, Inc.; 0-935473),* 7800 Wisconsin Ave., Bethesda, MD 20814 (SAN 695-9024) Tel 301-657-2473.

Shieldalloy, *(Shieldalloy Corp.-Metallurg Alloy Corp.; 0-9606196),* N. West Blvd., Newfield, NJ 08344 (SAN 220-3065) Tel 609-692-4200.

Shields, *(Shields Pubns.; 0-9600102; 0-914116),* P.O. Box 669, Eagle River, WI 54521 (SAN 204-5923) Tel 715-479-4810.

Shields Pub Co
See Publishers Consult

Shift Pub, *(Shift Publishing Co.; 0-931533),* P.O. Box 2242, Novato, CA 94948 (SAN 682-3122) Tel 415-892-4390.

Shikar Pub, *(Shikar Publishing Co.; 0-938199),* P.O. Box 9296, Santa Fe, NM 87501 (SAN 659-6606); Rte. 10, P.O. Box 1045, Santa Fe, NM 87501 (SAN 659-6614) Tel 505-988-4300.

Shillelagh, *(Shillelagh Books, Inc.; 0-9607838),* 8104 Wisner St., Niles, IL 60648 (SAN 238-1982) Tel 312-937-4257.

Shilo Pub Hse, *(Shilo Publishing House, Inc.; 0-88328),* 73 Canal St., New York, NY 10002 (SAN 205-9894) Tel 212-925-3468.

†Shining Star, *(Shining Star Press; 0-9613073),* P.O. Box 206, Goleta, CA 93116 (SAN 294-6599) Tel 805-968-1868; Dist. by: Bookpeople, 2929 Fifth St., Berkeley, CA 94710 (SAN 168-9517) Tel 415-549-3030; Dist. by: Inland Bk. Co., P.O. Box 261, 22 Hemingway Ave., East Haven, CT 06512 (SAN 200-4151) Tel 203-467-4257; *CIP.*

Shinn Music
See Duane Shinn

Shintaido, *(Shintaido of America; 0-942634),* 145 Judah, No. 6, San Francisco, CA 94122 (SAN 238-5805) Tel 415-731-9364.

Ship Inc, *(Ship, Inc., Pubns.),* 6206 S. First Avenue, Phoenix, AZ 85041 (SAN 208-1636) Tel 602-276-9654.

Ship-Shore, *(Ship to Shore; 0-9612686),* Div. of Robinson Yacht Co., Inc., 10500 Mt. Holly Rd., Charlotte, NC 28214 (SAN 289-419X) Tel 704-392-4740.

Shipley, *(Shipley Assocs.; 0-933427),* P.O. Box 40, Bountiful, UT 84010 (SAN 691-5175) Tel 801-295-2386; Toll free: 800-343-0009.

Shippers Natl, *(Shippers National Freight Claim Council, Inc.),* 120 Main St., Box Z, Huntington, NY 11743 (SAN 224-9553) Tel 516-549-8984.

273

Shire Pr, *(Shire Pr.; 0-918828),* P.O. Box 1728, Santa Cruz, CA 95061 (SAN 293-3942) Tel 408-425-0842; Dist. by: Bookpeople, 2929 Fifth St., Berkeley, CA 94710 (SAN 168-9517) Tel 415-549-3030.

Shirjieh Pubs, *(Shirjieh Pubs.; 0-912496),* P.O. Box 259, Menlo Park, CA 94025 (SAN 204-594X).

Shirk-Heath, *(Shirk-Heath, Sandra J.; 0-9615104),* 1935-42nd St. NW, Rochester, MN 55901 (SAN 694-2784) Tel 507-289-0711.

Shirlee, *(Shirlee Pubns.; 0-9613476),* P.O. Box 22122, Carmel, CA 93922 (SAN 657-3789) Tel 408-646-0600.

Shirleys Pub, *(Shirley's Publishing, Ltd.; 0-9609868),* 1608 Shenstone Ct., Virginia Beach, VA 23455 (SAN 275-3197) Tel 804-460-3668.

Shiver Mntn, *(Shiver Mountain Press, Inc.; 0-89488),* Rte. 47, Washington Depot, CT 06794 (SAN 210-0134) Tel 203-868-0533.

†**Shoal Creek Pub,** *(Shoal Creek Pubs.; 0-88319),* 406 Post Oak Rd., Fredericksburg, TX 78624 (SAN 203-2430) Tel 512-997-6529; Orders to: Shearer Publishing, 406 Post Oak Rd., Fredericksburg, TX 78624 (SAN 662-1449) Tel 512-447-6529; *CIP.*

Shoalwater Kitch, *(Shoalwater Kitchen; 0-9613895),* P.O. Box 624, Oysterville, WA 98641 (SAN 682-3130) Tel 206-665-4949; Dist. by: Pacific Pipeline, 19215 66th Ave., S., Kent, WA 98032 (SAN 208-2128) Tel 206-872-5523.

Shockley Pr, *(Shockley Pr.; 0-942048),* P.O. Box 36012, Los Angeles, CA 90036 (SAN 238-5937) Tel 213-933-4198.

Shoe Serv Inst, *(Shoe Service Institute of America; 0-931424),* 112 Calendar Court Mall, Lagrange, IL 60525 (SAN 211-5018) Tel 312-482-8010.

†**Shoe String,** *(Shoe String Pr., Inc.; 0-208),* P.O. Box 4327, Hamden, CT 06514 (SAN 213-2079) Tel 203-248-6307; 925 Sherman Ave., Hamden, CT 06514 (SAN 696-9410); *CIP. Imprints:* Archon Bks (Archon Books).(Archon Bks.); Cooper (Cooper); CT Academy (CT Academy); Lib Prof Pubns (Library Professional Publications).(Library Professional Pubns.); Linnet (Linnet); Pub. by Bingley England (Bingley, Clive, Limited (England)).(Bingley, Clive, Ltd. (England)); Pub. by Pembridge Pr UK (Pembridge Press (England)); Pub. by Thompson & Rutter, Inc. (Tompson & Rutter, Incorporated).(Tompson & Rutter, Inc.).

Shoe Tree Pr, *(Shoe Tree Pr.; 0-936915),* P.O. Box 356, Belvidere, NJ 07823 (SAN 658-375X) Tel 201-475-4751; 26 Parker St., Belvidere, NJ 07823 (SAN 658-3768).

Shofar Pubns, *(Shofar Pubns., Inc.; 0-936685),* P.O. Box 88711, Carol Stream, IL 60188 (SAN 699-7325) Tel 312-665-2150; 26 W 021 Astor Pl., Wheaton, IL 60187 (SAN 658-3024).

Sholars, *(Sholars, Robert E.; 0-9611178),* P.O. Box 2340, Mendocino, CA 95460 (SAN 283-4308).

Shopping Experience, *(Shopping Experience, Inc., The; 0-934758),* 2 Grace Ct., Brooklyn, NY 11201 (SAN 213-9472) Tel 718-625-2772.

†**Shopsmith,** *(Shopsmith, Inc.; 0-936611),* 6640 Poe Ave., Dayton, OH 45414 (SAN 686-2748) Tel 513-898-8070; Dist. by: Rodale Press Inc., 33 E. Minor St., Emmaus, PA 18049 (SAN 200-2477); *CIP.*

Shopware Educ, *(Shopware Educational Systems; 1-55669),* Rte. 1 Box 330-E, Aberdeen, WA 98520 (SAN 663-3838) Tel 206-532-3392.

Shore-Campbell, *(Shore/Campbell Publishing; 0-938297),* 1437 Lucile Ave., Los Angeles, CA 90026 (SAN 659-6592) Tel 213-666-6967; Dist. by: Baker & Taylor, Eastern Div., 50 Kirby Ave., Somerville, NJ 08876 (SAN 169-4901).

Shorewood Fine Art, *(Shorewood Fine Art Books, Inc.; 0-87230),* 27 Glen Rd., Sandy Hook, CT 06482 (SAN 219-9637) Tel 203-426-8100. *Imprints:* Woodbine Bks (Woodbine Books, Inc.).

Shorey, *(Shorey Pubns.; 0-8466),* 110 Union St., Seattle, WA 98101 (SAN 204-5958) Tel 206-624-0221.

Short Methods, *(Short Methods & Systems; 0-915800),* 1212 Hillsdale Dr., Claremont, CA 91711 (SAN 207-4842) Tel 714-626-3213.

Short Story Pr Imprint of **Holmes Pub**

Showcase, *(Showcase Charbo-Miles; 0-938201),* 3612 Stratford Rd., Topeka, KS 66604 (SAN 659-6622) Tel 913-272-5605.

Showcase Fairfield, *(Showcase Publishing Co.; 0-88205),* 1125 Missouri St., Fairfield, CA 94533 (SAN 213-6430) Tel 707-427-3130; Toll free: 800-526-0275.

†**Showcase Pubns,** *(Showcase Pubns.; 0-917800),* P.O. Box 40165, Pasadena, CA 91104 (SAN 213-5906) Tel 818-794-7782; *CIP.*

Shreveport Pub, *(Shreveport Publishing Corp.; 0-939042),* P.O. Box 31110, Shreveport, LA 71130 (SAN 216-1842).

Shrewd Pubns, *(Shrewd Pubns.; 0-936103),* Subs. of SourceWorks International, 2487 Samia Dr., Duluth, GA 30136 (SAN 696-7728) Tel 404-497-1100; P.O. Box 956277, Duluth, GA 30136 (SAN 699-6442).

Shroud of Turin, *(Shroud of Turin Research Project, Inc.; 0-9605516),* P.O. Box 7, Amston, CT 06231 (SAN 216-1834).

Shu Pub, *(Shu Publishing Co.; 0-938885),* 218 Dewey St., Worcester, MA 01610 (SAN 661-7158) Tel 617-756-6962.

Shulsinger Bros
See Shulsinger Sales

Shulsinger Sales, *(Shulsinger Sales, Inc.; 0-914080),* 50 Washington St., Brooklyn, NY 11201 (SAN 205-9851) Tel 718-852-0042.

†**Shumway,** *(Shumway, George, Pub.; 0-87387),* RD 7, Box 388B, York, PA 17402 (SAN 203-2422) Tel 717-755-1196; *CIP.*

Shumway Family Hist, *(Shumway Family History Services; 0-938717),* 1308 Cozy Terr., Anaheim, CA 92806 (SAN 661-616X) Tel 714-778-6199.

Shutts Minist, *(Shutts Ministries; 0-9614077),* P.O. Box 28, Marysville, OH 43040 (SAN 686-0648) Tel 513-644-9785.

SI Cont Ed Inc, *(Staten Island Continuum of Education, Inc.; 0-914639),* 130 Stuyvesant Pl., Staten Island, NY 10301 (SAN 289-6028) Tel 718-447-2600.

Si-sa-yong-o-sa, *(Si-sa-yong-o-sa, Inc.; 0-87296),* 115 W. 29th St., 5th Flr., New York, NY 10001 (SAN 673-1252) Tel 212-736-5092.

Siamese Imports, *(Siamese Imports Co., Inc.; 0-940202),* 148 Plandome Rd., Manhasset, NY 11030 (SAN 220-3545) Tel 516-365-8867.

Sibyl, *(Sibyl Jarvis Pischke; 0-9608532),* 1401 NE 35th St., Ft. Lauderdale, FL 33334 (SAN 240-7736) Tel 305-566-5078.

SICSA, *(Society for the Improvement of Stray Animals; 0-9615105),* 2600 Wilmington Pike, Dayton, OH 45419 (SAN 694-2709) Tel 513-294-6505; Box 82, Dayton, OH 45405 (SAN 694-2717).

SID, *(Society for Information Display),* 8055 W. Manchester Ave., No. 615, Playa Del Rey, CA 90293 (SAN 260-3446) Tel 213-305-1502.

Sidney Scott Ross, *(Ross, Sidney Scott; 0-9602028),* 1020 Meridian Ave., Suite 405, Miami Beach, FL 33139 (SAN 212-1379) Tel 305-538-1442.

SIECUS, *(Sex Information & Education Council of the U. S.; 0-9609212),* 80 Fifth Ave., Suite 801, New York, NY 10011 (SAN 224-2435) Tel 212-929-2300; Library, 715 Broadway, 2nd Flr., New York, NY 10003 (SAN 693-501X) Tel 212-673-3850.

Siegel, *(Siegel, Kenneth L., Publishing; 0-939848),* 19780 Ventura Blvd., Woodland Hills, CA 91364 (SAN 216-762X) Tel 818-999-6903.

Siemens Com Graphics, *(Siemens Communication Graphics; 0-936226),* 1501 Greenleaf, Evanston, IL 60602 (SAN 221-9956).

†**Sierra,** *(Sierra Club Bks.; 0-87156),* 730 Polk St., San Francisco, CA 94109 (SAN 203-2406) Tel 415-776-2211; Toll free: 800-638-6460; Dist. by: Random Hse., Inc., 400 Hahn Rd., Westminster, MD 21157 (SAN 202-5515); *CIP.*

Sierra Bks, *(Sierra Bks.; 0-916003),* Subs. of Sierra Records, P.O. Box 5853, Pasadena, CA 91107-0853 (SAN 294-6602) Tel 818-355-0181.

Sierra NV Chapter, *(Sierra Nevada Chapter),* Special Libraries Assn., P.O. Box 8159, Reno, NV 89507 (SAN 676-9659).

Sierra Pr, *(Sierra Pacific Press; 0-943238),* 1722 J St., Suite 19, Sacramento, CA 95814 (SAN 240-7744) Tel 916-444-9133.

Sierra Press, *(Sierra Pr., The; 0-939365),* P.O. Box 102, Yosemite National Park, CA 95389 (SAN 662-6955); Lot 60 El Portal Administrative Site, Yosemite National Park, CA 95389 (SAN 662-6963) Tel 209-379-2330. Do not confuse with Sierra Press, Phoenix, AZ.

Sierra Pub CA, *(Sierra Publishing (San Francisco); 0-932417),* 55 Sutter St., Suite 6, San Francisco, CA 94104 (SAN 686-7006) Tel 415-621-3652; Dist. by: Alchemy Bks., 717 Market St., Suite 514, San Francisco, CA 94101 (SAN 211-304X) Tel 415-777-2197.

Sierra Pub Co, *(Sierra Publishing Co.; 0-918493),* P.O. Box 213, Jackson, CA 95642 (SAN 676-9578) Tel 209-223-4238.

Sierra Pubns CA, *(Sierra Pubns.; 0-932848),* 70 Valley View Ave., San Jose, CA 95127 (SAN 211-6154) Tel 408-251-3799.

Sierra Pubns CO
See Sierra Pubns CA

Sierra Santa Fe, *(Sierra Club, Santa Fe Group; 0-9616458),* 1301 Luisa St., Santa Fe, NM 87501 (SAN 659-302X) Tel 505-983-2703.

Sierra Trading, *(Sierra Trading Post; 0-905890),* P.O. Box 2497, San Francisco, CA 94126 (SAN 216-6097) Tel 415-456-9378.

Siftsoft, *(Siftsoft; 0-936687),* 100 Valencia, San Francisco, CA 94103 (SAN 699-914X) Tel 415-824-0731; P.O. Box 260, San Francisco, CA 94103 (SAN 699-9158).

Sig Imprint of **NAL**

Sig Classics Imprint of **NAL**

†**Sigga Pr,** *(Sigga Press; 0-916348),* P.O. Box 25, Nottingham, NH 03290 (SAN 211-2698); *CIP.*

Sightseer, *(Sightseer Pubns.; 0-937928),* 7400 N. Kendall Dr., Miami, FL 33156 (SAN 220-1240).

Sigma Pr, *(Sigma Press Inc.; 0-9604516),* P.O. Box 379, South Bound Brook, NJ 08880 (SAN 215-8116).

Sigma Pr NY, *(Sigma Press),* P.O. Box 264, Manhasset, NY 11030 (SAN 240-9577).

Sigma Pub, *(Sigma Publishing Co., Inc.; 0-937027),* 1316 Broad St., Syracuse, NY 13224 (SAN 658-3474) Tel 315-446-0781.

Sigma Sci Inc, *(Sigma Scientific, Inc.; 0-915313),* 903 Myers Place, Blacksburg, VA 24060 (SAN 290-0416) Tel 703-951-0258.

Sigma Tau Gamma, *(Sigma Tau Gamma),* Box 54, Warrensburg, MO 64093 (SAN 224-5337) Tel 816-747-2222.

Signal Bks, *(Signal Bks.; 0-930095),* Subs. Of Compute Textual Services, 201-C E. Main St., Carrboro, NC 27510 (SAN 670-1795) Tel 919-929-5985.

Signal Media, *(Signal Media Corp.; 0-9616677),* 14951 Dallas Pkwy., Suite 1030, Dallas, TX 75240 (SAN 659-6789) Tel 214-458-8400.

Signals Pub, *(Signals Publishing Co.; 0-9615962),* P.O. Box 5071, Beverly Hills, CA 90210 (SAN 696-7760) Tel 213-650-0701; 2121 Kress St., Los Angeles, CA 90046 (SAN 697-3086).

Signature Bks, *(Signature Bks., Inc.; 0-941214),* 350 S. 400 E., Salt Lake City, UT 84111 (SAN 217-4391) Tel 801-531-1483. *Imprints:* Eden Hill Pub (Eden Hill Publishing); Orion (Orion).

Signature Pub, *(Signature Publishing Corp.; 0-939147),* 1155 Watson Way, No. 5, Sparks, NV 89431 (SAN 662-9059) Tel 702-331-1211.

Signmaker, *(Signmaker Press; 0-9605774),* Box 967, Ashland, OR 97520 (SAN 216-549X).

Signpost, *(Signpost Pr., Inc., The; 0-936563),* 412 N. State St., Bellingham, WA 98225 (SAN 698-097X) Tel 206-734-9781.

Signpost Bk Pub, *(Signpost Bk. Pub. Co.; 0-913140),* 8912 192nd St. SW, Edmonds, WA 98020 (SAN 204-5966) Tel 206-776-0370.

Signpost Pr, *(Signpost Pr.; 0-9609592),* N 56 W21414 Silver Spring Rd., Menomonee Falls, WI 53051 (SAN 275-3596) Tel 414-252-3219.

Signpost Pubns
See Signpost Bk Pub

Symbols/Abbreviations

Signs of Times, *(Signs of the Times Publishing Co.; 0-911380),* 407 Gilbert Ave., Cincinnati, OH 45202 (SAN 204-5974) Tel 513-421-2050; Toll free: 800-543-1925.

Signum Bks, *(Signum Books Limited; 0-9612034),* P.O. Box 5057, Oregon City, OR 97045-8057 (SAN 286-8768) Tel 503-657-3567.

Sigo Pr, *(Sigo Pr.; 0-938434),* 77 N. Washington St., No. 201, Boston, MA 02114 (SAN 216-3020) Tel 617-523-2321.

Sijthoff & Noordhoff
See Kluwer Academic

Silbert Bress, *(Silbert & Bress Pubns.; 0-89544),* P.O. Box 68, Mahopac, NY 10541 (SAN 210-5020) Tel 914-628-7910.

Silicon Pr, *(Silicon Pr.; 0-9615336),* 25 Beverly Rd., Summit, NJ 07901 (SAN 695-1538)
Tel 201-273-2272.

†**Siliconix Inc,** *(Siliconix Inc.; 0-930519),* 2201 Laurelwood Rd., Santa Clara, CA 95054 (SAN 692-7750) Tel 408-970-4066; Toll free: 800-554-5564; *CIP.*

Silk Butterfly Pr *Imprint of* **Panda Bks Pubs**

Silo Pubs, *(Silo Pubs., The; 0-937109),* P.O. Box 3662, Hesperia, CA 92345 (SAN 658-439X) Tel 619-244-1674; 18019 Danbury Ave., Hesperia, CA 92345 (SAN 658-4403).

Silv Dollar Pr, *(Silver Dollar Pr.; 0-9615146),* 5021 Arlington Dr., North Little Rock, AR 72116 (SAN 694-2725) Tel 501-753-4181.

†**Silver,** *(Silver Burdett Co.; 0-382),* Subs. of SFN Cos, Inc., 250 James St., Morristown, NJ 07960-1918 (SAN 204-5982) Tel 201-285-7700; Toll free: 800-631-8081; *CIP.*

Silver Age Pub, *(Silver Age Publishing; 0-940294),* P.O. Box 384, Rego Park, NY 11374 (SAN 217-5835) Tel 718-897-6938.

Silver & Gold, *(Silver & Gold Report; 0-935754; 0-916373),* P.O. Box 40, Bethel, CT 06801 (SAN 221-9972).

Silver App Pr, *(Silver Apples Press; 0-943710),* P.O. Box 292, Hainesport, NJ 08036 (SAN 238-3721).

†**Silver Buckle Pr,** *(Silver Buckle Pr.; 0-931101),* Memorial Library, Rm. 443, University of Wisconsin, 728 State St., Madison, WI 53706 (SAN 676-9497); *CIP.*

Silver D Invest Inc, *(Silver D. Investments, Inc.; 0-912497),* P.O. Box 833038, Richardson, TX 75083 (SAN 265-315X) Tel 214-699-0439.

Silver Dollar, *(Silver Dollar City, Inc.),* Silver Dollar City, MO 65616 (SAN 210-3699) Tel 417-388-2611.

Silver Fox, *(Silver Fox Connections; 0-9605910),* 1244 SW 301st St., Federal Way, WA 98003 (SAN 216-4485) Tel 206-839-3784.

Silver Sea, *(Silver Sea Pr.; 0-916005),* 820 Pacific Coast Hwy., Suite 103, Hermosa Beach, CA 90254 (SAN 294-6610) Tel 213-379-8959.

Silver Seal Bks, *(Silver Seal Books; 0-910867),* P.O. Box 106, Fox Island, WA 98333 (SAN 264-3871).

Silver Sg Pr, *(Silver Spring Press; 0-931953),* 15721 New Hampshire Ave, Silver Spring, MD 20904 (SAN 685-9674) Tel 301-384-9385.

Silver Skates *(Silver Skates Publishing Co.; 0-936105),* 1020 Santa Fe Ave., Albany, CA 94706 (SAN 696-7493) Tel 415-528-1302.

Silverado, *(Silverado Publishing Co.; 0-87938),* St. Helena, CA 94574 (SAN 213-3725); Dist. by: Motorbooks International, Pubs. & Wholesalers, 729 Prospect Ave., Osceola, WI 54020 (SAN 212-3304) Tel 715-294-3345.

Silverback, *(Silverback Books; 0-916747),* 323 Franklin Bldg. S., Suite 804/Department S-199, Chicago, IL 60606-7096 (SAN 654-4495) Tel 219-736-2112; Dist. by: The Distributors, 702 S. Michigan, South Bend, IN 46618 (SAN 169-2488) Tel 219-232-8500.

SilverBack
See Silverback

Silverbell Pr, *(Silverbell Pr.; 0-937489),* 25 Glenhaven, DeRidder, LA 70634 (SAN 659-1698) Tel 318-462-5105.

Silverfish Rev Pr, *(Silverfish Review Press; 0-9610508),* P.O. Box 3541, Eugene, OR 97403 (SAN 264-388X).

Silvergirl Bks
See Silvergirl Inc

†**Silvergirl Inc,** *(Silvergirl, Inc.),* P.O. Box 4858, Austin, TX 78765 (SAN 239-3875) Tel 512-473-2478; *CIP.*

†**Silverleaf Pr,** *(Silverleaf Press; 0-915591),* 19 Harding Lane, Westport, CT 06880 (SAN 292-6660) Tel 203-227-5727; *CIP.*

Silvermine, *(Silvermine Pubs.; 0-87231),* Comstock Hill, Silvermine, Norwalk, CT 06850 (SAN 209-6005) Tel 203-847-4732.

Simile II, *(Simile II),* 218 Twelfth St., P.O. Box 910, Del Mar, CA 92014 (SAN 208-8525) Tel 619-755-0272.

Simjac Pr, *(Simjac Press; 0-9615076),* Subs. of Danforth Publishing, Inc., 75 Russell St., Hamden, CT 06514 (SAN 694-048X) Tel 203-734-3331.

Simmons Boardman, *(Simmons-Boardman Bks., Inc.; 0-911382),* Subs. of Simmons-Boardman Publishing Corporation, New York, 1809 Capitol Ave., Omaha, NE 68102 (SAN 213-2605) Tel 402-346-4300; Toll free: 800-228-9670.

Simonetta Pr, *(Simonetta Pr.; 0-941594),* 15 W. Locust St., Bethlehem, PA 18018 (SAN 239-3883) Tel 215-867-5479.

Simons Bks, *(Simons Bks., Inc.; 0-937812),* P.O. Box 2145, Oceanside, CA 92054 (SAN 216-4493).

Simons Meredith, *(Simons & Meredith; 0-938277),* P.O. Box 554, Hasbrouck Heights, NJ 07604 (SAN 659-9141); 300 Speedwell Ave., Morris Plains, NJ 07950 (SAN 659-915X) Tel 201-538-1000.

Simontsits, *(Simontsits, Attila L.; 0-920004),* 4118 Ridge Rd., Apt. 6, Brooklyn, OH 44144 (SAN 283-409X) Tel 216-661-4319.

Simp Soft Computer, *(Simple Soft Computer Services; 0-939463),* 3208 Cahuenga Blvd. W., Suite 121, Los Angeles, CA 90068 (SAN 663-3382) Tel 818-505-9832.

Simple Prod, *(Simple Productions; 0-938497),* 12 E. 15th St., No. 3, Arcata, CA 95521 (SAN 661-0536) Tel 707-822-3148.

Simplex Comm, *(Simplex Communications, Inc.; 0-935248),* P.O. Box 9133, Fort Wayne, IN 46783 (SAN 213-3741) Tel 219-672-3702. Moved, left no forwarding address.

Simplicity, *(Simplicity Pattern Co., Inc.; 0-918178),* 200 Madison Ave., New York, NY 10016 (SAN 282-3179) Tel 212-576-0533; Orders to: Simplicity Educational Div., 901 Wayne St., Niles, MI 49121 (SAN 282-3187).

Simplified Reg, *(Simplified Regulations; 0-9607866),* W. 137 N. 8235 Parkview Dr., Menomonee Falls, WI 53051 (SAN 238-1990) Tel 414-255-2204.

Simply Delight, *(Simply Delightful Merchandising; 0-9614249),* 316 California Ave., Suite 304, Reno, NV 89509 (SAN 686-7308) Tel 702-673-0907.

Simply Elegant, *(Simply Elegant Co.; 0-9600492),* 3801 N. Mission Hills Rd., Northbrook, IL 60062 (SAN 204-5990) Tel 312-564-2221; Orders to: P.O. Box 74, Winnetka, IL 60093 (SAN 204-6008).

Simpson Pub, *(Simpson Publishing Co.),* 1115 S. Franklin St., Kirksville, MO 63501 (SAN 202-9928) Tel 816-665-7251.

Sims Pub, *(Sims Publishing; 0-930595),* P.O. Box 9576, Sacramento, CA 95823 (SAN 693-3726).

Simtek, *(Simtek; 0-933836),* P.O. Box 105, Carlisle, MA 01741-0105 (SAN 212-6907) Tel 617-369-5538.

Simul Learn, *(Simulation Learning Institute, Inc.; 0-918640),* 1 Adams Ct., Oyster Bay, NY 11771 (SAN 210-3702) Tel 516-922-6490.

Sinauer Assoc
See Sinauer Assocs

†**Sinauer Assocs,** *(Sinauer Assocs., Inc.; 0-87893),* N. Main St., Sunderland, MA 01375 (SAN 203-2392) Tel 413-665-3722; *CIP.*

Sinclair Ent, *(Sinclair, Dorothy, Enterprises; 0-9615311),* P.O. Box 782, Bellaire, TX 77401-0782 (SAN 694-5996) Tel 713-664-9809.

Sinclaire Pr, *(Sinclaire Pr.; 0-9616886),* 42 Bay View Rd., Wellesley, MA 02181 (SAN 661-6542) Tel 617-237-0140.

Sindowilf Ltd, *(Sindwilf Ltd. Pr.; 0-939580),* 110 La Bolsa Rd., Walnut Creek, CA 94598 (SAN 216-695X) Tel 415-932-7612.

Singer Pr, *(Singer Press; 0-9610922),* 1540 Rollins Dr., Los Angeles, CA 90063 (SAN 265-1106) Tel 213-263-2640.

Singing Bone Pr, *(Singing Bone Pr.; 0-933439),* 2318 Albion Pl., St. Louis, MO 63104 (SAN 691-5221) Tel 314-865-2789.

Singing Horse, *(Singing Horse Pr.; 0-935162),* P.O. Box 40034, Philadelphia, PA 19106 (SAN 219-2810) Tel 215-844-7429.

Singing River, *(Singing River Pubs.),* 4310 Twin Oaks Ave., Pascagoula, MS 39567 (SAN 239-4855).

Singing Stars Pr, *(Singing Stars Pr.; 0-936319),* P.O. Box 217, Rosemont, NJ 08556 (SAN 697-3159) Tel 609-397-8311.

Single Action Prod, *(Single Action Productions; 0-938887),* Div. of Images, 60 E. 135th St., Suite 7C, New York, NY 10037 (SAN 662-6572) Tel 212-690-2472.

Single Graph, *(Single Graphics; 0-914067),* 5043 N. 20th Ave., Phoenix, AZ 85015 (SAN 287-5535) Tel 602-246-7499.

Single Impressions, *(Single Impressions; 0-938562),* 1240 W. Eureka, Tucson, AZ 85704 (SAN 215-8132).

Single Source
See SourceView

Single Vision, *(Single Vision Pubns.; 0-9608960),* Box No. 804, Lebanon, OR 97355 (SAN 241-2519) Tel 503-258-5888.

Singlejack Bks, *(Singlejack Bks., of Miles & Weir, Ltd.; 0-917300),* Div. of Miles & Weir Ltd., P.O. Box 1906, San Pedro, CA 90733 (SAN 208-8541) Tel 213-548-5964; 839 S. Beacon St., Suite 308, San Pedro, CA 90733 (SAN 662-1465); Dist. by: Baker & Taylor Co., Eastern Div., 50 Kirby Ave., Somerville, NJ 08876 (SAN 169-4901); Dist. by: Baker & Taylor Co., Southeast Div., Mt. Olive Rd., Commerce, GA 30529 (SAN 169-1503); Dist. by: Baker & Taylor Co., Western Div., 380 Edison Way, Reno, NV 89564 (SAN 169-4464) Tel 206-872-5523; Dist. by: Baker & Taylor Co., Midwest Div., 501 Gladiola Ave., Momence, IL 60954 (SAN 169-2100); Dist. by: The Distributors, 702 S. Michigan, South Bend, IN 46618 (SAN 169-2488) Tel 219-232-8500.

Singles World, *(Singles World Publishing Co.; 0-936890),* 1094 Cudahy, No. 102, San Diego, CA 92110 (SAN 214-4735); Dist. by: Communication Creativity, P.O. Box 213, Saguache, CO 81149 (SAN 210-3478) Tel 303-655-2502.

Singular Hse Pr, *(Singular Hse. Pr.; 0-9616388),* 1302 Meridene Dr., Baltimore, MD 21239 (SAN 659-1736) Tel 301-435-0392.

Singular Speech Pr, *(Singular Speech Press; 0-9607756),* 507 Dowd Ave., Canton, CT 06019 (SAN 238-115X) Tel 203-693-6059.

Sinister Wisdom Bks, *(Sinister Wisdom Bks.; 0-931103),* P.O. Box 1308, Montpelier, VT 05602 (SAN 694-2199) Tel 802-229-9104.

†**Sipapu-Konocti Bks,** *(Sipapu/Konocti Books; 0-914134),* Subs. of Konocti Books, Rte. 1, Box 216, Winters, CA 95694 (SAN 206-5517) Tel 916-662-3364; *CIP.*

SIPRI *Imprint of* **Taylor & Francis**

SIR Inc, *(SIR Inc.; 1-55534),* 5215 Old Orchard, Suite 800, Skokie, IL 60077 (SAN 695-8605) Tel 312-470-9770.

Siren, *(Siren Publisher; 0-9613395),* 1034 Valota Rd., Redwood City, CA 94061 (SAN 657-114X) Tel 415-367-7755.

Sirius Bks, *(Sirius Books; 0-917108),* 4745 Anderson Ln., Eureka, CA 95501 (SAN 275-3766) Tel 707-442-8481.

Sirius Leag, *(Sirius League, The; 0-9610762),* P.O. Box 40507, Albuquerque, NM 87196 (SAN 264-6366) Tel 505-262-0720.

Sirius Pubns, *(Sirius Pubns.),* P.O. Box 1201, Agoura Hills, CA 91301 (SAN 282-3195) Tel 818-706-8838 (SAN 282-3209).

Siriusware, *(Siriusware; 0-926848),* 6 Turning Mill Rd., Lexington, MA 02173 (SAN 653-8606) Tel 617-862-9570.

Sis Kenny Inst, *(Sister Kenny Institute; 0-88440),* Pubns. Office, 800 E. 28th St., Minneapolis, MN 55407 (SAN 203-0705) Tel 612-874-4175.

Sisters, *(Sisters; 0-9610930),* P.O. Box 14593, Minneapolis, MN 55414 (SAN 265-2080) Tel 612-729-5383.

Sisters Choice, *(Sisters' Choice Press; 0-932164),* 1450-Sixth St., Berkeley, CA 94710 (SAN 211-7126) Tel 415-524-5804; Dist. by: Childrens Small Pr. Collection, 719 N. Fourth Ave., Ann Arbor, MI 48104 (SAN 200-514X).

Sisters Christ Charity, *(Sisters of Christian Charity; 0-9616887),* 1041 Ridge Rd., Wilmette, IL 60091-1560 (SAN 661-6402) Tel 312-256-1060.

Sisters Divine, *(Sisters of the Divine Savior; 0-9616092),* 4311 N. 100th St., Milwaukee, WI 53222 (SAN 698-1232) Tel 414-466-0810.

Sisters Grim Pr, *(Sisters Grim Pr., The; 0-9614371),* 140 Wylie Dr., No. 12, Baton Rouge, LA 70808 (SAN 688-6124) Tel 504-891-3458.

Sisters St Mary OR, *(Sisters of St. Mary of Oregon; 0-9616750),* 4440 SW, 148th Ave., Beaverton, OR 97007 (SAN 661-0420) Tel 503-644-9181.

Sitare Inc, *(Sitare, Inc.; 0-940178),* 1888 Century Park E., No. 10, Los Angeles, CA 90067 (SAN 217-0833).

SITES, *(SITES; 0-86528),* P.O. Box 1949, Washington, DC 20013 (SAN 692-7513) Tel 202-357-3168; Dist. by: Smithsonian Institution Traveling Exhibition Service, 1100 Jefferson Dr., SW, Suite 3147, Washington, DC 20560 (SAN 206-8044) Tel 202-357-3168.

†Sitnalta Pr, *(Sitnalta Press; 0-931826),* P.O. Box 2730, San Francisco, CA 94126 (SAN 211-5026); *CIP.*

Six Lights, *(Six Lights; 0-938919),* P.O. Box 357, Cutler, ME 04626 (SAN 661-7409) Tel 207-259-4424.

Six Pr, *(6 Press; 0-943310),* 11889 Dogwood Ave., Fountain Valley, CA 92708 (SAN 240-7752) Tel 714-839-1857.

Sixteenth Cent, *(Sixteenth Century Journal Pubs., Inc.; 0-940474),* NE Missouri State Univ., Laughlin Bldg., No. 115, Kirksville, MO 63501 (SAN 223-159X) Tel 816-785-4665.

Sixth House Pr Inc, *(Sixth House Press, Inc., The; 0-913911),* P.O. Box 10458, St. Petersburg, FL 33733 (SAN 286-8741) Tel 813-864-1630.

SJB Pub Co, *(SJB Publishing Co.; 0-912287),* 26632 Valpariso Rd., Mission Viejo, CA 92691 (SAN 265-0975) Tel 714-768-7238.

SK Pubns, *(SK Pubns.; 0-936306),* 7149 Natalie Blvd., Northfield, OH 44067 (SAN 214-1396).

Skagit Cnty Hist, *(Skagit County Historical Society; 0-914989),* P.O. Box 424, Mount Vernon, WA 98273 (SAN 289-4297) Tel 206-424-1328.

Skandia, *(Skandia America Group; 0-9609050),* 280 Park Ave., New York, NY 10017 (SAN 240-9062).

Skandisk, *(Skandisk, Inc.; 0-9615394),* 3424 19th Ave. S., Minneapolis, MN 55407 (SAN 695-4405) Tel 612-724-6561.

SKD Publishing, *(Sharon Kimberly Damon Publishing Co.; 0-937875),* 4201 Via Marina, No. 160, Marina del Rey, CA 90292 (SAN 659-5855); 624 S. Central Expressway, Richardson, TX 75080 (SAN 663-320X).

SKE Pub, *(SKE Publishing; 0-942080),* Subs. of Sherman Keene Pubns., P.O. Box 2519, Sedona, AZ 86336 (SAN 238-6046) Tel 602-282-1258.

Skies Call, *(Skies Call; 0-9503341),* 6339 31st Pl., NW, Washington, DC 20015 (SAN 207-5385) Tel 202-966-5186; Orders to: P.O. Box 57238, Washington, DC 20037 (SAN 207-5393).

Skill Builders, *(Skill Builders, Inc.; 0-915625),* 1800 Penfield Rd., Penfield, NY 14526 (SAN 292-6695).

Skillcorp, *(Skillcorp Pubs; 0-88085),* 203 Eighth St., Honesdale, PA 18431 (SAN 240-2807) Tel 717-253-4558; Orders to: 2300 W. Fifth Ave., P.O. Box 712, Columbus, OH 43216 (SAN 669-2656) Tel 614-486-0631.

Skills Improvement, *(Skills Improvement; 0-939570),* P.O. Box 595, Aurora, CO 80040 (SAN 216-6968) Tel 303-695-6187.

Skinner Hse Bks *Imprint of* **Unitarian Univ**

Skinny Bks, *(Skinny Books; 0-912499),* Box A 94, New York, NY 10272 (SAN 265-2110) Tel 212-732-0358.

Sko Studios, *(SKO Studios; 0-9615546),* 482 15th Ave., San Francisco, CA 94118 (SAN 695-9172) Tel 415-752-5053.

Skokie Valley Pr, *(Skokie Valley Pr.; 0-9614516),* 4250 N. Marine Dr., Chicago, IL 60613 (SAN 689-8106) Tel 312-549-1412.

Skribent, *(Skribent Press; 0-9609374),* 9700 SW Lakeside Dr., Tigard, OR 97223 (SAN 283-2542) Tel 503-620-0471; Dist. by: Pacific Pipeline Distributors, 19215 66th ave., S, Kent, WA 98032 (SAN 208-2128) Tel 206-872-5523.

Sky Bks, *(Sky Bks.; 0-9612274),* 2352 Ogden, No. Two, Denver, CO 80205 (SAN 289-5692) Tel 303-837-9235.

†Sky Pub, *(Sky Publishing Corp.; 0-933346),* 49 Bay State Rd., Cambridge, MA 02238 (SAN 212-4556) Tel 617-864-7360. Not to be confused with Sky Publications in Ringwood, NJ; *CIP.*

Sky Pubns NJ, *(Sky Pubns.; 0-941566),* 210 Skylands Rd., Ringwood, NJ 07456 (SAN 239-3123) Tel 201-962-6606. Not to be confused with Sky Publishing Corp. in Cambridge, MA.

Sky River Pr, *(Sky River Pr.; 0-918475),* 236 E. Main St., Ashland, OR 97520 (SAN 657-7164) Tel 503-488-0645.

Sky Road Pr, *(Sky Road Pr.; 0-9616544),* 940 Mathews Dr., Chico, CA 95926 (SAN 659-5340) Tel 916-343-6719.

Skybridge Pub Inc, *(Skybridge Publishing, Inc.; 0-911675),* 238 Smith Ridge Rd., New Canaan, CT 06840 (SAN 264-391X) Tel 203-966-8585.

Skydog OR, *(Skydog),* 6735 SE 78th St., Portland, OR 97206 (SAN 226-8019).

Skydog WA
See Skydog OR

Skye Terrier, *(Skye Terrier Club of America; 0-9600722),* Affil. of American Kennel Club, 2222 S. 12th St., St. Louis, MO 63104 (SAN 206-5681) Tel 314-773-4444.

Skyer Consul, *(Skyer Consultation Ctr.; 0-943106),* P.O. Box 121, Rockaway Park, NY 11694 (SAN 240-4427) Tel 718-634-7206.

Skylark *Imprint of* **Bantam**

Skylight, *(Skylight Pr., Inc.; 0-910423),* 3603 Hamilton St., Philadelphia, PA 19104 (SAN 240-9070).

Skylight Prod, *(Skylight Productions; 0-938111),* P.O. Box 6129, San Rafael, CA 94903 (SAN 659-7726); 617 Wakerobin Ln., San Rafael, CA 94983 (SAN 659-7734) Tel 415-499-1023.

Skyline Press, *(Skyline Pr.),* Div. of David White, Inc., 1 Pleasant Ave., Port Washington, NY 11050 (SAN 678-9021) Tel 516-944-9325.

Skyline Pub, *(Skyline Publishing; 0-918981),* P.O. Box 1880, Columbia Falls, MT 59912 (SAN 669-8662) Tel 406-892-5560.

Skyline West Pr, *(Skyline West Pr.; 0-914767),* Affil. of Calendars Unlimited, 4311 Woodland Park Ave. N., Seattle, WA 98103 (SAN 295-0472) Tel 206-633-2485; Dist. by: Medicine Bow Post, P.O. Box 56, Medicine Bow, WY 82329 (SAN 200-7053) Tel 307-379-2255; Dist. by: Calendars Unlimited, 4930 Everglade Dr., Santa Rosa, CA 95405 (SAN 200-7061) Tel 707-538-2503; Dist. by: Pacific Pipeline, Inc., 19215 66th Ave., S., Kent, WA 98032 (SAN 208-2128) Tel 206-872-5523.

Skyview Pub, *(Skyview Publishing; 0-934618),* Drawer L, Bellmore, NY 11710 (SAN 214-2015) Tel 212-255-5550.

Skyward Bound Pub, *(Skyward Bound Publishing; 0-9617212),* 6000 California St., San Francisco, CA 94121 (SAN 663-4230) Tel 415-751-4962.

†SLA, *(Special Libraries Assn.; 0-9613358),* 1700 18th St., NW, Washington, DC 20009 (SAN 680-0882) Tel 202-234-4700; *CIP.*

Slack Inc, *(Slack, Inc.; 0-913590; 0-943432; 1-55642),* 6900 Grove Rd., Thorofare, NJ 08086 (SAN 201-8632) Tel 609-848-1000; Toll free: 800-257-8290.

Slash Burn Pr, *(Slash & Burn Pr.; 0-938345),* 1016 N. Fifth St., Philadelphia, PA 19123 (SAN 660-9643) Tel 215-625-0570.

Slate Pr, *(Slate Pr.; 0-9616193),* Box 1421 Cooper Station, New York, NY 10276 (SAN 699-9409) Tel 212-475-8067.

Slate Servs, *(Slate Services; 0-913448),* P.O. Box 80, Westminster, CA 92684 (SAN 203-2384) Tel 714-892-0889.

Slater Pub, *(Slater, Jaye, Publisher; 0-9607454),* 12911 Newhope St., Garden Grove, CA 92640 (SAN 239-801X) Tel 714-530-8825.

Slavia Lib, *(Slavia Library; 0-918884),* 418 W. Nittany Ave., State College, PA 16801 (SAN 211-0598).

Slavica, *(Slavica Pubs., Inc.; 0-89357),* P.O. Box 14388, Columbus, OH 43214 (SAN 208-8576) Tel 614-268-4002.

†Slawson Comm, *(Slawson Communications, Inc.; 0-915391),* 3719 Sixth Ave., San Diego, CA 92103-4316 (SAN 200-6901) Tel 619-291-9126; *CIP.*

Slaybaugh & Assocs, *(Slaybaugh, C. S., & Assocs.; 0-917509),* 285 Manning Rd., Mogadore, OH 44260 (SAN 656-1047) Tel 216-699-4578.

SLE, *(S.L.E. Pubns.; 0-9608230),* P.O. Box 52, Kingston, RI 02881 (SAN 240-3250) Tel 401-783-4503.

Sleeping Bird, *(Sleeping Bird Pr.; 0-9611424),* R.R. 1, Box 67, Wingdale, NY 12594-9801 (SAN 284-9143) Tel 914-832-6019.

†Sleepy Hollow, *(Sleepy Hollow Pr.; 0-912882),* 150 White Plains Rd., Tarrytown, NY 10591 (SAN 202-0750) Tel 914-631-8200; Dist. by: Independent Pubs. Group, 1 Pleasant Ave., Pt. Washington, NY 11050 (SAN 202-0769); *CIP.*

Sliabhair, *(Sliabhair; 0-937785),* P.O. Box 34096, Bethesda, MD 20817 (SAN 659-3151) Tel 202-475-2297; 9011 Lindale Dr., Bethesda, MD 20817 (SAN 659-316X).

Slick *Imprint of* **Seattle Bk**

Slideways Pubns, *(Slideways Pubns.; 0-931105),* P.O. Box 188, Marne, MI 49435 (SAN 678-9463) Tel 616-784-2571.

Slingerland, *(Slingerland-Comstock Co.; 0-9613097),* 5881 Cold Brook Rd., Homer, NY 13077 (SAN 293-4485) Tel 607-749-3655.

Slingerland
See Slingerland

Slohm Assoc, *(Slohm, Natalie, Assocs., Inc.; 0-916840),* 49 W. Main St., Cambridge, NY 12816 (SAN 282-3217) Tel 518-677-3040; P.O. Box 273, Cambridge, NY 12816 (SAN 282-3225).

Slough Pr TX, *(Slough Pr.; 0-941720),* Subs. of Slough Productions, Box 1385, Austin, TX 78767 (SAN 239-3131) Tel 512-474-5488.

Slov Ins, *(Slovak Institute of Cleveland, Ohio; 0-9610908),* 2900 E. Blvd., Cleveland, OH 44107 (SAN 265-1122) Tel 216-721-5300.

Slow Loris, *(Slow Loris Pr.; 0-918366),* 923 Highview St., Pittsburgh, PA 15206 (SAN 209-6803).

SLPOTCI, *(Sacred Lands Project of the Christic Institute; 0-9616823),* 1831 Belmont Rd., NW, Washington, DC 20009 (SAN 661-1249) Tel 202-234-1856.

Slumbering, *(Slumbering Giant Publishing Co.; 0-9614702),* 2812 Fogarty Ave., Key West, FL 33040 (SAN 692-6118) Tel 305-294-3985.

Slurry Tech, *(Slurry Technology; 0-932066),* 1800 Connecticut Ave., NW, Suite 300, Washington, DC 20009 (SAN 211-7134) Tel 202-332-5751.

Slurry Transport
See Slurry Tech

SLUSA, *(SLUSA; 0-917129; 0-9606758),* 88 Eastern Ave., Somerville, NJ 08876 (SAN 216-1931) Tel 201-725-6789.

Sm Busn Clinic, *(Small Businessman's Clinic; 0-914285),* 113 Vista Del Lago, Scotts Valley, CA 95066 (SAN 287-5608) Tel 408-438-1411.

SMC Corp, *(SMC Corp.; 0-939547),* 3475 Washington Dr., No. 201, Eagan, MN 55122 (SAN 663-3412) Tel 612-452-9270.

Small Busn Success Pr *Imprint of* **First Intl Pub**

Small Helm Pr, *(Small Helm Pr.; 0-938453),* 622 Baker St., Petaluma, CA 94952 (SAN 660-9805) Tel 707-763-5757.

Small Master, *(Small-Scale Master Builder, The; 0-911215),* P.O. Box 5, San Luis Obispo, CA 93406 (SAN 283-3395).

Small Pr Dist, *(Small Pr. Distribution, Inc.; 0-914068),* 1814 San Pablo Ave., Berkeley, CA 94702 (SAN 204-5826) Tel 415-549-3336.

Small-Small Pr, *(Small-Small Pr.; 0-9616143),* 226 Linden St., Rumford, ME 04276 (SAN 699-9506) Tel 207-364-7237; Orders to: Maine Writers & Pubs., Alliance, 19D Mason St., Brunswick, ME 04011 (SAN 662-4081) Tel 207-729-6333.

Smart, *(Smart; 0-942912),* Central Missouri State Univ., Dept. of English, Warrensburg, MO 64093 (SAN 240-3242).

SMARTCO, *(SMARTCO; 0-917619),* Drawer C, Rocheport, MO 65279 (SAN 657-1654) Tel 314-698-4535.

SME, *(Society of Manufacturing Engineers; 0-87263),* P.O. Box 930, 1 SME Dr., Dearborn, MI 48121 (SAN 203-2376) Tel 313-271-1500.

Smile Pubns, *(Smile Pubns.; 0-9616018),* 612 W. Michigan Ave., Paw Paw, MI 49079 (SAN 699-7619) Tel 616-657-3121.

Smith & Assoc, *(Smith & Associates; 0-938260),* Box 61648, Houston, TX 77208 (SAN 215-8140) Tel 713-932-0518.

Smith & Smith Pub, *(Smith & Smith Publishing Co.; 0-9609230),* 119 N. Fourth St., Suite 411, Minneapolis, MN 55401 (SAN 241-4570) Tel 612-338-8235.

†Smith Coll, *(Smith College, Pubns.; 0-87391),* Office of the Director of Technical Services, Northampton, MA 01063 (SAN 204-6032) Tel 413-584-2700; Dist. by: Neilson Library, Office of the Director of Technical Services, Northampton, MA 01063 (SAN 204-6040) Tel 413-584-2700; *CIP.*

Smith Coll Mus Art, *(Smith College Museum of Art),* Elm at Bedford Terr., Northampton, MA 01063 (SAN 282-3233) Tel 413-584-2700; Toll free: 800-621-2736; Dist. by: Univ. of Chicago Pr., 5801 Ellis Ave., 3rd flr. S., Chicago, IL 60637 (SAN 202-5280) Tel 312-568-1550.

Smith F E, *(Smith, Frank E., Inc.; 0-9602288),* 12846 Ironwood Cir., Beacon Woods, Hudson, FL 33567 (SAN 222-3791).

Smith Gary
See G E Smith

Smith J C, *(Smith, Joe C., Jr.; 0-9615176),* Affil. of Bit/s Software, P.O. Box B-36085, Phoenix, AZ 85232 (SAN 694-2822); Orders to: BIT/S Software, 3202 W. Fillmore, Florence, AZ 85009 (SAN 662-3352) Tel 602-269-8234.

Smith Lib, *(Smith, Warren Hunting, Library; 0-939624),* Hobart & William Smith Colleges, Geneva, NY 14456 (SAN 216-6275) Tel 315-789-5500.

Smith Prod, *(Smith Productions; 0-9616545),* Affil. of Hatha Yoga Center, 4550 11th Ave., NE, Seattle, WA 98105 (SAN 659-5359) Tel 206-632-1706; Orders to: Smith Productios, 2116 N. 122, Seattle, WA 98133 (SAN 662-4286) Tel 206-363-1051.

Smith Pubs, *(Smith, W. H., Pubs., Inc.; 0-8317),* Subs. of W. H. Smith & Son, Ltd., 112 Madison Ave., New York, NY 10016 (SAN 216-3241) Tel 212-532-6600; Toll free: 800-932-0070; 80 Distribution Blvd., Edison, NJ 08817 (SAN 658-1625). *Imprints:* Mayflower Bks (Mayflower Books).(Mayflower Bks.); Rutledge Pr (Rutledge Press).(Rutledge Pr.); Sunflower Bks (Sunflower Books).(Sunflower Bks.).

Smith Slogans, *(Smith's Slogans & Sayings; 0-939403),* 3014 Melina Ct., Bensalem, PA 19020 (SAN 663-138X) Tel 215-757-0844.

†Smithsonian, *(Smithsonian Institution Pr.; 0-87474),* 955 L'Enfant Plaza, Suite 2100, Washington, DC 20560 (SAN 206-8044) Tel 202-287-3765; Orders to: Customer Services, P.O. Box 4866, Hampden Sta., Baltimore, MD 21211 (SAN 206-8052) Tel 301-338-6963; *CIP.*

†Smithsonian Bks, *(Smithsonian Bks.; 0-89599),* 955 L'Enfant Plaza, Rm. 2100, Washington, DC 20560 (SAN 216-1974) Tel 202-287-3388; Toll free: 800-223-2584; Dist. by: W. W. Norton & Co., 500 Fifth Ave., New York, NY 10110 (SAN 202-5795) Tel 212-354-5500; Dist. by: Harmony Bks., 1 Park Ave., New York, NY 10016 (SAN 282-7360) Tel 212-532-9200; Dist. by: Harry N. Abrams, 100 Fifth Ave., New York, NY 10011 (SAN 200-2434) Tel 212-206-7715; Dist. by: Cambridge Univ. Pr., 32 E. 57th St., New York, NY 10022 (SAN 281-3750) Tel 212-688-8888; *CIP.*

Smoky Hill, *(Smoky Hill River Pr.; 0-932199),* P.O. Box 2181, Salina, KS 67402-2181 (SAN 686-595X) Tel 913-827-4640.

†Smoky Valley Hist, *(Smoky Valley Historical Pubns.; 0-918331),* Subs. of Smoky Valley Historical Assn., Inc., P.O. Box 255, Lindsborg, KS 67456-0255 (SAN 657-3037) Tel 913-227-2302; *CIP.*

Smoley, *(Smoley, C. K., & Sons; 0-911390),* Div. of Lewis Pubs., Inc., P.O. Box 531, Chelsea, MI 48118 (SAN 204-6059) Tel 313-475-8610.

Smoloskyp, *(Smoloskyp Pubs., Inc.; 0-914834),* P.O. Box 561, Ellicott City, MD 21043 (SAN 206-1260) Tel 301-461-1764.

†SMU Press, *(Southern Methodist Univ. Pr.; 0-87074),* P.O. Box 415, Dallas, TX 75275 (SAN 203-3615); 6410 Airline Dr., Dallas, TX 75205 (SAN 658-1641) Tel 214-739-5959; *CIP.*

Smugglers, *(Smugglers Cove Pub.; 0-918484),* Ben Dennis & Assoc., 107 W. John St., Seattle, WA 98119 (SAN 209-8857) Tel 206-285-3171. Out of business.

Smyres Pubns, *(Smyres Pubns.; 0-9616952),* P.O. Box 4796, Ithaca, NY 14852 (SAN 661-7565); 818 Hanshaw Rd., Ithaca, NY 14850 (SAN 661-7573) Tel 607-257-7517.

Smyrna, *(Smyrna Pr.; 0-918266),* P.O. Box 1803, GPO, Brooklyn, NY 11202 (SAN 207-897X) Tel 718-638-8939.

SNAG, *(Society of North American Goldsmiths; 0-9604446),* 6707 N. Santa Monica Blvd.,, Milwaukee, WI 53217 (SAN 215-1081).

SNB
See SNB Pub

SNB Pub, *(SNB Publishing; 0-932909),* 10603 Glen Forest Trail, Brecksville, OH 44141 (SAN 688-9093) Tel 216-526-6552.

Sneak-A-Peek Bks, *(Sneek-A-Peek Books; 0-943944),* Fontenelle Dam, Kemmerer, WY 83101 (SAN 241-1512) Tel 307-877-9615.

Snipe, *(Snipe International; 0-938740),* 210 Crystal Park Rd., Manitou Springs, CO 80829 (SAN 238-7514) Tel 303-685-9044.

Snipe Pub, *(Snipe Publishing Co., The; 0-9617027),* P.O. Box 1280, Friendswood, TX 77546 (SAN 662-6459); 2 Narnia Way, Friendswood, TX 77546 (SAN 662-6467) Tel 713-482-0669.

SNM Pub, *(SNM Publishing Co.; 0-9614613),* 102 W. Sixth St., Box 29, Larned, KS 67550 (SAN 691-8336) Tel 316-285-3177.

SnO Pubns, *(SnO Pubns.; 0-937814),* Stockbridge, MA 01262 (SAN 217-1325). *Imprints:* Lenox Lib Assn (Lenox Library Assn.).

Snohomish Pub, *(Snohomish Publishing),* P.O. Box 2188, Soldotna, AK 99669 (SAN 262-0804).

†Snow Lion, *(Snow Lion Pubns.; 0-937938),* P.O. Box 6483, Ithaca, NY 14851 (SAN 281-7292) Tel 607-273-8506; Dist. by: Bookpeople, 2929 Fifth St., Berkeley, CA 94710 (SAN 168-9517) Tel 415-549-3030; Dist. by: Inland Bk. Co., Inc., P.O. Box 261, 22 Hemingway Ave., East Haven, CT 06512 (SAN 200-4151) Tel 203-467-4257; Dist. by: Samuel Weiser, Inc., P.O. Box 612, York Beach, ME 03910 (SAN 202-9588) Tel 207-363-4393; Dist. by: The Great Tradition, 750 Adrian Way, Suite 111, San Rafael, CA 94903 (SAN 200-5743) Tel 415-492-9382; Dist. by: New Leaf Distributors, The, 1020 White St. SW, Atlanta, GA 30310 (SAN 169-1449) Tel 404-755-2665; Dist. by: Book Dynamics, 836 Broadway, New York, NY 10003 (SAN 169-5649) Tel 212-254-7798; Dist. by: Distributors, The, 702 S. Michigan, South Bend, IN 46618 (SAN 169-2488) Tel 219-232-8500; *CIP.*

Snow Lion Graphics, *(Snow Lion Graphics; 0-9617066),* P.O. Box 9465, Berkeley, CA 94709 (SAN 662-8729); 1526 Walnut, Berkeley, CA 94709 (SAN 662-8737) Tel 415-841-5525.

Snow Pr, *(Snow Press; 0-9601148),* 9300 Home Court, Des Plaines, IL 60016 (SAN 210-3729) Tel 312-299-7605.

SNOWCO, *(Snowco-Publishing; 0-939230),* 266 N. El Camino Real, Suite D-12, Oceanside, CA 92054 (SAN 216-5112).

Snowstorm, *(Snowstorm Pubns.; 0-9605366),* Box 2310, Breckenridge, CO 80424 (SAN 216-194X).

†Snug Harbor NY, *(Snug Harbor Cultural Ctr.; 0-9604254),* 914 Richmond Terr., Staten Island, NY 10301 (SAN 214-4751) Tel 718-448-2500; *CIP.*

Snuggle & Read *Imprint of Avon*

Snyder Inc, *(Snyder, Walter, Printer, Inc.; 0-9601556),* Troy, NY 12180 (SAN 239-5789).

Snyder Inst Res, *(Snyder Institute of Research; 0-940714),* 508 N. Pacific Coast Hwy., Redondo Beach, CA 90277 (SAN 204-9694) Tel 213-372-4469.

Snyder Pub Co, *(Snyder Publishing Co.; 0-9609526),* No. 250, 1275 Fourth St., Santa Rosa, CA 95404 (SAN 260-2660) Tel 707-829-1388.

So Assn Child Six, *(Southern Association on Children Under Six; 0-942388),* P.O. Box 5403, Brady Sta., Little Rock, AR 72215 (SAN 236-8560) Tel 501-227-6404.

SO Metro, *(SO Metro; 0-9616398),* P.O. Box 44089, Indianapolis, IN 46204 (SAN 659-1272) Tel 317-924-3663; 118 E. 33rd St., Indianapolis, IN 46205 (SAN 659-1280).

So&So Pr, *(So & So Pr.; 0-918842),* 1003 Kieth Ave., Berkeley, CA 94708 (SAN 210-3893) Tel 415-525-2781.

Soap & Detergent, *(Soap & Detergent Assn.; 0-9601394),* 475 Park Ave. S., New York, NY 10016 (SAN 224-7089) Tel 212-725-1262.

Soaring Soc, *(Soaring Society of America),* 3200 Airport Ave., No. 12, Santa Monica, CA 90405 (SAN 229-2742) Tel 213-390-4447; P.O. Box 66071, Los Angeles, CA 90066 (SAN 669-2664).

Sobell Assocs, *(Sobell Assocs.; 0-937613),* 521 Ross Ct., Palo Alto, CA 94303 (SAN 659-1760) Tel 415-856-3460.

Soc Actuaries, *(Society of Actuaries; 0-938959),* 500 Park Blvd., Itasca, IL 60143 (SAN 224-8387) Tel 312-773-3010.

Soc Adv Cont Ed, *(Society for the Advancement of Continuing Education for Ministry; 0-918983),* 855 Locust St., Collegeville, PA 19426 (SAN 224-2184) Tel 215-489-6358.

Soc Adv Material, *(Society for the Advancement of Materials & Process Engineering; 0-938994),* 843 W. Glentana, Covina, CA 91722 (SAN 295-3528); P.O. Box 2459, Covina, CA 91722 (SAN 295-3536) Tel 818-331-0616.

Soc Alu Wm, *(Society of the Alumni of the College of William & Mary in Virginia, Inc.; 0-9615670),* 500 Richmond Rd., Williamsburg, VA 23187 (SAN 695-9652) Tel 804-229-1693; P.O. Box GO, Williamsburg, VA 23187 (SAN 699-6167).

Soc Am Arch, *(Society for American Archaeology; 0-932839),* 1511 K St. NW, Washington, DC 20005 (SAN 275-5211) Tel 202-638-6079; Dist. by: Kraus Reprint & Periodicals, Rte. 100, Millwood, NY 10546 (SAN 227-3233) Tel 914-762-2200.

†Soc Am Archivists, *(Society of American Archivists; 0-931828),* 600 S. Federal, Suite 504, Chicago, IL 60605 (SAN 211-7614) Tel 312-922-0140; *CIP.*

Soc Am Baseball Res, *(Society for American Baseball Research; 0-910137),* P.O. Box 1010, Cooperstown, NY 13326 (SAN 224-5434) Tel 607-547-9160.

Soc Am Foresters, *(Society of American Foresters; 0-939970),* 5400 Grosvenor Ln., Bethesda, MD 20814 (SAN 216-8561) Tel 301-897-8720.

Soc Am Mil Eng, *(Society of American Military Engineers),* 607 Prince St., Alexandria, VA 22314 (SAN 669-2680) Tel 703-549-3800.

Soc Am Travel Writers, *(Society of American Travel Writers),* 1120 Connecticut Ave. NW,, Washington, DC 20036 (SAN 224-9758) Tel 202-785-5567.

Soc Am Value E, *(Society of American Value Engineers),* 220 N. Story Rd., Suite 114, Irving, TX 75061 (SAN 223-968X) Tel 214-253-5171.

Soc Animal Rights, *(International Society for Animal Rights, Inc.; 0-9602632),* 421 S. State St., Clarks Summit, PA 18411 (SAN 214-1418) Tel 717-586-2200.

†Soc Auto Engineers, *(Society of Automotive Engineers; 0-89883),* 400 Commonwealth Dr., Warrendale, PA 15096 (SAN 232-5721) Tel 412-776-4841; *CIP.*

Soc Change Pr, *(Social Change Pr.; 0-9609376),* Box 2212, Sun City, AZ 85372 (SAN 260-1370) Tel 602-972-8346.

Soc Charter Prop Underwriters, *(Society of Chartered Property & Casualty Underwriters),* Kahler Hall, 720 Providence Rd., CB No. 9, Malvern, PA 19355 (SAN 263-9287) Tel 215-251-2728.

Soc Christian Ethics, *(Society of Christian Ethics),* Vancouver Schl. of Theology, 6000 Iona Dr., Vancouver, BC V6T 1L4, (SAN 223-9701).

Symbols/Abbreviations

Soc Common Insights, *(Society for Commo Insights Pr., Inc.; 0-940888),* 481 Eighth Ave., Suite 926, New York, NY 10001 (SAN 223-1158) Tel 212-947-1657.

Soc Comp Eng, *(Society for Computer Applications in Engineering, Planning & Architecture, Inc.; 0-933007),* 15713 Crabbs Branch Way, Rockville, MD 20855 (SAN 654-9802) Tel 301-926-7070.

Soc Computer S
See Soc Computer Sim

Soc Computer Sim, *(Society for Computer Simulation; 0-911801),* P.O. Box 17900, San Diego, CA 92117 (SAN 225-1973) Tel 619-277-3888.

Soc Descend Wash Army, *(Society of the Descendants of Washington's Army at Valley Forge; 0-9606828),* P.O. Box 915, Valley Forge, PA 19482 (SAN 224-4896) Tel 617-335-7670.

Soc Ethnomusicology, *(Society for Ethnomusicology, Inc.),* P.O. Box 2984, Ann Arbor, MI 48106 (SAN 225-3615) Tel 313-665-9400.

Soc Expl Geophys, *(Society of Exploration Geophysicists; 0-931830),* P.O. Box 702740, Tulsa, OK 74170-2740 (SAN 206-2844) Tel 918-493-3516.

Soc Exploration
See Soc Expl Geophys

Soc for Visual, *(Society for Visual Education, Inc.; 0-89290),* 1345 Diversey Pkwy., Chicago, IL 60614 (SAN 208-3930) Tel 312-525-1500; Toll free: 800-621-1900.

Soc German-Amer Studies *Imprint of North Central*

Soc Humanistic, *(Society for Humanistic Judaism; 0-912645),* 28611 W. Twelve Mile Rd., Farmington Hills, MI 48018 (SAN 275-4576) Tel 313-478-7610.

Soc Indus-Appl Math, *(Society for Industrial & Applied Mathematics; 0-89871),* 117 S. 17th St., Suite 1400, Philadelphia, PA 19103-5052 (SAN 206-5207) Tel 215-564-2929.

Soc Indus Micro, *(Society for Industrial Microbiology),* P.O. Box 12534, Arlington, VA 22209-8534 (SAN 223-8306) Tel 703-941-5373.

Soc Industrial Realtors, *(Society of Industrial Realtors Educational Fund),* 777 14th St., NW, Washington, DC 20005-3271 (SAN 202-0718) Tel 202-383-1150.

Soc Inter Celtic, *(Society of Inter-Celtic Arts & Culture; 0-936651),* 96 Marguerite Ave., Waltham, MA 02154 (SAN 699-7120) Tel 617-899-2204.

Soc Intercult Ed Train & Res, *(International Society for Intercultural Education, Training & Research; 0-933934),* Div. of Georgetown Univ., 1414 22nd St., NW, Washington, DC 20037 (SAN 214-1426) Tel 202-296-4710.

†Soc Issues, *(Social Issues Resources Series, Inc.; 0-89777),* P.O. Box 2348, Boca Raton, FL 33427 (SAN 222-8920) Tel 305-994-0079; Toll free: 800-327-0513; *CIP.*

Soc Libertarian Life, *(Society for Libertarian Life),* Box 4, Fullerton, CA 92632 (SAN 225-6770) Tel 714-962-6491.

Soc Logistics Engrs, *(Society of Logistics Engineers),* 303 Williams Ave., Park Plaza, Suite 922, Huntsville, AL 35801 (SAN 223-8314) Tel 205-539-3800 Tel 205-539-3833; Dist. by: Prentice Hall, Inc., Rte. 9W, Englewood Cliffs, NJ 07632 (SAN 200-2175) Tel 201-592-2352.

Soc Mad Poets, *(Society for Mad Poets Pr.; 0-9615250),* P.O. Box 14095, Chicago, IL 60614 (SAN 694-6070) Tel 312-975-1547; Dist. by: Bookslinger, 213 E. Fourth St., ST. Paul, MN 55101 (SAN 169-4154) Tel 612-221-0429.

Soc Mining Eng, *(Society of Mining Engineers, Inc.; 0-87335),* 8307 Shaffer Pkwy., Caller No. D., Littleton, CO 80127 (SAN 225-2163) Tel 303-973-9550.

Soc Motion Pic & TV Engrs, *(Society of Motion Picture & Television Engineers; 0-940690),* 862 Scarsdale Ave., Scarsdale, NY 10583 (SAN 224-0173) Tel 914-472-6600.

Soc Naval Arch, *(Society of Naval Architects & Marine Engineers; 0-9603048; 0-939773),* 1 World Trade Ctr., Suite 1369, New York, NY 10048 (SAN 202-0572) Tel 212-432-0310.

Soc Neuroscience, *(Society of Neuroscience),* 9650 Rockville Pike, Bethesda, MD 20014 (SAN 224-0165) Tel 301-530-8955.

Soc New Lang Study, *(Society for New Language Study, Inc.; 0-9502699; 0-936072),* P.O. Box 10596, Denver, CO 80210 (SAN 203-2368) Tel 303-777-6115.

†Soc Nuclear Med, *(Society of Nuclear Medicine, Inc.; 0-932004),* 136 Madison Ave., New York, NY 10016 (SAN 212-5625) Tel 212-889-0717; *CIP.*

Soc Nursing Prof, *(Society of Nursing Professionals, The),* P.O. Box 50822, Washington, DC 20004 (SAN 661-4558).

Soc Nutrition Ed, *(Society for Nutrition Education; 0-910869),* 1736 Franklin St., Oakland, CA 94612 (SAN 225-8552) Tel 415-444-7133.

†Soc Phil Pol, *(Bowling Green State Univ., Social Philosophy & Policy Ctr.; 0-912051),* Social Philosophy & Policy Ctr., Bowling Green, OH 43403 (SAN 264-6048) Tel 419-372-2536; *CIP.*

Soc Plastic Ind, *(Society of the Plastic Industry, Inc),* 355 Lexington Ave., New York, NY 10017 (SAN 224-9162) Tel 212-573-9400.

Soc Pres Old Mills
See Soc Preservation

†Soc Preservation, *(Society for the Preservation of Old Mills; 0-930497),* 604 Ensley Dr. Rte. 29, Knoxville, TN 37920 (SAN 670-9621) Tel 615-577-7757; *CIP.*

Soc Pro, *(Society of Professional Journalists, Sigma Delta Chi; 0-9613340),* 840 N. Lake Shore Dr., Suite 801W, Chicago, IL 60611 (SAN 275-6072) Tel 312-649-0224.

Soc Profs Ed, *(Society of Professors of Education; 0-933669),* Portland State Univ., P.O. Box 751, Portland, OR 97207 (SAN 224-0181) Tel 503-229-4750.

Soc Range Mgmt, *(Society for Range Management; 0-9603692),* 2760 W. Fifth Ave., Denver, CO 80204 (SAN 225-0586) Tel 303-571-0174.

Soc Real Estate Appraisers, *(Society of Real Estate Appraisers; 0-934737),* 645 N. Michigan Ave., Chicago, IL 60611 (SAN 682-9430) Tel 312-346-7422; Toll free: 800-331-7732.

Soc Right to Die, *(Society for the Right to Die, Inc.; 0-9613825),* 250 W. 57th St., New York, NY 10107 (SAN 225-9354) Tel 212-246-6973.

Soc Schol Pub, *(Society for Scholarly Publishing),* 2000 Florida Ave., NW, Washington, DC 20009 (SAN 225-1949) Tel 202-328-3555.

Soc Sci & Soc Res, *(Social Science & Sociological Resources; 0-915574),* P.O. Box 241, Aurora, IL 60507 (SAN 203-235X).

†Soc Sci Ed, *(Social Science Education Consortium, Inc.; 0-89994),* 855 Broadway, Boulder, CO 80302 (SAN 213-1684) Tel 303-492-8154; *CIP.*

Soc Sci Inst, *(Social Science Institute; 0-911394),* Harborside, ME 04642 (SAN 206-3158).

Soc Sci Pr, *(Social Science Press, Inc.; 0-911396),* 100 Oakdale Rd., Athens, GA 30606 (SAN 204-6083) Tel 404-542-4581.

Soc Sci Res, *(Social Science Research Council; 0-911400),* 605 Third Ave., New York, NY 10016 (SAN 204-6091).

Soc Sci Stud Rel, *(Society for the Scientific Study of Religion; 0-932566),* Catholic Univ. of America, Marist Hall, Rm. 108, Storrs, CT 06268 (SAN 212-1670).

Soc Slovene Studies, *(Society for Slovene Studies),* 420 W. 118th St., New York, NY 10027 (SAN 225-8706).

Soc Tchrs Fam Med, *(Society for Teachers of Family Medicine),* 1740 W. 92nd St., Kansas City, MO 64114 (SAN 224-3199) Tel 816-333-9700; Toll free: 800-821-2512.

Soc Tech Comm, *(Society for Technical Communication; 0-914548),* 815 15th St., NW, Washington, DC 20005 (SAN 206-569X) Tel 202-737-0035; Orders to: Univelt, Inc., P.O. Box 28130, San Diego, CA 92128 (SAN 204-8868) Tel 619-746-4005.

Soc Vertebrate, *(Society of Vertebrate Paleontology; 0-918799),* University of California, Museum of Paleontology, c/o Joseph T. Gregory, Berkeley, CA 94720 (SAN 669-7062) Tel 415-642-1730; Orders to: Society of Vertebrate Paleontology, LACM of Natural History, 900 Exposition Blvd., Los Angeles, CA 90007 (SAN 662-2410) Tel 213-744-3445.

Soc Wine Educators, *(Society of Wine Educators; 0-935347),* 132 Shaker Rd., Suite 14, East Longmeadow, MA 01028 (SAN 225-8846) Tel 413-567-8282.

Soc Wld Serv, *(Society For A World Service Federation; 0-9614149),* P.O. Box 1362, Dunedin, FL 34296-1362 (SAN 686-2101); 2058 Alpine Rd., No. 20, Clearwater, FL 33515 (SAN 662-2674) Tel 813-447-5673.

Soc Wood, *(Society of Wood Science & Technology),* P.O. Box 5062, Madison, WI 53705 (SAN 260-3470) Tel 608-264-5747.

†Soccer Bk Co, *(Soccer Book Co., The; 0-916019),* 32 W. Anapanu St., Suite 285, Santa Barbara, CA 93101 (SAN 294-0892) Tel 805-969-5051; *CIP.*

Soccer Ed, *(Soccer Education; 0-9616953),* 509 Laurel Dr., Thiensville, WI 53092 (SAN 661-7638) Tel 414-242-3137.

Soccer for Am, *(Soccer for Americans; 0-916802),* P.O. Box 836, Manhattan Beach, CA 90266 (SAN 208-3787) Tel 213-372-9000. Do Not Confuse with Sport-Shelf.

Soccer Pub Inc
See Soccer Pubns Inc

Soccer Pubns Inc, *(Soccer Publications, Inc.; 0-943752),* 3530 Greer Rd., Palo Alto, CA 94303 (SAN 216-3217) Tel 415-494-6338.

†Social Matrix, *(Social Matrix Research, Inc.; 0-89995),* P.O. Box 9128, Boston, MA 02114 (SAN 213-5922) Tel 617-247-2181; *CIP.*

Social Sys Pr, *(Social Systems Pr.; 0-935563),* P.O. Box 1091, Jeffersonville, IN 47131 (SAN 696-060X) Tel 502-423-8006.

Society Fire Protect, *(Society of Fire Protection Engineers),* 60 Batterymarch St., Boston, MA 02110 (SAN 209-3863) Tel 617-482-0686.

Society Indiv Lib, *(Society for Individual Liberty of the Genesee Valley; 0-9608490),* P.O. Box 10224, Rochester, NY 14610 (SAN 240-7760) Tel 716-671-2077.

Society Sp & Sp-Am, *(Society of Spanish & Spanish-American Studies; 0-89295),* Univ. of Colorado, Dept. of Spanish and Portuguese, Boulder, CO 80309-0278 (SAN 208-3221) Tel 303-492-7308.

†Society Vascular Surgery, *(Society For Vascular Surgery, The; 0-9612978),* 13 Elm St., Manchester, MA 01944 (SAN 292-6741) Tel 617-927-8330; *CIP.*

Sociology Pr, *(Sociology Pr.),* P.O. Box 400, Mill Valley, CA 94942 (SAN 212-7962).

SOCO Pubns, *(S.O.C.O. Pubns.; 0-910119),* Box 733, Herkimer, NY 13350 (SAN 241-5720).

SocSP *Imprint of B&N Imports*

Soda-Licious, *(Soda-Licious; 0-9616340),* 8625 NE Weidler, Portland, OR 97220 (SAN 659-1930) Tel 503-254-6132.

Soft Direct, *(Software Directions, Inc.; 0-936517),* 1572 Sussex Tpk., Randolph, NJ 07869 (SAN 697-8126) Tel 201-584-8466; Toll free: 800-346-7638.

Soft Energy
See Joydeism Pr

Soft Resources
See Tech Data Corp

Soft Shop Pr, *(Software Shop Pr., The; 0-937405),* 4977 Livernois, Troy, MI 48098 (SAN 659-1779) Tel 313-524-1581.

Soft Source, *(Software Source; 0-930241),* 2701-C W. 15th St., Suite 109, Plano, TX 75075 (SAN 653-4341) Tel 214-424-0758.

Soft Tech MI, *(Soft Tech, Inc.; 0-938087),* 18505 W. Eight Mile Rd., Suite 104, Detroit, MI 48219 (SAN 659-7025) Tel 313-544-8544.

SoftCorp FL, *(SoftCorp, Inc.; 0-937701),* 2340 State Rd. 580, Suite 244, Clearwater, FL 33575 (SAN 697-5356) Tel 813-799-3984; Toll free: 800-255-7526.

†Softext Pub, *(Softext Pubishing Corp.; 0-934577),* 17 E. 45th St., 6th Flr., New York, NY 10017 (SAN 693-9023) Tel 212-986-5985; *CIP.*

Softlaw Pub, *(Softlaw Publishing Co.; 0-9616248),* 2136 Matthews Ave., Bronx, NY 10462 (SAN 658-3628) Tel 212-597-3746.

Software Dev, *(Software Development Corp.; 0-937333),* Div. of City Software Development Corp., 735 W. Wisconsin Ave., Milwaukee, WI 53233 (SAN 658-8131) Tel 414-291-5466.

Software Hse, *(Software Hse.; 0-912055)*, 1105 Massachusetts Ave., Cambridge, MA 02138 (SAN 264-6374) Tel 617-661-7023.

Software Inc, *(Software Digest, Inc.; 0-916543)*, One Winding Rd., Philadelphia, PA 19131 (SAN 295-1185) Tel 215-878-9300.

Software Inst Am, *(Software Institute of America Inc.)*, 8 Windsor St., Andover, MA 01810 (SAN 291-851X) Tel 617-470-3870.

Softwriters Dev, *(Softwriters Development Corp.; 0-9616781; 0-939673)*, 4718 Harford Rd., Baltimore, MD 21214 (SAN 660-9678) Tel 301-426-4466.

Soho Press, *(Soho Pr., Inc., The; 0-939149)*, One Union Sq., New York, NY 10003 (SAN 662-5088) Tel 212-243-1527; Dist. by: Farrar, Straus & Giroux, 19 Union Sq., W., New York, NY 10003 (SAN 206-782X) Tel 212-741-6900.

†**Soil Conservation,** *(Soil Conservation Society of America; 0-935734)*, 7515 NE. Ankeny Rd., Ankeny, IA 50021-9764 (SAN 213-6961) Tel 515-289-2331; *CIP.*

Soil Sci Soc Am, *(Soil Science Society of America; 0-89118)*, Affil. of American Society of Agronomy Crop Science Society of America, 677 S. Segoe Rd., Madison, WI 53711 (SAN 206-2879) Tel 608-273-8080.

Sojourners Pr Ltd, *(Sojourners Press, Ltd.; 0-936768)*, 601 W. Tonopah, Suite 5, Phoenix, AZ 85027 (SAN 221-8933) Tel 602-582-1439.

Sokoloff, *(Sokoloff, Valentin A.; 0-9607438)*, 773 Cypress Ave., San Bruno, CA 94066 (SAN 239-4863) Tel 415-589-4511.

Sol Press *Imprint of* **Wisconsin Bks**

Solano Pr, *(Solano Pr.; 0-9614657)*, P.O. Box 7629, Berkeley, CA 94707-0629 (SAN 692-2236) Tel 415-527-8668.

Solar Age Pr, *(Solar Age Pr.; 0-914304)*, Indian Mills, WV 24949 (SAN 208-8630).

Solar Pr, *(Solar Pr.; 0-9616785)*, 1120 Frontenac Rd., Naperville, IL 60566 (SAN 660-9708) Tel 312-983-1400.

Solar Studio, *(Solar Studio, The; 0-932320)*, 178 Cowles Rd., Woodbury, CT 06798 (SAN 222-8823) Tel 203-263-3147.

Solar Training, *(Solar Training Pubns.; 0-940894)*, 10921 W. Exposition Dr. P.O. Box 26241, Lakewood, CO 80226 (SAN 219-6360) Tel 303-989-1611.

SOLARC, *(SOLARC - Solar Energy in Architecture)*, 2300 Cliff Dr., Newport Beach, CA 92663 (SAN 209-1283) Tel 714-631-3182.

†**Solaris Pr,** *(Solaris Pr., Inc.; 0-933760)*, P.O. Box 1009, Rochester, MI 48063 (SAN 262-0820) Tel 313-656-0667; *CIP.*

Solarium Analy, *(Solarium Analytika; 0-935861)*, P.O. Box 3594, West Sedona, AZ 86336 (SAN 696-0529); 105 Mountain Shadows Dr., Sedonax, AZ 86336 (SAN 699-6205) Tel 602-282-1903.

SolarVision, *(SolarVision, Inc.; 0-918984)*, 7 Church Hill, Harrisville, NH 03450 (SAN 210-508X) Tel 603-827-3347.

†**Soldier Creek,** *(Soldier Creek Pr.; 0-936996)*, Drawer U, Lake Crystal, MN 56055 (SAN 215-9171) Tel 507-726-2985; 642 S Hunt St., Lake Crystal, MN 56055 (SAN 658-1633); *CIP.*

Solidarity, *(Solidarity Pubns.; 0-942638)*, P.O. Box 40874, San Francisco, CA 94140 (SAN 238-5724) Tel 415-626-6626.

Solipaz Pub Co, *(Solipaz Publishing Co.; 0-913999)*, P.O. Box 366, Lodi, CA 95241 (SAN 286-8814) Tel 209-368-1595.

Solitaire Pub, *(Solitaire Publishing; 0-933143)*, 216 S. Bungalow , P.O. Box 14508, Tampa, FL 33690 (SAN 670-6975) Tel 813-876-0286.

Solo, *(Solo Music, Inc.; 0-913754)*, P.O. Box 1333, Sedona, AZ 86336 (SAN 206-7692) Tel 602-282-4023.

Solo Pr, *(Solo Pr.)*, 7975 San Marcos, Atascadero, CA 93422 (SAN 206-3794) Tel 805-466-3083.

Solo Press MA, *(Solo Pr.; 0-941866)*, 1009 Mass. Ave., Lexington, MA 02173 (SAN 239-3158) Tel 617-861-1340.

Solomon Assocs, *(Solomon Assocs.; 0-9617198)*, 9240 Broken Timber Way, Columbia, MD 21045 (SAN 663-2483) Tel 301-596-4433.

Solomon Intl, *(Solomon Intl Pub. Co.; 0-946155)*, P.O. Box 7164, Huntington Beach, CA 92615-7164 (SAN 655-1327).

Solpub, *(Solpub Co.; 0-931912)*, 16311 Heatherdale Dr.,, Houston, TX 77059 (SAN 212-7970) Tel 713-280-0454.

Solson Pubns, *(Solson Pubns.; 0-9615671)*, P.O. Box 274, Brooklyn, NY 11235 (SAN 696-057X) Tel 718-846-6553; 2362 E. 13th St., Brooklyn, NY 11229 (SAN 699-6213).

Solus Impress, *(Solus Impress)*, Porthill, ID 83853 (SAN 262-0839).

Soma Pr, *(Soma Pr.; 0-932510)*, P.O. Box 416, Yellow Springs, OH 45387 (SAN 222-8858) Tel 513-767-1573.

Soma Pr Cal, *(Soma Pr. of California; 0-943564)*, P.O. Box 3682, Pinedale, CA 93650 (SAN 238-3772) Tel 209-439-4829.

Some Place
See Lacis Pubns

Somerset Hse, *(Somerset Hse. Corp.; 0-938941)*, 515 Post Oak Blvd., No. 600, Houston, TX 77027 (SAN 661-7646) Tel 713-963-0300.

Somerset Pr IL, *(Somerset Pr.; 0-916642)*, Div. of Hope Publishing Co., Executive Dr., Carol Stream, IL 60188 (SAN 214-3267) Tel 312-665-3200; Toll free: 800-323-1049.

Somerset Pub, *(Somerset Pubs.)*, 200 Park Ave., Suite 303 E., New York, NY 10017 (SAN 204-6105) Tel 313-884-0400.

Somerton Pr, *(Somerton Pr.; 0-934129)*, P.O. Box 1746, Somerton, AZ 85350 (SAN 693-2665).

Sometime Pr, *(Sometime Pr., Inc.; 0-936230)*, 216 Pleasant St., Marblehead, MA 01945 (SAN 214-1442).

Somm, *(Somm; 0-9615807)*, 3017 Santa Monica Blvd., No. 155, Santa Monica, CA 90404 (SAN 696-5911) Tel 213-839-9691.

Somrie Pr, *(Somrie Pr.; 0-9603950; 0-933749)*, Ryder St. Sta. Box 328, Brooklyn, NY 11234-0328 (SAN 214-1450) Tel 718-251-3690; 1134 E. 72nd St., Brooklyn, NY 11234 (SAN 692-6304).

Son-Rise Pubns, *(Son-Rise Pubns.; 0-936369)*, Rte. 3, Box 202, New Wilmington, PA 16142 (SAN 698-0031) Tel 412-946-8334; Dist. by: Spring Arbor, 10885 Textile, Belleville, MI 48111 (SAN 158-9016) Tel 717-234-5041; Dist. by: Whitaker Hse., Pittsburgh & Colfax Sts., Springdale, PA 15144 (SAN 203-2104) Tel 412-274-4440.

Son Rise Williston, *(Son Rise Pubns.; 0-938355)*, 119 Industrial Pkwy., Williston, VT 05495 (SAN 659-8358) Tel 802-864-0724.

Son West Pubs, *(Son/West Pubs.; 0-9616546)*, P.O. Box 2122, Clovis, NM 88101 (SAN 659-5367) Tel 505-762-4020; 204 W. Christopher, Clovis, NM 88101 (SAN 659-5375).

Soncino Pr, *(Soncino Pr.)*, 5 Essex St., New York, NY 10002 (SAN 681-2740).

Sonflower Bks *Imprint of* **SP Pubns**

Songa Pubns, *(Songa Pubns.; 0-936017)*, Div. of Songa Braids, 2053 McGraw Ave., Apt. 1H, Bronx, NY 10462 (SAN 696-592X) Tel 212-409-2132; Orders to: Professional Secrets, P.O. Box 1566, GPO, Bronx, NY 10451 (SAN 662-3778) Tel 212-409-2132.

Songs & Stories, *(Songs & Stories Children Love; 0-934591)*, 4243 Carpenter Ave., Bronx, NY 10466 (SAN 694-0609) Tel 212-325-9004.

Sonica Pr, *(Sonica Press)*, P.O. Box 42720, Los Angeles, CA 90042 (SAN 216-1966) Tel 213-666-7197.

Sonoma County, *(Sonoma County Bike Trails)*, 50 Crest Way, Penngrove, CA 94951 (SAN 215-7098) Tel 707-795-8911.

Sonoma Lea Hist, *(Sonoma League for Historic Preservation; 0-9616547)*, P.O. Box 766, Sonoma, CA 95476 (SAN 659-5383) Tel 707-938-2996; 465 E. MacArthur, Sonoma, CA 95476 (SAN 659-5391).

Sonoran, *(Sonoran Pr.; 0-943332)*, Box 423, Youngtown, AZ 85363 (SAN 240-5687) Tel 602-974-0720.

Sons Lib, *(Sons of Liberty; 0-89562)*, Div. of New Christian Crusade Church, Box 214, Metairie, LA 70004 (SAN 210-6663) Tel 504-887-3217.

Sons Prophets Pr, *(Sons of the Prophets Pr.; 0-915315)*, 12359 Falling Leaves Ct., St. Louis, MO 63141 (SAN 290-0440) Tel 314-878-9270.

Sooty-Face, *(Sooty-Face Publishing Co.; 0-9602366)*, P.O. Box 26, Clairton, PA 15025 (SAN 212-5633) Tel 412-233-6141.

Sophia Bks, *(Sophia Bks.; 0-933981)*, 191 W. Rosslynn Ave., Columbus, OH 43214-1445 (SAN 693-0824) Tel 614-885-0823.

†**Sophia Inst Pr,** *(Sophia Institute Pr.; 0-918477)*, P.O. Box 5284, Manchester, NH 03108 (SAN 657-7172); *CIP.*

Sophia Pr, *(Sophia Press; 0-9609378)*, P.O. Box 533, Durham, NH 03824 (SAN 260-1397) Tel 603-868-2318.

Soque, *(Soque Publishers; 0-9608770)*, Div. of Mark of the Potter, Rte. 3, Box 83, Clarkesville, GA 30523 (SAN 238-3780) Tel 404-947-3440.

Sore Dove Pubs, *(Sore Dove Pubs.; 0-9611976)*, P.O. Box 6332, San Mateo, CA 94403 (SAN 286-7737) Tel 415-571-1632.

Sorger Assocs, *(Sorger Assocs., Inc.; 0-9604072)*, 229 Humphrey St., Marblehead, MA 01945 (SAN 214-1469).

SOS Minist Pr, *(SOS Ministries Pr.; 0-938573)*, Div. of Shama Sound Ministries, P.O. Box 27054, San Francisco, CA 94127 (SAN 661-4701); 78 Sycamore St., San Francisco, CA 94110 (SAN 661-471X) Tel 415-552-2300.

SOS Pub OR, *(SOS Publishing; 0-931689)*, P.O. Box 68290, Oak Grove, OR 97268 (SAN 686-1814) Tel 503-654-9123.

SOS Pubns
See SOS Pubns CA

SOS Pubns CA, *(SOS Pubns.; 0-938422)*, 4223 W. Jefferson Blvd., Los Angeles, CA 90016-4112 (SAN 238-5317) Tel 213-730-1815; Toll free: 800-325-7953 (Orders).

SOSREF, *(Save Our Schools Research & Education Foundation; 0-938159)*, 777 14th St., NW, Washington, DC 20005 (SAN 659-9001) Tel 703-356-0440.

Sotheby Pubns, *(Sotheby Pubns.)*, 1035 Fifth Ave., New York, NY 10028 (SAN 678-9188) Tel 212-737-0242; Orders to: Scala Bks., Keystone Industrial Pk., Scranton, PA 18512 (SAN 215-3742).

SOTOA
See O T O

Soul Pubns, *(Soul Pubns.; 0-937327)*, 6041 Cleveland Ave., Columbus, OH 43227 (SAN 658-8050) Tel 614-497-8536.

Soulbook, *(Soulbook)*, P.O. Box 61213, Los Angeles, CA 90061 (SAN 218-401X); c/o Community Resources Inc., 927 15th st., Suite 605 NW, Washington, DC 20005 (SAN 692-8412).

Sound Advice, *(Sound Advice Enterprises; 0-943668)*, 40 Holly Lane, Roslyn Heights, NY 11577 (SAN 238-3799) Tel 516-621-2445.

Sound Approach, *(Sound Approach, Inc.; 0-939265)*, 109 Caernarvon Ct., Exton, PA 19341 (SAN 662-524X) Tel 215-363-2900.

Sound Ent, *(Sound Enterprises Publishing Co.; 0-935565)*, 970 Cornwallis Dr., West Chester, PA 19380 (SAN 696-1886) Tel 215-431-4512.

Sound Feelings, *(Sound Feelings Publishing; 0-9615963)*, 24266 Walnut St., Newhall, CA 91321 (SAN 697-3167) Tel 805-254-4938.

Sound Food Co, *(Sound Food Co.; 0-9615672)*, Rte. 2, Box 298, Vashon, WA 98070 (SAN 696-1371) Tel 206-463-3842.

Sound Nut, *(Sound Nutrition; 0-9609226)*, 2560 N. 560 E., Provo, UT 84604 (SAN 241-4597) Tel 801-375-8227; Dist. by: Nutri-Books, P.O. Box 5793, Denver, CO 80223 (SAN 169-054X) Tel 303-778-8383.

Sound Pub, *(Sound Publishing Co.)*, P.O. Box 920, Great Neck, NY 10022 (SAN 206-2909) Tel 516-466-5750.

Sound View Pr, *(Sound View Pr.; 0-932087)*, Div. of P. Hastings Falk, Inc., 20 Wall St., Suite 150, Madison, CT 06443 (SAN 686-5240) Tel 203-245-2246.

Soundprint, *(Soundprint; 0-9611938)*, 2250 N. 800 E., Provo, UT 84604 (SAN 286-0554) Tel 801-377-0553.

Sounds Kansas, *(Sounds of Kansas; 0-9615597)*, Rte. 1, Inman, KS 67546 (SAN 696-1657) Tel 316-585-2389.

Soup to Nuts, *(Soup to Nuts Press; 0-9604780)*, 582 Fernando Dr., Novato, CA 94947 (SAN 215-918X).

Source Prods, *(Source Productions; 0-9614966)*, 10415 Sarah St., Toluca Lake, CA 91602 (SAN 693-7470) Tel 818-506-0236.

Source Pub, *(Source Publishing; 0-9615719)*, 1812 NW Flanders, Apt. 41, Portland, OR 97209 (SAN 696-1282) Tel 503-224-5529.

Source Pubns, *(Source Pubns.; 0-937589),* P.O. Box 1543, Colorado Springs, CO 80901 (SAN 659-1787) Tel 303-632-1419; 515 N. Custer, Colorado Springs, CO 80903 (SAN 659-1795).

Sourcebook, *(Sourcebook Project, The; 0-9600712; 0-915554),* P.O. Box 107, Glen Arm, MD 21057 (SAN 201-7652) Tel 301-668-6047.

†SourceFinders, *(SourceFinders Information Corp.; 0-917097),* 68 Sandra Rd., Voorhees, NJ 08043 (SAN 655-1157) Tel 609-772-2355; *CIP.*

SourceNet, *(SourceNet; 0-915051),* P.O. Box 6767, Santa Barbara, CA 93160 (SAN 289-0224) Tel 805-964-6066.

Sources, *(Sources; 0-9603232),* 26 Hart Ave., Hopewell, NJ 08525 (SAN 211-5182) Tel 609-466-0051.

SourceView, *(SourceView Software International; 0-87007; 0-87017),* Subs. of SourceView Corp., 835 Castro St., Martinez, CA 94553 (SAN 654-3073) Tel 415-228-6228; Toll free: 800-443-0100.

Sourdough, *(Sourdough Enterprises; 0-911803),* 16401 3rd Ave. SW, Seattle, WA 98166 (SAN 264-3987) Tel 206-244-8115.

South Asia Bks, *(South Asia Books E; 0-88386; 0-8364),* P.O. Box 502, Columbia, MO 65205 (SAN 207-4044) Tel 314-449-1359.

South Asia Bks, *(South Asia Bks.; 0-88386; 0-8364),* P.O. Box 502, Columbia, MO 65205 (SAN 207-4044) Tel 314-449-1359.

South Asia Bks, *(South Asia Books a; 0-88386; 0-8364),* P.O. Box 502, Columbia, MO 65205 (SAN 207-4044) Tel 314-449-1359.

†South End Pr, *(South End Pr.; 0-89608),* 116 St. Botolph St., Boston, MA 02115 (SAN 211-979X) Tel 617-266-0629; Orders to: 300 Raritan Ctr. Pkwy., CN-3137, Edison, NJ 08818 (SAN 695-4502) Tel 201-225-1900; *CIP.*

South Forty, *(South Forty Publishing; 0-9615291),* 20626 Whitewing Ct., P.O. Box 7735, Bend, OR 97708 (SAN 694-4175) Tel 503-382-3866.

South Georgia Coll, *(South Georgia College),* William S Smith Library, Douglas, GA 31533 (SAN 682-2479).

South Group, *(South Group Pubs., Ltd.; 0-940842),* 30 Main St., Port Washington, NY 11050 (SAN 219-6379) Tel 516-944-6161.

South Moulton Pr, *(New South Moulton Pr.; 0-939731),* 96 Rumsey Rd., Buffalo, NY 14209 (SAN 663-5873) Tel 716-881-3626.

South Mtn Pr, *(South Mountain Pr.; 0-937339),* 17 W. Pomfret St., Suite 7, Carlisle, PA 17013 (SAN 659-1809) Tel 717-245-2933.

South Oregon, *(Southern Oregon Historical Society; 0-943388),* P.O. Box 480, 206 N. Fifth St., Jacksonville, OR 97530 (SAN 240-7779) Tel 503-899-1847.

South Platte, *(South Platte Pr.; 0-9609568),* P.O. Box 163, David City, NE 68632 (SAN 262-0855) Tel 402-367-4734.

South Pub Assn, *(Southern Publishing Assn.; 0-8127),* Div. of Review & Herald Pub. Assn., 6856 Eastern Ave., Washington, DC 20012 (SAN 658-6473) Tel 202-723-3700.

South St Sea Mus, *(South Street Seaport Museum; 0-913344),* 203 Front St., New York, NY 10038 (SAN 282-3322) Tel 212-766-9020.

South Star Pub, *(South Star Publishing Co.; 0-938637),* P.O. Box 821, Gainesville, FL 32604 (SAN 661-6313); 1130 NW Third Ave., Gainesville, FL 32601 (SAN 661-6321) Tel 305-294-3156; Dist. by: Langley Pr., 821 Georgia St., Key West, FL 33040 (SAN 264-164X).

South Utah St, *(Southern Utah State College Library; 0-935615),* 351 W. Center, Cedar City, UT 84720 (SAN 696-0642) Tel 801-586-7939.

SouthArt Inc, *(SouthArt, Inc.; 0-9610698),* P.O. Box 5304, Hilton Head Island, SC 29938 (SAN 264-7931) Tel 803-671-2576.

Southco, *(Southco; 0-9614058),* 1724 Wildcat Ln., Ogden, UT 84403-3238 (SAN 685-9631) Tel 801-621-5520.

Southern Ctr Intl Stud, *(Southern Center for International Studies, Inc.; 0-935082),* 320 W. Paces Ferry Rd., NW, Atlanta, GA 30305 (SAN 213-375X) Tel 404-261-5763.

Southern Exposure, *(Southern Exposure; 0-943810),* c/o Institute for Southern Studies, P.O. Box 531, Durham, NC 27702 (SAN 275-6994) Tel 919-688-8167.

Southern Hist Pr, *(Southern Historical Pr., Inc.; 0-89308),* P.O. Box 738, Easley, SC 29641-0738 (SAN 208-8657) Tel 803-859-2346.

Southern IL Univ Sch, *(Southern Illinois Univ., Schl. of Medicine; 0-931369),* P.O. Box 3926, Springfield, IL 62708 Tel 217-782-4055.

Southern Ill U, *(Southern Illinois Univ. at Edwardsville; 0-933991),* P.O. Box 74, Dept. of Art & Design, Edwardsville, IL 62026 (SAN 692-8919) Tel 618-692-3071.

Southern Inst Pr, *(Southern Institute Pr.; 0-9615502),* P.O. Box 533, Indian Rocks Beach, FL 33535 (SAN 695-9237) Tel 904-262-1883.

Southern Pines, *(Southern Pines Centennial Committee; 0-9617019),* P.O. Box 870, Southern Pines, NC 28387 (SAN 662-9369); 500 W. Morganton Rd., Southern Pines, NC 28387 (SAN 662-9377) Tel 919-692-7021.

Southern Prog Alliance
See Alliance Pubs

Southern Pub, *(Southern Publishing Co.; 0-9616517),* 954 W. Tropical Way, Plantation, FL 33063 (SAN 659-5863) Tel 305-974-2029.

Southern Pubns, *(Southern Pubns.; 0-9617083),* P.O. Box 750, Fairhope, AL 36532 (SAN 662-6262); 159 S. School St., Fairhope, AL 36532 (SAN 662-6270) Tel 205-928-7681.

Southern Resources, *(Southern Resources Unlimited; 0-915575),* P.O. Box 29, Nashville, TN 37221 (SAN 292-6776) Tel 615-646-0199.

Southern U Pr, *(Southern Univ. Pr.; 0-87651),* 130 S. 19th St., Birmingham, AL 35233 (SAN 204-6148).

Southfarm, *(Southfarm Pr., The; 0-913337),* Subs. of Haan Graphi Pub. Services, Ltd., P.O. Box 1296, Middletown, CT 06457 (SAN 283-4146) Tel 203-344-9137; Dist. by: Stackpole Books, P.O. Box 1831, Cameron & Kelker Sts., Harrisburg, PA 17105 (SAN 202-5396) Tel 717-234-5041.

Southland Spec, *(Southland Specialty Publications Companies; 0-911041),* 2170 W. Broadway, No. 202, Anaheim, CA 92804 (SAN 263-0087) Tel 714-999-0299.

†Southwest Mus, *(Southwest Museum; 0-916561),* P.O. Box 128, Highland Park Sta., Los Angeles, CA 90042 (SAN 203-0683) Tel 213-221-2164; *CIP.*

Southwest Pub, *(Southwest Publishing Co.; 0-9615438),* 1814 Leisure World, Mesa, AZ 85206 (SAN 696-107X) Tel 602-981-2843.

Southwest Screen Print
See US Screen

Sovereign Pr, *(Sovereign Pr.; 0-914752),* 326 Harris Rd., Rochester, WA 98579 (SAN 206-1279) Tel 206-273-5109.

Sovereign VA, *(Sovereign Bks.; 0-9614715),* 2272 Pimmit Run La., No. 104, Falls Church, VA 22043 (SAN 692-6606) Tel 703-356-5377.

Sovereignty, *(Sovereignty, Inc.; 0-932201),* P.O. Box 909, Eastsound, WA 98245-0483 (SAN 686-5968) Tel 206-376-2177.

Soviet Studies, *(Soviet Studies; 0-930232),* P.O. Box 16, Hayward, CA 94543 (SAN 210-6671).

Sowa Bks, *(Sowa Books; 0-9605638),* 9637 Huntress Ln., San Antonio, TX 78255 (SAN 216-1826) Tel 512-695-2411.

Soyfoods Center, *(Soyfoods Ctr.; 0-933332),* P.O. Box 234, Lafayette, CA 94549 (SAN 212-8411); 1021 Dolores Dr., Lafayette, CA 94549 (SAN 658-165X) Tel 415-283-2991.

Sozo Pub Co, *(Sozo Pub. Co.; 0-9614465),* P.O. Box 23541, Nashville, TN 37202-3541 (SAN 678-917X) Tel 615-885-0198.

SP *Imprint* of **B&N Imports**

Sp Barb Breeders, *(Spanish Barb Breeders Association),* 2888 Bluff St., P.O. Box 487, Boulder, CO 80301 (SAN 225-039X) Tel 303-452-5951.

†SP Med & Sci Bks, *(SP Medical & Scientific Bks.; 0-89335),* Div. of Spectrum Pubns., Inc., 175-20 Wexford Terr., Jamaica, NY 11432 (SAN 213-5574) Tel 718-658-0888; *CIP.*

SP Press Intl, *(SP Pr., International, Inc.; 0-9617129),* 7806 Honeybee Ct., Bethesda, MD 20817 (SAN 662-6939) Tel 301-365-2739.

SP Pubns, *(Scripture Press Pubns., Inc.; 0-89207; 0-89693),* 1825 College Ave., Wheaton, IL 60187 (SAN 222-9471) Tel 312-668-6000; Toll free: 800-323-9409. *Imprints:* Sonflower Bks (Sonflower Books).

SPA Creek, *(SPA Creek Co.; 0-911551),* Div. of Spa Creek Instruments, 612 Third St., Annapolis, MD 21401 (SAN 264-3650) Tel 301-267-6565; Orders to: Spa Creek Inc., 616 Third St., Annapolis, MD 21403 (SAN 685-3587) Tel 301-267-6565.

†Space And, *(Space & Time; 0-917053),* 138 W. 70th St., Apt. 4B, New York, NY 10023-4432 (SAN 218-4095) Tel 212-595-0894; *CIP.*

Space News Pub, *(Space News Publishing Co.; 0-936591),* P.O. Box 66521, Baton Rouge, LA 70896 (SAN 698-1259).

Space-Time, *(Space-Time Assocs.; 0-918159),* 2039 Country Club Dr., Manchester, NH 03102 (SAN 296-8258) Tel 603-625-1094. Do not confuse with Space/Time Designs, Inc., Redmond, WA.

Space-Time WA, *(Space/Time Designs, Inc.; 0-9603570),* P.O. Box 2286, Redmond, WA 98073 (SAN 213-3776) Tel 206-392-9879. Do not confuse with Space-Time Assocs., Manchester, NH.

Space Travel
See Space Travel & Astron Res

Space Travel & Astron Res, *(Space Travel & Astronautic Research Society; 0-935313),* P.O. Box 92254, Pasadena, CA 91109-2254 (SAN 695-7153) Tel 818-795-8133; 2384 E. Orange Grove Blvd., Pasadena, CA 91104 (SAN 699-6108).

Spad Sys, *(Spad Systems, Ltd.; 0-913913),* P.O. Box 571, Williamsville, NY 14221 (SAN 286-8873) Tel 716-688-4259.

Spadra Pr, *(Spadra Pr.; 0-937161),* 126 Heritage Ln., Denton, TX 76201 (SAN 658-5019) Tel 817-382-5334; P.O. Box 23434, Denton, TX 76204 (SAN 658-5027).

Span Inc, *(Span, Inc.; 0-938281),* 2805 W. Seventh St., Little Rock, AR 72205 (SAN 658-9269) Tel 501-562-4307.

Spanish Lit Pubns, *(Spanish Literature Pubns. Co., Inc.; 0-938972),* P.O. Box 707, York, SC 29745 (SAN 216-3039) Tel 803-323-2231.

SPAR, *(SPAR),* 1123 Broadway, New York, NY 10010 (SAN 694-5325).

Sparhawk, *(Sparhawk Books, Inc.; 0-9605776),* Div. of Pawprints, Inc., Pierce Crossing Rd., Jaffrey, NH 03452 (SAN 216-5538) Tel 603-532-9337; Toll free: 633-2900; Orders to: Box 446, Jaffrey, NH 03452 (SAN 699-5608).

Sparkiestuff, *(Sparkiestuff; 0-9616616),* P.O. Box 1005, Augusta, ME 04330 (SAN 659-7750) Tel 207-623-2101; Worster Hse., Apt. 17, Hallowell, ME 04347 (SAN 659-7769).

Sparks Pr, *(Sparks Press; 0-916822),* 900 W. Morgan St., P.O. Box 26747, Raleigh, NC 27611 (SAN 208-8673) Tel 919-834-8283.

Sparrow Pr, *(Sparrow Pr.; 0-935552),* 103 Waldron St., West Lafayette, IN 47906 (SAN 205-0730) Tel 317-743-1991.

Sparrow Pr CA, *(Sparrow Press of California; 0-917143),* Subs. of Sparrow Corporation, 9255 Deering Ave., Chatsworth, CA 91311 (SAN 655-8844) Tel 818-703-6599.

Sparrow Pub, *(Sparrow Publishing; 0-942818),* W. 308 S. 7144 Hwy I, Mukwonago, WI 53149 (SAN 238-8634) Tel 414-968-2803.

Sparrow Pub NY, *(Sparrow Pubns.; 0-9611460),* 799 Sixth Ave., New York, NY 10001 (SAN 285-1296) Tel 212-741-0254.

Spartan *Imprint* of **Hayden**

Spartan Pr, *(Spartan Press; 0-912924),* P.O. Box 221, East Lansing, MI 48823 (SAN 204-6172).

Spaulding Hse Pubns, *(Spaulding Hse. Pubns.; 0-9613692),* 3217 Potterton Dr., Falls Church, VA 22044 (SAN 670-977X) Tel 703-241-7870.

Speak Yourself, *(Speak for Yourself, Inc.; 0-9614864),* 2925 Lindaloa Lane, Pasadena, CA 91107 (SAN 693-0603) Tel 818-791-5150.

Spears, *(Spears, W. H., Jr.; 0-9600106),* 426 N. Kennicott, Arlington Heights, IL 60004 (SAN 204-6180).

Spirit Am Day, *(Spirit of America Day, The),* P.O. Box 3333, Jackson, MS 39207 (SAN 225-6320) Tel 601-373-4400; Dist. by: Barrett & Co., P.O. Box 6700, Jackson, MS 39212 (SAN 240-8732) Tel 601-373-4400.

Spirit Christ, *(Spirit of Christ Ministries; 0-9615536),* Box 10952, Suite 194, Houston, TX 77292 (SAN 696-1002) Tel 713-757-3509.

Spirit Faith, *(Spirit of Faith Ministries; 0-936371),* 7040 SW 47th St., Miami, FL 33155 (SAN 698-0147) Tel 305-662-5778.

Spirit Front Fellow, *(Spiritual Frontiers Fellowship; 0-914071),* 3310 Baring St., Philadelphia, PA 19104 (SAN 287-0282) Tel 215-222-0619; 10819 Winner Rd., Independence, MO 64052 (SAN 287-0290); Dist. by: Samuel Weiser, Inc., P.O. Box 612, York Beach, ME 03910 (SAN 202-9588) Tel 207-363-4393.

Spirit Mount Pr, *(Spirit Mountain Press; 0-910871),* P.O. Box 1214, Fairbanks, AK 99707 (SAN 283-9156).

Spirit Pr *Imprint of* **J L Golz Co**

Spirit Prophecy, *(Spirit of Prophecy Ministries; 0-930351),* 1350 E. Flamingo, Las Vegas, NV 89132 (SAN 670-7661) Tel 702-737-0040; P.O. Box 19020-277, Las Vegas, NV 89132 (SAN 658-2591).

Spirit Speaks, *(Spirit Speaks; 0-938283),* P.O. Box 84304, Los Angeles, CA 90073 (SAN 663-1908).

†**Spirit That Moves,** *(Spirit that Moves Us Pr., The; 0-930370),* P.O. Box 1585, Iowa City, IA 52244 (SAN 210-8585) Tel 319-338-7502; *CIP.*

Spiritual, *(Spiritual Union; 0-9614275),* 237 Rivoli St., San Francisco, CA 94117 (SAN 687-407X) Tel 415-564-1826; Dist. by: Bookpeople, 2929 Fifth St., Berkeley, CA 94710 (SAN 168-9517) Tel 415-549-3030.

Spiritual Advisory *See* TMH Pub

Spiritual Comm *See* Arcline Pubns

Spiritual Fiction *Imprint of* **Garber Comm**

Spiritual Growth, *(Spiritual Growth Resources; 0-938180),* Div. of Organization Resoures Press Ltd., P.O. Box 977, Indianapolis, IN 46206 (SAN 692-8951).

Spiritual Renaissance, *(Spiritual Renaissance Press; 0-938380),* Affil. of Highreach Press, 315 Harvard Ln., Boulder, CO 80303 (SAN 220-1259) Tel 303-494-7577; Dist. by: Bookpeople, 2929 Fifth St., Berkeley, CA 94710 (SAN 168-9517) Tel 415-549-3030; Dist. by: DeVorss & Co., P.O. Box 550, 1046 Princeton Dr., Marina Del Rey, CA 90291 (SAN 168-9886) Tel 213-870-7478.

Spiritual Sci Lib *Imprint of* **Garber Comm**

Spiritual Warfare, *(Spiritual Warfare Ministries; 0-9615445),* P.O. Box 6515, Lakeland, FL 33807 (SAN 695-7064); Toll free: 800-282-8490; 730 Creative Dr., No. 1, Lakeland, FL 33803 (SAN 699-6094) Tel 813-644-7506; Dist. by: Spring Arbor, 10885 Textile Rd., Belleville, MI 48111 (SAN 158-9016) Tel 313-481-0900; Orders to: Whitaker House, Pittsburg & Colfax Sts., Springdale, PA 15144 (SAN 662-3549) Tel 412-274-4440.

Spiritwarrior Pub, *(Spiritwarrior Publishing Co.; 0-940298),* 306 Cecil St., Waynoka, OK 73880 (SAN 217-5851).

Spiritwood Pub, *(Spiritwood Publishers; 0-9611928),* 421 Queen N., Minneapolis, MN 55405 (SAN 283-3409) Tel 612-377-4259.

Spizzirri, *(Spizzirri Pub. Co., Inc.; 0-86545),* P.O. Box 664, Medinah, IL 60157 (SAN 215-2851) Tel 312-529-1181; Toll free: 800-325-9819.

Splittgerber, *(Splittgerber; 0-9614321),* 333 Old Mill Rd., No. 118, Santa Barbara, CA 93110 (SAN 687-5300) Tel 805-964-6161.

†**Spoken Lang Serv,** *(Spoken Language Services, Inc.; 0-87950),* P.O. Box 783, Ithaca, NY 14851 (SAN 203-2279) Tel 607-257-0500; *CIP.*

Spoon Riv Poetry, *(Spoon River Poetry Pr.; 0-933180),* P.O. Box 1443, Peoria, IL 61655 (SAN 210-8593) Tel 507-537-6463. Do Not Confuse with the Spoon River Press.

Spoon River, *(Spoon River Pr., The; 0-930358),* P.O. Box 3635, Peoria, IL 61614 (SAN 211-5190) Tel 309-673-2266. Do not confuse with Spoon River Poetry Pr.

Spoonwood Pr, *(Spoonwood Press; 0-939026),* 99 Pratt St., Suite 408, Hartford, CT 06103 (SAN 219-855X) Tel 203-246-7200; Orders to: Publishers Business Service, P.O. Box 643, Cambridge, MA 02139 (SAN 693-9767) Tel 617-481-6562.

Spore Prints, *(Spore Prints; 0-9612020),* 2985 Sacramento Dr., Redding, CA 96001 (SAN 283-3433) Tel 916-246-4834.

Sport Fishing, *(Sports Fishing Institute; 0-9602382),* 1010 Massachusetts Ave., NW Suite 100, Washington, DC 20001 (SAN 210-9719) Tel 202-898-0770.

Sporting News, *(Sporting News Publishing Co.; 0-89204),* Subs. of Times Mirror Co., P.O. Box 56, St. Louis, MO 63166 (SAN 203-2260); 1212 N. Lindbergh Blvd., St. Louis, MO 63132 (SAN 699-5616); Orders to: P.O. Box 44, St. Louis, MO 63166 (SAN 662-1481).

Sportnet, *(Sportnet, Inc.; 0-9616011),* 1680 38th St., Suite 100, Boulder, CO 80303 (SAN 697-3175) Tel 303-442-5565; P.O. Box 4064, Boulder, CO 80306 (SAN 699-6507).

Sports Hall Oblivion, *(Sports Hall of Oblivion; 0-938455),* P.O. Box 69025, Pleasant Ridge, MI 48069-0025 (SAN 660-9732); 959 W. Drayton, Ferndale, MI 48220 (SAN 660-9740) Tel 313-543-9412.

Sports Info Pr, *(Sports Information Press; 0-916533),* 2240 Harlan St., Denver, CO 80214 (SAN 295-4745) Tel 303-237-8613.

Sports Info Serv, *(Sports Information Service; 0-936301),* 471 W. Longlake Dr., Harrison, MI 48625 (SAN 696-8333) Tel 517-539-2611; Dist. by: Balfour Inc., 22 County Rd., Attleboro, MA 02703 (SAN 200-8246).

Sports Market, *(Sports Marketing, Inc.; 0-936169),* 2734 Hunters Forest, Germantown, TN 38138 (SAN 696-7590) Tel 901-755-7297.

Sports Med Bks Inc., *(Sports Medicine Bks., Inc.; 0-914363),* 22-1B Mulford Pl., Hempstead, NY 11550 (SAN 289-6818) Tel 516-481-8688.

Sports Psych Pubns, *(Sports Psychology Pubns.; 0-9616954),* P.O. Box 80632-2387, Greeley, CO 80631 (SAN 661-7670); 2623 17th Ave., Greeley, CO 80631 (SAN 661-7689) Tel 303-352-8947.

Sports Rec, *(Sports Records Bureau; 0-934175),* 528 Turf Ln., Wheaton, IL 60187 (SAN 803-367X) Tel 312-668-2484.

Sports Vision, *(Sports Vision, Inc.; 0-9614895),* 3114 NE 125th, Seattle, WA 98125 (SAN 693-2088) Tel 206-363-9111.

Sportsbks, *(Sportsbooks; 0-939468),* P.O. Box 494, Bolivar, NY 14715 (SAN 220-1887) Tel 716-928-2825.

Sportsguide, *(Sportsguide, Inc.; 0-935644),* P.O. Box 1417, Princeton, NJ 08542 (SAN 213-5590) Tel 609-921-8599.

Sportsminded Pubns, *(Sportsminded Pubns.; 0-9601912),* 2000 Center St., Suite 1330, Berkeley, CA 94704 (SAN 211-9803).

SportSoft, *(SportSoft, Inc.; 0-939267),* P.O. Drawer 160, Atlantic Beach, NC 28512 (SAN 662-6300) Tel 919-726-2865.

Sportsrite Pub Co, *(Sportsrite Publishing Co. Ltd; 0-930097),* 2601 Elliott Ave. Suite 5139, Seattle, WA 98121 (SAN 670-1841) Tel 206-448-4448.

SportsWare, *(SportsWare; 0-938709),* P.O. Box 18734, Washington, DC 20036-8734 (SAN 661-566X); 139 D St. SE, Washington, DC 20036 (SAN 661-5678) Tel 202-543-2114.

SPOSS, *(Society for the Promotion of Science & Scholarship, Inc.; 0-930664),* 4139 El Camino Way, Palo Alto, CA 94306 (SAN 211-3473) Tel 415-325-3958; Dist. by: Arcata Graphics, P.O. Box 711, Kingsport, TN 37662 (SAN 200-7304) Tel 615-246-7131.

Spraysaver Pubns, *(Spraysaver Pubns.; 0-9616523),* P.O. Box 392, Rockport, ME 04856 (SAN 659-588X); 7 Summer St., Rockport, ME 04856 (SAN 659-5898) Tel 207-236-3656.

Spring Harbor, *(Spring Harbor Pr.; 0-935891),* Div. of Spring Harbor, Ltd., P.O. Box 346, Delmar, NY 12054 (SAN 695-9768); 29 Bennett Terr., Delmar, NY 12054 (SAN 699-6175) Tel 518-439-5978.

Spring Hill, *(Spring Hill Center; 0-932676),* P.O. Box 288, Wayzata, MN 55391 (SAN 212-2332); Dist. by: Publishing Center for Cultural Resources, 625 Broadway, New York, NY 10012 (SAN 685-3617) Tel 212-260-2010.

Spring Historical, *(Springfield Historical Commission; 0-943572),* Planning Dept., Springfield City Hall, Springfield, OR 97477 (SAN 240-7787) Tel 503-686-9961.

Spring Manufac, *(Spring Manufacturers Institute; 0-9604120),* 380 W. Palatine Rd., Wheeling, IL 60090 (SAN 691-3326) Tel 312-520-3290.

Spring Pubns, *(Spring Pubns., Inc.; 0-88214),* P.O. Box 222069, Dallas, TX 75222 (SAN 203-2244); 408 N. Bishop, Suite 108, Dallas, TX 75208 (SAN 658-1692) Tel 214-943-4093.

†**Spring St Pr,** *(Spring Street Pr.; 0-931691),* 104 Spring St., Amherst, MA 01002 (SAN 682-4722) Tel 413-253-7748; *CIP.*

†**Springer Pub,** *(Springer Publishing Co., Inc.; 0-8261),* 536 Broadway, New York, NY 10012 (SAN 203-2236) Tel 212-431-4370; *CIP.*

†**Springer-Verlag,** *(Springer-Verlag New York, Inc.; 0-387),* Subs. of Springer-Verlag GmbH & Co. KG, 175 Fifth Ave., New York, NY 10010 (SAN 203-2228) Tel 212-460-1500; Toll free: 800-526-7254; *CIP.*

Springfellow Bks *See* Dutton

Springfield, *(Springfield Art Museum; 0-934306),* 1111 E. Brookside Dr., Springfield, MO 65807 (SAN 213-5957) Tel 417-866-2716.

Springfield Lib & Mus, *(Springfield Library & Museum Assn.; 0-916746),* 49 Chestnut St., Springfield, MA 01103 (SAN 214-2228).

Springfield Pub Co, *(Springfield Publishing Co.; 0-937500),* 9041 Newcastle Ave., Northridge, CA 91325 (SAN 220-0937) Tel 818-701-6821.

Springfield Res Serv, *(Springfield Research Service; 0-9603306),* P.O. Box 4181, Silver Spring, MD 20904 (SAN 221-7058); 724 Springloch Rd., Silver Spring, MD 20904 (SAN 662-149X) Tel 301-622-2247.

Springhouse *See* Springhouse Pub

Springhouse Corp *See* Springhouse Pub

†**Springhouse Pub,** *(Springhouse Publishing Co.; 0-916730; 0-87434),* 1111 Bethlehem Pike, Springhouse, PA 19477 (SAN 208-1202) Tel 215-646-8700; Toll free: 800-346-7844; 711 E. Union, West Chester, PA 19380 (SAN 658-0971); *CIP.*

Springmeadow Pub, *(Springmeadow Pubs.; 0-9614703),* P.O. Box 31038, Seattle, WA 98103 (SAN 692-6126) Tel 206-633-1087.

Springtide, *(Springtide Books; 0-910873),* 30 Watkins Rd., Brick, NJ 08724 (SAN 262-4230) Tel 201-458-1543.

Springtime *See* Springtime Inter

Springtime Inter, *(Springtime Interprises, Inc.; 0-9606462),* 11832 Timmy Ln., Garden Grove, CA 92640 (SAN 218-5067) Tel 714-971-7833.

Sproing, *(Sproing Books; 0-916176),* 10612 Altman St., Tampa, FL 33612 (SAN 206-3816).

Sprout Pubns, *(Sprout Pubns. Inc.; 0-932972),* P.O. Box 4064, Sarasota, FL 33578 (SAN 212-6931) Tel 813-349-1714; Dist. by: Nutri Bks., P.O. Box 5793, Denver, CO 80223 (SAN 169-054X) Tel 303-778-8383; Dist. by: Bookpeople, 2929 Fifth St., Berkeley, CA 94710 (SAN 662-1503) Tel 415-549-3030.

SPSS Inc, *(SPSS, Inc.; 0-926673; 0-918469),* 444 N. Michigan Ave., Suite 3000, Chicago, IL 60611 (SAN 653-8975) Tel 312-329-3600.

Spur Pubs, *(Spur Pubs.; 0-9615503),* P.O. Box 5895, Columbia, SC 29250 (SAN 695-9229) Tel 803-799-4540.

Sputz, *(Sputz, David; 0-9604312),* 611 Bedford Ave., Brooklyn, NY 11211 (SAN 215-1847).

Spyglass Ent *See* Spyglass Pro

Spyglass Pro, *(Spyglass Productions; 0-913487),* 6 Thelma Ave., Glen Burnie, MD 21061 (SAN 285-1938) Tel 301-768-3157.

Sq One Pubs, *(Square One Pubs., Inc.; 0-938961),* P.O. Box 4385, Madison, WI 53711 (SAN 661-7271); 501 S. Prospect, Madison, WI 53711 (SAN 662-4340) Tel 608-255-8425. *Imprints:* Stamp Out Sheep Pr (Stamp Out Sheep Press).

Squad Sig Pubns, *(Squadron Signal Pubns.; 0-89747),* 1115 Crowley Dr., Carrollton, TX 75006 (SAN 400-3748) Tel 214-242-1485; Toll free: 800-527-7427.

Squalor Prod, *(Squalor Productions; 0-9611426),* 2711 W. Adams St., Chicago, IL 60612 (SAN 284-9208) Tel 312-826-5126.

Squantum Pr, *(Squantum Press; 0-9607532),* 92 Old Colony Ave., Quincy, MA 02170 (SAN 238-4817) Tel 617-471-8380.

Square Circle, *(Square Circle Press; 0-930159),* 137 Granada Dr., Corte Madera, CA 94925 (SAN 669-7054) Tel 415-924-6045.

Squarebooks, *(Squarebooks; 0-916290),* P.O. Box 1000, Mill Valley, CA 94942 (SAN 209-1062) Tel 415-383-0202.

Squeezer, *(Squeezer Press; 0-9608270),* 311 Lake, San Francisco, CA 94118 (SAN 240-4451) Tel 415-751-7373.

Squire, *(Squire, Ron),* Orders to: Shirley Squire, 174 Calle Cuervo, San Clemente, CA 92672 (SAN 204-8728) Tel 714-492-7068.

†SRA, *(Science Research Assocs.; 0-574),* Subs. of IBM, 155 N. Wacker Dr., Chicago, IL 60606 (SAN 295-3498) Tel 312-984-7226; Toll free: 800-621-0476; *CIP.*

Sri Aurobindo, *(Sri Aurobindo Universal; 0-935075),* 331 E. 14th St., Apt 6C, New York, NY 10003 (SAN 695-0000) Tel 212-254-3321.

Sri Rama, *(Sri Rama Publishing; 0-918100),* 161 Robles Dr., Santa Cruz, CA 95060 (SAN 282-3578) Tel 408-426-5098; Orders to: P.O. Box 2550, Santa Cruz, CA 95063 (SAN 282-3586) Tel 408-426-5098.

Sri Shirdi Sai, *(Sri Shirdi Sai Pubns.; 0-938924),* 251 Wilbur Ave., Pittsburgh, PA 15145 (SAN 220-2751) Tel 412-823-1296.

SRL Pub Co, *(SRL Publishing Co.; 0-918152),* P.O. Box 2277, Sta. A, Champaign, IL 61820 (SAN 209-3871) Tel 217-356-1523.

Sroge M, *(Sroge, Maxwell, Publishing, Inc.; 0-942674),* 731 N. Cascade, The Sroge Bldg., Colorado Springs, CO 80903-3205 (SAN 238-5732) Tel 303-633-5556.

SSC *Imprint of Unipub*

SSPC, *(Steel Structures Painting Council),* 4400 Fifth Ave., Pittsburgh, PA 15213 (SAN 260-3187) Tel 412-578-3327; Orders to: Publications Department, SSPC-4400 Fifth Ave., Pittsburgh, PA 15213 (SAN 662-1538) Tel 412-268-3455.

SSSR
See Soc Sci & Soc Res

St Alban Pr, *(St. Alban Press; 0-918980),* 10606 Parrot Ave. Apt. A., Downey, CA 90241 (SAN 210-492X) Tel 213-861-7569; Orders to: Gene/Smith, P.O. Box 598, Ojai, CA 93023 (SAN 210-4938) Tel 805-646-6790.

St Alban Pr CA, *(St. Alban Pr., San Diego; 0-935461),* Subs. of Liberal Catholic Church, 741 Cerro Gordo Ave., San Diego, CA 92102 (SAN 695-8664) Tel 619-239-0637.

St Andrew Pr, *(St. Andrew Pr.; 0-939485),* Rt. 1, Box 283, Big Island, VA 24526 (SAN 663-3951) Tel 804-299-5956. Do not confuse with St. Andrews Press in Laurinburg, NC or in New York, NY.

St Andrews NC, *(St. Andrews Press; 0-932662),* St. Andrews Presbyterian College, Laurinburg, NC 28352 (SAN 207-8902) Tel 919-276-3652.

St Anthony Mess Pr, *(St. Anthony Messenger Pr.; 0-912228; 0-86716),* 1615 Republic St., Cincinnati, OH 45210 (SAN 204-6237) Tel 513-241-5616; Toll free: 800-325-9521.

St Anthony Northport, *(St. Anthony of Padua Schl.; 0-9616243),* 6 Fifth Ave., East Northport, NY 11731 (SAN 658-6880) Tel 516-261-5130.

St Anthony Orthodox, *(Saint Anthony Orthodox Pubns.; 0-936649),* Div. of Kellion of St. Anthony the Great, P.O. Box 1432, Alamogordo, NM 88311-1432 (SAN 699-7031).

St Augeo Pub, *(St. Augeo Publishing Co.; 0-9606900),* P.O. Box 567, Cross Keys Rd., R.D. 1, Glassboro, NJ 08028 (SAN 217-4308) Tel 609-881-4958.

St Augustine Hist, *(Saint Augustine Historical Society; 0-9612744; 0-917553),* 271 Charlotte St., St. Augustine, FL 32084 (SAN 289-8306) Tel 904-824-2872.

St Basil Pr, *(St. Basil Press; 0-9604278),* 4106 N. Ozark Ave., Norridge, IL 60634 (SAN 215-1057).

†St Bedes Pubns, *(St. Bede's Pubns.; 0-932506),* P.O. Box 545, Petersham, MA 01366-0545 (SAN 222-9692) Tel 617-724-3407; *CIP.*

St Clair Pr
See Wiley

St Clair Pub, *(St. Clair Publishing; 0-9616319),* Rte. 1, Box 371A, Cottontown, TN 37048 (SAN 658-6635) Tel 615-672-4844.

St Cuthberts, *(St. Cuthbert's Treasury Press; 0-914724),* 1290 Maricopa Dr., Oshkosh, WI 54901 (SAN 206-1287) Tel 414-235-2057.

St David's Bks, *(St. David's Bks.; 0-9613616),* 537 Hilaire Rd., Saint Davids, PA 19087 (SAN 677-0053).

ST David's Soc of WY Val, *(St. David's Society of Wyoming Valley),* 205 Maple St., Trucksville, PA 18708 (SAN 663-1916).

St Edns, *(Street Editions; 0-935694),* 20 Desbrosses St., New York, NY 10013 (SAN 282-373X).

St Edwards Univ, *(Saint Edward's Univ.; 0-938472),* 3001 S. Congress Ave., Austin, TX 78704 (SAN 215-9155).

St Francis Hosp, *(St. Francis Hospital, Dr. William G. Eckert Laboratory),* Wichita, KS 67214 (SAN 226-7403).

St Genesius Pr Ltd, *(St. Genesius Press, Ltd.; 0-911673),* 519 Seventh St., Rapid City, SD 57701 (SAN 264-3669) Tel 605-348-5465.

St George Bk Serv, *(St. George Book Service, Inc.; 0-916786),* P.O. Box 225, Spring Valley, NY 10977 (SAN 208-8371) Tel 914-623-7852.

St George IA, *(Saint George Pr., The; 0-939846),* 2814 Summit St., Sioux City, IA 51104-3743 (SAN 216-2989) Tel 309-676-4799.

St George Pr, *(St. George Pr.; 0-932104),* 3500 N. Coltrane Rd., Oklahoma City, OK 73121 (SAN 209-6773) Tel 405-427-5005.

St Georges Episcopal, *(St. George's Episcopal Church; 0-9613533),* 8250 Hwy. 72, P.O. Box 38447, Germantown, TN 38138-0447 (SAN 657-3819) Tel 901-525-2494.

St Giles, *(Saint Giles Pr.; 0-9607382),* Box 1416, Lafayette, CA 94549 (SAN 239-4901) Tel 415-939-3485.

St Herman AK, *(St. Herman of Alaska Brotherhood; 0-938635),* P.O. Box 70, Platina, CA 96076 (SAN 661-583X); Beegum Gorge Rd., Platina, CA 96076 (SAN 661-5848).

St James Pr, *(St. James Pr.; 0-912289),* 425 N. Michigan Ave., Chicago, IL 60611 (SAN 205-9258) Tel 312-329-0806.

St Joans Pr, *(St. Joan's Pr.; 0-942160),* 215 E. 80th St., New York, NY 10021 (SAN 226-2797).

St John Evang, *(St. John the Evangelist Church; 0-9616134),* 126 W. Georgia St., Indianapolis, IN 46225 (SAN 699-959X) Tel 317-635-2021.

St John Gallery, *(St. John, John, Gallery; 0-9605946),* 1683 Copenhagen Dr., Solvang, CA 93463 (SAN 216-6445).

St John-Oklawaha
See J V Hays

St Johns Pub, *(St. John's Publishing; 0-938577),* 6824 Oaklawn Ave., Edina, MN 55435 (SAN 661-1125) Tel 612-920-9044.

St Johns Univ Christ Hum, *(St. John's Univ., Christian Humanism Project; 0-9613867),* P.O. Box 5766, Collegeville, MN 56321 (SAN 685-2246) Tel 612-363-2417.

St Joseph, *(St. Joseph's Univ. Pr.; 0-916101),* 5600 City Ave., Philadelphia, PA 19131 (SAN 240-8368) Tel 215-879-7325.

St Joseph Hosp, *(St. Joseph Hospital; 0-9616857),* Div. of St. Joseph Health System, 1100 W. Stewart, Orange, CA 92668 (SAN 661-597X) Tel 714-771-8040.

St Local Inter, *(State, Local, & Intergovernmental Center; 0-943142),* Div. of Harvard University, 53 Church St., Cambridge, MA 02138 (SAN 240-5385) Tel 617-495-7908.

St Louis Human, *(St. Louis Humanities Forum; 0-9616369),* 711 N. 11th St., St. Louis, MO 63101 (SAN 659-0012) Tel 314-241-5109.

St Louis Metro Bar, *(Bar Assn. of Metropolitan St. Louis),* 1 Mercantile Ctr., Rm. 3600, St. Louis, MO 63101 (SAN 226-3149).

St Louis Pub Lib, *(St. Louis Public Library, Pubns. Dept; 0-937322),* 1301 Olive St., St. Louis, MO 63103 (SAN 205-9215) Tel 314-241-2288.

St Luke Pub, *(St. Luke's Publishing Co.; 0-939502),* Subs. of St. Luke's Pr./Fine Arts Productions, P.O. Box 1378, South Bend, IN 46624 (SAN 216-6925) Tel 219-234-5115.

†St Luke TN, *(St. Luke's Pr.; 0-918518),* Mid-Memphis Tower, 1407 Union Ave., Suite 401, Memphis, TN 38104 (SAN 210-0029) Tel 901-357-5441; Toll free: 800-524-5554 (dial 4617, orders); *CIP.*

St Marg Hse Hosp, *(St. Margaret's Hse. & hospital for Babies; 0-9611828),* 27 Hackett Blvd., Albany, NY 12208 (SAN 286-1941) Tel 518-465-2461.

St Margaret's, *(St. Margaret's Hospital),* Administrator's Office, 90 Cushing Ave., Boston, MA 02125 (SAN 207-5156).

St Mark Coptic Orthodox, *(St. Mark Coptic Orthodox Church),* P.O. Box 692, Troy, MI 48094 (SAN 240-1533) Tel 313-764-0350.

†St Martin, *(St. Martin's Pr., Inc.; 0-312; 0-9603648),* Subs. of Macmillan Pubs., 175 Fifth Ave., New York, NY 10010 (SAN 200-2132) Tel 212-674-5151; Toll free: 800-221-7945; 165 Marlborough St., Boston, MA 02116 (SAN 650-0560); *CIP. Imprints:* J Kahn (Kahn, Joann, Book, A).(Kahn, Joan, Bk., A); Papermac (Papermac Books).(Papermac Bks.).

St Mary's, *(St. Mary's Pr.; 0-88489),* Subs. of Christian Brothers of Minnesota, Terrace Heights, Winona, MN 55987 (SAN 203-073X) Tel 507-452-9090; Toll free: 800-533-8095.

St Matthew's, *(Saint Matthew's Episcopal Church),* 1401 W. Broad St., Savannah, GA 31401 (SAN 219-0966).

St Maurice Church, *(St. Maurice Church; 0-9615563),* 32 Hebron Rd., Bolton, CT 06040 (SAN 696-7272); Dist. by: Kathleen J. Callahan, 53 Burnt Hill Rd., Hebron, CT 06248 (SAN 200-8203) Tel 203-228-0873.

St Michael VA, *(St. Michael's Pr.; 0-910581),* P.O. Box 6009, Portsmouth, VA 23703 (SAN 260-2601) Tel 804-484-3690.

St Michaels, *(St. Michaels Historical Museum),* St. Michaels Mission, Drawer D, St. Michaels, AZ 86511 (SAN 239-5290) Tel 602-871-4172.

St Nectarios, *(St. Nectarios Pr.; 0-913026),* 10300 Ashworth Ave. N., Seattle, WA 98133-9410 (SAN 203-3542) Tel 206-522-4471. *Imprints:* Holy Transfiguration (Holy Transfiguration Monastery).

St Paul Area, *(American Red Cross, St. Paul Area Chapter; 0-9605584),* 100 S. Robert St., St. Paul, MN 55107 (SAN 240-8392).

St Paul the Apostle, *(Saint Paul the Apostle Church; 0-9602352),* 202 E. Washington St., Greencastle, IN 46135 (SAN 212-6206).

St Peters Pr, *(St. Peter's Pr.),* Kaduna/Dept. of State, Washington, DC 20520 (SAN 240-8376).

ST Pubns
See Signs of Times

St Sophia Religious, *(St. Sophia Religious Assn. of Ukrainian Catholics),* 7911 Whitewood Rd., Philadelphia, PA 19117 (SAN 204-949X) Tel 215-635-1555.

St Thomas, *(St. Thomas Pr.; 0-940648),* P.O. Box 1036 SMS, Fairfield, CT 06430 (SAN 204-6288) Tel 713-666-3111.

St Thomas Aca, *(St. Thomas Academy; 0-9615710),* 949 Mendota Heights Rd., Mendota Heights, MN 55120 (SAN 695-9385) Tel 612-454-0090.

St Thomas Pub, *(St. Thomas Pubs.; 0-9615048),* 4831 SE Powell Blvd., Suite 1043, Portland, OR 97206 (SAN 693-8612) Tel 503-231-9080.

St Thomas Seminary
See Vincentian

ST Two, *(ST2; 0-943542),* 203 Si Town Rd., Castle Rock, WA 98611 (SAN 238-3810) Tel 206-636-2645.

St Vartan
See D O A C

St Vincent Hosp, *(St. Vincent Hospital),* Dept. D., P.O. Box 2107, Santa Fe, NM 87501 (SAN 211-4003).

†**St Vladimirs,** *(St. Vladimir's Seminary Pr.; 0-913836; 0-88141),* 575 Scarsdale Rd., Crestwood, NY 10707 (SAN 204-6296) Tel 914-961-8313; *CIP.*

Stack the Deck, *(Stack the Deck, Inc.; 0-933282),* 9126 Sandpiper Ct., Orland Park, IL 60462 (SAN 659-7203) Tel 312-349-8345.

†**Stackpole,** *(Stackpole Bks., Inc.; 0-8117),* P.O. Box 1831, Cameron & Kelker Sts., Harrisburg, PA 17105 (SAN 202-5396) Tel 717-234-5041; Toll free: 800-READ-NOW; *CIP.* Imprints: K S Giniger (Giniger, K. S., Books).(Giniger, K. S., Bks.).

Stafford Co, *(Stafford Publishing Co., Inc.; 0-9612954),* 2876 Putting Green, Memphis, TN 38115 (SAN 292-6830) Tel 901-794-9682.

Staffort Hart, *(Staffort Hart Publishing Co.; 0-932301),* 70 E. Sixth Ave., Denver, CO 80206 (SAN 686-6646) Tel 303-781-7883.

Stage Guild, *(Stage Guild; 0-9612330),* 820 E. Genesee St., Syracuse, NY 13210 (SAN 289-4998) Tel 315-423-4008.

Staging & Stuff, *(Staging & Stuff; 0-935723),* P.O. Box 158545, Nashville, TN 37215 (SAN 695-961X) Tel 615-297-7883; 1806 Primrose Ave., Nashville, TN 37212 (SAN 699-6159) Tel 615-251-2544; Dist. by: Broadman-Holman, 127 Ninth Ave. N, Nashville, TN 37234 (SAN 281-3440).

Stained Glass, *(Stained Glass Images, Inc.; 0-936459),* 135 Dolton Ave., San Carlos, CA 94070 (SAN 698-0163) Tel 415-592-4858.

Staked Plains, *(Staked Plains Press; 0-918028),* P.O. Box 779, Canyon, TX 79015 (SAN 209-360X) Tel 806-655-7121.

Stalcup, *(Stalcup's Unlimited; 0-933501),* 413 W. Gaston Ave., Bessemer City, NC 28016 (SAN 691-8840) Tel 704-629-3940.

Stallcup R, *(Stallcup, Richard W.; 0-9615073),* P.O. Box 36, Inverness, CA 94937 (SAN 693-9244) Tel 415-669-1568.

Stalsby-Wilson, *(Stalsby/Wilson Pr.; 0-911299),* P.O. Box 19976, Houston, TX 77224 (SAN 693-3750).

Stamberger Pub, *(Stamberger Publishing Co.; 0-9614372),* 2330 Severn St., Baltimore, MD 21230 (SAN 688-6264) Tel 301-752-6035.

Stamlyn Pub Co, *(Stamlyn Publishing Co.; 0-9614339),* Div. of Stamlyn Corp., 3 West End Ave., P.O. Box 402, Old Greenwich, CT 06870-0402 (SAN 687-8385) Tel 203-637-9470.

Stamp Journal, *(Stamp Journals Index Co., The; 0-9608004),* 177 Columbia Heights, Brooklyn, NY 11201 (SAN 238-5740).

Stamp Out Sheep Pr *Imprint of* **Sq One Pubs**

Standard Arts, *(Standard Arts Pr.; 0-911426),* 2324 Butler Rd., Butler, MD 21023 (SAN 204-6318) Tel 301-472-4698.

†**Standard Ed,** *(Standard Educational Corp.; 0-87392),* 200 W. Monroe, Chicago, IL 60606 (SAN 204-6326) Tel 312-346-7440; *CIP.*

Standard Poors, *(Standard & Poor's Corp.; 0-927201),* Subs. of McGraw-Hill Inc., 25 Broadway, New York, NY 10004 (SAN 205-0900) Tel 212-208-8000.

†**Standard Pub,** *(Standard Publishing Co.; 0-87239; 0-87403),* Div. of Standex International, 8121 Hamilton Ave., Cincinnati, OH 45231 (SAN 220-0147) Tel 513-931-4050; Toll free: 800-543-1353; Toll free: 800-582-1385 in Ohio; *CIP.*

Standards Eng, *(Standards Engineering Society; 0-9616825),* 6700 Penn Ave. S., Minneapolis, MN 55423 (SAN 661-1265) Tel 612-861-4990.

Standish *Imprint of* **Dell**

Stanford Alumni Assn, *(Stanford Alumni Assn.; 0-916318),* Bowman Alumni House, Stanford, CA 94305 (SAN 222-8513).

Stanford Enviro, *(Stanford Environmental Law Society),* Stanford, CA 94305 (SAN 226-3483).

Stanford U Law
See Stanford Enviro

†**Stanford U Pr,** *(Stanford Univ. Pr.; 0-8047),* Stanford, CA 94305 (SAN 203-3526) Tel 415-723-9434; *CIP.*

StanGib
See S Gibbons

Stanley Found, *(Stanley Foundation, The; 0-9603112),* 420 E. Third St., Muscatine, IA 52761 (SAN 221-7066).

Stanley Pub Co, *(Stanley Publishing Co., The; 0-9613291),* P.O. Box 689, Westboro, MA 01581 (SAN 653-8444) Tel 617-366-9442.

†**Stanton & Lee,** *(Stanton & Lee Pubs., Inc.; 0-88361),* Subs. of Carley Capital Group, 44 E. Mifflin St., Madison, WI 53703 (SAN 211-2744) Tel 608-255-3254; Toll free: 800-356-4600; Toll free: 800-362-5464 (WI); *CIP.*

Stanton Production, *(Stanton, Allaben, Production; 0-913109),* 70 Little Pond Rd., Londonderry, VT 05148 (SAN 283-3441).

StanzaPr, *(StanzaPress),* 706 Fifth St., Steilacoom, WA 98388 (SAN 295-6381).

Star & Elephant Bks *Imprint of* **Green Tiger Pr**

Star Athlete, *(Star Athlete; 0-937566),* P.O. Box 1815, Laredo, TX 78044-1815 (SAN 659-1841) Tel 512-722-6391; 910 Cedar, No. 16, Laredo, TX 78040 (SAN 659-185X).

Star Bks Inc, *(Star Bks., Inc.; 0-915541),* 408 Pearson St., Wilson, NC 27893 (SAN 291-4468) Tel 919-237-1591.

Star City Pubns, *(Star City Pubns.; 0-9615937),* 1735 S. 20th St., Lincoln, NE 68502 (SAN 696-8244) Tel 402-477-5025; Orders to: Star City Publications, P.O. Box 2914, Lincoln, NE 68502 (SAN 662-3883).

Star-Gate, *(Star-Gate Enterprises; 0-911167),* P.O. Box 1006, Orinda, CA 94563 (SAN 281-5125) Tel 415-945-1210; Toll free: 800-824-2222 Ext. 35; Dist. by: Bookpeople, 2929 Fifth St., Berkeley, CA 94710 (SAN 168-9517) Tel 415-549-3030; Dist. by: U.S. Game Systems, 38 E. 32nd St., New York, NY 10016 (SAN 282-7336) Tel 212-685-4300; Dist. by: DeVorss & Co., P.O. Box 550, 1046 Princeton Dr., Marina del Rey, CA 90294 (SAN 692-6266); Dist. by: Publishers Group West, 5855 Beaudry St., Emeryville, CA 94608 (SAN 692-6274) Tel 415-658-3453.

Star-Gate Ent
See Star-Gate

Star Power Prod, *(Star Power Productions; 0-938641),* 636 Hermosa, Chaparral, NM 88021 (SAN 661-5856) Tel 505-824-4213.

Star Pr, *(Star Pr.; 0-937038),* P.O. Box 835, Friday Harbor, WA 98250 (SAN 226-8035) Tel 206-378-5871.

Star Pub CA, *(Star Publishing Co.; 0-89863),* 940 Emmett Ave., Belmont, CA 94002 (SAN 212-6958) Tel 415-591-3505.

Star Pub Fla, *(Star Publishing Co., Inc.),* 609 N. Railroad Ave. P.O. Drawer BB, Boynton Beach, FL 33435 (SAN 207-2904).

Star Pub TX, *(Star Publishing Co.; 0-935103),* P.O. Box 3537-168, Austin, TX 78764 (SAN 695-1775) Tel 512-327-8310.

Star Pubns MO, *(Star Pubns.; 0-932356),* 1211 W. 60th Terrace, Kansas City, MO 64113 (SAN 212-4564) Tel 816-523-8228.

Star Rover, *(Star Rover Hse. at Jack London Heritage Hse.; 0-932458),* 1914 Foothill Blvd., Oakland, CA 94606 (SAN 212-4572) Tel 415-532-8408.

Star System, *(Star System Press; 0-932890),* P.O. Box 15202, Wedgwood Sta., Seattle, WA 98115 (SAN 207-5059) Tel 206-522-2589.

Star Tree, *(Star Tree Pr.; 0-940506),* 114 Honeyspot Rd., Stratford, CT 06497 (SAN 219-0982).

Star Valley, *(Star Valley Pubns.; 0-911223),* P.O. Box 421, Noti, OR 97461 (SAN 287-7562) Tel 503-935-2974.

Starblaze *Imprint of* **Donning Co**

Starbright, *(Starbright Bks.; 0-9606248),* P.O. Box 353, Freeland, WA 98249 (SAN 282-3632) Tel 206-321-6138; Orders to: 1611 E. Dow Rd., Freeland, WA 98249 (SAN 282-3640) Tel 206-321-6138.

Starchand Pr, *(Starchand Press; 0-910425),* P.O. Box 468, Wainscott, NY 11975 (SAN 260-1419) Tel 516-324-2632.

Starfield Pr, *(Starfield Pr.; 0-9616826),* P.O. Box 3247, Shawnee, KS 66203 (SAN 661-4671); 5930 Barton, Shawnee, KS 66203 (SAN 661-468X) Tel 913-631-6060.

Starfire *Imprint of* **Bantam**

Starfire Bks, *(Starfire Books; 0-9608006),* 9502 Indian Hills Dr.,, Sun City, AZ 85351 (SAN 238-5759) Tel 602-972-0547.

Starhaven, *(Starhaven; 0-936315),* P.O. Box 3045, La Jolla, CA 92038 (SAN 697-3191).

Starkey Labs, *(Starkey Laboratories, Inc.; 0-9601970),* 6700 Washington Ave. S., Eden Prairie, MN 55344 (SAN 215-1111); Toll free: 800-328-8602.

Starlight Houston, *(Starlight Publishing Co.; 0-9616401),* P.O. Box 41275, Houston, TX 77241-1275 (SAN 659-1868) Tel 713-937-7465; 7850 Greenedge Dr., Houston, TX 77040 (SAN 659-1876).

Starlight Pr, *(Starlight Pr.; 0-9605438),* P.O. Box 3102, Long Island City, NY 11103 (SAN 216-0633).

Starlight Pubns, *(Starlight Pubns.; 0-9615667),* 1438 Epping Forest Dr., Atlanta, GA 30319 (SAN 695-9644) Tel 404-237-7125.

Starline *Imprint of* **Scholastic Inc**

Starlite, *(Starlite Distributors; 0-931941),* P.O. Box 20729, Reno, NV 89515 (SAN 200-7789).

Starlog
See Starlog Group

Starlog Group, *(Starlog Pr.; 0-931064; 0-934551),* Div. of Starlog Group, 475 Park Ave. South, New York, NY 10016 (SAN 212-1247) Tel 212-689-2830.

Starmark, *(Starmark Publishing; 0-936572),* Div. of Starmark, Inc., 706 N. Dearborn St., Chicago, IL 60610 (SAN 214-2236) Tel 312-922-3388.

†**Starmont Hse,** *(Starmont Hse.; 0-916732; 0-930261),* P.O. Box 851, Mercer Island, WA 98040 (SAN 208-8703) Tel 206-232-8484; *CIP.*

Starogubski, *(Starogubski Pr.; 0-9603234),* Westbeth, 55 Bethune St., Suite H658, New York, NY 10025 (SAN 207-2912) Tel 212-255-3322.

†**Starpath,** *(Starpath School of Navigation; 0-914025),* 2101 N. 34th St., Seattle, WA 98103 (SAN 286-889X) Tel 206-632-1293; *CIP.*

Starports Pub, *(Starports Publishing; 0-9616977),* 13624 Crestway Dr., Brook Park, OH 44142 (SAN 661-7743) Tel 216-362-0122.

Starr Pubns, *(Starr Pubns.; 0-9613292),* 4015 SE Franklin St., Portland, OR 97202 (SAN 653-8487) Tel 503-234-4185.

Starr Studios, *(Starr Studios; 0-9612548),* P.O. Box 5604, Missoula, MT 59806 (SAN 287-7643) Tel 406-543-4638; Dist. by: Publisher's Group West, 5855 Beaudry St., Emeryville, CA 94608 (SAN 202-8522) Tel 415-658-3453.

Starr TX, *(Starr, Arnold, & Co.; 0-9607194),* 1334 Country Place Cir., Houston, TX 77079 (SAN 239-1317) Tel 713-497-0004; Dist. by: Richardson's Educators, 2014 Lou Ellen Ln., Houston, TX 77018 (SAN 169-829X) Tel 713-688-2244.

Starrett Pub Co, *(Starrett Publishing Co.; 0-911983),* 550 Hilbar Lane, Palo Alto, CA 94303 (SAN 276-9409) Tel 415-327-1472.

Starry Messenger Bks, *(Starry Messenger Books, Inc.; 0-930179),* Div. of National Toxicology Monitor Inc., 262 Kalmia Ave., No. 12, Lexington, KY 40508 (SAN 670-6916).

Starseed Pubns, *(Starseed Pubns., Inc.; 0-915763),* P.O. Box 2258, Gearhart, OR 97138 (SAN 293-8863) Tel 503-738-3659.

Starshooter
See J P Werner

Start Now Pr, *(Start Now Press; 0-913819),* 4811 Lomitas Dr., San Diego, CA 92116 (SAN 286-0589) Tel 619-294-2239.

Stasiuk Ent, *(Stasiuk Enterprises; 0-932421),* 3150 NE 30th Ave., Portland, OR 97212 (SAN 687-4088) Tel 503-284-6887.

Stat Med Pub, *(Stat Medical Publishing Co.; 0-935463),* 1527 Pine St., Philadelphia, PA 19102 (SAN 695-8648) Tel 215-735-5175.

State AK Nat Res, *(State of Alaska, Dept. of Natural Resources; 0-9616003),* Div. of Parks, Pouch 7-001, Anchorage, AK 99510 (SAN 699-7627) Tel 907-762-4530.

State Arbor, *(Univ. of Utah, State Arboretum of Utah; 0-942830),* Univ. of Utah, Bldg. 436, Salt Lake City, UT 84112 (SAN 240-2971) Tel 801-581-5322.

State Bar TX, *(State Bar of Texas; 0-938160),* P.O. Box 12487, Capitol Sta., Austin, TX 78711 (SAN 216-4531) Tel 512-463-1481.

†**State Hist Iowa,** *(State Historical Society of Iowa; 0-89033),* 402 Iowa Ave., Iowa City, IA 52240 (SAN 206-5770) Tel 319-353-6689; *CIP.*

†**State Hist Soc Wis,** *(State Historical Society of Wisconsin; 0-87020),* 816 State St., Madison, WI 53706 (SAN 203-350X) Tel 608-262-1368; *CIP.*

State House Pr, *(State Hse. Pr.; 0-938349),* P.O. Drawer 15247, Austin, TX 78761 (SAN 660-9651); 1604 S. Congress, Austin, TX 78704 (SAN 660-966X) Tel 512-448-0770.

State Mutual Bk, *(State Mutual Bk. & Periodical Service, Ltd.; 0-89771),* 521 Fifth Ave., 17th Flr., New York, NY 10017 (SAN 658-3849) Tel 212-682-5844.

State Revenue Soc, *(State Revenue Society; 0-934939),* 51 Westchester Ave., Thornwood, NY 10594 (SAN 225-6053) Tel 914-747-0882.

State Street Pr, *(State Street Pr.; 0-933581),* P.O. Box 252, Pittsford, NY 14534 (SAN 692-2252) Tel 716-244-4850.

State U NY Buffalo, *(State Univ. of New York at Buffalo Music Department; 0-931111),* 222 Baird Hall, Buffalo, NY 14260 (SAN 678-9498) Tel 716-636-2765.

†**State U NY Pr,** *(State Univ. of New York Pr.; 0-87395; 0-88706),* State Univ. Plaza, Albany, NY 12246 (SAN 658-1730) Tel 518-472-5000; Orders to: P.O. Box 6525, Ithaca, NY 14850 (SAN 203-3496) Tel 607-277-2211; *CIP.*

Statelaw Guides, *(Statelaw Guides, Inc.; 0-934055),* P.O. Box 28962, St. Louis, MO 63132 (SAN 693-0867) Tel 314-993-2610.

Staten Island, *(Staten Island Historical Society; 0-9606756),* 441 Clarke Tpke., Richmondtown, NY 10306 (SAN 205-0641) Tel 212-351-1611.

†**Station Hill Pr,** *(Station Hill Pr.; 0-930794),* Station Hill Rd., Barrytown, NY 12507 (SAN 214-1485); Dist. by: Small Press Dist., 1814 San Pablo Ave., Berkeley, CA 94702 (SAN 204-5826) Tel 415-549-3336; Dist. by: Inland Bk. Co., P.O. Box 261, 22 Hemingway St., East Haven, CT 06512 (SAN 200-4151) Tel 203-467-4257; Dist. by: Station Hill Pr., Sta. Hill Rd., Barrytown, NY 12507 (SAN 214-1485); Dist. by: Writers & Bks., 740 University Ave., Rochester, NY 14607 (SAN 662-152X) Tel 716-473-2590; *CIP.*

Station Reps Assn, *(Station Representatives Assn., Inc.),* 230 Park Ave., New York, NY 10017 (SAN 224-6600) Tel 212-687-2484.

Statistical Pr, *(Statistical Pr.; 0-9610700),* P.O. Box 11019, San Francisco, CA 94101 (SAN 264-7958) Tel 415-922-1267.

Statistikon Corp, *(Statistikon Corp., The),* P.O. Box 246, East Norwich, NY 11732 (SAN 696-6721) Tel 516-922-0882.

Stay Away, *(Stay Away Joe Pubs.; 0-911436),* P.O. Box 2054, Great Falls, MT 59403 (SAN 204-6350).

STDS Pub *See* TVR Pub Co

Steam Pr MA, *(Steam Pr.; 0-942820),* 15 Warwick Rd., Watertown, MA 02172 (SAN 238-8642) Tel 617-923-1046; Dist. by: Kampmann & Company, 9 E. 40th St., New York, NY 10016 (SAN 202-5191) Tel 212-685-2928.

Steamship Hist Soc, *(Steamship Historical Society of America, Inc.; 0-913423),* 414 Pelton Ave., Staten Island, NY 10310 (SAN 285-0915) Tel 718-727-9583; Orders to: Steamship Hist. Soc, HC Hall Bldg., 345 Blackstone Blvd., Providence, RI 02906 (SAN 285-0923) Tel 401-274-0805.

Stearn Pubs, *(Stearn Publishers Ltd.; 0-9612186),* 500 E. 77th St., New York, NY 10162 (SAN 289-5005) Tel 212-737-9304.

Steaven Res & Pub, *(Steaven Research & Publishing; 0-932609),* 9860 SW Davies Rd., Beaverton, OR 97005 (SAN 687-5319) Tel 503-626-3693.

Steel Founders, *(Steel Founders' Society of America; 0-9604674),* 455 State St., Des Plaines, IL 60016 (SAN 215-2002) Tel 312-299-9160.

Steel Joist Inst, *(Steel Joist Institute),* 1205 48th Ave. N., Suite A, Myrtle Beach, SC 29577 (SAN 229-7841) Tel 803-449-0487.

SteelDragon Pr, *(SteelDragon Pr.; 0-916595),* P.O. Box 7253, Powderhorn Sta., Minneapolis, MN 55407 (SAN 296-6727) Tel 612-721-6076.

Steelstone, *(Steelstone Pr.; 0-9605678),* 4607 Claussen Lane, Valparaiso, IN 46383 (SAN 216-1877) Tel 219-464-1792.

Steffanides, *(Steffanides, George F.; 0-9600114),* 66 Lourdes Dr., Fitchburg, MA 01420 (SAN 204-6369) Tel 617-342-1997.

Steffen Pub Co, *(Steffen Publishing Co.; 0-911913),* Main St., Holland Patent, NY 13354 (SAN 283-9199) Tel 315-865-4132.

Stehsel, *(Stehsel, Donald; 0-9606582),* 2600 S. Third Ave., Arcadia, CA 91006 (SAN 206-3824) Tel 818-446-3679.

Steimatzky Pub *See* Shapolsky Steimatzky

†**Stein & Day,** *(Stein & Day; 0-8128),* Scarborough Hse., Briarcliff Manor, NY 10510 (SAN 203-3461) Tel 914-762-2151; *CIP.*

Stein Coll Intl, *(Stein Collectors International),* P.O. Box 463, Kingston, NJ 08528 (SAN 225-5456) Tel 201-329-2567.

Steiner *Imprint of* Garber Comm

Steiner Co *See* Haldor Co

Steiner Inst, *(Steiner, Rudolf, Institute; 0-9615304),* RD 2, Box 199, Phoenixville, PA 19460 (SAN 694-5422) Tel 215-495-5406.

Steiner R, *(Steiner, Ralph, Incorporated; 0-9615132),* Thetford, VT 05074 (SAN 694-2644) Tel 802-785-2476; Dist. by: Univ. of New Mexico Pr., Journalism Bldg., Rm. 220, Albuquerque, NM 87131 (SAN 213-9588) Tel 505-277-2346.

Steinerbks *Imprint of* Garber Comm

Steinlage, *(Steinlage Products; 0-914754),* 4766 Kremer Hoying Rd., St. Henry, OH 45883 (SAN 206-1295) Tel 419-678-4125.

Steinlitz-Hammacher, *(Steinlitz-Hammacher Co.; 0-917208),* P.O. Box 187, Hasbrouck Heights, NJ 07604 (SAN 293-3985) Tel 201-667-1429; Dist. by: Nacscorp, 528 E. Lorain St., Oberlin, OH 44074 (SAN 293-3993) Tel 216-775-8084; Dist. by: The Distributors, 702 S. Michigan, South Bend, IN 46618 (SAN 169-2488) Tel 219-232-8500.

Steinway, *(Steinway & Sons; 0-9607196),* Subs. of Steinway Musical Properties, Inc., Steinway Place, Long Island City, NY 11105 (SAN 239-1325) Tel 718-721-2600; Toll free: 800-223-6017.

Steketee-Van Huis *Imprint of* Holland Jr Welfare

Stel-Mar, *(Stel-Mar; 0-935456),* 329 Rhoda Dr., Lancaster, PA 17601 (SAN 215-1855).

Stella Maris Bks, *(Stella Maris Books; 0-912103),* P.O. Box 11483, Ft. Worth, TX 76110 (SAN 264-7613) Tel 817-924-7221.

Stelle, *(Stelle Group; 0-9600308),* P.O. Box 75, Quinlan, TX 75474 (SAN 204-6385) Tel 214-864-0799.

†**Stemmer Hse,** *(Stemmer Hse. Pub., Inc.; 0-916144; 0-88045),* 2627 Caves Rd., Owings Mills, MD 21117 (SAN 207-9623) Tel 301-363-3690; *CIP. Imprints:* Intl Design (International Design Library); Story-to-Color (Story-to-Color).

Stenotype Educ, *(Stenotype Educational Products, Inc.; 0-938643),* P.O. Box 959, Melrose, FL 32666 (SAN 661-6356); Rte. 1, P.O. Box 1235, Melrose, FL 32666 (SAN 661-6364) Tel 904-475-3332.

STEP, *(Specialized Training & Education Programs, Inc.; 0-934937),* 20 Golf Rd., P.O. Box 7414, Springfield, IL 62704 (SAN 694-2954) Tel 217-546-7493.

Step Ahead Pr, *(Step Ahead Pr.; 0-934941),* Affil. of Heartlite, Inc., 6509 Breckville Rd., P.O. Box 31360, Cleveland, OH 44131 (SAN 695-0159) Tel 216-526-6727.

Step By Step Pubns, *(Step By Step Pubns.; 0-9615611),* 2209 Madison, Norfolk, NE 68701 (SAN 695-8818) Tel 402-371-5023.

Step Stones Pr, *(Stepping Stones Pr.; 0-9616502),* P.O. Box 4585, McAllen, TX 78502 (SAN 659-3429) Tel 512-686-6829; 221 N. Main St., McAllen, TX 78502 (SAN 659-3437).

Stephen Wright, *(Wright, Stephen, Press; 0-9601904),* Box 1341, F.D.R. Post Office Sta., New York, NY 10150 (SAN 211-8785) Tel 212-927-2869.

Stephens Eng Assocs, *(Stephens Engineering Associates, Inc.; 0-911677),* 7030 220th SW., Mountlake Terrace, WA 98043 (SAN 264-4126) Tel 206-771-2182.

Stephens Pr, *(Stephens Press),* Drawer 1441, Spokane, WA 99210 (SAN 210-9573) Tel 509-838-8222.

Steppingstone Ent, *(Steppingstone Enterprises, Inc.; 0-939728),* 2108 S. University Dr., Park Place Plaza, Suite 103, Fargo, ND 58103 (SAN 216-7646) Tel 701-237-4742.

Steppingstones *See* Bibliophile

Stereopticon Pr, *(Stereopticon Press; 0-9608824),* 534 Wahlmont Dr., Webster, NY 14580 (SAN 238-3829) Tel 716-671-2342.

†**Sterling,** *(Sterling Publishing Co., Inc.; 0-8069),* 2 Park Ave., New York, NY 10016 (SAN 211-6324) Tel 212-532-7160; 900 Magnolia Ave., Elizabeth, NJ 07201 (SAN 658-1773); *CIP. Imprints:* Davis Pubns (Davis Publications).

Sterling Hgts Geneal, *(Sterling Heights Genealogical & Historical Society; 0-9616495),* 40255 Dodge Pk. Rd., Sterling Heights, MI 48078 (SAN 659-3380) Tel 313-731-3778.

Sterling Instru, *(Sterling Instrument),* 2101 Jericho Tpke., New Hyde Park, NY 11040 (SAN 207-2920).

Sterling Life Ins, *(Sterling Life Insurance Co.; 0-9617162),* One S. Limestone St., Springfield, OH 45502 (SAN 662-8087) Tel 602-953-1564.

Sterling Magic, *(Sterling Magic Creations, Inc.; 0-941658),* P.O. Box 251, San Bruno, CA 94066 (SAN 239-3174) Tel 415-871-8626.

Sterling Pubns Ltd *See* Bryce-Waterton Pubns

Sterling Swift *See* Heath

Sterling Swift *Imprint of* Heath

Sterling Travel Pubn, *(Sterling Travel Pubns.; 0-913303),* 12616-12th Ave. S., Seattle, WA 98168 (SAN 285-8592) Tel 206-246-4092.

Stern, *(Stern, Clarence Ames; 0-9600116),* P.O. Box 2294, Oshkosh, WI 54903 (SAN 204-6393) Tel 414-231-6786.

Stevens & Shea, *(Stevens & Shea Pubs.; 0-89550),* P.O. Box 794, Stockton, CA 95201 (SAN 206-3670) Tel 209-465-1880.

Stevens & Sons UK, *(Stevens & Sons Ltd.; 0-420),* 11 New Fetter Ln., London EC4P 4EE, .

Stevens Bk Pr, *(Stevens Bk., Pr.; 0-913029),* Div. of Stevens Book Shop, P.O. Box 71, Wake Forest, NC 27587 (SAN 159-1126) Tel 919-556-3830.

Stevens Irving *See* Moosehead Prods

Stevens Pub, *(Stevens, Gareth, Publishing; 0-918831; 1-55532),* 7221 W. Green Tree Rd., Milwaukee, WI 53223 (SAN 696-1592) Tel 414-466-7550.

Stevenson Intl, *(Stevenson International; 0-9606252),* 525 Princeton Circle W., Fullerton, CA 92631 (SAN 217-5878).

Stevenson Lang Skills, *(Stevenson Language Skills, Inc.; 0-941112),* 85 Upland Rd., Attleboro, MA 02703 (SAN 217-4413) Tel 617-222-1133.

†**Stevenson Pr,** *(Stevenson Pr.; 0-89482),* P.O. Box 10021, Austin, TX 78766 (SAN 209-8873); *CIP.*

Stevenson Sch *Imprint of* U of Tex Pr

Steves Wide World, *(Steves Wide World Studios),* 111 Fourth Ave. N., Edmonds, WA 98020 (SAN 214-2244). Deceased.

Steward & Sons, *(Steward & Sons; 0-917144),* P.O. Box 24-8583, Coral Gables, FL 33124 (SAN 208-8789).

Stewardship Enters, *(Stewardship Enterprises; 0-9611282),* P.O. Box 29403, Richmond, VA 23229 (SAN 283-3468) Tel 804-740-2608.

†**Stewart Tabori & Chang,** *(Stewart, Tabori & Chang, Pubs.; 0-941434; 1-55670),* 740 Broadway, New York, NY 10003 (SAN 293-4000) Tel 212-460-5000; Dist. by: Workman Publishing Co., Inc., One W. 39th St., New York, NY 10018 (SAN 203-2821) Tel 212-398-9160; Dist. by: Random House, Inc., 201 E. 50th St., New York, NY 10022 (SAN 202-5507) Tel 212-572-8030; *CIP.*

STHV, *(Science, Technology, & Human Values; 0-932564),* Massachusetts Institute of Technology, Bldg. 14, Cambridge, MA 02139 (SAN 212-2286) Tel 617-253-4010.

Still News, *(Still News Pubns.; 0-940828),* P.O. Box 353, Port Ludlow, WA 98365 (SAN 219-6417).

Still Point TX, *(Still Point Pr.; 0-933841),* 4222 Willow Grove Rd., Dallas, TX 75220 (SAN 692-6746) Tel 214-352-8282.

Stillgate, *(Stillgate Pubs.; 0-938286),* P.O. Box 67, Alstead, NH 03602 (SAN 216-1885).

Stillpoint, *(Stillpoint Publishing; 0-913299),* P.O. Box 640, Walpole, NH 03608 (SAN 285-8630) Tel 603-756-3508; Toll free: 800-526-0275; Orders to: Dutton-NAL, 34 Engelhard Dr., Cranbury, NJ 08512 (SAN 694-9622); Dist. by: New American Library, P.O. Box 999, Bergenfield, NJ 07621 (SAN 206-8087) Tel 201-387-0600.

Stilwell Studio, *(Stilwell Studio, The; 0-9605862),* P.O. Box 50, Carmel, CA 93921 (SAN 220-1895) Tel 408-624-0340.

Stimler Assoc, *(Stimler Associates; 0-9600770),* 33 W. Second St., Moorestown, NJ 08057 (SAN 206-7994).

Stindt Bks, *(Stindt Bks.; 0-9615465),* 3363 Riviera West Dr., Kelseyville, CA 95451 (SAN 695-7145) Tel 707-279-8581.

Stinson Beach, *(Stinson Beach Press; 0-918540),* P.O. Box 475, Stinson Beach, CA 94970 (SAN 209-8881) Tel 415-868-1424.

Stipes, *(Stipes Publishing Co.; 0-87563),* P.O. Box 526, 10-12 Chester St., Champaign, IL 61820 (SAN 206-8664) Tel 217-356-8391.

Stirrup Assoc, *(Stirrup Associates, Inc.; 0-937420),* 115 Church St., Decatur, GA 30030 (SAN 215-1863) Tel 404-378-4372.

Stivers, *(Stivers, Stephen N.; 0-9615274),* 4725 SE 49th St., Portland, OR 97206 (SAN 695-2194) Tel 503-775-2816; Dist. by: Stinna Co., 4725 SE 49th St., Portland, OR 97206 (SAN 200-5778).

STL Intl, *(STL International Inc.; 0-936215),* 12101 E. 51st St., No. 107, Tulsa, OK 74146 (SAN 696-8783) Tel 918-250-1488; Dist. by: International Cassette Corp., P.O. Box 1928, Greenville, TX 75401 (SAN 200-5824).

STO Pub, *(STO Pubns.; 0-9614540),* 6224 N. 13th St., Philadelphia, PA 19141 (SAN 691-7240) Tel 215-927-3392.

Stock-Breznau, *(Stock & Breznau Publishing Co.; 0-936525),* 12335 Santa Monica Blvd., Suite 207, Los Angeles, CA 90025 (SAN 698-018X).

Stock Drive, *(Stock Drive Products; 0-9609878),* 2101 Jericho Turnpike, New Hyde Park, NY 11040 (SAN 204-6415).

†**Stockton Pr,** *(Stockton Pr.; 0-935859; 0-943299),* Div. of Grove's Dictionaries of Music, Inc., 15 E. 26th St., New York, NY 10010 (SAN 696-0545) Tel 212-481-1334; Toll free: 800-221-2123; *CIP.*

Stockton Unified Schl Dist, *(Stockton Unified School District, The; 0-9607134),* 701 N. Madison St., Stockton, CA 95203 (SAN 239-037X).

†**Stoeger Pub Co,** *(Stoeger Publishing Co.; 0-88317),* Subs. of Stoeger Industries, 55 Ruta Ct., South Hackensack, NJ 07606 (SAN 206-118X) Tel 201-440-2700; Toll free: 800-631-0723; *CIP.*

Stokes, *(Stokes Publishing Co.; 0-914534),* 1125 Robin Way, Suite E, Sunnyvale, CA 94087 (SAN 206-5789) Tel 408-736-4637.

Stokesville Pub, *(Stokesville Publishing Co.; 0-936030),* P.O. Box 14401, Atlanta, GA 30324 (SAN 211-3333) Tel 404-261-5316.

Stoma Pr, *(Stoma Pr., Inc.; 0-89939),* 13231 42nd Ave., NE., Seattle, WA 98125 (SAN 222-8432).

Stone Age Pr, *(Stone Age Pr. of Alaska; 0-9615808),* 1649 Bannister Dr., Anchorage, AK 99508 (SAN 696-5938) Tel 907-279-3740.

Stone Canyon Pr, *(Stone Canyon Pr.; 0-937641),* 10635 Stone Canyon Rd., Dallas, TX 75230 (SAN 659-1884) Tel 214-360-9848.

Stone Country, *(Stone Country Pr.; 0-930020),* P.O. Box 132, Menemsha, MA 02552 (SAN 209-7788) Tel 617-693-5832.

Stone Hse NY, *(Stone Hse. Pr.; 0-937035),* P.O. Box 196, Roslyn, NY 11576 (SAN 658-7062) Tel 516-621-7145; 35 Post Dr., Roslyn Harbor, NY 11576 (SAN 658-7070). Do not confuse with with Stone House Pr., Fairfax VT.

Stone Man Pr, *(Stone Man Pr.; 0-914473),* Lubec, ME 04652 (SAN 289-6826) Tel 207-733-2194.

Stone-Marrow Pr, *(Stone-Marrow Press),* P.O. Box 1157, Anacortes, WA 98221 (SAN 203-3429).

Stone Pr CA, *(Stone Pr.; 0-916889),* 6800 Pacific View Dr., Los Angeles, CA 90068 (SAN 656-0377) Tel 213-876-3054.

Stone St Pr, *(Stone St. Pr., The; 0-943984),* 1 Stone St., Staten Island, NY 10304 (SAN 219-8185) Tel 718-447-1436.

Stone Trail Pr, *(Stone Trail Pr.; 0-932123),* P.O. Box 34320, Bethesda, MD 20817 (SAN 686-5259) Tel 301-365-2238.

†**Stone Wall Pr,** *(Stone Wall Pr., Inc.; 0-913276),* 1241 30th St. NW, Washington, DC 20007 (SAN 203-3402) Tel 202-333-1860; Dist. by: Independent Pubs. Group, 1 Pleasant Ave., Port Washington, NY 11050 (SAN 287-2544); *CIP.*

Stoneback Pub, *(Stoneback, Jean, Publishing Co.; 0-931440),* 588 Franklin St., Alburtis, PA 18011 (SAN 222-8440).

Stonecrest Pr, *(Stonecrest Pr.; 0-9616004),* P.O. Box 5927, Napa, CA 94558 (SAN 699-7643) Tel 707-255-8702.

Stonegate Pub, *(Stonegate Publishing),* P.O. Box 4853, Topeka, KS 66604 (SAN 291-8528).

Stoneground Pub, *(Stoneground Publishing; 0-933145),* 127 Piedra Loop, Los Alamos, NM 87544 (SAN 692-3380) Tel 505-672-9310.

Stonehaven Pubs, *(Stonehaven Pubs.; 0-937775),* Box 367, Lena, IL 61048 (SAN 659-347X); 602 Oak St., Lena, IL 61048 (SAN 659-3488) Tel 815-369-2823.

Stonehill Pr, *(Stonehill Pr.; 0-937167),* 24-B Bigelow St., Cambridge, MA 02139 (SAN 658-5108) Tel 617-723-8300; Orders to: Stonehill Press, P.O. Box 1362, Boston, MA 02104 (SAN 662-4103) Tel 617-497-9577.

Stonehouse, *(Stonehouse Pubns.; 0-9603236),* Sweet, ID 83670 (SAN 206-1058).

Stoneridge Inst, *(Stoneridge Institute of Politico-Socio-Economics Press; 0-937300),* 7703 Baltimore National Pike, Frederick, MD 21701 (SAN 215-112X) Tel 301-473-8287.

Stoneridge Pub, *(Stoneridge Publishing; 0-938767),* P.O. Box 1495, Pleasanton, CA 94566 (SAN 661-7778); 6000 Stoneridge Mall Rd., Suite 390, Pleasanton, CA 94566 (SAN 661-7786) Tel 415-462-3470.

Stoney Brook, *(Stoney Brook Publishing Co.; 0-912928),* 186 Main St. W., Chelmsford, MA 01863 (SAN 204-6423).

Stoneydale Pr Pub, *(Stoneydale Pr. Publishing Co.; 0-912867),* 304 Main St., P.O. Drawer B, Stevensville, MT 59870 (SAN 265-3168) Tel 406-777-2729.

Stony Brook Pr, *(Stony Brook Press; 0-9603726),* Box 158A, St. James, NY 11780 (SAN 209-5955) Tel 516-862-9296.

Stony Point Pubns, *(Stony Point Pubns.; 0-931293),* P.O. Box 4467, Petaluma, CA 94953 (SAN 682-0220) Tel 707-778-8754.

†**Storey Comm Inc,** *(Storey Communications, Inc.; 0-88266),* Schoolhouse Rd., Pownal, VT 05261 (SAN 203-4158) Tel 802-823-5811; Toll free: 800-441-5700; Dist. by: Harper & Row Pubs., 10 E. 53rd St., New York, NY 10022 (SAN 200-2086) Tel 212-207-7099; *CIP.* Imprints: Garden Way Pub (Garden Way Publishing); Storey Pub (Storey Publishing).

Storey Pub *Imprint of* **Storey Comm Inc**

Storie McOwen, *(Storie/McOwen Pubs., Inc.; 0-912367),* P.O. Box 308, Manteo, NC 27954 (SAN 265-0940) Tel 919-473-5881.

Stories Westports Past, *(Stories from Westport's Past; 0-9615410),* Div. of Joanna Foster Assocs., 32 Narrow Rocks Rd., Westport, CT 06880 (SAN 695-5142) Tel 203-226-0397.

Storm King
  See Storm King Pr

Storm King Pr, *(Storm King Pr.; 0-935166),* P.O. Box 3566, Washington, DC 20007 (SAN 213-6988) Tel 202-944-4224.

Storm Mtn Pubs, *(Storm Mountain Pubs.; 0-939167),* Subs. of LTM Design, 8791 Wolff Ct., Suite 200, Westminister, CO 80030 (SAN 662-8540) Tel 303-426-1671.

Stormline Pr, *(Stormline Pr., Inc.; 0-935153),* P.O. Box 593, Urbana, IL 61801 (SAN 695-3506); 403 E. Washington St., Urbana, IL 61801 (SAN 662-3476) Tel 217-328-2665.

†**Story Hse Corp,** *(Story Hse. Corp.; 0-87157),* Bindery Ln., Charlotteville, NY 12036 (SAN 169-5193) Tel 607-397-8725; Toll free: 800-428-1008 (NY State); Toll free: 800-847-2105 (Outside NY); *CIP.*

Story Line, *(Story Line Pr.; 0-934257),* c/o The Reaper, 325 Ocean View Ave., Santa Cruz, CA 95062 (SAN 693-3289) Tel 408-426-5539.

†**Story Pr,** *(Story Press; 0-931704),* P.O. Box 10040, Chicago, IL 60610 (SAN 212-6982) Tel 312-246-1064; *CIP.*

Story-to-Color *Imprint of* **Stemmer Hse**

Storypole, *(Storypole Pr.; 0-9609940),* 11015 Bingham Ave., E., Tacoma, WA 98446 (SAN 275-8199) Tel 206-531-2032.

Storyviews Pub, *(Storyviews Publishing Co.; 0-9617057),* 136 E. 55th St., New York, NY 10022 (SAN 662-8354) Tel 212-751-7307; Dist. by: Bookazine Co., 303 W. 10th St., New York, NY 10014 (SAN 169-5665) Tel 212-675-8877.

Stough Inst, *(Stough Institute, Inc., The; 0-940830),* 54 W. 16th St., New York, NY 10011 (SAN 219-8193).

†**Stowe-Day,** *(Stowe-Day Foundation; 0-917482),* 77 Forest St., Hartford, CT 06105 (SAN 209-052X) Tel 203-522-9258; *CIP.*

Stpngstns Pr NY, *(Steppingstones Pr.; 0-935821),* P.O. Box 1856, New York, NY 10027 (SAN 695-992X) Tel 718-474-5063; 247 Beach 122nd St., Belle Harbor, NY 11694 (SAN 699-6191).

Str Software, *(Strider Software; 0-936921),* Beecher Lake Rd., Pembine, WI 54156 (SAN 658-3776) Tel 715-324-5487.

Strafford Pubns, *(Strafford Pubns., Inc.; 0-9616858),* 1375 Peachtree St., NE, No. 260, Atlanta, GA 30367 (SAN 661-5953) Tel 404-881-1141.

Strahm, *(Strahm, Virgil; 0-9606050),* P.O. Box 900, Branson, MO 65616 (SAN 216-9347) Tel 417-334-4381.

Straight Pubs, *(Straight Arrow Pubs.; 0-9613653),* P.O. Box 1236, Los Altos, CA 94023 (SAN 670-7785) Tel 415-949-5243; Dist. by: Mustang Publishing, P.O. Box 9327, New Haven, CT 06533 (SAN 289-6702) Tel 203-624-5485.

Straight St Pub, *(Straight Street Publishing, Inc.; 0-936309),* 1500 NW Seventh Ct., Miami, FL 33136 (SAN 697-3221) Tel 305-326-8966.

Strang Comms Co, *(Strang Communications Co.; 0-930525),* 190 N. Westmonte Dr., Altamonte Springs, FL 32714 (SAN 677-5640) Tel 305-869-5005.

Strategic Assessments, *(Strategic Assessments, Inc.; 0-915669),* P.O. Box 8005-265, Boulder, CO 80306 (SAN 292-6873) Tel 303-444-1343.

Strategic Moves, *(Strategic Moves; 0-915375),* Div. of Strategic Corporation, The, 2188 SW Park Place, Portland, OR 97205 (SAN 291-4476) Tel 503-222-9028; Toll free: 800-992-2911 (Oregon only); Toll free: Y.

Strategic Systs, *(Strategic Learning Systems; 0-937037),* 18-15 215th St., Suite 2S, Bayside, NY 11360 (SAN 658-5094) Tel 718-631-1453.

Stratford Hse, *(Stratford Hse. Publishing Co.; 0-938614),* 5761 Whitnall Highway, Suite 202, North Hollywood, CA 91601 (SAN 216-1893); Orders to: P.O. Box 7077, Burbank, CA 91510 (SAN 669-2753) Tel 818-761-5752.

Stratford Pubns, *(Stratford Pubns., Inc.; 0-941568),* 8614 Camden St., Alexandria, VA 22308 (SAN 239-3204) Tel 703-780-4104.

Strathcona, *(Strathcona Publishing Co.; 0-931554),* 77 Bleecker St., New York, NY 10012 (SAN 211-4550) Tel 212-505-2546.

Symbols/Abbreviations

Summit Cnty OH, *(Summit County Chapter O G S),* 410 Bonshire Rd., Akron, OH 44319 (SAN 219-9823) Tel 216-644-8660.
Summit Ent, *(Summit Enterprises, Inc.; 0-934174),* 4500 N. 32nd St., Suite 201, Phoenix, AZ 85018 (SAN 213-6465); Toll free: 800-321-5378.
Summit Jr Fort, *(Summit Junior Fortnightly Club; 0-9608052),* 214 Springfield Ave., Summit, NJ 07901 (SAN 238-8650) Tel 201-665-1796.
Summit Pr CO, *(Summit Pr.; 0-936163),* P.O. Box 207, Manitou Springs, CO 80829 (SAN 696-7620) Tel 303-685-9103.
Summit Pub Co
  See Gold Penny
Summit Pub Co
  See Ohio-Summit Pub
Summit Univ, *(Summit Univ. Pr.; 0-916766),* Box A, Malibu, CA 90265 (SAN 208-4120) Tel 818-991-4751.
Summy
  See Summy-Birchard
†**Summy-Birchard,** *(Summy-Birchard Music; 0-87487),* Div. of Birch Tree Group, Ltd., 180 Alexander Rd., Box 2072, Princeton, NJ 08540 (SAN 202-7461) Tel 609-683-0090; *CIP. Imprints:* Suzuki Method (Suzuki Method International).
SUN, *(SUN; 0-915342),* 347 W. 39th St., New York, NY 10018 (SAN 206-3832) Tel 212-594-8428.
Sun & Moon CA, *(Sun & Moon Pr.; 0-940650),* P.O. Box 481170, Los Angeles, CA 90048 (SAN 216-3063) Tel 213-653-6711; 6363 Wilshire Blvd., Suite 115, Los Angeles, CA 90048 (SAN 658-179X).
Sun & Moon MD
  See Sun & Moon CA
Sun Dance Bks, *(Sun Dance Books; 0-913330),* 1520 N. Crescent Heights, Hollywood, CA 90046 (SAN 204-6474) Tel 213-654-2383; Dist. by: The Borgo Press, P.O. Box 2845, San Bernardino, CA 92406-2845 (SAN 208-9459) Tel 714-884-5813.
Sun Dance Pr
  See Sun Dance Bks
Sun Designs, *(Sun Designs; 0-912355),* Subs. of Rexstrom Co., Inc., P.O. Box 206, Delafield, WI 53018 (SAN 265-1181); 36802 Genesee Lake Rd., Oconomowoc, WI 53066 (SAN 265-119X) Tel 414-567-4255; Dist. by: Sterling Publishing Co., Two Park Ave., New York, NY 10016 (SAN 669-3083) Tel 212-532-7160.
Sun Features, *(Sun Features, Inc.; 0-937238),* Suite 2C, 7720 El Camino Real, Rancho La Costa, CA 92008 (SAN 282-3764) Tel 619-753-3489; Orders to: Box 368-P, Cardiff, CA 92007 (SAN 282-3772) Tel 619-753-3489.
Sun-Gemini Pr, *(SUN/Gemini Pr.; 0-933313),* P.O. Box 42170, Tucson, AZ 85733 (SAN 692-3747) Tel 602-299-1097.
Sun Life, *(Sun Life; 0-937930),* Greystone, Thaxton, VA 24174 (SAN 240-8333) Tel 703-586-4898.
Sun Litho Frazetta, *(Sun Litho-Print/Frazetta Prints; 0-9607060),* P.O. Box R, Marshall Creek, PA 18335 (SAN 239-0396) Tel 717-424-2692.
Sun Man Moon, *(Sun, Man, Moon, Inc.; 0-917738),* 4891 Pearce St. No. 1, Huntington Beach, CA 92649 (SAN 210-3745) Tel 714-840-9192; Orders to: P.O. Box 5084, Huntington Beach, CA 92646 (SAN 662-1554).
Sun Pr FL, *(Sun Pr. of Florida; 0-937039),* 35 Trotters Cir., Kissimmee, FL 32743 (SAN 658-702X) Tel 305-933-1586.
Sun Pub, *(Sun Publishing Co.; 0-914172; 0-89540),* P.O. Box 5588, Santa Fe, NM 87502-5588 (SAN 206-1325) Tel 505-988-2033.
Sun Pub GA, *(Sun Publishing, Inc.; 0-942970),* P.O. Box 450776, Atlanta, GA 30345 (SAN 238-8669).
Sun Ray Pub, *(Sun Ray Publishing Co.; 0-9614249),* 27885 SE Sun Ray Dr., Boring, OR 97009 (SAN 686-7014) Tel 503-663-3228.
Sun-Scape Pubns, *(Sun-Scape Pubns.; 0-919842),* P.O. Box 42725, Tucson, AZ 85733 (SAN 211-870X) Tel 602-744-0257.
Sun Scope, *(Sun Scope Publishing Co.; 0-9609188),* 9 Sunrise Rd., Danbury, CT 06810 (SAN 241-4635) Tel 203-743-6943.

Sun Seeker Bks, *(Sun Seeker Bks.; 0-9614662),* P.O. Box 4246, Clearlake, CA 95422 (SAN 692-4751) Tel 707-994-9161.
Sun Shine Pr
  See Sunshine TX
Sun Star Pubns, *(Sun Star Pubns.; 0-937787),* P.O. Box 519, Phoenix, AZ 85016 (SAN 659-3550) Tel 602-948-4346; 3104 E. Camelback Rd., Phoenix, AZ 85016 (SAN 659-3569).
Sun Tracks, *(Sun Tracks; 0-936350),* Univ. of Arizona, Dept. of English, Tucson, AZ 85721 (SAN 214-2007).
Sun Valley, *(Sun Valley Book; 0-9605212),* P.O. Box 1688, Sun Valley, ID 83353 (SAN 240-8406).
Sun Valley Pub, *(Sun Valley Publishing; 0-915803),* P.O. Box 1081, Ketchum, ID 83340 (SAN 294-1333) Tel 208-726-9685.
Sunbank Pub
  See Sunbank Pub Co
Sunbank Pub Co, *(Sunbank Publishing Co.; 0-9616190),* 3100 Damon Way, Burbank, CA 91504 (SAN 699-928X) Tel 213-849-1191.
Sunbeam, *(Sunbeam Pubns.; 0-9609514),* 780 N. 2250 W., Provo, UT 84601 (SAN 262-0928) Tel 801-374-6987.
Sunbeam Bks, *(Sunbeam Books; 0-916433),* 23630 Old Owen Rd., Monroe, WA 98272 (SAN 296-0036).
Sunbelt Pub Co, *(Sunbelt Publishing Co.; 0-9616247),* 6833 Lemon Rd., McLean, VA 22101 (SAN 658-6953) Tel 703-821-3195.
†**Sunbelt Pubns,** *(Sunbelt Pubns.; 0-932653),* P.O. Box 191126, San Diego, CA 92119 (SAN 687-8407) Tel 619-697-4811; *CIP.*
Sunberry Bks, *(Sunberry Books; 0-9613151),* P.O. Box 697, West Acton, MA 01720 (SAN 283-4294).
Sunbow Pubns, *(Sunbow Pubns.; 0-9615610),* P.O. Box 8936, Detroit, MI 48224 (SAN 695-8869) Tel 313-882-2269; 10718 Marne, Detroit, MI 48224 (SAN 699-6124).
†**SunBox,** *(SunBox Press; 0-930052),* 750 Alta Vista Way, Laguna Beach, CA 92651 (SAN 210-511X) Tel 714-494-2203; *CIP.*
Sunbright Bks
  See J Melek
Sunbright Bks *Imprint of* J Melek
Sunburst, *(Sunburst; 0-9609618),* P.O. Box 1433, Tacoma, WA 98401 (SAN 275-8571) Tel 206-565-2041.
Sunburst *Imprint of* FS&G
Sunburst *Imprint of* Sunburst Pub
Sunburst Comm, *(Sunburst Communications, Inc.; 0-911831; 1-55636),* 39 Washington Ave., Pleasantville, NY 10570 (SAN 213-5620) Tel 914-769-5030; Toll free: 800-431-1934.
Sunburst Farms
  See Builders Pub
Sunburst Pr, *(Sunburst Pr.; 0-934648),* P.O. Box 14205, Portland, OR 97214 (SAN 206-3840).
Sunburst Pr CA, *(Sunburst Pr.; 0-9615673),* P.O. Box 3129, Pacoima, CA 91333-3129 (SAN 695-9512); 13024 Sunburst St., Pacoima, CA 91331 (SAN 699-6140) Tel 818-899-0818.
Sunburst Prod
  See Sunburst Pub
Sunburst Pub, *(Sunburst Publishing; 0-9614865),* P.O. Box 11671, Zephyr Cove, NV 89448 (SAN 693-286X) Tel 916-544-1346; Dist. by: Bookpeople, 2929 Fifth St., Berkeley, CA 94710 (SAN 168-9517) Tel 415-549-3030. *Imprints:* Sunburst (Sunburst).
Sunburst Taco
  See Sunburst
Suncoast Prof Pub, *(Suncoast Professional Publishing Corp.; 0-937569),* 8800 49th St., N., Suite 102, Pinellas Park, FL 33565 (SAN 659-1922) Tel 813-545-1327.
Sundance, *(Sundance Pubns., Ltd.; 0-913582),* 250 Broadway, Denver, CO 80203 (SAN 203-0721) Tel 303-777-2880.
Sundance OR, *(Sundance Publishing Co.; 0-942822),* P.O. Box 604, Salem, OR 97308 (SAN 240-2858) Tel 503-378-0465.
Sundance Vent, *(Sundance/Venture Resources; 0-935389),* Div. of Sundance West, Inc., 7515 Cabrillo Ave., La Jolla, CA 92037 (SAN 696-1045); P.O. Box 1396, La Jolla, CA 92038 (SAN 699-6248) Tel 619-454-4700.

Sunday Edition, *(Sunday Edition, The; 0-932655),* P.O. Box 312, Tiburon, CA 94920 (SAN 687-8415) Tel 415-388-1298.
Sunday Paper, *(Sunday Paper, The; 0-9614022),* 188 Willow St., New Haven, CT 06511 (SAN 683-6259) Tel 203-624-2520.
Sunday Pubns, *(Sunday Pubns., Inc.; 0-941850),* 1937 10th Ave. N., Lake Worth, FL 33461 (SAN 239-3220) Tel 305-533-0990.
Sunday School, *(Sunday School Publishing Board; 0-910683),* 330 Charlotte Ave., Nashville, TN 37201 (SAN 275-8598) Tel 615-256-0856.
Sundial Bks *Imprint of* Sunstone Pr
Sundog Pr, *(Sundog Pr.; 0-9603640),* P. O. Box 111022, Anchorage, AK 99511 (SAN 221-699X).
Sundown *Imprint of* New Readers
Sundowner Serv, *(Sundowner Services; 0-932241),* 2559-47th Ave., San Francisco, CA 94116 (SAN 215-9228) Tel 415-564-0068.
Sunfire *Imprint of* Scholastic Inc
Sunfisher Bks, *(Sunfisher Books; 0-915413),* 105 Upper Sunset, Sonora, CA 95370 (SAN 683-4361); Dist. by: Baker & Taylor Co., Western Div., 380 Edison Way, Reno, NV 89502 (SAN 169-4464) Tel 206-872-5523.
Sunflower Bks *Imprint of* Smith Pubs
Sunflower Ink, *(Sunflower Ink; 0-931104),* Palo Colorado Canyon, Carmel, CA 93923 (SAN 212-9728) Tel 408-625-0588.
Sunflower U Pr, *(Sunflower Univ. Pr.; 0-89745),* 1531 Yuma, Manhattan, KS 66502-4228 (SAN 218-5075); 1531 Yuma, Manhattan, KS 66502-4228 (SAN 658-1811) Tel 913-532-6733.
Sunkist Hse, *(Sunkist House; 0-9614705),* 196 Sunkist, Los Altos, CA 94022 (SAN 692-6142) Tel 415-948-3594.
Sunlakes Pub, *(Sunlakes Publishing Co.; 0-9615884),* 4153 Bayard Rd., South Euclid, OH 44121 (SAN 696-7663) Tel 216-951-9100.
Sunland Pub, *(Sunland Publishing; 0-915621),* Rancho Don Carmel, P.O. Box 27552, Rancho Bernardo, CA 92128 (SAN 292-6903) Tel 619-746-5800.
SunMoon Pr, *(SunMoon Press; 0-942064),* P.O. Box 1516, Eugene, OR 97440 (SAN 238-4825) Tel 503-343-9544.
Sunnycrest Pub, *(Sunnycrest Publishing; 0-9610012),* Rte. 1, Box 1, Clements, MN 56224 (SAN 264-424X) Tel 507-692-2246.
Sunnyside, *(Sunnyside Publishing Co.; 0-934650),* Box 29, 51 Willow St., Lynn, MA 01903 (SAN 213-1757) Tel 617-595-4742.
Sunnyvale Mkting, *(Sunnyvale Marketing; 0-941662),* 2627 19th St., Rockford, IL 61109 (SAN 239-3239) Tel 815-397-3344.
Sunnyvale Psy, *(Sunnyvale Psychotherapy; 0-9615762),* 783 Steuben Dr., Sunnyvale, CA 94087 (SAN 695-9687) Tel 408-245-2677.
Sunrise Artistries, *(Sunrise Artistries, Inc.; 0-936519),* 64-24 Grand Ave., Maspeth, NY 11378 (SAN 698-0252) Tel 718-894-7683; Orders to: Sunrise Artistries, Inc., Box 125, Maspeth, NY 11378 (SAN 662-3964).
Sunrise Bks
  See Sunrise Chr Bks
Sunrise Chr Bks, *(Sunrise Christian Bks.; 0-940652),* c/o One Way, Ltd., 1707 "E" St., Eureka, CA 95501 (SAN 211-8254) Tel 707-442-4004.
Sunrise Found
  See Sunrise Museums
SunRise Hse, *(SunRise House; 0-915764),* P.O. Box 217, Longwood, FL 32750 (SAN 211-6529) Tel 305-830-7333.
Sunrise Museums, *(Sunrise Museums, Inc.; 0-9607962),* 746 Myrtle Rd., Charleston, WV 25314 (SAN 241-5852) Tel 304-344-8035.
Sunrise Paper
  See Sunrise Chr Bks
Sunrise Pr, *(Sunrise Press; 0-9606896),* 4984 Arboleda Dr., Fair Oaks, CA 95628 (SAN 237-9953) Tel 916-961-5551.
Sunrise Pr IL, *(Sunrise Press; 0-935800),* 2004 Grant St., Evanston, IL 60201 (SAN 215-286X) Tel 312-475-3651.
Sunrise Pub Hse, *(Sunrise Publishing House; 0-9607672),* 12021 Wilshire Blvd., Suite 225, Los Angeles, CA 90025 (SAN 240-1010).

288

Symbols/Abbreviations

Sunrise Pub NY, *(Sunrise Publishing Co. Inc.; 0-934401),* P.O. Box 408, New York, NY 10019 (SAN 693-4269) Tel 212-541-7143; Orders to: Sunrise Pub., 170 NE 33rd St., Ft. Lauderdale, FL 33334 (SAN 662-3220) Tel 305-563-1844.

Sunrise Pub OR, *(Sunrise Publishing; 0-9604344),* P.O. Box 38, Lincoln City, OR 97367 (SAN 215-1871) Tel 503-994-6723.

Sunrise Publ, *(Sunrise Publications (CO); 0-9614786),* P.O. Box 5075, Littleton, CO 80123 (SAN 692-9907) Tel 303-979-6096.

Sunrise Pubns *Imprint of* **J Melek**

Sunrise Pubns
See **J Melek**

Sunrise Pubns TX
See **Sunrise Texas**

Sunrise Texas, *(Sunrise Pubns.; 0-937789),* P.O. Box 34512, San Antonio, TX 78265 (SAN 659-3585) Tel 512-656-2055; 14502 Waddesdon Bluff, San Antonio, TX 78233 (SAN 659-3593).

Sunrise Tortoise, *(Sunrise Tortoise Books; 0-932222),* Box 61, Sandpoint, ID 83864 (SAN 212-5684).

Sunrise Vent, *(Sunrise Ventures; 0-9615674),* 708 Parkman Dr., Bloomfield Hills, MI 48013 (SAN 696-1428) Tel 313-645-6741.

Sunset-Lane, *(Sunset Bks./Lane Publishing Co.; 0-376),* 80 Willow Rd., Menlo Park, CA 94025 (SAN 201-0658) Tel 415-321-3600; Toll free: 800-227-7346; 1320 Willow Rd., Menlo Park, CA 94025 (SAN 658-182X).

Sunset Prods
See **Educ & Trainin**

Sunset Pubns
See **Sunset Pubns HI**

Sunset Pubns HI, *(Sunset Pubns.; 0-9601256; 0-941244),* 1655 Makaloa St., Suite 906, Honolulu, HI 96814 (SAN 215-1146).

Sunset Video, *(Sunset Video, Inc.; 0-936155),* 2210 Wilshire Blvd., Suite 542, Santa Monica, CA 90403 (SAN 696-7639) Tel 213-459-5826.

SunShine, *(SunShine; 0-937710),* Box 4351, Austin, TX 78765 (SAN 220-0945) Tel 512-453-2334.

Sunshine, *(Sunshine Computer Software Co.; 0-927286),* 1101 Post Oak Blvd., Suite 9-493, Houston, TX 77056 (SAN 277-6359) Tel 713-552-0949.

Sunshine
See **SunShine**

Sunshine Acad, *(Sunshine Academic Press, Inc.; 0-933064),* 304 27th St., West Palm Beach, FL 33407 (SAN 212-4602).

Sunshine Arts WA, *(Sunshine Arts; 0-938244),* W. 1018 Shannon, Spokane, WA 99205 (SAN 215-8183).

Sunshine Pr, *(Sunshine Pr.; 0-936223),* 3830 N. Oakland St., Arlington, VA 22207 (SAN 696-8252) Tel 703-243-8768.

Sunshine Serv, *(Sunshine Services Corp.; 0-942236),* Div. of Sunshine News Services, 325 Pennsylvania Ave. SE, Washington, DC 20003 (SAN 239-9830) Tel 202-544-3647.

Sunshine TX, *(Sunshine Pr.; 0-9615743),* P.O. Box 851, Comfort, TX 78013 (SAN 696-0510) Tel 512-995-2599; Dist. by: Quality Books, Inc., 918 Sherwood Dr., Lake Bluff, IL 60044-2204 (SAN 169-2127); Dist. by: The Distributors, 702 South Michigan, South Bend, IN 46618 (SAN 213-9502) Tel 219-232-8500.

Sunstone Found, *(Sunstone Foundation; 0-9606760),* 59 West First South, Salt Lake City, UT 84101 (SAN 213-9693) Tel 801-355-5926.

†Sunstone Pr, *(Sunstone Pr., The; 0-913270; 0-86534),* Subs. of Sunstone Corp., P.O. Box 2321, Santa Fe, NM 87504-2321 (SAN 214-2090) Tel 505-988-4418; *CIP.* *Imprints:* Sundial Bks (Sundial Books).

Sunstone Pubns, *(Sunstone Publications; 0-913319),* Div. of Sunstone, Inc., R.D. 3, Box 100A, Cooperstown, NY 13326 (SAN 283-4227) Tel 607-547-8207.

Sunwise Turn, *(Sunwise Turn, Ltd.; 0-88004),* P.O. Box 117, New York, NY 10003 (SAN 222-9838) Tel 718-230-8479.

SUNY Albany U Art, *(State Univ. of New York at Albany, Univ. Art Gallery; 0-910763),* 1400 Washington Ave., Albany, NY 12222 (SAN 260-2679) Tel 518-457-3375.

SUNY Buffalo, *(State University of New York at Buffalo),* Capen Hall, Amherst Campus, Buffalo, NY 14260 (SAN 227-0234).

SUNY Buffalo Univ Lib, *(State Univ. of New York at Buffalo, Univ. Libraries; 0-915769),* Amherst Campus, Capen Hall, Rm. 410, Buffalo, NY 14260 (SAN 294-1317) Tel 716-636-2818.

SUNY Compar Educ Ctr, *(State Univ. of New York at Buffalo, Comparative Education Ctr.; 0-937033),* SUNY Buffalo, Faculty of Educational Studies, Comparative Education Ctr., 428 Baldy Hall, Amherst, NY 14260 (SAN 659-4573).

SUNY Environ, *(State Univ. of New York, College of Environmental Science & Forestry at Syracuse Univ.),* Bray Hall, Rm. 123, Syracuse, NY 13210 (SAN 205-0633) Tel 315-470-6647.

†SUNYP Brainerd, *(State Univ. of New York at Potsdam, Brainerd Art Gallery; 0-942746),* State Univ. College of Arts & Sciences, Potsdam, NY 13676 (SAN 240-1959) Tel 315-267-2254; *CIP.*

†Superior Pub, *(Superior Publishing; 0-87564),* 708 Sixth Ave. N., Seattle, WA 98111 (SAN 202-747X) Tel 206-282-4310; Dist. by: Harbor Hse. Pubs., 221 Water St., Boyne City, MI 49712 (SAN 200-5751) Tel 616-582-2814; *CIP.*

Superior WI, *(Superior Pubns.),* 5510 Tower Ave., Superior, WI 54880 (SAN 209-682X) Tel 715-392-8060.

Superlove, *(Superlove; 0-9602334),* 4245 Ladoga Ave., Lakewood, CA 90713 (SAN 211-982X) Tel 213-429-6447.

Suratao, *(Suratao, Incorporated; 0-932286),* 4763 W. 12th St., Los Angeles, CA 90019 (SAN 212-1441) Tel 213-931-0371.

Sure Fire, *(Sure Fire Press; 0-916411),* Subs. of Holmes Publishing Group, c/o Holmes Publishing Group, P.O. Box 623, Edmonds, WA 98020 (SAN 656-9102) Tel 206-771-2701.

Sure Found, *(Sure Foundation; 0-936595),* Rte. 2, Box 74, Cloverdale, IN 46120 (SAN 698-1054) Tel 317-795-3136.

Surevelation, *(Surevelation; 0-917302),* P.O. Box 2193, Concord, CA 94521 (SAN 208-8800) Tel 415-687-2703.

Surf Chek, *(Surface Checking Gage Co.; 0-911464),* P.O. Box 1912, Prescott, AZ 86302 (SAN 204-6482) Tel 602-778-3160.

Surf Trav Pubns, *(Surface Travel Pubns. Co.; 0-915821),* 385 Brighton Ave., Long Branch, NJ 07740 (SAN 294-1341) Tel 201-222-9196; Orders to: P.O. Box 616, Long Branch, NJ 07740 (SAN 663-3056) Tel 609-853-7940.

Surfer Pubns, *(Surfer Pubns., Inc.; 0-939337),* Div. of For Better Living, Inc., 33046 Calle Aviador, San Juan Capistrano, CA 92675 (SAN 662-5096) Tel 714-496-5922; P.O. Box 1028, Dana Point, CA 92629 (SAN 662-510X); Dist. by: Select Magazine, 8 E. 40th St., New York, NY 10016 (SAN 200-7436).

†Surrey Bks, *(Surrey Bks., Inc.; 0-9609516),* 500 N. Michigan Ave., Suite 1940, Chicago, IL 60611 (SAN 275-8857) Tel 312-661-0050; Dist. by: Publishers Group West, 5855 Beaudry St., Emeryville, CA 94608 (SAN 202-8522) Tel 415-658-3453; *CIP.*

Surrey Pr, *(Surrey Press; 0-9610652),* 224 Surrey Rd., Warminster, PA 18974 (SAN 264-696X) Tel 215-675-4569.

Survival CT, *(Survival; 0-9604256),* Turkey Hills, Haddam, CT 06438 (SAN 213-9480).

Survival Ed Assoc, *(Survival Education Assn.; 0-913724),* 9035 Golden Givens Rd., Tacoma, WA 98445 (SAN 204-6490) Tel 206-531-3156.

Susan Hunter, *(Hunter, Susan, Publishing; 0-932419),* 1447 Peachtree St., NE, No. 807, Atlanta, GA 30309 (SAN 687-4126) Tel 404-874-5473.

Susedik Meth, *(Susedik Method, Inc. The; 0-914717),* P.O. Box 997, Cambridge, OH 43725 (SAN 287-766X) Tel 614-432-5204.

Susquehanna, *(Susquehanna Publisning Co.; 0-9609382),* 709 Apache Dr., Independence, MO 64056 (SAN 260-2695) Tel 816-257-0280.

Susquehanna U Pr, *(Susquehanna Univ. Pr.; 0-941664),* Dist. by: Associated University Presses, 440 Forsgate Dr., Cranbury, NJ 08512 (SAN 281-2959) Tel 609-655-4770.

Sussex Prints, *(Sussex Prints, Inc.; 0-911145),* P.O. Box 469, Georgetown, DE 19947 (SAN 275-8873) Tel 302-856-0026.

Sustaining Syst, *(Sustaining Systems; 0-939335),* 4300 4th Ave., NE, Seattle, WA 98105 (SAN 662-8893) Tel 206-547-7104.

Sutherland FL, *(Sutherland Publishing; 0-930942),* Div. of Sutherland Printing Company, Inc., 16956-6 McGregor Blvd., Ft. Myers, FL 33908 (SAN 222-8335) Tel 813-466-1626; Orders to: P.O. Box 426, Grinnell, IA 50112 (SAN 662-1570) Tel 515-236-6589.

Sutherland Learn Assocs, *(Sutherland Learning Assocs., Inc.; 0-934100),* 8700 Reseda Blvd., No. 108, Northridge, CA 91324 (SAN 212-8152) Tel 818-701-1344.

†Sutter House, *(Sutter House; 0-915010),* 77 Main St., P.O. Box 212, Lititz, PA 17543 (SAN 207-1207) Tel 717-626-0800; *CIP.*

Sutton Avn Pr, *(Sutton Aviation Press; 0-940300),* 3631-22nd Ave. S., Minneapolis, MN 55407 (SAN 217-1333) Tel 612-729-1175.

Sutton Pr
See **Sutton Avn Pr**

Sutton Pubns, *(Sutton Pubns.; 0-9617199),* 13 Thicket, Irvine, CA 92714 (SAN 663-2610) Tel 914-786-8054.

Suwannee Poetry, *(Suwannee Poetry; 0-938285),* P.O. Box 2902, Florence, AL 35630 (SAN 659-882X); Rte. 9, Florence, AL 35630 (SAN 659-8838) Tel 615-722-5404.

Suzuki Intl, *(Suzuki Method International; 0-87487),* Div. of Birch Tree Group Ltd., 180 Alexander Rd., Box 2072, Princeton, NJ 08540 (SAN 693-3718) Tel 609-683-0090.

Suzuki Method *Imprint of* **Summy-Birchard**

Sverge-Haus, *(Sverge-Haus Pubs.; 0-933348),* Div. of Sverge Rijks Haus, 11 Indian Spring Rd., Milton, MA 02186 (SAN 212-4610) Tel 617-773-2709.

SW Amer Pub Co, *(Southwest American Publishing Co.; 0-911217),* 5720 North 1-35 Industrial Blvd., Edmond, OK 73034 (SAN 264-4010).

SW Art Assn
See **Philbrook Art**

SW Educ Ent, *(Southwest Educational Enterprises; 0-937029),* 10711 Auldine, San Antonio, TX 78230 (SAN 658-7089) Tel 512-342-2297.

SW Legal Found, *(Southwestern Legal Foundation),* P.O. Box 830707, Richardson, TX 75083 (SAN 232-380X) Tel 214-690-2377; 2601 N. Floyd Rd., Richardson, TX 75080 (SAN 669-2702).

SW Mission, *(Southwestern Mission Research Ctr.; 0-915076),* Arizona State Museum, Tucson, AZ 85721 (SAN 215-8167) Tel 602-621-4898.

SW Nat Hist Assn, *(Southwest Natural History Association, The; 0-9610126),* P.O. Box 35141, Phoenix, AZ 85069 (SAN 275-7214) Tel 602-973-0591.

SW Pks Mnmts, *(Southwest Parks & Monuments Assn.; 0-911408),* 221 N. Court, Tucson, AZ 85701 (SAN 202-750X) Tel 602-622-1999.

SW Pub, *(South-Western Publishing Co.; 0-538),* Subs. of SFN Cos INC., 5101 Madison Rd., Cincinnati, OH 45227 (SAN 202-7518) Tel 513-271-8811; Toll free: 800-543-0487.

SW Sci Pub, *(Southwest Scientific Publishing; 0-9606246),* P.O. Drawer 3 AM, University Park, NM 88003 (SAN 220-3553) Tel 505-525-1370.

SW Univ Press, *(Southwest Univ. Pr.; 0-937681),* Div. of Southwest Univ., 4532 W. Napoleon Ave., Metairie, LA 70001 (SAN 659-3305) Tel 504-455-2900; 1021 N. Carrollton Ave., New Orleans, LA 70119 (SAN 659-3313).

SWAC Pr, *(SWAC Pr.),* Div. of Swac, Inc., Box 236, South Elgin, IL 60177 (SAN 699-7848) Tel 312-741-0500.

Swallow Pubns, *(Swallow Publications; 0-9614225),* P.O. Drawer 10, Ville Platte, LA 70536 (SAN 686-7030) Tel 318-363-2139.

Swallows Tale Pr, *(Swallow's Tale Pr.; 0-930501),* P.O. Box 930040, Norcross, GA 30093 (SAN 670-9206) Tel 404-493-4932.

Swampgas, *(Swampgas Press; 0-933838),* 3201 St. Charles Ave., No. 313, New Orleans, LA 70115 (SAN 212-7008) Tel 504-897-3413.

†Swan Books, *(Swan Bks.; 0-934048),* P.O. Box 332, Fair Oaks, CA 95628 (SAN 212-7016) Tel 916-961-8778; *CIP.*

Swan Pr, *(Swan Pr.; 0-9615530)*, 10443 N. Cave Creek Rd., Suite 211, Phoenix, AZ 85020 (SAN 695-8990) Tel 602-943-5492; P.O.Box 33517, Phoenix, AZ 85067 (SAN 699-6132).

Swansea, *(Swansea Publishing Co.; 0-916315)*, 45 Tamarack Dr., Windsor, CT 06095 (SAN 295-8325) Tel 203-242-0254.

Swansea Pr, *(Swansea Pr., Inc.)*, P.O. Box 27785, Philadelphia, PA 19118 (SAN 292-4757) Tel 215-836-1400; Toll free: 800-792-6732; 803 E. Willow Grove Ave., Philadelphia, PA 19118 (SAN 658-2494).

Swanson, *(Swanson Publishing Co.; 0-911466)*, P.O. Box 334, Moline, IL 61265 (SAN 204-6520).

Swearingen & Co.
   See Vaughan Edwards

†Swedenborg, *(Swedenborg Foundation, Inc.; 0-87785)*, 139 E. 23rd St., New York, NY 10010 (SAN 202-7526) Tel 212-673-7310; CIP.

Swedenborg Sci Assn, *(Swedenborg Scientific Association; 0-915221)*, 654 Dale Rd., P.O. Box 11, Bryn Athyn, PA 19009 (SAN 289-8454) Tel 215-947-4200.

Swedish-Am, *(Swedish-American Historical Society; 0-914819)*, 5125 N. Spaulding Ave., Chicago, IL 60625 (SAN 225-3828) Tel 312-583-5722.

Swedish Council, *(Swedish Council of America; 0-9609620)*, c/o American Swedish Institute, 2600 Park Ave., Minneapolis, MN 55407 (SAN 277-9668) Tel 612-871-4907.

Swedish Pioneer
   See Swedish-Am

†Sweet, *(Sweet Publishing; 0-8344)*, 3934 Sandshell, Ft. Worth, TX 76137 (SAN 206-8958) Tel 817-232-5661; Toll free: 800-531-5220; Toll free: 800-252-9213 (in Texas); CIP.

Sweet Ch'l Pr, *(Sweet CH'I Pr.; 0-912059)*, 662 Union St., Brooklyn, NY 11215 (SAN 264-6382) Tel 718-857-0449.

Sweetbrier, *(Sweetbrier Pr.; 0-936736)*, 536 Emerson St., Palo Alto, CA 94301 (SAN 216-1915) Tel 415-323-7822.

Sweeter Than Honey, *(Sweeter Than Honey; 0-934244)*, P.O. Box 7110, Tyler, TX 75711 (SAN 685-3625) Tel 214-561-6415.

Sweetlight, *(Sweetlight Bks.; 0-9604462)*, P.O. Box 307, Arcata, CA 95521 (SAN 215-1154) Tel 707-786-9328; Dist. by: Bookpeople, 2929 Fifth St., Berkeley, CA 94710 (SAN 168-9517) Tel 415-549-3030; Dist. by: Naturegraph Publishers, P.O. Box 1075, Happy Camp, CA 96039 (SAN 202-8999) Tel 916-493-5353.

Sweets Corners, *(Sweets Corners Press; 0-9611284)*, 1321 Sweets Corners Rd., Penfield, NY 14526 (SAN 283-3476) Tel 716-377-2962.

Sweetwater Pr, *(Sweetwater Pr.; 0-9615504)*, 1071 Duna Dr., Laramie, WY 82070 (SAN 695-9199) Tel 307-742-3082.

Sweetwater River Pr, *(Sweetwater River Press; 0-931950)*, P.O. Box 985, National City, CA 92050 (SAN 222-8289).

Swenson Pinckney, *(Swenson & Pinckney; 0-9610190)*, 2850 Mesa Verde Dr. E., Costa Mesa, CA 92626 (SAN 289-7121) Tel 714-979-8073; Dist. by: Publishers Marketing Group, 1104 Summit Ave., Plainview, TX 75074 (SAN 289-713X) Tel 214-423-0312.

Swenson Pub, *(Swenson Publishing; 0-9615688)*, 430 Magnolia Ln., N., Plymouth, MN 55441 (SAN 696-4427) Tel 612-545-6659.

Swets North Am, *(Swets North America)*, P.O. Box 517, Berwyn, PA 19312 (SAN 295-3544); Dist. by: C. J. Hogrefe Inc., P.O. Box 51, Lewiston, NY 14092 (SAN 295-3552) Tel 215-644-4944.

Swets Pub Nor
   See Swets North Am

Swim Safe, *(Swim Safe; 0-939627)*, P.O. Box 1017, Longwood, FL 32750 (SAN 663-6012); 1350 Hobson St., Longwood, FL 32750 (SAN 663-6020) Tel 305-339-1003.

Swimfants, *(Swimfants; 0-9604096)*, 1517 Lenox Dr., Modesto, CA 95350 (SAN 213-3105) Tel 209-526-2820.

Swimming, *(Swimming World; 0-911822)*, 116 W. Hazel, Inglewood, CA 90302-2905 (SAN 204-6539) Tel 213-674-2120.

Swiss Village, *(Swiss Village Bk. Store; 0-9615744)*, 907 Main St., Highland, IL 62249 (SAN 126-9925) Tel 618-654-2521; Box 412, Highland, IL 62249

Switz Pr, *(Switz Press, The; 0-930333)*, RR 3, P.O. Box 311, Vevay, IN 47043 (SAN 670-8439) Tel 812-427-2529.

Swollen Magpie, *(Swollen Magpie Pr.; 0-9609090)*, Rte. 2, Box 499, Putnam Valley, NY 10579 (SAN 240-933X) Tel 914-526-3392.

Sword & Stone, *(Sword & Stone Press; 0-939086)*, 4330 Windward Circle, Dallas, TX 75252 (SAN 216-3071) Tel 214-380-1433.

Sword of Lord, *(Sword of the Lord Pubs.; 0-87398)*, P.O. Box 1099, 224 Bridge Ave., Murfreesboro, TN 37130 (SAN 203-5642) Tel 615-893-6700.

Sword Shield Release, *(Sword & Shield Release; 0-938471)*, P.O. Box 128, Fairmont, WV 26554 (SAN 661-0641); 109 Linda Ln., Fairmont, WV 26554 (SAN 661-065X) Tel 304-363-6925.

Swordsman Pr, *(Swordsman Pr., Inc.; 0-940018)*, 15445 Ventura Blvd., No. 10, Sherman Oaks, CA 91413 (SAN 216-860X) Tel 818-888-2688; Box 5973, Sherman Oaks, CA 91413 (SAN 658-1838); Dist. by: Contemporary Bks., 180 N. Michigan Ave., Chicago, IL 60601 (SAN 202-5493) Tel 312-782-9181; Dist. by: Warner Bros. Pubns., 9000 Sunset Blvd., Penthouse, Los Angeles, CA 90069 (SAN 200-7347) Tel 213-273-3323.

Swordsman Pubns, *(Swordsman Pubns.; 0-913493)*, P.O. Box 111, Burnt Hills, NY 12027 (SAN 285-869X) Tel 518-399-0677.

Sybar Pub, *(Sybar Publishing; 0-936791)*, 2344 Sixth St., Berkeley, CA 94710 (SAN 690-260X) Tel 415-848-8233. Do not confuse with Sybex, Inc., same address.

Sybex, *(Sybex, Inc.; 0-89588)*, 2344 Sixth St., Berkeley, CA 94710 (SAN 211-1667) Tel 415-848-8233; Toll free: 800-227-2346; Interstate 80 at Maple Ave., Pine Brook, NJ 07058 (SAN 658-1846). *Imprints:* Sybex Computer Bks (Sybex Computer Bks.).

Sybex Computer Bks *Imprint of* Sybex
Sycamore Island *Imprint of* Paladin Pr
Sycamore Pr, *(Sycamore Pr., Inc.; 0-916768)*, P.O. Box 552, Terre Haute, IN 47808 (SAN 208-8827) Tel 812-299-2784.

SYDA Found, *(SYDA Foundation; 0-914602)*, Div. of Sushila Blackman, P.O. Box 600, South Fallsburg, NY 12779 (SAN 206-5649) Tel 914-434-2000.

Syder Pr, *(Syder Press; 0-939470)*, 5893 Kahara Court, Sacramento, CA 95822 (SAN 216-4590).

Sydon, *(Sydon, Inc)*, 3725 Monitor Circle N., Stockton, CA 95209 (SAN 202-070X).

Syentek Bks, *(Syentek Books Co., Inc.; 0-914082)*, P.O. Box 26588, San Francisco, CA 94126 (SAN 202-7534) Tel 415-928-0471.

Sylvan Bks, *(Sylvan Bks.; 0-916317)*, P.O. Box 481, Syracuse, IN 46567 (SAN 295-8457) Tel 219-457-5647.

Sylvan Inst, *(Sylvan Institute of Mental Health; 0-918428)*, 7104 NE Hazel Dell Ave., Vancouver, WA 98665 (SAN 209-6838) Tel 206-694-0911.

Sylvan Pubns, *(Sylvan Pubns.; 0-9606678)*, 42185 Baintree Circle, Northville, MI 48167 (SAN 219-4531) Tel 313-349-4827.

Sym & Sign, *(Symbols & Signs; 0-912504)*, P.O. Box 4536, North Hollywood, CA 91607 (SAN 205-4094).

Sym League, *(Symphony League of Jackson, Mississippi; 0-9608552)*, P.O. Box 9402, Jackson, MS 39206 (SAN 240-7833) Tel 601-960-1565.

Symbiosis Bks, *(Symbiosis Bks.; 0-9615903)*, 8 Midhill Dr., Mill Valley, CA 94941 (SAN 696-8457) Tel 415-383-7722.

Symbol Exc Pubs, *(Symbol of Excellence Publishers, Inc.; 0-932437)*, 3169 Cahaba Heights Rd., Birmingham, AL 35243 (SAN 686-7316) Tel 205-967-8402; Toll free: 800-231-0503.

Symmes Syst, *(Symmes Systems; 0-916352)*, P.O. Box 8101, Atlanta, GA 30306 (SAN 169-1465) Tel 404-876-7260.

Sympatico Pr, *(Sympatico Pr.; 0-9612666)*, 17 Rising Pl., Rochester, NY 14607 (SAN 289-4408) Tel 716-442-7851.

Symphony, *(Symphony Pr., Inc.)*, P.O. Box 515, Tenafly, NJ 07670 (SAN 210-6310).

Symposia Pr, *(Symposia Press; 0-918542)*, P.O. Box 418, Moorestown, NJ 08057 (SAN 209-892X) Tel 609-235-8439.

Symposium Pr, *(Symposium Pr.; 0-936576)*, 1620 Greenfield, Los Angeles, CA 90025 (SAN 213-1943) Tel 213-473-1758.

Synaptic Pr, *(Synaptic Pr.; 0-9616988)*, 220 S. Rose, No. 13, Los Angeles, CA 90012 (SAN 661-728X) Tel 213-687-4172.

Synaxis Pr, *(Synaxis Pr.; 0-911523)*, P.O. Box 689, Lynden, WA 98264 (SAN 685-4338).

Syncline, *(Syncline; 0-9603794)*, 7825 S. Ridgeway, Chicago, IL 60652 (SAN 214-1515).

Syncretic Prod, *(Syncretic Productions, Inc.; 0-935863)*, 1821 Hyde St., San Francisco, CA 94109 (SAN 695-9792) Tel 415-474-6366; P.O. Box 16012, San Francisco, CA 94116 (SAN 696-5172).

Syndactics, *(Syndactics, Inc.; 0-9614322)*, 8900 N. Central, No. 212, Phoenix, AZ 85020 (SAN 670-7084) Tel 602-944-4976; Orders to: P.O. Box 10004, Phoenix, AZ 85064 (SAN 699-5829) Tel 602-944-4976.

Syndicate, *(Syndicate Books; 0-911474)*, 551 Fifth Ave., Rm 1600, New York, NY 10176 (SAN 205-4108) Tel 212-682-0546.

Synergetics, *(Synergetics; 0-936501)*, 65 Meetinghouse Ridge, Meriden, CT 06450 (SAN 698-0627) Tel 203-235-3452; Dist. by: Roland Corp, 7200 Dominion Cir., Los Angeles, CA 90040 (SAN 200-5956).

Synergetics WV, *(Synergetics Pr., The; 0-910217)*, Box 2091, Parkersburg, WV 26102 (SAN 241-4643) Tel 304-485-0460.

†Synergistic Pr, *(Synergistic Pr., Inc.; 0-912184)*, 3965 Sacramento St., San Francisco, CA 94118 (SAN 205-4116) Tel 415-387-8180; CIP.

Synergy Bks *Imprint of* P Walsh Pr
Synergy Group, *(Synergy Group, Inc.; 0-916899)*, 4766 Park Granada, Suite 106, Calabasas, CA 91302 (SAN 691-8786) Tel 818-887-9100.

Synergy Hse, *(Synergy House; 0-934962)*, P.O. Box 1827, Costa Mesa, CA 92626 (SAN 213-3792) Tel 714-549-4484.

Synergy Pr, *(Synergy Pr.; 0-9616548)*, 3420 Holly Rd., Annandale, VA 22003 (SAN 659-5405) Tel 703-573-0909.

Synergy Pubs, *(Synergy Pubs.; 0-915223)*, P.O. Box 18268, Denver, CO 80218 (SAN 289-8489).

Synod NC Church, *(Synod of North Carolina, Presbyterian Church (U.S.A.))*, 1015 Wade Ave. P.O. Box 10785, Raleigh, NC 27605 (SAN 206-2356) Tel 919-834-4379.

Syntax Pubns, *(Syntax Pubns.; 0-910687)*, 340 Norton St., Boulder, CO 80303 (SAN 240-9879).

SYNTEC Inc, *(SYNTEC Inc; 0-943494)*, P.O. Box 1402, Bowie, MD 20716 (SAN 240-6780) Tel 301-249-9265.

†Synthesis Pubns, *(Synthesis Pubns.; 0-89935)*, P.O. Box 40099, San Francisco, CA 94140 (SAN 282-3888) Tel 415-824-1665; CIP.

Synthetix, *(Synthetix; 0-9612174; 0-937637)*, P.O. Box 1080, Berkeley, CA 94701 (SAN 291-8536) Tel 415-339-0601; 20 Villanova Dr., Oakland, CA 94611 (SAN 658-2486).

Syntony Inc Pub, *(Syntony Publishing, Inc.; 0-9613172; 0-933347)*, 1450 Bryon St., Palo Alto, CA 94301 (SAN 294-9997) Tel 415-326-5615; Dist. by: Publishers Group West, 5855 Beaudry St., Emeryville, CA 94698 (SAN 202-8522) Tel 415-658-3453.

Syracuse Cultural, *(Syracuse Cultural Workers; 0-935155)*, 601 Allen St., Syracuse, NY 13210 (SAN 695-3484) Tel 315-474-1132; Box 6367, Syracuse, NY 13217 (SAN 695-3492); Orders to: Syracuse Cultural Workers, P.O. Box 6367, Syracuse, NY 13217 (SAN 662-3468) Tel 315-474-1132.

Syracuse U Cont Ed, *(Syracuse Univ. Pubns. in Continuing Education; 0-87060)*, Syracuse, NY 13210 (SAN 202-7577) Tel 315-423-3421.

Syracuse U Foreign Comp, *(Syracuse Univ., Foreign & Comparative Studies Program; 0-915984)*, 724 Comstock Ave., Syracuse, NY 13244 (SAN 220-0082) Tel 315-423-2552.

T Smith, *(Smith, Toby; 0-9608762),* First Presbyterian Church, 215 Locust NE., Albuquerque, NM 87102 (SAN 241-0710) Tel 505-247-9594.

T T Taber, *(Taber, Thomas T.; 0-9603398),* Muncy, PA 17756 (SAN 211-9838).

T Thevenin, *(Thevenin, Tine; 0-9602010),* P.O. Box 16004, Minneapolis, MN 55416 (SAN 210-9603) Tel 612-922-4024.

T V Music, *(T.V. Music Co.; 0-918806),* 1650 Broadway, New York, NY 10019 (SAN 210-5136) Tel 212-246-3126.

T Vidal
See Edns Alba

T Voigt, *(Voigt, Tracy),* P.O. Box 76382, Los Angeles, CA 90076 (SAN 239-5746).

T W Holsinger, *(Holsinger, Terry Wayne; 0-9607966),* 150 S. Magnolia, No. 231, Anaheim, CA 92804 (SAN 239-6548) Tel 714-826-7505.

T W Khiralla, *(Khiralla, T. W.; 0-9601752),* 12400 Rye St., Studio City, CA 91604 (SAN 211-531X) Tel 213-763-2679.

T W Pubs, *(TW Pubs),* P.O. Box 152, River Forest, IL 60305 (SAN 205-4124).

T Weatherby, *(Weatherby, Thomas, Pub.),* 115 Billings St., Sharon, MA 02067 (SAN 212-582X).

T Weinberg
See Gordons & Weinberg

†T Y Crowell, *(Crowell, Thomas Y., Co.; 0-690),* 10 E. 53rd St., New York, NY 10022 (SAN 210-5918) Tel 212-593-3900; Toll free: 800-242-7737; Dist. by: Harper & Row Pubs., Keystone Industrial Pk., Scranton, PA 18512 (SAN 215-3742); *CIP.*

T Y Crowell
See Funk & W

TA Assocs, *(TA Assocs.; 0-9617020),* 815 Indian Rd., Glenview, IL 60025 (SAN 662-8648) Tel 312-729-5133.

TA Hughes Pubns, *(Hughes, T. A., Pubns.; 0-9614866),* 905 Aaron Dr., Columbia, SC 29203 (SAN 693-3327) Tel 803-754-4855.

†TA Press, *(TA Pr.; 0-89489),* Div. of International Transactional Analysis Assn., 1772 Vallejo St., San Francisco, CA 94123 (SAN 209-6846) Tel 415-885-5992; *CIP.*

TAB-Aero *Imprint of* **TAB Bks**

†TAB Bks, *(TAB Bks., Inc.; 0-8306; 0-8168),* P.O. Box 40, Blue Ridge Summit, PA 17214 (SAN 202-568X) Tel 717-794-2191; Toll free: 800-233-1128. Acquired Windcrest Software; *CIP.* Imprints: Gernshack (Gernshack Library); TAB-Aero (TAB-Aero); TAB/TPR (T A B/T P R).

TAB, TPR *Imprint of* **TAB Bks**

Tabard Pr, *(Tabard Pr.; 0-914427),* Div. of W. S. Konecky Assocs., 27 W. 20th St., New York, NY 10011 (SAN 663-2432) Tel 212-807-8230; Dist. by: Marboro Bks., 205 Moonachie Rd., Moonachie, NJ 07074 (SAN 150-8059).

Tabb Thetford Pubs, *(Tabb, Jeanne J., & Margaret Ann Thetford, Pubs.; 0-9616931),* 3725 Mockingbird Ln., Dallas, TX 75205-2124 (SAN 661-6674) Tel 214-522-3806.

Table Talk Bridge, *(Table Talk Bridge Club; 0-9616705),* 404 Lamar Dr., Macon, GA 31204 (SAN 659-8943) Tel 912-474-0586.

Table Two
See S Jersey Dining

Tabor Sarah Bks, *(Tabor Sarah Bks.; 0-935079),* 2419 Jefferson Ave., Berkeley, CA 94703 (SAN 695-0353) Tel 415-845-2540.

TACL, *(T.A.C.L.),* 641 Towle Way, Palo Alto, CA 94306 (SAN 211-5778) Tel 415-493-3628.

Tadpole, *(Tadpole; 0-9615253),* 6030 Autumn Arbor, Houston, TX 77092 (SAN 695-0965) Tel 713-681-8377.

Tafnews, *(Tafnews Pr.; 0-911520; 0-911521),* Div. of Track & Field News, Inc., P.O. Box 296, Los Altos, CA 94022 (SAN 202-7593) Tel 415-948-8188.

Taft Corp
See Taft Group

Taft Group, *(Taft Group, The; 0-914756),* 5130 MacArthur Blvd., NW, Washington, DC 20016 (SAN 206-5215) Tel 202-966-7086; Toll free: 800-424-3761.

Taft Museum, *(Taft Museum, The; 0-915577),* 316 Pike St., Cincinnati, OH 45202 (SAN 292-6946) Tel 513-241-0343.

Tahoma Pubns, *(Tahoma Pubns.; 0-9616969),* P.O. Box 44306, Tacoma, WA 98444 (SAN 661-7905); 9609 S. Sheridan, Tacoma, WA 98444 (SAN 661-7913) Tel 206-537-7877.

Tahrike Tarsile Quran, *(Tahrike Tarsile Quran; 0-940368),* P.O. Box 1115, Elmhurst, NY 11373 (SAN 217-1341) Tel 718-779-6505; 80-10 51 Ave., Elmhurst, NY 11373 (SAN 658-1870).

Tai Chi Ctr NY, *(Tai Chi Chuan Ctr. of New York; 0-9616586),* 1117 Ave. of the Americas, New York, NY 10036 (SAN 659-7785) Tel 212-221-6110.

†Tail Feather, *(Tail Feather; 0-911756),* c/o Card Lake Services, 3600 S. Harbor Blvd., No. 178, Oxnard, CA 93030 (SAN 205-4132) Tel 805-483-0689; *CIP.* Imprints: Neptune Bks (Neptune Books).

Take Five Pubs, *(Take Five Pubs.; 0-930099),* P.O. Box 1094, Arlington, IL 60006 (SAN 670-1884) Tel 312-577-2966.

Talent-Ed, *(Talent-Ed; 0-935003),* P.O. Box 455, Manlius, NY 13104-0455 (SAN 694-6577) Tel 315-682-7872.

Tales Mojave Rd, *(Tales of the Mojave Road Pub., Co.; 0-914224),* P.O. Box 307, Norco, CA 91760 (SAN 202-7607) Tel 714-737-3150.

Taliesin Pubs Inc
See HDL Pubs

Talisman, *(Talisman Pr.; 0-934612),* P.O. Box 455, Georgetown, CA 95634 (SAN 205-4140) Tel 916-333-4486.

Talisman Research, *(Talisman Literary Research, Inc.; 0-934614),* P.O. Box 455, Georgetown, CA 95634 (SAN 206-9547) Tel 916-333-4486.

Talk Town, *(Talk of the Town; 0-9612668),* 1313 Sunset Rd., Colorado Springs, CO 80909 (SAN 289-4416) Tel 303-633-2724.

Talking Leaves Pub, *(Talking Leaves Publishing Co.; 0-932077),* P.O. Box 84, Urbana, IL 61801 (SAN 686-2624) Tel 217-564-2462.

Talking Roots, *(Talking Your Roots; 0-9614867),* P.O. Box 3452, Washington, DC 20010 (SAN 693-3238) Tel 202-232-7892.

Talking Seal, *(Talking Seal Pr.; 0-9606322),* P.O. Box 4301, Flint, MI 48504 (SAN 218-5083).

Talking Tree Pr, *(Talking Tree Pr.; 0-9616957),* 19288 Galen Rd., Bend, OR 97702 (SAN 661-793X) Tel 503-389-0604.

Tall Oaks Pub, *(Tall Oaks Publishing, Inc.; 0-927188),* 1507 Evesham Rd., Voorhees, NJ 08043 (SAN 294-8583) Tel 609-795-1454.

Talley Assoc, *(Talley Assocs. Corp.; 0-932059),* 4107 Spice Wood Springs Rd., Austin, TX 78759 (SAN 686-2594) Tel 512-573-2128.

Talley Prods, *(Talley Productions; 0-9606588),* 1626 N. Wilcox, Suite 200, Hollywood, CA 90028 (SAN 219-8207).

Tallstone Pub, *(Tallstone Publishing; 0-936191),* 10 Vine Ave., Sharon, PA 16146 (SAN 696-7604) Tel 412-347-5857.

Talmis, *(Talmis, Inc.),* Subs. of Link Resources, 215 Park Ave. S., New York, NY 10003 (SAN 654-4487) Tel 212-473-5600.

Talmud Pr, *(Talmud Pr.; 0-9604554),* P.O. Box 3453, San Mateo, CA 94403 (SAN 213-9081) Tel 415-347-5751.

TAM Assoc, *(TAM Assocs.; 0-913005),* 911 Chicago, Oak Park, IL 60302 (SAN 283-4235) Tel 312-848-6760.

Tamal Land, *(Tamal Land Pr.; 0-912908),* 39 Merwin Ave., Fairfax, CA 94930 (SAN 207-0162) Tel 415-456-4705.

Tamal Vista, *(Tamal Vista Pubns.; 0-917436),* 222 Madrone Ave., Larkspur, CA 94939 (SAN 218-9844) Tel 415-924-7289.

Tamalpais Pr, *(Tamalpais Press; 0-916596),* 601 Van Ness Ave., No. 708, San Francisco, CA 94102 (SAN 209-2573) Tel 415-885-6613.

Tamara Pr, *(Tamara Pr.; 0-914991),* c/o Cannon, 440 E. 75th St., New York, NY 10021 (SAN 289-4424) Tel 516-625-0549.

Tamarack Edns, *(Tamarack Editions; 0-918092),* P.O. Box 6773, Ithaca, NY 14851 (SAN 210-170X).

†Tamarack Pr, *(Tamarack Pr.; 0-915024),* P.O. Box 5650, Madison, WI 53705 (SAN 209-2425) Tel 608-231-2444; *CIP.*

Tamas & Brownson, *(Tamas & Brownson Pubs.; 0-915603),* Subs. of Tamas & Assocs., Inc., 18251 McDurmott St., Suite A, Irvine, CA 92714 (SAN 291-4506) Tel 714-660-8822.

Tambra Pub, *(Tambra Publishing; 0-9615698),* P.O. Box3355, Covina, CA 91722 (SAN 200-562X) Tel 818-332-1983; Dist. by: Baker & Taylor, Eastern Div., 50 Kirby Ave., Somerville, NJ 08876 (SAN 169-4901).

Tamburitza, *(Tamburitza Pr.; 0-936922),* 1801 Blvd. of the Allies, Pittsburgh, PA 15219 (SAN 216-065X).

Tamerlane *Imprint of* **Underwood-Miller**

TAMS, *(Token & Medal Society, Inc.; 0-918492),* P.O. Box 366, Bryantown, MD 20617 (SAN 685-3641) Tel 301-274-3441; Orders to: Dorothy Baver, 611 Oakwood Way, El Cajon, CA 92021 (SAN 200-8238).

Tam's Bks, *(Tam's Books, Inc.; 0-89179),* 3333 S. Hoover St., Los Angeles, CA 90007 (SAN 207-6497) Tel 213-746-1141.

TAN Bks Pubs, *(TAN Bks. & Pubs., Inc.; 0-89555),* 2135 N. Central Ave., Rockford, IL 61103 (SAN 282-390X) Tel 815-962-2662; Orders to: P.O. Box 424, Rockford, IL 61105 (SAN 282-3918).

Tan Pr, *(Tan Pr.; 0-9615754),* P.O. Box 3721, Washington, DC 20007 (SAN 695-894X) Tel 202-333-6501.

Tanadgusix Corp, *(Tanadgusix Corp.; 0-9601948),* St. Paul, AK 99660 (SAN 211-7630).

Tanam Pr, *(Tanam Pr.; 0-934378),* 40 White St., New York, NY 10013 (SAN 215-3467) Tel 212-431-9183.

†Tandem Pr, *(Tandem Pr. Pubs.; 0-913024),* P.O. Box 237, Tannersville, PA 18372 (SAN 202-7615) Tel 717-629-0940; *CIP.*

Tandem Pubs VA, *(Tandem Pubs.; 0-9606244),* 5821 Banning Place, Burke, VA 22015 (SAN 218-5091).

Tangelwuld, *(Tangelwuld Pr.; 0-934667),* P.O. Box 160361, Las Colinas, TX 75016 (SAN 695-8982) Tel 214-686-5332.

Tangent Pr, *(Tangent Pr.; 0-932165),* Subs. of Tangent Toy Co., 140 Carl St., Suite 146, San Francisco, CA 94117 (SAN 687-6307); Dist. by: Bookpeople, 2929 Fifth St., Berkeley, CA 94710 (SAN 168-9517) Tel 219-232-8500; Dist. by: Publishers Group West, 5855 Beaudry St., Emeryville, CA 94608 (SAN 202-8522).

Tangents, *(Tangents; 0-9611742),* 328 W. Mulberry, Kankakee, IL 60901 (SAN 285-3809) Tel 815-932-5130.

Tanglewood Press, *(Tanglewood Pr.; 0-9614553),* 5012 Tanglewood Dr., Raleigh, NC 27612 (SAN 678-9153) Tel 919-787-2287.

Tanglewuld Pr
See Tangelwuld

Tanner *Imprint of* **U of Utah Pr**

Tanro Co, *(Tanro Co.; 0-9617220),* 1020 Rilma Ln., Los Altos, CA 94022 (SAN 663-4176) Tel 415-941-2623.

Tanstaafl, *(Tanstaafl; 0-931358),* P.O. Box 60026, Sunnyvale, CA 94086 (SAN 211-3805) Tel 408-280-1776.

Tao of Wing, *(Tao of Wing Chun Do; 0-918642),* 11023 NE. 131st, Kirkland, WA 98034 (SAN 211-9854) Tel 206-821-1487.

Tao Pub, *(Tao Pub.; 0-942196),* 2700 Ocean Ave., San Francisco, CA 94132 (SAN 239-9865) Tel 415-771-7181.

Taoist Pubs, *(Taoist Pubs.; 0-9608030),* Dist. by: EDT, Inc., P.O. Box 979, Royal Oak, MI 48068 (SAN 239-4928) Tel 313-399-4926; Dist. by: New Leaf Distributing Co., 1020 White St., SW, Atlanta, GA 30310 (SAN 169-1449) Tel 404-755-2665.

Taos Heritage, *(Taos Heritage Publishing Co.; 0-9615177),* P.O. Box NNN, Taos, NM 87571 (SAN 694-2830) Tel 505-758-2450.

Taosedon Pr, *(Taosedon Pr.; 0-9615915),* P.O. Box 2252, Taos, NM 87571 (SAN 696-7787) Tel 505-758-1029.

Tape Data Mkt
See TDM Audio

†Taplinger, *(Taplinger Publishing Co., Inc.; 0-8008),* 132 W. 22nd St., New York, NY 10011 (SAN 213-6821) Tel 212-741-0801; *CIP.* Imprints: Crescendo (Crescendo); Pentalic (Pentalic); Pivot (Pivot).

TAPPI, *(Technical Assn. of the Pulp & Paper Industry; 0-89852),* P.O. Box 105113, Atlanta, GA 30348 (SAN 676-5629) Tel 404-446-1400.

TARA
See Anthro Research

Tara Ctr, *(Tara Ctr., The; 0-936604),* Subs. of Share International Magazine (Amsterdam, Netherlands), P.O. Box 6001, North Hollywood, CA 91603 (SAN 282-3950) Tel 818-785-6300; Dist. by: DeVorss & Co., P.O. Box 550, 1046 Princeton Dr., Marina del Rey, CA 90294 (SAN 168-9886).

Taran House Pub, *(Taran Hse. Publishing; 0-933315),* 3703 E. Cornell Woods Dr., Suite C, Dayton, OH 45406 (SAN 692-3704) Tel 513-274-2942.

Tarantula Pr, *(Tarantula Pr.; 0-935737),* 1359 Conalea, Tucson, AZ 85748 (SAN 695-9032) Tel 602-296-5332; Orders to: Tara-Press, P.O. Box 17211, Tucson, AZ 85731 (SAN 662-3611).

Taraxacum, *(Taraxacum; 0-9602822),* 1227 30th St. NW, Washington, DC 20007 (SAN 213-8255) Tel 202-357-2681.

Target Comm, *(Target Communications Corp.; 0-913305),* 7626 W. Donges Bay Rd., P.O. Box 188, Mequon, WI 53092 (SAN 289-1913) Tel 414-242-3990.

Targeted Comm, *(Targeted Communications; 0-933117),* P.O. Box 1148, Cleveland, OH 44120-0868 (SAN 689-4674); 3644 Rolliston Rd., Cleveland, OH 44120-5137 (SAN 662-7730) Tel 216-921-8074.

Tari Bk Pubs, *(Tari Bk. Pubs.; 0-9604258),* 146 E. 34th St., Eugene, OR 97405 (SAN 214-1523).

Tarnhelm *Imprint of CSA Pr*

TarPar, *(TarPar, Ltd.; 0-933193),* P.O. Box 3, Kernersville, NC 27284 (SAN 207-494X) Tel 919-523-5369.

Tarquin *Imprint of Parkwest Pubns*

Tarrant, *(Tarrant, Patrick; 0-9608850),* 1907 Castle Ave., Bloomington, IL 61701 (SAN 241-080X).

Tartan Tiger, *(Tartan Tiger; 0-935827),* 2320 144th SE, Bellevue, WA 98007 (SAN 696-6535) Tel 206-747-7655.

Tarten *Imprint of McKay*

Tartu Pubns, *(Tartu Pubns; 0-9614357),* P.O. Box 85208, Seattle, WA 98145 (SAN 687-7427) Tel 206-547-7678.

Tasa Pub Co, *(Tasa Publishing Co.; 0-935698),* P.O. Box 35053, Edina, MN 55435 (SAN 216-0668).

Tasco
See M Shanken Comm

Tashmoo, *(Tashmoo Pr.; 0-932384),* RFD Box 590, Vineyard Haven, MA 02568 (SAN 212-5706) Tel 617-693-3199.

Tastes of Tahoe, *(Tastes of Tahoe; 0-934181),* P.O. Box 6114, Incline Village, NV 89450 (SAN 693-3807) Tel 702-831-5182.

Tatnic Pr, *(Tatnic Pr., The; 0-9615599),* R. D. 1, Box 528, South Berwick, ME 03908 (SAN 695-9938) Tel 207-676-2276.

Tatsch, *(Tatsch Assocs.; 0-912890),* P.O. Box 622, Fredericksburg, TX 78624 (SAN 202-7623) Tel 512-997-8785.

TAU Pr, *(TAU Pr.; 0-916453),* P.O. Box 2283, Rolling Hills, CA 90274 (SAN 209-3022).

Taunton, *(Taunton Pr., Inc.; 0-918804),* Box 355, Newtown, CT 06470 (SAN 210-5144) Tel 203-426-8171; Toll free: 800-243-7252; Dist. by: W.W. Norton & Co. Inc., 500 Fifth Ave., New York, NY 10110 (SAN 202-5795) Tel 212-354-5500.

Taurus Ed, *(Taurus Editions; 0-913925),* 96 Grand St., New York, NY 10013 (SAN 286-0597) Tel 212-966-1222.

Taurus Pub Co, *(Taurus Publishing Co.; 0-913495),* 56 Doris Rd., Box 492, Halifax, MA 02338 (SAN 283-8753) Tel 617-293-9110.

Taven-Lourveney, *(Taven-Lourveney Publishing Co.; 0-932167),* Subs. of Taven-Lourveney Enterprises, 105 Lawrence St., Hackensack, NJ 07601 (SAN 686-421X) Tel 201-343-5674.

Taverly-Churchill, *(Taverly-Churchill; 0-9616595),* P.O. Box 2097, Wawona, CA 95389 (SAN 659-5413) Tel 209-375-6300.

Tavistock Bks
See Tavistock Poetry

Tavistock Poetry, *(Tavistock Poetry Pr.; 0-9613117),* 5475 Pire Ave., San Diego, CA 92122 (SAN 655-1378) Tel 619-450-0120. Do not confuse with Tavistock Publications (UK), an imprint of Methuen, Inc.

Tax Analysts, *(Tax Analysts; 0-918255),* 6830 N. Fairfax Dr., Arlington, VA 22213 (SAN 226-4781) Tel 703-532-1850; Toll free: 800-336-0439.

Tax Found, *(Tax Foundation, Inc.; 0-9606762),* 1 Thomas Cir., NW, Suite 500, Washington, DC 20005 (SAN 225-1302) Tel 202-822-9050.

†**Tax Mgmt,** *(Tax Management Inc.),* 1231 25th St., NW, Washington, DC 20037 (SAN 240-1630); *CIP.*

Tax Reform Res, *(Tax Reform Research Group),* 215 Pennsylvania Ave., SE, Washington, DC 20003 (SAN 225-7246) Tel 202-546-4996.

Taxpayers Found, *(Taxpayers' Foundation; 0-911415),* 325 Pennsylvania Ave. SE, Washington, DC 20003 (SAN 265-3648) Tel 202-543-3070.

Taxwise Pubns
See Blair McGill Co

†**Taylor & Francis,** *(Taylor & Francis, Inc.; 0-85066; 0-905273; 1-85000; 0-335-; 0-86353; 0-903796),* 242 Cherry St., Philadelphia, PA 19106-1906 (SAN 286-2182) Tel 215-238-0939; Toll free: 800-821-8312; *CIP. Imprints:* Falmer Pr (Falmer Press).(Falmer Pr.); Open Univ Pr (Open University Press).(Open Univ. Pr.); SIPRI (S I P R I).(SIPRI).

Taylor & Friends
See S Taylor & Friends

Taylor & Ng, *(Taylor & Ng; 0-912738),* Subs. of Environmental Ceramics, Inc., 271 Sutter St., San Francisco, CA 94108 (SAN 208-3396) Tel 415-398-8548; Toll free: 800-227-4090; Box 8888, Fairfield, CA 94533 (SAN 658-1889); 2700 Maxwell Way, Fairfield, CA 94533 (SAN 658-1897).

Taylor-Carlisle, *(Taylor-Carlisle),* 451 Greenwich St., New York, NY 10013 (SAN 169-6017) Tel 212-226-0707.

Taylor Cty Hist Soc, *(Taylor County & Historical Society; 0-9617105),* Grafton, WV 26354 (SAN 662-5118) Tel 304-265-5015.

Taylor Homestead
See M Wetherbee

Taylor James
See J Taylor CA

Taylor Museum *Imprint of CO Springs Fine Arts*

Taylor Museum
See CO Springs Fine Arts

†**Taylor Pub,** *(Taylor Publishing Co.; 0-87833),* Subs. of Insilco, 1550 Mockingbird Ln., Dallas, TX 75235 (SAN 202-7631) Tel 214-637-2800; *CIP.*

Taylor Pub WA, *(Taylor Publishing; 0-9609056),* 1525 Lincoln St., Bellingham, WA 98226 (SAN 240-9860) Tel 206-734-6073.

Taylor Pubns, *(Taylor Pubns.; 0-935881),* P.O. Box 464, Ripley, TN 38063 (SAN 695-9970) Tel 901-635-0263.

Taylor Pubs, *(Taylor Pubs.; 0-935947),* 2336 Market St., Suite 41, San Francisco, CA 94114 (SAN 696-7779) Tel 415-392-8822.

Taylor Street, *(Taylor Street Pr.; 0-911407),* 60 Taylor Dr., Fairfax, CA 94930 (SAN 275-9403) Tel 415-453-2765.

Taylor Taylor, *(Taylor, Taylor & Taylor; 0-9616149),* 6644 Hellman Ave., Alta Loma, CA 91701 (SAN 699-9727) Tel 714-987-2769.

Tayu Pr, *(Tayu Pr.; 0-934350),* Div. of Tayu Center for Gay Spirituality, P.O. Box 11554, Santa Rosa, CA 95406 (SAN 213-1773) Tel 707-887-2490.

Tazelaar, *(Tazelaar; 0-9613792),* P.O. Box 68603, Seattle, WA 98168 (SAN 678-9897) Tel 206-246-6753.

TBC Inc, *(Technology & Business Communications, Inc.; 0-914849),* 730 Boston Post Rd., Order Dept., P.O. Box 915, Sudbury, MA 01776 (SAN 289-4491) Tel 617-443-4671.

†**TBN Ent,** *(TBN Enterprises; 0-935554),* Box 55, Alexandria, VA 22313 (SAN 206-2380) Tel 703-684-6111; *CIP.*

TBW Bks, *(TBW Bks.; 0-931474),* 36 Old Mill Rd., Falmouth, ME 04105 (SAN 224-2303) Tel 207-781-3002; Orders to: Harpswell Press, 132 Water St., Gardiner, ME 04345 (SAN 208-1199) Tel 207-582-1899.

†**Tchrs & Writers Coll,** *(Teachers & Writers Collaborative; 0-915924),* 5 Union Sq. W., New York, NY 10003 (SAN 206-3859) Tel 212-691-6590; *CIP.*

†**Tchrs Coll,** *(Columbia Univ., Teachers College, Teachers College Pr.; 0-8077),* 1234 Amsterdam Ave., New York, NY 10027 (SAN 282-3985) Tel 212-678-3929; Orders to: Harper & Row, Keystone Industrial Pk., Scranton, PA 18512 (SAN 282-3993); *CIP.*

Tchrs Eng Spkrs, *(Teachers of English to Speakers of Other Languages; 0-939791),* Tesol Suite 205 1118 22nd St. NW, Washington, DC 20037 (SAN 225-7858) Tel 202-625-4569.

†**Tchrs Insurance,** *(Teachers Insurance & Annuity Assn.; 0-9613704),* 730 Third Ave., New York, NY 10017 (SAN 677-5705) Tel 212-490-9000; *CIP.*

TCNFPC, *(Twin Cities Natural Family Planning Ctr., Inc.; 0-9616827),* 2414 S. Seventh St., Minneapolis, MN 55454 (SAN 661-1273) Tel 612-340-9830.

TDM Audio, *(TDM Audio; 0-88749),* 560 S. State College Blvd., Fullerton, CA 92631 (SAN 292-6970) Tel 714-441-0782.

Te Cum Tom, *(Te-Cum-Tom Enterprises; 0-913508),* 5770 Franson Ct., North Bend, OR 97459 (SAN 205-4183) Tel 503-756-5757.

Teach Me, *(Teach Me Tapes, Inc.; 0-934633),* 6024 Walnut Dr., Edina, MN 55436 (SAN 693-9309) Tel 612-938-8583.

Teach'em, *(Teach'em, Inc.; 0-931028),* 160 E. Illinois St., Chicago, IL 60611 (SAN 211-2787) Tel 312-467-0424.

Teacher Update, *(Teacher Update, Inc.; 0-89780),* P.O. Box 205, Saddle River, NJ 07458 (SAN 212-3878) Tel 201-342-9024.

Teachers Load, *(Teacher's Load Pr.; 0-9603750),* 2631 Farber Dr., St. Louis, MO 63136 (SAN 213-8735) Tel 314-653-0761.

Teachers Tax, *(Teacher's Tax Service; 0-912772),* 1303 E. Balboa Blvd., Newport Beach, CA 92661 (SAN 202-0394) Tel 714-675-9891.

Teak Wood Pr, *(Teak Wood Pr.; 0-937281),* 160 Fiesta Dr., Kissimmee, FL 32743 (SAN 659-0640) Tel 305-348-7330.

Teal Pr, *(Teal Pr.; 0-913793),* P.O. Box 4346, Portsmouth, NH 03801 (SAN 286-2042); 40 Pleasant St., Portsmouth, NH 03801 (SAN 662-2097) Tel 603-431-2319.

Tealwood Press
See Pierremont Press

Teaparty Bks, *(Teaparty Bks.; 0-9610602),* 10 Loring Ave., Box 232, Kingston, MA 02364 (SAN 265-3656) Tel 617-585-4666.

TEC Pubns, *(TEC Pubns.; 0-937533),* 1410 Robertson Way, Sacramento, CA 95818 (SAN 659-0322) Tel 916-443-3315.

Tech Analysis, *(Technical Analysis, Inc.; 0-938773),* 9131 California Ave., SW, Seattle, WA 98146 (SAN 661-5317) Tel 206-938-0570.

Tech And Bus C
See TBC Inc

Tech & Ed Ctr Graph Arts RIT, *(Technical & Education Center of the Graphic Arts, Rochester Institute of Technology (T&E Center); 0-89938),* 1 Lomb Memorial Dr., Rochester, NY 14623 (SAN 205-2334) Tel 716-475-2761.

Tech Assn Graphic, *(Technical Assn. of the Graphic Arts),* Rochester Institute of Technology, T & E Ctr., 1 Lomb Memorial Dr., P.O. Box 9887, Rochester, NY 14623-0887 (SAN 224-7836) Tel 716-272-0557.

Tech Asst Info
See Am Intl Action

Tech Comm Assoc, *(Technical Communications Assocs., Inc.; 0-9611694),* 1250 Oakmead Pkwy, Suite 210, Sunnyvale, CA 94086 (SAN 284-9097).

Tech Conf Assoc
See T-C Pubns CA

Tech Data, *(Tech Data Pubns.; 0-937816),* 6324 W. Fond Du Lac Ave., Milwaukee, WI 53218 (SAN 216-0129).

Tech Data Corp, *(Technical Data Corp.; 0-927469),* 330 Congress St., Boston, MA 02210 (SAN 286-5378) Tel 617-482-3341; Toll free: 800-343-7745.

Tech Data TX, *(Technical Database Corp.; 0-910747),* P.O. Box 720, Conroe, TX 77305 (SAN 262-4281) Tel 713-439-1687.

Tech Dict, *(Technical Dictionaries Co.; 0-911484),* Box 2130, Mt. Vernon, ME 04352 (SAN 205-4191).

Tech Direct, *(Technical Directions, Inc.; 0-918876),* P.O. Box 2221, West Lafayette, IN 47906 (SAN 207-1924) Tel 317-494-3888.

Tech Ed Pr, *(Technical Education Pr.; 0-911908),* P.O. Box 342, Seal Beach, CA 90740 (SAN 205-4205) Tel 213-431-8515.

Tech Ed Pub, *(Tech Ed Publishing; 0-933554),* P.O. Box 28262, Tempe, AZ 85282 (SAN 212-6842) Tel 602-838-3974; Toll free: 800-323-3133.

Tech Ed Serv, *(Technical Education Services; 0-930552),* Univ. of Missouri, School of Journalism, Kappa Alpha Mu, Box 838, Columbia, MO 65201 (SAN 213-3849) Tel 314-442-3161; Dist. by: Running Press, 125 S. 22nd St., Philadelphia, PA 19103 (SAN 204-5702) Tel 215-567-5080.

Tech Educ Conslt, *(Technical Educational Consultants; 0-939247),* 76 N. Broadway, Hicksville, NY 11801 (SAN 662-6343) Tel 516-681-1773; Dist. by: Bio Learning Systems, Inc., Rte. 106, Jericho, NY 11753 (SAN 200-8262) Tel 516-433-2992.

Tech Group, *(Technology Group, The; 0-939856),* P.O. Box 93124, Pasadena, CA 91109 (SAN 220-195X) Tel 818-794-6013. *Imprints:* Magick Circle (Magick Circle, The).

Tech Info Proj, *(Technical Information Project, Inc.; 0-939578),* P.O. Box 39185, Washington, DC 20016 (SAN 214-2619) Tel 202-363-1133.

Tech Info Pubn, *(Technical Information Pubn. Service; 0-930747),* 707 Ellis St., Ridgecrest, CA 93555 (SAN 679-1484).

Tech Insights, *(Technical Insights, Inc.; 0-914993),* P.O. Box 1304, Fort Lee, NJ 07024 (SAN 289-4459) Tel 201-568-4744.

Tech Marketing, *(Technology Marketing Corp.; 0-936840),* One Technology Plaza, Norwalk, CT 06854-1924 (SAN 212-4629) Tel 203-852-6800; Toll free: 800-243-6002.

†Tech Pr Inc, *(Technology Press, Inc., The; 0-89321),* P.O. Box 380, Fairfax Station, VA 22039-0380 (SAN 208-8851) Tel 703-978-5299; *CIP.*

Tech Pubns
See Intertec Pub

Tech Search Intl, *(Technology Search International, Inc.; 0-943420),* 500 East Higgins Rd., Elk Grove Village, IL 60007 (SAN 240-7868) Tel 312-593-2111.

Tech Tran Consult, *(Tech Tran Consultants, Inc.),* P.O. Box 206, Lake Geneva, WI 53147 (SAN 296-0656) Tel 414-248-9510.

Tech Tran Corp
See Tech Tran Consult

Tech Trans Inst, *(Technology Transfer Institute; 0-942948),* 741 10th St., Santa Monica, CA 90402 (SAN 240-4516) Tel 213-394-8305.

Techkits, *(Techkits, Inc.; 0-918662),* P.O. Box 105, Demarest, NJ 07627 (SAN 210-3753) Tel 201-768-7334.

Technicon Pubs, *(Technicon Pubs.; 0-915428),* P.O. Box 1413, Novato, CA 94947 (SAN 207-3560) Tel 415-897-7638.

Technics Pubns, *(Technics Pubns., Inc.; 0-935159),* 75-19 Vleigh Pl., Flushing, NY 11367 (SAN 696-1290).

Technipubs, *(Technipubs, Inc.; 0-936743),* 7002 Boulevard E., Suite 360, Guttenberg, NJ 07093 (SAN 699-9603) Tel 201-869-4452.

Technique Assoc, *(Technique Assocs.; 0-9614034),* P.O. Box 25330, Milwaukee, WI 53225 (SAN 683-5201) Tel 414-771-1450.

Technocracy, *(Technocracy, Inc.; 0-9606470),* P.O. Box 238, Savannah, OH 44874 (SAN 209-7842) Tel 419-962-4712.

TechnoLiteracy Assocs, *(TechnoLiteracy Assocs., Inc.; 0-9614335),* 1001 Connecticut Ave. NW, Suite 628, Washington, DC 20036 (SAN 687-8423) Tel 202-293-0909.

†Technomic, *(Technomic Publishing Co.; 0-87762),* 851 New Holland Ave., Box 3535, Lancaster, PA 17604 (SAN 202-764X) Tel 717-291-5609; Toll free: 800-233-9936 (For orders); *CIP.*

Techscience Inc, *(Techscience, Inc.; 0-918910),* P.O. Box 1100, Hawthorne, CA 90250 (SAN 208-1733) Tel 503-926-5739.

Techsonic Ind, *(Techsonic Industries, Inc.; 0-9616859),* 1 Hummingbird Ln., Eufaula, AL 36027 (SAN 661-5945) Tel 205-687-6613.

Tecohio Pub Co, *(Tecohio Publishing Co.; 0-9616116),* 27900 Fairmount Blvd., Cleveland, OH 44124 (SAN 699-7309) Tel 216-831-1884.

Tecolote Pubns, *(Tecolote Pubns.; 0-938711),* 4978 Coronado Ave., San Diego, CA 92107 (SAN 661-5058) Tel 619-222-6066.

Tee Loftin, *(Tee Loftin Pubs., Inc.; 0-934812),* 3100 R St., NW, Washington, DC 20007 (SAN 215-9635).

Teen Round-Up, *(Teen Round-Up, Inc.; 0-9614268),* Rte. 1, Box 226A, Duncan, OK 73533 (SAN 687-1534) Tel 405-255-5207.

Teitan Pr, *(Teitan Pr., Inc., The; 0-933429),* 339 W. Barry, Suite 16B, Chicago, IL 60657 (SAN 200-8211) Tel 312-929-7892.

Tekakwitha Ins, *(Tekakwitha Institute of Ancient Man; 0-935569),* 1812 Warren Dr., Woodbridge, VA 22191-2421 (SAN 696-1363) Tel 703-841-2569.

Teknek, *(Teknek; 0-930363),* 19936 Lorne St., Canoga Park, CA 91306 (SAN 670-7793) Tel 818-882-7122; Dist. by: Baker & Taylor Co., Eastern Div., 50 Kirby Ave., Somerville, NJ 08876 (SAN 169-4901).

TEL Pr, *(TEL Pr.; 0-9613839),* 245 N. Oakland Ave., Indianapolis, IN 46201 (SAN 682-0239) Tel 317-638-1641.

TEL Pubs, *(TEL Pubs., Ltd.; 1-55588),* 2516 S. Alpine, Rockford, IL 61125 (SAN 658-5116) Tel 815-398-6730; Toll free: 800-835-5835; P.O. Box 5471, Rockford, IL 61125 (SAN 658-5124).

Tele Cable, *(Telegraphic Cable & Radio Registrations, Inc.; 0-916446),* P.O. Box 14, Larchmont, NY 10538 (SAN 208-886X); 2076 Boston Post Rd., Larchmont, NY 10538 (SAN 662-1589) Tel 914-834-7888.

Tele-Viewer *Imprint of* Garber Comm

Telecom Lib, *(Telecom Library, The; 0-936648),* 12 W. 21st St., New York, NY 10010 (SAN 211-9862) Tel 212-691-8215; Toll free: 800-542-279. *Imprints:* Personal Achievement (Personal Achievement Library).

Teleflite Corp, *(Teleflite Corp., The; 0-930387),* 11620 Kitching St., Sunnymead, CA 92388 (SAN 295-7973) Tel 714-242-0500.

Telegraph Bks, *(Telegraph Bks.; 0-89760),* Box 38, Norwood, PA 19074 (SAN 213-8042) Tel 215-583-4550.

Teleometrics, *(Teleometrics International, Inc.; 0-937932),* 1755 Woodstead Court, The Woodlands, TX 77380 (SAN 220-0953) Tel 713-367-0060; Toll free: 800-527-0406.

†Telephone Bks, *(Telephone Bks. Pr.; 0-916382),* 109 Dunk Rock Rd., Guilford, CT 06437 (SAN 208-2462) Tel 203-453-1921; Dist. by: Inland Book Co., P.O. Box 261, 22 Hemingway Ave., East Haven, CT 06512 (SAN 200-4151) Tel 203-467-4257; Dist. by: Small Press Traffic, 3841-B 24th St., San Francisco, CA 94114 (SAN 200-7371); *CIP.*

Telephony, *(Telephony Publishing Corp.; 0-917845),* 55 E. Jackson Blvd., Chicago, IL 60604 (SAN 657-1174) Tel 312-922-2435.

Televisionary Pr, *(Televisionary Press; 0-915857),* 32 Union Sq., Room 805, New York, NY 10003 (SAN 670-7130).

Telex Russian Educ Bks, *(Telex-Russian Educational Bks., Inc.; 0-938181),* 730 Newark Ave., Jersey City, NJ 07306 (SAN 659-7238) Tel 201-332-3807.

Telford Pr, *(Telford Pr., The; 0-936923),* 285 Bloomfield Ave., Caldwell, NJ 07006 (SAN 683-3652) Tel 201-228-1487.

TELL Pubns, *(T. E. L. L. Pubns.; 0-939028),* P.O. Box 9044, Hampton, VA 23670 (SAN 217-2712).

Telos Pr, *(Telos Press Ltd.; 0-914386),* 431 E. 12th St., New York, NY 10009 (SAN 282-4027) Tel 212-228-6479.

†TelShare Pub Co, *(Telshare Publishing Co., Inc.; 0-910287),* P.O. Box 679, Marshfield, MA 02050 (SAN 241-4651); Toll free: 800-343-9707; *CIP.*

Telstar Inc, *(Telstar Inc.; 0-943000),* 366 N. Prior Ave., St. Paul, MN 55104 (SAN 240-4524) Tel 612-644-4726.

Tembo Prod, *(Tembo Productions, Inc.; 0-938177),* 15 Oakland Ave., Harrison, NY 10528 (SAN 659-722X) Tel 914-825-0900.

Tembrook Pr, *(Tembrook Pr.; 0-9614080),* 23 Copper Beech Dr., Lafayette Hill, PA 19444 (SAN 685-9445) Tel 215-825-9333.

Temescal Bks, *(Temescal Bks.; 0-914289),* P.O. Box 20067, Oakland, CA 94620-0067 (SAN 293-4795) Tel 415-655-5240.

Tempe Pubs
See Tech Ed Pub

Tempest Brookline, *(Tempest Bks.),* P.O. Box 492, Brookline, MA 02146 Tel 617-629-2397.

Templar Pr OH, *(Templar Pr.; 0-939039),* 187 E. Duncan St., Columbus, OH 43202-2675 (SAN 662-6556) Tel 614-261-7241. Do not confuse with Templar Pr. of New York, NY.

Temple Geneal, *(Temple Genealogical Society; 0-9616195),* 101 Main St., Temple, TX 76501 (SAN 699-8291) Tel 817-774-8435.

Temple Kriya Yoga, *(Temple of Kriya Yoga, The; 0-9613099),* 2414 N. Kedzie Ave., Chicago, IL 60647 (SAN 240-9348) Tel 312-795-0031.

Temple Pubns, *(Temple Pubns., Inc.; 0-918341),* 3327 SW Dosch Rd., Portland, OR 97201 (SAN 657-3045) Tel 503-223-8863; Dist. by: New Leaf Distr. Co., 1020 White St., SW, Atlanta, GA 30310 (SAN 169-1449) Tel 404-755-2665.

†Temple U Pr, *(Temple Univ. Pr.; 0-87722),* Broad & Oxford Sts., University Services Bldg., Philadelphia, PA 19122 (SAN 202-7666) Tel 215-787-8787; *CIP.*

Temple Univ Gallery, *(Temple Univ., Temple Gallery, The; 0-939351),* 1619 Walnut St., Philadelphia, PA 19103 (SAN 662-5126) Tel 215-787-5041.

Templegate, *(Templegate Pubs.; 0-87243),* 302 E. Adams St., P.O. Box 5152, Springfield, IL 62705 (SAN 213-1994) Tel 217-522-3361.

Templeman, *(Templeman, Eleanor Lee; 0-911044),* 3001 N. Pollard St., Arlington, VA 22207 (SAN 207-0189) Tel 703-528-1112.

Templeton, *(Templeton, Larry D.; 0-9608914),* 320 W. Algre Dr., Litchfield Park, AZ 85340 (SAN 241-1571) Tel 602-935-4346.

Templeton Pubs, *(Templeton Pubns.; 0-934405),* Div. of Templeton Investment Counsel, 1 Financial Plaza, Suite 2202, Ft. Lauderdale, FL 33394 (SAN 693-8272) Tel 305-764-7390.

Temporal, *(Temporal Acuity Products, Inc.; 0-911723),* 300-120th Ave. NE, Bldg. No.1, Bellevue, WA 98005 (SAN 264-4274) Tel 206-462-1007; Toll free: 800-426-2673.

Ten Penny, *(Ten Penny Players, Inc.; 0-934830),* 799 Greenwich St., New York, NY 10014 (SAN 213-8743) Tel 212-929-3169; Dist. by: Waterways Project, 799 Greenwich St., New York, NY 10014 (SAN 219-5402).

Ten Pound Isl Bk, *(Ten Pound Island Bk. Co.; 0-938459),* 108 Main St., Gloucester, MA 01930 (SAN 660-9821) Tel 617-283-5299.

†Ten Speed Pr, *(Ten Speed Pr.; 0-89815),* P.O. Box 7123, Berkeley, CA 94707 (SAN 202-7674) Tel 415-845-8414; Toll free: 800-841-BOOK; *CIP.*

Ten Talents, *(Ten Talents; 0-9603532),* P.O. Box 86A, Rte. 1, Chisholm, MN 55719 (SAN 207-9364) Tel 218-254-5357.

Ten-Thirty Pr, *(Ten-Thirty Pr., The; 0-916153),* Div. of Ten-Thirty Corp., 77-12 35th Ave., Suite 56A, Jackson Heights, NY 11372 (SAN 295-0022) Tel 718-476-8881.

Tenameca, *(Tenameca, Inc.; 0-918582),* P.O. Box 44436, Indianapolis, IN 46244 (SAN 210-3761) Tel 317-631-6304.

Tenderfoot Pr, *(Tenderfoot Pr.; 0-9615397),* P.O. Box 780, Narberth, PA 19072 (SAN 695-4669) Tel 215-667-4769.

Tendril, *(Tendril; 0-937504),* P.O. Box 512, Green Harbor, MA 02041 (SAN 215-188X).

Tenn Arts, *(Tennessee Arts Commission),* 320 Sixth Ave. N., Nashville, TN 37219 (SAN 239-4936).

Tenn Bar Assn, *(Tennessee Bar Assn.),* 3622 West End Ave., Nashville, TN 37205 (SAN 226-9694) Tel 615-383-7421.

Tenn Fed Garden, *(Tennessee Federation of Garden Clubs; 0-939114),* 3325 Lakewood Dr., Memphis, TN 38128 (SAN 219-8215).

Tenn Muni League, *(Tennessee Municipal League),* 226 Capitol Blvd, Nashville, TN 37219 (SAN 226-4862).

Tennis Manual, *(Tennis Manual; 0-9606066),* 9241 W. Broward Blvd., Plantation, FL 33324 (SAN 216-4620) Tel 305-474-6642.

†Tensleep Pubs, *(Tensleep Pubns.; 0-9610130),* Div. of Video Resources, Inc., P.O. Box 925, Aberdeen, SD 57401 (SAN 262-7477) Tel 605-226-0488; 202 S. Main, Citizen Bldg., Suite 524, Aberdeen, SD 57401 (SAN 658-1900); *CIP.*

Tent Meeting, *(Tent of Meeting, The; 0-9615531),* P.O. Box 8518, Santa Fe, NM 87504 (SAN 696-1479) Tel 505-988-8084.

Theobald, *(Theobald, Paul, & Co.; 0-911498),* 5 N. Wabash Ave., Rm. 1406, Chicago, IL 60602 (SAN 205-4280) Tel 312-236-3994.

Theodore Front, *(Front, Theodore, Musical Literature; 0-934082),* 16122 Cohasset St., Van Nuys, CA 91406 (SAN 221-167X) Tel 818-994-1902.

†**Theophrastus,** *(Theophrastus; 0-913728),* P.O. Box 458, Little Compton, RI 02837 (SAN 202-7771) Tel 401-635-4348; *CIP.*

†**Theorex,** *(Theorex; 0-916004),* 8327 La Jolla Scenic Dr., La Jolla, CA 92037 (SAN 207-6632) Tel 619-453-6988; *CIP.*

†**Theos Pub Hse,** *(Theosophical Publishing Hse.; 0-8356),* Div. of Theosophical Society in America., 306 W. Geneva Rd., Wheaton, IL 60187-0270 (SAN 202-5698) Tel 312-665-0123; P.O. Box 270, Wheaton, IL 60189-0270 (SAN 699-5667); *CIP.* Imprints: Quest (Quest Books).

Theos U Pr, *(Theosophical Univ. Pr.; 0-911500),* P.O. Bin C, Pasadena, CA 91109 (SAN 205-4299) Tel 818-798-3378.

Theoscience Found, *(Theoscience Foundation Pub.; 0-917802),* 193 Los Robles Dr., Burlingame, CA 94010 (SAN 209-0260).

Theosophy, *(Theosophy Co.; 0-938998),* 245 W. 33rd St., Los Angeles, CA 90007 (SAN 295-3560) Tel 213-748-7244; 347 E. 72nd St., New York, NY 10021 (SAN 295-3579).

Theotes, *(Theotes-Logos Research, Inc.; 0-911806),* 4318 York Ave. S., Minneapolis, MN 55410 (SAN 205-4310) Tel 612-922-3202.

These Jokes, *(These Are the Jokes Folks; 0-9613443),* P.O. Box 1806, Ross, CA 94957 (SAN 657-1182) Tel 415-924-1665.

Thibodaux, *(Thibodaux Service League; 0-9608800),* P.O. Box 305, Thibodaux, LA 70302 (SAN 241-0818) Tel 504-446-9818.

†**Thieme Inc,** *(Thieme, Inc.; 0-913258; 0-86577),* Subs. of Georg Thieme Verlag, 381 Park Ave., S., New York, NY 10016 (SAN 169-5983) Tel 212-683-5088; *CIP.*

Thieme-Stratton
See Thieme Inc

Thigpen, *(Thigpen, S. G.; 0-911892),* P.O. Box 819, Picayune, MS 39466 (SAN 205-4329).

Think Net Inc, *(Think Network, Inc.; 0-936673),* P.O. Box 6124, New York, NY 10128 (SAN 699-6892) Tel 212-348-3894; 171 E. 89th St., New York, NY 10128 (SAN 699-6906).

Think Shop, *(Think Shop, Inc.; 0-937871),* P.O. Box 114, Gallina, NM 87017 (SAN 659-5944) Tel 505-638-5678.

Thinking Caps, *(Thinking Caps; 0-9610876),* P.O. Box 7239, Phoenix, AZ 85011 (SAN 239-4960) Tel 602-956-1515.

Thinking Gnomes, *(Thinking Gnomes Pr.; 0-931945),* 1724 Sacramento St., Suite 49, San Francisco, CA 94109 (SAN 685-9410) Tel 415-673-1079.

Thinking Ink Pubns
See Thinking Pubns

Thinking Kids Pr, *(Thinking Kids' Pr.; 0-939707),* 1921 Alta Vista Dr., Alhambra, CA 91803 (SAN 663-5172) Tel 818-282-7339.

Thinking Pubns, *(Thinking Pubns.; 0-9610370; 0-930599),* 10 Platt St., P.O. Box 163, Eau Claire, WI 54702-0163 (SAN 264-4320) Tel 715-832-2488; Toll free: 800-225-GROW; P.O. Box 163, Eau Claire, WI 54702-0163 (SAN 658-1935); Toll free: 800-362-GROW (In Wisconsin).

Third Natl Corp, *(Third National Corp.; 0-9615676),* 201 Fourth Ave. N., Nashville, TN 37244 (SAN 696-1568) Tel 615-748-5317.

Third Party Pub, *(Third Party Pub. Co.; 0-89914),* Div. of Third Party Assocs., Inc., P.O. Box 13306, Montclair Sta., Oakland, CA 94661-0306 (SAN 127-7294) Tel 415-339-2323.

Third Pyramid, *(Third Pyramid, Inc.; 0-916479),* P.O. Box 260, Watertown, WI 53094 (SAN 296-0052); Dist. by: Third Pyramid Corporation, P.O. Box 260, Watertown, WI 53094-0260 (SAN 296-0052) Tel 414-699-2441.

Third Sector, *(Third Sector Pr.; 0-939120),* P.O. Box 18044, Cleveland, OH 44118 (SAN 217-2720) Tel 216-831-9300.

Third World, *(Third World Press; 0-88378),* 7524 S. Cottage Grove, Chicago, IL 60019 (SAN 202-778X) Tel 312-651-0700.

Third World Bk, *(Third World Bk. Shop; 0-9616005),* 3001 Hickory St., Alexandria, VA 22305 (SAN 697-967X) Tel 703-548-0387.

Thirteen Colonies Pr, *(Thirteen Colonies Pr.; 0-934943),* 710 S. Henry St., Williamsburg, VA 23185 (SAN 695-0361) Tel 804-229-1775.

Thirteenth Hse, *(Thirteenth House; 0-935458),* 71 Vondran St., Huntington Station, NY 11746 (SAN 213-5639).

Thirteenth Moon, *(13th Moon, Inc.; 0-9601224),* Box 309 Cathedral Station, New York, NY 10025 (SAN 208-9831) Tel 212-678-1074.

Thirty-three Pr, *(Thirty-Three Press; 0-9611912),* P.O. Box 456, Topsham, ME 04086 (SAN 286-2069) Tel 207-725-5263.

This N That, *(This 'N That Press; 0-941900),* 334 Crescent Dr., Galt, CA 95632 (SAN 239-8001) Tel 209-745-1000.

Thistlerose, *(Thistlerose Pubns.; 0-9605630),* 1007 Greenbrier St., St. Paul, MN 55106 (SAN 216-3098).

Thoburn Pr, *(Thoburn Pr.; 0-932029),* P.O. Box 6941, Tyler, TX 75711 (SAN 686-0818) Tel 214-581-0677.

Thomas Bros Maps, *(Thomas Brothers Maps; 0-88130),* 17731 Cowan, Irvine, CA 92714 (SAN 158-8192) Tel 714-863-1984; Toll free: 800-432-8430 (CA Only).

Thomas Co, *(Thomas Co., The),* 1669 Maple, No. 6, Box 718, Solvang, CA 93463 (SAN 696-7175) Tel 805-688-7026.

Thomas County His, *(Thomas County Historical Society; 0-9615822),* 725 N. Dawson St., Thomasville, GA 31792 (SAN 696-6675) Tel 912-226-7664.

Thomas Ent, *(Thomas Enterprises International; 0-935243),* 6580 W. 49th St., Mission, KS 66202 (SAN 695-7269) Tel 913-362-0405.

Thomas Geale, *(Thomas Geale Pubns., Inc.; 0-912781),* Drawer C.P. 223, 1142 Manhattan Ave., Manhattan Beach, CA 90226 (SAN 283-3735) Tel 213-379-4405.

Thomas Intl DC, *(Thomas International; 0-9612128),* P.O. Box 6376, Washington, DC 20015 (SAN 277-7088) Tel 301-657-2910.

Thomas Intl Pub, *(Thomas International Publishing Co., Inc.; 0-937200),* Subs. of Thomas Publishing Co., 1 Penn Plaza, New York, NY 10001 (SAN 213-8263) Tel 212-695-0500.

Thomas Jefferson Res
See T Jefferson Res Ctr

Thomas Merritt Island, *(Thomas Pubns.; 0-9616889),* P.O. Box 1736, Merritt Island, FL 32952 (SAN 661-6429); 60 Parnell St., Merritt Island, FL 32952 (SAN 661-6437) Tel 305-452-1979.

Thomas More, *(More, Thomas, Pr.; 0-88347),* Subs. of Thomas More Assn., 223 W. Erie St., Chicago, IL 60611 (SAN 203-0675) Tel 312-951-2100; Toll free: 800-835-8965.

Thomas-Newell, *(Thomas-Newell; 0-9600690),* 1201 Monroe St., P.O. Box 329, Endicott, NY 13760 (SAN 205-4337) Tel 607-754-0410.

Thomas Paine Pr, *(Thomas Paine Press; 0-934162),* 9528 Miramar Rd., Suite 130, San Diego, CA 92126 (SAN 212-9760) Tel 619-484-4798.

Thomas Partners, *(Thomas Partners Advertising, Inc.; 0-9616602),* 3255 Wilshire Blvd., Suite 1034, Los Angeles, CA 90010 (SAN 659-7793) Tel 213-385-6285.

Thomas Pr, *(Thomas Pr., Inc.; 0-911487),* 2030 Ferdon Rd., Ann Arbor, MI 48104 (SAN 682-8706) Tel 313-662-1275.

Thomas Pubns FL
See Thomas Merritt Island

Thomas Pubns TX, *(Thomas Pubns.; 0-918487),* 8200 Cameron Rd., No. D, Suite 100B, Austin, TX 78753 (SAN 657-6990); P.O. Box 33244, Austin, TX 78764 (SAN 662-2399).

Thomas W Taylor
See W T Taylor

Thomasson-Grant, *(Thomasson-Grant, Inc.; 0-934738),* 505 Faulconer Dr., Suite 1-C, Charlottesville, VA 22901 (SAN 239-3948) Tel 804-977-1780.

Thomond Pr Imprint of Elsevier

Thompson, *(Thompson Pubs.; 0-933479),* 2555 N. 19th St., Milwaukee, WI 53206 (SAN 691-8972) Tel 414-264-9241.

Thompson & Co
See Thompson Co Inc

Thompson & Forbes Co
See Thompson Forbes Co

†**Thompson Co Inc,** *(Thompson & Co., Inc.; 0-918351),* 1313 Fifth St., SE, Suite 301, Minneapolis, MN 55414-1524 (SAN 657-3843) Tel 612-331-3963; *CIP.*

Thompson Forbes Co, *(Thompson & Forbes Company; 0-9613694),* P.O. Box 2405, Duxbury, MA 02331 (SAN 670-9850) Tel 617-477-9208.

Thompson Pr, *(Thompson Pr.; 0-931947),* P.O. Box 263, Conway, NH 03818 (SAN 685-9399) Tel 603-447-5569.

Thompson Pub Group, *(Thompson Publishing Group),* 1725 K St., Suite 200 NW, Washington, DC 20006 (SAN 287-2986) Tel 202-872-1766.

Thompson Rutter Inc
See Tompson Rutter Inc

Thompson's, *(Thompson's),* P.O. Box 550, Albertville, AL 35950 (SAN 207-4656) Tel 205-878-2021.

Thomson, *(Thomson, Phillip; 0-911504),* 836 Georgia St., Williamston, MI 48895 (SAN 202-7798) Tel 517-655-2930.

Thomson Pub CA
See Thomson Pubns

Thomson Pubns, *(Thomson Pubns.; 0-913702),* P.O. Box 9335, Fresno, CA 93791 (SAN 210-377X) Tel 209-435-2163.

Thomson-Shore, *(Thomson-Shore, Inc.),* 7300 W. Joy Rd., Dexter, MI 48130 (SAN 262-0952) Tel 313-426-3939; Dist. by: D. B. Stiles, P.O. Box 812, Gautier, MS 39553 (SAN 262-0960).

†**Thor,** *(Thor Publishing Co.; 0-87407),* P.O. Box 1782, Ventura, CA 93002 (SAN 202-7801) Tel 805-648-4560; *CIP.*

Thoreau Found, *(Thoreau Foundation, Inc.; 0-912130),* Subs. of Thoreau Society, Inc., 156 Belknap St., Concord, MA 01742 (SAN 205-4353) Tel 617-369-5912.

Thorn Creek Pr, *(Thorn Creek Press; 0-915664),* Rte. 2, Box 160, Genesee, ID 83832 (SAN 264-4339) Tel 208-224-6924.

Thorn Hse Pr, *(Thorn Hse. Pr.; 0-937385),* 5764 Morley St., Los Angeles, CA 90045 (SAN 659-0500) Tel 818-347-5446; P.O. Box 45264, Los Angeles, CA 90045 (SAN 659-0519); Dist. by: White-Hatch Group, 6625 Springpark, Suite 14, Los Angeles, CA 90056 (SAN 200-6405).

†**Thorndike Pr,** *(Thorndike Pr.; 0-89621),* P.O. Box 159, Thorndike, ME 04986 (SAN 212-2375) Tel 207-948-2962; Toll free: 800-223-6121; *CIP.*

Thornfield Pr, *(Thornfield Pr.; 0-9613075),* P.O. Box 192, Castleton, VT 05735 (SAN 294-6815) Tel 802-468-5812; Dist. by: Baker & Taylor Co., Eastern Div., 50 Kirby Ave., Somerville, NJ 08876 (SAN 169-4901).

Thornton Pubns, *(Thornton Pubns.; 0-9613035),* 407 Levering Mill Rd., Bala Cynwyd, PA 19004 (SAN 294-1376) Tel 215-667-0887.

Thorntree Pr, *(Thorntree Pr.; 0-939395),* 547 Hawthorn Ln., Winnetka, IL 60093 (SAN 663-1371) Tel 312-446-8099.

Thornwood Bk, *(Thornwood Book Publishers; 0-943054),* P.O. Box 1442, Florence, AL 35631 (SAN 240-4540) Tel 205-766-4100.

Thoro, *(Thoro Press; 0-9613455),* 7454 Warrior Ct., Dayton, OH 45415 (SAN 657-3053) Tel 513-836-1386; Orders to: 3936 Salem Ave., Suite 275, Dayton, OH 45406 (SAN 662-2364).

†**Thorp Springs,** *(Thorp Springs Pr.; 0-914476),* 803 Red River St., Austin, TX 78701 (SAN 202-781X); 1002 Lorrain, Austin, TX 78703 (SAN 694-6348) Tel 804-476-8078; *CIP.*

†**Thorsons Pubs,** *(Thorsons Pubs., Inc.; 0-7225),* Subs. of Thorsons Publishing Group (Great Britain), 1 Park St., Rochester, VT 05767 (SAN 277-7398) Tel 802-767-3174; Dist. by: Inner Traditions, Park St., Rochester, VT 05767 (SAN 208-6948); Orders to: Harper & Row Pubs., Inc., Keystone Industrial Pk., Scranton, PA 18512 (SAN 215-3742); *CIP.*

Thoughts by Bonnie, *(Thoughts by Bonnie; 0-9616611),* Rte. 2, Oslo, MN 56744 (SAN 659-7963) Tel 218-695-5111.

Thrash Pubns, *(Thrash; 0-942658),* Rte. 1, Box 273, Seale, AL 36875 (SAN 277-7096).

Thrasher, *(Thrasher Balloons; 0-9601514),* P.O. Box 1111, Homestead, FL 33030 (SAN 211-5425) Tel 305-247-8412.

†**Three Continents,** *(Three Continents Pr.;* *0-89410; 0-914478),* 1636 Connecticut Ave., NW, Suite 501, Washington, DC 20009 (SAN 212-0070) Tel 202-332-3885; *CIP.*

Three Crowns Indus, *(Three Crowns Industries, Inc.; 0-9613100),* 7831 Temple Rd., Philadelphia, PA 19150 (SAN 294-6793) Tel 215-549-4497.

Three D Pubs, *(3-D Pubs.; 0-9600500),* P.O. Box 428, Edgerton, OH 43517 (SAN 205-4361).

Three Dimensional, *(Three Dimensional Thinking; 0-9613613),* 1420 Iroquois Ave., Long Beach, CA 90815 (SAN 669-8212) Tel 213-423-1441.

Three L Pr, *(Three L Press; 0-9601938),* 3142 La Mesa Dr., San Carlos, CA 94070 (SAN 212-0518).

Three Meadows Pr, *(Three Meadows Press; 0-942892),* 861 Oak Knoll Dr., Perrysburg, OH 43551 (SAN 240-1649) Tel 419-874-8489.

Three Mtn Pr, *(Three Mountains Pr.; 0-930986),* P.O. Box 50, Cooper Sta., New York, NY 10003 (SAN 209-7885) Tel 212-989-2737.

Three River Ctr, *(Three River Ctr.; 0-9615677),* 607 Menlo Ave., Menlo Park, CA 94025 (SAN 696-1622) Tel 415-328-2013.

Three Rivers Pr, *(Three Rivers Pr.; 0-915606),* P.O. Box 21, Carnegie Mellon Univ., Pittsburgh, PA 15213 (SAN 207-9097).

Three Squares, *(Three Squares Corp.; 0-9615678),* 217 S. Orange St., Suite No. 4, Glendale, CA 91204 (SAN 696-1681) Tel 213-661-0420.

Three Star Ent, *(Three Star Enterprises; 0-912507),* 9709 Raymond Dr., Belleville, IL 62223 (SAN 265-2293) Tel 618-397-1155.

Three-Stones Pubns, *(Three-Stones Pubns., Ltd.; 0-933673),* P.O. Box 6143, Seattle, WA 98168 (SAN 692-5421) Tel 206-431-0195.

Threshold VT, *(Threshold Bks.; 0-939660),* RFD 3, Box 1350, Putney, VT 05346 (SAN 216-6496) Tel 802-254-8300; Dist. by: Great Tradition, The, 750 Adrian Way, Suite 111, San Rafael, CA 94903 (SAN 200-5743) Tel 415-492-9382; Dist. by: Bookpeople, 2929 Fifth St., Berkeley, CA 94710 (SAN 168-9517).

Through Thick & Thin, *(Through Thick & Thin; 0-9608638),* 6216 Hills Dr., Birmingham, MI 48010 (SAN 239-5649) Tel 313-642-4252.

Throughbred Own & Breed
See Blood-Horse

Thrown Winds Pr, *(Thrown to the Winds Pr.; 0-9616301),* 171 Jackson St., Newton, MA 02159 (SAN 658-5140) Tel 617-964-7448.

Thueson, *(Thueson, James D.; 0-911506),* P.O. Box 14474, University Sta., Minneapolis, MN 55414 (SAN 239-4979).

Thum Print, *(Thum Printing; 0-932920),* 116 W. Pierce St., Elburn, IL 60119 (SAN 212-3150).

Thunder River, *(Thunder River Press; 0-9604274),* P.O. Box 10935, Aspen, CO 81611 (SAN 214-4786).

Thunderbird, *(Thunderbird Circle Pubs. Co.; 0-9615140),* OS350 Winfield Rd., Winfield, IL 60190 (SAN 694-2091) Tel 312-462-1768.

Thunderbolt Pubns, *(Thunderbolt Publications; 0-9612538),* Box 70427, 141 S. Taaffe, Sunnyvale, CA 94086 (SAN 289-5722) Tel 415-960-0146.

Thunderchief, *(Thunderchief Corp.),* P.O. Box 85, Troutdale, OR 97060 (SAN 212-8683).

†**Thunder's Mouth,** *(Thunder's Mouth Pr.; 0-938410),* P.O. Box 780, New York, NY 10025 (SAN 216-4663) Tel 212-595-2025; *CIP.*

Thurau Pr, *(Thurau Pr.; 0-914291),* Div. of Wild International Corp., P.O. Box 8482, Asheville, NC 28814 (SAN 287-5780) Tel 704-254-5000.

Thurnbriar Pr, *(Thurnbriar Pr.; 0-937163),* Robinhood, SR 2, Box 420, Bath, ME 04530 (SAN 658-5167).

Thursday Pubs, *(Thursday Pubs.; 0-934502),* 1846N Pine Bluff Rd., Stevens Point, WI 54481-8905 (SAN 212-9779) Tel 715-344-6441.

Thut World Ed Ctr
See I N Thut World Educ Ctr

Tia Mia, *(Tia Mia, Inc.; 0-9612880),* 720 N. Walnut St., El Paso, TX 79903 (SAN 291-4581) Tel 915-533-0464.

Tiare Pubns, *(Tiare Pubns.; 0-936653),* P.O. Box 493, Lake Geneva, WI 53147 (SAN 699-7066) Tel 414-248-4845; Rte. 4, Box 110, Lake Geneva, WI 53147 (SAN 699-7074).

Tiberias Inst, *(Tiberias Institute, The; 0-917873),* 1212 LaSombra Ct., El Cajon, CA 92020 (SAN 657-0240) Tel 619-444-8200.

Tiburon
See Word Power

Tichenor Pub, *(Tichenor Publishing; 0-89917),* Div. of T.I.S., Inc., 1928 Arlington Rd., Bloomington, IN 47402 (SAN 283-8818) Tel 812-332-3307; Toll free: 367-4002.

†**Ticknor & Fields,** *(Ticknor & Fields; 0-89919),* Affil. of Houghton Mifflin Co., 52 Vanderbilt Ave., New York, NY 10017 (SAN 282-4043) Tel 212-687-8996; Toll free: 800-225-3362; Dist. by: Houghton Mifflin Co., 1 Beacon St., Boston, MA 02108 (SAN 200-2388) Tel 617-725-5000; *CIP. Imprints:* Pub. by Clarion (Clarion Books).(Clarion Bks.).

Tidal Pr, *(Tidal Pr., The; 0-930954),* P.O. Box 150, Portsmouth, NH 03801 (SAN 211-3783) Tel 603-430-9475.

†**Tide Bk Pub Co,** *(Tide Bk. Publishing Co.; 0-9602786),* P.O. Box 101, York Harbor, ME 03911-0101 (SAN 282-406X) Tel 207-363-4534; Orders to: The Distributors, Inc., 702 S. Michigan, South Bend, IN 46618 (SAN 282-4078) Tel 219-232-8500; *CIP.*

Tide-Mark, *(Tide-Mark Pr., Ltd; 0-936846),* P.O. Box 813, Hartford, CT 06142 (SAN 222-1802) Tel 203-289-0363.

Tide Pr, *(Tide Pr.; 0-912931),* P.O. Box 4224, Linden, NJ 07036 (SAN 283-3158) Tel 201-862-0762.

†**Tidewater,** *(Tidewater Pubs.; 0-87033),* Div. of Cormell Maritime Pr., Inc., P.O. Box 456, Centreville, MD 21617 (SAN 202-0459) Tel 301-758-1075; Toll free: 800-638-7641; *CIP.*

Tiffany, *(Tiffany Press; 0-914800),* P.O. Box 304, Newton, MA 02158 (SAN 206-5819) Tel 617-527-9395.

Tiffany Pub, *(Tiffany Publishing Co.; 0-9616079),* 98 Puritan Ave., Worcester, MA 01604 (SAN 698-1321) Tel 617-756-1911.

Tiger Pubn, *(Tiger Pubns.; 0-9611318),* 32 Friendship Ct., Red Bank, NJ 07701 (SAN 283-3506) Tel 201-747-9042.

Tiger Stream Pr, *(Tiger Stream Pr.; 0-935829),* P.O. Box 96, Pismo Beach, CA 93449 (SAN 696-6519) Tel 805-541-6969.

Tigereyes Pr, *(Tigereyes Pr.; 0-931763),* P.O. Box 172, Lemoyne, PA 17043 (SAN 683-7921) Tel 717-774-6352.

Tigertail Ent, *(Tigertail Enterprises; 0-938921),* P.O. Box 1914, Santa Monica, CA 90402 (SAN 661-6690) Tel 805-683-2938.

Tilden Pr, *(Tilden Pr.; 0-9605750),* 1001 Connecticut Ave, NW, Suite 310, Washington, DC 20036 (SAN 217-135X) Tel 202-659-5855.

Till Pr, *(Till Press; 0-931208),* P.O. Box 27816, Los Angeles, CA 90027 (SAN 211-4569).

Tiller Pub NJ, *(Tiller Publishing; 0-9616671),* P.O. Box 4014, Dunellen, NJ 08812 (SAN 659-9109) Tel 201-968-2672.

Tillman Pubns, *(Tillman Pubns.; 0-9605752),* P.O. Box 488, Arverne, NY 11692 (SAN 239-8125).

†**Tilted Planet,** *(Tilted Planet Pr.; 0-912973),* P.O. Box 8646, Austin, TX 78173 (SAN 283-3808) Tel 512-447-7619; *CIP.*

Tilth, *(Tilth; 0-931380),* 4649 Sunnyside No., Seattle, WA 98103 (SAN 220-4096).

Timco Intl, *(Timco International; 0-915624),* P.O. Box 431, Berkeley, CA 94701 (SAN 207-3331).

Timco Mfg, *(Timco Manufacturing, Inc.; 0-9611060),* 851 15th St., Prairie du Sac, WI 53578 (SAN 282-8901) Tel 608-643-8534.

†**Timber,** *(Timber Pr.; 0-917304; 0-88192),* 9999 SW Wilshire, Portland, OR 97225 (SAN 216-082X) Tel 503-287-3093; Dist. by: International Specialized Bk. Services, Inc., 5602 NE Hassalo, Portland, OR 97213-3640 (SAN 169-7129) Tel 503-287-3093; *CIP.*

Timberline Bks, *(Timberline Books; 0-913488),* 25890 Weld Rd. 53, Kersey, CO 80644-8802 (SAN 202-0416) Tel 303-353-3785.

Timberline CO, *(Timberline Pr., Inc.; 0-931235),* 7207 Lipan St., Denver, CO 80221 (SAN 693-7713) Tel 303-429-4053. Do not confuse with Timberline Pr., Fulton, MO.

Timberline Pr, *(Timberline Pr.(CO); 0-9608284),* Box 70011, Eugene, OR 97401 (SAN 240-4619) Tel 503-345-1771.

Timbertrails *Imprint of* **Capstan Pubns**

Timberwind, *(Timberwind Publishing; 0-912849),* 7073 Maplewood Ave., Englewood, CO 80110 (SAN 283-3832) Tel 303-781-6366.

Timberwood, *(Timberwood Industries, Inc.; 0-9602298),* Div. of Books on Music Div., P.O. Box 82, South Salem, NY 10590 (SAN 212-6079) Tel 914-533-2020.

Time & Space
See T S L Pr

†**Time-Life,** *(Time-Life Bks.; 0-8094),* Div. of Time, Inc., 777 Duke St., Alexandria, VA 22314 (SAN 202-7836) Tel 703-960-5421; Toll free: 800-621-7026; 4200 N Industrial Blvd., Indianapolis, IN 46254 (SAN 658-1951); Toll free: 800-631-8081; Toll free: 800-343-9204; Dist. by: Little, Brown & Co., 34 Beacon St., Boston, MA 02106 (SAN 281-8892) Tel 617-227-0730; Dist. by: Morgan & Morgan Co., 145 Palisades St., Dobbs Ferry, NY 10522 (SAN 202-5620); Orders to: Silver Burdett Co., 250 James St., Morristown, NJ 07960 (SAN 204-5982). Lib. & School Orders to: Silver Burdett Co; *CIP.*

Time Mgr Intl, *(Time Manager International USA, Inc.; 0-937079),* 3727 Buchanan St., San Francisco, CA 94123 (SAN 658-5256) Tel 415-931-1100.

Time Museum, *(Time Museum, The; 0-912947),* Div. of United Realty Corp., 7801 E. State St., P.O. Box 5285, Rockford, IL 61125 (SAN 283-3522) Tel 815-398-6000.

Time Out, *(Time Out to Enjoy, Inc.; 0-9608010),* 715 Lake St., Suite 100, Oak Park, IL 60301 (SAN 238-5864) Tel 312-383-9017.

Time Share Corp, *(Time Share Corp.; 0-89466),* Subs. of Houghton-Mifflin, 3 Lebanon St., Hanover, NH 03755 (SAN 658-3830) Tel 603-643-3640.

Time Table Bks, *(Time Table Bks.; 0-9614208),* 1015 Cadillac Way, Suite 106, Burlingame, CA 94010 (SAN 686-7359) Tel 415-579-5632.

Time Warp Pub, *(Time Warp Publishing; 0-938889),* 7956 White Oak Ave., Northridge, CA 91325 (SAN 661-7948) Tel 818-344-2286.

Time-Wise, *(Time-Wise Pubns.; 0-918826),* P.O. Box 597, Yucca Valley, CA 92284 (SAN 208-2543) Tel 619-365-5888.

†**Timeless Bks,** *(Timeless Bks.; 0-931454),* Div. of Association for the Development of Human Potential, P.O. Box 160, Porthill, ID 83853 (SAN 211-6502) Tel 604-227-9224; *CIP.*

Timely Bks, *(Timely Bks.; 0-931328),* P.O. Box 267, New Milford, CT 06776 (SAN 211-3791) Tel 203-744-4719.

†**Times Bks,** *(Times Bks.; 0-8129),* Subs. of Random Hse., Inc., 201 E. 50th St., New York, NY 10022 (SAN 202-5558) Tel 212-751-2600; Toll free: 800-242-7737; Orders to: Random Hse., 400 Hahn Rd., Westminster, MD 21157 (SAN 200-2086); *CIP. Imprints:* Demeter (Demeter Press).(Demeter Pr.); Enctr (Encounter Books).(Encounter Bks.).

†**Times Change,** *(Times Change Pr.; 0-87810),* Publishers Services, P.O. Box 2510, Novato, CA 94948 (SAN 202-7860) Tel 415-883-3530; *CIP.*

Times Mirror, *(Times Mirror Pr.; 0-911510),* P.O. Box 23951, Los Angeles, CA 90023 (SAN 207-3765) Tel 213-265-6767.

Times Pr, *(Times Press, The; 0-9606608),* 11661 San Vicente Blvd., No. 901, Los Angeles, CA 90049 (SAN 219-8223) Tel 213-820-8767.

Times Pub, *(Times Publishing Group, Inc.; 0-9615476),* Affil. of Celebrity Service, International, Inc., 305 Washington Ave., Towson, MD 21204 (SAN 696-1754) Tel 301-337-2640; Toll free: 800-223-1796; C/O Celebrity Service, Inc., 1780 Broadway, Suite 300, New York, NY 10019 (SAN 662-3670) Tel 212-245-1460.

Timescape *Imprint of* **PB**

Timetable Pr, *(Timetable Pr.; 0-87974),* 50 Sagamore Dr., Syosset, NY 11791 (SAN 205-440X) Tel 516-921-2137.

Timpanogos Pub, *(Timpanogos Pubs.; 0-935329),* 683 South 1040 West, Orem, UT 84058 (SAN 695-7285) Tel 801-225-5898; P.O. Box 776, Orem, UT 84058 (SAN 696-5148).

Tin Man CT, *(Tin Man; 0-9610604),* 194 North St., Willimantic, CT 06226 (SAN 264-4363) Tel 203-423-7370; Dist. by: Holos Gallery, 194 North St., Willimantic, CT 06226 (SAN 264-4363) Tel 203-423-7370.

Tin Man Pr, *(Tin Man Pr.; 0-936110),* Box 219, Stanwood, WA 98292 (SAN 222-0156).

Tin Penny Pubs, *(Tin Penny Pubs.; 0-937285),* 407 Magnolia, Garden, KS 67846 (SAN 659-0578) Tel 316-276-4265.

Tinkers Dam Pr, *(Tinkers Dam Pr.; 0-943608),* 1703 E. Michigan Ave., Jackson, MI 49202 (SAN 240-7884) Tel 517-784-6158.

Tinnon-Brown, *(Tinnon-Brown Publishing Co.; 0-87252),* Orders to: Borden Publishing Co., 1855 W. Main St., Alhambra, CA 91801 (SAN 201-419X).

Tinys Self Help Bks, *(Tiny's Self Help Bks. for Children; 0-9616549),* 174 Main St., Apt. 108W, Bangor, ME 04401 (SAN 659-5421) Tel 207-947-2279; Orders to: Paperback Book Stores, Airport Mall, Bangor, ME 04401 (SAN 662-4294) Tel 207-942-9191.

†**Tioga Pub Co,** *(Tioga Pub. Co.; 0-935382),* P.O. Box 98, Palo Alto, CA 94302 (SAN 669-280X) Tel 415-854-2445; Dist. by: William Kaufmann, Inc., 95 First St., Los Altos, CA 94022 (SAN 202-9383) Tel 415-948-5810; *CIP.*

Tioga Pubns, *(Tioga Pubns.; 0-9616890),* 101 N. Fenton Rd., Chenango Forks, NY 13746 (SAN 661-6445) Tel 607-648-8578.

Tip Pubns, *(Tip Pubns.; 0-935567),* Subs. of Hunter Enterprises, P.O. Box 514, El Segundo, CA 90245 (SAN 696-1762) Tel 213-322-8437; 305 Richmond, El Segundo, CA 90245 (SAN 662-3689).

Tip-top, *(Tip-top; 0-9610000),* Box 442, New York, NY 10025 (SAN 263-2306).

Tipi Wkshp Bks, *(Tipi Workshop Bks.; 0-942914),* 1377 Quaker, Golden, CO 80401 (SAN 240-3277) Tel 303-278-7777; Orders to: P.O. Box 84, Allenspark, CO 80510 (SAN 693-9775).

†**Tippers Intl,** *(Tippers International, Ltd.; 0-9612552),* P.O. Box 1934, Wausau, WI 54401 (SAN 225-6460) Tel 715-842-4616; *CIP.*

Tiptoe Pub, *(Tiptoe Publishing; 0-937953),* P.O. Box 206, Naselle, WA 98638-0206 (SAN 659-7971) Tel 206-484-7722; 110 Wildwood Dr., Naselle, WA 98638 (SAN 659-798X).

Tire Mgmt, *(Tire Management Consultants, Ltd.; 0-937377),* P.O. Box 1069, Eugene, OR 97440 (SAN 659-0608) Tel 503-683-0163; 1277 SE Reservoir, Roseburg, OR 97470 (SAN 659-0616).

Tiresias Pr, *(Tiresias Pr., Inc.; 0-913292),* 116 Pinehurst Ave., New York, NY 10033 (SAN 202-7879) Tel 212-568-9570.

TIS Inc, *(T.I.S., Inc.; 0-89917),* Div. of T.I.S. Enterprises, P.O. Box 669, 1928 Arlington Rd., Bloomington, IN 47402 (SAN 169-2313) Tel 812-332-3307; Toll free: 800-367-4002.

Tisdale Pub, *(Tisdale Publishing Co.; 0-9616672),* P.O. Box 888, Mars Hill, NC 28754 (SAN 659-9087); Brook St., Mars Hill, NC 28754 (SAN 659-9095) Tel 704-689-2934.

Tissa Inc, *(TISSA, Inc.; 0-9616162),* Rte. 1, Box 349A, Culpepper, VA 22701 (SAN 699-8313) Tel 703-547-2989.

Tissue Culture Assn, *(Tissue Culture Assn.; 0-931767),* 19110 Montgomery Village Ave., Suite 300, Gaithersburg, MD 20879 (SAN 225-2546) Tel 301-869-2900.

Titan Pub Co, *(Titan Publishing Co.; 0-9603314),* P.O. Box 506, Mesilla, NM 88046 (SAN 211-7142).

Titanium, *(Titanium Development Assn.; 0-935297),* 11 W. Monument Ave., Suite 510, Dayton, OH 45402 (SAN 696-1827) Tel 513-223-8432; P.O. Box 2307, Dayton, OH 45401 (SAN 696-1835).

Title Books, *(Title Bks., Inc.),* P.O. Box 31170, Birmingham, AL 35233 (SAN 168-9207) Tel 205-324-2596.

Titus Pub Co, *(Titus Publishing Co.; 0-9610792),* 433 Sunbelt Dr., Suite E, P.O. Box 6788, Corpus Christi, TX 78411-0788 (SAN 265-1432) Tel 512-289-8282.

Tivoli Pub, *(Tivoli Publishing Co.; 0-9614788),* P.O. Box 19164, Kansas City, MO 64141 (SAN 692-9893) Tel 816-923-2546.

Tixcacalcupul, *(Tixcacalcupul Pr.; 0-938531),* P.O. Box 709, Summerland, CA 93067 (SAN 661-1427); 200 Greenwell Ave., Summerland, CA 93067 (SAN 661-1435) Tel 805-969-0525; Dist. by: Printed Matter, Inc., 7 Lispenard St., New York, NY 10013 (SAN 169-5924) Tel 212-925-0325.

TJ Enter IL, *(T.J. Enterprises; 0-936503),* 8000 S. Archer Rd., A106, Willow Springs, IL 60480 (SAN 698-0619) Tel 312-839-2611; P.O. Box 255, Chicago Ridge, IL 60415-0255 (SAN 698-2484).

TK Pubs, *(T. K. Publishers; 0-9614023),* P.O. Box 779, Cocoa, FL 32922 (SAN 683-6232) Tel 305-636-1952.

TKM Pubns, *(TKM Publications; 0-915301),* Rte. 6, Box 143-A, Abingdon, VA 24210 (SAN 290-0483) Tel 703-628-4887.

TL Enterprises, *(TL Enterprises, Inc.; 0-934798),* 29901 Agoura Rd., Agoura, CA 91301 (SAN 213-1803) Tel 818-991-4980.

TLC Bks, *(TLC Bks.; 0-9617081),* 416 N. Byrkit St., Mishawaka, IN 46544 (SAN 662-6165) Tel 219-959-1775; P.O. Box 1391, Mishawaka, IN 46544 (SAN 662-6173).

TLC Enterprises, *(TLC Enterprises; 0-9614922),* P.O. Box 3372, Englewood, CO 80112 (SAN 693-1278) Tel 303-799-5424.

TLC Pr
    See TechnoLiteracy Assocs

TLT, *(TLT Pubns.; 0-943314),* 202 S. Fifth St., Goshen, IN 46526 (SAN 240-7841) Tel 616-361-8013.

TM Prods, *(TM Productions; 0-937522),* Box 189, Wilmette, IL 60091 (SAN 215-2096) Tel 312-869-9242.

TMH Pub, *(TMH Publishing, Ltd.; 0-939386),* P.O. Box 6344, Santa Barbara, CA 93160-6344 (SAN 216-3047).

To Begin With, *(To Begin With; 0-9606764),* 1142 Hornell Dr., Silver Spring, MD 20904 (SAN 662-1597) Tel 301-421-9406; c/o Gordon Pledger, 1142 Hornell Dr., Silver Spring, MD 20904 (SAN 219-645X) Tel 301-421-9406.

To-the-Point, *(To-the-Point Press; 0-9606476),* Drawer 546, Dana Point, CA 92629 (SAN 223-0127) Tel 714-496-6677.

Toadwood Pubs, *(Toadwood Publishers; 0-9610878),* R.R.6, Box 63, Edwardsville, IL 62025 (SAN 282-5775) Tel 618-656-0531; Dist. by: Southwestern Stringed Instruments & Accessories, 1228 E. Prince Rd., Tucson, AZ 85719 (SAN 200-4003); Dist. by: Ability Development, Inc., Box 4260, Athens, OH 45701-4260 (SAN 111-9125) Tel 614-954-3547.

Today Bible, *(Today in Bible Prophecy, Inc.; 0-937682),* 113 S. Delano St. No. 1, Anaheim, CA 92804 (SAN 293-4566) Tel 714-995-1869; Orders to: P.O. Box 5700, Huntington Beach, CA 92615 (SAN 293-4574) Tel 714-963-7766.

Today Bible & You, *(Today, the Bible, and You; 0-9617286),* P.O. Box 1722, Broken Arrow, OK 74013 (SAN 663-5997); 13422 E. 131st St., Broken Arrow, OK 74011 (SAN 663-6004) Tel 918-455-2047.

Today News, *(Today News Service, Inc.; 0-932746),* National Press Bldg., Washington, DC 20045 (SAN 202-7887) Tel 202-628-6999.

Today Pubn
    See Today News

Todd & Honeywell, *(Todd & Honeywell, Inc.; 0-89962),* 10 Cuttermill Rd., Great Neck, NY 11021 (SAN 213-179X) Tel 516-487-9777; Toll free: 800-233-3361.

Todd Pub, *(Todd Publishing, Inc.; 0-935988),* P.O. Box 5837, Scottsdale, AZ 85261 (SAN 222-0172) Tel 602-998-3000.

Todd Pubns, *(Todd Pubns.; 0-915344),* 10 Rapids Rd., Stamford, CT 06905 (SAN 207-0804) Tel 203-322-5488.

Todd Pubns
    See Todd Pubns NY

Todd Pubns NY, *(Todd Publications),* P.O. Box 92, Lenox Hill Station, New York, NY 10021 (SAN 226-3599).

Todd Tarbox, *(Todd Tarbox Bks.; 0-89297),* 2424 Lancelot Dr., Baton Rouge, LA 70816 (SAN 208-2012) Tel 504-293-6308.

Toe Run Pr, *(Toe Run Pr.; 0-9615857),* P.O. Box 271606, Houston, TX 77277 (SAN 696-186X) Tel 713-961-7681; 4040 San Felipe, No. 108, Houston, TX 77027 (SAN 699-6264).

Tofua Pr
    See Rand-Tofua

Toggitt, *(Toggitt, Joan, Ltd.; 0-911514),* 35 Fairfield Pl., West Caldwell, NJ 07006 (SAN 205-4418); Toll free: 800-922-0808.

Toledo Blade, *(Toledo Blade Co., The; 0-9614554),* 541 Superior St., Toledo, OH 43660 (SAN 691-8115) Tel 419-245-6280.

Toledo Mus Art, *(Toledo Museum of Art, The; 0-935172),* Box 1013, Toledo, OH 43697 (SAN 213-8980) Tel 419-255-8000; Dist. by: Pennsylvania State Univ. Press, 215 Wagner Bldg., University Park, PA 16802 (SAN 213-5760) Tel 814-865-1327.

Tolemac, *(Tolemac, Inc.; 0-9609520),* P.O. Box 418, Ashland, OR 97520 (SAN 263-2314) Tel 503-482-2720.

Tolff, *(Tolff Pubs.; 0-916498),* Div. of Trinity of Light Fellowship Foundation., 5750 Via Real, No. 230, Carpinteria, CA 93013 (SAN 208-8916) Tel 805-684-6363.

Tolle Pubns, *(Tolle Pubns.; 0-915378),* P.O. Box 6243, Beaumont, TX 77705 (SAN 211-0970) Tel 713-860-5628; 7920 Wilcox Lane, Beaumont, TX 77706 (SAN 211-0989).

Tolstoy Found, *(Tolstoy Foundation, Inc.),* 200 Park Ave. S., Rm. 1612, New York, NY 10003 (SAN 209-2778) Tel 212-677-7770.

Tolteca Pubns, *(Tolteca Pubns.; 0-938461),* Div. of Centro Cultural de la Raza, P.O. Box 8251, San Diego, CA 92102 (SAN 660-983X); 2004 Park Blvd., San Diego, CA 92101 (SAN 660-9848) Tel 619-235-6135.

Tolvan Co, *(Tolvan Co.; 0-916774),* P.O. Box 1933, Appleton, WI 54911 (SAN 208-8924) Tel 414-766-1828.

Tom Tuttle, *(Tuttle, Tom, & Associates; 0-930556),* P.O. Box 91529, Santa Barbara, CA 93190 (SAN 208-2551) Tel 805-683-2812.

Tom Weisser, *(Weisser, Thomas; 0-9610710),* Box 53, Monmouth, OR 97361 (SAN 264-8105) Tel 503-838-6051.

Tomart Pubns, *(Tomart Pubns.; 0-914293),* P.O. Box 2102, Dayton, OH 45429 (SAN 287-5810) Tel 513-299-3785.

Tomash Pubs, *(Tomash Pubs.; 0-938228),* P.O. Box 49613, Los Angeles, CA 90049 (SAN 239-4987).

Tombouctou, *(Tombouctou Bks.; 0-939180),* P.O. Box 265, Bolinas, CA 94924 (SAN 282-6447) Tel 415-868-2738; Dist. by: Subterranean Bk. Co., P.O. Box 10233, 1327 W. Second, Eugene, OR 97440 (SAN 200-4917) Tel 503-343-6324; Dist. by: Bookpeople, 2929 Fifth St., Berkeley, CA 94710 (SAN 168-9517); Dist. by: Inland Book Co., P.O. Box 261, 22 Hemingway Ave., East Haven, CT 06512 (SAN 200-4151) Tel 203-467-4257; Dist. by: Small Press, 1814 San Pablo Ave., Berkeley, CA 94702 (SAN 204-5826) Tel 415-549-3336.

†**Tompson Rutter Inc,** *(Tompson & Rutter, Inc.; 0-936988),* P.O. Box 297, Grantham, NH 03753 (SAN 220-1380); Dunbar Hill Rd., Grantham, NH 03753-0297 (SAN 658-196X) Tel 603-863-4392; Dist. by: Shoe String Pr., Inc., P.O. Box 4327, Hamden, CT 06514 (SAN 213-2079) Tel 203-248-6307925 Sherman Ave., Hamden, CT 06514 (SAN 699-5675); *CIP.*

Toms Guide, *(Tom's Guide; 0-938557),* Div. of Martom Investments, Inc., P.O. Box 669, Pearl River, LA 70452-0669 (SAN 661-4647); 292 Oak St., Pearl River, LA 70452 (SAN 661-4655) Tel 504-863-2570.

Tonatiuh Intl
    See Tonatiuh-Quinto Sol Intl

Tonatiuh-Quinto Sol Intl, *(Tonatiuh/Quinto Sol International, Inc.; 0-88412; 0-89229),* P.O. Box 9275, Berkeley, CA 94709 (SAN 203-3984) Tel 415-655-8036.

†**Tonnis,** *(Tonnis Productions Inc.; 0-917057),* P.O. Box 311, Harleyville, PA 19438 (SAN 655-1319) Tel 215-256-9633; *CIP.*

Tony Pr-Ent, *(Tony Press/Tony B. Enterprises),* 2168 Candelero, Santa Fe, NM 87505 (SAN 239-507X).

Too Young, *(Too Young to Retire; 0-935703),* 321 W. 78th St., New York, NY 10024 (SAN 696-1916) Tel 212-496-8151.

Toolbox, *(Toolbox, The; 0-9606548),* 8219 Old Petersburg Rd., Evansville, IN 47711 (SAN 223-0135).

Tools Bks, *(Tools & Bks., Ltd.; 0-938089),* Old Potter Hill Rd., Westerly, RI 02891 (SAN 659-7998) Tel 401-377-8270.

†**Tools for Inner,** *(Tools for Inner Growth; 0-914073),* P.O. Box 520, Chiloquin, OR 97624 (SAN 287-5829); *CIP.*

Tools Techniques, *(Tools & Techniques, Inc.; 0-939283),* 1620 W. 12th St., Austin, TX 78703-3945 (SAN 662-5134) Tel 512-482-0824.

Tooth of Time, *(Tooth of Time Bks.; 0-940510),* 634 Garcia St., Santa Fe, NM 87501 (SAN 219-8231); Dist. by: Bookpeople, 2929 Fifth St., Berkeley, CA 94710 (SAN 168-9517) (SAN 200-4151); Dist. by: Bookslinger, 213 E. Forth St., St. Paul, MN 55101 (SAN 169-4154) Tel 612-221-0429; Dist. by: S.D.P., 1784 Shattuck, Berkeley, CA 94709 (SAN 292-823X).

Toothpaste
See Coffee Hse

Top-Ecol Pr, *(Top-Ecol Press),* 3025 Highridge Rd., La Crescenta, CA 91214 (SAN 218-9976) Tel 818-248-6369.

Top Stories, *(Top Stories, Inc.; 0-917061),* 228 Seventh Ave., New York, NY 10011 (SAN 655-3419) Tel 212-989-3869.

Topaz Pr, *(Topaz Press; 0-915767),* P.O. Box 5066, Billerica, MA 01821 (SAN 294-1392) Tel 617-663-7173.

Topaz Pr LA, *(Topaz Pr.; 0-9616733),* 3855 Partridge Ln., Baton Rouge, LA 70809 (SAN 659-8900) Tel 504-924-0983.

Topeka Geneal Soc, *(Topeka Genealogical Society, The),* P.O. Box 4048, Topeka, KS 66604-0048 (SAN 218-9984) Tel 913-233-5762.

†**Topgallant,** *(Topgallant Publishing Co., Ltd.; 0-914916),* 547 Halekauwila St., Suite 101, Honolulu, HI 96813 (SAN 209-4932) Tel 808-524-0884; *CIP.*

Topix Pr, *(Topix Press; 0-911269),* 420 S. Harbor Dr.s, Venice, FL 33595 (SAN 670-7114); Dist. by: Dracula Press, 29 Washington Sq. W., New York, NY 10011 (SAN 219-4228).

Topping Inst, *(Topping International Institute; 0-935299),* 4278 King Ave., Bellingham, WA 98226 (SAN 696-1932) Tel 206-647-2703; Orders to: 4291 Rural Ave., Bellingham, WA 98226 (SAN 662-3697) Tel 206-647-2703.

Tops Learning, *(Tops Learning Systems; 0-941008),* 10970 S. Mulino Rd., Canby, OR 97013 (SAN 217-4456) Tel 503-266-8550.

Topside Pubs, *(Topside Pubs.; 0-9617157),* P.O. Box 129, Dillard, GA 30537 (SAN 663-1568); Betty's Creek Rd., Dillard, GA 30537 (SAN 663-1576) Tel 404-746-2134.

Tor Bks, *(Tor Bks.; 0-8125),* Div. of Tom Doherty Assocs., Inc., 49 W. 24th St., New York, NY 10010 (SAN 239-3956) Tel 212-741-3100; Dist. by: St. Martin's Pr., 175 Fifth Ave., New York, NY 10010 (SAN 200-2132) Tel 212-674-5151; Dist. by: Warner Pub. Services, 75 Rockefeller Plaza, 9th Flr., New York, NY 10019 (SAN 200-5522).

Torah Aura, *(Torah Aura Productions; 0-933873),* 4423 Fruitland Ave., Los Angeles, CA 90058 (SAN 692-7025) Tel 213-585-7312; Toll free: 800-238-6724.

†**Torah Res,** *(Torah Resources; 0-9603100),* 951-56th St., Brooklyn, NY 11219 (SAN 213-702X); *CIP.*

Torah Umesorah, *(Torah Umesorah Pubns.; 0-914131),* 160 Broadway, New York, NY 10003 (SAN 218-9992) Tel 212-227-1000.

Torch *Imprint of* Har-Row
Torch Lib *Imprint of* Har-Row

Torey Pr, *(Torey Press; 0-941318),* P.O. Box 2114, Glen Ellyn, IL 60137 (SAN 239-0426) Tel 312-620-5641.

Tosaw, *(Tosaw Publishing Co.; 0-9609016),* 7305 Delcielo Way, P.O. Box 939, Ceres, CA 95307 (SAN 240-9097).

Tosefos, *(Tosefos Media, Inc.; 0-936617),* 824 Eastern Pkwy., Brooklyn, NY 11213 (SAN 696-7167) Tel 718-756-1498.

Total Comm, *(Total Communications; 0-932801),* 16408 Brandsford Pt., Chesterfield, MO 63017 (SAN 688-6167) Tel 314-537-1100.

Total Comm Ministries, *(Total Commitment Ministries),* Box 242, Harrisburg, OR 97446 (SAN 689-6499).

†**Total Concepts,** *(Total Concepts; 0-915805),* P.O. Box 90607, Honolulu, HI 96835-0607 (SAN 294-1406) Tel 808-595-4410; *CIP.*

Total Environ Action
See EAF NH

Total Graphics, *(Total Graphics; 0-912860),* 1251 Rowena Ave., San Marcos, CA 92069 (SAN 207-0243) Tel 619-744-6599.

Total Pub, *(Total Publishing; 0-914997),* 657 W. Milford Ave., Unit 19, Glendale, CA 91203 (SAN 289-453X) Tel 818-244-2758.

Total Train, *(Total Training; 0-9613123),* 657 W. Milford Ave., Glendale, CA 91203 (SAN 294-6823) Tel 818-244-2758.

Total Trial, *(Total Trial System, The; 0-9605222),* P.O. Box 3663, St. Paul, MN 55165 (SAN 215-8191).

Totem Shooters
See Ascii

Touch Art Magic, *(Touchstone Art Magic, Inc.; 0-9616550),* 1106 Paradise Ln., Ashland, OR 97520 (SAN 659-543X) Tel 503-488-0001.

Touch Heart, *(Touch the Heart Press; 0-9605492),* Div. of Louis Foundation Pubs., Box 210, Eastsound, WA 98245 (SAN 216-1575) Tel 206-376-2250.

Touch Prods Inc, *(Touch Productions, Inc.; 0-9615810),* P.O. Box 505, Lincolnton, NC 28092 (SAN 696-6462) Tel 704-735-4316; Rte. 1, Box 410, Iron Station, NC 28080 (SAN 699-640X).

Touche Co, *(Touche Ross & Co.; 0-942640),* 1633 Broadway, 9th Flr., New York, NY 10019 (SAN 239-5657) Tel 212-489-1600.

Touchstone Ctr Child, *(Touchstone Ctr. for Children, Inc., The),* 141 E. 88th St., New York, NY 10028 (SAN 265-3664) Tel 212-831-7717; Dist. by: Publishing Ctr. for Cultural Resources, 625 Broadway, New York, NY 10012 (SAN 685-3692) Tel 212-260-2010.

Touchstone Ent ND
See Steppingstone Ent

Touchstone Oregon, *(Touchstone Pr.; 0-911518),* P.O. Box 81, Beaverton, OR 97075 (SAN 205-4442) Tel 503-646-8081.

Touchstone Pr OR
See Touchstone Oregon

Touchstone Prog, *(Touchstone Programs; 0-939467),* P.O. Box 3446, Granada Hills, CA 91344; 10550 Encino Ave., Granada Hills, CA 91344 Tel 213-829-2102.

Tough Dove, *(Tough Dove Bks.; 0-9615129),* P.O. Box 548, Little River, CA 95456 (SAN 694-1818).

Tourism Ctr
See Travel & Tourism

Tout De Suite, *(Tout De Suite A la Microwave, Inc.; 0-9605362),* P. O. Box 30121, 305 Wood Bluff, Lafayette, LA 70503 (SAN 238-7565) Tel 318-984-2903.

Tout Pr, *(Tout Press; 0-932412),* 420 E. College St., Kent, OH 44240 (SAN 693-7799); Dist. by: Mayapple Press, P.O. Box 3185, Kent, OH 44240 (SAN 212-1913).

Tower Ent, *(Tower Enterprises; 0-910431),* 3380 S. Fourth Ave., No. 18, Yuma, AZ 85365 (SAN 260-1478) Tel 602-726-0471.

Tower Hill Pr, *(Tower Hill Press; 0-941668),* P.O. Box 1132, 301 S. Main St., Doylestown, PA 18901 (SAN 239-3298) Tel 215-345-1856.

Tower Pr PA, *(Tower Pr.; 0-932153),* 410 Penn St., Hollidaysburg, PA 16648 (SAN 686-4333) Tel 814-946-7310.

Tower Pub Co, *(Tower Publishing Co.; 0-89442),* 34 Diamond St., P.O. Box 7220, Portland, ME 04112 (SAN 210-2811) Tel 207-774-9813.

Towers Club, *(TOWERS Club, U. S. A.; 0-930668),* P.O. Box 2038, Vancouver, WA 98668-2038 (SAN 209-6072); 9107 NW 11th St., Vancouver, WA 98665 (SAN 699-5683) Tel 206-574-3084.

Town Concord Mass, *(Town of Concord, Massachusetts; 0-9614575),* P.O. Box 535, Concord, MA 01742 (SAN 691-8352) Tel 617-371-0350; 46 Kenney St., Concord, MA 01742 (SAN 662-295X) Tel 617-369-8352.

Town Islip, *(Town of Islip; 0-9615532),* Islip Town Hall, Islip, NY 11751 (SAN 696-1967) Tel 516-224-5500.

Town of Andover MA, *(Town of Andover, MA; 0-9603160),* Town Clerk, 20 Main St., Andover, MA 01810 (SAN 211-4836) Tel 617-475-3205.

Towncourt Ent, *(Towncourt Enterprises, Inc.; 0-9608928),* P.O. Box 9151, Coral Springs, FL 33075 (SAN 281-8671).

Townhouse Pub, *(Townhouse Publishing; 0-939219),* 301 N. Harrison St., Bldg. B, Suite 115, Princeton, NJ 08540 (SAN 662-6254) Tel 609-585-5539.

Townsend Harbor, *(Townsend Harbor Pr.; 0-9613629),* P.O. Box 119, Townsend, MA 01469 (SAN 670-8676) Tel 617-597-6396.

Toy Works Pr, *(Toy Works Pr.; 0-938715),* Div. of The Toy Works, 902 Broadway, Penthouse, New York, NY 10010 (SAN 661-6216) Tel 212-982-2269.

Toys 'n Things, *(Toys 'n Things Pr.; 0-934140),* Div. of Resources for Child Caring, Inc., 906 N. Dale St., St. Paul, MN 55103 (SAN 212-8691) Tel 612-488-7284.

TP Assocs, *(TP Assocs./TP Pr.; 0-913939),* P.O. Box 3226, Newport Beach, CA 92663 (SAN 286-8962) Tel 714-963-4482; 22181 Wood Island Ln., Huntington Beach, CA 92646 (SAN 286-8970) Tel 714-963-4482.

TPA Pub, *(TPA Publishing Ltd.; 0-9609996),* 540 W. 112th St., Los Angeles, CA 90044 (SAN 263-2349).

TPP *Imprint of* Lieber-Atherton

TPR Pub Inc, *(TPR Publishing Co., Inc.; 0-918000),* 81 Montgomery St., Scarsdale, NY 10583 (SAN 210-282X) Tel 914-472-0366.

TPW Pub Co, *(TPW Publishing Co.; 0-914475),* P.O. Box 4467, Mountain View, CA 94040-0467 (SAN 289-6834) Tel 408-243-1300.

TQS Pubns
See Tonatiuh-Quinto Sol Intl

Trabuco Creek Pr, *(Trabuco Creek Pr.; 0-939107),* 109 E. Ave., San Clemente, CA 92672 (SAN 662-5967) Tel 714-498-3783.

Traces Inst, *(Traces Institute Pubns.; 0-934185),* 705 Park Ave., No. 203, Plainfield, NJ 07060 (SAN 693-3874) Tel 201-755-5070.

Trackaday, *(Trackaday; 0-9606522),* Rte. 1, Box 330, New Market, VA 22844 (SAN 201-8624).

Traction Slides, *(Traction Slides International; 0-9610414),* Div. of Graphic Concepts, 2160 Washington St., Merrick, NY 11566 (SAN 264-438X) Tel 516-221-3629.

Tracy Pub, *(Tracy Publishing; 0-933984),* 1627 Boathouse Circle, Suite No. H-228, Sarasota, FL 33581 (SAN 209-5750) Tel 813-966-3797.

Trad Acupuncture, *(Traditional Acupuncture Foundation, Inc., The; 0-912381),* American City Bldg., Suite 100, Columbia, MD 21044 (SAN 265-2366) Tel 301-997-4888.

Trad Pr, *(Traditionalist Press; 0-9610736),* P.O. Box 1611, Louisville, KY 40201 (SAN 265-4148) Tel 502-636-0959.

Trad Pub, *(Traditional Publishing; 0-915377),* 1354 Bel Nor Rd., McKinleyville, CA 95521 (SAN 291-459X) Tel 707-839-1162.

Tradd St Pr, *(Tradd Street Pr.; 0-937684),* 1042B Hwy. 17 Bypass, Mt. Pleasant, SC 29464 (SAN 205-4469) Tel 803-881-3016.

Trade House, *(Trade House Publishing Co.; 0-943600),* P.O. Box 17845, Denver, CO 80217 (SAN 240-7906) Tel 303-469-7200.

Trade Rte Antiq, *(Trade Routes Antiques),* 8462 San Fernando Way, Dallas, TX 75218 (SAN 696-7221) Tel 214-559-4440.

Trade Serv
See Trade Srv Pubns

Trade Ship Pub Co
See Tradeship Pub Co

Trade Srv Pubns, *(Trade Service Publications, Inc.; 0-915955),* Div. of Trade Service Publications, Inc., 10996 Torreyana, San Diego, CA 92121 (SAN 293-9533) Tel 619-457-5920; Toll free: 800-542-6421.

Trade Wind, *(Trade Wind Impressions; 0-9616251),* 865 Hao St., Honolulu, HI 96821 (SAN 658-7127) Tel 808-373-1141.

Trademark Reg, *(Trademark Register; 0-911522),* 300 Washington Sq., Washington, DC 20036 (SAN 205-4477); 1050 Connecticut Ave., NW, Washington, DC 20036 (SAN 658-1978) Tel 202-429-6668.

Traders Pr, *(Traders Pr, Inc.; 0-934380),* P.O. Box 10344, Greenville, SC 29603 (SAN 212-9795) Tel 803-288-3900.

Tradeship Pub Co, *(Tradeship Publishing Co.; 0-934592),* 60 State St., 34th Fl. Tower, Boston, MA 02109 (SAN 213-876X).

Tradesman Pr, *(Tradesman Publishing; 0-935831),* 5363 Estrade Dr., San Jose, CA 95118 (SAN 696-6500) Tel 408-269-1176; Orders to: Tradesman Publishing, P.O. Box 7654, San Jose, CA 95150 (SAN 662-3808).

Tradewhims, *(Tradewhims; 0-936701),* 1741 20th St., Kingsburg, CA 93631 (SAN 699-9654) Tel 209-897-3286.

Tradewinds Pub, *(Tradewinds Publishing; 0-938379),* 1441 Woodland Dr., Deerfield, IL 60015 (SAN 661-0331) Tel 312-945-4101.

Tradex Pubns, *(Tradex Pubns.; 0-931528),* P.O. Box 27561, Houston, TX 77027 (SAN 212-1743) Tel 713-961-4432.

Traditional Pr, *(Traditional Pr., Inc.; 0-933711),* 1022 51st St., Brooklyn, NY 11219 (SAN 692-4980).

Traditional Stud, *(Traditional Studies Pr.; 0-919608),* 423 E. 84th St., New York, NY 10028 (SAN 215-2592).

Traditions Pr, *(Traditions Pr.; 0-937745),* P.O. Box 1296, Lexington, SC 29073 (SAN 659-364X) Tel 803-359-0045; Rte. 6, Box 261, Shirway Rd., Lexington, SC 29072 (SAN 659-3658).

†**Trado-Medic,** *(Trado-Medic Bks.; 0-932426),* Div. of Conch Magazine, Ltd., Pubs., 102 Normal Ave., Buffalo, NY 14213 (SAN 212-5722); *CIP.*

Traffic Inst, *(Northwestern Univ. Traffic Institute; 0-912642),* 405 Church St., P.O. Box 1409, Evanston, IL 60204-1409 (SAN 202-7909) Tel 312-492-5408; Toll free: 800-323-4011.

Traffic Serv, *(Traffic Service Corp.; 0-87408),* 1325 G St., NW, Suite 900, Washington, DC 20005 (SAN 202-7917) Tel 202-626-4540.

Trafunish Pub, *(Travfunish Publishing; 0-9612022),* P.O. Box 1018, Decatur, AL 35602 (SAN 286-8865) Tel 205-355-2603.

Trailer Life
   See TL Enterprises

Trailer Vis, *(Trailer Visions; 0-914483),* 1326 Santa Anita Ave., S. El Monte, CA 91733 (SAN 289-6877) Tel 213-575-3224.

Trails End, *(Trails End Bks.; 0-9614896),* 3232 S. Clifton, Suite 134, Wichita, KS 67216 (SAN 693-2118) Tel 316-686-9311.

Train Res Corp, *(Training Resource Corporation; 0-933794),* Five S. Miller Rd., Harrisburg, PA 17109 (SAN 216-0684) Tel 717-652-6300; Toll free: 800-222-9909.

Trainex Pr, *(Trainex Pr.; 0-8463),* P.O. Box 116, Garden Grove, CA 92641 (SAN 205-4515); Toll free: 800-854-2485.

Tramway Pr, *(Tramway Pr., Inc.; 0-932497),* 3611 Newton St., Denver, CO 80211 (SAN 687-4134) Tel 303-238-5614.

Tranquil Pr, *(Tranquility Pr.; 0-9614923),* 200 Leslie Dr., Box 516, Hallandale, FL 33009 (SAN 693-465X) Tel 305-454-8082.

Trans *Imprint of* **Northwestern U Pr**

†**Trans-Anglo,** *(Trans-Anglo Bks.; 0-87046),* P.O. Box 38, Corona del Mar, CA 92625 (SAN 276-0851) Tel 714-645-7393; *CIP.*

Trans-Atl Phila, *(Trans-Atlantic Pubns., Inc.),* 311 Bainbridge St., Philadelphia, PA 19147 (SAN 694-0234) Tel 215-925-5083. Do not confuse with Transatlantic Arts, Inc., Albuquerque, NM.

Trans-Atlantic
   See Trans-Atl Phila

Trans-Cal Pub, *(Trans-Cal Publishing; 0-936567),* P.O. Box 377, North Palm Springs, CA 92258 (SAN 698-0902) Tel 619-329-2221; 70-200 Dillon Rd., Desert Hot Springs, CA 92240 (SAN 698-0910).

Trans Data Rep, *(Transnational Data Reporting Service, Inc.; 0-936107),* P.O. Box 2039, Springfield, VA 22152 (SAN 696-7701) Tel 202-488-3434.

Trans Gala Pubns, *(Trans-Galactic Pubns.; 0-9616078),* 20 Sunnyside Ave., Suite A134, Mill Valley, CA 94941 (SAN 698-0899) Tel 415-388-7554.

Trans Inter Serv, *(Translation & Interpretation Service; 0-9615505),* 355 W. Fourth St., Winona, MN 55987 (SAN 695-2089) Tel 507-452-1038.

Trans-Media Pub
   See Condyne-Oceana

Trans Syst Group, *(Transportation Systems Group; 0-9615600),* 1850 K St., NW, Suite 950, Washington, DC 20006 (SAN 696-1975) Tel 202-862-1105.

Trans Tech, *(Trans Tech Pubns.; 0-87849),* 16 Bear Skin Neck, Rockport, MA 01966 (SAN 202-7933) Tel 617-546-6426.

Trans Tech Mgmt, *(Trans Tech Management Press; 0-938398),* P.O. Box 23032, Sacramento, CA 95823 (SAN 216-0692).

†**Transaction Bks,** *(Transaction Bks.; 0-87855; 0-88738),* Rutgers Univ., New Brunswick, NJ 08903 (SAN 202-7941) Tel 201-932-2280; *CIP.*

Transaction Pubs
   See Transaction Bks

Transatl Arts, *(Transatlantic Arts, Inc.; 0-693),* P.O. Box 6086, Albuquerque, NM 87197 (SAN 202-7968) Tel 505-898-2289. Do not confuse with Trans-Atlantic Pubns., Inc., Philadelphia, PA.

Transatlantic
   See Transatl Arts

Transbooks
   See Interbk Inc

Transculture Inc, *(Transculture, Inc.; 0-935862),* Village Box 104, New York, NY 10014 (SAN 213-8050).

Transemantics, *(Transemantics, Inc.; 0-930124),* 1601 Connecticut Ave., NW, Suite 500, Washington, DC 20009 (SAN 293-4043) Tel 202-659-9640; 5151 Wisconsin Ave., NW, Washington, DC 20016 (SAN 662-1600) Tel 202-362-2505.

Transform Berkeley, *(Transformations Press; 0-930162),* 1625 Jaynes St., Berkeley, CA 94703 (SAN 210-6744) Tel 415-524-8391.

Transform Inc, *(Transformations, Inc.; 0-9604856),* 2728 N. Prospect Ave., Milwaukee, WI 53211 (SAN 215-8906) Tel 414-962-0213; Orders to: 4200 W. Good Hope Rd., Milwaukee, WI 53209 (SAN 662-085X) Tel 414-351-5770.

Transitions, *(Transitions),* P.O. Box 478, Peoria, AZ 85345 (SAN 287-282X) Tel 602-972-7504.

Translation Pr, *(Translation Pr.; 0-931556),* 2901 Heatherway, Ann Arbor, MI 48104 (SAN 211-4739).

Transmediacom, *(Transmediacom, Inc.; 0-942696),* 300 Corporate Court, P.O. Box 408, South Plainfield, NJ 07080 (SAN 239-944X) Tel 201-756-6868.

TransMedica, *(TransMedica; 0-88137),* Div. of CBS, Inc., 41 Madison Ave., New York, NY 10010 (SAN 241-466X) Tel 212-951-8900.

Transnational Pub, *(Transnational Publishing Co.; 0-935949),* P.O. Box 19908, Los Angeles, CA 90019 (SAN 696-6551) Tel 213-731-3127; 3841 W. Washington Blvd., Los Angeles, CA 90018 (SAN 696-656X).

†**Transnatl Pubs,** *(Transnational Pubs., Inc.; 0-941320),* P.O. Box 7282, Ardsley-on-Hudson, NY 10503 (SAN 226-2967) Tel 914-693-0089; 22 Myrtle Ave., Dobbs Ferry, NY 10522 (SAN 658-1986); *CIP.*

Transport Chr, *(Transport for Christ International),* 3200 Gilichrist Rd., Mogadore, OH 44260 (SAN 225-4697) Tel 216-794-0587; P.O. Box 6242, Akron, OH 44312 (SAN 658-1994).

Transport Env, *(Transport Environment, The; 0-9608112),* SR 285 Old Squaw Dr., Kitty Hawk, NC 27949 (SAN 240-1657) Tel 919-261-2267.

Transport Res Bd, *(Transportation Research Board; 0-309),* 2101 Constitution Ave., NW, Washington, DC 20418 (SAN 225-2554).

Transrep, *(Transrep/Bibliographics; 0-918370),* P.O. Box 22678, Denver, CO 80222 (SAN 209-8997).

TransWorld, *(TransWorld Productions; 0-917517),* Orders to: Box 1842, Orange, CA 92668-0842 (SAN 656-108X).

Transylvania, *(Transylvania Publications Inc.; 0-911959),* 2 Stewart Ave., Eastchester, NY 10707 (SAN 672-3985).

Trask Hse Bks, *(Trask House Books, Inc.; 0-932264),* 2754 SE 27th Ave., Portland, OR 97202 (SAN 211-9889) Tel 503-235-1898.

Traumwald Pr, *(Traumwald Press; 0-913676),* 3550 N. Lake Shore Dr., Suite 10, Chicago, IL 60657 (SAN 205-454X) Tel 312-525-5303.

Travel & Tour Res, *(Travel & Tourism Research Assn.),* P.O. Box 8066, Foothill Sta., Salt Lake City, UT 84108 (SAN 224-0254) Tel 801-581-6333.

Travel & Tourism, *(Travel & Tourism Press; 0-935638),* P.O. Box 1188, Santa Cruz, CA 95061 (SAN 213-7038) Tel 408-429-1709.

Travel Digest
   See Travel Digests

Travel Digests, *(Travel Digests; 0-912640),* Div. of Paul Richmond & Co., Pubs., 73-465 Ironwood St., Palm Desert, CA 92260 (SAN 202-7976) Tel 619-346-4792.

†**Travel Discover,** *(Travel Discoveries; 0-930570),* 10 Fenway N., Milford, CT 06460 (SAN 211-0067); *CIP.*

Travel Fit, *(Travel Fit, Inc.; 0-935753),* 225 E. 86th St., Suite 902, New York, NY 10028 (SAN 696-2017) Tel 212-369-5627.

†**Travel Guides Pub,** *(Travel Guides Publishing; 0-930103),* P.O. Box 430, Redondo Beach, CA 90277 (SAN 670-2147) Tel 213-534-1536; *CIP.*

Travel Guildes Pub
   See Travel Guides Pub

Travel Info, *(Travel Information Bureau; 0-914072),* 44 County Line Rd., Farmingdale, NY 11735 (SAN 202-7992) Tel 516-454-0880.

Travel Inter, *(Travel Interludes; 0-9609388),* P.O. Box 4276, Carmel, CA 93921 (SAN 260-2725) Tel 408-624-0928.

†**Travel Keys,** *(Travel Keys; 0-931367),* P.O. Box 160691, Sacramento, CA 95816 (SAN 682-2452) Tel 916-452-5200; *CIP.*

Travel Photo, *(Travel Photography Pubns.; 0-9616197),* P.O. Box 1251, Los Altos, CA 94023-1251 (SAN 699-8305) Tel 415-969-4375.

Travel Pr, *(Travel Pr; 0-930328),* Affil. of MacMillan Publishing Co., P.O. Box 70 16 E. Third Ave., Suite 1A, San Mateo, CA 94401 (SAN 210-6760) Tel 415-342-9117; Dist. by: Charles Scribner's & Sons, Front & Brown Sts., Riverside, NJ 08075 (SAN 201-002X); Dist. by: MacMillan Publishing Company, Incorporated, 866 Third Ave., New YorK, NY 10022 (SAN 202-5574) Tel 212-702-2000.

Travel Right, *(Traveling Right; 0-936109),* P.O. Box 805, New York, NY 10002 (SAN 696-768X) Tel 212-228-2517.

Travel Text, *(Travel Text Assocs.; 0-917063),* 12605 E. State Fair, Detroit, MI 48205 (SAN 297-1704) Tel 313-527-6971.

Travel World, *(Travel World Pubns.; 0-89416),* Box 2818, Dublin, CA 94568 (SAN 210-5462) Tel 415-829-2728.

Travelers Pr, *(Traveler's Pr.; 0-9617158),* Drawer L, Red Lodge, MT 59068 (SAN 663-3633); Lazy S L Estates, Red Lodge, MT 59068 (SAN 663-3641) Tel 406-446-3026.

Travellers Bed, *(Travellers' Bed & Breakfast; 0-9613481),* P.O. Box 492, Mercer Island, WA 98040 (SAN 657-3851) Tel 206-232-2345.

Travis, *(Travis Piano Service; 0-9600394),* P.O. Box 5359-0359, 8012 Carroll Ave., Takoma Park, MD 20912 (SAN 205-4558) Tel 301-439-4111.

Travis Pub Co, *(Travis Publishing Co.; 0-917065),* Orders to: 19528 Ventura Blvd., Suite 336, Tarzana, CA 91356 (SAN 685-3951) Tel 818-995-3329.

Treacle
   See McPherson & Co

Treadle Pr, *(Treadle Pr.; 0-935143),* Div. of Binding & Printing Co., Box D, Sheperdstown, WV 25443 (SAN 695-2070) Tel 304-876-2557.

Treas Chest Ent, *(Treasure Chest Enterprises, Inc.; 0-939161),* 1710 Carrie Hills Ln., La Habra Heights, CA 90631 (SAN 662-9385) Tel 213-694-4486; Dist. by: Santillana, 942 Gerhart, Los Angeles, CA 90022 (SAN 200-7606).

Treasure Chest, *(Treasure Chest Pubns.; 0-918080),* 1850 W. Grant Rd., Suite 101, Tucson, AZ 85745 (SAN 209-3243) Tel 602-623-9558; Toll free: 800-223-5369 EXT 239; Orders to: P.O. Box 5250, Tucson, AZ 85703 (SAN 209-3251).

Treasure Guide
   See Treasure Guide Pub

Treasure Guide Pub, *(Treasure Guide Publishing Co.),* P.O. Box 368, Mesilla Park, NM 88047 (SAN 209-1747).

Treasure Hunt Pubns, *(Treasure Hunt Pubns.; 0-937111),* P.O. Box 1710, Temple City, CA 91780 (SAN 658-4446) Tel 818-285-5905; 5816 N. Rowland Ave., Temple City, CA 91780 (SAN 658-4454).

Treasure Publications, *(Treasure Pubns.; 0-912119),* P.O. Box 3300, Roanoke, VA 24015-1300 (SAN 264-8016) Tel 703-774-5144.

Treasured Co, *(Treasured Receipts Co.; 0-918489),* P.O. Box 381097, Germantown, TN 38183-1097 (SAN 657-7288) Tel 901-362-8900.

Tree Bks, *(Tree Bks.),* Box 9005, Berkeley, CA 94709 (SAN 203-6576).

Tree Comm, *(Tree Communications, Inc.; 0-934504),* 250 Fifth Ave., New York, NY 10001 (SAN 282-714X) Tel 212-213-9670; Toll free: 800-242-7737.

Tree House, *(Tree Hse. Enterprises; 0-935571),* 34316 Thornbrook Dr., Farmington Hills, MI 48018 (SAN 696-2025) Tel 313-474-8467; Orders to: 9739 Calgary Dr., Stanwood, MI 49346 (SAN 699-6272) Tel 313-474-8467. Do not confuse with Tree House Pr., of Shelter Island, NY & Treehouse Pr., of Chagrin Falls, OH.

Tree Hse Pr, *(Tree Hse. Pr.; 0-9615628),* P.O. Box 1032, Shelter Island Heights, NY 11965 (SAN 696-2041) Tel 516-749-2394. Do not confuse with Tree House Enterprises of Farmington Hills, MI & Treehouse Pr., of Chagrin Falls, OH.

Tree Life Pubns, *(Tree of Life Pubns.; 0-930852),* P.O. Box 5688, Santa Monica, CA 90405 (SAN 222-5395) Tel 213-393-0350; Toll free: 800-628-2828, ext. 628.

Tree of Life, *(Tree of Life Publishing Co.; 0-9615679),* P.O. Box 1851, Eagle River, WI 54521 (SAN 696-2068); 3975 Columbus Rd., Eagle River, WI 54521 (SAN 699-6280) Tel 715-479-6030.

Tree Roots
See Treeroots

Treehouse Pr, *(Treehouse Pr.; 0-9614789),* 369 N. Main St., Chagrin Falls, OH 44022 (SAN 692-9850) Tel 216-247-8554. Do not confuse with Tree House Pr., of Shelter Island, NY & Tree House Enterprises of Farmington, MI.

Treeroots, *(Treeroots Pr.; 0-9604450),* P.O. Box 2302, Los Angeles, CA 90078 (SAN 215-1170); Dist. by: Bookpeople, 2929 Fifth St., Berkeley, CA 94710 (SAN 168-9517) Tel 415-549-3030.

Trees Co Pr, *(Trees Co. Pr.; 0-937401),* 49 Van Buren Way, San Francisco, CA 94131 (SAN 659-0659) Tel 415-334-8352.

Trejos Lit Agy, *(Trejos Literary Agency; 0-939551),* 18235 Avalon Blvd., Carson, CA 90746 (SAN 663-3471) Tel 213-538-2945.

Trek-CIR, *(TREK-CIR Pubns.; 0-932464),* Box 898, Valley Forge, PA 19481 (SAN 212-2383) Tel 215-337-3110.

Tremaine Graph & Pub, *(Tremaine Graphic & Publishing; 0-939860),* 2727 Front St., Klamath Falls, OR 97601 (SAN 216-9398) Tel 503-884-4193.

Tremar Prod, *(Tremar Productions; 0-9616587),* 2306 Seminary Rd., Silver Spring, MD 20910 (SAN 659-8005) Tel 301-588-3107.

Tremont Pr, *(Tremont Pr., The; 0-943954),* P.O. Box 2307, Silver Spring, MD 20902 (SAN 241-1601) Tel 301-649-6666.

Trempealeau, *(Trempealeau Press; 0-912540),* 800 Hillcrest Dr., Santa Fe, NM 87501 (SAN 211-9897) Tel 505-983-1947.

Tremper, *(Tremper, W.J.; 0-9604166),* 340 Fairmount Ave., Jersey City, NJ 07306 (SAN 214-4794).

Trend House
See Florida Trend

Trends & Custom, *(Trends & Customs, Inc.; 0-910879),* P.O. Box 170008, Overland Plaza, Arlington, TX 76017 (SAN 262-0987); Dist. by: Publishers Marketing Group, 1104 Summit Ave., Plainview, TX 75074 (SAN 262-0995) Tel 214-423-0312.

Trends & Events, *(Trends & Events, Inc.; 0-942698),* P.O. Box 158, Fayette, IA 52142 (SAN 240-2882) Tel 319-425-4411.

Trends Pub, *(Trends Publishing Co.; 0-9602426),* 31731 Northwestern Hwy., Suite 258, Farmington Hills, MI 48018 (SAN 206-2445) Tel 313-851-7726.

Trenna Prods, *(Trenna Productions; 0-918519),* Div. of One to Grow On!, P.O. Box 2484, Malibu, CA 90265 (SAN 657-730X) Tel 213-457-2583.

Tres Amigos Pubns, *(Tres Amigos Pubns.; 0-930277),* 26325 Carmelo, Carmel, CA 93923 (SAN 670-8668) Tel 408-625-1579.

Trestleetree Pubns, *(Trestleetree Pubns.; 0-939109),* P.O. Box 295, Albany, NY 12201 (SAN 662-5940); 445 Broadway, Albany, NY 12201 (SAN 662-5959) Tel 518-456-7028.

Trevor Hill Pr, *(Trevor Hill Pr.; 0-9616695),* P.O. Box 1851, Davis, CA 95616 (SAN 659-8498); 2163 Bella Casa, Davis, CA 95616 (SAN 659-8501) Tel 916-752-1272.

Trg Abuse Prevention, *(Training in Abuse Prevention Project; 0-9616782),* P.O. Box 5340, Charleston, WV 25361-0340 (SAN 661-0552); 1614 Washington St., E., Charleston, WV 25361-0340 (SAN 661-0560) Tel 304-340-3695.

Tri-Color Pr, *(Tri-Color Pr; 0-9614604),* P.O. Box 36851, Los Angeles, CA 90036-0851 (SAN 691-8387) Tel 805-393-5902.

Tri-County, *(Tri-County Special Services; 0-943390),* P.O. Box 145, St. Anthony, ID 83445 (SAN 241-5887) Tel 208-624-3146.

Tri-District
See Tri-County

Tri-Med, *(Tri-Med Press),* 65 Christopher St., Montclair, NJ 07042 (SAN 216-0706) Tel 201-746-9132.

Tri-Oak, *(Tri-Oak Education; 0-9609732),* 24663 Dry Canyon Colocrk, Calabasas, CA 91302 (SAN 262-1002).

Tri State Prom, *(Tri State Promotions; 0-9607868),* P.O. Box 30926, Amarillo, TX 79120 (SAN 239-5665) Tel 806-372-6614.

Tri-State Rail, *(Tri-State Railway Historical Society Inc.; 0-9607444),* P.O. Box 2243, Clifton, NJ 07015-2243 (SAN 239-3301) Tel 201-488-5429.

Triad III Pub, *(Triad III Publishing Co.; 0-938891),* P.O. Box 535, Desert Hot Springs, CA 92240 (SAN 662-6580).

†**Triad Pr TX,** *(Triad Press),* P.O. Box 42006-K, Houston, TX 77242 (SAN 214-2023) Tel 713-789-0424; *CIP.*

Triad Pub, *(Triad Publishing Co., The; 0-936703),* 128 Brookmoor Rd., West Hartford, CT 06107 (SAN 699-9794) Tel 203-521-3390.

†**Triad Pub FL,** *(Triad Publishing Co., Inc.; 0-9600472; 0-937404),* Subs. of Triad Communications, Inc., 1110 NW Eighth Ave., Gainesville, FL 32601 (SAN 205-4574) Tel 904-373-5800; Toll free: 800-874-7777 (SAN 658-201X); Orders to: P.O. Box 13096, Gainesville, FL 32604 (SAN 662-1619); *CIP.*

Triad Pubs, *(Triad Pubs., Ltd.; 0-935673),* 1 S. Pinckeny St., Suite 313, Madison, WI 53703 (SAN 696-2114) Tel 608-255-0659.

Triad Sci Pubs
See Triad Pub FL

Triadoption Lib, *(Triadoption Library, Inc.; 0-941770),* P.O. Box 638, Westminster, CA 92684 (SAN 239-331X) Tel 714-892-4098.

Triadvocates Assoc, *(Triadvocates Associated; 0-9616806),* P.O. Box 336, Springfield, PA 19064 (SAN 661-4639) Tel 215-544-6927.

TriAm Pr, *(TriAm Press, Inc.; 0-914075),* 5015 McKean Ave., Philadelphia, PA 19144 (SAN 287-5853) Tel 215-849-2286.

Triang Pr, *(Triang Pr., The; 0-931513),* 5850 Hubbard Dr., Rockville, MD 20852 (SAN 682-3149) Tel 301-984-5730; Dist. by: W. W. Norton Co., Inc., 500 Fifth Ave,, New York, NY 10110 (SAN 202-5795) Tel 212-354-5500.

Triangle Pr, *(Triangle Pr.; 0-937144),* 211 North La Salle St., Suite 2026, Chicago, IL 60601 (SAN 216-2016) Tel 312-346-3265.

Triangle Pubns.
See TV Guide

Tribal Pr, *(Tribal Pr.; 0-9607044),* c/o Lowell Jensen, Rte. 2 Box 599, Cable, WI 54821 (SAN 239-0442) Tel 715-794-2247.

†**Tribeca Comm,** *(Tribeca Communications, Inc.; 0-943392),* 401 Broadway, Suite 1907, New York, NY 10013 (SAN 240-7922) Tel 212-226-6047; 44 W 74th St., New York, NY 10023 (SAN 658-2028) Tel 212-496-1923; *CIP. Imprints:* Tripro Bks (Tripro Books).

Tribune Pub, *(Tribune Publishing Co., Inc.; 0-940654),* 18 Okner Pkwy., Livingston, NJ 07039 (SAN 219-8258) Tel 201-992-1060.

Trico Pr, *(Trico Pr.; 0-916751),* 97 Franklin St., Stamford, CT 06902 (SAN 654-4002) Tel 203-324-5441.

Tricore Assoc, *(Tricore Associates, Inc.; 0-9607132),* 170 Kinnelon Rd., Suite 5, Kinnelon, NJ 07405 (SAN 239-0469) Tel 201-492-2798.

Trifecta Charley, *(Trifecta Charley, Ltd.),* P.O. Box 0215, Roseville, MI 48066 (SAN 659-2120).

Trike, *(Trike Pub.; 0-917588),* 201 Martin, Novato, CA 94947 (SAN 210-3273) Tel 415-382-1591; Dist. by: Small Press Distribution, Incorporated, 1814 San Pablo Ave., Berkeley, CA 94702 (SAN 204-5826) Tel 415-549-3336.

†**Trilateral Comm,** *(Trilateral Commission; 0-930503),* 345 E. 46th St., New York, NY 10017 (SAN 225-6703); *CIP.*

Trill Pr, *(Trill Press; 0-914485),* 2523 V St., Sacramento, CA 95818 (SAN 240-1673) Tel 916-736-2339.

Trillium Pr, *(Trillium Pr.; 0-89824),* P.O. Box 921, New York, NY 10159 (SAN 212-4637) Tel 212-684-7399; Orders to: P.O. Box 209, Monroe, NY 10950 (SAN 662-1627) Tel 914-783-2999.

Trilogy Pubs, *(Trilogy Pubs.; 0-931558),* 2901 Heatherway, Ann Arbor, MI 48104 (SAN 211-4747).

Trimark Pub Co, *(Trimark Publishing Co., Inc; 0-914663),* 184 Quigley Blvd., New Castle, DE 19720 (SAN 287-7686) Tel 302-322-2143; Toll free: 800-TRIMARK.

Trinas Pr, *(Dr. Trina's Pr.; 0-9615840),* P.O. Box 4777, Laguna Beach, CA 92651 (SAN 697-0109) Tel 714-497-5071.

†**Trine Bks,** *(Trine Books; 0-912361),* P.O. Box 446, Wallingford, CT 06492 (SAN 265-1459) Tel 203-269-6262; *CIP.*

Trinet, *(Trinet, Inc.; 0-86692),* Subs. of Control Data Corporation, Nine Campus Dr., Parsippany, NJ 07054 (SAN 216-3721) Tel 201-267-3600; Toll free: 800-Trinet-1.

Tringa Pr, *(Tringa Pr.; 0-9615255),* 217 N. Ashley St., Ann Arbor, MI 48104 (SAN 694-4027) Tel 313-665-6792.

Trinity Comns, *(Trinity Communications; 0-937495),* P.O. Box 3610, Manassas, VA 22110 (SAN 659-0675) Tel 703-369-2429; 9380 C1 Forestwood Ln., Manassas, VA 22110 (SAN 659-0683).

Trinity County, *(Trinity County of Office of Education; 0-9613243),* P.O. Box AH-201, Memorial Dr., Weaverville, CA 96093 (SAN 295-4478) Tel 916-623-2861.

Trinity Ent, *(Trinity Enterprises; 0-9617233),* 7590 Stanwick Ct., Dublin, OH 43017 (SAN 663-5806) Tel 614-766-4887.

Trinity House, *(Trinity House, Inc.; 0-913309),* P.O. Box 104, Crestwood, KY 40014 (SAN 283-3182) Tel 502-241-1492.

Trinity Luth Pr, *(Trinity Lutheran Pr.; 0-9616252),* P.O. Box Z, Brewster, MA 02631 (SAN 658-4489) Tel 617-896-3396.

Trinity Pub Hse, *(Trinity Publishing House, Inc.; 0-933656),* 107 Lafayette, Winona, MN 55987 (SAN 215-1189).

Trinity Pubns, *(Trinity Pubns.; 0-9610132),* P.O. Box 15608, Cincinnati, OH 45215 (SAN 226-8051) Tel 513-821-9770.

Trinity Trail Pubns, *(Trinity Trail Pubns.; 0-934409),* P.O. Box 267, Delores, CO 81323 (SAN 693-8299) Tel 303-882-4979.

†**Trinity U Pr,** *(Trinity Univ. Pr.; 0-911536; 0-939980),* 715 Stadium Dr., San Antonio, TX 78284 (SAN 205-4590) Tel 512-736-7619; *CIP.*

Triple B, *(Triple B Sales),* 44 Butternut Dr., Pittsford, NY 14534 (SAN 210-3788) Tel 716-381-7767.

Triple Play Pubns, *(Triple Play Pubns.; 0-934289),* 177-F Riverside Dr., Newport Beach, CA 92663 (SAN 693-2894) Tel 714-548-2045.

Triple Pr, *(Triple Press; 0-941264),* 33 N. Main St., Medford, NJ 08055 (SAN 239-3964).

Triple Pub, *(Triple S Publishing Co.; 0-9615539),* 426 Felix Ln., West St. Paul, MN 55118 (SAN 696-2122) Tel 612-457-9321.

Triple Seven, *(Triple Seven International; 0-9614870),* R2, Box 221, Gaston, IN 47342 (SAN 693-2134) Tel 317-358-3713.

Triplett Ents, *(Triplett Enterprises, Ltd.),* Munday-Brohard Rd., Macfarlan, WV 26148 (SAN 207-2947) Tel 304-477-3246.

Trippensee Pub, *(Trippensee Corp.; 0-943956),* 301 Cass St., Saginaw, MI 48602 (SAN 206-2518) Tel 517-799-8102.

Trippon Fash, *(Trippon Fashion Center; 0-935245),* 5656 Carlton Way, Hollywood, CA 90028 (SAN 696-2149) Tel 213-463-3471.

Tripro Bks *Imprint of Tribeca Comm*

TriQuarterly, *(TriQuarterly Books; 0-916384),* Northwestern Univ., 1735 Benson Ave., Evanston, IL 60201 (SAN 208-8959) Tel 312-492-3490.

Triton Bks, *(Triton Books; 0-943958),* P.O. Box 27934, Los Angeles, CA 90027 (SAN 241-161X) Tel 213-247-4177.

Triton Coll, *(Triton College Press, English Dept.; 0-931672),* 2000 Fifth Ave., River Grove, IL 60171 (SAN 211-2779).

Tritone Music, *(Tritone Music; 0-9603470),* 155 Montclair Ave., Montclair, NJ 07042 (SAN 213-6023) Tel 201-746-7946.

Triumph Pr, *(Triumph Pr., Inc.; 0-931515),* 1062 Edison NW, Grand Rapids, MI 49504 (SAN 682-3157) Tel 616-453-6891.

Triumph Pub, *(Triumph Publishing Co.; 0-917182),* P.O. Box 292, Altadena, CA 91001 (SAN 207-3927).

Triune Bks, *(Triune Bks.; 0-9613602),* 8 Ullman Terrace, Monsey, NY 10952 (SAN 669-7100) Tel 914-352-6950.

Trogon Pubns, *(Trogon Pubns.; 0-9600578),* 1210 Loucks Ave., Scottdale, PA 15683 (SAN 205-4604) Tel 412-887-9436.

Trojan Bks, *(Trojan Books; 0-9610986),* 1330 Cleveland Ave., Wyomissing, PA 19610 (SAN 265-3176) Tel 215-372-4692.

Trojan Pr, *(Trojan Press, Inc.; 0-913914),* 310 E. 18th St., North Kansas City, MO 64116 (SAN 202-8069) Tel 816-421-3858.

†Troll Assocs, *(Troll Assocs.; 0-89375; 0-8167),* Subs. of Educational Reading Services, 320 State Hwy. 17, Mahwah, NJ 07430 (SAN 169-4758) Tel 201-529-4000; Toll free: 800-526-5289; *CIP.*

Trolley Talk, *(Trolley Talk; 0-914196),* 59 Euclid Ave., Cincinnati, OH 45215 (SAN 205-4612).

Trollpost, *(Trollpost Greetings),* 2285 Norwegian Dr. No. 57, Clearwarter, FL 33575 (SAN 262-1010).

Troost Pr
See Troostwyk Pr

Troostwyk Pr, *(Troostwyk Pr.; 0-914487),* Box 22292, Denton, TX 76204 (SAN 289-5757).

Trophy *Imprint of HarpJ*

Tropic Isle Pub, *(Tropic Isle Pubs., Inc.; 0-937379),* P.O. Box 343, Rumson, NJ 07760 (SAN 659-0713); 130 Maple Ave., Suite 3H, Red Bank, NJ 07701 (SAN 659-0721) Tel 201-842-6004; Orders to: P.O. Box 610935, North Miami, FL 33261-0935 (SAN 662-4219) Tel 305-893-4277.

Trotevale, *(Trotevale, Inc.; 0-915333),* P.O. Box 58, Lander, WY 82520 (SAN 294-2895) Tel 307-332-6532.

†Troubador Pr, *(Troubador Pr.; 0-912300; 0-89844),* 410 N. La Cienega Blvd., Los Angeles, CA 90048 (SAN 285-0931) Tel 415-397-3716; One Sutter St., San Francisco, CA 94104 (SAN 658-2044); Dist. by: Price/Stern/Sloan Pubs., 410 N. La Cienega Blvd., Los Angeles, CA 90048 (SAN 202-0246) Tel 213-657-6100; *CIP.*

Trout Creek, *(Trout Creek Pr.; 0-9616155),* 5976 Billings Rd., Parkdale, OR 97041 (SAN 294-9881) Tel 503-352-6494.

Trout Gulch Pr, *(Trout Gulch Pr.; 0-9614605),* P.O. Box 20904, Castro Valley, CA 94546 (SAN 691-8379) Tel 415-581-0789.

†Troy State Univ, *(Troy State University Press; 0-916624),* Wallace Hall, Troy, AL 36082 (SAN 208-8967) Tel 205-566-3000; *CIP.*

Tru-Faith, *(Tru-Faith Publishing Co.; 0-937498),* P.O. Box 2283, Gainesville, GA 30503 (SAN 216-3101).

Truck Pr, *(Truck Press; 0-916562),* P.O. Box 2204, Short Beach, CT 06405 (SAN 208-3531) Tel 203-467-4257; Orders to: Inland Book Co., 22 Hemingway Ave., E. Haven, CT 06512 (SAN 204-1871).

Truck Trailer Mfrs, *(Truck Trailer Manufacturers Assn.),* 1020 Princess St., Alexandria, VA 22314 (SAN 224-8867).

Trudco Pub, *(Trudco Publishing; 0-937571),* 12155B Nottingham Ln., St. Louis, MO 63044 (SAN 659-0756) Tel 314-291-4402.

True Ent, *(True Enterprises; 0-9613360),* 9324 McFall Dr., El Paso, TX 79925 (SAN 656-1519) Tel 915-591-8385.

True Grid, *(True Grid Editions; 0-9610880),* 2600 S. 16th St., No. 729, Arlington, VA 22204 (SAN 265-2870) Tel 703-979-2432.

True Heitz, *(True Heitz-Thelma Yes Press),* 1400 McAndrew Rd., Ojai, CA 93023 (SAN 262-1029).

True Life Found, *(True Life Foundation, The; 0-912753),* 14510 Cordary Ave., Hawthorne, CA 90250 (SAN 283-3557) Tel 213-676-7567.

True Vine Pubns, *(True Vine Pubns.; 0-939269),* 140 S. Volusia Ave., Arcadia, FL 33821 (SAN 662-5258) Tel 813-993-0630.

†Truedog, *(Trudog Pr.; 0-937212),* 216 W. Academy St., Loanoke, AR 72086 (SAN 215-3475); *CIP.*

Trust Hidden Villa, *(Trust for Hidden Villa, The),* 26870 Moody Rd., Los Altos, CA 94022 (SAN 661-4566).

Truth CA, *(Truth Publishers, Inc. (Orange, CA; 0-913621),* 146 S. Trevor Ave., Anaheim, CA 92806 (SAN 285-3841) Tel 714-632-9554; Dist. by: Living Books, 12155 Magnolia Ave., Bldg. 11-B, Riverside, CA 92503 (SAN 669-330X) Tel 714-354-7330.

Truth Cons Pub, *(Truth or Consequences Publishing Co.; 0-937409),* P.O. Box 1643, Truth or Consequences, NM 87901 (SAN 659-0772) Tel 505-523-8856; 501 Main St., Truth or Consequences, NM 87901 (SAN 659-0780).

Truth Consciousness, *(Truth Consciousness; 0-933572),* Gold Hill, Salina Star Rte., Boulder, CO 80302 (SAN 212-7083) Tel 303-447-1637.

Truth in Money, *(Truth in Money, Inc.; 0-9606938),* P.O. Box 30, Chagrin Falls, OH 44022 (SAN 219-8266) Tel 216-247-8772.

Truth Missions, *(Truth Missions; 0-910607),* P.O. Box 3849, Manhattan Beach, CA 90266 (SAN 264-1909) Tel 213-546-3689.

Truth Pub MN, *(Truth Publishing Inc.),* 3802 W. Malapi Dr., Phoenix, AZ 85021 (SAN 214-1558) Tel 602-938-9019.

Truth Seeker, *(Truth Seeker Company Inc.; 0-939040),* P.O. Box 2832, San Diego, CA 92112 (SAN 226-3645) Tel 619-574-7600.

TSink Pub, *(TSink Publishing; 0-9613949),* P.O. Box 2402, Norcross, GA 30091 (SAN 686-2705).

TSM Books, *(TSM Bks., Inc.; 0-941316),* 555 Broad Hollow Rd., Suite 271, Melville, NY 11747 (SAN 239-040X) Tel 516-420-0961.

TSM Prods
See TSM Books

TSR Inc, *(TSR, Inc.; 0-935696; 0-88038),* Box 756, Lake Geneva, WI 53147 (SAN 222-0091) Tel 414-248-3625; Toll free: 800-372-4667; Dist. by: Random Hse., Inc., 400 Hahn Rd., Westminster, MD 21157 (SAN 202-5515).

TSS Inc
See Official Shit Co

TSU Pr
See Troy State Univ

TTR Pub, *(TTR Publishing; 0-938771),* 513 W. Florence, Tucson, AZ 85705 (SAN 661-7891) Tel 602-622-5718.

Tube Toys, *(Tube Toys; 0-9616305),* 929 Moana Dr., San Diego, CA 92106 (SAN 658-5183) Tel 619-223-4182; P.O. Box 60451, San Diego, CA 92106 (SAN 658-5191).

Tubular Exch, *(Tubular Exchange Manufacturers Assn.; 0-9609214),* 25 N. Broadway, Tarrytown, NY 10591 (SAN 224-8042) Tel 914-332-0040.

Tucker Pubns, *(Tucker Pubns.),* 409 Hill St., Fayetteville, TN 37334 (SAN 213-6031).

Tucson Mus Art, *(Tucson Museum of Art; 0-911611),* 140 N. Main, Tucson, AZ 85705 (SAN 280-798X) Tel 602-624-2333.

Tudor Pubs, *(Tudor Pubs., Inc.; 0-936389),* P.O. Box 3443, Greensboro, NC 27402 (SAN 697-3035); 3712 Old Battleground Rd., Greensboro, NC 27408 (SAN 697-3043) Tel 919-282-5907.

Tuffy Bks, *(Tuffy Bks., Inc.; 0-89828),* 84 Calvert St., P.O. Box 838, Harrison, NY 10528 (SAN 213-3903) Tel 914-835-5603.

Tulane Romance Lang, *(Tulane Studies in Romance Languages & Literature; 0-912788),* Newcomb Coll., Tulane Univ., New Orleans, LA 70118 (SAN 206-1333) Tel 504-865-5115.

Tulane SE Arch, *(Tulane Univ. Library/Southeastern Architectural Archive),* 7001 Freret St., New Orleans, LA 70118 (SAN 697-2446).

Tulane Stud Pol, *(Tulane University, Tulane Studies in Political Science; 0-930598),* Tulane Univ., College of Arts & Sciences, Dept. of Political Science, New Orleans, LA 70118 (SAN 276-1246) Tel 504-865-6191.

Tulane U Conf Hispanic Lit, *(Tulane University, Louisiana Conference on Hispanic Languages & Literatures; 0-9607798),* 300C Newcomb Hall Tulane Univ., New Orleans, LA 70118 (SAN 226-2118) Tel 504-865-5524.

Tulane U Ctr Busn
See Tulane Univ

Tulane U Ctr Lat, *(Center for Latin American Studies & Howard-Tilton Memorial Library; 0-9603212),* Tulane Univ., New Orleans, LA 70118 (SAN 287-7732).

Tulane Univ, *(Tulane Univ.; 0-87409),* Dist. by: Tulane University, Howard-Tilton Memorial Library, Special Collections Division, New Orleans, LA 70118 (SAN 207-5458).

Tulip Pr, *(Tulip Press; 0-941800),* P.O. Box J, Truckee, CA 95734 (SAN 239-3328) Tel 916-587-2995.

Tulip Pr IL
See Tulip Pr MN

Tulip Pr MN, *(Tulip Press; 0-9608766),* 1018 Chester Park Dr., Duluth, MN 55812 (SAN 241-0826) Tel 312-864-6747.

Tullis Prods, *(Tullis Productions),* 4310 Normal Ave., Hollywood, CA 90029 (SAN 209-195X); Orders to: P.O. Box 54119, Los Angeles, CA 90054 (SAN 209-1968).

†Tullous, *(Tullos Books; 0-916913),* P.O. Box 6322, Macon, GA 31208 (SAN 656-0369) Tel 912-742-0833; *CIP.*

Tumble Prods, *(Tumbleweed Productions, Inc.; 0-9611004),* 101 E. Park Blvd., Plano, TX 75074 (SAN 282-8979) Tel 214-881-1505.

Tumbleweed Pr, *(Tumbleweed Pr.; 0-938091),* 11503 Carrollwood Dr., Tampa, FL 33618 (SAN 659-705X) Tel 813-932-8487.

Tumbleweed Pub Co, *(Tumbleweed Publishing Co.; 0-9612160),* 3112 Van Ave., Eugene, OR 97401 (SAN 289-5102) Tel 503-345-7770.

Tundra Bks, *(Tundra Bks. of Northern New York; 0-912766; 0-88776),* Affil. of Tundra Books (Canada), P.O. Box 1030, Plattsburgh, NY 12901 (SAN 202-8085); Dist. by: Univ. of Toronto Pr., 33 E. Tupper St., Buffalo, NY 14203 (SAN 200-4224) Tel 716-852-0342.

Tundra Pubns, *(Tundra Pubns.; 0-9606768),* Moraine Rte., Estes Park, CO 80517 (SAN 219-6492) Tel 303-586-5794.

Tungs Gourmet Delight
See P Tungs Intl G

Tungs Pub, *(Tung's Publishing Co.; 0-9616253),* Affil. of Asia Food Co., 5224-28 York Rd., Baltimore, MD 21212 (SAN 658-7119) Tel 301-823-3738.

Tunick Inc, *(Tunick, David, Inc.; 0-9605298),* 12 E. 81st St., New York, NY 10028 (SAN 216-311X).

Tunnel Pr, *(Tunnel Press, Incorporated; 0-916597),* 2888 Bluff St. Suite 184, Boulder, CO 80302 (SAN 296-6786) Tel 213-874-3816.

Tunstede, *(Tunstede; 0-9616526),* 212 Vaughn's Gap Rd., Nashville, TN 37205 (SAN 292-3416) Tel 615-352-0971.

TUNU *Imprint of Unipub*

Tuppence, *(Tuppence, Inc.; 0-939662),* 2701 S. 35th, Lincoln, NE 68506 (SAN 220-1607) Tel 402-488-3655.

†Turbo Intl Pubn, *(Turbomachinery International Publications; 0-937506),* Div. of Business Journals, Inc., P.O. Box 5550, Norwalk, CT 06856 (SAN 205-3055) Tel 203-853-6015; *CIP.*

Turbomachinery, *(Turbomachinery Maintenance Institute, Inc.; 0-9615256),* P.O. Box 5550, Norwalk, CT 06850 (SAN 695-1619) Tel 203-853-6015.

Tureen R M, *(Tureen, Richard M., Publishing Co.; 0-9613113),* 8566 NW 19th Dr., Coral Springs, FL 33065 (SAN 294-1074) Tel 305-753-9733.

Turkey Hill Pr, *(Turkey Hill Press; 0-9608050),* 3 Turkey Hill Ln., Westport, CT 06880 (SAN 240-4966); Dist. by: Inland Book Co., P.O. Box 261, 22 Hemingway Ave., East Haven, CT 06512 (SAN 200-4151) Tel 203-467-4257.

Turkey Pr.; *(Turkey Pr.; 0-918824),* 6746 Sueno Rd., Isla Vista, CA 93117 (SAN 210-5195) Tel 805-685-3603.

Turn of Cent, *(Turn of the Century Editions; 0-940326),* 250 W. Broadway, New York, NY 10013 (SAN 220-3529) Tel 212-925-6587.

Turn the Page, *(Turn the Page Pr.; 0-931540; 0-931793),* 203 Baldwin Ave., Roseville, CA 95678 (SAN 281-3629) Tel 916-444-7933.

Turnaround Pr, *(Turnaround Pr.; 0-936203),* 384 Everett Ave., Palo Alto, CA 94301 (SAN 696-8554) Tel 415-325-9348.

Turnbull & Co, *(Turnbull & Company; 0-914999),* 19 Mt. Auburn St., Cambridge, MA 02138 (SAN 289-4602) Tel 617-864-1110.

Turnbull & Willoughby, *(Turnbull & Willoughby Pubs., Inc.; 0-943084),* 1151 W. Webster, Chicago, IL 60614 (SAN 240-4311) Tel 312-348-3181; Orders to: Contemporary Bk., Inc., 180 N. Michigan Ave., Chicago, IL 60601 (SAN 669-2478) Tel 312-782-9181.

Turner Assocs
See Turner Pub KY

Turner Pub KY, *(Turner Publishing Co.; 0-938021),* 555 Jefferson, Suite 201, Paducah, KY 42001 (SAN 659-803X) Tel 502-443-0121.

Turner Pub NY, *(Turner Publishing; 0-9615464),* 124 Highview Ave., Eastchester, NY 10709 (SAN 695-7277) Tel 914-337-9387; P.O. Box 261, Eastchester, NY 10709 (SAN 696-513X).

Turning Pubns, *(Turning Point Pubns.; 0-934947),* 1122 M St., Eureka, CA 95501 (SAN 694-4272) Tel 707-445-2290.

Turning Wheel Pr, *(Turning Wheel Pr.; 0-9602590),* 4 Washington Sq. Village 17-0, New York, NY 10012 (SAN 214-1566).

Turock Pub
See Excel Fitness

Turpin & Assocs, *(Turpin, John C., & Assocs.; 0-939506),* 1825 E. Faunsdale Dr., Sandy, UT 84092-3817 (SAN 216-700X) Tel 801-572-0999.

Turquoise Bks, *(Turquoise Books; 0-917834),* 1202 Austin Bluffs Pkwy., Colorado Springs, CO 80907 (SAN 206-5223) Tel 303-634-1556.

Turquoise Mount, *(Turquoise Mountain Pubns.; 0-917947),* P.O. Box 10153, Berkeley, CA 94709 (SAN 657-0267) Tel 415-525-7853.

Turret, *(Turret Publishing; 0-931952),* 5346 N. Enid Ave., Azusa, CA 91702 (SAN 211-4577) Tel 818-334-9534.

Turtle Bks, *(Turtle Bks.; 0-937693),* 2540 S. Zephyr Ct., Lakewood, CO 80227 (SAN 659-3704) Tel 303-989-7459; Orders to: Turtle Bks., P.O. Box 27799, Denver, CO 80227 (SAN 662-4251) Tel 303-989-7459.

Turtle Isl Foun, *(Turtle Island Foundation, Netzahaulcoyotl Historical Society; 0-913666),* 2845 Buena Vista Way, Berkeley, CA 94708 (SAN 205-4639) Tel 415-654-7020.

Turtle Lodge, *(Turtle Lodge Pr.; 0-934182),* 10628 Arabian Park Dr., Scottsdale, AZ 85259 (SAN 213-1811).

Turtle Pr, *(Turtle Pr.; 0-916844),* 333 E. 49th St., New York, NY 10017 (SAN 208-8975) Tel 212-753-7957.

Turtles Quill, *(Turtles Quill Scriptorium; 0-937686),* P.O. Box 643, Mendocino, CA 95460 (SAN 206-8966) Tel 707-937-4328.

Tusa McColl
See T & M

Tusayan Gospel, *(Tusayan Gospel Ministries, Inc.; 0-9601124),* P.O. Box 9861, Phoenix, AZ 85068 (SAN 209-3391) Tel 602-878-2838; Dist. by: Living Books, Inc., 12155 Magnolia Ave. 11-B, Riverside, CA 92503 (SAN 169-006X) Tel 714-354-7330.

Tusker Pr, *(Tusker Pr.; 0-937633),* P.O. Box 597004, San Francisco, CA 94159 (SAN 659-0799) Tel 415-931-7877; 1405-1/2 Lyon St., San Francisco, CA 94115 (SAN 659-0802).

TUSPCO, *(Universal Scientific Pubns. Co., Inc., The; 0-88078),* P.O. Box 60943, Terminal Annex, Los Angeles, CA 90060 (SAN 220-309X) Tel 213-723-1776.

Tustin Inst, *(Tustin Institute of Technology, Inc.; 0-918247),* 22 E. Los Olivos St., Santa Barbara, CA 93105 (SAN 670-7092) Tel 805-682-7171.

Tutorial IL, *(Tutorial Pr.; 0-9613076),* 323 S. Franklin Bldg., Suite T-206, Chicago, IL 60606-7096 (SAN 294-6858).

Tutorial Press, *(Tutorial Pr., The; 0-912329),* 711-A Encino Pl. NE, Albuquerque, NM 87123 (SAN 265-1467) Tel 505-296-8636.

TUVOTI, *(Unspeakable Visions of the Individual; 0-934660),* P.O. Box 439, California, PA 15419 (SAN 207-916X) Tel 412-938-8956; Dist. by: Bookslinger, 213 E. Fourth St., St. Paul, MN 55101 (SAN 669-2893) Tel 612-221-0429; Dist. by: Bookpeople, 2929 Fifth St., Berkeley, CA 94710 (SAN 669-2907).

TV Digest, *(Television Digest, Inc.; 0-911486),* 1836 Jefferson Place, NW, Washington, DC 20036 (SAN 207-2955) Tel 202-872-9200.

TV Factbk
See TV Digest

TV Guide, *(TV Guide; 0-9603684),* Div. of Triangle Publications, Inc., 4 Radnor Corporate Ctr., Radnor, PA 19088 (SAN 214-4808) Tel 215-293-8947.

TV Info Off, *(Television Information Office; 0-937361),* 745 Fifth Ave., New York, NY 10151 (SAN 275-9624) Tel 212-759-6800.

TV Music Arch, *(Television Music Archives Pr.; 0-9615965),* 3000 Bronx Pk., E., Bronx, NY 10467 (SAN 697-3019) Tel 212-882-5989.

TVR Pub Co, *(TVR Publishing Co.; 0-9614079),* 5682 Oak Dr., La Palma, CA 90623 (SAN 693-3769) Tel 714-739-2125.

TVRT, *(TVRT; 0-931106),* 25 E. Fourth St., New York, NY 10003 (SAN 206-1341) Tel 212-260-4254; Dist. by: Printed Matter, 7 Lispenard St., New York, NY 10013 (SAN 169-5924) Tel 212-925-0325.

Twain Pub, *(Twain Publishing; 0-9609194),* 35 E St., NW, Washington, DC 20001 (SAN 241-4678) Tel 202-382-3802.

Twayne *Imprint of* **New Coll U Pr**

Twelvetrees Pr, *(Twelvetrees Pr.; 0-942642),* P.O. Box 188, Pasadena, CA 91102 (SAN 239-9458) Tel 818-798-5207.

Twen Fir Cent, *(Twenty First Century Pubns.; 0-933278),* P.O. Box 702, 401 N. 4th St., Fairfield, IA 52556 (SAN 211-8181) Tel 515-472-5105.

†Twen Fir Pr, *(Twenty-First Century Pr.; 0-918357),* P.O. Box 5010, Madison, WI 53705 (SAN 657-3878) Tel 608-231-2765; *CIP.*

Twentieth Fund
See Priority Pr Pubns

Twenty-Third, *(Twenty-Third Pubns.; 0-89622),* P.O. Box 180, Mystic, CT 06355 (SAN 210-9204); Toll free: 800-321-0411; 185 Willow St., Mystic, CT 06355 (SAN 658-2052); Toll free: 800-321-0411.

TWG Pub, *(TWG Publishing; 0-937077),* P.O. Box 2359, Daly City, CA 94017 (SAN 658-4470) Tel 415-333-9966.

†Twickenham Pr, *(Twickenham Pr.; 0-936726),* 31 Jane St., Suite 17B, New York, NY 10014 (SAN 214-3291); Dist. by: Daedalus Bk., 2260 25th Pl., NE, Washington, DC 20018 (SAN 158-9202) Tel 202-526-0558; *CIP.*

Twiggs Comm, *(Twiggs Communications; 0-914003),* 5366 Breeze Hill, Troy, MI 48098 (SAN 286-9039) Tel 313-641-8248.

Twin Cir, *(Twin Circle Publishing Co.; 0-937045),* 6404 Wilshire Blvd., Suite 900, Los Angeles, CA 90048 (SAN 658-7135) Tel 213-653-2200.

Twin City, *(Twin City Printery; 0-9609914),* Box 890, Lewiston, ME 04240 (SAN 206-2577) Tel 207-784-9181.

Twin Oaks Bks, *(Twin Oaks Books; 0-9608918),* 4343 Causeway Dr., Lowell, MI 49331 (SAN 238-0862).

Twin Oaks Co
See J & B Bks

Twin Peaks Pr, *(Twin Peaks Pr.; 0-933261),* P.O. Box 8097, Portland, OR 97207 (SAN 692-4034) Tel 206-256-1670; 8608 NE Mason Dr., Suite 10, Vancouver, WA 98662 (SAN 697-6018).

Twin Pines Pr, *(Twin Pines Press; 0-9609840),* 851 Rivervale Rd., River Vale, NJ 07675 (SAN 264-4428) Tel 201-391-6860.

Twines Catskill
See Catskill Art

Twining Pr, *(Twining Pr., The; 0-936877),* 319 Lovell Ave., Mill Valley, CA 94941 (SAN 699-9700) Tel 415-383-7464.

Two A's, *(Two A's Industries, Inc.; 0-915001),* 285 S. Dr., Mt. View, CA 94040 (SAN 289-4564) Tel 415-968-3111.

Two Edit, *(II Editions),* 488 Madison Ave., New York, NY 10022 (SAN 276-9417).

Two Eighteen, *(Two-Eighteen Press; 0-938690),* P.O. Box 218, Village Sta., New York, NY 10014 (SAN 207-9127) Tel 212-966-5877.

Two Ems, *(Two Ems, Inc.; 0-936652),* 18 Harkness Dr., Madison, CT 06443 (SAN 222-1853); P.O.Box 1083, Madison, CT 06443 (SAN 658-2060).

Two Riders, *(Two Riders Pr.; 0-915860),* P.O. Box 31, Chestnut Hill, MA 02167 (SAN 207-6179) Tel 617-232-8819.

Two Rivers, *(Two Rivers Press; 0-89756),* 28070 S. Meridan Rd., Aurora, OR 97002 (SAN 211-6510).

Two Trees Pr, *(Two Trees Pr.; 0-935725),* P.O. Box 8190-18, Fargo, ND 58102 (SAN 696-2181) Tel 701-235-1120.

Two Trees Pub, *(Two Trees Publishing; 0-938183),* 1272 Bear Mountain Ct., Boulder, CO 80303 (SAN 659-7262) Tel 303-494-5192.

Two Zees, *(Two Zee's Enterprises, Ltd.; 0-9606054),* 2010 Jones Rd., Fort Lee, NJ 07024 (SAN 216-9401) Tel 212-988-7813.

TwoAM Pubns, *(2AM Pubns.; 0-937491),* Div. of Anderson & McCombs Advertising & Marketing, P.O. Box 50444, Chicago, IL 60650 (SAN 659-0837) Tel 312-652-0013; 1406 S. 51st Ct., Chicago, IL 60650 (SAN 659-0845).

TwoPeninsula Pr, *(TwoPeninsula Pr.; 0-941912),* Box 30034, Lansing, MI 48909 (SAN 676-990X).

Twos Co-Cookbks, *(Two's Co./Cookbooks),* P.O. Box 977, Pebble Beach, CA 93953 (SAN 689-6464) Tel 408-624-7600.

Twowindows Pr, *(Twowindows Pr.; 0-912136),* 2644 Fulton St., Berkeley, CA 94704 (SAN 205-4671).

TX Gardener Pr, *(Texas Gardener Pr.; 0-914641),* Div. of Suntex Communications, Inc., P.O. Box 9005, Waco, TX 76714-9005 (SAN 289-615X); Dist. by: Texas Monthly Pr., P.O. Box 1569, Austin, TX 78767 (SAN 200-2531).

TX S & S Pr, *(S&S Pr.; 0-934646),* P.O. Box 5931, Austin, TX 78763 (SAN 212-6885). Do Not Confuse with (S&S) Simon & Schuster.

†TX Womans U Pr, *(Texas Woman's University Press; 0-9607488),* P.O. Box 23866, Denton, TX 76204 (SAN 238-4833) Tel 817-382-1531; *CIP.*

TY Pub Ltd, *(TY Publishing, Ltd.; 0-930613),* P.O. Box 2589, Littleton, CO 80161-2589 (SAN 686-2691).

Tycooli Intl
See Tycooly Pub

Tycooly Pub, *(Tycooly Publishing USA),* Affil. of Tycooly Int'l, P.O. Box C-166, Riverton, NJ 08077 (SAN 659-4557) Tel 609-829-6830.

Tyler-Gibson, *(Tyler-Gibson Pubs.; 0-9605520),* P.O. Box 1266, Boston, MA 02205 (SAN 220-1437) Tel 617-734-7049.

Tyndale, *(Tyndale Hse. Pubs.; 0-8423),* 336 Gundersen Dr., P.O. Box 80, Wheaton, IL 60189 (SAN 206-7749) Tel 312-668-8300; Toll free: 800-323-9400.

TYP *Imprint of* **Unipub**

Typographeum, *(Typographeum Bookshop, The; 0-930126),* The Stone Cottage, Bennington Rd., Francestown, NH 03043 (SAN 211-3031).

Typrofile Pr, *(Typrofile Pr.; 0-943316),* Church Rd., Box 223, Wernersville, PA 19565 (SAN 240-7930) Tel 215-678-3886.

U *Imprint of* **B&N Imports**

U AL Dept Mech Eng, *(University of Alabama in Huntsville, Department of Mechanical Engineering; 0-942166),* Huntsville, AL 35899 (SAN 239-989X) Tel 205-895-6154.

U AL Law, *(University of Alabama School of Law),* P.O. Box 1976, University, AL 35486 (SAN 226-8949).

U Alaska Inst Res, *(Univ. of Alaska, Institute of Social & Economic Research; 0-88353),* Div. of Univ. of Alaska, 3211 Providence Dr., Anchorage, AK 99508 (SAN 203-0144) Tel 907-786-7710.

U Alaska Rasmuson Lib, *(University of Alaska, Elmer E. Rasmuson Library; 0-935792),* Fairbanks, AK 99701 (SAN 206-1082) Tel 907-479-7224.

U Alta Pr, *(Univ. of Alberta Pr.; 0-88864),* 123 Administration Bldgs., Edmonton, AB T6G 2E2, .

U & K Pub, *(U & K Publishing Co.; 0-9616357),* 806 Carter Rd., Rockville, MD 20852 (SAN 659-090X) Tel 301-762-8980.

U & U Pubns, *(U&U Pubns., Inc.; 0-912163),* 3435 Ridgewood Rd., NW, Atlanta, GA 30327 (SAN 264-8040) Tel 404-921-7814.

U AR Acc Dept, *(Univ. of Arkansas, Accounting Dept. Foundation; 0-935951),* Business Administration, Rm. 204, Fayetteville, AR 72701 (SAN 696-7817) Tel 501-575-6123.

U Ariz Ctr Photog, *(Univ. of Arizona, Ctr. for Creative Photograhy; 0-938262),* 843 E. University, Tucson, AZ 85719 (SAN 285-1032) Tel 602-621-7968; Dist. by: Univ. of Arizona Pr., 1615 E. Speedway, Tucson, AZ 85719 (SAN 285-1040) Tel 602-795-0583.

U Assocs, *(U Assocs., Inc.; 0-9615393),* 1160 N. Federal Hwy., Suite 721, Ft. Lauderdale, FL 33304 (SAN 695-3530) Tel 305-763-5991.

U-Bild, *(U-Bild Enterprises; 0-910495),* Div. of U-B Newspaper Syndicate, Box 2383, 15233 Stagg St., Van Nuys, CA 91409 (SAN 260-1508) Tel 818-785-6368.

U Cal AISC, *(Univ. of California, American Indian Studies Ctr.; 0-935626),* 3220 Campbell Hall, Los Angeles, CA 90024 (SAN 220-1283) Tel 213-825-7315.

U Cal Grad Sch Mgmt
    See UCLA Mgmt

U Cal Hist Sci Tech, *(Univ. of California, Office for History of Science & Technology; 0-918102),* 470 Stephens Hall, Univ. of California, Berkeley, CA 94720 (SAN 210-1394) Tel 415-642-4581.

U Cal LA Indus Rel, *(Univ. of California, Institute of Industrial Relations; 0-89215),* 405 Hilgard Ave., Los Angeles, CA 90024 (SAN 205-4698) Tel 213-825-9191.

U Cal Risk Management
    See J Morris

U Chi Ctr Policy, *(University of Chicago, Center for Policy Study),* 5801 S. Ellis Ave., Rm. 200, Chicago, IL 60637 (SAN 220-102X) Tel 312-962-8352.

U Chi Dept Anthro, *(Univ. of Chicago, Dept. of Anthropology; 0-916256),* 1126 E. 59th St., Chicago, IL 60637 (SAN 208-0583) Tel 312-962-7314.

U Chi Dept Educ, *(Univ. of Chicago, Dept. of Education; 0-936745),* 5835 S. Kimbark Ave., Chicago, IL 60637 (SAN 699-9719) Tel 312-962-9457.

†U Chicago Dept Geog, *(Univ. of Chicago, Department of Geography, Research Papers; 0-89065),* 5828 S. University Ave., Chicago, IL 60637 (SAN 203-3003) Tel 312-962-8314; *CIP.*

U Chicago Grad Sch Busn, *(University of Chicago, Graduate School of Business; 0-918584),* 1101 E. 58th St., Chicago, IL 60637 (SAN 211-4585) Tel 312-962-7431.

U Chicago Midwest Admin, *(University of Chicago, Midwest Administration Center; 0-931080),* 5835 S. Kimbark Ave., Chicago, IL 60637 (SAN 206-0906) Tel 312-962-1565.

U CO at Colorado Springs
    See Writers Forum

U CO Busn Res Div, *(Univ. of Colorado, Business Research Div.; 0-89478),* Div. of College of Business, Box 420, Univ. of Colorado, Boulder, CO 80309 (SAN 209-9047) Tel 303-492-8227.

U Conn Sch Law, *(University of Connecticut, School of Law Press; 0-939328),* 35 Elizabeth St., Hartford, CT 06105 (SAN 216-5554) Tel 203-241-4609.

†U Delaware Pr, *(Univ. of Delaware Pr.; 0-87413),* c/o Associated Univ. Presses, Inc., 440 Forsgate Dr., Cranbury, NJ 08512 (SAN 203-4476) Tel 609-655-4770; *CIP.*

U Exten-U of Cal
    See Univ Extension Pubns

U Field Staff Intl, *(Universities Field Staff International, Inc.; 0-910116; 0-88333),* P.O. Box 150, Hanover, NH 03755 (SAN 202-4764) Tel 603-448-5741.

U Fla Law, *(University of Florida, College of Law),* Law Ctr., Gainesville, FL 32611 (SAN 227-0536).

U Hawaii, *(Univ. of Hawaii at Manoa, Industrial Relations Ctr.),* 2425 Campus Rd., Honolulu, HI 96822 (SAN 280-8773).

U HI at Manoa Korean
    See Ctr Korean U HI at Manoa

U IA Audiovisual, *(Univ. of Iowa, Audiovisual Ctr.),* C215 Seashore Hall, Iowa City, IA 52242 (SAN 264-5909) Tel 319-353-7368.

U IA Ctr Ed Experiment, *(Univ. of Iowa, Ctr. for Educational Experimentation, Development & Evaluation; 0-939984; 0-88670),* N345 Oakdale Hall, Oakdale, IA 52319 (SAN 216-8677) Tel 319-353-4200.

U ID Ctr Busn, *(Univ. of Idaho, Ctr. for Business Development & Research; 0-940982),* Moscow, ID 83843 (SAN 205-9673) Tel 208-885-6611.

†U IL-Archaeological, *(Univ. of Illinois, at Urbana-Champaign, Archaeological Survey, Inc.; 0-942704),* 109 Davenport Hall, 607 S. Mathews Ave., Urbana, IL 61801 (SAN 240-1037); *CIP.*

U Il Natl Ad
    See NAAHP Inc

U IL Sch Music, *(University of Illinois, School of Music),* University of Illinois, Urbana, IL 61801 (SAN 240-5024) Tel 217-333-1027; 1114 W. Nevada, Urbana, IL 61801 (SAN 662-1708).

U Intel Data Bank, *(Universal Intelligence Data Bank of America; 0-9610740),* P.O. Box 865, Railroad RT No. 2, Independence, MO 64050 (SAN 264-8067) Tel 816-249-3374; 866 Twyman Rd., Independence, MO 64050 (SAN 693-5079) Tel 816-249-5933.

U Iowa IPA, *(Univ. of Iowa, Institute of Public Affairs),* Div. of Continuing Education, 507 N. Clinton, Iowa City, IA 52242 (SAN 262-1231) Tel 319-353-3270.

U Iowa Law, *(Univ. of Iowa, College of Law),* Iowa City, IA 52240 (SAN 226-9155).

U Kan Music
    See U KS Dept Art Music

U KS Dept Art Music, *(Univ. of Kansas, Dept. of Art & Music Education & Music Therapy; 0-936117),* 311 Bailey Hall, Lawrence, KS 66045-4322 (SAN 696-7655) Tel 913-864-4784.

U Ky Lib Assocs, *(University of Kentucky, Library Associates; 0-919123),* Lexington, KY 40506 (SAN 241-4686) Tel 606-257-9401.

U M H & C, *(Univ. of Minnesota Hospital & Clinic, Consultation/Education Div.; 0-937423),* Div. of Univ. of Minnesota, Box 603, Harvard St. at East River Rd., Minneapolis, MN 55455 (SAN 659-0934) Tel 612-626-6356; Orders to: Pritchett & Hall Assocs., Inc., 3440 Oakcliff Rd., NE, Suite 110, Atlanta, GA 30340 (SAN 662-4227) Tel 404-451-0602.

U Maine Orono, *(Univ. of Maine, at Orono Pr.; 0-89101),* PICS Bldg., Univ. of Maine at Orono, Orono, ME 04469 (SAN 207-2971) Tel 207-581-1700.

U MD Geography, *(Univ. of Maryland, Dept. of Geography; 0-918512),* 1113 Lefrak Hall, College Park, MD 20742 (SAN 209-9055) Tel 301-454-2241.

U MD Inst, *(Univ. of Maryland, College Park, Institute for Urban Studies; 0-913749),* 1113 Lefrak Hall, Univ. of Maryland, College Park, MD 20742 (SAN 286-2107) Tel 301-454-2662.

U MD Law, *(Univ. of Maryland, Schl. of Law),* 500 W. Baltimore St., Baltimore, MD 21201 (SAN 226-9260).

†U MI Japan, *(Univ. of Michigan, Ctr. for Japanese Studies; 0-939512),* 108 Lane Hall, Ann Arbor, MI 48109 (SAN 216-7018) Tel 313-763-7265; *CIP.*

U MI Law CLE, *(Univ. of Michigan, Law Schl., Institute of Continuing Legal Education; 0-88288),* 625 S. State, Ann Arbor, MI 48104 (SAN 226-9295).

U Miami Marine, *(Univ. of Miami, Rosenstiel School of Marine & Atmospheric Science; 0-930050),* Orders to: Publications-STO Sales, 4600 Rickenbacker Causeway, Miami, FL 33149 (SAN 276-4210) Tel 305-361-4616.

U Miami N-S Ctr, *(Univ. of Miami North/South Ctr., Graduate Schl. of International Studies; 0-935501),* P.O. Box 248123, Coral Gables, FL 33124 (SAN 695-8834) Tel 305-284-4303.

U Mich Arch, *(Univ. of Michigan, College of Architecture & Urban Planning; 0-9614792),* 292 Harmon St., Birmingham, MI 48009 (SAN 693-0182) Tel 313-644-0604.

†U Mich Busn Div Res, *(Univ. of Michigan, Div. of Research, Graduate Schl. of Business Administration; 0-87712),* Ann Arbor, MI 48109 (SAN 204-8736) Tel 313-764-1366; *CIP.*

U Mich-Dearborn, *(Univ. of Michigan-Dearborn; 0-933691),* Branch of Univ. of Michigan, 4901 Evergreen Rd., Dearborn, MI 48128-1491 (SAN 291-3615) Tel 313-593-5075; Orders to: Follett's Bookstore, 4901 Evergreen Rd., Dearborn, MI 48128-1491 (SAN 662-2224) Tel 313-593-5530.

U Mich Div Res
    See U Mich Busn Div Res

U Mich Mus Anthro, *(Univ. of Michigan, Museum of Anthropology, Pubns. Dept.; 0-932206),* 4009 Museums Bldg., 1109 Geddes, Ann Arbor, MI 48109 (SAN 203-0489) Tel 313-764-6867.

U Mich SE Asia Stud
    See Ctr S&SE Asian

U Minn Law, *(Univ. of Minnesota, Law Schl.),* Minneapolis, MN 55455 (SAN 227-3276).

U Minn Pediatric, *(Univ. of Minnesota; 0-940210),* Div. of Pediatric Nephrology & the Minnesota Medical Foundation, P.O. Box 73, Mayo Bldg., Minneapolis, MN 55455 (SAN 262-1037); 420 Delaware St., SE, Minneapolis, MN 55455 (SAN 658-2168).

U MO Plant Bio, *(University of Missouri-Columbia, Interdisciplinary Plant Biochemistry & Physiology Group; 0-936463),* Univ. of Missouri-Columbia, 322 Chemistry Bldg., Columbia, MO 65203 (SAN 697-9769) Tel 314-882-7606.

U MO Poli Sci
    See MO Poli Sci

U MO-St Louis, *(University of Missouri-Saint Louis; 0-9601616),* 8001 Natural Bridge Rd., St. Louis, MO 63121 (SAN 211-8726) Tel 314-553-5168.

U MS Bus Econ, *(Univ. of Mississippi, Bureau of Business & Economic Research; 0-938004),* 300 LaBauve A, University, MS 38677 (SAN 206-0841) Tel 601-232-7481.

U MS Law Ctr, *(Univ. of Mississippi, Law Ctr.; 0-8377),* University, MS 38677 (SAN 213-3938); Dist. by: Fred B. Rothman & Co., 10368 W. Centennial Rd., Littleton, CO 80123 (SAN 159-9437) Tel 303-979-5657.

U NC Dept Statistics, *(Univ. of North Carolina at Chapel Hill, Dept. of Statistics),* 322 Phillips Hall, Chapel Hill, NC 27514 (SAN 239-5673).

U NC Inst Res Soc Sci, *(Univ. of North Carolina, Institute for Research in Social Science; 0-89143),* IRSS Pubns., Manning Hall 026A, Chapel Hill, NC 27514 (SAN 206-0795) Tel 919-966-3204.

U ND Pr, *(Univ. of North Dakota Pr.),* P.O. Box 8006, Grand Forks, ND 58202 (SAN 206-0787) Tel 701-777-2544.

U Nebr Dept Human, *(Univ. of Nebraska, Dept. of Human Development & the Family, Ctr. for Family Strengths; 0-934949),* Univ. of Nebraska, Center for Family Strengths, Lincoln, NE 68583-0830 (SAN 695-071X) Tel 402-472-1672.

U Nebr IANR, *(Univ. of Nebraska, Institute of Agriculture & Natural Resources; 0-9616828),* Univ. of Nebraska, 108 ACB, Lincoln, NE 68583-0918 (SAN 661-1672) Tel 402-472-3007.

U Nevada
    See Natl Judicial Coll

U New Haven Pr, *(Univ. of New Haven Pr.; 0-936285),* 300 Orange Ave., West Haven, CT 06516 (SAN 697-9785) Tel 203-932-7118.

U NM Law, *(Univ. of New Mexico, Schl. of Law),* 1117 Stanford NE, Albuquerque, NM 87131 (SAN 227-3357).

U of AK Inst Marine, *(Univ. of Alaska, Institute of Marine Science; 0-914500),* Publications Office, Fairbanks, AK 99775-1080 (SAN 208-1032) Tel 907-474-7843.

U of Ala Ctr Bus, *(University of Alabama, Center for Business & Economic Research; 0-943394),* P.O. Box AK, University, AL 35486 (SAN 206-1074) Tel 205-348-6191.

†**U of Ala Pr,** *(Univ. of Alabama Pr.; 0-8173),* P.O. Box 2877, University, AL 35486 (SAN 202-5272) Tel 205-348-5180; *CIP.*

U of Alaska Pr, *(Univ. of Alaska Pr.; 0-912006),* Univ. of Alaska, Vice Chancellor of Research & Advanced Study, Signer's Hall, Fairbanks, AK 99775-1580 (SAN 203-3011) Tel 907-474-6389.

†**U of Ariz Pr,** *(Univ. of Arizona Pr.; 0-8165),* 1615 E. Speedway, Tucson, AZ 85719 (SAN 205-468X) Tel 602-795-0583; 250 E Valencia, Tucson, AZ 85706 (SAN 658-2125); *CIP.*

†**U of Ark Pr,** *(Univ. of Arkansas Pr.; 0-938626),* Univ. of Arkansas, Fayetteville, AR 72701 (SAN 239-3972) Tel 501-575-3246; Toll free: 800-242-7737; Dist. by: Texas A & M Univ. Pr., Drawer C, College Station, TX 77843 (SAN 207-5237) Tel 409-845-1436; *CIP.*

U of AZ Ed Mat, *(Univ. of Arizona, Arizona Educational Materials Ctr.; 0-940870),* College of Education, P.O. Box 601, Tucson, AZ 85721 (SAN 219-6514) Tel 602-621-3724.

U of CA Inst Global, *(Univ. of California, Institute on Global Conflict and Cooperation; 0-934637),* Univ. of Cal., San Diego, IGCC Central Office, Q-60, La Jolla, CA 92093 (SAN 693-9163) Tel 619-452-3352.

†**U of Cal Intl St,** *(Univ. of California, Institute of International Studies; 0-87725),* 215 Moses Hall, Berkeley, CA 94720 (SAN 203-3038) Tel 415-642-7189; *CIP.*

†**U of Cal Pr,** *(Univ. of California Pr.; 0-520),* 2120 Berkeley Way, Berkeley, CA 94720 (SAN 203-3046) Tel 415-642-6683; Toll free: 800-822-6657 (For orders); 1095 Essex St., Richmond, CA 94801 (SAN 658-2133). Do not confuse U of Cal Pr, Berkeley, CA, with the Univ. of Calgary Pr., Calgary, AB, Canada; *CIP.*

U of Cal Sch Law, *(University of California, School of Law; 0-935076),* Davis, CA 95616 (SAN 206-7374); Dist. by: Fred B. Rothman & Co., 10368 W. Centennial Rd., Littleton, CO 80127 (SAN 159-9437) Tel 303-979-5657.

†**U of Chicago Pr,** *(Univ. of Chicago Pr.; 0-226),* Div. of Univ. of Chicago, 5801 Ellis Ave., 3rd Flr., S., Chicago, IL 60637 (SAN 205-5280) Tel 312-962-7693; Toll free: 800-621-2736; Orders to: 11030 S. Langley Ave., Chicago, IL 60628 (SAN 202-5299) Tel 312-568-1550; *CIP.* *Imprints:* Chicago Original Paperback (Chicago Original Paperback); Chicago Visual Lib (Chicago Visual Library); Midway Reprint (Midway Reprint).

U of Dallas Pr, *(Univ. of Dallas Pr.; 0-918306),* 1845 E. Northgate, Irving, TX 75062 (SAN 209-4940) Tel 214-721-5226.

U of Denver Intl
See Monograph Series

U of Denver Teach, *(Univ. of Denver, Ctr. for Teaching, International Relations Pubns.; 0-943804),* GSIS, Univ. of Denver, Denver, CO 80208 (SAN 241-0877) Tel 303-871-2426.

U of Detroit Pr, *(Univ. of Detroit Pr.; 0-911550),* 4001 W. McNichols, Detroit, MI 48221 (SAN 205-471X).

U of Evansville Pr, *(Univ. of Evansville Pr.; 0-930982),* 1800 Lincoln Ave., Evansville, IN 47722 (SAN 265-413X) Tel 812-479-2488.

U of FL African Studies, *(Univ. of Flordia Ctr. for African Studies; 0-935833),* 470 Grinter Hall, Gainesville, FL 32611 (SAN 695-8796) Tel 904-392-2187.

U of Fla Pr
See U Presses Fla

†**U of GA Inst Govt,** *(Univ. of Georgia, Carl Vinson Institute of Government; 0-89854),* Terrell Hall, Athens, GA 30602 (SAN 212-8012); *CIP.*

†**U of Ga Pr,** *(Univ. of Georgia Pr.; 0-8203),* Terrell Hall, Athens, GA 30602 (SAN 203-3054) Tel 404-542-2830; *CIP.*

U of Healing, *(Univ. of Healing Pr.; 0-940480),* 32750 Hwy. 94, Campo, CA 92006 (SAN 211-7983) Tel 619-478-5111; 1101 Far Valley Rd., Campo, CA 92006 (SAN 693-9783) Tel 619-478-5111.

U of Idaho Pr, *(Univ. of Idaho Pr.; 0-89301),* Div. of Idaho Research Foundation, Inc., University Sta., Box 3368, Moscow, ID 83843 (SAN 208-905X) Tel 208-885-6245.

U of Ill Lib Info Sci, *(Univ. of Illinois at Urbana-Champaign, Graduate Schl. of Library & Information Science; 0-87845),* Pubns. Office, 249 Armory Bldg, 505 E. Armory St., Champaign, IL 61820 (SAN 277-4917) Tel 217-333-1359.

†**U of Ill Pr,** *(Univ. of Illinois Pr.; 0-252),* 54 E. Gregory Dr., Champaign, IL 61820 (SAN 202-5310) Tel 217-333-0950; Toll free: 800-242-7737; Orders to: Harper & Row, Inc., Keystone Industrial Pk., Scranton, PA 18512 (SAN 215-3742); Orders to: Univ. of Illinois Pr., P.O. Box 1650, Hagerstown, MD 21741; *CIP. Imprints:* IB (Illini Books).(Illini Bks.).

†**U of Iowa Pr,** *(Univ. of Iowa Pr.; 0-87745),* Univ. of Iowa, Iowa City, IA 52242 (SAN 282-4868) Tel 319-353-3181; Orders to: Graphic Services Bldg., Iowa City, IA 52242 (SAN 282-4876) Tel 319-353-4171; *CIP.*

U of Iowa Sch Soc Wk, *(Univ. of Iowa, Schl. of Social Work; 0-934936),* Iowa City, IA 52242 (SAN 214-1612).

U of KS Cont Ed, *(University of Kansas, Division of Continuing Education; 0-936352),* Continuing Education Bldg., Lawrence, KS 66045 (SAN 214-1620).

U of KS Ind Stud
See U of KS Cont Ed

U of KS Mus Nat Hist, *(Univ. of Kansas, Museum of Natural History; 0-89338),* 602 Dyche Hall, Lawrence, KS 66045 (SAN 206-0957) Tel 913-864-4540.

U of KS Pubns, *(Univ. of Kansas Pubns.),* Exchange & Gift Dept., Watson Library, Univ. of Kansas, Lawrence, KS 66045 (SAN 215-7101).

U of KY Libs, *(Univ. of Kentucky Libraries; 0-917519),* Department of Special Collections & Archives, Lexington, KY 40506-0059 (SAN 656-1098) Tel 606-257-1466.

U of LA Ctr LA Studies
See U of SW LA Ctr LA Studies

†**U of Mass Pr,** *(Univ. of Massachusetts Pr.; 0-87023),* P.O. Box 429, Amherst, MA 01004 (SAN 203-3089) Tel 413-545-2217; *CIP.*

U of Md Lib Serv, *(Univ. of Maryland, College of Library & Information Services; 0-911808),* 3116 Hornbake Library Bldg., College Park, MD 20742 (SAN 203-3097) Tel 301-454-2590; Orders to: University of Maryland, Univ. Bk. Ctr., College Park, MD 20742 (SAN 203-3100).

†**U of Miami Pr,** *(Univ. of Miami Pr.; 0-87024),* P.O. Box 4836, Hampden Sta., Baltimore, MD 21211 (SAN 203-3119) Tel 301-338-6952; *CIP.*

U of Mich Alumnae, *(Univ. of Michigan Alumnae Council; 0-9613460),* Subs. of Alumni Assn. of the Univ. of Michigan, 200 Fletcher St., Ann Arbor, MI 48109 (SAN 657-307X) Tel 313-763-9708.

U of Mich Busn Res
See U Mich Busn Div Res

U of Mich Ctr Chinese, *(Univ. of Michigan, Ctr. for Chinese Studies; 0-89264),* 104 Lane Hall, Ann Arbor, MI 48109 (SAN 208-2772) Tel 313-763-7181.

U of Mich Inst Labor, *(Univ. of Michigan, Institute of Labor & Industrial Relations; 0-87736),* University of Michigan, Victor Vaughn Bldg., 1111 E. Catherine, Ann Arbor, MI 48109 (SAN 662-1716) Tel 313-747-0699; Dist. by: ILIR Pubns., Univ. of Michigan, Victor Vaughn Bldg., 1111 E. Catherine, Ann Arbor, MI 48109-2054 (SAN 203-3127) Tel 313-763-1187.

†**U of Mich Pr,** *(Univ. of Michigan Pr.; 0-472),* P.O. Box 1104, Ann Arbor, MI 48106 (SAN 282-4884) Tel 313-764-4330; Orders to: 839 Greene St., Ann Arbor, MI 48106 (SAN 282-4892) Tel 313-764-4392; *CIP. Imprints:* AA (Ann Arbor Books).(Ann Arbor Bks.).

U of Minn Bell, *(Univ. of Minnesota, Bell Institute of Pathology; 0-912922),* P.O. Box 302, Mayo Memorial Bldg., Minneapolis, MN 55455 (SAN 204-8744).

U of Minn Comp Ctr, *(Univ. of Minnesota, Computer Ctr.; 0-936992),* Univ. of Minnesota, Duluth, MN 55812 (SAN 215-1200).

†**U of Minn Pr,** *(Univ. of Minnesota Pr.; 0-8166),* 2037 University Ave., SE, Minneapolis, MN 55414 (SAN 213-2648) Tel 612-624-6055; *CIP.*

U of Missouri Mus Art Arch, *(Univ. of Missouri, Museum of Art & Archaeology; 0-910501),* 1 Pickard Hall, Univ. Of Missouri, Columbia, MO 65211 (SAN 260-2733) Tel 314-882-3591.

U of MN College Lib Arts, *(Univ. of Minnesota, College of Liberal Arts, Ctr. for Humanistic Studies; 0-9607884),* 117 Pleasant St., SE, Minneapolis, MN 55118 (SAN 238-4027) Tel 612-624-0003.

†**U of Mo Pr,** *(Univ. of Missouri Pr.; 0-8262),* 200 Lewis, Columbia, MO 65211 (SAN 203-3143) Tel 314-882-7641; Toll free: 800-242-7737; Dist. by: Harper & Row Pubs., Inc., 10 E. 53rd St., New York, NY 10022 (SAN 215-3742) Tel 212-207-7099; *CIP.*

U of MT Pubns Hist, *(Univ. of Montana Pubns. in History; 0-934054),* Missoula, MT 59812 (SAN 208-080X) Tel 406-243-2231.

U of MT Sch Arts, *(Univ. of Montana, School of Fine Arts; 0-9615029),* Univ. of Montana, Missoula, MT 59812 (SAN 693-7853) Tel 406-243-4970.

U of NC Dept Health, *(Univ. of North Carolina at Chapel Hill, Dept. of Health Administration, Schl. of Public Health; 0-89055),* 263 Rosenau 201H, Chapel Hill, NC 27514 (SAN 207-7574) Tel 919-966-4091.

U of NC Inst Gov, *(Univ. of North Carolina, Institute of Government),* Knapp Bldg. 059A, Chapel Hill, NC 27514 (SAN 204-8752) Tel 919-966-4119.

†**U of NC Pr,** *(Univ. of North Carolina Pr.; 0-8078),* P.O. Box 2288, Chapel Hill, NC 27514 (SAN 203-3151) Tel 919-966-3561; *CIP.*

†**U of Nebr Pr,** *(Univ. of Nebraska Pr.; 0-8032),* 901 N. 17th St., Lincoln, NE 68588-0520 (SAN 202-5337) Tel 402-472-3581; *CIP. Imprints:* Bison (Bison Books).

U of Nev Bur Busn, *(Univ. of Nevada, Reno Bureau of Business & Economic Research; 0-942828),* Reno, NV 89557 (SAN 240-1711) Tel 702-784-6877.

†**U of Nev Pr,** *(Univ. of Nevada Pr.; 0-87417),* Reno, NV 89557 (SAN 203-316X) Tel 702-784-6573; *CIP.*

U of NI Dept Art, *(Univ. of Northern Iowa, Dept. of Art; 0-932660),* Cedar Falls, IA 50614-0362 (SAN 212-2391) Tel 319-273-2077.

U of NM Nat Am Std, *(Univ. of New Mexico, Native American Studies; 0-934090),* 1812 Las Lomas NE, Albuquerque, NM 87131 (SAN 212-8446).

†**U of NM Pr,** *(Univ. of New Mexico Pr.; 0-8263),* Journalism Bldg., Rm. 220, Albuquerque, NM 87131 (SAN 213-9588) Tel 505-277-2346; *CIP.*

†**U of Notre Dame Pr,** *(Univ. of Notre Dame Pr.; 0-268),* P.O. Box L, Notre Dame, IN 46556 (SAN 203-3178) Tel 219-239-6346; Toll free: 800-242-7737; Dist. by: Harper & Row Pubs., Keystone Industrial Pk., Scranton, PA 18512 (SAN 215-3742); *CIP.*

†**U of Okla Pr,** *(Univ. of Oklahoma Pr.; 0-8061),* 1005 Asp Ave., Norman, OK 73019 (SAN 203-3194) Tel 405-325-5111; Toll free: 800-242-7737; Dist. by: Harper & Row, Inc., Keystone Industrial Pk., Scranton, PA 18512 (SAN 215-3742); Orders to: Univ. of Oklahoma Pr., P.O. Box 1657, Hagerstown, MD 21741 (SAN 203-3194); *CIP.*

U of Oreg Bks, *(Univ. of Oregon Bks.; 0-87114),* Univ. Pubns., 101 Chapman Hall, Univ. of Oregon, Eugene, OR 97403 (SAN 206-7757) Tel 503-686-5396.

U of Oreg ERIC, *(Univ. of Oregon ERIC Clearinghouse on Educational Management; 0-86552),* Div. of U. S. Dept. of Education, University of Oregon, 1787 Agate St., Eugene, OR 97403 (SAN 226-806X) Tel 503-686-5043.

U of Oreg Health Sci
See Oregon Hlth Sci Univ

U of Pa Contemp Art, *(Univ. of Pennsylvania, Institute of Contemporary Art; 0-88454),* 34th & Walnut Sts., Philadelphia, PA 19104 (SAN 203-3208) Tel 215-898-7108.

†**U of Pa Pr,** *(Univ. of Pennsylvania Pr.; 0-8122),* 418 Service Dr., Blockley Hall, 13th Flr., Philadelphia, PA 19104 (SAN 202-5345) Tel 215-898-6261; *CIP. Imprints:* Pa Paperbks (Pennsylvania Paperbooks).

U of Pacific
See Holt-Atherton

†**U of Pittsburgh Pr,** *(Univ. of Pittsburgh Pr.; 0-8229),* 127 N. Bellefield Ave., Pittsburgh, PA 15260 (SAN 203-3216) Tel 412-624-4110; Toll free: 800-242-7737; Dist. by: Harper & Row Pubs., Inc., Keystone Industrial Pk., Scranton, PA 18512 (SAN 215-3742); *CIP.*

†**U of PR Pr,** *(Univ. of Puerto Rico Pr.; 0-8477),* P.O. Box X, U.P.R. Sta., Rio Piedras, PR 00931 (SAN 208-1245) Tel 809-763-0812; *CIP.*

†**U of Queensland Pr,** *(Univ. of Queensland Pr.; 0-7022),* P.O. Box 1365, New York, NY 10023 (SAN 206-8540) Tel 212-799-3854; Orders to: Publishers Distribution Services, Inc., 250 Commercial St., Manchester, NH 03101 (SAN 206-8559) Tel 603-623-0305; *CIP.*

U of S Cal Pr, *(Univ. of Southern California Press; 0-88474),* Student Union 400, Univ. of Southern California, Los Angeles, CA 90007 (SAN 203-1892).

U of S Dakota Pr
See Dakota Pr

†**U of SC Pr,** *(Univ. of South Carolina Pr.; 0-87249),* Columbia, SC 29208 (SAN 203-3224) Tel 803-777-5243; *CIP.*

U of SD Gov Res Bur, *(Univ. of South Dakota, Governmental Research Bureau; 1-55614),* 233 Dakota Hall, Vermillion, SD 57069 (SAN 206-0698) Tel 605-677-5242.

U of St Thomas, *(Univ. of St. Thomas),* 3812 Montrose Blvd., Houston, TX 77006 (SAN 206-0701) Tel 713-522-7911.

U of SW LA Ctr LA Studies, *(Univ. of Southwestern Louisiana Ctr. Louisiana Studies; 0-940984),* P.O. Box 40831, USL, Lafayette, LA 70504 (SAN 217-4502) Tel 318-231-6027.

U of Tenn Geo, *(Univ. of Tennessee, Dept. of Geological Sciences; 0-910249),* Div. of University of Tennessee, Knoxville, Rm 306, Geography & Geology Bldg., Knoxville, TN 37996-1410 (SAN 241-4694) Tel 615-974-2366.

†**U of Tenn Pr,** *(Univ. of Tennessee Pr.; 0-87049),* Div. of Univ. of Tennessee & Member of Assn. of American University Presses, 293 Communications Bldg., Knoxville, TN 37996-0325 (SAN 212-9930) Tel 615-974-3321; Orders to: P.O. Box 6525, Ithaca, NY 14850 (SAN 662-1740) Tel 607-277-2211; *CIP.*

U of Tex Arlington Pr, *(Univ. of Texas at Arlington Pr., The; 0-87706),* Box 19075, Arlington, TX 76019 (SAN 213-9707); Orders to: English Dept., Box 19035, Arlington, TX 76019 (SAN 213-9715).

U of Tex Dept Astron, *(Univ. of Texas, Dept. of Astronomy; 0-9603796),* RLM 15.308, Austin, TX 78712 (SAN 214-1647) Tel 512-471-4461.

U of Tex H Ransom Ctr, *(Univ. of Texas, Harry Ransom Humanities Research Ctr.; 0-87959),* Div. of Univ. of Texas at Austin, P.O. Box 7219, Austin, TX 78713 (SAN 203-1906) Tel 512-471-9113.

U of Tex Hum Res
See U of Tex H Ransom Ctr

†**U of Tex Inst Tex Culture,** *(Univ. of Texas, Institute of Texan Cultures; 0-86701),* P.O. Box 1226, San Antonio, TX 78294 (SAN 213-8778) Tel 512-226-7651; *CIP.*

†**U of Tex Pr,** *(Univ. of Texas Pr.; 0-292),* P.O. Box 7819, Austin, TX 78713-7819 (SAN 212-9876) Tel 512-471-7233; Toll free: 800-252-3206 (Orders Only); *CIP. Imprints:* Stevenson Sch (Stevenson, Robert Louis, School, The).(Stevenson, Robert Louis, Schl., The).

U of Tex Tarlton Law Lib, *(Univ. of Texas, Tarlton Law Library; 0-935630),* 727 E. 26th St., Austin, TX 78705-5799 (SAN 214-1655) Tel 512-471-7726.

†**U of Toronto Pr,** *(Univ. of Toronto Pr.; 0-8020),* 33 E. Tupper St., Buffalo, NY 14203 (SAN 214-2651) Tel 716-852-0342; *CIP.*

†**U of Utah Pr,** *(Univ. of Utah Pr.; 0-87480),* 101 University Services Bldg., Salt Lake City, UT 84112 (SAN 220-0023) Tel 801-581-6771; Toll free: 800-662-0062 Ext. 6771; *CIP. Imprints:* Tanner (Tanner Trust Fund).

U of VT Dept Hist, *(Univ. of Vermont, Dept. of History; 0-9614365),* 442 Main St., Burlington, VT 05405 (SAN 688-5721) Tel 802-656-3180.

U of VT Psych, *(Univ. of Vermont, Dept. of Psychiatry; 0-9611898; 0-938685),* One S. Prospect St., Burlington, VT 05401 (SAN 286-2123) Tel 802-656-4563.

U of W Fla, *(Univ. of West Florida, Gulf Coast History & Humanities Conference; 0-940836),* Univ. of West Florida, Bldg. 32, Pensacola, FL 32514 (SAN 219-6522) Tel 904-474-2492.

U of Wash Grad Sch Busn, *(Univ. of Washington, Graduate School of Business),* Mackenzie Hall, DJ-10, Seattle, WA 98195 (SAN 203-0187) Tel 206-543-4598.

†**U of Wash Pr,** *(Univ. of Washington Pr.; 0-295),* P.O. Box 50096, Seattle, WA 98145-5096 (SAN 212-2502) Tel 206-543-4050; Toll free: 800-441-4115; *CIP.*

U of WI-Superior
See UWIS CLSES

U of Wis Arch-Urban Pl
See U of Wis Ctr Arch-Urban

U of Wis Ctr Arch-Urban, *(Univ. of Wisconsin-Milwaukee, Center for Architecture & Urban Planning Research; 0-938744),* Subs. of School of Architecture and Urban Planning, UW-Milwaukee, P.O. Box 413, Milwaukee, WI 53201 (SAN 211-9900) Tel 414-963-4014.

†**U of Wis Land,** *(Univ. of Wisconsin-Madison, Land Tenure Ctr.; 0-934519),* Univ. of Wisconsin, 1300 University Ave., Madison, WI 53706 (SAN 693-4927) Tel 608-262-3657; *CIP.*

†**U of Wis Pr,** *(Univ. of Wisconsin Pr.; 0-299),* 114 N. Murray St., Madison, WI 53715 (SAN 203-3259) Tel 608-262-8782; *CIP.*

U of Wis-Stevens Point, *(Univ. of Wisconsin-Stevens Point Foundation Pr.; 0-932310),* 428 COPS Bldg., Stevens Point, WI 54481 (SAN 212-2405) Tel 715-346-4496.

U of Wis Sys Ethnic, *(Univ. of Wisconsin System American Ethnic Studies Coordinating Committee (AESCC); 0-942672),* c/o UW-Milwaukee - SHP-304, P.O. Box 413, Milwaukee, WI 53201 (SAN 282-4922) Tel 414-963-4700.

U of Wyoming, *(Univ. of Wyoming; 0-941570),* P.O. Box 3315, University Sta., Laramie, WY 82071 (SAN 206-0620) Tel 307-766-2379.

U OK Ctr Econ, *(Univ. of Oklahoma, Ctr. for Economic & Management Research; 0-931880),* College of Business Administration, 307 W. Brooks St., Rm. 4, Norman, OK 73019 (SAN 212-3916) Tel 405-325-2931.

U OR BGR, *(Univ. of Oregon, Bureau of Governmental Research & Service),* P.O. Box 3177, Eugene, OR 97403 (SAN 227-339X) Tel 503-686-5232.

U OR Ctr Leisure
See Inst Recreation Res

U Penn Law, *(Univ. of Pennsylvania, Law School),* 3400 Chestnut St., Philadelphia, PA 19174 (SAN 227-3411).

U Penn South Asia, *(Univ. of Pennsylvania, Dept. of South Asia Regional Studies; 0-936115),* Univ. of Pennsylvania, 820 Williams Hall/CU, Philadelphia, PA 19104 (SAN 697-001X) Tel 215-898-7475.

†**U Pr of Amer,** *(University Pr. of America; 0-8191),* 4720 Boston Way, Lanham, MD 20706 (SAN 200-2256) Tel 301-459-3366; *CIP.*

U Pr of Cal, *(Univ. Press of California; 0-935048),* 1000 N. Coast Hwy., No. 3, Laguna Beach, CA 92651 (SAN 212-3215) Tel 714-497-4861.

U Pr of Hawaii
See UH Pr

U Pr of Idaho
See U of Idaho Pr

†**U Pr of KS,** *(Univ. Pr. of Kansas; 0-7006),* 329 Carruth, Lawrence, KS 66045 (SAN 203-3267) Tel 913-864-4154; *CIP.*

†**U Pr of Ky,** *(Univ. Pr. of Kentucky; 0-8131),* Univ. of Kentucky, 102 Lafferty Hall, Lexington, KY 40506-0024 (SAN 203-3275) Tel 606-257-2951; Dist. by: Harper & Row Pubs., Inc., Keystone Industrial Pk., Scranton, PA 18512 (SAN 215-3742); *CIP.*

†**U Pr of Miss,** *(Univ. Pr. of Mississippi; 0-87805),* 3825 Ridgewood Rd., Jackson, MS 39211 (SAN 203-1914) Tel 601-982-6205; *CIP.*

†**U Pr of New Eng,** *(Univ. Pr. of New England; 0-87451),* 3 Lebanon St., Hanover, NH 03755 (SAN 203-3283) Tel 603-646-3349; *CIP.*

†**U Pr of Va,** *(Univ. Pr. of Virginia; 0-8139),* P.O. Box 3608, Univ. Sta., Charlottesville, VA 22903 (SAN 202-5361) Tel 804-924-3468; *CIP. Imprints:* Bird & Bull Pr (Bird & Bull Press, The); Colonial Soc MA (Colonial Society of Massachusetts); Friends U Rochester (Friends of the University of Rochester Libraries).(Friends of the Univ. of Rochester Libraries); Maya Pub Co (Maya Publishing Company).(Maya Publishing Co.).

†**U Pr of Wash,** *(Univ. Press of Washington, D.C.; 0-87419),* University Press Bldg., Delbrook Campus C.A.S., Riverton, VA 22651 (SAN 204-8760) Tel 703-635-4029; Dist. by: Coronet Press, The, 41 Morton St., New York, NY 10014 (SAN 241-2934) Tel 212-924-3986; *CIP.*

U Pr Wisc River Falls, *(Univ. Press, Univ. of Wisconsin-River Falls),* 118 N. Hall, River Falls, WI 54022 (SAN 214-1663).

†**U Presses Fla,** *(Univ. Presses of Florida; 0-8130),* 15 NW 15th St., Gainesville, FL 32603 (SAN 207-9275) Tel 904-392-1351; *CIP. Imprints:* Univ Gallery U of FL (University of Florida, University Gallery).

†**U Pubns Amer,** *(University Pubns. of America, Inc.; 0-89093; 1-55655),* 44 N. Market St., Frederick, MD 21701 (SAN 210-5802) Tel 301-694-0100; Toll free: 800-692-6300; *CIP. Imprints:* Aletheia Bks (Aletheia Books).(Aletheia Bks.).

U-Read Pubns, *(U-Read Pubns.; 0-938925),* 389 Marin Ave., Mill Valley, CA 94941 (SAN 661-7956) Tel 415-383-5638; Dist. by: Publishers Group West, 5855 Beaudry St., Emeryville, CA 94608 (SAN 202-8522) Tel 415-658-3453.

U Rochester Policy, *(Univ. of Rochester Policy Center Pubns.; 0-932468),* 105 Dewey Hall, Univ. of Rochester, Rochester, NY 14627 (SAN 212-3924) Tel 716-275-3218.

U S A Pub Co, *(U.S.A. Publishing Co.; 0-9612124),* c/o Northwest Title & Escrow, Inc., 165 Cook St., No. 202, Denver, CO 80206 (SAN 289-5110).

U S Standard Inc, *(U.S. Standard, Inc.; 0-915229),* 309 Garden Ct., Sycamore, IL 60178 (SAN 289-8667) Tel 815-895-2646; P.O. Box 131, Sycamore, IL 60178 (SAN 658-246X); Dist. by: Pan American Navigation, P.O. Box 9046, Van Nuys, CA 91409 (SAN 202-8506) Tel 213-345-2744; Dist. by: Sportsman's Market, Clermont County Airport, Batavia, OH 41503 (SAN 205-0803) Tel 513-732-2411; Dist. by: Aviation Bk. Co., 1640 Victory Blvd., Glendale, CA 91201 (SAN 289-8691) Tel 818-240-1771.

U S Strat Inst, *(U. S. Strategic Institute; 0-913187),* 265 Winter St., Waltham, MA 02154 (SAN 287-7759) Tel 617-890-5030.

U Scranton Ethnic, *(Univ. of Scranton, Ethnic Studies Program; 0-9607870),* Univ. of Scranton, Dept. of Hist. & Political Sci., Scranton, PA 18510 (SAN 239-7498) Tel 717-961-7443.

U St NY Zd
See NYS Ed Dept

U Temecula Pr, *(Univ. of Temecula Pr.; 0-936283),* 29860 Camino del Sol, Temecula, CA 92390 (SAN 697-9793) Tel 714-676-5234; P.O. Box 1239, Temecula, CA 92390 (SAN 698-2352).

U Tenn CSW, *(Univ. of Tennessee, College of Social Work, Office of Research & Public Service; 0-89695),* 1838 Terrace Ave., Knoxville, TN 37996-3920 (SAN 287-2994) Tel 615-974-6015.

U Tenn SSW
See U Tenn CSW

U Tex Austin Ctr
See UTX CSAA

U Tex Austin Film Lib, *(Univ. of Texas at Austin Film Library; 0-913648),* Drawer W, University Sta., Austin, TX 78713-7448 (SAN 203-0446) Tel 512-471-3572.

U Tex Studia
See Studia Hispanica

U Tulsa Info Serv, *(Univ. of Tulsa, Information Services Div.; 0-932602),* 600 S. College Ave., Tulsa, OK 74104 (SAN 206-0671) Tel 918-939-6351.

U TX Arl TX Hum, *(University of Texas At Arlington, Texas Humanities Resource Center; 0-942484),* Library, P.O. Box 19497, Arlington, TX 76019 (SAN 238-5880) Tel 817-273-2767.

U TX Austin Gen Libs, *(Univ. of Texas at Austin, General Libraries; 0-930214),* Univ. of Texas at Austin, P.O. Box P, Austin, TX 78713-7330 (SAN 210-6795) Tel 512-471-3811; Orders to: University of Texas at Austin, General Libraries, Publications, P.O. Box P, Austin, TX 78713-7330 (SAN 662-1759) Tel 512-471-3811.

U TX Inst Lat Am Stud, *(Univ. of Texas at Austin, Institute of Latin American Studies; 0-86728),* Sid Richardson Hall 1-310, Austin, TX 78712 (SAN 220-3103) Tel 512-471-5551.

U VA CLE Law, *(University of Virginia Committee on Continuing Legal Education School of Law),* Charlottesville, VA 22901 (SAN 226-2819) Tel 804-924-3416.

U VA Inst Gov, *(University of Virginia Institute of Government),* 207 Minor Hall, Charlottesville, VA 22903 (SAN 227-1001) Tel 804-924-3396.

U VA Law CLE
See U VA CLE Law

U WA Ctr Soc Welfare, *(Univ. of Washington, Ctr. for Social Welfare Research; 0-935035),* Univ. of Washington, Schl. of Social Work, 4101 15th Ave. NE, Box JH-30, Seattle, WA 98195 (SAN 694-5252) Tel 206-545-1632.

U Wake Forest, *(Wake Forest Univ.; 0-918401),* 7227 Reynolda Sta., Winston-Salem, NC 27109 (SAN 657-3908) Tel 919-761-5769.

U WI Ctr Coop, *(Univ. of Wisconsin, Univ. Ctr. for Cooperatives; 0-942288),* 514 Lowell Hall, 610 Langdon St., Madison, WI 53703 (SAN 240-1681) Tel 608-262-3251.

U WI Sea Grant, *(Univ. of Wisconsin Sea Grant Institute; 0-936287),* Div. of Univ. of Wisconsin, 1800 University Ave., Madison, WI 53705 (SAN 697-9831) Tel 608-263-3259.

U Wis Lib Sch
See U Wis Sch Lib

U Wis-Mil Ctr Latin Am, *(Univ. of Wisconsin-Milwaukee, Ctr. for Latin America; 0-930450),* Univ. of Wisconsin-Milwaukee, P.O. Box 413, Milwaukee, WI 53201 (SAN 224-0939) Tel 414-963-4401; 3243 N. Downer Ave., Milwaukee, WI 53211 (SAN 669-036X).

U Wis Sch Lib, *(Univ. of Wisconsin-Madison, Schl. of Library & Information Studies; 0-936442),* 600 N. Park St., Madison, WI 53706 (SAN 219-9874).

U Wisc Indus Rel
See Indus Relations Res

U Wisc Law Madison, *(Univ. of Wisconsin-Madison Law Schl.; 0-933431),* 975 Bascom Mall, Madison, WI 53706 (SAN 237-8876) Tel 608-262-2240.

UAH Pr, *(UAH Press; 0-933958),* P.O. Box 1247, Huntsville, AL 35807 (SAN 212-8160).

†UAHC, *(Union of American Hebrew Congregations; 0-8074),* 838 Fifth Ave., New York, NY 10021 (SAN 203-3291) Tel 212-249-0100; *CIP.*

UB *Imprint of* **Unipub**

Ubu Repertory, *(Ubu Repertory Theater Pubns.; 0-913745),* 149 Mercer St., New York, NY 10012 (SAN 286-2077) Tel 212-925-0999; Dist. by: Publishing Ctr. for Cultural Resources, 625 Broadway, New York, NY 10012 (SAN 274-9025) Tel 212-260-2010.

†UC Chicano, *(Univ. of California, Berkeley, Chicano Studies Library; 0-918520),* 3404 Dwinelle Hall, Berkeley, CA 94720 (SAN 209-9039) Tel 415-642-3859; *CIP.*

UC-Wm Andrews Clark, *(University of California, Wm. Andrews Clark Memorial Library; 0-88330),* 2520 Cimarron St., Los Angeles, CA 90018 (SAN 206-1104) Tel 213-731-8529.

UCal Berk CLRE, *(Univ. of California, Berkeley, Ctr. for Labor Research & Education; 0-937817),* 2521 Channing Way, Berkeley, CA 94720 (SAN 659-4336) Tel 415-642-0323.

UCB Real Estate, *(University of California at Berkeley, Center for Real Estate & Urban Economics),* 156 Barrows Hall, Berkeley, CA 94720 (SAN 237-6482).

UCC UCC
See Union Cong Church

UCDLA, *(Univ. of California; 0-913248),* Div. of Library Automation, 186 University Hall, Berkeley, CA 94720 (SAN 207-3617) Tel 415-642-9485.

Uchill, *(Uchill, Ida Libert; 0-9604468),* 795 S. Jersey St., Denver, CO 80224 (SAN 214-3305) Tel 303-355-9829; Dist. by: L & B Enterprises, 1205 S. Ivy Way, Denver, CO 80224 (SAN 200-7681) Tel 303-756-4563.

†UCLA Arch, *(Univ. of California, Los Angeles, Institute of Archaeology; 0-917956),* 405 Hilgard Ave., Los Angeles, CA 90024 (SAN 210-3281) Tel 213-825-7411; *CIP.*

UCLA Busn Forecasting, *(University of California, Los Angeles, Business Forecasting Project; 0-913404),* Graduate School of Management, Rm. 4371-C, Los Angeles, CA 90024 (SAN 203-0160) Tel 213-825-1623.

†UCLA CAAS, *(Center for Afro-American Studies at UCLA; 0-934934),* Univ. of California at Los Angeles, 3111 Campbell Hall, 405 Hilgard Ave., Los Angeles, CA 90024 (SAN 214-2899) Tel 213-825-3528; Orders to: CAAS Pubns., Publishers Services, P.O. Box 2510, Novato, CA 94948 (SAN 661-9711) Tel 415-883-3140; *CIP.*

UCLA Chicano Stud, *(Univ. of California, Los Angeles, Chicano Studies Research Ctr., Pubns. Unit; 0-89551),* 3126 Campbell Hall, 405 Hilgard Ave., Los Angeles, CA 90024 (SAN 209-097X) Tel 213-825-2642.

UCLA Hist Mus
See UCLA Mus Hist

UCLA Lat Am Ctr, *(Univ. of California, Latin American Ctr.; 0-87903),* 405 Hilgard Ave., Los Angeles, CA 90024 (SAN 201-0704) Tel 213-825-6634.

UCLA Law, *(Univ. of California at Los Angeles, Schl. of Law),* Rm. 2125C, Los Angeles, CA 90024 (SAN 226-3637).

UCLA Mgmt, *(UCLA, Grad, School of Management, GSM Pubns. Services; 0-911798),* 405 Hilgard Ave., Los Angeles, CA 90024 (SAN 203-0179) Tel 213-206-8197.

UCLA Mus Hist, *(Univ. of California Los Angeles, Museum of Cultural History; 0-930741),* 405 Hilgard Ave., 55A Haines Hall, Los Angeles, CA 90024 (SAN 280-8501) Tel 213-825-4361.

UCLA Tissue, *(UCLA Tissue Typing Laboratory; 0-9604606),* UCLA School of Medicine, Los Angeles, CA 90024 (SAN 282-4752); Orders to: 1000 Veteran Ave., Los Angeles, CA 90024 (SAN 282-4760) Tel 213-825-7651.

UCO BGR, *(University of Colorado, Bureau of Governmental, Research & Science),* 125 Ketchum Bldg., Boulder, CO 80302 (SAN 226-9163).

UCP NYC, *(United Cerebral Palsy of New York City, Inc.; 0-9616554),* 122 E. 23rd St., New York, NY 10010 (SAN 659-6061) Tel 212-677-7400.

UCPANB, *(United Cerebral Palsy Assn. of the North Bay; 0-9616891),* 1057 College Ave., No. 104, Santa Rosa, CA 95404 (SAN 661-6453) Tel 707-544-3448.

Ucross Bks, *(Ucross Bks.; 0-9614024),* P.O. Box 764, Los Alamos, NM 87544 (SAN 683-7344) Tel 505-662-6591.

UFB Pubns
See Seven Suns

UFO Photo, *(UFO Photo Archives; 0-9608558; 0-934269),* P.O. Box 17206, Tuscon, AZ 85710 (SAN 240-7949) Tel 602-296-6753.

UFO Schools, *(UFO Schools, Inc.; 0-933938),* 31800 Schoenherr, Apt. H9, Warren, MI 48093 (SAN 213-182X) Tel 313-293-5867.

UH CRDG, *(Univ. of Hawaii at Manoa, Curriculum Research & Development Group; 0-937049),* 1776 University Ave., CM 103, Honolulu, HI 96822 (SAN 658-6597) Tel 808-948-6823; Dist. by: Educational Merchandising & Consulting, 8912 Mineral King Ct., Elk Grove, CA 95624 (SAN 200-6308).

†UH Pr, *(Univ. of Hawaii Pr., The; 0-8248),* 2840 Kolowalu St., Honolulu, HI 96822 (SAN 202-5353) Tel 808-948-8697; 1330 Lower Campus Rd., Honolulu, HI 96822 (SAN 658-215X); *CIP. Imprints:* Consort Pac Arts (Consortium for Pacific Arts & Cultures); Eastwest Ctr (Eastwest Center Press).(Eastwest Ctr. Press); Kolowalu Bk (Kolowalu Book); Korea Devel Inst (Korea Development Institute); Pac Telecomm (Pacific Telecommunications Council); Seaweeds & Cons (Seaweeds & Constructions).

UHLs Pub, *(UHL's Publishing Co. (U-L); 0-943240),* RD 1, Box 119, Spencer, NY 14883 (SAN 240-7957) Tel 607-589-6594.

UI Law Urbana, *(Univ. of Illinois at Urbana-Champaign, College of Law),* 209 Law Bldg., Champaign, IL 61820 (SAN 226-8779).

UI Urbana
See UI Law Urbana

UIE *Imprint of* **Unipub**

Ujjaini Pubs, *(SI; 0-9610134),* 8911 Leamont, Houston, TX 77099 (SAN 276-1432) Tel 713-495-5849.

Ukiyo-e Soc, *(Ukiyo-e Society of America, Inc.; 0-9610398),* 1692 Second Ave., New York, NY 10028 (SAN 264-4479).

Ukrainian Acad, *(Ukrainian Academic Press; 0-87287),* Div. of Libraries Unlimited, Inc., P.O. Box 263, Littleton, CO 80160 (SAN 203-3305) Tel 303-770-1220.

Ukrainian Arts Sci, *(Ukrainian Academy of Arts & Sciences in the U.S., The; 0-916381),* 206 W. 100 St., New York, NY 10025 (SAN 206-2607) Tel 212-222-1866.

Ukrainian Cult Inst, *(Ukrainian Cultural Institute),* Dickinson State College, Dickinson, ND 58601 (SAN 287-2366).

Ukrainian Ed Assn, *(Ukrainian Education Assn. of Maryland, Inc.; 0-9606178),* 518 S. Wolfe St., Baltimore, MD 21231 (SAN 220-3537) Tel 301-252-3051.

Ukrainian Her Co, *(Ukrainian Heritage Co.; 0-936113),* 8444 Kraay, Munster, IN 46321 (SAN 696-7671) Tel 219-972-3108.

Ukrainian News, *(Ukrainian News, Inc.; 0-912601),* 19411 W. Warren Ave., Detroit, MI 48228 (SAN 282-8413).

Ukrainian Pol, *(Ukrainian Political Science Assn. in the U. S.),* P.O. Box 12963, Philadelphia, PA 19108 (SAN 236-5537).

Ukrainian Res, *(Ukrainian Research Foundation; 0-934760),* 6931 S. Yosemite St., Englewood, CO 80112 (SAN 213-5647).

Ukrainian St
See Ukrainian Arts Sci

Uleck Assoc
See Prospect Pr

Ulrich, *(Ulrich's Bks., Inc.; 0-914004),* 549 E. University Ave., Ann Arbor, MI 48107-8607 (SAN 100-2945) Tel 313-662-3201.

Ultima Thule Pub, *(Ultima Thule Publishing Co.; 0-938203),* P.O. Box 100731, Anchorage, AK 99510 (SAN 659-6657); 524 W. Fourth Ave., Suite 204C, Anchorage, AK 99510 (SAN 659-6665) Tel 907-277-0875.

Ultra-Nutri, *(Ultra Nutrimol Technical Pubs.; 0-9612386),* 19 Westglow St., A2, Boston, MA 02122 (SAN 287-7694) Tel 617-825-0595.

†Ultralight Pubns, *(Ultralight Pubns.; 0-938716),* P.O. Box 234, Hummelstown, PA 17036 (SAN 220-2786) Tel 717-566-0468; Toll free: 800-441-7527; *CIP. Imprints:* AViation Pubs (AViation Publishers).

Ultramarine Pub, *(Ultramarine Publishing Co., Inc.; 0-89366),* P.O. Box 303, Hastings-on-Hudson, NY 10706 (SAN 208-8762) Tel 914-478-2522.

Ulysses Pr, *(Ulysses Pr.; 0-915233),* Box 4000 H, Berkeley, CA 94704 (SAN 289-8764) Tel 415-644-0915; 3019 Deakin St., Berkeley, CA 94705 (SAN 289-8772); Dist. by: Publishers Group West, 5855 Beaudry St., Emeryville, CA 94608 (SAN 202-8522) Tel 415-658-3453.

UM Ctr NENAS, *(Univ. of Michigan, Ctr. for Near Eastern & North African Studies; 0-932098),* 144 Lane Hall, Ann Arbor, MI 48109-1290 (SAN 211-7150) Tel 313-764-0350; Orders to: Univ. of Michigan Resources Ctr., 204 S. Fourth St., Ann Arbor, MI 48103 (SAN 653-483X) Tel 313-764-8288; Dist. by: Univ. of Michigan Pr., Pubns. Distribution Ctr., 839 Greene St., Ann Arbor, MI 48106 (SAN 285-1075) Tel 313-764-4394; Dist. by: Cambridge Univ. Pr., 510 North Ave., New Rochelle, NY 10801 (SAN 285-1083) Tel 914-235-0300; Dist. by: International Bk. Ctr., P.O. Box 295, Troy, MI 48099 (SAN 208-7022) Tel 313-879-8436. Do not confuse with Univ. of Michigan, Dept. of Near Eastern Studies.

UM Dept NES, *(Univ. of Michigan, Dept. of Near Eastern Studies; 0-916798),* Div. of Univ. of Michigan, 3074 Frieze Bldg., Ann Arbor, MI 48109 (SAN 285-1059) Tel 313-764-0314; Dist. by: Eisenbrauns, P.O. Box 275, Winona Lake, IN 46590 (SAN 285-1067) Tel 219-269-2011. Do not confuse with Univ. of Michigan, Ctr. for Near Eastern & North African Studies.

UM Eastern Stud
See UM Dept NES

UM Near Eastern Studies
See UM Dept NES

UMCD, *(United Methodist Church of the Dunes; 0-9608642),* 943 Lake Ave., Grand Haven, MI 49417 (SAN 238-3993) Tel 616-846-5429.

UMHB Pr, *(Univ. of Mary Hardin-Baylor Pr.; 0-9616297),* 11th & College St., Belton, TX 76513 (SAN 658-5310) Tel 817-939-5811; P.O. Box 431, UMHB Sta., Belton, TX 76513 (SAN 658-5329).

UMI
See UMI Charlotte

UMI Charlotte, *(UMI Pubns., Inc.; 0-943860),* P.O. Box 30036, Charlotte, NC 28230 (SAN 241-0834) Tel 704-374-0420. Do not confuse with UMI Research Pr., Ann Arbor, MI.

UMI Mus Anthro, *(Univ. of Michigan, Museum of Anthropology; 0-915703),* 4009 Museums, Ann Arbor, MI 48109 (SAN 280-901X).

†**UMI Res Pr,** *(UMI Research Pr.; 0-8357),* Div. of University Microfilms, International, 300 N. Zeeb Rd., Ann Arbor, MI 48106 (SAN 212-2464) Tel 313-761-4700; Toll free: 800-521-0600. Do not confuse with UMI Publications, Inc., Charlotte, NC; *CIP.*

UN, *(United Nations; 0-680),* Sales Section, Publishing Div., Rm. DC2-853, New York, NY 10017 (SAN 206-6718) Tel 212-754-8302.

†**UNA-USA,** *(United Nations Assn. of the United States of America, Inc.; 0-934654),* 300 E. 42nd St, New York, NY 10017 (SAN 204-8892) Tel 212-697-3232; *CIP.*

UNABASHED Lib, *(UNABASHED Librarian; 0-916444),* G.P.O. Box 2631, New York, NY 10116-2631 (SAN 208-8983).

Unarius
See Unarius Pubns

Unarius Pubns, *(Unarius Pubns.; 0-932642; 0-935097),* 145 S. Magnolia Ave., El Cajon, CA 92020 (SAN 168-9614) Tel 619-447-4170.

UNC Inst Res Soc Sci
See U NC Inst Res Soc Sci

Undena Pubns, *(Undena Pubns.; 0-89003),* P.O. Box 97, Malibu, CA 90265 (SAN 293-406X) Tel 818-366-1744; Dist. by: Eisenbrauns, P.O. Box 275, Winona Lake, IN 46590-0278 (SAN 293-4078) Tel 219-269-2011.

Underhill, *(C. S. Underhill; 0-9600268),* P.O. Box 127, East Aurora, NY 14052 (SAN 206-670X) Tel 716-652-0185.

Underhill Enter, *(Underhill Enterprises; 0-9616734),* 1815 Russell Ave., Cheyenne, WY 82001 (SAN 659-8889) Tel 307-632-5197.

Underwater Spec Ltd, *(Underwater Specialists, Ltd.; 0-936655),* 5700 Sheridan St., Hollywood, FL 33021 (SAN 699-7236).

Underwood B, *(Underwood, Barry; 0-9614790),* 5504 Dobbs St., No. 77, Los Angeles, CA 90032 (SAN 692-9869) Tel 213-225-9352.

Underwood-Miller, *(Underwood/Miller; 0-934438; 0-88733),* 651 Chestnut St., Columbia, PA 17512 (SAN 282-4795) Tel 717-684-7335. *Imprints:* Tamerlane (Tamerlane Press).

Undiscovered, *(Undiscovered Denver Dining; 0-9610064),* 940 Emerson, Denver, CO 80218 (SAN 285-1008); Dist. by: Gordon's, 5450 Valley Hwy., Denver, CO 80216 (SAN 285-1016) Tel 303-296-1830; Dist. by: Dillon's, P.O. Drawer J, Boulder, CO 80306 (SAN 285-1024) Tel 303-442-5323.

Une Pub, *(Une Publishing),* 9 Moss Ave., Danbury, CT 06810 (SAN 217-1368).

Uneeda Pr, *(Uneeda Pr.; 0-9617283),* 701 Howe Ave., Suite G-48, Sacramento, CA 95825 (SAN 663-5202) Tel 916-922-2066.

UNESCO *Imprint of* **Unipub**

†**Ungar,** *(Ungar Publishing Co.; 0-8044),* 370 Lexington Ave., New York, NY 10017 (SAN 202-5256) Tel 212-532-3650; Orders to: Harper & Row, Keystone Industrial Park, Scranton, PA 18512 (SAN 662-1635); *CIP.*

Uni-Sun, *(UNI-SUN; 0-912949),* P.O. Box 25421, 4005 NE 49th Terrace, Kansas City, MO 64119 (SAN 283-4332) Tel 816-454-8705.

Unibra Pub Co, *(Unibra Publishing Co.; 0-933077),* P.O. Box 901079, Memphis, TN 38109 (SAN 689-8122) Tel 901-785-1902; Orders to: Robert Lee, Book Order Dept. - A, P.O. Box 901079, Memphis, TN 38109 (SAN 662-2860) Tel 901-785-4589.

Unicon Ent, *(Unicon Enterprises; 0-912327),* 3602 W. Glen Branch, Peoria, IL 61614 (SAN 265-1475) Tel 309-688-3772.

Unicorn Bkshop, *(Unicorn Bookshop; 0-9615275),* P.O. Box 154, Trappe, MD 21673 (SAN 695-2178) Tel 301-476-3838.

Unicorn Comm, *(Unicorn Communications; 0-913311),* P.O. Box 2507, Billings, MT 59103 (SAN 287-7708) Tel 406-657-1200.

Unicorn Ent, *(Unicorn Enterprises; 0-87884),* 1620 Collinsdale Ave., Cincinnati, OH 45230 (SAN 206-6696).

Unicorn NJ, *(Unicorn Pr.; 0-937004),* P.O. Box 138, Monmouth Junction, NJ 08852 (SAN 213-4772) Tel 215-968-0155.

†**Unicorn Pr,** *(Unicorn Pr.; 0-87775),* P.O. Box 3307, Greensboro, NC 27402 (SAN 203-3313) Tel 919-852-0281; *CIP.*

Unicorn Pub, *(Unicorn Publishing Hse., Inc., The; 0-88101),* 1148 Parsippany Blvd., Parsippany, NJ 07054 (SAN 240-4567) Tel 201-334-0353; 300 Raritan Ctr. Pkwy., Edison, NJ 08818 (SAN 658-2087).

Unicorn Rising, *(Unicorn Rising Ltd.; 0-913313),* Rte. 2, P.O. Box 360, Sheridan, OR 97378 (SAN 285-8924) Tel 503-843-3902.

Unicorn VA
See Fitzg Unicorn

UNIDO *Imprint of* **Unipub**

Unif Theol Seminary, *(Unification Theological Seminary; 0-932894),* G.P.O. Box 2432, New York, NY 10116 (SAN 212-3193) Tel 914-758-6881; Dist. by: Rose of Sharon Press Inc., G.P.O. Box 2432, New York, NY 10116 (SAN 212-3207) Tel 914-758-6881.

Unification Church, *(Unification Church Pubns.),* 4 W. 43rd St., New York, NY 10036 (SAN 211-8270).

UNIFO Pubs, *(UNIFO Pubs., Ltd.; 0-89111),* P.O. Box 37, Pleasantville, NY 10570 (SAN 219-8290); 28 Lower Main St., Ossining, NY 10562 (SAN 658-2079) Tel 914-941-1330.

Unikorn Magik, *(Unikorn Magik; 0-9604016),* Three Gregg St., Beverly, MA 01915-2913 (SAN 214-1582) Tel 617-927-9388.

Unikorn Majik
See Unikorn Magik

Unilaw *Imprint of* **Donning Co**

Uniline Div, *(Uniline Division John Klein &Assoc. Inc.; 0-912904),* John Klein Assocs., Inc., 20700 Miles Ave., Cleveland, OH 44128 (SAN 203-0497) Tel 216-587-3070.

Union & Confed Inc., *(Union & Confederacy Inc.; 0-911679),* Route 1, Box 267, College Grove, TN 37046 (SAN 276-9425) Tel 615-368-7175.

†**Union Coll,** *(Union College Press; 0-912756),* Orders to: Union College Press, College Grounds, Schenectady, NY 12308 (SAN 206-9776) Tel 518-370-6096; *CIP.*

Union Conc Sci, *(Union of Concerned Scientists),* 26 Church St., Cambridge, MA 02238 (SAN 225-6894) Tel 617-547-5552; 1346 Connecticut Ave., NW, Washington, DC 20036 (SAN 650-0633).

Union Cong Church, *(Union Congregational Church; 0-9610366),* 176 Cooper Ave., Upper Montclair, NJ 07043 (SAN 264-4509).

Union League PA, *(Union League of Philadelphia; 0-915810),* 140 S. Broad St., Philadelphia, PA 19102 (SAN 207-687X) Tel 215-563-6500.

Union Messianic Jew Pub, *(Union of Messianic Jewish Congregations Publishing; 0-9614555),* 2208 Rockland Ave., Rockville, MD 20851 (SAN 691-8123) Tel 301-770-2494.

Union Park, *(Union Park Press; 0-9601570),* P.O. Box 2737, Boston, MA 02208 (SAN 211-5808) Tel 617-754-0708.

Union Pr, *(Union Press; 0-9603384),* 3009 Hillegass Ave., Berkeley, CA 94705 (SAN 212-3088) Tel 415-845-9658.

Union Printers Hist Soc, *(Union Printers Historical Society),* 1726 West Jarvis Ave., Chicago, IL 60626 (SAN 240-4990).

Union Rep, *(Union Representative; 0-918515),* 430 S. Michigan Ave., Chicago, IL 60605 (SAN 657-7334) Tel 312-798-1660.

Union Square Bks *Imprint of* **Crittenden Pub**

Union Sta, *(Union Station, The; 0-9615257),* 785 Murrah Rd., North Augusta, SC 29841 (SAN 694-3810) Tel 803-279-5975.

Unipub, *(Unipub; 0-89059; 0-400; 0-527),* Div. of Kraus-Thomson Organization, Ltd., 9730E George Palmer Hwy., Lanham, MD 20706 (SAN 210-7562) Tel 301-459-7666. Toll free: 800-521-8110;
Imprints: AMPC (American Productivity Center); ED (Editions Delta); EUR (Europa); FUJI (F U J I).(FUJI); ICJ (International Court of Justice (ICJ)); IFPA (Institute for Foreign Policy Analysis (IFPA)); ISES (International Solar Energy Society (ISES)); JCP (JCP); Venture Econo (Venture Economics). Capital Pub Corp (Capital Publishing Corporation (CPC)).(Capital Publishing Corp. (CPC)); CAB (Commonwealth Agricultural Bureau (CAB)); CRD (United Nations Center for Regional Development (CRD)); ILO (International Labor Organization (ILO)); Owen's Pub Co (Owen's Publishing Company (OD)); PDC (Centre for Agricultural Publishing & Documentation); PUB (Publitek); TUNU (United Nations University, The (TUNU)).(United Nations Univ., The (TUNU)); TYP (Tycooly Publishing); UB (UNESCO Regional Office for Education in Asia & the Pacific (Bangkok)); UR (Unesco Records); US (Unesco Slides); Worldwide Furbearer Con (Worldwide Furbearer Conference Inc.); WWIR (Who's Who in the International Red Series (WWIR)).

CIP. Imprints: APO (Asian Productivity Organization); DUO (D U O).(DUO); Edns Delta (Editions Delta); FAO (Food & Agriculture Organization); FMME (Fund for Multinational Management Education); FMME-COA (Fund for Multinational Management Education - Council of the Americas); FNB (Fishing News Books, Limited). (Fishing News Bks., Ltd.); GATT (General Agreement on Tariffs & Trade); IAEA (International Atomic Energy Agency); ICSU (International Council of Scientific Unions, Abstracting Board of Publications).(International Council of Scientific Unions, Abstracting Board of Pubns.); IUCN (International Union for Conservation of Nature & Natural Resources); ORDINA (O R D I N A).(ORDINA); SSC (Supplies & Services, Government of Canada); UIE (U I E).(UIE); UNESCO (United Nations Educational, Scientific & Cultural Organization); UNIDO (United Nations Industrial Development Organization); WIPO (World Intellectual Property Organization).

Unique Bks
See Landrum & Assocs

Unique Golf Res, *(Unique Golf Resorts of The World Inc.; 0-9612294),* 4501 Camden Dr., Corona Del Mar, CA 92625 (SAN 289-5137) Tel 714-760-0208.

Unique Pub CA, *(Unique Publishing Co.; 0-934189),* 1825 Clinton Ave., Suite D, Alameda, CA 94501 (SAN 693-403X) Tel 415-865-1987; 7941 La Riviera Dr., Sacramento, CA 95826 (SAN 662-3212) Tel 916-381-4783.

Unique Pubns, *(Unique Pubns.; 0-86568),* Subs. of CFW Enterprises,INC., 4201 W. Vanowen Pl., Burbank, CA 91505 (SAN 214-3313) Tel 818-845-2656; Toll free: 800-332-3330.

Unique Pubs, *(Unique Pubs.; 0-936811),* 11901 Andrew St., Wheaton, MD 20902 (SAN 699-9514) Tel 202-755-6961.

UNITAR, *(United Nations Institute for Training & Research),* 801 UN Plaza, New York, NY 10017 (SAN 227-1214).

Unitarian, *(Unitarian Universalist Church, The),* E. Main St., Canton, NY 13617 (SAN 213-1838).

†**Unitarian Univ,** *(Unitarian Universalist Assn.; 0-933840),* 25 Beacon St, Boston, MA 02108 (SAN 225-4840) Tel 617-742-2100; *CIP. Imprints:* Skinner Hse Bks (Skinner House Bks).

United Aloe
See Erde Intl

†**United Bible,** *(United Bible Societies; 0-8267),* 1865 Broadway, New York, NY 10023 (SAN 204-8787) Tel 212-581-7400; Orders to: American Bible Society, P.O. Box 5656, Grand Central Station, New York, NY 10163 (SAN 662-1643); *CIP.*

United Busn
See Media Horizons

United Church Pr
See Pilgrim NY

United Comns, *(United Communications of America, Inc.; 0-937047),* 2445 Hartrey Ave., Evanston, IL 60201 (SAN 658-6627) Tel 312-869-9888; Dist. by: Kampmann & Co., 9 E. 40th St., New York, NY 10016 (SAN 202-5191) Tel 212-685-2928.

United CP, *(United Cerebral Palsy Assns., Inc.),* 66 E. 34th St., New York, NY 10016 (SAN 224-2869).

United Ed, *(United Educators, Inc.; 0-87566),* 900 Armour Dr., Lake Bluff, IL 60044 (SAN 204-8795) Tel 312-234-3700.

United Elec R&M, *(United Electrical Radio & Machine Workers of America; 0-916180),* 11 E. 51st St., New York, NY 10022 (SAN 208-3973) Tel 212-753-1960.

United Galactic Pub *Imprint of* First Intl Pub

United Health, *(United Health Resource, Inc.),* 2082 Michelson Dr., Irvine, CA 92715 (SAN 670-6789) Tel 714-476-2167.

United Learn, *(United Learning Corp.; 0-915671),* P.O. Box 5441, Eugene, OR 97405 (SAN 207-298X) Tel 503-683-3383.

United Meth Archives, *(United Methodist Church, Commission on Archives & History; 0-915466),* P.O. Box 127, Madison, NJ 07940 (SAN 203-0578) Tel 201-822-2787.

United Meth Educ, *(United Methodist Board of Higher Education & Ministry; 0-938162),* Box 871, Nashville, TN 37202 (SAN 216-3136) Tel 615-327-2700.

United Ostomy, *(United Ostomy Assn.),* 2001 W. Beverly Blvd., Los Angeles, CA 90057 (SAN 224-408X) Tel 213-413-5510.

United Piece, *(United Piece Dye Works; 0-911546),* 11 W. 40th St., New York, NY 10018 (SAN 204-8809) Tel 212-840-0400.

United Pub Co, *(United Publishing Co.; 0-937323),* 11 Elm Pl., Albany, NY 12203 (SAN 658-8077) Tel 518-456-1321.

United Pubs Intl, *(United Publishers International, Ltd.; 0-939499),* 252 W. 47th St., Suite 6, New York, NY 10036 (SAN 663-4044) Tel 212-921-7664.

United Res, *(United Research; 0-915235),* P.O. Box 1146, Black Mountain, NC 28711 (SAN 289-8780) Tel 704-669-6845.

United Res CA, *(United Research; 0-9614924),* Div. of Solar Products, Inc., 2816 Atadero Ct., Carlsbad, CA 92008 (SAN 693-5834) Tel 619-942-0335.

United Res Pub, *(United Resources Publishing; 0-932307),* 1100 Quail St., Suite 100, Newport Beach, CA 92660-2701 (SAN 686-726X) Tel 714-851-2717.

United Seminars Amer, *(United Seminars of America, Inc.; 0-938093),* P.O. Box 19324, San Diego, CA 92119 (SAN 659-7068); 7290 Navajo Rd., No. 212, San Diego, CA 92119 (SAN 659-7076) Tel 619-463-6405.

United Spirit, *(United Spiritual Temple; 0-935611),* 249412 Sumner Ave., Brooklyn, NY 11206 (SAN 695-7978) Tel 718-424-5275; P.O. Box 249, Metro Sta., Brooklyn, NY 11206 (SAN 696-0413).

United Syn Bk, *(United Synagogue Book Service; 0-8381),* Subs. of United Synagogue of America, 155 Fifth Ave., New York, NY 10010 (SAN 203-0551) Tel 212-533-7800.

United Synagogue, *(United Synagogue Commission on Jewish Education; 0-8381),* 155 Fifth Ave., New York, NY 10010 (SAN 236-4174)

United Thoroughbred Trnrs, *(United Thoroughbred Trainers of America, Inc.),* 19363 James Couzens Hwy., Detroit, MI 48235 (SAN 224-5728).

United West Pr, *(United West Pr.; 0-9612488),* 611 Dell St., P.O. Box 337, Solana Beach, CA 92075 (SAN 291-8609) Tel 619-481-1990.

Unity Bks
See Unity School

Unity Church Denver, *(Unity Church of Denver; 0-942482),* 3021 S. University, Denver, CO 80210 (SAN 161-4541) Tel 303-758-5664.

Unity Pr, *(Unity Pr.; 0-9615041),* P.O. Box 5500 Jasmine St., Castro Valley, CA 94552 (SAN 693-8302) Tel 415-538-5291.

Unity School, *(Unity School of Christianity; 0-87159),* Unity School of Christianity, Unity Village, MO 64065 (SAN 204-8817) Tel 816-524-3550.

Univ Alaska, *(University of Alaska; 0-943712),* Museum, Fairbanks, AK 99501 (SAN 200-4240).

Univ Assocs, *(University Assocs.; 0-88390),* 8517 Production Ave., San Diego, CA 92121 (SAN 203-393X) Tel 619-578-5900; 8535 Production Ave., San Diego, CA 92121 (SAN 658-2109).

Univ Autograph, *(Universal Autograph Collectors Club; 0-9608816),* P.O. Box 467, Rockville Centre, NY 11571 (SAN 260-3675) Tel 516-766-0093.

Univ AZ Agriculture, *(Univ. of Arizona, College of Agriculture; 0-932913),* Univ. of Arizona, Tucson, AZ 85721 (SAN 689-9706) Tel 602-621-7180.

Univ AZ Mex Amer Studies, *(Univ. of Arizona, Mexican American Studies & Research Ctr.; 0-939363),* 1625 E. Speedway, No. 8, Tucson, AZ 85719 (SAN 662-6971) Tel 602-621-5121.

Univ Bk Serv, *(Univ. Bk. Service; 0-942644),* 2162 Gerritsen Ave., Brooklyn, NY 11229 (SAN 206-4014) Tel 718-280-5066.

Univ Bks, *(University Books, Inc.; 0-8216),* Div. of Lyle Stuart, Inc., 120 Enterprise Ave., Secaucus, NJ 07094 (SAN 203-3348) Tel 201-866-0490; Toll free: 800-572-6657.

Univ Bks *Imprint of* G K Hall

Univ Black Pr, *(Universal Black Writer Pr., The; 0-930569),* P.O. Box 5, Radio City Station, New York, NY 10101 (SAN 219-5658) Tel 212-622-5996.

Univ Book Hse, *(Univ. Bk. Hse.; 0-936461),* 112 Russell Woods Dr., Lynchburg, VA 24502 (SAN 697-9742) Tel 804-237-1486.

Univ CA Dutch Studies, *(Univ. of California, Dutch Studies Program; 0-9616744),* Dept. of German, 5317 Dwinelle Hall, Berkeley, CA 94720 (SAN 661-0447) Tel 415-642-2941.

Univ Central AR Pr, *(Univ. of Central Arkansas Pr.; 0-9615143),* Box S, UCA, Conway, AR 72032 (SAN 694-2083) Tel 501-450-3180.

Univ Chi Ctr Hlth, *(Univ. of Chicago, Ctr. for Health Administration Studies; 0-9616519),* 1101 E. 58th St., Chicago, IL 60637 (SAN 659-5960) Tel 312-962-7104.

Univ Cinn Coll Ed, *(Univ. of Cincinnati, College of Educ.; 0-915645),* Office Of The Dean, Cincinnati, OH 45221 (SAN 292-7187).

Univ Class, *(University Classics, Ltd., Publishers; 0-914127),* 1 Bryan Rd., Briarwood, Athens, OH 45701 (SAN 287-5934) Tel 614-592-4543. *Imprints:* Univ Classics Ltd (University Classics, Limited).

Univ Classics Ltd *Imprint of* Univ Class

Univ CO Dept Hist, *(Univ. of Colorado-Denver, Dept. of History; 0-937859),* P.O. Box 105, Denver, CO 80202 (SAN 659-5979); 1100 14th St., Denver, CO 80202 (SAN 659-5987) Tel 303-556-3442.

Univ Co-Op Soc, *(University Co-Operative Society; 0-916048),* P.O. Box 7520, Austin, TX 78712 (SAN 207-5083) Tel 512-476-7211.

Univ Conn Ed
See I N Thut World Educ Ctr

†**Univ Conn Lib,** *(Univ. of Connecticut Library Business Services, U-5B; 0-917590),* Fairfield Ave., Box U-5BO, Storrs, CT 06268 (SAN 209-3901) Tel 203-486-2520; *CIP.*

Univ Coterie Pipe, *(Universal Coterie of Pipe Smokers),* 20-37 120th St., College Point, NY 11356 (SAN 223-8543).

Univ Diversified
See U Pr of Cal

Univ Edns, *(University Editions; 0-916383),* Subs. of Aegina Press, 4937 Humphrey Rd., Huntington, WV 25704 (SAN 295-8287) Tel 304-736-1027.

Univ Edns *Imprint of* New Benjamin

Univ Extension Pubns, *(University Extension Pubns, Univ. of California, Berkeley; 0-917936),* 2223 Fulton St., Berkeley, CA 94720 (SAN 208-0311) Tel 415-642-3112.

†**Univ Fla Food,** *(Univ. of Florida, Institute of Food & Agricultural Sciences; 0-916287),* Bldg. 459 Shealy Dr., Gainesville, FL 32611 (SAN 295-6055) Tel 904-392-2186; *CIP.*

Univ GA Nat Res, *(Univ. of Georgia Institute of Natural Resources; 0-935835),* Univ. of Georgia, Athens, GA 30602 (SAN 696-6497) Tel 404-542-1555.

Univ Gallery U of FL *Imprint of* U Presses Fla

Univ Games, *(University Games; 0-935145),* 4055 Bohannon Dr., Menlo Park, CA 94025 (SAN 695-2321) Tel 415-322-3953.

Univ Goddess, *(Universal Goddess Center Inc.; 0-937946),* P.O. Box 671, Malibu, CA 90265 (SAN 220-0996) Tel 213-457-7119; Dist. by: The Distributors, 702 S. Michigan, South Bend, IN 46618 (SAN 212-0364) Tel 219-232-8500.

Univ Great Brother, *(Universal Great Brotherhood, Inc.; 0-915594),* P.O. Box 9154, St. Louis, MO 63117 (SAN 207-3447).

Univ Health Ctr, *(Univ. of Oklahoma Health/Science Ctr., Department of Family Medicine; 0-9617230),* P.O. Box 26901, Oklahoma City, OK 73190 (SAN 663-6322); 800 NE 15th St., Oklahoma City, OK 73190 (SAN 663-6330) Tel 405-271-6388; Dist. by: Society for Teachers of Family Medicine, 1740 W. 92nd St., Kansas City, MO 64114 (SAN 224-3199).

Univ Houston Mex Amer, *(Univ. of Houston, Mexican American Studies Program; 0-939709),* 4800 Calhoun Rd., Houston, TX 77004 (SAN 663-0766).

Univ Life Sci, *(Universal Life & Science Foundation; 0-914295),* Foundation Book Store, 2980 E. Bay Dr., Largo, FL 33541 (SAN 287-590X) Tel 813-531-1670.

Symbols/Abbreviations

Univ Lions Club, *(University Lions Club Foundation of Seattle, The; 0-9617052),* 4312 NE 85th St., Seattle, WA 98115 (SAN 662-8842) Tel 206-523-1557.

Univ Maryland, *(University of Maryland, School of Medicine-Anatomy Department; 0-9608786),* 655 W. Baltimore St., Baltimore, MD 21201 (SAN 238-4019) Tel 301-528-3532.

Univ Mass Grad, *(University of Massachusetts, Graduate School; 0-9604712),* Amherst, MA 01003 (SAN 240-9836); Dist. by: Department of Geology & Geography, Univ. of Massachusetts, Amherst, MA 01003 (SAN 282-6143).

Univ MI Dental, *(Univ. of Michigan Program in Dental Public Health; 0-935837),* 109 Observatory, Ann Arbor, MI 48109 (SAN 696-6632) Tel 313-764-5477.

Univ Miami A R C, *(Atlantic Reef Committee, The; 0-932981),* Div. of Marine Geology & Geophysics, Univ. of Miami, Fisher Island Sta., Miami Beach, FL 33139 (SAN 239-5134) Tel 305-672-1840.

Univ Miami CSL, *(Univ. of Miami, Comparative Sedimentology Laboratory; 0-932981),* Div. of Marine Geology and Geophysics (MGG-RSMAS), Fisher Island Sta., Miami Beach, FL 33139 (SAN 219-0141) Tel 305-672-1840.

†**Univ Microfilms,** *(University Microfilms, Inc.; 0-8357),* Div. of Bell & Howell, 300 N. Zeeb Rd., Ann Arbor, MI 48106 (SAN 212-2464) Tel 313-761-4700; Toll free: 800-521-0600; Toll free: 800-343-5299 (Canada). Serials and newspapers in microform, reprints of articles and issues, dissertations published and available on demand. Imprints: Books on Demand, reprinting of out-of-print books, and UMI Research Press, scholarly and professional book publishing; *CIP.*

Univ Minn Sch, *(Univ. of Minnesota, Schl. of Architecture; 0-943352),* Dist. by: Univ. of Minnesota Press, 2037 University Ave. SE, Minneapolis, MN 55414 (SAN 213-2648) Tel 612-376-2972.

Univ Miss-KS Art, *(Univ. of Missouri-Kansas City, Gallery of Art; 0-914489),* Dept. of Art & Art History, Kansas City, MO 64110 (SAN 289-6893) Tel 816-276-1502.

Univ MN Art Mus, *(Univ. of Minnesota, Univ. Art Museum; 0-938713),* 84 Church St., SE, Minneapolis, MN 55455 (SAN 661-5066) Tel 612-624-9052.

Univ Monographs, *(University Monographs; 0-932429),* Subs. of Wright State Univ., Wright State Univ., Rm. 442 Millett, Dayton, OH 45435 (SAN 687-4355) Tel 513-873-3023.

Univ MS Natl Opera
See Natl Opera Assn

Univ MS Schl Engin, *(Univ. of Mississippi Schl. of Engineering, The; 0-937099),* Univ. of Mississippi, University, MS 38677 (SAN 658-4373) Tel 601-232-5374.

Univ Mus of U PA, *(Univ. of Pennsylvania, Univ. Museum; 0-934718),* 33rd & Spruce Sts., Philadelphia, PA 19104 (SAN 207-9283) Tel 215-898-4090.

Univ of Cincinnati, *(Univ. of Cincinnati; 0-9611212),* Dept. of Geography, Mail Location 131, Cincinnati, OH 45221 (SAN 283-8842).

†**Univ of Trees,** *(Univ. of the Trees Pr.; 0-916438),* P.O. Box 66, Boulder Creek, CA 95006 (SAN 212-9965); 13165 Pine St., Boulder Creek, CA 95006 (SAN 658-2176) Tel 408-338-2161 (SAN 264-2441); *CIP.*

Univ OK Gov Res, *(Univ. of Oklahoma, Bureau of Government Research; 0-942646),* 455 West Lindsey, Rm. 304, Norman, OK 73019 (SAN 209-6102) Tel 405-325-6621.

Univ Place, *(University Place Book Shop; 0-911556),* 821 Broadway, New York, NY 10003 (SAN 204-8841) Tel 212-254-5998.

Univ Pr
See University Pr

Univ Pr San Francisco, *(University Pr.; 0-9616978),* 6521 California St., San Francisco, CA 94121 (SAN 661-8014) Tel 415-731-1702.

Univ Pub, *(Univ. Pubs.; 0-931117),* P.O. Box 3571, Chattanooga, TN 37404 (SAN 678-9528) Tel 615-624-3784.

Univ Pub
See Univ Pub Hse

Univ Pub Assocs, *(University Publishing Assocs., Inc.; 0-8026),* Subs. of University Pr. of America, 4720 Boston Way, Lanham, MD 20706 (SAN 662-6394) Tel 301-459-3366.

Univ Pub Bureau
See Summa Pub Bur

Univ Pub CA, *(Universal Publishing; 0-9617022),* 15760 Ventura Blvd., Suite 1700, Encino, CA 91436 (SAN 662-5568) Tel 818-783-2934. Do not confuse with other companies with the same name in Maitland, FL, Oak Park, IL, Stoughton, MA.

Univ Pub Group, *(University Publishing Group; 1-55572),* 107 E. Church St., Frederick, MD 21701 (SAN 699-7171) Tel 301-694-8531.

Univ Pub Hse, *(Univ. Publishing Hse.; 0-9614194),* 6319 St. Henry Dr., Nashville, TN 37205 (SAN 686-7367) Tel 615-352-7192.

Univ Pub Inc, *(University Publishing, Inc.; 0-938381),* 2400 Broadway, Beaumont, TX 77702 (SAN 661-0323) Tel 713-748-8690; Dist. by: Lone Star College Bk., P.O. Box 19569, Austin, TX 78760 (SAN 200-6626).

Univ Pub MA, *(Universal Publishing Co., Massachusetts; 0-932427),* 264 Tosca Dr., Stoughton, MA 02072 (SAN 687-4347) Tel 617-821-0398.

Univ Pubns, *(Universal Pubns.; 0-941116),* P.O. Box 117, Fawnskin, CA 92333 (SAN 217-4480) Tel 714-585-9636.

Univ Pubs NY, *(University Pubns.; 0-911463),* P.O. Box 219, Sayville, NY 11782 (SAN 264-4592).

Univ RI Ocean Mgt, *(Univ. of Rhode Island, Ctr. for Ocean Management Studies; 0-938095),* 19 Upper College Rd., Kingston, RI 02881 (SAN 659-7084) Tel 401-792-2145.

Univ SC Natl Info
See Natl Info Ctr NM

Univ Sci Bks, *(University Science Bks.; 0-935702),* 20 Edgehill Rd., Mill Valley, CA 94941 (SAN 213-8085) Tel 415-383-1430.

Univ Sci Ctrs, *(Universal Science Pr., Inc.; 0-934669),* Div. of Universal Science Centers, Inc., 10604 Santa Monica Blvd., Los Angeles, CA 90025 (SAN 694-0765) Tel 805-581-3244; Orders to: Sam Sonders, P.O. Box 420, Simi Valley, CA 93062 (SAN 662-3301) Tel 805-581-3244.

Univ Servs Inc, *(University Services; 0-913535),* 1159 Second Ave., Salt Lake City, UT 84103 (SAN 285-2012).

Univ South, *(Univ. of the South, The; 0-918769),* SPO 1145, Sewanee, TN 37375 (SAN 287-2676).

Univ South ME, *(Univ. of Southern Maine, College of Education; 0-939561),* University of Southern Maine, College of Education, Bailey Hall 400, Gorham, ME 04038 (SAN 663-4281) Tel 207-780-5316.

Univ Stat Tracts, *(University Statistical Tracts; 0-931316),* 75-19 171st St., Flushing, NY 11366 (SAN 211-3341) Tel 718-969-7553.

Univ Tech, *(Universal Technology Corp.; 0-912426),* Corporate Headquaters, 1616 Mardon Dr., Dayton, OH 45432 (SAN 204-885X) Tel 513-426-8530; Orders to: Technology & Audiovisual Complex, 2700 N. Fairfield Rd., Dayton, OH 45432 (SAN 650-0641) Tel 513-426-2808.

Univ TN Alumni, *(Univ. of Tennessee National Alumni Assn., The; 0-9616311),* Univ. of Tennessee, 600 Andy Holt Tower, Knoxville, TN 37996 (SAN 658-716X) Tel 615-974-6071.

Univ Utah, *(University of Utah, Bureau of Economic & Business Research; 0-942486),* 401 Kendall D. Garff Bldg., Salt Lake City, UT 84112 (SAN 238-5899) Tel 801-581-7274.

Univ VT Dept Psych
See U of VT Psych

Univ-Wide Lib
See UCDLA

Univ Wis-Mad Law, *(University of Wisconsin-Madison Law School, Disputes Processing Research Center; 0-915305),* Room 209 Law School, Madison, WI 53706 (SAN 290-0521) Tel 608-263-2545.

Univelt Inc, *(Univelt, Inc.; 0-912183; 0-87703; 0-914548),* P.O. Box 28130, San Diego, CA 92128 (SAN 204-8868) Tel 619-746-4005; 740 Metcalf St., Suite 13, Escondido, CA 92025 (SAN 658-2095).

Universal Bks, *(Universal Books, Inc.; 0-9608865),* 526 Silver Leaf Dr., Oroville, CA 95965 (SAN 241-0850) Tel 916-589-3171.

Universal Book Co, *(Universal Bk. Co., The),* P.O. Box 60943, Terminal Annex, Los Angeles, CA 90060 (SAN 219-8983) Tel 213-723-1776.

Universal Develop, *(Universal Developments Publishing; 0-935624),* 2855 Velasco Lane, Costa Mesa, CA 92626 (SAN 205-9835) Tel 714-641-0188; Orders to: P.O. Box 5253, Orange, CA 92667 (SAN 662-1678).

Universal Elect, *(Universal Electronics Inc.; 0-916661),* 4555 Grove Rd., Suite 3, Columbus, OH 43232 (SAN 296-6859) Tel 614-866-4605.

Universal Ministries, *(Universal Ministries, Inc., Publishing House; 0-942428),* P.O. Box 9017, Pittsburgh, PA 15224 (SAN 238-2032) Tel 301-622-9238.

Universal Pr, *(Universal Pr.; 0-918950),* 6609 Cherrywood Ave., Bakersfield, CA 93308 (SAN 210-5225) Tel 805-393-0381.

†**Universe,** *(Universe Bks., Inc.; 0-87663; 1-55550),* Div. of South Park Pr., 381 Park Ave. S., New York, NY 10016 (SAN 202-537X) Tel 212-685-7400; *CIP.* Imprints: Free Life (Free Life Editions); Main St (Main Street Press); Man Inst Pol Res (Manhattan Institute for Policy Research Book); Pica Pr (Pica Press); Pica Spec Stud (Pica Special Studies).

Universe Pub Co, *(Universe Publishing Co.; 0-935484),* 185 W. Demarest Ave., Englewood, NJ 07631 (SAN 214-3321) Tel 201-567-4296.

University Imprint of **Exposition Pr FL**

University Pr, *(University Pr.; 0-8418),* Drawer N, Wolfe City, TX 75496 (SAN 203-3356) Tel 214-496-2226.

Unlimited Golden Pr, *(Unlimited Golden Opportunities Pr.; 0-934521),* P.O. Box 27218, Oakland, CA 94602 (SAN 693-8434) Tel 415-534-6472.

Unltd. Mktg. Pubns., *(Unlimited Marketing Pubns.; 0-912305),* Div. of Unlimited Marketing & Research Services, Inc., 190 Angell St., P.O. Box 944 Annex Sta., Providence, RI 02901 (SAN 265-2897) Tel 401-421-7080.

Unmuzzled Ox, *(Unmuzzled Ox Pr.; 0-934450),* 105 Hudson St., New York, NY 10013 (SAN 207-9151) Tel 212-226-7170.

Unnameable Pr, *(Unnameable Pr.; 0-934227),* P.O. Box 11689, Atlanta, GA 30355-1689 (SAN 693-1170); 594 Wimbledon Rd., NE Apt. G-3, Atlanta, GA 30324 (SAN 662-314X) Tel 404-892-2424.

Unpublished Edns
See Printed Edns

Unsinn Pubns, *(Unsinn Pubns., Inc.; 0-9615386),* P.O. Box 672, Drexel Hill, PA 19026 (SAN 695-3522) Tel 215-543-0999.

UNWLA, *(Ukrainian National Women's League of America; 0-9610788),* 108 Second Ave., New York, NY 10003 (SAN 234-1298) Tel 212-533-4646.

UOI Co, *(UOI Co.; 0-913929),* 15445 Ventura Blvd., Sherman Oaks, CA 91403 (SAN 286-9047) Tel 818-785-5050.

UP Imprint of **B&N Imports**

UPB, *(University Pr. Bks.; 0-8295),* Box 460, Middletown, NY 10940 (SAN 207-4907) Tel 914-343-5323.

UPBS
See UPB

Updegraff, *(Updegraff Pr., The; 0-9613203),* 2564 Cherosen Rd., Louisville, KY 40205 (SAN 283-3530) Tel 502-454-3206.

Upjohn Inst
See W E Upjohn

Uplift Bks, *(Uplift Books; 0-88005),* 760-C N. Golden Springs Dr., Diamond Bar, CA 91765 (SAN 219-8312) Tel 714-595-8409.

Upper Country, *(Upper Country People Probe),* 204 Andrews Ave., Hartsville, TN 37074 (SAN 239-5002).

Upper Crust, *(Upper Crust Cookbook, The; 0-9613757),* P.O. Box 5363, Scottsdale, AZ 85261 (SAN 692-7599) Tel 602-483-0755.

Upper Rm Pub, *(Upper Room Publishing Co.; 0-938645),* P.O. Box 629, Alamo, GA 30411 (SAN 661-633X); Pine St., Alamo, GA 30311 (SAN 661-6348) Tel 912-568-7249.

Used Car Pubns, (Used Car Pubns.; 0-932675), Subs. of J. L. Sales, 5502 Englishman Place, Rockville, MD 20852 (SAN 687-844X) Tel 301-493-5686.

Useful Maps
See J J Gately

USGPO
See Gov Printing Office

USL Art Museum, (Univ. of Southwestern Louisiana, Univ. Art Museum; 0-936819), USL Drawer 42571, Lafayette, LA 70504 (SAN 280-9532).

Usonia Pr, (Usonia Pr.; 0-9615348), P.O. 19440 Diamond Lake Sta., Minneapolis, MN 55419 (SAN 695-1007) Tel 612-824-7258.

USPC, (United States Pharmacopeial Convention, Inc.; 0-913595), USPC, Inc., Order Processing Dept. P.O. Box 2248, Rockville, MD 20852 (SAN 220-2794) Tel 301-881-0666.

USPS, (United States Postal Service, Philatelic Marketing Division; 0-9604756), 475 L'Enfant Plaza, Washington, DC 20260-6355 (SAN 219-8304) Tel 202-268-2350.

USR Group, (USR Group; 0-936593), 4655 Old Ironsides Dr., Suite 200, Santa Clara, CA 95054 (SAN 698-1305) Tel 408-986-8840.

USS North Car, (USS North Carolina, Battleship Commission; 0-9608538), P.O. Box 417, Wilmington, NC 28402 (SAN 240-7973) Tel 919-762-1829.

USTA-CERT, (U. S. Tennis Assn./Ctr. for Education & Recreational Tennis; 0-938822), 729 Alexander Rd., Princeton, NJ 08540 (SAN 207-6551) Tel 609-452-2580.

UT Arts Festival, (Utah Arts Festival Foundation, Inc.; 0-939011), 168 W. 500 N., Salt Lake City, UT 84103 (SAN 662-5835) Tel 801-322-2428.

UTA Pr, (UTA Pr., The; 0-932408), Affil. of Univ. of Texas at Arlington, Box 19929, Univ. of Texas at Arlington, Arlington, TX 76019-0929 (SAN 212-0542) Tel 817-273-3391; Orders to: Univ. of Texas at Arlington, Univ. Bookstore, Box 19075, Arlington, TX 76019 (SAN 662-1767) Tel 817-273-2785.

Utah Folklife Ctr, (Utah Folklife Center; 0-9614561), Subs. of Utah Arts Council, 617 E. South Temple, Salt Lake City, UT 84102 (SAN 691-814X) Tel 801-533-5760.

Utah Geo Series, (Utah Geographic Series, Inc.; 0-936331), Box 8325, Salt Lake City, UT 84108 (SAN 697-9866) Tel 801-583-2333; 1308 S. 1700 E., No. 207, Salt Lake City, UT 84105 (SAN 698-2360).

Utah Mus Natural Hist, (Utah Museum of Natural History; 0-940378), University of Utah, Salt Lake City, UT 84112 (SAN 213-5663).

Utah St Hist Soc, (Utah State Historical Society; 0-913738), 300 Rio Grande, Salt Lake City, UT 84101 (SAN 204-8930) Tel 801-533-6024.

†Utah St U Pr, (Utah State Univ. Pr.; 0-87421), Logan, UT 84322-9515 (SAN 202-9294) Tel 801-750-1362; CIP.

Utama Pubns Inc, (Utama Pubns., Inc.; 0-911527), Tano Rd., Box 236, Santa Fe, NM 87501 (SAN 282-4779) Tel 505-988-7321.

Utica Hse, (Utica House Publishing Co.; 0-9609296), RR No. 1, Utica, IL 61373 (SAN 260-1532) Tel 815-223-3200.

Utopia Pr, (Utopia Press; 0-911947), 4480 Annie Oakley Dr., Las Vegas, NV 89121 (SAN 264-4622).

Utopian Universe, (Utopian Universe Publishing Co.), P.O. Box 26, East Elmhurst, NY 11369 (SAN 207-4923) Tel 718-478-3291.

UTX CSAA, (Univ. of Texas at Austin, Ctr. for the Study of American Architechture; 0-934951), Univ. of Texas at Austin, Schl. of Architecture, Austin, TX 78712 (SAN 695-0671) Tel 512-471-1922.

UTX SLIS, (Univ. of Texas at Austin, Graduate Schl. of Library & Information Science; 0-938729), Austin, TX 78712-1276 (SAN 661-5872) Tel 512-471-3821.

UWIM CCA, (Univ. of Wisconsin-Milwaukee, Ctr. for Consumer Affairs), 929 N. Sixth St., Milwaukee, WI 53203 (SAN 235-5671) Tel 414-224-4177.

UWIS CLSES, (Univ. of Wisconsin-Superior Ctr. for Lake Superior Environmental Studies; 0-9614968), Univ. of Wisconsin-Superior, Superior, WI 54880 (SAN 693-7306) Tel 715-394-8422.

UWSP Found Pr
See U of Wis-Stevens Point

Uxor Pr, (Uxor Pr., Inc.; 0-932555), 425 E. 51st St., New York, NY 10022 (SAN 687-4916) Tel 212-688-9199.

Uzzano Pr, (Uzzano Pr.; 0-930600), 511 Sunset Dr., Menomonie, WI 54751 (SAN 211-1020).

V A Bradford, (Bradford, Vance A.; 0-9615983), 4707 Memory Ln., Oklahoma City, OK 73112 (SAN 697-3531) Tel 405-947-1408.

V A Ostendorf, (Ostendor, Virginia A., Inc.; 0-937007), P.O. Box 2896, Littleton, CO 80161-2896 (SAN 696-2564); 7085 S. Pennsylvania St., Littleton, CO 80161 (SAN 658-2923) Tel 303-797-3131.

V Amati, (Venti Amati; 0-9614119), 202 Park, Marshall, MN 56258 (SAN 656-9072) Tel 507-532-3647.

V & A Comm
See C B Vega

V & M World Wide, (V & M World Wide Bks., Corp.; 0-933517), 22 Sunset Ave., Lynbrook, NY 11563 (SAN 691-9235).

V B Carter, (Carter, Virginia B.; 0-9603862), Five Geyerwood Lane, St. Louis, MO 63131 (SAN 214-1132) Tel 314-965-0577.

V B Ricard, (Ricard, Virginia B.; 0-9613508), 1826 Indian Meadows Ln., Fort Collins, CO 80525 (SAN 657-3096) Tel 303-493-1922.

V C Jantz, (Jantz, Virginia C.; 0-9607170), Rte. 12 Box 450, Waco, TX 76710 (SAN 239-1031) Tel 817-848-4786.

V Campo, (Campo, Vincent), 1223 Newkirk Ave., Brooklyn, NY 11230 (SAN 237-9945).

V Danca, (Danca, Vince; 0-9602390), 1191 Roxbury Close, Rockford, IL 61107 (SAN 212-4971).

V Dumond, (Dumond, Val; 0-9613673), P.O. Box 97124, Tacoma, WA 98497 (SAN 683-2172).

V E Wysinger, (Wysinger, Vossa E.), P.O. Box 158, Berkeley, CA 94704 (SAN 203-1140) Tel 415-655-1742.

V G Rosenberg, (Rosenberg, Vivian Graff), R.D. 2 Box 274, Walkers Mill Rd., Germantown, NY 12526 (SAN 212-1360) Tel 518-537-6159.

V Greene, (Vaughn, Greene M.), 548 Elm Ave., San Bruno, CA 94066 (SAN 683-2784) Tel 415-589-4224.

V H Ho, (Ho, Van H., Assocs.; 0-9602904), P.O. Box 130, Harbor City, CA 90710 (SAN 213-5124).

V H Pub, (VHW Publishing; 0-9610912), 3780 Hope Terr., Santa Barbara, CA 93110 (SAN 265-153X) Tel 805-687-4087.

V H Weisberg
See V H Pub

V I Anderson, (Anderson, Velma Irene; 0-89279), Stanhope, IA 50246 (SAN 283-295X).

†V I Pr, (V.I. Pr., Inc.; 0-916945), P.O. Box 1403, Pompano Beach, FL 33061 (SAN 655-7813) Tel 305-785-5588; CIP.

V J Nelson, (Nelson, Vera Joyce), 1969 SW Park, No. 310, Portland, OR 97201 (SAN 207-6829).

V J P Enter, (VJP Enterprises; 0-9615924), 636 Cleveland, Missoula, MT 59801 (SAN 696-7825) Tel 406-728-6968; Dist. by: Pacific Pipeline, 19215 66th Ave. S., Kent, WA 98032-1171 (SAN 208-2128) Tel 206-872-5523; Dist. by: Pictorial Histories Publishing Co., 713 South Third W., Missoula, MT 59801 (SAN 212-4351) Tel 406-549-8488.

V Lockman, (Lockman, Vic; 0-936175), P.O. Box 1916, Ramona, CA 92065 (SAN 697-2063) Tel 619-789-9572.

V Lopez, (Lopez, Violet; 0-9615909), 119-20 Union Tpke., Apt. E3-A3, Kew Gardens, NY 11415 (SAN 697-2233) Tel 718-544-4194.

V Luker, (Luker, Vera G.; 0-9615733), 6715 Tulip Ln., Dallas, TX 75230 (SAN 695-863X) Tel 214-361-6478.

V Parr Pub, (Parr, V., Publishing; 0-9613991), P.O. Box 727, Santa Paula, CA 93060 (SAN 682-1626) Tel 805-646-0063.

V Parrish Pub, (Parrish, Vernon, Publishing; 0-9615774), 1900 S. Eads St., Arlington, VA 22202 (SAN 696-6306) Tel 703-892-1993.

V Plezia, (Plezia, Valerie; 0-9609368), 14009 Mohawk Trail, Cleveland, OH 44130 (SAN 260-2490) Tel 216-842-4581.

V Quade, (Quade, Vicki; 0-9602604), 3000 N. Sheridon Rd., Apt 5-E, Chicago, IL 60657 (SAN 213-151X) Tel 312-528-2569.

V R McLaughlin, (McLaughlin, Vicki & Roger; 0-9613456), Rt. 1, P.O. Box 114G, Weston, WV 26452 (SAN 677-4997).

V S Epstein, (Epstein, Vivian Sheldon; 0-9601002), 212 S. Dexter St., Denver, CO 80222 (SAN 208-6425) Tel 303-322-7450.

V S FitzPatrick, (FitzPatrick, V. S.; 0-937173), Arriba, CO 80804 (SAN 658-5221) Tel 303-768-3468.

V S Morris, (Morris, Victoria S., Bks.; 0-914318), 39 Gleneden Ave., Oakland, CA 94611 (SAN 202-2125) Tel 415-652-2013.

V Scoper, (Scoper, Vincent, Jr.; 0-9600514), P.O. Box 2366, Laurel, MS 39440 (SAN 205-4736).

V Sharp Pub, (Sharp, Vera, Publishing Co.; 0-9616987), 204C Edgewater Towers, 17350 Sunset Blvd., Pacific Palisades, CA 90272 (SAN 658-8360) Tel 213-454-2111.

V Young, (Young, Victor A.; 0-9603694), 548 S. Main St., Red Lion, PA 17356 (SAN 213-5736) Tel 717-244-6816.

VA Army Natl Guard, (Virginia Army National Guard Foundation; 0-9616860), 501 E. Franklin St., Richmond, VA 23219 (SAN 661-5937) Tel 804-344-4103.

VA Atty Genl, (Virginia Office of the Attorney General), Supreme Court Bldg., 101 N. Eighth St., Richmond, VA 23219 (SAN 226-7888).

VA Bk, (Virginia Book Co.; 0-911578), Box 431, Berryville, VA 22611 (SAN 206-7773) Tel 703-955-1428.

VA Cardinal Pubns, (Virginia Cardinal Pubns, Inc.; 0-938951), P.O. Box 1177, Vienna, VA 22180 (SAN 661-7220); 135 Park St., NE, Vienna, VA 22180 (SAN 661-7239) Tel 703-938-0666.

Va CARES, (Virginia Community Action Re-Entry Systems, Inc.; 0-9613647), P.O. Box 2868, Roanoke, VA 24001 (SAN 670-7807) Tel 703-342-1880.

VA Chamber Com, (Virginia Chamber of Commerce, Publishing Div.; 0-918529), 9 S. Fifth St., Richmond, VA 23219 (SAN 219-0354) Tel 804-644-1607.

VA City Rest, (Virginia City Restoration Corp.; 0-9604560), P.O. Box 221691, Carmel, CA 93922 (SAN 215-1901).

VA Ctr Creative Arts, (Virginia Ctr. for Creative Arts), Dist. by: Associated University. Presses, 440 Forsgate Dr., Cranbury, NJ 08512 (SAN 281-2959) Tel 609-655-4770.

VA Muni League, (Virginia Municipal League; 0-932993), P.O. Box 12203, Richmond, VA 23241 (SAN 226-787X) Tel 804-649-8471.

†Va Mus Arts, (Virginia Museum of Fine Arts; 0-917046), Blvd. & Grove, Richmond, VA 23221 (SAN 281-0204) Tel 804-257-0818; Blvd. & Grove Ave., Office of Publications, Richmond, VA 23221 (SAN 661-9282) Tel 804-257-0534; Dist. by: University of Washington Press, P.O. Box C50096, Seattle, WA 98145-0096 (SAN 212-2502) Tel 206-543-8870; CIP.

VA St Chamber Com
See VA Chamber Com

†VA State Lib, (Virginia State Library; 0-88490), 11th St. at Capitol Sq., Richmond, VA 23219 (SAN 203-0543) Tel 804-786-2312; CIP.

VA Surveyors, (Virginia Surveyors Foundation; 0-9604076), 6001 Lakeside Ave., Richmond, VA 23228 (SAN 282-5120) Tel 804-262-1351.

Vadare, (Vadare Publishing Co.; 0-9610782; 0-933725), 4 Burnham Ln., Dix Hills, NY 11746 (SAN 265-1491) Tel 516-661-3855; Toll free: 800-645-1112.

Vagabond Imprint of Scholastic Inc

†Vagabond Pr, (Vagabond Press; 0-912824), 1610 N. Water St., Ellensburg, WA 98926 (SAN 203-0535) Tel 509-925-5634; CIP.

Vail Ballou, (Vail-Ballou Press, Inc.; 0-9600868), 187 Clinton St., Binghamton, NY 13902 (SAN 239-5681).

Vail Pub, (Vail Publishing; 0-9607872), 8285 SW Brookridge, Portland, OR 97225 (SAN 240-0766) Tel 503-292-9964.

Vaishnava, (Vaishnava Research Institute; 0-935485), 5825 Telegraph Ave., No. 21, Oakland, CA 94609 (SAN 695-7927) Tel 415-540-7665; Dist. by New Leaf Distributing, 1020 White St., SW, Atlanta, GA 30310 (SAN 169-1449) Tel 404-755-2665.

VAL Ent
See Classic Hse

Val Geol Pubns, *(Valley Geological Pubns.;*
0-9616520), 36 Plantation Cir., Greenfield,
MA 01301 (SAN 659-5995)
Tel 413-774-4827.

Val-Hse Pub, *(Val-House Publishing; 0-936354),*
2903 Carriage Lane, P.O. Box 490443,
College Park, GA 30349 (SAN 214-4816)
Tel 404-957-9802.

Valaske Pub, *(Valaske Publishing; 0-9616601),*
6118 Fourth Ave., Kenosha, WI 53142
(SAN 659-5448) Tel 414-654-6007.

Vale Pr, *(Vale Pr.; 0-916475),* P.O. Box 6519,
Newport News, VA 23606 (SAN 295-1320)
Tel 804-599-4256.

Valee Studios, *(Valee Studios; 0-9615939),* 4103
Scripps Ave., Palo Alto, CA 94306
(SAN 696-8589) Tel 415-493-1617.

Valen Pub, *(Valen Publishing Co.; 0-9613897),*
23243 Spires St., Canoga Park, CA 91304
(SAN 682-3203) Tel 818-348-9034.

Valencia, *(Valencia, Jerry; 0-9604784),* 7525
Raytheon Rd., San Diego, CA 92111
(SAN 220-1038); Orders to: P.O. Box 758,
La Jolla, CA 92038 (SAN 220-1046)
Tel 619-729-3344.

Valentine Pub, *(Valentine Publishing & Drama*
Co.; 0-941672), P.O. Box 1378, Ashland,
OR 97520 (SAN 239-3379)
Tel 503-773-7035. *Imprints:* Bardavon Bks
(Bardavon Books).

Valhalla Pr, *(Valhalla Press; 0-9607070),* Box
301, Chicago, IL 60690 (SAN 282-4981)
Tel 312-761-1888.

Valhalla Rehab, *(Valhalla Rehabilitation Pubns.,*
Ltd.; 0-911681), P.O. Box 1053, Valhalla, NY
10595 (SAN 262-1053) Tel 914-948-1004.

Valiant Pubns, *(Valiant Pubns.; 0-9608244),*
1200 Beneficial Life Tower, Salt Lake City,
UT 84111 (SAN 240-4656)
Tel 801-538-2000.

Valkyrie Pr
See Valkyrie Pub Hse

Valkyrie Pub Hse, *(Valkyrie Publishing Hse.;*
0-912760; 0-934616; 0-912589), Subs. of
Freedom Press, 8245 26th Ave. N., St.
Petersburg, FL 33710 (SAN 203-1671)
Tel 813-345-8864.

Vallentine Mitchell
See Biblio Dist

Valley Bk, *(Valley Bk. Co.; 0-9616255),* 502
Cranwell Cir., Blacksburg, VA 24060
(SAN 658-5280) Tel 703-951-7984; P.O.
Box 884, Blacksburg, VA 24060
(SAN 658-5299).

Valley Calif *Imprint of* Western Tanager
Valley Calif
See Western Tanager

Valley Guild, *(Valley Guild, The; 0-9612742),*
Non Profit Organization of The Steinbeck
House of Salinas, 132 Central Ave., Salinas,
CA 93901 (SAN 289-8802)
Tel 408-424-7672; Orders to: Steinbeck
House, 132 Central Ave., Salinas, CA 93901
(SAN 289-5498).

Valley Lights, *(Valley Lights Pubns.; 0-9606482),*
P.O. Box 1537, Ojai, CA 93023
(SAN 219-8320) Tel 805-646-9888.

Valley Presbyterian, *(Valley Presbyterian*
Hospital; 0-9605718), 15107 Vanowen St.,
Van Nuys, CA 91405 (SAN 216-4701)
Tel 818-981-1300.

†Valley Publishing, *(Valley Publishing;*
0-9612990), P.O. Box 2223, Lower Burrell,
PA 15068 (SAN 292-7209)
Tel 412-337-0635; *CIP.*

Valley Sun, *(Valley of the Sun Publishing Co.;*
0-911842; 0-87554), Div. of Sutphen Corp.,
P.O. Box 38, Malibu, CA 90265
(SAN 206-8974) Tel 818-889-1575; Toll
free: 800-421-6603; Dist. by: Pocket Bks.,
1230 Ave. of the Americas, New York, NY
10020 (SAN 202-5922) Tel 212-246-2121;
Orders to: Box 2010, Malibu, CA 90265.

Valley View, *(Valley View Blueberry Press;*
0-9608432), 21717 N.E. 68th St.,
Vancouver, WA 98662 (SAN 240-7981)
Tel 206-892-2839.

Valor Pub, *(Valor Publishing Co.; 0-941052),*
Affil. of Game Marketing, 3355 Birch Cir.,
Allentown, PA 18103-4512
(SAN 217-3662) Tel 215-437-3622.

Valuation, *(Valuation Pr., Inc.; 0-930458),*
131-60 Mindanao Way, Suite 270, Marina
del Rey, CA 90292 (SAN 210-6809);
Orders to: P.O. Box 1080, Marina del Rey,
CA 90291 (SAN 210-6817)
Tel 213-822-3691.

†Value Comm, *(Value Communications;*
0-916392), Subs. of Oak Tree Pubns., Inc.,
9601 Aero Dr., San Diego, CA 92123
(SAN 208-0990) Tel 619-560-5163; *CIP.*

ValuWrite, *(Valuwrite Pubns.; 0-940986),* P.O.
Box E, Provo, UT 84603 (SAN 223-2022)
Tel 801-373-1111.

Van Allen Pub
See Ocean Allen Pub

Van Arsdale Video, *(Van Arsdales Video Travel*
Guides; 0-939005), P.O. Box 3175, Naples,
FL 33939 (SAN 662-5436); 281 11th Ave.
S., Naples, FL 33940 (SAN 662-5444)
Tel 813-649-5828.

Van Dean, *(Van Dean Educators Inc),* Box
1422, Malvern, PA 19355 (SAN 240-8996).

Van der Marck, *(Van der Marck, Alfred,*
Editions; 0-912383), 1133 Broadway, Suite
301, New York, NY 10033
(SAN 265-2919) Tel 212-645-5150; Orders
to: Harper & Row Pubs., Inc., Keystone
Industrial Park, Scranton, PA 18512
(SAN 693-9821); Dist. by: Harper & Row
Pubs., Inc., 10 E. 53rd St., New York, NY
10022 (SAN 200-2086) Tel 212-207-7099.

Van Diver, *(Van Diver, Bradford B.; 0-9601106),*
The State University College of Arts &
Science at Potsdam, Dept. of Geology,
Potsdam, NY 13676 (SAN 209-908X)
Tel 315-267-2288.

Van Dyk, *(Van Dyk Pubns.),* 816 W. White
Oak, Independence, MO 64050
(SAN 209-6129) Tel 816-836-3290.

Van Koevering
See Caballero Pr

Van Ness LOT
See Van Ness LOTCO

Van Ness LOTCO, *(Van Ness LOTCO;*
0-9608648), 2309 Newmarket Dr.,
Louisville, KY 40222 (SAN 238-4094)
Tel 502-425-5118.

†Van Nos Reinhold, *(Van Nostrand Reinhold*
Co., Inc.; 0-442; 0-8436), Div. of
International Thomson Organisation, Inc.,
115 Fifth Ave., New York, NY 10003
(SAN 202-5183) Tel 212-254-3232; Orders
to: VNR Order Processing, 7625 Empire Dr.,
Florence, KY 41042 (SAN 202-5191)
Tel 606-525-6600; *CIP. Imprints:* Lark
Comms (Lark Communications); Lifetime
Pubns. (Lifetime Learning Pubns.).

Van Siclen Bks, *(Van Siclen Bks.; 0-933175),*
111 Winnetka Rd., San Antonio, TX 78229
(SAN 692-3399) Tel 512-349-2913.

†Van Vactor & Goodheart, *(Van Vactor &*
Goodheart; 0-941324), 24 Lee St.,
Cambridge, MA 02139 (SAN 282-5007)
Tel 617-497-5277; *CIP.*

Van Veer Nursery *Imprint of*
Binford-Metropolitan

Van Winkle, *(Van Winkle Pub. Co., Inc.;*
0-918664), Box 2000, 140 River Ave.,
Holland, MI 49423 (SAN 210-6833)
Tel 616-396-1546.

Vance Biblios, *(Vance Bibliographies; 0-88066;*
0-89028; 1-55590), P.O. Box 229, 112 N.
Charter St., Monticello, IL 61856
(SAN 212-6273) Tel 217-762-3831.

Vance Pubns, *(Vance Pubns.; 0-938595),* P.O.
Box 2158, Mansfield, OH 44905
(SAN 661-1400); Toll free: 800-423-9074;
1016 N. Stewart Rd., Mansfield, OH 44905
(SAN 661-1419) Tel 419-589-8401; Dist.
by: Publishers Marketing Group, 1104
Summit Ave., Plainview, TX 75074
(SAN 262-0995) Tel 214-423-0312.

Vancento Pub, *(Vancento Pub. Co.; 0-934142),*
62 Court St., Reno, NV 89501
(SAN 238-7697).

Vanderbilt Pr, *(Vanderbilt Press Inc.; 0-916815),*
65 N.W. 21st St., Miami, FL 33127
(SAN 654-2603) Tel 305-573-0906.

Vanderbilt Pubns, *(Vanderbilt Univ. Pubns. in*
Anthropolgy; 0-935462), Box 1532 Sta. B,
Vanderbilt Univ., Nashville, TN 37235
(SAN 695-7986) Tel 615-322-7522.

†Vanderbilt U Pr, *(Vanderbilt Univ. Pr.; 0-8265),*
1211 18th Ave. S., Nashville, TN 37212
(SAN 202-9308) Tel 615-322-3585; Dist.
by: Univ. of Illinois Pr., c/o Harper & Row
Pubs., Inc., Keystone Industrial Pk.,
Scranton, PA 18512 (SAN 202-5310)
Tel 217-333-0950; Orders to: Univ. of
Illinois Pr., P.O. Box 1650, Hagerstown, MD
21741; *CIP.*

Vanderkolk, *(Vanderkolk Publishing; 0-9617269),*
4555 Acacia, La Mesa, CA 92041
(SAN 663-5083) Tel 619-589-6201.

Vanessa-Ann Collec, *(Vanessa-Ann Collection,*
The; 0-913921), P.O. Box 9113, Ogden, UT
84409 (SAN 286-6897) Tel 801-621-2777.

Vanessapress, *(Vanessapress),* P.O. Box 81335,
Fairbanks, AK 99708 (SAN 696-5040);
1560 Farmer's Loop, Fairbanks, AK 99708
Tel 907-479-0172.

Vanguard, *(Vanguard Pr., Inc.; 0-8149),* 424
Madison Ave., New York, NY 10017
(SAN 202-9316) Tel 212-753-3906; Dist.
by: Columbia Publishing Co., Inc., Drawer A,
Frenchtown, NJ 08825 (SAN 202-9316)
Tel 201-996-2141.

Vanguard *Imprint of* **Noontide**

†Vanguard Bks, *(Vanguard Books; 0-917702),*
P.O. Box 3566, Chicago, IL 60654
(SAN 213-8212) Tel 312-342-3425; *CIP.*

Vanguard Inst, *(Vanguard Institutional Pubs.;*
0-934725), 1011 4th St., Suite 305, Santa
Monica, CA 90403 (SAN 694-1508)
Tel 213-394-1284.

VanMeer Pubns, *(VanMeer Pubns., Inc.;*
0-937826), P.O. Box 1289, Clearwater, FL
33517 (SAN 220-1054) Tel 813-531-6047.

Vanous, *(Vanous, Arthur, Co.; 0-89918),* P.O.
Box 650279, Vero Beach, FL 32965
(SAN 169-4871) Tel 305-562-9186.

Vantage, *(Vantage Pr., Inc.; 0-533),* 516 W. 34th
St., New York, NY 10001 (SAN 206-8893)
Tel 212-736-1767.

Vantage Info, *(Vantage Information; 0-914791),*
P.O. Box 22684, Lexington, KY 40522
(SAN 655-1459).

Vantage Printing, *(Vantage Printing Company;*
0-943110), 2003 Broadway, Houston, TX
77012 (SAN 240-4672) Tel 713-644-1994.

Vardaman Pr, *(Vardaman Press; 0-942648),*
2720 E. 176th St., Tacoma, WA 98445
(SAN 239-9482).

Varfley, *(Varfley, Edwin B.; 0-9609570),* P.O.
Box 2916, Providence, RI 02908
(SAN 276-4806).

Variena Publishing, *(Variena Publishing;*
0-939225), 6796 Lowell Blvd., Denver, CO
80221 (SAN 663-4974) Tel 303-650-0910.

Varietal Fair, *(Varietal Fair; 0-9614025),* 4022
Harrison Grade Rd., Sebastopol, CA 95472
(SAN 683-6216) Tel 707-874-3105.

Variety Artists Bks, *(Variety Artists Bks.;*
0-939639), 4232 Herschel Ave., Suite 209,
Dallas, TX 75219 (SAN 663-5792)
Tel 214-521-7177.

Varnes Pubs, *(Varnes Pubs.; 0-943584),* 9404
Genesee Ave., No. 284, La Jolla, CA 92037
(SAN 240-8007) Tel 619-453-3081; Orders
to: P.O. Box 9655, Marina del Rey, CA
90295 (SAN 662-1775).

Varsity Pubs, *(Varsity Publishing; 0-9614872),*
RD 1, Box 326, Valatie, NY 12184
(SAN 693-2266) Tel 518-784-3025.

Vashon Pt Prod, *(Vashon Point Productions;*
0-9616103), Rte. 1, P.O. Box 432, Vashon,
WA 98070 (SAN 659-5642).

Vassilion, *(Vassilion, Harry J.; 0-9606180),* 5519
N. Hills Dr., Raleigh, NC 27612
(SAN 216-471X).

Vaughan Edwards, *(Vaughan, Edwards, Pubs.;*
0-911237), Box 2015, Dusty Bend Sta.,
Camden, SC 29020 (SAN 275-8903)
Tel 803-432-3849.

Vaughan Pubns, *(Vaughan Pubns.; 0-9613951),*
P.O. Box 1527, Chandler Heights, AZ 85224
(SAN 686-1628) Tel 602-838-1924.

Vaughn Pub KY, *(Vanghn Pubs.),* P.O. Box 97,
London, KY 40741 (SAN 693-1006).

VC Pub, *(VC Publishing; 0-935333),* 7506 New
Jersey Ave., Hudson, FL 33567
(SAN 695-8044) Tel 813-863-2738; Toll
free: 800-472-9336; Dist. by: Veronica Cass,
Inc., P.O. Box 5519, Hudson, FL 33567
(SAN 200-5808).

†VCH Pubs, *(VCH Pubs., Inc.; 0-89573),* 220 E.
23rd St., Suite 109, New York, NY 10010
(SAN 212-2421); Orders to: 303 NW 12th
Ave., Deerfield Beach, FL 33442-1705
(SAN 662-1783) Tel 305-426-5566; *CIP.*

VEATU, *(VEATU Press; 0-9610276),* 7126 Morgan Ave. S, Richfield, MN 55423 (SAN 264-4649) Tel 612-869-8324.

Vector Assocs, *(Vector Associates; 0-930808),* P.O. Box 6215, Bellevue, WA 98007 (SAN 211-1039) Tel 206-747-5881.

Vector Counsel, *(Vector Counseling Institute; 0-913596),* P.O. Box 1271, Mt. Vernon, WA 98273 (SAN 205-4752) Tel 206-855-0630.

Vector Golf, *(Vector Golf, Inc.; 0-9613027),* 6608 Genoa Rd., Fort Worth, TX 76116 (SAN 293-9053) Tel 817-731-0424.

Vector Inter, *(Vector Intercontinental; 0-937907),* P.O. Box 20820, Cleveland, OH 44120 (SAN 659-6002); 13221 Shaker Sq., Cleveland, OH 44120 (SAN 659-6010) Tel 216-561-3677.

Vedanta Ctr, *(Vedanta Centre Pubs.; 0-911564),* Div. of Vedanta Centre, Inc., 130 Beechwood St., Cohasset, MA 02025 (SAN 206-7781) Tel 617-383-0940.

Vedanta Pr, *(Vedanta Pr.; 0-87481),* Div. of Vedanta Society, 1946 Vedanta Pl., Hollywood, CA 90068-3996 (SAN 202-9340) Tel 213-465-7114.

Vedanta Soc St Louis, *(Vedanta Society of St. Louis; 0-916356),* 205 S. Skinker Blvd., St. Louis, MO 63105 (SAN 208-1180) Tel 314-721-5118.

Vedette Print, *(Vedette Printing Co.),* Greenfield, MO 65661 (SAN 239-5703).

Veep, *(VEEP, Incorporated; 0-9614166),* P.O. Box 882, Norristown, PA 19404 (SAN 686-6719) Tel 215-277-3778.

Vehicle Edns, *(Vehicle Editions; 0-931428),* 238 Mott St., New York, NY 10012 (SAN 212-5773) Tel 212-226-1769; Dist. by: Talman Company, The, 150 Fifth Ave., Rm. 514, New York, NY 10011 (SAN 200-5204) Tel 212-620-3182.

Vel-or Co, *(Vel-or Co.; 0-9615906),* 2141 Lakeview Rd., Vista, CA 92084 (SAN 696-7612) Tel 619-727-2230.

Veldt Protea
   See Veldt Protea Inst

Veldt Protea Inst, *(Veldt Protea Institute; 0-917538),* 3207 Las Palmas St., Houston, TX 77027 (SAN 209-3626); Dist. by: British Market Inc., 2366 Rice Blvd., Houston, TX 77005 (SAN 200-8289) Tel 713-529-9889.

Velo-News, *(Velo-News; 0-941950),* Box 1257, Brattleboro, VT 05301 (SAN 239-5711) Tel 802-254-2305; Dist. by: Countryman Press, Inc., P.O. Box 175, Woodstock, VT 05091 (SAN 206-4901) Tel 802-457-1049.

Velocities, *(Velocities; 0-930231),* 2740 College, No. 302, Berkeley, CA 94705 (SAN 679-1522).

VeNard Pubs, *(VeNard Pubs.; 0-9610342),* 4812 Folson Blvd. No. H, Sacramento, CA 95819 (SAN 264-469X) Tel 916-739-8343.

†Vendome, *(Vendome Pr., The; 0-86565),* 515 Madison Ave., Suite 1906, New York, NY 10022 (SAN 215-2347) Tel 212-838-8991; Dist. by: Rizzoli International Pubns., 597 Fifth Ave., New York, NY 10017 (SAN 207-7000) Tel 212-223-0100; *CIP.*

Venice West, *(Venice West Pubs.),* 319 North Cordova St., Burbank, CA 91505 (SAN 210-2986) Tel 818-843-5515; Dist. by: Capra Press, P.O. Box 2068, Santa Barbara, CA 93120 (SAN 208-0494) Tel 805-966-4590.

Ventnor, *(Ventnor Pubs.; 0-911566),* Drawer G, Ventnor Post Office,, Ventnor, NJ 08406-0078 (SAN 205-4760).

Ventura Pr, *(Ventura Pr.; 0-917438),* P.O. Box 1076, Guerneville, CA 95446 (SAN 205-4779).

Venture Assocs, *(Venture Assocs., Inc.; 0-9616346),* P.O. Box 140165, Nashville, TN 37214 (SAN 658-7976) Tel 615-758-0430; 704 Valley Brook Dr., Mt. Juliet, TN 37122 (SAN 658-7984).

Venture Bks, *(Venture Books; 0-9600432),* P.O. Box 131, Coopersburg, PA 18036 (SAN 205-4787) Tel 215-965-2891.

Venture CA, *(Venture Pubns.; 0-9612478),* 2687 Montrose Pl., Santa Barbara, CA 93105 (SAN 289-6427) Tel 805-682-5074.

Venture Con Pr, *(Venture Concepts Press; 0-9611214),* 806 15th St. NW Suite 421, Washington, DC 20005 (SAN 282-9304) Tel 212-783-1166.

Venture Econ Inc, *(Venture Economics Inc.; 0-914470),* P.O. Box 348, 16 Laurel Ave., Wellesley Hills, MA 02181 (SAN 206-2240) Tel 617-431-8100; Toll free: 800-521-8110.

Venture Econo *Imprint of* **Unipub**

Venture Indus, *(Venture Industries, Inc.; 0-937051),* P.O. Box 393, St. Augustine, FL 32085 (SAN 658-6678) Tel 904-829-0221; 117A King St., St. Augustine, FL 32085 (SAN 658-6686).

Venture PA
   See Venture Pub PA

Venture Persp Pr, *(Venture Perspective Pr.; 0-932309),* 4300 Stevens Creek Blvd., Suite 155, San Jose, CA 95129 (SAN 686-7375) Tel 408-247-1325.

Venture Pr AZ, *(Venture Pr.; 0-936465),* 1626 Ventura Dr., Tempe, AZ 85281 (SAN 697-9904) Tel 602-966-2116.

Venture Pub PA, *(Venture Publishing; 0-910251),* 1640 Oxford Cir., State College, PA 16801 (SAN 240-897X) Tel 814-234-4561.

Venturecraft Co, *(Venturecraft Kits Co.; 0-941326),* 47 Great River Dr., Sound Beach, NY 11789 (SAN 239-5738) Tel 516-744-4395.

Ventures Intl, *(Ventures International; 0-917437),* P.O. Box 6539, San Diego, CA 92106 (SAN 656-1381) Tel 619-223-6787.

Ventures Pub
   See D L Barber Ventures

Venus Bks, *(Venus Bks.; 0-939352),* 9655 Chimney Hill, Suite 2118, Dallas, TX 75243 (SAN 216-4728) Tel 214-644-7482.

Verbatim
   See Verbatim Bks

Verbatim Bks, *(Verbatim; 0-930454),* Box 668, Essex, CT 06426 (SAN 211-1047) Tel 203-767-8248.

VerDugo Pr, *(VerDugo Pr.; 0-941140),* 6715 Sunset Blvd., Hollywood, CA 90028 (SAN 239-572X); Dist. by: Hollywood Reporter, 6715 Sunset Blvd., Hollywood, CA 90028 (SAN 217-3824) Tel 213-464-7411.

Vergin Pr, *(Vergin Pr.; 0-935839),* 1101 Avalon Dr., Apt. J, El Paso, TX 79925 (SAN 696-6411) Tel 915-779-8678.

Veridon Edns, *(Veridon Editions; 0-912061),* P.O. Box 65, New Rochelle, NY 10804 (SAN 264-7028).

Veritas, *(Veritas Foundation; 0-911568),* P.O. Box 111, West Sayville, NY 11796 (SAN 206-3107). Formerly Named Probe.

Veritas Pr, *(Veritas Press; 0-932208),* 3310 Rochambeau Ave., New York, NY 10467 (SAN 212-2413) Tel 212-655-7566.

†Veritat Found, *(Veritat Foundation, Inc.; 0-938760),* 3910 Los Feliz Blvd., Los Angeles, CA 90027 (SAN 205-6348); *CIP.*

Veritie Pr, *(Veritie Press, Inc.; 0-915964),* P.O. Box 222, Novelty, OH 44072 (SAN 207-6977) Tel 216-338-3374.

Verlag Chemie
   See VCH Pubs

Vermont Bks, *(Vermont Bks., Inc.; 0-911570),* Div. of TL. Vermont Book Shop, 38 Main St., Middlebury, VT 05753 (SAN 205-4817) Tel 802-388-2061.

Vermont Herit Pr, *(Vermont Heritage Press; 0-911853),* 124 Elm St., Bennington, VT 05201 (SAN 264-472X) Tel 802-442-6873.

Vernal Equinox, *(Vernal Equinox Pr.; 0-942380),* P.O. Box 581, San Anselmo, CA 94960 (SAN 240-1762).

Verry, *(Verry, Lawrence, Inc.; 0-8426),* P.O. Box 215, Mystic, CT 06355 (SAN 202-5205) Tel 203-536-3104.

Versailles, *(Versailles, Elizabeth Starr; 0-9606002),* 42 Nash Hill Rd., Williamsburg, MA 01096 (SAN 203-0330) Tel 413-268-7576.

Version One Point Zero
   See Mid Coast Pub

Vert Milon Pr, *(Vert Milon Pr.; 0-9613980),* P.O. Box 332, Alexandria, VA 22313 (SAN 682-2061) Tel 703-549-8330.

Vertex, *(Vertex Co.),* 4438 Manzanita Dr., San Jose, CA 95129 (SAN 209-4096) Tel 408-252-2592.

Verve Pr, *(Verve Pr.; 0-937363),* P.O. Box 1997, Huntington Beach, CA 92647 (SAN 659-0985) Tel 714-846-9640; 17171 Sims, Huntington Beach, CA 92649 (SAN 659-0993).

Vervir, *(Vervir, Inc.; 0-935247),* 251 Willows Dr., Laguna Hills, CA 92653 (SAN 695-832X) Tel 714-458-6442.

Very Best, *(Very Best Publishers, The; 0-911729),* Cranehill, 194 Maple Ave., Great Barrington, MA 01230 (SAN 293-4086) Tel 617-262-3477.

Very Healthy Ent, *(Very Healthy Enterprises; 0-9615452),* P.O. Box 4728, Inglewood, CA 90309 (SAN 696-2254) Tel 213-672-3269.

Very Idea, *(Very Idea, The; 0-9615130),* 1604 Ave J, Box 53, Abernathy, TX 79311 (SAN 694-1869) Tel 806-298-4252.

Very Vera, *(Very Vera; 0-937747),* P.O. Box 2311, Honolulu, HI 96804 (SAN 659-3739) Tel 808-988-3395; 2804 Manoa Rd., Honolulu, HI 96822 (SAN 659-3747); Dist. by: Mediatech, 737 Bishop St., Suite 2790, Honolulu, HI 96813 (SAN 200-6456).

†Vestal, *(Vestal Pr., Ltd.; 0-911572),* P.O. Box 97, 320 N. Jensen Rd., Vestal, NY 13850 (SAN 205-4825) Tel 607-797-4872; *CIP.*

Vestron Video, *(Vestron Video, Inc.; 0-8051),* 1011 High Ridge Rd., Stamford, CT 06907 (SAN 658-6430) Tel 203-968-0000; P.O. Box 4000, Stamford, CT 06907.

Vetco Printing, *(Vetco Printing & Publishing; 0-9616448),* 4217 N. Main St., Suite 110, Dayton, OH 45405 (SAN 659-1000) Tel 513-275-2837.

Veterans Info, *(Veterans Information Service),* P.O. Box 111, East Moline, IL 61244 (SAN 205-4833) Tel 309-797-1868.

Veterinary Med, *(Veterinary Medicine Publishing Co.; 0-935078),* Subs. of Medical Economics Co., 9073 Lenexa Dr., Lenexa, KS 66215 (SAN 209-0074) Tel 913-492-4300; Toll free: 800-255-6864.

Veterinary Textbks, *(Veterinary Textbooks; 0-9601152),* 36 Woodcrest Ave., Ithaca, NY 14850 (SAN 207-2998) Tel 607-272-1860.

Vets Ed Proj, *(Veterans Education Project, Inc.; 0-941486),* P.O. Box 42130, Washington, DC 20015 (SAN 239-054X) Tel 202-686-2741.

Vets Prof Mgmt, *(Veterinarians Professional Management Co.; 0-936233),* 5722 San Miguel Rd., Bonita, CA 92002 (SAN 696-8562) Tel 619-479-5555.

Vibrante Pr, *(Vibrante Pr.; 0-935301),* 2430 Juan Tabo, NE, Suite 110, Albuquerque, NM 87112 (SAN 696-2351) Tel 505-298-4793.

Vichitra Pr, *(Vichitra Pr.; 0-941582),* 10582 Cheviot Dr., Los Angeles, CA 90064 (SAN 239-3387) Tel 213-839-8547; Dist. by: Asian Humanities Pr., 3204 Adeline St., P.O. Box 3056, Berkeley, CA 94703 (SAN 213-6503).

Vicious Cir Pr, *(Vicious Circle Pr.; 0-936393),* Box 18244, Louisville, KY 40218 (SAN 697-3051) Tel 502-538-7222; Rte. 2, Armstrong Ln. Box 158, Mt. Washington, KY 40047 (SAN 699-6493).

Vicksburg Jr Aux, *(Vicksburg Junior Auxiliary; 0-9614988),* No. 5 Lakewood, Vicksburg, MS 39180 (SAN 693-7691) Tel 601-638-8562.

Vicky Bird Bks
   See V S Morris

Vicris Pubn, *(Vicris Pubn.; 0-9616644),* 4502 W. Ashlan Ave., Fresno, CA 93711 (SAN 659-669X) Tel 209-276-0345.

Victimology, *(Victimology Inc.; 0-916818; 0-943242),* 2333 N. Vernon St., Arlington, VA 22207 (SAN 208-3728) Tel 703-528-8872.

Victims Pr, *(Victim's Pr.; 0-935261),* 640 Turk St., Suite 46, San Francisco, CA 94102 (SAN 695-5274) Tel 415-673-5460.

Victor Bks, *(Victor Bks.; 0-88207; 0-89693),* Div. of Scripture Pr. Pubns., Inc., P.O. Box 1825, Wheaton, IL 60187 (SAN 207-7302) Tel 312-668-6000; Toll free: 800-323-9409 (For orders); Order to: 1825 College Ave., Wheaton, IL 60187 (SAN 207-7310).

Victor Pub Co
   See M Victor Pub

†Victoria Hse, *(Victoria House, Pubs.; 0-918480),* 2218 N.E. 8th Ave., Portland, OR 97212 (SAN 209-9101) Tel 503-284-4801; *CIP.*

Victoria Isl
   See J T Brown & Assocs

Victoria Pr, *(Victoria Pr., The; 0-9613204),* 39865 Cedar Blvd., Suite 240, Newark, CA 94560 (SAN 295-6128).

Victorian Design, *(Victorian Design Pr.; 0-913693),* P.O. Box 5186, Mill Valley, CA 94942 (SAN 286-2158); 382 Throckmorton Ave., Mill Valley, CA 94941 (SAN 286-2166) Tel 415-388-4990.

Victorian Video, *(Victorian Video Productions; 0-936225),* P.O. Box 1328, Port Townsend, WA 98368 (SAN 696-8570) Tel 916-961-9359.

Victorious Ministry, *(Victorious Ministry Through Christ, Inc.; 0-9605178),* P.O. Box 1804, Winter Park, FL 32790 (SAN 215-823X); Dist. by: Impact Books, 137 W. Jefferson, Kirkwood, MO 63122 (SAN 214-0330) Tel 314-833-3309.

Victory Hse, *(Victory Hse., Inc.; 0-932081),* P.O. Box 700238, Tulsa, OK 74170 (SAN 686-2667) Tel 918-747-5009.

Victory Pub, *(Victory Publishing; 0-935303),* 1068 Del Norte Ave., Menlo, CA 94025 (SAN 696-2408) Tel 415-322-4402.

VICY, *(Virgin Islands Commission on Youth; 0-937421),* P.O. Box 580, Charlotte Amalie, St. Thomas, VI 00801 (SAN 659-1019) Tel 809-774-6012.

Vida Pubs
See Life Pubs Intl

Video Assocs, *(Video Assocs., Inc.; 1-55593),* 5419 Sunset Blvd., Los Angeles, CA 90028 (SAN 658-7151) Tel 213-463-3255.

Video Athlete, *(Video Athlete Corp.; 0-915659),* 120 W. Mifflin, Madison, WI 53703 (SAN 287-2358).

Video Award, *(Video Award Motion Pictures, Inc.; 0-936311),* 1585 Broadway, New York, NY 10036 (SAN 697-3094) Tel 212-315-2600.

Video-Forum, *(Video-Forum; 0-88432),* Div. of Jeffrey Norton Pubs., 96 Broad St., Guilford, CT 06437 (SAN 217-4707) Tel 203-453-9794; Toll free: 800-243-1234.

Video-Info, *(Video-Info Pubns.; 0-931294),* P.O. Box 2685, Santa Fe, NM 87501 (SAN 212-5781) Tel 505-983-6422.

Video Pubns Ltd, *(Video Pubns., Ltd.; 0-935667),* 915 Oliver St., Suite 821, St. Louis, MO 63101 (SAN 696-2467) Tel 314-231-9550.

Video Travel, *(Video Travel, Inc.; 1-55629),* 153 W. Fourth St., Williamsport, PA 17701 (SAN 659-9311) Tel 717-326-6525; Toll free: 800-828-6888.

Video Treas, *(Video Treasures; 1-55529),* 200 Robbins Ln., Jericho, NY 11753 (SAN 696-2521) Tel 201-778-0877.

Video Wizard, *(Video Wizard Co.; 0-943320),* 134 St. Charles Ave., San Francisco, CA 94132 (SAN 240-8023) Tel 415-952-4990.

Vienna Hse, *(Vienna Hse, Inc.; 0-8443),* 342 Madison Ave., New York, NY 10017 (SAN 202-9367) Tel 212-986-7724.

Viet Nam Mar, *(Vietnam Marine Pubns.; 0-9611880),* P.O. Box 201, Lancaster, TX 75146 (SAN 286-0694) Tel 214-227-3365; Dist. by: Presidio Pr., 31 Pamaron Way, Novato, CA 94947 (SAN 214-2759) Tel 415-883-1373.

VIEW Inc, *(VIEW, Inc.; 0-8030),* 34 E. 23rd St., New York, NY 10010 Tel 212-674-5550.

Viewpoint Pr, *(Viewpoint Pr.; 0-943962),* P.O. Box P, Tehachapi, CA 93561 (SAN 241-1644) Tel 213-318-3645.

Vigilantero Pr, *(Vigilantero Pr.; 0-9616829),* P.O. Box 7513, Boulder, CO 80306 (SAN 661-1656); 1627 Columbine, Boulder, CO 80306 (SAN 661-1664) Tel 303-440-0713.

†**Viking,** *(Viking-Penguin, Inc.; 0-670),* 40 W. 23rd St., New York, NY 10010 (SAN 200-2442) Tel 212-337-5200; Toll free: 800-631-3577; Orders to: 299 Murray Hill Pkwy., East Rutherford, NJ 07073 (SAN 282-5074); CIP. Imprints: Comp (Compass Books).(Compass Bks.); E Sifton Bks (Elisabeth Sifton Books); Exp (Explorer Books).(Explorer Bks.); Studio (Studio Books).(Studio Bks.); Viking Kestrel (Viking Kestrel).

Viking Import, *(Viking Import House, Inc.; 0-911576),* 412 SE Sixth St., Ft. Lauderdale, FL 33301 (SAN 205-485X).

Viking Kestrel *Imprint of* **Viking**

Viking Pr
See Viking

Vil Oak Pk, *(Village of Oak Park; 0-9616915),* 1 Village Hall Plaza, Oak Park, IL 60302 (SAN 661-6593) Tel 312-383-6400; Dist. by: Chicago Review Pr., 814 N. Franklin, Chicago, IL 60610 (SAN 213-5744) Tel 312-337-0747.

Villa Pr, *(Villa Pr.; 0-913472),* Affil. of Schoolhouse Software, 69-10 164th St., Fresh Meadows, NY 11365 (SAN 203-0322) Tel 718-591-0894.

Villa Pr AZ, *(Villa Pr.; 0-933843),* 4506 W. Citrus Way, Glendale, AZ 85301 (SAN 692-6878) Tel 602-934-3607.

Village AL, *(Village Press (AL), The; 0-9613152),* P.O. Box 787, Daphne, AL 36526 (SAN 294-9911) Tel 205-626-3505.

Village Hse Pubs, *(Village Hse. Pubs.; 0-9617255),* 3541 Brookwood Rd., Birmingham, AL 35223 (SAN 663-5466) Tel 205-967-2284.

Village Pr, *(Village Pr., The; 0-940310),* P.O. Box 174, Unionville, CT 06085 (SAN 217-5770) Tel 203-673-9827.

Village Voice, *(Village Voice; 0-934465),* 842 Broadway, New York, NY 10003 (SAN 205-4868) Tel 212-475-3300.

Villanova Law, *(Villanova Univ. Law Schl.),* Villanova Univ., Villanova, PA 19085 (SAN 226-7810).

Villanova U Ath, *(Villanova Univ., Athletic Dept.; 0-9615910),* Field Hse., Villanova, PA 19085 (SAN 696-7647) Tel 215-647-9590.

Vimach Assocs, *(Vimach Associates; 0-917949),* 3039 Indianola Ave., Columbus, OH 43202 (SAN 657-0283) Tel 614-262-0471.

†**Vin Image,** *(Vintage Image; 0-918666),* 1335 Main St., St. Helena, CA 94574 (SAN 210-329X) Tel 707-963-3883; CIP.

Vincente Bks, *(Vincente Bks.; 0-915241),* P.O. Box 7388, Berkeley, CA 94707-0388 (SAN 289-8829) Tel 415-528-5648.

Vincentian, *(Vincentian Evangelization; 0-9608630),* 1025 Napoleon Ave., New Orleans, LA 70115 (SAN 219-0974) Tel 504-899-1130.

Vinco Pr, *(Vinco Pr.; 0-9603836),* 1553 Woodward, Detroit, MI 48226 (SAN 213-8093).

VinMar Agency, *(VinMar Agency, Inc.; 0-943964),* P.O. Box 1329, Avon Park, FL 33825 (SAN 241-1652) Tel 813-453-7412.

Vintage Am, *(Vintage America Publishing Co.; 0-932930),* P.O. Box 57361, Washington, DC 20037 (SAN 212-1689). Do Not Confuse with Vintage Trade Books, Imprint of Random.

Vintage Forty-Five, *(Vintage '45 Pr.; 0-9614375),* P.O. Box 266, Orinda, CA 94563 (SAN 688-6302) Tel 415-254-7266; Dist. by: Bookpeople, 2929 Fifth St., Berkeley, CA 94710 (SAN 168-9517); Dist. by: Inland Book Company, P.O. Box 261, 22 Hemingway Ave., East Haven, CT 06512 (SAN 200-4151) Tel 203-467-4257.

Vintage Pr
See Vintage Press

Vintage Press, *(Vintage Pr.; 0-9615324),* 40 Christine Dr., East Hanover, NJ 07936 (SAN 695-0493) Tel 201-887-5020. Do not confuse with 'Vintage' imprints of Random House, New York, NY.

Vintage Pubns, *(Vintage Pubns.; 0-931973),* 806 Adobe Dr., Santa Rosa, CA 95404 (SAN 686-0761) Tel 707-539-1699.

Vintage Radio, *(Vintage Radio Co.; 0-914126),* 26451 Dunwood Rd., P.O. Box 2045, Rolling Hills Estates, CA 90274 (SAN 282-5104) Tel 213-375-4272; Dist. by: McMahon Vintage Radio, P.O. Box 1331,, N. Highlands, CA 95660 (SAN 282-6356) Tel 916-332-8262.

Vinton, *(Vinton Publishing),* 1244 Wyoming St., Boulder City, NV 89005 (SAN 277-710X).

Violet Pr, *(Violet Pr.; 0-912968),* P.O. Box 398, New York, NY 10009 (SAN 203-1701).

Violetta Bks, *(Violetta Bks.; 0-915913),* 76 Byers St., Springfield, MA 01105 (SAN 294-1090) Tel 413-737-8118; Orders to: Box 15151, Springfield, MA 01115 (SAN 693-5117).

Vip Aero Pubs, *(Vip Aero Publishers Inc.; 0-934575),* P.O. Box 16103, Colorado Springs, CO 80935 (SAN 693-8442) Tel 303-596-4172.

VIP Directory, *(VIP Directory, The; 0-937955),* Div. of Ads Agency, Inc., P.O. Box 6030, Stateline, NV 89449 (SAN 659-8080); 200 Kingsbury Grade, Suite A, Stateline, NV 89449 (SAN 659-8099) Tel 702-588-6445.

VIP Int, *(VIP International, Inc.; 0-9615601),* 6342 SW Macadam Ave., Portland, OR 97201 (SAN 695-8109) Tel 503-245-3390; Orders to: P.O. Box 383, Marylhurst, OR 97036 (SAN 662-3581).

Virago *Imprint of* **Doubleday**

Vireo Pr, *(Vireo Press; 0-9612144),* Box 898, Waycross, GA 31501 (SAN 287-7783).

Virginia Bar, *(Virginia State Bar),* 801 E. Main St., Ross Bldg., 10th Flr., Richmond, VA 23219 (SAN 226-7829) Tel 804-293-6618.

Virginia State
See Virginia Bar

Virgo Pr, *(Virgo Press; 0-930558),* 975 Arthur Godfrey Rd., Suite 401, Miami Beach, FL 33140 (SAN 211-1063) Tel 305-538-6324.

Virtue Notagraph, *(Virtue Notagraph Editions; 0-914596),* 4940 Beaumont Dr., La Mesa, CA 92041 (SAN 206-1376) Tel 619-469-6634.

Virtuoso, *(Virtuoso Pubns., Inc.; 0-918624),* 206 SE 46th Lane, Cape Coral, FL 33904 (SAN 210-153X) Tel 813-549-1802.

Visa Pub, *(Visa Publishing Corp.; 0-9606802),* 50 E. 42nd St., New York, NY 10017 (SAN 217-2739); Dist. by: Bookazine Co., Inc., 303 W. Tenth St., New York, NY 10014 (SAN 169-5665) Tel 212-675-8877.

Visa Pub FL
See Nova Pub IL

Visage Pr
See Victimology

Vishwa, *(Vishwa Dharma Pubns.; 0-942508),* 174 Santa Clara Ave., Oakland, CA 94610 (SAN 238-2075) Tel 415-654-4683.

Visibility Ent, *(Visibility Enterprises; 0-9603740),* 450 West End Ave., New York, NY 10024 (SAN 214-4832) Tel 212-787-9239.

Visible Diff, *(Visible Difference International, A; 0-933675),* P.O. Box 175, Selden, NY 11784-0175 (SAN 692-543X) Tel 516-924-1786.

VisiCorp
See Paladin

Vision *Imprint of* **FS&G**

Vision Bks, *(Vision Books; 0-942024),* 790 Commercial Ave., Coos Bay, OR 97420 (SAN 293-4256) Tel 503-267-4232 (SAN 168-9886) (SAN 212-0364); Dist. by: Vision Books, 790 Commercial Ave., Coos Bay, OR 97420 (SAN 293-4264) Tel 503-267-4232; Dist. by: DeVorss & Co.,Inc., P.O. Box 550, 1046 Princeton Dr., Marina del Rey, CA 90294 (SAN 168-9886); Dist. by: Bookpeople, 2929 Fifth St., Berkeley, CA 94710 (SAN 168-9517); Dist. by: Publishers Group West, 5855 Beaudry St., Emeryville, CA 94608 (SAN 202-8522); Dist. by: New Leaf Distributing, 1020 White St. SW, Atlanta, GA 30310 (SAN 169-1449) Tel 404-755-2665; Dist. by: Ingram Book Co., 347 Reedwood Dr., Nashville, TN 37217 (SAN 169-7978).

Vision Found, *(Vision Foundation, Incorporated; 0-9606836),* 818 Mt. Auburn St., Watertown, MA 02172 (SAN 217-1376) Tel 617-926-4232; Toll free: 800-852-3029 Massachusetts only.

Vision Hse, *(Vision Hse.; 0-88449),* 2300 Knoll Dr., Ventura, CA 93003 (SAN 282-5155) Tel 805-644-9721; Orders to: Gospel Light Publications, P.O. Box 6309, Oxnard, CA 93031 (SAN 282-5163).

Vision Pubns, *(Vision Pubns.; 0-912063),* P.O. Box 8555, St. Louis, MO 63126 (SAN 289-0267) Tel 314-962-7600; 951 Briarton, Crestwood, MO 63126 (SAN 289-0275).

Vision Ventures, *(Vision Ventures, Inc.; 0-9616958),* Div. of Vision Services-An Agency for the Visually Impaired, 1401 Madison St., Suite 284, Seattle, WA 98104 (SAN 661-8049) Tel 206-386-6666.

Visionaide Pr, *(Visionaide Pr.; 0-9612134),* 3 White Oak Rd., Roseland, NJ 07068 (SAN 286-8881) Tel 201-226-0958.

Visionary Pub, *(Visionary Publishing, Inc.; 0-937223),* P.O. Box 2440, San Anselmo, CA 94960 (SAN 658-7178) Tel 415-461-4784; 500 V. F. Vista Grande, Greenbrae, CA 94904 (SAN 658-7186).

Visions Success, *(Visions for Success, Inc.; 0-9616406),* P.O. Box 1616, Richmond, VA 23214 (SAN 659-1027) Tel 804-740-9178; 1223A Gaskins Rd., Richmond, VA 23214 (SAN 659-1035).

Vismar, *(Vismar Publishing Co.; 0-9602206),* P.O. Box 29034, Parma, OH 44129 (SAN 212-3932).

Vista Pubns, *(Vista Pubns.; 0-930938),* 1108 McAdams Ave., Dallas, TX 75224 (SAN 211-2817). Do Not Confuse with Vista Pubns. in California.

Vistara Pubns, *(Vistara Pubns.; 0-930551; 0-935384),* P.O. Box 30577, Phoenix, AZ 85032 (SAN 677-4180).

Visual Attraction, *(Visual Attraction; 0-9617201),* 114 Holly Way, Pismo Beach, CA 93449 (SAN 663-267X) Tel 805-546-8836.

Visual Comm, *(Visual Communications, Inc.; 0-9615759),* 518 Fifth Ave. Suite 305, Moline, IL 61265 (SAN 695-8095) Tel 309-762-9076; Orders to: Peoria Historical Society, 942 NE, Glen Oak Ave., Peoria, IL 61603 (SAN 662-3573) Tel 309-674-1921.

Visual Communication *Imprint of* **Hastings**

Visual Educ Assn, *(Visual Education Assn.; 1-55637),* Div. of Graphic Paper Products Corp., P.O. Box 1666, Springfield, OH 45501 (SAN 660-9775); Toll free: 800-543-5947; 581 W. Leffel Ln., Springfield, OH 45501 (SAN 660-9783); Dist. by: Southern California Bk. Co., 2219 S. Union Ave., Los Angeles, CA 90007 (SAN 168-9827); Dist. by: Marshall/Mangold, 4805 Nelson Ave., Baltimore, MD 21215 (SAN 169-3115).

Visual Evangels, *(Visual Evangels Publishing Co.; 0-915398),* 1401 Ohio St., Michigan City, IN 46360 (SAN 212-002X) Tel 219-874-3902.

Visual Impact, *(Visual Impact Pubs., Communicators; 0-913426),* 723 S. Wells St., Chicago, IL 60607 (SAN 206-8591) Tel 312-922-2083.

Visual Purple, *(Visual Purple; 0-917198),* Box 996, Berkeley, CA 94701 (SAN 208-9114); Dist. by: Bookpeople, 2929 Fifth St., Berkeley, CA 94710 (SAN 168-9517) Tel 415-549-3030.

Visual Resources Assn, *(Visual Resources Assn.; 0-938852),* 20 W. 31st Ave., Eugene, OR 97405-3326 (SAN 215-9686) Tel 503-686-3052; Orders to: Visual Resources Assn., Christina Updike, Treas., c/o James Madison Univ., Art Dept., Harrisonburg, VA 22807 (SAN 662-0817).

†Visual Studies, *(Visual Studies Workshop; 0-89822),* 31 Prince St., Rochester, NY 14607 (SAN 218-1606); *CIP.*

VITA
See Vols Tech Asst

Vita Pr TN, *(Vita Pr.),* 2143 Poplar Ave., Memphis, TN 38104 (SAN 214-4840) Tel 901-725-4072.

Vita Sign, *(Vita-Sign; 0-939389),* Subs. of Copy Write, 3412 Dodge St., Omaha, NE 68131 (SAN 663-1274) Tel 402-341-1647.

Vital Pr, *(Vital Pr.; 0-915660),* Box 38341, Sacramento, CA 95838 (SAN 213-1846).

Vitality Assocs, *(Vitality Assocs.; 0-930918),* P.O. Box 2154, Saratoga, CA 95070 (SAN 211-2809); 14600 Wild Oak Way, Saratoga, CA 95070 (SAN 669-294X) Tel 408-867-1241.

Vitality Hse Int Inc, *(Vitality House International, Inc.; 0-912547),* 3707 N. Canyon Rd.,No. 8C, Provo, UT 84604-4568 (SAN 265-2935) Tel 801-224-9214.

Vitriol Pubns, *(Vitriol Pubns.; 0-930635),* 110 E. 23rd St., Suite 801, New York, NY 10010 (SAN 676-3200) Tel 212-254-4538.

Viv-Poo, *(Viv-Poo; 0-9611952),* P.O. Box 32327, Washington, DC 20007 (SAN 286-0791) Tel 703-524-0627.

Vivekananda, *(Vivekananda Vedanta Society; 0-9600826),* 5423 S. Hyde Park Blvd., Chicago, IL 60615 (SAN 222-190X).

VJP Enter
See V J P Enter

VLE Ltd, *(VLE, Ltd.; 0-912693),* P.O. Box 547, Tenafly, NJ 07670 (SAN 282-8472) Tel 201-567-5536.

Voc Career Assess, *(Vocational & Career Assessment; 0-940150),* P.O. Box 1566, Lakeside, CA 92040 (SAN 220-3111) Tel 619-561-2092.

Voc Indus Clubs, *(Vocational Industrial Clubs of America, Inc.; 0-933263),* P.O. Box 3000, Leesburg, VA 22075 (SAN 225-8137) Tel 703-777-8810.

Voc-Offers, *(Voc-Offers; 0-918995),* P.O. Box 4273, Hayward, CA 94540 (SAN 669-8247) Tel 408-255-6579.

Voc Pub, *(Vocational Publishing; 0-934635),* 10620 Fillmore St., Blaine, MN 55434 (SAN 693-9317) Tel 612-784-1846.

Vocal Power, *(Vocal Power; 0-934419),* Div. of Voice Works Institude., 17200 Burbank Blvd., Encino, CA 91316 (SAN 693-4471) Tel 818-994-1060; Dist. by: Cherry Lane Bks., P.O. Box 430, Port Chester, NY 10573-0430 (SAN 219-0788).

Voice of Liberty, *(Voice of Liberty Pubns.; 0-934762),* 3 Borger Place, Pearl River, NY 10965 (SAN 213-568X) Tel 914-735-8140.

Vol Lawyers Arts, *(Volunteer Lawyers for the Arts; 0-917103),* 1285 Ave. of the Americas, 3rd Flr., New York, NY 10019 (SAN 227-0617) Tel 212-575-1150.

Volaphon Bks, *(Volaphon Bks.; 0-916258),* Div. of Woodbine Press, 73 Fox Ridge Crescent, Warwick, RI 02886 (SAN 208-0559) Tel 401-738-2638.

Volare Bks, *(Volare Books; 0-915243),* 781 S. Stillwater Lane, Anaheim, CA 92807 (SAN 289-8845) Tel 714-998-7901.

Volcanda Educ, *(Volcanda Educational Pubns.),* 211 Deerfoot Rd., DeLand, FL 32720 (SAN 211-3368).

†Volcano Pr, *(Volcano Press, Incorporated; 0-912078),* 330 Ellis St., San Francisco, CA 94102 (SAN 220-0015) Tel 415-664-5600; *CIP.*

Voldstad Ent, *(Voldstad Enterprise; 0-9603906),* 688 S. Hobart Blvd., Los Angeles, CA 90005 (SAN 209-0791).

Volkwein Bros
See Columbia Pictures

Vollbracht Ent
See Elliott Graph

Vols Tech Asst, *(Volunteers in Technical Assistance; 0-86619),* 1815 N. Lynn St., Suite 200, Arlington, VA 22209 (SAN 225-6711) Tel 703-276-1800.

Volunteer Council, *(Volunteer Council of the Tulsa Philharmonic Society, Inc.; 0-9617004),* 8177 S. Harvard, Suite 431, Tulsa, OK 74137 (SAN 662-5479) Tel 918-663-2226.

Volunteer Mgmt, *(Volunteer Management Assocs.; 0-9603362),* 279 S. Cedar Brook Rd., Boulder, CO 80302 (SAN 221-6914).

Volunteer Pubns, *(Volunteer Pubns.; 0-938310),* P.O. Box 240786, Memphis, TN 38124-0786 (SAN 215-9287) Tel 901-685-9577.

Volunteers Asia
See Appropriate Techn Proj

Volute Bks *Imprint of* **Naiad Pr**

Von-Bogckmann, *(Von-Bogckmann Jones, Printers),* Austin, TX 78742 (SAN 262-1061).

Von Gehr, *(Von Gehr Pr., The; 0-9601470),* P.O. Box 7654, Menlo Park, CA 94026 (SAN 211-3376) Tel 415-342-2631.

Von Hurland-Swenson
See Hurland-Swenson

Von Palisaden Pubns, *(Von Palisaden Publications, Incorporated; 0-932375),* 195 Spring Valley Rd., Paramus, NJ 07652 (SAN 687-3812) Tel 201-262-4919.

Vongrutnorv Og, *(Vongrutnorv Og Press; 0-9603504),* Randall Flat Rd. P.O. Box 411, Troy, ID 83871 (SAN 211-7169) Tel 208-835-4902.

Voter Ed Proj, *(Voter Education Project),* 52 Fairlie St. NW, Atlanta, GA 30303 (SAN 235-8336).

Voters Serv Educ, *(Voters Service Education Fund of the League of Women Voters of the Cincinnati Area, The; 0-9608724),* 103 Wm. Howard Taft Rd., Cincinnati, OH 45219 (SAN 238-4108) Tel 513-281-8683.

Voyager Pub FL, *(Voyager Publishing, Inc.; 0-938161),* 1950 Lee Rd., Suite 223, Winter Park, FL 32789 (SAN 659-9036) Tel 305-740-8348.

Voyager Pub Hse, *(Voyager Publishing Hse.; 0-9616761),* 23131 State Rte. 2, Monroe, WA 98272 (SAN 659-9419) Tel 206-794-7453.

Voyager Pubns, *(Voyager Pubns., Inc.; 0-9603020),* 2604 First National Bank Tower, Atlanta, GA 30303 (SAN 213-1854) Tel 404-658-1228; Orders to: P.O. Box 229, Lansing, NY 14882 (SAN 213-1862) Tel 607-257-1648.

Voyageur Pr Inc, *(Voyageur Pr., Inc.; 0-89658),* 7225 Wash Ave., Edina, MN 55435 (SAN 287-2668).

Voyaging Pr, *(Voyaging Pr.; 0-910711),* 669 N. 400 W., West Lafayette, IN 47906 (SAN 260-275X) Tel 317-743-2042.

VoyB *Imprint of* **HarBraceJ**

VSBE, *(Very Serious Business Enterprises; 0-9605304),* P.O. Box 356, Newark, NJ 07101 (SAN 215-8221).

VT Council Arts, *(Vermont Council on the Arts, Inc.; 0-916718),* 136 State St., Montpelier, VT 05602 (SAN 208-9092) Tel 802-828-3291.

†VT Hist Soc, *(Vermont Historical Society; 0-934720),* 109 State St., Montpelier, VT 05602 (SAN 206-0442) Tel 802-828-2291; *CIP.*

†VT Life Mag, *(Vermont Life Magazine; 0-936896),* 61 Elm St., Montpelier, VT 05602 (SAN 215-8213); *CIP.*

VTNC Arlington, *(Volunteer The National Center; 0-939239),* 1111 N. 19th St., Suite 500, Arlington, VA 22209 (SAN 276-5330) Tel 703-276-0542.

VTR Pub, *(VTR Publishing Co.; 0-915146),* 23 Eaton Rd., Syosset, NY 11791 (SAN 207-0979) Tel 516-938-0878.

Vu-Point Pubs, *(Vu-Point Pubs.; 0-9614557),* P.O. Box 3006, West Chester, PA 19381 (SAN 691-8158) Tel 215-696-8461.

Vulcan Bks, *(Vulcan Bks., Inc.; 0-914350),* 12722 Lake City Way, NE, Seattle, WA 98125 (SAN 203-1728) Tel 206-362-2606; Orders to: P.O. Box 25616, Seattle, WA 98125 (SAN 201-1736).

VUV Assocs, *(VUV Associates),* 1600 Regency Dr., Lincoln, NE 68506 (SAN 282-583X).

Vydex Mgmt, *(Vydex Management Group, Inc.; 0-935663),* 125 Worth Ave., Suite 112, Palm Beach, FL 33480 (SAN 695-8400) Tel 305-659-3288.

W A Barber, *(Barber, William A.; 0-9613725),* 42 Simsbury Rd., Stamford, CT 06905 (SAN 240-9186).

W A Benjamin
See Benjamin-Cummings

W A Hutchinson, *(Hutchinson, William A.; 0-9615427),* 52 Jeffrey Ln., Amherst, MA 01002 (SAN 696-2432) Tel 413-253-7036; Dist. by: AVI Publishing Co., Inc., 250 Post Rd. E., P.O. Box 831, Westport, CT 06881 (SAN 201-4017) Tel 203-226-0738.

W A Jewell
See Jewell-Johnson

W A Linder, *(Linder, William A., Co., Pubs.; 0-934844),* P.O. Box 443, Lindsborg, KS 67456 (SAN 205-4892) Tel 913-227-2514.

W A Reilly
See S F Learnard

W A Tieck, *(Tieck, W. A.; 0-9600398),* 3930 Bailey Ave., Bronx, NY 10463 (SAN 205-4906) Tel 212-549-5566.

W Amos, *(Amos, Winsom, Pub.; 0-9600520),* P.O. Box 416, C/O Soma Press, Yellow Springs, OH 45387 (SAN 222-8858) Tel 513-767-1573.

W & M Pr, *(W&M Press; 0-942240),* 6301 Colby, Des Moines, IA 50311 (SAN 241-5925) Tel 515-277-4354.

W & W Pubs, *(W & W Publishers; 0-9614026),* P.O. Box 905, Fort Valley, GA 31030 (SAN 683-616X) Tel 912-825-5850.

W Anglia Pubns, *(West Anglia; 0-942424),* c/o Ben Sen Pr., P.O. Box 2683, La Jolla, CA 92038 (SAN 238-2091) Tel 714-453-0706.

W B Patterson, *(Patterson, W. B.; 0-9606968),* 3080 Alaneo Pl., Wailuku, Maui, HI 96793 (SAN 205-4914) Tel 808-244-5437.

W B Rich, *(Rich, Will B.; 0-9612468),* 606 W. Barry St. 166, Chicago, IL 60657 (SAN 289-5714).

W Bailey Pub, *(Bailey, William, Pub.; 0-9604196),* P.O. Box 331, West Point, CA 95255 (SAN 214-2317) Tel 209-293-4303.

W Bittinger, *(Bittinger, Wayne; 0-9616990),* P.O. Box 220, Parsons, WV 26287 (SAN 661-8421) Tel 304-478-2881.

W Blake Pr, *(Blake, William, Press, Inc., The; 0-942868),* 140 Tenn. Ave. NE., Washington, DC 20002 (SAN 238-843X) Tel 202-546-3237.

W C Cullar, *(Cullar, W. Clytes; 0-9616504),* 1222 Ferndale Ave., Dallas, TX 75224 (SAN 659-4387) Tel 214-943-8339.

W C Darrah, *(Darrah, William Culp; 0-913116),* 2235 Baltimore Pike, Gettysburg, PA 17325 (SAN 205-4922) Tel 717-334-2272.

W C Hannan, *(Hannan, W. C., Graphics; 0-9611652),* P.O. Box A, Escondido, CA 92025 (SAN 285-3027) Tel 619-746-4959.

W C Hays, (Hays, William C.; 0-9616625), 3601 Wedgewood, Lansing, MI 48910 (SAN 661-2040) Tel 517-393-7026.

W C Howell, (Howell, Will C.; 0-9601140), 185 E. Norton, Sherwood, OR 97140 (SAN 210-2110) Tel 503-625-7409.

W C Stump, (Stump, William C.; 0-9613487), 108 Mapother St., Loyall, KY 40854 (SAN 657-3894) Tel 606-573-6868.

W Club Denton, (Woman's Club of Denton, Inc.; 0-9612076), P.O. Box 35, Denton, MD 21629 (SAN 286-8938) Tel 301-479-1186.

W D Andersen, (Andersen, William D., & Associates; 0-930373), 2935 Cordell St., Memphis, TN 38118 (SAN 295-0421) Tel 901-794-9566.

W D Farmer, (Farmer, W. D., Residence Designer, Inc.; 0-931518), P.O. Box 450025, Atlanta, GA 30345 (SAN 204-1219) Tel 404-934-7380; Toll free: 800-225-7526; Toll free: 800-221-7526 (In Georgia).

W D Lantz, (Lantz, Walter D.; 0-9610364), 1424 Marietta Ave., Lancaster, PA 17603 (SAN 264-1666) Tel 717-299-2943.

W D Leyerle
See Leyerle Pubns

W D Linscott, (Linscott, William D.; 0-9604920), 40 Glen Dr., Mill Valley, CA 94941 (SAN 214-4018) Tel 415-383-2666.

W D Staples, (Staples, Walter D.; 0-9616385), 12 Country Meadow, Rolling Hills Estates, CA 90274 (SAN 659-1833) Tel 213-541-3497.

W Dean Editions, (Dean, Wayne, Editions; 0-9616161), 3217 Petunia Ct., San Diego, CA 92117 (SAN 699-8364) Tel 619-272-6075.

W E C Plant Ent, (Plant, W.E.C., Enterprises; 0-913611), P.O. Box 030096, Ft. Lauderdale, FL 33303 (SAN 285-3612) Tel 305-467-3512; Dist. by: W. E. C. Plant Enterprises, P.O. Box 030096, Ft. Lauderdale, FL 33303 (SAN 285-3612).

W E May, (May, William E.; 0-9616086), 380 Hospital Dr., Suite 460, Macon, GA 31201 (SAN 661-2024) Tel 912-742-0833.

W E Siegmond, (Siegmond, W. E., Enterprises; 0-916610), 382 Central Park West, New York, NY 10025 (SAN 208-225X).

†W E Upjohn, (Upjohn, W. E., Institute for Employment Research; 0-911558), 300 S. Westnedge Ave., Kalamazoo, MI 49007 (SAN 236-9486) Tel 616-343-5541; CIP.

W Evans & Cogswell
See Walker Evans & Cogswell

W F Brinton, (Brinton, William F.; 0-9603554), Old Rome Rd., Box 4050, Mt. Vernon, ME 04352 (SAN 694-311X) Tel 207-293-2357.

W F Cox, (Cox, Willis F.; 0-9610758), Box 47, James Store, VA 23080 (SAN 264-7060) Tel 804-693-4533.

W F M T Inc, (WFMT, Inc.; 0-9613952), Affil. of Chicago Magazine, 303 E. Wacker Dr., Chicago, IL 60601 (SAN 682-1642) Tel 312-565-5139; Dist. by: Charles Levy Circ. Co., 1200 N. Branch, Chicago, IL 60622 (SAN 159-835X) Tel 312-440-4400.

W FLoyd, (Floyd, Wayne; 0-9613160), 1407 Darlene, Arlington, TX 76010 (SAN 294-9288) Tel 817-861-1683.

W Fourth St Block, (West Fourth Street Block Assn.), 285 W. Fourth St., New York, NY 10014 (SAN 208-077X) Tel 212-929-1452.

W Fox, (Fox, Wesley; 0-9604122), P.O. Box 26976, Lakewood, CO 80226-0976 (SAN 214-3739) Tel 303-936-9016.

W G Arader, (Arader, W. Graham; 0-934626), 1000 Boxwood Ct., King of Prussia, PA 19406 (SAN 212-8497) Tel 215-825-6570.

W G M Pub, (W.G.M. Publishing Co.; 0-934439), P.O. Box 312, Maplewood, NJ 07040 (SAN 694-5295) Tel 201-761-6667.

W G Weger, (Weger, William G.; 0-9617058), P.O. Box 976, Ottumwa, IA 52501 (SAN 662-8400); 425 N. Green, Apt. 5, Ottumwa, IA 52501 (SAN 662-8419) Tel 515-683-3014.

W Griffin Assocs, (Griffin, Wesley, Assocs.; 0-9617144), 976 Denhart St., Norfolk, VA 23504 (SAN 663-3390) Tel 804-827-8299.

W H Anderson
See Anderson Pub Co

†W H Freeman, (Freeman, W. H., & Co.; 0-7167), Subs. of Scientific American, Inc., 41 Madison Ave., 37th Flr., New York, NY 10010 (SAN 290-6864) Tel 212-532-7660; Orders to: 4419 W. 1980, S, Salt Lake City, UT 84104 (SAN 290-6872) Tel 801-973-4660; CIP.

W H Hull, (Hull, William H., Pub.; 0-939330), 6833 Creston Rd., Minneapolis, MN 55435 (SAN 220-1690) Tel 612-926-1327.

W H Lord, (Lord, William H.; 0-9606320), 9210 N. College Ave., Indianapolis, IN 46240 (SAN 214-0497) Tel 317-846-3907.

W H Marshall, (Marshall, Walter H.), 931 Knight, Helena, MT 59601 (SAN 264-1992).

W H Mathers Mus, (William Hammond Mathers Museum; 0-9605982), 601 E. Eighth St., Indiana University, Bloomington, IN 47405 (SAN 216-7379) Tel 812-335-6873.

W Henderson, (Henderson, William; 0-9612580), 16015 Gault St. Apt. A, Van Nuys, CA 91406 (SAN 289-579X) Tel 818-780-9718.

W I S H
See Wish Pubns

W J Johnson
See Walter J Johnson

W J Stewart, (Stewart, William J.; 0-9615440), P.O. Box 793, Mill Valley, CA 94942 (SAN 696-1169) Tel 415-456-8415.

W James Pr, (James, William, Pr.; 0-938537), Harvard Medical Schl., Laboratory of Neurophysiology/Mass Mental Health Ctr., 74 Fenwood Dr., Boston, MA 02115 (SAN 661-4809) Tel 617-734-1300.

W Jewish Hist
See Magnes Mus

W Jones, (Jones, Wendy), Box 7186, Canyon Lake, CA 92380 (SAN 264-1410).

W K Walthers, (Walthers, William K., Inc.; 0-941952), 5601 W. Florist Ave., P.O. Box 18676, Milwaukee, WI 53218 (SAN 238-4868) Tel 414-527-0770; Toll free: 800-558-5478.

†W Kaufmann, (Kaufmann, William, Inc.; 0-913232; 0-86576), 95 First St., Los Altos, CA 94022 (SAN 202-9383) Tel 415-948-5810; Dist. by: Publishers Group West, 5855 Beaudry St., Emeryville, CA 94608 (SAN 202-8522) Tel 415-658-3453; CIP.

W Keast, (Keast, Winifred; 0-9613847), 740 Memorial Dr., Winthrop, ME 04364 (SAN 655-4326) Tel 207-377-8087.

W L Bates, (Bates, William L., Pub.; 0-9615781), 317 Ave. B, Snohomish, WA 98290 (SAN 699-7988) Tel 206-568-2508.

W L Dowler, (Dowler, Warren L.; 0-930188), 526 Camillo St., Sierra Madre, CA 91024 (SAN 210-721X) Tel 818-355-9707.

W L Meagher, (Meagher, Walter L.; 0-913115), Subs. of Leo Books, Ltd., P.O. Box 4365, Ann Arbor, MI 48106 (SAN 283-2011).

W L Morford, (Morford, Wanda L.; 0-9616543), 3310 Queen City Ave., Apt. 6, Cincinnati, OH 45238 (SAN 659-5243) Tel 513-632-3126; Orders to: P.O. Box 118734, Cincinnati, OH 45211 (SAN 662-4278) Tel 513-481-0982.

W L Sheppard, (Sheppard, W. L.; 0-9607610), 923 Old Manoa Rd., Havertown, PA 19083 (SAN 216-3225) Tel 215-449-2167.

W M Owen, (Owen, William M; 0-9613247), 885 Heather Rd., Deerfield, IL 60015 (SAN 295-4370) Tel 312-945-9290.

W M Taylor, (Taylor, William M.), 412 Red Hill Ave., San Anselmo, CA 94960 (SAN 212-9736) Tel 415-457-2214.

W Moore Pub, (Moore, Wendell, Pub.; 0-934281), 3085 W. Hwy. 89A, Sedona, AZ 86336 (SAN 693-3114) Tel 602-282-3419; Dist. by: EPM Pubns., 3085 W. Hwy. 89A, Sedona, AZ (SAN 200-8025).

W N Becht, (Becht, W. Nicholas; 0-9617254), P.O. Box 56, Owensville, IN 47665 (SAN 663-5814) Tel 812-724-4601; 405 S. Main St., Owensville, IN 47665 (SAN 663-5822).

W N Hoffman, (Hoffman, William N.; 0-9612050), 53 Claire Ave., New Rochelle, NY 10804 (SAN 286-7923) Tel 914-636-7597.

W N Stryker, (Stryker, William Norman; 0-9602936), 3804 Adrienne Dr., Alexandria, VA 22309 (SAN 212-7989).

W Nehmer, (Nehmer, Wilford; 0-9616386), 5362 Cedardale Dr., West Bend, WI 53095 (SAN 658-9782) Tel 414-644-8175.

W P Allen, (Allen, W. P., & Co., Inc.; 0-916777), P.O. Box 702, Portland, OR 97207 (SAN 654-2921) Tel 503-538-2311.

W P Brownell, (Brownell, W. P., Associates, Inc.), 3675 Clark Rd., Sarasota, FL 33583 (SAN 295-0499).

W P Ouber
See E P Oubre

W P S Pub Co, (WPS Publishing Co.; 0-935841), 7655 Redfield, Suite 5, Scottsdale, AZ 85260 (SAN 696-6438) Tel 602-951-4001.

W P Smedley, (Smedley, W. P., Co.; 0-938279), 60 W. Vaughn St., Kingston, PA 18704 (SAN 659-820X) Tel 717-288-8386.

W Perry, (Perry, Warner; 0-9603962), 23 Knickerbocker St., Newark, DE 19713 (SAN 213-5450).

W Phila Womens Comm, (West Philadelphia Women's Committee for the Philadelphia Orchestra, The; 0-9607586), P.O. Box 685, Bryn Mawr, PA 19010 (SAN 217-2887) Tel 215-688-4930.

W R C Smith, (Smith, W. R. C., Publishing Co.; 0-912476), 1760 Peachtree Rd., N.W., Atlanta, GA 30357 (SAN 202-9391) Tel 404-874-4462.

W R Corliss
See Sourcebook

W R Gordon, (Gordon, William R.; 0-910662), 232 Beresford Rd., Rochester, NY 14610 (SAN 202-9405) Tel 716-288-8549; Orders to: Harold E. Cox, 80 Virginia Terrace, Forty Fort, PA 18704 (SAN 202-1943); Dist. by: National RR Historical Society, P.O. Box 664, Rochester, NY 14602 (SAN 282-0447) Tel 716-244-6438.

W R I T E, (WRITE; 0-915441), 160 S. Springer Rd., Los Altos, CA 94022 (SAN 276-8623) Tel 415-964-8923; Orders to: Roberta Speer, 4665 Shady Ln., Colorado Springs, CO 80908 (SAN 662-1929) Tel 303-495-3875.

W R Inman, (Inman, W. Richard), 996-C Ponderosa Ave., Sunnyvale, CA 94086 (SAN 208-4198).

W S Hein, (Hein, William S., & Co., Inc.; 0-89941; 0-930342), Hein Bldg., 1285 Main St., Buffalo, NY 14209 (SAN 210-9212) Tel 716-882-2600; Toll free: 800-828-7571.

W S Sullwold, (Sullwold, William S., Publishing, Inc.; 0-88492), 18 Pearl St., Taunton, MA 02780 (SAN 203-1744) Tel 617-823-0924.

W Schocken, (Schocken, Wolfgang A.; 0-9615883), 18 Traill St., Cambridge, MA 02138 (SAN 696-7698) Tel 617-354-6192.

W States Historical, (Western States Historical Pubs., Inc.; 0-912506), 4020 W. 77th Pl., Westminster, CO 80030 (SAN 203-0217) Tel 303-429-1927.

W States Shelter, (Western States Shelter/Western Ctr. on Domestic Violence; 0-912309), 870 Market St., Suite 1058, San Francisco, CA 94102 (SAN 265-3001) Tel 415-362-0454.

W Stery, (Stery, William, Co.; 0-937913), P.O. Box 371595, Decatur, GA 30037-1595 (SAN 659-5901); 2897 Bradmoor Ct., Decatur, GA 30034 (SAN 659-591X) Tel 404-241-5003.

W Stice, (Stice, Will; 0-9610512), P.O. Box 12886, Salem, OR 97309 (SAN 264-4142) Tel 503-588-0344.

W Sutton, (Sutton, Weldon L., Publisher; 0-9607388), 5481 Kingsly Ave., Apt.A, Montclair, CA 91763 (SAN 239-7994) Tel 714-626-8600.

W T Doyle, (Doyle, William T.; 0-9615486), Murry Rd., Montpelier, VT 05602 (SAN 696-3749) Tel 802-223-2851.

W T Pancoast
See Blazing Flowers

W T Taylor, (Taylor, W. Thomas, Bookseller; 0-935072), 708 Colorado, Suite 704, Austin, TX 78701 (SAN 211-1454) Tel 512-478-7628.

W Va U Ctr Exten, (West Virginia University, Center for Extension & Continuing Education), 308 Knapp Hall, Morgantown, WV 26506 (SAN 213-4039).

W VA Wesleyan, (West Virginia Wesleyan College), Department of English, West Virginia Wesleyan College, Buckhannon, WV 26201 (SAN 239-5762) Tel 304-473-8000.

†W W Gaunt, (Gaunt, William W., & Sons, Inc.; 0-912004), 3011 Gulf Dr., Holmes Beach, FL 33510-2199 (SAN 202-9413) Tel 813-778-5211; CIP.

W Whitney, (Wheelock Whitney & Company; 0-917105), 123 E. 62nd St., New York, NY 10021 (SAN 655-3648) Tel 212-688-4474.

WA County Hist, (Washington County Historical Society; 0-9608434), Box 456, Chatom, AL 36518 (SAN 240-8058).

WA Museum Arts, (Washington County Museum of Fine Arts; 0-914495), P.O. Box 423, Hagerstown, MD 21741 (SAN 281-0565) Tel 301-739-5727.

WA State U Vet, (Washington State Univ., Dept. of Veterinary Microbiology & Pathology; 0-936375), Washington State Univ., Pullman, WA 99164-7040 (SAN 697-9912) Tel 509-335-6850.

Waconia Heritage, (Waconia Heritage Assn.; 0-9615181), 119 Cherry St., Waconia, MN 55387 (SAN 694-3500) Tel 612-442-4234; Orders to: P.O. Box 241, Waconia, MN 55387 (SAN 662-3379) Tel 612-442-4234.

Waddell, (Waddell, Ward, Jr.; 0-9600130), 495 San Fernando St., San Diego, CA 92106 (SAN 205-4973).

Wade Bks, (Wade Books), P.O. Box 847, Kentfield, CA 94914 (SAN 241-5933).

†Wadley Inst Molecular Med, (Wadley Institutes of Molecular Medicine; 0-935994), 9000 Harry Hines, Dallas, TX 75235 (SAN 213-8794); CIP.

Wadsworth
See Wadsworth Pub

Wadsworth Atheneum, (Wadsworth Atheneum; 0-918333), 600 Main St., Hartford, CT 06103 (SAN 205-4981) Tel 203-278-2670.

Wadsworth Inc
See Wadsworth Pub

†Wadsworth Pub, (Wadsworth Publishing Co.; 0-534; 0-927794; 0-7150), Subs. of International Thomson Organization, Ltd., 10 Davis Dr., Belmont, CA 94002 (SAN 200-2213) Tel 415-595-2350; Toll free: 800-831-6996; CIP. Imprints: Continuing Ed (Continuing Education Division).(Continuing Education Div.).

Wag On Wall, (Wag On The Wall; 0-9609628), 2005 Valle Vista, National City, CA 92050 (SAN 262-4419).

Wagapaw Pr, (Wagapaw Pr., The; 0-918999), P.O. Box 1381, San Luis Obispo, CA 93406 (SAN 669-7968) Tel 805-544-5339.

Waggoner Cent, (Waggoner Centennial '86 Committee; 0-9616552), Box 46, Waggoner, IL 62572 (SAN 659-5456) Tel 217-227-3321; 251 E. Main St., Waggoner, IL 62572 (SAN 659-5464).

Wagon & Star, (Wagon & Star Pubs.), 4032 W. Century Blvd., Inglewood, CA 90304 (SAN 202-9421).

Wahr, (Wahr, George, Publishing Co.; 0-911586), 304 1/2 S. State St., Ann Arbor, MI 48104 (SAN 205-5015) Tel 313-668-6097.

Wainwright, (Wainwright; 0-934553), c/o Ostrics, P.O. Box 11309, West Park, OH 44111 (SAN 693-8310).

Wake-Brook, (Wake-Brook Hse.; 0-87482), 990 NW 53rd St., Ft. Lauderdale, FL 33309 (SAN 205-5023) Tel 305-776-5884; P.O. Box 153, Hyannis, MA 02601 (SAN 694-4744) Tel 617-775-5860.

Wake Forest, (Wake Forest Univ. Pr.; 0-916390), Box 7333, Winston-Salem, NC 27109 (SAN 658-2206) Tel 919-761-5448; Dist. by: Univ. of North Carolina Pr., Box 2288, Chapel Hill, NC 27514 (SAN 203-3151) Tel 919-966-3561.

Wake Forest Law, (Wake Forest Univ., Schl. of Law, Continuing Legal Education), P.O. Box 7206, Reynolda Sta., Winston-Salem, NC 27109 (SAN 237-9074) Tel 919-761-5560.

Wakestone Bks, (Wakestone Bks.; 0-9613859), 405 Clifton Heights, Newport, TN 37821 (SAN 683-2199) Tel 615-623-7394.

†Walck, (Walck, Henry Z., Inc.; 0-8098), Div. of David McKay Co. Inc., 2 Park Ave., New York, NY 10016 (SAN 285-1121) Tel 212-340-9800; Toll free: 800-327-4801 (Orders).

Walden Pr, (Walden Press; 0-911938), 423 S. Franklin Ave., Flint, MI 48503 (SAN 205-5031).

†Waldman Hse Pr, (Waldman Hse. Pr.; 0-931674), 525 N. Third St., Minneapolis, MN 55401 (SAN 295-0243); Dist. by: Bookmen, Inc., 525 N. Third St., Minneapolis, MN 55401 (SAN 169-409X); CIP.

Waldo Bruce Pubns, (Waldo Bruce Pubs.; 0-9607338), P.O. Box 140906, Dallas, TX 75214 (SAN 239-3409) Tel 214-368-2614.

Waldos Pr, (Waldos Pr.; 0-9613882), 309 North 36th 12A, Seattle, WA 98103 (SAN 682-6350).

Waldron, (Waldron, A. James, Enterprises; 0-911590), 371 Kings Hwy., W., Haddonfield, NJ 08033 (SAN 205-504X) Tel 609-428-3742.

†Walker & Co, (Walker & Co.; 0-8027), Div. of Walker Publishing Co., Inc., 720 Fifth Ave., New York, NY 10019 (SAN 202-5213) Tel 212-265-3632; CIP.

Walker Educ, (Walker Educational Bk. Corp.; 0-8027), Affil. of Walker & Co., 720 Fifth Ave., New York, NY 10019 (SAN 206-1899) Tel 212-265-3632.

Walker Evans & Cogswell, (Walker, Evans & Cogswell Co.), 5300 Rivers Ave., North Charleston, SC 29405 (SAN 265-4121) Tel 803-747-8761.

Walkers Manual, (Walkers Manual, Inc.; 0-916234), C/O National Standards Assn., Inc., 5161 River Rd., Bethesda, MD 20816 (SAN 211-2833).

Walking Bird OR, (Walking Bird Publishing; 0-9615387), 340 N. Grand St., Eugene, OR 97402 (SAN 695-4642) Tel 503-485-6312.

Walking News Inc, (Walking News, Inc.; 0-915850), P.O. Box 352 - Canal St. Sta., New York, NY 10013 (SAN 239-5436) Tel 212-925-2632.

Wallaby Imprint of **PB**

Wallace-Homestead, (Wallace-Homestead Bk. Co.; 0-87069), Subs. of Capital Cities/ABC, Inc., 580 WatersEdge Rd., Lombard, IL 60148 (SAN 205-5058) Tel 312-953-1100; Toll free: 800-323-2596.

Wallace Pub, (Wallace Publishing; 0-9606804), 2307 Shoreland Ave., Toledo, OH 43611 (SAN 217-4529) Tel 419-729-9065.

Wallcur Inc, (Wallcur, Inc.; 0-918082), 3287 F St., Suite G, San Diego, CA 92102 (SAN 209-3642) Tel 619-233-9628.

Wallingford NJ, (Wallingford Pr.; 0-930988), 500 Grand Ave., Englewood, NJ 07631 (SAN 211-3821) Tel 201-568-5111.

Walloon Pr, (Walloon Press), 4260 Ridgecrest Dr., El Paso, TX 79902 (SAN 207-5539) Tel 915-533-3166.

Walmyr, (Walmyr Publishing Co.; 0-942390), P.O. Box 3554, Leon Sta., Tallahassee, FL 32303 (SAN 238-1249) Tel 904-386-5796.

†Walnut AZ, (Walnut Pr.; 0-931318), 12010 Hillcrest Dr., Sun City, AZ 85351 (SAN 285-113X) Tel 602-972-5814; Orders to: LTO Enterprises, 6036 N. 10th Way, Phoenix, AZ 85014 (SAN 662-1805) Tel 602-265-7765; CIP.

†Walnut Pr, (Walnut Pr.), Tully, NY 13159 (SAN 207-9992) Tel 607-842-6668; CIP.

Walrus Pr, (Walrus Pr.; 0-932033), 73 Pine St., Haworth, NJ 07641 (SAN 686-0796) Tel 201-385-0364.

Walsh Pub
See Walsh Pub Hse

Walsh Pub Hse, (Walsh Publishing Hse.; 0-9610254), P.O. Box 120, Kew Gardens, NY 11415 (SAN 264-4789) Tel 718-544-8692.

Walsworth's, (Walsworth Publishing Co., Inc.), Marceline, MO 64658 (SAN 295-0251).

Walt-Buch Pub
See Waltman & Buckner Pub

Walt Whitman, (Whitman, Walt Ctr. for the Atrs & humanties; 0-9615683), Second & Cooper Sts., Camden, NJ 08102 (SAN 695-8303) Tel 609-757-7276.

Walter & Colleen, (Walter & Colleen Spivey; 0-87418), Rte. 2, Box 58, New Market, VA 22844 (SAN 693-4293); Dist. by: Coleman Publishing, Inc., 99 Milbar Blvd., Farmingdale, NY 11735 (SAN 238-1508) Tel 516-293-0383.

Walter Griffin, (Griffin, Walter; 0-9616153), 2518 Maple St., East Point, GA 30344 (SAN 699-9921) Tel 404-529-8794.

Walter J Johnson, (Johnson, Walter J., Inc.; 0-8472), 355 Chestnut St., Norwood, NJ 07648 (SAN 209-1828) Tel 201-767-1303.

Walterick Pubs, (Walterick Pubs., Inc.; 0-937396), Box 2216, Kansas City, KS 66110-0216 (SAN 211-9366) Tel 913-371-3273; Toll free: 800-255-4097.

Walters
See Walters Pub

Walters Art, (Walters Art Gallery; 0-911886), 600 N. Charles St., Baltimore, MD 21201 (SAN 202-9448) Tel 301-547-9000.

Walters Pub, (Walters Publishing Co.; 0-940412), 90 Abbotsford Rd., Brookline, MA 02146 (SAN 211-1136).

Walther, (Walther, Lou; 0-9612672), 210 W. Sixth Ave., Broomfield, CO 80020 (SAN 289-4580) Tel 303-466-7757.

Waltman & Buckner Pub, (Waltman & Buckner Pubs. Inc; 0-934191), 3651 Lancaster, P.O. Box 41478, Plymouth, MN 55441 (SAN 693-4390) Tel 612-544-1762.

Wampeter Pr, (Wampeter Pr.; 0-931694), P.O. Box 512, Green Harbor, MA 02041 (SAN 212-3231) Tel 305-296-4244.

W&E Orr, (Orr, William N. & Elizabeth; 0-9606502), P.O. Box 5286, Eugene, OR 97405 (SAN 226-2053).

†Wanderer Bks, (Wanderer Bks.; 0-671), Div. of Simon & Schuster, 1230 Ave. of the Americas, New York, NY 10020 (SAN 212-5803) Tel 212-245-6400; Toll free: 800-223-2336; CIP.

Wanderer Pr, (Wanderer Pr., The; 0-915245), Subs. of The Wanderer Printing Co., 201 Ohio St., St. Paul, MN 55107-9984 (SAN 240-8961) Tel 612-224-5733.

Wandering You Pr, (Wandering You Pr.; 0-9617104), Subs. of Creative Resources, Inc., P.O. Box 20, Lodi, NJ 07644-0020 (SAN 662-5142); 70 Outwater Ln., Garfield, NJ 07026 (SAN 662-5150) Tel 201-772-1052.

Want Pub, (Want Publishing Co.; 0-942008), 1511 K St., NW, Washington, DC 20005 (SAN 238-7727) Tel 202-783-1887.

War Eagle Cooks, (War Eagle Cooks; 0-9616521), Rte. 6, P.O. Box 127A, Rogers, AR 72756 (SAN 659-6029) Tel 501-789-5343.

Ward Pr, (Ward Pr., The; 0-932142), P.O. Box 1712, Rochester, NY 14603 (SAN 212-6281) Tel 716-467-8400.

Wards Comm, (Wards Communications, Inc.; 0-910589), 28 W. Adams, Detroit, MI 48226 (SAN 206-3905) Tel 313-962-4433.

Ward's Natl Sci, (Ward's Natural Science Establishment, Inc.; 0-89873), P.O. Box 92912, Rochester, NY 14692-9012 (SAN 658-8409) Tel 716-359-2502.

Ware Pr
See Acad Guild

Warehouse Pub, (Warehouse Publishing Co.; 0-9616841), 1456 E. Philadelphia St., No. 22, Ontario, CA 91761 (SAN 661-4604) Tel 714-947-3210.

Waring & Assocs, (Waring & Associates; 0-912307), 845 Heathermoor Lane, Perrysburg, OH 43551 (SAN 265-2978) Tel 419-874-6044.

Warman, (Warman Publishing Co., Inc.; 0-911594), P.O. Box 1112, Willow Grove, PA 19090 (SAN 202-9464) Tel 215-657-1812; Dist. by: Kampmann & Co., 9 E. 40th St., New York, NY 10016 (SAN 202-5191) Tel 212-685-2928.

†Warne, (Warne, Frederick, & Co., Inc.; 0-7232), 40 W. 23rd. St., New York, NY 10010 (SAN 212-9884) Tel 212-337-5200; CIP.

†Warner Bks, (Warner Bks., Inc.; 0-446), Div. of Warner Communications, 666 Fifth Ave., New York, NY 10103 (SAN 282-5368) Tel 212-484-2900; Toll free: 800-638-6460; Dist. by: Ballantine Bks., Inc., 201 E. 50th St., New York, NY 10022 (SAN 214-1183) Tel 212-751-2600; CIP.

†Warner Pr, (Warner Pr. Pubs.; 0-87162), 1200 E. Fifth St., Anderson, IN 46012 (SAN 202-9472) Tel 317-644-7721; Toll free: 800-428-6409; Orders to: P.O. Box 2499, Anderson, IN 46018 (SAN 691-4241); CIP.

Warrbek Video, (Warrbek Video Productions; 0-937403), Rte. 6, Box 806, Cleburne, TX 76031 (SAN 659-1086) Tel 817-645-6961.

†Warren, (Warren, Gorham & Lamont, Inc.; 0-88262; 0-88712), Subs. of International Thomson Organisation, Ltd. (London), 210 South St., Boston, MA 02111 (SAN 202-9480); Toll free: 800-922-0066; CIP.

Warren Bk Pub, (Warren Bk. Publishing Co.; 0-938287), P.O. Box 1376, Warren, MI 48090-1376 (SAN 659-8846) Tel 313-756-7886; 7515 Yacht St., Warren, MI 48091 (SAN 659-8854) Tel 313-756-7886.

†**Watts,** *(Watts, Franklin, Inc.; 0-531),* Subs. of Grolier, Inc., Shermann Tpke., Danbury, CT 06816 (SAN 285-1156) Tel 212-686-7070; Toll free: 800-672-6672; *CIP. Imprints:* Busn Travel (Business Travelers, Incorporated).(Business Travelers, Inc.); College Div (College Division).(College Div.); Fontana Pap (Fontana Paperbacks); Gloucester Pr (Gloucester Press).(Gloucester Pr.); Intl Communications (International Communications); MacRae (MacRae, Julia); Warwick (Warwick Press).(Warwick Pr.).

Waukesha, *(Waukesha County Historical Society; 0-9613624),* 101 W. Main St., Waukesha, WI 53186 (SAN 281-0700) Tel 414-548-7186.

Waumbek, *(Waumbek Books; 0-9603106),* P.O. Box 573, Ashland, NH 03217 (SAN 213-5701) Tel 603-968-7959.

Waveland Pr, *(Waveland Pr., Inc.; 0-917974; 0-88133),* P.O. Box 400, Prospect Heights, IL 60070 (SAN 209-0961) Tel 312-634-0081.

Waverly Comm Hse, *(Waverly Community Hse., Inc.; 0-9616433),* Main St., Waverly, PA 18471 (SAN 659-1124) Tel 717-587-5811.

Waverly Pr
See Williams & Wilkins

Waverly Pub, *(Waverly Pubs.; 0-9615681),* 235 West End Ave., New York, NY 10023 (SAN 695-8184) Tel 212-873-8571.

Way
See Am Christian

Way of Seeing, *(Way of Seeing, Inc., A),* 2869 Grant Dr., Ann Arbor, MI 48104 (SAN 216-3152) Tel 313-973-7717.

Way Up Firm, *(Way Up, Firm & High Tail It Bright Out of Town Detective Agency Poetry Press, The; 0-933326),* 2620 F St., No. 5, Sacramento, CA 95816 (SAN 212-5846). Moved, left no forwarding address.

Wayfarer Pubns, *(Wayfarer Pubns.; 0-935099),* P.O. Box 26156, Los Angeles, CA 90026 (SAN 695-054X) Tel 213-665-7773.

Wayfinder Pr, *(Wayfinder Pr.; 0-9608764),* Box 1877, Ouray, CO 81427 (SAN 241-0796) Tel 303-325-4150; Dist. by: Johnson Books, 1880 S. 57th Ct., Boulder, CO 80301 (SAN 658-1013) Tel 415-658-3453.

Wayland Pr, *(Wayland Pr.; 0-933573),* 2640 E. 12th Ave., Box 715, Denver, CO 80206 (SAN 691-9065) Tel 303-233-5453.

Waymark *Imprint of* **Doubleday**

Wayne Omari Ed Game, *(Wayne-Omari Educational Game Co.; 0-9616325),* 25 Eastern Pkwy., Brooklyn, NY 11238 (SAN 658-7909) Tel 718-638-1617.

†**Wayne St U Pr,** *(Wayne State Univ. Pr.; 0-8143),* Leonard N. Simons Bldg., 5959 Woodward Ave., Detroit, MI 48202 (SAN 202-5221) Tel 313-577-4601; *CIP. Imprints:* Savoyard (Savoyard Books).(Savoyard Bks.).

Waynor, *(Waynor Publishing Co.; 0-917070),* P.O. Box 699, Goshen, NH 03752 (SAN 208-9165) Tel 603-863-1364.

WB&A Pubns, *(WB&A Pubns.; 0-942834),* Div. of William Bloomfield & Associates, Inc., 456 Pond St., Boston, MA 02130 (SAN 240-298X) Tel 617-524-3938.

WBT *Imprint of* **Wash Bk Trad**

WCC Direct
See Concord Ref Bks

WCF Pubns, *(WCF Pubns.; 0-9615904),* Box 568, Waterloo, IA 50704 (SAN 696-7833) Tel 319-233-1267.

WCP Pubns, *(WCP Pubns.; 0-937365),* 9528 Miramar Rd., Suite 106, San Diego, CA 92126 (SAN 659-1043) Tel 619-271-9445; 8767 Covina St., San Diego, CA 92126 (SAN 659-1051).

WCTU, *(National Woman's Christian Temperance Union),* 1730 Chicago Ave., Evanston, IL 60201 (SAN 225-8935).

WD Pr, *(WD Pr.; 0-9614272),* P.O. Box 24115, St. Louis, MO 63130 (SAN 687-4142) Tel 314-727-8554.

WDW Pubns
See Wittman Pubns

Weather Wkbk, *(Weather Workbook Co.; 0-931778),* 827 N.W. 31st St., Corvallis, OR 97330 (SAN 206-393X).

Weatherford, *(Weatherford, R.M., Press; 0-9604078),* 10902 Woods Creek Rd., Monroe, WA 98272 (SAN 126-4206) Tel 206-794-4318.

†**Weatherhill,** *(Weatherhill, John, Inc.; 0-8348),* 6 E. 39th St., New York, NY 10016 (SAN 202-9529) Tel 212-686-2857; Dist. by: Charles E. Tuttle, Co., Inc., 28 S. Main St., P.O. Box 410, Rutland, VT 05701-0410 (SAN 213-2621) Tel 802-773-8930; *CIP.*

Weatherly Pr, *(Weatherly Pr.; 0-935727),* 1840-130th Ave. NE, Suite 10, Bellevue, WA 98005 (SAN 695-8230) Tel 206-881-5212.

Weatherman, *(Weatherman, Hazel Marie; 0-913074),* c/o Glassbooks, Inc., Rte. 1, Box 357A, Ozark, MO 65721 (SAN 237-9554) Tel 417-485-7812.

†**Weathervane CA,** *(Weathervane Bks.; 0-943246),* P.O. Box 2157, Walnut Creek, CA 94595 (SAN 240-5040); *CIP.*

Webb Country, *(Webb Country Kennel),* Div. of Webb Country Farms, Rte. 2, Box 201, Mocksville, NC 27028 (SAN 663-6098) Tel 919-998-3908.

Webb-Newcomb, *(Webb-Newcomb Co., Inc.; 0-935054),* 308 N.E. Vance St., Wilson, NC 27893 (SAN 213-4004) Tel 919-291-7231.

Weber Oil, *(Weber Oil Co.; 0-9616358),* 700 Main St., Bangor, ME 04401 (SAN 659-1140) Tel 207-942-5501.

Weber Pub
See Conestoga Pr

†**Weber Systems,** *(Weber Systems, Inc.; 0-938862),* 8437 Mayfield Rd., No. 102, Chesterland, OH 44026 (SAN 240-8201) Tel 216-729-2858; Toll free: 800-851-6018; *CIP.*

Webfoot Inc, *(Webfoot, Inc.; 0-9610358),* Box 248, Wendell, NC 27591 (SAN 264-4851) Tel 919-365-5088.

Webster Pub Co FL, *(Webster Publishing Co.; 0-930814),* 2108 S. Crystal Lake Dr., Lakeland, FL 33801 (SAN 683-2326) Tel 813-665-1024.

Weddy Rail Bks *Imprint of* **David & Charles**

Wedge Pub, *(Wedge Publishing),* c/o Radix Books, Inc., 11 Knickerbocker Ln., Orindand, CA 94563 (SAN 209-1364) Tel 415-254-3039.

†**Wedgestone Pr,** *(Wedgestone Pr.; 0-911459),* P.O. Box 175, Winfield, KS 67156 (SAN 276-5888) Tel 316-221-2779; *CIP.*

Wee Smile, *(Wee Smile Books; 0-9605444),* P.O. Box 1329, Sparks, NV 89431 (SAN 215-983X) Tel 702-356-0216.

Weed Sci Soc, *(Weed Science Society of America; 0-911733),* 309 W. Clark St., Champaign, IL 61820 (SAN 276-5918).

Weeg Comp, *(Weeg Computing Center; 0-937114),* Univ. of Iowa, 120 LC, Iowa City, IA 52242 (SAN 215-2630).

Weeks Ent, *(Weeks Enterprises; 0-9615604),* 9408 Thomas Rd., Bloomington, MN 55431 (SAN 695-8125) Tel 612-881-5145.

Weeks Pubs, *(Weeks Pubs.; 0-9614492),* P.O. Box 10282, Arlington, VA 22210 (SAN 689-4720) Tel 703-528-2304.

Wegferd Pubns, *(Wegferd Pubns.; 0-937861),* 2021 Sherman Ave., North Bend, OR 97459 (SAN 659-6037) Tel 503-756-7401.

Wehawken Bk, *(Wehawken Book Co.; 0-916386),* 4221 45th St., NW, Washington, DC 20016 (SAN 207-5512) Tel 202-362-3185.

Wehman, *(Wehman Brothers, Inc.; 0-911604),* Ridgedale Ave., Morris County Mall, Cedar Knolls, NJ 07927 (SAN 206-779X) Tel 201-539-6300.

Wehmeyer Print, *(Wehmeyer Printing Co.),* Ste. Genevieve, MO 63670 (SAN 239-5444).

Wei-Chuan's Cooking, *(Wei-Chuan's Cooking; 0-941676),* 1455 Monterey Pass Rd., No. 110B, Monterey Park, CA 91754 (SAN 239-5096) Tel 213-261-3880.

Weidenfeld, *(Weidenfeld & Nicolson; 1-55584),* 10 E. 53rd St., 14th Flr., New York, NY 10022 (SAN 658-4497) Tel 212-207-6900.

Weills
See Berkley Pub

Weinberg, *(Weinberg, Michael Aron; 0-9601014),* P.O. Box 27957, Los Angeles, CA 90027 (SAN 208-2314) Tel 213-661-9844.

Weinberg Bks, *(Weinberg Bks.; 0-907053),* P.O. Box 438, Sudbury, MA 01776 (SAN 695-5444).

Weiner
See Public Relations

Weinstock, *(Weinstock, Beatrice C.; 0-9600568),* 1971 San Marco Blvd., Jacksonville, FL 32207 (SAN 205-5139) Tel 904-396-7597.

Weisberg, *(Weisberg, Harold; 0-911606),* 7627 Old Receiver Rd., Frederick, MD 21701 (SAN 205-5147) Tel 301-473-8186.

†**Weiser,** *(Weiser, Samuel, Inc.; 0-87728),* P.O. Box 612, York Beach, ME 03910 (SAN 202-9588) Tel 207-363-4393; Toll free: 800-843-6666; Toll free: 800-423-7087 orders; *CIP.*

Weiss Pub, *(Weiss Publishing Co., Inc.; 0-916720),* 5309 W. Grace St., Richmond, VA 23226 (SAN 208-4775) Tel 804-282-4641.

Weiss S & D, *(Weiss, Sigmund),* 11 Lancaster Place, Stony Brook, NY 11790 (SAN 219-3035).

Weist Pub OH, *(Weist Publishing Co., The; 0-938166),* P.O. Box 164, Englewood, OH 45322 (SAN 215-8256).

Welcome Pr, *(Welcome Pr.; 0-916871),* 2701 Queen Anne Ave. N., Seattle, WA 98109 (SAN 654-5114) Tel 206-282-5336.

Welcome Pub, *(Welcome Publishing; 0-932849),* P.O. Box 549, Santa Ynez, CA 93460-0574 (SAN 691-2966) Tel 805-688-3574.

Welding Res Coun, *(Welding Research Council),* 345 E. 47th St., New York, NY 10017 (SAN 225-2562) Tel 212-705-7956.

Welding Spec, *(Welding Specialist; 0-9613213),* 3101 Ensign Ave.N, New Hope, MN 55427 (SAN 295-6659) Tel 612-545-7681.

Welkin Bks, *(Welkin Bks.; 0-9614873),* 28 Watkins Ave., Oneonta, NY 13820 (SAN 693-2908) Tel 607-432-1915.

Well Aware, *(Well Aware About Health; 0-943562),* P.O. Box 43338, Tuscon, AZ 85733 (SAN 238-4140) Tel 602-297-2960.

Well-Made Prod, *(Well-Made Products),* 832 N.E. 104th, Seattle, WA 98125 (SAN 238-7719).

Wellbeing Bks, *(Wellbeing Bks., Tapes, Seminars; 0-943450),* Div. of Open Marketing Group, P.O. Box 396, 17 Omar Tr., Newtonville, MA 02160 (SAN 240-4680) Tel 617-332-7845.

Weller Inst, *(Weller Institute for the Cure of Design, Inc.; 0-916873),* 2427 Park Oak Dr., Los Angeles, CA 90068 (SAN 654-5149) Tel 213-467-4576.

Wellesley-Cambridge Pr, *(Wellesley-Cambridge Pr.; 0-9614084),* Rm. 2-240, Massachusetts Inst. of Technology, Cambridge, MA 02139 (SAN 686-0699) Tel 617-253-4383; P.O. Box 157, Wellesley, MA 02181 (SAN 686-0702) Tel 617-235-9537.

Wellingham-Jones, *(Wellingham-Jones, Patricia; 0-939221),* P.O. Box 238, Tehama, CA 96090 (SAN 662-670X); 8619 Sherwood Blvd., Los Molinos, CA 96055 (SAN 662-6718) Tel 916-384-1341.

Wellington Pr, *(Wellington Pr.; 0-910959),* P.O. Box 13504, Tallahassee, FL 32317 (SAN 264-4878) Tel 904-878-6500; Dist. by: The Baker & Taylor Co., 1515 Broadway, New York, NY 10036 (SAN 169-5606) Tel 212-730-7650; Dist. by: Book Dynamics, 836 Broadway, New York, NY 10003 (SAN 169-5649) Tel 212-254-7798; Dist. by: Distributors The, 702 S. Michigan, South Bend, IN 46618 (SAN 212-0364) Tel 219-232-8500; Dist. by: Bookpeople, 2929 Fifth St., Berkeley, CA 94710 (SAN 168-9517) Tel 415-549-3030; Dist. by: The New Leaf Distributors, 1020 White St., SW, Atlanta, GA 30310 (SAN 169-1449) Tel 404-755-2665; Dist. by: Inland Book Co., P.O. Box 261, 22 Hemingway Ave., East Haven, CT 06512 (SAN 200-4151) Tel 203-467-4257.

Wellington Pubns, *(Wellington Pubns.; 0-915915),* P.O. Box 223159, Carmel, CA 93923 (SAN 294-1104) Tel 408-624-7871.

Wellness Inst, *(Wellness Institute, Inc.; 0-9617202),* 2901 General DeGaulle St., Ste. 106B, New Orleans, LA 70114 (SAN 663-382X) Tel 504-361-1845.

Wellness Pubns, *(Wellness Pubns.; 0-934957),* 225 W. 30th, P.O. Box 3021, Holland, MI 49423 (SAN 694-468X) Tel 616-396-5477.

Wellpower, *(Wellpower Pubns.; 0-917073),* 11346 W. Jefferson, River Rouge, MI 48229 (SAN 655-5659) Tel 313-841-4849.

Wells & West Pubs, *(Wells & West Pubs.; 0-917545),* 1166 Winsor, North Bend, OR 97459 (SAN 669-7119).

Wellspring Bks, *(Wellspring Bks.; 0-9614712),* Rte. 1, Box 27, Groton, VT 05046 (SAN 692-6614) Tel 802-584-3674. Do not confuse wit Wellspring Bks., Ukiah, CA.

Wellspring CA
See Wellspring Utah
Wellspring Ent, *(Wellspring Enterprises; 0-937575),* 9921 Carmel Mountain Rd., Suite 188, San Diego, CA 92129 (SAN 659-1167) Tel 619-484-4479; 9008 Sundance Ct., San Diego, CA 92129 (SAN 659-1175).
Wellspring Pr, *(Wellspring Press; 0-914688),* Page Rd., Lincoln, MA 01773 (SAN 203-2171).
Wellspring Ukiah, *(Wellspring Bks.; 0-9616568),* 144 Clara Ave., Ukiah, CA 95482 (SAN 659-5472) Tel 707-463-0165. Do not confuse with Wellspring Bks., Groton, CT.
Wellspring Utah, *(Wellspring Publishing; 0-9608658),* P.O. Box 1113, Sandy, UT 84091 (SAN 239-5800) Tel 415-571-8662.
Wellton Bks, *(Wellton Bks.; 0-943678),* P.O. Box 989, Citrus Heights, CA 95610 (SAN 238-4159) Tel 916-783-8536.
WELS Board, *(WELS Board for Parish Education; 0-938272),* 2929 N. Mayfair Rd., Milwaukee, WI 53222 (SAN 216-3160) Tel 414-771-9357.
Welsh Soc Phila, *(Welsh Society of Philadelphia),* 450 Broadway, Camden, NJ 08103 (SAN 225-4158).
Welstar Pubns, *(Welstar Pubns.; 0-938503),* Div. of Occupational Hygiene Center of NY, Inc., 20 Colonel Robert Magaw Pl., New York, NY 10033 (SAN 660-9791) Tel 212-928-7528.
Wendover
See Biobehavioral Pr
Werner Pubn, *(Werner Pubns.; 0-933147),* 2020 18th Ave., Greeley, CO 80631 (SAN 692-3429) Tel 303-352-8566.
Wertz Pubns, *(Wertz Pubns; 0-9609196),* 6007 Lockport Rd., Niagara Falls, NY 14305 (SAN 240-9003) Tel 716-297-0455.
Wescott Cove, *(Wescott Cove Publishing Co.; 0-918752),* Box 130, Stamford, CT 06904 (SAN 210-5810) Tel 203-322-0998.
Wesis Pubns, *(Wesis Pubns.),* 29 Meadowbrook Lane, Cedar Grove, NJ 07009 (SAN 209-6153) Tel 201-256-7997.
Weslee Pub, *(Weslee Publishing; 0-933319),* 808 Fourth & Battery Bldg., Seattle, WA 98121 (SAN 692-2937) Tel 206-789-4931.
Wesley Found, *(Wesley Foundation, The; 0-9606652),* 211 N. School St., Normal, IL 61761 (SAN 219-6557) Tel 309-452-1435.
Wesley Inst, *(Wesley Institute Inc.; 0-9614501),* 243 Johnston Rd., Pittsburgh, PA 15241 (SAN 689-9625) Tel 412-831-9390; Orders to: Wesley Institute, P.O. Box 113445, Pittsburgh, PA 15241 (SAN 662-2879) Tel 412-831-9390.
†**Wesleyan U Pr,** *(Wesleyan Univ. Pr.; 0-8195),* 110 Mt. Vernon St., Middletown, CT 06457 (SAN 282-5414) Tel 203-344-7918; Toll free: 800-242-7737; Orders to: Harper & Row Pubs., Inc., Keystone Industrial Pk., Scranton, PA 18512 (SAN 215-3742) Tel 717-343-4761; CIP.
West-Art, *(West-Art; 0-914301),* P.O. Box 279, Clarence, NY 14031 (SAN 287-6124) Tel 716-634-8805; 8555 Main St., Williamsville, NY 14221 (SAN 287-6132).
West Atlantic, *(West Atlantic Pubns.; 0-935262),* 426 Columbia Ave., Mount Joy, PA 17552 (SAN 213-4012) Tel 717-653-2296; Orders to: P.O. Box 273, Mount Joy, PA 17552 (SAN 213-4020) Tel 717-653-5619.
West Boston, *(West of Boston; 0-911155),* 14 Bayfield Rd., Wayland, MA 01778 (SAN 284-978X) Tel 617-653-7241; Orders to: P.O. Box 2 Cochituate Station, Wayland, MA 01778 (SAN 689-8289).
West Cent KY Family Re Assoc, *(West-Central Kentucky Family Research Assn.),* P.O. Box 1932, Owensboro, KY 42302 (SAN 219-0508) Tel 502-684-4150.
West Coast, *(West Coast Poetry Review; 0-915596),* 1335 Dartmouth Dr., Reno, NV 89509 (SAN 207-3684) Tel 702-322-4467.
West Coast Plays
See CA Thea-Westcoast
West End, *(West End Pr.; 0-931122),* Box 291477, Los Angeles, CA 90029 (SAN 211-3406); Box 27334, Albuquerque, NM 87125 (SAN 662-1864) Tel 505-242-9762; Orders to: Publishers Services, P.O. Box 3914, San Rafael, CA 94902 (SAN 201-3037).

West Gate Pr, *(West Gate Press; 0-942836),* P.O. Box 961, Portland, ME 04104-0961 (SAN 240-5059).
West Pasco Genealogical, *(West Pasco Genealogical Society; 0-9614369),* 1016 Club House Dr., New Port Richey, FL 33552 (SAN 688-6310) Tel 813-847-7513; Orders to: Ethel Sweitzer, 122 E. Brentwood Dr., Port Richey, FL 33568 (SAN 662-2801) Tel 813-848-4795.
West Press, *(West Pr.; 0-930743),* P.O. Box 99717, San Diego, CA 92109 (SAN 676-5580) Tel 619-270-9096.
†**West Pub,** *(West Publishing Co.; 0-8299; 0-314),* P.O. Box 64526, 50 W. Kellogg Blvd., St. Paul, MN 55102-1611 (SAN 202-9618) Tel 612-228-2500; Toll free: 800-328-9352; CIP.
West Pubns CA, *(West Pubns.; 0-930109),* P.O. Box 487, Anaheim, CA 92805 (SAN 669-7127) Tel 714-772-0227.
West River, *(West River Press; 0-9602190),* 3530 W. Huron River Dr., Ann Arbor, MI 48103 (SAN 212-324X) Tel 313-668-8170.
West Side Pr, *(West Side Pr.; 0-935073),* Div. of Eagle Eye Maps, P.O. Box 1457, Glenwood Springs, CO 81602 (SAN 694-6933); 8261/2 Grand Ave. No. 29, Glenwood Springs, CO 81601 (SAN 694-6941) Tel 303-945-8857.
West Summit, *(West Summit Pr.; 0-9601356),* 26400 George Zeiger Drive, Suite 216, Beachwood, OH 44122 (SAN 295-3587) Tel 216-765-1028; Summit Pl., Suite C-206, 500 Old Highway 441, Mt. Dora, FL 32757 (SAN 295-3595) Tel 904-383-1708. Second address: alternate winter contact.
West SW Pub Co, *(West Southwest Publishing Co.; 0-938658),* 2755 Irwin Rd., Redding, CA 96002 (SAN 214-4883) Tel 916-221-4421.
West Tex Mus, *(West Texas Museum Assn.; 0-911618),* P.O. Box 4499, Lubbock, TX 79409 (SAN 206-667X) Tel 806-742-2443.
West Va U Lib
See West Va U Pr
West Va U Pr, *(West Virginia Univ. Pr.; 0-937058),* Main Library, P.O. Box 6069, Morgantown, WV 26506 (SAN 205-5163) Tel 304-293-4040.
West Village, *(West Village Publishing Co.; 0-933308),* 2904 E. Vanowen Ave., Orange, CA 92667 (SAN 213-1870) Tel 714-633-1420.
West Wind Prod, *(West Winds Productions, Inc.; 0-935969),* P.O. Box 3532, Boulder, CO 80307 (SAN 696-6594) Tel 303-443-2800; 855 Broadway, Boulder, CO 80307 (SAN 696-6608).
West World Pr, *(Western World Pr.; 0-88189),* Box 366, Sun City, CA 92381 (SAN 290-6945); 980 N. State, D-6, Hemet, CA 92343 (SAN 290-6953) Tel 714-652-8288.
Westbourne Ent, *(Westbourne Enterprises; 0-9613885),* P.O. Box 3623, Hollywood, CA 90028 (SAN 682-6393) Tel 213-876-1338.
Westbrook Pubns, *(Westbrook Publications; 0-9614247),* P.O. Box 869, Millbrook, AL 36054 (SAN 686-6778) Tel 205-285-5407.
Westburg, *(Westburg Assocs., Pubs.; 0-87423),* 1745 Madison St., Fennimore, WI 53809 (SAN 205-5171) Tel 608-822-6237.
Westbury Hse *Imprint of* Butterworth
Westcliff Pubns, *(Westcliff Pubns.; 0-932896),* 1441 Avocado, No. 408, Newport Beach, CA 92660 (SAN 212-2448).
Westcliffe Pubs Inc, *(Westcliffe Pubs., Inc.; 0-942394),* P.O. Box 1261, Englewood, CO 80150 (SAN 239-7528) Tel 303-935-0900; Toll free: 800-523-3692; 2650 S. Zuni St., Englewood, CO 80110 (SAN 660-9473).
Westcoast Pub, *(Westcoast Publishing Co.; 0-937957),* P.O. Box 1046, Port Richey, FL 34288 (SAN 659-5499) Tel 813-847-3066; 105 Royal Palm Ave., New Port Richey, FL 33553 (SAN 659-5502).
Westcott, *(Westcott Pubs.; 0-911620),* P.O. Box 803, Springfield, MO 65801 (SAN 205-518X) Tel 417-466-7455.
Westerfield, *(Westerfield, Scott; 0-9615537),* 7418 Nottoway Cir., Louisville, KY 40214 (SAN 695-8079) Tel 502-361-3998.

†**Western Assn Map,** *(Western Assn. of Map Libraries; 0-939112),* Univ. of California Library, C-075-P, c/o Larry Cruse, La Jolla, CA 92093 (SAN 216-3179) Tel 619-452-3338; Orders to: Western Assn. of Map Libraries, Univ. of California Library, c/o Stanley D. Stevens, Santa Cruz, CA 95064 (SAN 662-1872) Tel 408-429-2364; CIP.
Western Bk Journ, *(Western Bk. Journal Pr.; 0-936029),* 1470 Woodberry Ave., San Mateo, CA 94403 (SAN 206-2305) Tel 415-573-8877.
Western Bks, *(Western Bks.; 0-938463),* P.O. Box 1, Woodston, KS 67675 (SAN 660-9856) Tel 913-994-6253.
Western Educ Serv, *(Western Educational Services; 0-916236),* 168 N. Main St., P.O. 596, Centerville, UT 84014 (SAN 207-7426).
Western Enter, *(Western Enterprises; 0-9613461),* 3538 Oak Cliff Dr., Fallbrook, CA 92028 (SAN 679-1611) Tel 619-728-6465.
Western Epics, *(Western Epics Publishing Co.; 0-914740),* 254 S. Main St., Salt Lake City, UT 84101 (SAN 206-1384) Tel 801-328-2586.
Western Fish Pr, *(Western Fisherman's Pr.; 0-9617059),* P.O. Box 23943, Portland, OR 97223 (SAN 662-8508); 14355 SW Pacific Hwy., Tigard, OR 97223 (SAN 662-8516) Tel 503-639-4848.
Western Guideways, *(Western Guideways, Ltd.; 0-931788),* P.O. Box 15532, Lakewood, CO 80215 (SAN 210-6264) Tel 303-237-0583.
Western Gull Pub, *(Western Gull Publishing, Book Div. of the Daily News; 0-9610910),* Subs. of Longview Pub Co., P.O. Box 1330, 305 W. First St., Port Angeles, WA 98362 (SAN 265-1556) Tel 206-452-2345.
Western Heritage
See Pintores Pr
Western Horizons Bks, *(Western Horizons Bks.; 0-934959),* P.O. Box 4068, Helena, MT 59604 (SAN 692-7262) Tel 406-442-7795; Dist. by: Pacific Pipeline, Inc., 19215 66th Ave. S., Kent, WA 98032 (SAN 699-5942) Tel 206-872-5523.
Western Horseman, *(Western Horseman, Inc., The; 0-911647),* P.O. Box 7980, Colorado Springs, CO 80933 (SAN 264-4894) Tel 303-633-5525.
Western Ill Univ
See WIU Essays Lit
†**Western Imprints,** *(Western Imprints, Pr. of the Oregon Historical Society, The; 0-87595),* 1230 SW Park Ave., Portland, OR 97205-2483 (SAN 202-8301) Tel 503-222-1741; CIP. Imprints: Western Imprints (Western Imprints).
Western Imprints *Imprint of* Western Imprints
Western Islands, *(Western Islands; 0-88279),* 395 Concord Ave., Belmont, MA 02178 (SAN 206-8435) Tel 617-489-0606.
Western MA Pubs, *(Western Massachusetts Pubs.; 0-9616486),* 101 Caseland St., Springfield, MA 01107 (SAN 659-3720) Tel 413-787-6050.
†**Western Marine Ent,** *(Western Marine Enterprises Inc.; 0-930030),* Box Q, Ventura, CA 93002 (SAN 210-525X) Tel 805-644-6043; CIP.
Western Michigan, *(Western Michigan News),* P.O. Box 7264, Seymour Sq. Sta., Grand Rapids, MI 49508 (SAN 169-3875); P.O. Box 10, 301 S. Rath Ave., Ludington, MI 49431 (SAN 169-3905).
Western Mtn, *(Western Mountain Press; 0-911265),* 524C Cardenas S. E., Albuquerque, NM 87108 (SAN 275-1143) Tel 505-268-8776.
Western NC Pr, *(Western North Carolina Pr., Inc.; 0-915948),* Affil. of Books of Distinction, 16 Tahquitz Ct., Camarillo, CA 93010 (SAN 208-9181) Tel 805-987-5760.
Western Prof, *(Western Profiles Publishing Co.; 0-937231),* 1616 Champa St., Suite 210, Denver, CO 80202 (SAN 658-7232) Tel 303-623-2828; Orders to: P.O. Box 1026, Denver, CO 80201-1026 (SAN 662-4162).
Western Psych, *(Western Psychological Services; 0-87424),* Div. of Manson Western Corp., 12031 Wilshire Blvd., Los Angeles, CA 90025 (SAN 202-9634) Tel 213-478-2061.

†**Western Pub,** *(Western Pub. Co., Inc.; 0-307),*
850 Third Ave., New York, NY 10022
(SAN 202-523X) Tel 212-753-8500; 1220
Mound Ave., Racine, WI 53401
(SAN 669-2982) Tel 414-633-2431; Orders
to: Dept. M, P.O. Box 700, Racine, WI
53401; Dist. by: Childrens Pr., 1224 W. Van
Buren St., Chicago, IL 60607
(SAN 201-9264) Tel 312-666-4200. Do not
confuse with Western Publisher, Lake Worth,
FL; *CIP. Imprints:* Golden Pr (Golden
Press).(Golden Pr.).

Western Pubs FL, *(Western Pubs.; 0-9602218),*
1711 S. Lakeside Dr., Lake Worth, FL 33460
(SAN 212-8039) Tel 305-588-6848. Not to
be confused with Western Publishing, New
York, NY.

Western Res Pr, *(Western Reserve Pr., The;
0-912400),* P.O. Box 675, Ashtabula, OH
44004 (SAN 205-5201) Tel 216-997-5851.

Western Son Acad, *(Western Son Academy;
0-938647),* P.O. Box 4080, Irvine, CA
92716 (SAN 661-6119); 2 Hopkins, Irvine,
CA 92715 (SAN 661-6127)
Tel 714-786-9585.

Western States, *(Western States Arts
Foundation; 0-9611710),* 207 Shelby St.,
Sante Fe, NM 87501 (SAN 285-3531)
Tel 505-988-1166.

Western Sun Pubns, *(Western Sun Pubns.;
0-9608146),* P.O. Box 1470, Yuma, AZ
85364 (SAN 240-5067) Tel 602-726-6239.

Western Tanager, *(Western Tanger Pr.;
0-934136),* 1111 Pacific Ave., Santa Cruz,
CA 95060 (SAN 220-0155)
Tel 408-425-1111. *Imprints:* Paper Vision
(Paper Vision Press); Valley Calif (Valley
Publishers).(Valley Pubs.).

Western Union, *(Western Union Corp.),* 1 Lake
St., Upper Saddle River, NJ 07458
(SAN 694-6968) Tel 201-825-6246.

Western Wood, *(Western Wood Products
Association; 0-9600912),* Portland, OR
97204 (SAN 276-6426).

Western World, *(Western World Pubs.;
0-931864),* P.O. Box 23785, Pleasant Hill,
CA 94523 (SAN 207-6616)
Tel 415-825-1042.

Westerners Intl, *(Westerners International),* Box
3485, Tucson, AZ 85722 (SAN 233-7797).

Westernlore, *(Westernlore Pubns.; 0-87026),* 609
No. 4th Ave., Tucson, AZ 85705
(SAN 202-9642) Tel 602-297-5491; Orders
to: Westernlore Press, P.O. Box 35305,
Tucson, AZ 85740 (SAN 202-9650)
Tel 602-297-5491.

Westfield Ctr Early Keyboard, *(Westfield Ctr.
for Early Keyboard Studies, Inc.; 0-9616755),*
1 Cottage St., Easthampton, MA 01027
(SAN 659-8374) Tel 413-527-7664.

Westgate Hse, *(Westgate Hse.; 0-9607320),* 56
Westgate Dr., San Franciso, CA 94127
(SAN 239-5819) Tel 415-584-8338.

Westgate OR Pr, *(Westgate Pr. (Oregon);
0-9614926),* 225 Westgate Sq., 3800 SW
Cedar Hills Blvd., Beaverton, OR 97005
(SAN 693-5869) Tel 503-646-0820; Dist.
by: Pacific Pipeline, 19215 66th Ave., S.,
Kent, WA 98032 (SAN 208-2128)
Tel 206-872-5523.

Westgate Pr, *(Westgate Pr.),* Div. of Westgate
Group, Ltd., 8 Bernstein Blvd., Center
Moriches, NY 11934 (SAN 687-6579)
Tel 516-878-2901.

†**Westin Comm,** *(Westin Communications;
0-86620),* 5760 Owensmouth Ave., Suite 31,
Woodland Hills, CA 91367
(SAN 297-1968); Toll free: 800-421-1893;
Orders to: Westin Communications, Jonathan
Industrial Ctr., Chaska, MN 55318
(SAN 212-3681) Tel 612-448-5773; Orders
to: NACSCORP, Oberlin, OH 44074
(SAN 209-2824) Tel 216-775-8048; Orders
to: Wybel Distribution Co., Inc., 101 S.
Hough St., Barrington, IL 60010
(SAN 159-3668); *CIP.*

Westlake Pub, *(Westlake Publishing Co.;
0-935709),* 11601 Wilshire Blvd., Suite 720,
Los Angeles, CA 90025 (SAN 695-8346)
Tel 213-824-0330.

Westland Pubns, *(Westland Pubns.; 0-915162),*
P.O. Box 117, McNeal, AZ 85617-0117
(SAN 207-1169).

Westloch Pubns, *(Westloch Pubns.; 0-9616964),*
2440 NW 57th St., No. 2, Seattle, WA
98107 (SAN 661-8073) Tel 206-783-5671.

Westmail Pr, *(Westmail Pr.),* 179 Westmoreland
Ave., White Plains, NY 10606
(SAN 207-5326) Tel 914-948-1116.

†**Westminster,** *(Westminster Pr.; 0-664),* 925
Chestnut St., Philadelphia, PA 19107
(SAN 202-9669) Tel 215-928-2700; Toll
free: 800-523-1631; Toll free: 800-942-4405
(In Pennsylvania); Orders to: P.O. Box 718,
William Penn Annex, Philadelphia, PA 19105
(SAN 202-9677) Tel 215-928-2760; *CIP.*

Westminster Trading, *(Westminster Trading
Corp., The; 0-938953),* 5 Northern Blvd.,
Amherst, NH 03031 (SAN 661-7212)
Tel 603-886-5041.

Westmoreland, *(Westmoreland Museum of Art;
0-931241),* 221 N. Main St., Greensburg,
PA 15601 (SAN 264-4916); Toll free:
800-242-7737; Dist. by: Univ. of Pittsburgh
Pr., 127 N. Bellefield Ave., Pittsburgh, PA
15260 (SAN 203-3216).

Westover *Imprint of* **Barre**

Westover Pr, *(Westover Press; 0-9612836),* P.O.
Box 1667, Murray Hill Sta., New York, NY
10156 (SAN 290-0602) Tel 212-889-3591;
Seven Park Ave., New York, NY 10016
(SAN 290-0610).

Westpark Bks, *(Westpark Bks.; 0-936205),* 1819
Birdseye Creek Rd., Gold Hill, OR 97525
(SAN 696-8600) Tel 503-582-1234; Dist.
by: Quality Bks., Inc., 918 Sherwood Dr.,
Lake Bluff, IL 60044-2204 (SAN 169-2127);
Dist. by: Southwest Parks & Monuments
Assn., 221 N. Court St., Tucson, AZ 85701
(SAN 202-750X) Tel 602-622-1999.

Westphal Pub, *(Westphal Publishing; 0-9610520),*
P.O. Box 19542, Irvine, CA 92713
(SAN 262-1088) Tel 714-660-0727.

Westphalia Pr, *(Westphalia Pr., The; 0-915637),*
Rte. 1, P.O. Box 96, Loose Creek, MO
65054 (SAN 292-7284) Tel 314-897-3526;
Dist. by: Paperback Supply Co., 4121 Forest
Park Ave., St. Louis, MO 63108
(SAN 169-426X); Dist. by: Cowley
Distributing Co., 732 Heisenger Rd.,
Jefferson City, MO 65101
(SAN 169-426X).

†**Westport Pubs,** *(Westport Pubs., Inc.;
0-9611286; 0-933701),* Subs. of Test
Corporation of America, 330 W. 47th St.,
Suite 205, Kansas City, MO 64112
(SAN 283-3492) Tel 816-756-1490; *CIP.
Imprints:* Test Corp America (Test
Corporation of America).

Westrail Pubns, *(Westrail Pubns.; 0-9602466),*
Box 300, Glendora, CA 91740
(SAN 212-7091).

Westridge, *(Westridge Pr., Ltd.; 0-918832),*
1090 Southridge Pl., S., Salem, OR 97302
(SAN 210-5268) Tel 503-363-2422.

Westrom, *(Westrom Co., The; 0-938230),* P.O.
Box 85527, Los Angeles, CA 90072
(SAN 215-8264).

Westroots, *(Westroots; 0-936580),* 3131a Via
Alicante, La Jolla, CA 92037
(SAN 222-0296).

WestSea Pub, *(WestSea Pub. Co., Inc.;
0-937820),* 149D Allen Blvd., Farmingdale,
NY 11735 (SAN 215-7144)
Tel 516-420-1110.

†**Westview,** *(Westview Pr.; 0-89158; 0-86531;
0-8133),* 5500 Central Ave., Boulder, CO
80301 (SAN 219-970X) Tel 303-444-3541;
CIP.

WestView Pub, *(WestView Publishing Co.;
0-937535),* 6065 Mission Gorge Rd., Suite
425, San Diego, CA 92120
(SAN 659-123X) Tel 619-444-6807.

Westville Pub Co, *(Westville Pub. Co. Ltd.;
0-938860),* P.O. Box 81, Old Westbury, NY
11568 (SAN 240-0359).

Westwater, *(Westwater Bks.; 0-916370),* Div. of
Belknap Photographic Services, Inc., P.O.
Box 365, Boulder City, NV 89005
(SAN 208-3698) Tel 702-293-1406.

Westwind Pr, *(Westwind Pr.; 0-9602342),* Rte.
1, Box 208, Farmington, WV 26571
(SAN 215-7152).

Westwind Pubns, *(Westwind Pubns.; 0-9613379),*
89 Kearney St., S. San Francisco, CA 94080
(SAN 657-1204) Tel 415-588-6493.

Westwood Ent, *(Westwood Enterprises;
0-9617118),* 5302 N. 79th Pl., Scottsdale,
AZ 85253 (SAN 662-8028)
Tel 602-994-8244.

Westwood Pr, *(Westwood Pr., Inc.; 0-936159),*
251 Park Ave. S., New York, NY 10010
(SAN 696-7183) Tel 212-420-8008.

Westwood Pub Co, *(Westwood Publishing Co.;
0-930298),* 312 Riverdale Dr., Glendale, CA
91204 (SAN 211-8769) Tel 818-242-3497.

Weybridge, *(Weybridge Publishing Co.;
0-939356),* 16911 Brushfield Dr., Dallas, TX
75248 (SAN 216-4965) Tel 214-931-7770.

Weybright
See McKay

Wffn Proof, *(Wff'n Proof Pubs.; 0-911624),*
1490 South Blvd., Ann Arbor, MI 48104
(SAN 205-521X) Tel 313-665-2269.

WFHAAVSC, *(World Federation of Health
Agencies for the Advancement of Voluntary
Surgical Contraception; 0-935955),* 122 E.
42nd St., New York, NY 10168
(SAN 696-7809) Tel 212-573-8338.

WFI Pub Co, *(WFI Publishing Co.; 0-933560),*
Div. of WFI Corporation, 2049 Century Park
E., Suite 3330, Los Angeles, CA 90067
(SAN 212-9817) Tel 213-553-8700.

WFS, *(Women for Sobriety, Inc.),* P.O. Box 618,
Quakertown, PA 18951 (SAN 216-4779)
Tel 215-536-8026.

Whale Museum, *(Whale Museum/Moclips
Cetological Society, The; 0-933331),* P.O.
Box 945, Friday Harbor, WA 98250
(SAN 692-2864) Tel 206-378-4710.

Whale Pub, *(Whale Publishing; 0-9616487),*
P.O. Box 21696, St. Louis, MO 63109
(SAN 659-3755); 6015 Potomac, St. Louis,
MO 63139 (SAN 659-3763)
Tel 314-832-5734.

Whale Pubns, *(Whale Pubns.; 0-9615448),* 526
W. 123rd St., New York, NY 10027
(SAN 695-7528) Tel 212-316-3862.

What to Do, *(What to Do County Pubns., Inc.;
0-930520),* Div. of Hardscrabble Pubns.,
Inc., P.O. Box 396, Pleasantville, NY 10570
(SAN 213-5728).

Whatcom Cty Opp, *(Whatcom County
Opportunity Council; 0-934671),* 314 E.
Holly St., Bellingham, WA 98225
(SAN 694-0781) Tel 206-734-5121.

†**Whatever Pub,** *(Whatever Publishing Inc.;
0-931432),* P.O. Box 137, Mill Valley, CA
94942 (SAN 211-8777) Tel 415-388-2100;
Toll free: 800-227-3900 (Retail orders only);
Dist. by: Publishers Group West, 5855
Beaudry, Emeryville, CA 94608
(SAN 202-8522) Tel 415-658-3453; Dist.
by: Bookpeople, 2929 Fifth St., Berkeley, CA
94710 (SAN 168-9517) Tel 415-549-3030;
CIP.

Whats Cooking, *(What's Cooking Pubns., Inc.;
0-9614250),* 226 Birchwood Rd., P.O. Box
323, Hinsdale, IL 60521 (SAN 686-7391)
Tel 312-986-1595.

Wheal Grace, *(Wheal-Grace Inc.; 0-933433),*
420 Valley Brook Ave., Lyndhurst, NJ 07071
(SAN 691-5310) Tel 201-933-7092.

Wheat Forders, *(Wheat Forder's Press;
0-917888),* P.O. Box 6317, Washington, DC
20015 (SAN 209-9187) Tel 202-362-1588.

Wheatherstone Pr, *(Wheatherstone Press;
0-9613011),* 20 Wheatherstone, Lake
Oswego, OR 97034 (SAN 292-7292)
Tel 503-635-2646.

Wheat'N Flower, *(Wheat'N Flower Designs;
0-9613993),* P.O. Box 2433, Springfield, IL
62705 (SAN 683-129X) Tel 217-546-5096.

Wheaton Resource, *(Wheaton Resource Corp.;
0-936657),* 1800 N. Main St., Wheaton, IL
60187 (SAN 699-7090) Tel 312-665-6200;
Dist. by: Chicago Review Press, 814 N.
Franklin St., Chicago, IL 60610
(SAN 213-5744) Tel 312-337-0747.

Wheedle Inc, *(Wheedle, Inc.; 0-936873),* P.O.
Box 4053, Wenatchee, WA 98801
(SAN 699-9638) Tel 509-662-8737; 23 S.
Wenatchee Ave., Suite 115, Wenatchee, WA
98801 (SAN 699-9646).

Wheel Pr, *(Wheel Pr.; 0-936747),* P.O. Box
23233, Tigard, OR 97223 (SAN 697-2594);
9203 SE Mitchell, Portland, OR 97266
(SAN 699-6485).

Wheeler Prods, *(Wheeler Productions;
0-9614362),* 2183 Payne Ave., St. Paul, MN
55117 (SAN 688-573X) Tel 612-774-3057.

Wheelgun Pr, *(Wheelgun Pr.; 0-937289),* Div. of
FR3 Enterprises, P.O. Box 2022, Simi Valley,
CA 93065 (SAN 659-1256)
Tel 805-527-7693; 2046 Sheridan Ct., Simi
Valley, CA 93065 (SAN 659-1264).

Wheelock
See W Whitney

Wheelwright Pr, *(Wheelwright Press; 0-935706),*
300 Page St., San Francisco, CA 94102
(SAN 222-0326) Tel 415-863-3136.

Wheelwright UT, *(Wheelwright Press, Ltd.; 0-937512),* 1836 Sunnyside Ave., Salt Lake City, UT 84108 (SAN 205-9533) Tel 801-582-8158.

Where to Find OR in OR, *(Where to Find The Oregon in Oregon; 0-9616696),* 7277 SW Barnes Rd., Portland, OR 97225 (SAN 659-8382) Tel 503-292-4549; Dist. by: Bay News Co., 3155 NW Yeon Ave., Portland, OR 97210 (SAN 169-7153)19215 66th Ave., S., Kent, WA 98032 (SAN 208-2128).

Where To Go, *(Where To Go, Inc.; 0-912785),* P.O. Box 204, Excelsior, MN 55331 (SAN 282-8219) Tel 612-474-7000.

Whimsie Pr, *(Whimsie Pr.; 0-916178),* P.O. Box 70, Mill Creek Rd., Otego, NY 13825 (SAN 239-5770).

Whipporwill, *(Whipporwill; 0-917012),* c/o R. I. Pubns. Society, 189 Wickenden St., Providence, RI 02903 (SAN 239-4006).

Whirling Vortices, *(Whirling Vortices; 0-9616147),* 408 Sixth Ave., Clarence, IA 52216 (SAN 699-976X) Tel 319-452-3293.

Whirlpool, *(Whirlpool Corp.; 0-938336),* Home Study Department, La Porte, IN 46350 (SAN 215-8272) Tel 219-325-2345.

Whispering Sands Pubns, *(Whispering Sands Pubns.; 0-9608718),* P.O. Box 181t., P.O. Box 181, Santa Fe, NM 87501 (SAN 238-0870).

Whispers, *(Whispers Pr.; 0-918372),* 70 Highland Ave., Binghamtom, NY 13905 (SAN 210-6272) Tel 607-729-6920.

Whitaker Hse, *(Whitaker Hse.; 0-88368),* Pittsburgh & Colfax Sts., Springdale, PA 15144 (SAN 203-2104) Tel 412-274-4440; Toll free: 800-245-2422.

White & Spencer, *(White, Laurie A., & Steven L. Spencer; 0-9612024),* 4340 Tamarac Trail, Harbor Springs, MI 49740 (SAN 287-7791) Tel 616-347-6701.

White Consult, *(White Consultants Inc.; 0-932263),* State Rd. 625, P.O. Box D, Gainesville, VA 22065 (SAN 686-6328) Tel 703-347-0030.

White Crane Pubns, *(White Crane Pubns.; 0-9604880),* P.O. Box 3081, Eugene, OR 97403 (SAN 237-9708) Tel 503-342-2759.

White Cross, *(White Cross Press; 0-918186),* Route One, Box 592, Granger, TX 76530 (SAN 210-2862) Tel 512-859-2814.

White Deer Bks, *(White Deer Bks.; 0-931567),* 80 Beekman St., New York, NY 10038 (SAN 687-6560).

White Dove Pr, *(White Dove Pr.; 0-9614576),* 2120 Haskell Ave., Lawrence, KS 66046 (SAN 691-8395) Tel 913-842-1937.

White Dove Pub Co, *(White Dove Publishing Co.; 0-914541),* 4640 Jewell St., Suite 104, San Diego, CA 92109 (SAN 289-6443) Tel 619-581-2266; Toll free: 800-621-0852.

White Eagle Pub, *(White Eagle Pub., The; 0-941804),* P.O. Box 1332, Dept. BP-0111, Lowell, MA 01853 (SAN 239-3441); Dist. by: Baker & Taylor Co., Eastern Div., 50 Kirby Ave., Somerville, NJ 08876 (SAN 169-4901).

White Ewe, *(White Ewe Press; 0-917976),* P.O. Box 1614, Baltimore, MD 21203 (SAN 209-410X).

White G E F, *(White, Glenn E. F.; 0-9611926),* 101 Buckingham St., Meriden, CT 06450 (SAN 286-1011) Tel 203-235-7462.

White Hall Bks *Imprint of* Betterway Pubns

White Horse, *(White Horse Productions, Inc.; 0-940376),* 286 Cabot St., Beverly, MA 01915 (SAN 219-8355) Tel 617-927-3677.

White House Hist, *(White House Historical Assn.; 0-912308),* 740 Jackson Pl. NW, Washington, DC 20506 (SAN 226-8108) Tel 202-737-8292.

White Hse, *(White Hse. Theater, The; 0-9615860),* 3017 Brighton Sixth St., Brooklyn, NY 11235 (SAN 696-7795) Tel 718-769-1013; P.O. Box 245, New York, NY 10013 (SAN 660-9570). *Imprints:* Double Trouble Day (Double Trouble Day).

White Lion Pr, *(White Lion Pr.; 0-9615707),* 225 E. Fifth St. No. 4-D, New York, NY 10003 (SAN 695-7919) Tel 212-260-1677.

White Meadow, *(White Meadow Pr.; 0-933855),* P.O. Box 582, Rockaway, NJ 07866 (SAN 692-7408) Tel 201-696-1666.

White Peony, *(White Peony Pr.; 0-917951),* Rte. 1, Box 90, Cairnbrook, PA 15924 (SAN 657-0305) Tel 814-754-4944.

White Pine, *(White Pine Pr.; 0-934834),* 76 Center St., Fredonia, NY 14063 (SAN 209-8067) Tel 716-672-5743.

White Pine OR, *(White Pine Pr.; 0-9610988),* 505 SW Long Farm Rd., West Linn, OR 97068 (SAN 265-301X) Tel 503-638-0500; Dist. by: International Specialized Bk. Services, Inc., 5602 NE Hassalo St., Portland, OR 97213-3640 (SAN 169-7129) Tel 503-287-3093.

White Rhino Pr, *(White Rhinoceros Pr., The; 0-9616760),* 804 Gracelyn Ct., Blacksburg, VA 24060 (SAN 659-851X) Tel 703-552-2976; Dist. by: Pocahontas Press, Inc., 2805 Wellesley Ct., Blacksburg, VA 24060 (SAN 696-6195); Dist. by: Virginia Polytechnic Institute & State Univ. Bookstore, Blacksburg, VA 24061 (SAN 291-6134).

†White River, *(White River Pr., Inc.; 0-932431),* 1857 N. Pennsylvania St., Indianapolis, IN 46202 (SAN 687-4150) Tel 317-925-6668; *CIP.*

White Rose, *(White Rose Marketing; 0-9605128),* 23101 Moulton Pkwy., Suite 110, Laguna Hills, CA 92653 (SAN 216-3233).

White S Bks, *(White Saddle Bks.; 0-912142),* 9144 Knauf Rd., Canfield, OH 44406 (SAN 205-5236).

White S W, *(White, Stewart W.; 0-9614794),* 105 Shore Acres SW, Tacoma, WA 98498 (SAN 693-0018) Tel 206-584-7893.

White Sound, *(White Sound Pr.; 0-932265),* 1615 W. Harrison Ave., Decatur, IL 62526 (SAN 686-6336) Tel 217-423-0511.

White Wing Pub, *(White Wing Publishing Hse. & Pr.; 0-934942),* P.O. Box 3000, Cleveland, TN 37311 (SAN 203-2198) Tel 615-476-8536.

Whitebrook Bks, *(Whitebrook Bks.; 0-9608934),* P.O. Box 746, Easthampton, MA 01027 (SAN 237-9694).

Whitefield Pub
See G Whitefield Pub

Whitehall Co, *(Whitehall Co.; 0-87655),* 1200 S. Willis Ave., Wheeling, IL 60090 (SAN 696-737X) Tel 312-541-9290.

Whitehall Pr, *(Whitehall Pr.-Budget Pubns.; 0-916565),* Whitehall, Rt. 1, Box 603, Sandersville, GA 31082 (SAN 295-5512) Tel 912-552-7455.

Whitehaven Pub, *(Whitehaven Publishing; 0-936291),* 2924 Brakley, Suite B-6, Baton Rouge, LA 70816 (SAN 697-9971) Tel 504-291-7942.

Whitehead Photo, *(Whitehead Photography; 0-9603486),* 13 S. Foushee St., Richmond, VA 23220 (SAN 213-7054) Tel 804-648-3219.

Whitehorse, *(Whitehorse; 0-937591),* 4154 Ticonderoga Way, Boise, ID 83706 (SAN 659-1299) Tel 208-336-8650.

Whitenwife Pubns, *(Whitenwife Pubns.; 0-9603656),* 149 Magellan St., Capitola, CA 95010 (SAN 213-8816) Tel 408-476-2730.

Whites Creek Pr, *(Whites Creek Pr.; 0-9616918),* P.O. Box 266, Whites Creek, TN 37189 (SAN 661-5430); 4772 Lickton Pike, Whites Creek, TN 37189 (SAN 661-5449) Tel 615-876-2622.

Whitewater, *(Whitewater; 0-9612286),* 509 E. 73rd St., No. 18, New York, NY 10021 (SAN 289-5765).

Whitfield, *(Whitfield; 0-930920),* 1841 Pleasant Hill Rd., Pleasant Hill, CA 94523 (SAN 210-6280) Tel 415-938-6759.

Whitfield Pub, *(Whitfield Publishing Co.; 0-938649),* P.O. Box 53617, San Jose, CA 95153 (SAN 661-6372); 5343 Birch Grove Dr., San Jose, CA 95153 (SAN 661-6380) Tel 408-282-9991.

Whitinsville Bk, *(Whitinsville Bk. Co.; 0-915949),* 20 Steele St., Worcester, MA 01607 (SAN 294-1120) Tel 617-754-1115.

Whitlaker, *(Whitlaker Marketing; 0-914303),* P.O. Box 661, Whitmore Lake, MI 48189 (SAN 287-6175) Tel 313-552-3764; 10329 Cedar Crest, Whitmore Lake, MI 48189 (SAN 287-6183).

Whitlock SC
See Makin Do Ent

Whitman-Walker, *(Whitman-Walker Clinic, Inc., the),* 2335 18th St., NW, Washington, DC 20009 (SAN 237-9775).

†Whitmore, *(Whitmore Publishing Co.; 0-87426),* 35 Cricket Terrace, Ardmore, PA 19003 (SAN 203-2112) Tel 215-896-6116; *CIP.*

Whitney Lib *Imprint of* Watson-Guptill

Whitney PB, *(Whitney, Philip B.; 0-9612992),* Rte. 2, Stephens City, VA 22655 (SAN 292-7349) Tel 703-869-1713.

Whitston Pub, *(Whitston Pub. Co., Inc.; 0-87875),* P.O. Box 958, Troy, NY 12181 (SAN 203-2120) Tel 518-283-4363.

Whitt, *(Whitt, Jane Chapman; 0-9615446),* 3332 Glenmore Dr., Falls Church, VA 22041 (SAN 695-7307) Tel 703-578-1861.

Whitten Pub Co, *(Whitten Publishing Co.; 0-9602766),* P.O. Box 513, Flatonia, TX 78941 (SAN 213-1889).

Whitts Three Ent, *(Whitt's Three Enterprises; 0-9617082),* RR 1, Box 301, North Liberty, IN 46554 (SAN 662-6432); 59105 Crumstown Hwy., North Liberty, IN 46554 (SAN 662-6440).

Whole Person, *(Whole Person Assocs., Inc./Whole Person Pr.; 0-938586),* P.O. Box 3151, Duluth, MN 55803 (SAN 282-5430) Tel 218-728-6807; Dist. by: Bookpeople, 2929 Fifth St., Berkeley, CA 94710 (SAN 168-9517) Tel 415-549-3030; Orders to: Whole Person Pr., P.O. Box 3249, Duluth, MN 55803 (SAN 282-5457) Tel 218-728-4077.

Whole World, *(Whole World Publishing, Inc.; 0-938184),* 400 Lake Cook Rd., No. 207, Deerfield, IL 60015 (SAN 217-1422) Tel 312-945-8050; Toll free: 800-323-4305.

Wholeo Bks, *(Wholeo Bks.; 0-942488),* 565 Willow Rd., No. 26, Menlo Park, CA 94025 (SAN 239-9547) Tel 415-324-3462.

Who's Black Mill, *(Who's Who of Black Millionaires, Inc.; 0-915021),* P.O. Box 12092, Fresno, CA 93776 (SAN 289-4661) Tel 209-266-5438.

Who's What Where, *(Who's What and Where; 0-9614418),* P.O. Box 921, Detroit, MI 48231 (SAN 689-0512) Tel 313-886-5611.

Whos Who & Why
See Currier-Davis

Who's Who Black Am, *(Who's Who Among Black Americans, Inc.),* 721 N. McKinley, Lake Forest, IL 60045 (SAN 207-9968) Tel 312-295-6650.

Who's Who Electro, *(Who's Who in Consumer Electronics, Inc.; 0-935305),* Div. of Martin Porter Associate Publications, 76 Court St., Brooklyn, NY 11201 (SAN 695-8443) Tel 718-875-7616.

Who's Who Hist Soc, *(Who's Who Historical Society; 0-9603166),* P.O. Box 4240, San Clemente, CA 92672 (SAN 213-7062) Tel 714-498-0600.

Whos Who Rest, *(Who's Who in America's Restaurants; 0-910297),* Div. of Who's Who in Restaurants, 1841 Broadway, Suite 808, New York, NY 10023 (SAN 241-4775) Tel 212-581-0360.

WI Conf United Meth Ch, *(Wisconsin Annual Conference of the United Methodist Church, The; 0-938779),* 750 Windsor St., Sun Prairie, WI 53590 (SAN 661-647X) Tel 608-837-3367; P.O. Box 220, Sun Prairie, WI 53590 (SAN 661-6488).

WIA
See Women Arts Found

Wibat Pubns, *(Wibat Pubns.; 0-935996),* P.O. Box 60, Forestville, CA 95436 (SAN 214-1698).

WIBC, *(Women's International Bowling Congress),* 5301 S. 76th St., Greendale, WI 53129 (SAN 216-4787) Tel 414-421-9000.

WICC Bks, *(WICC Books, Inc.; 0-918878),* Div. of Worth Intl Communications Corp., P.O. Box 69-3780, Miami, FL 33169 (SAN 210-5292) Tel 305-653-0123.

Wichita Art Mus, *(Wichita Art Museum; 0-939324),* Div. of City of Wichita, 619 Stackman Dr., Wichita, KS 67203 (SAN 205-5260) Tel 316-268-4921.

Wichita Ctr Entrep SBM, *(Center for Entrepreneurship & Small Business Management; 0-941958),* Wichita State Univ., P.O. Box 48, Wichita, KS 67208 (SAN 239-5193).

Wicker Park, *(Wicker Park Pr.; 0-911595),* Box 5597, Chicago, IL 60680 (SAN 264-4967) Tel 312-486-2191.

Wicker Pubns, *(Wicker Pubns.; 0-930111),* 28833 SE Amisted Lane, Eagle Creek, OR 97022 (SAN 670-2570) Tel 503-637-3412.

Wickstrom, *(Wickstrom Pubs., Inc.; 0-936240),* 5901 SW 74th St., Suite 310, Miami, FL 33143 (SAN 206-0345) Tel 305-661-4222; Dist. by: Banyan Books, Inc., P.O. Box 431160, Miami, FL 33243 (SAN 208-340X) Tel 305-665-6011.

Wickwire Pr, *(Wickwire Pr.; 0-9612556),* Rd. 1, Sutton, VT 05867 (SAN 289-467X) Tel 802-467-3218; Dist. by: Countryman Press, Inc., Maxham Meadows, Box 175, VT 05091 (SAN 206-4901) Tel 802-457-1049.

Widdy Pub, *(Widdy Publishing; 0-9614981),* 731 Cascade Dr., Woodburn, OR 97071 (SAN 693-6792) Tel 503-981-3378.

Wide Horiz Pr, *(Wide Horizons Pr.; 0-938109),* 13 Meadowsweet, Irvine, CA 92715 (SAN 659-8137) Tel 714-786-7922.

Wide Skies, *(Wide Skies Pr.),* P.O. Box 7, Rte. 1, Polk, NE 68654 (SAN 205-5279) Tel 402-765-3798.

Wide World Publishing
See Wide World-Tetra

Wide World-Tetra, *(Wide World Publishing/Tetra; 0-933174),* P.O. Box 476, San Carlos, CA 94070 (SAN 211-1462) Tel 415-593-2839; Dist. by: Bookpeople, 2929 Fifth St., Berkeley, CA 94710 (SAN 168-9517) Tel 415-549-3030; Dist. by: Publishers Group West, 5855 Beaudry St., Emeryville, CA 94608 (SAN 202-8522) Tel 415-658-3453.

Widening Horizons, *(Widening Horizons, Inc.; 0-9616310),* 9582 Hamilton Ave., Suite 241, Huntington Beach, CA 92646 (SAN 658-7208) Tel 714-964-2363; 9622 Chevy Chase Dr., Huntington Beach, CA 92646 (SAN 658-7216).

Wideview *Imprint of* Putnam Pub Group

Wiener Pub Inc, *(Wiener, Markus, Publishing, Inc.; 0-910129),* 2901 Broadway, Suite 107, New York, NY 10025 (SAN 282-5465) Tel 212-678-7138; Dist. by: Schocken Bks. (Masterworks of Jewish Writing Ser. only), 62 Cooper Sq., New York, NY 10003 (SAN 213-7585) Tel 212-475-4900; Dist. by: M & B Fulfillment Services, 540 Barnum Ave., Bridgeport, CT 06610 (SAN 282-6062) Tel 203-366-1900.

Wieser & Wieser, *(Wieser & Wieser, Inc.; 0-914373),* 118 E 25th St., New York, NY 10010 (SAN 289-6958) Tel 212-260-0860.

Wigan Pier, *(Wigan Pier Press; 0-934594),* 1283 Page St., San Francisco, CA 94117 (SAN 213-1897) Tel 415-863-6664.

Wiggins
See J H Wiggins

Wiide Pubns Co, *(Wiide Pubns., Co.; 0-933151),* 1100 Center Point., Stevens Point, WI 54481 (SAN 200-4771) Tel 715-344-9600.

Wilcord Pubns, *(Wilcord Pubns., Ltd.; 0-920986),* c/o Robert Silver Assocs., 307 E. 37th St., New York, NY 10016 (SAN 241-5801) Tel 212-686-5630.

Wild Clover Bks, *(Wild Clover Bks.; 0-9616008),* Rte. 2, Inavale, NE 68952 (SAN 697-9998) Tel 402-746-3589.

Wild Duck Pr, *(Wild Duck Press; 0-9612542),* Porterville Rd., East Aurora, NY 14052 (SAN 289-7075) Tel 716-652-8246.

Wild Geese, *(Wild Geese Publishing Co., The; 0-918379),* 116 Elessa Dr., Hendersonville, TN 37075 (SAN 657-3916) Tel 615-822-7177.

Wild Horses, *(Wild Horses Publishing Co.; 0-9601088; 0-937148),* 12310 Concepcion Rd., Los Altos Hills, CA 94022 (SAN 211-8289) Tel 415-941-3396.

Wild Horses Potted Plant
See Wild Horses

Wild Rose, *(Wild Rose; 0-915507),* P.O. Box 29234, Los Angeles, CA 90029 (SAN 291-4654) Tel 213-241-0284; 1355 Cedar Court Rd., Glendale, CA 91207 (SAN 291-4662).

Wild Skies Pr *Imprint of* Entheos

Wild Trees Press, *(Wild Trees Pr.; 0-931125),* P.O. Box 378, Navarro, CA 95463 (SAN 678-9552); Dist. by: Bookpeople, 2929 Fifth St., Berkeley, CA 94710 (SAN 168-9517) Tel 415-549-3030; Dist. by: Publishers Group West, 5855 Beaudry St., Emeryville, CA 94608 (SAN 202-8522) Tel 415-658-3453; Dist. by: Inland Bk. Co., P.O. Box 261, 22 Hemingway, East Haven, CT 06512 (SAN 200-4151) Tel 203-467-4257.

Wild Willow, *(Wild Willow Pr.; 0-9614795),* P.O. Box 438, Baraboo, WI 53913 (SAN 693-0301); 700 Second St., Baraboo, WI 53913 (SAN 662-3077) Tel 608-356-9048.

Wilder Advent Bks, *(Wilderness Adventure Books; 0-9611596),* 320 Garden Ln., P.O. Box 968, Fowlerville, MI 48836 (SAN 285-6662) Tel 517-223-9581.

Wilder Hse Bks
See Wilder Advent Bks

Wilderness Hse, *(Wilderness House; 0-931798),* 11129 Caves Hwy., Cave Junction, OR 97523 (SAN 208-0907) Tel 503-592-2106.

†Wilderness Pr, *(Wilderness Pr.; 0-89997; 0-911824),* 2440 Bancroft Way, Berkeley, CA 94704-1676 (SAN 203-2139) Tel 415-843-8080; *CIP.*

Wilderness Pr
See Way Up Firm

Wilderness Soc, *(Wilderness Society, The),* 1400 Eye St. NW, 10th Flr., Washington, DC 20005 (SAN 225-0128) Tel 202-842-3400.

Wildfire *Imprint of* Scholastic Inc

Wildfire Pub, *(Wildfire Publishing Co.; 0-938444),* 5797 Honors Drive, San Diego, CA 92122 (SAN 216-2040) Tel 619-458-1728.

Wildflower, *(Wildflower Pr.; 0-938370),* P.O. Box 1027, Woodland Hills, CA 91365 (SAN 215-8280).

Wildhaunt Bks
See B Butler

Wildlife Educ, *(Wildlife Education, Ltd.; 0-937934),* 930 W. Washington, Suite 14, San Diego, CA 92103 (SAN 215-8299) Tel 619-299-5034.

Wildlife Mgmt, *(Wildlife Management Institute),* Suite 725, 1101 14th St., NW, Washington, DC 20005 (SAN 225-0136) Tel 202-347-1774.

†Wildlife Soc, *(Wildlife Society, Inc. The; 0-933564),* 5410 Grosvenor Ln., Bethesda, MD 20814 (SAN 203-0225) Tel 301-897-9770; *CIP.*

Wildlife Soc
See N Central Sect Wildlife

Wildlife-Wildlands, *(Wildlife-Wildlands Institute; 0-910439),* 5200 Upper Miller Creek Rd., Missoula, MT 59803 (SAN 260-1575) Tel 406-251-3867.

Wildwater Designs, *(Wildwater Designs Ltd.),* 230 Penllyn Pike, Penllyn, PA 19422 (SAN 219-8371).

Wildwood, *(Wildwood Pr.; 0-918944),* 2110 Wood Ave., Colorado Springs, CO 80907 (SAN 210-5284) Tel 303-634-8078.

Wildwood Pr, *(Wildwood Pr.; 0-9607260),* 209 SW Wildwood, Grants Pass, OR 97526 (SAN 239-345X) Tel 503-479-3434.

Wildwood Pub Co, *(Wildwood Publishing Co.; 0-915251),* 6851 Ream's Rd., Alanson, MI 49706 (SAN 289-8926).

Wildwood Pubns MI, *(Wildwood Pubns.; 0-914104),* Div. of Live Stream, Inc., P.O. Box 629, Traverse City, MI 49684 (SAN 206-5916) Tel 616-941-7160; Toll free: 800-447-7367.

Wiley, *(Wiley, John, & Sons, Inc.; 0-471; 0-8260),* 605 Third Ave., New York, NY 10158 (SAN 200-2272) Tel 212-850-6418. *Imprints:* Harwal Pub Co (Harwal Publishing Company).

Wilk Pub, *(Wilk Publishing Co.),* P.O. Box 320, Park Ridge, IL 60068 (SAN 203-221X) Tel 312-725-4878.

Wilkerson Pub Co, *(J. L. Wilkerson Publishing Co.; 0-915253),* 731 Franklin St., Westbury, NY 11590 (SAN 289-8950) Tel 516-334-6297.

Wilkinson, *(Wilkinson, Paul H.; 0-911710),* 5900 Kingswood Rd., NW, Washington, DC 20014 (SAN 205-5295) Tel 301-530-0888.

Will Eisner Stds
See Poorhouse Pr

Willamette, *(Willamette Pr.; 0-913695),* P.O. Box 2065, Beaverton, OR 97075 (SAN 286-2174) Tel 503-643-1357.

Willamette Kayak Canoe Club, *(Willamette Kayak & Canoe Club; 0-9616257),* P.O. Box 1062, Corvallis, OR 97339 (SAN 658-3784) Tel 503-754-4323; 218 NW 28th, Corvallis, OR 97330 (SAN 658-3792).

Willamette River, *(Willamette River Press; 0-915443),* P.O. Box 317, W. Linn, OR 97068 (SAN 291-4697) Tel 503-656-6300.

Willard-Bower, *(Willard/Bower; 0-9606810),* 100 Marilyn Ave., Roseville, CA 95678 (SAN 211-9943) Tel 916-786-2632.

Willard Pr, *(Willard Pr.; 0-9615349),* P.O. Box 1254, Summit, NJ 07901 (SAN 695-099X) Tel 201-273-5143.

Willco Pub, *(Willco Publishing; 0-937579),* 325 N. 33rd Ave., Suite 104, St. Cloud, MN 56301 (SAN 658-8352) Tel 612-393-2829.

Willcraft, *(Willcraft Pubs.; 0-910585),* 5093 Williamsport Dr., Norcross, GA 30092 (SAN 260-2784) Tel 404-449-4758.

Willer, *(Willer, Ed; 0-9614931),* 2606 Lewis Farm Rd., Raleigh, NC 27608 (SAN 693-4463) Tel 919-832-8881; Orders to: Village Book and Stationery, Inc., P.O. Box 10485, Raleigh, NC 27605 (SAN 662-3239) Tel 919-834-6234.

Willett Pub Co, *(Willett Publishing Co.; 0-915005),* 388 Berkeley Ave., Winnetka, IL 60093 (SAN 289-4688) Tel 312-441-8818.

William & Allen, *(William & Allen; 0-9614403),* P.O. Box 6147, Olympia, WA 98502 (SAN 688-7058) Tel 206-866-7417.

†William & Rich, *(William & Richards, Pubs.; 0-9600202),* P.O. Box 2546, San Francisco, CA 94126 (SAN 282-5481) Tel 415-461-2835; *CIP.*

†William Carey Lib, *(Carey, William, Library Pubs.; 0-87808),* 1705 N. Sierra Bonita Ave., P.O. Box 40129, Pasadena, CA 91104 (SAN 208-2101) Tel 818-798-0819; *CIP. Imprints:* Ecclesia (Ecclesia Pubns.); Mandate (Mandate Press); World Christ (World Christian Bookshelf).

William Dana, *(William & Dana Co.; 0-9616258),* 518 N. Nevada, Suite 210, Colorado Springs, CO 80903 (SAN 658-7305) Tel 303-632-2213.

William of Orange, *(William of Orange Publications),* N84 W16033 Menomonee Ave., No. 109, Menomonee Falls, WI 53051 (SAN 264-4983) Tel 414-255-4309; Orders to: Gerry Max or Carole Rahn, 1450 Vallejo St., No. 205, San Francisco, CA 54109 (SAN 662-748X) Tel 415-771-2364.

William Tyndale Col Pr, *(Tyndale, William, College Pr.; 0-912407),* 35700 W. 12 Mile Rd., Farmington Hills, MI 48018 (SAN 265-3702) Tel 313-553-7200.

Williams & Assocs
See Wms & Assocs IA

†Williams & Wilkins, *(Williams & Wilkins Co.; 0-683),* Div. of Waverly Pr., Inc., 428 E. Preston St., Baltimore, MD 21202 (SAN 202-5175) Tel 301-528-8521; Toll free: 800-638-0672; *CIP.*

Williams Coll, *(Williams College; 0-915081),* P.O. Box 676, Williamstown, MA 01267 (SAN 289-8993) Tel 413-597-2278; 75 Park St., Williamstown, MA 01267 (SAN 289-9000).

Williams Com, *(Williams Communications, Inc.; 0-9612296),* P.O. Box 1849, Orangeburg, SC 29115 (SAN 263-2365).

Williams Pr, *(Williams Press),* 417 Commerce St., Nashville, TN 37219 (SAN 211-1438).

Williams Pub Co, *(Williams, Edward, Publishing Co.; 0-934411),* P.O. Box 33280, No. 231, Austin, TX 78764 (SAN 693-8345) Tel 512-258-5884. *Imprints:* Banned Bks (Banned Books).

Williams-Wright Pub, *(Williams/Wright Pubs.; 0-937961),* 18402 SW 89th Pl., Miami, FL 33157 (SAN 659-5510) Tel 305-251-2756.

†Williamsburg, *(Colonial Williamsburg Foundation; 0-910412; 0-87935),* Pubns. Dept., P.O. Box C, Williamsburg, VA 23187 (SAN 203-297X) Tel 804-229-1000; Dist. by: Henry Holt & Co., 521 Fifth Ave., New York, NY 10175 (SAN 200-6472) Tel 212-599-7600; Dist. by: University Pr. of Virginia, (SAN 202-5361); *CIP.*

Williamson Ad Agcy, *(Williamson & Assocs. Advertising Agency; 0-934033),* 3004 16th Street, Suite 304, San Francisco, CA 94108 (SAN 692-9710) Tel 415-981-0911.

†Williamson Pub Co, *(Williamson Publishing Co.; 0-913589),* Church Hill Rd., P.O. Box 185, Charlotte, VT 05445 (SAN 285-3884) Tel 802-425-2102; *CIP.*

Williamson Sch, *(Williamson School of Horsemanship; 0-9600144),* P.O. Box 506, Hamilton, MT 59840 (SAN 205-5317) Tel 406-363-2874.

Winequest, *(Winequest; 0-9615063),* 31 Belford Ave., Bay Shore, NY 11706 (SAN 694-1516) Tel 516-666-4216.

Winfoto, *(Winfoto; 0-9605522),* 1790 Kearney St., Denver, CO 80220 (SAN 216-2067).

Wingate HS Pr, *(Wingate High School Pr.; 0-9613681),* 600 Kingston Ave., Brooklyn, NY 11203 (SAN 692-7505).

†**Wingbow Pr,** *(Wingbow Pr.; 0-914640),* Dist. by: Bookpeople, 2929 Fifth St., Berkeley, CA 94710 (SAN 168-9517) Tel 415-549-3030; *CIP.*

Winged Lion, *(Winged Lion Publishing Ltd.; 0-915922),* 414 S. Western Ave., P.O. Box 75936, Los Angeles, CA 90075 (SAN 208-0346).

Wings Faith Pub, *(Wings of Faith Publishing Hse.; 0-930555),* 500 Bruns Ave., Charlotte, NC 28208 (SAN 677-4687) Tel 704-332-8923.

Wings ME, *(Wings Pr.; 0-939736),* R.F.D 2, P.O. Box 730, Belfast, ME 04915 (SAN 216-7689) Tel 207-338-2005.

Wings Pr, *(Wings Pr.; 0-930324),* P.O. Box 25296, Houston, TX 77005 (SAN 209-4975) Tel 713-668-7953.

Wings Pub Prod, *(Wings Publishing & Production Co.; 0-9616010),* P.O. Box 683, Severna Park, MD 21146 (SAN 696-7205) Tel 301-987-6244; 732 Benfield Rd., Severna Park, MD 21146 (SAN 698-2158).

Winicorp, *(Winicorp; 0-9610634),* P.O. Box 3314, San Leandro, CA 94578 (SAN 276-9476) Tel 415-483-3029.

Winmar Pr, *(Winmar Pr.; 0-9613253),* 5800 W. Century Blvd., P.O. Box 91157-1157, Los Angeles, CA 90009 (SAN 686-1601) Tel 213-672-0735.

Winmark Pr, *(Winmark Pr.; 0-9608278),* P.O. Box 148, Stratford, CT 06497 (SAN 240-5083).

Winn Bks, *(Winn Bks.; 0-916947),* Div. of The Winn Corporation, P.O. Box 80157, Seattle, WA 98108 (SAN 655-7864) Tel 206-763-9544; Toll free: 800-426-5589; Dist. by: Ingram, 1125 Heil Quaker Blvd., LaVergne, TN 37086 (SAN 169-7978) Tel 615-793-5000; Dist. by: Publishers Group West, 5855 Beaudry St., Emeryville, CA 94608 (SAN 202-8522) Tel 415-658-3453; Dist. by: Bookpeople, 2929 Fifth St., Berkeley, CA 94710 (SAN 168-9517) Tel 415-549-3030; Dist. by: Pacific Pipeline, 19215 66th Ave. S., Kent, WA 98032 (SAN 208-2128) Tel 206-872-5523; Dist. by: Pacific Trade Group, P.O. Box 668, Pearl City, HI 96782-0668 (SAN 169-1635).

Winn Pub
See Winn Bks

Winners Pub, *(Winners Publishing Co.; 0-938099),* P.O. Box 1335, Coronado, CA 92118 (SAN 659-7114); 842 H Ave., Coronado, CA 92118 (SAN 659-7122) Tel 619-435-6407.

Winnetka Pr, *(Winnetka Pr.; 0-938901),* 5101 Suffield Ct., Skokie, IL 60077 (SAN 662-6548) Tel 312-966-2730.

WINNEWS, *(Women's International Network News Quarterly; 0-942096),* 187 Grant St., Lexington, MA 02173 (SAN 237-9740) Tel 617-862-9430.

Winning Pubns MN
See Winning St Paul

Winning St Paul, *(Winning Pubns.; 0-9617124),* 1439 Arcade St., Suite 120, St. Paul, MN 55106 (SAN 662-6831) Tel 612-774-0678. Do not confuse with Winning Pubns., Oakland, CA.

Winning Ways Pr, *(Winning Ways Pr.; 0-931501),* 2888 Bluff, Suite 433, Boulder, CO 80301 (SAN 683-1230) Tel 303-447-8483.

Winrock Intl, *(Winrock International; 0-933595),* Rte. 3, Morrilton, AR 72110-9537 (SAN 692-7165) Tel 501-727-5435; Dist. by: Agribookstore/Winrock, Rosslyn Plaza, 1611 N. Kent St., Suite 600, Arlington, VA 22209 (SAN 200-6693) Tel 703-525-9455.

Winship Pr, *(Winship Pr.; 0-915430),* 2324 Clayton St., Macon, GA 31204 (SAN 207-3005) Tel 912-743-0029.

Winslow Wolverton, *(Winslow Wolverton & Kornegay; 0-9614874),* Div. of Triad Publications, P.O. Box 283, Herford, NC 27944 (SAN 693-2304) Tel 919-426-7665; Dist. by: Wimmer Brothers Books, 4210 BF Goodrich Blvd., Memphis, TN 38181 (SAN 662-3174) Tel 901-362-8900.

Winston & Beck, *(Winston & Beck; 0-9615921),* 3504 Chaucer Pl., Raleigh, NC 27609 (SAN 696-7736) Tel 919-782-4615.

Winston-Derek, *(Winston-Derek Pubs.,Inc.; 0-938232; 1-55523),* P.O. Box 90883, Nashville, TN 37209 (SAN 216-4760) Tel 615-321-0535; Toll free: 800-826-1888; Dist. by: Baker & Taylor Co., Midwest Div., 5 Gladiola Ave., Momence, IL 60954 (SAN 169-2100).

Winston Pr, *(Winston Pr., Inc.; 0-86683),* Div. of Harper & Row, Inc., c/o Harper & Row Pubs., Inc., 1700 Montgomery St., San Francisco, CA 94111 (SAN 215-3734) Tel 415-989-9000; Toll free: 800-242-7737 (Bookstores & schools); Toll free: 800-638-3030 (Individuals); Orders to: Harper & Row Pubs., Inc., Keystone Industrial Pk., Scranton, PA 18512 (SAN 215-3742). Harper & Row acquired Winston-Seabury from CBS Educational Publishing. Now considered an 'imprint' of Harper & Row. Please use San Francisco address for editorial inquiries.

Winter Brook, *(Winter Brook Publishing Co.; 0-9602204),* P.O. Box 1106, Covina, CA 91722 (SAN 212-7121) Tel 714-585-7101.

Winter Pub Co, *(Winter Publishing Co.; 0-938372),* P.O. Box 36536, Tucson, AZ 85740 (SAN 220-1100); 6632 N. Willowbrook Dr., Tucson, AZ 85704 (SAN 220-1119) Tel 602-742-4104.

Winterbourne Pr, *(Winterbourne Pr.; 0-9609172),* 1407 Gilman St., Berkeley, CA 94706 (SAN 241-4201) Tel 415-527-9885.

†**Wintergreen,** *(Wintergreen & Advance Pubs.; 0-933460),* 1131 Tellem Drive, Pacific Palisades, CA 90272 (SAN 212-713X) Tel 213-459-1341; *CIP.*

Wintergreen P, *(Wintergreen Pr.),* 4105 Oak St., Long Lake, MN 55356 (SAN 694-101X) Tel 612-476-1303.

Winters Pubns, *(Winters' Pubns.; 0-935011),* P.O. Box 156, North Adams, MI 49262 (SAN 695-1929) Tel 517-287-5712.

WinterSpring Pr, *(WinterSpring Pr.; 0-938651),* 406 Second St., Davis, CA 95616 (SAN 661-6305) Tel 916-753-2262.

Winterthur, *(Winterthur Museum & Gardens; 0-912724),* Rte. 52, Winterthur, DE 19735 (SAN 205-5406) Tel 302-656-8591; Dist. by: W. W. Norton & Co., 500 Fifth Ave., New York, NY 10110 (SAN 202-5795) Tel 212-354-5500; Dist. by: Harry N. Abrams, 100 Fifth Ave., New York, NY 10011 (SAN 200-2434) Tel 212-206-7715; Dist. by: Garland Press, 1611 Hilton Ave., Columbia, GA 31906 (SAN 223-1840); Dist. by: University Press of Virginia, P.O. Box 3608, University Station, Charlottesville, VA 22903 (SAN 202-5361) Tel 804-924-3468.

WIPO *Imprint of* Unipub

Wire Assn Intl, *(Wire Association International),* 1570 Boston Post Rd., Guilford, CT 06437 (SAN 224-8778) Tel 203-453-2777; P.O. Box H, Guilford, CT 06510 (SAN 669-3008).

Wires Ltd, *(Wires, Ltd.; 0-9616173),* 1717 K St. NW, Suite 706, Washington, DC 20006 (SAN 699-9913) Tel 202-293-5540.

Wis Ed Fund, *(Wisconsin Education Fund; 0-9600358),* P.O. Box 321, Port Washington, WI 53074 (SAN 205-5414) Tel 414-284-9066.

Wis Ev Luth
See WELS Board

Wis Inst Drug Abuse, *(Wisconsin Institute on Drug Abuse; 0-9615363),* Div. of Tellurian Community, Inc., 300 Femrite Dr., Madison, WI 53716 (SAN 695-2690) Tel 608-222-7311.

Wisc T & T
See Tamarack Pr

Wisconsin Bks, *(Wisconsin Bks.; 0-913370),* 2769 Marshall Pkwy., Madison, WI 53713 (SAN 213-8875) Tel 608-257-4126. *Imprints:* R B Allison Co (Allison, R. B., Co.); Sol Press (Sol Press).

Wisconsin Gen, *(Wisconsin State Genealogical Society, Inc.; 0-910255),* 5049 LaCrosse Ln., Madison, WI 53705 (SAN 223-0623) Tel 608-233-8018; c/o Hedberg, P.O. Box 685, Madison, WI 53701 (SAN 662-7498).

Wisconsin Sptmn, *(Wisconsin Sportsman; 0-932558),* P.O. Box 2266, Oshkosh, WI 54903 (SAN 207-3013) Tel 414-233-1327.

Wiscott Ent, *(Wiscott Enterprises; 0-938533),* 401 S. Kingsley Dr., Suite 126, Los Angeles, CA 90020 (SAN 661-1540) Tel 213-387-2283.

Wisdom Bk Pubs, *(Wisdom Bk. Pubs., Inc.; 0-930509),* 2854 Angelo Dr., Los Angeles, CA 90077 (SAN 670-9702) Tel 213-271-1380.

Wisdom Garden, *(Wisdom Garden Bks.; 0-914794),* P.O. Box 29448, Los Angeles, CA 90029 (SAN 206-5584) Tel 213-380-1968.

Wisdom House, *(Wisdom Hse. Pr.; 0-932560),* 43222 SE Tapp Rd., Sandy, OR 97055 (SAN 212-2022) Tel 503-668-3119.

Wisdom Pr, *(Wisdom Pr.; 0-9615050),* P.O. Box 28031, Las Vegas, NV 89126 (SAN 693-8469) Tel 702-382-3009.

Wisdom Pubns *Imprint of* **Great Traditions**

Wise Pub, *(Wise Publishing Co.; 0-915766),* 5625 Wilhelmina Ave., Woodland Hills, CA 91367 (SAN 203-1876) Tel 818-883-7527.

Wish Bklets, *(Wish Booklets; 0-913786),* 3807 Meredith Dr., Greensboro, NC 27408 (SAN 205-5430) Tel 919-282-2122.

Wish Pubns, *(WISH Pubns.; 0-917392),* 113 W. 60th St., New York, NY 10023 (SAN 276-7090) Tel 212-841-5514.

Wishing Rm, *(Wishing Room, Inc., The; 0-931563),* P.O. Box 337, Mechanicsville, VA 23111 (SAN 682-207X) Tel 804-746-0375.

Wishing Star Bks *Imprint of* **Scholastic Inc**

Wisla Pubs, *(Wisla Pubs.; 0-9614274),* 1404 Twisted Oak Ln., Baton Rouge, LA 70810 (SAN 687-4169) Tel 504-766-6036; Orders to: P.O. Box 65042, Baton Rouge, LA 70896-5042 (SAN 662-2763).

Wistaria Pr, *(Wistaria Pr.; 0-916930),* 4373 NE Wistaria Dr., Portland, OR 97213 (SAN 237-9732) Tel 503-281-5945.

With Kids, *(With Kids; 0-9611292),* P.O. Box 353, West Sand Lake, NY 12196 (SAN 283-9903).

With Love Foun, *(With Love Foundation, Inc.; 0-9614082),* 535 Cordova Rd., Suite 182, Santa Fe, NM 87501 (SAN 685-9321) Tel 505-983-1809.

Witkower, *(Witkower Pr., Inc.; 0-911638),* P.O. Box 2296, Bishop's Corner, West Hartford, CT 06117 (SAN 205-5449) Tel 203-232-1127.

Witness Holocaust, *(Witness to the Holocaust Project; 0-912313),* Emory University, Atlanta, GA 30322 (SAN 264-5025) Tel 404-727-7525.

Wittenborn, *(Wittenborn, George, Inc.; 0-8150),* 1018 Madison Ave., New York, NY 10021 (SAN 125-0957) Tel 212-288-1558.

Wittman Pubns, *(Wittman Pubns., Inc.),* P.O. Box 3689, Baltimore, MD 21214 (SAN 210-9905) Tel 301-254-0273.

WIU Essays Lit, *(Western Illinois Univ. Essays in Literature; 0-934312),* 114 Simpkins Hall, Macomb, IL 61455 (SAN 215-7128) Tel 309-298-2212.

Wizards, *(Wizards Bookshelf; 0-913510),* P.O. Box 6600, San Diego, CA 92106 (SAN 203-2872) Tel 619-235-0340; Dist. by: DeVorss & Co., P.O. Box 550, 1046 Princeton Dr., Marina del Rey, CA 90291 (SAN 282-6151); Dist. by: New Leaf Distributing, 1020 White St., SW, Atlanta, GA 30310 (SAN 294-1449).

Wkshops Innovative Teach, *(Workshops for Innovative Teaching; 0-9604042),* 191 Edgewood Ave., San Francisco, CA 94117 (SAN 214-1744) Tel 415-665-4932.

WLCJ, *(Women's League for Conservative Judaism; 0-936293),* 48 E. 74th St., New York, NY 10021 (SAN 697-9661) Tel 212-628-1600.

Wm B ONeill, *(O'Neill, William B.; 0-9615243),* P.O. Box 2275, Reston, VA 22090 (SAN 693-1014) Tel 703-860-0782.

Wm C Brown, *(Brown, William C., Pubs.; 0-697),* 2460 Kerper Blvd., Dubuque, IA 52001 (SAN 203-2864) Tel 319-589-2822.

Wm Dailey Antiq, *(Dailey, William, Antiquarian Books; 0-915148),* P.O. Box 69160, Los Angeles, CA 90069 (SAN 223-7504) Tel 213-658-8515.

Wm F Penoyar
See G T M Co

Wm H T Fam, *(William Henry Thomas Family; 0-9614787),* 8 Central Highlands, Tuscaloosa, AL 35404 (SAN 692-7610) Tel 205-556-9330.

Wm Morris Soc, *(Morris, William, Society; 0-931332),* 420 Riverside Dr., 12G, New York, NY 10025 (SAN 225-2899).

WMC Serv, *(WMC Service Corp.; 0-942198),* Subs. of Wisconsin Manufacturers & Commerce, P.O. Box 352, Madison, WI 53701 (SAN 687-6544); 501 E. Washington Ave., Madison, WI 53703 (SAN 662-278X) Tel 608-258-3400.

Wms & Assocs IA, *(Williams & Assocs.; 0-938185),* Subs. of South Seas Visuals, 4068 Tanglefoot Terr., Bettendorf, IA 52722 (SAN 659-7335) Tel 319-355-7142.

Wndsr Locks Hist Soc, *(Windsor Locks Historical Society),* Noden-Reed Pk., 58 West St., Windsor Locks, CT 06096 (SAN 663-4583).

Woburn Pr
See Biblio Dist

WOLA, *(Washington Office on Latin America; 0-9613249),* 110 Maryland Ave. NE, Suite 40404, Washington, DC 20002 (SAN 225-6630) Tel 202-544-8045.

Wolcotts, *(Wolcotts, Inc.; 0-910531),* 15124 Downey Ave., Paramount, CA 90723 (SAN 260-2792); Toll free: 800-421-2220; Toll free: 800-262-1538 (In California).

Wolf Creek Pr, *(Wolf Creek Pr.; 0-9611886),* P.O. Box 327, Canyondam, CA 95923 (SAN 286-0848) Tel 916-596-3412.

†**Wolf Hse,** *(Wolf Hse. Bks.; 0-915046),* P.O. Box 6657, Grand Rapids, MI 49506 (SAN 203-2856) Tel 616-245-8812; *CIP.*

Wolf Run Bks, *(Wolf Run Bks.; 0-942296),* P.O. Box 9620, Minneapolis, MN 55440 (SAN 206-9571).

Wolfdog Pubns, *(Wolfdog Pubns.; 0-9616191),* P.O. Box 142506, Anchorage, AK 99514-2506 (SAN 699-9824); 4938 Mills Dr., Anchorage, AK 99508 (SAN 699-9832) Tel 907-333-1481.

Wolfe Pub Co, *(Wolfe Publishing Co., Inc.; 0-935632),* 6471 Airpark Dr., Prescott, AZ 86301 (SAN 289-7083) Tel 602-445-7810.

Wolfenbarger, *(Wolfenbarger Publishing; 0-913127),* P.O. Box 277, Phoenix City, AL 36867 (SAN 283-3344).

Wolfson, *(Wolfson Publishing Co.; 0-916114),* Seven Wood St., Conestoga Bldg., Pittsburgh, PA 15222 (SAN 208-922X) Tel 412-391-6190.

Wolk & Rais, *(Wolk & Rais; 0-947647),* 1 Longford St., Philadelphia, PA 19136 (SAN 695-2437).

Wolverine Pr, *(Wolverine Pr.; 0-9615395),* Box 962, Hellgate Sta., New York, NY 10029 (SAN 695-4626) Tel 212-369-4394; 430 E. 105th St., Apt. 2C, New York, NY 10029 (SAN 695-4634).

Womack Assoc, *(Womack Associates; 0-9605530),* 512 Westwood Dr., Prescott, AZ 86301 (SAN 215-9864).

Womack Educ Pubns, *(Womack Educational Pubns.; 0-9605644),* Div. of Womack Machine Supply Co., 2010 Shea Rd., P.O. Box 35027, Dallas, TX 75235 (SAN 205-9657) Tel 214-357-3871.

Woman Activist, *(Woman Activist, Inc.; 0-917560),* 2310 Barbour Rd., Falls Church, VA 22043 (SAN 209-617X) Tel 703-573-8716.

Woman Time Mgmt, *(Woman Time Management; 0-9610530),* 4719 Taft, Wichita Falls, TX 76308 (SAN 264-5033) Tel 817-691-1196; Dist. by: Baker & Taylor Co., Midwest Div., 501 Gladiola Ave., Momence, IL 60954 (SAN 169-2100); Dist. by: Baker & Taylor Co., Southeast Div., Mt. Olive Rd., Commerce, GA 30529 (SAN 169-1503); Dist. by: Dot Gibson, 161 Knight Ave. Cir., Waycross, GA 31501 (SAN 200-4143) Tel 912-285-2848; Dist. by: Southwest Cookbook Distributors, 1901 S. Shore Dr., Bonham, TX 75418 (SAN 200-4925) Tel 214-583-8898.

Womans Inst-Cont Jewish Ed, *(Woman's Institute for Continuing Jewish Education; 0-9608054),* 4079 54th St., San Diego, CA 92105 (SAN 240-1061).

Woman's Pr, *(Woman's Pr., The; 0-9614878),* 245 W. 107th St., Apt. 12B, New York, NY 10029 (SAN 659-3631) Tel 212-427-1816; Orders to: P. B. S., P.O. Box 643, Cambridge, MA 02139 (SAN 662-4243) Tel 617-491-6562.

Womansource
See Metrosource Pubns

Wombat Ent, *(Wombat Enterprises, Unlimited; 0-9605722),* P.O. Box 428, Latham, NY 12110 (SAN 239-5029).

Women Arts Found, *(Women in the Arts Foundation, Inc),* 325 Spring St., New York, NY 10013 (SAN 225-3941) Tel 212-691-0988.

Women-in-Lit, *(Women-in-Literature, Inc.; 0-935634),* P.O. Box 60550, Reno, NV 89506 (SAN 213-8824) Tel 702-972-1671.

Women on Words, *(Women on Words & Images; 0-9600724),* 30 Valley Rd., Princeton, NJ 08540 (SAN 206-622X) Tel 609-921-8653; Orders to: P.O. Box 2163, Princeton, NJ 08540 (SAN 206-6238).

Women Writers Alliance, *(Women Writers Alliance; 0-915675),* P.O. Box 1083, Springfield, MA 01101 (SAN 292-7381) Tel 413-737-4888.

Women Yellow CO, *(Women's Yellow Pages, Inc.; 0-932439),* 1758 Emersen, Denver, CO 80218 (SAN 686-7405) Tel 303-861-2568.

†**Women's Action,** *(Women's Action Alliance, Inc.; 0-9605828),* 370 Lexington Ave., New York, NY 10017 (SAN 207-6950) Tel 212-532-8330; *CIP.*

Womens Auxiliary Cancer, *(Women's Auxiliary of the American Cancer Society; 0-9607282),* Affil. of American Cancer Society, 241 Fourth Ave., Pittsburgh, PA 15222 (SAN 239-3506) Tel 412-261-4352; Orders to: WAACS Cookbook, 838 Golfview Dr., McKeasport, PA 15135 (SAN 662-1910) Tel 412-751-3535.

Women's Club Denton
See W Club Denton

Womens Com Buffalo, *(Women's Committee of the Buffalo Philharmonic Orchestra Society, Inc.; 0-9607538),* 26 Richmond Ave., Buffalo, NY 14222 (SAN 239-7986) Tel 716-839-1482.

Womens Com Rich, *(Women's Committee of the Richmond Symphony; 0-9613752),* 211 W. Franklin St., Richmond, VA 23220 (SAN 677-8224) Tel 804-740-8180.

Women's Div, *(Central Sephardic Jewish Community of America, Inc., Women's Div.; 0-9611294),* 8 W. 70th St., New York, NY 10023 (SAN 283-9911) Tel 212-873-2100.

Women's Hist, *(Women's History Research Center, Inc.; 0-912374),* 2325 Oak St., Berkeley, CA 94708 (SAN 207-7175) Tel 415-548-1770.

Womens Inst Free Press, *(Women's Institute for Freedom of the Press; 0-930470),* 3306 Ross Pl., NW, Washington, DC 20008 (SAN 225-7114) Tel 202-966-7783.

Womens Intl
See WINNEWS

Women's Legal Defense, *(Women's Legal Defense Fund; 0-932689),* Box 6189, Santa Barbara, CA 93160 (SAN 212-9892) Tel 805-965-7039.

Womens Referral Serv, *(Women's Referral Service, Inc.; 0-937121),* P.O. Box 3093, Van Nuys, CA 91407 (SAN 658-5337) Tel 818-995-6646.

Womens Research Act, *(Women's Research Action Project; 0-930522),* 72 Cornell St., Roslindale, MA 02131 (SAN 209-6900) Tel 617-327-5016.

Womens Serv, *(Women's Service League of West Feliciana Parish; 0-9609422),* P.O. Box 904, 205 Pine St., St. Francisville, LA 70775 (SAN 276-7589) Tel 504-635-6162.

Womens Times, *(Women's Times Publishing; 0-910259),* Box 215, Grand Marais, MN 55604 (SAN 240-8945) Tel 218-387-2509.

Womens Yellow Pgs, *(Women's Yellow Pages; 0-9610748),* P.O. Box 66093, Los Angeles, CA 90066 (SAN 282-5562) Tel 213-398-5761.

Wonder, *(Wonder-Treasure Bks., Inc.; 0-448),* Div. of Price-Stern-Sloan, Price/Stern/Sloan Publishers, 410 N. La Cienega Blvd., Los Angeles, CA 90048 (SAN 205-5457) Tel 213-657-6100; Toll free: 800-421-0892; Toll free: 800-227-8801 (In California).

Wonder View Pr, *(Wonder View Pr.; 0-930117),* P.O. Box 3301, Mililani, HI 96789 (SAN 670-2813) Tel 808-623-5337.

Wood & Jones, *(Wood & Jones Pubs.; 0-9606114),* 139 W. Colorado Blvd., Pasadena, CA 91105 (SAN 216-8707) Tel 818-449-1144.

Wood Fire, *(Wood Fire Ashes Pr.; 0-9613338),* 9230 E. Shore, Big Fork, MT 59911 (SAN 655-7872) Tel 406-837-5134.

Wood Inst
See C P P

Wood Lake Pr, *(Wood Lake Pr.; 0-919599),* Dist. by: Friendship Pr., 475 Riverside Dr., Rm. 772, New York, NY 10027 (SAN 682-2754) Tel 212-870-2497.

Wood Lib-Mus, *(Wood Library-Museum of Anesthesiology; 0-9614932),* Subs. of American Society of Anesthesiologists, 515 Busse Hwy., Park Ridge, IL 60068 (SAN 693-4048) Tel 312-825-5586.

Wood Machinery, *(Wood Machinery Manufacturers of America),* 1900 Arch St., Philadelphia, PA 19103 (SAN 224-8514).

Wood Moor Ent, *(Wood Moor Enterprises; 0-936307),* Box 100, Nelson Rd., Brighton, IN 38011 (SAN 696-8619) Tel 901-476-5618. Out of Business.

Wood Pond, *(Wood Pond Pr.; 0-934260),* 365 Ridgewood Rd., West Hartford, CT 06107 (SAN 217-1112) Tel 203-521-0389.

Wood Pubns, *(Wood Pubns., Inc.),* P.O. Box 963, Rancho Santa Fe, CA 92067 (SAN 670-7254) Tel 619-756-3382.

Woodall, *(Woodall Publishing Co.; 0-912082),* 11 N. Skokie Hwy., Suite 205, Lake Bluff, IL 60044 (SAN 205-5465) Tel 312-295-7799; Dist. by: Simon & Schuster, Inc., 1230 Ave. of the Americas, New York, NY 10020 (SAN 200-2450) Tel 212-245-6400.

Woodbine Bks Imprint of Shorewood Fine Art

Woodbine House, *(Woodbine Hse.; 0-933149),* 10400 Connecticut Ave., Suite 512, Kensington, MD 20895 (SAN 692-3445) Tel 301-949-3590.

Woodbine-Volaphon
See Volaphon Bks

†**Woodbridge Pr,** *(Woodbridge Pr. Publishing Co.; 0-912800; 0-88007),* P.O. Box 6189, Santa Barbara, CA 93160 (SAN 212-9892) Tel 805-965-7039; *CIP.*

Woodburn Pr, *(Woodburn Press; 0-9612798),* P.O. Box 5653, Duke Sta., Durham, NC 27706 (SAN 289-906X) Tel 919-493-2655.

Woodbury Pr, *(Woodbury Pr.; 0-912123),* Whippoorwill Rd., P.O. Box 700, R.F.D No. 1, Litchfield, ME 04350 (SAN 264-6463) Tel 207-268-4604; Dist. by: Portland News, 270 Western Ave., S. Portland, ME 04106 (SAN 688-413X) Tel 207-774-2633; Dist. by: Maine Writers & Pubs. Alliance, 25A Forest Ave., Portland, ME 04101 (SAN 693-9805) Tel 207-775-6260.

Woodcock, *(Woodcock Pubns.; 0-9605352),* P. O. Box 985, Pacific Grove, CA 93950 (SAN 217-1430).

Woodcock Pr, *(Woodcock Press; 0-941674),* P.O. Box 4744, Santa Rosa, CA 95402 (SAN 239-3514) Tel 707-542-6326.

Woodcraft Supply, *(Woodcraft Supply Corp.; 0-918036),* 41 Atlantic Ave., P.O. Box 4000, Woburn, MA 01888 (SAN 210-2900) Tel 617-935-5860; Toll free: 800-225-1153.

Wooden Nutmeg, *(Wooden Nutmeg Press; 0-918164),* 74 Waller Rd., Bridgeport, CT 06606 (SAN 210-2919) Tel 203-372-8806.

Wooden Shoe, *(Wooden Shoe),* P.O. Box 174, Pleasantville, NY 10570 (SAN 207-3021) Tel 914-769-5580.

Woodford Mem, *(Woodford Memorial Editions, Inc.; 0-9601574),* P.O. Box 55085, Seattle, WA 98155 (SAN 210-9727) Tel 206-364-4167.

Woodgreene Pr, *(Woodgreene Pr.; 0-910257),* 6915 Greenfield Way, Salt Lake City, UT 84121 (SAN 241-4791) Tel 801-942-0761.

Woodhill, *(Woodhill Pr., Inc.; 0-532),* 300 W. 43rd St., New York, NY 10036 (SAN 202-6066) Tel 212-397-5200.

†**Woodland,** *(Woodland Publishing Co., Inc.; 0-934104),* 230 Manitoba Ave., Wayzata, MN 55391 (SAN 213-1900) Tel 612-473-2725; *CIP.*

Woodland ID, *(Woodland Pr., The; 0-9615031),* Box 3524 Univ., Sta., Moscow, ID 83843 (SAN 693-8833) Tel 208-882-6668.

Woodlands Pr, *(Woodlands Pr.; 0-917627),* 79 San Marino Dr., San Rafael, CA 94901 (SAN 657-1697) Tel 415-258-0729.

Woodlawn Plant, *(Woodlawn Plantation-Wright Hse. Council; 0-9608708),* P.O. Box 37, Mt. Vernon, VA 22121 (SAN 281-1863).

Woodlawn Pubs, *(Woodlawn Pubs., Inc.; 0-914111),* P.O. Box 2334, Wichita, KS 67201 (SAN 287-623X) Tel 316-788-3293.

Woodley Pubns, *(Woodley Pubns.; 0-937623),* 4620 DeRussey Pkwy., Chevy Chase, MD 20815 (SAN 659-1418) Tel 301-986-9276.

Woodmere Press, *(Woodmere Pr.),* P.O. Box 20190, Cathedral Finance Sta., New York, NY 10025 (SAN 678-3058) Tel 212-678-7839.

Woodmont Pr, *(Woodmont Pr., The; 0-9607762),* P.O. Box 108, Green Village, NJ 07935 (SAN 217-2755) Tel 201-377-6243.

Woodpile Pub
See Woodpile Pubs

Woodpile Pubs, *(Woodpile Pubs.; 0-9608118),* 1046 N. Herbert Ave., Tuscon, AZ 85705 (SAN 240-303X) Tel 602-628-1260.

Woodruff Pub, *(Woodruff Publishing Co.; 0-9616165),* 4153 Kennesaw Dr., Birmingham, AL 35213 (SAN 699-9891) Tel 205-879-8102.

Woods Books & Music Publishing
See Woods Mus Bks Pub

Woods Colt Pr, *(Woods Colt Pr.),* 5900 Ward Pkwy., Kansas City, MO 64113 (SAN 663-0790).

Woods Creek Pr, *(Woods Creek Pr.; 0-916541),* P.O. Box 339, Ridgecrest, CA 93555 (SAN 295-5571) Tel 619-375-1988.

Woods End, *(Woods End Agricultural Institute; 0-9603554),* Orchard Hill Rd., Temple, ME 04982 (SAN 239-5037).

Woods Hole Hist, *(Woods Hole Historical Collection; 0-9611374),* P.O. Box 185, Woods Hole, MA 02543 (SAN 283-1791) Tel 617-548-2768.

Woods Hole Pr, *(Woods Hole Pr.; 0-915176),* Subs. of Job Shop, 3 Water St. P.O. Box 305, Woods Hole, MA 02543 (SAN 210-332X) Tel 617-548-9600.

Woods Lib Pub, *(Woods Library Publishing Co.; 0-912304),* 9159 Clifton Park, Evergreen Park, IL 60642 (SAN 205-5473) Tel 312-423-5986.

Woods Mus Bks Pub, *(Woods Music & Bks. Publishing; 0-9602990; 0-936661),* P.O. Box 29521, Los Angeles, CA 90029 (SAN 213-1919) Tel 818-247-4177.

Woods Pubns, *(Woods Pubns.; 0-943168),* 2200 Guadalupe, Austin, TX 78705 (SAN 240-5105).

Woodside-Atherton, *(Woodside-Atherton Auxiliary to Stanford Children's Hospital; 0-9615260),* 75 Arbor Rd., Menlo Park, CA 94025 (SAN 694-4124) Tel 415-326-0880.

Woodside Pr, *(Woodside Pr.; 0-9615870),* Div. of Applied Human Development, Inc., 105 South Dr., Mountain View, CA 94040 (SAN 696-7078) Tel 415-989-8226; Dist. by: Publishers Group West, 5855 Beaudry St., Emeryville, CA 94608 (SAN 662-3816) Tel 415-658-3453.

Woodside Pr ID, *(Woodside Pr.; 0-938191),* P.O. Box 1935, Sun Valley, ID 83353 (SAN 659-7181); 1018 Baldy View Dr., Hailey, ID 83333 (SAN 659-719X) Tel 208-788-2306.

Woodsong Graph, *(Woodsong Graphics, Inc.; 0-912661),* P.O. Box 238, New Hope, PA 18938-0238 (SAN 282-8235) Tel 215-794-8321; Orders to: P M G International, 1104 Summit Ave., 100B, Plano, TX 75074 (SAN 662-202X) Tel 214-423-0312.

Woodstone Bks, *(Woodstone Bks.; 0-939866),* 3217-Villanova St., Dallas, TX 75225 (SAN 216-9436) Tel 214-824-0527.

Woodward Centennial, *(Woodward Centennial Committee),* Woodward, IA 50276 (SAN 291-8722).

Woodworkers Index, *(Woodworker's Index; 0-9616050),* P.O. Box 2376, West Lafayette, IN 47906 (SAN 698-0074) Tel 317-463-9883; 1833 Summit Dr., West Lafayette, IN 47906 (SAN 698-2379).

Woodworking Mach Mfrs
See Wood Machinery

Woodworth-Barnes, *(Woodworth-Barnes, E. L.; 0-9613798),* 150 Downs Blvd., Clemson Downs Apts., B-209, Clemson, SC 29631 (SAN 678-965X) Tel 803-654-5454.

Woolf UT Sys, *(Woolf, Eugene T., Utah System of High Education; 0-910153),* 355 W. North Temple, 3 Triad Ctr., Suite 550, Salt Lake City, UT 84180-1205 (SAN 669-2788); Orders to: Tanner Ctr. for Human Values, Southern Utah State College, Cedar City, UT 84720 (SAN 280-5782) Tel 801-533-5617.

†**Woolmer-Brotherson,** *(Woolmer/Brotherson, Ltd.; 0-913506),* Revere, PA 18953 (SAN 205-5481) Tel 215-847-5074; *CIP.*

Worcest Art, *(Worcester Art Museum; 0-936042),* 55 Salisbury St., Worcester, MA 01609-3196 (SAN 281-1936) Tel 617-799-4406; Dist. by: University of Massachusetts Press, P.O. Box 429, Amherst, MA 01004 (SAN 203-3089) Tel 413-545-2217.

Worcester County, *(Worcester County Newspapers; 0-917523),* 25 Elm St., Southbridge, MA 01550 (SAN 656-111X) Tel 617-764-4325.

Word Aflame, *(Word Aflame Pr.; 0-912315),* Subs. of Pentecostal Publishing House, 8855 Dunn Rd., Hazelwood, MO 63042 (SAN 212-0046) Tel 314-837-7300.

Word Among Us, *(Word Among Us Pr.; 0-932085),* P.O. Box 3646, Washington, DC 20007 (SAN 686-4651) Tel 301-977-2500; Toll free: 800-638-8539.

Word Beat, *(Word Beat Pr.; 0-912527),* P.O. Box 22310, Flagstaff, AZ 86002 (SAN 265-3060).

†**Word Bks,** *(Word, Inc.; 0-87680; 0-8499),* Subs. of Capital Cities/American Broadcasting Co., 4800 W. Waco Dr., Waco, TX 76796 (SAN 203-283X) Tel 817-772-7650; Orders to: Customer Service, P.O. Box 1790, Waco, TX 76796; *CIP.*

Word Doctor, *(Word Doctor Publications; 0-918248),* P.O. Box 9761, 6516 Ben Ave., N. Hollywood, CA 91609 (SAN 207-5865) Tel 818-980-3576.

Word Dynamics, *(Word Dynamics Concept; 0-939023),* P.O. Box 5256, Sacramento, CA 95817-0256 (SAN 662-5541); 6115 Ctr. Mall Way, Sacramento, CA 95823 (SAN 662-555X) Tel 916-427-6836.

Word Ent, *(Word Enterprise; 0-938722),* 574 Auten Rd., Suite 3F, South Somerville, NJ 08876 (SAN 215-9325) Tel 201-874-5323.

Word Factory, *(Word Factory; 0-936854),* 2029-F Cerrissa Ct., San Diego, CA 92154 (SAN 214-4913).

Word Faith, *(Word of Faith; 0-914307),* P.O. Box 819000, Dallas, TX 75381 (SAN 287-6272) Tel 214-620-1586.

Word for Today, *(Word for Today, The; 0-936728),* P.O. Box 8000, Costa Mesa, CA 92628 (SAN 214-2260) Tel 714-979-0706; Dist. by: Living Books, 12155 Magnolia Ave., Bldg. 11-B, Riverside, CA 92503 (SAN 169-006X) Tel 714-354-7330.

Word Foun, *(Word Foundation, Inc., The; 0-911650),* P. O. Box 18235, Dallas, TX 75218 (SAN 205-549X) Tel 214-348-5006.

Word-Fraction, *(Word-Fraction Math Aid Co.; 0-911642),* P.O. Box 475, Woodland Hills, CA 91366 (SAN 205-5503).

Word In Rhyme, *(Word In Rhyme Publishing Co., The; 0-936377),* 320 Lithia, St. Louis, MO 63119 (SAN 697-9688) Tel 314-968-0177.

Word Lab, *(Word Lab Inc.; 0-916579),* P.O. Box 53462, Houston, TX 77052 (SAN 289-7091) Tel 713-621-4984.

Word Merchant Pr, *(Word Merchant Press; 0-931482),* 40 Clinton St., No. 6C, Brooklyn, NY 11201 (SAN 265-4113).

Word Ministries Inc, *(Word Ministries Inc.; 0-9613051),* P.O. Box 145, Greenville, SC 29602 (SAN 294-295X) Tel 912-746-3223; Dist. by: First Presbyterian Church, 682 Mulberry St., Macon, GA 31201 (SAN 200-4550).

Word of Life
See Servant

Word of Mouth, *(Word of Mouth Pr.; 0-910027),* Box 824, Yonkers, NY 10701 (SAN 240-8937) Tel 212-519-6325; Dist. by: Baker & Taylor Co., Eastern Div., 50 Kirby Ave., Somerville, NJ 08876 (SAN 169-4901); Dist. by: Quality Books, 918 Sherwood Dr., Lake Bluff, IL 60044-2204 (SAN 169-2127).

Word Picture Prod, *(Word Picture Productions; 0-937865),* 5859 Brighton Pl., New Orleans, LA 70114 (SAN 659-6053) Tel 504-393-2761.

Word Play DC, *(Word Play; 0-938761),* P.O. Box 5810, Washington, DC 20016 (SAN 661-6739) Tel 202-244-6631; 4537 44th St., NW, Washington, DC 20016 (SAN 661-6747).

Word Power, *(Word Power, Inc.; 0-934832),* Lockbox 17034, Seattle, WA 98107 (SAN 213-3881) Tel 206-782-1437.

Word Serv, *(Word Services & Pied Pubns. Publishing Co.; 0-918626),* 1927 S. 26th St., Lincoln, NE 68502 (SAN 210-5519).

Word Store, *(Word Store; 0-934961),* Div. of Legal Education Ltd., 1047 Emmet St., Charlottesville, VA 22905 (SAN 695-0515) Tel 804-971-4741.

Word Weavers, *(Word Weavers; 0-9615605),* P.O. Box 8742, Minneapolis, MN 55408 (SAN 695-2305) Tel 612-824-9243.

Word Wheel, *(Word Wheel Books, Inc.; 0-913700),* 181 Stanford Ave., Menlo Park, CA 94025 (SAN 203-1868) Tel 415-854-2496.

Word Works, *(Word Works, Inc.; 0-915380),* P.O. Box 42164, Washington, DC 20015 (SAN 293-4426) Tel 202-554-3014.

Wordcraft MD, *(Wordcrafter Pubns.; 0-941448),* 15804 White Rock Rd., Gaithersburg, MD 20878 (SAN 239-0590) Tel 301-948-2539.

Worden Pr, *(Worden Pr.; 0-914821),* Main St., Brookfield, NY 13314-0010 (SAN 289-4718) Tel 315-899-3366.

Wordoctor
See Word Doctor

Wordpix Serv, *(Wordpix Services; 0-9615971),* 1379 Biscayne Way, Haslett, MI 48840 (SAN 697-2616) Tel 517-339-9357.

Wordpower, *(Wordpower; 0-915257),* 637-C Shalimar Dr., Costa Mesa, CA 92627 (SAN 290-0629) Tel 714-642-2142.

Words Living Minis, *(Words for Living Ministries Inc.; 0-934527),* 102 W. Carlisle St., Marion, KY 42064 (SAN 693-8477) Tel 502-965-5060.

Words Pr, *(Words Press; 0-9607390),* P.O. Box 1935, Beaverton, OR 97075 (SAN 239-7951).

Wordscope Assoc
See Wordscope Inc

Wordscope Inc, *(Wordscope, Inc.; 0-930121),* 8040 Floral Ave., Suite 304, Skokie, IL 60077 (SAN 670-3194) Tel 312-677-0506; Orders to: P.O. Box 1594, Skokie, IL 60076 (SAN 214-204X) Tel 312-677-0506; Dist. by: Bloch Pub. Co., 19 W. 21st St., New York, NY 10010 (SAN 169-2124) Tel 212-989-9104; Dist. by: Jonathan David Co., 68-22 Eliot Ave., Middle Village, NY 11379 (SAN 662-2445) Tel 718-456-8611.

Wordshop Pubns
See G S Pubs

Wordsmith
See Wordsmith Pubns

WordSmith Inc, *(WordSmith, Inc.; 0-936295),* 806 Mullins Hill Dr., Huntsville, AL 35802 (SAN 697-970X) Tel 205-535-4033P.O. Box 16021, Huntsville, AL 35802 (SAN 662-3956).

Wordsmith Pub
See Wrdsmith Pubns

Wordsmith Pubns, *(Wordsmith Pubns.),* 3317 Mayfield Ave., San Bernardino, CA 92405 (SAN 219-1032). Do not confuse with Wordsmith Pubns., Charlotte, NC.

Wordsmiths, *(Wordsmiths, The; 0-9606108),* P.O. Box 2231, Evergreen, CO 80439 (SAN 216-8715) Tel 303-674-8017.

Wordspinner Pr, *(Wordspinner Pr.; 0-939043),* 752 E. 1700 S., Salt Lake City, UT 84105 (SAN 662-6483) Tel 801-484-0863; Dist. by: Sounds of Zion, 5180 S. 300 W, Unit U, Murray, UT 84107 (SAN 200-7525).

†**Wordtree,** *(Wordtree, The; 0-936312),* 10876 Bradshaw, Overland Park, KS 66210-1148 (SAN 214-1752) Tel 913-469-1010; *CIP.*

World View Pr, *(World View Press; 0-931610),* P.O. Box 15, Fort Lee, NJ 07024 (SAN 686-1598).

†**World View Pubs,** *(World View Pubs.; 0-89567),* 46 W. 21st St., New York, NY 10010 (SAN 223-8764) Tel 212-255-0352; *CIP.*

World Vision Intl, *(World Vision International; 0-918261),* 919 W. Huntington Dr., Monrovia, CA 91016 (SAN 225-4719) Tel 818-303-8811.

World Wide
See Island Herit-Wrldwide Dist

World Wide Mini, *(World Wide Ministry of Deliverance, Inc.; 0-9612676),* 104 S. Main, Hersey, MI 49639 (SAN 289-4769) Tel 616-796-5958.

World Wide OR, *(World Wide Publishing Corp.; 0-930294),* P.O. Box 105, Ashland, OR 97520 (SAN 207-4818) Tel 503-482-3800.

World Wide Prods, *(World Wide Products; 0-934062),* 740 Pine St., San Francisco, CA 94108 (SAN 212-8721) Tel 415-391-6324.

World Wide Pubs, *(World Wide Publications; 0-89066),* 1303 Hennepin Ave., Minneapolis, MN 55403 (SAN 203-185X) Tel 612-333-0940.

World-Wide Tampa, *(World-Wide Pubns.; 0-911977),* P.O. Box 24339, Tampa, FL 33623 (SAN 276-9492) Tel 813-858-6034.

World Without War Pubns, *(World Without War Council; 0-912018),* 421 S. Wabash, Chicago, IL 60605 (SAN 203-2805) Tel 312-663-4250.

World Yesterday, *(World of Yesterday, The; 0-936505),* Rte. 3, Box 263H, Waynesville, NC 28786 (SAN 698-0597) Tel 704-648-5647.

Worlds Wonder, *(Worlds of Wonder; 1-55578),* 4209 Technology Dr., Fremont, CA 94538 (SAN 699-993X) Tel 415-659-4300.

Worldwatch Inst, *(Worldwatch Institute; 0-916468),* 1776 Massachusetts Ave., NW, Washington, DC 20036 (SAN 209-2727) Tel 202-452-1999.

Worldwest Invest, *(Worldwide Investment & Tax Management Service, Inc.; 0-930891),* P.O. Box 18414-123, Las Vegas, NV 89114 (SAN 677-8240) Tel 702-735-3658.

Worldwide Furbearer Con *Imprint of Unipub*

Worldwide Travel, *(Worldwide Travel & Tourism Ctr.; 0-9690625),* 3 Roosevelt Terr., Plattsburgh, NY 12901 (SAN 696-5601). Do not confuse with Worldwide Travel Series, Santa Barbara, CA.

Wormhoudt, *(Wormhoudt, Arthur; 0-916358),* William Penn College, Oskaloosa, IA 52577 (SAN 207-5547) Tel 515-673-3091.

Wormwood Pr, *(Wormwood Pr.; 0-937523),* P.O. Box 8125, Calabasas, CA 91302-8125 (SAN 659-1434) Tel 213-455-1791.

Wormwood Rev, *(Wormwood Review Pr.; 0-935390),* P.O. Box 8840, Stockton, CA 95208-0840 (SAN 209-8113) Tel 209-466-8231.

Worth, *(Worth Pubs., Inc.; 0-87901),* 33 Irving Pl., New York, NY 10003 (SAN 205-5546) Tel 212-475-6000.

Worth Co
See H S Worth

Worth Print
See Worthprinting

Worthington Co
See M & W Inc

Worthprinting, *(Worthprinting Pubs.; 0-9609734),* 1791 D Rolling Hills Dr., Twinsburg, OH 44087 (SAN 670-6762) Tel 216-425-9571.

Worzalla Pub
See Wiide Pubns Co

WOS, *(Wells of Salvation),* 6821 SR 366, Huntsville, OH 43324 (SAN 217-1414).

Wounded Coot, *(Wounded Coot Greetings; 0-935583),* 1825 15th Ave. SE No., 205, St. Cloud, MN 56301 (SAN 695-796X) Tel 612-363-5771; P.O. Box 418, St. Cloud, MN 56374 (SAN 696-5156).

WOW Inc, *(Wider Opportunities for Women; 0-934966),* 1325 G St., NW, Lower Level, Washington, DC 20005 (SAN 213-4047) Tel 202-638-3143.

WPL Assocs, *(WPL Assocs., Inc.; 0-9605442),* Affil. of Construction Industry Press, 1105-G Spring St., Silver Spring, MD 20910 (SAN 662-4375) Tel 301-589-8588.

WPL Assocs
See Constr Ind Pr

WPTI, *(Wildlife & Preservation Trust International, Inc.),* Affil. of Jersey Wildlife Preservation Trust, 34th St. & Girard Ave., Philadelphia, PA 19104 (SAN 260-3306) Tel 215-222-3636.

Wrdsmith Pubns, *(Wordsmith Pubns.; 0-9615608),* 1600 La Salle St., Charlotte, NC 28216 (SAN 695-8257) Tel 704-536-6558. Do not confuse with Wordsmith Pubns., San Bernardino, CA.

Wredco Pr, *(Wredco Pr.; 0-931705),* Div. of Writing & Editing Consultants, P.O. Box 3387, Flagstaff, AZ 86003 (SAN 683-7476) Tel 602-526-4941; Toll free: 800-423-5819 (Arizona only).

Wreden, *(Wreden, William P.; 0-9600574),* P.O. Box 56, Palo Alto, CA 94302 (SAN 123-4048) Tel 415-325-6851.

Wright-Armstead, *(Wright-Armstead; 0-931505),* 2410 Barker Ave., Suite 14-G, Bronx, NY 10467 (SAN 686-158X) Tel 212-654-9445.

Wright Group, *(Wright Group, The; 0-940156; 1-55624),* Div. of Thomas C. Wright, Inc., 10949 Technology Pl., San Diego, CA 92127 (SAN 201-9884) Tel 619-487-8820; Toll free: 800-523-2371; Toll free: 800-331-4524 (In California).

Wright Hand, *(Wright Hand Book Keeping; 0-9616960),* 15640 Alum Rock Ave., San Jose, CA 95127 (SAN 661-8138) Tel 408-258-0841.

Wright Pr, *(Wright Pr., The; 0-915263),* P.O. Box 94, Paris, TX 75460 (SAN 289-9159) Tel 214-785-4060.

Wright-PSG
See PSG Pub Co

Wright Pub, *(Wright, Curtis, Publishing; 0-935249),* 1019 University Ave., Honolulu, HI 96826 (SAN 695-8060) Tel 808-942-2928.

Wright Pub VA, *(Wright Publishing Co.; 0-9617119),* 205 68th St., Virginia Beach, VA 23451 (SAN 662-801X) Tel 804-422-4921. Do not confuse with other companies with the same name in Atlanta, GA, and Costa Mesa, CA.

Wright R E, *(Wright, Richard E.; 0-9604210),* Dist. by: Caucasian Rugs, 5666 Northcumberland St., Pittsburgh, PA 15217 (SAN 276-8615) Tel 412-422-0300.

Wrinkles, *(Wrinkles; 0-9616463),* 48 Pulliam Dr., Pleasanton, TX 78064 (SAN 659-3771) Tel 512-569-5751.

Writ Pr, *(Writ Pr.; 0-914653),* P.O. Drawer 1970, Decatur, GA 30031-1970 (SAN 289-6508) Tel 404-377-3200.

Write-On Creations, *(Write-On Creations, Inc.; 0-9611916),* 15801 Providence Dr. No. 2C, Southfield, MI 48075 (SAN 286-2204) Tel 313-569-1446.

Write Protect, *(Write Protect Publishing, Co.; 0-935393),* 135 Charles St., Suite 4E, New York, NY 10014 (SAN 695-7897) Tel 212-243-7212.

Write Staff
See Write Stuff

Write Stuff, *(Write Stuff, The; 0-9613899),* 3512 NE 51st St. 4, Vancouver, WA 98661 (SAN 678-9161) Tel 206-687-5171.

Write to Sell, *(Write to Sell; 0-9605078),* Div. of Communication Unlimited, P.O. Box 1001, Carpinteria, CA 93013 (SAN 215-7187) Tel 805-684-2469.

Write Words, *(Write Words, Inc., The; 0-938597),* P.O. Box 6446, Arlington, VA 22206 (SAN 661-1478); 1440 S. Greenbrier St., Arlington, VA 22206 (SAN 661-1486) Tel 703-820-5019.

Write Your Life, *(Write for Your Life; 0-9616259),* 3750 Estero Blvd., Ft. Myers Beach, FL 33931 (SAN 658-7372) Tel 813-765-1904.

†**Writer,** *(Writer, Inc.; 0-87116),* 120 Boylston St., Boston, MA 02116 (SAN 203-2791) Tel 617-423-3157; *CIP.*

Writer Serv FL, *(Writer's Service, Inc.; 0-911229),* P.O. Box 152, Miami Springs, FL 33166 (SAN 276-9654).

Writers & Readers, *(Writers & Readers Publishing Inc.),* c/o W.W. Norton Co., 500 Fifth Ave., New York, NY 10110 (SAN 216-4795) Tel 212-354-5500.

†**Writers Digest,** *(Writers Digest Bks.; 0-89879; 0-911654),* Div. of F&W Publications, Inc., 9933 Alliance Rd., Cincinnati, OH 45242 (SAN 212-064X) Tel 513-984-0717; Toll free: 800-543-4644; *CIP.*

Writers Forum, *(Writers' Forum; 0-9602992),* Affil. of University of Colorado at Colorado Springs, P.O. Box 7150, Colorado Springs, CO 80933-7150 (SAN 213-392X) Tel 303-599-4023.

Writers Guide Pubns *Imprint of Gabriel Hse*

Writers Help, *(Writer's Helpers, The; 0-9603666),* 422 Perkins Bldg., 1103 A St., Tacoma, WA 98402 (SAN 221-6442) Tel 206-272-1609; Dist. by: Quality Books, 918 Sherwood Dr., Lake Bluff, IL 60044-2204 (SAN 169-2127).

Writers Pr, *(Writers Press; 0-931536),* Box 805, 2000 Connecticut Ave., Washington, DC 20008 (SAN 212-2030) Tel 202-232-0440.

†**Writers Pub Coop,** *(Writers Publishing Cooperative; 0-931751),* 220 Canal St., No. 43, San Rafael, CA 94901 (SAN 687-6854); *CIP.*

Writers Pub Hse, *(Writer's Publishing House; 0-9606510),* 615 N.E. 15th Court, Ft. Lauderdale, FL 33304 (SAN 217-2186) Tel 305-764-4824.

Writers W Alameda, *(Writers West of Alameda, Inc.; 0-9616107),* P.O. Box 2692, Alameda, CA 94501 (SAN 699-6795) Tel 415-522-5038.

Writers Workshp, *(Writer's Workshop, Inc.; 0-915543),* 1117 W. Broad St., Stratford, CT 06497 (SAN 291-4808) Tel 203-377-0024.

†**Writing,** *(Writing Works Inc.; 0-916076),* 3441 Thorndyke Ave. W., Seattle, WA 98119 (SAN 209-4118) Tel 206-282-9988; *CIP.*

Writing & More, *(Writing & More; 0-9614666),* Affil. of Accurate Writing & More, P.O. Box 1164, Northampton, MA 01061 (SAN 692-4786) Tel 413-586-2388.

Writing Con, *(Writing Consultant, The; 0-911683),* P.O. Box 20244, Finance Sta., New York, NY 10025 (SAN 264-5122) Tel 212-864-6415.

Writing Consult, *(Writing Consultants; 0-931295),* Div. of Microlytics, Inc., 300 Main St., East Rochester, NY 11445 (SAN 681-7289) Tel 716-377-0130; Toll free: 800-828-6293.

Writing Soft Intl, *(Writing Software International; 0-939227),* 110 E. Broadway, Suite 600, Missoula, MT 59802 (SAN 662-6181) Tel 406-543-3141.

Written Word, *(Written Word, The),* 6735 The Paseo, Kansas City, MO 64132 (SAN 295-0278).

WRK Prods, *(WRK Productions; 0-939579),* Subs. of Sutherland Productions, Inc., P.O. Box 7127, Eugene, OR 97401 (SAN 663-4826); 2175 Debra Dr., Springfield, OR 97477 (SAN 663-4834) Tel 503-343-3771.

Wrld Coun Churches, *(World Council of Churches),* 475 Riverside Dr., Rm. 1062, New York, NY 10115 (SAN 234-3207) Tel 212-870-2533.

Wrld Info NY, *(World Information Corp., The; 0-916006),* 1 World Trade Ctr., Suite 7800, New York, NY 10048 (SAN 208-1903) Tel 212-432-8072.

Wrld Link Bks, *(World Link Bks.; 0-932093),* 919 N. 19th St., Colorado Springs, CO 80904 (SAN 686-4643) Tel 303-633-7525.

Wrld Mission Crusade, *(World Mission Crusade; 0-938351),* 5930 18th St., NE, St. Petersburg, FL 33703-1739 (SAN 661-0676) Tel 813-527-5205.

Wrld-Wide Bks, *(World-Wide Bks.; 0-9614296),* 2027 Grand Canal Blvd. 20, Stockton, CA 95207 (SAN 687-4606) Tel 209-957-9601.

Wrld Wide Trade, *(World Wide Trade Service; 0-911652),* P.O. Box 283, Medina, WA 98039 (SAN 204-9953).

Wrld Wisdom Bks, *(World Wisdom Books; 0-941532),* P.O. Box 2682, Bloomington, IN 47402-2682 (SAN 239-1406) Tel 812-332-1663; Dist. by: Bookpeople, 2929 Fifth St., Berkeley, CA 94710 (SAN 168-9517) Tel 415-549-3030; Dist. by: New Leaf, 1020 White St., SW, Atlanta, GA 30310 (SAN 169-1449) Tel 404-755-2665; Dist. by: Great Tradition, The, 750 Adrian Way, Suite 111, San Rafael, CA 94903 (SAN 200-5743) Tel 415-492-9382.

Wrldwide Trav SB, *(Worldwide Travel Series; 0-938653),* 133 E. de la Guerra, Santa Barbara, CA 93101 (SAN 661-6291) Tel 805-963-3180. Do not confuse with Worldwide Travel & Tourism Ctr., Plattsburgh, NY.

Wrobleski, (Wrobleski; 0-935585), 5124 Grove St., Minneapolis, MN 55436-2481 (SAN 695-8087) Tel 612-929-6448.

WRP, (Water Resources Pubns.; 0-918334), P.O. Box 2841, Littleton, CO 80161 (SAN 209-9136) Tel 303-790-1836.

Wry-Bred Pr, (Wry-Bred Pr.; 0-9606190), 10 Waterside Plaza, Suite 20B, New York, NY 10010 (SAN 220-3138) Tel 212-689-5473; Orders to: P.O. Box 1454, Madison Square Sta., New York, NY 10159 (SAN 662-1945).

Wry Idea, (Wry Idea Co.; 0-9606814), 3150 Ducommun, San Diego, CA 92122 (SAN 223-2049) Tel 619-452-7465.

WS Imprint of **Pyramid Pubns**

WSP, (Washington Square Pr., Inc.; 0-671), Div. of Simon & Schuster, Inc., 1230 Ave. of the Americas, New York, NY 10020 (SAN 206-9784) Tel 212-246-2121; Toll free: 800-223-2336; Orders to: 200 Old Tappan Rd., Old Tappan, NJ 07675 (SAN 662-1821) Tel 201-767-5000. Imprints: ANTA (A N T A Series of Distinguished Plays).(ANTA Series of Distinguished Plays); CC (Collateral Classics Series); RE (Readers Enrichment Series).

WSU Bur Bus Res, (Wayne State University, Bureau of Business Research, Schl. of Business Admin.; 0-942650), Wayne State Univ., Schl of Business Admin., Prentis Bldg. 209, Detroit, MI 48202 (SAN 239-9512) Tel 313-577-4213.

Wunderle Outdoor, (Wunderle Outdoor Books; 0-9611162), 86 Eight Mile Prairie Rd., Carterville, IL 62918 (SAN 283-426X).

WV Business Pub, (West Virginia Business Publishing Corp.; 0-937683), P.O. Box 5173, Charleston, WV 25361 (SAN 659-3666) Tel 304-345-8283; 1614 Washington St. E., Charleston, WV 25361 (SAN 659-3674).

WV Highlands, (West Virginia Highlands Conservancy; 0-9616553), 1206 Virginia St., E, Suite 201, Charleston, WV 25301 (SAN 659-5480) Tel 304-645-6028.

WV Pubs
See World View Pubs

WV Univ Coop Ext, (West Virginia Univ. Cooperative Extension Service; 0-9616194), Div. of West Virginia Univ. Pr., 506 Knapp Hall, Morgantown, WV 26506-6031 (SAN 699-9522) Tel 304-293-4221.

WV Womens Found, (West Virginia Women's Foundation; 0-9617031), P.O. Box 5069, Charleston, WV 25311 (SAN 662-8761); WB-9 Capitol Complex, Charleston, WV 25305 (SAN 662-877X) Tel 304-348-0070.

WWAI, (Who's Who in Artificial Intelligence; 0-937287), P.O. Box 620098, Woodside, CA 94062 (SAN 659-106X) Tel 415-493-7905; 275 Ventura Blvd., Apt. 31, Palo Alto, CA 94305 (SAN 659-1078).

WWF Bks, (WWF Bks.; 0-9616263), Div. of Titan Sports, Inc., P.O. Box 4520, Greenwich, CT 06830 (SAN 658-3687); 81 Holly Hill Ln., Greenwich, CT 06830 (SAN 658-3695) Tel 203-869-4100.

WWH Pr, (WWH Press; 0-939240), 41 Hampton Rd., Scarsdale, NY 10583 (SAN 216-5163) Tel 914-725-3632.

WWIR Imprint of **Unipub**

WWUCEAS, (Western Washington Univ., Ctr. for East Asian Studies; 0-914584), Bellingham, WA 98225 (SAN 203-218X) Tel 206-676-3041.

WWW Pubs, (WWW Pubs.; 0-9613654), 4501 Camino Del Obispo, Tucson, AZ 85718 (SAN 670-7815) Tel 602-299-6105; P.O. Box 42224, Tucson, AZ 85733 (SAN 670-7823).

WWWWW Info Serv, (WWWWW Information Services; 0-912688), P.O. Box 10046, Rochester, NY 14610 (SAN 203-2783) Tel 716-482-2022.

Wychwood Pr, (Wychwood Pr.; 0-932386), P.O. Box 10, College Park, MD 20740 (SAN 211-7711) Tel 301-779-1569.

†Wyden, (Wyden Books; 0-87223), Div. of P.E.I. Books, Inc., P.O. Box 151, Ridgefield, CT 06877 (SAN 210-9794) Tel 203-438-9631; Dist. by: Harper & Row Pubs., Inc., Keystone Industrial Park, Scranton, PA 18512 (SAN 215-3742); CIP.

Wyden Imprint of **McKay**

wY'east Consulting, (wY'east Consulting; 0-9616865), 6917 SW 33rd, Portland, OR 97219 (SAN 661-1680) Tel 503-244-0902.

Wyndham Hall, (Wyndham Hall Pr.; 0-932269; 1-55605), P.O. Box 877, 52857 C.R. 21, Bristol, IN 46507 (SAN 686-6743) Tel 219-848-7920.

Wyndham Hse, (Wyndham Hse.; 0-911755), 4740 Von Karman, Newport Beach, CA 92660 (SAN 263-9793) Tel 714-851-1668.

Wyndham Pub, (Wyndham Publishing Co.; 0-938775), 223 Pearl St., Sulphur, LA 70663-4453 (SAN 661-8162) Tel 318-625-3111.

Wynnehaven, (Wynnehaven Publishing Co.; 0-9601476), 212 Ocean St., Beach Haven, NJ 08008 (SAN 210-1416) Tel 609-492-3601.

Wyo Writers, (Wyoming Writers, Inc.; 0-917557), 2545 E. Ninth St., Casper, WY 82609 (SAN 657-1239) Tel 307-235-6248.

†Wyoming Law Inst, (Wyoming Law Institute; 0-915876), P.O. Box 3035, University Sta., Laramie, WY 82071 (SAN 207-6926); CIP.

Wyoming Pub, (Wyoming Publishing; 0-913701), c/o Cheyenne Frontier Days, P.O. Box 2666, Cheyenne, WY 82003 (SAN 286-0880) Tel 307-634-3321.

Wyoming Specialities
See Powder River

Wyoming State Press, (Wyoming State Museums & Historical Department; 0-943398), Barrett Bldg., Cheyenne, WY 82002 (SAN 240-8104) Tel 307-777-7518.

Wyvern, (Wyvern Pubns.; 0-9602404), P.O. Box 188, Dumfries, VA 22026 (SAN 215-9872) Tel 703-670-3527.

X-Log, (X-Log Corp.; 0-9603162), 393 Main St., Catskill, NY 12414 (SAN 212-3290) Tel 518-943-4771.

X Press Pr
See Downtown Poets

Xanadu Ent, (Xanadu Enterprises; 0-933638), 2012 Grove Ave., Richmond, VA 23220 (SAN 213-4063).

Xavier Moreau, (Moreau, Xavier, Inc.; 0-937950), 437 Madison Ave., New York, NY 10022 (SAN 264-2174) Tel 212-355-1410.

Xavier Pr, (Xavier Press; 0-912977), 3122 Jerome, Dallas, TX 75223 (SAN 283-4057) Tel 214-826-5835.

Xenos Bks, (Xenos Bks.; 0-934724), 13620 Normandie Ave., Gardena, CA 90249 (SAN 213-4071) Tel 213-538-5000.

Xerox Ed Pubns
See Field Pubns

Xerox Learning
See Learn Int

XPrime, (XPrime Corp.; 0-937185), 10835 Santa Monica Blvd., Suite 204A, Los Angeles, CA 90025 (SAN 658-537X) Tel 213-470-4663.

XyloPub Ltd, (XyloPub, Ltd.; 0-9616862), P.O. Box 1167, Edenton, NC 27932-1167 (SAN 661-5880); 309 N. Granville St., Apt. 1, Edenton, NC 27932 (SAN 661-5899) Tel 919-482-7021.

Y A Salaam, (Salaam, Yusef A.; 0-9613032), 167 W. 136th, Suite 5, New York, NY 10030 (SAN 287-3001).

Y C B A C, (You Can Be a Classic, Inc.; 0-939285), P.O. Box 5369, Louisville, KY 40205 (SAN 662-5169); 1701 Sulgrave Rd., Louisville, KY 40205 (SAN 662-5177) Tel 502-454-6699.

Y Cent Inter Area, (Yale Center for International & Area Studies; 0-934611), P.O. Box 13A Yale Station, New Haven, CT 06520 (SAN 693-8825) Tel 203-436-3416.

Y V Bissette, (Bissette, Yoma V.), Dist. by: Historical Research Assocs., Box 4275, Bisbee, AZ 85603 (SAN 240-1355).

Y W A W C E, (Young Woman's Auxiliary of the Woman's Club of Evanston; 0-9613115), 1702 Chicago Ave., Evanston, IL 60201 (SAN 294-1198); 1204 Milford St., Evanston, IL 60202 (SAN 294-1201) Tel 312-475-0932.

Y Z Pubns, (Y.Z. Pubns.; 0-9614730), P.O. Box 46033, Los Angeles, CA 90046 (SAN 692-6207) Tel 213-654-9782.

Yacht Imp, (Yacht Import Services; 0-935471), P.O. Box 187, LaPorte, TX 77571 (SAN 695-8028) Tel 713-471-8433.

Yacht Owners, (Yacht Owners Register, Inc., The; 0-915953), 275 Washington St., Newton, MA 02158-1630 (SAN 294-1155) Tel 617-536-8534.

Yaker Enviro, (Yaker Environmental Systems, Inc.; 0-937055), P.O. Box 18, Stanton, NJ 08885 (SAN 697-7618) Tel 201-735-7056; Box 157 Hamden Rd., Annandale, NJ 08801 (SAN 658-2966) Tel 201-735-7056.

Yale Art Gallery, (Yale Univ. Art Gallery; 0-89467), Div. of Yale University, 2006 Yale Sta., New Haven, CT 06520 (SAN 209-6927) Tel 203-436-0574.

Yale Russian, (Yale Russsian & East European Pubns.; 0-936586), P.O. Box 13A ,85 Trumbull St., New Haven, CT 06520 (SAN 283-9806); Dist. by Slavica Pubs., Inc., P.O. Box 14388, Columbus, OH 43214 (SAN 208-8576) Tel 614-268-4002.

Yale U Anthro, (Yale Univ. Pubns. in Anthropology; 0-913516), Subs. of Yale University, P.O. Box 2114, Yale Sta., New Haven, CT 06520 (SAN 205-5562) Tel 203-436-7807.

Yale U Lib, (Yale Univ. Library Pubns.; 0-8457), P.O. Box 1603A Yale Sta., New Haven, CT 06520 (SAN 202-1226) Tel 203-436-8336.

Yale U Observ, (Yale University, Observatory; 0-914753), 260 Whitney Ave., P.O. Box 6666, New Haven, CT 06511 (SAN 276-878X) Tel 203-436-3460.

†Yale U Pr, (Yale Univ. Pr.; 0-300), 302 Temple St., New Haven, CT 06520 (SAN 203-2740) Tel 203-436-7584; Orders to: 92A Yale Sta., New Haven, CT 06520 (SAN 203-2759) Tel 203-436-7582; CIP.

Yale U SE Asia, (Yale Univ. Southeast Asia Studies; 0-938692), Box 13A, Yale University, New Haven, CT 06520 (SAN 206-0027) Tel 203-436-8897.

†Yama Pub, (Yama Publishing Co.; 0-937290), 2266 Fifth Ave., No. 136, New York, NY 10037 (SAN 219-984X) Tel 212-283-5220; CIP.

Yankee Bks, (Yankee Bks.; 0-911658; 0-89909), Div. of Yankee Publishing, Inc., Main St., Dublin, NH 03444 (SAN 293-4434) Tel 603-563-8111; Toll free: 800-258-5327; Orders to: Yankee Bks., Trade Sales Div., Depot Sq., Peterborough, NH 03458 (SAN 293-4442) Tel 603-924-3807.

Yankee Bookmen
See Heritage Bk

Yankee Group, (Yankee Group, The), 89 Broad St., 14th Flr., Boston, MA 02110 (SAN 223-8772) Tel 617-542-0100.

Yankee Inc
See Yankee Bks

Yankee Ped Bkshop, (Yankee Peddler Bookshop; 0-918426), 4299 E. Lake Rd., Box 118, Pultneyville, NY 14538 (SAN 209-925X) Tel 315-589-2063.

Yankee Peddler, (Yankee Peddler Book Co.; 0-911660), Drawer O, Southampton, NY 11968 (SAN 205-5570) Tel 516-283-1612.

Yara Pr, (Yara Press; 0-913038), P.O. Box 1295, Mendocino, CA 95460 (SAN 205-5589) Tel 707-937-0866.

Yardbird Wing, (Yardbird Wing Editions; 0-918412), Dist. by: Yardbird Pub. Co., Inc., P.O. Box 2370, Station A, Berkeley, CA 94702 (SAN 208-9343) Tel 415-841-6500.

Yates Vent, (Yates Ventures; 0-917195), 3350 W. Bayshore Rd. Suite 201, Palo Alto, CA 94303 (SAN 655-9190) Tel 415-424-8844.

YB Imprint of **Dell**

Y'bird
See Reed & Youngs Quilt

†Ye Galleon, (Ye Galleon Pr.; 0-87770), P.O. Box 287, Fairfield, WA 99012 (SAN 205-5597) Tel 509-283-2422; CIP.

Ye Olde Print, (Ye Olde Printery; 0-932606), 5815 Cherokee Dr., Cincinnati, OH 45243 (SAN 213-408X) Tel 513-561-4338.

†Year Bk Med, (Year Bk. Medical Pubs., Inc.; 0-8151), Subs. of Times Mirror, 35 E. Wacker Dr., Chicago, IL 60601 (SAN 205-5600) Tel 312-726-9733; Toll free: 800-621-9262; CIP.

Yearround Pr, (Yearround Pr.; 0-9615262), Div. of Mary Ann Trombold Enterprises, P.O. Box 371, Mercer Island, WA 98040 (SAN 695-0485) Tel 206-232-7023.

Yellow Bk PA, (Yellow Book of Pennsylvania, Inc.; 0-9604612), 1 Fairway Plaza, P.O. Box 315, Huntingdon Valley, PA 19006 (SAN 219-9858) Tel 215-938-0600.

Yellow Jacket, (Yellow Jacket Pr.; 0-915626), 1101 N. Lewis, Stillwater, OK 74075 (SAN 207-3048) Tel 405-743-2566.

Yellow Moon, *(Yellow Moon Pr.; 0-938756),* P. O. Box 1316, Cambridge, MA 02238 (SAN 216-4809) Tel 617-628-7894.

†Yellow Pr, *(Yellow Press; 0-916328),* 2394 Blue Island Ave., Chicago, IL 60608 (SAN 207-9631); Dist. by: Small Press Dist., Inc., 1814 San Pablo Ave., Berkeley, CA 94702 (SAN 204-5826) Tel 415-549-3336; *CIP.*

Yellow Rose Fin, *(Yellow Rose Financial Corp.; 0-930631),* 221 N. Monroe St., San Angelo, TX 76901 (SAN 683-4280).

Yellow Rose Pr, *(Yellow Rose Pr.; 0-912854),* P.O. Box 160221, Irving, TX 75016 (SAN 203-4271) Tel 214-233-6610.

Yellow Springs, *(Yellow Springs Computer Camp, Inc.; 0-912529),* P.O. Box 292, Yellow Springs, OH 45387 (SAN 265-3087) Tel 513-767-7717.

Yellow Stone Pr, *(Yellowstone Pr.; 0-9617253),* Div. of Dan Bailey, P.O. Box 1019, Livingston, MT 59047 (SAN 663-5733); 209 W. Park St., Livingston, MT 59047 (SAN 663-5741) Tel 406-222-1673.

Yellow Umb Pr, *(Yellow Umbrella Press; 0-942654),* 501 Main St., Chatham, MA 02633 (SAN 223-1018).

Yellowstone Lib, *(Yellowstone Library & Museum Assn., The; 0-934948),* Yellowstone Park, WY 82190 (SAN 214-4921).

Yerba Buena
See Taylor & Ng

YES Bks Imprint of Youth Ed

Yes Inc, *(Yes! Inc.; 0-936119),* 1035 31st St., NW, Washington, DC 20007 (SAN 223-064X) Tel 202-338-6969; Dist. by: Random Hse., Inc., 201 E. 50th St., New York, NY 10022 (SAN 202-5507) Tel 212-872-8036.

Yes Intl *(Yes International; 0-936663),* 449 Portland Ave., St. Paul, MN 55102 (SAN 699-6787) Tel 612-224-0503.

Yes Pr Imprint of Down There Pr

Yesnaby Inc, *(Yesnaby Inc.; 0-9606262),* P.O. Box 213, RD 8, Danville, PA 17821 (SAN 220-3499) Tel 717-437-3488.

Yesnaby Pubs
See Yesnaby Inc

Yesod Pubs, *(Yesod Pubs.),* 75 Prospect Park W., Brooklyn, NY 11215 (SAN 211-8300) Tel 718-768-5591.

Yiddish Arch Pr, *(Yiddish Archivist Press; 0-942656),* 27 Halls Point Rd., Stonycreek, CT 06450 (SAN 239-9571) Tel 203-481-0888.

Yivo Inst, *(Yivo Institute for Jewish Research; 0-914512),* 1048 Fifth Ave., New York, NY 10028 (SAN 207-1614) Tel 212-535-6700.

YMCA USA, *(YMCA Program Store; 0-88035),* 1607 N. Market, Champaign, IL (SAN 662-1953).

Yng Peoples Pr, *(Young People's Pr.; 0-9606964),* Box 1005, Avon, CT 06001 (SAN 239-4022) Tel 203-677-6409.

Yo-Mark Prodn, *(Yo-Mark Production Co.; 0-9604607),* P.O. Box 765, Gettysburg, PA 17325 (SAN 691-8409) Tel 717-334-0751.

Yoder, *(Ida, Yoder; 0-9614083),* 180 Hall Drive, Wadsworth, OH 44281 (SAN 685-9291) Tel 216-336-0261.

Yoga, *(Yoga Pubn. Society; 0-911662),* P.O. Box 8885, Jacksonville, FL 32239-8885 (SAN 203-2724); Dist. by: Landau Bk. Co., Inc., 272 W. Park Ave., Long Beach, NY 11561 (SAN 201-064X); Dist. by: De Vorss & Company, P.O. Box 550, 1046 Princeton Dr., Marina del Rey, CA 90294 (SAN 200-4321).

Yoga Res Foun, *(Yoga Research Foundation; 0-934664),* 6111 SW 74th Ave., Miami, FL 33143 (SAN 209-0279) Tel 305-666-2006.

Yogi Gupta, *(Yogi Gupta New York Center; 0-911664),* 90-16 51st Ave., Elmhurst, NY 11373 (SAN 205-5619).

Yokefellow Pr, *(Yokefellow Press; 0-932970; 0-914005),* 230 College Ave., Richmond, IN 47374 (SAN 276-9336) Tel 317-962-6810.

Yoknapatawpha, *(Yoknapatawpha Pr.; 0-916242),* Box 248, Oxford, MS 38655 (SAN 213-7593) Tel 601-234-0909.

York Hse, *(York Hse.; 0-9615389),* 148 York Ave., Kensington, CA 94708 (SAN 276-9468) Tel 415-525-7167.

†York Pr, *(York Press, Inc.; 0-912752),* 2712 Mt. Carmel Rd., Parkton, MD 21120 (SAN 203-2708) Tel 301-343-1417; *CIP.*

†Yorke Med, *(Yorke Medical Bks.; 0-914316),* Div. of Technical Publishing, 875 Third Ave., New York, NY 10022 (SAN 207-155X) Tel 212-605-9620; Orders to: Box C-757, Brooklyn, NY 11205 (SAN 662-1961); *CIP.*

Yorkville Bk
See Kapitan Szabo

Yosemite D, *(Yosemite-Di-Maggio; 0-911819),* 618 Grand Ave., Oakland, CA 94610 (SAN 264-5173) Tel 415-839-9780; Dist. by: Bookpeople, 2929 Fifth Ave., Berkeley, CA 94710 (SAN 168-9517) Tel 415-549-3030; Dist. by: L & S Distributors, 480 Ninth St., San Francisco, CA 94103 (SAN 169-0213) Tel 415-861-6300.

Yosemite Natl Hist, *(Yosemite Natural History Assn.; 0-939666),* Box 545, Yosemite National Park, CA 95389 (SAN 225-2201) Tel 209-379-2646; Orders to: P.O. Box 230, El Portal, CA 95318 (SAN 662-197X) Tel 209-379-2646.

You Are Winner, *(You Are a Winner; 0-9615778),* 74 Basinside Way, Alameda, CA 94501 (SAN 696-6659) Tel 415-523-4109.

You Can Make It Ent, *(You Can Make It Enterprises; 0-9606328),* 121 Bank St., Grass Valley, CA 95945 (SAN 219-1040) Tel 415-947-1767.

You Can Pub, *(You Can Publishing; 0-916819),* 3219 Fourth St., N., Minneapolis, MN 55412 (SAN 654-505X) Tel 612-823-9044.

Young, *(Young, Thomas; 0-9614151),* P.O. Box 550, Bellaire, TX 77401 (SAN 686-418X) Tel 713-667-3356.

Young Creations
See New Boundary Design

Young Ideas, *(Young Ideas; 0-9616786),* 2928 Hill Dr., Troy, MI 48098 (SAN 660-9767) Tel 313-689-3618.

Young Life, *(Young Life National Services; 0-932856),* Box 520, Colorado Springs, CO 80901 (SAN 211-8319) Tel 303-473-4262.

Young People's Pr
See Yng Peoples Pr

Young Pine Pr, *(Young Pine Pr.; 0-9608280),* c/o Asian Multi-Media, 6036 Upland Terrace S., Seattle, WA 98118 (SAN 200-433X) Tel 206-344-7580.

Young Pr Idaho, *(Young Pr.; 0-9616273),* Rte. 4, Box 76, St. Maries, ID 83861 (SAN 658-4330) Tel 208-245-3645.

Young Womans
See Y W A W C E

Younique Pr, *(Younique Pr.; 0-9601920),* 2550 Long Lake Rd., St. Paul, MN 55112 (SAN 221-296X).

Your New Beginning, *(Your New Beginning; 0-9616892),* 10312 E. Freer St., Temple City, CA 91780 (SAN 661-6461) Tel 818-443-2637.

†Yourdon, *(Yourdon Pr.; 0-917072),* 1501 Broadway, New York, NY 10036 (SAN 208-2136) Tel 212-391-2828; Toll free: 800-223-2452; *CIP.*

Yours Truly, *(Yours Truly, Inc.; 0-932946),* Div. of Burdett Pubns., 5455 Garden Grove Blvd., Westminster, CA 92683 (SAN 295-1045); Toll free: 800-845-7076.

Youth Challenge, *(Youth Challenge Pub.; 0-9606116),* P.O. Box 4567, Topeka, KS 66604 (SAN 216-4817) Tel 913-478-3300.

Youth Ed, *(Youth Education Systems, Inc.; 0-87738),* Box 223, Scarborough Sta., Scarborough, NY 10510 (SAN 205-5635) Tel 212-599-8417. Imprints: YES Bks (YES Books).

Youth Mission, *(Youth with a Mission International; 0-9615534),* P.O. Box 4407, Kailua Kona, HI 96745 (SAN 695-8265) Tel 808-329-1621.

Youth Special, *(Youth Specialties; 0-910125),* 1224 Greenfield Dr., El Cajon, CA 92021 (SAN 211-8327) Tel 619-440-2333.

Yuchi Pines, *(Yuchi Pines Institute),* P.O. Box 319, Fort Mitchell, AL 36856 (SAN 239-5053).

Yuganta Pr, *(Yuganta Pr.; 0-938999),* 85 Midland Ave., Stamford, CT 06906 (SAN 662-541X) Tel 203-323-7160.

Yuletide Intl, *(Yuletide International; 0-911049),* 9665 Malad St., Boise, ID 83709 (SAN 264-5181) Tel 208-322-1260.

Yummy Designs, *(Yummy Designs; 0-936467),* P.O. Box 2033, Chino, CA 91708 (SAN 697-9718) Tel 714-591-5256; 12836 12th St., No. 44, Chino, CA 91710 (SAN 697-9726); Orders to: Character Medical Co., 390 Swift, South San Francisco, CA 94080 (SAN 698-2344).

YWCA, *(Young Women's Christian Assn., National Board),* 726 Broadway, New York, NY 10003 (SAN 207-9674) Tel 212-614-2700.

YWCA WA, *(Young Womens Christian Assn. of Seattle; 0-9615533),* 1118 Fifth Ave., Seattle, WA 98101 (SAN 695-8249) Tel 206-447-4855.

YWCO, *(Young Women's Christian Organization (YWCO); 0-9608282),* 201 St. Charles St., Baton Rouge, LA 70802 (SAN 240-4613).

Z Graphic Pubns, *(Z-Graphic Pubns.; 0-941572),* 833 Joost Ave., San Francisco, CA 94127 (SAN 239-3522) Tel 415-584-4048.

Z H Wright, *(Wright, Zelma H., Jr.),* 140 Briggs, Beaumont, TX 77707-2329 (SAN 209-133X) Tel 409-832-2308.

Z Main, *(Main, Zilpha P.; 0-9601584),* 2701 Wilshire Blvd. No. 809, Los Angeles, CA 90057 (SAN 222-0644) Tel 213-387-9762.

Z P Wesolowski, *(Wesolowski, Zdzislaw P.; 0-937527),* 3702 NE 171st St., Apt. 13, North Miami Beach, FL 33160 (SAN 695-1191) Tel 305-945-5087; Dist. by: Printing Services, Inc., 3249 NW 38th St., Miami, FL 33142 (SAN 200-7096) Tel 305-633-2571.

Z Pr, *(Z Pr., Inc.; 0-915990),* Calais, VT 05648 (SAN 289-0240); Dist. by: Inland Bks. Co., P.O. Box 261, 22 Hemingway Ave., East Haven, CT 06512 (SAN 200-4151) Tel 203-467-4257.

Zachry Pubns, *(Zachry Pubns.),* 502 E. N. 16th, Abilene, TX 79601 (SAN 203-1825) Tel 915-673-2356.

Zalo, *(Zalo Pubns. & Services, Inc.; 0-931200),* Dist. by: Frangipani Press, Div. of T.I.S. Enterprises, P.O. Box 669, 1928 Arlington Rd., Bloomington, IN 47402 (SAN 169-2313) Tel 812-332-3307.

Zalonka Pubns
See Spencer Inst

Zalozba Prometej, *(Zalozba Prometej; 0-934158),* P.O. Box 8391, New Orleans, LA 70182 (SAN 212-8462) Tel 504-283-7177.

Zamisdat Pr, *(Zamisdat Pr.; 0-934727),* P.O. Box 1255, Gracie Sta., New York, NY 10028 (SAN 694-1524) Tel 212-473-4888.

Zanel Pubns, *(Zanel Pubns.; 0-936914),* P.O. Box 255867, Sacramento, CA 95865-5867 (SAN 212-985X) Tel 916-973-8050.

Zaner-Bloser, *(Zaner-Bloser, Inc.; 0-88309),* Subs. of Highlights for Children, 2300 W. Fifth Ave., P.O. Box 16764, Columbus, OH 43216-6764 (SAN 282-5678) Tel 614-486-0221.

ZapoDel Inc, *(ZapoDel Inc.; 0-934545),* P.O. Box 1049, Del Mar, CA 92014 (SAN 693-8361) Tel 619-481-7337; Dist. by: Quality Books, Inc., 918 Sherwood Dr., Lake Bluff, IL 60044-2204 (SAN 169-2127) Tel 312-498-4000; Dist. by: Publishers Group West, 5855 Beaudry St., Emeryville, CA 94608 (SAN 202-8522) Tel 415-658-3453.

Zaram Promo, *(Zaram Promotional Concepts; 0-935395),* 1400 N. Lake Shore Dr., Chicago, IL 60610 (SAN 695-815X) Tel 312-943-2277.

Zarathustrotemo Pr, *(Zarathustrotemo Pr., The; 0-937581),* 601-2 Harwood Rd., Suite 172, Bedford, TX 76021 (SAN 658-8301) Tel 817-831-2586; 2900 Haltom Rd., Ft. Worth, TX 76117 (SAN 658-831X) Tel 817-831-2586.

Zarcon Pr, *(Zarcon Pr.; 0-9604916),* 2000 Allston Way, Berkeley, CA 94701 (SAN 658-8336); P.O. Box 428, Berkeley, CA 94701 (SAN 658-8344).

Zartscorp, *(Zartscorp, Inc. Books; 0-9605610),* 333 West End Ave., New York, NY 10023 (SAN 209-5017) Tel 212-724-5071.

Zebra, *(Zebra Bks.; 0-89083; 0-8217),* 475 Park Ave. S., New York, NY 10016 (SAN 207-9860) Tel 212-889-2299; Toll free: 800-221-2649; Dist. by: Simon & Schuster Mass Merchandise Sales Co., 1230 Ave. of the Americas, New York, NY 10020 (SAN 169-5835) Tel 212-245-6400.

Symbols/Abbreviations

NAME INDEX

The *Name Index* is arranged alphabetically and contains the following elements in the same sequence as listed, when applicable: company name; name abbreviation used in many of Bowker's bibliographies; International Standard Book Number prefix(es) (ISBN); Standard Address Number(s) (SAN); business affiliation; editorial address(es); telephone number(s); toll-free telephone number(s); ordering/distribution address(es); telephone number(s); and imprint(s) with their name abbreviation(s).

Cross-references are provided from imprints and variant names to the main company name.

Abingdon Pr. *(Abingdon; 0-687),* Div. of United Methodist Publishing Hse., 201 Eighth Ave., S., Nashville, TN 37202 (SAN 201-0054). Tel 615-749-6301; Toll-free: 800-251-3320; 1015 Visco Dr., Nashville, TN 37210 (SAN 699-9956). *Imprints:* Apex Books (Apex); Festival Books (Festival).
Apex Books *See* **Abingdon Press**

Names

Names

AFUA Enterprises, Inc., *(AFUA Ent; 0-918088),* P.O. Box 9026, General Lafayette Sta., Jersey City, NJ 07304 (SAN 210-1599) Tel 201-451-0599.

AG Pr., *(AG Pr),* 16th & Yuma, P.O. Box 1009, Manhattan, KS 66502 (SAN 204-7632) Tel 913-539-7558.

A Gentle Wind, *(Gentle Wind; 0-939065),* P.O. Box 3103, Albany, NY 12203; 186 Partridge St., Albany, NY 12203 Tel 518-482-9023.

AG2 Pr., *(Agtwo Pr; 0-9606552),* 6234 N. Central Ave., Phoenix, AZ 85012 (SAN 222-9897) Tel 602-265-9407.

AIMS, *(AIMS; 0-915357),* 2701 Fondren Dr., Dallas, TX 75206 (SAN 291-0527) Tel 214-691-6451. Do not confuse with AIMS International Bks., Cincinnati, OH.

A. J. Publishing Co., *(A J Pub; 0-914190),* P.O. Box 3012, Duluth, MN 55803 (SAN 201-1840) Tel 218-727-3998.

A.J. Publishing Co., *(AJ Pub Co; 0-9612332),* 4200 Peachway, Boulder, CO 80301 (SAN 289-095X) Tel 303-444-7748.

AKLM Publications, *(A K L M Pubns; 0-9612430),* 42 Lake St., Wakefield, MA 01880 (SAN 289-0771) Tel 617-245-2914.

ALB Assocs., *(ALB Assocs; 0-913405),* 1420 Centre Avenue, Suite 1106, Washington Plaza, Pittsburgh, PA 15219 (SAN 285-8096) Tel 412-566-2525.

ALM Assocs., Inc., *(ALM Assocs),* 3264 Cove Rd., Jupiter, FL 33458 (SAN 287-2897).

†**AMACOM,** Div. of American Management Assn., *(AMACOM; 0-8144),* 135 W. 50th St., New York, NY 10020 (SAN 201-1670) Tel 212-903-8087; *CIP.*

AMCO International, *(AMCO Intl; 0-9602406),* P.O. Box 347, Staten Island, NY 10301 (SAN 212-6534) Tel 718-489-6736.

A M D G Press *See* Sugden, Sherwood, & Co.

AMG Pubs., *(AMG Pubs; 0-89957),* 6815 Shallowford Rd., Chattanooga, TN 37421 (SAN 211-3074).

AMIGOS Bibliographic Council, *(AMIGOS Biblio; 0-938288),* 11300 N. Central Expressway, Suite 321, Dallas, TX 75243 (SAN 219-7596) Tel 214-750-6130.

AMI International Pr., *(AMI Pr; 0-911988),* Mountain View Rd., Washington, NJ 07822 (SAN 213-6791) Tel 201-689-1700.

AMJ Graffica, Inc., *(AMJ Graffica; 0-935575),* P.O. Box 16552, St. Louis Park, MN 55416-0552 (SAN 696-4761) Tel 612-922-0746.

AMORC, Div. of Supreme Grand Lodge of AMORC, Inc., *(AMORC; 0-912057),* Rosicrucian Order, Park Naglee, San Jose, CA 95191 (SAN 211-3864) Tel 408-287-9171.

AMP Educational Services, *(AMP Educ Servs; 0-937429),* 18 Edstone Dr., Staten Island, NY 10301 (SAN 659-0004) Tel 718-390-1119.

AMR Educational Systems, *(AMR Educ Sys; 1-55536),* 4825-C 140th Ave., N., Clearwater, FL 33520 (SAN 695-9458) Tel 813-539-6555.

AMR Publishing Co., *(AMR Pub Co; 0-913698; 0-913599; 0-939971),* P.O. Box 3007, Arlington, WA 98223 (SAN 281-272X) Tel 206-659-6434; 3816 168th Pl., NE, Arlington, WA 98223.

AMSCO School Pubns., Inc., *(AMSCO Sch; 0-87720),* 315 Hudson St., New York, NY 10013 (SAN 201-1751) Tel 212-675-7000.

†**AMS Pr., Inc.,** *(AMS Pr; 0-404),* 56 E. 13th St., New York, NY 10003 (SAN 201-1743) Tel 212-777-4700; *CIP.*

AMS Publishing, *(AMS Kansas; 0-936869),* 31st & Louisiana, Lawrence, KS 66046 (SAN 699-8992) Tel 913-843-1199; P.O. Box 1, Rte. 6, Lawrence, KS 66046 (SAN 699-900X).

ANA of Pleasanton, *(ANA Pleasanton; 0-930673),* P.O. Box 5091, Pleasanton, CA 94566 (SAN 677-0584) Tel 415-658-3110.

ANC Enterprises, *(A N C Ent; 0-9606134),* 15050 Camden Ave., San Jose, CA 95124 (SAN 223-209X) Tel 408-377-1121; 1901 Bascom Ave., No. 327, Campbell, CA 95008 (SAN 223-2103).

AN, Inc., *(AN Inc; 0-9605316),* P.O. Box 81369, Corpus Christi, TX 78412 (SAN 214-0888).

ANZ Religious Pubns., Div. of KOI Trust, *(ANZ Religious Pubns),* RFD 1, Box 1717, Canterbury, NH 03224 (SAN 659-204X) Tel 603-753-4802.

AOI Corp., *(AOI Corp; 0-936074),* Ogden Dunes, Box 1109, Portage, IN 46368 (SAN 223-3932).

APF, Div. of Advanced Personal Finances, *(APF; 0-932515),* P.O. Box 1525, Bellevue, WA 98009 (SAN 687-4614) Tel 206-455-4663.

APLIC International, *(APLIC Intl; 0-933438),* Population Council Library, One Dag Hamarskjold Plaza, New York, NY 10017 (SAN 205-1486) Tel 212-644-1620.

†**APL Pr.,** Div. of STSC, Inc., *(APL Pr; 0-917326),* 215 E. Jefferson St., Rockville, MD 20852 (SAN 208-5070) Tel 301-984-5000; Toll free: 800-592-0050; *CIP.*

A.P.M. Pr., *(A P M Pr; 0-937612),* 502 E. 17th St., Brooklyn, NY 11226 (SAN 214-3356).

APSA, *(APSA),* P.O. Box 5503, Washington, DC 20016 (SAN 212-4009).

ARAS Publishing, *(ARAS Pub; 0-9612164),* 1380 156th St., NE, No. 2060, Bellevue, WA 98007 (SAN 289-1131) Tel 206-643-2757.

ARCI Assocs., *(ARCI Assocs; 0-934045),* Spring Canyon Trail, P.O. Box 2724, Rapid City, SD 57709 (SAN 693-0107) Tel 605-341-7397.

ARC Press, *(ARC Pr; 0-9600884),* 254 W. 71 St., New York, NY 10023-3710 (SAN 263-9033).

ARC Publishing Co., *(A R C Pub; 0-917187),* P.O. Box 1138, Glendale, CA 91209 (SAN 655-8704) Tel 818-244-0113; Dist. by: DeVorss & Co., P.O. Box 550, 1046 Princeton Dr., Marina del Rey, CA 90294 (SAN 168-9886).

ARCS Inc., *(ARCS Inc; 0-9615213),* 2628 E. Cannon Dr., Phoenix, AZ 85028 (SAN 695-1139) Tel 602-971-2867.

ARCsoft Publishers, *(ARCSoft; 0-86668),* P.O. Box 132, Woodsboro, MD 21798 (SAN 216-2210) Tel 301-845-8856.

A.R.E. Pr., *(ARE Pr; 0-87604),* 215 67th St., Virginia Beach, VA 23451 (SAN 201-1484) Tel 804-428-3588; Toll free: 800-368-2727; P.O. Box 595, Virginia Beach, VA 23451 (SAN 692-8234).

†**A-R Editions, Inc.,** *(A-R Eds; 0-89579),* 315 W. Gorham St., Madison, WI 53703 (SAN 289-7067) Tel 608-251-2114; *CIP.*

ARI Publishing Co., *(ARI Pub Co; 0-9616419),* 6 Sheraton Ln., No. 7, Norwich, CT 06360 (SAN 659-0144) Tel 203-889-3733.

ARL Publishing, *(ARL Pub; 0-936419),* P.O. Box 59983, Dallas, TX 75229-1983 (SAN 698-1747) Tel 214-243-7604; 10836 Grissom, Suite 104, Dallas, TX 75229 (SAN 698-1755).

ARO Publishing Co., *(ARO Pub; 0-89868),* Box 193, 398 S. 1100 West, Provo, UT 84601 (SAN 212-6370) Tel 801-377-8218. Imprints: Reading Research (Read Res).

AROY, Inc., *(Amateur Radio; 0-9615633),* P.O. Box 257, Malden, MO 63863 (SAN 696-0561) Tel 314-276-5476; 1012 E. Almar St., Malden, MO 63863 (SAN 696-5199).

ARS Enterprises, *(ARS Enterprises; 0-938630),* P.O. Box 997, Mercer Island, WA 98040 (SAN 238-9088) Tel 206-236-1755.

ART Productions, *(ART Prod; 0-938671),* P.O. Box 503, Ft. Pierre, SD 57532 (SAN 661-5007); 2004 E. Sully, Fort Pierre, SD 57501 (SAN 661-5015) Tel 605-224-1425.

A Raw One Shot *See* Raw Bks. & Graphics

ASC Holding Corp., *(ASC Holding; 0-935578),* P.O. Box 2230, Hollywood, CA 90078 (SAN 287-2889) Tel 213-876-5080.

†**ASI Pubs., Inc.,** *(ASI Pubs Inc; 0-88231),* 63 W. 38th St., Suite 505, New York, NY 10018 (SAN 201-1395) Tel 212-719-2919; *CIP.*

ASQC Quality Pr., Div. of American Society for Quality Control, *(ASQC Qual Pr; 0-87389),* 230 W. Wells St., Milwaukee, WI 53203 (SAN 684-5467) Tel 414-272-8575; Toll free: 800-952-6587.

A System Pubns., *(A System Pubns; 0-935739),* P.O. Box 8681, Trenton, NJ 08650 (SAN 696-1894) Tel 609-588-9022.

ATG Co., *(ATG Co Parma; 0-9616072),* P.O. Box 29508, Parma, OH 44129 (SAN 697-8215) Tel 216-582-4134; 11691 Mapleridge Dr., North Royalton, OH 44133 (SAN 697-8223).

ATQ American Transcendental Quarterly, *(ATQ; 0-9607894),* Univ. of Rhode Island, Dept. of English, Kingston, RI 02881 (SAN 237-9325).

ATR Pubns., *(A T R Pubns; 0-938955),* 3320 Mount Vista Dr., San Jose, CA 95127 (SAN 663-5040) Tel 408-251-5093.

A Thomas Publishing Co., *(A Thomas Pub; 0-937329; 0-9613884),* 19827 W. 12 Mile Rd., Suite 354, Southfield, MI 48076 (SAN 200-2795) Tel 313-559-4846; Toll free: 800-331-6871; Dist. by: Reca International Corp., 150 Haven, P.O. Box 951, Port Washington, NY 11050 (SAN 200-6332). Acquired titles published by Patricia E. Hutt.

A to Z Bk. Serv., *(A to Z Bk Serv; 0-9614716),* P.O. Box 610813, North Miami, FL 33261 (SAN 692-946X).

AV Enterprises Pr., *(AV Enter Pr; 0-9615715),* P.O. Box 6778, Oxnard, CA 93030 (SAN 695-9520) Tel 805-984-5800; 60 W. Fiesta Green, Port Hueneme, CA 93041 (SAN 695-9539).

†**AVI Publishing Co., Inc.,** *(AVI; 0-87055),* 250 Post Rd. E., P.O. Box 831, Westport, CT 06881 (SAN 201-4017) Tel 203-226-0738; *CIP.*

A, E Solutions, Inc. *See* Hunt & Assocs., Consulting Engineers

†**Aames-Allen Publishing Co.,** *(Aames-Allen; 0-936930),* 1106 Main St., Huntington Beach, CA 92648 (SAN 214-4395) Tel 714-536-4926; Dist. by: I.S.B.S., 5602 NE Hassalo, Portland, OR 97213 (SAN 200-8181) Tel 503-287-3093; Toll free: 800-547-7734; *CIP.*

AARD AMES Pr., *(AARD AMES Pr; 0-939013),* P.O. Box 12110, San Antonio, TX 78212 (SAN 662-5584); 121 E. Mariposa, San Antonio, TX 78212 (SAN 662-5592) Tel 512-822-3930.

Aardvark Adventures, *(Aardvark; 0-933877),* P.O. Box 2449, Livermore, CA 94550 (SAN 692-7882) Tel 415-443-2687.

Aardvark Bks., *(Aardvark Bks; 0-936619),* 4782 First Ave., Hibbing, MN 55746 (SAN 698-116X) Tel 218-262-1236; P.O. Box 469-B, Hibbing, MN 55746 (SAN 698-2573).

Aaron Blake Pubs., *(Aaron Blake Pubs; 0-937609),* 9854 Vidor Dr., Los Angeles, CA 90035 (SAN 659-042X) Tel 213-553-4535; Dist. by: Bookpeople, 2929 Fifth St., Berkeley, CA 94710 (SAN 168-9517) Tel 415-549-3030; Toll free: 800-227-1516.

Aaron-Jay Publishing Co., *(Aaron Jay; 0-9615888),* Box 36984, Tucson, AZ 85740 (SAN 696-9984) Tel 602-744-2041; 4150 W. Old Father Pl., Tucson, AZ 85741 (SAN 696-9992).

Aaron-Jenkins Pr., *(Aaron-Jenkins),* P.O. Box 998, Lawndale, CA 90260 (SAN 210-9891) Tel 213-324-9083.

aatec Pubns., *(aatec Pubns; 0-937948),* P.O. Box 7119, Ann Arbor, MI 48107 (SAN 215-7217) Tel 313-995-1470.

Aazunna Publishing, *(Aazunna; 0-934444),* P.O. Box 3736, Ventura, CA 93006 (SAN 213-716X).

Abaca Bks., *(Abaca Bks; 0-933759),* 10 Clinton Pl., Normal, IL 61761 (SAN 692-6967) Tel 309-454-7141.

Abacus Publishing Co., *(Abacus Pub; 0-936171),* P.O. Box 1686, McComb, MS 39648 (SAN 696-9895) Tel 601-684-0001; 1408 Wren Ave., McComb, MS 39648 (SAN 696-9909).

Abacus Software, Inc., *(Abacus Soft; 0-916439),* P.O. Box 7219, Grand Rapids, MI 49510 (SAN 285-4066) Tel 616-241-5510.

Abage Pubns., *(Abage; 0-917350),* 6430 N. Western Ave., Chicago, IL 60645 (SAN 206-3972) Tel 312-274-3531.

Abak Press, *(Abak Pr; 0-914214),* 500 Pepper Ridge Rd., Stamford, CT 06905 (SAN 201-1166) Tel 203-329-9009.

Abalache Bookshop Publishing Co., *(Abalache Bkshop; 0-910453),* 311 S. Klein, Oklahoma City, OK 73108 (SAN 260-0110) Tel 405-235-3288.

†**Abaris Bks., Inc.,** *(Abaris Bks; 0-913870; 0-89835),* 24 W. 40th St., New York, NY 10018 (SAN 206-4588) Tel 212-354-1313; *CIP.*

†**Abattoir Editions,** *(Abattoir; 0-914034),* University of Nebraska at Omaha, Omaha, NE 68182-0190 (SAN 204-7454) Tel 402-554-2787; Dist. by: Granary Bks., 212 North Second St., Minneapolis, MN 55401 (SAN 200-6227) Tel 612-338-4376; *CIP.*

Abbetira Pubns., *(Abbetira Pubns; 0-913407),* P.O. Box 27297, Tucson, AZ 85726-7297 (SAN 697-709X) Tel 602-628-9949; Dist. by: Samuel Weiser, Inc., P.O. Box 612, York Beach, ME 03910 (SAN 202-9588); Dist. by: Starlite Distributors, P.O. Box 20729, Las Vegas, NV 89515 (SAN 662-7544).

Abbeville Pr., Inc., *(Abbeville Pr; 0-89659),* 505 Park Ave., New York, NY 10022 (SAN 211-4755) Tel 212-888-1969; Toll free: 800-227-7210.

Abbey, Stella K., *(S K Abbey),* 2840 80th St., NE, Bellevue, WA 98004 (SAN 204-7152).

Abbey Pr. Printing & Publishing, *(Abbey; 0-87029),* Hwy. 545, St. Meinrad, IN 47577 (SAN 201-2057) Tel 812-357-8011.

Abbincott Publishing Co., *(Abbincott; 0-938490),* 1501 Broadway, Rm. 1414, New York, NY 10036 (SAN 215-8345).

Abbotsford Pr., *(Abbotsford Pr; 0-933011),* P.O. Box 2097, Southbury, CT 06488 (SAN 689-5247) Tel 203-262-6642.

Abbott, Delila M., *(D M Abbott; 0-9607336),* 4775 Bon Air St., Salt Lake City, UT 84117 (SAN 239-1449) Tel 801-277-2733; Dist. by: Zion's Book Store, 254 S. Main St., Salt Lake City, UT 84101 (SAN 239-1457) Tel 801-328-2586; Dist. by: Deseret Book Store, 44 ES. Temple, Salt Lake City, UT 84111 (SAN 200-4097) Tel 801-328-8191; Dist. by: Country Furniture, Old Gardner Mill, 1050 W. 7800 S., West Jordan, UT 84084 (SAN 200-4100) Tel 801-566-2842.

Abbott, Joseph Jr., *(J Abbott; 0-9615351),* P.O. Box 343, Woodridge, NJ 07075-0343 (SAN 695-1988) Tel 201-939-2871.

Abbott, Stanley R., Div. of Word International, *(S R Abbott Mini; 0-915545),* P.O. Box 54975, Tulsa, OK 74155 (SAN 291-0586) Tel 918-455-2111.

Abbott Laboratories, Diagnostics Div., Div. of Abbott Laboratories, North Chicago, IL, *(Abbott Laboratories; 0-9614903),* 1921 Hurd St., P.O. Box 152020, Irving, TX 75015 (SAN 693-3912) Tel 214-257-6474.

Abbott, Langer & Assocs., *(Abbott Langer Assocs; 0-916506),* 548 First St., Crete, IL 60417 (SAN 207-9305) Tel 312-672-4200.

Abbott Loop Pubns., *(Abbott Loop; 0-911739),* 2626 Abbott Rd., Anchorage, AK 99507-4299 (SAN 263-905X) Tel 907-349-9641.

Abbott Pr., *(Abbott Pr; 0-9612678),* P.O. Box 433, Ridgefield, NJ 07657 (SAN 289-0445) Tel 201-943-4867.

Abbott Pr., Subs. of Lynch Assocs., *(Abbott Pr WA; 0-933445),* 4207 Corliss Ave. N., Seattle, WA 98103 (SAN 691-7569) Tel 206-547-1269.

ABC-CLIO Pr. *See* **ABC-Clio Information Services**

Abdo & Daughters, *(Abdo Daughters; 0-939179),* P.O. Box 36036, Minneapolis, MN 55435 (SAN 662-9164); 6537 Cecilia Cir., Edina, MN 55435 (SAN 662-9172) Tel 612-944-5522; Dist. by: Children Pr., 1224 W. Van Buren St., Chicago, IL 60607 (SAN 201-9264) Tel 312-666-4200; Dist. by: Rockbottom Bks., 1224 W. Van Buren St., Chicago, IL 60607 (SAN 200-769X).

Abegg Grillot Enterprises, *(Abegg Grillot Ent; 0-9614131),* P.O. Box 72486, Roselle, IL 60172 (SAN 686-5062) Tel 312-980-6367.

Abigail Publishing Co., *(Abigail Pub; 0-9616650),* 9956 84th St., N., Seminole, FL 33543 (SAN 659-6673) Tel 813-393-8185.

Abilene Christian Univ. Pr., Div. of Abilene Christian University, *(Abilene Christ U; 0-915547; 0-89112),* 1634 Campus Ct., Abilene, TX 79601 (SAN 207-1681) Tel 915-674-2720; Toll free: 800-527-0575; Toll free: 800-592-1404 (TX). *Imprints:* Biblical Research Press (Bibl Res Pr).

Abingdon Pr., Div. of United Methodist Publishing Hse., *(Abingdon; 0-687),* 201 Eighth Ave., S., Nashville, TN 37202 (SAN 201-0054) Tel 615-749-6290; Toll free: 800-251-3320; 1015 Visco Dr., Nashville, TN 37210 (SAN 699-9956). *Imprints:* Apex Books (Apex); Festival Books (Festival).

Abingdon Publishing Co, Inc., *(Abingdon Pub; 0-937915),* 6315 Kingston Pike, Suite 1107, Knoxville, TN 37919 (SAN 659-4824) Tel 615-584-5445. Do not confuse with Abingdon Pr., Nashville, TN.

†**Ablex Publishing Corp.,** *(Ablex Pub; 0-89391),* 355 Chestnut St., Norwood, NJ 07648 (SAN 209-3332) Tel 201-767-8450; *CIP.*

Abmor Publishing, *(Abmor Pub; 0-915359),* P.O. Box 547, Aberdeen, MD 21001 (SAN 291-0594) Tel 301-272-0692.

Abner Schram Ltd., *(Abner Schram Ltd; 0-8390),* 36 Park St., Montclair, NJ 07042 (SAN 685-3129) Tel 201-744-7755; c/o Biblio Distribution Ctr., 81 Adams Dr., Totowa, NJ 07512 (SAN 680-0025) Tel 201-256-8600. *Imprints:* Allanheld & Schram (Allanheld & Schram).

About Faces Publishing Co., Inc., *(About Faces Pub; 0-931977),* 913 Collins Dr., West Chester, PA 19380 (SAN 686-1164) Tel 215-692-9911.

About Time Publishing Co., The, Affil. of Friends of Freedom, *(About Time MA; 0-913683),* P.O. Box 836, Northampton, MA 01061 (SAN 286-1186) Tel 413-545-2145; P.O. Box 1060, Amherst, MA 01004 (SAN 662-2070) Tel 413-545-2148; Orders to: P.O. Box 160, Hadley, MA 01035 (SAN 200-7304) Tel 413-586-5487; Dist. by: Richard Rawe, P.O. Box 443, Soap Lake, WA 98851 (SAN 290-7054) Tel 509-246-1559; Dist. by: Love Ministries, Inc., P.O. Box 69, Worthville, KY 41098 (SAN 662-2089).

Abracadabra Pr., *(Abracadabra Pr; 0-934542),* P.O. Box 334, Balboa Island, CA 92662 (SAN 238-0099) Tel 714-675-0966.

Abracadata Ltd., *(Abracadata; 0-939377),* P.O. Box 2352, Eugene, OR 97402 (SAN 662-9547); 2055 W. 25th, Eugene, OR 97405 (SAN 662-9555) Tel 503-342-3030.

Abraham, George J., *(G J Abraham; 0-9617177),* 23 Monroe Ave., Geneva, NY 14456 (SAN 663-1657) Tel 315-789-6126.

†**Abrams, Harry N., Inc.,** Subs. of Times Mirror Co., *(Abrams; 0-8109),* 100 Fifth Ave., New York, NY 10011 (SAN 200-2434) Tel 212-206-7715; Toll free: 800-345-1359; Orders to: Wayne Public Warehouse, 150 Parish Dr., Wayne, NJ 07470 (SAN 699-9964); *CIP.*

Abraxas Press, Inc., *(Abraxas; 0-932868),* 2518 Gregory St., Madison, WI 53711 (SAN 207-7744) Tel 608-238-0175; Dist. by: Bookslinger, 213 E. Fourth St., Saint Paul, MN 55101 (SAN 169-4154) Tel 612-221-0429.

Abraxas Publishing, *(Abraxas Pub WA; 0-939768),* 10245 Main St., Suite 1-3, Bellevue, WA 98004 (SAN 216-8731) Tel 206-455-8608; Orders to: P.O. Box 312, Kirkland, WA 98038-0312 (SAN 662-7099) Tel 206-455-8608.

Abrell, Diana F., *(D F Abrell; 0-9616706),* Star Rte. 308, Box 29A, Mt. Desert, ME 04660 (SAN 659-6703) Tel 207-288-3311.

†**Abt Bks.,** Subs. of Abt Assocs., Inc., *(Abt Bks; 0-89011),* 55 Wheeler St., Cambridge, MA 02138 (SAN 207-9402) Tel 617-492-7100; *CIP.*

Abundant Life Communications, *(Abundant Li Comm; 0-936471),* 106 Lamarck Dr., Ft. Washington, MD 20744 (SAN 698-1291) Tel 301-839-6777; P.O. Box 55487, Ft. Washington, MD 20744 (SAN 698-2603).

Abundant Life Pubns., Subs. of Perry Gaspard Ministries, *(Abundant Life Pubns; 0-931867),* P.O. Box 336, Lake Charles, LA 70602 (SAN 686-0532) Tel 318-478-1112.

Abyss Pubns., *(Abyss; 0-911856),* P.O. Box C, Somerville, MA 02143 (SAN 201-1859) Tel 617-666-1804.

Academia Pr., *(Academia; 0-911880),* P.O. Box 125, Oshkosh, WI 54901 (SAN 201-2146) Tel 414-235-8362.

Academic Assoc., *(Acad Assoc; 0-918260),* P.O. Box 628, Van Nuys, CA 91408 (SAN 210-1556) Tel 818-988-2479.

Academic Book Club, *(Acad Bk Club),* N. 5411 Post St., Spokane, WA 99208 (SAN 213-6058) Tel 509-325-1435.

Academic Communication Assocs., *(Acad Comm; 0-930951),* 3917 Marvin St., P.O. Box 6044, Oceanside, CA 92056 (SAN 678-8726) Tel 619-758-9593.

†**Academic Enterprises,** *(Academic Enter; 0-931399),* P.O. Box 666-A, Pullman, WA 99163-0666 (SAN 682-1804) Tel 509-334-4826; *CIP.*

†**Academic Guild Publishers,** *(Acad Guild; 0-938550; 0-938552),* 28 Hurlbut St., Cambridge, MA 02138 (SAN 216-7085) Tel 617-491-1837; Orders to: P.O. Box 397B, Cambridge, MA 02238 (SAN 688-4075) Tel 617-491-1837; Toll free: 800-428-4825; Toll free: 800-428-4824 in CA; *CIP.*

Academic Information Service, Inc., *(Acad Info Serv; 0-916018),* P.O. Box 6296, Washington, DC 20015 (SAN 222-4755).

Academic International, *(Academic Intl; 0-87569),* P.O. Box 1111, Gulf Breeze, FL 32561 (SAN 201-212X).

†**Academic Pr., Inc.,** Subs. of Harcourt Brace Jovanovich, Inc., *(Acad Pr; 0-12),* Orlando, FL 32887 (SAN 206-8990) Tel 305-345-4143; Toll free: 800-321-5068; *CIP.*

Academic Pr./Vilencia Productions, *(Academic Pr; 0-939155),* P.O. Box 946, Bellflower, CA 90706 (SAN 662-9229); 6208 Ibbetson Ave., Lakewood, CA 90713 (SAN 662-9237) Tel 213-920-7205.

Academic Pubns., *(Academic Pubns; 0-937647),* P.O. Box 478, Notre Dame, IN 46556 (SAN 659-2678) Tel 219-239-5423; Hagger Hall, Notre Dame, IN 46556 (SAN 659-2686).

Academic Publishers of America, *(Acad Pub Amer; 0-911337),* 6458 Lake Shore Dr., San Diego, CA 92119 (SAN 266-0245) Tel 619-698-0066.

Academic Therapy Pubns., *(Acad Therapy; 0-87879),* 20 Commercial Blvd., Novato, CA 94947 (SAN 201-2111) Tel 415-883-3314. *Imprints:* High Noon Books (High Noon Books).

Academie Press Inc., *(Academie Pr; 0-933136),* 1250 Sixth Ave, San Diego, CA 92112 (SAN 223-680X) Tel 714-459-1743.

Academy Bks., *(Academy Bks; 0-914960),* P.O. Box 757, Rutland, VT 05701 (SAN 208-4325) Tel 802-773-9194; Dist. by: Charles E. Tuttle Co., Inc, P.O. Box 410, 28 S. Main St., Rutland, VT 05701-0410 (SAN 213-2621) Tel 802-773-8930.

Academy Chicago Pubs., *(Academy Chi Pubs; 0-915864; 0-89733),* 425 N. Michigan Ave., Chicago, IL 60611 (SAN 213-2001) Tel 312-644-1723.

Academy Enterprises of New Orleans, Inc., *(Acad Ent; 0-912541),* P.O. Box 73354, Metairie, LA 70033 (SAN 282-7387).

Academy for Educational Development, Inc., *(Acad Educ Dev; 0-89492),* 680 Fifth Ave., New York, NY 10019 (SAN 210-0185) Tel 212-397-0040; 1414-22nd St., NW, Washington, DC 20037 (SAN 215-0379).

Academy Hill Pr., *(Academy Hill; 0-932312),* RD Two, P.O. Box 357, Red Hook, NY 12571 (SAN 211-4607) Tel 914-758-0402.

Academy of American Franciscan History, *(AAFH; 0-88382),* P.O. Box 34440, West Bethesda, MD 20817 (SAN 201-1964) Tel 301-365-1763.

Academy of Dentistry for the Handicapped, *(Acad Dentistry Handicap),* 211 E. Chicago, Suite 2133, Chicago, IL 60611 (SAN 224-2966) Tel 312-440-2660.

Academy of General Dentistry, *(Acad Genl Dentistry),* 211 E. Chicago Ave., Suite 1200, Chicago, IL 60611-2670 (SAN 224-2974) Tel 312-440-4300.

Academy of Management, *(Acad of Mgmt; 0-915350),* Dept. of Management, College of Business Administration, Wichita State Univ., Wichita, KS 67208 (SAN 207-3463) Tel 601-325-3928; Orders to: Dennis F. Ray, The Academy of Management College of Business, Mississippi State University, Mississippi State, MS 39762 (SAN 207-3471).

Academy of Motion Picture Arts & Sciences, *(Acad Motion Pic; 0-942102),* 8949 Wilshire Blvd., Beverly Hills, CA 90211-1972 (SAN 210-5845) Tel 213-278-8990.

Academy of Natural Sciences Philadelphia, *(Acad Nat Sci Phila; 0-910006),* Scientific Pubns., 19th & The Pkwy., Philadelphia, PA 19103 (SAN 204-7497) Tel 215-299-1050.

Names

337

Academy of Political Science, *(Acad Poli Sci),* 2852 Broadway, New York, NY 10025 (SAN 227-1745) Tel 212-866-6752.

Academy of Prison Arts, The, *(Acad Prison Arts; 0-939406),* P.O. Box 99901, Pittsburgh, PA 15233 (SAN 216-5651) Tel 412-761-1955; Dist. by: Motheroot, P.O. Box 8306, Pittsburgh, PA 15218-0306 (SAN 216-4205) Tel 412-731-4453.

Academy of Professional Art Conservation & Science, *(Acad Prof Art; 0-911877),* 165 W. Napa St., P.O. Box 192, Sonoma, CA 95476 (SAN 263-9076) Tel 707-938-3801.

Academy of the New Church, *(Acad New Church; 0-910557),* P.O. Box 278, Bryn Athyn, PA 19009 (SAN 266-0512) Tel 215-947-4200.

Academy Professional Information Services, Inc., *(Academy Prof Inform; 0-934205),* 116 W. 32nd St., 8th Flr., New York, NY 10001 (SAN 693-0085) Tel 212-736-6688.

Academy Pubns., *(Academy Pubns; 0-931560),* P.O. Box 5224, Sherman Oaks, CA 91413 (SAN 212-1778) Tel 818-788-6662; Dist. by: Bookpeople, 2929 Fifth St., Berkeley, CA 94710 (SAN 168-9517) Tel 415-549-3030; Toll free: 800-227-1516.

Academy Santa Clara, *(Academy Santa Clara; 0-912314),* 2464 El Camino Real, Suite 407, Santa Clara, CA 95051 (SAN 201-2162) Tel 408-241-6799.

Acadia Publishing Co., Div. of World Three, Inc., *(Acadia Pub Co; 0-934745),* P.O. Box 770, Bar Harbor, ME 04609 (SAN 694-1648) Tel 207-288-9025.

Acadian Genealogy Exchange, *(Acadian Genealogy; 0-939444),* 863 Wayman Branch Rd., Covington, KY 41015 (SAN 216-325X) Tel 606-356-9825.

Acadian Publishing Enterprise, Inc., *(Acadian Pub; 0-914216),* Rte. Four, P.O. Box 470, Church Point, LA 70525 (SAN 202-3199) Tel 318-684-5871.

Acadiana Pr., The, *(Acadiana Pr; 0-937614),* P.O. Box 42290, USL, Lafayette, LA 70504 (SAN 215-6156) Tel 318-662-3468.

Acaworld, Div. of Acaworld Corp., *(Acaworld; 0-915582),* Drawer 4037, Greenville, NC 27836-4037 (SAN 208-1350) Tel 919-355-6555.

Accelerated Development Inc., *(Accel Devel; 0-915202),* 3400 Kilgore Ave., Muncie, IN 47304 (SAN 210-3346) Tel 317-284-7511.

Accelerated Indexing Systems, Inc., *(Accelerated Index; 0-89593),* P.O. Box 2127, Salt Lake City, UT 84110 (SAN 211-8793) Tel 801-531-0100.

Accent Bks., Div. of Accent Pubns., *(Accent Bks; 0-89636; 0-916406),* P.O. Box 15337, Lakewood Sta., Denver, CO 80215 (SAN 208-9087) Tel 303-988-5300; Toll free: 800-525-5550; 12100 W. Sixth Ave., Denver, CO 80215 (SAN 208-5100).

Accent on Music, *(Accent Music; 0-936799),* P.O. Box 417, Palo Alto, CA 94302 (SAN 699-8151) Tel 415-321-3248; 1044 Beech St., East Palo Alto, CA 94303 (SAN 699-816X).

Accent Pubns., *(Accent Pubns; 0-9613104),* 13 Circuit Ave., Scituate, MA 02066 (SAN 293-9525) Tel 617-545-4486; Toll free: 800-525-5550.

Accent Studios, *(Accent Studios; 0-917205),* P.O. Box 6929, San Diego, CA 92106 (SAN 656-1500) Tel 619-222-0386.

Access Pr., Ltd., *(Access Pr; 0-9604858; 0-915461),* 59 Wooster St., New York, NY 10012 (SAN 263-2500) Tel 212-219-8993; Toll free: 800-222-3774 (Orders); Dist. by: Simon & Schuster, Inc., 1230 Ave. of the Americas, New York, NY 10020 (SAN 200-2450) Tel 212-245-6400.

Accolade, Inc., *(Accolade Inc; 0-935345),* 20863 Stevens Creek Blvd., B-5/E, Cupertino, CA 95014 (SAN 695-9598) Tel 408-446-5757.

Accord, Inc., *(Accord; 0-937301),* 481 Eighth Ave., New York, NY 10001 (SAN 658-7704) Tel 212-714-1099.

Accord, Inc., *(Accord Inc; 0-939581),* P.O. Box 5208, Louisville, KY 40205 (SAN 663-5091); 2210 Dundee Rd., No. 204, Louisville, KY 40205 (SAN 663-5105) Tel 502-589-2889. Do not confuse with Accord, Inc., New York, NY.

Accord Pr., *(Accord Pr; 0-9606078),* P.O. Box 9432, San Jose, CA 95157 (SAN 216-7794) Tel 408-255-8894.

Accord Publishing Ltd., *(Accord Publishing; 0-939251),* 1391 Carr St., Denver, CO 80215 (SAN 663-5032) Tel 303-232-8377; Dist. by: Weather Channel, The, 2840 Mt. Wilkinson Pkwy., Suite 200, Atlanta, GA 30339 (SAN 200-8165).

†**Accountants Pr.,** *(Accountants Pr; 0-930001),* P.O. Box 753, Mississippi State, MS 39762-0753 (SAN 669-7135) Tel 601-324-0985; *CIP.*

Accounting Publications *See* **B of A Communications Co.**

Accounting Pubns., Inc, *(Accounting; 0-917537),* P.O. Box 12848, University Sta., Gainesville, FL 32604 (SAN 656-0555) Tel 904-375-0772.

Accreditation Board for Engineering & Technology, Inc., *(Accred Bd Eng & Tech),* 345 E. 47th St., New York, NY 10017 (SAN 224-0297).

Accura Music, Inc., *(Accura; 0-918194),* P.O. Box 4260, Athens, OH 45701-4260 (SAN 210-1564) Tel 614-594-3547; Toll free: 800-221-9254.

Ace Bks., Div. of Berkley Publishing Group, *(Ace Bks; 0-441),* Orders to: Berkeley Publishing Group, 200 Madison Ave., New York, NY 10016 (SAN 169-5800) Tel 212-686-9820; Dist. by: Kable Books, 777 Third Ave., New York, NY 10017 (SAN 220-6978).

Ace Reid Enterprises, *(Reid Ent; 0-917207),* P.O. Box 868, Kerrville, TX 78028 (SAN 656-089X) Tel 512-257-7446.

Acheron Pr., *(Acheron Pr; 0-941452),* Bear Creek at the Kettle, Friendsville, MD 21531 (SAN 239-0612) Tel 301-746-5885.

Achievement Hse., *(Achievement Hse; 0-9615629),* 103 Great Plain Rd., Danbury, CT 06811 (SAN 695-9857) Tel 203-748-0277; Toll free: 800-551-1133.

Achievement Institute, The, *(Achievement Inst; 0-936452),* 3772 Plaza Dr., Suite S, Ann Arbor, MI 48104 (SAN 214-2783); Orders to: Airport Business Services, 704 Airport Blvd., Suite 4, Ann Arbor, MI 48104 (SAN 661-9290).

Achievement Pr., *(Achievement Pr; 0-932707),* Box 608, Sheridan, WY 82801 (SAN 687-8571) Tel 307-672-8475.

Acid Rain Foundation, Inc., The, *(Acid Rain Found; 0-935577),* 1630 Blackhawk Hills, St. Paul, MN 55122 (SAN 695-9946) Tel 612-455-7719.

Ackerman, Jan, *(J Ackerman; 0-9616199),* 1019 Columbia St., Hood River, OR 97031 (SAN 658-3369) Tel 503-386-5970.

Acoma Bks., *(Acoma Bks; 0-916552),* P.O. Box 4, Ramona, CA 92065 (SAN 207-7221) Tel 619-789-1288.

Acorn, *(Acorn OH; 0-9604194),* 1778 Radnor Rd., Cleveland, OH 44118 (SAN 216-213X).

Acorn Bks. *See* **Macmillan Publishing Co., Inc.**

Acorn Music Press *See* **Music Sales Corp.**

Acorn Pr., *(Acorn NC; 0-89386),* 1318 Broad St., Box 4007, Duke Sta., Durham, NC 27706 (SAN 216-4833) Tel 919-286-9830.

Acorn Pubns., *(Acorn Pubns; 0-931442),* Nine Victory Rd., Suffern, NY 10901 (SAN 211-3058).

Acorn Publishing, *(Acorn Pub; 0-937921),* P.O. Box 7067, Syracuse, NY 13261 (SAN 659-4832) Tel 315-689-7072; 100 S. Clinton St., Syracuse, NY 13261 (SAN 659-4840).

Acorn Publishing, *(Acorn Pub MN; 0-938399),* 15150 Scenic Heights Rd., Eden Prairie, MN 55344 (SAN 659-6738) Tel 612-934-6614.

Acosep Corp., *(Acosep Corp; 0-9616402),* 401 N. Plum St., Springfield, OH 45504 (SAN 658-9677) Tel 513-323-0777.

Acoustical Society of America, *(Acoustical Soc Am),* 335 E. 45th St., New York, NY 10017 (SAN 226-0026) Tel 516-349-7800.

Acquisition Planning, Inc., *(Acquisition Plan; 0-940694),* 30 E. Huron St., Suite 4506, Chicago, IL 60611 (SAN 218-5598) Tel 312-943-1715.

Acrobat Bks., *(Acrobat; 0-918226),* P.O. Box 480820, Los Angeles, CA 90048 (SAN 209-3936).

†**Acropolis Bks.,** Subs. of Colortone Pr., Inc., *(Acropolis; 0-87491),* 2400 17th St. NW, Washington, DC 20009 (SAN 201-2227) Tel 202-387-6805; Toll free: 800-621-5199; *CIP.*

Actex Pubns., *(Actex Pubns; 0-936031),* A-12 Wallens Hill Rd., Winsted, CT 06098 (SAN 696-9879) Tel 203-379-5470; Dist. by: Actuarial Bookstore, The, P.O. Box 318, Abington, CT 06230 (SAN 200-5867) Tel 203-975-3540.

Acting World Bks., *(Acting World Bks; 0-9615288),* P.O. Box 3044, Hollywood, CA 90078 (SAN 694-5430) Tel 213-466-4297.

Action & Life Pubns., *(Action Life Pubns; 0-9607590; 0-936707),* 504 E. Palace Ave., Santa Fe, NM 87501 (SAN 238-6607) Tel 505-983-1960.

Action for Independent Maturity *See* **American Assn. of Retired Persons**

Action Link Pubns., *(Action Link; 0-936148),* 53 Condon Court, San Mateo, CA 94403 (SAN 214-090X).

Action Press, *(Action Pr; 0-9610794),* P.O. Box 25738, Tempe, AZ 85282 (SAN 296-1180).

Action Productions, *(Action Prods; 0-9608868),* 1102 17th St., NW, Puyallup, WA 98371 (SAN 241-0915) Tel 206-845-3627.

Action Publishing Co., *(Action Pub; 0-935677),* 11304 1/2 Pico Blvd., West Los Angeles, CA 90064 (SAN 696-0006) Tel 213-477-4067.

Actonizing, Inc., *(Actionizing; 0-912137),* 910 NW 92nd St., Oklahoma City, OK 73114 (SAN 264-7109) Tel 405-840-9546.

Active Learning, *(Active Learning; 0-914460),* P.O. Box 64992, Lubbock, TX 79464 (SAN 201-1174).

Active Learning Corp., *(Active Lrn; 0-912813),* P.O. Box 254, New Paltz, NY 12561 (SAN 282-7794); 125 Springtown Rd., New Paltz, NY 12561 (SAN 660-949X) Tel 914-255-0844.

Activities for Learning, *(Activities Learning; 0-9609636),* 2684 Sumac Ridge, St. Paul, MN 55110 (SAN 283-2445).

Activity Factory, The, *(Activity Factory; 0-936885),* 1551 Key Ct., Kissimmee, FL 32743 (SAN 658-4586) Tel 305-846-1443.

Activity Resources Co., Inc., *(Activity Resources; 0-918932),* P.O. Box 4875, 20655 Hathaway Ave., Hayward, CA 94541 (SAN 209-0201) Tel 415-782-1300.

Actor Training & Research Institute Pr., *(Actor Train Res; 0-9616087),* 451 W. Melrose, No. 404, Chicago, IL 60657 (SAN 698-0767) Tel 312-871-0349; Dist. by: Baker & Taylor (Midwest Div.), 501 Gladiola Ave., Momence, IL 60954 (SAN 169-2100); Dist. by: Blackwell N. America, 1001 Fries Mill Rd., Blackwell, NJ 08012 (SAN 169-4596) Tel 609-629-0700; Toll free: 800-257-7341; Dist. by: The Book House, 208 W. Chicago St., Jonesville, MI 49250-0125 (SAN 169-3859) Tel 517-849-2117; Toll free: 800-248-1146.

Acupinch Outreach Ctr., *(Acupinch; 0-9607456),* 2989 McCully Dr., NE, Atlanta, GA 30345 (SAN 238-2113) Tel 404-939-1678.

Ad-Dee Publishers, Inc., *(Ad-dee Pubs Inc; 0-9600982),* P.O. Box 5426-B, Eugene, OR 97405 (SAN 208-6638) Tel 503-343-5868.

†**Ad-Lib Pubns.,** *(Ad-Lib; 0-912411),* P.O. Box 1102, Fairfield, IA 52556 (SAN 265-170X) Tel 515-472-6617; Toll free: 800-624-5893; 51 N. Fifth St., Fairfield, IA 52556 (SAN 663-3005); *CIP.*

Ad Verbum Corp., *(Ad Verbum; 0-939203),* 438 Hill Rd., Box 569, West Acton, MA 01720 (SAN 662-6157) Tel 617-263-5113.

Adam Publishing Co., Subs. of Adam Art Assocs., *(Adam Pub Co; 0-9614209),* 537 Brobst St., Shillington, PA 19607 (SAN 686-9378) Tel 215-775-2739.

Adama Pubs., Inc., *(Adama Pubs Inc; 0-915361),* 306 W. 38th St., New York, NY 10018 (SAN 291-0640) Tel 212-594-5770; Toll free: 800-672-6672; Dist. by: Franklin Watts, Inc., 387 Park Ave., S., New York, NY 10016 (SAN 200-7002) Tel 212-594-5770.

Adamant Pr., Div. of Precision Paper,Inc., *(Adamant Pr; 0-912362),* P.O. Box Seven, Adamant, VT 05640 (SAN 201-2235).

Adamas Pubns., *(Adamas Pubs; 0-9607892),* P.O. Box 5504, Washington, DC 20016 (SAN 238-1362) Tel 301-656-0008.

Adams, Bob, Inc., *(Adams Inc MA; 0-937860),* 840 Summer St., Boston, MA 02127 (SAN 215-2886) Tel 617-268-9570.

Adams, Charles J. III, *(C J Adams; 0-9610008),* 14 E. 34th St., Reading, PA 19606 (SAN 266-0865) Tel 215-779-8173.

Adams, Earl, *(E Adams; 0-9612748),* P.O. Box 5145, Vienna, WV 26105 (SAN 289-7172); Dist. by: Gambler's Bk. Club, 630 S. 11th St., P.O. Box 4115, Las Vegas, NV 89127 (SAN 203-414X) Tel 702-382-7555.

Adams, Florence J., *(F J Adams; 0-9617276),* 504 E. Knotts Ave., Grafton, WV 26354 (SAN 663-4699); Dist. by: McClain Printing Co., 212 Main St., Parsons, WV 26287 (SAN 203-9478) Tel 304-478-2881.

Adams, Thomas Dean, *(T Adams; 0-9609242),* 2817 Darrow Ave., Klamath, OR 97603 (SAN 241-2624) Tel 213-271-0938.

Adams, Bannister, Cox Pubs., *(Adams Bannister Cox; 0-937431),* 460 Riverside Dr., Suite 52, New York, NY 10027 (SAN 658-9707) Tel 212-749-6709.

†**Adams County Historical Society,** *(Adams County; 0-934858),* P.O. Box 102, Hastings, NE 68901-0102 (SAN 209-1917) Tel 402-463-5838; *CIP.*

Adams Press, *(Adams Minn; 0-914828),* 59 Seymour Ave., SE, Minneapolis, MN 55414 (SAN 201-1867) Tel 612-378-9076; Orders to: Lerner Publications Co., 241 First Ave. N., Minneapolis, MN 55401 (SAN 201-0828).

Adams Publishing Co., *(Adams Pub Co; 0-9615868),* P.O. Box 356, Eastsound, WA 98245 (SAN 696-6799) Tel 206-376-5256 (SAN 698-2085).

Adamson, Douglas, *(D Adamson),* New Boston Rd., Box 173, Sanbornton, NH 03269 (SAN 208-1288) Tel 603-934-5333; Orders to: Douglas Adamson, P.O. Box 41, First New Hamshire Bank Bldg., Franklin, NH 03235 (SAN 661-9304) Tel 603-934-6226.

Adar Pubns., *(Adar Pubns; 0-916169),* 8434 Main St., Interlaken, NY 14847 (SAN 294-8842) Tel 607-532-4404.

Adastra Pr., *(Adastra Pr; 0-938566),* 101 Strong St., Easthampton, MA 01027 (SAN 207-7752).

Add-Effect Assocs., Inc., *(Add-Effect Assoc; 0-940896),* P.O. Box 401, 1093 Radnor Rd., Wayne, PA 19087 (SAN 219-0761) Tel 215-688-6489.

Addison Gallery of American Art, *(Addison Gallery),* Phillips Academy, Andover, MA 01810 (SAN 206-8583).

Addison House, Subs. of American Showcase, Inc., *(Addison Hse; 0-89169),* 724 Fifth Ave., Tenth Floor, New York, NY 10019 (SAN 210-5543) Tel 212-245-0981.

Addor Assocs., Inc., *(Addor),* P.O. Box 2128, Westport, CT 06880 (SAN 200-5948) Tel 203-226-9791; 115 Roseville Rd., Westport, CT 06880 (SAN 658-2982).

Addresso'set Pubns., *(Addresso'set; 0-916944),* P.O. Box 3009, Vallejo, CA 94590 (SAN 208-5127) Tel 707-644-6358.

Adelantre, *(Adelantre; 0-917288),* 4594 Bedford Ave., Brooklyn, NY 11235 (SAN 208-2268).

Adelphi Pr., *(Adelphi Pr; 0-9610796),* P.O. Box 867, Hyattsville, MD 20783 (SAN 265-0541) Tel 301-622-9158.

Adelphi Pr., *(Adelphi Pr PA; 0-9615832),* 1533 Garfield Ave., Wyomissing, PA 19610 (SAN 697-0001) Tel 215-373-3510.

Adelphi Univ. Press, *(Adelphi Univ; 0-88461),* S. Ave., Garden City, NY 11530 (SAN 201-6826) Tel 516-663-1120.

Adenine Pr., Inc., *(Adenine Pr; 0-940030),* 11A Fullerton Ave., Schenectady, NY 12304 (SAN 281-241X) Tel 518-372-0006; Orders to: P.O. Box 355, Guilderland, NY 12084 (SAN 281-2428).

†**Adinkra Press,** *(Adinkra Pr; 0-9611900),* 431 Coffield Ave., Napa, CA 94558 (SAN 208-0279) Tel 707-224-3300; *CIP.*

Adirondack Conservancy Committee/The Adirondack Council, *(Adiron Conserv; 0-9613403),* P.O. Box 188, Elizabethtown, NY 12932 (SAN 656-9595) Tel 518-873-2610; Dist. by: Adirondack Mountain Club, Inc., 174 Glen St., Glens Falls, NY 12801 (SAN 204-7691) Tel 518-793-7737.

†**Adirondack Mountain Club, Inc.,** *(ADK Mtn Club; 0-935272),* 174 Glen St., Glens Falls, NY 12801 (SAN 204-7691) Tel 518-793-7737; *CIP.*

Adirondack Museum, The, *(Adirondack Mus; 0-910020),* Rte. 28 N., Blue Mountain Lake, NY 12812 (SAN 201-7105) Tel 518-352-7311; P.O. Box 99, Blue Mountain Lake, NY 12812 (SAN 699-9972).

Adirondack Sports Pubns., *(Adirondack S P; 0-9616439),* Rte. 86, Wilmington, NY 12997 (SAN 658-9715) Tel 518-946-2605.

Adirondack Yesteryears, Incorporated, *(Adirondack Yes; 0-9601158),* 246 Lake St., Saranac Lake, NY 12983 (SAN 209-4126) Tel 518-891-3206 Tel 518-891-3206.

Adizes Institute, Inc., The, *(Adizes Inst Inc; 0-89074),* 2001 Wilshire Blvd., Santa Monica, CA 90403 (SAN 265-3729) Tel 213-453-5593.

Adlen, R. N., Publishing Co., *(R N Adlen; 0-938113),* 7822 Comanche Ave., Canoga Park, CA 91306 (SAN 659-6762) Tel 818-500-9898.

Adlen Bks., *(Adlen Bks; 0-9615371),* 3303 Kerckhoff Ave., Fresno, CA 93702 (SAN 696-6322) Tel 209-264-5421.

Adler, Alfred, Institute of Chicago, Inc., *(A Adler Inst; 0-918560),* 618 S. Michigan Ave., Chicago, IL 60605 (SAN 201-1956) Tel 312-294-7100.

Adler & Adler Pubs., Inc., *(Adler & Adler; 0-917561),* 4550 Montgomery Ave., Suite 705, Bethesda, MD 20814 (SAN 656-5298) Tel 301-654-4271; Dist. by: Harper & Row Pubs., Inc., Keystone Industrial Pk., Scranton, PA 18512 (SAN 200-688X); Toll free: 800-253-3677.

Adler Publishing Co., *(Adler Pub Co; 0-913623),* Panorama Plaza, Box 25333, Rochester, NY 14625 (SAN 285-6808) Tel 716-377-5804; Dist. by: Writers & Bks., 740 University Ave., Rochester, NY 14607 (SAN 156-9678) Tel 716-473-2590. Do not confuse with Adler's Foreign Bks., Inc., New York, NY. *Imprints:* Nightsun Books (Nightsun Bks).

Adler's Foreign Bks., Inc., *(Adlers Foreign Bks; 0-8417),* 915 Foster St., Evanston, IL 60201 (SAN 201-2251) Tel 312-866-6329; Toll free: 800-235-3771. Do not confuse with Adler Publishing Co., Rochester, NY.

Admark, Inc., *(Admark),* 200 Lakeside Dr., Horsham, PA 19044 (SAN 699-7996) Tel 215-443-9892.

†**Admates,** *(Admates CA; 0-935236),* P.O. Box 210, Venice, CA 90294-0210 (SAN 215-689X) Tel 213-392-4911; *CIP.*

Administrative Management Society, *(Admin Mgmt; 0-916875),* International Headquarters, 2360 Maryland Rd., Willow Grove, PA 19090 (SAN 224-8530) Tel 215-659-4300.

Administrative Research Associates, *(ARA; 0-910022),* Irvine Town Ctr., Box 4211, Irvine, CA 92716 (SAN 201-1891) Tel 714-499-3939.

Admiral Nimitz Foundation, *(Adm Nimitz Foun; 0-934841),* P.O. Box 777, Fredericksburg, TX 78624 (SAN 201-1883); 340 E. Main, Fredericksburg, TX 78624 (SAN 661-9312) Tel 512-997-4379.

Admont Corp., *(Admont Corp; 0-939421),* P.O. Box 3148, Staunton, VA 24401-6259; 198 Kalorama St., Suite B, Staunton, VA 24401 Tel 703-886-4777.

Adner Productions, *(Adner Prods; 0-941454),* 2497 New York Ave., Melville, NY 11747 (SAN 238-9037).

Adonis Press, *(Adonis Pr; 0-932776),* Hawthorne Valley, Ghentdale, NY 12075 (SAN 218-463X); Orders to: Christy Barnes, R.D., Hillsdale, NY 12529 (SAN 661-9320) Tel 518-325-7182.

Adonis Studio, *(Adonis Studio; 0-914827),* P.O. Box 6626, Cleveland, OH 44101 (SAN 289-0461) Tel 216-526-5713.

Adrenal Metabolic Research Society Society of Hypoglycemia Foundation, *(Hypoglycemia Foun),* 153 Pawling Ave., Troy, NY 12180 (SAN 266-0946) Tel 518-272-7154.

Adrienne Pubns., Inc., *(Adrienne Pubns Inc; 0-9610534),* 123 Cheshire Rd., Bethany, CT 06525 (SAN 263-9092) Tel 203-393-2323.

Adrift Editions, *(Adrift Edns; 0-916351),* 239 E. Fifth St., No. 4D, New York, NY 10003 (SAN 295-1029).

Adult Development and Learning, *(Adult Dev Learn; 0-9613245),* 40 McDivitt Rd., Manchester, CT 06040 (SAN 295-5156) Tel 203-643-0468.

Advance Book Program *See* **Benjamin-Cummings Publishing Co.**

Advance Group, The, *(Adv Group; 0-9613500),* 400 N. Noble, Chicago, IL 60622 (SAN 657-2472) Tel 312-942-8538; Orders to: Advance Screen Printing Institute, 1401 W. Hubbard, Chicago, IL 60622 (SAN 662-7633).

Advance Memory Research, Inc. *See* **AMR Educational Systems**

Advance Planning Publications, *(Advance Planning; 0-9600524),* Rte. 3, St. Croix Cove, Hudson, WI 54016 (SAN 209-1070) Tel 715-386-9007.

AdvanceAbility Publishing Co., *(AdvanceAbility; 0-913833),* P.O. Box 12, Carnelian Bay, CA 95711 (SAN 286-7125) Tel 916-583-5687.

Advanced Acceptance, *(Adv Accept),* P.O. Box 3692, Quincy, IL 62301 (SAN 217-2216).

Advanced Backgammon Enterprises, *(Advanced Back; 0-9608566),* 256 S. Robertson Blvd., Beverly Hills, CA 90211 (SAN 238-2210) Tel 213-820-0678.

Advanced Information Concepts, *(Advanced Info; 0-938031),* 400 S. Romona, Suite 110-120, Corona, CA 91719 (SAN 661-4124) Tel 714-737-7699.

Advance Instructional Systems, Inc., *(Advance Instr Sys; 0-935477),* 300 Deerfield Rd., Camp Hill, PA 17011 (SAN 696-0049) Tel 717-737-5988.

Advanced International Studies Institute, in association with the Univ. of Miami, *(AISI; 0-933074),* P.O. Box 1705, Fort Wayne, IN 46885 (SAN 201-8675) Tel 219-447-9927.

Advanced Learning Products, *(Advan Learning; 0-916881),* 10615 Cullman Ave., Whittier, CA 90603 (SAN 654-519X) Tel 213-947-8138.

Advanced Professional Development, Inc., *(Adv Prof Dev; 0-912907),* 5519 Carpenter Ave., North Hollywood, CA 91607 (SAN 282-9576) Tel 818-506-7765.

Advanced Professional Seminars, Inc., *(Adv Prof Seminars; 0-9604532),* 7033 Ramsgate Place, Suite "A", Los Angeles, CA 90045 (SAN 220-0279); Orders to: P.O. Box 45791, Los Angeles, CA 90045 (SAN 220-0287) Tel 213-776-0113.

Advanced Systems Publishing Co., *(Advanced Syst Pub; 0-9616871),* 243 S. Mathilda, Suite 104, Sunnyvale, CA 94086 (SAN 661-1516) Tel 408-733-0381.

Advanced Therapeutics Communications, *(Advanced Thera Comm; 0-911741),* 515 Madison Ave., New York, NY 10022 (SAN 263-9084) Tel 212-752-4530.

Advantage Pr., *(Advantage Pr; 0-9615341),* P.O. Box 51, Rocklin, CA 95677 (SAN 695-1090) Tel 916-624-0845.

Adven Group, The, *(Adven Group; 0-938825),* 261 Oakhurst Ln., Arcadia, CA 91006 (SAN 661-7034) Tel 818-447-3816.

Advent Bks., Inc, *(Advent NY; 0-89891),* 141 E. 44th St., Suite 511, New York, NY 10017 (SAN 212-9973) Tel 212-697-0887. *Imprints:* Plutarch Press (Plutarch Pr).

Advent: Pubs., Inc., *(Advent; 0-911682),* P.O. Box A3228, Chicago, IL 60690 (SAN 201-2286).

Adventure Capital Corp., *(Adventure Cap Corp),* P.O. Box 88, Canyon, CA 94516 (SAN 692-7416); 8343 Skyline Blvd., Oakland, CA 94611 (SAN 692-7424); Dist. by: Brown Book, Inc., P.O. Box 3490, Santa Barbara, CA 93130 (SAN 202-4276).

Adventure Productions, Inc., *(Adventure Prods; 0-9614904),* 1401 Duff Dr., Suite 600, Ft. Collins, CO 80524 (SAN 693-3955) Tel 303-493-8776.

Adventure Pubns., Div. of Nordell Graphic Communication, Inc., *(Adventure Pubns; 0-934860),* P.O. Box 96, Staples, MN 56479 (SAN 212-7199) Tel 218-894-3592.

Adventures in Living, *(Adventures in Living; 0-9605868),* 10659 Caminito Cascara,, San Diego, CA 92108 (SAN 216-2148) Tel 619-281-6174; Dist. by: DeVorss & Company, P.O. Box 550, 1046 Princeton Dr., Marina del Rey, CA 90294 (SAN 168-9886) Tel 213-870-7478.

Adventures Unlimited Pr., *(Adventures Unltd; 0-932813),* P.O. Box 22, Stelle, IL 60919 (SAN 688-6442) Tel 815-253-6390.

Names

339

Advertising Council, Inc., *(Ad Council),* 825 Third Ave., New York, NY 10022 (SAN 224-6082) Tel 212-758-0400; 1730 Rhode Island Ave. NW, Washington, DC 20036 (SAN 668-9515) Tel 202-331-9153; 1717 N. Highland Ave., Los Angeles, CA 90028 (SAN 668-9523) Tel 213-462-0988.

Advertising Planners, Inc., *(Ad Planners; 0-937769),* 31050 Wallace Ave., Aptos, CA 95003 (SAN 659-2708) Tel 408-688-0768.

Advisory Publishing, *(Advisory Pub; 0-913409),* P.O. Box 668, Crestline, CA 92325-0668 (SAN 285-807X) Tel 714-338-5103.

Advocacy Pr., Div. of Girls Club of Santa Barbara, *(Advocacy Pr; 0-911655),* P.O. Box 236, Santa Barbara, CA 93102 (SAN 263-9114) Tel 805-962-2728; Dist. by: Ingram Book Co., P.O. Box 17266, Nashville, TN 37217 (SAN 169-7978) Tel 615-361-5000; Toll free: 800-251-5900; Dist. by: Publishers Group West, 5855 Beaudry St., Emeryville, CA 94608 (SAN 202-8522).

Advocate House, *(Advocate Hse; 0-910029),* P.O. Box 731, Ben Lomond, CA 95005 (SAN 241-1946) Tel 408-338-3354.

Advocate Press, *(Advocate; 0-911866),* Hwy. 29, Franklin Springs, GA 30639 (SAN 201-2294) Tel 404-245-7272.

†Advocate Publishing Group, Subs. of Avatar Media Assocs., *(Advocate Pub Group; 0-89894),* P.O. Box 351, Reynoldsburg, OH 43068-0351 (SAN 213-0238) Tel 614-861-7738; *CIP.*

Aegean Park Pr., *(Aegean Park Pr; 0-89412),* P.O. Box 2837, Laguna Hills, CA 92654-0837 (SAN 210-0231) Tel 714-586-8811.

Aegis Publishing Co., *(Aegis Pub Co; 0-933013),* 3290 Sixth Ave., 1F, San Diego, CA 92103 (SAN 213-9030) Tel 619-296-6751.

Aeolus Pr., *(Aeolus Pr VA; 0-9616166),* 7126 Merrimac Dr., McLean, VA 22101 (SAN 699-8933) Tel 703-893-7103. Do not confuse with Aeolus Pr., Inc., Baltimore, MD.

Aeolus Pr., Inc., *(Aeolus Pr MD; 0-937315),* 7106 Campfield Rd., Baltimore, MD 21207 (SAN 658-7682) Tel 301-484-6287. Do not confuse with Aeolus Pr., McLean, VA.

Aerial Photography Services, Inc., *(Aerial Photo; 0-936672),* 2511 S. Tryon St., Charlotte, NC 28203 (SAN 214-2791).

Aerial Pr., Inc., *(Aerial Pr; 0-942344),* P.O. Box 1360, Santa Cruz, CA 95061 (SAN 239-7056) Tel 408-425-8619.

Aerie Bks., Ltd., *(Aerie Bks Ltd; 0-938819),* 49 W. 24th St., 9th Flr., New York, NY 10010 (SAN 661-8189) Tel 212-741-3100.

Aero Associates, *(Aero Assocs; 0-9613088),* 705-1/2 W. Hillcrest Ave., Inglewood, CA 90301 (SAN 294-6637) Tel 213-677-4965.

Aero-Medical Consultants, Inc., *(Aero-Medical; 0-912522),* 10912 Hamlin Blvd., Largo, FL 33544 (SAN 201-2316) Tel 813-596-2551.

Aero Pr. Pubs., *(Aero Pr; 0-936450),* P.O. Box 2091, Fall River, MA 02722 (SAN 207-0650) Tel 617-644-2058.

Aero Products Research, Inc., *(Aero Products; 0-912682),* 11201 Hindry Ave., Los Angeles, CA 90045 (SAN 205-5996) Tel 213-641-7242.

Aero Visions, Inc., *(Aero Vis; 0-941730),* 14962 Merced Circle, Irvine, CA 92714 (SAN 239-1473) Tel 714-559-7113.

Aerobic and Fitness Association of America, *(Aerobic Fitness Assn; 0-9614719),* 15250 Ventura Blvd., Suite 802, Sherman Oaks, CA 91403 (SAN 692-5170) Tel 818-905-0040.

Aerodrome Pr., *(Aerodrome Pr; 0-935092),* P.O. Box 44, Story City, IA 50248 (SAN 213-4519) Tel 515-733-2589.

Aeroemblem Pubns., Ltd., *(Aeroemblem Pubns; 0-9615456),* 7 March Dr., Wichita Falls, TX 76306 (SAN 695-7455) Tel 817-855-0988.

Aerofax, Inc., *(Aerofax; 0-942548),* P.O. Box 120127, Arlington, TX 76012 (SAN 240-0642) Tel 214-647-1105.

AeroGraphics, *(AeroGraphics; 0-9607814),* P.O. Box 1520, Deland, FL 32721 (SAN 238-1370) Tel 904-736-9779.

Aerospace Medical Assn., *(Aerospace Med Assn),* Washington Natl Airport, Washington, DC 20001 (SAN 224-2583) Tel 703-892-2240.

AeroTravel Research, *(AeroTravel Res; 0-914553),* P.O. Box 3694, Cranston, RI 02910 (SAN 219-3442) Tel 401-941-6140.

Aesculapius Pubs., Inc., *(Aesculapius Pubs; 0-918228),* 240 E. 76th St., Apt. 1-B, New York, NY 10021 (SAN 210-1572) Tel 212-628-1797.

Aestas Pr., *(Aestas Pr; 0-9616414),* P.O. Box 11134, Shore Wood, WI 53211 (SAN 658-9723) Tel 414-332-5004; 1700 E. Chateau Pl., No. 11, Shore Wood, WI 53211 (SAN 658-9731).

Aesthetic Realism Foundation Incorporated, *(Aesthetic Realism; 0-911492),* 141 Greene St., New York, NY 10012 (SAN 205-423X) Tel 212-777-4490.

Aesthetics West, *(Aesthetics; 0-934673),* 2732 Harris St., P.O. Box 5149, Eugene, OR 97405 (SAN 694-1877) Tel 503-343-8278.

Aetherius Society, *(Aetherius Soc; 0-937249),* 6202 Afton Pl., Hollywood, CA 90028-8298 (SAN 266-1209) Tel 213-465-9652.

Affinity Publishers Services, Publishing Division, *(Affinity Pub Serv),* Orders to: Box 600531, Houston, TX 77260 (SAN 650-9940).

†Affirmation Bks., *(Affirmation; 0-89571),* 109 Woodland St., Natick, MA 01760 (SAN 209-5211) Tel 617-651-3893; Orders to: 120 Hill St., Whitinsville, MA 01588 (SAN 668-9531) Tel 617-234-6266; *CIP.*

Affordable Adventures, Inc., *(Affordable Adven; 0-935201),* 924 W. Eula Ct., Glendale, WI 53209 (SAN 695-7323) Tel 414-964-3753.

Africa Fund, *(Africa Fund; 0-943428),* 198 Broadway, New York, NY 10038 (SAN 224-0319) Tel 212-962-1210.

Africa News Service Inc., *(Africa News Serv; 0-9614368),* P.O. Box 3851, Durham, NC 27702 (SAN 217-5924) Tel 919-286-0747.

Africa World Pr., *(Africa World; 0-86543),* P.O. Box 1892, Trenton, NJ 08607 (SAN 692-3925) Tel 609-695-3766; 556 Bellevue Ave., Trenton, NJ 08618 (SAN 658-2753). Do not confuse with Africa Research & Pubns. Project, Inc. at the same address.

African American Images, *(African Am Imag; 0-913543),* 910 S. Michigan Ave., Rm. 556, Chicago, IL 60605 (SAN 201-2332) Tel 312-922-1147.

African-American Institute, *(AAI; 0-87862),* 833 United Nations Plaza, New York, NY 10017 (SAN 204-5540) Tel 212-949-5666.

African Development Information, *(African Develop),* 1346 Connecticut Ave. NW, Suite 903, Washington, DC 20036 (SAN 240-9437). Moved, left no forwarding address.

African Studies Assn., *(African Studies Assn; 0-918456),* 405 Hilgard Ave., 255 Kinsey Hall, Los Angeles, CA 90024 (SAN 212-260X) Tel 213-206-8011. *Imprints:* Crossroads Press (Crossroads).

African Studies Ctr., Boston Univ., *(Boston U African; 0-915118),* 270 Bay State Rd., Boston, MA 02215 (SAN 223-5927) Tel 617-353-7306.

Africana Pub. See Holmes & Meier Pubs., Inc.

†Africana Publishing Co., Div. of Holmes & Meier, *(Africana Pub; 0-8419),* 30 Irving Pl., New York, NY 10003 (SAN 219-5828) Tel 212-687-8155; *CIP.*

Africana Research Pubns., *(Africana Res; 0-933524),* 2580 Seventh Ave., New York, NY 10039 (SAN 212-470X).

Afro-Am Publishing Co., Inc., *(Afro-Am; 0-910030),* 910 S. Michigan Ave., Rm. 556, Chicago, IL 60605 (SAN 201-2332) Tel 312-922-1147.

Afro-Hispanic Institute, *(Afro Hispanic Inst; 0-939423),* 3306 Ross Pl., NW, Washington, DC 20008 (SAN 663-3994) Tel 202-966-7783.

†Afro Resources Inc., *(Afro Res Inc; 0-915549),* P.O. Box 192, Temple Hills, MD 20748 (SAN 291-0659) Tel 301-894-3855; *CIP.*

Aftermath, *(Aftermath; 0-936579),* P.O. Box 420374, Sacramento, CA 95842 (SAN 698-0864) Tel 916-331-0600; 7005 Buskirk Dr., Sacramento, CA 95842 (SAN 698-0872).

Afton Oaks Typesetting & Publishing Co., *(Afton Oaks; 0-912217),* Box 2098, Corpus Christi, TX 78403 (SAN 265-0576) Tel 512-881-8207.

AG Access Publishing Corp., *(AG Access Pub; 0-932857),* P.O. Box 2008, Davis, CA 95617 (SAN 688-9123) Tel 916-756-7177; 2655 Portage Bay Ave., Davis, CA 95616 (SAN 658-2729).

Agadir Pr., *(Agadir Pr; 0-913627),* P.O. Box 2015, Corvallis, OR 97339 (SAN 286-0309) Tel 503-929-5918; 424 S. 17th St., Philomath, OR 97370 (SAN 286-0317).

Agapao Unlimited, Inc., Div. of ABC Institute for Better Living, Inc., *(Agapao; 0-937305),* 228 Bidwell Ave., Jersey City, NJ 07305 (SAN 658-7690) Tel 201-434-8098; Dist. by: Terrell's Bindery, 3620 Buena Vista, Nashville, TN 37218 (SAN 200-6324) Tel 615-242-1051.

Agape, Div. of Hope Publishing Co., *(Agape IL; 0-916642),* 380 S. Main Place, Carol Stream, IL 60188 (SAN 217-2224); Toll free: 800-323-1049.

Agape Pr., Div. of KINGCommunications, *(Agape Pr; 0-915459),* 1900 Tribune Tower, 409 13th St., Oakland, CA 94612 (SAN 291-0675) Tel 415-763-5208.

†Agathon Pr. Inc., *(Agathon; 0-87586),* 111 Eighth Ave., New York, NY 10011 (SAN 201-2367) Tel 212-741-3087; *CIP.*

Agee Pubs., Inc., *(Agee Pub; 0-935265),* P.O. Box 526, Athens, GA 30603 (SAN 695-7498) Tel 404-548-5269; 425 N. Lumpkin St., Athens, GA 30603 (SAN 696-7035).

Ageless Bks., *(Ageless Bks; 0-918482),* P.O. Box 6300, Beverly Hills, CA 90212 (SAN 210-0215) Tel 213-933-6338.

Agency for Instructional Technology, *(Agency Instr Tech; 0-9603244),* P.O. Box A, Bloomington, IN 47402 (SAN 225-7564) Tel 812-339-2203; Toll free: 800-457-4509; 1111 W. 17th St., Bloomington, IN 47401 (SAN 668-954X).

Agency Pr., Div. of Agency Services, *(Agency Pr; 0-910887),* P.O. Box 1602, Greenville, SC 29602 (SAN 266-1446) Tel 803-242-5400.

Aging/Alcoholism Information Committee, *(Aging Alcoholism; 0-9612426),* 173 Windsor Dr., Daly City, CA 94015 (SAN 289-0984) Tel 415-986-4510.

Aglow Pubns., Div. of Women's Aglow Fellowship International, *(Aglow Pubns; 0-930756; 0-932305),* P.O. Box I, Lynnwood, WA 98046-1557 (SAN 211-8297) Tel 206-775-7282.

Agnes Press, The, *(Agnes Press; 0-936033),* 3739 Cottontail Ln., Utica, MI 48087 (SAN 696-995X) Tel 313-731-3239.

Agnew Tech-Tran, Inc., *(Agnew Tech-Tran; 0-9606636),* P.O. Box 789, Woodland Hills, CA 91365 (SAN 212-7202) Tel 818-340-5147.

Agni Review, *(Agni Review),* P.O. Box 660, Amherst, MA 01004 (SAN 219-4600).

Agni Yoga Society, Inc., *(Agni Yoga Soc; 0-933574),* 319 W. 107th St., New York, NY 10025-2799 (SAN 201-7121) Tel 212-864-7752.

Agri-Fence, *(Agri-Fence),* P.O. Box 521, Rough & Ready, CA 96975 (SAN 263-2519) Tel 916-273-5492.

Agribookstore/Winrock, Affil. of Winrock International, *(Agribookstore),* Rosslyn Plaza, 1611 N. Kent St., Suite 600, Arlington, VA 22209 (SAN 200-6693) Tel 703-525-9455.

Agriculture & Natural Resources, Univ. of California, *(Ag & Nat Res; 0-931876),* 6701 San Pablo Ave., Oakland, CA 94608-1239 (SAN 211-4771) Tel 415-642-2431.

Agricutural Publishing Co., *(Agri Pub Co; 0-914669),* P.O. Box 1572, Eugene, OR 97440 (SAN 287-783X) Tel 503-345-4312.

AgriData Resources, Inc., *(AgriData; 0-910939),* 330 E. Kilbourn Ave., Milwaukee, WI 53202 (SAN 209-6706) Tel 414-278-7676; Toll free: 800-558-9044.

†Agrinde Pubns., Ltd., *(Agrinde Pubns; 0-9601068),* 220 Church St., New York, NY 10013 (SAN 281-2452) Tel 212-227-1005; Toll free: 800-251-4000; Dist. by: Dodd, Mead & Co., 79 Madison Ave., New York, NY 10016 (SAN 201-3339) Tel 212-685-6464; *CIP.*

Agronomy Pubns., *(Agronomy Pubns; 0-9616847),* P.O. Box 83, River Falls, WI 54022 (SAN 661-1494) Tel 715-425-2353.

AGT Publishing Inc., *(AGT Pub; 0-933521),* 230 Park Ave., New York, NY 10169 (SAN 691-845X) Tel 212-687-8155.

Aharonian, Aharon G., *(A G Aharonian; 0-9613300),* P.O. Box 67, Shrewsbury, MA 01545 (SAN 654-1569) Tel 617-791-3261.

Ahio Publishing Co., *(Ahio Pub Co; 0-914347),* 4313 W. 43rd St., Tulsa, OK 74107 (SAN 289-582X) Tel 918-446-9278.

Ahsahta Pr., *(Ahsahta Pr; 0-916272),* Dept. of English, Boise State Univ., Boise, ID 83725 (SAN 207-9461) Tel 208-385-1246; Orders to: Univ. Bookstore, Boise State Univ., Boise, ID 83725 (SAN 207-947X) Tel 208-385-1276.

Aid-U Publishing Co., *(Aid-U Pub; 0-940370),* P.O. Box 47226, Oak Park, MI 48237 (SAN 217-149X) Tel 313-569-8288.

Aiga Pubns., *(AIGA Pubns; 0-943980),* P.O. Box 148, Laie, HI 96762 (SAN 241-094X) Tel 808-293-5277.

Aikido Federation of California, *(Aikido Fed),* P.O. Box 10962, Costa Mesa, CA 92627 (SAN 263-9122).

Air Age, Inc., *(Air Age; 0-911295),* 632 Danbury Rd., Wilton, CT 06897 (SAN 266-1667) Tel 203-834-2900.

Air Conditioning & Refrigeration Institute, *(ACR Inst),* 1501 Wilson Blvd., Suite 600, Arlington, VA 22209 (SAN 230-6263) Tel 703-524-8800.

Air Diffusion Council, *(Air Diffusion),* 230 N. Michigan Ave., Suite 1200, Chicago, IL 60601 (SAN 229-4362) Tel 312-372-9800.

Air Force Museum Foundation, Inc., The, *(US Air Force Mus; 0-9611634),* P.O. Box 33624, Wright Patterson Air Force Base, OH 45433 (SAN 284-8953) Tel 513-258-1218.

Air Movement & Control Assn., Inc., *(Air Mvmt & Cont),* 30 W. University Dr., Arlington Heights, IL 60004 (SAN 224-618X) Tel 312-394-0150.

Air-Plus Enterprises, *(Air-Plus Ent; 0-940726),* P.O. Box 367, Glassboro, NJ 08028 (SAN 219-7545) Tel 609-881-0724; Dist. by: Quality Books, 400 Anthony Trail, Northbrook, IL 60062 (SAN 668-9558).

Air Pollution Control Assn., *(Air Pollution Control Assoc),* Box 2861, Pittsburgh, PA 15230 (SAN 225-1701) Tel 412-232-3444.

Air Science Co., *(Air Sci Co; 0-903608),* P.O. Box 143, Corning, NY 14830 (SAN 210-7791) Tel 607-962-5591.

Air Taxi Charter & Rental Directory of North America, The, *(Air Taxi Chart & Rent; 0-9603908),* Box 3000, Oak Park, IL 60303 (SAN 213-9049) Tel 217-546-1491.

Airborne Pr., *(Airborne Pr; 0-934145),* 3055 Clay St., San Francisco, CA 94115 (SAN 693-3076) Tel 415-921-5617.

Airman Universal Pubns., *(Airman Universal; 0-941978),* P.O. Box 310027, Atlanta, GA 30331 (SAN 239-5118).

Airmont Publishing Co., Inc., *(Airmont; 0-8049),* 401 Lafayette St., New York, NY 10003 (SAN 206-8710).

Airport Bk. Pr., *(Airport Bk Pr; 0-935866),* 11205 Farmland Dr., Rockville, MD 20852 (SAN 213-7178) Tel 301-881-4996.

Airsho Pubs., *(Airsho Pubs; 0-9601506),* 349 Homeland S. Way, 1B, Baltimore, MD 21212 (SAN 201-6974) Tel 301-323-3314.

Airth Pubns., *(Airth Pubns; 0-9616720),* Birdwood, 1015-1/2 Lovers Ln., Ocean Springs, MS 39564 (SAN 659-6770) Tel 601-875-6028.

AJAY Enterprises, *(AJAY Ent; 0-939440),* P.O. Box 2018, Mosby Branch, Falls Church, VA 22042-0018 (SAN 211-1209) Tel 703-573-8220.

AK Enterprises, *(AK Enterprises; 0-9614814),* 13540 Venus Way, Anchorage, AK 99515-3919 (SAN 692-9184) Tel 907-345-4948.

Akers, Mona J. Coole, *(M Akers; 0-912706),* 219 S. Williams St., Denver, CO 80209 (SAN 206-9075) Tel 303-722-1892.

Akhtar, Salman, *(S Akhtar; 0-9615818),* 1015 Chestnut St. 2nd Flr., Philadelphia, PA 19107 (SAN 696-6705) Tel 215-928-8420.

Akiba Pr., *(Akiba Pr; 0-934764),* Box 13086, Oakland, CA 94661 (SAN 212-0666) Tel 415-339-1283.

Akili Books of America, *(Akili Bks of Amer; 0-9607296),* P.O. Box 1291, South Gate, CA 90280 (SAN 239-1481) Tel 213-635-7191.

Aksunai Pr., *(Aksunai Pr; 0-930939),* P.O. Box 326B, Wakefield, MA 01880 (SAN 684-2593).

†**Al-Anon Family Group Headquarters,** *(Al-Anon; 0-910034),* 1372 Broadway, 7th flr., New York, NY 10018-6106 (SAN 201-2391) Tel 212-302-7240; P.O. Box 862 Midtown Station, New York, NY 10018-0862 (SAN 662-7110); *CIP.*

AL-DEL Hobbies, Inc., *(AL-DEL; 0-933360),* 528 SE 6th St., College Place, WA 99324 (SAN 212-4718) Tel 503-378-7909.

Al Fresco Enterprise, *(Al Fresco; 0-9612596),* Postal Drawer 11530, Pueblo, CO 81001 (SAN 211-5832) Tel 303-545-9524.

Alabama Cattlemen's Assn., *(AL Cattlemen; 0-9616023),* P.O. Box 1746, Montgomery, AL 36197 (SAN 698-1720) Tel 205-265-1867; 600 Adams Ave., Montgomery, AL 36197 (SAN 698-1739).

Alabama Department of Revenue, *(AL Revenue),* Administrative Bldg., Montgomery, AL 36130 (SAN 266-1934).

Alabama Law Institute, *(AL Law Inst),* P.O. Box 1425 Law Ctr., Rm. 326, University, AL 35486 (SAN 290-683X).

Aladdin Bks. *See* Atheneum Pubs.

Aladdin Bks. *See* Macmillan Publishing Co., Inc.

Aladdin Pr., *(Aladdin Pr; 0-916607),* 318 Harvard St., Suite 10, Brookline, MA 02146 (SAN 296-4422); Dist. by: Redwing Bk. Co., 44 Linden St., Brookline, MA 02146 (SAN 163-3597) Tel 617-738-4664.

Alamo Press, *(Alamo Pr; 0-9605140),* 104 Garydale Court, Alamo, CA 94507 (SAN 216-2164).

Alan I. Pr., *(Alan I Press; 0-938827),* 99-555 Honohina St., Aiea, HI 96701 (SAN 661-6984) Tel 808-488-4674.

Alandale Pr., *(Alandale Pr; 0-937748),* R.D. 5, Ballston Rd., Amsterdam, NY 12010 (SAN 216-0978) Tel 518-842-5189.

Alaska Angler Publications, *(Alaska Angler; 0-916771),* P.O. Box 82222, Fairbanks, AK 99708 (SAN 654-1453) Tel 907-455-6691; Orders to: P.O. Box 83550, Fairbanks, AK 99708 (SAN 693-9929) Tel 907-456-8212; Dist. by: Alaska News Agency, 325 W. Potter Dr., Anchorage, AK 99502 (SAN 168-9274) Tel 907-563-3251. *Imprints:* Alaska Hunter Publications (Alaska Hunter Pubns).

Alaska Department of Labor/Research & Analysis, *(Alaska Labor),* P.O. Box 25501, Juneau, AK 99802-5501 (SAN 266-2035) Tel 907-465-4500.

Alaska Fieldbooks Co., Ltd., *(Alaska Fieldbks; 0-918745),* P.O. Box 1044, Anchorage, AK 99510 (SAN 657-5676) Tel 907-274-5742.

Alaska Heritage Enterprises, Inc., *(Alaska Heritage; 0-930571),* 7404 Sand Lake Rd., Anchorage, AK 99502 (SAN 677-2196) Tel 907-243-4120; Dist. by: Pacific Pipeline, Inc., 19215 66th Ave. S., Kent, WA 98032 (SAN 208-2128).

Alaska Historical Commission, Div. of State of Alaska, *(Alaska Hist; 0-943712),* Dept. of Education, Old City Hall, 524 W. Fourth Ave., Suite 207, Anchorage, AK 99501 (SAN 240-9933) Tel 907-274-6222; Dist. by: Alaska Pacific Univ., 4101 University Dr., Anchorage, AK 99508 (SAN 215-2908).

Alaska Hunter Publications *See* **Alaska Angler Publications**

Alaska Missionary Conference of the United Methodist Church, Conference Council on Ministries, *(AMCUMC Ministries; 0-9616802),* 501 W. Northern Lights Blvd., Anchorage, AK 99503 (SAN 661-034X) Tel 907-789-7354.

Alaska Native Language Ctr., *(Alaska Native; 0-933769; 1-55500),* Univ. of Alaska, P.O. Box 111, Fairbanks, AK 99775-0120 (SAN 692-9796) Tel 907-474-6577.

Alaska Natural History Assn., *(Alaska Natural; 0-9602876),* 2525 Gambell St., Anchorage, AK 99503 (SAN 223-5269) Tel 907-274-8440.

†**Alaska Northwest Publishing Co.,** *(Alaska Northwst; 0-88240),* 130 Second Ave., S., Edmonds, WA 98020 (SAN 201-2383) Tel 206-774-4111; *CIP.*

Alaska Pacific Univ. Pr., *(Alaska Pacific; 0-935094),* A.P.U., 4101 University Dr., Anchorage, AK 99508 (SAN 215-2908) Tel 907-564-8291.

Alaska State Council on the Arts, *(Alaska St Coun; 0-910615),* 619 Warehouse Ave., Suite 220, Anchorage, AK 99501 (SAN 260-1591) Tel 907-279-1558.

Alaska State Legislature, *(Alaska Legis; 0-935511),* State Capitol Bldg, Juneau, AK 99811 (SAN 266-2108).

Alaska Travel Pubns., Inc., *(Alaska Travel; 0-914164),* P.O. Box 4-2031, Anchorage, AK 99509 (SAN 201-1913) Tel 907-272-2869.

Alaskabooks, *(Alaskabks),* P.O. Box 1494, Juneau, AK 99802 (SAN 201-6990) Tel 907-586-3067.

Alba Hse., Div. of the Society of St. Paul, *(Alba; 0-8189),* 2187 Victory Blvd., Staten Island, NY 10314 (SAN 201-2405) Tel 718-761-0047.

Albacore Pr., *(Albacore Pr; 0-9601716),* P.O. Box 355, Eastsound, WA 98245 (SAN 223-4181).

Albanian Catholic Information Ctr., *(Albanian Cath Info; 0-9614744),* P.O. Box 1217, Santa Clara, CA 95053 (SAN 692-7319) Tel 415-387-2020.

Albany County Historical Assn., *(Albany County; 0-89062),* 9 Ten Broeck Pl., Albany, NY 12210 (SAN 219-7553); Dist. by: Publishing Ctr. for Cultural Resources, 625 Broadway, New York, NY 10012 (SAN 274-9025) Tel 212-260-2010.

Albany Institute of History & Art, *(Albany Hist & Art),* 125 Washington Ave., Albany, NY 12210 (SAN 204-7764) Tel 518-463-4478.

Albany Public Library, *(Albany Pub Lib; 0-9605090),* 161 Washington Ave., Albany, NY 12210 (SAN 215-8361).

Albatross, *(Albatross; 0-932759),* P.O. Box 333, Urbana, IL 61801 (SAN 688-5403) Tel 217-367-1598.

Albert, Nancy E., *(N E Albert; 0-9613998),* Evanston Law Ctr., P.O. Box 110, Evanston, IL 60204 (SAN 687-6633).

Albert Hse. Publishing, *(Albert Hse Pub; 0-913553),* 30 Ayles Rd., Hyde Park, MA 02136 (SAN 285-2071) Tel 617-361-4398.

Albin, James R., *(J R Albin; 0-916210),* 431 Bridgeway, Sausalito, CA 94965 (SAN 207-4850) Tel 415-332-6438.

Albion, *(Albion NC; 0-932530),* Dept. of History, Appalachian State Univ., Boone, NC 28608 (SAN 212-2626) Tel 704-262-6004.

Albion Albums, *(Albion Albums; 0-9604100),* P.O. Box 301, Albion, CA 95410 (SAN 216-2172).

Albion-American Bks., *(Albion Am Bks),* P.O. Box 217, Elfrida, AZ 85610 (SAN 215-7225).

Albion Pr., *(Albion PA; 0-930953),* P.O. Box 445, Exton, PA 19341 (SAN 678-8734) Tel 215-431-3362.

Albion Pr., *(Albion Pr; 0-9606846),* 582 Stratford Ave., St. Louis, MO 63130 (SAN 217-3220) Tel 314-863-9285; Dist. by: Baker & Taylor Co., Midwest Div., 501 Gladiola Ave., Momence, IL 60954 (SAN 169-2100); Dist. by: The Distributors, 702 S. Michigan, South Bend, IN 46618 (SAN 169-2488) Tel 219-232-8500; Dist. by: Book Dynamics, 836 Broadway, New York, NY 10003 (SAN 169-5649) Tel 212-254-7798; Dist. by: Koen Book Distributors, Inc., 514 N. Read Ave., Cinnaminson, NJ 08077 (SAN 169-4642) Tel 609-786-1111; Dist. by: Paperback Supply, Inc., 4121 Forest Park Ave., St. Louis, MO 63108 (SAN 169-4324) Tel 314-652-1000.

Albion Review Pr., *(Albion Review Pr; 0-9613841),* Albion College, Albion, MI 49224 (SAN 681-9591) Tel 517-629-5511.

Albright & Co., *(Albright & Co; 0-932919),* P.O. Box 2011, Huntsville, AL 35804 (SAN 688-9174) Tel 205-539-3288.

Albright Pr., *(Albright; 0-918301),* 12240 Blythen Way, Oakland, CA 94619 (SAN 657-2480); Dist. by: Bookpeople, 2929 Fifth St., Berkeley, CA 94710 (SAN 168-9517) Tel 415-549-3030.

Alchemist/Light Publishing, *(Alchemist-Light; 0-9600650),* P.O. Box 881444, San Francisco, CA 94188 (SAN 201-7164) Tel 415-345-7021.

Alchemy Bks., *(Alchemy Bks; 0-931290),* 717 Market, Suite 514, San Francisco, CA 94103 (SAN 211-304X) Tel 415-777-2197.

Names

Alchemy Communications Group, Ltd., Subs. of Alchemy II, Inc., *(Alchemy Comms; 0-934323),* 9207 Eton Ave., Chatsworth, CA 91311 (SAN 693-5990) Tel 818-700-8300; Dist. by: Worlds of Wonder, Inc., 4209 Technology Dr., Fremont, CA 94538 (SAN 699-993X) Tel 415-659-4300.

Alcoholics Anonymous World Services, Inc., *(AAWS; 0-916856),* 468 Park Ave., S., New York, NY 10016 (SAN 210-7678) Tel 212-686-1100; Orders to: P.O. Box 459, Grand Central Sta., New York, NY 10163 (SAN 215-0441).

Alcoholism Consultation Service, *(Alcohol Con Serv; 0-930427),* 1504 NW Blvd., Suite H, Spokane, WA 99205 (SAN 670-9931) Tel 509-326-2301.

Alcoholism Trust Committee, *(Alcohol Comm; 0-912399),* P.O. Box 1877, Carlsbad, CA 92008 (SAN 265-1718) Tel 619-729-2572.

Alcom, Inc., *(Alcom Inc; 0-936129),* 1005 NE 72nd St., Seattle, WA 98115 (SAN 696-9860) Tel 206-527-8999.

Alcott Pr., The, *(Alcott Pr WA; 0-9616180),* W. 1114 Spofford Ave., Spokane, WA 99205 (SAN 699-8526) Tel 509-326-3373; P.O. Box 857, Spokane, WA 99210 (SAN 699-8534).

Alcove Publishing Co., *(Alcove Pub Co OR; 0-937473),* P.O. Box 362, West Linn, OR 97068 (SAN 658-9766) Tel 503-655-5564; 6385 Barclay St., West Linn, OR 97068 (SAN 658-9774).

Alcyone Pubns., *(Alcyone Pubns; 0-916669),* Triphammer Mall, P.O. Box 4764, Ithaca, NY 14852 (SAN 656-8785).

Alden, Jay, Pubs., *(J Alden; 0-914844),* P.O. Box 1295, 546 S. Hofgaarden St., La Puente, CA 91749 (SAN 204-7780) Tel 818-968-6424.

Alden, John, Bks., *(John Alden Bks; 0-9605818),* 187 Barmont Dr., P.O. Box 26668, Rochester, NY 14626 (SAN 216-5678) Tel 716-225-8534.

Alden Electronics & IRE Co., Inc., *(Alden Electronics; 0-9607004),* Washington St., Westboro, MA 01581 (SAN 237-9287) Tel 617-366-8851.

Aldredg-Blair Inc., *(Aldredg-Blair; 0-942446),* P.O. Box 7195, Dallas, TX 75209 (SAN 238-1389) Tel 214-521-6724.

Aldridge Group, The, *(Aldridge Group; 0-9612834),* 2148 Seminole, Detroit, MI 48214 (SAN 289-9647) Tel 313-876-0086.

Alef Bet Communications, *(Alef Bet Comns; 0-9616488),* 14809 Bremer Rd., New Haven, IN 46774 (SAN 659-2740) Tel 219-749-0182.

Alegra Hse. Pubs., Affil. of Kaya Books, *(Alegra Hse Pubs; 0-933879),* P.O. Box 1443-B, Warren, OH 44482 (SAN 692-7858) Tel 216-372-2951.

Alek Publishing Co., *(Alek Pub; 0-9613963),* 223 Tenafly Rd., Englewood, NJ 07631 (SAN 682-2843) Tel 201-569-4174.

Alemany Pr., Inc., Div. of Janus Bk. Pubs., Inc., *(Alemany Pr; 0-88084),* 2501 Industrial Pkwy. W., Hayward, CA 94545 (SAN 240-1312) Tel 415-887-7070; Toll free: 800-227-2375.

Alembic Marketing Partners, *(Alembic Mktg; 0-9616368),* 538 Camino del Monte Sol, Santa Fe, NM 87501 (SAN 658-9804) Tel 505-984-2766.

†**Alembic Pr.,** *(Alembic Pr; 0-934184),* 1424 Stanley Rd., Plainfield, IN 46168 (SAN 281-2479) Tel 317-839-8312; CIP.

Alert Pubs., *(Alert Pubs; 0-938033),* P.O. Drawer 2459, Hemet, CA 92343 (SAN 659-6819) Tel 714-929-2062; 261 W. Susan Ln., Hemet, CA 92343 (SAN 659-6827).

Aletheia Bks. See **University Pubns. of America, Inc.**

Aletheia Pubs., Inc., Div. of Alpha Omega Pub., *(Aletheia Pubs; 0-86717),* P.O. Box 1437, Tempe, AZ 85281 (SAN 216-7824) Tel 602-438-2702.

Alethes, *(Alethes; 0-930254),* P.O. Box 5842, Carmel, CA 93921 (SAN 202-3598).

Aleutian Pribilof Islands Assn., Inc. (AANG ANGAGIN), *(Aleutian; 0-9609308),* 1689 C St., Anchorage, AK 99501 (SAN 260-0102) Tel 907-276-2700.

Alexander & Alexander Pubs., *(Alexander & Alexander; 0-939353),* 1012 Fair Oaks, Suite 392, South Pasadena, CA 91030 (SAN 662-6912) Tel 818-799-0839.

Alexander Communications, *(Alexander Comms; 0-942454),* 212 W. Superior., Chicago, IL 60610 (SAN 238-1494) Tel 312-944-5115.

Alexander Publishing, *(Alexander Pub; 0-939067),* 14536 Roscoe Blvd., Suite 105, Panorama City, CA 91402 (SAN 662-9415) Tel 818-891-9831.

Alexandria Assn., The, *(Alexandria Assn; 0-9616541),* P.O. Box 178, City Hall, Alexandria, VA 22313 (SAN 659-4085) Tel 703-838-4554; Orders to: Lyceum Museum Shop, 201 S. Washington St., Alexandria, VA 22314 (SAN 662-7862) Tel 703-548-1812.

†**Alexandrian Pr.,** Div. of Computer Curriculum Corporation, *(Alexandrian Pr; 0-916485),* 1070 Avastradero Rd., Palo Alto, CA 94303 (SAN 295-5423) Tel 415-494-8450; Toll free: 800-227-8324; Dist. by: Baker & Taylor Co., Western Div., 380 Edison Way, Reno, NV 89564 (SAN 169-4464); Dist. by: Publishers Group West, 5855 Beaudry St., Emeryville, CA 94608 (SAN 202-8522); Dist. by: Bookpeople, 2929 Fifth St., Berkeley, CA 94710 (SAN 168-9517); Dist. by: Ingram Industries, 347 Reedwood Dr., Nashville, TN 37217 (SAN 169-7978); CIP.

Alexandrian Pr., Subs. of Holmes Publishing Group, *(Alexandrian WA; 0-916411),* P.O. Box 623, Edmonds, WA 98020 (SAN 656-9080) Tel 206-771-2701.

Alfa Sierra Pubs., *(Alfa Sierra; 0-9604728),* P.O. Box 9636, San Diego, CA 92109 (SAN 216-0137) Tel 619-276-6291.

Alfred & Alfred Co., *(Alfred),* 5260 Figueroa St., Suite 114, Los Angeles, CA 90037 (SAN 206-9636).

Alfred Publishing Co., Inc., *(Alfred Pub; 0-88284),* 15335 Morrison St., Sherman Oaks, CA 91413 (SAN 201-243X) Tel 818-995-8811; Toll free: 800-821-6083.

Alger County Historical Society, *(Alger Cnty Hist Soc; 0-9617008),* 203 W. Onota St., Munising, MI 49862 (SAN 662-9067) Tel 906-387-2607.

†**Algol Pr.,** *(Algol Pr; 0-916186),* P.O. Box 4175, New York, NY 10163 (SAN 207-9445) Tel 718-643-9011; CIP.

†**Algonquin Bks. of Chapel Hill,** *(Algonquin Bks; 0-912697),* P.O. Box 2225, Chapel Hill, NC 27515 (SAN 282-7506); 501 W. Franklin St., Suite 104, Chapel Hill, NC 27514 (SAN 662-2011) Tel 919-967-0108; Dist. by: Taylor Publishing Co., 1550 Mockingbird Ln., P.O. Box 597, Dallas, TX 75221 (SAN 202-7631) Tel 214-637-2800; CIP.

†**Algonquin Enterprises,** *(Algonquin Enter; 0-931979),* P.O. Box 1410, Muskegon, MI 49443 (SAN 686-1148) Tel 616-780-3815; CIP.

Algorithmics, Inc., *(Algorithmics; 0-917448),* 44 W. 62nd St., New York, NY 10023 (SAN 201-2448) Tel 212-246-2366.

Alicejamesbooks, Div. of Alice James Poetry Cooperative, *(Alicejamesbooks; 0-914086),* 138 Mt. Auburn St., Cambridge, MA 02138 (SAN 201-1158) Tel 617-354-1408.

Alimar Publishing Co., *(Alimar Pub; 0-9616034),* 8920 Wilshire Blvd., No. 316, Beverly Hills, CA 90211 (SAN 698-0449) Tel 213-271-3113.

Alin Foundation Press, *(Alin Found Pr; 0-9606924),* 2107 Dwight Way, Berkeley, CA 94704 (SAN 212-0682) Tel 415-845-4907.

Alinda Pr., *(Alinda Pr; 0-933076),* Box 553, Eureka, CA 95502 (SAN 212-4734) Tel 707-443-2510.

Alised Enterprises, *(Alised; 0-913377),* 7808 Maryknoll Ave., Bethesda, MD 20817 (SAN 209-522X) Tel 301-320-3306.

Alistair Pr., *(Alistair Pr; 0-9616489),* 374 Shadow Rd., Greenwood, IN 46142 (SAN 659-2767) Tel 317-888-6581.

Alive Assocs., *(Alive Assocs; 0-915467),* 2516 Swift Run St., Vienna, VA 22180 (SAN 291-0683) Tel 703-573-4608.

Alive Films, Inc., *(Alive Films; 0-937113),* 1414 Seabright Dr., Beverly Hills, CA 90210 (SAN 658-5469) Tel 213-275-5711.

Alive Polarity Pubns., *(Alive Polarity; 0-941732),* 28779 Via Las Flores, Murrieta, CA 92362 (SAN 239-149X) Tel 714-677-7451.

Alive Pubns. Ltd., *(Alive Pubns; 0-935572),* 11 Park Place, New York, NY 10007 (SAN 281-2495) Tel 212-962-0316.

Alivening Pubns., *(Alivening Pubns; 0-9616707),* P.O. Box 1368, Land O Lakes, FL 33539 (SAN 659-6835) Tel 813-996-3659; 315 Geneva Rd., Land O Lakes, FL 33539 (SAN 659-6843).

Allabout Bks., *(Allabout Bks; 0-930003),* P.O. Box 14155, Fremont, CA 94539 (SAN 669-7143) Tel 415-657-3613.

Allan-Michaels Corp., The, *(Allan-Michaels; 1-55621),* 120036 Ackler Sta., Nashville, TN 37212 (SAN 659-6851) Tel 615-791-2880.

Allanheld & Schram See **Abner Schram Ltd.**

Allanheld & Schram See **Rowman & Littlefield, Pubs.**

Allanheld, Osmun & Co. Pubs., Inc., Div. of Littlefield, Adams & Co., *(Allanheld; 0-916672; 0-86598),* 81 Adams Dr., Totowa, NJ 07512 (SAN 211-724X) Tel 201-256-8600.

Allan's, *(Allans; 0-88100),* P.O. Box 4806, Inglewood, CA 90309 (SAN 265-3753).

Allbooks, *(Allbooks; 0-9616527),* 4341 Majestic Ln., Fairfax, VA 22033 (SAN 659-4093) Tel 703-968-7396.

†**Allegany Mountain Pr.,** *(Allegany Mtn Pr; 0-931588),* 111 N. Tenth St., Olean, NY 14760 (SAN 211-5034) Tel 716-372-0935; CIP.

Allegheny County Bar Assn., *(Allegheny Co Bar),* 620 Second Ave., Pittsburgh, PA 15219 (SAN 227-1893).

Allegheny Pr., *(Allegheny; 0-910042),* P.O. Box 220, Elgin, PA 16413 (SAN 201-2456) Tel 814-664-8504.

Allegheny Pubns., *(Allegheny Pubns; 0-938037),* 2161 Woodsdale Rd., Salem, OH 44460 (SAN 659-686X) Tel 216-337-6403.

Allegro Publishing Co., *(Allegro Pub; 0-9601042),* P.O. Box 39892, Los Angeles, CA 90039 (SAN 201-2464) Tel 213-665-6783.

Alleluia Pr., *(Alleluia Pr; 0-911726),* P.O. Box 103, Allendale, NJ 07401 (SAN 202-3601) Tel 201-327-3513; 672 Franklin Turnpike, Allendale, NJ 07401 (SAN 202-361X).

Allen, J. A., & Co. Ltd., *(J A Allen; 0-85131),* Dist. by: Sporting Bk. Ctr., Inc., Canaan, NY 12029 (SAN 222-8734) Tel 518-794-8998.

Allen, J. K. & A. C., Publishing, *(J K & A C Allen; 0-9616913),* 207 Burnett Dr., Baytown, TX 77520 (SAN 661-4833) Tel 713-665-7088.

Allen, Nathan, Publishing Co., *(N Allen Pub; 0-943586),* 1503 Van Stone Dr., Milford, MI 48042 (SAN 240-5806) Tel 313-363-2206.

Allen, W. P., & Co., Inc., *(W P Allen; 0-916777),* P.O. Box 702, Portland, OR 97207 (SAN 654-2921) Tel 503-538-2311.

†**Allen & Unwin, Inc.,** Div. of Allen & Unwin, Ltd., *(Allen Unwin; 0-04; 0-86861),* 8 Winchester Pl., Winchester, MA 01890 (SAN 210-3362) Tel 617-729-0830; Toll free: 800-547-8889; CIP.

Allen Group, The, *(Allen Group; 0-943402),* 145 E. Center St., Provo, UT 84061 (SAN 240-5792) Tel 801-373-8000.

Allen Lane, Dist. by: Viking Penguin, Inc., 40 W. 23rd St., New York, NY 10010 (SAN 200-2442) Tel 212-337-5200.

Allen Pr., Inc., *(Allen Pr; 0-935868),* P.O. Box 368, Lawrence, KS 66044 (SAN 213-7186).

Allen Publishing, *(Allen Pub; 0-9614419),* P.O. Box 2129, New York, NY 10185 (SAN 689-1012) Tel 718-522-2858.

Allenby Pr., *(Allenby Pr; 0-9615419),* 701 S. First Ave., Suite 272, Arcadia, CA 91006 (SAN 695-7544) Tel 818-446-6700.

Allenson, Alec R., Inc., *(A R Allenson; 0-8401),* P.O. Box 447, Geneva, AL 36340 (SAN 162-4903).

Allergan Humphrey, Inc., Div. of Smithkline Bechman, *(Allergan Humphrey; 0-939425),* 3081 Teagarden St., San Leandro, CA 94577 (SAN 663-351X) Tel 415-895-9110.

†**Allerton Press, Inc.,** *(Allerton Pr; 0-89864),* 150 Fifth Ave., New York, NY 10011 (SAN 239-4049); CIP.

Allgau Bks., *(Allgau Bks; 0-936887),* 2945 Lincoln Way, San Francisco, CA 94122 (SAN 658-3504) Tel 415-681-3471.

Allgood Books, *(Allgood Bks),* P.O. Box 1329, Jackson, MS 39205 (SAN 208-1318) Tel 601-355-5419.

Alliance College, *(Alliance Coll),* Cambridge Springs, PA 16403 (SAN 216-0862).

Alliance for School Health, *(Alliance Schl Health; 0-9616270),* P.O. Box 2041, Fair Oaks, CA 95628-2041 (SAN 658-5434) Tel 916-487-5560; 1748 Park Pl. Dr., Carmichael, CA 95608 (SAN 658-5442).

Alliance for the Arts, *(Alliance Arts; 0-912443),* 330 W. 42nd St., New York, NY 10036 (SAN 211-8939) Tel 212-947-6340; Dist. by: Publishing Center for Cultural Resources, 625 Broadway, New York, NY 10012 (SAN 274-9025) Tel 212-260-2010.

Alliance Plus, *(Alliance Plus; 0-9617034),* 22151 Bianco, Laguna Hills, CA 92653 (SAN 662-846X) Tel 714-581-4235.

Alliance Pubs., Div. of Southern Program Alliance, *(Alliance Pubs),* P.O. Box 25004, Fort Lauderdale, FL 33320 (SAN 213-3768) Tel 305-722-5361.

Alliance to Save Energy, *(Alliance Save ener),* 1925 K St., NW, No. 206, Washington, DC 20006 (SAN 266-2426) Tel 202-857-0666.

Allied Artists of America, Inc, *(Allied Artists America),* 15 Gramercy Park S., New York, NY 10003 (SAN 225-2732) Tel 516-437-4369.

Allied Enterprises, *(Allied Ent; 0-9605082),* P.O. Box 8050, Chicago, IL 60680 (SAN 238-9045).

Allied Research Society, Inc., *(Allied Res Soc; 0-912984),* 11057 New River Circle, Rancho Cordova, CA 95670 (SAN 201-2480) Tel 916-635-7728.

Allin Enterprises, *(Allin Ent; 0-936181),* P.O. Box 284, Orono, ME 04473 (SAN 696-9968) Tel 207-866-2579; 7 Mayo St., Orono, ME 04473 (SAN 696-9976).

Allison, R. B., Co. *See Wisconsin Bks.*

Allison Enterprises, *(Allison Ent; 0-918324),* P.O. Box 200, Franklin, NJ 07416 (SAN 210-024X) Tel 201-827-5104.

Allison Pubs., *(Allison Pubs; 0-9607936),* 1 La Playa, Box 733, Cochise, AZ 85606 (SAN 207-2009) Tel 602-384-2047.

Allnutt Publishing, *(Allnutt Pub; 0-934374),* P.O. Box 879, Evergreen, CO 80439 (SAN 221-962X) Tel 303-670-3390.

Allowance, Inc., *(Allowance; 0-9604228),* 1516 Bonnie Brae, Denton, TX 76201 (SAN 214-2805).

Allred, O. M., Pubns., *(O M Allred; 0-936035),* 2201 Sunrise Blvd., Ft. Myers, FL 33907 (SAN 696-9941) Tel 813-939-3606.

Allum, Faith T., *(F T Allum; 0-9613349),* 1104 Larke Ave., Rogers City, MI 49779 (SAN 655-8739) Tel 517-734-4517.

†**Ally Pr.,** *(Ally Pr; 0-915408),* 524 Orleans St., St. Paul, MN 55107 (SAN 207-7116); *CIP.*

Allyn & Bacon, Inc., Div. of Simon & Schuster, *(Allyn; 0-205),* 7 Wells Ave., Newton, MA 02159 (SAN 201-2510) Tel 617-964-5530; Toll free: 800-526-4799; Orders to: College Div., 1 Pond Rd., Rockleigh, NJ 07647 (SAN 201-2529).

Alma Historical Society, *(Alma Hist Soc; 0-9604684),* P.O. Box 87, Alma, WI 54610 (SAN 216-0986).

Almaas Pubns., *(Almaas Pubns; 0-936713),* 5975 Park Ave., Richmond, CA 94805 (SAN 699-8771) Tel 415-652-1243; P.O. Box 10114, Berkeley, CA 94709 (SAN 699-878X); Dist. by: Bookpeople, 2929 Fifth St., Berkeley, CA 94710 (SAN 168-9517) Tel 415-549-3030; Toll free: 800-227-1516. *Imprints:* Diamond Books (Diamond Bks).

Almanac-Pr., *(Almanac Pr; 0-935090),* P.O. Box 480264, Los Angeles, CA 90048 (SAN 213-4551).

†**Almar Pr.,** *(Almar; 0-930256),* 4105 Marietta Dr., Binghamton, NY 13903 (SAN 210-5713) Tel 607-722-0265; *CIP.*

Almin Pr., *(Almin; 0-9615631),* P.O. Box 363, Willingboro, NJ 08046 (SAN 696-0065) Tel 609-871-0422; 24 Needlepoint Ln., Willingboro, NJ 08046 (SAN 696-5180).

Almo Pubns., *(Almo Pubns; 0-89705),* 1358 N. La Brea, Hollywood, CA 90028 (SAN 211-6995); Dist. by: Columbia Pictures Pubns., 15800 NW 48th Ave., Miami, FL 33014 (SAN 203-042X) Tel 305-620-1500.

Alms Hse. Pr., *(Alms Hse Pr; 0-939689),* 23 Grotke Rd., Spring Valley, NY 10977 (SAN 663-5776) Tel 914-735-9548.

Aloha Press, *(Aloha Pr; 0-943758),* P.O. Box 26214, Honolulu, HI 96825 (SAN 238-0382) Tel 808-395-7369.

†**Aloray Inc.,** *(Aloray; 0-913690),* 215 Greenwich Ave., Goshen, NY 10924 (SAN 201-1190) Tel 516-595-2235; *CIP.*

Alpenglow Pr., *(Alpenglow Pr; 0-935997),* P.O. Box 1841, Santa Maria, CA 93456 (SAN 696-6748) Tel 805-928-4904.

Alpenrose Pr., *(Alpenrose Pr; 0-9603624),* Box 499, Silverthorne, CO 80498 (SAN 222-2612) Tel 303-468-6273.

Alpenstock Publishing, *(Alpenstock; 0-9614521),* P.O. Box 1759, Santa Ana, CA 92702 (SAN 691-7380) Tel 714-750-7621.

Alpert, Burt, *(Alpert; 0-9600642),* 877 26th Ave., San Francisco, CA 94121 (SAN 201-1204).

Alpha-Beto Music, *(Alpha Beto Music; 0-9616528),* 152 Sabine, Portland, TX 78374 (SAN 659-4107) Tel 512-643-6309.

Alpha Centauri Pubs., *(Alpha Centauri; 0-940332),* P.O. Box 1011, Highland, NY 12528 (SAN 220-3162) Tel 914-691-7014.

Alpha Chi, National College Honor Scholarship Society, *(Alpha Chi),* Sta. A, Box 773, Searcy, AR 72143 (SAN 224-5086) Tel 501-268-3121.

Alpha Gamma Arts, *(Alpha Gamma; 0-941716),* 2625 Kiowa Ct., P.O. Box 4671, Walnut Creek, CA 94596 (SAN 281-2517) Tel 415-935-7409; Dist. by: China Bks., & Periodicals, Inc., 2929 24th St., San Francisco, CA 94110 (SAN 145-0557) Tel 415-282-2994.

Alpha Iota of Pi Lambda Theta, Pubns., *(Alpha Iota; 0-914622),* 2260 N. Orange Grove Ave., Pomona, CA 91767 (SAN 206-3204) Tel 714-626-5065.

Alpha Media Publishing, *(Alpha Media; 0-918539),* 113 Fescue Ln., Roseburg, OR 97470 (SAN 657-5684) Tel 503-672-3280.

Alpha Omega, *(Alpha and Omega; 0-941734),* 1026 E. Garden Ave., Coeur d'Alene, ID 83814 (SAN 239-1503) Tel 208-664-2954.

Alpha Omega Pub., *(Alpha Omega Pub; 0-937059),* 5500 Boca Raton, Suite 427, Fort Worth, TX 76112 (SAN 658-5396) Tel 817-654-2082; P.O. Box 8383, Fort Worth, TX 76124-1383 (SAN 658-540X).

Alpha Press, *(Alpha Pr; 0-914620),* 3574 Clinton St., Gardenville, NY 14224 (SAN 201-1212) Tel 716-674-6183.

Alpha Pubns., *(Alpha Pubns OH; 0-939427),* 1818 Wilbur Rd., Medina, OH 44256 (SAN 663-401X) Tel 216-239-1881. Do not confuse with Alpha Pubns. in Blue Bell, PA or in Winona Lake, IN.

Alpha Pubns., *(Alpha Pub MN; 0-9615632),* Box 6328, Minneapolis, MN 55406-0328 (SAN 696-0618) Tel 612-721-7856; Dist. by: Spring Arbor Distributors, 10885 Textile Rd., Belleville, MI 48111 (SAN 158-9016) Tel 313-481-0900; Toll free: 800-521-3990; Dist. by: Successful Living, Inc., 9905 Hamilton Rd., Eden Prarie, MN 55344 (SAN 213-0939) Tel 612-944-2511.

Alpha Publishing Co., Div. of Special Edition Inc., *(Alpha Pub Co; 0-933771),* 3497 E. Livingston Ave., Columbus, OH 43227 (SAN 692-8048) Tel 614-231-4088.

Alpha Publishing Trust, *(Alpha Pub Trust; 0-931753),* 897 Washington St., P.O. Box 82, Newtonville, MA 02160 (SAN 683-6135) Tel 617-864-9859; 96 Prescott St., Cambridge, MA 02138 (SAN 683-6143).

Alpha Pubns., Inc., *(Alpha Pubns; 0-912404),* 1079 De Kalb Pike, Blue Bell, PA 19422 (SAN 201-2537) Tel 215-277-6342.

Alphabet Pr., *(Alphabet MA; 0-940032),* 60 N. Main St., Natick, MA 01760 (SAN 217-1449) Tel 617-655-9696; Toll free: 800-462-1252.

Alphabet Pr., *(Alphabet Pr; 0-9602690),* P.O. Box 6180, Boston, MA 02209 (SAN 213-2753) Tel 617-323-7942. Do not confuse with Alphabet MA of Natick, MA.

Alpine Guild, *(Alpine Guild; 0-931712),* P.O. Box 183, Oak Park, IL 60303 (SAN 281-255X) Tel 312-386-3507.

Alpine Pr., *(Alpine WY; 0-9615114),* P.O. Box 1930, Mills, WY 82644 (SAN 697-2454).

Alpine Pubns., *(Alpine Pubns; 0-931866),* 214 19th St., SE, Loveland, CO 80537 (SAN 211-478X) Tel 303-667-2017. *Imprints:* Blue Ribbon Books (Blue Rib Books).

Alpine-Tahoe Pr., *(Alpine-Tahoe; 0-9604574),* Box 1484, Tahoe City, CA 95730 (SAN 211-2108) Tel 916-583-3273.

Alson Publishing Co., *(Alson Pub; 0-916943),* 931 Santiago St., Santa Ana, CA 92701 (SAN 655-5500) Tel 714-730-5102.

Alstad, Ken, Co., *(K Alstad; 0-9616985),* 9096 E. Bellevue, Tucson, AZ 85715 (SAN 661-7190) Tel 602-298-0175.

Alsterda, Grayce Harper, *(G H Alsterda; 0-9617035),* 915 W. White Gate Dr., Mt. Prospect, IL 60056 (SAN 662-8214) Tel 312-394-0023.

Alta Gaia Books, *(Alta Gaia Bks; 0-933432),* P.O. Box 541, Millerton, NY 12546 (SAN 222-6642).

Alta Hse., *(Alta House; 0-9616970),* P.O. Box 147, Port Townsend, WA 98368 (SAN 661-7115); 2208 Waltnut St., Port Townsend, WA 98368 (SAN 661-7123) Tel 206-385-4303.

Alta Napa Pr., *(Alta Napa; 0-931926),* 1969 Mora Ave., Calistoga, CA 94515 (SAN 216-3276) Tel 707-942-4444.

Alta Publishing Co., Inc., *(Alta Pub Co; 0-914855),* 6113 Robinwood Rd., Bethesda, MD 20817 (SAN 289-0488) Tel 301-320-5184; Orders to: P.O. Box 42107, Washington, DC 20015-0707 (SAN 669-3512).

Alta Vista Bks., *(Alta Vista Bks; 0-936761),* 550 W. Vista Way, Suite 109, Vista, CA 92083 (SAN 699-8879) Tel 619-758-4584; P.O. Box 1728, Vista, CA 92083 (SAN 699-8887).

Altacom, Inc., *(Altacom; 0-918391),* 608 Pendleton St., P.O. Box 19070, Alexandria, VA 22314 (SAN 657-3193) Tel 703-683-1442.

Altai Publishers, *(Altai Pub; 0-9609710),* P.O. Box 1972, Flagstaff, AZ 86002 (SAN 263-0281) Tel 602-779-0491.

Altair Pr., *(Altair Pr; 0-934768),* P.O. Box 1286, Boulder, CO 80306 (SAN 209-1585) Tel 303-494-6405.

Altair Publishing Co., *(Altair Pub Co; 0-9604976),* 508 S. Can-Dota, Mt. Prospect, IL 60056 (SAN 215-935X) Tel 312-255-8029.

Altair Publishing Co., *(Altair Pub UT; 0-938117),* P.O. Box 20024, West Valley City, UT 84120 (SAN 659-6983); 3585 Cochise, West Valley City, UT 84120 (SAN 659-6991) Tel 801-967-3308.

Altara Group, The, *(Altara Group; 0-9607106),* 7 Charles Ct., P.O. Box 24, North Haven, CT 06473 (SAN 238-9363) Tel 203-239-9400.

Altarinda Books, *(Altarinda Bks; 0-9607896),* 13 Estates Dr., Orinda, CA 94563 (SAN 238-1397) Tel 415-254-3830.

Alternate Energy Publishing Co., *(Alternate Energy; 0-930086),* P.O. Box 26507, Albuquerque, NM 87125 (SAN 210-6981) Tel 505-873-2084.

Alternate Source, The, *(Alter Source; 0-915363),* 704 N. Pennsylvania Ave., Lansing, MI 48906 (SAN 265-6833) Tel 517-482-8270; Toll free: 800-253-3200 ext 700.

Alternating Currents, *(Alt Currents; 0-937435),* P.O. Box 2121, Jamestown, NC 27282 (SAN 658-9820) Tel 919-379-5233; 4613 McKnight Mill Rd., Greensboro, NC 27405 (SAN 658-9839).

Alternating Currents Pr., *(Alter Currents; 0-9617221),* Box 525, Capitola, CA 95010 (SAN 663-4184); 644 Stewart St., Boulder Creek, CA (SAN 663-4192) Tel 408-338-4169.

†**Alternative Museum,** *(Alternative Mus; 0-932075),* 17 White St., New York, NY 10013 (SAN 686-2616) Tel 212-226-2158; *CIP.*

Alternative Parenting Pubns., *(Alter Parent; 0-935693),* 1298 W. Shady Mill Rd., Corona, CA 91720 (SAN 696-673X) Tel 714-736-8702; P.O. Box 2619, Corona, CA 91718 (SAN 696-7086).

Alternative Sources of Energy, Inc., *(ASEI; 0-917328),* 107 S. Central Ave., Milaca, MN 56353 (SAN 208-5151) Tel 612-983-6892.

Alternative World Foundation, Inc., *(Altern World; 0-938035),* AWF-1, Goshen, IN 46526 (SAN 659-7033) Tel 219-534-3402; 803 N. Main, Goshen, IN 46526 (SAN 659-7041).

Alternatives, *(Alternatives; 0-914966),* P.O. Box 429, 5263 Bouldercrest Rd., Ellenwood, GA 30049 (SAN 206-8915) Tel 404-961-0102.

Names

Alternatives for the Eighties, *(Altern Eighties; 0-9617089),* 122 Stanley Hall, Columbia, MO 65202 (SAN 662-636X) Tel 314-882-6439. Do not confuse with Alternatives of Ellenwood, GA.

Alternatives in Religious Education, Inc., *(AIRE; 0-86705),* 3945 S. Oneida St., Denver, CO 80237 (SAN 216-6534) Tel 303-363-7779.

Alternatives to Abortion, Inc., *(Alter Abortion; 0-9615457),* P.O. Box 15271, Pittsburgh, PA 15237 (SAN 695-7471) Tel 412-731-2420.

Alternatives To Violence of the Cleveland Friends Meeting Commitee, *(Alternatives Vio),* 10916 Magnolia Dr., Cleveland, OH 44106 (SAN 689-0204).

Altitude Publishing Co., *(Altitude; 0-917441),* 7866 S. Windermere Cir., Littleton, CO 80120 (SAN 657-0593) Tel 303-388-4989.

Altro Health & Rehabilitation Service, *(Altro Health Rehab; 0-937607),* 40 E. 30th St., New York, NY 10016 (SAN 658-988X) Tel 212-684-0600.

Alumni Assn. of the US Army War College, *(Alumni Assn US; 0-9613301),* Alumni Assn., USAWC, Box 462 USAWC, Carlisle Barracks, PA 17013-5050 (SAN 654-1968) Tel 717-243-0884.

Alyson Pubns., Inc., *(Alyson Pubns; 0-932870; 1-55583),* 40 Plympton St., Boston, MA 02118 (SAN 213-6546) Tel 617-542-5679.

Am-Fem Co., *(AM-FEM Co; 0-9607232),* P.O. Box 93, Cooper Sta., New York, NY 10276 (SAN 239-152X).

Am-Law Publishing Corp., *(Am Law Pub; 0-9606682),* 205 Lexington Ave., New York, NY 10016 (SAN 219-7049) Tel 212-696-8900.

AM/PM Publishing Co., *(AM-PM Pub Co; 0-933875),* 2376 Union St., San Francisco, CA 94123 (SAN 692-7866) Tel 415-621-8100.

Amadeo Concha Pr., *(Amadeo Concha; 0-939448),* 832 Arkansas St., Lawrence, KS 66044 (SAN 216-5864) Tel 913-842-6393.

Amadeus Pr., Inc., *(Amadeus Oregon; 0-931340),* 9999 SW Wilshire, Suite 124, Portland, OR 97225 (SAN 659-3909) Tel 503-292-0745.

Amador Pubs., *(Amador Pubs; 0-938513),* P.O. Box 12335, Albuquerque, NM 87195 (SAN 661-3055); 607 Isleta Blvd. SW, Albuquerque, NM 87105 (SAN 661-3063) Tel 505-877-4395.

Amana Bks., *(Amana Bks; 0-915597),* 58 Elliot St., Brattleboro, VT 05301 (SAN 292-4307) Tel 802-257-0872.

Amana Preservation Foundation, *(Amana Found; 0-9616200),* Box 97, Middle, IA 52307 (SAN 658-4578) Tel 319-622-3435.

Amarta Pr., *(Amarta Pr; 0-935100),* P.O. Box 202, West Franklin, NH 03235 (SAN 213-2761) Tel 603-934-2420.

Amaryllis Pr., *(Amaryllis Pr; 0-89275; 0-943276),* 212 W. 79 St., New York, NY 10024 (SAN 201-4300) Tel 212-496-6460.

Amata Graphics, *(Amata Graphics; 0-931224),* P.O. Box 12313, Portland, OR 97212 (SAN 211-2094) Tel 503-231-8540.

Amateur Athletic Union of the United States, *(AAU Pubns; 0-89710),* 3400 W. 86th St., Indianapolis, IN 46268 (SAN 204-7853) Tel 317-872-2900.

Amateur Hockey Assn. of the U. S., *(Amateur Hockey Assn),* 2997 Broadmoor Valley Rd., Colorado Springs, CO 80906 (SAN 224-5698) Tel 303-576-4900.

Amateur Radio Operator's Yearbook, Inc. *See* AROY, Inc.

Amato, Frank, Pubns., *(F Amato Pubns; 0-936608),* P.O. Box 02112, Portland, OR 97202 (SAN 214-3372) Tel 503-653-8108.

Amaya Publishing Co., *(Amaya Pub; 0-916949),* P.O. Box 227, Shiloh, NJ 08353 (SAN 655-5543) Tel 609-455-6637.

Amazing Events Unlimited, *(Amazing Even; 0-936237),* 459 Hamilton St., Suite 105, Palo Alto, CA 94301 (SAN 696-9380) Tel 415-327-3236.

AMB Pr., Inc., *(AMB Pr; 0-913171),* P.O. Box 459, Riverside, PA 17868 (SAN 282-9460) Tel 717-286-5466.

Ambassador Pr., Inc., *(Ambassador Pr; 0-935019),* P.O. Box 216, Edgemont, PA 19028-0216 (SAN 694-3977) Tel 215-356-1893; Orders to: Warehouse, 947 Plumsock Rd., Edgemont, PA 19028-0216 (SAN 696-0340).

Amber Co. Pr., *(Amber Co Pr; 0-934965),* 2324 Prince St., Berkeley, CA 94705 (SAN 695-1112) Tel 415-549-2587.

Amber Publishing Corp., *(Amber Pub; 0-916788),* 82 W. University, Alfred, NY 14802 (SAN 208-5178) Tel 212-736-2288.

Amberly Pubns., *(Amberly Pubns; 0-9612334),* P.O. Box 4153, Chapel Hill, NC 27515-4153 (SAN 289-1018) Tel 919-493-6050.

Ambleside Publishers, Inc., *(Ambleside; 0-913011),* 2122 E. Concorda Dr., Tempe, AZ 85282 (SAN 283-2887) Tel 602-967-3457.

Amchan Pubns., *(Amchan Pubns; 0-9617132),* P.O. Box 3648, Alexandria, VA 22302 (SAN 663-1835); 4425 S. 36th St., Arlington, VA 22206 (SAN 663-1843) Tel 703-931-8520.

Amdulaine Pubns., Inc., *(Amdulaine Pubns; 0-9615780),* 5800 One Perkins Pl. Dr., Suite 8A, Baton Rouge, LA 70808 (SAN 696-6691) Tel 504-769-0010.

Ameco Publishing Corp., *(Ameco; 0-912146),* 220 E. Jericho Tpke., Mineola, NY 11501 (SAN 202-4799) Tel 516-741-5030.

Amelia, *(Amelia; 0-936545),* 329 E St., Bakersfield, CA 93304 (SAN 697-9920) Tel 805-323-4064.

Amen Publishing Co., *(Amen Pub; 0-941204),* Box 3612, Arcadia, CA 91006 (SAN 217-3239) Tel 818-355-9336.

Amereon, Ltd., *(Amereon Ltd; 0-88411; 0-89190; 0-8488),* P.O. Box 1200, Mattituck, NY 11952 (SAN 201-2413) Tel 516-298-5100.

American Academic Assn. for Peace in the Middle East, *(AAAPME; 0-917158),* 330 Seventh Ave., Suite 606, New York, NY 10001 (SAN 208-5186) Tel 212-563-2580.

American Academy & Institute of Arts & Letters, *(Am Acad Inst Arts; 0-915974),* 633 W. 155th St., New York, NY 10032 (SAN 204-7888) Tel 212-368-5900.

American Academy in Rome, *(Am Acad Rome),* 41 E. 65th St., New York, NY 10021 (SAN 225-3801) Tel 212-535-4250.

American Academy of Advertising, *(Am Acad Advert; 0-931030),* Brigham Young Univ., Graduate Schl. of Management, Provo, UT 84602 (SAN 236-073X) Tel 801-378-2080.

American Academy of Gnathologic Orthopedics, *(Am Acad Gnatho; 0-913011),* 211 E. Chicago Ave., No. 915, Chicago, IL 60611 (SAN 227-7646) Tel 312-642-5834.

American Academy of Orthopaedic Surgeons, *(Amer Acad Ortho Surg; 0-89203),* 222 S. Prospect Ave., Park Ridge, IL 60068 (SAN 228-2097) Tel 312-823-7186.

American Academy of Osteopathy, *(Am Acad Osteopathy; 0-940668),* P.O. Box 750, Newark, OH 43055 (SAN 218-5296) Tel 614-349-8701.

American Academy of Otolaryngic Allergy, *(Am Acad Otolary),* 1101 Vermont Ave. NW, Suite 302, Washington, DC 20005 (SAN 228-2348) Tel 202-682-0546.

American Academy of Pediatrics, *(AM Acad Pediat; 0-910761),* 141 Northwest Point Rd., Elk Grove Village, IL 60007 (SAN 265-3540) Tel 312-228-5005.

American Academy of Political & Social Science, *(Am Acad Pol Soc Sci; 0-87761),* 3937 Chestnut St., Philadelphia, PA 19104 (SAN 201-1239) Tel 215-386-4594; Dist. by: Sage Pubns., Inc., 275 S. Beverly Dr., Beverly Hills, CA 90212 (SAN 204-7217) Tel 213-274-8003.

American Accounting Assn., *(Am Accounting),* 5717 Bessie Dr., Sarasota, FL 33583 (SAN 204-790X) Tel 813-921-7747.

American Advisory Pr., Inc., *(American Ad Pr; 0-937387),* P.O. Box 57, Clearwater, FL 33517-0057 (SAN 658-991X) Tel 813-446-6840.

American Air Mail Society, *(Am Air Mail; 0-939429),* 102 Arbor Rd., Cinnaminson, NJ 08077-3859 (SAN 225-5847) Tel 609-829-6792.

American Allergy Association, *(Am Allergy Assn),* P.O. Box 7273, Menlo Park, CA 94026 (SAN 224-2621) Tel 415-322-1663.

American Alliance for Health, Physical Education, Recreation & Dance, Affil. of National Education Assn., *(AAHPERD; 0-88314),* 1900 Association Dr., Reston, VA 22091 (SAN 202-3237) Tel 703-476-3400.

American Animal Hospital Assn., *(Am Animal Hosp Assoc; 0-9616498),* 1746 Cole Blvd., Golden, CO 80401 (SAN 224-4799) Tel 303-279-2500.

American Anthropological Assn., *(Am Anthro Assn; 0-913167),* Pubns. Dept., 1703 New Hampshire Ave., NW, Washington, DC 20009 (SAN 202-4284) Tel 202-232-8800.

American Antiquarian Society, *(Am Antiquarian; 0-912296),* 185 Salisbury St., Worcester, MA 01609 (SAN 206-474X) Tel 617-752-5813; Dist. by: Univ. Pr. of Virginia, P.O. Box 3608, University Sta., Charlottesville, VA 22903 (SAN 202-5361) Tel 804-924-3468.

American Applied Technologies, Div. of Erde International (U.S.A.), *(American Ap Tech; 0-937425),* P.O. Box 25007, Phoenix, AZ 85002 (SAN 658-9952) Tel 602-285-1661; 3600 N. Sixth Ave., No. 16, Phoenix, AZ 85013 (SAN 658-9960).

American Arab Affairs Council, *(Am-Arab Affairs; 0-943182),* 1730 M St. NW, Suite 512, Washington, DC 20036 (SAN 240-5814) Tel 202-296-6767.

American Arbitration Assn., *(Am Arbitration),* 140 W. 51st St., New York, NY 10020 (SAN 225-0802) Tel 212-484-4000.

American Archives Pubs., *(Am Archives Pubs; 0-938039),* 208 Ember Glow Cir., College Station, TX 77840 (SAN 659-7092) Tel 409-268-0725.

American Art Therapy Assn., *(Am Art Therapy),* 1980 Isaac Newton Sq. S., Reston, VA 22090 (SAN 688-7686) Tel 703-370-3223.

American Assembly, *(Am Assembly),* Columbia University, New York, NY 10027-6598 (SAN 209-6471).

American Assn. for Adult & Continuing Education, *(A A A C E; 0-88379),* 1201 16th St., NW, Suite 301, Washington, DC 20036 (SAN 201-2278) Tel 202-822-7866.

American Assn. for Artificial Intelligence, *(Amer Artificial; 0-86576),* 445 Burgess Dr., Menlo Park, CA 94025 (SAN 679-1905) Tel 415-328-3123; Dist. by: Morgan Kaufman, Inc., 95 First St., Los Altos, CA 94022 (SAN 662-7668) Tel 415-941-4960.

American Assn. for Chinese Studies, *(Am Assn Chinese Stud),* Asian Studies Program, Ohio State Univ., Columbus, OH 43210 (SAN 219-757X) Tel 614-422-6681.

†**American Assn. for Clinical Chemistry,** *(Am Assn Clinical Chem; 0-915274),* 1725 K St., NW, Suite 1010, Washington, DC 20006 (SAN 214-2813); *CIP.*

American Assn. for Counseling & Development, *(Am Assn Coun Dev; 0-911547; 1-55620),* 5999 Stevenson Ave., Alexandria, VA 22304 (SAN 291-9141) Tel 703-823-9800.

American Association for Gifted Children, *(Am Assn Gifted Children),* 15 Gramercy Park, New York, NY 10016 (SAN 225-798X) Tel 212-473-4266.

American Assn. for Medical Transcription, *(Am Assoc Med; 0-935229),* 3460 OakdaleRd., Suite F, Modesto, CA 95355 (SAN 696-0715) Tel 209-576-0883; Toll free: 800-982-2182; P.O. Box 6187, Modesto, CA 95355 (SAN 696-5202).

American Assn. for Parapsychology, *(AAP Calif; 0-930149),* Box 8447, Calabasas, CA 91302 (SAN 669-6384) Tel 818-888-6570.

†**American Assn. for State & Local History Pr.,** *(AASLH Pr; 0-910050),* 172 Second Ave. N., Suite 102, Nashville, TN 37201 (SAN 201-1972) Tel 615-225-2971; Orders to: 154 Second Ave., N., Nashville, TN 37201 (SAN 658-0114); *CIP.*

†**American Assn. for the Advancement of Science,** *(AAAS; 0-87168),* 1333 H St. NW, 8th Flr., Washington, DC 20005 (SAN 201-193X) Tel 202-223-6695 (SAN 688-3842); *CIP.*

American Assn. for the Advancement of Science, Pacific Div., *(AAASPD; 0-934394),* c/o California Academy of Sciences, Golden Gate Park, San Francisco, CA 94118 (SAN 204-3661).

American Assn. for the International Commission of Jurists, Inc., *(Am Assn Intl Comm Jurists; 0-916265),* 777 United Nations Plaza, New York, NY 10017 (SAN 235-6473) Tel 212-972-0883.

American Assn. for Vocational Instructional Materials, *(Am Assn Voc Materials; 0-89606; 0-914452),* 120 Engineering, Athens, GA 30602 (SAN 225-8811) Tel 404-542-2586.

†American Assn. of Blood Banks, *(Am Assn Blood; 0-914404; 0-915355),* 1117 N. 19th St., Suite 600, Arlington, VA 22209 (SAN 201-1573) Tel 703-528-8200; *CIP.*

American Assn. of Botanical Gardens & Arboreta, Inc., *(Am Assn Botanical Gdns; 0-934843),* P.O. Box 206, Swarthmore, PA 19081 (SAN 225-1493) Tel 215-328-9145.

American Assn. of Cereal Chemists, *(Am Assn Cereal Chem; 0-913250),* 3340 Pilot Knob Rd., St. Paul, MN 55121 (SAN 204-7934) Tel 612-454-7250.

American Assn. of Colleges for Teacher Education, *(AACTE; 0-910052; 0-89333),* 1 Dupont Cir., Suite 610, Washington, DC 20036 (SAN 204-3882) Tel 202-293-2450.

American Assn. of Colleges of Pharmacy, *(AACP Bethesda; 0-937526),* 4630 Montgomery Ave., Suite 201, Bethesda, MD 20814 (SAN 202-4292) Tel 301-654-9060.

†American Assn. of Collegiate Registrars & Officers, *(Am Assn Coll Registrars; 0-910054),* 1 Dupont Cir., NW, Suite 330, Washington, DC 20036 (SAN 225-7394) Tel 202-293-9161; *CIP.*

American Assn. of Community & Junior Colleges, *(Am Assn Comm Jr Coll; 0-87117),* 1 Dupont Cir. NW, Suite 410, Washington, DC 20036 (SAN 293-2253) Tel 202-293-7050; Dist. by: AACJC Pubn. Sales, 80 S. Early St., Alexandria, VA 22304 (SAN 293-2261) Tel 703-823-6966.

American Assn. of Correctional Officers, *(Amer Correct Officers),* 1474 Willow Ave., Des Plaines, IL 60016 (SAN 224-036X) Tel 312-751-6068.

American Assn. of Cost Engineers, *(Am Assn Cost Engineers),* 308 Monongahela Bldg., Morgantown, WV 26505 (SAN 214-0942) Tel 304-296-8444.

American Assn. of Diabetes Educators, *(Am Assn Diabetes Ed),* 500 N. Michigan Ave., Suite 1400, Chicago, IL 60611 (SAN 224-3091) Tel 312-661-1700.

American Assn. of Engineering Societies, *(AAES; 0-87615),* 415 Second St., NE, Suite 200, Washington, DC 20002 (SAN 201-386X) Tel 202-546-2237.

American Assn. of Equipment Lessors, *(Am Assn Equip Lessors; 0-912413),* 1300 N. 17th St., No. 1010, Arlington, VA 22209 (SAN 224-9359) Tel 703-527-8655.

American Assn. of Homes for the Aging, *(Am Assn Homes; 0-943774),* 1129 20th St. NW, Suite 400, Washington, DC 20036 (SAN 260-3918) Tel 202-296-5960.

American Assn. of Law Libraries, *(Am Assn Law Libs),* 53 W. Jackson Blvd., Chicago, IL 60604 (SAN 680-005X) Tel 312-939-4764.

American Assn. of Medical Assistants, *(Am Med Assts; 0-942732),* 20 N. Wacker Dr., Suite 1575, Chicago, IL 60606 (SAN 224-3520) Tel 312-899-1500.

†American Assn. of Museums, *(Am Assn Mus; 0-931201),* 1055 Thomas Jefferson St., NW, Washington, DC 20007 (SAN 233-5255) Tel 202-338-5300; *CIP.*

American Assn. of Nurserymen, *(Am Nurserymen),* 1250 Eye St., NW, Suite 500, Washington, DC 20005 (SAN 225-0462) Tel 202-789-2900.

American Assn. of Petroleum Landmen, *(AAPL),* 2408 Continental Life Bldg., Fort Worth, TX 76102 (SAN 266-4917) Tel 817-335-9751.

American Assn. of Retired Persons, *(Am Assn Retire),* 1909 K St., NW, Washington, DC 20049 (SAN 260-3985) Tel 202-872-4700; P.O. Box 19269-K, Washington, DC 20036 (SAN 668-9663); Orders to: AARP Pubns., Scott-Foresman & Co., 400 S. Edward St., Mt. Prospect, IL 60056 (SAN 697-595X).

American Assn. of Schl. Administrators, *(Am Assn Sch Admin; 0-87652),* 1801 N. Moore St., Arlington, VA 22209 (SAN 202-3628) Tel 703-528-0700.

American Assn. of State Highway & Transportation Officials, *(AASHTO),* 444 N. Capitol St., NW, Washington, DC 20001 (SAN 204-7969) Tel 202-624-5800.

American Assn. of Stratigraphic Palynologists Foundation, *(Am Assn Strat; 0-931871),* C.O. Mobil Research - DRL, P.O. Box 819047, Dallas, TX 75381-9047 (SAN 686-0524) Tel 214-851-8481.

American Assn. of Teachers of Spanish & Portuguese, *(AATSP),* Mississippi State Univ., Mississippi State, MS 39762-6349 (SAN 225-8722) Tel 601-325-2041.

American Assn. of Textile Chemists and Colorists, *(Am Assn Text; 0-9613350),* 1 Davis Dr., P.O. Box 12215, Research Triangle Park, NC 27709 (SAN 655-8747) Tel 919-549-8141.

American Assn. of University Women, *(Am Assn U; 0-9611476),* 2401 Virginia Ave., NW, Washington, DC 20037 (SAN 291-8617) Tel 202-785-7700; Toll free: 800-424-9717.

American Assn. of Univ. Women, Corpus Christi Branch, Div. of American Assn. of University Women, *(Am Assn U Women; 0-9615283),* P.O. Box 8151, Corpus Christi, TX 78412 (SAN 694-5449) Tel 512-853-4573.

American Association of University Women Educational Foundation, *(Am Assn Univ Women),* 2401 Virginia Ave., NW, Washington, DC 20037 (SAN 225-8854) Tel 202-785-7763.

American Assn. of Zoological Parks & Aquariums, *(Am Assoc Z Pk),* Oglebay Pk., Wheeling, WV 26003 (SAN 684-5363) Tel 304-242-2160.

†American Assn. on Mental Deficiency, *(Am Assn Mental; 0-940898),* 1719 Kalorama Rd., Washington, DC 20009 (SAN 206-961X) Tel 202-387-1968; Toll free: 800-424-3688; *CIP.*

American Astronautical Society, *(Am Astronaut; 0-87703),* P.O. Box 28130, San Diego, CA 92128 (SAN 661-9339) Tel 619-746-4005; Orders to: Univelt, Inc., P.O. Box 28130, San Diego, CA 92128 (SAN 201-2561) Tel 619-746-4005.

American Atheist Pr., *(Am Atheist; 0-911826; 0-910309),* P.O. Box 2117, Austin, TX 78768-2117 (SAN 206-7188) Tel 512-458-1244. *Imprints:* Broukal, Gustav, Press (Gustav Broukal).

American Automobile Assn., *(AAA; 0-916748),* 8111 Gatehouse Rd., Falls Church, VA 22047 (SAN 208-5194) Tel 703-222-6190; Dist. by: Random Hse., Inc., 201 E. 50th St., New York, NY 10022 (SAN 202-5507).

American Bando Assn., *(Am Bando Assn; 0-9608394),* Catonsville Community College, Catonsville, MD 21228 (SAN 240-5830) Tel 301-788-6149.

American Bankers Assn., *(Am Bankers; 0-89982),* 1120 Connecticut Ave., NW, Washington, DC 20036 (SAN 208-4554) Tel 202-467-6660.

American Baptist Historical Society, *(Am Baptist; 0-910056),* 1106 S. Goodman St., Rochester, NY 14620 (SAN 201-257X) Tel 716-473-1740.

American Bar Assn., *(Amer Bar Assn; 0-89707),* 750 N. Lake Shore Dr., Chicago, IL 60611 (SAN 211-4798) Tel 312-988-5000; 1800 M St., NW, Washington, DC 20036 (SAN 668-968X) Tel 202-331-2200. *Imprints:* American Bar Association Journal (ABA Jrnl); American Bar Endowment (ABA Endowment); American Bar Retirement Association (ABA Retirement); Department of Professional Standards (ABA Prof Stds); Division of Bar Services (ABA Bar Servs); Judicial Administration Division (ABA Judicial Admin); Law Student Division (ABA LSD); Section of Administrative Law (ABA Admin Law); Section of Antitrust Law (ABA Antitrust); Section of Bar Activities (ABA Bar Activities); Section of Corporation Banking & Business Law (ABA Corp Banking); Section of Criminal Justice (ABA Crim Just); Section of Economics of Law Practice (ABA Econ Law); Section of General Practice (ABA Genl Prac); Section of Individual Rights & Responsibilities (ABA Indiv Rts); Section of Insurance Negligence & Compensation Law (ABA Ins Neg); Section of International Law (ABA Intl Law); Section of Labor Relations Law (ABA Labor); Section of Legal Education and Admissions to the Bar (ABA Legal Ed); Section of Litigation (ABA Litigation); Section of Natural Resources Law (ABA Natl Res); Section of Patent, Trademark, & Copyright Law (ABA Patent); Section of Public Contract Law (ABA Pub Contract); Section of Public Utility Law (ABA Pub Utility); Section of Real Property Probate & Trust Law (ABA Real Prop); Section of Science & Technology (ABA Sci Tech); Section of Taxation (ABA Tax); Section of Tort & Insurance Practice Law (ABA Tort); Section of Urban, State, & Local Government Law (ABA Urban). Special Committee on Environmental Law (ABA Environ); Standing Committee on Lawyers Title Guaranty Funds (ABA Title); Standing Committee on Legal Assistance for Military Personnel (ABA Assist); Standing Committee on Unauthorized Practice of Law (ABA Unauth); Young Lawyers Section (ABA Young Lawyers).

American Bar Association Journal *See American Bar Assn.*

American Bar Endowment *See American Bar Assn.*

American Bar Foundation, Subs. of American Bar Assn., *(Am Bar Foun; 0-910058; 0-910059),* 750 N. Lake Shore Dr., Chicago, IL 60611 (SAN 201-2588) Tel 312-998-6400; Dist. by: Little, Brown & Co., 34 Beacon St., Boston, MA 02108 (SAN 200-2205).

American Bar Retirement Assn. *See American Bar Assn.*

American Bartenders' Assn., Inc., *(Am Bartenders; 0-916689),* P.O. Box 11447, Bradenton, FL 34282 (SAN 653-7383) Tel 813-756-5265.

American Bed & Breakfast Assn., Div. of Hearth & Home Enterprises, *(Am Bed & Breakfast; 0-934473),* P.O. Box 23294, Washington, DC 20026 (SAN 693-8647) Tel 703-237-9777; Dist. by: National Press, Inc., 7508 Wisconsin Ave., Bethesda, MD 20814 (SAN 293-8839) Tel 301-657-1616.

American Bible Society, Member of United Bible Societies, *(Am Bible; 0-8267),* 1865 Broadway, New York, NY 10023 (SAN 203-5189) Tel 212-581-7400; Orders to: P.O. Box 5656, Grand Central Sta., New York, NY 10163 (SAN 662-7129) Tel 212-581-7400; Toll free: 800-543-8000.

American Biographical Ctr., *(Am Biog Ctr; 0-9601168),* P.O. Box 473, Williamsburg, VA 23187 (SAN 210-0266) Tel 804-725-2234.

American Biographical Institute, *(Am Biog Inst; 0-934544),* 5126 Bur Oak Cir., Raleigh, NC 27612 (SAN 213-0092) Tel 919-781-8710; P.O. Box 31226, Raleigh, NC 27622 (SAN 696-5067).

American Biography Service Inc., *(Am Biog Serv; 0-932051),* 14722 Newport C 184, Tustin, CA 92680 (SAN 686-2640) Tel 714-832-4382.

Names

Names

American Blade Book Service, *(Am Blade Bk Serv; 0-911881),* 2835 Hickory Valley Rd., P.O. Box 22007, Chattanooga, TN 37422 (SAN 265-3559) Tel 615-894-0339.

†**American Blood Commission,** *(Am Blood Comm; 0-935498),* 1117 N. 19th St., Suite 501, Arlington, VA 22209 (SAN 213-7194) Tel 703-522-8414; *CIP.*

American Board of Medical Specialties, *(Am Bd Med Spec; 0-934277),* 1 American Plaza, No. 805, Evanston, IL 60201-4889 (SAN 228-0477) Tel 312-491-9091; Dist. by: Login Brothers Bk. Co., 1450 W. Randolph St., Chicago, IL 60607 (SAN 169-183X) Tel 312-733-6424; Toll free: 800-621-4249.

†**American Book Co.,** Div. of International Thomson Educational Publishing, Inc., *(ABC; 0-278),* 135 W. 50th St., New York, NY 10020 (SAN 201-534X) Tel 212-265-8700; Orders to: 7625 Empire Dr., Florence, KY 41042 (SAN 201-5358) Tel 800-354-9815; *CIP.*

American Brahman Breeders Association, *(Am Brahman Breeders),* 1313 La Concha Lane, Houston, TX 77054 (SAN 224-9901) Tel 713-794-4444.

American Buddhist Shim Gum Do Assn., Inc., *(Am Buddhist Shim Do; 0-9614427),* 203 Chestnut Hill Ave., Brighton, MA 02135 (SAN 690-050X) Tel 617-787-1506.

American Bureau for Medical Advancement in China, *(A B M A C),* 2 E. 103rd St., New York, NY 10029 (SAN 266-6332) Tel 212-860-1990.

American Bureau of Economic Research, *(Am Bur Eco Res; 0-930462),* P.O. Box 7999, Tyler, TX 75711 (SAN 222-5069) Tel 214-593-7447.

American Bureau of Metal Statistics, *(Am Bur Metal; 0-910064),* 400 Plaza Dr., Harmon Meadow, P.O. Box 1405, Secaucus, NJ 07094-0405 (SAN 201-1581) Tel 201-863-6900.

American Business Consultants, Inc., *(Am Busn Consult; 0-937152),* 1540 Nuthatch Lane, Sunnyvale, CA 94087-4999 (SAN 214-3399) Tel 408-732-8931.

†**American Camping Assn.,** *(Am Camping; 0-87603),* Bradford Woods 5000 State Rd. 67, N., Martinsville, IN 46151-7902 (SAN 201-2596) Tel 317-342-8456; *CIP.*

American-Canadian Pubs., Inc., *(Am Canadian; 0-913844),* Box 4575, Santa Fe, NM 87502 (SAN 201-260X) Tel 505-471-7863.

†**American Canal & Transportation Ctr.,** *(Am Canal & Transport; 0-933788),* 809 Rathton Rd., York, PA 17403 Tel 717-843-4035. Do not confuse with American Canal Society, same address. ACS is a non-profit, educational organization. American Canal & Transportation Ctr. is a publishing firm; *CIP.*

American Cancer Society, Colorado Div., Inc., *(Am Cancer Colo),* 2255 S. Oneida St., Denver, CO 80224 (SAN 217-300X).

American Cancer Society Inc., *(Am Cancer NY),* 777 Third Ave., New York, NY 10017 (SAN 227-6941) Tel 212-371-2900.

American Cancer Society, Iowa Div., Inc., *(Am Cancer Iowa),* Box 980, Mason City, IA 50401 (SAN 217-2771).

American Cancer Society, Maryland Div., Inc., *(Am Cancer MD),* 200 E. Joppa Rd., Towson, MD 21204 (SAN 217-2860).

American Cancer Society, Massachusetts Div., Inc., *(Am Cancer Mass),* 247 Commonwealth Ave., Boston, MA 02116 (SAN 217-278X).

American Cancer Society, Michigan Div., Inc., *(Am Cancer Mich),* 1205 E. Saginaw St., Lansing, MI 48906 (SAN 217-2852).

American Cancer Society, Minnesota Div., Inc., *(Am Cancer Minn; 0-9602796),* 3316 W. 66th St., Minneapolis, MN 55435 (SAN 219-9963) Tel 612-925-2772; Toll free: 800-582-5152; Dist. by: Bookman, Inc., 525 N. Third St., Minneapolis, MN 55401 (SAN 282-7352) Tel 612-341-3333; Toll free: 800-328-8411.

American Cancer Society, Mississippi Div., Inc., *(Am Cancer MS),* 345 N. Mart Plaza, Jackson, MS 39206 (SAN 217-2828).

American Cancer Society, New Hampshire Div., Inc., *(Am Cancer NH),* 686 Mast Rd., Manchester, NH 03102 (SAN 217-2836).

American Cancer Society, New York Div., Inc., *(Am Cancer Forest Hills),* 111-15 Queens Blvd., Forest Hills, NY 11375 (SAN 217-2763).

American Cancer Society, New York Div., Inc., *(Am Cancer Syracuse),* 6725 Lyons St., East Syracuse, NY 13057 (SAN 217-2801) Tel 607-437-7025.

American Cancer Society, Oregon Division, *(Amer Cancer Soc OR; 0-9617128),* 0330 SW Curry St., Portland, OR 97201 (SAN 662-6750) Tel 503-295-6422.

American Cancer Society, Westchester Div., Inc., *(Am Cancer Westchester; 0-9616598),* 901 N. Broadway, White Plains, NY 10603 (SAN 659-4859) Tel 914-949-4800.

American Cancer Society, Wyoming Div., Inc., *(Am Cancer WY),* 506 Shoshoni, Cheyenne, WY 82001 (SAN 217-2798).

American Casting Education Foundation, Inc., *(Am Casting; 0-9605960),* 4910 Woodmere Dr., Lakeland, FL 33803 (SAN 281-2614) Tel 813-644-3104; Dist. by: ACEF Publications, P.O. Box 261, Great Falls, VA 22066-0261 (SAN 282-6666).

American Cat Fanciers Assn., *(Am Cat Fanciers),* P.O. Box 203, Point Lookout, MO 65726 (SAN 234-9620).

American Catholic Philosophical Assn., *(Am Cath Philo; 0-918090),* Catholic Univ. of America, Administration Bldg., Rm. 403, Washington, DC 20064 (SAN 204-2626).

American Catholic Pr., *(Am Cath Pr; 0-915866),* 1223 Rossell Ave., Oak Park, IL 60302 (SAN 202-4411) Tel 312-386-1366.

†**American Ceramic Society, Inc,** *(Am Ceramic; 0-916094),* 65 Ceramic Dr., Columbus, OH 43214 (SAN 201-6958) Tel 614-268-8645; *CIP.*

American Chemical Dependency Society, *(Am Chem Dep Soc),* 5001 Olson Memorial Hwy., Minneapolis, MN 55422 (SAN 277-6537) Tel 612-546-5001.

American Chemical Society, *(Am Chemical; 0-8412),* 1155 16th St., NW, Washington, DC 20036 (SAN 201-2626) Tel 202-872-4600; Toll free: 800-424-6747.

American Chemical Society, Inc., Rubber Div., *(Rubber Division; 0-912415),* Univ. of Akron, Akron, OH 44325 (SAN 265-1726).

American Chiropractic Academic Press, *(Am Chiro Acad; 0-936948),* 6840 NW 16th, Suite 146, Oklahoma City, OK 73127 (SAN 215-6180); Dist. by: American Chiropratic Assn., 1916 Wilson Blvd., Arlington, VA 22201 (SAN 215-6180) Tel 703-276-8800.

†**American Chiropractic Assn.,** *(Am Chiro Assn; 0-9606618),* 1916 Wilson Blvd., Suite 300, Arlington, VA 22201 (SAN 215-6180) Tel 703-276-8800; *CIP.*

American Choral Directors Assn., *(Am Choral Dirs),* P.O. Box 6310, Lawton, OK 73506 (SAN 266-6715) Tel 405-355-8161. Please use postal box for all correspondence. No mail receptacle at street address.

American Christian History Institute, *(Amer Christian Hist Inst; 0-9616201),* 1093 Beechwood St., Camarillo, CA 93010 (SAN 658-3482).

American Christian Pr., The Way International, *(Am Christian; 0-910068),* P.O. Box 328, New Knoxville, OH 45871 (SAN 206-9628) Tel 419-753-2523.

American Civil Liberties Union, Washington Office, Div. of National American Civil Liberties Union, *(ACLU DC; 0-914031),* 122 Maryland Ave., NE, Washington, DC 20002 (SAN 227-2032) Tel 202-544-1681.

†**American Classical College Pr.,** *(Am Classical Coll Pr; 0-913314; 0-89266),* P.O. Box 4526, Albuquerque, NM 87196 (SAN 201-2618) Tel 505-843-7749; *CIP.*

American Classical League, The, *(Amer Classical; 0-939507),* Miami University, Oxford, OH 45056 (SAN 225-8358) Tel 513-529-3991.

American Coalition of Citizens with Disabilities, Inc., *(Am Coalition Citizens Disabil; 0-933526),* 1012 14th St., NW, Suite 901, Washington, DC 20005 (SAN 223-677X) Tel 202-628-3470.

American College of Apothecaries, *(Am Coll Apothecaries; 0-934322),* 874 Union Ave., Memphis, TN 38163 (SAN 217-0868) Tel 901-528-6037.

American College of Chest Physicians, *(Am Chest Phys; 0-916609),* 911 Busse Hwy., Park Ridge, IL 60068 (SAN 227-7123) Tel 312-698-2200.

American College of Health Care Administrators, *(Am Coll Health),* 4650 East-West Hwy, P.O. Box 5890, Bethesda, MD 20814 (SAN 224-3857) Tel 301-652-8384.

American College of Healthcare Executives, *(ACHE),* 840 N. Lake Shore Dr., Chicago, IL 60611 (SAN 224-330X) Tel 312-943-0544.

American College of Heraldry, Inc., The, *(Am Coll Heraldry; 0-9605668),* P.O. Box CG, University, AL 35486 (SAN 216-0994).

American College of Laboratory Animal Medicine, *(ACLAM),* The Milton S. Hershey Medical Center, P.O. Box 850, Hershey, PA 17033 (SAN 224-4810) Tel 717-531-8462; Dist. by: Academic Press, Inc., Orlando, FL 32887 (SAN 206-8990) Tel 305-345-4143; Toll free: 800-321-5068.

American College of Obstetricians & Gynecologists, *(Am Coll Obstetric; 0-915473),* 600 Maryland Ave., SW, No. 300E, Washington, DC 20024 (SAN 284-9623) Tel 202-638-5577.

American College of Probate Counsel, *(Am Coll Probate),* 10964 W Pico Blvd, Los Angeles, CA 90064 (SAN 227-2083).

American College of Radiology, *(Am Coll Radiology),* 20 N. Wacker Dr., Chicago, IL 60606 (SAN 224-4462) Tel 312-236-4963.

American College Testing Program, *(Am Coll Testing; 0-937734),* 2201 N. Dodge St., Iowa City, IA 52243 (SAN 204-8027) Tel 319-337-1410; P.O Box 168, Iowa City, IA 52243 (SAN 696-5075).

American College, The, *(Amer College; 0-943590),* 270 Bryn Mawr Ave., Bryn Mawr, PA 19010 (SAN 240-5822) Tel 215-896-4544.

American Committee on East-West Accord, *(Amer Com E W Accord),* 109 11th St., SE, Washington, DC 20003 (SAN 235-7801) Tel 202-546-1700.

American Community Cultural Ctr. Assn., *(Am Community Cultural; 0-9614619),* 19 Foothills Dr., Pompton Plains, NJ 07444 (SAN 225-3011) Tel 201-835-2661.

American Computer Pr., *(Am Comp Pr; 0-934433),* 5511 Wisteria Way, Livermore, CA 94550 (SAN 693-6008) Tel 415-455-5560.

American Concrete Institute, *(ACI; 0-87031),* 22400 W. Seven Mile Rd., P.O. Box 19150, Detroit, MI 48219 (SAN 203-1450) Tel 313-532-2600.

American Congress of Jews from Poland & Survivors of Conc; 0-9616450), 6534 Moore Dr., Los Angeles, CA 90048 (SAN 659-2791) Tel 213-938-7881.

American Congress on Surveying & Mapping, *(Am Congrs Survey; 0-9613459),* 210 Little Falls St., Falls Church, VA 22046 (SAN 225-1531) Tel 703-241-2446.

American Consulting Engineers Council, *(Am Consul Eng; 0-910090),* 1015 15th St., NW, Suite 802, Washington, DC 20005 (SAN 206-8508) Tel 202-347-7474.

American Cooking Guild, The, Div. of WRC Publishing, *(Am Cooking; 0-942320),* 2915 Fenimore Rd., Silver Spring, MD 20902 (SAN 239-751X) Tel 301-949-6787.

American Correctional Assn., *(Am Correctional; 0-942974),* 4321 Hartwick Rd., Suite L-208, College Park, MD 20740 (SAN 204-8051) Tel 301-699-7600; Toll free: 800-ACA-JOIN.

American Council for Capital Formation, *(Am Coun Cap Form),* 1850 K St., NW, Washington, DC 20006 (SAN 225-6479) Tel 202-293-5811.

American Council for Construction Education, *(Am Coun Const Ed),* 1015 15th St., NW, Suite 700, Washington, DC 20005 (SAN 225-7688) Tel 202-347-5875.

American Council for Drug Education, Inc., *(Am Council Drug Ed; 0-942348),* 5820 Hubbard Dr., Rockville, MD 20852 (SAN 239-7099) Tel 301-984-5700.

American Council for Nationalities Service, *(ACNS; 0-915384),* 20 W. 40th St., New York, NY 10018 (SAN 218-4613).

†**American Council for the Arts,** *(Am Council Arts; 0-915400),* 1285 Ave. of the Americas, 3F, New York, NY 10019 (SAN 207-3706) Tel 212-245-4510; *CIP.*

American Council for Voluntary International Action, *(Am Intl Action; 0-932140),* 200 Park Ave. S., New York, NY 10003 (SAN 225-9508) Tel 212-777-8210. *Imprints:* Inneraction (Inneraction).

American Council on Consumer Interests, *(Am Coun Consumer),* Univ. of Missouri, 240 Stanley Hall, Columbia, MO 65211 (SAN 225-641X) Tel 314-882-3817.

†**American Council on Education,** *(ACE; 0-8268),* 1 Dupont Cir., Washington, DC 20036 (SAN 201-2170) Tel 202-939-9380; Toll free: 800-257-5755; Dist. by: Macmillan Publishing Co., Inc., 866 Third Ave., New York, NY 10022 (SAN 202-5574) Tel 212-702-2000; *CIP.*

American Council on Pharmaceutical Education, *(Am Council Pharmaceutical Educ),* 311 W. Superior St., Suite 512, Chicago, IL 60610 (SAN 224-4179) Tel 312-664-3575.

American Craft Council, *(Am Craft; 0-88321),* 45 W. 45th St., New York, NY 10036 (SAN 201-2634) Tel 212-696-0710; Orders to: Pubns. Dept., 40 W. 53rd St., New York, NY 10019 (SAN 661-9355).

American Dairy Goat Assn., *(Am Dairy Goat),* Box 865, Spindale, NC 28160 (SAN 224-9847).

American Dance Guild, *(Am Dance Guild; 0-934994),* 570 Seventh Ave., New York, NY 10018 (SAN 233-3236) Tel 212-944-0557.

American Deafness & Rehabilitation Assn., *(Am Deaf & Rehab; 0-914494),* 814 Thayer Ave., Silver Spring, MD 20910 (SAN 201-8918) Tel 301-589-0880.

American Demographics, *(American Demo; 0-936889),* P.O. Box 68, Ithaca, NY 14851 (SAN 658-4594) Tel 607-273-6343; 127 W. State St., Ithaca, NY 14851 (SAN 658-4608).

American Dental Assn., *(Am Dental; 0-910074),* 211 E. Chicago Ave., Chicago, IL 60611 (SAN 202-4519) Tel 312-440-2642.

American Dental Assn. Health Foundation, *(Am Dent Health; 0-934510),* 211 E. Chicago Ave., Suite 412, Chicago, IL 60611 (SAN 696-5520) Tel 312-440-2516.

American Dental Hygienists Assn., *(Am Dental Hygienists),* 444 N. Michigan Ave., Suite 3400, Chicago, IL 60611 (SAN 224-3032) Tel 312-440-8900.

American Developing Industries, *(Am Developing; 0-8187),* 10520 First Way N., St. Petersburg, FL 33702 (SAN 217-2232) Tel 813-576-2027.

American Diabetes Assn., *(Am Diabetes),* 1660 Duke St., P.O. Box 25757, Alexandria, VA 22313 (SAN 224-3105) Tel 703-549-7444.

American Dietetic Assn., *(Am Dietetic Assn; 0-88091),* 430 N. Michigan Ave., Chicago, IL 60611 (SAN 228-1341) Tel 312-280-5000.

American Donkey & Mule Society, *(Am Donkey),* Rte. 5, Box 65, Denton, TX 76201 (SAN 224-9855) Tel 817-382-6845.

American Dynamics Corp., *(Am Dynamics NY; 0-9608962),* Box 11, Cathedral Sta., New York, NY 10025 (SAN 218-6160) Tel 212-749-3546.

American Eagle Publishing, *(Am Eagle Pub; 0-935431),* 119 Sylvan Rd., Needham, MA 02192 (SAN 696-4990) Tel 201-440-5220.

American Economic Assn., *(Am Economic Assn; 0-917290),* 1313 21st Ave. S., Suite 809, Oxford Hse., Nashville, TN 37212 (SAN 225-6487) Tel 615-322-2595.

American Economic Development Council, *(Amer Econ Dev Council; 0-9616567),* 4849 N. Scott St., Suite 10, Schiller Park, IL 60176 (SAN 225-8129) Tel 312-671-5646.

American Education Assn., *(Am Educ Assn),* 663 Fifth Ave., New York, NY 10022 (SAN 225-7734) Tel 212-687-6865.

American Educational Music Pubns., Inc., *(Am Ed Mus Pubns; 0-942542),* 8400 Grand Lake Rd., Presque Isle, MI 49777 (SAN 239-6599) Tel 517-595-2000.

American Educational Research Assn., *(Am Educ Res; 0-935302),* 1230 17th St. NW, Washington, DC 20036 (SAN 676-8784) Tel 202-223-9485.

American Educational Trust, The, *(Am Educ Trust; 0-937165),* P.O. Box 53062, Washington, DC 20009 (SAN 296-1172) Tel 202-939-6050; Toll free: 800-368-5788; Toll free: 800-368-5788.

American Egg Board, *(Am Egg Bd),* 1460 Renaissance Dr., Park Ridge, IL 60068 (SAN 225-0543) Tel 312-296-7043.

American Electroplaters & Surface Finishers Society, *(Am Electro Surface; 0-936569),* 12644 Research Pkwy., Orlando, FL 32826 (SAN 225-1604) Tel 305-281-6441.

American Electroplaters' Society, Inc. *See* **American Electroplaters & Surface Finishers Society**

American Engineering Model Society, *(Am Eng Model Soc),* Box 2066, Aiken, SC 29802 (SAN 225-1647) Tel 803-649-6710; 117 Grace Cir., Aiken, SC 29801 (SAN 668-9744).

†**American Enterprise Institute for Public Policy Research,** *(Am Enterprise; 0-8447),* 1150 17th St., NW, Washington, DC 20036 (SAN 202-4527) Tel 202-862-5800; Toll free: 800-424-2873. Do not confuse with American Enterprise Pubns., Mercer, PA; *CIP.*

American Enterprise Pubns., *(A E P; 0-9612198),* Box 6690, R.D. 6, Mercer, PA 16137 (SAN 202-4454) Tel 412-748-3726. Do not confuse with American Enterprise Institute for Public Policy Research, Washington, DC.

American Entomological Institute, *(Am Entom Inst),* 3005 SW 56th Ave., Gainesville, FL 32608 (SAN 202-4535) Tel 904-377-6458.

American Entrepreneurs Assn., *(Am Entrepreneurs),* 2311 Pontius Ave., Los Angeles, CA 90064 (SAN 241-3558).

American Express Food & Wine Magazine Corp., Affil. of American Express Publishing Co., *(Am Express Food; 0-916103),* 1120 Ave. of the Americas, New York, NY 10036 (SAN 294-8923) Tel 212-382-5000.

American Express Pubns. *See* **Better Home & Gardens Bks.**

American Faculty Pr., Inc., *(Am Faculty Pr; 0-912834),* 44 Lake Shore Dr., Rockaway, NJ 07866 (SAN 201-2650) Tel 201-627-2727.

American Family Communiversity Pr., *(Am Family; 0-910574),* 5242 W. North Ave., Chicago, IL 60639 (SAN 210-7708) Tel 312-237-4793.

American Family Records Assn., *(AFRA; 0-913233),* 311 E. 12th St., Kansas City, MO 64106 (SAN 241-3566) Tel 816-453-1294.

American Fan Assn., *(AFA),* Box 1481, East Lansing, MI 48864 (SAN 688-9565) Tel 517-339-2900.

American Federation of Arts, *(Am Fed Arts; 0-917418),* 41 E. 65th St., New York, NY 10021 (SAN 201-2669) Tel 212-988-7700.

American Federation of Astrologers, *(Am Fed Astrologers; 0-86690),* Box 22040, Tempe, AZ 85282 (SAN 225-1396) Tel 602-838-1751.

American Federation of Labor & Congress of Industrial Organizations, *(AFL-CIO),* 815 16th St. NW, Washington, DC 20006 (SAN 224-246X) Tel 202-637-5041.

American Feed Industry Assn., *(Am Feed Industry),* 1701 N. Ft. Myer Dr., Arlington, VA 22209 (SAN 224-7283) Tel 703-524-0810.

American First Day Cover Society, *(Am First Day),* 16S31 Abbey Dr., Mitchellville, MD 20716 (SAN 225-5855).

American Fisheries Society, *(Am Fisheries Soc; 0-913235),* P.O. Box 1150, Columbia, MD 21044 (SAN 284-964X) Tel 301-596-3458; 5410 Grosvenor Ln., Suite 110, Bethesda, MD 20814 (SAN 284-9658) Tel 301-897-8616.

American Fisheries Society, Florida Chapter, *(Am Fish FL; 0-9616679),* Univ. of Florida, Bldg. 803, Gainesville, FL 32611 (SAN 659-7130) Tel 904-392-5870.

American Fishing Tackle Manufacturers Assn., *(Am Fish Tackle; 0-933986),* 2625 Clearbrook Dr., Arlington Heights, IL 60005 (SAN 224-6287) Tel 312-364-4666.

American Forestry Assn., *(Am Forestry; 0-935050),* Bk. Editorial Dept., 1319 18th St., NW, Washington, DC 20036 (SAN 204-8175) Tel 202-467-5810.

†**American Foundation for the Blind,** *(Am Foun Blind; 0-89128),* 15 W. 16th St., New York, NY 10011 (SAN 201-2677) Tel 212-620-2150; *CIP.*

American Foundrymen's Society, *(Am Foundrymen; 0-87433),* Golf & Wolf Rds., Des Plaines, IL 60016 (SAN 224-0424) Tel 312-824-0181.

American Friends Service Committee, *(Am Fr Serv Comm; 0-910082),* 1501 Cherry St., Philadelphia, PA 19102 (SAN 201-2685) Tel 215-241-7000.

American Fuchsia Society, *(Am Fuchsia; 0-9613167),* Hall of Flowers, Ninth Ave. & Lincoln Way, San Francisco, CA 94122 (SAN 294-8931) Tel 707-442-3994.

American Gas Assn., *(Am Gas Assn; 0-87257),* 1515 Wilson Blvd., Arlington, VA 22209 (SAN 224-7623) Tel 703-841-8400.

†**American Geographical Society,** *(Am Geographical),* 156 Fifth Ave., New York, NY 10010 (SAN 225-1906) Tel 212-242-0214; *CIP.*

†**American Geological Institute,** *(Am Geol; 0-913312),* 4220 King St., Alexandria, VA 22302 (SAN 202-4543) Tel 703-379-2480; Toll free: 800-336-4764; *CIP.*

†**American Geophysical Union,** *(Am Geophysical; 0-87590),* 2000 Florida Ave. NW, Washington, DC 20009 (SAN 202-4489) Tel 202-462-6903; Toll free: 800-424-2488; *CIP.*

American Guidance Service, Inc., *(Am Guidance; 0-913476; 0-88671),* Publishers' Bldg., Circle Pines, MN 55014 (SAN 201-694X) Tel 612-786-4343; Toll free: 800-328-2560.

American Hasbourgh Dynasty Co., *(Am Hasbourgh; 0-936037),* P.O. Box 2203, Long Island City, NY 11102 (SAN 696-9925) Tel 718-626-0389; 4-33 27th Ave., Astoria, NY 11102 (SAN 696-9933).

American Health & Nutrition, Inc., *(Amer Health Nutri; 0-914851),* 262 Larkspur Plaza Dr., Larkspur, CA 94939 (SAN 289-0496) Tel 415-924-5702; Dist. by: New Leaf Distributing, The, 1020 White St. SW, Atlanta, GA 30310 (SAN 169-1449) Tel 404-755-2665; Toll free: 800-241-3829.

American Health Care Assn., *(Am Health Care Assn)* 1200 15th St., NW, Washington, DC 20005 (SAN 224-3865) Tel 202-833-2050.

American Health Consultants, Inc., Subs. of Medical Economics, Inc., *(Am Health Consults; 0-9603332),* 67 Peachtree Park Dr., NE, Atlanta, GA 30309 (SAN 222-2655) Tel 404-351-4523; Toll free: 800-559-1032.

American Heart Assn., Inc., *(Am Heart; 0-87493),* 7320 Greenville Ave., Dallas, TX 75231 (SAN 202-4551) Tel 214-706-1464; Dist. by: American Heart Association, Distribution Center, 2005 Hightower, Garland, TX 75401 (SAN 662-7137) Tel 214-278-1346; Dist. by: American Heart Association, Materials Resource Center, 4808 Eastover Cir., Mesquite, TX 75149 (SAN 662-7145).

†**American Heritage, Inc.,** *(Am Heritage; 0-8281),* 60 Fifth Ave., New York, NY 10020 (SAN 206-9032) Tel 212-399-8900; Dist. by: Houghton Mifflin Co., 1 Beacon St., Boston, MA 02108 (SAN 200-2388) Tel 617-725-5000; *CIP.*

American Hispanist, Inc., *(American Hispanist; 0-89217),* P.O. Box 64, Clear Creek, IN 47426 (SAN 209-3944).

American Historic Homes, *(American Hist; 0-9615481),* P.O. Box 336, Dana Point, CA 92629 (SAN 696-0731) Tel 714-496-7050.

American Historical Assn., *(Am Hist Assn; 0-87229),* 400 A St., SE, Washington, DC 20003 (SAN 201-159X) Tel 202-544-2422.

American Historical Foundation, The, *(Amer Hist Found; 0-933489),* P.O. Box 6622, Richmond, VA 23230 (SAN 692-7386) Tel 804-353-1812.

American Historical Society of Germans from Russia, *(Am Hist Soc Ger; 0-914222),* 631 D St., Lincoln, NE 68502 (SAN 204-7543) Tel 402-474-3363.

American History Pr., Div. of Northwoods Pr., *(Am Hist Pr; 0-89002),* P.O. Box 123, S. Thomaston, ME 04858 (SAN 217-0876).

American History Research Associates, *(Am Hist Res; 0-910086),* P.O. Box 140, Brookeville, MD 20833 (SAN 206-717X) Tel 301-774-3573.

†**American Home Economics Assn.,** *(Am Home Eco; 0-8461),* 2010 Massachusetts Ave., NW, Washington, DC 20036 (SAN 266-9277) Tel 202-862-8344; *CIP.*

Names

American Horse Council, *(Am Horse Coun),* 1700 K St. NW, Suite 300, Washington, DC 20006 (SAN 225-025X) Tel 202-296-4031.

†**American Hospital Assn.,** *(Am Hospital; 0-87258),* 840 N. Lake Shore Dr., Chicago, IL 60611 (SAN 295-2955) Tel 312-280-6000; Toll free: 800-242-2626 (Orders); *CIP.*

†**American Hospital Publishing, Inc.,** Subs. of American Hospital Assn., *(AHPI; 0-939450; 1-55648),* 211 E. Chicago Ave., Chicago, IL 60611 (SAN 216-5872) Tel 312-440-6800; Toll free: 800-242-2626; Orders to: AHA Services, Inc., P.O. Box 99376, 4444 W. Ferdinande, Chicago, IL 60624 (SAN 661-9363) Tel 312-280-6020; *CIP.*

American Hot Dip Galvanizers Assn., *(Am Hot Dip),* Suite 700 1101 Connecticut Ave., NW, Washington, DC 20036-4303 (SAN 224-6805) Tel 202-857-1119.

American Hotel & Motel Assn., *(Am Hotel & Motel Assn; 0-86612),* 888 Seventh Ave., New York, NY 10019 (SAN 224-7917) Tel 212-265-4506.

†**American Hotel & Motel Assn., Educational Institute,** *(Educ Inst Am Hotel; 0-86612),* 1407 S. Harrison Rd., East Lansing, MI 48823 (SAN 215-8590) Tel 517-353-5500; Warehouse, 2113 N. High St., Lansing, MI 48906 (SAN 669-0726); *CIP.*

†**American Humane Assn.,** *(Am Humane Assn; 0-930915),* P.O. Box 1266, Denver, CO 80201 (SAN 227-2156) Tel 303-695-0811; *CIP.*

American Hungarian Foundation, *(Am Hungarian Foun),* 177 Somerset St., New Brunswick, NJ 08903 (SAN 211-2086) Tel 201-846-5777.

American Hungarian Review, *(Hungarian Rev; 0-911862),* 5410 Kerth Rd., St. Louis, MO 63128 (SAN 204-0816) Tel 314-487-7566.

American Imagery Institute, *(American Imagery; 0-9616350),* P.O. Box 13453, Milwaukee, WI 53213 (SAN 659-0039) Tel 414-781-4045; 4375 Meadow View E., Brookfield, WI 53005 (SAN 659-0047).

American Immigration Control Foundation, *(Amer Immigration; 0-936247),* P.O. Box 525, Monterey, VA 24465 (SAN 697-3205) Tel 703-468-2022; 3 Water St., Monterey, VA 24465 (SAN 697-3213).

American Impressions Book Co., *(Am Impress Bk Co; 0-942550),* 417 Cleveland Ave., Plainfield, NJ 07060 (SAN 238-7654) Tel 201-757-2600.

†**American Indian Archaeological Institute,** *(Am Indian Arch; 0-936322),* P.O. Box 260, Washington, CT 06793 (SAN 221-2536) Tel 203-868-0518; *CIP.*

American Indian Pubs., Inc., *(Am Indian Pubs; 0-937862),* 177 F Riverside Dr., Newport Beach, CA 92663 (SAN 216-3284).

American Industrial Hygiene Assn., *(Am Indus Hygiene; 0-932627),* 475 Wolf Ledges Pkwy., Akron, OH 44311-1087 (SAN 224-3970) Tel 216-762-7294.

American Inheritance Pr., *(Am Inheritance Pr; 0-932037),* 2314 Arctic Ave., Atlantic City, NJ 08401 (SAN 686-0729) Tel 609-344-0383.

American Institute for Archaeological Research, Inc., *(Am Inst Arch Res; 0-937923),* 220 Main St., Salem, NH 03079 (SAN 659-4867) Tel 617-267-6906.

American Institute for Character Education, *(Am Inst Char Ed; 0-913413),* 342 W. Woodlawn, San Antonio, TX 78212 (SAN 236-154X) Tel 512-734-5091; Orders to: P.O. Box 12617, San Antonio, TX 78212 (SAN 680-0114).

American Institute for Conservation of Historical & Artistic Works, *(Am Inst Conser Hist),* 3545 Williamsburg Lane, NW, Washington, DC 20008 (SAN 225-4972) Tel 202-364-1036.

American Institute for Economic Research, *(Am Inst Econ Res; 0-913610),* Division St., Great Barrington, MA 01230 (SAN 225-6509) Tel 413-528-1216.

American Institute for Marxist Studies, *(Am Inst Marxist; 0-89977),* 85 E. Fourth St., New York, NY 10013 (SAN 202-4594) Tel 212-689-4530.

American Institute for Property & Liability Underwriters, Inc., *(Am Inst Property; 0-89463),* 720 Providence Rd., Malvern, PA 19355 (SAN 210-1629) Tel 215-644-2100.

American Institute for Psychological Research, The, *(Am Inst Psych; 0-89920),* 614 Indian School Rd. NW, Albuquerque, NM 87102 (SAN 212-9302) Tel 505-843-7749.

American Institute for Writing Research, Corp., *(Am Inst Writing Res; 0-917944),* P.O. Box 1364, Grand Central Sta., New York, NY 10163 (SAN 210-0290) Tel 718-266-2897.

American Institute of Adlerian Studies, The, *(AIAS; 0-918287),* 600 N. McClurg Ct., Suite 2502A, Chicago, IL 60611 (SAN 657-2502) Tel 312-337-5066.

†**American Institute of Aeronautics & Astronautics,** *(AIAA; 0-915928),* 1633 Broadway, New York, NY 10019 (SAN 204-529X) Tel 212-581-4300; *CIP.*

American Institute of Architects, *(Am Inst Arch; 0-913962),* 1735 New York Ave., NW, Washington, DC 20006 Tel 202-626-7474; Orders to: AIA Service Corp., 44 Industrial Pk. Dr., Box 753, Waldorf, MD 20601 (SAN 661-9371).

American Institute of Architects, San Antonio Chapter, *(AIA San Antonio; 0-9616842),* 720 6PM S. Tower, San Antonio, TX 78216 (SAN 662-5673) Tel 512-349-9971.

American Institute of Baking, *(Am Inst Baking),* 1213 Bakers Way, Manhattan, KS 66502 (SAN 224-6449) Tel 913-537-4750.

American Institute of Banking, Affil. of ABA, *(Amer Inst Bank; 0-935183),* 550 Kearny St., Suite 310, San Francisco, CA 94108 (SAN 696-9003) Tel 415-392-5286.

American Institute of Certified Public Accountants, *(Am Inst CPA; 0-87051),* 1211 Ave. of the Americas, New York, NY 10036 (SAN 202-4578) Tel 212-575-6200.

†**American Institute of Chemical Engineers,** *(Am Inst Chem Eng; 0-8169),* 345 E. 47th St., New York, NY 10017 (SAN 204-7551) Tel 212-705-7657; *CIP.*

American Institute of Chemists, Inc., *(Amer Inst Chem; 0-939293),* 7315 Wisconsin Ave., Bethesda, MD 20814 (SAN 232-6280) Tel 301-652-2447.

American Institute of Cooperation, *(Am Inst Cooperation; 0-938868),* 1800 Massachusetts Ave., NW, Suite 508, Washington, DC 20036 (SAN 204-5281) Tel 202-296-6825.

American Institute of Discussion, *(Am Inst Disc; 0-910092),* P.O. Box 103, Oklahoma City, OK 73101 (SAN 202-4586) Tel 405-235-9681.

American Institute of Food Distribution, Inc., *(Am Inst Food Distr),* 28-12 Broadway, Fair Lawn, NJ 07410 (SAN 224-7372) Tel 201-791-5570.

†**American Institute of Islamic Studies,** *(Am Inst Islamic; 0-933017),* P.O. Box 10398, Denver, CO 80210 (SAN 266-9811) Tel 303-936-0108; *CIP.*

American Institute of Italian Studies, *(Am Inst Ital Stud; 0-916322),* Villa Walsh, Morristown, NJ 07960 (SAN 220-2298) Tel 201-538-2886; Dist. by: Kraus Reprint & Periodicals, Rte. 100, Millwood, NY 10546 (SAN 201-0542) Tel 914-762-2200.

American Institute of Maintenance, *(Am Inst Maint; 0-9609052),* 1120 E. Chevy Chase Dr., P.O. Box 2068, Glendale, CA 91205 (SAN 260-3179) Tel 818-244-1176.

American Institute of Management, *(Amer Inst Mgmt; 0-935517),* 33 Market St., No. 46, Poughkeepsie, NY 12601 (SAN 696-074X) Tel 914-471-3240.

American Institute of Mining, Metallurgical, & Petroleum Engineers, *(Am Inst Mining Metal; 0-89520),* 345 E. 47th St., New York, NY 10017 (SAN 688-9921) Tel 212-705-7695.

American Institute of Musical Studies *See* **AIMS**

American Institute of Parliamentarians, *(Am Inst Parliamentarians; 0-942736),* 124 W. Washington Blvd., Suite 144, Ft. Wayne, IN 46802 (SAN 225-3690) Tel 219-422-3680.

American Institute of Physics, *(Am Inst Physics; 0-88318),* 335 E. 45th St., New York, NY 10017 (SAN 201-162X) Tel 212-661-9404; Toll free: 800-247-7497. Publisher of scholarly journals, books and databases in physics and related sciences in hardcopy, 16mm and 35mm microfilm, reel and cartridge, and microfiche. North American distributor of journals from the Institute of Physics (UK), Annals of the Israel Physical Society, Physics Briefs from the Fachinformationszentrum (West Germany), and Physica Scripta (Royal Swedish Academy of Sciences).

†**American Institute of Real Estate Appraisers,** Affil. of National Assn. of Realtors, *(Am Inst Real Estate Appraisers; 0-911780),* 430 N. Michigan Ave., Chicago, IL 60611 (SAN 206-7153) Tel 312-329-8533; Dist. by: Regnery Gateway, Inc., 940-950 N. Shore Dr., Lake Bluff, IL (SAN 210-5578); *CIP.*

American Institute of Small Business, *(Amer Inst Small Bus; 0-939069),* 7515 Wayzata Blvd., Suite 201, Minneapolis, MN 55426 (SAN 662-9407) Tel 612-545-7001; Toll free: 800-328-2906.

American Institute of Steel Construction, Inc., *(Am Inst Steel Construct),* 400 N. Michigan Ave., Chicago, IL 60611 (SAN 224-6872) Tel 312-670-2400.

American Institute of Taxidermy, Inc., *(Am Inst Taxidermy; 0-9616088),* 3232 McCormick Dr., Janesville, WI 53545 (SAN 698-0775) Tel 608-755-5160.

American Institute of the History of Pharmacy, *(Am Inst Hist Pharm; 0-931292),* 425 N. Charter St., Pharmacy Bldg., Madison, WI 53706 (SAN 204-5257) Tel 608-262-5378.

American Institute of Timber Construction, *(Am Inst Timber),* 333 W. Hampden Ave., Englewood, CO 80110 (SAN 230-287X) Tel 303-761-3212.

American Institute of Ultrasound in Medicine, *(Am Inst Ultrasound),* 4405 East-West Hwy., Bethesda, MD 20814 (SAN 224-4756) Tel 301-656-6117.

American Institutes for Research, *(Am Inst Res; 0-89785),* P.O. Box 1113, Palo Alto, CA 94302 (SAN 202-442X).

American Institutes for Research, Systems Division, *(AIR Systems; 0-89785),* 41 North Rd., Bedford, MA 01730 (SAN 215-9368) Tel 617-275-0800.

American Insurance Assn., *(Am Ins NY),* 85 John St., New York, NY 10038 (SAN 266-9900) Tel 212-433-4400.

American International Development Studies, Inc., *(Am Intl Dev; 0-9616279),* P.O. Box 490249, Miami, FL 33149 (SAN 658-5345) Tel 305-444-5678.

American Iris Society, *(Am Iris; 0-9601242),* 7414 E. 60th St., Tulsa, OK 74145 (SAN 210-3826) Tel 918-627-0706; Orders to: Rte. 3, Box 270, Vinita, OK 74301 (SAN 210-3834) Tel 918-782-3133.

American Iron & Steel Institute, *(Am Iron & Steel),* 1000 16th St. NW, Washington, DC 20036 (SAN 224-8719) Tel 202-452-7100.

American Italian Historical Assn., Inc., *(Am Italian; 0-934675),* 209 Flagg Pl., Staten Island, NY 10304 (SAN 210-8828) Tel 718-454-9326.

American Ivy Society, The, *(Am Ivy Soc; 0-937233),* P.O. Box 520, West Carrollton, OH 45449-0520 (SAN 225-5685) Tel 513-434-7069.

American Jewish Commission on the Holocaust, *(Am Jewish Holo; 0-9613537),* Ralph Bunche, Graduate Institute School Cuny, 33 W. 42nd St., New York, NY 10036 (SAN 669-7178) Tel 212-790-4222.

American Jewish Committee, *(Am Jewish Comm; 0-87495),* 165 E. 56 St., New York, NY 10022 (SAN 675-0079) Tel 212-751-4000.

American Jewish Historical Society, *(Am Jewish Hist Soc; 0-911934),* Two Thornton Rd., Waltham, MA 02154 (SAN 202-4608) Tel 617-891-8110.

American Journal of Forensic Psychiatry, Div. of American College of Forensic Psychiatry, *(AJFP; 0-935645),* 26701 Quail Creek, No. 295, Laguna Hills, CA 92656 (SAN 696-0774) Tel 714-831-0236.

Names

American Journal of Nursing Co., Educational Services Div., *(Am Journal Nurse; 0-937126)*, 555 W. 57th St., New York, NY 10019 (SAN 202-4616) Tel 212-582-8820.

†American Judicature Society, *(Am Judicature; 0-938870)*, 25 E. Washington, Suite 1600, Chicago, IL 60602 (SAN 201-7202) Tel 312-558-6900; *CIP.*

American Language Academy, *(Am Lang Acad; 0-934270)*, Regents/ALA., 2 Park Ave., New York, NY 10016 (SAN 281-2665); Toll free: 800-822-8202.

American Law Enforcement Officers Assn., *(Am Law Enforce Off; 0-936320)*, 1100 125th St. NE, North Miami, FL 33161 (SAN 225-1175).

American Law Institute, *(Am Law Inst; 0-8318)*, 4025 Chestnut St., Philadelphia, PA 19104 (SAN 204-756X) Tel 215-243-1600; Toll free: 800-CLE-NEWS.

American Legacy Press *See* Crown Pubs., Inc.

American Legislative Exchange Council, *(Am Legislative; 0-89483)*, 214 Massachusetts Ave., NE, Washington, DC 20002 (SAN 210-0274) Tel 202-547-4646.

American Leprosy Missions, Inc., *(Am Leprosy Mission)*, c/o ALM Inc., One Broadway, Elmwood Park, NJ 07407 (SAN 224-3474) Tel 201-794-8650.

American Liberty Pubns., *(Am Liberty; 0-917209)*, 1912 Waltzer Rd., Santa Rosa, CA 95401 (SAN 656-0385) Tel 707-544-3141.

American Liberty Publishing *See* Jackson, Don, Assocs.

American Library Publishing Co., Inc., *(Am Lib Pub Co; 0-934598)*, 275 Central Park W., New York, NY 10024 (SAN 201-9868) Tel 212-362-1442.

†American Life Foundation & Study Institute, *(Am Life Foun; 0-89257)*, P.O. Box 349, Watkins Glen, NY 14891 (SAN 201-1646) Tel 607-535-4737; *CIP.*

American Life Foundations-Century House Books, *(ALF-CHB; 0-87282)*, Old Irelandville, P.O. Box 306, Watkins Glen, NY 14891 (SAN 201-9736) Tel 607-535-4004.

American Literary Translators Assn., *(Am Lit Trans)*, P.O. Box 830688, Richardson, TX 75083-0688 (SAN 260-3497) Tel 214-690-2093.

American Logistics Assn., *(Am Logistics Assn; 0-915959)*, 1133 15th St. NW, Suite 500, Washington, DC 20005 (SAN 225-1027) Tel 202-466-2520.

American Lung Assn., *(Am Lung Assn; 0-915116)*, 1740 Broadway, New York, NY 10019 (SAN 211-3503).

American Malacologists, Inc., *(Am Malacologists; 0-915826)*, Box 2255, Melbourne, FL 32902-2255 (SAN 207-6403) Tel 305-725-2260.

American Management Reviews, *(Am Manage Rev; 0-9613385)*, P.O. Box 45500, Phoenix, AZ 85064 (SAN 657-0623) Tel 602-252-7622.

†American Map Corp., Subs. of Langenscheidt Pubs,Inc., *(Am Map; 0-8416)*, 46-35 54th Rd., Maspeth, NY 11378 (SAN 202-4624) Tel 718-784-0055; *CIP.*

American Marine Corp., *(Am Marine Corp; 0-9615134)*, 1 Burlington Woods Dr., Suite 302, Burlington, MA 01803 (SAN 694-2504) Tel 617-273-1326.

†American Marketing Assn., *(Am Mktg; 0-87757)*, 250 S. Wacker Dr., No. 200, Chicago, IL 60606 (SAN 202-4667) Tel 312-648-0536; *CIP.*

American Martial Arts Publishing, *(Am Martial Arts Pub; 0-932981)*, P.O. Box 4097, Greenville, NC 27836 (SAN 686-113X) Tel 919-758-2055.

†American Mathematical Society, *(Am Math; 0-8218)*, P.O. Box 6248, Providence, RI 02940 (SAN 201-1654) Tel 401-272-9500; Toll free: 800-556-7774; Orders to: P.O. Box 1571, Annex Sta., Providence, RI 02901-1571 (SAN 201-1662); *CIP.*

American Media, *(Am Media; 0-912986)*, P.O. Box 4646, Westlake Village, CA 91359 (SAN 202-4632) Tel 805-496-1649.

†American Medical Assn., *(AMA; 0-89970)*, 535 N. Dearborn St., Chicago, IL 60610 (SAN 206-8516) Tel 312-751-6000; *CIP.*

American Medical Publishing Assn., *(Am Med Pub; 0-911411)*, c/o Louis Reines, 1560 Broadway, New York, NY 10036 (SAN 691-4136) Tel 212-819-5400.

American Medical Record Assn., *(Am Med Record Assn)*, P.O. Box 97349, Chicago, IL 60690 (SAN 224-4489) Tel 312-787-2672.

American Mental Health Foundation, *(Am Mental Health Found)*, 2 E. 86th St., New York, NY 10028 (SAN 228-0531).

American Metal Market/Metalworking News, *(AMM; 0-910094)*, Dist. by: Fairchild Pubns., Inc., 7 E. 12th St., New York, NY 10003 (SAN 201-470X) Tel 212-741-4280.

American Meteorite Laboratory, *(Am Meteorite; 0-910096)*, P.O. Box 2098, Denver, CO 80201 (SAN 202-4659) Tel 303-428-1371.

American Metric Journal, *(Am Metric; 0-917240)*, P.O. Box 847, Tarzana, CA 91356 (SAN 209-4134) Tel 805-484-5787.

American Mideast Research, *(Am Mideast; 0-9604562)*, 3315 Sacramento St., Suite 511, San Francisco, CA 94118 (SAN 215-0506) Tel 415-346-9222.

American Mosquito Control Assn., *(Am Mosquito)*, P.O. Box 5416, Lake Charles, LA 70606 (SAN 224-3652) Tel 318-474-4736.

American Motor Logs, *(Amer Motor; 0-936207)*, 2099 LaCrosse Ave., St. Paul, MN 55119 (SAN 696-933X) Tel 612-735-1410.

American Museum of Natural History, *(Am Mus Natl Hist; 0-913424)*, Central Park W. at 79th St., New York, NY 10024 (SAN 208-2160) Tel 212-873-1498.

American Museum Science Books *See* Natural History Pr.

American Museum Sourcebooks in Anthropology *See* Natural History Pr.

American Music Ctr., Inc., *(Am Music Ctr; 0-916052)*, 250 W. 54th St., New York, NY 10019 (SAN 225-3518).

American Music Conference, *(American Music; 0-918196)*, 150 E. Huron St., Chicago, IL 60611 (SAN 209-3952) Tel 312-266-8670.

American Mutuality Foundation, *(Am Mutuality; 0-938844)*, 9428 S. Western Ave., Los Angeles, CA 90047 (SAN 216-0153).

American National Metric Council, *(Am Natl; 0-916148)*, 1010 Vermont Ave., NW, Suite 320-21, Washington, DC 20005-4960 (SAN 207-9380) Tel 202-628-5757.

†American National Standards Institute, *(ANSI)*, 1430 Broadway, New York, NY 10018 (SAN 203-4778) Tel 212-354-3311; *CIP.*

American Natural Hygiene Society, *(Am Nat Hygiene; 0-914532)*, 12816 Race Track Rd., Tampa, FL 33625 (SAN 224-3660).

American-Nepal Education Foundation, *(Am-Nepal Ed)*, 2790 Cape Meares Lp., Tillamook, OR 97141 (SAN 236-5049) Tel 503-842-4024.

American New Church Sunday School Assn., *(Am New Church Sunday; 0-917426)*, 48 Highland St., Sharon, MA 02067 (SAN 208-9432) Tel 617-784-5041; Dist. by: Swedenborg Library, 79 Newbury St., Boston, MA 02116 (SAN 208-9440).

American Nonsmokers' Rights Foundation, *(Am Nonsmokers Rights; 0-9616473)*, 2054 University Ave., Suite 500, Berkeley, CA 94704 (SAN 659-2821) Tel 415-841-3032.

†American Nuclear Society, *(Am Nuclear Soc)*, 555 N. Kensington Ave., La Grange Park, IL 60525 (SAN 207-5172) Tel 312-352-6611; *CIP.*

American Numismatic Assn., *(American Numismatic; 0-89637)*, 818 N. Cascade Ave., P.O. Box 2366, Colorado Springs, CO 80901-2366 (SAN 211-3481) Tel 303-632-2646; Toll free: 800-367-9723.

American Numismatic Society, *(Am Numismatic; 0-89722)*, Broadway at 155th St., New York, NY 10032 (SAN 201-7067) Tel 212-234-3130.

†American Nurses Assn., *(ANA)*, 2420 Pershing Rd., Kansas City, MO 64108 (SAN 204-5176) Tel 816-474-5720; Toll free: 800-368-5643; *CIP.*

†American Occupational Therapy Assn., Inc., *(Am Occup Therapy; 0-910317)*, P.O. Box 1725, Rockville, MD 20850-4375 (SAN 224-4705); 1383 Piccard Dr., Rockville, MD 20850-4375 (SAN 662-7153) Tel 301-948-9626; *CIP.*

American Oil Chemists Society, *(Am Oil Chemists; 0-935315)*, 508 S. Sixth St., Champaign, IL 61820 (SAN 225-1558) Tel 217-359-2344.

American Oral Health Institute Pr., *(Amer Oral Health Inst Pr; 0-936837)*, P.O. Box 151528, Columbus, OH 43215-8528 (SAN 658-3296) Tel 614-447-0038; 3746 Granden Rd., Columbus, OH 43214 (SAN 658-330X).

American Orff-Schulwerk Assn., *(Amer Orff)*, 332 Gerard Ave., Elkins Park, PA 19117 (SAN 260-3519) Tel 215-635-2622; Orders to: P.O. Box 391089, Cleveland, OH 44139-1089 (SAN 661-938X).

American Oriental Society, *(Am Orient Soc; 0-940490)*, 329 Sterling Memorial Library, Yale Sta., New Haven, CT 06520 (SAN 211-3082) Tel 203-436-1040.

American Ornithologists Union, *(Am Ornithologists; 0-943610)*, National Museum of Natural History, Washington, DC 20560 (SAN 225-2252) Tel 202-381-5286.

American Parapsychological Research Fellowship *See* American Assn. for Parapsychology

American Passage Mktg. Corp., *(Am Passage Mktg; 0-937649)*, 500 Third Ave. W., Seattle, WA 98119 (SAN 659-2848) Tel 206-282-8111.

American Patent Law Assn., *(Am Patent Law)*, 2001 Jefferson Davis Hwy., Rm. 203, Arlington, VA 22202 (SAN 227-3586).

†American Petroleum Institute Pubns., *(Am Petroleum; 0-89364)*, 1220 L St. NW, Washington, DC 20005 (SAN 204-5141) Tel 202-682-8375; *CIP.*

†American Pharmaceutical Assn., *(Am Pharm Assn; 0-917330)*, 2215 Constitution Ave., NW, Washington, DC 20037 (SAN 202-4446) Tel 202-628-4410; *CIP.*

American Philatelic Society, *(Am Philatelic Society; 0-933580)*, P.O. Box 8000, State College, PA 16803 (SAN 225-5863) Tel 814-237-3803; 100 Oakwood Ave., State College, PA 16803 (SAN 668-9876).

American Philosophical Society, *(Am Philos; 0-87169)*, 104 S. Fifth St., Philadelphia, PA 19106 (SAN 206-9016) Tel 215-627-0706; Orders to: P.O. Box 40227-5227, Philadelphia, PA 19106 (SAN 661-9398).

American Physical Therapy Assn., *(Am Phys Therapy Assn; 0-912452)*, 1111 N. Fairfax St., Alexandria, VA 22314 (SAN 202-4683) Tel 202-466-2070.

†American Physiological Society, *(Am Physiological)*, 9650 Rockville Pike, Bethesda, MD 20814 (SAN 225-2341) Tel 301-530-7070; *CIP.*

American Phytopathological Society, *(Am Phytopathol Soc; 0-89054)*, 3340 Pilot Knob Rd., St. Paul, MN 55121 (SAN 212-0704) Tel 612-454-7250; Toll free: 800-328-7560.

American Pictures Foundation, *(Amer Pictures)*, P.O. Box 2123, New York, NY 10009 (SAN 659-1957) Tel 212-614-0438.

American Pine Barrens Pub. Co., *(Am Pine Barrens; 0-937438)*, P.O. Box 22820, 1400 Washington Ave., Albany, NY 12222 (SAN 215-1278).

American Planning Assn., *(Am Plan Assn)*, 1776 Massachusetts Ave., NW, Washington, DC 20036 (SAN 267-176X) Tel 202-872-0611; Orders to: Planners Bkstore, 1313 E. 60th St., Chicago, IL 60637 (SAN 650-003X) Tel 312-947-2115.

American Plant Life Society, *(Am Plant Life; 0-930653)*, P.O. Box 985, National City, CA 92050 (SAN 225-1507) Tel 619-477-0295.

American Poetry & Literature Pr., *(Am Poetry & Lit; 0-933486)*, P.O. Box 2013, Upper Darby, PA 19082 (SAN 212-6397) Tel 215-352-5438.

American Political Items Collectors, *(Am Political Collect)*, P.O. Box 340339, San Antonio, TX 78234 (SAN 225-5308) Tel 512-655-5213.

American Political Science Assn., *(Am Political; 0-915654)*, 1527 New Hampshire Ave., NW, Washington, DC 20036 (SAN 207-3382) Tel 202-483-2512.

American Polygraph Assn., *(Am Polygraph)*, P.O. Box 1061, Severna Park, MD 21146 (SAN 225-1205); Toll free: 800-272-8037; P.O. Box 794, Severna Park, MD 21146 (SAN 693-479X); Orders to: American Polygraph Assn. Pubns., P.O. Box 1061, Severna Park, MD 21146 (SAN 661-9401) Tel 301-647-0936.

Names

American Pomological Society, *(Am Pomological),* 103 Tyson Bldg., University Park, PA 16802 (SAN 225-0195) Tel 814-863-2198; Dist. by: Michigan State Univ. Pr., 1405 S. Harrison Rd., 25 Manly Miles Bldg., East Lansing, MI 48824 (SAN 202-6295) Tel 517-355-9543.

American Poultry Historical Society, *(Am Poultry Soc),* Dept. of Poultry Science, 1675 Observatory Dr., Madison, WI 53706-1284 (SAN 267-1891).

American Powder Metallurgy Institute, *(Am Powder Metal),* 105 College Rd. E., Princeton, NJ 08540 (SAN 211-0652).

American Power Boat Association, *(Am Power Boat),* 17640 E. Nine Mile Rd., P.O. Box 377, East Detroit, MI 48021 (SAN 224-5442) Tel 313-773-9700.

American Practice Builders, *(Amer Practice Build; 0-939111),* 6725 Papermill Dr., Knoxville, TN 37919 Tel 615-584-0500.

American Prepaid Legal Services Institute, *(Am Prepaid; 0-913955),* 750 N. Lake Shore Dr., Chicago, IL 60611 (SAN 241-1709) Tel 312-988-5752.

American Pr., *(American Pr; 0-89641),* 520 Commonwealth Ave., Boston, MA 02215-2605 (SAN 210-7007) Tel 617-247-0022.

American Production & Inventory Control Society, Inc., *(Am Prod & Inventory; 0-935406),* 500 W. Annándale Rd., Falls Church, VA 22046-4274 (SAN 213-7208) Tel 703-237-8344.

American Productivity Center *See* **Unipub b**

American Professional Education, Inc., *(Am Pro Educ; 0-938401),* P.O. Box 705, Hackensack, NJ 07602 (SAN 659-7165) Tel 201-489-4900; 552 Summit Ave., Hackensack, NJ 07601 (SAN 659-7173).

American Prudential Enterprises, *(Am Prudential; 0-9608346),* P.O. Box 4506, Salisbury, NC 28144 (SAN 238-9053) Tel 704-637-4407.

†**American Psychiatric Pr., Inc.,** Subs. of American Psychiatric Assn., *(Am Psychiatric; 0-89042; 0-88048),* 1400 K St., NW, Washington, DC 20005 (SAN 293-2288) Tel 202-682-6262; Toll free: 800-368-5777. Publishing arm of the American Psychiatric Assn; *CIP.*

American Psychoanalytic Association, *(Am Psychoanalytic),* 309 E. 49 St., New York, NY 10017 (SAN 224-4381) Tel 212-752-0450.

American Psychological Assn., *(Am Psychol; 0-912704),* 1200 17th St., NW, Washington, DC 20036 (SAN 202-4705) Tel 202-955-7600; Orders to: P.O. Box 2710, Hyattsville, MD 20784 (SAN 685-3137) Tel 703-247-7705.

†**American Public Health Assn. Pubns.,** *(Am Pub Health; 0-87553),* 1015 15th St., NW, Washington, DC 20005 (SAN 202-4713) Tel 202-789-5660; *CIP.*

American Public Power Assn., *(APPA),* 2301 M St., NW, Washington, DC 20037 (SAN 267-2073) Tel 202-795-8300.

American Public Welfare Assn., *(Am Pub Welfare; 0-910106),* 1125 15th St., NW, Washington, DC 20005 (SAN 202-4721) Tel 202-293-7550.

American Public Works Assn., *(Am Public Works; 0-917084),* 1313 E. 60th St., Chicago, IL 60637 (SAN 208-130X) Tel 312-667-2200.

American Pub., *(Am Pub; 0-916036),* P.O. Box 102, Oxford, IN 47971 (SAN 207-7019).

American Publishing Today, Inc., *(Am Pub Today; 0-911975),* P.O. Box 31059, Sarasota, FL 33582 (SAN 264-6501) Tel 813-377-2048.

American Quality Bks., *(Am Quality; 0-936956),* 1775 SE Columbia Dr., No. 238, Richland, WA 99352 (SAN 214-2821) Tel 509-783-7976.

American Quarter Horse Assn., *(Am Qtr Horse),* P.O. Box 200, Amarillo, TX 79168 (SAN 225-0306) Tel 806-376-4811.

American Quaternary Assn., *(Am Quaternary Assn),* Illinois State Museum, Springfield, IL 62706 (SAN 225-2198) Tel 313-764-1473.

American Quilt Study Group, *(Am Quilt; 0-9606590),* 105 Molino Ave., Mill Valley, CA 94941 (SAN 219-6867) Tel 415-388-1382.

American Rabbit Breeders Association, Inc., *(Am Rabbit Breeders),* 1925 S. Main, Bloomington, IL 61701 (SAN 225-056X) Tel 309-827-6623.

American Radio Relay League, Inc., *(Am Radio; 0-87259),* 225 Main St., Newington, CT 06111 (SAN 202-473X) Tel 203-666-1541.

American Record Collectors Exchange, *(Am Record; 0-914652),* P.O. Box 1377, F.D.R. Sta., New York, NY 10022 (SAN 201-1689) Tel 212-688-8426.

American Red Cross, St. Paul Area Chapter, *(St Paul Area; 0-9605584),* 100 S. Robert St., St. Paul, MN 55107 (SAN 240-8392).

American Registry of Professional Entomologists, *(Am Reg Pro Entomologists),* 4603 Calvert Rd., P.O. Box AJ, College Park, MD 20740 (SAN 225-1698) Tel 301-864-1336.

American Rental Assn., *(Am Rent Assn; 0-916487),* 1900 19th St., Moline, IL 61265 (SAN 231-3987) Tel 309-764-2475.

†**American Reprint Co./Rivercity Pr.,** *(Am Repr-Rivercity Pr; 0-89190),* Dist. by: Amereon Ltd., P.O. Box 1200, Mattituck, NY 11952 (SAN 201-2413) Tel 516-298-5100; *CIP.*

†**American Reprints Co.,** *(Am Reprints; 0-915706),* 2200 Eldridge Ave., P.O. Box 6011, Bellingham, WA 98227 (SAN 207-5008) Tel 206-647-0107. Do not confuse us with American Reprint Co./Rivercity Pr., Mattituck, NY; *CIP.*

American Research Council, *(American Res; 0-8282),* Box 183, Rye, NY 10580 (SAN 658-6325).

American Resort & Residential Development Assn., *(ARRDA),* 1220 L St. NW., 5th Flr., Washington, DC 20005 (SAN 225-4379) Tel 202-371-6700.

American Resources Group, Ltd., *(Am Resources; 0-913415),* 127 N. Washington St., Carbondale, IL 62901 (SAN 285-8134) Tel 618-529-2741.

American Rivers Conservation Council, *(Am River Conser Coun),* 322 4th St., NE, Washington, DC 20002 (SAN 223-8829) Tel 202-547-6900.

American Romanian Academy of Arts & Sciences, *(Am Romanian; 0-912131),* 4310 Finley Ave., No. 6, Los Angeles, CA 90027 (SAN 211-2116) Tel 213-666-8379.

American-Scandinavian Foundation, *(Am Scandinavian; 0-89067),* 127 E. 73rd St., New York, NY 10021 (SAN 201-7075) Tel 212-879-9779; Orders to: Heritage Resource Ctr., P.O. Box 26305, Minneapolis, MN 55426 (SAN 201-7083).

†**American School Health Assn.,** *(Am Sch Health; 0-917160),* 1521 S. Water St., Kent, OH 44240 (SAN 208-5240) Tel 216-678-1601; P.O. Box 708, Kent, OH 44240 (SAN 662-7161); *CIP.*

American School of Astrology, *(Am Sch Astrol),* 21 Mellon Ave., West Orange, NJ 07052 (SAN 211-2868) Tel 201-731-2255.

†**American School of Classical Studies at Athens,** *(Am Sch Athens; 0-87661),* c/o Institute for Advanced Study, Princeton, NJ 08543-0631 (SAN 201-1697) Tel 609-734-8387; *CIP.*

†**American Schls. of Oriental Research,** *(Am Sch Orient Res; 0-89757),* P.O. Box HM, Duke Sta., Durham, NC 27706 (SAN 239-4057) Tel 219-269-2011; Dist. by: Eisenbrauns, P.O. Box 275, Winona Lake, IN 46590-0278 (SAN 213-4365) Tel 219-269-2011; *CIP.*

American Sciences Pr., Inc., *(Am Sciences Pr; 0-935950),* 20 Cross Rd., Syracuse, NY 13224-2144 (SAN 213-8883).

American Scientific Corp., *(Amer Scientific; 0-9617163),* 3250 Holly Way, Chula Vista, CA 92010 (SAN 662-9466) Tel 619-426-1280.

American Scientist, *(American Scientist),* c/o Sigma Xi the Scientific Research Society, 345 Whitney Ave., New Haven, CT 06511 (SAN 275-357X).

American Short Line Railroad Assn., *(Am Short Line),* 2000 Massachusetts Ave., NW, Washington, DC 20036 (SAN 267-2790) Tel 202-785-2250.

American Showcase, Inc., *(Am Showcase; 0-931144),* 724 Fifth Ave., New York, NY 10019 (SAN 281-2681) Tel 212-245-0981; Dist. by: Watson Guptill Pubns., 1515 Broadway, New York, NY 10036 (SAN 282-5384).

American Society for Advancement of Anesthesia in Dentistry, *(Am Soc Ad Anesthesia Dentistry),* 475 White Plains Rd., Eastchester, NY 10707 (SAN 225-4964) Tel 914-961-8136.

American Society for Education & Religion, Inc., *(Am Soc Ed & Rel; 0-942978),* 29 Beaver Oak Ct., Baltimore, MD 21236 (SAN 240-334X) Tel 301-256-1349.

American Society for Engineering Education, *(Am Soc Eng Ed; 0-87823),* 11 Dupont Cir., Suite 200, Washington, DC 20036 (SAN 225-7831) Tel 202-293-7080.

American Society for Hospital Materials Management, Div. of American Hospital Assn., *(ASHMM),* 840 N. Lake Shore Dr., Chicago, IL 60611 (SAN 224-3326) Tel 312-280-6137.

†**American Society for Information Science,** *(Am Soc Info Sci; 0-87715),* 1424 16th St., NW, Suite 404, Washington, DC 20036 (SAN 202-4748) Tel 202-462-1000; Toll free: 800-248-5474; *CIP.*

American Society for Information Science *See* **Knowledge Industry Pubns., Inc.**

†**American Society for International Law,** *(Am Soc Intl Law),* 2223 Massachusetts Ave., NW, Washington, DC 20008 (SAN 227-3640) Tel 202-265-4313; *CIP.*

American Society for Metals, *(ASM; 0-87170),* 9639 Kinsman Rd., Metals Park, OH 44073 (SAN 204-7586) Tel 216-338-5151.

†**American Society for Microbiology,** *(Am Soc Microbio; 0-914826; 1-55581),* 1913 Eye St., NW, Washington, DC 20006 (SAN 202-1153) Tel 202-833-9680; *CIP.*

American Society for Neurochemistry, *(Am Soc Neuro),* 3801 Miranda Ave., VA Medical Center, Palo Alto, CA 94304 (SAN 260-3454) Tel 415-493-5000.

American Society for Nondestructive Testing, *(Am Soc Nondestructive),* 4153 Arlingate Plaza, Caller No. 28518, Columbus, OH 43228 (SAN 267-3193) Tel 614-274-6003.

American Society for Personnel Administration, *(Am Soc Personnel; 0-939900),* 606 N. Washington St., Alexandria, VA 22314 (SAN 224-8964) Tel 703-548-3449.

American Society for Pharmacology & Experimental Therapeutics, *(Am Phar & Ex; 0-9609094),* 9650 Rockville Pike, Bethesda, MD 20014 (SAN 267-3223) Tel 301-530-7060.

†**American Society for Photogrammetry and Remote Sensing,** *(ASP & RS; 0-937294),* 210 Little Falls St., Falls Church, VA 22046 (SAN 204-5044) Tel 703-534-6617; *CIP.*

American Society for Public Administration, *(Am Soc Pub Admin; 0-936678),* 1120 G St., NW, Suite 500, Washington, DC 20005 (SAN 693-8396) Tel 202-393-7878.

†**American Society for Testing & Materials,** *(ASTM; 0-8031),* 1916 Race St., Philadelphia, PA 19103 (SAN 201-1344) Tel 215-299-5400; *CIP.*

American Society for Training & Development, *(Am Soc Train & Devel; 0-201; 0-7755),* 1630 Duke St., Alexandria, VA 22313 (SAN 224-8972) Tel 703-683-8100; P.O. Box 1443, Alexandria, VA 22313 (SAN 658-0122); Dist. by: Ballinger Publishing Co., 54 Church St., Harvard Sq., Cambridge, MA 02138 (SAN 201-4084) Tel 617-492-0670; Dist. by: Random House, Inc., 201 E. 50th St., New York, NY 10022 (SAN 202-5507) Tel 212-751-2600; Dist. by: Scott, Foresman & Co., 1900 E. Lake Ave., Glenview, IL 60025 (SAN 200-2140) Tel 312-729-3000; Dist. by: Van Nostrand Reinhold Co., Inc., 115 Fifth Ave., New York, NY 10003 (SAN 202-5183) Tel 212-254-3232; Dist. by: McGraw-Hill Bk. Co., 1221 Ave. of the Americas, New York, NY 10020 (SAN 200-2248) Tel 212-512-2000.

American Society of Abdominal Surgery, *(Am Soc Abdominal Surg),* 675 Main St., Melrose, MA 02176 (SAN 224-2575) Tel 617-655-6102.

American Society of Agricultural Engineers, *(Am Soc Ag Eng; 0-916150),* 2950 Niles Rd., St. Joseph, MI 49085 (SAN 223-6087) Tel 616-429-0300.

†**American Society of Agronomy,** *(Am Soc Agron; 0-89118),* 677 S. Segoe Rd., Madison, WI 53711 (SAN 204-5060) Tel 608-273-8080; *CIP.*

American Society of Appraisers, *(Am Soc Appraisers; 0-937828),* P.O. Box 17265, Washington, DC 20041 (SAN 206-2194) Tel 703-620-3838.

American Society of Assn. Executives, *(Am Soc Assn Execs; 0-88034),* 1575 Eye St. NW, Washington, DC 20005 (SAN 224-8182) Tel 202-626-2723.

†**American Society of Civil Engineers,** *(Am Soc Civil Eng; 0-87262),* 345 E. 47th St., New York, NY 10017 (SAN 204-7594) Tel 212-705-7538; Toll free: 800-548-2723; *CIP.*

American Society of Clinical Pathologists Pr., Div. of American Society of Clinical Pathologists, *(Am Soc Clinical; 0-89189),* Educational Products Div., 2100 W. Harrison St., Chicago, IL 60612 (SAN 207-9429) Tel 312-738-1336; Toll free: 800-621-4142 (Orders); Dist. by: Appleton-Century-Crofts, 25 Van Zant St., East Norwalk, CT 06855 (SAN 209-1488).

American Society of Consultant Pharmacists, *(Am Soc Consult Phar; 0-934322),* 2300 Ninth St., S., Arlington, VA 22204 (SAN 223-7350).

American Society of Heating, Refrigerating & Air Conditioning Engineers, Inc., *(Am Heat Ref & Air Eng; 0-910110),* 1791 Tullie Cir. NE, Atlanta, GA 30329 (SAN 223-9809) Tel 404-636-8400.

American Society of Hospital Pharmacists, *(Am Soc Hosp Pharm; 0-930530),* 4630 Montgomery Ave., Bethesda, MD 20814 (SAN 204-5052) Tel 301-657-3000.

American Society of Indexers, *(Am Soc Indexers),* 1700 18th St., NW, Washington, DC 20009 (SAN 225-3283).

American Society of Internal Medicine, *(Am Soc Intern Med; 0-9607006),* 1101 Vermont Ave., NW, Suite 500, Washington, DC 20005 (SAN 223-9817) Tel 202-289-1700.

American Society of Journalists & Authors, *(Am Soc Jrnl & Auth; 0-9612200),* 1501 Broadway, Suite 1907, New York, NY 10036 (SAN 225-4441) Tel 212-997-0947.

American Society of Lubrication Engineers, *(Am Lubrication Engs),* 838 Busse Hwy., Park Ridge, IL 60068 (SAN 225-2031) Tel 312-825-5536.

American Society of Mammalogists, *(Am Soc Mammalogists; 0-943612),* Vertebrate Museum Shippensburg Univ., Shippensburg, PA 17257 (SAN 225-204X) Tel 717-532-1407.

†**American Society of Mechanical Engineers,** *(ASME; 0-87053),* 345 E. 47th St., New York, NY 10017 (SAN 201-1379) Tel 212-705-7722; *CIP.*

American Society of Newspaper Editors, *(Am Soc News; 0-943086),* Box 17004, Washington, DC 20041 (SAN 240-3358).

American Society of Notaries, *(Am Soc Notaries),* 918 16th St., NW, Washington, DC 20006 (SAN 223-9833).

†**American Society of Plant Physiologists,** *(Am Soc of Plant; 0-943082),* 155-018-A Monona Dr., Rockville, MD 20855 (SAN 240-3366) Tel 301-251-0560; *CIP.*

†**American Society of Plant Taxonomists, The,** *(Am Soc Plant; 0-912861),* Univ. of Michigan Herbarium, N. Univ., Bldg., Ann Arbor, MI 48109-1057 (SAN 282-969X) Tel 313-764-2407; *CIP.*

American Society of Plumbing Engineers, *(Am Soc Plumb Eng),* 15233 Ventura Blvd., Suite 811, Sherman Oaks, CA 91403 (SAN 224-0475) Tel 818-893-4845.

American Society of Polar Philatelists, *(Am Soc Polar),* 8700 Darlina Dr., El Paso, TX 79925 (SAN 235-2729) Tel 915-772-7814; Orders to: David Warfel, 463 Spruce Dr., Exton, PA 19341 (SAN 235-2737).

American Society of Quality Control, *(Am Soc QC),* 230 W. Wells St., Suite 7000, Milwaukee, WI 53203 (SAN 225-2406) Tel 713-790-0795.

American Society of Real Estate Counselors, Affil. of National Assn. of Realtors, *(Am Soc REC; 0-939653),* 430 N. Michigan Ave., Chicago, IL 60611 (SAN 204-5036) Tel 312-329-8431.

American Society of Safety Engineers, *(ASSE; 0-939874),* 1800 E. Oakton Blvd., Des Plaines, IL 60018 (SAN 201-7032) Tel 312-692-4121.

American Society of Transportation & Logistics, Inc., *(Am Soc Transport),* P.O. Box 33095, Louisville, KY 40232 (SAN 231-634X) Tel 502-451-8150.

American Sociological Assn., *(Am Sociological; 0-912764),* 1772 N St., NW, Washington, DC 20036 (SAN 226-0093) Tel 202-833-3410.

†**American Solar Energy Society, Inc.,** U. S. Section of International Solar Energy Society, *(Am Solar Energy; 0-89553),* 2030 17th St., Boulder, CO 80302 (SAN 210-3842) Tel 303-443-3130; *CIP.*

American Southwest Publishing Co., *(Am Southwest Pub Co; 0-933177),* 2800 Third Ave., San Diego, CA 92103 (SAN 689-7339) Tel 619-295-9595.

American Speech-Language Hearing Assn., *(Am Speech Lang Hearing; 0-910329),* 10801 Rockville Pike, Rockville, MD 20852 (SAN 224-4608) Tel 301-897-5700.

American Spice Trade Assn., *(Am Spice Trade),* 580 Sylvan Ave., Englewood Cliffs, NJ 07632 (SAN 224-7380) Tel 201-568-2163.

American Sports Sales, Inc., *(Am Sports Sales; 0-912354),* P.O. Box 160, Orangeburg, NY 10962 (SAN 203-4964) Tel 914-359-5300.

American Stamp Dealers Assn., *(Am Stamp Dealer; 0-912219),* 5 Dakota Dr., Lake Success, NY 11042 (SAN 267-4254).

American String Teachers Assn., Affil. of Music Educators National Conference, *(Am String Tchrs),* 2740 Spicewood Ln., Bloomington, IN 47401 (SAN 236-4913) Tel 812-339-4904; Orders to: Theodore Presser Co., Presser Pl., Bryn Mawr, PA 19010 (SAN 661-941X) Tel 215-525-3636.

American Student Dental Assn., *(Am Student Dent),* 211 E. Chicago Ave., Chicago, IL 60611 (SAN 267-4327) Tel 312-440-2795.

American Studies Ctr., The, *(Am Studies Ctr; 0-931727),* 499 South Capitol St., S.W. Suite 404, Washington, DC 20002 (SAN 658-3814) Tel 202-488-7122.

American Studies Pr., Inc., *(American Studies Pr; 0-934996),* 13511 Palmwood Ln., Tampa, FL 33624 (SAN 213-2788) Tel 813-974-2857.

American Studies Publishing Co., *(Amer Studies; 0-942738),* 19496 Sandcastle Ln., Huntington Beach, CA 92648 (SAN 240-1851) Tel 714-960-2117.

American Sunbathing Assn., *(Am Sunbathing),* 1703 N. Main St., Suite E, Kissimmee, FL 32743-3396 (SAN 225-3666) Tel 305-933-2064.

American Teaching Aids, *(Am Teaching; 0-88037),* P.O. Box 1406, Covina, CA 91722 (SAN 238-9398) Tel 818-967-4128.

American Technical Pubs., Inc., *(Am Technical; 0-8269),* 1155 W. 175th St., Homewood, IL 60430 (SAN 206-8141); Toll free: 800-323-3471.

American Telephone & Telegraph-Communications, Div. of AT&T Co., *(AT&T Comns; 0-938963),* 295 N. Maple Ave., Rm. 5237A3, Basking Ridge, NJ 07920 (SAN 661-7166) Tel 201-221-5351. Do not confuse with AT&T Co. of New York, NY.

American Theatre Assn., *(Am Theatre Assn; 0-940528),* 1010 Wisconsin Ave. NW, Suite 620, Washington, DC 20007 (SAN 206-8133) Tel 202-342-7530.

American Topical Assn., Inc., *(Am Topical Assn; 0-935991),* 416 Lincoln St., P.O. Box 630, Johnstown, PA 15907 (SAN 267-4629) Tel 814-539-6301.

American Training & Research Assocs., Inc., *(ATRA; 0-9613999),* 147 Range Rd., Windham, NH 03087 (SAN 683-5694) Tel 603-898-1280.

American Translators Assn., Mid-America Chapter, *(MICATA; 0-9616557),* 323 Brush Creek Blvd., Apt. 805, Kansas City, MO 64112 (SAN 659-4816) Tel 816-561-8441.

American Travel Pubns., Inc., *(Am Travel Pubns; 0-936929),* 1856 Lilac Ct., Carlsbad, CA 92008 (SAN 658-6848) Tel 619-438-0514; Dist. by: American Travel Publications, Inc., 6992 El Camino Real, Suite 104-199, Carlsbad, CA 92008 (SAN 658-6848) Tel 619-438-0514; Dist. by: Sunset Books, 80 Willow Rd., Menlo Park, CA 94025 (SAN 201-0658) Tel 415-321-3600; Toll free: 800-227-7346.

American Trend Publishing Co., The, *(Am Trend Pub; 0-941388),* 645 Emporia Rd., Boulder, CO 80303 (SAN 238-9401) Tel 303-499-4582.

American Trial Lawyers Assn. *See* Association of Trial Lawyers of America

American Trucking Assns., *(Am Trucking Assns; 0-88711),* 2200 Mill Rd., Alexandria, VA 22314 (SAN 224-9693).

American Trust Pubns., *(Am Trust Pubns; 0-89259),* Dist. by: Islamic Bk. Service, 10900 W. Washington St., Indianapolis, IN 46231 (SAN 169-2453) Tel 317-839-8150.

American Universal Artforms Corp., *(Am Univ Artforms; 0-913632),* 6208 Quail Hollow, Austin, TX 78750 (SAN 202-4772) Tel 512-345-6235.

American Univ., Dept. of History, Organization of Historical Studies, *(Dept Hist Org),* American Univ., Massachusetts & Nebraska Aves., NW, Washington, DC 20016 (SAN 283-2666).

American V. Mueller, *(American Mueller; 0-937433),* 7280 N. Caldwell Ave., Chicago, IL 60648 (SAN 659-0063) Tel 312-774-6800.

American Vecturist Assn., *(Am Vecturist),* P.O. Box 1204, Boston, MA 02104 (SAN 235-0017) Tel 617-277-8111.

American Veterinary Pubns., Inc., *(Am Vet Pubns; 0-939674),* Drawer KK, Santa Barbara, CA 93102 (SAN 277-6545) Tel 805-963-6561; Toll free: 800-235-6947.

American Watchmakers Institute, *(Am Watchmakers; 0-918845),* 3700 Harrison Ave., Cincinnati, OH 45211 (SAN 267-498X) Tel 513-661-3838.

American Water Ski Assn., *(Am Water Ski),* 799 Overlook Dr., Winter Haven, FL 33880 (SAN 267-5005) Tel 813-324-4341; P.O. Box 191, Winter Haven, FL 33882 (SAN 668-9957).

American Water Works Assn., *(Am Water Wks Assn; 0-89867),* 6666 W. Quincy Ave., Denver, CO 80234 (SAN 212-8241) Tel 303-794-7711.

American Welcome Serv. Pr., Subs. of American Welcome Services, *(Am Welcome Serv; 0-9612432),* 180 E. End Ave., New York, NY 10028 (SAN 289-1077) Tel 212-734-9210.

American Welding Society, *(Am Welding; 0-87171),* P.O. Box 351040 Rd., Miami, FL 33135 (SAN 201-1700) Tel 305-443-9353.

American Wooden Money Guild, *(Am Wooden Money),* P.O. Box 30444, Tucson, AZ 85751 (SAN 235-2494).

American Yoga Assn., *(Am Yoga Assn),* 3130 Mayfield Rd., W103, Cleveland, OH 44118 (SAN 225-4867) Tel 216-371-0078.

American Youth Sports Publishing Co., *(Am Youth Sports Pub; 0-933715),* 24365 San Fernando Rd., Suite 193, Newhall, CA 91321 (SAN 692-5014) Tel 805-259-6206.

Americana *See* Crown Pubs., Inc.

Americana Books, *(Americana Bks; 0-917902),* P.O. Box 481, Pinellas Park, FL 33565 (SAN 210-0282).

Americana Pr., *(Americana Pr; 0-9616144),* 3516 Albemarle St., NW, Washington, DC 20008 (SAN 658-7550) Tel 202-362-8538.

Americana Pubns., *(Americana Pubns; 0-935407),* 1121 Marion St., Manteca, CA 95336 (SAN 696-0790) Tel 209-823-7526; P.O. Box 1528, Manteca, CA 95336 (SAN 696-5210).

Americana Review, *(Americana Rev; 0-914166),* 10 Socha Ln., Scotia, NY 12302 (SAN 206-3220) Tel 518-399-6482.

Americanist Pr., *(Americanist; 0-910120),* 1525 Shenkel Rd., Pottstown, PA 19464 (SAN 205-6003) Tel 215-323-5289.

Americans For Due Process, Inc., *(Amer Due Process; 0-9617222),* P.O. Box 85, Woodhaven, NY 11421 (SAN 663-3862); 304 Bayville Rd., Locust Valley, NY 11560 (SAN 663-3870) Tel 516-671-7975.

Americans For Energy Independence, *(Americans Energy Ind; 0-934458),* 1629 K St. NW, Suite 302, Washington, DC 20006 (SAN 212-999X) Tel 202-466-2105.

Americans for Second Bill of Rights, *(Amer Sec Bill; 0-936527),* P.O. Box 550, Sour Lake, TX 77659 (SAN 658-8239).

America's Society of Separated & Divorced Men, Inc., *(Am Soc Separated),* 575 Keep St., Elgin, IL 60120 (SAN 241-3590) Tel 312-695-2200.

Names

Names

Americas Watch *See* **Fund for Free Expression**

Amerimark, Inc., *(Amerimark Inc; 1-55537),* 740 N. Blue Pkwy., Suite 312, Midland Bank Bldg., Lee's Summit, MO 64063 (SAN 696-0839) Tel 816-525-5227.

Ames Publishing Co., *(Ames Pub Co; 0-9615263),* 21172 Aspen Ave., Castro Valley, CA 94546 (SAN 695-1945) Tel 415-537-3250.

Amethyst, *(Amethyst; 0-912865),* 2800 Woodley Rd., N.W., No. 423, Washington, DC 20008 (SAN 265-377X) Tel 202-797-9707.

Amhara Corp., *(Amhara Corp; 0-917450),* 6990 S. 1700 E., Salt Lake City, UT 84121 (SAN 208-063X).

Amherst College, Mead Art Museum, *(Mead Art Mus; 0-914337),* Amherst, MA 01002 (SAN 277-9730) Tel 413-542-2335.

Amherst College Pr., *(Amherst Coll Pr; 0-943184),* Amherst College, Amherst, MA 01002 (SAN 201-7008) Tel 413-542-2299.

Amherst Media, *(Amherst Media; 0-936262),* 418 Homecrest Dr., Amherst, NY 14226 (SAN 214-0950).

Amherst Podium Pr., *(Amherst Podium; 0-9615133),* P.O. Box 64, Amherst, NY 14226 (SAN 694-2490).

Amherst Pr., *(Amherst Pr),* P.O. Box 296, Amherst, WI 54406 (SAN 213-9820) Tel 715-824-5890.

Amicus Pr., *(Amicus Pr; 0-914861),* 4201 Underwood Ave., Baltimore, MD 21218 (SAN 289-0518) Tel 301-889-5056.

Amideast, *(Amideast; 0-913957),* 1100 17th St. NW, Suite 300, Washington, DC 20036 (SAN 286-7184) Tel 202-785-0022.

Amiel, Leon, Pub., *(L Amiel Pub; 0-8148),* 31 W. 46th St., New York, NY 10036 (SAN 207-0766) Tel 212-575-0010.

Ami's Publishing, *(Amis Pub; 0-935131),* 13221 Valleyheart Dr., Sherman Oaks, CA 91423 (SAN 695-1953) Tel 818-784-6756; Orders to: P.O. Box 4306-P, North Hollywood, CA 91607 (SAN 662-345X).

Amish Mennonite Pubns., *(Amish Men Pub; 0-935409),* 8117 Magnet Rd., Minerva, OH 44657 (SAN 696-0901) Tel 216-895-4721.

Amisted Brands, Inc., *(Amistad Brands; 0-9610432),* 22 Division Ave., NE, Washington, DC 20019 (SAN 263-9165); Dist. by: Somba Bookstore, Capital Plaza, 3155 Main St., Hartford, CT 01614 (SAN 200-5441).

Amity Books, *(Amity Bks MO; 0-934864),* 1702 Magnolia, Liberty, MO 64048 (SAN 213-7216).

Amity Foundation, *(Amity Found; 0-9612716),* P.O. Box 11048, Eugene, OR 97440 (SAN 289-7210) Tel 503-683-5927.

Amity Hallmark, Ltd., *(Amity Hallmark),* 40-09 149th Place, Flushing, NY 11354 (SAN 210-766X).

Amity House, Inc., *(Amity Hous Inc; 0-916349),* 106 Newport Bridge Rd., Warwick, NY 10990 (SAN 295-1037) Tel 914-258-4078.

Amity Publications, *(Amity Pubns; 0-943814),* 78688 Sears Rd., Cottage Grove, OR 97424 (SAN 285-6794).

Amity Publishing Co., *(Amity Pub Co; 0-934011),* P.O. Box 933, Allston, MA 02134 (SAN 692-7653) Tel 617-628-6816; Dist. by: Inland Book Co., 22 Hemingway Ave., P.O. Box 261, East Haven, CT 06512 (SAN 200-4151) Tel 203-467-4257.

Ammie Enterprises, *(Ammie Enter; 0-932825),* P.O. Box 2132, Vista, CA 92083 (SAN 691-3008) Tel 619-758-4561.

Amnesty International of the USA, Inc., Div. of Amnesty International, *(Amnesty Intl USA; 0-939994),* 304 W. 58th St., New York, NY 10024 (SAN 225-6266) Tel 212-582-4440; Toll free: 800-251-4000.

Amo-Sino Bks., *(Amo Sino Bks; 0-9615160),* P.O. Box 10013, Newark, NJ 07101 (SAN 694-3861) Tel 201-787-6600.

†**Amon Carter Museum of Western Art,** *(Amon Carter; 0-88360),* P.O. Box 2365, Fort Worth, TX 76113 (SAN 204-7608) Tel 817-738-1933; Dist. by: Univ. of Texas Pr., P.O. Box 7819, Austin, TX 78713 (SAN 212-9876) Tel 512-471-7233; *CIP.*

Amonics, *(Amonics; 0-918166),* 2530 Cypress Ave., Norman, OK 73069 (SAN 209-3707) Tel 405-321-8076.

Amory & Pugh, *(Amory & Pugh; 0-9607492),* 79 Raymond St., Cambridge, MA 02140 (SAN 238-0056).

Amos, Winsom, Pub., *(W Amos; 0-9600520),* P.O. Box 416, C/O Soma Press, Yellow Springs, OH 45387 (SAN 222-8858) Tel 513-767-1573.

Amoskeag Pr., Inc., *(Amoskeag Pr),* P.O. Box 666, Hooksett, NH 03106 (SAN 208-2721) Tel 603-622-6626.

Ampersand Pr., *(Ampersand RI; 0-9604740; 0-935331),* Roger Williams College Creative Writing Program, Bristol, RI 02809 (SAN 216-2202) Tel 401-253-1040.

Ampersand Publishing, *(Ampersand Pub; 0-9607234),* 3609 Mukilteo Blvd., Everett, WA 98203 (SAN 239-1546) Tel 206-353-7593.

Amphibian Pubns., *(Amphibian Pubns),* Three Bell St., Providence, RI 02909 (SAN 240-0812).

Amrita Foundation, Inc., *(Amrita Found; 0-937134),* P.O. Box 8080, Dallas, TX 75205 (SAN 284-9666) Tel 214-521-1072.

Amsco Music *See* **Music Sales Corp.**

Amulefi Publishing Co., *(Amulefi; 0-936360),* 11 E. Utica St., Buffalo, NY 14209 (SAN 214-0969).

Amusement & Music Operators Assn., *(AMOA),* 111 E. Wacker Dr., Chicago, IL 60601 (SAN 230-0923) Tel 312-644-6610.

Amusement Park Bks., Inc., *(Amusement Pk Bks; 0-935408),* 20925 Mastick Rd., Fairview Park, OH 44126 (SAN 222-7673) Tel 216-331-6429.

Amward Pubns., Inc., *(Amward Pubns; 0-939676),* 824 National Press Bldg., Washington, DC 20045 (SAN 216-7131) Tel 202-628-6710.

Amy's, *(Amys; 0-9614581),* P.O. Box 1718, Fort Myers, FL 33902 (SAN 691-7585) Tel 813-334-6048; Dist. by: Spring Arbor Distributors, 10885 Textile Rd., Belleville, MI 48111 (SAN 158-9016) Tel 313-481-0900.

An Inch at a Time Productions, *(An Inch Prods; 0-9613655),* P.O. Box 8133, Des Moines, IA 50306 (SAN 670-7556) Tel 515-274-5081.

Ana, Mele Inc., Publishing, *(Mele Ana; 0-934509),* 3960 Laurel Canyon Blvd., Suite 170, Studio City, CA 91604 (SAN 693-8523) Tel 818-509-1196.

Ana-Doug Publishing, *(Ana-Doug Pub; 0-916946),* 424 W. Commonwealth, Fullerton, CA 92632 (SAN 208-4821) Tel 714-738-1655.

†**Anaheim Publishing Company, a Division of Wadsworth, Incorporated,** Subs. of International Thomson Organization, Inc., *(Anaheim Pub Co; 0-88236),* 10 Davis Dr., Belmont, CA 94002 (SAN 202-4802); Toll free: 800-831-6996; Orders to: Wadsworth, Inc., 7625 Empire Dr., Florence, KY 41042 (SAN 663-2858) Tel 606-525-2230; Toll free: 800-354-9706; *CIP.*

Anais Nin Foundation, The, *(Anais Nin Found; 0-9611238),* P.O. Box 276, Becket, MA 01223 (SAN 283-068X) Tel 413-623-5170; Orders to: 2335 Hidalgo Ave., Los Angeles, CA 90039 (SAN 658-2338).

Anais Pr., *(Anais Pr; 0-9608858),* P.O. Box 9635, Denver, CO 80209 (SAN 240-9976) Tel 303-778-0524.

Analog Devices, Inc., *(Analog Devices; 0-916550),* 2 Technology Way, Norwood, MA 02062 (SAN 210-3389) Tel 617-461-3294; Orders to: P.O. Box 796, Norwood, MA 02062 (SAN 210-3397) Tel 617-461-3392.

Analysis Pr., Subs. of Merrill Analysis, Inc., *(Analysis; 0-911894),* Box 228, Chappaqua, NY 10514 (SAN 210-9549) Tel 914-238-3641.

Analytech Management Consulting, *(Analytech; 0-9610932),* 15 Russell Rd., Alexandria, VA 22301 (SAN 265-1734) Tel 703-836-7830.

Analytic Investment Management, Inc., *(Analytic Invest; 0-9606348),* 2222 Martin St., No. 230, Irvine, CA 92715 (SAN 210-8844) Tel 714-833-0294.

†**Analytic Pr., The,** *(Analytic Pr; 0-88163),* 365 Broadway, Suite 102, Hillsdale, NJ 07642 (SAN 267-5455) Tel 201-666-4110; Dist. by: Lawrence Erlbaum Associates, Inc., 365 Broadway, Hillsdale, NJ 07642 (SAN 213-960X) Tel 201-666-4110; *CIP.*

Analytical Psychology Club of Los Angeles, *(Analytic Psych; 0-9600936),* 10349 W. Pico Blvd., Los Angeles, CA 90064 (SAN 223-663X) Tel 213-556-1193; Orders to: C.J. Jung Institute, 10349 W. Pico Blvd., Los Angeles, CA 90064 (SAN 200-464X).

Analytical Psychology Club of New York, Inc., The, *(Analytical Psych),* 28 E. 39th St., New York, NY 10016 (SAN 267-5463) Tel 212-697-7877.

Analytical Psychology Club of San Francisco, Inc., The, *(Analyt Psych SF; 0-9611232),* 2411 Octavia St., San Francisco, CA 94109 (SAN 283-2461) Tel 415-524-9433; Orders to: Ivon der Hude, 615 Beloit Ave., Kensington, CA 94708 (SAN 662-751X) Tel 415-524-9433.

Analytichem International, Inc., *(Analytichem; 0-9616096),* 24201 Frampton Ave., Harbor City, CA 90710 (SAN 698-1186) Tel 213-539-6490.

Anand, Raj K., *(Raj Anand),* 210 Lincoln St., Worcester, MA 01605 (SAN 692-6819).

Ananda Marga Pubns., *(Ananda Marga; 0-88476),* 854 Pearl St., Denver, CO 80203 (SAN 206-3239) Tel 303-832-6465.

Ananda Pubns., *(Ananda; 0-916124),* 14618 Tyler Foote Rd., Nevada City, CA 95959 (SAN 201-1778) Tel 916-292-3482.

Ananse Pr., *(Ananse Pr; 0-9605670),* P.O. Box 22565, Seattle, WA 98122 (SAN 216-3292) Tel 206-325-8205.

Anapauo Farm, Inc., *(Anapauo Farm; 0-9616899),* Star Rte., P.O. Box 1BC, Lakemont, GA 30552 (SAN 661-4922) Tel 404-782-6442.

Anatomical Chart Co., *(Anatomical Chart; 0-9603730),* 7124 N. Clark St., Chicago, IL 60626 (SAN 223-5315).

Ancestral Historian Society, *(Ancestral Hist; 0-939774),* Postal Unit 529, Evans, GA 30809 (SAN 216-8774) Tel 404-863-2863.

Ancestry Inc., *(Ancestry; 0-916489),* 350 S. 400 East, Suite 110, Salt Lake City, UT 84111 (SAN 687-6528) Tel 801-531-1790; Toll free: 800-531-1790 (Orders only); Orders to: P.O. Box 476, Salt Lake City, UT 84110 (SAN 662-7706).

Anchor & Acorn Pr., *(Anchor & Acorn; 0-936931),* 15 Kent St., Petaluma, CA 94952 (SAN 658-6872) Tel 707-762-0510.

Anchor & Dolphin Publishing Co., The, *(Anchor & Dolphin; 0-9615944),* 435 N. Seventh St., Allentown, PA 18102 (SAN 696-9852) Tel 215-821-7913.

Anchor Books *See* **Doubleday & Co., Inc.**

Anchor Communications, Div. of Imagination Unlimited, *(Anchor Comm; 0-935633),* 110 Quince Ave., Highland Springs, VA 23075 (SAN 696-0944) Tel 804-737-4498; P.O. Box 70, Highland Springs, VA 23075 (SAN 696-5229).

Anchor Foundation, Inc., The, *(Anchor Found; 0-913460; 0-937091),* Dist. by: Pathfinder Press, 410 West St., New York, NY 10014 (SAN 202-5906) Tel 212-741-0690.

Anchor Press *See* **Doubleday & Co., Inc.**

Anchorage Pr., *(Anchorage; 0-87602),* P.O. Box 8067, New Orleans, LA 70182 (SAN 203-4727) Tel 504-283-8868.

Ancient City Pr., *(Ancient City Pr; 0-941270),* P.O. Box 5401, Santa Fe, NM 87502 (SAN 164-5552) Tel 505-982-8195.

ANCLA Productions, *(ANCLA Prods; 0-9612202),* 7903 Randy Rd., Rockford, IL 61103 (SAN 289-1042) Tel 815-633-3840.

And Bks., *(And Bks; 0-89708),* 702 S. Michigan, Suite 836, South Bend, IN 46618 (SAN 213-9502) Tel 219-232-3134; Dist. by: The Distributors, 702 S. Michigan, South Bend, IN 46618 (SAN 169-2488) Tel 219-232-8500; Toll free: 800-348-5200 (orders only).

And/Or Pr., Inc., *(And-Or Pr; 0-915904),* P.O. Box 2246, Berkeley, CA 94702 (SAN 206-9458) Tel 415-548-2124.

Andacht, Sandra, Pub., *(S Andacht; 0-9607616),* P.O. Box 94, Little Neck, NY 11363 (SAN 238-6402) Tel 718-229-6593.

Andante Pubs., *(Andante Pub; 0-940038),* 1812 E. 32nd St., Brooklyn, NY 11234 (SAN 220-1992) Tel 718-336-9490.

Andent, Inc., *(Andent Inc; 0-914555),* 1000 North Ave., Waukegan, IL 60085 (SAN 291-8560) Tel 312-223-5077.

Andersen, Arthur, & Co., *(A Andersen),* 69 W. Washington St., Chicago, IL 60602 (SAN 226-8817) Tel 312-580-0069.

Andersen, Paul, *(P Andersen; 0-9604720),* P.O. Box 2184, Laguna Hills, CA 92654 (SAN 215-1286).

Andersen, William D. , & Associates, *(W D Andersen; 0-930373),* 2935 Cordell St., Memphis, TN 38118 (SAN 295-0421) Tel 901-794-9566.

Anderson, Arthur W., *(A W Anderson; 0-9614420),* 175 Fisher St., Needham, MA 02192 (SAN 689-0989) Tel 617-449-0556; Orders to: The Windsor Press, P.O. Box 87, Wellesley Hills, MA 02181 (SAN 662-7722) Tel 617-235-0265.

Anderson, Dan, *(Dan Anderson; 0-9614527),* 6083 Fred Dr., Cypress, CA 90630-3905 (SAN 692-2791).

Anderson, David, Gallery, Inc., *(D Anderson; 0-915956),* 521 W. 57th St., New York, NY 10019 (SAN 281-2746).

Anderson, Edis J., *(Edis Anderson; 0-9616097),* P.O. Box 160, RR 3, Geneseo, IL 61254 (SAN 698-1208) Tel 309-944-6682; 2050 N. 900 E. Rural, Geneseo, IL 61254 (SAN 698-1216).

Anderson, Elizabeth Y., *(E Y Anderson; 0-9614002),* 8302 Stevens Rd., Thurmont, MD 21788 (SAN 694-5333).

Anderson, John MacKenzie, *(J Mac Anderson; 0-9615813),* 2717 Johnston Pl., Cincinnati, OH 45206 (SAN 696-6713) Tel 513-221-8015; Toll free: 800-732-2663; Dist. by: American Scotch Highland Breeders Assn., P.O. Box 81, Remer, MN 56672 (SAN 689-2574) Tel 218-566-1321.

Anderson, L. W., Genealogical Library, *(L W Anderson Genealogical; 0-935187),* 2218 17th St., P.O. Box 1647, Gulfport, MS 39502 (SAN 692-672X) Tel 601-863-3598.

Anderson, Robert D., Publishing Co., *(Anderson R; 0-942028),* P.O. Box 22324, Sacramento, CA 95822 (SAN 238-4434) Tel 916-369-0223; Toll free: 800-222-3030; 9323 Tech Center Dr., Suite 1700, Sacramento, CA 95826 (SAN 661-9428).

Anderson, Velma Irene, *(V I Anderson; 0-89279),* Stanhope, IA 50246 (SAN 283-295X).

Anderson, W. H. See **Anderson Publishing Co.**

Anderson & Daughters, *(Anderson & Daughters; 0-9615338),* P.O. Box 2008, Beverly Hills, CA 90213 (SAN 695-1120) Tel 213-456-9696.

Anderson Gallery, Div. of Virginia Commonwealth Univ., *(Anderson Gal; 0-935519),* 907 1/2 W. Franklin St., Richmond, VA 23284 (SAN 277-982X) Tel 804-257-1522.

Anderson House Museum of the Society of the Cincinnati, *(Anderson Hse Mus),* 2118 Massachusetts Ave., NW, Washington, DC 20008 (SAN 277-9838) Tel 202-785-0540.

Anderson Kramer Associates, Inc., Affil. of Siancy Kramer Books, Inc., *(Anderson Kramer; 0-910136),* 1722 H St., NW, Washington, DC 20006 (SAN 203-4735) Tel 202-298-8015.

Anderson Negotiations/Communications, *(Anderson Negotiations; 0-938515),* 1295 Monterey Blvd., San Francisco, CA 94127 (SAN 661-1176) Tel 415-834-6610.

†**Anderson Pubns.,** *(Anderson MI; 0-9610088),* Box 423, Davison, MI 48423 (SAN 267-5633) Tel 313-653-0984; *CIP.*

Anderson Publishing, *(Anderson Publ; 0-9602128),* P.O. Box 1751, Naples, FL 33939 (SAN 209-5238) Tel 813-262-5592.

†**Anderson Publishing Co.,** *(Anderson Pub Co; 0-87084),* P.O. Box 1576, Cincinnati, OH 45201 (SAN 208-2799); Toll free: 800-543-0883; 646 Main. St., Cincinnati, OH 45202 (SAN 661-9436) Tel 513-421-4393; *CIP.*

Anderson World, Inc., *(Anderson World; 0-89073),* 1400 Stierlin Rd., Mountain View, CA 94043 (SAN 281-2754) Tel 415-965-8777; Toll free: 800-257-5755; Orders to: P.O. Box 366, Mountain View, CA 94042 (SAN 281-2762).

Anderson's Pubns., *(Andersons Pubns; 0-931353),* P.O. Box 11338, Santa Rosa, CA 95406 (SAN 693-7829) Tel 707-575-1280.

Andesign, *(Andesign; 0-9615556),* 3925 Edenborn Ave., Metairie, LA 70002 (SAN 696-4826) Tel 504-455-1210.

Andor Publishing Co., Inc., *(Andor Pub; 0-89319),* P.O. Box 19, Wilton, CT 06897-0019 (SAN 208-5267). Out of business.

†**Andover Press,** *(Andover Pr; 0-939014),* 516 W. 34th St., New York, NY 10001 (SAN 216-1001); *CIP.*

Andre's & Co., *(Andre's & Co; 0-936264),* 289 Varick St., Jersey City, NJ 07302 (SAN 214-0977).

†**Andrew Mountain Pr.,** *(Andrew Mtn Pr; 0-9603840; 0-916897),* 81 Allendale Rd., Hartford, CT 06114 (SAN 213-7232) Tel 203-549-6723; P.O. Box 14353, Hartford, CT 06114 (SAN 658-0130); *CIP.*

Andrews, Anotol N., *(A N Andrews; 0-9616592),* 6033 Dauphin Ave., Los Angeles, CA 90034 (SAN 659-4883) Tel 213-935-4058.

Andrews, James, & Co., Inc., Publishing, *(James Andrews Co; 0-9614643),* 1942 Mt. Zion Dr., Golden, CO 80401 (SAN 691-8670) Tel 303-279-1277.

Andrews, McMeel & Parker, Subs. of Universal Press Syndicate, *(Andrews McMeel Parker; 0-8362),* 4900 Main St., Kansas City, MO 64112 (SAN 202-540X) Tel 816-932-6700; Toll free: 800-826-4216. *Imprints:* Search Books (Search).

Andrews Univ. Pr., *(Andrews Univ Pr; 0-943872),* Berrien Springs, MI 49104 (SAN 241-0958) Tel 616-471-3392.

Andrion Bks., *(Andrion Bks; 0-933773; 0-9606826),* 230 Park Ave., Suite 1624, New York, NY 10169 (SAN 692-770X) Tel 212-986-5842.

Andromeda Pr., *(Andromeda; 0-9602996),* 111 E. Platt, Maquoketa, IA 52060 (SAN 213-0017).

Andujar Communication Technologies, Inc., *(Andujar Comn Tech; 0-938086),* 7720A Herschel Ave., P.O. Box 2622, La Jolla, CA 92037 (SAN 663-5326).

Andy Keech See **Skies Call**

Anechron Three Press See **First International Publishing Corp.**

Anemone Editions, Ltd., *(Anemone Edns; 0-9604818),* P.O. Box 6056, Carmel, CA 93921 (SAN 216-0161).

Angel City Books, *(Angel City; 0-9605416),* 8033 Sunset Blvd., No. 366, Hollywood, CA 90046 (SAN 216-0951).

Angel Press Publications, *(Angel Pubns; 0-9612324),* P.O. Box 1431, Travis AFB, CA 94535 (SAN 289-1085) Tel 707-447-3374; Orders to: Angel Press, P.O. Box 1072, Mt Angel, OR 97362 (SAN 688-4164) Tel 503-845-2569.

Angel Pr. Pubs., *(Angel Pr; 0-912216),* 561 Tyler St., Monterey, CA 93940 (SAN 205-3330) Tel 408-372-1658.

Angelica Pr., The, *(Angelica Pr; 0-9617261),* 142 W. 24th St., 12th flr., New York, NY 10011 (SAN 663-5709) Tel 212-255-5155.

Angell, Robert W., *(R W Angell),* 11501 NE 11th Pl., Biscayne Park, FL 33161 (SAN 686-175X).

Angels of Easter Seal, *(Angels Easter; 0-9613501),* 4177 Fairway Dr., Canfield, OH 44406 (SAN 657-8306) Tel 216-533-6353; 299 Edwards St., Youngstown, OH 44502 (SAN 662-2402) Tel 216-743-1168.

Angers Publishing Corp., *(Angers Pub; 0-939524),* Box H.H., Lafayette, LA 70502 (SAN 216-6542) Tel 318-981-0859.

Angriff Pr., *(Angriff Pr; 0-913022),* P.O. Box 2726, Hollywood, CA 90078 (SAN 203-4743) Tel 213-386-9826.

Angst World Library, *(Angst World; 0-914580),* 1160 Forest Creek Rd., Selma, OR 97538 (SAN 201-1786).

Angus Cupar Publishers, *(Angus Cupar; 0-9612524),* 117 Hunt Dr., Princeton, NJ 08540 (SAN 287-7848) Tel 609-924-3358.

Anhinga Pr., *(Anhinga Pr; 0-938078),* Apalachee Poetry Ctr., P.O. Box 10423, Tallahassee, FL 32302 (SAN 216-0943).

Anima Books See **Anima Pubns.**

Anima Pubns., Div. of Conococheague Associates, Inc., *(Anima Pubns; 0-89012),* 1053 Wilson Ave., Chambersburg, PA 17201 (SAN 281-2770) Tel 717-263-8303. *Imprints:* Anima Books (Anima Bks).

Animal Cracker Pr., *(Animal Cracker),* R 6, Box 329, Bemidji, MN 56601 (SAN 210-9123).

Animal Owners Motivation Programs, *(Animal Owners; 0-9604576),* P.O. Box 16,, Frankfort, IL 60423 (SAN 215-1294) Tel 815-469-2284.

Animal Protection Institute of America, *(Animal Prot Inst),* P.O. Box 22505, 5894 S. Land Park Dr., Sacramento, CA 95822 (SAN 225-8951) Tel 916-422-1921.

Animal Stories, *(Animal Stories; 0-9616202),* 16783 Beach Blvd., Huntington Beach, CA 92647 (SAN 692-7327) Tel 213-322-5495.

Animal Welfare Institute, *(Animal Welfare),* P.O. Box 3650, Washington, DC 20007 (SAN 201-7156) Tel 202-337-2333.

Anirt Pr., *(Anirt Pr; 0-9605878),* 15707 Eastwood Ave., Lawndale, CA 90260 (SAN 216-6550) Tel 213-678-9753.

Anma Libri, *(Anma Libri; 0-915838),* P.O. Box 876, Saratoga, CA 95071 (SAN 212-5889) Tel 415-851-3375.

Ann Arbor Bks. See **Univ. of Michigan Pr.**

Ann Arbor Bk. Co., *(Ann Arbor Bk; 0-932364),* P.O. Box 8064, Ann Arbor, MI 48107 (SAN 212-0712).

Ann Arbor Pubs., *(Ann Arbor FL; 0-89039),* P.O. Box 7249, Naples, FL 33940 (SAN 213-8271) Tel 813-775-3528.

Anna Publishing, Inc., *(Anna Pub; 0-89305),* P.O. Box 218, Eight S. Bluford Ave., Ocoee, FL 32761 (SAN 281-2789) Tel 305-656-6998.

Annand Enterprises, Inc., *(Annand Ent),* Ball Hill Rd., Milford, NH 03055 (SAN 240-9666).

Annandale-International, *(Annandale-Intl; 0-9602562),* Box 384, Bronx, NY 10472 (SAN 212-8470) Tel 212-292-8067.

Annegan, Charles, *(C Annegan; 0-9605200),* P.O. Box 1304, San Marcos, CA 92069 (SAN 215-8469).

†**Annual Reviews, Inc.,** *(Annual Reviews; 0-8243),* P.O. Box 10139, Palo Alto, CA 94303-0897 (SAN 201-1816) Tel 415-493-4400; Toll free: 800-523-8635; P.O Box 1039, Palo Alto, CA 94303-0897 (SAN 658-0149); *CIP.*

Annuals Publishing Co., *(Annuals Pub Co; 0-912417),* 10 E. 23rd St., New York, NY 10010 (SAN 265-1742) Tel 212-475-1620; Dist. by: Robert Silver Assocs., 307 E. 37th St., New York, NY 10016 (SAN 241-5801) Tel 212-686-5630.

Another Chicago Pr., *(Another Chicago Pr; 0-9614644),* P.O. Box 11223, Chicago, IL 60611 (SAN 691-8468) Tel 312-248-7665.

Another View, Inc., *(Another View; 0-913564),* P.O. Box 1921, Brooklyn, NY 11202 (SAN 201-4351) Tel 212-624-0939.

Another Way Publishing, *(Another Way; 0-937251),* 400 E. Las Palmas Dr., Fullerton, CA 92635 (SAN 699-8070).

Anozira Agency, *(Anozira),* 1725 Farmer Ave., Tempe, AZ 85281 (SAN 206-4596).

Anro Communications, *(Anro Comm; 0-930623),* 100 Tamal Plaza, Suite 195, Corte Madera, CA 94925 (SAN 693-0255) Tel 415-924-1875.

Ansal Pr., *(ANSAL Pr; 0-910455),* 8620 Olympic View Dr., Edmonds, WA 98020 (SAN 260-0137) Tel 206-774-4645.

Ansayre Pr., *(Ansayre Pr; 0-937369),* 284 Huron Ave., Cambridge, MA 02138 (SAN 659-0071) Tel 617-547-0339.

Ansley Pubns., *(Ansley Pubns; 0-939113),* Rte. 1, Box 248, Hoboken, GA 31542 (SAN 662-4707) Tel 912-458-2602.

Answer-Book Library, *(Answer-Bk; 0-9608460; 0-915559),* 2000 Center St., Box 1470, Berkeley, CA 94704 (SAN 240-5857) Tel 415-845-5964.

Answer Group, The, *(Answer Grp; 0-916827),* 833 Park Rd. N., Wyomissing, PA 19610 (SAN 654-1240) Tel 215-378-1835; Dist. by: Liberty Publishing Co., Inc., 50 Scott Adam Rd., Cockeysville, MD 21030 (SAN 211-030X) Tel 301-667-6680.

Answering the Call, *(Answering the Call; 0-9616490),* P.O. Box 6597, Biloxi, MS 39532 (SAN 659-2864) Tel 601-388-1319; 115 Canterbury, Biloxi, MS 39532 (SAN 659-2872).

Answers Period, Inc., *(Answers Period; 0-917875),* P.O. Box 72666, Corpus Christi, TX 78472 (SAN 656-9617) Tel 512-852-8927; Dist. by: Baker & Taylor Co., Midwest Div., 501 Gladiola Ave., Momence, IL 60954 (SAN 169-2100) Tel 815-472-2444; Dist. by: Ingram Industries, 347 Reedwood Dr., Nashville, TN 37217 (SAN 169-7978) Tel 615-360-2819; Toll free: 800-251-5902.

Names

353

Names

Answers Pr., *(Answers Pr; 0-937651),* 5725 Calmor Ave., Suite 4, San Jose, CA 95123 (SAN 659-2880) Tel 408-554-9200.
ANTA Series of Distinguished Plays *See* **Washington Square Pr., Inc.**
Antaeus Pr., Div. of Antaeus Inc., *(Antaeus Pr; 0-933085),* P.O. Box 44225, Indianapolis, IN 46204 (SAN 689-5344) Tel 317-293-5323.
Antarctic Pr., *(Antarctic Pr; 0-930655),* P.O. Box 7134, Bellevue, WA 98008 (SAN 684-2631) Tel 206-747-2016; Dist. by: Pacific Pipeline, Inc., 19215 66th Ave. S., Kent, WA 98032 (SAN 208-2128) Tel 206-872-5523; Toll free: 800-426-4727.
†Antelope Island Pr., *(Antelope Island; 0-917946),* 2406 Mckinley Ave., Berkeley, CA 94703 (SAN 209-2921) Tel 415-832-4392; *CIP.*
Anthoensen Pr., *(Anthoensen Pr; 0-937703),* 37 Exchange St., Portland, ME 04112 (SAN 659-2910) Tel 207-774-3301.
Anthology Film Archives, *(Anthology Film; 0-911689),* 491 Broadway, New York, NY 10012 (SAN 263-9181) Tel 212-226-0010.
Anthony, Dorothy Malone, *(Anthony D M; 0-9607944),* 802 S. Eddy, Fort Scott, KS 66701 (SAN 239-6130) Tel 316-223-3404.
Anthony, Travis D., *(T D Anthony; 0-9604686),* P.O. Box 646, Rush Springs, OK 73082 (SAN 214-2295) Tel 405-476-2211.
Anthony Pr., *(Anthony Pr CA; 0-9606850),* Box 3722, Alhambra, CA 91803 (SAN 217-2240) Tel 213-942-4945.
Anthony Pr., *(Anthony Pr NV; 0-9615557),* 2000 Manzanita Ln., Reno, NV 89509 (SAN 696-4850) Tel 702-825-1684; P.O. Box 836, Reno, NV (SAN 696-4869). Do not confuse with Anthony Pr., Alhambra, CA.
Anthony Publishing, *(Anthony Pub TX; 0-9612996),* P.O. Box 70, Breckenridge, TX 76024 (SAN 297-1682).
Anthony Publishing Co., *(Anthony Pub Co; 0-9603832),* 218 Gleasondale Rd., Stow, MA 01775 (SAN 213-9073) Tel 617-897-7191; Dist. by: Bookpeople, 2929 Fifth St., Berkeley, CA 94710 (SAN 168-9517); Dist. by: DeVorss & Co., P.O. Box 550, 1046 Princeton Dr., Marina del Rey, CA 90294 (SAN 168-9886) Tel 213-870-7478; Dist. by: Inland Books, 22 Hemingway St., East Haven, CT 06512 (SAN 200-4151) Tel 203-467-4257; Dist. by: New Leaf Distributing Co., 1020 White St., SW, Atlanta, GA 30310 (SAN 169-1449) Tel 404-755-2665; Dist. by: The Distributors, 702 S. Michigan, South Bend, IN 46618 (SAN 169-2488) Tel 219-232-8500; Dist. by: Samuel Weiser, P.O. Box 612, York Beach, ME 03910 (SAN 202-9588) Tel 207-363-4393.
Anthracite Museum Pr., Div. of Scanton Anthracite Museum & Iron Furnaces Associates., *(Anthracite; 0-917445),* RD 1, Bald Mountain Rd., Scranton, PA 18504 (SAN 657-0631) Tel 717-963-4804.
Anthropological Research Associates, *(Anthro Research; 0-940148),* 59389 County Rd. 13, Elkhart, IN 46517-3503 (SAN 220-3081) Tel 219-875-7237.
Anthropology Museum, The, *(N Ill Anthro; 0-917039),* Northern Illinois University, Dekalb, IL 60115 (SAN 655-4962) Tel 815-753-0246.
Anthroposophic Pr., Inc., *(Anthroposophic; 0-910142; 0-88010),* Bell's Pond, Star Route, Hudson, NY 12534 (SAN 201-1824) Tel 518-851-2054.
Anti-Defamation League of B'nai B'rith, *(ADL; 0-88464),* 823 United Nations Plaza, New York, NY 10017 (SAN 204-7616) Tel 212-490-2525; Dist. by: Hippocrene Bks., Inc., 171 Madison Ave., New York, NY 10016 (SAN 213-2060).
Antietam Pr., *(Antietam Pr; 0-931590),* P.O. Box 62, Boonsboro, MD 21713 (SAN 211-5859) Tel 301-432-8079.
Antilles Pr., *(Antilles Pr; 0-916611),* P.O. Box 6684 Sunny Isle, St. Croix, VI 00820 (SAN 296-4414) Tel 809-773-1849.
Antioch Publishing Co., *(Antioch Pub Co; 0-89954),* 888 Dayton St., Yellow Springs, OH 45387 (SAN 654-7214) Tel 513-767-7379; Toll free: 800-543-2397.
Antiquarium, The, *(Antiquarium; 0-9603990),* 66 Humiston Dr., Bethany, CT 06525 (SAN 201-6850) Tel 203-393-2723.

Antiquary Pr., *(Antiquary Pr; 0-937864),* P.O. Box 9505, Baltimore, MD 21237 (SAN 220-0309) Tel 301-836-3409.
Antique Acres Pr., *(Antique Acres; 0-9615861),* 98 Jacksonville Rd., Ivyland, PA 18974 (SAN 696-6764) Tel 215-675-4567.
Antique & Historical Glass Foundation, *(Ant & Hist Glass),* P.O. Box 7413, Toledo, OH 43615 (SAN 225-5766).
Antique Classic Reprints, *(Antique Classic; 0-930088),* 144 Red Mill Rd., Peekskill, NY 10566 (SAN 210-7015) Tel 914-528-4074.
Antique Clocks Publishing, *(Antique Clocks; 0-933396),* P.O. Box 21387, Concord, CA 94521 (SAN 284-9682) Tel 415-687-8252; Dist. by: Scanlon Clocks, P.O. Box 379, Modesto, CA 95353 (SAN 284-9690) Tel 204-524-9789.
Antique Collectors' Club, *(Antique Collect; 0-902028; 0-907462),* 529 Ellis Hollow Creek Pk., Ithaca, NY 14850 (SAN 208-5003).
Antique Doorknob Publishing Company, The, *(Ant Doorknob Pub; 0-9610800),* 3900 Latimer Rd. N., Tillamook, OR 97141 (SAN 265-0665) Tel 503-842-2244.
Antique Pubns., *(Antique Pubns; 0-915410),* P.O. Box 655, Marietta, OH 45750 (SAN 216-3306).
Antiquity Reprints, *(Antiquity Re; 0-937214),* Box 370, Rockville Centre, NY 11571 (SAN 237-9295) Tel 516-766-5585.
Antler Books, *(Antler Bks; 0-914349),* 650 Market St., San Francisco, CA 94104 (SAN 289-5803) Tel 415-392-7378.
Antoinette Enterprises, *(Antoinette Ent; 0-9612098),* 5500 Trumbull Ave., Detroit, MI 48208 (SAN 286-7346) Tel 313-871-5748.
Antwayne Publishing Company, *(Antwayne Pub; 0-9610934),* 7030 Raintree Rd., Ft. Wayne, IN 46825 (SAN 265-1750) Tel 219-489-9565.
Anundsen Publishing Co., *(Anundsen Pub),* 108 Washington St., Decorah, IA 52101 (SAN 698-1860) Tel 319-382-4295.
Anura Publishing, *(Anura Pub; 0-9607074),* 12077 Wilshire Blvd., Suite 611, Los Angeles, CA 90025 (SAN 238-941X) Tel 213-395-4161; Dist. by: DeVorss & Co., P.O. Box 550, 1046 Princeton Dr., Marina del Rey, CA 90294 (SAN 168-9886) Tel 213-870-7478.
†Anzinger-Cain, Kay, *(K Anzinger-Cain; 0-9603188),* 18432 Las Cumbres Rd., Los Gatos, CA 95030 (SAN 694-3128) Tel 408-354-1628; P.O. Box 434, Los Gatos, CA 95031 (SAN 213-4748) Tel 408-354-8557; *CIP.*
Aozora Publishing, *(Aozora Pub; 0-9605962),* P.O. Box 95, 131 Ash St., Myrtle Point, OR 97458 (SAN 216-714X) Tel 503-572-5089.
APCO Pubns., *(APCO Pubns; 0-913237),* 6269 Varial Ave., Suite D5, Woodland Hills, CA 91367 (SAN 285-8142) Tel 818-887-2347.
†Aperture Foundation, Inc., *(Aperture; 0-89381; 0-912334),* 20 E. 23rd St., New York, NY 10010 (SAN 201-1832) Tel 212-505-5555; Toll free: 800-631-3577; Dist. by: Farrar Straus & Giroux, 19 Union Sq. W., New York, NY 10003 (SAN 206-782X) Tel 212-741-6900; *CIP.*
Apex Books *See* **Abingdon Pr.**
Apex Univ. Press, *(Apex U Pr; 0-916146),* c/o Castle-Pierce Printing Co., P.O. Box 2247, Oshkosh, WI 54903 (SAN 201-1565).
Aphra Behn Pr., *(DMSO News Serv; 0-940530),* 9513 SW Barbur Blvd., Suite 103, Portland, OR 97219 (SAN 223-7571) Tel 503-646-0471.
Apocalypse Publishing Co., *(Apocalypse Pub; 0-941614),* P.O. Box 1, Niagara Falls, NY 14305 (SAN 239-1562).
Apollo Bk., *(Apollo; 0-938290),* 5 Schoolhouse Ln., Poughkeepsie, NY 12603 (SAN 216-101X) Tel 914-462-0040; Toll free: 800-431-5003.
Apollo Books, Inc. (MN), *(Apollo Bks; 0-916829),* 107 Lafayette, Winona, MN 55987 (SAN 654-1283); Toll free: 800-328-8963.
Apollo Computer Systems, Inc., *(Apollo Com; 0-9610582),* 616 14th St., Arcata, CA 95521 (SAN 264-651X) Tel 707-822-0318.

Apollo Editions, *(Apollo Eds; 0-8152),* C/O Harper & Row Pubs., 10 E. 53rd St., New York, NY 10022 (SAN 211-691X); Toll free: 800-242-7737; Dist. by: Harper & Row Pubs., Keystone Industrial Park, Scranton, PA 18512 (SAN 215-3742). *Imprints:* Apollo Editions Juvenile Books (AE-J); Apollo Editions Trade Books (AE-T).
Apollo Editions Juvenile Books *See* **Apollo Editions**
Apollo Editions Trade Books *See* **Apollo Editions**
Apologetics Press Inc., *(Apologetic Pr; 0-932859),* 230 Landmark Dr., Montgomery, AL 36117-2752 (SAN 688-9190) Tel 205-272-8558.
Apostolate for Family Consecration, The, *(AFC; 0-932406),* Box 220, Kenosha, WI 53141 (SAN 223-6702).
Apostrophe Pr., *(Apostrophe Pr; 0-9607752),* 330 Mountain Ave., N. Plainfield, NJ 07060 (SAN 239-7455) Tel 201-769-1526.
Appalachian Assocs., *(Appalach Assoc; 0-940414),* 615 Pasteur Ave., Bowling Green, OH 43402 (SAN 219-760X) Tel 419-352-9111.
Appalachian Background, Inc., *(Appalach Bkground; 0-939115),* P.O. Box 143, Oakland, MD 21550 (SAN 662-4715); 301 S. Second St., Oakland, MD 21550 (SAN 662-4723) Tel 301-334-4334.
Appalachian Bks., *(Appalachian Bks; 0-912660),* P.O. Box 249, Oakton, VA 22124 (SAN 204-5524) Tel 703-281-2464.
†Appalachian Consortium Pr., Div. of Appalachian Consortium, Inc., *(Appalach Consortium; 0-913239),* Appalachian State Univ., University Hall, Boone, NC 28608 (SAN 285-8150) Tel 704-262-2064; *CIP.*
†Appalachian Mountain Club Bks., *(Appalach Mtn; 0-910146),* 5 Joy St., Boston, MA 02108 (SAN 203-4808) Tel 617-523-0636; *CIP.*
†Appel, Paul P., Pub., *(Appel; 0-911858),* 216 Washington St., Mt. Vernon, NY 10553 (SAN 202-3253) Tel 914-667-7365; *CIP.*
Applause Pubns., *(Applause Pubns; 0-932352),* 2234 S. Shady Hills Dr., Diamond Bar, CA 91765 (SAN 211-8807).
Applause Pubs., *(Applause Pub),* P.O. Box 441, Naples, FL 33939-0441 (SAN 692-3941).
Applause Theater Bk. Pubs., *(Applause Theater Bk Pubs; 0-936839),* 211 W. 71st St., New York, NY 10023 (SAN 658-3245) Tel 212-595-4735; Dist. by: Harper & Row, Keystone Industrial Pk., Scranton, PA 18512 (SAN 215-3742); Toll free: 800-242-7737.
Apple Computer, Inc., *(Apple Comp; 0-9609780),* 20525 Mariani Ave., Mail Stop 23-AX, Cupertino, CA 95014 (SAN 267-6044) Tel 408-996-1010.
Apple-Gems, *(Apple-Gems; 0-9602122),* P.O. Box 16292, San Francisco, CA 94116 (SAN 212-4769) Tel 415-587-9752.
Apple Hut Publishing Co., *(Apple Hut; 0-931148),* 1047 Park Hill Dr., P.O. Box 2704, Escondido, CA 92025 (SAN 211-2159) Tel 619-741-3565. Out of business.
Apple Paperbacks *See* **Scholastic, Inc.**
Apple Pie Bks., *(Apple Pie Bks; 0-934207),* 2740 Greenwich No. 416, San Francisco, CA 94123 (SAN 693-1243) Tel 415-921-4471. Do not confuse with Apple Pie Publishing, of Englewood, CO.
Apple Pie Publishing Co., *(Apple Pie Pub Co; 0-911149),* 7521 E. Costilla Ave., Englewood, CO 80112 (SAN 267-6052) Tel 303-770-1784.
Apple Pr., *(Apple Pr; 0-9602238),* 5536 SE Harlow, Milwaukie, OR 97222 (SAN 212-8489) Tel 503-659-2475.
Apple Pr. Publishing, *(Apple Pr Pub; 0-9615833),* 6975 SW Sandburg Rd., Portland, OR 97223 (SAN 697-2713) Tel 503-684-3398.
Apple Publishing Co., *(Apple Pub Co; 0-9604134),* Box 624 Grand Central Station, New York, NY 10163 (SAN 215-0549).
Apple Publishing Co., Subs. of Educational Assessment Service, Inc., *(Apple Pub Wisc; 0-937891),* W. 6050 Apple Rd., Watertown, WI 53094 (SAN 659-4123) Tel 414-261-1118.
Apple Tree Lane, *(Apple Tree Ln; 0-9601602),* 801 La Honda Rd., Woodside, CA 94062 (SAN 211-7177).

†**Apple Tree Pr., Inc.,** *(Apple Tree; 0-913082),* P.O. Box 1012, Flint, MI 48501 (SAN 206-7366) Tel 313-234-5451; *CIP.*

Apple-Wood Bks., *(Apple Wood; 0-918222),* Box 2870, Cambridge, MA 02139 (SAN 210-3419) Tel 617-350-0311; Dist. by: Arbor House Publishing Co., 235 E. 45th St., New York, NY 10017 (SAN 201-1522) Tel 212-599-3131.

Applegate Computer Enterprises, *(Applegate Comp Ent),* 470 Slagle Creek, Grants Pass, OR 97527 (SAN 285-6840).

†**Appleman, Robert C.,** *(R C Appleman; 0-9607718),* 7216 57th NE, Seattle, WA 98115 (SAN 211-0520) Tel 206-525-7909; *CIP.*

Appleseeds, *(Appleseeds; 0-9608944),* 4508 W. Ponds View Dr., Littleton, CO 80123 (SAN 240-9674).

†**Appleton & Lange,** Subs. of Simon & Schuster, A Gulf & Western Co., *(Appleton & Lange; 0-8385),* 25 Van Zant St., East Norwalk, CT 06855 (SAN 209-1488) Tel 203-838-4400; Toll free: 800-826-2618; Drawer L, Los Altos, CA 94022 (SAN 663-2866); Orders to: Appleton & Lange, 25 Van Zant St., East Norwalk, CT 06855 (SAN 209-1488); Dist. by: Prentice-Hall, Inc., Englewood Cliffs, NJ 07632 (SAN 200-2175) Tel 201-592-2000; *CIP.*

Appleton-Century-Crofts See **Prentice-Hall, Inc.**

Appleton Davies, *(Appleton Davies; 0-941022),* 32 S. Raymond Ave., Suite 10, Pasadena, CA 91105 (SAN 217-3255) Tel 818-792-3046.

Appletree Pr., *(Appletree Pr; 0-9611956),* 5903 Highland Pass, Austin, TX 78731 (SAN 286-7354) Tel 512-459-0606.

Applewhite, Karen Miller, *(Applewhite; 0-9603472),* 5942 E. Sage Dr., Scottsdale, AZ 85253 (SAN 213-6074) Tel 602-941-4753.

Appleyard, John, Agency, Inc., *(Appleyard Agency),* Box 1902, Pensacola, FL 32589 (SAN 211-2167) Tel 904-432-8396.

†**Applezaba Pr.,** *(Applezaba; 0-930090),* P.O. Box 4134, Long Beach, CA 90804 (SAN 210-7023) Tel 213-591-0015; *CIP.*

Application Engineering Corp., *(Application Eng Corp; 0-910447),* 850 Pratt Blvd.,, Elk Grove Village, IL 60007 (SAN 260-0145) Tel 312-593-5000.

Applied Arts Pubs., Div. of Sowers Printing Co., *(Applied Arts; 0-911410),* Box 479, Lebanon, PA 17042 (SAN 204-4838) Tel 717-272-9442.

Applied Concepts, *(Appl Concepts; 0-930011),* 5430 S. 12th Ave., Suite C, Tucson, AZ 85706 (SAN 669-7186) Tel 602-294-1188.

Applied Innovations, *(Applied Innovations; 0-938831),* 2515 39th Ave., SW, Seattle, WA 98116 (SAN 661-7018) Tel 206-937-1626.

Applied Pressure Techniques, Wm. J. Bales, *(Applied Press; 0-9600560),* P.O. Box 12248, Phoenix, AZ 85002 (SAN 205-1532).

Applied Publishing, Div. of Applied Software, Inc., *(Applied Pub MN; 0-935679),* 3402 Columbus Ave., S., Suite 225, Minneapolis, MN 55407 (SAN 696-0979) Tel 612-822-1998.

Applied Publishing Ltd., *(Applied Pub; 0-915834),* P.O. Box 261, Wilmette, IL 60091 (SAN 207-608X).

Applied Science Publications, Inc., *(Applied Sci Pubns; 0-915061),* P.O. Box 5399 Grand Central Station, New York, NY 10163 (SAN 670-7165) Tel 212-756-6440.

Applied Systems Institute, Inc., *(Applied Sys Inst; 0-935731),* 1910 K St., NW, Suite 600, Washington, DC 20006 (SAN 696-1037) Tel 202-785-0920.

Applied Therapeutics, Inc., *(Applied Therapeutics; 0-915486),* P.O. Box 1903, Spokane, WA 99210 (SAN 212-2057) Tel 509-534-5713.

Apprentices of Perception Pr., *(Apprentices; 0-9608792),* P.O. Box 3084, Berkeley, CA 94703 (SAN 240-9984). Moved, left no forwarding address.

Appropriate Technology Project, Volunteers in Asia, Inc., *(Appropriate Techn Proj; 0-917704; 0-8048),* P.O. Box 4543 (Rm 5, Clubhouse, Old Union, Stanford Univ.), Stanford, CA 94305 (SAN 210-9638) Tel 415-497-3228.

April Enterprises, Inc., *(April Enterp; 0-9608772),* 14136 Janna Way, Sylmar, CA 91342 (SAN 238-2385) Tel 818-367-1666.

April Hill Pubs., *(April Hill; 0-917780),* 79 Elm St., Springfield, VT 05156 (SAN 213-6554) Tel 802-885-3151.

April Publishing, *(April Pub; 0-939122),* P.O. Box 480000, Los Angeles, CA 90048 (SAN 238-0048).

Apt Bks., Inc., *(Apt Bks; 0-86590),* 141 E. 44th St., Suite 511, New York, NY 10017 (SAN 215-7209) Tel 212-697-0887.

Aptitude Inventory Measurement Service, *(Aptitude Inventory; 0-9602710),* 2506 McKinney Ave., Suite B, Dallas, TX 75201 (SAN 215-6202).

Aptos Publishing Co., *(Aptos Pub; 0-938187),* P.O. Box 2278, Aptos, CA 95001 (SAN 659-7246); 106 San Benito Ave., Aptos, CA 95003 (SAN 659-7254) Tel 408-688-0280.

Aqua Explorers, Inc., *(Aqua Explorers; 0-9616167),* 22 Maiden Ln., Lynbrook, NY 11563 (SAN 699-9050) Tel 516-596-0482.

Aquarelle Pr., *(Aquarelle Pr; 0-9616679),* P.O. Box 3676, Baton Rouge, LA 70808 (SAN 659-7270); 5036 Hyacinth Ave., Baton Rouge, LA 70808 (SAN 659-7289) Tel 504-926-4220; Dist. by: F & W Pubns., Inc., 9933 Alliance Rd., Cincinnati, OH 45242 (SAN 287-0274) Tel 513-984-0717.

Aquari Corp., *(Aquari Corp; 0-916204),* P.O. Box 2008, Rose City, MI 48654 (SAN 207-9917) Tel 517-685-2086.

Aquarian Book Pubs., *(Aquarian Bk Pubs; 0-9605126),* 7011 Hammond Ave., Dallas, TX 75223 (SAN 216-096X) Tel 214-328-5144.

Aquarian Educational Group, *(Aqua Educ; 0-911794),* P.O. Box 267, Sedona, AZ 86336 (SAN 203-4816) Tel 602-282-2655.

Aquarian League, The, *(Aquarian League; 0-931607),* P.O. Box 537, Louisville, KY 40201 (SAN 683-6747).

Aquarian Research Foundation, *(Aquarian Res; 0-916726),* 5620 Morton St., Philadelphia, PA 19144 (SAN 208-5305) Tel 215-849-3237; Dist. by: Bookpeople, 2929 Fifth St., Berkeley, CA 94710 (SAN 168-9517) Tel 415-549-3030.

AQUARIUS Enterprises, *(AQUARIUS; 0-922051),* 801 Harbor Dr., Suite A, Forked River, NJ 08731 (SAN 286-4304) Tel 609-693-0513.

Aquarius Enterprises, *(Aquarius; 0-941200),* 53 Central Ave. 15, Wailuku, Maui, HI 96793 (SAN 203-4824) Tel 808-244-7347.

Aquarius Rising Pr., *(Aquarius Rising Pr; 0-933883),* 2035 S. State, P.O. Box 16438, Chicago, IL 60616 (SAN 692-6622) Tel 312-337-1607.

Aquatic Adventure Pubns., *(Aquatic Adv Pubns; 0-9616150),* P.O. Box 60494, Palo Alto, CA 94306 (SAN 699-8712) Tel 415-856-2363.

Aquatic Specialists, *(Aquatic Spec; 0-912867),* 3405 E. Redbud Dr., Knoxville, TN 37920 (SAN 282-972X).

Aquilevie, *(Aquilevie; 0-9616035),* P.O. Box 231, Hopkins Park, IL 60944 (SAN 698-0406) Tel 815-944-5416; R.R. 4, Box 499, St. Anne, IL 60944 (SAN 698-2441).

Aquin Publishing Co., *(Aquin Pub; 0-915352),* 4412 Laurelgrove Ave., Studio City, CA 91604 (SAN 203-4085) Tel 213-508-7169.

Arab Petroleum Research Inst., *(Arab Petro Res; 0-913177),* P.O. Box 535, Shelburne, VT 05482 (SAN 282-9584) Tel 802-985-3851.

Arachne's Muse Foundation, The, *(Arachnes Muse; 0-9611940),* 57 Christopher St., New York, NY 10014 (SAN 286-0244) Tel 212-874-5300.

Arader, W. Graham, *(W G Arader; 0-934626),* 1000 Boxwood Ct., King of Prussia, PA 19406 (SAN 212-8497) Tel 215-825-6570.

Aragorn Bks., Inc., *(Aragorn Bks; 0-913862),* 14698 Nordhoff St., Panorama City, CA 91402 (SAN 203-4832) Tel 213-894-3104.

Arana Pr., Inc., *(Arana Press; 0-9617108),* P.O. Box 14238, St. Paul, MN 55114 (SAN 662-698X) Tel 612-646-7445.

†**Ararat Pr.,** Div. of Armenian General Benevolent Union, *(Ararat Pr; 0-933706),* 585 Saddle River Rd., Saddle Brook, NJ 07662 (SAN 212-8268) Tel 201-797-7600; *CIP.*

†**Arbit Bks., Inc.,** *(Arbit; 0-930038),* 8050 N. Pt. Washington Rd., Milwaukee, WI 53217 (SAN 210-4695) Tel 414-352-4404; Toll free: 800-558-6908; *CIP.*

Arbogast Publishing Co., *(Arbogast Pub; 1-55598),* P.O. Box 56, Hannawa Falls, NY 13647 (SAN 659-008X) Tel 315-265-8317; Outer Grove St., Hannawa Falls, NY 13647 (SAN 659-0098).

Arbolyn Pubns., *(Arbolyn Pubns; 0-937909),* P.O. Box 2412, Columbia, SC 29202 (SAN 659-4131) Tel 803-794-3215; 1708 Holly Hill Dr., West Columbia, SC 29169 (SAN 659-414X).

Arbor Hse. Pub. Co., Div. of Hearst Corp., *(Arbor Hse; 0-87795),* 235 E. 45th St., New York, NY 10017 (SAN 201-1522) Tel 212-599-3131.

Arbor Pubns., *(Arbor Pubns; 0-9602556),* P.O. Box 8185, Ann Arbor, MI 48107 (SAN 212-8276) Tel 313-668-6673.

Arc Pr., *(Arc Pr AR; 0-938041),* P.O. Box 88, Cane Hill, AR 72717 (SAN 659-7297); Cold Springs Rd., Cane Hill, AR 72717 (SAN 659-7300) Tel 501-824-3821.

Arcade Pubs., *(Arcade Pubs; 0-933885),* Box 5365, Berkeley, CA 94705 (SAN 692-767X) Tel 415-848-8656.

Arcadia Corp., *(Arcadia Corp; 0-9614745),* P.O. Box 324, Franklin, NH 03235 (SAN 692-9206) Tel 603-934-6186.

Arcadia Pr., *(Arcadia Pr; 0-938186),* 37 Washington Square West, Apt. 4C, New York, NY 10011 (SAN 215-6210) Tel 212-477-5331.

Arcadia Pubns., *(Arcadia Pubns; 0-938829),* 6030 W. Coldspring Rd., Greenfield, WI 53220 (SAN 661-7026) Tel 414-327-5258.

Arcana Publishing, Div. of Lotus Light Publications, *(Arcana Pub; 0-910261),* P.O. Box Two, Wilmot, WI 53192 (SAN 241-3604) Tel 414-862-2395.

Arcane Order Studio of Contemplation, *(Arcane Order),* 2904 Rosemary Ln., Falls Church, VA 22042 (SAN 225-4743) Tel 703-536-8863.

Arcane Pubns., *(Arcane Pubns; 0-912240),* Box 36, York Harbor, ME 03911 (SAN 203-4840).

Arcas Pr., *(Arcas Pr; 0-9615753),* P.O. Box 90984, San Diego, CA 92109 (SAN 696-110X) Tel 619-488-2666.

Arceneaux, Thelma Hoffman Tyler, *(T H Arceneaux; 0-9600870),* 115 Apricot St., Thibodaux, LA 70301 (SAN 207-5342) Tel 504-446-1037.

Archaeological Institute of America, *(Archaeological Inst; 0-9605042),* 15 Park Row, Suite 1732, New York, NY 10038 (SAN 232-542X); P.O. Box 1901, Kenmore Sta., Boston, MA 02215 (SAN 693-952X).

Archaeological News, Inc., *(Arch News Inc; 0-943254),* Florida State Univ., Dept. of Classics, Tallahassee, FL 32306 (SAN 240-3374) Tel 904-644-3033.

Archangel Publishing, *(Archangel Pub; 0-932661),* 310 W. Washington, Parisette, IL 61944 (SAN 687-7664) Tel 217-463-7895.

†**Archdiocesan Historical Commission,** Div. of Archdiocese of Portland in Oregon, *(Archdiocesan; 0-9613644),* 5000 N. Williamette Blvd., Portland, OR 97203-5798 (SAN 670-7882) Tel 503-283-7111; 2838 E. Burnside, Portland, OR 97207-0351 (SAN 200-5417) Tel 503-234-5334; Dist. by: Pacific Northwest Books, P.O. Box 314, Medford, OR 97501 (SAN 200-5263); *CIP.*

†**Archer Editions Pr.,** *(Archer Edns; 0-89097),* 318 Fry Branch Rd., Lynnville, TN 38472 (SAN 207-7124) Tel 615-527-3643; *CIP.*

†**Archibald Publishing,** *(Archibald Pub; 0-937819),* P.O. Box 6573, Minneapolis, MN 55406 (SAN 659-4158) Tel 612-724-6431; 3336 35th Ave. S., Minneapolis, MN 55406 (SAN 659-4166).

†**Archinform,** *(Archinform; 0-937254),* P.O. Box 27732, Los Angeles, CA 90027 (SAN 212-3320) Tel 213-662-0216; *CIP.*

†**Architectural Bk. Publishing Co., Inc.,** *(Architectural; 0-8038),* 268 Dogwood Ln., Stamford, CT 06903 (SAN 658-0157) Tel 203-322-1460; Dist. by: Kampmann & Co., 9 E. 40th St., New York, NY 10016 (SAN 202-5191) Tel 212-685-2928; Toll free: 800-526-7626; *CIP.*

355

Names

Architectural License Seminars, Inc., *(Arch Lic Seminar; 0-937705),* P.O. Box 64188, Los Angeles, CA 90064 (SAN 659-2937) Tel 213-208-7112; 924 Westwood Blvd., Suite 840, Los Angeles, CA 90024 (SAN 659-2945).

Architectural Pubns., *(Arch Pubns; 0-9608208),* 103 MacDougal St., New York, NY 10012 (SAN 240-3382) Tel 212-477-6385.

Architectural Record Bks. *See* McGraw-Hill Bk. Co.

Archival Pr., Inc., *(Archival Pr; 0-915882),* P.O. Box 93, MIT Branch Sta., Cambridge, MA 02139 (SAN 214-283X).

†**Archival Services, Inc.,** *(Archival Servs; 0-910653),* P.O. Box 78191, Shreveport, LA 71137-8191 (SAN 270-1774) Tel 318-222-7655; P.O. Box 112, Blanchard, LA 71009 (SAN 662-0108) Tel 318-929-4707; *CIP.*

Archive Corp., *(Archive Corp; 0-9608810),* 1650 Sunflower Ave., Costa Mesa, CA 92626 (SAN 693-1669) Tel 714-641-0279.

Archive Press, The, *(Archive Pr; 0-910720),* 2101 192nd Ave., S.E., Issaquah, WA 98027 (SAN 217-2259).

Archives of Belmont Abbey, The, *(Archives Belmont; 0-9614976),* Belmont Abbey, Belmont, NC 28012 (SAN 693-6016) Tel 704-825-7031.

Archives of Social History, *(Archives Soc Hist; 0-914924),* P.O. Box 763, Stony Brook, NY 11790 (SAN 204-4889) Tel 516-751-3709.

Archives, The, *(Archives Pr; 0-918501),* 1259 El Camino Real, No. 188, Menlo Park, CA 94025 (SAN 657-3207) Tel 415-326-6997.

Archon Bks. *See* Shoe String Pr., Inc.

Archon Institute for Leadership Development, Inc., The, *(Archon Inst Leader Dev; 0-9616203),* 3700 Massachusetts Ave., No. 121, Washington, DC 20016 (SAN 658-3415) Tel 202-342-7710.

†**Archway Paperbacks,** *(Archway; 0-671),* ; Toll free: 800-223-2336; c/o Pocket Bks., 1230 Ave. of the Americas, New York, NY 10020 (SAN 202-5922) Tel 212-246-2121; *CIP.*

Arcline Pubns., *(Arcline Pubns; 0-913852),* P.O. Box 1550, Pomona, CA 91769 (SAN 203-2287) Tel 714-623-1738.

Arco Publishing, Inc., Div. of Prentice-Hall, Inc., *(Arco; 0-668),* 1 Gulf & Western Bldg., New York, NY 10023 (SAN 201-0003) Tel 212-333-5800. *Imprints:* Morgan Aviation Books (Morgan Aviation).

Arctinurus Co., Inc., *(Arctinurus Co; 0-915386),* P.O. Box 275, Bellmawr, NJ 08031-0275 (SAN 276-9719) Tel 609-933-0212.

Arcturus Pubs., Inc., *(Arcturus Pubs; 0-916877),* P.O. Box 606, Cherry Hill, NJ 08003 (SAN 653-9718) Tel 609-428-3863.

Arcus Publishing Co., *(Arcus Pub; 0-916955),* P.O. Box 228, Sonoma, CA 95476 (SAN 655-5667) Tel 707-996-9529.

†**Arden Library,** *(Arden Lib; 0-8495),* Mill & Main Sts., Darby, PA 19023 (SAN 207-477X) Tel 215-726-5505; *CIP.*

Arden Pr., *(Arden Pr; 0-912869),* P. O. Box 418, Denver, CO 80201 (SAN 277-6553) Tel 303-433-1448.

†**Ardis Pubs.,** *(Ardis Pubs; 0-88233; 0-87501),* 2901 Heatherway, Ann Arbor, MI 48104 (SAN 201-1492) Tel 313-971-2367; *CIP.*

Ardsley Hse. Pubs., Inc., *(Ardsley; 0-912675),* 320 Central Park, W., New York, NY 10025 (SAN 282-7549) Tel 212-496-7040.

Ardsley Pr., *(Ardsley Pr; 0-937253),* 110 Maple St., Suite 211, Springfield, MA 01105 (SAN 659-0128) Tel 413-737-4797.

Arena *See* Pyramid Pubns., Inc.

Arena Lettres, Div. of John Taylor, Inc., *(Arena Lettres; 0-88479),* 8 Lincoln Pl., Waldwick, NJ 07463 (SAN 206-3247) Tel 201-445-7154.

Arendson, Peter, *(P Arendson),* 1151 Xenia St., Denver, CO 80220 (SAN 239-586X) Tel 303-320-4448.

Ares Pubs., Inc., *(Ares; 0-89005),* 7020 N. Western Ave., Chicago, IL 60645-3416 (SAN 205-6011) Tel 312-743-1405.

†**Arete Pr.,** *(Arete Pr; 0-941736),* 480 W. Sixth St., Claremont, CA 91711 (SAN 239-1570) Tel 714-624-7757; *CIP.*

Arete' Pr., of Colorado, *(Arete CO; 0-9614341),* P.O. Box 440477, Aurora, CO 80044 (SAN 687-8547) Tel 303-337-3113.

Argee Pub. Co., *(Argee Pub; 0-917961),* 14125 Haynes St., Van Nuys, CA 91401 (SAN 211-8815) Tel 818-994-9040.

Argent Press, *(Argent Pr; 0-915417),* 215 E. 61st St., New York, NY 10021 (SAN 291-0748) Tel 212-838-6509.

Argo Bks. *See* Atheneum Pubs.

Argo Books, *(Argo Bks; 0-912148),* Main St., Norwich, VT 05055 (SAN 203-4867) Tel 802-649-1000.

Argonaut Publishing, *(Argonaut Pub; 0-918777),* P.O. Box 50123, Santa Barbara, CA 93108 (SAN 657-3215) Tel 805-684-6977; 1050 Cindy Ln., Carpinteria, CA 93013 (SAN 657-3223); Dist. by: Harper & Row, Publishers, Inc., 1700 Montgomery St., San Francisco, CA 94111 (SAN 215-3734) Tel 415-989-9000.

Argonne Bks., *(Argonne Bks; 0-915063),* 1083 Austin Ave. NE, Atlanta, GA 30307 (SAN 289-7245) Tel 404-872-0780.

Argos Hse., *(Argos House; 0-9607082),* Crescent Ave., Saratoga Springs, NY 12866 (SAN 238-9428) Tel 518-584-5817.

Argos Publishing Co., Subs. of Aaron E. Freeman, Inc., *(Argos Pub Co; 0-915509),* 1156 Sidonia Ct., Leucadia, CA 92024 (SAN 291-0764) Tel 619-436-4271.

Argosy, *(Argosy; 0-87266),* 116 E. 59th St., New York, NY 10022 (SAN 203-4875).

Argus Archives, *(Argus Archives; 0-916858),* 228 E. 49th St, New York, NY 10017 (SAN 208-4244) Tel 212-355-6140.

Argus Books & Graphics, *(Argus Bks),* 1714 Capitol Ave., Sacramento, CA 95814 (SAN 203-4883).

Argus Communications, Div. of DLM, Inc., *(Argus Comm; 0-89505; 0-913592),* 1 DLM Park, P.O. Box 8000, Allen, TX 75002 (SAN 201-1476) Tel 214-727-3346; Toll free: 800-527-4748.

Argyle Press, *(Argyle Pr; 0-9610272),* P.O. Box 3215, Silver Spring, MD 20901 (SAN 291-0195).

Ariadne Books *See* Beacon Pr., Inc.

†**Ariadne Pr.,** *(Ariadne Pr; 0-918056),* 4817 Tallahassee Ave., Rockville, MD 20853 (SAN 210-1661) Tel 301-949-2514; *CIP.*

Ariana Productions, *(Ariana Prods; 0-916549),* P.O. Box 18627, Cleveland, OH 44118 (SAN 295-5350) Tel 216-283-5563.

Arica Institute Pr., *(Arica Inst Pr; 0-916554),* 150 Fifth Ave., Suite 912, New York, NY 10011 (SAN 208-5321) Tel 212-807-9600.

Ariel Bks., *(Ariel Bks; 0-9614304),* 820 Miramar Ave., Berkeley, CA 94707 (SAN 687-4738) Tel 415-525-2098; Dist. by: Blue Wind Pr., P.O. Box 7175, Berkeley, CA 94707 (SAN 206-7099) Tel 415-525-2098.

Ariel Pr., Subs. of Light, *(Ariel OH; 0-89804),* 4082 Clotts Rd., Columbus, OH 43230 (SAN 219-8460) Tel 614-471-1163; Toll free: 800-336-7769; Toll free: 800-336-7768 (OH).

Ariel Pr., *(Ariel Pr CA; 0-914863),* 1541 Pkwy. Loop, Suite D, P.O. Box 3723, Tustin, CA 92680 (SAN 289-0534) Tel 714-259-4800.

Ariel Pubns., *(Ariel Pubns; 0-917656),* 14417 SE 19th Pl., Bellevue, WA 98007 (SAN 207-5334) Tel 206-641-0518. Do not confuse with Ariel Bks., Berkeley, CA, or Ariel Pr., Tustin, CA, or Ariel Pr., Columbus, OH.

Aries Plus Pubns., *(Aries CA; 0-9612570),* 6719 Hollywood Blvd., Hollywood, CA 90028 (SAN 289-0542).

Aries Productions, Inc., *(Aries Prod; 0-910035),* 9633 Cinnabar Dr., Sappington, MO 63126 (SAN 241-2004) Tel 314-849-3722; P.O. Box 29396, Sappington, MO 63126 (SAN 669-0009).

†**Aries Rising Pr.,** *(Aries Rising; 0-917211),* 2132 Alcyona Dr., Los Angeles, CA 90068 (SAN 655-9573) Tel 818-957-8751; P.O. Box 29532, Los Angeles, CA 90029 (SAN 662-2313); *CIP.*

Arif, *(Arif; 0-913537),* 2748 Ninth St., Berkeley, CA 94710 (SAN 206-944X) Tel 415-848-5386.

Arion Pr., *(Arion Pr; 0-910457),* 460 Bryant St., San Francisco, CA 94107 (SAN 203-1361) Tel 415-777-9651.

†**Aris Bks./Harris Publishing Co.,** *(Aris Bks Harris; 0-943186),* 1621 Fifth St., Berkeley, CA 94710 (SAN 219-7626) Tel 415-527-5171; Dist. by: Simon & Schuster, 1230 Ave. of the Americas, New York, NY 10020 (SAN 200-2450) Tel 212-245-6400; *CIP.*

Arista Corp., Subs. of Hachette SA (France), *(Arista Corp NY; 0-89796; 0-914876; 0-8073),* 2 Park Ave., New York, NY 10016 (SAN 207-7078) Tel 212-889-2780; Toll free: 800-227-1606.

Aristan Pr., *(Aristan Pr; 0-931407),* P.O. Box 395, Placentia, CA 92670 (SAN 686-9327).

Arithmetic of God, The, *(AOG; 0-940532),* P.O. Box 573, Kings Mountain, NC 28086 (SAN 219-7642) Tel 704-739-7986.

Arizona Antique Directory, The, *(AZ Antique Direct; 0-9615549),* 943 W. Keating, Mesa, AZ 85202 (SAN 696-4907) Tel 602-831-9493; Dist. by: Treasure Chest Publications, P.O. Box 5250, Tucson, AZ 85703 (SAN 209-3243); Dist. by: Central Arizona Distributing, 4932 W. Pasedana Ave., Glendale, AZ 85301 (SAN 200-7630).

Arizona Archaeological Society, *(AZ Archaeol; 0-939071),* P.O. Box 9665, Phoenix, AZ 85068 (SAN 662-9342); 2602 W. Bloomfield Rd., Phoenix, AZ 85029 (SAN 662-9350) Tel 602-944-6034.

Arizona Daily Star, Subs. of Pulitzer Pub. Co., *(Ariz Daily Star; 0-9607758),* P.O. Box 26807, 4850 S. Park Ave., Tucson, AZ 85726 (SAN 239-748X) Tel 602-573-4400; Toll free: 800-362-4890.

Arizona Game & Fish Dept., *(AZ Game & Fish; 0-917563),* 2222 W. Greenway Rd., Phoenix, AZ 85023 (SAN 273-9194) Tel 602-942-3000.

Arizona Highways, Div. of Arizona Department of Transportation, *(Ariz Hwy; 0-916179),* 2039 W. Lewis Ave., Phoenix, AZ 85009 (SAN 294-8974) Tel 602-258-6641.

Arizona Historical Foundation, *(AZ Hist Foun; 0-910152),* Hayden Memorial Library, Arizona State University, Tempe, AZ 85287 (SAN 201-7040) Tel 602-966-8331.

†**Arizona Historical Society,** *(AZ Hist Soc; 0-910037),* 949 E. Second St., Tucson, AZ 85719 (SAN 201-6982) Tel 602-628-5774; *CIP.*

Arizona Law Institute College of Law, *(AZ Law Inst; 0-910039),* Univ. of Arizona, Tucson, AZ 85721 (SAN 227-3535) Tel 602-621-5522.

Arizona State Univ. Anthropological Research Papers, *(AZ Univ ARP; 0-936249),* Arizona State Univ., Anthropology Dept., Tempe, AZ 85287 (SAN 697-323X) Tel 602-965-7596.

Arizona State Univ. Ctr. for Asian Studies, *(ASU Ctr Asian; 0-939252),* Tempe, AZ 85287 (SAN 220-1623) Tel 602-965-7184.

†**Arizona State Univ., Ctr. for Latin American Studies,** *(ASU Lat Am St; 0-87918),* Social Sciences Bldg., Rm. 213, Tempe, AZ 85287 (SAN 201-1336) Tel 602-965-5127; *CIP.*

Arizona State Univ., Dept. of Theatre, *(AZSU Theatre; 0-938675),* Arizona State Univ., Dept. of Theatre, Tempe, AZ 85287 (SAN 661-3802) Tel 602-965-2661.

Ark & Arbor Press, *(Ark & Arbor; 0-9606234),* Box 901, Little Compton, RI 02837 (SAN 238-907X).

Ark Communications Institute, *(Ark Comm Inst; 0-934325),* P.O. Box 1010, Bolinas, CA 94924 (SAN 693-0905) Tel 415-868-2222.

Ark Paperbacks *See* Methuen, Inc.

Arkansas Commemorative Commission, Trapnall Hall, *(AR Commemorative; 0-9606278),* 300 W. Markham, Little Rock, AR 72201 (SAN 223-2111) Tel 501-371-1749.

Arkansas Legislative Digest, Inc., *(AR Legis Digest; 0-935765),* 500 E. Markham, No. 219, Little Rock, AR 72201 (SAN 695-8362) Tel 501-376-2843.

†**Arkansas State Univ.,** *(Ark St Univ; 0-930677),* P.O. Box 1990, State University, AR 72467 (SAN 677-0002) Tel 501-972-3056; *CIP.*

Arkansas Symphony Orchestra Society Guild, *(AR Symphony Orch; 0-9615625),* P.O. Box 7328, Little Rock, AR 72217 (SAN 696-1150) Tel 501-666-1761.

Arkbridge Assn., *(Arkbridge Assn; 0-9616312),* P.O. Box 3533, Pompano Beach, FL 33072 (SAN 699-8178) Tel 305-785-2257.

Arkham Hse. Pubs., *(Arkham; 0-87054),* P.O. Box 546, Sauk City, WI 53583 (SAN 206-9741) Tel 608-643-4500. *Imprints:* Mycroft & Moran (Mycroft & Moran).

Arlen Communications, Inc., *(Arlen Comm Inc; 0-9609768),* 7315 Wisconsin Ave., Suite 600 E, Bethesda, MD 20814 (SAN 267-6451) Tel 301-656-7940.

†**Arlington Bk. Co.,** *(Arlington Bk; 0-930163),* P.O. Box 327, Arlington, VA 22210-0327 (SAN 200-786X) Tel 202-296-6750; *CIP.*

Arlington Hse. *See* **Crown Pubs., Inc.**

Arlotta Pr., *(Arlotta; 0-918838),* 6340 Millbank Dr., Dayton, OH 45459 (SAN 210-3877) Tel 513-434-1518.

Arma Press, *(Arma Pr; 0-9603662),* Rte. 139, North Branford, CT 06471 (SAN 203-4093).

Armado & Moth, *(Armado & Moth; 0-9603626),* 2131 Arapahoe, Boulder, CO 80302 (SAN 213-4586) Tel 303-442-1415.

Armagh Pr., The, *(Armagh Press; 0-9617109),* 7816 Turning Creek Ct., Potomac, MD 20854 (SAN 662-6998) Tel 301-469-0393.

Arman, M., Pub. Inc., *(M Arman; 0-933078),* P.O. Box 785, Ormond Beach, FL 32074 (SAN 293-230X) Tel 904-673-5576; Orders to: 28 N. Ridgewood Ave., Rio Vista, Ormond Beach, FL 32074 (SAN 293-2318).

Arman Enterprises, Inc., *(Arman Ent; 0-915438),* RD No. 1 Box 353A, Woodstock, CT 06281 (SAN 207-1673) Tel 203-928-5838.

Armedia Consultants, Subs. of Armedia Corporating, Inc., *(Armedia Con; 0-916903; 0-9607626),* 508 Colquitt St. Suite A, Houston, TX 77006 (SAN 656-1632) Tel 702-739-6612.

Armenian Heritage Pr., Div. of National Assn. for Armenian Studies & Research, *(Armenian Her; 0-935411),* 175 Mt. Auburn St., Cambridge, MA 02138 (SAN 696-1193) Tel 617-876-7630.

Armenian Numismatic Society, *(ANS; 0-9606842),* 8511 Beverly Park Pl., Pico Rivera, CA 90660 (SAN 217-3263) Tel 213-695-0380.

Armenian Reference Bks., Co., *(Armenian Ref Bks; 0-931539),* P.O. Box 7106, Glendale, CA 91205 (SAN 683-2407) Tel 818-507-1525.

Armenian Review, Inc., *(Armen Review; 0-935353),* P.O. Box 2629, Cambridge, MA 02238 (SAN 696-1231) Tel 617-926-4037; 80 Bigelow Ave., Watertown, MA 02172 (SAN 696-5237).

Armond Dalton Publishers, Inc., *(Armond-Dalton; 0-912503),* P.O. Box 318, Haslett, MI 48840 (SAN 656-8580) Tel 517-349-4695.

Armory Pubns., *(Armory Pubns; 0-9604982; 0-939683),* P.O. Box 44372, Tacoma, WA 98444 (SAN 215-725X) Tel 206-531-4632.

Arms Control Assn., *(Arms Control; 0-934766),* 11 Dupont Cir., NW, Washington, DC 20036 (SAN 224-053X) Tel 202-797-6450.

Armstrong, Alan, & Assocs., *(A Arm Assoc; 0-946291),* 5827 Columbia Pike, Suite 501, Falls Church, VA 22041 (SAN 679-1913).

†**Armstrong, D., Co., Inc.,** *(D Armstrong),* 2000-B Governor's Cir., Houston, TX 77092 (SAN 210-0320) Tel 713-688-1441; *CIP.*

Armstrong, Irma M., *(I M Armstrong; 0-9611106),* 1188 Harrison Ave., Salt Lake City, UT 84105 (SAN 283-2925) Tel 801-484-7123.

Armstrong Books, Inc. *See* **Armstrong Publishing Co.**

Armstrong Browning Library, *(Armstrong Browning; 0-914108),* P.O. Box 6336, Waco, TX 76706 (SAN 206-3263) Tel 817-755-3566.

Armstrong Chapel, *(Armstrong Chapel; 0-9616073),* 5125 Drake Rd., Cincinnati, OH 45243 (SAN 698-133X) Tel 513-575-2256.

Armstrong Press, The, *(Armstrong Pr; 0-915739),* Rte. Two, Box 509, Notasulga, AL 36866 (SAN 216-3314) Tel 205-257-3670.

Armstrong Publishing Co. Div. of Croesus Co. Inc., *(Armstrong Pub; 0-915936),* 5514 Wilshire Blvd., Los Angeles, CA 90036 (SAN 208-533X) Tel 213-937-3600.

Arnall, Franklin, *(Arnall; 0-914638),* P.O. Box 253, Claremont, CA 91711 (SAN 204-482X) Tel 714-621-2461.

Arner Pubns., *(Arner Pubns; 0-914124),* P.O. Drawer A, Clark Mills, NY 13321 (SAN 201-145X) Tel 315-853-8375.

Arnold, Edward, Pubs., Ltd., *(E Arnold; 0-7131),* 3 E. Read St., Baltimore, MD 21202 (SAN 263-9203) Tel 301-539-1529; Toll free: 800-638-7511; York County Industrial Pk., Connolly Rd., Emigsville, PA 17318 (SAN 200-6367).

Arnold, James, & Co., *(Arnold & Co; 0-913013),* 18533 Burbank Blvd., Suite 138, Tarzana, CA 91356 (SAN 282-9630) Tel 818-888-4883.

Arnold, Luis, *(L Arnold; 0-9610434),* 13 Loma Vista Pl., San Rafael, CA 94901 (SAN 263-9211) Tel 415-454-5075.

Arnold, William, Assocs., Inc., *(Arnold Assocs; 0-9615458),* P.O. Box 36786, Grosse Pointe, MI 48236 (SAN 695-7420) Tel 313-886-8001.

Arnold-Porter Publishing Co., *(Arnold-Porter Pub; 0-9605048),* P.O. Box 646, Keego Harbor, MI 48033 (SAN 220-0325) Tel 313-338-4478.

Aronson, Charles N., Writer-Publisher, *(C N Aronson; 0-915736),* 11520 Bixby Hill Rd., Arcade, NY 14009 (SAN 207-6144) Tel 716-496-6002.

Aronson, J. H., *(J H Aronson; 0-9613348),* P.O. Box 302, Highmount, NY 12441 (SAN 655-816X) Tel 914-254-5701. Do not confuse with Jason Aronson, Northvale, NJ.

†**Aronson, Jason, Inc.,** *(Aronson; 0-87668),* 230 Livingston St., Northvale, NJ 07647 (SAN 201-0127) Tel 201-767-4093; Orders to: Jason Aronson, Inc., 1205 O'Neill Hwy., Dunmore, PA 18512 (SAN 200-7746) Tel 717-342-1449; Dist. by: Haddon Craftsmen Distribution Ctr., 1205 O'Neil Hwy., Dunmore, PA 18512 (SAN 663-2874) Tel 717-342-1449. Do not confuse with J. H. Aronson, Highmount, NY; *CIP.*

Arpel Graphics, Inc., *(Arpel Graphic; 0-916567),* 32 E. Micheltorena, Santa Barbara, CA 93101 (SAN 297-1836) Tel 805-687-5658.

Arrants & Associate, *(Arrants & Assoc; 0-943704),* P.O. Box 6606, Bellevue, WA 98008 (SAN 238-3675) Tel 206-644-1664.

†**Arrays, Inc./Continental Software,** *(Arrays-Continent; 0-88688),* 6711 Valjean Ave., Van Nuys, CA 91406 (SAN 265-0398) Tel 818-994-1899; *CIP.*

Arriaga Pubns., *(Arriaga Pubns; 0-9606356),* P.O. Box 652, Booneville, AR 72927 (SAN 214-0985).

Arriflex Corp., *(Arriflex; 0-936763),* 500 Rte. 303, Blauvelt, NY 10913 (SAN 699-8828) Tel 914-353-1400.

Arrigo, Hargreaves, Nishimura, *(Arrigo CA),* 10175 Bunting Ave., Fountain Valley, CA 92708 (SAN 663-4680).

Arrow Publishing, *(Arrow P; 0-9614631),* 405 W. Washington St., Suite 26, San Diego, CA 92103 (SAN 691-893X) Tel 619-296-3201.

Arrow Publishing Co., Inc., *(Arrow Pub; 0-913450),* 1020 Turnpike St., Canton, MA 02021 (SAN 201-6753) Tel 617-828-8013.

Arroway Pubs., *(Arroway; 0-9600284),* 242 S. Alta Vista Blvd., Los Angelas, CA 90036 (SAN 203-4913) Tel 213-875-3730.

Arrowhead Pr., *(Arrowhead Pr; 0-9604152),* 3005 Fulton, Berkeley, CA 94705 (SAN 214-2562) Tel 415-540-7010.

Arrowood Bks., *(Arrowood Bks; 0-934847),* P.O. Box 2100, Corvallis, OR 97339 (SAN 694-4531) Tel 503-753-9539; Dist. by: Pacific Pipeline, Inc., 19215 66th Ave. S., Kent, WA 98032 (SAN 208-2128) Tel 206-872-5523; Toll free: 800-426-4727; Dist. by: Far West Book Service, 3515 NE Hassalo, Portland, OR 97232 (SAN 107-7650) Tel 503-234-7664.

Arrowood Pr., Div. of A & W Promotional Bk. Corp., *(Arrowood Pr; 0-88486),* 166 Fifth Ave., New York, NY 10010 (SAN 661-8758) Tel 212-691-4688. *Imprints:* Inspirational Press (Inspirational Pr).

Arrowstar Publishing, *(Arrowstar Pub; 0-935151),* 10134 University Pk. Sta., Denver, CO 80210-1034 (SAN 695-3379) Tel 303-692-6579.

Ars Ceramica, *(Ars Ceramica; 0-89344),* P.O. Box 7366, Ann Arbor, MI 48107 (SAN 209-343X) Tel 313-429-7864; Dist. by: Keramos, P.O. Box 7500, Ann Arbor, MI 48107 (SAN 169-3670).

Ars Edition Inc., *(Ars Edition; 0-86724),* 70 Air Park Dr., Ronkonkoma, NY 11779 (SAN 220-2018) Tel 516-467-2300.

Ars Eterna Pr., *(Ars Eterna; 0-9602170),* 7627 Glen Prairie, Houston, TX 77061 (SAN 212-4785).

Ars Publishing Co., *(ARS Pub; 0-941616),* 6 W. Main St., Suite 1, Stockton, CA 95202 (SAN 239-1422) Tel 209-465-8243.

Arsenal Pr., *(Arsenal Pr; 0-9609022),* Box 12244, Atlanta, GA 30355 (SAN 241-2012) Tel 404-261-7696.

Art Adventures Press, *(Art Adventure; 0-918326),* 1286 Grizzly Peak, Berkeley, CA 94708 (SAN 210-0339) Tel 415-843-6197.

Art Alliance Pr., *(Art Alliance; 0-87982),* Dist. by: Associated University Presses, 440 Forsgate Dr., Cranbury, NJ 08512 (SAN 281-2959) Tel 609-665-4770.

Art & Antique Bks. *See* **Watson-Guptill Pubns., Inc.**

Art & Communications, *(Art & Comm; 0-943188),* 812 N. Edwards, Carlsbad, NM 88220 (SAN 240-5865) Tel 505-885-3295.

Art & Reference Hse., *(Art & Ref; 0-910156),* Brownsboro, TX 75756 (SAN 203-4921).

Art Bks. International, Ltd., *(Art Bks Intl; 0-933516; 0-88168),* 9 E. 32nd St., Suite 9C, New York, NY 10016 (SAN 214-1809) Tel 212-213-9393. *Imprints:* Pennsylvania Academy of Fine Arts, The (PA Acad Fine Arts).

Art Direction Bk. Co., Div. of Advertising Trade Pubns., Inc., *(Art Dir; 0-910158; 0-88108),* 10 E. 39th St., 6th Flr., New York, NY 10016 (SAN 208-4023) Tel 212-889-6500.

Art Directors Club of Los Angeles, *(Art Dir Club; 0-931963),* 1258 N. Highland Ave., Los Angeles, CA 90038 (SAN 686-0443) Tel 213-465-8707.

Art Education, Inc., *(Art Educ; 0-912242),* 28 E. Erie St., Blauvelt, NY 10913 (SAN 203-493X) Tel 914-359-2233.

Art Farm Gallery The, *(Art Farm Gal; 0-9611726),* RFD Five, Box 85, Lexington, VA 24450 (SAN 285-3361) Tel 703-463-7961.

Art History Pubs., *(Art History; 0-9600002),* Rte. Two, Red Wing, MN 55066 (SAN 203-4948) Tel 612-388-4046.

Art in Motion, *(Art in Motion; 0-915653),* 1092 Harlan Dr., San Jose, CA 95129 (SAN 292-3912) Tel 408-255-8843.

†**Art Institute of Chicago,** *(Art Inst Chi; 0-86559),* Michigan Ave. & Adams St., Chicago, IL 60603 (SAN 204-479X) Tel 312-443-3540; Toll free: 800-621-2736; Dist. by: Univ. of Wash. Pr., P.O. Box 50096, Seattle, WA 98105 (SAN 212-2502) Tel 206-543-8870; *CIP.*

Art Libraries Society of North America, *(Art Libs Soc; 0-942740),* 3900 E. Timrod St., Tucson, AZ 85711 (SAN 225-3291) Tel 602-881-8479.

Art Series *See* **Barnes & Noble Bks.-Imports**

Art Students League of New York, The, *(Art Students; 0-937750),* 215 W. 57th St., New York, NY 10019 (SAN 278-0593) Tel 212-247-4510.

Art/Tech, Inc., *(Art/Tech; 0-939181),* 4560 127th St., Butler, WI 53007 (SAN 662-9180) Tel 414-783-4222.

†**Art Therapy Pubns.,** *(Art Therapy; 0-9611462),* Craftsbury Common, VT 05827 (SAN 212-4017); *CIP.*

Arte Publico Pr., *(Arte Publico; 0-934770),* The Americas Review, Univ. of Houston Central Campus, Houston, TX 77004 (SAN 213-4594) Tel 713-749-4768.

Artech Assocs., *(Artech Assocs; 0-936539),* 1120 1/2 N. Kickapoo, Shawnee, OK 74801 (SAN 697-8207) Tel 405-273-0942.

†**Artech Hse., Inc.,** Subs. of Horizon Hse. Microwave, Inc., *(Artech Hse; 0-89006),* 625 Canton St., Norwood, MA 02062 (SAN 201-1441) Tel 617-769-9730; *CIP.*

†**Artefact Co., The,** *(Artefact Co; 0-943190),* 5537 Germantown Ave., Philadelphia, PA 19144 (SAN 240-5873) Tel 215-849-0100; *CIP.*

Artex Pr., *(Artex Pr; 0-930401),* 1525 Elk St., Stevens Point, WI 54481 (SAN 670-9397) Tel 715-341-6959.

Arthouse Hawaii Publishing, *(Arthse HI Pub; 0-935021),* 1436 Young St., Honolulu, HI 96814 (SAN 694-5457) Tel 808-942-7100; P.O. Box 61544, Honolulu, HI 96822 (SAN 699-6043).

Arthritis Foundation, *(Arthritis Found; 0-912423),* 1314 Spring St., NW, Atlanta, GA 30309 (SAN 267-677X) Tel 404-872-7100.

Arthur Owned Publishing, *(Arthur Owned; 0-9602112),* 606A Adams Ave., Philadelphia, PA 19120 (SAN 212-2650).

357

Names

Arthur Pubns., Inc., *(Arthur Pubns; 0-932782),* P.O. Box 23101, Jacksonville, FL 32241-3101 (SAN 211-8823) Tel 904-737-8732.

Arthur Publishing, *(Arthur Pub; 0-934849),* P.O. Box 749, Clayton, CA 94517-0749 (SAN 694-454X) Tel 415-672-4112.

Arthurian Pr., The, *(Arthurian Pr; 0-9608198),* 6 E. 45 St., Penthouse, New York City, NY 10017 (SAN 240-169X) Tel 212-286-0260.

Arti Grafiche Il Torchio, *(Arti Grafiche; 0-935194),* 123 Townsend St., Suite 450, San Francisco, CA 94107 (SAN 213-4608).

Artichoke Pr., *(Artichoke; 0-9603916),* 3274 Parkhurst Dr., Rancho Palos Verdes, CA 90274 (SAN 213-6562).

Artichoke Pubns., *(Artichoke Pub; 0-910163),* 7410 Baxtershire Dr., Dallas, TX 75230 (SAN 241-2020) Tel 214-233-9479.

Article I, *(Article One),* Merrill Rd., McCammon, ID 83250 (SAN 216-1028).

Artisan Sales, *(Artisan Sales; 0-934666),* P.O. Box 1497, Thousand Oaks, CA 91360 (SAN 211-8408) Tel 805-482-8076.

Artistic Endeavors, *(Artistic Endeavors; 0-9604500),* 24 Emerson Place, Boston, MA 02114 (SAN 207-5733) Tel 617-227-1967.

Artists & Alchemists Pubns., *(Artists & Alchemists; 0-915600),* 215 Bridgeway, Sausalito, CA 94965 (SAN 207-3978) Tel 415-332-0326; Dist. by: Swallow Press, 811 Junior Terrace, Chicago, IL 60613 (SAN 202-5671).

Artists Foundation, Inc., The, *(Artists Found; 0-932246),* 110 Broad St., Boston, MA 02110 (SAN 212-2073) Tel 617-482-8100.

Artman's Pr., *(Artmans Pr; 0-9605468),* 1511 McGee Ave., Berkeley, CA 94703 (SAN 206-8923) Tel 415-527-2710.

Artra Publishing, Inc., *(Artra Pub; 0-936725),* 628 San Dieguito Dr., Encinitas, CA 92024 (SAN 699-8666) Tel 619-436-1140; P.O. Box 575, Encinitas, CA 92024 (SAN 699-8674).

Artronix Data Corp., *(Artronix; 0-935479),* 9 E. 96th St., New York, NY 10128 (SAN 696-1304) Tel 212-860-5479.

Arts Administration Research Institute, *(Arts Admin Res Inst; 0-915440),* 75 Spark St., Cambridge, MA 02138 (SAN 223-6222); Dist. by: Publishing Center for Cultural Resources, 625 Broadway, New York, NY 10012 (SAN 274-9025).

Arts & Architecture Pr., *(Arts & Arch; 0-931228),* 2730 Wilshire Blvd., Suite 300, Santa Monica, CA 90403 (SAN 211-5050) Tel 213-395-0732.

Arts & Culture of the North, *(Arts & Culture; 0-9605898),* Box 1333, Gracie Square Sta., New York, NY 10028 (SAN 216-3322) Tel 212-879-9019.

Arts & Humanities Council of Tulsa, *(Art & Human Council Tulsa; 0-942374),* 2210 S. Main, Tulsa, OK 74114 (SAN 238-0064).

Arts & Learning Services Foundation, *(Arts & Learning; 0-938541),* 4632 Vincent Ave. S., Minneapolis, MN 55410 (SAN 661-3047) Tel 612-922-8175; Dist. by: Gary E. McCuen Pubns., Inc., 411 Mallalieu Dr., Hudson, WI 54016 (SAN 691-909X) Tel 715-386-5662.

Arts Communications, *(Arts Comm; 0-918840),* 14 E. 11th St., New York, NY 10003 (SAN 210-3427).

Arts End Bks., *(Arts End; 0-933292),* P.O. Box 162, Newton, MA 02168 (SAN 213-6082) Tel 617-965-2478.

Arts Factory, The, *(Arts Factory; 0-9615873),* 23604 49th Pl., W., Mountlake Terrace, WA 98043 (SAN 696-6802) Tel 206-778-7857; P.O. Box 55547, Seattle, WA 98155 (SAN 696-9836).

Arts Pubns, *(Arts Pubns; 0-9607458),* 80 Piedmont Ct., Larkspur, CA 94939 (SAN 238-003X) Tel 415-924-2633; Dist. by: Educational Bk. Distributor, P.O. Box 551, San Mateo, CA 94401 (SAN 158-2259).

Artus Co., The, *(Artus Co; 0-9606684),* P.O. Box 81245, Lincoln, NE 68501 (SAN 215-6687) Tel 402-477-7952.

Aruba Publishing Co., *(Aruba Pub; 0-936251),* P.O. Box 1296, Solana Beach, CA 92075 (SAN 697-3248) Tel 619-259-9867; 1106 Second St., No. 203, Encinitas, CA 92024 (SAN 697-3256).

Arvada Historical Society, *(Arvada Hist; 0-9615540),* P.O. Box 419, Arvada, CO 80001 (SAN 696-1339) Tel 303-421-0842; 3864 Hoyt St., Wheat Ridge, CO 80033 (SAN 696-1347).

Arvidson, J., Press, *(J Arvidson; 0-9602098),* P.O. Box 4022, Helena, MT 59601 (SAN 209-0848) Tel 406-442-0354.

Arwyn Map Co., *(Arwyn Map; 0-936039),* 9090 W. 74th Ave., Arvada, CO 80005 (SAN 696-9917) Tel 303-428-2864.

As-Siddiquyah Pubs., *(As-Siddiquyah; 0-935631),* 482 Franklin St., Buffalo, NY 14202 (SAN 696-1401) Tel 716-884-2606.

†**Asante Pubns.,** *(Asante Pubns; 0-9614210),* P.O. Box 1085, San Diego, CA 92112 (SAN 686-9599) Tel 619-448-6179; *CIP.*

Asbury Theological Seminary, *(Asbury Theological; 0-914368),* Wilmore, KY 40390 (SAN 208-2616).

Ascend Motivational Pubs., *(Ascend Motivational; 0-936891),* 1817 N. Hills Blvd., Suite 3004, Knoxville, TN 37917 (SAN 658-4616) Tel 615-525-5017.

Ascended Master Teaching Foundation, *(AMTF; 0-939051),* 1439 Timber Hills Rd., Mount Shasta, CA 96067 (SAN 662-8680) Tel 916-926-4913.

Aschley Pr., The, *(Aschley Pr; 0-940900),* 2898 Kingsley Rd., Cleveland, OH 44122 (SAN 223-1735) Tel 216-752-3535.

Ascii, *(Ascii; 0-9603432; 0-939414),* P.O. Box 770222, Eagle River, AK 99577-0222 (SAN 213-6015) Tel 907-688-9485.

Asclepiad Pubns., Inc., *(Asclepiad; 0-935718),* 2257 Independence, Ann Arbor, MI 48104 (SAN 213-7240).

Ascot Pr., *(Ascot Pr; 0-9613538),* P.O. Box 1304, Hartford, CT 06143-1304 (SAN 669-7194) Tel 203-633-6911.

Ascot Publishing Co., *(Ascot Pub; 0-936621),* 14001 Goldmark, Suite 240, Dallas, TX 75240 (SAN 698-1097) Tel 214-680-0170.

Ash-Kar Pr., *(Ash-Kar Pr; 0-9605308),* P.O. Box 14547, San Francisco, CA 94114 (SAN 213-0025) Tel 415-864-2430; Dist. by: Bookpeople, 2929 Fifth St., Berkeley, CA 94710 (SAN 168-9517) Tel 415-549-3030; Toll free: 800-227-1516.

Ash Lad Pr., *(Ash Lad Pr; 0-915492),* P.O. Box 396, Canton, NY 13617 (SAN 207-4265) Tel 315-386-8820.

Ash Tree, *(Ash Tree; 0-9614620),* P.O. Box 64, Woodstock, NY 12498 (SAN 691-8964) Tel 914-246-8081; Dist. by: Ash Tree Publishing, P.O. Box 64, Woodstock, NY 12498 (SAN 662-7749) Tel 914-246-8081.

Ashby, Helena, Bks., *(H Ashby Bks; 0-9614781),* Box 187, Roachdale, IN 46172 (SAN 692-9230) Tel 317-522-1309.

†**Asher-Gallant Pr.,** Div. of Caddylak Systems, Inc., *(Asher-Gallant; 0-87280),* 201 Montrose Rd., Westbury, NY 11590 (SAN 670-7947) Tel 516-333-7440; *CIP.*

Ashford Pr., *(Ashford Pr CT; 0-937992),* RFD 1, Box 182-A, Willimantic, CT 06226 (SAN 219-7650).

Ashiedu Pubns., Div. of Whiz-Z-Books, *(Ashiedu Pubns; 0-933889),* P.O. Box 741151, Dallas, TX 75374 (SAN 692-7270) Tel 214-991-7148.

Ashland Poetry Pr., *(Ashland Poetry; 0-912592),* Ashland College, Ashland, OH 44805 (SAN 203-4972) Tel 419-289-4142.

Ashlee Publishing Co., Inc., *(Ashlee Pub Co; 0-911993),* 310 Madison Ave., New York, NY 10017 (SAN 264-7125) Tel 212-682-7681.

†**Ashley Bks., Inc.,** *(Ashley Bks; 0-87949),* 30 Main St., Pt. Washington, NY 11050 (SAN 201-1409) Tel 516-883-2221; Orders to: P.O. Box 768, Pt. Washington, NY 11050 (SAN 201-1417); *CIP.*

ASHO Pr. See Bridge Pubns. Inc.

†**Ashod Pr.,** *(Ashod Pr; 0-935102),* 620 E. 20th St., 11F, New York, NY 10009 (SAN 281-2894) Tel 212-475-0711; Orders to: P.O. Box 1147 Madison Sq. Sta., New York, NY 10159 (SAN 281-2908); *CIP.*

Ashton-Tate Publishing Group, *(Ashton-Tate Pub; 0-912677),* 20101 Hamilton Ave., Torrance, CA 90502 (SAN 265-4628) Tel 213-329-8000; Toll free: 800-437-4329. Now handles all Multimate Products.

Ashworth, Lee & Assoc., *(L Ashworth; 0-918409),* P.O. Box 465, Beaumont, TX 77704 (SAN 657-6451) Tel 409-769-3410.

Asia Bk. Corp. of America, *(Asia Bk Corp; 0-940500),* 94-41 218th St., Queens Village, NY 11426 (SAN 214-493X) Tel 718-740-4612.

Asia Fellows, *(Asia Fellows; 0-9617287),* 2029 National Press Bldg., Washington, DC 20045 (SAN 663-5911) Tel 703-522-5122.

Asia Publishing Hse., *(Asia; 0-210),* Dist. by: Apt Bks., Inc., 141 E. 44th St., Suite 511, New York, NY 10017 (SAN 215-7209) Tel 212-697-0887.

Asia Resource Ctr., *(Asia Resource; 0-9604518),* P.O. Box 15275, Washington, DC 20003 (SAN 207-7647) Tel 202-547-1114.

†**Asia Society, Inc.,** *(Asia Soc; 0-87848),* 725 Park Ave., New York, NY 10021 (SAN 281-2916) Tel 212-288-6400; Dist. by: Charles E. Tuttle, Co., P.O. Box 410, 28 S. Main St., Rutland, VT 05701-0410 (SAN 213-2621) Tel 802-773-8930; *CIP.*

Asia Watch See **Fund for Free Expression**

Asian American Studies Center, UCLA, *(Asian Am Stud),* 3232 Campbell Hall, Univ. of California, Los Angeles, CA 90024 (SAN 210-7759) Tel 213-825-2968.

Asian Conservation Laboratory, *(Asian Conserv Lab; 0-940492),* Dist. by: Raiko Corp., P.O. Box 597, New York, NY 10003 (SAN 240-9542) Tel 212-783-2597.

Asian Humanities Pr., *(Asian Human Pr; 0-89581; 0-87573),* 2512 Ninth St., Suite 8, Berkeley, CA 94710 (SAN 213-6503) Tel 415-485-8065; Dist. by: Great Tradition, The, 750 Adrian Way, Suite 11, San Rafael, CA 94903 (SAN 200-5743) Tel 415-492-9382.

†**Asian Music Pubns.,** *(Asian Music Pub; 0-913360),* Dist. by Theodore Front Musical Literature, Inc., 16122 Cohasset St., Van Nuys, CA 91406 (SAN 124-2601) Tel 818-994-1902; *CIP.*

Asian Productivity Organization See **Unipub**

Asigan Limited, *(Asigan Ltd; 0-910333),* P.O. Box 10688, Beverly Hills, CA 90213 (SAN 241-2667) Tel 213-550-1982.

Askenasy, Hans, *(H Askenasy; 0-9613497),* P.O. Box 4197, Laguna Beach, CA 92652 (SAN 657-3479) Tel 714-896-7251.

Askon Publishing Co., Subs. of Askon Corp., *(Askon Pub; 0-931609),* P.O. Box 3156, Abilene, TX 79604 (SAN 683-678X) Tel 915-672-3640; 1025 Cypress, Abilene, TX 79604 (SAN 658-2702).

ASME Gear Research Institute, *(ASME Gear Res; 0-9617215),* P.O. Box 353, Naperville, IL 60566 (SAN 663-4125); N. Washington at East-West Tollway, Naperville, IL 60566 (SAN 663-4133) Tel 312-355-4200.

Asociacion nacional pro personas mayores, *(Assn Personas Mayores; 0-913139),* 2727 W. Sixth St., Suite 270, Los Angeles, CA 90057 (SAN 223-7768).

Aspect Foundation, *(Aspect Found; 0-939073),* 39 W. 14th St., Rm. 404, New York, NY 10011 (SAN 662-913X) Tel 212-206-8463.

Aspen Art, *(Aspen Art; 0-9601120),* 401 Ctr., Evanston, WY 82930 (SAN 210-167X) Tel 307-789-9879.

Aspen Ctr. for Visual Arts, *(Aspen Ctr Visual Arts; 0-934324),* 590 N. Mill St., Aspen, CO 81611 (SAN 274-9025) Tel 303-925-8050; Dist. by: Publishing Ctr. for Cultural Resources, 625 Broadway, New York, NY 10012 (SAN 274-9025).

†**Aspen Institute for Humanistic Studies,** *(Aspen Inst Human; 0-89843; 0-915436),* P.O. Box 150, Queenstown, MD 21658 (SAN 213-0033); *CIP.*

Aspen Productions, *(Aspen Prods; 0-913635),* 7501 Monogram Dr., Sacramento, CA 95842 (SAN 286-0384) Tel 916-344-2246.

Aspen Pubs., Inc., Affil. of Wolters Samson Group, *(Aspen Pub; 0-912862; 0-89443; 0-87189; 0-912654),* 1600 Research Blvd., Rockville, MD 20850 (SAN 203-4999) Tel 301-251-5000; Toll free: 800-638-8437.

Aspen West Publishing, *(Aspen West Pub; 0-9615390),* P.O. Box 1245, Sandy, UT 84091 (SAN 694-2318) Tel 801-571-7435; Orders to: 9267 S. Tortellini Dr., Sandy, UT 84902 (SAN 699-6019).

Asphalt Institute, *(Asphalt Inst),* Asphalt Inst Bldg., College Park, MD 20740 (SAN 224-6627) Tel 301-277-4258.

Assembling Pr., Affil. of Rutgers University Mason Gross School of the Arts, (Assembling Pr; 0-915066), P.O. Box 1967, Brooklyn, NY 11202 (SAN 201-1360).

Assessment Research, (Assessment Res; 0-937987), P.O. Box 8900-330, Salem, OR 97303-0890 (SAN 659-7319); 2335 Manzanita Dr., NE, Salem, OR 97303 (SAN 659-7327) Tel 503-390-6690.

Assistance League of Corvallis, (Assistance League; 0-9616597), 534 NW Fourth St., Corvallis, OR 97330 (SAN 659-4891) Tel 503-753-0408.

Associated Air Balance Council, (Assoc Air Bal; 0-910289), 1518 K Street, N.W., Washington, DC 20005 (SAN 267-7113) Tel 202-737-0202.

Associated Bk. Pubs., Inc., (Assoc Bk Pubs; 0-910164), P.O. Box 5657, Scottsdale, AZ 85261 (SAN 212-2081) Tel 602-998-5223.

Associated Booksellers, Affil. of Merrimack Publishing Corp., (Assoc Bk; 0-87497), 562 Boston Ave., Bridgeport, CT 06610 (SAN 203-5014) Tel 203-333-7268; Toll free: 800-232-2224.

Associated Collegiate Press, Div. of National Scholastic Press Association, (Assoc Collegiate Pr), 620 Rarig Center, 330 21st Ave. S., Univ. of Minnesota, Minneapolis, MN 55455 (SAN 225-8323).

Associated Creative Writers, (Assoc Creative Writers; 0-933362), 9231 Molly Woods Ave., La Mesa, CA 92041 (SAN 212-8292) Tel 619-460-4107.

Associated Equipment Distributors, (Assn Equip Distrs), 615 W. 22nd St., Oak Brook, IL 60521 (SAN 224-0548) Tel 312-574-0650.

Associated Faculty Pr., Affil. of Kraus Reprint & Periodical, (Assoc Faculty Pr; 0-86733; 0-87198; 0-8046), Rte. 100, Millwood, NY 10546 (SAN 217-4979) Tel 914-762-2200; Orders to: 19 W. 36th St., New York, NY 10018 (SAN 694-9495) Tel 212-307-1300. Imprints: National University Publications (Natl U).

Associated General Contractors of America, (Assn Gen Con), 1957 E St. NW, Washington, DC 20006 (SAN 224-6880) Tel 203-393-2040.

Associated Grantmakers of Massachusetts, Inc., (Assoc Grant; 0-912427), Suite 840, 294 Washington St., Boston, MA 02108 (SAN 265-1807) Tel 617-426-2606.

Associated Human Resources, Subs. of Ingram Laboratories, Inc., (Assoc Human Res; 0-9613878), 3 Meade St., Buckhannon, WV 26201 (SAN 681-9621) Tel 304-472-3261.

Associated Marine, Affil. of Associated Insurance Administrators, Inc., (Assoc Marine; 0-9613304), P.O. Box 5421, San Mateo, CA 94402 (SAN 654-2131) Tel 415-349-1341.

Associated Media Cos., Ltd, (Assoc Media Cos; 0-938731), 4350 Via Dolce, No. 311, Marina del Rey, CA 90292 (SAN 661-7107) Tel 213-821-2011.

Associated Parents Group of Hillsborough, Inc., (Assoc Parents; 0-9616566), 300 El Cerito Ave., Hillsborough, CA 94010 (SAN 659-4174) Tel 415-340-1565.

†Associated Press, (Assoc Pr; 0-917360), 50 Rockefeller Plaza, New York, NY 10020 (SAN 206-7137) Tel 212-621-1500; CIP.

Associated Printers, (Assoc Print), Grafton-Grand Forks, Box 471, Grafton, ND 58237 (SAN 209-5254) Tel 701-352-0640.

Associated Pubns., (Assoc Pubns; 0-9608806), P.O. Box 728, Glendora, CA 91740 (SAN 238-2407).

Associated University Presses, (Assoc Univ Prs; 0-8453), 440 Forsgate Dr., Cranbury, NJ 08512 (SAN 281-2959) Tel 609-655-4770. Imprints: Cornwall Books (Cornwall Bks).

Associated Writing Programs, (Assoc Writing Progs; 0-936266), c/o Old Dominion Univ., Norfolk, VA 23508 (SAN 214-0993) Tel 804-440-3840.

Associates for Youth Dev., Inc., (Assocs Youth Dev; 0-913951), P.O. Box 36748, Tucson, AZ 85740 (SAN 286-7214) Tel 602-297-1056; 1935 Harran Cir., Tucson, AZ 85704 (SAN 286-7222).

Associates in Thanatology, (Assocs Thanatology; 0-9607928), 115 Blue Rock Rd., South Yarmouth, MA 02664 (SAN 281-2967) Tel 617-394-6520; Dist. by: DeVorss & Co., P.O. Box 550, 1046 Princeton Dr., Marina del Rey, CA 90294 (SAN 168-9886) Tel 213-870-7487; Dist. by: Inland Bk. Co., P.O. Box 261, East Haven, CT 06512 (SAN 200-4151) Tel 203-467-4257.

Associates of the James Ford Bell Library, (Assocs James Bell; 0-9601798), 472 Wilson Library, Univ. of Minnesota, 309 19th Ave. S., Minneapolis, MN 55455 (SAN 209-1763) Tel 612-373-2888.

Associates of Urbanus, (Assocs Urbanus; 0-930957), P.O. Box 457, 36200 Freedom Rd., Farmington, MI 48024 (SAN 678-8750) Tel 313-474-9110.

Association for Advancement of Behavior Therapy, (Assn Advance Behav Therapy), 15 W. 36th St., New York, NY 10018 (SAN 224-4357).

†Association for Birth Psychology, (Assn Birth Psych; 0-9612182), 444 E. 82nd St., New York, NY 10028 (SAN 289-114X) Tel 212-988-6617; CIP.

Association for Brain Tumor Research, (Assn Brain Tumor; 0-9616451), 6232 N Pulaski Rd., Suite 200, Chicago, IL 60646 (SAN 224-280X) Tel 312-544-4941.

Association for Business Communication, The, (Assn Busn Comm; 0-931874), 100 English Bldg., 608 S. Wright St., Urbana, IL 61801 (SAN 211-9382) Tel 217-333-1007.

†Association for Childhood Education International, (ACEI; 0-87173), 11141 Georgia Ave., Suite 200, Wheaton, MD 20902 (SAN 201-2200) Tel 301-942-2443; CIP.

Association for Consumer Research, (Assn Consumer Res; 0-915552), Graduate School of Managment, 632 TNRB, Brigham Young Univ., Provo, UT 84602 (SAN 207-3838) Tel 801-378-2080.

Association for Education & Rehabilitation of the Blind & Visually Impaired, (Assn Ed Rehab Blind; 0-934677), 206 N. Washington St., Suite 320, Alexandria, VA 22314 (SAN 227-6372) Tel 703-548-1884.

†Association for Educational Communications & Technology, (Assn Ed Comm Tech; 0-89240), 1126 16th St., NW, Washington, DC 20036 (SAN 207-3277) Tel 202-466-4780; CIP.

Association for Educational Data Systems, (Assn Educ Data), 1201 16th St. NW, Washington, DC 20036 (SAN 236-2074) Tel 202-822-7845.

Association for Experiential Education, (Assn Exper Ed), Box 249 CU, Boulder, CO 80309 (SAN 225-7742) Tel 303-492-1547.

Association for Holistic Health, (Assn Holistic; 0-915407), P.O. Box 9532, San Diego, CA 92109 (SAN 263-9246) Tel 619-275-2694.

†Association for Information & Image Management, (Assn Inform & Image Mgmt; 0-89258), 1100 Wayne Ave., Silver Spring, MD 20910 (SAN 202-1021) Tel 301-587-8202; CIP.

Assn. for Integrative Studies, The, (Assoc Integ; 0-9615764), Miami Univ., Schl. of Interdisciplinary Studies, 185 Peabody Hall, Oxford, OH 45056 (SAN 696-1460) Tel 513-529-6992.

Association for Jewish Studies, (Assn for Jewish Studies; 0-915938), Queens College, Dept. of History, Flushing, NY 11367 (SAN 669-0084); Dist. by: Ktav Publishing Hse., 900 Jefferson St., Box 6249, Hoboken, NJ 07030 (SAN 669-0092) Tel 201-963-9524.

Association for Library Service to Children, Div. of American Library Association, (Assn Library Serv), 50 E. Huron St., Chicago, IL 60611 (SAN 233-464X) Tel 312-944-6780; Toll free: 800-545-2433.

Association for Northern California Records & Research, (Assn NC Records), P.O. Box 3024, Chico, CA 95927 (SAN 267-8063) Tel 916-895-5710.

Association for Population Family Planning International, (Assn Pop Lib), 105 Madison Ave., New York, NY 10016 (SAN 267-808X).

Association for Practitioners in Infection Control, (Assn Practic Infection), 505 E. Hawley St., Mundelein, IL 60060 (SAN 689-4585) Tel 312-949-6052.

Association for Public Justice Education Fund, (Assn Public Justice; 0-936456), 806 15th St. NW, Suite 218, Washington, DC 20005 (SAN 214-1000) Tel 202-737-2110.

Association for Research & Enlightenment, Inc. See A.R.E. Pr.

Association for Retarded Citizens of the U. S., (Assn Retarded Citizens), 2501 Ave. J, P.O. Box 6109, Arlington, TX 76011 (SAN 224-0564) Tel 817-640-0204.

Association for Study of Higher Education, (Assn Study Higher Ed; 0-913317), 1 Dupont Cir., Suite 630, Washington, DC 20036 (SAN 225-803X) Tel 202-296-2597.

Association for Supervision & Curriculum Development, (Assn Supervision; 0-87120), 125 N. West St., Alexandria, VA 22314 (SAN 201-1352) Tel 703-549-9110.

†Association for Systems Management, (Assn Syst Mgmt; 0-934356), 24587 Bagley Rd., Cleveland, OH 44138 (SAN 201-7091) Tel 216-243-6900; CIP.

Association for the Advancement of Medical Instrumentation, (Assn Adv Med Instrn; 0-910275), 1901 N. Ft. Myer Dr., Suite 602, Arlington, VA 22209-1699 (SAN 224-3407) Tel 703-525-4890.

Association for the Care of Children's Health, (Assn Care Child), 3615 Wisconsin Ave., NW, Washington, DC 20016 (SAN 267-8314) Tel 202-244-1801.

Association for the Preservation of Virginia Antiquities, The, (Assn Preserv VA; 0-917565), 2300 E. Grace St., Richmond, VA 23230 (SAN 657-1247) Tel 804-359-0239.

Association for the Study of Family Living, The, (Assn Family Living; 0-9602670), P.O. Box 130, Brooklyn, NY 11208 (SAN 212-8772) Tel 718-647-7406.

Association for the Study of the Nationalities (USSR) & East Europe, (Assn Study Nat; 0-910895), City College of New York, Russian Area Studies Program, Convent Ave. at 138th St., New York, NY 10031 (SAN 263-2470) Tel 212-690-6739.

Association for Transarmament Studies, (Assn Trans; 0-9614256), 3636 Lafayette, Omaha, NE 68131 (SAN 687-1127) Tel 402-558-2085.

Association for Union Democracy, (Assn Union Demo; 0-9602244), 30 Third Ave., Brooklyn, NY 11217 (SAN 227-4337) Tel 718-855-6650.

Association for University Business & Economic Research, (Assn U Busn & Econ Res), Univ. of Alabama, Ctr. for Business & Economic Research, P.O. Box AK, University, AL 35486 (SAN 236-1299) Tel 205-348-6191.

Assn. of Academic Health Sciences Library Directors, (AAHSLD; 0-938505), 1133 M.D. Anderson Blvd., Houston, TX 77030 (SAN 267-8373) Tel 713-797-1230; Stanford Univ. Medical Ctr., Stanford, CA 94305 (SAN 658-0165).

Assn. of American Colleges, (Assn Am Coll; 0-911696), 1818 R St. NW, Washington, DC 20009 (SAN 224-0572) Tel 202-387-3760.

†Association of American Geographers, (Assn Am Geographers; 0-89291), 1710 16th St., NW, Washington, DC 20009 (SAN 201-6796) Tel 202-234-1450; CIP.

†Association of American Law Schls., (Assn Am Law Schls), 1 Dupont Cir., NW, Suite 370, Washington, DC 20036 (SAN 225-8382) Tel 202-296-8891; CIP.

†Assn. of American Pubs., Inc., (AAP; 0-933636), 220 E. 23rd St., 2nd Flr., New York, NY 10010 (SAN 204-4714) Tel 212-689-8920; CIP.

Association of American State Geologists, (FL Bureau Geology), Dept. of Natural Resources, Geological Survey, P.O. Box 30028, Lansing, MI 48909 (SAN 224-0580) Tel 517-373-3014.

Association of Arab-American University Graduates, (Assn Arab-Amer U Grads; 0-937694), 556 Trapelo Rd., Belmont, MA 02178 (SAN 240-0820) Tel 617-484-5483. Imprints: A A U G Press (AAUG Pr).

Association of Artist-Run Galleries, (Assn Artist Gal), 152 Wooster St., New York, NY 10012 (SAN 267-8632).

Names

Association of Bay Area Governments, *(Assn Bay Area)*, Metrocenter, Eighth & Oak Sts., Oakland, CA 94604 (SAN 226-4374) Tel 415-464-7914; P.O. Box 2050, Oakland, CA 94604 (SAN 669-0114).

Association of Black Psychologists, *(Assn Black Psych)*, 1118 Ninth St., NW, Washington, DC 20001 (SAN 224-0610) Tel 202-289-3663; P.O. Box 2929, Washington, DC 20013 (SAN 669-0122).

Association of California School Administrators, *(Assn Calif Sch Admin)*, Old Bayshore Hwy., Burlingame, CA 94010 (SAN 203-1310) Tel 415-692-4300.

Association of Christian Librarians, *(Assn Chr Libs)*, Houghton College - Buffalo Suburban Campus, 910 Union Rd., West Seneca, NY 14224 (SAN 217-2267).

Association of Christian Pubs. & Booksellers, Inc., *(Assn Christian Pub; 0-943258)*, 3360 NW 110th St., Miami, FL 33167 (SAN 240-3390).

Association of College & Research Libraries, Div. of American Library Assn., *(Assn Coll & Res Libs; 0-8389)*, 50 E. Huron St., Chicago, IL 60611 (SAN 225-3305) Tel 312-944-6780; Toll free: 800-545-2433; Toll free: 800-545-2445 (in IL); Orders to: ALA Publishing Services, 50 E. Huron St., Chicago, IL 60611 (SAN 662-717X).

Association of College, University & Community Arts Administrators, *(Assn Coll Arts Admin)*, 6225 University Ave., Madison, WI 53705-1099 (SAN 225-8498) Tel 608-233-7400.

Association of Consulting Chemists & Chemical Engineers, *(Assn Chemists)*, 50 E. 41st St., Suite 92, New York, NY 10017 (SAN 267-9000) Tel 212-684-6255.

Association of Departments of Foreign Languages, *(Assn Dept Lang)*, 10 Astor Pl., New York, NY 10003 (SAN 267-9094) Tel 212-614-6319.

Association of Energy Engineers, *(Assn Energy Eng)*, 4025 Pleasantdale Rd., Suite 340, Atlanta, GA 30340 (SAN 225-1663) Tel 404-447-5083.

Association of Environmental Engineering Professors, *(Assn Environ Eng; 0-917567)*, Univ. of Texas, Austin, Dept. of Civil Engineering, ECJ8.6, Austin, TX 78712 (SAN 236-2554).

Association of Federal Investigators, *(Assn Fed Investigators)*, 810 18th St., NW, Washington, DC 20006 (SAN 225-0799).

Assn. of Former Intelligence Officers, *(Assn Former Inter)*, 6723 Whittier Ave., Suite 303A, McLean, VA 22101 (SAN 689-6197) Tel 703-790-0320.

Association of Governing Boards of Universities & Colleges, *(Assn Gov Bds)*, 1 Dupont Cir., Suite 400, Washington, DC 20036 (SAN 267-9361) Tel 202-296-8400.

Association of Independent Camps, Inc., *(Assn Ind Camps)*, 60 Madison Ave., New York, NY 10010 (SAN 224-5531) Tel 212-679-3230.

Association of Information Systems Professionals, *(Assn Info Sys; 0-935220; 0-928397)*, 1015 N. York Rd., Willow Grove, PA 19090 (SAN 213-5191) Tel 215-657-6300.

Association of Interpretive Naturalists Incorporated, *(Assn Interp Naturalist)*, 6700 Needwood Rd., Derwood, MD 20855 (SAN 226-6644) Tel 301-948-8844.

Association of Interstate Commerce Commission Practitioners, *(Assn ICC Practitioners)*, 1112 ICC Bldg., 12th St. & Constitution Ave. NW., Suite 310, Washington, DC 20423 (SAN 224-2230) Tel 202-783-9432.

Association of Labor-Management Administrators & Consultants on Alcoholism, *(ALMACA)*, 1800 N. Kent St., Suite 907, Arlington, VA 22209 (SAN 689-6383) Tel 703-522-6272.

Association of Muslim Scientists & Engineers, *(Assn Muslim Sci; 0-916581)*, P.O. Box 38, Plainfield, IN 46168 (SAN 296-4449) Tel 317-839-8157.

Association of National Advertisers, Inc., *(Assn Natl Advertisers)*, 155 E. 44th St., New York, NY 10017 (SAN 224-6112).

†Association of Official Analytical Chemists, *(Assoc Official; 0-935584)*, 1111 N. 19th St., Suite 210, Arlington, VA 22209 (SAN 260-3411) Tel 703-522-3032; *CIP.*

Association of Operating Room Nurses, Inc., *(Assn Oper Rm Nurses; 0-939583)*, 10170 E. Mississippi Ave., Denver, CO 80231 (SAN 224-3814) Tel 303-755-6300.

Association of Part-Time Professionals, *(Assn Part-Time; 0-917449)*, Box 3419, Alexandria, VA 22302 (SAN 689-6618) Tel 703-734-7975.

Association of Physical Plant Administrators of Universities & Colleges, *(Assn Phys Plant Admin; 0-913359)*, 1446 Duke St, Alexandria, VA 22314-3492 (SAN 223-7776) Tel 703-684-1446.

Association of Physicians Assistant Programs, *(Assn Phys Asst Prog)*, 1117 N. 19th St., Arlington, VA 22209 (SAN 224-3539).

Association of Professional Genealogists, *(Assn Prof Genealogists)*, 57 WS Temple, Suite 225, Salt Lake City, UT 84101 (SAN 224-0750) Tel 801-532-3327; P.O. Box 11601, Salt Lake City, UT 84147 (SAN 669-0157); Dist. by: Genealogical Institute, 57 WS Temple, Suite 255, Salt Lake City, UT 84101 (SAN 207-1959).

Association of Records Managers & Administrators, Inc., *(Assn Recs Mgrs & Admin; 0-933887)*, 4200 Somerset Dr., Suite 215, Prairie Village, KS 66208 (SAN 224-9316) Tel 913-341-3808.

Association of Research Libraries, *(Assn Res Lib)*, 1527 New Hampshire Ave. NW, Washington, DC 20036 (SAN 225-3321).

Association of Schl. Business Officials International, *(Assn Sch Busn; 0-910170)*, 1760 Reston Ave., Suite 411, Reston, VA 22090 (SAN 204-5478) Tel 703-478-0405.

Association of School Business Officials of the United States & Canada *See Association of Schl. Business Officials International*

Association of Sexologists, The, *(Assn Sexologists; 0-939902)*, 1523 Franklin St., San Francisco, CA 94109 (SAN 216-7867).

Association of Soil & Foundation Engineers, *(Assn Soil & Found Engrs)*, 8811 Coleville Rd., Suite 225, Silver Spring, MD 20910 (SAN 224-0769) Tel 301-565-2733.

Assn. of Specialized Cooperative Library Agencies, *(ASCLA)*, 50 E. Huron St., Chicago, IL 60611 (SAN 233-4658).

Association of Systematics Collections, *(Assn Syst Coll; 0-942924)*, C/O Univ. of Kansas, Museum of Natural History, Lawrence, KS 66045 (SAN 232-5853) Tel 913-864-4867.

Association of Teacher Educators, *(Assn Tchr Ed)*, 1900 Association Dr., Suite ATE, Reston, VA 22091 (SAN 203-7904) Tel 703-620-3110.

Association of Teachers of Latin American Studies, *(Assn Tchrs Latin Amer; 0-938305)*, 252-58 63rd Ave., Little Neck, NY 11362 (SAN 689-7428) Tel 718-428-1237.

Association of the Bar of the City of New York, *(Assn Bar NYC)*, 42 W. 44th St., New York, NY 10036 (SAN 204-4706) Tel 212-382-6650.

Association of Third World Studies, *(Assn Third Wld; 0-931971)*, P.O. Box 1232, Americus, GA 31709 (SAN 685-3072) Tel 912-924-8287.

Association of Trial Lawyers of America, *(Assn Trial Lawyers; 0-933067)*, 1050 31st St., NW, Washington, DC 20007 (SAN 226-4625).

Association of Trial Lawyers of America, Education Fund, *(Assn Trial Ed; 0-941916)*, 1050 31st St., NW, Washington, DC 20007 (SAN 238-2156) Tel 202-965-3500; Orders to: P.O. Box 3717, Washington, DC 20007 (SAN 661-9487).

Association of Ukrainian Writers in Exile Slovo, *(Assn Ukrainian Writers; 0-930013)*, 6509 Lawnton Ave., Philadelphia, PA 19126 (SAN 669-7208) Tel 215-924-9147.

†Association on American Indian Affairs, Inc., *(Assn Am Indian)*, 95 Madison Ave., New York, NY 10016 (SAN 204-4730) Tel 212-689-8720; *CIP.*

Assurance Pubs., *(Assurance Pubs; 0-932940)*, 330 Clover Ln., Garland, TX 75043 (SAN 213-005X).

Astara, Inc., *(Astara; 0-918936)*, 800 W. Arrow Hwy., P.O. Box 5003, Upland, CA 91785 (SAN 207-6446) Tel 714-981-4941.

†Aster Publishing Co., Div. of Health Management Institute, *(Aster Pub Co; 0-933019)*, P.O. Box 10752, Merrillville, IN 46411 (SAN 689-5387) Tel 219-980-6554; Dist. by: Biofeedback & Stress Management Services, P.O. Box 95, Schererville, IN 46375 (SAN 200-5271) Tel 503-726-1200; *CIP.*

Aster Publishing Corp., *(Aster Pub Corp; 0-943330)*, 320 N. A St., Springfield, OR 97477 (SAN 240-4869).

Asthma & Allergy Foundation of America, *(Asthma & Allergy)*, 1835 K St. NW, Suite P-900, Washington, DC 20006 (SAN 227-6011) Tel 202-293-2950.

Astonisher Pr., *(Astonisher Pr; 0-937255)*, P.O. Box 80635, Lincoln, NE 68501 (SAN 659-0152) Tel 402-474-6227; 540 W. Joel, Lincoln, NE 68521 (SAN 659-0160).

Astor-Honor, Inc., *(Astor-Honor; 0-8392)*, 48 E. 43rd St., New York, NY 10017 (SAN 203-5022).

Astro Artz, *(Astro Artz; 0-937122)*, 240 S. Broadway, 5th Fl., Los Angeles, CA 90012 (SAN 215-6229) Tel 213-687-7362.

Astro Dynasty Publishing Hse., *(Astro Dynasty Pub Hse; 0-914725)*, 270 N. Canon Dr., No. 1021, Beverly Hills, CA 90210 (SAN 291-8307) Tel 213-274-7249.

Astro Press, *(Astro Pr TX; 0-9608568)*, P.O. Box 820399, Dallas, TX 75382 (SAN 238-2415).

Astro Pubs., *(Astro Pubs; 0-941272)*, 1332 University Blvd. N., Jacksonville, FL 32211 (SAN 238-9096) Tel 904-743-7344.

Astroart Enterprises, *(Astroart Ent; 0-917814)*, P.O. Box 503, South Houston, TX 77587 (SAN 203-5030) Tel 713-649-6601.

Astrolabe, Div. of Astro-Graphics Services, Inc., *(Astrolabe SW; 0-87199; 0-913637)*, P.O. Box 28, Orleans, MA 02653 (SAN 670-7416); 45 S. Orleans Rd., Orleans, MA 02653 (SAN 662-2038) Tel 617-255-0510; Dist. by: ACS Pubns., Inc., P.O. Box 16430, San Diego, CA 92116-0430 (SAN 208-5380) Tel 619-297-9203; Toll free: 800-826-1085; Toll free: 800-525-1786 (in CA).

Astrologer on Wheels, Inc., *(Astrol Wheels; 0-940044)*, 141 E. 55th St., New York, NY 10022 (SAN 220-2034); P.O. Box 5255, F. D. R. Sta., New York, NY 10150 (SAN 220-2042).

Astrologer's Library *See Inner Traditions International, Ltd.*

Astrologize America, *(Astrologize Am; 0-939585)*, P.O. Box 884561, San Francisco, CA 94188 (SAN 663-5113); 68 Sycamore St., San Francisco, CA 94110 (SAN 663-5121) Tel 415-558-8004.

†AstroMedia, Div. of Kalmbach Publishing Co., *(AstroMedia; 0-913135)*, 1027 N 7th St., Milwaukee, WI 53233 (SAN 282-9703) Tel 414-272-2060; Dist. by: Tide-Mark Pr., P.O. Box 813, Hartford, CT 06142 (SAN 222-1802) Tel 203-289-0363; *CIP.*

Astronomical Society of the Pacific, *(Astron Soc Pacific; 0-937707)*, 1290 24th Ave., San Francisco, CA 94122 (SAN 225-1426) Tel 415-661-8660.

Astronomical Workshop, *(Astron Wkshp; 0-934546)*, Furman Univ., Greenville, SC 29613 (SAN 209-5602) Tel 803-294-2208.

Astropoint Research Assocs., *(Astropoint Res; 0-9615454)*, 5020 S. Lake Shore Dr., Chicago, IL 60615 (SAN 695-7382) Tel 312-493-3595.

Astrosonics Research Institute, *(Astrosonics; 0-939192)*, 11037 1/2 Freeman Ave., Lennox, CA 90304 (SAN 220-1631) Tel 213-673-4649.

Astrosophical Research & Esoteric Publishing Oddities Corp., *(AREPO; 0-938359)*, P.O. Box 6334, FDR Sta., New York, NY 10150 (SAN 659-736X); 618 49th St., Brooklyn, NY 11220 (SAN 659-7378) Tel 718-426-2957.

Asylum's Press/Language, *(Asylums Pr-Language; 0-940220)*, 464 Amsterdam Ave., New York, NY 10024 (SAN 220-3235) Tel 212-799-4475.

At Speed Press, *(At Speed Pr; 0-940046)*, P.O. Box 5400, Santa Barbara, CA 93108 (SAN 220-2050) Tel 805-966-2814; Dist. by: Motorbooks International, P.O. Box 2, 729 Prospect Ave., Osceola, WI 54020 (SAN 212-3304) Tel 715-294-3345.

Names

At-Swim Pr., *(At-Swim; 0-939254),* c/o Facsimile Book Shop, 16 W. 55th St., New York, NY 10019 (SAN 215-3084) Tel 212-581-2672.

At The Sign Of The Cock, *(At The Sign; 0-9613491),* 2341 Brixton Rd., Columbus, OH 43221 (SAN 657-3231) Tel 614-488-3986.

Ata Books, *(Ata Bks; 0-931688),* 1928 Stuart St., Berkeley, CA 94703 (SAN 211-4801) Tel 415-841-9613.

A T A P Corp., *(ATAP Corp; 0-942026),* 7125 Stagecoach Trail, Knoxville, TN 37919 (SAN 238-6313) Tel 615-690-3130.

Ataraxia, *(Ataraxia; 0-915109),* 5401 Hyde Park Blvd., Chicago, IL 60615 (SAN 289-7296) Tel 312-241-7694.

Atcom, Inc., *(Atcom; 0-915260),* 2315 Broadway, New York, NY 10024 (SAN 208-4252) Tel 212-873-5900.

Atheist Association, *(Atheist Assn),* Box 2832, San Diego, CA 92112 (SAN 226-0077).

Athena Press, Inc., *(Athena Pr; 0-9602736),* P.O. Box 776, Vienna, VA 22180 (SAN 213-0076).

Athena Pr., The, *(Athena Pr ND; 0-940730),* 602 S. Fourth St., Grand Forks, ND 58201 (SAN 219-7081) Tel 701-775-9156.

Athena Pubns., *(Athena Pubns; 0-932950),* P.O. Box 61, West Peterborough, NH 03468 (SAN 212-7156).

†**Athenaeum of Philadelphia,** *(Athenaeum Phila; 0-916530),* 219 S. Sixth St., E. Washington Square, Philadelphia, PA 19106 (SAN 208-5402) Tel 215-925-2688; *CIP.*

Atheneum Pubs., Subs. of Scribner Bk. Cos., Inc., *(Atheneum; 0-689),* 115 Fifth Ave., New York, NY 10003 (SAN 201-0011) Tel 212-614-1300; Toll free: 800-257-5755; Dist. by: Riverside Distribution Ctr., Front & Brown Sts., Riverside, NJ 08075 (SAN 200-5018). *Imprints:* Aladdin Books (Aladdin); Argo Books (Argo); Children's Books (Childrens Bk); McElderry Book (McElderry Bk).

Athletic Institute, *(Athletic Inst; 0-87670),* 200 N. Castlewood Dr., North Palm Beach, FL 33408 (SAN 203-5065) Tel 305-842-3600; Dist. by: Sterling Publishing Co., 2 Park Ave., New York, NY 10016 (SAN 211-6324) Tel 212-502-7160.

Athletic Pr., *(Athletic; 0-87095),* P.O. Box 80250, Pasadena, CA 91108 (SAN 203-5057) Tel 213-283-3446.

Athletics Congress/USA, The, *(Athletics Cong; 0-939254),* P.O. Box 120, Indianapolis, IN 46206 (SAN 220-164X) Tel 317-638-9155.

Atkins, A., Publishing Co., *(A Atkins Pub; 0-9617122),* 612 W. Illinois St., Oblong, IL 62449 (SAN 662-6866) Tel 618-592-4288.

Atkins Video Society, *(Atkins Video; 0-9616437),* P.O. Box 120355, Nashville, TN 37212 (SAN 659-0179) Tel 914-763-8177; 1013 17th Ave., S., Nashville, TN 37212 (SAN 659-0187).

Atkinson, Mary D., *(Atkinson; 0-937436),* 10405B 46th Ave., Beltsville, MD 20705 (SAN 215-6091) Tel 301-595-5138.

Atlanta Professional Women's Directory, Inc., *(Atlanta Pro; 0-935197),* 1103 N. Hill Pkwy., Atlanta, GA 30341 (SAN 695-7331) Tel 404-524-5121; Orders to: P.O. Box 28122, Atlanta, GA 30358 (SAN 662-779X).

Atlanta TakeOut, Div. of Lifestyle Publications Inc., *(Atlanta TakeOut; 0-9614544),* P.O. Box 720635, Atlanta, GA 30358 (SAN 691-7925) Tel 404-256-6455.

Atlanta's Best Buys, *(Atlantas Best; 0-9608196),* P.O. Box 11662, Atlanta, GA 30355 (SAN 240-1878) Tel 404-261-0566.

Atlantic Coastal Equity Corp., *(Atlantic Coast; 0-935635),* 936 47th Ave., Vero Beach, FL 32960 (SAN 696-1584) Tel 305-569-4364.

Atlantic Council of the United States, *(Atlantic Council US; 0-88410),* 1616 H St. NW, Washington, DC 20006 (SAN 225-6282) Tel 202-347-9353; Dist. by: Oelgeschlager, Gunn & Hain, 131 Clarendon St., Boston, MA 02116 (SAN 213-6937) Tel 617-437-9620.

Atlantic Law Bk. Co., *(Atlantic Law),* 445 Capitol Ave., Hartford, CT 06106 (SAN 204-4692) Tel 203-527-1313.

†**Atlantic Monthly Pr.,** Div. of Atlantic Monthly Co., *(Atlantic Monthly; 0-87113),* 8 Arlington St., Boston, MA 02116 (SAN 226-4587) Tel 617-536-9500; Toll free: 800-343-9204; Dist. by: Little, Brown & Co., 34 Beacon St., Boston, MA 02108 (SAN 200-2205) Tel 617-227-0730; *CIP.*

Atlantic Publishing, *(Atlantic Lakeland; 0-938677),* 1034 S. Florida Ave., Lakeland, FL 33803 (SAN 661-3829) Tel 813-688-8000.

†**Atlantic Publishing Co.,** *(Atlantic Pub; 0-932349),* P.O. Box 18126, Jacksonville, FL 32229 (SAN 687-3618) Tel 912-638-3559; *CIP.*

Atlantic Publishing Co., *(Atlantic Pub Co; 0-937866),* P.O. Box 67, Tabor City, NC 28463 (SAN 215-6237) Tel 919-653-3153.

Atlantic Publishing Co., *(Atlantic FL; 0-910627),* P.O. Box 1197, Silver Springs, FL 32688 (SAN 268-1250) Tel 904-351-0991.

Atlantic Reef Committee, The, Div. of Marine Geology & Geophysics, *(Univ Miami A R C; 0-932981),* Univ. of Miami, Fisher Island Sta., Miami Beach, FL 33139 (SAN 239-5134) Tel 305-672-1840.

Atlantic Sunrise Publishing, Affil. of Atlantic City Diary, *(Atlantic Sunrise; 0-9614585),* 165 Atlantic Ave., McKee City, NJ 08232 (SAN 691-764X) Tel 609-641-1222; Orders to: P.O. Box 574, Pleasantville, NJ 08232 (SAN 662-2895) Tel 609-641-1222.

Atlantis Editions, *(Atlantis),* 11 E. 73rd St., New York, NY 10021 (SAN 209-312X).

Atlantis Editions, *(Atlantis Edns; 0-910174; 0-917183),* P.O. Box 18326, Philadelphia, PA 19120 (SAN 207-5849) Tel 408-625-6697.

Atlantis Publishing Corp., *(Atlan Pub Corp; 0-936158),* P.O. Box 59467, Dallas, TX 75229 (SAN 223-3959).

Atlas Powder Co., Div. of Tyler Corp., *(Atlas Powder; 0-9616284),* 15301 Dallas Pkwy. Colonnade, Suite 1200, Dallas, TX 75248-4692 (SAN 658-5833) Tel 717-386-4121.

Atlas Publishing Corp., *(Atlas Pub),* 2121 S. 48th St. ,Suite 102, Scottsdale, AZ 85253 (SAN 686-2950).

†**Atma Bks.,** *(Atma Bks; 0-914557),* Box 432, Fallsburg, NY 12733 (SAN 289-1425) Tel 914-434-6707; *CIP.*

Atomic Industrial Forum, Inc., *(Atomic Indus Forum),* 7101 Wisconsin Ave., Bethesda, MD 20814-4805 (SAN 225-221X).

Atonement Enterprises, *(Atonement Ent; 0-9616739),* P.O. Box 660460, Sacramento, CA 95866-0460 (SAN 659-7386); 616 25th St., Apt. 1, Sacramento, CA 95816 (SAN 659-7394) Tel 916-443-5540.

Atre Software, Inc., *(Atre Soft; 0-937989),* P.O. Box 727, Rye, NY 10580 (SAN 659-7408) Tel 914-967-2037; 16 Elm Pl., Rye, NY 10580 (SAN 659-7416).

Attention Span Advancement Registry Service, *(ASA; 0-9606990),* 1940 Fifth Ave., Sacramento, CA 95818 (SAN 238-910X).

Attic Books Ltd., Subs. of Alex G. Malloy, Inc., *(Attic Bks; 0-915018),* P.O.Box 38, S. Salem, NY 10590 (SAN 206-8931) Tel 203-438-0396.

Attic Discoveries, *(Attic Discoveries; 0-936253),* 342 E. 50th St., Suites 1A-2F, New York, NY 10022 (SAN 697-3264) Tel 212-758-0678.

Attic Pr., *(Attic Pr; 0-87921),* Stony Point, Rte. 2, Greenwood, SC 29646 (SAN 201-1328) Tel 803-374-3013.

Attic Salt Pr., The, Div. of Inscript, Inc., *(Attic Salt; 0-9615512),* P.O. Box 8335, Mobile, AL 36689 (SAN 696-1630); 4501 Old Shell Rd., Mobile, AL 36608 (SAN 696-1649) Tel 205-343-4691.

Atticus Pr., *(Atticus Pr; 0-912377),* 720 Heber Ave., Calexico, CA 92231 (SAN 265-1815) Tel 619-357-3721; Dist. by: Bookpeople, 2929 Fifth St., Berkeley, CA 94710 (SAN 168-9517) Tel 415-549-3030; Dist. by: Small Press Distribution, Inc., 1814 San Pablo Ave., Berkeley, CA 94702 (SAN 204-5826) Tel 415-549-3336.

†**Auburn Hse. Publishing Co., Inc.,** Affil. of Affiliated Publications, *(Auburn Hse; 0-86569),* 14 Dedham, Dover, MA 02030 (SAN 220-0341) Tel 617-785-2220; *CIP.*

Auburn Pr., Inc., *(Auburn Pr; 0-938205),* 9167 Chesapeake Dr., San Diego, CA 92123 (SAN 659-7424) Tel 619-560-6431.

Auburn-Wolfe Publishing, *(Auburn-Wolfe; 0-912385),* 584 Castro St., No. 351, San Francisco, CA 94114 (SAN 265-1823) Tel 415-665-2025.

Auction Index, Inc., *(Auction Index; 0-918819),* 30 Valentine Park, West Newton, MA 02165 (SAN 682-773X).

Auction Pr., *(Auction Pr; 0-9613483),* 96 S. Clermont, Denver, CO 80222 (SAN 657-324X) Tel 303-399-0049.

Audio-Forum Division See Norton, Jeffrey, Pubs., Inc.

Audio Pr., The, *(Audio Pr; 0-939643),* 930 Sherman St., Suite 101, Denver, CO 80203 (SAN 663-5717) Tel 303-839-1112.

Audio-Visual Designs, *(Audio-Visual; 0-917451),* P.O. Box 24, Earlton, NY 12058-0024 (SAN 656-8793) Tel 518-731-2054.

Audit Investments Inc., *(Audit Investments; 0-912840),* 136 Summit Ave., Montvale, NJ 07645 (SAN 201-1301) Tel 201-358-2735.

Audubon Naturalist Society of the Central Atlantic States, Inc., *(Audubon MD; 0-939587),* 8940 Jones Mill Rd., Chevy Chase, MD 20815 (SAN 663-6195) Tel 301-652-9188.

Audubon Naturalists Society of the Central Altantic States, Inc., *(Audubon Naturalist),* 8940 Jones Mill Rd., Chevy Chase, MD 20815 (SAN 225-0012) Tel 301-652-9188.

Audubon Park Pr., *(Audubon Pk Pr; 0-9616452),* P.O. Box 4327, New Orleans, LA 70178 (SAN 659-2988) Tel 504-861-2537; 6500 Magazine St., New Orleans, LA 70118 (SAN 659-2996).

Audubon Society of Portland, *(Audubon Soc Portland; 0-931686),* 5151 NW Cornell Rd., Portland, OR 97210 (SAN 211-2132).

†**Auerbach Pubs., Inc.,** Subs. of Warren, Gorham & Lamont, *(Auerbach; 0-87769),* 1 Penn Center, New York, NY 10119 (SAN 213-0084) Tel 212-760-7500; Toll free: 800-257-8162; Orders to: 210 South St., Boston, MA 02111 (SAN 662-7188); Toll free: 800-922-0066; *CIP.*

†**Augsburg Publishing Hse.,** *(Augsburg; 0-8066),* 426 S. Fifth St., P.O. Box 1209, Minneapolis, MN 55440 (SAN 169-4081) Tel 612-330-3300; Toll free: 800-328-4648; Orders to: 57 E. Main St., Columbus, OH 43215 (SAN 146-3365) Tel 604-221-7411; Orders to: 5210 N. Lamar, P.O. Box 49337, Austin, TX 78765 (SAN 661-9495) Tel 512-459-1112; Orders to: 3224 Beverly Blvd., Box 57974, Los Angeles, CA 90057 (SAN 661-9509) Tel 213-386-3722; *CIP.*

August Corp., *(August Corp; 0-933482),* P.O. Box 582, Scottsdale, AZ 85252 (SAN 215-2940) Tel 602-949-7366.

August Hse., *(August Hse; 0-935304; 0-87483),* P.O. Box 3223, Little Rock, AR 72203-3223 (SAN 223-7288) Tel 501-663-7300.

August Pubns., *(August Pubns; 0-9613902),* P.O. Box 67, San Rafael, CA 94915 (SAN 686-290X) Tel 415-454-7772.

Augusta Junior Woman's Club, Inc., *(Augusta Jr Womans; 0-9615980),* P.O. Box 3133, Augusta, GA 30904 (SAN 698-1682) Tel 404-736-0557.

Augusta Pubs., *(Augusta Pubs; 0-9613217),* P.O. Box 1257, Woodbridge, CA 95258 (SAN 291-8625) Tel 209-368-2496.

Augustana College Library, *(Augustana Coll; 0-910182),* 35th St. & Seventh Ave., Rock Island, IL 61201 (SAN 203-5073) Tel 309-794-7266.

Augustana College Pr., The, *(Aug Col Pr; 0-9615558),* P.O. Box 2172, Humanities Ctr., Sioux Falls, SD 57197 (SAN 696-4834) Tel 605-336-5436.

Augustana Historical Society, *(Augustana; 0-910184),* Augustana College Library, Rock Island, IL 61201 (SAN 206-6378) Tel 309-794-7266.

Augustin, J. J., Inc., Pub., *(J J Augustin; 0-87439),* 123 Buckram Rd., Locust Valley, NY 11560 (SAN 204-5451) Tel 516-676-1510.

Augustine Fellowship, Sex & Love Addicts Anonymous, Fellowship-wide Services, Inc., The, *(Augustine Fellow; 0-9615701),* P.O. Box 119, New Town Branch, Boston, MA 02258 (SAN 696-169X) Tel 617-332-1845; Orders to: P.O. Box 88, New Town Branch, Boston, MA 02258 (SAN 696-1711).

Names

Names

Augustinian College Press, *(Augustinian Coll Pr; 0-9612336),* 3900 Harewood Rd. NE, Washington, DC 20017 (SAN 289-1174) Tel 202-526-4580.

Aum Pubns., Subs. of Agni Press, *(Aum Pubns; 0-88497),* P.O. Box 32433, Jamaica, NY 11431 (SAN 201-128X) Tel 718-523-3471.

Aunt Ellen's *See* **Modern Handcraft, Inc.**

Aunt Louise Publishing Co., *(Aunt Louise Pub; 0-9616652),* P.O. Box 164, Highland Park, IL 60035 (SAN 659-7432) Tel 312-433-0204; 1229 Eaton Ct., Highland Park, IL 60035 (SAN 659-7440).

Aunt Lute Bk., Co., *(Aunt Lute Bk Co; 0-918040),* P.O. Box 2568, Iowa City, IA 52244 (SAN 210-217X) Tel 319-338-7022.

Aura Books, *(Aura Bks; 0-937736),* 7911 Willoughby Ave., Los Angeles, CA 90046 (SAN 215-7268) Tel 213-656-9373; Toll free: 800-843-6666; Dist. by: Bookpeople, 2929 Fifth St., Berkeley, CA 94710 (SAN 168-9517) Tel 415-549-3030; Toll free: 800-227-1516; Dist. by: Samuel Weiser, Inc., P.O. Box 612, York Beach, ME 03910 (SAN 202-9588) Tel 207-363-4393; Toll free: 800-843-6666.

Aura Publishing Co., *(Aura Pub Co; 0-9615513),* 707 Mill St., Santa Rosa, CA 95404 (SAN 696-1878) Tel 707-527-0270. Do not confuse with Aura Publishing Co. of New Haven, CT or Aura Publishing Co. of Brooklyn, NY.

Aurea Pubns., *(Aurea; 0-87174),* P.O. Box 176, Allenhurst, NJ 07711 (SAN 203-5081) Tel 201-531-4535.

Aurelon Tales, *(Aurelon; 0-912388),* R.F.D. No. 3, 177 Sarles St., Mt. Kisco, NY 10549 (SAN 203-509X).

Aureon Publishing Co., *(Aureon Pub; 0-9613386),* 716 Mountain Dr., Kerrville, TX 79057 (SAN 657-0674) Tel 512-896-1650.

Aurico Publishing Co., *(Aurico; 0-910186),* 87 Elmwood St., Somerville, MA 02144 (SAN 203-1442) Tel 617-491-4992.

Auromere, Inc., *(Auromere; 0-89744),* 1291 Weber St., Pomona, CA 91768 (SAN 169-0043) Tel 714-629-8255; Toll free: 800-243-0138; Dist. by: Bookpeople, 2929 Fifth St., Berkeley, CA 94710 (SAN 168-9517) Tel 415-549-3030; Dist. by: Devorss & Co., Bk. Pubs. & Distributors, P.O. Box 550, 1040 Princeton Dr., Marina del Rey, CA 90294 (SAN 168-9886) Tel 213-870-7478; Dist. by: New Leaf Distributing Co., 1020 White St. SW, Atlanta, GA 30310 (SAN 169-1449) Tel 404-755-2665; Dist. by: Samuel Weiser, P.O. Box 612, York Beach, ME 03910 (SAN 202-9588) Tel 207-363-4393; Dist. by: Inland Bk. Co., P.O. Box 261, 22 Hemingway Ave., East Haven, CT 06512 (SAN 200-4151) Tel 203-467-4257; Dist. by: Distributors, 702 S. Michigan St., South Bend, IN 46618 (SAN 212-0364) Tel 219-232-8500; Dist. by: Starlite Distributors, P.O. Box 20729, Reno, NV 89515 (SAN 131-1921).

Aurora Assocs., Inc., *(Aurora Assocs; 0-931211),* 1140 Connecticut Ave., NW Suite 1200, Washington, DC 20036 (SAN 681-9672) Tel 202-463-0950.

Aurora News Register Publishing Co., *(Aurora News Reg; 0-8300),* 1320 K, Aurora, NE 68818 (SAN 281-2991); Dist. by Shirley Lueth, 1409 9th St., Aurora, NE 68818 (SAN 282-5910) Tel 402-694-3988.

Aurora Pr., *(Aurora Press; 0-943358),* 205 Third Ave., Apt 2-A, New York, NY 10003 (SAN 240-5881) Tel 212-673-1831; Dist. by: New Leaf Distributing, The, 1020 White St., SW, Atlanta, GA 30310 (SAN 169-1449) Tel 404-755-2665; Toll free: 800-241-3829; Dist. by: Samuel Weiser, Inc., P.O. Box 612, York Beach, ME 03910 (SAN 202-9588) Tel 207-363-4393; Dist. by: Bookpeople, 2929 Fifth St., Berkeley, CA 94710 (SAN 168-9517) Tel 415-549-3030; Toll free: 800-227-1516.

Aurora Pubns., Div. of Pacific Empire Corporation, *(Aurora Pubns; 0-913417),* 6214 Meridian Ave., San Jose, CA 95120 (SAN 285-8207) Tel 408-997-0437

†**Aurora Pubs.,** *(Aurora Pubs; 0-87695),* 118 16th Ave., S, Nashville, TN 37203 (SAN 201-1271) Tel 615-254-5842; *CIP.*

Ausonia Press, *(Ausonia Pr; 0-912429),* 100 Thorndale Dr., No. 457, San Rafael, CA 94903 (SAN 265-1831) Tel 415-931-5553.

Austin, Stephen F., State Univ., Schl. of Forestry, *(Austin Univ Forestry; 0-938361),* P.O. Box 6109, Nacogdoches, TX 75952 (SAN 659-7459) Tel 409-569-3304; North St. & E. College Ave., Nacogdoches, TX 75961 (SAN 659-7467).

Austin Bilingual Language Editions, *(Austin Bilingual Lang Ed; 0-940048),* P.O. Box 3864, Austin, TX 78764 (SAN 220-2069) Tel 512-441-1436.

†**Austin Hill Pr., Inc.,** *(Austin Hill Pr; 0-89690),* 2955 Renault Pl., San Diego, CA 92122 (SAN 211-8831) Tel 619-453-6486; *CIP.*

Austin Junior Forum, Inc., *(Austin Junior; 0-9607152),* P.O. Box 26628, Austin, TX 78755-0628 (SAN 238-9436) Tel 512-474-1311.

Austin Pr., Div. of Lone Star Pubs. Inc., *(Austin Pr; 0-914872),* P.O. Box 9774, Austin, TX 78766 (SAN 206-7870) Tel 512-453-8611.

Australiana Pubns., *(Australiana; 0-909162),* 6511 Riviera Dr., Coral Gables, FL 33146 (SAN 209-3235) Tel 305-666-9404. Name formerly Dryden Pr. of Australia.

Authentic American Art, Inc., *(Authentic Am Art; 0-9614524),* 142 Helios Ave., Metairie, LA 70130 (SAN 689-7347) Tel 504-837-0882.

Author Aid/Research Associates International, Div. of Research Associates International, *(Author Aid; 0-911085),* 340 E. 52nd St., New York, NY 10022 (SAN 263-0672) Tel 212-758-4213.

Authors Edition, Inc., *(Authors Edn MA; 0-918058),* Box 803, Lenox, MA 01240 (SAN 210-1696) Tel 413-637-0666.

Author's Note, *(Authors Note; 0-938927),* P.O. Box 30117, Long Beach, CA 90853 (SAN 661-7085); 2800 Neilson Way, No.715, Santa Monica, CA 90405 (SAN 661-7093) Tel 213-399-7528.

Authors Unlimited, *(Authors Unltd; 1-55666),* 3330 Barham Blvd., Suite 204, Los Angeles, CA 90068 (SAN 662-8044) Tel 213-874-0902.

†**Auto Bk. Pr.,** *(Auto Bk; 0-910390),* P.O. Bin 711, San Marcos, CA 92069 (SAN 201-1263) Tel 619-744-3582; *CIP.*

Auto Logic Publns., Inc., *(Auto Logic Pubns; 0-915845),* P.O. Box 9187, San Jose, CA 95157 (SAN 293-9606) Tel 408-435-1101.

Auto Publishing, *(Auto Pub; 0-938517),* P.O. Box 425, Mira Loma, CA 91752 (SAN 661-115X); 9430 Mission Blvd., Riverside, CA 92509 (SAN 661-1168) Tel 714-685-8570.

Automated TrainingSystems, *(Automated TrainingSyst),* 21250 Califast, No. 107, Woodland Hills, CA 91367 (SAN 694-3985).

Automation in Housing, *(Automation in Housing Mag; 0-9607408),* P.O. Box 120, Carpinteria, CA 93014 (SAN 239-1589) Tel 805-684-7659.

Automobile Quarterly Pubns., Div. of Princeton Publishing, *(Auto Quarterly; 0-911968),* 221 Nassau St, Princeton, NJ 08542 (SAN 281-3017) Tel 609-924-7555; Orders to: Rte. 222 & Sharadin Rd., P.O. Box 348, Kutztown, PA 19530 (SAN 281-3025) Tel 215-683-8352; Toll free: 800-523-0236.

Automotive Contact, Inc., *(Auto Contact Inc; 1-55527),* 3075 Canal Rd., Suite 2, Terre Haute, IN 47802 (SAN 695-4995) Tel 812-232-2441.

Autonomy House Publications, *(Autonomy Hse; 0-9612204),* 417 N. Main St., Monticello, IN 47960 (SAN 263-9254) Tel 219-583-8593.

Autotronic Conversions, *(Autotronic Conversions),* P.O. Box 17249, El Paso, TX 79917 (SAN 208-2241).

Autumngold Publishing, *(Autumngold Pub; 0-931253),* P.O. Box 634, Beverly Hills, CA 90213 (SAN 681-9664) Tel 818-783-2477.

Auvinen, Jewell Shelly, *(J S Auvinen; 0-9610158),* P.O. Box 5185, Santa Cruz, CA 95063 (SAN 263-9262) Tel 408-335-3543.

Auxiliary of Burdette Tomlin Memorial Hospital, *(B T Memorial Hospital; 0-9608326),* Cape May Court House, Cape May, NJ 08210 (SAN 240-5156) Tel 609-368-5068.

Auxiliary Univ. Pr., *(Auxiliary U Pr; 0-913034),* Box 772, Barrington, IL 60010 (SAN 202-327X) Tel 312-381-7888.

Auxosia/Gold Bks., *(Auxosia Gold Bks; 0-935374),* P.O. Box 4275, Houston, TX 77210 (SAN 221-2846).

AV-Text Corporation, *(AV Text Corp; 0-914865),* 733 Kings Rd., Suite 140, Los Angeles, CA 90069 (SAN 289-0577) Tel 213-658-5260.

Avalon Communications, Inc., *(Avalon Comm; 0-88041),* 1705 Broadway, Hewlett, NY 11557 (SAN 281-3033) Tel 516-599-4555; Dist. by: Doubleday & Co., Inc., 501 Franklin Ave., Garden City, NY 11530 (SAN 281-6083) Tel 516-873-4561.

Avalon Hill Pubs., *(Avalon Hill),* 4517 Harford Rd., Baltimore, MD 21214 (SAN 204-4633) Tel 301-254-5300.

Avant-Garde Media, Inc., *(Avant-Garde; 0-913568),* 251 W. 57th St., New York, NY 10019 (SAN 206-9563) Tel 212-581-2000. Do not confuse with Avant-Garde Publishing Corp., Novato, CA.

Avant-Garde Publishing Corp., *(Avant-Garde Pub; 0-930182; 0-87275),* 37B Commercial Blvd., Novato, CA 94947 (SAN 210-5853) Tel 415-883-8083; Toll free: 800-874-6544. Do not confuse with Avant-Garde Media, Inc., New York, NY.

Avantage Publishing, *(Avantage Pub; 0-938733),* 85 School St., Shrewsbury, MA 01545 (SAN 661-7069) Tel 617-842-2052.

Avanyu Publishing, Inc., *(Avanyu Pub; 0-936755),* Adobe Gallery, 413 Romero NW, Albuquerque, NM 87104 (SAN 699-8550) Tel 505-243-8485; P.O. Box 27134, Albuquerque, NM 87125 (SAN 699-8569).

Avatar, *(Avatar MO; 0-936040),* P.O. Box 16703, Raytown, MO 64133 (SAN 220-2328).

Avatar Pr., *(Avatar Pr; 0-914790),* P.O. Box 7727, Atlanta, GA 30357 (SAN 206-7579) Tel 404-892-8511.

Avatar Pr., *(Avatar NY; 0-9614674),* 41-50 48th St., Sunnyside, NY 11104 (SAN 692-5138) Tel 718-937-1933.

Avcom International Inc., *(Avcom Intl; 0-941024),* P.O. Box 2398, Wichita, KS 67201 (SAN 223-1743) Tel 316-262-1491.

Ave Maria Institute Press *See* **AMI International Pr.**

Ave Maria Pr., *(Ave Maria; 0-87793),* Notre Dame, IN 46556 (SAN 201-1255) Tel 219-287-2831.

Avenel *See* **Outlet Bk. Co.**

Avenue B, *(Avenue B; 0-939691),* P.O. Box 542, Bolinas, CA 94924 (SAN 663-4753); 87 Brighton Ave., Bolinas, CA 94924 (SAN 663-4761) Tel 415-868-0681; Dist. by: Small Press Distribution, 1814 San Pablo Ave., Berkeley, CA 94702 (SAN 658-179X) Tel 415-549-3336 (SAN 204-5826).

Avenue Publishing Co., *(Avenue Pub; 0-910977),* 9417 Conant Ave., Hamtramck, MI 48212 (SAN 268-1811) Tel 313-875-6635; 9417 Conant Ave., Hamtramck, MI 48212 (SAN 699-5144).

Avery Color Studios, *(Avery Color; 0-932212),* Star Rte., Box 275, Au Train, MI 49806 (SAN 211-1470) Tel 906-892-8251.

Avery Pr., Inc., *(Avery Pr Inc; 0-937321),* 600 Kalmia Ave., Boulder, CO 80302 (SAN 658-8042) Tel 303-443-1592. Do not confuse with Avery Pr., Atlanta, GA.

†**Avery Pub. Group, Inc.,** *(Avery Pub; 0-89529),* 350 Thorens Ave., Garden City Park, NY 11040 (SAN 210-3915) Tel 516-741-2155; *CIP.*

Avian Pubns., *(Avian Pubns; 0-910335),* 310 Maria Dr., Wausau, WI 54401 (SAN 241-2691) Tel 715-845-5101.

Aviation Bk. Co., *(Aviation; 0-911720; 0-911721; 0-916413),* 1640 Victory Blvd., Glendale, CA 91201 (SAN 212-0259) Tel 818-240-1771; Toll free: 800-423-2708. *Imprints:* Bomber Books (Pub. by Bomber).

Aviation Bk. Co., *(Aviation; 0-911720; 0-911721),* 1640 Victory Blvd., Glendale, CA 91201 (SAN 120-1530) Tel 818-240-1771; Toll free: 800-423-2708; Toll free: 800-542-6657 (in California). *Imprints:* Progressive Pilot Seminars (Progressive Pilot Sem).

Aviation Language School Inc., *(Aviation Lang Sch; 0-941456),* 4031 Woodridge Rd., Miami, FL 33133 (SAN 239-0639) Tel 305-665-9041.

Aviation Pubns., *(Aviat Pub; 0-87994),* P.O. Box 357, Appleton, WI 54912 (SAN 201-713X).

Aviation Pubns., Inc., *(Aviation Pubns; 0-917539),* P.O. Box 12848, University Sta., Gainesville, FL 32604 (SAN 656-0563) Tel 904-375-0772.

AViation Publishers *See* **Ultralight Pubns.**

Avocet, Inc., *(Avocet Inc.; 0-9607236),* Box 7615, Menlo Park, CA 94025 (SAN 239-1597) Tel 415-321-8501.

Avon Bard Bks. *See* **Avon Bks.**

Avon Bks., Div. of Hearst Corp., *(Avon; 0-380),* 1790 Broadway, New York, NY 10019 (SAN 201-4009) Tel 212-399-4500; Toll free: 800-247-5470. *Imprints:* Avon Bard Books (Bard); Avon Camelot Books (Camelot); Avon Discus Books (Discus); Avon Flare Books (Flare); Avon Library (Avon Lib); Banner Books (Banner); Snuggle & Read (Snuggle & Read).

Avon Camelot Bks. *See* **Avon Bks.**

Avon Discus Bks. *See* **Avon Bks.**

Avon Flare Bks. *See* **Avon Bks.**

Avon Library *See* **Avon Bks.**

†**Avons Research Pubns.,** *(Avons Res; 0-913772),* P.O. Box 40, La Canada, CA 91011 (SAN 202-3644) Tel 818-790-5370; *CIP.*

Avva, Inc., *(Avva; 0-938013),* 735 Dolores St., Stanford, CA 94305 (SAN 659-7475) Tel 415-328-0852.

Awakening Heart Pubns., *(Awakening Heart Pubns; 0-9616529),* P.O. Box 10092, Burbank, CA 91506 (SAN 659-4182) Tel 818-353-1584; 1512 1/2 W. Alameda Ave., Burbank, CA 91506 (SAN 659-4190).

Awakening Productions Inc., *(Awakening Prods; 0-914706),* 4132 Tuller Ave., Culver City, CA 90230 (SAN 205-6046).

Awani Pr., *(Awani Pr; 0-915266),* P.O. Box 881, Fredericksburg, TX 78624 (SAN 206-4626) Tel 512-997-5514.

†**AWARE,** *(AWARE; 0-916831),* P.O. Box 8371, Los Angeles, CA 90008 (SAN 654-1275) Tel 213-215-1881; *CIP.*

Awareness Marketing, *(Awareness Marketing; 0-915961),* P.O. Box 11822, Costa Mesa, CA 92627 (SAN 293-9622) Tel 714-642-3401.

AWWA Research Foundation, *(AWWA Res Found; 0-915295),* 6666 W. Quincy Ave., Denver, CO 80235 (SAN 289-9655) Tel 303-794-7711; Orders to: Computer Services, 6666 W. Quincy Ave., Denver, CO 80235 (SAN 662-7560) Tel 303-794-7711.

Axcess Software, Inc., *(Axcess Soft; 0-938929),* 6303 S. Rural Rd., Suite 9, Tempe, AZ 85283 (SAN 697-5658) Tel 602-838-3030; Toll free: 800-AXCENTS.

Axelrod Publishing of Tampa Bay, *(Axelrod Pub; 0-936417),* 1410 N. 21st St., Tampa, FL 33605 (SAN 698-1658) Tel 813-251-5269; P.O. Box 14248, Tampa, FL 33690 (SAN 698-2611).

Axiom Pr. Pubs., *(Axiom Pr Pubs; 0-933800),* P.O. Box 1668, Burlingame, CA 94011-1668 (SAN 213-2354) Tel 415-441-1211; Dist. by: J. A. Majors Co. California, 11511 Tennessee Ave., Los Angeles, CA 90064 (SAN 168-9800) Tel 213-879-1607; Toll free: 800-421-7149; 800-352-7277 (in California).

Axlon, Inc., *(Axlon Inc; 0-934571),* 1287 Lawrence Station Rd., Sunnyvale, CA 94089 (SAN 694-4353) Tel 408-747-1900.

†**Ayd Medical Communications,** *(Ayd Medical Comm; 0-931858),* 1130 E. Cold Spring Lane, Baltimore, MD 21239 (SAN 222-4712); *CIP.*

Ayer Co. Pubs., Inc., *(Ayer Co Pubs; 0-88143),* 382 Main St., P.O. Box 958, Salem, NH 03079 (SAN 211-6936) Tel 603-898-1200.

Aylesworth, Owen R., *(O R Aylesworth; 0-9609312),* 621 W. Arrellaga St., Santa Barbara, CA 93101 (SAN 260-0161) Tel 805-962-4252.

Aylmer Pr., *(Aylmer Pr; 0-932314),* P.O. Box 2735, Madison, WI 53701 (SAN 212-6044) Tel 608-233-2259.

Aylsworth Publishing Co., *(Aylsworth; 0-916572),* 21 Fairview Rd., Wilbraham, MA 01095 (SAN 208-516X) Tel 413-596-9234.

Ayt Ventures Pubs., *(Ayt Ventures Pubs; 0-937895),* 6863 E. Mary Dr., Tucson, AZ 85730 (SAN 659-4077) Tel 602-790-1989.

Azimuth Pr., *(Azimuth Pr; 0-913179),* P.O. Box 660, Arnold, MD 21012 (SAN 282-9754) Tel 301-757-4455. Do not confuse with Azimuth Pr., Houston, TX.

Aztex Corp., *(Aztex; 0-89404),* 1126 N. Sixth Ave., P.O. Box 50046, Tucson, AZ 85703 (SAN 210-0371) Tel 602-882-4656.

Azure Coast Publishing Co., Div. of Werner R. Hashagen Architect & Assocs., *(Azure Coast; 0-942514),* 7480 La Jolla Blvd., La Jolla, CA 92037 (SAN 238-1419) Tel 619-459-0122; Dist. by: Quality Bks., 918 Sherwood Dr., Lake Bluff, FL 60044-2204 (SAN 169-2127) Tel 312-498-4000.

Azure Zephyr Pubns., *(Azure Zephyr; 0-9614833),* P.O. Box 1917, Lakeside, CA 92040-0979 (SAN 693-0840); 9395 Harriet Rd., No. 105, Lakeside, CA 92040 (SAN 696-7000) Tel 619-561-0690.

BAH Publishing Co., *(B A H Publishing; 0-9617236),* P.O. Box 302, Ashville, OH 43103 (SAN 663-5431) Tel 614-983-3735; Lot 24, Lockbourne Lodge, Rte. 1, 10610 Ashville Pike, Lockbourne, OH 43137 (SAN 663-544X).

BAN Publishing Co., *(BAN Pub Boston; 0-938357),* 6 Rollins Pl., Boston, MA 02114 (SAN 698-178X) Tel 617-227-1332; Orders to: Bettina A. Norton, 6 Rollins Pl., Boston, MA 02114 (SAN 662-7846).

B. A. S. I. C./Bedell Advertising Selling Improvement Corp., *(BASIC Bedell; 0-916014),* 2040 Alameda Padre Serra, Santa Barbara, CA 93103 (SAN 223-6648).

B & B Productions, *(B & B Prod; 0-9614578),* Box 295, St. Helena, CA 94574 (SAN 692-2880) Tel 707-963-0852.

B&B Pubs., *(B & B Pubs; 0-9608674),* P.O. Box 1062, Brooksville, FL 33512 (SAN 240-5903) Tel 904-796-7712. Do not confuse with B&B Pub., Saugus, CA.

B. & B. Publishing, *(B & B Pub CA; 0-9607008),* P.O. Box 165, Saugus, CA 91350 (SAN 238-9452) Tel 805-255-3422. Do not confuse with either B&B Pub., Inc., Westminster, CO.

B & C Publishing, *(B & C Pub; 0-937239),* 1224 SW Lakeview Dr., Sebring, FL 33870 (SAN 658-666X) Tel 813-385-8693.

B & D Publishing, *(B & D Pub; 0-9613328),* 1915 Solano St., Suite B, Corning, CA 96021 (SAN 289-5854) Tel 916-824-1410.

B & G Associates, *(B & G Assoc; 0-9604230),* 408 Larkwood Dr., Montgomery, AL 36109 (SAN 215-0565).

B & K Enterprises, Inc., *(B & K Ent; 0-941458),* 1053 Montview Rd., Ft. Collins, CO 80521 (SAN 239-0647) Tel 303-484-4254.

B & R Samizdat Express, *(B & R Samizdat; 0-915232),* P.O. Box 161, West Roxbury, MA 02132 (SAN 207-1037) Tel 617-469-2269.

B & W Bks., *(B & W Bks; 0-9614996),* 445 Meadowcrest Cir., Memphis, TN 38117 (SAN 693-0980) Tel 901-682-8009.

B-B Leather, *(B-B Leather; 0-9616569),* P.O. Box 478, Blackfoot, ID 83221 (SAN 659-7645) Tel 208-785-1731; 719 W. Pacific, Blackfoot, ID 83221 (SAN 659-7653).

BCG Ltd., Div. of DPMS, *(BCG Ltd; 0-9615201),* 1209 NW Blvd., Spokane, WA 99205 (SAN 694-3578) Tel 509-328-7307.

BDR Learning Products, Inc., *(BDR Learn Prods; 0-934698),* P.O. Box 3356, Annapolis, MD 21403 (SAN 212-2227) Tel 301-263-1775.

BEK Pr., *(BEK Pr; 0-9613766),* No. 1 Woodbury Hills, Woodbury, CT 06798 (SAN 656-8807) Tel 203-263-4389.

BE Pubs., *(BE Pubs; 0-9617074),* 955 Connecticut Ave., Bridgeport, CT 06607 (SAN 662-6246) Tel 203-576-1007; Toll free: 800-826-8692.

BH Enterprises, *(BH Ent; 0-9604896),* P.O. Box 216, Midwood Sta., Brooklyn, NY 11230 (SAN 220-0562) Tel 718-336-0521.

BHRA Fluid Engineering, *(BHRA Fluid; 0-900983),* Dist. by: Air Science Co., P.O. Box 143, Corning, NY 14830 (SAN 210-7791) Tel 607-962-5591.

BILR Corp., The, *(BILR Corp; 0-937177),* P.O. Box 22918, Denver, CO 80222 (SAN 658-4624) Tel 303-789-9974; 43 Sunset Dr., Englewood, CO 80110 (SAN 658-4632).

B.I. Pubs., *(B I Pubs; 0-933021),* P.O. Box 1606, Indianapolis, IN 46206 (SAN 689-5433) Tel 317-312-1716.

B.I.Z. Publishing, *(BIZ Pub; 0-9615544),* 2424 Congress Ave., Suite G, San Diego, CA 92110 (SAN 696-0480) Tel 619-295-6337.

BJA Family Pubns., *(BJA Family; 0-9615320),* 136 Washington St., Paterson, NJ 07505 (SAN 694-6518) Tel 201-684-3119.

BJIS Publishing, *(BJIS Pub; 0-9614211),* 1000 Olive Dr., Suite 22, P.O. Box 6718, Bakersfield, CA 93386 (SAN 670-6991) Tel 805-393-7022.

BJ Service, *(B J Serv; 0-911535),* 152 S. Reeves Dr., Suite 105, Beverly Hills, CA 90212 (SAN 263-9270) Tel 213-276-8945.

BLOC Development Corp., *(BLOC Devel; 0-938843),* 1301 Dade Blvd., Miami Beach, FL 33139 (SAN 697-8452) Tel 305-531-5486; Toll free: 800-231-1149.

BMB Publishing Co., *(BMB Pub Co; 0-930924),* P.O. Box 1622, Boston, MA 02105 (SAN 201-4270) Tel 617-492-5762.

BMC International, Inc., *(BCM Intl Inc; 0-86508),* 237 Fairfield Ave., Upper Darby, PA 19082 (SAN 211-7762) Tel 215-352-7177.

BMDP Statistical Software, *(BMDP Stat; 0-935386),* 1440 Sepulveda Blvd., Los Angeles, CA 90025 (SAN 213-8069) Tel 213-479-7799.

BMH Bks., Div. of Brethren Missionary Herald, Inc., *(BMH Bks; 0-88469),* P.O. Box 544, Winona Lake, IN 46590 (SAN 201-7571) Tel 219-267-7158; Toll free: 800-348-2756.

B-Movie Publishing, *(B Movie; 0-930959),* 743 N. Harper Ave., Los Angeles, CA 90046 (SAN 678-8769) Tel 213-651-3217.

†**BNA Bks.,** Div. of Bureau of National Affairs, Inc., *(BNA; 0-87179),* 2550 M St., NW, Suite 699, Washington, DC 20037 (SAN 201-4262) Tel 202-452-5742; Toll free: 800-372-6033; Toll free: 800-3521400; Orders to: BNA Bks. Distribution Ctr., 300 Raritan Ctr. Pkwy., CN94, Edison, NJ 08818 (SAN 661-9649) Tel 201-225-1900; Orders to: BNA Customer Service (Reports & Services), 9435 Key West Ave., Rockville, MD 20850-3397 (SAN 661-9657) Tel 301-258-1033; *CIP.*

BNR Pr., *(BNR Pr; 0-931960),* 132 E. Second St., Port Clinton, OH 43452 (SAN 211-5948) Tel 419-734-2422.

BOA Editions, Ltd., *(BOA Edns; 0-918526),* 92 Park Ave., Brockport, NY 14420 (SAN 281-3351) Tel 716-637-3844; Dist. by: Bookslinger, 213 E. Fourth St., St. Paul, MN 55101 (SAN 169-4154) Tel 612-221-0429.

BOS Pubns., *(BOS Pubns; 0-9616119),* 3 First National Plaza, Suite 3650, Chicago, IL 60602 (SAN 699-6914) Tel 312-673-6464.

B of A Communications Co., *(B of A; 0-911238),* P.O. Box 22252, Louisiana State Univ., Baton Rouge, LA 70893 (SAN 204-6776) Tel 504-272-6600; Pelican Office Ctr., 11628 S. Choctaw Dr., Baton Rouge, LA 70815 (SAN 200-4208); Orders to: P.O. Box 15809, Broadview Sta., Pelican Office Products Ctr., Baton Rouge, LA 70895 (SAN 669-2567). *Imprints:* Accounting Publications (Acct Pubns); Malibu Publications (Malibu Pubns); Regent House (Regent House).

B.R.E. Pubs., Affil. of Non-Denominational Bible Prophesy Study Assn., *(B R E Pub; 0-9611368),* 339 E. Laguna Dr., Tempe, AZ 85282 (SAN 265-380X) Tel 602-967-3066.

B.R.K. Enterprises, Inc., *(B R K Ent),* 336 S. Donald Ave., Arlington Heights, IL 60004 (SAN 285-6859) Tel 312-259-8376.

BR-3 Pr., *(Br-Three Pr; 0-9607566),* 1129 S. Seventh St., Ann Arbor, MI 48103 (SAN 238-4469) Tel 313-665-2330.

B. S. Productions, *(B S Prods; 0-939565),* P.O. Box 4465, Sparks, NV 89432 (SAN 663-4931); 5200 Pyramid Lake Hwy., Spanish Springs, NV 89432 (SAN 663-494X) Tel 702-673-9425.

B. Success Pr., *(B Success Press; 0-933523),* 5030 Arundel Dr., Woodland Hills, CA 91364 (SAN 691-8506) Tel 818-346-3829; Box 812, Tarzana, CA 91356 (SAN 698-2077).

BUC International Corp., *(BUC Intl; 0-911778),* 1314 NE. 17 Ct., Fort Lauderdale, FL 33305 (SAN 201-9426) Tel 305-565-6715; Toll free: 800-327-6929.

Names

BW Enterprises Publishing Co., *(BW Enterprises; 0-9616280)*, 2289 Berrydale Rd., Cantonment, FL 32533 (SAN 658-554X) Tel 904-968-6244.

BYLS Pr., *(BYLS Pr; 0-934402)*, 6247 N. Francisco Ave., Chicago, IL 60659 (SAN 212-7253) Tel 312-262-8959.

Babies Milk Fund Children's & Prenatal Clinics, *(Babies Milk Fund; 0-9614115)*, 231 Bethesda Ave., Rm. 6109, Cincinnati, OH 45267 (SAN 686-256X) Tel 513-281-8000; Dist. by: Seven Hills Bks., 49 Central Ave., Suite 300, Cincinnati, OH 45202 (SAN 169-6629) Tel 513-381-3881.

Babineaux, Floyd, *(F Babineaux; 0-9616648)*, P.O. Box 3468, Irving, TX 75061 (SAN 659-7718) Tel 214-438-3000.

Babka Publishing Co., *(Babka Pub; 0-930625)*, P.O. Box 1050, Dubuque, IA 52001 (SAN 204-4609); 100 Bryant, Dubuque, IA 52001 (SAN 661-9525) Tel 319-588-2073.

Babson College Ctr. for Entrepreneurial Studies, *(Babson College; 0-910897)*, Babson College, Wellesley, MA 02157 (SAN 263-0737) Tel 617-239-4332.

Baby Grande Productions, *(Baby Grande Prods; 0-9614348)*, 352 N. Columbus St., Galion, OH 44833 (SAN 687-7699) Tel 419-468-9672.

Bacadaa, Ltd., *(Bacadaa; 0-9616763)*, 18928 Sorrento, Detroit, MI 48235 (SAN 659-7742) Tel 313-864-1320.

Bacchus Press, *(Bacchus Pr; 0-940416)*, 4225 Candleberry Ave., Seal Beach, CA 90740 (SAN 219-7669) Tel 213-430-5245; Dist. by: Publishers Group West, 5835 Beaudry Ave, Emeryville, CA 94608 (SAN 202-8522) Tel 415-658-3453; Dist. by: GBC Press, 630 S. 11th St., Las Vegas, NV 89127 (SAN 203-414X) Tel 702-382-7555.

Bacchus Wine Pr., Div. of Bacchus Press, Ltd., *(Bacchus Wine; 0-9613525)*, 1421 Jordan St., Baltimore, MD 21217 (SAN 657-5773) Tel 301-576-0762.

Back Bay Bks., Inc., *(Back Bay; 0-939126)*, P.O. Box 1396, Newport Beach, CA 92663 (SAN 216-1060) Tel 714-645-4900.

Back Door Pr., *(Back Door Pr; 0-9605568)*, 124B Fourth Ave., N., Edmonds, WA 98020 (SAN 241-3620).

Back Fork Bks., *(Back Fork Bks)*, Drawer 752, Webster Springs, WV 26288 (SAN 240-4699).

†Back Row Pr., *(Back Row Pr; 0-917162)*, 1803 Venus Ave., St. Paul, MN 55112 (SAN 208-5569) Tel 612-633-1685; *CIP.*

Back To Eden Bks., Publishing Co., *(Back to Eden; 0-940676)*, P.O. Box 1439, Loma Linda, CA 92354 (SAN 218-5318) Tel 714-796-9615.

†Backcountry Pubns., Inc., *(Backcountry Pubns; 0-942440)*, P.O. Box 175, Woodstock, VT 05091 (SAN 238-1427) Tel 802-457-1049; Toll free: 800-635-5009; Dist. by: Countryman Pr., P.O. Box 175, Woodstock, VT 05091 (SAN 206-4901) Tel 802-457-1049; *CIP.*

†Backeddy Bks., *(Backeddy Bks; 0-9603566)*, Box 301, Cambridge, ID 83610 (SAN 211-4655); *CIP.*

Backroads, *(Backroads; 0-933294)*, Box 14, Kelly, WY 83011 (SAN 213-831X).

Backside Pr., *(Backside Pr; 0-915855)*, P.O. Box 112412, San Diego, CA 92111 (SAN 293-9630) Tel 619-291-1740.

Backspace Ink, *(Backspace Ink; 0-9616675)*, 372 Second Ave., San Francisco, CA 94118 (SAN 659-7777) Tel 415-387-6892.

Backstreet Editions, Inc., *(Backstreet; 0-943018)*, Box 555, Port Jefferson, NY 11777 (SAN 240-3404) Tel 516-821-0678.

†Backwater Corp., *(Backwater Corp; 0-913539)*, 7438 SE 40th St., Mercer Island, WA 98040 (SAN 285-1520) Tel 206-232-2171; *CIP.*

Backwoods Bks., *(Backwoods Bks; 0-938833)*, P.O. Box 9, Gibbon Glade, PA 15440 (SAN 661-700X) Tel 412-329-4581.

Backwoods Pubns., Div. of Backwoods Films, *(Backwoods Pubns; 0-911997)*, 130 Watervliet Ave, Dayton, OH 45420 (SAN 263-9289) Tel 513-254-5299.

Backyard Music, *(Backyard Music; 0-9614939)*, P.O. Box 9047, New Haven, CT 06532 (SAN 693-6776) Tel 203-469-5756.

Bacon St. Pr., *(Bacon St Pr; 0-9610438)*, 46 Western Ave., Sherborn, MA 01770 (SAN 238-0390).

†Badger Books, *(Badger Bks; 0-930478)*, P.O. Box 40336, San Francisco, CA 94140 (SAN 211-0008) Tel 415-285-2708; *CIP.*

Badlands Natural History Assn., *(Badlands Natl Hist; 0-912410)*, P.O. Box 6, Interior, SD 57750 (SAN 202-3695) Tel 605-433-5361.

Bae Publishing Co., *(Bae Pub Co; 0-9613363)*, P.O. Box 225, Higley, AZ 85236 (SAN 292-3270) Tel 602-988-2182.

Baen Bks., Div. of Baen Publishing Enterprises, *(Baen Bks; 1-55594)*, 260 Fifth Ave., New York, NY 10001 (SAN 658-8417) Tel 212-532-4111; Dist. by: Simon & Schuster, Inc., 1230 Ave. of the Americas, New York, NY 10020 (SAN 200-2450) Tel 212-245-6400.

Baese, Geary L., *(Geary L Baese; 0-9615510)*, 610 W. Mountain Ave., Ft. Collins, CO 80521 (SAN 696-0588) Tel 303-221-5802.

Baffico/Breger Video, Inc., *(Baffico Breger; 0-939243)*, 915 Broadway, New York, NY 10010 Tel 212-254-3900.

Baggeboda Pr., *(Baggeboda Pr; 0-932591)*, 1128 Rhode Island St., Lawrence, KS 66044 (SAN 687-505X) Tel 913-842-0490.

Baggiani-Tewell Educational Materials, Inc., *(Baggiani-Tewell; 0-934329)*, 4 Spring Hill Ct., Chevy Chase, MD 20815 (SAN 693-6024) Tel 301-656-3353.

Baha'i Publishing Trust, *(Baha'i; 0-87743)*, 415 Linden Ave., Wilmette, IL 60091 (SAN 213-7496) Tel 312-251-1854; Toll free: 800-323-1880.

Bahm, Archie J., *(Bahm; 0-911714)*, 1915 Las Lomas Rd., NE, Albuquerque, NM 87106 (SAN 212-5854) Tel 505-242-9983. *Imprints:* World Books (World).

Baikar Assn., Inc., *(Baikar Assn; 0-936893)*, 468 Mt. Auburn St., Watertown, MA 02172 (SAN 658-4748) Tel 617-924-4420.

Baikie, Kenneth, *(K Baikie; 0-9607790)*, 4613 N. 74th Pl., Scottsdale, AZ 85251 (SAN 207-6985) Tel 602-994-4083.

Bailey, Emma, *(E Bailey; 0-9615823)*, 27 Western Ave., Brattleboro, VT 05301 (SAN 696-6829) Tel 802-254-8214.

Bailey, William, Pub., *(W Bailey Pub; 0-9604196)*, P.O. Box 331, West Point, CA 95255 (SAN 214-2317) Tel 209-293-4303.

Bailliere-Tindall See Saunders, W. B., Co.

Baines, Gwendolyn, *(Baines; 0-9614505)*, 1800 Meade St., Nashville, TN 37207 (SAN 691-7429) Tel 615-262-9615.

Baja Bks., *(Baja Bks; 0-9602838; 0-9615829)*, P.O. Box 4151, Santa Barbara, CA 93140 (SAN 213-0122) Tel 805-962-4029; Dist. by: Ingram Bk. Co., P.O. Box 17266, Nashville, TN 37217 (SAN 169-7978); Toll free: 800-251-5900; Dist. by: Cogan Bks., 4332 W. Artesia Ave., Fullerton, CA 92633 (SAN 168-9649); Dist. by: Publishers Group West, 5855 Beaudry St., Emeryville, CA 94608 (SAN 202-8522) Tel 415-658-3453.

Baja Enterprises, *(Baja Enter; 0-9609470)*, P.O. Box 11988, Costa Mesa, CA 92627 (SAN 260-163X) Tel 714-760-7036.

Baja Pr., *(Baja Pr; 0-910041)*, 2829 Nipoma St., San Diego, CA 92106 (SAN 241-2055) Tel 619-223-1563.

Baja Trail Pubns., Inc., *(Baja Trail; 0-914622)*, P.O. Box 6088, Huntington Beach, CA 92615 (SAN 206-3301) Tel 714-847-2252.

Bakar Pr., *(Bakar Press; 0-939295)*, P.O. Box 496, Cape Neddick, ME 03902 (SAN 662-7927); Old Mountain Rd., Cape Neddick, ME 03902 (SAN 662-7935) Tel 207-646-6210.

Bakebooks & Cookbooks, Inc., *(Bakebks & Cookbks; 0-9606686)*, P.O. Box 92185, Milwaukee, WI 53202 (SAN 219-7111) Tel 414-461-9813.

Baker, Walter H., Co., *(Baker's Plays; 0-87440)*, 100 Chauncy St., Boston, MA 02111 (SAN 202-3717) Tel 617-482-1280.

Baker-Berwick Pubns., Inc., *(Baker-Berwick; 0-938403)*, 304 S. Prospect St., Kent, OH 44240 (SAN 659-7807) Tel 216-673-5162.

Baker Bk. Hse., *(Baker Bk; 0-8010)*, P.O. Box 6287, Grand Rapids, MI 49516-6287 (SAN 201-4041) Tel 616-676-9186.

Baker Co. See Baker Gallery Pr.

Baker Gallery Pr., *(Baker Gallery; 0-912196)*, P.O. Box 1920, Lubbock, TX 79408 (SAN 202-3709) Tel 806-763-2500.

Baker Library See Kelley, Augustus M., Pubs.

Baker Publishing, *(Baker Pub; 0-913193)*, 9348 Monogram Ave. Suite 120, Sepulveda, CA 91343 (SAN 282-9762) Tel 818-892-5747.

†Baker Street Production, Ltd., *(Baker St Prod; 0-914867)*, 502 Range St., Box 3610, Mankato, MN 56001 (SAN 289-0585) Tel 507-625-2482; *CIP.*

Baker Street Pub., *(Baker St Pub; 0-9594025)*, 402 Hemingway Dr., Bel Air, MD 21014 (SAN 687-6471).

Baker, Voorhis & Co., Inc., *(Baker Voorhis; 0-8320)*, 30 Smith Ave., Mount Kisco, NY 10549 (SAN 658-6384).

†Bala Bks., *(Bala Bks; 0-89647)*, 268 W. 23rd St., New York, NY 10011 (SAN 284-9747) Tel 212-929-8073; *CIP.*

Balaban International Science Services, *(Balaban Intl Sci Serv; 0-86689)*, Dist. by: International Pubs. Service, P.O. Box 230, Accord, MA 02018 (SAN 654-9357) Tel 617-749-2966.

Balaban Publishing Co., *(Balaban Pub; 0-9617121)*, 163 Joralemon St., Suite 1502, Brooklyn, NY 11201 (SAN 662-4731) Tel 718-403-9743.

†Balamp Publishing, *(Balamp Pub; 0-913642)*, 4205 Fullerton Ave., Detroit, MI 48238 (SAN 202-4330) Tel 313-491-1950; Orders to: P.O. Box 02367, North End, Detroit, MI 48202 (SAN 202-4349); *CIP.*

Balance Beam Pr., Inc., *(Balance Beam Pr; 0-912701)*, 12711 Stoneridge Rd., Dayton, MN 55327 (SAN 282-9770) Tel 612-427-3168.

Balassanian, Sonia, *(S Balassanian; 0-9608388)*, 81 Murray St., New York, NY 10007 (SAN 240-5172) Tel 212-732-3598.

Balboa Publishing, *(Balboa Pub; 0-935902)*, 101 Larkspur Landing Cir., Larkspur, CA 94939 (SAN 220-035X) Tel 415-461-8884.

Balch Institute, *(Balch I E S; 0-937437)*, 18 S. Seventh St., Philadelphia, PA 19106 (SAN 695-7838).

Balcom Bks., *(Balcom; 0-9600008)*, 320 Bawden St., Apt. 401, Ketchikan, AK 99901 (SAN 202-3725) Tel 907-225-2496.

Balcones Co., *(Balcones Co; 0-9615782)*, 225 Congress Ave., No. 153, Austin, TX 78711 (SAN 696-6837) Tel 512-346-8337; P.O. Box 2143, Austin, TX 78711 (SAN 698-2093).

Baldner, Jean V., *(Baldner J V; 0-9615317)*, 19203 N. 29th Ave., Phoenix, AZ 85027 (SAN 694-6526) Tel 602-582-0312.

Baldwin Manor Pr., *(Baldwin Manor Pr; 0-9617094)*, 4722 Baptist Rd., Pittsburgh, PA 15227 (SAN 662-474X) Tel 412-881-4384.

Bale Bks., Div. of Bale Pubns., *(Bale Bks; 0-912070)*, P.O. Box 2727, New Orleans, LA 70176 (SAN 201-405X); 5121 St. Charles Ave., Suite 13, New Orleans, LA 70115 (SAN 661-9533).

Balensiefer, F. H., *(F H Balensiefer; 0-9617228)*, 8337 Orchard St., Alta Loma, CA 91701 (SAN 663-4273) Tel 714-987-4991.

Balick, Lillian R., *(L R Balick; 0-9615834)*, 15 Clermont Rd., Wilmington, DE 19803 (SAN 200-5875) Tel 302-571-3540.

Ball State Univ., Ctr. for Environmental Design, Research & Service, *(Ctr Env Des Res; 0-912431)*, College of Architecture and Planning /AB104, Muncie, IN 47306-1099 (SAN 265-1890) Tel 317-285-5859.

†Ball State Univ., *(Ball State Univ; 0-937994)*, Muncie, IN 47306 (SAN 239-4081); *CIP.*

Ball State Univ. Art Gallery, *(Ball State Art; 0-915511)*, Muncie, IN 47306 (SAN 278-1344) Tel 317-285-5242.

Ballantine Bks., Inc., Div. of Random Hse., Inc., *(Ballantine; 0-345)*, 201 E. 50th St., New York, NY 10022 (SAN 214-1175) Tel 212-751-2600; Toll free: 800-638-6460; Orders to: 400 Hahn Rd., Westminster, MD 21157 (SAN 214-1183). *Imprints:* Del Rey Books (Del Rey).

Ballantrae Technical Bks., *(Ballantrae Tech; 0-936333)*, 9 Grandview Rd., Suite 2201, Windham, NH 03087 (SAN 697-8231) Tel 603-434-1246.

Ballena Pr., *(Ballena Pr; 0-87919)*, 823 Valparaiso Ave., Menlo Park, CA 94025 (SAN 201-4076) Tel 415-323-9261; Orders to: Ballena Press Publishers Service, P.O. Box 2510, Novato, CA 94948 (SAN 669-0181) Tel 415-883-3530.

Balletmonographs, *(Balletmonographs; 0-9604232)*, 2545 Pomeroy Ct., S, San Francisco, CA 94080 (SAN 214-3054).

†**Ballinger Publishing Co.,** Subs. of Harper & Row, Inc., *(Ballinger Pub; 0-88410; 0-88730),* 54 Church St., Harvard Sq., Cambridge, MA 02138 (SAN 201-4084) Tel 617-492-0670; Toll free: 800-638-3030; *CIP.*

Ballyhoo Bks., *(Ballyhoo Bks; 0-936335),* P.O. Box 534, Shoreham, NY 11786 (SAN 697-8487) Tel 516-929-8148; R.R. 1, Box 447C, Sylvan Dr., Wading River, NY 11792 (SAN 698-2239).

†**Balsam Pr., Inc.,** Div. of Rutledge Bks., *(Balsam Pr; 0-917439),* 122 E. 25th St., 4th Flr., New York, NY 10010 (SAN 208-4503) Tel 212-598-6976; Dist. by: Kampmann & Co., Inc., 9 E. 40th St., New York, NY 10016 (SAN 202-5191) Tel 212-685-2928; Toll free: 800-526-7626; *CIP.*

Baltic Cinematographic Research Centre Press, The, *(Baltic Cinema; 0-941618),* 921 Norwood, Melrose Park, IL 60160 (SAN 239-1619) Tel 312-343-8857.

Baltimore County Fire Service Centennial Committee, *(Baltimore CFSCC; 0-9608952),* 800 York Rd., Towson, MD 21204 (SAN 241-2063) Tel 301-494-4531.

Baltimore County Public Library, *(Baltimore Co Pub Lib; 0-937076),* 320 York Rd., Towson, MD 21204 (SAN 214-3429).

†**Baltimore Museum of Art,** *(Baltimore Mus; 0-912298),* Art Museum Dr., Baltimore, MD 21218 (SAN 201-7431) Tel 301-396-6316; Orders to: The Museum Shop, Art Museum Dr., Baltimore, MD 21218 (SAN 201-744X) Tel 301-396-6338; *CIP.*

Baltimore NRHS Pubns., *(Baltimore NRHS; 0-9601320),* 4710 Keswick Rd., Baltimore, MD 21210 (SAN 202-4365) Tel 301-467-8849; Orders to: 2107 N. Charles St., Baltimore, MD 21218 (SAN 202-4373) Tel 301-685-6161.

Baltimore Streetcar Museum, *(Baltimore Streetcar; 0-9609638),* Box 7184, Baltimore, MD 21218 (SAN 262-5857) Tel 301-484-7773.

Baltimore Vegetarians, *(Baltimore Veg; 0-931411),* P.O. Box 1463, Baltimore, MD 21203 (SAN 686-2098) Tel 301-752-8348; Dist. by: New Leaf Distributing, The, 1020 White St., SW, Atlanta, GA 30310 (SAN 169-1449) Tel 404-755-2665; Toll free: 800-241-3829.

Bamberger Bks., *(Bamberger; 0-917453),* P.O. Box 1126, Flint, MI 48501-1126 (SAN 657-0690) Tel 313-234-8069; Dist. by: Small Pr. Distribution, 1814 San Pablo Ave., Berkeley, CA 94702 (SAN 204-5826) Tel 415-549-5336; Dist. by: Inland Bk. Co., P.O. Box 261, 22 Hemingway Ave., East Haven, CT 06512 (SAN 200-4151) Tel 203-467-4257; Toll free: 800=243-0138; Dist. by: Bookslinger, 213 E. Fourth St., St. Paul, MN 55101 (SAN 169-4154) Tel 612-221-0429.

Bamboo Ridge Pr., *(Bamboo Ridge Pr; 0-910043),* P.O. Box 61781, Honolulu, HI 96822-8781 (SAN 240-8740) Tel 808-395-7098.

Bambook Pubns., *(Bambook Pubns; 0-939567),* P.O. Box 1403, Weatherford, TX 76086-1403 (SAN 663-4648); 405 Valley Ln., Weatherford, TX 76086 (SAN 663-4656) Tel 817-594-8202.

Banbury *See* **Dell Publishing Co., Inc.**

Banbury Publishing Co., *(Banbury Pub Co; 0-9609598),* P.O. Box 926, 302 W. Jefferson, Effingham, IL 62401 (SAN 260-1648) Tel 217-347-7555.

Bancroft, John C., *(J C Bancroft),* 5855 Sheridan Rd., Apt. 7D, Chicago, IL 60660 (SAN 207-6071) Tel 312-271-7747.

Bancroft Parkman, Inc., *(Bancroft Parkman; 0-914022),* P.O. Box 236, Washington, CT 06793 (SAN 215-0581) Tel 212-737-2715.

Bancroft Press, *(Bancroft Pr; 0-914888),* 27 McNear Dr., San Rafael, CA 94901 (SAN 206-4634) Tel 415-454-7094.

Bancroft-Whitney Co., *(Bancroft Whitney Co; 0-8321),* 301 Brannan St., San Francisco, CA 94107 (SAN 204-5389) Tel 415-986-4410.

Bandanna Bks., *(Bandanna Bks; 0-942208),* 209 W. de la Guerra, Santa Barbara, CA 93101 (SAN 238-7956) Tel 805-962-9996.

Bandar Log, Inc., *(Bandar Log; 0-9617036),* P.O. Box 86, Magdalena, NM 87825 (SAN 662-8222).

Bande House Publishing Co., *(Bande Hse Pub; 0-943760),* 1142 Manhattan Ave., Manhattan Beach, CA 90266 (SAN 238-2458) Tel 213-379-6924.

Bandon Historical Society, *(Bandon Hist; 0-932368),* P.O. Box 737, Bandon, OR 97411 (SAN 232-2677) Tel 503-347-2164.

Banjar Pubns., *(Banjar Pubns; 0-9617181),* Box 32164, Minneapolis, MN 55432 (SAN 663-6292).

Bank Administration Institute, *(Bank Admin Inst; 1-55520),* 60 Gould Ctr., Rolling Meadows, IL 60008 (SAN 204-4552) Tel 312-228-2308.

Bank Lease Consultants Financial Pubns., Div. of Bank Lease Consultants Inc., *(Bank Lease Pubns; 0-933355),* 2950 Merced St., San Leandro, CA 94577 (SAN 691-7658) Tel 415-895-1900; 3401 W. End Ave., Suite 706, Nashville, TN 37203 (SAN 662-2909) Tel 615-383-1930.

Bank Marketing Assn., *(Bank Mktg Assn),* 309 W. Washington St., Chicago, IL 60606 (SAN 224-8611) Tel 312-782-1442.

Bank Street Pr., The, *(Bank St Pr; 0-935505),* 24 Bank St., New York, NY 10014 (SAN 696-0634) Tel 212-255-0692.

Bankers Pr., Inc., *(Bankers Pr; 0-9602414),* 5810 S. Green St., Chicago, IL 60621 (SAN 213-0130).

†**Bankers Publishing Co.,** *(Bankers; 0-87267),* 210 South St., Boston, MA 02111 (SAN 201-4564) Tel 617-426-4495; *CIP.*

Banks-Baldwin Law Publishing Co., *(Banks-Baldwin; 0-8322),* University Ctr., P.O. Box 1974, Cleveland, OH 44106 (SAN 204-5370) Tel 216-721-7373; Toll free: 800-362-4500 (OH).

Banmar Inc., *(Banmar Inc; 0-9614989),* 4239 Monroe St., Toledo, OH 43606 (SAN 693-7594) Tel 419-473-2940.

Bannack Publishing Co., *(Bannack Pub Co; 0-916027),* 207 Iowa Dr., Golden, CO 80403 (SAN 294-6785) Tel 303-279-2207.

Banned Books *See* **Williams, Edward, Publishing Co.**

Banner *See* **Exposition Pr. of Florida, Inc.**

Banner Bks. *See* **Avon Bks.**

Banner Bks., *(Banner Books CA; 0-939693),* 6458 Lake Shore Dr., San Diego, CA 92119 (SAN 663-4745) Tel 619-697-4182. Do not confuse with Banner Bks. Intl., Sherman Oaks, CA.

Banner Bks., Inc., *(Banner Bks; 0-9615938),* P.O. Box 70302, Reno, NV 89570 (SAN 697-0184) Tel 702-825-6363.

Banner of Truth, The, *(Banner of Truth; 0-85151),* P.O. Box 621, Carlisle, PA 17013 (SAN 211-7738) Tel 717-249-5747.

†**Banner Pr.,** *(Banner Pr NY; 0-916650),* P.O. Box 6469, Chicago, IL 60680 (SAN 212-0119) Tel 312-663-1843; *CIP.*

†**Banner Pr., Inc.,** *(Banner Pr AL; 0-87121),* P.O. Box 20180, Birmingham, AL 35216 (SAN 204-5362) Tel 205-822-4783; *CIP.*

Banning, Arthur J., Pr., *(Banning Pr; 0-938060),* 509 Foshay Tower, Minneapolis, MN 55402 (SAN 220-0368) Tel 612-788-9248.

Banquet Hse. Pubs., *(Banquet Hse; 0-934109),* 184 Main St., Lancaster, NH 03584 (SAN 693-2800) Tel 603-788-4427.

Banster Pr., The, *(Banster Pr; 0-9604620),* P.O. Box 7326, Menlo Park, CA 94025 (SAN 218-4656) Tel 415-851-8032.

Bantam Bks., Inc., *(Bantam; 0-553),* 666 Fifth Ave., New York, NY 10019 (SAN 201-3975) Tel 212-765-6500; Toll free: 800-323-9872; Orders to: 414 E. Golf Rd., Des Plaines, IL 60016 (SAN 201-3983). *Imprints:* Minibooks (Minibooks); Pathfinder Books (Pathfinder); Peacock (Peacock); Skylark (Skylark); Spectra (Spectra); Starfire (Starfire); Windstone (Windstone).

†**Banyan Books,** *(Banyan Bks; 0-916224),* P.O. Box 431160, Miami, FL 33243 (SAN 208-340X) Tel 305-665-6011; *CIP.*

Banyan Tree Bks., *(Banyan Tree; 0-9604320),* 1963 El Dorado Ave., Berkeley, CA 94707 (SAN 207-3862); Dist. by: Bookpeople, 2929 Fifth St., Berkeley, CA 94710 (SAN 168-9517) Tel 415-549-3030; Toll free: 800-227-1516.

Baptist Publishing Hse., *(Baptist Pub Hse; 0-89114),* 1319 Magnolia St., Texarkana, TX 75501-4493 (SAN 183-6544) Tel 214-793-6531.

Bar Assn. of Metropolitan St. Louis, *(St Louis Metro Bar),* 1 Mercantile Ctr., Rm. 3600, St. Louis, MO 63101 (SAN 226-3149).

Bar Co., *(Bar Co; 0-9615482),* 1900 Westlake Ave., N., Seattle, WA 98109 (SAN 696-0669) Tel 206-282-0212.

Bar Guide Enterprises, *(Bar Guide; 0-918338),* P.O. Box 4044, Terminal Annex, Los Angeles, CA 90051 (SAN 210-041X) Tel 818-883-5369.

Barah Publishing, *(Barah; 0-930292),* P.O. Box 697, San Anselmo, CA 94960 (SAN 209-3480) Tel 415-459-1165.

Baraka Bks., Subs. of Movement of Spiritual Inner Awareness, *(Baraka Bk; 0-914829),* P.O. Box 3935, Los Angeles, CA 90051 (SAN 289-1395) Tel 213-737-4055; 3500 W. Adams Blvd., Los Angeles, CA 90018 (SAN 289-1409).

Baranski Pub. Co., *(Baranski Pub Co; 0-941974),* P.O. Box 4527, Topeka, KS 66604 (SAN 238-0005).

Barbacoa Pr., *(Barbacoa Pr; 0-933579),* P.O. Box 32576, Kansas City, MO 64111 (SAN 692-2058) Tel 816-753-3208; Toll free: 800-255-0513; Dist. by: Ingram Industries, 347 Reedwood Dr., Nashville, TN 37217 (SAN 169-7978); Dist. by: Publishers Group West, 5855 Beaudry St., Emeryville, CA 94608 (SAN 202-8522) Tel 415-658-3453; Toll free: 800-9828319.

Barbara Dolls, *(Barbara Dolls; 0-918564),* Box 736, Bowie, MD 20715 (SAN 210-0665); 2700 Balsam Pl., Bowie, MD 20715 (SAN 210-0673) Tel 301-262-2968.

Barbarossa Pr., *(Bararossa Pr; 0-9617086),* P.O. Box 4, Victor, CO 80860 (SAN 662-5908); 200 N. Third St., Victor, CO 80860 (SAN 662-7900) Tel 303-689-2714.

Barbary Coast Bks., *(Barbary Coast Bks; 0-936041),* P.O. Box 3645, Oakland, CA 94609 (SAN 697-0060) Tel 415-653-8048; 5362 Miles Ave., Oakland, CA 94618 (SAN 697-0079).

Barbed Wire Pr., Subs. of Western Pubns., Inc., *(Barbed Wire Pr; 0-935269),* P.O. Box 2107, Stillwater, OK 74076 (SAN 695-748X) Tel 405-743-3370.

Barber, D. L., Ventures, *(D L Barber Ventures; 0-938895),* 13351 Benton St., Garden Grove, CA 92643 (SAN 662-6637) Tel 213-425-3460; P.O. Box 2248, Garden Grove, CA 92642-2248 (SAN 663-3242) Tel 714-530-6716.

Barber, Lilian, Pr., *(Barber Pr; 0-936508),* P.O. Box 232, Grand Central Sta., New York, NY 10163 (SAN 214-1817) Tel 212-874-2678. *Imprints:* Ethnographica (Ethnographica).

Barber, William A., *(W A Barber; 0-913725),* 42 Simsbury Rd., Stamford, CT 06905 (SAN 240-9186).

Barber Co., *(Barber Co; 0-937125),* 2203 NW 63rd St., Seattle, WA 98107 (SAN 658-4713) Tel 206-782-2779.

Barbour, James L., *(J L Barbour; 0-939128),* P.O. Box 326, Port Tobacco, MD 20677 (SAN 215-6245) Tel 301-934-8045.

Barbour & Co., Inc., Div. of Book Bargains, Inc., *(Barbour & Co; 0-916441),* 164 Mill St., Westwood, NJ 07675 (SAN 295-7094) Tel 201-664-0577; Toll free: 800-221-2648; Dist. by: Spring Arbor Distributors, 10885 Textile Rd., Belleville, MI 48111 (SAN 158-9016) Tel 313-481-0900; Dist. by: Ingram Industries, 347 Reedwood Dr., Nashville, TN 37217 (SAN 169-7978) Tel 615-361-5000; Dist. by: Baker & Taylor Cos., The, 1515 Broadway, New York, NY 10036 (SAN 169-5606) Tel 212-730-7650; Dist. by: Riverside Bk. & Bible Hse., Inc., 1500 Riverside Dr., P.O. Box 370, Iowa Falls, IA 50126 (SAN 169-2666) Tel 515-648-4269; Dist. by: Living Bks., Inc., 12155 Magnolia Ave., Bldg. 11-B, Riverside, CA 92503 (SAN 169-006X) Tel 714-354-7330; Dist. by: Cicero Bible Pr., 1901 Airport Rd., Harrison, AR 72601 (SAN 200-7231) Tel 501-741-3400.

Barclay Bridge Supplies, Inc., *(Barclay Bridge; 0-87643),* 8 Bush Ave., Port Chester, NY 10573 (SAN 202-3768) Tel 914-937-4200.

Barclay Pr., *(Barclay Pr; 0-913342),* P.O. Box 232, Newberg, OR 97132 (SAN 201-7520) Tel 503-538-7345.

Barclay Pubs., Inc., *(Barclay Pubs; 0-9614429),* 203 Gary Rd., Carrboro, NC 27510 (SAN 690-0410) Tel 919-967-5350.

Barcus, Earlynne, *(E Barcus; 0-9611922),* P.O. Box 794, Fruita, CO 81521 (SAN 286-0449) Tel 303-858-3558; Rte. 1, P.O. Box 22B, Crawford, CO 81415 (SAN 286-0457).

Bard Games/Arcanum, Inc., *(Bard Games; 0-9610770),* P.O. Box 7729, Greenwich, CT 06836 (SAN 265-0789) Tel 203-661-4547.

Bard Hall Pr., *(Bard Hall Pr; 0-916491),* 32 Nickerbocker at Oak, Tenafly, NJ 07670 (SAN 295-2459) Tel 201-567-7629; Dist. by: Persea Books, Inc., 225 Lafayette St., New York, NY 10012 (SAN 212-8233) Tel 212-431-5270.

Bard Pr., *(Bard Pr; 0-934776),* 799 Greenwich St., New York, NY 10014 (SAN 214-1035) Tel 212-929-3169. Do not confuse with Avon Bard, an imprint of Avon Bks.

Bardavon Books *See* Valentine Publishing & Drama Co.

Bardic Echoes Pubns., *(Bardic; 0-915020),* P.O. Box 5339, Ft. Wayne, IN 46895 (SAN 207-0952) Tel 219-484-3718.

Barding, L.F., Publishing, *(Barding Pub; 0-9605848),* P.O. Box 06264, Ft. Myers, FL 33906 (SAN 216-5880) Tel 813-936-2774.

Bargain Hunter's Notebooks, *(Bargain Hunt Ntebks; 0-9613971),* P.O. Box 157, Old Greenwich, CT 06870 (SAN 682-2851) Tel 203-637-3320.

Bargara Press, *(Bargara Pr; 0-911087),* 1523 Fillmore St., Lynchburg, VA 24501 (SAN 268-2176) Tel 804-332-5147; Rte. 2, Box 444, Rustburg, VA 24588 (SAN 268-2184) Tel 804-332-0961.

Bark-Back, *(Bark-Back; 0-9603338),* P.O. Box 235, Glenshaw, PA 15116 (SAN 213-4624) Tel 412-364-3743.

Barker, Gray, Books, *(G Barker Bks; 0-911306),* Box D, Jane Lew, WV 26378 (SAN 204-7292) Tel 304-269-2719.

Barking Dog Pr., *(Barking Dog; 0-937131),* Box 253, Storm Lake, IA 50588 (SAN 658-4675) Tel 712-732-5671.

Barks Pubns., Inc., *(Barks Pubns; 0-943876),* 400 N. Michigan Ave., Suite No. 1016, Chicago, IL 60611-4198 (SAN 241-0974) Tel 312-321-9440.

Barksdale Foundation, *(Barksdale Foun; 0-918588),* P.O. Box 187, Idyllwild, CA 92349 (SAN 210-1718) Tel 714-659-4676.

†Barlenmir House, Pubs., *(Barlenmir; 0-87929),* 413 City Island Ave., New York, NY 10464 (SAN 201-4556) Tel 212-885-2120; *CIP.*

Barleycorn Books, *(Barleycorn; 0-935566),* 290 SW Tualatin Loop, West Linn, OR 97068 (SAN 213-6104) Tel 503-225-0234.

Barlina Bks., Inc., *(Barlina Bks; 0-937525),* 7405 Colshire Dr., Suite 240, McLean, VA 22102 (SAN 659-0217) Tel 703-442-8870.

Barlow-Kaiser Publishing Co., *(Kaiser Pub Co; 0-9610166),* P.O. Box 265, Windham, NH 03087 (SAN 268-2206) Tel 802-888-4066; Dist. by: Schiffer Publishing, Ltd., 1469 Morstein Rd., West Chester, PA 19380 (SAN 208-8428) Tel 215-696-1001.

Barn Owl Books, *(Barn Owl Bks; 0-9609626),* Box 7727, Berkeley, CA 94707 (SAN 268-2214) Tel 415-848-1395.

Barnaby Books, *(Barnaby Bks; 0-940350),* 3290 Pacific Heights Rd., Honolulu, HI 96813 (SAN 217-5010) Tel 808-524-1490.

Barnard, Jerry, Ministries, *(J Barnard; 0-938043),* P.O. Box 413, San Diego, CA 92112 (SAN 659-784X); 6550 Soledad Mountain Rd., La Jolla, CA 92037 (SAN 659-7858) Tel 619-275-1944.

Barnard, Roberts & Co., Inc., *(Barnard Roberts; 0-934118),* 305 Gun Rd., Baltimore, MD 21227 (SAN 213-4632) Tel 301-247-2242.

Barnegat Light Pr., *(Barnegat; 0-937996),* P.O. Box 305, Barnegat Light, NJ 08006 (SAN 215-6253); 7 Wynnewood Dr., Cranbury, NJ 08512 (SAN 661-9541) Tel 609-395-0316. *Imprints:* Pine Barrens Pr. (Pine Barrens Pr).

Barnes, A. S., & Co., Inc., Subs. of Oak Tree Pubns., Inc., *(A S Barnes; 0-498),* 9601 Aero Dr., San Diego, CA 92123 (SAN 201-2030) Tel 619-560-5163.

Barnes, C. Virginia, *(C V Barnes),* 2 Fifth Ave.-16M, New York, NY 10011 (SAN 218-6438).

Barnes, John W., Publishing, Inc., *(Barnes Pub; 0-914822),* P.O. Box 323, Scarsdale, NY 10583 (SAN 223-6281).

Barnes, Richard S., & Co. Books, *(R S Barnes; 0-942448),* 821 Foster St., Evanston, IL 60201 (SAN 209-2395) Tel 312-869-2272.

Barnes, Robert H., *(R H Barnes; 0-930480),* P.O. Box 418, Grayland, WA 98547 (SAN 210-3532) Tel 206-267-3601.

Barnes & Noble Books *See* Harper & Row Pubs., Inc.

Barnes & Noble Bks.-Imports, Div. of Littlefield, Adams & Co., *(B&N Imports; 0-389),* 81 Adams Dr., Totowa, NJ 07512 (SAN 206-7803) Tel 201-256-8600. *Imprints:* Art Series (Art); Focus Books (FB); Keynote Series (Key); Science Paperbacks (SP); Social Science Paperbacks (SocSP); U Books (U); University Paperbacks (UP).

Barnes-Bks., Div. of MOIC, *(Barnes-Bks; 0-917732),* R.R. 1, Box 14340, Ft. Ann, NY 12827 (SAN 682-2622) Tel 518-793-4791; Orders to: Baker & Taylor, 501 S. Gladiolus St., Momence, IL 60954 (SAN 169-4901).

Barney Press, *(Barney Pr; 0-9607888),* 8300 Kern Canyon Rd. No. 60, Bakersfield, CA 93306 (SAN 238-1443) Tel 805-395-4433.

Barniak Pubns, *(Barniak Pubns; 0-9613803),* 424 S. Kentucky Ave., Evansville, IN 47714 (SAN 679-3959) Tel 812-425-1272.

Barnstable Bks., *(Barnstable; 0-918230),* 799 Broadway, Rm. 506A, New York, NY 10003 (SAN 210-1726) Tel 212-473-8681.

Barnwood Pr. Cooperative, The, *(Barnwood Pr; 0-935306),* River Hse., R.R. 2, Box 11C, Daleville, IN 47334 (SAN 223-7245).

Baron Publishing Co., Inc., *(Baron Pub Co; 0-935843),* P.O. C-230, Scottsdale, AZ 85252 (SAN 696-0693) Tel 602-941-2418; 7777 E. Main St., Suite 161, Scottsdale, AZ 85251 (SAN 696-0707).

Baron/Scott Enterprises, Inc., *(Baron-Scott Enterp; 0-943568),* 8804 Monard Dr., Silver Spring, MD 20910 (SAN 240-5938) Tel 301-587-2444.

Barone & Co., *(Barone & Co; 0-89234; 0-89234),* 3530 Edmunds St. NW, Washington, DC 20007 (SAN 293-2326) Tel 202-337-0076; c/o 1984 Almanac National Journal, 1730 M St. NW, Washington, DC 20036 (SAN 293-2334) Tel 202-857-1400.

Baroness Pubns., Ltd., Inc., *(Baroness FL; 0-938568),* 1442 Gulf-to-Bay, Clearwater, FL 33515 (SAN 238-714X).

Barr-Randol Publishing Co., *(Barr-Randol Pub; 0-934581),* 136A N. Grand Ave., West Covina, CA 91791 (SAN 694-0714) Tel 818-339-0270.

Barre Publishing Co., *(Barre),* ; Toll free: 800-526-4264; Dist. by: Crown Publishers, Inc., 225 Park Ave., New York, NY 10003 (SAN 200-2639) Tel 212-254-1600. *Imprints:* Westover Pub Co. (Westover).

Barrett & Co., Pubs., *(Barrett; 0-9609396),* P.O. Box 6700, Jackson, MS 39212 (SAN 240-8732) Tel 601-373-4400; P.O. Box 1182, Houston, TX 77251 (SAN 685-3161) Tel 713-641-6335.

Barrett Bk. Co., *(Barrett Bk; 0-932684),* 1123 High Ridge Rd., Stamford, CT 06905 (SAN 211-5883).

Barrie Road Bks., *(Barrie Rd Bks; 0-937293),* 6400 Barrie Rd., No. 611, Edina, MN 55435 (SAN 658-7771) Tel 612-929-7692.

Barrier & Kennedy, ESL, *(Barrier & Kennedy; 0-911743),* P.O. Box 58273, Raleigh, NC 27658 (SAN 276-9689) Tel 919-847-1079.

Barrington Hall Pr., *(Barrington IA; 0-942066),* Box 118, Greeley, IA 52050 (SAN 238-6429) Tel 319-925-2962.

Barrington Hse. Publishing Co., *(Barrington Hse; 0-935323),* 1119 Lorne Way, Sunnyvale, CA 94087 (SAN 695-7501) Tel 408-241-8422.

Barrington Pr., *(Barrington AZ; 0-916229),* 4102 E. 27th St., Tucson, AZ 85711 (SAN 294-8990) Tel 602-745-0070; Dist. by: Pacific Literary Assocs., 4102 E. 27th St., Tucson, AZ 85711 (SAN 200-7770).

Barrington Pr., *(Barrington MA; 0-9616920),* P.O. Box 291, Boston Univ. Sta., Boston, MA 02215 (SAN 661-3942); 28 Lakewood Rd., Newton Highlands, MA 02161 (SAN 661-3950) Tel 617-969-9346.

Barron Enterprises, *(Barron Enter; 0-9603446),* 714 Willow Glen Rd., Santa Barbara, CA 93105 (SAN 222-2787) Tel 805-687-5873.

Barrows Co., Inc., *(Barrows Co; 0-89069),* 116 E. 66th St., New York, NY 10021 (SAN 203-137X) Tel 212-772-1199.

Barry, M. J. P., *(M J P Barry; 0-9617009),* 323 W. Harvard Ave., Anchorage, AK 99501 (SAN 662-9148) Tel 907-272-0668.

Barth, Robert L., *(Barth; 0-941150),* 14 Lucas St., Florence, KY 41042 (SAN 238-9126).

Bartholomew Bks., *(Bartholomew Bks; 0-933123),* P.O. Box 634, Inverness, CA 94937 (SAN 689-7363) Tel 415-669-1664.

Bartleby Pr., *(Bartleby Pr; 0-910155),* 11141 Georgia Ave., No. A6, Silver Spring, MD 20902 (SAN 241-2098) Tel 301-949-2443.

Bartleby, The, a Cape Elizabeth Journal, *(Bartleby; 0-937981),* Cape Elizabeth High Schl., Ocean House Rd., Cape Elizabeth, ME 04107 (SAN 659-4905) Tel 207-799-3309.

Barton, Cyril, *(C Barton; 0-9613277),* Rte. One, Waltonville, IL 62894 (SAN 654-357X) Tel 618-279-3475.

Barton-Jay, David, Projects, The, *(Barton-Jay Proj; 0-910409),* 175 Fifth Ave., Suite 3156, New York, NY 10010 (SAN 260-1168) Tel 212-929-4576.

Barton Publishing Co., *(Barton Pub; 0-9616702),* P.O. Box 160786, Austin, TX 78746 (SAN 659-7939); 1406-B Rabb Rd., Austin, TX 78704 (SAN 659-7947) Tel 512-447-2871.

Baruch, Bernard M., College Alumni Assn., Inc., *(Alumni Assn; 0-9606858),* 17 Lexington Ave., College Box 280, New York, NY 10010 (SAN 217-2275).

Basal Books, Div. of Basal-Tech, Inc., *(Basal Books; 0-916961),* 726 Lafayette Ave, Cincinnati, OH 45220 (SAN 292-3289) Tel 513-751-2723.

Basbery Publishing Co., *(Basbery Pub; 0-912875),* 2349 Seven Pines Dr., Suite 4, St. Louis, MO 63146 (SAN 283-2941) Tel 314-434-0329.

Base 8 Publishing, *(Base Eight; 0-938207),* P.O. Box 1211, Carpinteria, CA 93013 (SAN 659-7874); 4415-A Catlin Cir., Carpinteria, CA 93013 (SAN 659-7882) Tel 805-684-1153.

Baseball Histories, Inc., *(Baseball Hist; 0-9608534),* P.O. Box 15168, St. Louis, MO 63110 (SAN 240-5954) Tel 314-535-4215.

Basement Pr., *(Basement Pr; 0-9611240),* P.O. Box 284, Columbus, NE 68601 (SAN 283-0825) Tel 402-564-5054.

Bash Educational Services, Inc., *(Bash Educ Serv; 0-938408),* P.O. Box 2115, San Leandro, CA 94577 (SAN 218-4664) Tel 415-278-8275.

†Basic Bks., Inc., Subs. of Harper & Row Pubs., Inc., *(Basic; 0-465),* 10 E. 53rd St., New York, NY 10022 (SAN 201-4521) Tel 212-207-7292; Toll free: 800-242-7737; *CIP.*

Basic Computer Literacy Inc., *(Basic Comp Lit; 0-931983),* 370 N. Locust, Manteno, IL 60950 (SAN 686-0931) Tel 815-468-8178.

Basic English Revisited, *(Basic Eng Rev; 0-9605312; 0-939045),* P.O. Box J, Burlington, WI 53105 (SAN 215-2959) Tel 414-763-8258.

Basic Science Pr., *(Basic Sci Pr; 0-917410),* 1608 Via Lazo, Palos Verdes Estates, CA 90274 (SAN 209-6498) Tel 213-375-6740.

Basil Blackwell (England) *See* Porcupine Pr., Inc.

Basil Hill, Inc., *(Basil Hill Inc; 0-910207; 0-930299),* R.D. 1, Morris, PA 16938 (SAN 238-0625) Tel 301-622-3289.

Basin/Plateau Pr., *(Basin Plateau Pr; 0-9617133),* P.O. Box 155, Eureka, UT 84628 (SAN 662-9563); Hatfield at Emerald Alley, Eureka, UT 84628 (SAN 662-9571) Tel 801-248-0709.

Basin Publishing Co., *(Basin Pub),* 168 Weyford Terrace, Garden City, NY 11530 (SAN 208-4622) Tel 516-741-0668.

Basis Bks., *(Basis Bks; 0-9614676),* P.O. Box 5254, Lake Station, IN 46405 (SAN 690-0402) Tel 219-962-3502.

†Bask Industries, *(Bask Indus; 0-917746),* 400 Dwight Rd., Burlingame, CA 94010 (SAN 209-1992) Tel 415-347-8396; *CIP.*

Bass, Clarence, Ripped Enterprises, *(Clarence Bass; 0-9609714),* 528 Chama NE, Albuquerque, NM 87108 (SAN 268-229X) Tel 505-266-5858.

Bassett & Brush, *(Bassett & Brush; 0-9605548),* W. 4108 Francis Ave., Spokane, WA 99205 (SAN 216-3349).

Bastian, Marlene Y., *(M Y Bastian; 0-9609058),* 240 SE 87th, Portland, OR 97216 (SAN 241-2101) Tel 503-252-0989.

Basu, Romen, *(R Basu),* Rm. DC1-1215, P.O. Box 20, New York, NY 10163-0020 (SAN 276-9670) Tel 212-249-6743.

Bataan Bk. Pubs., Inc., *(Bataan Bk Pubs; 0-9608294),* P.O. Box 18238, Pittsburgh, PA 15236 (SAN 240-1339) Tel 412-653-3884.

Bates, William L., Pub., *(W L Bates; 0-9615781),* 317 Ave. B, Snohomish, WA 98290 (SAN 699-7988) Tel 206-568-2508.

Bath Street Press, *(Bath St Pr; 0-937618),* 1016 Bath St., Ann Arbor, MI 48103 (SAN 215-2967) Tel 313-663-2071.

Battaglia Enterprises Inc., *(Battaglia Ent; 0-9614063),* 3280 Turner Hill Rd., Lithonia, GA 30058 (SAN 686-0540) Tel 404-482-2603.

†**Battelle Pr.,** Div. of Battelle Memorial Institute, *(Battelle; 0-935470),* 505 King Ave., Columbus, OH 43201-2693 (SAN 213-4640) Tel 614-424-6393; Toll free: 800-526-7254; *CIP.*

Batterers Anonymous Press, *(Batterers Anon; 0-9612754),* 1269 North E St., San Bernardino, CA 92405 (SAN 289-730X) Tel 714-884-6809.

Battery Park Book Co., *(Battery Pk; 0-89782),* Box 710, Forest Hills, NY 11375 (SAN 211-5891).

Battery Pr., *(Battery Pr; 0-89839),* P.O. Box 3107, Uptown Sta., Nashville, TN 37219 (SAN 212-5897) Tel 615-298-1401.

Baublitz, Jacinth Ivie, *(J I Baublitz; 0-9610316),* 3708 Westbrier Terrace, Midland, MI 48640 (SAN 263-9327) Tel 517-835-6351.

Bauer, Mary Anne, Productions, *(M A Bauer; 0-9613619),* 7311 SE 31st St., Portland, OR 97202 (SAN 671-0085) Tel 503-777-0373.

Bauer, Richard E., *(R E Bauer),* 1524 Pleasant Court, Sheldon, IA 51201 (SAN 656-0431).

Bauer, Rosemarie, *(Bauer),* Rte. 1, Box 1438, Granite City, IL 62040 (SAN 217-2984).

†**Bauhan, William L., Inc.,** *(Bauhan; 0-87233),* Old County Rd., Dublin, NH 03444 (SAN 204-384X) Tel 603-563-8020; *CIP.*

Bawden Bros, Inc., *(Bawden Bros),* 400 S. 14th Ave., Eldridge, IA 52748 (SAN 212-0585) Tel 319-285-4800.

Baxter Group, The, *(Baxter Group; 0-938949),* P.O. Box 61672, Sunnyvale, CA 94086 (SAN 661-7247); 2966 Moorpark, No. 36, San Jose, CA 95128 (SAN 661-7255) Tel 408-248-8308.

Bay, Alfred, *(Alfred Bay; 0-9615634),* 2390 El Camino Real, No. 1, Palo Alto, CA 94306 (SAN 696-0723) Tel 415-494-1374.

Bay Area Cross Cultural Consultants, *(Bay Area Cross; 0-932211),* 10344 San Pablo Ave., El Cerrito, CA 94530 (SAN 686-600X) Tel 415-526-1633.

Bay Area Explorers, *(Bay Area CA; 0-9615635),* P.O. Box 519, San Ramon, CA 94583 (SAN 696-0782) Tel 415-828-4957.

Bay Area Pilipino Writers, *(Bay Area Pilipino; 0-9616181),* P.O. Box 5646, San Francisco, CA 94101 (SAN 658-3148) Tel 415-626-1650.

†**Bay Bks., of Brewster,** *(Bay Brewster; 0-918781),* P.O. Box L, Brewster, MA 02631 (SAN 657-3290) Tel 617-255-7591; *CIP.*

Bay Institute of San Francisco, *(Bay Inst SF; 0-937995),* 5080 Paradise Dr., Tiburon, CA 94920 (SAN 659-7890) Tel 415-435-5922.

Bay Pr., *(Bay Pr; 0-941920),* 3710 Discovery Rd., N, Port Townsend, WA 98368 (SAN 237-9902) Tel 206-385-1270.

Bay Pubns., *(Bay Pubns; 0-9615014),* P.O. Box 404, Panama City, FL 32401 (SAN 694-034X) Tel 904-785-7870; Dist. by: Wimmer Brothers Bks., 4210 B.F. Goodrich Blvd., Memphis, TN 38181 (SAN 209-6544) Tel 901-362-8900.

Bay Village Women's Club & Foundation, *(Bay Vil Womens; 0-9616678),* 343 Walmar Dr., Bay Village, OH 44140 (SAN 659-7904) Tel 216-871-3075.

Bayard Pubns., Inc., *(Bayard Pubns; 0-933268),* 500 Summer St., Stamford, CT 06901 (SAN 212-4033) Tel 203-327-0800.

Bayberry Pr., *(Bayberry NY; 0-936403),* 7 Colonial Rd., Port Washington, NY 11050 (SAN 698-164X) Tel 516-767-0633.

Bayberry Pr., *(Bayberry Pr; 0-916326),* 21 Little Fox Ln., Westport, CT 06880 (SAN 222-562X).

Bayland Publishing, Inc., *(Bayland Pub; 0-934018),* P.O. Box 25386, Houston, TX 77005 (SAN 214-1051) Tel 713-524-3000. *Imprints:* Houston Home/Garden Magazine Books (Houston Home-Garden Mag).

Baylin/Gale Productions, *(Baylin Gale; 0-917893),* 1905 Mariposa, Boulder, CO 80302 (SAN 697-2721) Tel 303-449-4551.

Baylor Univ. Pr., *(Baylor Univ Pr; 0-918954),* Academic Pubns., CSB 547, Baylor Univ., Waco, TX 76798 (SAN 685-317X) Tel 817-755-3164; Orders to: Book Dept., Baylor Bk. Store, P.O. Box 6325, Waco, TX 76706 (SAN 204-4404) Tel 817-755-2161.

Bayou Cuisine, *(Bayou Cuisine; 0-9606490),* P.O. Box 1005, Indianola, MS 38751 (SAN 208-0613) Tel 601-887-4365.

Bayou Pr., Div. of Angleton Investments, Inc., *(Bayou Pr; 0-9615254),* P.O. Box 1086, Angleton, TX 77515 (SAN 694-4574) Tel 409-849-4874.

Bayou Publishing Co., *(Bayou Pub Co; 0-9602570),* 5200 Bon Air Dr., Monroe, LA 71203 (SAN 213-2850) Tel 318-343-1964.

†**Bayshore Books,** *(Bayshore Bks; 0-9602314),* Box 848, Nokomis, FL 33555 (SAN 212-7237) Tel 813-485-2564; *CIP.*

Bayside Publishing Co., *(Bayside; 0-913794),* 1350 77th Ave., N., St. Petersburg, FL 33702 (SAN 202-3806).

Bayway Bks., *(Bayway Bks; 0-938363),* P.O. Box 66436, St. Petersburg Beach, FL 33736 (SAN 659-7912); 4900 Brittany Dr. S., Suite 901, St. Petersburg, FL 33715 (SAN 659-7920) Tel 813-867-0025.

†**Baywood Publishing, Co., Inc.,** *(Baywood Pub; 0-89503),* 120 Marine St., P.O. Box D, Farmingdale, NY 11735 (SAN 206-9326) Tel 516-293-7130; *CIP.*

BCS Associates, *(BCS Assocs; 0-914515),* P.O. Box 3614, Univ. Sta., Moscow, ID 83843 (SAN 289-5838) Tel 208-855-6692.

BCS Educational Aids, Inc., *(BCS Educ Aids; 0-938416),* P.O. Box 100, Bothell, WA 98041 (SAN 239-9326) Tel 206-485-4110.

Be All Bks., *(Be All Bks; 0-9601848),* P.O. Box 941, Sonoma, CA 95476 (SAN 212-1476).

Beacham, Roger, Pub., *(Beacham; 0-911796),* 4509 Balcones Dr., Austin, TX 78731 (SAN 202-3814) Tel 512-451-4572.

Beachcomber Books, *(Beachcomber Bks; 0-913076),* P.O. Box 197, Cortaro, AZ 85652 (SAN 202-3822) Tel 602-744-1619.

Beachcomber Press, *(Beachcomber Pr; 0-9614628),* Box 1313 Belgrade Rd., Oakland, ME 04963 (SAN 691-8891) Tel 207-465-7197.

Beacon Hill Pr. of Kansas City, Subs. of Nazarene Publishing Hse., *(Beacon Hill; 0-8341),* Dist. by: Nazarene Publishing Hse., P.O. Box 527, Kansas City, MO 64141 (SAN 202-9022) Tel 816-931-1900.

Beacon Hse., Inc., *(Beacon Hse; 0-87648),* Welsh Rd. & Butler Pk., Ambler, PA 19002 (SAN 202-3830) Tel 215-643-7800.

Beacon Pr., Inc., *(Beacon Pr; 0-8070),* 25 Beacon St., Boston, MA 02108 (SAN 201-4483) Tel 617-742-2110; Orders to: Harper & Row Pubs., Inc., 10 E. 53rd St., New York, NY 10022 (SAN 200-2086) Tel 212-207-7099; Toll free: 800-242-7737. *Imprints:* Ariadne Books (Ariadne Bks).

Beacon West Pubns., *(Beacon West; 0-9613168),* P.O. Box 1176, Encinitas, CA 92024 (SAN 294-9008) Tel 619-753-4707.

Bead-Craft, *(Bead-Craft; 0-9613503),* 1549 Ashland Ave., St. Paul, MN 55104 (SAN 657-2510) Tel 612-645-1216.

Bead Society, The, *(Bead Society; 0-939678),* 6500 Romaine St., No.7, Los Angeles, CA 90038 (SAN 216-7166) Tel 213-467-8982; Orders to: P.O. Box 2513, Culver City, CA 90231 (SAN 661-955X) Tel 213-838-0110.

Beagle Bks., Inc., *(Beagle Bks NY; 0-8441),* 101 Fifth Ave., New York, NY 10003 (SAN 658-6295) Tel 212-691-7131.

Beale, B. DeRoy, *(B D Beale; 0-9602132),* 8529 Spalding Dr., Richmond, VA 23229 (SAN 223-4971) Tel 804-741-1836.

Beale, Guthrie, Pr., *(G Beale Pr; 0-937781),* 7508 42nd Ave., NE, Seattle, WA 98115 (SAN 659-2279) Tel 206-525-6596.

Bean Publishing Co., *(Bean Pub Co; 0-935905),* 2624 Green Oak Pl., Los Angeles, CA 90068 (SAN 696-6888) Tel 213-463-2033.

Beanie Bks., *(Beanie Bks; 0-933530),* 7443 Stanford, St. Louis, MO 63130 (SAN 281-3130).

Beanstalk Productions, Inc., *(Beanstalk Prod; 0-937629),* 160 Madison Ave., 6th Flr., New York, NY 10016 (SAN 659-0241) Tel 212-686-3270.

Bear, Clair, Publishing Co., *(Bear Pub Co; 0-934857),* P.O. Box 13623, Kansas City, MO 64199 (SAN 694-5589) Tel 913-648-6017; Dist. by: Distributors, The, 702 S. Michigan, South Bend, IN 46618 (SAN 169-2488) Tel 219-232-8500.

Bear & Co., Inc., *(Bear & Co; 0-939680),* P.O. Drawer 2860, Santa Fe, NM 87504-2860 (SAN 216-7174) Tel 505-983-5968; Toll free: 800-932-3277; Dist. by: Bookpeople, 2929 Fifth St., Berkeley, CA 94710 (SAN 168-9517) Tel 415-549-3030; Dist. by: Spring Arbor Distributors, 10885 Textile Rd., Belleville, MI 48111 (SAN 158-9016) Tel 313-481-0900; Dist. by: New Leaf Distributing, 1020 White St., SW, Atlanta, GA 30310 (SAN 169-1449) Tel 404-755-3454; Dist. by: Distributors, The, 702 S. Michigan, South Bend, IN 46618 (SAN 212-0364) Tel 404-755-3454; Dist. by: Inland Bk. Co., 22 Hemingway Ave., East Haven, CT 06512 (SAN 200-4151) Tel 203-467-4257; Dist. by: Quality Bks., 400 Anthony Trail, Northbrook, IL 60062 (SAN 169-2127).

Bear Creek Pubns., *(Bear Crk Pubns; 0-936005),* 2507 Minor Ave. E., Seattle, WA 98102 (SAN 696-687X) Tel 206-885-0864.

Bear Creek Publishing Co., *(Bear Creek Pub; 0-941026),* P.O. Box 254, Ouray, CO 81427 (SAN 217-3298) Tel 303-325-4700; P.O. Box 2024, Cottonwood, AZ 86326 (SAN 692-4166) Tel 602-634-9636.

Bear Flag Bks., *(Bear Flag Bks; 0-933271),* 941 Populus Pl., Sunnyvale, CA 94086 (SAN 691-7941) Tel 408-739-7508.

Bear Hollow Pr., Subs. of Shuttle Hill Herb Shop, Inc., *(Bear Hollow Pr; 0-938209),* 110 Salisbury Rd., Delmar, NY 12054 (SAN 659-459X) Tel 518-439-9065.

Bear Pubns., *(Bear; 0-912934),* P.O. Box 16, Cambridge, NY 12816 (SAN 202-3857) Tel 518-677-2766.

Bear State Books, *(Bear State),* 304 High St., Santa Cruz, CA 95060 (SAN 213-6112) Tel 408-426-3272.

Bear Tribe Publishing, *(Bear Tribe; 0-943404),* P.O. Box 9167, Spokane, WA 99209 (SAN 207-8643) Tel 509-326-6561.

Bear Wallow Publishing Co., The, *(Bear Wallow Pub; 0-936376),* High Valley Foothill Rd., Union, OR 97883 (SAN 223-3916) Tel 503-562-5687.

Beardsley Pr., The, *(Beardsley Pr; 0-9616445),* P.O. Box 32, Sanford, FL 32772-0032 (SAN 659-0268) Tel 305-321-5283; 827 Rosalia Dr., Sanford, FL 32771 (SAN 659-0276).

Bearly Ltd., *(Bearly Ltd; 0-943456),* 149 York St., Buffalo, NY 14213 (SAN 239-3549) Tel 716-883-4571.

Beatitude, *(Beatitude SF; 0-9617010),* 575 Columbus Ave., No. 27, San Francisco, CA 94133 (SAN 662-8966) Tel 415-986-9684. Do not confuse wity Beatitude Pr., Berkeley, CA.

Beatty, R. O., & Assocs., *(R O Beatty Assocs; 0-916238),* P.O. Box 763, Boise, ID 83701 (SAN 207-9909) Tel 208-343-4949.

Beatty, R. W., *(Beatty; 0-87948),* P.O. Box 26, Arlington, VA 22210 (SAN 206-7110).

Beau Bayou Publishing Co., *(Beau Bayou; 0-935619),* P.O. Box 53089, Lafayette, LA 70505 (SAN 696-0804) Tel 318-234-5991; Toll free: 800-624-0466; 227 LaRue France, Lafayette, LA 70508 (SAN 696-0812).

Beau Lac Pubs., *(Beau Lac; 0-911980),* P.O. Box 248, Chuluota, FL 32766 (SAN 202-3865) Tel 305-365-3830.

Beau Rivage Press, *(Beau Rivage; 0-931174),* Seven E. 14th St., Suite 1112, New York, NY 10003 (SAN 211-3090) Tel 212-989-1625.

Beaufort Bk. Co., *(Beaufort SC; 0-910206),* Box 1127, Beaufort, SC 29902 (SAN 202-3873) Tel 803-524-5172. Do not confuse with Beaufort Bks., Inc., New York, NY.

Names

†**Beaufort Bks., Inc.,** *(Beaufort Bks NY; 0-8253),* 9 E. 40th St., New York, NY 10016 (SAN 215-2304) Tel 212-685-8588; Toll free: 800-526-7626; Dist. by: Kampmann & Co., 9 E. 40th St., New York, NY 10016 (SAN 202-5191) Tel 212-685-2928; Toll free: 800-526-7626; *CIP.*

Beaufort County Open Land Trust, Inc., *(Beaufort County),* Box 75, Beaufort, SC 29902 (SAN 217-2879).

Beaulieu, Beth Sea, *(B S Beaulieu; 0-9608796),* 22 Wells Ave., Chicopee, MA 01020 (SAN 241-0001) Tel 413-598-8551.

Beaumont Bks., Affil. of Malsam Marketing, *(Beaumont Bks; 0-9616108),* 3333 W. 55th Ave., Denver, CO 80221 (SAN 699-7155) Tel 303-433-9192.

†**Beautiful America Publishing Co.,** *(Beautiful Am; 0-89802; 0-915796),* 9725 SW Commerce Cir., Wilsonville, OR 97070 (SAN 211-4623) Tel 503-682-0173; *CIP.*

Beautiful Day Bks., *(Beautiful Day; 0-930296),* 3318 Gumwood Dr., Hyattsville, MD 20783 (SAN 210-587X) Tel 301-442-3609.

Beauty Without Cruelty, *(Beauty Without Cruelty),* 175 W. 12th St., New York, NY 10011 (SAN 225-896X).

Beaux Arts, Inc., *(Beaux Arts; 0-9607010),* c/o Lowe Art Museum, 1301 Stanford Dr., Coral Gables, FL 33146 (SAN 279-4357) Tel 305-667-9346.

†**Beaux-Arts Pr./BAP Bks.,** *(Beaux-Arts Pr; 0-916965),* 808 Post St., Suite 1106, San Francisco, CA 94109 (SAN 655-5713) Tel 415-474-4900; Dist. by: Bookpeople, 2929 Fifth St., Berkeley, CA 94710 (SAN 168-9517) Tel 415-549-3030; *CIP.*

Beaver Publications, *(Beaver Pubns; 0-9611234),* 15605 NW. Cornell Rd., Beaverton, OR 97006 (SAN 282-8286) Tel 503-645-8425.

Beaver Tails & Dorsal Fins, *(Beaver Tails; 0-9615949),* P.O. Box 615, Menominee, MI 49858 (SAN 697-3353) Tel 906-863-3820; 3301 15th St., Menominee, MI 49858 (SAN 697-3361).

Beavers, *(Beavers; 0-910208),* Star Rte., Box 537, Laporte, MN 56461 (SAN 202-389X) Tel 218-224-2182.

Becht, W. Nicholas, *(W N Becht; 0-9617254),* P.O. Box 56, Owensville, IN 47665 (SAN 663-5814) Tel 812-724-4601; 405 S. Main St., Owensville, IN 47665 (SAN 663-5822).

Beck, Donald, *(D Beck),* P.O. Box 53, Maple Glen, PA 19002 (SAN 693-3998).

Becker, Beverly, *(B Becker; 0-9602000),* P.O. Box 360, Park Ridge, IL 60068 (SAN 212-2693) Tel 312-635-0306.

Beckham Hse. Pubs., Inc., *(Beckham House; 0-931761),* 77 Ives St., Suite 49, Providence, RI 02906 (SAN 683-2237).

Beckman, Steven D., *(S D Beckman; 0-9609434),* 621 Palm Ave., Lodi, CA 95240 (SAN 284-9755) Tel 209-369-3903.

Beckman, Tom, & Assoc., *(T Beckman & Assoc; 0-937204),* P.O. Box 20081, Cincinnati, OH 45219 (SAN 213-2710).

Beckwith, Burnham Putnam, *(Beckwith; 0-9603262),* 656 Lytton Ave., (C430), Palo Alto, CA 94301 (SAN 211-884X) Tel 415-324-0342.

Becoming Pr., *(Becoming Pr; 0-9616204),* P.O. Box 221383, Carmel, CA 93922 (SAN 658-3172) Tel 408-625-3188.

Becraft, Melvin E., *(M E Becraft; 0-9615981),* 1240 Holly Ave., Rohnert Park, CA 94928 (SAN 698-1631) Tel 707-585-2095; Orders to: P.O. Box 2236, Rohnert Park, CA 94928 (SAN 662-4014).

Bed & Breakfast Registry, *(Bed & Breakfast; 0-9616205),* P.O. Box 8174, St. Paul, MN 55108 (SAN 658-3210) Tel 612-646-4238; 1519 Grantham, St. Paul, MN 55108 (SAN 658-3229).

Beddoe Publishing, *(Beddoe Pub; 0-9606106),* 430 Closter Dock Rd., Closter, NJ 07624 (SAN 220-2344).

Beddow, F. Lorlene, *(F L Beddow; 0-9615982),* 1437 SW 37th St., No. 2, Pendleton, OR 97801 (SAN 698-1623) Tel 503-276-2610; Dist. by: Pacific Northwest Bks., P.O. Box 314, Medford, OR 97501 (SAN 200-5263) Tel 503-664-4442.

Bedford Bks., *(Bedford Bks; 0-935199),* P.O. Box 709, Bedford, TX 76021 (SAN 695-7366) Tel 817-540-0346.

Bedford Hills Publishing Co., Inc., *(Bedford Hills Pub; 0-936153),* 205 Adams St., Bedford Hills, NY 10507 (SAN 697-0087) Tel 914-241-7007.

Bedford Pr. Pubs., *(Bedford Pr; 0-938491),* 472 Jackson St., San Francisco, CA 94133 (SAN 659-7955) Tel 415-362-3730.

Bedford Publishers, Inc., *(Bedford Publishers; 0-911557),* 779 Kirts, Troy, MI 48084 (SAN 268-2435) Tel 313-362-0369.

Bedous Press, *(Bedous; 0-918094),* P.O. Box K, Beaverton, OR 97075 (SAN 210-1742) Tel 503-649-7844.

Bedpress Books *See* **New Bedford Pr.**

Bedrick, Peter, Bks., *(P Bedrick Bks; 0-911745; 0-87226),* 125 E. 23rd St., New York, NY 10010 (SAN 263-9335) Tel 212-777-1187; Dist. by: Harper & Row Pubs., Inc., Keystone Industrial Pk., Scranton, PA 18512 (SAN 215-3742); Toll free: 800-C-HARPER. *Imprints:* Bedrick/Blackie (Bedrick Blackie).

Bedrick, Blackie *See* **Bedrick, Peter, Bks.**

Bee Tree Productions, *(Bee Tree; 0-937083),* P.O. Box 9156, Asheville, NC 28815 (SAN 699-7767) Tel 704-298-2877; 298 Long Branch Rd., Swannanoa, NC 28778 (SAN 658-3032).

Beeberry Books, *(Beeberry Bks; 0-9601996),* 230 Maclane, Palo Alto, CA 94306 (SAN 216-017X) Tel 415-494-2969.

†**Beech Hill Publishing Co.,** *(Beech Hill; 0-933786),* Box 136, Southwest Harbor, ME 04679 (SAN 212-6419) Tel 207-244-3931; *CIP.*

Beech Leaf Press, *(Beech Leaf; 0-939294),* Dist. by: Kalamazoo Nature Ctr., Inc., 7000 N. Westnedge Ave., Kalamazoo, MI 49007 (SAN 268-2478) Tel 616-381-1574.

Beech Tree Farm Publications, *(Beech Tree; 0-910210),* 702 Edwards Rd. No. 121, Greenville, SC 29615 (SAN 201-4475) Tel 803-268-7888.

Beechcliff Bks., *(Beechcliff Bks; 0-9608930),* 100 Severn Ave., Suite 605, Annapolis, MD 21403 (SAN 241-001X) Tel 301-263-3580.

Beecher, Willard & Marguerite, Foundation, *(Beecher Found; 0-942350),* 8400 Westchester, Suite 300, Dallas, TX 75225 (SAN 281-3165); c/o Today's Books, 3775 Walnut Hill Lane, Dallas, TX 75229-6139 (SAN 281-3173).

Beechtree Pr., *(Beechtree Pr),* P.O. Box 15669, Long Beach, CA 90815 (SAN 669-6465) Tel 213-429-5210.

Beechwood Bks., *(Beechwood; 0-912221),* P.O. Box 20484, Birmingham, AL 35216 (SAN 265-0797) Tel 205-823-2376.

Beefmasters Breeders Universal, *(Beefmasters),* 11201 Morning Court, San Antonio, TX 78213 (SAN 224-9936) Tel 512-344-3132.

Beekman Hill, Pr., *(Beekman Hill; 0-940534),* 342 E. 51st St., Apt. 3A, New York, NY 10022 (SAN 222-9919) Tel 212-755-0218.

†**Beekman Publishers, Inc.,** *(Beekman Pubs; 0-8464),* P.O. Box 888, Woodstock, NY 12498 (SAN 201-4467) Tel 914-679-2300; *CIP.*

Beeline Bks., *(Beeline Bks; 0-9611020),* P.O. Box 6121, Albany, NY 12206 (SAN 285-127X) Tel 518-434-3236; 169 Central Ave., Albany, NY 12206 (SAN 285-1288).

Beer Can Collectors of America, *(Beer Can Coll),* 747 Merus Ct., Fenton, MO 63026 (SAN 268-2486) Tel 314-343-6486.

Beer Flat Music, *(Beer Flat; 0-911999),* 3451 Riviera Dr., San Diego, CA 92109 (SAN 264-6021) Tel 619-272-2514.

†**Beginner Books,** Div. of Random House, Inc., *(Beginner; 0-394),* 201 E. 50th St., New York, NY 10022 (SAN 202-3288) Tel 212-751-2600; Toll free: 800-638-6460; Orders to: 400 Hahn Rd., Westminster, MD 21157 (SAN 202-3296); *CIP.*

Beginning Pr., *(Beginning Pr; 0-9615514),* 1000 Union, No. 202, Seattle, WA 98101 (SAN 296-0855) Tel 206-682-3622; Dist. by: Pacific Pipeline, Inc., 19215 66th Ave., S., Kent, WA 98032 (SAN 208-2128) Tel 206-872-5523; Toll free: 800-426-3711.

Behavior Science Systems, Inc., *(Behavior Sci Systs; 0-936787),* P.O. Box 1108, Minneapolis, MN 55440 (SAN 699-8976) Tel 612-929-6220; 4860 W. 39th St., No. 317, St. Louis Park, MN 55416 (SAN 699-8984).

Behavioral Medicine Press, *(Behavioral Med Pr; 0-9613198),* 3390 Andover, Ann Arbor, MI 48105 (SAN 295-6519).

Behavioral Publications, Inc. *See* **Human Sciences Pr., Inc.**

Behavioral Publishing Co., Div. of Behavioral Therapy Institute, *(Behavioral Pub; 0-940904),* 1736 Old Grove Rd., Pasadena, CA 91107 (SAN 217-3301) Tel 818-791-7999.

Behavioral Research Council, Div. of American Institute for Economic Research, *(Behavioral Mass; 0-913610),* Division St., Great Barrington, MA 01230 (SAN 201-7458) Tel 413-528-1216.

Behavioral Science Ctr., Inc., Pubs., Div. of Behavioral Science Ctr., Inc., *(Behav Sci Ctr Pubns; 0-938837),* 2522 Highland Ave., Cincinnati, OH 45219 (SAN 661-6895) Tel 513-221-8545.

Behavioral Science Research Pr., Inc., *(Behavioral Sci; 0-935907),* 2695 Villa Creek Dr., No. 180, Dallas, TX 75234 (SAN 696-6896) Tel 214-243-8543.

Behavioral Studies Press, *(Behavioral Studies; 0-911958),* P.O. Box 5323, Beverly Hills, CA 90210 (SAN 202-3903) Tel 213-472-2662.

Behavioral Systems, Inc., *(Behavorial Sys Inc; 0-9610136),* Rte. 2, P.O. Box 630, Marshall, VA 22115 (SAN 268-2559) Tel 703-435-8181.

Behavioronics, *(Behavioronics; 0-938679),* P.O. Box 8207, Corpus Christi, TX 78412-0207 (SAN 661-3837); 1746 Star Cove Dr., Corpus Christi, TX 78412 (SAN 661-3845) Tel 512-993-8297.

Behemoth Publishing, *(Behemoth Pub; 0-9606782),* Star Rte., Oasis, UT 84650 (SAN 217-331X) Tel 801-864-2842.

Behemoth Publishing *See* **Media & Travel Pubns.**

†**Behrman Hse., Inc.,** *(Behrman; 0-87441),* 235 Watchung Ave., West Orange, NJ 07052 (SAN 201-4459) Tel 201-669-0447; Toll free: 800-221-2755; *CIP.*

Beil, Frederic C., Publishing Co., *(Beil; 0-913720),* 321 E. 43rd St., New York, NY 10017 (SAN 240-9909) Tel 212-682-5519. *Imprints:* Sandstone Press (Sandstone Pr).

Being Books, *(Being Bks; 0-938292),* 19834 Gresham St., Northridge, CA 91324 (SAN 215-7292) Tel 818-341-0283.

Being Pubns, *(Being Pubns),* 1530 Valley Ave. NW, Grand Rapids, MI 49504 (SAN 207-7876).

Beitzell, Edwin W., *(E W Beitzell; 0-9604502),* P.O. Box 107, Abell, MD 20606 (SAN 204-4374) Tel 301-769-3279; Dist. by: St. Mary's County Historical Society, P.O. Box 212, Leonardtown, MD 20650 (SAN 200-545X) Tel 301-475-2467.

Bek Technical Pubns., Inc., *(Bek Tech; 0-912884),* 1700 Painters Run Rd., Pittsburgh, PA 15243 (SAN 202-3911) Tel 412-221-0900.

Bel-Air Publishing Co., *(Bel-Air),* 249 S. Camden Drive, Beverly Hills, CA 90212 (SAN 263-2454).

Bel-Del Enterprises, Ltd., The, *(Bel-Del Ent; 0-9616893),* 1016 Vista Grande Dr. NW, Albuquerque, NM 87105 (SAN 661-3217) Tel 505-836-4353; Dist. by: Tri-State Railway Historical Society, Inc., P.O. Box 2243, Clifton, NJ 07015-2243 (SAN 239-3301) Tel 201-857-2987.

Bel Esprit Press, *(Bel Esprit; 0-9607118),* 10 E. 23rd St., New York, NY 10010 (SAN 239-409X).

Belforte Assocs., *(Belforte Assoc; 0-916389),* P.O. Box 245, Sturbridge, MA 01566 (SAN 295-9429) Tel 617-347-9324.

Belier Pr., Inc., *(Belier Pr; 0-914646),* P.O. Box 1234 Old Chelsea Sta., New York, NY 10113 (SAN 206-4766) Tel 212-620-4276.

Believers Bookshelf, *(Believers Bkshelf; 0-941202),* Box 261, Sunbury, PA 17801 (SAN 211-7746) Tel 717-672-2134.

Believers Faith Center, *(Believers Faith; 0-912573),* 148 E. 22nd St., Costa Mesa, CA 92627 (SAN 277-657X) Tel 714-650-0447.

Bell, Alexander Graham, Assn. for the Deaf, *(Alexander Graham; 0-88200),* 3417 Volta Pl., NW, Washington, DC 20007 (SAN 203-6924) Tel 202-337-5220.

Bell, D. Rayford, Bishop, *(D R Bell; 0-9604820; 0-938195),* 1225 McDaniel Ave., Evanston, IL 60202 (SAN 215-8388) Tel 618-869-1907.

Bell, James W., Publisher, *(J W Bell; 0-939130),* 7611 Briarwood Dr., Little Rock, AR 72205 (SAN 216-1044); Dist. by: Publishers Distribution Service, 7509 Cantrell Rd., Little Rock, AR 72207 (SAN 282-5937).

Bell, Robert L., *(R L Bell; 0-9602450),* 669 Main St., Melrose, MA 02176 (SAN 211-8866) Tel 617-665-4998.

Bell *See* **Outlet Bk. Co.**

Bell Bks. *See* **Farrar, Straus & Giroux, Inc.**

Bell Enterprises, Inc., *(Bell Ent; 0-918340),* P.O. Box 9054, Pine Bluff, AR 71611 (SAN 209-1895) Tel 501-247-1922.

Bell Gallery *See* **Brown Univ., David Winton Bell Gallery**

†**Bell Publishing,** *(Bell Pub; 0-943064),* 15 Surrey Ln., East Brunswick, NJ 08816 (SAN 240-1266) Tel 201-257-7793; *CIP.*

Bell Springs Publishing, *(Bell Springs Pub; 0-917510),* P.O. Box 640, Laytonville, CA 95454 (SAN 209-3138); Bell Springs Rd., Laytonville, CA 95454 (SAN 661-9576) Tel 707-984-6746.

Bell Telephone Laboratories, Inc., *(Bell Telephone; 0-932764),* 600 Mountain Ave., Rm. 6G-301A, Murray Hill, NJ 07974 (SAN 223-6346).

Belle Grove, Inc., *(Belle Grove; 0-9616530),* P.O. Box 137, Middletown, VA 22645 (SAN 659-4204) Tel 703-869-2028; Rte. 11 S., Middletown, VA 22645 (SAN 659-4212).

Belle Mead, Pr., *(Belle Mead Pr; 0-9610346),* 306 Dutchtown Rd., Belle Mead, NJ 08502 (SAN 263-9351) Tel 201-359-5683.

Belle Pubns., *(Belle Pubns; 0-9605732),* 172 Pathway Ln., West Lafayette, IN 47906 (SAN 216-1036) Tel 317-463-6361.

Belle Trac Corp., *(Belle Trac; 0-9615835),* 306 W. Wabash Ave., Effingham, IL 62401 (SAN 697-0125) Tel 217-347-7090.

Bellefontaine Books, *(Bellefontaine Bks; 0-932786),* P.O. Box 1554, Arroyo Grande, CA 93420 (SAN 212-5900) Tel 805-481-8357.

Belleraphon Pr., *(Belleraphon; 0-9613906),* 20317 Farmington Rd., Bldg. D, Suite B, Livonia, MI 48152 (SAN 683-2318) Tel 313-478-7860.

†**Bellerophon Bks,** *(Bellerophon Bks; 0-88388),* 36 Anacapa St., Santa Barbara, CA 93101 (SAN 202-392X) Tel 805-965-7034; *CIP.*

†**Belles-Lettres Bks.,** *(Belles-Lettres; 0-917747),* P.O. Box 20405, Oakland, CA 94620-0405 (SAN 656-9633) Tel 415-655-9783; *CIP.*

Bellestri, Joseph, *(J Bellestri; 0-9615777),* 2819 Yost Blvd., Ann Arbor, MI 48104 (SAN 696-6810) Tel 313-971-2170.

Bellevue Art Museum, *(Bellevue Art; 0-942342),* 310 Bellevue Sq., Bellevue, WA 98004 (SAN 278-1670) Tel 206-454-3322.

†**Bellevue Press,** *(Bellevue Pr; 0-933466),* 60 Schubert St., Binghamton, NY 13905 (SAN 207-7884) Tel 607-729-0819; *CIP.*

Bellflower Pr., *(Bellflower; 0-934958),* Case Western Reserve Univ., Dept. of English, Cleveland, OH 44106 (SAN 213-2346) Tel 216-368-2340.

Bellman Publishing Co., *(Bellman; 0-87442),* P.O. Box 34937, Bethesda, MD 20817 (SAN 202-3938) Tel 301-897-0033.

Bellwether Books *See* **EJP Publishing Co.**

Bellwether Publishing Co., *(Bellwether Pub; 0-913144),* 167 E. 67th St., New York, NY 10021 (SAN 209-0880).

Belmary Press, *(Belmary; 0-910214),* 4652 E. Pinewood, Mobile, AL 36618 (SAN 697-3396) Tel 205-342-7171.

Belmont Historic District Commission, *(Belmont Hist Dist Comm),* Town Hall, Belmont, MA 02178 (SAN 292-3661).

Belnice Bks., *(Belnice Bks; 0-941274),* Box 1325, Claremont, CA 91711 (SAN 239-4103) Tel 714-626-1167.

Belo, A. H., Corp., The Dallas Morning News, *(Dallas Morning; 0-914511),* Texas Almanac Div., Communications Ctr., Dallas, TX 75265 (SAN 289-5986) Tel 214-977-8261.

Beloved Rebecca, Pubns., *(Beloved Bks; 0-9613907),* 3103 Wells Drive, Parlin, NJ 08859 (SAN 683-2296) Tel 201-721-2435.

Belvoir Pubns., Inc., *(Belvoir Pubns; 0-9615196),* 1111 E. Putnam Ave., Riverside, CT 06878 (SAN 694-3586) Tel 203-637-5900.

Ben Royal Pr., *(B Royal Pr; 0-9603198),* 19 Highland Ave., Randolph, VT 05060 (SAN 222-2817).

Ben-Simon Pubns., *(Ben-Simon; 0-914539),* P.O. Box 2124, Port Angeles, WA 98362 (SAN 289-1492) Tel 604-652-6332.

Benbow, D. R., *(D R Benbow; 0-931611),* 441 Clairmont Ave., Apt. 1014, Decatur, GA 30030 (SAN 206-7293) Tel 404-378-7028.

Bench Mark Publications, *(Bench Mark IL; 0-9610892),* P.O. Box 755, Charleston, IL 61920 (SAN 265-0819) Tel 217-345-7581.

Bench Pr., *(Bench Pr NY; 0-9616160),* P.O. Box 1446, Sag Harbor, NY 11963 (SAN 699-8321) Tel 516-725-4593; 200 Noyac Ave., Sag Harbor, NY 11963 (SAN 699-833X).

Bench Pr., The, *(Bench Press Pa; 0-930769),* 1355 Raintree Dr., Columbia, SC 29210 (SAN 677-6663) Tel 803-781-7232.

Benchmark Books, Inc., *(Benchmark Inc; 0-9615052),* P.O. Box 27004, Chinatown Sta., Honolulu, HI 96827 (SAN 694-0706) Tel 808-833-7563.

Benchmark Pr., Inc., *(Benchmark Pr; 0-936157),* 8435 Keystone Crossing, Suite 175, Indianapolis, IN 46240 (SAN 697-0095) Tel 317-253-3763.

Benchmark Publications, *(Benchmark Winnetka; 0-928520),* P.O. Box 154-B, Winnetka, IL 60093 (SAN 672-2547) Tel 312-446-0430.

Benchmark Pubns., Ltd., *(Benchmark Ltd; 0-9615467),* 1 First St., Suite N, Los Altos, CA 94022 (SAN 696-088X) Tel 415-941-3823.

Bender, Matthew, & Co., Inc., Subs. of Times Mirror Co., *(Bender; 0-87571),* ; Toll free: 800-821-2232; Orders to: 235 E. 45th St., New York, NY 10017 (SAN 202-330X) Tel 212-661-5050.

Bender, R. James, Publishing, *(Bender Pub CA; 0-912138),* P.O. Box 23456, San Jose, CA 95153 (SAN 201-7296) Tel 408-225-5777.

Benedictine Convent of Perpetual Adoration, *(Benedict Con Adoration; 0-913180),* 3888 Paducah Dr., San Diego, CA 92117 (SAN 204-5346) Tel 619-274-1030.

Benefield, M.E., Publishing, *(M E Benefield Pub; 0-9607326),* P.O. Box 395, 200 Jennifer, Jonesboro, AR 72401 • (SAN 239-1635) Tel 501-972-1376.

Bengal Pr., Inc., *(Bengal Pr; 0-935650),* P.O. Box 1128, Grand Rapids, MI 49501 (SAN 213-7259).

Bengor Pubns., Inc., *(Bengor Pubns; 0-913799),* 3827 NE 100th, Seattle, WA 98125 (SAN 286-0473) Tel 206-622-4090.

Benin Press, Ltd., *(Benin; 0-910216),* 5225 S. Blackstone Ave., Chicago, IL 60615 (SAN 203-3962).

Beninda Books, *(Beninda; 0-931868),* 173 SE Fifth Ave., No. 2, Delray Beach, FL 33444 (SAN 211-8874).

Benjamin Bks., *(Benjamin Bks; 0-916967),* 7238 Munsee Ln., Indianapolis, IN 46260 (SAN 655-5756) Tel 317-253-1032.

Benjamin Co., Inc., *(Benjamin Co; 0-87502),* 1 Westchester Plaza, Elmsford, NY 10523 (SAN 202-3970) Tel 914-592-8088.

Benjamin-Cummings Publishing Co., Subs. of Addison-Wesley Pub. Co., *(Benjamin-Cummings; 0-8053),* 2727 Sand Hill Rd., Menlo Park, CA 94025 (SAN 200-2353) Tel 415-854-6020; Orders to: South St., Reading, MA 01867 (SAN 206-7862). *Imprints:* Advance Book Program (Adv Bk Prog).

Benjamin Pr., *(Benjamin Pr; 0-936317),* P.O. Box 112, Northampton, MA 01061 (SAN 697-3396) Tel 413-586-6272; 88 Turkey Hill Rd., Northampton, MA 01060 (SAN 697-340X) Tel 413-586-6272.

Benjamins, John, North America, Inc., *(Benjamins North Am; 90-272; 1-55619),* 1 Buttonwood Sq., No. 101, Philadelphia, PA 19130 (SAN 219-7677) Tel 215-564-6379.

Benmir Bks., *(Benmir Bks; 0-917883),* 570 Vistamont Ave., Berkeley, CA 94718 (SAN 656-9641) Tel 415-527-0266.

Benn Brothers, Inc. *See* **Lyons, Nick, Bks.**

Bennet, Rebecca, Pubns., Inc., *(Bennet Pub; 0-910218),* 5409 18th Ave., Brooklyn, NY 11204 (SAN 206-8443) Tel 718-256-1954.

Bennett, Hal Z., *(Hal Z Bennett),* 124 Ardmore Rd., Kensington, CA 94707 (SAN 212-6052).

Bennett, James R., *(J R Bennett; 0-9617257),* Rte. 1, Box 124, McCalla, AL 35111 (SAN 663-5458) Tel 205-477-5711.

Bennett, Robert, Architect & Engineer, *(Bennett Arch & Eng; 0-9601718),* 6 Snowden Rd., Bala Cynwyd, PA 19004 (SAN 211-657X) Tel 215-667-7365.

Bennett-Edwards, *(Bennett-Edwards; 0-9617271),* 337 W. 36th St., New York, NY 10018 (SAN 663-4508) Tel 212-675-5053.

Bennett Pub. Co., Div. of Macmillan, Inc., *(Bennett Il),* 866 Third Ave., New York, NY 10022 (SAN 201-4440) Tel 309-691-4454.

Bennington, Ed, Jr., *(E Bennington; 0-9607776),* 1604 Argonne Ave. N., Sterling, VA 22170 (SAN 207-5482) Tel 703-430-8579.

Bennington College, *(Bennington Coll; 0-9614940),* Bennington College, Bennington, VT 05201 (SAN 693-675X) Tel 802-442-5401.

Benshaw Pubns., *(Benshaw Pub; 0-9607508),* 940 Princeton Dr., Marina del Rey, CA 90291 (SAN 238-633X) Tel 213-821-7871.

Benson, W. S., & Co., Inc., *(Benson; 0-87443),* P.O. Box 1866, Austin, TX 78767 (SAN 202-3989) Tel 512-476-5050.

Bentley, Robert, Inc., *(Bentley; 0-8376),* 1000 Massachusetts Ave., Cambridge, MA 02138 (SAN 213-9839) Tel 617-547-4170; Toll free: 800-423-4595.

Benton, Linn, Genealogical Services, *(L Benton Geneal; 0-939509),* 1117 SE 9th St., Albany, OR 97321 (SAN 663-3501) Tel 503-928-2582.

Benton-Cutter Pr., The, Div. of Kaminari Design, *(Benton Cutter Pr; 0-9615702),* 515-A W. Lambert Rd., Brea, CA 92621 (SAN 696-091X) Tel 714-529-6399.

Bentwood Pr., *(Bentwood Pr; 0-938839),* P.O. Box 172, Sutton, AK 99674 (SAN 661-6909) Tel 907-745-6840.

Bentz, Edna M., *(E M Bentz; 0-9615420),* 13139 Old West Ave., San Diego, CA 92129 (SAN 696-0936) Tel 619-484-1708.

Bentz, John D., *(J D Bentz; 0-9612438),* 13139 Old West Ave., San Diego, CA 92129 (SAN 289-0801) Tel 619-484-1708.

Benziger Publishing Co., Div. of Glencoe Publishing Co., *(Benziger Pub Co; 0-02; 0-8460),* c/o Macmillan Publishing Co., Inc., 866 Third Ave., New York, NY 10022 (SAN 202-5574) Tel 212-935-2000.

Benziger Sisters Pubns., *(Benziger Sis),* 466 E. Mariposa St., Altadena, CA 91001 (SAN 209-5297).

Berea College Pr., *(Berea College Pr; 0-938211),* Berea College Box 2317, Berea, KY 40404 (SAN 659-8218) Tel 606-986-9341; Berea College, Chestnut St., Lincoln Hall, Berea, KY 40404 (SAN 659-8226); Dist. by: Gnomon Pr., P.O. Box 106, Frankfort, KY 40602-0106 (SAN 209-0104) Tel 502-223-1858.

Bereny Bear, Bks., *(Bereny Bear; 0-914345),* 333 E. 79th St., New York, NY 10021 (SAN 289-601X) Tel 212-744-7433; Orders to: P.O. Box 1601, F.D.R. Sta., New York, NY 10150 (SAN 693-9856) Tel 212-744-7433.

Berg, Norman S. , Publisher, Ltd., *(Berg; 0-910220),* P.O. Box 15232, Atlanta, GA 30333 (SAN 226-8086).

Berg, R. J., & Co., *(R J Berg & Co; 0-89730),* P.O. Box 20450, Indianapolis, IN 46220 (SAN 286-3502) Tel 317-259-0569. *Imprints:* Berg, R. J., & Company, Pubs. (R. J. Berg); New Books, Incorporated (New Bks); News & Features Press (News & Features).

Berg, R. J., & Company, Pubs. *See* **Berg, R. J., & Co.**

Berg America Co., Ltd., *(Berg Am; 0-9616074),* 1136 SE Third Ave., Ft. Lauderdale, FL 33316 (SAN 697-998X) Tel 305-764-3636.

Berg Publishing Co., *(Berg Pub Co; 0-932861),* Box 359, Shakopee, MN 55379 (SAN 688-9212) Tel 612-445-4425.

Bergano Bk. Co., *(Bergano Bk Co; 0-917408),* P.O. Box 06430, Fairfield, CT 06430 (SAN 659-6118) Tel 203-254-2054.

Bergbower, Cornelius, *(C Bergbower; 0-9616653),* Louie Ave., Bluford, IL 62814 (SAN 659-8250) Tel 618-732-6195.

Bergee Corp., A, *(Bergee Corp; 0-935413),* Publishers' Bldg., Circle Pines, MN 55014 (SAN 696-4893) Tel 612-786-5720.

Names

Berger, Margaret L., *(M L Berger; 0-9605914),* Orders to: E. Weyhe, Inc., 794 Lexington Ave., New York, NY 10021 (SAN 699-5152) Tel 212-838-5466.

Berger Publishing Co., The, *(Berger Pub; 0-9616397),* 52 Penn Cir. W., Pittsburgh, PA 15206 (SAN 699-8267).

Bergerie, Maurine, *(M Bergerie; 0-9604234),* 201 Pollard Ave., New Iberia, LA 70560 (SAN 214-2848).

†**Bergh Publishing, Inc.,** *(Bergh Pub; 0-930267),* 1049 Park Ave., New York, NY 10028 (SAN 670-8633) Tel 212-860-8599; *CIP.*

†**Bergin & Garvey Pubs., Inc.,** *(Bergin & Garvey; 0-89789),* 670 Amherst Rd., South Hadley, MA 01075 (SAN 213-6120) Tel 413-467-3113; *CIP.*

Bergquist Publishing, *(Bergquist Pub; 0-9615483),* 414 W. Seventh, Willmar, MN 56201 (SAN 696-0952) Tel 612-235-4516.

Bergwall Educational Software, Inc., *(Bergwall Ed Soft; 0-943008; 0-8064),* 106 Charles Lindbergh Blvd., Uniondale, NY 11553 (SAN 659-3879) Tel 516-222-1130; Toll free: 800-645-1737.

Bergwall Productions, Inc., *(Bergwall; 0-943008; 0-8064),* P.O. Box 238, Garden City, NY 11530 (SAN 240-3064) Tel 516-222-1130; Toll free: 800-645-1737; 106 Charles Lindbergh Blvd., Uniondale, NY 11553 (SAN 696-9399).

Berke, Carl, *(C Berke),* 20 Simmons Dr., Milford, MA 01757 (SAN 216-2105) Tel 617-473-8034.

Berkel, Boyce N., M.D., *(B Berkel; 0-9603184),* 2245 McMullen Booth Rd., Clearwater, FL 33519 (SAN 213-4667).

Berkeley Art Center, *(Berkeley Art; 0-942744),* 1275 Walnut St., Berkeley, CA 94709 (SAN 240-1916) Tel 415-644-6893.

Berkeley Electronic Publishing, Subs. of International Publishing & Computer Services, Inc., *(Berkeley Elect; 0-933859),* P.O. Box 3056, Berkeley, CA 94703 (SAN 692-8692) Tel 415-652-6004.

Berkeley Poets' Workshop & Press (BPW & P), *(BPW & P; 0-917658),* P.O. Box 459, Berkeley, CA 94701 (SAN 208-5488) Tel 415-528-2252.

Berkeley Scientific Pubns., *(Berkeley Sci; 0-910224),* P.O. Box 4546, Anaheim, CA 92803 (SAN 211-7231) Tel 714-497-3522.

Berkeley Slavic Specialties, *(Berkeley Slavic; 0-933884),* P.O. Box 3034, Oakland, CA 94609 (SAN 212-7245) Tel 415-653-8048.

BerkeleyMorgan/Pubs, *(BerkeleyMorgan; 0-9615186),* 1742 Riggs Pl., NW, Washington, DC 20009 (SAN 694-3357) Tel 202-797-0647.

Berkley Publishing Group, Affil. of G.P. Putnam's Sons, *(Berkley Pub; 0-425; 0-515),* 200 Madison Ave., New York, NY 10016 (SAN 201-3991) Tel 212-686-9820; Toll free: 800-223-0510; Dist. by: ICD, 250 W. 55th St., New York, NY 10019 (SAN 169-5800) Tel 212-262-7444. *Imprints:* Highland Books (Highland); Medallion Books (Medallion); Windhover (Windhover).

Berkshire Hse. Pubs., *(Berkshire Hse; 0-936399),* P.O. Box 28, Great Barrington, MA 01230 (SAN 698-1666) Tel 413-528-3156; 315 W. 102nd St., New York, NY 10025 (SAN 698-1674); Dist. by: Ingram Industries, 347 Reedwood Dr., Nashville, TN 37217 (SAN 169-7978) Tel 615-360-2819; Toll free: 800-251-5902.

Berkshire Publishing Co., Ltd., *(Berkshire Pub Co; 0-910555),* P.O. Box 27910, St. Louis, MO 63146 (SAN 260-1656).

Berkshire Software Co., *(Berkshire Soft; 0-938213),* 72-61 113th St., Suite 5-K, Forest Hills, NY 11375 (SAN 659-8234) Tel 718-263-1221.

†**Berkshire Traveller, Pr.,** *(Berkshire Traveller; 0-912944),* Pine St., Stockbridge, MA 01262 (SAN 201-4424) Tel 413-298-3636; *CIP.*

Berle Bks., *(Berle Bks; 0-9617296),* 2700 Neilson Way, No. 1735, Santa Monica, CA 90405 (SAN 663-4354) Tel 213-396-5111.

Berlitz *See* **Macmillan Publishing Co., Inc.**

Berman, Morris, Studio, Inc., *(M Berman; 0-939197),* 1170 Broadway, Suite 410, New York, NY 10001 (SAN 662-9008) Tel 212-213-5960.

Bermont Bks., Inc., *(Bermont Bks; 0-930686),* P.O. Box 309, Glenelg, MD 21737 (SAN 211-1705) Tel 301-531-3560.

Bermuda Biological Station, *(Bermuda Bio; 0-917642),* c/o Prof. James N. Butler, Pierce Hall, 29 Oxford St., Cambridge, MA 02138 (SAN 206-4995) Tel 617-495-2845.

Bern, Karl, Pubs., *(Karl Bern Pubs; 0-9601524),* 9939 Riviera Dr., Sun City, AZ 85351 (SAN 211-1497) Tel 602-933-0854.

Bernard, Claude, Gallery, Ltd., *(C Bernard Gallery Ltd; 0-936827),* 33 E. 74th St., New York, NY 10021 (SAN 699-9042) Tel 212-988-2050.

Bernard, Ros, Pubns., *(R Bernard; 0-935872),* 24 Minell Pl., Teaneck, NJ 07666 (SAN 281-319X) Tel 201-837-7258; Orders to: P.O. Box 2177, Teaneck, NJ 07666 (SAN 281-3203).

Bernardo Press, Div. of Mayo & Associates, Inc., *(Bernardo Press),* 16496 Bernardo Center Dr., San Diego, CA 92128 (SAN 679-1875) Tel 619-451-3790.

Bernstein, R. B., *(R B Bernstein; 0-9613614),* P.O. Box 817, Hermosa Beach, CA 90254 (SAN 678-9080).

Berot Book, Inc., The, *(Berot Bk; 0-940372),* 220 E. Hillsdale St., Lansing, MI 48933 (SAN 217-1589) Tel 517-371-4647.

Berrick, R., Engineering Co., Inc., *(R Berrick; 0-910045),* 2312 Tilbury Ave., Pittsburgh, PA 15213 (SAN 241-3639).

Berringer Publishing, *(Berringer Pub; 0-9614987),* 15335 Morrison St. No. 100, Sherman Oaks, CA 91403 (SAN 693-7608) Tel 818-990-1700.

Berry, John R., Evangelistic Assn., *(J R Berry; 0-9616900),* P.O. Box 8252, Philadelphia, PA 19101 (SAN 661-4949); 5622 Florence Ave., Philadelphia, PA 19143 (SAN 661-4957) Tel 215-727-4325.

Berry Bks., *(Berry Bks; 0-9614746),* 1114 SE 22nd Terr., Cape Coral, FL 33904-4626 (SAN 692-9214).

Berry Good Children's Bks., *(Berry Good Child Bks; 0-9616555),* RR 2, P.O. Box 823, Lot 342, Coconut Creek, FL 33067 (SAN 659-4220); 6800 NW 39th Ave., Coconut Creek, FL 33067 (SAN 659-4239).

Berry Hill, Pr., *(Berry Hill Pr; 0-933863),* 7336 Berry Hill, Rancho Palos Verdes, CA 90274 (SAN 692-7041) Tel 213-377-7040.

Berry Patch Pr., *(Berry Patch; 0-9609912),* 3350 NW Luray Terr., Portland, OR 97210 (SAN 268-2729) Tel 503-224-3350; Dist. by: Far West Bk. Service, 3515 NE Hassalo, Portland, OR 97232 (SAN 107-6760) Tel 503-234-7664; Dist. by: Pacific Pipeline, Inc., 19215 66th Ave., S., Kent, WA 98032 (SAN 208-2128); Toll free: 800-562-4647.

Berry Publishing, *(Berry Pub; 0-942556),* Box 33, Hazel Crest, IL 60429 (SAN 240-0669) Tel 312-335-0347.

Bert & I, Inc., *(Bert & I Inc; 0-9607546),* 35 Mill Rd., Ipswich, MA 01938 (SAN 238-2202) Tel 617-356-0151.

Berwyn-London Pubs., *(Berwyn-London; 0-916536),* 2401 Calumet St., Flint, MI 48503 (SAN 208-550X).

Bess Pr., Inc., *(Bess Pr; 0-935848),* P.O. Box 22388, Honolulu, HI 96822 (SAN 239-4111); 2555 Makaulii Pl., Honolulu, HI 96816 (SAN 661-9584) Tel 808-734-7159.

Bessandy Pubns., *(Bessandy Pubns; 0-9610936),* 49 N. Main, P.O. Box 87, Clawson, UT 84516 (SAN 265-1912) Tel 801-384-2608.

Bessemer Junior Service League, *(Bessemer Jr Serv Leag; 0-9614351),* P.O. Box 928, Bessemer, AL 35021-0928 (SAN 687-8083) Tel 205-938-7713.

Best, A. M., Co., *(A M Best; 0-89408),* Ambest Rd., Oldwick, NJ 08858 (SAN 201-7407) Tel 201-439-2200.

Best, Charles, Antiques, *(Best Antiques; 0-914346),* 6288 S. Pontiac, Englewood, CO 80111 (SAN 202-9723) Tel 303-771-3153.

Best Bks., Inc., *(Best Bks; 0-910228),* P.O. Box 2309, Henderson, NV 89015 (SAN 202-4012) Tel 702-565-7182.

Best Bks. Pubs., *(Best Bks Pub; 0-88429),* P.O. Box 1895, McAlister, OK 74502 (SAN 202-1730) Tel 918-423-7296.

Best Bks. Publishing, *(Best Bks CA; 0-936255),* 1993 Orchard Rd., Hollister, CA 95023 (SAN 697-3426) Tel 408-991-5493.

Best Cookbooks, Inc., *(Best Cookbks; 0-935687),* 2721 Church St., Zachary, LA 70791 (SAN 696-0995) Tel 504-654-6523.

Best of Friends, *(Best Friends; 0-9615950),* P.O. Box 5573, Kingwood, TX 77325 (SAN 697-3450) Tel 713-359-6733; 4006 Oak Gardens Dr., Kingwood, TX 77339 (SAN 697-3469).

Best Publishing, Co., *(Best Pub Co; 0-941332),* P.O. Box 1978, San Pedro, CA 90732 (SAN 238-9509) Tel 213-548-4545.

Best Western Press, *(Best West Pr; 0-941192),* P.O. Box 494, Bakersfield, CA 93302 (SAN 238-9134).

Bestsell Pubns., *(Bestsell Pubns; 0-9616807),* RFD 1, Box 662, New Seabury, MA 02649 (SAN 661-2962); 337 High Wood Way, New Seabury, MA 02649 (SAN 661-2970) Tel 617-477-1774.

Bet-Ken Productions, *(Bet-Ken Prods; 0-9603698),* 4363 Cherry Ave., San Jose, CA 95118 (SAN 213-683X) Tel 408-267-3425.

Beta Phi Mu Chapbooks, *(Beta Phi Mu; 0-910230),* School of Library and Information Science; Univ. of Pittsburgh, Pittsburgh, PA 15260 (SAN 202-4020) Tel 412-624-5234; Toll free: Univ. of Pittsburgh, Schl. of Library & Information Science.

Beth Israel Sisterhood, *(Beth Israel; 0-9613256),* 9411 Liberty Rd., Randallstown, MD 21133 (SAN 296-452X) Tel 301-922-6565.

Beth Jacob Hebrew Teachers College Inc., *(B J Hebrew Tchrs; 0-934390),* 1213 Elm Ave., Brooklyn, NY 11230 (SAN 222-741X).

†**Bethany College Pr-Kansas,** *(Bethany Coll KS; 0-916030),* 421 N. First St., Lindsborg, KS 67456-1897 (SAN 211-8882) Tel 913-227-3311; *CIP.*

†**Bethany Hse. Pubs.,** Div. of Bethany Fellowship, Inc., *(Bethany Hse; 0-87123; 1-55661),* 6820 Auto Club Rd., Minneapolis, MN 55438 (SAN 201-4416) Tel 612-944-2121; Toll free: 800-328-6109; *CIP.*

Bethel Historical Society Inc., *(Bethel Hist Soc; 0-9614153),* 15 Broad St., Bethel, ME 04217 (SAN 686-5305) Tel 207-824-2908.

Bethel Pubns., *(Bethel Pub OR; 0-9600096),* 4803 Kathy, Temple, TX 76502 (SAN 241-273X) Tel 503-859-8365:

Bethel Publishing Co., Div. of Missionary Church, Inc., *(Bethel Pub; 0-934998),* 1819 S. Main St., Elkhart, IN 46516 (SAN 201-7555) Tel 219-293-8585; Toll free: 800-348-7657.

Bethsheva's Concern, *(Bethsheva's Concern; 0-9610802),* P.O. Box 276, Clifton, NJ 07011-9990 (SAN 265-0878); Dist. by: Starlite Distributors, P.O. Box 20729, Reno, NV 89515 (SAN 200-7789) Tel 702-359-5676; Dist. by: New Leaf Distributing, The, 1020 White St. SW, Atlanta, GA 30310 (SAN 169-1449) Tel 404-755-2665; Toll free: 800-241-3829.

BETOM Pubns., *(BETOM Pubns; 0-9605172),* P.O. Box 1873, Appleton, WI 54913 (SAN 238-5198) Tel 414-731-2947.

Betsy Ross Pr., *(Betsy Ross Pr; 0-934120),* P.O. Box 986, Fort Collins, CO 80522 (SAN 222-7428).

Bette Stoler Gallery, *(Bette Stoler Gallery; 0-9614551),* 13 White St., New York, NY 10038 (SAN 691-795X) Tel 212-966-5090.

Better Baby Pr., The, Div. of Institutes for the Achievement of Human Potential, *(Better Baby; 0-936676),* 8801 Stenton Ave., Philadelphia, PA 19118 (SAN 215-7314) Tel 215-233-2050.

Better Baseball, *(Better Baseball; 0-913557),* 2309 Colcord Ave., Waco, TX 76707 (SAN 285-2152); Dist. by: Publishers Marketing Group, 1104 Summit Ave., Plainview, TX 75074 (SAN 285-2160) Tel 214-423-0312.

Better Bks. Pub., *(Better Bks),* Rte. 2, Box 2574, Vale, OR 97918 (SAN 215-7322) Tel 503-473-2133.

Better Health Programs, *(Better H Prog; 0-933161),* 2107 Van Ness Ave., Suite 408, San Francisco, CA 94109 (SAN 692-2597) Tel 415-775-5921.

Better Health Pubs., Inc., *(Better Health; 0-932213),* 3368 Governor Dr., Suite F-224, San Diego, CA 92122 (SAN 686-6018) Tel 619-549-8897; Dist. by: Baker & Taylor Co., Eastern Div., 50 Kirby Ave., Somerville, NJ 08876 (SAN 169-4901) Tel 201-526-8000; Dist. by: Publishers Group West, 5855 Beaudry St., Emeryville, CA 94608 (SAN 202-8522) Tel 415-658-3453; Dist. by: Nutri-Books Corp., P.O. Box 5793, Denver, CO 80223 (SAN 169-054X) Tel 303-778-8383; Dist. by: Gordon's Bks., Inc., 5450 N. Valley Hwy., Denver, CO 80216 (SAN 169-0531) Tel 303-296-1830; Dist. by: Living Bks., Inc., 12155 Magnolia Ave., Bldg. 11-B, Riverside, CA 92503 (SAN 169-006X) Tel 714-354-7330; Dist. by: Spring Arbor Distributors, 10885 Textile Rd., Belleville, MI 48111 (SAN 158-9016) Tel 313-481-0900; Toll free: 800-521-3990.

Better Home & Gardens Bks., Div. of Meredith Corp., *(BH&G; 0-696),* 1716 Locust St., Des Moines, IA 50336 (SAN 202-4055) Tel 515-284-2844. *Imprints:* American Express Pubns. (Am Express).

Better Life Products, *(Better Life; 0-9614258),* 421 N. Pleasant Hill Blvd., Des Moines, IA 50317 (SAN 687-116X) Tel 515-262-6040.

Betterway Pubns., Inc., *(Betterway Pubns; 0-932620),* White Hall, VA 22987 (SAN 215-2975) Tel 804-823-5661. *Imprints:* White Hall Books (White Hall Bks).

Bettienal Pubs., *(Bettienal; 0-914037),* 3212 Gleneagles Dr., Silver Spring, MD 20906 (SAN 287-489X) Tel 301-598-7934.

Betty's Soup Shop Pr., *(Betty's Soup; 0-9612914),* 847 Junipero Ave., Pacific Grove, CA 93950 (SAN 291-0780) Tel 408-375-1873.

Between Hours Press, *(Between Hours; 0-910232),* 29 E. 63rd St., New York, NY 10021 (SAN 202-4039).

Betz Publishing, Co., Inc., *(Betz Pub Co Inc; 0-941406),* P.O. Box 34631, Bethesda, MD 20817 (SAN 238-9886) Tel 301-340-0030.

Betzina, Sandra, *(S Betzina; 0-9615614),* 95 Fifth Ave., San Francisco, CA 94118 (SAN 696-1010) Tel 415-221-7736; Dist. by: Bookpeople, 2929 Fifth St., Berkeley, CA 94710 (SAN 168-9517) Tel 415-549-3030; Toll free: 800-227-1516.

Betzold, Michael, *(Betzold; 0-9602452),* 20025 Renfrew St., Detroit, MI 48221 (SAN 211-6170) Tel 313-864-1496.

Beulah Records & Publishing Co., *(Beulah; 0-911870),* Rte. 1, Crossville, IL 62827 (SAN 202-4047) Tel 618-966-3405.

Beverage Media, Ltd., *(Beverage Media; 0-9602566),* 161 Sixth Ave., New York, NY 10013 (SAN 214-106X).

Beverly Foundation, The, *(Beverly Found; 0-938485),* 841 S. Fair Oaks, Pasadena, CA 91105 (SAN 659-8277) Tel 818-792-2292.

Bewick Editions, *(Bewick Edns; 0-935590),* P.O. Box 14140, Detroit, MI 48214 (SAN 213-6139) Tel 313-521-5049.

Bey-Len Cat Bks., *(Bey-Len Cat Bks; 0-9615398),* P.O. Box 628, Maspeth, NY 11378 (SAN 696-1053).

Beyond Words Publishing Co., *(Beyond Words Pub; 0-89610),* 112 Meleana Pl., Honolulu, HI 96817 (SAN 211-1403) Tel 808-595-8166.

Bezkorovainy, Anatoly, *(Bezkorovainy; 0-9607600),* 6801 N. Kilpatrick, Chicago, IL 60646 (SAN 218-4672) Tel 312-942-5429.

BFP (Bks. for Professionals) *See* **Harcourt Brace Jovanovich, Inc.**

Bhaktipada Bks., Div. of Palace Press, *(Bhaktipada Bks; 0-932215),* Rd 1, Box 331, Moundsville,, VA 26041 (SAN 686-5763) Tel 304-845-3890.

†**Bhaktivedanta Bk. Trust,** *(Bhaktivedanta; 0-912776),* 3764 Watseka Ave., Los Angeles, CA 90034 (SAN 203-8560) Tel 213-559-4455; Toll free: 800-356-3000; *CIP.*

Bhaktivedanta Institute of Religion & Culture, The, *(Bhaktive Inst; 0-936405),* 11693 N. Shore Dr., No. 11B, Reston, VA 22090 (SAN 698-1607).

Bi World Industries, Inc., *(Bi World Indus; 0-89557),* P.O. Box 1143, 671 N. State St., Orem, UT 84057 (SAN 210-5888) Tel 801-224-5803.

Bibb, Mary, *(M Bibb; 0-9608778),* 1002 Fall Dr. NE, Grants Pass, OR 97526 (SAN 238-0420) Tel 503-474-2581.

Bible Baptist Church, *(Bible Baptist),* Cross St. at Lock St., P.O. Box 1348, Nashua, NH 03061 (SAN 656-044X) Tel 603-888-4020.

Bible Light Pubns., *(Bible Light; 0-937078),* P.O. Box 168, Jerome Ave. Sta., Bronx, NY 10468 (SAN 214-3445).

Bible Memory Assn., Inc., *(Bible Memory; 0-89323),* P.O. Box 12000, Ringgold, LA 71068 (SAN 214-1019).

Bible-Speak Enterprises, *(Bible-Speak; 0-911423),* 1940 Mount Vernon Ct., No. 4, Mountain View, CA 94040 (SAN 268-2931) Tel 415-965-9020.

Bible Study, Pr., *(Bible Study Pr; 0-9600154),* 9017 N. 70th St., Milwaukee, WI 53223 (SAN 281-3211) Tel 414-354-3504; Dist. by: Omnibook Co., N. 57 W. 136 88 Carmen Ave., Menomonee Falls, WI 53051 (SAN 281-322X) Tel 414-781-2866. *Imprints:* Omnibook, Company (Omnibook).

Bible Temple Pubns., *(Bible Temple; 0-914936),* 7545 NE Glisan St., Portland, OR 97213 (SAN 206-1953) Tel 503-253-9020.

Bibli O'Phile Publishing Co, *(Bibli O'Phile Pub Co; 0-942104),* 156 E. 61st St., New York, NY 10021 (SAN 238-6437) Tel 212-888-1008; Toll free: 800-255-1660; Dist. by: E. P. Dutton & Co., 2 Park Ave., New York, NY 10016 (SAN 201-0070) Tel 212-725-1818.

Biblia Candida, *(Biblia Candida; 0-9617134),* 4466 Winterville Rd., Spring Hill, FL 33526 (SAN 663-1878) Tel 904-686-3527.

Biblical Archaeology Society, *(Biblical Arch Soc; 0-9613089),* 3000 Connecticut Ave. NW., Suite 300, Washington, DC 20008 (SAN 293-9673) Tel 202-387-8888.

Biblical Research Assocs., Inc., *(Biblical Res Assocs; 0-935106),* The College of Wooster, Wooster, OH 44691 (SAN 211-2876) Tel 216-263-2470.

Biblical Research Press *See* **Abilene Christian Univ. Pr.**

Biblio Distribution Ctr., Div. of Littlefield, Adams & Co., *(Biblio Dist),* 81 Adams Dr., Totowa, NJ 07512 (SAN 211-724X) Tel 201-256-8600. Do not confuse with Biblio Pr. in Fresh Meadows, NY.

Biblio Pr., *(Biblio NY; 0-9602036),* P.O. Box 22, Fresh Meadows, NY 11365-0022 (SAN 217-0892) Tel 718-361-3141; 50-17 40th St., Sunnyside, NY 11104 (SAN 695-4464). Do not confuse with Biblio Distribution Centre of Totowa, NJ.

Bibliographic Guides *See* **Hall, G. K., & Co.**

Bibliographic Press, The, *(Bibliographic Pr; 0-930429),* 154-61 22nd Ave., Whitestone, NY 11357 (SAN 670-9788).

Bibliographical Society of America, *(Biblio Soc Am),* P.O. Box 397, Grand Central Sta., New York, NY 10163 (SAN 225-333X) Tel 718-638-7957; Dist. by: Univ. Pr. of Virginia, P.O. Box 3608, University Sta., Charlottesville, VA 22903 (SAN 680-019X) Tel 804-924-3468.

Bibliophile Legion Bks, Inc., *(Bibliophile; 0-918184),* P.O. Box 612, Silver Spring, MD 20901 (SAN 207-6322) Tel 301-490-4367.

Biblioteca Siglo de Oro, *(Biblio Siglo; 0-916613),* 530 N. First St., Charlottesville, VA 22901 (SAN 208-2705) Tel 804-295-1021.

Bibliotechnology Systems & Publishing Co., *(Bibliotec Systems & Pub; 0-936857),* P.O. Box 657, Lincoln, MA 01773 (SAN 699-8690) Tel 617-259-0524; 16 Blueberry Ln., Lincoln, MA 01773 (SAN 699-8704).

Bibliotheca Islamica, Inc., *(Bibliotheca; 0-88297),* P.O. Box 14474, University Sta., Minneapolis, MN 55414 (SAN 202-4063) Tel 612-221-9883.

Bibliotheca Persica, *(Bibliotheca Persica; 0-933273),* 450 Riverside Dr., No. 4, New York, NY 10027 (SAN 691-7968) Tel 212-280-4366; Dist. by: Caravan Bks., P.O. Box 344, Delmar, NY 12054 (SAN 206-7323) Tel 518-439-5978.

†**Biblo & Tannen Booksellers & Pubs., Inc.,** *(Biblo; 0-8196),* 321 Sandbank Rd., P.O. Box 302, Cheshire, CT 06410 (SAN 202-4071) Tel 213-272-2308; *CIP.*

Bibulophile Pr., *(Bibulophile Pr; 0-911153),* P.O. Box 399, Bantam, CT 06750-0399 (SAN 268-2990) Tel 203-567-5543.

Bicentennial Era Enterprises, *(Bicent Era; 0-9605734),* P.O. Box 1148, Scappoose, OR 97056 (SAN 216-2245) Tel 503-684-3937.

Bicycle Bks., Inc., *(Bicycle Books; 0-933201),* 1282a Seventh Ave., San Francisco, CA 94122 (SAN 692-2600) Tel 415-665-8214; Dist. by: Kampmann & Co., Inc., 9 E. 40th St., New York, NY 10016 (SAN 202-5191) Tel 212-685-2928; Toll free: 800-526-7627; Dist. by: Raincoast Bk. Distributors, Ltd., 112 E. Third Ave., Vancouver, BC V5T 1C8, (SAN 200-6170) Tel 604-873-6581.

Bid Publishing, Div. of Beyond Interior Design, Inc., *(Bid Pub Co; 0-915587),* 606 Wilshire Blvd., No. 404, Santa Monica, CA 90401 (SAN 291-0810) Tel 213-215-3400.

Bielawski, Maxwell, *(Bielawski; 0-9600014),* 320 Lakeshore Dr., Dunkirk, NY 14048 (SAN 204-5338) Tel 716-366-2241.

†**Bieler Pr.,** *(Bieler; 0-931460),* 212 Second St., N., Studio 1, 4th Flr., Minneapolis, MN 55401 (SAN 209-7087) Tel 612-339-1978; *CIP.*

Big Apple Co.,The, *(Big Apple Co; 0-918853),* 195 Claremont, Suite 391, Long Beach, CA 90803 (SAN 670-0578) Tel 714-879-0452.

Big Bend Natural History Assn., Inc., *(Big Bend; 0-912001),* Box 68, Big Bend National Park, TX 79834 (SAN 268-3075) Tel 915-477-2236.

Big Blue Bks., *(Big Blue Bks; 0-916969),* 13239 Vanguard Way, Lakeside, CA 92040 (SAN 655-5772) Tel 619-443-6397.

†**Big Brothers-Big Sisters of America,** *(Big Brothers-Big Sisters; 0-9613820),* 230 N. 13th St., Philadelphia, PA 19107 (SAN 681-9648) Tel 215-567-2748; *CIP.*

Big Daddy Pr., *(Big Daddy Pr; 0-939771),* 14033 Burbank No. 128, Van Nuys, CA 91401 (SAN 677-6221) Tel 818-994-2139.

Big Foot Pr., *(Big Foot NY; 0-917455),* 57 Seafield Ln., Bay Shore, NY 11706 (SAN 657-0720) Tel 516-666-8512.

Big Horn Book Co. *See* **International Aviation Pubs., Inc.**

Big House Publishing Co., *(Big Hse Pub; 0-937529),* P.O. Box 202, Steger, IL 60475 (SAN 659-0373) Tel 312-758-8786; 22901 Sherman Rd., Chicago Heights, IL 60411 (SAN 659-0381).

Big Island Club Hawaii, Inc., *(Big Island; 0-9608396),* P.O. Box 344, Paauilo, HI 96776 (SAN 240-5962) Tel 808-775-7331.

Big Kids Publishing, Inc., *(Big Kids Pub; 0-930249),* P.O. Box 10237, Rochester, NY 14610 (SAN 670-8617) Tel 716-248-3498.

Big Moose Pr., *(Big Moose; 0-914692),* P.O. Box 180, Big Moose, NY 13331 (SAN 206-3336) Tel 315-357-2821.

Big Morning Pr, *(Big Morning Pr; 0-935056),* Box 3342, Lawrence, KS 66044 (SAN 211-4100) Tel 913-843-0012.

Big Nickel Pubns., *(Big Nickel; 0-936433),* P.O. Box 157, Milford, NH 03055 (SAN 697-8495) Tel 617-486-8971.

Big Red Cartoon Co., *(Big Red Cartoon; 0-9616098),* P.O. Box 27112, Ralston, NE 68127 (SAN 698-1380) Tel 402-592-4291; 8636 "S" Plaza, No. 10, Omaha, NE 68127 (SAN 698-1399); Dist. by: Nelson News, Inc., 4651 F St., Omaha, NE 68117 (SAN 169-443X).

Big Santa Anita Historical Society, *(Big Santa Hist; 0-9615421),* 7 N. Fifth Ave., Arcadia, CA 91006 (SAN 696-2955) Tel 818-967-8008.

Big Sur Pubs., *(Big Sur Pubs; 0-9613141),* 8300 Delongpre Ave., Los Angeles, CA 90069 (SAN 294-9415) Tel 213-654-8677.

Big Sur Women Pr, *(Big Sur Women; 0-9614678),* P.O. Box 40, Big Sur, CA 93920 (SAN 692-5073) Tel 408-667-2498.

Big Toad Press, *(Big Toad Pr; 0-940536),* 617 25th St., Sacramento, CA 95816 (SAN 209-5300) Tel 916-446-7363.

Big Valley Publishing Co., *(Big Valley Pub; 0-9616795),* 18024 Ventura Blvd., Encino, CA 91316 (SAN 659-8293) Tel 818-345-0773.

Bigelow Society, Inc., The, *(Bigelow Soc; 0-9616682),* 1516 Evergreen St., Fairbanks, AK 99709 (SAN 659-8323) Tel 907-456-6272.

Biggs, Marge, *(M Biggs; 0-9603218),* 12475 Willet, Grand Terrace, CA 92324 (SAN 213-2400).

Names

Biggs Pubs., *(Biggs Pubs; 0-9616590),* P.O. Box 105, Newalla, OK 74857 (SAN 659-4913) Tel 405-391-3144; 11008 Squirmy Dr., Newalla, OK 74857 (SAN 659-4921).

Bigoni Bks., *(Bigoni Bks; 0-938996),* 4121 NE Highland, Portland, OR 97211 (SAN 216-3357) Tel 503-288-0997.

Bijon, *(Bijon; 0-938391),* 9 Sumner Pl., Piscataway, NJ 08854 (SAN 659-8366) Tel 201-463-1505; P.O. Box 91, Piscataway, NJ 08854 (SAN 660-9589).

Bilingual Bks., Inc., *(Bilingual Bks; 0-916682),* 6018 Seaview NW., Seattle, WA 98107 (SAN 220-2352) Tel 206-789-7544; Toll free: 800-228-4078; Dist. by: Cliffs Notes Inc., P.O. Box 80728, Lincoln, NE 68501 (SAN 200-4275) Tel 402-477-6971.

Bilingual Educ. Servs., Inc., *(Bilingual Ed Serv; 0-86624),* 2514 S. Grand Ave., Los Angeles, CA 90007 (SAN 218-4680) Tel 213-749-6213.

Bilingual Review/Pr., *(Biling Rev-Pr; 0-916950),* Hispanic Research Ctr., Arizona State Univ., Tempe, AZ 85287 (SAN 208-5526) Tel 607-724-9495.

Bilingue Pubns., *(Bilingue Pubns; 0-933196),* P.O. Drawer H, Las Cruces, NM 88004 (SAN 223-6389) Tel 505-526-1557.

Bill Coats Ltd., *(B Coats; 0-931709),* 1406 Grandview Dr., Nashville, TN 37215 (SAN 683-6046) Tel 615-383-8536; Dist. by: Publishers Marketing Group, 1104 Summit Ave., Plainview, TX 75074 (SAN 262-0995) Tel 214-423-0312.

Bill Matthews, Inc., *(B Matthews Inc; 0-9613734),* P.O. Box 26727, Lakewood, CO 80226 (SAN 677-5446) Tel 303-922-0055.

BillArt Pubns., *(BillArt; 0-9611112),* 23 Overlook Rd., Woodbridge, CT 06525 (SAN 282-8693) Tel 203-397-0338; Orders to: P.O. Box 124, Rowayton, CT 06853 (SAN 699-5713).

Billboard Bks. *See* **Watson-Guptill Pubns., Inc.**

Billib Pr., *(Billib Press; 0-9613767),* P.O. Box 340026, Boca Raton, FL 33434 (SAN 678-9595) Tel 305-487-1494.

Billings, Harold C., Jr., *(H C Billings; 0-9613642),* 35 Woolson Ave., Springfield, VT 05156 (SAN 670-8021) Tel 802-885-4764.

†**Billner & Rouse, Inc.,** *(Billner & Rouse; 0-932755),* P.O. Box 20465, Hammarskjold Ctr., New York, NY 10017 (SAN 688-5462) Tel 212-868-1121; Dist. by: Longwood Publishing Group, Inc., 27 S. Main St., Wolfeboro, NH 03894-2069 (SAN 209-3170) Tel 603-569-4576; Toll free: 800-343-9444; *CIP.*

Binary Engineering Assocs., Inc., *(Binary Eng Assocs; 0-932217),* P.O. Box 528, Holden, MA 01520 (SAN 686-6026) Tel 617-829-4361.

Binford & Mort Publishing; Metropolitan Pr., *(Binford-Metropolitan; 0-8323),* 1202 NW 17th Ave., Portland, OR 97209 (SAN 201-4386) Tel 503-221-0866. *Imprints:* Van Veer Nursery (Van Veer Nursery).

Bingley, Clive, Ltd. (England) *See* **Shoe String Pr., Inc.**

Binney & Smith, Inc., *(Binney & Smith; 0-86696),* P.O. Box 431, Easton, PA 18042 (SAN 216-5899).

Binns, Joseph J., *(J J Binns; 0-89674),* 6919 Radnor Rd., Bethesda, MD 20817 (SAN 213-2095) Tel 301-320-3327; Toll free: 800-243-2790; Dist. by: Robert B. Luce, Inc., 540 Barnum Ave., Bridgeport, CT 06608 (SAN 201-1077) Tel 203-366-1900.

Bio Dynamic Farming & Gardening Assn., Inc., *(Bio-Dynamic Farm; 0-938250),* P.O. Box 253, Wyoming, RI 02898 (SAN 224-9871) Tel 401-539-2320; Richmond Townhouse Rd., Wyoming, RI 02898 (SAN 669-0203).

Bio Energy Council, *(Bio Energy),* c/o Volunteers in Technical Assistance, P.O Box 12438, Arlington, VA 22209-8438 (SAN 209-6145) Tel 703-276-1800.

Bio-Graphics Publishing, *(Bio Graphics; 0-935649),* 4095 Adrian St., Tucker, GA 30084 (SAN 696-1088) Tel 404-934-7855.

Bio-Marine Images, *(Bio Marine; 0-9617106),* 22906 Edmonds Way, No. 14, Edmonds, WA 98020 (SAN 662-4758) Tel 206-775-8578.

Bio-Publishing Co., *(Bio-Pub; 0-916833),* 2200 Sunderland Rd., Winston-Salem, NC 27103 (SAN 654-3758) Tel 919-760-0944.

Biobehavioral Pr., *(Biobehavioral Pr; 0-938176),* 9725 Louedd Ave., Houston, TX 77070 (SAN 214-4875) Tel 713-890-8575.

Biocomm, *(Biocomm; 0-938841),* P.O. Box 2151, Seal Beach, CA 90740 (SAN 661-6933); 5042 Hampton Ct., Westminster, CA 92683 (SAN 661-6941) Tel 714-892-3930.

Bioenergetics Pr., Subs. of Bioenergetics, Inc., *(Bioenergetics Pr; 0-9613177),* 1129 Drake St., Madison, WI 53715 (SAN 295-6624) Tel 608-255-4028.

Biofeedback & Advanced Therapy Institute, Inc., *(BATI; 0-942558),* 5979 W. Third St., Suite 205, Los Angeles, CA 90036 (SAN 239-6181) Tel 213-938-0478.

Biofeedback Pr., *(Biofeed Pr; 0-9606358),* 3428 Sacramento St., San Francisco, CA 94118 (SAN 212-8187) Tel 415-921-5455.

Biofeedback Research Institute Inc., *(Biofeedback Research; 0-930758),* 6399 Wilshire Blvd., Suite 900, Los Angeles, CA 90048 (SAN 208-2225) Tel 213-933-9451.

Biograf Pubns. *See* **Garber Communications, Inc.**

Biograph Bks., *(Biograph Bks; 0-938311),* 260 W. 35th St., Suite 607, New York, NY 10001 (SAN 659-8390) Tel 212-330-0970.

BioGuide Pr., *(BioGuide Pr; 0-9615277),* P.O. Box 16072, Alexandria, VA 22302 (SAN 694-4582) Tel 703-820-9045; 1225 Martha Custis Dr., Apt. 411, Alexandria, VA 22302 (SAN 699-6027).

Biohydrant Pubns., *(Biohydrant; 0-918562),* 56 Congress St., St. Albans, VT 05478 (SAN 209-6374) Tel 802-524-6307.

Biokinesiology Institute, *(Biokinesiology Institute; 0-937216),* P.O. Box 910, Monticello, UT 84535 (SAN 214-3437) Tel 801-587-2972; Orders to: The Nutrition Place, 5432 Hwy. 227, Trail, OR 97541 (SAN 661-9592) Tel 503-878-2080.

Biological Illustrations Inc., *(Bio Illustra; 0-932353),* P.O. Box 15292, Gainesville, FL 32604 (SAN 687-3669) Tel 904-375-4582.

Biomateria Publishing, Co., Inc., *(Biomat Pub Co; 0-9609098),* P.O. Box 523, Stony Brook, NY 11790 (SAN 241-2748) Tel 516-689-9492.

Biomedical Engineering Society, *(Biomedical Eng),* P.O. Box 2399, Culver City, CA 90231 (SAN 225-1477) Tel 213-206-6443.

†**Biomedical Information Corp.,** *(Biomedical Info; 0-935404),* 800 Second Ave., New York, NY 10017 (SAN 223-7172) Tel 212-599-3400; *CIP.*

Bionomic Publishers, Inc., *(Bionomic; 0-912987),* 28306 Industrial Blvd. Suite M, Hayward, CA 94545 (SAN 283-2879).

Bios Publishers, *(Bios Pubs; 0-9610636),* Box 159, Aransas Pass, TX 78336 (SAN 264-6528) Tel 512-758-2105.

BioSciences Information Services, *(BioSci Info; 0-916246),* 2100 Arch St., Philadelphia, PA 19103 (SAN 287-6809) Tel 215-587-4800. Microfilm & microfiche editions of & indexes to Biological Abstracts & Biological Abstracts/RRM (Reports, Reviews, Meetings).

BioService Corp., *(BioServ Corp; 0-938278),* 500 S. Racine Ave., Suite 302, Chicago, IL 60607 (SAN 215-7330).

BIOSIS *See* **BioSciences Information Services**

Biotechnical Veterinary Consultants, *(Biotech Vet; 0-9612756),* P.O. Box 789, Cardiff-by-the-Sea, CA 92007 (SAN 289-7334) Tel 619-756-1344.

Birch Ballast Notificatory (BBN), *(Birch Ballast; 0-915271),* 1319 Pitkin Ave., Akron, OH 44310 (SAN 289-968X) Tel 216-929-5097.

Birch Portage Pr., *(Birch Portage; 0-916691),* 502 Leicester Ave., Duluth, MN 55803 (SAN 654-1305) Tel 218-728-1991; Orders to: P.O. Box 3055, Duluth, MN 55803 (SAN 654-1313).

Birch Run Publishing, *(Birch Run Pub; 0-931964),* 19 Sycamore Ln., Madison, CT 06443 (SAN 211-5921).

Birchfield Bks., *(Birchfield Bks; 0-912871),* P.O. Box 1305, N. Conway, NH 03860 (SAN 277-6510) Tel 603-447-3086.

Bird & Bull Press, The *See* **Univ. Pr. of Virginia**

Bird In Hand Publishing, *(Bird Hand Pub; 0-9613994),* 3620 Weston Pl., Long Beach, CA 90807 (SAN 683-2261) Tel 213-427-4393.

Bird Professional Pubns., *(Bird Prof Pubns; 0-9616174),* 2320 Lynx Way, Boise, ID 83705 (SAN 699-8607) Tel 208-384-1600.

Bird-Sci Books *See* **Foris Pubns., USA**

Bird Shoal Bks., *(Bird Shoal Bks; 0-9617135),* P.O. Box 503, Harkers Island, NC 28531 (SAN 663-1622); Pentecostal Church Rd., Harkers Island, NC 28531 (SAN 663-1630) Tel 919-728-4635.

Birds' Meadow Publishing Co., Inc., *(Birds' Meadow Pub; 0-9606360),* 1150 N. Olson Rd., Coupeville, WA 98239-9776 (SAN 208-0710).

Birdseed, *(Birdseed; 0-933006),* 1560-C Lincoln Ave., Alameda, CA 94501 (SAN 212-3339).

Birkby, Evelyn, *(E Birkby; 0-9615636),* 1301 Maple St., Sidney, IA 51652 (SAN 696-1126) Tel 712-374-2335.

Birkhauser Boston, Inc., *(Birkhauser; 0-8176),* 380 Green St., Cambridge, MA 02139 (SAN 213-2869) Tel 617-876-2333.

Birmingham Historical Society, *(Birmingham Hist Soc; 0-943994),* 1 Sloss Quarters, Birmingham, AL 35222-1243 (SAN 240-1347).

Birth & Parenting Pubns., *(Birth & Parenting; 0-9615484),* Rte. 1, Box 137, Earlysville, VA 22936 (SAN 696-1134) Tel 804-973-1529.

Birth Day Publishing Co., *(Birth Day; 0-9600958),* P.O. Box 7722, San Diego, CA 92107 (SAN 208-5542) Tel 619-296-3194.

Bisbee Pr., Collective, *(Bisbee Pr; 0-938196),* Drawer HA, Bisbee, AZ 85603 (SAN 215-8418).

Bisel George T., Co., *(Bisel Co),* 710 S. Washington Sq., Philadelphia, PA 19106 (SAN 201-727X) Tel 215-922-5760; Toll free: 800-247-3526 in Pennsylvania.

Bishop, Charles Lawrence, *(C L Bishop; 0-9616120),* 13014 Open Hearth Way, Germantown, MD 20874 (SAN 699-7422) Tel 301-496-6411.

†**Bishop Graphics, Inc.,** *(Bishop Graphics; 0-9601748; 0-938009),* P.O. Box 5007, Westlake Village, CA 91359 (SAN 658-0181); Toll free: 800-222-5808; Dist. by: PMS Industries (mail orders), 1790 Hembree Rd., Alpharetta, GA 30201 (SAN 683-1486) Tel 404-475-1818; Orders to: 538 Sterling Center Dr., Westlake Village, CA 91359 (SAN 663-2882) Tel 818-991-2600; *CIP.*

Bishop Museum Pr., *(Bishop Mus; 0-910240),* P.O. Box 19000-A, Honolulu, HI 96819 (SAN 202-408X) Tel 808-847-3511.

Bishop Pine Press, *(Bishop Pine; 0-9612760),* P.O. Box 128, Inverness, CA 94937 (SAN 289-7342) Tel 415-663-1744; Dist. by: Nancy Kleban, Box 486, Point Reyes Station, CA 94956 (SAN 200-4283).

Bishop Pr. The, *(Bishop Pr; 0-911329),* P.O. Box 894, Rancho Santa Fe, CA 92067 (SAN 268-3334) Tel 619-756-4667.

Bishop-Rogers Pubns., *(Bishop-Rogers; 0-914727),* P.O. Box 85152-276, San Diego, CA 92138 (SAN 287-7813) Tel 619-278-9695.

Bismarck-Mandan Symphony League, *(Bismarck Mandan; 0-9612998),* P.O. Box 131, Bismarck, ND 58502 (SAN 293-4922) Tel 701-258-2867; 2217 Ave. E, Bismarck, ND 58501 (SAN 293-4930) Tel 701-223-6571.

Bison Books *See* **Univ. of Nebraska Pr.**

Bissell, Charles B., III, *(C Bissell; 0-9612604),* 1911 Flintwood Dr., Richmond, VA 23233 (SAN 289-0631) Tel 804-741-6008.

Bissette, Yoma V., *(Y V Bissette),* Dist. by: Historical Research Assocs., Box 4275, Bisbee, AZ 85603 (SAN 240-1355).

Biting Idge Miracle Pr., *(Biting Idge; 0-942352),* c/o Chrysalis Pubns., P.O. Box 151493, Columbus, OH 43215 (SAN 239-7153) Tel 614-221-6827.

Bits Pr., *(Bits Pr; 0-933248),* Case Western Reserve Univ., Dept. of English, Cleveland, OH 44106 (SAN 212-5927) Tel 216-795-2810.

Bitterroot Educational Resources for Women, *(Bitterroot Ed; 0-915111),* 315 S. Fourth East, Missoula, MT 59801 (SAN 289-7350) Tel 406-728-3041.

Bittersweet Pr., *(Bittersweet Evanston; 0-9611962),* 819 Clinton Pl., Evanston, IL 60201 (SAN 286-7451) Tel 312-492-9472. Do not confuse with Bittersweet Publishing Co., Livermore, CA.

Bittersweet Publishing Co., Subs. of Bittersweet Enterprises, *(Bittersweet Pub; 0-931255),* 5658 Oakmont Cir., Livermore, CA 94550 (SAN 681-9656) Tel 415-455-5816. Do not confuse with Bittersweet Pr., Evanston, IL.

Bittinger, Wayne, *(W Bittinger; 0-9616990),* P.O. Box 220, Parsons, WV 26287 (SAN 661-8421) Tel 304-478-2881.

Biviano, Ronald, *(Biviano; 0-9605476),* 909 Charles, Crete, IL 60417 (SAN 215-9880).

Bixler, Herbert E., *(H E Bixler; 0-9610066),* 13 South Hill Rd., Jaffrey Center, NH 03454 (SAN 268-3415) Tel 603-532-6918.

Bixter Bks., Div. of Allan M. Keene & Co., *(Bixter Bks; 0-936933),* 250 E. 63rd St., New York, NY 10021 (SAN 658-6929) Tel 212-308-3698.

Bizarre Butterfly Publishing, Subs. of Green Davis & Assocs., *(Bizarre Butterfly; 0-915113),* 1347 E. San Miguel, Phoenix, AZ 85014 (SAN 289-5900).

Bjoerling, Jussi, Memorial Archive, Inc., The, *(J Bjoerling; 0-9608546),* P.O. Box 2638, Indianapolis, IN 46206 (SAN 240-5989) Tel 317-635-2021.

†**BkMk Pr., (Univ., of Missouri-Kansas City),** *(BkMk; 0-933532),* UMKC, 5216 Rockhill Rd., Suite 204, Kansas City, MO 64110 (SAN 207-7914) Tel 816-276-2258; Dist. by: Baker & Taylor Co., Midwest Div., 501 Gladiola Ave., Momence, IL 60954 (SAN 169-2100) Tel 815-472-2444; Dist. by: Blackwell North America, 1001 Fries Mill Rd., Blackwood, NJ 08012 (SAN 169-4596) Tel 609-629-0700; Toll free: 800-257-7341; *CIP.*

Bks. New China *See* **Hippocrene Bks., Inc.**

Black, A. & C., Pubs., Ltd., *(A & C Black; 0-7136; 0-7137),* 35 Bedford Row, London WC1R 4JH,

Black, Gloria, *(G Black; 0-9616466),* 2039 NE 98th St., Seattle, WA 98115 (SAN 659-3038) Tel 206-524-6636.

Black, Robert G., Pub., *(R G Black; 0-910631),* P. O. Box 587, Franklin, NC 28734 (SAN 268-3423) Tel 704-488-6920.

Black, Tzvi, *(T Black; 0-9609752),* 125 Carey Street, Lakewood, NJ 08701 (SAN 283-2968) Tel 201-363-2127.

†**Black-A-Moors, Inc., The,** *(Black-A-Moors; 0-933886),* 2339 N. Fairhill St., Philadelphia, PA 19133 (SAN 223-7180) Tel 215-634-1440; *CIP.*

Black & Red, *(Black & Red; 0-934868),* P.O. Box 02374, Detroit, MI 48202 (SAN 208-5550).

Black & White Publishing, Subs. of Sun-Rose Assocs., Inc., *(Black & White; 0-940050),* 18 Cogswell Ave., Cambridge, MA 02140 (SAN 220-2077) Tel 617-576-3863.

Black Bear Pubns., *(Black Bear; 0-932593),* 1916 Lincoln St., Croydon, PA 19020-8026 (SAN 687-5068) Tel 215-788-3543.

Black Box Corp., Subs. of Micom Systems, *(Black Box),* Mayview Rd. at Park Dr., P.O. Box 12800, Pittsburgh, PA 15241 (SAN 277-1985) Tel 412-746-5530.

Black Buzzard, Pr., *(Black Buzzard; 0-938872),* 4705 S. Eighth Rd., Arlington, VA 22204 (SAN 216-0196).

Black Cat Bks. *See* **Grove Pr.**

Black Caucus of the American Library Assn., *(Black Caucus Am Lib),* 499 Wilson Library, Univ. of Minneapolis Libraries, Minneapolis, MN 55455 (SAN 211-8890) Tel 612-373-3097.

Black Classic, Pr., *(Black Classic; 0-933121),* P.O. Box 13414, Baltimore, MD 21203 (SAN 219-5836) Tel 301-728-4595.

Black Current Pr., The, *(Black Current; 0-938975),* P.O. Box 1149, Haines, AK 99827 (SAN 659-8552); Second St., Haines, AK 99827 (SAN 659-8560) Tel 907-766-2146.

Black Dog, Pr., *(Black Dog Pr; 0-933525),* P.O. Box 1213, Capitola, CA 95010 (SAN 691-8514) Tel 408-462-4162.

Black Experience Publishing Co., *(Black Experience; 0-9611778),* P.O. Box 224244, Dallas, TX 75216 (SAN 285-2195).

Black Family Institute Pubs., *(Blk Fam Inst Pub; 0-939205),* P.O. Box 24739, Oakland, CA 94623 (SAN 662-6130); 155 Filbert St., Oakland, CA 94607 (SAN 662-6149) Tel 415-836-3245.

Black Flag Pr., *(Black Flag Pr; 0-937259),* 638 Main St., Woburn, MA 01801 (SAN 659-039X) Tel 617-933-5260.

Black Graphics, *(Black Graphics; 0-939569),* 3023 Woodcreek Ln., Suite 209, Houston, TX 77073 (SAN 663-4958) Tel 713-821-1576.

Black Heron, Pr., *(Black Heron Pr; 0-930773),* P.O. Box 95676, Seattle, WA 98145 (SAN 677-623X) Tel 206-523-2637.

Black Ice, Pr., *(Black I Press; 0-918411),* 6022 Sunnyview Rd., NE, Salem, OR 97305 (SAN 657-5781) Tel 503-363-6064; Dist. by: Bookslinger, 213 E. Fourth St., St. Paul, MN 55101 (SAN 169-4154) Tel 612-221-0429.

Black Ice Pubs., *(Black Ice; 0-939250),* 100 Prescott St., Worcester, MA 01605 (SAN 216-0889) Tel 617-755-1525.

Black Letter Pr., *(Black Letter; 0-912382),* 601 Bridge St., NW, Grand Rapids, MI 49504 (SAN 201-436X) Tel 616-538-2516.

Black Light Fellowship, *(Black Light Fellow; 0-933176),* P.O. Box 5369, Chicago, IL 60680 (SAN 212-3347) Tel 312-722-1441; 2859 W. Wilcox, Chicago, IL 60612 (SAN 669-0211).

Black Mountain Bks., *(Black Mntn; 0-936310),* P.O. Box 601, State College, PA 16804 (SAN 216-3365) Tel 814-234-1967.

Black Oak, Pr., *(Black Oak; 0-930674),* Box 4663, Univ. Pl. Sta., Lincoln, NE 68504 (SAN 212-7261).

Black Oak Pubs, *(Black Oak NY; 0-9608834),* Lloyd Harbor Rd., Huntington, NY 11743 (SAN 241-0044) Tel 516-421-5646.

Black Oak Publishing, *(Blk Oak Pub CA; 0-939392),* P.O. Box DB, Bloomington, CA 92316 (SAN 216-5597).

Black Oyster, Pr., *(Black Oyster; 0-9605966),* 821 Hampshire St., San Francisco, CA 94110 (SAN 216-7182) Tel 415-285-8367.

Black Plankton, Pr., *(Black Plankton; 0-9611236),* P.O. Box 521, Fulton, CA 95439 (SAN 277-6588).

Black Pumpkin Pr., *(Blk Pumpkin Pr; 0-9616206),* Main St., Dunstable, MA 01827 (SAN 658-3326) Tel 617-649-9057.

Black Pursuit, Inc., *(Black Pursuit; 0-935979),* 1809 Hal Ave., Huntington, WV 25701 (SAN 696-6861) Tel 304-523-5392; P.O. Box 5524, Huntington, WV 25703 (SAN 698-2123).

Black Resource Guide, Inc., *(Black Resource; 0-9608374),* 501 Oneida Place, NW, Washington, DC 20011 (SAN 240-1363) Tel 202-291-4373.

Black Rose Bks., *(Black Rose Bks; 0-919618; 0-919619; 0-920057),* 33 E. Tupper St., Buffalo, NY 14230 (SAN 661-9606). U. S. office of Black Rose Bks. Canadian address: 3981 boul. St.-Laurent, Montreal, PQ H2W 1T7. Tel 514-844-4076.

Black Scholar Pr., *(Black Scholar Pr; 0-933296),* P.O. Box 2869, Oakland, CA 94609 (SAN 222-5816) Tel 415-547-6633.

†**Black Sparrow Pr.,** *(Black Sparrow; 0-87685),* 24 Tenth St., Santa Rosa, CA 95401 (SAN 201-4343) Tel 707-579-4011; *CIP.*

Black Stallion Country Press, *(Black Stallion Ctry Pr; 0-9607694),* P.O. Box 2250, Culver City, CA 90231 (SAN 237-9376).

Black Star Publishing Co., *(Black Star Pub; 0-9605426),* 450 Park Ave., S., New York, NY 10016 (SAN 204-4153) Tel 212-679-3288.

Black Star Series, *(Black Star; 0-9607630),* 16 Clipper St., San Francisco, CA 94114 (SAN 293-2369); Dist. by: Subco., P.O. Box 10233, Eugene, OR 97440 (SAN 293-2377).

Black Stone Pr., *(Black Stone; 0-937002),* (SAN 209-5319); Dist. by: Small Press Distribution, Inc., 1814 San Pablo Ave., Berkeley, CA 94702 (SAN 204-5826).

†**Black Swan Bks., Ltd.,** *(Black Swan CT; 0-933806),* P.O. Box 327, Redding Ridge, CT 06876 (SAN 213-4675) Tel 203-938-9548; *CIP.*

Black Swan Pr./Surrealist Editions, *(Black Swan Pr; 0-941194),* 1726 W. Jarvis Ave., Chicago, IL 60626 (SAN 211-593X).

Black Think Tank, *(Black T T; 0-915921),* 1801 Bush St., Suite 127, San Francisco, CA 94109 (SAN 293-969X) Tel 415-929-0204.

†**Black Thorn Bks.,** *(Black Thorn Bks; 0-932366),* 1 Camp St., Cambridge, MA 02140 (SAN 213-2877); *CIP.*

Black Willow Poetry, *(Black Willow; 0-910047),* 401 Independence Dr., Sunrise Towamencin Township, Harleysville, PA 19438 (SAN 240-9682) Tel 215-368-0163.

Blackberry Bks., *(Blackberry Bks),* 26 Stonecrest Rd., Ridgefield, CT 06877 (SAN 208-4201). Do not confuse with Blackberry-Salted in the Shell, South Harpswell, ME.

Blackberry - Salted in the Shell, *(Blackberry ME; 0-942396),* P.O. Box 687, South Harpswell, ME 04079 (SAN 207-7949) Tel 207-833-6051. Do not confuse with Blackberry Bks., Ridgefield, CT.

Blackbird Pr., *(Blackbird Pr; 0-933473),* 1812 Keyway, Dubuque, IA 52001 (SAN 692-4069) Tel 319-556-8474.

Blackbird Pr. Pubns., *(A C Libro Blackbird; 0-940538),* 613 Howard Ave., Pitman, NJ 08071 (SAN 218-5334) Tel 609-589-6963; Dist. by: Joanne Nobes Hoey, 33 E. Centennial Dr., Medford, NJ 08055 (SAN 238-7921) Tel 609-983-5120.

Blackman, Kallick, Co. Ltd., Certified Public Accountants, *(Blackman Kallick; 0-916181),* 300 S. Riverside Plaza, Chicago, IL 60606 (SAN 294-9024) Tel 312-207-1040.

Blackman, *(B Blackman; 0-9615074),* P.O. Box 414, Tarzana, CA 91356 (SAN 693-9481) Tel 818-708-8877.

Blackpot Enterprises, *(Blackpot Enterprises; 0-937823),* P.O. Box 1773, Zephyrhills, FL 34283-1773 (SAN 659-4247) Tel 813-788-4455; 737 Tucker Rd., Zephyrhills, FL 34248 (SAN 659-4255).

Blacksmith Corp., *(Blacksmith Corp; 0-941540),* P.O. Box 424, Southport, CT 06490 (SAN 239-0671) Tel 203-367-4041; Toll free: 800-531-2665.

Blackstone Publishing Co., *(Blackstone Pub; 0-9615836),* 1507 Cochise Dr., Arlington, TX 76012 (SAN 697-0117) Tel 817-274-6915.

Blackwater Publishing Co., Inc., *(Blackwater Pub Co; 0-910341),* 530 Allison Ave., SW, Roanoke, VA 24016 (SAN 241-2756) Tel 703-362-4810.

†**Blackwell, Basil, Inc.,** Subs. of Basil Blackwell, Ltd. (UK), *(Basil Blackwell; 0-631; 0-85520; 0-423; 0-900186; 0-904679; 0-7456; 0-233),* 432 Park Ave., S., Suite 1503, New York, NY 10016 (SAN 680-5035) Tel 212-684-2890; Orders to: (Individuals' orders only), P.O. Box 1655, Hagerstown, MD 21741 (SAN 658-2656) Tel 301-824-7300; Orders to: Harper & Row Pubs., Inc. (Trade orders), Keystone Industrial Pk., Scranton, PA 18512 (SAN 215-3742); Toll free: 800-242-7737; *CIP.*

Blackwell North America, *(NA Blackwell; 0-946344),* 1001 Fries Mill Rd., Blackwood, NJ 08012 (SAN 169-4596) Tel 609-629-0700; Toll free: 800-257-7341; 6024 SW. Jean Rd., Bldg. G, Lake Oswego, OR 97034 (SAN 169-7048) Tel 503-684-1140; Toll free: 800-547-6426.

Blackwell Scientific Pubns., Inc., Div. of Blackwell Scientific Pubns, Ltd. (UK), *(Blackwell Pubns; 0-632; 0-86542),* 667 Lytton Ave., Palo Alto, CA 94301 (SAN 673-2569) Tel 415-324-1688; Orders to: P.O. Box 50009, Palo Alto, CA 94303 (SAN 688-4245) Tel 415-965-4081. Palo Alto, CA offices of Blackwell Scientific Pubns., Inc.: publishers of earth and life science books. See Boston, MA offices of Blackwell Scientific Pubns., for books on medicine and nursing.

†**Blackwell Scientific Pubns., Inc.,** Subs. of Blackwell Scientific Publications, Ltd., *(Blackwell Sci; 0-86542),* 52 Beacon St., Boston, MA 02108 (SAN 215-2029) Tel 617-720-0761; Toll free: 800-325-4177; Dist. by: C. V. Mosby Co., 11830 Westline Industrial Dr., St. Louis, MO 63146 (SAN 200-2280) Tel 314-872-8370; Orders to: Research Report Ctr., 411 Fairchild Ave., Mountain View, CA 94043 (SAN 661-9614) Tel 415-965-4081. Boston, MA office of Blackwell Scientific Pubns., Inc.: publishers of medical and nursing books. See Palo Alto, CA office of Blackwell Scientific Pubns., Inc. for books on the earth and life sciences; *CIP.*

Blackwells Pr., *(Blackwells Pr; 0-930513),* 2925B Freedom Blvd., Watsonville, CA 95076 (SAN 696-5024) Tel 408-722-4534.

Blaffer, Sarah Campbell, Foundation, *(S C Blaffer Found; 0-9615615),* 2001 Kirby Dr., Suite 913, Houston, TX 77019 (SAN 696-1142) Tel 713-528-5279.

Names

Blagrove Pubns., *(Blagrove Pubns; 0-9604466; 0-939776),* 80 Pitkin St., P.O. Box 584, Manchester, CT 06040 (SAN 215-1316) Tel 203-647-1785.

Blair, John, *(J Blair; 0-9601880),* P.O. Box 70043, Riverside, CA 92513 (SAN 211-8858) Tel 714-785-4975.

†**Blair, John F., Pub.,** *(Blair; 0-910244; 0-89587),* 1406 Plaza Dr., Winston-Salem, NC 27103 (SAN 201-4319) Tel 919-768-1374; Toll free: 800-222-9796; *CIP.*

Blair, McGill & Company, *(Blair McGill Co; 0-915771),* 5101-13 S. New Hope Rd., Gastonia, NC 28054 (SAN 294-1368) Tel 704-824-2597.

Blair of Columbus, Inc., Div. of Country Cakes, *(Blair Columbus; 0-9613709),* P.O. Box 7852, Columbus, GA 31908 (SAN 677-1882) Tel 404-561-1144.

Blake, William, Press, Inc., The, *(W Blake Pr; 0-942868),* 140 Tenn. Ave. NE., Washington, DC 20002 (SAN 238-843X) Tel 202-546-3237.

Blake Printing & Publishing, Inc., *(Blake Print Pub; 0-918303),* 2222 Beebee St., San Luis Obispo, CA 93401 (SAN 657-2618) Tel 805-543-6843; Toll free: 800-792-6946.

Blake Schls., The, *(Blake Schools; 0-933023),* 511 Kenwood Pkwy., Minneapolis, MN 55403 (SAN 689-5441) Tel 612-339-1700.

Blakely, Jordan, *(Blakely; 0-9614582),* (SAN 692-3291); Dist. by: The Pullum Corp., G3500 Flushing Rd., Suite 450, Flint, MI 48504 (SAN 200-7797) Tel 313-733-2662.

Blakely, Richard P., *(R P Blakely; 0-9607110),* Rte. 6, Box 163, Astoria, OR 97103 (SAN 238-9517) Tel 503-458-6849.

Blalock, Jack, *(J Blalock; 0-9605156),* P.O. Box 8746, Pembroke Pines, FL 33084-0746 (SAN 215-8396).

Blanck, Helen E., *(H E Blanck; 0-9603700),* 1228 108th Ave., NE., Minneapolis, MN 55434 (SAN 208-0702) Tel 612-757-5374.

Bland, Charles, *(C L Bland; 0-9610804),* 154 Delamere Rd., Williamsville, NY 14221 (SAN 265-0886) Tel 716-631-3193.

Blandin Foundation, *(Blandin Found; 0-9613861),* 100 Pokeyama Ave. N., Grand Rapids, MN 55744 (SAN 685-1932) Tel 218-326-0523.

Blankenship & Co, *(Blankenship & Co.; 0-9613038),* 16418 Kleinwood, Spring, TX 77379 (SAN 293-9088) Tel 713-370-0006.

Blarney Books, *(Blarney Bks; 0-935420),* 6129 Shenandoah Dr., Sacramento, CA 95841 (SAN 213-4683).

Blarney Co., The, *(Blarney Co; 0-9616083),* 334 Old Joppa, Fallston, MD 21047 (SAN 698-1151) Tel 301-879-7967; Box 127, Bel Air, MD 21014 (SAN 698-2565).

Blazing Flowers Pr., *(Blazing Flowers; 0-9610562),* 358 Willowdell, Mansfield, OH 44906 (SAN 263-9378) Tel 419-529-2649.

Blazon Bks., *(Blazon Bks; 0-913017),* 1934 W. Belle Plaine, Chicago, IL 60613 (SAN 283-2860) Tel 312-975-0317; Dist. by: Bookpeople, 2929 Fifth St., Berkeley, CA 94710 (SAN 168-9517) Tel 415-549-3030; Dist. by: Inland Bk. Co., P.O. Box 261, 22 Hemingway Ave., East Haven, CT 06512 (SAN 200-4151) Tel 203-467-4257.

Bleecker Street Publishing Corp., *(Bleecker St Pub; 0-941376),* P.O. Box 13066, 18 Koger Executive Ctr., Norfolk, VA 23506 (SAN 238-9525) Tel 804-461-1212.

Blenderman, Doretta K., *(D K Blenderman; 0-9615637),* 9972 Duffy, Temple City, CA 91780 (SAN 696-1185) Tel 818-286-4757.

Bless Israel Today Ministries, Inc., *(Bless Israel; 0-913961),* P.O. Box 39, New City, NY 10956 (SAN 286-7257) Tel 914-634-1255.

Blessitt Publishing, *(Blessitt Pub; 0-934461),* P.O. Box 69544, Hollywood, CA 90069 (SAN 693-7616) Tel 213-659-8683.

Blewstone Pr., Div. of Allergenco, *(Blewstone Pr; 0-930961),* P.O. Box 8571, Wainwright Sta., San Antonio, TX 78208 (SAN 678-8777) Tel 512-822-4116.

Blind John Pubns., *(Blind John; 0-940388),* 2740 Onyx St., Eugene, OR 97403 (SAN 217-0906).

Blip Productions, *(Blip Prods; 0-936917),* 10656 Riverview Pl., Minneapolis, MN 55433 (SAN 268-3253) Tel 612-426-7442.

Blithedale Press, *(Blithedale; 0-917637),* 321 W. Blithedale Ave., Mill Valley, CA 94941 (SAN 656-8815) Tel 415-383-2886.

Blitz Publishing Co., *(Blitz Pub Co; 0-928404; 0-9606344),* 1600 Verona St., Middleton, WI 53562 (SAN 215-1324) Tel 608-836-7550.

Bloch & Co., *(Bloch & Co OH; 0-914276),* P.O. Box 18058, Cleveland, OH 44118 (SAN 201-7261) Tel 216-371-0979.

Bloch Publishing, Co., *(Bloch; 0-8197),* 19 W. 21st St., New York, NY 10010 (SAN 214-204X) Tel 212-989-9104.

Block Pubs., *(Block; 0-916864),* P.O. Box 1802, Palm Springs, CA 92263 (SAN 208-5577) Tel 619-327-0321.

Blom, Benjamin See Amaryllis Pr.

Blondo/Campbell, *(Blondo-Campbell; 0-9616654),* 2325 Tenth Ave. E., Apt. 101, Seattle, WA 98102 (SAN 659-8595) Tel 206-323-4775.

Blood-Horse, Inc., Subs. of Thoroughbred Owners & Breeders Assn., *(Blood-Horse; 0-936032; 0-939049),* P.O. Box 4038, Lexington, KY 40544 (SAN 203-5294) Tel 606-278-2361; Toll free: 800-354-9207.

Blood Information Service, *(Blood Info; 0-914508),* 508 Getzville Rd., Buffalo, NY 14226 (SAN 206-3344) Tel 716-832-7997.

Bloom Books Inc., *(Bloom Bks; 0-935000),* 1020 Broad St., Newark, NJ 07102 (SAN 215-1332) Tel 201-642-1130.

Blooming Prairie Warehouse, *(Blooming; 0-9608298),* 2340 Heinz Rd., Iowa City, IA 52240 (SAN 240-3420) Tel 319-337-6448.

Bloomsberry Pr., *(Bloomsberry Pr)* 839 Williamson St., No. 1, Madison, WI 53703 (SAN 291-8161).

Blossom Bks., *(Blossom Bks; 0-943280),* 9842 Hibert St., Suite 234, San Diego, CA 92131 (SAN 240-5997) Tel 619-695-8472.

Blossom Valley Press, *(Blossom Valley; 0-939894),* P.O. Box 4044, Blossom Valley Sta., Mountain View, CA 94040 (SAN 216-7905) Tel 415-941-7525.

Blue Begonia Press, *(Blue Begonia; 0-911287),* 225 S. 15th Ave., Yakima, WA 98902 (SAN 268-3652) Tel 509-452-9748.

†**Blue Bird Publishing,** *(Blue Bird Pub; 0-933025),* 1428 W. Broad, No. 202, Columbus, OH 43222 (SAN 200-5603) Tel 614-275-6275; Toll free: 800-255-2665; *CIP.*

Blue Boar Pr., The, *(Blue Boar Pr; 0-9617182),* P.O. Box 964, Manchaca, TX 78652 (SAN 663-2645); 11040 Manchaca Rd., Manchaca, TX 78652 (SAN 663-2653) Tel 512-282-3493.

Blue-Book Pubs., *(Blue Book; 0-918698),* 64 Prospect St., White Plains, NY 10606 (SAN 210-2935) Tel 914-949-0890.

Blue Cat, *(Blue Cat; 0-936200; 0-932679),* 349 Paseo Tesoro, Walnut, CA 91789 (SAN 214-0322) Tel 714-594-3317; Dist. by: Ingram Industries, 347 Reedwood Dr., Nashville, TN 37217 (SAN 169-7978); Dist. by: Baker & Taylor Co., Eastern Div., 50 Kirby Ave., Somerville, NJ 08876 (SAN 169-4901); Dist. by: Baker & Taylor Co., Midwest Div., 501 Gladiola Ave., Momence, IL 60954 (SAN 169-2100); Dist. by: Baker & Taylor Co., Southeast Div., Mt. Olive Rd., Commerce, GA 30529 (SAN 169-1503).

Blue Cloud Quarterly Press, *(Blue Cloud; 0-9612864),* Blue Cloud Abbey, Marvin, SD 57251 (SAN 208-5585) Tel 605-432-5528.

†**Blue Cross & Blue Shield Assn.,** *(Blue Cross & Shield; 0-914818),* 840 N. Lake Shore Dr., Chicago, IL 60611 (SAN 223-629X) Tel 312-440-6182; *CIP.*

Blue Diamond Press, The, *(Blue Diamond; 0-930856),* 801 Tilden St., Bronx, NY 10467 (SAN 220-4142).

Blue Dolphin Publishing, Inc., *(B Dolphin Pub; 0-931892),* P.O. Box 1908, Nevada City, CA 95959 (SAN 223-2480) Tel 916-265-6923; 12380 Nevada City Hwy., Grass Valley, CA 95945 (SAN 696-009X).

Blue Dragon Press, *(Blue Dragon),* 1515 Poplar Ave., Richmond Heights, CA 94805 (SAN 214-3453) Tel 415-235-0361.

Blue Engine Express, The, *(Blue Engine; 0-9611370),* 173 E. Iroquois, Pontiac, MI 48053 (SAN 283-2852) Tel 313-338-3275.

†**Blue Feather Press,** *(Blue Feather; 0-932482),* P.O. Box 5113, Santa Fe, NM 87502 (SAN 211-9293) Tel 505-983-2776; *CIP.*

Blue Flower, *(Blue Flower; 0-9603924),* Dist. by: Han Bks., 3607 Baring St., Philadelphia, PA 19104 (SAN 214-2864) Tel 215-382-1410.

Blue Giant Press, *(Blue Giant Pr; 0-940054),* 24 Concord Ave., No. 308, Cambridge, MA 02138 (SAN 220-2093) Tel 617-661-2591.

Blue Harbor Press, *(Blue Harbor; 0-9605278),* P.O. Box 1028, Lomita, CA 90717-0280 (SAN 215-8442).

Blue Haven Area Foundation, Inc., *(Blue Haven; 0-9609210),* Rte. 3, Box 629, Marble Falls, TX 78654 (SAN 241-2764) Tel 512-598-5727; Dist. by: Collection, Inc., 2101 Kansas City Rd., Olathe, KS 66061 (SAN 200-6359) Tel 913-764-5900; Dist. by: Southwest Cookbook Distributors, 1901 South Shore Dr., Bonham, TX 75418 (SAN 200-4925) Tel 214-583-8898.

Blue Heron Pr., *(Blue Heron WA; 0-935317),* P.O. Box 5182, Bellingham, WA 98227 (SAN 695-7536); 5 Harbor Mall, Bellingham, WA 98225 (SAN 662-3565) Tel 206-671-1155; Dist. by: Robert Hale & Co., 1840 130th Ave., NE, Suite 10, Bellevue, WA 98005 (SAN 200-6995) Tel 206-881-5212; Dist. by: Pacific Pipeline, Inc., 19215 66th Ave., S., Kent, WA 98032 (SAN 208-2128) Tel 206-872-5523; Toll free: 800-426-4727.

Blue Heron Pr., Inc., *(Blue Heron; 0-939198),* 1728 Herrick, NE, Grand Rapids, MI 49505 (SAN 220-0376) Tel 616-363-7810.

Blue Horizon Press, *(Blue Horizon; 0-9607622),* 1517 Crestwood Dr., Greenville, TN 37743 (SAN 213-0254) Tel 615-639-1264.

Blue J, Inc., *(Blue J; 0-936531),* 3808 S. Calhoun St., Fort Wayne, IN 46807 (SAN 697-8509) Tel 219-432-5776.

Blue Lagoon Pubs., *(Blue Lagoon; 0-9605338),* 3960 Laurel Canyon, Studio City, CA 91604 (SAN 215-9899) Tel 818-761-2114.

Blue Leaf Editions, *(Blue Leaf; 0-915206),* P.O. Box 857, New London, CT 06320 (SAN 207-205X) Tel 203-445-7391.

Blue Moon, Pr., *(Blue Moon Pr; 0-933188),* Orders to: College of Arts & Science, Spalding Hall, Lewis-Clark State College, Lewis-Clark State College, Lewiston, ID 83501 (SAN 213-0157); Dist. by: Kampmann & Co., Inc., 9 E. 40th St., New York, NY 10016 (SAN 202-5191) Tel 212-685-2928; Toll free: 800-526-7626.

Blue Mountain Computer, Inc., *(Blue Mtn Com; 0-914729),* 6818 Woodstream Circle, Seabrook, MD 20706 (SAN 289-5919).

Blue Mountain Pr., *(Blue Mtn MI; 0-9602408),* 2005 Academy St., Kalamazoo, MI 49007 (SAN 207-7965) Tel 616-349-3924.

Blue Mountain Pr., Inc., *(Blue Mtn Pr CO; 0-88396),* P.O. Box 4549, Boulder, CO 80306 (SAN 169-0477) Tel 303-449-0536; Toll free: 800-525-0642.

Blue Mouse Studio, The, *(Blue Mouse; 0-9609640),* P.O. Box 312, Union, MI 49130 (SAN 268-3725) Tel 616-641-5468.

Blue-Note Press, *(Blue Note; 0-9610658),* 54 Cherrywood Lane, Erie, PA 16509 (SAN 264-7168) Tel 814-864-9759.

Blue Oak Pr., *(Blue Oak; 0-912950),* P.O. Box 27, Sattley, CA 96124 (SAN 207-0383).

Blue Poppy Enterprises Pr., *(Blue Poppy; 0-936185),* 2140 Pine St., Boulder, CO 80302 (SAN 697-0168) Tel 303-442-0796; Dist. by: Bookpeople, 2929 Fifth St., Berkeley, CA 94710 (SAN 168-9517) Tel 415-549-3030; Dist. by: Redwing Bk. Co., 44 Linden St., Brookline, MA 02146 (SAN 163-3597) Tel 617-738-4664.

Blue Raven Publishing Co., *(Blue Raven Pub Co; 0-916029),* P.O. Box 5641, Bellevue, WA 98006 (SAN 294-6920) Tel 206-643-2203.

Blue Reed Arts Inc., *(Blue Reed; 0-916783),* 839 Williamson St., No. 1, Madison, WI 53703 (SAN 654-2069) Tel 608-251-2206.

Blue Ribbon Bks. See Alpine Pubns.

Blue Ribbon Books See Scholastic, Inc.

Blue Ridge Press of Boone, *(Blue Ridge; 0-938980),* Route 2, Vilas, NC 28692 (SAN 216-3373).

Blue River Pubns., *(Blue River Pubns; 0-930431),* P.O. Box 684, Anoka, MN 55303 (SAN 671-0107).

Blue River Publishing Co., *(Blue River; 0-936324),* P.O. Box 882, Sheboygan, WI 53082-0882 (SAN 215-627X).

Blue Rooster Pr., *(Blue Rooster Pr; 0-9617075),* Rte. 4, Box 540, Perry, FL 32347 (SAN 662-6289); Green Farm Rd., Perry, FL 32347 (SAN 662-6297) Tel 904-584-8589.

Blue Scarab Pr., *(Blue Scarab; 0-937179),* 243 S. Eighth St., Pocatello, ID 83201 (SAN 658-4640) Tel 208-232-5118.

Blue Sea Press, *(Blue Sea; 0-917549),* P.O. Box 9426, Arlington, VA 22209-0426 (SAN 657-0747) Tel 703-522-8826.

Blue Sky Marketing, Inc., *(Blue Sky; 0-911493),* P.O. Box 17003, St. Paul, MN 55117 (SAN 263-9394) Tel 612-774-2920.

Blue Star Pr., *(Blue Star; 0-939602),* 163 Joralemon St., Suite 1144, Brooklyn, NY 11201 (SAN 216-616X) Tel 718-237-9497.

Blue Tulip Pr., *(Blue Tulip Pr; 0-9616163),* 110 S. El Camino, Suite 113, San Mateo, CA 94401 (SAN 699-8372) Tel 415-348-4356.

Blue Unicorn, *(Blue Unicorn; 0-9608574),* 22 Avon Rd., Kensington, CA 94707 (SAN 238-0447) Tel 415-526-8439.

Blue Whale Pr., *(Blue Whale Pr; 0-9615303),* 2980 Edgewick Rd., Glendale, CA 91206 (SAN 694-5236) Tel 213-245-5624; Dist. by: Bookpeople, 2929 Fifth St., Berkeley, CA 94710 (SAN 168-9517) Tel 415-549-3030; Toll free: 800-227-1516; Dist. by: Baker & Taylor Co., Western Div., 380 Edison Way, Reno, NV 89564 (SAN 169-4464) Tel 702-786-6700; Dist. by: Pacific Pipeline, Inc., 19215 66th Ave., S., Kent, WA 98032 (SAN 208-2128) Tel 206-872-5523; Toll free: 800-426-4727.

†**Blue Wind Press,** *(Blue Wind; 0-912652),* P.O. Box 7175, Berkeley, CA 94707 (SAN 206-7099) Tel 415-525-2098; *CIP.*

Bluebird Press (CA), *(Bluebird Pr CA; 0-934003),* P.O. Box 1000, Wildomar, CA 92395 (SAN 692-669X) Tel 714-674-4888.

Bluebird Pr., Inc., *(Bluebird Pr; 0-930169),* P.O. Box 941, Eunice, LA 70535 (SAN 670-7335) Tel 318-546-6100.

Bluefish, *(Bluefish; 0-914102),* Box 1601, Southampton, NY 11968 (SAN 201-6346) Tel 516-283-8811.

Bluejay Bks., *(Bluejay Bks; 0-312),* 1123 Broadway, Suite 306, New York, NY 10010 (SAN 293-0188) Tel 212-206-1538; Dist. by: St. Martin's Pr., 175 Fifth Ave., New York, NY 10010 (SAN 200-2132) Tel 212-674-5151; Toll free: 800-221-7945. Do not confuse with Bluejay Pr., Kokomo, IN.

Bluejay Pr., *(Bluejay Pr IN; 0-939132),* 5900 Dartmouth Ct., Kokomo, IN 46902 (SAN 216-3381) Tel 317-453-2240. Do not confuse with Bluejay Books, New York, NY.

Bluestem Productions, *(Bluestem Prod; 0-9609064),* Box 334, 2327 Lafayette Rd., Wayzata, MN 55391 (SAN 240-9747); Dist. by: Bluestem & the Bookmen, Inc., 525 N. Third St., Minneapolis, MN 55401 (SAN 169-409X) Tel 612-471-7795; Dist. by: Badger Periodicals Distributors, Inc., 2420 W. Fourth St., Appleton, WI 54914 (SAN 169-9024) Tel 414-731-9521; Dist. by: Voelz Educational Services, 1528 Vista Ave., Janesville, WI 53545 (SAN 200-4291) Tel 608-752-0211; Dist. by: The Distributors, 702 South Michigan, South Bend, IN 46618 (SAN 169-2488) Tel 219-232-8500.

Bluetick Publishing, *(Bluetick Pub; 0-9612102),* 2014 Carroll Ave., San Francisco, CA 94124 (SAN 285-6824) Tel 415-467-2719.

Blumarts, Inc., *(Blumarts Inc; 0-935875),* 14 W. Tenth St., New York, NY 10011 (SAN 696-1223) Tel 212-475-0227.

Blume, Augie, & Assocs., *(Blume & Assocs; 0-932521),* P.O. Box 190, San Anselmo, CA 94960 (SAN 687-4649) Tel 415-457-0215.

Blustein/Geary Associates, *(Blustein-Geary; 0-9605248),* 46 Glen Circle, Waltham, MA 02154 (SAN 215-8450).

Blyden, Edward W., Pr., Inc., *(Blyden Pr; 0-914110),* P.O. Box 621, Manhattanville Sta., New York, NY 10027 (SAN 206-4804) Tel 212-222-6000.

Blythe-Pennington, Ltd., *(Blythe-Pennington; 0-943778),* P.O. Box 338, Croton-on-Hudson, NY 10520 (SAN 241-0060) Tel 914-271-4905.

BM Consumer Pubns, *(BM Consumer Pubns; 0-942662),* 556 Sunnymount Ave., Sunnyvale, CA 94087 (SAN 239-6165) Tel 408-737-2950.

B'nai B'rith Hillel Foundations, *(B'nai B'rith-Hillel; 0-9603058),* 1640 Rhode Island Ave., NW, Washington, DC 20036 (SAN 204-4080) Tel 202-857-6556.

Bnos Zion of Bobov, Inc., *(Bnos Zion; 0-937143),* 5000 14th Ave., Brooklyn, NY 11219 (SAN 658-4659) Tel 718-438-3080.

Bo-Tree Productions, Inc., *(Bo-Tree Prods; 0-933714),* 1137 San Antonio Rd., Suite E, Palo Alto, CA 94303 (SAN 216-7050) Tel 415-967-1817.

Boals, Prudencia, Publishing Co., *(Boals Pub; 0-9604270),* R no.6, P.O. Box 89A, Ripley, TN 38063 (SAN 214-2104).

Board for Publications of The Evangelical Lutheran Synod, *(Board Pub Evang; 0-89279),* 734 Marsh St., Mankato, MN 56001 (SAN 262-0030).

Board of Certified Safety Professionals, *(Bd Cert Safety),* 208 Burwash Ave., Savoy, IL 61874 (SAN 225-2422) Tel 217-359-9263.

Board of Church & Society of United Methodist Church, *(Bd Church & Soc),* 100 Maryland Ave. NE., Washington, DC 20002 (SAN 234-5625); Dist. by: Discipleship Resources for Church and Society, 1908 Grand Ave., P.O. Box 189, Nashville, TN 37202 (SAN 661-9932).

Board of Jewish Education of Greater New York, *(Board Jewish Educ; 0-88384),* 426 W. 58th St., New York, NY 10019 (SAN 213-0165) Tel 212-245-8200.

Board of Pubn., LCA, *(Bd of Pubn LCA; 0-8006),* 2900 Queen Lane, Philadelphia, PA 19129 (SAN 213-1110) Tel 215-848-6800; Toll free: 800-367-8737.

†**Boardman, Clark, Co., Ltd.,** Subs. of International Thomson Organization, Inc., *(Boardman; 0-87632),* 435 Hudson St., New York, NY 10014 (SAN 202-4136) Tel 212-929-7500; Toll free: 800-221-9428; *CIP.*

†**Boardroom Bks.,** Div. of Boardroom Reports, Inc., *(Boardroom; 0-932648; 0-88723),* 330 W. 42nd St., New York, NY 10036 (SAN 211-5956) Tel 212-239-9000; Orders to: P.O. Box 1026, Millburn, NJ 07041 (SAN 662-7196) Tel 201-379-4642; *CIP.*

Boardworks Publishing, *(Boardworks Pub; 0-934863),* 35 Eldridge Rd. No. 110, Jamaica Plain, MA 02130 (SAN 694-5619) Tel 617-522-5493; Orders to: Boardworks Publishing, P.O. Box 1241, Jamaica Plain, MA 02130 (SAN 200-7118); Dist. by: Bryant Altman, 84 Beaconfield Rd., Brookline, MA 02146 (SAN 662-3409) Tel 617-232-6818.

Boar's Head Press, *(Boars Head; 0-932114; 0-9606674),* P.O. Box 16413, St. Louis, MO 63125 (SAN 211-1489) Tel 314-846-2694.

Boast, Carol, & Cheryl Rae Nyberg, *(C Boast & C Nyberg; 0-9616293),* 716 W. Indiana Ave., Urbana, IL 61808 (SAN 658-4683) Tel 217-367-4583.

Boat Owners Association of the United States, *(Boat Own Assn US),* 880 S. Pickett St., Alexandria, VA 22304 (SAN 224-5450).

Boathouse Pr., *(Boathouse Pr; 0-9614829),* P.O. Box 58907, Philadelphia, PA 19102 (SAN 693-0123) Tel 215-333-9632.

Boatner Norton Pr., *(Boatner-Norton; 0-9606654),* c/o The Million Year Picknick, 99 Mt. Auburn St., Cambridge, MA 02138 (SAN 219-7162) Tel 617-492-7896.

Bob Bk. Pubns., *(Bob Bks; 0-9612104),* 6516 SW Barnes Rd., Portland, OR 97225 (SAN 685-3781) Tel 503-292-6248.

Bobbeh Meisehs Pr., *(Bobbeh Meisehs; 0-9616933),* 137 Tremont St., Cambridge, MA 02139 (SAN 661-7077) Tel 617-547-2874; Dist. by: Inland Bk. Co., 22 Hemingway St., P.O. Box 261, East Haven, CT 06512 (SAN 200-4151) Tel 203-467-4257; Dist. by: Bookpeople, 2929 Fifth St., Berkeley, CA 94710 (SAN 168-9517) Tel 415-549-3030; Toll free: 800-227-1516.

Bobbi Enterprises, *(Bobbi Ent; 0-9603200),* Rte. 1, Box 44, Mt. Iron, MN 55768 (SAN 213-2885) Tel 218-735-8364.

Bobbs-Merrill Co., Subs. of Macmillan Publishing Co., Inc., *(Bobbs; 0-672),* 866 Third Ave., New York, NY 10022 (SAN 201-3959) Tel 212-702-2000. *Imprints:* Charter Books (Chart); Liberal Arts Press (Lib).

Bobets Publishing Co., *(Bobets; 0-9609782),* P.O. Box 8385, Scottsdale, AZ 85251 (SAN 263-2446) Tel 602-948-2756.

Bobley Publishing Corp., Subs. of Illustrated World Encyclopedia, Inc., *(Bobley; 0-8324),* 311 Crossways Park Dr., Woodbury, NY 11797 (SAN 202-3334) Tel 516-364-1800.

Boca Raton Museum of Art, *(Boca Raton Museum; 0-936859),* 801 W. Palmetto Park Rd., Boca Raton, FL 33432 (SAN 278-2251) Tel 305-392-2500.

Bock Publishing, *(Bock Pub; 0-9614747),* 1777 Sheridan Ave., St. Paul, MN 55116 (SAN 692-9222) Tel 612-699-3252.

Bodhi Press, *(Bodhi; 0-914187),* P.O. Box 44914, Phoenix, AZ 85064 (SAN 287-492X) Tel 602-840-7116.

Bodima, *(Bodima; 0-88875),* Dist. by: Altarinda Books, 13 Estates Dr., Orinda, CA 94563 (SAN 238-1397) Tel 415-254-3830.

Bodine & Assocs., Inc., Pubs., *(Bodine; 0-910254),* The Quadrangle, Suite 132, Village of Cross Keys, Baltimore, MD 21210 (SAN 201-4246) Tel 301-433-7491.

Body Blueprints, *(Body Blueprints; 0-9617110),* 1213 W. California Ave., Mill Valley, CA 94941 (SAN 662-7005) Tel 415-388-1155.

Body Enterprises, *(Body Enterprises; 0-941460),* P.O. Box 80577, Lincoln, NE 68501 (SAN 239-068X) Tel 402-466-8877.

Body Sculpture, *(Body Sculpt; 0-918227),* 1419 Superior Ave., Suite 2, Newport Beach, CA 92663 (SAN 657-2545) Tel 714-760-8235; Dist. by: PMG International, 1343 Columbia, Suite 405, Richardson, TX 75081 (SAN 200-4763).

Bodymind Bks., *(Bodymind Bks; 0-938405),* 450 Hillside Ave., Mill Valley, CA 94941 (SAN 659-8625) Tel 415-383-4017; Dist. by: Bookpeople, 2929 Fifth St., Berkeley, CA 94710 (SAN 168-9517) Tel 415-549-3030.

Boehm, Edward Marshall, Inc., *(E M Boehm; 0-918096),* 25 Fairfacts St., P.O. Box 5051, Trenton, NJ 08638 (SAN 210-1777) Tel 609-392-2207; Toll free: 800-257-9410.

Boehmer Publishing, *(Boehmer Pub; 0-9601728),* 134 Beechwood Rd., Braintree, MA 02184 (SAN 211-5964) Tel 617-848-0486.

Bogden, George A., & Sons, Inc., *(Bogden & Son; 0-942068),* P.O. Box 3, Ridgewood, NJ 07451 (SAN 237-9813) Tel 201-652-3755.

Boggaston Bk. Co., The, *(Boggaston; 0-937085),* 21 Blandin Ave., Framingham, MA 01701 (SAN 658-4802) Tel 617-620-1332.

Bohemica, *(Bohemica; 0-935504),* Columbia Univ. Dept. of Slavic Languages, New York, NY 10027 (SAN 223-7148).

Bohn & Bland Pubs., Inc., *(Bohn Bland Pubs; 0-930965),* 750 Menlo Ave., Suite 250, Menlo Park, CA 94025 (SAN 678-8793) Tel 415-324-0622.

Boian Bks., *(Boian Bks; 0-9604420),* 780 Riverside Dr., Apt. 5E, New York, NY 10032 (SAN 220-1305) Tel 212-234-0173.

Boies, Robert Brice, *(R B Boies; 0-9616981),* 1300 Hibiscus, McAllen, TX 78501 (SAN 663-5622) Tel 512-682-0956.

Boise State Univ., *(Boise St Univ; 0-88430; 0-932129),* 1910 University Dr., Boise, ID 83725 (SAN 206-7080) Tel 208-385-1182; Orders to: BSU Bookstore, 1910 University Dr., Boise, ID 83725 Tel 208-385-1274.

Bola Pr., *(Bola Pr; 0-9608062),* P.O. Box 96, Village Sta., New York, NY 10014 (SAN 295-2971).

Bola Pubns., *(Bola Pubns; 0-943118),* 2378 Willowbrae Dr., Eagle Pass, TX 78852 (SAN 240-3439).

Bolchazy-Carducci Pubs., *(Bolchazy-Carducci; 0-86516),* 44 Lake St., Oak Park, IL 60302 (SAN 219-7685) Tel 312-386-8360.

Bold Age Pr., *(Bold Age Pr; 0-936841),* 10475 Bruceville Rd., Suite G, Elk Grove, CA 95624 (SAN 658-3423) Tel 916-685-3929.

Bold Blue Jay Pubns., *(Bold Blue Jay Pubns; 0-9608182),* 229 Moonlite Dr., Circle Pines, MN 55014 (SAN 238-0412) Tel 612-784-7522.

Bold Productions, *(Bold Prodns; 0-938267),* P.O. Box 328, Oviedo, FL 32765 (SAN 659-8684); 475 Carrigan Ave., Oviedo, FL 32765 (SAN 659-8692) Tel 305-365-8957.

Bold Strummer, Ltd, *(Bold Strummer Ltd; 0-933224),* 1 Webb Rd., Westport, CT 06880 (SAN 213-0262) Tel 203-226-8230.

Bollenbaugh Hill Bks., *(Bollenbaugh Hill; 0-937653),* 10910 Bollenbaugh Rd., Monroe, WA 98272 (SAN 659-3054) Tel 206-794-8065.

375

Bolton, D. Joyce, *(D J Bolton; 0-9602368),* 700 Paseo De Peralta, Santa Fe, NM 87501 (SAN 211-2922) Tel 505-982-4953.

Bolton Pr., *(Bolton Pr; 0-9616326),* 1325 Belmore Way, NE, Atlanta, GA 30338 (SAN 659-0446) Tel 404-237-1577.

Bolz, Roger W., & Assocs., *(R W Bolz),* 205 Wyntfield Dr., Lewisville, NC 27023 (SAN 654-8857) Tel 919-945-5695.

Bomb Shelter Propaganda, *(Bomb Shelter Prop; 0-938309),* P.O. Box 1393, Tempe, AZ 85281 (SAN 659-7696) Tel 602-275-6473.

Bomber Bks. *See Aviation Bk. Co.*

Bon Chance Enterprises, *(Bon Chance Ent; 0-941922),* 14547 Titus St. Suite 102, Panorama City, CA 91412 (SAN 238-6356) Tel 213-785-3149.

Bon Mot Pubns., *(Bon Mot Pubns; 0-9601044),* Rte. 15, P.O. Box 857, Pigeon Force, TN 37863 (SAN 209-3472) Tel 615-436-3919.

Bonanza *See Outlet Bk. Co.*

Bond, Dorothy, *(D Bond; 0-9606086),* 34706 Row River Rd., Cottage Grove, OR 97424 (SAN 216-7913) Tel 503-942-3236.

Bond, E., Pubs., Inc., *(E Bond Pubs; 0-935521),* 2970 Bridgehampton Ln., Orlando, FL 32806 (SAN 696-124X) Tel 305-843-4786.

Bond Publishing, Co., Div. of Progressive Artistic Communications Enterprises, Inc., *(Bond Pub Co; 0-939296),* P.O. Box 1217, Landover, MD 20785 (SAN 220-1488) Tel 301-946-8152.

Bond Research, *(Bond Res; 0-939511),* 592 Baird St., Akron, OH 44311 (SAN 663-3528) Tel 216-773-5682.

BondsCourt Pr., *(Bondscourt Pr; 0-914377),* P.O. Box 23160, Ft. Lauderdale, FL 33307 (SAN 289-6044) Tel 305-772-1072.

Bone Bks., *(Bone Bks; 0-9611174),* 45 Canyon Wren, Sedona, AZ 86336 (SAN 277-6596) Tel 602-282-7707; Dist. by: Missouri Archaeological Society, P.O. Box 958, Columbia, MO 65205 (SAN 238-8316).

Bonjour Bks., *(Bonjour Books; 0-915785),* 6221 Carlson Dr., New Orleans, LA 70122 (SAN 293-9096) Tel 504-282-4660.

Bonner Pr., Subs. of Bonner Communications, Inc., *(Bonner Pr; 0-933705),* 5524-C Old National Hwy., Atlanta, GA 30349 (SAN 692-5308) Tel 404-766-5653; Dist. by: Independent Publishers Group, 1 Pleasant Ave., Port Washington, NY 11050 (SAN 287-2544) Tel 516-944-9325.

Bonney, Orrin H. & Lorraine G., *(Bonney; 0-931620),* P.O. Box 139, Kelly, WY 83011 (SAN 206-7072) Tel 307-733-6392.

Bonnie Prudden Pr., *(Bonnie Prudden; 0-902146),* P.O. Box 59, Stockbridge, MA 01262 (SAN 212-825X) Tel 413-298-3066.

Bonsall Pubns., *(Bonsall Pub; 0-9602066),* 4339 Holly Lane, Bonsall, CA 92003 (SAN 223-4939) Tel 619-758-0054.

Bonus Bks., Inc., *(Bonus Books; 0-933893),* 160 E. Illinois St., Chicago, IL 60611 (SAN 692-7157) Tel 312-467-0580.

Boofish Bks., *(Boofish Bks; 0-9616709),* P.O. Box 69, Chester, CA 96020 (SAN 659-8714) Tel 916-342-1055; 801 Main St., Chester, CA 95926 (SAN 659-8722).

Book & Paper Group, The, *(Bk Paper Group; 0-937685),* Univ. of Chicago Library, 1100 E. 57th St., Chicago, IL 60637 (SAN 659-3062) Tel 312-962-8705.

†**Book & Tackle Shop,** *(Book & Tackle; 0-910258),* 29 Old Colony Rd., Chestnut Hill, MA 02167 (SAN 208-0389) Tel 617-965-0459; 7 Bay St., Watch Hill, RI 02891 (SAN 669-0254) Tel 401-596-0700; *CIP.*

Book Arts *See Menasha Ridge Pr., Inc.*

Book Binder, The, *(Book Binder; 0-915783),* 1560 Tamarack Ave., Atwater, CA 95301 (SAN 293-907X) Tel 209-358-2058.

†**Book Co., The,** Subs. of Arrays, Inc., *(Bk Co; 0-912003),* 11223 S. Hindry Ave., Los Angeles, CA 90045 (SAN 264-603X) Tel 213-410-3977; *CIP.*

Book Department, The, *(Book Dept; 0-9606080),* P.O. Box 241, Hartford, CT 06141-0241 (SAN 216-7921) Tel 203-728-3470.

Bk. Distribution Ctr., *(Book Dist Ctr; 0-941722),* P.O. Box 31669, Houston, TX 77235 (SAN 226-2770) Tel 713-721-1980.

Book Express, *(Bk Express; 0-9612322),* P.O. Box 1249, Bellflower, CA 90706 (SAN 289-1301) Tel 213-867-3723; Dist. by: Publishers Group West, 5855 Beaudry Ave., Emeryville, CA 94608 (SAN 202-8522) Tel 415-658-3453; Dist. by: Ingram Book Co., P.O. Box 17266, Nashville, TN 37217 (SAN 169-7978); Toll free: 800-251-5900; Dist. by: Baker & Taylor (Western Div.), 380 Edison Way, Reno, NV 89564 (SAN 169-4464) Tel 702-786-6700; Toll free: 800-648-3540; Dist. by: Gordons Books, Inc., 5450 N. Valley Hwy., Denver, CO 80216 (SAN 169-0531) Tel 303-296-1830.

Book Industry Study Group, Inc., *(Bk Indus Study; 0-940016),* 160 Fifth Ave., New York, NY 10010 (SAN 216-793X) Tel 212-929-1393.

†**Book-Lab,** *(Book-Lab; 0-87594),* 500 74th St., North Bergen, NJ 07047 (SAN 201-422X) Tel 201-861-6763; *CIP.*

Book Latvia, Inc., The, *(Book Latvia; 0-9614091),* 4N013 Randall Rd., St. Charles, IL 60174 (SAN 685-9933) Tel 312-393-9614.

Book Look, *(Bk Look; 0-934781),* 51 Maple Ave., Warwick, NY 10990 (SAN 694-2474) Tel 914-986-1981.

†**Book Nest, The,** *(Book Nest),* 366 Second St., Los Altos, CA 94022 (SAN 214-1086); *CIP.*

Book Page, *(Bk Page; 0-910266),* 904 Silver Spur Rd., Suite 120, Rolling Hills Estate, CA 90274 (SAN 158-8869) Tel 213-373-1914.

Book Peddlers, The, *(Book Peddlers; 0-916773),* 18326 Minnetonka Blvd., Deephaven, MN 55391 (SAN 653-9548) Tel 612-475-3527; Dist. by: Quality Bks., 918 Sherwood Dr., Lake Bluff, IL 60044-2204 (SAN 169-2127).

Bk. Promotions Pr., *(Book Promo Pr; 0-933586),* P.O. Box 122, Flushing, MI 48433 (SAN 212-7288) Tel 313-659-6683.

Bk. Pubs., Inc., *(Bk Pubs; 0-931541),* P.O. Box 21492, Tampa, FL 33622 (SAN 682-286X) Tel 813-876-1521.

Book Publishing Co., The, *(Book Pub Co; 0-913990),* P.O. Box 99, Summertown, TN 38483 (SAN 202-439X) Tel 615-964-3571.

Bk., Searchers, *(Book Searchers; 0-932484),* 2622 15th Ave., Forest Grove, OR 97116 (SAN 212-0739) Tel 503-357-6948.

Book Service Assocs., Inc., *(Bk Serv Assocs; 0-916253),* P.O. Box 10830, Winston-Salem, NC 27108 (SAN 294-9059) Tel 919-725-7557; 612 S. Main St., Winston-Salem, NC 27101 (SAN 294-9067).

Book Value International *See Quality Books, Inc.*

Bookaset Editions, *(Bookaset Edns; 0-936043),* 223 E. 70th St., New York, NY 10021 (SAN 697-0052) Tel 212-988-0196; Orders to: R.R. 1, Box 374, Kent, CT 06757-9755 (SAN 697-0044) Tel 203-927-3978.

Bookcraft, Inc., *(Bookcraft Inc; 0-88494),* 1848 W. 2300, S., Salt Lake City, UT 84119 (SAN 204-3998) Tel 801-972-6180.

Bookery, *(Bookery; 0-930822),* 8193 Riata Dr., Redding, CA 96002 (SAN 211-8904) Tel 916-365-8068.

Bookfinger, *(Bookfinger; 0-913774),* P.O. Box 487, Peter Stuyvesant Sta., New York, NY 10009 (SAN 202-4144).

Bkhaus, *(Bkhaus; 0-931613),* P.O. Box 299, East Detroit, MI 48021 (SAN 683-681X); 23323 Teppert, East Detroit, MI 48021 (SAN 662-2631) Tel 313-778-5688; Dist. by: Quality Books, Inc., 918 Sherwood Dr., Lake Bluff, IL 60044-2204 (SAN 169-2127) Tel 312-295-2010; Toll free: 800-323-4241; Dist. by: Publishers Group West, 5855 Beaudry St., Emeryville, CA 94608 (SAN 202-8522) Tel 415-658-3453; Toll free: 800-982-8319.

†**Booklegger Pr.,** *(Booklegger Pr; 0-912932),* 555 29th St., San Francisco, CA 94131 (SAN 206-2232) Tel 415-647-9074; Dist. by: Bookpeople, 2929 Fifth St., Berkeley, CA 94710 (SAN 168-9517) Tel 415-549-3030; Toll free: 800-227-1516; *CIP.*

Bookling Pubs., The, *(Bookling Pubs; 0-910717),* 54 Flat Swamp Rd., Newtown, CT 06470 (SAN 268-4047) Tel 203-426-3021.

†**Bookmaker Publishing,** *(Bookmaker; 0-934778),* 1212 E. 131st St., Burnsville, MN 55337 (SAN 213-2907); *CIP.*

Bookmaker, The, *(Bookmaker WA; 0-939075),* Star Rte., Box 38, Winthrop, WA 98862 (SAN 662-8362) Tel 509-996-2576. Do not confuse with Bookmaker Pub. in Burnsville, MN or Bookmakers Guild in Longmont, CO.

Bookmakers Guild, Inc., *(Bookmakers Guild; 0-917665),* 1430 Florida Ave., Suite 202, Longmont, CO 80501 (SAN 657-1255) Tel 303-442-5774; Dist. by: Independent Publishers Group, 1 Pleasant Ave., Port Washington, NY 11050 (SAN 287-2544) Tel 516-944-9325.

Bookman Hse., *(Bookman Hse; 0-918464),* P.O. Box 271804, Houston, TX 77277 (SAN 687-6617).

Bookman Publishing, Subs. of Bookman Dan!, Inc., *(Bookman Pub; 0-934780),* 1601 St. Paul St., Baltimore, MD 21202 (SAN 238-6453) Tel 301-625-0067; P.O. Box 13492, Baltimore, MD 21203 (SAN 658-0203); Orders to: Motorbooks International, Pubs. & Wholesalers, Inc., P.O. Box 2, Osceola, WI 54020 (SAN 169-9164) Tel 715-294-3345; Toll free: 800-826-6600. Do not confuse with Bookman Publishing Co., Waianae, HI.

Bookman Publishing Co., *(Bookman Waianae; 0-942070),* P.O. Box 754, Waianae, HI 96792 (SAN 662-4995) Tel 808-696-4659. Do not confuse with Bookman Publishing, Baltimore, MD.

Bookmark, Div. of Mayhill Pubns, *(Bookmark),* P.O. Box 74, Knightstown, IN 46148 (SAN 203-5278) Tel 317-345-5335.

Bookmarks/USA, *(Bookmarks-USA; 0-935867),* P.O. Box 16085, Chicago, IL 60616 (SAN 696-1266) Tel 312-947-0755; 1605 E. 55th St., No. 2, Chicago, IL 60615 (SAN 696-1274) Tel 312-752-1500.

BookMasters, *(BkMaster; 0-917889),* P.O. Box 159-Z, Ashland, OH 44805 (SAN 656-9668) Tel 419-289-6051.

Bookmates International, Inc., *(Bookmates Intl; 0-933082),* P.O. Box 9883, Fresno, CA 93795 (SAN 212-8799) Tel 209-298-3308; Dist. by: Spring Arbor Distributors, 10885 Textile Rd., Belleville, MI 48111 (SAN 158-9016) Tel 313-481-0900.

Bookplate, Inc., The, *(Bookplate; 0-918413),* 2080 Chestnut St., San Francisco, CA 94123 (SAN 657-5803) Tel 415-563-0888.

Bookpress Ltd., *(BkPr Ltd; 0-916271),* P.O. Box KP, Williamsburg, VA 23187 (SAN 295-6721) Tel 804-229-1260.

Books, *(Books; 0-910268),* 635 N. Elmwood Ave., Waukegan, IL 60085 (SAN 202-4152) Tel 312-623-6963.

Bks. Americana, Inc., *(Bks Americana; 0-89689),* P.O. Box 2326, Florence, AL 35630 (SAN 212-1816) Tel 205-757-9966; Dist. by: Collector Books, 5801 Kentucky Dam Rd., Paducah, KY 42001 (SAN 213-2621) Tel 502-898-6211; Dist. by: Charles E. Tuttle Co., Inc., 28 S. Main St., Rutland, VT 05701-0410 (SAN 213-2621) Tel 802-773-8229; Dist. by: Ingram Book Co., P.O. Box 17266r, Nashville, TN 37217 (SAN 651-1163) Tel 615-361-5000.

Books by Brooks, *(Bks By Brooks; 0-9616207),* 2946 Housley Dr., Dallas, TX 75228 (SAN 658-3288) Tel 817-898-2169.

Books by Kellogg, *(Bks by Kellogg; 0-9603972),* P.O. Box 487, Annandale, VA 22003 (SAN 214-0454) Tel 703-256-2483.

Books for All Times, Inc., *(Bks for All Times; 0-939360),* P.O. Box 2, Alexandria, VA 22313 (SAN 216-2253) Tel 703-548-0457.

Books for Business, *(Bks Business; 0-89499),* Box 5474, New York, NY 10163 (SAN 210-0436).

Books for Professionals, *(Bks for Profs; 0-935422),* 4600 Valley Hi Dr., Sacramento, CA 95823 (SAN 212-3355) Tel 916-428-5984.

Books International of DH-TE International, Inc., *(Bks Intl DH-TE),* P.O. Box 14487, St. Louis, MO 63178 (SAN 202-4101) Tel 314-721-8787.

Books Marcus, *(Books Marcus; 0-916020),* P.O. Box 788, Ojai, CA 93023 (SAN 207-9763).

Books Of A Feather, *(Bks Of A Feather; 0-9613060),* P.O. Box 3095, Terminal Annex, Los Angeles, CA 90051 (SAN 293-972X) Tel 213-797-5551.

Books of Science, *(Bks of Sci; 0-916615),* P.O. Box 462, Columbia, MD 21045 (SAN 296-4589) Tel 301-730-8391.

Books of The New Universe, *(Bks of New Univ; 0-9611638),* P.O. Box 982, Centereach, NY 11720 (SAN 285-1350) Tel 516-585-7261; 164 Noel Dr., Centereach, NY 11720 (SAN 285-1369).

Bks. of The World, *(Books World; 0-915657),* P.O. Box 677, Sterling, VA 22170 (SAN 292-4196) Tel 703-450-4194.

Bks. of Truth, *(Bks of Truth; 0-939399),* P.O. Box 2324, Bath, OH 44210 (SAN 663-1304); 1742 Orchard Dr., Akron, OH 44313 (SAN 663-1312) Tel 216-666-3852.

Books of Value, *(Bks of Value; 0-9603174),* 2458 Chislehurst Dr., Los Angeles, CA 90027 (SAN 210-5896) Tel 213-664-8981.

Books On Business, *(Bks On Bus; 0-932355),* P.O. Box 113, Buena Park, CA 90621 (SAN 687-3685) Tel 714-523-0357.

Books on Demand, Div. of University Microfilms, International, *(Bks Demand UMI; 0-8357),* 300 N. Zeeb Rd., Ann Arbor, MI 48106 (SAN 212-2464) Tel 313-761-4700; Toll free: 800-521-0600. On-demand reprints of out-of-print books reproduced by xerography and bound in paper covers (cloth covers are available for 6.00 additional). Imprint of University Microfilms International.

Bks. on Special Children, *(BOSC; 0-9613860),* P.O. Box 305, Congers, NY 10920 (SAN 682-2649); 49 Woodside Dr., New City, NY 10956 (SAN 688-430X) Tel 914-638-1236.

Books on Tape, Inc., *(Bks on Tape; 0-913369),* P.O. Box 7900, Newport Beach, CA 92660 (SAN 285-8959) Tel 714-548-5525; Toll free: 800-626-3333.

†**Bks. With Ideas, Inc.,** *(Bks With Ideas; 0-917569),* 74 Arguello Cir., San Rafael, CA 94901 (SAN 657-1263) Tel 415-456-5463; *CIP.*

Bookcraft, Inc., *(Bookcraft; 0-937137),* 4909 Eastbourne Dr., Indianapolis, IN 46226 (SAN 658-4667) Tel 317-545-0467.

Bookslinger, *(Bookslinger),* 213 E. Fourth St., Saint Paul, MN 55101 (SAN 169-4154) Tel 612-221-0429.

Bookstore Pr., *(Bookstore Pr; 0-912846),* Box 191, RFD 1, Freeport, ME 04032 (SAN 201-4211).

Bookthrift, Inc., Div. of Simon & Schuster, Inc., *(Bookthrift; 0-89673),* 45 W. 36th St., New York, NY 10018 (SAN 158-8109) Tel 212-947-0909. Hardcover & paperback remainders & special promotional book publishing, hardcover reprints & imports.

Bookworks, *(Bookworks),* Dist. by: Random House, Inc., 400 Hahn Rd., Westminster, MD 21157 (SAN 202-5515).

Bookworld Publishing Co., Inc., *(Bkworld Pub; 1-55633),* 3165 McCrory Pl., Suite 260, Orlando, FL 32803 (SAN 663-3854) Tel 305-894-0661.

Bookworm Pub., *(Bookworm NY; 0-9609624),* 52 Wahl Rd., Rochester, NY 14609 (SAN 268-4098) Tel 716-544-2439. Do not confuse with Bookworm Publishing Co., Russelville, AR.

Bookworm Publishing Co., Inc., *(Bookworm Pub; 0-916302),* P.O. Box 1792, Russelville, AR 72801 (SAN 207-978X) Tel 501-284-4153. Do not confuse with Bookworm Pub., Rochester, NY.

Boomerang Pubs., *(Boomerang; 0-9605900),* 6164 W. 83rd Way, Arvada, CO 80003 (SAN 216-3403) Tel 303-423-5706.

Boone, Lalia, *(L Boone; 0-9612758),* 519 N. Grant, Moscow, ID 83843 (SAN 289-7431) Tel 208-882-4267.

Boone & Crockett Club, *(Boone & Crockett; 0-940864),* 205 S. Patrick St., Alexandria, VA 22314 (SAN 219-7693).

Boone-Thomas Enterprises, *(Boone-Thomas; 0-9611780),* P.O. Box 1093, College Park, MD 20740 (SAN 285-2225) Tel 301-935-5348; 8801 35th Ave., College Park, MD 20740 (SAN 285-2233).

Boonin, Joseph, Inc. *See* **European American Music**

Boosey & Hawkes, Inc., *(Boosey & Hawkes; 0-913932),* 200 Smith St., Farmingdale, NY 11735 (SAN 213-6805) Tel 516-752-1122.

Borden Publishing Co., *(Borden; 0-87505),* 1855 W. Main St., Alhambra, CA 91801 (SAN 201-419X) Tel 818-283-5031.

Borderline Pr., *(Borderline NY; 0-9614941),* 27 W. 11th St., New York, NY 10011 (SAN 693-6644) Tel 212-989-9248; Dist. by: Samuel Weiser, Inc., P.O. Box 612, York Beach, ME 03910 (SAN 202-9588) Tel 207-363-4393; Dist. by: New Leaf Distributing, The, 1020 White St., SW, Atlanta, GA 30310 (SAN 169-1449) Tel 404-755-2665; Toll free: 800-241-3829.

Boreal Pubns., *(Boreal Pubns; 0-9615212),* RFD 2, Box 65A, Landaff, NH 03585 (SAN 694-4612) Tel 603-838-6473.

Bored Feet Pubns., *(Bored Feet Pubns; 0-939431),* P.O. Box 1832, Mendocino, CA 95460 (SAN 661-6992); 31500 N. Mitchell Creek Rd., Fort Bragg, CA 95437 (SAN 663-3226) Tel 707-964-6629.

Borf Bks., *(Borf Bks; 0-9604894),* Mohawk Rd., Brownsville, KY 42210 (SAN 214-3496) Tel 502-597-2187.

Borger Pubns., *(Borger Pubns; 0-9611838),* 385 Eighth St., San Francisco, CA 94103 (SAN 285-2241) Tel 415-863-3427.

†**Borgo Pr.,** *(Borgo Pr; 0-89370; 0-8095),* P.O. Box 2845, San Bernardino, CA 92406-2845 (SAN 208-9459) Tel 714-884-5813; *CIP.*

Boring Software Co., *(Boring Soft; 0-936793),* P.O. Box 568, Boring, OR 97009 (SAN 699-8348) Tel 503-663-4464; 8721 SE 307th Ave., Boring, OR 97009 (SAN 699-8356).

Bork Research, *(Bork Res; 0-939258),* P.O. Box 2654, Quincy, MA 02269 (SAN 220-1658) Tel 617-471-6254.

Born-Hawes Pub. Ltd., *(Born-Hawes Pub; 0-85667),* 55 Vandam St., New York, NY 10013 (SAN 211-2213) Tel 212-929-5275.

Bornstein Memory Training Schls., *(Bornstein Memory; 0-9602610),* 11693 San Vicente Blvd., W. Los Angeles, CA 90049 (SAN 213-0181) Tel 213-478-2056.

Borogove Pr., *(Borogove Pr; 0-9608246),* 78 Bay View Ave., Belvedere, CA 94920 (SAN 240-3447) Tel 415-772-6730.

†**Boss Bks.,** *(Boss Bks; 0-932430),* P.O. Box 370, Madison Sq. Sta., New York, NY 10159 (SAN 211-8920) Tel 212-683-3274; *CIP.*

Boss Performance, *(Boss Perform; 0-931417),* P.O. Box 8035, S. 4228 Conklin, Spokane, WA 99203 (SAN 689-898X).

Boston African American National Historical Site, *(Boston Afro Am; 0-934441),* 46 Joy St., Boston, MA 02114 (SAN 693-5672) Tel 617-742-5415; Orders to: Suffolk Univ., Sawyer Library, 8 Ashburton Pl., Boston, MA 02108 (SAN 662-3255) Tel 617-723-4700.

Boston Athenaeum Library, *(Boston Athenaeum; 0-934552),* 10 1/2 Beacon St., Boston, MA 02108-3777 (SAN 213-019X) Tel 617-227-0270.

Boston Bk. & Art Pubs., *(Boston Bk & Art; 0-8435),* 657 Boylston St., Boston, MA 02116 (SAN 658-6260).

Boston Bks., *(Boston Bks; 0-9616683),* P.O. Box 9909, Spokane, WA 99209-0909 (SAN 659-8757) Tel 509-326-3604.

Boston College, *(Boston Coll),* Chestnut Hill, MA 02167 (SAN 202-3342); Dist. by: Consortium Press, 821 15th St., NW., Washington, DC 20005 (SAN 202-3350).

Boston College Mathematics Institute, *(Boston Coll Math; 0-917916),* Boston College, Chestnut Hill, MA 02167 (SAN 209-9551) Tel 617-552-3775.

Boston Map Co., The, *(Boston Map; 0-938543),* P.O. Box 299, Boston, MA 02118 (SAN 661-2857); 45 W. Newton St., Boston, MA 02118 (SAN 661-2865) Tel 617-267-3001.

Boston Music Company, The, *(Boston Music; 0-88121),* 116 Boylston St., Boston, MA 02116 (SAN 201-7326) Tel 617-426-5100.

Boston Organ Club Chapter, Organ Historical Society, *(Boston Organ Club; 0-9610092),* P.O. Box 104, Harrisville, NH 03450 (SAN 268-4128) Tel 603-827-3055.

†**Boston Public Library,** *(Boston Public Lib; 0-89073),* P.O. Box 286, Boston, MA 02117 (SAN 204-3971) Tel 617-536-5400; *CIP.*

Boston Publishing, Co., *(Boston Pub Co; 0-939526),* 314 Dartmouth St., Boston, MA 02116 (SAN 216-6577) Tel 617-267-8800; Dist. by: Addison-Wesley Publishing Co., 5 Jacob Way, Reading, MA 01867 (SAN 200-2000) Tel 617-944-3700; Dist. by: Time-Life Books, 777 Duke St., Rm. 204, Alexandria, VA 22314 (SAN 202-7836) Tel 703-960-5421.

Boston Risk Management Corp., *(Boston Risk Mgmt; 0-9607398),* 70 Chestnut St., Boston, MA 02108 (SAN 239-5142) Tel 617-723-5592.

Boston Street Railway Assn., *(Boston St Rwy; 0-938315),* P.O. Box 102, Cambridge, MA 02238-0102 (SAN 239-5150) Tel 617-749-1540; 207 South St., Hingham, MA 02043 (SAN 658-0211).

Bostonian Society, *(Bostonian Soc; 0-934865),* 206 Washington St., Old State House, Boston, MA 02109 (SAN 225-2937) Tel 617-242-5610; Orders to: Bostonian Society Gift Shop, 206 Washington Street, Old State House, Boston, MA 02109 (SAN 661-9622) Tel 617-242-5619.

Botanical Society of America, Inc., *(Botanical Soc; 0-939201),* Indiana Univ., Dept. of Biology, Bloomington, IN 47405 (SAN 224-0866) Tel 812-335-9455; Univ. of Texas, Dept. of Botany, Austin, TX 78712 (SAN 661-9630).

Botany Bks., *(Botany Bks; 0-9611966),* 1518 Hayward Ave., Bremerton, WA 98310 (SAN 286-7494) Tel 206-377-6489.

Bottom Dog, Pr., *(Bottom Dog Pr; 0-933087),* c/o Firelands College of Bowling Green State Univ., Huron, OH 44839 (SAN 689-5492) Tel 419-433-5560.

Bottom Line Pr., *(Bottom Line Pr; 0-943020),* P.O. Box 31420, San Francisco, CA 94131 (SAN 240-3455) Tel 415-661-1040.

Bottom Line Software, *(Bottom Line Soft; 0-937973),* P.O. Box 10545, Eugene, OR 97440 (SAN 659-4948) Tel 503-484-0520; 474 Willamette, Suite 201, Eugene, OR 97401 (SAN 659-4956).

Boulevard Books, *(Boulevard; 0-910278),* P.O. Box 89, Topanga, CA 90290 (SAN 202-4179) Tel 213-445-1036.

Bouregy, Thomas, & Co., Inc., *(Bouregy; 0-8034),* 401 Lafayette St., 2nd Flr., New York, NY 10003 (SAN 201-4173) Tel 212-598-0222.

Bove, Susan Barber, *(S B Bove; 0-9611720),* 3344 Rte. 89, Seneca Falls, NY 13148 (SAN 284-9151) Tel 315-549-7152.

Bovin Publishing, *(Bovin; 0-910280),* 68-36 108th St., Forest Hills, NY 11375 (SAN 202-4187) Tel 718-268-2292.

Bowden Publishing, *(Bowden Pub; 0-9616177),* 6252 Cedarwood Rd., Mentor, OH 44060 (SAN 699-8895) Tel 216-942-8729.

Bowen, F A., Reports, Inc., *(F A Bowen; 0-9602830),* P.O. Box 213, Janesville, WI 53547 (SAN 212-8810) Tel 608-752-6333.

Bowen, Glen, Communications, *(G Bowen Comm; 0-910173),* 2415 Villa Creek, Kingwood, TX 77339 (SAN 241-2772) Tel 713-359-3039.

Bowen, Robert Goss, Jr., *(R G Bowen; 0-9607512),* 31 Cobb Rd., Mountain Lakes, NJ 07046 (SAN 237-983X).

Bowen's Publishing Division, *(Bowens Pub Div.; 0-942354),* P.O. Box 270, Bedford, MA 01730-0270 (SAN 239-717X) Tel 617-275-1660.

Bowers, Eddie, Publishing Co., *(E Bowers Pub; 0-912855),* 2884 Hickory Hill, Dubuque, IA 52001 (SAN 282-9878) Tel 319-556-4586; 576 Central Ave., Dubuque, IA 52001 (SAN 663-3013) Tel 319-588-4801.

Bowers, John D., *(J D Bowers; 0-9601360),* P.O. Box 101, Radnor, PA 19087 (SAN 208-0028) Tel 215-688-5541.

Bowers, Sampson, *(Sampson Bowers; 0-916448),* P.O. Box 731, Carmel Valley, CA 93924 (SAN 208-4058).

Names

Bowker, R. R., Co., Div. of Reed Publishing USA, *(Bowker; 0-8352; 0-911255),* 205 E. 42nd St., New York, NY 10017 (SAN 214-1191) Tel 212-916-1600; Toll free: 800-521-8110 US; Toll free: 800-537-8416 Canada. On April 1, 1986, R. R. Bowker Co. became the sole supplier for all Bowker annuals & continuation books. Any orders or standing orders for these titles placed with wholesalers should be changed, & ordered directly from Bowker from the address above. BOWKER NOW OFFERS A 5 PERCENT DISCOUNT FOR ALL STANDING ORDERS. This new policy does not affect subscriptions and non-continuation titles. On or about Oct. 15, 1986, R. R. Bowker Co. will move to a new location. NEW ADDRESS: 245 W. 17TH ST., NEW YORK, NY 10011.

Bowling Green Pr., *(Bowling Gr Pr; 0-9614621),* P.O. Box 582, Bowling Green, OH 43402 (SAN 691-9138) Tel 419-352-0493.

Bowling Green State Univ., Dept. of Philosophy, *(BGSU Dept Phil; 0-935756),* Bowling Green State Univ., Bowling Green, OH 43403 (SAN 213-2923) Tel 419-372-2117.

Bowling Green State Univ., Philosophy Documentation Ctr., *(Philos Document; 0-912632),* Bowling Green State Univ., Bowling Green, OH 43403-0189 (SAN 218-6586) Tel 419-372-2419.

†Bowling Green State Univ., Social Philosophy & Policy Ctr., *(Soc Phil Pol; 0-912051),* Social Philosophy & Policy Ctr., Bowling Green, OH 43403 (SAN 264-6048) Tel 419-372-2536; *CIP.*

Bowling Green Univ. Popular Pr., *(Bowling Green Univ; 0-87972),* Bowling Green State Univ., Popular Culture Ctr., Bowling Green, OH 43403 (SAN 201-4165) Tel 419-372-7865.

Bowling Proprietors' Assn. of America, *(Bowling Prop Assn),* P.O. Box 5802, Arlington, TX 76005 (SAN 268-4241) Tel 817-649-5105.

Bowman Publishing, Inc., *(Bowman Pub Inc; 0-934969),* 743 Harvard Ave., St. Louis, MO 63130 (SAN 695-1147) Tel 314-726-0353.

Bowmar/Noble Pubs., Div. of Economy Co, *(Bowmar-Noble; 0-8372; 0-8107),* P.O. Box 25308, 1901 N. Walnut St., Oklahoma City, OK 73125 (SAN 201-4157) Tel 405-528-8444.

Box Four Twenty-Four Press, *(Box Four Twenty-Four; 0-9614506),* Box 424, Pacific Grove, CA 93950 (SAN 691-7364) Tel 408-649-8215.

Box 21, Inc., *(Box Twenty One; 0-918846),* Tucson, AZ 85702 (SAN 210-394X) Tel 602-325-9602.

Boxes & Arrows, *(Boxes & Arrows; 0-939479),* P.O. Box 792, Jacksonville, FL 32201 (SAN 663-2726); 8150 Baytree Towne Cir., Jacksonville, FL 32201 (SAN 663-2734) Tel 904-642-5388.

†Boxwood Pr., *(Boxwood; 0-910286; 0-940168),* 183 Ocean View Blvd., Pacific Grove, CA 93950 (SAN 201-4149) Tel 408-375-9110; *CIP.*

Boy Scouts of America, *(BSA; 0-8395),* 1325 Walnut Hill Ln., Irving, TX 75038-3096 (SAN 284-9798) Tel 214-659-2273; Orders to: Eastern Distribution Ctr., 2109 Westinghouse Blvd., P.O. Box 7143, Charlotte, NC 28217 (SAN 284-9801) Tel 704-588-4260.

Boyar Bks., *(Boyar; 0-9608464),* 2802 E. Locust St., Davenport, IA 52803 (SAN 240-6039) Tel 319-355-7246.

†Boyars, Marion, Pubs., Inc., *(M Boyars Pubs; 0-7145; 0-905223; 0-906890),* 262 W. 22nd St., New York, NY 10011 (SAN 284-981X) Tel 212-807-6574; Dist. by: Kampmann & Co., Inc., 9 E. 40th St., New York, NY 10016 (SAN 201-002X) Tel 212-685-2928; Toll free: 800-526-7626; *CIP.*

†Boyce-Pubns., *(Boyce-Pubns; 0-918823),* 1023 Oxford, Clovis, CA 93612 (SAN 669-652X) Tel 209-299-8495; *CIP.*

Boyd, Ima Gene (Guthery), *(Ima Boyd; 0-9600502),* 370 E. Archwood Ave., Akron, OH 44301 (SAN 203-7998) Tel 216-773-1757.

†Boyd & Fraser Publishing Co., Subs. of International Thomson Organization, Ltd., *(Boyd & Fraser; 0-87835; 0-87709),* 20 Park Pl., Boston, MA 02116 (SAN 201-4130) Tel 617-426-2292; *CIP.*

Boyd Co., The, *(Boyd Co; 0-9616796),* P.O. Box 5280, Austin, TX 78763-5280 (SAN 659-8803); 16007 Scenic Oak Trail, Buda, TX 78610 (SAN 659-8811) Tel 512-478-7707. *Imprints:* Patch & Frazzle Press (Patch & Frazzle).

Boyer, Carl, *(C Boyer; 0-936124),* P.O. Box 333, Newhall, CA 91322-0333 (SAN 215-7349) Tel 805-259-3154.

Boyertown Area Historical Society, *(Boyertown Hist; 0-9616068),* 43 S. Chestnut St., Boyertown, PA 19512 (SAN 697-824X) Tel 215-369-1868.

Boyink, Betty, Publishing, *(B Boyink; 0-9612608),* 818 Sheldon Rd., Grand Haven, MI 49417 (SAN 289-0658) Tel 616-842-3304.

Boykin, James H., *(Boykin; 0-9603342),* 1260 NW 122nd St., Miami, FL 33167 (SAN 215-0603) Tel 305-681-7663.

Boyle, Michael, Publisher, *(M Boyle Pub; 0-911097),* 155 Afleck St., Hartford, CT 06106 (SAN 268-4284) Tel 203-728-3828.

Boyne Bks., *(Boyne Bks; 0-9615889),* 1526 Sheffield, Jackson, MS 39211 (SAN 697-0176) Tel 601-362-7297.

Boynton & Assocs., *(Boynton & Assocs; 0-933168),* Clifton Hse., Clifton, VA 22024 (SAN 212-9310); Dist. by Hobby Bk. Distributors, 3150 State Line Rd., North Bend, OH 45052 (SAN 200-6669) Tel 513-353-3390.

Boynton Cook Pubs., Inc., *(Boynton Cook Pubs; 0-86709),* P.O. Box 860, 52 Upper Montclair Plaza, Upper Montclair, NJ 07043 (SAN 216-6186) Tel 201-783-3310.

Boys Clubs of America, *(Boys Clubs; 0-9604288),* 771 First Ave., New York, NY 10017 (SAN 204-3920) Tel 212-557-7755.

†Boys Town, Nebraska Ctr., Communications & Public Service Div., Div. of Father Flanagan's Boys' Home, *(Boys Town Ctr; 0-938510),* Boys Town, NE 68010 (SAN 215-8477) Tel 402-498-1580; *CIP.*

Brace, Beverly W., *(B W Brace),* 6352 St. Joseph Ave. NW, Albuquerque, NM 87120 (SAN 210-3435) Tel 505-831-5551.

Brace-Park Pr., *(Brace-Park; 0-942560),* P.O. Box 526, Lake Forest, IL 60045 (SAN 239-412X).

†Bradbury Pr., Affil. of Macmillan, Inc., *(Bradbury Pr; 0-87888),* 866 Third Ave., New York, NY 10022 (SAN 201-4114) Tel 212-702-3598; Toll free: 800-257-5755; Dist. by: Macmillan Pub. Co., Inc., Front & Brown Sts., Riverside, NJ 08370 (SAN 202-5582); *CIP.*

†Braddock Pubns., Inc., *(Braddock Pubns; 0-931147),* 1001 Connecticut Ave., NW, Rm 210, Washington, DC 20036 (SAN 237-7772) Tel 202-296-3630; *CIP.*

Bradford, Vance A., *(V A Bradford; 0-9615983),* 4707 Memory Ln., Oklahoma City, OK 73112 (SAN 697-3531) Tel 405-947-1408.

Bradford & Wilson, Ltd., *(Bradford & Wilson; 0-915073),* Box 7189 University Sta., Provo, UT 84602 (SAN 289-7466) Tel 801-377-4819.

Bradford Co., The, *(Bradford Co),* P.O. Box 256, Scituate, MA 02066 (SAN 263-242X) Tel 617-545-5750.

Bradford Mountain Bk. Enterprises, Inc., *(Bradford Mtn Bk; 0-945610),* 125 E. 23rd St. No. 300, New York, NY 10010 (SAN 289-7237) Tel 212-473-2990.

Bradford Pr., *(Bradford Pr MA; 0-9615783),* 502 Boxford Rd., Bradford, MA 01830 (SAN 696-6845) Tel 617-372-1775; P.O. Box 224, Bradford, MA 01830 (SAN 698-2107).

Bradford Pubs., *(Bradford Pubs; 0-936935),* 2843 Ash Dr., Springfield, OH 45504 (SAN 658-3466).

Bradford Publishing Co., *(Brad Pub Co; 0-935355),* 360 Pine St., 6th Flr., San Francisco, CA 94104 (SAN 696-1320) Tel 415-362-0435.

Bradford Software, *(Bradford Soft; 0-935507),* 6216 E. Ensenada St., Mesa, AZ 85205 (SAN 696-4958) Tel 602-985-7455.

Bradford's Directory of Marketing Research Agencies & Management Consultants, Div. of Denlinger's Publishers, Ltd., *(Bradfords VA; 0-910290),* P.O. Box 276, Dept. B-15, Fairfax, VA 22030 (SAN 204-2754) Tel 703-830-4646.

Bradgate Centennial Committee, *(Bradgate Cent; 0-89279),* Bradgate, IA 50520 (SAN 283-9342).

Bradley Bks., *(Bradley Bks; 0-936765),* 4310 Valli Vista Rd., Colorado Springs, CO 80915 (SAN 699-8518) Tel 303-596-5709.

Bradley Communications, *(Bradley Comm; 0-936045),* P.O. Box 299, Haverford, PA 19041 (SAN 697-0028) Tel 215-896-6146; 1 Coopertown Rd., Haverford, PA 19041 (SAN 697-0036).

Bradley-Nord Sun Enterprises, *(Bradley-Nord; 0-941278),* HC 72 Box 31,, Coldwater, KS 67029 (SAN 238-9169); 323 Pacific St., Bakersfield, CA 93305 (SAN 238-9177).

Bradley Pubns., *(Bradley Pubns; 0-89748),* 80 Eighth Ave., New York, NY 10011 (SAN 696-2912); Dist. by: Warner Brothers Publications, Incorporated, 265 Secaucus Rd., Secaucus, NJ 07094 (SAN 203-0586) Tel 201-348-0700.

Bradley Publishing, *(Bradley Pub; 0-940716),* P.O. Box 7383, Little Rock, AR 72217 (SAN 219-6891) Tel 501-224-0692.

Bradshaw, Jim, Ltd., *(J Bradshaw; 0-9616474),* 186 Catherine St., Lafayette, LA 70503 (SAN 659-3070) Tel 318-234-0393.

Bradson Pr., *(Bradson; 0-9603574),* 31200 LaBaya Dr., Suite 304, Westlake Village, CA 91362 (SAN 213-7267) Tel 818-707-0471.

Bradt Enterprises Pubns., *(Bradt Ent; 0-9339822; 0-9505797),* 93 Harvey St., Apt. 8, Cambridge, MA 02140 (SAN 169-328X) Tel 617-492-8776.

Brady, Frank, *(Brady; 0-9614639),* P.O. Box 4653, Annnapolis, MD 21403-6653 (SAN 691-9219) Tel 301-263-8388.

Brady, Larry G., Publishing, *(Larry G Brady; 0-935489),* 424 E. H St., No. 1103, Chula Vista, CA 92101 (SAN 694-5392) Tel 619-585-9184.

†Brady Communications Co., Inc., Subs. of Prentice-Hall, Inc., *(Brady Comm; 0-87618; 0-87619; 0-89303),* Rte. 9W, Englewood Cliffs, NJ 07632 (SAN 200-2175) Tel 201-592-2352; Toll free: 800-638-0220; Orders to: P.O. Box 500, Englewood Cliffs, NJ 07632 (SAN 215-3939) Tel 201-592-2000; *CIP.*

Brady Street Pr., *(Brady St Pr; 0-9616168),* 1808 N. Farwell Ave., Milwaukee, WI 53202 (SAN 699-9123) Tel 414-272-1232.

Braemar Bks., *(Braemar OR; 0-9612044),* P.O. Box 25296, Portland, OR 97225 (SAN 286-7524) Tel 503-292-4226.

Braemar Pr., *(Braemar Pr; 0-9616791),* 130 Prospect Blvd., St. Paul, MN 55107 (SAN 659-8897) Tel 612-224-6211.

†Bragdon, Allen D., Pubs., Inc., *(A D Bragdon; 0-916410),* Brownstone Library, Munchie Bks., 153 W. 82nd St., New York, NY 10024 (SAN 208-5623) Tel 212-787-6886; Dist. by: Kampmann & Co., 9 E. 40th St., New York, NY 10016 (SAN 202-5191) Tel 212-685-2928; Dist. by: Dodd, Mead & Co., 79 Madison Ave., New York, NY 10016 (SAN 201-3339) Tel 212-685-6464; *CIP.*

Bragg, Emma White, Ph. D., *(E W Bragg; 0-9611930),* 707 Ringgold Dr., Nashville, TN 37207 (SAN 286-0732) Tel 615-227-8923.

Braidwood Publishing Co., *(Braidwood Pub; 0-9616790),* P.O. Box 232, Harwich, MA 02645 (SAN 659-8927); 740 Main St., Harwich Center, MA 02645 (SAN 659-8935) Tel 617-432-0350.

Brain Age Pubs., Subs. of Rolles Edan, Inc, *(Brain Age Pubs; 0-933125),* P.O. Box 427, New Rochelle, NY 10802 (SAN 689-7371) Tel 914-632-9029.

Brain-Image Power Pr., *(Brain-Image; 0-9609246),* P.O. Box 1723, Hollywood, CA 90078 (SAN 260-0218).

Brain Research Pubns., *(Brain Res; 0-916088),* Highbridge Terrace, Fayetteville, NY 13066 (SAN 207-9666).

†Brainchild Bks., *(Brainchild Bks; 0-9613286),* P.O. Box 837, Paia, Maui, HI 96779 (SAN 654-3383) Tel 808-572-9102; *CIP.*

Brancaleone Educational Co, *(Brancaleone Educ; 0-9601186),* 18 Plymouth St., Montclair, NJ 07042 (SAN 209-6218) Tel 201-746-4021.

Branch, Paul R., *(P Branch; 0-9614000),* 209 Land's End Rd., Morehead City, NC 28557 (SAN 686-922X).

Branch Libraries *See* New York Public Library

Branch Redd, *(Branch Redd; 0-9615784),* P.O. Box 46466, Philadelphia, PA 19160 (SAN 696-6853) Tel 215-324-1462.

Branch-Smith, Inc., *(Branch-Smith; 0-87706),* P.O. Box 1868, Fort Worth, TX 76101 (SAN 201-7237) Tel 817-332-6377; 120 St. Louis Ave., Fort Worth, TX 76101 (SAN 201-7245).

Branchemco, Inc., *(Branchemco; 0-9610178),* 8286 Western Way Cir., C-2, Jacksonville, FL 32216-8389 (SAN 268-442X) Tel 904-737-0984; Toll free: 800-874-5990; Toll free: 800-342-1259 (In Florida).

Brand, Irene B., *(Brand; 0-9615285),* Rte. 1, Box 110, Southside, WV 25187 (SAN 694-5465) Tel 304-675-2977.

Brand, Robert F., *(R F Brand; 0-9615727),* 1029 Lake Ln., Pennsburg, PA 18073 (SAN 696-1355) Tel 215-679-8134.

Brandeis-Bardin Institute Pubns., The, *(Brandeis-Bardin Inst; 0-916952),* Brandeis, CA 93064 (SAN 208-5666) Tel 213-348-7201.

Branden Publishing Co., *(Branden Pub Co; 0-8283),* Box 843, Brookline Village, Boston, MA 02147 (SAN 201-4106) Tel 617-734-2045.

Brandon Hse., Inc., *(Brandon Hse; 0-913412),* P.O. Box 240, Bronx, NY 10471 (SAN 201-4092).

Brandt Bks., *(Brandt Bks; 0-9616327),* 1134 Willits Dr., Corona, CA 91720 (SAN 659-0454) Tel 714-735-6167.

Brandywine Conservancy, *(Brandywine Conserv; 0-940540),* P.O. Box 141, Chadds Ford, PA 19317 (SAN 214-3518) Tel 215-388-7601.

Brandywine Pr., Inc., The, *(Brandywine; 0-89616),* c/o E. P. Dutton, 2 Park Ave, New York, NY 10016 (SAN 201-0070).

†**Branford, Charles T., Co.,** *(Branford; 0-8231),* P.O. Box 41, Newton Centre, MA 02159 (SAN 201-9302) Tel 617-964-2441; *CIP.*

Brant, Michelle, *(Brant; 0-9611346),* 2435 Gough St., San Francisco, CA 94123 (SAN 283-2518) Tel 415-775-3024; Dist. by: Bookpeople, 2929 Fifth St., Berkeley, CA 94710 (SAN 168-9517) Tel 415-549-3030; Dist. by: L & S Distributors, 480 9th St., San Francisco, CA 94103 (SAN 169-0213) Tel 415-861-6300.

Brashears, Deya, *(Deya Brashears; 0-9614717),* 1 Corte Del Rey, Orinda, CA 94563 (SAN 692-641X) Tel 415-376-3516; Dist. by: Gryphon House, Inc., 3706 Otis Street, P.O. Box 275, Mt. Rainier, MD 20712 (SAN 169-3190) Tel 301-779-6200.

Brason-Sargar Pubns., *(Brason-Sargar; 0-9602534),* P.O. Box 872, Reseda, CA 91335 (SAN 281-3416) Tel 213-305-7726; Dist. by: DeVorss & Co., P.O. Box 550, 1046 Princeton Dr., Marina del Rey, CA 90294 (SAN 168-9886) Tel 213-870-7478.

†**Brass Pr.,** *(Brass Pr; 0-914282),* 136 Eighth Ave., N., Nashville, TN 37203-3798 (SAN 201-8608) Tel 615-254-8969; *CIP.*

Brattle Pubns., *(Brattle; 0-918938),* 1753 Massachusetts Ave., Cambridge, MA 02140 (SAN 210-3958) Tel 617-661-7467.

Brayden Bks., *(Brayden; 0-9610994),* 719 Post Rd. E., Westport, CT 06880 (SAN 265-1939) Tel 203-227-9667.

Braynard, Frank O., *(F O Braynard; 0-9606204),* 98 Du Bois Ave., Sea Cliff, NY 11579 (SAN 223-2138) Tel 516-676-0733.

†**Braziller, George, Inc.,** *(Braziller; 0-8076),* 1 Park Ave., New York, NY 10016 (SAN 201-9310) Tel 212-889-0909; *CIP.*

Breachwood Publications *See* Riverrun Pr.

Bread & Butter, Pr., *(Bread and Butter; 0-912549),* 2582 S. Clayton, Denver, CO 80210 (SAN 223-1700) Tel 303-753-0912.

Bread for the World, *(Bread for the World),* 32 Union Sq. E., New York, NY 10003 (SAN 226-0182).

Breaking Point, Inc., *(Breaking Point; 0-917020),* P.O. Box 328, Wharton, NJ 07885 (SAN 208-0699) Tel 201-361-7238.

Breakthrough Pubns., Inc., *(Breakthrough; 0-914327),* Scarborough Sta. Plaza, Briarcliff, NY 10510 (SAN 287-4946) Tel 914-762-5111; Toll free: 800-824-5000; Orders to: P.O. Box 594, Millwood, NY 10546 (SAN 662-2127).

Breakthru Publishing, *(Breakthru Pub; 0-942540),* 3603 Piedmont Ave., Oakland, CA 94611 (SAN 293-2407) Tel 415-547-4724; Dist. by: Publishers Group West, 5855 Beaudry, Emeryville, CA 94608 (SAN 202-8522) Tel 415-658-3453.

Brean-Jones Publishing Co., *(Brean-Jones Pub; 0-9615785),* 445 N. Pennsylvania, Suite 709, P.O. Box 449081, Indianapolis, IN 46202 (SAN 694-5317) Tel 317-632-1984; Dist. by: R.W. Haldeman & Assoc., 445 N. Pennsylvania, Indianapolis, IN 46202 (SAN 200-576X).

Breck Schl., *(Breck School; 0-9617136),* 123 Ottawa Ave., N., Minneapolis, MN 55422 (SAN 663-1770) Tel 612-377-5000.

Breed Manual Pubns., *(Breed Manual Pubns; 0-938681),* 3370 Jackson Dr., Jackson, WI 53037 (SAN 661-387X) Tel 414-677-3112.

Breeland, Samuel, *(S Breeland; 0-9615422),* 7842 Playa del Rey Ct., Jacksonville, FL 32216 (SAN 696-141X) Tel 904-731-3754.

Breese, Gerald, *(G Breese),* Princeton Univ., Princeton, NJ 08540 (SAN 206-1007).

Breezewood Publishing Co., *(Breezewood Pub; 0-9606984),* P.O. Box 5421, Greenville, SC 29606 (SAN 691-2648) Tel 803-834-9836.

Breise, Frederic H., *(F H Breise; 0-938576),* 5750 Severin Dr., La Mesa, CA 92041 (SAN 215-8485).

†**Breitenbush Bks.,** *(Breitenbush Bks; 0-932576),* P.O. Box 02137, Portland, OR 97202 (SAN 219-7707) Tel 503-230-1900; *CIP.*

Breland & Farmer, Designers, Inc., *(Breland & Farmer; 0-938007),* 631 Lakeland East Dr., Jackson, MS 39208 (SAN 661-2512) Tel 601-932-3232.

Bremer Bks., *(Bremer Bks; 0-9615766),* 83 Proteus Ave., Groton, CT 06340 (SAN 696-1436) Tel 203-446-1540.

Brendon Hill Publishing Co., *(Brendon Hill Pub; 0-937751),* 6116 Merced Ave., Suite 192, Oakland, CA 94611 (SAN 659-2473) Tel 415-895-7033.

Brennan Bks., Inc., *(Brennan Bks; 0-89270),* 18660 Bonnie Ln., Brookfield, WI 53005 (SAN 208-5674) Tel 414-786-4092.

Brentwood Communications Group, *(Brentwood Comm; 0-916573; 1-55630),* 3914 Cody Rd., Columbus, GA 31907 (SAN 297-1895) Tel 404-561-1772; Toll free: 800-334-8861.

Brentwood Publishing Corp., *(Brentwood Pub; 0-939442),* 825 S. Barrington Ave., Los Angeles, CA 90049 (SAN 216-3438).

Breslau, Nathan, Publishing Co., *(N Breslau; 0-9610716),* 918 A. Savannas Point Dr., Fort Pierce, FL 33450 (SAN 264-6544) Tel 305-466-3439.

Breslov Research Institute, *(Breslov Res Inst; 0-930213),* 3100 Brighton Third St., Brooklyn, NY 11235 (SAN 670-7890) Tel 718-777-5252.

B'Ret Publications, *(Bret Pubns; 0-933357),* 1810 Michael Faraday Dr., Suite 101, Reston, VA 22090 (SAN 691-7666) Tel 703-471-7388.

†**Brethren Encyclopedia,** *(Brethren Encyclopedia; 0-936693),* Bethany Theological Seminary, Oak Brook, IL 60521 (SAN 291-817X); Orders to: 313 Fairview Ave., Ambler, PA 19002 (SAN 685-3803); *CIP.*

†**Brethren Pr.,** Div. of Church of the Brethren, *(Brethren; 0-87178),* 1451 Dundee Ave., Elgin, IL 60120 (SAN 201-9329) Tel 312-742-5100; Toll free: 800-323-8039. Do not confuse with Brethren Publishing Co., Ashland, Ohio; *CIP.*

Brethren Publishing Co., *(Brethren Ohio; 0-934970),* 524 College Ave., Ashland, OH 44805 (SAN 201-730X) Tel 419-289-1708. Do not confuse with Brethren Pr., Elgin, Illinois.

†**Breton Pubs.,** Div. of Wadsworth Publishing Co., Inc., *(Breton Pubs; 0-534),* Statler Office Bldg., 20 Park Plaza, Boston, MA 02116 (SAN 213-4691) Tel 617-482-2344; Toll free: 800-343-2204; Toll free: 800-354-9706 (Orders); Dist. by: Wadsworth Publishing Co., Inc., 10 Davis Dr., Belmont, CA 94002 (SAN 200-2213) Tel 415-595-2350; Dist. by: Delmar Publishers, Inc., 2 Computer Dr., W., Albany, NY 11212 (SAN 206-7544); Toll free: 800-833-3350; *CIP.*

Brevet Pr., *(Brevet Pr; 0-88498),* Box 1404, Sioux Falls, SD 57101 (SAN 201-7563) Tel 605-361-6121.

Brevis Corp., *(Brevis Corp; 0-9617125),* 3310 S. 2700 E., Salt Lake City, UT 84109 (SAN 662-6785) Tel 801-466-6677.

Brevity Press, *(Brevity; 0-917838),* P.O. Box 120622, Nashville, TN 37212 (SAN 209-3979) Tel 615-292-0211.

Brewers Pubns., *(Brewers Pubns; 0-937381),* P.O. Box 4888, Boulder, CO 80306 (SAN 659-0462) Tel 303-441-0840; 7349 Pebble Ct., Longmont, CO 80501 (SAN 659-0470).

Brewster, Janet Bradham, *(J B Brewster; 0-9616934),* P.O. Box 269, Manning, SC 29102 (SAN 662-5606); 316 Brockington St., Manning, SC 29102 (SAN 662-5614) Tel 803-435-4016.

Brian's House, Inc., *(Brian's Hse; 0-9606970),* Box 736, West Chester, PA 19381 (SAN 238-9185).

Briarcliff Pr., Subs. of Settel Associates Inc., *(Briarcliff Pr; 0-932523),* 11 Wimbledon Ct., Jericho, NY 11753 (SAN 687-4703) Tel 516-681-1505.

Briarcliff Pub. Co., *(Briarcliff; 0-915754),* 8111 Timberlodge Trail, Dayton, OH 45459 (SAN 210-573X).

Bric-a-Brac Bookworks, *(Bric-A-Brac),* Box 887, Forked River, NJ 08731 (SAN 282-6364) Tel 609-693-4053.

Brick Alley Bks. Pr., *(Brick Alley Books Press; 0-933647),* 423 S. Main St., Stillwater, MN 55082 (SAN 691-8824) Tel 612-439-0266.

Brick Hse. Publishing, Co., Subs. of Mont Chat, Inc., *(Brick Hse Pub; 0-931790),* 3 Main St., Andover, MA 01810 (SAN 213-201X) Tel 617-475-9568.

Brick Institute of America, *(Brick Inst Amer),* 11490 Commercial Pk. Dr., Suite 300, Reston, VA 22091 (SAN 241-3647) Tel 703-620-0010.

Brick Row Bk. Shop, *(Brick Row),* 278 Post St., No. 303, San Francisco, CA 94108-5071 (SAN 692-3917) Tel 415-398-0414.

Brickel, Estelle D. & Stephen B., *(E & S Brickel; 0-9609844),* c/o Brickel Associates, Inc., 515 Madison Ave., New York, NY 10022 (SAN 284-9836).

Bricker's International Directory, *(Bricker's Intl; 0-916404),* 425 Family Farm Rd., Woodside, CA 94062 (SAN 208-5682) Tel 415-851-3090.

Brickley, James E., *(J E Brickley; 0-9611514),* 914 N. 35th St., Renton, WA 98056 (SAN 284-9224).

Bridal Sense Pubns., *(Bridal Sense; 0-933359),* P.O. Box 765, Framingham, MA 01701 (SAN 691-7674) Tel 617-435-3504.

Bride Guide Enterprises, *(Bride Guide; 0-939884),* 15301 Ventura Blvd., Suite 500, Sherman Oaks, CA 91403 (SAN 695-6750) Tel 213-907-0218; Dist. by: United Bk. Service, 1310 San Fernando Rd., Los Angeles, CA 90065 (SAN 168-986X); Dist. by: Cogan Bks., 4332 W. Artesia Ave., Fullerton, CA 92633 (SAN 168-9649).

Bridge Pubns. Inc., *(Bridge Pubns Inc; 0-88404),* 1414 N. Catalina St., Los Angeles, CA 90027 (SAN 208-3884) Tel 213-382-0382; Toll free: 800-722-1733; Toll free: 800-843-7389 (in California). *Imprints:* ASHO Pubns. (ASHO).

Bridge Publisnting, Inc., *(Bridge Pub; 0-88270),* 2500 Hamilton Blvd., South Plainfield, NJ 07080 (SAN 239-5061) Tel 201-754-0745; Toll free: 800-631-5802. *Imprints:* Haven Books (Haven Bks); Open Scroll (Open Scroll).

Bridgeberg Books, *(Bridgeberg; 0-915358),* 2163 Ewing, Los Angeles, CA 90039 (SAN 210-3028) Tel 213-469-9972.

Bridgehead Pr., *(Bridgehead Pr; 0-912543; 0-915271),* P.O. Box 850125, New Orleans, LA 70185-0125 (SAN 265-1963); Dist. by: Adler Publishing Co., Panorama Plaza, Box 25333, Rochester, NY 14625 (SAN 285-6808) Tel 716-377-5804.

Bridges to the Sound Publishing Corp., *(Bridges Sound; 0-938316),* P.O. Box 260607, Tampa, FL 33685 (SAN 215-7357).

Bridgeview Bks., *(Bridgeview; 0-9613365),* 1065 Central Blvd., Hayward, CA 94542 (SAN 657-0755) Tel 415-889-6355.

Bridgewater Publishing Co., *(Brdgwtr Pub Co; 0-911563),* P.O. Box 336, Glen Ellyn, IL 60137 (SAN 263-9459) Tel 312-469-6078.

Brigadoon Pubns., Inc., *(Brigadoon; 0-938512),* 52 Otis Ave., Staten Island, NY 10306 (SAN 216-0218).

Names

Briggs, Everett F., (E F Briggs; 0-9615976),
Maple Terr., Monongah, WV 26554
(SAN 697-3566) Tel 304-534-5220.

Briggs, Roberts, Assocs., (Rob Briggs;
0-9609850; 0-931191), Box 9, Mill Valley,
CA 94942 (SAN 268-4632)
Tel 415-461-7051; Dist. by: Publishers
Services, 11A Commercial Blvd., Novato,
CA 94947 (SAN 200-7223)
Tel 415-883-3140.

Brigham Young Univ., Family & Community
History Ctr., (BYU Family Commun Hist;
0-938605), Brigham Young Univ., 335
KMB, Provo, UT 84602 (SAN 661-3489)
Tel 801-378-4386.

Brigham Young Univ., J. Reuben Clark Law
Schl., (BYU Clark Law), Brigham Young
Univ., Provo, UT 84602 (SAN 226-4188).

Brigham Young Univ. Law Library, (BYU Law
Lib), Brigham Young University, Provo, UT
84602 (SAN 268-4640).

Bright Baby, Bks., (Bright Baby; 0-930681), 101
Star Lane, Whitethorn, CA 95489
(SAN 676-9608) Tel 707-986-7693.

Bright Books, (Bright Bks; 0-9605968), P.O.
Box 428, Akron, IN 46910 (SAN 216-7204)
Tel 219-893-4113.

Bright Morning Pubns., (Bright Morning;
0-937101), P.O. Box 5338, Kailua Kona, HI
96745 (SAN 658-5809) Tel 808-325-6699.

Bright Mountain Bks., (Bright Mtn Bks;
0-914875), 138 Springside Rd., Asheville,
NC 28803 (SAN 289-0674)
Tel 704-684-8840; Dist. by: Bright Horizons,
138 Springside Rd., Asheville, NC 28803
(SAN 200-7193) Tel 704-684-8840.

Bright Ring Publishing, (Bright Ring; 0-935607),
P.O. Box 5768-B, Bellingham, WA 98227
(SAN 696-0537) Tel 206-733-0722; Dist.
by: Pacific Pipeline, Inc., 19215 66th Ave. S.,
Kent, WA 98032 (SAN 208-2128)
Tel 206-872-5523; Toll free: 800-426-4727;
Dist. by: Baker & Taylor, Eastern Div., 50
Kirby Ave., Somerville, NJ 08876
(SAN 169-4901) Tel 201-526-8000.

Brightfield Publishing Co., (Brightfield Pub Co;
0-939777), 2531 Sawtelle Blvd., No. 38A,
Los Angeles, CA 90064 Tel 213-477-6130.

Brighton Hse. Pubns., (Brighton House;
0-9603256), 500 Bright Water Ct., Brooklyn,
NY 11235 (SAN 213-6570).

Brighton Pubns., (Brighton Pubns; 0-918420),
P.O. Box 12706, New Brighton, MN 55112
(SAN 210-0452) Tel 612-636-2220.

Brighton Street Press, The, (Brighton St Pr;
0-9609642), 53 Flastaff Rd., Rochester, NY
14609 (SAN 268-4667) Tel 716-889-5564.

Brightwaters Pr., Inc., (Brightwaters; 0-918305),
235 Park Ave. S., New York, NY 10003
(SAN 657-2626) Tel 212-777-1711.

Brillig Works Pub., Co., (Brillig Works;
0-89681), 1322 College Ave., Boulder, CO
80302 (SAN 211-5999).

Brinton, William F., (W F Brinton; 0-9603554),
Old Rome Rd., Box 4050, Mt. Vernon, ME
04352 (SAN 694-311X) Tel 207-293-2357.

Bristen Pr., (Bristen Pr; 0-936337), P.O. Box
336, New Hartford, NY 13413
(SAN 697-8517) Tel 315-724-5463; 109
Patricia Ln., Utica, NY 13501
(SAN 697-8525).

†British Book Center, (British Bk Ctr; 0-8277),
Fairview Park, Elmsford, NY 10523
(SAN 201-9361) Tel 914-592-7700; CIP.

Brittany Hse., (Brittany Hse; 0-9613982), 1721
Carr St., Palatka, FL 32077
(SAN 682-1812) Tel 904-325-7834.

Brittany Press, (Brittany Pr; 0-912749), P.O.
Box 888311, Atlanta, GA 30356-0311
(SAN 283-9350) Tel 404-433-5711.

Brittany Pubns., Ltd., (Brittany Pubns;
0-941394), P.O. Box 11572, Ontario Station,
Chicago, IL 60611 (SAN 238-9541)
Tel 312-645-1017.

Brittingham, Janet R., (J R Brittingham;
0-9613351), 2143 Harmony Lane, Jamison,
PA 18929 (SAN 655-8755)
Tel 215-343-6838.

Britton, Inc., (Britton Inc; 0-9611782), 507
Main St., Hingham, MA 02043
(SAN 285-225X) Tel 617-749-9175.

Broadblade Pr., (Broadblade Pr; 0-9614640),
11314 Miller Rd., Swartz Creek, MI 48473
(SAN 691-9227) Tel 313-635-3156; Dist.
by: Baker & Taylor, Midwest Div., 501
Gladiola Ave., Momence, IL 60954
(SAN 169-2100).

Broadcast Information Bureau, Inc., Div. of
National Video Clearinghouse, Inc.,
(Broadcast Info; 0-943174), 100 Lafayette
Dr., Syosset, NY 11791 (SAN 240-3463)
Tel 516-496-3355.

Broadcast Interview Source, (Broadcast Inter;
0-934333), 2500 Wisconsin No. 930,
Washington, DC 20007 (SAN 693-6040)
Tel 202-333-4904.

Broadfoot Publishing, Co., (Broadfoot;
0-916107), Rte. 4, Box 508C, Wilmington,
NC 28405 (SAN 294-9075)
Tel 919-686-4379.

†Broadman Pr., Div. of Southern Baptist
Convention, Sunday School Board,
(Broadman; 0-8054), 127 Ninth Ave. N.,
Nashville, TN 37234 (SAN 201-937X)
Tel 615-251-2544; Toll free: 800-251-3225;
CIP.

Broadsheet Pubns., (Broadsheet Pubns;
0-941142), P.O. Box 616, McMinnville, OR
97128 (SAN 223-1751) Tel 503-472-5524.

†Broadside Press Pubns., (Broadside; 0-910296),
P.O. Box 04257, Detroit, MI 48204
(SAN 201-9388) Tel 313-935-8396; CIP.

Broadway Play Publishing, (Broadway Play;
0-88145), 357 W. 20th St., New York, NY
10011 (SAN 260-1699) Tel 212-627-1055;
Toll free: 800-752-9782 (except NY, HI,
AK).

Broadway Pr., (Broadway Pr; 0-911747), 120
Duane St., Suite 407, New York, NY 10007
(SAN 263-9467) Tel 212-693-0570.

Brob Hse. Bks., (Brob Hse Bks; 0-938407), P.O.
Box 7829, Atlanta, GA 30309
(SAN 659-9117); 242 12th St., Atlanta, GA
30309 (SAN 659-9125) Tel 404-876-1311.

Brock Publishing Co., (Brock Pub; 0-930534),
P.O. Box 1685, Chico, CA 95927
(SAN 201-8616) Tel 714-673-6310.

Brockton Art Museum/Fuller Memorial,
(Brockton Art-Fuller; 0-934358), Oak St.,
Brockton, MA 02401 (SAN 262-0049)
Tel 617-588-6000.

†Brodart Co., (Brodart; 0-87272), 500 Arch St.,
Williamsport, PA 17705 (SAN 203-6711)
Tel 717-326-2461; Toll free: 800-233-8467;
CIP.

Brodkey, Robert S., (R S Brodkey; 0-9616374),
1315 Kinnear Rd., Columbus, OH 43214
(SAN 659-0497) Tel 614-422-2609; Dist.
by: Ohio State Univ. Bookstores, 154 N.
Oval Mall, Columbus, OH 43212
(SAN 209-5637) Tel 614-422-4539.

Brodsky & Treadway, (B&T; 0-9610914), 10-R
Oxford St., Somerville, MA 02143
(SAN 265-0924) Tel 617-666-3372.

Broken Moon Press, (Broken Moon; 0-913089),
330 Del Monte Ave., Tacoma, WA 98466
(SAN 283-2844).

Broken Whisker Studio, (Broken Whisker;
0-932220), P.O. Box 1303, Chicago, IL
60690 (SAN 209-0856) Tel 312-987-0906.

Brokering Press, (Brokering Pr; 0-942562),
11641 Palmer Rd., Bloomington, MN 55437
(SAN 239-622X) Tel 612-888-5281.

Brolet Pr., Div. of Van Valkenburgh Nooger &
Neville, Inc., (Brolet; 0-910298), 33 Gold
St., New York, NY 10038 (SAN 202-425X)
Tel 212-227-6280.

Bronwen Pr., Div. of Jennifer James, Inc.,
(Bronwen Pr; 0-915423), 3903 E. James,
Seattle, WA 98122 (SAN 291-2287)
Tel 206-329-8157; Dist. by: Pacific Pipeline,
19215 66th Ave. S., Kent, WA 98032
(SAN 208-2128) Tel 206-872-5523.

Bronx Bks., (Bronx Bks; 0-9616765), P.O. Box
100, Bronx, NY 10463 (SAN 659-9192); 98
Van Cortland Park S., Bronx, NY 10463
(SAN 659-9206) Tel 212-796-3677.

†Bronx County Historical Society, The, (Bronx
County; 0-941980), 3309 Bainbridge Ave.,
Bronx, NY 10467 (SAN 238-4485)
Tel 212-881-8900; CIP.

†Bronx Museum of the Arts, The, (Bronx Mus;
0-917535), 1040 Grand Concourse, Bronx,
NY 10456 (SAN 656-0598)
Tel 212-681-6000; Dist. by: Publishing
Center, for Cultural Resources, Inc., 625
Broadway, New York, NY 10012
(SAN 274-9025) Tel 212-260-2010; CIP.

Brooding Heron Pr., (Brooding Heron Pr;
0-918116), Waldron Island, WA 98297
(SAN 210-2188).

†Brookes, Paul H., Pubs., (P H Brookes;
0-933716), P.O. Box 10624, Baltimore, MD
21285-0624 (SAN 212-730X)
Tel 301-377-0883; Toll free: 800-638-3775;
CIP.

Brookfield Pub. Co., (Brookfield Pub Co), Old
Post Rd., Brookfield, VT 05036
(SAN 213-4446) Tel 802-276-3162.
Imprints: Multiscience Publications Ltd.
(Pub. by Multisci Pubns Ltd); Online
Publications Ltd (Online Pubns Ltd).

†Brookings Institution, (Brookings; 0-8157),
1775 Massachusetts Ave., NW, Washington,
DC 20036-2188 (SAN 201-9396)
Tel 202-797-6000; CIP.

Brookline Bks., (Brookline Bks; 0-914797), P.O.
Box 1046, Cambridge, MA 02238
(SAN 289-0690)
Tel 617-868-0360.

Brooklyn Botanic Garden, (Bklyn Botanic),
1000 Washington Ave., Brooklyn, NY 11225
(SAN 203-1094)
Tel 718-622-4433.

Brooklyn College Conservatory of Music, (Bklyn
Coll Music; 0-9600976), Brooklyn College,
Brooklyn, NY 11210 (SAN 208-4813)
Tel 718-780-5286.

Brooklyn College, Pr., (Brooklyn Coll Pr;
0-930888), 2227 Boylan Hall, Society In
Change, Brooklyn, NY 11210
(SAN 281-3467); Orders to: 136 S.
Broadway, Irvington-on-Hudson, NY 10533
(SAN 281-3475) Tel 914-591-9111.

Brooklyn Educational & Cultural Alliance,
(Bklyn Educ; 0-933250), Pratt Institute, 200
Willoughby Ave., Brooklyn, NY 11205
(SAN 212-4858) Tel 718-636-3600.

†Brooklyn Museum, (Bklyn Mus; 0-87273;
0-913696), Pubns. & Marketing Services,
Eastern Pkwy., Brooklyn, NY 11238
(SAN 206-3387) Tel 718-638-5000; CIP.

Brookman Stamp Co., Div. of Barrett &
Worthen, Inc., (Brookman Stamp; 0-936937),
215 Middlesex Tpke., Burlington, MA 01803
(SAN 658-6902) Tel 617-229-6097.

Brooks, Peter, (Peter Brooks; 0-9617203), 221
San Bernardino Rd., Covina, CA 91722
(SAN 663-2556) Tel 818-966-1708.

Brooks, Stanley J., Co., (S J Brooks; 0-941806),
1416 Westwood Blvd. Suite 201, Los
Angeles, CA 90024 (SAN 213-7275)
Tel 213-470-2849.

†Brooks/Cole Publishing, Co., (Brooks-Cole; 0-8185;
0-534), 555 Abrego St., Monterey, CA
93940 (SAN 202-3369) Tel 408-373-0728;
Orders to: Wadsworth, Inc., Customer
Service Ctr., 7625 Empire Dr., Florence, KY
41042 (SAN 200-2213); CIP.

†Brooks Publishing Co., (Brooks Pub Co;
0-932370), 2740 Fulton Ave., Suite 113,
Sacramento, CA 95821 (SAN 212-8829)
Tel 916-972-0633; Orders to: P.O. Box 1066,
Carmichael, CA 95609 (SAN 212-8837)
Tel 916-972-0633; CIP.

Broome Closet, The, (Broome Closet;
0-9608130), 34-892 Rancho Vista, Cathedral
City, CA 92234 (SAN 238-8340)
Tel 619-328-4694.

Brossart Pub., (Brossart Pub; 0-9615153), 20715
Viento Valle, Escondido, CA 92025
(SAN 694-3349) Tel 619-741-3255.

Brost-Heus, (Brost Heus; 0-9616109), 384
Elizabeth St., San Francisco, CA 94114
(SAN 699-7392) Tel 415-641-8864.

Brotherhood Aum, Div. of David Miilphen
Assn., (Brotherhood Aum; 0-939777), 556A
W. 110th St., New York, NY 10025
(SAN 677-6213) Tel 212-663-8977.

Brotherhood Commission, (Brotherhood Comm),
1548 Poplar Ave., Memphis, TN 38104
(SAN 225-4662) Tel 901-272-2461.

Brotherhood of Life, Inc., (Bro Life Inc;
0-914732), 110 Dartmouth, SE,
Albuquerque, NM 87106 (SAN 202-4233)
Tel 505-255-8980.

Broude Brothers Ltd., Music, (Broude; 0-8450),
170 Varick St., New York, NY 10013
(SAN 281-3483) Tel 212-242-7001; Toll
free: 800-225-3197; 141 White Oaks Rd.,
Williamstown, MA 01267 (SAN 281-3491).

Broude International Editions, Inc., (Broude Intl
Edns; 0-89371), 141 White Oaks Rd.,
Williamstown, MA 01267 (SAN 208-9483)
Tel 413-458-8131.

Names

Brouhaha Publishing Co., *(Brouhaha Pub; 0-9616036),* 180 Richmond Ave., Buffalo, NY 14222 (SAN 697-8533) Tel 716-884-0248.

Broukal, Gustav, Pr. *See American Atheist Pr.*

Brown, Arlin J., *(Arlin J Brown),* The Arlin J. Brown Info. Ctr., P.O. Box 251, Ft. Belvoir, VA 22060 (SAN 203-4891) Tel 703-451-8638.

Brown, Arthur E., Co., *(E A Brown Co; 0-912579),* 1702 Oak Knoll Dr., Alexandria, MN 56308 (SAN 282-7581) Tel 612-762-8847.

Brown, C. C., Publishing Co., *(C C Brown Pub; 0-9600378),* Box 462, Airway Heights, WA 99001 (SAN 203-6789) Tel 509-244-5807.

Brown, Cathy J., *(C J Brown; 0-9614796),* Dist. by: Creative Expressions, P.O. Box 456, Colchester, VT 05446 (SAN 200-5816).

Brown, D., Books, *(D Brown Bks),* 511 Capp St., San Francisco, CA 94110 (SAN 209-4290) Tel 415-648-3653.

Brown, David C., *(D C Brown; 0-9613415),* 931 North Negley Ave., Pittsburgh, PA 15206 (SAN 656-9730) Tel 412-363-2390; Dist. by: Bruce Shatswell, 10 Phillips Ave., Apt. 2, Lynn, MA 01902 (SAN 200-6103) Tel 617-595-8511.

Brown, Dorothy E., *(D E Brown; 0-9603420),* 3166 Ridge Court, Placerville, CA 95667 (SAN 213-8492) Tel 916-622-9035.

Brown, J. W., Publishing, Inc., *(J W Brown Pub; 0-938215),* P.O. Box 1592, Sedona, AZ 86336 (SAN 659-9214); 55 Southwest Dr., Sedona, AZ 86336 (SAN 659-9222) Tel 602-282-6715.

Brown, James L., *(J L Brown; 0-912314),* Orders to: Old Town News, 308 N. Irwin St., Hanford, CA 93230 (SAN 223-1646).

Brown, Jerald R., *(Jerald Brown; 0-9614679),* 17440 Taylor Ln., Occidental, CA 95465 (SAN 692-5081) Tel 707-874-3344; Dist. by: Bookpeople, 2929 Fifth St., Berkeley, CA 94710 (SAN 168-9517) Tel 415-549-3030; Toll free: 800-227-1516; Dist. by: Inland Book Co., P.O. Box 261, 22 Hemingway Ave., East Haven, CT 06512 (SAN 200-4151) Tel 203-467-4257.

Brown, John Carter, Library, *(J C Brown; 0-916617),* P.O. Box 1894, Providence, RI 02912 (SAN 203-6797) Tel 401-863-2725.

Brown, Katharine, *(Brown Katharine; 0-9613959),* RFD No 1 Old Warner Rd., Henniker, NH 03242 (SAN 688-4318) Tel 603-428-7516; 2101 S. Pine St., Englewood, FL 33533 (SAN 693-5176) Tel 813-474-4470. Use the Second Address for First Only.

Brown, Kenneth J., *(K J Brown; 0-9613137),* 2114 McClellan St., Philadelphia, PA 19145-1911 (SAN 294-698X) Tel 215-462-7876.

Brown, Lewis S., Publisher, *(L S Brown Pub; 0-9608542),* 124 W. Pierpont St., Kingston, NY 12401 (SAN 240-6047) Tel 914-338-4352.

Brown, William C., Pubs., *(Wm C Brown; 0-697),* 2460 Kerper Blvd., Dubuque, IA 52001 (SAN 203-2864) Tel 319-589-2822.

Brown & Assocs., *(J T Brown & Assocs; 0-938742),* 2951 N. Clark St., Chicago, IL 60657 (SAN 216-4736) Tel 312-248-3092.

Brown Book Co., *(Brown Bk; 0-910294),* P.O. Box 69-3883, Miami, FL 33269 (SAN 202-4276) Tel 305-932-0707.

Brown Cherry Pubns, *(Brown Cherry Pub; 0-910515),* 738 Plum Ave., Hampton, VA 23661 (SAN 260-1702) Tel 804-247-3230.

Brown County Historical Society, Inc., *(Brown Cnty Hist Soc; 0-9616808),* P.O. Box 668, Nashville, IN 47448 (SAN 661-0846); State Rd. 135 N., Nashville, IN 47448 (SAN 661-0854) Tel 812-988-4297.

Brown Hse. Communications, *(Brown House; 0-936895),* P.O. Box 15457, Stamford, CT 06901 (SAN 658-4772) Tel 203-834-0050; 108 Pond Rd., Wilton, CT 06897 (SAN 658-4780).

Brown Hse. Galleries Ltd., *(Brown Hse Gall; 0-9604534),* 5717 Hammersley Rd., P.O. Box 4243, Madison, WI 53711 (SAN 215-7365).

Brown Rabbit Press, *(Brown Rabbit; 0-933988),* No. 3 Smithdale Ct., Houston, TX 77024 (SAN 213-0246) Tel 713-465-1168.

Brown Univ., David Winton Bell Gallery, *(D W Bell Gallery; 0-933519),* 64 College St., Providence, RI 02912 (SAN 278-2758) Tel 401-863-2421.

Brown Unlimited, *(Brown Unlimited; 0-9615755),* P.O. Box 6357, Arlington, VA 22206 (SAN 696-1495) Tel 703-931-6068; 3700 N. Rosser St., Alexandria, VA 22311 (SAN 696-1509).

Brownell, W. P., Associates, Inc., *(W P Brownell),* 3675 Clark Rd., Sarasota, FL 33583 (SAN 295-0499).

†Browning Institute, Inc., *(Browning Inst; 0-930252),* P.O. Box 2983, Grand Central Sta., New York, NY 10163 (SAN 210-704X); Dist. by: Wedgestone Pr., P.O. Box 1757, Winfield, KS 67156 (SAN 276-5888) Tel 316-221-2779; *CIP.*

Browning Pubns., *(Browning Pubns; 0-933718),* 4850 Gaidrew Rd., Alpharetta, GA 30201 (SAN 212-8845) Tel 404-475-3430.

Brownlee Books, *(Brownlee Books; 0-9613049),* P.O. Box 489, Hooks, TX 75561 (SAN 293-9126).

Brownlow Publishing Co., Inc., *(Brownlow Pub Co; 0-915720),* 6309 Airport Freeway, Fort Worth, TX 76117 (SAN 207-5105) Tel 817-831-3831; Toll free: 800-433-7610.

Brown's Studio, *(Brown's Studio; 0-9604822),* 4004 Seven Springs Blvd., New Port Richey, FL 33552 (SAN 215-6288) Tel 813-376-5711.

Brownstone Bks., *(Brownstone Bks; 0-941028),* 1711 Clifty Dr., Madison, IN 47250 (SAN 217-3387) Tel 812-273-6908.

Brownstone Pubns., *(Brownstone Pubns; 0-9613101),* P.O. Box 8185, Rolling Meadows, IL 60008 (SAN 293-9800) Tel 312-934-0144.

B'ruach HaTorah Pubns., *(Bruach HaTorah; 0-89655),* 7617 Reading Rd., Cincinnati, OH 45237 (SAN 284-9844) Tel 513-821-8941; P.O. Box 37366, Cincinnati, OH 45222 (SAN 284-9852).

Brubaker, E. S., *(Brubaker; 0-9613496),* 645 N. President Ave., Lancaster, PA 17603 (SAN 209-5343) Tel 717-397-3120.

†Bruccoli Clark Pubns., *(Bruccoli; 0-89723),* 2006 Summer St., Columbia, SC 29201 (SAN 209-3987) Tel 803-771-4642; *CIP.*

Bruce, Martin M., Pubs., *(M M Bruce; 0-935198),* 50 Larchwood Rd., Box 248, Larchmont, NY 10538 (SAN 203-6819) Tel 914-834-1555.

Bruce, Russell, M. D., *(R M D Bruce; 0-961724I),* Lattawoods, Dyersburg, TN 38024 (SAN 663-5555) Tel 901-285-7347.

Bruce Bks. *See Glencoe Publishing Co.*

Bruce McGaw Graphics, Inc., *(B McGaw Graphics; 0-9613932),* 230 Fifth Ave., New York, NY 10001 (SAN 683-5600) Tel 212-679-7823.

Bruhn, John G., *(J G Bruhn; 0-9616570),* 7521 Beluche Dr., Galveston, TX 77551 (SAN 659-9230) Tel 409-761-3001.

Bruington, F. M., *(F M Bruington; 0-9616838),* 1201 Eighth Ave. W., Lot M-4, Palmetto, FL 33561 (SAN 661-2822) Tel 813-729-3704.

Brummel Publishing Company, *(G Brummel Pub; 0-9613041),* P.O. Box 198, Richmond Hill, NY 11419 (SAN 293-3765) Tel 718-835-1155; 116-10 103rd Ave., Richmond Hill, NY 11419 (SAN 295-3773).

Brun Pr., Inc., *(Brun Pr; 0-932574),* 701 NE 67th St., Miami, FL 33138 (SAN 293-2423) Tel 305-756-6249.

Brune, Gunnar, *(G Brune; 0-9604766),* 2014 Royal Club Ct., Arlington, TX 76017 (SAN 215-0611) Tel 817-465-3171.

Bruner, William T., *(Bruner; 0-9606566),* 3848 Southern Pkwy., Louisville, KY 40214 (SAN 211-2884) Tel 502-367-7089.

†Brunner/Mazel, Inc., *(Brunner-Mazel; 0-87630),* 19 Union Sq. W., New York, NY 10003 (SAN 164-9167) Tel 212-924-3344; *CIP.*

Brunswick Historical Society, *(Brunswick Hist Soc),* P.O. Box 1776, Cropseyville, NY 12052 (SAN 213-0289).

Brunswick Publishing Co., *(Brunswick Pub; 0-931494; 1-55618),* Rte. 1, Box 1A1, Lawrenceville, VA 23868 (SAN 211-6332) Tel 804-848-3865.

Brush Hill Pr., Inc., *(Brush Hill; 0-915087),* P.O. Box 96, Boston, MA 02137 (SAN 289-758X) Tel 617-333-0612.

Bryan, R. L., *(R L Bryan; 0-934870),* P. O. Drawer 368, Columbia, SC 29202 (SAN 203-6827).

Bryan-Lee Publishing, *(Bryan-Lee Pub; 0-9614494),* 581 Paseo Miramar, Pacific Palisades, CA 90272 (SAN 689-3422) Tel 213-454-9461.

Bryans *See Dell Publishing Co., Inc.*

Bryant, James M., *(J M Bryant),* P.O. Box 412, Normangee, TX 77871 (SAN 206-2070) Tel 713-828-4265.

Bryant, Lawrence C., *(L C Bryant),* 467 Palmetto Pkwy., NE, Orangeburg, SC 29115 (SAN 201-0550) Tel 803-536-1305.

Bryant Library, The, *(Bryant Library; 0-9602242),* Paper Mill Rd., Roslyn, NY 11576 (SAN 223-484X) Tel 516-621-2240.

Bryce-Waterton Pubns., *(Bryce-Waterton Pubns; 0-913339),* 6411 Mulberry Ave., Portage, IN 46368 (SAN 283-9202) Tel 219-762-5106; Dist. by: Independent Publishers Group, 1 Pleasant Ave., Port Washington, NY 11050 (SAN 287-2544) Tel 516-944-9325; Dist. by: Quality Bks., 918 Sherwood Dr., Lake Bluff, IL 60044-2204 (SAN 169-2127); Toll free: 800-323-4241.

Bryn Ffyliaid Pubns., *(Bryn Ffyliaid; 0-9611114),* 5600 Bellaire Dr., New Orleans, LA 70124 (SAN 283-2720) Tel 504-486-7036.

Brynmorgen Pr., Inc., *(Brynmorgen; 0-9615984),* P.O. Box 405, Boylston, MA 01505 (SAN 698-1585) Tel 617-869-2624; 23 Mill Rd. Circuit, Boylston, MA 01505 (SAN 698-1593).

Brynwood Publishing Co., *(Brynwood Pub; 0-937615),* 13567 Brynwood Ln., Ft. Myers, FL 33912 (SAN 659-0527) Tel 813-369-2117.

B2C Adventures, *(B-TwoC; 0-939368),* 2 Carvel Rd., Annapolis, MD 21401 (SAN 212-2103) Tel 301-974-0642.

Bubba Pr., *(Bubba Pr; 0-9607240),* 560 Hartz Ave., Suite 406, Danville, CA 94526 (SAN 239-4138) Tel 415-820-6237.

Bubbling-Well Pr., *(Bubbling-Well; 0-938045),* P.O. Box 961, St. Cloud, MN 56302 (SAN 659-9257); 701 Germain Mall, Rm. 201, St. Cloud, MN 56301 (SAN 659-9265) Tel 612-253-0426.

Buber, Martin, Press, *(M Buber Pr),* G.P.O. Box 2009, Brooklyn, NY 11202 (SAN 212-7318).

Buccaneer Bks., *(Buccaneer Bks; 0-89966),* P.O. Box 168, Cutchogue, NY 11935 (SAN 209-1542).

Buccaneer Bks., *(Buccaneer CA; 0-934765),* P.O. Box 518, Laguna Beach, CA 92652 (SAN 694-1907) Tel 714-494-4243.

Buch, Judy, *(Judy Buch; 0-9614749),* 111 Olson Dr., Southington, CT 06489 (SAN 692-9249) Tel 203-628-4535; Dist. by: Gryphon House Inc., 3706 Otis St., P.O. Box 275, Mt. Rainier, MD 20712 (SAN 169-3190) Tel 301-779-6200.

Buchan Pubns., *(Buchan Pubns; 0-915067),* P.O. Box 7218, St. Petersburg, FL 33734 (SAN 289-761X) Tel 813-526-9121.

Buchanan, Laurie, Div. of Pages to Go, *(Buchanan L; 0-943102),* 12540 Oak Knoll Rd., Suite B-11, Poway, CA 92064 (SAN 240-8236) Tel 619-748-1056.

Buchs, J., Pubns., *(J Buchs),* 5301 Richmond, No. 24B, Houston, TX 77027 (SAN 208-256X).

Buck Hill Assocs., *(Buck Hill; 0-917420),* 129 Garnet Lake Rd., Johnsburg, NY 12843 (SAN 202-4403) Tel 518-251-2743.

Buck Mountain Pr., *(Buck Mntn Pr; 0-9616710),* P.O. Box 774407, Steamboat Springs, CO 80477 (SAN 659-9281); 3005 Trails Edge Rd., Steamboat Springs, CO 80477 (SAN 659-929X) Tel 303-879-4204.

Buck Publishing Co., *(Buck Pub; 0-934530),* 2409 Vestavia Dr., Birmingham, AL 35216 (SAN 213-0203) Tel 205-979-2296.

Buckeye Pr., *(Buckeye Pr; 0-9615559),* 1803 Park Dr., Columbus, OH 43906 (SAN 696-1533) Tel 404-324-3823; Toll free: 800-241-8981.

Buckingham Assocs., *(Buckingham Assoc),* 591 Parker Hill Rd., Springfield, VT 05156 (SAN 692-3771) Tel 802-885-5052.

Buckle Pr., *(Buckle Pr; 0-9616809),* RR 2, P.O. Box 2283, Lake George, NY 12845 (SAN 661-0862); Schermerhorn Dr., Lake George, NY 12845 (SAN 661-0870) Tel 518-668-2530.

Names

Buckley-Little Bk. Catalogue Co., Inc., *(Buckley-Little; 0-916667),* Canal St. Sta., P.O. Box 512, New York, NY 10013 (SAN 297-0104) Tel 212-982-9357; Dist. by: New York Zoetrope, 80 E. 11th St., Suite 516, New York, NY 10003 (SAN 209-6293) Tel 212-420-0590; Toll free: 800-242-7546.

Buckley Pubns., Inc., *(Buckley Pubns; 0-915388),* 4848 N. Clark St., Chicago, IL 60640-4711 (SAN 208-1954) Tel 312-271-0202.

Bucknell Univ. Pr., *(Bucknell U Pr; 0-8387),* Dist. by: Associated University Presses, 440 Forsgate Dr., Cranbury, NJ 08512 (SAN 281-2959) Tel 609-655-4770.

Bucks County Genealogical Society, *(Bucks Cnty Gen; 0-9612804),* P.O. Box 1092, Doylestown, PA 18901 (SAN 289-9698) Tel 215-345-0210.

Bucks County Historical Society, *(Bucks Co Hist; 0-910302),* Pine & Ashland Sts., Doylestown, PA 18901 (SAN 203-6835) Tel 215-345-0210.

Bucyrus-Erie Co., *(Bucyrus-Erie Co; 0-9604136),* P.O. Box 56, South Milwaukee, WI 53172 (SAN 214-1825).

Buddhist Assn. of the U.S., The, *(Buddhist Assn US; 0-915078),* Dist. by: Institute for Advanced Studies of World Religions, 2150 Center Ave., Fort Lee, NJ 07024 (SAN 265-3885).

†**Buddhist Bks. International,** *(Buddhist Bks; 0-914910),* 9701 Wilshire Blvd., Suite 850, Beverly Hills, CA 90212 (SAN 281-3548); CIP.

†**Buddhist Study Center, The,** *(Buddhist Study; 0-938474),* c/o Press Pacifica, P.O. Box 47, Kailua, HI 96734 (SAN 284-9860) Tel 808-538-3805; Offices of Buddhist Education, 1727 Pali Hwy., Honolulu, HI 96813 (SAN 284-9879); CIP.

Buddhist Text Translation Society, *(Buddhist Text; 0-917512),* Box 217, City of Ten Thousand Buddhas, Talmage, CA 95481 (SAN 281-3556) Tel 707-462-0939.

Budgate Press, *(Budgate Pr; 0-9610746),* 7421 Day Forest Rd., Empire, MI 49630 (SAN 264-7192) Tel 616-334-3387.

Budlong Pr. Co., *(Budlong; 0-910304),* 5915 N. Northwest Hwy., Chicago, IL 60631 (SAN 202-4837).

†**Buffalo Fine Arts Academy,** *(Buffalo Acad; 0-914782),* Albright-Knox Art Gallery, 1285 Elmwood Ave., Buffalo, NY 14222 (SAN 202-4845) Tel 716-882-8700; Dist. by: Univ. of Washington Pr., P.O. Box C50096, Seattle, WA 98145 (SAN 212-2502) Tel 206-543-4050; Toll free: 800-441-4115; CIP.

Buggy Whip Press, *(Buggy Whip; 0-9612824),* 121 Park Ave., Lexington, KY 40508 (SAN 289-5927) Tel 606-233-7176.

Builders of the Adytum, Ltd., *(Builders of Adytum; 0-938002),* 5105 N. Figueroa St., Los Angeles, CA 90042 (SAN 202-4853) Tel 213-255-7141; Orders to: P.O. Box 42278, Dept., O, Los Angeles, CA 90042 (SAN 202-4861).

Builders Publishing Co., The, *(Builders Pub; 0-941000),* P.O. Box 2278, Salt Lake City, UT 84110 (SAN 212-8675) Tel 801-364-7396; Dist. by: New Leaf Distributing, The, 1020 White St. SW, Atlanta, GA 30310 (SAN 169-1449) Tel 404-755-2665; Toll free: 800-241-3829; Dist. by: Bookpeople, 2929 Fifth St., Berkeley, CA 94710 (SAN 168-9517) Tel 415-549-3030; Toll free: 800-227-1516; Dist. by: The Distributors, 702 S. Michigan, South Bend, IN 46618 (SAN 169-2488) Tel 219-232-8500; Dist. by: Devorss & Co., P.O. Box 550, 1046 Princeton Dr., Marina del Rey, CA 90294 (SAN 168-9886) Tel 213-870-7478.

Building Blocks, *(Building Blocks; 0-943452),* 3893 Brindlewood Ln., Elgin, IL 60120 (SAN 240-6063) Tel 312-742-1013.

Building Cost File, Inc., *(Building Cost File; 0-942564),* 2906 Anthony St., Wantagh, NY 11793 (SAN 238-0293) Tel 516-785-1676.

Building Institute, The, *(Building Inst; 0-911749),* 855 Piermont Rd., Piermont, NY 10968 (SAN 263-9483) Tel 914-359-0299; Dist. by: Caroline House, Inc., 5S 250 Frontenac Rd., Naperville, IL 60540 (SAN 211-2280) Tel 312-983-6400.

Bull City, *(Bull City; 0-933974),* 3425 B. Randolph Rd., Durham, NC 27705 (SAN 222-7223).

†**Bull Publishing, Co.,** *(Bull Pub; 0-915950),* P.O. Box 208, Palo Alto, CA 94302 (SAN 208-5712) Tel 415-322-2855; Dist. by: Kampmann & Co., Inc., 9 E. 40th St., New York, NY 10016 (SAN 202-5191) Tel 212-685-2928; Toll free: 800-526-7626; CIP.

Bullbrier Pr., *(Bullbrier Pr; 0-9612610),* 10 Snyder Heights, Ithaca, NY 14850 (SAN 289-0704) Tel 607-273-5109.

Bulldog Club of America, Div. III, *(Bulldog Club Amer; 0-9616531),* 4345 Army St., San Francisco, CA 94131 (SAN 659-4263) Tel 415-282-9079.

Bullet Pubns., Inc., Subs. of Bullet Word Processing, *(Bullet Pubns; 0-9614186),* P.O. Box 7657, Phoenix, AZ 85011 (SAN 686-6034) Tel 602-265-0678.

Bullworks, *(Bullworks; 0-9601190),* 20 Fairway Dr., Stamford, CT 06903 (SAN 211-4097) Tel 203-968-1925.

Bumann, Richard L., *(Bumann Spec Works; 0-9607112),* 2139 Ranch View Terrace, Olivenhain, CA 92024 (SAN 238-9568) Tel 714-753-7279.

†**Bumper Crop Pr.,** *(Bumper Crop Pr; 0-932769),* 12960 State Rte. 700, Hiram, OH 44234 (SAN 688-5497) Tel 216-569-3129; CIP.

Bunkhouse Pubns., Inc., *(Bunkhouse; 0-918628),* 123 N. Sultana Ave., Ontario, CA 91764 (SAN 215-062X).

Bunney's Guides, *(Bunneys Guides; 0-9616711),* P.O. Box 75655, Northgate Sta., Seattle, WA 98125 (SAN 659-932X); 10800 Roosevelt Way, NE, Seattle, WA 98125 (SAN 659-9338) Tel 206-367-3219.

Bunting & Lyon, Inc., *(Bunting; 0-913094),* 238 N. Main St., Wallingford, CT 06492 (SAN 202-487X) Tel 203-269-3333.

Burda Pubns., *(Burda Pubns; 0-914926),* Rockefeller Ctr., Suite 1918, 1270 Ave. of the Americas, New York, NY 10020 (SAN 206-7595).

Burdette & Co., Inc., *(Burdette; 0-910306),* c/o T. Thomte & Co., Inc., 661 Massachusetts Ave., Arlington, MA 02174 (SAN 202-4888) Tel 617-641-2700.

Burdick Ancestry Library, The, *(Burdick Ancestry Lib; 0-9609100),* 2317 Riverbluff Pkwy., No. 249, Sarasota, FL 33581-5032 (SAN 241-2802).

Bureau Issues Assn., *(Bureau Issues; 0-930412),* 7070 Wolftree Ln., Rockville, MD 20852 (SAN 213-0483).

Bureau of Business Practice, Inc., Div. of Simon & Schuster, Inc. A Gulf & Western Co., *(Bur Busn Prac; 0-87622),* 24 Rope Ferry Rd., Waterford, CT 06386 (SAN 204-3742) Tel 203-442-4365.

Bureau of Economic Geology, Div. of Univ. of Texas at Austin, *(Bur Econ Geology),* University Sta., Box X, Austin, TX 78713 (SAN 207-432X) Tel 512-471-1534.

Bureau of Governmental Research & Services, *(Bur Univ Gov SC; 0-917069),* University of South Carolina, Gambrell Hall, Columbia, SC 29208 (SAN 655-4849) Tel 803-777-8156.

Bureau of Health & Hospital Careers Counseling, *(Bur Health Hosp; 0-917364),* Lincoln Hospital Medical Ctr., P.O. Box 238, Scarsdale, NY 10583 (SAN 208-5720) Tel 914-241-0610.

Bureau of International Affairs, *(Bur Intl Aff; 0-938780),* 1613 Chelsea Rd., San Marino, CA 91108 (SAN 201-9442) Tel 818-793-2841.

Bureau of Public Secrets, *(Bur Public Secrets; 0-939682),* P.O. Box 1044, Berkeley, CA 94701 (SAN 216-2261).

Burger, Joanne, *(J Burger; 0-916188),* 57 Blue Bonnet Court, Lake Jackson, TX 77566 (SAN 211-2191).

Burger Pubns., *(Burger Pubns; 0-914561),* Suite 210, 1515 Pacific Ave., Venice, CA 93001 (SAN 289-1549) Tel 213-392-5165.

Burgess, Jack K., Inc., *(J K Burgess; 0-937218),* 2175 Lemoine Ave., Fort Lee, NJ 07024 (SAN 220-1356) Tel 201-592-0739.

Burgess International Group, Inc., *(Burgess MN Intl; 0-8087),* 7110 Ohms Ln., Edina, MN 55435 (SAN 212-6001) Tel 612-831-1344. *Imprints:* Continuing Education Pubn., Co. (CEPCO); Feffer & Simons (Feffer & Simons).

Burgundy Pr., *(Burgundy Pr; 0-917574),* P.O. Box 313, Southampton, PA 18966 (SAN 212-1859).

Burk, Margaret, *(M Burk; 0-937806),* P.O. Box 22, Ambassador Sta., Los Angeles, CA 90070 (SAN 214-2880).

Burkehaven Press, *(Burkehaven Pr; 0-914062),* Penacook Rd., Contoocook, NH 03229 (SAN 202-4896) Tel 603-746-3625.

Burke's Book Store, Inc., *(Burke's Bk Store; 0-937130),* 634 Poplar Ave., Memphis, TN 38105 (SAN 127-3124) Tel 901-527-7484.

Burkett, Jeff, *(Jeff Burkett; 0-9616303),* 2700 W. 44th St., Apt. 207, Minneapolis, MN 55410 (SAN 658-4543) Tel 612-922-6324.

Burkhart's, *(Burkharts; 0-9615199),* 259 Midway Ave., P.O. Box 807, Blandon, PA 19510 (SAN 694-3594) Tel 215-926-2564.

Burlage Corp., *(Burlage Corp; 0-9616208),* 800 Atlantic Ave., Virginia Beach, VA 23451 (SAN 658-3377) Tel 804-480-3673.

Burman, M. L., *(M L Burman),* Box 72, Pineland, FL 33945 (SAN 655-3834) Tel 813-283-0777.

Burn, Billie, Bks., *(Burn Books; 0-9614670),* P.O. Box 29, Daufuskie Island, SC 29915 (SAN 692-4565) Tel 803-842-6801.

Burn, Hart & Co., Pubs., *(Burn Hart; 0-918060),* 632 Calle Yucca, Box 1772, Thousand Oaks, CA 91360 (SAN 210-1823) Tel 805-498-3985.

Burnell Co./Publishers, Inc., The, *(Burnell Co; 0-916973),* P.O. Box 304, Mankato, MN 56001 (SAN 655-587X) Tel 507-625-4302.

Burnett Microfiche Co., *(Burnett Micro; 0-916497),* 3891 Commander Dr., Atlanta, GA 30341-0016 (SAN 295-5547) Tel 404-455-6445.

Burning Deck, Div. of ANTART Contemporary Art Ctr., *(Burning Deck; 0-930900; 0-930901),* 71 Elmgrove Ave., Providence, RI 02906 (SAN 207-7981); Dist. by: Small Pr. Distribution, Inc., 1814 San Pablo Ave., Berkeley, CA 94702 (SAN 204-5826) Tel 415-549-3336.

Burns, H. Keith, Publishing, *(H Keith Burns; 0-943842),* 6026 Mesa Ave., Los Angeles, CA 90042 (SAN 241-0079) Tel 213-256-5436.

Burns, J. B., *(J B Burns; 0-9602998),* 4250 Lauderdale Ave., La Crescenta, CA 91214 (SAN 213-473X).

†**Buros Institute of Mental Measurements,** Div. of Univ. of Nebraska-Lincoln, *(Buros Inst Mental; 0-910674),* Univ. of Nebraska-Lincoln, 135 Bancroft, Lincoln, NE 68588-0348 (SAN 698-1895) Tel 402-472-6203; Orders to: Univ. of Nebraska Pr., 901 N. 17th St., Lincoln, NE 68588-0520 (SAN 662-4022) Tel 402-472-3581; CIP.

Burr, Aaron, Assn., *(Aaron Burr Assn),* R.D. 1, Rte. 33, Box 429, Hightstown, NJ 08520 (SAN 225-395X) Tel 609-448-2218.

Burr, Betty Fagan, *(B F Burr; 0-911619),* 613 Bostwick, Nacogdoches, TX 75961 (SAN 263-9491) Tel 409-564-7478.

Burr Pubns., Ltd., *(Burr Pubns; 0-911994),* RD 1, Rte. 33, Box 429, Hightstown, NJ 08520 (SAN 207-2068).

Burrell Center, Inc., *(Burrell Ctr Inc; 0-9606362),* P.O. Box 1611 SSS, Springfield, MO 65805 (SAN 223-7520) Tel 417-883-5400.

†**Burill-Ellsworth Assocs.,** *(Burrill-Ellsworth; 0-935310),* 26 Birchwood Pl., Tenafly, NJ 07670 (SAN 281-3602); Orders to: Box 295, Tenafly, NJ 07670 (SAN 281-3610); CIP.

Burrows, Hal D., /Inner Press, *(H D Burrows; 0-916886),* 429 E. 98th St., No. 1, Inglewood, CA 90301 (SAN 211-0180) Tel 213-671-5959.

Burrows & Baker, *(Burrows & Baker; 0-930414),* 201 E. 21st St., New York, NY 10010 (SAN 223-2618).

Burtis Enterprises, Pubs., *(Burtis Ent; 0-939530),* 23651 Gerrad Way, Canoga Park, CA 91307 (SAN 216-6593) Tel 818-346-8534.

Burtt, E. A., *(E A Burtt; 0-9616132),* 227 Willard Way, Ithaca, NY 14850 (SAN 699-8429) Tel 607-273-5421.

Burtt & Co., *(Burtt Co; 0-937087),* 9 Hampden St., Wellesley, MA 02181 (SAN 658-4853) Tel 617-235-7616.

Burwell Enterprises, *(Burwell Ent; 0-938519),* 5106 F.M. 1960, Suite 349, Houston, TX 77069 (SAN 674-7078) Tel 713-537-9051.

Buryn, Ed, Pub., *(Ed Buryn Pub; 0-916804),* Box 31123, San Francisco, CA 94131 (SAN 211-3880) Tel 415-824-8938; Dist. by: Bookpeople, 2929 Fifth St., Berkeley, CA 94710 (SAN 168-9517) Tel 415-549-3030; Toll free: 800-227-1516; Dist. by: Pacific Pipeline, Inc., 19215 66th Ave., S., Kent, WA 98032 (SAN 208-2128) Tel 206-872-5523; Dist. by: The Distributors, 702 S. Michigan, South Bend, IN 46618 (SAN 169-2488) Tel 219-232-8500; Dist. by: Book Dynamics, 836 Broadway, New York, NY 10003 (SAN 169-5649) Tel 212-254-7798.

Busby Pubns., *(Busby Pubns; 0-9610288),* APO PSC Box 5766, New York, NY 09179-5379 (SAN 263-9505).

Busch, Ernestine G., *(E G Busch; 0-9614750),* 8717 Echo St., El Paso, TX 79904 (SAN 692-9257) Tel 915-755-5991.

Busche-Waugh-Henry Pubns., *(B W H Pubns; 0-931511),* P.O. Box 10382, Seattle, WA 98101 (SAN 682-2878) Tel 206-382-0386.

Bush, Elsie R. & Dale L., *(D & E Bush; 0-9609440),* 29222 Highway 41, Coarsegold, CA 93614 (SAN 260-0234) Tel 209-683-6387.

Bush, Joseph V., Inc., *(J V Bush; 0-9616684),* P.O. Box 626, Bonita, CA 92002 (SAN 659-9362); 4554 Cresta Verde, Bonita, CA 92002 (SAN 659-9370) Tel 619-479-0874.

Business & Institutional Furniture Manufacturers Assn., *(Busn Inst Furn),* 2335 Burton SE, Grand Rapids, MI 49506 (SAN 224-0890) Tel 616-243-1681.

Business & Legal Reports, *(Busn Legal Reports; 1-55645),* 64 Wall St., Madison, CT 06443 (SAN 661-504X) Tel 203-245-7448.

Business & Professional Bks., Inc., *(Busn Pro Bks; 0-9608576),* P.O. Box 9671, San Jose, CA 95157 (SAN 238-2539) Tel 408-294-3960.

Business & Professional Div. See **Prentice-Hall, Inc.**

Business Bks. International, *(Business Bks CT; 0-916673),* P.O. Box 1587, New Canaan, CT 06840 (SAN 297-1860) Tel 203-966-9645.

Business Communications Co., Inc., *(BCC; 0-89336),* P.O. Box 2070C, 9 Viaduct Rd., Stamford, CT 06906 (SAN 207-706X) Tel 203-325-2208.

Business Computers, *(Busn Comp CO),* 1315 N. Main Ave., Suite 230, Durango, CO 81301 (SAN 675-3744).

Business International Corporation, *(Busn Intl Corp; 0-87180),* 1 Dag Hammerskjold Plaza, New York, NY 10017 (SAN 237-7896).

Business Journals, *(Busn Journals),* 22 S. Smith St., P.O. Box 5550, E. Norwalk, CT 06856 (SAN 204-2053).

Business Media Resources, *(Busn Media Res; 0-938545),* 150 Shoreline Hwy., Bldg. B, Suite 27, Mill Valley, CA 94941 (SAN 661-2806) Tel 415-331-6021.

†**Business News Publishing Co.,** *(Busn News; 0-912524),* P.O. Box 2600, Troy, MI 48007 (SAN 201-9450) Tel 313-362-3700; CIP.

Business Plan Publishing, *(Business Plan; 0-936257),* P.O. Box 3841, St. Augustine, FL 32084 (SAN 697-3574) Tel 904-471-6779; Oceanside Condominium, No. 402, St. Augustine, FL 32084 (SAN 698-2220).

Business Psychology International, *(Busn Psych; 0-931918),* P.O. Box 235-6, Boston, MA 02159 (SAN 211-6014) Tel 617-332-3820.

Business Pubns., Inc., Subs. of Richard D. Irwin, Inc., *(Business Pubns; 0-256),* 1700 Alma Rd., Suite 390, Plano, TX 75075 (SAN 202-4926) Tel 214-422-4389; Dist. by: Richard D. Irwin, Inc., 1818 Ridge Rd., Homewood, IL 60430 (SAN 206-8400) Tel 312-798-6000; Toll free: 800-323-4560.

Business Pubns., Inc., *(Busn Pubns CA; 0-9610808),* 8505 Commerce Ave., San Diego, CA 92121-2610 (SAN 683-2229).

Business Publishing Co., *(Busn Pub TX),* 2631A Gwendolyn Ln., Austin, TX 78748 (SAN 659-5626).

Business Research Services Inc., *(Business Research; 0-933527),* 2 E. 22nd St., Suite 308, Lombard, IL 60148 (SAN 691-8522) Tel 312-495-8787; Toll free: 800-325-8720.

Business Sale Institute, *(Busn Sale Inst; 0-933808),* 170 Park Center Plaza, Suite 202, San Jose, CA 95113 (SAN 212-8853) Tel 408-286-4850.

Business/Technology Information Service, *(Busn Tech Info Serv; 0-930978; 0-89934),* P.O. Box 574, Orinda, CA 94563 (SAN 282-5902) Tel 415-254-2913; Orders to: Manufacturing Productivity Ctr., IIT Ctr., 10 W. 35th St., Chicago, IL 60616 (SAN 694-9606) Tel 312-567-4808.

Business Travelers, Inc. See **Watts, Franklin, Inc.**

Business Trend Analysts, *(Busn Trend; 0-88073),* 2171 Jericho Tpke., Commack, NY 11725 (SAN 217-2313) Tel 516-462-5454.

Buskens, Joy Callaway, *(J C Buskens; 0-9616351),* Rte. 1, Box 2690, Gulf Shores, AL 36542 (SAN 658-8948) Tel 205-968-7026.

Busy Bees, *(Busy Bees; 0-9617073),* 8041 Lake Waunatta Dr., Winter Park, FL 32792 (SAN 662-6084) Tel 305-671-6127.

Butcher Block Pr., *(Butcher Block Pr; 0-9614367),* 2932 Benjamin, Wichita, KS 67204 (SAN 688-5527) Tel 316-838-7717.

Buten Museum, *(Buten Mus; 0-912014),* 246 N. Bowman Ave., Merion Station, PA 19066 (SAN 202-4942) Tel 215-664-6601.

Buteo Bks., *(Buteo; 0-931130),* P.O. Box 481, Vermillion, SD 57069 (SAN 212-0054).

Butler, Barbara, *(B Butler; 0-9614105),* P.O. Box 1044, Sisters, OR 97759 (SAN 685-9755) Tel 503-382-0755.

Butler, Doug, *(Doug Butler; 0-916992),* P.O. Box 370, Maryville, MO 64468 (SAN 206-3999) Tel 816-582-3202.

Butler, JoNett, /Bea Farwell, *(Butler-Farwell; 0-9614834),* 1117 Second Ave., S. Crescent Dr., Clinton, IA 52732 (SAN 693-0875) Tel 319-242-8378; Orders to: America's Best Appetizers, P.O. Box 335, Clinton, IA 52732-0335 (SAN 662-3115) Tel 319-242-8378.

Butler, Larry D., *(L D Butler; 0-9616497),* 1260 Louisiana Ave., Port Allen, LA 70767 (SAN 659-3089) Tel 504-355-3070.

Butler Publishing Hse., Inc., *(Butler Pub Hse; 0-932315),* P.O. Box 21212, Detroit, MI 48221 (SAN 687-0384) Tel 313-891-5877.

Butte Historical Society, *(Butte Hist Soc; 0-930683),* P.O. Box 3913, Butte, MT 59703 (SAN 676-9209) Tel 406-782-3113; Dist. by: Pacific Pipeline, Inc., 19215 66th Ave S., Kent, WA 98032 (SAN 208-2128) Tel 206-872-5523.

Buttercup Bks., *(Buttercup Bks; 0-9614997),* 3641 Kimworth Ln., Shingle Springs, CA 95682 (SAN 693-9503) Tel 916-677-9142.

Butterfield Pr., *(Butterfield; 0-935767),* 304 Federal Rd., Brookfield, CT 06804 (SAN 695-8354) Tel 203-775-0939.

Butterfield Pr., *(Butterfield Pr; 0-932579),* 140 Stuyvesant Dr., San Anselmo, CA 94960 (SAN 689-6472) Tel 415-485-5568.

Butterfly & The Eagle Publishing Co., The, *(B & E Pub Co; 0-9615560),* Box 38002, Los Angeles, CA 90038 (SAN 696-480X) Tel 213-737-6143.

Butterfly Bks., *(Butterfly Bks; 0-939077),* 4526 Queens Way, Sierra Vista, AZ 85635 (SAN 661-6925) Tel 602-458-0869.

Butterfly Press, *(Butterfly Pr; 0-918766),* 13635 Queensbury, Houston, TX 77079 (SAN 209-7133) Tel 713-464-7570; Orders to: P.O. Box 19571, Houston, TX 77224-9571 (SAN 661-9665) Tel 713-464-7579; Dist. by: Richardson Educators, 2014 Lou Ellen Ln., Houston, TX 77018 (SAN 200-7177) Tel 713-688-2244. Formerly Terzarima System.

Butterfly Publishing Co., *(Butterfly Santa Monica; 0-9614637),* 2210 Wilshire Blvd., Suite 845, Santa Monica, CA 90403 (SAN 691-9146) Tel 213-829-2002; Dist. by: Nutri-Books Corp., P.O. Box 5793, Denver, CO 80223 (SAN 169-054X) Tel 303-778-8383; Dist. by: New Leaf Distributing, The, 1020 White St., SW, Atlanta, GA 30310 (SAN 169-1449) Tel 404-755-2665; Toll free: 800-241-3829; Dist. by: Baker & Taylor Co., Western Div., 380 Edison Way, Reno, NV 89564 (SAN 169-4464) Tel 702-786-6700; Toll free: 800-648-3540; Dist. by: Great Tradition, The, 750 Adrian Way, Suite 111, San Refael, CA 94903 (SAN 200-5743) Tel 415-492-9382; Toll free: 800-634-2665.

Butterfly Publishing, Inc., *(Butterfly Pub; 0-941254),* P.O. Box 21116, Salt Lake City, UT 84121 (SAN 237-935X) Tel 801-263-3577.

Butternut & Blue, *(Butternut & Blue; 0-935523),* 2804 Maple Ave., Baltimore, MD 21234 (SAN 696-1576) Tel 301-668-0824.

Butternut Press, Div. of Zullo & Van Sickle Bks., *(Butternut Pr; 0-913419),* 18761 (W) N. Frederick, Gaithersburg, MD 20879 (SAN 285-8991) Tel 301-963-7878.

Butterworth Co. of Cape Cod, Inc., The, *(Butterworth of Cape Cod; 0-937338),* 350 Main St., West Yarmouth, MA 02673 (SAN 239-524X).

†**Butterworth Legal Pubs.,** *(Butterworth MN; 0-917126; 0-86678),* 289 E. Fifth St., St. Paul, MN 55101-1989 (SAN 205-8839) Tel 612-227-4200; CIP.

Butterworth Legal Pubs., Div. of Reed Holdings, Inc., *(Butterworth TX; 0-409),* 1321 Rutherford Ln., Suite 180, Austin, TX 78753-6798 (SAN 654-6692) Tel 512-835-7921.

†**Butterworth Legal Pubs.,** Div. of Reed International, *(Butterworth WA),* 15014 NE 40th St., Suite 205, Redmond, WA 98052-5325 (SAN 695-670X) Tel 206-881-3900; Orders to: 80 Montvale Ave., Stoneham, MA 02180-2471 (SAN 662-3522) Tel 617-438-8464; Toll free: 800-544-1013; CIP.

Butterworth's (Scientific, Technical, Medical), Subs. of Reed International, *(Butterworth; 0-408; 0-250; 0-409; 0-407),* 80 Montvale Ave., Stoneham, MA 02180 (SAN 206-3964) Tel 617-438-8464; Toll free: 800-544-1013. *Imprints:* Newnes-Butterworth (Newnes-Butterworth); Westbury House (Westbury Hse).

†**Butterworths U. S., Legal Pubs., Inc., New England Div.,** *(Butterworth Legal Pubs; 0-88063; 0-86673; 0-406; 0-409),* 84 Montvale Ave., Stoneham, MA 02180-2471 (SAN 238-1451) Tel 617-438-8464; CIP.

Button Publishing, Subs. of Michael F. Ingbar Art Co., Inc., *(Button Pub; 0-915115),* 7 E. 20th St., 4th Fl., New York, NY 10003 (SAN 289-7636).

Buttonwood Pr., *(Buttonwood Pr; 0-934867),* 41 Park Ave., Suite 5D, New York, NY 10016 (SAN 694-5635) Tel 212-689-4643.

Buttrill & Reid, *(Buttrill Reid; 0-9612214),* 5515 Hooks St., Beaumont, TX 77706 (SAN 289-1522) Tel 301-320-6781; 5506 Ridgefield Rd., Bethesda, MD 20816 (SAN 289-1530).

Buxbaum, Edwin C., *(Buxbaum; 0-9600494),* P.O. Box 465, Wilmington, DE 19899 (SAN 201-7482) Tel 302-994-2663.

Buyer's Directory, *(Buyer's Directory; 0-936588),* R.D. 3, Box 533, Olean, NY 14760 (SAN 214-1108) Tel 716-372-0514.

By By Productions, *(By By Prods; 0-938826),* P.O. Box 1676, Glendora, CA 91740 (SAN 216-0242).

By Hand & Foot, Ltd., Div. of Green River Tools, Inc., *(By Hand & Foot; 0-938670),* 5 Cotton Mill-Hill, P.O. Box 611, Brattleboro, VT 05301 (SAN 215-8493).

Byelorussian-American Association, *(Byelorussian-Am),* 166-34 Gothic Dr, Jamaica, NY 11432 (SAN 225-4042) Tel 718-397-5341.

Byrd, Harold E., *(Byrd; 0-9601972),* P.O. Box 191278, Los Angeles, CA 90019 (SAN 212-2707) Tel 213-931-9094.

Byrd/S D and I/1.0 Communications, *(Byrd SDI; 0-9613299)*, 480-60th St., Oakland, CA 94609 (SAN 654-2344) Tel 415-548-6177; Orders to: P.O. Box 5925, Berkeley, CA 94705 (SAN 654-2352).

Byrnam Press, *(Byrnam Pr; 0-9613268)*, 484 Lake Park Ave., Box 220, Oakland, CA 94610 (SAN 297-021X) Tel 415-658-9146.

Byron-Davenport Pubs., *(Byron Daven Pubs; 0-930895)*, P.O. Box 34165, Bethesda, MD 20817 (SAN 679-2022) Tel 301-983-0742.

Byron Pr., *(Byron Pr; 0-935101)*, 1840 N. Beverly Glen Blvd., Los Angeles, CA 90077 (SAN 695-0639) Tel 213-470-2817.

BYTE Bks. *See* McGraw-Hill Bk. Co.

Bytecraft, Inc., Div. of Future Byte, *(Bytecraft; 0-935033)*, P.O. Box 1860, Casper, WY 82602-1860 (SAN 693-7950) Tel 307-235-6010.

Byzantine Pr., *(Byzantine Pr; 0-913168)*, 115 N. Seventh St., Las Vegas, NV 89101 (SAN 204-3785) Tel 702-384-4200.

Byzantium Pr., *(Byzantium Pr; 0-937439)*, 5 Mayfair Ln., Westport, CT 06880 (SAN 659-0543) Tel 203-227-5503.

CAFH Foundation, Inc., *(CAFH Found Inc; 0-9609102)*, P.O. Box 4665, Berkeley, CA 94704 (SAN 281-3696) Tel 415-620-0222; 1510 White Hill Rd., Yorktown, NY 10598 (SAN 662-3530); Dist. by: Bookpeople, 2929 Fifth St., Berkeley, CA 94710 (SAN 168-9517) Tel 415-549-3030.

CAK Associates, *(CAK Assocs Inc; 0-911245)*, P.O. Box 16042, Albuquerque, NM 87191 (SAN 268-5612) Tel 505-293-2293.

C.A.M Co., *(C A M Co; 0-942752)*, P.O. Box 352, Hortonville, WI 54944 (SAN 281-3645) Tel 414-982-2856; Dist. by: The Distributors, 702 S. Michigan, South Bend, IN 46618 (SAN 169-2488) Tel 219-232-8500; Dist. by: Baker & Taylor, Midwest Div., 501 Gladiola Ave., Momence, IL 60954 (SAN 169-2100) Tel 815-472-2444.

CAO Times, Inc., *(CAO Times)*, P.O. Box 75, Old Chelsea Sta., New York, NY 10113 (SAN 657-1298).

C.A.P.P. Bks., *(CAPP Bks; 0-9606824)*, P.O. Box 416, Williamsburg, VA 23187 (SAN 209-1984) Tel 804-253-1393.

CASE/Third Wave Publishing, *(CASE Third Wave; 0-937951)*, 80 Grand St., Jersey City, NJ 07302 (SAN 659-9389) Tel 201-333-0227.

C.A.S., Inc., *(CAS Inc)*, 2525 Murworth Dr., No. 202, Houston, TX 77054 (SAN 692-2562) Tel 713-661-0346; P.O. Box 20762, Houston, TX 77225-0762 (SAN 659-5926).

CAUSE, *(CAUSE; 0-933783)*, 737 29th St., Boulder, CO 80303 (SAN 225-7378) Tel 303-449-4430.

CAVU Pr., *(CAVU Pr; 0-9616265)*, P.O. Box 23, Harrison, NY 10528 (SAN 658-3156).

CAYC Learning Tree, *(CAYC Learning Tree; 0-940908)*, 9998 Ferguson Rd., Dallas, TX 75228 (SAN 212-8861) Tel 214-321-6484.

C & A Kiser, *(C & A Kiser; 0-9611920)*, P.O. Box 154, Bessemer City, NC 28016 (SAN 286-1275) Tel 704-629-4674.

C & E Enterprises, Pubs., *(C & E Ent Pub; 0-9610096)*, 980 West St., San Luis Obispo, CA 93401 (SAN 268-5620) Tel 805-543-8187.

C & G Enterprises, *(C & G Ent; 0-9607154)*, P.O. Box 58567, Tukwila, WA 98188 (SAN 238-9576) Tel 206-937-3378.

C & G Publishing, *(C&G Pub; 0-941030)*, 941 Sherwood Ave., Los Altos, CA 94022 (SAN 217-3395) Tel 415-941-4082.

C & I Pubns., *(C & I Pubns; 0-916835)*, 2101 14th Ave. SW, Largo, FL 33540 (SAN 654-2506) Tel 813-585-1164.

C & L Books, *(C and L Bks; 0-9614751)*, P.O. Box 955, Medina, OH 44258 (SAN 692-9273) Tel 216-722-3610.

C&L Publishing Co., *(C & L Pub Co; 0-9605724)*, 2525 Wilson Blvd., Arlington, VA 22201 (SAN 216-3462).

C&M Pubns., *(C&M Pubns; 0-938934)*, 6110 Hwy. 290 W., Austin, TX 78735 (SAN 216-227X).

C & P Pubns., *(C P Pubns TN; 0-9617092)*, P.O. Box 381813, Germantown, TN 38183-1813 (SAN 662-5266); 1485 Stonegate Pass, Germantown, TN 38183-1813 (SAN 662-5274) Tel 901-756-1641. Do not confuse with C P Pubns., Port Angeles, WA.

C. & R. Anthony, Inc., *(C & R Anthony; 0-910140)*, 300 Park Ave. S., P.O. Box 781, Madison Sq. Sta., New York, NY 10157 (SAN 203-4786) Tel 212-986-7693. Do Not Confuse with Anthony Pub Co.

C & S Enterprises, *(C & S Ent; 0-9609028)*, 5169 Wheelis Dr., Memphis, TN 38117 (SAN 281-367X) Tel 901-767-7961.

C & T Publishing, *(C & T Pub; 0-914881)*, P.O. Box 1456, Lafayette, CA 94549 (SAN 289-0720) Tel 415-284-1177; Dist. by: Gutcheon Patchworks, 611 Broadway, New York, NY 10012 (SAN 200-5352) Tel 212-505-0305; Dist. by: Dicmar Trading Co., Inc., 4057 Highwood Ct., NW, Washington, DC 20007 (SAN 200-5298).

CB City International, *(CB City Intl; 0-943132)*, P.O. Box 31500, Phoenix, AZ 85046 (SAN 240-5199) Tel 602-996-8700.

CB Enterprises, Div. of A. M. Communications, *(C B Enterprises; 0-9616997)*, 9304 Mill Hollow, Dallas, TX 75243 (SAN 663-5008).

CBH Publishing, Inc., *(CBH Pub; 0-9604538)*, 446 Central Ave., Northfield, IL 60093 (SAN 216-2288) Tel 312-446-6346.

CBN Univ., *(CBN Univ; 1-55574)*, Centerville Tpke., Virginia Beach, VA 23463 (SAN 699-9484) Tel 804-424-7000.

†CBP Pr., Div. of Christian Board of Publication, *(CBP; 0-8272)*, P.O. Box 179, St. Louis, MO 63166 (SAN 201-4408) Tel 314-371-6900; Toll free: 800-351-2665; *CIP*.

†CBS Educational & Professional Publishing, Div. of CBS, Inc., *(CBS Ed; 0-03)*, 383 Madison Ave., New York, NY 10017 (SAN 200-2108) Tel 201-947-3306; Toll free: 800-CBS-ASK4; *CIP*.

CBSI, *(CBSI)*, 3390 Peachtree Rd. NE, Suite 1148, Atlanta, GA 30326 (SAN 670-7386).

C Bks., Div. of Cartographic Enterprises, *(C Bks; 0-941786)*, P.O. Box 548, Del Mar, CA 92014 (SAN 239-4154) Tel 619-755-2505; Dist. by: Publishers Group West, 5855 Beaudry St., Emeryville, CA 94608 (SAN 202-8522) Tel 415-658-3453.

CCC Pubns., *(CCC Pubns; 0-918259)*, 20306 Tau Pl., Chatsworth, CA 91311 (SAN 669-666X) Tel 818-407-1661. Imprints: Magic Publishing (Magic Publish).

CC Exchange, *(CC Exchange; 0-939078)*, P.O. Box 1251, Laguna Beach, CA 92652 (SAN 239-7536) Tel 714-494-4310.

CCFL Bahamian Field Station, *(CCFL Bahamian; 0-935909)*, 270 SW 34th St., Ft. Lauderdale, FL 33315 (SAN 696-7191) Tel 305-524-3009.

CCM Co., The, *(CCM; 0-914393)*, 1308 E. Eighth St., Tucson, AZ 85719 (SAN 289-6192) Tel 602-622-2796.

C.C. Pubns., Inc., *(C C Pubns; 0-88120)*, P.O. Box 23699, Tigard, OR 97223 (SAN 241-0990) Tel 503-692-6880; Toll free: 800-547-4800. Do not confuse with C C Pubs., Clearwater FL.

CC Pubs., *(C C Pubs; 0-9603766)*, P.O. Box 4044, Clearwater, FL 33518 (SAN 223-5471) Tel 813-797-3321. Do not confuse with CC Pubns., Tigard OR.

CC Studios, Inc., *(CC Studios; 1-55592)*, 389 Newton Tpke., Weston, CT 06883 (SAN 658-652X) Tel 203-226-3355.

CCVI Publishing, *(CCVI Pub; 0-935579)*, 120 E. 34th St., New York, NY 10016 (SAN 696-1606) Tel 212-683-1185.

CCW Pubns., *(CCW Pubns; 0-9615561)*, 3401 NE 11th St., Renton, WA 98056 (SAN 695-8478) Tel 206-228-8707.

C.C.W. Publishing, *(CCW Pub; 0-9613206)*, P.O. Box 2069, Chapel Hill, NC 27514 (SAN 295-6861) Tel 919-967-7254.

CDC Pr., *(CDC Pr; 0-935769)*, 88 Bradley Rd., Woodbridge, CT 06525 (SAN 695-8338) Tel 203-387-8887.

CDI, Inc., *(CDI Inc; 0-939021)*, P.O. Box 11065, Birmingham, AL 35202 (SAN 662-5495); 5560 Cahaba Valley Rd., Birmingham, AL 35243 (SAN 662-5509) Tel 205-991-7315.

CDS Publishing Co., Subs. of Man-Computer Systems, Inc., *(CDS Pub; 0-916376)*, 84-13 168th St., Jamaica, NY 11432 (SAN 208-5755) Tel 718-739-4242.

CDT Publishing Co., *(CDT Pub; 0-9616998)*, 27103 E. Millpond, Capistrano Beach, CA 92624 (SAN 662-5533) Tel 714-240-8131.

CEA Bks. Pr., *(CEA Bks Pr; 0-933588)*, George Mason Univ., 129 Boyd Dr., Box 1329, Flat Rock, NC 28731 (SAN 211-8459) Tel 601-324-2340.

CEG Pr., *(CEG Pr; 0-9614566)*, P.O. Box 384, Lake Oswego, OR 97034 (SAN 691-7690) Tel 503-636-7704; Dist. by: Western States Bookservice, P.O. 855, Clackamas, OR 97015 (SAN 200-5662).

CEL Educational Resources, Div. of CEL Communications, Inc., *(CEL Educ Resc; 0-938815)*, 515 Madison Ave., New York, NY 10022 (SAN 661-8391) Tel 212-421-4030.

C. E. M. Co., *(C E M Comp; 0-930004)*, 3154 Coventry Dr., Bay City, MI 48706 (SAN 209-5378) Tel 517-686-4208.

CEO Pubns., *(CEO Pubns; 0-937415)*, 2429 Rio Lindo, Healdsburg, CA 95448 (SAN 659-0594) Tel 707-431-7474; Dist. by: Publishers Group West, 5855 Beaudry St., Emeryville, CA 94608 (SAN 202-8522) Tel 415-658-3453; Toll free: 800-982-8319.

CEPA Gallery, *(CEPA Gall; 0-939784)*, 700 Main St., 4th Fl., Buffalo, NY 14202 (SAN 216-8839) Tel 716-856-2717.

CE Publishing, *(C E Pub; 0-912227)*, P.O. Box 488, Plantsville, CT 06479 (SAN 265-0983) Tel 203-621-6811.

C. E. R. I. Press, Subs. of Communication & Education Resources, Inc., *(C E R I Pr; 0-941822)*, 5513 Forrestal Ave., Alexandria, VA 22311 (SAN 239-1678) Tel 703-820-7459.

CES Industries, Inc., *(CES Industries; 0-86711)*, 130 Central Ave., Farmingdale, NY 11735 (SAN 237-9864) Tel 516-293-1420.

CFA Co., *(CFA Co; 0-933897)*, 11208 Korman Dr, Potomac, MD 20854 (SAN 692-6630) Tel 301-299-5060.

CFKR Career Materials, Inc., *(CFKR Career; 0-934783)*, P.O. Box 437, Meadow Vista, CA 95722 (SAN 694-2547) Tel 916-878-0118.

CFPR Pubns., *(CFPR Pubns; 0-9613278)*, P.O. Box 19446, Portland, OR 97219 (SAN 654-1534) Tel 503-246-6184.

CFS Publishing Corp., *(C F S Pub Corp; 0-913095)*, 122 E. 25th St., 4th Fl., New York, NY 10010 (SAN 282-9894); Dist. by: Kampmann & Co., 9 E. 40th St., New York, NY 10016 (SAN 202-5191) Tel 212-685-2928.

C-4 Resources, *(C-Four Res; 0-914527)*, 115 Neil St., Champaign, IL 61820 (SAN 289-1565) Tel 217-395-6242.

CHAMAH Pubs., *(CHAMAH Pubs; 0-938666)*, 25 Broadway, Suite 1042, New York, NY 10004 (SAN 215-9430).

CIBA Medical Education Div., Div. of CIBA-Geigy Corp., *(CIBA Med; 0-914168)*, 14 Henderson Dr., West Caldwell, NJ 07006 (SAN 207-2084); Toll free: 800-631-1181 (Orders) 800-631-1162 (Editorial); Orders to: P.O. Box 18060, Newark, NJ 07101 (SAN 207-2092).

C.I.L., Inc., Bks., *(C I L Inc; 0-9613326)*, P.O. Box 27-3855, Boca Raton, FL 33427 (SAN 655-6205) Tel 305-392-3936.

CIM Systems, Inc., *(C I M Systems)*, 9451 LBJ Freeway, Dallas, TX 75243 (SAN 669-3598) Tel 214-437-5171.

CIPRA Advertising, *(CIPRA; 0-9613520)*, 314 E. Curling Dr., Boise, ID 83702 (SAN 657-6761) Tel 208-344-7770.

CIS Communications, Inc., *(CIS Comm; 0-935063)*, 674 Eighth St., P.O. Box 26, Lakewood, NJ 08701 (SAN 694-5953) Tel 201-367-7858.

CIS, Inc., *(C I S; 0-914891)*, P.O. Box 7741, Philadelphia, PA 19101 (SAN 289-0852).

CIS, Inc., *(CIS Inc; 0-9615562)*, 5415 The Estates Dr., Oakland, CA 94618 (SAN 696-4788) Tel 415-547-7655.

CIVITAS, Inc., *(Civitas; 0-9610016)*, 60 E. 42nd St., Suite 411, New York, NY 10165 (SAN 268-5647) Tel 212-752-4530.

C J Books, *(C J Bks; 0-942878)*, P.O. Box 922, Gig Harbor, WA 98335 (SAN 263-9548) Tel 206-851-3778; Dist. by: Pacific Pipline, Inc., 19215 66th Ave., S., Kent, WA 98032 (SAN 208-2128) Tel 206-872-5523.

CKE Pubns., Div. of Carolyn Kyle Enterprises, *(CKE Pubns; 0-935133)*, 2030 N. Milroy St., Olympia, WA 98502 (SAN 695-197X) Tel 206-943-4323.

CLCB Pr., Div. of CLCBI International Inc. of Scotland, *(CLCB Pr)*, P.O. Box 99, Newell, NC 28126 (SAN 211-2892).

CLC Pr., *(C L C Press; 0-930779)*, P.O. Box 478, San Andreas, CA 95249 (SAN 677-8437) Tel 209-369-2781.

C.L.I.M.B.(Creative Learning is More Beautiful), *(CLIMB; 0-914191)*, Nine Heritage Dr., Freehold, NJ 07728 (SAN 287-511X) Tel 201-431-2264.

CL Pubns., Inc., *(CL Pubns Inc; 0-9615697)*, 131 Townsend St., San Francisco, CA 94107 (SAN 696-1673) Tel 415-957-9353.

C M Publishing, *(C M Pub; 0-9607514)*, 330 Eubank, El Paso, TX 79902 (SAN 237-9856) Tel 915-584-3008.

CMS Publishing, Inc., Subs. of Communication Management Services, *(CMS Pub; 0-932311)*, 3570 N. Rice St., St. Paul, MN 55112 (SAN 687-0414) Tel 612-484-5893.

COB Assocs., Inc., *(COB Assocs; 0-938409)*, P.O. Box 21416, Philadelphia, PA 19126 (SAN 661-0153); 6501 N. Gratz St., Philadelphia, PA 19126 (SAN 661-0161) Tel 215-548-6684.

COMAL Users Group, USA, Ltd., *(COMAL Users; 0-928411)*, 6041 Monona Dr., Madison, WI 53716 (SAN 669-5256) Tel 608-222-4432.

COMAP , Inc., *(C O M A P Inc; 0-912843)*, 60 Lowell St., Arlington, MA 02174 (SAN 282-9991) Tel 617-641-2600.

COSMEP (THe International Assn. of Independent Pubs.), *(COSMEP; 0-9611378)*, P.O. Box 703, San Francisco, CA 94101 (SAN 209-7222) Tel 415-922-9490.

†CPI Publishing, Inc., *(CPI Pub; 0-675)*, 145 E. 49th St., New York, NY 10017 (SAN 218-6896) Tel 212-753-3800; Dist. by: Modern Curriculum Pr., 13900 Prospect Rd., Cleveland, OH 44136 (SAN 206-6572); Toll free: 800-321-3106; *CIP.*

†CPL Bibliographies, *(CPL Biblios)*, 1313 E. 60th St., Merriam Ctr., Chicago, IL 60637-2897 (SAN 210-3516) Tel 312-947-2007; *CIP.*

C. P. Press, *(C P Pr; 0-9600452)*, 31 Woodmont Rd., Upper Montclair, NJ 07043 (SAN 202-4985).

CRA Readers Service, *(CRA Readers Serv; 0-9616505)*, RD 1, P.O. Box 278, Claysville, PA 15323 (SAN 659-4271) Tel 412-948-3588.

CRB Research, *(CRB Res; 0-939780)*, P.O. Box 56, Commack, NY 11725 (SAN 216-8812) Tel 516-543-7486.

†CRC Pr., Inc., *(CRC Pr; 0-87819; 0-8493)*, 2000 Corporate Blvd., Boca Raton, FL 33431 (SAN 202-1994) Tel 305-994-0555; Toll free: 800-272-7737; *CIP.*

†CRC Pubns., *(CRC Pubns; 0-933140; 0-930265)*, 2850 Kalamazoo Ave. SE, Grand Rapids, MI 49560 (SAN 212-727X) Tel 616-246-0752; *CIP.*

†CRCS Pubns., *(CRCS Pubns NV; 0-916360)*, P.O. Box 20850, Reno, NV 89515 (SAN 200-626X) Tel 702-358-2850. Do Not Confuse with CRC Pr, Florida; *CIP.*

CRG Pr., *(CRG Pr; 0-939686)*, 1000 16th St., NW, Suite 400, Washington, DC 20036 (SAN 216-7239) Tel 202-223-2400.

CRI/Communication Research, Inc., *(CRI-Comm Res; 0-934547)*, 4156 Danvers Ct., S6, Grand Rapids, MI 49508 (SAN 693-8663) Tel 616-949-6743.

CRI Pubns., Div. of CrossRoads of Ames, Ltd., *(CRI Pubns; 0-935689)*, P.O. Box 565, Ames, IA 50010 (SAN 696-172X) Tel 515-292-7700.

CR Publishing, Inc., *(CR Pub; 0-938467)*, 805 E. State Ave., Terra Alta, WV 26764 (SAN 659-9397) Tel 304-789-2464.

CRS Consultants Pr., *(CRS Pr; 0-911127)*, P.O. Box 490175, Key Biscayne, FL 33149 (SAN 268-5663) Tel 305-361-9573.

CSA Pr., *(CSA Pr; 0-87707)*, Lake Ravun Rd., Lakemont, GA 30552 (SAN 207-7329) Tel 404-782-4723; P.O. Box 7, Lakemont, GA 30552 (SAN 658-0408). *Imprints:* Tarnhelm Press (Tarnhelm).

CSA Pubns., Subs. of the State Univ. of New York at Binghamton, *(CSA Pubn; 0-933199)*, SUNY-Binghamton, Ctr. for Education & Social Research, Binghamton, NY 13901 (SAN 692-2619) Tel 607-777-2116.

CSPP-Fresno Pubns., *(CSPP-Fresno Pubns; 0-931309)*, 1350 M St., Fresno, CA 93721 (SAN 685-2572) Tel 209-486-8420.

CS Pubns., *(CS Pubns; 0-934206)*, 1791 Primrose Dr., El Cajon, CA 92020 (SAN 213-0459).

C.S.S. of Ohio, *(CSS of Ohio; 0-89536; 1-55673)*, 628 S. Main St., Lima, OH 45804 (SAN 207-0707) Tel 419-227-1818; Toll free: 800-537-1030.

C2F, Inc., *(C Two F Inc; 0-9616328)*, 6600 SW 111th Ct., Beaverton, OR 97005 (SAN 659-0624) Tel 503-643-9050; P.O. Box 1417, Beaverton, OR 97075 (SAN 659-0632).

CWS & Assocs., *(CWS Assocs)*, P.O. Box 2300, Pine Island, FL 33945 (SAN 693-0948) Tel 813-283-1061.

CWS Group Pr., *(CWS Group Pr; 0-9604324)*, P.O. Box 28753, 6025 N. Jefferson, Apt. 2, Kansas City, MO 64118-8753 (SAN 214-3526) Tel 816-453-5095.

Caann Verlag Gmbtt, *(Caann Verlag)*, Dist. by: Associated Booksellers, 147 McKinley Ave., Bridgeport, CT 06606 (SAN 206-9717).

Cabala Press, *(Cabala Pr; 0-941542)*, 2421 W. Pratt Ave., Chicago, IL 60645 (SAN 239-071X) Tel 312-761-0682.

Caballero Press, *(Caballero Pr; 0-9601346)*, 1936 Caballero Way, Las Vegas, NV 89109 (SAN 210-6825) Tel 702-735-3406.

Cabashon Publishing, *(Cabashon Pub; 0-937825)*, 11770 Bernardo Plaza Ct., San Diego, CA 92128 (SAN 659-428X) Tel 619-451-0377.

Cabat Studio Pubns., *(Cabat Studio Pubns; 0-913521)*, 627 N. Fourth Ave., Tucson, AZ 85705 (SAN 285-1539) Tel 602-622-6362.

Cabell County Medical Society, *(Cabell Cty Med Soc; 0-9616839)*, 1340 Hal Green Blvd., Huntington, WV 25701 (SAN 661-2792) Tel 304-522-3450.

Cabell Publishing, Co., *(Cabell Pub; 0-911753)*, Box 7173, Tobe Hahn Station, Beaumont, TX 77706 (SAN 263-9564) Tel 409-898-0575.

Cabin Publishing MN, *(Cabin Pub MN; 0-933363)*, P.O. Box 73, Long Lake, MN 55356 (SAN 691-6678) Tel 612-472-6434.

Cable Television Information Ctr., The, *(Cable TV Info Ctr; 0-943336)*, 1500 N. Beauregard St., Suite 205, Alexandria, VA 22311 (SAN 240-6071) Tel 703-845-1700.

Caboose Pr., *(Caboose Pr; 0-9608064)*, 499 Embarcadero, Oakland, CA 94606 (SAN 240-1983) Tel 415-465-6323.

Cachalot Books, *(Cachalot Bks; 0-913023)*, 4959 Hollywood Blvd., Suite 409, Hollywood, CA 90027 (SAN 283-0000) Tel 213-466-9724.

Cache Pr., *(Cache Pr)*, 801 Juniper Ave., Boulder, CO 80302 (SAN 212-0763).

Cache Valley Newsletter Publishing Co., *(Cache Valley; 0-941462)*, 1219 West Oneida, Preston, ID 83263 (SAN 239-0728) Tel 208-852-3167.

Cactus Max Pr., Div. of Cactus Max, Inc., *(Cactus Max; 0-932925)*, P.O. Box 12477, El Paso, TX 79913 (SAN 688-9263) Tel 915-584-7649.

CAD-CAM Decisions, *(Cad Cam; 0-938800)*, P.O. Box 76042, Atlanta, GA 30328 (SAN 240-012X) Tel 404-255-5271.

Cad/Cam Publishing, Inc., *(Cad-Cam Pub; 0-934692)*, 841 Turquoise St., Suites D & E, San Diego, CA 92109 (SAN 694-5643) Tel 619-488-0533.

Caddylack Publishing *See Asher-Gallant Pr.*

Cadmus Editions, *(Cadmus Eds; 0-932274)*, P.O. Box 687, Tiburon, CA 94920 (SAN 212-887X) Tel 707-894-3048; Dist. by: The Subterranean Co., 1327 W. Second, P.O. Box 10233, Eugene, OR 97440 (SAN 169-7102) Tel 503-343-6324.

Cadmus Pr., *(Cadmus Press; 0-930685)*, 25 Waterview Dr., Port Jefferson, NY 11777 (SAN 677-1300) Tel 516-928-9896.

†Caedmon, Div. of Raytheon Co., *(Caedmon; 0-9601156; 0-89845)*, 1995 Broadway, New York, NY 10023 (SAN 206-278X) Tel 212-580-3400; Toll free: 800-223-0420; *CIP.*

Cagg, Richard D., *(Cagg; 0-9605636)*, 423 W. Fourth, Cameron, MO 64429 (SAN 215-6296) Tel 816-632-2973.

Cahill Publishing Co., *(Cahill Pub Co; 0-9610810)*, P.O. Box 91053, Houston, TX 77088 (SAN 263-9572) Tel 713-447-4550.

Cain, Mike, *(M Cain; 0-9601458)*, 192 Terra Manor Dr., Wintersville, OH 43952 (SAN 211-2221) Tel 614-264-3687.

Cain-Lockhart Pr., *(Cain Lockhart; 0-937133)*, P.O. Box 1129, Issaquah, WA 98027-1129 (SAN 658-4977); 19510 SE 51st St., Issaquah, WA 98027-1129 (SAN 658-4985) Tel 206-392-0508.

Caislan Pr., *(Caislan Pr; 0-937444)*, Box 28371, San Jose, CA 95159 (SAN 295-3048) Tel 408-723-8514; Dist. by: Baker & Taylor, Eastern Div., 50 Kirby Ave., Somerville, NJ 08876 (SAN 169-4901); Dist. by: Baker & Taylor, Midwest Div., 501 Gladiola Ave., Momence, IL 60954 (SAN 169-2100); Dist. by: Blackwell N. America, 1001 Fries Mill Rd., Blackwood, NJ 08012 (SAN 169-4596) Tel 609-629-0700; Dist. by: Bk. Hse., Inc., 208 W. Chicago St., Jonesville, MI 49250-0125 (SAN 295-3099) Tel 517-849-2117.

Caissa Editions, Div. of Dale Brandeth Bks., *(Caissa Edit; 0-939433)*, P.O. Box 151, Yorklyn, DE 19736 (SAN 659-1965); Box 461, White Briar Rd., Hockessin, DE 19707 (SAN 663-317X) Tel 302-239-4608.

Cajun Bayou Distributors & Management, Inc., *(Cajun Bayou; 0-9613196)*, 7110 Airline Hwy., Baton Rouge, LA 70805 (SAN 294-9105) Tel 504-356-5482.

Cajun Pubs., *(Cajun Pubs; 0-933727)*, Rte. 4, Box 88, New Iberia, LA 70560 (SAN 692-4948) Tel 318-363-6653; Toll free: 800-551-3076.

Cal-Syl Press, *(Cal-Syl Pr; 0-930638)*, 3960 E. 14th St., Oakland, CA 94601 (SAN 211-8424) Tel 415-534-5032.

Calabasas Publishing, Co., *(Calabasas Pub; 0-930025)*, P.O. Box 9002, Calabasas, CA 91302-9002 (SAN 669-7429) Tel 818-888-1079.

Calaciura Pr., *(Calaciura Pr; 0-9614464)*, P.O. Box 25544, Cleveland, OH 44125 (SAN 688-6507); 12500 Oakview Blvd., Cleveland, OH 44125 (SAN 662-7714) Tel 216-921-8074; Dist. by: Quality Bks., Inc., 918 Sherwood Dr., Lake Bluff, IL 60044-2204 (SAN 169-2127) Tel 312-295-2010; Dist. by: Targeted Communications, 3644 Rolliston Rd., Cleveland, OH 44120-5137 (SAN 689-4674) Tel 216-921-8074.

Calaloux Pubns., *(Calaloux Pubns; 0-911565)*, P.O. Box 6803, Ithaca, NY 14850 (SAN 263-9599); 470 Broome St., New York, NY 10013 (SAN 263-9602) Tel 212-799-7749.

Calamus Bks., *(Calamus Bks; 0-930762)*, Box 689, Cooper Sta., New York, NY 10276 (SAN 211-7002).

Calapooia Pubns., *(Calapooia Pubns; 0-934784)*, 27006 Gap Rd., Brownsville, OR 97327 (SAN 223-7040) Tel 503-466-5208.

Calapooya Bks., *(Calapooya Bks; 0-935004)*, 136 High St., Eugene, OR 97401 (SAN 213-6147) Tel 503-344-4301.

Calcon Press, *(Calcon Pr; 0-9600740)*, P.O. Box 536, Bruce, MS 38915 (SAN 201-8683).

Caldwell Pubns., Inc., *(Caldwell Pubns; 0-932777)*, P.O. Box 5332, Arlington, VA 22205 (SAN 688-475X) Tel 703-533-1567.

Caledonia Pr., *(Caledonia Pr; 0-932282)*, P.O. Box 245, Racine, WI 53401 (SAN 211-8432) Tel 414-637-6200.

Calem Publishing Co., *(Calem Pub Co; 0-9616444)*, 444 Appleton St., Holyoke, MA 01040 (SAN 659-0705) Tel 413-533-0338.

Caliban Pr., *(Caliban; 0-936897)*, 114 Montview Rd., Montclair, NJ 07043 (SAN 658-490X) Tel 201-744-4453.

†Calbre Pr., Inc., *(Calibre Pr; 0-935878)*, 666 Dundee Rd., Suite 1607, Northbrook, IL 60062 (SAN 213-9146) Tel 312-498-5680; Toll free: 800-323-0037 outside Illinois; *CIP.*

Calico Barn, *(Calico Barn; 0-9616848)*, 626 Shadowwood Ln., SE, Warren, OH 44484 (SAN 661-3071) Tel 216-856-7384.

Names

Calico Pr., *(Calico Pr; 0-912714),* P.O. Box 758, Twentynine Palms, CA 92277 (SAN 202-4993) Tel 619-367-7661.

Califia Productions, *(Califia Prod; 0-938521),* 22982 La Cadena, Suite 15, Laguna Hills, CA 92653 (SAN 661-1230) Tel 714-855-4319.

California Academy of Sciences Pubns., *(Calif Acad Sci; 0-940228),* Golden Gate Park, San Francisco, CA 94118 (SAN 204-3661) Tel 415-221-5100.

California Aero Pr., *(Cal Aero Pr; 0-914379),* P.O. Box 1365, Carlsbad, CA 92008 (SAN 289-5943) Tel 619-729-6002.

California Agricultural Lands Project, Subs. of Round Valley, *(CA Agri Lnd Pr; 0-912005),* 227 Clayton St., San Francisco, CA 94117 (SAN 264-6056) Tel 415-664-5600.

California Association for Older Americans, *(CA Assn Older; 0-917154),* Tel 415-386-3500; Orders to: Volcano Press, 330 Ellis St., San Francisco, CA 94102 (SAN 268-5795) Tel 415-664-5600.

California Bks., *(Calif Books; 0-934112),* Box 9551, Stanford, CA 94305 (SAN 212-8888).

California Bks., *(Calif Irvine; 0-939478),* Seven Bridgewood, Irvine, CA 92714 (SAN 216-5910) Tel 714-551-2795.

California Cambrian Pr., *(Calif Cam; 0-911247),* P.O. Box 2331, Carlsbad, CA 92008 (SAN 268-5817) Tel 619-729-0050.

California Childrens Publication, *(Calif Child Pubns; 0-9610442),* P.O. Box 91102, Long Beach, CA 90809-1102 (SAN 285-6867).

California Clock Co., *(CA Clock; 0-939513),* 26131 Avenida Aeropuerto, San Juan Capistrano, CA 92675 (SAN 663-3544) Tel 714-493-4552.

California College Pr., *(Cal College Pr; 0-933195),* 222 W. 24th St., National City, CA 92050 (SAN 692-2643) Tel 619-477-4800; Toll free: 800-221-7374.

California Continuing Education of the Bar, *(Cal Cont Ed Bar; 0-88124),* 2300 Shattuck Ave., Berkeley, CA 94704 (SAN 237-6105) Tel 415-642-3973.

†California Creative, Pubns., *(Cal Creative Pubns; 0-9613962),* 14252 Culver Dr., Ste. A-159, Irvine, CA 92714 (SAN 682-2894) Tel 714-679-1855; *CIP.*

California Dept. of Consumer Affairs, Div. of Consumer Services, *(Calif Dept CA),* 1020 N St., Room 419, Sacramento, CA 95814 (SAN 223-8853) Tel 916-445-7450.

California Department of Consumer Affairs Co-op Development Program, *(Calif Dept Co; 0-910427),* 1020 N St., Rm. 509, Sacramento, CA 95814 (SAN 262-0057) Tel 916-322-7674; Orders to: Co-op Pubns., P.O. Box 310, Sacramento, CA 95802 (SAN 661-9673).

California Dreamers, Inc., *(CA Dreamers; 0-939471),* 3505 N. Kimball, Chicago, IL 60618 (SAN 663-2696) Tel 312-478-0660.

California Education Plan, *(CA Ed Plan; 0-936047),* 942 Acacia Ave., Los Altos, CA 94022 (SAN 697-0265) Tel 415-948-6412.

California Farm Bureau Federation, *(Cal Farm Bureau),* 1601 Exposition Blvd., Sacramento, CA 95815 (SAN 217-2976).

California Farmer Publishing Co., *(CA Farmer Pub; 0-936815),* 731 Market St., San Francisco, CA 94103-2011 (SAN 699-8720) Tel 415-495-3340.

California Features Inc., *(Cal Features; 0-933781),* P.O. Box 58, Beverly Hills, CA 90213 (SAN 692-6975) Tel 213-939-3200.

California Financial Pubns. *See* California Health Pubns.

California Folklore Society, The, *(CA Folklore Soc; 0-914563),* P.O. Box 4552, Glendale, CA 91202 (SAN 289-1603) Tel 818-244-3229.

California Guitar Archives, *(CA Guitar Archv; 0-939297),* P.O. Box 7000-166, Palos Verdes Peninsula, CA 90274 (SAN 662-7943); 25126 Walnut St., Lomita, CA 90717 (SAN 662-7951) Tel 213-539-0738.

California Health Pubns., Subs. of California Financial Pubns., *(Calif Health; 0-930926),* Box 220, Carlsbad, CA 92008 (SAN 211-6588). *Imprints:* California Financial Pubns. (CA Finan Pubns).

California Historical Society, *(Calif Hist; 0-910312),* 2090 Jackson St., San Francisco, CA 94109 (SAN 281-3734) Tel 415-567-1848 Tel 415-567-1848.

California Institute of International Studies, *(Cal Inst Intl; 0-912098),* 766 Santa Ynez, Stanford, CA 94305 (SAN 206-8532) Tel 415-322-2026.

†California Institute of Public Affairs, Affil. of the Claremont Colleges, *(Cal Inst Public; 0-912102),* P.O. Box 10, Claremont, CA 91711 (SAN 202-2087) Tel 714-624-5212; *CIP.*

California Institute of Technology, Munger Africana Library, *(Munger Africana Lib; 0-934912),* Pasadena, CA 91125 (SAN 211-1195) Tel 818-356-4469.

California Institute of the Arts, *(CA Inst Arts),* Placement Office, 24700 McBean Pkwy., Valencia, CA 91355 (SAN 658-8263) Tel 805-253-7871.

California/International Arts Foundation, *(CA Intl Arts; 0-917571),* 2737 Outpost Dr., Los Angeles, CA 90068 (SAN 657-128X) Tel 213-874-4107.

California Journal Pr., *(Cal Journal; 0-930302),* 1714 Capitol Ave., Sacramento, CA 95814 (SAN 210-1122) Tel 916-444-2840.

California Landmark Pubns., *(CA Landmark; 0-9613382),* 1450 Koll Circle, No. 110, San Jose, CA 95112 (SAN 657-0798) Tel 408-293-7291.

California Lathing & Plastering Contractors Assn., *(Cal Lath & Plaster),* 25332 Narbonne Ave., Suite 170, Lomita, CA 90717 (SAN 224-0912) Tel 213-539-6080.

California Lawyer's Press, Inc., *(Cal Lawyers Pr),* P.O. Box 2435, Los Angeles, CA 90051 (SAN 219-7715); Orders to: Living Books, Inc., 12155 Magnolia Ave., Bldg. 11B, Riverside, CA 92503 (SAN 219-7723).

California Library Media Consortium for Classroom Evaluation of Microcomputer Courseware, *(CA Lib Media),* 333 Main St., Redwood City, CA 94063 (SAN 674-8937) Tel 415-363-5471.

California Medical Pubns., *(CA Med Pubns; 0-9615638),* 715 E. Chapman Ave., Orange, CA 92666 (SAN 695-8788) Tel 714-639-3519.

†California Native Plant Society, the, *(Calif Native; 0-943460),* 909 12th St., Suite 116, Sacramento, CA 95814 (SAN 240-6098) Tel 916-447-2677; *CIP.*

California Photo Service, *(Calif Photo; 0-9615357),* 5760 Hollis St., Emeryville, CA 94608 (SAN 695-3409) Tel 415-658-9200.

California Poetry Pubns., *(Cal Poet; 0-916183),* P.O. Box 12323, Santa Ava, CA 92701 (SAN 294-9113) Tel 714-646-6592.

California Pubns., *(Calif Pubns; 0-917306),* P.O. Box 8014, Calabasas, CA 91302 (SAN 208-578X) Tel 213-880-4181.

California Rocketry, *(CA Rocketry; 0-912468),* P.O. Box 1242, Claremont, CA 91711 (SAN 204-692X) Tel 714-620-1733.

California State Legislature, Joint Committee on Rules, *(Cal State Leg; 0-9611168),* State Capitol, Rm. 124, Sacramento, CA 95814 (SAN 289-0313) Tel 916-324-2089.

California State Univ. at Chico, Center for Business & Economic Research, *(CSU Ctr Busn Econ; 0-9602894),* Chico, CA 95929 (SAN 215-9481).

California State Univ., Dominguez Hills Educational Resources Center, *(CSUDH),* 800 E. Victoria, Dominguez Hills, CA 90747 (SAN 211-4887).

California State Univ. Fullerton, Oral History Program, *(CSUF Oral Hist; 0-930046),* Fullerton, CA 92634 (SAN 210-3982) Tel 714-773-3580.

California State Univ., Northridge Library, *(CSUN; 0-937048),* 18111 Nordhoff St., Northridge, CA 91330 (SAN 203-8722) Tel 818-885-2271.

California State Univ. at Fullerton Foundation, *(CSU Fullerton),* Fullerton, CA 92634 (SAN 215-1952); Dist. by: Hackett Publishing Co., Inc., P.O. Box 55573, 4047 N. Pennsylvania St., Indianapolis, IN 46205 (SAN 201-6044) Tel 317-283-8187.

California State Univ. at Northridge, Office of Disabled Student Services, *(CSUN Disabled; 0-937475),* 18111 Nordhoff St., Northridge, CA 91330 (SAN 659-0020) Tel 818-885-2869.

California State Univ. Fullerton, Dept. of Religious Studies, *(CA St U Religious; 0-9615339),* 800 N. State College Blvd., Fullerton, CA 92634 (SAN 695-1155) Tel 714-773-3722.

California State Univ., Fullerton, Visual Arts Ctr., *(CSU Art Gallery; 0-935314),* 800 N. State College Blvd., Fullerton, CA 92634 (SAN 223-7059).

California State Univ., Sacramento Library, *(CSU Sacto Lib; 0-938847),* 2000 Jed Smith Dr., Sacramento, CA 95819 (SAN 661-6976) Tel 916-278-6201.

California Street, *(Calif Street; 0-915090),* 723 Dwight Way, Berkeley, CA 94710 (SAN 207-673X) Tel 415-549-2461.

California Supreme Court, Div. of the State of California, *(CA Supreme Ct; 0-936629),* 350 McAllister St., Suite 3000, San Francisco, CA 94102 (SAN 699-7252) Tel 415-557-0205; Orders to: P.O. Box 1015, N. Highlands, CA 95660 (SAN 662-4049).

California Theatre Council/Westcoast Plays, *(CA Thea-Westcoast; 0-934782),* 849 S. Broadway, Suite 621, Los Angeles, CA 90014 (SAN 263-9629) Tel 213-622-6727.

California Weekly Explorer, Inc., *(Calif Weekly; 0-936778),* Suite 305-4521 Campus Dr. P.O. Box 19553, Irvine, CA 92713 (SAN 217-0914) Tel 714-786-7604; Dist. by: R. C. Law Co., 579 S. State College Blvd., Fullerton, CA 92631 (SAN 200-609X) Tel 714-871-0940.

Call Publishing Co., *(Call Pub Co; 0-939589),* P.O. Box 52130, Raleigh, NC 27612 (SAN 663-6160); 2532 Boothbay Ct., Raleigh, NC 27612 (SAN 663-6179) Tel 919-847-0311.

†Callaghan & Co., *(Callaghan; 0-8366),* 3201 Old Glenview Rd., Wilmette, IL 60091 (SAN 206-9393) Tel 312-256-7000; Toll free: 800-323-1336 (Orders); Toll free: 800-323-8067 (Editorial); *CIP.*

Callahan, John D., *(Callahan CA; 0-9615767),* P.O. Box 1281, LaCanada, CA 91011 (SAN 696-1789) Tel 818-767-5362; 8601 Sunland Blvd., Suite 44, Sun Valley, CA 91352 (SAN 696-1797).

Callahan, Kathleen J., Affil. of St. Maurice Church, *(K J Callahan; 0-9615563),* 53 Burnt Hill Rd., Hebron, CT 06248 (SAN 200-8203) Tel 203-228-0873.

Callahan's Guides, *(Callahans Guides; 0-910967),* 20 Main St., P.O. Box 116, Essex Junction, VT 05452 (SAN 263-2411).

Callaloo Fiction Series/Poetry Series, *(Callaloo Fic Poetry; 0-912759),* Univ. of Virginia, Dept. of English, Charlottesville, VA 22903 (SAN 282-7654) Tel 804-924-7105.

Callarman Hse., *(Callarman Hse; 0-930092),* 2582 Anchor, Port Hueneme, CA 93041 (SAN 210-7066) Tel 805-985-9500.

†Callaway Editions, *(Callaway Edns; 0-935112),* 108 W. 18th St., New York, NY 10011 (SAN 213-2931) Tel 212-929-5212; *CIP.*

Calli Callul, *(Calli Callul; 0-9617223),* c/o D. Beaver, 8135 W. Floyd Ave. 9-201, Lakewood, CO 80227 (SAN 663-3927) Tel 303-987-8545.

Calligrafree-The Calligraphy Co., *(Calligrafree; 0-942032),* P.O. Box 98, Brookville, OH 45309 (SAN 240-9496); Dist. by: Hunt Manufacturing Co., 1405 Locust St., Philadelphia, PA 19102 (SAN 678-7339) Tel 215-732-7700.

Calligraphy by Donna, *(Calligraphy Donna; 0-9604308),* 565 SE Airpark Dr., Bend, OR 97702 (SAN 216-0250) Tel 503-382-8215.

Calliope Music, *(Calliope Music; 0-9605912),* P.O. Box 1460, Ansonia Sta., New York, NY 10023 (SAN 216-6607).

Calliope Pr., *(Calliope Pr; 0-939684),* P.O. Box 2273, N. Hollywood, CA 91602 (SAN 216-7212) Tel 818-841-5119.

Calliopes Corner, 3 A.M. Pr., *(Calliopes Corner; 0-938219),* P.O. Box 110647, Anchorage, AK 99511-0647 (SAN 659-946X); 450 Daily, Anchorage, AK 99511 (SAN 659-9478) Tel 907-349-7170.

Callwyn Bks. U. S. A., Div. of Simple Classics, Inc., *(Callwyn; 0-9615639),* P.O. Box 4131, Louisville, KY 40204 (SAN 696-2157) Tel 502-451-7996; 933 Baxter Ave., Louisville, KY 40204 (SAN 696-2165).

CalMedia, *(CalMedia; 0-939782),* P.O. Box 156, La Mirada, CA 90637 (SAN 216-8820) Tel 714-522-7575.

Calvary Episcopal Church, *(Calvary Episcopal),* Box 67, Cleveland, MS 38732 (SAN 217-2895).

Calvary Missionary Pr., Div. of Calvary
Missionary Fellowship, (Calvary Miss Pr;
0-912375), P.O. Box 13532, Tucson, AZ
85732 (SAN 265-2021) Tel 602-745-3822.

Calvary Pr., (Calvary Pr; 0-9604138), 400 S.
Bennett St., Southern Pines, NC 28387
(SAN 223-4505).

Calvert, Mary, (M Calvert; 0-9609914), Lincoln
St., East Boothbay, ME 04544
(SAN 268-6120) Tel 207-633-3693.

Calwood Pubns., (Calwood Pubns), P.O. Box
284, Monsey, NY 10952 (SAN 210-9557)
Tel 914-352-7760.

Calyx Bks., Div. of Calyx Inc., (Calyx Bks;
0-934971), P.O. Box B, Corvallis, OR 97339
(SAN 695-1171) Tel 503-753-9384; Dist.
by: Inland Bk. Co., P.O. Box 261, 22
Hemingway Ave., East Haven, CT 06512
(SAN 200-4151) Tel 203-467-4257; Dist.
by: Bookpeople, 2929 Fifth St., Berkeley, CA
94710 (SAN 168-9517) Tel 415-549-3030;
Dist. by: Small Press Dist., 1814 San Pablo
Ave., Berkeley, CA 94702 (SAN 204-5826)
Tel 415-549-3336; Dist. by: Pacific Pipeline,
19215 66th Ave., S., Kent, WA 98032
(SAN 208-2128) Tel 206-872-5523.

Cam-Tri Productions, (Cam-Tri Prods;
0-9606218), 1895 Tigertail Rd., Eugene, OR
97405 (SAN 217-5045) Tel 503-344-0118.

†Camaro Publishing, Co., (Camaro Pub;
0-913290), 90430 World Way Ctr., Los
Angeles, CA 90009 (SAN 201-7865)
Tel 213-837-7500; CIP.

Camas Pr., The, (Camas Pr; 0-9616066), P.O.
Box 41, Camas Valley, OR 97416
(SAN 697-8541) Tel 503-445-2327; 1061
Main Camas Rd., Camas Valley, OR 97416
(SAN 697-855X).

Cambia, (Cambia WA; 0-938221), 4040 148th
Ave., SE, Bellevue, WA 98006
(SAN 659-9508) Tel 206-643-1681.

Cambita Bks., (Cambita Bks; 0-9610444), 2214
W. Appletree Rd., Milwaukee, WI 53209
(SAN 263-9637) Tel 414-351-0263; P.O.
Box 09330, Milwaukee, WI 53209
(SAN 699-5187).

Cambria Records & Publishing, (Cambria
Records; 0-936939), 2625 Colt Rd., Rancho
Palos Verdes, CA 90274 (SAN 658-6937)
Tel 213-427-1494; P.O. Box 374, Lomita,
CA 90717 (SAN 658-6945).

Cambrian Pr., (Cambrian Pr; 0-936669), 3681
Union Ave., San Jose, CA 95124
(SAN 699-7430) Tel 408-266-3030.

Cambrian Pubns., (Cambrian; 0-912548), P.O.
Box 191, Little River Sta., Miami, FL 33138
(SAN 202-5019) Tel 305-751-1122.

Cambric Pr., (Cambric; 0-918342), 901 Rye
Beach Rd., Huron, OH 44839
(SAN 210-0460) Tel 419-433-5560.

Cambridge Architectural Pr., (Cambridge Arch
Pr; 0-937999), 300 Franklin St., Cambridge,
MA 02139 (SAN 659-9516)
Tel 617-491-8386.

Cambridge Bk. Co., Div. of Simon & Schuster
(Gulf & Western), (Cambridge Bk; 0-8428),
888 Seventh Ave., New York, NY 10106
(SAN 169-5703) Tel 212-957-5300; Toll
free: 800-221-4764.

Cambridge Scientific Abstracts, (Cambridge Sci),
stern), (Cambridge Bk; 0-8428; 0-88387),
5161 River Rd., Bethesda, MD 20816
(SAN 201-2995) Tel 301-951-1400.

Cambridge Stratford, Ltd., (Cambridge Strat;
0-935637), 867 Hopkins Rd., Suite 101,
Amherst, NY 14221 (SAN 696-2173)
Tel 716-688-4927.

Cambridge Univ. Pr., (Cambridge U Pr; 0-521),
32 E. 57th St., New York, NY 10022
(SAN 200-206X) Tel 212-688-8888; Toll
free: 800-431-1580; Orders to: 510 North
Ave., New Rochelle, NY 10801
(SAN 281-3769) Tel 914-235-0300.

Camda, (Camda; 0-9600434), P.O. Box 2467,
Staunton, VA 24401 (SAN 202-5027).

Camden Harbor Pr., (Camden Harbor Pr;
0-935853), 13160 Mindanao Way, Suite 270,
Marina del Rey, CA 90292
(SAN 696-2246) Tel 213-305-9783.

Camden Hse., Inc., (Camden Hse; 0-938100),
Drawer 2025, Columbia, SC 29202
(SAN 215-9376) Tel 803-788-8689; Dist.
by: Camden Hse., Inc., P.O. Box 4836,
Hampden Sta., Baltimore, MD 21211
(SAN 661-9681) Tel 301-338-6950.

†Camelback Records, Inc., (Camelback Inc;
0-917215), P.O. Box 2245, Scottsdale, AZ
85252-2245 (SAN 656-1535)
Tel 602-945-1101; CIP.

Camelot Consultants, (Camelot Consult;
0-938481), 50 N. 21st St., Las Vegas, NV
89101 (SAN 659-9524) Tel 702-384-5262.

†Camelot Publishing, (Camelot Pub MN;
0-942450), 1551 Camelot Lane NE, Fridley,
MN 55432 (SAN 240-0855); CIP.

Camelot Publishing Co., (Camelot Pub; 0-89218),
P.O. Box 1357, Ormond Beach, FL 32074
(SAN 202-5035) Tel 904-672-5672.

Cameo Publishing, Co., Subs. of Val J. Webb
Numismatics, (Cameo Pub GA; 0-9614430),
P.O. Box 723064, Atlanta, GA 30339
(SAN 689-3430) Tel 404-952-8741.

Cameron & Co., (Cameron & Co; 0-918684),
543 Howard St., San Francisco, CA 94105
(SAN 210-9700) Tel 415-777-5582.

Cameron Pr., (Cameron Pr), P.O. Box 535,
Alexandria, VA 22313 (SAN 679-2014).

Camex Inc., (Camex; 0-932565), 489 Fifth Ave.,
New York, NY 10017 (SAN 687-4746)
Tel 212-682-8400.

Camin, (Camin; 0-9614123), 3123 Childers St.,
Raleigh, NC 27612 (SAN 686-5089)
Tel 919-782-4686.

Camino E. E. & B. Company, (Camino E E & B;
0-940808), P.O. Box 510, Camino, CA
95709 (SAN 219-841X).

Camm Publishing Co., (Camm Pub; 0-9608400),
P.O. Box 640358, Uleta Branch, Miami, FL
33164 (SAN 240-6101) Tel 305-949-7536.

Camp Denali Publishing, (Camp Denali;
0-9602792), P.O. Box 67, McKinley Park,
AK 99755 (SAN 213-0297).

Campaign for World Government, (Campaign
World Gvt), 331 Park Ave., Suite 304,
Glencoe, IL 60022 (SAN 224-0920)
Tel 312-835-3685 Tel 312-835-1377.

Campana Art Co. Inc., (Campana Art;
0-939608), 721 W. Wilks St., Pampa, TX
79065 (SAN 204-3572) Tel 806-665-3618.

Campanile Press See San Diego State Univ., Pr.

Campbell, Arthur, Inc., (Campbell Inc;
0-932775), P.O. Box 2549, Portland, OR
97208 (SAN 688-4768) Tel 503-635-7894.

Campbell, Lucile M., (L M Campbell;
0-9607114), c/o Mrs. Joe Richardson, 615
Sixth Ave. SW, Decatur, AL 35601
(SAN 238-9592) Tel 205-355-8895.

Campbell, Robert M., (R M Campbell;
0-9613542), P.O. Box 7906, Ann Arbor, MI
48107 (SAN 670-1752) Tel 313-482-6571.

Campbell, Sandy M., (S Campbell; 0-917366),
230 Central Park S., New York, NY 10019
(SAN 204-7128) Tel 212-582-6286.

Campbell's List, (Campbells List; 0-933089),
P.O. Box 428, 100 E. Ventris Ave., Maitland,
FL 32751 (SAN 237-6288)
Tel 305-644-8298; Toll free: 800-624-2232.

Camping Guideposts, (Camp Guidepts;
0-942684), Whiteface Woods, Cotton, MN
55724 (SAN 239-6246) Tel 218-482-3446.

Campo, Vincent, (V Campo), 1223 Newkirk
Ave., Brooklyn, NY 11230
(SAN 237-9945).

Campus Crusade for Christ, International,
(Campus Crusade; 0-918956), c/o Heres Life
Pub., P.O. Box 1576, San Bernardino, CA
92402 (SAN 212-4254) Tel 714-886-7981.

Campus Pubs., (Campus; 0-87506), 713 W.
Ellsworth Rd., Ann Arbor, MI 48104
(SAN 201-9558) Tel 313-663-4033.

Campus Scope Pr., (Campus Scope; 0-915858),
2928 Dean Pkwy., Apt. 4D, Minneapolis,
MN 55416 (SAN 216-0269).

Can Do Pubns., (Can Do Pubns; 0-943024),
P.O. Box 396, Shrewsbury, MA 01545
(SAN 240-3501) Tel 617-842-7322.

Can-to-Pan Cookery, (Can-to-Pan; 0-9605536),
143 Benson Ave., Vallejo, CA 94590
(SAN 240-9461) Tel 707-557-0578.

Canal Captains Pr., (Canal Captains; 0-9613675),
103 Dogwood Ln., Berkeley Heights, NJ
07922 (SAN 670-9680) Tel 201-464-9335.

Canal Pr., (Canal Pr; 0-9611116), Box 28, Canal
Winchester, OH 43110 (SAN 282-8774)
Tel 614-885-9757.

Cancer Care, Inc., (Cancer Care; 0-9606494),
1180 Sixth Ave., New York, NY 10036
(SAN 225-9087) Tel 212-221-3300.

Cancer Control Society, (Cancer Control Soc;
0-943080), 2043 N. Berendo St., Los
Angeles, CA 90027 (SAN 216-2296)
Tel 213-663-7801.

Cancer Research, Inc., Affil. of American Assn.
for Cancer Research, (Cancer Res;
0-938547), Temple Univ., Schl. of Medicine,
3440 N. Broad St., Philadelphia, PA 19140
(SAN 661-3284) Tel 215-221-4720.

Candle Bks., Inc., (Candle Bks; 0-9609644),
1010 Grey Oak, San Antonio, TX 78213
(SAN 262-0065) Tel 512-342-5880.

Candy Apple Publishing Co., (Candy Apple Pub;
0-9616464), P.O. Box 48421, St. Petersburg,
FL 33743-8421 (SAN 659-3178)
Tel 813-544-0355; 6575 Bonnie Bay Cir. N.,
Pinellas Park, FL 33565 (SAN 659-3186).

Cane Curiosa, (Cane Curiosa), 4121 Forest Park,
St. Louis, MO 63108 (SAN 289-5951).

Cane Patch, The, (Cane Patch; 0-9615765), P.O.
Box 1382, Myrtle Beach, SC 29578
(SAN 696-2270) Tel 803-448-3461; 1102
N. Oak St., Myrtle Beach, SC 29578
(SAN 696-2289).

Cane River Pecan Co., (Cane River; 0-9613404),
P.O. Box 161, New Iberia, LA 70560
(SAN 656-8831) Tel 318-364-2591; Orders
to: 101 Taylor St., New Iberia, LA 70560
(SAN 662-233X) Tel 318-365-4136.

Caney Station Bk., Inc., (Caney Station Bks;
0-9613634), Route 1, Box 1, Greenville, KY
42345 (SAN 682-2584) Tel 502-338-4880.

Canfield Pr. See Harper & Row Pubs., Inc.

Canipe, Kenneth W., (K W Canipe; 0-9616329),
Rte. 12, Box 474, Hickory, NC 28602
(SAN 659-0748) Tel 704-294-3322.

Canner, J. S., & Co., Div. of Plenum Publishing
Corp., (Canner; 0-910324), 49-65
Lansdowne St., Boston, MA 02215
(SAN 202-5094) Tel 617-437-1923.
Microcards; also microfilm of Plenum
journals only.

Canning Pubns., Inc., (Canning Pubns;
0-938516), 925 Anza Ave., Vista, CA 92084
(SAN 215-9384) Tel 619-724-5900.

Canning Trade Inc,The, (Canning Trade Inc;
0-930027), 2619 Maryland Ave, Baltimore,
MD 21218 (SAN 669-7437)
Tel 301-467-3338.

Cannon, Timothy L., & Nancy F. Whitmore, (T
L Cannon & N F Whitmore; 0-9602816),
7916 Juniper Dr., Frederick, MD 21701
(SAN 213-4756).

Cannon/S & K, Inc., (Cannon-S & K;
0-9616991), 1732 Glade St., Muskegon, MI
49441 (SAN 656-8359) Tel 616-722-6036.

Canoe Pr., (Canoe Press; 0-9613768), 537 S.
Elmwood, Oak Park, IL 60304
(SAN 678-9633) Tel 312-989-2626; Orders
to: P.O. Box 1443, Oak Park, IL 60304
(SAN 685-4117) Tel 312-386-5279.

Canon Law Society of America, (Canon Law
Soc; 0-943616), Catholic Univ., Caldwell
Hall, Rm. 431, Washington, DC 20064
(SAN 237-6296) Tel 202-269-3491.

Canon Pr., (Canon Pr; 0-939651), P.O. Box 213,
Centerville, UT 84014-0213
(SAN 663-5830); 497 E. 400 N., Bountiful,
UT 84010 (SAN 663-5849)
Tel 801-295-6003.

Canon Publications, (Canon Pubns; 0-88181),
P.O. Box 698, Talent, OR 97540
(SAN 264-7206) Tel 503-535-1490.

Canon Pubs., Ltd., (Canon Pubs; 0-9616591),
29056 Histead Dr., Evergreen, CO 80439
(SAN 659-4972) Tel 303-674-0472.

Canter & Assocs., (Canter & Assoc; 0-9608978;
0-939007), 1553 Euclid Ave., Santa Monica,
CA 90404 (SAN 240-8716); Toll free:
800-262-4347.

Canterbury Pr., (Canterbury; 0-933753), 2318
Eighth St., Berkeley, CA 94710
(SAN 692-6045) Tel 415-843-1860; Dist.
by: Bookpeople, 2929 Fifth St., Berkeley, CA
94710 (SAN 168-9517) Tel 415-549-3030;
Dist. by: Inland Bk Co., P.O. Box261, 22
Hemingway Ave., East Haven, CT 06512
(SAN 200-4151) Tel 203-467-4257; Toll
free: 800-243-0138.

Canterbury Pr., (Canterbury Pr; 0-933990),
5540 Vista Del Amigo, Anaheim, CA 92807
(SAN 212-890X).

Canticle Pr., (Canticle Pr; 0-941396), 1986 S.
2600, E., Salt Lake City, UT 84106
(SAN 238-9606) Tel 801-466-4028.

Cantine & Kilpatrick, Pubns., (Cantine &
Kilpatrick; 0-940548), P.O. Box 798,
Huntington, NY 11743 (SAN 222-9927)
Tel 516-271-8990.

387

Cantor, B.G., Art Foundation, *(Cantor Art Found; 0-939912),* 1 World Trade Ctr., 105th Fl., New York, NY 10048 (SAN 216-7964) Tel 212-938-5136.

Cantor & Company, Inc., *(Cantor & Co; 0-9608980),* Suburban Station Bldg., Philadelphia, PA 19103 (SAN 237-630X).

Canyon Pr., *(Canyon Pr; 0-936899),* 162 Ruby Ave., San Carlos, CA 94070 (SAN 658-4918) Tel 415-593-5639.

Canyon Publishing Co., *(Canyon Pub Co; 0-942568),* 8561 Eatough Ave., Canoga Park, CA 91304 (SAN 240-0685) Tel 818-702-0171.

Canyonlands Natural History Assn., *(Canyonlands; 0-937407),* 125 W. 200 S., Moab, UT 84532 (SAN 659-0764) Tel 801-259-8161.

Cap & Gown Pr., Inc., *(Cap & Gown; 0-88105),* Sales Office, P.O Box 58825, Houston, TX 77258 (SAN 240-611X); 4519 Woodrow Ave., Galveston, TX 77550 (SAN 661-969X) Tel 409-763-3410.

Cap K Pubns., *(Cap K Pubns; 0-9616532),* 358 S. Bentley Ave., Los Angeles, CA 90049 (SAN 659-4298) Tel 213-472-9206.

Capability's Bks., *(Capability's; 0-913643),* P.O. Box 114, Hwy. No. 46, Deer Park, WI 54007 (SAN 286-0759) Tel 715-269-5346.

Capablanca *See* **Imprint Editions**

Capaco, *(Capaco; 0-9615837),* 7825 Patriot Dr., Annandale, VA 22003 (SAN 697-0338) Tel 703-941-8558.

Cape Ann Antiques, *(Cape Ann Antiques; 0-9616832),* P.O. Box 3502, Peabody, MA 01960 (SAN 661-2733); 15 Mildred Rd., Danvers, MA 01923 (SAN 661-2741) Tel 617-777-3011.

Cape Ann Historical Assn., *(Cape Ann Hist Assoc; 0-938791),* 27 Pleasant St., Gloucester, MA 01930 (SAN 278-3401) Tel 617-283-0455.

Cape Cod Historical Pubns., *(Cape Cod Hist Pubns; 0-9616740),* P.O. Box 281, Yarmouth Port, MA 02675 (SAN 659-9532); 425 Main St., Yarmouth Port, MA 02675 (SAN 659-9540) Tel 617-362-4761.

†**Cape Cod Museum of Natural History,** *(Cape Cod Mus Nat His; 0-916275),* Brewster, MA 02631 (SAN 295-6942) Tel 617-896-3867; *CIP.*

†**Capistrano Pr., Ltd.,** *(Capistrano Pr; 0-912433),* 12882 Valley Hwy, Suite 15, Garden Grove, CA 92465 (SAN 265-2064) Tel 714-891-7451; *CIP.*

Capital Futures Assocs., Ltd., *(Capital Futures Assocs; 0-939397),* P.O. Box 2618, Chicago, IL 60690 (SAN 663-1320); 1605 W. Chase, Chicago, IL 60626 (SAN 663-1339) Tel 312-274-9254.

Capital Pr., *(Capital Press),* Six Kennedy St., Alexandria, VA 22305 (SAN 678-9102).

Capital Publishing Co., *(Capital Pub Co; 0-9615703),* P.O. Box 19655, Sacramento, CA 95819 (SAN 696-317X) Tel 916-455-0846; 84 Sandburg Dr., Sacramento, CA 95819 (SAN 696-3188).

Capital Publishing Corp. (CPC) *See* **Unipub a**

Capital Technology, Inc., *(Capital Tech; 0-9603460),* P.O. Box 2428, Charlotte, NC 28211-8240 (SAN 213-294X).

Capitalist Pr., *(Capitalist Pr OH; 0-938770),* P.O. Box 2753, North Canton, OH 44720 (SAN 696-9194).

Capitol Enquiry, *(Capitol Enquiry; 0-917982),* P.O. Box 22246, Sacramento, CA 95822 (SAN 211-5077) Tel 916-428-3271.

Capitol Pubns., Ltd., Education Research Group, *(Capitol VA; 0-937925),* 1101 King St., P.O. Box 1453, Alexandria, VA 22313-2053 (SAN 659-4980) Tel 703-683-4100; Toll free: 800-827-7204 (Orders only).

Capitola Bk. Co., *(Capitola Bk; 0-932319),* 1475 41st Ave., Capitola, CA 95010 (SAN 687-0449) Tel 408-475-9042.

Capra Pr., *(Capra Pr; 0-88496; 0-912264),* P.O. Box 2068, Santa Barbara, CA 93120 (SAN 201-9620) Tel 805-966-4590.

†**Capricorn Bks.,** *(Capricorn Bks),* 2 Aztec Ct., Toms River, NJ 08757 (SAN 260-0013) Tel 201-349-0725; *CIP.*

Capricorn Corp., *(Capricorn Corp; 0-910719),* 4961 Rebel Trail NW, Atlanta, GA 30327 (SAN 262-0073) Tel 404-843-8668.

Capricornus Pr., *(Capricornus Pr; 0-9608544),* P.O. Box 1023, Boulder, CO 80306 (SAN 240-6128) Tel 303-442-2663.

Caprine Pr., *(Caprine Pr; 0-914381),* 1878 E. 15th St., Tulsa, OK 74104 (SAN 289-596X) Tel 918-743-4936.

Caprock Pr., *(Caprock Pr; 0-912570),* 4806 17th St., Lubbock, TX 79416 (SAN 201-9639) Tel 806-795-7599.

Capstan Pubns., *(Capstan Pubns; 0-914565),* P.O. Box 306, Basin, WY 82410 (SAN 289-162X) Tel 307-568-2604. *Imprints:* Glenndale Books (Glenndale Bks); Timbertrails (Timbertrails).

Capstone Editions, *(Capstone Edns; 0-9610662),* P.O. Box 13143, Tucson, AZ 85732 (SAN 264-6552) Tel 602-745-6750.

Captain Fiddle Pubns., *(Captain Fiddle Pubns; 0-931877),* 4 Elm Ct., Newmarket, NH 03857 (SAN 686-0508) Tel 603-659-2658.

Captain Stanislaus Mlotkowski Memorial Brigade Society, *(Cptn Stanislaus; 0-9600814),* 247 Philadelphia Pike, Wilmington, DE 19809 (SAN 207-124X).

Captain's Lady Collections, The, *(Captains Lady; 0-9609534),* 65-69 High St., Springfield, MA 01105 (SAN 260-1729) Tel 413-739-6655.

†**Carabelle Bks.,** *(Carabelle; 0-938634),* Box 1611, Shepherdstown, WV 25443 (SAN 281-3785) Tel 304-876-2723; *CIP.*

Carabis, Anne J., *(Carabis; 0-9605802),* 25 Nelson Ave., Latham, NY 12110 (SAN 216-5600) Tel 518-783-9807.

†**Caratzas, Aristide D., Pub.,** Affil. of C.B.P. Publishing & Distributing CO. Inc., *(Caratzas; 0-89241),* 481 Main St., New Rochelle, NY 10802 (SAN 201-3134) Tel 914-632-8487; P.O. Box 210, New Rochelle, NY 10802 (SAN 658-0238); *CIP.*

†**Caravan Bks.,** Subs. of Scholar's Facsimiles & Reprints, *(Caravan Bks; 0-88206),* P.O. Box 344, Delmar, NY 12054 (SAN 206-7323) Tel 518-439-5978; *CIP.*

Caravan-Maritime Bks., *(Caravan-Maritime; 0-917368),* 87-06 168th Pl., Jamaica, NY 11432 (SAN 201-8705) Tel 718-526-1380. Do not confuse with Caravan Bks.

Caravan Pr., *(Caravan Pr; 0-912159),* 343 S. Broadway, Los Angeles, CA 90013 (SAN 264-7222) Tel 213-628-2563.

Caravelle Bks., Inc., *(Caravelle NY; 0-501),* 207 E. 37th St., New York, NY 10016 (SAN 658-6236).

Carbarn Press, *(Carbarn Press; 0-934406),* P.O. Box 255, Tiburon, CA 94920 (SAN 223-7024) Tel 415-435-9073.

CARBEN Surveying Reprints, *(CARBEN Survey),* 1403 Woodmont Dr., Johnson City, TN 37601 (SAN 209-5327).

Carcanet Pr., Subs. of Carcanet Press, (UK), *(Carcanet; 0-85635; 0-902145),* 108 E. 31st St., New York, NY 10016 (SAN 686-192X) Tel 212-686-1033; Toll free: 800-242-7737; Dist. by: Harper & Row Pubs., Inc., Keystone Industrial Pk., Scranton, PA 18512 (SAN 215-3742).

Carcosa, *(Carcosa; 0-913796),* P.O. Box 1064, Chapel Hill, NC 27514 (SAN 202-5124) Tel 919-929-2974.

Cardamom Pr., *(Cardamom; 0-9611118),* P.O. Box D, Richmond, ME 04357 (SAN 283-2836) Tel 207-666-5645.

Cardamone, Helen M., Pub., *(H M Cardamone; 0-9608330),* 2108 Genesee St., Utica, NY 13502 (SAN 240-5229) Tel 315-735-0363.

Carden & Cherry Advertising, *(Carden Cherry Adv; 0-934319),* 1220 McGavock St., Nashville, TN 37203 (SAN 693-4633) Tel 615-255-6696; Dist. by: Ballantine Bks., 201 E. 50th St., New York, NY 10022 (SAN 214-1175) Tel 212-751-2600.

Carderock Pr., *(Carderock Pr; 0-938813),* P.O. Box 56, Cabin John, MD 20818 (SAN 662-5630); 8305 Fenway Rd., Bethesda, MD 20817 (SAN 662-5649) Tel 301-365-0768.

Cardi-Bel, Inc., *(Cardi-Bel; 0-938119),* G.P.O. Box 2073, San Juan, PR 00936 (SAN 659-9559); Perseo & Sirio St., Urb. Altamira, San Juan, PR 00922 (SAN 659-9567) Tel 809-783-6857.

Cardiff-By-The-Sea Publishing Co., *(Cardiff; 0-9608038),* 6065 Mission Gorge Rd., San Diego, CA 92120 (SAN 240-2009) Tel 619-286-6902.

Cardinal Point, Inc., *(Cardinal Pt; 0-932065),* P.O. Box 596, Ellettsville, IN 47429 (SAN 685-4273) Tel 812-876-7811; Toll free: 800-628-2828.

Cardinal Pr., Inc., *(Cardinal Pr; 0-943594),* 76 N. Yorktown, Tulsa, OK 74110 (SAN 219-1385) Tel 918-583-3651.

Cardinal Productions, *(Cardinal Prod; 0-939245),* 3636 Lemmon Ave., Suite 205, Dallas, TX 75219 (SAN 662-6351) Tel 214-528-5750.

Cardinal Pubs., *(Cardinal Pubs; 0-912930),* P.O. Box 207, Davis, CA 95616 (SAN 201-9647).

Cardot Enterprises, *(Cardot Entpr Inc; 0-9607516),* 214 Avenida Barbera, Sonoma, CA 95476 (SAN 238-6283).

Cardoza Publishing, *(Cardoza Pub; 0-9607618),* P.O. Box 1484, Studio City, CA 91604 (SAN 281-3904) Tel 818-980-4471; Dist. by: Bookazine, 303 West 10th St., New York, NY 10014 (SAN 169-5665); Dist. by: Book Dynamics, 836 Broadway, New York, NY 10003 (SAN 169-5649) Tel 212-254-7798; Dist. by: Koen Distributors, 514 N. Read Ave., Cinnaminson, NJ 08077 (SAN 169-4642); Dist. by: Publishers Group West, 5855 Beaudry Street, Emeryville, CA 94608 (SAN 202-8522) Tel 415-658-3453. *Imprints:* Cardoza Schl of Blackjack (Cardoza Sch Blackjk); Gambling Research Institute (Gambling Res).

Cardoza Schl of Blackjack *See* **Cardoza Publishing**

Care Communications, Incorporated, *(Care Comm Inc; 0-916499),* 200 E. Ontario, Chicago, IL 60611 (SAN 295-5180) Tel 312-943-0463.

Care/Share Productions, *(Care-Share; 0-9611628),* P.O. Box 12245, Charleston, SC 29412 (SAN 284-9267) Tel 803-795-7234; Orders to: Gene Dillard Ministries, P.O. Box 90546, Charleston, SC 29410 (SAN 688-4156) Tel 803-747-6967.

Career Directions Pr., *(Career Directions; 0-933163),* 171 Rte. 34, Holmdel, NJ 07733 (SAN 692-2783) Tel 201-946-8457.

Career Management Assocs., *(Career Mgmt; 0-937595),* 39505 Luckiamute Rd., Philomath, OR 97370 (SAN 659-0829) Tel 503-929-2254.

Career Management Consultants, *(Career Mgmt Consult; 0-9616157),* 544 NW 28th St., Corvallis, OR 97330 (SAN 699-9360) Tel 503-753-6478; P.O. Box 1802, Corvallis, OR 97330 (SAN 699-9379).

Career Management Pr., Subs. of Career Management Ctr., *(Career Manage Pr; 0-9613630),* 8301 State Line, No. 202, Kansas City, MO 64114 (SAN 670-8560) Tel 816-363-1500; Dist. by: Talman Co., 150 Fifth Ave., Rm. 514, New York, NY 10011 (SAN 200-5204) Tel 212-620-3182.

Career Planning Pubs., *(Career Plan; 0-910595),* 7101 York Ave. S. No. 100, Edina, MN 55435 (SAN 260-0242) Tel 612-921-3379.

Career Publishing Corp., *(Career Pub Corp; 0-934829),* 505 Fifth Ave., Suite 1003, New York, NY 10017 (SAN 694-3640) Tel 212-840-7011; Toll free: 800-835-2246.

†**Career Publishing, Inc.,** *(Career Pub; 0-89262),* 910 N. Main St., Orange, CA 92667 (SAN 208-581X) Tel 714-771-5155; Toll free: 800-854-4014; P.O. Box 5486, Orange, CA 92613-5486 (SAN 658-0246); *CIP.*

Career Publishing, Inc., *(Career Pub IL; 0-911744),* 905 Allanson Rd., Mundelein, IL 60060 (SAN 202-5132) Tel 312-949-0011.

Career Resources Co., *(Career Resources; 0-9616617),* Drawer 29388, Richmond, VA 23229 (SAN 659-9575); 1543-C Honey Grove Dr., Richmond, VA 23229 (SAN 659-9583) Tel 804-285-4410.

Careers Unlimited, *(Careers Unltd; 0-916275),* P.O. Box 470886, Tulsa, OK 74147 (SAN 295-6993) Tel 918-622-2811.

CareerTrack Pubns., Inc., *(CareerTrack Pubns; 0-943066),* 1800 38th St., Boulder, CO 80301 (SAN 240-4133) Tel 303-440-7440; Toll free: 800-334-1018; Dist. by: Acropolis Bks., 2400 17th St. NW, Washington, DC 20009 (SAN 201-2227) Tel 202-387-6805.

Carefree Living Co., *(Carefree Living; 0-938411),* 2509 E. Thousand Oaks Blvd., No. 160, Thousand Oaks, CA 91362-3249 (SAN 659-9613); 642 Camino Manzanas, Thousand Oaks, CA 91360 (SAN 659-9621) Tel 805-498-2654.

Caregiving Resources, *(Caregiving Resc; 0-939273),* 29 Oberlin St., Maplewood, NJ 07040 (SAN 662-8834) Tel 201-761-0456.

CareInstitute, Subs. of Comprehensive Care Corp., *(CareInst; 0-917877),* 660 Newport Ctr. Dr., Newport Beach, CA 92660 (SAN 657-0682) Tel 714-640-8950.

Carey, William, Library Pubs., *(William Carey Lib; 0-87808),* 1705 N. Sierra Bonita Ave., P.O. Box 40129, Pasadena, CA 91104 (SAN 208-2101) Tel 818-798-0819. *Imprints:* Ecclesia Pubns. (Ecclesia); Mandate Press (Mandate); World Christian Bookshelf (World Christ).

Cargo Service Inc., *(Cargo Serv Inc; 0-9610616),* Box 466, Middletown, OH 45042 (SAN 276-959X) Tel 513-746-3993.

Carib Hse. (USA), *(Carib Hse; 0-936378),* P.O. Box 38834, Hollywood, CA 90038 (SAN 214-1124) Tel 818-890-1056.

Carib Pubns. *See Casa Bautista de Publicaciones*

Caribbean Bks., *(Caribbean Bks; 0-931209),* 801 4th Ave, Parkersburg, IA 50665 (SAN 681-9680) Tel 319-346-2048.

Carikean Publishing, *(Carikean Pub; 0-9616741),* P.O. Box 11771, Chicago, IL 60611-0771 (SAN 659-963X); 833 W. Buena, No. 1909, Chicago, IL 60613 (SAN 659-9648) Tel 312-327-3743.

Carillon Bks., Div. of Catholic Digest, *(Carillon Bks; 0-89310),* 2115 Summit Ave., St. Paul, MN 55105 (SAN 208-5828) Tel 612-647-5251.

Caring, Inc., *(Caring; 0-911163),* P.O. Box 400, Milton, WA 98354 (SAN 268-6597) Tel 206-922-8194.

Carith Hse., *(Carith Hse; 0-9616697),* 514 Warren St., Brookline, MA 02146 (SAN 659-9656); Marylake, Rte. 4, Box 1150, Little Rock, AR 72206 (SAN 659-9664) Tel 501-888-3052.

Carleton College, *(Carleton Coll; 0-9613911),* NorthField, MN 55057 (SAN 683-244X) Tel 507-663-4267.

Carleton Pr., *(Carleton Pr; 0-9615890),* Lambs Ln., Cresskill, NJ 07626 (SAN 697-029X) Tel 201-567-3858.

Carlette Publishing, *(Carlette Pub; 0-9615423),* 2416 N. Fairview, Rochester Hills, MI 48064 (SAN 696-2297) Tel 313-456-8506.

Carlino & Co., *(Carlino Co; 0-937827),* P.O. Box 15182, Honolulu, HI 96815 (SAN 659-4301) Tel 808-926-1752; 711 Ulili St., Honolulu, HI 96816 (SAN 659-431X).

Carlinshar & Assoc. Applied Research Corp., *(Carlinshar; 0-934872),* 519 E. Briarcliff, Bolingbrook, IL 60439 (SAN 212-8918) Tel 312-739-7720.

Carlisle Industries, *(Carlisle Indus; 0-9600344),* 31000 Tower Rd., Visalia, CA 93291 (SAN 202-5140) Tel 209-798-1544.

Carlisle Pub., Inc., *(Carlisle Pub; 0-910177),* P.O. Box 112, Hartsdale, NY 10530 (SAN 240-9739) Tel 914-725-0408.

Carlsbad Caverns Natural History Assn., *(Carlsbad His; 0-916907),* 3225 National Parks Hwy, Carlsbad, NM 88220 (SAN 268-6627) Tel 505-785-2318.

Carlton Pr., *(Carlton; 0-8062),* 11 W. 32nd St., New York, NY 10001 (SAN 201-9655) Tel 212-714-0300.

Carlton Pubns., Inc., *(Carlton Pubns CA; 0-937348),* 10949 Fruitland Dr., Studio City, CA 91604 (SAN 215-9414).

Carlyle Assocs., *(Carlyle Assocs; 0-935084),* 1236 Ninth St., Santa Monica, CA 90403 (SAN 213-4764) Tel 213-393-3323; P.O. Box 3391, Santa Monica, CA 90403 (SAN 658-0262); Dist. by: Wallaby Books, 1230 Ave. of the Americas, New York, NY 10020 (SAN 202-2450) Tel 212-245-6400.

Carlyle Sports, Inc., *(Carlyle Sports; 0-9616136),* 958 Alexandria Dr., Newark, DE 19711 (SAN 699-9174) Tel 302-366-8047.

Carma Pr., Inc., *(Carma; 0-918328),* Box 12633, St. Paul, MN 55112 (SAN 209-5351) Tel 612-631-9417.

Carmarthen Oak Pr., *(Carmarthen Oak; 0-915117),* 1835 University Ave., No. A, Berkeley, CA 94703 (SAN 289-7768) Tel 415-848-0648.

Carmel, Simon J., *(S Carmel; 0-9600886),* 10500 Rockville Pike, Apt. 1028, Rockville, MD 20852 (SAN 209-536X).

Carmonelle Pubns., *(Carmonelle Pubns; 0-943334),* P.O. Box 74, 304 Main St., Cameron, WI 54822 (SAN 240-5237) Tel 715-458-2684.

Carnation Pr., *(Carnation; 0-87601),* P.O. Box 101, State College, PA 16804 (SAN 203-5103); 346 W. Hillcrest Ave., State College, PA 16803 (SAN 661-9703) Tel 814-238-3577.

Carnegie Council on Ethics & International Affairs, *(Carnegie Ethics & Intl Affairs; 0-87641),* 170 E. 64th St., New York, NY 10021 (SAN 203-5960) Tel 212-838-4120.

Carnegie Endowment for International Peace, *(Carnegie Endow; 0-87003),* 11 Dupont Cir., NW, Washington, DC 20036 (SAN 281-3955) Tel 202-797-6424.

Carnegie Forum on Education & the Economy, Affil. of Carnegie Corp. of New York, *(Carnegie Forum Ed Eco; 0-9616685),* 1001 Connecticut Ave., NW, Suite 301, Washington, DC 20036 (SAN 660-9945) Tel 202-463-0747.

†**Carnegie Foundation for the Advancement of Teaching,** *(Carnegie Found),* 5 Ivy Ln., Princeton, NJ 08540 (SAN 268-6643) Tel 609-452-1780; Dist. by: Princeton Univ. Pr., 3175 Princeton Pike, Lawrenceville, NJ 08648 (SAN 202-0254) Tel 609-896-1344; *CIP.*

Carnegie Institute, Board of Trustees, The, *(Carnegie Board; 0-911239),* 4400 Forbes Ave., Pittsburgh, PA 15213 (SAN 268-6686) Tel 412-622-3377.

†**Carnegie Institution of Washington,** *(Carnegie Inst; 0-87279),* 1530 P St. NW, Washington, DC 20005 (SAN 201-9663) Tel 202-387-6411; *CIP.*

Carnegie-Mellon Univ., Pr., *(Carnegie-Mellon; 0-915604),* P.O. Box 21, Schenley Park, Pittsburgh, PA 15216 (SAN 211-2329) Tel 412-578-2861; Dist. by: Harper & Row, 10 E. 53rd St., New York, NY 10022 (SAN 200-2086) Tel 212-207-7099.

Carnegie Pr., Inc., *(Carnegie Pr; 0-935506),* 100 Kings Rd., Madison, NJ 07940 (SAN 223-7032).

Carnot Press, *(Carnot Pr; 0-917308),* P.O. Box 1544, Lake Oswego, OR 97034 (SAN 208-5852) Tel 503-636-6894.

Carnton Association, Inc., *(Carnton Assn),* Rte. 2, Carton Lane, Franklin, TN 37064 (SAN 277-5794).

Carolando Pr., *(Carolando; 0-940542),* 6545 W. N Ave., Oak Park, IL 60302 (SAN 219-3426) Tel 312-383-6480.

Carolina Academic Pr., *(Carolina Acad Pr; 0-89089),* P.O. Box 8795, Forest Hills Sta., Durham, NC 27707 (SAN 210-7848) Tel 919-489-7486.

†**Carolina Art Assn.,** Affil. of Gibbes Art Gallery, *(Carolina Art; 0-910326),* Orders to: Gibbes Gallery Shop, 135 Meeting St., Charleston, SC 29401 (SAN 203-512X) Tel 803-722-2706; *CIP.*

Carolina Banks Publishing, *(Carolina Banks Pub; 0-9617003),* 196 Ocean Blvd., Southern Shores, Kitty Hawk, NC 27949 (SAN 662-653X) Tel 919-261-2478.

Carolina Biological Supply Co., *(Carolina Biological; 0-89278),* 2700 York Rd., Burlington, NC 27215 (SAN 208-5860) Tel 919-584-0381; Toll free: 800-334-5551.

Carolina Cornucopia Educational Publishing Company, *(Cornucop Pub; 0-935911),* 5610 Laurel Crest Dr., Durham, NC 27712 (SAN 696-7213) Tel 919-471-1873; Dist. by: Nancy Robert's Collection, 3600 Chevington Rd., Charlotte, NC 28211 (SAN 200-5786).

Carolina Editions, Inc., *(Carolina Edns; 0-914056),* P.O. Box 3169, Greenwood, SC 29646 (SAN 201-8721) Tel 803-229-3503.

Carolina Independent Publications, Inc., *(Carolina Ind; 0-916975),* P.O. Box 2690, 2824 Hillsborough Rd., Durham, NC 27705 (SAN 655-6108) Tel 919-286-9692.

Carolina Pr., *(Carolina Pr; 0-9616475),* 2660 Nantucket Dr., Winston-Salem, NC 27103 (SAN 659-3194) Tel 919-760-0944.

†**Carolina Wren, Pr., The,** Affil. of Durham Arts Council, *(Carolina Wren; 0-932112),* 300 Barclay Rd., Chapel Hill, NC 27514 (SAN 213-0327) Tel 919-967-8666; *CIP.*

Caroline Hse., Inc., *(Caroline Hse),* 5S 250 Frontenac Rd., Naperville, IL 60540 (SAN 211-2280) Tel 312-983-6400; Toll free: 800-245-2665.

†**Carolrhoda Bks., Inc.,** *(Carolrhoda Bks; 0-87614),* 241 First Ave., N., Minneapolis, MN 55401 (SAN 201-9671) Tel 612-332-3344; Toll free: 800-328-4929; *CIP.*

†**Carolyn Bean Publishing, Ltd.,** *(Bean Pub; 0-916860),* 120 Second St., San Francisco, CA 94105 (SAN 208-5445) Tel 415-957-9574; *CIP.*

Carothers Co., *(Carothers; 0-943026),* Box 2518, Escondido, CA 92025 (SAN 240-3536) Tel 619-741-2755.

Carousel Art, Inc., *(Carousel Art; 0-914507),* P.O. Box 150, Green Village, NJ 07935 (SAN 290-697X) Tel 201-377-1483.

†**Carousel Pr.,** *(Carousel Pr; 0-917120),* P.O. Box 6061, Albany, CA 94706 (SAN 209-2646) Tel 415-527-5849; *CIP.*

Carousel Publishing Corp., *(Carousel Pub Corp; 0-935474),* 27 Union St., Brighton, MA 02135 (SAN 287-7333).

Carpe Librum, *(Carpe Librum; 0-9617242),* 3277 Roswell Rd., Suite 447, Atlanta, GA 30319 (SAN 663-5512) Tel 404-458-2441.

Carpenter Ctr. for the Visual Arts & Peabody Museum, *(Carpenter Ctr),* c/o Harvard Univ. Pr., 79 Garden St., Cambridge, MA 02138 (SAN 200-2043) Tel 617-495-2480.

†**Carpenter Pr.,** *(Carpenter Pr; 0-914140),* Rte. 4, Pomeroy, OH 45769 (SAN 206-4650) Tel 614-992-7520; *CIP.*

Carpet & Rug Institute, Inc., *(Carpet Rug Inst; 0-89275),* 310 Holiday Dr., Box 2048, Dalton, GA 30720 (SAN 268-6724) Tel 404-278-3176.

Carr, Claudia, *(C Carr),* Box 205, Ketchum, ID 83340 (SAN 696-9178).

Carrera International, Inc., *(Carrera Intl; 0-910597),* RFD 1682, Laurel Hollow, NY 11791 (SAN 263-967X) Tel 516-487-1616.

Carreta Pr., *(Carreta; 0-914199),* P.O. Box 5153, Mesa, AZ 85202 (SAN 287-5330) Tel 602-274-7480.

Carrey, Dixeann W., *(D W Carrey; 0-931882),* 6256 NW 16th Ct., Margate, FL 33063 (SAN 212-4068) Tel 305-975-0113.

Carri Publishing, *(Carri Pub; 0-935771),* 1696 Morning Glory Ln., San Jose, CA 95124 (SAN 695-8389) Tel 408-723-7535.

Carriage House Press, *(Carriage Hse Pr; 0-9612216),* Eight Evans Rd., Brookline, MA 02146 (SAN 287-7279) Tel 617-232-1636.

Carriage House Pr. (NY), *(Carriage House; 0-939713),* 1 Carriage Ln., East Hampton, NY 11937 (SAN 663-6152) Tel 516-267-8773. Do not confuse with Carriage House Pr. of Brookline, MA.

Carrier's Beekeeping Supplies, *(Carriers Bees; 0-9607550),* 601 S. Baywood Ave., San Jose, CA 95128 (SAN 238-6291) Tel 408-296-6100.

Carrington Hse., Ltd., *(Carrington Hse Ltd; 0-936695),* 1124 W. Barry Ave., Chicago, IL 60657 (SAN 699-9093) Tel 312-348-8613.

Carrol Gate Press, The, *(Carrol Gate Pr; 0-9608714),* 951 W. Liberty Dr., Wheaton, IL 60187 (SAN 238-048X) Tel 312-690-8574.

Carroll, Lewis, Society of North America, *(Lewis Carroll Soc; 0-930326),* 617 Rockford Rd., Silver Spring, MD 20902 (SAN 213-1064).

Carroll & Graf Pubs., *(Carroll & Graf; 0-88184),* 260 Fifth Ave., New York, NY 10001 (SAN 264-6560) Tel 212-889-8772; Toll free: 800-982-8319; Dist. by: Publishers Group West, 5855 Beaudry St., Emeryville, CA 94608 (SAN 202-8522) Tel 415-658-3453.

Carroll College Press, *(Carroll Coll; 0-916120),* 100 NE Ave., Waukesha, WI 53186 (SAN 208-5879) Tel 414-547-1211.

†**Carroll Pr.,** *(Carroll Pr; 0-910328),* 43 Squantum St., Cranston, RI 02920 (SAN 203-6231) Tel 401-942-1587; P.O. Box 8113, Cranston, RI 02920 (SAN 658-0270); *CIP.*

Carroll St., Pr., *(Carroll St Pr; 0-918869),* P.O. Box 70743, Sunnyvale, CA 94086 (SAN 670-073X); Dist. by: Dai Sing Distributing, P.O. Box 884, Feltor, CA 95018 (SAN 200-4879).

Carron, L.P., Pubs., *(Carron Pubs; 0-9607241),* 205 Ridgewood Rd., Easton, PA 18042 (SAN 238-9207).

Names

Carrousel Pubns., Inc., *(Carrousel Pubns; 0-939826)*, P.O. Box 225, Springfield, NJ 07081 (SAN 216-910X) Tel 201-379-2515.

Carrousels & Dreams Publishing, *(Carrousels D; 0-9615874)*, 4664 Pasadena, Sacramento, CA 95821 (SAN 697-0354) Tel 916-485-6831.

Carson, H. Glenn, Enterprises, Ltd., *(H G Carson Ent; 0-941620)*, Drawer 71, Deming, NM 88031 (SAN 239-1716) Tel 505-546-6100.

Carson, Ray, *(R Carson)*, 711 E. Camden Ave., El Cajon, CA 92020 (SAN 206-8222) Tel 619-440-7647.

Carson-Dellosa Publishing Co., Inc., *(Carson-Dellos; 0-88724)*, 207 Creek Ridge, Greensboro, NC 27406 (SAN 287-5896) Tel 919-274-1150.

†Carson Press, *(Carson Pr; 0-934360)*, 733 W. Carson St., Torrance, CA 90502 (SAN 213-2958) Tel 213-328-3180; *CIP.*

Carstens Pubns., Inc., *(Carstens Pubns; 0-911868)*, P.O. Box 700, Newton, NJ 07860 (SAN 281-3971) Tel 201-383-3355; Orders to: Shipments to UPS, Purolator Etc., Fredon Stringdale Rd., Fredon Township, Newton, NJ 07860-0700 (SAN 281-398X).

Carter, Virginia B., *(V B Carter; 0-9603862)*, Five Geyerwood Lane, St. Louis, MO 63131 (SAN 214-1132) Tel 314-645-0577.

Carter Craft Doll House, *(Carter Craft; 0-9604404)*, 5505 42nd Ave., Hyattsville, MD 20781 (SAN 203-624X) Tel 301-277-3051.

Carter's, Fred F., Free & Easy Publications, *(Carter's Free & Easy Pubns; 0-916391)*, 212 Race St., Suite 3A, Philadelphia, PA 19106 (SAN 295-7019) Tel 215-925-6766.

CartoGraphics, Inc., *(CartoGraphics; 0-937441)*, 2729-E Merrilee Dr., Fairfax, VA 22031 (SAN 659-0853) Tel 703-573-9342.

Cartwright, Nellie Parodi, *(N P Cartwright; 0-9601482)*, 4348 Via Frascati, Rancho Palos Verdes, CA 90274 (SAN 210-9883) Tel 213-833-7586.

Carver Publishing, Inc., *(Carver Pub; 0-915044)*, P.O. Box 6002, Hampton Institute, Hampton, VA 23668 (SAN 201-0143) Tel 804-727-5000.

Carves Cards, *(Carves)*, 179 S St., Chestnut Hill, MA 02167 (SAN 209-4177) Tel 617-469-9175.

Carvin Publishing, Inc., *(Carvin Pub; 0-9616390)*, P.O. Box 850200, New Orleans, LA 70185-0200 (SAN 659-0888) Tel 504-866-4351; 57 Neron Pl., New Orleans, LA 70118 (SAN 659-0896).

Casa Bautista de Publicaciones, Div. of Southern Baptist Convention, *(Casa Bautista; 0-311)*, P.O. Box 4255, 7000 Alabama St., El Paso, TX 79914 (SAN 220-0139) Tel 915-566-9656; Dist. by: Broadman Press, 127 Ninth Ave., N., Nashville, TN 37234 (SAN 201-937X) Tel 615-251-2606. *Imprints:* Carib Publications (Carib Pubns); Centre De Publications Baptistes (Centre De Pubns Baptistes); Editorial Mundo Hispano (Edit Mundo).

Casa de Unidad, *(Casa Unidad; 0-9615977)*, 1920 Scotten, Detroit, MI 48209 (SAN 697-2071) Tel 313-843-9598.

Cascade Photographics, *(Cascade Photo; 0-935818)*, 6906 Martin Way, Olympia, WA 98506 (SAN 213-7291) Tel 206-491-5473.

Cascade Publishing Co., The, *(Cascade Pub; 0-9610664)*, P.O. Box 27343, Seattle, WA 98125 (SAN 264-7249) Tel 206-668-2467.

Case Publishing See Lord Publishing

Case Western Reserve Univ., Dept. of Surgery, *(CWRU Dept Surgery; 0-9616613)*, 2065 Adelbert Rd., Cleveland, OH 44106 (SAN 660-9910) Tel 216-658-2620.

†Case Western Reserve Univ., Schl. of Law, *(Case Western)*, 11075 East Blvd., Cleveland, OH 44106 (SAN 227-0218) Tel 216-368-3280; *CIP.*

Casenotes Publishing Co., Inc., *(Casenotes Pub; 0-87457)*, P.O. Box 3946, Beverly Hills, CA 90212 (SAN 688-931X) Tel 213-475-1141; Dist. by: Law Distributors, Inc., 14415 S. Main St., Gardena, CA 90248 (SAN 212-3681) Tel 213-321-3275; Toll free: 800-421-1893.

Casino Gaming Seminars, *(Casino Gam Seminars)*, P.O. Box 718, Solvang, CA 93463 (SAN 239-5304).

Casino Publishing, *(Casino; 0-9611120)*, P.O. Box 54081, San Jose, CA 95154 (SAN 277-6626) Tel 408-365-1538.

Casino Research Productions, *(Casino Res; 0-916619)*, c/o Norby Walters Associates, 1650 Broadway-Suite 1410, New York, NY 10019 (SAN 296-4724) Tel 212-245-3939.

Casino Schools Pr. (CSI Pr.), *(CSI Pr; 0-913421)*, 1923 Bacharach Blvd., Atlantic City, NJ 08401 (SAN 285-9017) Tel 609-345-0303.

Caspers Wine Press, *(Caspers Wine; 0-933298)*, 15222 Magnolia Blvd., Suite 107, Sherman Oaks, CA 91403 (SAN 212-1492) Tel 818-788-1481.

Cass County Historical Commission, *(Cass County His; 0-9615358)*, P.O. Box 98, Vandalia, MI 49095 (SAN 695-2283) Tel 616-445-8651.

Cassady, Jim, & Fryar Calhoun, *(Cassady & Calhoun; 0-9613650)*, P.O. Box 3580, Berkeley, CA 94703 (SAN 670-7572) Tel 415-540-0800.

Cassandra Pr., *(Cassandra Pr; 0-9615875)*, P.O. Box 2044, Boulder, CO 80306 (SAN 697-0389) Tel 303-499-7651; 445 43rd St., Boulder, CO 80306 (SAN 697-0397); Dist. by: Bookpeople, 2929 Fifth St., Berkeley, CA 94710 (SAN 168-9517) Tel 415-549-3030; Dist. by: New Leaf Distributing, The, 1020 White St., SW, Atlanta, GA 30310 (SAN 169-1449) Tel 404-755-2665; Dist. by: Publishers Group West, 5855 Beaudry St., Emeryville, CA 94608 (SAN 202-8522) Tel 415-658-3453; Dist. by: Samuel Weiser, Inc., P.O. Box 612, York Beach, ME 03910 (SAN 202-9588) Tel 415-658-3453; Dist. by: Inland Bk. Co., P.O. Box 261, 22 Hemingway Ave., East Haven, CT 06512 (SAN 200-4151) Tel 203-467-4257; Dist. by: Nutri-Bks., Corp., P.O. Box 5793, Denver, CO 80223 (SAN 295-3404); Dist. by: Starlite, P.O. Box 20729, Reno, NV 89515 (SAN 131-1921) Tel 702-359-5676.

Cassell Communications Inc., *(Cassell Commun Inc; 0-942980)*, P.O. Box 9844, Fort Lauderdale, FL 33310 (SAN 240-138X) Tel 305-485-0795; Toll free: 800-351-9278; Toll free: 800-851-3392 (FL).

Cassette Concepts, Inc., *(Cassette Concepts; 0-935525)*, 28-A Lee Rd., Crozier, VA 23039 (SAN 696-2300) Tel 804-784-3978.

Cassizzi, Vic, *(Cassizzi)*, P.O. Box 8788, 710 Town Mtn. Rd., Asheville, NC 28804 (SAN 217-0922) Tel 704-253-5016.

Cassone Press, *(Cassone Pr; 0-9610082)*, 3028 Emerson Ave. S. Suite 3, Minneapolis, MN 55408 (SAN 268-6813) Tel 612-827-4774.

†Castalia Publishing Co., *(Castalia Pub; 0-916154)*, P.O. Box 1587, Eugene, OR 97440 (SAN 208-2403); *CIP.*

Castelli Graphics/Artspace, *(Castelli-Artspace; 0-9604140)*, 4 E. 77th St., New York, NY 10021 (SAN 214-1140).

Castenholz & Sons, *(Castenholz Sons; 0-9603498)*, 1055 Hartzell St., Pacific Palisades, CA 90272 (SAN 237-9449).

Castle & Cooke, Inc., *(Castle & Cooke; 0-9611512)*, 50 California St., San Francisco, CA 94111 (SAN 285-6816) Tel 415-986-3000.

Castle Bks., Inc., Div. of Book Sales, Inc., *(Castle Bks; 0-916693)*, P.O. Box 12506, Memphis, TN 38182 (SAN 204-4005); 233 Crestmere Pl., Memphis, TN 38112 (SAN 658-2575) Tel 901-276-1968.

Castle Distributors, *(Castle Dist)*, 316 Estes Dr., Chapel Hill, NC 27514 (SAN 239-3530) Tel 919-967-6439.

Castle Press See Dahlstrom, Grant, , Castle Press

Castle Pubns., Ltd., *(Castle Pubns; 0-943178)*, P.O. Box 580, Van Nuys, CA 91408 (SAN 240-3544) Tel 818-629-7823.

†Castle Publishing Co., *(Castle Pub Co; 0-9603372)*, P.O. Box 188, Portland, ME 04112 (SAN 209-2565) Tel 207-772-7851; *CIP.*

Castle Publishing Co., Ltd., *(Castle NY; 0-9611078)*, 505 W. End Ave., New York, NY 10024 (SAN 213-0343) Tel 212-362-5209.

†Castle Ventures, *(Castle Vent; 0-930211)*, 1111 Blanche St., No. 307, Pasadena, CA 91106 (SAN 670-7955) Tel 818-793-0935; *CIP.*

Castlemarsh Pubns., *(Castlemarsh; 0-942250)*, P.O. Box 30340, Savannah, GA 31410-0340 (SAN 240-8708) Tel 912-897-3455.

Castleton Publishing, *(Castleton Pub; 0-935885)*, P.O. Box 2197, Corona, CA 91718 (SAN 696-2319) Tel 714-734-8587; 1997 Starfire Ave., Corona, CA 91719-2946 (SAN 696-2327).

Castro, Mercedes, *(Castro; 0-9604748)*, 78-10 147th St., Apt. 3D, Flushing, NY 11367 (SAN 215-6113).

Cat-Tales Pr., *(Cat-Tales Pr; 0-917107)*, 229 St. Johns Pl., No. 2-D, Brooklyn, NY 11217 (SAN 655-6132) Tel 718-230-0724.

Catalan Communications, *(Catalan Communs; 0-87416)*, 43 E. 19th St., Suite 200, New York, NY 10003 (SAN 687-7753) Tel 212-254-4996; Dist. by: Bud Plant, Inc., 12555 Loma Rica Dr., No. 10, Grass Valley, CA 95945 (SAN 268-5086) Tel 916-273-9588; Dist. by: Glenwood Distributors, 1624 Vandalia, Collinsville, IL 62234 (SAN 158-1740); Dist. by: Capital City, 2827 Perry St., Madison, WI 53713 (SAN 200-5328).

Catalina, Lynn J., *(L J Catalina; 0-9613769)*, P.O. Box 20121, Albuquerque, NM 87154-0121 (SAN 679-0003); 7405 Luella Anne Dr. NE, Albuquerque, NM 87109 (SAN 662-2569) Tel 505-821-2151.

Catalyst, *(Catalyst; 0-89584)*, 250 Park Ave. S., New York, NY 10003 (SAN 203-6258) Tel 212-777-8900.

Catalyst Pubns., *(Catalyst Pubns; 0-931143)*, 143 Dolores St., San Francisco, CA 94103 (SAN 687-6498) Tel 415-552-5045.

Catan, Omero C., *(Catan; 0-9600618)*, 1901 SW 87th Terr., Ft. Lauderdale, FL 33324 (SAN 203-6266).

Catering to You, Inc., *(Catering; 0-935271)*, P.O. Box 2161, Del Mar, CA 92014 (SAN 695-7390) Tel 619-295-5801.

Cathedral of Knowledge, *(Cathedral of Knowledge)*, 235 NE 84th Ave., Portland, OR 97220 (SAN 211-6022) Tel 503-255-3859.

Cathedral Shop, The, *(Cathedral Shop; 0-915075)*, The Cathedral of St. John the Divine 112th St. & Amsterdam Ave., New York, NY 10025 (SAN 289-7792) Tel 212-222-7448.

Catholic Authors Press, *(Cath Authors; 0-910334)*, 1201 S. Kirkwood Rd., · Kirkwood, MO 63122 (SAN 203-6274) Tel 314-965-4801.

†Catholic Biblical Assn. of America, *(Catholic Bibl Assn; 0-915170)*, Catholic Univ., 620 Michigan Ave. NE, Washington, DC 20064 (SAN 210-7856) Tel 202-635-5519; *CIP.*

Catholic Bk. Publishing Co., *(Catholic Bk Pub; 0-89942)*, 257 W. 17th St., New York, NY 10011 (SAN 204-3432) Tel 212-243-4515.

Catholic Bulletin Publishing Co., *(Catholic Bulletin Pub; 0-935587)*, 244 Dayton Ave., St. Paul, MN 55102 (SAN 696-2378) Tel 612-291-4444; Dist. by: Paulist Pr., 997 MacArthur Blvd., Mahwah, NJ 07430 (SAN 202-5159) Tel 201-825-7300.

Catholic Charities, U.S.A., *(Catholic Charities; 0-938748)*, 1319 F St., NW, Washington, DC 20004 (SAN 202-0890) Tel 202-639-8400.

†Catholic Health Assn. of the U.S., *(Cath Health; 0-87125)*, 4455 Woodson Rd., St. Louis, MO 63134-0889 (SAN 201-968X) Tel 314-427-2500; *CIP.*

Catholic Library Assn., *(Cath Lib Assn; 0-87507)*, 461 W. Lancaster Ave., Haverford, PA 19041 (SAN 203-6282) Tel 215-649-5251.

Catholic News Publishing Co., *(Cath News Pub Co; 0-910635)*, 210 North Ave., New Rochelle, NY 10801 (SAN 268-7240) Tel 914-632-7771.

Catholic Peace Fellowship, Affil. of Fellowship of Reconciliation, *(Cath Peace Fell; 0-942252)*, 339 Lafayette St, New York, NY 10012 (SAN 225-6932) Tel 212-673-8990.

Catholic Pr. Assn., *(Cath Pr Assn)*, 119 N. Park Ave., Rockville Centre, NY 11570 (SAN 204-3335) Tel 516-766-3400.

†Catholic Univ. of America Pr., *(Cath U Pr; 0-8132)*, 620 Michigan Ave., NE, Washington, DC 20064 (SAN 203-6290) Tel 202-635-5052; Orders to: P.O. Box 4852, Hampden Sta., Baltimore, MD 21211 (SAN 203-6304) Tel 301-338-6953; *CIP.*

Catholics for a Free Choice, *(Cath Free Choice; 0-915365),* 2008 17th St. NW, Washington, DC 20009 (SAN 291-1116) Tel 202-638-1706.

Catmaral Publishing Co., *(Catmaral Pub Co; 0-9611598),* 2401 Burridge Rd., Baltimore, MD 21234 (SAN 284-9283) Tel 301-661-7389.

Catnip Pr., *(Catnip Pr; 0-9615475),* 117 Garth Rd., Apt. 2D, Scarsdale, NY 10583 (SAN 696-3161) Tel 914-472-2157.

†**Cato Institute,** *(Cato Inst; 0-932790),* 224 Second St., SE, Washington, DC 20003 (SAN 212-6095) Tel 202-546-0200; *CIP.*

Cato Pr., *(Cato Pr; 0-916621),* 2 Bryn Mawr Ave., Suite 205, P.O. Box 205, Bryn Mawr, PA 19010 (SAN 296-4767) Tel 215-527-3939.

Catoctin Press, *(Catoctin Pr; 0-914385),* 709 E. Main St., Middletown, MD 21769 (SAN 289-6117) Tel 301-371-6293.

Cat's Pajamas Press, *(Cats Pajamas; 0-916866),* 527 Lyman Ave., Oak Park, IL 60304 (SAN 207-8015) Tel 312-386-5137.

Catskill Art Supply, *(Catskill Art; 0-9600350),* 35 Mill Hill Rd., Woodstock, NY 12498 (SAN 205-4663).

Catskill Ctr. for Conservation & Development, Inc., *(Catskill Ctr Conserv; 0-9616712),* General Delivery, Arkville, NY 12406 (SAN 660-9953); Rte. 28, Arkville, NY 12406 (SAN 660-9961) Tel 914-586-2611.

Catspaw, Inc., *(Catspaw Inc; 0-939793),* P.O. Box 1123, Salida, CO 81201; 9395 County Rd. 160, Salida, CO 81201 Tel 303-539-3884.

Cauce, Cesar, Pubs. & Distributors, *(Cauce Pubs; 0-86686),* 44 Fifth Ave. Box 120, Brooklyn, NY 11217 (SAN 216-5287).

Causa International, *(Causa Intl; 0-933901),* 401 Fifth Ave., New York, NY 10016 (SAN 692-7793) Tel 212-684-6122.

Cavalier Press, *(Cavalier; 0-910338),* P.O. Box 111, Matteson, IL 60443 (SAN 203-6312).

Cavanaugh, *(Cavanaugh; 0-9614212),* 3833 Calvert St. NW, Washington, DC 20007 (SAN 687-0511) Tel 202-338-7257.

Cavco Pubns., *(Cavco Pubns; 0-932137),* 1829 E. Franklin St., Chapel Hill, NC 27514 (SAN 686-4260) Tel 919-929-0222; Orders to: Health Science Consortium, 103 Laurel Ave., Carrboro, NC 27510 (SAN 662-2690) Tel 919-942-8731.

Cave Bks., Subs. of Cave Research Foundation, *(Cave Bks MO; 0-939748),* 756 Harvard Ave., St. Louis, MO 63130 (SAN 216-7220) Tel 314-862-7646; Orders to: 901 Buford Pl., Nashville, TN 37204 (SAN 699-5195) Tel 615-269-3921.

†**Cavendish, Marshall, Corp.,** Subs. of Marshall Cavendish, Ltd., *(Marshall Cavendish; 0-85685; 0-86307),* 147 W. Merrick Rd., Freeport, NY 11520 (SAN 238-437X); Toll free: 800-821-9881; P.O. Box 410, Freeport, NY 11520 (SAN 658-0289) Tel 516-546-4200; *CIP.*

Caxton Club, *(Caxton Club; 0-940550),* 60 W. Walton St., Chicago, IL 60610 (SAN 216-3195) Tel 312-943-9090.

†**Caxton Printers, Ltd.,** *(Caxton; 0-87004),* P.O. Box 700, Caldwell, ID 83605 (SAN 201-9698) Tel 208-459-7421; Toll free: 800-451-8791 (Idaho only); *CIP.*

Cay-Bel Publishing Co., *(Cay-Bel; 0-941216),* 45 Center St., Brewer, ME 04412 (SAN 238-9215) Tel 207-989-3820.

Cayo Del Grullo Press, *(C Del Grullo; 0-9611604),* c/o History Dept., Texas A & I Univ., Kingsville, TX 78363 (SAN 284-9313) Tel 512-595-3603.

Cayucos Books, *(Cayucos; 0-9600372),* P.O. Box 2113, Monterey, CA 93940 (SAN 208-5887) Tel 408-375-5289.

Cayuse Pr., *(Cayuse Pr; 0-933529),* P.O. Box 9086, Berkeley, CA 94709 (SAN 693-8744) Tel 415-525-8515; Dist. by: Bookpeople, 2929 Fifth St., Berkeley, CA 94710 (SAN 168-9517) Tel 415-549-3030; Dist. by: The Distributors, 702 South Michigan, South Bend, IN 46618 (SAN 169-2488) Tel 219-232-8500.

CEBCO Standard Publishing, *(CEBCO; 0-88320; 0-8278),* 9 Kulick Rd., Fairfield, NJ 07006 (SAN 207-1568) Tel 201-575-8153.

Cecrle, Ruth Fay Straub, *(R F S Cecrle; 0-9616159),* 3308 Vernon Ave., Brookfield, IL 60513 (SAN 699-8399) Tel 312-485-7567.

Cedar Creek Pubs., *(Cedar Creek IN; 0-935316),* 2310 Sawmill Rd., Fort Wayne, IN 46825 (SAN 213-4780) Tel 219-637-3856.

Cedar Crest Bks., *(Cedar Crest Bks; 0-910291),* P.O. Box 15, Cochituate, MA 01778 (SAN 241-2837) Tel 617-491-0683.

Cedar Data Communications, *(Cedar Data; 0-916977),* 150 Pamela Rd., Monrovia, CA 91016 (SAN 655-6140) Tel 818-244-1387.

Cedar Elm Publishing Co., *(Cedar Elm Pub; 0-9617161),* 3312 Barklate Pk. Ct., Fort Worth, TX 76109 (SAN 663-1517) Tel 817-927-8160.

Cedar River Publishing Co., *(Cedar River Pub; 0-938047),* 5619 S. Augusta, Seattle, WA 98178 (SAN 660-997X) Tel 206-723-3127; Dist. by: Adams News Co., Inc., 1555 W. Galer St., Seattle, WA 98119 (SAN 169-8842) Tel 206-284-7617.

Cedars Pr., *(Cedars Pr; 0-936326),* P.O. Box 29351, Columbus, OH 43229 (SAN 223-3835).

Cedars Pr., The, *(Cedars WI; 0-917575),* Rte. 2, Box 336, Green Lake, WI 54941 (SAN 657-1301) Tel 414-294-6754.

Cedarshouse Pr., *(Cedarshouse; 0-912435),* 406 W. 28th St., Bryan, TX 77803 (SAN 265-2099) Tel 409-822-5615.

Cedarwinds Publishing Co., *(Cedarwinds; 0-915297),* P.O. Box 13618, Tallahassee, FL 32317 (SAN 212-1700) Tel 904-224-9261.

Cedarwood Pr., *(Cedarwood Pr; 0-930417),* 1115 E. Wylie St., Bloomington, IN 47401 (SAN 268-750X) Tel 812-332-3017.

Celcom Press, *(Celcom Pr),* 901 Boren Ave., Cabrini Medical Tower, Suite 1036, Seattle, WA 98104 (SAN 208-2411).

Celebrate Life Enterprises, *(Celebrate Life Ent; 0-9614507),* P.O. Box 95127, Seattle, WA 98145-2127 (SAN 691-7372) Tel 206-527-5406.

Celebrate One, *(Celebrate One; 0-937893),* 9422 SW 55th St., Portland, OR 97219 (SAN 659-4328) Tel 503-246-1591.

Celebrity Pr., Inc., *(Celebrity Pr; 0-9607412),* 6656 W. Fifth St., Los Angeles, CA 90048 (SAN 239-1759) Tel 213-653-4012.

Celestial Arts Pub. Co., Subs. of Ten Speed Press, *(Celestial Arts; 0-912310; 0-89087),* P.O. Box 7327, Berkeley, CA 94707 (SAN 159-8333) Tel 415-524-1801; Toll free: 800-841-2665.

Celestial Gems, *(Celestial Gems; 0-914154),* 404 State St., Centralia, WA 98531 (SAN 201-1948) Tel 206-736-5083.

Celestial Gifts, *(Celestial Gifts),* Rd. 1, Box 150, Chestertown, MD 21620 (SAN 219-1431) Tel 301-778-0309.

Celestial Pr., *(Celestial Pr; 0-910340),* 441 NE 24th St., Boca Raton, FL 33432 (SAN 203-6320) Tel 305-368-1309.

Celia Totus Enterprises Inc., *(Celia Totus Enter; 0-931363),* P.O. Box 539, Toppenish, WA 98948 (SAN 682-5567) Tel 509-865-2480; Rte. 1, Box 1207, Toppenish, WA 98948 (SAN 662-2593).

Celilo Pubns., *(Celilo Pubns; 0-9614529),* 6819 SW 32nd Ave., Portland, OR 97219 (SAN 689-738X) Tel 503-244-2688.

Cellar Bk. Shop, *(Cellar),* 18090 Wyoming, Detroit, MI 48221 (SAN 213-4330) Tel 313-861-1776.

†**Celo Pr.,** *(Celo Pr; 0-914064),* 1901 Hannah Branch Rd., Burnsville, NC 28714 (SAN 201-971X) Tel 704-675-4925; *CIP.*

Celorio, Cesar Alberto, *(C A Celorio; 0-918168),* 28-02 Ditmars Blvd., Astoria, NY 11105 (SAN 210-1858) Tel 718-278-7890.

Celtic Heritage Pr., Inc., *(Celt Heritage Pr; 0-9614753),* 59-10 Queens Blvd., No. 9B, Woodside, NY 11377 (SAN 692-929X) Tel 718-478-8162.

Cembura, Al, *(Cembura; 0-912454),* 139 Arlington Ave., Berkeley, CA 94707 (SAN 201-9728) Tel 415-524-0478.

CeMoMedServ Pubns., Div. of Central Missouri Medical Servs., *(CeMoMedServ; 0-916109),* 516 E. Capitol Ave. No. E, Jefferson City, MO 65101 (SAN 294-9083) Tel 314-634-2925; Dist. by: Cowley Distributing, Inc., 732 Heisinger Rd., Jefferson City, MO 65101 (SAN 169-426X) Tel 314-636-6511.

Cenotto Pubns., *(Cenotto Pubns; 0-938121),* P.O. Box 623, Jackson, CA 95642 (SAN 660-9988); 557 Clinton Rd., Jackson, CA 95642 (SAN 660-9996) Tel 209-223-3196.

Centaur Bks., Inc., *(Centaur; 0-87818),* 799 Broadway, New York, NY 10003 (SAN 201-7725) Tel 212-677-1720.

Centennial Photo Service, *(Centennial Photo Serv; 0-931838),* Rte. 3, Box 1125, Grantsburg, WI 54840 (SAN 212-6443) Tel 715-689-2153; Dist. by: Watson-Guptill, 1515 Broadway, New York, NY 10036 (SAN 282-5384) Tel 212-764-7457.

Centennial Pr., Div. of Cliff's Notes, Inc., *(Centennial; 0-8220),* P.O. Box 80728, Lincoln, NE 68501 (SAN 203-6339) Tel 402-477-6971; Toll free: 800-228-4078.

Centennial Reproductions, *(Centennial Repros; 0-9606474),* 27 E. Cache la Poudre, Colorado Springs, CO 80707 (SAN 239-4162).

Center City Financial Group, *(Center City; 0-937341),* 8637 Navajo Rd., San Diego, CA 92119 (SAN 659-0950) Tel 619-465-7400.

Center for Action on Endangered Species, *(Ctr Action Endangered),* 175 W Main St, Ayer, MA 01432 (SAN 231-844X).

†**Center for Advanced Psychic Research & Development, The,** *(Ctr Adv Psychic Res; 0-9611788),* P.O. Box 1000, Cutchogue, NY 11935 (SAN 285-2284) Tel 516-727-4270; *CIP.*

Center for African Art, The, *(Center African Art; 0-9614587),* 54 E. 68th St., New York, NY 10021 (SAN 691-7712) Tel 212-861-1200.

Center For African Studies, *(Ctr for African; 0-932219),* P.O. Box 689, New York, NY 10030 (SAN 686-6042) Tel 212-678-7184.

Center for Afro-American Studies at UCLA, *(UCLA CAAS; 0-934934),* Univ. of California at Los Angeles, 3111 Campbell Hall, 405 Hilgard Ave., Los Angeles, CA 90024 (SAN 214-2899) Tel 213-825-3528; Orders to: CAAS Pubns., Publishers Services, P.O. Box 2510, Novato, CA 94948 (SAN 661-9711) Tel 415-883-3140.

Center for Agricultural & Rural Development, *(Ctr Agri & Rural Dev; 0-936911),* Iowa State Univ., 578 Heady Hall, Ames, IA 50010 (SAN 658-3121) Tel 515-294-1183.

†**Center for American Archeology Pr.,** *(Ctr Amer Arche; 0-942118),* Kampsville Archeological Ctr., Kampsville, IL 62053 (SAN 237-9457) Tel 618-653-4532; Orders to: P.O. Box 366, Kampsville, IL 62053 (SAN 694-9517) Tel 618-653-4316; *CIP.*

Center for Analysis of Public Issues, *(Ctr Analysis Public Issues; 0-943136),* 16 Vandeventer Ave., Princeton, NJ 08540 (SAN 209-3227) Tel 609-924-9750.

†**Center for Applications of Psychological Type, Inc.,** *(Ctr Applications Psych; 0-935652),* 2720 NW Sixth St., Gainesville, FL 32609 (SAN 213-9162) Tel 904-375-0160; *CIP.*

Center for Applied Linguistics, *(Ctr Appl Ling; 0-87281),* 1118 22nd St., NW, Washington, DC 20037 (SAN 281-3998) Tel 202-429-9292; Dist. by: Harcourt Brace Jovanovich, International Div., Orlando, FL 32887 (SAN 200-2299) Tel 305-345-3800.

†**Center for Applied Research in Education, Inc., The,** Subs. of Prentice-Hall, *(Ctr Appl Res; 0-87628),* Englewood Cliffs, NJ 07632 (SAN 206-6424) Tel 201-592-2494; Orders to: P.O. Box 430, West Nyack, NY 10995 (SAN 206-6432) Tel 201-767-5030; *CIP.*

†**Center for Arts Information,** Subs. of Clearinghouse for Arts Information, Inc., *(Ctr for Arts Info; 0-935654),* 625 Broadway, New York, NY 10012 (SAN 282-7034) Tel 212-677-7548; *CIP.*

Center for Bio-Gerontology, The, *(Ctr Bio-Gerontology; 0-937777),* 8760 Sunset Blvd., Los Angeles, CA 90069 (SAN 659-3208) Tel 213-652-5731.

Center for Black Studies, *(Ctr Black Studies; 0-939242),* Wayne State University, Detroit, MI 48202 (SAN 216-5171) Tel 313-577-2321.

Center for Black Success, The, *(Ctr Black Success; 0-9616936),* 250 W. 54th St., Suite 811, New York, NY 10019 (SAN 661-8375) Tel 212-541-7600.

Center for Business and Economic Research, *(Center Bus Eco Res; 0-931497),* Western Illinois University, Macomb, IL 61455 (SAN 683-2180) Tel 309-298-1594.

Names

Center for Business Information, *(Ctr Busn Info; 0-936936)*, P.O. Box 2404, Meriden, CT 06450 (SAN 214-2902) Tel 203-481-0888.

†Center for Canal History & Technology, *(Ctr Canal Hist; 0-930973)*, P.O. Box 877, Easton, PA 18044-0877 (SAN 678-8831) Tel 215-250-6700; *CIP.*

Center for Communications Management, The (CCMI), *(C C M I)*, 76 Arch St., Ramsey, NJ 07446 (SAN 239-5185) Tel 201-825-3311.

Center for Communications Ministry, *(Ctr Comm Ministry; 0-9606188)*, 1962 S. Shenandoah, Los Angeles, CA 90034 (SAN 220-293X) Tel 213-559-2944.

Center for Community Economic Development, *(Center Community)*, P.O. 13065, Washington, DC 20009 (SAN 217-6742) Tel 202-659-3986.

Center for Computer Assisted Research in the Humanities, *(Ctr Comp Assisted; 0-936943)*, 525 Middlefield Rd., Suite 120, Menlo Park, CA 94025 (SAN 658-6708) Tel 415-322-7050.

Center for Computer/Law, *(Ctr Comp Law; 0-935200)*, P.O. Box 3549, Manhattan Beach, CA 90266 (SAN 223-7008).

Center for Conflict Resolution, *(Ctr Conflict Resol; 0-941492)*, 731 State St., Madison, WI 53703 (SAN 239-0736) Tel 608-255-0479.

Center for Connecticut Studies, *(Ctr CT Studies)*, Eastern Connecticut State Univ., Willimantic, CT 06226 (SAN 212-4874) Tel 203-456-2231.

Center for Contemporary Poetry, Div. of Murphy Library, University of Wisconsin at La Crosse, *(Ctr Cont Poetry; 0-917540)*, Murphy Library, Univ. of Wisconsin at La Crosse, La Crosse, WI 54601 (SAN 201-906X) Tel 608-785-8511.

Center for Creative Leadership, Affil. of Smith Richardson Foundation, *(Ctr Creat Leader; 0-912879)*, P.O. Box P-1, 5000 Laurinda Dr., Greensboro, NC 27402-1660 (SAN 282-9924) Tel 919-288-7210.

Center for Creative Life Pubns., *(Center Creative Life; 0-9614588)*, 415 Ave. A, E., Rm. 2, Bismarck, ND 58501 (SAN 691-7747) Tel 701-224-0102.

Center for Defense Information, *(CDI)*, 1500 Massachusetts Ave., Washington, DC 20005 (SAN 260-3322) Tel 202-862-0700.

Center for Economic Analysis *See* CEA Bks. Pr.

Center for Economic Conversion, *(Ctr Econ Conversion; 0-930471)*, 222c View St., Mountain View, CA 94041 (SAN 670-8951) Tel 415-968-8798.

Center for Education & Research in Free Enterprise, *(Ctr Educ Res; 0-86599)*, Texas A&M Univ., College Station, TX 77843 (SAN 215-0646).

Center for Educational Alternatives, *(Ctr Ed Alternatives; 0-943346)*, 908 Ridgecrest Circle, Anaheim, CA 92807 (SAN 240-5245) Tel 714-974-6476.

Center for Entrepreneurship & Small Business Management, *(Wichita Ctr Entrep SBM; 0-941958)*, Wichita State Univ., P.O. Box 48, Wichita, KS 67208 (SAN 239-5193).

Center for Environmental Education, *(Ctr Env Educ; 0-9615294)*, 624 Ninth St., NW, Washington, DC 20001 (SAN 694-566X) Tel 202-737-3600.

Center for Futures Education, Inc., *(Ctr Futures Ed; 0-915513)*, P.O. Box 489, Cedar Falls, IA 50613 (SAN 291-1132) Tel 319-277-7529.

Center for Health Information, *(Ctr Health Info; 0-932567)*, P.O. Box 4636, Foster City, CA 94404 (SAN 687-4754) Tel 415-345-6669.

Center for Holocaust Studies, Documentation & Research, *(Ctr Holo; 0-9609970)*, 1610 Ave. J, Brooklyn, NY 11230 (SAN 268-7755) Tel 718-338-6494.

Center for Independent Living, Inc., *(Center Independent; 0-942846)*, Access Project, 2539 Telegraph Ave., Berkeley, CA 94704 (SAN 240-2025) Tel 415-841-4776.

Center for Information Sharing, *(Ctr Info Sharing; 0-939532)*, 77 N. Washington St., Boston, MA 02114 (SAN 216-3489) Tel 617-742-3222.

Center for Innovation in Education, *(Ctr Innovation; 0-9614646)*, 19225 Vineyard Ln., Saratoga, CA 95070 (SAN 691-8530) Tel 408-867-6873.

Center for International Policy, Subs. of Fund for Peace, *(Ctr Intl Policy)*, 236 Massachusetts Ave., NE, Washington, DC 20002 (SAN 225-6592) Tel 202-544-4666.

Center for International Training & Education, *(CITE; 0-938960)*, 777 United Nations Plaza, Suite 9-A, New York, NY 10017 (SAN 217-0957).

Center for Judaic-Christian Studies, *(Ctr Judaic-Christ Studies; 0-918873)*, P.O. Box 202707, Austin, TX 78720 (SAN 669-9979) Tel 512-343-3101.

Center for Jurisdictional Studies, *(Ctr Juris Stud; 0-9614259)*, 323 E. William St., Suite 205, Ann Arbor, MI 48104 (SAN 687-1208) Tel 313-582-4782.

Center for Korean Studies, Univ. of Hawaii at Manoa, *(Ctr Korean U HI at Manoa; 0-917536)*, 1881 East-West Rd., Honolulu, HI 96822 (SAN 208-0044) Tel 808-949-1833.

Center for Land Grant Studies, The, *(Ctr Land Grant; 0-9605202)*, 136 Grant Ave., Santa Fe, NM 87501 (SAN 216-3497).

Center for Latin American Studies & Howard-Tilton Memorial Library, *(Tulane U Ctr Lat; 0-9603212)*, Tulane Univ., New Orleans, LA 70118 (SAN 287-7732).

Center for Law & Education, Incorporated, *(Ctr Law & Ed; 0-912585)*, 14 Appian Way, 6th Flr., Cambridge, MA 02138 (SAN 237-6431) Tel 617-495-4666.

Center for Law-Related Education, *(Ctr Law Related; 0-937709)*, 4400 Cathedral Oaks Rd., Santa Barbara, CA 93160 (SAN 659-3216) Tel 805-964-4711.

†Center for Leadership Studies, Div. of Leadership Studies, Inc., *(Ctr Leadership; 0-931619)*, 230 W. Third Ave., Escondido, CA 92025 (SAN 683-7131) Tel 619-741-6595; Dist. by: University Assocs., Inc., 8517 Production Ave., San Diego, CA 92121 (SAN 203-333X) Tel 619-578-5900; *CIP.*

Center for Marital & Sexual Studies, *(Ctr Marital Sexual; 0-9600626)*, 5251 Los Altos Plaza, Long Beach, CA 90815 (SAN 203-8587) Tel 213-597-4425.

Center for Mazzei Studies, *(Mazzei; 0-916322)*, c/o Kraus Reprint & Periodicals, Rte. 100, Millwood, NY 10546 (SAN 201-0542) Tel 914-762-2200.

†Center for Migration Studies, *(Ctr Migration; 0-913256; 0-934733)*, 209 Flagg Pl., Staten Island, NY 10304 (SAN 281-4013) Tel 718-351-8800; *CIP.*

Center for Modern Psychoanalytic Studies, *(CMPS NYC; 0-916850)*, 16 W. Tenth St., New York, NY 10011 (SAN 208-7537) Tel 212-260-7050.

Center for National Policy Review, *(Ctr Natl Pol Rev)*, 1025 Vermont Ave., NW, Suite 360, Washington, DC 20005 (SAN 237-6350) Tel 202-783-5640.

Center for National Security Studies, *(Ctr Natl Security; 0-86566)*, 122 Maryland Ave. NE, Washington, DC 20002 (SAN 215-2991) Tel 202-544-1681.

Center for Neo-Hellenic Studies, *(Ctr Neo Hellenic; 0-932242)*, 1010 W. 22nd St., Austin, TX 78705 (SAN 211-8467) Tel 512-477-5526.

†Center for Occupational Hazards, *(Ctr Occupational Hazards; 0-918875)*, 5 Beekman St., New York, NY 10038 (SAN 669-9936) Tel 212-227-6220; *CIP.*

Center for Occupational Research & Development, *(Ctr Res & Dev; 1-55502)*, 601C Lake Air Dr., Waco, TX 76710 (SAN 694-2121) Tel 817-772-8756.

Center for Philosophy & Public Policy, Div. of University of Maryland, *(Ctr Philos & Pub Policy)*, Univ. of Maryland, Woods Hall, Rm. 0123, College Park, MD 20742 (SAN 225-7009) Tel 301-454-4103.

Center for Polish Studies & Culture, Div. of Orchard Lake Schls., *(Ctr Polish; 0-9615564)*, Orchard Lake Schls., 3355 Indian Trail, Orchard Lake, MI 48033 (SAN 696-2440) Tel 313-682-1885.

†Center for Professional Advancement, *(Ctr Prof Adv; 0-86563)*, 197 Rt. 18, P.O. Box H, E. Brunswick, NJ 08816 (SAN 214-185X) Tel 201-249-1400; *CIP.*

Center for Professional Development, *(Center Prof; 0-9608190)*, P.O. Box 1283, USU, Logan, UT 84322 (SAN 240-2033) Tel 801-750-1810.

Center for Public Advocacy Research, Inc., *(Ctr Pub; 0-943138)*, 12 W. 37th St., New York, NY 10018 (SAN 240-5253) Tel 212-736-7440.

Center for Reformation Research, *(Center Reform; 0-910345)*, 6477 San Bonita Ave., St. Louis, MO 63105 (SAN 241-2845) Tel 314-727-6655.

Center for Renewable Resources, *(Ctr Renew Resources; 0-937446)*, 1001 Connecticut Ave., NW, Suite 638, Washington, DC 20036 (SAN 223-9876) Tel 202-466-6880.

Center for Research & Documentation on World Language Problems, *(CRDWLP; 0-934973)*, 777 United Nations Plaza, New York, NY 10017 (SAN 695-118X) Tel 212-687-7041.

Center for Research in Ambulatory Health Care Administration, Affil. of Medical Group Management Association, *(Ctr Res Ambulatory; 0-933948)*, 1355 S. Colorado Blvd., Suite 900, Denver, CO 80222 (SAN 230-9459) Tel 303-753-1111.

Center for Research in Social Change, *(Ctr Res Soc Chg; 0-89937)*, Emory Univ., Fred Roberts Crawford Witness to the Holocaust Project, Atlanta, GA 30322 (SAN 211-5247) Tel 404-727-7525; Dist. by: Witness to the Holocaust Project, Emory University, Atlanta, GA 30322 (SAN 264-5025) Tel 404-727-7525.

Ctr. for Research Libraries, The, *(Ctr Res Lib; 0-932486)*, 6050 S. Kenwood Ave., Chicago, IL 60637 (SAN 225-3348) Tel 312-955-4545.

Center for Research on Population & Security, *(CRPS; 0-937307)*, 322 Azalea Dr., Chapel Hill, NC 27514 (SAN 658-7712) Tel 919-933-7491; P.O. Box 13067, Research Triangle Park, NC 27709 (SAN 658-7720).

Center for Responsive Politics, *(Ctr Politics; 0-939715)*, 2001 O St. NW, Washington, DC 20036 (SAN 663-6144) Tel 202-857-0044.

Center for Responsive Psychology, *(Ctr Respon Psych; 1-55524)*, Brooklyn College, CUNY, Brooklyn, NY 11210 (SAN 225-7165) Tel 718-780-5960.

Center for Sacred Healing Arts Publishing Co., *(Ctr Sacred Healing; 0-936901)*, 1329 W. 37th Dr., Los Angeles, CA 90007 (SAN 658-5558) Tel 213-733-1272.

Center for Science in the Public Interest, *(Ctr Sci Public; 0-89329)*, 1501 16th St. NW, Washington, DC 20036 (SAN 207-6543) Tel 202-332-9110.

Center for SE Asian Studies, Northern Illinois Univ., *(North Ill U Ctr SE Asian)*, Dist. by: Cellar Book Shop, 18090 Wyoming, Detroit, MI 48221 (SAN 213-4330) Tel 313-861-1776.

Center for Self-Sufficiency Publishing, *(Ctr Self Suff; 0-910811)*, Box 7234, Houston, TX 77248 (SAN 698-1828).

Ctr. for Sexual Communication, *(Ctr Sexual Comm)*, 195 Claremont, Suite 374, Long Beach, CA 90803 (SAN 687-6595).

†Center for Southern Folklore, *(Ctr South Folklore; 0-89267)*, 1216 Peabody Ave., P.O. Box 40105, Memphis, TN 38104 (SAN 209-2247) Tel 901-726-4205; *CIP.*

Center for Study of Responsive Law, *(Ctr Responsive Law; 0-936758)*, P.O. Box 19367, Washington, DC 20036 (SAN 281-403X) Tel 202-387-8030.

Center For Sutton Movement Writing, Incorporated, The, *(Ctr Sutton Movement; 0-914336)*, P.O. Box 7344, Newport Beach, CA 92658-7344 (SAN 203-154X) Tel 714-644-8342.

Center for Technology, Environment, & Development, *(Ctr Tech Environ; 0-939436)*, Clark Univ., 950 Main St., Worcester, MA 01610 (SAN 216-5708).

Center for Thanatology Research & Education, Inc., *(Ctr Thanatology; 0-930194)*, 391 Atlantic Ave., Brooklyn, NY 11217-1701 (SAN 210-7414) Tel 718-858-3026; Orders to: P.O. Box 989, Brooklyn, NY 11202-1202 (SAN 215-0425).

Center for the Art of Living, Subs. of Training Systems, *(Ctr Art Living; 0-9602552)*, P.O. Box 788, Evanston, IL 60204 (SAN 212-8926) Tel 312-864-8664.

Center for the History of American Needlework, *(Ctr Hist Am Needle; 0-934074)*, P.O. Box 359, Valencia, PA 16059 (SAN 225-3003) Tel 412-586-5325.

Center for the Scientific Study of Religion, *(Ctr Sci Study; 0-913348)*, 5757 University Ave., Chicago, IL 60637 (SAN 203-8749) Tel 312-752-5757.

Center for the Study of Aging, Inc., *(Ctr Study Aging; 0-937829)*, 706 Madison Ave., Albany, NY 12208 (SAN 659-4344) Tel 518-465-6927.

Center for the Study of Christian Values in Literature, *(BYU CSCVL; 0-939555)*, Brigham Young University, Center for the Study of Christian Values in Literature, 3134 JKHB, Provo, UT 84602 (SAN 663-4257) Tel 801-378-2304.

Center for the Study of Elephants, The, *(Ctr Study Elephants; 0-942074)*, P.O. Box 4444, Carson, CA 90749 (SAN 239-5177).

Center for the Study of Language & Information, *(Ctr Study Language; 0-937073)*, Stanford Univ., Ventura Hall, Stanford, CA 94305 (SAN 658-5582) Tel 415-723-1712; Dist. by: Univ. of Chicago Pr., 5801 Ellis Ave., 3rd Flr., Chicago, IL 60637 (SAN 202-5280) Tel 312-962-7723.

†Center for the Study of Multiple Birth, *(Ctr Multiple Birth; 0-932254)*, 333 E. Superior St., Suite 476, Chicago, IL 60611 (SAN 274-1997) Tel 312-266-9093; *CIP.*

Center for the Study of Services, *(Ctr Study Serv; 0-9611432)*, 806 15th St. NW, Suite 925, Washington, DC 20005 (SAN 287-2862) Tel 202-347-9612.

Center for the Study of the Presidency, *(Ctr Study Presidency; 0-938204)*, 208 E. 75 St., New York, NY 10021 (SAN 225-6339) Tel 212-249-1200.

Center for Traditionalist Orthodox Studies, *(Ctr Trad Orthodox; 0-911165)*, P.O. Box 398, Etna, CA 96027 (SAN 287-0029) Tel 916-467-3228; c/o St. Gregory Palamas Monastery, P.O. Box 398, Etna, CA 96027 (SAN 287-0037).

Center for Transnational Accounting & Financial Research, *(Ctr Trans Acct Fin; 0-913795)*, Univ. of Connecticut, U-41A, Storrs, CT 06268 (SAN 291-9273).

Center for U. S.-Mexican Studies, *(Ctr Mex Studies; 0-935391)*, Univ. of California, San Diego, CA 92093 (SAN 696-2483) Tel 619-452-4503; 10111 N. Torrey Pines Rd., La Jolla, CA 92037 (SAN 696-2491).

†Center for Urban Policy Research, *(Ctr Urban Pol Res; 0-88285)*, Rutgers Univ., Kilmer Campus, Bldg. 4051, New Brunswick, NJ 08903 (SAN 206-6297) Tel 201-932-3133; *CIP.*

Center for Western Studies, *(Ctr Western Studies; 0-931170)*, Augustana College, Box 727, Sioux Falls, SD 57197 (SAN 211-4844) Tel 605-336-4007.

Center for Women's Studies & Services, *(Ctr Women's Studies; 0-9600856)*, 2467 E St., San Diego, CA 92102 (SAN 225-7297) Tel 619-233-8984.

Center Gallery of Bucknell University, *(Cntr Gallery Buck Univ; 0-916279)*, Bucknell Univ., Center Gallery, Lewisburg, PA 17837 (SAN 295-706X) Tel 717-524-3792.

Center of Concern, *(Center Concern; 0-934255)*, 3700 13th St., NE, Washington, DC 20017 (SAN 268-8115) Tel 202-635-2757.

Center Pr., *(Center Pr; 0-934320)*, 2045 Francisco St., Berkeley, CA 94709 (SAN 213-0351) Tel 415-526-8373.

†Center Pubns., Div. of Zen Center of Los Angeles, Inc., *(Center Pubns; 0-916820)*, 923 S. Normandie Ave., Los Angeles, CA 90006 (SAN 208-9386) Tel 213-387-2351; Dist. by: Bookpeople, 2929 Fifth St., Berkeley, CA 94710 (SAN 168-9517) Tel 415-549-3030; *CIP.*

Center Pubns., Inc., *(Center Pubns Inc; 0-942452)*, 2025 Zonal Ave., Los Angeles, CA 90033 (SAN 238-1478) Tel 213-224-7384.

Centerline Pr., *(Centerline; 0-913111)*, 2005 Palo Verde, Suite 325, Long Beach, CA 90815 (SAN 283-9369) Tel 213-421-0220.

Centerpoint Pr., *(Centerpoint Pr; 0-937897)*, P.O. Box 4771, Bryan, TX 77805 (SAN 659-4352) Tel 409-775-7887.

Centerstream Publishing, *(Centerstream Pub; 0-931759)*, P.O. Box 5066, Fullerton, CA 92635 (SAN 683-8022) Tel 714-738-6489.

Centra Pubns., *(Centra Pubns; 0-9617288)*, 4705 Laurel St., San Diego, CA 92105 (SAN 663-6136) Tel 619-263-7942.

Central Agency For Jewish Education, *(Central Agency; 0-930029)*, 4200 Biscayne Blvd., Miami, FL 33137 (SAN 669-747X) Tel 305-576-4030.

Central America Resource Ctr., *(Central Am Res; 0-938049)*, P.O. Box 2327, Austin, TX 78768 (SAN 661-0005); 600 W. 28th St., Suite 203, Austin, TX 78705 (SAN 661-0013) Tel 512-476-9841.

Central Coast Women's Yellow Pages, *(C C W Y P; 0-934335)*, 301 S. Miller, Suite 214, Santa Maria, CA 93454 (SAN 693-6067) Tel 805-928-8563; Dist. by: Tri-County News, 1376 W. Main St., Santa Maria, CA 93454 (SAN 169-0345) Tel 805-925-6541.

Central Committee for Conscientious Objectors, *(CCCO; 0-933368)*, 2208 South St., Philadelphia, PA 19146 (SAN 207-9852) Tel 215-545-4626; 1251 Second Ave., San Francisco, CA 94122 (SAN 680-0238) Tel 415-566-0500.

†Central Conference of American Rabbis, *(Central Conf; 0-916694)*, 21 E. 40th St., New York, NY 10016 (SAN 204-3262) Tel 212-684-4990; *CIP.*

Central Electrial Railfans' Assn., *(Central Electric; 0-915348)*, P.O. Box 503, Chicago, IL 60690 (SAN 207-3110) Tel 312-346-3723.

Central Florida Voters Congress, *(Central FL Voters)*, P.O. Box 1172, Orlando, FL 32802 (SAN 212-4882).

Central Sephardic Jewish Community of America, Inc., Women's Div., *(Women's Div; 0-9611294)*, 8 W. 70th St., New York, NY 10023 (SAN 283-9911) Tel 212-873-2100.

Centralia Press, *(Centralia Pr; 0-9611008)*, P.O. Box 607, Floral Park, NY 11002 (SAN 283-9857) Tel 516-328-0239.

Centre De Publications Baptistes *See* Casa Bautista de Publicaciones

Centre Enterprise, The, *(Centre Ent; 0-932876)*, Box 640506 Station "O", San Francisco, CA 94164-0506 (SAN 212-3401) Tel 415-673-1377.

Centre for Agricultural Publishing & Documentation *See* Unipub a

Centro de Investigaciones Regionales de Mesoamerica, Affil. of Plumsock Mesoamerican Studies, *(CIRMA; 0-910443)*, P.O. Box 38, S. Woodstock, VT 05071 (SAN 260-0269) Tel 802-457-1199.

Centurion Press, *(Centurion Pr)*, Drawer 62, Los Angeles, CA 90028 (SAN 206-4839).

Centurion Pr., *(Centurion Pr AZ; 0-935527)*, 4360 N. Bear Claw Way, Tucson, AZ 85749 (SAN 696-2580) Tel 602-749-2245.

Century Bookbindery, *(Century Bookbindery; 0-89984)*, P.O. Box 6471, Philadelphia, PA 19145 (SAN 209-2441) Tel 215-583-4550.

Century Communications, Inc., *(Century Comm; 0-930264)*, 5520 W. Touhy, Suite G, Skokie, IL 60077 (SAN 208-1911) Tel 312-676-4060.

Century Farms Heritage Committee, *(Century Farms; 0-9615152)*, 743 17th St., SE, Owatonna, MN 55060 (SAN 694-3381) Tel 507-455-1674.

Century One Pr., *(Century One; 0-937080)*, 2325 E. Platte Ave., Colorado Springs, CO 80909 (SAN 214-3534) Tel 303-471-1322.

Century Press, *(Century Pr; 0-915680)*, 412 N. Hudson, Oklahoma City, OK 73102 (SAN 207-382X).

Century Publisher, *(Century Pub; 0-9614739)*, Box 204, Holts Summit, MO 65043 (SAN 692-7246) Tel 314-896-4968; Dist. by: Cowley Distributing Inc., 732 Heisinger Rd., Jefferson City, MO 65101 (SAN 169-426X).

Cerberus Assocs., Inc., *(Cerberus Assocs; 0-936397)*, 9 Willow St., Douglaston, NY 11363 (SAN 698-1577) Tel 718-224-4343.

†Cerberus Bk. Co., The, *(Cerberus; 0-933590)*, 2009 North Mckinley, Hobbsragg, NH 88240 (SAN 213-8352) Tel 505-393-5612; *CIP.*

Ceres Pr., *(Ceres Pr; 0-9606138)*, Box 87, Woodstock, NY 12498 (SAN 217-0949) Tel 914-679-8561; Dist. by: Bookpeople, 2929 Fifth St., Berkeley, CA 94710 (SAN 168-9517) Tel 415-549-3030; Toll free: 800-227-1516; Dist. by: Great Tradition, The, 750 Adrian Way, Suite 111, San Rafael, CA 94903 (SAN 200-5743) Tel 415-492-9382; Dist. by: New Leaf Ditributing, The, 1020 White St., SW, Atlanta, GA 30310 (SAN 169-1449) Tel 404-755-2665; Toll free: 800-241-3829; Dist. by: Nutri-Books Corp., P.O. Box 5793, Denver, CO 80223 (SAN 295-3404); Toll free: 800-525-9030.

Certain Ethnic Publishing, *(Certain Ethnic; 0-9615918)*, c/o Malrite Creative Services, 1200 Statler Office Tower, Cleveland, OH 44115 (SAN 697-0303) Tel 216-781-3010.

Certified Feelings, Inc., *(Certified Feelings; 0-936903)*, P.O. Box 799 Times Square Sta., New York, NY 10108 (SAN 658-5663).

Cerulean Pr., *(Cerulean Pr; 0-917458)*, c/o Kent Pubns., 18301 Halsted St., Northbridge, CA 91325 (SAN 209-0597) Tel 818-349-2080.

Cesareans/Support, Education & Concern, *(Cesareans Ed)*, 22 Forest Rd., Framingham, MA 01701 (SAN 268-5698) Tel 617-877-8266.

Chaco Pr., *(Chaco Pr; 0-9616019)*, 5218 Donna Maria Ln., La Canada-Flintridge, CA 91011 (SAN 697-1784) Tel 818-952-0108; Orders to: Treasure Chest, P.O. Box 5250, Tucson, AZ 85703 (SAN 662-3913) Tel 602-623-9558; Toll free: 800-223-5369.

†Chadwyck-Healey, Inc., *(Chadwyck-Healey; 0-914146; 0-89887; 0-85964)*, 1021 Prince St., Alexandria, VA 22314 (SAN 282-3306) Tel 203-683-4890; *CIP.*

Chaffey Communities Cultural Center, *(Chaffey Commun Cult Ctr; 0-9603586)*, P.O. Box 772, Upland, CA 91785 (SAN 213-8360) Tel 714-982-8010.

†Chalfant Pr., Inc., *(Chalfant Pr; 0-912494)*, P.O. Box 787, Bishop, CA 93514 (SAN 203-6347) Tel 619-873-3535; *CIP.*

Challenge Expedition Co., *(Challenge Exp; 0-9608120)*, P.O. Box 1852, Boise, ID 83701 (SAN 240-0871) Tel 208-386-9300.

†Challenge Pr., Div. of Economic Research Ctr., Inc., *(Challenge Pr; 0-89421)*, 1107 Lexington Ave., Dayton, OH 45407 (SAN 210-0509) Tel 513-275-8637; *CIP.*

Challenge Pubns., Inc., *(Chal Public; 0-935415)*, 7950 Deering Ave., Canoga Park, CA 91304 (SAN 696-2602) Tel 818-887-0550.

Challenge Publishing, Co., *(Challenge Pub Co; 0-916115)*, 2750 Bellflower Blvd., Suite 210, Long Beach, CA 90815 (SAN 294-9148) Tel 213-429-5265.

Chalmers, Irena, Cookbooks, Inc., *(I Chalmers; 0-941034)*, 23 E. 92nd St., New York, NY 10128 (SAN 217-3425) Tel 212-289-3105; Toll free: 800-334-8128; Orders to: P.O. Box 988, Denton, NC 27239 (SAN 661-972X).

Chamber of Commerce, *(COC)*, P.O. Box 51, Philadelphia, MS 39350 (SAN 217-2968).

Chamber of Commerce of the United States, *(Chamber Comm US; 0-89834)*, Special Pubns. Office, 1615 H St., NW, Washington, DC 20062 (SAN 225-6134) Tel 202-659-6111.

Chambers, Melvett G., *(M G Chambers; 0-9616522)*, 2231 Dawson Cir., Aurora, CO 80011 (SAN 659-4360) Tel 303-363-7429.

Chambliss, Madelon, *(Madelon Chamb; 0-9612420)*, P.O. Box 36B 81, 510 S. Sierra Bonita Ave., Los Angeles, CA 90025 (SAN 289-1743) Tel 213-935-3770.

Chameleon Productions, Inc., *(Chameleon Prods; 0-9613843)*, 5800 Arlington Ave., Studio 3M, Bronx, NY 10471 (SAN 681-9702) Tel 212-548-2932.

Champagne Pr., *(Champagne Pr; 0-9612146)*, 313 Walnuthaven Dr., West Covina, CA 91790 (SAN 290-6996) Tel 818-814-2052; P.O. Box 631, West Covina, CA 91793 (SAN 290-7003).

Champaign County Historical Archives Illinois, *(Champaign County; 0-9609646)*, The Urbana Free Library, 201 S. Race St., Urbana, IL 61801 (SAN 268-8476) Tel 217-367-4057.

Champaign Public Library & Information Ctr., *(Champaign Pub Lib; 0-9617184)*, 505 S. Randolph, Champaign, IL 61820 (SAN 663-2629) Tel 217-356-7243.

Names

Champaign Systems, Inc., *(Champaign Syst; 0-937547)*, 2518 Brett Dr., Champaign, IL 61821 (SAN 659-0977) Tel 217-359-9013.

Champion Athlete Publishing Co., *(Champion Athlete; 0-938074)*, Box 2936, Richmond, VA 23235 (SAN 215-6148) Tel 804-794-6034.

Champion Pr., *(Champ Pr Inglewood; 0-936691)*, Centinela Hospital, 555 E. Hardy St., Inglewood, CA 90301 (SAN 699-7228) Tel 213-673-2086. Do not confuse with Champion Pr., Scottsdale, AZ.

Champion Pr., *(Champion Pr; 0-938636)*, P.O. Box 1969, Scottsdale, AZ 85252 (SAN 218-4710) Tel 602-949-0786; Dist. by: Tom Hopkins International, Inc., 7531 E. Second St., Scottsdale, AZ 85252 (SAN 200-5174) Tel 602-949-0786. Do not confuse with Champion Pr. of Inglewood, CA.

Championship Bks., *(Championship Bks; 0-89279)*, 2109 N. Western, Ames, IA 50010 (SAN 656-1217) Tel 515-232-1101.

†Champlain College Pr., *(Champlain Coll Pr; 0-9612704)*, P.O. Box 670, Burlington, VT 05402-9990 (SAN 289-8144) Tel 802-658-0800; 163 S. Willard St., Burlington, VT 05402 (SAN 658-2451); *CIP.*

Champlin Museum, Pr., *(Champlin Museum; 0-912173)*, 4636 Fighter Aces Dr., Mesa, AZ 85205 (SAN 264-7257) Tel 602-830-4540.

Chan Shal Imi Society Press, *(Chan Shal Imi; 0-936380)*, P.O. Box 1365, Stone Mountain, GA 30086 (SAN 213-2974).

Chandler, Tertius, *(Chandler Tertius; 0-9693872)*, 2500 Buena Vista, Berkeley, CA 94708 (SAN 693-9961) Tel 415-849-1850.

†Chandler & Sharp Pubs., Inc., *(Chandler & Sharp; 0-88316)*, 11A Commercial Blvd., Novato, CA 94947 (SAN 205-6127) Tel 415-883-2353; *CIP.*

Chandler Institute, *(Chandler Inst; 0-918877)*, P.O. Box 394, Mission, SD 57555 (SAN 669-9758) Tel 605-856-4472.

Chandler-Smith Publishing Hse., Inc., *(Chandler-Smith; 0-916787)*, 132 Lowell St., Peabody, MA 01960 (SAN 654-3936) Tel 617-531-4952.

Chang, Paul K., *(P K Chang; 0-9612410)*, 8005 Falstaff Rd., McLean, VA 22102 (SAN 287-735X) Tel 703-356-1135.

†Changing Times Education Service, Div. of EMC Corp., *(Changing Times; 0-89247)*, 300 York Ave., St. Paul, MN 55101 (SAN 208-4015) Tel 612-771-1555; *CIP.*

Channels to Children, *(Channels Children; 0-9616396)*, P.O. Box 25834, Colorado Springs, CO 80936 (SAN 658-9936) Tel 303-223-4317; 2625 Dunbar Ave., Ft. Collins, CO 80526 (SAN 658-9944).

Channing Bks. & Whaleship Plans, *(Channing Bks; 0-9600496)*, P.O. Box 552, Marion, MA 02738 (SAN 203-6363) Tel 617-748-0087; 35 Main St., Marion, MA 02738 (SAN 658-0297).

Chan's Corp., *(Chans Corp; 0-914322)*, 230 S. Garfield Ave., Monterey Park, CA 91754 (SAN 201-8764) Tel 213-572-0425.

Chanteloup, Paul Francis, *(P F Chanteloup; 0-9616655)*, 1479 Blackhawk Ct., Sunnyvale, CA 94087 (SAN 661-0021) Tel 408-245-9421.

Chanteyman Pr., *(Chanteyman; 0-9601250)*, 42 Crocus St., Woodbridge, NJ 07095 (SAN 210-4008) Tel 201-634-4123.

Chanticleer Pr., *(Chanticleer CA; 0-9615876)*, 4974 N. Fresno St., Suite 242, Fresno, CA 93726 (SAN 697-0346) Tel 209-275-9040.

Chanticleer Pr., *(Chanticleer FL; 0-9612442)*, 1428 State St., Suite 107, Sarasota, FL 33577 (SAN 289-176X) Tel 813-371-8544.

Chanticleer Pr., Inc., *(Chanticleer; 0-918810)*, 424 Madison Ave., New York, NY 10017 (SAN 201-5749) Tel 212-486-3900.

Chantry Pr., *(Chantry Pr; 0-941608)*, P.O. Box 144, Midland Park, NJ 07432 (SAN 239-0752) Tel 201-423-5882.

Chaosium Inc., *(Chaosium; 0-933635)*, P.O. Box 6302, Albany, CA 94706 (SAN 692-6460) Tel 415-527-7361.

Chapel Bks. *See* Dell Publishing Co., Inc.

Chapel Hill Pr., *(Chapel Hill Pr; 0-934001)*, P.O. Box 958, Murray Hill Sta., 115 E. 34th St., New York, NY 10156 (SAN 692-6649) Tel 212-425-1153.

Chapin PTO, *(Chapin PTO; 0-9611640)*, Rte. 3, Box 384, Chapin, SC 29036 (SAN 284-9348) Tel 803-345-3590.

Chapman & Bookman, *(Chapman & Bkman; 0-9613544)*, 2409 NE 12th Ct., Ft. Lauderdale, FL 33304 (SAN 669-7488) Tel 305-564-1650.

Chapman Assocs., *(Chapman Assocs; 0-937243)*, 9 Farrington Pkwy., Burlington, VT 05401 (SAN 658-6740) Tel 802-862-8633.

Chapman, Brook & Kent, Div. of Institute for Reading Research, *(Chapman Brook; 0-930687)*, P.O. Box 21008, Santa Barbara, CA 93121 (SAN 677-1173) Tel 805-962-0055.

Chapter & Cask, Div. of Collart Enterprises, *(Chapter & Cask; 0-940056)*, P.O. Box 3604, Glyndon, MD 21071 (SAN 217-0663) Tel 301-833-7172.

†Char-L Pub. Co., *(Char-L; 0-9605654)*, P.O. Box 121, Niantic, IL 62551 (SAN 238-7751); *CIP.*

Character Research Pr., *(Character Res; 0-915744)*, 266 State St., Schenectady, NY 12305 (SAN 209-1240) Tel 518-370-0025.

Chariot Books *See* Cook, David C., Publishing Co.

Charioteer Press, *(Charioteer; 0-910350)*, P.O. Box 57223, Washington, DC 20037 (SAN 203-6371) Tel 202-965-5046.

Charisma Pr., *(Charisma Pr; 0-933402)*, P.O. Box 263, Andover, MA 01810 (SAN 212-6478) Tel 617-851-7910.

Charisma Pubns., Inc., *(Charisma Pubns; 0-937008)*, P.O. Box 40321, Indianapolis, IN 46240 (SAN 214-3542) Tel 317-843-4143.

Charismatic Renewal Services, *(Charismatic Ren Servs; 0-943780)*, 237 N. Michigan, South Bend, IN 46601 (SAN 268-8492) Tel 219-234-6021; Toll free: 800-348-2227.

†Chariton Review Pr., *(Chariton Review; 0-933428)*, Northeast Missouri State Univ., Kirksville, MO 63501 (SAN 212-4890) Tel 816-785-4499; *CIP.*

Charland, Thomas C., *(T C Charland; 0-9610754)*, P.O. Box 7112, Falls Church, VA 22046-1268 (SAN 264-7265) Tel 703-830-4892.

Charlemarie Pr., *(Charlemarie; 0-937181)*, 707 Watkins, Conway, AR 72032 (SAN 658-4896) Tel 501-327-2181.

†Charles Pr. Pubs., *(Charles; 0-914783; 0-89303)*, P.O. Box 15715, Philadelphia, PA 19103 (SAN 203-638X) Tel 215-735-3665; *CIP.*

†Charles Publishing Co., *(Charles Pub; 0-912880)*, 5039 Bluebell, North Hollywood, CA 91607 (SAN 201-9779) Tel 818-763-2031; *CIP.*

Charles River Bks., *(Charles River Bks; 0-89182)*, 1 Thompson Sq., Boston, MA 02129 (SAN 209-2530) Tel 617-259-8857. *Imprints:* Charles River Reprints (CRR).

Charles River Reprints *See* Charles River Bks.

Charleston Pr., *(Charleston Pr; 0-935773)*, 4911 S. Sherwood Forest Blvd., Baton Rouge, LA 70816 (SAN 695-8311) Tel 504-293-9472.

Charlotte Drug Education Ctr. Pubns., *(Charlotte Drug; 0-934337)*, 1416 E. Morehead St., Charlotte, NC 28204 (SAN 693-6083) Tel 704-336-3211.

Charlotte Latin Schls., Inc., *(C Latin Schls; 0-9615616)*, P.O. Box 6143, Charlotte, NC 28207 (SAN 696-2742) Tel 704-366-7260; 9900 Providence Rd., Matthews, NC 28105 (SAN 696-5261).

Charlton Hse. Publishing, Div. of Charlton Industries, Ltd., *(Charlton Hse; 0-916697)*, P.O. Box 2474, Newport Beach, CA 92663 (SAN 654-2360) Tel 714-760-8528.

Charm City Assocs., *(Charm City Assocs; 0-9617229)*, 401 Hawthorn Rd., Baltimore, MD 21210 (SAN 663-4265) Tel 301-243-5997.

Charred Norton Publishing Co., *(Charred Norton; 0-930975)*, 43 Elm St., Camillus, NY 13031 (SAN 678-884X) Tel 315-672-8012.

Chartcrafters Pubs., *(Chartcrafters Pubs; 0-930151)*, P.O. Box 26136, Baltimore, MD 21210 (SAN 669-6678) Tel 301-889-2628; Dist. by: Yankee Inc., Main St., Dublin, NH 03444 (SAN 293-4434) Tel 603-563-8111; Toll free: 800-258-5327.

Charter Bks. *See* Bobbs-Merrill Co.

Charter Oak Pr., *(Charter Oak Pr; 0-87521)*, P.O. Box 7783, Lancaster, PA 17604 (SAN 692-4581) Tel 717-656-4293.

Charter Press, Subs. of James B. Warkentin, Realtor, *(Charter Pr; 0-9614681)*, 2429 Martindale Rd., Shelburne, VT 05482 (SAN 692-5103) Tel 802-985-3862.

†Charters West, *(Charters W; 0-9613913)*, P.O. Box 675, Goleta, CA 93116 (SAN 682-2355); *CIP.*

ChartGuide Ltd., *(ChartGuide Ltd; 0-938206)*, 300 N. Wilshire Ave., Suite 5, Anaheim, CA 92801 (SAN 215-7373) Tel 714-533-1423.

Chartmasters, *(Chartmasters; 0-917190)*, P.O. Box 1264, Covington, LA 70434 (SAN 208-5917) Tel 504-892-9135.

Chartrand, Robert Lee, *(Chartrand)*, 5406 Dorset Ave., Chevy Chase, MD 20815 (SAN 211-1152).

Chartwell Hse., Inc., *(Chartwell; 0-910354)*, P.O. Box 166, Bowling Green Sta., New York, NY 10004 (SAN 203-6398).

Chase, Don M., *(D M Chase; 0-918634)*, 8569 Lawrence Lane, Sebastopol, CA 95472 (SAN 209-4215) Tel 707-823-7670.

Chase, Peter, Productions, *(P C Prods; 0-9617243)*, 701 Island Ave., Apt. 2B, San Diego, CA 92101 (SAN 663-5504) Tel 619-235-4238.

Chase Communications, *(Chase Comns; 0-9615565)*, 1776 Nancy Creek Bluff, NW, Atlanta, GA 30327 (SAN 696-2610) Tel 404-355-4142.

†Chase Pubns., *(Chase Pubns; 0-914779)*, 1654-33rd Ave., San Francisco, CA 94122 (SAN 297-1720) Tel 415-731-0158; Dist. by: Bookpeople, 2929 Fifth St., Berkeley, CA 94710 (SAN 168-9517) Tel 415-549-3030; Toll free: 800-227-1516; Dist. by: Publishers Group West, 5855 Beaudry St., Emeryville, CA 94608 (SAN 202-8522) Tel 415-658-3453; Toll free: 800-982-8319; *CIP.*

Chasse Pubns., *(Chasse Pubns; 0-913930)*, 8760 Grand, Beulah, CO 81023 (SAN 203-6401) Tel 303-485-3136; P.O. Box 38, Beulah, CO 81023 (SAN 699-5209).

Chateau Publishing, Inc., *(Chateau Pub; 0-88435)*, P.O. Box 20432, Herndon Sta., Orlando, FL 32814 (SAN 201-7814) Tel 305-898-1641.

Chateau Thierry Pr., *(Chateau Thierry; 0-935046)*, 1668 W. Olive Ave., Chicago, IL 60660 (SAN 281-4056) Tel 312-262-2234.

†Chatham Bookseller, *(Chatham Bkseller; 0-911860)*, 8 Green Village Rd., Madison, NJ 07940 (SAN 203-641X) Tel 201-822-1361; *CIP.*

Chatham Communicators, Inc., *(Chatham Comm Inc; 0-910347)*, 3857 N. High St., P.O. Box 14091, Columbus, OH 43214 (SAN 241-2861) Tel 614-268-8989.

Chatham Historical Society Inc., *(Chatham His Soc; 0-9615051)*, Box 381, Chatham, MA 02633 (SAN 683-8795) Tel 617-945-9812; Dist. by: Pabnassus Imprint, 21 Camal Rd., Box 335, Orleans, MA 02653 (SAN 200-5158).

†Chatham Hse., Pubs., Inc., *(Chatham Hse Pubs; 0-934540)*, Box 1, Chatham, NJ 07928 (SAN 213-036X) Tel 201-635-2059; Orders to: Chatham Hse. Distributors, 540 Barnum Ave., Bridgeport, CT 06608 (SAN 281-4080) Tel 203-366-1900; *CIP.*

†Chatham Pr., *(Chatham Pr; 0-85699)*, P.O. Box A, Old Greenwich, CT 06870 (SAN 201-9795) Tel 203-531-7880; Dist. by: Devin-Adair Pubs., Inc., 6 N. Water St., Greenwich, CT 06830 (SAN 213-750X) Tel 203-531-7755; *CIP.*

Chatham Pub. Co., *(Chatham Pub CA; 0-89685)*, P.O. Box 283, Burlingame, CA 94010 (SAN 210-4016) Tel 415-348-0331.

Chatham River Press *See* Outlet Bk. Co.

†Chatham Square Press, Inc., *(Chatham Sq; 0-89456)*, 401 Broadway, 23rd Fl., New York, NY 10013 (SAN 210-1874) Tel 212-226-3368; *CIP.*

Chatsworth Pr., Subs. of Woodland Media, Inc., *(Chatsworth; 0-917181)*, 21540 Prairie St., Chatsworth, CA 91311 (SAN 696-9186) Tel 818-341-3156; Toll free: 800-262-7367; Dist. by: Media Products, 21540 Prairie, Suite C, Chatsworth, CA 91311 (SAN 200-6960) Tel 818-341-3156; Dist. by: Publishers Group West, 5855 Beaudry St., Emeryville, CA 94608 (SAN 202-8522) Tel 415-658-3453; Toll free: 800-982-8319.

Names

Chattanooga Christian Schl., *(Chattanooga Christ; 0-9615039),* 3354 Broad St., Chattanooga, TN 37409 (SAN 656-0415) Tel 615-266-3296.

Chatterbox Voice Learning Systems, *(Chatterbox Voice Lrn Syst; 0-939557),* 29 Elk Ridge Ln., Boulder, CO 80302 (SAN 661-888X) Tel 303-444-4654; Toll free: 800-531-5314.

Chatterton Pr., *(Chatterton Pr; 0-930574),* 2471 Berthbrook Dr., Cincinnati, OH 45231 (SAN 211-4631).

Chauncy Pr., The, Div. of M & M Pubns. & Sails, Ltd., *(Chauncy Pr; 0-918517),* Turtle Pond Rd., Saranac Lake, NY 12983 (SAN 657-6842) Tel 518-891-1650.

Chaves County Historical Society, *(Chaves Hist; 0-9615310),* 200 N. Lea Ave., Roswell, NM 88201 (SAN 694-5988) Tel 505-622-8333.

Cheap St., *(Cheap St; 0-941826),* Rte. 2, Box 293, New Castle, VA 24127 (SAN 239-1783) Tel 703-864-6288.

Checkmark *See* **Facts on File, Inc.**

Chedney Pr., *(Chedney; 0-910358),* P.O. Box 1148, Auburn, ME 04210 (SAN 203-6428).

Cheeruppet World, Inc., *(Cheeruppet; 0-914201),* 2264 Calle Iglesia, Mesa, AZ 85202 (SAN 287-6000) Tel 602-839-3319; Orders to: 2405 E. Southern Ave., Sta., Tempe, AZ 85282 (SAN 287-6019) Tel 602-831-6088.

Cheese Pr., The, *(Cheese Pr; 0-9607404),* P.O. Box 85, Main St., Ashfield, MA 01330 (SAN 239-1791) Tel 413-628-3808.

Cheetah Publishing Co., *(Cheetah Pub; 0-936241),* 275 N. Forest Lake Dr., Altamonte Springs, FL 32714 (SAN 697-0443) Tel 305-862-2951.

Cheever Publishing, Inc., *(Cheever Pub; 0-915708),* P.O. Box 700, Bloomington, IL 61702 (SAN 207-9410) Tel 309-378-2961.

Chefs Publishing, Co., *(Chefs Pub Co; 0-933903),* P.O. Box 541202, Houston, TX 77254-1202 (SAN 692-7556) Tel 713-664-0884.

Chelonia Pr., *(Chelonia Pr; 0-938947),* 1850 Union St., Suite 196, San Francisco, CA 94123 (SAN 661-8367) Tel 415-665-0621.

Chelsea Green Publishing Co., *(Chelsea Green Pub; 0-930031),* P.O. Box 283, Chelsea, VT 05038 (SAN 669-7631) Tel 802-685-3108; 1 Court St., Chelsea, VT 05038 (SAN 658-2583).

†**Chelsea Hse. Pubs.,** Div. of Chelsea Hse. Educational Communications, Inc., *(Chelsea Hse; 0-87754; 1-55546),* 5014 West Chester Pike, Edgemont, PA 19028 (SAN 206-7609) Tel 215-353-6625; Toll free: 800-523-0458; *CIP.*

Chelsea-Lee Bks., *(Chelsea-Lee Bks; 0-913974),* P.O. Box 66273, Los Angeles, CA 90066 (SAN 201-9817) Tel 213-616-0391.

†**Chelsea Pub. Co.,** *(Chelsea Pub; 0-8284),* 15 E. 26 St., New York, NY 10010 (SAN 201-9825) Tel 212-889-8095; *CIP.*

Cheltenham Pr., *(Cheltenham Pr; 0-9615838),* Box 591046, San Francisco, CA 94159-1046 (SAN 697-0311) Tel 415-552-2994; 1673 Oak St., San Francisco, CA 94117 (SAN 697-032X).

Chem-Orbital, *(Chem-Orbital; 0-930376),* P.O. Box 134, Park Forest, IL 60466 (SAN 213-3466) Tel 312-755-2080.

Chemical Engineering *See* **McGraw-Hill Bk. Co.**

Chemical Information Management, Inc., *(CIMI),* P.O. Box 2740, Cherry Hill, NJ 08034 (SAN 212-9345) Tel 609-795-6767.

†**Chemical Publishing Co., Inc.,** *(Chem Pub; 0-8206),* 80 Eighth Ave., New York, NY 10011 (SAN 203-6444) Tel 212-255-1950; *CIP.*

Chen Chi Studio, *(Chen Chi Studio; 0-9604652),* 15 Gramercy Park, New York, NY 10003 (SAN 215-1359).

Chen Fu Tien, *(Chen Fu),* P.O. Box 1854, Norwalk, CA 90650 (SAN 287-2870).

Cheng & Tsui Co., *(Cheng & Tsui; 0-917056; 0-88727),* 25-31 West St., Boston, MA 02111 (SAN 169-3387) Tel 617-426-6074.

Chenonta, Inc., *(Chenonta; 0-938845),* P.O. Box 3727, West Sedona, AZ 86340 (SAN 661-695X).

Cherniak/Damele Publishing Co., *(Cherniak-Damele; 0-911093),* P.O. Box 19077, Oakland, CA 94619 (SAN 268-8670) Tel 415-533-1598; Dist. by: Informedia, 103 Godwin Ave., Midland Park, NJ 07432 (SAN 268-8689) Tel 201-447-2569.

Cherokee Pubns., *(Cherokee Pubns; 0-935741),* P.O. Box 256, Cherokee, NC 28719 (SAN 696-2785) Tel 704-488-2988.

†**Cherokee Publishing Co.,** *(Cherokee; 0-87787),* P.O. Box 1523, Marietta, GA 30061 (SAN 650-0404) Tel 404-424-6210; *CIP.*

Cherry County Centennial Committee, *(Cherry County Cent; 0-9614508),* Box 284, Valentine, NE 69201 (SAN 691-7275) Tel 402-376-1477.

†**Cherry Lane Bks.,** Div. of Cherry Lane Music Co., Inc., *(Cherry Lane; 0-89524),* 110 Midland Ave., Port Chester, NY 10573 (SAN 219-0788) Tel 914-937-8601; Toll free: 800-354-4004; P.O. Box 430, Port Chester, NY 10573; *CIP.*

†**Cherry Valley Editions,** *(Cherry Valley; 0-916156),* P.O. Box 303, Cherry Valley, NY 13320 (SAN 208-1482) Tel 607-264-3707; Orders to: Beach & Co., Pubs., P.O. Box 303, Cherry Valley, NY 13320 (SAN 206-6847); *CIP.*

Cherryable Brothers, *(Cherryable; 0-930689),* 130 Seventh St., Suite 448, Garden City, NY 11530 (SAN 677-1106) Tel 516-486-5090.

Cherubim, *(Cherubim; 0-938574),* P.O. Box 75, Ft. Tilden, NY 11695 (SAN 215-8523).

Chesapeake & Ohio Historical Society, Inc., *(Ches & OH Hist; 0-939487),* P.O. Box 417, Alderson, WV 24910 (SAN 225-3798) Tel 804-444-5252.

Chesapeake Bay Pr., Div. of WJBM Assocs., Inc., *(Chesapeake Bay Pr; 0-938225),* P.O. Box 951, Rockville, MD 20851 (SAN 661-003X); 2214 McAuliffe Dr., Rockville, MD 20851 (SAN 661-0048) Tel 301-424-9677.

Chesbro Pr., *(Chesbro; 0-938006),* 230 Longview Ave., Morgan Hill, CA 95037 (SAN 220-0392) Tel 408-779-5930; P.O. Box 1326, Morgan Hill, CA 95037 (SAN 658-0300).

Chesire Bks., *(Cheshire; 0-917352),* 514 Bryant St., Palo Alto, CA 94301 (SAN 208-5925) Tel 415-321-2449; Dist. by: Bookpeople, 2929 Fifth St., Berkeley, CA 94710 (SAN 168-9517) Tel 415-549-3030.

Chess Enterprises, Inc., *(Chess Ent Inc; 0-931462),* 107 Crosstree Rd., Coraopolis, PA 15108 (SAN 277-5808) Tel 412-262-2138.

Chess Information & Research Ctr., *(Chess Info Res Ctr; 0-9617207),* P.O. Box 534, Gracie Sta., New York, NY 10028 (SAN 663-2793); 512 E. 83rd St., Apt. 3D, New York, NY 10028 (SAN 663-2807) Tel 212-754-8706.

Chess Pubns., *(Chess Pub; 0-935273),* 6007 Beech Ave., Bethesda, MD 20817 (SAN 695-7404) Tel 301-243-5943; Dist. by: Betty Cox Assocs., 232 E. University Pkwy., Baltimore, MD 21218 (SAN 200-7819).

Chester Hse. Pubs., *(Chester Hse Pubs; 0-935763),* P.O. Box 1469, Grand Central Station, New York, NY 10163 (SAN 696-284X) Tel 914-478-4256; 160-01 77th Ave., Flushing, NY 11366 (SAN 696-2858) Tel 718-591-8579.

†**Chestnut Hill Pr.,** *(Chestnut Hill Pr; 0-9608132),* 5320 Groveland Rd., Geneseo, NY 14454 (SAN 238-0498) Tel 716-243-3616.

Chestnut Hill Senior Services Ctr., *(CHSSC Phila; 0-9616330),* 8434 Germantown Ave., Philadelphia, PA 19118 (SAN 659-0225) Tel 215-248-0180.

Cheswick Pr., *(Cheswick Pr; 0-9616686),* 8106 Three Chopt Rd., Richmond, VA 23229 (SAN 661-0056) Tel 804-288-7795.

Cheval Bks., *(Cheval Bks; 0-910368),* P.O. Box 2783, Hollywood, CA 90028 (SAN 208-306X) Tel 213-657-7311.

Cheyenne Corral, *(Cheyenne Cor; 0-9609648),* 7101 Tumbleweed Dr., Cheyenne, WY 82009 (SAN 281-4099).

Chicago Architectural Club, The, *(Chicago Arch; 0-9614052),* 4 W. Burton Place, Chicago, IL 60610 (SAN 684-9113) Tel 312-266-1783.

Chicago Board of Trade, *(Chicago Bd Trade; 0-917456),* 141 W. Jackson, Chicago, IL 60604 (SAN 203-6460) Tel 312-435-7210.

Chicago Center for Afro-American Studies & Research, Inc., *(Chi Ctr Afro-Am Stud; 0-937954),* P.O. Box 7610, Chicago, IL 60680 (SAN 215-9449).

†**Chicago Historical Society,** *(Chicago Hist; 0-913820),* Clark St. at North Ave., Chicago, IL 60614 (SAN 203-6479) Tel 312-642-4600; Toll free: 800-621-2736; *CIP.*

Chicago Horticultural Society, *(Chi Horticult; 0-939914),* P.O. Box 400, Glencoe, IL 60022 (SAN 216-7980) Tel 312-835-5440.

Chicago Institute for Psychoanalysis, *(Chicago Psych; 0-918568),* 180 N. Michigan Ave., Chicago, IL 60601 (SAN 210-1432) Tel 312-726-6300.

Chicago Law Bk. Rare, *(Chicago Law Bk; 0-9610650),* 4814 S. Pulaski Rd., Chicago, IL 60632 (SAN 264-648X) Tel 312-376-1713.

Chicago Linguistic Society, *(Chicago Ling; 0-914203),* c/o Univ. of Chicago, Classics 314A, 1050 E. 59th St., Chicago, IL 60637 (SAN 287-6027) Tel 312-962-8529.

Chicago Map Society, The, *(Chicago Map; 0-916789),* 60 W. Walton, Chicago, IL 60610 (SAN 654-200X) Tel 312-943-9090.

Chicago Office of Fine Arts, Dept. of Cultural Affairs, *(Chi Ofc Fine Arts; 0-938903),* Cultural Ctr., 78 Washington St., Chicago, IL 60608 (SAN 661-8340) Tel 312-744-8927.

Chicago Original Paperback *See* **Univ. of Chicago Pr.**

Chicago Publishing Co., *(Chicago Publishing; 0-9603264),* P.O. Box 635, Chicago, IL 60690 (SAN 209-5394) Tel 312-528-1523.

Chicago Reporter, The, Div. of Community Renewal Society, *(Chicago Rep; 0-9615553),* 18 S. Michigan Ave., Chicago, IL 60603 (SAN 696-4842) Tel 312-236-4830.

Chicago Review Pr., Inc., *(Chicago Review; 0-914090; 1-55652),* 814 N. Franklin St., Chicago, IL 60610 (SAN 213-5744) Tel 312-337-0747. *Imprints:* Landmarks Commission Village of Oak Park (Landmarks Comm Village Oak Pk).

Chicago Tribune Books Today, *(Chicago Trib),* 435 N. Michigan Ave., Chicago, IL 60611 (SAN 204-2959) Tel 312-222-3232.

Chicago Visual Library *See* **Univ. of Chicago Pr.**

Chicago Zoological Society, *(Chicago Zoo; 0-913934),* 3300 Golf Rd., Brookfield, IL 60513 (SAN 663-4672).

Chick Pubns., *(Chick Pubns; 0-937958),* P.O. Box 662, Chino, CA 91710 (SAN 211-7770) Tel 714-987-0771.

Chickasaw Bayou Press, *(Chickasaw Bayou; 0-9606372),* 103 Trace Harbor Rd., Madison, MS 39110 (SAN 217-1651) Tel 601-856-7062.

†**Chicot Pr., The,** *(Chicot Pr; 0-913845),* P.O. Box 21988, Baton Rouge, LA 70893 (SAN 286-7389) Tel 813-933-7098; Orders to: 13014 N. Dale Mabry, Suite 249, Tampa, FL 33618 (SAN 662-2100) Tel 813-933-7098; *CIP.*

Chiefton Publishing, Inc., Div. of Chiefton Enterprises, Inc., *(Chiefton Pub; 0-9615945),* 5125 Blake Rd., Edina, MN 55436 (SAN 697-046X) Tel 612-935-0564.

Child & Family Enterprises, Inc., *(Child & Family Ent; 0-935202),* 7 Leonard Pl., Albany, NY 12202 (SAN 213-8379) Tel 518-449-5735.

Child & Waters Incorporated, *(Child & Waters Inc; 0-9611200),* 516 Fifth Ave., New York, NY 10036 (SAN 283-2569) Tel 212-840-1935.

Child Care Administrative Services, *(Child Care Admin; 0-937261),* 11742 W. Pico Blvd., Suite 202, Los Angeles, CA 90064 (SAN 659-025X) Tel 213-477-2177.

Child Care Information Exchange, *(Child Care; 0-942702),* P.O. Box 2890, Redmond, WA 98073 (SAN 240-3072) Tel 206-882-1066.

Child Evangelism Fellowship Press, *(CEF Press),* Highway M, Warrenton, MO 63383 (SAN 211-7789) Tel 314-456-4321.

Child Focus Co., *(Child Focus Co; 0-933892),* P.O. Box 1885, Fallbrook, CA 92028 (SAN 207-5199) Tel 619-723-8542.

Child Health Assn. of Sewickley, Inc., *(Child Health Assn; 0-9607634),* 1108 Ohio River Blvd., Sewickley, PA 15143 (SAN 240-088X) Tel 412-741-3221.

Child Safe Products, Inc., Publishing Div., *(Child Safe; 0-917461),* 449 N. University Dr., Plantation, FL 33324 (SAN 657-0836); Toll free: 800-334-0090.

Child-Savers, Inc., *(Child Savers; 0-936049),* 30 W. 61st St., Suite 27c, New York, NY 10023 (SAN 697-0230) Tel 212-247-6580.

Names

Child Trends Inc., *(Child Trends; 0-932359),*
1990 M St. NW, Washington, DC 20036
(SAN 687-3707) Tel 202-223-6288.

†**Child Welfare League of America, Inc.,** *(Child Welfare; 0-87868),* 440 First St., NW,
Washington, DC 20001 (SAN 201-9876)
Tel 202-638-2952; *CIP.*

Childbirth Graphics, Ltd., *(Childbirth Graphics; 0-943114),* 1210 Cluver Rd., Rochester, NY
14609 (SAN 240-3587) Tel 716-482-7940.

Children First Press, *(Children First; 0-9603696),* Box 8008, Ann Arbor, MI
48107 (SAN 212-4904) Tel 313-668-8056.

Children of Mary, *(Children; 0-933731),* P.O.
Box 40, Pearblossom, CA 93553
(SAN 692-6053) Tel 805-944-1132.

Children's Art Foundation, Inc., *(Childrens Art; 0-89409),* Box 83, Santa Cruz, CA 95063
(SAN 210-0533) Tel 408-426-5557.

Childrens Bk. Co., Inc., Div. of Creative
Education, Inc., *(Childrens Bk Co; 0-89813),*
P.O. Box 227, Mankato, MN 56001
(SAN 204-5532) Tel 507-625-2490. Out of
business.

Children's Bk. Council, Inc., The, *(Child Bk Coun; 0-933633),* 67 Irving Pl., New York,
NY 10003 (SAN 225-2929)
Tel 212-254-2666.

Children's Book Press/Imprenta de Libros Infantiles, *(Childrens Book Pr; 0-89239),*
1461 9th Ave., San Francisco, CA 94122
(SAN 210-7864) Tel 415-664-8500.

Children's Books *See* **Atheneum Pubs.**

†**Children's Ctr. Pubns. of California,** *(Childrens Ctr; 0-915861),* Creativity Ctr. S., P.O. Box
885, Bonita, CA 92002 (SAN 293-9878)
Tel 619-479-0602; *CIP.*

Children's Council of San Francisco, *(Child Council SF; 0-937711),* 3896 24th St., San
Francisco, CA 94114 (SAN 659-3240)
Tel 415-647-0778.

Children's Defense Fund, *(Children's Defense; 0-938008),* 122 C St., NW, Washington, DC
20001 (SAN 216-1133) Tel 202-628-8787;
Toll free: 800-424-9602.

Children's Hospice Intl., *(Child Hospice VA; 0-932321),* 501 Slaters Ln., Suite 207,
Alexandria, VA 22314 (SAN 687-0570)
Tel 703-549-1811.

Childrens Hospital of Buffalo, Josephine Goodyear Memorial Committee, *(CHB Goodyear Comm; 0-9616699),* 219 Bryant St., Buffalo,
NY 14222 (SAN 661-227X)
Tel 716-634-7778.

Children's Hospital of San Francisco, Pubn. Dept., *(Childrens Hosp; 0-931421),* P.O.
Box 3805, San Francisco, CA 94119
(SAN 683-5422); 3700 California St.,
OPR-110, San Francisco, CA 94119
(SAN 658-2699) Tel 415-387-8700.

Children's Learning Center, Inc., *(Children Learn Ctr; 0-917206),* 4660 E. 62nd St.,
Indianapolis, IN 46220 (SAN 208-5933)
Tel 317-251-6241.

Childrens Literature Assn. Pubns., *(CHLA Pubns; 0-937263),* Purdue Univ., 210
Education, West Lafayette, IN 47907
(SAN 225-297X) Tel 317-494-2355.

Children's Memorial Hospital, The, *(Children's Memorial; 0-9607400),* 2300 Children's
Plaza, Chicago, IL 60614 (SAN 239-4189).

Children's Museum of Denver, Inc., *(Childrens Mus Denver; 0-933027),* 2121 Cresent Dr.,
Denver, CO 80211 (SAN 689-5514)
Tel 303-433-7444.

Children's Museum of Indianapolis, *(Child Mus; 0-9608982),* 30th & Meridian, Indianapolis,
IN 46208 (SAN 268-9057).

Children's Museum of Oak Ridge, *(Children's Mus; 0-9606832),* P.O. Box 3066, Oak
Ridge, TN 37830 (SAN 219-7227)
Tel 615-482-1075.

Childrens Pr., Div. of Regensteiner Publishing
Enterprises, Inc., *(Childrens; 0-516),* 1224
W. Van Buren St., Chicago, IL 60607
(SAN 201-9264) Tel 312-666-4200; Toll
free: 800-621-1115. *Imprints:* Elk Grove
Books (Elk Grove Bks); Golden Gate
(Golden Gate); Sextant (Sextant).

Children's Theatre Assn. of America, Div. of
American Theatre Assn., *(Childrens Theatre; 0-940528),* 1010 Wisconsin Ave., NW,
Washington, DC 20007 (SAN 239-3581)
Tel 202-342-7530.

Children's Ventures, Inc., *(Child Ventures; 0-9615985),* P.O. Box 3000, Grants Pass,
OR 97526 (SAN 698-1569)
Tel 503-479-2929; Dist. by: Pacific Pipeline,
Inc., 19215 66th Ave, S., Kent, WA 98032
(SAN 208-2128) Tel 206-872-5523; Toll
free: 800-426-4727.

Children's Yellow Pages, *(Childrens Yellow; 0-9613059),* P.O. Box 48636, Los Angeles,
CA 90048 (SAN 293-9916); 542 S. Lorraine
Blvd., Los Angeles, CA 90020
(SAN 293-9924) Tel 213-930-1733; Dist.
by: Publishers Group West, 5855 Beaudry
St., Emeryville, CA 94608 (SAN 202-8522)
Tel 415-658-3453.

Childs Play, *(Childs Play; 0-931749),* 12423
Fleet Ct., Sterling Heights, MI 48077
(SAN 683-5120) Tel 313-939-9245.

†**Child's World, Inc., The,** *(Childs World; 0-89565; 0-913778),* 980 N. McLean Blvd.,
Elgin, IL 60121 (SAN 211-0032)
Tel 312-741-7591; P.O. Box 989, Elgin, IL
60121 (SAN 661-9738); Dist. by: Children's
Pr., 1224 W. Van Buren St., Chicago, IL
60607 (SAN 201-9264) Tel 312-666-4200;
CIP.

Childwrite, Inc., *(Childwrite; 0-943194),* 26409
Timberlane Dr., SE, Kent, WA 98042
(SAN 240-527X) Tel 206-631-8972.

Chilmark House, *(Chilmark Hse; 0-937532),*
4224 38th St. NW, Washington, DC 20016
(SAN 215-9457) Tel 202-363-4222.

Chiltern Yoga Foundation, *(Chiltern Yoga; 0-9612762),* 1029 Hyde St., Suite 6, San
Francisco, CA 94109 (SAN 289-8284)
Tel 415-776-1158.

Chilton Bk. Co., Subs. of ABC Publishing,
(Chilton; 0-8019), Chilton Way, Radnor, PA
19089 (SAN 658-0319) Tel 215-964-4000;
Orders to: Schl., Library Services, Chilton
Way, Radnor, PA 19089 (SAN 202-1552)
Tel 215-964-4729; Dist. by: Hobby Bk.
Distributors, 3150 State Line Rd.,
(SAN 200-6669).

Chilton Corp., *(Chilton Corp; 0-9616037),*
12606 Greenville, Dallas, TX 75243
(SAN 698-0384) Tel 214-699-6320.

China Bks. & Periodicals, Inc., *(China Bks; 0-8351),* 2929 24th St., San Francisco, CA
94110 (SAN 145-0057) Tel 415-282-2994.

China House of Arts, *(China Hse Arts; 0-9609104),* 1100 Madison Ave., New York,
NY 10028 (SAN 241-287X)
Tel 212-794-9652.

China Phone Book Co. Ltd., The, *(China Phone),* P.O. Box 2385-N, Menlo Park, CA
94025 (SAN 268-9146).

China Research, *(China Res; 0-9605190),* 1500
NW 103rd Lane, Coral Springs, FL 33065
(SAN 223-1654) Tel 305-752-6274.

China West Bks., *(China West; 0-941340),* P.O.
Box 2804, San Francisco, CA 94126
(SAN 238-9231) Tel 415-755-3715.

Chinese Academic & Professional Society of Mid-America, *(Chinese Acad Prof Soc; 0-9616137),* 6711 Innsbruck Ct., Naperville,
IL 60532 (SAN 699-8577)
Tel 312-996-4860.

Chinese-American Librarians Assn., *(Chinese Lib; 0-930691),* c/o Ohio University Library,
Athens, OH 45701 (SAN 677-0991)
Tel 614-594-5228.

Chinese Art Appraisers Assn., *(Chinese Art App; 0-930940),* Box 734, 633 Post St., San
Francisco, CA 94109 (SAN 211-495X)
Tel 415-673-6023.

Chinese Culture Service, Inc., *(Chinese Cult Serv; 0-937256),* P.O. Box 444, Oak Park,
IL 60303 (SAN 215-2401)
Tel 312-848-2210.

Chinese Historical Society of Southern California, Inc., *(Chinese Hist CA; 0-930377),* 1648 Redcliff St., Los Angeles,
CA 90026 (SAN 670-7580)
Tel 213-828-6911.

Chinkapin Press, Inc., *(Chinkapin; 0-938874),*
P.O. Box 10565, Eugene, OR 97401
(SAN 220-2360).

Chip's Bookshop, Inc., *(Chips; 0-912378),* Box
639, Cooper Sta., New York, NY 10003
(SAN 203-6517) Tel 212-362-9336.

Chiron Pr., Inc., *(Chiron Pr; 0-913462),* 24 W.
96th St., New York, NY 10025
(SAN 202-1560) Tel 212-662-5486; Orders
to: Chiron Pr., Inc., Publishers Storage &
Shipping Co., 231 Industrial Pk., Fitchburg,
MA 01420 (SAN 202-1579)
Tel 617-491-1727.

Chiron Publications, *(Chiron Pubns; 0-933029),*
400 Linden Ave., Wilmette, IL 60091
(SAN 689-1659) Tel 312-256-7551; Dist.
by: Open Court Publishing Co., P.O. box
599, Peru, IL 61354 (SAN 202-5876)
Tel 815-223-2520; Toll free: 800-435-6850.

Chiron Publishing, Co., *(Chiron Pub Co; 0-915053),* P.O. Box 575, Bethel Park, PA
15102 (SAN 289-8330) Tel 412-831-2929.

†**Chiropractic Publishing Services,** *(Chiropractic Pub; 0-914893),* 2017 S. Ventura, Tempe,
AZ 85282 (SAN 289-0879)
Tel 602-277-6293; *CIP.*

Chisos Mountain Pr., *(Chisos Mount; 0-9614040),* P.O. Box 6268, Pasadena, TX
77506 (SAN 684-7293) Tel 713-943-3203.

Chisum Publishing, Inc., *(Chisum Pub; 0-937689),* 1000 E. 14th St., Suite 388,
Plano, TX 75074 (SAN 659-0284)
Tel 214-423-2120; 1541 Ave. K, Plano, TX
75074 (SAN 659-0292) Tel 214-422-7066.

Chiuzac, Ltd., *(Chiuzac Ltd),* 630 First Ave.,
New York, NY 10016 (SAN 699-7775).

Chiwaukee Publishing Co., *(Chiwaukee Pub Co; 0-9613129),* 11745 First Ave., Kenosha, WI
53140 (SAN 294-703X) Tel 414-694-9532.

Chlorine Institute, *(Chlorine Inst; 0-940230),* 70
W. 40th St., New York, NY 10018
(SAN 204-2983) Tel 212-819-1677.

Cho, Jun Young, *(J Y Cho; 0-9617185),* 1801
Edgewater Dr., Plano, TX 75075
(SAN 663-2688) Tel 214-828-8143.

Choate, Betty Burton, *(B B Choate; 0-9616352),*
Rte. 2, Box 156, Winona, MS 38967
(SAN 659-0330) Tel 601-283-1192; Burton
Dr., Winona, MS 38967 (SAN 659-0349).

†**Chockstone Pr.,** *(Chockstone Pr; 0-9609452; 0-934641),* 526 Franklin St., Denver, CO
80218 (SAN 276-6809) Tel 303-377-1970;
CIP.

Chogie Pubs., *(Chogie Pubs; 0-9610818),* 123
Virginia Rd., Oak Ridge, TN 37830
(SAN 285-1199) Tel 615-482-7320; Orders
to: Rte. 5, Box 286A, Paris, TN 38242
(SAN 285-1202) Tel 901-642-9752.

†**CHOICE,** *(Choice; 0-930659),* 125 S. Ninth
St., Suite 603, Philadelphia, PA 19107
(SAN 260-3969) Tel 215-592-0550; *CIP.*

Choice Pubns., *(Choice Pubns; 0-934685),* 1335
Rosewood, Ferndale, MI 48220
(SAN 694-3438) Tel 313-399-0711.

Choice Publishing Co., *(Choice Pub CA; 0-9615891),* P.O. Box 3568, Santa Monica,
CA 90403-3568 (SAN 696-2998)
Tel 213-394-2313.

Chopping Board, Inc., *(Chopping Board Inc; 0-915747),* P.O. Box 2549, Gainesville, FL
32602 (SAN 292-3319).

Choral Resource Seminars, *(Choral Resource; 0-9616618),* P.O. Box 15068, San Francisco,
CA 94115 (SAN 661-0064); 1332 Dolores,
No. 2, San Francisco, CA 94110
(SAN 661-0072) Tel 415-648-6854.

Chou-Chou Pr., *(Chou-Chou; 0-9606140),* P.O.
Box 152, Shoreham, NY 11786
(SAN 220-2379).

Chowder Pr., *(Chowder Pr; 0-9614546),* 13
Schuyler Dr., Saratoga Springs, NY 12866
(SAN 691-7984) Tel 518-587-2808.

Chrisolith Books, *(Chrisolith Bks; 0-916085),*
Box 9437, New Haven, CT 06534
(SAN 294-7099) Tel 203-789-7347.

Christ for the Nations, Inc., *(Christ Nations; 0-89985),* P.O. Box 769000, Dallas, TX
75376-9000 (SAN 211-7800)
Tel 214-376-1711.

Christ Foundation, The, *(Christ Found; 0-910315),* P.O. Box 10, Port Angeles, WA
98362 (SAN 241-4872) Tel 206-452-5249.

Christ United Methodist Church, *(Christ United Meth Ch; 0-9616507),* 4488 Poplar Ave.,
Memphis, TN 38117 (SAN 659-4379)
Tel 901-682-8299.

Christendom College Press *See* **Christendom Pubns.**

Christendom Pubns., *(Christendom Pubns; 0-931888),* Rte. 3, Box 87, Front Royal, VA
22630 (SAN 214-2570) Tel 703-636-2908.
Imprints: Christendom College Press (Chr
Coll Pr); Crossroads Books (Crossroads).

Christian Academy of Success, *(Chr Acad Success; 0-941280),* 5428 W. Barbara Ave.,
Glendale, AZ 85302 (SAN 238-924X).

Christian Book Club of America *See* **Noontide Pr., The**

Christian Bks. Pub. Hse., *(Christian Bks; 0-940232),* P.O. Box 959, Gardiner, ME 04345 (SAN 201-8942); Toll free: 800-228-2665.

Christian Booksellers Assn., *(Chr Bksellers),* 2620 Venetucci Blvd., P.O. Box 200, Colorado Springs, CO 80901 (SAN 216-3519) Tel 303-576-7880.

Christian Classics, Inc., *(Chr Classics; 0-87061),* P.O. Box 30, Westminster, MD 21157 (SAN 203-6525) Tel 301-848-3065.

Christian College Coalition, *(Christ Coll Coal)* 1776 Massachusetts Ave. NW, No. 700, Washington, DC 20036 (SAN 268-9499) Tel 202-293-6177.

Christian Conciliation Service, *(Chr Concil Serv),* P.O. Box 2069, Oak Park, IL 60303 (SAN 277-6634).

Christian Education Research Institute, *(Chr Educ Res Inst; 0-943708),* Box 888-747, Atlanta, GA 30356 (SAN 238-0501) Tel 404-972-3888.

Christian Fellowship Pubs., Inc., *(Christian Fellow Pubs; 0-935008),* 11515 Allecingie Pkwy., Richmond, VA 23235 (SAN 207-4885) Tel 804-794-5333.

Christian Freedom Press, Inc., *(Christian Freedom),* 518 Lincoln Ave., West Chicago, IL 60185 (SAN 289-7059).

Christian Heritage Press *See* **Holmes Publishing Group**

Christian International Pubs., *(Chr Intl Pubs; 0-939868),* Rt. 2 Box 351, Point Washington, FL 32454 (SAN 281-4102).

Christian Light Pubns., Inc., *(Christian Light; 0-87813),* P.O. Box 1126, Harrisonburg, VA 22801 (SAN 206-7315) Tel 703-434-0768.

Christian Literature Crusade, Inc., *(Chr Lit; 0-87508),* P.O. Box 1449, Fort Washington, PA 19034-8449 (SAN 169-7358) Tel 215-542-1240.

Christian Marriage Enrichment, *(Chr Marriage; 0-938786),* 1913 E. 17th St., Suite 118, Santa Ana, CA 92701 (SAN 216-1141) Tel 714-542-3506.

Christian Ministries Pubns., *(Christian Mini; 0-911567),* 173 Woodland Ave., Lexington, KY 40502 (SAN 264-2115) Tel 606-254-6003.

Christian Pubns., Inc., *(Chr Pubns; 0-87509),* 3825 Hartzdale Dr., Camp Hill, PA 17011-8870 (SAN 202-1617) Tel 717-761-7044; Toll free: 800-932-0382.

Christian Pub CA, *(Chrstn Pub Palm Springs; 0-939501),* P.O. Box 828, Palm Springs, CA 92263 (SAN 663-4095); 2250 Alhambra Dr., Palm Springs, CA 92262 (SAN 663-4109) Tel 619-327-1866.

Christian Publishing Services, Inc., Subs. of Harrison House Pubs., *(Christian Pub; 0-88144),* Box 35388, Tulsa, OK 74155 (SAN 260-0285) Tel 918-584-5535; Toll free: 800-826-5992.

†**Christian Research, Pr., The,** *(Christian Res Pr; 0-915923),* P.O. Box 2013, Des Moines, IA 50310 (SAN 293-4868) Tel 515-255-8854; 3825 Kingman, Des Moines, IA 50311 (SAN 293-4876); *CIP.*

Christian Restoration Assn., *(Chr Restor Assn; 0-9614213),* 5664 Cheviot Rd., Cincinnati, OH 45247 (SAN 687-0635) Tel 513-385-0461.

Christian Service Ctrs., Inc., *(Christ Serv Ctrs; 0-936801),* 5300 Ulmerton Rd., Clearwater, FL 33520 (SAN 699-8798) Tel 813-535-4532.

Christian Studies Center, *(Chr Stud Ctr; 0-939200),* P.O. Box 11110, Memphis, TN 38111 (SAN 220-0406) Tel 901-458-0738.

Christian Univ. Pr. *See* **Eerdmans, William B., Publishing Co.**

Christianica Ctr., *(Christianica; 0-911346),* 6 N. Michigan Ave., Chicago, IL 60602 (SAN 204-739X) Tel 312-782-4230.

†**Christianity Today, Inc.,** *(Chr Today; 0-917463),* 465 Gundersen Dr., Carol Stream, IL 60188 (SAN 656-884X) Tel 312-260-6200; *CIP.*

Christian's Library Pr., Inc., *(Chr Lib Pr; 0-934874),* P.O. Box 2226, Grand Rapids, MI 49501 (SAN 222-7061).

Christlife Pubs., *(Christlife Pubs; 0-939079),* 1909 Willowbend, Deer Park, TX 77536 (SAN 662-9199) Tel 713-476-9916.

Christmas Star Church, *(Christmas Star; 0-9613670),* P.O. Box 3921, St. Augustine, FL 32085 (SAN 676-2085).

Christopher Publishing, *(Chris Pub UT; 0-936863),* P.O. Box 412, Springville, UT 84663 (SAN 200-2787) Tel 801-489-4254; Dist. by: Bookpeople, 2929 Fifth St., Berkeley, CA 94710 (SAN 168-9517); Dist. by: The Distributors, 702 S. Michigan Ave., South Bend, IN 46618 (SAN 169-2488) Tel 219-232-8500; Dist. by: New Leaf Distributing, Co., 1020 White Street SW, Atlanta, GA 30310 (SAN 169-1449) Tel 404-755-2665; Dist. by: Nutri-Books Corporation, P.O. Box 5793, Denver, CO 80223 (SAN 169-054X) Tel 303-778-8383 (SAN 169-8834); Dist. by: Pacific Pipeline, Inc., 19215 66th Ave. South, Kent, WA 98032 (SAN 169-2127) Tel 206-872-5523. *Imprints:* Littlegreen (Littlegreen).

Christopher Publishing Hse. (Massachusetts), *(Chris Mass; 0-8158),* 106 Longwater Dr., Norwell, MA 02061 (SAN 202-1625) Tel 617-878-9336.

Christopher Resources, Inc., *(Christopher Res; 0-9610034),* 34 N. White St., P.O. Box E, Frankfort, IL 60423 (SAN 268-9707) Tel 312-655-4923.

†**Christopher's Bks.,** *(Christophers Bks; 0-87922),* 390 62nd St., Oakland, CA 94618 (SAN 212-5870) Tel 415-428-1120; *CIP.*

Christophers, The, *(Chrstphrs NY; 0-939055),* 12 E. 48th St., New York, NY 10017 (SAN 226-6679) Tel 212-759-4050.

Christ's Mission, *(Christs Mission; 0-935120),* P.O. Box 203, Prospect Heights, IL 60070 (SAN 211-7819) Tel 312-870-3800.

Christward Ministry, *(Christward; 0-910378),* 20560 Questhaven Rd., Escondido, CA 92025 (SAN 202-1633) Tel 619-744-1500.

Chromatic Communications Enterprises, Inc., *(Chromatic Comm; 0-912673),* P.O. Box 3249, Walnut Creek, CA 94598 (SAN 277-6642) Tel 415-945-1602.

Chrome Yellow Private Pr./Nords Studio, *(Chrome Yellow; 0-935656),* 125 Central Ave., Crescent City, FL 32012 (SAN 200-7614) Tel 904-698-2430; Dist. by: Educational Trade Publishing, 124 Central Ave., Crescent City, FL 32012 (SAN 200-7606).

†**Chronicle Bks.,** Div. of Chronicle Publishing Co., *(Chronicle Bks; 0-87701),* 1 Hallidie Plaza, Suite 806, San Francisco, CA 94102 (SAN 202-165X) Tel 415-777-7240; Toll free: 800-652-1657; *CIP.*

Chronicle Guidance Pubns., Inc., *(Chron Guide; 0-912578; 1-55631),* P.O. Box 1190, Moravia, NY 13118-1190 (SAN 202-1641) Tel 315-497-0330.

Chrysalis Publishing, Ltd., *(Chrysalis; 0-940402),* P.O. Box 10690, Phoenix, AZ 85064 (SAN 218-4729) Tel 602-944-8804.

Chrysler Museum, The, *(Chrysler Museum; 0-940744),* Olney Rd., & Mowbray Arch, Norfolk, VA 23510 (SAN 278-4289) Tel 804-622-1211.

Chrysopylon Pubs., *(Chrysopylon; 0-9615640),* 1832 Lexington, San Mateo, CA 94402 (SAN 696-7116) Tel 415-574-2028; P.O. Box 3113, San Mateo, CA 94403 (SAN 698-2131).

Chthon Pr., *(Chthon Pr)* 77 Mark Vincent Dr., Westford, MA 01886 (SAN 208-2438).

Chulainn Press, Inc., *(Chulainn Press; 0-917600),* 1040 Butterfield Rd., P.O. Box 770, San Anselmo, CA 94960 (SAN 209-3286).

Church, Jim & Cathy, *(J-C Church; 0-9616093),* 7230 Trenton Pl., Gilroy, CA 95020 (SAN 698-1062) Tel 408-842-9682; P.O. Box 80, Gilroy, CA 95021 (SAN 698-2549).

†**Church & Synagogue Library Assn.,** *(CSLA; 0-915324),* P.O. Box 1130, Bryn Mawr, PA 19010 (SAN 210-7872) Tel 215-853-2870; *CIP.*

Church Bytes, Inc., *(Church Bytes; 0-9615086),* 201 W. Laflin, Waukesha, WI 53186 (SAN 694-3411) Tel 414-542-0905.

Church History Research & Archives, *(Church History; 0-935122),* 220 Graystone Dr., Gallatin, TN 37066 (SAN 211-7827) Tel 615-452-7027.

†**Church Library Council,** *(Church Lib; 0-9603060),* 5406 Quintana St., Riverdale, MD 20737 (SAN 210-5322) Tel 301-864-9308; *CIP.*

Church of God, Dept. of General Education, *(Church God; 0-937443),* Keith & 25th St., Cleveland, TN 37311 (SAN 659-1949) Tel 615-472-3361.

Church of Light, *(Church of Light; 0-87887),* Box 76862, Sanford Sta., Los Angeles, CA 90076 (SAN 209-150X) Tel 818-352-9335.

Church of Man Publishing Co., *(Church Man Pub; 0-936435),* 6112 N. Mesa No., 210, El Paso, TX 79912 (SAN 697-8568) Tel 915-533-5777.

Church of St. Leo the Great Press, *(Church St. Leo; 0-9607014),* 227 S. Exeter St., Baltimore, MD 21202 (SAN 238-9630) Tel 301-727-8600.

Church of Scientology Information Service-Pubns., *(Church of Scient Info; 0-915598),* c/o Bridge Pubns., Inc., 4833 Fountain Ave., Los Angeles, CA 90029 (SAN 268-9774).

Church of Scientology of California, *(C Scientol LA),* 2723 W. Temple St., Los Angeles, CA 90026 (SAN 209-6501) Tel 213-380-0710; Dist. by: Grosset & Dunlap, Inc., 51 Madison Ave., New York, NY 10010 (SAN 205-5457) Tel 212-689-9200.

Church of Scientology of New York, The, *(Church Scient NY),* 227 W. 46th St., New York, NY 10036 (SAN 211-786X).

Church of the Cross, *(Church Cross; 0-9601178),* 4068 S. Willow Way, Denver, CO 80237 (SAN 210-055X) Tel 303-770-2272.

Church of the Open Door, *(Church Open Door; 0-935729),* 701 W. Sierra Madre Ave., Glendora, CA 91740 (SAN 693-9465) Tel 818-914-4646.

Churches Alive, International, *(Churches Alive; 0-934396),* P.O. Box 3800, San Bernardino, CA 92413 (SAN 213-2982) Tel 714-886-5361.

†**Churchill Livingstone, Inc.,** Subs. of Longman Holdings, Inc., *(Churchill; 0-443),* 1560 Broadway, New York, NY 10036 (SAN 281-501X) Tel 212-819-5400; Dist. by: J.A. Majors Co., 3770A Zip Industrial Blvd., Atlanta, GA 30354 (SAN 169-1406) Tel 404-768-4956; Dist. by: Brown & Connolly, Inc., 2 Keith Way, Hingham, MA 02043 (SAN 169-3298) Tel 617-749-8570; Dist. by: Login Brothers Bk. Co., 1450 W. Randolph St., Chicago, IL 60607 (SAN 169-183X); Dist. by: J.A. Majors Co., P.O. Box 819074, Dallas, TX 75061-9074 (SAN 169-8117); Dist. by: J.A. Majors Co., 1806 Southgate Blvd., Houston, TX 77030 (SAN 169-8281); *CIP.*

Churchill Pr., *(Churchill Pr; 0-932223),* 2948 Dothan Ln., Dallas, TX 75229 (SAN 686-6069) Tel 214-247-5390.

Churchilliana Co., *(Churchilliana; 0-917684),* 4629 Sunset Dr., Sacramento, CA 95822 (SAN 211-2248) Tel 916-448-8053.

Chute, Phillip B., Corporation, *(Chute Corp; 0-930981),* 3585 Main St., Riverside, CA 92501 (SAN 678-8866) Tel 714-686-6970.

Cichy, Helen J., *(H J Cichy; 0-9601852),* Brandon, MN 56315 (SAN 211-190X).

†**Cider Mill Pr.,** *(Cider Mill; 0-910380),* P.O. Box 211, Stratford, CT 06497 (SAN 201-7792) Tel 203-378-4066; *CIP.*

Ciga Pr., *(Ciga Pr; 0-942574),* Box 654, Fallbrook, CA 92028 (SAN 239-6289) Tel 619-728-9308.

Cimarron Pr., Inc., *(Cimarron Pr; 0-9609106),* 1721 S. Tyler, Amarillo, TX 79105 (SAN 241-2888) Tel 806-372-2364.

Cincinnati Post, The, Div. of Scripps Howard, *(Cin Post; 0-933002),* 125 E. Court St., Cincinnati, OH 45202 (SAN 220-4703) Tel 513-352-2787.

Cincinnati Schl. of Hypnosis, The, *(Cincinnati Schl; 0-936139),* 5827 Happy Hollow Rd., Suite 101, Cincinnati, OH 45150 (SAN 697-0206) Tel 513-831-3600.

Cinco Puntos Pr., *(Cinco Puntos; 0-938317),* 2709 Louisville, El Paso, TX 79930 (SAN 661-0080) Tel 915-566-9072.

CineBooks, Inc., *(Cinebooks; 0-933997),* 6135 N. Sheridan Rd., Chicago, IL 60660 (SAN 692-8838) Tel 312-274-2617; Dist. by: R. R. Bowker Co. (selected titles), 205 E. 42nd St., New York, NY 10017 (SAN 214-1191) Tel 212-916-1600; Toll free: 800-521-8110.

Circa Pr., *(Circa Pr Portland; 0-936339),* 11015 SW Collina, Portland, OR 97219 (SAN 697-8258) Tel 503-636-7241.

Circinatum Pr., *(Circinatum Pr; 0-931594),* Box 99309, Tacoma, WA 98499 (SAN 211-5522) Tel 206-588-2503.

Circle-A Pubs., *(Circle-A Pubs; 0-9614415),* 8608 E. Hubbell, Scottsdale, AZ 85257 (SAN 691-2869) Tel 602-947-8233.

Circle Fine Art Corp., *(Circle Fine Art; 0-932240),* 875 N. Michigan Ave., Suite 3160, Chicago, IL 60611 (SAN 216-1168) Tel 312-943-0664.

Circular Ltd., *(Circular Ltd; 0-916067),* One Public Square, Cleveland, OH 44113 (SAN 294-7153) Tel 216-241-2600.

Circulo de cultura panamericano, *(Circulo Cult Panam; 0-917370),* 16 Malvern Place, Verona, NJ 07044 (SAN 226-6687) Tel 201-239-3125.

Ciri-Beth, *(CIRI-BETH; 0-9609834),* P.O. Box 1331, Tacoma, WA 98401 (SAN 268-9936) Tel 206-627-0434.

Cistercian Pubns., Inc., *(Cistercian Pubns; 0-87907),* WMU Sta., Kalamazoo, MI 49008 (SAN 202-1668) Tel 616-383-4985.

†Citadel Pr., Subs. of Lyle Stuart, Inc., *(Citadel Pr; 0-8065),* 120 Enterprise Ave., Secaucus, NJ 07094 (SAN 202-1676) Tel 201-866-4199; Toll free: 800-572-6657; *CIP.*

Citation Press *See* Scholastic, Inc.

Cite Press, *(CITE Pr; 0-9611122),* P.O. Box, Huntington Station, NY 11746 (SAN 282-8812) Tel 516-673-8187.

Citizen Involvement Training Project, *(Citizen Involve; 0-934210),* c/o Univ. of Massachusetts, 225 Schl. of Education, Amherst, MA 01003 (SAN 203-3089) Tel 413-545-2038.

Citizen Publishing, *(Citizen Pub; 0-9615867),* Box 44, Chapel Hill, NC 27514 (SAN 696-3021) Tel 919-942-2194.

Citizens' Energy Project, *(Citizens Energy; 0-89988),* 1110 Sixth St. NW, No. 300, Washington, DC 20001-3687 (SAN 213-4799) Tel 202-289-4999.

Citizens Forum on Self-Government, National Municipal League, *(Citizens Forum Gov),* 55 W. 44th St., New York, NY 10036 (SAN 225-073X) Tel 212-730-7930.

Citizens in Defense of Civil Liberties, *(Citizens Defense; 0-9608328),* Suite 918, 343 S. Dearborn St., Chicago, IL 60604 (SAN 240-5288) Tel 312-939-2492.

City College of New York, Physics, *(City Coll Physics; 0-9611452),* Convent Ave. at 138th St., New York, NY 10031 (SAN 283-1074) Tel 212-690-6923.

City College Workshop Ctr., *(City Coll Wk; 0-918374),* Convent Ave. & 136th St., N. Academic Ctr. 4th Flr. Rm.200, New York, NY 10031 (SAN 209-9233) Tel 212-690-4162.

City Desk Inc. The, *(City Desk; 0-9614280),* 1346 Connecticut Ave. NW, Washington, DC 20036 (SAN 687-4398) Tel 202-775-8587.

City in Print Bibliography, *(City in Print-Bibl Proj; 0-918010; 0-88874),* P.O. Box 40157, Tucson, AZ 85717 (SAN 209-231X) Tel 602-795-9719; Dist. by: ICU Publisher, P.O. Box 40157, Tucson, AZ 85717 (SAN 219-368X).

†City Lights Bks., *(City Lights; 0-87286),* 261 Columbus Ave., San Francisco, CA 94133 (SAN 202-1684) Tel 415-362-8193; Dist. by: Subterranean Co., 1327 W. Second, P.O. Box 10233, Eugene, OR 97440 (SAN 169-7102) Tel 503-343-6324; *CIP.*

City Miner Bks., *(City Miner Bks; 0-933944),* P.O. Box 176, Berkeley, CA 94701 (SAN 222-7010) Tel 415-841-1511; Dist. by: Bookpeople, 2929 Fifth St., Berkeley, CA 94710 (SAN 168-9517); Dist. by: Publishers Group West, 5855 Beaudry St., Emeryville, CA 94608 (SAN 202-8522) Tel 415-658-3453.

City National Bank & Trust Co. of Rockford, *(City Bank-Rockford; 0-9602150),* Box 1628, 1100 Broadway, Rockford, IL 61110 (SAN 212-4920).

†City of Baltimore, Dept. of Legislative Reference, *(City Baltimore; 0-916623),* City Archives & Records Management Office , 211 E. Pleasant St., Rm. 201, Baltimore, MD 21202 (SAN 296-4791) Tel 301-396-4861; *CIP.*

City of Cleveland, *(City of Cleveland; 0-9615479),* Bolivar County Library, 104 Leflore Ave., Cleveland, MS 38732 (SAN 696-3099) Tel 601-843-2774.

City of Cocoa Beach, Florida, *(City of Cocoa Beach; 0-9616571),* P.O. Box 280, Cocoa Beach, FL 32923 (SAN 661-0099); 2 S. Orlando Ave., Cocoa Beach, FL 32931 (SAN 661-0102) Tel 305-783-4911.

City of Edina, *(City Edina; 0-9605054),* 4801 W. 50th St., Edina, MN 55424 (SAN 219-774X) Tel 612-927-8861.

City of Hope, *(City Hope; 0-940876),* 1500 E. Duarte Rd., Duarte, CA 91010 (SAN 209-1267) Tel 818-359-8111.

Cityhill Publishing, Div. of Christian Fellowship of Columbia, *(Cityhill Pub; 0-939159),* 4600 Christian Fellowship Rd., Columbia, MO 65203 (SAN 662-9393) Tel 314-445-8561.

Civic-Data Corp., *(Civic Data; 0-937628),* 523 Superior Ave., Newport Beach, CA 92663 (SAN 204-3351) Tel 714-646-1623; Orders to: Southern California Business Directory, 523 Superior Ave., Newport Beach, CA 92663 (SAN 661-9754) Tel 714-646-1623; Toll free: 800-824-9896.

Civil War Round Table of New York, *(Civil War; 0-910382),* 168 Weyford Terr., Garden City, NY 11530 (SAN 202-3490).

Civilized Pubns., *(Civilized Pubns; 0-933405),* 2019 S. Seventh St., Philadelphia, PA 19148 (SAN 691-4829) Tel 215-467-0744; Dist. by: New Leaf Distributing, The, 1020 White St., SW, Atlanta, GA 30310 (SAN 169-1449) Tel 404-755-2665; Toll free: 800-241-3829.

Claitors Publishing Div., *(Claitors; 0-87511),* 3165 S. Acadian at Interstate 10, Box 239, Baton Rouge, LA 70821 (SAN 206-8346).

Clar, Raymond C., *(C R Clar; 0-9613635),* 1681 Parkmead Way, Sacramento, CA 95822 (SAN 678-9110); Dist. by: River Mist Distributors, 624 University Ave., Palo Alto, CA 94301 (SAN 200-7827).

Clare Co., *(Clare Co; 0-918848),* 8001 Lockwood Ave., Skokie, IL 60077 (SAN 210-4040).

Claremont Graduate School, Ctr. for Developmental Studies in Education, *(Claremont Grad; 0-941742),* Harper Hall 200, Claremont, CA 91711 (SAN 239-1813) Tel 714-621-8075.

Claremont Hse., *(Claremont House; 0-913860),* 231 E. San Fernando No. 1, San Jose, CA 95112 (SAN 203-6606) Tel 408-293-8650.

Claremont Institute for the Study of Statesmanship and Political Philosophy, The, *(Claremont Inst; 0-930783),* 4650 Arrow Hwy., Suite D-6, Montclair, CA 91763-1223 (SAN 677-6191) Tel 714-621-6825.

Claremont Pr., *(Claremont CA; 0-941358),* 2819 Arizona, Suite D, Santa Monica, CA 90404-1527 (SAN 240-8694) Tel 213-828-2868; Orders to: Box 3434, Will Rogers Sta., Santa Monica, CA 90403 (SAN 661-9762).

Claremont Research & Pubns., Inc., *(Claremont; 0-912439),* 160 Claremont Ave., New York, NY 10027 (SAN 265-2196) Tel 212-662-0707.

Claremount Press, *(Claremount Pr),* Box 177, Cooper Sta., New York, NY 10003 (SAN 219-466X)

Claretian Pubns., *(Claretian Pubns; 0-89570),* 221 W. Madison St., Chicago, IL 60606 (SAN 207-5598) Tel 312-236-7782.

Clarion Bks. *See* Ticknor & Fields

Clarion Call Bks., Subs. of Clarion Call Music, *(Clar Call Bks; 0-935993),* 102 Bluebonnet Tr., Keene, TX 76059 (SAN 696-7140) Tel 817-645-8785; P.O. Box 45, Keene, TX 76059 (SAN 696-214X).

Clarion Classics *See* Zondervan Publishing Hse.

Clarion's Call Publishing, *(Clarions Call Pub; 0-9617176),* 225 Cory Ave., Prescott, AZ 86301 (SAN 663-1703) Tel 602-778-2090.

Clarity Pr., *(Clarity Pr; 0-932863),* 3277 Roswell Rd., NE, Suite 469, Atlanta, GA 30305 (SAN 688-9530) Tel 404-662-6806.

†Clarity Publishing, *(Clarity Pub; 0-915488),* 75 Champlain St., Albany, NY 12204 (SAN 211-5093) Tel 518-465-4591; *CIP.*

Clark, Arthur H., Co., *(A H Clark; 0-87062),* P.O. Box 230, Glendale, CA 91209 (SAN 201-2006) Tel 213-254-1600.

Clark, Dean, Pubs., Div. of Dean Clark Communications, *(Dean Clark; 0-935091),* P.O. Box 3192, Palmer, PA 18043 (SAN 695-0647) Tel 215-253-8263.

Clark, Eunice Newbold, *(E N Clark; 0-9614199),* 6474 Tulip Ln., Dallas, TX 75230 (SAN 688-2625) Tel 214-361-2972.

Clark, I. E., Inc., *(I E Clark; 0-88680),* St. Johns Rd., Schulenburg, TX 78956 (SAN 282-7433) Tel 409-743-3232; Orders to: P.O. Box 246, Schulenburg, TX 78956 (SAN 662-2003).

Clark, Merrian E., *(M Clark; 0-910384),* 22151 Clarendon St., P.O. Box 505, Woodland Hills, CA 91365 (SAN 203-9419) Tel 818-347-1677.

Clark, Rosemarie, *(R Clark; 0-9508551),* 435 City Centre Mart, Middletown, OH 45042 (SAN 682-7764).

Clark, Sterling & Francine, Art Institute, *(S & F Clark Art; 0-931102),* P.O. Box 8, Williamstown, MA 01267 (SAN 222-8491).

Clark County Historical Society, *(Clark County Hist Soc),* 300 W. Main St., Springfield, OH 45504 (SAN 204-3378) Tel 513-324-0657.

Clark Publishing, *(Clark Pub KY; 0-939053),* P.O. Box 435, Henderson, KY 42420 (SAN 662-9296); 3020 Zion Rd., Henderson, KY 42420 (SAN 662-930X) Tel 502-827-8995.

Clark Publishing Co., *(Clark Pub; 0-931054),* Dist. by: The Caxton Printers, Ltd., P.O. Box 700, Caldwell, ID 83605 (SAN 201-9698) Tel 208-459-7421.

Clark Publishing, Inc., *(Clark Inc; 0-913821),* P.O. Box 11003, Tacoma, WA 98411 (SAN 286-0481) Tel 206-472-4469; Orders to: P.O. Box 5603, Tacoma, WA 98405 (SAN 286-049X).

†Clark Univ. Pr., *(Clark U Pr; 0-914206),* 950 Main St., Worcester, MA 01610 (SAN 205-6135) Tel 617-793-7206; *CIP.*

Clarke, Peter, *(P Clarke; 0-9612162),* P.O. Box 38, Sugar Hill, NH 03585 (SAN 287-7376) Tel 603-823-5976.

Clarke Historical Library, Div. of Central Michigan Univ., *(Clarke His; 0-916699),* Central Michigan Univ., Pk. 408, Mt. Pleasant, MI 48859 (SAN 218-6799) Tel 517-774-3352.

Clarke Memorial Museum, Inc., *(Clarke Memorial; 0-9615641),* 240 E St., Eureka, CA 95501 (SAN 278-4505) Tel 707-443-1947.

Clarksburg-Harrison Bicentennial Committee, *(Clarksburg-Harrison; 0-9615566),* 404 W. Pike St., Clarksburg, WV 26301 (SAN 696-4877) Tel 304-624-6512.

Clarus Music, Ltd., *(Clarus Music; 0-86704),* 340 Bellevue Ave., Yonkers, NY 10703 (SAN 216-6615) Tel 914-591-7715.

Class Media Productions, *(Class Media Prod; 0-942098),* P.O. Box 26465, Los Angeles, CA 90026 (SAN 237-9961) Tel 213-665-2970; Dist. by: Publishers Group West, 58 Beaudry St., Emeryville, CA 94608 (SAN 202-8522) Tel 415-658-3453.

Classic *See* Exposition Pr. of Florida, Inc.

Classic Car Club of America, *(Classic Car),* P.O. Box 443, Madison, NJ 07940 (SAN 225-5057).

Classic Consultants Pr., Div. of Classic Consultants, Ltd., *(Classic Cons; 0-935499),* 3402 E. Libby, Phoenix, AZ 85032 (SAN 696-4966) Tel 602-992-7441.

Classic Fire Pictures, *(Classic Fire; 0-938229),* P.O. Box 240382, Memphis, TN 38124 (SAN 661-0110); 4503 Charleswood, Memphis, TN 38117 (SAN 661-0129) Tel 901-767-9367.

Classic Furniture Kits, *(Classic Furn Kits),* 343 Lantana St., Camarillo, CA 93010 (SAN 203-6614).

Classic House, *(Classic Hse; 0-931954),* P.O. Box 87564, San Diego, CA 92138-7564 (SAN 211-5816); 3409 Waco St., Suite 1, San Diego, CA 92117 (SAN 660-9457) Tel 619-275-3112.

Classic Nonfiction Library, *(Classic Nonfic; 0-9606540),* Woodward, PA 16882 (SAN 203-6622).

Classic Press *See* Gold Book, Publications

Classic Pubs., *(Classic CA; 0-9609762),* P.O. Box 49454, Los Angeles, CA 90049 (SAN 264-326X) Tel 213-476-6869.

Classic Publishers/Louisville, *(Classic Pub; 0-937222),* Prospect, KY 40059 (SAN 215-0662) Tel 502-228-4446.

Classic Theatre for Children, *(Classic Theatre Child; 0-938735),* 146 York St., New Haven, CT 06511 (SAN 661-5031) Tel 203-624-7636.

Classical Folia, *(Classical Folia),* College of the Holy Cross, Worcester, MA 01610 (SAN 207-5369).

Classics on Computer, *(Classics Comp; 0-938523),* 5435 Columbus Ave., Van Nuys, CA 91411 (SAN 661-1222) Tel 818-785-7340.

Classics Unlimited, Inc., *(Classics Unltd; 0-936660),* 2121 Arlington Ave., Caldwell, ID 83605 (SAN 214-1868).

Clatworthy Colorvues, *(Clatworthy; 0-918290),* 111 1/2 Riverview, Santa Cruz, CA 95062 (SAN 209-5424) Tel 408-426-6401.

Clausen, Muriel C., *(M C Clausen; 0-9603664),* 780 W. Grand Ave., Oakland, CA 94612 (SAN 213-7305).

Claussen Books, *(Claussen Bks; 0-9603266),* 434 Arballo Dr., San Francisco, CA 94132 (SAN 211-9412) Tel 415-585-0716.

Clawson Printing Co., *(Clawson),* 107 W. Second, Frankfort, KS 66427 (SAN 215-1367).

Clay-Jon Publishers, *(Clay-Jon Pubs; 0-913103),* P.O. Box 59221, Birmingham, AL 35259-9221 (SAN 283-0310) Tel 205-951-3681; 5140 Crowley Dr., Birmingham, AL 35259-9221 (SAN 699-5721).

Claymont Communications, *(Claymont Comm; 0-934254),* Box 112, Charles Town, WV 25414 (SAN 211-7010) Tel 304-725-1523.

Clayton Publishing House, Inc., *(Clayton Pub Hse; 0-915644),* 3438 Russell Blvd., Suite 203, St. Louis, MO 63104 (SAN 158-6807) Tel 314-772-5757; Dist. by: People Lovers Bks, 27 N. Gore, Webster Groves, MO 63117 (SAN 200-6138).

Cleaning Consultant Services, Inc., *(Cleaning Cons; 0-9601054),* 1512 Western Ave., Seattle, WA 98101 (SAN 208-2179) Tel 206-682-9748.

Clear Creek Pubs., Inc., *(Clear Creek; 0-9609318),* P.O. Box 8008, Boulder, CO 80306 (SAN 260-1753) Tel 303-449-1278.

Clear Fork Publishing, *(Clear Fork Pub),* P.O. Box 569, Tomball, TX 77375 (SAN 698-1879).

Clear Fork Ranch, Inc., *(Clear Fork Ranch; 0-9616868),* 4800 Bryant Irvin Ct., Ft. Worth, TX 76109-4103 (SAN 661-1575) Tel 817-737-3703.

Clear View Pubns., *(Clear View Pubns; 0-941156),* P.O. Box 3008, Fox Valley Mall, Aurora, IL 60505 (SAN 237-9929).

Clearview Press, *(Clearview Pr; 0-9606976),* 1927 N Hudson Ave., Chicago, IL 60614 (SAN 238-9258).

Clearwater Junior Woman's Club, *(Clearwater; 0-9615642),* P.O. Box 4061, Clearwater, FL 33518 (SAN 696-3102) Tel 813-725-2802; 105 Woodburn Ct., Safety Harbor, FL 33572 (SAN 696-3110).

Clearwater Publishing Co., Inc., *(Clearwater Pub; 0-8287; 0-88354),* 1995 Broadway, New York, NY 10023 (SAN 201-8969) Tel 212-873-2100. Primarily microfilm & microfiche, but also books, audiocassettes & videocassettes on American Indian studies, art, & architechture, history, Judaica, Latin American studies, law & peace studies, material culture. Microform distributor for ACRPP, Alpha COM GmbH, Bibliotheque Nationale, CREDOC, Emmett Microforms, France Expansion, Hachette Microeditions, Inter Documentation Co. (IDC), Irish Microforms, The Irish Times, MFO Mikrofilm Gmbh, Microform Academic Publishers, Mikropress GmbH, Mindata Ltd., Georg Olms Verlag, Studio Harcourt, World Microfilms Pubns., Yushudo Booksellers.

Cleckley-Thigpen Psychiatric Associates, The, *(Cleckley-Thigpen),* P.O. Box 2619, Augusta, GA 30904 (SAN 238-051X) Tel 404-724-7492.

Cleis Pr., *(Cleis Pr; 0-939416),* P.O. Box 8933, Pittsburgh, PA 15221 (SAN 284-9968) Tel 412-731-3863; P.O. Box 14684, San Francisco, CA 94114 (SAN 284-9976); Dist. by: Bookpeople, 2929 Fifth St., Berkeley, CA 94710 (SAN 168-9517) Tel 415-549-3030; Dist. by: Baker & Taylor, Eastern Div., 50 Kirby Ave., Somerville, NJ 08876 (SAN 169-4901); Dist. by: Inland Bk. Co., 22 Hemingway St., East Haven, CT 06512 (SAN 200-4151) Tel 203-467-4257.

Clement, David D. & Dorothy Z., , *(D Clement; 0-9601618),* 3931 Villa Ct., Fair Oaks, CA 95628 (SAN 210-7112) Tel 916-966-1666.

Clementine Press, *(Clementine Pr; 0-943880),* 2342 SW Thorton, Des Moines, IA 50321 (SAN 241-1024) Tel 515-285-0588.

Clene Publications, *(Clene Pubns),* 620 Michigan Ave. NE, Washington, DC 20064 (SAN 277-6650). Out of business.

Clergy And Laity Concerned Chicago, *(Clergy & Laity; 0-931879),* 17 N State No. 904, Chicago, IL 60602 (SAN 686-0494) Tel 312-899-1800.

Cleveland-Cliffs, *(Cleveland Cliffs; 0-9607174),* 1460 Union Congress Bldg., Cleveland, OH 44115 (SAN 239-0760) Tel 216-241-2356.

Cleveland Clinic Foundation, *(Clvlnd Clinic Found; 0-9615424),* 9500 Euclid Ave., Cleveland, OH 44106 (SAN 696-3196) Tel 216-444-2662.

Cleveland Landmarks, Pr., Inc., *(Cleveland Landmarks; 0-936760),* 4601 E. Pleasant Valley Rd., Cleveland, OH 44131 (SAN 214-2929).

Cleveland State Univ. Poetry Ctr., *(Cleveland St Univ Poetry Ctr; 0-914946),* Cleveland State Univ., Cleveland, OH 44115 (SAN 209-2816) Tel 216-687-3986; Dist. by: Nacscorp, Inc., 528 E. Lorain St., Oberlin, OH 44074 (SAN 169-6823) Tel 216-775-1561.

Cleworth, Charles W., Pub., *(C W Cleworth; 0-934212),* 1736 Downing St., Denver, CO 80218 (SAN 212-7326) Tel 303-832-5000.

Cleydale Engineering, *(Cleydale Engineering; 0-937303),* Rte. 1, Box 217-B, Blacksburg, VA 24060 (SAN 658-7739) Tel 708-775-4915.

Click!, Inc., *(Click Inc; 0-937187),* 7398 Washington Ave., S., Eden Prairie, MN 55344 (SAN 658-697X) Tel 612-944-8977.

Click's Cookbooks, *(Click's Cookbooks; 0-9612920),* 2714 NE 95th St., Seattle, WA 98115 (SAN 292-3300).

Cliffhanger Press *See Ed-it Productions*

Cliff's Notes, Inc., *(Cliffs; 0-8220),* 1701 P St., Lincoln, NE 68501 (SAN 202-1706) Tel 402-477-6971; Toll free: 800-228-4078.

Cline-Sigmon Pubs., *(Cline-Sigmon; 0-914760),* P.O. Box 367-T, Hickory, NC 28601 (SAN 205-6151) Tel 704-322-5090.

Clinical Hearing Consultants, *(Clinical Hearing Consults; 0-9614656),* 8100 E. Indian School Rd., P.O. Box 398, Scottsdale, AZ 85252 (SAN 692-2031) Tel 602-941-1200.

Clinical Psychology Publishing Co., Inc. (CPPC), *(Clinical Psych; 0-88422),* 4 Conant Square, Brandon, VT 05733 (SAN 201-7679) Tel 802-247-6871.

Clinical Sociology Assn., *(Clin Soc Assn; 0-942756),* c/o General Hall, Inc., 5 Talon Way, Dix Hills, NY 11746 (SAN 692-8315) Tel 516-243-0155.

Clinitemp, Inc., *(Clinitemp; 0-937450),* P.O. Box 40273, Indianapolis, IN 46240 (SAN 215-1375) Tel 317-872-4155.

Clipboard Pubns., *(Clipboard; 0-9606084),* 606 Pine St., Coulee Dam, WA 99116 (SAN 216-8006) Tel 509-633-1546.

Cliveden Pr., The, *(Cliveden Pr; 0-941694),* Suite COMM. 2, 1133 13th St., NW, Washington, DC 20005 (SAN 277-6669) Tel 202-789-0231.

Cloak & Dagger Pubns., *(Cloak Dagger; 0-937617),* 825 25th St., Ogden, UT 84401 (SAN 659-1302) Tel 801-394-4162.

Clodele Enterprises, Inc., *(Clodele; 0-930416),* 2004 Vaugine Ave., Pine Bluff, AR 71601 (SAN 209-5432) Tel 501-534-8804.

Clone Records, Inc., *(Clone Records; 0-9606222),* 44 Maple Rd., Rocky Point, NY 11778 (SAN 219-7766).

Close Up Foundation, *(Close Up Foun; 0-932765),* 1235 Jefferson Davis Hwy., Arlington, VA 22202 (SAN 679-1980) Tel 703-892-5400; Toll free: 800-336-5479; Dist. by: Social Studies Schl. Services, 10000 Culver Blvd., Box 802, Culver City, CA 90232 (SAN 168-9592) Tel 213-839-2436; Dist. by: Close Up Foundation, 1235 Jefferson Davis Hwy., Arlington, VA 22202 (SAN 679-1980) Tel 703-892-5400; Toll free: 800-336-5479.

Closing the Gap, Inc., *(Closing Gap; 0-932719),* P.O. Box 68, Henderson, MN 56044 (SAN 669-5833) Tel 612-248-3294.

Closson Pr., *(Closson Pr; 0-933227),* 1935 Sampson Dr., Apollo, PA 15613-9238 (SAN 297-1712) Tel 412-337-4482.

Clothespin Fever Pr., *(Clothespin Fever Pr; 0-9616572),* 5529 N. Figueroa, Los Angeles, CA 90042 (SAN 699-8119) Tel 213-257-4968.

Clothing Manufacturers Assn. of the U. S. A., *(Clothing Mfrs),* 1290 Ave. of the Americas, New York, NY 10104 (SAN 224-6198) Tel 212-757-6664.

Cloud Marauder Pr., *(Cloud Marauder),* Dist. by: SBD: Small Press Distribution, 1814 San Pablo Ave., Berkeley n, CA 94702 (SAN 204-5826) Tel 415-549-3336.

Cloud Pr., *(Cloud Pr; 0-935713),* 1422 Bonita Ave., Berkeley, CA 94709 (SAN 696-3226) Tel 415-526-1969.

Cloud Ridge Pr., *(Cloud Ridge Pr; 0-9615617),* P.O. Box 926, Boulder, CO 80306-0926 (SAN 696-3242) Tel 303-442-6163; Sugarloaf Star Rte., Boulder, CO 80302 (SAN 696-3250).

Cloud 10 Creations Inc., *(Cloud Ten; 0-910349),* P.O. Box 99, Cazenovia, NY 13035 (SAN 241-2896) Tel 315-655-9517.

Cloudcap, Div. of Alpenbooks, *(Cloudcap; 0-938567),* P.O. Box 27344, Seattle, WA 98125 (SAN 661-2598); 11309 Durland Pl. NE, Seattle, WA 98125 (SAN 661-2601) Tel 206-365-9192.

Cloudcrest, *(Cloudcrest; 0-9612340),* Box 333, Nashville, IN 47448 (SAN 263-9726).

Clover International, *(Clover Intl; 0-911249),* P.O. Box 928, Adelphi, MD 20783-0928 (SAN 269-0373) Tel 301-431-6617.

Clyde Pr., The, *(Clyde Pr; 0-933190),* 373 Lincoln Pkwy, Buffalo, NY 14216 (SAN 213-8395) Tel 716-875-4713.

Clymer Pubns., *(Clymer Pubns; 0-89287),* P.O. Box 4520, Arleta, CA 91333-4520 (SAN 204-3416) Tel 818-767-7660; 12860 Muscatine St., Arleta, CA 91333 (SAN 658-0327).

CMDRS-Rusty's Maps, *(Cmdrs-Rusty's; 0-943714),* P.O. Box 5, Arvada, CO 80001-0005 (SAN 241-0087) Tel 303-421-8833.

Coach Hse. Pr., Inc., *(Coach Hse; 0-88020),* P.O. Box 458, Morton Grove, IL 60053 (SAN 201-7709) Tel 312-967-1777.

Coal Information Network of Kentucky, *(Coal Info Net),* Ashland Community College, 1400 College Dr., Ashland, KY 41101 (SAN 679-1999).

Coalition for Equity of New York & New Jersey, *(C E NY NJ; 0-9617090),* 32 Washington Pl., Rm. 72, New York, NY 10003 (SAN 662-5851) Tel 212-598-2705.

Coalition of Independent College-University Students, *(Coalition Ind Coll),* 1 Dupont Cir., NE, Washington, DC 20036 (SAN 225-7815) Tel 202-659-1747.

Coalition of Northeastern Governors Policy Research Ctr., *(Coalition NE Govn; 0-914193),* 400 N. Capitol St. NW, Suite 382, Washington, DC 20001 (SAN 287-7317).

Coalition on Women & Religion, *(Coalition Women-Relig; 0-9603042),* 4759 15th Ave. NE, Seattle, WA 98105 (SAN 210-7880) Tel 206-525-1213.

Coalson-Kuhn Publishing Co., *(Coalson-Kuhn; 0-915551),* P.O. Box 913, Denton, TX 76201 (SAN 291-1183) Tel 817-387-4006.

Coast Aire Pubns., *(Coast Aire; 0-9606874),* 2823 N. Yucca St., Chandler, AZ 85224 (SAN 217-3433) Tel 602-899-6151.

Coast to Coast, Bks., *(Coast to Coast; 0-9602664),* 2934 NE 16th Ave., Portland, OR 97212 (SAN 212-7334) Tel 503-282-5891.

Coast to Coast Pubns., Inc., *(Coast Pubns NY; 0-915816),* 679A Hempstead Turnpike, Franklin Square, NY 11010 (SAN 223-3053) Tel 516-485-4234.

Coastal Education & Research Foundation, Inc., *(CERF Inc; 0-938415),* P.O. Box 8068, Charlottesville, VA 22906 (SAN 661-0137); 355 W. Rio Rd., Charlottesville, VA 22901 (SAN 661-0145) Tel 305-523-6768.

Coastal Plains Publishing Co., *(Coastal Plains; 0-9607300),* P.O. Box 1101, Danville, VA 24541 (SAN 239-183X) Tel 919-299-7581.

Coastal Pr., *(Coastal Pr FL; 0-9615728),* P.O. Box 5343, Sarasota, FL 33579 (SAN 695-2887) Tel 813-922-6960; 4014 Red Rock Ln., Sarasota, FL 33581 (SAN 696-0375).

Names

Coastlight Pr., *(Coastlight Pr; 0-9606288),* 210 A California Ave., Palo Alto, CA 94306 (SAN 223-2146) Tel 415-325-9088; Dist. by: Bookpeople, 2929 Fifth St., Berkeley, CA 94710 (SAN 168-9517) Tel 415-549-3030.

Coastline Assoc., *(Coastline Assoc; 0-9615425),* 3111 Camino del Rio N., Suite 407, San Diego, CA 92123 (SAN 695-7374) Tel 619-563-0304.

Coastline Publishing, Co., *(Coastline Pub Co; 0-932927),* P.O. Box 223062, Carmel, CA 93922 (SAN 692-9508) Tel 408-625-9388; Dist. by: Bookpeople, 2929 Fifth St., Berkeley, CA 94710 (SAN 168-9517) Tel 415-549-3030; Toll free: 800-227-1516; Dist. by: Inland Book Co., 22 Hemingway Ave., P.O. Box 261, East Haven, CT 06512 (SAN 200-4151) Tel 203-467-4257; Toll free: 800-243-0138; Dist. by: Baker & Taylor Co., Eastern Div., 50 Kirby Ave., Somerville, NJ 08876 (SAN 169-4901) Tel 201-526-8000.

Coates, Pamela, Antiques, *(P Coates; 0-9600678),* 1506 Harvey Rd., Ardencroft, DE 19810 (SAN 207-3919).

Cobb Group, Inc., The, *(Cobb Group; 0-936767),* 301 N. Hurstbourne Ln., Suite 115, Louisville, KY 40222 (SAN 699-8860) Tel 502-425-7756.

Cobble & Mickle Bks., *(Cobble Mickle Bks),* P.O. Box 3521, San Diego, CA 92103-0160 (SAN 659-395X) Tel 619-291-4235; 4285 Maryland St., San Diego, CA 92103 (SAN 659-3968); Dist. by: Quality Bks., Inc., 918 Sherwood Dr., Lake Bluff, IL 60044-2204 (SAN 169-2127).

Cobblesmith, *(Cobblesmith; 0-89166),* Box 191, RFD 1, Freeport, ME 04032 (SAN 210-346X) Tel 207-865-6495.

Cobblestone Publishing, Inc., *(Cobblestone Pub; 0-9607638),* 20 Grove Street, Peterborough, NH 03458 (SAN 237-9937).

Cobra Co., The, *(Cobra Co; 0-933907),* 8842 SW 72 St., Apt. J-258, Miami, FL 33173 (SAN 692-7459) Tel 305-596-2887.

Cobra Press, *(Cobra Pr; 0-9600384),* 15381 Chelsea Dr., San Jose, CA 95124 (SAN 203-6657) Tel 408-559-4899.

Coburn, Warren, *(Coburn; 0-9614044),* 516 N. 11th St. Apt. D, Las Vegas, NV 89101 (SAN 684-7846).

Cochran, Debby, *(D Cochran; 0-9606142),* 513 E. Main St., Thurmont, MD 21788 (SAN 217-5096) Tel 301-271-2143.

Cochran Publishing Co., *(Cochran Pub; 0-936259),* Suburban Rte., Box 193, Rapid City, SD 57701 (SAN 697-3582) Tel 605-232-7242.

Cochrun, Inc., *(Cochrun; 0-9601050),* 11933 72nd Ave., N., Seminole, FL 33542 (SAN 209-0627) Tel 813-398-5939.

Cocinero Press, *(Cocinero Pr; 0-9606366),* Box 11583, Phoenix, AZ 85061 (SAN 219-7774).

Cockle, George R., Assocs., *(G R Cockle; 0-916160),* P.O. Box 1224, Downtown Sta., Omaha, NE 68101 (SAN 211-3104).

Cockpit Management Training, Inc., *(Cockpit Mgmt Trng; 0-938051),* P.O. Box 205, Piedmont, OK 73078 (SAN 661-017X); 1209 Blugil Dr., NE, Piedmont, OK 73078 (SAN 661-0188) Tel 405-373-1357.

Cocoa Beach Woman's Club, *(Cocoa Beach W; 0-9615567),* 215 Beachwood Blvd., Melbourne Beach, FL 32951 (SAN 696-3285) Tel 305-724-6952.

Coda Pr., Inc., *(Coda Pr; 0-930956),* 700 W. Badger Rd., Suite 101, Madison, WI 53713 (SAN 211-4968). Moved, left no forwarding address.

CoDe North, Inc., *(CoDe North; 0-9614942),* 622 Keel Ave., Rear, Memphis, TN 38107 (SAN 693-661X) Tel 901-527-7704.

Coelacanth Pubns., *(Coelacanth; 0-918239),* 55 Bluecoat, Irvine, CA 92720 (SAN 657-5846) Tel 714-544-0914.

Coffee Break Press, *(Coffee Break; 0-933992),* P.O. Box 103, Burley, WA 98322 (SAN 212-341X) Tel 206-857-4329.

Coffee Hse. Pr./Toothpaste Pr., *(Coffee Hse; 0-915124; 0-918273),* P.O. Box 10870, Minneapolis, MN 55440 (SAN 206-3883) Tel 612-338-0125; Dist. by: Consortium Bk. Sales & Distribution, 213 E. Fourth St., St. Paul, MN 55101 (SAN 200-6049) Tel 612-221-9035. *Imprints:* Hot Chocolate Books (Hot Choco); Morning Coffee Chapbooks (Morning Coffee).

Coffeetable Pubns., *(Coffeetable; 0-938252),* P.O. Box 884, Bay Minette, AL 36507 (SAN 215-739X) Tel 205-937-6432.

Coffin, George, *(Coffin; 0-939452),* 257 Trapelo Rd., Waltham, MA 02154 (SAN 202-1714) Tel 617-893-0057.

Cogan Productions, *(Cogan Prod; 0-939025),* 555 W. Illinois Ave., Aurora, IL 60506 (SAN 662-6491) Tel 312-896-6555.

Cogill, Burgess, *(B Cogill; 0-9617227),* 350 University Ave., San Francisco, CA 94134 (SAN 663-3943) Tel 415-644-1571.

Cohasco, Inc., Div. of Snyder Graphics, *(Cohasco; 0-940746),* P.O. Drawer 821, Yonkers, NY 10702 (SAN 219-7243) Tel 914-476-8500.

Cohen, Alan, *(A Cohen; 0-910367),* P.O. Box 1036, New Brunswick, NJ 08903 (SAN 239-4227) Tel 201-699-1744; Dist. by: Coleman Graphics, 99 Milbar Blvd., Farmingdale, NY 11735 (SAN 238-1508) Tel 516-293-0383; Dist. by: New Leaf Distributing, 1020 White St. SW, Atlanta, GA 30310 (SAN 169-1449) Tel 404-755-2665; Toll free: 800-241-3829; Dist. by: DeVorss & Co., P.O. Box 550, 1046 Princeton Dr., Marina del Rey, CA 90294 (SAN 168-9886).

Cohen, Leo, *(L Cohen; 0-9613366),* P.O. Box 3402, La Jolla, CA 92038 (SAN 657-1492) Tel 619-453-4163.

Cohen Publisher, *(Cohen Pub; 0-9614943),* 1855 Sanford St., Philadelphia, PA 19116 (SAN 693-6555) Tel 215-698-7726.

Coin & Currency Institute, Inc., *(Coin & Curr; 0-87184),* P.O. Box 1057, Clifton, NJ 07014 (SAN 203-5650) Tel 201-471-1441.

Coit & Assocs., *(Coit & Assocs; 0-936475),* P.O. Box 296, South Laguna, CA 92677 (SAN 698-1283) Tel 714-499-5848.

Coker Publishing, Hse., *(Coker Pub; 0-933012),* 135 Gran-de Ct., Fayetteville, GA 30214 (SAN 284-9984) Tel 404-461-3386.

Colbben Publishing Co., *(Colbben Pub; 0-938123),* 8455 W. 38th Ave., Wheat Ridge, CO 80033 (SAN 661-0196) Tel 303-431-7552.

Colburn & Tegg, *(Colburn & Tegg; 0-9600594),* 19709 Hollis Ave., Hollis, NY 11412 (SAN 209-1003) Tel 718-468-3278.

Colby College, *(Colby College; 0-910394),* College Editor's Office, Waterville, ME 04901 (SAN 203-5669) Tel 207-872-3000.

Cold Dreams Enterprises, *(Cold Dreams Ent; 0-937549),* P.O. Box 6022, Denver, CO 80206 (SAN 659-1213) Tel 303-973-0593; 8007 Culebra Peak, Littleton, CO 80127 (SAN 659-1221).

†Cold Spring Harbor Laboratory, *(Cold Spring Harbor; 0-87969),* P.O. Box 100, Cold Spring Harbor, NY 11724 (SAN 203-6185) Tel 516-367-8351; Toll free: 800-843-4388; *CIP.*

Colden United Methodist Women, *(Colden Method; 0-9615568),* P.O. Box 177, Colden, NY 14033 (SAN 696-3331) Tel 716-941-3197; 8476 Blanchard Rd., Colden, NY 14033 (SAN 696-334X).

Cole, David M./Outreach Books, *(Cole-Outreach),* P.O. Box 425, Corona, CA 91718 (SAN 214-2589).

Cole, Jim, *(J Cole; 0-9601200),* 627 Kay St., Fairbanks, AK 99701 (SAN 661-9770) Tel 907-479-6107; Orders to: Ed & Janet Reynolds, Drawer D., Mill Valley, CA 94941 (SAN 269-0713) Tel 415-388-1621.

Cole Hse., Inc., *(Cole Hse Inc; 0-936297),* P.O. Box 19526, Alexandria, VA 22320-0526 (SAN 697-3302); 702 Prince St., Alexandria, VA 22314 (SAN 697-3310) Tel 703-548-3347.

Coleman, Candy, Enterprises, *(C Coleman; 0-943768),* 1309 Main St.,Suite 103, Dallas, TX 75202 (SAN 238-2628) Tel 214-747-0429.

Coleman, Dorothy S., *(D S Coleman; 0-910396),* 4315 Van Ness St., Washington, DC 20016 (SAN 203-8811) Tel 202-966-2655.

†Coleman, Earl M., Enterprises, Inc., *(E M Coleman Ent; 0-930576),* P.O. Box T, Crugers, NY 10521 (SAN 211-1381); *CIP.*

Coleman Publishing, Inc., *(Coleman Pub; 0-942494; 0-87418),* 99 Milbar Blvd., Farmingdale, NY 11735 (SAN 238-1508) Tel 516-293-0383; Toll free: 800-227-3489.

Coles-Cumberland Pr., International Inc., *(Coles Cumber; 0-930893),* P.O. Box 9925, Phoenix, AZ 85068 (SAN 679-1964) Tel 602-943-2643.

Colgate Univ. Pr., *(Colgate U Pr; 0-912568),* 304 Lawrence Hall, Hamilton, NY 13346 (SAN 204-3181) Tel 315-824-1000.

Colgin Publishing, *(Colgin Pub; 0-9604582),* Box 301, Manlius, NY 13104 (SAN 240-0898) Tel 315-682-6081.

Colin-Pr., *(Colin-Pr; 0-9613844),* 128 Dean St., Brooklyn, NY 11201 (SAN 681-9710) Tel 718-852-7270; Dist. by: Baker & Taylor Co., Midwest Div., 501 Gladiola Ave., Momence, IL 60954 (SAN 169-2100) Tel 815-472-2444; Dist. by: The Distributors, 702 S. Michigan, South Bend, IN 46618 (SAN 169-2488) Tel 219-232-8500.

Collaborare Publishing, *(Collaborare Pub; 0-931881),* 354 Front, Upper Sandusky, OH 43351 (SAN 686-0486) Tel 419-294-3207; Dist. by: Gallopade: Carole Marsh Bks., General Delivery, Bath, NC 27808 (SAN 213-8441) Tel 919-923-4291.

Collaborative Learning Systems, *(Collaborative Learn; 0-910817),* P.O. Box 37043, Tucson, AZ 85740 (SAN 269-0721) Tel 602-626-1019.

Collage, Inc., Subs. of Whitehall Co., *(Collage Inc; 0-938728),* 1200 S. Willis Ave., Wheeling, IL 60090 (SAN 205-5244) Tel 312-541-9290.

Collateral Classics Series *See* **Washington Square Pr., Inc.**

Colleagues Pr., Inc., *(Colleagues Pr Inc; 0-937191),* Box 4007, East Lansing, MI 48823 (SAN 658-487X) Tel 517-337-1054; 311 Kensington Rd., East Lansing, MI 48823 (SAN 658-4888).

Colleasius Press, *(Colleasius Pr; 0-941036),* P.O. Box 514, Goffstown, NH 03045 (SAN 212-1522) Tel 603-529-2222.

Collector Bks., Div. of Schroeder Publishing Co., Inc., *(Collector Bks; 0-89145),* 5801 Kentucky Dam Rd., Paducah, KY 42001 (SAN 157-5368) Tel 502-898-6211; Toll free: 800-626-5420; P.O. Box 3009, Paducah, KY 42001 (SAN 200-7479).

Collector's Choice, *(Collectors Choice; 0-9602742),* c/o French-Bray Inc., P.O. Box 698, Glen Burnie, MD 21061 (SAN 204-2479) Tel 301-768-6000.

Collectors Club, Inc., *(Collectors; 0-912574),* 22 E. 35th St., New York, NY 10016-3806 (SAN 202-1722) Tel 212-683-0559.

Collector's Club of Chicago, Inc., *(Collectors Club IL; 0-916675),* 1029 N. Dearborn, Chicago, IL 60610 (SAN 297-0325) Tel 312-441-7790.

Colleen Enterprises, Inc., *(Colleen Ent; 0-9616698),* Box 23417, Honolulu, HI 96822 (SAN 661-020X); 1030D Awawamalu St., Honolulu, HI 96821 (SAN 661-0218) Tel 808-946-1226.

College Acceptance, *(Coll Acceptance; 0-9615165),* 2 Clover Ln., Randolph, NJ 07869 (SAN 694-3624) Tel 201-895-3390.

College Administration Pubns., Inc., *(Coll Admin Pubns; 0-912557),* Box 8492, Asheville, NC 28814 (SAN 240-8155) Tel 704-252-0883.

College & Univ. Personnel Assn., *(Coll & U Personnel; 0-910402),* 11 Dupont Cir., Suite 120, Washington, DC (SAN 236-5170).

College Board, The, *(College Bd; 0-87447),* 888 Seventh Ave., New York, NY 10106 (SAN 203-5677) Tel 212-582-6210; Orders to: College Board Pubns., P.O. Box 886, New York, NY 10101 (SAN 203-5685).

College Choice Pubns., *(College Choice; 0-935275),* 55 Wedgewood Rd., West Newton, MA 02165 (SAN 695-7439) Tel 617-965-4828.

College Course Guides *See* **Doubleday & Co., Inc.**

College Div. *See* **Watts, Franklin, Inc.**

†College-Hill Pr., Inc., Subs. of Little, Brown & Co., *(College-Hill; 0-316),* 4284 41st St., San Diego, CA 92105 (SAN 220-0414) Tel 619-563-8899; Toll free: 800-854-2541; Orders to: Little, Brown & Co., 200 West St., Waltham, MA 02254 (SAN 661-9789) Tel 617-890-0250; Toll free: 800-343-9204; *CIP.*

College Kids Cookbooks, *(Coll Kids Cook; 0-912848),* 624 N. Bailey Ave., Fort Worth, TX 76107 (SAN 201-761X) Tel 817-626-4083.

Names

College of American Pathologists, *(Coll Am Pathol; 0-930304),* 7400 N. Skokie Blvd., Skokie, IL 60077 (SAN 224-4160) Tel 312-677-3500.

College of Community Health Sciences, *(Coll Comm Health),* P.O. Box 6291, University, AL 35486 (SAN 287-2684); Dist. by: Univ. of Alabama Pr., P.O. Box 2877, University, AL 35486 (SAN 287-2692).

College of Physicians of Philadelphia, The, *(C P P; 0-943060),* 19 S. 22nd St., Philadelphia, PA 19103 (SAN 240-4591) Tel 215-561-6050.

College of St. Thomas, Ctr. for Jewish-Christian Learning, *(CST Jewish-Christian; 0-9616619),* P.O. Box 5010, St. Paul, MN 55105 (SAN 661-0234); 2115 Summit Ave., St. Paul, MN 55105 (SAN 661-0242) Tel 612-647-5715.

College of the Atlantic, *(Coll Atlantic; 0-9601024),* 105 Eden St., Bar Harbor, ME 04609 (SAN 208-7235) Tel 207-288-5015.

College of the Holy Cross, Cantor Art Gallery, *(Cantor Art Gallery; 0-9616183),* 1 College St., Worcester, MA 01610 (SAN 658-3202) Tel 617-793-3356.

College of Wooster, Office of Pubns., *(Coll Wooster; 0-9604658),* Wooster, OH 44691 (SAN 203-5707) Tel 216-263-2000.

†**College Placement Council, Inc.,** *(Coll Placement; 0-913936),* 62 Highland Ave., Bethlehem, PA 18017 (SAN 201-7822) Tel 215-868-1421; CIP.

College Pr. Publishing Co., Inc., *(College Pr Pub; 0-89900),* Box 1132, 205 N. Main, Joplin, MO 64802 (SAN 211-9951) Tel 417-623-6280; Toll free: 800-641-7148.

College Readings, Inc., *(College Readings; 0-916580),* P.O. Box 168, Clifton, VA 22024 (SAN 206-8354).

College Skills Ctr., *(College Skills; 0-89026),* 320 W. 29th St., Baltimore, MD 21211 (SAN 206-3433) Tel 301-235-1700; Toll free: 800-638-1010; 2936 Remington Ave., Baltimore, MD 21211 (SAN 661-9797) Tel 301-235-1722.

College Store, *(Coll Store; 0-910408),* Middlebury College, 5 Hillcrest Rd., Middlebury, VT 05753 (SAN 203-5693) Tel 802-388-3711.

College Survival, Inc., *(Coll Survival; 0-942456),* 2650 Jackson Blvd., Rapid City, SD 57702 (SAN 238-1516); Toll free: 800-528-8323 Tel 605-341-3901.

Collegiate Visitors Guides, *(Collegiate Visitors; 0-9600260),* 170 Bridge Rd., Hillsborough, CA 94010 (SAN 203-5723).

†**Collegium Bk. Pub., Inc.,** *(Collegium Bk Pubs; 0-89669),* 525 Executive Blvd., Elmsford, NY 10523 (SAN 214-2341); CIP.

Collier, Robert, Pub., Inc., *(R Collier; 0-912576),* P.O. Box 3684, Indialantic, FL 32903 (SAN 204-2908) Tel 305-723-3228.

Collier Bks. *See* **Macmillan Publishing Co., Inc.**

Collings, Adam Randolph, Inc., *(A R Collings; 0-933692),* 1829 S. Janette Ln., P.O. Box 8658, Anaheim, CA 92802 (SAN 220-4851) Tel 714-969-0415.

Collins, B., *(B Collins; 0-9615515),* 718 N. 23rd St., Philadelphia, PA 19130 (SAN 696-3358) Tel 215-765-5708.

Collopy, C. T., *(C T Collopy; 0-9617234),* 1200 E. Elizabeth St., Ft. Collins, CO 80524 (SAN 663-477X) Tel 303-493-0112.

Colman Pubs., *(Colman Pubs; 0-9602456),* 1147 Elmwood, Stockton, CA 95204 (SAN 212-4939) Tel 209-464-9503.

†**Cologne Pr.,** *(Cologne Pr; 0-9602310),* P.O. Box 682, Cologne, NJ 08213 (SAN 214-2937) Tel 609-965-5163; CIP.

Colon, Fernando L., Jr., *(F L Colon; 0-9615643),* 232 Seventh St., Jersey City, NJ 07302 (SAN 696-3374) Tel 201-656-0782.

Colon Health Ctr. Publishing Co., *(CHC Pub; 0-9616184),* 105 Locust, Larkspur, CA 94939 (SAN 658-3261) Tel 415-924-6106; P.O. Box 1013, Larkspur, CA 94939 (SAN 658-327X); Dist. by: Nutri-books Corp., P.O. Box 5793, Denver, CO 80223 (SAN 169-054X) Tel 303-778-8383; Toll free: 800-525-9030; Dist. by: Bookpeople, 2929 Fifth St., Berkeley, CA 94710 (SAN 168-9517) Tel 415-548-3030; Toll free: 800-227-1516.

Colonial Pr., *(Colonial Pr AL; 0-938991),* 1237 Stevens Rd, SE, Bessemer, AL 35023 (SAN 662-6599) Tel 205-428-8327. Do not confuse with Colonial Pr. of Cedar Knolls, NJ.

Colonial Publishing, Inc., *(Colonial Pub; 0-939435),* 65 Oakway Rd., Timonium, MD 21093 (SAN 663-4079) Tel 301-666-3380.

Colonial Society of Massachusetts *See* **Univ. Pr. of Virginia**

†**Colonial Williamsburg Foundation,** *(Williamsburg; 0-910412; 0-87935),* Pubns. Dept., P.O. Box C, Williamsburg, VA 23187 (SAN 203-297X) Tel 804-229-1000; Dist. by: Henry Holt & Co., 521 Fifth Ave., New York, NY 10175 (SAN 200-6472) Tel 212-599-7600; Dist. by: University Pr. of Virginia, (SAN 202-5361); CIP.

Colony Publishing, Ltd., Div. of Eastern Marketing, *(Colony Pub; 0-934651),* 8000 Franklin Farms Dr., Richmond, VA 23288 (SAN 694-0749) Tel 804-288-2884; Dist. by: Talman Co., 150 Fifth Ave., Rm. 514, New York, NY 10011 (SAN 200-5204) Tel 212-620-3182.

Colophon Bks. *See* **Harper & Row Pubs., Inc.**

Colophon Book Shop, The, *(Colophon),* P.O. Box E, Epping, NH 03042 (SAN 213-8409) Tel 603-679-8006.

Colophone Publishing, *(Colophone Pub; 0-937873),* 217 Sampson St., Clinton, NC 28328 (SAN 659-4581) Tel 919-592-2170.

Color Center U. S. A., Inc., *(Color Center; 0-9615447),* 610 E. 250 N., Centerville, UT 84014 (SAN 695-7463) Tel 801-298-0621.

Color Charisma Pr., *(Color Pr; 0-916359),* 3127 Presidential Dr., Atlanta, GA 30340 (SAN 295-7213) Tel 404-458-3580; Dist. by: PMG International, 1343 Columbia, No. 405, Richardson, TX 75081 (SAN 200-4763).

Color Coded Charting & Filing Systems, *(Color Coded Charting; 0-9605902),* 7759 California Ave., Riverside, CA 92504 (SAN 211-1888) Tel 714-688-0800.

Color Market, Inc., The, *(Color Market; 0-940014),* 3177 MacArthur Blvd., Northbrook, IL 60062 (SAN 216-8049) Tel 312-564-3770.

Colorado Associated Univ. Pr., Univ. of Colorado, *(Colo Assoc; 0-87081),* 1344 Grandview Ave., Univ. of Colorado, Boulder, CO 80309 (SAN 202-1749) Tel 303-492-7191; P.O. Box 480, Univ. of Colorado, Boulder, CO 80309 (SAN 658-0343).

Colorado Big Game Trophy Records, Inc., *(Colo Big Game; 0-9611376),* 2707 Holiday Lane, Colorado Springs, CO 80909 (SAN 283-9385) Tel 703-590-3638.

Colorado Classics, *(Colo Classics; 0-9607198),* Rt. One, P.O. Box 434, Calhoun, LA 71225 (SAN 239-0779) Tel 318-396-1457.

Colorado College Music Pr., *(Colo Coll Music; 0-933894),* Colorado Springs, CO 80903 (SAN 213-6600) Tel 303-473-2233.

Colorado Creative Supply, Inc., *(Colo Creat Supply; 0-911613),* 2900 Cherryridge Rd., Englewood, CO 80110 (SAN 263-9734) Tel 303-761-1798.

Colorado Express, The, *(Colorado Expr; 0-939396),* 18214 Capitol Hill Sta., Denver, CO 80218 (SAN 216-5929) Tel 303-320-6976.

Colorado Holistic Health Network, *(Colo Holistic; 0-912539),* P.O. Box 61297, Denver, CO 80206 (SAN 265-2218) Tel 303-399-1840.

Colorado Legal Publishing Co., Inc., *(CO Legal Pub; 0-936381),* 1360 S. Clarkson St., Suite 300, Denver, CO 80210 (SAN 697-3337) Tel 303-778-6811.

Colorado Leisure Sports, *(Colo Leisure; 0-9613458),* Box 1953, Estes Park, CO 80517 (SAN 669-6686) Tel 303-586-6846.

Colorado Mountain Club Foundation, The, *(CO Mtn Club Found; 0-9617023),* 2530 W. Alameda, Denver, CO 80219 (SAN 662-6513) Tel 303-355-9620.

†**Colorado Railroad Museum,** *(CO RR Mus; 0-918654),* P.O. Box 10, Golden, CO 80402 (SAN 201-7830) Tel 303-279-4591; CIP.

Colorado River Pr., *(Colo River Pr; 0-931302),* P.O. Box 7547, Austin, TX 78713 (SAN 211-1179) Tel 512-452-0989.

Colorado Schl. of Mines, *(Colo Sch Mines; 0-918062),* Pubns. Dept. Sales, Golden, CO 80401 (SAN 201-7962) Tel 303-273-3607; Toll free: 800-446-9488.

Colorado Springs Fine Arts Ctr., *(CO Springs Fine Arts; 0-916537),* 30 W. Dale St., Colorado Springs, CO 80903 (SAN 240-9372) Tel 303-634-5581. *Imprints:* Taylor Museum of the Colorado Springs Fine Arts Ctr. (Taylor Museum).

Colorado State Univ., Geotechnical Engineering Program, *(Geotech Engineer Prog; 0-910069),* Dept. of Civil Engineering, Ft. Collins, CO 80523 (SAN 241-3272) Tel 303-491-6081.

Colourpicture Pubs., Inc., *(Colourpicture; 0-938440),* 76 Atherton St., Boston, MA 02130 (SAN 216-2318); Dist. by: Smith Novelty Co., 460 Ninth St., San Francisco, CA 94103 (SAN 216-2326) Tel 415-861-4900.

Coltharp Publishing Co., *(Coltharp Pub),* P.O. Box 7461, Amarillo, TX 79109 (SAN 240-1398).

Colton, Ann Ree, Foundation, *(Colton Found; 0-917189),* 336 W. Colorado St., P.O. Box 2057, Glendale, CA 91209 (SAN 655-8798) Tel 818-244-0113; Dist. by: DeVorss & Co., P.O. Box 550, 1046 Princeton Dr., Marina del Rey, CA 90294 (SAN 168-9886).

Colton Bk. Imports, *(Colton Bk),* 908 Southgate Ave., Daly City, CA 94015 (SAN 204-7136).

†**Coltrane & Beach Bk.,** *(Coltrane & Beach; 0-913425),* Box 6249, Westlake Village, CA 91359 (SAN 285-9025) Tel 213-889-4052; Dist. by: Kampmann & Co., Nine E. 40th St., New York, NY 10016 (SAN 202-5191) Tel 212-685-2928; CIP.

Columba Publishing Co., Div. of V. C. Kistler & Assocs., *(Columba Pub; 0-938655),* 2661 W. Market St., Fairlawn, OH 44313 (SAN 661-132X) Tel 216-836-2805.

Columbia Bks. Inc., Pubs., *(Columbia Bks; 0-910416),* 1350 New York Ave., NW, Suite 207, Washington, DC 20005 (SAN 202-1757) Tel 202-737-3777.

Columbia Business Systems Inc., *(Columbia Busn Sys; 0-9604828),* 21 George St., Lowell, MA 01852 (SAN 215-8531) Tel 617-453-0154.

Columbia College Chicago, *(Columbia College Chi; 0-932026),* c/o Columbia College, 600 S. Michigan Ave., Chicago, IL 60605 (SAN 204-3041) Tel 312-663-1600.

†**Columbia County Historical Society,** *(Columbia County Hist Soc; 0-88023),* P.O. Box 197, Orangeville, PA 17859 (SAN 217-345X) Tel 717-683-6011; CIP.

Columbia Enterprise, *(Columbia Enter; 0-937343),* 20 Jules Dr., Albany, NY 12205 (SAN 699-8097) Tel 518-438-2069; Orders to: Bookhouse, Inc., 208 W. Chicago St., Jonesville, MI 49250-0125 (SAN 662-4073) Tel 517-849-2117.

Columbia Hse. Publishing Corp., *(Columbia Hse Pub; 0-942200),* P.O. Box 1711, Clemson, SC 29633 (SAN 237-9422).

Columbia Language Services, *(Columbia Lang Serv; 0-9604126),* P.O. Box 28365, Washington, DC 20038 (SAN 213-9936) Tel 301-587-4979.

Columbia Pictures Pubns., *(Columbia Pictures; 0-913650),* 15800 NW 48th Ave., Miami, FL 33014 (SAN 203-042X) Tel 305-620-1500; Toll free: 800-327-7643 (outside FL).

Columbia Pr., *(Colum Pr MD; 0-936051),* 7304 Silent Bird Ct., Columbia, MD 21045 (SAN 697-0257) Tel 202-387-4398.

†**Columbia Publishing Co., Inc.,** *(Columbia Pub; 0-914366),* Drawer AA, Frenchtown, NJ 08825 (SAN 201-8977) Tel 201-996-2141; Dist. by: Vanguard Press, Inc., 424 Madison Ave., New York, NY 10017 (SAN 202-9316) Tel 212-753-3906; CIP.

Columbia Scholastic Pr. Assn., Div. of Columbia University, *(Columbia Scholastic; 0-916084),* Box 11, Central Mailroom, Columbia Univ., New York, NY 10027 (SAN 127-9750) Tel 212-280-3311.

Columbia Univ., Ctr. for Career Research & Human Resource Management, *(CU Ctr Career Res),* 314 Uris Hall, Graduate School of Business Administration, New York, NY 10027 (SAN 289-6141) Tel 212-280-5570.

Columbia Univ., Center for the Social Sciences, *(Columbia U Ctr Soc Sci; 0-938436),* 420 W. 118th St., 814 I.A.B., New York, NY 10027 (SAN 215-7403) Tel 212-280-3621. Do Not Confuse with Columbia Univ. Pr., Columbia Schl of Social Work, or Teachers College.

Columbia Univ., East Asian Institute, *(Columbia U E Asian Inst; 0-913418),* 420 W. 118th St., New York, NY 10027 (SAN 204-1790) Tel 212-280-2591.

Columbia Univ., Graduate Program in Public Policy & Administration, *(Columbia U GPPPA; 0-910955),* 400 W. 119th St., Apt. 10J, New York, NY 10027 (SAN 269-1183).

Columbia Univ., Graduate Schl. of Business, *(Grad Sch Bus NY; 0-9612584),* 801 Uris Hall, New York, NY 10027 (SAN 204-305X) Tel 212-280-3423.

Columbia Univ. Libraries, *(Columbia U Libs; 0-9607862),* 535 W. 114th St., New York, NY 10027 (SAN 211-1896) Tel 212-280-2231.

Columbia Univ., Oral History Research Office, *(Columbia U Oral Hist Res; 0-9602492),* Box 20, Butler Library, New York, NY 10027 (SAN 223-4742) Tel 212-280-2273.

Columbia Univ. Pr., *(Columbia U Pr; 0-231),* 562 W. 113th St., New York, NY 10025 (SAN 212-2472) Tel 212-316-7100; Orders to: 136 S. Broadway, Irvington-on-Hudson, NY 10533 (SAN 212-2480) Tel 914-591-9111. *Imprints:* King's Crown Paperbacks (King's Crown Paperbacks).

Columbia University School of Law, *(Columbia Law),* 435 W 116th St, New York, NY 10027 (SAN 237-6601).

Columbia Univ., Teachers College, Teachers College Pr., *(Tchrs Coll; 0-8077),* 1234 Amsterdam Ave., New York, NY 10027 (SAN 282-3985) Tel 212-678-3929; Orders to: Harper & Row, Keystone Industrial Pk., Scranton, PA 18512 (SAN 282-3993); Toll free: 800-242-7737.

Columbine *See* Fawcett Bk. Group

Columbine Press, *(Columbine Pr; 0-9609108),* Box 845, Aspen, CO 81612 (SAN 241-483X) Tel 303-925-6025.

Columbine Pubns., Subs. of Jacquelyn Peake Assocs., *(Columbine Pubns; 0-9613830),* 1013 Mirrormere Cir., Ft. Collins, CO 80526 (SAN 681-9745) Tel 303-493-6755.

Columbus Council of American Youth Hostels, *(Columbus Youth Hostels; 0-9616175),* P.O. Box 23111, Columbus, OH 43223 (SAN 699-8658); 629 Dennison, Columbus, OH 43215 (SAN 658-3059) Tel 406-721-1776.

Columbus Museum of Art, *(Columbus Mus Art; 0-918881),* 480 E. Broad St., Columbus, OH 43215 (SAN 278-5102).

Columbus Single Scene, *(Columbus Single; 0-935913),* 55 Caren Ave. Suite 202, Worthington, OH 43085 (SAN 696-7248) Tel 614-436-2076.

Columella Pr., *(Columella Pr; 0-9605972),* 5040 N. 15th Ave. No. 408, Phoenix, AZ 85015 (SAN 216-7247) Tel 602-254-5015.

Colutron Research Corporation, *(Colutron Research; 0-933407),* 5420 Arapahoe Ave., Boulder, CO 80303 (SAN 691-4888) Tel 303-443-5211.

Colwell Systems, Inc., Subs. of Deluxe Check Printer, Inc., *(Colwell Syst; 0-940012),* 201 Kenyon Rd., Champaign, IL 61820 (SAN 208-1431) Tel 217-351-5400; Toll free: 800-248-7000; Toll free: 800-233-7777.

Colwyn-Tangno, *(Colwyn-Tangno),* 96 Old River Rd., Wilkes Barre, PA 18702 (SAN 215-7411).

Coman Assocs., *(Coman Assocs),* P.O. Box 9602, Tulsa, OK 74157 (SAN 698-1887).

Combustion Engineering Power Systems Group, *(Combustion Eng; 0-9605974),* 1000 Prospect Hill Rd., Dept. 7015-1921, Windsor, CT 06095 (SAN 216-7255) Tel 203-285-2344.

Comedy Ctr., The, Div. of Assocs. International, *(Comedy Ctr),* 700 Orange St., Wilmington, DE 19801 (SAN 276-9751) Tel 302-656-2209; Toll free: 800-441-7098.

Comedy Writings & Co., *(Comedy Writ; 0-9609224),* 2034 Grace Ave., Los Angeles, CA 90068 (SAN 240-9771).

Comenius World Council, *(Comenius World; 0-916824),* 247 South St., Hartford, CT 06114 (SAN 208-6050) Tel 203-524-5741.

Comet Pr., *(Comet Pr; 0-939517),* 1259 El Camino Real, Suite 251, Menlo Park, CA 94025 (SAN 663-3595) Tel 408-294-1948.

Comet Publishing Co., The, *(Comet Pub; 0-9616742),* Box 6507, Napa, CA 94581 (SAN 661-0250); 2400 Silverado Trail, St. Helena, CA 94574 (SAN 661-0269) Tel 707-963-2559.

Comicana, Inc., Book Div., Div. of Comicana, Inc., *(Comicana; 0-940420),* RFD 2, Box 242, Hickory Kingdom Rd., Bedford, NY 10506 (SAN 219-7782) Tel 914-939-3035; Dist. by: Henry Holt & Co., 521 Fifth Ave., 6th Flr., New York, NY 10175 (SAN 200-6472) Tel 212-599-7600.

Comico The Comic Co., *(Comico Comic Co; 0-938965),* 1547 DeKalb St., Norristown, PA 19401 (SAN 661-6836) Tel 215-277-4305.

Command Computer Corp., *(Command Comp),* 36 Columbia Terr., Weehawken, NJ 07087 (SAN 694-2970) Tel 201-865-8500.

Command Productions, *(Command Prods; 0-933132),* Box 26348, San Francisco, CA 94126 (SAN 223-3150).

Commentary Pr., *(Comment Pr; 0-914675),* P.O. Box 43532, Atlanta, GA 30336 (SAN 289-7040) Tel 404-949-4947.

Commerce Clearing Hse., Inc., *(Commerce; 0-8080),* 4025 W. Peterson Ave., Chicago, IL 60646 (SAN 202-3504) Tel 312-583-8500.

Commercial Law League of America, *(Commercial Law),* 222 W. Adams St., Chicago, IL 60606 (SAN 225-0845) Tel 312-236-4942.

Commission for the Advancement of Public Interest Organizations, *(Comm Adv Public Interest; 0-9602744),* 1875 Connecticut Ave., NW, No. 1010, Washington, DC 20009 (SAN 213-0408).

Commission of the European Communities, *(Comm Europe Comm),* 2100 M St. NW, Suite 707, Washington, DC 20037 (SAN 680-0297) Tel 202-862-9500.

Commission on Chicago Historical & Architectural Landmarks, *(Comm Chi Hist & Arch; 0-934076),* 320 N. Clark, Chicago, IL 60610 (SAN 213-7313); Dist. by: Chicago Review Pr., 820 N. Franklin, Chicago, IL 60610 (SAN 213-5744) Tel 312-337-0747.

Commission on Voluntary Service & Action, *(Comm Voluntary Serv & Action),* 475 Riverside Dr., Rm. 1126, New York, NY 10115 (SAN 210-7899) Tel 212-870-2801.

Commission to Study the Organization of Peace, *(Comm Peace),* 866 United Nations Plaza, New York, NY 10017 (SAN 203-5324).

†**Committee for Economic Development,** *(Comm Econ Dev; 0-87186),* 477 Madison Ave., New York, NY 10022 (SAN 202-1765) Tel 212-688-2063; CIP.

Committee for Human Rights in Rumania, *(Comm Rights Rumania; 0-9605258),* P.O. Box J, Gracie Sta., New York, NY 10028 (SAN 225-6606) Tel 212-289-5488.

Committee for National Security, The, *(Comm Natl Security; 0-937115),* 1601 Connecticut Ave., NW, Washington, DC 20009 (SAN 658-4934) Tel 202-745-2450.

Committee for Nuclear Responsibility, Inc., *(Comm Nuclear Respon; 0-932682),* Main P.O. Box 11207, San Francisco, CA 94101 (SAN 212-1530) Tel 415-776-8299.

Committee for Scientific Investigation of Claims of Paranormal, *(Comm Sci Investigation),* 3151 Bailey Ave., Buffalo, NY 14215 (SAN 285-0001); P.O. Box 229, Central Park Sta., Buffalo, NY 14215 (SAN 285-001X) Tel 716-834-3223.

Committee for Single Adoptive Parents, *(Comm Single Adopt),* P.O. Box 15084, Chevy Chase, MD 20815 (SAN 225-8862).

Committee in Support of Solidarity, Inc., *(Comm Support Solidarity; 0-935417),* 275 Seventh Ave. 25th Flr., New York, NY 10001 (SAN 696-3463) Tel 212-989-0909.

Committee on Institutional Cooperation, *(Comm Inst Coop),* 302 E. John St., Suite 1705, Champaign, IL 61820 (SAN 269-1744).

Committee on the Present Danger, *(Comm Present Danger),* 905 16th St., NW, Washington, DC 20006 (SAN 224-0971) Tel 202-628-2409.

Committee, The, *(Committee IL; 0-937352),* 2901 S. King Dr., No. 515, Chicago, IL 60616 (SAN 217-0965) Tel 312-567-9522.

Committee to Abolish Prison Slavery, *(Comm Abol Prison; 0-910007),* P.O. Box 3207, Washington, DC 20010 (SAN 241-3280) Tel 202-797-7721.

Committee to Restore the Constitution, Inc., *(Comm Restore Const),* P.O. Box 986, Fort Collins, CO 80522 (SAN 225-6398).

Commodity Ctr. Corp., *(Commodity Ctr; 0-9615644),* 600 S. Dearborn, No. 1911, Chicago, IL 60605 (SAN 696-3528) Tel 312-663-1368.

Commodity Research Bureau, Inc., Subs. of Knight-Ridder Business Information Service, *(Commodity Res; 0-910418),* 75 Montgomery St., Jersey City, NJ 07302 (SAN 204-3092) Tel 201-451-7500.

Common Cause, *(Common Cause; 0-914389),* 2030 M St. NW, Washington, DC 20036 (SAN 219-7790) Tel 202-833-1200.

Common Knowledge Press, Subs. of Commonweal, *(Common Knowledge; 0-943004),* P.O. Box 316, Bolinas, CA 94924 (SAN 240-3080) Tel 415-868-0970.

Common-Sense Happiness, *(Common Hap; 0-9615786),* 4470 SW Hall Blvd., Suite 294, Beaverton, OR 97005 (SAN 696-7124) Tel 503-620-8691.

Common Sense Press, Inc., *(Common Sense; 0-917572),* P.O. Box 417, Corona del Mar, CA 92625 (SAN 209-424X).

Common Sense Pubns., *(Common Sen Pubns; 0-916979),* P.O. Box 130275, Tyler, TX 75713 (SAN 655-6213) Tel 214-561-0110.

Common Women Collective, *(Common Women; 0-9601122),* c/o Women's Center, 46 Pleasant St., Cambridge, MA 02139 (SAN 210-1890) Tel 617-354-8807.

Commonground Pr., *(Commonground Pr; 0-9610348),* 546 Albany Post Rd., New Paltz, NY 12561 (SAN 211-1187).

Commonwealth Agricultural Bureau (CAB) *See* Unipub a

Commonweatlh Bks., Inc., *(Comwealth Bks NJ; 0-940390),* P.O. Box 66, Palisades Park, NJ 07650 (SAN 217-1635).

Commonwealth of Pennsylvania, Dept. of General Services, Bureau of Pubns. & Paperwork Management, *(Commonweal PA; 0-8182),* P.O. Box 1365, Harrisburg, PA 17105 (SAN 656-8858) Tel 717-787-3978. *Imprints:* Commonwealth of Pennsylvania, Dept. of Environmental Resources, Bureau of Topographic & Geologic Survey (Enviro Resources).

Commonwealth of Pennsylvania, Dept. of Environmental Resources, Bureau of Topographic & Geologic Survey *See* **Commonwealth of Pennsylvania, Dept. of General Services, Bureau of Pubns. & Paperwork Management**

Commonwealth Press, *(Cmnwlth Pr Worcester; 0-914274),* 44 Portland St., Worcester, MA 01608 (SAN 204-3076) Tel 617-755-4391.

Commonwealth Pr., Inc., *(Commonwealth Pr; 0-89227),* 415 First St., Radford, VA 24141 (SAN 281-515X) Tel 703-639-2475.

Commonwealth Publishing Co., Inc., *(Commonwlth Pub; 0-943882),* 3657 Thousand Oaks Blvd., Westlake Village, CA 91362 (SAN 241-1032) Tel 805-496-6642.

Commonwealth Scientific Corp., *(Cmnwlth Sci; 0-930787),* 500 Pendleton St., Alexandria, VA 22314 (SAN 677-6094) Tel 303-221-5026.

CommTek Publishing Co., Div. of Commtek, Inc., *(CommTek Pub; 0-934543),* P.O. Box 53, Boise, ID 83707 (SAN 693-8671) Tel 208-322-2800.

Communication & Learning Innovators Ltd., *(Comm & Learning; 0-932361),* 4906 Painters St., New Orleans, LA 70122 (SAN 687-3723) Tel 504-282-1174.

Communication Architects, *(Comm Architects; 0-935597),* P.O. Box 300, Lynnwood, WA 98046-0300 (SAN 696-3544) Tel 206-774-4461.

Communication Arts Books *See* Hastings Hse. Pubs.

Communication Channels, Inc., *(Comm Channels; 0-915962; 0-916164),* 6255 Barfield Rd., Atlanta, GA 30328 (SAN 203-8641) Tel 404-256-1490; Toll free: 800-241-9834.

Communication Consultants International, *(Comm Consultants; 0-938320),* P.O. Box 1212, San Diego, CA 92112 (SAN 215-742X).

Communication Creativity, *(Comm Creat; 0-918880),* P.O. Box 213, Saguache, CO 81149 (SAN 210-3478) Tel 303-589-8223.

Communication Materials Center, *(Comm Materials; 0-940912),* 110 Rices Mill Rd., Wyncote, PA 19095 (SAN 207-9356) Tel 215-884-0928.

Communication Networks, Inc., *(Comm Networks; 0-935419),* 102 W. Leigh St., Richmond, VA 23220 (SAN 696-3587) Tel 804-225-7868; Toll free: 800-882-4800.

†**Communication Pr.,** *(Comm Pr CA; 0-918850),* Box 22541, Sunset Sta., San Francisco, CA 94122 (SAN 210-4067) Tel 415-383-1914; *CIP.*

Communication Research Assocs., Inc., *(Comm Research Assocs; 0-9615952),* 7100 Baltimore Blvd., Suite 500, College Park, MD 20740 (SAN 697-3418) Tel 301-927-3998.

Communication Resources, *(Comm Res OH; 0-930921),* 1425 W. Maple St. P.O. Box 2625, North Canton, OH 44720 (SAN 686-1830) Tel 216-499-1950.

†**Communication Skill Builders,** *(Communication Skill; 0-88450),* 3130 N. Dodge Blvd., P.O. Box 42050, Tucson, AZ 85733 (SAN 201-7768) Tel 602-323-7500; *CIP.*

Communication Skills/Press, *(Comm Skills; 0-911703),* 926 Coachella Ave., Sunnyvale, CA 94086 (SAN 263-9742) Tel 408-738-2434.

Communication Strategies Inc., *(Comm Strat Inc; 0-930353),* P.O. Box 14773, Albuquerque, NM 87191 (SAN 670-7599) Tel 505-293-9159.

Communication Studies, *(Comn Studies; 0-931814),* 6145 Anita St., Dallas, TX 75214-2612 (SAN 211-5530) Tel 214-823-1981.

Communication Unltd. (CA), *(Comm Unltd CA; 0-910167),* P.O. Box 1001, Carpinteria, CA 93013 (SAN 682-2568).

Communications Academy, The, *(Communacad),* P.O. Box 541, Wilton, CT 06897 (SAN 241-3671) Tel 203-762-9538.

Communications by Design/MLM, *(Commun Design-MLM; 0-9615477),* 1354 Hancock St., Quincy, MA 02169 (SAN 696-3625) Tel 617-770-4341.

Communications Library, Div. of Communications Institute, *(Comm Lib; 0-934339),* Lockbox 5891, San Francisco, CA 94101-5891 (SAN 693-6091) Tel 415-626-5050.

Communications Media Ctr., *(Comm Media; 0-941888),* New York Law Schl., 57 Worth St., New York, NY 10013 (SAN 238-227X) Tel 212-966-2053.

Communications Monitor Press *See* **First International Publishing Corp.**

†**Communications Pr., Inc.,** *(Comm Pr Inc; 0-89461),* 1735 DeSales St., NW, Washington, DC 20036 (SAN 210-3486) Tel 202-639-8822; *CIP.*

†**Communications Research,** *(Comm Res; 0-9611910),* 12267 Natural Bridge Rd., Bridgeton, MO 63044 (SAN 286-0813) Tel 314-739-1742; *CIP.*

Communications Research Institute, *(CRI),* 25 Central Park West, New York, NY 10023 (SAN 211-9420) Tel 212-752-5566.

Communications Technology, Inc., *(Comm Tech; 0-918232),* Main St., Greenville, NH 03048 (SAN 159-8198) Tel 603-878-1441.

Communications Trends, Inc., *(Comm Trends Inc; 0-88709),* 2 East Ave., Larchmont, NY 10538 (SAN 285-9092) Tel 914-833-0600.

Communicative Arts Group, Div. of Beautiful You, Inc., *(Comm Arts; 0-941874),* 1343 Columbia Suite 405, Richardson, TX 75081 (SAN 239-1848) Tel 214-690-1200.

Communicatons Unlimited, *(Comm Unltd),* 11032 Pinyon Dr., Northglenn, CO 80234 (SAN 209-5459).

†**Communicom Publishing Co.,** *(Communicom; 0-932617),* 548 NE 43rd Ave., Portland, OR 97213 (SAN 680-4438) Tel 503-239-5141; *CIP.*

Communigraphics of Oconomowoc, Inc., *(Communigraphics; 0-9615001),* 225 W. Wisconsin Ave., Oconomowoc, WI 53066 (SAN 694-0250) Tel 414-567-8904; Dist. by: The Distributors, 702 S. Michigan, South Bend, IN 46618 (SAN 169-2488) Tel 219-232-8500.

Communitarian Press, *(Comm Pr; 0-932225),* Rt. 1, Box 159, Kyle, TX 78640 (SAN 686-6077) Tel 512-398-7513.

Community Arts, Inc., *(Cmnty Arts; 0-9617165),* 15 Douglass St., San Francisco, CA 94114 (SAN 662-9474) Tel 415-771-7020.

Community Builders, *(Comm Builders; 0-9604422),* Canterbury, Shaker Rd., NH 03224 (SAN 215-3009) Tel 603-783-4743.

Community Collaborators, *(Comm Collaborators; 0-930388),* P.O. Box 5429, Charlottesville, VA 22905 (SAN 213-3008) Tel 804-977-1126.

Community Council of Greater New York, *(Comm Coun Great NY; 0-86671),* 275 Seventh Ave. 12th Fl., New York, NY 10001 (SAN 203-0047) Tel 212-741-8844.

Community for Conscious Evolution, The, *(Comm Con Ev; 0-9607066),* 171 Jackson St., Newton, MA 02159 (SAN 238-9657) Tel 617-964-7448.

Community for Creative Non-Violence, *(Comm Creat Non-Violence; 0-9611972),* 1345 Euclid St., NW, Washington, DC 20009 (SAN 277-6677) Tel 202-332-4332.

Community Foundation of Greater Washington Inc., *(Comm Foun DC; 0-933409),* 3221 M St. NW, Washington, DC 20007 (SAN 686-1873) Tel 202-338-8993.

Community Intervention, Inc., *(Comm Intervention; 0-9613416),* 529 S. Seventh St., Suite 570, Minneapolis, MN 55415 (SAN 656-9706) Tel 612-332-6537.

†**Community Law Reports, Inc.,** *(Community Law; 0-89035),* 8771 Elm Ave., Orangevale, CA 95662 (SAN 206-3441) Tel 916-988-7576; *CIP.*

†**Community Publishing Co.,** *(Community Pub),* 103 Lewis St., Perth Amboy, NJ 08861 (SAN 201-8993); *CIP.*

Community Service, Inc., *(Comm Serv OH; 0-910420),* 114 E. Whiteman, Yellow Springs, OH 45387 (SAN 203-5758) Tel 513-767-2161; P.O. Box 243, Yellow Springs, OH 45387 (SAN 669-0483).

Community Service Pubns., *(Commun Service; 0-9615812),* 2104 Park Ave., Minneapolis, MN 55401 (SAN 696-7094) Tel 612-871-3333.

Community Service Society of New York, *(Comm Serv Soc NY; 0-88156),* Office of Information 105 E. 22nd St., New York, NY 10010 (SAN 204-3149) Tel 212-254-8900.

†**Community Wholistic Growth Center Inc,** *(Comm Wholistic Growth; 0-918833),* 10 W. Lockwood, Webster Groves, St Louis, MO 63119 (SAN 682-2363); *CIP.*

†**Compact Bks.,** *(Compact Bks; 0-936320),* 2500 Hollywood Blvd., Hollywood, FL 33020 (SAN 215-0670) Tel 305-925-5242; Dist. by: Interbook, Inc., 14895 E. 14th St., Suite 370, San Leandro, CA 94577 (SAN 662-3034) Tel 415-352-9221; *CIP.*

Comparable Worth Project, *(Comparable Worth; 0-9615953),* 488 41st St., No. 5, Oakland, CA 94609 (SAN 697-3434) Tel 415-658-1808.

Comparahatch Ltd., Inc., *(Comparahatch; 0-914521),* RD 1, Box 102, Tannersville, PA 18372 (SAN 289-6184) Tel 717-629-2962.

Compass Bks. See Viking-Penguin, Inc.

Compass Bk. Pubs., *(Compass Bk Pub; 0-937507),* Box 9996, Phoenix, AZ 85068 (SAN 659-1310) Tel 602-944-8526.

Compass Pubns., *(Compass Pubns NY; 0-9606282),* 115 E. 87th St., Box 12-F, New York, NY 10128 (SAN 220-3286) Tel 212-289-2368.

Compass Pubns., Inc., *(Compass Va; 0-910422),* 1117 N. 19th St., Arlington, VA 22209 (SAN 203-5774) Tel 703-524-3136.

†**CompCare Pubns.,** Div. of Comprehensive Care Corp., *(CompCare; 0-89638),* 2415 Annapolis Ln., Minneapolis, MN 55441 (SAN 211-464X) Tel 612-559-4800; Toll free: 800-328-3330; *CIP.*

Competence Assurance Systems, Div. of Whole Brain Corp., *(CAS; 0-89147),* Harvard Sq., P.O. Box 81, Cambridge, MA 02138 (SAN 208-0001) Tel 617-661-9151.

Competency Pr., *(Comp Pr; 0-9602800),* P.O.. Box 95, White Plains, NY 10605 (SAN 223-5579).

Composers' Graphics, *(Comp Graphics; 0-931553),* 5702 N. Ave., Carmichael, CA 95608 (SAN 682-1847) Tel 916-489-7889.

Comprehensive Health Education Foundation, *(Comprehen Health Educ; 0-935529),* 20832 Pacific Hwy., S., Seattle, WA 98188 (SAN 696-3668) Tel 206-824-2907.

Comprehensive Information Sciences, Inc., *(Comp Info Sci; 0-936477),* P.O. Box 622, Huntington, NY 11743 (SAN 698-1135) Tel 516-423-7528.

COMPress, Div. of Wadsworth, Inc., *(COMPress; 0-933694; 0-88720),* P.O. Box 102, Wentworth, NH 03282 (SAN 284-9887); Toll free: 800-221-0419 Tel 603-764-5831.

Compressed Gas Association, *(Compress Gas),* 1235 Jefferson Davis Highway, Arlington, VA 22202 (SAN 260-3136) Tel 703-979-0900.

CompTech Pubs., Inc., *(CompTech; 0-935397),* 663 S. Bernardo Ave., Suite 173, Sunnyvale, CA 94087-1020 (SAN 696-3684) Tel 408-736-8082; 125-73 Connemara Way, Sunnyvale, CA 94087-3226 (SAN 696-3692) Tel 408-736-8082; Dist. by: George L. Oliver Co., P.O. Box 1842, Fremont, CA 94538-0184 (SAN 200-6111) Tel 415-651-6720; Dist. by: George L. Oliver Co., 44834 S. Grimmer Blvd., Fremont, CA 94538 (SAN 200-612X).

Comptex Associates, Inc., *(Comptex Assocs Inc; 0-911849),* P.O. Box 6745, Washington, DC 20020 (SAN 265-3710).

Compton Pr., *(Compton Pr; 0-9607302),* P.O. Box 871, Cathedral Sta., New York, NY 10025 (SAN 239-1856) Tel 212-749-5377.

Compu-Sultants, *(Compu-Sul; 0-9610734),* 940 Wild Forest Dr., Gaithersburg, MD 20879 (SAN 264-6609) Tel 301-977-3511.

Compu-Tech Publishing, Inc., *(Compu-Tech Pub; 0-917531),* 615 South St., Garden City, NY 11530 (SAN 669-6708) Tel 516-222-1637.

CompuSoft Publishing, Div. of CompuSoft, Inc., *(CompuSoft; 0-932760),* 3719 Sixth Ave., San Diego, CA 92103-4316 (SAN 287-0045) Tel 619-299-8511; Toll free: 800-854-6505; Dist. by: Ingram Bk., Co., 347 Reedwood Dr., Box 17266, Nashville, TN 37217 (SAN 169-7978); Dist. by: Golden-Lee Bk. Distributors, 1000 Dean St., Brooklyn, NY 11238 (SAN 169-5126) Tel 718-857-6333; Dist. by: Micromedia Marketing, 6060 Rickenbacker Rd., Los Angeles, CA 90040-3030 (SAN 282-6445) Tel 213-721-3083; Dist. by: Slawson Communications, Inc., 3719 Sixth Ave., San Diego, CA 92103-4316 (SAN 200-6901) Tel 619-291-9126.

Computational Mechanics, Inc., *(Computational Mech MA; 0-931215),* 400 W. Cummings Pk., Suite 6200, Woburn, MA 01801 (SAN 653-6425) Tel 617-933-7374. No longer publishes software.

Compute! Pubns., Inc., Subs. of American Broadcasting Companies, Inc., *(Compute Pubns; 0-87455; 0-942386),* 825 Seventh Ave., 9th flr., New York, NY 10019 (SAN 284-320X) Tel 212-887-5928.

Computeach Press, Inc., *(Computeach; 0-9607864),* P.O. Box 20851, San Jose, CA 95160 (SAN 238-1532) Tel 408-268-4240.

Computech, Inc., *(Computech Inc; 0-936165),* 4401 East-West Hwy., Bethesda, MD 20814 (SAN 697-0273) Tel 301-656-4030.

Computech (VA), *(Computech VA; 0-932997),* 55 Charles Parish Dr., Poquoson, VA 23662 (SAN 670-7343) Tel 804-868-8055.

Computer Aided Design Ventures Unlimited, *(CAD Ventures Unltd; 0-937687),* P.O. Box 1816, Glendora, CA 91740 (SAN 659-3259) Tel 818-445-1359; 1344 S. Bruning Ave., Glendora, CA 91740 (SAN 659-3267).

Computer & Business Equipment Manufacturers Assn., *(CBEMA; 0-912797),* 311 First St. NW, Suite 500, Washington, DC 20001 (SAN 269-2341) Tel 202-737-8888 Tel 202-638-4922.

Computer Assisted Library Instruction Co., Inc. (CALICO), *(Computer Assis; 0-916625),* P.O. Box 15916, St. Louis, MO 63114 (SAN 296-4856) Tel 314-863-8028.

Computer Awareness, *(Comp Awareness; 0-934531),* 43612 Greenview Dr., Mt. Clemens, MI 48043 (SAN 693-7896) Tel 313-468-8585.

Names

Computer Directions for Schools, *(Computer Direct; 0-912007),* P.O. Box 1136, Livermore, CA 94550 (SAN 264-6072) Tel 415-455-8326; 714 Alden Ln., Livermore, CA 94550 (SAN 264-6080) Tel 415-455-8326.

Computer Entrepreneur Publishing Co., The, *(Comp Entrepreneur),* P.O. Box 456, Grand Central Station, New York, NY 10163 (SAN 677-8941).

Computer Information Ltd., *(Comp Info Ltd; 0-9614906),* P.O. Box 60369, San Diego, CA 92106-8369 (SAN 693-4692) Tel 619-266-9141; Toll free: 800-528-3665.

Computer Language Co., Inc., The, *(Computer Lang; 0-941878),* 140 W. 30th St., New York, NY 10001 (SAN 239-1864) Tel 212-736-8364.

Computer Law Reporter, *(Comp Law Rep),* 1519 Connecticut Ave., NW Suite 200, Washington, DC 20036 (SAN 692-8765).

Computer Management Research Inc, *(Computer Res; 0-930411),* 20 Waterside Plaza Level A, New York, NY 10010 (SAN 669-6694) Tel 212-683-0606.

Computer Options, *(Comp Options; 0-9614937),* 198 Amherst Ave., Berkeley, CA 94708 (SAN 693-5311) Tel 415-525-5033.

Computer Research Corp., *(Comp Res; 0-939559),* 500 West End Ave., Suite 11E, New York, NY 10024 (SAN 663-429X) Tel 212-580-2633.

Computer Resources, Inc., *(CRI NH; 0-938193),* Barrington Mall, Barrington, NH 03820 (SAN 661-0285) Tel 603-664-5811.

Computer Science Pr., Inc., *(Computer Sci; 0-914894; 0-88175),* 1803 Research Blvd., Suite 500, Rockville, MD 20850 (SAN 200-2361) Tel 301-251-9050.

Computer Times, *(Computer Times; 0-935743),* 197 Marion Dr., McMurray, PA 15317 (SAN 696-3757) Tel 412-941-1188.

Computerist, Inc., The, *(Computerist; 0-938222),* P.O. Box 6502, Chelmsford, MA 01824 (SAN 217-2542) Tel 617-256-3649.

Computers & ME, Ltd., *(Computers & ME; 0-935349),* Ashbrook Rd., Exeter, NH 03833-9733 (SAN 696-3781) Tel 603-772-4399 (SAN 285-5690).

Computext Inc., *(Computext Inc; 0-913847),* 7947 Teel Way, Indianapolis, IN 46256 (SAN 286-7419) Tel 317-842-1956.

Computing!, *(Computing; 0-913733),* 2519 Greenwich St., San Francisco, CA 94123 (SAN 265-0363) Tel 415-567-1634; Toll free: 800-428-7824.

Computing Trends, *(Computing Trends),* P.O. Box 22012, Seattle, WA 98122 (SAN 212-2111) Tel 206-523-6685.

Comstock Bonanza Pr., *(Comstock Bon; 0-933994),* 18919 William Quirk Memorial Dr., Grass Valley, CA 95945 (SAN 223-694X) Tel 916-272-7054.

Comstock Editions, Inc., *(Comstock Edns; 0-89174),* 3030 Bridgeway Blvd., Sausalito, CA 94965 (SAN 207-6454) Tel 415-332-3216; Orders to: 1380 W. Second Ave., Eugene, OR 97402 (SAN 207-6462) Tel 503-686-8001.

Comstock Nevada Publishing Co., *(Comstock NV Pub Co; 0-915933),* P.O. Box 6431, Incline Village, NV 89450 (SAN 293-9991) Tel 702-831-5858; P.O. Box W, Tahoe City, CA 95730 (SAN 294-0000) Tel 916-583-3644.

†**Comstock Publishing Assocs.,** *(Comstock),* Dist. by: Cornell Univ. Pr., Sales Manager, 124 Roberts Pl., P.O. Box 250, Ithaca, NY 14851 (SAN 281-5672); *CIP.*

Comtech, Publishing Division, *(Comtech Pub Div; 0-9616370),* P.O. Box 456, Pittsford, NY 14534 (SAN 659-1388) Tel 716-586-3365; 225 Long Meadow Cir., Pittsford, NY 14534 (SAN 659-1396).

Comptemporary Research Assocs., Inc., *(Contemp Res; 0-935061),* P.O. Box 7240, Dallas, TX 75209 (SAN 694-5937) Tel 214-690-5882; 1218 Glen Cove, Richardson, TX 75080 (SAN 694-5945).

Comware Publishing, *(Comware Pub; 0-912441),* 1272 Olwyn Dr., Tustin, CA 92680 (SAN 265-2226) Tel 714-838-8876.

Con Brio Pr., *(Con Brio; 0-9602068),* 8708 Morris Rd., Minneapolis, MN 55437 (SAN 212-3428) Tel 612-835-2905.

Con-Cor International, *(Con Cor Intl; 0-930983),* 1025 Industrial Dr., Bensenville, IL 60106 (SAN 678-8874) Tel 312-595-0210.

Conagree Pubns., *(Conagree Pubns; 0-938599),* P.O. Box 11874, Capitol Sta., Columbia, SC 29211 (SAN 661-3535) Tel 803-356-1860.

Conarc, *(Conarc),* P.O. Box 339, Bethel Island, CA 94511 (SAN 241-368X) Tel 415-684-3362.

Concept Development Assocs., Inc., *(Concept Develop; 0-935745),* 7960 Old Georgetown Rd., Bethesda, MD 20814 (SAN 696-3811) Tel 301-951-0997; Dist. by: Ingram Software Distribution Services, 2128 Elmwood Ave., Buffalo, NY 14207 (SAN 285-760X) Tel 716-874-1874; Toll free: 800-828-7250.

†**Concept Publishing,** *(Concept Pub; 0-930726),* P.O. Box 500, York, NY 14592 (SAN 211-5549) Tel 716-243-3148; *CIP.*

Concept Spelling,Inc., *(Concept Spelling; 0-935276),* P.O. Box 7200, Costa Mesa, CA 92626 (SAN 213-909X) Tel 714-770-0811.

Concept: Synergy, *(Concept Synergy; 1-55638),* P.O. Box 159 (M), Fairfax, CA 94930 (SAN 661-0307); 500 VP Vista Grande, Greenbrae, CA 94904 (SAN 661-0315) Tel 415-456-4857.

Concepts, *(Concepts; 0-910533),* P.O. Box 6750, Ithaca, NY 14851 (SAN 240-821X) Tel 607-272-3346.

Concepts ETI Inc., *(Concepts ETI; 0-933283),* Main St., P.O. Box 643, Norwich, VT 05055 (SAN 692-3607) Tel 802-649-8875.

Concepts in Criminal Justice, *(Concepts Crim Just; 0-931621),* P.O. Box 5415, San Luis Obispo, CA 93403 (SAN 683-7247) Tel 805-481-4496.

Concepts Publishing, *(Concepts Pub MA; 0-9611712),* P.O. Box 358, Stockbridge, MA 01262 (SAN 663-0898); Dist. by: W. W. Norton & Co., 500 Fifth Ave., New York, NY 10110 (SAN 202-5795) Tel 212-354-5500.

Concepts Unlimited, *(Concepts Unlmted; 0-88075),* 150 E. Fountainview Ln., Lombard, IL 60148 (SAN 237-9414).

Conceptual Design, *(Concept Design; 0-9604902),* Nine Glenmore Rd., Troy, NY 12180 (SAN 214-3577) Tel 518-283-6467.

Concern, Inc., *(Concern; 0-937345),* 1794 Columbia Rd. NW, Washington, DC 20009 (SAN 225-1728) Tel 202-328-8160.

Concerned Communications, *(Concerned Comms; 0-936785),* P.O. Box 700, Arroyo Grande, CA 93420 (SAN 699-8623) Tel 805-489-4848; 200 Traffic Way, Arroyo Grande, CA 93420 (SAN 699-8631).

Concerned Pubns., Inc., *(Concerned Pubns; 0-939286),* P.O. Box 1024, Clermont, FL 32711 (SAN 220-1496) Tel 904-429-3022.

Concerned United Birthparents, Inc., *(CUB),* 595 Central Ave., Dover, NH 03820 (SAN 241-3736) Tel 603-749-3744.

†**Conch Magazine Ltd. Pubs.,** Div. of Conch Communications Co., *(Conch Mag; 0-914970),* 102 Normal Ave., Buffalo, NY 14213 (SAN 206-4855) Tel 716-885-3686; *CIP.*

Concho Corp., *(Concho Corp; 0-916791),* 610 Ralston Ave., Mill Valley, CA 94941 (SAN 654-1992) Tel 415-388-1383.

Concord Bks., *(Concord Bks),* P.O. Box 2707, Seal Beach, CA 90740 (SAN 158-0337) Tel 808-326-2514.

Concord Friends Meeting, *(Concord Friends; 0-9617060),* P.O. Box 23, Concordville, PA 19331 (SAN 662-8427); Concord Rd., Concordville, PA 19331 (SAN 662-8435) Tel 215-388-7268.

Concord Grove Pr., Subs. of Institute of World Culture, *(Concord Grove; 0-88695),* Concord Hse., 1407 Chapala St., Santa Barbara, CA 93101 (SAN 283-0388) Tel 805-966-3941.

Concord Pr., *(Concord Pr),* P.O. Box 2686, Seal Beach, CA 90740 (SAN 206-4669) Tel 213-431-5711.

Concord Reference Bks., Inc., Subs. of Whitney Communications Corp., *(Concord Ref Bks; 0-940994),* 850 Third Ave., 13th Fl., New York, NY 10022-6203 (SAN 219-6530) Tel 212-223-5100.

Concordant Publishing Concern, *(Concordant; 0-910424),* 15570 W. Knochaven Rd., Canyon Country, CA 91351 (SAN 203-5790) Tel 805-252-2112.

Concordia Historical Institute, *(Concordia Hist),* 801 DeMun Ave., St. Louis, MO 63105 (SAN 225-459X) Tel 314-721-5934.

†**Concordia Publishing Hse.,** *(Concordia; 0-570),* 3558 S. Jefferson Ave., St. Louis, MO 63118 (SAN 202-1781) Tel 314-664-7000; Toll free: 800-325-3040; *CIP.*

Concordia Seminary, School for Graduate Studies, *(Concordia Schl Grad Studies; 0-911770),* 801 DeMun Ave., St. Louis, MO 63105 (SAN 204-3165) Tel 314-721-5934.

Concordia Theological Seminary, *(Concordia Theo Sem; 0-9615927),* 6600 N. Clinton St., Ft. Wayne, IN 46825 (SAN 696-9216) Tel 219-482-9611.

Concours Publishing, *(Concours Pub; 0-9602644),* 7271 Jurupa Rd., Riverside, CA 92509 (SAN 212-8950).

Concourse Pr., *(Concourse Pr; 0-911323),* Box 28600, Overbrook Sta., Philadelphia, PA 19151 (SAN 269-249X) Tel 215-649-2207.

Concrete Reinforcing Steel Institute, *(Concrete Reinforcing),* 933 Plum Grove Rd., Schaumburg, IL 60195 (SAN 224-6902) Tel 312-490-1700.

Conde Centennial Bk. Committee, *(Conde Cent Bk Comm),* Rte. 1, P.O. Box 99, Conde, SD 57434 (SAN 658-8255).

Condido Pr., *(Condido Pr; 0-911863),* P.O. Box 27551, Rancho Bernardo, San Diego, CA 92128 (SAN 685-3196) Tel 619-743-2122.

Conditions, *(Conditions),* P.O. Box 56, Van Brunt Sta., Brooklyn, NY 11215 (SAN 219-0796).

Condo Management Maintenance Corp., *(Condo Mgmt; 0-910049),* P.O. Box 4908, 65 Hwy. 22, Suite 4B, Clinton, NJ 08809 (SAN 240-8686).

Condor Publishing, *(Condor MA; 0-9606370),* 7 Macarthur Rd., Ashland, MA 01721 (SAN 219-080X).

Conduit, Div. of Univ. of Iowa, *(Conduit; 0-937332),* Univ. of Iowa, Oakdale Campus, Iowa City, IA 52242 (SAN 214-235X) Tel 319-353-5789.

Condyne-The Oceana Group, Div. of Oceana Pubns., *(Condyne-Oceana; 0-913338),* 75 Main St., Dobbs Ferry, NY 10522 (SAN 202-7925) Tel 914-693-5944.

Cone-Heiden, *(Cone-Heiden),* 417 E. Pine St., Seattle, WA 98122 (SAN 201-9000).

Conestoga Pr., *(Conestoga Pr; 0-9613297),* 555 Lang Creek Rd., Marion, MT 59925 (SAN 653-9513) Tel 406-858-2430.

Confederate Calender Works, *(Confed Calendar; 0-943030),* P.O. Drawer 2084, Austin, TX 78768 (SAN 240-3625) Tel 512-474-2097.

Conference Board, Inc., The, *(Conference Bd; 0-8237),* 845 Third Ave., New York, NY 10022 (SAN 202-179X) Tel 212-759-0900; Toll free: 800-872-6273.

Conference for Chinese Oral & Performing Literature, *(Chinoperl),* 140 Uris Hall, Cornell Univ., Ithaca, NY 14853 (SAN 269-2570) Tel 607-255-6222.

Conference of State Bank Supervisors, *(Conf St Bank; 0-916361),* 1015 18th St. NW, Washington, DC 20036 (SAN 269-2805) Tel 202-296-2849.

Conference on Economic Progress, *(Conf Econ Prog; 0-910428),* 2610 Upton St., N.W., Washington, DC 20008 (SAN 203-5804) Tel 202-363-6222.

Conference on Faith & History, *(Conf Faith & Hist; 0-913446),* Indiana State Univ., Dept. of History, Terre Haute, IN 47809 (SAN 203-5812) Tel 812-232-6311.

†**Confluence Pr., Inc.,** *(Confluence Pr; 0-917652),* Spalding Hall, Lewis-Clark Campus, Lewiston, ID 83501 (SAN 209-5467) Tel 208-746-2341; Dist. by: Kampmann & Co., 9 E. 40th St., New York, NY 10016 (SAN 202-5191) Tel 212-685-2928; *CIP.*

†**Congdon & Weed,** *(Congdon & Weed; 0-86553),* 298 Fifth Ave., 7th Flr., New York, NY 10001 (SAN 214-3585) Tel 212-736-4883; Toll free: 800-221-7945; Dist. by: Contemporary Bks., 180 N. Michigan Ave., Chicago, IL 60601 (SAN 202-5493) Tel 312-782-9181; *CIP.*

Congeros Pubns., Affil. of Stump's Printing, *(Congeros Pubns; 0-918628),* P.O. Box 1387, Ontario, CA 91762 (SAN 213-733X).

†**Congregation Shaarai Shomayim,** *(Cong Shaarai),* 508 N. Duke St., Lancaster, PA 17602 (SAN 215-7438) Tel 717-397-5575; *CIP.*

Congregation Sons of Israel, *(Congr Sons Israel; 0-9603994),* 116 Grandview Ave., Chambersburg, PA 17201 (SAN 239-5215).

Names

Congress of Racial Equality, *(CORE; 0-917354),* 1916-38 Park Ave., New York, NY 10037 (SAN 204-2886) Tel 212-694-9300.

Congress Square Pr., *(Congress Sq; 0-9611320),* P.O. Box 4060, Portland, ME 04101 (SAN 283-2763) Tel 207-772-0181.

†**Congressional Quarterly, Inc.,** *(Congr Quarterly; 0-87187),* 1414 22nd St., NW, Washington, DC 20037 (SAN 202-1803) Tel 202-887-8500; *CIP.*

Congressional Staff Directory, Ltd., *(Congr Staff; 0-87289),* P.O. Box 62, Mount Vernon, VA 22121 (SAN 203-5820) Tel 703-765-3400.

Conjunctions, *(Conjunctions; 0-941964),* 33 W. Ninth St., New York, NY 10011 (SAN 239-5169) Tel 212-477-1136.

Conmar Publishing, Co., *(Conmar Pub; 0-9613784),* P.O. Box 641, Citrus Heights, CA 95610 (SAN 678-9617) Tel 916-962-2028; Dist. by: Wellman Publishing, P.O. Box 484, Folsom, CA 95630 (SAN 683-7441) Tel 916-985-7064.

Connecticut Farm Bureau Assn., Inc., *(CT Farm Bureau Assn; 0-9615485),* 101 Reserve Rd., Hartford, CT 06114 (SAN 696-3870) Tel 203-247-7394.

Connecticut Fireside Pr., *(Conn Fireside),* P.O. Box 5293, Hamden, CT 06518 (SAN 207-8090) Tel 203-248-1023.

Connecticut Historical Commission, *(Conn Hist Com; 0-918676),* 59 S. Prospect St., Hartford, CT 06106 (SAN 223-3223).

Connecticut Historical Society Pr., The, *(Conn Hist Soc; 0-940748),* 1 Elizabeth St., Hartford, CT 06105 (SAN 204-2843) Tel 203-236-5621.

Connecticut Hospice, Inc., The, *(Conn Hospice; 0-936479),* 61 Burban Dr., Branford, CT 06405 (SAN 698-1070) Tel 203-481-6231.

Connecticut Law Tribune, *(CT Law Trib; 0-910051),* 179 Allyn St., Hartford, CT 06103-1418 (SAN 237-675X).

Connecticut River Watershed Council, Inc., *(CT River Water; 0-9616371),* 125 Combs Rd., Easthampton, MA 01027 (SAN 659-1426) Tel 413-584-0057.

Connecticut Yankee Publishers, Inc., *(Conn Yankee; 0-915129),* 17 Blue Mountain Rd., Norwalk, CT 06851 (SAN 289-9035) Tel 203-847-6512.

Connecting Link, The, *(Connecting Link; 0-9608678),* P.O. Box 716, Stone Mountain, GA 30086-0716 (SAN 238-2636) Tel 404-979-8013.

Connections, *(Connections CA; 0-911719),* 5009 San Joaquin Dr., San Diego, CA 92109 (SAN 263-9815) Tel 619-272-6565.

Connell & Connell, Inc., *(Connell & Connell; 0-9616573),* 39 Desoto Cir., Texarkana, TX 75503 (SAN 661-0374) Tel 214-793-7845.

Conner & Sanderson Publications, *(Conner & Sanderson; 0-9606904),* Dist. by: Coleman Publishing Inc., 99 Milbar Blvd., Farmingdale, NY 11735 (SAN 238-1508) Tel 516-293-0383.

Connery, Liz Newkirk, *(L Newkirk Connery; 0-9614333),* 411 Wingrave Dr., Charlotte, NC 28226 (SAN 688-1211) Tel 704-366-4747.

Connoisseur Enterprises, *(Connoisseur; 0-912605),* 12540 SE Linwood, Apt. 26, Milwaukie, OR 97222 (SAN 277-6685) Tel 503-655-2070.

Connolly Secretary of the Commonwealth, *(Connolly Sec Commonw; 0-9613915),* State House Rm. 340, Boston, MA 02133 (SAN 683-1796) Tel 617-727-9121.

Conquest Corp., *(Conquest Corp MI; 0-936682),* 32724 Friartuck, Birmingham, MI 48010 (SAN 219-9734) Tel 313-646-1344.

Conroy, Barbara, *(B Conroy),* P.O. Box 9331, Santa Fe, NM 87504 (SAN 214-2961) Tel 505-983-9217.

Conscience & Military Tax Campaign-U. S., Affil. of National War Tax Resistance Co-ordinating Commitee and Mobilization For Survival, *(Conscience & Military Tax; 0-9616313),* 4534 1/2 University Way, Seattle, WA 98105 (SAN 658-6503) Tel 206-547-0952.

†**Conservation Foundation,** *(Conservation Foun; 0-89164),* 1255 23rd St., NW, Washington, DC 20037 (SAN 207-6640) Tel 202-293-4800; *CIP.*

Conservation Press, *(Conserv Pr),* Australian Government Trade Commission, 636 Fifth Ave., New York, NY 10111 (SAN 238-0528).

ConSol Network, Inc., *(ConSol; 0-917893),* 1905 Mariposa St., Boulder, CO 80302 (SAN 656-9714) Tel 303-449-4551; Dist. by: Baker & Taylor., Midwest Div., 501 Gladiola Ave., Momence, IL 60954 (SAN 169-2100).

Consolidated Athletic Commission, *(Consol Athletic Comm),* 851 N Leavitt St, Chicago, IL 60622 (SAN 224-5388).

†**Consolidated Capital Communications Group, Inc. (CCCG),** *(Consol Cap Comm Grp; 0-930032),* 2000 Powell St., Emeryville, CA 94608 (SAN 283-9407); *CIP.*

Consortium for Mathematics & its Applications See COMAP , Inc.

Consortium for Pacific Arts & Cultures See Univ. of Hawaii Pr., The

Consortium Soft, *(Consortium Soft; 0-939519),* 504 East Walnut, Nevada, MO 64772 (SAN 663-3625) Tel 417-667-9489.

Constant Society, *(Constant Soc; 0-931894),* P. O. Box 45513, Seattle, WA 98105 (SAN 211-4976) Tel 206-525-5947.

Constellation Pr., Inc., *(Constellation Pr; 0-9616620),* Box 1271, Manhattan Beach, CA 90266 (SAN 661-0404); 1817 Agnes Rd., Manhattan Beach, CA 90266 (SAN 661-0412) Tel 213-545-2284.

Constitutional Rights Foundation, *(Constitutional Rights Found),* 601 S. Kingsley Dr., Los Angeles, CA 90005 (SAN 225-6401) Tel 213-487-5590.

Construction Bookstore, Inc., *(Construct Bkstore; 0-935715),* P.O. Box 2959, Gainesville, FL 32602-2959 (SAN 696-3935) Tel 904-378-9784; 1830 NE Second St., Gainesville, FL 32609 (SAN 696-3943).

Construction Industry Pr., Affil. of WPL Assocs., Inc., *(Constr Ind Pr; 0-9605442),* 1105-F Spring St., Silver Spring, MD 20910 (SAN 238-7549) Tel 301-589-4884.

Construction Products Manufacturers Council, *(Constr Prod Manuf),* 1600 Wilson Blvd., Suite 1005, Arlington, VA 22209 (SAN 224-1013) Tel 703-522-0613.

Construction Pubns., *(Construct Pubns; 0-912324),* 4552 E. Palomino Rd., Phoenix, AZ 85018 (SAN 201-7970) Tel 602-840-3947.

Construction Trade Pubns., *(Construct Trade; 0-9616849),* 24611 Tabuenca, Mission Viejo, CA 92692 (SAN 661-308X) Tel 714-770-6334.

Constructive Action, Inc., *(Constructive Action; 0-911956),* P.O. Box 4006, Whittier, CA 90607 (SAN 203-5839) Tel 213-947-5707.

Constructive Educational Concepts, Inc., *(Construct Educ; 0-934734),* 213 Duncaster Rd., Box 667, Bloomfield, CT 06002 (SAN 215-7446).

Consultant Services Northwest, Inc., *(Consult Serv NW; 0-9617216),* 839 NE 96th St., Seattle, WA 98115 (SAN 663-4249) Tel 206-524-1950.

Consultants Bureau See Plenum Publishing Corp.

Consultants News, Subs. of Kennedy & Kennedy, Inc., *(Consultants News; 0-916654),* Templeton Rd., Fitzwilliam, NH 03447 (SAN 206-4871) Tel 603-585-2200.

†**Consulting Psychologists Pr., Inc.,** *(Consulting Psychol; 0-89106),* 577 College Ave., Palo Alto, CA 94306 (SAN 201-7849) Tel 415-857-1444; *CIP.*

Consumer Awareness Learning Laboratory, *(Consumer Aware; 0-910599),* RD 3, Box 237, Fort Elfsborg Rd., Salem, NJ 08079 (SAN 260-1761) Tel 609-935-6264.

Consumer Communications, Ltd., *(Consumer Comm Ltd; 0-940060),* P.O. Box 35429, Station D, Albuquerque, NM 87176 (SAN 217-0671) Tel 505-881-0313.

Consumer Energy Council of America, *(Consumer Energy Coun),* 2000 L St. NW, Suite 320, Washington, DC 20036 (SAN 224-103X) Tel 202-659-0404.

Consumer Guide Bks./Pubns. Intl., Ltd., Div. of Pubs. Intl., Ltd., *(Pubns Intl Ltd; 0-88176),* 3841 W. Oakton St., Skokie, IL 60076 (SAN 263-9823) Tel 312-676-3470; Toll free: 800-526-4264; Dist. by: Crown Publishers, Inc., 225 Park Ave., S, New York, NY 10003 (SAN 200-2639) Tel 212-254-1600; Dist. by: Harper & Row Publishers, Inc., 10 E. 53rd St., NewYork, NY 10022 (SAN 200-2086) Tel 212-207-7099; Dist. by: Simon & Schuster, Inc., 1230 Ave. of the Americas, New York, NY 10020 (SAN 200-2450) Tel 212-245-6400.

Consumer Information Pubns., *(Consumer Info Pubns; 0-940062),* 2245 Curlew Rd., Palm Harbor, FL 33563 (SAN 220-2395) Tel 813-784-7795.

Consumer Publications, *(Consumer Pubn; 0-914087),* P.O. Box 465, Kings Park, NY 11754 (SAN 283-9431) Tel 516-979-9183.

Consumer Publishing Co., *(Consumer Pub; 0-9600270),* New & Friendship Rds., Vincentown, NJ 08088 (SAN 206-927X).

Consumer Reports Bks., Div. of Consumers Union of US, Inc., *(Consumer Reports; 0-89043),* 110 E. 42nd St., No. 1301, New York, NY 10017 (SAN 224-1048) Tel 212-682-9280.

Consumer's Advisory, Pr., *(Consumers Advisory; 0-9606340),* P.O. Box 77107, Greensboro, NC 27407 (SAN 219-0818).

Consumers Checkbk., *(Consumers Checkbk),* 806 15th St. NW 925, Washington, DC 20005 (SAN 678-9137).

Consumers Union of U. S., Inc., Div. of Comsumer Reports Bks., *(Consumers Union; 0-89043),* 256 Washington St., Mt. Vernon, NY 10553 (SAN 269-3518) Tel 914-667-9400; Orders to: Consumer Reports Bks., 540 Barnum Ave., Bridgeport, CT 06608 (SAN 661-9800).

Consumertronics Co., *(Consumertronics; 0-934274),* 2011 Crescent Dr., Alamogordo, NM 88310 (SAN 212-7369); P.O. Drawer 537, Alamogordo, NM 88310 (SAN 658-036X) (SAN 661-9819).

Contact Editions, *(Contact Edit; 0-937645),* P.O. Box 603, Northampton, MA 01061 (SAN 659-1450) Tel 413-586-1181; 30 N. Maple St., Florence, MA 01060 (SAN 659-1469).

Contact/II Pubns., *(Contact Two; 0-936556),* P.O. Box 451, Bowling Green, New York, NY 10004 (SAN 200-4151) Tel 212-674-0911; Dist. by: Small Press Distribution, Inc., 1814 San Pablo Ave., Berkeley, CA 94702 (SAN 204-5826) Tel 415-549-3336; Dist. by: NY New Papers, 611 Broadway, New York, NY 10012 (SAN 200-8130) Tel 212-777-6157; Dist. by: Ingram Industries, 347 Reedwood Dr., Nashville, TN 37217 (SAN 169-7978) Tel 615-793-5000.

Contemplative Bks., *(Contemplative Bks; 0-939419),* P.O. Box 8065, Columbus, GA 31908 (SAN 663-1819); 3400 St. Mary's Rd., Columbus, GA 31906 (SAN 663-1827) Tel 404-689-1892.

Contemporary Arts Ctr., The, *(Contemp Arts; 0-917562),* 115 E. Fifth St., Cincinnati, OH 45202 (SAN 210-5551) Tel 513-721-0390.

†**Contemporary Arts Pr.,** Div. of La Mamelle, Inc., *(Contemporary Arts; 0-931818),* P.O. Box 3123, Rincon Annex, San Francisco, CA 94119 (SAN 213-3016); *CIP.*

Contemporary Bks., Inc., *(Contemp Bks; 0-8092),* 180 N. Michigan Ave., Chicago, IL 60601 (SAN 202-5493) Tel 312-782-9181. Formerly: Henry Regnery Co. *Imprints:* Gateway Editions (Gate); Great Debate Series (GrDeb); Logos Books (Logos).

Contemporary Image Advertising, Ltd., *(Contemp Image; 0-9616743),* 300 S. Washington Ave., Suite 380 J, Lansing, MI 48933 (SAN 661-0463) Tel 517-484-4922.

Contemporary Issues Clearinghouse, *(Contemp Issues; 0-914677),* 1410 S. Second St., Pocatello, ID 83201 (SAN 289-7024).

Contemporary Literature Pr., *(Contemp Lit Pr; 0-930266),* P.O. Box 26462, San Francisco, CA 94126 (SAN 201-9027).

Contemporary Perspectives, Inc. See CPI Publishing, Inc.

Contemporary Publishing, Co. of Raleigh, *(Contemp Pub Co of Raleigh; 0-89892),* 508 St. Mary's St., Raleigh, NC 27605 (SAN 213-0424) Tel 919-821-4566.

Names

Content, Derek J., Rare Bks., Inc., *(D J Content; 0-935681),* Crow Hill, Houlton, ME 04730 (SAN 696-3986) Tel 207-532-7794.

†**Context Pubns.,** *(Context Pubns; 0-932654),* P.O. Box 2909, Rohnert Park, CA 94928-6506 (SAN 212-8977) Tel 707-584-4423; Dist. by: Bookpeople, 2929 Fifth St., Berkeley, CA 94710 (SAN 168-9517) Tel 415-549-3030; Toll free: 800-227-1516; *CIP.*

Continent Pubns., *(Cntnt Pubs SF; 0-9616169),* 110 Pacific Ave., Suite 218, San Francisco, CA 94111 (SAN 699-7783).

Continental Association of Funeral & Memorial Societies, Inc., *(Continent Assn Funeral),* 2001 S St. NW, Suite 530, Washington, DC 20009 (SAN 202-6201) Tel 202-745-0634.

Continental Divide Trail Society, *(Continent Divide; 0-934326),* P.O. Box 30002, Bethesda, MD 20814 (SAN 213-0432) Tel 301-493-4080.

Continental Editions, *(Continent Edns; 0-916868),* 2300 Indian Hills Dr., 3-231, Sioux City, IA 51104 (SAN 208-192X) Tel 712-239-5954.

Continental Heritage Pr., *(Continent Herit; 0-932986),* 6 E. Fifth, Suite 410, Tulsa, OK 74103 (SAN 212-0348) Tel 918-582-5100.

Continental Historical Society, *(Cont Hist Soc; 0-9609900),* 3145 Geary Blvd., No. 126, San Francisco, CA 94118 (SAN 269-3607) Tel 415-751-1253.

Continental Media Co., *(Continent Media; 0-912349),* P.O. Box 31256, Hartford, CT 06103 (SAN 265-1114) Tel 203-247-0300.

Continental Pubns. Ltd., *(Continental CA; 0-916096),* P.O. Box 1729, Carlsbad, CA 92008 (SAN 208-6093) Tel 619-434-7017.

Continental Services, Ltd., *(Continental Servs; 0-9616277),* 301 W 53rd. St., Apt. 6C, New York, NY 10019 (SAN 658-5604) Tel 212-333-7348.

Continuing Education Div. *See* **Wadsworth Publishing Co.**

Continuing Education Pubns., Subs. of Portland State University, *(Continuing Ed Pubns; 0-930253),* 1633 SW Pk., Portland, OR 97207 (SAN 670-8552) Tel 503-229-4846.

Continuing Education Pubn., Co. *See* **Burgess International Group, Inc.**

Continuing Education Systems, Inc., *(CES; 0-916780),* 112 S. Grant St., Hinsdale, IL 60521 (SAN 208-6107) Tel 312-654-2596.

Continuing SAGA Pr., *(Continuing SAGA),* P.O. Box 194, San Anselmo, CA 94960 (SAN 215-7454) Tel 415-454-4411.

Continuity Press, The, *(Continuity Pr; 0-939408),* P.O. Box 677, Gualala, CA 95445 (SAN 216-5724) Tel 707-884-3766.

†**Continuum Pub. Co.,** *(Continuum; 0-8264),* 370 Lexington Ave., New York, NY 10017 (SAN 213-8220) Tel 212-532-3650 (SAN 201-002X); Dist. by: Harper & Row, Keystone Industrial Pk., Scranton, PA 18512 (SAN 215-3742); Toll free: 800-242-7737; *CIP.*

Contract Data Pubs., *(Contract Data; 0-939260),* P.O. Box 366, Alta Loma, CA 91701 (SAN 220-1666) Tel 714-987-6850.

Control Data Patents & Trademarks Dept., *(Control Patents; 0-918852),* 1225 Conneticut Ave.,N.W. Suit 202, Washington, DC 20036 (SAN 204-2525) Tel 202-296-4523.

Control Engineering Technical Publishing, Subs. of Dun & Bradstreet Corp., *(Control Eng; 0-914331),* 1301 S. Grove Ave., Barrington, IL 60010 (SAN 287-587X) Tel 312-381-1840.

Convention of American Instructors of the Deaf, *(Con Am Inst Deaf; 0-942896),* 814 Thayer Ave., Silver Spring, MD 20910 (SAN 227-7417).

Convex Industries, Inc., *(Convex Indus; 0-913920),* 4720 Cheyenne, Boulder, CO 80303 (SAN 203-5871) Tel 303-494-4176.

Conveyor Equipment Manufacturers Assn., *(Conveyor Equip Mfrs),* 152 Rollins Ave., Suite 208, Rockville, MD 20852 (SAN 224-8492) Tel 301-984-9080.

Conway Data, Inc., *(Conway Data; 0-910436),* 40 Technology Park, Norcross, GA 30092 (SAN 203-1183) Tel 404-446-6996.

Conway House, *(Conway Hse; 0-914402),* P.O. Box 424, Bellaire, MI 49615 (SAN 203-6207).

Conyers Bonner, Publishing Co., *(Bonner Pub Co; 0-914007),* P.O. Box 17812, Raleigh, NC 27619-7812 (SAN 286-7435) Tel 919-878-8697.

Cook, Chester L., *(C L Cook; 0-9604670),* P.O. Box 1511, Slidell, LA 70458 (SAN 220-1194) Tel 504-643-3254.

Cook, David C., Publishing Co., *(Cook; 0-89191; 0-912692; 1-55513),* 850 N. Grove Ave., Elgin, IL 60120 (SAN 206-0981) Tel 312-741-2400; Toll free: 800-323-7543. *Imprints:* Chariot Books (Chariot Bks).

Cook, Fred B., *(Cook MO; 0-9614001),* 2433 E. Edgewood, Springfield, MO 65804 (SAN 683-5724) Tel 417-881-5055.

Cook, Jim, Pub., *(Jim Cook; 0-936941),* 494 Conejo Rd., Santa Barbara, CA 93103 (SAN 658-5051) Tel 805-962-7879.

Cook, Ray G., *(R G Cook; 0-9602002),* 366 Hooker Ave., Poughkeepsie, NY 12603 (SAN 223-4009).

Cookbook Factory, The, *(Cookbook Fact; 0-910983),* P.O. Box 11515, Eugene, OR 97440 (SAN 262-012X) Tel 503-344-7759.

Cookbook Pubs., *(Cookbook Pubs; 0-934474),* Lenexa, KS 66215 (SAN 213-2427) Tel 501-741-7340; Dist. by: Southern Star, Inc., P.O. Box 968, Harrison, AR 72601 (SAN 213-2435).

Cookbooks Unlimited, *(Cookbks Unltd; 0-932443),* 1 Wind Poppy Ct., The Woodlands, TX 77381 (SAN 687-083X) Tel 713-363-2661.

Cooke City Store, *(Cooke City; 0-9608876),* Box 1097, Cooke City, MT 59020 (SAN 241-1040) Tel 406-838-2234.

Coolidge Pr., Div. of Chattanooga Printing & Engraving Co., *(Coolidge Pr; 0-9615343),* 110 Somerville Ave., Chattanooga, TN 37405 (SAN 695-121X) Tel 615-484-8788.

Cooling Spring Pr., The, Div. of Challenge Hse., *(Cooling Spring; 0-935883),* 405 Jefferson St., Saluda, SC 29138 (SAN 696-3412) Tel 704-669-2782 (SAN 696-3420) Tel 803-445-2351.

Cooper *See* **Shoe String Pr., Inc.**

Cooper & Cooper Pub., *(Cooper & Cooper Pub; 0-931429),* P.O. Box 1516, Palo Alto, CA 94302 (SAN 683-2121) Tel 415-327-6472.

†**Cooper-Hewitt Museum,** Affil. of Smithsonian Institution, *(Cooper-Hewitt Museum; 0-910503),* 2 E. 91st St., New York, NY 10128 (SAN 260-0366) Tel 212-860-6868; *CIP.*

Cooper Hse. Publishing Co., *(Cooper Hse Pub; 0-939121),* P.O. Box 44021, Shreveport, LA 71134 (SAN 662-4766); 160 Prospect, Shreveport, LA 71104 (SAN 662-4774) Tel 318-424-8036.

Cooper-Morgan, Inc., *(Cooper-Morgan; 0-9614801),* 6649 E. Roswell Rd., Ste. 659, Atlanta, GA 30328 (SAN 692-6665) Tel 404-636-7508.

†**Cooper Sq. Pubs., Inc.,** Div. of Littlefield, Adams & Co., *(Cooper Sq; 0-8154),* 81 Adams Dr., Totowa, NJ 07512 (SAN 281-5621) Tel 201-256-8600; *CIP.*

Cooperative Power, Inc., Subs. of Cooperation Corporation, *(Coop Power),* R. R. 1, Box 24A, Springfield, IL 62707 (SAN 210-7473) Tel 217-523-8663.

Coordinating Council of Literary Magazines, *(Coord Coun Lit Mags; 0-942332),* 666 Broadway, 11th flr., New York, NY 10012 (SAN 225-3410) Tel 212-614-6551; Dist. by: Moyer Bell Ltd., Colonial Hill, RFD 1, Mt. Kisco, NY 10549 (SAN 669-6961) Tel 914-666-0084.

Cop-A-Form, Inc., *(Cop-A-Form; 0-914567),* P.O. Box 02227, 443 Crestview Rd., Columbus, OH 43202 (SAN 289-1875) Tel 614-261-9917.

Cope, L, Publishing, *(L Cope Pub; 0-9617214),* 134-6 W. 32nd St., Suite 602, New York, NY 10001 (SAN 663-4028); 86 Myrtle Ave., Irvington, NJ 07111 (SAN 663-4036) Tel 201-315-8667.

Copesthetic, *(Copesthetic),* 2032 Belmont Rd. NW, No. 612, Washington, DC 20009 (SAN 295-0103) Tel 202-667-0470.

Copley, Frank O., *(F O Copley; 0-9615724),* 1291 Forest Ave., Rogers City, MI 49779 (SAN 696-4001) Tel 517-734-4381; Box 216, Rogers City, MI 49779 (SAN 696-5369).

†**Copley Bks.,** Subs. of The Copley Press, Inc., *(Copley Bks; 0-913938),* P.O. Box 957, La Jolla, CA 92038 (SAN 202-1846); 7776 Ivanhoe Ave., La Jolla, CA 92037 (SAN 662-720X) Tel 619-454-1842; *CIP.*

Copouts Ink, *(Copouts Ink; 0-938417),* P.O. Box 6223, Anaheim, CA 92806 (SAN 661-051X); 1733 Chelsea, Anaheim, CA 92805 (SAN 661-0528) Tel 714-776-2718.

Coppage, A. Maxim, *(A M Coppage),* 2225 Hillsborough Ct. No. 3, Concord, CA 94520 (SAN 238-0536).

†**Copper Beech Pr.,** *(Copper Beech; 0-914278),* Box 1852, Brown Univ., Providence, RI 02912 (SAN 212-8063); *CIP.*

†**Copper Canyon Pr.,** *(Copper Canyon; 0-914742; 1-55659),* P.O. Box 271, Port Townsend, WA 98368 (SAN 206-488X) Tel 206-385-4925; Dist. by: Consortium Bk. Sales & Distribution, 213 E. Fourth St., St. Paul, MN 55101 (SAN 200-6049) Tel 612-221-9035; *CIP.*

Copper Development Assn., *(Copper Devel Assn),* Greenwich Office Pk. 2, Box 1840, Greenwich, CT 06836-1840 (SAN 230-9793) Tel 203-625-8210.

Copper Orchid Publishing Co., The, *(Copper Orchid; 0-9608522),* 1966 Westbrook Dr., Jackson, MI 49201 (SAN 240-6195) Tel 517-750-4625.

Copperfield Pr., *(Copperfield Pr; 0-933857),* P.O. Box 15025, Austin, TX 78761 (SAN 692-7351) Tel 512-837-2931.

Copperfield Pr., The, *(Copprfld NYC; 0-9617037),* 80-85 Dumfries Pl., Jamaica, NY 11432 (SAN 662-5843) Tel 718-969-1797. Do not confuse with Copperfield Pr., Austin, TX.

Copple Hse. Bks., *(Copple Hse; 0-932298),* Roads' End, Lakemont, GA 30552 (SAN 658-0378) Tel 404-782-2134 (SAN 281-5648).

Copy & Concepts, Ltd., *(Copy Concepts; 0-937983),* 22 Grove St., New York, NY 10014 (SAN 659-4999) Tel 212-243-8065.

Copy Fast Printing, *(Copy Fast; 0-9612032),* 246 King St., Pottstown, PA 19464 (SAN 286-7710) Tel 215-326-7456.

Copy Fast Printing Ctr., Inc., *(Copy Fast Ctr; 0-930579),* 505 Worcester Rd., Rt. 9, Framingham, MA 01702 (SAN 678-4445) Tel 617-875-0621.

Copy-Write Artograph Co., Div. of E. Wynn Vogel Co., *(Copy-Write; 0-912392),* 1865 77th St., Brooklyn, NY 11214-1233 (SAN 203-588X) Tel 718-331-1045.

Copyright Information Services, *(Copyright Info; 0-914143),* P.O. Box 1460, Friday Harbor, WA 98250 (SAN 287-6388) Tel 206-378-5128.

Coraco, *(Coraco; 0-917628),* 1017 S. Arlington Ave., Los Angeles, CA 90019 (SAN 203-5898) Tel 213-737-1066.

Coral Gables Publishing Co., Inc., *(Coral Gables Pub; 0-938993),* 8065 SW 107th Ave., Miami, FL 33173 (SAN 662-5320) Tel 305-279-9049.

Corban Productions, *(Corban Prods; 0-9608710),* P.O. Box 215, Worthington, OH 43089 (SAN 238-0544) Tel 614-889-0102.

Corbett, Bayliss, *(Bayliss Corbett; 0-933152),* 762 Ave N. SE, Winter Haven, FL 33880 (SAN 212-5935) Tel 813-294-5555.

Corbett, H. Roger, Jr., *(Corbett),* 8100 Cardiff St., Lorton, VA 22079 (SAN 211-1160) Tel 703-550-7317.

Corcoran, Lawrence, *(L Corcoran),* 7801 Sand Bay Rd., Sturgeon Bay, WI 54235 (SAN 212-6494).

†**Corcoran Gallery of Art,** *(Corcoran; 0-88675),* 17th St. & New York Ave. NW, Washington, DC 20006 (SAN 204-2797) Tel 202-638-3211; *CIP.*

Cordner, John, *(J Cordner; 0-9617224),* 3712 35th Ave. SW, Seattle, WA 98126 (SAN 663-365X) Tel 206-935-8403.

Cordovan Pr., *(Cordovan Pr; 0-89123),* 5314 Bingle Rd. P.O. Box 920973, Houston, TX 77292 (SAN 204-2789) Tel 713-688-8811.

Cordus Press, *(Cordus Pr; 0-935118),* P.O. Box 587, North Amherst, MA 01059 (SAN 203-3108) Tel 413-549-6888.

Coren Assocs., *(Coren Assocs; 0-9611642),* P.O. Box 58, Mamaroneck, NY 10543 (SAN 284-947X) Tel 914-698-9113.

Corey & Co. Designers, *(Corey & Co; 0-9615538),* 249 Newbury St., Boston, MA 02116 (SAN 696-4028) Tel 617-266-1850.

Corey/Stevens Bks., *(Corey-Stevens Bks; 0-942866),* 7958 SW Barbur Blvd., Portland, OR 97219 (SAN 240-2106) Tel 503-246-7418.

†**Coriander Pr.,** *(Coriander Pr; 0-912837),* 361 Scenic Dr., Ashland, OR 97520 (SAN 283-0051) Tel 503-488-1016; P.O. Box 337, Ashland, OR 97520 (SAN 658-232X); *CIP.*

Corinth Bks., *(Corinth Bks; 0-87091),* 4008 EW Hwy., Chevy Chase, MD 20815 (SAN 281-5656) Tel 301-652-1016; Orders to: Bookslinger, 213 E. Fourth St., St. Paul, MN 55101 (SAN 169-4154) Tel 612-221-0429.

Corinth Hse. Pubs., *(Corinth Hse; 0-938280),* 2238 E. Vermont Ave., Anaheim, CA 92806 (SAN 214-3607) Tel 714-635-6930.

Corinthian Pr., The, Div. of EDR Corp., *(Corinthian; 0-86551),* 3592 Lee Rd., Shaker Heights, OH 44120 (SAN 216-1214) Tel 216-751-7300.

Corinthian Pubns., *(Corinth Pub; 0-935915),* 2518 E. Ocean View Ave., Norfolk, VA 23518 (SAN 696-7256) Tel 804-587-2671; P.O. Box 8279, Norfolk, VA 23503 (SAN 698-2166).

Corita Communications, *(Corita Comm; 0-933016),* 1301 N. Kenter Ave., Los Angeles, CA 90049 (SAN 212-2723).

Corja Bks., *(Corja Bks; 0-916887),* 2726 Blenheim Ave., Redwood City, CA 94063 (SAN 655-9565) Tel 415-365-8939.

Cormorant Bks., *(Cormorant Bks; 0-936261),* 405 E. 300 S., Lehi, UT 84043 (SAN 697-3442) Tel 801-968-3232.

Cornelia & Michael Bessie Books *See* **Harper & Row Pubs., Inc.**

Cornell, George D. & Harriet W., Fine Arts Center *See* **Rollins College, George D. & Harriet W. Cornell Fine Arts Ctr.**

Cornell Daily Sun, Inc., The, *(Cornell Daily; 0-938304),* 109 E. State St., Ithaca, NY 14850 (SAN 239-8370) Tel 607-273-3606.

Cornell Design Publishers, *(Cornell Des; 0-914397),* P.O. Box 278, East Hanover, NJ 07936 (SAN 289-6281) Tel 201-884-0330.

Cornell Laboratory of Ornithology, *(Cornell Ornithology; 0-938027),* Cornell Univ., 159 Sapsucker Woods Rd., Ithaca, NY 14850 Tel 607-255-5056; Dist. by: Houghton Mifflin Co., 1 Beacon St., Boston, MA 02108 (SAN 200-2388) Tel 617-725-5000.

†**Cornell Maritime Pr., Inc.,** *(Cornell Maritime; 0-87033),* P.O. Box 456, Centreville, MD 21617 (SAN 203-5901) Tel 301-758-1075; Toll free: 800-638-7641; *CIP.*

Cornell Modern Indonesia Project, Affil. of Cornell University, *(Cornell Mod Indo; 0-87763),* 102 West Ave., Ithaca, NY 14850 (SAN 203-591X) Tel 607-255-4359.

Cornell Univ. China-Japan Program, East Asia Papers, *(Cornell China-Japan Pgm; 0-939657),* 140 Uris Hall, Cornell Univ., Ithaca, NY 14853 (SAN 219-3604) Tel 607-255-6222.

Cornell Univ., Dept. of Agronomy, *(Cornell U Dept; 0-932865),* 1008 Bradfield Hall, Ithaca, NY 14853 (SAN 688-9158) Tel 607-255-1736; Orders to: International Soils/Dept. of Agronomy, Cornell Univ., 1014 Bradford Hall, Ithaca, NY 14853 (SAN 662-2828).

Cornell Univ. Libraries, Dept. of Manuscripts & Univ. Archives, *(Cornell Manu; 0-935995),* 101 Olin Library, Ithaca, NY 14853-5301 (SAN 696-7159) Tel 607-255-3530.

Cornell Univ. Pr., *(Cornell U Pr; 0-8014),* 124 Roberts Pl., P.O. Box 250, Ithaca, NY 14851 (SAN 202-1862) Tel 607-257-7000; Orders to: 714 Cascadilla St., Ithaca, NY 14851 (SAN 281-5680) Tel 607-277-2211.

Cornell Univ., Schl. of Hotel Administration, *(Cornell U Sch Hotel; 0-937056),* 327 Statler Hall, Ithaca, NY 14853 (SAN 204-2746) Tel 607-255-5093.

Cornell Univ., Southeast Asia Program, *(Cornell SE Asia; 0-87727),* 120 Uris Hall, Ithaca, NY 14853 (SAN 206-6416) Tel 607-256-2378.

Cornell Widow, Inc., *(Cornell Widow; 0-9605870),* 104 Willard Straight Hall, Cornell University, Ithaca, NY 14853 (SAN 216-356X).

Corner Hse. Pubs., *(Corner Hse; 0-87928),* 1321 Green River Rd., Williamstown, MA 01267 (SAN 203-5936) Tel 413-458-8561.

CornerBrook Pr., *(CornerBrook Pr; 0-913523),* Box 106, Lansing, NY 14882 (SAN 285-1563) Tel 607-533-4056; 178 N. Lansing School Rd., RD 1, Groton, NY 13073 (SAN 285-1571) Tel 607-255-3182.

Cornerstone Library, Inc., Div. of Simon & Schuster, Inc., *(Cornerstone; 0-346),* ; Toll free: 800-223-2336; Orders to: Simon & Schuster, Inc., 1230 Ave. of the Americas, New York, NY 10020 (SAN 200-2450) Tel 212-245-6400.

Cornerstone Pr., *(Cornerstone Pr; 0-918476),* P.O. Box 28048, St. Louis, MO 63119 (SAN 210-0584) Tel 314-296-9662.

Cornhusker Pr., Subs. of Dutton-Lainson Co., *(Cornhusker Pr; 0-933909),* P.O. Box 729, Hastings, NE 68901 (SAN 682-2819); 426 W. Second St., Hastings, NE 68901 (SAN 692-6363) Tel 402-463-6702.

Cornick Concepts, Inc., *(Cornick; 0-9615516),* 437 Midsummer Ct., West Palm Beach, FL 33411 (SAN 696-4036) Tel 305-798-3550.

Corning Museum of Glass, *(Corning; 0-87290),* 1 Museum Way, Corning, NY 14830-2253 (SAN 202-1897) Tel 607-937-5371; Dist. by: Associated University Presses, 440 Forsgate Dr., Cranbury, NJ 08512 (SAN 281-2959) Tel 609-655-4770.

Corning Publishing Co., *(Corning Pub Co; 0-9614945),* 171 Ontario Ave., Holyoke, MA 01040 (SAN 693-6512) Tel 413-536-1947.

Cornrows & Co., *(Cornrows & Co; 0-939183),* 5401 14th St. NW, Washington, DC 20011 (SAN 662-8303) Tel 202-723-1827.

Cornucopia Pubns., *(Cornucopia Pubns; 0-914207),* 2515 E. Thomas Rd., Suite 16, Phoenix, AZ 85016 (SAN 287-6396) Tel 602-279-1122.

Cornwall Books *See* **Associated University Presses**

Corona, Belva, *(B Corona; 0-9616840),* 1629 SW 81st, Oklahoma City, OK 73159 (SAN 661-5384) Tel 405-681-9731.

Corona Publishing Co., *(Corona Pub; 0-931722),* 1037 S. Alamo, San Antonio, TX 78210 (SAN 211-8491) Tel 512-227-1771.

Coronado Pr., Inc., *(Coronado Pr; 0-87291),* P.O. Box 3232, Lawrence, KS 66044 (SAN 201-7776) Tel 913-843-5988.

Coronet Bks., *(Coronet Bks; 0-89563),* 311 Bainbridge St., Philadelphia, PA 19147 (SAN 210-6043) Tel 215-925-2762.

Corporate Communication Studies, Inc., *(Corporate Comm Studies; 0-915683),* P.O. Box 9538, Daytona Beach, FL 32020 (SAN 292-4528) Tel 904-673-3848.

Corporate Organizing Project, Subs. of Ctr. for Urban Education, *(Corp Organ Pro; 0-931987),* 611 Vanderbilt St., Brooklyn, NY 11218 (SAN 683-2458) Tel 718-871-5356.

Corporate Support Systems, *(Corporate Support Systs; 0-936879),* 615 W. Kirby Ave., Champaign, IL 61820 (SAN 658-3237) Tel 217-398-2077.

Corporate Technology Information Services, Inc., *(CorpTech; 0-936507),* 2 Laurel Ave., Wellesley Hills, MA 02181 (SAN 697-8576) Tel 617-235-5330 (SAN 697-8584).

Corporate West, Inc., *(Corporate West Inc; 0-9613119),* 2602 N. 20th Ave., Phoenix, AZ 85009 (SAN 294-7285) Tel 602-253-0514.

Corporation for Community College Television, *(Corp Cmnt Col TV; 0-9617111),* 5400 Orange Ave., Suite 109, Cypress, CA 90630 (SAN 662-7013) Tel 714-828-5770.

Corporation for Enterprise Development, The, *(Corp Ent Dev; 0-9605804),* 1725 K St., NW, Suite 1401, Washington, DC 20006 (SAN 216-5619) Tel 202-293-7963.

Corpus Christi Area Garden Council, Inc., *(Corpus Christi Area),* P.O. Box 6165, Corpus Christi, TX 78411 (SAN 663-088X).

Corral, Apache, Publishing Co., *(A Corral; 0-9616932),* 3048 Champion, No. 2, Oakland, CA 94602 (SAN 661-8332) Tel 415-261-5592.

†**Correlan Pubns.,** *(Correlan Pubns; 0-913842),* P.O. Box 337, Watsonville, CA 95077 (SAN 202-0386) Tel 408-728-1766; *CIP.*

Corridor Publishing Co., *(Corridor Pub; 0-936053),* P.O. Box 1008, Crawfordsville, IN 47933 (SAN 697-0249) Tel 317-362-1509.

Corrieri, Michael, Jr., *(M Corrieri; 0-9615686),* 19 Russell St., Lockport, NY 14094 (SAN 696-4044) Tel 716-433-8897; Orders to: Corrieri Home Inspections, P.O. Box 3262, Lockport, NY 14094 (SAN 662-3735).

Corroboree Pr., *(Corroboree Pr; 0-911169),* 2729 Bloomington Ave. S., Minneapolis, MN 55407 (SAN 269-3925) Tel 612-724-1355.

Corser, Frank Rose, *(F & R Corser; 0-9608636),* 215 Baseline, San Dimas, CA 91773 (SAN 263-984X).

Corsi, Petro, *(Corsi; 0-9615871),* 4404 Sherman Oaks Ave., Sherman Oaks, CA 91403 (SAN 696-6187) Tel 213-553-9761.

Cortland Publishing, Inc., *(Cortland Pub; 0-914825),* 5775 Wayzata Blvd., Rm. 700, Minneapolis, MN 55416 (SAN 289-0941) Tel 612-544-1375.

Corvallis Software, Inc., *(Corvallis Software; 0-942358),* P.O. Box 1412, Corvallis, OR 97339 (SAN 237-9406) Tel 503-754-9245.

Corwin Pubs., Inc., *(Corwin Pubs; 0-938569),* P.O. Box 2806, San Francisco, CA 94126 (SAN 661-2571); 123 Corwin St., Suite C, San Francisco, CA 94114 (SAN 661-258X) Tel 415-621-4346.

Cos Cob Pr., *(Cos Cob Pr; 0-915639),* 82 Valleywood Rd, Cos Cob, CT 06807 (SAN 292-4676) Tel 203-661-7918.

Cosmic Communication Co., *(Cosmic Comm; 0-912038),* 100 Elm Ct., Decorah, IA 52101 (SAN 201-9043) Tel 319-382-8350.

Cosmic Hse., *(Cosmic Hse NM; 0-932492),* P.O. Box 10515, Alameda, NM 87184 (SAN 211-9331) Tel 505-897-2240.

Cosmic Science Pub., *(Cos Sci Orange; 0-9615921),* 12932 Malma Dr., Santa Ana, CA 92705 (SAN 696-785X) Tel 714-771-0448. Do not confuse with Cosmic Science Pub. of Louisville, KY.

Cosmoenergetics Pubns., *(Cosmoenergetics Pubns; 0-938954),* P.O. Box 86353, San Diego, CA 92138 (SAN 239-8184) Tel 619-295-1664; Dist. by: New Leaf, 1020 White St, SW, Atlanta, GA 30310 (SAN 169-1449) Tel 404-755-3454; Toll free: 800-241-3829.

†**Cosmos Of Humanists Pr.,** *(Cosmos Humanists; 0-913429),* P.O. Box 11143, San Francisco, CA 94101 (SAN 285-8827) Tel 415-337-1787; *CIP.*

Cosmotic Concerns, *(Cosmotic Concerns; 0-938104),* c/o Jacef Relations, P.O. Box 621, Langley, WA 98260-0621 (SAN 238-0552) Tel 206-221-2617.

Cosray Research Institute, *(Cosray Res; 0-9606374),* 2505 S. Fourth East, P.O. Box 151045, Salt Lake City, UT 84115 (SAN 216-3578).

Costa, *(Costa),* 23 Old Field Pl., Red Bank, NJ 07701 (SAN 263-9858).

Costano Bks., *(Costano; 0-930268),* P.O. Box 355, Petaluma, CA 94953 (SAN 210-3508) Tel 707-762-4848.

Costello, Ralph H., *(R H Costello; 0-9612900),* 101 Grand Ave., No. 16, Capitola, CA 95010 (SAN 291-1264) Tel 408-476-8868.

Cottage Bks., *(Cottage Bks; 0-911253),* P.O. Box 2071, Silver Spring, MD 20902 (SAN 285-0044) Tel 301-649-5433; Dist. by: LIDCO, 2849 Georgia Ave., NW, Washington, DC 20001 (SAN 282-6011) Tel 202-328-0191; Dist. by: Acropolis Books Ltd., 2400 17th St., NW, Washington, DC 20009 (SAN 201-2227) Tel 202-387-6805.

Cottage Craft, *(Cottage; 0-935203),* P.O. Box 505, Mableton, GA 30059 (SAN 695-7315) Tel 404-426-4004.

Cottage Industries, *(Cottage Indus; 0-938348),* Box 244, Cobalt, CT 06414 (SAN 215-7462) Tel 203-342-2599.

Cottage Industry, Inc., *(Cott Ind Phoenix; 0-9615721),* 5112 N. 40th St., Phoenix, AZ 85018 (SAN 696-4052) Tel 602-951-8989.

Cottage Pr., Inc., *(Cottage Pr; 0-918343),* P.O. Box 1265, Englewood Cliffs, NJ 07632 (SAN 657-3339) Tel 201-894-1011.

Cottage Publishing Co., *(Cottage Pub Co; 0-915479),* 566 Wyckoff Ave., Wyckoff, NJ 07481 (SAN 291-1299) Tel 201-891-8295; Orders to: P.O. Box 21, Ridgefield, CT 06877 (SAN 291-1302).

Cotton Lane Pr., *(Cotton Lane; 0-9604810),* Cotton Ln. at 18 Eighth St., Augusta, GA 30901. (SAN 281-5699) Tel 404-722-0232.

Cottontail Pubns., *(Cottontail Pubns; 0-942124),* R.R. 1, Box 198, Bennington, IN 47011 (SAN 238-6526) Tel 812-427-3914.

Cottonwood Bks., *(Cottonwood Bks; 0-935775),* 1216 Lillie Cir., Salt Lake City, UT 84121 (SAN 696-4079) Tel 801-262-4586.

†Cottonwood Pubns., *(Cottonwood Pubns; 0-918887),* 1091 Morning St., Worthington, OH 43085 (SAN 669-9820); Orders to: Cottonwood Publications, P.O. Box 264, Worthington, OH 43085 (SAN 662-2429) Tel 614-885-8132; *CIP.*

Cougar Bks., *(Cougar Bks; 0-917982),* P.O. Box 22246, Sacramento, CA 95822 (SAN 209-4266) Tel 916-428-3271.

Coughlin, Michael E., Pub., *(M E Coughlin; 0-9602574),* 1985 Selby Ave., St. Paul, MN 55104 (SAN 211-5220) Tel 612-646-8917.

Coulee Pr., *(Coulee Pr; 0-9611456),* Box 1744, La Crosse, WI 54602-1744 (SAN 283-1171) Tel 608-788-6253.

Couleur, Inc. & Assocs., *(Couleur Inc Assoc; 0-9613208),* 27830 Ten Oaks Ctr., Conroe, TX 77302 (SAN 295-7272) Tel 713-363-3116.

Council for Advancement & Support of Education, *(Coun Adv & Supp Ed; 0-89964),* 11 Dupont Cir., Suite 400, Washington, DC 20036 (SAN 225-8641) Tel 202-328-5900; Orders to: CASE Pubns. Order Dept., 80 S. Early St., Alexandria, VA 22304 (SAN 202-4500) Tel 703-823-6966.

Council for Agricultural Science & Technology, *(Coun Agri Sci),* P.O. Box 1550, Iowa State Univ. Sta., Ames, IA 50010-1550 (SAN 225-7416) Tel 515-292-2125.

Council for Basic Education, *(Coun Basic Educ; 0-931989),* 725 15th St., NW, Washington, DC 20005 (SAN 269-4093) Tel 202-347-4171.

Council for Career Planning, Inc., *(Coun Career Plan; 0-916340),* P.O. Box 2466, New York, NY 10168-2466 (SAN 201-2545) Tel 212-687-9490.

Council for Indian Education, *(Coun India Ed; 0-89992),* 517 Rimrock Rd., Billings, MT 59102 (SAN 202-2117) Tel 406-252-1800; Orders to: Box 31215, Billings, MT 59107 (SAN 689-836X) Tel 406-252-1800.

†Council for Inter-American Security, *(Coun Inter-Am; 0-943624),* 122 C St., NW, Suite 330, Washington, DC 20001 (SAN 238-2660) Tel 202-543-6622; *CIP.*

Council for Inter-American Security, Educational Institute, *(Coun Inter Ed; 0-910637),* 122 C St., NW, Suite 330, Washington, DC 20001 (SAN 269-4174) Tel 202-543-6622.

Council for Intercultural Studies & Programs, *(CISP; 0-939288),* 777 United Nations Plaza, Suite 9H, New York, NY 10017 (SAN 220-2417).

Council for Public Television, Channel 6, Inc., *(Council Public TV; 0-9616209),* 1261 Glenarm Pl., Denver, CO 80227 (SAN 658-3318) Tel 303-892-6666.

Council for Social & Economic Studies, Inc., *(Coun Soc Econ; 0-930690),* 1133 13th St., NW, Suite COMM. 2, Washington, DC 20005 (SAN 210-1130) Tel 202-789-0231.

Council for Unified Research & Education, *(CURE),* 617 W. 113th St., New York, NY 10025 (SAN 233-0091) Tel 212-666-4766.

Council Oak Bks., Ltd., *(Coun Oak Bks; 0-933031),* 1428 S. St. Louis, Tulsa, OK 74120 (SAN 689-5522) Tel 918-587-6454; Toll free: 800-526-7626; Dist. by: Kampmann & Co., 9 E. 40th St., New York, NY 10016 (SAN 202-5191).

Council of American Revolutionary Sites, *(CARS; 0-9616323),* Pennsylvania Rte. 32, Washington Crossing, PA 18977 (SAN 658-6643) Tel 215-493-4076; P.O. Box 103, Washington Crossing, PA 18977-0103 (SAN 658-6651).

Council of Biology Editors, *(Coun Biology Eds; 0-914340),* 9650 Rockville Pike, Bethesda, MD 20814 (SAN 207-0693) Tel 301-530-7036.

Council of Europe, Directorate of Legal Affairs, *(Coun Europe Direct),* Dist. by: Manhattan Publishing Co., 225 Lafayette St., New York, NY 10012 (SAN 213-442X).

Council of Independent Colleges, *(Coun Indep Colleges; 0-937012),* 1 Dupont Cir., NW, Suite 320, Washington, DC 20036 (SAN 690-0291) Tel 202-466-7230.

Council of Jewish Federations & Welfare Funds, Inc., *(Coun Jewish Feds),* 575 Lexington Ave., New York, NY 10022 (SAN 225-9532).

Council of Logistics Management, *(Coun Logistics Mgt),* 2803 Butterfield Rd, Oak Brook, IL 60521 (SAN 224-7100) Tel 312-574-0985.

Council of New York Law Associates, *(Coun NY Law; 0-910639),* 99 Hudson St., New York, NY 10013 (SAN 237-6997).

†Council of Planning Librarians, *(Coun Plan Librarians; 0-86602),* 1313 E. 60th St., Chicago, IL 60637-2897 (SAN 225-3364) Tel 312-947-2007; *CIP.*

Council of State Governments, *(Coun State Govts; 0-87292),* Iron Works Pike, P.O. Box 11910, Lexington, KY 40578 (SAN 225-1264) Tel 606-252-2291.

†Council of State Policy & Planning Agencies, Affil. of National Governor's Association, *(CSPA; 0-934842),* 400 N. Capitol St. NW, Suite 291, Washington, DC 20001 (SAN 213-3032) Tel 202-624-5386; *CIP.*

Council on American Affairs *See* Council for Social & Economic Studies, Inc.

Council on Economic Priorities, *(CEP; 0-87871),* 30 Irving Pl., New York, NY 10003 (SAN 204-269X) Tel 212-420-1133.

†Council on Foreign Relations, *(Coun Foreign; 0-87609),* 58 E. 68th St., New York, NY 10021 (SAN 201-7784) Tel 212-734-0400; Orders to: 540 Barnum Ave., Bridgeport, CT 06608 (SAN 661-9835) Tel 203-334-8500; *CIP.*

Council on Foundations, Inc., *(Coun Found; 0-913892),* 1828 L St., NW, Suite 1200, Washington, DC 20036 (SAN 210-3524) Tel 202-466-6512; Orders to: P.O. Box 0002, Washington, DC 20055 (SAN 661-9843).

Council on Hemispheric Affairs, *(Coun Hemispheric Aff; 0-937551),* 1612 20th St., NW, Washington, DC 20009 (SAN 235-7674) Tel 202-745-7000.

Council on Interracial Bks. for Children, Inc., *(CIBC; 0-930040),* 1841 Broadway, Rm. 500, New York, NY 10023 (SAN 210-7155) Tel 212-757-5339.

Council on Municipal Performance, *(Coun on Municipal; 0-916450),* 30 Irving Pl., New York, NY 10003 (SAN 208-6166) Tel 212-420-5950; Dist. by: John Wiley & Sons, Inc., 605 Third Ave., New York, NY 10158 (SAN 200-2272) Tel 212-850-6418.

Council on Postsecondary Accreditation, *(Coun Postsecondary Accredit),* 1 Dupont Cir., Suite 305, Washington, DC 20036 (SAN 225-736X) Tel 202-452-1433.

Council on Religion and Law, *(Coun Rel & Law),* P.O. Box 30, Cambridge, MA 02140 (SAN 237-5842).

†Council on Social Work Education, *(Coun Soc Wk Ed; 0-87293),* P.O. Box 43469, Columbia Heights Sta., Washington, DC 20009 (SAN 225-8714); *CIP.*

Council on Tall Buildings & Urban Habitat, *(Coun Tall Bldg; 0-939493),* Bldg. 13, Lehigh University, Bethlehem, PA 18015 (SAN 663-4168) Tel 215-861-3515.

Counseling & Consulting Services (CCS) Publications, *(Counsel & Consult; 0-910819),* 4020 Moorpark Ave., Suite 204, San Jose, CA 95117 (SAN 262-0146) Tel 408-246-1128.

Counseling & Stress Research Center, *(Counsel & Stress; 0-912561),* 21 Montauk Ave, New London, CT 06320 (SAN 283-9466) Tel 203-447-9935.

Counseling Research Institute, *(Counseling Res; 0-935205),* 8000 W. 14th Ave., Suite 1 & 2, Lakewood, CO 80215 (SAN 695-1066) Tel 303-237-9159; Dist. by: Institue for Rational Living, Inc., 45 E. 65th St., New York, NY 10021 (SAN 218-7833) Tel 212-535-0822.

†Counter-Propaganda Pr., The, *(Counter-Prop Pr; 0-943468),* P.O. Box 365, Park Forest, IL 60466 (SAN 240-6217) Tel 312-534-8679; *CIP.*

Country Bazaar Publishing & Distributing, *(Country Bazaar; 0-936744),* Honey, Inc. Bldg., Rte. 2, Box 190, Berryville, AR 72616 (SAN 215-1669) Tel 501-423-3131.

Country Cooking, *(Country Cooking; 0-940750),* P.O. Box 1563, Woodbridge, VA 22193 (SAN 223-128X) Tel 703-670-9093.

Country Dance & Song Society of America, *(Country Dance & Song; 0-917024),* 505 Eighth Ave., Suite 2500, New York, NY 10018-6505 (SAN 208-1423) Tel 212-594-8833.

Country Garden Pr., *(Country Garden; 0-9611974),* 4412 McCulloch St., Duluth, MN 55804 (SAN 220-2425) Tel 218-525-3294.

Country Hse., The, *(Country Hse; 0-940554),* 15 Thomas Ave., Topsham, ME 04086 (SAN 216-3586) Tel 207-729-8941.

Country Music Foundation Pr., *(Country Music Found; 0-915608),* 4 Music Sq. E., Nashville, TN 37203 (SAN 207-5121) Tel 615-256-1639.

Country Pr., *(Country Pr Mohawk; 0-9616225),* Ward Rd., Mohawk, NY 13407 (SAN 663-0855).

Country Press, The, *(Country Pr NY; 0-913174),* Rte. One, P.O. Box 7652, Henderson, NY 13650 (SAN 203-5995) Tel 315-938-5481.

Country Pub., *(Country Pub; 0-935777),* P.O. Box 12153, Tallahassee, FL 32308 (SAN 696-4087) Tel 904-878-2837; 324 Louvinia Ct., Tallahassee, FL 32308 (SAN 696-5377).

Country Pubs., Inc., The, *(Country Pub Inc; 0-9610772; 0-939685),* P.O. Box 432, Middleburg, VA 22117 (SAN 265-1130) Tel 703-687-6306.

Country Road Press, *(Country Rd; 0-939596),* 414 W. Jonquil Rd., Santa Ana, CA 92706 (SAN 216-6194) Tel 714-836-0458.

Country Squire, The, *(Country Squire; 0-9609228),* 11 Lake St., Granville, MA 01034 (SAN 241-4864) Tel 413-357-8525.

Countryman, J., Pubs., *(J Countryman Pubs; 0-937347),* 4420 FM 1960 W., Suite 120, Houston, TX 77068 (SAN 659-1523) Tel 214-630-4300.

Countryman Pr., Inc., *(Countryman; 0-914378; 0-88150),* Box 175, Woodstock, VT 05091 (SAN 206-4901) Tel 802-457-1049; Toll free: 800-635-5009 (orders only). Imprints: Foul Play Press (Foul Play).

Countryside Bks., *(Countryside Bks; 0-88453),* Northwood Plaza Sta., Clearwater, FL 33519-0360 (SAN 201-7954) Tel 813-796-7337.

Countryside Studio, Inc., *(Countryside Studio; 0-9605428),* P.O. Box 88, Hwy. 25 W., Cottontown, TN 37048 (SAN 216-1222).

Countway, Francis A., Library of Medicine, *(F A Countway),* 10 Shattuck St., Boston, MA 02115 (SAN 206-4057).

County Super Assn., of California, *(County Super Assn CA),* 1100 K St., Suite 101, Sacramento, CA 95814 (SAN 680-0300) Tel 916-441-4011.

Couple to Couple League, The, *(Couple to Couple; 0-9601036),* P.O. Box 111184, Cincinnati, OH 45211 (SAN 208-1490) Tel 513-661-7612; 3621 Glenmore Ave., Cincinnati, OH 45211 (SAN 669-0564).

Courier Press, *(Courier Pr; 0-917310),* C/O First American National Bank, Trust Dept., First American Center, Nashville, TN 37237 (SAN 208-4139) Tel 615-748-2341.

Courier Press, *(Courier Pr FL; 0-934602),* 428 NE 82nd St., Suite 1, Miami, FL 33138 (SAN 212-9949).

Courseware, Inc., *(Courseware; 0-89805),* 10075 Carroll Canyon Rd., San Diego, CA 92131 (SAN 212-4955) Tel 619-578-1700.

Court Interpreters & Translators Assn., Inc., *(CITA NY; 0-939733),* Peck Slip Sta., P.O. Box 406, New York, NY 10172 (SAN 663-6128) Tel 718-965-0217.

Court Scribe, The, *(Court Scribe; 0-9601572),* 2201 Friendly St., Eugene, OR 97405 (SAN 210-8879) Tel 503-343-7562.

Courtroom Compendiums, *(Courtroom Comp; 0-910355),* 22106 Clarendon, P.O. Box 705, Woodland Hills, CA 91365 (SAN 260-0374) Tel 818-884-9039.

Couturier Pr., Div. of Dori's Bears, *(Couturier Pr; 0-934875),* 10636 Main St., Suite 498, Bellevue, WA 98004 (SAN 694-4620) Tel 206-746-3385.

†Cove View Pr., *(Cove View; 0-931896),* P.O. Box 3234, Ashland, OR 97520 (SAN 220-0422); *CIP.*

Coven, Susan B. Anthony, *(SBA Coven; 0-937081),* P.O. Box 11363, Oakland, CA 94611 (SAN 658-4551) Tel 415-444-7724; 2927 Harrison St., Oakland, CA 94611 (SAN 658-456X).

Covenant Pr., *(Covenant; 0-910452),* 3200 W. Foster Ave., Chicago, IL 60625 (SAN 203-6029) Tel 312-478-4676; Toll free: 800-621-1290.

Coventry *See* **Fawcett Bk. Group**

Coventry Hse., *(Coventry Hse; 0-933761),* 490 E. Walnut Ave., Pasadena, CA 91101 (SAN 692-7688) Tel 818-304-6804.

Cover Publishing Co., *(Cover Pub; 0-912912),* P.O. Box 1092, Tampa, FL 33601 (SAN 203-6037) Tel 813-237-0266.

Cow Puddle Pr., *(Cow Puddle; 0-9600672),* Sunset Trading Post, Sunset, TX 76270 (SAN 206-5282) Tel 817-872-2027.

Cowan, Robert G., *(Cowan; 0-910456),* 1650 Redcliff St., Los Angeles, CA 90026 (SAN 203-6045) Tel 213-664-7401.

Coward, McCann & Geoghegan *See* **Putnam Publishing Group, The**

Cowboy Poet Pub Co., *(Cowboy Poet; 0-9614907),* 4475 Memphis St., Dallas, TX 75207 (SAN 693-5346) Tel 214-631-5770.

Cowley Pubns., Div. of Society of St. John the Evangelist, *(Cowley Pubns; 0-936384),* 980 Memorial Dr., Cambridge, MA 02138 (SAN 213-9987) Tel 617-876-3507.

Cox, Harold E., *(Cox; 0-911940),* 80 Virginia Terrace, Forty Fort, PA 18704 (SAN 202-1943) Tel 717-287-7647.

Cox, Willis F., *(W F Cox; 0-9610758),* Box 47, James Store, VA 23080 (SAN 264-7060) Tel 804-693-4533.

Cox-Miller Ltd., *(C M Ltd; 0-9617244),* P.O. Box 5741, Phoenix, AZ 85010 (SAN 663-5482); 2317 W. Dahlia Dr., Phoenix, AZ 85029 (SAN 663-5490) Tel 602-997-9118.

Cox Pubns., *(Cox Pubns; 0-912665),* P.O. Box 958, El Cerrito, CA 94530 (SAN 282-7573) Tel 415-527-2552.

Coyne & Chenoweth, *(Coyne & Chenoweth; 0-941038),* P.O. Box 81905, Pittsburgh, PA 15217 (SAN 217-3476) Tel 412-321-4528.

Coyote Bks., *(Coyote; 0-940556),* P.O. Box 629, Brunswick, ME 04011 (SAN 212-6060).

Coyote Bks., *(Coyote Bks MN; 0-9616901),* 3953 Alabama Ave., S., St. Louis Park, MN 55416 (SAN 661-4930) Tel 612-925-9244. Do not confuse with Coyote Bks., in Brunswick, ME.

Coyote Love Pr., *(Coyote Love; 0-913341),* 87 State St., No. 2, Portland, ME 04101 (SAN 283-040X) Tel 207-774-8451; Dist. by: Small Press Distribution, 1814 San Pablo Ave., Berkeley, CA 94702 (SAN 204-5826) Tel 415-549-3336.

Coyote Pr., *(Coyote Press; 1-55567),* P.O. Box 3377, Salinas, CA 93912 (SAN 699-6752) Tel 408-422-4912 (SAN 699-6760).

Coyote Productions, *(Coyote Prod; 0-936147),* P.O. Box 167, Auburn, ME 04210 (SAN 697-0214) Tel 207-934-2588; 25 Cookman Ave., Old Orchard Beach, ME 04064 (SAN 697-0222).

Crabtree Publishing, *(Crabtree; 0-937070),* P.O. Box 3451, Federal Way, WA 98063 (SAN 214-3615) Tel 206-927-3777.

Cracker Bks. Publishing, Inc., *(Cracker Bks Pub; 0-932827),* P.O. Box 214, Winter Beach, FL 32971 (SAN 688-6205) Tel 305-231-4871.

Craftree, Div. of McCall's (A.B.C.) Needlework & Crafts Magazines, *(Craftree; 1-55564),* 825 Seventh Ave., New York, NY 10019 (SAN 699-7082) Tel 212-887-8462; Dist. by: Gaylenot Publishing, 740 Monroe Way, Placentia, CA 92670 (SAN 200-5972).

†**Craftsman Bk. Co.,** *(Craftsman; 0-910460; 0-934041),* 6058 Corte del Cedro, Box 6500, Carlsbad, CA 92008 (SAN 159-7000) Tel 619-438-7828; *CIP.*

Craftways Pubns., *(Craftways; 0-9607224),* 1465 Fourth St., Berkeley, CA 94710 (SAN 239-0809) Tel 415-527-4561.

†**Cragmont Pubns.,** *(Cragmont Pubns; 0-89666),* 1308 E. 38th St., Oakland, CA 94602 (SAN 211-4860) Tel 415-530-8436; *CIP.*

Craig, James D., *(J D Craig; 0-9602042),* P.O. Box 42, Pebble Beach, CA 93953 (SAN 212-0356).

Craig, James R., *(J R Craig),* 1542 S. Cody, Lakewood, CO 80226 (SAN 263-9874) Tel 303-985-0790.

Craig Inc., *(Craig Inc; 0-9614816),* P.O. Box 05383, Detroit, MI 48205 (SAN 693-0131) Tel 313-526-3204.

Craig Publications, *(Craig Pubns; 0-9613396),* P.O. Box 4382, San Clemente, CA 92672 (SAN 676-9071).

Craig Publishing Hse., *(Craig Pub Hse; 0-9615135),* 100 S. Kanawha St., Buckhannon, WV 26201 (SAN 694-2512) Tel 304-472-5543.

Crain Bks., Div. of Crain Communications, Inc., *(Crain Bks; 0-87251),* 740 Rush St., Chicago, IL 60611 (SAN 207-1967) Tel 312-649-5250; Toll free: 800-621-6877.

Cram Cassettes, *(Cram Cassettes; 1-55651),* P.O. Box 1275, South Bend, IN 46624 (SAN 661-8316); 2118 Renfrew Ct., South Bend, IN 46614 (SAN 661-8324) Tel 219-291-2645.

Crambruck Pr., *(Crambruck; 0-87699),* 381 Park Ave. S., New York, NY 10016 (SAN 204-2622) Tel 212-532-0871.

Cramer Bk. Store, *(Cramer Bkstore; 0-913118),* Box 7235, Kansas City, MO 64113 (SAN 203-607X).

Crampton Assocs., Inc., *(Crampton Assoc; 0-9610142),* Box 1214, Homewood, IL 60430 (SAN 269-5049) Tel 312-798-3710.

Cranberry Knoll Pubs., Subs. of Mary Webber, Inc., *(Cranberry Knoll; 0-9614737),* P.O. Box 293, Yarmouth, ME 04096 (SAN 692-7149) Tel 207-846-4954.

Cranberry Pr., The, *(Cranberry Pr; 0-9615645),* 276 East St., Pittsford, NY 14534 (SAN 696-4117) Tel 716-318-1928.

Cranbrook Institute of Science, *(Cranbrook; 0-87737),* 500 Lone Pine Rd., P.O. Box 801, Bloomfield Hills, MI 48013 (SAN 203-6088) Tel 313-645-3255.

Cranbrook Publishing, *(Cranbrook Pub; 0-9604690),* 2302 Windemere, Flint, MI 48503 (SAN 215-7470).

Crane Pubns. (CA), *(Crane Pubns CA; 0-915561),* Box 90155, San Diego, CA 92109 (SAN 292-3297) Tel 619-273-7018.

Crane Publishing Co., Div. of MLP, *(Crane Pub Co; 0-89075),* 1301 Hamilton Ave., Box 3713, Trenton, NJ 08629 (SAN 207-1053) Tel 609-586-6400.

†**Crane, Russak & Co., Inc.,** Affil. of Taylor & Francis, Ltd. (London), *(Crane Russak & Co; 0-8448),* 3 E. 44th St., New York, NY 10017 (SAN 202-1978) Tel 212-867-1490; *CIP.*

Crank, David, Pubns., *(D Crank Pubns; 0-936437),* 1416 Larkin Williams Rd., Fenton, MO 63026 (SAN 697-8266) Tel 314-343-4359.

Cranky Nell Book, A *See* **Kane, Miller Bk. Pubs.**

Crawford, Claud C., *(Claud Crawford; 0-933697),* 4627 Martin Mill Pike, Knoxville, TN 37920 (SAN 692-5200) Tel 615-573-7248.

Crawford, F. Marion, Memorial Society, *(F M Crawford),* Saracinesca House 3610 Meadowbrook Ave., Nashville, TN 37205 (SAN 225-2821) Tel 615-292-9695.

Crawford Aviation, *(Crawford Aviation; 0-9603934),* P.O. Box 1262, Torrance, CA 90505 (SAN 213-4810); Dist. by: Aviation Bk. Co., 1640 Victory Blvd., Glendale, CA 91201 (SAN 212-0259) Tel 818-240-1771.

Crawford Press, Div. of American Companies, Inc., *(Econo-Clad Bks-Crawford Pr; 0-88103; 0-8085),* Box 1777, Topeka, KS 66601 (SAN 240-365X) Tel 913-233-4252; Toll free: 800-255-3502.

Crazy Horse Memorial Foundation, *(Crazy Horse),* Crazy Horse, Black Hills, SD 57730 (SAN 233-4089) Tel 605-673-4681.

Crazy Sam Enterprises, *(Crazy Sam),* 8301 Ambassador Rd, Dallas, TX 75247 (SAN 678-9056).

Creamer, Lyle R., *(L R Creamer),* 8206 Mulberry St., Cypress, CA 90630 (SAN 670-719X).

Creation Hse., *(Creation Hse; 0-88419),* 396 E. St. Charles Rd., Wheaton, IL 60188 (SAN 202-2001) Tel 312-653-1472.

Creation Research Society Bks., Div. of Creation Research Society, *(Creation Research; 0-940384),* 5093 Williamsport Dr., Norcross, GA 30092 (SAN 216-2873) Tel 404-449-4758.

Creation Science Fellowship, Inc., *(Creation Sci Fellowship; 0-9617068),* 362 Ashland Ave., Pittsburgh, PA 15228 (SAN 662-8559) Tel 412-341-4908.

Creations Unlimited, *(Creations Unltd; 0-938900),* P.O. Box 2591, Farmington Hills, MI 48018 (SAN 216-1109).

Creative Alternatives Pr., *(Creative Alter Pr; 0-932041),* P.O. Box 50142, Jacksonville Beach, FL 32240 (SAN 685-3013) Tel 904-249-7721.

†**Creative Arts Bk. Co.,** *(Creative Arts Bk; 0-88739; 0-916870),* 833 Bancroft Way, Berkeley, CA 94710 (SAN 208-4880) Tel 415-848-4777; *CIP.*

Creative Arts Development, *(Creat Arts Dev; 0-912801),* P.O. Box 1240, Soquel, CA 95073 (SAN 277-6693) Tel 408-475-2396.

Creative Arts Rehabilitation Ctr., *(CARC; 0-9606876),* 251 W. 51st St., New York, NY 10019 (SAN 217-3484) Tel 212-246-3113.

Creative AV Things, Inc., *(Creative AV; 0-937927),* P.O. Box 582, Glen Rock, NJ 07452 (SAN 659-3941).

Creative Black Bk., Inc., *(Creat Black Bk; 0-916098),* 401 Park Ave. S., New York, NY 10016 (SAN 207-9496) Tel 212-684-4255.

†**Creative Books/Creative Services,** *(Creative Bks; 0-914606),* P.O. Box 5162, Carmel, CA 93921 (SAN 203-6215) Tel 408-624-7573; Dist. by: Peanut Butter Publishing, 911 Western Ave., Suite 401, Maritime Bldg., Seattle, WA 98104 (SAN 212-7881); *CIP.*

Creative Cataylist, *(Creative Cataylist; 1-55663),* 6023 Majestic Ave., Oakland, CA 94605 Tel 415-562-8617; Dist. by: Bookpeople, 2929 Fifth St., Berkeley, CA 94710 (SAN 168-9517) Tel 415-549-3030; Toll free: 800-227-1516; Dist. by: Alchemy Bks., 717 Market St., Suite 514, San Francisco, CA 94101 (SAN 211-304X) Tel 415-777-2197.

Creative Communications, *(Creative Comm; 0-939116),* 529 Dayton St., Edmonds, WA 98020 (SAN 239-684X) Tel 206-775-5877.

†**Creative Computing Pr.,** *(Creative Comp; 0-916688; 0-87194),* 1 Park Ave., New York, NY 10016 (SAN 281-5737) Tel 212-503-5315; Toll free: 800-631-8112; 39 E. Hanover Ave., Morris Plains, NJ 07950 (SAN 281-5745) Tel 201-540-0445; *CIP.*

Creative Concepts for Children, *(Creat Conc Children; 0-938231),* 1214 Ensenada Ave., Orlando, FL 32825 (SAN 661-0587) Tel 305-273-6259.

Creative Concepts In Communications Ltd., *(Creat Concepts MO; 0-9614433),* 1250 W. 63rd St., Kansas City, MO 64113 (SAN 689-3457) Tel 816-523-9207.

Creative Concepts, Inc., *(Creative Concepts; 0-9614356),* 3400 First St., N., Suite 203, St. Cloud, MN 56301 (SAN 687-7443) Tel 612-252-1220.

Creative Concern Pubns., *(Creat Concern; 0-917117),* 3208 E. Mayaguana Ln., Lantana, FL 33462 (SAN 655-6221) Tel 305-433-5735.

Creative Cuisine Inc., *(Creative Cuisine; 0-9614122),* P.O. Box 518, Naples, FL 33939 (SAN 686-5100) Tel 813-263-7121.

Creative Curriculum, *(Creative Curriculum),* 4302 Rolla Lane, Madison, WI 53711 (SAN 240-8678).

Creative Developmental Pr., *(Creative Develop Pr; 0-9615723),* 2431 Petaluma Ave., Long Beach, CA 90815 (SAN 696-4125) Tel 213-596-0026; P.O. Box 33, Long Beach, CA 90801 (SAN 696-7051).

Creative Education Foundation, Inc., *(Creat Educ Found; 0-930222),* 437 Franklin St., Buffalo, NY 14202 (SAN 685-3218) Tel 716-884-2774; c/o State Univ. College at Buffalo, 437 Franklin St., Buffalo, NY 14202 (SAN 210-7163) Tel 716-884-2774.

Creative Education, Inc., *(Creative Ed; 0-87191; 0-88682),* 123 S. Broad St., P.O. Box 227, Mankato, MN 56001 (SAN 202-201X) Tel 507-388-6273.

Creative Foods, Ltd., *(Creative Foods; 0-9615708),* 1700 Vine St., West Des Moines, IA 50265 (SAN 696-4133) Tel 515-223-4888.

Creative Forum Publishing, *(Creative Forum; 0-936411),* 4900 SW Centralwood Ave., Lake Oswego, OR 97034 (SAN 698-1550) Tel 503-639-9210.

Creative Gospel Productions, Incorporated, *(Creat Gospel Prod; 0-931965),* 23381 L'Enfant Plaza, SW, Washington, DC 20026 (SAN 686-0753) Tel 202-563-6319.

†Creative Homeowner Pr., Div. of Federal Marketing Corp., *(Creative Homeowner; 0-932944),* 24 Park Way, Upper Saddle River, NJ 07458 (SAN 213-6627) Tel 201-934-7100; Toll free: 800-631-7795; *CIP.*

Creative Images Ltd., *(Creative Images; 0-941378),* 12000 Windflower Place, Oklahoma City, OK 73120 (SAN 238-9266) Tel 405-755-0099.

Creative Infomatics, Inc., *(Creative Infomatics; 0-917634),* P.O. Box 1607, Durant, OK 74702-1607 (SAN 211-5557) Tel 405-924-0643.

Creative Learning Assn., *(Create Learn; 0-88193),* R.R. 4, Box 330, Charleston, IL 61920 (SAN 669-4101) Tel 217-345-1010.

Creative Learning Pr., Inc., *(Creative Learning; 0-936386),* P.O. Box 320, Mansfield Center, CT 06250 (SAN 214-2368) Tel 203-281-4036.

Creative Literature, *(Creative Lit; 0-9609110),* 1521 E. Flower St., Phoenix, AZ 85014 (SAN 281-5753) Tel 602-274-4151.

Creative Media Works, *(Creat Media; 0-89411),* 692 Elkader St., Ashland, OR 97520 (SAN 209-3561) Tel 503-482-0088.

Creative Options Publishing Co., Div. of Laing Communications, Inc., *(Creative Options; 0-938106),* 110-110th NE, Suite 309, Bellevue, WA 98004 (SAN 240-0901) Tel 206-451-9331.

Creative Partners, *(Creative Part; 0-9615930),* P.O. Box 84, Little Neck, NY 11363 (SAN 697-0419) Tel 516-482-5309; 254-09 West End Dr., Great Neck, NY 11363 (SAN 697-0427).

Creative Programming, Inc., *(Creat Prog Inc; 0-912079),* 28990 W. Pacific Coast Hwy., Suite 109, Malibu, CA 90265 (SAN 264-7303); Toll free: 800-323-6354.

Creative Pubns., *(Creatv Pubns UT; 0-9616992),* 370 E. 230th S., Orem, UT 84058 (SAN 661-6852) Tel 801-224-0724; P.O. Box 1104, Orem, UT 84058 (SAN 661-6860). Do not confuse with Creative Pubns., Oak Lawn, CA, Quincy, MA, Concord, CA.

†Creative Publishing, Co., *(Creative Texas; 0-932702),* P.O. Box 9292, College Station, TX 77840 (SAN 209-3499) Tel 409-775-6047; *CIP.*

Creative Publishing Corp. of America, *(Creative Amer Pub; 0-9608340),* 633 Jefferson Heights Ave., Jefferson, LA 70121 (SAN 239-5320) Tel 504-733-1275.

Creative Pubns B P C M, *(Creat Pubns B P C M; 0-914569),* 1431 St. James Pkwy., Concord, CA 94521 (SAN 289-1921) Tel 415-687-6401.

Creative Research & Educational Systems for Today, *(Creative Res & Educ; 0-935770),* 168-02 Jewel Ave., Flushing, NY 11365 (SAN 213-9170).

Creative Research Systems, *(Creative Res; 0-918577),* 1649 Del Oro, Petaluma, CA 94952 (SAN 284-6071) Tel 707-765-1001.

Creative Resource Systems, Inc., *(Creat Resource; 0-938772),* P.O. Box 890, 116 Railroad St., Winterville, NC 28590 (SAN 238-7301) Tel 919-756-9658.

Creative Resources, *(Creat Res OH; 0-910601),* 683 Riddle Rd., Cincinnati, OH 45220 (SAN 260-1788) Tel 513-559-1481.

Creative Resources, Inc., *(Creat Res NC; 0-937306),* 3548 Round Oak Rd., Charlotte, NC 28210 (SAN 200-2779) Tel 704-554-8357.

†Creative Roots, Inc., *(Creative Roots; 0-940508),* P.O. Box 401, Planetarium Sta., New York, NY 10024 (SAN 218-4737) Tel 212-799-2294; *CIP.*

Creative Sales Corp., *(Creative Sales; 0-933162),* 762 W. Algonquin Rd., Arlington Heights, IL 60005 (SAN 212-3436).

Creative Services, Inc., *(Creative Serv; 0-939975),* P.O. Box 6008, High Point, NC 27262 (SAN 694-2385) Tel 919-889-3010; 502 Blake Ave., High Point, NC 27262.

Creative Storytime Pr., *(Creative Storytime; 0-934876),* P.O. Box 572, Minneapolis, MN 55440 (SAN 211-6634) Tel 612-926-9740.

Creative Teaching Pr., Inc., *(Creat Teach Pr; 0-916119),* 15598 Producer Ln., Huntington Beach, CA 92649 (SAN 294-9180) Tel 714-892-5523; Toll free: 800-732-1548.

†Creative Therapeutics, *(Creative Therapeutics; 0-933812),* 155 County Rd., Cresskill, NJ 07626-0317 (SAN 212-6508) Tel 201-567-7295; *CIP.*

†Creative Ventures, *(Creative Vent; 0-917166),* 1709 Dickenson, Olympia, WA 98502 (SAN 208-6190) Tel 206-754-4019; Orders to: 1721 Conger NW, Olympia, WA 98502 (SAN 208-6204) Tel 206-352-2755; *CIP.*

Creative Ventures, Inc., *(Creat Ventures IN; 0-942034),* P.O. Box 2286, West Lafayette, IN 47906 (SAN 239-5231).

Creative Ventures International, *(Creative Intl; 0-9615787),* 3341 Hidden Acres Dr., Atlanta, GA 30340 (SAN 696-7132) Tel 404-496-0988.

Creative Walking, Inc., *(Creative Walking; 0-939041),* 175 Elkton Rd., Newark, DE 19711 (SAN 662-6521) Tel 302-368-2222.

Creative with Words Pubns., *(Creative Words Pubns; 0-936945),* P.O. Box 223226, Carmel, CA 93922 (SAN 658-6961) Tel 408-625-3542.

Creativity Unlimited Pr., *(Creativity Unltd Pr; 0-912559),* 30819 Casilina, Rancho Palos Verdes, CA 90274 (SAN 282-7646) Tel 213-377-7908.

Creatures at Large, *(Creatures at Large; 0-940064),* 1082 Grand Teton Dr., Pacifica, CA 94044 (SAN 281-577X) Tel 415-359-4341; P.O. Box 687, Pacifica, CA 94044 (SAN 281-5788).

Credence Publishing Hse., *(Credence Pub Hse; 0-9606226),* P.O. Box 6125, Olympia, WA 98502 (SAN 217-5126) Tel 206-866-4648.

Credit Research Foundation, Inc., *(Credit Res NYS; 0-939050),* 3000 Marcus Ave., Lake Success, NY 11042 (SAN 204-2606) Tel 516-488-1166.

Credit Union Executives Society, *(Credit Union Execs),* 6320 Monona Dr., Madison, WI 53716 (SAN 224-697X).

Creek House, *(Creek Hse; 0-9600490),* P.O. Box 793, Ojai, CA 93023 (SAN 203-6126) Tel 805-646-3200.

Cregier, Don M., *(Don Cregier; 0-9614536),* 301 S. 15th St., Murray, KY 42071 (SAN 692-2848); Dist. by: Lorrah & Hitchcock Publishers Inc., 301 S. 15th St., Murray, KY 42071 (SAN 220-7915).

Creighton Publishing, *(Creighton Pub; 0-9617139),* P.O. Box 1509, Port Aransas, TX 78373 (SAN 663-3447); 405 Ruthie Ln., Port Aransas, TX 78373 (SAN 663-3455) Tel 512-749-5550.

Cremona Foundation, Inc., The, *(Cremona Found; 0-936325),* Cremona Farm, Mechanicsville, MD 20659 (SAN 697-3477) Tel 301-884-3140.

Crescendo *See* Taplinger Publishing Co., Inc.

†Crescent Bks., *(Crescent Bks; 0-9614251),* Box 10000, New Orleans, LA 70181 (SAN 687-0864) Tel 504-626-4168; *CIP.*

Crescent Heart Publishing, *(Crescent Heart; 0-9609916),* 150 Cerro Crest Dr., Novato, CA 94947 (SAN 262-4664) Tel 415-897-6763.

Creso, Irene, *(Creso; 0-9613916),* Irene Creso Herbarium, William O. Rieke Science Ctr., Pacific Lutheran University, Tacoma, WA 98447 (SAN 683-1915) Tel 206-535-7571.

Cresset Pubs., *(Cresset Pubs; 0-936082),* 519 E. Tabor Rd., Philadelphia, PA 19120 (SAN 215-9473).

Cresswell Enterprises, *(Cresswell Ent; 0-930943),* 335 E. 11th St., Casper, WY 82601 (SAN 693-0417).

Crest Bks. *See* Fawcett Bk. Group

Crest Challenge Books, *(Crest Challenge; 0-913776),* 42 Dart St., Loma Linda, CA 92354 (SAN 203-6142) Tel 714-796-1536; Orders to: P.O. Box 993, Loma Linda, CA 92354 (SAN 203-6150).

Crest Pr., Inc., *(Crest Pr Inc; 0-9615359),* 5 Crestway, Silver City, NM 88061 (SAN 655-2275) Tel 505-538-2324; Dist. by: Many Feathers SW Bks. & Maps Distributor, 5738 N. Central, Phoenix, AZ 85012 (SAN 158-8877).

Crest Software, *(Crest Sftware; 0-930615),* 2132 Crestview Dr., Durango, CO 81301 (SAN 676-262X) Tel 303-247-9518.

Crestline Publishing Co., *(Crestline; 0-912612),* 1251 N. Jefferson Ave., Sarasota, FL 33577 (SAN 202-2044) Tel 813-955-8080.

†Crestwood Hse., Inc., *(Crestwood Hse; 0-89686; 0-913940),* P.O. Box 3427, Mankato, MN 56002 (SAN 206-3492) Tel 507-388-1616; Toll free: 800-535-4393; *CIP.*

CRIC Productions, Inc., *(CRIC Prod; 0-935357),* Box 1214, Kingshill, St. Croix, VI 00850 (SAN 696-4141) Tel 809-778-2043.

Cricket Pubns., *(Cricket Pubns; 0-912883),* P.O. Box 8771, Toledo, OH 43623 (SAN 283-0116) Tel 419-535-8739.

Cricket Software, *(Cricket Software; 0-936727),* 3508 Market St., Phildelphia, PA 19104 (SAN 699-9298) Tel 215-387-7955.

Cricketfield Pr., *(Cricketfield Pr; 0-9614281),* 39 Megunticook St., Camden, ME 04843 (SAN 687-4401) Tel 207-236-3083.

Crime & Social Justice, *(Crime & Soc Justice; 0-935206),* P.O. Box 40601, San Francisco, CA 94140 (SAN 213-2133) Tel 415-550-1703.

Criminal Justice Ctr., Office of Pubns., *(Criminal Jus Ctr; 0-935530),* Sam Houston State Univ., Huntsville, TX 77341 (SAN 217-2348) Tel 409-294-1692.

Criminal Justice Department, *(Crim Jus Dept; 0-942754),* Loyola Univ. of Chicago, 820 N. Michigan Ave., Chicago, IL 60611 (SAN 679-1956).

Crises Research Pr., *(Crises Res Pr; 0-86627),* 301 W. 45th St., New York, NY 10036 (SAN 238-9274).

†Crisp Pubns., Inc., *(Crisp Pubns; 0-931961),* 95 First St., Los Altos, CA 94022 (SAN 686-0400) Tel 415-949-4888; *CIP.*

Crispo, Andrew, Gallery, Inc., *(Crispo Gallery; 0-937014),* 41 E. 57th St., New York, NY 10022 (SAN 214-297X).

Crissey, Harrington E., Jr., *(H E Crissey; 0-9608878),* 1806 Benton St., No. 1, Philadelphia, PA 19152 (SAN 241-1059) Tel 215-745-8503.

Criterion Music Corp., *(Criterion Mus; 0-910468),* 6124 Selma Ave., Hollywood, CA 90028 (SAN 203-6177) Tel 213-469-2296; Dist. by: Joe Goldfeder Music Enterprises, P.O. Box 660, Lynbrook, NY 11563 (SAN 203-6177).

Criterion Press, *(Criterion Pr; 0-9609428),* P.O. Box 1014, Torrance, CA 90505 (SAN 260-0382) Tel 213-326-3503.

Criterion Pubns., *(Criterion Pubns; 0-937969),* 209 N. Beckley, De Sotoer, TX 75115 (SAN 659-5006) Tel 214-223-9348; Orders to: P.O. Box 214749, Dallas, TX 75221-4749 (SAN 662-426X).

Critical Mass Energy Project of Public Citizen, *(Critical Mass),* 215 Pennsylvania Ave., SE, Washington, DC 20003 (SAN 225-6878) Tel 202-546-4996.

Critical Thinking Bk. Co., *(Critical Book; 0-935475),* 110 Sarah Dr., Mill Valley, CA 94941 (SAN 696-415X) Tel 405-383-8805.

Critics Choice Paperbacks, *(Critics Choice Paper; 0-931773; 1-55547),* 31 E. 28th St., New York, NY 10016 (SAN 684-7412) Tel 212-685-1550; Dist. by: Kable News Co., 777 Third Ave., New York, NY 10017 (SAN 169-5835); Dist. by: World Wide Media Services, Inc., 386 Park Ave. S., New York, NY 10016 (SAN 165-1684).

Critique Publishing, *(Critique Pub; 0-911485),* P.O. Box 11451, Santa Rosa, CA 95406 (SAN 692-6738).

Crittenden Publishing, Inc., *(Crittenden Pub; 0-913153),* P.O. Box 1150, 85 Galli, Novato, CA 94948 (SAN 283-2771) Tel 415-883-8771; Toll free: 800-421-3483. *Imprints:* Union Square Books (Union Square Bks).

Crockett Publishing Co., *(Crockett Pub Co; 0-915131),* 1319 Fremont Dr., Twin Falls, ID 83301 (SAN 289-9094) Tel 208-733-6531; Dist. by: Perry Enterprises, 2666 N. 650 E., Provo, UT 84601 (SAN 689-2485) Tel 801-375-9529.

Crofton Publishing Corp., *(Crofton Pub; 0-89020),* 21 Wilson Ave., Belmont, MA 02178 (SAN 206-7560) Tel 617-489-2149.

†Croissant & Co., *(Croissant & Co; 0-912348),* P.O. Box 282, Athens, OH 45701 (SAN 204-255X) Tel 614-593-3008; *CIP.*

Cromwel Press, *(Cromwel; 0-916298),* P.O. Box 335, Santa Margarita, CA 93453 (SAN 210-3540) Tel 805-543-1581.

Names

Cromwell-Smith Services, *(Cromwell-Smith; 0-933086),* 60 Montego Ct., No. 26MB, Coronado, CA 92118 (SAN 213-2443) Tel 619-435-1928; Orders to: P.O. Box 1714, La Jolla, CA 92038 (SAN 661-9851) Tel 619-935-1928.

Croner Pubns., *(Croner; 0-87514),* 211-03 Jamaica Ave., Queens Village, NY 11428 (SAN 203-8706) Tel 718-464-0866.

Crop Dust Pr., *(Crop Dust Pr; 0-9616621),* Rte. 5, Box 75, Warrenton, VA 22186 (SAN 661-0617) Tel 703-642-6255.

Crop Science Society of America, *(Crop Sci Soc Am),* 677 S. Segoe Rd., Madison, WI 53711 (SAN 213-8247) Tel 608-273-8080.

Crosby County Pioneer Memorial, *(Crosby County; 0-9606940),* P.O. Box 386, Crosbyton, TX 79322 (SAN 220-116X) Tel 806-675-2331.

Crosley, Inc., *(Crosley; 0-9603268),* 1515 Kitchen, Jonesboro, AR 72401 (SAN 212-8985) Tel 501-935-3928.

Cross, Laurella B., *(L B Cross; 0-9612806),* P.O. Box 2933, Roswell, NM 88201 (SAN 289-9760) Tel 505-625-1095.

Cross, Richard B., Co., *(R B Cross Co),* 103 S. Howard St., P.O. Box 405, Oxford, IN 47971 (SAN 662-4359) Tel 317-385-2255.

Cross Books, *(Cross Bks; 0-9601672),* 50 MacArthur Dr., North Providence, RI 02911 (SAN 211-5239) Tel 401-231-0874.

Cross Country Pr., *(Cross Country; 0-916696),* P.O. Box 492, Ridgefield, CT 06877 (SAN 208-3094) Tel 203-431-8225.

†**Cross-Cultural Communications,** *(Cross Cult; 0-89304),* 239 Wynsum Ave., Merrick, NY 11566 (SAN 208-6212) Tel 516-868-5635; *CIP.*

Cross Cultural Pr., *(Cross Cult Pr; 0-930693),* 1166 S. 42nd St., Springfield, OR 97478 (SAN 677-0754) Tel 503-746-7401.

Cross Harp Pr., *(Cross Harp; 0-930948),* 530 Ranch Rd., Visalia, CA 93291 (SAN 223-1050) Tel 209-733-1679 Tel 213-851-7438.

Cross Information Co., *(Cross Info; 0-923426),* 1881 Ninth St., Suite 311, Boulder, CO 80302-5151 (SAN 286-3898) Tel 303-444-7799.

Crossbar Enterprises, *(Crossbar Ent; 0-9604994),* 9522 Stevebrook Rd., Fairfax, VA 22032 (SAN 215-6326) Tel 703-978-0288.

CrossBow Bks., *(Crossbow Bks; 0-915973),* P.O. Box 857, Easton, PA 18042 (SAN 293-941X) Tel 201-859-3512.

Crosscurrents, *(Crosscurrents),* 2200 Glastonbury Rd., Westlake Village, CA 91361 (SAN 659-6401).

Crosscut Saw Pr., *(Crosscut Saw; 0-931020),* Tel 415-843-7869; Orders to: Bookpeople, 2929 Fifth St., Berkeley, CA 94710 (SAN 168-9517).

†**Crossing Pr., The,** *(Crossing Pr; 0-89594; 0-912278),* Box 640, Trumansburg, NY 14886 (SAN 202-2060) Tel 607-387-6217; *CIP.*

†**Crossroad Pub. Co.,** *(Crossroad NY; 0-8245),* 370 Lexington Ave., New York, NY 10017 (SAN 287-0118) Tel 212-532-3650; Dist. by: Harper & Row Pubs., Inc., Keystone Industrial Pk., Scranton, PA 08075 (SAN 215-3742); Toll free: 800-242-7737; *CIP.*

Crossroads Books *See* **Christendom Pubns.**

Crossroads Books with the Public Library of Cincinnati & Hamilton County, *(Crossroad Bks Public; 0-9611380),* 485 Wood Ave., Cincinnati, OH 45220 (SAN 283-9490).

Crossroads Communications, *(Crossroads Comm; 0-916445),* P.O. Box 7, Carpentersville, IL 60110 (SAN 295-1258) Tel 312-587-1658.

Crossroads Press *See* **African Studies Assn.**

Crossway Books *See* **Good News Pubs.**

Crow Canyon Press, *(Crow Canyon; 0-937760),* 2050 Ridgewood Road, Alamo, CA 94507 (SAN 215-6334).

†**Crowell, Thomas Y., Co.,** *(T Y Crowell; 0-690),* 10 E. 53rd St., New York, NY 10022 (SAN 210-5918) Tel 212-593-3900; Toll free: 800-242-7737; Dist. by: Harper & Row Pubs., Keystone Industrial Pk., Scranton, PA 18512 (SAN 215-3742); *CIP.*

Crowell, Thomas Y., Junior Bks., Div. of Harper Junior Bks. Group, *(Crowell Jr Bks; 0-690),* 10 E. 53rd St., New York, NY 10022 (SAN 200-2086) Tel 212-207-7000; Toll free: 800-638-3030; 1700 Montgomery St., San Francisco, CA 94111 (SAN 215-3734) Tel 415-989-9000; Orders to: Keystone Industrial Pk., Scranton, PA 18512 (SAN 215-3742).

Crowell-Collier Pr. *See* **Macmillan Publishing Co., Inc.**

Crown Ark Pubns., *(Crown Ark Pubns; 0-943762),* P.O. Box 23941, Webster Groves, MO 63119 (SAN 238-2679).

Crown Ministries International, *(Crown Min; 0-935779),* P.O. Box 49, Euclid, MN 56722 (SAN 696-7108) Tel 218-745-5826.

Crown Pubs., Inc., *(Crown; 0-517),* 225 Park Ave., S, New York, NY 10003 (SAN 200-2639) Tel 212-254-1600; Toll free: 800-526-4264. *Imprints:* American Legacy Press (AM Legacy Pr.); Americana (Americana); Arlington House (Arlington Hse); Harmony Books (Harmony); Julian Press (Julian Pr.); Knapp Press (Knapp Pr.); Michelman, Herbert, Books (Michelman Books); Outdoor Life Books (Outdoor Life); Potter, Clarkson N., Books (C N Potter Bks); Prince Paperback (Prince Paper).

Cruikshank, Eleanor P., *(Cruikshank; 0-9605284),* 194 San Carlos Ave., Sausalito, CA 94965 (SAN 215-7489).

Cruising Chef, *(Cruising; 0-931297),* 421 Gerona Ave., Coral Gables, FL 33146 (SAN 683-2474) Tel 305-665-8376.

Crumb Elbow Publishing, *(Crumb Elbow Pub),* P.O. Box 294, Rhododendron, OR 97049 (SAN 679-128X) Tel 503-622-4798.

Crusade Pubns, *(Crusade Pubs),* 11326 Ranchito St., El Monte, CA 91732 (SAN 203-8595). Religious Publications Only.

Cruzada Spanish Pubns., *(Cruzada Span Pubns; 0-933648),* P.O. Box 650909, Miami, FL 33165 (SAN 214-2376).

Cryptologia, Div. of Rose-Hulman Institute of Technology, *(Cryptologia; 0-9610560),* 5500 Wabash Ave., Terre Haute, IN 47803 (SAN 263-9920) Tel 812-877-1511.

Crystal Butterfly Prints & Pr., *(Crystal Butterfly; 0-938233),* P.O. Box 672, Oak Lawn, IL 60454-0672 (SAN 661-0625); 8420 S. Knox, Chicago, IL 60652 (SAN 661-0633) Tel 312-767-3881.

Crystal Co., The, *(Crystal Co; 0-9614094),* P.O. Box 348, Sunol, CA 94586 (SAN 656-0407) Tel 415-862-2332; Dist. by: Samuel Weiser, P.O. Box 612, York Beach, ME 03910 (SAN 202-9588) Tel 207-363-4393; Dist. by: Starlite Dist., P.O. Box 20729, Reno, NV 89515 (SAN 131-1921); Dist. by: New Leaf Dist., 1020 White St. SW, Atlanta, GA 30310 (SAN 169-1449) Tel 404-755-2665; Dist. by: Bookpeople, 2929 Fifth St., Berkeley, CA 94710 (SAN 168-9517) Tel 415-549-3030; Dist. by: Brotherhood of Life, 110 Dartmouth SE, Albuquerque, NM 87106 (SAN 202-4233) Tel 505-255-8980.

Crystal Cove Pr., *(Crystal Cove; 0-9616787),* 4011 Calle Abril, San Clemente, CA 92672 (SAN 661-0668) Tel 714-496-0830.

Crystal International Publishing Co., *(Crystal Intl Pub; 0-9616622),* 2622 Woodlake, No. 1, Wyoming, MI 49509 (SAN 661-0714) Tel 616-530-9615.

Crystal Pr., *(Crystal MI; 0-930402),* 1909 Proctor St., Flint, MI 48504 (SAN 220-522X) Tel 313-239-8281.

Crystal Pr., Ltd., *(Crystal Pr; 0-938108),* P.O. Box 215, Crystal Bay, NV 89402 (SAN 239-5282).

Crystal Pubns., *(Crystal Pubns; 0-9610820),* 827 Arlington Ave., Berkeley, CA 94707 (SAN 265-2269) Tel 415-526-8736.

Crystal Pubs., *(Crystal Pubs; 0-934687),* 140 Garfield Ave., Colonia, NJ 07067 (SAN 694-1443) Tel 201-382-1315.

Crystal Rainbow Publishing Co., *(Crystal Rainbow; 0-938125),* 3712 Fort Hill Dr., Alexandria, VA 22310 (SAN 661-0684) Tel 703-960-3859.

CSIS *See* **Georgetown Univ., Ctr. for Strategic & International Studies**

†**CSS Pubns.,** *(CSS Pubns; 0-942170),* P.O. Box 23, Iowa Falls, IA 50126 (SAN 238-0471); *CIP.*

CSUDH *See* **California State Univ., Dominguez Hills Educational Resources Center**

CT Academy *See* **Shoe String Pr., Inc.**

CTB, McGraw-Hill *See* **McGraw-Hill Bk. Co.**

Cuban Museum *See* **Museum of Arts & Sciences**

Cube Pubns., Inc., *(Cube Pubns; 0-911603),* 1 Buena Vista Rd., Pt. Jefferson, NY 11777 (SAN 263-9939) Tel 516-331-4990; P.O. Box 665, Pt. Jefferson, NY 11777 (SAN 696-5083).

Cuckoo Bird Pr. *See* **Andrion Bks.**

Cuisinart Cooking Club, *(Cuisinart Cooking; 0-936662),* 15 Valley Dr., Greenwich, CT 06830 (SAN 214-2287) Tel 203-622-4689; P.O. Box 2150, Greenwich, CT 06836-2150 (SAN 658-0416).

Cuisine Productions, *(Cuisine Prods; 0-910327),* P.O. Box 795217, Dallas, TX 75379 (SAN 241-4902) Tel 214-386-6708.

Cuissential Arts, *(Cuissential; 0-9615136),* P.O. Box 22337, Sacramento, CA 95822 (SAN 694-2520) Tel 916-421-1957.

Culinary Arts, Ltd., *(Culinary Arts; 0-914667),* 8050 SW 85th St., Portland, OR 97223 (SAN 289-1972) Tel 503-639-4549.

Cullar, W. Clytes, *(W C Cullar; 0-9616504),* 1222 Ferndale Ave., Dallas, TX 75224 (SAN 659-4387) Tel 214-943-8339.

Cullins & Cullins, *(Cullins; 0-9608386),* P.O. Box 241, Sloughhouse, CA 95683 (SAN 240-530X) Tel 916-687-6745.

Cultural Resource, *(Cultural Res; 0-918421),* 120 Tuscarora Dr., Hillsborough, NC 27278 (SAN 657-5854) Tel 919-732-6206.

Cultural Services, Inc., *(Cultural Serv; 0-913169),* P.O. Box 30435, Bethesda, MD 20814 (SAN 283-0469) Tel 301-654-2092; Dist. by: Oryx Pr., 2214 N. Central, Phoenix, AZ 85004 (SAN 692-8420).

Cultural Studies Institute, *(CSI Campbell; 0-9606058),* 999 W. Hamilton Ave., Suite 104, Campell, CA 95008 (SAN 216-8863) Tel 408-370-2267; Dist. by: Professional Pubns., P.O. Box 199, San Carlos, CA 94070 (SAN 264-6315) Tel 415-595-8437.

Culver Pubns., *(Culver Pubns; 0-9615155),* P.O. Box 3103, Kingston, NY 12401 (SAN 693-126X) Tel 914-331-6215.

Cumberland Pr., *(Cumberland Pr; 0-87027),* 136 Main St., Freeport, ME 04032 (SAN 203-2090) Tel 207-865-6045.

Cumulative Index to Nursing & Allied Health Literature, Div. of Glendale Adventist Medical Ctr., *(Cum Index Nursing; 0-910478),* Box 871, Glendale, CA 91209 (SAN 217-2356) Tel 818-240-2819.

Cunningham, Eileen S., *(E S Cunningham),* R.R. 2, Carrollton, IL 62016 (SAN 213-0467).

Cunningham Press, *(Cunningham Pr),* 3063 W. Main, Alhambra, CA 91801 (SAN 203-8773) Tel 818-283-8838; Dist. by: Theosophy Co., 245 W. 33rd St., Los Angeles, CA 90007 (SAN 295-3560) Tel 213-748-7244.

Cunningham Publishing Co., *(Cunningham Pub Co; 0-911659),* 701 Washington, Box 1345, Buffalo, NY 14205 (SAN 263-9947) Tel 519-587-5143.

Cupboard Cookbook, The, *(Cupbd Cookbk; 0-9613676),* Box 444, Salem, IL 62881 (SAN 238-0455) Tel 618-548-3049.

†**Curbstone Pr.,** *(Curbstone; 0-915306),* 321 Jackson St., Willimantic, CT 06226 (SAN 209-4282) Tel 203-423-9190; Dist. by: Talman Co., 150 Fifth Ave., Rm. 514, New York, NY 10011 (SAN 200-5204) Tel 212-620-3182; *CIP.*

Curbstone Publishing, *(Curbstone Pub TX; 0-931604),* P.O. Box 7445 Univ. Sta., Austin, TX 78712 (SAN 281-5796) Tel 512-263-3237.

Curl, *(Curl; 0-9614282),* Edgemont, SD 57735 (SAN 687-441X) Tel 307-325-6545.

Curran, Alfred A., *(A A Curran; 0-9617186),* 119 Sefton Dr., New Britain, CT 06053 (SAN 663-2637) Tel 203-827-8023.

Curran, D. F., Productions, *(D F Curran Prods),* P.O. Box 776, Wausau, WI 54401-0776 (SAN 287-2854).

Current Digest of the Soviet Press, The, Affil. of American Assn. for the Advancement of Slavic Studies & American Council of Learned Societies, *(Current Digest; 0-913601),* 1480 W. Lane Ave., Columbus, OH 43221 (SAN 282-7069) Tel 614-422-4234.

†**Current Issues Pubns.,** *(Current Issues; 0-936012),* 2214 Stuart St., Berkeley, CA 94705 (SAN 213-9189) Tel 415-549-1451; *CIP.*

Names

Current Literature Pubns., Inc., *(Current Lit Pubns; 0-914899),* 1513 E. St., Bellingham, WA 98225 (SAN 289-0976) Tel 206-734-9233.

Current Nine Publishing, *(Current Nine Pub; 0-9615413),* 4167 S. Four Mile Run Dr., No. 203, Arlington, VA 22204 (SAN 695-4979) Tel 703-920-9587; P.O. Box 6089, Arlington, VA 22206 (SAN 695-4987).

Curriculum Information Ctr., Inc., *(Curriculum Info Ctr; 0-914608; 0-89770),* Ketchum Pl., P.O. Box 510, Westport, CT 06880 (SAN 206-3506) Tel 203-226-8941. Purchased by Market Data Retrieval in 1979.

Currier, Philip J., *(P J Currier; 0-9613636),* Patterson Hill Rd., Henniker, NH 03242 (SAN 693-5141) Tel 603-428-7214.

Currier Davis Publishing, *(Currier-Davis; 0-930507),* P.O. Box 58, Winter Park, FL 32790-0058 (SAN 670-963X) Tel 305-788-8677; 1180 Spring Ctr., S. Blvd., Suite 120, Altamonte Springs, FL 32714 (SAN 670-9648).

Currier's Fine Art Appraisals & Publishing, *(Curriers Fine Art; 0-935277),* P.O. Box 2098-A, Brockton, MA 02402 (SAN 695-751X) Tel 617-588-4509; 22 Martland Ave., Brockton, MA 02401 (SAN 696-9518) Tel 617-588-4509.

Curry County Historical Society, *(Curry County; 0-932368),* 920 S. Ellensburg, Gold Beach, OR 97444 (SAN 215-7500) Tel 503-247-2165.

Curson House, Inc. Publishers, *(Curson Hse; 0-913694),* 250 S. 18th St. Chestnut St., Philadelphia, PA 19103 (SAN 203-8781) Tel 215-732-7111.

†**Curtin & London, Inc.,** *(Curtin & London; 0-930764),* P.O. Box 363, Marblehead, MA 01945 (SAN 212-0151) Tel 617-631-0762; Orders to: (Computer & business titles), P.O. Box 363, Marblehead, MA 01945 (SAN 212-0151); Orders to: Focal Pr. (Photography titles), 80 Montvale Ave., Stoneham, MA 02180 (SAN 220-0066) Tel 617-438-8464; Dist. by: Van Nostrand Reinhold, 115 Fifth Ave., New York, NY 10003 (SAN 202-5183) Tel 212-254-3232; CIP.

Curtis, Donald A., *(D A Curtis; 0-9610284),* 904 W. Main St., East Palestine, OH 44413 (SAN 263-9971) Tel 216-426-4389.

Curtis, Ralph, Bks., *(R Curtis Bks; 0-88359),* P.O. Box 183, Sanibel, FL 33957 (SAN 281-5834) Tel 813-472-5490.

Curtis Instruments, Inc., *(Curtis Instruments; 0-939488),* 200 Kisco Ave., Mt. Kisco, NY 10549 (SAN 216-3616) Tel 914-666-2971.

Curtis-Lieberman Bks., *(Curtis Lieberman; 0-930985),* Box 186, Woodstock, VT 05091 (SAN 678-9285) Tel 802-457-2877.

Curtis Media Corp., *(Curtis Media; 0-88107),* 9954 Brockbank Dr., Dallas, TX 75220 (SAN 240-7310).

Curtis Publishing Co., The, Div. of Saturday Evening Post, *(Curtis Pub Co; 0-89387),* 1100 Waterway Blvd., Indianapolis, IN 46206 (SAN 216-3624) Tel 317-634-1100.

Cushing, Helen Grant, *(H G Cushing; 0-9603588),* 339 E. 58th St., New York, NY 10022 (SAN 213-9995) Tel 212-355-6048; Orders to: G. H. Cushing, 16237 Gledhill St., Sepulveda, CA 91343 (SAN 214-0004).

Cushman Pubs., *(Cushman Pubs; 0-9607084),* 7720 Brandeis Way, Springfield, VA 22153 (SAN 238-9681) Tel 703-243-4960.

Custer, Marquis, Pubns., *(Custer; 0-9600274),* 1021 S. Lee Ave., Lodi, CA 95240 (SAN 206-9261) Tel 209-368-0502.

Custom Curriculum Concepts, *(Custom Curriculum; 0-9611480),* P.O. Box 2813, Denton, TX 76202 (SAN 285-2373) Tel 214-466-0104.

Custom Cycle Fitments, *(CCF; 0-940558),* 726 Madrone Ave., Sunnyvale, CA 94086 (SAN 223-7644) Tel 408-734-9426.

Custom Graphics Pr., *(Custom Graphics; 0-9616766),* 501 N. Sixth St., Cornell, IL 61319 (SAN 661-0722) Tel 815-358-2888.

Custom House Press, *(Custom Hse; 0-940560),* 2900 Newark Rd., P.O. Box 2369, Zanesville, OH 43701 (SAN 216-3632).

Custom Publishing Co., *(Custom Pub Co; 0-942728),* P.O. Box 1412, Costa Mesa, CA 92628 (SAN 281-5850); 338 Bucknell Rd., Costa Mesa, CA 92626 (SAN 669-0580) Tel 714-545-4653; Orders to: 11 Starglow Cir., Sacramento, CA 95831 (SAN 281-5869) Tel 916-424-4726.

Custom Taping, Inc., *(Custom Taping; 0-935059),* 3940 Montclair Rd., Birmingham, AL 35213 (SAN 694-6100) Tel 205-879-7902.

Cutaway Press, *(Cutaway Pr; 0-9610304),* 476 Bluebird Canon Dr., Laguna Beach, CA 92651 (SAN 263-998X) Tel 714-494-1370.

Cutting Tool Manufacturers Assn., *(Cutting Tool Mfg),* 1230 Keith Bldg., Cleveland, OH 44115 (SAN 230-5240) Tel 216-241-7333.

Cwieka, R., *(R Cwieka; 0-915277),* 1375 Clinton Ave., Irvington, NJ 07111 (SAN 289-9779) Tel 201-375-4589.

Cy De Cosse, Inc., *(Cy De Cosse; 0-86573),* 5900 Green Oak Dr., Minnetonka, MN 55343 (SAN 289-7148) Tel 612-936-4700; Toll free: 800-328-3895.

Cyber Research Inc., *(Cyber Res Inc; 0-931193),* P.O. Box 9565, New Haven, CT 06520 (SAN 681-9753) Tel 203-786-5151.

CyberIconics Institutes, *(CyberIconics; 0-9606980),* 1640 E. Hale St., Mesa, AZ 85203 (SAN 237-9430).

Cyclopedia Publishing Co., *(Cyclopedia; 0-914226),* 6 Freedom Rd., Pleasant Valley, NY 12569 (SAN 206-6327).

Cykxbooks, Div. of Cykkincorp, *(Cykx; 0-932436),* P.O. Box 299, Lenox Hill Sta., New York, NY 10021 (SAN 212-1557).

Cynthia Publishing Co., *(Cynthia Pub Co; 0-9614168),* 4455 Los Feliz Blvd., Suite 1106 W., Los Angeles, CA 90027 (SAN 686-6484) Tel 213-664-3165.

Cyometrics, Inc., *(Cyometrics; 0-943284),* 25 W. Courtland St., Bel Air, MD 21014 (SAN 240-6225) Tel 301-838-1144.

CyPress, *(CyPr NY; 0-930269),* c/o Cybex, 2100 Smithtown Ave., Ronkonkoma, NY 11779 (SAN 670-8544) Tel 516-585-9000.

Cypress, *(Cypress CA; 0-938995),* P.O. Box 223179, Carmel-by-the-Sea, CA 93922 (SAN 662-5398) Tel 408-625-6164.

Cypress Book Company, Inc., Subs. of China International Bk. Trading Corp., *(Cypress Co; 0-934643),* Paramus Pl., 205 Robin Rd., Suite 225, Paramus, NJ 07652 (SAN 694-0285) Tel 201-967-7820.

Cypress Creek Pubns., *(Cypress Creek Pubns; 0-937755),* P.O. Box 2009, Florence, AL 35630 (SAN 659-3356) Tel 205-764-8861; Rte. 6, Box 6, Florence, AL 35630 (SAN 659-3364).

DAW Bks., Affil. of New American Library, *(DAW Bks; 0-8099),* ; Toll free: 800-526-0275; c/o New American Library, 1633 Broadway, New York, NY 10019 (SAN 206-8079) Tel 212-397-8000.

D & A Publishing Co., *(D & A Pub; 0-931578),* 3123 N. 20th St., Phoenix, AZ 85016 (SAN 211-4119) Tel 602-955-8469.

D & B Corp., *(D & B Corp; 0-936905),* 13815 SE Rust Way, Boring, OR 97009 (SAN 658-3563) Tel 503-658-5451.

D & B Enterprises, *(D B Enterprises; 0-937349),* P.O. Box 1121, Longmont, CO 80501 (SAN 659-1531) Tel 303-772-7902; 9 Seattle Ln., Longmont, CO 80501 (SAN 659-154X).

D & J Pr., *(D & J Pr; 0-937757),* P.O. Box 29834, San Antonio, TX 78229 (SAN 697-1024) Tel 512-492-9699.

D & K Dists., *(D & K Dists; 0-918889),* 6645 Delbarton St., San Diego, CA 92120 (SAN 669-9847) Tel 619-265-0158.

D & L Publishing, *(D & L Pub; 0-88100),* 660 Fort Hill Dr., Vicksburg, MS 39180 (SAN 682-8701) Tel 601-636-5624.

D & M Publishing Co., *(D & M Pub; 0-9616713),* P.O. Box 375, Slatersville, RI 02876 (SAN 661-0757); 237 N. Main, Slatersville, RI 02876 (SAN 661-0765) Tel 401-765-5936.

D & P Publishing Co., *(D & P Pub; 0-938319),* P.O. Box 1236, Slidell, LA 70459 (SAN 661-0773); 500 Pontchartrain Dr., Slidell, LA 70459 (SAN 661-0781) Tel 504-641-5586; Dist. by: Forest Sales & Distributing, 2616 Spain St., New Orleans, LA 70117 (SAN 157-5511).

D & R Publishing, Div. of D & R Enterprises, *(D R Pub; 0-937445),* 3141 33rd Ave. S., Minneapolis, MN 55406 (SAN 659-1558) Tel 612-729-0897.

D&S Pubns., *(D&S Pubns; 0-9607090),* 6334 St. Andrews Cir., Ft. Myers, FL 33907 (SAN 238-9290).

D & S Pubs., Member of Butterworth Legal Publishing Group, *(D & S Pub),* 2030 Calumet St., P.O. Box 5105, Clearwater, FL 33518 (SAN 226-983X) Tel 813-441-8933; Toll free: 800-237-9707; Toll free: 800-282-8118 in Florida.

D & S Publishing, *(D&S Publishing; 0-9615954),* P.O. Box 7343 Indian Creek Sta., Shawnee Mission, KS 66207 (SAN 697-3493) Tel 913-764-5900; 11901 Canterbury, Leawood, KS 66209 (SAN 697-3507).

DBA Bks., *(DBA Bks; 0-9605276),* 323 Beacon St., Boston, MA 02116 (SAN 281-5877) Tel 617-739-2200; 358 Chestnut Hill Ave., Brookline, MA 02146 (SAN 281-5885).

DBA Monte Vista Centennial Commission, *(DBA Monte Vista; 0-943640),* P.O. Box 63, Monte Vista, CO 81144 (SAN 238-3012) Tel 303-852-2525.

DBA Pr., *(DBA Pr; 0-914399),* P.O. Box 2932, Toledo, OH 43606 (SAN 289-629X) Tel 419-474-2140.

DBC, *(DBC; 0-9608798),* 1164 Wall Rd., Webster, NY 14580 (SAN 241-0109) Tel 716-872-0393.

DBI Bks., Inc., *(DBI; 0-910676; 0-87349),* 4092 Commercial Ave., Northbrook, IL 60062 (SAN 202-9960) Tel 312-272-6310.

DBJ Publishing, *(DBJ Pub; 0-9616870),* 200 Moraga Way, Orinda, CA 94563 (SAN 661-1508) Tel 415-254-1290.

DC Publishing Co., Inc., *(DC Pub Co; 0-933911),* 1686 Tustin Avenue, Suite A-163, Costa Mesa, CA 92627 (SAN 692-7785) Tel 714-645-2036.

DFM Assocs., *(DFM Assoc; 0-9616870),* 10 Chrysler, Irvine, CA 92718 (SAN 239-8508) Tel 714-859-8700.

D Fox Head Press, *(Fox Head; 0-910521),* 28 Vandeventer Ave., Princeton, NJ 08540 (SAN 260-1893) Tel 609-924-9316.

DGC Assocs., Inc., *(D G C Assocs Inc; 0-930941),* 1450 Preston Forest Sq., Dallas, TX 75230 (SAN 679-4033) Tel 214-991-4044.

DGL InfoWrite, *(DGL InfoWrite; 0-9614944),* 3010 Vassar Dr., Boulder, CO 80303 (SAN 693-6520) Tel 303-499-1749.

DITO Publishing, *(DITO Pub; 0-937929),* 15051 N. 20th St., Phoenix, AZ 85022 (SAN 659-5014) Tel 602-867-4587.

D.I.Y. Bks., Inc., *(DIY Bks; 0-9604036),* P.O. Box 2055, Hollywood, CA 90028 (SAN 239-4219).

D.J.A.'s Writing Circle, *(DJA Writ Circle; 0-9608924),* 2900 Country Club Rd., Jacksonville, NC 28540 (SAN 241-0117) Tel 919-346-8976.

DJC, Inc., A Witty Enterprise, *(Costello and Witty; 0-9609894),* 16222 Monterey Ln., No. 114, Huntington Beach, CA 92649-2236 (SAN 269-5596).

D. J. S. Enterprises, *(DJS Ent; 0-933634),* 1027 E. College St., Iowa City, IA 52240-5545 (SAN 692-0640) Tel 319-338-0148; Orders to: 31244 Palos Verdes Dr. W., Suite 229, Rancho Palos Verdes, CA 90274 (SAN 692-0659) Tel 213-377-5017.

DJ's Guides, Div. of Eicurean Delight, *(DJs Guides; 0-9615919),* 138 SE 53rd, Portland, OR 97215 (SAN 697-0540) Tel 503-232-1324; P.O. Box 06472, Portland, OR 97206 (SAN 697-0559).

DK Halcyon Group, Div. of Thom Doran & Partners, Inc., *(DK Halcyon; 0-939550),* 2640 Lance Dr., Dayton, OH 45409 (SAN 216-678X) Tel 513-293-9211.

DL, Inc., *(DL Inc; 0-937075),* P.O. Box 17356, Tucson, AZ 85731 (SAN 658-5698) Tel 602-291-7412; 9450 Paseo Tierra Verde, Tucson, AZ 85731 (SAN 658-5701).

DLM/CPA, *(DLM CPA; 0-935730),* P.O. Box 70125, Sunnyvale, CA 94086 (SAN 223-1662).

DMC Pubns., *(DMC Pubns; 0-9616810),* 45 Fairlawn Ave., Black Rock, CT 06605 (SAN 661-0900) Tel 203-368-1742.

Names

D.M. Publishing Co., *(DM Pub; 0-938419),* P.O. Box 5064, Sioux City, IA 51102 (SAN 661-0730); 901 N. St. Mary's, Sioux City, IA 51102 (SAN 661-0749) Tel 712-258-3133.

D.M.R. Pubns., Inc., *(DMR Pubns; 0-89552),* 1020 N. Broadway, Suite 111, Milwaukee, WI 53202 (SAN 205-325X) Tel 414-272-9977.

DMS Publishing Co., *(DMS Publishing Co; 0-914731),* 28311 S. Ridge Haven Ct., Rancho Palos Verdes, CA 90274 (SAN 291-8188) Tel 213-541-9441; Orders to: Holy Shroud Shrine, c/o Marcia Mascia, Corpus Christi Church, 136 S. Regent St., Port Chester, NY 10573 (SAN 662-2232) Tel 914-939-2553.

D.N.R. Pr., *(DNR Pr; 0-9604682),* 441 Hillsmont Pl., El Cajon, CA 92020 (SAN 216-7107) Tel 619-442-4647.

DOK Pubs., Inc., Div. of United Educational Services, Inc., *(DOK Pubs; 0-914634),* Box 605,, East Aurora, NY 14052 (SAN 201-3347) Tel 716-652-9131; Toll free: 800-458-7900.

DP Bks., *(DP Bks; 0-939299),* 7545 Katella, No. 118, Stanton, CA 90680 (SAN 662-796X) Tel 714-761-3496.

D.P. Enterprises, *(D P Enter; 0-935208),* P.O. Box 23241, Phoenix, AZ 85063 (SAN 213-4837).

D-Q University Pr., *(D-Q Univ Pr; 0-935279),* P.O. Box 409, Davis, CA 95617 (SAN 695-7250) Tel 916-758-0470.

DRACO, *(DRACO; 0-9617189),* 410 E. Indiana St., Princeton, IN 47670 (SAN 663-2580) Tel 812-386-7142.

DRC Graphics Service, *(DRC Graphics Serv; 0-9614887),* P.O. Box 4594, Portland, OR 97208 (SAN 693-2347) Tel 503-244-5026.

D.S.C. Publishing, Div. of D.S.C., Inc., *(D S C Pub; 0-910985),* 2 Dogwood Dr. & Hayestown Rd., P.O. Box 769, Danbury, CT 06811 (SAN 269-7696) Tel 203-748-3231.

DTM International, *(DTM Intl; 0-9616210),* Box 5, Lake Orion, MI 48035 (SAN 658-5078) Tel 313-693-7300; 1081 Indianwood Rd., Lake Orion, MI 48035 (SAN 658-5086).

DT Pubs., *(DT Pubs; 0-9616069),* P.O. Box 657, Princeton Junction, NJ 08550 (SAN 697-8606) Tel 609-443-4222.

DTW Pubns./Dance Theater Workshop, *(Dance Theater; 0-9611382),* 219 W. 19th St., New York, NY 10011 (SAN 283-121X) Tel 212-691-6500.

†**Da Capo Pr., Inc.,** Subs. of Plenum Publishing Corp., *(Da Capo; 0-306),* 233 Spring St., New York, NY 10013 (SAN 201-2944) Tel 212-620-8000; Toll free: 800-221-9369; Toll free: 800-221-9369; *CIP.*

Daan Graphics, *(Daan Grap; 0-9609788),* 906 Lincoln Blvd., Middlesex, NJ 08846 (SAN 269-5634) Tel 201-469-1887.

Dabbs, Jack A., *(Dabbs; 0-911494),* 2806 Cherry Lane, Austin, TX 78703 (SAN 205-4248) Tel 512-472-7463.

Dabney, A. L., *(A L Dabney),* 10441 Goodyear Dr., Dallas, TX 75229 (SAN 212-4092).

Dabney, *(Dabney; 0-9614155),* 2000 Hawkins Lane, Eugene, OR 97405 (SAN 686-5410) Tel 503-485-5847; Orders to: Human Creative Services, 2000 Hawkins Lane, Eugene, OR 97405 (SAN 693-5192) Tel 503-485-5847.

†**DaCa Publishing Co.,** *(DaCa Pub; 0-917904),* 1636 Monaco Dr., St. Louis, MO 63122 (SAN 209-3634) Tel 314-966-5678; *CIP.*

Dace Publishing, Inc., *(Dace Pub; 0-932045),* P.O. Box 60, Quinque, VA 22965 (SAN 686-0001) Tel 804-985-3183.

Dada Center Pubns., *(Dada Ctr; 0-930608),* 2319 W. Dry Creek Rd., Healdsburg, CA 95448 (SAN 211-1225) Tel 707-433-1237.

†**Dadant & Sons,** *(Dadant & Sons; 0-915698),* Hamilton, IL 62341 (SAN 224-1137); *CIP.*

Dade Variety Press, *(Dade Variety Pr),* 18154 NW Second Ave., Miami, FL 33169 (SAN 206-7005).

Daedalus Acting Lab, *(Daedalus Act; 0-9615815),* 629 Park Ave., No. 2A, New York, NY 10021 (SAN 696-7302) Tel 212-249-5356; P.O. Box 667, Lenox Hill Sta., New York, NY 10021 (SAN 698-2182).

D'Agostino, Lena V., *(L V D'Agostino; 0-9601076),* Davenport Center, NY 13751 (SAN 209-2085) Tel 607-278-5808.

Dah-A-Dee, Inc., *(Dah A Dee; 0-9616561),* 5644 40th Ave., SW, Seattle, WA 98136 (SAN 659-4395) Tel 206-937-5524.

Daheshist Publishing Co., The, *(Daheshist; 0-935359),* 575 Lexington Ave., New York, NY 10022 (SAN 696-298X) Tel 212-751-6700.

Dahlstrom, Grant, /Castle Press, *(Grant Dahlstrom),* 516 N. Fair Oaks Ave., Pasadena, CA 91103 (SAN 206-7455).

Dahlstrom & Co., Inc., *(Dahlstrom & Co; 0-940712),* 76 Prospect St., Franklin, MA 02038 (SAN 239-5088) Tel 617-528-1043. *Imprints:* Study Buddy Books (Study Buddy).

Dailey, William, Antiquarian Books, *(Wm Dailey Antiq; 0-915148),* P.O. Box 69160, Los Angeles, CA 90069 (SAN 223-7504) Tel 213-658-8515.

Daily Planet Almanac, Inc., The, *(Daily Planet; 0-939882),* P.O. Box 1641, Boulder, CO 80306 (SAN 281-5893) Tel 303-440-0268; Dist. by: Planet Productions, P.O. Box 1641, Boulder, CO 80306 (SAN 282-5899) Tel 415-549-3030.

†**Daimax Publishing House,** *(Daimax Pub Hse),* Dist. by: Press Pacifica, Ltd., P.O. Box 47, Kailua, HI 96734 (SAN 169-1635); *CIP.*

Dairy Goat Journal Publishing Corp., *(Dairy Goat; 0-930848),* Box 1808, Scottsdale, AZ 85252 (SAN 223-5730) Tel 602-991-4628.

Daisy Publishing, Inc., *(Daisy Pub WA; 0-943470),* P.O. Box 67A, Mukilteo, WA 98275 (SAN 240-6233) Tel 206-347-1414.

Dajan Enterprises, *(Dajan Ent; 0-9615542),* P.O. Box 4647, Huntsville, AL 35815 (SAN 696-3064) Tel 205-881-5034; 12025 Chicamauga Trail, Huntsville, AL 35803 (SAN 696-527X).

Dakin, H. S., Co., *(H S Dakin; 0-930420),* 3101 Washington St., San Francisco, CA 94115 (SAN 210-5934).

Dakota Kids Co., *(Dakota Kids; 0-938165),* P.O. Box 189, Sturgis, SD 57785 (SAN 200-6731); S. Blucksberg Mt. Rd., Sturgis, SD 57785 (SAN 202-9243) Tel 605-347-5668; Dist. by: North Plains Pr., P.O. Box 1830, Aberdeen, SD 57402-1830 (SAN 661-0811) Tel 605-225-5360.

Dakota Pr., *(Dakota Pr; 0-88249),* Univ. of South Dakota, Vermillion, SD 57069 (SAN 207-7345) Tel 605-677-5281.

Dakota Specialties, *(Dakota Special; 0-935337),* P.O. Box 307, Mandan, ND 58554 (SAN 696-3080) Tel 701-663-5047; 410 E. Main St., Mandan, ND 58554 (SAN 696-5288).

Dale Bks., Inc., *(Dale Bks CA; 0-935917),* 901 H St. Suite 307, Sacramento, CA 95814 (SAN 696-7337) Tel 916-652-0206; 9403 Whiskey Bar Rd., Loomis, CA 95650 (SAN 662-3832) Tel 916-652-0206; Orders to: Books & Things, 9403 Whiskey Bar Rd., Loomis, CA 95650 (SAN 662-7838).

†**Dalkey Archive Pr., The,** *(Dalkey Arch; 0-916583),* 1817 79th Ave., Elmwood Park, IL 60635 (SAN 296-4910) Tel 312-453-2024; Dist. by: Inland Book Co., P.O. Box 261, 22 Hemingway Ave., East Haven, CT 06512 (SAN 200-4151); Toll free: 800-243-0138; Dist. by: Small Press Distribution, Inc., 1814 San Pablo Ave., Berkeley, CA 94702 (SAN 204-5826) Tel 415-549-3336; *CIP.*

Dallas A & M Univ. Mothers' Club, *(Dallas A & M Mothers; 0-9612446),* 6209 Pineview Rd., Dallas, TX 75248 (SAN 289-2014) Tel 214-980-6488; Orders to: Hullabaloo in the Kitchen, P.O. Box 796212, Dallas, TX 75379 (SAN 662-2151) Tel 214-980-6488.

Dallas Inst Pubns., The, *(Dallas Inst Pubns; 0-911005),* 2719 Routh St., Dallas, TX 75201 (SAN 274-4872) Tel 214-698-9090.

Dallas Junior Forum, *(Dallas Jr Forum; 0-9617187),* 4666 Chapel Hill Rd., Dallas, TX 75214 (SAN 663-2564) Tel 214-821-4025.

Dallas Museum of Art, *(Dallas Mus; 0-9609622; 0-936227),* 1717 N. Harwood, Dallas, TX 75201 (SAN 204-2436) Tel 214-922-0220; Dist. by: Univ. of Texas Pr., P.O. Box 7819, Austin, TX 78713 (SAN 652-186X) Tel 512-471-7233.

Dallas Sandt Co., *(Dallas Sandt; 0-936263),* 3104 E. Camelback Rd., Suite 301, Phoenix, AZ 85016 (SAN 697-3515) Tel 602-224-5410.

Dallas Southern Memorial Assn., The, *(Dallas South Memorial; 0-9615569),* P.O. Box 252232, Dallas, TX 75225 (SAN 696-4885) Tel 214-696-4831.

Dallum, Linda Brinkman, *(L B Dallum; 0-9616937),* P.O. Box 6894, Great Falls, MT 59405 (SAN 661-8294); 4051 Sixth Ave. S., Great Falls, MT 59405 (SAN 661-8308) Tel 406-452-3114.

Dalmas & Ricour, *(Dalmas & Ricour; 0-940066),* 6322 Cool Shade Dr., Fayetteville, NC 28303 (SAN 220-2433).

Dalton, Pat, *(Dalton),* 410 Lancaster Ave., Haverford, PA 19041 (SAN 215-9902).

Dalyn Pr., *(Dalyn Pr; 0-9613200),* 820 Alhambra Blvd., Sacramento, CA 95816 (SAN 295-7302) Tel 916-446-2757.

Damar Publishing, *(Damar Pub; 0-938421),* P.O. Box 660, Lake Worth, FL 33460-0660 (SAN 661-0889); 1519 14th Ave., North Lake Worth, FL 33460 (SAN 661-0897) Tel 305-586-8623.

Damas Publishing Co., *(Damas Pub; 0-917268),* 6515 Sunset Blvd., Suite 202, Hollywood, CA 90028 (SAN 208-4783) Tel 213-851-4653.

Damascus Hse., *(Damascus Hse),* Dist. by: Doubleday, 501 Franklin Ave., Garden City, NY 11530 (SAN 201-3231).

Dame Pubns., Inc., *(Dame Pubns; 0-931920),* 7800 Bissonnet, Suite 415, Houston, TX 77074 (SAN 214-3623) Tel 713-995-1000.

Damgood Books, *(Damgood Bks; 0-912659),* 5870 Green Valley Circle, Apt. 333, Fox Hills, CA 90230 (SAN 277-6715) Tel 213-838-7445.

D'amico, Paul M., *(D'amico; 0-9607270),* Main St., Livingston Manor, NY 12758 (SAN 239-4200).

Damien-Dutton Society for Leprosy Aid, Inc., *(Damien-Dutton Soc; 0-9606330),* 616 Bedford Ave., Bellmore, NY 11710 (SAN 217-1694) Tel 516-221-5829.

Damon Press, Inc., *(Damon Pr; 0-910641),* Box 224, Leonia, NJ 07605 (SAN 262-6144) Tel 201-944-3393.

Dan River Pr., Div. of Conservatory of American Letters, *(Dan River Pr; 0-89754),* P.O. Box 123, South Thomaston, ME 04858 (SAN 212-7377); P.O. Box 88, Thomaston, ME 04861 (SAN 661-9878) Tel 207-354-6550.

Dana, William B., Co., *(Dana Co; 0-9614837),* 45 John St., Suite 911, New York, NY 10038 (SAN 693-0999) Tel 212-233-5200.

DaNa Pubns., *(DaNa Pubns; 0-937103),* 1050 Austin Ave., Idaho Falls, ID 83401 (SAN 658-568X) Tel 208-524-1067.

Danbury Hse., Bks., *(DanBury Hse Bks; 0-935207),* P.O. Box 253, Oakland, ME 04963 (SAN 669-6724) Tel 207-465-2610.

Danca, Vince, *(V Danca; 0-9602390),* 1191 Roxbury Close, Rockford, IL 61107 (SAN 212-4971).

Dance Films Association, Inc., *(Dance Films; 0-914438),* 241 E. 34th St., New York, NY 10016 (SAN 206-3522) Tel 212-686-7019.

Dance Magazine, Inc., *(Dance Mag Inc; 0-930036),* 33 W. 60th St., New York, NY 10023 (SAN 210-4091) Tel 212-245-9050; Toll free: 800-331-1750.

Dance Notation Bureau, Inc., *(Dance Notation; 0-932582),* 33 W. 21st St., 3rd Flr., New York, NY 10010 (SAN 212-3452) Tel 212-807-7899.

Danceways Books, *(Danceway Bks; 0-937180),* 393 West End Ave. 14F, New York, NY 10024 (SAN 219-4724) Tel 212-799-2860; Dist. by: Variety Arts, Inc., 305 Riverside Dr., Suite 4A, New York, NY 10025 (SAN 200-691X); Toll free: 800-221-2154.

Dancin' Bee Co., *(Dancin Bee; 0-933192),* 107 Maple Ave., P.O. Box 237, Ridgely, MD 21660 (SAN 213-4845).

Dancing Bear Pubns., *(Dancing Bear Pubns; 0-931139),* P.O. Box 3013, Del Mar, CA 92014 (SAN 679-3991) Tel 619-942-2291.

†**Dandelion Hse., The,** Div. of Child's World, Inc., *(Dandelion Hse; 0-89693),* P.O. Box 989, Elgin, IL 60121 (SAN 240-8910) Tel 312-741-7591; Dist. by: Scripture Pr., 1825 College Ave., Wheaton, IL 60187 (SAN 222-9471) Tel 312-668-6000; *CIP.*

Dandelion Pr., *(Dandelion Pr; 0-89799),* 184 Fifth Ave., New York, NY 10010 (SAN 212-0836) Tel 212-929-0090.

Names

Dandick Co., The, *(Dandick Co; 0-917546),* P.O. Box 55, Scottsdale, AZ 85252 (SAN 223-5765).

Dandy Lion Pubns., *(Dandy Lion; 0-931724),* P.O. Box 190, San Luis Obispo, CA 93406 (SAN 211-5565) Tel 805-543-3332.

†**Dane Books,** *(Dane Bks; 0-917655),* 15 St. Regis Circle, Salinas, CA 93905 (SAN 657-1336) Tel 415-956-5966; *CIP.*

Daneco Pubns., *(Daneco Pubns; 0-910519),* 3451 18th Ave. S., Minneapolis, MN 55407 (SAN 260-180X) Tel 612-724-6285.

Danella Pubns., *(Danella Pubns; 0-940562),* P.O. Box C, Sausalito, CA 94966 (SAN 218-5407) Tel 415-332-9601.

Danforth, Edward J., *(E J Danforth; 0-9601174),* 20 Westwood Dr., Orono, ME 04473 (SAN 210-0622) Tel 207-866-2846.

Dangary Publishing, Co., *(Dangary Pub; 0-910484),* 205 S. Smallwood St., Baltimore, MD 21223 (SAN 204-2398) Tel 301-685-8894 Tel 202-621-5732.

Dangberg, Grace, Foundation, Inc., The, *(Grace Dangberg; 0-913205),* P.O. Box 9621, University Sta., Reno, NV 89507-0621 (SAN 283-0493) Tel 702-883-2017.

Daniel, John, Pub., *(J Daniel; 0-936784),* P.O. Box 21922, Santa Barbara, CA 93121 (SAN 215-1995) Tel 805-962-1780.

Danly Productions, Inc., *(Danly Prods; 0-9617278),* 7609 W. Industrial Dr., Forest Park, IL 60130 Tel 312-771-0200.

Danmark Enterprises, Ltd., *(Danmark Enterprises; 0-9616596),* 1221 Minor Ave., No. 201, Seattle, WA 98101 (SAN 659-5022) Tel 206-682-1734.

Dante Univ. of America Pr., Inc., *(Dante U Am; 0-937832),* P.O. Box 843, Brookline Village, Boston, MA 02147 (SAN 220-150X) Tel 617-734-2045.

†**Danubian Pr., Inc.,** *(Danubian; 0-87934),* Rte. 1, Box 59, Astor, FL 32002 (SAN 201-8047) Tel 904-759-2255; *CIP.*

DAR Systems International, *(DAR Syst; 0-916163; 1-55616),* P.O. Box 4925, Berkeley, CA 94704-4925 (SAN 294-7323) Tel 415-689-1312; Dist. by: Baker & Taylor, Midwest Div., 501 Gladiolus Ave., Momence, IL 60954 (SAN 169-2100) Tel 815-472-2444; Orders to: Micro Data Products (Software orders only), 537 S. Olathe Ct., Aurora, CO 80011 (SAN 662-2267) Tel 303-360-6200.

Daratech, Inc., *(Daratech; 0-938484),* 16 Myrtle Ave., Cambridge, MA 02138 (SAN 281-5915) Tel 617-354-2339; Orders to: P.O. Box 410, Cambridge, MA 02238 (SAN 281-5923). No longer publishes software.

Darby Bks., *(Darby Bks; 0-89987),* P.O. Box 148, Darby, PA 19023 (SAN 204-2371) Tel 215-583-4550.

Dare-Co., Div. of Daisy R. & E. Co., *(Dare Co; 0-936729),* 2508 Nottingham Ave., Los Angeles, CA 90027 (SAN 699-8909) Tel 213-662-3204; P.O. Box 27164, Los Angeles, CA 90027 (SAN 699-8917).

Dare, Inc., *(DARE; 0-943690),* 3628 Grant Ave., Rockford, IL 61103 (SAN 238-2695) Tel 815-877-8511.

Dargaud Publishing International, Ltd., *(Dargaud Pub; 0-917201),* 2 Lafayette Ct., Greenwich, CT 06830 (SAN 655-8100) Tel 203-661-0707.

Darian Books, *(Darian Bks; 0-910899),* 9027 N. 52nd Ave., Glendale, AZ 85302 (SAN 269-5898) Tel 602-931-3788.

Darien Community Assn., Inc., *(DCA),* Orders to: Tory Hole, 274 Middlesex Rd., Darien, CT 06820 (SAN 208-4902) Tel 203-655-9050.

Darien House Books, *(Darien Hse; 0-88201),* c/o Images Graphiques, 37 Riverside Dr., New York, NY 10023 (SAN 210-4415) Tel 212-787-4000.

†**Daring Bks.,** Div. of Daring Publishing Group, *(Daring Bks; 0-938936),* 2020 Ninth St., SW, Canton, OH 44706 (SAN 216-0293) Tel 216-454-7519; Orders to: P.O. Box 526, Canton, OH 47701 (SAN 685-3242); *CIP.*

Dark Child Pr., *(Dark Child Pr; 0-932139),* 1329 N. Garfield, Pocatello, ID 83204 (SAN 686-4279) Tel 208-233-1283; Dist. by: Inland Bk. Co., P.O. Box 261. 22 Hemingway Ave., East Haven, CT 06512 (SAN 200-4151) Tel 203-467-4257.

Dark Harvest Bks., *(Dark Harvest; 0-913165),* P.O. Box 48134, Niles, IL 60648-0134 (SAN 283-0558) Tel 312-991-6290.

Dark Sun Pr., *(Dark Sun; 0-937968),* c/o MFA Photography, Rochester Institute of Technology, 1 Lomb Mem. Dr., Rochester, NY 14623 (SAN 220-0430) Tel 716-475-2616.

Darrah, William Culp, *(W C Darrah; 0-913116),* 2235 Baltimore Pike, Gettysburg, PA 17325 (SAN 205-4922) Tel 717-334-2272.

Darrow, Frank M., *(Darrow; 0-912636),* P.O. Box 305, Trona, CA 93562 (SAN 201-4661); 82194 7th St., Argus, CA 93562 (SAN 201-467X).

Dart Publishing Co., *(Dart Pub Co; 0-931243),* 19344 Wyandotte St., Suite 122, Reseda, CA 91335 (SAN 681-977X) Tel 818-885-6169.

Dartnell Corp., *(Dartnell Corp; 0-85013),* 4660 Ravenswood Ave., Chicago, IL 60640 (SAN 205-5407) Tel 312-561-4000; Toll free: 800-621-5463.

†**Darwin Pr., Inc.,** *(Darwin Pr; 0-87850),* P.O. Box 2202, Princeton, NJ 08540 (SAN 201-2987) Tel 609-737-1349; *CIP.*

Darwin Pubns., Div. of Howell North-Darwin-Superior, *(Darwin Pubns; 0-933506),* 850 N. Hollywood Way, Burbank, CA 91505 (SAN 207-4370) Tel 818-848-0944.

Data Analysis Group, *(Data Analysis; 0-936677),* 8263 Vista Dr., La Mesa, CA 92041 (SAN 697-7588) Tel 619-464-6888.

Data & Research Technology Corp., *(Data & Res Tech; 0-935025),* 1102 McNeilly Ave., Pittsburgh, PA 15216 (SAN 694-5503) Tel 412-563-2212.

†**Data Courier Inc.,** *(Data Courier; 0-914604),* 620 S. Fifth St., Louisville, KY 40202 (SAN 289-7016); *CIP.*

Data Decisions, *(Data Dec),* 20 Brace Rd., Cherry Hill, NJ 08034 (SAN 670-7378) Tel 609-429-7100.

Data Description, Inc., *(Data Description; 0-935321),* P.O. Box 4555, Ithaca, NY 14852 (SAN 695-7358) Tel 607-257-1000 (SAN 696-9496).

Data Financial Press, *(Data Financial; 0-933088),* P.O. Box 668, Menlo Park, CA 94025 (SAN 212-4106); Dist. by: Caroline House, P.O. Box 801, Menlo Park, CA 94025 (SAN 212-4114) Tel 415-321-4553.

Data House Publishing Co., Inc., *(Data Hse; 0-935922),* 5724 N. Pulaski Ave.,, Chicago, IL 60646 (SAN 214-0020) Tel 312-478-0900.

Data Processing Management Assn., *(Data Process Mgmt),* 505 Busse Hwy., Park Ridge, IL 60068-3191 (SAN 654-1046) Tel 312-825-8124.

Data Research, Inc., *(Data Res MN; 0-939675),* 4635 Nicols Rd., Suite 100, Eagan, MN 55122 (SAN 663-5857) Tel 612-452-8267.

Database Services, *(Database Serv; 0-939920),* 2685 Marine Way., No. 1305, Mountain View, CA 94043-1125 (SAN 216-8073) Tel 415-961-2880; Orders to: P.O. Box 50545, Suite 1305, Mountain View, CA 94043 (SAN 663-2890) Tel 415-961-2880; Dist. by: Online, Inc., 11 Tannery Ln., Weston, CT 06883 (SAN 200-822X) Tel 203-227-8466.

Datacom Computer Sales & Supplies, 144 D Canterbury Lane, Medina, OH 44256-2563 (SAN 287-5896) Tel 216-225-0600; Toll free: 800-604-5553; 216-725-0500, .

DataCompatable, *(DataCompatable; 0-938793),* 2423 Willowbend Dr., Richmond, TX 77469 (SAN 661-4906) Tel 713-232-4372.

Datafax Corp., *(Datafax Corp; 0-935169),* 511 11th Ave. S., No. 54, Minneapolis, MN 55415 (SAN 695-846X).

Datalan, Inc., *(Datalan Inc; 0-9617245),* 21054 Sherman Way, Canoga Park, CA 91303 (SAN 698-455X) Tel 818-702-9744.

†**Datametrics Systems Corp.,** *(Datametrics Syst; 0-932853),* 5270 Lyngate Ct., Burke, VA 22015 (SAN 691-2885) Tel 703-425-1006; *CIP.*

Datamost, Inc., *(Datamost; 0-88190),* 21040 Nordhoff St., Chatsworth, CA 91311 (SAN 264-7311) Tel 818-709-1202; Toll free: 800-692-1649.

DataMyte Corp., *(DataMyte Corp; 0-930345),* 14960 Industrial Rd., Minnetonka, MN 55345 (SAN 669-7070) Tel 612-935-7704.

Dataplan, *(Dataplan; 0-9606878),* 2450 Foothill Blvd., Calistoga, CA 94515 (SAN 217-3506) Tel 707-942-0217.

†**Datapro Research Corp.,** Div. of McGraw-Hill Information Systems Co., *(Datapro Res; 0-07),* 1805 Underwood Blvd., Delran, NJ 08075 (SAN 226-7179); *CIP.*

Dataquest Inc., *(Dataquest),* 1290 Ridder Park Dr., San Jose, CA 95131 (SAN 201-825X) Tel 408-971-9001.

Datar Publishing Co., *(Datar Pub; 0-931572),* 9351 Ewers Dr., Crestwood, MO 63126 (SAN 211-4135) Tel 314-843-5343; Toll free: 800-633-8378.

Datarule Pub. Co., Inc., *(Datarule; 0-911740),* Rte. 4, Box 7, West Rd., South Salem, NY 10590 (SAN 201-2693) Tel 914-533-2263; Orders to: P.O. Box 448, New Canaan, CT 06840 (SAN 661-9886).

Datatext Co., *(Datatext; 0-916187),* P.O. Box 2097, 540 Brook Lane, Warminster, PA 18974 (SAN 294-9202) Tel 215-674-3030.

Daughter Culture Pubns., *(Daughter Cult; 0-935281),* 3109 Scotts Valley Dr., Suite 168, Scotts Valley, CA 95066 (SAN 695-7447) Tel 408-438-7412.

Daughters of Hawaii, *(Daughters of HI; 0-938851),* 2913 Pali Hwy., Honolulu, HI 96817 (SAN 662-5789) Tel 808-598-6291.

†**Daughters of St. Paul,** *(Dghtrs St Paul; 0-8198),* 50 St. Paul's Ave., Boston, MA 02130 (SAN 203-8900) Tel 617-522-8911; *CIP.*

Daughters of Utah Pioneers, *(Daughters Utah),* 300 N. Main St., Salt Lake City, UT 84103 (SAN 240-8465) Tel 801-533-5759.

D'Aurora Press, *(DAurora Pr; 0-933022),* 190 Cascade Dr., Mill Valley, CA 94941 (SAN 212-4122).

Dav-A-Lyn Enterprise, *(Dav-A-Lynn Ent; 0-9614798),* P.O. Box 88682, Seattle, WA 98188 (SAN 692-6681) Tel 206-433-2747.

Davar Publishing Co., Inc., *(Davar Pub; 0-937831),* P.O. Box 854, Pacific Palisades, CA 90272 (SAN 659-4409) Tel 213-459-8600; 16015 Northfield, Pacific Palisades, CA 90272 (SAN 659-4417).

Davenport, Donald Jordan, *(D J Davenport; 0-9606640),* 17700 Northland Pk. Ct., Southfield, MI 48075 (SAN 219-7278) Tel 313-443-9000.

Davenport, May, Pubs., *(Davenport; 0-9603118; 0-943864),* 26313 Purissima Rd., Los Altos Hills, CA 94022 (SAN 212-467X) Tel 415-948-6499.

Davenport Publishing, *(Davenport Pub; 0-9616110),* 1302 Beachmont, Ventura, CA 93001 (SAN 696-9224) Tel 805-644-7054.

Davey, Daniel, & Co., Inc., Pubs., *(Davey; 0-8088),* P.O. Box 6088, Hartford, CT 06106 (SAN 203-882X) Tel 203-525-4334.

Davicone Inc., *(Davicone Inc; 0-937089),* 1075 Lullwater Rd., NE, Atlanta, GA 30307 (SAN 658-5159) Tel 404-377-0208.

David, Deborah, Press, *(D David Pr; 0-930890),* 11 Arthur's Round Table, Wynnewood, PA 19096 (SAN 211-2914) Tel 215-649-0998.

David, E., & Assocs., *(E David Assoc; 0-928107),* 22 Russett Ln., Storrs, CT 06268 (SAN 657-4394) Tel 203-429-1785.

David & Charles, Inc., *(David & Charles; 0-7153),* P.O. Box 257, North Pomfret, VT 05053 (SAN 213-8859) Tel 802-457-1911; Toll free: 800-423-4525. *Imprints:* Weedy Rail Books (Weddy Rail Bks).

David Publishing, *(David Pub MN; 0-9616767),* Box 7, St. Bonifacius, MN 55375-0007 (SAN 661-0935); 6425 County Rd. 30, St. Bonifacius, MN 55375 (SAN 661-0943) Tel 612-472-7126.

Davida Pubns., *(Davida Pubns; 0-9603022),* 32 Longate Rd., Clinton, CT 06413 (SAN 212-1565) Tel 203-669-0656; Dist. by: Devorss & Co., P.O. Box 550, 1046 Princeton Dr., Marina del Rey, CA 90294 (SAN 282-6151).

†**Davidson, Harlan, Inc.,** *(Harlan Davidson; 0-88295),* 3110 N. Arlington Heights Rd., Arlington Heights, IL 60004 (SAN 201-2375) Tel 312-253-9720; *CIP.*

Davidson, Mary Frances, *(M F Davidson; 0-9607792),* Rte. 3, Gatlinburg, TN 37738 (SAN 203-8668) Tel 615-436-5429.

Davio, Dorothy F., *(D F Davio; 0-9615718),* Box 34, Barton, VT 05822 (SAN 696-3137) Tel 802-525-3430.

Davis, Beau Robert, Professional Enterprises, Inc., *(Beau R D Prof Ent; 0-9603644),* 4535 W. Sahara Ave. Suite 105, Las Vegas, NV 89102 (SAN 221-6949) Tel 818-998-3611.

Davis, Elsie Spry, *(E S Davis; 0-9605618),* 710 Second St., Coronado, CA 92118 (SAN 216-129X).

†**Davis, F. A., Co.,** *(Davis Co; 0-8036),* 1915 Arch St., Philadelphia, PA 19103 (SAN 295-3250) Tel 215-568-2270; Toll free: 800-523-4049; Dist. by: Brown & Connolly, Inc., 2 Keith Way, Hingham, MA 02043 (SAN 169-3298) Tel 617-749-8590; Dist. by: Login Brothers Bk. Co., Inc., 1450 W. Randolph St., Chicago, IL 60607 (SAN 169-183X) Tel 312-733-6424; Dist. by: J. A. Majors Co., P.O. Box 819074, Dallas, TX 75061-9074 (SAN 169-8117) Tel 214-247-2929; Dist. by: Login Brothers NJ, 135 New Dutch Ln., Box 2700, Fairfield, NJ 07006 (SAN 157-1427); Dist. by: Rittenhouse Bk. Distributors, Inc., 511 Feheley Dr., King of Prussia, PA 19406 (SAN 213-4454); Dist. by: J. A. Majors Co., 3770A Zip Industrial Blvd., Atlanta, GA 00354 (SAN 169-1406) Tel 404-786-4956; Dist. by: Login Brothers East, 1550 Enterprise Rd., Twinsburg, OH 44087 (SAN 156-4439); Dist. by: J. A. Majors Co., 1806 Southgate, Houston, TX 77030 (SAN 169-8281) Tel 713-526-5757; Dist. by: J. A. Majors Co., 3909 Bienville, New Orleans, LA 70119 (SAN 169-2984) Tel 504-486-5956; *CIP.*

Davis, Grant, Co., Inc., *(G Davis; 0-934786),* P.O. Box 692, Lewisville, TX 75067 (SAN 213-2141).

Davis, H.B., Co., *(H B Davis; 0-942016),* 480 Canal Street, New York, NY 10013 (SAN 239-5223).

Davis, L., Pr., Inc., *(Davis Pr; 0-9607902; 0-933485),* 1125 Oxford Pl., Schenectady, NY 12308 (SAN 238-1540) Tel 518-374-5636.

Davis, Leonard, Institute of Health Economics, Div. of University of Pennsylvania, *(L Davis Inst; 0-937695),* 3641 Locust Walk, Philadelphia, PA 19104-6218 (SAN 659-3410) Tel 215-898-4750.

Davis, O. K., *(O K Davis; 0-9610262),* P.O. Box 1427, Ruston, LA 71270 (SAN 264-0015) Tel 318-255-3990.

Davis, Robert E., *(R E Davis; 0-9614255),* 21 John Maddox Dr., Rome, GA 30161 (SAN 686-6980) Tel 404-234-0718.

Davis, Steve, Publishing, *(S Davis Pub; 0-911061),* P.O. Box 190831, Dallas, TX 75219 (SAN 262-8422) Tel 214-821-8821.

Davis & Assocs., Inc., *(Davis Assocs; 0-923643),* 1655 Peachtree St., NE, No. 1104, Atlanta, GA 30309 (SAN 654-8644) Tel 404-875-0793.

Davis & Co., *(Davis & Co; 0-9614214),* P.O. Box 26318, Colorado Springs, CO 80936-6318 (SAN 687-0899) Tel 303-574-1874.

Davis Assocs., *(Davis Ascs PA; 0-931431),* 1143 Wright Dr., Huntingdon Valley, PA 19006 (SAN 683-1729) Tel 215-947-1752.

Davis Mathematics Pr., *(Davis Math Pr; 0-916327),* P.O. Box 1212, Davis, CA 95617-1212 (SAN 295-7310) Tel 916-753-3587.

Davis Publications *See* **Sterling Publishing Co., Inc.**

Davis Pubns., Inc., *(Davis Mass; 0-87192),* 50 Portland St., Worcester, MA 01608 (SAN 201-3002) Tel 617-754-7201; Dist. by: Sterling Publishing Co., Inc., 2 Park Ave., New York, NY 10016 (SAN 211-6324) Tel 212-532-7160.

Davis Pubns., Inc., *(Davis Pubns; 0-89559),* 380 Lexington Ave., New York, NY 10017 (SAN 290-6848) Tel 212-557-9100; Dist. by: Doubleday & Co., 501 Franklin Ave., Garden City, NY 11530 (SAN 281-6075).

Davis Publishing Co., Inc., *(Davis Pub Co; 0-89368),* 250 Potrero St., Santa Cruz, CA 95060 (SAN 201-8152) Tel 408-423-4968; Orders to: P.O. Box 841, Santa Cruz, CA 95061 (SAN 201-8160).

Davis Publishing Co., *(Davis Pub; 0-9615877),* 4112 Hart Rd., Richfield, OH 44286 (SAN 697-0591) Tel 216-659-4449.

Davison, Marguerite P., *(M P Davison; 0-9603172),* P.O. Box 263, Swarthmore, PA 19081 (SAN 212-498X) Tel 215-876-4191.

Davison Publishing Co., Inc., *(Davison; 0-87515),* P.O. Box 477, Ridgewood, NJ 07451 (SAN 204-2339) Tel 201-445-3135.

Davus Publishing, *(Davus Pub; 0-915317),* P.O. Box 280, Madison Square Sta., New York, NY 10159 (SAN 289-9787); 141 E. 26th St., New York, NY 10010 (SAN 650-9975) Tel 212-685-0957.

Dawn Heron Pr., Subs. of Dashiell Hammett Tour, *(Dawn Heron; 0-939790),* 537 Jones St., No. 9207, San Francisco, CA 94102 (SAN 216-8871) Tel 415-564-7021.

†**Dawn Horse Pr.,** Div. of Advaitayana Buddhist Communion, *(Dawn Horse Pr; 0-913922; 0-918801),* 750 Adrian Way, San Rafael, CA 94903 (SAN 201-3029) Tel 415-492-0922; Toll free: 800-521-4785; *CIP.*

Dawn Ministries, *(Dawn Ministries; 0-9605892),* 2789 Mendel Way, Sacramento, CA 95833 (SAN 216-5937).

†**Dawn Press,** *(Dawn Pr; 0-933704),* 1011 Jeffrey Rd., Wilmington, DE 19810 (SAN 221-2269); *CIP.*

Dawn Valley, Pr., *(Dawn Valley; 0-936014),* P.O. Box 58, New Wilmington, PA 16142 (SAN 208-9734) Tel 412-946-2948.

Dawnfire Books, *(Dawnfire; 0-942058),* 2218 24th St., No. B, Santa Monica, CA 90405 (SAN 239-4332) Tel 213-450-2911; Dist. by: Bookpeople, 2929 Fifth St., Berkeley, CA 94710 Tel 415-549-3030.

†**Dawnwood Pr.,** *(Dawnwood Pr; 0-911025),* c/o Sterling Publishing Co., 2 Park Ave., Suite 2650, New York, NY 10016 (SAN 211-6324) Tel 212-532-7160; *CIP.*

Dawson, J. B., *(J B Dawson CA; 0-9615084),* P.O. Box 50457, Phoenix, AZ 85076 (SAN 694-4337) Tel 602-893-0108.

Dawson's Bk. Shop, *(Dawsons; 0-87093),* 535 N. Larchmont Blvd., Los Angeles, CA 90004 (SAN 201-3045) Tel 213-469-2186.

Day Book Company, *(Day Bk Co; 0-9611310),* 3641 N Maple Ave., Fresno, CA 93726 (SAN 277-6723).

Day Star, *(Day Star NV; 0-939614),* P.O. Box 14052, Las Vegas, NV 89114 (SAN 216-6208) Tel 702-361-3022.

Day Star Pubs., *(Day Star; 0-932994),* 1550 View Dr., San Leandro, CA 94577 (SAN 212-4130).

Daybreak Press, *(Daybreak Pr; 0-940916),* 646 Dale Court S., St. Paul, MN 55112 (SAN 217-2372).

Daymaker Publishing Co., *(Daymaker Pub; 0-938601),* 1512 Berkeley St., Suite B, Santa Monica, CA 90404 (SAN 661-1397) Tel 213-453-2457.

Daystar Communications, *(Daystar Comm; 0-930037),* P.O. Box 748, Millville, NJ 08332 (SAN 669-7798) Tel 609-327-1231.

Daystar Press *See* **White, Laurie A., & Steven L. Spencer**

Daystar Publishing Co., *(Daystar Co Carson; 0-933650),* 21405 Lostime Ave., Carson, CA 90745 (SAN 221-2277).

Daystar Publishing Co., *(Daystar Pub Co; 0-938962),* P.O. Box 707, Angwin, CA 94508 (SAN 281-5974) Tel 707-965-2085; Dist. by: Bookpeople, 2929 Fifth St., Berkeley, CA 94710 (SAN 168-9517) Tel 415-549-3030; Dist. by: Publisher's Group West, 5855 Beaudry St., Emeryville, CA 94608 (SAN 202-8522) Tel 415-658-3453.

Dayton Art Institute, *(Dayton Art; 0-937809),* P.O. Box 941, Dayton, OH 45401 (SAN 278-6206) Tel 513-223-5277.

Dayton Hudson Foundation, *(Dayton Hudson; 0-9607450),* 777 Nicollet Mall, Minneapolis, MN 55402 (SAN 238-2326) Tel 612-370-6555.

Dayton Laboratories, *(Dayton Labs; 0-916750),* 3235 Dayton Ave., Lorain, OH 44055 (SAN 208-1946) Tel 216-246-1397.

Dayton Newspapers, Inc., Div. of Cox Newspapers, Inc., *(Dayton Newspapers; 0-938492; 0-9616347),* Fourth & Ludlow Sts., Dayton, OH 45401 (SAN 215-8809) Tel 513-225-2184.

Dayton Philharmonic Women's Assn., *(Dayton Phil; 0-9614169),* 125 E. First St., Dayton, OH 45402 (SAN 686-6506) Tel 513-224-3521.

Dazet Creations, Inc., *(Dazet Creations; 0-936209),* 15775 N. Hillcrest, Suite 508, Dallas, TX 75248 (SAN 697-1083) Tel 214-380-1987.

D'Carlin Publishing, *(DCarlin Pub; 0-939342),* 2729 Carlsbad Blvd., Carlsbad, CA 92008 (SAN 216-2369) Tel 619-729-7758.

De Bussy, Carvel, *(C de Bussy; 0-9602260),* 3901 Connecticut Ave., NW, Suite 208, Washington, DC 20008 (SAN 212-6516).

De Graff, John, ,Inc., *(J De Graff; 0-8286),* Clinton Corners, NY 12514 (SAN 201-3061) Tel 914-266-5800; Dist. by: International Marine Publishing Co., 21 Elm St., Camden, ME 04843 (SAN 202-716X) Tel 207-236-4342.

†**De Gruyter, Walter, Inc.,** Div. of Walter de Gruyter & Co., *(De Gruyter; 3-11; 0-89925),* 200 Saw Mill River Rd., Hawthorne, NY 10532 (SAN 201-3088) Tel 914-747-0110; *CIP.*

De Gruyter/Aldine, Div. of Walter De Gruyter, Inc., *(De Gruyter Aldine; 0-202),* 200 Saw Mill River Rd., Hawthorne, NY 10532 (SAN 212-4726) Tel 914-747-0110.

De Karsan Publishing Co., *(De Karsan; 0-9602308),* P.O. Box 28404, San Diego, CA 92128 (SAN 210-8941) Tel 619-280-3334.

De Leuw, Cather & Co., *(DeLeuw-Cather Co),* 600 Fifth Street, NW, Washington, DC 20001 (SAN 283-1813).

De Mortmain Bks., *(De Mortmain; 0-932501),* 2259 University Ave., Sacramento, CA 95825 (SAN 687-391X) Tel 916-481-5614.

De Novo Pr., *(De Novo Pr; 0-912357),* Box 5106, Berkeley, CA 94705 (SAN 265-1173) Tel 415-849-9382; Dist. by: Bookpeople, 2929 Fifth St., Berkeley, CA 94710 (SAN 168-9517) Tel 415-549-3030.

De Serio, Louis F., *(De Serio; 0-9603568),* P.O. Box 1163, Sedona, AZ 86336 (SAN 213-6163) Tel 602-282-2634.

De Vorss & Co., *(De Vorss; 0-87516),* P.O. Box 550, Marina del Rey, CA 90292 (SAN 168-9886) Tel 213-870-7478.

De Young Pr., *(De Young Pr; 0-936128),* P.O. Box 7252, Spencer, IA 51301-7252 (SAN 212-7652).

Deacon Press, The, *(Deacon Pr; 0-940684),* 1244 Brian St., Placentia, CA 92670 (SAN 218-5415) Tel 714-524-0939.

Dead Angel, *(Dead Angel; 0-911757),* 1206 Lyndale Dr. SE, Atlanta, GA 30316 (SAN 264-0031).

Dead Reckoning Pr., *(Dead Reckoning; 0-935733),* P.O. Box 31, Cambria, CA 93428 (SAN 696-3153) Tel 805-927-3054; 2677 Tipton St., Cambria, CA 93428 (SAN 696-5296).

Deal, S., Associates, *(S Deal Assoc; 0-930006),* 1629 Guizot St., San Diego, CA 92107 (SAN 210-4105) Tel 619-226-1731.

Dealer's Choice Bks., Inc., *(Dealers Choice),* 6402 N. Nebraska Ave., Tampa, FL 33604 (SAN 687-6390); Toll free: 800-238-8288.

Dean, Wayne, Editions, *(W Dean Editions; 0-9616161),* 3217 Petunia Ct., San Diego, CA 92117 (SAN 699-8364) Tel 619-272-6075.

Dean Pubns., *(Dean Pubns; 0-939052),* 2204 El Canto Circle, Rancho Cordova, CA 95670 (SAN 217-0744).

Deanne II Inc., *(Deanne Inc; 0-9611584),* Rte. 4, P.O. Box 82A, No. 3 Quil Run, Carthage, MO 64836 (SAN 285-6654) Tel 417-358-7814; Dist. by: Dot Gibson Pubns., 161 Knight Ave., Cir., Waycross, GA 31501 (SAN 200-4143) Tel 912-285-2848; Dist. by: Southwest Cookbook Distributors, Inc., 1901 South Shore Dr., Bonham, TX 75418 (SAN 200-4925) Tel 214-583-8898.

Dear Kids Pubs., *(Dear Kids),* Currierville Rd., Newton, NH 03858 (SAN 206-4677) Tel 603-382-7503.

Dearen, Leah, Publishing, *(Dearen Pub; 0-938575),* P.O. Box 162, Alpine, CA 92001 (SAN 661-1036); 3330 Zumbrota Rd., Alpine, CA 92001 (SAN 661-1044) Tel 619-445-9611.

Dearhorse Pubns., *(Dearhorse Pubns; 0-9614170),* P.O. Box 15121, Portland, OR 97215 (SAN 686-6522) Tel 503-233-1206.

Death Valley 49ers, Inc., *(Death Valley Fortyniners; 0-936932),* c/o Chalfant Press, Box 787, Bishop, CA 93514 (SAN 203-6347) Tel 619-873-3535.

Deaver Corp., *(Deaver Corp; 0-932665),* 155 W. 68th St., Suite 630, New York, NY 10023 (SAN 687-7923) Tel 212-799-9835.

Names

Debron Enterprises, *(Debron; 0-911347),* P.O. Box 8242, Witchita, KS 67208 (SAN 269-6118) Tel 316-262-0695.

Debton Pubns., Inc., *(Debton Pubns; 0-916321),* 1731 Vulcan St., El Cajon, CA 92021 (SAN 295-737X).

Decade Media Bks. Communications, Inc., *(Decade Media; 0-910365),* 1133 Broadway, Suite 707, New York, NY 10010 (SAN 263-2152) Tel 212-929-8044.

†**Decatur House Press, Ltd,** *(Decatur Hse; 0-916276),* 2122 Decatur Place, NW, Washington, DC 20008 (SAN 208-1539) Tel 202-387-3913; *CIP.*

Decatur Junior Service League, Inc., *(Decatur Jr Serv; 0-9614406),* P.O. Box 486, Decatur, AL 35602 (SAN 688-6221) Tel 205-350-1917.

December Pr., Inc., *(December Pr; 0-913204),* 3093 Dato,, Highland Park, IL 60035 (SAN 203-8854) Tel 312-432-6804; Dist. by: Chicago Review Pr., 814 N. Franklin St.., Chicago, IL 60610 (SAN 213-5744) Tel 312-337-0747.

December Rose Publishing House, Div. of Retirement Housing Foundation, *(December Rose; 0-9612730),* 255 S. Hill St., Suite 407, Los Angeles, CA 90012 (SAN 289-9191) Tel 213-617-7002.

Deciduous, *(Deciduous; 0-9601640),* 1456 W. 54th St., Cleveland, OH 44102 (SAN 211-4143) Tel 216-651-7725.

Decision-Making Ctr., *(Decision-Making; 0-9616604),* 761 Wells Rd., Wethersfield, CT 06109 (SAN 661-1052) Tel 203-529-8747.

Decker, B. C., Inc., *(B C Decker; 0-941158; 1-55664),* P.O. Box 30246, Philadelphia, PA 19103 (SAN 663-1584); 1919 Chestnut St., Philadelphia, PA 19103 (SAN 663-1592) Tel 215-963-9456. Canadian office: 3228 S. Service Rd., Burlington, ON L7N 3H8. Tel: 416-639-6215.

†**Decker Pr., Inc.,** *(Decker Pr Inc; 0-933724),* P.O. Box 3838, Grand Junction, CO 81502 (SAN 216-115X) Tel 303-241-6193; Toll free: 800-525-3454; *CIP.*

Deco-Press Publishing Co., *(Deco-Pr Pub; 0-937016),* 500 E. 84th Ave., Box 29489, Denver, CO 80229 (SAN 220-2441).

Decorative Design Studio, Inc., *(Deco Design Studio; 0-941284),* Rte. 3, Box 155, Smithsburg, MD 21783 (SAN 238-9320) Tel 301-824-7592.

Dectur Corp., *(Dectur Corp; 0-9602228),* 2878 Forest St., Denver, CO 80207 (SAN 212-4149).

Dedeaux Publishing, Inc., *(Dedeaux; 0-930987),* 907 Rve Dauphine St., New Orleans, LA 70116 (SAN 678-8882) Tel 504-529-3406.

Dee Publishing Co., *(Dee Pub Co; 0-934476),* 864 S. Commercial, Salem, OR 97302 (SAN 206-4685) Tel 503-363-2410.

DEEJ Publishing Co., *(Deej Pub; 0-9608832),* 8200 Rosewood Lane, Prairie Village, KS 66208 (SAN 241-0133) Tel 816-474-8120.

Deep River Press, *(Deep River Pr; 0-935232),* 51141/2 E. Second St., P.O. Box 3444, Long Beach, CA 90803 (SAN 213-8425) Tel 213-433-8738.

Deep Sea Pr., *(Deep Sea Pr; 0-939591),* Collington Rd., P.O. Box 48, Kitty Hawk, NC 27949 (SAN 663-6187) Tel 919-441-4637.

†**Deepak, A., Publishing,** Div. of Science & Technology Corp., *(A Deepak Pub; 0-937194),* P.O. Box 7390, 101 Research Dr., Hampton, VA 23666 (SAN 240-1606) Tel 804-865-0332; *CIP.*

Deepstar Pubns., *(Deepstar Pubns; 0-918888),* P.O. Box 1266, Crestine, CA 92325 (SAN 210-4121) Tel 714-338-4440.

Deer Creek Pr., Div. of California School of Design, *(Deer Creek Pr; 0-913596),* 516 Olive St, Sausalito, CA 94965 (SAN 669-6732) Tel 415-332-1990.

Deer Crossing Camp Pr., *(Deer Xing Camp; 0-938525),* 940 Providence Ct., Cupertino, CA 95014 (SAN 661-146X) Tel 408-996-9448.

Deer Crossing Press, *(Deer Crossing; 0-932792),* Rte. 1, Box 18, Paducah, KY 42001 (SAN 212-1867).

Deercreek Pubs., *(Deercreek Pubs; 0-9616768),* 197 Road 154, Carpenter, WY 82054 (SAN 661-1060) Tel 307-549-2296.

Deere & Co. Technical Services, *(Deere & Co; 0-86691),* Dept. 333, John Deere Rd., Moline, IL 61265 (SAN 216-3659) Tel 309-752-6941; Orders to: 1400 Third Ave., Moline, IL 61265 (SAN 661-9894) Tel 309-757-5903.

Deermouse Press, *(Deermouse; 0-9600596),* 4 Berkeley Place, Cambridge, MA 02138 (SAN 201-8039) Tel 617-876-0836.

Dee's Delights, Inc., Div. of Hobby Bk. Distributors, *(Dees Delights; 0-938685),* 3150 State Line Rd., North Bend, OH 45052 (SAN 661-3969) Tel 513-353-3390.

Defenders Pubns., *(Defenders Pubns; 0-910643),* P.O. Box 11134, Las Vegas, NV 89111 (SAN 269-6207) Tel 702-451-5773.

Defense & Foreign Affairs Publications Ltd., *(Defense & Foreign Aff; 0-9605932),* 1777 T St. NW, Washington, DC 20009 (SAN 216-3551) Tel 202-223-4934.

Defensive Tips, *(Defensive Tips; 0-933531),* P.O. Box 6033, Concord, CA 94524-1033 (SAN 679-1700) Tel 415-689-0159.

Definition Pr., Subs. of Eli Siegel-Martha Baird Foundation, *(Definition; 0-910492),* 141 Greene St., New York, NY 10012 (SAN 201-310X) Tel 212-777-4490.

Defoggi, Ernest, *(E Defoggi; 0-9602372),* Rt. 1, Box 514-A, Newport, NC 28570 (SAN 211-3120) Tel 919-726-7047.

Dehack Effort, *(Dehack),* P.O. Box 922, Campbell, CA 95009 (SAN 208-1512) Tel 408-265-8799.

Deinotation-7 Press, *(Deinotation Seven; 0-9602044),* P.O. Box 204, Susquehanna, PA 18847-0204 (SAN 223-4661); 220 Exchange Pl., Susquehanna, PA 18847 (SAN 658-0424); Orders to: Brodart Books, 500 Arch St., Williamsport, PA 17705 (SAN 669-0637).

Dekalb Historical Society, *(Dekalb; 0-9615459),* Old Courthouse on the Square, Decatur, GA 30030 (SAN 695-734X) Tel 404-373-1088.

†**Dekker, Marcel, Inc.,** *(Dekker; 0-8247),* 270 Madison Ave., New York, NY 10016 (SAN 201-3118) Tel 212-696-9000; Toll free: 800-228-1160; *CIP.*

Del Casa Educational Productions, *(Del Casa Educ; 0-910183),* 175 Fifth Ave., New York, NY 10010 (SAN 238-132X) Tel 212-677-2200.

Del Mar Press, *(Del Mar Pr; 0-9611124),* P.O. Box 2508, Del Mar, CA 92014 (SAN 283-2682) Tel 619-481-1808.

Del Mar Publishing, *(Delmar Pub; 0-935361),* 389 Rainer Dr., Salinas, CA 93906 (SAN 696-320X) Tel 408-449-3260.

Del Rey Bks. *See* **Ballantine Bks., Inc.**

Del Sol Editores, *(Del Sol Editores; 0-9616267),* 53 Stephen Hopkins Ct., University Heights, Providence, RI 02904 (SAN 658-3547) Tel 401-272-3566.

Delacorte Pr., *(Delacorte; 0-87459),* 1 Dag Hammarskjold Plaza, New York, NY 10017 (SAN 201-0097) Tel 212-605-3000; Toll free: 800-221-4676. *Imprints:* Friede, Eleanor (E Friede); Lawrence, Seymour (Sey Lawr.)

Delafield Press, *(Delafield Pr; 0-916872),* P.O. Box 335, Suttons Bay, MI 49682 (SAN 208-3817) Tel 616-271-3826.

Delaney, John, Pubns., *(J Delaney Pubns; 0-9608514),* P.O. Box 404, Bogota, NJ 07603-0404 (SAN 240-625X) Tel 201-836-2543.

Delapeake Publishing, Co., *(Delapeake Pub Co; 0-911293),* P.O. Box 1148, Wilmington, DE 19899 (SAN 269-6274) Tel 302-571-6979.

Delapress, Inc., *(Delapr Inc; 0-87571),* Rte. 1, Hwy. 304, Delaplaine, AR 72425 (SAN 692-896X) Tel 501-249-3392.

deLatour, Ruggles, Inc., *(R deLatour; 0-938291),* 176 E. 77th St., New York, NY 10021 (SAN 659-6754) Tel 212-861-7589.

Delaware Valley Poets, *(Del Valley; 0-937158),* P.O. Box 6203, Lawrenceville, NJ 08648 (SAN 215-1391) Tel 609-737-0222.

Delbridge Publishing, *(Delbridge Pub Co; 0-88232),* P.O. Box 2989, Stanford, CA 94305-0028 (SAN 207-2122) Tel 408-446-3131.

Delcon Corp., *(Delcon; 0-934856),* P.O. Box 323, Harlan St. Rte., Eddyville, OR 97343 (SAN 213-4853).

DeLethein Pr., The, *(DeLethein Pr),* Dept. BP, 4605 Holborn Ave., Annandale, VA 22003 (SAN 287-2846).

Delford Pr., *(Delford Pr; 0-931726),* P.O. Box 27, Oradell, NJ 07649 (SAN 209-7311) Tel 201-262-0647.

Delgren Bks., *(Delgren Bks; 0-943472),* 3000 N. Romero Rd., No. A29, Tuscon, AZ 85705 (SAN 240-4702) Tel 602-887-8730; Toll free: 800-528-4923.

Delilah Bks., *(Delilah Bks; 0-933328),* 118 E. 25th St., New York, NY 10010 (SAN 238-9339); Toll free: 800-847-5515; Dist. by: Putnam Publishing Group, 200 Madison Ave., New York, NY 10016 (SAN 202-5531).

Delilah Communications, Ltd., *(Delilah Comm; 0-933348; 0-88715),* 118 E. 25th St., New York, NY 10010 (SAN 212-4157) Tel 212-477-2100; Dist. by: Dell Publishing Co., 1 Dag Hammarskjold Plaza, 245 E. 47th St., New York, NY 10017 (SAN 201-0097).

Dell Publishing Co., Inc., Subs. of Doubleday & Co., Inc., *(Dell; 0-440),* 1 Dag Hammarskjold Plaza, 245 E. 47th St., New York, NY 10017 (SAN 201-0097) Tel 212-605-3000; Toll free: 800-932-0070. *Imprints:* Banbury (Banbury); Bryans (Bryans); Chapel Books (Chapel); Dell Trade Paperbacks (Dell Trade Pbks); Delta Books (Delta); Emerald (Emerald); Laurel Editions (LE); Laurel Leaf Library (LFL); Mayflower Books (MB); Standish (Standish); Yearling Books (YB).

Dell Trade Paperbacks *See* **Dell Publishing Co., Inc.**

†**Dellen Publishing Co.,** Subs. of Macmillan Publishing Co., *(Dellen Pub; 0-89517),* 3600 Pruneridge Ave., Santa Clara, CA 95051 (SAN 219-0834) Tel 408-246-4215; *CIP.*

Delmar Co., The, Subs. of Republic Corp., *(Delmar Co; 0-912081),* P.O. Box 220025, 9601 Monroe Rd., Charlotte, NC 28222 (SAN 264-732X) Tel 704-847-9801; Toll free: 800-438-1504.

†**Delmar Pubs., Inc.,** Div. of International Thomson Educational Pub., Inc., *(Delmar; 0-8273),* 2 Computer Dr. W., Albany, NY 12212 (SAN 206-7544) Tel 518-459-1150; Toll free: 800-833-3350; P.O. Box 15-015, Albany, NY 12212 (SAN 658-0440); *CIP.*

DeLong & Assocs., *(DeLong & Assocs; 0-9603414),* P.O. Box 1732, Annapolis, MD 21404 (SAN 213-215X) Tel 301-263-5592.

deLorenzo & diSalvo Inc., *(deLorenzo diSalvo; 0-933709),* 2130 Jackson St., No. 306, San Francisco, CA 94115 (SAN 692-5219) Tel 415-346-2519.

Delorme Publishing Co., *(DeLorme Pub; 0-89933),* P.O. Box 298, Freeport, ME 04032 (SAN 220-1208) Tel 207-865-4171; Toll free: 800-227-1656.

Delphi Pr., *(Delphi Pr WA; 0-939202),* 1750 K St., NW, Suite 1110, Washington, DC 20006 (SAN 220-1674) Tel 202-466-7951.

Delphi Research Center, *(Delphi Res; 0-916987),* P.O. Box 428, Lincoln, MA 01773 (SAN 655-6248) Tel 617-259-0527.

Delta Bks. *See* **Dell Publishing Co., Inc.**

Delta Group Pr., *(Delta G Pr; 0-913787),* 245 Ponderosa Way, Evergreen, CO 80439 (SAN 286-0902) Tel 303-674-9850.

Delta Pi Epsilon, Inc., *(Delta Pi Epsilon; 0-9603064),* National Office, Gustavus Adolphus College, St. Peter, MN 56082 (SAN 223-565X) Tel 507-931-4184.

Delta Queen Steamboat Co., The, *(Delta Queen; 0-937331),* 30 Robin St. Wharf, New Orleans, LA 70130 (SAN 658-8085) Tel 504-586-0631.

Delta Sales, *(Delta Sales; 0-931626),* 399 Southgate Ave., Daly City, CA 94015 (SAN 212-2510).

Delta Systems Co., Inc., *(Delta Systems; 0-937354),* 570 Rock Road Dr., Unit H, Dundee, IL 60118 (SAN 220-0457) Tel 312-551-9595.

Deltiologists of America, *(Deltiologists Am; 0-913782),* 10 Felton Ave., Ridley Park, PA 19078 (SAN 225-607X) Tel 215-521-1092.

Demaris Studio Press, Inc., *(Demarais Studio; 0-9607462),* 64 Lawn Park Ave., Trenton, NJ 08648 (SAN 238-6224) Tel 609-833-1737.

†**Dembner Bks.,** Div. of Red Dembner
Enterprises Corp., *(Dembner Bks; 0-934878)*,
80 Eighth Ave., New York, NY 10011
(SAN 211-5573) Tel 212-924-2525; Dist.
by: W. W. Norton & Co., Inc., 500 Fifth
Ave., New York, NY 10110
(SAN 202-5795) Tel 212-354-5500; Toll
free: 800-233-4830; *CIP.*

Demecon Pubs., *(Demecon; 0-943700)*, P.O.
Box 13759, Reading, PA 19612
(SAN 212-8314) Tel 215-929-8336.

Demeter Pr. *See* **Times Bks.**

DemoNet, Inc., *(DemoNet; 0-933337)*, 7310 C
Adams, Paramount, CA 90723
(SAN 107-9476) Tel 213-408-1966.

DeMos Music Pubns., *(DeMos Music;
0-940026)*, P.O. Box 14125, Houston, TX
77221 (SAN 217-0698) Tel 713-433-5235.

Demou, Morris, & Assocs., *(M Demou & Assocs;
0-9604794)*, 2013 Big Oak Dr., Burnsville,
MN 55337 (SAN 209-1798)
Tel 612-890-3579.

Den Rey Pubns., *(Den Rey Pubns; 0-9617113)*,
Rte 3, St. Agusta, St. Cloud, MN 56301
(SAN 662-8036) Tel 612-255-0480.

Denali Pr., The, *(Denali Press; 0-938737)*, P.O.
Box 1535, Juneau, AK 99802
(SAN 661-8278); 1950 Glacier Hwy.,
Juneau, AK 99802 (SAN 661-8286)
Tel 907-586-6014.

Denco International, *(Denco Intl)*, P.O. Box
1052, Deerfield Beach, FL 33441-1052
(SAN 213-6171) Tel 305-822-6666.

Dendle & Schraibman, *(Dendle & Schraibman;
0-9608168)*, 272 S. Hanover, Lexington, KY
40502 (SAN 240-4729).

Dendrobium Bks., *(Dendrobium Bks; 0-936831)*,
387 Ivy St., San Francisco, CA 94102
(SAN 699-8542) Tel 415-558-8444.

Denhamwood, Inc., *(Den Hamwood; 0-931544)*,
16944 Ventura Blvd., Encino, CA 91316
(SAN 223-3665) Tel 818-783-2758.

Denison, T. S., & Co., Inc., *(Denison; 0-513)*,
9601 Newton Ave. S., Minneapolis, MN
55431 (SAN 201-3142) Tel 612-888-1460;
Toll free: 800-328-3831. Do Not Confuse
with Dennison Pubns.

Dennis-Landman Pubs., *(Dennis-Landman;
0-930422)*, 1150 18th St., Santa Monica, CA
90403 (SAN 210-9352) Tel 213-453-4643.

Dennison Pubns., *(Dennison)*, Dist. by: Borden
Publishing Co., 1855 W. Main St., Alhambra,
CA 91801 (SAN 201-419X)
Tel 818-283-5031.

Denoyer-Geppert Co., *(Denoyer; 0-87453)*, 5235
N. Ravenswood Ave., Chicago, IL 60640
(SAN 204-2215) Tel 312-561-9200; Toll
free: 800-323-1887.

Denson Pr., *(Denson Pr; 0-9614188)*, P.O. Box
29165, San Francisco, CA 94129
(SAN 686-6530); 1200 Gough St., Suite 5D,
San Francisco, CA 94109 (SAN 662-2720)
Tel 415-441-1804.

Dental Folklore, Bks. of K.C., Div. of Dental
Folklore, *(Dental Folk; 0-930989)*, 7612 W.
95th St., Apt. A, Overland Park, KS 66212
(SAN 678-8890) Tel 913-341-0855; Orders
to: Dental Folklore of K.C., P.O. Box 25642,
Overland Park, KS 66225 (SAN 688-4261).

Dental-Info, *(Dental-Info; 0-9607518)*, 2509 N.
Campbell, No. 9, Tucson, AZ 85719
(SAN 239-4340).

Dentan Press, *(Dentan Pr; 0-9610080)*, 1404
Buchanan St.,P.O. Box 1745, Novato, CA
94948 (SAN 269-6738) Tel 415-897-1483.

Denti, Elisabetta, *(Elisabetta Denti; 0-9614723)*,
7545 Bradburn, No. 403, Westminister, CO
80030 (SAN 692-5235) Tel. 403-429-2213.

Denton Senior Center, *(Denton Senior Ctr;
0-9606146)*, c/o Department Of Parks And
Recreation, 215 E. Mckinney, Denton, TX
76201 (SAN 218-4745).

Denver Art Museum, *(Denver Art Mus;
0-914738)*, Pubns. Dept. 100 W. 14th Ave.
Pkwy., Denver, CO 80204 (SAN 206-3530)
Tel 303-575-5282; Dist. by: Museum Shop,
100 W. 14th Ave., Denver, CO 80204
(SAN 200-4704) Tel 303-575-2253; Dist.
by: Univ. of Washington Pr., P.O. Box
C-50096, Seattle, WA 98145
(SAN 212-2502).

Denver Ctr. for Performing Arts, The, *(Denver
Ctr Performing Arts; 0-936947)*, 1245
Champa St., Denver, CO 80204
(SAN 658-6732) Tel 303-893-4000.

Denver Museum of Natural History, *(Denver
Mus Natl Hist; 0-916278)*, City Park,
Denver, CO 80205 (SAN 204-2193)
Tel 303-370-6302.

Denver Public Library, *(Denver Public;
0-942214)*, 3840 York St., Denver, CO
80205 (SAN 208-1504) Tel 303-571-2367.

Denzer, Ron, Publishing, *(Ron Denzer;
0-9616331)*, 2540 Roy Ave., Crescent City,
CA 95531 (SAN 659-1566)
Tel 707-464-3278.

DePauw Univ., *(DePauw Univ; 0-936631)*,
Office of Pubns., Charter Hse., Greencastle,
IN 46135 (SAN 699-6973)
Tel 317-658-4629.

Depot Pr., *(Depot Pr; 0-910151)*, P.O. Box
60072, Nashville, TN 37206
(SAN 240-1401) Tel 615-226-1890.

Dept. of Professional Standards *See* **American
Bar Assn.**

Derby Publishing Co., *(Derby Pub; 0-940424)*,
P.O. Box 221474, Charlotte, NC 28222
(SAN 217-1716) Tel 704-366-7029.

Dermody, Gail R. & Eugene M., *(Dermody)*,
P.O. Box 324, Lakewood, OH 90714
(SAN 212-0860).

Derrick, Sara M., *(S M Derrick; 0-89279)*, 1323
Johnson St., Sandusky, OH 44870
(SAN 283-9881).

Derry Literary Guild, *(Derry Lit; 0-9612586)*,
P.O. Box U, Hershey, PA 17033
(SAN 289-1034); Orders to: One of A Kind,
Hershey's Chocolate World, Box 800,
Hershey, PA 17033 (SAN 692-8439)
Tel 717-534-5439.

DeRu's Fine Art Bks., Div. of DeRu's Fine Art
Gallery, *(DeRu's Fine Art; 0-939370)*, 9100
E. Artesia Blvd., Bellflower, CA 90706
(SAN 216-3667) Tel 213-920-1312.

Deseret Bk. Co., Div. of Deseret Management
Corp., *(Deseret Bk; 0-87747; 0-87579)*, P.O.
Box 30178, Salt Lake City, UT 84130
(SAN 201-3185) Tel 801-534-1515; Toll
free: 800-453-3876.

Deseret News Publishing Company, *(Deseret
News; 0-910901)*, 30 E. First S. St., P.O.
Box 1257, Salt Lake City, UT 84110
(SAN 269-6835) Tel 801-237-2137.

Desert Arthritis Medical Clinic, *(Desert
Arthritis; 0-930703)*, 13630 Mountain View
Dr., Desert Hot Springs, CA 92240
(SAN 677-1947) Tel 619-329-6422.

Desert Biological Publications, *(Desert Bio
Pubns; 0-9614003)*, P.O. Box 291, Dona
Ana, NM 88032 (SAN 686-1784).

Desert Botanical Garden, *(Desert Botanical;
0-9605656)*, 1201 N. Galvin Parkway,
Phoenix, AZ 85008 (SAN 212-9000)
Tel 602-941-1225.

Desert First Works, Inc., *(Desert First;
0-916556)*, 3870 N. Vine Ave., Tucson, AZ
85719 (SAN 208-6263) Tel 602-326-1041.

Desert Light Pub., *(Desert Light; 0-942128)*,
Lorraine Wood, Phoenix, AZ 85283
(SAN 238-6550) Tel 602-840-2217.

Desert Ministries, Inc., *(Desert Min; 0-914733)*,
P.O. Box 13235, Pittsburgh, PA 15243
(SAN 657-6036) Tel 412-854-3311.

Desert Pr., The, *(Desert Pr; 0-937764)*, Box K,
Bouse, AZ 85325 (SAN 215-6342).

Desert Tortoise Council, *(Desert Tortoise Coun)*,
5319 Cerritos Ave., Long Beach, CA 90805
(SAN 225-0039) Tel 213-422-6172.

Desert Wind Publishing Co., Div. of Signature
Galleries, *(Desert Wind Pub; 0-9615217)*,
7534 First St., Scottsdale, AZ 85251
(SAN 695-1295) Tel 602-946-0270.

Design Enterprises of San Francisco, *(Design
Ent SF; 0-932538)*, P.O. Box 14695, San
Francisco, CA 94114 (SAN 211-6359)
Tel 415-282-8813.

Design Methods Group, The, *(Design Meth;
0-910821)*, P.O. Box 5, San Luis Obispo,
CA 93406 (SAN 269-6886)
Tel 805-546-1321.

Design Publications, Inc., *(Design Pubns;
0-934341)*, 330 W. 42nd St., New York, NY
10036 (SAN 693-6113) Tel 212-695-4955.

Design Schools, The, *(Design Schools;
0-9607016)*, 101 Park Ave., New York, NY
10178 (SAN 238-969X) Tel 212-972-1505.

Designed Impacts, *(Designed Impacts;
0-930791)*, 910 Woodmont Blvd., H-6,
Nashville, TN 37204 (SAN 677-8488)
Tel 615-269-5580.

Designer Bks., *(Designer Bks; 0-9616966)*, P.O.
Box 18181, Garden City, GA 31418-0181
(SAN 661-8251); 618 Hwy. 80, Garden City,
GA 31408 (SAN 661-826X)
Tel 912-772-5183.

Designs III Pubs., *(Designs Three; 0-9609254)*,
515 W. Commonwealth Ave., Fullerton, CA
92632 (SAN 209-2336) Tel 714-871-9100.

Desperation Pr., *(Desperation Pr; 0-9609112)*,
Los Alamos Technical Equipment Co., P.O.
Box 659, Los Alamos, NM 87544
(SAN 241-4929) Tel 505-662-4815.

Desserco Publishing, *(Desserco Pub; 0-916698)*,
P.O. Box 2433, Culver City, CA 90230
(SAN 208-3914) Tel 213-827-4600.

Destiny Books *See* **Inner Traditions
International, Ltd.**

Destiny Pubs., *(Destiny; 0-910500)*, 43 Grove
St., Merrimac, MA 01860 (SAN 203-8889)
Tel 617-346-9311.

Determined Productions, Inc., *(Determined
Prods; 0-915696)*, 315 Pacific Ave. at
Battery, P.O. Box 2150, San Francisco, CA
94126 (SAN 212-7385) Tel 415-433-0660.

Detroit Black Writers' Guild, *(Detroit Black;
0-9613078)*, 5601 W. Warren, Detroit, MI
48210 (SAN 294-7315) Tel 313-898-7629.

Detroit Guide, *(Detroit Guide; 0-9600448)*,
15365 Glastonbury, Detroit, MI 48223
(SAN 218-4567).

†**Detroit Institute of Arts,** *(Detroit Inst Arts;
0-89558)*, 5200 Woodward Ave., Detroit,
MI 48202 (SAN 204-2150)
Tel 313-833-7960; *CIP.*

Detroit Symphony League, *(Detroit Symphony;
0-9611348)*, 5567 Westwood Ln.,
Birmingham, MI 48010 (SAN 282-8847)
Tel 313-851-3485.

Deus Bks. *See* **Paulist Pr.**

Deutsch, Andre, *(Andre Deutsch; 0-233)*, c/o E.
P. Dutton, 2 Park Ave., New York, NY
10016 (SAN 201-0070) Tel 212-725-1818;
Toll free: 800-526-0275 (Orders only);
Orders to: New American Library, P.O. Box
120, Bergenfield, NJ 07261
(SAN 661-9444) Tel 201-387-0600; Toll
free: 800-526-0275.

Devco Pr., *(Devco Pr; 0-9611790)*, P.O. Box
842, Golden, CO 80402 (SAN 285-2330)
Tel 303-278-0736.

Developing Markets, Inc., *(Dev Markets;
0-936949)*, 40 High St., Hamilton, OH
45011 (SAN 658-6996) Tel 513-896-1539.

Development of Research & Human Services,
Div. of Development of Research & Human
Services, *(Develop Res; 0-9609114)*, P.O.
Box 1865, Albuquerque, NM 87103
(SAN 241-4937); 5501 Kettle, NW,
Albuquerque, NM 87120 (SAN 661-9908)
Tel 505-898-3739.

Development through Self-Reliance, Inc., *(Devel
Self Rel; 0-936731)*, 9527 Good Lion Rd.,
Columbia, MD 21045 (SAN 699-9077)
Tel 301-596-0794; Box 281, Columbia, MD
21045 (SAN 699-9085) Tel 301-964-1647.

Developmental Arts, *(Developmental Arts;
0-9605372)*, P.O. Box 389, Arlington, MA
02174 (SAN 215-8566).

Developmental Reading Distributors, *(Develop
Read Dist; 0-910504)*, P.O. Box 1451, Cape
Coral, FL 33910 (SAN 201-8187).

Devida Pubns., *(Devida Pubns; 0-9607498)*, Six
Darby Rd., E. Brunswick, NJ 08816
(SAN 238-7964)P.O. Box 761, Princeton, NJ
08550 (SAN 238-7972) Tel 201-257-7257.

†**Devil Mountain Bks.,** *(Devil Mountain Bks;
0-915685)*, P.O. Box 4115, Walnut Creek,
CA 94596 (SAN 292-4803)
Tel 415-939-3415; *CIP.*

Devin-Adair Pubs., Inc., *(Devin; 0-8159)*, 6 N.
Water St., Greenwich, CT 06830
(SAN 213-750X) Tel 203-531-7755.

DeVito Enterprises, *(De Vito; 0-910506)*, 28
Dean St., Box 11, East Windsor, CT 06088
(SAN 203-8846) Tel 203-623-3152.

†**Devon Pr., Inc.,** *(Devon Pr; 0-934160)*, 820
Miramar, Berkeley, CA 94707
(SAN 212-8500) Tel 415-525-2098; *CIP.*

Devon Publishing Co., Inc., The, *(Devon Pub;
0-941402)*, 2700 Virginia Ave., NW,
Washington, DC 20037 (SAN 238-9703)
Tel 202-337-5197.

Names

Devonshire Publishing Co., The, *(Devonshire Pub; 0-918897)*, P.O. Box 7066, Chicago, IL 60680 (SAN 669-9987); 11 N. Batavia Rd., Batavia, IL 60510-1722 (SAN 662-2437) Tel 312-242-3846; Dist. by: New Leaf Distributing, 1020 White St, SW, Atlanta, GA 30310 (SAN 169-1449) Tel 404-755-2665; Dist. by: Baker & Taylor (Southeast Div.), Mt. Olive Rd., Commerce, GA 30529 (SAN 169-1503); Dist. by: Baker & Taylor (Midwest Div.), 501 Gladiola Ave, Momence, IL 60954 (SAN 169-2100).

DeVore & Sons, Inc., *(DeVore & Sons; 1-55665)*, P.O. Box 118, Wichita, KS 67201; Toll free: 800-835-1051; 1199 E. Central, Wichita, KS 67214; Dist. by: Riverside Bk. & Bible Hse., P.O. Box 370, Iowa Falls, IA 50126 (SAN 169-2666) Tel 515-648-4269; Toll free: 800-247-5111.

DeWaters, Lillian, Pubns., *(L De Waters)*, Old Greenwich, CT 06870 (SAN 203-8633) Tel 203-637-0658.

Dewey Pubns., Inc., *(Dewey Pubns; 0-9615053)*, 353 N. Edison St., Arlington, VA 22203 (SAN 694-1451) Tel 703-522-4761; Orders to: 1717 K St., NW, Suite 1102, Washington, DC 20006 (SAN 662-3328).

DeWitt & Sheppard Pubs., *(DeWitt & Sheppard; 0-932365)*, P.O. Box 5603, Tacoma, WA 98405 (SAN 687-3758) Tel 206-272-7588.

†**DeWitt Historical Society,** *(DeWitt Hist; 0-942690)*, Clinton House, 116 N. Cayuga, Ithaca, NY 14850 (SAN 264-004X); *CIP.*

Dews, Robert Porter, *(R P Dews; 0-940184)*, P.O. Box 302, Edison, GA 31746 (SAN 213-652X) Tel 912-835-2282.

Dexter, Lincoln A., *(L A Dexter; 0-9601210)*, 4002 Dexter Way, Middleburg, FL 32068-8786 (SAN 207-057X) Tel 904-282-2470.

Dharma Drum Pubns., *(Dharma Drum Pubs; 0-9609854)*, 90-31 Corona Ave., Elmhurst, NY 11373 (SAN 269-6967) Tel 718-592-6593.

†**Dharma Publishing,** *(Dharma Pub; 0-913546; 0-89800)*, 2425 Hillside Ave., Berkeley, CA 94704 (SAN 201-2723) Tel 415-548-5407; *CIP.*

Dhillon, Harinder J., *(H J Dhillon; 0-9617188)*, 2907 Bristol Channel Ct., Pasadena, MD 21122 (SAN 663-2572) Tel 301-437-7978; Dist. by: U. S. Government Printing Office, Stop SSMR, Washington, DC 20401 (SAN 206-152X) Tel 202-783-3238.

Di-Tri Bks., *(Di-Tri Bks; 0-9603374)*, 261 Waubesa St., Madison, WI 53704 (SAN 209-1712).

Dia Pr., *(Dia Press; 0-9615517)*, P.O. Box 71326, Reno, NV 89570 (SAN 696-3269) Tel 702-827-6753.

Diabetes Ctr., Inc., Div. of Park Nicollet Medical Foundation, *(Diabetes Ctr MN; 0-937721)*, 13911 Ridgedale Dr., Minnetonka, MN 55343 (SAN 659-252X) Tel 612-541-0239.

Diablo Bks., *(Diablo Bks; 0-9607520)*, 1317 Cayonwood Ct., No. 1, Walnut Creek, CA 94595 (SAN 238-6232) Tel 415-939-8644.

†**Diablo Pr.,** *(Diablo; 0-87297)*, P.O. Box 7042, Berkeley, CA 94707 (SAN 201-3223) Tel 415-524-9624; *CIP.*

Diablo Western Pr., *(Diablo West Pr; 0-932438)*, P.O. Box 5364, Walnut Creek, CA 94596 (SAN 211-9471).

Dial Bks. for Young Readers, Div. of E. P. Dutton, *(Dial Bks Young)*, 2 Park Ave., New York, NY 10016 (SAN 264-0058) Tel 212-725-1818; Toll free: 800-526-0275; Orders to: New American Library, P.O. Box 120, Bergenfield, NJ 07261 (SAN 200-6758) Tel 201-387-0600; Toll free: 800-526-0275. *Imprints:* Hillside Books (Hillside Bks).

Dial Pr. *See* Doubleday & Co., Inc.

Dialectics Workshop, *(Dialectics Workshop; 0-939275)*, 53 Hickory Hill Rd., Tappan, NY 10983 (SAN 662-8869) Tel 914-359-2283.

†**Dialog Pr.,** Subs. of Feature Group, Inc., *(Dialog; 0-9614153)*, Dept. 856, P.O. Box 59072, Chicago, IL 60659 (SAN 669-3474); *CIP.*

†**Dialogue Hse. Library,** *(Dialogue Hse; 0-87941)*, 80 E. 11th St., New York, NY 10003 (SAN 201-8195) Tel 212-673-5880; Toll free: 800-221-5844; *CIP.*

†**Dialogue Pr. of Man & World, The,** *(Dialogue Pr Man World; 0-932540)*, 246 Sparks Bldg., University Park, PA 16802 (SAN 211-9447) *CIP.*

Diamond Bks. *See* Almaas Pubns.

Diamond Communications, Inc., *(Diamond Communications; 0-912083)*, P.O. Box 88, South Bend, IN 46624 (SAN 264-7346) Tel 219-287-5008.

Diamond Farm Bk. Pubs., Div. of Diamond Enterprises, *(Diamond Farm Bk; 0-9506932)*, P.O. Box 537, Alexandria Bay, NY 13607 (SAN 674-9054) Tel 613-475-1771.

Diamond Heights Publishing Co.,, *(Diamond Heights; 0-936182)*, 25 Grand View Ave., San Francisco, CA 94114 (SAN 215-3017) Tel 415-821-9133.

Diamond Pr., *(Diamond Pr PA; 0-9615843)*, Regency Woods G-5, Doylestown, PA 18901 (SAN 696-7329) Tel 215-345-6094.

Diamond Pubs., Div. of Landmark International, *(Diamond Pubs; 0-936519)*, 23818 Twin Pines Ln., Diamond Bar, CA 91765 (SAN 216-0307) Tel 714-595-4977.

Diamondis, P. J., *(P J Diamondis; 0-9612110)*, 255 Redwood Rd., Merritt Island, FL 32952 (SAN 289-1905) Tel 305-453-6496.

Diana's Bimonthly Pr., *(Dianas Bimonthly; 0-933442)*, 23 N. Fair St., Warwick, RI 02888 (SAN 207-8147) Tel 401-274-5417.

Diane Bks. Publishing, Inc., *(Diane Bks; 0-88264)*, 2807 Oregon Ct., No. E, Torrance, CA 90503 (SAN 201-2731) Tel 213-320-2591; P.O. Box 2948, Torrance, CA 90509 (SAN 661-9916); Orders to: Diane Books, P.O. Box 2948, Torrance, CA 90509 (SAN 693-4862) Tel 213-533-5872.

Dickay Publishing, *(Dickay Pub; 0-9611068)*, P.O. Box 664, Buckeye Lake, OH 43008 (SAN 282-8596) Tel 614-928-4566.

Dickenson Pr., *(Dickenson Pr; 0-9615487)*, 1012 Chesapeake Ct., Huntington, WV 25701 (SAN 696-3307) Tel 304-525-9561.

Dickerson Pr., *(Dickerson Pr; 0-9615621)*, 2215 Lincolnwood Dr., Evanston, IL 60201 (SAN 696-3323) Tel 312-869-0132.

Dickey, Grover C., *(G C Dickey)*, 200 Gill Dr., Midwest City, OK 73110 (SAN 208-3612).

Diction Bks., *(Diction Bks; 0-9609198)*, 1313 Fifth St., SE, Suite 223, Minneapolis, MN 55414 (SAN 241-4945) Tel 612-379-3888.

Dictionary Society of North America, *(Dict Soc NA)*, Indiana State Univ., Dept. of Instructional Services, Terre Haute, IN 47809 (SAN 233-4755) Tel 812-237-2330.

Dicul Publishing, *(Dicul Pub; 0-938784)*, P.O. Box 091111, Columbus, OH 43209-7111 (SAN 216-0315) Tel 614-231-4670; Dist. by: DeVorss & Co., Inc., P.O. Box 550, 1046 Princeton Dr., Marina del Rey, CA 90294 (SAN 168-9886) Tel 213-870-7478; Dist. by: PEP Distributors, 2070 Rosewood Ln., Lima, OH 45806 (SAN 200-4194); Dist. by: Toastmaster International, 2200 N. Grand Ave., Santa Ana, CA 92711 (SAN 206-1112) Tel 714-542-6793.

Didactic Systems Inc., *(Didactic Syst; 0-89401)*, P.O. Box 457, Cranford, NJ 07016 (SAN 209-1739) Tel 212-789-2194.

Diefendorf, R. J., *(R J Diefendorf; 0-913125)*, RFD 546, West Lebanon, ME 04027 (SAN 283-264X) Tel 207-658-9715.

Diehl, Kathryn, *(K Diehl; 0-9603552)*, 554 N. McDonel, Lima, OH 45801 (SAN 285-0079) Tel 419-223-7207.

Diemar, Eleanor, *(E Diemar; 0-9601046)*, P.O. Box 24, Cedarhurst, NY 11516 (SAN 202-4969) Tel 516-374-2020.

Diemer, Smith Publishing Co., Inc., *(Diemer-Smith; 0-941138)*, 3377 Solano Ave., Suite 322, Napa, CA 94558 (SAN 238-874X) Tel 707-224-0813.

Diesel Engine Manufacturers Assn., *(Diesel Engine)*, 712 Lakewood Ctr., N., 14600 Detroit Ave., Cleveland, OH 44107 (SAN 224-7232).

Diet Teaching Programs, Inc., The, *(Diet Teach Progs; 0-941040)*, P.O. Box 1832, Sun City, AZ 85372 (SAN 217-3522) Tel 602-977-6677.

Dietz Pr., *(Dietz; 0-87517)*, 109 E. Cary, Richmond, VA 23219 (SAN 201-3258) Tel 804-648-0195.

Diffendal & Johnson, *(Diffendal & Johnson; 0-9614260)*, 614 Eighth St., NE, Washington, DC 20002 (SAN 687-1224) Tel 202-546-4103; Orders to: P.O. Box 76985, Washington, DC 20013 (SAN 662-2739).

Different Drummer Press, *(Different Drum; 0-9609580)*, 306 Eighth St., Des Moines, IA 50309 (SAN 262-6217) Tel 515-243-8105.

Digital Concept Systems, Inc., *(Digit Concept; 0-936327)*, 4826 Bucknell, Suite 201, San Antonio, TX 78249 (SAN 697-354X) Tel 512-692-1201.

Digital Equipment Corp., *(Digital Equip; 1-55558)*, 12 Crosby Dr., Bedford, MA 01730 (SAN 677-8968).

†**Digital Pr./Digital Equipment Corp.,** *(Digital Pr; 0-932376; 1-55558)*, 12 Crosby Dr., Bedford, MA 01730 (SAN 212-2529) Tel 617-276-1536; Toll free: 800-343-8322; Orders to: 12-A Esquire Rd., North Billerica, MA 01862 (SAN 212-2537); *CIP.*

Dignatus Co., *(Dignatus Co; 0-9605820)*, P.O. Box 2254, Mission Viejo, CA 92690 (SAN 216-5732) Tel 714-493-0710.

Dignity, Inc., *(Dignity Inc; 0-940680)*, 1500 Massachusetts Ave., NW, No. 11, Washington, DC 20005 (SAN 223-7431) Tel 202-861-0017.

Dilettante Pr., Inc., *(Dilettante; 0-935421)*, 1826 St. Claude Ave., New Orleans, LA 70116 (SAN 696-3366) Tel 504-943-3822.

†**Dilithium Pr.,** *(Dilithium Pr; 0-918398; 0-88056; 0-930206)*, P.O. Box 606, Beaverton, OR 97075 (SAN 210-0649) Tel 503-243-3313; Toll free: 800-547-1842; *CIP.*

Dillingham Pr., *(Dillingham Pr; 0-9616071)*, Box 2601, Santa Fe, NM 87501 (SAN 697-8592) Tel 505-983-3447.

Dillon, Lacy A., *(L A Dillon; 0-9616811)*, P.O. Box 222, Ravencliff, WV 25913 (SAN 661-0927) Tel 304-294-6559.

Dillon-Donnelly, *(Dillon-Donnelly; 0-933508)*, 7058 Lindell Blvd., St. Louis, MO 63130 (SAN 208-4589) Tel 314-862-6239.

Dillon/Liederbach, Inc., *(Dillon-Liederbach; 0-913228)*, 4953 Stonington Rd., Winston-Salem, NC 27103 (SAN 201-3274) Tel 919-768-7014.

Dillon Pr., Inc., *(Dillon; 0-87518)*, 242 Portland Ave., S., Minneapolis, MN 55415 (SAN 201-3266) Tel 612-333-2691; Toll free: 800-328-8322. *Imprints:* Gemstone Books (Gemstone Bks).

Dillon-Tyler Pubs., *(Dillon-Tyler Pubs; 0-916280)*, 1041 W. Salvador Ave., Napa, CA 94558 (SAN 208-1075) Tel 707-224-2525.

Dilman Pr., *(Dilman Pr; 0-9615301)*, 773 Cole, No. 8, San Francisco, CA 94117 (SAN 694-4639) Tel 415-386-6072; Dist. by: Bookpeople, 2929 Fifth St., Berkeley, CA 94710 (SAN 168-9517) Tel 415-549-3030.

Dimedia, Inc., *(Dimedia; 0-89300)*, 162 Washington St., Newark, NJ 07102 (SAN 240-057X); Dist. by: Publishers Group West, 5855 Beaudry St., Emeryville, CA 94608 (SAN 202-8522) Tel 415-658-3453; Toll free: 800-982-8319.

Dimedinha, Inc., *(Dimedinha Inc; 0-9616453)*, P.O. Box 71566, Madison Heights, MI 48071-0566 (SAN 658-8387) Tel 313-368-3983.

Dimension Bks., *(Dimension Bks; 0-87193)*, P.O. Box 811, Denville, NJ 07834 (SAN 211-7916) Tel 201-627-4334.

Dimension Four Unlimited, *(Dimension Four Unltd; 0-937805)*, 6821 Convoy Ct., Suite B, San Diego, CA 92111 (SAN 659-3372) Tel 619-541-1170.

Dimension Pr., The, *(Dimension Pr; 0-911173)*, 4205 Far West Blvd., Austin, TX 78755 (SAN 269-7114) Tel 512-345-0622; P.O. Box 26673, Austin, TX 78755 (SAN 658-0459).

Dimensional Graphics International, Ltd., *(Dimen Graphics Intl; 0-941444)*, 1154 Fort St. Mau, Suite 308, Honolulu, HI 96813 (SAN 238-9711) Tel 808-521-2000.

Dimensionist Press, *(Dimensionist Pr; 0-9602374)*, 5931 Stanton Ave., Highland, CA 92346 (SAN 212-2545) Tel 714-946-9687.

Dimes Group *See* U. S. Information Moscow

Dimond Pubs., *(Dimond Pubs; 0-937610)*, 3431 Fruitvale Ave., Oakland, CA 94602 (SAN 215-1405).

Dinograph Southwest, Inc., *(Dinograph SW; 0-932680),* P.O. Box 1600, Alamogordo, NM 88310 (SAN 212-1573).

†**Dinosaur Pr., The,** *(Dinosaur; 0-9605458),* 86 Leverett Rd., Amherst, MA 01002 (SAN 213-618X) Tel 413-549-0404; *CIP.*

Diocese of Armenian Church, *(D O A C; 0-934728),* 630 Second Ave., New York, NY 10016 (SAN 216-0625).

Dionex Corp., *(Dionex Corp; 0-9617173),* P.O. Box 3603, Sunnyvale, CA 94088 (SAN 663-1347); 1228 Titan Way, Sunnyvale, CA 94088 (SAN 663-1355) Tel 408-737-0700.

Dioscorides Pr., Inc., *(Dioscorides Pr; 0-931146),* 9999 SW Wilshire, Suite 124, Portland, OR 97225 (SAN 659-3917) Tel 503-292-0745.

Diotima Bks., *(Diotima Bks; 0-935772),* Box H, Glen Carbon, IL 62034 (SAN 214-3631).

DiPaul, H. Bert, *(DiPaul; 0-9605418),* 1066 Brennan Dr., Warminster, PA 18974 (SAN 216-0323).

†**Diplomatic Pr.,** *(Diplomatic IN; 0-910512),* Indiana Univ., Goodbody Hall 344, Bloomington, IN 47405 (SAN 201-3290) Tel 812-335-1605; *CIP.*

Direct International, Inc., *(Direct Intl; 0-9616409),* 150 E. 74th St., New York, NY 10021 (SAN 659-1574) Tel 212-861-4188.

Direct Mail Marketing Assn., Inc., *(Direct Mail Market; 0-933641),* 6 E. 43rd St., New York, NY 10017 (SAN 224-862X) Tel 212-689-4977.

Direct Market Designs, *(Direct Market; 0-9609790),* P.O. Box 142, Island Lake, IL 60042 (SAN 293-2466) Tel 312-526-5141; Dist. by: Publishers Group West, 5855 Beaudry St., Emeryville, CA 94608 (SAN 202-8522) Tel 415-658-3453.

Directed Media Inc., *(Directed Media; 0-939688),* P.O. Box 3005, Wenatchee, WA 98801 (SAN 216-7263) Tel 509-662-7693.

Direction Dynamics, *(Direction Dynamics; 0-933583),* 309 Honeycutt Dr., Wilmington, NC 28403 (SAN 692-2082) Tel 919-799-6544.

Directions Pr., *(Directions Pr; 0-940564),* 523 Gainsborough, No. 101, Thousand Oaks, CA 91360 (SAN 215-6350).

Directories, *(Directories; 0-9607992),* 436 E. 88th St., New York, NY 10128 (SAN 238-5635) Tel 212-722-8460.

Directories Publishing Co., Inc., *(Directories Pub; 0-937020),* P.O. Box 1824, Clemson, SC 29633-1824 (SAN 203-8919) Tel 803-646-7840; Toll free: 800-222-4531.

Directory of Directors Co., Inc., *(DODC; 0-936612),* P.O. Box 462, Southport, CT 06490 (SAN 204-2037) Tel 203-255-8525.

Directory of Washington Creative Services, *(Directory Creat Servs DC; 0-938053),* 1506 19th St., NW, Washington, DC 20036 (SAN 661-1087) Tel 202-462-6110; Dist. by: Ross Bk. Service, 3718 Seminary Rd., Alexandria, VA 22304 (SAN 200-6634).

Directory Systems, Inc., *(Directory Systems Inc; 0-942036),* 51 Bank St., Stamford, CT 06901 (SAN 238-6240) Tel 203-348-6319.

Disa Pr., Inc., *(Disa Press Inc; 0-913255),* P.O. Box 9284, Wilmington, DE 19809 (SAN 285-8681) Tel 302-475-4509.

Discipleship Resources, Subs. of Board of Discipleship of the United Methodist Church, *(Discipleship Res; 0-88177),* P.O. Box 840, 1908 Grand Ave., Nashville, TN 37202 (SAN 264-0074) Tel 615-327-2700; Orders to: P.O. Box 189, Nashville, TN 37202 (SAN 661-9932).

Discount America Guide, *(Discount America; 0-942528),* 51 E. 42 St., Rm, 417, New York, NY 10017 (SAN 239-6343) Tel 212-687-0810.

Discoveries Publishing Co., *(Discoveries; 0-934000),* P.O. Box 424, Glastonbury, CT 06033 (SAN 212-7393).

Discovery Bks., *(Discovery Bks; 0-913976),* Star Route, Mountain View, Owls Heads, NY 12969 (SAN 206-9512) Tel 518-483-0079.

Discovery Pr., *(Discovery Calif; 0-9617131),* P.O. Box 3461, Mission Viejo, CA 92690 (SAN 662-8052); 3459 Via Verde, No. B, Capistrano Beach, CA 92624 (SAN 662-8060) Tel 714-496-3503. Do not confuse with Discovery Pr., Portland, OR.

Discovery Pr., *(Discovery Pr; 0-9614261),* P.O. Box 12241, Portland, OR 97212 (SAN 687-1240) Tel 503-282-9372.

Discovery Stuff, *(Discovery Stuff; 0-930484),* 5328 W. 67th St., Shawnee Mission, KS 66208 (SAN 211-0636).

Discovery Toys, *(Discovery Toys; 0-939979),* P.O. Box 232008, Pleasant Hill, CA 94523; 400 Ellinwood Way, Suite 300, Pleasant Hill, CA 94523 Tel 415-680-8697.

Disharmony Bks. See **Moonstone Pr.**

Displays for Schools, Inc., *(Displays Sch; 0-9600962),* P.O. Box 163, Gainesville, FL 32602 (SAN 157-9711) Tel 904-373-2030.

Dissemination & Assessment Ctr. for Bilingual Education, *(Dissemination & Assessment; 0-89417),* 7703 N. Lamar, Austin, TX 78752 (SAN 209-3073) Tel 512-458-9131.

Distant Thunder Pr., *(Distant Pr; 0-9614525),* 301 Racine Rd., Madison, WI 53705 (SAN 650-0218) Tel 608-231-3625.

Distant Thunder Pr., *(Distant Thunder; 0-9614360),* 906 Pine St., Seattle, WA 98101 (SAN 688-4792) Tel 206-622-0996.

Distributors, The, *(distributors; 0-942520),* 702 S. Michigan, South Bend, IN 46618 (SAN 169-2488) Tel 219-232-8500; Toll free: 800-348-5200.

District of Columbia Bar Assn., *(DC Bar Assn),* 1426 H St. NW, Rm. 840, Washington, DC 20005 (SAN 226-7314).

Div. of G.P. Enterprises See **Job Hunters Forum**

Diversified Industries, Div. of Dicom Corp, *(Diversified Ind; 0-89534),* 2841 Index Rd., Madison, WI 53713 (SAN 210-301X) Tel 608-271-6544.

Diversified Pubns., *(Divers Pubns; 0-939593),* P.O. Box 548, Colorado City, CO 81019 (SAN 663-6209); 3041 Lunar Dr., Colorado City, CO 81019 (SAN 663-6217) Tel 303-676-3090.

Diversified Pub. Co, *(Diversified Pub Co; 0-942306),* 5301-44, Lubbock, TX 79414 (SAN 239-8494).

Diversity Pr., *(Diversity Okla; 0-936715),* 1000 SE Adams, Idabel, OK 74745 (SAN 699-9131) Tel 405-286-3148. Do not confuse with Diversity Pr., Chicago, IL.

Diversity Pr., *(Diversity Pr; 0-941906),* 2738 N. Racine St., Chicago, IL 60614 (SAN 239-197X) Tel 312-472-5662.

Divesports Publishing, *(Divesports Pub; 0-9611522),* P.O. Box 1397, Austin, TX 78767-1397 (SAN 285-2462) Tel 512-443-5883.

Divine Love Publishing Co., *(Divine Love Pub; 0-9617038),* P.O. Box 1844, Soquel, CA 95073 (SAN 662-8230); 4631 Soquel Dr., Soquel, CA 95073 (SAN 662-8249) Tel 408-462-6282.

Divine Science Federation International, *(Divine Sci Fed),* 1819 E. 14th Ave., Denver, CO 80218 (SAN 204-1103) Tel 303-322-7730.

Diving Safety Digest, *(Diving Safety; 0-9614638),* P.O. Box 2735, Menlo Park, CA 94026 (SAN 691-9200) Tel 415-322-6984.

Division of Bar Services See **American Bar Assn.**

Divisions, *(Divisions; 0-934276),* P.O. Box 18647, Cleveland Heights, OH 44118 (SAN 223-579X).

Divorce Research Ctr., *(Divorce Res),* P.O. Box 18-1515, Coronado, CA 92118 (SAN 285-5373).

Divry, D. C., Inc., *(Divry; 0-910516),* 148 W. 24th St., New York, NY 10011 (SAN 201-3320) Tel 212-255-2153.

Dixon Enterprises, *(Dixon Enter; 0-9614394),* P.O. Box 1231, Oak Ridge, TN 37831 (SAN 688-668X) Tel 615-482-6721; Dist. by: Baker & Taylor, Eastern Div., 50 Kirby Ave., Somerville, NJ 08876 (SAN 169-4901).

Dlaw Pubns., *(Dlaw Pubns; 0-9614350),* 5243 Tacoma Way, Tacoma, WA 98409 (SAN 687-7931) Tel 206-475-9200; Orders to: 1614 S. 74th St., Tacoma, WA 98408 (SAN 662-2798).

Dnomro Pubns., *(Dnomro Pubns; 0-913565),* 40 Fairmont Ave., Waltham, MA 02154 (SAN 201-274X) Tel 617-893-5631.

Do It Now Foundation, *(Do It Now; 0-89230),* P.O. Box 21126, Phoenix, AZ 85036 (SAN 225-9265) Tel 602-257-0797; 2050 E. University, No. 7, Phoenix, AZ 85034 (SAN 669-0661).

Do-It Publishing Group, *(Do-It Pub Group; 0-936265),* 211 Franklin St., Alexandria, VA 22314 (SAN 697-3280) Tel 703-549-5192.

†**Do-It-Yourself Legal Pubs.,** *(Do It Yourself Legal Pubs; 0-932704),* 150 Fifth Ave., New York, NY 10011 (SAN 214-1876) Tel 212-242-2840; *CIP.*

Doane Publishing, *(Doane Pub; 0-932250),* 11701 Borman Dr., St. Louis, MO 63146 (SAN 207-2149) Tel 314-569-2700.

Dobbins, Joan H., *(J H Dobbins; 0-9610540),* 419 Windover Circle, Meridian, MS 39305 (SAN 264-0082) Tel 601-483-5081.

Dobbins, M. F., *(M F Dobbins; 0-9607176),* 3045 Pennypack Rd., Hatboro, PA 19040 (SAN 239-0841) Tel 215-884-8057.

Dobry Enterprise, *(Dobry Enter; 0-9615218),* 2152 Poplar Ridge Rd., Pasadena, MD 21122 (SAN 695-1309) Tel 301-437-0297.

Docket Series See **Oceana Pubns., Inc.**

Dr. Trina's Pr., *(Trinas Pr; 0-9615840),* P.O. Box 4777, Laguna Beach, CA 92651 (SAN 697-0109) Tel 714-497-5071.

Doctors' Ophthalmic Pr., *(Doctors Pr; 0-9617262),* 401 China Basin St., San Francisco, CA 94107 (SAN 663-5687) Tel 415-777-2020.

Doctrine of Christ Pubns., *(Doctrine Christ; 0-940068),* 2215 Bourbon St., Beaumont, TX 77705 (SAN 220-2131).

Documan Pr., Ltd., *(Documan; 0-932076),* 3201 Lorraine Ave., Kalamazoo, MI 49008 (SAN 281-6032) Tel 616-344-0805; Orders to: Box 387, Kalamazoo, MI 49005 (SAN 281-6040).

Document Reprocessors Pubns., *(Doc Reprocessors; 0-9616850),* 41 Sutter St., Suite 1120, San Francisco, CA 94104 (SAN 661-3101) Tel 415-362-1298.

Documentary Bk. Pubs. Corp., *(Doc Bk Pubs; 0-935503),* 11661 SE First, Suite 201, Bellevue, WA 98005 (SAN 696-4818) Tel 206-462-7400.

Documentary Pubns., *(Documentary Pubns; 0-89712),* 106 Kenan St., Chapel Hill, NC 27514 (SAN 211-559X) Tel 919-929-1833.

Documentary Research Inc., *(Documentary Res; 0-931627),* 96 Rumsey Rd., Buffalo, NY 14209 (SAN 683-7298) Tel 716-885-9777.

Dodd-Blair & Assocs., *(Dodd-Blair Assocs; 0-930205),* P.O. Box 644, Rangeley, ME 04970 (SAN 670-7874) Tel 207-864-5195.

Dodd, Mead & Co., *(Dodd; 0-396; 0-89696),* 79 Madison Ave., New York, NY 10016 (SAN 201-3339) Tel 212-685-6464; Toll free: 800-251-4000; Orders to: P.O. Box 141000, Nashville, TN 37214 (SAN 287-0177).

Dodson, Rita, *(R Dodson; 0-9615511),* Rte. 5, Dodson Rd., Cartersville, GA 30120 (SAN 696-6382) Tel 404-382-0965.

Doe, John, Pr., *(J Doe Pr; 0-9609476),* 420 13th Ave. E., Seattle, WA 98105 (SAN 263-2233) Tel 206-525-7901.

Dog Ear Pr., The, *(Dog Ear; 0-937966),* P.O. Box 143, South Harpswell, ME 04079 (SAN 216-3675) Tel 207-729-7791.

Dog-Eared Pubns., *(Dog Eared Pubns; 0-941042),* P.O. Box 814, Corvallis, OR 97339 (SAN 281-6059) Tel 503-753-4274; Dist. by: Pacific Pipeline, Inc., 19215 66th Ave., S., Kent, WA 98032 (SAN 208-2128) Tel 206-872-5523; Toll free: 800-426-4727.

Dog-Master Systems, Div. of Environmental Research Labs, *(Dog Master),* 1020 K-9 Way, P.O. Box 250, Agoura Hills, CA 91301 (SAN 209-181X); Toll free: 800-824-7888.

Dog River Publishing, *(Dog River; 0-932509),* P.O. Box 1922, Douglasville, GA 30133-1922 (SAN 687-4428) Tel 404-942-5090.

Dogwood Pr., Inc., *(Dogwood Pr; 0-9614978),* P.O. Box 2023, Stone Mountain, GA 30086 (SAN 693-6121) Tel 404-296-1073.

Dole Pub., *(Dole Pub; 0-9614216),* 1503 Franklin Ave., Redlands, CA 92373 (SAN 687-0953) Tel 714-793-9768.

Dolice Graphics, *(Dolice Graphics; 0-935901),* 3 W. 19th St., New York, NY 10011 (SAN 696-7280) Tel 212-206-0770.

Doll Collectors of America, Inc., *(Doll Collect Am; 0-9603210),* Dist. by: Patry/Edgar, 11 Charlemont Rd., Medford, MA 02155 (SAN 282-695X).

†**Doll Works, The,** *(Doll Works; 0-940070),* P.O. Box 91910, Santa Barbara, CA 93190 (SAN 220-214X) Tel 805-966-6692; *CIP.*

Dollar's Info Bks., *(Dollar's Info Bks; 0-915453),* 1500 Pecan Pl. Dr., Plaquemine, LA 70764 (SAN 291-2279) Tel 504-687-6516.

Names

Names

Dolores Pr., *(Dolores Pr; 0-934117),* 69 Rensselaer Dr., Commack, NY 11725 (SAN 693-2916) Tel 516-499-4281.

Dolphin, Deon K., *(D K Dolphin; 0-9613157),* 2130 Hwy 101 D12, Greenbrae, CA 94904 (SAN 294-9229) Tel 415-461-7916.

Dolphin Books *See* Doubleday & Co., Inc.

Doma Pr./SPI, Affil. of Spritual Pathways Institute, *(Doma; 0-917816),* P.O. Box 564, Lisle, IL 60532 (SAN 210-0681) Tel 312-969-0734.

Dome Pubns., *(Dome Pubns; 0-88267),* 1169 Logan Ave., Elgin, IL 60120 (SAN 203-8927) Tel 312-697-4814.

Domesday Bks., *(Domesday Bks; 0-912195),* P.O. Box 734, Peter Stuyvesant Sta., New York, NY 10009 (SAN 264-6102) Tel 212-254-1004.

Dominguez, Richard, *(R Dominguez; 0-9616928),* P.O. Box 1860, New York, NY 10185 (SAN 661-6666) Tel 212-803-3009.

Dominica Institute, The, *(Dominica Inst; 0-935959),* 2516 Christie Pl., Owensboro, KY 42301 (SAN 697-2357) Tel 809-449-3346.

Dominion Pr., Div. of The Invisible Ministry, *(Dominion Pr; 0-912132),* P.O. Box 37, San Marcos, CA 92069-0025 (SAN 203-8935) Tel 619-746-9430.

Dominion Publishing, *(Dominion Pub; 0-913431),* P.O. Box 1293, Parker, CO 80134 (SAN 285-8711) Tel 303-841-2215.

Dominus Vobiscum Publishing, Inc., *(Dominus Vobiscum Pub; 0-9617076),* P.O. Box 62, Stuart St. P.O., Back Bay Annex, Boston, MA 02117 (SAN 662-622X); 257 Commonwealth Ave., Suite 03, Boston, MA 02116 (SAN 662-6238) Tel 617-262-4400.

Domjan Studio, *(Domjan Studio; 0-933652),* West Lake Rd., Tuxedo Park, NY 10987 (SAN 293-2512) Tel 914-351-4596.

Domus Books *See* Quality Books, Inc.

Don Bosco Multimedia, Div. of Salesian Society, Inc., *(Don Bosco Multimedia; 0-89944),* 457 North Ave., Box T, New Rochelle, NY 10802 (SAN 213-2613) Tel 914-576-0122. *Imprints:* Don Bosco Publications (D Bosco Pubns); Patron Books (Patron); Salesiana Publishers (Salesiana).

Don Bosco Publications *See* Don Bosco Multimedia

Don Quixote Publishing Co., Inc., *(D Quixote Pub; 0-943078),* P.O. Box 9442, Amarillo, TX 79105 (SAN 240-3676).

Donaghey, John, Pubns., *(J Donaghey; 0-9604298),* P.O. Box 402021, Garland, TX 75046 (SAN 214-364X) Tel 214-272-7607; Dist. by: Baker & Taylor Co., Eastern Div., 50 Kirby Ave., Somerville, NJ 08876 (SAN 169-4901) Tel 201-526-8000.

Donahoe, Edward D., Pubs., *(Donahoe Pubs; 0-938400),* P.O. Box 22011, Louisville, KY 40222 (SAN 217-0973) Tel 502-423-9638.

Donahue-Gandy, Marlene M., *(M M Donahue-Gandy; 0-9613514),* 6228 Westbrook Dr., Citrus Heights, CA 95610 (SAN 657-6508) Tel 916-722-5611.

Donaldson, Belzano & Associates, *(D B Assoc; 0-9611386),* 2102 Business Ctr. Dr., Suite 130, Irvine, CA 92715 (SAN 285-2519) Tel 714-752-2322.

Donchian, Peter, Pubns., *(P Donchian Pubns; 0-9615881),* 64 Crosslands, Kennett Square, PA 19348 (SAN 697-063X) Tel 215-388-1652.

Donel, D. E., Co., The, *(D E Donel; 0-913657),* P.O. Box 376, Loma Linda, CA 92354 (SAN 286-0929) Tel 714-796-5598.

Dong Nam P & C Inc., *(Dong Nam P & C; 0-914524),* 2946 N. Lincoln Ave., Chicago, IL 60657 (SAN 206-3557) Tel 312-549-4660.

Donnan Publications, *(Donnan Pubns; 0-931299),* P.O. Box 773, Martinez, CA 94553 (SAN 685-1975) Tel 415-229-3581.

Donnell Publishing Co., *(Donnell Pub Co; 0-9613091),* P.O. Box 5055, Willowick, OH 44094 (SAN 294-734X) Tel 216-944-0318.

Donnelly, Mary Louise, *(Donnelly; 0-939142),* P.O. Box 306, Burke, VA 22015 (SAN 214-0039) Tel 703-250-4967.

Donning Co. Pubs., Subs. of Walsworth Publishing Co., *(Donning Co; 0-915442; 0-89865),* 5659 Virginia Beach Blvd., Norfolk, VA 23502 (SAN 211-6316) Tel 804-461-8090; Toll free: 800-446-8572; 801 S. Missouri Ave., Marceline, MO 64658 (SAN 661-9940). *Imprints:* Starblaze (Starblaze); Unilaw (Unilaw).

Donoghue Organization, Inc., The, *(Donoghue Organ Inc; 0-913755),* Box 540, 360 Woodland St., Holliston, MA 01746 (SAN 285-2365).

Donovan, Anthony J., *(A J Donovan; 0-9617258),* 35 W. 82nd St., Apt. 3A, New York, NY 10024 (SAN 663-5393) Tel 212-724-7400.

Doodly-Squat Pr., The *See* Drift Group, The

Doolco, Inc., *(Doolco Inc; 0-914626),* 11252 Goodnight Ln., Suite 600, Dallas, TX 75229 (SAN 205-6178) Tel 214-241-2326.

Dooryard Pr., *(Dooryard; 0-937160),* P.O. Box 221, Story, WY 82842 (SAN 216-1230) Tel 307-683-2937.

D'OR Pr., *(D-OR Pr; 0-935045),* 200 N. Pickett St., No. 1113, Alexandria, VA 22304 (SAN 694-4671) Tel 703-751-7140.

Dorchester Publishing Co., Inc., *(Dorchester Pub Co; 0-8439),* 6 E. 39th St., Suite 900, New York, NY 10016 (SAN 264-0090) Tel 212-725-8811; Dist. by: Kable News Co., 777 Third Ave., New York, NY 10017 (SAN 169-5835).

Dordt College Pr., *(Dordt Coll Pr; 0-932914),* 498 Fourth Ave., NE, Sioux Center, IA 51250 (SAN 221-2110) Tel 712-722-6420.

Dorf, Marilyn, *(Marilyn Dorf; 0-9616211),* 4149 E St., Lincoln, NE 68510 (SAN 658-5132) Tel 402-489-3104.

Doris Pubns., *(Doris Pubns; 0-933865),* P.O. Box 1576, Louisville, KY 40201 (SAN 692-7033) Tel 502-774-3297.

†Dorison Hse. Pubs., Inc., *(Dorison Hse; 0-916752),* 31 St. James Ave., Boston, MA 02116 (SAN 208-3140) Tel 617-426-1715; *CIP.*

Dorje Ling Pubs., *(Dorje Ling; 0-915880),* P.O. Box 287, Lagunitas, CA 94938 (SAN 208-2144) Tel 415-488-9017.

Dorland, Wayne E., Publishing Co., *(Dorland Pub Co; 0-9603250),* Box 264, Mendham, NJ 07945 (SAN 213-2451) Tel 201-543-2694.

Dorleac-MacLeish, *(Dorleac-MacLeish; 0-916329),* 5100 Longfellow St., Los Angeles, CA 90042 (SAN 295-7442) Tel 213-255-6730.

Dormac, Inc., *(Dormac; 0-86575),* P.O. Box 1699, Beaverton, OR 97075 (SAN 209-3502) Tel 503-641-3128; Toll free: 800-547-8032.

Dormant Brain Research & Development Laboratory, *(Dormant Brain Res; 0-938967),* Laughing Coyote Mountain, Box 10, Black Hawk, CO 80422 (SAN 219-7820).

Dormition Skete Pubns., *(Dormition Pubns; 0-935889),* 29060 County Rd. 185, Buena Vista, CO 81211 (SAN 696-3439) Tel 303-395-6395.

Dorrance & Co., *(Dorrance; 0-8059),* 828 Lancaster Ave., Bryn Mawr, PA 19010 (SAN 201-3363) Tel 215-527-7880.

Dorset Hse. Publishing Co., Inc., *(Dorset Hse Pub Co; 0-932633),* 353 W. 12th St., New York, NY 10014 (SAN 687-794X) Tel 212-620-4053; Toll free: 800-342-6657.

Dorset Pr., Subs. of Marboro Bks., *(Dorset Pr; 0-88029),* c/o Marboro Bks., 105 Fifth Ave., New York, NY 10003 (SAN 287-6663) Tel 212-924-8395.

Dorset Publishing Co., Inc., *(Dorset Pub Co; 0-533),* P.O. Box 907, Boulder City, NV 89005 (SAN 689-0555) Tel 702-294-1048.

Dorsey Pr., The, Div. of Richard D. Irwin, Inc., *(Dorsey; 0-256),* 224 S. Michigan Ave., Chicago, IL 60604 (SAN 203-8943) Tel 312-322-8400; Toll free: 800-323-4560; Orders to: Richard D. Irwin, Inc., 1818 Ridge Rd., Homewood, IL 60430 (SAN 661-9959) Tel 312-798-6000.

Dorward, D. M., Photography, *(Dorward Photo; 0-9615729),* Box 1620, Ketchum, ID 83340 (SAN 696-3455) Tel 208-788-2376; 301 Canyon East Fork Rd., Ketchum, ID 83340 (SAN 696-9690).

Dos Pasos Editores, Inc., *(Dos Pasos Ed; 0-9615403),* P.O. Box 261 UTEP, El Paso, TX 79968 (SAN 696-351X) Tel 915-584-2475.

Dos Tejedoras Fiber Arts Pubns., *(Dos Tejedoras; 0-932394),* 3036 N. Snelling Ave., St. Paul, MN 55113 (SAN 213-4861) Tel 612-646-7445.

Dots Pubns., *(Dots Pubns; 0-9605204),* 625 Mahoney Ave., Oakview, CA 93022 (SAN 215-7535) Tel 805-649-3126; Orders to: P.O. Box 563, Ventura, CA 93002 (SAN 661-9967).

Double A Pubns., *(Double A; 0-9615550),* 18000 Pacific Hwy. S., No. 1105, Seattle, WA 98188 (SAN 696-3617) Tel 206-243-9115.

Double C Publishing, *(Double C Pub; 0-943288; 0-937844),* 1401-G E. Fourth St., Long Beach, CA 90802 (SAN 240-6292) Tel 213-432-0882.

Double Crown, *(Double Crown; 0-935010),* 51995 Hernley Road, Aguanga, CA 92302 (SAN 212-0372) Tel 714-763-5174.

Double Detectives *See* Godine, David R., Pub., Inc.

Double E Pubs., *(Double E Pubs; 0-936195),* 277 NE Conifer, No. 12, Corvallis, OR 97330 (SAN 697-1091) Tel 503-753-7085.

Double Eagle Bk. Co., *(Double Eagle; 0-935781),* 160 Eileen Ln., Orcutt, CA 93455 (SAN 696-7299) Tel 805-937-0241; P.O. Box 2262, Orcutt, CA 93455 (SAN 698-2174).

Double Elephant Press, *(Double Elephant),* Dist. by: Ten Speed Press, P.O. Box 7123, Berkeley, CA 94707 (SAN 202-7674) Tel 415-845-8414.

Double H Pubns., *(Double H Pubns; 0-9615469),* 2879 E. Valley View, Holladay, UT 84117 (SAN 696-3641) Tel 801-277-1997.

Double Helix Press, *(Double Helix; 0-930578),* 1300 Tigertail Rd., Los Angeles, CA 90049 (SAN 211-0083) Tel 213-472-6452; Toll free: 800-631-3577; Dist. by: International Universities Press, Inc., 59 Boston Post Rd., P.O. Box 1524, Madison, CT 06443-1524 (SAN 202-7186); Dist. by: Penguin Books, 40 W. 23rd St., New York, NY 10010 (SAN 202-5914) Tel 212-807-7300.

Double Lee Productions, *(Double Lee; 0-9607540),* 401 First Ave., New York, NY 10010 (SAN 239-5339).

Double M Pr., *(Double M Pr; 0-916634),* 16455 Tuba St., Sepulveda, CA 91343 (SAN 213-9510) Tel 818-360-3166.

Double M Publishing Co., *(Double M Pub; 0-913379),* Rte. 1, Nadia Dr., Joliet, IL 60436 (SAN 285-872X) Tel 815-741-0576; Dist. by: Baker & Taylor Co., Midwest Div., 501 Gladiola Ave., Momence, IL 60954 (SAN 169-2100) Tel 815-472-2444.

Double Page, *(Double Page; 0-935711),* c/o AVI Group, 1211 Sixth Ave., 14th Flr., New York, NY 10036 (SAN 696-3676) Tel 212-575-0707 P.O. Box 939, Radio City Sta., New York, NY 10101 (SAN 696-5326); Dist. by: Como Sales, Inc., 799 Broadway, New York, NY 10003 (SAN 202-8549).

Double Talk, *(Double Talk; 0-9615839),* P.O. Box 412, Amelia, OH 45102 (SAN 697-0575) Tel 513-753-7117.

Double Trouble Day *See* White Hse. Theater, The

Doubleday & Co., Inc., *(Doubleday; 0-385),* 245 Park Ave., New York, NY 10017 (SAN 201-0089) Tel 212-953-4561; Toll free: 800-645-6156 (Orders); Toll free: 800-457-7605 (Sales Service); Orders to: 501 Franklin Ave., Garden City, NY 11530 (SAN 281-6083) Tel 516-873-4561. *Imprints:* Anchor Books (Anch); Anchor Press (Anchor Pr); College Course Guides (CCG); Dial Press (Dial); Dolphin Books (Dolp); Echo Books (Echo); Galilee (Galilee); Image Books (Image Bks); Lyons, Nick, Books (NLB); Made Simple Books (Made); Quantum Press (Quantum Pr); Virago (Virago); Waymark Books (Waymark); Windfall (Windfall); Zenith Books (Zenith); Zephyr (Zephyr); Zephyr-BFYR (Zephyr-BFYR).

DoubLeo Pubns., *(DoubLeo Pubns; 0-936560),* 227 E. 11th St., New York, NY 10003 (SAN 214-0047) Tel 212-473-2739.

Dougherty, F. Robert, *(F R Dougherty; 0-936267),* 4809 Horseshoe Pike, Downingtown, PA 19335 (SAN 698-1542) Tel 215-269-1146.

Doughty, Al, *(A Doughty; 0-9617246),* Rte. 1, Pinckneyville, IL 62274 (SAN 663-5601) Tel 618-357-9839.

Douglas County Planning Dept., *(Douglas Cty Planning; 0-9616574),* Courthouse Annex No. 2, 205 SE Jackson St., Roseburg, OR 97470 (SAN 661-1109) Tel 503-440-4289.

Douglass Pubns., Inc., *(Douglass Pubs; 0-935392),* P.O. Box 3270, Alexandria, VA 22302 (SAN 211-7037) Tel 703-998-6948.

Dove Bks. *See Macmillan Publishing Co., Inc.*

Dove Ecclesiastical Ministries, *(Dove Ecclesiastical; 0-9611978),* 25974 S. River Rd., Mount Clemons, MI 48045 (SAN 286-7753) Tel 313-468-7038.

Dove Pubns., *(Dove Pubns; 0-917123),* P.O. Box 33, Cass City, MI 48726 (SAN 655-8119) Tel 517-872-4581.

Dove Systems, *(Dove Sys),* 1199 4th St., Los Osos, CA 93402 (SAN 683-2482).

Dovebooks, *(Dovebks; 0-9613450),* 3740 Silver Leaf Ct., Marietta, GA 30060 (SAN 657-2553) Tel 404-436-7911; Dist. by: Writers & Books, 740 University, Rochester, NY 14609 (SAN 156-9678).

Dovehaven Pr., Ltd., *(Dovehaven Pr Ltd),* Box HH, Jackson, WY 83001 (SAN 693-2231) Tel 307-733-8050.

†**Dover Pubns., Inc.,** *(Dover; 0-486),* 180 Varick St., New York, NY 10014; Toll free: 800-223-3130; Orders to: 31 E. Second St., Mineola, NY 11501 (SAN 201-338X) Tel 516-294-7000; CIP.

Dovetail Pr., *(Dovetail; 0-935468),* 250 W. 94th St., New York, NY 10025 (SAN 209-6609) Tel 212-865-9216.

†**Dow Jones & Co., Inc.,** *(Dow Jones; 0-87128),* P.O. Box 300, Princeton, NJ 08549 (SAN 201-8055) Tel 609-452-2000. *Formerly known as Dow Jones Bks; CIP.*

Dow Jones-Irwin, Inc., Div. of Richard D. Irwin, Inc., *(Dow Jones-Irwin; 0-87094; 0-256; 1-55623),* 1818 Ridge Rd., Homewood, IL 60430 (SAN 220-0236) Tel 312-798-6000; Toll free: 800-323-4566.

Dowler, Warren L., *(W L Dowler; 0-930188),* 526 Camillo St., Sierra Madre, CA 91024 (SAN 210-721X) Tel 818-355-9707.

Dowling College Pr., *(Dowling; 0-917428),* Oakdale, NY 11769 (SAN 208-9521) Tel 516-589-6100.

Down East Bks., Div. of Down East Enterprise Inc., *(Down East; 0-89272),* P.O. Box 679, Camden, ME 04843 (SAN 208-6301) Tel 207-594-9544; Toll free: 800-432-1670 (In ME only); Roxmont, Rte. One, Rockport, ME 04856 (SAN 658-0467).

Down Home Pr., *(Down Home Pr; 0-937697),* P.O. Box 408, Stony Brook, NY 11790 (SAN 659-3453) Tel 516-689-3221; 2 William Penn Dr., Stony Brook, NY 11790 (SAN 659-3461).

Down the Shore Publishing, *(Down the Shore Pub; 0-9615208),* 72 Maiden Ln., Harvey Cedars, NJ 08008 (SAN 661-082X) Tel 609-494-3346; P.O. Box 353, Harvey Cedars, NJ 08008 (SAN 661-0838).

Down There Pr., *(Down There Pr; 0-9602324; 0-940208),* P.O. Box 2086, Burlingame, CA 94010 (SAN 212-3312) Tel 415-342-9867; Dist. by: Bookpeople, 2929 Fifth St., Berkeley, CA 94710 (SAN 168-9517); Dist. by: Children's Small Pr. Collection, The, 719 N. Fourth Ave,, Ann Arbor, MI 48104 (SAN 200-514X); Dist. by: Distributors, The, 702 S. Michigan, South Bend, IN 46618 (SAN 169-2488) Tel 219-232-8500; Dist. by: Ingram Industries, 347 Reedwood Dr., Nashville, TN 37217 (SAN 169-7978); Dist. by: Inland Bk. Co., P.O. Box 261, 22 Hemingway Ave., East Haven, CT 06512 (SAN 200-4151) Tel 203-467-4257; Dist. by: New Leaf Distributing, The, 1020 White St., SW, Atlanta, GA (SAN 169-1449). *Imprints:* Yes Press (Yes Pr).

Down to Earth Pubns., *(Down to Earth Pubns; 0-939301),* 873 Lincoln, St. Paul, MN 55105 (SAN 662-8079) Tel 612-222-6576.

Downey, Joel, *(J Downey; 0-9601284),* 7625 Hutchinson Ave., Pittsburgh, PA 15218 (SAN 210-4156) Tel 412-371-5880.

†**Downey Place Publishing Hse., Inc.,** *(Downey Place; 0-910823),* P.O. Box 1352, El Cerrito, CA 94530-1352 (SAN 269-753X) Tel 415-529-1012; CIP.

Downs, Angus, Ltd., *(Angus Downs; 0-910053),* 4101 Lake Ridge Dr., Holland, MI 49423 (SAN 241-2950) Tel 616-399-1813.

Downsbrough, Peter, *(P Downsbrough; 0-9602192),* 305 E. Houston St, New York, NY 10012 (SAN 212-3460); Dist. by: Printed Matter, 7 Lispenard St., New York, NY 10013 (SAN 169-5924) Tel 212-925-0325.

Downtown Bk. Ctr., Inc., *(Downtown Bk; 0-941010),* 245 SE First St., Suites 236-237, Miami, FL 33131 (SAN 169-1112) Tel 305-377-9941.

Downtown Poets Co-Op, *(Downtown Poets; 0-917402),* c/o Home Planet News, P.O. Box 415, Stuyvesant Sta., New York, NY 10009 (SAN 208-9653) Tel 212-625-4245.

Downtown Research & Development Ctr., *(Downtown Res; 0-915910),* 1133 Broadway , Suite 1407, New York, NY 10010 (SAN 207-9658) Tel 212-206-7979.

Dowsing Institute of America, *(Dowsing Inst; 0-931740),* 414 Biscayne Dr., Wilmington, NC 28405 (SAN 211-643X).

Doxey, W. S., *(Doxey),* 550 N. White, Carrollton, GA 30117 (SAN 211-8955).

Doyle, Howard A., Publishing Co., *(Howard Doyle; 0-87299),* P.O. Box 555, East Dennis, MA 02641 (SAN 204-0751) Tel 617-385-2000.

Doyle, William T., *(W T Doyle; 0-9615486),* Murry Rd., Montpelier, VT 05602 (SAN 696-3749) Tel 802-223-2851.

Dozenal Society of America, *(Dozenal; 0-933789),* Nassau Community College, Math Dept., Garden City, NY 11530 (SAN 224-1145) Tel 516-222-7611; 6 Brancatelli, West Islip, NY 11795 (SAN 693-4870) Tel 516-669-0273.

Dr. Pepper Co., The, *(Dr Pepper; 0-9607448),* P.O. Box 225086, Dallas, TX 75231 (SAN 239-1996) Tel 214-824-0331.

Draco Productions & Pubns., *(Draco Prod Pubns; 0-936121),* 2036 Pauoa Rd., Honolulu, HI 96813 (SAN 697-0664) Tel 808-523-1752; P.O. Box 27373, Honolulu, HI 96827 (SAN 697-0672).

Dracula Pr., Subs. of Dracula, Unlimited, *(Dracula Pr; 0-9611944),* 29 Washington Sq. W., Penthouse, New York, NY 10011 (SAN 219-4228) Tel 212-533-5018.

Dragon Enterprises, *(Dragon Ent; 0-9606382),* P.O. Box 200, Genoa, NV 89411 (SAN 215-3025) Tel 702-782-2486.

†**Dragon Gate, Inc.,** *(Dragon Gate; 0-937872),* 6532 Phinney Ave., N., Seattle, WA 98103 (SAN 217-099X) Tel 206-783-8387; Orders to: 508 Lincoln St., Pt. Townsend, WA 98368 (SAN 697-7073) Tel 206-385-5848; CIP.

Dragon Tree Pr., The, *(Dragon Tree; 0-940918),* 1310 College Ave., Suite 1102, Boulder, CO 80302 (SAN 217-3557) Tel 303-444-7926.

Dragonlord Pr., *(Dragonlord Pr; 0-9614201),* 311 MsCalley St., Chapel Hill, NC 27514 (SAN 687-1054) Tel 919-781-8580.

Dragon's Lair, *(Dragon's Lair; 0-910987),* P.O. Box 14197, San Francisco, CA 94114-0917 (SAN 264-0104) Tel 415-921-7054.

Dragons Teeth Pr., *(Dragons Teeth; 0-934218),* El Dorado National Forest, Georgetown, CA 95634 (SAN 201-3398).

Dragonsbreath Pr., The, *(Dragonsbreath; 0-943120),* 10905 Bay Shore Dr., Sister Bay, WI 54234 (SAN 219-3612) Tel 414-854-2742.

Dragonscales & Mane Publishing, *(Dragonscales & Mane Pub; 0-918899),* 151 Chenery St., San Francisco, CA 94131 (SAN 669-974X) Tel 415-821-6846.

Dragonwyck Publishing, Inc., *(Dragonwyck Pub; 0-9606148),* Burrage Rd., Contoocook, NH 03229 (SAN 281-6113) Tel 603-746-5606; Orders to: P.O. Box 385, Contoocook, NH 03229 (SAN 281-6121).

Drain Enterprise, The, *(Drain Enterprise; 0-930419),* 309 First St., Drain, OR 97435 (SAN 240-902X).

Drake-Hurst Pubns., *(Drake-Hurst Pubns; 0-9614156),* 4596 Bridlewood Terr., St. Louis, MO 63116 (SAN 686-5356) Tel 314-892-0501.

Drake's Printing & Publishing, *(Drake's Ptg & Pub; 0-912013),* 225 N. Magnolia Ave., Orlando, FL 32801 (SAN 216-1249) Tel 305-841-3491.

Drakes View Publishing, *(Drakes View Publishing; 0-939123),* P.O. Box 438, Inverness, CA 94937 (SAN 663-5016); 245 Drakes View Dr., Inverness, CA 94937 (SAN 663-5024) Tel 415-663-1730; Dist. by: Bookpeople, 2929 Fifth St., Berkeley, CA 94720 (SAN 168-9517); Toll free: 800-227-1516.

Drama Bk. Pubs., *(Drama Bk; 0-910482; 0-89676),* 821 Broadway, New York, NY 10003 (SAN 213-5752) Tel 212-627-2158.

Drama Jazz Hse., Inc., *(Drama Jazz Hse Inc; 0-915833),* 33 Heritage Ct., Annapolis, MD 21401 (SAN 293-924X) Tel 202-636-7050.

Dramaline Pubns., *(Dramaline Pubns; 0-9611792),* 10470 Riverside Dr., Suite 201, Toluca Lake, CA 91602 (SAN 285-239X) Tel 818-985-9148; Dist. by: Samuel French, Inc., 45 W. 25th St., New York, NY 10010 (SAN 206-4170) Tel 212-206-8990; Dist. by: Samuel French, Inc., 7625 Sunset Blvd., Hollywood, CA 90046 (SAN 200-6855) Tel 213-876-0570.

Dramatika, *(Dramatika; 0-9604000),* 429 Hope St., Tarpon Springs, FL 33589 (SAN 207-8155).

Dramatists Play Service, Inc., *(Dramatists Play; 0-8222),* 440 Park Ave. S., New York, NY 10016 (SAN 207-5717) Tel 212-683-8960.

Drame Pr., *(Drame Pr; 0-9617190),* 2928 W. Washington, Phoenix, AZ 85009 (SAN 663-2599).

Drasnar, George, Productions, *(G Drasnar; 0-936951),* 706-A S. Pacific Coast Hwy., Redondo Beach, CA 90277 (SAN 658-7003) Tel 213-316-9065.

Drawing Board, Computer Supplies Div., The, Div. of Pitney Bowes, Greenwoods Industrial Pk., P.O. Box 2995, Hartford, CT 06104 (SAN 695-2933); Toll free: 800-243-3207.

Draydel Pr., *(Draydel Pr; 0-9614112),* 36 W. 56th St., New York, NY 10014 (SAN 685-3048) Tel 212-489-9874.

Dream Garden Pr., *(Dream Garden; 0-9604402; 0-942688),* P.O. Box 27076, Salt Lake City, UT 84127 (SAN 217-1007) Tel 801-972-0663; 1042 S. Seventh W., Salt Lake City, UT 84104 (SAN 696-5547).

Dream Research, *(Dream Res; 0-9607172),* P.O. Box 1142, Tacoma, WA 98401 (SAN 239-085X) Tel 206-565-4999; Dist. by: Pacific Pipeline, Inc., 19215 66th Ave. S., Kent, WA 98032 (SAN 208-2128) Tel 206-872-5523; Toll free: 800-426-4727; Dist. by: DeVorss & Co., P.O. Box 550, 1046 Princeton Dr., Marina del Rey, CA 90294 (SAN 168-9886) Tel 203-870-7478; Dist. by: New Leaf Distributing, The, 1020 White St., SW, Atlanta, GA 30310 (SAN 169-1449) Tel 404-755-2665; Toll free: 800-241-3829.

Dreaming Spring Pr., The, Div. of The Dreaming Spring Corp., *(Dreaming; 0-9611923),* 510 Woodgate Dr., Marietta, GA 30066 (SAN 283-2658) Tel 404-427-1238; Dist. by: DeVorss & Co., P.O. Box 550, 1046 Princeton Dr., Marina del Rey, CA 90294 (SAN 282-6151) Tel 203-870-7478; Dist. by: Starlite Distributors, P.O. Box 20729, Reno, NV 89515 (SAN 200-7789) Tel 702-359-5676.

Dreenan Pr., Ltd., *(Dreenan Pr; 0-88376),* P.O. Box 385, Croton-on-Hudson, NY 10520 (SAN 201-808X) Tel 914-271-5085.

Drelwood Pubns., *(Drelwood Pubns; 0-937766),* P.O. Box 10605, Portland, OR 97210 (SAN 215-756X); Orders to: Communication Creativity, P.O. Box 213, Saguache, CO 81149 (SAN 210-3478) Tel 303-655-2504.

Dremel, Div. of Emerson Electric Co., *(DREMEL; 0-9606512),* 4915 21st St., Racine, WI 53406 (SAN 223-1530) Tel 414-554-1390.

Drewry, Betty, *(B Drewry; 0-9615928),* 3025 Dale Dr., NE, Atlanta, GA 30305 (SAN 697-1059) Tel 404-233-6281.

Drift Group, The, *(Drift Group; 0-938365),* P.O. Box 5144, Helena, MT 59604 (SAN 661-1117) Tel 406-442-2746.

Driscoll, Robert Bruce, *(R B Driscoll; 0-9601374),* P.O. Box 637, Oakland, CA 94604 (SAN 204-1936) Tel 415-451-4870.

Drivers License Guide Co., *(Drivers License Guide; 0-938964),* 1492 Oddstad Dr., Redwood City, CA 94063 (SAN 215-949X); Toll free: 800-227-8827.

Names

Names

Drollery Pr., *(Drollery Pr; 0-940920),* 1615 Encinal Ave., Alameda, CA 94501 (SAN 223-1808) Tel 415-521-4087; Dist. by: Publishers Group West, 5855 Beaudry St., Emeryville, CA 94608 (SAN 202-8522) Tel 415-658-3453; Toll free: 800-982-8319.

Dropsie College, *(Dropsie Coll; 0-9602686; 0-935135),* 250 N. Highland, Merion, PA 19066 (SAN 223-4602); Dist. by: Eisenbrauns, P.O. Box 275, Winona Lake, IN 46590-0278 (SAN 200-7835) Tel 219-269-2011.

Dropzone Pr., *(Dropzone Pr; 0-913257),* P.O. Box 882222, San Francisco, CA 94188 (SAN 285-6638) Tel 415-776-7164; Dist. by: Publishers Group West, 5855 Beaudry St., Emeryville, CA 94608 (SAN 202-8522) Tel 415-658-3453.

†Drug Intelligence Pubns., *(Drug Intell Pubns; 0-914768),* 4720 Montgomery Ln. Suite 807, Bethesda, MD 20814 (SAN 201-2804) Tel 301-654-8736; Orders to: 1241 Broadway, Hamilton, IL 62341 (SAN 201-2812) Tel 217-847-2504; *CIP.*

Drug Store Market Guide, *(Drug Store Mkt; 0-9606064),* 1739 Horton Ave., Mohegan Lake, NY 10547 (SAN 216-888X) Tel 914-528-7147.

Druid Bks., *(Druid Bks; 0-912518),* P.O. Box 231, Ephraim, WI 54211 (SAN 210-797X).

Druid Heights Books, *(Druid Heights; 0-9606568),* 685 Camino del Canyon, Muir Woods, Mill Valley, CA 94941 (SAN 206-4693) Tel 415-388-2111.

Drum Associates, Affil. of John Scherer & Assocs., *(Drum Assocs; 0-9611024),* W. 201 Sumner, Spokane, WA 99204 (SAN 277-674X) Tel 509-747-1029.

Drumbeat *See* **Longman, Inc.**

Drumm, Chris, Bks., *(C Drumm Bks; 0-936055),* P.O. Box 445, Polk City, IA 50226 (SAN 697-0478) Tel 515-984-6749.

Dry Color Manufacturers Assn., *(Dry Color Mfrs),* 206 N. Washington St., Suite 202, Alexandria, VA 22314 (SAN 224-683X) Tel 703-684-4044.

Dry Eye Institute, *(Dry Eye Inst; 0-9616938),* P.O. Box 98069, Lubbock, TX 79499 (SAN 661-8235); 301 York Ave., Lubbock, TX 79416 (SAN 661-8243) Tel 806-799-1862.

Dry Ridge Co., *(Dry Ridge; 0-9613545),* 733 James Ln., Walton, KY 41094 (SAN 669-7801) Tel 606-485-6193.

†Dryad Pr., *(Dryad Pr; 0-931848),* 15 Sherman Ave., Takoma Park, MD 20912 (SAN 206-197X) Tel 301-891-3729; *CIP.*

†Dryden Pr., Div. of Holt, Rinehart & Winston, Inc., *(Dryden Pr; 0-8498),* 901 N. Elm, Hinsdale, IL 60521 (SAN 281-613X) Tel 312-325-2985; Toll free: 800-323-7437; 1 Salt Creek Ln., Hinsdale, IL 60521 (SAN 658-0483); Orders to: CBS College Publishing, 383 Madison Ave., New York, NY 10017 (SAN 281-6148) Tel 212-872-2219; *CIP.*

Dryden Press of Australia *See* **Australiana Pubns.**

Du Ewa, *(Du Ewa; 0-933033),* Box 6300108, Spuyten Duyvil Sta., New York, NY 10463 (SAN 690-0364) Tel 212-796-3070.

Du Sable Museum Press, *(Du Sable Mus),* 740 E. 56th Place, Chicago, IL 60637 (SAN 201-8004) Tel 312-947-0600.

Du Vall Pr. Financial Pubns., *(Du Vall Financial; 0-931232),* 920 W. Grand River, Williamston, MI 48895 (SAN 212-0380).

Dual Pubns., Inc., *(Dual Pubns; 0-914041),* 1542 Sunflower Ct. S., Palm Springs, CA 92262 (SAN 287-6493) Tel 619-320-5330.

Dube, Brian, Inc., *(B Dube; 0-917643),* 25 Park Place, New York, NY 10007 (SAN 657-0704) Tel 212-619-2182.

Dubis Assocs., Inc., *(Dubis Assoc; 0-942076),* 2043 W. Rock Rd., Perkasie, PA 18944 (SAN 238-4558) Tel 904-756-4937.

DuBose Publishing, *(DuBose Pub; 0-938072),* P.O. Box 924, Atlanta, GA 30301 (SAN 215-7586).

Duck Distributing, *(Duck Dist; 0-9616420),* 11103 Clear Fork, Humble, TX 77338 (SAN 659-1582) Tel 713-454-7294.

Duck Down, Pr., *(Duck Down; 0-916918),* P.O. Box 1047, Fallon, NV 89406 (SAN 208-502X) Tel 702-423-6643.

Duck Tale Productions, *(Duck Tale Prods; 0-9610374),* P.O. Box 11159, Memphis, TN 38111 (SAN 264-0155) Tel 901-452-8944.

Duco, Joyce, *(J Duco; 0-9612896),* BNA Corporate Center, Bldg. 200, Suite 207, Nashville, TN 37217 (SAN 291-140X) Tel 615-366-0455; Dist. by: DeVorss & Co., P.O. Box 550, 1046 Princeton Dr., Marina del Rey, CA 90294 (SAN 168-9886) Tel 213-870-7478; Dist. by: Spring Arbor Distributors, 10885 Textile Rd., Belleville, MI 48111 (SAN 158-9016) Tel 313-481-0900; Toll free: 800-521-3990.

Duende Pr, *(Duende; 0-915008),* 6434 Raymond St, Oakland, CA 94609 (SAN 207-8163).

Dufour Editions, Inc., *(Dufour; 0-8023),* Box 449, Chester Springs, PA 19425-0449 (SAN 201-341X) Tel 215-458-5005.

Dugdale, Kathleen, *(Dugdale; 0-9600028),* C/O Indiana University Foundation, P.O. Box 500, Bloomington, IN 47402 (SAN 201-3428) Tel 812-335-8311.

Duggan & Duggan Pubns., *(Duggan Pubns; 0-916989),* P.O. Box 282, New Lenox, IL 60451 (SAN 168-9886) Tel 815-485-9519.

Duir Pr., *(Duir Press; 0-9602912),* 919 Sutter St., Apt. 9, San Francisco, CA 94109 (SAN 223-5722).

Dujarie Pr., *(Dujarie Pr; 0-8275),* Columbia Hall, Notre Dame, IN 46556 (SAN 658-6309) Tel 219-283-7133.

Duke, David A., *(D A Duke; 0-9605056),* P.O. Box 725, Whitehouse, TX 75791 (SAN 220-0465) Tel 214-839-4837.

Duke Publishing Co., *(Duke Pub Co; 0-9613727),* P.O. Box 210368, San Francisco, CA 94121 (SAN 677-5187) Tel 415-759-0118.

†Duke Univ., Ctr. for International Studies, *(Ctr Intl Stud Duke; 0-916994),* 2122 Campus Dr., Durham, NC 27706 (SAN 213-5795); *CIP.*

Duke Univ. Pr., *(Duke; 0-8223),* Box 6697 College Sta., Durham, NC 27708 (SAN 201-3436) Tel 919-684-2173.

Dultz, Ron, Publishing, *(R Dultz; 0-9601636),* P.O. Box 985, Reseda, CA 91335 (SAN 211-5603) Tel 818-993-7932.

†Dumbarton Oaks, *(Dumbarton Oaks; 0-88402),* 1703 32nd St., NW, Washington, DC 20007 (SAN 293-2547) Tel 202-342-3259; Dist. by: Dumbarton Oaks Publishing Service, P.O. Box 4866, Hampden Sta., Baltimore, MD 21211 (SAN 293-2555) Tel 301-338-6954; *CIP.*

Dumond, Val, *(V Dumond; 0-9613673),* P.O. Box 97124, Tacoma, WA 98497 (SAN 683-2172).

Dun & Bradstreet Corp., *(Dun),* 299 Park Ave., New York, NY 10171 (SAN 287-0134) Tel 212-593-6800; Orders to: 99 Church St., New York, NY 10007 (SAN 287-0142).

Duna Studios, Inc., *(Duna Studios; 0-942928),* P.O. Box 24051, Minneapolis, MN 55424 (SAN 240-1428) Tel 612-926-5201.

Dunbar Publishing Co., *(Dunbar Pub; 0-931680),* P.O. Box 13368, Jamaica, NY 11413 (SAN 221-2048).

Duncan & Gladstone Publishing Co., *(Duncan & Gladstone; 0-9616212),* P.O. Box 50355, Austin, TX 78763 (SAN 698-1852) Tel 512-477-1080; 1209 W. 10th St., Austin, TX 78703 (SAN 658-3008).

Duncan Gun Shop Inc., *(Duncan Gun; 0-9613502),* 414 Second St., North Wilkesboro, NC 28659 (SAN 683-2490).

Duncan-Holmes Publishing Co., *(Duncan-Holmes; 0-9609480),* P.O. Box 481, Syracuse, IN 46567 (SAN 269-7750).

Duncliff's International, *(Duncliffs Intl; 0-911663),* 3662 Katella Ave., Los Alamitos, CA 90720 (SAN 264-018X).

Dunconor Books, *(Dunconor Bks; 0-918820),* P.O. Box 106, Crestone, CO 81131 (SAN 208-1776).

Dundas, Richard J., Pubns., *(R J Dundas Pubns; 0-9617093),* 31 North St. Extension, Rutland, VT 05701 (SAN 662-4782) Tel 802-775-4558; Dist. by: Queen City Brass Pubns., Box 75054, Cincinnati, OH 45275 (SAN 200-7436).

Dundee Publishing, *(Dundee Pub; 0-935210),* P.O. Box 202, Dundee, NY 14837 (SAN 213-6848) Tel 301-432-8079.

Dunedin Youth Guild Inc., *(Dunedin Youth; 0-9613858),* P.O. Box 1453, Dunedin, FL 34296-1453 (SAN 683-2504) Tel 813-734-0394.

Dunes Enterprises, *(Dunes; 0-9613419),* P.O. Box 601, Beverly Shores, IN 46301 (SAN 207-0146) Tel 219-872-8077.

Dunk Rock Books *See* **Four Quarters Publishing Co.**

†Dunlap Society, *(Dunlap Soc; 0-89481),* Lake Champlain Rd., Essex, NY 12936 (SAN 281-6156) Tel 518-963-7373; Orders to: Princeton Univ. Pr., 41 Williams St., Princeton, NJ 07302 (SAN 281-6164) Tel 609-452-4879; *CIP.*

Dunlay, Kate E., *(K E Dunlay; 0-9617024),* 27 sherman Bridge Rd., Wayland, MA 01778 (SAN 662-5746) Tel 617-358-4039; Dist. by: Fiddlecase Bks., HC 63 Box 104, East Alstead, NH 03602 (SAN 200-7495).

Dunn, Iris, *(Iris Dunn; 0-9616135),* HCR 8, Box 455, Beeville, TX 78102 (SAN 699-8593) Tel 512-358-3750.

Dunne, Carol, *(Carol Dunne; 0-9616138),* 220 NE 51st Ct., Fort Lauderdale, FL 33334 (SAN 699-864X) Tel 305-771-5646.

Dun's Marketing Services, *(Dun's Mktg; 0-918257),* 49 Old Bloomfield Ave., Mountain Lakes, NJ 07046 (SAN 226-5508) Tel 201-299-0181; Toll free: 800-526-0651; 3 Century Dr., Parsippany, NJ 07054 (SAN 661-9975) Tel 201-455-0900.

Dunsmuir Centennial Committee, *(Dunsmuir Centennial; 0-9614838),* P.O. Box 605, Dunsmuir, CA 96025 (SAN 693-0212) Tel 916-235-2144.

Dunstan Pr., *(Dunstan Pr; 0-930995),* 30 Linden St., Rockland, ME 04841 (SAN 678-8920) Tel 207-596-0064.

Dunwoody Pr., Div. of MRM, Language Research Ctr., Inc., *(Dunwoody Pr; 0-931745),* P.O. Box 1825, Silver Spring, MD 20902 (SAN 683-5309) Tel 301-946-7006.

Dunwoody Pubs., *(Dunwoody Pubs; 0-9616895),* Mt. Vernon Rd., Dunwoody, GA 30338 (SAN 661-3403) Tel 404-425-9112.

DUO *See* **Unipub**

Duobooks, Inc., *(Duobooks; 0-918394),* 154 W. 57th St., New York, NY 10019 (SAN 210-0703) Tel 212-757-4438; Orders to: 300 Fairfield Rd., Fairfield, NJ 07006 (SAN 210-0711).

Duodecimal Society of America *See* **Dozenal Society of America**

Dupont & Disend, *(Dupont & Disend; 0-9614927),* 2137 Mt. Vernon Rd., Atlanta, GA 30338 (SAN 693-4005) Tel 404-395-7483.

Duquesne Publishing Co., *(Duquesne Pub; 0-89653),* P.O. Box 222, West Brookfield, MA 01585 (SAN 211-1233) Tel 617-867-9341.

†Duquesne Univ. Pr., *(Duquesne; 0-8207),* 600 Forbes Ave., Pittsburgh, PA 15282 (SAN 658-0491) Tel 412-434-6610; Toll free: 800-221-3845; Dist. by: Humanities Pr. International, Inc., 171 First Ave., Atlantic Highlands, NJ 07716-1289 (SAN 201-9272) Tel 201-872-1441; *CIP.*

Durand International, *(Durand Intl; 0-9604056),* P.O. Box 925, Lynwood, CA 90262 (SAN 214-1884).

Durant Publishing Co., *(Durant Pub; 0-9606128),* 1208 Tatum Dr., Alexandria, VA 22307 (SAN 217-488X) Tel 703-765-4311.

Durbin Assocs., *(Durbin Assoc; 0-936786),* 3711 Southwood Dr., Easton, PA 18042 (SAN 215-0697).

Duren, Joyce, *(J Duren; 0-9616196),* 328 Myers Pl., Inglewood, CA 90301 (SAN 699-9018) Tel 213-671-5271.

Durrell Pubns., Inc., *(Durrell; 0-911764),* P.O. Box 743, Kennebunkport, ME 04046 (SAN 201-3452) Tel 207-985-3904.

Durst, Sanford J., *(S J Durst; 0-915262; 0-942666),* 29-28 41st Ave., Long Island City, NY 11101 (SAN 211-6987) Tel 718-706-0303.

Dushkin Publishing Group, Inc., *(Dushkin Pub; 0-87967),* Sluice Dock, Guilford, CT 06437 (SAN 213-3460) Tel 203-453-4351; Toll free: 800-243-6532.

†Dustbooks, *(Dustbooks; 0-913218; 0-916685),* P.O. Box 100, Paradise, CA 95969 (SAN 204-1871) Tel 916-877-6110; *CIP.*

Dustin Pubns., *(Dustin Pubns; 0-9614622),* 935 W. Mountain St., Glendale, CA 91202 (SAN 679-1840) Tel 818-242-7000.

Dutch Fork Press, *(Dutch Fork Pr; 0-9611610),* P.O. Box 21766-A, Columbia, SC 29221 (SAN 285-2640) Tel 803-772-6919.

Dutton, E. P., *(Dutton; 0-525),* 2 Park Ave., New York, NY 10016 (SAN 201-0070) Tel 212-725-1818; Toll free: 800-221-4676. *Imprints:* Elsevier-Phaidon (Elsevier-Phaidon); Gingerbread House (Gingerbread); Hawthorn Books (Hawthorn); Phaidon (Pub. by Phaidon); Windmill Books (Windmill).

Duval-Bibb Publishing Co., *(Duval Bibb Pub; 0-937713),* P.O. Box 23704, Tampa, FL 33623 (SAN 659-3119) Tel 813-870-1970; 200 N. Westshore Blvd., Tampa, FL 33609 (SAN 659-3127).

Duverus Publishing Corp., *(Duverus Pub; 0-918700),* P.O. Box 107, Seligman, MO 65745 (SAN 209-1305) Tel 417-662-3690.

Duvivier, Paul, *(P Duvivier; 0-9616873),* 3013 Cleveland Ave., NW, Washington, DC 20008 (SAN 661-3365) Tel 202-234-2631.

Duxbury Pr. *See* **PWS Pubs.**

Dvorak International Federation, *(Dvorak Intl; 0-9615788),* 11 Pearl St., Brandon, VT 05733 (SAN 696-7310) Tel 802-247-6020.

Dvorion Bks., *(Dvorion Bks; 0-9611328),* 508 Fifth Ave., Bethlehem, PA 18018 (SAN 282-888X) Tel 215-691-6318.

Dwapara Herald Pubs., Inc., *(Dwapara; 0-917952),* P.O. Box 429, Marble Hill, MO 63764 (SAN 209-5513) Tel 314-238-4273.

Dwight D. Eisenhower Presidential Library *See* **Eisenhower, Dwight D., Library**

Dwyer, Jeffrey P., *(J P Dwyer),* 30 Pleasant St., Box 426, Northampton, MA 01061 (SAN 209-5521) Tel 413-584-7909.

Dyco, Inc., *(Dyco Inc; 0-937224),* 6702 E. Cactus Rd., Scottsdale, AZ 85254 (SAN 216-1257) Tel 602-948-4784.

Dynabyte Bks., *(Dynabyte Books; 0-9610220),* 281 Morning Sun Ave., Mill Valley, CA 94941 (SAN 264-0198) Tel 415-381-9108.

Dynamic Communications, *(Dynamic Comm; 0-9613917),* 1001 Slayton Ave., Grand Haven, MI 49417 (SAN 683-2083) Tel 616-842-8466.

Dynamic Graphics, Inc., *(Dynamic Graph; 0-939437),* 6000 N. Forest Park Dr., Peoria, IL 61614 (SAN 663-3463) Tel 309-688-8800.

Dynamic Information Publishing, *(Dynamic Info; 0-941286),* 8311 Greeley Blvd., Springfield, VA 22152 (SAN 240-091X).

Dynamic Ink Publishing, Co., *(Dynamic Ink Pub; 0-934089),* 8900 Keystone Crossing, No. 680 Tower, Indianapolis, IN 46240 (SAN 693-0239) Tel 317-841-7884.

Dynamic Pubns., Inc., *(Dynamic Pubns; 0-915569),* 901 Bonifant Rd., Silver Spring, MD 20904 (SAN 291-1418) Tel 301-236-6800; Toll free: 800-255-1777.

Dynamic Reflections, *(Dynamic Reflections; 0-9616971),* P.O. Box 881, East Brunswick, NJ 08816 (SAN 661-8219); 24 Colonial Dr., New Brunswick, NJ 08816 (SAN 661-8227) Tel 201-254-0415.

Dynamic Teaching Co., *(Dynamic Teaching; 0-937899),* 2247 Palmwood Ct., Rancho Cordova, CA 95670 (SAN 659-4425) Tel 916-638-1136.

Dynamics of Christian Living Inc., *(Dynamics Chr Liv; 0-940386),* Box 1053, Akron, OH 44309 (SAN 219-7839).

Dynamis Corp., *(Dynamis Corp; 0-936173),* P.O. Box 1900, Ansonia Station, NY 10023 (SAN 697-0486) Tel 914-234-9217.

†Dynamo, Inc., *(Dynamo Inc; 0-936294; 0-913659),* P.O. Box 173, Wheaton, IL 60189 (SAN 214-0675) Tel 312-665-0060; *CIP.*

Dynasty Publishing, *(Dynasty Pub; 0-936541),* 1188 Bishop St., Suite 3011, Honolulu, HI 96813 (SAN 697-8614) Tel 808-527-4995.

D'Zign Land Survey & Development, *(D'Zign Land Survey Dev; 0-9616846),* 747 Geary St., No. 203, San Francisco, CA 94109 (SAN 661-1710) Tel 415-775-2275.

E & B Enterprise, *(E B Enterprise; 0-9616364),* Rte. 2, Box 128-B, Hempstead, TX 77445 (SAN 659-1590) Tel 409-826-6303.

E&C Bks., *(E & C Bks; 0-935126),* 20 Atwater Pl., Massapequa, NY 11758 (SAN 213-8433).

†E&E Enterprises, *(E & E Enterprises; 0-917954),* 1203 Pomelo Ct., Longwood, FL 32779 (SAN 208-3906) Tel 305-862-2823; *CIP.*

E & P Enterprises, *(E & P Enter; 0-9614095),* P.O. Box 2613, Lawton, OK 73502 (SAN 685-9895) Tel 512-224-4431.

†EBHA Press, Div. of Economic and Business History Assocs., *(EBHA Pr; 0-935662),* 5919 Cullen Dr., Lincoln, NE 68506-1433 (SAN 213-6201) Tel 402-488-0684; *CIP.*

EBSCO Industries, Inc., *(EBSCO Ind; 0-913956),* P.O. Box 1943, Birmingham, AL 35201 (SAN 201-3584) Tel 205-991-6600; Toll free: 800-633-6088.

ECA Assocs., *(ECA Assoc; 0-938818),* P.O. Box 15004, Great Bridge Sta., Chesapeake, VA 23320 (SAN 215-9503) Tel 804-547-5542; P.O. Box 20186, Cathedral Finance Sta., New York, NY 10025 (SAN 215-9511) Tel 212-866-8694.

ECR Associates, *(ECR Assocs; 0-9600352),* 4832 Park Rd Suite 125, Charlotte, NC 28209 (SAN 201-9752) Tel 704-372-3227.

ECRI, *(ECRI),* 5200 Butler Pike, Plymouth Meeting, PA 19462 (SAN 224-1234) Tel 215-825-6000.

EDC Publishing, Div. of Educational Development Corp., *(EDC; 0-88110),* 10302 E. 55th Pl., Tulsa, OK 74146 (SAN 226-2134) Tel 918-622-4522; Toll free: 800-331-4418; P.O. Box 470663, Tulsa, OK 74147 (SAN 658-0505); P.O. Box 702253, Tulsa, OK 74170 (SAN 658-0513). *Imprints:* Usborne-Hayes (Usborne-Hayes).

EDITS Pubs., *(EDITS Pubs),* P.O. Box 7234, San Diego, CA 92107 (SAN 208-4600) Tel 619-488-1666.

E D M Digest Co., *(EDM Digest; 0-9614302),* 31505 Grand River, Suite 1, Farmington, MI 48024 (SAN 687-4762) Tel 313-474-3489.

EDUCOM, *(EDUCOM),* P.O. Box 364, Rosedale & Carter Rds., Princeton, NJ 08540 (SAN 223-0321) Tel 609-734-1915.

EEPC Publishing Co., *(EEPC Pub; 0-937699),* 653 E. 118, Cleveland, OH 44108 (SAN 659-3496) Tel 216-451-5242.

EFQ Pubns., *(EFQ Pubns; 0-937265),* P.O. Box 4958, San Francisco, CA 94101 (SAN 659-1620).

EG Booksellers & Pubs., *(EG Bkslr Pubs; 0-938979),* 99 Sanchez St., San Francisco, CA 94114 (SAN 661-6828) Tel 415-863-5864; Dist. by: Small Pr. Distribution, 1814 San Pablo Ave., Berkeley, CA 94702 (SAN 204-5826) Tel 415-549-3336.

EGM Enterprises, *(EGM Ent; 0-9604586),* 1223 S. 155th St., Omaha, NE 68144 (SAN 215-1448) Tel 402-333-3698.

EHUD International Language Foundation, *(EHUD),* 1755 Trinity Ave., No. 79, Walnut Creek, CA 94596 (SAN 281-6172) Tel 415-937-4841; Orders to: Box 2082, Dollar Ranch Sta., Walnut Creek, CA 94595 (SAN 281-6180) Tel 415-937-4841.

E-Heart Pr., Inc., *(E-Heart Pr; 0-935014),* 3700 Mockingbird Ln., Dallas, TX 75205 (SAN 216-3691) Tel 214-528-2655.

EIC/Intelligence, Inc., *(EIC Intell; 0-89947),* 48 W. 38th St., New York, NY 10018 (SAN 211-1276) Tel 212-944-8500; Toll free: 800-223-6275.

EJP Publishing Co., *(EJP Pub Co; 0-934883),* P.O. Box 44268, Tucson, AZ 85733 (SAN 694-4426); 4420 E. Speedway, Suite 202, Tucson, AZ 85719 (SAN 662-3387) Tel 602-628-7678. *Imprints:* Bellwether Books (Bellwether Bks); Gecko Press (Gecko Pr).

EKB Bks., *(EKB Bks; 0-9616714),* P.O. Box 608291, Chicago, IL 60626 (SAN 661-2075); 7613 N. Paulina, Chicago, IL 60626 (SAN 661-2083) Tel 312-973-4317.

EK Publishing Co., *(EK Pub Co; 0-937833),* 535 NE Adams, Chehalis, WA 98532 (SAN 659-4433) Tel 206-748-0545.

EKS Publishing, Co., *(EKS Pub Co; 0-939144),* 5336 College Ave., Oakland, CA 94618 (SAN 216-1281) Tel 415-653-5183.

EMC Controls, Inc., *(EMC Controls; 0-9609256),* P.O. Box 242, Cockeysville, MD 21030 (SAN 260-0455) Tel 301-667-8162.

EMC Publishing, Div. of EMC Corp., *(EMC; 0-88436; 0-912022; 0-8219),* 300 York Ave., St. Paul, MN 55101 (SAN 201-3800) Tel 612-771-1555; Toll free: 800-328-1452.

†ENAAQ Pubns., *(ENAAQ Pubns; 0-915867),* P.O. Box 1375, Chicago, IL 60690 (SAN 293-9339) Tel 312-643-4247; 5226 S. Ingleside, Chicago, IL 60615 (SAN 293-9347); *CIP.*

ENR Wordsmiths, *(ENR Word; 0-911511),* P.O. Box 160081, Miami, FL 33116 (SAN 264-2468) Tel 305-596-4523.

EO Pr., *(EO Pr; 0-935830),* RR 1, Box 353-A Minuet Ln., Kingston, NY 12401 (SAN 221-1858) Tel 914-336-8797.

†EPM Pubns., *(EPM Pubns; 0-914440; 0-939009),* 1003 Turkey Run Rd., McLean, VA 22101 (SAN 206-7498) Tel 703-442-7810; Orders to: P.O. Box 490, McLean, VA 22101 (SAN 206-7501); *CIP.*

E.P. Pr., Inc., *(E P Press),* P.O. Box 1172, Gastonia, NC 28052 (SAN 297-1771).

ERA/CCR Corp., *(ERA-CCR; 0-913935),* P.O. Box 650, Nyack, NY 10960 (SAN 217-5622) Tel 914-358-6806; Toll free: 800-845-8402.

E R S *See* **Educational Research Service**

ESE California, *(ESE Calif; 0-912076),* 509 N. Harbor Blvd., La Habra, CA 90631 (SAN 201-4629) Tel 213-691-0737.

ESP Corp., *(ESP Corp; 0-9601610),* 195 Cortlandt St., Belleville, NJ 07109 (SAN 211-4194).

ESP, Inc., *(ESP; 0-8209),* P.O. Drawer 5037, 1201 E. Johnson Ave., Jonesboro, AR 72401 (SAN 241-497X); Toll free: 800-643-0280.

ETC Assocs., *(ETC Assocs; 0-910565),* 507 Rider Rd., Clayville, NY 13322 (SAN 269-9796) Tel 315-839-5184.

†ETC Pubns., *(ETC Pubns; 0-88280),* 700 E. Vereda del Sur, Palm Springs, CA 92262 (SAN 201-4637) Tel 619-325-5352; Orders to: Order Dept., Box ETC, Palm Springs, CA 92263-1608 (SAN 201-4645); *CIP.*

EVKAR Publishing, *(EVKAR Pub; 0-9616965),* 842 Eastfield Rd., Westbury, NY 11590 (SAN 661-8197) Tel 516-334-4101.

E. W. Clautice, Pubs., *(Clautice Pubs; 0-9614359),* 231 Lynbrok Dr. N., York, PA 17402 (SAN 688-4776) Tel 717-755-6809.

EW Engineering, Inc., *(EW Eng; 0-931728),* P.O. Box 28, Dunn Loring, VA 22027 (SAN 212-3487).

E-Z Learning Methods, *(E-Z Learning; 0-931924),* P.O. Box 2582, Pomona, CA 91766 (SAN 212-3495) Tel 714-622-6835.

E.T.T.A. *See* **Evangelical Teacher Training Assn.**

Eades Publishing Co., *(Eades Pub; 0-9615892),* 126 Lummi, LaConner, WA 98257 (SAN 697-0915) Tel 206-466-3472.

Eagle Bank Pr., Div. of Greentree Pictures, *(Eagle Bank Pr; 0-937501),* Jan Del, Box 63030, Bronx, NY 10463-9992 (SAN 659-1663) Tel 212-796-5792; 4705 Henry Hudson Pkwy., No. 2K, Riverdale, NY 10471 (SAN 659-1671).

Eagle Bks., *(Eagle Bks; 0-910971),* 1900 W. B St., Joplin, MO 64801 (SAN 263-2160).

Eagle Communications, *(Eagle Comm; 0-9605462),* 340 W. Main St., Missoula, MT 59806 (SAN 216-1303).

Eagle Foundation, The, *(Eagle Foun),* Box 155, Apple River, IL 61001 (SAN 225-1736) Tel 815-594-2259; 300 E. Hickory, Apple River, IL 61001 (SAN 669-070X).

Eagle Peak Publishing Co., *(Eagle Peak Pub; 0-9611102),* 15703 Vista Vicente Dr., Ramona, CA 92065 (SAN 282-8634) Tel 619-789-4177.

Eagle Pr., *(Eagle Pr CA; 0-9615068),* 3315 Sacramento St., No 427, San Francisco, CA 94115 (SAN 693-9414) Tel 415-591-6815.

Eagle Publishing Co., *(Eagle Pub; 0-941624),* 7283 Kolb Pl., Dublin, CA 94568 (SAN 239-2011) Tel 415-828-1350.

Eaglenest Publishing Co., *(Eaglenest Pub; 0-9616392),* 2120 Crestmoor Rd., Suite 398, Nashville, TN 37215 (SAN 659-171X) Tel 615-385-0101.

Eagles 5, The, *(Eagles Five; 0-9616745),* 45-057 Waikalualoko Loop, Kaneohe, HI 96744 (SAN 661-2202) Tel 808-263-5182.

†Eagles View Publishing, Subs. of Eagle Feather Trading Post, Inc., *(Eagles View; 0-943604),* 706 W. Riverdale Rd., Ogden, UT 84405 (SAN 240-6330) Tel 801-393-3991; *CIP.*

†Eakin Pubns., Inc., *(Eakin Pubns; 0-89015),* P.O. Box 23066, Austin, TX 78735 (SAN 207-3633) Tel 512-288-1771; *CIP.*

†Eakins Pr. Foundation, *(Eakins; 0-87130),* 5 W. 73rd St., New York, NY 10023 (SAN 201-3541) Tel 212-496-2255; *CIP.*

Ear-Literature *See* **Pierce-Ellis Enterprises**

Ear Say Bks., *(Ear Say; 0-9613871),* 29-06210 St., Bayside, NY 11360 (SAN 656-8874); Dist. by: Ear-Say, Main P.O. Box 299, Purchase, NY 10577 (SAN 685-1886) Tel 914-342-0234.

Eardley Pubns., *(Eardley Pubns; 0-937630),* P.O. Box 281, Rochelle Park, NJ 07662 (SAN 215-6377) Tel 201-791-5014.

Earendil Pr., *(Earendil Pr; 0-914577),* 1958 Manzanita, Oakland, CA 94611 (SAN 289-2235) Tel 415-339-1352.

Earhart Pr., *(Earhart Pr; 0-937061),* 424 Hilldale, Ann Arbor, MI 48105 (SAN 658-5744) Tel 313-665-9261.

Earl Enterprises, *(Earl Ent; 0-9602504),* P.O. Box 1254, 7400 Cutting Blvd., El Cerrito, CA 94530 (SAN 223-4645).

Earle, Arthur, *(A Earle; 0-9600788),* 10922 Nandina Ct., Philadelphia, PA 19116 (SAN 207-4648) Tel 215-676-9762.

†Early American Industries Assn., Inc., *(Early Am Indus; 0-943196),* P.O. Box 2128, Empire State Plaza, Albany, NY 12220-0128 (SAN 669-0718) Tel 518-439-2215; *CIP.*

Early Educators Pr., *(Early Educators; 0-9604390),* P.O. Box 1177, Lake Alfred, FL 33850 (SAN 216-2407) Tel 813-956-1569; Dist. by: Gryphon Hse., Inc., 3706 Otis St., P.O.Box 275, Mt. Rainier, MD 20712 (SAN 169-3190) Tel 301-779-6200; Toll free: 800-638-0928.

Early Learning Assocs., Inc., *(Early Learn Assoc; 0-933373),* 25118 35th Ave., S, Kent, WA 98032 (SAN 691-6732) Tel 206-839-3156.

Early Stages Press, Inc., *(Early Stages; 0-915786),* P.O. Box 31463, San Francisco, CA 94131 (SAN 209-0155).

Early Winters Press, *(Early Winters; 0-941984),* 110 Prefontaine S., Seattle, WA 98104 (SAN 238-0110).

Earnest Pubns., *(Earnest Pubns; 0-9616789),* P.O. Box 1302, Chicago Heights, IL 60411 (SAN 661-2210); 161 Kathleen Ln., Chicago Heights, IL 60411 (SAN 661-2229) Tel 312-756-2719.

Earpacker Press, *(Earpacker Pr; 0-9611304),* P.O. Box 5029, Philadelphia, PA 19111 (SAN 277-6766).

Earth Basics Pr., *(Earth Basics; 0-910361),* P.O. Box 1021, Milpitas, CA 95035 (SAN 260-0463) Tel 408-945-9134.

Earth First!, *(Earth First; 0-933285),* P.O. Box 5871, Tucson, AZ 85703 (SAN 692-3585) Tel 602-744-0623.

Earth Heart, *(Earth Heart; 0-934747),* 30 Manana Way, Point Reyes Station, CA 94956 (SAN 694-1966) Tel 415-663-8010; P.O. Box 1027, Point Reyes Station, CA 94956 (SAN 658-2818); Dist. by: Bookpeople, 2929 Fifth St., Berkeley, CA 94710 (SAN 168-9517) Tel 415-549-3030; Toll free: 800-227-1516.

Earth Science Assocs., *(Earth Sci Assocs; 0-9616753),* 6321 Cate Rd., Powell, TN 37849 (SAN 661-2245) Tel 615-947-9698.

Earth-Song Pr., *(Earth-Song; 0-9605170),* 202 Hartnell Pl., Sacramento, CA 95825 (SAN 220-0473) Tel 916-927-6863.

Earth-Space Innovations, *(Earth Space),* P.O. Box 43, Van Etten, NY 14889 (SAN 241-3779).

†Earth View, Inc, *(Earth View; 0-932898),* 6514 18th Ave., NE, Seattle, WA 98115 (SAN 213-0491) Tel 206-527-3168; *CIP.*

Earthlight Pubs., *(Earthlight; 0-935128),* 5539 Jackson, Kansas City, MO 64130 (SAN 213-3059).

Earthquake Engineering Research Ctr., *(Earthquake Eng; 0-943198),* 6431 Fairmount Ave., Suite 7, El Cerrito, CA 94530 (SAN 224-117X) Tel 415-848-0972.

Earthquake Ready Now, *(Earthquake Ready; 0-9615360),* P.O. Box 7360, Santa Cruz, CA 95061 (SAN 695-2631) Tel 408-458-1966.

Earthstewards Publications, *(Earthstewards Pubns),* Box 873, Monte Rio, CA 95462 (SAN 240-1436).

†Earthview Pr., *(Earthview Press; 0-930705),* 1818 Samos Cir., Lafayette, CO 80026 (SAN 677-2072) Tel 303-666-8130; Orders to: P.O. Box 11036, Boulder, CO 80301 (SAN 662-2526); *CIP.*

Earthwise Pubns., *(Earthwise Pubns; 0-933494),* P.O. Box 680-536, Miami, FL 33168 (SAN 223-7407) Tel 305-688-8558.

EarthZ, *(EarthZ; 0-9614271),* 1575 S. Lincoln St., Kent, OH 44240 (SAN 687-1593) Tel 216-678-6108.

Easi-Bild Directions Simplified, Inc., *(Easi-Bild; 0-87733),* 529 N. State Rd., P.O. Box 215, Briarcliff Manor, NY 10510 (SAN 201-3304) Tel 914-941-6600.

East Brother Light Station, Inc., *(East Brother; 0-9614254),* 117 Park Place, Point Richmond, CA 94801 (SAN 686-6751).

East Dennis Publishing Co., *(East Dennis; 0-87299),* P.O. Box 555, East Dennis, MA 02641 (SAN 210-8011) Tel 617-385-2000.

East Eagle Press, *(East Eagle; 0-9605738),* P.O. Box 812, Huron, SD 57350 (SAN 216-3705) Tel 605-352-5875.

East European Quarterly, *(East Eur Quarterly; 0-914710; 0-88033),* Univ. of Colorado, Boulder, CO 80302 (SAN 661-9983); Dist. by: Columbia Univ. Pr., 136 S. Braodway, Irvington-on-Hudson, NY 10533 (SAN 212-2472) Tel 914-591-9111.

East Linden Pr., *(East Linden Pr; 0-9614902),* 905 Linden Ave., Boulder, CO 80302 (SAN 693-3262) Tel 303-444-0879.

East Montpelier Historical Society, *(E Montpelier Hist Soc; 0-9612222),* Marilyn S. Blackwell, East Montpelier Historical Society, RR1, East Montpelier, VT 05651 (SAN 289-1999) Tel 802-229-9588; Dist. by: Hill/Ellen C., RDI Box 64, E. Montpelier, VT 05651 (SAN 200-7851) Tel 802-223-2720.

East Oregonian, *(East Oregonian; 0-934880),* P.O. Box 1089, Pendleton, OR 97801 (SAN 201-2863) Tel 503-276-2211.

East Ridge Press, *(East Ridge Pr; 0-914896),* 126 Ridge Rd., Hankins, NY 12741 (SAN 201-2871) Tel 914-887-5161; Dist. by: Ridge Book Service, 161 Ridge Rd., Hankins, NY 12741 (SAN 282-6453).

East River Publishing Co., *(East River Pub CO; 0-915789),* P.O. Box 654, Crested Butte, CO 81224 (SAN 293-9274) Tel 303-349-7400.

East Rock Pr., Inc., *(E Rock Pr; 0-910825),* HCR 68, Box 42, Cushing, ME 04563 (SAN 650-0242) Tel 207-354-2467; Orders to: 251 Dwight St., New Haven, CT 06511 (SAN 688-3907) Tel 203-624-8619.

East Rock Pr., Ltd., *(East Rock Ltd; 0-9615543),* 150 Edgehill Rd., New Haven, CT 06511 (SAN 696-3471) Tel 203-776-7825.

†East-West Ctr., *(EW Ctr HI; 0-86638),* 1777 East-West Rd., Honolulu, HI 96848 (SAN 210-802X) Tel 808-944-7391; *CIP.*

East-West Cultural Ctr., *(E-W Cultural Ctr; 0-930736),* 2865 W. Ninth St., Los Angeles, CA 90006 (SAN 211-0121) Tel 213-480-8325.

East West Culture Exchange, *(East West Cult; 0-9601274),* 5204 N. Leicester Dr., Muncie, IN 47304 (SAN 210-3559) Tel 317-289-3123.

East West Health Bks., Div. of East West Journal, Inc., *(East West Health; 0-936184),* 17 Station St., Box 1200, Brookline, MA 02147 (SAN 221-1939) Tel 617-232-1000.

East West Pr., *(East West Pr; 0-9606090),* P.O. Box 4204, Minneapolis, MN 55414 (SAN 216-809X) Tel 612-379-2049.

East/West Publishing Co., *(E-W Pub Co; 0-934788),* 838 Grant Ave., Suite 302, San Francisco, CA 94108 (SAN 215-8574) Tel 415-781-3194.

East-West Publishing, Co., *(East-West Pub; 0-931955),* 988 Roslyn, Grosse Pointe, MI 48236 (SAN 686-0362) Tel 313-885-7308; 2413 S. Broadway, Santa Ana, CA 92707 (SAN 662-7692) Tel 714-549-1498.

East Windsor Historical Society, Inc., *(E Windsor; 0-910506),* P.O. Box 232, East Windsor, CT 06088 (SAN 218-7116).

†East Woods Pr./Fast & McMillan Pubs., *(East Woods; 0-914788; 0-88742),* 429 East Blvd., Charlotte, NC 28203 (SAN 212-0127) Tel 704-334-0897; Toll free: 800-438-1242; *CIP.*

Easter Seal Rehabilitation Center of Eastern Fairfield County, Inc., Affil. of National Easter Seal Society, *(Easter Rehabilitation Inc; 0-9613209),* 226 Mill Hill Ave., Bridgeport, CT 06610 (SAN 295-5639) Tel 203-366-7551; Dist. by: Dot Gibson Pubns., P.O. Box 117, Waycross, GA 31502 (SAN 200-4143) Tel 912-285-2848; Toll free: 800-223-1718; Dist. by: Collection, Inc., The, 2101 Kansas City Rd., Olathe, KS 66061 (SAN 200-6359) Tel 913-764-1811; Dist. by: Baker & Taylor Co., Eastern Div., 50 Kirby Ave., Somerville, NJ 08876 (SAN 169-4901) Tel 201-526-8000.

†Eastern Acorn Press, Div. of Eastern National Park & Monument Assn., *(Eastern Acorn; 0-915992),* 339 Walnut St., Philadelphia, PA 19106 (SAN 219-9793) Tel 215-597-7129; *CIP.*

Eastern Connecticut State College Foundation, *(Eastern CT St Coll Fdn; 0-915884),* P.O. Box 431, Willimantic, CT 06226 (SAN 207-4834) Tel 203-456-2231.

Eastern Mennonite Board Of Missions & Charities, *(E Mennonite Bd; 0-9613368),* Oak Ln. & Brandt Blvd., Salunga, PA 17538-0628 (SAN 657-1360) Tel 717-898-2251.

Eastern Mountain Sports, *(Eastern Mount),* 11312 Vose Farm Rd., Peterborough, NH 03458 (SAN 213-3067) Tel 603-924-9571; Dist. by: Appalachian Mountain Club, 5 Joy St., Boston, MA 02108 (SAN 203-4808) Tel 617-523-0636.

Eastern Orthodox Bks., *(Eastern Orthodox; 0-89981),* P.O. Box 302, Willits, CA 95490 (SAN 201-355X).

Eastern Pr., *(Eastern Pr; 0-939758),* 426 E Sixth St., Bloomington, IN 47402 (SAN 216-3713) Tel 812-336-5865; Orders to: P.O. Box 881, Bloomington, IN 47401 (SAN 661-9991).

Eastern School Press, *(East School Pr; 0-912181),* P.O. Box 684, Talent, OR 97540 (SAN 264-7362) Tel 503-535-1490.

†Eastern Washington State Historical Society, *(Eastern Wash; 0-910524),* W. 2316 First Ave., Spokane, WA 99204 (SAN 203-8293) Tel 506-456-3931; *CIP.*

Eastern Washington Univ. Press, *(East Wash Univ; 0-910055),* Eastern Washington Univ., Cheney, WA 99004 (SAN 241-2977) Tel 509-359-2201.

Eastham Editions, *(Eastham Edns; 0-915102),* P.O. Box 10, Prospect, NY 13435 (SAN 207-1258) Tel 315-896-6388.

Eastland Pr., *(Eastland; 0-939616),* P.O. Box 12689, Seattle, WA 98111 (SAN 216-6216) Tel 206-283-7085.

Eastman Kodak Co., *(Eastman Kodak; 0-87985),* 343 State St., Bldg. 16, 2nd Flr., Dept. 373, Rochester, NY 14650 (SAN 201-3568) Tel 716-724-4254; Toll free: 800-242-7737.

†Eastman School of Music Press, *(Eastman Sch Music; 0-9603186),* 26 Gibbs St., Rochester, NY 14604 (SAN 222-3260); *CIP.*

Eastview Editions, Inc., *(Eastview; 0-89860),* P.O. Box 783, Westfield, NJ 07091 (SAN 169-4952) Tel 201-964-9485.

Eastwest Ctr. Pr. See Univ. of Hawaii Pr., The

Eastwood Publishing Co., *(Eastwood Orem; 0-9617053),* 130 S. Eastwood Dr., Orem, UT 84058 (SAN 662-958X) Tel 801-224-8423. Do not confuse with Eastwood Pub. Co., Denver, CO.

Eastwood Publishing Co., *(Eastwood Pub Co; 0-9612692),* 2901 Blake St., Denver, CO 80205 (SAN 291-8323) Tel 303-296-1905.

Easy Banana Productions, *(Easy Banana Prods; 0-9613879),* 2000 Gough St., San Francisco, CA 94109 (SAN 681-9788) Tel 415-776-0868.

Easy Read Publishing Corp., *(Easy Read Pub; 0-937199),* 1522 N. Dixie, West Palm Beach, FL 33401 (SAN 658-7038) Tel 305-588-1612.

Easy Street Pubns., *(Easy St Pubns; 0-916009),* 12351 Osborne St., No. 13, Pacoima, CA 91331 (SAN 293-9266) Tel 213-899-6770.

Eaton Publishing, Inc., *(Eaton Pub; 0-9610904),* P.O. Box 729, Tinley Park, IL 60477 (SAN 265-1319) Tel 312-479-2345.

Eatongude Pr., *(Eatongude Pr; 0-9614721),* 227 W. 13th St., 4th Fl., New York, NY 10011 (SAN 692-5227) Tel 212-691-9384.

Ebaesay-Namreplican (EBN) Pubns., *(Ebaesay; 0-9608212),* 210 W. Lemon Ave. No. 22, Monrovia, CA 91016 (SAN 240-3692) Tel 818-358-1763.

Ebe, John, *(Ebe),* 445 Grand St., Brooklyn, NY 11211 (SAN 238-8758) Tel 718-388-7074.

Ebenezer Ctr. for Aging & Human Development, Subs. of Ebenezer Society, *(Ebenezer Ctr; 0-938846),* 2500 Park Ave., Minneapolis, MN 55404 (SAN 240-0162) Tel 612-879-1457.

Eberly Press, *(Eberly Pr; 0-932296),* 430 N. Harrison, East Lansing, MI 48823 (SAN 214-0055) Tel 517-351-7299.

Ebonics Publishers Internationale, *(Ebonics; 0-910363),* P.O. Box 36518, Atlanta, GA 30032 (SAN 240-9038) Tel 404-696-6357.

Eccles Pr., *(Eccles Pr; 0-9616812),* Newmark's Yacht Ctr., Berth 204, Wilmington, CA 90744 (SAN 658-8247) Tel 213-835-3760.

Ecclesia Pubns. *See* Carey, William, Library Pubs.

†Ecco Pr., *(Ecco Pr; 0-912946; 0-88001),* 18 W. 30th St., New York, NY 10001 (SAN 202-5795) Tel 212-685-8240; Toll free: 800-223-2584; Dist. by: W. W. Norton & Co., Inc., 500 Fifth Ave, New York, NY 10110 (SAN 202-5795) Tel 212-354-5500; *CIP.*

Echo Books *See* Doubleday & Co., Inc.

Echo Pubns., Inc., *(Echo Pubns; 0-940562),* P.O. Box 6548, New Orleans, LA 70174 (SAN 297-1690) Tel 504-368-4050.

Echo Publishers, *(Echo Pubs; 0-912852),* P.O. Box 7130, West Menlo Park, CA 94026 (SAN 201-3592) Tel 415-524-1575; Dist. by: B.Dalton Bookseller, P.O. Box 317, Minneapolis, MN 55440 (SAN 662-7218); Dist. by: SCHOENHOFS foreign books, P.O. Box 182, Cambridge, MA 02138 (SAN 662-7226).

†Echo Publishing Co., *(Echo Pub Co; 0-916121),* 8865 Laura Ln., Beaumont, TX 77707 (SAN 294-9237) Tel 409-866-0997; *CIP.*

Echo Stage Co., Ltd., *(Echo Stage Co; 0-9607886),* 250 W. 16th St., Suite 1A, New York, NY 10011 (SAN 239-5347) Tel 212-243-6865.

Echoes and Shadows, *(Echoes & Shadows; 0-942130),* P.O. Box 241, Elm Grove, WI 53122 (SAN 238-0129).

†Echolight Corp., The, *(Echolight Corp; 0-931547),* 151 Kentucky Ave., SE, Washington, DC 20003 (SAN 682-1685) Tel 202-546-1220; *CIP.*

Eckhardt, Fred, Associates, *(F Eckhardt Assocs; 0-9606302),* P.O. Box 546, Portland, OR 97207 (SAN 211-2930) Tel 503-289-7596.

Eclectic Pr., *(Eclectic Pr; 0-9605920),* P.O. Box 984, Ansonia Sta., New York, NY 10023 (SAN 216-6682) Tel 212-874-2867. Publishes poetry exclusively.

Eclectical Publishing Co., Inc., *(Eclectical; 0-912447),* P.O. Box 7326, New Orleans, LA 70186 (SAN 265-346X) Tel 504-246-5413.

Eclipse Bks., Div. of Eclipse Enterprises, Inc., *(Eclipse Bks; 0-913035),* P.O. Box 199, Guerneville, CA 95446 (SAN 283-0566).

Eco Images, *(Eco Images; 0-938423),* Box 61413, Virginia Beach, VA 23462 (SAN 661-230X); 4132 Blackwater Rd., Virginia Beach, VA 23451 (SAN 661-2318) Tel 804-421-3929.

Ecofunding Pr., *(Ecofunding; 0-936529),* 100 E. 85th St., New York, NY 10028 (SAN 697-8274) Tel 212-472-1214.

Econo Communications, *(Econo Comm; 0-913525),* 412 Edsam Ave., Pitman, NJ 08071 (SAN 285-158X); Dist. by: Baker & Taylor, Eastern Div., 50 Kirby Ave., Somerville, NJ 08876 (SAN 169-4901); Dist. by: Scholarly Bk. Ctr., 3828 Hawthorn Ct., Waukegan, IL 60087 (SAN 169-2259).

†Economics Institute, *(Econ Inst; 0-88036),* 1030 13th St., Boulder, CO 80302 (SAN 239-0493) Tel 303-492-8419; *CIP.*

Economics Pr., Inc., *(Economics Pr; 0-910187),* 12 Daniel Rd., Fairfield, NJ 07006 (SAN 204-1774) Tel 201-227-1224; Toll free: 800-526-2554; Toll free: 800-526-1128 (NJ).

Economics Research Center, *(Econ Res Ctr),* 1600 Campus Rd., Occidental College, Los Angeles, CA 90041 (SAN 203-8307).

Ecotope, Inc., *(Ecotope; 0-934478),* 2812 E. Madison, Seattle, WA 98112 (SAN 221-1955) Tel 206-322-3753.

Ecumenical Pr., *(Ecumenical Phila; 0-931214),* Temple Univ., 511 Humanities Bldg., Philadelphia, PA 19122 (SAN 222-8211); Dist. by: Hippocrene Bks., 171 Madison Ave., New York, NY 10016 (SAN 213-2060) Tel 718-454-2366.

Ecumenical Program for Interamerican Communication & Action, *(EPICA; 0-918346),* 1470 Irving St. NW, Washington, DC 20010 (SAN 207-8244) Tel 202-332-0292.

Ed-it Productions, *(Ed-it Prods),* P.O. Box 29527, Oakland, CA 94604-9527 (SAN 669-0408) Tel 415-763-3510; Dist. by: Strawberry Hill Pr., 2594 15th Ave., San Francisco, CA 94127 (SAN 238-8103) Tel 415-664-8112. *Imprints:* Cliffhanger Press (Cliffhanger Pr).

Ed-U Pr., Inc., *(Ed-U Pr; 0-934978),* P.O. Box 583, Fayetteville, NY 13066 (SAN 221-1866) Tel 315-637-9524.

Ed-Venture Films/Bks., *(Ed Venture CA; 0-935873),* 1122 Calada St., Los Angeles, CA 90023 (SAN 696-3498) Tel 213-261-1885; Orders to: P.O. Box 23214, Los Angeles, CA 90023-0214 (SAN 696-530X).

Edasi, *(Edasi; 0-9614148),* P.O. Box 286, Lenox Hill Sta., New York, NY 10021 (SAN 686-4295); 221 E. 70th St., New York, NY 10021 (SAN 663-3102).

EdCom-Jean Wiley Huyler Communications, *(EdCom; 0-941554),* 922 N. Pearl A-27, Tacoma, WA 98406 (SAN 264-021X) Tel 206-759-1579.

Eddowes, John, *(J Eddowes; 0-9615646),* 1716 Irvin St., Vienna, VA 22180 (SAN 696-4699) Tel 703-281-5994.

Eddy Tern Pr., *(Tern Pr; 0-9605388),* 430 SW 206th St., Seattle, WA 98166 (SAN 215-9791) Tel 206-824-4042.

Edelson, Mary Beth, *(Edelson; 0-9604650),* 110 Mercer St., New York, NY 10012 (SAN 215-7594) Tel 212-226-0832.

Edelweiss Pr., *(Edelweiss Pr; 0-9600874),* 124 Front St., Massapequa Park, NY 11762 (SAN 208-0419) Tel 516-799-1150.

Eden Games, Inc., *(Eden Games; 0-937655),* P.O. Box 148, Clackamas, OR 97015 (SAN 659-3518) Tel 503-656-9215.

Eden Hill Pr., *(Eden Hill Pr; 0-9614355),* P.O. Box 337, Cruz Bay, St. John, VI 00830 (SAN 687-7435) Tel 809-776-6573.

Eden Hill Publishing *See* Signature Bks., Inc.

Eden Pr., *(Eden Pr; 0-920792; 0-88831),* Dist. by: Univ. of Toronto Pr., 33 E. Tupper St., Buffalo, NY 14203 (SAN 214-2651) Tel 716-852-0342.

Eden Pr./Art Reproductions, *(Eden Press; 0-939373),* P.O. Box 745, Corona del Mar, CA 92625 (SAN 687-6455) Tel 714-675-1201.

Eden Project, Pubs., *(Eden Project Pubs; 0-939385),* P.O. Box 1348, Mt. Shasta, CA 96067 (SAN 663-3889); 111 McLoud Ave., No. 2, Mt. Shasta, CA 96067 (SAN 663-3897) Tel 916-926-4322; Dist. by: Bookpeople, 2929 Fifth St., Berkeley, CA 94710 (SAN 168-9517).

Edenite Society, Inc., *(Edenite; 0-938520),* Rte. 526, Imlaystown, NJ 08526 (SAN 239-9040) Tel 609-259-7517.

Eden's Work, *(Eden's Work; 0-937226),* RFD 1, Box 540A, Franklin, ME 04634 (SAN 219-998X) Tel 207-565-3533.

Edenwood Hse., *(Edenwood Hse),* P.O. Box 607, Garner, NC 27529 (SAN 263-2179) Tel 919-772-0107.

Eder Publishing, *(Eder Pub; 0-9614252),* 178 Commonwealth Ave., Boston, MA 02116 (SAN 687-1070) Tel 617-262-5367.

Edery, David, *(D Edery; 0-9610756),* P.O. Box 351024, Los Angeles, CA 90035 (SAN 264-6137) Tel 213-859-3974.

Edgar, Betsy J., *(B J Edgar),* Rte. 4, Box 130, Lewisburg, WV 24901 (SAN 204-174X) Tel 304-645-7642.

Edgemoor Publishing Co., *(Edgemoor; 0-88204),* 721 Durham Dr., Houston, TX 77007 (SAN 201-3681) Tel 713-861-3451; Orders to: P.O. Box 13612, Houston, TX 77019 (SAN 201-369X).

Edgepr., *(Edgepress; 0-918528),* P.O. Box 69, Point Reyes, CA 94956 (SAN 209-6625) Tel 415-663-1511.

Edgerton, William H., *(Edgerton; 0-9601172),* Box 88, Darien, CT 06820 (SAN 210-0738) Tel 203-655-9510.

Edges Design Co.-Eric's Pr., *(Eric's Pr; 0-911985),* Box 1680, Tahoe City, CA 95730 (SAN 264-6668) Tel 408-663-0633.

Edgewater Bk. Distributors, *(Edgewater; 0-937424),* P.O. Box 40238, Cleveland, OH 44140 (SAN 215-3033) Tel 216-835-3108.

Edgewood Pr., *(Edgewood; 0-9602472),* 2865 East Rock Rd., Clare, MI 48617 (SAN 212-6559).

Edgewood Pubs., *(Edgewood Pubs; 0-9616151),* 234 Park St., New Haven, CT 06511 (SAN 699-9190) Tel 203-865-0661.

Edgeworth Publishing Co., Ltd., *(Edgeworth Pub; 0-939191),* 226-10 137th Ave., Laurelton, NY 11413 (SAN 662-9040) Tel 718-978-1782.

Edging Ahead Pr., *(Edging Ahead Pr; 0-9615488),* P.O. Box 19071, San Diego, CA 92119 (SAN 696-3536) Tel 619-448-2206.

Ediciones Alba, *(Edns Alba; 0-9600714),* Encarnacion 1573, Caparra Heights, San Juan, PR 00920 (SAN 206-3581) Tel 809-781-5984.

Ediciones Arauco, *(Ediciones Arauco),* P.O. Box 5855, Collegeville, MN 56321 (SAN 659-1973) Tel 612-363-2748.

Ediciones Contra Viento y Marea, *(Ediciones Viento y Marea; 0-931852),* Box M-228, Hoboken, NJ 07030 (SAN 222-8157).

Ediciones Del Norte, *(Ediciones Norte; 0-910061),* P.O. Box A130, Hanover, NH 03755 (SAN 241-2993) Tel 603-795-2433; 13 Dartmouth College Hwy., Lyme, NH 03768 (SAN 658-053X).

Ediciones El Gato Tuerto, *(Ed El Gato Tuerto; 0-932367),* P.O. Box 210277, San Francisco, CA 94121 (SAN 687-3774); 205 16th Ave., Apt. 6, San Francisco, CA 94118 (SAN 662-2755) Tel 415-752-0473.

Ediciones Hispamerica, *(Edins Hispamerica; 0-935318),* 5 Pueblo Ct., Gaithersburg, MD 20878 (SAN 213-9200) Tel 301-948-3494.

Ediciones Huracan, Inc., *(Ediciones Huracan; 0-940238),* Avenida Gonzalez 1002, Rio Piedras, PR 00925 (SAN 217-5134) Tel 809-763-7407.

Ediciones Kerigma, *(Edicion Kerigma; 0-938127),* P.O. Box 557428, Miami, FL 33255 (SAN 661-2377); 4467 SW 75th Ave., Miami, FL 33155 (SAN 661-2385) Tel 305-261-5200.

Ediciones Universal, *(Ediciones; 0-89729),* 3090 SW Eighth St., Miami, FL 33135 (SAN 207-2203) Tel 305-642-3355; P. O. Box 450353, Shenandoah Sta., Miami, FL 33145 (SAN 658-0548).

†Edison Electric Institute, *(Edison Electric; 0-931032),* 1828 L St., Suite 709, Washington, DC 20036 (SAN 224-7119) Tel 202-828-7551; *CIP.*

Edison Institute, The, *(Edison Inst; 0-933728),* 20900 Oakwood Blvd., Dearborn, MI 48121 (SAN 216-4841). *Imprints:* Henry Ford Museum Press (Ford Mus).

Edith, Rusconi Kaltovich, *(E R Kaltovich; 0-9613989),* 351 E. Fourth St., Florence, NJ 08518 (SAN 686-2802).

Editions Delta *See* Unipub

Editions Delta *See* Unipub b

Editions des Deux Mondes, *(Edns Des Deux Mondes; 0-939586),* P.O. Box 56, Newark, DE 19711 (SAN 216-373X) Tel 302-398-2834.

Editions Francaises de Louisiane/Louisiana French Editions, Inc., *(Ed Francaises; 0-935085),* P.O. Box 1344, Jennings, LA 70546 (SAN 695-0779) Tel 318-824-7380; 302 E. Nezpique St., Jennings, LA 70546 (SAN 695-0787).

Editions, Ltd., *(Editions Ltd; 0-9607938),* 1123 Kapahulu Ave., Honolulu, HI 96816-5811 (SAN 691-9510) Tel 808-735-7644.

Editions Orphee, Inc., *(Edit Orphee; 0-936186),* P.O. Box 21291, Columbus, OH 43221 (SAN 221-1890).

Editorial AI, *(Editorial AI; 0-930795),* 2200 Hendon, St. Paul, MN 55108 (SAN 677-8267) Tel 612-644-5937.

Editorial Arcos, Inc., *(Edit Arcos; 0-937509),* P.O. Box 652253, Miami, FL 33265-2253 (SAN 659-1744) Tel 305-223-2344; 10850 W. Flagler St., Apt. D-103, Miami, FL 33174 (SAN 659-1752).

Editorial Asol, *(Edit Asol),* Box 21942, Univ. of Puerto Rico, Rio Piedras, PR 00931 (SAN 238-8766).

Names

Editorial Betania, Div. of Bethany Fellowship, Inc., *(Edit Betania; 0-88113),* 5541 NW 82nd Ave., Miami, FL 33166 (SAN 240-6349) Tel 305-592-5121.

Editorial Caribe, *(Edit Caribe; 0-89922),* 3934 SW Eighth St., Suite 303, Miami, FL 33134 (SAN 215-1421) Tel 305-445-0564; Toll free: 800-222-5342; 4243 NW 37 Ct., Miami, FL 33134 (SAN 658-0556).

Editorial Centro Pedagogico, Inc., *(Edit Centro Pedagogico; 0-934541),* Calle Luna No. 72, Box 310, Ponce, PR 00733 (SAN 693-790X) Tel 809-843-0686; 1144 E. Third St., Brooklyn, NY 11230 (SAN 693-7918).

Editorial Concepts, Inc., *(Edit Concepts; 0-939193),* 7116 SW 47th St., Miami, FL 33155 (SAN 662-8958) Tel 305-661-6588; Dist. by: Spanish Periodical & Bk. Sales, 10100 NW 25th St., Miami, FL 35127 (SAN 200-7576); Dist. by: Agencia de Publicaciones de Puerto Rico, GPO Box 4903, San Juan, PR 00936 (SAN 169-9296); Dist. by: Southeast Periodicals, P.O. Box 340008, Coral Gables, FL 33134 (SAN 238-6909) Tel 305-856-5011.

Editorial Consultants, Inc., *(Edit Consult; 0-917636),* 1728 Union St., San Francisco, CA 94123 (SAN 212-6567) Tel 415-474-5010.

Editorial Doble Omega, *(Editorial D O; 0-88696),* P.O. Box 650712, Miami, FL 33165 (SAN 283-0590) Tel 305-554-4865; 13895 SW 22nd St., Miami, FL 33175 (SAN 283-0604).

Editorial Experts, Inc., *(Edit Experts; 0-935012),* 85 S. Bragg St., Suite 400, Alexandria, VA 22312-2731 (SAN 216-3748) Tel 703-642-3040.

Editorial Justa Pubns. Inc., *(Editorial Justa; 0-915808),* 2831 Seventh St., Berkeley, CA 94710 (SAN 208-1962) Tel 415-848-3628; Orders to: P.O. Box 2131-C, Berkeley, CA 94702 (SAN 208-1970).

Editorial Mensaje, *(Edit Mensaje; 0-86515),* 125 Queen St., Staten Island, NY 10314 (SAN 214-0063) Tel 718-761-0056.

Editorial Mundo Hispano *See* Casa Bautista de Publicaciones

Editorial Research Service, *(Edit Res Serv; 0-933592),* P.O. Box 411832, Kansas City, MO 64141 (SAN 212-7407) Tel 913-829-0609.

Editorial Review, *(Edit Review; 0-916447),* 1009 Placer St., Butte, MT 59701 (SAN 295-1231) Tel 406-782-2546.

Editorial Roche, *(Edit Roche; 0-939081),* P.O. Box 3583, Haio Rey, PR 00919 (SAN 662-9083); Urb. Del Carmen 2, No. 19, Juana Diaz, PR 00665 (SAN 662-9091) Tel 809-837-2468.

Editors & Engineers, Ltd., *(Editors; 0-672),* Dist. by: Bobbs-Merrill Co., Inc., 866 Third Ave., New York lis, NY 10022 (SAN 201-3959) Tel 212-402-7809.

†Edlo Books, *(Edlo Bks; 0-9613007),* P.O. Box 259, RD 1, Marlton, NJ 08053 (SAN 292-482X) Tel 609-424-1305; *CIP.*

Edmunds, Adeline, *(A Edmunds; 0-9605846),* 421 N. Sixth Ave., Sturgeon Bay, WI 54235 (SAN 216-3756) Tel 414-743-9433.

EDPRESS *See* **Educational Press Assn. of America**

Ed's Publishing, Co., *(Eds Pub Co; 0-9612822),* 9366 Greenwell Springs Rd., Baton Rouge, LA 70814 (SAN 289-9809) Tel 504-925-0991.

EduCALC Pubns, *(EduCALC Pubns; 0-936356),* 27953 Cabot Rd,, South Laguna, CA 92677 (SAN 281-6229) Tel 714-831-2631; Dist. by: Publishers Group West, 5855 Beaudry St., Emeryville, CA 94608 (SAN 202-8522) Tel 415-658-3453.

Educated Eye Pr., The, *(Educated Eye; 0-9615607),* 2030 Park Newport, Newport Beach, CA 92660 (SAN 696-4923) Tel 714-759-0966; P.O. Box 9601, Newport Beach, CA 92660 (SAN 696-5474).

Education & Training Consultants Co., *(Ed & Training; 0-87657),* Box 2085, Sedona, AZ 86336-2085 (SAN 201-3665) Tel 602-282-3009.

Education & Training Consultants, Inc., Subs. of Education & Training Dev. Consultants-"Multi-Ethnic Bks. & Games", *(Educ & Trainin; 0-937196),* P.O. Box 1691, Ann Arbor, MI 48106 (SAN 282-3780); 1402 Astor Dr., Ann Arbor, MI 48104 (SAN 662-1562) Tel 313-668-0572.

Education Assocs., *(Ed Assocs; 0-918772),* P.O. Box 8021, Athens, GA 30603 (SAN 210-4180) Tel 404-542-4244.

Education Assocs., Inc., *(Ed Assocs KY; 0-940428; 1-55549),* 45 Fountain Pl., P.O. Box Y, Frankfort, KY 40602 (SAN 223-0674).

Education Commission of the States, *(Ed Comm States),* 1860 Lincoln St., Suite 300, Denver, CO 80295 (SAN 224-120X).

Education Design/Editorial Consultants, *(Educ Des Edit Cons; 0-9613138),* P.O. Box 31975, Aurora, CO 80041 (SAN 294-7722) Tel 303-442-5156.

Education Development Ctr., Inc., *(Educ Dev Ctr; 0-89292),* Orders to: EDC Publishing Ctr., 55 Chapel St., Newton, MA 02160 (SAN 207-821X) Tel 617-969-7100.

Education Foundation, Inc., *(Educ Found; 0-914448),* P.O. Box 1187, Charleston, WV 25324 (SAN 204-1685) Tel 304-342-0855.

Education Freedom Foundation, *(Ed Freedom),* 20 Parkland, St. Louis, MO 63122 (SAN 225-7955) Tel 314-966-3485.

Education Guide, Inc., *(Educ Guide; 0-914880),* P.O. Box 421, Randolph, MA 02368 (SAN 201-4580) Tel 617-961-2217.

Education News Service, *(Ed News Serv; 0-936423),* P.O. Box 1789, Carmichael, CA 95609 (SAN 693-6237) Tel 916-483-6159.

Education Pr., The, *(Ed Pr; 0-915481),* P.O. Box 19532, Greensboro, NC 27419 (SAN 291-1442) Tel 919-292-5903.

Education Pr., The, *(Educ Pr CA; 0-9601706),* Box 2358, Huntington Beach, CA 92647 (SAN 213-1323).

Education Research Assocs., *(Educ Res MA; 0-913636),* P.O. Box 767, Amherst, MA 01004 (SAN 215-3068) Tel 413-253-3582. *Imprints:* E R A Press (ERA Pr).

Education Resource Consortium Inc., *(Educ Res Consortium; 0-931263),* 190 E. Sweetbriar Dr., Claremont, CA 91711 (SAN 681-9796) Tel 714-621-6261.

Education Services, *(Education Serv; 0-936394),* P.O. Box 5281, Atlanta, GA 30307 (SAN 221-1920).

Education System Pub., *(Ed Sys Pub; 0-915676; 0-916011),* Terminal Annex, Box 54579, Los Angeles, CA 90054 (SAN 207-4028).

Educational Activities, Inc., *(Ed Activities; 0-914296; 0-89525),* 1937 Grand Ave., Baldwin, NY 11510 (SAN 207-4400) Tel 516-223-4666; Toll free: 800-645-3739; Orders to: P.O. Box 392, Freeport, NY 11520.

Educational Associates, *(Educational Assocs),* P.O. Box 35221, Phoenix, AZ 85069 (SAN 670-686X) Tel 602-869-9223.

Educational Book Pubs., *(Ed Bk Pubs OK; 0-932188),* P.O. Box 1219, Guthrie, OK 73044 (SAN 215-8582).

Educational Communications, Inc., *(Educ Comm; 0-915130; 0-930315),* 721 N. McKinley Rd., Lake Forest, IL 60045 (SAN 201-6540) Tel 312-295-6650.

Educational Computer Systems, Inc., *(Educ Comp Syst; 0-935919),* 17 Peacock Farm Rd., Lexington, MA 02173 (SAN 696-7396) Tel 617-863-8037.

Educational Data Resources, *(Ed Data Res; 0-9616851),* P.O. Box 23069, Washington, DC 20026-3069 (SAN 661-3454); 236 33rd St., NE, Washington, DC 20019 (SAN 661-3462) Tel 202-399-6253.

Educational Design, Inc., *(Ed Design Inc; 0-87694),* 47 W. 13th St., New York, NY 10011 (SAN 204-1588) Tel 212-255-7900; Toll free: 800-221-9372.

Educational Development, *(Educ Development; 0-914763),* 200 W. Bullard Ave., Suite E-1, Clovis, CA 93612 (SAN 677-4733) Tel 209-299-4131.

Educational Development Association, *(Ed Dev Assn),* P.O. Box 181, Hazel Crest, IL 60429 (SAN 205-6143).

Educational Development Corp., *(Ed Devel Corp; 0-913332; 0-89403),* 10302 E. 55th Pl., Tulsa, OK 74146 (SAN 204-1626) Tel 918-622-4522; Toll free: 800-331-4418.

Educational Direction, Inc., *(Educ Direction; 0-940432),* 150 N. Miller Rd., Bldg. 200, Akron, OH 44313 (SAN 217-1724).

Educational Directories Inc., *(Ed Direct; 0-910536),* P.O. Box 199, Mt. Prospect, IL 60056 (SAN 201-3614) Tel 312-392-1811.

Educational Editions, *(Educ Editions; 0-933092),* MS-293, P.O. Box 420240, Houston, TX 77243 (SAN 212-6575) Tel 713-467-2241.

†Educational Equity Concepts, Inc., *(Educ Equity Con; 0-931629),* 114 E. 32nd St., Suite 306, New York, NY 10016 (SAN 683-7328) Tel 212-725-1803; Dist. by: Gryphon Hse., 3706 Otis St., P.O. Box 275, Mount Rainier, MD 20712 (SAN 169-3190) Tel 301-779-6200; *CIP.*

†Educational Facilities Laboratories, *(Ed Facilities; 0-88481),* c/o Academy for Educational Development, 680 Fifth Ave., New York, NY 10019 (SAN 210-0185) Tel 212-397-0040; Dist. by: Publishing Center for Cultural Resources, 625 Broadway, New York, NY 10012 (SAN 274-9025) Tel 212-260-2010; *CIP.*

Educational Factors, Inc., *(Ed Factors; 0-936864),* 1462 Jenvey Ave., P.O. Box 6389, San Jose, CA 95150 (SAN 221-9204).

Educational Film Library Assn., *(EFLA; 0-87520),* 45 John St., Suite 301, New York, NY 10038 (SAN 201-8233) Tel 212-227-5599.

Educational Foundation for Nuclear Science, Inc., *(Educ Found for Nucl Sci; 0-941682),* 5801 S. Kenwood Ave., Chicago, IL 60637 (SAN 679-9876) Tel 312-363-5225; Dist. by: Univ. of Chicago Pr., 5801 Ellis Ave., 3rd Flr. S., Chicago, IL 60637 (SAN 202-5280) Tel 312-962-7693.

Educational Graphics Pr., *(Ed Graphics Pr; 0-916123),* P.O. Box 180476, Austin, TX 78718 (SAN 294-9245) Tel 512-251-9620.

Educational Insights, Inc., *(Educ Insights; 0-88679),* 150 W. Carob St., Compton, CA 90220 (SAN 283-8745) Tel 213-637-2131.

Educational Leadership & Counseling Dept., *(Educ Leadership; 0-911467),* Eastern Michigan Univ., Office of Community Educational Research, 34F Boone Hall, Ypsilanti, MI 48197 (SAN 264-0228).

Eucational Learning Systems, Inc., *(Educ Lrn Syst; 0-939303),* P.O. Box 225, Tulsa, OK 74101 (SAN 663-1738); 2407 E. 17th Pl., Tulsa, OK 74101 (SAN 663-1746) Tel 918-743-9494.

Educational Materials Co., *(Educ Materials; 0-937117),* R.R. 2, Box 89, River Rd., South Windham, ME 04082 (SAN 658-5175).

Educational Media Corp., *(Ed Media Corp; 0-932796),* P.O. Box 21311, Minneapolis, MN 55421 (SAN 212-4203) Tel 612-636-5098.

Educational Medical Pubs., *(Educ Medical; 0-930728),* 18 Kling St., West Orange, NJ 07052 (SAN 211-1268).

Educational Methods *See* **Longman Financial Services Publishing**

Educational Ministries, Inc., *(Ed Ministries; 0-940754),* 2861-C Saturn St., Brea, CA 92621 (SAN 219-7316) Tel 714-961-0622; Toll free: 800-221-0910.

Educational Planning Services Corp., *(Educ Plan Serv; 0-9609720),* P.O. Box 182, Newton Highlands, MA 02161 (SAN 263-2187) Tel 617-235-8101.

Educational Pr., *(Ed Pr FL; 0-9616075),* P.O. Box 21147, Sarasota, FL 33583 (SAN 697-9963) Tel 813-922-5051.

Educational Press Assn. of America, *(Educ Pr Assn; 0-89972),* Glassboro State College, Glassboro, NJ 08028 (SAN 204-1634) Tel 609-863-7349.

Educational Program Development Associates, Inc., *(Educ Prog Dev),* 2103 Crestmoor Rd., Nashville, TN 37215 (SAN 240-9895) Tel 615-269-5755.

Educational Pubns., *(Ed Pubns; 0-942930),* P.O. Box 41870, Tuscon, AZ 85717 (SAN 240-3706) Tel 602-791-9690.

Educational Pubns. *See* **Johnny Reads, Inc.**

Educational Research Service, *(Ed Research),* 1800 N. Kent St., Arlington, VA 22209 (SAN 203-7912) Tel 703-243-2100.

Educational Service, Inc., *(Educ Serv; 0-89273),* P.O. Box 219, Stevensville, MI 49127 (SAN 206-9423) Tel 616-429-1451; Toll free: 800-253-0763; 5060 St., Joe Rd., Stevensville, MI 49127 (SAN 658-0564).

Educational Service Publications, *(Educ Serv Pub; 0-9608250),* Box 205, Boones Mill, VA 24065 (SAN 240-3714) Tel 703-334-2269.

Educational Services Pr., *(Educ Serv Pr; 0-914911),* 99 Bank St., Suite 2F, New York, NY 10014 (SAN 289-1212); Dist. by: Children's Small Pr. Collection, 719 N. Fourth Ave., Ann Arbor, MI 48104 (SAN 200-514X); Dist. by: Blackwell North America, 1001 Fries Mill Rd., Blackwood, NJ 08012 (SAN 169-4596) Tel 609-629-0700; Dist. by: Baker & Taylor Co., Eastern Div., 50 Kirby Ave., Somerville, NJ 08876 (SAN 169-4901) Tel 201-526-8000; Dist. by: Baker & Taylor Co., Midwest Div., 501 Gladiola Ave., Momence, IL 60954 (SAN 169-2100); Dist. by: Baker & Taylor Co., Southeast Div., Mt. Olive Rd., Commerce, GA 30529 (SAN 169-1503); Dist. by: Baker & Taylor Co., Western Div., 380 Edison Way, Reno, NV (SAN 169-4464).

Educational Skills, *(Ed Skills Dallas; 0-9604058),* 9636 Hollow Way, Dallas, TX 75220 (SAN 221-6086).

Educational Solutions, Inc., *(Ed Solutions; 0-87825),* 95 University Pl., New York, NY 10003-4555 (SAN 205-6186) Tel 212-674-2988.

Educational Strategies, *(Edu Strategies; 0-9615789),* 223 W. Walnut St., Oneida, NY 13421 (SAN 696-7361) Tel 315-363-1716; P.O. Box 598, Oneida, NY 13421 (SAN 698-2190).

Educational Strategies, Inc., Div. of Antenna Products International Sales Corp., *(Educ Strategies; 0-938809),* 1815 Monetary Ln., Carrollton, TX 75006 (SAN 661-499X) Tel 214-241-6610. Do not confuse with Educational Strategies Oneida, NY.

†**Educational Studies Pr.,** *(Educ Stud Pr; 0-934328),* Northern Illinois Univ., L.E.P.S. Dept., 325 Graham Hall, DeKalb, IL 60115 (SAN 213-3083) Tel 815-753-1499; Orders to: ISURF, Inc., Iowa State Univ., 350 Beardshear Hall, Ames, IA 50011 (SAN 662-0000) Tel 515-294-4740; CIP.

Educational Technology, Subs. of Prescription Learning, *(Educ Tech IL; 1-55639),* P.O. Box 2372, Springfield, IL 62705 (SAN 659-8609) Tel 217-786-2500.

†**Educational Technology Pubns, Inc.,** *(Educ Tech Pubns; 0-87778),* 720 Palisade Ave., Englewood Cliffs, NJ 07632 (SAN 201-3738) Tel 201-871-4007; CIP.

Educational Testing Service, *(Educ Testing Serv; 0-88685),* Rosedale Rd., Princeton, NJ 08541-6000 (SAN 238-034X) Tel 609-921-9000.

Educator Bks., Inc., *(Educator Bks; 0-912092),* Drawer 32, San Angelo, TX 76901 (SAN 203-8382) Tel 915-653-0152.

Educator Pubns., *(Educator Pubns; 0-913558),* 1110 S. Pomona Ave., Fullerton, CA 92632 (SAN 201-3746) Tel 714-871-2950; P.O. Box 333, Fullerton, CA 92632 (SAN 201-3754).

Educator's Academy, *(Ed Acad; 0-9607160),* P.O. Box 75, Dayton, OH 45402 (SAN 238-9738) Tel 513-274-1662.

Educators Progress Service, Inc., *(Ed Prog; 0-87708),* 214 Center St., Randolph, WI 53956 (SAN 201-3649) Tel 414-326-3126.

Educators' Pubns., Inc., *(Educ Pubns; 0-935423),* 1585 Rosecrans St., San Diego, CA 92106 (SAN 696-4974) Tel 619-224-1955.

Educators United for Global Awareness, *(Educ Awareness; 0-9613024),* c/o Jackson State Univ., History Dept., Jackson, MS 39217 (SAN 295-768X).

†**Educomp Pubns.,** *(Educomp Pubns; 0-9612226),* 14242 Wyeth Ave., Irvine, CA 92714 (SAN 287-7384) Tel 714-551-4073; CIP.

Eduplay, Div. of EPI Corp., *(Eduplay; 0-935609),* 9707 Shelbyville Rd./Hold Box No. 60, Louisville, KY 40223 (SAN 696-3552) Tel 502-895-3547; Dist. by: Gelber Marketing, Inc., 200 Fifth Ave., New York, NY 10010 (SAN 200-5727).

EduTech Courseware, *(EduTech Courseware; 0-938581),* 7801 E. Bush Lake Rd., Suite 350, Minneapolis, MN 55331 (SAN 661-1133) Tel 612-831-0445.

EduTech, Inc., *(EduTech; 0-938082; 0-923809),* 303 Lamartine St., Jamaica Plain, MA 02130 (SAN 293-1184) Tel 617-524-1774.

EduTech Press, *(Edutech; 0-9610102),* 22158 Ramona, Apple Valley, CA 92307 (SAN 269-865X) Tel 619-247-7633.

Edutrends, Inc., *(Edutrends; 0-935987),* 6949 Park Dr. E., Kew Gardens, NY 11367 (SAN 696-7353) Tel 718-793-5262; Dist. by: Deltak Inc., East/West Technological Ctr., 1751 W. Diehl Rd., Naperville, IL 60566 (SAN 294-281X) Tel 312-369-3000.

Edward De Bono School of Thinking, The, *(E De Bono; 0-942580),* 205 E. 78th St., New York, NY 10021 (SAN 239-6319) Tel 212-249-9450.

Edward Pr., *(Edward Pr; 0-9606020),* 62 Brighton St., Rochester, NY 14607 (SAN 216-8898) Tel 716-271-4272.

Edwards, Carol L., & Kathleen E. B. Manley, Pubs., *(Edwards & Manley; 0-9615687),* California State Univ., Long Beach, Dept. of Comparative Literature, Long Beach, CA 90840 (SAN 696-3609).

Edwards, Elmer Eugene, *(Elmer Edwards; 0-9604834),* P.O. Box 584, Miami, FL 33161 (SAN 215-143X).

Edwards, Ernest P., *(E P Edwards; 0-911882),* P.O. Box AQ, Sweet Briar, VA 24595 (SAN 201-3525) Tel 804-381-5442.

Edwards, G. F., *(G F Edwards; 0-932318),* Box 1461, Lawton, OK 73502 (SAN 212-1719) Tel 405-248-6870.

Edwards, Lowell E., *(L E Edwards; 0-936024),* P.O. Box 255714, Sacramento, CA 95825 (SAN 213-7348).

Edwards, Thomas Clarke, *(T C Edwards NJ; 0-9611840),* 147 Midwood Rd., Paramus, NJ 07652 (SAN 286-1925) Tel 201-444-8580.

Edwards Brothers, Inc., *(Edwards Bros; 0-910546),* 2500 S. State St., P.O. Box 1007, Ann Arbor, MI 48106 (SAN 206-9814) Tel 313-769-1000.

Edwards Publishing Co., *(Edwards Pub Co; 0-911935),* P.O. Box 42218, Tacoma, WA 98442 (SAN 264-0236).

Edward's Publishing Co., Inc., *(Edward's CA; 0-935531),* 14115 Chadron Ave., P.O. Box 1668, Hawthorne, CA 90251-1668 (SAN 695-1015) Tel 213-644-5643.

EEBART, *(EEBART; 0-9614991),* Box 127, Leaf River, IL 61047 (SAN 693-7632) Tel 815-738-2237.

Eerdmans, William B., Publishing Co., *(Eerdmans; 0-8028),* 255 Jefferson Ave., SE, Grand Rapids, MI 49503 (SAN 220-0058) Tel 616-459-4591; Toll free: 800-253-7521. *Imprints:* Christian University Press (Chr Univ Pr).

Effect Publishing, Inc., *(Effect Pub; 0-911971),* 501 Fifth Ave., Suite 1612, New York, NY 10017 (SAN 264-665X) Tel 212-557-1321.

Effective Learning, Inc., *(Effective Learn; 0-915474),* 7 N. MacQuesten Pkwy., P.O. Box 2212, Mount Vernon, NY 10550 (SAN 208-4791) Tel 914-664-7944; 25 N. MacQuesten Pkwy., Mount Vernon, NY 10550 (SAN 658-0572).

Effective Learning Pubns., *(Effect Learning GA; 0-933594),* 218 Valley Rd., Statesboro, GA 30458 (SAN 213-487X).

Effective Learning Systems, Inc., *(Effect Learn Sys; 0-913261),* P.O. Box 85, Moraga, CA 94556 (SAN 283-0620) Tel 415-376-6162.

Effective Management Resources Corp., *(Effect Mgmt; 0-939740),* 2229 Nyon Ave., Anaheim, CA 92806 (SAN 216-3764).

Effectiveness Training Associates, *(Effectiveness Train; 0-918460),* 321 River St., Manistee, MI 49660 (SAN 209-553X) Tel 616-723-8422.

Eggplant Pr., *(Eggplant Pr; 0-935060),* c/o Cloud Woman/Chocolate Waters, 415 W. 44th St., No. 7, New York, NY 10036 (SAN 211-6030) Tel 212-581-6820.

Eggs Pr., *(Eggs Pr; 0-9602914),* 3038 41st Ave., S., Minneapolis, MN 55406 (SAN 213-6228).

Ego Bks., *(Ego Bks; 0-933540),* 6011 Meadowbrook Ln., Lincoln, NE 68510 (SAN 212-159X) Tel 402-489-6982.

Egret Pubns., *(Egret Pubns; 0-938425),* 594 Broadway, New York, NY 10012 (SAN 661-2393) Tel 212-226-1330.

Egret Publishing Co., The, *(Egret Pub Co; 0-9615730),* 369 Eighth St., Eureka, CA 95501 (SAN 694-3706) Tel 707-445-5475; P.O. Box 991, Eureka, CA 95501 (SAN 696-9704).

Ehde Publishing Co., *(Ehde Pub Co; 0-936188),* Sontag, MS 39665 (SAN 214-0071).

Ehling Clifton Bks., *(Ehling Clifton Bks),* 2401 Clifton Ave., Cincinnati, OH 45219 (SAN 240-1444).

EHM Publishing, *(EHM Pub; 0-9609828),* Box 3173, Tallahassee, FL 32315 (SAN 262-0170) Tel 904-539-9767.

Eichner, Debbie, *(D Eichner; 0-9615887),* 5936 Mercedes, Dallas, TX 75206 (SAN 697-0931) Tel 214-385-2300.

Eide, Lucille, *(L Eide; 0-9610668),* 1122 17th St., No. 319, Sacramento, CA 95814 (SAN 264-7370) Tel 916-443-9518.

Eidolon Pr., *(Eidolon Pr; 0-9609044),* P.O. Box 8204, Pensacola, FL 32505 (SAN 241-3787).

Eighth Mountain Pr., *(Eighth Mount Pr; 0-933377),* 624 SE 29th Ave., Portland, OR 97214 (SAN 691-6767) Tel 503-233-3936; Dist. by: Bookpeople, 2929 Fifth St., Berkeley, CA 94710 (SAN 168-9517) Tel 415-549-3030; Toll free: 800-227-1516; Dist. by: Inland Bk. Co, P.O. Box 261, 22 Hemingway Ave., East Haven, CT 06512 (SAN 200-4151) Tel 203-467-4257; Toll free: 800-243-0138.

Eighties Pr., *(Eighties Pr; 0-87390),* 308 First St., Moose Lake, MN 55767 (SAN 204-5869); Dist. by: Ally Press, 524 Orleans St., St. Paul, MN 55107 (SAN 207-7116).

Eileen's Enterprises, *(Eileens Enter; 0-934807),* 420 E. Patterson, Dunkirk, OH 45836 (SAN 694-3497) Tel 419-759-3081.

Eisenberg, Jerome M., *(Eisenberg Inc; 0-934749),* 153 E. 57th St., New York, NY 10022 (SAN 694-1974) Tel 212-355-2034; Orders to: Royal-Athena Galleries, 153 E. 57th St., New York, NY 10022 (SAN 694-1974).

Eisenberg Educational Enterprises, *(Eisenberg Ed; 0-930080),* Beleveedere Towers 108, 1190 W. Northern Pkwy, Baltimore, MD 21210 (SAN 210-5942) Tel 301-435-8351.

Eisenbrauns, *(Eisenbrauns; 0-931464),* P.O. Box 275, Winona Lake, IN 46590-0278 (SAN 200-7835) Tel 219-269-2011.

Eisenhower, Dwight D., Library, *(Eisenhower Lib; 0-9605728),* Abilene, KS 67410 (SAN 217-1015) Tel 913-263-4751.

Eiteljorg, Harrison, Pubns., *(Eiteljorg Pubns; 0-9607596),* 4567 Cold Spring Rd., Indianapolis, IN 46208 (SAN 239-4359); Dist. by: Independent Publishers Group, 1 Pleasant Ave., Port Washington, NY 11050 (SAN 287-2544).

Either-or Pr., *(Either-or Pr; 0-910931),* 122 North St., Pittsfield, MA 01201 (SAN 262-0189).

Ekay Music, Inc., *(Ekay Music; 0-943748),* 223 Katonah Ave., Katonah, NY 10536 (SAN 241-0680) Tel 914-232-8108; Orders to: Songbooks Unlimited, 352 Evelyn St., Paramus, NJ 07652 (SAN 662-1430) Tel 201-967-9495.

Eko Pubns., *(Eko Pubns),* P.O. Box 5492, Philadelphia, PA 19143 (SAN 201-4599).

El Camino Pubs., *(El Camino; 0-942060),* 4010 Calle Real, Suite 4, Santa Barbara, CA 93110 (SAN 238-6151) Tel 805-682-9340.

El-Hajj Malik El-Shabazz Pr., *(El-Shabazz Pr; 0-913358),* P.O. Box 1115, Washington, DC 20013 (SAN 201-2340).

El Moro Pubns., *(El Moro; 0-9602484),* P.O. Box 965, Morro Bay, CA 93442 (SAN 211-5255) Tel 805-772-3514.

El Renacimiento, *(El Renacimiento),* 1132 N. Washington Ave., Lansing, MI 48906 (SAN 219-2667) Tel 517-485-4389.

El Siglo Pubs., *(El Siglo Pubs; 0-9614985),* 2730 W. Los Reales, Tucson, AZ 85706 (SAN 693-224X) Tel 602-327-0506 Tel 602-578-2778.

Ela, Chipman P., *(C P Ela; 0-9607464),* 1841 Massachusetts Ave., Lexington, MA 02173 (SAN 238-616X) Tel 617-861-8332; Dist. by: Arlington Bk. Co., P.O. Box 327, Arlington, VA 22210-0327 (SAN 200-786X) Tel 202-296-6750.

Elan Northwest Pubs., *(Elan NW Pubs; 0-9603272),* P.O. Box 5442, Eugene, OR 97405 (SAN 204-6707) Tel 503-485-3462.

Elar Publishing Co.,Inc., *(Elar Pub Co; 0-914130),* 1120 Old Country Rd., Plainview, NY 11803 (SAN 215-952X) Tel 516-433-6530.

Names

Eldan Pr., *(Eldan Pr; 0-9615128),* 1259 El Camino, No. 288, Menlo Park, CA 94025 (SAN 694-1982) Tel 415-322-8777; Dist. by: Publishers Group West, 5855 Beaudry St., Emeryville, CA 94608 (SAN 202-8522) Tel 415-658-3453; Toll free: 800-982-8319.

Elder, Charles & Randy, Pubs., *(C Elder; 0-918450),* 2115 Elliston Place, Nashville, TN 37203 (SAN 201-8292) Tel 615-327-1867.

Elder Care, *(Elder),* P.O. Box 212, Chittenango, NY 13037 (SAN 655-184X) Tel 315-687-9764.

Eldridge Publishing Co., *(Eldridge Pub; 0-912963),* P. O. Drawer 216, Franklin, OH 45005 (SAN 204-1553) Tel 513-746-6531.

Electret Scientific Co., *(Electret Sci; 0-917406),* P.O. Box 4132, Morgantown, WV 26505 (SAN 206-4715) Tel 304-594-1639.

Electric Bank, The, *(Electric Bank; 0-938236),* 4225 University, Des Moines, IA 50311 (SAN 209-7214) Tel 515-255-3552.

Electric Pr., The, *(Electric Pr; 0-916919),* 3455 E. Lamona Ave., Fresno, CA 93703 (SAN 297-1658) Tel 209-264-6215.

Electricity Consumers Resource Council, *(Elec Consumers Res),* 1828 L St., Suite 403, Washington, DC 20036 (SAN 269-8846).

Electro-Horizons Pubns., *(Electro Horiz; 0-939527),* 114 Lincoln Rd. E., Plainview, NY 11803 (SAN 663-3757) Tel 516-938-1159.

Electro-Optical Research Co., *(Electro-Optical; 0-936581),* Suite 422, 2029 Century Park E., Los Angeles, CA 90067 (SAN 207-2211) Tel 213-277-7422.

Electrodata, Inc., *(Electrodata; 0-943890),* P.O. Box 206, Glen Echo, MD 20812 (SAN 241-1083) Tel 202-338-0669.

Electron Optics Publishing Group, Subs. of Philips Electronic Instruments, Inc., *(Electron Optics Pub Grp; 0-9612934),* 85 McKee Dr., Mahwah, NJ 07430 (SAN 292-4854) Tel 802-785-3042.

Electronic Bookshelf, Inc., The, *(Elect Bkshelf; 0-935325),* R.R. No. 9, Box 64, Frankfort, IN 46041 (SAN 695-765X) Tel 317-324-2182.

Electronic Courseware Systems, Inc., *(Electron Course; 0-942132; 1-55603),* 1210 Lancaster Dr., Champaign, IL 61821 (SAN 238-6577) Tel 217-359-7099.

Electronic Flea Market, *(Electronic Flea),* 2020 Girard Ave. S., Minneapolis, MN 55405 (SAN 206-4529).

Electronic Industries Assn., *(Elec Ind Assn),* 2001 Eye St., NW, Washington, DC 20006 (SAN 230-0702) Tel 202-457-4900.

Electronic Trend Publications, *(Electronic Trend; 0-944405),* 10080 N. Wolfe Rd., Suite 372, Cupertino, CA 95014 (SAN 287-7457) Tel 408-996-7416.

Elegant Stew Pr., *(Elegant Stew; 0-9612618),* General Delivery, Boston, MA 02205-9999 (SAN 289-1220).

Elek-Tek, Inc., 6557 N. Lincoln Ave., Chicago, IL 60645-3986 (SAN 695-5215) Tel 312-677-7660; Toll free: 800-621-1269.

ELEMENT Pubs., Inc., *(ELEMENT Pubs; 0-939393),* 708 Greenwich St., New York, NY 10014 (SAN 663-1363) Tel 212-929-8275.

Elenchus Enterprises, Inc., *(Elenchus Ent; 0-936953),* 87 Van Buren St., Woodbridge, NJ 07095 (SAN 658-7046) Tel 201-634-5140.

Elevation Pr., *(Elevation Pr; 0-932624),* 1031 24th St., Greeley, CO 80631 (SAN 212-1875) Tel 303-352-2979.

11th Hour Gospel, *(Eleventh Hour; 0-9608662),* Box 190, Prosser, WA 99350 (SAN 240-6365) Tel 509-786-4230.

Elghund Publishing Co., *(Elghund Pub; 0-9612112),* P.O. Box 158, Simpsonville, MD 21150 (SAN 289-0380) Tel 301-997-9490.

Eli Mail-Order, Inc., *(Eli Mail; 0-9602230),* P.O. Box 81, Brooklyn, NY 11208 (SAN 212-3509).

Elijah-John Pubns., *(Elijah-John; 0-9614311),* 103 Russell, Apt. 6, Saline, MI 48176 (SAN 687-5106) Tel 313-429-5717.

Eliopoulos, Nicholas C, Publishing, *(Eliopoulos; 0-9605396),* P.O. Box 65, Oak Park, IL 60303 (SAN 220-0856); 5711 W. School St., Chicago, IL 60634 (SAN 662-0027) Tel 312-725-1960.

Elisabeth Sifton Books *See* **Viking-Penguin, Inc.**

Elite Publishing Co., Inc., *(Elite Pub Co; 0-935589),* 2346 S. Lynhurst Dr., Indianapolis, IN 46241 (SAN 696-3773) Tel 317-244-5665.

†**Elite Publishing Corp.,** *(Elite; 0-918367),* 11-03 46th Ave., Long Island City, NY 11101 (SAN 657-338X) Tel 718-937-4606; *CIP.*

†**Elizabeth Pr.,** *(Elizabeth Pr),* 103 Van Etten Blvd., New Rochelle, NY 10804 (SAN 201-3789); *CIP.*

Elizabeth St. Pr., *(Elizabeth St Pr; 0-910323),* 240 Elizabeth St., New York, NY 10012 (SAN 241-5003) Tel 212-758-7400.

Elk Grove Books *See* **Childrens Pr.**

Elk Grove Village Public Library, *(Elk Grove Vill; 0-9605940),* 1 Morrison Blvd., Elk Grove Village, IL 60007 (SAN 216-6224) Tel 312-439-0447.

Elkins, J. A., Brothers Publishing Co., *(J A Elkins Brs),* P.O. Drawer 785, Porter, TX 77365 (SAN 669-6880).

Elks, Mary, *(M Elks; 0-9616039),* 2 Beech Trail, Durham, NC 27705 (SAN 698-0813) Tel 919-684-6570.

Ell Ell Diversified, Inc., *(Ell Ell Diversified; 0-937428),* P.O. Box 1702, Santa Rosa, CA 95402 (SAN 215-3076) Tel 707-542-8663.

Eller, Sylvia, *(S Eller; 0-9617012),* 727 E. Orange Grove, No. G, Pasadena, CA 91104 (SAN 662-8656) Tel 818-791-3258.

Ellerbach, John, *(J Ellerbach; 0-9616813),* 878 41st St., Des Moines, IA 50312 (SAN 661-0978) Tel 515-255-5604.

Ellingsworth Press, *(Ellingsworth; 0-9605698),* 20 E. Main St., Rm. 338, Waterbury, CT 06702 (SAN 211-1519).

Elliot's Bks., *(Elliots Bks; 0-911830),* P.O. Box 6, Northford, CT 06472 (SAN 204-1529) Tel 203-484-2184.

Elliott, Carroll, & Ellen Gale Hammett, *(Elliott & Hammett; 0-9615630),* R.F.D. 3, St. Mary's, WV 26170 (SAN 696-3803) Tel 304-665-2254.

Elliott, J. R., *(J R Elliott),* 9 Country Manor, Fergus Falls, MN 56537 (SAN 283-2380) Tel 218-736-3453.

Elliott, R. W., *(R W Elliott; 0-9616575),* Rte. 5, Box 1-B, Lindale, TX 75771 (SAN 661-2350) Tel 214-882-3312; Hwys. I-20 & FM 849, Lindale, TX 75771 (SAN 662-4324).

TEP, *(TEP; 0-911759),* 276 Cambridge St. Suite 4, Boston, MA 02114 (SAN 264-0252) Tel 617-227-7277.

Elliott Graphics, Inc., *(Elliott Graph; 0-9614793),* 1133 Broadway, New York, NY 10010 (SAN 692-9818).

Ellis, Edward, *(E Ellis; 0-9611126),* P.O. Box 661, Rangeley, ME 04970 (SAN 283-2429); 123 Welsh Rd., Ambler, PA 19002 (SAN 283-2437) Tel 215-646-3839.

Ellis & Stewart Pubs., *(Ellis & Stewart Pub; 0-942532),* 270 N. Canon Dr., Suite 103, Beverly Hills, CA 90210 (SAN 239-6386) Tel 213-276-5424.

Ellis Pr., The, *(Ellis Pr; 0-933180),* P.O. Box 1443, Peoria, IL 61655 (SAN 214-008X) Tel 217-xxx.

Ellison Enterprises, *(Ellison Ent; 0-930580),* 3466 N. Miami Ave., Miami, FL 33127 (SAN 211-0091) Tel 305-576-6600.

Elm Hollow Inc. Pubs., *(Elm Hollow Inc Pub; 0-916553),* S.R. Box 21A2, Elm Hollow Rd., Livingston Manor, NY 12758 (SAN 295-2602) Tel 914-439-5400.

Elm Pr., *(Elm Pr; 0-9613420),* 12859 Via Latina, Del Mar, CA 92014 (SAN 656-9781) Tel 619-452-8692.

Elm Pubns., *(Elm Pubns; 0-911175),* P.O. Box 23192, Knoxville, TN 37933-1192 (SAN 269-8986) Tel 615-966-5703.

Elmwood Park Publishing, Co., *(Elmwood Park Pub; 0-933181),* P.O. Box 35132, Elmwood Park, IL 60635-0132 (SAN 691-7178) Tel 312-453-5023.

Elmwood Publishing Co., The, *(Elmwood Pub Co; 0-931396),* 1509 Norman Ave., San Jose, CA 95125 (SAN 211-6650) Tel 408-267-2498.

Elon College Alumni Assn., *(Elon College Alum Assoc; 0-9605976),* P.O. Box 2116, Elon College, NC 27244 (SAN 216-7298) Tel 919-584-2380.

Elpenor Bks., *(Elpenor; 0-931972),* Box 3152, Merchandise Mart Plaza, Chicago, IL 60654 (SAN 222-8076).

Elra Press, *(Elra Pr; 0-933200),* 140 University Ave., Box 30, Palo Alto, CA 94301 (SAN 222-8009).

Elramco Enterprises, Inc., *(ELRAMCO Enter; 0-930355),* 1533 Central Ave., Albany, NY 12205 (SAN 670-7629) Tel 518-458-9095.

Elrod, Bruce C., *(B C Elrod; 0-9614805),* P.O. Box 363, White Rock, SC 29177 (SAN 692-7629) Tel 803-781-8690; Toll free: 800-729-8690.

Elsa II Pubns., *(Elsa II Pub; 0-939595),* 788 G. Laurel Walk, Goleta, CA 93117 (SAN 663-6225) Tel 805-687-6707.

Elsah Landing Restaurant, The, *(Elsah Landing; 0-9606150),* 10041 Conway Rd., St. Louis, MO 63124 (SAN 285-0095) Tel 314-993-4843; Orders to: Elsah Landing Restaurant Cookbook, P.O. Box 98, Elsah, IL 62028 (SAN 285-0117).

Elsevier-Nelson *See* **Lodestar Bks.**

Elsevier North-Holland Biomedical Pr. *See* **Elsevier Science Publishing Co., Inc.**

Elsevier-Phaidon *See* **Dutton, E. P.**

Elsevier Science Publishing Co., Inc., Subs. of Elsevier NDU NV, *(Elsevier; 0-444; 0-7204),* 52 Vanderbilt Ave., New York, NY 10017 (SAN 200-2051) Tel 212-370-5520. *Imprints:* Elsevier North-Holland Biomedical Press (Biomedical Pr); Excerpta-Medica (Excerpta Medica); North-Holland (North Holland); Thomond Press (Thomond Pr).

Elysian Pr., *(Elysian Pr; 0-941692),* P.O. Box 94, Cold Spring Harbor, NY 11724 (SAN 239-2844) Tel 212-831-0596.

Elysium Growth Pr., *(Elysium; 1-55599),* 700 Robinson Rd., Topanga, CA 90290 (SAN 210-5950) Tel 213-455-1000; 5436 Fernwood Ave., Los Angeles, CA 90027 (SAN 688-3915) Tel 213-465-7121.

Emami, Mary Lou & Suzanne Coulson, *(Emami-Coulson; 0-9602316),* 1691 Dickinson Dr., Wheaton, IL 60187 (SAN 213-9197).

Embassy Imprint, Inc., *(Embassy Imp; 0-930527),* Bridge Rd., Haddam, CT 06438 (SAN 682-7896) Tel 203-345-2574.

Embee Pr., *(Embee Pr; 0-89816),* 82 Pine Grove, Kingston, NY 12401 (SAN 212-1603).

Embroidery Themes Co., *(Embroidery; 0-9614004),* RD. 3, Lebanon, NJ 08833 (SAN 693-4013).

Emerald *See* **Dell Publishing Co., Inc.**

Emerald City Pr., *(Emerald City; 0-932531),* P.O. Box 21066, Little Rock, AR 72212 (SAN 687-4673) Tel 501-224-3897.

Emerald Forest Music, *(Emerald Forest; 0-9613159),* P.O. Box 161034, San Diego, CA 92116 (SAN 294-9261) Tel 619-298-5530.

Emerald House, *(Emerald Hse; 0-936958),* P.O. Box 1769, Sandpoint, ID 83864 (SAN 214-3682) Tel 208-263-1071; Dist. by: DeVorss & Co., P.O. Box 550, 1046 Princeton Dr., Marina del Rey, CA 90294 (SAN 168-9886); Dist. by: Angel Book Distribution Center, 561 Tyler St., Monterey, CA 93940 (SAN 200-5042); Dist. by: New Pathways, 103 Goldencrest Ave., Waltham, MA 02154 (SAN 200-5050).

Emerald People Productions, *(Emerald People; 0-938055),* P.O. Box 58996, 2 Penn Ctr., Philadelphia, PA 19102 (SAN 661-2407); 352 Keswick Ave., Glenside, PA 19038 (SAN 661-2415) Tel 215-886-8243.

Emerald Publishing, *(Emerald NV; 0-9615757),* P.O. Box 11830, Reno, NV 89510 (SAN 696-3846) Tel 415-658-6470.

Emerald Publishing, *(Emerald Pub MI; 0-9617095),* P.O. Box 906, Sterling Heights, MI 48311 (SAN 662-4790); 42275 Malbeck Dr., Sterling Heights, MI 48310 (SAN 662-4804) Tel 313-739-9497. Do not confuse with other companies with the same name in El Segundo, CA, Reno, NV.

Emerald Publishing Co., *(Emerald CA; 0-935675),* P.O. Box 2813, El Segundo, CA 90245-1913 (SAN 696-3862) Tel 213-322-8049.

Emerald Valley Publishing Co., *(Emerald Pub; 0-933094),* P.O. Box 70288, Eugene, OR 97401 (SAN 222-8025) Tel 503-485-8796.

†**Emergence Pubns.,** *(Emergence; 0-89465),* P.O. Box 1394, Hillsboro, OR 97123 (SAN 210-6299) Tel 503-648-2758; *CIP.*

Emergency Care Research Institute *See* **ECRI**

Emergency Department Nurses Association, *(Emerg Nurses IL; 0-935890),* 666 N. Lakeshore Dr., Chicago, IL 60511 (SAN 269-9036) Tel 312-649-0297.

Emergency Medical Technology Press *See* **First International Publishing Corp.**

Emergency Service Products & Productions, *(Emerg Service Products & Prod; 0-9606144),* P.O. Box 1513, Orange, CA 92668 (SAN 217-5142) Tel 714-830-1754.

Emerging Island Cultures Pr., *(Emerging Island; 0-931003),* 612 Second Ave., San Francisco, CA 94118 (SAN 678-8963) Tel 415-752-6347.

Emeritus Inc., Pub., *(Emeritus Inc; 0-943694),* 15 Jade Lane, Cherry Hill, NJ 08002 (SAN 238-2768) Tel 609-667-4278.

Emerson, R. C., Co., *(R C Emerson; 0-9614755),* 540 Latimer Rd., Santa Monica, CA 90402 (SAN 692-9168) Tel 213-454-5814.

Emerson Bks., Inc., *(Emerson; 0-87523),* 121 N. Hampton Dr., White Plains, NY 10603 (SAN 201-3819) Tel 914-739-3506; Madelyn Ave., Vrplanck, NY 10596 (SAN 658-0580).

Eminent Pubns. Enterprises, *(Eminent Pubns; 0-936955),* P.O. Box 1026, Jeffersonville, IN 47131 (SAN 658-6589) Tel 812-282-8338.

Emissaries of Divine Light, *(Emissaries Divine; 0-932869),* 5569 N. County Rd., Loveland, CO 80537 (SAN 688-9875) Tel 303-667-4675.

Emissary Pubns., *(Emissary Pubns; 0-941380),* P.O. Box 642, S. Pasadena, CA 91030 (SAN 238-9746) Tel 818-794-3400.

Emmanuel Christian Ministries, *(Emmanuel Christian; 0-9615955),* 1050 Barberry Rd., Yorktown Heights, NY 10598 (SAN 697-3299) Tel 914-245-5635.

Emmett Pub. Co., *(Emmett; 0-934682),* 2861 Burnham Blvd., Minneapolis, MN 55416 (SAN 210-556X).

Emmons-Fairfied Publishing Co., *(Emmons-Fairfied Pub; 0-9607956),* 18674 Fairfield, Detroit, MI 48221 (SAN 240-0707) Tel 313-284-0180.

Emory Publishing Co., *(Emory Pub Co; 0-934681),* P.O. Box 55022, Birmingham, AL 35255 (SAN 694-2008) Tel 205-979-0971.

Emotions Anonymous International, *(Emotions Anony Intl; 0-9607356),* P.O. Box 4245, St. Paul, MN 55104 (SAN 239-5495) Tel 612-647-9712; 1595 Selby Ave., St. Paul, MN 55104 (SAN 669-0734).

Empak Enterprises, Inc., *(Empak Enter; 0-9616156),* 520 N. Michigan Ave., Chicago, IL 60611 (SAN 699-9182) Tel 312-642-3434.

Empey Enterprises, *(Empey Ent; 0-9613084),* 810 Alexander St., Greenville, MI 48838 (SAN 293-9290) Tel 616-754-7036.

Empire Books, *(Empire Bks; 0-88015),* 527 Madison Ave., New York, NY 10022 (SAN 219-7324) Tel 212-752-6451; Toll free: 800-242-7737; Orders to: Harper & Row Pubs., Inc., Keystone Industrial Park, Scranton, PA 18512 (SAN 215-3742).

Empire Games Pr., Div. of Empire Games, Inc., *(Empire Games Pr; 0-913037),* P.O. Box 5462, Arlington, TX 76011 (SAN 283-0663) Tel 817-261-3666; 700 E. Abram, Arlington, TX 76010 (SAN 283-0671).

Empire Publishing Co., The, *(Empire Pub Co; 0-9616213),* 25 Bryant Ave., Milton, MA 02186 (SAN 658-5205) Tel 617-696-8592.

†**Employee Benefit Research Institute,** *(Employee Benefit; 0-86643),* 2121 K St., NW, Suite 860, Washington, DC 20037-2121 (SAN 216-2423) Tel 202-659-0670; Toll free: 800-354-5425; Orders to: P.O. Box 753, Waldorf, MD 20601 (SAN 662-0035) Tel 301-843-1020; *CIP.*

Employee Relocation Council, *(Employee; 0-912614),* 1720 N. St., NW, Washington, DC 20036 (SAN 201-3827) Tel 202-857-0857.

Emporia State Univ. Pr., *(Emporia State),* 1200 Commercial St., Emporia, KS 66801 (SAN 207-9771) Tel 316-343-1200.

Emprise Pubns., *(Emprise Pubns; 0-938129),* P.O. Box 456, Cayucos, CA 93430 (SAN 661-2423); 3499 Studio Dr., Cayucos, CA 93430 (SAN 661-2431) Tel 408-422-0415.

Empyrean Pubns., *(Empyrean Pubns; 0-935283),* P.O. Box 49, Portland, CT 06480 (SAN 696-6772) Tel 203-928-2301; 21 Highland Ave., Portland, CT 06480 (SAN 696-6780).

EMT Inc., *(EMT Inc; 0-916363),* 2026 Beechwood, Wilmatte, IL 60091 (SAN 295-7604) Tel 312-943-1900.

En Passant Poetry Press, *(En Passant Poet; 0-9605098),* 4612 Sylvanus Dr., Wilmington, DE 19803 (SAN 212-4211) Tel 302-774-4571.

Enabling Systems, Inc., *(Enabling Syst; 0-917688),* P.O. Box 2813, Honolulu, HI 96803 (SAN 207-2440) Tel 808-545-2646.

Enabling Technologies, Inc., *(Enabling Tech Inc; 0-936299),* 600 S. Dearborn, Suite 1304, Chicago, IL 60605 (SAN 697-3329) Tel 312-427-0386; Dist. by: Ashton-Tate Bks., 8901 S. La Cienega Blvd., Inglewood, CA 90301 (SAN 265-4628).

Enas, Enas A., *(EA Enas; 0-9616232),* 1935 Green Trails Dr., Lisle, IL 60532 (SAN 658-5752) Tel 312-961-0279.

Enchiridion International, *(Enchiridion; 0-916649),* Box 2589, Cullowhee, NC 28723 (SAN 296-5054).

Encino Press, *(Encino Pr; 0-88426),* 510 Baylor St., Austin, TX 78703 (SAN 201-3843) Tel 512-476-6821.

Encode Computer Services, *(Encode Comp Serv; 0-939439),* P.O. Box 5070, Kingwood, TX 77325 (SAN 663-348X); 2218 Running Spring, Kingwood, TX 77339 (SAN 663-3498) Tel 713-358-6687.

Encounter Bks. *See* **Times Bks.**

Encyclopaedia Britannica Educational Corp., Affil. of Encyclopaedia Britannica, Inc., *(Ency Brit Ed; 0-87827; 0-8347),* 425 N. Michigan Ave., Chicago, IL 60611 (SAN 201-3851) Tel 312-321-6800; Toll free: 800-554-9862.

Encyclopaedia Britannica, Inc., *(Ency Brit Inc; 0-85229),* 310 S. Michigan Ave., Chicago, IL 60604 (SAN 204-1464) Tel 312-347-7000; Toll free: 800-554-9862.

End is Here Pubns., The, *(End is Here Pubns; 0-9607640),* 1522 Micheltorena , No. 4, Los Angeles, CA 90026 (SAN 663-5350).

End of the Age Ministries, *(End Age Ministries; 0-936131),* P.O. Box 3321, Littleton, CO 80161 (SAN 697-0974) Tel 303-797-1000; 1508 W. Briarwood Ave., Littleton, CO 80120 (SAN 697-0982).

End-Time Ministries, *(End-Times Mini; 0-9615220),* P.O. Box 55127, Tulsa, OK 74155 (SAN 695-1503) Tel 918-258-4767.

End Violence Against the Next Generation, Inc., *(End Violence; 0-932141),* 977 Keeler Ave., Berkeley, CA 94708-1498 (SAN 225-9184) Tel 415-527-0454.

Endeavor Publishing Co., *(Endeavor Pub; 0-942172),* 30064 Annapolis Cir., Inkster, MI 48141 (SAN 204-1448); Dist. by: Baker & Taylor Co., Midwest Div., 501 Gladiola Ave., Momence, IL 60954 (SAN 169-2100) Tel 815-472-2444; Dist. by: Baker & Taylor Co., Eastern Div., 50 Kirby Ave., Somerville, NJ 08876 (SAN 169-4901) Tel 201-526-8000.

Endless Rhymes & Lines, *(Endless Rhymes; 0-9615717),* 3714 Russell Ave. N., Minneapolis, MN 55412 (SAN 696-3889) Tel 612-521-8243.

Endowment for Research in Human Biology, The, *(Endowment Res Human Bio; 0-938321),* 250 Longwood Ave.,c/o Center for Biochemical & Biophysical Science & Medical, Boston, MA 02115 (SAN 661-244X) Tel 617-732-1367.

Endurance Press, *(Endurance; 0-910552),* 5695 Lumley St., Detroit, MI 48210 (SAN 203-8412) Tel 313-843-0310.

Energize Bks., Div. of Energize Assocs., *(Energize; 0-940576),* 5450 Wissahickon Ave., Lobby A, Philadelphia, PA 19144 (SAN 218-5458) Tel 215-438-8342.

Energon Company, *(Energon Co; 0-9601552),* P. O. Box 1352, Laramie, WY 82070 (SAN 693-5443) Tel 307-742-3458.

Energy Blacksouth Press, *(Energy Blacksouth),* Box 441, Howard University, Washington, DC 20059 (SAN 208-1393); 2805 Southmore, Houston, TX 77004 (SAN 208-1407). Out of business.

Energy Education Pubs., *(Energy Educ),* 1151 Conlon SE, Grand Rapids, MI 49506 (SAN 211-0105) Tel 616-949-3666.

Energy Forum, Inc., *(Energy Forum; 0-917882),* P.O. Box 840, Lanham, MD 20706 (SAN 241-3795) Tel 301-927-5090; Dist. by: Maryland Historical Press, 9205 Tuckerman St., Lanham, MD 20706 (SAN 202-6147) Tel 301-577-2436.

Energy Self-Sufficiency, *(Energy Self Suff; 0-9608402),* P.O. Box 1410, Paso Robles, CA 93447 (SAN 240-639X) Tel 805-238-0437.

Energy Textbooks International, Inc., *(Energy Textbks; 0-910649),* 2809 NW Expressway, Suite 540, Oklahoma City, OK 73112 (SAN 262-0200) Tel 405-842-6676; Dist. by: Penwell Books, 1421 S. Sheridan, Tulsa, OK 74112 (SAN 282-1559) Tel 918-835-3161; Dist. by: Kraftbilt Products, 7659 E. 46th Pl., Tulsa, OK 74145 (SAN 662-7234) Tel 918-628-1260.

Enetai Pr., *(Enetai Pr; 0-9615811),* 105 S. Main St., Seattle, WA 98104 (SAN 696-7345) Tel 206-624-2540; Dist. by: Pacific Pipeline, 19215 66th Ave. S., Kent, WA 98032 (SAN 208-2128) Tel 206-872-5523.

Engdahl Typography, *(Engdahl Typo; 0-939489),* 829 St. Helena Ave., Santa Rosa, CA 95404 (SAN 663-3935) Tel 707-544-4532; Dist. by: Clamshell Press, 160 California Ave., Santa Rosa, CA 95404 (SAN 219-1512).

Engelmeier, Philip A., *(Engelmeier; 0-9605002),* 909 Geary-517, San Francisco, CA 94109 (SAN 215-6415).

Enger, Ronald L., *(R L Enger; 0-9601742),* 1853 Shadowbrook Dr., Merced, CA 95340 (SAN 211-948X).

Engineering Foundation, *(Eng Found; 0-939204),* 345 E. 47th St., New York, NY 10017 (SAN 216-3772).

Engineering Information, Inc., *(Eng Info; 0-911820; 0-87394),* 345 E. 47th St., New York, NY 10017 (SAN 203-8420) Tel 212-705-7615.

†**Engineering Pr., Inc.,** *(Engineering; 0-910554),* P.O. Box 1, San Jose, CA 95103-0001 (SAN 201-3878) Tel 408-258-4503; *CIP.*

Engineering Pubns., *(Eng Pubns; 0-9605004),* P.O. Box 302, Blacksburg, VA 24060 (SAN 220-0481).

Engineer's Pr., *(Engineers Pr; 0-930642),* P.O. Box 1651, Coral Gables, FL 33134 (SAN 201-5668) Tel 305-856-0031.

Englander Communications Inc., *(Eng Communi Inc; 0-9613139),* 1111 E. Putnam Ave., Riverside, CT 06878 (SAN 294-7765) Tel 203-637-5900.

Engler Publishing, *(Engler Pub; 0-9615003),* 6117 Linden Rd., Woodbury, MN 55125 (SAN 693-9430) Tel 612-735-7192.

English Cocker Spaniel Club of America, Inc., *(Eng Cocker Spaniel; 0-9613761),* P.O. Box 223, Sunderland, MA 01375 (SAN 225-5588) Tel 413-665-3567.

English Educational Services International, Inc., *(Eng Educ Serv; 0-936808),* 139 Massachusetts Ave., Boston, MA 02115 (SAN 215-160X) Tel 617-267-8063.

English Factory, The, *(English Fact; 0-911349),* 2202 N. Mitchel St., Phoenix, AZ 85006 (SAN 269-9257) Tel 602-258-7747.

English I Computer Tutorials, Inc., *(Eng Comp Tut; 0-915869),* 1617 N. Troy St., Chicago, IL 60647 (SAN 293-9363) Tel 312-489-1588.

English Language Services, Div. of Washington Educational Research Associates, Inc., *(Eng Language; 0-87789; 0-89285; 0-89318),* 5761 Buckingham Pkwy., Culver City, CA 90230 (SAN 281-6326) Tel 213-642-099414350 NW Science Park Dr., Portland, OR 97229 (SAN 281-6334).

Eno River Press, Inc., *(Eno River Pr; 0-88024),* P.O. Box 4900, Duke Sta., Durham, NC 27706 (SAN 217-3573) Tel 919-929-0078.

Enoch Pratt Free Library, *(Enoch Pratt; 0-910556),* 400 Cathedral St., Baltimore, MD 21201-4484 (SAN 201-3916) Tel 301-396-5494.

Enquiry Press, *(Enquiry Pr; 0-941494),* 799 Broadway, Suite 325, New York, NY 10003 (SAN 239-0876) Tel 212-982-2406.

Enrich, Subs. of Ohaus Scale Corp., *(Enrich; 0-933358; 0-86582),* 2325 Paragon Dr., San Jose, CA 95131 (SAN 213-2168) Tel 408-263-7111; Toll free: 800-ENRICH-1.

Enrichment Enterprises, *(Enrich Enter; 0-9609612),* 1424 Hacienda Pl., Pomona, CA 91768 (SAN 264-0260) Tel 714-622-4887.

Ensign Pr., *(Ensign Pr; 0-9608996),* P.O. Box 638, Camden, ME 04843 (SAN 240-866X) Tel 207-236-6545.

Ensign Publishing Co., *(Ensign Pub; 0-910558),* P.O. Box 298, Riverton, UT 84065 (SAN 686-287X).

Enslow, Ridley, Pubs *See* **Enslow Pubs., Inc.**

Enslow Pubs., Inc., *(Enslow Pubs; 0-89490),* Bloy St. & Ramsey Ave., Box 777, Hillside, NJ 07205 (SAN 213-7518) Tel 201-964-4116.

Ensminger Publishing Co., *(Ensminger; 0-941218),* 648 W. Sierra Ave., P.O. Box 429, Clovis, CA 93612 (SAN 239-4375).

Entelek, Inc., *(Entelek; 0-87567),* Ward-Whidden Hse., The Hill, P.O. Box 1303, Portsmouth, NH 03801 (SAN 201-3924) Tel 603-436-0439.

Enteracom, Inc., *(Enteracom Inc; 0-936509),* 5070 Parkside Ave., Suite 1420, Philadelphia, PA 19131 (SAN 697-8282) Tel 215-877-9409.

Enterline, J.R., *(J R Enterline),* 144 W. 95th St., New York, NY 10025 (SAN 208-399X) Tel 212-865-9648.

Enterpress Partners, *(Enterpress; 0-939355),* P.O. Box 7097, Redlands, CA 92374 (SAN 662-6815); 1322 San Pablo, Redlands, CA 92373 (SAN 662-6823) Tel 714-798-1155.

Enterprise Achievement Associates, *(Enter Achieve; 0-930305),* Hudson, OH 44236 (SAN 686-2837).

Enterprise Bks., *(Enterprise Bks UT; 0-936957),* 123 Westminster Ave., Salt Lake City, UT 84115 (SAN 658-6570) Tel 801-485-1585.

Enterprise for Education, Inc., *(Enterprise Educ; 0-934653; 0-928609),* 1320-A Santa Monica Mall, Suite 205, Santa Monica, CA 90401 (SAN 694-0730) Tel 213-394-9864.

Enterprise Pr., *(Enterprise Pr; 0-9604726),* Box 108, Bath, MI 48808 (SAN 214-2406) Tel 517-339-9564.

Enterprise Pubns., *(Enterprise Calif; 0-918558),* P.O. Box 4001, Downey, CA 90241 (SAN 207-222X).

Enterprise Pubns., *(Enterprise IL),* 20 N. Wacker Dr., Chicago, IL 60606 (SAN 204-1421) Tel 312-332-3571.

Enterprise Publishing Assn., *(Enterprise Pub; 0-939542),* Box 29, W. Second St., Coudersport, PA 16915 (SAN 216-6704) Tel 814-274-8044.

Enterprise Publishing, Inc., *(Enterprise Del; 0-913864),* 725 Market St., Wilmington, DE 19801 (SAN 201-3932) Tel 302-654-0110.

Enterprise Pubns. *See* **Newspaper Enterprise Assn., Inc.**

Enterprises for Emmanuel, *(Ent Emmanuel; 0-9616332),* P.O. Box 2450, Elkhart, IN 46515 (SAN 659-1647) Tel 219-262-3440; 53038 Faith Ave., Elkhart, IN 46514 (SAN 659-1655).

Entertainment Factory, The, *(Entertainment Factory; 0-936086),* P.O. Box 407, Cave Creek, AZ 85331 (SAN 214-0098) Tel 602-488-2510.

Entertainment Yellow Pages, *(Enter Yellow; 0-916909),* 6000 Sunset Blvd. No. 209, Hollywood, CA 90028 (SAN 655-8836) Tel 213-857-8326.

Entheos Communications, Div. of Entheos Mountain Agriculture, *(Entheos; 0-939750),* P.O. Box 370, Seabeck, WA 98380-0370 (SAN 216-3209) Tel 206-830-4758.
Imprints: Wild Skies Press (Wild Skies Pr.)

Entity Publishing Co., *(Entity Pub Co; 0-89913),* 1314 Larmor Ave., Rowland Heights, CA 91748 (SAN 213-3091) Tel 714-598-1755.

Entomography Pubns., *(Entomography; 0-9608404),* 1722 J St., Suite 19, Sacramento, CA 95814 (SAN 240-6403) Tel 916-444-9133.

†Entomological Reprint Specialists, *(Entomological Repr; 0-911836),* P.O. Box 77224, Dockweiler Sta., Los Angeles, CA 90007 (SAN 201-4602) Tel 213-227-1285; *CIP.*

Entomological Society of America, *(Entomol Soc; 0-938622),* 4603 Calvert Rd., College Park, MD 20740 (SAN 201-3940) Tel 301-864-1334; P.O. Box 4104, Hyattsville, MD 20781 (SAN 669-0769).

Entrepreneur Group, *(Entre Group; 0-936133),* 2311 Pontius St., Los Angeles, CA 90064 (SAN 697-0885) Tel 619-457-3260.

Entrepreneurs Productions, *(Entre Prods; 0-911665),* 5 White St., New York, NY 10013 (SAN 264-0279) Tel 212-966-6464.

Entropy, Ltd., *(Entropy Ltd; 0-938876),* S. Great Rd., Lincoln, MA 01773 (SAN 215-6423) Tel 617-259-8901.

Entry Publishing, Inc., *(Entry Pub; 0-941342),* 27 W. 96th St., New York, NY 10025 (SAN 238-9754) Tel 212-662-9703.

†Entwhistle Bks., *(Entwhistle Bks; 0-9601428; 0-934558),* P.O. Box 611, Glen Ellen, CA 95442 (SAN 211-0113) Tel 707-996-3901; *CIP.*

Entwood Publishing, Inc., *(Entwood Pub; 0-9605978),* P.O. Box 268, Wausau, WI 54402-0268 (SAN 216-7301) Tel 715-842-7250; Dist. by: Caroline Hse., Inc., 5S 250 Frontenac Rd., Naperville, IL 60540 (SAN 211-2280) Tel 312-983-6400; Toll free: 800-245-2665.

Enviro Press, *(Enviro Pr; 0-937976),* c/o Aware Inc., 621 Mainstream Dr., Nashville, TN 37228 (SAN 220-049X) Tel 615-255-2288; Dist. by: Butterworth Publishers, 80 Montvale Ave., Stoneham, MA 02180 (SAN 200-500X) Tel 617-438-8464.

Environmental Action Foundation, Inc, *(EAF NH),* Church Hill, Harrisville, NH 03450 (SAN 232-7635).

Environmental Design & Research Ctr., *(Environ Design; 0-915250),* 261 Port Royal Ave., Foster City, CA 94404 (SAN 285-0125).

Environmental Design Research Assn., *(EDRA; 0-939922),* L'Enfant Plaza Sta., P.O. Box 23129, Washington, DC 20026 (SAN 216-8103) Tel 301-657-2651.

†Environmental Law Institute, *(Environ Law Inst; 0-911937),* 1616 P. St., NW Suite 200, Washington, DC 20036 (SAN 225-0853) Tel 202-328-5150; *CIP.*

Environmental Pr., *(Environ Pr; 0-936960),* 1201 Dusky Thrush, Austin, TX 78746 (SAN 214-3003) Tel 512-327-5479.

Environmental Pubns. Associates, Ltd, *(Environ Pubns; 0-9606694),* 17 Jefryn Blvd. W., Deer Park, NY 11729 (SAN 209-5564) Tel 516-667-8896.

Environmental Research Institute of Michigan, *(Environ Res Inst; 0-9603590),* P.O. Box 8618, Ann Arbor, MI 48107 (SAN 213-2176).

Environmental Studies Council, Inc., *(Envir Studies Coun; 0-916629),* 2900 NE Indian River Dr., Jensen Beach, FL 33457 (SAN 296-5127) Tel 305-334-1262.

Envision Communications, *(Envision Comm; 0-9605942),* 10 Thurlow Terr., Albany, NY 12203 (SAN 216-6232) Tel 518-462-1135.

ENVO Publishing Co. Inc., *(Envo Pub Co; 0-932871),* P.O. Box 415, Bethlehem, PA 18016 (SAN 688-9913) Tel 215-691-1339.

Envoy Pr., Inc., *(Envoy Press; 0-938719),* 141 E. 44th St., Suite 511, New York, NY 10017 (SAN 661-5023) Tel 212-696-0887.

Enyi, Donatus O., Div. of World Trend, USA, *(D Enyi; 0-937171),* 1514 First St., NW, Washington, DC 20001 (SAN 658-5264) Tel 202-387-2019; Dist. by: World Trend USA, P.O. Box 1886, Washington, DC 20013 (SAN 200-6820) Tel 202-387-2619.

Epic Pubns., Inc., *(Epic Pubns; 0-914244),* 4420 Westover Dr., Orchard Lake, MI 48033 (SAN 203-8439) Tel 313-626-6217.

Epic Publishing, Inc., *(Epic Pub Inc; 0-9616122),* Country Green Shopette, 3055 E. Hwy. 50, Canon City, CO 81212 (SAN 699-6884) Tel 303-275-0555.

Epicurean Traveler Pr., *(Epicurean),* 229-A Upper Terr., San Francisco, CA 94117 (SAN 281-6741) Tel 415-731-0475.

Epidemiology Resources Inc., *(Epidemiology; 0-917227),* P.O. Box 57, Chestnut Hill, MA 02167 (SAN 656-0342) Tel 617-734-9100.

EPIGEM, *(EPIGEM; 0-916705),* 5914 Pulaski Ave., Philadelphia, PA 19144 (SAN 654-1445) Tel 215-849-4510.

Epimetheus Pr., Inc., *(Epimetheus Pr; 0-88008),* P.O. Box 565, Gracie Sq. Sta., New York, NY 10028 (SAN 285-0133) Tel 212-879-0553; P.O. Box 4508, Sunrise Sta., Ft. Lauderdale, FL 33338 (SAN 285-0141) Tel 305-522-4496; P.O. Box 361, Blackwood, NJ 08012 (SAN 658-0599).

Epiphany Press, *(Epiphany Pr; 0-916700),* P.O. Box 14606, San Francisco, CA 94114 (SAN 206-5037) Tel 415-431-1917.

Episcopal Ctr. for Evangelism, *(Episcopal Ctr; 0-918903),* P.O. Box 920, Live Oak, FL 32060 (SAN 208-1598).

Episcopal Churchwoman of All Saints, Inc., *(ECS Inc; 0-9606880),* 100 Rex Dr., River Ridge, LA 70123 (SAN 217-3581) Tel 504-737-1416; Orders to: La Bonne Cuisine, P.O. Box 23065, New Orleans, LA 70183 (SAN 662-0795); Dist. by: Publishers Group West, 5855 Beaudry St., Emeryville, CA 94608 (SAN 202-8522) Tel 415-658-3453; Toll free: 800-982-8319; Dist. by: Collection, Inc., The, 2101 Kansas City Rd., Olathe, KS 66061 (SAN 200-6359) Tel 913-764-1811.

Epistemics Institute Pr., Subs. of Institute for Applied Epistemics, *(Epistemics; 0-930371),* 8620 Wilshire Blvd., Suite 104, Beverly Hills, CA 90211 (SAN 670-7637) Tel 213-659-4541; Orders to: P.O. Box 18672, Los Angeles, CA 90007 (SAN 662-247X) Tel 213-389-0307.

Epistemology Publishers, *(Epistemology Pubs; 0-931889),* P.O. Box 564, Mableton, GA 30059 (SAN 686-0338) Tel 404-944-0917.

EPOC *See* **Equity Policy Center (EPOC)**

Epoch Pr., *(Epoch Pr; 0-9614068),* P.O. Box 3047, San Rafael, CA 94912 (SAN 693-9996) Tel 415-332-0685.

Epsilon Pi Tau, *(Epsilon Pi Tau),* Technology Building, Bowling Green State University, Bowling Green, OH 43403 (SAN 224-5140) Tel 419-372-2425.

Epstein, Max C., *(Epstein M C; 0-9612046),* 1 Montgomery Pl., Brooklyn, NY 11215 (SAN 286-7796) Tel 718-783-1605.

Epstein, Vivian Sheldon, *(V S Epstein; 0-9601002),* 212 S. Dexter St., Denver, CO 80222 (SAN 208-6425) Tel 303-322-7450.

Equal Employment Advisory Council, *(Equal Employ; 0-937856),* 1015 Fifteenth St. NW, Suite 1220, Washington, DC 20005 (SAN 220-0511).

Equal Justice Consultants & Educational Products, *(Equal Just Con; 0-930413),* P.O. Box 5582, Eugene, OR 97405 (SAN 682-0492) Tel 503-343-6761.

Equality Pr., *(Equality Pr; 0-938795),* 42 Ranchita Way, Chico, CA 95928 (SAN 661-4914) Tel 916-895-5249.

Equanimity Pr., *(Equanimity; 0-941362),* P.O. Box 839, Bolinas, CA 94924 (SAN 238-9762); Dist. by: Bookpeople, 2929 Fifth St., Berkeley, CA 94710 (SAN 168-9517) Tel 415-549-3030 (SAN 662-0051).

†Equity Institute The, *(Equity Inst; 0-932469),* P.O. Box 30245, Bethesda, MD 20814 (SAN 687-4215) Tel 301-654-2904; *CIP.*

Equity Policy Center (EPOC), *(Equity Policy; 0-941696),* 4818 Drummond Ave., Chevy Chase, MD 20815 (SAN 239-4235) Tel 301-656-4475.

Equity Pr., *(Equity; 0-931769),* P.O. Box 3841, Tallahassee, FL 32315-3841 (SAN 684-8877) Tel 904-385-5497.

Equity Publishing Corp., *(Equity Pub NH; 0-87454),* Main St., Orford, NH 03777 (SAN 204-1383) Tel 603-351-4374.

Era Press, *(Era Davidson; 0-9605270),* Box 548, Davidson, NC 28036 (SAN 215-8612).

ERA Press *See* **Education Research Assocs.**

Erde International, *(Erde Intl; 0-911973),* P.O. Box 25007, Phoenix, AZ 85002 (SAN 264-701X) Tel 602-285-1661.

Erens, Patricia, *(P Erens; 0-9603920),* 2920 Commonwealth Ave., Chicago, IL 60657 (SAN 213-7356); Dist. by: Chicago Review Press, 814 N. Franklin St., Chicago, IL 60610 (SAN 213-5744) Tel 312-337-0747.

Ergo Business Bks., *(ERGO Business Bks; 0-941046),* 1401 Pasadena Ave., Fillmore, CA 93015 (SAN 217-359X) Tel 805-495-3237.

ERIC Clearinghouse on Information Resources, *(ERIC Clear; 0-937597),* Syracuse Univ., Schl. of Education, Huntington Hall, Syracuse, NY 13244-2340 (SAN 672-8189) Tel 315-423-3640; Orders to: Syracuse Univ., 030 Huntington Hall, Syracuse, NY 13244-2340 (SAN 662-250X).

Erickson, Phoebe, *(P Erickson; 0-9613390),* P.O. Box 46, Hartland, VT 05048 (SAN 657-1077) Tel 802-436-2788.

Ericson, *(Ericson; 0-9605868),* 215 Foster Dr., Des Moines, IA 50312 (SAN 220-1682) Tel 515-255-0798.

Names

Ericson Bks., *(Ericson Bks; 0-911317),* 1614 Redbud St., Nacogdoches, TX 75961 (SAN 263-0923) Tel 409-564-3625.

Erie Art Museum, *(Erie Art Mus; 0-9616623),* 411 State St., Erie, PA 16501 (SAN 661-2458) Tel 814-459-5477.

Erie Street Pr., The, *(Erie St Pr; 0-942582),* 221 S. Clinton Ave., Oak Park, IL 60302 (SAN 285-015X) Tel 312-848-5716.

†Eriksson, Paul S., Pub., *(Eriksson; 0-8397),* 208 Battell Bldg., Middlebury, VT 05753 (SAN 201-6702) Tel 802-388-7303; Dist. by: Independent Publishers Group, 1 Pleasant Ave., Pt. Washington, NY 11050 (SAN 287-2544) Tel 516-944-9325; *CIP.*

Erin Hills Pubs., *(Erin Hills; 0-9600754),* 1390 Fairway Dr., San Luis Obispo, CA 93401 (SAN 206-4537) Tel 805-543-3050.

†Erlbaum, Lawrence, Assocs., Inc., *(L Erlbaum Assocs; 0-89859; 0-8058),* 365 Broadway, Hillsdale, NJ 07642 (SAN 213-960X) Tel 201-666-4110; *CIP.*

Ernst Katz, *(E Katz; 0-9613745),* 1923 Geddes Ave., Ann Arbor, MI 48104 (SAN 677-6272) Tel 313-662-9355.

Eros Publishing, Co., *(Eros Pub; 0-911571),* P.O. Box 355, Parkchester Sta., Bronx, NY 10462 (SAN 264-0317) Tel 212-828-5569.

Erskine, Kathryn A., *(Erskine; 0-9605058),* Box 398, Hurricane, WV 25526 (SAN 215-9538).

Erskine Pr., *(Erskine Pr; 0-914353),* P.O. Box 21622, Concord, CA 94518 (SAN 289-6214) Tel 415-687-8313.

Ervin, W & S, Publishing Co., *(Ervin Pub Co; 0-915447),* 739 Indian Hill Dr., Port Orange, FL 32019 (SAN 291-1531).

Erwin/Marvin & M., *(Erwin Marvin M; 0-914598),* 661 Mar Vista Dr., Los Osos, CA 93402 (SAN 670-6959) Tel 805-528-0783.

Escape Ventures, Inc., *(Escape Ventures; 0-930039),* P.O. Box 4330, Virginia Beach, VA 23454 (SAN 669-7844) Tel 804-481-1026.

Escortguide: The People Connection To New Mexico, *(Escortguide; 0-9607818),* 535 Cordova Rd., Suite 125, Santa Fe, NM 87501 (SAN 238-1583) Tel 505-988-7099.

Eshelman, Ruth, *(R Eshelman; 0-9617140),* 849 Coast Blvd (Casa de Manana), La Jolla, CA 92037 (SAN 663-3277) Tel 619-454-2151.

Esmond Julie Publishing, *(Esmond Julie Pub; 0-9616333),* 7787 Carraway Ct., Maineville, OH 45039 (SAN 659-1701) Tel 513-398-8395.

Esperance Enterprises, Inc., *(Esperance Enter; 0-930757),* Box 218, 14625 Watt Rd., Novelty, OH 44072 (SAN 679-1654) Tel 216-338-1625.

Esperanto League for North America, Inc., *(Esperanto League North Am; 0-939785),* P.O. Box 1129, El Cerrito, CA 94530 (SAN 201-8241) Tel 415-653-0998; 5712 Hollis St., Emeryville, CA 94608 (SAN 669-0785).

Esperanto Society of Chicago, *(Esperanto Soc; 0-9615986),* P.O. Box 1698, Chicago, IL 60690 (SAN 698-1534) Tel 312-549-0057.

ESPress, *(ESPress; 0-917200),* P.O. Box 8606, Washington, DC 20011 (SAN 206-748X) Tel 202-723-4578.

Esprit, *(Esprit; 0-9614437),* 900 Minnesota St., San Francisco, CA 94107 (SAN 689-352X) Tel 415-648-6900.

Esquire, Inc., Div. of Follett Corp., *(Esquire; 0-695),* 1010 W. Washington Blvd., Chicago, IL 60607 (SAN 200-2035).

Essai Seay Publishing Co., *(Essai Seay Pubns; 0-9607958),* P.O. Box 55, East St. Louis, IL 62202 (SAN 240-0715) Tel 618-271-5323.

Essays in Literature, *(Essays in Lit W Ill J; 0-934312),* Dept. of English, Western Illinois Univ., Macomb, IL 61455 (SAN 212-6583) Tel 309-298-2212.

Essence Pubns., *(Essence Pubns; 0-940756),* 168 Woodbridge Ave., Highland Park, NJ 08904 (SAN 211-4909) Tel 201-572-3120.

Essex County Board of Supervisors, *(Essex Cty Bd Sup),* P.O. Box 1079, Tappahannock, VA 22560 (SAN 669-6740).

Essex County History, *(Essex County MA),* P.O. Box 418, West Newbury, MA 01985 (SAN 209-3731) Tel 617-465-5397. Out of business.

Essex Institute, *(Essex Inst; 0-88389),* 132 Essex St., Salem, MA 01970 (SAN 203-8447) Tel 617-744-3390.

Essex Press, *(Essex Pr; 0-930381),* Rte. 1, P.O. Box 77C, Erwin, TN 37650 (SAN 670-7645) Tel 615-743-7685.

Essex Pubns., *(Essex Pubns; 0-930332),* Portsmouth, NH 03824 (SAN 694-3144) Tel 603-436-7974.

Essex Publishing, Ltd., *(Essex Pub Ltd; 0-912889),* P.O. Box 317, Ada, MI 49301 (SAN 283-2585) Tel 616-459-0031.

Estacado Books, *(Estacado Bks),* P.O. Box 4516, Lubbock, TX 79409 (SAN 207-6756) Tel 806-799-1986.

Estes, Hiawatha, & Assocs., *(H Estes; 0-911008),* P.O. Box 404-RR, Northridge, CA 91328 (SAN 206-8389) Tel 818-885-6588.

Estonian World Council Inc., *(Estonian Wrld; 0-932595),* 2206 Chilham Rd., Baltimore, MD 21209 (SAN 687-5114) Tel 301-542-1735.

Estrela Press, *(Estrela Pr; 0-943632),* 2318 2nd Ave., Box 23, Seattle, WA 98121 (SAN 238-2792) Tel 206-322-5402.

Estrilda Distributors Inc., *(Estrilda Dist),* 1005 W. Hill St., Champaign, IL 61821 (SAN 677-4806) Tel 217-398-6975.

Estuarine Research Federation, *(Estuarine Res; 0-9608990),* Belle Baruch Institute, Univ. of South Carolina, Columbia, SC 29208 (SAN 241-3027) Tel 803-777-3916.

ETC See Education & Training Consultants Co.

Eterna Pr., *(Eterna Pr; 0-934670),* P.O. Box 1344, Oak Brook, IL 60521 (SAN 221-1807).

Eternal Enterprises, *(Eternal Ent; 0-917578),* P.O. Box 60913, Sacramento, CA 95860 (SAN 206-4383). Name Formerly L P Price.

Etheridge, G. & M., Ministries, Inc., *(Etheridge Minist; 0-937417),* P.O. Box 564, Sikeston, MO 63801 (SAN 658-8581) Tel 314-471-9344; 415 Louise Ave., Sikeston, MO 63801 (SAN 658-859X).

Ethical Enterprises, *(Ethical Enterprises; 0-9614810),* 6083 Charlesworth St., Dearborn Heights, MI 48127 (SAN 692-9311) Tel 313-278-7074.

†Ethics & Public Policy Ctr., Inc., *(Ethics & Public Policy; 0-89633),* 1030 15th St., NW, Suite 300, Washington, DC 20005 (SAN 216-132X) Tel 202-682-1200; *CIP.*

Ethics Resource Ctr., Inc., *(Ethics Res Ctr; 0-916152),* 1025 Connecticut Ave., NW, Suite 1003, Washington, DC 20036 (SAN 201-6893) Tel 202-223-3411.

Ethiopian Cookbook Enterprise, *(Ethiopian Ent; 0-9616345),* 3800 Powell Ln., No. 404, Falls Church, VA 22041 (SAN 658-7747) Tel 703-823-0988.

Ethnographic Arts Pubns., *(Ethnographic Arts Pubns; 0-9611006),* 1040 Erica Rd., Mill Valley, CA 94941 (SAN 282-8650) Tel 415-383-2998.

Ethnographica See Barber, Lilian, Pr.

†Ethridge, Blaine, Bks., *(Ethridge; 0-87917),* 15 E. Kirby, No. 510, Detroit, MI 48202 (SAN 201-4327) Tel 313-872-3160; *CIP.*

Ettema, Ross K., *(R K Ettema),* 16420 Claire Ln., South Holland, IL 60473 (SAN 696-3919).

Ettinger, L. J., *(Ettinger; 0-9614840),* 16170 Rhyolite Cir., Reno, NV 89511 (SAN 693-1049) Tel 702-851-3061; Orders to: 3949 Knobhill Dr., Sherman Oaks, CA 91423 (SAN 699-5950) Tel 818-789-7724.

Eubanks International Pubns., Inc., *(Eubanks Intl Pubns; 0-9616214),* P.O. Box 3634, Silver Spring, MD 20901 (SAN 658-523X) Tel 301-496-4768; 1131 University Blvd., W., Silver Spring, MD 20902 (SAN 658-5248).

Eucalyptus Pr., *(Eucalyptus Pr; 0-9611980),* P.O. Box 7073, Kansas City, MO 64113 (SAN 287-7430)

Euclid Northwest Pubns., *(Euclid NW Pubns; 0-9615088),* 4227 Crestview St., Wenatchee, WA 98801 (SAN 694-1478) Tel 509-662-8131; Orders to: 4145 80th Ave., SE, Mercer Island, WA 98040 (SAN 662-3336).

Euclid Pr., *(Euclid Pr; 0-936583),* 900 Euclid Ave., Apt. 205, Santa Monica, CA 90403 (SAN 698-0805) Tel 213-394-2868.

Euclid Publishing Co., The, *(Euclid Pub; 0-935490),* Dist. by: Bond & Bacon Assocs., P.O. Box 121, Cathedral Sta., New York, NY 10025 (SAN 211-6057).

Eupsychian Pr., The, *(Eupsychian; 0-939344),* 950 Roadrunner Rd., Austin, TX 78746 (SAN 216-5627) Tel 512-327-2214; Orders to: P.O. Box 3090, Austin, TX 78764-3090 (SAN 662-006X).

Eurail Guide Annual, *(Eurail Guide; 0-912442),* 27540 Pacific Coast Hwy., Malibu, CA 90265 (SAN 207-9704) Tel 213-457-7286.

Euramerica Pr., *(Euramerica Pr; 0-916876),* 381 N. Main St., Pittston, PA 18640 (SAN 208-1563) Tel 717-693-4678.

Eurasia Pr., *(Eurasia Pr NY; 0-932030),* 168 State St., Teaneck, NJ 07666-3516 (SAN 222-7886) Tel 212-564-4099; Toll free: 800-242-7737; 302 Fifth Ave., New York, NY 48202 (SAN 658-0602); 21 Market St., Paterson, NJ 07509 (SAN 658-0610).

†Eureka Pubns., *(Eureka Pubns; 0-942848),* Box 372, Mantua, NJ 08051 (SAN 240-2165) Tel 609-468-4145; *CIP.*

Euro-Dutch, Pubs., *(Euro-Dutch Pub),* P.O. Box 1070, Buffalo, NY 14221-1070 (SAN 265-3826).

Eurofit Publishing Co., *(Eurofit Pub; 0-938821),* 70 E. Ridgewood Ave., Ridgewood, NJ 07450 (SAN 661-8200) Tel 201-652-2012.

Eurolingua, *(Eurolingua; 0-931922),* P.O. Box 101, Bloomington, IN 47402-0101 (SAN 222-7894).

Europa, *(Europa; 0-905118),* c/o Unipub, Customer Service Dept., P.O. Box 1222, Ann Arbor, MI 48106 (SAN 202-5264).

Europa See Unipub

Europa Co., *(Europa AZ; 0-937215),* 5645 W. Camelback Rd., Phoenix, AZ 85031 (SAN 658-7011) Tel 602-846-0124.

European American Music, *(Eur-Am Music; 0-913574),* P.O. Box 850, Valley Forge, PA 19482 (SAN 201-7393) Tel 215-648-0506.

Eustace, Herbert W., C.S.B., *(Eustace CSB),* P.O. Box 7328, Berkeley, CA 94707 (SAN 276-9743) Tel 415-524-0846.

Euterpe Pr., *(Euterpe Pr; 0-9616315),* 45 Buckingham Dr., Billerica, MA 01821 (SAN 658-7054) Tel 617-667-6377.

Evanel Assocs., *(Evanel; 0-918948),* Box 42, Northfield, OH 44067 (SAN 209-4347) Tel 216-467-1750.

Evangel Pr., (IN), Div. of Brethren in Christ Church, *(Evangel Indiana; 0-916035),* 301 N. Elm, Nappanee, IN 46550-0189 (SAN 211-7940) Tel 219-773-3164.

Evangel Pubns., *(Evangel Pubns; 0-935515),* P.O. Box 11007, Huntsville, AL 35814 (SAN 696-4931) Tel 205-533-0498; 1119 Retlaw St., Huntsville, AL 35816 (SAN 696-494X).

Evangelical & Reformed Historical Society, *(Evang & Ref; 0-910564),* 555 W. James St., Lancaster, PA 17603 (SAN 281-6849).

Evangelical Literature League, The, *(Evangelical Lit; 0-939125),* P.O. Box 6219, Grand Rapids, MI 49516-6219 (SAN 662-4812); 941 Wealthy, SE, Grand Rapids, MI 49516-6219 (SAN 662-4820) Tel 616-454-3196.

Evangelical Sisterhood of Mary, *(Evang Sisterhood Mary),* 9849 N. 40th St., Phoenix, AZ 85028 (SAN 211-8335) Tel 602-996-4040.

Evangelical Teacher Training Assn., *(Evang Tchr; 0-910566),* 110 Bridge St., P.O. Box 327, Wheaton, IL 60189 (SAN 203-8471) Tel 312-668-6400.

Evangeline Pr. & Dramatists Service, Inc., *(Evangel Pr & Drama Serv; 0-935425),* 1071 Sunny Dell Ln., Sunny Dell Acres, Hueytown, AL 35023 (SAN 696-4982) Tel 205-426-1034.

Evangelist Assn., *(Evang Assn; 0-9603014),* P.O. Box 368014, Chicago, IL 60636 (SAN 217-2380).

†Evans, M., & Co., Inc., *(M Evans; 0-87131),* 216 E. 49th St., New York, NY 10017 (SAN 203-4050) Tel 212-688-2810; Toll free: 800-526-0275; Dist. by: Henry Holt and Co., 521 Fifth Ave., New York, NY 10175 (SAN 200-6472) Tel 212-599-7600; *CIP.*

Evans, Norma P., *(N P Evans; 0-937418),* 2211 Liberty, Beaumont, TX 77701 (SAN 213-2184) Tel 409-835-7175.

Evans, Robert L., *(R L Evans; 0-9606698),* 2500 St. Anthony Blvd., Minneapolis, MN 55418 (SAN 208-3450) Tel 612-781-7384.

Evans, Rod L., *(Rod L Evans; 0-9616533),* RR 1, P.O. Box 33B, Conde, SD 57434 (SAN 659-4441) Tel 605-382-5963.

Names

Evans-Kimbrell, Frances, *(F Evans-Kimbrell; 0-9616264),* Star Rte., Box 102, Allardt, TN 38504 (SAN 658-3539) Tel 615-879-5299.

Evans Pubns., Subs. of Eva-Tone, Inc., *(Evans FL; 0-932715),* 4801 Ulmerton Rd., Clearwater, FL 33520 (SAN 687-7419) Tel 813-577-7000.

Evans Pubns., *(Evans Pubns; 0-934188),* P.O. Box 520, Perkins, OK 74059 (SAN 212-9019) Tel 405-547-2411.

Evans Publishing Co., *(Evans Pub; 0-9614583),* P.O. Box 26126, Denver, CO 80226 (SAN 692-7084).

Evans Publishing Hse., *(Evans Pub Hse; 0-934889),* P.O. Box 1042, Boca Raton, FL 33429 (SAN 694-4442).

Everest, F. Alton, *(F A Everest; 0-9608352),* 6275 South Rounhill Dr., Whittier, CA 90601 (SAN 662-0078) Tel 213-698-8831; Dist. by: Mix Pubns., Inc., 2608 Ninth St., Berkeley, CA 94710 (SAN 693-9562) Tel 415-843-7901; Toll free: 800-233-9604.

†**Everett/Edwards, Inc.,** *(Everett-Edwards; 0-912112),* P.O. Box 1060, DeLand, FL 32720 (SAN 201-4653) Tel 904-734-7458; *CIP.*

Everett Press *See* **Street Pr.**

Evergreen, *(J D Adams; 0-939523),* P.O. Box 794, Pico Rivera, CA 90660-0794 (SAN 663-4443); 1334 E. 216th St., Carson, CA 90745 (SAN 663-4451) Tel 213-948-6436.

Evergreen Bks. *See* **Grove Pr.**

Evergreen-Black Cat Bks. *See* **Grove Pr.**

Evergreen Book Distributors, *(Evergreen Dist; 0-903729),* 6513 Lankershim Blvd., Suite 37, N. Hollywood, CA 91606 (SAN 223-1522) Tel 818-986-9689.

Evergreen Communications, Inc., *(Evergreen Comm; 0-943782),* 301 W. Washington, Bloomington, IL 61701 (SAN 241-192X) Tel 309-829-9411. *Imprints:* Pantagraph Books (Pantagraph Bks).

Evergreen Educational Services, *(Evergreen Ed; 0-9616769),* P.O. Box 3863, Pinedale, CA 93650 (SAN 661-2482); 622 E. Tenaya, Fresno, CA 93710 (SAN 661-2490) Tel 209-439-6040.

Evergreen Enterprises, *(Evergreen Ent; 0-933183),* P.O. Box 763, Laurel, MD 20707-0763 (SAN 691-7186) Tel 301-953-1861.

Evergreen Pacific, *(Evergreen Pacific; 0-9609036),* 4535 Union Bay Place NE, Seattle, WA 98105 (SAN 240-9119).

Evergreen Paddleways, *(Evergreen Paddleways; 0-916166),* 1416 21st St., Two Rivers, WI 54241 (SAN 205-6208) Tel 414-794-8485.

Evergreen Pr., *(Evergreen Pr; 0-913056),* P.O. Box 306, Avalon, CA 90704 (SAN 206-9415) Tel 213-510-1700.

Evergreen Pr., Inc., *(Evergreen; 0-914510),* P.O. Box 4971, Walnut Creek, CA 94596 (SAN 206-3638) Tel 415-933-3700; 3380 Vincent Rd., Pleasant Hill, CA 94523 (SAN 658-0629).

Evergreen Productions, *(Evergreen Prods; 0-9613919),* 3300 16th St., NW, No. 714, Washington, DC 20010 (SAN 682-5249) Tel 202-483-4392.

Evergreen Publishing Co., *(Evergreen Co; 0-9611960),* 1665 Nome St., Aurora, CO 80010 (SAN 286-7427) Tel 303-366-0879.

Evergreen Publishing Co., *(Evergreen Calif; 0-939083),* 136 S. Atlantic Blvd., Monterey Park, CA 91754 (SAN 662-9113) Tel 818-281-3622; Dist. by: East Wind Bks. & Art, 1435 Stockton St., San Francisco, CA 94133 (SAN 200-7584). Do not confuse with Evergreen Pub., North Andover, MA, or Evergreen Pub., Seattle, WA.

Evergreen Publishing Co., *(Evergreen Pub WA; 0-937627),* 901 Lenora, Seattle, WA 98121 (SAN 659-1728) Tel 206-624-8400.

Everlast Pr., *(Everlast Pr; 0-9607262),* 365 Maple St., W. Hempstead, NY 11552 (SAN 239-0884) Tel 516-483-8581.

Everson Museum of Art, *(Everson Mus; 0-914407),* 401 Harrison St., Syracuse, NY 13202 (SAN 278-7458) Tel 315-474-6064.

Everybody's Press, *(Everybodys Pr),* Fame Ave., Hanover, PA 17331 (SAN 237-949X) Tel 717-632-3535.

Everyday Series, *(Everyday Ser; 0-915517),* 13 Riverview Terrace, Rensselaer, NY 12144 (SAN 291-154X) Tel 518-449-8737.

Evolving Pubns., *(Evolving Pubns; 0-912389),* 2531 Sawtelle Blvd., No. 42, Los Angeles, CA 90064 (SAN 265-2390) Tel 213-390-5993.

Ewing Pubns., *(Ewing Pubns),* 114 Main St., Kingston, NJ 08528 (SAN 212-9388).

Ex Libris, *(Ex Libris ID; 0-9605212),* Box 225, Sun Valley, ID 83353 (SAN 215-7608) Tel 208-622-8174.

Ex Libris, *(Ex Libris PA; 0-9617141),* Logan Square East, Apt. 2305, Philadelphia, PA 19103 (SAN 682-2800) Tel 215-563-1800.

Exanimo Pr., *(Exanimo Pr; 0-89316),* P.O. Box 18, 23520 Hwy. 12, Segundo, CO 81070 (SAN 209-0910).

Excel Fitness, Pubs., *(Excel Fitness; 0-916915),* P.O. Box 19257, Seattle, WA 98119 (SAN 656-0350) Tel 206-282-7476; Dist. by: Pacific Pipeline, 19215 66th Ave. S., Kent, WA 98032 (SAN 208-2128) Tel 206-872-5523; Toll free: 800-562-4647 (in WA); Toll free: 800-426-4727 (in OR, ID, MT, NV, & Northern CA).

Excel, Inc., *(Excel; 0-9608992),* 200 W. Station St., Barrington, IL 60010 (SAN 237-9503) Tel 312-382-7272.

Excel Pr., *(Excel Pr; 0-9609582),* 459 59th St., Brooklyn, NY 11220 (SAN 262-0227) Tel 718-492-4789.

Excelsior Music Publishing Co., *(Excelsior Music Pub Co; 0-935016),* 35-19 215th Pl., Bayside, NY 11361 (SAN 221-1742); Dist. by: STBS, 50 W. 23rd St., New York, NY 10010 (SAN 200-6162) Tel 212-206-8795.

Excelsior Publishing, *(Excelsior Pub; 0-9614096),* P.O. Box 141, Houston, DE 19954 (SAN 685-9879) Tel 302-422-3980.

Exceptional Parent, The, *(Excptnl Parent; 0-930958),* 605 Commonwealth Ave., Boston, MA 02215 (SAN 211-5611) Tel 617-536-8961.

Exceptional Press, Inc., *(Exceptional Pr Inc; 0-914420),* P.O. Box 344, San Juan Capistrano, CA 92675 (SAN 206-3646) Tel 714-493-8405.

Exceptional Resources Inc., *(Exceptional Res; 0-935594),* P.O. Box 9221, Austin, TX 78766 (SAN 221-1750); Dist. by: Pro-ED, 5341 Industrial Oaks Blvd., Austin, TX 78735 (SAN 222-1349) Tel 512-892-3142.

Excerpta-Medica *See* **Elsevier Science Publishing Co., Inc.**

Excerpta Medica-Princeton, *(Excerpta Princeton),* 3131 Princeton Pike, Lawrenceville, NJ 08648 (SAN 209-5041).

Excogitations, *(Excogitations; 0-939597),* P.O. Box 6260, Pasadena, TX 77506 (SAN 663-6241); 226 E. Oak, Deer Park, TX 77536 (SAN 663-625X) Tel 713-476-1767.

Execucom Systems Corp., *(Execucom Sys Corp; 0-911941),* 9442 Capital of Texas Hwy. N., Austin, TX 78759-6311 (SAN 264-0325) Tel 512-346-4980.

Executive Chauffeuring Schl., *(Exec Chauffeuring; 0-9616215),* 3115 Fujita St., Torrance, CA 90505 (SAN 658-4799) Tel 213-534-3535.

Executive Communications, *(Executive Comm; 0-917168),* 919 Third Ave., New York, NY 10022 (SAN 208-3043) Tel 212-421-3713.

Executive Education Press, Div. of Executive Education, Inc., *(Exec Ed Pr; 0-9606022),* P.O. Box 160, Camden, ME 04843 (SAN 216-8928) Tel 207-236-6782.

Executive Enterprises, *(Executive Ent),* 5811 La Jolla Corona Dr., La Jolla, CA 92037 (SAN 209-1259) Tel 619-459-4901. Do Not Confuse with Executive Enterprises Pubns. in NY.

†**Executive Enterprises, Inc.,** *(Exec Ent Inc; 0-917386; 0-88057),* 22 W. 21st St., New York, NY 10010 (SAN 208-953X); Toll free: 800-645-7880; *CIP.*

Executive Grapevine, Inc., Affil. of Executive Grapevine (London), *(Exec Grapevine),* 575 Madison Ave., Suite 1006, New York, NY 10022 (SAN 659-493X) Tel 212-605-0414.

Executive Publishing (MO), *(Executive Pub; 0-943338),* Box 3155, Springfield, MO 65804 (SAN 240-6438) Tel 417-883-0950.

†**Executive Reports Corp.,** Subs. of Prentice-Hall, Inc., *(Exec Reports; 0-13),* 190 Sylvan Ave., Englewood Cliffs, NJ 07632 (SAN 204-1294) Tel 201-592-2075; Orders to: Dept. 200-B, Englewood Cliffs, NJ 07632 (SAN 204-1308) Tel 201-767-5059; *CIP.*

Executive Salary Research Co., *(Exec Sal; 0-912716),* 1685 Sunrise Dr., Lima, OH 45805 (SAN 201-8268) Tel 419-991-3936; Orders to: P.O. Box 832, Lima, OH 45802 (SAN 201-8276).

Executive Speaker Co., The, *(Exec Speaker Co; 0-930255),* P.O. Box 292437, Dayton, OH 45429 (SAN 670-8528) Tel 513-294-8493.

Executive Standards, Inc., *(Exec Stand; 0-917818),* 811 East St., New Britain, CT 06051 (SAN 210-0797) Tel 203-224-3357.

Executive Systems, Inc., *(Exec Systems; 0-937867),* 15300 Ventura Blvd., Suite 305, Sherman Oaks, CA 91403 (SAN 659-445X) Tel 818-990-3457.

Executives West Publishing Co., *(Exec West; 0-939148),* 4250 E. Camelback, Suite 180K, Phoenix, AZ 85018 (SAN 219-9742).

Exelrod Press, *(Exelrod Pr; 0-917388),* P.O. Box 2303, Pleasant Hill, CA 94523 (SAN 208-1555) Tel 415-934-3357.

Exeter Publishing Co., *(Exeter Pub; 0-937193),* 3752 Motor Ave., Los Angeles, CA 90034 (SAN 699-8259) Tel 213-305-1762.

Exhibit Press, *(Exhibit Pr; 0-9607908),* P.O. Box 44844, Los Olivos Station, AZ 02130 (SAN 238-0315) Tel 413-528-4894.

Exhorters, Inc., The, *(Exhorters; 0-9609260),* P.O. Box 492, Vienna, VA 22180 (SAN 241-3825) Tel 703-698-6880.

Exile Pr., *(Exile Pr; 0-933515),* P.O. Box 1768, Novato, CA 94948 (SAN 297-1747) Tel 415-883-2132.

†**Existential Books,** *(Existential Bks; 0-89231),* 1816 Stevens Ave. S., Suite 25, Minneapolis, MN 55403 (SAN 208-1547) Tel 612-871-7275; *CIP.*

Exodus International North America, *(Exodus Intl N Am; 0-931593),* P.O. Box 2121, San Rafael, CA 94912 (SAN 682-5214) Tel 415-454-0960.

Expansion Pr., *(Expansion Pr; 0-9616099),* 852 Rosedale Ave., SE, Atlanta, GA 30312 (SAN 698-1224) Tel 404-622-7072.

Expedited Publishing Co., Div. of Patent Rights, Inc., *(Expedited; 0-9603122),* P.O. Box 67, Scarborough, NY 10510 (SAN 213-490X).

Experiment Pr., The, Div. of Experiment in International Living, *(Experiment Pr; 0-936141),* Kipling Rd., Brattleboro, VT 05301 (SAN 696-7388) Tel 802-257-7751.

Expim Co., *(EXPIM Co; 0-9611794),* P.O. Box 23084, Washington, DC 20026 (SAN 285-2446) Tel 202-426-8350; 7237 Hillmead Ct., Springfield, VA 22150 (SAN 285-2454).

Exploration Pr., Div. of Chicago Theological Seminary, *(Exploration Pr; 0-913552),* Chicago Theological Seminary, 5757 S. University Ave., Chicago, IL 60637 (SAN 203-851X) Tel 312-752-5757.

Explorations Institute, *(Explorations Inst; 0-918600),* P.O. Box 1254, Berkeley, CA 94701 (SAN 210-8968).

Explorations Pr., *(Explr Pr MA; 0-941830),* P.O. Box 907, Greenfield, MA 01302 (SAN 239-2054).

Explorer Bks. *See* **Viking-Penguin, Inc.**

Explorer Books, *(Explorer Bks; 0-9605938),* 601 LeGrand, Route 6, Panama City Beach, FL 32407 (SAN 216-6240) Tel 904-234-1378.

Exponent Ltd., *(Exponent; 0-935722),* Box 481, Bedford Hills, NY 10507 (SAN 214-3038).

Exposition Pr. of Florida, Inc., *(Exposition Pr FL; 0-682),* 1701 Blount Rd., Suite C, Pompano Beach, FL 33069 (SAN 207-0642) Tel 305-979-3200. *Imprints:* Banner (Banner); Classic (Classic); Lochinvar (Lochinvar); O.E.G. Foundation (OEG Found); Testament (Testament); University (University).

ExPress Publishing, *(ExPress; 0-932956),* P.O. Box 1639, El Cerrito, CA 94530-4639 (SAN 208-6433) Tel 415-236-5496; Dist. by: Bookpeople, 2929 Fifth St., Berkeley, CA 94710 (SAN 168-9517) Tel 415-549-3030; Dist. by: Distributors, The, 702 S. Michigan, South Bend, IN 46618 (SAN 169-2488) Tel 219-232-8500; Dist. by: Cogan Bks., 4332 W. Artesia Ave., Fullerton, CA 92633 (SAN 168-9649) Tel 714-523-0309; Dist. by: Law Distributors, 14415 S. Main St., Gardena, CA (SAN 212-3681).

ExPressAll, *(ExPressAll; 0-936190),* 260 Dean Rd., Brookline, MA 02146 (SAN 207-5903) Tel 617-734-3508.

Expression Co., *(Expression),* P.O. Box 153, Londonderry, NH 03053 (SAN 203-8536) Tel 603-432-5232.

Expressive Images Studio, *(Expressive Images Studio; 0-915701),* 1215 Kuehnle St., Ann Arbor, MI 48103 (SAN 292-4919) Tel 313-665-7804.

Expro Pr., *(Expro Pr; 0-936391),* Boston College, 519 B McGuinn Hall, Chestnut Hill, MA 02167 (SAN 697-3345) Tel 617-552-4198; Dist. by: Talman Co., 150 Fifth Ave., Rm. 514, New York, NY 10011 (SAN 200-5204) Tel 212-620-3182.

Extension Division, Univ., of Missouri, *(Extension Div; 0-933842),* Argricultural Editor's Office, 1-98 Agriculture Building, Univ. of Missouri, Columbia, MO 65211 (SAN 679-1638); Orders to: Extension Pubns., Univ. of Missouri, 222 S. Fifth St., Columbia, MO 65211 (SAN 688-427X) Tel 314-882-7216.

Extequer Pr., *(Extequer; 0-935892),* P.O. Box 60193, Pasadena, CA 91106 (SAN 281-6873) Tel 818-797-3627.

External Representation of the Ukrainian Helsinki Group, *(ERUHG; 0-86725),* P.O. Box 770, Canal Sta., New York, NY 10003 (SAN 217-0701) Tel 212-564-4334.

Exxon Corp., Human Resources, *(Exxon Human Resources; 0-938933),* 1251 Ave. of the Americas, New York, NY 10020 (SAN 661-8170) Tel 212-333-1921.

Eyecontact, *(Eyecontact; 0-938112),* 465 Lexington Ave., New York, NY 10017 (SAN 281-692X) Tel 212-683-1641; Dist. by: Golden Lee, 1000 Dean St., Brooklyn, NY 11238 (SAN 169-5126) Tel 212-857-6333; Dist. by: Publishers Group West, 5855 Beaudry St., Emeryville, CA 94608 (SAN 202-8522) Tel 415-658-3453.

EZ Cookin' Bk. Co., *(EZ Cookin; 0-937545),* 9925 Currant Ave., Fountain Valley, CA 92708 (SAN 240-9364).

FARMS, *(FARMS; 0-934893),* P.O. Box 7113, Univ. Sta., Provo, UT 84602 (SAN 694-4469) Tel 801-378-3295.

FAS Pubs., *(FAS Pubs),* P.O. Box 5453, Madison, WI 53705 (SAN 201-4750) Tel 608-274-1733.

F & F Publishing Co., *(F & F Pub; 0-9616875),* 50 Shady Glen Rd., Memphis, TN 38119 (SAN 661-3748) Tel 901-685-9915.

F&S Pr., Div. of Frost & Sullivan, *(F&S Pr; 0-86621),* 106 Fulton St., New York, NY 10038 (SAN 220-0538) Tel 212-233-1080. Out of business.

FBF Pubns., *(FBF Pubns; 0-9616026),* P.O. Box 3296, San Bernardino, CA 92413 (SAN 698-1518) Tel 714-864-0865; 5695 McKinley Ave., San Bernardino, CA 92413 (SAN 698-1526) Tel 714-820-2280.

FC&A Publishing, *(FC&A Pub; 0-915099),* 103 Clover Green, Peachtree City, GA 30269 (SAN 289-7946) Tel 404-487-6307.

F.D.C. Publishing Co., *(FDC Pub; 0-89794),* P.O. Box 206, Stewartsville, NJ 08886 (SAN 212-2758).

F.D.M. Distributor, *(FDM Distributor; 0-9615720),* 7807 Hohman Ave., Munster, IN 46321 (SAN 696-4168) Tel 219-836-8107.

FDP Assocs., *(FDP Assocs; 0-937209),* 461 Park Ave., S., New York, NY 10016 (SAN 658-7194) Tel 212-213-8730.

FDS Gourmet Enterprises, *(FDS Gourmet; 0-9616834),* 4136 Indiana Ave., Kenner, LA 70065 (SAN 661-2563) Tel 504-468-1834.

FER Publishing Co., *(FER Pub Co; 0-9614380),* 13 Vine St., Manchester, MA 01944 (SAN 688-4822) Tel 617-526-1529; Dist. by: Globe Pequot Pr., Old Chester Rd., Chester, CT 06412 (SAN 201-9892) Tel 203-526-9571.

F.E.S., Ltd., Publishing, *(FES Ltd; 0-937063),* P.O. Box 70, Bayside, NY 11361 (SAN 658-6066) Tel 718-423-6662.

F. I. Communications, *(F I Comm; 0-89553),* 45 Alhambra, Portola Valley, CA 94025 (SAN 201-8489) Tel 415-851-0254; Orders to: P.O. Box 3121, Stanford, CA 94305-0036 (SAN 201-8497).

F. I. G. Ltd., *(FIG Ltd; 0-9601452),* P.O. Box 23, Northbrook, IL 60062 (SAN 211-8971).

FMA Business Bks., *(FMA Bus; 0-930566),* 3928 Iowa St., San Diego, CA 92104 (SAN 221-1483) Tel 619-563-0599.

FM Atlas Publishing Co., *(F M Atlas; 0-917170),* P.O. Box 24, Adolph, MN 55701 (SAN 207-6764) Tel 218-879-7676.

FMI Publishing, *(FMI Pub; 0-9606164),* P.O. Box 26464, Tempe, AZ 85282 (SAN 217-5576).

F Magazine, Inc., *(F Magazine; 0-936959),* 1405 W. Belle Plaine, Chicago, IL 60613 (SAN 658-6511) Tel 312-929-8044.

FSSSN Colloquia & Symposia at the Univ. of Wisconsin, *(FSSSN Collo & Sympo),* FSSSN, Univ. of Wisconsin, P.O. Box 285, Brookfield, WI 53005 (SAN 682-2738).

F/22 Pr., *(F-Twenty-Two; 0-933596),* P.O. Box 141, Leonia, NJ 07605 (SAN 671-6830) Tel 201-568-6250.

FVN Corp., *(FVN Corp; 0-915687),* 1660 Dyerville Loop Rd., Redcrest, CA 95569 (SAN 292-496X) Tel 707-946-2206.

Faber, Carl, Audiotapes *See Perseus Pr.*

Faber & Faber, Inc., *(Faber & Faber; 0-571; 0-905209),* 50 Cross St., Winchester, MA 01890 (SAN 218-7256) Tel 617-721-1427; Dist. by: Harper & Row Pubs., Inc., Keystone Industrial Pk., Scranton, PA 18512 (SAN 215-3742).

Fablewaves, *(Fablewaves; 0-937578),* P.O. Box 7874, Van Nuys, CA 91409 (SAN 215-0719) Tel 213-372-2983.

Fabrication Pr., *(Fabrication Pr; 0-9616233),* 3446 Garfield Ave. S., Minneapolis, MN 55408 (SAN 658-5841) Tel 612-870-3574; 3446 Garfield Ave. S. No. 1, Minneapolis, MN 55408 (SAN 662-4138) Tel 612-825-3898.

Facets Multimedia, Inc., *(Facets Multimed; 0-9615518),* 1517 W. Fullerton Ave., Chicago, IL 60614 (SAN 696-4176) Tel 312-281-9075.

Facing History & Ourselves National Foundation, Inc., *(Facing Hist; 0-9615841),* 25 Kennard Rd., Brookline, MA 02146 (SAN 697-0710) Tel 617-232-1595; Dist. by: Reading Matters, Inc., 64 Walnut St., Brookline, MA 02146 (SAN 200-5891).

Facing Tile Institute, *(FTI),* Box 8880, Canton, OH 44711 (SAN 270-0239).

FACM Publishing Co., Inc., *(FACM Pub Co),* The JBI Bldg., Box 521, Mahwah, NJ 07430 (SAN 693-1030) Tel 201-529-3883.

Facsimile Bk. Shop, Inc., *(Facsimile Bk),* 16 W. 55th St., New York, NY 10019 (SAN 215-3084).

Fact Publishing, *(Fact Pub; 0-9613171),* 1310 N. Benton Way, Los Angeles, CA 90026 (SAN 294-927X) Tel 213-413-5524.

Factor Publishing Co., *(Factor Pub; 0-935629),* P.O. Box 815, Eastsound, WA 98245 (SAN 696-4184) Tel 206-276-2808.

Factory Mutual System, *(Factory Mutual),* 1151 Boston-Providence Tpke., P.O. Box 688, Norwood, MA 02062 (SAN 224-8115) Tel 617-762-4300.

Facts, *(Facts FL; 0-910991),* 727 Granada Dr.,, Boca Raton, FL 33432 (SAN 263-2209).

Facts on File, Inc., Subs. of Commerce Clearing Hse., *(Facts on File; 0-87196; 0-8160),* 460 Park Ave. S., New York, NY 10016 (SAN 201-4696) Tel 212-683-2244; Toll free: 800-322-8755. *Imprints:* Checkmark (Checkmark).

Faculty Publishing, *(Faculty Pub C A; 0-915141),* 1421 Tulane Dr., Davis, CA 95616 (SAN 289-923X) Tel 916-756-3195.

Fade in Pubs., *(Fade In; 0-936748),* 312 S. 6th, Bozeman, MT 59715 (SAN 215-0727).

Fads & Fashions Co., *(Fads Fashions; 0-9616534),* P.O. Box 9221, Forestville, CT 06010 (SAN 659-4468) Tel 203-582-9415; 15 Evergreen St., Forestville, CT 06010 (SAN 659-4476).

Fag Rag Bks., *(Fag Rag; 0-915480),* P.O. Box 331, Kenmore Sta., Boston, MA 02215 (SAN 207-3498).

Fahnestock Studios, *(Fahnestock; 0-936057),* 70 E. Clinton Ave., Tenafly, NJ 07670 (SAN 697-0680) Tel 201-568-2141.

Fainshaw Pr., Subs. of B. R. Smith & Assocs., Inc., *(Fainshaw Pr; 0-943290),* Box 961, Westmoreland, NH 03467 (SAN 240-6454) Tel 603-585-6654; Dist. by: Great Tradition, The, 750 Adrian Way, Suite 111, San Rafael, CA 94903 (SAN 200-5743) Tel 415-492-9382; Toll free: 800-634-2665.

Fair Haven Pr., *(Fair Haven Pr; 0-932227),* P.O. Box 2152, Meriden, CT 06450 (SAN 686-6093) Tel 203-634-8098.

Fairborn Observatory, *(Fairborn Observ),* 1357 N. 91st Pl., Mesa, AZ 85207 (SAN 270-0255) Tel 602-986-2828.

Fairchild Bks., Div. of Fairchild Pubns., *(Fairchild; 0-87005),* 7 E. 12th St., New York, NY 10003 (SAN 201-470X) Tel 212-741-4280.

Fairfax, C. H., Co., Inc., *(C H Fairfax; 0-935132),* P.O. Box 502, Columbia, MD 21045 (SAN 221-170X).

Fairfax County, *(Fairfax County; 0-9601630),* 4100 Chain Bridge Rd., Fairfax, VA 22030 (SAN 212-632X).

Fairfield House, *(Fairfield Hse; 0-9602048),* 3 Fairfield Dr., Baltimore, MD 21228 (SAN 209-374X) Tel 301-747-6590.

Fairfield Press, Inc., *(Fairfield; 0-913158),* 128 E. 62nd St., New York, NY 10021 (SAN 206-4049) Tel 212-838-7424.

Fairhurst, Jim, *(J Fairhurst),* P.O. Box 153, Dover, NH 03820 (SAN 697-1601) Tel 603-742-2715.

Fairleigh Dickinson Univ. Pr., *(Fairleigh Dickinson; 0-8386),* Dist. by: Associated University Presses, 440 Forsgate Dr., Cranbury, NJ 08512 (SAN 281-2959) Tel 609-655-4770.

FairMail Service, Inc., *(FairMail Serv; 0-9601262),* 417 Cleveland Ave., Plainfield, NJ 07060 (SAN 210-4210) Tel 201-754-7770.

Fairmont Pr., Inc., The, *(Fairmont Pr; 0-88173; 0-915586),* 700 Indian Trail, Lilburn, GA 30247 (SAN 207-5946) Tel 404-925-9388; Orders to: Prentice-Hall, P.O. Box 500, Englewood Cliffs, NJ 07632 (SAN 663-2904) Tel 201-592-2000.

Fairway House, *(Fairway Hse; 0-9603180),* P.O. Box 6344, Bakersfield, CA 93386 (SAN 213-6856); Dist. by: James A. Glynn, 2 Monte Vista Dr., Bakersfield, CA 93305 (SAN 200-7355).

Fairweather Pr. OR, *(Fairweather Pr OR; 0-9614005),* 1718 SW Myrtle St., Portland, OR 97201 (SAN 208-2128) Tel 503-223-4707; Dist. by: Far West Book Service, 3515 NE Hassalo, Portland, OR 97232 (SAN 282-6429) Tel 503-234-7664; Dist. by: Pacific Pipeline Inc., 19215 66th Ave. S., Kent, WA 98032 (SAN 208-2128) Tel 206-872-5523.

Fairy Publications, *(Fairy Pubns; 0-9611088),* P.O. Box 450, Laguna Beach, CA 92652 (SAN 282-8669) Tel 714-661-7533; Dist. by: Cogan Books, 4332 W. Artesia Ave., Fullerton, CA 92633 (SAN 168-9649); Dist. by: Distributors The, 702 S. Michigan, South Bend, IN 46618 (SAN 212-0364) Tel 219-232-8500.

Faith & Life Pr., *(Faith & Life; 0-87303),* 718 Main St., Newton, KS 67114-0347 (SAN 201-4726) Tel 316-283-5100; Box 347, Newton, KS 67114-0347 (SAN 658-0637).

Faith Messenger Pubns., *(Faith Messenger; 0-938544),* P.O. Box 641, Upland, CA 91785 (SAN 281-7020) Tel 714-946-3134.

Faith Printing Co., *(Faith Print; 0-939241),* Rte. 2, Hwy. 290, Taylors, SC 29687 (SAN 694-5341) Tel 803-895-3822.

Faith Publishing Hse., *(Faith Pub Hse),* P.O. Box 518, Guthrie, OK 73044 (SAN 204-1243) Tel 405-282-1479; 920 W. Mansur, Guthrie, OK 73044 (SAN 658-0645).

FaithAmerica Foundation, *(FaithAmerica; 0-942770),* Suite 216, 4130 N. 70th St., Scottsdale, AZ 85251 (SAN 240-1452).

Falcon Books *See Smith, Gibbs M., Inc.*

Falcon Co., *(Falcon Co; 0-935921),* 3675 Syracuse Ave., San Diego, CA 92122 (SAN 696-7442) Tel 619-453-8965; P.O. Box 22569, San Diego, CA 92122 (SAN 698-2204).

Falcon Enterprises, *(Falcon Ent; 0-9613551),* P.O.Box 210094, Anchorage, AK 99521 (SAN 669-7984) Tel 907-337-2646.

Falcon Head Press, Ltd., *(Falcon Head Pr; 0-914802),* P.O. Box 913, Golden, CO 80401 (SAN 206-4065).

Falcon Hill Pr., *(Falcon Hill Pr; 0-936332),* Box 1431, Sparks, NV 89432-1431 (SAN 221-1718) Tel 702-786-2134.

Names

Falcon Pr., *(Falcon Pr Az; 0-941404),* 3660 N. Third St., Phoenix, AZ 85012 (SAN 262-0243) Tel 602-246-3546; Dist. by: Inland Bk. Co., P.O. Box 261, 22 Hemingway Ave., East Haven, CT 06512 (SAN 200-4151) Tel 203-467-4257; Dist. by: Samuel Weiser, Inc., P.O. Box 612, York Beach, ME 03910 (SAN 202-9588) Tel 207-363-4393; Dist. by: Baker & Taylor Co., Western Div., 380 Edison Way, Reno, NV 89564 (SAN 169-4464) Tel 702-786-6700; Dist. by: Bookpeople, 2929 Fifth St., Berkeley, CA 94710 (SAN 168-9517); Dist. by: Great Tradition, The, 750 Adrian Way, Suite 111, San Rafael, CA 94903 (SAN 200-5743) Tel 415-492-9382; Dist. by: Nascorp, Inc., 528 E. Lorain St., Oberlin, OH 44074 (SAN 169-6823) Tel 216-775-8048.

Falcon Pr. Publishing Co., Inc., *(Falcon Pr MT; 0-934318; 0-937959),* P.O. Box 731, Helena, MT 59624 (SAN 221-1726) Tel 406-442-6597; 27 Neill Ave., Helena, MT 59624 (SAN 658-0653); Orders to: P.O. Box 279, Billings, MT 59103 (SAN 281-7047).

Falcon Publishing, *(Falcon Pub; 0-932542),* P.O. Box 688, Ben Lomond, CA 95005 (SAN 213-0513) Tel 408-336-2906.

Falcon Publishing, *(Falcon Pub Venice; 0-942764),* 2000 Strongs, Venice, CA 92091 (SAN 212-8322) Tel 213-399-4791.

Falk, *(Falk; 0-9614108),* 3470 Rolling View Ct., White Bear Lake, MN 55110 (SAN 685-2998) Tel 612-770-1922.

Fallen Angel Pr., *(Fallen Angel; 0-931598),* 17606 Muirland, Detroit, MI 48221 (SAN 211-8963) Tel 313-864-0982.

Fallen Leaf Pr., *(Fallen Leaf; 0-914913),* P.O. Box 10034, Berkeley, CA 94709 (SAN 289-1255) Tel 415-848-7805.

Falling Wall Pr., *(Falling Wall; 0-905046),* Dist. by: Flatiron Bk. Distributors, Inc., 1170 Broadway, Suite 807, New York, NY 10001 (SAN 240-9917) Tel 212-206-1118.

Falling Water Pr., *(Falling Water; 0-932229),* P.O. Box 4554, Ann Arbor, MI 48106 (SAN 686-5771) Tel 313-761-7605.

Falls of the Tar Pubns., *(Falls Tar; 0-938828),* P.O. Box 4194, Rocky Mount, NC 27801 (SAN 240-0189) Tel 919-442-7423.

Falmer Pr. *See Taylor & Francis, Inc.*

Falmouth Historical Commission, *(Falmouth Hist Com; 0-9616647),* 59 Town Hall Sq., Falmouth Town Hall, Falmouth, MA 02540 (SAN 659-5618) Tel 617-548-5800.

Falsoft, Inc., *(Falsoft; 0-932471),* P.O. Box 385, Prospect, KY 40059 (SAN 687-4223); 9509 U.S. Hwy. 42, Prospect, KY 40059 (SAN 662-2771).

Falztar Bks., *(Falztar Bks; 0-9616465),* P.O. Box 4462, Wichita, KS 67204 (SAN 659-2201).

Family Album, ABAA, The, *(Family Album; 0-934630),* RD 1, Box 42, Glen Rock, PA 17327 (SAN 212-5021).

Family & Health Improvement Society, *(Family Health; 0-9606024),* P.O. Box 952, Cambridge, OH 43725 (SAN 211-3562) Tel 614-432-3007.

Family Care Assocs., *(Family Care Assocs; 0-935467),* 201 Barclay Cir., Cheltenham, PA 19012 (SAN 696-4222) Tel 215-635-3553; Orders to: P.O. Box 37, Cheltenham, PA 19012 (SAN 662-3743).

Family Circle Bks., Subs. of Family Circle, Inc., *(Family Circle Bks; 0-933585),* 488 Madison Ave., New York, NY 10022 (SAN 692-2120) Tel 212-593-8419; Toll free: 800-247-2904; Orders to: P.O. Box 10814, Des Moines, IA 50381 (SAN 662-2976).

Family Friends Pubns., *(Family Friends; 0-9609324),* R.R. 1, Box 43A, Oelh, IA 52223 (SAN 240-849X) Tel 319-927-2377.

Family Health International, *(Fam Health Intl; 0-939704),* Triangle Dr., Research Triangle Park, NC 27709 (SAN 216-7409) Tel 919-549-0517.

Family Health Media, *(Fam Health Media; 0-931470),* 201 S. Lloyd, Suite 230 Physician's Plaza, Aberdeen, SD 57401 (SAN 211-965X) Tel 605-229-5990.

Family Heritage Publishing Co., *(Family Herit; 0-9615453),* 8275 Louisiana St., Merrillville, IN 46410 (SAN 695-7692) Tel 219-924-4124; Dist. by: Pratik Pubn., P.O. Box 11133, Merrillville, IN 46411 (SAN 200-7878).

Family Histories, *(Family Hist TX; 0-9616624),* 2320 Country Green Ln., Arlington, TX 76011 (SAN 661-2032) Tel 817-277-3281.

Family History & Genealogy Ctr., *(Fam Hist & Gen; 0-912017),* 1300 E. 109th St., Kansas City, MO 64131 (SAN 264-6145) Tel 816-942-5497.

Family History Foundation, *(Family History; 0-943162),* P.O. Drawer 4464, Bryan, TX 77805-4464 (SAN 240-3749) Tel 409-775-0809.

Family of God, The, *(Family God; 0-932873),* P.O. Box 19571, Las Vegas, NV 89132 (SAN 688-993X) Tel 702-731-4750.

Family Press, *(Family Pr; 0-9600666),* P. O. Box 16005, St. Paul, MN 55116 (SAN 205-5740) Tel 612-699-9108.

Family Process Pr., Div. of Family Process, Inc., *(Family Process; 0-9615519),* 149 E. 78th St., New York, NY 10021 (SAN 696-4249) Tel 212-861-6059; Dist. by: W. W. Norton & Co., 500 Fifth Ave., New York, NY 10110 (SAN 202-5795) Tel 212-354-5500; Toll free: 800-223-2584.

Family Pubns., *(Family Pubns; 0-931128),* P.O. Box 398, Maitland, FL 32751 (SAN 211-3147) Tel 305-894-7060.

Family Publishing Co., The, *(Family Pub CA; 0-937770),* P.O. Box 462, Bodega Bay, CA 94923 (SAN 215-3092) Tel 707-875-3373.

†**Family Relations Foundation,** *(Family Relat; 0-9614218),* P.O. Box 462, Sebastopol, CA 95472 (SAN 687-1097) Tel 707-823-0876; Dist. by: Bookpeople, 2929 Fifth St., Berkeley, CA 94710 (SAN 168-9517) Tel 415-549-3030; *CIP.*

Family Relations Learning Ctr., *(Family Relations; 0-9607250),* 450 Ord Dr., Boulder, CO 80303 (SAN 239-4243) Tel 303-499-1171.

Family Resource, Inc., The, *(Family Res; 0-914915),* 4901 W. Lovers Ln., Dallas, TX 75209 (SAN 289-128X) Tel 214-350-6621.

†**Family Service America,** *(Family Serv; 0-87304),* 44 E. 23rd St., New York, NY 10010 (SAN 206-4073) Tel 212-674-6100; *CIP.*

Family Skills, Inc., *(Fam Skills; 0-934275),* 1 Galleria Tower No. 1940, 13355 Noel Rd., Dallas, TX 75240 (SAN 693-2576) Tel 214-458-2867; Toll free: 800-543-7545; Dist. by: Kampmann & Co., Inc., 9 E. 40th St., New York, NY 10016 (SAN 202-5191) Tel 212-685-2928; Toll free: 800-526-7626.

Family Tree Pony Farm, Pubns. Div., *(Family Tree Pony Farm; 0-940074),* 2690 SE Lund Ave., Port Orchard, WA 98366 (SAN 220-2174) Tel 206-895-2116.

Family Visions, Inc., *(Family Visions; 0-934835),* 1400 Homer Rd., Winona, MN 55987 (SAN 694-3845) Tel 507-452-8966; P.O. Box 30067, Winona, MN 55987 (SAN 658-2834).

Family World Publishing House, Inc., *(Family World Pub Hse; 0-934176),* 3951 Providence Rd., New Town Square, PA 19073 (SAN 213-0521) Tel 215-353-3555.

Famous Last Words, *(Famous Last Wds; 0-916331),* 4815 Fairfax Ave., Oakland, CA 94601-4811 (SAN 654-7273) Tel 415-534-8468.

Famous Pr. Publishing, *(Famous Pr Pub; 0-942010),* P.O. Box 1673, Mansfield, OH 44901 (SAN 238-2377) Tel 419-522-4735; 200 N. Diamond St., Mansfield, OH 44901 (SAN 658-0661).

Fan Publishing Co., *(Fan Pub Co; 0-932179),* P.O. Box 20306, Raleigh, NC 27619 (SAN 686-5364) Tel 919-846-0607.

Fanferon Pr., *(Fanferon Pr; 0-9614841),* P.O. Box 5804, Bellingham, WA 98227 (SAN 693-1057) Tel 206-671-5808.

Fankhauser, Jerry, *(J Fankhauser; 0-9617006),* 2650 Fountainview, Suite 208, Houston, TX 77057 (SAN 662-5517) Tel 713-783-7264; Dist. by: DeVorss & Co., P.O. Box 550, 1046 Princeton Dr., Marina del Rey, CA 90294 (SAN 168-9886) Tel 213-870-7478; Dist. by: Miracle Pub. Co., 18 Charleston N., Sugar Land, TX 77478 (SAN 272-4618).

Fannin County Historical Commission, *(Fannin County; 0-9609602),* P.O. Box 338, Bonham, TX 75418 (SAN 260-1842) Tel 214-583-2832.

Fant, Freeman, Madson, *(Fant-Freeman-Madson; 0-87518),* 209 Shady Oak Rd., Hopkins, MN 55343 (SAN 223-0682); Dist. by: Alver R. Freeman, 8315 Dupont Ave., Minneapolis, MN 55420 (SAN 223-0690).

Fantaco Pubns., Affil. of Fantaco Enterprises, Inc., *(Fantaco; 0-938782),* 21 Central Ave., Albany, NY 12210-1391 (SAN 662-0086) Tel 518-463-1400; Orders to: Fantaco Enterprises, Inc., 21 Central Ave., Albany, NY 12210 (SAN 270-0379).

Fantasy Factory, Inc., *(Fantasy Fact; 0-939717),* 10344 Cheviot Dr., Los Angeles, CA 90064 (SAN 663-6276) Tel 213-559-7426.

Fantasy Publishing Co., Inc., *(Fantasy Pub Co),* c/o Borden Publishing Co., 1855 W. Main St., Alhambra, CA 91801 (SAN 201-419X) Tel 213-337-7947.

Far Eastern Research & Pubns. Center, *(Far Eastern Res; 0-912580),* P.O. Box 151, Prince Georges, MD 20748 (SAN 205-5759).

Far West Editions, *(Far West Edns; 0-914480),* P.O. Box 549, San Francisco, CA 94101 (SAN 207-0456) Tel 415-587-4951.

Far West Laboratory for Educational Research & Development, *(Far West Lab; 0-914409),* 1855 Folsom St., San Francisco, CA 94103 (SAN 289-6222) Tel 415-565-3139.

Far Western Philosophy of Education Society, *(Far Western Phil; 0-931702),* Arizona State Univ., College of Education, Hiram Bradford Farmer Education Bldg., Rm. 412, Tempe, AZ 85281 (SAN 210-8062) Tel 602-965-3674.

Faraday Press, *(Faraday; 0-939762),* P.O. Box 4098, Mountain View, CA 94040 (SAN 216-731X).

Farago Pubns., Div. of Vita Juice, *(Farago Pubns; 0-935363),* 6510 W. Sixth St., Los Angeles, CA 90048 (SAN 696-4192) Tel 213-655-8310.

Fare, Pam, Bks., *(P Fare Bks; 0-9615998),* 6 Osgood Ave., Claremont, NH 03743 (SAN 697-9351) Tel 603-542-7319.

Farm & Ranch Vacations, Inc., *(Farm & Ranch; 0-913214),* 36 E. 57th St., New York, NY 10022 (SAN 201-4734) Tel 212-355-6334.

†**Farm Journal, Inc.,** *(Farm Journal; 0-89795),* 230 W. Washington Sq., Philadelphia, PA 19105 (SAN 212-0887) Tel 215-829-4755; Toll free: 800-237-1212; *CIP.*

Farmer, W. D., Residence Designer, Inc., *(W D Farmer; 0-931518),* P.O. Box 450025, Atlanta, GA 30345 (SAN 204-1219) Tel 404-934-7380; Toll free: 800-225-7526; Toll free: 800-221-7526 (In Georgia).

Farmer, Wesley M., Enterprises,Inc., *(Farmer Ent; 0-937772),* P.O. Box 1323, Santee, CA 92071 (SAN 215-6431) Tel 619-448-8697.

Farmington Cookbook, The, *(Farmington Cookbook; 0-9602646),* 3033 Bardstown Rd., Louisville, KY 40205 (SAN 218-4486).

Farmworker Justice Fund, Inc., *(Farmworker Justice; 0-9616508),* 2001 S St., NW, No. 312, Washington, DC 20009 (SAN 659-4492) Tel 202-462-8192.

Farnum Films, *(Farnum Films; 0-915790),* Executive House, 225 E. 46th St., New York, NY 10017 (SAN 206-1988) Tel 212-371-8679; Orders to: P.O. Box 1094, New York, NY 10017 (SAN 206-1996).

Farr Pubs., *(Farr Pubs; 0-9614476),* P.O. Box 175, Gainesville, VA 22065 (SAN 689-3538) Tel 703-347-5785.

Farragut Publishing Co., *(Farragut Pub; 0-918535),* 810 18th St. NW, Washington, DC 20006 (SAN 657-6168) Tel 202-347-5415; Dist. by: Baker & Taylor Co., Eastern Div., 50 Kirby Ave., Somerville, NJ 08876 (SAN 169-4901) Tel 201-526-8000; Dist. by: Inland Bk. Co., P.O. Box 261, 22 Hemingway Ave., East Haven, CT 06512 (SAN 200-4151) Tel 203-467-4257; Toll free: 800-243-0138.

Farrah, Upland, Westmoreland & Granger, *(Farrah Upland; 0-943568),* Rte. 2, Box 384, Pittsboro, NC 27312 (SAN 240-6470) Tel 919-542-4052.

Names

Farrar, Straus & Giroux, Inc., *(FS&G; 0-374),* 19 Union Sq., W., New York, NY 10003 (SAN 206-782X) Tel 212-741-6900; Toll free: 800-242-7737. *Imprints:* Bell Books (Bell); FS&G Paperbacks (FS&G Pap); L. C. Page Co. (Page); Sunburst Books (Sunburst); Vision Books (Vision).

Farrell, John, Texas Slanguage Bks., *(J Farrell; 0-939305),* 2015 Stehle Rd., Rosenberg, TX 77471 (SAN 663-172X) Tel 713-232-7841.

Farris Publishing, *(Farris Pub; 0-9616391),* 2401 Repsdorph, No. 1711, Seabrook, TX 77586 (SAN 658-8530) Tel 713-532-1448.

†**Farwell, Brice,** *(B Farwell; 0-9600484),* 330 Heidi Ct., Morgan Hill, CA 95037 (SAN 206-7129) Tel 408-778-1650; *CIP.*

Fashion Imprints Assocs., *(Fashion Imprints; 0-9602860),* Box 3523, Merchandise Mart, Chicago, IL 60654 (SAN 213-0548) Tel 312-821-5922.

Fat Control Inc., *(Fat Control; 0-918275),* P.O. Box 10117, Towson, MD 21204 (SAN 682-2711).

Fat Wars Enterprises, *(Fat Wars Ent; 0-9614219),* 9842 Hibert St. Suite 264, San Diego, CA 92131 (SAN 687-1100) Tel 619-695-8771.

Father Tree Pr., Div. of WARP Graphics, Inc., *(Father Tree Pr; 0-936861),* 2 Reno Rd., Poughkeepsie, NY 12603 (SAN 699-9204) Tel 914-462-0588; Dist. by: Bud Plant, Inc., 12555 Loma Rica Dr., No. 10, Grass Valley, CA 95945 (SAN 268-5086) Tel 916-273-9588.

Fathom Eight, *(Fathom Eight; 0-910651),* P.O. Box 80505, San Marino, CA 91108-8505 (SAN 270-0611) Tel 818-289-5088.

Fathom Pr., *(Fathom Pr; 0-936849),* P.O. Box 191, Eastport, NY 11941 (SAN 658-358X) Tel 516-878-9825; 11 Beverly Ln., East Moriches, NY 11940 (SAN 658-3598).

Fathom Publishing Company, *(Fathom Pub; 0-9607358),* Box 821, Cordova, AK 99574 (SAN 239-7684) Tel 907-424-7770.

Faubus, Orval E., *(Faubus),* 114 E. 2nd St., Little Rock, AR 72203 (SAN 220-1526); c/o Pioneer Pr., P.O. Box 191, Little Rock, AR 72201 (SAN 220-1518) Tel 501-374-0271.

Faulkner Bks., *(Faulkner Bks; 0-916631),* 870 Seventh Ave., Suite 31E, New York, NY 10019 (SAN 296-6921) Tel 212-541-7459.

†**Fault Pubns.,** *(Fault Pubns; 0-930646),* 33513 6th St., Union City, CA 94587 (SAN 207-8252) Tel 415-487-1383; *CIP.*

Faust Publishing Co., *(Faust Pub Co; 0-917905),* 7523 Maple St., New Orleans, LA 70118 (SAN 656-9846) Tel 504-866-4916.

Fawcett Bk. Group, *(Fawcett; 0-449),* 201 E. 50th St., New York, NY 10022 (SAN 201-4572) Tel 212-751-2600; Toll free: 800-638-6460. *Imprints:* Columbine (Columbine); Coventry (Coventry); Crest Books (Crest); Gold Medal Books (GM); Juniper (Juniper); Premier Books (Prem).

Fax Collector's Editions, *(Fax Collect; 0-913960),* P.O. Box 851, Mercer Island, WA 98040 (SAN 208-6468) Tel 206-232-8484; Dist. by: Starmont House, Inc., P.O. Box 851, Mercer Island, WA 98040 (SAN 208-8703) Tel 206-232-8484; Dist. by: F & SF Bk., Co. P.O. Box 415, Staten Island, NY 10302 (SAN 169-6262) Tel 718-201-3526.

Fax Publishing Co., Subs. of Kadmos Corp., *(Fax Pub Co; 0-9614842),* 1119 Vermont, P.O. Box 808, Quincy, IL 62306 (SAN 693-1081) Tel 217-224-5105.

†**Faxon Co., The,** *(Faxon; 0-87305),* 15 SW Park, Westwood, MA 02090 (SAN 159-8619) Tel 617-329-3350; Toll free: 800-225-6055; *CIP.*

Fay-West Heritage Pubns., *(Fay-West Her; 0-9609326),* 247 Ironshire South, Laurel, MD 20707 (SAN 260-1850) Tel 301-725-1908.

Fayova Publications, *(Fayova Pubns; 0-932970),* 3052 Bayberry Ct., E., Carmel, IN 46032 (SAN 277-6790).

FDW Arts, *(FDW Arts; 0-9608354),* 1394 Old Quincy Lane, Reston, VA 22094 (SAN 240-6446) Tel 703-437-4818.

Fear Free Foundation, *(Fear Free; 0-939637),* P.O. Box 16119, North Hollywood, CA 91615 (SAN 663-575X); 900 E. Palmar, No. 10, Glendale, CA 91205 (SAN 663-5768) Tel 818-760-1113.

Feather & Good, *(Feather & Good; 0-9607642),* Box 141, Radnor, PA 19087 (SAN 239-8532).

Feather Press, *(Feather Pr; 0-9607960),* Box 1225, Dumas, TX 79029 (SAN 240-0723) Tel 806-935-4348.

Features Northwest, *(Features NW; 0-931435),* 5132 126th Pl., NE, Marysville, WA 98270 (SAN 683-2059) Tel 206-659-7559; Dist. by: Creative Communications, 529 Dayton St., Edmonds, WA 98020 (SAN 239-684X) Tel 206-775-5877.

F E B Press, *(F E B Pr; 0-9610144),* P.O. Box 2431, Ann Arbor, MI 48106 (SAN 270-0662) Tel 313-973-2282.

FEDAPT, *(FEDAPT; 0-9602942),* 165 W. 46th St., Suite 310, New York, NY 10036 (SAN 224-1307) Tel 212-869-9690.

Feder, Jay, Pub., *(Feder Pub; 0-9616084),* 910 16th St., Rm. 335, Denver, CO 80202 (SAN 698-1127) Tel 303-534-0251.

Feder, Michal E., *(Feder; 0-9615449),* 706 Hydra Ln., Foster City, CA 94404 (SAN 695-5781) Tel 415-345-0809.

Feder, T. H., Books, Div. of Art Resource, *(T H Feder Bks; 0-933772),* 65 Bleecker St., New York, NY 10012 (SAN 212-9396) Tel 212-505-8700.

Federal Aviation Exams Co., *(Fed Aviation; 0-938706),* Box 718, Solvang, CA 93463 (SAN 215-8620).

Federal Aviation Publishing, Inc., *(Fed Aviation Pub; 0-939357),* Four Embarcadero Center, Suite 5040, San Francisco, CA 94111 (SAN 662-6807) Tel 415-571-5458. Do not confuse with Federal Aviation Exams, in Solvang, CA.

Federal Bar Assn., *(Federal Bar),* 1815 H St., NW, Washington, DC 20006 (SAN 223-7784) Tel 202-638-0252.

Federal Bureau of Investigation, Laboratory Div., *(Fed Bu Invest; 0-932115),* U. S. Dept. of Justice, Washington, DC 20535 (SAN 686-4740) Tel 703-640-6131.

Federal Document Retrieval Inc., *(Fed Doc Retrieval; 0-932929),* 514 C St. NE, Washington, DC 20002 (SAN 689-1632) Tel 202-638-0520; Toll free: 800-368-1009.

Federal Employees Digest, Inc., *(Fed Employees; 0-910582),* P.O. Box 7528, Falls Church, VA 22046 (SAN 204-1170) Tel 703-533-3031.

Federal Employment Bulletin, *(Fed Employ Bul; 0-933791),* P.O. Box 11715, Washington, DC 20008 (SAN 692-8722) Tel 202-667-3050.

Federal Legal Pubns., Inc., *(Fed Legal Pubn; 0-87945),* 157 Chambers St., New York, NY 10007 (SAN 201-4769) Tel 212-243-5775.

Federal Pubns., Inc., *(Fed Pubns Inc),* 1120 20th St., NW, Washington, DC 20036 (SAN 237-7071) Tel 202-337-7000.

Federal Reserve Bank of Minneapolis, *(FRB Minneapolis; 0-915484),* Research Dept., 250 Marquette Ave., Minneapolis, MN 55480 (SAN 281-7063) Tel 612-340-2355; Orders to: Office of Public Information, 250 Marquette Ave., Minneapolis, MN 55480 (SAN 281-7071) Tel 612-340-2443.

Federation Employment & Guidance Service, *(Fed Employ & Guidance; 0-934186),* 510 Sixth Ave., 4th Flr., New York, NY 10011 (SAN 213-0556) Tel 212-741-7150.

Federation of American Health Systems, *(Fed Am Health Systs),* 1405 N. Pierce, Suite 311, Little Rock, AR 72207 (SAN 224-3334) Tel 501-661-9555.

Federation of Fly Fishers, *(Fed Fly Fishers; 0-9614193),* P.O. Box 1088, West Yellowstone, MT 59758 (SAN 686-8002) Tel 406-646-9541.

Federation of Jewish Men's Clubs, *(Fed Jewish Mens Clubs; 0-935665),* 475 Riverside Dr., Suite 244, New York, NY 10115 (SAN 273-4230) Tel 212-749-8100.

Federation of Societies for Coatings Technology, *(Fed Soc Coat Tech; 0-934010),* 1315 Walnut St., Suite 832, Philadelphia, PA 19107 (SAN 212-9035) Tel 215-545-1506.

Federlin, Tom, *(Federlin; 0-9603136),* 47 Cardinal Ct., Saratoga Springs, NY 12866 (SAN 213-4934) Tel 518-587-3704.

Feedback Theatrebooks, Div. of Feedback Services, *(Feedback Thea Bks; 0-937657),* P.O. Box 606, Nashville, IN 47448 (SAN 659-221X); Anandale Estates, Nashville, IN 47448 (SAN 659-2228).

FEELGREAT, *(FEELGREAT; 0-942106),* 1370 Windsor Rd., Teaneck, NJ 07666 (SAN 239-5363) Tel 201-833-0068.

Feeling Good Assocs., Div. of Barry Blum, M.D., Inc., *(Feeling Good Assocs; 0-9615412),* 507 Palma Way, Mill Valley, CA 94941 (SAN 695-5002) Tel 415-383-5439.

Feezor, Betty, Bks., *(Feezor Betty Bks; 0-915605),* 6217 Glenridge Rd., Charlotte, NC 28211 (SAN 292-501X) Tel 704-366-4147.

Feffer & Simons *See* **Burgess International Group, Inc.**

Feinsot, Bernice B., *(B B Feinsot; 0-915526),* 330 W. 28th St., Apt. 1F, New York, NY 10001 (SAN 207-351X) Tel 212-929-2918.

Feist Pubns., *(Feist Pubns),* 2827 Seventh St., Berkeley, CA 94710 (SAN 204-1138) Tel 415-841-5771.

Fejer, Paul Haralyi, *(P H Fejer; 0-9607422),* 1472 Timberview, Bloomfield Hills, MI 48013 (SAN 237-9511).

Feldheim, Philipp, Inc., *(Feldheim; 0-87306),* 200 Airport Executive Pk., Spring Valley, NY 10977 (SAN 164-9671) Tel 914-356-2282.

Feldman, Mildred L. B., *(Feldman; 0-9606700),* 1424 S. Alameda Dr., Baton Rouge, LA 70815 (SAN 209-1135) Tel 504-925-9666.

†**Feldman, Ronald, Fine Arts, Inc.,** *(Feldman Fine Arts; 0-914661),* 31 Mercer St., New York, NY 10013 (SAN 289-2421) Tel 212-226-3232; *CIP.*

Felicity Pr., *(Felicity; 0-9603846),* Box 14382, University Sta., Gainesville, FL 32604 (SAN 215-0743) Tel 904-475-2963.

Felicity Pr., *(Felicity Pr ME; 0-931265),* P.O. Box 2066, Augusta, ME 04330 (SAN 681-9826) Tel 207-622-0815.

Fell, Frederick, Pubs., Inc., *(Fell; 0-8119),* 2500 Hollywood Blvd., Suite 302, Hollywood, FL 33020 (SAN 208-2365) Tel 305-925-5242; Toll free: 800-526-7626; Dist. by: Pubs. Distribution Ctr., 25 Branca Rd., East Rutherford, NJ 07073 (SAN 200-5018) Tel 201-939-6064. *Imprints:* Pegasus Rex (Pegasus Rex).

Fellendorf Assocs., Inc., *(Fellendorf Assocs Inc; 0-9613033),* 1300 Ruppert Rd., Silver Spring, MD 20903 (SAN 295-3781) Tel 301-593-1636.

Fellows, Paul E., *(P E Fellows; 0-9612228),* 23 Chick St., Metropolis, IL 62960 (SAN 289-2227) Tel 618-524-7203.

Fellows of Contemporary Art, *(Fellows Cont Art; 0-911291),* 333 S. Hope St. 48th Fl., Los Angeles, CA 90071 (SAN 270-1219) Tel 213-620-1780; Orders to: Art Catalogues, 625 N. Almont Dr., Los Angeles, CA 90069 (SAN 662-0094) Tel 213-274-0160.

Fellowship of Reconciliation, *(Fellowship of Recon; 0-911810),* Box 271, Nyack, NY 10960 (SAN 210-7279) Tel 914-358-4601; 523 N. Broadway, Nyack, NY 10960 (SAN 669-0815).

Fellowship of the Crown, *(Fellowship Crown),* P.O. Box 3743, Carmel, CA 93921 (SAN 206-4103) Tel 408-624-5600.

Fellowship Pr., *(Fellowship Pr PA; 0-914390; 0-87728),* 5820 Overbrook Ave., Philadelphia, PA 19131 (SAN 201-6117) Tel 215-879-8604.

Fels & Firn Pr., *(Fels & Firn; 0-918704),* 2940 Seventh St., Berkeley, CA 94710 (SAN 293-2628) Tel 415-457-4361; Dist. by: The Distributors, 702 S. Michigan St., South Bend, IN 46618 (SAN 293-2636).

Felsun Pr., *(Felsun Pr; 0-940928),* 1800 Old Meadow Rd., Suite 305, McLean, VA 22102 (SAN 217-3611) Tel 703-356-7799.

Feltus, Peter R., *(P R Feltus; 0-9605286),* P.O. Box 5339, Berkeley, CA 94705 (SAN 215-3106).

Feminist Committee Pr., The, *(Feminist Comm; 0-9603330),* 1957 Westminster Way, NE, Atlanta, GA 30307 (SAN 211-1292) Tel 404-636-6436.

Feminist Pr. at the City Univ. of New York, The, *(Feminist Pr; 0-912670; 0-935312),* 311 E. 94th St., New York, NY 10128 (SAN 213-6813) Tel 212-360-5790; Dist. by: Harper & Row, Pubs., Inc., Keystone Industrial Pk., Scranton, PA 18512 (SAN 215-3742); Toll free: 800-242-7737.

Feminist Writers Guild-Milwaukee Chapter, *(Fem Writers Guild; 0-9606982),* c/o The Womens Coalition, 2211 E. Kenwood Blvd., Milwaukee, WI 53211 (SAN 238-0595).

Names

Fen Winnie Ink, *(Fen Winnie; 0-9614438),* P.O. Box 13658, San Luis Obispo, CA 93406 (SAN 689-1586) Tel 805-927-3979.

Fenimore Bk. Store, Affil. of New York State Historical Assn., *(Fenimore Bk),* P.O. Box 800 Lake Rd., Cooperstown, NY 13326 (SAN 285-0176) Tel 607-547-2533.

Fenn Publishing Co., *(Fenn Pub Co; 0-937634),* 1075 Paseo de Peralta, Santa Fe, NM 87501 (SAN 215-2436) Tel 505-982-4631.

Fennwyn Pr., *(Fennwyn Pr),* 920 E., St. Patrick, Rapid City, SD 57701 (SAN 207-1177); Dist. by: Honor Books, P.O. Box 641, Rapid City, SD 57709 (SAN 208-0877) Tel 605-348-9734.

Fenton, Mark A., *(M A Fenton; 0-9616217),* 4808 Colfax Ave. S, Minneapolis, MN 55409 (SAN 658-3644) Tel 612-822-7314.

Fenton Assocs., *(Fenton Assocs; 0-915345),* 3235 Columbia Pike, Westmont Shopping Ctr., Arlington, VA 22204 (SAN 289-9817) Tel 703-892-1232.

Fenton Valley Pr., *(Fenton Valley Pr; 0-9615149),* 657 Chaffeeville Rd., Storrs, CT 06268 (SAN 694-3683) Tel 203-429-0710; Dist. by: DeVorss & Co., P.O. Box 550, 1046 Princeton Dr., Marina del Rey, CA 90294 (SAN 168-9886); Dist. by: Inland Bk. Co., P.O. Box 261, 22 Hemingway Ave., East Haven, CT 06512 (SAN 200-4151) Tel 203-467-4257; Dist. by: New Leaf Distributing Co., 1020 White St. SW, Atlanta, GA 30310 (SAN 169-1449) Tel 404-755-2665; Dist. by: Baker & Taylor, Eastern Div., 50 Kirby Ave., Somerville, NJ 08876 (SAN 169-4901).

Fergeson, F., Productions, *(F Fergeson; 0-935510),* Mount Zion, IL 62526 (SAN 214-3704) Tel 217-869-5608.

Ferguson, Howard E., *(H E Ferguson; 0-9611180),* 22445 Lorain Rd., Fairview Park, OH 44126 (SAN 277-6863) Tel 216-734-3233.

†**Ferguson, J. G., Publishing Co.,** *(Ferguson; 0-89434),* 111 E. Wacker Dr., Suite 500, Chicago, IL 60601 (SAN 207-1363) Tel 312-861-0666; *CIP.*

Ferguson Communications Publishers, *(Ferguson Comns Pubs; 0-917231),* 1540 E. Moore Rd., Hillsdale, MI 49242 (SAN 656-0326) Tel 517-437-7205.

Ferguson-Florissant School District/Early Education, *(Ferguson-Florissant; 0-939418),* 1005 Waterford Dr., Florissant, MO 63033 (SAN 216-5740) Tel 314-831-8809.

Fermata Pr., *(Fermata; 0-939792),* 40 Harriett Rd., Gloucester, MA 01930 (SAN 216-8936) Tel 617-283-5849.

Ferment Pr., *(Ferment Pr; 0-9605318),* P.O. Box 2195, San Leandro, CA 94577 (SAN 293-2644) Tel 415-895-2739; Dist. by: Bookpeople, 2929 Fifth St., Berkeley, CA 94710 (SAN 168-9517) Tel 415-549-3030; Orders to: The Distributors, 702 S. Michigan, South Bend, IN 46618 (SAN 293-2660) Tel 219-232-8500.

Fern Pubns., Subs. of Mueller Assocs., *(Fern Pubns; 0-9614097),* 2117 S. High St., Bloomington, IN 47401 (SAN 685-3080) Tel 812-339-0347.

Fern Ridge Pr., *(Fern Ridge Pr; 0-9615332),* 1927 McLean Blvd., Eugene, OR 97405 (SAN 695-0868) Tel 503-485-8243.

†**Ferndale Hse.,** *(Ferndale Hse; 0-931637),* P.O. Box 1029, Ferndale Hse, CA 95536 (SAN 683-7735) Tel 707-786-9332; Dist. by: Spring Arbor Distributors, 10885 Textile Rd., Belleville, MI 48111 (SAN 158-9016) Tel 313-481-0900; *CIP.*

Ferndock Publishing, *(Ferndock Pub; 0-9616321),* P.O. Box 86, Rte. 1, Dennison, MN 55018 (SAN 658-7224) Tel 507-778-3357.

Fernglen Pr., *(Fernglen Pr; 0-9612630),* 473 Sixth St., Lake Oswego, OR 97034 (SAN 289-2790) Tel 503-635-4179.

Ferrari Pubns./Places of Interest, *(Ferrari Pubns; 0-942586),* P.O. Box 35575, Phoenix, AZ 85069 (SAN 239-6424) Tel 602-863-2408.

Ferri, Roger C., & Assocs., *(Ferri; 0-9605928),* 261 W. 22nd St., New York, NY 10011 (SAN 216-6712) Tel 212-929-8192.

Ferris State College, *(Ferris St Coll; 0-9615299),* Schl. of Graphic Arts Dept., Big Rapids, MI 49307 (SAN 694-4655) Tel 616-796-0461.

†**Fertig, Howard, Inc.,** *(Fertig; 0-86527),* 80 E. 11th St., New York, NY 10003 (SAN 201-4777) Tel 212-982-7922; *CIP.*

Festival Books *See Abingdon Pr.*

†**Festival Pubns.,** *(Festival Pubns; 0-930828),* P.O. Box 10180, Glendale, CA 91209 (SAN 211-1527) Tel 818-887-0034; *CIP.*

Fevertree Pr., *(Fevertree Pr; 0-911027),* Rte. 3, Box 216, Camilla, GA 31730 (SAN 270-1405) Tel 518-398-7764.

Fiasco Productions, *(Fiasco Prod; 0-935735),* 7062 14th Ave., NW, Seattle, WA 98117 (SAN 696-4230) Tel 206-789-4935.

Fibar Designs, *(Fibar Designs; 0-932086),* The Fannings, P.O. Box 2634, Menlo Park, CA 94026 (SAN 211-6847).

†**Fiction Collective, Inc.,** *(Fiction Coll; 0-914590; 0-932511),* Brooklyn College, c/o English Dept., Brooklyn, NY 11210 (SAN 201-4785) Tel 718-780-5547; Dist. by: Sun & Moon Pr., 6363 Wilshire Blvd., Suite 115, Los Angeles, CA 90048 (SAN 216-3063) Tel 213-653-6711; *CIP.*

Fiction International, *(Fiction Intl; 0-931362),* St. Lawrence Univ., Canton, NY 13617 (SAN 221-1548) Tel 315-379-5961.

Fictioneer Books, Ltd, *(Fictioneer Bks; 0-934882),* Box B.I.P, Screamer Mountain, Clayton, GA 30525 (SAN 213-3113) Tel 404-782-3318.

Fiddleback, Inc., *(Fiddleback; 0-939027),* 2861 Glen Oaks Dr., Salt Lake City, UT 84109 (SAN 662-6505) Tel 801-486-0454.

Fideler Co., *(Fideler; 0-88296),* 203 Logan St., SW, Grand Rapids, MI 49503 (SAN 201-4793) Tel 616-456-8577.

Fidelio Pr., *(Fidelio Pr; 0-912681),* 504 Second SE., Apt. 4, Washington, DC 20003 (SAN 283-2577) Tel 202-544-8321.

Fidelity Assocs., Inc., *(Fidelity Assoc; 0-9615570),* P.O. Box 3766, Gastonia, NC 28053 (SAN 696-4257) Tel 704-864-3766; 2936 Rousseau Ct., Gastonia, NC 28054 (SAN 696-5385).

Fidelity Hse., *(Fidelity Hse; 0-942254),* 42 Wenonah Ave., Rockaway, NJ 07866 (SAN 682-255X).

Fidelity Publishing Corp. of America, The, *(Fidelity Pub; 0-942496),* 2021 Business Ctr. Dr., Suite 107, Irvine, CA 92715 (SAN 238-1591) Tel 714-752-5544; Toll free:800-826-3830 (CA only).

Field & Wood, Inc., Medical Pubs., *(Field & Wood Med; 0-938607),* 1405 Locust St., 11th Flr., Philadelphia, PA 19102 (SAN 661-3519) Tel 215-828-4010.

Field Museum of Natural History, *(Field Mus; 0-914868),* Roosevelt Rd. at Lake Shore Dr., Chicago, IL 60605-2496 (SAN 211-3554) Tel 312-922-9410.

Field Publications, Div. of Field Corp., *(Field Pubns; 0-8374),* 245 Long Hill Rd., Middletown, CT 06457 (SAN 207-060X) Tel 203-638-2400; Toll free: 800-852-5000; Orders to: 1250 Fairwood Ave., Columbus, OH 43216 (SAN 207-0618) Tel 614-253-0892. Acquired in 1985 by the Field Corp.

Field Translation Series *See Oberlin College Pr.*

Fielding Travel Bks., *(Fielding Travel Bks),* c/o William Morrow & Co., Inc., 105 Madison Ave., New York, NY 10016 (SAN 201-4823) Tel 212-889-3050; Orders to: William Morrow & Co., Order Dept., 6 Henderson Dr., West Caldwell, NJ 07006 (SAN 202-5779).

Fields, A. S., *(A S Fields; 0-939307),* 4654 Hwy 6, N., Houston, TX 77084 (SAN 663-1495) Tel 713-859-2580.

Fields, Virginia B., *(Fields; 0-9614510),* 150 W. Forest, Slidell, LA 70458 (SAN 691-7410) Tel 504-643-4284.

Fieldston Co., Inc., *(Fieldston Co; 0-9613656),* 1133 15th St., NW, Suite 1000, Washington, DC 20005 (SAN 670-7653) Tel 202-775-0240.

Fiery Water Pr., *(Fiery Water; 0-9613401),* 1202 Loma Dr., No. 129, Ojai, CA 93023 (SAN 656-9854) Tel 805-646-1671; Dist. by: DeVorss & Co., P.O. Box 550, 1046 Princeton Dr., Marina del Rey, CA 90294 (SAN 168-9886) Tel 213-870-7478; Dist. by: Valley Lights Pubns., P.O. Box 1537, Ojai, CA 93023 (SAN 219-8320) Tel 805-646-9888.

Fiesta City Pubs., *(Fiesta City; 0-940076),* P.O. Box 5861, Santa Barbara, CA 93150-5861 (SAN 217-071X) Tel 805-969-2891.

Fiesta Publishing Corp., *(Fiesta Pub; 0-88473),* 6360 NE Fourth Ct., Miami, FL 33138 (SAN 201-8470) Tel 305-751-1181.

Fifth Avenue Brides, Inc., Affil. of Bridal Guide, Ltd., *(Fifth Ave Brides; 0-9615882),* P.O. Box 2091, La Crosse, WI 54601 (SAN 697-0729); 2820 Leonard St., La Crosse, WI 54602-2091 (SAN 697-0737) Tel 608-782-8580; Dist. by: Clergy Bk. Services, 12855 W. Silver Spring Dr., Butler, WI 53007 (SAN 169-9032) Tel 414-781-1234; Dist. by: Howard Gardiner, Inc., 1743 Dallas Trade Mart, Dallas, TX 75207 (SAN 200-6944) Tel 214-748-3387; Toll free: 800-527-5807; Dist. by: Primarily Paper, Inc., Orange UMAGA, Rm. 304, Minnetonka, MN 55343 (SAN 200-6952) Tel 612-462-3229.

Fifth Estate, Inc., The, *(Fifth Estate; 0-937217),* 1008 Dougals Ave., Providence, RI 02904 (SAN 658-7240) Tel 401-861-0361; P.O. Box 3172, Providence, RI 02906 (SAN 658-7259).

Fifth Wave Pr., *(Fifth Wave Pr; 0-911761),* P.O. Box 9355, San Rafael, CA 94912 (SAN 264-0368) Tel 415-457-2019.

Fig Leaf Creations, *(Fig Leaf; 0-918774),* 1706 Olive Ave., Santa Barbara, CA 93101 (SAN 210-4245) Tel 805-962-4987.

Fig Leaf Pr., *(Fig Leaf Pr; 0-912235),* 5791 E. Shields Ave., Fresno, CA 93727 (SAN 264-0376) Tel 209-292-4222.

Figures, The, *(Figures; 0-935724),* 27 1/2 Rosseter St., Great Barrington, MA 01230 (SAN 209-2468) Tel 413-528-2552; Dist. by: Small Pr. Distribution, 1814 San Pablo Ave., Berkeley, CA 94702 (SAN 204-5826) Tel 415-549-3336.

Fila's Designs Unlimited, Inc., *(Filas Des Unltd; 0-9610588),* 1013 Big Baer Dr., Glen Burnie, MD 21061 (SAN 264-7338) Tel 301-761-1471.

Filbrun, Daniel P., *(D P Filbrun; 0-9614439),* 12859 Euphemia-Castine Rd., West Manchester, OH 45382 (SAN 689-3465) Tel 513-678-4074.

Filkon Publishing, Ltd., *(Filkon Pub; 0-936807),* 21 W. 46th St., 2nd Flr., New York, NY 10036 (SAN 699-9433) Tel 212-719-4237.

Fill the Gap Pubns., *(Fill the Gap; 0-89858),* P.O. Box 30760, Lafayette, LA 70503 (SAN 211-9978) Tel 318-984-2004.

Film Classic Exchange, *(Film Classics; 0-9610916),* P.O. Box 77568 Dockweiler Stn., Los Angeles, CA 90007 (SAN 265-1351) Tel 213-731-3854.

Film Communicators, *(Film Communicators; 0-9606702),* 11136 Weddington St., N. Hollywood, CA 91601 (SAN 219-7359) Tel 818-766-3747; Toll free: 800-423-2400.

Film Instruction Co. of America, *(FICOA; 0-931974),* 2901 S. Wentworth Ave., Milwaukee, WI 53207 (SAN 206-2003).

Filmquest Bks., *(Filmquest Bks; 0-9610670),* 857 Partridge Ave., No. 1, Menlo Park, CA 94025 (SAN 264-7397).

Filsinger & Co., Ltd., *(Filsinger & Co; 0-916754),* 288 W. 12 St., New York, NY 10014 (SAN 208-3574) Tel 212-243-7421.

Filson Club, Inc., *(Filson Club; 0-9601072),* 1310 S. Third St., Louisville, KY 40208-2306 (SAN 205-5791) Tel 502-635-5083.

Filter Pr., *(Filter; 0-910584; 0-86541),* P.O. Box 5, Palmer Lake, CO 80133 (SAN 201-484X) Tel 303-481-2523.

Final Call Foundation, Inc., *(Final Call Found; 0-938483),* 4503 Seventh St., Lubbock, TX 79416 (SAN 661-3136) Tel 806-793-7234.

Financial Accounting Standards Board, *(Finan Acct; 0-910065),* High Ridge PK., P.O. Box 3821, Stamford, CT 06905-0831 (SAN 241-3051) Tel 203-329-8401.

Financial Aid Assistance Service, *(Financial Aid; 0-9610018),* P.O. Box 1497, Springfield, OR 97477 (SAN 270-1561) Tel 503-726-2205.

Financial Analysts Federation, the, *(Finan Analysts),* 1633 Broadway, 14th Floor, New York, NY 10019 (SAN 224-7305) Tel 212-957-2866.

Financial Data Corp., *(Finan Data Corp; 0-940758),* 1313 Fifth St. SE, Suite 124, Minneapolis, MN 55414 (SAN 219-7367) Tel 612-379-3866.

Financial Executives Research Foundation, *(Finan Exec; 0-910586),* 10 Madison Ave., Morristown, NJ 07960 (SAN 206-4111) Tel 201-898-4600; P.O. Box 1938, Morristown, NJ 07960 (SAN 660-9295).

Financial Freedom Pubs., *(Finan Freedom; 0-942360),* 9260 E. Colonville Rd., Clare, MI 48617 (SAN 281-7101) Tel 517-386-7729; Dist. by: Financial Freedom Consultants, P.O. Box 268, Clare, MI 48617 (SAN 281-711X) Tel 517-386-7720.

Financial Guidance Ctr., Inc., *(Financial Guidance; 0-938323),* 147 Main St., Maynard, MA 01754 (SAN 661-3187) Tel 617-897-6470.

Financial Guide Bks., *(Finan Guide Bks; 0-916407),* 12610 Bentree Rd., Minneapolis, MN 55343 (SAN 295-8031) Tel 612-544-8482.

Financial Management Association, *(Finan Mgmt Assn),* College of Business Administration, University of South Florida, Tampa, FL 33620 (SAN 236-2775) Tel 813-974-2084.

Financial Managers Society for Savings Institutions, Inc., *(Finan Mgrs Soc),* 111 E. Wacker Ave., Suite 2221, Chicago, IL 60601 (SAN 230-6174) Tel 312-938-2576.

Financial Marketing Assoc., *(Fin Mktg Assocs; 0-9616902),* 1011 E. Main St., Richmond, VA 23219 (SAN 661-4965) Tel 804-643-6069.

Financial Partners Publishing, *(Financial; 0-9607644),* 4929 S. 121st St., Omaha, NE 68137 (SAN 679-1530) Tel 402-895-0346.

Financial Pr., Inc., *(Financial Pr),* 4975 SW 82nd St., Miami, FL 33143 (SAN 206-4545).

Financial Pr., The, *(Finan Press; 0-9615066),* 2555 Kennedy Blvd., Jersey City, NJ 07304 (SAN 693-9325) Tel 201-434-6110.

Financial Publishing Co., *(Finan Pub; 0-87600),* 82 Brookline Ave., Boston, MA 02215 (SAN 205-5805) Tel 617-262-4040.

Finch Bks., *(Finch Bks; 0-9616491),* 340 Birch St., Titusville, FL 32780 (SAN 659-2236) Tel 305-268-5420.

FIND-SVP Information Clearing Hse., *(FIND-SVP; 0-931634),* 500 Fifth Ave., New York, NY 10110 (SAN 212-6680) Tel 212-354-2424; Toll free: 800-346-3787.

Fine, Donald I., *(D I Fine; 0-917657; 1-55611),* 128 E. 36th St., New York, NY 10016 (SAN 656-9749) Tel 212-696-1838; Orders to: Haddon Craftsmen, Inc., 1205K O'Neill Hwy., Dunmore, PA 18512 (SAN 662-7625) Tel 717-348-9292.

Fine Arts Museum of Long Island, The, *(FA Mus LI; 0-933535),* 295 Fulton Ave., New York, NY 11550 (SAN 691-8581) Tel 516-481-5700.

Fine Arts Museums of San Francisco, The, *(Fine Arts Mus; 0-88401),* M. H. De Young Memorial Museum, Golden Gate Pk., San Francisco, CA 94118 (SAN 206-524X) Tel 415-221-4811; Orders to: Museum Society Bookshops, M. H. De Young Memorial Museum, Golden Gate Pk., Sna Francisco, CA 94118 Tel 415-750-3642.

Fine Arts Society, *(Fine Arts Soc; 0-932192),* 50459 N. Portage Rd., South Bend, IN 46628 (SAN 211-3902) Tel 219-272-9290; Orders to: 2314 W. Sixth St., Mishawaka, IN 46544 (SAN 211-3910) Tel 219-255-8606.

Fine Edge Productions, *(Fine Edge; 0-938665),* Rte. 2, Box 303, Bishop, CA 93514 (SAN 661-3225); 303 Valley View Rd., Bishop, CA 93514 (SAN 661-3233) Tel 619-387-2412.

Fine Line Productions, *(Fine Line Prodns; 0-936413),* 3181-A Mission St., San Francisco, CA 94110 (SAN 698-150X) Tel 415-282-5502; Dist. by: Bookpeople, 2929 Fifth St., Berkeley, CA 94710 (SAN 168-9517) Tel 415-549-3030; Toll free: 800-227-1516; Dist. by: New Leaf Distributing, The, 1020 White St., SW, Atlanta, GA 30310 (SAN 169-1449) Tel 404-755-2665; Toll free: 800-241-3829.

Fine Print, *(Fine Print; 0-9607290),* P.O. Box 3394, San Francisco, CA 94119 (SAN 239-2070) Tel 415-776-1530.

Fine Tools, Inc., *(Fine Tools; 0-936059),* 2028 Backus Ave., Danbury, CT 06810 (SAN 697-0699) Tel 203-797-0183.

Fine View Pr., *(Fine View Pr; 0-9615571),* 474 Fineview, Kalamazoo, MI 49007 (SAN 696-4273) Tel 616-342-6048.

Fineline Co., *(Fineline; 0-913917; 0-917520),* 23501 Carlow Rd., Torraine, CA 90505 (SAN 286-8997) Tel 213-378-1904.

Finesse Pr., *(Finesse Pr; 0-938981),* 2068 Via Las Cumbres, No. 7, San Diego, CA 92111 (SAN 661-6798) Tel 619-569-7728.

Finestkind Bks., Div. of Connecticut Cane & Reed Co., *(Finestkind Bks; 0-938849),* 205 Hartford Rd., Manchester, CT 06040 (SAN 662-5576) Tel 203-646-6586.

Finkelstein, Adrian, *(A Finkelstein; 0-87418),* 855 E. Palatine Rd., Palatine, IL 60067 (SAN 693-4285); Dist. by: Coleman Publishing Co., 99 Milbar Blvd., Farmingdale, NY 11735 (SAN 238-1508) Tel 516-293-0383.

Finn Hill Arts, *(Finn Hill; 0-917270),* P.O. Box 542, Silverton, CO 81433 (SAN 208-5054) Tel 303-387-5729.

Finnerty, Mary T., *(M T Finnerty; 0-9602222),* 33 Johnson, West Roxbury, MA 02132 (SAN 212-2766); Orders to: P.O. Box 591, Astor Sta., Boston, MA 02123 (SAN 212-2774).

Finney Co., *(Finney Co; 0-912486),* 3350 Gorham Ave., Minneapolis, MN 55426 (SAN 206-412X) Tel 612-929-6165.

Finnish American Literary Heritage Foundation, *(Finnish Am Lit; 0-943478),* P.O. Box 1838, Portland, OR 97207 (SAN 240-6497) Tel 503-229-3064.

FinnRoots, Inc., *(FinnRoots; 0-940034),* 40 E.49th St. No. 1602, New York, NY 10017 (SAN 220-2190) Tel 212-832-8989.

Fins Pubns., *(Fins Pubns; 0-9615221),* Box 13005, Roseville, MN 55113 (SAN 695-1511) Tel 612-483-8187; Dist. by: Bookman, Inc., 519 N. Third St., Minneapolis, MN 55401 (SAN 282-7352) Tel 612-341-3333; Toll free: 800-328-8411.

Fiore Enterprises, *(Fiore Ent; 0-9616687),* P.O. Box 2164, River Grove, IL 60171 (SAN 661-3411); 2119 78th Ave., Elmwood Park, IL 60635 (SAN 661-342X) Tel 312-453-8964.

Fire & Light Bks., *(Fire & Light Bks; 0-911327),* P.O. Box 688, Madison, WI 53701 (SAN 270-1677).

Fire & Police Directory Press, The See **First International Publishing Corp.**

Fire Call Press, The See **First International Publishing Corp.**

Fire Engineering Bk. Service, Div. of Technical Publishing Co., A Dun & Bradstreet Co., *(Fire Eng; 0-912212),* 875 Third Ave., New York, NY 10022 (SAN 281-7128) Tel 212-605-9515; Orders to: Fire Engineering Bk. Service, 1301 S. Grove Ave., Barrington, IL 60010 (SAN 281-7136) Tel 312-381-1840; Toll free: 800-992-4447.

Fire in the Lake, *(Fire Lake; 0-9615693),* 1875 Oak St., No. 2, San Francisco, CA 94117 (SAN 696-429X) Tel 415-626-1708.

Fire Pr., The, *(Fire Pr; 0-912607),* P.O. Box 327, Metuchen, NJ 08840 (SAN 283-2593) Tel 201-964-8476.

Firebird Pr., *(Firebird Pr; 0-912019),* P.O. Box 69, Dunlap, IL 61525 (SAN 265-3834).

Firebrand Bks., *(Firebrand Bks; 0-932379),* 141 The Commons, Ithaca, NY 14850 (SAN 687-3855) Tel 607-272-0000.

FireBuilders, The, *(FireBuilders; 0-9601794),* RR1, Box 620, Stetson Rd., Brooklyn, CT 06234 (SAN 210-5977) Tel 203-774-4824.

Firelands Historical Society, *(Firelands Hist; 0-932535),* 4 Case Ave., Norwalk, OH 44857 (SAN 687-469X) Tel 419-668-6038; 45 N. Pleasant St., Norwalk, OH 44857 (SAN 693-5214) Tel 419-668-8031; Dist. by: Baker & Taylor Co., Eastern Div., 50 Kirby Ave, Somerville, NJ 08876 (SAN 169-4901).

†**Fireside Bks.,** Div. of Warren H. Green, Inc., *(Fireside Bks; 0-87527),* 8356 Olive Blvd., St. Louis, MO 63132 (SAN 201-8500) Tel 314-991-1335; Toll free: 800-223-2336; CIP.

Fireside Pr., *(Fireside Pr),* Box 5293, Hamden, CT 06518 (SAN 209-7400) Tel 203-248-1023.

Firestein Bks., *(Firestein Bks; 0-9602498),* P.O. Box 370643, El Paso, TX 79937-0643 (SAN 212-940X) Tel 915-594-2966.

Firestone, W. D., Press, *(Firestone; 0-934562),* 1313 S. Jefferson Ave., Springfield, MO 65807 (SAN 213-2478) Tel 417-866-5141.

Fireweed Pr., *(Fireweed; 0-912683),* P.O. Box 6011, Falls Church, VA 22046 (SAN 277-6839) Tel 703-560-0810.

Fireweed Pr., *(Fireweed Pr AK; 0-914221),* P.O. Box 83970, Fairbanks, AK 99708 (SAN 287-4911) Tel 907-479-2398.

Firey, Walter, *(Firey; 0-9603066),* 1307 Wilshire Blvd., Austin, TX 78722 (SAN 209-5572) Tel 512-454-2418.

Firm Foundation Publishing Hse., *(Firm Foun Pub; 0-88027),* P.O. Box 17200, Pensacola, FL 32522 (SAN 201-4858) Tel 904-433-4258.

First Amendment Press, *(First Amend),* P.O. Box 7334, Stanford, CA 94305 (SAN 215-7616) Tel 415-851-3391.

First American Bank for Savings, *(First Am Bank),* 154 East St., Dorchester, MA 02122 (SAN 207-5164) Tel 617-288-9491.

First Baptist Church AL, *(First Bapt AL; 0-9616158),* P.O. Box 400, Jacksonville, AL 36265 (SAN 699-9557) Tel 205-435-7263; 231 E. Seventh St., Jacksonville, AL 36265 (SAN 699-9565).

First Baptist Church of Steinhatchee, *(First Baptist),* P.O. Box 113, Steinhatchee, FL 32359 (SAN 240-1754) Tel 904-498-3242.

First Choice, *(First Choice; 0-9606704),* P.O. Box 1680, Ramona, CA 92065 (SAN 219-7375) Tel 619-789-8878.

First Church of Christ Scientist, *(First Church; 0-87952),* 1 Norway St., Boston, MA 02115 (SAN 206-6467) Tel 617-262-2300.

First Commonwealth Pr., *(First Commonwealth; 0-912709),* 1300 NE 157th St., North Miami Beach, FL 33162 (SAN 283-0280) Tel 305-949-7797.

First East Coast Theatre and Publishing Co., Inc., *(First East; 0-910829),* P.O. Box A244, Village Sta., New York, NY 10014 (SAN 270-1812) Tel 718-296-1979.

First Encounter Pr., The, *(First Encounter; 0-912609),* P.O. Box 946, N. Eastham, Cape Cod, MA 02651 (SAN 282-7697) Tel 617-255-3389.

First Impressions Publishing Co., *(First Impressions; 0-934794),* P.O. Box 9073, Madison, WI 53715 (SAN 213-0572) Tel 608-238-6254.

First International Publishing Corp., *(First Intl Pub; 1-55632),* P.O. Box 20279, Seattle, WA 98102-1279 (SAN 659-6126); 2803 Eighth Ave., Seattle, WA 98119 (SAN 659-6134) Tel 206-282-1438. *Imprints:* Anechron Three Press (Anechron Three Pr); Communications Monitor Press (Comns Monitor Pr); Emergency Medical Technology Press (Emerg Med Tech Pr); Fire & Police Directory Press, The (Fire Police Direct Pr); Fire Call Press, The (Fire Call Pr); Small Business Success Press (Small Busn Success Pr); United Galactic Publishing Foundation Press (United Galactic Pub).

First Love Ministries, *(First Love Min; 0-9614947),* P.O. Box 317, Linden, NJ 07036 (SAN 693-6482) Tel 201-862-7172.

First Mountain Foundation, The, *(First Mntn Foun; 0-916834),* Montclair State College, Upper Montclair, NJ 07042 (SAN 281-7144) Tel 201-893-4277; Orders to: P.O. Box 196, Montclair, NJ 07042 (SAN 281-7152).

First Ozark Pr., The, *(First Ozark Pr; 0-911559),* P.O. Box 1137, Harrison, AR 72601 (SAN 217-734X).

First Parish in Concord, *(First Parish Concord),* 20 Lexington Rd., Concord, MA 01742 (SAN 658-8220) Tel 617-369-9602; Orders to: Eric P. Smith, 35 Academy Ln., Concord, MA 01742 (SAN 662-4170).

First Person, *(First Person; 0-916452),* Box 604, Palisades, NY 10964 (SAN 208-0508) Tel 914-359-7340; Dist. by: Small Pr. Distribution, Inc., 1814 San Pablo Ave., Berkeley, CA 94702 (SAN 204-5826) Tel 415-549-3336.

First Pubns., Inc., *(First Pubns; 0-912891),* P.O. Box 1832, Evanston, IL 60204 (SAN 283-2607) Tel 312-869-7210.

First Stage Arts Project, *(First Stage; 0-939695),* 1800 S. Robertson Blvd., Suite 322, Los Angeles, CA 90035 (SAN 663-4729) Tel 213-836-6398; 4913 Indian Wood Rd., No. 507, Culver City, CA 90230 (SAN 663-4737).

First Step Enterprises, *(First Step Ent; 0-9614220),* P.O. Box 87265, San Diego, CA 92138-7265 (SAN 686-8010) Tel 619-224-0578.

Names

Names

Firsthand Press, *(Firsthand; 0-939620),* 137 Sixth St., Juneau, AK 99801 (SAN 295-3307) Tel 907-568-1411; Orders to: 137 Sixth St., Juneau, AK 99801 (SAN 295-3315) Tel 907-568-1411.

Firth, Robert H., Cable Cellarbook., *(Firth; 0-9605060),* 20351 Lake Erie Dr., Walnut, CA 91789 (SAN 293-2679); Dist. by: The Cellar Book Shop,, 18090 Wyoming, Detroit, MI 48221 (SAN 213-4330) Tel 313-861-1776.

Fiscal Policy Council, *(Fiscal Policy; 0-940494),* 100 E. 17th St., Riviera Beach, FL 33404 (SAN 217-1740) Tel 305-863-9701.

Fischer, Carl, Inc., *(Fischer Inc NY; 0-8258),* 62 Cooper Sq., New York, NY 10003 (SAN 215-1979).

Fischer, Henry G., *(Henry Fischer),* R.R. 1, Box 389, Sherman, CT 06784 (SAN 692-3135); Dist. by: Metropolitan Museum of Art, Book Sales Dept., 82nd St. & Fifth Ave., New York, NY 10028 (SAN 202-6279) Tel 212-879-5500.

Fischer, Inge, *(I Fischer; 0-9610238),* 1616 Kewalo St., No. 507, Honolulu, HI 96822 (SAN 264-0406) Tel 808-531-5764.

Fischer Publishing, *(Fischer Pub; 0-915421),* P.O. Box 116, 7851 Herbert Rd., Canfield, OH 44406 (SAN 291-1574) Tel 216-533-4446.

Fish, Harriet, *(H U Fish; 0-9612344),* P.O. Box 135, Carlsborg, WA 98324 (SAN 287-1726) Tel 206-452-9195.

Fishelis, Avraham, Pub., *(A Fishelis; 0-9605560),* 577 Grand St., New York, NY 10002 (SAN 240-0006) Tel 212-260-1760.

Fisher, Bill & Kay, *(B & K Fisher; 0-9603004),* P.O. Box 714, Colfax, CA 95713 (SAN 659-0918) Tel 916-346-2941.

Fisher, Clay C., *(C C Fisher),* 702 Tenth St., NE, Massillon, OH 44646 (SAN 202-4977).

Fisher, John B., *(J B Fisher; 0-9612308),* 2029 Robin Rd., Salisbury, NC 28144 (SAN 289-2251) Tel 704-637-0988.

Fisher, Raymond John, *(R J Fisher; 0-9616984),* 1271 Gaylord St., Denver, CO 80206 (SAN 661-7263) Tel 303-322-4959.

Fisher Bks., *(Fisher Bks; 1-55561),* 3499 N. Campbell Ave., No. 909, Tucson, AZ 85719 (SAN 698-1410) Tel 602-325-5263.

Fisher-Bradley, Inc., *(Fisher-Bradley; 0-934751),* 77 Bralan Ct., Gaithersburg, MD 20877 (SAN 694-1745) Tel 301-840-9755.

Fisher Hse. Pubns., *(Fisher Hse Pubns; 0-938325),* P.O. Box 863, Merrifield, VA 22116 (SAN 661-3241); 3366 Woodburn Rd., No. 21, Annandale, VA 22003 (SAN 661-325X) Tel 703-849-9654.

†Fisher Institute, The, *(Fisher Inst; 0-933028),* 6350 LBJ Freeway, Suite 183E, Dallas, TX 75240 (SAN 213-4942); *CIP.*

Fisher Pubns., *(Fisher Pubns; 0-911303),* 748 Springdale Rd., Statesville, NC 28677 (SAN 270-1871) Tel 704-873-3776.

Fishergate Publishing Co., Inc., *(Fishergate; 0-942720),* 2521 Riva Rd., Annapolis, MD 21401 (SAN 240-2181) Tel 301-841-6646.

Fisheries Communications, Inc., *(Fisheries Comm; 0-9608932),* Box 37, Dept B, Stonington, ME 04681 (SAN 241-0184) Tel 207-367-2396.

Fishing News Bks., Ltd. *See Unipub*

Fishing with Jack Pubns., *(Fishing with Jack Pubns; 0-9616975),* 1 Marvel Ct., San Francisco, CA 94121 (SAN 661-8146) Tel 415-221-1592.

Fishner Bks., *(Fishner Bks; 0-9606848),* P.O. Box 445, Vienna, VA 22180 (SAN 217-3638) Tel 703-281-4255.

Fiske, Jane F., *(J F Fiske; 0-9615790),* 44 Stonecleave Rd., Boxford, MA 01921 (SAN 696-7426) Tel 617-887-8787.

Fisons Corp., *(Fisons Corp; 0-914132),* 2 Preston Ct., Bedford, MA 01730 (SAN 220-5459) Tel 617-275-1000.

Fitchburg Pr., Inc., *(Fitchburg Pr; 0-9617191),* 2805 Florann Dr., Madison, WI 53711 (SAN 663-5865) Tel 608-273-3266.

Fitness Alternatives Pr., *(Fitness Alt Pr; 0-943364),* Box 761, Evergreen, CO 80439 (SAN 240-1096).

Fitness Ctr. Information Network, The, *(Fitness Ctr Info; 0-935783),* P.O. Box 906, Greenfield, MA 01302 (SAN 699-8089) Tel 413-773-8769.

Fitness Pubns., *(Fitness; 0-918278),* P.O. Box 1786, Poughkeepsie, NY 12601 (SAN 209-3995) Tel 914-463-1626.

FitzGerald, Jerry, & Associates, *(FitzGerald & Assocs; 0-932410),* 506 Barkentine Ln., Redwood City, CA 94065 (SAN 214-0128) Tel 415-591-5676.

Fitzgerald, Vincent, & Co., *(Fitzgerald & Co; 0-935581),* 11 E. 78th St., New York, NY 10021 (SAN 695-9261) Tel 212-249-1971.

Fitzgerald Unicorn, *(Fitzg Unicorn; 0-9604564),* 808 Charlotte, Fredericksburg, VA 22401 (SAN 214-2643) Tel 703-371-3253.

FitzPatrick, V. S., *(V S FitzPatrick; 0-937173),* Arriba, CO 80804 (SAN 658-5221) Tel 303-768-3468.

FitzSimons, H.T., Co., Inc., *(FitzSimons; 0-912222),* 357 W. Erie St., Chicago, IL 60610 (SAN 206-4200) Tel 312-944-1841.

517 Parachute Combat Team Assn., *(Five Hundred Seven Parachute; 0-9616015),* 6600 Josie Ln., Hudson, FL 33567 (SAN 697-3272) Tel 813-863-2995.

5 M Pubs., *(Five M Pubs; 0-9614306),* P.O. Box 6641, New Orleans, LA 70174 (SAN 687-4983) Tel 504-391-9412.

Five Starr Productions, *(Five Starr Prods; 0-9606026),* 1610 Christine, Wichita Falls, TX 76302 (SAN 216-8944) Tel 301-838-8059.

Five Windmills Pub. Co., *(Five Windmills; 0-9609600),* P.O. Box 5841, Scottsdale, AZ 85261 (SAN 260-1877) Tel 602-998-0713.

†Fjord Pr., *(Fjord Pr; 0-940242),* P.O. Box 16501, Seattle, WA 98116 (SAN 220-3332) Tel 206-625-9363; Dist. by: Academy Chicago Pubs., 425 N. Michigan Ave., Chicago, IL 60611 (SAN 213-2001) Tel 312-644-1723; *CIP.*

Flame International Inc., *(Flame Intl; 0-933184),* P.O. Box 305, Quantico, VA 22134 (SAN 215-3114).

Flaming Arrow Pubns., *(Flaming Arrow Pubns; 0-930043),* R.F.D, Walpole, NH 03608 (SAN 669-8123) Tel 603-756-4152.

Flaming Hooker Pr., Div. of Markin Medical Research, *(Flaming Hooker Pr; 0-9615223),* 1236 Ginger Crescent, Virginia Beach, VA 23456 (SAN 695-152X) Tel 804-427-0220; P.O. Box 9106, Virginia Beach, VA 23450 (SAN 662-3441).

Flamingo Pr., *(Flamingo Pr CA; 0-938905),* 2304 Altisma Way, No. 208, Carlsbad, CA 92008 (SAN 661-812X) Tel 619-438-3011. Do not confuse with Flamingo Pr., New York, NY.

Flashmaps Pubns., Inc., *(Flashmaps Pubns; 0-942226),* P.O. Box 13, Chappaqua, NY 10514 (SAN 239-8540) Tel 914-238-5116.

Flat Five Pr., *(Flat Five Pr; 0-935285),* 3214A Golden City Blvd., Roanoke, VA 24014 (SAN 696-4214) Tel 703-345-2151.

Flat Glass Marketing Assn., *(Flat Glass Mktg),* 3310 Harrison, Topeka, KS 66611 (SAN 224-7720) Tel 913-226-7013.

†Flatiron Bk. Distributors, *(Flatiron Book Dist),* 1170 Broadway, New York, NY 10001 (SAN 663-2998); *CIP.*

Flayderman, N., & Co., Inc., *(Flayderman; 0-910598),* Squash Hollow Rd., New Milford, CT 06776 (SAN 205-5813) Tel 203-354-5567.

†Fleet Pr. Corp., Subs. of Fleet Academic Editions, Inc., *(Fleet; 0-8303),* 160 Fifth Ave., New York, NY 10010 (SAN 201-4874) Tel 212-243-6100; *CIP.*

Fleet Street Corp., *(Fleet St Corp; 0-9611314),* 656 Quince Orchard Rd., Gaithersburg, MD 20878 (SAN 282-9053) Tel 301-977-3900.

Fleming, Don, Seminars & Publishing Co., *(D Fleming Sem; 0-9609264),* 1827 E. Rowland Ave., W. Covina, CA 91791 (SAN 260-0560) Tel 213-332-7226; Orders to: 527 N. Azuza Ave. Suite 225, Covina, CA 91722 (SAN 669-0823).

Fleming, Jim, Pubns., *(J Fleming; 0-939415),* P.O. Box 1211, Vail, CO 81658 (SAN 663-2513); 1860 W. Meadow, No. 8, Vail, CO 81658 (SAN 663-2521) Tel 303-934-3237.

Fleming Publishing, *(Fleming Pub; 0-937835),* 414 Glover Ave., Enterprise, AL 36330 (SAN 659-4506) Tel 205-393-3062.

Fleur-Di-Lee, *(Fleur-Di-Lee; 0-911579),* 5969 Donna, Tarzana, CA 91356 (SAN 264-0422).

Fleury Foundation Inc., *(Fleury Found; 0-933537),* P.O. Box 19352, Orlando, FL 32814 (SAN 691-859X) Tel 305-422-4999.

Flex-A-bility Inc., *(Flex-A-bility; 0-932931),* P.O. Box 7252, 890 S. Long, Freeport, NY 11520 (SAN 690-0348) Tel 516-223-7965.

Flight Safety Foundation, Inc., *(Flight Safety; 0-912768),* 5510 Columbia Pike, Arlington, VA 22204 (SAN 205-5821) Tel 703-820-2777.

Flint Hills Book Co., *(Flint Hills),* 1735 Fairview, Manhattan, KS 66502 (SAN 208-1806).

Flint Institute of Arts, *(Flint Inst Arts; 0-939896),* 1120 E. Kearsley St., Flint, MI 48503 (SAN 216-812X) Tel 313-234-1695.

FlipTrack Learning Systems, Div. of Mosaic Media, Inc., *(FlipTrack; 0-917792),* 999 Main St., Suite 200, Glen Ellyn, IL 60137 (SAN 286-9136) Tel 312-790-1117; Toll free: 800-222-3547.

Floating Island Pubns., *(Floating Island; 0-912449),* P.O. Box 516, Point Reyes Station, CA 94956 (SAN 212-9043) Tel 415-669-1612.

†Flora & Fauna Pubns., Div. E. J. Brill Publishing Co., *(Flora & Fauna; 0-916846),* 4300 NW 23rd Ave., Suite 100, Gainesville, FL 32606 (SAN 220-2468) Tel 904-371-9858; *CIP.*

Floral Publishing, *(Floral Pub; 0-938057),* P.O. Box 55282, Madison, WI 53705 (SAN 661-1842); 717 Eugenia Ave., Madison, WI 53705 (SAN 661-1850) Tel 603-238-5626.

Flores, J., Pubns., *(J O Flores; 0-918751),* P.O. Box 14, Rosemead, CA 91770 (SAN 679-1395) Tel 818-287-2195.

Flores De Papel Inc., *(Flores De Papel; 0-915475),* 12 Robyn Lane, Greenleaf Golf & Racquet Club, Haines City, FL 33844 (SAN 291-1582) Tel 813-422-8113.

Florham Park Press, Inc., *(Florham; 0-912598),* 12 Leslie Ave., P.O. Box 303, Florham Park, NJ 07932 (SAN 206-4219) Tel 201-377-3670.

Floricanto Pr., Div. of Hispanex, *(Floricanto Pr; 0-915745),* 604 William St., Oakland, CA 94612 (SAN 293-9169) Tel 415-893-8702.

Florida Bar Continuing Legal Education Pubns., The, *(FL Bar Legal Ed; 0-910373),* 600 Apalachee Pkwy., Tallahassee, FL 32301-8226 (SAN 260-0579) Tel 904-222-5286; Toll free: 800-874-0005.

Florida Ctr. for Public Management, *(FL Ctr Public; 0-932143),* Florida State Univ., Tallahassee, FL 32306-4025 (SAN 686-4287) Tel 904-644-6460.

Florida Classics Library, *(Florida Classics; 0-912451),* P.O. Drawer 1657, Pt. Salerno, FL 33492-1657 (SAN 265-2404) Tel 305-546-9380.

Florida Flair Bks., *(Florida Flair Bks; 0-9613236),* 8955 SW 93rd Ct., Miami, FL 33176 (SAN 295-4192) Tel 305-274-5734.

Florida Mail Pr., *(FL Mail Pr; 0-937759),* P.O. Box 6, Old Town, FL 32680 (SAN 659-2244) Tel 904-542-7904; 400 Madison Ave., Old Town, FL 32680 (SAN 659-2252).

Florida Medical Entomology Laboratory, *(Fla Med Entom; 0-9615224),* 200 Ninth St. SE, Vero Beach, FL 32962 (SAN 694-6453) Tel 305-562-5435.

Florida Rare Coin Galleries, *(Fla Rare Coin; 0-9614824),* P.O. Box 13193, Tallahassee, FL 32317 (SAN 693-0026) Tel 904-878-5779.

Florida Sea Grant College Program, *(FL Sea Grant Coll; 0-912747),* Univ. of Florida, G.O. 22, McCarty Hall, Gainesville, FL 32611 (SAN 282-7719) Tel 904-392-1771.

Florida Sinkhole Research Institute, *(FL Sinkhole Res; 0-937971),* Univ. of Central Florida, Orlando, FL 32765 (SAN 659-5030) Tel 305-275-2043.

Florida State Univ., Institute for Social Research, *(FL St U-Inst Soc Re),* Tallahassee, FL 32306 (SAN 204-1081) Tel 904-599-2525.

Florida State Univ. Institute of Science & Public Affairs, *(Florida State U Inst; 0-9606708),* 361 Bellamy Bldg, Florida State Univ., Tallahassee, FL 32306 (SAN 219-7405).

Florida State University, Geology Dept., *(FSU Geology; 0-938426),* Tallahassee, FL 32306 (SAN 239-9350) Tel 904-644-3208.

Florida Sun-Gator Publishing Co., *(Florida Sun-Gator),* P.O. Box 365, Oviedo, FL 32765 (SAN 209-3030) Tel 305-671-3633.

Florida Trend Bk. Division, Div. of Florida Trend, Inc., *(Florida Trend; 0-88251),* P.O. Box 611, St. Petersburg, FL 33731 (SAN 202-8018) Tel 813-821-5800.

Florida Women's Yellow Pages Directory, *(Florida Women; 0-935785),* P.O. Box 1523, Clearwater, FL 33517 (SAN 695-8133) Tel 813-443-1300; Dist. by: Surf & Sand, P.O. Box 1312, Largo, FL 33540 (SAN 200-7886).

Flourtown Publishing Co., *(Flourtown Pub; 0-9603376),* P.O. Box 148, Flourtown, PA 19031 (SAN 207-6381).

Flower & Garden *See* **Modern Handcraft, Inc.**

Flower Press, *(Flower Pr; 0-942256),* 10332 Shaver Rd., Kalamazoo, MI 49002 (SAN 217-7358) Tel 616-327-0108.

Floyd, Wayne, *(W FLoyd; 0-9613160),* 1407 Darlene, Arlington, TX 76010 (SAN 294-9288) Tel 817-861-1683.

†**Flume Press,** *(Flume Pr; 0-9613984),* 644 Citrus Ave., Chico, CA 95926 (SAN 682-1898) Tel 916-342-1583; *CIP.*

Flying Bks., *(Flying Bks; 0-911139),* 3850 Coronation Rd., Eagan, MN 55122 (SAN 270-2185) Tel 612-454-2493.

Flying Diamond Bks., *(Flying Diamond Bks; 0-918532),* Rte. 2, Box 612, Hettinger, ND 58639 (SAN 209-5580) Tel 701-567-2646.

Flying Enterprises, Inc, *(Flying Ent; 0-912470),* Box 7000, Dallas, TX 75209 (SAN 201-4882) Tel 214-358-3456.

Flying Fingers, *(Flying Fingers; 0-9612448),* P.O. Box 5455, Santa Monica, CA 90405 (SAN 289-2456) Tel 213-396-5648.

Flying Fox Pr., The, *(Flying Fox Pr; 0-9617225),* 4700 Jamestown Rd., Bethesda, MD 20816 (SAN 663-3692) Tel 301-229-8160.

Flying Pencil Pubns., *(Flying Pencil; 0-916473),* P.O. Box 19062, Portland, OR 97219 (SAN 295-1398) Tel 503-245-2314.

Flying Yankee Enterprises, *(Flying Yankee; 0-9615574),* 13 Nutting Rd., Groton, MA 01450 (SAN 696-4311) Tel 617-448-5339; P.O. Box 595, Littleton, MA 01460 (SAN 696-5393).

Flynn, George, *(G Flynn),* 145 W. Twelfth St., New York, NY 10011 (SAN 211-3929) Tel 212-929-6257.

Flynn, James H., *(J H Flynn; 0-9613258),* 1704 Drewlaine Dr., Vienna, VA 22180 (SAN 296-6891) Tel 703-938-2489.

Flyway Publishing Co., Inc., *(Flyway Pub; 0-9616657),* 137 Veto St., Chenoa, IL 61726 (SAN 661-3500) Tel 815-945-7862.

Focal Point Pr., *(Focal Point Pr),* 321 City Island Ave., City Island, NY 10464 (SAN 663-1894) Tel 212-885-1403.

Focal Pr., Div. of Butterworth Publishers, *(Focal Pr; 0-240; 0-480),* 80 Montvale Ave., Stoneham, MA 02180 (SAN 220-0066) Tel 617-438-8464.

Focus Bks. *See* **Barnes & Noble Bks.-Imports**

Focus Pubns., *(Focus Pubns MO; 0-911921),* P.O. Box 15853, St. Louis, MO 63114 (SAN 264-0449) Tel 314-426-7011.

Focus Pubns. (DC), *(Focus Pubns; 0-930197),* 4520 East-West Hwy., No. 600, Bethesda, MD 20814 (SAN 670-8005) Tel 301-656-0091.

Focus Pub. Co., *(Focus Pub; 0-938442),* 29175 Oak Point Dr., Farmington Hills, MI 48018 (SAN 281-7160) Tel 313-553-0298; Dist. by: Distributor, The, 702 S. Michigan, South Bend, IN 46618 (SAN 169-2488) Tel 219-232-8500.

Focus Quality Games Corp., *(Focus Quality; 0-915236),* P.O. Box 114, Blythebourne Sta., Brooklyn, NY 11219 (SAN 207-1266).

Fog Pubns., *(Fog Pubns; 0-9616535),* 413 Pennsylvania W., Albuquerque, NM 87108 (SAN 659-4484) Tel 505-255-3096.

Foggy Bottom Pubns., *(Foggy Bottom Pubns; 0-934891),* Box 57150 West End Sta., Washington, DC 20037 (SAN 694-4450) Tel 202-337-4352.

Foghorn Pr., *(Foghorn Pr; 0-935701),* 2687 45th Ave., San Francisco, CA 94116 (SAN 696-4346) Tel 415-564-4918; Orders to: 2022 Taraval, No. 9523, San Francisco, CA 94116 (SAN 662-782X) Tel 415-564-4918; Dist. by: Bookpeople, 2929 Fifth St., Berkeley, CA 94710 (SAN 168-9517); Toll free: 800-227-1516; Dist. by: Publishers Group West, 5855 Beaudry St., Emeryville, CA 94608 (SAN 202-8522) Tel 415-658-3453.

†**Folcroft Library Editions,** *(Folcroft; 0-8414; 0-88305; 0-8482),* P.O. Box 182, Folcroft, PA 19032 (SAN 206-8362) Tel 215-583-4550; *CIP.*

Foldabook Publishing Co., *(Foldabook Pub; 0-89726),* 111 N. Fuller Ave., Los Angeles, CA 90036 (SAN 217-2399) Tel 213-933-3009.

Folder Editions, *(Folder Edns; 0-913152),* 103-26 68th Rd., Apt. A 47, Forest Hills, NY 11375 (SAN 206-6475) Tel 718-275-3839.

Folger Bks., *(Folger Bks; 0-918016),* Dist. by: Associated University Presses, 440 Forsgate Dr., Cranbury, NJ 08512 (SAN 281-2959) Tel 609-655-4770.

Folio Pubs., *(Folio Pubs; 0-9613702),* Box 1807, Sta. B, Vanderbilt Univ., Nashville, TN 37235 (SAN 677-167X) Tel 615-322-2828.

Folio Publishing Corp., Subs. of Hanson Publishing Group, *(Folio; 0-918110),* P.O. Box 4949, Stamford, CT 06907-0949 (SAN 210-2021); 6 River Bend, Stamford, CT 06907-0949 (SAN 658-0718) Tel 203-358-9900.

Folk Art Studios, *(Folk Art; 0-930310),* 608 E. First St., Tustin, CA 92680 (SAN 207-5601) Tel 714-731-3355.

Folk-Legacy Records, Inc., *(Folk-Legacy),* Sharon Mountain Rd., Sharon, CT 06069 (SAN 207-3390) Tel 203-364-5661.

Folk-Life Books, *(Folk-Life; 0-914917),* P.O. Box 128, Princeton, LA 71067 (SAN 289-1336) Tel 318-949-3915; Rte. 4, Box 299, Haughton, LA 71037 (SAN 289-1344).

Folk Pr., The, *(Folk Press; 0-938603),* Kapiolani Community College, Office of Community Services, 4303 Diamond Head Rd., Honolulu, HI 96816 (SAN 661-356X) Tel 808-735-8256.

Folkestone Pr., *(Folkestone; 0-910600),* P.O. Box 3142, St. Louis, MO 63130 (SAN 206-4227) Tel 314-725-2767.

Folkloric Studies T.G.B. Pr., *(Folkloric Studies; 0-9615745),* P.O. Box 7484, Menlo Park, CA 94026 (SAN 696-4354) Tel 415-854-3184.

Folklorica Pr., Inc., *(Folklorica Pr; 0-939544),* 70 Greenwich Ave., Suite 377, New York, NY 10011 (SAN 216-6720) Tel 212-929-1921.

Folks Pubns., *(Folks Pubns; 0-941628),* P.O. Box 1121, N. Highland, CA 95660 (SAN 239-2089) Tel 916-331-2106.

Folksay Pr., *(Folksay Pr; 0-916454),* 67131 Mills Rd., R.R. 3, St. Clairsville, OH 43950 (SAN 208-6514) Tel 614-695-3348; Dist. by: Bookpeople, 2929 Fifth St., Berkeley, CA 94710 (SAN 168-9517) Tel 415-549-3030.

Folkstone Press, The, *(Folkstone Pr),* P.O. Box 3142, St. Louis, MO 63130 (SAN 285-6778); Dist. by: Paperback Supply, 4121 Forest Park Blvd., St. Louis, MO 63108 (SAN 285-6786).

Fontana, John M., Pub., *(J M Fontana; 0-9600034),* 4 Walnut Place, Huntington, NY 11743 (SAN 206-4235) Tel 516-549-0892.

Fontana Paperbacks *See* **Watts, Franklin, Inc.**

Fontastic, *(Fontastic; 0-9603596),* 157 Judd St., Madison, WI 53714 (SAN 222-3368) Tel 608-249-8701.

Fonville, Naomi, *(N Fonville; 0-9616421),* 905 Hinton Ave., Lumberton, MS 39455 (SAN 696-6578) Tel 601-796-4338.

Food & Agriculture Organization *See* **Unipub**

Food & Energy Council, *(Food & Energy Coun),* 409 Vandiver W., Suite 202, Columbia, MO 65202 (SAN 225-1884) Tel 314-875-7155.

Food Equipment Repair & Maintenance, *(FERM),* 462 Hillside, Rochester, NY 14610 (SAN 682-2681) Tel 716-244-5869.

Food First *See* **Institute for Food & Development Policy**

Food for Thought Pr., *(Food Thought Pr; 0-9616876),* 1712 Markham Ave. NE, Tacoma, WA 98422 (SAN 661-3675) Tel 206-952-2142.

Food for Thought Pubns., *(Food for Thought),* P.O. Box 331, Amherst, MA 01004 (SAN 209-4363) Tel 413-253-5432.

Food Learning Ctr., *(Food Lrn Ctr; 0-931149),* 6518 Fremont Ave. N., Seattle, WA 98103 (SAN 679-4173) Tel 206-783-9679.

†**Food Marketing Institute,** *(Food Marketing; 0-939813),* 1750 K St., NW, Washington, DC 20006 (SAN 224-7429) Tel 202-452-8444; *CIP.*

Food Processors Institute, The, *(Food Processors; 0-937774),* 1401 New York Ave. NW, Suite 400, Washington, DC 20005 (SAN 215-3122) Tel 202-393-0890.

†**Food Research & Action Ctr.,** *(Food Res; 0-934220),* 1319 F St., NW, Washington, DC 20004 (SAN 215-9937) Tel 202-393-5060; *CIP.*

Food Trends, *(Food Trends; 0-9615572),* 7953 First Ave. S., St. Petersburg, FL 33707 (SAN 696-4389) Tel 813-345-1166.

Foodwork, Inc., *(Foodwork; 0-9615573),* 1658 Cowling Ave., Louisville, KY 40205 (SAN 696-4486) Tel 502-459-0249.

Fool Court Pr., The, *(Fool Court; 0-910305),* P.O. Box 25824, Charlotte, NC 28212 (SAN 240-8503) Tel 704-537-7375.

Football Hobbies, Pubs., *(Football Hobbies; 0-912122),* 4216 McConnell, El Paso, TX 79904 (SAN 204-1057) Tel 915-565-7354.

Foothills Pr., *(Foothills; 0-936061),* P.O. Box 5194, Orange, CA 92613-5194 (SAN 697-0702) Tel 714-491-1372.

Footprint Publishing Co., *(Footprint Pub; 0-9613548),* P.O. Box 1542, Lima Linda, CA 92354 (SAN 677-4873) Tel 714-883-4114.

Footsteps Press, *(Footsteps; 0-934796),* 1327 E. Bender, Hobbs, NM 88240 (SAN 213-666X).

Footwear Industries of America, *(Footwear Indus),* 3700 Market St., Philadelphia, PA 19104 (SAN 679-3665) Tel 215-222-1484; Orders to: P.O. Box 6930, Falls Church, VA 22046 (SAN 662-2577).

For Us Pubns., *(For Us Pubns; 0-915383),* P.O. Box 33147 Farragut Sta., Washington, DC 20033 (SAN 291-1604) Tel 202-462-1465.

Foran Pubn., *(Foran Pubn; 0-912941),* P.O. Box 356, Elsie, MI 48831 (SAN 283-2615); Dist. by: Publishers Marketing Group, 1104 Summit Ave., Plainview, TX 75074 (SAN 262-0995) Tel 214-423-0312.

Forbes, George F., *(G F Forbes; 0-910604),* 22085 Alamogordo Rd., Saugus, CA 91350 (SAN 281-7209) Tel 805-254-0734.

Forbes, Inc., *(Forbes Inc; 0-935705),* 60 Fifth Ave., New York, NY 10011 (SAN 696-4494) Tel 212-206-5548.

Force Pub. Co., *(Force Pub; 0-942362),* P.O. Box 4037, Salinas, CA 93912 (SAN 239-8559) Tel 408-663-0537.

Ford, Edward E., Publishing, *(EE Ford; 0-9616716),* 10209 N. 56th St., Scottsdale, AZ 85253 (SAN 659-4964) Tel 602-991-4860.

Ford, Sondra, & Assoc., *(S Ford & Assoc; 0-913043),* 478 Hamilton Ave., No.173, Campbell, CA 95008 (SAN 283-0809) Tel 408-446-1351.

Ford Associates, *(Ford Assocs; 0-88017),* 824 E. Seventh St., Auburn, IN 46706 (SAN 201-6508) Tel 219-925-3378.

Ford-Brown & Co., Pubs., *(Ford-Brown; 0-918644),* P.O. Box 600574, Houston, TX 77260 (SAN 209-6048) Tel 713-526-8699.

†**Ford Foundation,** *(Ford Found; 0-916584),* 320 E. 43rd St., New York, NY 10017 (SAN 222-9730) Tel 212-573-5000; Orders to: Box 559, Naugatuck, CT 06770 (SAN 685-3277) Tel 203-729-3100; *CIP.*

Fordham Equipment & Publishing Co., *(Fordham Pub; 0-913308),* 3308 Edson Ave., Bronx, NY 10469 (SAN 207-2254) Tel 212-379-7300.

Fordham Univ. Pr., *(Fordham; 0-8232),* University Box L, Bronx, NY 10458 (SAN 201-6516) Tel 212-579-2319.

Fords Travel Guides, *(Fords Travel; 0-916486),* Box 505, 22151 Clarendon St., Woodland Hills, CA 91365 (SAN 212-9418) Tel 818-347-1677.

Forecast Public Artspace Productions, *(Forecast PAP; 0-9613083),* 2955 Bloomington Ave. S., Minneapolis, MN 55407 (SAN 294-0248) Tel 612-721-4394.

Forecaster Publishing Co., Inc., *(Forecaster Pub; 0-911353),* 19623 Ventura Blvd., Tarzana, CA 91356 (SAN 218-7272) Tel 818-345-4421.

Names

Names

Foreign Language for Young Children, *(Fgn Lang Young Child; 0-937531),* 21 Lake Ave., Newton Centre, MA 02159 (SAN 658-8522) Tel 617-332-2427; Dist. by: Long Play, Inc., 2611 E. Franklin Ave., Minneapolis, MN 55406 (SAN 200-6375).

Foreign Policy Assn., *(Foreign Policy; 0-87124),* 205 Lexington Ave., New York, NY 10016 (SAN 212-9426) Tel 212-481-8450.

†Foreign Policy Research Institute, *(For Policy Res; 0-910191),* 3508 Market St., Suite 350, Philadelphia, PA 19104 (SAN 218-7280) Tel 215-382-0685; *CIP.*

Foreign Trade Association of Southern California, *(Foreign Trade),* World Trade Center, 350 S. Figueroa St., Suite 226, Los Angeles, CA 90017 (SAN 224-1293) Tel 213-627-0634.

Foreman, Gloria, Publishing Co., *(G Foreman; 0-915198),* P.O. Box 405, Oklahoma City, OK 73101 (SAN 203-4263) Tel 918-723-5925.

Foreman Co., Pubs., The, *(Foreman Co; 0-936009),* 302 S. Plumer, Tucson, AZ 85719 (SAN 696-7469) Tel 602-623-5012.

Foremost Pubs., Inc., *(Foremost Pubs; 0-940078),* W. Main Rd., Little Compton, RI 02837 (SAN 220-2204) Tel 401-635-2900.

†Forest Hill Pr., *(Forest Hill; 0-9605472),* 3974 Forest Hill Ave., Oakland, CA 94602 (SAN 215-9945); *CIP.*

Forest History Society, Inc., *(Forest Hist Soc; 0-89030),* 701 Vickers Ave., Durham, NC 27701 (SAN 201-6524) Tel 919-682-9319; Dist. by: Duke Univ. Pr., 6697 College Sta., Durham, NC 27708 (SAN 201-3436) Tel 919-684-2173.

Forest Industries Committee on Timber Valuation & Taxation, *(Forest Ind Comm; 0-914272),* 1250 Connecticut Ave., Suite 800, Washington, DC 20036 (SAN 204-1049) Tel 202-223-2314; Dist. by: International Specialized Book Services Inc., 5602 NE Hassalo St., Portland, OR 97213-3640 (SAN 169-7129) Tel 503-287-3093.

Forest of Peace Bks., Inc., *(Forest Peace; 0-939516),* Rte. One, Box 247, Easton, KS 66020 (SAN 216-6739) Tel 913-773-8255.

Forest Pr., Div. of Lake Placid Educ. Foundation, *(Forest Pr; 0-910608),* 85 Watervliet Ave., Albany, NY 12206 (SAN 210-8070) Tel 518-489-8549.

Forest Products Research Society, *(Forest Prod; 0-935018),* 2801 Marshall Ct., Madison, WI 53705 (SAN 211-4216) Tel 608-231-1361.

Forest Publishing, Div. of National Speakers Bureau, *(Forest Pub; 0-9605118),* 222 Wisconsin, Suite 201, Lake Forest, IL 60045 (SAN 215-7624) Tel 312-295-1122; Toll free: 800-323-9442.

Forest Resources Systems Institute, *(Forest Res Syst; 0-9615391),* 201 N. Pine St., Suite 24, Florence, AL 35630 (SAN 695-3433) Tel 205-767-0250.

Foreverly Music, *(Foreverly; 0-9614221),* P.O. Box 3933, Seattle, WA 98124 (SAN 686-7146) Tel 206-783-1798.

Foris Pubns., USA, *(Foris Pubns; 0-938198),* Orders to: Box C-50, Cinnaminson, NJ 08077 (SAN 220-1151) Tel 609-829-6830. *Imprints:* Bird-Sci Books (Bird-Sci Bks).

Forkuo, Peter C., World Enterprises, *(P C Forkuo World Ent; 0-941928),* P.O. Box 402, Worchester, MA 01613 (SAN 238-6186) Tel 617-753-1769.

Forman Publishing Inc., *(Forman Pub),* 11661 San Vicente Blvd., Suite 206, Los Angeles, CA 90049 (SAN 692-980X) Tel 213-820-8672.

Formatcen, *(Formatcen; 0-8259),* Cultural Education Ctr., Albany, NY 12230 (SAN 658-6279) Tel 518-474-5801. **Formerly known as Xerox Educational Pubns.** See **Field Publications**

Formhals, Hugh, *(Hugh Formhals),* 542 Mullen Rd., NW, Albuquerque, NM 87107 (SAN 681-8285) Tel 505-344-8313.

Formur International, *(Formur Intl; 0-89378),* 4200 Laclede Ave., St. Louis, MO 63108 (SAN 207-5768).

Forrers, G. T., & Co., Ltd. See **Haynes Pubns., Inc.**

Forsan Books, *(Forsan Bks; 0-9612298),* 865 Karen Dr., Chico, CA 95926 (SAN 289-2286) Tel 916-343-7361.

Forster, Reginald Bishop, Assocs., Inc., *(R B Forster; 0-931398),* 3287 Ramos Cir., Sacramento, CA 95827 (SAN 211-2388) Tel 916-362-3276; Toll free: 800-328-5091; 800-321-9789 in California.

Forsyth Gallery, *(Forsyth Gall; 0-9601560),* P.O. Box 525, Cooper Sta., New York, NY 10003 (SAN 211-6677) Tel 212-925-6697.

Forsyth Travel Library, Inc., *(Forsyth Lib Travel; 0-931212),* P.O. Box 105, Coarsegold, CA 93614 (SAN 210-6051) Tel 209-683-5883.

Forsythe & Cromwell, *(Forsythe & Cromwell; 0-940390),* P.O. Box 217, Andover, NJ 07821 (SAN 217-3646) Tel 201-625-1989.

Fort Frederica Assn., Inc., *(Fort Frederica; 0-930803),* Rte. 9, Box 286-C, St. Simons Island, GA 31522 (SAN 677-6299) Tel 912-638-3639.

Forte, Robert L., *(R Forte; 0-9609328),* P.O. Box 1051, Flint, MI 48501 (SAN 260-1885) Tel 313-789-0244; Dist. by: Safeguard Security Inc., P.O. Box 1051, Dept. SMP, Flint, MI 48501 (SAN 696-5091).

Forth Interest Group, *(Forth Interest; 0-935533),* 1330 S. Bascom Ave., No. D, San Jose, CA 95155 (SAN 696-4508) Tel 408-277-0667; P.O. Box 8231, San Jose, CA 95155 (SAN 696-544X).

Forth Publishing, Inc., *(Forth Pub; 0-9615575),* 301 E. Grand Ave., San Francisco, CA 94080 (SAN 696-4516) Tel 415-583-0786.

Fortress Pr., *(Fortress; 0-8006),* 2900 Queen Ln., Philadelphia, PA 19129 (SAN 220-0074); Toll free: 800-367-8737.

Fortuna Book Sales, *(Fortuna; 0-910610),* 8035 Fairlane Ave., Brooksville, FL 33512 (SAN 206-4278).

Fortunato Bks., *(Fortunato Bks; 0-9612494),* 7 Halko Dr., Cedar Knolls, NJ 07927 (SAN 213-0599) Tel 201-540-8852.

Fortune Software, Co., *(Fortune Soft; 0-939277),* 70 Sierra Rd., Boston, MA 02136 (SAN 662-8192) Tel 617-361-0900.

Forum for Death Education & Counseling, *(Forum Death Educ; 0-9607394),* Millikin Univ., Decatur, IL 62522 (SAN 237-952X).

Forum for Scriptural Christianity, Inc., *(Forum Script; 0-917851),* P.O. Box 165, Wilmore, KY 40390 (SAN 225-4638) Tel 606-858-4661; Dist. by: Cokesbury, 201 Eighth Ave. S., Nashville, TN 37203 (SAN 200-6863); Toll free: 800-672-1789.

Forum Pr., Inc., Subs. of Harlan Davidson Inc., *(Forum Pr IL; 0-88273),* 3110 N. Arlington Heights Rd., Arlington Heights, IL 60004 (SAN 201-2375) Tel 312-253-9720. *Imprints:* Marston Press (Marston); Piraeus Publishers (Piraeus).

Forum Quorum, Div. of Forum School Foundation, *(Forum Quorum; 0-9606778),* P.O. Box 43, Waldwick, NJ 07463 (SAN 219-7413) Tel 201-444-0499; Orders to: The Collection, P.O. Box 1220, Olathe, KS 66061-1220 (SAN 662-0116); Toll free: 800-821-5745.

Forward Movement Pubns., *(Forward Movement; 0-88028),* 412 Sycamore St., Cincinnati, OH 45202-4195 (SAN 208-3841) Tel 513-721-6659; Toll free: 800-543-1813.

Forward Press, The, *(Forward Pr; 0-941262),* 30 S. First Ave., Suite 301, Arcadia, CA 91006 (SAN 239-426X) Tel 818-445-7204.

Forza Pr., *(Forza Pr; 0-9614045),* 521 Entrada Way, Menlo Park, CA 94025 (SAN 684-8028) Tel 415-322-9108.

Foster, Fred B., Pubns., *(F B Foster Pubns; 0-9613762),* 5670 Stockton Blvd., No. 21, Sacramento, CA 95824 (SAN 682-269X) Tel 916-383-8579.

Foster, Steven, Financial Pubns., *(S Foster Fin; 0-930567),* 6520 Selma Ave., Suite 332, Los Angeles, CA 90028 (SAN 695-6017).

Foster Parents Plan International, Inc., *(Foster Parents; 0-918397),* P.O. Box 804, East Greenwich, RI 02818 (SAN 657-341X) Tel 401-826-2500.

Fotonovel Pubns., *(Fotonovel; 0-89752),* 8831 Sunset Blvd., PH-W, Los Angeles, CA 90069 (SAN 213-2486) Tel 213-659-8888; Dist. by: The Independent News Co., 75 Rockefeller Plaza, New York, NY 10019 (SAN 208-6158).

Foul Play Press See **Countryman Pr., Inc.**

Foundation Bks., *(Fosun Bks; 0-934988),* P.O. Box 29229, Lincoln, NE 68529 (SAN 201-6567) Tel 402-466-4988.

Foundation Bks., *(Foundation Bks; 0-932477),* 151 Tremont St., P. H., Boston, MA 02111 (SAN 687-1291) Tel 617-423-4958; Dist. by: Baker & Taylor Co., Eastern Div., 151 Treamont St., Boston, MA 02111 (SAN 169-4901); Dist. by: Baker & Taylor Co., Western Div., 380 Edison Way, Reno, NV 89564 (SAN 169-4464) Tel 702-786-6700; Dist. by: Baker & Taylor Co., Midwest Div., 501 Gladiola Ave., Momence, IL 60954 (SAN 169-2100); Dist. by: Baker & Taylor Co., Southeast Div., Mt. Olive Rd., Commerce, GA 30529 (SAN 169-1503).

Foundation Ctr., The, *(Foundation Ctr; 0-87954),* 79 Fifth Ave., New York, NY 10003 (SAN 207-5687) Tel 212-620-4230; Toll free: 800-424-9836.

Foundation for "A Course In Miracles", *(Foun Miracles; 0-933291),* P.O. Box 783, Crompond, NY 10517 (SAN 692-2902) Tel 914-528-0101.

Foundation for Ameliorology, *(Found Amelio; 0-935923),* 6609 Hwy. 93, Golden, CO 80403 (SAN 696-7450) Tel 303-278-3215.

Foundation for American Christian Education, *(Found Am Christ; 0-912498),* 2946 25th Ave., San Francisco, CA 94132 (SAN 205-5856) Tel 415-661-1775.

Foundation for American Communications, *(Foun Am Comm; 0-910755),* 3383 Barham Blvd., Los Angeles, CA 90068 (SAN 270-2746) Tel 213-851-7372.

Foundation for American Resource Management, *(Found Am Res Mgmt; 0-8223),* Dist. by: Duke Univ. Pr., 6697 College Sta., Durham, NC 27708 (SAN 201-3436) Tel 919-684-2173.

Foundation for Auditability Research & Education, Inc. See **Institute of Internal Auditors, Inc.**

Foundation for Christian Self-Government See **Mayflower Institute**

Foundation for Christian Services Inc., *(Foun Christ Serv),* P.O. Box 1555, Altamonte Springs, FL 32715 (SAN 264-0457) Tel 305-830-7424.

†Foundation for Classical Reprints, The, *(Found Class Reprints; 0-89901),* 607 McKnight St. NW, Albuquerque, NM 87102 (SAN 212-9051) Tel 505-843-7749; *CIP.*

Foundation for Economic Education, Inc., *(Foun Econ Ed; 0-910614),* 30 S. Broadway, Irvington-on-Hudson, NY 10533 (SAN 311-3515) Tel 914-591-7230.

Foundation for Historic Restoration in Pendleton Area, *(Foun Hist Rest; 0-912462),* P.O. Box 444, Pendleton, SC 29670 (SAN 206-4286) Tel 803-654-3283.

Foundation for Human Understanding, *(Foun Human GA; 0-936396),* Box 5712, Athens, GA 30604 (SAN 214-3720).

Foundation for Inner Peace, *(Found Inner Peace; 0-9606388),* P.O. Box 635, Tiburon, CA 94920 (SAN 212-422X) Tel 415-435-2255.

Foundation for Interior Design Education Research, *(Foun Int Design; 0-931007),* 322 Eighth Ave., Suite 1501, New York, NY 10001 (SAN 225-8145) Tel 212-929-8366.

Foundation for Life Action, *(Found Life Act; 1-55531),* 902 S. Burnside Ave., Los Angeles, CA 90036 (SAN 696-4532) Tel 213-933-5591; Toll free: 800-367-2246; Toll free: 800-732-5489 (In California); Orders to: P.O. Box 36456, Los Angeles, CA 90036 (SAN 662-3751).

Foundation for Motivation in Dentistry, *(Foun Mot Dent; 0-913740),* Schooleys Mountain, NJ 07840 (SAN 201-6583).

Foundation for National Progress, *(Foun Natl Prog; 0-938806),* Housing Information Ctr., 4020 Blue Bonnet Blvd., Houston, TX 77025 (SAN 215-9554).

Foundation for Philosophy of Creativity, Inc., *(Foun Phil Creat),* North Texas State Univ., Dept. of Philosophy, Denton, TX 76203 (SAN 283-183X); Orders to: University Pr. of America, 4720 Boston Way, Lanham, MD 20706 (SAN 200-2256) Tel 301-459-3366.

Foundation for Positive Thought Judaism, *(Found Pos Jud; 0-935683),* P.O. Box 5512, New York, NY 10185 (SAN 696-4281) Tel 212-686-2904.

Foundation for the Advancement of Man, *(Foun Adv Man; 0-939790),* P.O. Box 2876, Escondido, CA 92025 (SAN 218-4761).

Foundation for the Community of Artists, *(Foun Commun Artists; 0-933032),* 280 Broadway, Suite 412, New York, NY 10017 (SAN 225-2678) Tel 212-227-3770.

Foundation for the Peoples of the South Pacific, *(Found PSP),* 2-12 W. Park Ave., Long Beach, NY 11561 (SAN 237-1626) Tel 516-432-3563; P.O. Box 727, Long Beach, NY 11561 (SAN 658-0726) Tel 516-432-3563.

Foundation Hse. Pubns., Inc., Div. of Emissary Foundation International, Inc., *(Foundation Hse; 0-935427),* 4817 N. Country Rd. 29, Loveland, CO 80537 (SAN 696-5512) Tel 303-669-2166.

Foundation of Human Understanding, The, *(Foun Human Under; 0-933900),* P.O. Box 811, 111 NE Evelyn St., Grants Pass, OR 97526-9997 (SAN 213-9545) Tel 503-479-0549; 8780 Venice Blvd., P.O. Box 34036, Los Angeles, CA 90034 (SAN 680-0327) Tel 213-559-3711.

†**Foundation Pr., Inc.,** *(Foundation Pr; 0-88277),* 170 Old Country Road, Mineola, NY 11501 (SAN 281-7225) Tel 516-248-5580; *CIP.*

Foundation Pubns., Inc., *(Foun Pubns; 0-910618),* P.O. Box 6439, Anaheim, CA 92806 (SAN 206-4294) Tel 714-630-6450.

Foundation Publishing, *(Found Pub; 0-932032),* P.O. Box 3243, Burlington, VT 05401 (SAN 211-6189) Tel 802-862-7386.

Fountain Hse. East, *(Fountain Hse East; 0-914736),* Box 99298, Jeffersontown, KY 40299 (SAN 206-6262) Tel 502-267-5414.

Fountain Press, Inc., *(Fountain Pr; 0-89350),* Dist. by: Inspirational Marketing Inc., Box 301, Indianola, IA 50125 (SAN 208-6557).

Fountain Pubns., *(Fountain Publications Oregon; 0-911376),* 3728 NW Thurman St., Portland, OR 97210 (SAN 205-5880) Tel 503-223-2232.

Fountain Valley Pubblishing Co., *(Fountain Valley Pub; 0-933039),* 16533 Sequoia St., Fountain Valley, CA 92708 (SAN 689-7509) Tel 714-839-1351.

Fountainhead Pubns., Inc., *(Fountainhead; 0-935497),* 155 E. 55th St., Suite 8C, New York, NY 10022 (SAN 206-4324) Tel 212-421-1556.

Four Circles Pr., *(Four Circles Pr; 0-938739),* 556-H102 Main St., N., Roosevelt Island, New York, NY 10044 (SAN 661-8111) Tel 212-759-5174.

Four D Publishing Co., *(Four D Pub Co; 0-9610006),* Box 381, Princeton, IL 61356 (SAN 270-3092).

Four Mile Historic Park, Inc., *(Four Mile Hist Pk; 0-9617039),* 715 S. Forest St., Denver, CO 80222 (SAN 662-8257) Tel 303-399-1859.

Four Peaks Enterprises, Inc., *(Four Peaks Ent; 0-9616872),* P.O. Box 17569, Fountain Hills, AZ 85268 (SAN 661-1524); 16705 E. Fairfax Dr., Fountain Hills, AZ 85268 (SAN 661-1532) Tel 602-837-9693.

Four Quarters Publishing Co., *(Four Quarters; 0-931500),* 1200 Boston Post Rd., Guilford, CT 06437 (SAN 213-8123). *Imprints:* Dunk Rock Books (Dunk Rock).

Four Seasons Book Pubs., *(Four Seas Bk; 0-9605400),* 220 Piney Point Landing, P.O. Box 576, Grasonville, MD 21638 (SAN 215-8639) Tel 301-827-7350.

†**Four Seasons Foundation,** *(Four Seasons Foun; 0-87704),* P.O. Box 31190, San Francisco, CA 94131 (SAN 201-6591) Tel 415-824-5774; Dist. by: Subterranean Co., 1327 W. Second, P.O. Box 10233, Eugene, OR 97440 (SAN 169-7102) Tel 503-343-6324; *CIP.*

Four Seasons Pubns., *(Four S Pubns; 0-9615987),* P.O. Box 125, Newark, DE 19715-0125 (SAN 698-1488) Tel 302-834-7522.

Four Six Zero Five Brandon Lane Press, *(Brandon-Lane-Pr),* 4605 Brandon Ln., Beltsville, MD 20705 (SAN 692-2066) Tel 301-937-1446.

Four Sons Pr., *(Four Sons; 0-918503),* 1545 E. Roberts Ave., Fresno, CA 93710 (SAN 657-3428) Tel 209-439-1677.

Four Trees Pubns., *(Four Trees Pubns; 0-936329),* P.O. Box 31220, San Francisco, CA 94131 (SAN 697-337X) Tel 415-641-4035; 1484 Dolores St., San Francisco, CA 94110 (SAN 697-3388); Dist. by: Bookpeople, 2929 Fifth St., Berkeley, CA 94710 (SAN 168-9517) Tel 415-549-3030; Toll free: 800-227-1516.

Four Ways West Pubns., *(Four Ways West; 0-9616874),* P.O. Box 1734, La Mirada, CA 90637-1734 (SAN 661-3195); 14618 Valley View, La Mirada, CA 90638 (SAN 661-3209) Tel 714-521-4259.

Four Zoas Night House, Ltd., *(Four Zoas Night Ltd; 0-939622),* P.O. Box 111, Ashuelot Village, NH 03441 (SAN 216-6267) Tel 603-239-6830.

Fournies, F., & Associates, Inc., *(F Fournies; 0-917472),* 129 Edgewood Dr., Bridgewater, NJ 08807 (SAN 205-5708) Tel 201-526-2442.

Foursquare Press, *(Foursquare Pr; 0-930616),* 648 Ransom Rd., Lancaster, NY 14086 (SAN 211-8998) Tel 716-681-2586.

†**Fourth North American Fur Trade Conference,** *(Fourth NA Am Fur; 0-9613451),* 240 Summit Ave., St. Paul, MN 55102 (SAN 657-2537) Tel 612-296-9393; *CIP.*

Fourth World, *(Fourth World; 0-9613920),* 110 West Geneva Drive, Tempe, AZ 85282 (SAN 669-6767) Tel 602-966-0039.

Fowler & Wells, Publisher, *(Fowler & Wells; 0-937776),* 2175 Hudson Terrace, No. 6P, Fort Lee, NJ 07024 (SAN 277-6804) Tel 201-592-8717; Dist. by: Inland Book Co., P.O. Box 261, Hemingway Ave., East Haven, CT 06512 (SAN 200-4151) Tel 203-467-4257.

Fowler Music Enterprises, *(Fowler Music; 0-943894),* 808 S. Alkire St., Lakewood, CO 80228 (SAN 241-113X) Tel 303-986-7309.

Fox, Randy, *(Randy Fox; 0-9616578),* 7001 Summerfield Dr., Indianapolis, IN 46224 (SAN 661-2288) Tel 317-298-7060.

Fox, Sanford, *(S Fox; 0-9603854),* 41-41 Christine Court, Fairlawn, NJ 07410 (SAN 214-0152).

Fox, Wesley, *(W Fox; 0-9604122),* P.O. Box 26976, Lakewood, CO 80226-0976 (SAN 214-3739) Tel 303-936-9016.

Fox Assocs./Fox Theatre, *(Fox Assocs; 0-9615933),* 527 N. Brand, St. Louis, MO 63103 (SAN 697-0745) Tel 314-534-1678; Dist. by: Paperback Supply, 4121 Forest Park Blvd., St. Louis, MO 63108 (SAN 169-4324).

†**Fox Hills Pr., The,** *(Fox Hills Pr; 0-914932),* 2676 Cunningham Hole Rd., Annapolis, MD 21401 (SAN 211-139X) Tel 301-266-6626; *CIP.*

Fox Hollow Fibres, *(Fox Hollow; 0-9608074),* 560 Milford Rd., Earlysville, VA 22936 (SAN 240-0928) Tel 804-973-9621.

Fox Reading Research Co., *(Fox Reading Res; 0-938131),* P.O. Box 1059, Coeur D'Alene, ID 83814 (SAN 213-0602) Tel 208-772-4524.

Fox River Publishing Co., *(Fox River; 0-939398),* Box 54, Princeton, WI 54968 (SAN 216-3802).

Fox Thoughts Pubns., *(Fox Thoughts; 0-912403),* 2640 East Twelfth Ave., Department 571, Denver, CO 80206 (SAN 265-4040) Tel 303-736-8238; Dist. by: DeVorss & Co., P.O. Box 550, 1046 Princeton Dr., Marina del Rey, CA 90294 (SAN 168-9886) Tel 203-870-7478.

Foxhall Press, *(Foxhall Pr; 0-9611128),* P.O. Box 9629, Washington, DC 20016 (SAN 282-9061) Tel 202-362-5870.

Foxhound Enterprises, *(Foxhound Ent; 0-940502),* 25 Tazewell St., Fredericksburg, VA 22405 (SAN 223-1034) Tel 703-371-7498; Dist. by: M. E. Repass, Box 68, Louisa, KY 41230 (SAN 223-1042).

Foxmoor Pr., *(Foxmoor; 0-938604),* Rte. 6, P.O. Box 28, Tahlequah, OK 74464 (SAN 215-8647).

Foxy Owl Pubns., *(Foxy Owl Pubns; 0-9613246),* 515 Dalton St., Emmaus, PA 18049 (SAN 295-2866) Tel 215-965-3405.

Fragments West/Valentine Pr., The, *(Fragments West; 0-9611890),* 3908 E. Fourth St., Long Beach, CA 90814 (SAN 286-1933) Tel 213-438-3424.

Fragonard Pr., *(Fragonard Pr; 0-930807),* Aspen Hill, P.O. Box 6365, Silver Spring, MD 20906 (SAN 677-6280) Tel 302-651-5005.

Framo Publishing, *(Framo Pub; 0-936398),* 561 W. Diversey Pkwy., Chicago, IL 60614 (SAN 214-0160) Tel 312-477-1485.

Franas Press, *(Franas Pr; 0-9600482),* 1116 Ocean Ave., Mantoloking, NJ 08738 (SAN 205-5899).

Francis, Reynold S., *(R S Francis; 0-9616349),* P.O. Box 8211, Minneapolis, MN 55408 (SAN 659-3925); 3319 Pleasant Ave., S., Minneapolis, MN 55408 (SAN 659-3933).

Franciscagraphics, *(Franciscagraphics; 0-933925),* P.O. Box 28322, Atlanta, GA 30358 (SAN 693-0298) Tel 404-252-1962.

†**Franciscan Herald Pr.,** *(Franciscan Herald; 0-8199),* 1434 W. 51st St., Chicago, IL 60609 (SAN 201-6621) Tel 312-254-4462; *CIP.*

Franciscan Institute Pubns., *(Franciscan Inst),* Drawer F, St. Bonaventure Univ., St. Bonaventure, NY 14778 (SAN 201-8543) Tel 716-375-2105.

Franje, *(Franje CA; 0-9601078),* 1175 Barbara Dr., Vista, CA 92084 (SAN 205-5902) Tel 619-726-7129.

Frank, Arlen W., *(Arlen Frank; 0-9614531),* 3812 Croydon St., Slidell, LA 70458 (SAN 692-2589) Tel 504-643-7513.

Frank, Leonard Roy, *(L R Frank; 0-9601376),* 2300 Webster St., San Francisco, CA 94115 (SAN 212-0917) Tel 415-922-3029.

Frank Pubns., *(Frank Pubns; 0-942952),* 60 E. 42nd St., Suite 757, New York, NY 10017 (SAN 240-4737) Tel 212-687-3383.

†**Franklin, Burt, Pubs.,** Affil. of Lenox Hill Publishing & Distributing Corp., *(B Franklin; 0-89102),* 235 E. 44th St., New York, NY 10017 (SAN 282-597X) Tel 212-687-5250; Toll free: 800-223-0766; *CIP.*

Franklin, Charles, Pr., The, *(Franklin Pr WA; 0-932091; 0-9603516),* 7821 175th St., SW, Edmonds, WA 98020 (SAN 692-9001) Tel 206-774-6979; Toll free: 800-99B-00KS.

Franklin, Donald, *(Donald Franklin; 0-914714),* 7852 Ducor Ave., Canoga Park, CA 91304 (SAN 201-2758) Tel 818-883-4247.

Franklin, J., Inc. Pub., *(J Franklin; 0-9616736),* P.O. Box 14057, Tulsa, OK 74159 (SAN 661-4302); 4123 S. Victor Ct., Tulsa, OK 74105 (SAN 661-4310) Tel 918-747-9858.

Franklin, Rasilon, *(R Franklin; 0-9616052),* 1805 N. Scottsdale, Tempe, AZ 85282 (SAN 698-0694) Tel 602-829-2403.

Franklin & Marshall College, *(Franklin & Marshall; 0-910626),* P.O. Box 3003, Lancaster, PA 17604-3003 (SAN 226-3408) Tel 717-291-3981.

Franklin, Beedle & Assocs., *(Franklin Beedle),* 4521 Campus Dr., Suite 327, Irvine, CA 92715 (SAN 661-3179) Tel 714-552-4155.

Franklin D. Roosevelt Philatelic Society, *(FDR Philatelic Soc; 0-9612272),* 154 Laguna Ct., St. Augustine Shores, FL 32086 (SAN 225-591X) Tel 904-797-3513.

Franklin-Hill Pr., *(Franklin-Hill Pr; 0-937447),* 6250 El Cajon Blvd., No. 805, San Diego, CA 92115 (SAN 658-8514) Tel 619-698-5333.

†**Franklin Institute Pr., The,** Div. of Lawrence Erlbaum Assocs., Inc., *(Franklin Inst Pr; 0-89168),* 365 Broadway, Hillsdale, NJ 07642 (SAN 209-5599) Tel 201-666-4110; *CIP.*

Franklin Pubns., *(Franklin Bryn Mawr; 0-916503),* Box 1338, Bryn Mawr, PA 19010 (SAN 295-4141) Tel 215-525-1225.

Franks, Ray, Publishing Ranch, *(R Franks Ranch; 0-943976),* P.O. Box 7068, Amarillo, TX 79114 (SAN 218-7329) Tel 806-355-6417.

Frantasy Workshop, *(Frantasy Wkshp; 0-942696),* 1400 W. Cross St., Lakewood, NJ 08701 (SAN 289-193X) Tel 201-363-3988.

Franzak & Foster Co., *(Franzak & Foster; 0-942588),* 4012 Bridge Ave., Cleveland, OH 44113 (SAN 240-0731) Tel 216-961-4134.

Frary Family Assn., *(Frary Family; 0-9616030),* Harmony Rd., No. 162, Northwood, NH 03261 (SAN 698-1461) Tel 603-942-8520.

Fraser, Inc., *(Fraser Inc; 0-930045),* P.O. Box 1507, Madison, CT 06443 (SAN 295-0464); 38 Academy St., Madison, CT 06443 (SAN 658-2540) Tel 203-245-3279; Dist. by: Williamson Publishing Co., P.O. Box 185, Charlotte, VT 05445 (SAN 285-3884) Tel 802-425-2102.

Fraser Products Co., *(Fraser Prods Co; 0-933379)*, 10730 Wheatland Ave., Sunland, CA 91040 (SAN 691-6775) Tel 818-767-3334; Dist. by: Baker & Taylor Co., Eastern Div., 50 Kirby Ave., Somerville, NJ 08876 (SAN 169-4901) Tel 201-526-8000.

Fraser Publishing Co., Div. of Fraser Management Assocs., Inc., *(Fraser Pub Co; 0-87034)*, 309 S. Willard St., Burlington, VT 05401 (SAN 213-9529) Tel 802-658-0322; Orders to: Box 494, Burlington, VT 05402 (SAN 213-9537).

Fraser Publishing Co. *See* Fraser, Inc.

Fraternity of Alpha Zeta, The, *(Alpha Zeta)*, P.O. Box 595, Lafayette, IN 47902 (SAN 224-1315) Tel 317-742-2538.

Fraulo, Anne, *(A Fraulo; 0-9616577)*, 488 Main St., East Haven, CT 06512 (SAN 661-2296) Tel 203-469-0220.

Fraunces Tavern Museum, *(Fraunces Tavern; 0-9616415)*, 54 Pearl St., New York, NY 10004 (SAN 669-6783) Tel 212-425-1778.

Frazier-Long Inc., *(Frazier-Long; 0-9614192)*, 288 Craig Dr., Lawrenceville, GA 30245 (SAN 686-6549) Tel 404-962-6345.

Fred Pr., *(Fred Pr; 0-937393)*, 59 Suydam St., New Brunswick, NJ 08901 (SAN 658-8573) Tel 201-878-7976; Orders to: 1178 Castleton Rd., Cleveland Heights, OH 44121 (SAN 662-4189).

Fredericks Publishing Co., *(Fredericks Pub; 0-939690)*, P.O. Box 97, Mertztown, PA 19539 (SAN 216-7328) Tel 215-682-7784.

Fredonia, *(Fredonia; 0-940204)*, 29169 W. Heathercliff, Suite 9490, Malibu, CA 90265 (SAN 217-104X).

Fred's Robot Factory Pr., *(Fred Robot Factory; 0-936733)*, P.O. Box 474, San Manuel, AZ 85631 (SAN 699-9611) Tel 602-896-2721; Redington Rd., San Manuel, AZ 85631 (SAN 699-962X).

Free-Bass Pr., *(Free-Bass; 0-8256)*, Box 563, Eugene, OR 97440 (SAN 217-1058) Tel 503-345-1795; Dist. by: Music Sales Corp., 5 Bellvale Rd., P.O. Box 572, Chester, NY 10918 (SAN 209-0988) Tel 914-469-2271.

Free Beginning Press, *(Free Begin Pr; 0-930707)*, 41 Beryl St, Roslindale, MA 02131 (SAN 677-2145) Tel 617-323-2561.

Free Church Pubns., Div. of Evangelical Free Church of America, *(Free Church Pubns; 0-911802)*, 1515 E. 66th St., Minneapolis, MN 55423 (SAN 206-4146) Tel 612-866-3343.

Free Congress Research & Education Foundation, *(Free Congr Res; 0-942522)*, 721 Second St., NE, Washington, DC 20002 (SAN 238-1605) Tel 202-546-3004.

Free Energy Pr., *(Free Ener Pr; 0-931009)*, 313A Noyac Rd., Sag Harbor, NY 11963 (SAN 678-9668) Tel 516-725-1211.

Free Enterprise Institute, Subs. of Amway Corp., *(Free Ent Inst; 0-940434)*, 7575 E. Fulton Rd., Ada, MI 49355 (SAN 217-1767) Tel 616-676-7946.

Free Enterprise Pr., The, *(Free Enter Pr; 0-939571)*, 12500 NE Tenth Pl., Bellevue, WA 98005 (SAN 663-5342) Tel 206-455-5038.

Free Enterprises Services, Inc., *(Free Ent System; 0-943636)*, 2120 Beneva Rd., Sarasota, FL 33582 (SAN 238-2849) Tel 813-924-4211.

Free Library of Philadelphia, *(Phila Free Lib; 0-911132)*, Rare Book Dept., Logan Square, Philadelphia, PA 19103 (SAN 205-3837) Tel 215-686-5416.

Free Life Editions *See* Universe Bks., Inc.

Free Market Books, *(Free Market; 0-930902)*, P.O. Box 186, Irvington, NY 10533 (SAN 209-1143) Tel 914-591-7769.

Free Market Institute, *(Free Market Ins; 0-935429)*, 9707 S. Gessner, No. 114, Houston, TX 77071 (SAN 696-4303) Tel 713-995-8228.

†Free Pr., Div. of Macmillan Publishing Co., Inc., *(Free Pr; 0-02)*, 866 Third Ave., New York, NY 10022 (SAN 201-6656) Tel 212-702-2004; Toll free: 800-257-5755; Dist. by: Macmillan Co., Front & Brown Sts., Riverside, NJ 08370 (SAN 202-5582) Tel 609-461-6500; *CIP.*

†Free Spirit Publishing Co., *(Free Spirit Pub Co; 0-915793)*, 123 N. Third St., Suite 716, Minneapolis, MN 55401 (SAN 293-9584) Tel 612-338-2068; *CIP.*

Free State Constitutionists Media Publishing Co., *(Free State Constitution; 0-934005)*, 640 Aldershot Rd., Baltimore, MD 21229 (SAN 692-7726) Tel 301-747-5025.

Freed, Roy N., *(Roy Freed; 0-9601030)*, 50 Winchester St. No. 103, Brookline, MA 02146 (SAN 201-8594) Tel 617-277-6211.

Freedeeds Books *See* Garber Communications, Inc.

Freedman, Jacob, Liturgy Research Foundation, *(J Freedman Liturgy)*, P.O. Box 317, Forest Park Sta., Springfield, MA 01108 (SAN 207-7582).

Freedman Gallery of Art, *(Freedman; 0-941972)*, Albright College, Reading, PA 19603 (SAN 278-856X) Tel 215-921-2381.

†Freedom Bks., *(Freedom Bks; 0-930374)*, P.O. Box 5303, Hamden, CT 06518 (SAN 210-9255) Tel 203-281-6791; *CIP.*

Freedom from Religion Foundation, *(Freedom Rel Found)*, P.O. Box 750, Madison, WI 53701 (SAN 276-9484) Tel 608-256-8900.

Freedom Hse., *(Freedom Hse; 0-932088)*, 48 E. 21st St., New York, NY 10010 (SAN 211-7339) Tel 212-473-9691.

Freedom Pr., *(Freedom Pr; 0-941630)*, P.O. Box 5503, Scottsdale, AZ 85261 (SAN 239-2100) Tel 607-991-5414.

Freedom Pr. International, Ltd., *(Freedom Intl; 0-917639)*, 1601 Northwest Expwy., Oklahoma City, OK 73118 (SAN 656-920X).

Freedom Press, Ltd., *(Freedom Ltd; 0-915031)*, 1601 Northwest Expressway, Oklahoma City, OK 73118 (SAN 289-9256).

Freedom, Pubns., Div. of Sedona Institute, *(Freedom Pubns; 0-915721)*, 2408 Arizona Biltmore Circle, No. 115, Phoenix, AZ 85016 (SAN 293-9614) Tel 602-956-8766.

Freedom Pubs., *(Freedom Pubs; 0-935787)*, 3960 S. Denker, Los Angeles, CA 90062 (SAN 696-432X) Tel 213-666-8093.

Freedom Tree, Inc., *(Freedom Tree; 0-938969)*, P.O. Box 2406, Cheyenne, WY 82003 (SAN 661-7131); 2232 Del Range Blvd., Suite 205, Cheyenne, WY 82003 (SAN 661-714X) Tel 307-635-0369.

Freedom University/Freedom Seminary Press, *(Freedom Univ-FSP)*, 5927 Windhover Dr., Orlando, FL 32819 (SAN 209-505X) Tel 305-351-0898.

Freedoms Foundation At Valley Forge, Los Angeles County Chapter, *(Freedoms Found Vall; 0-9612726)*, 17040 Rancho St., Encino, CA 91316 (SAN 289-9264) Tel 818-784-6626.

Freelance Communications, *(Freelance Comm; 0-935309)*, P.O. Box 1895, Upland, CA 91785 (SAN 695-7773) Tel 714-982-3199.

Freelance Pubns. Ltd, *(Freelance Pubns; 0-9602050)*, P.O. Box 1385, Meredith, NH 03253 (SAN 213-0734) Tel 603-279-8661.

Freeland Pr., *(Freeland Pr; 0-9615893)*, P.O. Box 26044, Santa Ana, CA 92799 (SAN 697-0850); 2727 S. Croddy Way, No. J, Santa Ana, CA 92704 Tel 714-979-5737.

Freeland Pubns., *(Freeland Pubns; 0-936868)*, P.O. Box 18941, Philadelphia, PA 19119 (SAN 215-3130).

Freelandia Institute, *(Freelandia; 0-914674)*, Star Rte., Cassville, MO 65625 (SAN 205-6216).

Freeman, H. P., Writer-Pub., *(H P Freeman CA; 0-9609920)*, 1125 Monroe St., Red Bluff, CA 96080 (SAN 270-3408) Tel 916-527-1679; P.O. Box 93, Red Bluff, CA 96080 (SAN 658-0742).

†Freeman, W. H., & Co., Subs. of Scientific American, Inc., *(W H Freeman; 0-7167)*, 41 Madison Ave., 37th Flr., New York, NY 10010 (SAN 206-6864) Tel 212-532-7660; Orders to: 4419 W. 1980, S, Salt Lake City, UT 84104 (SAN 290-6872) Tel 801-973-4660; *CIP.*

Freeman, Cooper & Co., *(Freeman Cooper; 0-87735)*, 1736 Stockton St., San Francisco, CA 94133 (SAN 201-6672) Tel 415-362-6171.

Freeman Farms Pr., *(Freeman Farms; 0-9617300)*, 4306 Freeman Rd., Orchard Park, NY 14127 (SAN 663-463X).

Freeperson, Div. of TH-EC, Inc., *(Freeperson; 0-918236)*, 455 Ridge Rd., Novato, CA 94947 (SAN 209-438X) Tel 415-897-0336.

Freeport Historical Society, *(Freeport Hist; 0-9613259)*, 45 Main St., Freeport, ME 04032 (SAN 296-5844); P.O. Box 358, Freeport, ME 04032 (SAN 699-5772).

†Freer Gallery of Art, Smithsonian Institution, *(Freer; 0-934686)*, 12th & Jefferson Dr., SW, Washington, DC 20560 (SAN 201-856X) Tel 202-357-2102; *CIP.*

Freestone Publishing Co., *(Freestone Pub Co; 0-913512)*, Box 398, Monroe, UT 84754 (SAN 206-4154) Tel 801-527-3738; Dist. by: Bookpeople, 2929 Fifth St., Berkeley, CA 94710 (SAN 168-9517) Tel 415-549-3030.

Freidus, Robert, Gallery, *(Freidus Gallery)*, 158 Lafayette St., New York, NY 10013 (SAN 223-2065) Tel 212-925-0113.

Freline, Inc., *(Freline; 0-913853)*, P.O. Box 889, 32 East Ave., Hagerstown, MD 21740 (SAN 286-7508) Tel 301-797-9689.

Fremar Press, The, *(Fremar Pr; 0-9612348)*, 160 Ravenswood Court, Vacaville, CA 95688 (SAN 290-7011) Tel 707-448-2870.

French, Samuel, Inc., *(French; 0-573)*, 45 W. 25th St., New York, NY 10010 (SAN 206-4170) Tel 212-206-8990; 7625 Sunset Blvd., Hollywood, CA 90046 (SAN 200-6855) Tel 213-876-0570.

French & European Pubns., Inc., *(French & Eur; 0-8288)*, 115 Fifth Ave., New York, NY 10003 (SAN 206-8109) Tel 212-673-7400.

French Bks. in Print, *(French Bks Print)*, P.O. Box 1445, Long Island City, NY 11101 (SAN 659-2007).

French Forum Pubns., Inc., *(French Forum; 0-917058)*, P.O. Box 5108, Lexington, KY 40505 (SAN 208-4996) Tel 606-299-9530.

French Institute-Alliance Francaise, *(French Inst; 0-933444)*, 22 E. 60th St., New York, NY 10022-1077 (SAN 204-207X) Tel 212-355-6100.

†Freneau, Philip, Press, *(Freneau; 0-912480)*, 18 Valentine St., Box 116, Monmouth Beach, NJ 07750 (SAN 201-6680) Tel 201-222-6458; *CIP.*

Fresh Press, *(Fresh Pr; 0-9601398)*, 3712 Ortega Ct., Palo Alto, CA 94303 (SAN 210-6000) Tel 415-493-3596.

FreshCut Pr., *(FreshCut; 0-9605550)*, 133 Clara Ave., Ukiah, CA 95482 (SAN 215-8655) Tel 707-462-6482; 410 Clara Ave., Ukiah, CA 95482 (SAN 215-8663).

Freshet Press, Inc., *(Freshet Pr; 0-88395)*, 90 Hamilton Rd., Rockville Centre, NY 11570 (SAN 205-5929) Tel 516-766-3011.

Freshman, Samuel K., *(S K Freshman; 0-9600708)*, 700 S. Flower St., Suite 2600, Los Angeles, CA 90017 (SAN 206-5266) Tel 213-629-1100.

Freshwater Pr., Inc., *(Freshwater; 0-912514)*, 1701 E. 12th St., Suite 3KW, Cleveland, OH 44114-3201 (SAN 201-6699) Tel 216-241-0373.

Freudy, Joan D., *(J D Freudy; 0-9616440)*, 24 Oakfield Ave., Freeport, NY 11520 (SAN 658-8468) Tel 516-623-6695.

†Freundlich Bks., Div. of Lawrence Freundlich Pubns., Inc., *(Freundlich; 0-88191)*, 212 Fifth Ave., Suite 1305, New York, NY 10010 (SAN 264-7419) Tel 212-532-9666; Dist. by: Kampmann & Co., Inc., 9 E. 40th St., New York, NY 10016 (SAN 202-5191) Tel 212-685-2928; Toll free: 800-526-7626; *CIP.*

Frick Art Museum, *(Frick Art Mus)*, 7227 Reynolds St., Pittsburgh, PA 15208 (SAN 278-8624) Tel 412-371-7766.

Fried, Al, Assocs., *(A Fried Assocs; 0-87445)*, 271 North Ave., New Rochelle, NY 10801 (SAN 201-8659).

Friede, Eleanor *See* Delacorte Pr.

Friede Pubns., *(Friede Pubns; 0-9608588)*, 2339 Venezia Dr., Davison, MI 48423 (SAN 238-2865) Tel 313-658-1955.

†Friedman, Ira J., Div. of Associated Faculty Pr., Inc., *(Friedman; 0-87198)*, Rte. 100, Millwood, NY 10546 (SAN 217-4979) Tel 914-762-2200; *CIP.*

Friedrich, Paul, *(P Friedrich)*, Benjamin & Martha Waite Press, 1126 E. 59th St., Chicago, IL 60637 (SAN 210-8992) Tel 312-753-3705.

Friendly City Publishing Co., *(Friendly City; 0-938212)*, 318 Cedar Springs Road, Athens, TN 37303 (SAN 215-6458) Tel 615-745-2960.

†Friendly Press, *(Friendly Oregon; 0-938070)*, 2744 Friendly St., Eugene, OR 97405 (SAN 215-8671); *CIP.*

†**Friendly Pr., Inc.,** *(Friendly Pr NY; 0-914919)*, 401 Park Ave. S, New York, NY 10016 (SAN 207-9496) Tel 212-684-4255; *CIP.*

Friendly Press (VA), The, *(Friendly VA; 0-916127)*, P.O. Box 1215, McLean, VA 22101 (SAN 294-930X) Tel 703-790-0428.

Friends for Long Island's Heritage, *(Friends Long Island; 0-911357)*, 1864 Muttontown Rd., Syosset, NY 11791 (SAN 270-3564) Tel 516-364-1050; Dist. by: Publishing Center for Cultural Resources, 625 Broadway, New York, NY 10012 (SAN 274-9025) Tel 212-260-2010.

Friends General Conference, *(Friends Genl Conf)*, 1520-B Race St., Philadelphia, PA 19102 (SAN 225-4484).

Friends Historical Assn., *(Friends Hist Assn; 0-9609122)*, Haverford College Library, Quaker Collection, Haverford, PA 19041 (SAN 225-4492) Tel 215-896-1161.

Friends of Arcadia Public Library, *(Friends Arcadia)*, 20 W. Duarte Rd., Arcadia, CA 91006 (SAN 216-3829) Tel 818-446-0351.

Friends of City Park, *(Friends City Park; 0-9610062)*, City Park Administration Bldg., New Orleans, LA 70119 (SAN 262-8643) Tel 504-561-8989.

Friends of Florida State Univ. Library, *(Friends Fla St)*, Florida State Univ., Tallahassee, FL 32306 (SAN 205-5937).

Friends of Freedom Pubs., *(Friend Freedom; 0-915854)*, P.O. Box 6124, Waco, TX 76706 (SAN 207-3757) Tel 817-662-4643.

Friends of Israel Gospel Ministry, Inc., The, *(Frnds Israel; 0-915540)*, 475 White Horse Pike, P.O. Box 908, Bellmawr, NJ 08031 (SAN 225-445X) Tel 609-853-5590.

Friends of Israel-Spearhead Press, The, *(Friends Israel-Spearhead Pr)*, P.O. Box 123, West Collingswood, NJ 08107 (SAN 212-5056) Tel 215-922-3030.

Friends of Mineralogy, *(Friends Mineralogy; 0-9614396)*, 1590 Olive Barber Rd., Coos Bay, OR 97420 (SAN 688-6833) Tel 503-267-2193; Orders to: Mineralogical Record, The, P.O. Box 1656, Carson City, NV 98702 (SAN 662-281X) Tel 702-883-2598.

Friends of Minnesota Music, Inc., *(Friends Minn Music; 0-9614757)*, Dinkytown Sta. Box 13405, Minneapolis, MN 55414 (SAN 692-9370) Tel 612-874-1491.

Friends of Nature, Inc., *(Friends Nature; 0-910636)*, Brookville, ME 04617 (SAN 205-5945). Canadian address: Chester, NS B0J 1J0.

Friends of Photography, The, *(Friends Photography; 0-933286)*, P.O. Box 500, Sunset Ctr., Carmel, CA 93921 (SAN 212-5064) Tel 408-624-6330.

†**Friends of Polish Music at USC,** *(Friends of Pol Mus; 0-916545)*, 3428 wrightview Dr., Studio City, CA 91604 Tel 213-877-1906; c/o Univ. of Southern California, Schl. of Music, University Park, Los Angeles, CA 90089-0851 (SAN 295-2815) Tel 213-743-6935; *CIP.*

Friends of Refugees of Eastern Europe, *(Friends Refugees; 0-86639)*, 1383 President St., Brooklyn, NY 11213 (SAN 215-9953) Tel 718-467-0860; Orders to: SVET Publishers, Inc., 455 Albany Ave., Brooklyn, NY 11213 (SAN 693-9589) Tel 718-774-0065.

Friends of the C.C.B.C., Inc, *(Friends CCBC; 0-931641)*, P.O. Box 5288, Madison, WI 53704-0288 (SAN 683-7638) Tel 608-251-7051.

Friends of the Commerce Public Library, *(Friends of Comm Lib; 0-9615374)*, P.O. Box 308, Commerce, TX 75428 (SAN 695-538X) Tel 214-886-6858.

Friends of the Earth, Inc., *(Friends of Earth; 0-913890)*, 1045 Sansome, San Francisco, CA 94111 (SAN 201-579X) Tel 415-433-7373.

Friends of the Folsom Library, *(Friends Fols Lib; 0-9610718)*, Rensselaer Polytechnic Institute, Troy, NY 12181 (SAN 264-7427) Tel 518-270-6706.

Friends of the Governor's Mansion, *(Friends Governors; 0-9615894)*, P.O. Box 13022, Austin, TX 78711 (SAN 697-077X); 200 E. Sixth St., Suite 201, Austin, TX 78701 (SAN 697-0788) Tel 512-474-9960; Dist. by: Univ. Texas Press, P.O. Box 7819, Austin, TX 78712 (SAN 212-9876) Tel 512-471-4032.

Friends of the Libraries of Kansas State Univ., *(Friends Lib KSU; 0-9616658)*, Kansas State Univ., Farrell Library, Manhattan, KS 66506 (SAN 661-1826) Tel 913-532-5693.

Friends of the Museum, Inc., *(Friends Mus Inc; 0-913965)*, 800 W. Wells St., Milwaukee, WI 53233 (SAN 286-7532) Tel 414-278-2787; Orders to: The Muses-Cookbook Milwaukee Public Museum, 800 W. Wells St., Milwaukee, WI 53233 (SAN 286-7540) Tel 414-278-2710.

Friends of the Ohio State Univ. Libraries, *(Friends Ohio St U Lib; 0-88215)*, Rm. 112, Main Lib., 1858 Neil Ave. Mall, Columbus, OH 43210 (SAN 202-814X) Tel 614-422-3387.

Friends of the Osterhout Free Library, *(Friends Osterhout; 0-9616411)*, 71 S. Franklin St., Wilkes-Barre, PA 18701 (SAN 658-8549) Tel 717-823-0156.

Friends of The Symphony Pubns., *(Friends Symphony Pubns; 0-9617142)*, P.O. Box 1603, Muskegan, MI 49443 (SAN 663-2491); 800 First St., Muskegan, MI 49443 (SAN 663-2505) Tel 616-780-2496.

Friends of the Towson Library, Inc., *(Friends Towson Lib; 0-9602326)*, 320 York Rd., Towson, MD 21204 (SAN 293-2695); c/o Baltimore County Public Library, Board of Library Trustees for Baltimore County, 320 York Road,, Towson, MD 21204 (SAN 293-2709).

Friends of the Tucson Public Library, *(Friends Tucson; 0-9608370)*, 110 E. Pennington St., Tuscon, AZ 85701 (SAN 662-0140) Tel 602-791-4391; c/o Tuscon Writes Project, Tuscon Public Library, Box 27470, Tuscon, AZ 85726 (SAN 240-3765).

Friends of the Univ. of Rochester Libraries *See* **Univ. Pr. of Virginia**

Friends of the Univ. of Toledo Libraries, *(Friends Univ Toledo; 0-918160)*, Univ. of Toledo Library, 2801 W. Bancroft St., Toledo, OH 43606 (SAN 208-1792) Tel 419-537-2326.

Friends of Truth, *(Friends Truth; 0-930682)*, 1509 Bruce Rd., Oreland, PA 19075 (SAN 211-0423) Tel 215-576-1450.

Friends of World Teaching, *(Friends World Teach; 0-9601550)*, P.O. Box 1049, San Diego, CA 92112 (SAN 212-906X) Tel 619-274-5282.

Friends Peace Committee, Nonviolence & Children Program, Div. of Philadelphia Yearly Meeting, *(Nonviol & Children; 0-9605062)*, 1515 Cherry St., Philadelphia, PA 19102 (SAN 215-868X) Tel 215-241-7239.

Friends' Pr., *(Friends Pr; 0-9615090)*, P.O. Box 1006, Weston, CT 06883 (SAN 694-3691) Tel 203-227-6643; Dist. by: DeVorss Distributors, P.O. Box 550, 1046 Princeton Dr., Marina del Rey, CA 90294 (SAN 168-9886) Tel 203-870-7478; Dist. by: Bookpeople, 2929 Fifth St., Berkeley, CA 94710 (SAN 168-9517) Tel 415-549-3030; Toll free: 800-227-1516; Dist. by: Starlite Distributors, P.O. Box 20729, Reno, NV 89515 (SAN 200-7789); Dist. by: Inland Book Company, 22 Hemingway Ave., East Haven, CT 06512 (SAN 200-4151) Tel 203-467-4257; Dist. by: New Leaf Distributing, 1020 White St., SW, Atlanta, GA 30310 (SAN 169-1449) Tel 404-755-2665; Toll free: 800-241-3829.

Friends Schl. of Baltimore, Inc., *(Friends Sch Balt; 0-9610826)*, 5114 N. Charles St., Baltimore, MD 21210 (SAN 265-2447) Tel 301-435-2800. In cooperation with Museum & Library of Maryland History-The Maryland Historical Society.

†**Friends United Pr.,** *(Friends United; 0-913408)*, 101 Quaker Hill Dr., Richmond, IN 47374 (SAN 201-5803) Tel 317-962-7573; *CIP.*

Friendship Pr., Subs. of National Council of the Churches of Christ USA, *(Friend Pr; 0-377)*, 475 Riverside Dr., Rm. 772, New York, NY 10027 (SAN 201-5773) Tel 212-870-2495; Orders to: Friendship Pr. Distribution, P.O. Box 37844, Cincinnati, OH 45237 (SAN 201-5781) Tel 513-761-2100.

Friis-Pioneer Press, *(Friis-Pioneer Pr; 0-943480)*, 1611 S. Minnie St., Santa Ana, CA 92707 (SAN 202-1498) Tel 714-835-3456.

Frisch, Howard, *(Frisch H; 0-910638)*, P.O. Box 128, Village Sta., New York, NY 10014 (SAN 220-5610) Tel 212-243-6188.

Frog Hair Pr., *(Frog Hair; 0-9616031)*, 16 Devonshire Blvd., San Carlos, CA 94070 (SAN 698-1453) Tel 415-592-5728.

†**Frog in the Well,** *(Frog in Well; 0-9603628)*, 25A Buena Vista Terr., San Francisco, CA 94117 (SAN 207-8295) Tel 415-431-2113; *CIP.*

From Here Pr., *(From Here; 0-89120)*, P.O. Box 219, Fanwood, NJ 07023 (SAN 209-746X) Tel 201-889-7886. *Imprints:* Old Plate Press (Old Plate).

From Me to You, *(From Me; 0-9608590)*, 811 Sioux Ave., Box 38, Mapleton, IA 51034 (SAN 238-2873) Tel 712-882-1517.

†**Fromm International Publishing Co.,** *(Fromm Intl Pub; 0-88064)*, 560 Lexington Ave., New York, NY 10022 (SAN 239-7269) Tel 212-308-4010; Dist. by: Kampmann & Co., Inc., 9 E. 40th St., New York, NY 10016 (SAN 202-5191) Tel 212-685-2928; *CIP.*

Frommer-Pasmantier Pubs., Div. of Simon & Schuster, *(Frommer-Pasmantier; 0-671)*, One Gulf & Western Plaza, New York, NY 10023 (SAN 205-2725) Tel 212-333-4101.

†**Frompovich, C. J., Pubns.,** *(C J Frompovich; 0-935322)*, R.D. 1, Chestnut Rd., Coopersburg, PA 18036 (SAN 213-3121) Tel 215-346-8461; *CIP.*

Front, Theodore, Musical Literature, *(Theodore Front; 0-934082)*, 16122 Cohasset St., Van Nuys, CA 91406 (SAN 221-167X) Tel 818-994-1902.

Front Row Experience, *(Front Row; 0-915256)*, 540 Discovery Bay Blvd., Byron, CA 94514 (SAN 207-1274) Tel 415-634-5710.

Frontal Lobe, *(Frontal Lobe; 0-931400)*, 836 Starlite Lane, Los Altos, CA 94022 (SAN 211-9013).

Frontier Cooperative Herbs, *(Frontier Coop Herbs; 0-9616218)*, Box 299, Norway, IA 52318 (SAN 658-6058) Tel 319-227-7991; Dist. by: International Distributors, RFD, Baker Hill Rd., Bradford, NH 03221 (SAN 200-6340); Dist. by: New Leaf Distributing, 1020 White St, SW, Atlanta, GA 30310 (SAN 169-1449).

Frontier Heritage Pr., *(Frontier Heritage)*, 1108 Davis St., Suite 109, Evanston, IL 60201 (SAN 659-199X).

Frontier Press, *(Frontier Press Calif)*, P.O. Box 5023, Santa Rosa, CA 95402 (SAN 206-653X) Tel 707-544-5174.

Frontier Pr. Co., *(Frontier Pr Co; 0-912168)*, P.O. Box 1098, Columbus, OH 43216 (SAN 205-5953) Tel 614-864-3737. *Imprints:* Lincoln Library (Lincoln Lib).

Frontier Pr., The, *(Frontier Pr; 0-932237)*, 15 Quintana Dr., Galveston, TX 77551 (SAN 686-578X) Tel 409-740-0138.

Frontier Pubns., *(Frontier Pubns; 0-9614948)*, 124 Ivy, Nampa, ID 83651 (SAN 693-6458) Tel 208-466-7439.

Frontline Pubns., *(Frontline; 0-910657)*, P.O. Box 1104, El Toro, CA 92630 (SAN 260-1907) Tel 714-837-6258.

Frontline Publishing, *(Frontline Pub; 0-935789)*, 203 Brimbal Ave., Beverly, MA 01915 (SAN 696-4338) Tel 617-927-2535; P.O. Box 327, Beverly, MA 01915 (SAN 696-5407).

Frost, O. W., *(O W Frost; 0-930766)*, 2141 Lord Baranof Dr., Anchorage, AK 99517 (SAN 211-3163).

Frost & Sullivan, Inc., *(Frost & Sullivan, 0-86621)*, 106 Fulton St., New York, NY 10038 (SAN 215-8698) Tel 212-233-1080; Toll free: 800-242-7737.

Frost Art Distributors, *(Frost Art; 0-9604802)*, 781 S. Kohler St., Los Angeles, CA 90021 (SAN 220-0546) Tel 213-626-3830.

Frosty Peak Bks., *(Frosty Peak Bks; 0-9607116)*, P.O. Box 4073, Malibu, CA 90265 (SAN 281-5591) Tel 213-457-2832; Orders to: P.O. Box 80584, Fairbanks, AK 99708 (SAN 699-5233) Tel 907-479-8411; Dist. by: Wilderness Pr., 2440 Bancroft Way, Berkeley, CA 94704-1676 (SAN 203-2139) Tel 415-843-8080.

Fruition Pubns., Inc., *(Fruition Pubns; 0-939926)*, Box 103, Blawenburg, NJ 08504 (SAN 216-8146) Tel 609-466-3196.

Fruitlands Museums, Inc., *(Fruitlands Mus; 0-941632)*, 102 Prospect Hill Rd., Harvard, MA 01451 (SAN 239-2119) Tel 617-456-3924.

Fruth, Florence Knight, *(F K Fruth)*, 64 St. Andrews Dr., Beaver Falls, PA 15010 (SAN 211-156X) Tel 412-846-5282.

Fry, Joan E., *(J E Fry; 0-9600984)*, 4025 State St., 22, Santa Barbara, CA 93110 (SAN 208-6565) Tel 805-967-8384.

FS&G Paperbacks *See* Farrar, Straus & Giroux, Inc.

Fudge, Edward, Publishing, *(E Fudge)*, P.O. Box 218026, Houston, TX 77218 (SAN 211-7975) Tel 713-578-7837.

FUJI *See* Unipub b

Fulcrum, Inc., *(Fulcrum Inc; 1-55591)*, 350 Indiana St., Suite 510, Golden, CO 80401 (SAN 200-2825) Tel 303-277-2623; Toll free: 800-992-2908.

Full Count Press, *(Full Count Pr OK; 0-936908)*, 223 N. Broadway, Edmond, OK 73034 (SAN 215-1456).

†Full Court Press, Inc., *(Full Court NY; 0-916190)*, 138-140 Watts St., New York, NY 10013 (SAN 211-9021) Tel 212-966-1831; CIP.

Full Court Pr., Inc., *(Full Court VA; 0-913767)*, Box 5177, Roanoke, VA 24012 (SAN 285-2527) Tel 703-345-5440.

Full Gospel Business Men's Fellowship International, *(Full Gospel; 0-86595)*, P.O. Box 5050, 3150 Bear St., Costa Mesa, CA 92626 (SAN 220-2476) Tel 714-754-1400.

Fuller, Aletha B., *(A B Fuller; 0-9616085)*, 742 Sandefer St., Abilene, TX 79601 (SAN 698-1178).

Fuller, Ben, Publishing Co., *(B Fuller Pub; 0-938807)*, P.O. Box 11669, Atlanta, GA 30355-1669 (SAN 661-4973); 334 Campbell Rd., Symrna, GA 30080 (SAN 661-4981) Tel 404-433-1037.

Fuller, Buckminster, Institute, *(Buckminster Fuller; 0-911573)*, 1743 S. La Cienega Blvd., Los Angeles, CA 90035-4601 (SAN 264-0511) Tel 213-837-7710.

Fuller Golden Gallery, *(Fuller Golden Gal; 0-9607452)*, 228 Grant Ave., San Francisco, CA 94108 (SAN 239-7749) Tel 415-982-6177.

Fuller Publishing Co., *(Fuller Pub; 0-9605850)*, 1060 Cragmont, Berkeley, CA 94708 (SAN 216-5953) Tel 415-527-4412.

Fuller Theological Seminary, *(Fuller Theol Soc; 0-9602638)*, 84 N. Los Robles, Pasadena, CA 91101 (SAN 221-8259).

Fulness Hse., Inc., *(Fulness Hse; 0-937778)*, P.O. Box 79350, Ft. Worth, TX 76179 (SAN 215-9961).

Fulton County Arts Council, *(Fulton Coun Art; 0-9606650)*, 501 William-Oliver Bldg., 32 Peachtree St., NW, Atlanta, GA 30303 (SAN 223-1328) Tel 404-577-7378.

Fun Bk. Enterprises, *(Fun Bk Enter; 0-937511)*, P.O. Box 50397, Atlanta, GA 30302-0397 (SAN 658-8492) Tel 404-987-2178; 1980 Overton Trail, Stone Mountain, GA 30088 (SAN 658-8506).

Fun Co., Inc. *See* Havin' Fun, Inc.

Fun in a Foreign Language, *(Fun Foreign Lang; 0-9615956)*, 3115 E. Mulberry Dr., Phoenix, AZ 85016 (SAN 697-3485) Tel 602-954-7075.

Fun Life Enterprises, *(Fun Life)*, P.O. Box 3481, Oak Brook, IL 60521 (SAN 657-8624).

Fun Publishing Co., *(Fun Pub AZ; 0-918858)*, P.O. Box 2049, Scottsdale, AZ 85252 (SAN 210-4261) Tel 602-946-2093. Do not confuse with Fun Publishing Co., Cincinnati, OH.

Fun Publishing Co., *(Fun Pub OH; 0-938293)*, 5860 Miami Rd., Cincinnati, OH 45243 (SAN 661-1761) Tel 513-272-3672. Do not confuse with Fun Publishing Co., Scottsdale, AZ.

Fun Reading Co., *(Fun Reading; 0-9608466)*, 2409 Glenwood Rd., Brooklyn, NY 11210 (SAN 240-6055) Tel 718-453-5582.

Function Industries Pr., *(Function Ind Pr; 0-930257)*, P.O. Box 9915, Seattle, WA 98109 (SAN 670-8498) Tel 206-284-3489.

Fund for Free Expression, *(Fund Free Expression; 0-938579)*, 36 W. 44th St., New York, NY 10036 (SAN 661-2555) Tel 212-840-9460. *Imprints:* Americas Watch (Americas Watch); Asia Watch (Asia Watch); Helsinki Watch (Helsinki Watch).

Fund for Multinational Management Education - Council of the Americas *See* Unipub

Fund for Multinational Management Education *See* Unipub

Fund Raisers, Inc., *(Fund Raisers Inc; 0-916555)*, 524 S. First Ave., Arcadia, CA 91006 (SAN 295-2904) Tel 818-445-0802.

Fund-Raising Institute, *(Fund Raising; 0-930807)*, Box 365, Ambler, PA 19002 (SAN 677-6302) Tel 215-628-8729.

Fundation, The, *(Fundation; 0-930451)*, 1404 Briarwood Rd. NE, Atlanta, GA 30319 (SAN 670-946X) Tel 404-321-1376.

Fundingsland Productions, *(Fundingsland; 0-932099)*, 1825-15 1/2 St., SW, Minot, ND 58701 (SAN 686-5127) Tel 701-839-5159.

Funk & Wagnalls Co., *(Funk & W; 0-308)*, C/O Harper & Row Pubs., 10 E. 53rd St., New York, NY 10022 (SAN 211-6944); Toll free: 800-242-7737; Dist. by: Harper & Row Pubs, Keystone Industrial Park, Scranton, PA 18512 (SAN 215-3742). *Imprints:* Funk & Wagnalls Juvenile Books (FW-J); Funk & Wagnalls Trade Books (FW-T).

Funk & Wagnalls Juvenile Books *See* Funk & Wagnalls Co.

Funk & Wagnalls Trade Books *See* Funk & Wagnalls Co.

Funky, Punky & Chic, *(Funky-Punky-Chic; 0-940762)*, P.O. Box 601, Cooper Sta., New York, NY 10276 (SAN 219-7448) Tel 212-533-1772.

Funn Music, *(Funn Music; 0-9611130)*, P.O. Box 5067, Garden Grove, CA 92645 (SAN 282-9142) Tel 714-895-3770.

FunPrax Associates, *(FunPrax; 0-9609972)*, 711 Skinner Building, Seattle, WA 98101 (SAN 270-4005).

Funston, Gwendolen, *(G Funston; 0-9615862)*, 3781 Lodge Ln., Trenton, MI 48183 (SAN 694-535X) Tel 313-676-9456.

Fur Line Press, *(Fur Line Pr; 0-912662)*, Dist. by: ManRoot Press, Box 982, South San Francisco, CA 94080 (SAN 201-5811).

Furman Univ. Bookstore, *(Furman U Bkstr)*, Greenville, SC 29613 (SAN 101-0670) Tel 803-294-2164.

Furst Pubns., *(Furst Pubns; 0-931612)*, 111 Kings Hwy. S., Westport, CT 06880 (SAN 211-4666).

Furuta/Associates, *(Furuta; 0-916129)*, P.O. Box 399, Fallbrook, CA 92028 (SAN 294-9318) Tel 619-723-8678.

Fusion Energy Foundation, *(Fusion Energy Found; 0-938460)*, 1010 16th St., NW,, Washington, DC 20036 (SAN 237-9538) Tel 703-689-2490; Box 17149, Washington, DC 20041-0149 (SAN 692-8307).

Fusion Groups, Inc., *(Fusion Groups; 0-912778)*, Indian Brook Rd., Garrison, NY 10524 (SAN 205-5988). Name Formerly Sonja.

Futura Publishing Co., Inc., *(Futura Pub; 0-87993)*, P.O. Box 330, Mt. Kisco, NY 10549 (SAN 201-582X) Tel 914-666-3505; 295 Main St., Mt. Kisco, NY 10549 (SAN 658-0750) Tel 914-666-3505.

Future Arts, Inc., *(Future Arts; 0-943122)*, Rt 2, Box 691, Baileys Harbor, WI 54202 (SAN 240-3781).

Future Directions, Inc., *(Future Direct; 0-914413)*, 9620 Chesapeake Dr., Suite 200, San Diego, CA 92123 (SAN 289-6249) Tel 619-698-5140.

Future Generations, *(Future Gen; 0-935791)*, 2936 Macomb St. NW, Washington, DC 20008 (SAN 696-4370) Tel 202-364-4363.

Future Homemakers of America, *(Future Home)*, 1910 Association Dr., Reston, VA 22091 (SAN 236-3135) Tel 703-476-4900.

Future Pr., *(Future Pr; 0-918406)*, P.O. Box 73, Canal St. Sta., New York, NY 10013 (SAN 210-0886).

Future Publishing Co., *(Future Pub FL)*, P.O. Box 1207, Oviedo, FL 32765 (SAN 223-081X).

Future Schools, Inc., *(Future Schls Inc; 0-936219)*, R.D. 2, Box 260, Hopewell Junction, NY 12533 (SAN 697-0958) Tel 914-897-5688; Dist. by: School Computers Systems, Inc., Jeanne Dr., Putnam Valley, NY 10579 (SAN 200-5905) Tel 914-528-2456.

Future Science Research Publishing Co., *(Future Sci Res; 0-941292)*, P.O. Box 06392, Portland, OR 97206 (SAN 239-4278) Tel 503-235-1971.

Future Shop, *(Future Shop; 0-930490)*, P.O. Box 3262, Santa Barbara, CA 93130 (SAN 211-2396) Tel 805-682-5460.

Future Systems, Inc., *(Future Syst; 0-938907)*, P.O. Box 26, Falls Church, VA 22046 (SAN 661-8081); 2209 N. Quintana, Arlington, VA 22205 (SAN 661-809X) Tel 703-241-1799.

FuturePace Inc., *(FuturePace; 0-932573)*, P.O. Box 1173, San Rafael, CA 94915 (SAN 687-4770) Tel 415-485-1200; Dist. by: Publishers Group West, 5855 Beaudry St., Emeryville, CA 94608 (SAN 202-8522) Tel 415-658-3453; Dist. by: Bookpeople, 2929 Fifth St., Berkeley, CA 94710 (SAN 168-9517) Tel 415-549-3030.

Futures Group, The, *(Futures Group; 0-9605196)*, 76 Eastern Blvd., Glastonbury, CT 06033-1264 (SAN 215-8701) Tel 203-633-3501.

Futures Publishing Group, Div. of LJR Communications, Inc., *(Futures Pub; 0-936624)*, 5513 Twin Knolls, Suite 213, Columbia, MD 21045 (SAN 215-2541) Tel 301-730-5365. *Imprints:* Managed Account Reports (Mngd Acct Reprts).

Futures Unlimited, Inc., *(Futures Unlimited Inc.; 0-940082)*, 5200 W. 73rd St., Minneapolis, MN 55435 (SAN 220-2220) Tel 612-835-7729.

Futuro Co., The, Div. of The Jung Corp., *(Futuro Ohio; 0-9617392)*, 5801 Mariemont Ave., Cincinnati, OH 45227 (SAN 663-6101) Tel 513-271-3400.

GAIA Services, *(GAIA Services; 0-9616496)*, P.O. Box 84, RFD 3, St. Johnsbury, VT 05819 (SAN 659-2341) Tel 802-633-4152.

GAMA Communications, *(GAMA Comns; 0-938853)*, P.O. Box 170, Salem, NH 03079 (SAN 661-8057); 35 Pelham Rd., Salem, NH 03079 (SAN 661-8065) Tel 603-898-2822.

G & G Pubs., *(G&G Pubs; 0-937534)*, Rte. 7, No. 63, Hopewell Junction, NY 12533 (SAN 215-2444).

G & G Publishing Co., *(G & G Pub Co; 0-9610028)*, P.O. Box 49231, Atlanta, GA 30359 (SAN 262-8708) Tel 404-992-1198.

G & H Bks., *(G & H Bks; 0-9616717)*, 2515 E. Thomas Rd., Suite 16, Phoenix, AZ 85016 (SAN 661-3780) Tel 602-955-3812.

GBC Publishing, *(GBC Pub; 0-9606228)*, 947 Garfield Ave., Oak Park, IL 60304 (SAN 217-5207) Tel 312-848-1995.

G B H Publishing, *(G B H Pub)*, 825 32nd Ave., Santa Cruz, CA 95062 (SAN 270-4153) Tel 408-462-4916.

GBM Books, Div. of God's Broadcaster Ministries, Inc., *(GBM Bks; 0-912695)*, P.O. Box 4895, 4850 Whisett Ave., North Hollywood, CA 91607 (SAN 277-6820) Tel 818-763-0942.

G.B. Pr., *(G B Pr; 0-9615406)*, 49 Wilbur St., Weatherly, PA 18255 (SAN 695-5010) Tel 717-427-8398.

GBS Pubns., *(GBS CA; 0-913855)*, 1969 Benecia Ave., Los Angeles, CA 90025 (SAN 287-7473) Tel 213-552-1440.

GBS Pubs., Div. of Gordon's Booksellers, *(GBS Pubs; 0-939928)*, 8 E. Baltimore St., Baltimore, MD 21202 (SAN 216-8154).

GCE Pubns., *(G C E Pubns; 0-915668)*, P.O. Box 539, Los Alamitos, CA 90720 (SAN 207-6772) Tel 213-493-4421.

GCT Publishing Co., Inc., *(GCT Pub; 0-937659)*, P.O. Box 6448, Mobile, AL 36660 (SAN 659-2325) Tel 205-478-4700; 350 Weinacker Ave., Mobile, AL 36660 (SAN 659-2333).

G. D. A. Pubns., *(GDA Pubns; 0-938640)*, P.O. Box 30119, Lafayette, LA 70503 (SAN 215-2452).

GDE Pubns., Div. of Glen Eley Enterprises, *(GDE Pubns OH; 0-940934)*, P.O. Box 304, Lima, OH 45802 (SAN 222-9749).

G.E.C. Publishing Firm, *(G E C; 0-9613391)*, 1613 Chelsea Rd., Suite 160, San Marino, CA 91108 (SAN 657-0895) Tel 818-445-6329.

GEC Research Pr., Div. of GEC Research, *(GEC Research; 0-939525)*, Box 3053, Santa Barbara, CA 93130 (SAN 658-8182) Tel 805-687-5480.

GED Institute, *(GED Inst; 0-937128)*, G St. NW, Waterville, WA 98858 (SAN 276-945X).

GEN Pubns., *(GEN Pubns; 0-914225)*, P.O. Box 291189, Los Angeles, CA 90029 (SAN 287-5012) Tel 213-413-3264.

GE-PS Cancer Memorial, *(GE-PS Cancer; 0-9601644),* 519 Austin Ave., Park Ridge, IL 60068 (SAN 215-7659) Tel 312-823-5425.

G.E.R.P.A. Pubns., *(G E R P A; 0-9613352),* 1404 Union St., Schenectady, NY 12308 (SAN 655-8763) Tel 518-346-6127.

†**GFI Assocs.,** Div. of The Republic Group, *(GFI Assocs; 0-915309),* 5801 Lee Hwy., Arlington, VA 22207 (SAN 289-985X) Tel 703-533-8555; P.O. Box 408, Middleburg, VA 22117 (SAN 662-2208) Tel 703-327-4866; Dist. by: Frederick Fell Pubs., 2500 Hollywood Blvd., Suite 302, Hollywood, FL 33020 (SAN 208-2365) Tel 305-925-5242; Toll free: 800-526-7626; Dist. by: Kampmann & Co., 9 E. 40th St., New York, NY 10016 (SAN 202-5191) Tel 212-685-2928; *CIP.*

GGL Educational Pr., *(GGL Educ Press; 0-915751),* 2555 E. Chapman, Suite 606, Fullerton, CA 92631 (SAN 293-9665) Tel 714-525-1256.

G.H.A. Pubns., *(GHA Pubns; 0-9614441),* 603 Fifth Ave., Juniata, Altoona, PA 16601 (SAN 689-0695) Tel 814-942-9855.

GHC Business Bks., Div. of GHC Sales, *(GHC; 0-9609046),* 4214 N. Post Rd., Omaha, NE 68112 (SAN 241-3183) Tel 402-453-1769; P.O. Box 299, Fort Calhoun, NE 68023 (SAN 662-0264).

G.I.A. Pubns., Inc., *(GIA Pubns),* 7404 S. Mason Ave., Chicago, IL 60638 (SAN 205-3217) Tel 312-496-3800.

G.J. Enterprises, *(G J Ent; 0-9612912),* 446 Old Stonebrook Rd., Acton, MA 01718 (SAN 291-1612) Tel 617-568-1401.

G-Jo Institute/Falkynor Bks., The, *(Falkynor Bks; 0-916878),* 4950 SW 70th Ave., Davie, FL 33314 (SAN 208-645X) Tel 305-791-1562; Dist. by: The Great Tradition, 750 Adrian Way, Suite 111, San Rafael, CA 94903 (SAN 200-5743) Tel 415-492-9382; Dist. by: Samuel Weiser, P.O. Box 612, York Beach, ME 03910 (SAN 202-9588) Tel 207-363-4393; Toll free: 800-843-6666; Dist. by: The Distributors, 702 S. Michigan, South Bend, IN 46618 (SAN 169-2488) Tel 219-232-8500.

G K Press, *(G K Pr; 0-910067),* 415 Sheffield Rd., Cherry Hill, NJ 08034 (SAN 241-3078) Tel 609-877-9115.

GLGLC Music, Subs. of La Costa Music Consultants, *(GLGLC Music; 0-9607558; 0-932303),* P.O. Box 147, Cardiff by the Sea, CA 92007 (SAN 238-6194) Tel 619-436-7219.

GMI Pubns., Inc., *(GMI Pubns Inc; 0-937408),* P.O. Box 16824, Jacksonville, FL 32216 (SAN 215-2479) Tel 904-359-2427.

GNK Pr., Div. of Good Natured Kitchen, *(GNK Pr; 0-9609266),* 453 Half Hollow Rd., Dix Hills, NY 11746 (SAN 260-0587) Tel 516-271-9565.

GNU Publishing, *(GNU; 0-915914),* P.O. Box 6820, San Francisco, CA 94101 (SAN 203-5367).

GP Courseware, Subs. of General Physics Corp., *(GP Courseware; 0-87683),* 10650 Hickory Ridge Rd., Columbia, MD 21044 (SAN 294-0264) Tel 301-964-6032; Toll free: 800-638-3838.

GRDA Pubns., Div. of Goldberg Research & Development Assocs. Corp., *(GRDA Pubns; 0-9614808),* 110 Tiburon Blvd., Mill Valley, CA 94941 (SAN 692-9524) Tel 415-388-6080.

GRQ, Inc., *(GRQ Inc),* 19 E. Central Ave., Paoli, PA 19301 (SAN 663-4621) Tel 215-251-9525.

GSJ Pr., Div. of Gray Endeavors, Inc., *(GSJ Press; 0-9609842),* 205 Willow St., South Hamilton, MA 01982 (SAN 270-577X) Tel 617-468-4486.

GS Pubs., *(G S Pubs; 0-9606338),* P.O. Box 6213, Laguna Niguel, CA 92677 (SAN 282-5619) Tel 714-951-9009; Orders to: 26355 Palomita Cir., Mission Viejo, CA 92691 (SAN 282-5627) Tel 714-951-9009.

GTM, Inc., *(G T M Co; 0-9615112),* P.O. Box 776, Arnold, MD 21012 (SAN 693-8221) Tel 301-757-7082.

Gabari Publishing Co., *(Gabari Pub Co; 0-916073),* 3612 21st Ave., Sacramento, CA 95820 (SAN 294-801X) Tel 916-454-6492.

Gabriel Books, Div. of Minnesota Scholarly Pr., Inc., *(Gabriel Bks),* P.O. Box 224, Mankato, MN 56001 (SAN 214-2627) Tel 507-387-4964; Dist. by: Independent Publishers Group, One Pleasant Ave., Port Washington, NY 11050 (SAN 287-2544).

Gabriel Hse., Inc., *(Gabriel Hse; 0-936192),* 5045 W. Oakton St., Suite 7, Skokie, IL 60077 (SAN 213-9219) Tel 312-675-1146. *Imprints:* Writer's Guide Pubns. (Writers Guide Pubns).

Gabriel Systems, Inc., *(Gabriel Syst; 0-934481),* 147 Main St., Box 357, Maynard, MA 01754 (SAN 693-885X) Tel 617-897-6470.

Gabrielle Press, *(Gabrielle Pr FL; 0-9608656),* 6829 Woodwind Dr., Sarasota, FL 33581 (SAN 240-7663) Tel 813-922-5317; Dist. by: Magna Books, Sannibel, FL 33957 (SAN 200-4267) Tel 813-472-6777.

Gabriel's Horn Publishing Co., *(Gabriel's Horn; 0-911861),* P.O. Box 141, Bowling Green, OH 43402 (SAN 283-4219) Tel 419-352-1338.

Gach, John, Books, *(Gach Bks),* 5620 Waterloo Rd., Columbia, MD 21045 (SAN 214-0195).

GAF International, *(GAF Intl; 0-942176),* P.O. Box 1722, Vista, CA 92083 (SAN 238-8367).

Gain Pubns., *(Gain Pubns; 0-910725),* P.O. Box 2204, Van Nuys, CA 91404 (SAN 270-4218) Tel 818-785-1895.

Gaines, P., Co., The, *(P Gaines Co; 0-936284),* P.O. Box 2253, Oak Park, IL 60303 (SAN 214-0209) Tel 312-996-7829.

Gajda, George J., *(G Gajda; 0-9608018),* P.O. Box 1846, Santa Monica, CA 90406 (SAN 209-4398).

Galactic Central Pubns., *(Galactic Central; 0-912613),* P.O. Box 40494, Albuquerque, NM 87196 (SAN 282-7689) Tel 505-255-9057.

Galahad Publishing, *(Galahad Pub; 0-918483),* 5124 S. 3245 W., Salt Lake City, UT 84118 (SAN 657-680X) Tel 801-969-8752.

Galahand Press, The, *(Galahand Pr; 0-940578),* P.O. Box 951, Austin, TX 78767 (SAN 223-7687) Tel 512-459-9384.

Galaxy Music Corp., *(Galaxy Music),* 131 W. 86th St., New York, NY 10023 (SAN 205-2628) Tel 212-874-2100; Dist. by: E.C. Schirmer Music Co., 138 Ipswich St., Boston, MA 02115 (SAN 222-9544) Tel 617-236-1935.

Galaxy Pr., *(Galaxy Pr; 0-916566),* P.O. Box 1640, Loma Linda 92354. Escondido, CA 92027 (SAN 208-0729) Tel 714-796-6921.

Galbraith/Scott Pubns., Inc., *(Galbraith-Scott; 0-9614844),* Box 296, Hartland, MI 48029 (SAN 693-112X) Tel 313-632-7691.

Gale, Hoyt Rodney, *(H R Gale),* 669 Sturtevant Dr., Sierra Madre, CA 91024 (SAN 212-8209) Tel 818-355-2988.

Gale Research Co., Subs. of International Thomson Information, Inc., *(Gale; 0-8103),* Book Tower, Detroit, MI 48226 (SAN 213-4373) Tel 313-961-2242; Toll free: 800-223-4253.

Galeria Pr., *(Galeria Pr; 0-9615137),* 401 Tilting T. Dr., P.O. Box 457, Borrego Springs, CA 92004 (SAN 694-2032) Tel 619-767-5956.

Galerie Pr., Inc., *(Galerie Pr; 0-917541),* P.O. Box 4608, Lafayette, LA 70502 (SAN 657-1409) Tel 318-234-5076.

Galilee See **Doubleday & Co., Inc.**

Galileo Pr., *(Galileo; 0-913123),* 15201 Wheeler Ln., Sparks, MD 21152 (SAN 240-6543) Tel 301-771-4544; Dist. by: Bookslinger, 213 E. Fourth St., St. Paul, MN 55101 (SAN 169-4154) Tel 612-221-0429; Dist. by: The Distributors, 702 S. Michigan, South Bend, IN 46618 (SAN 212-0364) Tel 219-232-8500; Dist. by: Small Pr. Distribution, Inc., 1814 San Pablo Ave., Berkeley, CA 94702 (SAN 204-5826) Tel 415-549-3336.

Galison Bks., *(Galison; 0-939456),* 25 W. 43rd St., New York, NY 10036 (SAN 216-3888) Tel 212-354-8840.

Gall Pubns., *(Gall Pubns; 0-88904),* 2965 Weston Ave., Niagara Falls, NY 14305 (SAN 212-6117).

Gallant Publishing Co., *(Gallant Pub CA; 0-9616219),* P.O. Box 5656, Essex Junction, VT 05453 (SAN 658-6082) Tel 802-879-6699; 3 Sugar Tree Ln., Essex Junction, VT 05453 (SAN 658-6090).

Gallaudet College Pr., *(Gallaudet Coll; 0-913580; 0-930323),* 800 Florida Ave. NE, Washington, DC 20002 (SAN 205-261X) Tel 202-651-5595; Toll free: 800-672-6720 (ext. 5595).

Gallen, Richard See **Pocket Bks., Inc.**

Gallen, Richard & Co., Inc., *(R Gallen & Co; 0-87760),* 260 Fifth Ave., New York, NY 10001 (SAN 294-7951); Dist. by: Dell Publishing Co., Inc., One Dag Hamarskjold Plaza, 245 E. 47th St., New York, NY 10017 (SAN 201-0097) Tel 212-605-3000. Trade Paperbacks, Formerly was a Packager.

Galleries of the Claremont Colleges, *(Galleries Coll; 0-915478),* Montgomery Art Gallery, Pomona College, Claremont, CA 91711 (SAN 158-0515) Tel 714-621-8283.

Gallery Arts Pr., *(Gallery Arts; 0-9608592),* P.O. Box 88, Rye, NY 10580 (SAN 238-2881).

Gallery Ellington, *(Gallery Ellington; 0-9614307),* 550 N. Rock Rd. Suite 52, Wichita, KS 67206 (SAN 687-4967) Tel 316-682-9051.

Gallery for Fine Photography, *(Gallery Fine; 0-9615647),* 5423 Magazine St., New Orleans, LA 70115 (SAN 696-3854) Tel 504-891-1002.

Gallery Graphics Press, *(Gallery Graphics; 0-943294; 0-933293),* P.O. Box 5457, Carmel, CA 93923 (SAN 240-6551); P.O. Box 7403, Carmel, CA 93921 (SAN 662-0159); 3757 Raymond Way, Carmel, CA 93923 (SAN 662-0167) Tel 408-625-0226.

Gallery of Fine Art of Ohio Univ., *(Gallery Fine Art Ohio U; 0-933041),* 48 East Union St., Athens, OH 45701-2979 (SAN 689-7525) Tel 614-594-6935.

Gallery Press, *(Gallery Pr; 0-913622),* 117 N. Main St., Essex, CT 06426 (SAN 207-0936) Tel 203-767-0313.

Gallery Schlesinger-Boisante, *(Gallery Schlesinger Boisante; 0-9614661),* 822 Madison Ave., New York, NY 10021 (SAN 661-6755).

Gallery West, Inc., *(Gallery West; 0-9610550),* P.O. Box 5688, Santa Fe, NM 87502 (SAN 262-026X) Tel 505-471-4443.

Galley Kitchen Shoppe, The, *(Galley Kitchen; 0-9612544),* 905 US Hwy. 1, Lake Park, FL 33403 (SAN 297-178X).

Galley Press, *(Galley OR; 0-9604800),* P.O. Box 892, Portland, OR 97207 (SAN 215-3149) Tel 206-693-1397; Toll free: 800-932-0070.

Gallimaufry, *(Gallimaufry; 0-916300),* Dist. by: Apple-Wood Pr., P.O. Box 2870, Cambridge, MA 02139 (SAN 210-3419) Tel 617-964-5150.

Gallo, John, *(J Gallo; 0-9615648),* R.D. 2, Oneonta, NY 13820 (SAN 696-5032) Tel 607-432-3022.

Gallopade: Carole Marsh Bks., *(Gallopade Carole Marsh Bks; 0-935326; 1-55609),* General Delivery, Bath, NC 27808 (SAN 213-8441) Tel 919-923-4291.

Galloway Pubns., *(Galloway; 0-87874),* 2940 NW Circle Blvd., Corvallis, OR 97330-3999 (SAN 201-5854) Tel 503-754-7464.

Gallup Organization, The, *(Gallup NJ),* 53 Bank St., Princeton, NJ 08540 (SAN 659-6096).

Galveston Arts, *(Gavelston Arts; 0-9616139),* P.O. Box 1105, Galveston, TX 77553 (SAN 699-9670) Tel 409-763-7173; 2020 Post Office, Galveston, TX 77553 (SAN 699-9689).

Gambler, *(Gambler; 0-930911),* P.O. Box 863, Metuchen, NJ 08840 (SAN 687-6587) Tel 201-789-3337.

Gamblers Anonymous Publishing, Inc./National Service Office, *(Gamblers Anon; 0-917839),* P.O. Box 17173, Los Angeles, CA 90017 (SAN 201-5870); 1543 W. Olympic Blvd. Suite 533, Los Angeles, CA 90015 (SAN 650-0285) Tel 213-386-8789.

Gambling Research Institute See **Cardoza Publishing**

Gambling Times, Inc., *(Gambling Times; 0-89746; 0-914314),* 1018 N. Cole Ave., Hollywood, CA 90038 (SAN 211-6383) Tel 213-466-5261.

Game Fields Press, *(Game Flds Pr; 0-9614007),* P.O. Box 238, Lake Oswego, OR 97034 (SAN 683-5643) Tel 503-636-0952.

Game Publishing *See* **Valor Publishing Co.**

Gamesmasters Pubs. Assn., *(Gamesmasters; 0-935426),* 20 Almont St., Nashua, NH 03060 (SAN 213-5000).

Gaming Bks. International, Inc., *(Gaming Bks Intl; 0-934047),* 810 E. Sahara, Suite 4, Las Vegas, NV 89104 (SAN 693-0387) Tel 702-369-8585.

Gamliel's Pub, *(Gamliels Pub; 0-9616579),* 24 Duxbury Rd., Newton Center, MA 02159 (SAN 660-9597) Tel 617-244-2351. *Imprints:* Windsor Press, Inc., The (Windsor Pr).

Gamma Books, *(Gamma Bks; 0-933124),* 400 Nelson Rd., Ithaca, NY 14850 (SAN 212-4688) Tel 607-273-8801.

Gamma Infinity, Inc., *(Gamma Infinity; 0-935869),* 932 MacKenzie Dr., Sunnyvale, CA 94087 (SAN 697-2705) Tel 408-559-0318.

Gamma Psi Chapter, Phi Alpha Theta, *(Gamma Psi; 0-9606168),* History Dept., Washington State Univ., Pullman, WA 99164-4030 (SAN 217-5525) Tel 509-335-8676.

Gamut Music Co., *(Gamut Music; 0-910648),* P.O. Box 454, Dedham, MA 02026 (SAN 205-2598) Tel 617-244-3305.

Gan-Tone Publishing Co., *(Gan-Tone Pub; 0-939458),* Carnegie Hall, 881 Seventh Ave., Studio 1105-6, New York, NY 10019 (SAN 216-5961) Tel 212-265-5690.

Ganek, Selene, *(S Ganek; 0-9616186),* 758 Strawberry Hill Dr., Glencoe, IL 60022 (SAN 658-3385) Tel 312-835-0830; Dist. by: Baker & Taylor (Midwest Div.), 501 Gladiola Ave., Momence, IL 60954 (SAN 169-2100).

Ganis & Harris, Inc., *(Ganis & Harris; 0-9605188),* 39 W. 14th St., New York, NY 10011 (SAN 216-0897).

Ganley Pub., *(Ganley Pub; 0-932445),* P.O. Box 149 Amherst Branch, Buffalo, NY 14226-0149 (SAN 686-7154) Tel 716-839-2415.

Gann Law Bks., *(Gann Law Bks; 0-933902),* 1180 Raymond Blvd., Newark, NJ 07102 (SAN 203-5375) Tel 201-624-5533.

Gannett Bks., Subs. of Guy Gannett Publishing Co., *(G Gannett; 0-930096),* P.O. Box 1460B, Portland, ME 04101 (SAN 210-7295) Tel 207-775-5811; Toll free: 800-442-6036.

Gannon, William, *(Gannon; 0-88307),* 205 E. Palace Ave., Santa Fe, NM 87501 (SAN 201-5889) Tel 505-983-1579.

°**Gannon Univ. Pr.,** *(Gannon U Pr; 0-936063),* Perry Sq., Erie, PA 16541 (SAN 697-0796) Tel 814-871-7437.

Ganong, W. L., Co., *(Ganong W L Co; 0-933036),* Homestead Hse., P.O. Box 2727, Chapel Hill, NC 27514 (SAN 221-1351) Tel 919-929-0421.

Gant, Margaret Elizabeth, *(M E Gant; 0-9603138),* 7500 Deer Track Dr., Raleigh, NC 27612 (SAN 212-7415) Tel 919-848-8062.

Gantzer, Howard J., *(Howard Gantzer; 0-9614532),* 1111 Archwood Dr., Olympia, WA 98502 (SAN 692-3143) Tel 206-754-4890.

Gap Mountain Bks., *(Gap Mountain; 0-9615520),* Rte. 2, Box 42, Newport, VA 24128 (SAN 696-3900) Tel 703-552-5943.

Garabed Books, *(Garabed; 0-9605102),* 23 Leroy St., New York, NY 10014 (SAN 281-7330) Tel 212-243-0768; Orders to: Zareh, Inc., 65 State St., Boston, MA 02109 (SAN 281-7349) Tel 617-227-6464.

Garber Communications, Inc., *(Garber Comm; 0-89345; 0-8334),* 5 Garber Hill Rd., Blauvelt, NY 10913 (SAN 226-2789) Tel 914-359-9292. *Imprints:* Biograf Pubns. (Biograf Pubns); Freedeeds Books (Freedeeds Bks); Spiritual Fiction Pubns. (Spiritual Fiction); Spiritual Science Library (Spiritual Sci Lib); Steiner, Rudolf, Pubns. (Steiner); Steinerbooks (Steinerbks); Tele-Viewer Pubns. (Tele-Viewer).

Garcia, Lois, *(L Garcia),* 2917 Shady Ave., Pittsburgh, PA 15217 (SAN 699-8275).

Garcia, Robert T., *(R T Garcia; 0-9610352),* P.O. Box 41714, Chicago, IL 60641 (SAN 264-0562) Tel 312-867-4143.

Gard & Co., *(Gard & Co; 0-9603316),* P.O. Box 34579, NW Sta., Omaha, NE 68134 (SAN 209-0198) Tel 402-493-1352.

Garden Bks., *(Garden Bks),* P.O. Box 3446, Oakland, CA 94609 (SAN 656-822X).

Garden City Historical Society, *(Garden City; 0-9604654),* Box 179, Garden City, NY 11530 (SAN 215-1472).

Garden Club of Georgia, Inc., The, *(Garden GA; 0-9612486),* 325 Lumpkin St., Athens, GA 30605 (SAN 289-2510) Tel 912-234-4106.

Garden Club of Lexington Inc., The, *(Garden Club Lex; 0-9614443),* P.O. Box 22091, Lexington, KY 40522 (SAN 689-3597) Tel 606-266-3438.

Garden Club of Savannah, *(Garden Club Sav; 0-9613370),* P.O. Box 8806, Savannah, GA 31412 (SAN 657-1417).

Garden Publishing Co. *See* **Hull, William H., Pub.**

Garden Way Publishing *See* **Storey Communications, Inc.**

†**Gardner, Isabella Stewart, Museum,** *(I S Gardner Mus; 0-914660),* 2 Palace Rd., Boston, MA 02115 (SAN 201-9221) Tel 617-566-1401; *CIP.*

Gardner-Farkas Pr., Inc., *(Gardner Farkas Pr; 0-9613874),* 1701 River Run, River Plaza Office Tower, Suite 603, Fort Worth, TX 76107 (SAN 681-9850); Orders to: P.O. Box 33229, Fort Worth, TX 76162 (SAN 662-2585) Tel 817-870-2113.

Gardner-O'Brien Fine Arts Research, Inc., *(Gardner-O'Brien; 0-9616580),* 17 Cortes St., Boston, MA 02116 (SAN 661-2326) Tel 617-329-9107.

†**Gardner Pr., Inc.,** *(Gardner Pr; 0-89876),* 19 Union Sq., W., New York, NY 10003 (SAN 214-1906) Tel 212-924-8293; *CIP.*

Gardner Publishing, Inc., *(Gardner Pub; 0-9617183),* 150 Marine St., City Island, NY 10464 (SAN 663-2661) Tel 212-885-1036.

Gardnor House, *(Gardnor Hse; 0-943602),* P.O. Box 1928, Spring, TX 77383 (SAN 240-6578).

Garfield Pubns., *(Garfield Pubns; 0-9609856),* 6095 Ripley Ln., Paradise, CA 95969 (SAN 270-4382) Tel 916-872-4184.

Garges, Beverly & Sherman, Pubs., *(B & S Garges; 0-9614041),* P.O. Box 811, Michigan Center, MI 49254 (SAN 684-8109) Tel 517-764-4183; 5235 Pine Dr., Jackson, MI 49201 (SAN 693-5184).

†**Garland Publishing, Inc.,** *(Garland Pub; 0-8240),* 136 Madison Ave., New York, NY 10016 (SAN 201-5897) Tel 212-686-7492; *CIP.*

Garland STPM Press *See* **Garland Publishing, Inc.**

Garlinghouse, L. F., Co., The, *(L F Garlinghouse Co; 0-938708),* P.O. Box 1717, Middletown, CT 06457 (SAN 238-7077) Tel 203-632-0500.

Garmer Pr., Inc., *(Garmer Pr Inc; 0-9612960),* 7800 Sandy Cove Dr., New Orleans, LA 70128 (SAN 292-5117) Tel 504-246-4023; Dist. by: Forest Sales & Distributors, 2616 Spain St., New Orleans, LA 70117 (SAN 157-5511) Tel 504-947-2106.

Garner, Alan, Publishing Group, *(A Garner Pub; 0-939515),* 100 Via Estrada, Suite P, Laguna Hills, CA 92653 (SAN 663-3560) Tel 714-770-8323.

Garner, Clifford S., *(C S Garner; 0-9612808),* 444 Saratoga Ave., No. 29H, Santa Clara, CA 95050 (SAN 289-9868) Tel 408-249-4192; Orders to: Enterprises Store, The, 1200 N. Lake Ave., Pasadena, CA 91104 (SAN 662-2216) Tel 818-798-7893; Toll free: 800-826-0364.

Garnet Pr., *(Garnet Pr; 0-938133),* P.O. Box 1094, North Falmouth, MA 02556 (SAN 661-2172); 35 Deep Pond Dr., East Falmouth, MA 02536 (SAN 661-2180) Tel 617-540-8639.

Garnet Pub. Co., *(Garnet Pub; 0-917475),* P.O. Box 14713, Spokane, WA 99214 (SAN 656-0600) Tel 509-926-4176.

Garnet Publishing Co., *(Garnet Pub CA; 0-935793),* 1177 Cielo Cir., Rohnert Park, CA 94928 (SAN 696-9275) Tel 707-792-2294.

†**Garrard Pub. Co.,** *(Garrard; 0-8116),* 29 Goldsborough St., Easton, MD 21601 (SAN 201-5900); Orders to: 1607 N. Market St., Champaign, IL 61820 (SAN 201-5919) Tel 217-352-7685; *CIP.*

Garrett & Stringer, Inc., *(Garrett & String; 0-9615791),* P.O. Box 330677, Coconut Grove Sta., Miami, FL 33233 (SAN 696-9259) Tel 305-447-1019; 3126 Center St., Coconut Grove, FL 33133 (SAN 696-9267).

Garrett Corp., The, Div. of Allied-Signal, Inc., *(Garrett Corp; 0-9617029),* 18200 Coastline Dr., Malibu, CA 90265 (SAN 662-8788) Tel 213-454-1041.

Garrett Park Pr., *(Garrett Pk; 0-912048),* P.O. Box 190 E, Garrett Park, MD 20896 (SAN 201-5927) Tel 301-946-2553.

Garrett Publishing Co., *(Garrett Pub; 0-939085),* 13117 Balboa Blvd., Granada Hills, CA 91344 (SAN 662-9288) Tel 818-360-5052.

Garric Pr., *(Garric Pr; 0-9609922),* P.O. Box 517, Glen Ellen, CA 95442 (SAN 270-4404) Tel 707-938-3625.

Garson Assocs., *(Garson Associates; 0-9614591),* 172 Babylon Tpke., Merrick, NY 11566 (SAN 691-7763) Tel 516-868-9833.

Gartner Group, Inc., *(Gartner Group; 0-9614408),* 72 Cummings Point Rd., Stamford, CT 06904 (SAN 688-2579) Tel 203-964-0096.

Garvin, A. J., & Assocs., *(A J Garvin; 0-9607252),* 720 E. Ann St., Ann Arbor, MI 48104 (SAN 281-7357) Tel 313-662-2734; Orders to: P.O. Box 7525, Ann Arbor, MI 48107 (SAN 281-7365).

Gaslight Pubns., *(Gaslight; 0-934468),* 112 E. Second St., Bloomington, IN 47401 (SAN 213-5019) Tel 812-332-5169. *Imprints:* McGuffin Books (McGuffin Bks).

Gasogene Pr., *(Gasogene Pr; 0-938501),* P.O. Box 1041, Dubuque, IA 52001 (SAN 661-2717) Tel 612-546-4671; 1325 Jersey Ave. S., 308, St. Louis Park, MN 55426 (SAN 663-3218).

Gately, James J., *(J J Gately; 0-916126),* Box 25, Haddonfield, NJ 08033 (SAN 219-3434).

Gateway Arts, *(Gateway Arts; 0-935327),* P.O. Box 3267, Oakland, CA 94609 (SAN 695-7668) Tel 415-655-5240.

Gateway Bks., *(Gateway Bks; 0-933469),* 66 Cleary Ct., Suite 1405, San Francisco, CA 94109 (SAN 691-8808) Tel 415-929-7134; Dist. by: Strawberry Hill Pr., 2594 15th Ave., San Francisco, 94127 (SAN 238-8103) Tel 415-664-8112; Dist. by: Publishers Group West, 5855 Beaudry St., Emeryville, CA 94608 (SAN 202-8522) Tel 415-658-3453; Dist. by: Ingram Bk. Co., 347 Reedwood Dr., Nashville, TN 37217 (SAN 169-7978); Dist. by: Book Dynamics, Inc., 836 Broadway, New York, NY 10003 (SAN 169-5649) Tel 212-254-7798.

Gateway Editions *See* **Contemporary Bks., Inc.**

Gateway Editions *See* **Regnery Bks.**

Gateway Pr., *(Gateway Pr; 0-936533),* P.O. Box 5180, Mill Valley, CA 94942 (SAN 697-8622) Tel 415-332-1428; Dist. by: Publishers Group West, 5855 Beaudry St., Emeryville, CA 94608 (SAN 202-8522) Tel 415-658-3453; Dist. by: Bookpeople, 2929 Fifth St., Berkeley, CA 94710 (SAN 168-9517) Tel 415-549-3030; Toll free: 800-277-1516.

Gateway Pr., *(Gateway Pr TX; 0-9613155),* P.O. Box 6867, Tyler, TX 75701 (SAN 294-8052) Tel 214-561-3479.

Gateway Productions, Inc., *(Gateway Prod; 0-936769),* 3011 Magazine St., New Orleans, LA 70115 (SAN 699-9808) Tel 504-891-2600.

Gateway Pubns., *(Gateway Pubns; 0-937661),* 1106 Greenbanks Dr., Mt. Pleasant, MI 48858 (SAN 659-235X) Tel 517-772-1432; Dist. by: Baha'i Distribution Service, 415 Linden Ave., Wilmette, IL 60091 (SAN 200-643X); Dist. by: Kalimat Pr., 10889 Wilshire Blvd., Suite 700, Los Angeles, CA 90024 (SAN 213-7666).

†**Gateway Publishing, Inc.,** *(Gateway MO; 0-9616128),* 1177 N. Warson Rd., St. Louis, MO 63132 (SAN 699-6809) Tel 314-997-7462. Do not confuse with Gateway Publishing, 4121 Forest Park Blvd., St. Louis, MO; *CIP.*

Gaunt, Bonnie, *(B Gaunt; 0-9602688),* 510 Golf Ave., Jackson, MI 49203 (SAN 221-8267).

Names

†**Gaunt, William W., & Sons, Inc.,** *(W W Gaunt; 0-912004),* 3011 Gulf Dr., Holmes Beach, FL 33510-2199 (SAN 202-9413) Tel 813-778-5211; *CIP.*

Gauntlet Books, *(Gauntlet Bks),* 144 King St., Franklin, MA 02038 (SAN 201-5935) Tel 617-528-4414.

Gauquier, Anthony V. & Beverly, *(A Gauquier; 0-9609574),* 335 Spring St., Rockland, MA 02370 (SAN 260-1915) Tel 617-878-4133; Orders to: P.O. Box 1215, Plymouth, MA 02360 (SAN 650-0293).

Gaus, Theo, Ltd., *(Gaus; 0-912444),* P.O. Box 1168, Brooklyn, NY 11202 (SAN 203-4174) Tel 718-625-4651.

Gavea-Brown Pubns., *(Gavea-Brown; 0-943722),* Box O, Brown Univ., Providence, RI 02912 (SAN 240-4788).

†**Gay Presses of New York,** *(Gay Pr NY; 0-9604724),* P.O. Box 294, New York, NY 10014 (SAN 215-210X) Tel 212-255-4713; *CIP.*

†**Gay Sunshine Pr.,** *(Gay Sunshine; 0-917342),* Box 40397, San Francisco, CA 94140 (SAN 208-0915) Tel 415-824-3184; Dist. by: Bookpeople, 2929 Fifth St., Berkeley, CA 94710 (SAN 168-9517); Dist. by: Inland Bk. Co., P.O. Box 261, 22 Hemingway Ave., East Haven, CT 06512 (SAN 200-4151) Tel 203-467-4257; Toll free: 800-243-0138; *CIP.*

Gaylord's Guides, Ltd., *(Gaylord's Guides; 0-936907),* 204 W. 20th St., New York, NY 10011 (SAN 658-3334).

Gazebo Pubns., *(Gazebo Pubns; 0-914161),* P.O. Box 368, Milton, IN 47357-0368 (SAN 287-4989).

Gazelle Pubns., *(Gazelle Pubns; 0-930192),* 5580 Stanley Dr., Auburn, CA 95603 (SAN 209-5610) Tel 916-878-1223.

Gazette International Networking Institute, *(Gazette Intl; 0-931301),* 4502 Maryland Ave., St. Louis, MO 63108 (SAN 683-2539) Tel 314-361-0475.

Gazette Press, Inc., *(Gazette Pr; 0-933390),* 225 Hunter Ave., North Tarrytown, NY 10591 (SAN 203-4182) Tel 914-631-8866.

Gazette Printing, *(Gazette Print),* 1114 Broadway, Wheaton, MN 56296 (SAN 679-1514).

Gazin, Patricia, *(P Gazin),* 1250 First St., Hermosa Beach, CA 90254 (SAN 211-4410) Tel 213-376-5765.

Geankoplis, Christie J., *(Geankoplis; 0-9603070),* 101 W. 35th St., Minneapolis, MN 55408 (SAN 209-5629) Tel 612-625-1586; Dist. by: Ohio State Univ. Bookstores, 1315 Kinnear Rd., Columbus, OH 43212 (SAN 209-5637) Tel 614-422-2991.

Gearhart-Edwards Press, *(Gearhart-Edwards),* 2917 N. Summit Ave., Milwaukee, WI 53211 (SAN 214-0217).

Gebbie Pr., *(Gebbie Pr),* P.O. Box 1000, New Paltz, NY 12561 (SAN 226-5443) Tel 914-255-7560.

Gebhardt, Chuck, *(C Gebhardt; 0-9601410),* P.O. Box 6821, San Jose, CA 95150 (SAN 211-1934).

Gecko Press *See* EJP Publishing Co.

Gee Tee Bee, *(Gee Tee Bee; 0-917232),* 11901 Sunset Blvd., No. 102, Los Angeles, CA 90049 (SAN 206-9652) Tel 213-476-2622.

Geer, Corinne C., *(C C Geer; 0-9601508),* 2222 Wallington Dr., Albany, GA 31707 (SAN 211-3937).

Geer, D.J.P., *(D J P Geer; 0-9613061),* 10731 Sinclair Ave., Dallas, TX 75218 (SAN 294-8095) Tel 214-327-4938.

Gehry Pr., *(Gehry Pr; 0-935020),* 1319 Pine St., Iowa City, IA 52240 (SAN 213-0629).

Gekko Pr., *(Gekko Press; 0-9616903),* 10745 Molony Rd., Culver City, CA 90230 (SAN 661-5147) Tel 213-824-4507.

Geller, Norman, Pubs., *(N Geller Pub; 0-915753),* P.O. Box 1283, Lewiston, ME 04240 (SAN 293-9681) Tel 207-783-2400.

Gem City College Pr., *(Gem City Coll; 0-910222),* 700 State St., P.O. Box 179, Quincy, IL 62306 (SAN 202-4004) Tel 217-222-0391.

Gem-O-Lite Plastics Co., *(Gem O Lite; 0-911888),* P.O. Box 985, N. Hollywood, CA 91603 (SAN 203-4204) Tel 213-877-3491.

Gem Press, *(Gem Pr; 0-9613554),* 731 Preston Ave, Lewiston, ID 83501 (SAN 669-8255) Tel 208-743-7422.

Gem Pubns., *(Gem Pubns; 0-941832),* P.O. Box 2499, Melbourne, FL 32902 (SAN 239-2143) Tel 305-727-3034.

Gemaia Press, *(Gemaia Pr; 0-9602232),* 209 Wilcox Lane, Sequim, WA 98382 (SAN 212-4238).

Gemak Publishing, *(Gemak Pub; 0-9608742),* 3084 S. Gavilan, Las Vegas, NV 89122 (SAN 262-0278) Tel 702-458-1770.

Gembooks, *(Gembooks; 0-910652),* 3677 San Gabriel Pkwy., Pico Rivera, CA 90660 (SAN 201-5943).

Gemfield Assn., Inc., *(Gemfield Assn; 0-9614845),* P.O. Box 610092, North Miami, FL 33161-0092 (SAN 693-1154) Tel 305-893-6223.

Gemini Music Division *See* Pilgrim Pr., The United Church Pr.

Gemini Press, *(Gemini Pr; 0-9601690),* 625 Pennsylvania Ave., Oakmont, PA 15139 (SAN 211-4933) Tel 412-828-3315.

Gemini Publications, *(Gemini Pub NY; 0-9613030),* 177-31 Edgerton Rd., Jamaica, NY 11432 (SAN 293-9711) Tel 718-380-1787; Dist. by: American Networking Resources, 177-31 Edgerton Rd., Jamaica Estates, NY 11432 (SAN 662-7579) Tel 718-380-1787.

Gemini Pubns., *(Gemini Pubns TX; 0-938427),* P.O. Box 60328, San Angelo, TX 76906 (SAN 661-2903); 3206 Grandview Dr., San Angelo, TX 76904 (SAN 661-2911) Tel 915-944-7262. Do not confuse with Gemini Pubns., St. Lukes, MO, New York, NY.

Gemini Publishing Co., *(Gemini Pub Co; 0-937164),* 11543 Gullwood Dr., Houston, TX 77089 (SAN 215-2460) Tel 713-484-2424.

Gemini Smith, Inc., *(Gemini Smith; 0-935022),* 5858 Desert View Dr., La Jolla, CA 92037 (SAN 212-6125) Tel 619-454-4321.

Gemmeg Pr., *(Gemmeg Pr; 0-9608076),* P.O. Box 322, Parkville Sta., Brooklyn, NY 11204 (SAN 240-4796) Tel 718-259-5379.

Gemological Institute of America, *(Gemological; 0-87311),* 1660 Stewart St., Santa Monica, CA 90404 (SAN 203-4212) Tel 213-829-2991.

Gems 'n' Gold Publishing Co., *(Gems N Gold Pub; 0-9614846),* P.O. Box 6577, Marietta, GA 30065-6577 (SAN 693-0263).

Gemstone Books *See* Dillon Pr., Inc.

Genaway & Assocs., Inc., *(Genaway; 0-943970),* 530 W. Regency Circle, P.O. Box 477, Canfield, OH 44406 (SAN 241-3833). Trade name: Business Technical Information Service.

Gene Pr., *(Gene Press; 0-939087),* 18 Donald Pl., Elizabeth, NJ 07208 (SAN 662-9121) Tel 201-353-1655.

Genealogical Assn. of Southwestern Michigan, Dept. C, *(Genealog Assn SW),* P.O. Box 573, St. Joseph, MI 49085 (SAN 223-0364) Tel 616-429-7914.

†**Genealogical Bks. in Print,** *(GBIP; 0-89157),* 6818 Lois Dr., Springfield, VA 22150 (SAN 220-2484) Tel 703-971-5877; *CIP.*

Genealogical Enterprises, *(Genealogic Ent; 0-9616020),* 1140 Windsong Ln., Siesta Key, Sarasota, FL 34242 (SAN 698-147X) Tel 813-349-8001.

Genealogical Institute, *(Genealog Inst; 0-940764),* P.O. Box 22045, Salt Lake City, UT 84122 (SAN 662-0175) Tel 801-532-3327; Dist. by: Family History World, P.O. Box 22045, Salt Lake City, UT 84122 (SAN 282-6402).

†**Genealogical Publishing Co., Inc.,** *(Genealog Pub; 0-8063),* 1001 N. Calvert St., Baltimore, MD 21202 (SAN 206-8370) Tel 301-837-8271; *CIP.*

Genealogical Sources, Unlimited, *(Genealog Sources; 0-913857),* 407 Regent Ct., Knoxville, TN 37923 (SAN 286-7583) Tel 615-690-7831.

General Agreement on Tariffs & Trade *See* Unipub

General Aviation Press, *(Gen Aviation Pr),* P.O. Box 110918, Carrollton, TX 75011 (SAN 214-446-2502; Dist. by: Airways Supply, P.O. Box 810469, Dallas, TX 75381 (SAN 200-5182) Tel 213-240-1771.

General Board of Church and Society of the United Methodist Church, *(General Board; 0-9613222),* 100 Maryland Ave. NE, Washington, DC 20002 (SAN 295-1266) Tel 202-488-5631.

General Commission on Archives & History, *(Gen Comm Arch),* 36 Madison Ave., P.O. Box 127, Madison, NJ 07940 (SAN 240-9410) Tel 201-822-2787.

General Communications Co. of America, *(Gen Comm Co; 0-914761),* 720 W. 8th St., Los Angeles, CA 90017 (SAN 655-4504).

General Communications, Inc., *(General Comns; 0-939185),* 100 Garfield St., Denver, CO 80206 (SAN 662-8338) Tel 303-322-6400.

General Edu-Media, Inc., *(Genl Edu Media; 0-939531),* P.O. Box 1549, Troy, MI 48099 (SAN 663-432X); 4349 Greensboro, Troy, MI 48099 (SAN 663-4338) Tel 313-524-2317.

General Education Pubns., *(General Educ; 0-914504),* 99 S. Van Ness Ave., San Francisco, CA 94103 (SAN 209-2182) Tel 415-621-5410.

General Electric Co., *(G E Company FL; 0-9617205),* P.O. Box 861, Gainesville, FL 32602-0861 (SAN 692-5154) Tel 904-462-3911.

General Electric Co., Technical Promotion & Training Services, *(GE Tech Prom & Train; 0-932078),* 1 River Rd., Bldg. 22, Rm. 232, Box MK, Schenectady, NY 12345 (SAN 206-9911).

General Hall, Inc., *(Gen Hall; 0-930390),* 5 Talon Way, Dix Hills, NY 11746 (SAN 211-1306) Tel 516-423-0155.

General Means, Inc., *(General Means; 0-9608852),* P.O. Box 3546, City of Industry, CA 91744 (SAN 241-0222) Tel 818-336-7763.

General Philatelic Corporation *See* General Trade Corp.

†**General Society of Mayflower Descendants,** *(Mayflower; 0-930270),* Orders to: Mayflower Families, P.O. Box 3297, Plymouth, MA 02361 (SAN 209-5823) Tel 617-746-3188. Do Not Confuse with Mayflower Books, Inc; *CIP.*

General Systems Science Corp., *(Gen Syst Sci; 0-938235),* 2611 Terrace View, Arcata, CA 95521 (SAN 661-4299) Tel 707-839-2861.

General Technical Services, Inc., *(Gen Tech Serv; 0-914780),* 1200 Lincoln Rd., Prospect Park, PA 19076 (SAN 201-5951) Tel 215-522-1500.

General Trade Corp., *(General Trade; 0-88219),* P.O. Box 402, Loveland, CO 80539 (SAN 209-3812) Tel 303-667-1133. *Imprints:* General Philatelic Corporation (General Philatelic).

General Welfare Publications, *(Gen Welfare Pubns; 0-87312),* Box 19098, Sacramento, CA 95819 (SAN 240-4753) Tel 916-677-1610.

Generations Publishing Co., *(Generations Pub; 0-9606392),* 901 Post Oak Ln., Charleston, IL 61920 (SAN 222-9978) Tel 217-258-2568.

Genesee Country Museum Pr., *(Genesee Ctry Mus Pr; 0-931535),* Flint Hill Rd., Mumford, NY 14511 (SAN 682-2940) Tel 716-538-6822.

Genesis, Inc., *(Genesis Inc; 0-9615457),* P.O. Box 42403, Pittsburgh, PA 15203 (SAN 696-3978) Tel 412-761-5505.

Genesis Pr., *(Genesis Pr; 0-9615923),* P.O. Box 66929, Baton Rouge, LA 70896 (SAN 697-0753) Tel 504-769-9627 (SAN 206-8346).

Genesis Project, The, *(Genesis Project; 0-86702),* P.O. Box 37282, Washington, DC 20013 (SAN 216-6747) Tel 703-998-0800.

Genesis Pubns., Inc., *(Genesis Pubns; 0-904351),* 1613 Spear St. Tower, 1 Market Plaza, San Francisco, CA 94105 (SAN 239-4286). Do not confuse with Genesis Pubns., Standardsville, VA or Genesis Pubns., Inc., Tuscon, AZ.

Genesis Pubns., Inc., *(Gnsis Pubns Tucson; 0-936633),* 2509 N. Campbell, No. 287, Tuscon, AZ 85719 (SAN 699-7260) Tel 602-795-8751. Do not confuse with Genesis Pubns., Inc. of San Francisco, CA, or Genesis Pubns., Inc. of Standardsville, VA.

Genesis Pubs., *(Genesis Pubs Inc; 0-913331)*, 8825 Roswell Rd., No. 161, Atlanta, GA 30338-1140 (SAN 283-0914); Dist. by: Llewellyn Pubns., P.O. Box 64383, St. Paul, MN 55101 (SAN 281-9155) Tel 612-291-1970.

Genesis II, *(Genesis Two; 0-9615649)*, 99 Bishop Allen Dr., Cambridge, MA 02139 (SAN 696-3994) Tel 617-576-1801.

Geneva Historical Society & Museum, The, *(Geneva Hist Soc Mus; 0-9613821)*, 543 S. Main St., Geneva, NY 14456 (SAN 278-9078) Tel 315-789-5151.

Geneva Ministries, *(Geneva Ministr; 0-939404)*, 708 Hamvassy Rd., Tyler, TX 75701 (SAN 216-5759) Tel 214-592-0620.

†Geneva Pr., The, *(Geneva Pr; 0-664)*, 925 Chestnut St., Philadelphia, PA 19107 (SAN 215-076X) Tel 215-928-2700; Toll free: 800-523-1631; *CIP.*

†Genitron Pr., *(Genitron Press; 0-915781)*, P.O. Box 31391, Seattle, WA 98103 (SAN 293-9746) Tel 206-382-1711; *CIP.*

Genium Publishing Corp., *(Genium Pub; 0-931690)*, 1145 Catalyn St., Schenectady, NY 12303 (SAN 213-5027) Tel 518-377-8855.

Genius Publishing, *(Genius Pub; 0-935925)*, 1450 S. Rexford Dr., Los Angeles, CA 90035 (SAN 697-094X) Tel 213-553-8009.

Genny Smith Bks., *(Genny Smith Bks; 0-931378)*, 1304 Pitman Ave., Palo Alto, CA 94301 (SAN 211-3570) Tel 415-321-7247; Dist. by: William Kaufmann Inc., 95 First St., Los Altos, CA 94022 (SAN 202-9383) Tel 415-948-5810.

†Genotype, *(Genotype; 0-936618)*, 15042 Montebello Rd., Cupertino, CA 95014 (SAN 214-3089); *CIP.*

Genova, Inc., *(Genova Inc; 0-9616509)*, 7034 E. Court St., Davison, MI 48423-0309 (SAN 659-4514); Toll free: 800-521-7488; P.O. Box 309, Davison, MI 48423 (SAN 659-4522).

Genre Communications, *(Genre Comms; 0-9610948)*, 5697 Xenon Court, Arvada, CO 80002 (SAN 265-2463) Tel 303-425-4214.

Gentle Touch Pr., *(Gentle Touch; 0-9610894)*, P.O. Box 12305, Boulder, CO 80303 (SAN 265-1386) Tel 303-449-7499.

Gentle World, Inc., *(Gentle World; 0-9614248)*, P.O. Box 1418, Umatilla, FL 32784 (SAN 686-7448) Tel 904-669-2822; Dist. by: New Leaf, 1020 White St., SW, Atlanta, GA 30310 (SAN 169-1449) Tel 404-755-2665; Toll free: 800-241-3829; Dist. by: Nutri-Books Corp., P.O. Box 5793, Denver, CO 80223 (SAN 169-054X) Tel 303-778-8383.

Gentrace Assocs., Inc., *(Gentrace Assocs; 0-936065)*, 2810 Babe Ruth Dr., San Jose, CA 95132 (SAN 697-080X) Tel 408-923-7885.

Genun Pubs., Div. of Genealogy Unlimited Inc., *(Genun Pubs; 0-912811)*, 789 S. Buffalo Grove Rd., Buffalo Grove, IL 60089 (SAN 282-7700) Tel 312-541-3175.

Geo-Space Research Foundation, *(Geo Space; 0-936961)*, 4120 Rio Bravo, No. 104, El Paso, TX 79902 (SAN 658-649X) Tel 915-532-1136.

Geo Speleo Pubns., *(Geo Speleo Pubns; 0-9613107)*, P.O. Box 52, East Texas, PA 18046 (SAN 294-0124) Tel 215-683-4367.

GeoApp Publishing Co., *(GeoApp Pub Co; 0-9615842)*, Appalachian State Univ., Geography Dept., Boone, NC 28608 (SAN 697-0966) Tel 704-262-3001.

Geographics, *(Geographics; 0-930722)*, Box 133, Easton, CT 06612 (SAN 211-1810).

Geologic Pubns, Div. of Geology & Earth Resources, *(Geologic Pubns)*, Department of Natural Resources, Olympia, WA 98504 (SAN 240-0936).

Geological Society of America, Inc., *(Geol Soc; 0-8137)*, P.O. Box 9140, 3300 Penrose Pl., Boulder, CO 80301 (SAN 201-5978).

Geophysical Institute, *(Geophysical Inst; 0-915360)*, Univ. of Alaska, 611 C. T. Elvey Bldg., Fairbanks, AK 99701 (SAN 216-2482) Tel 907-474-7798.

Geopolymer Institute, The, *(Geopolymer Inst)*, 16863 Lenore, Detroit, MI 48219 (SAN 663-3048) Tel 313-592-0216; Dist. by: US Distribution Ctr., 13119 Glenfield, Detroit, MI 48213 (SAN 289-145X).

Geoprint, Inc., *(Geoprint; 0-9616454)*, 11431 W. River Hills Dr., Burnsville, MN 55337 (SAN 659-2368) Tel 612-890-0110; Dist. by: Bookmen, 525 N. 3rd St., Minneapolis, MN 55401 (SAN 169-409X); Dist. by: Pacific Trade Group, P.O. Box 668, Pearl City, HI 96782-0668 (SAN 169-1635).

George, Alexander, *(G Alexander; 0-930923)*, 79 Washington St., Hempstead, NY 11550 (SAN 683-2563).

George, Gorin, *(G Gorin; 0-9613974)*, 11 Fifth Ave., New York, NY 10003 (SAN 682-2401) Tel 212-260-5422.

George Peabody College for Teachers of Vanderbilt Univ., *(Peabody Coll; 0-933436)*, 21st Ave., S., Box 164, Nashville, TN 37203 (SAN 216-3837).

George Washington Univ., Ctr. for Telecommunications Studies, *(CTS-GWU; 0-932768)*, 2130 H St., NW, Rm. W1, Washington, DC 20052 (SAN 212-4491) Tel 202-676-6455.

George Washington Univ. Law Schl., *(GWU Law)*, 720 20th St., NW, Washington, DC 20006 (SAN 227-3004).

George Washington Univ. National Law Ctr., Government Contracts Program, *(GWU Natl Law; 0-935165)*, Academic Ctr., Rm. T412, 801 22nd St. NW, Washington, DC 20052 (SAN 227-3012) Tel 202-676-6815; Toll free: 800-446-2221.

Georgetown Heritage Society, *(Georgetown Herit; 0-936149)*, P.O. Box 467, Georgetown, TX 78627 (SAN 697-0990) Tel 512-863-1980; 109 E. Eighth St., Georgetown, TX 78626 (SAN 697-1008).

Georgetown Pr., *(Georgetown Pr; 0-914558)*, 483 Francisco St., San Francisco, CA 94133 (SAN 206-7463) Tel 415-397-4753.

Georgetown Univ., Center for Peace Studies, *(Ctr Peace Stud; 0-912239)*, 410 Maguire Bldg., Georgetown Univ., Washington, DC 20057 (SAN 265-1394) Tel 202-625-4240.

†Georgetown Univ., Ctr. for Strategic & International Studies, *(CSI Studies; 0-89206)*, 1800 K St. NW, Suite 400, Washington, DC 20006 (SAN 281-4021) Tel 202-775-3119; *CIP.*

Georgetown Univ., Ctr. for Strategic & International Studies, World Power & Pacific Program, *(World Power Prog; 0-89206)*, 1800 K St. NW, Suite 1102, Washington, DC 20006 (SAN 695-104X).

Georgetown Univ., Kennedy Institute of Ethics, *(Geo U Kennedy Inst; 0-9614448)*, Georgetown Univ., Washington, DC 20057 (SAN 689-3775) Tel 202-625-8709.

Georgetown Univ. Law Ctr., *(Grgtwn U Law Ctr)*, 600 New Jersey Ave., NW, Washington, DC 20001 (SAN 663-6314) Tel 202-624-8230.

†Georgetown Univ. Pr., *(Georgetown U Pr; 0-87840)*, Intercultural Ctr., Rm. 111, Washington, DC 20057 (SAN 203-4247) Tel 202-625-8041; *CIP.*

Georgetown Univ., School for Summer & Continuing Education, *(GU-Sch Summer & Cont Ed; 0-939998)*, Washington, DC 20057 (SAN 216-8162).

Georgetown Univ., Schl. of Foreign Service, *(Geo U Sch For Serv; 0-934742)*, Georgetown Univ., Institute for the Study of Diplomacy, Washington, DC 20057 (SAN 221-1580) Tel 202-625-3784. *Imprints:* Institute for the Study of Diplomacy (Inst Study Diplomacy); School of Foreign Service (Sch For Serv).

Georgia Agricultural Commission for Peanuts, *(GA Peanut Comm)*, P.O. Box 967, Tifton, GA 31793 (SAN 225-0535) Tel 912-386-3470; 110 E. Fourth St., Tifton, GA 31794 (SAN 650-0307).

Georgia Assn. of Historians, *(GA Assn Hist; 0-939346)*, Kennesaw College, History Dept., Marietta, GA 30061 (SAN 216-5643) Tel 404-429-2945.

Georgia Department of Archives & History, *(GA Dept Archives)*, 330 Capitol Ave., Atlanta, GA 30334 (SAN 218-7426) Tel 404-656-2358.

Georgia Institute of Continuing Legal Education, *(GA Inst CLE)*, Univ. of Georgia, Athens, GA 30602 (SAN 262-124X) Tel 404-542-2522.

Georgia Municipal Assn., *(GA Municipal)*, 34 Peachtree St., Suite 2300, Atlanta, GA 30303 (SAN 227-3047).

†Georgia State Univ., College of Business Administration, Business Publishing Div., *(GA St U Busn Pub; 0-88406)*, University Plaza, Atlanta, GA 30303-3093 (SAN 201-5838) Tel 404-658-4253; *CIP.*

Georgian International, Ltd., Inc., *(Georgian Intl; 0-9611392)*, P.O. Box 24346, Fort Lauderdale, FL 33307 (SAN 285-3035); 2725 Center Ave., Fort Lauderdale, FL 33308 (SAN 662-2054) Tel 305-564-1011.

†Georgian Pr. Co., The, *(Georgian Pr; 0-9603408)*, 2620 SW Georgian Pl., Portland, OR 97201 (SAN 213-9766) Tel 503-223-9899; Dist. by: Pacific Pipeline, Inc., 19215 66th Ave., S., Kent, WA 98032 (SAN 208-2128) Tel 206-872-5523; *CIP.*

Geoscience Analytical, *(Geoscience Analytical; 0-941054)*, Chemistry UCLA, Los Angeles, CA 90024 (SAN 217-3670) Tel 213-825-7675.

Geoscience Information Society, *(Geosci Info; 0-934485)*, c/o American Geological Institute, 4220 King St., Alexandria, VA 22302 (SAN 266-8467).

Geothermal Resources Council, *(Geothermal; 0-934412)*, P.O. Box 1350, Davis, CA 95617-1350 (SAN 213-0637); 111 G St., Suite 28, Davis, CA 95616 (SAN 669-0874) Tel 916-758-2360.

Geothermal World Publishers, *(Geothermal World)*, 5762 Firebird Court, Mission Oaks, Camarillo, CA 93010 (SAN 226-2061) Tel 805-482-6288.

Gerard, Leona B., *(L B Gerard; 0-9606394)*, 222 E. Broadway, Apt. 709, Eugene, OR 97401 (SAN 218-5482) Tel 503-345-3029.

Geraventure Corp., *(Geraventure; 0-938524)*, P.O. Box 2131, Melbourne, FL 32902-2131 (SAN 216-0331).

Gerecor, Ltd., *(Gerecor; 0-935613)*, 232 Madison Ave., New York, NY 10016 (SAN 696-401X) Tel 212-725-2350.

Geri-Rehab, Inc., *(Geri-Rehab; 0-941930)*, Box 170, Hibbler Rd., Lebanon, NJ 08833 (SAN 239-4383) Tel 201-735-8918.

Geriatric Educational Consultants, *(Geriatric Educ; 0-937663)*, 43 Middleton Ln., Willingboro, NJ 08046 (SAN 659-2376) Tel 609-877-5972.

Gerisch Publishing Co., *(Gerisch Pub Co; 0-934201)*, 1217 David Whitney Bldg., Detroit, MI 48226 (SAN 693-028X) Tel 313-962-3969.

Germainbooks, *(Germainbooks; 0-914142)*, 91 St. Germain Ave., San Francisco, CA 94114 (SAN 201-5986) Tel 415-731-8155.

German American Chamber of Commerce, Inc., *(German Am Chamber; 0-86640)*, 666 Fifth Ave., New York, NY 10103 (SAN 216-3845).

Gernshack Library *See* TAB Bks., Inc.

Geron-X, Inc., *(Geron-X; 0-87672)*, P.O. Box 1108, Los Altos, CA 94023-1108 (SAN 201-5994) Tel 415-941-1692.

Geronima Pr., *(Geronima; 0-943164)*, 2216 Cliff Dr., Santa Barbara, CA 93109 (SAN 240-7191) Tel 805-966-7563.

Gerontological Society of America, *(Gerontological Soc)*, 1411 K St. NW, Suite 300, Washington, DC 20005 (SAN 224-2591) Tel 202-393-1411.

Gerosota Pubns., *(Gerosota Pub; 0-9609126)*, 3530 Pine Valley Dr., Sarasota, FL 33579-4335 (SAN 241-5046) Tel 813-924-3251.

Gerry's Frankly Speaking, *(G's Frankly Speaking; 0-9612578)*, P.O. Box 2225, Salem, OR 97308 (SAN 289-2138) Tel 503-585-8411; 475 Cottage, Salem, OR 97301 (SAN 289-2146).

Gershman, Norman H., Gallery, Inc., *(N H Gershman; 0-9617237)*, 710 Broadway, New York, NY 10003 (SAN 663-5660) Tel 212-349-8606.

Gersna, Charles, *(C Gersna; 0-9615747)*, 130 Sixth Ave., New Eagle, PA 15067 (SAN 696-4362) Tel 412-258-9731.

Gessert, George, *(G Gessert; 0-9615895)*, 1230 W. Broadway, Eugene, OR 97402 (SAN 697-1032) Tel 503-343-2920.

Gestalt Journal, *(Gestalt Journal; 0-939266)*, P.O. Box 990, Highland, NY 12528 (SAN 216-5317) Tel 914-691-7192.

Getal Inc., *(Getal; 0-916131)*, P.O. Box 25242, Portland, OR 97225 (SAN 294-9326) Tel 503-292-3201.

†**Getty, J. Paul, Museum,** *(J P Getty Mus; 0-89236),* 17985 Pacific Coast Hwy., Malibu, CA 90265 (SAN 208-2276) Tel 213-459-7611; Dist. by: J P Getty Museum Bookstore, P.O. Box 2112, Santa Monica, CA 90406 (SAN 662-7242) Tel 213-459-7611; *CIP.*

Getwell Church of Christ, *(Getwell Church; 0-9615751),* 1511 Getwell Rd., Memphis, TN 38111 (SAN 696-4397) Tel 901-743-0464.

Ghirardelli Chocolate Co., *(Ghirardelli Choc; 0-9610218),* 1111 139th Ave., San Leandro, CA 94578 (SAN 270-5028) Tel 415-483-6970.

Ghosh, A., *(Ghosh A; 0-9611614),* 5720 W. Little York, Suite 216, Houston, TX 77091 (SAN 285-2780) Tel 713-445-5526.

Ghost Dance Pr., *(Ghost Dance; 0-939520),* ATL EBH MSU, East Lansing, MI 48824 (SAN 207-8317) Tel 517-351-5977.

Ghost Pony Pr., *(Ghost Pony Pr; 0-941160),* 2518 Gregory St., Madison, WI 53711 (SAN 237-9546) Tel 608-238-0175; Dist. by: Small Pr. Distribution, Inc., 1816 San Pablo Ave., Berkeley, CA 94702 (SAN 204-5826) Tel 415-549-3336.

Ghost Town Pubns., *(Ghost Town; 0-933818),* P.O. Drawer 5998, Carmel, CA 93921 (SAN 209-4401) Tel 408-373-2885.

Giant Poplar Pr., *(Giant Poplar Pr; 0-9616536),* 452 Sylva Hwy., Franklin, NC 28734 (SAN 659-4530) Tel 704-369-6486.

Gibbelins Gazatte Pubns./Silver EEL Pr., The, *(Gibbelin's Gazatte; 0-9610452),* 3217-G Whisper Lake, Winter Park, FL 32792 (SAN 264-0589) Tel 305-657-2236.

Gibbes Art Gallery *See* **Carolina Art Assn.**

Gibbons, Stanley, Inc., *(S Gibbons; 0-85259),* 124 Charlotte Ave., Hicksville, NY 11801 (SAN 213-3784) Tel 516-935-9490.

Gibbs Publishing Co., *(Gibbs Pub OH; 0-932924),* P.O. Box 2345, Toledo, OH 43603 (SAN 212-2138) Tel 419-592-4581.

Giblin, Les, *(L Giblin; 0-9616416),* 3790 Quail Ridge Dr., Boynton Beach, FL 33436 (SAN 658-8662) Tel 305-737-7076; Dist. by: Executive Bks., 210 W. Allen St., Mechanicsburg, PA 17055 (SAN 156-5419).

Giboney, Daniel W., *(D Giboney; 0-9606396),* P.O. Box 5432, Spokane, WA 99205 (SAN 218-5490) Tel 509-326-3602.

Gibraltar Pr., *(Gibraltar; 0-9606284),* P.O. Box 121425, Nashville, TN 37212 (SAN 216-3853); 171 Fuller St., Brookline, MA 02146 (SAN 216-3861).

Gibson, C. R., Co., *(Gibson; 0-8378),* 32 Knight St., Norwalk, CT 06856 (SAN 201-5765) Tel 203-847-4543; Toll free: 800-243-6004; Dist. by: C.R. Gibson, Distribution Ctr., Beacon Falls, CT 06403 (SAN 281-7462).

Gibson, Dot, Pubns., *(D Gibson; 0-941162),* P.O. Box 117, Waycross, GA 31502 (SAN 200-4143); 161 Knight Ave. Cir., Waycross, GA 31501 (SAN 660-9287) Tel 912-285-2848.

Gibson-Hiller Co., *(Gibson Hiller; 0-918892),* P.O. Box 22, Dayton, OH 45406 (SAN 210-427X) Tel 513-277-2427.

Gick Publishing Inc., *(Gick; 0-918170),* 9 Studebaker Dr., Irvine, CA 92718 (SAN 209-6641) Tel 714-581-5830.

Giddings Studio Publishing, *(Giddings Studio Pub; 0-9615226),* 2700 Wakonda Dr., Ft. Collins, CO 80521 (SAN 695-1406) Tel 303-484-5028; Dist. by: Vet Text, Colorado State Univ., Veterinary Teaching Hospital, Fort Collins, CO 80523 (SAN 200-7150) Tel 303-491-7101.

Gielow, Fred C., *(Gielow; 0-9603938),* 110 Crestview Ct., Cary, NC 27511 (SAN 215-0778) Tel 914-254-0639.

Giffard Pubns., *(Giffard Pubns; 0-937411),* 11011 SW 117th Ave., Miami, FL 33176 (SAN 658-8697) Tel 305-596-3460.

Gifford, Frederick L, *(Gifford F L; 0-9613464),* 52 W. Main St., Clifton Springs, NY 14432 (SAN 692-9826).

Gifford, George E., Memorial Committee, *(G E Gifford Memorial),* Calvert School, Rising Sun, MD 21911 (SAN 281-739X); Orders to: Frances M. Hubis, 24 Hubis Lane, Rising Sun, MD 21911 (SAN 281-7403) Tel 301-658-6479.

Gift Pubns., *(Gift Pubns; 0-86595),* 3150 Bear St., Costa Mesa, CA 92626 (SAN 216-387X).

Gifted Child Program, *(Gifted Child Prog),* P.O. Box 2503, Berkeley, CA 94702 (SAN 670-7033).

Gifted Education Pr., *(Gifted Educ Pr),* 10201 Yuma Ct., Manassas, VA 22110 (SAN 694-132X) Tel 703-369-5017; P.O. Box 1586, Manassas, VA 22110 (SAN 658-280X).

Gilbert, Pedro L., *(P L Gilbert; 0-9616124),* 1668 Belle Isle Cir., NE, Atlanta, GA 30329 (SAN 699-7384) Tel 404-873-2707.

Gilbert, Skeet, *(S Gilbert; 0-9600548),* Fuquay-Varina, NC 27526 (SAN 204-7144) Tel 919-552-4623.

Gilbert Research, Div. of Don Gilbert Industries, Inc., *(Gilbert Res; 0-937975),* P.O. Box 2188, Jonesboro, AR 72402 (SAN 659-5049) Tel 501-932-6070; 5611 Krueger Dr., Jonesboro, AR 72402 (SAN 659-5057).

Gilchem Corp., *(Gilchem Corp; 0-917122),* Woodlawn Rd., Suite 112, Bldg. 3, Woodlawn Green, Box 11291, Charlotte, NC 28209 (SAN 208-659X) Tel 704-523-2889.

Gilfer Assocs., Inc., *(Gilfer; 0-914542),* P.O. Box 239, Park Ridge, NJ 07656 (SAN 208-3981) Tel 201-391-7887.

Gilgal Pubns., *(Gilgal Pubns; 0-916895),* P.O. Box 3386, Sunriver, OR 97707 (SAN 655-8801) Tel 503-593-8639.

Gilgamesh Pr. Ltd., *(Gilgamesh Pr IL; 0-936684),* 1059 W. Ardmore Ave., Chicago, IL 60660 (SAN 219-9882) Tel 312-334-0327.

Gilgamesh Publishing Co., *(Gilgamesh Pub; 0-914246),* 6050 Blvd. East, West New York, NJ 07093 (SAN 203-6916).

Giligia Pr., *(Giligia; 0-87791),* P.O. Box 126, East Chatham, NY 12002 (SAN 203-4255) Tel 518-312-3793.

Gill, Bernard, *(B Gill),* 4204 W. Warren, Apt. 1, Detroit, MI 48210 (SAN 699-7961).

Gill, Bernard Jamil, *(B J Gill; 0-9616510),* 5012 Ridgewood, Detroit, MI 48204 (SAN 659-4549) Tel 313-898-1074.

Gillen, Jack, Seminars, Inc., *(J Gillen; 0-9617143),* P.O. Box 5179, Orlando, FL 32855 (SAN 663-3285); 2822 Oranole Way, Apopka, FL 32703 (SAN 663-3293) Tel 305-299-1260.

Gillespie, Charles A., *(C A Gillespie; 0-9609974),* 3 Lynwood Ave., Titusville, FL 32796 (SAN 263-1032) Tel 305-269-0643.

Gillespie & Co., *(Gillespie Co; 0-9616404),* P.O. Box 2376, Daly City, CA 94017 (SAN 658-8735) Tel 415-755-5123.

Gillig, Harry, *(Harry Gillig; 0-9600848),* 2624 NE 26th Ave., Fort Lauderdale, FL 33306 (SAN 207-3242) Tel 305-564-8432.

Gilman, Jane L., *(J L Gilman; 0-9612800),* Lott Rd., Sussex, NJ 07461 (SAN 289-9892); Five Cornelia St., New York, NY 10014 (SAN 289-9906) Tel 212-924-8908.

Gilmar Enterprises, *(Gilmar Pr; 0-936402),* P.O. Box 597, Newcastle, CA 95658 (SAN 214-2430).

Gilmore City Centennial Committee, *(Gilmore City; 0-89279),* c/o Mrs. Eugene Dunn, Box 393, Gilmore City, IA 50541 (SAN 645-1750).

Gilmore, Genevieve & Donald, Art Center *See* **Kalamazoo Institute of Arts**

Gim-Ho Enterprises, *(Gim-Ho; 0-9615006),* 5781 Calaveras Cir., La Palma, CA 90623 (SAN 692-3038) Tel 714-531-4108.

Gimbaling Gourmet Pr., *(Gimbaling Gourmet; 0-9617263),* P.O. Box 4264, Annapolis, MD 21403 (SAN 663 5644); 11C President Point Dr., Annapolis, MD 21403 (SAN 663-5652) Tel 301-267-8511.

Gindick, Jon, *(J Gindick),* 530 Ranch Rd., Visalia, CA 93291 (SAN 211-0741) Tel 209-733-1679; Orders to: 530 Ranch Rd., Visalia, CA 93291 (SAN 211-075X).

Gingerbread Hse. *See* **Dutton, E. P.**

Gingery, David J., *(D J Gingery; 0-9604330),* 2045 Boonville, Springfield, MO 65803 (SAN 214-3771) Tel 417-866-7770.

Giniger, K. S., Co., Inc., *(Giniger; 0-934025),* 1133 Broadway, Suite 1301, New York, NY 10010 (SAN 201-8381) Tel 212-645-5150; Orders to: Regnery Gateway Distributors, 940-950- North Shore Dr., Lake Bluff, IL 60044 (SAN 662-0183) Tel 312-295-8088.

Giniger, K. S., Bks. *See* **Stackpole Bks., Inc.**

Ginkgo Hut, *(Ginkgo Hut; 0-936620),* 13 Augusta Dr., Lincroft, NJ 07738 (SAN 215-3157) Tel 201-530-9572.

Ginn Pr., Div. of Ginn & Co., *(Ginn Pr; 0-536),* 191 Spring St., Lexington, MA 02173 (SAN 214-0225) Tel 617-863-2700; Toll free: 800-848-9500.

Ginseng Pr., *(Ginseng Pr; 0-932800),* 74 Poplar Grove Rd., Franklin, NC 28734 (SAN 211-4224) Tel 704-369-9735.

Ginseng Research Institute, *(Ginseng Res Inst; 0-9613800),* P.O. Box 42, Roxbury, NY 12474 (SAN 679-419X) Tel 607-326-7888.

Giordano-Webb Pubns., *(Giordano-Webb; 0-935795),* P.O. Box 1668, Bakersfield, CA 93302 (SAN 697-1377) Tel 805-325-9431; 1930 Truxtun Ave., Bakersfield, CA 93301 (SAN 697-1385).

Giorgi, *(Giorgi; 0-9614222),* 4168 Woodland St., Santa Maria, CA 93455 (SAN 686-807X) Tel 805-937-3518.

Giorno Poetry Systems, *(Giorno Poetry),* 222 Bowery, New York, NY 10012 (SAN 207-8325) Tel 212-925-6372.

Giovanni's Tours, Inc., *(Giovanni's Tour; 0-9612528),* P.O. Box 24, Agoura, CA 91301 (SAN 297-1763).

Girl Scouts of the USA, *(Girl Scouts USA; 0-88441),* 830 Third Ave., New York, NY 10022 (SAN 203-4611) Tel 212-940-7500.

Girs Press, *(Girs Pr),* Streeter Hill Rd., West Chesterfield, NH 03466 (SAN 206-202X) Tel 603-256-8484; Orders to: P.O. Box 91, West Chesterfield, NH 03466 (SAN 206-2038).

Girtman Pr., *(Girtman Pr; 0-9616220),* 1900 Hollyoaks Lake Rd., E, Jacksonville, FL 32211 (SAN 658-5388) Tel 904-641-9751.

†**Gita-Nagari Pr.,** *(Gita-Nagari; 0-911233),* 10310 Oaklyn Rd., Potomac, MD 20854 (SAN 262-8759) Tel 301-983-3386; *CIP.*

†**Glacier Natural History Assn., Inc.,** *(Glacier Nat Hist Assn; 0-916792),* Glacier National Park, West Glacier, MT 59936 (SAN 208-6603) Tel 406-888-5441; *CIP.*

Glahn, Peggy Blanchard, *(P B Glahn; 0-9615821),* 8626 N. Fowler, Clovis, CA 93612 (SAN 696-9291) Tel 209-299-7284.

Glanville Pubs., Inc., Div. of Ocean Group, *(Glanville; 0-87802),* 75 Main St., Dobbs Ferry, NY 10522 (SAN 201-6478) Tel 914-693-1733.

Glaser, Anton, *(A Glaser; 0-9600324),* 1237 Whitney Rd., Southampton, PA 18966 (SAN 201-1999).

Glass Art Pubns., *(Glass Art; 0-9608356),* P.O. Box 2244, Van Nuys, CA 91404 (SAN 240-6594) Tel 818-769-6410.

Glass Publishing Co., *(Glass Pub Co; 0-9614759),* 8711 Village Dr., Suite 112, San Antonio, TX 78217 (SAN 676-5947) Tel 512-653-9555.

Glass Tempering Assn., *(Glass Tempering),* 3310 Harrison St., Topeka, KS 66611 (SAN 224-7739).

Glass Works Press, *(Glass Works; 0-934280),* P.O. Box 81782, San Diego, CA 92138 (SAN 207-2297) Tel 619-563-8165.

Glassbooks, *(Glassbooks Mo; 0-913074),* Rte. 1, Box 357a, Ozark, MO 65721 (SAN 237-9554).

Glassman, Barbara, *(B Glassman; 0-9614443),* P.O. Box 1058, Makawao, Maui, HI 96768 (SAN 689-3619) Tel 808-572-7132.

Glastonbury Pr., *(Glastonbury Pr; 0-932145),* 12816 E. Rose Dr., Whittier, CA 90601 (SAN 686-4309) Tel 213-698-4243; Dist. by: Publishers Group West, 5855 Beaudry St., Emeryville, CA 94608 (SAN 202-8522) Tel 415-658-3453; Toll free: 800-982-8319; Dist. by: Quality Books, Inc., 918 Sherwood Dr., Lake Bluff, IL 60044-2204 (SAN 169-2704) Tel 312-498-4000.

Glazier, Michael, Inc., *(M Glazier; 0-89453),* 1935 W. Fourth St., Wilmington, DE 19805 (SAN 210-2056) Tel 302-654-1635.

Gleason, David King, *(D K Gleason; 0-9612038),* 1766 Nicholson Dr., Baton Rouge, LA 70802 (SAN 286-7869) Tel 504-383-8989.

Glen-Bartlett Publishing Co., *(Glen-Bartlett; 0-9602802),* 105 W. Main St., Westboro, MA 01581 (SAN 213-0645) Tel 617-366-7669.

Glen Hse. Communications, Subs. of Stanley Chase Productions, Inc., *(Glen Hse; 0-918269),* 1937 S. Beverly Glen Blvd., Los Angeles, CA 90025 (SAN 657-257X) Tel 213-475-4236.

Glen-L Marine Design, *(Glen-L Marine),* 9152 Rosecrans, Bellflower, CA 90706 (SAN 203-428X) Tel 213-630-6258.

Names

Glen Pr., *(Glen Pr; 0-9603518),* 2247 Glen Ave., Berkeley, CA 94709 (SAN 215-7667).

Glencoe Publishing Co., Affil. of Macmillan Publishing Co., *(Glencoe; 0-02),* 17337 Ventura Blvd., Encino, CA 91316 (SAN 201-6451) Tel 818-990-3080; Toll free: 800-257-5755.

Glendessary Pr., Inc. *See* **Boyd & Fraser Publishing Co.**

Glenhurst Pubns., Inc., *(Glenhurst Pubns; 0-914227),* Central Community Ctr., 6300 Walker St., St. Louis Park, MN 55416 (SAN 295-365X) Tel 612-925-3632.

Glenmary Research Ctr., *(Glenmary Res Ctr; 0-914422),* 750 Piedmont Ave., NE, Atlanta, GA 30308 (SAN 201-6443) Tel 404-876-6518.

Glenn, Peter, Pubns., Inc., *(Peter Glenn; 0-87314),* 17 E. 48th St., New York, NY 10017 (SAN 201-9930) Tel 212-688-7940; Toll free: 800-223-1254.

Glenn Educational Medical Services, Inc., *(Glenn Educ Med; 0-937449),* P.O. Box 690028, Houston, TX 77269-0028 (SAN 658-876X) Tel 713-586-9056; 176 Old Bridge Lake, Houston, TX 77069 (SAN 658-8778).

Glenn-Ryan Publishing, *(Glenn-Ryan Pub; 0-936963),* 1729 Bette, Mesquite, TX 75149 (SAN 658-6538) Tel 214-222-8409.

Glenndale Books *See* **Capstan Pubns.**

Glennon Publishing Co., *(Glennon Pub; 0-918523),* 636 23rd St., Manhattan Beach, CA 90266 (SAN 657-3452) Tel 213-545-4349.

Glenson Publishing, *(Glenson Pub; 0-934884),* P.O. Box 298, Sterling Heights, MI 48077 (SAN 214-378X).

Global Academic Pubs., Div. of Eden Cross, *(Global Acad Pubs; 1-55633),* 234 Fifth Ave., New York, NY 10001 (SAN 661-3276); Dist. by: Inland Bk. Co., P.O. Box 261, 22 Hemingway Ave., East Haven, CT 06512 (SAN 200-4151) Tel 203-467-4257.

Global Bks., *(Global Bks; 0-9617235),* P.O. Box 2025, Gaithersburg, MD 20879 (SAN 663-5539); 10747 Wayridge Dr., Gaithersburg, MD 20879 (SAN 663-5547) Tel 301-869-1888.

Global Communications, *(Global Comm; 0-938294),* 316 Fifth Ave., New York, NY 10001 (SAN 216-3896) Tel 212-685-4080; Orders to: Box 753, New Brunswick, NJ 08903 (SAN 662-0191).

Global Engineering Documents, Div. of Information Handling Services, *(Global Eng; 0-912702),* 2625 Hickory St., P.O. Box 2504, Santa Ana, CA 92707 (SAN 205-2873) Tel 714-540-9870; Toll free: 800-854-7179.

Global Games, Inc., *(Global Games; 0-9616154),* E. 8112 Sprague Ave., Spokane, WA 99212 (SAN 699-8496) Tel 509-927-0555.

Global Management, Inc., *(Global Man; 0-935871),* P.O. Box 975, Mathews, VA 23109 (SAN 696-4400) Tel 804-725-7795; R.D. Box 107A, Mathews County, Newpoint, VA 23125 (SAN 696-9712).

Global Perspectives in Education, *(Global Perspectives),* 218 E. 18th St., New York, NY 10003 (SAN 236-364X) Tel 212-674-4167.

Global Pr., The, *(Global Pr CO; 0-911285),* 1510 York St., Suite 204, Denver, CO 80206 (SAN 263-1059) Tel 303-393-7647.

Global Pubns., *(Global Pubns CA; 0-9604752),* P.O. Box 2112, Palm Springs, CA 92263 (SAN 215-2207) Tel 619-323-4204.

Global Risk Assessments, Inc., *(Global Risk; 0-914325),* 3638 University Ave., Suite 215, Riverside, CA 92501 (SAN 287-4806) Tel 714-788-0672.

Global Studies Ctr., The, *(Global Studies Ctr; 0-937585),* 1611 N. Kent St., Suite 600, Arlington, VA 22209 (SAN 658-8794) Tel 703-841-0048.

Globe Pequot Pr., Subs. of Boston Globe, *(Globe Pequot; 0-87106),* Old Chester Rd., Chester, CT 06412 (SAN 201-9892) Tel 203-526-9572; Toll free: 800-243-0495 Orders only; P.O. Box Q, Chester, CT 06412 (SAN 658-0769) Tel 203-526-9572; Toll free: 800-962-0973 (CT only).

Globe Pr. Bks., *(Globe Pr Bks; 0-936385),* P.O. Box 2045, Madison Sq. Sta., New York, NY 10159 (SAN 697-3523) Tel 212-807-7540.

Globe Pr., The, *(Globe Pr; 0-910321),* 18803 N. Park Blvd., Cleveland, OH 44122 (SAN 241-5062).

Globe Three, Inc., *(Globe Three; 0-934647),* P.O. Box 265, Middletown, OH 45042 (SAN 694-0293) Tel 513-422-4155.

Globus Pubs., *(Globus Pubs; 0-88669),* P.O. Box 27086, San Francisco, CA 94127 (SAN 265-1416); 332 Balboa St., San Francisco, CA 94118 (SAN 265-1424) Tel 415-668-4723. deceased.

Gloria Pubs., *(Gloria Pubs; 0-9604080),* 2489 East Lake Rd., Livonia, NY 14487 (SAN 221-6132).

Glorycliff Publishing Co., *(Glorycliff Pub; 0-938571),* 4325 Hwy. 91 N., Dillon, MT 59725 (SAN 661-6224) Tel 406-683-5219.

†**Gloucester Art Pr.,** *(Gloucester Art; 0-930582; 0-86650),* P.O. Box 4526, Albuquerque, NM 87196 (SAN 205-2865); 607 McKnight St., NW, Albuquerque, NM 87102 (SAN 662-0205) Tel 505-843-7749; *CIP.*

Gloucester Crescent, *(Gloucester Cres; 0-931151),* 961 Pheasant Run Dr., Spring Valley, OH 45370 (SAN 670-6681) Tel 513-885-4764.

Gloucester Pr. *See* **Watts, Franklin, Inc.**

Glover Pubns., *(Glover Pubns; 0-9602328),* P.O. Box 21745, Seattle, WA 98111 (SAN 221-8275).

Gloy Enterprises, *(Gloy Enter; 0-9616051),* 4336 Market, Suite 504, Riverside, CA 92501 (SAN 698-0716) Tel 714-683-2850.

Gluten Co., Inc., The, *(Gluten Co; 0-935596),* 509 E. 2100 N., Box 482, Provo, UT 84604 (SAN 213-0653) Tel 801-377-6390.

Glyndwr Resources, *(Glyndwr Resc; 0-937505),* 43779 Valley Rd., Decatur, MI 49045 (SAN 658-8832) Tel 616-423-8639.

Glynn Pubns., *(Glynn Pubns; 0-9616342),* P.O. Box 38, Donaldson, IN 46513 (SAN 658-781X) Tel 219-936-3385; 20893 Ninth Rd., Plymouth, IN 46563 (SAN 658-7828).

Glyphic Pr., *(Glyphic Pr; 0-935964),* 665 Killarney Dr., Morgantown, WV 26505 (SAN 213-9235) Tel 304-599-3659.

Gnomon Pr., *(Gnomon Pr; 0-917788),* P.O. Box 106, Frankfort, KY 40602-0106 (SAN 209-0104) Tel 502-223-1858.

Gnosis Pubns., *(Gnosis Pubns; 0-940988),* 1440 Tyler Ave., San Diego, CA 92103 (SAN 223-7709) Tel 619-296-1628.

Goal Enterprises & Associates, *(Goal Ent; 0-9612350),* 6354 N. 11th, Fresno, CA 93710 (SAN 297-1755).

Goat Rock Pubns., *(Goat Rock; 0-9610240),* P.O. Box 21, Jenner, CA 95450 (SAN 264-0600) Tel 707-865-2762.

Godine, David R., Pub., *(Godine; 0-87923),* 300 Massachusetts Ave., Horticultural Hall, Boston, MA 02115 (SAN 213-4381) Tel 617-536-0761; Dist. by: Harper & Row Pubs., Inc., Keystone Industrial Pk., Scranton, PA 18512 (SAN 215-3742); Toll free: 800-242-7737. *Imprints:* Double Detectives (Double Det); Godine Storytellers (Godine Storytellers); Nonpareil Books (Nonpareil Bks).

Godine Storytellers *See* **Godine, David R., Pub., Inc.**

Godiva Publishing, *(Godiva Pub; 0-938018),* P.O. Box 305, Portland, OR 97242 (SAN 214-3097) Tel 503-233-1228.

Gods of the Universe, *(Gods Universe; 0-9607228),* P.O. Box 1543, Highland, IN 46322 (SAN 239-0957) Tel 219-924-8200.

Goehringer & Sons Associates, *(Goehringer & Sons; 0-9601704),* Box 9626, Pittsburgh, PA 15226 (SAN 211-562X) Tel 412-531-9549; 2194 Pauline Ave., Pittsburgh, PA 15216 (SAN 211-5638).

Goethe, Meredyth, Pubs. Ltd., *(Goethe Pubs; 0-9606714),* 3200 Lenox Rd., NE, E411, Atlanta, GA 30324 (SAN 223-7636) Tel 404-237-3735. deceased.

Gold Book, Publications, *(Gold Bk; 0-915493),* P.O. Box 2361, Redding, CA 96099 (SAN 291-171X). *Imprints:* Classic Press (Classic Press).

Gold Circle Productions, *(Gold Circle; 0-943986),* 10783 Eagle Cir., Nevada City, CA 95959 (SAN 241-3841) Tel 916-265-9218.

Gold Crest Productions, *(Gold Crest; 0-941790),* 834 Tyvola Rd., Suite 110, Charlotte, NC 28210 (SAN 239-4294) Tel 704-523-2118.

Gold Hill Publishing Co., Inc., *(Gold Hill; 0-940936),* Drawer F, Virginia City, NV 89440 (SAN 217-3697) Tel 702-847-0222.

Gold Horse Publishing, Inc., *(Gold Horse; 0-912823),* 1981 Moreland Pkwy., Annapolis, MD 21401 (SAN 285-3957) Tel 301-269-0680.

Gold/Kane Enterprises, *(Gold-Kane Ent; 0-9604430),* 1580 Garfield St., Denver, CO 80206 (SAN 220-0554) Tel 303-333-9659.

Gold Medal Bks. *See* **Fawcett Bk. Group**

Gold Penny Press, The, *(Gold Penny; 0-87786),* Box 2177, Canoga Park, CA 91306 (SAN 281-7470) Tel 213-368-1417; Orders to: Associated Booksellers, 147 McKinley Ave., Bridgeport, CT 06606 (SAN 281-7489) Tel 203-366-5494.

Gold Run Pubs., *(Gold Run Pubs; 0-9615975),* 4234 Pueblo St., Carmichael, CA 95608 (SAN 697-3558) Tel 916-481-5733.

Gold Rush Sourdough Co., Inc., *(Gold Rush; 0-912936),* 122 E. Grand Ave., S. San Francisco, CA 94080 (SAN 203-4336) Tel 415-871-0340.

Gold Star Pr., *(Gold Star Pr; 0-915153),* P.O. Box 433, New London, NC 28127 (SAN 289-9337) Tel 704-983-2287.

Gold Star Pubns., *(Gold Star Pubns; 0-941508),* P.O. Box 1451, Sioux Falls, SD 57101 (SAN 239-0965) Tel 605-332-4582.

Gold Stein Pr., *(Gold Stein Pr; 0-938237),* P.O. Box 12280, Santa Ana, CA 91712-2280 (SAN 661-4272); 1600 Galaxy Dr., Newport Beach, CA 92660 (SAN 661-4280) Tel 714-631-4053.

Goldberg, James M., *(J M Goldberg; 0-9603074),* 1828 L St., NW, Suite 660, Washington, DC 20036 (SAN 211-4321) Tel 202-785-2050.

Golden Adler Bks., *(Golden Adler; 0-9616094),* P.O. Box 641, Issaquah, WA 98027-0641 (SAN 698-1089) Tel 206-392-1823.

Golden Aires, Inc., *(Golden Aires; 0-9607910),* 615 W. Deer St., Glenrock, WY 82637 (SAN 239-6513) Tel 307-634-3391.

Golden Aloha, *(Golden Aloha; 0-9614202),* 3450 Meadowbrook Dr., Napa, CA 94558 (SAN 686-7170) Tel 707-255-7042; Dist. by: Gedare Enterprises, Inc., 3450 Meadowbrook Dr., Napa, CA 94558 (SAN 200-5433) Tel 707-255-7042.

Golden Argosy Publishing Co., *(Golden Argosy; 0-9615618),* 112 E. Burnett, Stayton, OR 97383 (SAN 696-4419) Tel 503-769-6088.

Golden Bear Publishing, Inc., Div. of Golden Bear, Inc., *(Golden Bear Pub; 0-938295),* P.O. Box 573, Westport, CT 06881 (SAN 661-1745) Tel 203-226-6022; 56 Hermit Ln., Westport, CT 06881 (SAN 661-1753) Tel 203-226-0892.

Golden Bell Press, *(Golden Bell; 0-87315),* 2403 Champa St., Denver, CO 80205 (SAN 203-4344) Tel 303-572-1777.

Golden Coast Publishing Co., *(Golden Coast; 0-932958),* 22 Waite Dr., Savannah, GA 31406 (SAN 212-355X).

Golden Door, Inc., *(Gold Door Inc; 0-9610790),* P.O. Box 1567, Escondido, CA 92025 (SAN 265-1203) Tel 619-295-5791; 3085 Reynard Way, San Diego, CA 92103 (SAN 265-1211). *Imprints:* Len Forman Publishing Co., Inc. (Len Forman Pub Co).

Golden Dragon Pubs., Inc., *(Golden Dragon Pub; 0-910295),* P.O. Box 1529, Princeton, NJ 08540 (SAN 241-5070) Tel 609-896-1332.

Golden Gambit Bks., *(Golden Gambit; 0-918862),* 76 Weaton Dr., Attleboro, MA 02703 (SAN 210-1181).

Golden Gate *See* **Childrens Pr.**

Golden Gate Pr., *(Golden Gate SF; 0-9616288),* 2022 Taraval, No. 2185, San Francisco, CA 94116 (SAN 658-6074) Tel 415-586-3388.

Golden Gate Productions/KQED, Inc., *(Golden Gate Prod; 0-912333),* 500 Eighth St., San Francisco, CA 94103 (SAN 265-1246) Tel 415-553-2221.

Golden Gate Univ. Press, *(Golden Gate Law; 0-943844),* 536 Mission St., San Francisco, CA 94105 (SAN 241-0249) Tel 415-442-7204.

Golden Glow Pr., *(Golden Glow Pr; 0-931355),* P.O. Box 1689, Aptos, CA 95001 (SAN 688-2633) Tel 408-425-3208. Do not confuse with Golden Glow Publishing, Sturgeon Bay, WI.

Golden Glow Publishing, *(Golden Glow; 0-933072),* 9240 Limekiln Rd., Sturgeon Bay, WI 54235 (SAN 212-3568) Tel 414-824-5774. Do not confuse with Golden Glow Pr., Aptos, CA.

Golden Hands Pr., *(Golden Hands Pr; 0-9616422),* 29505 Sugarspring Rd., Farmington Hills, MI 48018 (SAN 658-8859) Tel 313-626-4093.

Golden Hill Books, *(Golden Hill; 0-9605364),* P.O. Box 5598, Helena, MT 59604 (SAN 216-1354) Tel 406-443-0678.

Golden Hill Pr., *(Golden Hl Pr NY; 0-9614876),* Box 122, Spencertown, NY 12165 (SAN 623-031X) Tel 518-392-2358. Do not confuse with Golden Pr of Racine, WI.

Golden Hind Pr., *(Golden Hind Pr; 0-931267),* 3 Church Cir., Suite 206, Annapolis, MD 21401 (SAN 681-9869) Tel 301-263-7330.

Golden Hinde Publishing, *(Golden Hinde Pub; 0-936717),* 760 Market St., No. 1036, San Francisco, CA 94102 (SAN 699-847X) Tel 415-956-5966.

Golden Horseshoe, *(Golden Horseshoe; 0-9617096),* P.O. Drawer O, Emory, VA 24327 (SAN 662-4839) Tel 703-944-3529.

Golden Key Pubns., *(Golden Key; 0-9602166),* P.O. Box 1463, Mesa, AZ 85201-0270 (SAN 212-3576) Tel 602-834-7000; Dist. by: DeVorss & Co., P.O. Box 550, Marina del Rey, CA 90291 (SAN 662-7250) Tel 213-870-7478.

Golden Keys Success Seminar, Inc., *(Gold Key Succ),* P.O. Box 9358, Salt Lake City, UT 84109 (SAN 240-852X).

†**Golden-Lee Bk.,** Div. of Golden-Lee Book Distributors, Inc., *(Golden-Lee Bk; 0-912331),* 1000 Dean St., Brooklyn, NY 11238 (SAN 265-1254) Tel 718-857-6333; Toll free: 800-221-0960; *CIP.*

Golden Light Press, *(Golden Light; 0-940086),* 4956 Sable Pine Circle C-1, West Palm Beach, FL 33409 (SAN 217-0728).

Golden Mean Pubs., The, *(Golden Mean; 0-937698),* 271 Beach St., Ashland, OR 97520 (SAN 216-2490) Tel 503-482-9771.

Golden Owl Pubs., *(Golden Owl Pub; 0-9601258),* 182 Chestnut Rd., Lexington Park, MD 20653 (SAN 210-4288) Tel 301-863-9253.

Golden Palm Pr., Div. of Educational Services Unltd., *(Golden Palm Pr; 0-937319),* P.O. Box 3822, Santa Ana, CA 92703 (SAN 658-7836) Tel 714-834-9225; 2525 N. Park Blvd., Santa Ana, CA 92706 (SAN 658-7844).

Golden Phoenix Pr., *(Golden Phoenix; 0-910727),* 1300 LaPlaya No. 1, San Francisco, CA 94122 (SAN 262-6772) Tel 415-681-1563.

Golden Poplar Pr., *(Golden Poplar Pr; 0-918907),* Box 792, East Lansing, MI 48823 (SAN 670-1043) Tel 517-351-6751.

Golden Pr. See Western Pub. Co., Inc.

Golden Publications, *(Golden Pubns; 0-918783),* 21393 Back Alley Rd., Bend, OR 97702 (SAN 657-3460) Tel 503-382-1622.

Golden Puffer Press, *(Golden Puffer; 0-9607022),* 3150 W. Tucana, Tucson, AZ 85745 (SAN 238-8774) Tel 602-743-7827.

Golden Quill Pr., The, Subs. of Audio Amateur Pubns., *(Golden Quill; 0-8233),* Avery Rd., Francestown, NH 03043 (SAN 201-6419) Tel 603-547-6622.

†**Golden Quill Pubs., Inc.,** *(Gold Quill Pubs CA; 0-933904),* P.O. Box 1278-R, Colton, CA 92324 (SAN 213-0726) Tel 714-783-0119; *CIP.*

Golden Rainbow Press, *(Golden Rainbow Pr),* P.O. Box 106, Houston, TX 77001 (SAN 212-6605).

Golden Robes Pr., *(Gold Robes Pr; 0-9616140),* P.O. Box 632, Siletz, OR 97380 (SAN 699-9743) Tel 503-444-2778; 5137 Logsden Rd., Siletz, OR 97380 (SAN 699-9751).

Golden Sceptre Publishing, *(Golden Sceptre; 0-9615117),* 1442A Walnut St., Suite 61, Berkeley, CA 94706 (SAN 694-1532) Tel 415-525-1481; Dist. by: Bookpeople, 2929 Fifth St., Berkeley, CA 94710 (SAN 168-9517); Toll free: 800-227-1516; Dist. by: New Leaf Distributing, 1020 White St., SW, Atlanta, GA 30310 (SAN 169-1449) Tel 404-755-2665; Toll free: 800-624-4466 in California.

Golden Seal Research Headquarters, *(Golden Seal; 0-912368),* P.O. Box 27821, Hollywood, CA 90027 (SAN 201-8365).

Golden State Dance Teachers Assn., Affil. of Alterra Publishing, *(Golden St Dance Teach Assn; 0-932980),* 10804 Woodruff Ave., Downey, CA 90241-3910 (SAN 212-6613) Tel 213-869-8949.

Golden State Industries Corp., *(Golden State Indus),* 5042 E. Third St., Los Angeles, CA 90022 (SAN 211-9536).

Golden West Historical Pubns., *(Golden West Hist; 0-930960),* P.O. Box 1906, Ventura, CA 93002-1906 (SAN 212-6621).

†**Golden West Pubs.,** *(Golden West Pub; 0-914846),* 4113 N. Longview, Phoenix, AZ 85014 (SAN 207-5652) Tel 602-265-4392; *CIP.*

†**Goldenleaf Pub,** *(Goldenleaf Pub Co; 0-930047),* P.O. Box 405, Valley Center, CA 92082 (SAN 669-8344) Tel 619-749-0023; *CIP.*

Goldermood Rainbow, *(Goldermood Rainbow; 0-916402),* 331 W. Bonneville St., Pasco, WA 99301 (SAN 207-835X) Tel 509-547-5525.

Goldfield Pubns., Inc., *(Goldfield San Diego; 0-936341),* 1501 Goldfield St., San Diego, CA 92122 (SAN 697-8630) Tel 619-276-5035.

Goldfield Publishing, *(Goldfield Pub),* 8400 Melrose Ave., Los Angeles, CA 90069 (SAN 241-385X).

Goldstein Gallery, Univ. of Minnesota, *(Goldstein MN; 0-939719),* 1985 Buford St., 240 McNeal Hall, St. Paul, MN 55108 (SAN 663-6268) Tel 612-624-3292.

Goldstein Software, Inc., *(Goldstein Soft; 0-939933),* 12520 Prosperity Dr., Suite 340, Silver Spring, MD 20904 (SAN 661-8782) Tel 301-622-9020.

†**Golem Pr.,** *(Golem; 0-911762),* P.O. Box 1342, Boulder, CO 80306 (SAN 203-4379) Tel 303-444-0841; *CIP.*

Golembe Assocs., Inc., *(Golembe Assocs; 0-9608840),* 1025 Thomas Jefferson St. NW, Suite 301, Washington, DC 20007 (SAN 238-8235) Tel 202-337-5550.

Golf Assocs., *(Golf Assoc; 0-9607140),* P.O. Box 2244, Menlo Park, CA 94025 (SAN 238-9835) Tel 415-854-4621.

Golf Digest/Tennis, Inc., Subs. of New York Times, *(Golf Digest; 0-914178),* 5520 Park Ave., Box 395, Trumbull, CT 06611-0395 (SAN 212-7431) Tel 203-373-7119; P.O. Box 0395, Trumbull, CT 06611-0395 (SAN 699-5276); Dist. by: Simon & Schuster, 1230 Ave. of the Americas, New York, NY 10020 (SAN 200-2450) Tel 212-245-6400.

Golf Sports Publishing, *(Golf Sports Pub; 0-930049),* P.O. Box 3687, Lacey, WA 98503 (SAN 669-8387) Tel 206-491-8067.

Goliards Press, *(Goliards Pr),* 3515 18th St., Bellingham, WA 98225 (SAN 206-9903).

Goll, Reinhold W., *(R W Goll; 0-9606716),* 1942B Mather Way, Elkins Park, PA 19117 (SAN 212-4246).

Gollehon Pr., Inc., *(Gollehon Pr; 0-914839),* 3105 Madison Ave. SE, Grand Rapids, MI 49508 (SAN 289-2170) Tel 616-247-8231; Toll free: 800-262-4947.

GoLo Pr., Div. of Golo Enterprises, *(GoLo Press; 0-9614983),* P.O. Box 1500, Shepherdstown, WV 25443 (SAN 693-756X) Tel 304-876-3254.

Golz, J.L., Co., *(J L Golz Co; 0-914123),* 975 S. Laurelwood Ln., Anaheim, CA 92806 (SAN 287-4822) Tel 714-774-0551. Imprints: Spirit Press (Spirit Pr).

Gondolier Pr., *(Gondolier; 0-935824),* P.O. Box QQQ, Southampton, NY 11968 (SAN 214-0233).

Gondwana Books, Div. of Alta Napa Pr., *(Gondwana Bks; 0-931926),* 1969 Mora Ave., Calistoga, CA 94515 (SAN 212-0208) Tel 707-942-4444.

Gong Enterprise Incorporated, *(Gong Ent; 0-916713),* P.O. Box 1753, Bristol, VA 24203 (SAN 654-5122) Tel 703-466-4672.

Gong Productions, *(Gong Prods),* 3525 Diamond Ave., Suite 309, Oakland, CA 94602 (SAN 289-1581).

Gonzaga Univ. Press, *(Gonzaga U Pr),* Spokane, WA 99202 (SAN 206-4480).

Gonzalez, Fernando L., *(F L Gonzalez; 0-9601090),* P.O. Box 1812, Flushing, NY 11352 (SAN 210-0924).

Good Apple, Inc., *(Good Apple; 0-916456; 0-86653),* P.O. Box 299, Carthage, IL 62321 (SAN 208-6646) Tel 217-357-3981; Toll free: 800-435-7234.

†**Good Bks.,** Subs. of Good Enterprises, Ltd., *(Good Bks PA; 0-934672),* Main St., Intercourse, PA 17534 (SAN 693-9597) Tel 717-768-7171; Toll free: 800-762-7171; *CIP.*

Good Food Books, *(Good Food Bks; 0-932398),* 17 Colonial Terrace, Maplewood, NJ 07040 (SAN 212-8535) Tel 201-762-0841.

Good Friends See Ideals Publishing Corp.

†**Good Gay Poets,** *(Good Gay),* P.O. Box 277, Astor Sta., Boston, MA 02123 (SAN 207-3536) Tel 617-661-7534; *CIP.*

Good Hope Press, *(Good Hope GA; 0-9608596),* 75 Silverwood Rd., NE, Atlanta, GA 30342 (SAN 240-6608) Tel 404-255-7416.

Good Hope Publishing Co., The, *(Good Hope Pub; 0-9608562),* 16541 Warwick, Detroit, MI 48219 (SAN 240-6616) Tel 313-532-2531.

Good Ideas Co., *(Good Ideas; 0-9603940),* Box 296, Berea, OH 44017 (SAN 212-5072) Tel 216-234-5411.

Good Life Pr., Div. of Charing Cross Publishing Co., *(Good Life; 0-89074),* 658 S. Bonnie Brae St., Los Angeles, CA 90057 (SAN 206-4944) Tel 213-483-5832.

Good Life Publishers, *(Good Life VA; 0-917374),* 14200 Nash Rd., Chesterfield, VA 23832 (SAN 208-6654) Tel 804-794-4954.

Good Money Pubns., Inc., *(Good Money Pubns; 0-933609),* Box 363, Worcester, VT 05682 (SAN 692-459X) Tel 802-223-3911; Toll free: 800-535-3551.

Good News: A Forum For Scriptual Christianity, Inc., *(Good News KY),* 308 E. Main St., Wilmore, KY 40390 (SAN 657-1441) Tel 606-858-4661.

Good News Pubs., *(Good News; 0-89107),* 9825 W. Roosevelt Rd., Westchester, IL 60153 (SAN 211-7991) Tel 312-345-7474; Toll free: 800-323-3890 Sales only. Imprints: Crossway Books (Crossway Bks).

Good Old Spot Pr., *(Good Old Spot Pr; 0-9616718),* 10727 20th Ave. NE, Seattle, WA 98125 (SAN 661-3764) Tel 206-363-2685; Dist. by: Pacific Pipeline, Inc., 19215 66th Ave. S, Kent, WA 98032 (SAN 208-2128) Tel 206-872-5523; Toll free: 800-562-4647 (WA).

Good Sign Pubns., *(Good Sign; 0-937730),* 457 Ruthven Ave., Palo Alto, CA 94301 (SAN 215-6482).

Good Soldier Pubns., *(Good Soldier Pubns; 0-9616499),* 4817 Crestwood, Waco, TX 76710 (SAN 659-2384) Tel 817-772-5630.

Goodale Publishing, *(Goodale Pub; 0-9609662),* 1903 Kenwood Pkwy., Minneapolis, MN 55405 (SAN 262-0294) Tel 612-377-5783.

Goode, J. Norman, *(J N Goode; 0-914811),* 4121 Buckthorn St., Lewisville, TX 75028 (SAN 289-2154) Tel 214-539-1115.

Goode/Steely Associates, *(Goode-Steely Assocs; 0-9612620),* 31473 Rudolph Rd., Cottage Grove, OR 97424 (SAN 289-2162) Tel 503-942-7361.

Goodfellow Catalog Pr., Inc., *(Goodfellow; 0-936016),* P.O. Box 4520, Berkeley, CA 94704 (SAN 206-4499) Tel 415-845-2062. Imprints: Liplop Press (Pub. by Liplop).

†**Goodheart-Willcox Co.,** *(Goodheart; 0-87006),* 123 W. Taft Dr., South Holland, IL 60473 (SAN 203-4387) Tel 312-333-7200; Toll free: 800-323-0440; *CIP.*

Goodkind, Herbert K., Estate of, *(H K Goodkind; 0-9600498),* 151 Fenimore Rd., Apt. 63B, Mamaroneck, NY 10543 (SAN 203-4700) Tel 914-698-7854.

Goodlife Pubs., *(Goodlife Pubs; 0-938593),* 323 Franklin Bldg., Suite 804/J-55, Chicago, IL 60606-7095 (SAN 661-1559); 50 Broome St., Brooklyn, NY 11222 (SAN 661-1567) Tel 718-384-7015.

Goodlife Resources, Inc., *(Good Life Resources),* 5764 Mill St., Erie, PA 16509 (SAN 241-3868) Tel 814-868-3349.

†**Goodman, Thomas H.,** *(T H Goodman; 0-9601252),* 3218 Shelburne Rd., Baltimore, MD 21208 (SAN 210-4296) Tel 301-358-2817; *CIP.*

Goodmaster Bks., *(Goodmaster Bks; 0-937235),* 1490 Rte. 23, Wayne, NJ 07470 (SAN 658-6481) Tel 201-284-1963.

Names

Names

Goodrich Press, *(Goodrich Pr; 0-9612734),* P.O. Box 2265, Ann Arbor, MI 48106 (SAN 289-9345) Tel 313-665-6597.

Goose Pond Pr., *(Goose Pond Pr; 0-910835),* 11600 Southwest Freeway, Suite 179, Houston, TX 77031 (SAN 270-5419) Tel 617-259-9842.

Gopher Graphics, *(Gopher; 0-936511),* RD 2, Box 323, Greene, NY 13778 (SAN 697-8649) Tel 607-656-4531.

†**Gorak Bks.,** *(Gorak Bks; 0-918803),* P.O. Box 5411, Pasadena, CA 91107 (SAN 669-6856) Tel 818-795-5520; *CIP.*

Goranson Press, *(Goranson Pr),* 7624 W. Raschen Ave., Chicago, IL 60656 (SAN 207-2300).

†**Gordian Pr., Inc.,** *(Gordian; 0-87752),* P.O. Box 304, Staten Island, NY 10304 (SAN 201-6389) Tel 718-273-4700; *CIP.*

Gordon, David C., *(D C Gordon; 0-9616919),* 7056 Dryer Rd., Victor, NY 14564 (SAN 662-5681) Tel 716-924-3116.

Gordon, Harry G., *(H G Gordon; 0-9612184),* 711 Coleridge Dr., Greensboro, NC 27410 (SAN 287-2935) Tel 919-279-6400.

Gordon, Marilyn, ,Pub., *(M Gordon Pub; 0-9609542),* 2153 Westchester Ave., Bronx, NY 10462 (SAN 260-1923) Tel 212-829-0830.

Gordon, William R., *(W R Gordon; 0-910662),* 232 Beresford Rd., Rochester, NY 14610 (SAN 202-9405) Tel 716-288-8549; Orders to: Harold E. Cox, 80 Virginia Terrace, Forty Fort, PA 18704 (SAN 202-1943); Dist. by: National RR Historical Society, P.O. Box 664, Rochester, NY 14602 (SAN 282-0447) Tel 716-244-6438.

Gordon & Breach Science Pubs., Inc., *(Gordon & Breach; 0-677),* P.O. Box 786 Cooper Sta., New York, NY 10276 (SAN 201-6370) Tel 212-206-8900.

Gordon-Cremonesi Book, *(Gordon-Cremonesi),* 115 Fifth Ave., New York, NY 10003 (SAN 694-9541) Tel 212-486-2700.

†**Gordon Pr. Pubs.,** *(Gordon Pr; 0-87968; 0-8490),* P.O. Box 459, Bowling Green Sta., New York, NY 10004 (SAN 201-6362); *CIP.*

Gordons & T. Weinberg, *(Gordons & Weinberg; 0-9603484),* P.O. Box 3101, Princeville, HI 96722 (SAN 213-571X) Tel 808-826-6380.

Gordonstown Press, *(Gordonstown; 0-9603942),* Box U, Dillon, CO 80435 (SAN 214-3100).

Gordy Press, *(Gordy Pr; 0-936472),* 330 Pine Ridge Rd., Jackson, MS 39206 (SAN 216-1362) Tel 601-362-6518.

Gorsuch Scarisbrick, Pubs., *(Gorsuch Scarisbrick; 0-89787),* 8233 Via Paseo del Norte, Suite E400, Scottsdale, AZ 85258 (SAN 220-5920) Tel 602-991-7881.

Gos Inc., *(Gos Inc; 0-942258),* P.O. Box 3912, Missoula, MT 59806 (SAN 237-9562).

Goshen College, *(Goshen Coll; 0-913859),* 1700 S. Main St., Goshen, IN 46526 (SAN 287-7260) Tel 219-533-3161.

Goshindo Martial Arts, *(Goshindo Martial; 0-9613678),* 11 Sterling Ave., Tappan, NY 10983 (SAN 670-9427) Tel 914-359-7023.

†**Gospel Advocate Co., Inc.,** *(Gospel Advocate; 0-89225),* P.O. Box 150, Nashville, TN 37202 (SAN 205-2792); Toll free: 800-251-8446; 1006 Elm Hill Pike, Nashville, TN 37210 (SAN 662-0213); Toll free: 800-242-8006 in Tennesee; Dist. by: Christian Communications, P.O. Box 150, Nashville, TN 37202 (SAN 200-7207); Toll free: 800-251-8446; Toll free: 800-342-8006 in Tennessee; *CIP.*

Gospel Place, The, *(Gospel Place),* P.O. Box 110304, Nashville, TN 37211 (SAN 277-6847) Tel 615-377-3910.

†**Gospel Publishing Hse.,** Div. of General Council of the Assemblies of God, *(Gospel Pub; 0-88243),* 1445 Boonville Ave., Springfield, MO 65802 (SAN 206-8826) Tel 417-862-2781; Toll free: 800-641-4310; Toll free: 800-492-7625 in Missouri; *CIP.*

Gospel Themes Pr., *(Gospel Themes Pr; 0-938855),* 710 S. 140th, Seattle, WA 93168 (SAN 662-5797) Tel 206-243-8591.

Gospic Realty Corp., *(Gospic Realty; 0-943898),* 63 Little Clove Rd., Staten Island, NY 10301 (SAN 241-1172) Tel 718-981-6361.

Goss & Co., Pubs., *(Goss; 0-912010),* 396 Redwood Dr., Pasadena, CA 91105 (SAN 203-4409) Tel 213-257-1773.

Gotham Book Mart, *(Gotham; 0-910664),* 41 W. 47th St., New York, NY 10036 (SAN 203-4417) Tel 212-719-4448.

Gothic Bookshop, *(Gothic; 0-917585),* P.O. Box LM, Durham, NC 27706 (SAN 656-8866) Tel 919-684-3986.

Gottlieb & Allen, *(Gottlieb & Allen; 0-930768),* 200 E. 27th St., New York, NY 10016 (SAN 211-4232).

Gottlieb's Bakery, *(Gottlieb's Bakery),* 1601 Bull St., Savannah, GA 31401 (SAN 655-8372); Dist. by: Wimmer Brothers, 4120 B.F. Goodrich Blvd., Memphis, TN 38181 (SAN 209-6544) Tel 901-362-8900.

Gotuit Enterprises, *(Gotuit Ent; 0-931490),* 13342 El Dorado Dr., No. 191-A., P.O. Box 2568, Seal Beach, CA 90740 (SAN 211-3597) Tel 213-430-5198.

Gould, Bruce, Pubns., *(B Gould Pubns; 0-918706),* P.O. Box 16, Seattle, WA 98111 (SAN 210-9964).

Gould, Jay, Enterprises, *(J Gould; 0-9608332),* 7840 Old Auburn Rd., Fort Wayne, IN 46825 (SAN 240-5334) Tel 219-489-4441.

Gould Pubns., *(Gould; 0-87526),* 199/300 State St., Binghamton, NY 13901 (SAN 201-6354) Tel 607-724-3000.

Gourmet Guides, *(Gourmet Guides; 0-937024),* 1767 Stockton St., San Francisco, CA 94133 (SAN 214-3798).

Gourmet Publications, *(Gourmet Pubns; 0-9611388),* 1401 W. Calle Kino, Tucson, AZ 85704 (SAN 283-9024) Tel 602-297-1281.

Gousha, H. M., Co., The, *(H M Gousha; 0-88098),* 2001 The Alameda, San Jose, CA 95150 (SAN 281-7519) Tel 408-296-1060; Orders to: Dept. TM, P.O. Box 6227, San Jose, CA 95150 (SAN 281-7527).

Government Data Pubns., *(Gov Data Pubns),* 1120 Connecticut Ave., NW, Washington, DC 20036 (SAN 207-3439).

Government Institutes, Inc., *(Gov Insts; 0-86587),* 966 Hungerford Dr., Suite 24, Rockville, MD 20850 (SAN 214-3801).

Government Product News, *(Gov Prod News; 0-9611182),* 1111 Chester Ave., Cleveland, OH 44114 (SAN 277-6855) Tel 216-696-7000.

†**Government Research Pubns.,** *(Gov Res Pubns; 0-931684),* Box 122, Newton Center, MA 02159 (SAN 211-4674); *CIP.*

Government Research Service, *(Govt Res Serv; 0-9615227),* 701 Jackson, Rm. 304, Topeka, KS 66603 (SAN 695-1430) Tel 913-232-7720.

Governmental Research Assn., Inc., *(GRA; 0-931684),* 24 Province St., Boston, MA 02108 (SAN 205-275X) Tel 617-720-1000.

Gowan, J. C., *(Gowan; 0-9606822),* 1426 Southwind, Westlake Village, CA 91361 (SAN 202-0343) Tel 818-991-0342.

Gower, Herschel, *(Herschel Gower; 0-9613156),* 1006 Estes Rd., Nashville, TN 37215 (SAN 294-9334) Tel 615-269-0669; Dist. by: Austin Periodical Services, 499 Merritt Ave., Nashville, TN 37203 (SAN 169-5576).

Gower Publishing Co., Div. of Gower Publishing Co., Ltd. (UK), *(Gower Pub Co; 0-566),* Old Post Rd., Brookfield, VT 05036 (SAN 262-0308) Tel 802-276-3162.

Grace, Louise P., *(L P Grace; 0-9613652),* 8338 San Leandro, Dallas, TX 75218 (SAN 679-1808) Tel 214-327-5207.

Grace Lutheran Foundation of Boulder Colorado, Inc., *(G Lutheran Foun; 0-9606516),* 1001 13th St., Boulder, CO 80302 (SAN 217-1783) Tel 303-442-1883.

Grace Pubns., *(Grace Pubns; 0-911925),* P.O. Box 1383, San Marcos, CA 92069 (SAN 264-0635) Tel 619-722-4161.

†**Grace Publishing Co.,** *(Grace Pub Co),* P.O. Box 23385, Tampa, FL 33622 (SAN 211-8017) Tel 813-884-8003; *CIP.*

Grace Publishing House, *(Grace Pub House; 0-9605576),* 10505 Cole Rd., Whittier, CA 90604 (SAN 238-3543) Tel 213-944-7372.

Grace World Outreach Ctr., *(Grace World Outreach; 0-933643),* 2695 Creve Coeur Mill Rd., Maryland Heights, MO 63043 (SAN 692-6495) Tel 314-291-6647.

Gracelaine Pubns., *(Gracelaine; 0-932984),* 3001 Ashley Ave., Montgomery, AL 36109 (SAN 212-2804).

Graceway Publishing Co., Inc., *(Graceway; 0-932126),* P.O. Box 159, Sta."C", Flushing, NY 11367 (SAN 212-0976) Tel 718-261-0759.

Gracie Enterprises, Inc., *(Gracie Ent; 0-9606398),* P.O. Box 506, Chula Vista, CA 92012 (SAN 226-7934) Tel 619-421-8055.

Grade Finders, Inc., *(Grade Finders),* 642 Lancaster Ave., Berwyn, PA 19312 (SAN 208-2322) Tel 215-644-4159; Orders to: P.O. Box 444, Bala-Cynwyd, PA 19004 (SAN 208-2330).

Graduate Group, The, Div. of Whitman Assocs., *(Graduate Group; 0-938609),* 86 Norwood Rd., West Hartford, CT 06117 (SAN 661-5902) Tel 203-232-3100.

Graduate Management Admission Council, *(Grad Mgmt Admin; 0-943846),* 11601 Wilshire Blvd., Los Angeles, CA 90025-1748 (SAN 218-7469); Dist. by: Educational Testing Service, P.O. Box 966, Princeton, NJ 08541 (SAN 238-034X) Tel 609-921-9000.

Graduate School Pr., *(Grad School; 0-87771),* U.S. Dept. of Agriculture, South Bldg., Rm. 1404, Washington, DC 20250 (SAN 203-4425) Tel 202-447-7123; Orders to: 600 Maryland Ave., SW, Rm. 142, Washington, DC 20024 (SAN 662-0221) Tel 202-382-8635.

Graeff, Roderick W., Dr.-Ing., *(Graeff; 0-9604570),* 607 Church, Ann Arbor, MI 48104 (SAN 215-2126) Tel 313-769-6588.

Graeme Publishing Corp., *(Graeme Pub; 0-937587),* P.O. Box 549, Wilbraham, MA 01095 (SAN 658-8883) Tel 413-596-3176.

Graffeo's Hostess Helper, Inc., *(Graffeo's Hostess; 0-9616869),* 705 S. Guegnon, Abbeville, LA 70510 (SAN 661-1311) Tel 318-893-3897.

Graham, Gordon, & Co., *(G Graham; 0-9616353),* P.O. Box 608, Fall City, WA 98024 (SAN 658-9464) Tel 206-222-9840; 5815 Preston Hwy., Fall City, WA 98024 (SAN 658-9472).

Graham, Josephine, *(J Graham),* c/o Suggin Productions, 7710 Choctaw Rd., Little Rock, AR 72205 (SAN 209-8911).

Graham & Trotman, Inc., Subs. of Graham & Trotman Ltd., *(Graham & Trotman; 0-86010),* 13 Park Ave., Gaithersburg, MD 20877 (SAN 699-5284) Tel 301-670-1767.

Graham Conley Pr., *(Graham Conley; 0-912087),* Box 2968, New Haven, CT 06515 (SAN 224-746X) Tel 203-389-0183.

Graham Pubns., Inc., *(Graham Pubns; 0-936167),* Winsted Ctr., Rte. 59 N., Joliet, IL 60435 (SAN 697-0923) Tel 815-436-8988.

†**Gramercy Books Press, Inc.,** *(Gramercy Bks; 0-935134),* 354 George St, New Brunswick, NJ 08901 (SAN 213-845X); *CIP.*

Gramm, E. F., Pr., *(E F Gramm Pr; 0-912989),* 130 Simsbury Dr., Ithaca, NY 14850 (SAN 283-0965) Tel 607-257-1328.

Grammar Simplified, *(Grammar; 0-9616040),* 4010 N. Brandywine Dr., No. 318, Peoria, IL 61614 (SAN 698-0260) Tel 309-685-7025.

Grammatical Sciences, *(Grammatical Sci),* 1236 Jackson St., Santa Clara, CA 95050 (SAN 203-4433).

Granberg, Ronald Scott, *(R S Granberg),* c/o Law Distributors, 14415 S. Main St., Gardena, CA 90248 (SAN 212-3681).

Grand Bks., Inc., *(Grand Bks Inc; 0-930809),* P.O. Box 7, Middleton, MI 48856 (SAN 677-6361) Tel 517-875-4249.

Grand Canyon Natural History Assn., *(GCNHA; 0-938216),* P.O. Box 399, Grand Canyon, AZ 86023 (SAN 215-7675).

Grand River Pr., *(Grand River; 0-936343),* P.O. Box 1342, East Lansing, MI 48823 (SAN 697-8657) Tel 517-351-3641; 144 Highland Ave., East Lansing, MI 48823 (SAN 698-2255).

Grand Strand Humane Society, *(Grand Strand; 0-9616053),* 6300 N. Ocean Blvd., Myrtle Beach, SC 29577 (SAN 698-0686) Tel 803-449-5206.

Grandin, E. B., Bk. Co., Inc., *(E B Grandin; 0-910523),* 148 N. 100 W., Provo, UT 84601 (SAN 260-1931) Tel 801-224-6706.

Granite Hill Corp., *(Granite Hill),* RFD No. 1, P.O. Box 210, Hallowell, ME 04347 (SAN 287-1718).

Granite Pr., *(Granite Pr; 0-9614886)*, P.O. Box 7, Penobscot, ME 04476 (SAN 693-2428) Tel 207-326-9322; Dist. by: Bookslinger, 213 E. Fourth St., St. Paul, MN 55101 (SAN 169-4154); Dist. by: Bookpeople, 2929 Fifth St., Berkeley, CA 94710 (SAN 168-9517); Dist. by: Inland Bk. Co., P.O. Box 261, 22 Hemingway Ave., East Haven, CT 06512 (SAN 200-4151); Toll free: 800-243-0138.

Granite Pubs., *(Granite Pubs; 0-935669)*, 2717 B Houma Blvd., Metairie, LA 70006 (SAN 696-4435) Tel 504-455-3380.

Grannis, Alberta M., *(A M Grannis; 0-9613774)*, 790 NE 97th St., Miami Shores, FL 33138 (SAN 678-9579) Tel 305-759-0584.

Grant, Donald M., Publisher, Inc, *(D M Grant; 0-937986)*, West Kingston, RI 02892 (SAN 281-7535) Tel 401-783-3266; Dist. by: Pacific Comics, Inc., 4887 Ronson Ct., Suite E, San Diego, CA 95945 (SAN 169-0124); Dist. by: Bud Plant Inc., 13393 Grass Valley Dr., Suite 7, P.O. Box 1886, Grass Valley, CA 95945 (SAN 268-5086); Dist. by: F & S.F. Book Co., P.O. Box 415, Staten Island, NY 10302 (SAN 169-6270).

Grant Corner Inn, *(Grant Corner Inn; 0-9616719)*, 122 Grant Ave., Santa Fe, NM 87501 (SAN 661-373X) Tel 505-983-6678.

Granville Pubns., *(Granville Pubns; 0-931349)*, 10960 Wilshire, Suite 826, Los Angeles, CA 90024 (SAN 682-5796) Tel 213-477-3924.

†Grapetree Productions, Inc., *(Grapetree Prods; 0-941374)*, Box 10cn, 600 Grapetree Dr., Key Biscayne, FL 33149 (SAN 239-3638) Tel 305-361-2060; *CIP*.

Grapevine, Inc., *(Grapevine Inc; 0-937931)*, P.O. Box 706, Ooltewah, TN 37363 (SAN 659-5065) Tel 615-238-5586; 9515 Lee Way, Suite E, Ooltewah, TN 37363 (SAN 659-5073).

Grapevine Pubns, Inc., *(Grapevine Pubns; 0-931011)*, P.O. Box 118, Corvallis, OR 97339 (SAN 678-9714) Tel 503-754-0583.

Graphic Artists Guild, *(Graphic Artists; 0-932102)*, c/o Robert Silver Associates, 307 E. 37th St., New York, NY 10016 (SAN 295-334X).

Graphic Arts Ctr. Publishing Co., *(Gr Arts Ctr Pub; 0-912856; 0-932575)*, P.O. Box 10306, Portland, OR 97210 (SAN 201-6338) Tel 503-226-2402; Toll free: 800-452-3032.

Graphic Arts Technical Foundation, *(Graphic Arts Tech Found)*, 4615 Forbes Ave., Pittsburgh, PA 15213 (SAN 224-778X) Tel 412-621-6941.

Graphic Arts Trade Journals, *(Graph Arts Trade; 0-910762)*, 399 Conklin St., Suite 306, P.O. Box 81, Farmingdale, NY 11735 (SAN 206-8281) Tel 516-694-4842.

Graphic Communications Assn., *(Graph Comm Assn; 0-933505)*, 1730 N. Lynn St., Suite 604, Arlington, VA 22209 (SAN 224-7798).

Graphic Communications Ctr., *(Graphic Comm Ctr; 0-89667)*, P.O Box 357, Appleton, WI 54912 (SAN 201-632X).

Graphic Communications, Inc., *(Graphic Comm; 0-924247)*, 200 Fifth Ave., Waltham, MA 02254 (SAN 284-8880) Tel 617-890-8778.

Graphic Crafts, Inc., *(Graphic Crafts; 0-9605622)*, P.O. Box 327, 300 Beaver Valley Pike, Willow Street, PA 17584 (SAN 209-3294) Tel 717-464-2733.

Graphic Dimensions, *(Graphic Dimensions; 0-930904)*, 8 Frederick Rd., Pittsford, NY 14534 (SAN 213-067X) Tel 716-381-3428.

Graphic Enterprises, Inc., Div. of North Texas Printing Company, *(Graphic Ent; 0-914921)*, 316 E. Abram St., Arlington, TX 76010 (SAN 289-2189) Tel 817-277-9442.

Graphic Enterprises of the Carolinas, *(Graphic Enter NC; 0-936135)*, P.O. Box 18251, Greensboro, NC 27419 (SAN 697-0648) Tel 919-855-6880; 402 Edwardia Dr., Greensboro, NC 27419 (SAN 697-0656).

Graphic Image Pubns., *(Graphic Image; 0-912457)*, P.O. Box 1740, La Jolla, CA 92038 (SAN 265-4059) Tel 619-755-6558.

Graphic Impressions, *(Graphic Impress; 0-914628)*, 1939 W. 32nd Ave., Denver, CO 80211 (SAN 201-6311) Tel 303-458-7475.

Graphic Learning Corp., Subs. of Graphic Learning of Canada, *(Graphic Learning; 0-943068; 0-87746)*, 855 Broadway, Boulder, CO 80302 (SAN 240-3803) Tel 303-492-8197; P.O. Box 13829, Tallahassee, FL 32317 (SAN 650-0315) Tel 904-878-8284.

Graphic Press, Div. of Carl Nelson Associates, *(Graphic Pr; 0-89284)*, P.O. Box 13056, Washington, DC 20009 (SAN 208-6662) Tel 202-232-2927.

Graphic Pr., Inc., *(Graphic Pr LA; 0-936183)*, 3719 Magazine St., New Orleans, LA 70115 (SAN 697-1016) Tel 504-891-6377.

Graphic Publishing Co., Inc., *(Graphic Pub; 0-89279)*, 204 N. Second Ave., W., Lake Mills, IA 50450 (SAN 202-4306) Tel 515-592-2000.

Graphic World, *(Graphic World)*, Harding St., Minneapolis, MN 55413 (SAN 663-0863).

Graphics-Communication Associates, *(Graphics Comm)*, P.O. Drawer 10549, Tallahassee, FL 32302 (SAN 240-9356).

Graphics Marketing Systems, Inc., *(Graphics Mktg Syst; 0-934093)*, P.O. Box 260686, Tampa, FL 33685 (SAN 693-0344) Tel 813-968-1475.

Graphics Press, *(Graphics Calif; 0-937536)*, 3010 Santa Monica Blvd. Suite 406, Santa Monica, CA 90404 (SAN 215-2487) Tel 213-393-9029.

Graphics Pr., *(Graphics Pr; 0-9613921)*, P.O. Box 430, Cheshire, CT 06410 (SAN 670-7289) Tel 203-272-9187.

Graphie International Inc., *(Graphie Intl; 0-916189)*, 349 Paseo Tesoro, Walnut, CA 91789 (SAN 294-9342) Tel 714-981-1072.

Graphitti Designs, *(Graphitti Designs; 0-936211)*, 515 W. Valencia Dr., Unit E, Fullerton, CA 92632 (SAN 697-1105) Tel 714-738-5480.

Grass Hooper Press, *(Grass Hooper Pr; 0-933038)*, 4030 Connecticut St., St. Louis, MO 63116 (SAN 221-1157) Tel 314-772-8164; Dist. by: Paperback Supply, 4121 Forest Park Ave., St. Louis, MO 63108 (SAN 169-4324) Tel 314-652-1000.

Grass Roots Productions, *(Grass Roots Productions; 0-9614589)*, 444 W. 54th St., New York, NY 10019 (SAN 691-7771) Tel 212-957-8386.

Grass Roots Publishing, *(Grass Roots Montana; 0-9616221)*, P.O. Drawer 789, Red Lodge, MT 59068 (SAN 658-5418) Tel 406-446-1687; 1500 S. Broadway, Red Lodge, MT 59068 (SAN 658-5426).

Grassdale Pubs., Inc., *(Grassdale Pubs; 0-939798)*, 1002 Lincoln Green, Norman, OK 73072 (SAN 216-8960) Tel 405-329-7071; Orders to: P.O. Box 53158, Oklahoma City, OK 73152 (SAN 662-023X) Tel 405-525-9458.

Grasshopper Pubns., *(Grasshopper Pubns; 0-937139)*, 604 E. Third, Hennessey, OK 73742 (SAN 658-5302) Tel 405-853-6689.

Grassroots Educational Service, *(Grassroots Ed Serv; 0-933426)*, 102 1/2 Broadway, Glendale, CA 91205 (SAN 212-5099) Tel 818-240-1683.

Grastorf, Lang & Co., Inc., *(Grastorf & Lang; 0-933408)*, 142 W. 24th St., New York, NY 10011 (SAN 215-0786) Tel 212-255-5693.

Grauer, Jack, *(J Grauer; 0-930584)*, 2005 S.E. 58th, Portland, OR 97215 (SAN 208-0885) Tel 503-232-5596.

Gravel-Kellogg Publishing Co., *(Gravel-Kellogg; 0-9608684)*, 235 W. 20th St., Fremont, NE 68025 (SAN 238-292X) Tel 402-727-4859.

Gravesend Press, *(Gravesend Pr; 0-9608508)*, 4392 Bussey Rd., Syracuse, NY 13215 (SAN 240-6632).

Gravity Publishing, *(Gravity Pub; 0-936067)*, 6324 Heather Ridge, Oakland, CA 94611 (SAN 696-9240) Tel 415-339-3774; Dist. by: Publishers Group West, 5855 Beaudry St., Emeryville, CA 94608 (SAN 202-8522) Tel 415-658-3453; Dist. by: Quality Bks., 918 Sherwood Dr., Lake Bluff, IL 60044-2204 (SAN 169-2127); Dist. by: Bookpeople, 2929 Fifth St., Berkeley, CA 94710 (SAN 663-3145) Tel 415-549-3030; Toll free: 800-227-1516.

Gravity Research Pubns., *(Gravity Research; 0-913001)*, 1237 Camino Del Mar, Suite C-131, Del Mar, CA 92014 (SAN 283-0981).

Gray, Herbi, *(H Gray; 0-9608406)*, P.O. Box 2343, Olympia, WA 98507 (SAN 240-6640) Tel 206-491-4138.

Gray & Associates, *(Gray Assoc; 0-937636)*, P.O. Box 961, Madison, WI 53701 (SAN 215-2118) Tel 608-274-7458.

†Gray Beard Publishing, *(Gray Beard; 0-933686)*, 107 W. John St., Seattle, WA 98119 (SAN 212-8543); *CIP*.

Gray Data, *(Gray Data; 0-924256)*, 3071 Palmer Sq., Chicago, IL 60647 (SAN 653-4201) Tel 312-278-8080.

Gray Falcon Pr., *(Gray Falcon Pr; 0-935335)*, P.O. Box 3, Martinsville, NJ 08836 (SAN 696-4443) Tel 201-685-2063; 901 Brown Rd., Bridgewater, NJ 08807 (SAN 696-5423).

Gray Moose Press, The, *(Gray Moose; 0-9608078)*, 19 Elmwood Ave., Rye, NY 10580 (SAN 239-4308) Tel 914-967-0665.

Gray Pubns., *(Gray Pubns CA)*, 31300 Via Colinas, No. 102, Westlake Village, CA 91362 (SAN 663-5369).

Gray Pubns., *(Gray Pubns WV; 0-934805)*, Box 460, Franklin, WV 26807 (SAN 694-3721) Tel 304-358-2791.

Grayking Publishing, *(Grayking Pub; 0-9610786)*, 124 Webster Rd., Spencerport, NY 14559 (SAN 265-1580) Tel 716-352-5152.

Graylock Press, *(Graylock; 0-910670)*, 428 E. Preston St., Baltimore, MD 21202 (SAN 203-445X) Tel 301-528-4105.

†Graywolf Pr., *(Graywolf; 0-915308; 1-55597)*, P.O. Box 75006, St. Paul, MN 55175 (SAN 207-1665) Tel 612-222-8342; 370 Selby Ave., No. 203, St. Paul, MN 55102 (SAN 658-0793); Dist. by: Consortium Bk. Sales & Distribution, 213 E. Fourth St., St. Paul, MN 55101 (SAN 200-6049) Tel 612-221-9035; *CIP*.

Grdinic, Eva, *(Grdinic; 0-9604176)*, 6661 Vista del Mar Dr., Playa del Rey, CA 93001 (SAN 214-2449).

Great Adventure Publishing, Inc., *(Great Advent Pub; 0-936069)*, 921 Douglas Ave., Altamonte Springs, FL 32714 (SAN 697-0893) Tel 305-862-4101.

†Great American Books, *(Great Am Bks; 0-936790)*, 256 S. Robertson Blvd., Beverly Hills, CA 90211 (SAN 215-1499); *CIP*.

Great American Gift Co., The, *(Great Am Gift; 1-55569)*, 33 Portman Rd., New Rochelle, NY 10801 (SAN 699-7198) Tel 914-576-7660.

Great & Small Pubns., Subs. of Great & Small Enterprise, *(Great & Sm Pubs; 0-930907)*, P.O. Box 13115, Houston, TX 77219 (SAN 679-6818) Tel 713-961-5134.

Great Basin Pr., *(Great Basin; 0-930830)*, Box 11162, Reno, NV 89510 (SAN 211-1144) Tel 702-826-7729.

Great Bear Pr., The, *(Great Bear Pr; 0-938559)*, P.O. Box 5164, Eugene, OR 97405 (SAN 661-6232); 2437 Miami Ln., Eugene, OR 97403 (SAN 661-6240) Tel 503-485-3683.

Great Commission Pubns., *(Great Comm Pubns; 0-934688)*, 7401 Old York Rd., Philadelphia, PA 19126 (SAN 215-1502) Tel 215-635-6510.

Great Debate Series *See* **Contemporary Bks., Inc.**

Great Eastern Books *See* **Shambhala Pubns., Inc.**

Great Elm Pr., *(Great Elm; 0-9613465)*, RD 2, P.O. Box 37, Rexville, NY 14877 (SAN 657-2588) Tel 607-225-4592.

Great Game Products, *(Great Game Pro; 0-935307)*, 8804 Chalon Dr., Bethesda, MD 20817 (SAN 695-7765) Tel 301-365-3297; Toll free: 800-426-3748.

Great Lakes Bks., *(Great Lakes Bks; 0-9606400)*, P.O. Box 164, Brighton, MI 48116 (SAN 222-9994) Tel 313-227-7471.

Great Lakes Pr., Inc., *(Grt Lks Pr; 0-9614760)*, 4662 Vanatta Rd., Okemos, MI 48864 (SAN 692-9745) Tel 517-349-3302.

Great Northwest Publishing Co., Inc., *(Great Northwest; 0-937708)*, P.O. Box 103902, Anchorage, AK 99510 (SAN 219-9890).

Great Oak Press of Virginia, *(Great Oak Pr VA; 0-9608234)*, Box 6541, Falls Church, VA 22046 (SAN 240-3129) Tel 703-560-6347.

†Great Ocean Pubns., *(Great Ocean; 0-915556)*, 1823 N. Lincoln St., Arlington, VA 22207 (SAN 207-527X) Tel 703-525-0909; *CIP*.

Names

†**Great Outdoors Publishing Co.**, *(Great Outdoors; 0-8200)*, 4747 28th St., N., St. Petersburg, FL 33714 (SAN 201-6273) Tel 813-525-6609; Toll free: 800-433-5560 (Florida only); *CIP.*

Great Plains Emporium, *(Grt Plains Emporium; 0-9616365)*, P.O. Box 416, Schaller, IA 51053 (SAN 658-9448) Tel 712-275-4542; 303 Berwick, Schaller, IA 51053 (SAN 658-9456).

Great Plains National Instructional Television Library, *(Great Plains; 0-9614949)*, Box 80669, Lincoln, NE 68501 (SAN 213-0696); Toll free: 800-228-4630.

Great Plains Software, *(Great Plains Soft; 0-924261)*, 1701 SW 38th St., Fargo, ND 58103 (SAN 264-8830) Tel 701-281-0550; Toll free: 800-345-3276.

Great Pyramid Press, *(Great Pyramid; 0-9605822)*, P.O. Box 2745, Augusta, GA 30904 (SAN 220-1704) Tel 404-736-3514.

Great Raven Press, *(Great Raven Pr)*, Box 858, Lewiston, ME 04240 (SAN 211-9595).

Great Smoky Mountains Natural History Assn., *(GSMNH; 0-937207)*, Rte. 2, Gatlinburg, TN 37738 (SAN 658-7267) Tel 615-436-7318.

Great Traditions, *(Great Traditions)*, P.O. Box 3680, Clearlake, CA 95422 (SAN 679-1301). *Imprints:* Wisdom Publications (Wisdom Pubns).

†**Great Wine Grapes,** *(Great Wine Grapes)*, 157 24th Ave., San Francisco, CA 94121 (SAN 211-5271); Dist. by: Wine Appreciation Guild Ltd., 155 Connecticut St., San Francisco, CA 94107 (SAN 201-9515) Tel 415-864-1202; *CIP.*

Greater Golden Hill Poetry Express, The, *(Greater Gold; 0-9611842)*, 4604 Niagara Ave., San Diego, CA 92107 (SAN 286-195X) Tel 619-224-5951.

Greater Philadelphia Women's Yellow Pages, The, *(Greater PWYP; 0-9611844)*, P.O. Box 42397, Philadelphia, PA 19101 (SAN 286-1968) Tel 215-235-4042.

Greater Portland Landmarks, Inc., *(Greater Portland; 0-9600612; 0-939761)*, 165 State St., Portland, ME 04101 (SAN 203-4484) Tel 207-774-5561.

Greater Washington Research Ctr., *(Great Wash Re; 0-935535)*, 1717 Massachusetts Ave., NW, Suite 403, Washington, DC 20036 (SAN 696-4451) Tel 202-387-0900.

Greater Works Outreach, *(Greater Works; 0-9616324)*, 301 College Pk. Dr., Monroeville, PA 15146 (SAN 658-778X) Tel 412-327-6500.

Greatest Graphics, Inc., *(Greatest Graphics; 0-936120)*, 1904 B East Meadowmere, Springfield, MO 65804 (SAN 213-7410); Orders to: P.O. Box 4467gs, Springfield, MO 65804 (SAN 213-7429) Tel 417-862-6500.

Greatland Graphics/Puffin Pr., *(Greatland Graphics; 0-936425)*, Box 100333, Anchorage, AK 99510 (SAN 698-1763) Tel 907-271-5555; 450 Atlantis, Anchorage, AK 99518 (SAN 698-1771).

Green, Bill, Pubns., *(Green Pubns; 0-9616095)*, 1210c Quarry Rd., Marion, IN 46259 (SAN 698-0996) Tel 317-664-2941.

Green, Robert Alan, *(R A Green; 0-9600266; 0-9615281)*, 214 Key Haven Rd., Key West, FL 33040 (SAN 204-6563) Tel 305-296-6736.

†**Green, Warren H., Inc.,** *(Green; 0-87527)*, 8356 Olive Blvd., St. Louis, MO 63132 (SAN 201-4939) Tel 314-991-1335; *CIP.*

Green, Wayne, Ents., Subs. of International Data Group, *(Green Pub Inc; 0-88006)*, Rte. 202, N., Peterborough, NH 03458 (SAN 219-7855) Tel 603-525-4201.

Green Acres School, *(Green Acres Schl; 0-9608998)*, 11701 Danville Dr., Rockville, MD 20852 (SAN 206-2046) Tel 301-881-4100.

Green Apple Pr., *(Green Apple; 0-933381)*, P.O. Box 1908, North Myrtle Beach, SC 29582 (SAN 691-6791) Tel 803-249-5402.

Green Ball Press, The, *(Green Ball Pr; 0-9610950)*, P.O. Box 29771, Elkins Park, PA 19117 (SAN 287-7368) Tel 215-379-6449.

Green Block Publishing, *(Green Block; 0-9609748)*, Rte. 2, Carthage, TN 37030 (SAN 263-1520).

Green Bough Pr., *(Green Bough Pr; 0-9615007)*, 3156 W. Laurelhurst Dr., NE, Seattle, WA 98105 (SAN 693-9333) Tel 206-523-0022.

Green Briar Pr., *(Green Briar Pr; 0-9614511)*, 6612 Green Briar Rd., Middleton, WI 53562 (SAN 691-7291) Tel 608-831-3530.

Green Creek Publishing Co., *(Green Creek Pub Co; 0-930051)*, 2251 Van Antwerp Rd., Schenectady, NY 12309 (SAN 669-831X) Tel 518-372-7156.

Green Crown Pr., *(Green Crown Pr; 0-9613804)*, P.O. Box 15445, 7035 Laurel Canyon, North Hollywood, CA 91615-5445 (SAN 679-4084).

Green Dolphin Bookshop, *(Green Dolphin; 0-911904)*, 1300 SW Washington St., Portland, OR 97205 (SAN 205-3268) Tel 503-224-3060.

Green Eagle Press, *(Green Eagle Pr; 0-914018)*, 241 W. 97th St., New York, NY 10025 (SAN 203-4492) Tel 212-663-2167.

Green Fields Bks., *(Green Fields Bks; 0-937715)*, P.O. Box 8228, Washington, DC 20024 (SAN 659-2287) Tel 202-863-1564; 240 M St., SW, Washington, DC 20024 (SAN 659-2295).

Green Hill Pubs., *(Green Hill; 0-916054; 0-89803; 0-915463)*, 722 Columbus St., Ottawa, IL 61350 (SAN 281-7578) Tel 815-434-7905; Dist. by: Kampmann & Co., 9 E. 40th St., New York, NY 10016 (SAN 202-5191) Tel 212-685-2928. *Imprints:* Jameson Books (Pub. by Jameson Bks); Pegma Books (Pegma Bks).

Green Hut Pr., *(Green Hut; 0-916678)*, 1015 Jardin St. E., Appleton, WI 54911 (SAN 208-2888) Tel 414-734-9728.

Green Key Pr., *(Green Key Pr; 0-910783)*, P.O. Box 3801, Seminole, FL 33542 (SAN 264-0708).

Green Leaf Pr., *(Green Leaf CA; 0-938462)*, P.O. Box 6880, Alhambra, CA 91802 (SAN 239-3646) Tel 818-281-6809; 20 W. Commonwealth Ave., Alhambra, CA 91801 (SAN 239-3654).

Green Meadow Bks., *(Green Meadow Bks; 0-9614817)*, Weld Rd. Offices, Phillips, ME 04966 (SAN 693-0441) Tel 207-639-3814.

Green Mountain Club, The, *(Green Mtn Club)*, P.O. Box 889, 43 State St., Montpelier, VT 05602 (SAN 695-5436).

Green Mountain Micro, *(Green Mountain; 0-916015)*, Bathory Rd., Roxbury, VT 05669 (SAN 294-0140) Tel 802-485-6112.

†**Green Oak Pr.,** *(Green Oak Pr; 0-931600)*, 9339 Spicer Rd., Brighton, MI 48116 (SAN 211-9544) Tel 313-449-4802; *CIP.*

Green Oak Township Historical Society, *(Green Oak Township; 0-936792)*, P.O. Box 84, Brighton, MI 48116 (SAN 218-477X).

Green River Press, Inc., *(Green River; 0-940580)*, Saginaw Valley State College, University Center, MI 48710 (SAN 207-5881) Tel 517-790-4376.

Green Street Pr., The, *(Green St Pr; 0-9614285)*, P.O. Box 1957, Cambridge, MA 02238 (SAN 687-4460) Tel 617-628-0539.

Green Tiger Pr., The, *(Green Tiger Pr; 0-88138; 0-915676)*, 1061 India St., San Diego, CA 92101 (SAN 219-4775) Tel 619-238-1001. *Imprints:* Star & Elephant Books (Star & Elephant Bks).

Green Valley Film and Art Center, *(Green Valley; 0-9614313)*, 300 Maple St., Burlington, VT 05401 (SAN 687-5149) Tel 802-862-4929; Dist. by: Countryman Press, P.O. Box 175, Woodstock, VT 05091 (SAN 206-4901) Tel 802-457-1049.

Green Valley Pr., *(Green Valley Pr; 0-932047)*, P.O. Box 816, Williamson, WV 25661 (SAN 683-2601) Tel 304-235-5561.

Green Valley World, Inc., *(Green Val World; 0-913444)*, 41 S. Ocean Ave., Cayucos, CA 93430 (SAN 663-0758) Tel 805-995-1378.

Greenbeck, *(Greenbeck; 0-9613079)*, 849 S. Mountain Ave., Ontario, CA 91762 (SAN 294-8133) Tel 714-988-9513.

†**Greenberg Publishing Co.,** *(Greenberg Pub Co; 0-89778)*, 7543 Main St., Sykesville, MD 21784 (SAN 211-9552) Tel 301-795-7447; *CIP.*

Greenbriar Books, *(Greenbriar Bks; 0-932970)*, 5906 Hodgman Dr., Cleveland, OH 44130 (SAN 264-0716).

Greencastle Pr., The, *(Greencastle Pr; 0-934347)*, 5 Hanna Court, Greencastle, IN 46135 (SAN 693-6105) Tel 317-653-4770.

Greencrest Pr., Inc., *(Greencrest; 0-939800)*, P.O. Box 7745, Winston-Salem, NC 27109 (SAN 216-8979) Tel 919-722-6463.

Greene, Bill, *(B Greene; 0-934668)*, Box 810, Mill Valley, CA 94942 (SAN 213-0149).

Greene, J. R., *(J R Greene; 0-9609404)*, 33 Bearsden Rd., Athol, MA 01331 (SAN 262-6845) Tel 617-249-9376.

Greene, R. M., & Assocs., *(Greene & Assocs; 0-934487)*, 14291 Prospect Ave., Tustin, CA 92680 (SAN 693-8892) Tel 714-731-7419.

Greene, Robert E., *(R E Greene; 0-9603320)*, 120 U St. NW, Washington, DC 20001 (SAN 213-313X).

Greene, Stephen, Pr., Div. of Viking Penguin, Inc., *(Greene; 0-8289; 0-86616)*, 15 Muzzey St., Lexington, MA 02173 (SAN 201-6222) Tel 617-861-0170; Dist. by: Viking Penguin, Inc., 40 W. 23rd St., New York, NY 10010 (SAN 200-2442) Tel 212-337-5200; Toll free: 800-631-3577.

Greene County Homemakers Extension Assn., *(Greene Coun Home Ext Assn; 0-9613043)*, P.O. Box 56, Wrights, IL 62098 (SAN 293-9827) Tel 217-368-2162.

Greene Pubns., *(Greene Pubns; 0-9608892)*, 1412 Glendale Blvd., Los Angeles, CA 90026 (SAN 241-1180) Tel 213-413-2150.

Greene Publishing, *(Greene Pub; 0-913371)*, P.O. Box 22715, Knoxville, TN 37933-0715 (SAN 657-1433) Tel 615-574-1532.

Greene's Publishing Co., Inc., *(Greenes Pub; 0-917233)*, P.O. Box 69249, Los Angeles, CA 90069 (SAN 655-8577) Tel 818-985-2877; Dist. by: Publishers Group West, 5855 Beaudry St., Emeryville, CA 94608 (SAN 202-8522) Tel 415-658-3453.

Greenfield Bks., *(Greenfield Bks; 0-9615576)*, P.O. Box 4682, Greenwich, CT 06836 (SAN 696-446X) Tel 203-625-5045; 27 Indian Field Rd., Greenwich, CT 06830 (SAN 696-5431).

Greenfield Books *See* Pierian Pr.

Greenfield Press, *(Greenfield Pr; 0-9611846)*, P.O. Box 176, Southport, CT 06490 (SAN 286-1798) Tel 203-268-4878.

Greenfield Pubns., *(Greenfield Pubns; 0-9606666)*, 8720 E. Forrest Dr., Scottsdale, AZ 85257 (SAN 223-7717) Tel 602-994-1452.

Greenfield Review Pr., *(Greenfld Rev Pr; 0-912678)*, R.D.1, Box 80, Greenfield Ctr., NY 12833 (SAN 203-4506) Tel 518-584-1728.

†**Greenhaven Pr.,** *(Greenhaven; 0-912616; 0-89908)*, 577 Shoreview Park Rd., St. Paul, MN 55126 (SAN 201-6214) Tel 612-482-1582; Toll free: 800-231-5163; *CIP.*

Greenhigh Pubs., *(Greenhigh; 0-9615770)*, Rte. 9, Box 390-A, Tyler, TX 75706 (SAN 696-4478) Tel 214-597-0757.

Greenhouse Pr., *(Greenhse Pr; 0-9615912)*, 1239 Sunset Ave., Clinton, NC 28328 (SAN 697-0907) Tel 919-592-3725.

Greenhouse Publishing Co., *(Greenhouse Pub; 0-9616844)*, P.O. Box 525, Marshall, VA 22115 (SAN 661-1729) Tel 703-364-1959.

Greenlawn Pr., Div. of LaSalle Co., *(Greenlawn Pr; 0-937779)*, 107 S. Greenlawn Ave., South Bend, IN 46617 (SAN 659-2309); Dist. by: CRS/Communication Ctr., 107 N. Michigan, South Bend, IN 46606 (SAN 200-6421).

Greenleaf Bks., *(Greenlf Bks; 0-934676)*, Canton, ME 04221 (SAN 203-4514).

Greenleaf Co., *(Greenleaf Co; 0-940582)*, P.O. Box 11393, Chicago, IL 60611 (SAN 223-0011) Tel 312-288-2205.

Greenleaf Pubns., *(Greenlf Pubns; 0-9608812)*, P.O. Box 50357, Pasadena, CA 91105 (SAN 238-2938).

Greenlight Press, *(Greenlight Pr; 0-930864)*, P.O. Box 360, 1230 Grant Ave., San Francisco, CA 94133 (SAN 211-6669).

Greenpeace/Center for Investigative Reporting, *(Greenpeace-Ctr Invest Re; 0-9607166)*, 54 Mint St., 4th Floor, San Francisco, CA 94103 (SAN 239-0973) Tel 415-543-1200.

Green's Creek Press, *(Greens Creek; 0-9609406)*, Rte. 5, Dublin, TX 76446 (SAN 262-0316).

Greensboro Symphony Guild, *(Greensboro Symphony; 0-9617247)*, 3607 Sagamore Dr., Greensboro, NC 27410 (SAN 663-5563) Tel 919-668-2072.

Greenspires Bks., *(Greenspires; 0-9601028)*, 2 Chestnut St., Andover, MA 01810 (SAN 208-1571) Tel 617-475-1020.

Greenspring Pubns., *(Greenspring; 0-915351),* 3 Barstad Court, Lutherville, MD 21093 (SAN 289-9914) Tel 301-828-9316; Dist. by: Liberty Publishing Co., Inc., P.O. Box 298, Cockeysville, MD 21030 (SAN 211-030X) Tel 301-667-6680.

†**Greenswamp Pubns.,** *(Greenswamp; 0-917431),* 4216 Blackwater Rd., Virginia Beach, VA 23457 (SAN 656-1438) Tel 804-421-3397; *CIP.*

Greensward Pr., *(Greensward Pr; 0-930165),* P.O. Box 640472, San Francisco, CA 94109 (SAN 670-7149) Tel 213-663-7801; Dist. by: Nutri Books, P.O. Box 5793, Denver, CO 80223 (SAN 169-054X) Tel 303-778-8383; Toll free: 800-525-9030; Dist. by: Bookpeople, 2929 Fifth St., Berkeley, CA 94710 (SAN 168-9517) Tel 415-549-3030.

GreenTower Pr., *(GreenTower Pr; 0-9616467),* Northwest Missouri State Univ., 113 Colden Hall, Maryville, MO 64468 (SAN 659-2317) Tel 816-562-1559.

Greenvale Press, *(Greenvale; 0-911876),* P.O. Box 242, Kopperl, TX 76652 (SAN 203-4522) Tel 817-772-8576.

Greenview Pubns, *(Greenview Pubns; 0-9606994),* Box 7051, Chicago, IL 60680 (SAN 238-8782).

Greenville County Medical Society Aux., *(Greenville County Med; 0-9613679),* 2407 Augusta St., Greenville, SC 29605 (SAN 685-4354) Tel 803-233-3205.

Greenwich Design, *(Greenwich Des; 0-9603892),* Box 611, Hopkins, MN 55343 (SAN 210-7333) Tel 612-935-2574; 910 1/2 Excelsior Ave. W., Hopkins, MN 55343 (SAN 210-7341).

Greenwich House See Outlet Bk. Co.

Greenwich House, Chatham River Press See Outlet Bk. Co.

Greenwich Pr., Ltd., *(Greenw Pr Ltd; 0-86713),* 30 Lindeman Dr., Trumbull, CT 06611 (SAN 216-8170) Tel 203-371-6568; Toll free: 800-243-4246.

†**Greenwillow Bks.,** Div. of William Morrow & Co., Inc., *(Greenwillow; 0-688),* 105 Madison Ave., New York, NY 10016 (SAN 202-5760) Tel 212-889-3050; Toll free: 800-631-1199; Orders to: William Morrow & Co., Inc., Wilmor Warehouse, 6 Henderson Dr., West Caldwell, NJ 07006 (SAN 202-5779); *CIP.*

Greenwood Hse., *(Greenwood Hse; 0-9601982),* 1655 Flatbush Ave., Apt. B1902, Brooklyn, NY 11210 (SAN 212-3584) Tel 718-253-9299.

Greenwood Pr., Div. of Congressional Information Services, Inc., *(Greenwood; 0-8371; 0-313; 0-89930),* 88 Post Rd., W., Westport, CT 06881 (SAN 213-2028) Tel 203-226-3571; P.O. Box 5007, Westport, CT 06881 (SAN 696-5555). *Imprints:* Quorum Books (Quorum Bks).

Greer/Martha Pr., *(M Greer; 0-9617179),* 2710 Woodscrest Ave., Lincoln, NE 68502 (SAN 663-186X) Tel 402-435-2710.

Greeting Card Assn., *(Greeting Card Assn; 0-938369),* 1350 New York Ave., NW, Suite 615, Washington, DC 20005 (SAN 661-275X) Tel 202-393-1778.

Greetings Publishing Co., *(Greetings Pub Co; 0-9611848),* P.O. Box 107, Asbury Park, NJ 07712 (SAN 286-1844) Tel 201-222-4667.

Greeves, R. V., Art Gallery, *(R V Greeves; 0-9616999),* P.O. Box 428, Fort Washakie, WY 82514 (SAN 662-5339); 53 N. Fork Rd., Fort Washakie, WY 82514 (SAN 662-5347) Tel 307-332-3557.

Greger, Margaret, *(M Greger; 0-9613680),* 1425 Marshall, Richland, WA 99352 (SAN 670-8994).

Gregg-Hamilton, *(Gregg-Hamilton; 0-934800),* 410 S. Meridian, Aberdeen, MS 39730 (SAN 211-9560) Tel 601-369-8120.

Gregg, Inc., *(Gregg Inc; 0-9615229),* 693 Maple, Plymouth, MI 48170 (SAN 694-3780) Tel 313-455-0606.

Gregg International, *(Gregg Intl; 0-576),* Old Post Rd., Brookfield, VT 05036 (SAN 695-2046) Tel 802-276-3162.

Gregory, Howard, Associates, *(H Gregory; 0-9607086),* 640 The Village No. 209, Redondo Beach, CA 90277 (SAN 206-4502) Tel 213-379-7190.

Gregory Pubns., *(Gregory Pubns; 0-917224),* Gateway Sta., Box 440950, Aurora, CO 80044 (SAN 208-6689).

Gregory Publishing Co., *(Gregory Pub; 0-911541),* 806 N. Maple St., Itasca, IL 60143 (SAN 211-5646).

Grenadier Bks., Inc., *(Grenadier Bks; 0-935691),* 7001 Ulmerton Rd., Suite 4205, Largo, FL 33541 (SAN 696-4524) Tel 813-535-2674; P.O. Box 17327, Airport Sta., Clearwater, FL 33520 (SAN 696-5458).

Grendhal Poetry Review Pr., The, *(Grendhal Poetry Review; 0-938781),* 116 Tamarack St., Vandenberg AFB, Lompoc, CA 93437 (SAN 661-5457) Tel 805-734-1987.

Grenridge Publishing, *(Grenridge Pub; 0-943410),* P.O. Box 4587, Greenville, SC 29608 (SAN 240-6659) Tel 803-294-2207.

†**Greta Bear Enterprises,** *(Greta Bear; 0-931452),* P.O. Box 9525, Berkeley, CA 94709 (SAN 209-6420); Dist. by: Bookpeople, 2929 Fifth St., Berkeley, CA 94610 (SAN 168-9517); *CIP.*

Grey Art Gallery & Study Ctr., New York Univ., *(Grey Art Gallery Study Ctr; 0-934349),* 33 Washington Pl., New York, NY 10003 (SAN 279-8697) Tel 212-598-7603.

Grey Book, *(Grey Bk; 0-912021),* P.O. Box 1237, Flagstaff, AZ 86002 (SAN 264-617X) Tel 602-774-2923.

†**Grey Fox Pr.,** *(Grey Fox; 0-912516),* Box 31190, San Francisco, CA 94131 (SAN 201-6176); Dist. by: Subterranean Co., 1327 W. Second, P.O. Box 10233, Eugene, OR 97440 (SAN 169-7102) Tel 503-343-6324; *CIP.*

Grey Gull Publications, *(Grey Gull Pubns; 0-9614592),* P.O. Box 69, Damariscotta, ME 04543 (SAN 691-778X) Tel 207-563-1625.

Grey Home Pr., *(Grey Home Pr),* 8 Court Rd., Westford, MA 01886 (SAN 683-2636).

†**Grey Hse., Publishing, Inc.,** *(Grey Hse Pub; 0-939300),* Colonial Bank Bldg., Sharon, CT 06069 (SAN 216-390X) Tel 203-364-0533; *CIP.*

Grey Towers Pr., *(Grey Towers Pr; 0-938549),* P.O. Box 188, Milford, PA 18337 (SAN 661-6259); Grey Towers, Milford, PA 18337 (SAN 661-6267) Tel 717-296-6401.

Greycliff Publishing Co., *(Greycliff Pub),* P.O. Box 1273, Helena, MT 59624 (SAN 663-0804) Tel 406-443-4171.

Greyfalcon House, *(Greyfalcon Hse; 0-914870),* 496 Hudson St., Suite 443, New York, NY 10014 (SAN 207-0723) Tel 212-777-9042.

Greystone Pr., *(Greystone Pr; 0-9615376),* 306 Mecherle, Apt. 7, Bloomington, IL 61701 (SAN 695-5339) Tel 309-438-2528.

Greystone Pubs., *(Greystone Pubs; 0-9614761),* 46 Monument Ave., Harrisonburg, VA 22801 (SAN 692-9060) Tel 703-434-2019.

Grieco, *(Grieco; 0-931843),* P.O. Box 1262, San Juan Capistrano, CA 92693 (SAN 686-0273) Tel 714-498-1536.

Griefworks Publishing Company, *(Griefworks Pub Co; 0-932667),* 1119 Sylvania Ave., Toledo, OH 43612 (SAN 687-7974) Tel 419-478-2100.

Griesinger Films, *(Griesinger Films; 0-9616762),* Rte. 2, P.O. Box 1986, French Creek, WV 26218 (SAN 661-3918) Tel 304-924-5035.

Griffin, Boyd, Inc., *(Boyd Griffin; 0-941726),* 425 E. 51st St., New York, NY 10022 (SAN 239-2194) Tel 212-399-4226.

Griffin, Walter, *(Walter Griffin; 0-9616153),* 2518 Maple St., East Point, GA 30344 (SAN 699-9921) Tel 404-529-8794.

Griffin, Wesley, Assocs., *(W Griffin Assocs; 0-9617144),* 976 Denhart St., Norfolk, VA 23504 (SAN 663-3390) 1el 804-827-8299.

Griffin Bks., *(Griffin Bks; 0-9604770),* 743 11th Ave., Huntington, WV 25701 (SAN 215-8558).

Griffin Heritage Assn., The, *(Griffin Herit),* RFD 2, Box 49, Ochlocknee, GA 31773 (SAN 694-5376).

Griffon Hse. Pubns./Bagehot Council, *(Griffon Hse; 0-918680),* P.O. Box 81, Whitestone, NY 11357 (SAN 211-6685) Tel 718-767-8380.

Griggs Printing & Publishing, *(Griggs Print; 0-918292),* Box 1351, 426 First St., Havre, MT 59501 (SAN 209-441X) Tel 406-265-7431.

Grindle Pr., Div. of Avalon Corp., *(Grindle Pr; 0-937065),* 8340 E. Raintree Dr., Suite B2, Scottsdale, AZ 85260 (SAN 658-6104) Tel 602-483-3901.

Grinnell College, *(Grinnell Coll; 0-9607182),* Grinnell, IA 50112 (SAN 216-3918).

Grinnen-Barrett Publishing Co., *(Grinnen-Barrett Pub Co; 0-9613063),* 36 Winchester St., No. 8, Brookline, MA 02146 (SAN 294-8184) Tel 617-232-1993.

Grinning Idiot Press, *(Grinning; 0-88100),* P.O. Box 1577, Brooklyn, NY 11202 (SAN 283-2674).

Gris Gris Pr., *(Gris Gris Pr; 0-9614138),* 2431 S. Acadian, No. 590, Baton Rouge, LA 70808 (SAN 686-5135) Tel 504-927-5437.

Grist Mill, *(Grist Mill; 0-917820),* Energy Conservation Services, 90 Depot Rd., Eliot, ME 03903 (SAN 207-4710) Tel 207-439-3873.

Gritz La Ritz, *(Gritz La Ritz; 0-939679),* P.O. Box 42619, Portland, OR 97242 (SAN 663-4850); 3212 SE 9th St., No. 8, Portland, OR 97202 (SAN 663-4869) Tel 503-232-6800; Dist. by: Far West Book Services, 3515 NE Hassalo, Portland, OR 97232 (SAN 107-6760) Tel 503-234-7664.

Grolier, Inc., *(Grolier Inc; 0-7172),* Sherman Tpke., Danbury, CT 06816 (SAN 205-3195) Tel 203-797-3500.

Groome Center, *(Groome Ctr; 0-916964),* 5225 Loughboro Rd., NW., Washington, DC 20016 (SAN 208-6697) Tel 202-362-7644.

Grooming Made E-Z, *(Grooming; 0-9615460),* 8306 Wilshire Blvd., Suite 840, Beverly Hills, CA 90211 (SAN 695-7641) Tel 213-389-5400.

Gros Ventre Treaty Committee, *(Gros Ventre Treaty),* Ft. Belknap Agency, Harlem, MT 59526 (SAN 210-900X).

Gross, Joseph, *(J Gross; 0-9616476),* 28 Parkhurst Dr., Spencerport, NY 14559 (SAN 659-2260) Tel 716-552-6766.

Gross, Ruth T., *(R T Gross; 0-9606946),* 1815 Tigertail Ave., Miami, FL 33133 (SAN 212-0402).

Gross & Johnson Publishing Co., *(Gross Johnson; 0-935351),* 989 Woodbourne Dr., Suite 500, Atlanta, GA 30310 (SAN 696-4540) Tel 404-977-5350.

Gross Enterprises, *(Gross Ent; 0-913854),* 1705 The Strand, Manhattan Beach, CA 90266 (SAN 203-4573) Tel 213-545-5410.

Grossett & Dunlap, Inc. See Putnam Publishing Group, The

Grossman, David, Press, *(D Grossman Pr; 0-910563),* 212 E. 47th St., Apt. 33a, New York, NY 10017 (SAN 260-1958) Tel 212-486-9598.

Grosvenor Society, The (Friends of the Buffalo & Erie County Public Library), *(Grosvenor Soc; 0-9615896),* Lafayette Sq., Buffalo, NY 14203 (SAN 697-1040) Tel 716-856-7525.

Grosvenor Square Assocs, USA, *(Grosvenor Sq; 0-9611472),* P.O. Box 153, Wilkinsonville, MA 01590 (SAN 283-1341) Tel 714-458-1869.

Grosvenor U. S. A., Subs. of Grosvenor Bks., London, UK, *(Grosvenor USA; 0-901269),* P.O. Box 8647, Richmond, VA 23226 (SAN 663-1606) Tel 703-288-7624; Dist. by: M & B Fulfillment, 540 Barnum Ave., Bridgeport, CT 06610 (SAN 282-6062) Tel 203-366-1900.

Grounder Publishing, *(Grounder Pub; 0-930271),* P.O. Box 42399, Houston, TX 77242-2399 (SAN 670-8447) Tel 713-784-8739.

Group Bks., *(Group Bks; 0-936664; 0-931529),* P.O. Box 481, Loveland, CO 80539 (SAN 214-4689); 2890 N. Monroe, Loveland, CO 80539 (SAN 662-1376) Tel 303-669-3836.

Group Four Pubns., Inc., *(Group Four Pubns; 0-934125),* 1307 N. 45th St., Seattle, WA 98103 (SAN 693-2630) Tel 206-526-8577.

Group Health Assn. of America, *(Group Health Assoc of Amer; 0-936164),* 1129 20th St., NW, Washington, DC 20036 (SAN 270-627X).

Groupwork Today Inc., *(Groupwork Today; 0-916068),* P.O. Box 258, South Plainfield, NJ 07080 (SAN 208-0370) Tel 201-755-4803.

Grove Educational Technologies, *(Grove Educ Tech; 0-936735),* P.O. Box 405, Lake Grove, NY 11755 (SAN 699-9840) Tel 516-588-5948; 27 Hy Pl., Lake Grove, NY 11755 (SAN 699-9859).

Grove Farm Homestead & Waioli Mission Hse., *(Grove Farm Home; 0-9617174),* P.O. Box 1631, Lihue, Kauai, HI 96766 (SAN 663-1282) Tel 808-245-3202.

Names

Grove Pr., *(Grove; 0-8021; 0-394),* 920 Broadway, New York, NY 10010 (SAN 201-4890) Tel 212-529-3600; Toll free: 800-638-6460. *Imprints:* Black Cat Books (BC); Evergreen Books (Ever); Evergreen-Black Cat Books (EverBC); Zebra Books (Zebra).

Groves Dictionaries of Music, Inc., Div. of Peninsula Publishers Ltd., *(Groves Dict Music; 0-943818),* 15 E. 26th St., New York, NY 10010 (SAN 211-9579) Tel 212-481-1332; Toll free: 800-221-2123. *Imprints:* Stockton Press (Pub. by Stockton Pr).

Growing Pains Press, *(Growing Pains Pr; 0-941834),* 90 Club Rd., Riverside, CT 06878 (SAN 239-2208) Tel 203-637-9771.

Growing Together Press, *(Growing Together; 0-9604118),* P.O. Box 2983, Stanford, CA 94305 (SAN 215-7683).

Growth Assocs., *(Growth Assoc; 0-918834),* P.O. Box 18429, Rochester, NY 14618-0429 (SAN 210-430X) Tel 716-244-1225.

Growth Associates, Inc., *(Growth Assocs Inc; 0-915469),* P.O. Box 38705, Germantown, TN 38183-0705 (SAN 291-1825) Tel 901-754-6678; 7698 Blackberry Ridge Cove, Germantown, TN 38138 (SAN 291-1833).

Growth Publishing, *(Growth Pub; 0-931225),* P.O. Box 661, Herndon, VA 22070 (SAN 682-9112) Tel 703-471-1160.

Growth Resources, Inc., *(Growth Resources; 0-936965),* 22322 Pineapple Walk, Boca Raton, FL 33433 (SAN 658-6546) Tel 305-394-5915.

Growth Unlimited, Inc., *(Growth Unltd; 0-9601334; 0-916927),* 31 East Ave., S., Battle Creek, MI 49017 (SAN 210-8976) Tel 616-965-2229.

Gruenwald, Myron E., *(M E Gruenwald; 0-9601536),* 1260 Westhaven Dr., Oshkosh, WI 54904 (SAN 221-5144) Tel 414-235-7398.

Grumbacher, M., Inc., Subs. of CPG International Co., *(M Grumbacher),* 460 W. 34th St., New York, NY 10001 (SAN 205-3179) Tel 212-279-6400; Toll free: 800-346-3278; Orders to: Engelhard Dr., Cranbury, NJ 08512 (SAN 662-0248) Tel 609-655-8282.

†Grune & Stratton, Inc., Subs. of Harcourt Brace Jovanovich Inc., *(Grune; 0-8089),* ; Toll free: 800-321-5068; c/o Promotion Dept., Orlando, FL 32887-0018 (SAN 206-8990) Tel 305-345-4212; *CIP.*

Gruter Institute for Law & Behavioral Research, *(Gruter Inst),* 158 Goya Rd., Portola Valley, CA 94025 (SAN 200-5859) Tel 415-854-2034.

Grynberg Publishing Corp., *(Grynberg Pub; 0-935537),* 5000 S. Quebec, Suite 500, Denver, CO 80237 (SAN 696-4559) Tel 303-850-7497.

Gryphon Bks., *(Gryphon Bks; 0-936071),* P.O. Box 209, Brooklyn, NY 11228 (SAN 697-0834); 1148 73rd St., Brooklyn, NY 11228 (SAN 697-0842) Tel 718-745-1811.

Gryphon Hse., Inc., *(Gryphon Hse; 0-87659),* 3706 Otis St., P.O. Box 275, Mount Rainier, MD 20712 (SAN 169-3190) Tel 301-779-6200; Toll free: 800-638-0928.

Gryphon West Pubs., *(Gryphon West Pubs; 0-943482),* P.O. Box 12096, Seattle, WA 98102 (SAN 240-4818).

Guadalupe River Press, *(Guadalupe River Pr),* c/o Trinity University Bookstore, 715 Stadium Rd., San Antonio, TX 78284 (SAN 238-0617).

Guappone's Pubs., *(Guappones Pubs; 0-9615230),* R.D. 1, Box 10, McClellandtown, PA 15458 (SAN 209-4428) Tel 412-737-5172.

Guarionex Pr., Ltd., *(Guarionex Pr; 0-935966),* 201 W. 77th St., New York, NY 10024 (SAN 216-1370) Tel 212-724-5259; Dist. by: Bookpeople, 2929 Fifth St., Berkeley, CA 94710 (SAN 168-9517) Tel 415-549-3030.

Guastella Pubns., *(Guastella Pubns; 0-9607230),* P.O. Box 6082, Tallahassee, FL 32301 (SAN 239-0981).

Guffey Books, Inc., *(Guffey Bks),* 6634 S. Broadway, Littleton, CO 80120 (SAN 203-462X) Tel 303-798-6406.

†Guggenheim, Solomon R., Museum, *(S R Guggenheim; 0-89207),* 1071 Fifth Ave., New York, NY 10128 (SAN 205-3152) Tel 212-360-3573; *CIP.*

Guggenheim Research Assn., *(Guggenheim; 0-910377),* 444 SW Birdsdale Dr., Gresham, OR 97030 (SAN 262-0324); Dist. by: Salem Press of Oregon, 1021 Oregon National Bldg., 610 SW Adler, Gresham, OR 97205 (SAN 262-0332).

Guggenrobin Pubs., *(Guggenrobin Pubs; 0-936967),* 30-08 Broadway, Astoria, NY 11106 (SAN 658-7798) Tel 718-956-4476; P.O. Box 156, Astoria, NY 11106 (SAN 658-7801).

Guidance Enterprises, *(Guidance Ent; 0-930199),* P.O. Box 4500, Prescott, AZ 86302 (SAN 670-7920) Tel 602-776-0277.

Guide Pr., *(Guide Pr WI; 0-9615699),* 50 Whitcomb Cir., No. 5, Madison, WI 53705 (SAN 696-4567) Tel 608-273-2914; P.O. Box 173, Verona, WI 53593 (SAN 696-5466).

Guide-Pro Assocs., *(Guide-Pro Assocs; 0-9615947),* P.O. Box 402, Massapequa Park, NY 11762 (SAN 697-1113) Tel 516-798-9481; 21 Ave. Louise, Massapequa Park, NY 11762 (SAN 697-1121).

Guide to Reprints, Inc., *(Guide to Reprints; 0-918086),* P.O. Box 249, Kent, CT 06757 (SAN 210-2080) Tel 203-927-4588.

Guide to Richmond, *(Guide to Rich; 0-9607442),* P.O. Box 242, Midlothian, VA 23113 (SAN 239-2216) Tel 804-794-8068.

Guideline Publishing Co., *(Guideline Pub; 0-917474),* 336 S. Occidental Blvd., Los Angeles, CA 90057 (SAN 203-4638) Tel 213-382-4500.

Guidelines Press, *(Guidelines Pr; 0-932570),* 1307 S. Killian Dr., Lake Park, FL 33403 (SAN 212-0984) Tel 305-842-9411.

Guidepost Pubs. & Distributors, Inc., *(Guidepost Pubs & Dists; 0-936217),* P.O. Box 93112, Cleveland, OH 44101 (SAN 697-1067) Tel 216-268-1356; 1 Public Sq., Suite 802, Cleveland, OH 44113-2101 (SAN 697-1075); Dist. by: Circular, Ltd., 1 Public Sq., Suite 802, Cleveland, OH 44113-2101 (SAN 294-7153) Tel 216-241-2600.

Guides to Multinational Business, Inc., *(Guides Multinatl Busn; 0-931000),* P.O. Box 92, Harvard Sq., Cambridge, MA 02138 (SAN 212-2561).

Guifford-Hill Publishing Co., *(Guifford-Hill),* Rte. 8, Box 264, London, KY 40741 (SAN 211-5123).

†Guignol Bks., *(Guignol Bks; 0-941062),* P.O. Box 247, Rhinebeck, NY 12572 (SAN 281-7594) Tel 914-876-2141; *CIP.*

Guild Books, Catholic Polls, Inc., *(Guild Bks; 0-912080),* 86 Riverside Dr., New York, NY 10024 (SAN 203-4646) Tel 212-799-2600.

†Guild for Psychological Studies Publishing Hse., *(Guild Psy; 0-917479),* 2230 Divisadero St., San Francisco, CA 94115 (SAN 656-0687) Tel 415-788-3035; *CIP.*

Guild Hall Museum, *(Guild Hall; 0-933793),* 158 Main St., East Hampton, NY 11937 (SAN 278-9698) Tel 516-324-0806.

Guild Pr., *(Guild Pr; 0-940248),* P.O. Box 22583, Robbinsdale, MN 55422 (SAN 220-3340) Tel 612-566-1842.

Guildhall Pubs., Ltd., *(Guildhall Pubs; 0-940518),* P.O. Box 325, Peoria, IL 61651 (SAN 219-838X); 231 Oak Ct, Peoria, IL 61614 (SAN 662-0256) Tel 309-688-5985.

†Guilford Pr., The, Div. of Guilford Pubns. Inc., *(Guilford Pr; 0-89862),* 200 Park Ave., S., New York, NY 10003 (SAN 212-9442) Tel 212-674-1900; Toll free: 800-221-3966; *CIP.*

Guinea Hollow Press/Films, *(Guinea Hollow; 0-916344),* P.O. Box 59, Stanhope, NJ 07874 (SAN 281-7624); Orders to: 190 Waverly Place, New York, NY 10014 (SAN 281-7616) Tel 212-924-4586.

Guitar & Song Publications, *(Guitar & Song; 0-932327),* 1015 Highland Ave., Dayton, OH 45410 (SAN 686-8088) Tel 513-252-0424.

Guitar Editions, Inc., *(Guitar Editions; 0-939721),* P.O. Box 2042, Charlottesville, VA 22902 (SAN 663-592X); 1116 E. Market St., Charlottesville, VA 22901 (SAN 663-5938) Tel 804-296-0105.

Guitar Foundation of America, *(Guitar Found Amer; 0-9616877),* P.O. Box 1090A, Garden Grove, CA 92642 (SAN 661-6631) Tel 415-326-3809; 604 Tennyson Ave., Palo Alto, CA 94301 (SAN 661-664X).

Gulf Coast Educators Press, *(Gulf Coast Ed),* 4430 Piedmont Rd., Pensacola, FL 32503 (SAN 262-0340).

Gulf Coast Publishing Co., *(Gulf Coast Pub; 0-939127),* P.O. Box 66940, St. Petersburg, FL 33736 (SAN 662-4847); 7645 Sun Island Dr., St. Petersburg, FL 33707 (SAN 662-4855) Tel 813-360-1495.

†Gulf Coast Research Laboratory, *(Gulf Coast Lab; 0-917235),* E. Beach, Ocean Springs, MS 39564 (SAN 655-8593) Tel 601-875-2244; *CIP.*

Gulf Publishing Co., *(Gulf Pub; 0-87201; 0-88415),* P.O. Box 2608, Houston, TX 77252 (SAN 201-6125) Tel 713-529-4301. *Imprints:* Hutchins House (Hutchins Hse); Lone Star Books (Lone Star Bks).

Gulfport Historical Society, *(Gulfport Hist; 0-9615746),* 3134 Beach Blvd., Saint Petersburg, FL 33707 (SAN 696-4575) Tel 813-321-7095.

Gull Bks., *(Gull Bks; 0-940584),* Box 273A, Prattsville, NY 12468 (SAN 281-7632) Tel 518-299-3171.

Gumbs & Thomas Pubs., *(Gumbs & Thomas; 0-936073),* 2067 Broadway, Suite 41, New York, NY 10023 (SAN 697-0877) Tel 212-870-0969.

Gun Hill Publishing Co., *(Gun Hill; 0-9600228),* P.O. Box 539, Yazoo City, MS 39194 (SAN 203-4654) Tel 601-746-3196.

Gun Owners Foundation, *(Gun Ownrs Fund; 0-9613968),* 5881 Leesburg Pike, Suite 204, Falls Church, VA 22041 (SAN 682-2959) Tel 703-931-5033.

Gun Room Pr., *(Gun Room; 0-88227),* 127 Raritan Ave., Highland Park, NJ 08904 (SAN 201-8357) Tel 201-545-4344.

Gundersen, Dr. Richard O., *(Gunderson; 0-9608080),* 350 W. 66th St., Yuma, AZ 85364 (SAN 240-2270) Tel 602-726-9229.

Gunnerman Pr., *(Gunnerman Pr; 0-936075),* P.O. Box 4292, Auburn Hills, MI 48057 (SAN 695-541X); 6444 Malvern, Troy, MI 48098 (SAN 696-9461) Tel 313-879-2779.

Gunther Pubs., *(Gunther Pubs; 0-916191),* P.O. Box 75932, Washington, DC 20013 (SAN 294-9350) Tel 202-722-5111.

Guptill Music, *(Guptill; 0-916715),* P.O. Box 521, Orange, CA 92666 (SAN 653-8657) Tel 714-538-2667; 1419 Joana Dr., Santa Ana, CA 92701 (SAN 653-8665).

Gurze Bks., *(Gurze Bks; 0-936077),* P.O. Box 20066, Santa Barbara, CA 93120 (SAN 697-0818) Tel 805-687-7922; 1727 Mountain Ave., Santa Barbara, CA 93101 (SAN 697-0826) Tel 805-682-0956.

Gusto Press, *(Gusto Pr; 0-933906),* P.O. Box 1009, 2960 Philip Ave., Bronx, NY 10465 (SAN 212-9450) Tel 212-931-8964.

Gut-Level Publishing, *(Gut Level Pub; 0-9616814),* 296 Bonefish Ct., Aptos, CA 95003 (SAN 661-0986) Tel 408-688-6547.

†Gutenberg Press, The, *(Gutenberg; 0-9603872),* P.O. Box 26345, San Francisco, CA 94126 (SAN 213-9278) Tel 415-548-3776; *CIP.*

Guthrie, Al, *(A Guthrie; 0-9606526),* P.O. Box 443, Carmichael, CA 95608 (SAN 209-4436) Tel 916-483-6543.

Guthrie, Gary, *(Gary Guthrie; 0-9612980),* 977 Myra Ave., Chula Vista, CA 92011 (SAN 292-515X) Tel 619-427-8098.

Guthrie, James M., *(J M Guthrie; 0-9614671),* Box 260. R. R. 15, Bedford, IN 47421 (SAN 682-2657) Tel 812-279-8004.

Guthrie Publishing Co., *(Guthrie Pub; 0-941064),* P.O. Box 152, Dalbo, MN 55017 (SAN 217-3751) Tel 612-689-4350.

Gwendolyn Pr., *(Gwendolyn Pr; 0-937503),* 107 Gwendolyn Dr., Vidalia, GA 30474 (SAN 658-9480) Tel 912-537-0195.

Gwethine Publishing Co., *(Gwethine Pub Co; 0-9605288),* 201 N. Wells St., Chicago, IL 60606 (SAN 220-0007) Tel 312-372-8105.

Gwinnett, Button, Publishers, Inc., *(Button Gwin; 0-938386),* 125 Scott St., P.O. Box 508, Buford, GA 30518 (SAN 264-0732).

Gwinnett Historical Society, *(Gwinnett Hist; 0-914923),* P.O. Box 261, Lawrenceville, GA 30246 (SAN 289-2197) Tel 404-962-1450.

Names

Gypsum Assn., *(Gypsum Assn),* 1603 Orrington Ave., Suite 1210, Evanston, IL 60201 (SAN 224-8808) Tel 312-491-1744.

Gypsy Lore Society, North American Chapter, Affil. of Gypsy Lore Society, *(Gypsy Lore Soc),* 2104 Dexter Ave., No. 203, Silver Spring, MD 20902 (SAN 241-3876) Tel 301-681-3123.

HALT, Inc., *(HALT DC; 0-910073),* 201 Massachusetts Ave., NE, Suite 319, Washington, DC 20002 (SAN 223-7873) Tel 202-546-4258.

H & B Hess Co., *(H & B Hess Co; 0-916507),* P.O. Box 12653, Jackson, MS 39211 (SAN 295-4184) Tel 601-956-0717.

H & D Pr., *(H & D Pr; 0-9614223),* P.O. Box 1284, Staten Island, NY 10314 (SAN 686-7189) Tel 718-447-5647.

H & H Pubns., *(H & H Pubns CA; 0-910197),* 1524 Hudson St., Redwood City, CA 94061 (SAN 241-5364) Tel 415-364-3402.

H & H Pubns., *(H-&-H Pubs),* P.O. Box 555, Hope Mills, NC 28348 (SAN 670-6940) Tel 919-425-2241.

H&H Pub. Co., Inc., *(H & H Pub; 0-943202),* 2165 Sunnydale Blvd., Suite N, Clearwater, FL 33575 (SAN 240-5350) Tel 813-442-7760.

H & S Publishing Co., *(H & S Pub Co; 0-9609268),* P.O. Box 304, Allenhurst, NJ 07711 (SAN 260-0641) Tel 201-775-3251.

Heirloom Bks., *(Heirloom Bks; 0-914925),* 3039 McClellan, Detroit, MI 48214 (SAN 289-2332) Tel 313-331-7244; Box 15472, Detroit, MI 48215 (SAN 669-3555).

H. B. C., *(HBC; 0-9601276),* Box 626, Lansing, IL 60438 (SAN 210-4318) Tel 312-474-7999.

HCP Research, *(HCP Res; 0-941210),* 20655 Sunrise Dr., Cupertino, CA 95014 (SAN 217-376X) Tel 408-446-1565.

HCP Systems, Inc., *(HCP Systems; 0-930945),* 11905 Whistler Ct., Potomac, MD 20854 (SAN 692-8226) Tel 301-340-9794.

HDL Publishing Co., Div. of HDL Communications, *(HDL Pubs; 0-937359),* 599 Adamsdale Rd., North Attleboro, MA 02760 (SAN 659-0403).

HEH Medical Pubns., *(HEH Med Pubns; 0-9614173),* 2227 W. Lindsey, Suite 1401, Norman, OK 73069 (SAN 686-6557) Tel 405-329-4457.

H. E. Howard, Inc., *(H E Howard; 0-930919),* P.O. Box 4161, Lynchburg, VA 24502 (SAN 679-680X) Tel 804-846-1146.

HEMA Publishing, *(HEMA Pub; 0-938805),* P.O. Box 23977, Rochester, NY 14623 (SAN 661-5120); 56 Wildbriar Rd., Rochester, NY 14623 (SAN 661-5139) Tel 716-334-7697.

HHH Horticultural, *(HHH Horticultural),* 68 Brooktree Rd., Hightstown, NJ 08520 (SAN 213-1951).

HIMACHAL, *(HIMACHAL; 0-9617065),* 304 Franklin Pk. Apt. Deerfield Rd., East Syracuse, NY 13057 (SAN 662-894X) Tel 607-273-2798.

HI Pr. of Cold Spring, Inc., *(HI Pr Cold Spring; 0-9615988),* Box 361, Cold Spring, NY 10516 (SAN 697-8894) Tel 914-265-3098.

HIT Pubns., *(HIT pubns; 0-910993),* P.O. Box 11198, Costa Mesa, CA 92627 (SAN 270-6482) Tel 714-722-7458.

HK Publishing Co., *(HK Pub Co; 0-913809),* P.O. Box 610053, Houston, TX 77208 (SAN 283-9598) Tel 713-827-1651.

HMB Pubns., *(HMB Pubns; 0-937086),* 7406 Monroe Ave., Hammond, IN 46324 (SAN 214-3836) Tel 219-932-1798; Dist. by: The Distributors, 702 S. Michigan, South Bend, IN 46618 (SAN 169-2488) Tel 219-232-8500.

HP Bks., Subs. of Knight-Ridder Newspapers, Inc., *(HP Bks; 0-912656; 0-89586),* P.O. Box 5367, Tucson, AZ 85703 (SAN 201-6087) Tel 602-888-2150; Toll free: 800-528-4923.

HR Assocs., *(HR Assocs; 0-9616423),* 6520 Misty Creek Dr., Citrus Heights, CA 95610 (SAN 658-9499) Tel 916-722-9398; P.O. Box 95866-0876, Sacramento, CA 95866 (SAN 658-9502).

HRH Systems, Inc., *(HRH Systems; 0-936737),* P.O. Box 4496, Silver Spring, MD 20904 (SAN 699-8801) Tel 301-384-7159; 12918 Allerton Ln., Silver Spring, MD 20904 (SAN 699-881X) Tel 301-384-7159.

HRM Communications, Inc., *(H R M Comm Inc; 0-9611254),* 201 E. 77th St., New York, NY 10021 (SAN 282-8723) Tel 212-734-4958.

HSA Pubns., *(HSA Pubns; 0-910621),* 4 W. 43rd St., New York, NY 10036 (SAN 270-6490) Tel 212-977-0050.

†HTH Pubs., *(HTH Pubs; 0-916658),* P.O. Box 550, Coupeville, WA 98239 (SAN 208-1148) Tel 206-678-4447; *CIP.*

H3 Enterprises, *(H Three; 0-943578),* 7 Victoria Vale, Monterey, CA 93940 (SAN 240-8317) Tel 408-372-4054.

H/U Pubns., *(H-U Public; 0-917292),* 1121 S. Redwood Rd., P.O. Box 27042, Salt Lake City, UT 84127-0042 (SAN 208-6816) Tel 801-973-4620.

HWH Creative Productions, Inc., *(HWH Creative Prod; 0-936969),* 87-53 167th St., Jamaica, NY 11432 (SAN 658-7887) Tel 718-297-2208.

Haas, Frederick C., *(Haas; 0-9601180),* Rte. 2 Box 78A, Blackstone, VA 23824 (SAN 210-0932) Tel 804-292-4726.

Haas Enterprises, *(Haas Ent NH; 0-9605552),* 7 N. Main, Box 218, Ashland, NH 03217 (SAN 216-034X) Tel 603-968-7177.

Haase-Mumm Publishing Co., Inc., *(Haase-Mumm Pub Co; 0-940114),* 100 E. Ohio St., Rm. B20, Chicago, IL 60611 (SAN 220-2867) Tel 312-951-5267; Dist. by: Amart Bk. & Catalog Dist. Co., Inc., 100 E. Ohio St., Rm. B20, Chicago, IL 60611 (SAN 276-9778).

Habel, Robert E., *(Habel; 0-9600444),* 1529 Ellis Hollow Rd., Ithaca, NY 14850 (SAN 203-4719) Tel 607-272-3199.

Haberman Pr., *(Haberman Pr; 0-9617000),* P.O. Box 71, Merrick, NY 11566 (SAN 662-5355); 67-15 Parsons Blvd., No. 6H, Flushing, NY 11365 (SAN 662-5363) Tel 718-591-0916.

Hach, Phila, *(Hach; 0-9606192),* 1601 Madison St., Clarksville, TN 37040 (SAN 217-0736) Tel 615-647-4084.

Hacker Art Bks., *(Hacker; 0-87817),* 54 W. 57th St., New York, NY 10019 (SAN 201-6052) Tel 212-757-1450.

†Hackett Publishing Co., Inc., *(Hackett Pub; 0-915144; 0-915145; 0-87220),* P.O. Box 44937, Indianapolis, IN 46204 (SAN 201-6044) Tel 317-635-9250; *CIP.*

Haddad's Fine Arts, Inc., *(Haddad's Fine Arts; 0-88445),* P.O. Box 3016 C, Anaheim, CA 92803 (SAN 206-5312) Tel 714-996-2100; 3855 E. Mira Loma Ave., Anaheim, CA 92803 (SAN 206-5320).

Hadley, R. G., Co., *(R G Hadley; 0-9600988),* 615 E. Main St., Silverton, OR 97381 (SAN 207-1282) Tel 503-873-4241.

Hadronic Pr., Inc., *(Hadronic Pr Inc; 0-911767),* Nonantum, MA 02195 (SAN 264-0740) Tel 617-864-9859.

Hady, Edmund Carl, *(E C Hady; 0-9600794),* 128 N. Main St., Ashley, PA 18706 (SAN 201-3509).

Haer Institute for Electro Physiological Research, *(Haer Inst; 0-940090),* P.O. Box 337 4 Industrial Pkwy, Brunswick, ME 04011 (SAN 220-2255).

Haffenreffer Museum of Anthropology, *(Haffenreffer Mus Anthro; 0-912089),* Brown University, Mt. Hope Grant, Bristol, RI 02809 (SAN 278-9817) Tel 401-253-8388.

†Hafner Pr., Div. of Macmillan Publishing Co., Inc., *(Hafner; 0-02),* 866 Third Ave., New York, NY 10022 (SAN 201-6001) Tel 212-702-2000; Toll free: 800-257-5755; Dist. by: Collier-Macmillan Distribution Ctr., Front & Brown Sts., Riverside, NJ 08075 (SAN 202-5582); *CIP.*

Hage Pubns., *(Hage Pubns; 0-933619),* P.O. Box 21, Somerville, NJ 08876 (SAN 692-4654) Tel 201-722-2933.

Hagin, Kenneth, Ministries, Inc., *(Hagin Ministries; 0-89276),* P.O. Box 50126, Tulsa, OK 74150-0126 (SAN 208-2578) Tel 918-258-1588.

Hagley Museum & Library, *(Hagley Museum; 0-914650),* P.O. Box 3630, Wilmington, DE 19807 (SAN 204-1545) Tel 302-658-2400.

Hagley Volunteers Cookbook Committee, *(Hagley Vol Ckbk; 0-9610990),* Hagley Museum & Library, P.O. Box 3 630, Greenville, DE 19807 (SAN 265-2501) Tel 302-658-2400.

Hagstrom Map Co., Inc., Subs. of American Map Corp., *(Hagstrom Map; 0-910684),* 46-35 54th Rd., Maspeth, NY 11378 (SAN 203-543X) Tel 718-784-0055.

Hague Pr., The, *(Hague Pr; 0-936851),* 965 Norview Ave., Norfolk, VA 23513 (SAN 658-3393) Tel 804-853-4661; P.O. Box 385, Norfolk, VA 23501 (SAN 658-3407).

Haigwood, John E., *(J E Haigwood; 0-9614500),* P.O. Box 5001, Rome, GA 30162 (SAN 690-0100) Tel 404-234-6414.

Hailstone, *(Hailstone; 0-9616979),* 2601 NW Expwy., No. 1210W, Oklahoma City, OK 73112 (SAN 661-8022) Tel 405-842-0131.

Haimo, Oscar, *(Haimo),* 252 E. 61st St., New York, NY 10021 (SAN 202-2664) Tel 212-838-6627.

Haimowoods Press, *(Haimowoods; 0-917790),* 1101 Forest Ave., Evanston, IL 60202 (SAN 210-296X) Tel 312-864-7209.

Haines, Ben M., *(B Haines; 0-9600586),* Box 1111, Lawrence, KS 66044 (SAN 202-3660) Tel 816-525-2579.

Haines, Leland M., *(L M Haines),* P.O. Box 54, Wayne, MI 48184 (SAN 661-4531).

Haker Books, *(Haker Books; 0-9609964),* 2707 First Ave. N., Great Falls, MT 59401 (SAN 262-0359) Tel 406-454-1487.

Hake's Americana & Collectibles, *(Hake; 0-918708),* P.O. Box 1444, York, PA 17405 (SAN 210-3575) Tel 717-843-3731.

Hakim's Pubs., *(Hakims Pubs),* 210 S. 52nd St., Philadelphia, PA 19139 (SAN 207-2327).

Halbur Publishing, *(Halbur; 0-9603520),* P.O. Box 11354, Santa Rosa, CA 95406 (SAN 212-9469) Tel 707-544-7537.

Halcyon Bk. Concern/The Temple of the People, *(Halcyon Bk; 0-933797),* P.O. Box 7095, Halcyon, CA 93420 (SAN 692-8773) Tel 805-489-2822; Dist. by: DeVorss & Co., P.O. Box 550, 1046 Princeton Dr., Marina del Rey, CA 90294-0550 (SAN 168-9886); Dist. by: The Philosophical Research Society, 3910 Los Feliz Blvd., Los Angeles, CA 90027 (SAN 205-3829); Dist. by: Starlite Distributors, P.O. Box 20729, Reno, NV 89515 (SAN 200-7789) Tel 702-359-5676.

Halcyon House *See National Bk. Co.*

Halcyon House, Publishers, Inc., *(Halcyon Hse; 0-911311),* P.O. Box 9547, Kansas City, MO 64133 (SAN 270-6555) Tel 816-737-0064.

Halcyon Press of Ithaca, *(Halcyon Ithaca; 0-9604006),* 111 Halcyon Hill Rd., Ithaca, NY 14850 (SAN 215-1510) Tel 607-257-1864.

Haldor Co., *(Haldor Co; 0-9614517),* P.O. Box 12354, Las Vegas, NV 89112 (SAN 689-6006) Tel 702-458-1723.

Hale, Nathan, Institute, The, Affil. of The Hale Foundation, *(Nathan Hale Inst; 0-935067),* 422 First St. SE, Suite 208, Washington, DC 20003 (SAN 694-6631) Tel 202-546-2293.

Hale and Hawthorne Publishers, *(Hale and Hawthorne; 0-931647),* P.O. Box 1394, Williamsburg, VA 23187-1394 (SAN 683-7336).

Halevy Financial Pubns., *(Halevy Finan Pubns; 0-935651),* 13431 Pepperdine Cir., Westminster, CA 92683 (SAN 695-958X) Tel 714-891-9084.

Half Court Press, *(Half Court; 0-911179),* 1122 18th St. No. 201, Santa Monica, CA 90403 (SAN 270-6563) Tel 213-453-5029.

Half Court Pr., *(Half Court Pr; 0-937619),* 16475 Dallas Pkwy., Suite 650, Dallas, TX 75248 (SAN 658-9510) Tel 214-248-3902.

Half Halt Pr., *(Half Halt Pr; 0-939481),* P.O. Box 3512, Gaithersburg, MD 20878 (SAN 663-270X); 125 Lamont Ln., Gaithersburg, MD 20878 (SAN 663-2718) Tel 301-948-2187.

Halfcourt Pr., *(Halfcourt Pr; 0-914585),* 3299 N. Fourth Ave., Wausau, WI 54401 (SAN 287-7481) Tel 715-675-3710; Orders to: P.O. Box 137, Iola, WI 54945 (SAN 662-2143).

Halgo, Inc., *(Halgo Inc; 0-9613805),* 2732 Maryland Ave., Baltimore, MD 21218 (SAN 679-4157) Tel 301-467-8186 (SAN 699-5861); Orders to: P.O. Box 4866, Hampden Sta., Baltimore, MD 21211 (SAN 202-7048).

Haljan Pubns., *(Haljan Pubns; 0-910907),* P.O. Box 291, 136 S. Main St., LaMoille, IL 61330 (SAN 270-6571) Tel 815-638-2152.

Hall, C. Mitchel, *(C M Hall; 0-914574)*, 3401 Bangor St., SE, Washington, DC 20020 (SAN 206-5339) Tel 202-583-3297.

Hall, Clarence H., *(C H Hall; 0-9604084)*, 3409 Altwater Rd., Avon Park, FL 33825 (SAN 214-3119).

Hall, Eva Litchfield, *(E L Hall; 0-9604398)*, 1400 S. Plymouth Ave., Apt. 321, Rochester, NY 14611 (SAN 207-2181).

Hall, G. K., & Co., Div. of Macmillian Publishing Co., *(G K Hall; 0-8161)*, 70 Lincoln St., Boston, MA 02111 (SAN 206-8427); Toll free: 800-343-2806. *Imprints:* Bibliographic Guides (Pub. by Biblio Guides); Hall Library Catalogs (Hall Library); Hall Reference Books (Hall Reference); Hall, G. K., Medical Pubs. (Hall Medical); Large Print Books (Large Print Bks); University Books (Univ Bks).

Hall, G. K., Medical Pubs. See Hall, G. K., & Co.

Hall, H. W., *(H W Hall; 0-935064)*, 3608 Meadow Oaks Lane, Bryan, TX 77802 (SAN 208-4678) Tel 409-845-2316.

Hall, James M., *(J M Hall; 0-9614762)*, 3500 Tallyho Dr., Kokomo, IN 46902 (SAN 692-9079) Tel 317-453-2693.

Hall, Joseph S, *(Hall J; 0-910738)*, 1654 N. Cherokee Ave., Hollywood, CA 90028 (SAN 204-0646) Tel 213-464-4164.

Hall, Norman, Ministries, *(N Hall; 0-938429)*, N. 1658 Fairmont Loop, Coeur d'Alene, ID 83814 (SAN 661-292X) Tel 208-664-4576.

Hall Library Catalogs See Hall, G. K., & Co.

Hall of Fame Management, Inc., *(Hall Fame Mgt; 0-9612238)*, P.O. Box 396, New York, NY 10185 (SAN 287-7392) Tel 212-534-4102.

Hall Pr., *(Hall Pr; 0-932218)*, P.O. Box 5375, San Bernardino, CA 92412 (SAN 211-7061) Tel 714-887-3466.

Hall Publishing Co., *(Hall Pub AL; 0-931859)*, 919 Greenboro Ave. Central Sq. 104, Tuscaloosa, AL 35401 (SAN 686-0265).

Hall Reference Bks. See Hall, G. K., & Co.

Hall Reunion, The, *(Hall Reunion; 0-9617071)*, 5720 Nella Blvd., NW, Canton, OH 44720 (SAN 662-8915) Tel 813-446-0206.

Hallberg Publishing Corp., *(C Hallberg; 0-87319)*, P.O. Box 547, Delavan, WI 53115 (SAN 205-3063) Tel 414-728-3173.

Halldin, A. G., Publishing Co., *(Halldin Pub; 0-935648)*, P.O. Box 667, Indiana, PA 15701 (SAN 208-208X) Tel 412-463-8450.

Haller, Lynda, *(L Haller; 0-9614174)*, 3400 SE 15th, Edmond, OK 73034 (SAN 686-6204) Tel 405-341-0853.

Halley's Comet, *(Halleys Comet; 0-937451)*, P.O. Box 706, Andover, ME (SAN 658-9529); 10 Barney St., Andover, NY 14806 (SAN 658-9537) Tel 607-478-8868.

Hallmark Card, Inc., *(Hallmark; 0-87529)*, 25th & McGee Sts., Kansas City, MO 64108 (SAN 202-2672) Tel 816-274-5111.

Hallowell, H. Thomas, *(H T Hallowell)*, 916 The Benson East, Jenkintown, PA 19046 (SAN 695-6351) Tel 215-572-3030.

Halls of Ivy Press, *(Halls of Ivy; 0-912256)*, 3445 Leora Ave., Simi Valley, CA 93063 (SAN 204-0204) Tel 805-527-0525.

Hallum, Boen, *(B Hallum; 0-9608854)*, 4977 Lockbourne Rd., Columbus, OH 43207 (SAN 241-0265) Tel 614-491-3886.

Hallwalls, Inc., *(Hallwalls Inc; 0-936739)*, 700 Main St., Buffalo, NY 14202 (SAN 699-9026) Tel 716-854-5828.

Halpern & Simon, Div. of AaronCorp, *(Halpern & Simon Publishing; 0-942898)*, P.O. Box 9399, Coral Springs, FL 33075 (SAN 240-3137); 3255 NW 94th Ave., Coral Springs, FL 33075 (SAN 662-0272); Orders to: P.O. Box 697, New York, NY 10272 (SAN 662-0280) Tel 718-712-5258.

†Halsted Pr., Div. of John Wiley & Sons, Inc., *(Halsted Pr; 0-470)*, 605 Third Ave., New York, NY 10158 (SAN 202-2680) Tel 212-850-6465; Toll free: 800-526-5368; *CIP.*

Halty Ferguson, *(Halty Ferguson; 0-912604)*, 376 Harvard St., Cambridge, MA 02138 (SAN 202-2699) Tel 617-868-6190.

Halyburton Pr., *(Halyburton; 0-916717)*, P.O. Box 2973, Ann Arbor, MI 48106 (SAN 653-7480) Tel 313-662-0060; 931 Hockey Ln., Ann Arbor, MI 48103 (SAN 653-7499).

Hamaker-Weaver Pubs., *(Hamaker-Weaver; 0-941550)*, Rt. 1, Box 158, Seymour, MO 65746 (SAN 239-2224) Tel 417-935-2116.

HamanD Publishing Co., *(HamanD Pub)*, 525 B St., Suite 342, San Diego, CA 92101 (SAN 208-1172) Tel 619-234-8393.

Hamaya U.S.A., Inc., *(Hamaya USA; 0-9615266)*, 929 E. Second St., Suite 108, Los Angeles, CA 90012 (SAN 694-647X) Tel 213-626-1017.

Hamba Books, *(Hamba Bks; 0-9606152)*, 1901 Creekwood Dr., Conway, AR 72032 (SAN 217-5223) Tel 501-329-6147.

Hambledon Pr., The, *(Hambledon Press; 0-907628)*, 309 Greenbrier Ave., Ronceverte, WV 24970 (SAN 677-4946) Tel 304-645-1058.

Hamburg Pr., The, *(Hamburg Pr; 0-916587)*, P.O. Box 171, Augusta, GA 30903 (SAN 296-693X) Tel 404-724-0364.

Hamilton, Alexander, Institute, Inc., *(Hamilton Inst; 0-86604)*, 1633 Broadway, New York, NY 10019 (SAN 205-311X) Tel 212-397-3580; Orders to: 1501 Broadway, New York, NY 10036 (SAN 689-8319) Tel 212-397-3580.

Hamilton Hse., *(Hamilton Hse; 0-917908)*, 936 N. Fifth, Philadelphia, PA 19123 (SAN 209-3308) Tel 215-923-9161.

Hamilton's, *(Hamiltons; 0-9608598)*, P.O. Box 932, Bedford, VA 24523 (SAN 264-0759) Tel 703-586-5592.

Hamilton's Publishing, *(Hamiltons Pub; 0-939129)*, 390 Oak Ave., Suite D, Carlsbad, CA 92008 (SAN 662-8583) Tel 619-434-6911. Do not confuse with Hamilton's in Bedford, VA.

Hamlet House, *(Hamlet Hse; 0-913861)*, P.O. Box 791044, New Orleans, LA 70179-1044 (SAN 286-7699) Tel 504-482-4903; 631 N. Carrollton Ave., New Orleans, LA 70119 (SAN 286-7702).

Hamline Univ. Schl. of Law, Advanced Legal Education, *(Hamline Law; 0-88055)*, 1536 Hewitt Ave., St. Paul, MN 55104 (SAN 293-9851) Tel 612-641-2122.

Hamma Library of Trinity Lutheran Seminary, *(Hamma)*, 2199 E. Main St., Columbus, OH 43209 (SAN 677-1602).

Hammer Galleries, Subs. of Knoedler Art Galleries, *(Hammer Gal; 0-9611570)*, 33 W. 57th St., New York, NY 10019 (SAN 283-1414) Tel 212-644-6373.

Hammer Mountain Bk. Halls, *(Hammer Mntn Bk; 0-9616659)*, 841 Union St., Schenectady, NY 12308 (SAN 661-3497) Tel 518-393-5266.

Hammill, J. H., III, *(J H Hammill; 0-9600652)*, 1081 Bollinger Canyon Rd., Moraga, CA 94556 (SAN 203-8986) Tel 415-376-0210.

Hammond-Harwood House Assn., Inc., *(Hammond-Harwood; 0-910688)*, Orders to: Maryland's Way, Hammond Harwood House, 19 Maryland Ave., Annapolis, MD 21401 (SAN 204-0220) Tel 301-267-6891.

†Hammond Inc., *(Hammond Inc; 0-8437)*, 515 Valley St., Maplewood, NJ 07040 (SAN 202-2702) Tel 201-763-6000; Toll free: 800-526-4953; *CIP.*

Hammond Pubns., *(Hammond Pubns; 0-937979)*, P.O. Box 8212, Wichita, KS 67208 (SAN 659-5081) Tel 316-683-3077; 6622 Aberdeen, Wichita, KS 67208 (SAN 659-509X).

Hammond Records, *(Hammond Records; 0-942874)*, P.O. Box 3431, Thousand Oaks, CA 91360 (SAN 239-5517) Tel 805-495-1143; 874 Chelterham Cir., Thousand Oaks, CA 91360 (SAN 658-0815).

Hamoroh Pr., *(Hamoroh Pr; 0-9604754)*, P.O. Box 48862, Los Angeles, CA 90048 (SAN 215-6512).

Hampol Publishing Co., *(Hampol Pub Co; 0-9609330)*, Box 36, 47 Harvard Ave., Boston, MA 02134 (SAN 260-1990) Tel 617-232-2430; Orders to: 1284 Beacon St., Brookline, MA 02146 (SAN 662-0299).

Hampshire Pacific Pr., *(Hampshire Pacific; 0-939930)*, 3043 SW Hampshire St., Portland, OR 97201 (SAN 216-8189).

Hampshire Pr., The, *(Hampshire Pr)*, 900 Main St., Wilmington, MA 01887 (SAN 296-127X); Dist. by: Henrietta Howard-Moineau, P.O. Box 235, West Boylston, MA 01505 (SAN 296-1288).

Hampton, Patricia Kay, *(P K Hampton; 0-9614397)*, Rte. 1, Box 98-D, Paeonian Springs, VA 22129 (SAN 688-6868) Tel 703-777-5821.

Hampton-Brown Co., *(Hampton-Brown; 0-917837)*, 200 Clock Tower Pl., Suite 201-A, Carmel, CA 93923 (SAN 657-145X) Tel 408-625-3666.

Hampton Court Pubs., *(Hampton Court Pub; 0-910569)*, Wixon Pond Rd., Mahopac, NY 10541 (SAN 264-0767) Tel 914-628-6155; Orders to: P.O. Box 655, Mahopac, NY 10541 (SAN 662-0302) Tel 914-628-6155.

Hampton Mae Institute, *(Hampton Mae; 0-9616511)*, 4104 Lynn Ave., Tampa, FL 33603 (SAN 659-4611) Tel 813-238-2221.

Hampton Pr., *(Hampton Pr MI; 0-938352)*, P.O. Box 805, Rochester, MI 48063 (SAN 216-0358) Tel 313-852-0980.

Hampton Publishing Co., *(Hampton Pub Co; 0-934895)*, 927 Cybus Way, Southampton, PA 18966 (SAN 694-4485) Tel 215-357-4531.

Hampton Univ., Univ. Museum, *(Hampton Univ Muse; 0-9616982)*, Hampton, VA 23668 (SAN 279-0009) Tel 804-727-5308.

†Hancock Hse. Pubs., *(Hancock House; 0-88839)*, 1431 Harrison Ave., Blaine, WA 98230 (SAN 240-8546) Tel 604-538-1114; Dist. by: Big Country Books, Inc., 1431 Harrison Ave., Blaine, WA 98230 (SAN 200-7215) Tel 604-538-1114; *CIP.*

Hancraft Studios, *(Hancraft; 0-941248)*, P.O. Box 578, Claremont, CA 91711 (SAN 219-9556) Tel 714-621-7046.

Hand Pr., *(Hand Pr; 0-9605620)*, 12015 Coyne St., Los Angeles, CA 90049 (SAN 218-4788) Tel 213-472-9691; Dist. by: Aperture, Millerton, NY 12546 (SAN 201-1832).

Hand Tools Institute, *(Hand Tools Inst; 0-9609220)*, 25 N. Broadway, Tarrytown, NY 10591 (SAN 224-7852).

Hands Off, *(Hands off; 0-9609596)*, P.O. Box 68, Tacoma, WA 98401 (SAN 260-2016) Tel 206-752-2525.

Hands on Pubns., *(Hands on Pubns; 0-931178)*, 451 Silvera Ave., Long Beach, CA 90803 (SAN 213-9286) Tel 213-596-4738.

Hands-On Publishing Co., *(Hands-On Pub Co; 0-934789)*, 1539 Lexington Ave., New York, NY 10029 (SAN 694-2075) Tel 212-876-9252.

Handwerk, Gordon, Pubs., *(G Handwerk; 0-940524)*, P.O. Box 685, Madison, NJ 07940 (SAN 217-1791) Tel 201-377-1644.

Handy Bk. Co., *(Handy Bk Co; 0-934049)*, 2509 S. Padre Island Dr. P.O. Box 721203, Corpus Christi, TX 78472-1203 (SAN 693-0484) Tel 512-851-2240; Dist. by: Baker & Taylor, Eastern Div., 50 Kirby Ave., Somerville, NJ 08876 (SAN 169-4901) Tel 201-526-8000.

Handy Books See Harcourt Brace Jovanovich, Inc.

Haney Bks., *(Haney Bks; 0-9609552)*, P.O. Box 552, Salem, IL 62881 (SAN 283-9059) Tel 618-548-1276.

Hang Gliding Pr., *(Hang Gliding; 0-938282)*, Box 22552, San Diego, CA 92122 (SAN 215-6520) Tel 619-452-1768.

†Hanging Loose Pr., *(Hanging Loose; 0-914610)*, 231 Wyckoff St., Brooklyn, NY 11217 (SAN 206-4960) Tel 718-643-9559; Dist. by: Inland Book Co., P.O. Box 261, 22 Hemingway Ave., East Haven, CT 06512 (SAN 200-4151) Tel 203-467-4257; Dist. by: Bookslinger, 213 E. Fourth St., St. Paul, MN 55101 (SAN 169-4154) Tel 612-221-0429; Dist. by: Small Press Dist., Inc., 1814 San Pablo Ave., Berkeley, CA 94702 (SAN 204-5826) Tel 415-549-3336; *CIP.*

Hanley & Belfus Inc., *(Hanley & Belfus; 0-932883)*, 210 S. 13th St., Philadelphia, PA 19107 (SAN 689-0032) Tel 215-546-7293.

Hanmer, R. F., *(R F Hanmer)*, P.O. Box 614, Wallingford, CT 06492 (SAN 681-820X).

Hanna, J. S., House, Div. of Reports for Government, *(J S Hanna; 0-9607024)*, 183 Gifford Way, Sacramento, CA 95864 (SAN 238-986X) Tel 916-486-1670.

Hanna-Barbera Productions, Inc., *(Hanna-Barbera Prod; 0-936817)*, 3400 Cahuenga Blvd., Los Angeles, CA 90068-1376 (SAN 699-8615) Tel 213-721-1414; Dist. by: Worldvision Enterprises, 660 Madison Ave., New York, NY 10021 (SAN 200-6235).

Hannan, W. C., Graphics, *(W C Hannan; 0-9611652),* P.O. Box A, Escondido, CA 92025 (SAN 285-3027) Tel 619-746-4959.

Hannon, Douglas, *(D Hannon; 0-937866),* Rte. 2, Box 991, Odessa, FL 33556 (SAN 215-7705); Dist. by: Great Outdoors Publishing Co., St. Petersburg, FL 33714 (SAN 201-6273); Dist. by: Atlantic Publishing Company, P.O. Box 67, Tabor City, NC 28463 (SAN 215-6237) Tel 919-653-3153.

Hanover Publishing Co., *(Hanover Pub KY; 0-936021),* P.O. Box 591, Ashland, KY 41105 (SAN 696-7957) Tel 606-329-0077; 1505 Carter Ave., Ashland, KY 41105 (SAN 696-7965).

Hansa Publishing, *(Hansa Pub; 0-933593),* 2124 Kittredge St., No. 76, Berkeley, CA 94704 (SAN 692-2147) Tel 415-528-6377; Dist. by: Bookpeople, 2929 Fifth St., Berkeley, CA 94710 (SAN 168-9517) Tel 415-549-3030.

Hansen, Charles, Educational Music & Bks., Inc., *(Hansen Ed Mus; 0-8494),* 1860 West Ave., Miami Beach, FL 33139 (SAN 205-0609) Tel 305-673-4612; Dist. by: Hansen Hse., 1860 West Ave., Miami Beach, FL 33139 (SAN 200-7908) Tel 305-532-5461; Toll free: 800-327-8202. *Imprints:* Maestro Publication (Maestro Pubn); Musica para Ninos (Musica Ninos); Shattinger International (Shattinger).

Hansen, Kathryn, *(K Hansen),* 24055 Paseo del Lago W., Tower 2, No. 1057, Laguna Hills, CA 92653 (SAN 696-7981) Tel 714-830-7777; P.O. Box 2323, Laguna Hills, CA 92653 (SAN 662-3875).

Hansen, Ludela, Enterprises, *(L Hansen Enter; 0-935685),* P.O. Box 340, Claymont, DE 19703 (SAN 695-9547) Tel 302-475-7382; 1511 Forsythia Ave., Wilmington, DE 19810 (SAN 695-9555).

Hansen, Mack, *(M Hansen; 0-9606672),* 207 Hill Blvd., Petaluma, CA 94952 (SAN 219-7499) Tel 707-763-1489.

Hansen, Mark Victor, *(M V Hansen),* P.O. Box 7665, Newport Beach, CA 92658-7665 (SAN 694-2407) Tel 714-759-9304.

Hansen Publishing Co., *(Hansen Pub MI; 0-930098),* P.O. Box 1723, East Lansing, MI 48823 (SAN 210-735X) Tel 517-332-5946; Dist. by: Holley International Co., 63 Kercheval, Suite 204A, Grosse Pointe Farms, MI 48236 (SAN 241-5178) Tel 313-882-0405.

Hansen-Reshanov Consultants, Inc., *(Hansen Reshanov; 0-937553),* P.O. Box 27541, Golden Valley, MN 55402 (SAN 658-9545) Tel 612-544-1211; 8009 40th Ave., N., New Hope, MN 55427 (SAN 658-9553).

Hansi Ministries, Inc., *(Hansi; 0-932878),* P.O. Box 3009, Fallbrook, CA 92028-0945 (SAN 213-5086) Tel 619-728-7847.

Hanson, Margaret B., *(Hanson; 0-9605834),* Mayoworth Rte., Kaycee, WY 82639 (SAN 216-4884) Tel 307-738-2215.

Hanson, Paul *See* **Martin Pr., The**

Hanuman Bks., *(Hanuman Bks; 0-937815),* P.O. Box 1070, Old Chelsea Sta., New York, NY 10113 (SAN 659-462X) Tel 212-645-1840; 222 W. 23rd St., Suite 807, New York, NY 10011 (SAN 659-4638).

Hanuman Foundation, Div. of Prison-Ashram Project, *(Hanuman Foun; 0-9614444),* Rte. 1, Box 201-N, Durham, NC 27705 (SAN 689-3635) Tel 919-942-2138.

Hapi Pr., *(Hapi Pr; 0-913244),* 512 SW Maplecrest Dr., Portland, OR 97219 (SAN 699-5292) Tel 503-246-9632.

Happibook Pr., *(Happibook Pr; 0-937395),* P.O. Box 218, Montgomery, NY 12549-0218 (SAN 658-9561) Tel 914-457-9328; E. Kaisertown Rd., Montgomery, NY 12549 (SAN 658-957X).

Happiness Pr., *(Happiness Pr; 0-916508),* 14351 Wycliff, Postal Drawer DD, Magalia, CA 95954 (SAN 208-6719) Tel 916-873-0294; Orders to: P.O. Box B-DD, Magalia, CA 95954 (SAN 662-0329).

Happiness Unlimited Pubns., *(Happiness Unltd; 0-939372),* 4317 Tillman Dr., Virginia Beach, VA 23452 (SAN 220-1550) Tel 804-498-1552; Toll free: 800-525-5018, Ext 552.

Happy Hands Publishing Co., *(Happy Hands Pub Co; 0-941468),* 3750 S. University Dr., Suite 201, Fort Worth, TX 76109 (SAN 264-0775) Tel 817-932-9081.

Happy Health Pubs., *(Happy Health; 0-9606402),* 13048 Delmonte Dr. 42-D, Seal Beach, CA 90740 (SAN 206-4979) Tel 213-431-0069.

Happy History, Inc., *(Happy History; 0-918430),* P.O. Box 2160, Boca Raton, FL 33432 (SAN 210-0940) Tel 305-483-8093.

Happy Thoughts & Rainbow Co., The, *(Happy Thoughts & Rainbow; 0-9608686),* Rte. 2, P.O. Box 419, Aurora, MN 55705 (SAN 238-2954) Tel 218-229-3451.

Happy Valley Apple, *(Happy Valley Apple; 0-913758),* Dist. by: Bookpeople, 2929 Fifth St., Berkeley, CA 94710 (SAN 168-9517) Tel 415-549-3030.

Happy Valley Pubs., *(Happy Val Whittier; 0-936805),* 12413 Cullman Ave., Whittier, CA 90604 (SAN 699-8763) Tel 213-943-5660.

Haralson Publishing Co., *(Haralson Pub Co; 0-934534),* P.O. Box 20366, Atlanta, GA 30325 (SAN 221-1076) Tel 404-872-6471.

Harben Publishing Company, *(Harben Pub; 0-9608158),* P.O. Box 1055, Safety Harbor, FL 33572 (SAN 238-8375).

Harbin Communications Group Inc., *(Harbin Comm; 0-932539),* 7420 FDR Sta., New York, NY 10150 (SAN 687-4789) Tel 212-319-9085.

Harbinger Books *See* **Harcourt Brace Jovanovich, Inc.**

Harbinger Group, Inc., Div. of Xerox Corp., *(Harbinger Group; 0-935963),* 17 North Ave., Norwalk, CT 06851 (SAN 696-8007) Tel 203-849-5000.

Harbinger Medical Pr., *(Harbinger Med Pr NC; 0-9612242),* P.O. Box 17201, Winston-Salem, NC 27116 (SAN 291-834X).

Harbinger Pubns., *(Harbinger Pubns; 0-933611),* 23815 Pine Lake Dr., P.O. Box 164, Sugar Pine, CA 95346 (SAN 692-4603) Tel 209-586-5740.

Harbinger Publishing, *(Harbinger FL; 0-939441),* 2413 NW 40th Circle, Boca Raton, FL 33431 (SAN 663-3536); Dist. by: Banyan Bks., P.O. Box 431160, Miami, FL 33143 (SAN 208-340X).

†**Harbor Hill Bks., Inc.,** *(Harbor Hill Bks; 0-916346; 0-915585),* P.O. Box 407, Harrison, NY 10528 (SAN 201-9159) Tel 914-698-3495; *CIP.*

Harbor Hse. Pubs., Subs. of Seaway Review, Inc., *(Harbor Hse MI; 0-937360),* 221 Water St., Boyne City, MI 49712 (SAN 200-5751) Tel 616-582-2814.

Harbor Pr., *(Harbor Pr; 0-936197),* P.O. Box 1656, Gig Harbor, WA 98335 (SAN 696-8953); 1602 Lucille Pkwy., NW, Gig Harbor, WA 98335 (SAN 696-8961) Tel 206-851-9598.

†**Harbor Publishing Co.,** *(Harbor Pub; 0-937638),* 80 N. Moore St., Suite 4J, New York, NY 10013 (SAN 656-8882) Tel 212-349-1818; *CIP.*

Harboridge Press, *(Harboridge Pr),* 455 E. Ridge St.,.Marquette, MI 49855 (SAN 201-9167).

Harbottle Pr., *(Harbottle Pr; 0-9615145),* 3601 Allen Pkwy., No. 97, Houston, TX 77019 (SAN 694-2059) Tel 713-529-7079.

Harbrace Paperback Library *See* **Harcourt Brace Jovanovich, Inc.**

HarBraceJ Juvenile Bks. *See* **Harcourt Brace Jovanovich, Inc.**

Harburn, Todd & Gerald E., Pubs., *(T & G Harburn; 0-9617171),* 2417-8 E. Jolly Rd., Lansing, MI 48910 (SAN 663-1800) Tel 517-394-6856.

Harcourt Brace Jovanovich, Inc., *(HarBraceJ; 0-15),* 1250 Sixth Ave., San Diego, CA 92101 (SAN 200-2736) Tel 619-699-6335; Toll free: 800-543-1918; Harcourt Brace Jovanovich Bldg., Orlando, FL 32887 (SAN 200-2299). *Imprints:* B F P (Books for Professionals) (BFP); Handy Books (Handy); Harbinger Books (Hbgr); Harbrace Paperback Library (HPL); Harcourt Brace Jovanovich, Inc., College Dept. (HC); Harvest Books (Harv); HarBraceJ Juvenile Books (HJ); Law & Business, Inc. (Law & Business); Psychological Corporation (Psych Corp); Voyager Books (VoyB).

Harcourt Brace Jovanovich, Inc., College Dept. *See* **Harcourt Brace Jovanovich, Inc.**

†**Hard Pr.,** *(Hard Pr; 0-938878),* 340 E. 11th St., New York, NY 10003 (SAN 219-1849); *CIP.*

Hard/Soft Pr., Div. of Hard/Soft, Inc., *(Hard Soft Pr; 0-938611),* P.O. Box 1277, Riverdale, NY 10471 (SAN 661-5759) Tel 212-543-9313.

Hardin, Albert N., Jr., *(Hardin; 0-9601778),* 5414 Lexington Ave., Pennsauken, NJ 08109 (SAN 210-9026) Tel 609-662-2221.

Hardin Publishing Co., *(Hardin Pub Co; 0-916255),* P.O. Box 269, Avera, GA 30803 (SAN 294-9369) Tel 404-598-2312.

Hardin-Simmons Univ. Pr., *(Hardin-Simmons; 0-910075),* Box 896, HSU, Abilene, TX 79698 (SAN 241-3205) Tel 915-677-7281.

Harding, A. R., Publishing Co., *(A R Harding Pub; 0-936622),* 2878 E. Main St., Columbus, OH 43209 (SAN 206-4936) Tel 614-231-9585.

Hardscrabble Bks., *(Hardscrabble Bks; 0-915056),* Rte. 2, Box 285, Berrien Springs, MI 49103 (SAN 207-0960) Tel 616-473-5570.

Hardscrabble House Publications, *(Hardscrabble Hse Pubns; 0-9613995),* 60 Franklin St, Malone, NY 12953 (SAN 682-5095) Tel 518-483-5595.

Hardwick, M. Warren, *(M W Hardwick; 0-9616067),* 1126 E. Cedar St., Angleton, TX 77515 (SAN 697-8665) Tel 409-849-6227.

Hardwood Plywood Manufacturers Assn., *(Hardwd Ply),* Box 2789, 1825 Michael Faraday Dr., Reston, VA 22090 (SAN 224-7569) Tel 703-435-2900.

Hardy, Arthur, & Associates, *(A Hardy & Assocs; 0-930892),* P.O. Box 8058, New Orleans, LA 70182 (SAN 210-9913) Tel 504-282-2326.

Hardy, Max, Pub., *(M Hardy; 0-939460),* P.O. Box 28219, Las Vegas, NV 89126-2219 (SAN 216-597X) Tel 702-368-0379.

Hardy House Publishing Co., A Hardy-Roberts Enterprise, *(Hardy Hse; 0-917844),* P.O. Box 705, South Laguna Beach, CA 92677 (SAN 210-0959) Tel 714-497-2670.

Hardywill Group, Inc., *(Hardywill Grp; 0-916797),* 2108 Lafayette Tower E., Detroit, MI 48207 (SAN 654-3480) Tel 313-259-0504; Dist. by: The Distributors, 702 S. Michigan, South Bend, IN 46618 (SAN 169-2488) Tel 219-232-8500; Dist. by: Ludington News Co., 1600 E. Grand Blvd., Detroit, MI 48207 (SAN 169-3972) Tel 313-925-7600.

Harian Bks., *(Harian; 0-87036),* 1 Vernon Ave., Floral Park, NY 11001 (SAN 202-2729).

Harian Creative Pr.-Bks., Subs. of Harian Creative Assocs., *(Harian Creative; 0-911906),* 47 Hyde Blvd., Ballston Spa, NY 12020 (SAN 204-0255) Tel 518-885-7397.

Harker & Van Pelt Hse., *(Harker Van Pelt; 0-930639),* 65 Larchwood Ave., West Long Branch, NJ 07764 (SAN 676-3014) Tel 201-222-3608; 145 E. 49th St., New York, NY 10017 (SAN 676-3022).

Harlequin Bks., *(Harlequin Bks; 0-373),* Dist. by: Simon & Schuster, Inc., 1230 Ave. of the Americas, New York, NY 10020 (SAN 200-2450) Tel 212-245-6400.

Harlin Jacque Pubns., *(Harlin Jacque; 0-940938),* 89 Surrey Ln., Hempstead, NY 11550 (SAN 281-7659) Tel 516-489-8564; Orders to: 71 N. Franklin St., Suite 207, Hempstead, NY 11550 (SAN 281-7667) Tel 516-489-0120.

Harling, Donn & Deborah, *(D & D Harling; 0-9617013),* 6932 N. Topeka Ave., Topeka, KS 66617 (SAN 662-880X) Tel 913-288-1990.

Harlo Pr., *(Harlo Pr; 0-8187),* 50 Victor Ave., Detroit, MI 48203 (SAN 202-2745) Tel 313-883-3600.

Harmon-Meek Gallery, *(Harmon-Meek Gal; 0-911431),* 1258 Third St., S., Naples, FL 33940 (SAN 264-0791) Tel 813-261-2637.

Harmonious Circle Pr., *(Harmonious Pr; 0-9610544),* 15 Ozone Ave., Apt. 2, Venice, CA 90291 (SAN 264-0813).

Harmony Bks. *See* **Crown Pubs., Inc.**

Harmony Hse. Pubs.-Louisville, *(Harmony Hse Pub LO; 0-916509),* 1008 Kent Rd., Goshen, KY 40026 (SAN 295-4257) Tel 502-228-4446; Orders to: P.O. Box 90, Prospect, KY 40059 (SAN 662-2275) Tel 502-228-2010.

Harmony Institute Pr., *(Harmony Inst Pr; 0-938687),* P.O. Box 210, Tollhouse, CA 93667 (SAN 661-5538); 28974 Harmony Ranch Rd., Tollhouse, CA 93667 (SAN 661-5546) Tel 209-855-3643.

Harmony Mark, Inc., *(Harmony Mark; 0-9616761),* 604 N. Burghley Ave., Ventnor, NJ 08406 (SAN 661-3756) Tel 609-822-0287.

Harmony Pr., Inc., *(Harmony Pr; 0-941600),* P.O. Box 122, North Granby, CT 06060 (SAN 238-8790) Tel 203-653-2722.

Harmony Raine & Co., Div. of Buccaneer Books, Inc., *(Harmony Raine; 0-89967),* Box 133, Greenport, NY 11944 (SAN 262-0367) Tel 516-734-5650.

Harmony Society Pr., *(Harmony Soc; 0-937640),* Clark Univ., Worcester, MA 01610 (SAN 215-6539) Tel 617-793-7351.

Harmsen Publishing Co., *(Harmsen; 0-9601322),* 1331 E. Alameda Ave., Denver, CO 80209 (SAN 213-0742).

Haroldsen, Mark O., *(M O Haroldsen; 0-932444),* 1831 E. Fourth Union Blvd., Salt Lake City, UT 84121 (SAN 281-7675).

Harp & Lion Pr., *(Harp & Lion; 0-936345),* 197 Main St., Annapolis, MD 21401 (SAN 697-8673) Tel 301-267-7094.

Harp & Thistle, Ltd. of Warner Robins Georgia, *(Harp & Thistle),* P.O. Drawer BO, Agana, GU 96910 (SAN 270-6792).

Harp 'N Harmonica Music Publishing Co., *(Harp N Harmonica; 0-936601),* 2160 Monterey, B1, Hermosa Beach, CA 90254 (SAN 698-0562) Tel 213-372-8727; Orders to: P.O. Box 671, Hermosa Beach, CA 90254.

Harp Press, *(Harp Pr; 0-9610456),* 822 Magdeline Dr., Madison, WI 53704 (SAN 264-0821) Tel 608-249-3458.

Harper, Phyllis, *(P Harper; 0-9615704),* 2720 Lawndale, Tupelo, MS 38801 (SAN 695-9474) Tel 601-842-2611.

Harper & Assocs., Inc., *(Harper Assocs; 0-9612352),* 2221 Acacia Dr., Wilmington, NC 28403 (SAN 289-5471) Tel 919-762-4962.

Harper & Row Junior Bks., Div. of Harper Junior Bks. Group, *(HarpJ; 0-06),* 10 E. 53rd St., New York, NY 10022 (SAN 200-2086) Tel 212-207-7000; Orders to: Keystone Industrial Pk., Scranton, PA 18512 (SAN 215-3742). *Imprints:* Trophy (Trophy).

Harper & Row Pubs., Inc., *(Har-Row; 0-06),* 10 E. 53rd St., New York, NY 10022 (SAN 200-2086) Tel 212-207-7099; Toll free: 800-242-7737; 1700 Montgomery St., San Francisco, CA 94111 (SAN 215-3734) Tel 415-989-9000; Dist. by: Harper & Row Pubs. Inc., Keystone Industrial Pk., Scranton, PA 18512 (SAN 215-3742). *Imprints:* Barnes & Noble Books (B&N Bks); Canfield Press (Canfield Pr); Colophon Books (CN); Cornelia & Michael Bessie Books (C&M Bessie Bks); Harper Crest (HarCrest); Harper Religious Books (HarpR); Harper Trade Books (HarpT); Harper's College Division (HarpC); Harrow Books Paperback Department (HW); Icon Editions (Icon Edns); International Department (IntlDept); Lippincott, J. B., /Harper & Row Medical Division (Harper Medical); Open University (Open U); Perennial Fiction Library (Perennial Fiction Lib); Perennial Library (PL); Perennial Mystery Library (Perennial Mystery Library); School Department (SchDept); Torchbooks (Torch); Torchbooks Library Binding (Torch Lib).

Harper Coloron, *(Harper Coloron; 0-9616278),* 604 State St., Bldg. 6, Box 48, Kings L., Brewster, MA 02631 (SAN 658-621X) Tel 617-896-5613.

Harper Crest *See* **Harper & Row Pubs., Inc.**

Harper Religious Bks. *See* **Harper & Row Pubs., Inc.**

Harper Square Press, Artcrest Products Co., Inc., *(Harper Sq Pr; 0-933908),* c/o Artcrest Products Co., Inc., 500 E. Cermak Rd., Chicago, IL 60616 (SAN 212-9086) Tel 312-733-7117.

Harper Trade Bks. *See* **Harper & Row Pubs., Inc.**

Harper's College Division *See* **Harper & Row Pubs., Inc.**

Harpers Ferry Pr., Div. of Harpers Ferry Enterprises, Inc., *(Harpers Ferry Pr; 0-9616354),* P.O. Box 304, Harpers Ferry, WV 25425 (SAN 658-9588) Tel 304-535-2593; Rte. 3, Box 120, Harpers Ferry, WV 25425 (SAN 658-9596).

Harpswell Pr., *(Harpswell Pr; 0-88448),* 132 Water St., Gardiner, ME 04345 (SAN 208-1199) Tel 207-582-1899.

Harrane Publishing Co., *(Harrane Pub; 0-931897),* P.O. Box 1855, Kailua, HI 96734 (SAN 686-0257) Tel 808-261-0050.

Harriet's Kitchen, *(Harriet's Kitchen; 0-938592),* P.O. Box 424, Forest Hills, NY 11375 (SAN 216-2520).

†**Harrington Park Pr., Inc.,** Subs. of Haworth Pr., *(Harrington Pk; 0-918393),* 28 E. 22nd St., New York, NY 10010-6194 (SAN 657-3487) Tel 212-228-2800; Orders to: Kim LaBarre, 75 Griswold St., Binghamton, NY 13904 (SAN 211-0156) Tel 607-722-7068; Dist. by: The Haworth Pr., Inc., 28 E. 22 St., New York, NY 10010-6194 (SAN 662-2372) Tel 212-228-2800; *CIP.*

Harris, Barbara, *(B Harris; 0-9601060),* P.O. Box 2992, Portland, OR 97208 (SAN 281-7691) Tel 503-223-6434.

Harris, Frank, *(F Harris; 0-9610458),* 2129 Rose St., Berkeley, CA 94709 (SAN 264-0848) Tel 415-548-8709.

Harris, H. E., & Co., Inc., *(Harris & Co; 0-937458),* Lafayette West Industrial Pk., P.O. Box 7087, Portsmouth, NH 03801 (SAN 202-1137) Tel 603-433-0400; Orders to: P.O. Box 7086, Portsmouth, NH 03801 (SAN 662-0337).

Harris Learning Academy, *(Harris Academy; 0-911181),* 2402 S. Newberry Ct., Denver, CO 80222 (SAN 264-0856); Dist. by: Publishers Group West, 5855 Beaudry St., Emeryville, CA 94608 (SAN 202-8522) Tel 415-658-3453.

Harris Publishing Company, *(Harris Pub; 0-916512),* 2057-2 E. Aurora Rd., Twinsburg, OH 44087 (SAN 208-3280) Tel 216-425-9000; Toll free: 800-321-9136.

Harrison, E. Bruce, Co., *(E B Harrison; 0-9609130),* 605 14th St., NW, Washington, DC 20005 (SAN 241-5119).

Harrison Co., *(Harrison Co GA; 0-910694),* 3110 Crossing Park, Norcross, GA 30071 (SAN 205-0536) Tel 404-447-9150; Toll free: 800-241-3561; Toll free: 800-282-9867 (In Georgia).

Harrison Education Motivation Enterprises, *(HEMECO; 0-9611440),* 21863 Brill Rd., Riverside, CA 92508 (SAN 212-744X) Tel 714-653-4779.

†**Harrison Hse., Inc.,** *(Harrison Hse; 0-89274),* P.O. Box 35035, Tulsa, OK 74153 (SAN 208-676X) Tel 918-582-2126; Toll free: 800-331-3647; *CIP.*

Harrison Pubns., *(Harrison Pubns; 0-916089),* P.O. Box 252, Williamstown, MA 01267 (SAN 294-8230) Tel 413-689-3230.

Harrow & Heston, *(Harrow & Heston; 0-911577),* Stuyvesant Plaza, P.O. Box 3934, Albany, NY 12203 (SAN 264-0872) Tel 518-442-5223.

Harrow Bks. Paperback Dept. *See* **Harper & Row Pubs., Inc.**

†**Harrowood Books,** *(Harrowood Bks; 0-915180),* 3943 N. Providence Rd., Newtown Square, PA 19073 (SAN 207-1622) Tel 215-353-5585; *CIP.*

Harsand Pr., *(Harsand Pr; 0-9612310),* N. 8565 Holseth Rd., Holmen, WI 54636 (SAN 287-7309) Tel 608-526-3848; Dist. by: Publishers Group West, 5855 Beaudry St., Emeryville, CA 94608 (SAN 202-8522) Tel 415-658-3453; Dist. by: Hardsand Distributing, P.O. Box 515, Holmen, WI 54636 (SAN 200-7223) Tel 608-526-3848.

Hart, R. S., *(R S Hart; 0-9604226),* 6636 Washington Blvd., Box 53, Elkridge, MD 21227 (SAN 214-2465).

Hart, Richard, *(R Hart; 0-9602100),* P.O. Box 649, Berkeley, CA 94701-0649 (SAN 281-7705).

Hart Brothers Publishing, *(Hart Bro Pub; 0-910077),* P.O. Box 205, Williston, VT 05495 (SAN 240-8562) Tel 802-879-4670.

Hart-Eden Pr., *(Hart Eden Pr; 0-937497),* 6114 LaSalle, Suite 283, Oakland, CA 94611 (SAN 658-9626) Tel 415-339-1753.

Hart Graphics, *(Hart Graphics; 0-9605422),* P.O. Box 968, Austin, TX 78767 (SAN 217-1074).

Hart Pubns., Inc., *(Hart Pubns; 0-912553),* 1900 Grant St., Suite 400, P.O. Box 1917, Denver, CO 80201 (SAN 282-7883) Tel 303-837-1917.

Hartley & Marks, Inc., *(Hartley & Marks; 0-88179),* P.O. Box 147, Point Roberts, WA 98281 (SAN 264-0880) Tel 206-945-2017; Dist. by: Kampmann & Co., 9 E. 40th St., New York, NY 10016 (SAN 202-5191) Tel 212-685-2928. *Imprints:* A Cloudburst Press Book (Cloudburst Press Bk).

Hartley Enterprises, *(Hartley Ent),* P.O. Box 701, Rancho Mirage, CA 92270 (SAN 209-3278).

Hartley House, *(Hartley Hse; 0-937518),* P.O. Box 1352, Hartford, CT 06143 (SAN 220-0570) Tel 203-525-2376.

†**Hartmore Hse.,** Subs. of Media Judaica, Inc., *(Hartmore; 0-87677),* 304 E. 49th St., New York, NY 10017 (SAN 293-2717) Tel 212-319-6666; Orders to: Media Judaica, Inc., 1363 Fairfield Ave., Bridgeport, CT 06605 (SAN 207-0022) Tel 203-384-2284; *CIP.*

Hartnell Pubns., *(Hartnell Pubns; 0-9605754),* 195 Hartnell Place, Sacramento, CA 95825 (SAN 219-7863) Tel 916-925-6064.

Hartnett, Marian, Pr., *(Hartnett Marian Pr; 0-9613008),* 5 W. Alexandria Ave., Alexandria, VA 22301 (SAN 292-5281) Tel 703-683-4972.

Hart's Spring Works, *(Harts Spring Wks; 0-943096),* P.O. Box 330178, San Francisco, CA 94133 (SAN 240-3846) Tel 415-982-8043.

Hartt Publishing of Indiana, *(Hartt Pub Indiana; 0-9614495),* P.O. Box 5078, Fort Wayne, IN 46895 (SAN 682-2703) Tel 219-484-4473.

Harvard Business Schl. Pr., *(Harvard Busn; 0-87584),* Harvard Business Schl., Gallatin E117, Boston, MA 02163 (SAN 202-277X) Tel 617-495-6700; Dist. by: Harper & Row Pubs., Inc., Keystone Industrial Pk., Scranton, PA 18512 (SAN 215-3742); Toll free: 800-638-3030.

Harvard Common Pr., *(Harvard Common Pr; 0-916782; 0-87645),* 535 Albany St., Boston, MA 02118 (SAN 208-6718) Tel 617-423-5803; Dist. by: Kampmann & Co., 9 E. 40th St., New York, NY 10016 (SAN 202-5191) Tel 212-685-2928.

Harvard Educational Review, *(Harvard Educ Rev; 0-916690),* 13 Appian Way, Cambridge, MA 02138 (SAN 208-3426) Tel 617-495-3432.

†**Harvard Law School, International Tax Program,** *(Harvard Law Intl Tax; 0-915506),* Harvard Law School, Cambridge, MA 02138 (SAN 207-3803) Tel 617-495-4407; *CIP.*

Harvard Series in Ukrainian Studies *See* **Harvard Ukrainian Research Institute**

Harvard Ukrainian Research Institute, *(Harvard Ukrainian; 0-916458),* 1583 Massachusetts Ave., Cambridge, MA 02138 (SAN 208-967X) Tel 617-495-3692.

Harvard Univ. Ctr. for International Affairs, *(Harvard U Intl Aff; 0-87674),* Coolidge Hall-International Studies, 1737 Cambridge St., Cambridge, MA 02138 (SAN 204-0271) Tel 617-495-2137.

Harvard Univ. Ctr. for Jewish Studies, *(Harvard U Ctr Jewish),* Dist. by: Harvard Univ. Pr., 79 Garden St., Cambridge, MA 02138 (SAN 200-2043) Tel 617-495-2600.

Harvard Univ., Ctr. for Middle Eastern Studies, *(Harvard CMES; 0-932885),* 1737 Cambridge St., Cambridge, MA 02138 (SAN 688-9409) Tel 617-495-4051.

†**Harvard Univ., Council on East Asian Studies,** *(Harvard E Asian),* Dist. by: Harvard Univ. Pr., 79 Garden St., Cambridge, MA 02138 (SAN 200-2043) Tel 617-495-2600; *CIP.*

†**Harvard Univ., Dept. of Romance Languages & Literatures,** *(Harvard U Romance Lang & Lit; 0-940940),* 201 Boylston Hall, Cambridge, MA 02138 (SAN 217-3786) Tel 617-495-2546; c/o French Forum, Inc., P.O. Box 5108, Lexington, KY 40505 (SAN 208-4996) Tel 606-299-9530; *CIP.*

†**Harvard Univ. Fogg Art Museum,** *(Harvard Art Mus; 0-916724),* 32 Quincy St., Cambridge, MA 02138 (SAN 270-6865) Tel 617-495-2397; *CIP.*

Names

Harvard Univ. Graduate Schl. of Design, Div. of Harvard Univ., *(Harvard U GSD; 0-935617),* 48 Quincy St., Cambridge, MA 02138 (SAN 695-9210) Tel 617-495-4004.

Harvard University, Gutman Library, *(Gutman Lib; 0-943484),* Educational Technology Ctr., Appian Way, Cambridge, MA 02138 (SAN 658-0807) Tel 617-495-4225.

Harvard Univ., Harvard Law Schl. Library, Pubns. Dept., *(Harvard U Har Law; 0-88086),* Langdell Hall, Cambridge, MA 02138 (SAN 218-7558) Tel 617-495-3170.

Harvard University, Museum of Comparative Zoology, *(Mus Comp Zoo; 0-910999),* Harvard University, 26 Oxford St., Cambridge, MA 02138 (SAN 270-6873) Tel 617-495-2471.

Harvard Univ. Pr., *(Harvard U Pr; 0-674),* 79 Garden St., Cambridge, MA 02138 (SAN 200-2043) Tel 617-495-2600.

Harvest Age Ministries, *(Harvest Age; 0-9616405),* 803 Ebenezer Rd., Kannapolis, NC 28081 (SAN 658-9650) Tel 704-938-7250.

Harvest Books *See* Harcourt Brace Jovanovich, Inc.

Harvest House Press, *(Harvest NJ; 0-89523),* Eden West, 30 Nassau St., Princeton, NJ 08540 (SAN 212-7768) Tel 609-924-8715.

Harvest Hse. Pubs., Inc., *(Harvest Hse; 0-89081),* 1075 Arrowsmith, Eugene, OR 97402 (SAN 207-4745) Tel 503-343-0123; Toll free: 800-547-8979.

Harvest Moon Books, *(Harvest Moon; 0-9602886),* P.O. Box 172, Riverside, CA 92502 (SAN 213-0750) Tel 714-682-4907.

Harvest Press, *(Harvest Pr; 0-917332),* 480 Nelson Road, Santa Cruz, CA 95066 (SAN 208-6794) Tel 408-335-5015.

Harvest Pubns., Div. of Baptist General Conference, *(Harvest IL; 0-935797),* 2002 S. Arlington Heights Rd., Arlington Heights, IL 60005 (SAN 696-8023) Tel 312-228-0200.

Harvest Pubns., Div. of Baptist General *(Harvest Pubns; 0-939074),* Box 2466, Hollywood, CA 90078 (SAN 209-2964) Tel 213-469-0786.

Harvestman & Associates, *(Harvestman),* P.O. Box 271, Menlo Park, CA 94026 (SAN 212-1662) Tel 415-326-6997.

Harvey, Arnold, Assocs., *(A Harvey; 0-913014),* P.O. Box 89, Commack, NY 11725 (SAN 204-028X) Tel 516-543-2738.

Harvey, James M., *(Harvey J M; 0-933799),* 825 N-Lamb Blvd., Las Vegas, NV 89110 (SAN 692-8943) Tel 702-452-1217.

Harvey Woman's Club, *(Harvey Womans Club; 0-9611654),* P.O. Box 1058, Palestine, TX 75801 (SAN 285-306X) Tel 214-723-7342; Dist. by: Southwest Cookbook Distributors Inc., 1901 South Shore Dr., Bonham, TX 75418 (SAN 200-4925) Tel 214-583-8898; Dist. by: The Collection, P.O. Box 15624, Kansas City, MO 64106 (SAN 689-8440); Toll free: 800-821-5745.

Harwal Publishing Company *See* Wiley, John, & Sons, Inc.

†Harwood Academic Pubs., *(Harwood Academic; 3-7186),* P.O. Box 786, Cooper Sta., New York, NY 10276 (SAN 213-9294) Tel 212-206-8900; *CIP.*

Hascom Pubs., *(Hascom Pubs; 0-935927),* P.O. Box 1396, Provo, UT 84603 (SAN 696-804X) Tel 801-375-0790.

Hashim, A. S., *(AS Hashim; 0-9611132),* 6407 Tuckerman Lane, Rockville, MD 20852 (SAN 282-9282) Tel 301-530-4466; Dist. by: Publisher's Marketing Group, 1104 Summit Ave., Plainview, TX 75074 (SAN 262-0995) Tel 214-423-0312.

Haskala Pr., *(Haskala Pr; 0-9613846),* 640 Orange Ave., Los Altos, CA 94022 (SAN 681-9885) Tel 415-948-4648.

Haskell Booksellers, Inc., *(Haskell; 0-8383),* P.O. Box Y20, Blythebourne Sta., Brooklyn, NY 11219 (SAN 202-2818) Tel 718-435-7878.

Haskett Specialties, Inc., *(Haskett Spec; 0-9609724),* 26 E. Harrison St., Mooresville, IN 46158 (SAN 270-6946) Tel 317-831-1668.

Hass, Ed, *(E Hass; 0-9611166),* 966 Ponderosa Ave., No. 56, Sunnyvale, CA 94086 (SAN 277-6758) Tel 408-735-7188.

Hastings Bks., *(Hastings Bks; 0-940846),* 116 N. Wayne Ave., Wayne, PA 19087 (SAN 205-048X).

†Hastings Center, *(Hastings Ctr; 0-916558),* 360 Broadway, Hastings-on-Hudson, NY 10706 (SAN 208-6980) Tel 914-478-0500; *CIP.*

Hastings Hse. Pubs., Div. of Gallen Fund, Inc., *(Hastings; 0-8038),* 260 Fifth Ave., New York, NY 10001 (SAN 213-9561) Tel 212-889-9624; Toll free: 800-52607626; Dist. by: Kampmann & Co, Inc., 9 E. 40 St., New York, NY 10016 (SAN 202-5191) Tel 212-685-2928. *Imprints:* Communication Arts Books (Communication Arts); Visual Communication Books (Visual Communication).

Hastings Pr., *(Hastings Pr; 0-935799),* 693 Columbus Ave., New York, NY 10025 (SAN 696-4664) Tel 518-465-5222; Box 20108, New York, NY 10025 (SAN 699-6337).

Hat Tree Studio, *(Hat Tree Studio),* 2713 W. 96th Pl., Evergreen Park, IL 60642 (SAN 663-0782).

Hatch's Distributors, Subs. of Hatch's Card Shops, Inc., *(Hatch's Dist; 0-939723),* 15677 E. 17th Ave., Aurora, CO 80011 (SAN 663-5946) Tel 303-341-7240.

Hatfield, Glen, *(Hatfield; 0-9600216),* P.O. Box 329, Kankakee, IL 60901 (SAN 204-0298) Tel 815-939-1818.

Hatfield Hse. Bks., *(Hatfield Hse; 0-931015),* 783 Concord, Richmond, KY 40475 (SAN 678-9757) Tel 606-369-3919.

Hatfield Hse., Publishing Co., *(Hatfield Hse Pub; 0-9617030),* P.O. Box 24175, San Jose, CA 95124 (SAN 662-8664); 1655 York St., San Jose, CA 95124 (SAN 662-8672) Tel 408-266-2615.

Hathaway Hse., Inc., *(Hathaway Hse; 0-912241),* 601 Memorial Pkwy., Rochester, MN 55902 (SAN 265-1270) Tel 507-288-8483.

Hathor Hse. Bks., *(Hathor House Bks; 0-934482),* 138 N. Third St., Douglas, WY 82633 (SAN 221-1033) Tel 307-358-2166.

Hattori Corp. of America, *(Hattori Corp; 0-936971),* 555 W. 57th St., New York, NY 10019 (SAN 658-7852) Tel 212-977-7755.

Haunted Bookshop, The, *(Haunted Bk Shop; 0-940882),* 214 St. Francis St., Mobile, AL 36602 (SAN 223-1344) Tel 205-432-6606.

Hausladen Publishing, *(Hausladen Pub; 0-9617130),* 820 6th Ave. NW, Apt. 5, New Brighton, MN 55112 (SAN 662-6947) Tel 612-639-1130.

Havasupai Tribal Coucil, *(Havasupai Council; 0-9614648),* P.O. Box 10, Supai, AZ 86435 (SAN 691-8603) Tel 602-448-2731.

Havemeyer Books, *(Havemeyer Bks; 0-911397),* 12 Havemeyer Place, Greenwich, CT 06830 (SAN 270-6962) Tel 203-661-3823.

Haven Books *See* Bridge Publisnting, Inc.

Haven Corp., *(Haven Corp; 0-911361),* 802 Madison, Evanston, IL 60202 (SAN 275-9977) Tel 312-869-3434.

Haven Pubns., *(Haven Pubns; 0-930586),* G.P.O. Box 2046, New York, NY 10001 (SAN 220-6293) Tel 212-219-0672.

Haverford Hse., *(Haverford; 0-910702),* 347 E. Conestoga Rd., P.O. Box 408, Wayne, PA 19087 (SAN 204-0301) Tel 215-688-5191.

Havertown Books, *(Havertown Bks)* P.O. Box 711, Havertown, PA 19083 (SAN 208-4384).

Havin' Fun, Inc., *(Havin Fun Inc; 0-937513),* P.O. Box 70468, Eugene, OR 97401-0124 (SAN 658-8476) Tel 503-726-5327; 650 Harlow Rd., No. 123, Springfield, OR 97477 (SAN 658-8484).

Hawaii Council of Teachers of English, *(Hawaii CTE; 0-9616581),* Windward Community College, 45-720 Keaahala St., Kaneohe, HI 96744 (SAN 661-2369) Tel 808-235-7424.

Hawaii Legislative Reference Bureau, *(HI Legis Ref),* State Capitol, Honolulu, HI 96813 (SAN 227-2741).

Hawaii Office of the Auditor, *(HI Auditor),* State Capitol, Honolulu, HI 96813 (SAN 227-2733).

Hawaiian Service, Inc., *(Hawaiian Serv; 0-930492),* P.O. Box 2835, Honolulu, HI 96803 (SAN 205-0463) Tel 808-841-0134.

Hawaiian Sugar Planters Assn., *(Hawaiian Sugar),* 99-193 Aiea Heights Dr., Aiea, HI 96701 (SAN 270-7012) Tel 808-487-5561; P.O. Box 1057, Aiea, HI 96701 (SAN 669-0939).

Hawk Hands Pr., *(Hawk Hands Pr; 0-9615827),* 2661 California St., No. 4, San Francisco, CA 94115 (SAN 696-8066) Tel 415-446-7125.

Hawk-Island Associates, *(Hawk-Island; 0-937342),* 2630 N. 8th St., Sheboygan, WI 53081 (SAN 215-0794).

Hawk Migration Assn. of North America, *(Hawk Migration Assn; 0-938239),* 254 Arlington St., Medford, MA 02155 (SAN 661-4264) Tel 617-895-6924.

Hawkes Publishing Inc., *(Hawkes Pub Inc; 0-89036),* Box 15711, Salt Lake City, UT 84115 (SAN 205-6232) Tel 801-262-5555.

Hawkins, Beverly, Studio & Gallery, *(B Hawkins Studio; 0-9608084),* 20104 Halloway Ave., Matoaca, VA 23803 (SAN 240-1495) Tel 804-861-9403.

Hawkins, Robert L., *(R L Hawkins; 0-9607764),* P.O. Box 430, Litchfield Park, AZ 86432 (SAN 212-6648) Tel 602-247-5070.

Hawkins Publishing, *(Hawkins Pub; 0-9612770),* 310 Tahiti Way, No. 108, Marina del Rey, CA 90291 (SAN 289-9426) Tel 213-821-2971.

Hawkland Pr., Ltd., *(Hawkland Pr; 0-918431),* P.O. Box 15599, 5822 Taylor, Davenport, IA 52806 (SAN 657-6184) Tel 319-386-3815.

Hawkline Books, *(Hawkline Bks; 0-9609860),* 520 Military Way, Palo Alto, CA 94306 (SAN 270-7020) Tel 415-493-4387.

Hawks Inn Historical Society Inc., *(Hawks Inn Hist Soc; 0-9613121),* P.O. Box 104, Delafield, WI 53018 (SAN 294-8265); 500 Mill Rd., Delafield, WI 53018 (SAN 294-8273) Tel 414-646-8540.

Hawkshead Bk. Distribution Co., *(Hawkshead Bk),* P.O. Box 294, Old Westbury, NY 11568 (SAN 212-8217) Tel 516-333-6325.

Hawley Pubns., *(Hawley; 0-910704),* 8200 Gould Ave., Hollywood, CA 90046 (SAN 204-0328) Tel 213-654-1573.

†Haworth Pr., Inc., The, *(Haworth Pr; 0-917724; 0-86656),* 28 E. 22nd St., New York, NY 10010-6194 (SAN 211-0156) Tel 212-228-2800; *CIP.*

Hawthorn Bks. *See* Dutton, E. P.

Hawthorne Publishing Co., Div. of Vantage Companies, *(Hawthorne Co; 0-9617238),* 2777 Stemmons Freeway, Suite 2000, Dallas, TX 75207 (SAN 663-5695) Tel 214-631-0600.

Hay Hse., *(Hay House; 0-937611),* 1242 Berkeley St., Santa Monica, CA 90404 (SAN 658-9618) Tel 213-828-3666.

Hayashi, Hiroshi, *(H Hayashi; 0-9616815),* 112 Allston St., Allston, MA 02134 (SAN 661-0994) Tel 617-354-0365.

Hayden Bk. Co., Div. of Hayden Publishing Co, *(Hayden; 0-8104),* 10 Mulholland Dr., Hasbrouck Heights, NJ 07604 (SAN 200-2094) Tel 201-393-6300; Toll free: 800-631-0856. *Imprints:* Rider, John F. (Rider); Spartan Books, Incorporated (Spartan).

Hayden Enterprises, *(Hayden Enter; 0-9613969),* 2999 Twin Oaks Place, Salem, OR 97304 (SAN 682-241X).

Hayes, Gordon, *(G H Hayes; 0-9605880),* 3626 Meyler St., San Pedro, CA 90731 (SAN 216-6798) Tel 213-833-7066.

Hayes, T. I., Publishing Co., *(T I Hayes Pub Co; 0-938402),* P.O. Box 98, Hueysville, KY 41640 (SAN 293-2733) Tel 606-358-9844; Orders to: P.O. Box 17352, Ft. Mitchell, KY 41017 (SAN 293-2741) Tel 606-341-3201.

Hayes Publishing Co., Inc., *(Hayes; 0-910728),* 6304 Hamilton Ave., Cincinnati, OH 45224 (SAN 277-6154) Tel 513-681-7559.

Hayes Publishing, Ltd., *(Hayes Pub; 0-88625),* 219 N. Mllwaukee St., Milwaukee, WI 53202 (SAN 696-4591).

Hayfield Publishing Co., *(Hayfield Pub; 0-913856),* Box 11, Hayfield, MN 55940 (SAN 204-0336) Tel 507-477-2511.

Haymark Pubns., *(Haymark; 0-933910),* P.O. Box 243, Fredericksburg, VA 22401 (SAN 213-2508) Tel 703-373-1144.

Haymart Books, *(Haymart Bks; 0-9613826),* RR 1, Box 8, Giltner, NE 68841 (SAN 681-9966) Tel 402-849-2288.

Haynes Owners Workshop Manuals *See* Haynes Pubns., Inc.

Haynes Pubns., Inc., *(Haynes Pubns; 0-85696),* P.O. Box 456, 859 Lawrence Dr., Newbury Park, CA 91320 (SAN 212-1611) Tel 805-498-6703; Dist. by: Interbook, 14895 E. 14th St., Suite 370, San Leandro, CA 94577 (SAN 692-7564) Tel 415-352-9221. *Imprints:* Forrers, G. T., & Co. Ltd. (G T Forrers); Haynes Owners Workshop Manuals (Hayes Owners Workshop Manuals).

Hays, Helen Ireland, *(H I Hays; 0-9611798),* 108 S. William St., Johnstown, NY 12095 (SAN 285-2675) Tel 212-757-1176.

Hays, J. V., Inc., *(J V Hays; 0-941948),* 531 W. Pennsylvania Ave., Deland, FL 32720-3338 (SAN 238-4809) Tel 904-734-8944.

Hays, William C., *(W C Hays; 0-9616625),* 3601 Wedgewood, Lansing, MI 48910 (SAN 661-2040) Tel 517-393-7026.

Hays Humane Society, *(Hays Humane Soc; 0-9616537),* P.O. Box 311, Hays, KS 67601 (SAN 659-4646) Tel 913-625-7685; 3504 Hillcrest Dr., Hays, KS 67601 (SAN 659-4654).

Hays, Rolfes & Assocs., *(Hays Rolfes; 0-9602448),* P.O. Box 11465, Memphis, TN 38111 (SAN 212-6656) Tel 901-682-8128; Dist. by: The Collection, Inc., P.O. Box 1220, 2101 Kansas City Rd., Olathe, KS 66061 (SAN 200-6359) Tel 913-764-5900; Toll free: 800-223-1781.

Hayward Area Historical Society, *(Hayward Area Hist; 0-936427),* 22701 Main St., Hayward, CA 94541 (SAN 697-869X) Tel 415-581-0223.

†Haywire Press, *(Haywire Pr),* 44 S. Mountain Rd., New City, NY 10956 (SAN 210-8100) Tel 914-634-5214; CIP.

Haywood Pr., *(Haywood Pr; 0-9609892),* Box 176, Brooklyn, NY 11205-0176 (SAN 270-7055) Tel 718-891-6460.

Hazard Management Co., Inc., *(Hazard Mgmt; 0-935623),* P.O. Box 468, Cazenovia, NY 13035 (SAN 695-9431) Tel 315-655-3486; 3957 Rippleton Rd., Cazenovia, NY 13035 (SAN 695-944X).

Hazardous Materials Control Research Institute, *(Hazardous Mat Control),* 9300 Columbia Blvd., Silver Spring, MD 20910 (SAN 276-9433) Tel 301-587-9390.

Hazelden Foundation, *(Hazelden; 0-89486),* Box 176, Center City, MN 55012 (SAN 209-4010) Tel 612-257-4010; Toll free: 800-328-9000.

Hazlett Printing & Publishing, Inc., Div. of Valkyrie-Hazlett Printing, Inc., *(Hazlett Print; 0-940588),* 2135 First Ave. S., St. Petersburg, FL 33712 (SAN 264-0902) Tel 813-822-6069.

HCC Enterprises, *(HCC Enter; 0-9614847),* 2501 Greenwood Ave., Sacramento, CA 95821 (SAN 693-1197) Tel 916-488-8409.

Headlands Pr., Inc., *(Headlands Pr; 0-915500),* P.O. Box 862, Tiburon, CA 94920 (SAN 207-3234) Tel 415-435-0770.

Headwaters Press, *(Headwaters Pr; 0-932428),* 3734 131st Ave. N., Suite 7, Clearwater, FL 33520 (SAN 211-9609).

Headway Pubns., *(Headway Pubns; 0-89537),* 1700 Port Manleigh Circle, Newport Beach, CA 92660 (SAN 210-4342) Tel 714-644-9126.

Heahstan Press, The, *(Heahstan Pr; 0-9604244),* P.O. Box 954, Denton, TX 76202 (SAN 214-3127).

Heal, *(Heal; 0-9614132),* P.O. Box 385, Pratt, WV 25162 (SAN 686-5143) Tel 304-442-4759.

Heald Pubns., *(Heald Pubns; 0-9613127),* 420 Rutgers Ave., Swarthmore, PA 19081 (SAN 294-8281) Tel 215-447-7255. Out of business.

Healing Tao Bks., *(Heal Tao Bks; 0-935621),* 2 Creskill Pl., Huntington, NY 11743 (SAN 695-9318) Tel 516-549-9452; Dist. by: The Talman Co., 150 Fifth Ave., Rm. 514, New York, NY 10011 (SAN 200-5204) Tel 212-620-3182.

Health Action Press, Subs. of Center for Health Action, *(Health Act Pr; 0-913571),* 6439 Taggart Rd., Delaware, OH 43015 (SAN 285-2691) Tel 614-548-5340.

Health Administration Pr., Div. of Foundation of the American College of Healthcare Executives, *(Health Admin Pr; 0-914904; 0-910701),* 1021 E. Huron St., Ann Arbor, MI 48104-9990 (SAN 207-0464) Tel 313-764-1380.

Health Alert Pr., *(Health Alert Pr; 0-936571),* P.O. Box 2060, Cambridge, MA 02238 (SAN 698-0732) Tel 617-497-4190 (SAN 698-0740).

Health & Homeopathy Publishing, Inc., *(Hlth Homeopathy; 0-9616800),* 515 S. Tenth St., Unit J, Philadelphia, PA 19147 (SAN 661-3314) Tel 215-592-0854.

Health Challenge Pr., *(Hlth Challenge; 0-935929),* 7601 Calle Sin Envidia, No. 14, Tucson, AZ 85718 (SAN 696-8074) Tel 602-742-4594.

Health Communications, Inc., *(Health Comm; 0-932194),* 1721 Blount Rd., Suite 1, Pompano Beach, FL 33069 (SAN 212-100X); Toll free: 800-857-9100.

Health Education Aids, *(Health Ed Aids; 0-89829),* 8 S. Lakeview Dr., Goddard, KS 67052 (SAN 220-6323) Tel 316-794-2216.

Health Education & Life Expansion Research, *(Health Ed & Life Exp Res; 0-9607142),* Box 70027, Los Angeles, CA 90309 (SAN 238-9878) Tel 213-738-9940.

Health Education Training and Administration Consortium, Inc., The, *(Health Ed Train; 0-911067),* 1764 Bising Ave., No. 4, North College Hill, OH 45239 (SAN 270-711X) Tel 513-931-9227.

Health Educator Publications Inc., *(Health Ed Pubns; 0-932887),* 525 Lincoln St., Rockville, MD 20850 (SAN 689-0059) Tel 301-424-1363.

Health Explosion, The, *(Health Explo; 0-9613424),* P.O. Box 2375, Owensboro, KY 42302 (SAN 656-8890) Tel 502-684-4439.

Health Information Library, Krames Communications, *(Health Info Lib; 0-911931),* 312 90th St., Daly City, CA 94015 (SAN 264-2816) Tel 415-994-8800.

Health Media of America, *(Health Med Amer; 0-937325),* 11300 Sorrento Valley Rd., No. 250, San Diego, CA 92121 (SAN 658-8069) Tel 619-453-3887.

Health Physics Society, Columbia Chapter, *(Health Phys Soc; 0-9613108),* P.O. Box 564, Richland, WA 99352 (SAN 294-0183) Tel 509-376-8085.

Health Plus, Pubs., *(Health Plus; 0-932090),* P.O. Box 22001, Phoenix, AZ 85028 (SAN 211-4984) Tel 602-992-0589; Dist. by: Contemporary Bks., 180 N. Michigan Ave., Chicago, IL 60601 (SAN 202-5493) Tel 312-782-9181.

Health Policy Advisory Center, *(Health PAC),* 17 Murray St, New York, NY 10007 (SAN 224-3288) Tel 212-267-8890.

Health Promotion Group, Inc., The, *(Health Prom Group; 0-935105),* P.O. Box 59687, Homewood, AL 35259 (SAN 695-1449) Tel 205-934-6020.

Health Psychology Pubns., *(Hlth Psy Pubns; 0-9617145),* 710 11th Ave., Suite 106, Greeley, CO 80631 (SAN 663-3366) Tel 303-587-2543.

Health Publishing Co., *(Health Pub Co; 0-917591),* P.O. Box 1922, Chula Vista, CA 92012 (SAN 657-1468) Tel 706-612-1941.

Health Research, *(Health Res Las Vegas; 0-9601978),* Box 19420, Las Vegas, NV 89132 (SAN 212-2553) Tel 702-733-8476.

Health Science, Div. of Live Food Products, Inc., *(Health Sci; 0-87790),* Box 7, Santa Barbara, CA 93102 (SAN 208-1016) Tel 805-968-1028.

Health Sciences Communications Assn., *(Health Sci Comm),* 6105 Lindell Blvd., St. Louis, MO 63112 (SAN 224-2915) Tel 314-725-4722.

Healthcare Financial Management Assn., *(Healthcare Fin Mgmt Assn; 0-930228),* 1900 Spring Rd., Suite 500, Oak Brook, IL 60521 (SAN 207-5911) Tel 312-655-4600.

Healthcare Pr., *(Healthcare Pr; 0-9613775),* P.O. Box 4488, Rollingbay, WA 98061 (SAN 678-9749) Tel 206-842-5243.

HealthProInk Publishing, Div. of Spelman Productions, Inc., *(HealthProInk; 0-933803),* P.O. Box 3333, Farmington Hills, MI 48018 (SAN 692-8803); Toll free: 800-802-4966 in Michigan; 26941 Pebblestone Rd., Southfield, MI 48034 (SAN 662-3050) Tel 313-355-3686.

Healthtalk, *(Healthtalk; 0-936439),* 1888 Century Pk. E., Suite 405, Los Angeles, CA 90067 (SAN 697-8711) Tel 213-556-0603.

Healthwise, Inc., *(Healthwise; 0-9612690),* P.O. Box 1989, Boise, ID 83701 (SAN 289-2367) Tel 208-345-1161; 904 W. Fort St., Boise, ID 83702 (SAN 289-2375).

Healthworks, Inc., *(Healthworks; 0-938480),* 30131 Town Ctr. Dr., Suite 135, Laguna Niguel, CA 92677-2034 (SAN 215-7721) Tel 714-495-8550.

Hearn Assocs., *(Hearn Assocs; 0-9615450),* 1270 Covington Rd., Los Altos, CA 94022 (SAN 695-7676) Tel 415-968-4713.

Hearne-Books U.S.A., *(Hearne Bks; 0-918760),* 22 River St., Braintree, MA 02184 (SAN 210-4350) Tel 617-843-5702.

HearSay Pr., *(HearSay Pr; 0-938613),* P.O. Box 42265, Portland, OR 97242 (SAN 661-5805); 2916 SE 21st Ave., Portland, OR 97202 (SAN 661-5813) Tel 503-233-2637.

Hearst Bks., Div. of William Morrow & Co., Inc., *(Hearst Bks; 0-910992; 0-87851; 0-910990; 0-688),* 105 Madison Ave., New York, NY 10016 (SAN 202-2842) Tel 212-889-3050.

Heart Country Tennessee Pubns., *(Heart Ctry TN Pubns; 0-9616334),* Rte. 1, Box 196-B, Big Sandy, TN 38221 (SAN 658-960X) Tel 901-584-2038.

Heart of America Pr., *(Heart Am Pr; 0-913902),* 10101 Blue Ridge Blvd., Kansas City, MO 64134 (SAN 204-0379) Tel 816-761-0080.

Heart of the Lakes Publishing, *(Heart of the Lakes; 0-932334),* 2989 Lodi Rd., Interlaken, NY 14847-0299 (SAN 213-0769) Tel 607-532-4997.

Heartfire Marketing, *(Heartfire Mktg; 0-935211),* Box 2004, Grants Pass, OR 97526 (SAN 695-7722).

Hearthstone, Inc., *(Hearthstone CO; 0-9616308),* 506 N. Cascade, Colorado Springs, CO 80903 (SAN 658-7283) Tel 303-473-4413.

Hearthstone Press, *(Hearthstone; 0-937308),* 708 Inglewood Dr., Broderick, CA 95605 (SAN 209-4460) Tel 916-372-0250.

Hearthstone Pubns., *(Hearth Pub; 0-943098),* 145 Quinn St., Naugatuck, CT 06770 (SAN 240-3854) Tel 203-734-5398.

Heartland Image, *(Heartland Image; 0-915945),* P.O. Box 69, Big Fork, MT 59911 (SAN 294-0302) Tel 406-837-5587; 162 Lake Hills Dr., Big Fork, MT 59911 (SAN 294-0310).

HeartLight Pubns., *(HeartLight Pubns; 0-9615911),* 193 W. Mariposa St., Altadena, CA 91001 (SAN 696-8120) Tel 818-791-1597.

Hearts & Crafts, *(Hearts & Crafts; 0-9617072),* 5585 E. Pacific Coast Hwy, No. 132, Long Beach, CA 90804 (SAN 662-9105) Tel 213-498-3506.

Heartspring Unlimited, *(Heartspring Unltd; 0-9615606),* P.O. Box 10385, Glendale, CA 91209 (SAN 695-9725) Tel 818-507-8800; 321 W. Milford St., Suite 8, Glendale, CA 91203 (SAN 695-9733).

Heartstart Pubns., *(Heartstart; 0-912825),* 2392 Nancy Pl., St. Paul, MN 55113 (SAN 282-7913) Tel 612-484-3443.

Heartwind Pubns., *(Heartwind Pubns; 0-916193),* P.O. Box 4833, Shreveport, LA 71104 (SAN 294-9377) Tel 318-222-4697.

†Heartwork Press, *(Heartwork Pr; 0-935598),* 220 Redwood Hwy., Mill Valley, CA 94941 (SAN 214-025X); CIP.

Heath, D. C., Co., *(Heath; 0-669; 0-278; 0-88408),* 125 Spring St., Lexington, MA 02173 (SAN 213-7526) Tel 617-862-6650; Toll free: 800-428-8071; Orders to: D. C. Heath & Co. Distribution Ctr., 2700 Richardt Ave., Indianapolis, IN 46219 (SAN 202-2885) Tel 317-359-5585. *Imprints:* Swift, Sterling (Sterling Swift).

Heather Foundation, *(Heather Foun; 0-9600300),* P.O. Box 48, San Pedro, CA 90733 (SAN 204-0387) Tel 213-831-6269.

Heather Publishing Co., *(Heather Pub Co; 0-9613837),* P.O. Box 77347, Oklahoma City, OK 73177 (SAN 682-8922) Tel 405-751-2922.

Heatherdown Press, *(Heatherdown Pr; 0-9610038),* 3450 Brantford Rd., Toledo, OH 43606 (SAN 270-7284) Tel 419-877-0073.

†Heathkit/Zenith Educational System, Div. of Zenith Electronics Corp., *(Heathkit-Zenith Ed; 0-87119),* P.O. Box 1288, Benton Harbor, MI 49022 (SAN 296-6476) Tel 616-982-3641; CIP.

Heavenow Productions, *(Heavenow Prod; 0-9616770),* 7800 185th Pl., SW, Edmonds, WA 98020 (SAN 661-339X) Tel 206-775-8365.

Hebraeus Press, *(Hebraeus Pr; 0-910511),* Box 32 HBLL Brigham Young Univ., Provo, UT 84603 (SAN 260-0692) Tel 801-347-8839.

†Hebrew Publishing Co., *(Hebrew Pub; 0-88482),* 100 Water St., Brooklyn, NY 11202-0875 (SAN 201-5404) Tel 718-858-6928; CIP.

†**Hebrew Union College Press,** *(Hebrew Union Coll Pr; 0-87820),* Clifton Ave., Cincinnati, OH 45220 (SAN 220-6358) Tel 513-221-1875; Dist. by: Ktav Publishing Hse., Inc., 900 Jefferson St., Hoboken, NJ 07030 (SAN 658-1056) Tel 201-963-9524; *CIP.*

Hebrew Union College Press *See* **Ktav Publishing Hse., Inc.**

Hedgehog Press, *(Hedgehog Pr; 0-943486),* 3041 Lopez, Pebble Beach, CA 93953 (SAN 240-6705) Tel 408-649-3415.

Hedman Stenotype, *(Hedman Steno; 0-939056),* 1158 W. Armitage Ave., Chicago, IL 60614 (SAN 239-7579)
Tel 312-871-6500.

Heeday's Pubns., *(Heedays; 0-917822),* 94-12 Kipaa Pl., Waipahu, HI 96797 (SAN 209-5653).

Heene Enterprises, *(Heene Enter; 0-9616054),* 3420 Ediwhar St., San Diego, CA 92123 (SAN 698-0651)
Tel 619-268-8090.

Heffron, Dan, Enterprises, *(Heffron Ent; 0-9605104),* P.O. Box 9019, Cleveland, OH 44137 (SAN 216-0366).

Hegeler Institute, The, *(Hegeler Inst; 0-914417),* The Monist, School of Philosophy, University of Southern California, Los Angeles, CA 90089 (SAN 289-6346) Tel 815-223-1231; Orders to: The Monist, P.O. Box 600, La Salle, IL 61301 (SAN 662-7552) Tel 815-223-1231; Toll free: 800-435-6850.

Heian International Publishing, Inc., *(Heian Intl; 0-89346),* P.O. Box 1013, Union City, CA 94587 (SAN 213-2036)
Tel 415-471-8440.

†**Heidelberg Graphics,** *(Heidelberg Graph; 0-918606),* P.O. Box 3606, Chico, CA 95927 (SAN 211-5654) Tel 916-342-6582; Orders to: 1116 Wendy Way, Chico, CA 95926-1511 (SAN 662-0345); *CIP.*

Heidenreich House, *(Heidenreich; 0-9600428),* 5012 Oak Point Way, Fair Oaks, CA 95628 (SAN 204-0395)
Tel 916-961-3297.

Heilman, Carl E., *(C E Heilman; 0-9613161),* P.O. Box 213A, Rte. 8, Brant Lake, NY 12815 (SAN 294-9385)
Tel 518-494-3072.

Heimburger House Publishing Co., *(Heimburger Hse Pub; 0-911581),* 310 Lathrop Ave., River Forest, IL 60305 (SAN 264-0929) Tel 312-366-1973.

Hein, G., *(G Hein; 0-9614649),* 141 N. 11th St., Lehighton, PA 18235 (SAN 691-862X) Tel 215-377-3595.

Hein, William S., & Co., Inc., *(W S Hein; 0-89941; 0-930342),* Hein Bldg., 1285 Main St., Buffalo, NY 14209 (SAN 210-9212) Tel 716-882-2600; Toll free: 800-828-7571.

†**Heineman, James H., Inc., Pub.,** *(Heineman; 0-87008),* 475 Park Ave., New York, NY 10022 (SAN 204-0409) Tel 212-688-2028; *CIP.*

Heinemann Educational Bks., Inc., *(Heinemann Ed; 0-435),* 70 Court St., Portsmouth, NH 03801 (SAN 210-5829) Tel 603-431-7894.

Heinle & Heinle Pubs., Inc., *(Heinle & Heinle; 0-8384),* 20 Park Plaza, Boston, MA 02116 (SAN 216-0730) Tel 617-451-1940; Toll free: 800-225-3782.

Heinman, W. S., Imported Bks., *(Heinman; 0-88431),* 225 W. 57th St., Rm. 404, New York, NY 10019 (SAN 121-6201) Tel 212-757-7628; P.O. Box 926, New York, NY 10023 (SAN 660-935X).

Heirloom Pr., *(Heirloom Pr; 0-9615377),* 3430 Georgia Ave. N., Minneapolis, MN 55427 (SAN 695-5347) Tel 612-536-0564; Orders to: P.O. Box 28168, Minneapolis, MN 55428 (SAN 662-3492).

Heirloom Pubns. Ltd., *(Heirloom Pubns; 0-9609488),* P.O. Box 667, Cedar Rapids, IA 52406 (SAN 270-7403)
Tel 319-366-4690.

Heirloom Publishing, *(Heirloom Pub; 0-938015),* P.O. Box 183, Mills, WY 82644 (SAN 661-2334); 4340 Hideaway Ln., Mills, WY 82644 (SAN 661-2342)
Tel 307-235-3561.

Heirs International, *(Heirs Intl; 0-915970),* 444 Lombard St., No. 6, San Francisco, CA 94133 (SAN 207-8414) Tel 415-956-8752.

Heisler, Suzanne, *(S Heisler; 0-9617054),* P.O. Box 212, Menlo Park, CA 94025 (SAN 662-9318); 800 Roble Ave., Menlo Park, CA 94025 (SAN 662-9326)
Tel 415-323-2716.

Helander, Joel E., *(Helander; 0-935600),* 36 Norton Ave., Guilford, CT 06437 (SAN 213-7445) Tel 203-453-6626.

Heldon Pr., *(Heldon Pr; 0-933169),* 9146 Arrington Ave., Downey, CA 90240 (SAN 692-3127) Tel 213-869-5741.

Heldref Pubns., Div. of The Helen Dwight Reid Educational Foundation, *(Heldref Pubns; 0-916882),* 4000 Albemarle St., NW, Washington, DC 20016 (SAN 208-0788) Tel 202-362-6445.

Helen Publishing Co., *(Helen Pub; 0-9617192),* 25 Lake St., Apt. 5A, White Plains, NY 10603 (SAN 663-2823) Tel 914-682-0555.

Heli-World Pr., *(Heli World Pr; 0-939177),* 3229 Sunset Way, Bellingham, WA 98226 (SAN 662-9156) Tel 206-758-7396.

Helikon Press, *(Helikon NY; 0-914496),* 120 W. 71st St., New York, NY 10023 (SAN 201-9175) Tel 212-873-6884.

Helix Books *See* **Rowman & Littlefield, Pubs.**

Helix House Pubs., *(Helix Hse; 0-930866),* 9231 Molly Woods Ave., La Mesa, CA 92041 (SAN 211-3171). Out of business.

Helix Pr., *(Helix Pr; 0-914587),* 4410 Hickey, Corpus Christi, TX 78413 (SAN 289-2669) Tel 512-852-8834.

Helix Pr., Div. of RGS, Inc., *(Helix Pr VA; 0-935653),* P.O. Box 5144, Springfield, VA 22150 (SAN 695-9393); 7606 Chancellor Way, Springfield, VA 22153 (SAN 695-9407) Tel 703-455-7614.

hell box, the, *(hell box; 0-9614593),* 4022 Greenhill Pl., Austin, TX 78759 (SAN 691-7798) Tel 512-345-0776.

Hellcoal Press, *(Hellcoal Pr; 0-916912),* P.O. Box 4, S. A. O. , Brown Univ., Providence, RI 02912 (SAN 208-6808)
Tel 401-863-2341.

Hellenes-English Biblical Foundation, *(Hellenes; 0-910710),* P.O. Box 10412, Jackson, MS 39209 (SAN 204-0433).

†**Hellenic College Press,** Div. of Holy Cross Orthodox Press, *(Hellenic Coll Pr; 0-917653),* 50 Goddard St., Brookline, MA 02146 (SAN 213-6694)
Tel 617-731-3500; *CIP.*

Hello Reader *See* **Scholastic, Inc.**

Helmers & Howard, Pubs., Inc., *(Helmers Howard Pub; 0-939443),* 1221 E. Madison St., Colorado Springs, CO 80907 (SAN 663-3552) Tel 303-520-1559.

Helotes Area Volunteers Fire Dept. Inc., *(Helotes Area; 0-9612736),* P.O. Box 186, Helotes, TX 78023 (SAN 289-9434) Tel 512-695-3254.

H.E.L.P. Bks., Inc., *(HELP Bks; 0-918500),* 1201 E. Calle Elena, Tucson, AZ 85718 (SAN 209-665X) Tel 602-297-6452.

Helpful Beginnings, *(Helpful Beginnings; 0-938783),* P.O. Box 1684, Clovis, CA 93613-1684 (SAN 661-5465); 1502 Celeste, Clovis, CA 93612 (SAN 661-5473) Tel 209-299-1876.

HelpLine, *(HelpLine; 0-930053),* 200 Ross St, Pittsburgh, PA 15219 (SAN 669-8522) Tel 412-255-1140.

Helsinki Watch *See* **Fund for Free Expression**

Hemingway, Donald W., *(D W Hemingway),* 309 S. Tenth W., Salt Lake City, UT 84104 (SAN 220-2506); Dist. by: George Mc. Co. Inc., P.O. Box 15671, Salt Lake City, UT 84115 (SAN 220-2514).

Hemingway Western Studies Research Ctr., *(Heming W Studies; 0-932129),* Boise State Univ., 1910 University Dr., Boise, ID 83725 Tel 208-385-1572.

Hemisphere House Books, *(Hemisphere Hse; 0-930770),* P.O. Box 1934, Corpus Christi, TX 78403 (SAN 211-0717).

Hemisphere Publishing Corp., *(Hemisphere Pub; 0-89116),* 79 Madison Ave., Suite 1110, New York, NY 10016 (SAN 207-4001) Tel 212-725-1999; Toll free: 800-242-7737 (Ordering).

Hemlock Society, *(Hemlock Soc; 0-9606030),* P.O. Box 66218, Los Angeles, CA 90066 (SAN 293-275X) Tel 213-391-1871; Dist. by: Grove Pr., 196 W. Houston St., New York, NY 10014 (SAN 201-4890) Tel 212-242-4900.

Hemming, H. & G., *(Hemming; 0-9614224),* 14812 N. Cameo Dr., Sun City, AZ 85351 (SAN 686-8096) Tel 602-977-9488.

Hemmings Motor News, *(Hemmings; 0-917808),* Box 256, Bennington, VT 05201 (SAN 210-3060) Tel 802-442-3101.

Hemphill Publishing Co., *(Hemphill; 0-914696),* 1400 Wathen Ave., Austin, TX 78703 (SAN 204-0441) Tel 512-476-9422.

Hemphills, The, *(The Hemphills; 0-9600948),* P.O. Box 8302, Nashville, TN 37207 (SAN 208-4856) Tel 615-865-7100.

Hempstead House, *(Hempstead House; 0-940094),* 1019 Jerome St., Houston, TX 77009 (SAN 220-2271) Tel 713-864-6130.

Henart Bks., *(Henart Bks; 0-938059),* 4711 NW 24th Ct., Lauderdale Lakes, FL 33313 (SAN 661-1885) Tel 305-485-4286; Dist. by: Banyan Bks., P.O. Box 431160, Miami, FL 33243 (SAN 208-340X) Tel 305-665-6011.

Henceforth Pubns., *(Henceforth; 0-913437; 0-913439),* c/o Berkshire Christian College, Lenox, MA 01240 (SAN 285-1628) Tel 413-637-1451.

Henchanted Bks., *(Henchanted Bks; 0-9615756),* P.O. Box H, Calpella, CA 95418 (SAN 696-4648) Tel 707-485-7551.

Henderikse, *(Henderikse; 0-932455),* 110 Christopher St., New York, NY 10014 (SAN 686-8118) Tel 212-242-7513.

Hendershot Bibliography, *(Hendershot; 0-911832),* 4114 Ridgewood Dr., Bay City, MI 48706-2499 (SAN 204-045X) Tel 517-684-3148.

Henderson, Albert, *(A Henderson; 0-917237),* 2423 Noble Sta., Bridgeport, CT 06608 (SAN 655-8607) Tel 203-367-1555.

Henderson, Mahlon Lucas, *(M L Henderson; 0-9616434),* 4533 Flower Valley Dr., Rockville, MD 20853 (SAN 659-2023).

†**Henderson, T. Emmett,** *(T E Henderson; 0-940590),* 130 W. Main St., Middletown, NY 10940 (SAN 208-0834)
Tel 914-343-1038; *CIP.*

Henderson, William, *(W Henderson; 0-9612580),* 16015 Gault St. Apt. A, Van Nuys, CA 91406 (SAN 289-579X) Tel 818-780-9718.

†**Hendrick-Long Publishing Co.,** *(Hendrick-Long; 0-937460),* 4811 W. Lovers Ln., Dallas, TX 75209 (SAN 281-7748) Tel 214-358-4677; P.O. Box 25123, Dallas, TX 75225 (SAN 281-7756); *CIP.*

Hendricks-Ferguson, *(Hendricks-Ferguson; 0-9615468),* 3521 Heyward St., Columbia, SC 29205 (SAN 695-9334)
Tel 803-254-3875.

Hendricks Hse., Inc., *(Hendricks House; 0-87532),* Main St., Putney, VT 05346 (SAN 206-9830) Tel 802-387-4185.

Hendricks Publishing, *(Hendricks Pub; 0-943764),* P.O. Box 724026, Atlanta, GA 30339 (SAN 264-0945).

Henke, Mary Alice, *(Henke M A; 0-9611032),* Box 327, Enders, NE 69027 (SAN 282-8782) Tel 308-882-4004.

Hennepin Hall Pubns., *(Hennepin Hall; 0-912243),* P.O. Box 84, Rockford, IL 61105 (SAN 265-1289) Tel 815-877-5345.

Hennessey & Ingalls, Inc., *(Hennessey; 0-912158),* 1254 Third St. Mall, Santa Monica, CA 90401 (SAN 293-2776) Tel 213-458-9074; Dist. by: Hennessy, 8325 Campion Dr., Los Angeles, CA 90045 (SAN 293-2784) Tel 213-458-9074.

Henry, John, Company, Div. of American Printers & Lithographers, *(Floraprint USA),* 5800 W. Grand River Ave., Lansing, MI 48901 (SAN 216-7069) Tel 312-966-6500; Dist. by: International Specialized Bk., Servs., Inc., 5602 NE Hassalo St., Portland ove, OR 97213-3640 (SAN 169-7129) Tel 503-287-3093.

Henry Art Gallery, *(Henry Art; 0-935558),* DE-15, Univ. of Washington, Seattle, WA 98195 (SAN 213-6708) Tel 206-543-2280.

Henry Ford Museum Press *See* **Edison Institute, The**

Henry John & Co., *(Henry John & Co; 0-937028),* P.O. Box 10235, Dillingham, AK 99576 (SAN 214-3909) Tel 907-842-5458.

Names

Heptangle Books, *(Heptangle; 0-935214),* P.O. Box 283, Berkeley Heights, NJ 07922 (SAN 210-6329) Tel 201-647-4449.

Her Publishing Co., Inc., *(Her Pub Co; 0-930676),* P.O. Box 1168, Oakwood Shopping Ctr., Gretna, LA 70053 (SAN 211-0164).

Herald Bks., *(Herald Bks; 0-910714),* P.O. Box 17, Pelham, NY 10803 (SAN 202-2893) Tel 914-576-1121.

Herald Books, *(Herald NC),* Kings at Canterbury, Kings Mountain, NC 28086 (SAN 656-8904).

Herald Hse., *(Herald Hse; 0-8309),* P.O. Box HH, Independence, MO 64055 (SAN 202-2907) Tel 816-252-5010; Toll free: 800-821-7550.

Herald Pr., Div. of Mennonite Publishing Hse., Inc., *(Herald Pr; 0-8361),* 616 Walnut Ave., Scottdale, PA 15683 (SAN 202-2915) Tel 412-887-8500; Toll free: 800-245-7894.

†Heraldic Publishing Co., Inc., *(Heraldic Pub; 0-910716),* 305 West End Ave., New York, NY 10023 (SAN 204-0476) Tel 212-874-1511; *CIP.*

Herb Farm Pr., *(Herb Farm Pr; 0-9614650),* Rte. 123A, New Ipswich, NH 03071 (SAN 691-8638) Tel 603-878-1151.

Herb Society of America, Inc., *(Herb Society),* 2 Independence Ct., Concord, MA 01742 (SAN 232-6078) Tel 617-371-1486.

Herbal Perception, The, *(Herbal Perception; 0-943638),* Box 143, Mt. Clemens, MI 48043 (SAN 238-2997) Tel 313-949-7932.

Herbal Research Publishing, *(Herbal Res Pub; 0-937643),* 25 Leonard Rd., Lexington, MA 02173 (SAN 658-8565) Tel 617-862-0171.

†Here's Life Pubs., Inc., *(Here's Life; 0-89840),* P.O. Box 1576, San Bernardino, CA 92402 (SAN 212-4254) Tel 714-886-7981; *CIP.*

Heresy Press, *(Heresy Pr; 0-9603276),* 713 Paul St., Newport News, VA 23605 (SAN 213-2516).

Heritage Academy, *(Heritage Acad; 0-9612048),* P.O. Box 9251, Columbus, MS 39701 (SAN 286-7907) Tel 601-327-4004.

Heritage Arts, *(Heritage Arts; 0-911029),* 1807 Prairie Ave., Downers Grove, IL 60515 (SAN 270-7543) Tel 312-964-1194.

Heritage Assocs., Inc., *(Heritage Assocs; 0-910467),* P.O. Box 6291, Albuquerque, NM 87197 (SAN 260-0706); 2217 Lead SE, Albuquerque, NM 87106 (SAN 662-0353) Tel 505-268-0155.

Heritage Books, *(Heritage Books),* 5176 E. Country Club Rd., Salina, KS 67401 (SAN 212-0410) Tel 913-827-7861.

Heritage Bks., Inc., *(Heritage Bk; 0-917890; 1-55613),* 3602 Maureen Ln., Bowie, MD 20715 (SAN 209-3367) Tel 301-464-1159.

Heritage Computer Corp., Div. of Heritage Mutual Insurance Co., *(Heritage Computer; 0-935433),* 2800 S. Taylor Dr., Sheboygan, WI 53081 (SAN 696-1924) Tel 414-457-1422.

Heritage Foundation, *(Heritage Found; 0-89195),* 214 Massachusetts Ave., NE, Washington, DC 20002 (SAN 209-3758) Tel 202-546-4400.

Heritage North Press, *(Heritage N Pr; 0-913905),* 3809 Barbara Dr., Anchorage, AK 99517 (SAN 286-8679).

†Heritage Press, *(Heritage Pr; 0-935428),* P.O. Box 18625, Baltimore, MD 21216 (SAN 221-2684) Tel 301-383-8521; *CIP.*

Heritage Press of Pacific, *(Heritage Pac; 0-9609132),* 1279-203 Ala Kapuna St., Honolulu, HI 96819 (SAN 264-0961) Tel 808-839-1238.

Heritage Pubns., *(Heritage Margaretville; 0-937213),* P.O. Box 642, Main St., Margaretville, NY 12455 (SAN 658-7291) Tel 914-586-3810.

Heritage Pubs. Services, *(Herit Pubs Servs; 0-939379),* 2000 S. Dairy Ashford, Suite 685, Houston, TX 77077 (SAN 662-9539) Tel 713-589-7080.

Heritage Publishing Co., *(Herit Pub CA; 0-936011),* 1056 McClellan Way, Stockton, CA 95207 (SAN 696-8147) Tel 209-951-2238. Do Not Confuse With Heritage Publishing Co., Matthews, NC.

Heritage Publishing Co., *(Herit Pub NC; 0-936013),* 207 Kimrod Ln., Matthews, NC 28105 (SAN 696-818X) Tel 704-867-8729. Do Not Confuse With Heritage Publishing Co., Stockton, CA.

Heritage Publishing Co., *(Heritage; 0-9613922),* 202 Lexington Pl., Uniontown, PA 15401 (SAN 682-5087) Tel 412-439-0560.

Heritage Pubns., *(Heritage Pubns; 0-9612868),* P.O. Box 76072, Birmingham, AL 35253 (SAN 291-1876); 400 Office Pk. Dr., Suite 111, Birmingham, AL 35223 (SAN 291-1884) Tel 205-871-4233; Dist. by: Dot Gibson Pubns., P.O. Box 117, Waycross, GA 31502 (SAN 200-4143); Dist. by: The Collection, Inc., P.O. Box 1220, Olathe, KS 66061 (SAN 658-277X) Tel 913-764-5900.

Heritage Recording, *(Heritage Rec; 0-9602888),* P.O. Box 13232, St. Paul, MN 55113 (SAN 211-1942) Tel 612-780-4058.

Heritage Research Hse., Inc., *(Heritage Res Hse; 0-912617),* Box 64003, Virginia Beach, VA 23464 (SAN 282-7956) Tel 804-467-4777.

Heritage Technical Services, *(Heritage Tech Serv; 0-914769),* P.O. Box 5635, Kent, WA 98031 (SAN 291-8374).

Heritage Trails, *(Heritage PA; 0-936441),* P.O. Box 307, Turbotville, PA 17772 (SAN 697-8746) Tel 717-649-5846; 82 Main St., Turbotville, PA 17772 (SAN 697-8754).

Heritage Trails Pr., *(Heritage Trails; 0-910083),* 94 Santa Maria Dr., Novato, CA 94947 (SAN 240-8589) Tel 415-897-5679.

Hermagoras Pr., *(Hermagoras Pr; 0-9611800),* P.O. Box 1555, Davis, CA 95617 (SAN 285-2802); Dist. by: Univ. of California, Davis, UCD Bookstore, Davis, CA 95616 (SAN 200-4267) Tel 916-752-1984.

Herman, Hal, Promotions, *(Hal Herman Promo; 0-9613201),* Rte. 19, P.O. Box 1152, Tallahassee, FL 32308 (SAN 295-8260) Tel 904-893-4343.

Hermes House *See* **Shambhala Pubns., Inc.**

Hermes Hse. Pr., *(Hermes Hse; 0-9605008),* 39 Adare Pl., Northampton, MA 01060 (SAN 220-0589) Tel 413-584-8402; Dist. by: Associated Booksellers, 562 Boston Ave., Bridgeport, CT 06610 (SAN 203-5014) Tel 203-333-7268; Dist. by: The Distributors, 702 S. Michigan, South Bend, IN 46618 (SAN 169-2488) Tel 219-232-8500.

Hermes Publishing Company, *(Hermes Pub Co; 0-930421),* P.O. Box 100819, Fort Lauderdale, FL 33310-0819 (SAN 682-0506) Tel 305-735-3141.

Hermetician Pr., *(Hermetician Pr; 0-935895),* P.O. Box 611381, North Miami, FL 33261-1381 (SAN 696-8198) Tel 305-891-7312; 1048 NE 128 St. No. 5, North Miami, FL 33161 (SAN 696-8201); Dist. by: New Leaf Distributing, 1020 White St. SW, Atlanta, GA 30310 (SAN 169-1449) Tel 404-755-2665; Toll free: 800-241-3829; Dist. by: Starlite, P.O. Box 20739, Reno, NV 89515 (SAN 685-9593) Tel 702-359-5676; Dist. by: Astro Computing Services, P.O. Box 16430, San Diego, CA 92116 (SAN 200-8149) Tel 619-297-9209.

Hermit Pr., *(Hermit Pr FL; 0-939017),* P.O. Box 933, Marianna, FL 32446 (SAN 662-5452); 121 S. Madison St., Marianna, FL 32446 (SAN 662-5460) Tel 904-482-2300. Do not confuse with Hermit Press in Terre Haute, IN.

†Hermitage, *(Hermitage; 0-938920),* P.O. Box 410, Tenafly, NJ 07670 (SAN 239-4413) Tel 201-894-8247; *CIP.*

Hermosa Pubns., *(Hermosa; 0-913478),* P.O. Box 8172, Albuquerque, NM 87198 (SAN 203-0012) Tel 505-262-0440.

Hero Bks., *(Hero Books; 0-915979),* 8316 Arlington Blvd., Fairfax, VA 22031 (SAN 294-0345) Tel 703-560-6427.

Hero Games, Affil. of Iron Crown Enterprises, Inc., *(Hero Games; 0-917481; 0-915795),* P.O. Box 1605, Charlottesville, VA 22902 (SAN 656-0695) Tel 804-295-3917; Toll free: 800-325-0479; Orders to: Iron Crown Enterprises, Inc., P.O. Box 1605, Charlottesville, VA 22902 (SAN 663-3064).

Heroic Publishing, Inc., *(Heroic Pub Inc; 0-936079),* P.O. Box 13735, Milwaukee, WI 53213 (SAN 696-8228) Tel 414-547-2671; 1402 Josephine, Waukesha, WI 53186 (SAN 696-8236).

Heroica Bks., *(Heroica Bks; 0-935539),* Box 12718, Northgate Sta., San Rafael, CA 94913 (SAN 696-1940) Tel 415-897-6067; Dist. by: Baker & Taylor Co., Western Div., 380 Edison Way, Reno, NV 89564 (SAN 169-4464) Tel 702-786-6700; Dist. by: Blackwell North America, 1001 Fries Mill Rd., Blackwood, NJ 08012 (SAN 169-4596) Tel 609-629-0700; Dist. by: Blackwell North America, 6024 SW Jean Rd., Bldg. G, Lake Oswego, OR 97034 (SAN 169-7048) Tel 503-684-1140; Dist. by: Key Bk. Service, 425 Asylum St., Bridgeport, CT 06610 (SAN 169-0671) Tel 203-334-2165. *Imprints:* Modern Studies Group (Modern Studies Group).

Heron Bks., *(Heron Bks; 0-89739),* P.O. Box 1230, McMinnville, OR 97128 (SAN 678-4917).

Heron House Pubs., *(Heron Hse; 0-916920),* 9610 Manitou Beach Dr., NE, Bainbridge Island, WA 98110 (SAN 208-4767) Tel 206-842-3768.

Heron Pr., *(Heron Pr CA; 0-935999),* P.O. Box 31539, San Francisco, CA 94131 (SAN 696-8260) Tel 415-695-0323; Dist. by: Publishers Group West, 5855 Beaudry St., Emeryville, CA 94608 (SAN 202-8522) Tel 415-658-3453; Dist. by: Ingram Bk. Co., P.O. Box 17266, Nashville, TN 37217 (SAN 169-7978) Tel 615-361-5000; Toll free: 800-251-5700.

Heron Press, The, *(Heron Pr; 0-931246),* 36 Bromfield St., Boston, MA 02108 (SAN 206-5002) Tel 617-482-3615.

Herpetological Search Service & Exchange, *(Herpetological Search),* 117 E. Santa Barbara Rd., Lindenhurst, NY 11757 (SAN 287-7406).

Herren, Janet M, *(J M Herren; 0-9613025),* 4750 Crystal Springs Dr., Bainbridge Island, WA 98110 (SAN 293-9967) Tel 206-842-3484.

Herring Design Press, *(Herring Design; 0-917001),* 1216 Hawthorne, Houston, TX 77006 (SAN 655-6426) Tel 713-526-1250; Dist. by: Publishers Marketing Group, 1104 Summit Ave., Plainview, TX 75074 (SAN 262-0995).

Herring Pr., *(Herring Pr),* 1216 Hawthorne, Houston, TX 77006 (SAN 696-1983) Tel 713-526-1250.

Herrold, Stephen & Rebecca, *(S R Herrold),* 1530 Montalban Dr., San Jose, CA 95120 (SAN 676-3502).

Hershey, Virginia Sharpe, *(Hershey; 0-9605320),* 5325 Wikiup Bridgeway, Santa Rosa, CA 95404 (SAN 216-2024).

Hershey Foods Corporation, *(Hershey Foods; 0-943296),* 14 E. Chocolate Ave., Hershey, PA 17033 (SAN 240-6713) Tel 717-534-4912.

Herzl Pr., Subs. of World Zionist Organization, *(Herzl Pr; 0-930832),* 515 Park Ave., New York, NY 10022 (SAN 201-5374) Tel 212-752-0600.

Hesher Publishing, *(Hesher Publ; 0-914013),* P.O. Box 402, Grand Island, NY 14072 (SAN 286-7745) Tel 716-773-1327.

†Hesperian Foundation, The, *(Hesperian Found; 0-942364),* P.O. Box 1692, Palo Alto, CA 94302 (SAN 239-8567) Tel 415-325-9017; *CIP.*

Hesperides Paperbacks *See* **Oxford Univ. Pr., Inc.**

Heuristicus Publishing Co., *(Heuristicus; 0-934016),* 401 Tolbert St., Brea, CA 92621 (SAN 212-8551).

Hewlett-Packard Co., *(Hewlett-Packard; 0-9612030),* 3410 Central Expwy., Santa Clara, CA 95051 (SAN 285-1253) Tel 408-749-9500; Toll free: 800-367-4772; 3003 Scott Blvd., Santa Clara, CA 95050 (SAN 285-1261) Tel 408-988-7000.

Heyday Bks., *(Heyday Bks; 0-930588),* P.O. Box 9145, Berkeley, CA 94709 (SAN 207-2351) Tel 415-549-3564.

Heye Foundation *See* **Museum of the American Indian**

Heyeck Pr., The, *(Heyeck Pr; 0-940592),* 25 Patrol Ct., Woodside, CA 94062 (SAN 217-7692) Tel 415-851-7491.

Heyman, Barbara G., *(B G Heyman; 0-9616831),* 2530 E. 30th St., Tulsa, OK 74114 (SAN 661-3322) Tel 918-742-7100.

Heywood Pubs., *(Heywood Pubs; 0-9614314),* 4523 Lonsdale Blvd., Northfield, MN 55057 (SAN 687-5157) Tel 507-645-6453.

Hi Barbaree Pr., *(Hi Barbaree Pr; 0-9614477),* 17 Golf View Dr., Hingham, MA 02043 (SAN 689-3651) Tel 617-749-5467.

Hi-Country Pubs., *(Hi Country Pubs; 0-938354),* P.O. Box 2362, Littleton, CO 80161 (SAN 216-0374).

Hi-Tech Publishing House, Inc., *(Hi Tech Pub; 0-912619),* P.O. Box 19656, Atlanta, GA 30325 (SAN 282-8006).

Hi-Time Publishing Corp., *(Hi-Time Pub; 0-937997),* P.O. Box 13337, Milwaukee, WI 53213 (SAN 661-2520); Toll free: 800-558-2292; 12040-F W. Feerick St., Wauwatosa, WI 53222 (SAN 661-2539) Tel 414-466-2420.

Hi Willow Research & Publishing, *(Hi Willow; 0-931510),* Box 1801, Fayetteville, AR 72702 (SAN 211-3945) Tel 501-751-9096.

Hiawatha Bk. Co., *(Hiawatha Bks),* 7567 NE 102nd Ave., Bondurant, IA 50035 (SAN 162-8348) Tel 515-967-4025.

Hiawatha Pr, *(Hiawatha Pr; 0-930276),* 3505 St. Paul Ave., Minneapolis, MN 55416 (SAN 211-1799).

Hice, Bethell Whitley, *(B W Hice; 0-9608046),* 1344 Fairview Ave., Bridgeport, WA 98813 (SAN 240-1509).

Hickman Systems, *(Hickman Systems; 0-915689),* 4 Woodland Ln., Kirksville, MO 63501 (SAN 292-5311) Tel 816-665-1836.

Hickox, Ron G., *(R G Hickox; 0-9613064),* c/o Antique Arms & Military Research, P.O. Box 360010, Tampa, FL 33673-0006 (SAN 294-8346) Tel 813-237-0764.

Hidden Assets, *(Hidden Assets; 0-941552),* P.O. Box 22011, Seattle, WA 98122 (SAN 239-4324).

Hidden House *See Music Sales Corp.*

Hidden Studio, *(Hidden Studio; 0-942722),* 305A Main St., Falmouth, MA 02540 (SAN 238-8480) Tel 617-540-4439.

Hidden Valley Books., *(Hidden Valley Bks; 0-915807),* P.O. Box 5766, Scottsdale, AZ 85261 (SAN 295-3803) Tel 602-998-8085; 8431 E. Lincoln Dr., Scottsdale, AZ 85253 (SAN 295-3811).

†Hidden Valley Pr., *(Hid Valley MD; 0-935710),* P.O. Box 606, 7051 Poole Jones Rd., Frederick, MD 21701 (SAN 213-5094) Tel 301-662-6745; *CIP.*

Hiddigeigei Books, *(Hiddigeigei; 0-915560),* 1751 Grove St., San Francisco, CA 94117 (SAN 207-981X) Tel 415-563-3936.

Hideaways International, *(Hideaways Intl; 0-933613),* 15 Goldsmith St., Littleton, MA 01460 (SAN 692-4662) Tel 617-486-8955; Toll free: 800-843-4433.

Hieroglyphics Pr., *(Hieroglyphics; 0-916395),* P.O. Box 906, Maggie Valley, NC 28751 (SAN 295-8309) Tel 704-926-3245.

Higgins, Mae L., *(M L Higgins; 0-9616410),* 1809 Oriole Ct., Severn, MD 21144 (SAN 658-8611) Tel 301-672-2896.

High/Coo Pr., *(High-Coo Pr; 0-913719),* Rte. 1, Battle Ground, IN 47920 (SAN 217-7706) Tel 317-567-2596.

High Country Bks., *(High Country Bks; 0-932773),* P.O. Box 45060, Boise, ID 83711-5060 (SAN 688-4830) Tel 208-655-3925.

High-Energy Electrostatics Research, *(High Energy Res; 0-936199),* 7420 Dickenson St., Springfield, VA 22150 (SAN 696-8732) Tel 703-451-6184.

High Falls Pubs., *(High Falls Pubns; 0-9617217),* 4408 E. Groveland Rd., Geneseo, NY 14454 (SAN 663-4117) Tel 716-243-0753.

High Goals Press, *(High Goals Pr; 0-9602576),* P.O. Box 2103, Tallahassee, FL 32316 (SAN 221-8186).

High Impact Pr., *(High Impact; 0-935435),* P.O. Box 262, Cheney, WA 99004 (SAN 696-1991) Tel 509-235-4029; Eastern Washington Univ., 310 WLM Hall No. 90, Cheney, WA 99004 (SAN 696-2009).

High Mesa Pr., *(High Mesa Pr; 0-9614010),* P.O. Box 2267, Taos, NM 87571 (SAN 693-3815) Tel 505-758-8769.

High Mountain Publishing Inc., *(High Mount Pub; 0-9614190),* P.O. Box 147, Irasburg, VT 05845 (SAN 686-6174) Tel 802-754-2183.

High Museum of Art, The, *(High Mus Art; 0-939802),* 1280 Peachtree St., Atlanta, GA 30309 (SAN 216-9002) Tel 404-892-3600.

High Noon Books *See Academic Therapy Pubns.*

High Pubs., *(High Pubs; 0-9604216),* 65 MacAlester Rd., Pueblo, CO 81001 (SAN 281-7780) Tel 303-542-7028; Orders to: P.O. Box 11411, Pueblo, CO 81001 (SAN 281-7799).

High Q Pubns., *(High Q; 0-931820),* P.O. Box 133H, Scarsdale, NY 10583 (SAN 207-3900).

High Rockies Enterprises, Inc., *(High Rockies; 0-937166),* P.O. Box 4809, Dept. 2002, Boulder, CO 80306 (SAN 215-1529).

†High-Scope Educational Research Foundation, Div. of High-Scope Pr., *(High-Scope; 0-931114),* 600 N. River St., Ypsilanti, MI 48198 (SAN 211-9617) Tel 313-485-2000; 306 W. Cross, Ypsilanti, MI 48197 (SAN 669-0947); *CIP.*

High Score, Inc., *(High Scores; 0-940182),* Box 522, Long Beach, MS 39560 (SAN 220-228X).

High Sierra Photos, *(High Sierra; 0-9613329),* Box 557, Lone Pine, CA 93545 (SAN 655-6450) Tel 619-876-5995.

High South Pubns., Div. of Jr. League of Johnson City, *(High South Pubns; 0-9616492),* P.O. Box 4485, CRS, Johnson City, TN 37602 (SAN 659-2392) Tel 615-929-7747; 705 E. Holston, Johnson City, TN 37601 (SAN 659-2406).

High-Touch Publications, *(High Touch; 0-914419),* New England Bldg., Suite 450 or 611, P.O. Box 2712, Winter Park, FL 32790 (SAN 289-6354) Tel 305-628-4176.

Higher Education Pubns., Inc., *(Higher Ed Pubns; 0-914927),* 2946 Sleepy Hollow Rd., Suite 2E, Falls Church, VA 22044 (SAN 289-2391) Tel 703-532-2300.

Higher Self Publishing, *(Higher Self Pub; 0-938241),* P.O. Box 1715, Lexington, KY 40592 (SAN 661-4248); 3346 Commodore Dr., Lexington, KY 40592 (SAN 661-4256) Tel 606-269-2744.

Highflyer Press, *(Highflyer Pr; 0-9605010),* P.O. Box 23081, Kansas City, MO 64141 (SAN 240-1517).

Highgate Hse. Pubs., *(Highgate Hse; 0-934215),* 180 Cabrini Blvd., New York, NY 10033 (SAN 693-1200) Tel 212-927-4561.

Highland Bks. *See Berkley Publishing Group*

Highland Bks., *(Highland Bks; 0-934769),* P.O. Box 567, Littleton, CO 80160-0567 (SAN 694-1753) Tel 303-795-8410; Dist. by: Baker & Taylor, Midwest Div., 501 S. Gladiola Ave., Momence, IL 60954 (SAN 169-2100); Dist. by: Quality Bks., 918 Sherwood Dr., Lake Bluff, IL 60044-2204 (SAN 158-9016).

Highland Enterprises, *(Highland Ent; 0-913490),* Box 7000, Dallas, TX 75209 (SAN 204-0514) Tel 214-358-3456.

Highland Hse. Publishing, Inc., *(Highland NY; 0-938988),* 74 Hunters Lane, Westbury, NY 11590 (SAN 201-1082) Tel 516-334-6497.

Highland Press, *(Highland; 0-914335),* 321 Bello Rio, Sacramento, CA 95809 (SAN 287-5462) Tel 415-878-8836.

Highland Pr., *(Highland Pr; 0-910722),* Rte. 3, Box 3125, Boerne, TX 78006 (SAN 204-0522).

Highland Pubns., *(Highland Pubns; 0-916261),* P.O. Box 861, Oak Park, IL 60303 (SAN 294-9393) Tel 312-383-4463.

Highland Publishing, *(Highland Pub; 0-9615009),* 5226 Green Farms Rd., Edina, MN 55436 (SAN 694-0307) Tel 612-933-5797.

Highlander Research & Education Center, *(Highlander; 0-9602226),* Rte. 3 Box 370, New Market, TN 37820 (SAN 212-6664).

Highlands Development Co., *(Highlands Dev; 0-9616816),* 7373 N. Scottsdale Rd., Suite 274B, Scottsdale, AZ 85253 (SAN 661-1001) Tel 602-991-5426.

Highlands Publishing Co., *(Highlands Pub; 0-943328),* 424 NW Lakeview Dr., Sebring, FL 33870 (SAN 240-4826).

Highlight Bks., *(Highlight Bks; 0-9616715),* P.O. Box 1076, Crawfordville, FL 32327 (SAN 661-4485) Tel 904-926-5944.

Highlights, *(Highlights NJ; 0-9616366),* P.O. Box 25, Gibbsboro, NJ 08026 (SAN 658-862X) Tel 609-767-2644; 15 Amherst Rd., Berlin, NJ 08009 (SAN 658-8638).

Highlights for Children, Inc., *(Highlights; 0-87534; 0-87534),* 803 Church Ave., Honesdale, PA 18431 (SAN 281-7810) Tel 614-486-0631; 2300 W. Fifth Ave., P.O. Box 269, Columbus, OH 43272-0002 (SAN 281-7802).

Hightech Pubns., *(Hightech Pubns; 0-936551),* 23868 Hawthorne Blvd., Torrance, CA 90505 (SAN 697-9858) Tel 213-378-0261.

Higley Publishing Corp., *(Higley; 0-9614116),* P.O. Box 2470, Jacksonville, FL 32203 (SAN 211-8041) Tel 904-396-1918; Dist. by: Appalachian Bible Co. & Christian Bks., 604 Rolling Hills Dr., Johnson City, TN 37601 (SAN 169-7889) Tel 615-926-0128; Dist. by: Spring Arbor, 10885 Textile Rd., Belleville, MI 48111 (SAN 158-9016) Tel 313-481-0900; Toll free: 800-521-4340.

Hilary Hse. Pubs., Inc., *(Hilary Hse Pubs; 0-934464),* 1033 Channel Dr., Hewlett, NY 11557 (SAN 213-2524) Tel 516-295-2376.

Hiles & Hardin Pubs., *(Hiles & Hardin Pubs; 0-931373),* 4870 Topanga Canyon Blvd., Woodland Hills, CA 91364 (SAN 682-2665).

Hill, E.J., & Co. Inc., *(E J Hill & Co Inc; 0-940316),* 5000 Willow Spring Dr., Racine, WI 53402 (SAN 217-5258) Tel 414-639-9355.

Hill, Grace, *(G Hill; 0-9604506),* 3 Haskins Rd., Hanover, NH 03755 (SAN 213-0785) Tel 603-643-4059.

Hill, Hortense Gettys, Memorial Fund, *(Hort Gettys Hill Mem; 0-9613799),* Box 2153, Rockford, IL 61130 (SAN 682-2614).

Hill, Joyce, Assn., *(J Hill Assocs; 0-914685),* 1023 South 24th St., Kingsville, TX 78363 (SAN 292-3335).

Hill, Lawrence, & Co., Inc., *(Lawrence Hill; 0-88208),* 520 Riverside Ave., Westport, CT 06880 (SAN 214-1221) Tel 203-226-5980; Dist. by: Independent Publishers Group, 1 Pleasant Ave., Port Washington, NY 11050 (SAN 287-2544) Tel 516-944-9325; Dist. by: Lawrence Hill & Co., Inc., 520 Riverside Ave., Westport, CT 06880 (SAN 214-1221) Tel 203-226-5980.

†Hill & Wang, Inc., Div. of Farrar, Straus & Giroux, Inc., *(Hill & Wang; 0-8090),* 19 Union Sq., W., New York, NY 10003 (SAN 201-9299) Tel 212-741-6900; Toll free: 800-242-7737; *CIP.*

Hill College Pr., Affil. of Hill College, *(Hill Coll Pr; 0-912172),* P.O. Box 619, Hillsboro, TX 76645 (SAN 201-5463) Tel 817-582-2555.

Hill Monastic Manuscript Library, *(Hill Monastic; 0-940250),* Bush Ctr., St. John's Univ., Collegeville, MN 56321 (SAN 238-8839).

Hill Pubns., *(Hill Pubns; 0-9602704),* P.O. Box 1236, Boca Raton, FL 33433 (SAN 213-0831).

Hill Springs Pubns., *(Hill Springs Pubns; 0-931856),* 5023 Kentucky St., South Charleston, WV 25309 (SAN 211-5735) Tel 304-768-8223.

Hillary Pr., *(Hillary Pr; 0-935367),* 2821 S. Hillock Ave., Chicago, IL 60608 (SAN 696-2033) Tel 312-523-2098.

Hillcrest Pr., *(Hillcrest Pr; 0-914589),* 609 Mountain Dr., Beverly Hills, CA 90210 (SAN 290-702X) Tel 213-276-4592; P.O. Box 10636, Beverly Hills, CA 90210 (SAN 290-7038).

Hillel Jewish Student Center, *(Hillel Jewish; 0-9611580),* 2615 Clifton Ave., Cincinnati, OH 45220 (SAN 285-3175) Tel 513-621-6728.

Hillman Co., *(Hillman CT; 0-938307),* 29 taconic Rd., Greenwich, CT 06830 (SAN 661-4426) Tel 203-661-3698.

Hillman Press, *(Hillman Pr; 0-9601176),* 12 Broad Cove Rd., Cape Elizabeth, ME 04107 (SAN 210-0983) Tel 207-799-7666; Dist. by: ICEL, University of San Francisco, San Francisco, CA 94117 (SAN 210-0991).

Hillman Pubns., *(Hillman Pubns; 0-931649),* 424 Stonewood St, Canal Fulton, OH 44614 (SAN 683-731X) Tel 216-854-6537.

Hillmer Graphics Co., *(Hillmer Graph Co; 0-916065),* 2020 California St., Omaha, NE 68102 (SAN 294-8362) Tel 402-422-1167.

Hills Medical/Sports, The, *(Hills Med),* 4615 Bee Cave Road, Austin, TX 78746 (SAN 264-097X).

Hillsdale Educational Pubs., Inc., *(Hillsdale Educ; 0-910726),* 39 North St., Box 245, Hillsdale, MI 49242 (SAN 159-8759) Tel 517-437-3179.

Hillside Bks. *See* Dial Bks. for Young Readers

Hillside Bks., *(Hillside Bks; 0-9611350),* P.O. Box 601, Lynnfield, MA 01940 (SAN 283-2364) Tel 617-581-2961.

Hillside Press, *(Hillside; 0-918462),* P.O. Box 785, Vista, CA 92084 (SAN 209-5661) Tel 619-726-1853.

Hillside Press, The, *(Hillside Pr; 0-941066),* P.O. Box 42, Carversville, PA 18913 (SAN 217-3808) Tel 215-297-5800.

Hillside Publications, *(Hillside Pubns; 0-915755),* P.O. Box 385, Keasbey, NJ 08832 (SAN 295-382X) Tel 201-686-9410; 358 Long Ave., Hillside, NJ 07205 (SAN 295-3838).

Hilltop House, *(Hilltop Hse; 0-9613717),* 12842 Francine Ct., Poway, CA 92064 (SAN 676-2948) Tel 619-566-2675.

Hilltop Press, *(Hilltop Pr CA; 0-941470),* P.O. Box 14592, San Francisco, CA 94114 (SAN 239-1007).

Hilltop Pubns., Inc., *(Hilltop Pubns; 0-937782),* 127 E. 69th St., New York, NY 10021 (SAN 215-6547); Dist. by Dell Publishing Co. Inc., 1 Dag Hammarskjold Plaza, 245 E. 47th St., New York, NY 10017 (SAN 201-0097) Tel 212-605-3000.

Hilltop Publishing Co., *(Hilltop Pub Co; 0-912133),* P.O. Box 654, Sonoma, CA 95476 (SAN 264-6706) Tel 707-938-1700; Dist. by: Bookpeople, 2929 Fifth St., Berkeley, CA 94710 (SAN 168-9517) Tel 415-549-3030; Toll free: 800-227-1516.

Hilltop Publishing Co., *(Hilltop Publishing; 0-913397),* P.O. Box 148, 446 Monroe Rd., Sarver, PA 16055-0148 (SAN 285-8487) Tel 412-353-1411.

Hilmarton Manor Press, *(Hilmarton Manor),* 27 Harrison St., Bridgeport, CT 06604 (SAN 210-9751).

Hilton Head Elementary PTA, Div. of Hilton Head Elementary School, *(Hilton Head PTA; 0-9615726),* 25 School Rd., Hilton Head Island, SC 29928 (SAN 696-4729) Tel 803-681-6600.

Himalayan Pubs., Div. of Himalayan International Institute of Yoga Science & Philosophy, *(Himalayan Pubs; 0-89389),* RR 1, Box 405, Honesdale, PA 18431 (SAN 207-5067) Tel 717-253-3022.

Hinckley, Clive, *(C Hinckley; 0-9602984),* 106 E. Sunset Dr., S., Redlands, CA 92373 (SAN 207-480X).

Hindman, Janice McClure, *(McClure Hindman Bks; 0-9611034),* P.O. Box 208, Durkee, OR 97905 (SAN 282-8804) Tel 503-877-2430.

Hinds, Norman C., Jr., Publishing Co., *(N C Hinds Pub; 0-935541),* P.O. Box 456, Newburyport, MA 01950 (SAN 695-9636) Tel 617-465-2697; Dist. by: New Leaf Distributing, The, 1020 White St., SW, Atlanta, GA 30310 (SAN 169-1449) Tel 404-755-2665; Toll free: 800-241-3829.

Hinds, Tom, *(T Hinds; 0-9614911),* 8932 Falling Creek Court, Annandale, VA 22003-4108 (SAN 693-4137) Tel 703-425-4275.

Hine's Legal Directory Incorporated, *(Hines Legal Dir; 0-910911),* 443 Duane St, P.O. Box 71, Glen Ellyn, IL 60138 (SAN 226-4331) Tel 312-469-3983.

Hinkle, Ray, Pubs., *(Ray Hinkle; 0-9616373),* 123 W. McKinley, Blackwell, OK 74631 (SAN 658-8646) Tel 405-363-3831; P.O. Box 572, Blackwell, OK 74631 (SAN 658-8654).

Hinman, Marjory B., *(M B Hinman),* P. O. Box 345, Windsor, NY 13865 (SAN 208-1237) Tel 607-655-3174.

Hinman-Snyder Productions, *(Hinman-Synder; 0-9613472),* 1881 Louden Heights, Charleston, WV 25314 (SAN 657-2707) Tel 304-346-0609.

Hinsdale Pr., *(Hinsdale Pr; 0-931375),* 526 Third Ave., San Francisco, CA 94118 (SAN 682-594X) Tel 415-752-8748.

Hinshaw Music, Inc., *(Hinshaw Mus; 0-937276),* P.O. Box 470, Chapel Hill, NC 27514 (SAN 693-4072) Tel 919-933-1691.

Hippocrene Bks., Inc., *(Hippocrene Bks; 0-87052; 0-88254),* 171 Madison Ave., New York, NY 10016 (SAN 213-2060) Tel 212-685-4371. *Imprints:* Books New China (Bks New China); Northwest Illustrated (NW Illus).

Hippogriff Pubns., *(Hippogriff Pubns; 0-936973),* 111 E. Fifth, Bonham, TX 75418 (SAN 658-7860) Tel 214-583-3218.

Hired Hand Press, *(Hired Hand; 0-9602256),* P.O. Box 426, Dover, MA 02030 (SAN 212-4262) Tel 617-325-8155.

Hirsch, A. Jay, *(Hirsch A J; 0-9610920),* 1711 Dana Place, Fullerton, CA 92631 (SAN 285-662X) Tel 714-871-5512.

Hispanic Bk. Distributors & Pubs., Inc., *(Hispanic Bk Dist; 0-938243),* 1870 W. Prince Rd., Suite 8, Tucson, AZ 85705 (SAN 661-423X) Tel 602-887-8879.

Hispanic Institute in the United States, *(Hispanic Inst),* 612 W 116th St, New York, NY 10027 (SAN 225-3100).

Hispanic Policy Development Project, *(Hispanic Policy Dev Proj; 0-918911),* 1001 Connecticut Ave., Suite 310, Washington, DC 20036 (SAN 670-0861) Tel 202-822-8414.

Hispanic Seminary of Medieval Studies, *(Hispanic Seminary; 0-942260),* 3734 Ross St., Madison, WI 53705 (SAN 207-9836).

†Hispanic Society of America, *(Hispanic Soc; 0-87535),* 613 W. 155th St., New York, NY 10032 (SAN 204-0573) Tel 212-926-2234; CIP.

Historic Baltimore Society, Inc., *(Hist Balt Soc; 0-942460),* 4 Willow Brook Ct., Randallstown, MD 21133 (SAN 285-0257) Tel 301-922-3649; Dist. by: LMC, P.O. Box 355, Linthicum Heights, MD 21090-0355 (SAN 200-7169) Tel 301-766-1211.

Historic Cherry Hill, *(Hist Cherry Hill; 0-943366),* 523 1/2 S. Pearl St., Albany, NY 12202 (SAN 240-6721) Tel 518-434-4791.

Historic Denver Inc., *(Hist Denver; 0-914248),* 1701 Wynkoop, Suite 200, Denver, CO 80202 (SAN 220-651X).

Historic Florida Keys Preservation Board, *(Hist Fl Keys; 0-943528),* 500 Whitehead, Monroe County Courthouse, Key West, FL 33040 (SAN 240-6748) Tel 305-294-7511.

Historic Frankfort, Inc., *(Historic Frankfort; 0-9615489),* P.O. Box 775, Frankfort, KY 40602 (SAN 696-205X) Tel 502-223-0870.

Historic Heartland Assn., Inc., *(Hist Heart Assn Inc; 0-910623),* P.O. Box 1, Brainerd, MN 56401 (SAN 260-2024) Tel 218-963-2218; 6410 Murray Hill Rd., Baltimore, MD 21212 (SAN 699-5306) Tel 301-377-7294.

Historic Jefferson Foundation, *(Hist Jefferson Found; 0-935077),* Drawer 2049, Marshall, TX 75671 (SAN 695-0914) Tel 214-938-4332; Orders to: P.O. Box 1088, Hughes Springs, TX 75656 (SAN 662-3425) Tel 214-639-2012.

Historic Kansas City Foundation, *(Hist Kansas City; 0-913504),* 20 W. Ninth St., Kansas City, MO 64105 (SAN 239-4421) Tel 816-471-3391.

Historic Natchez Foundation, The, *(Hist Natchez; 0-936549),* P.O. Box 1761, Natchez, MS 39120 (SAN 697-9874) Tel 601-442-2500; 107 N. Commerce St., Natchez, MS 39120 (SAN 697-9882).

Historic New Orleans Collection, The, *(Historic New Orleans; 0-917860),* 533 Royal St., New Orleans, LA 70130 (SAN 281-7829) Tel 504-523-4662.

Historic Photos, *(Historic Photos; 0-933206),* 3460 St. Helena Hwy. N., St. Helena, CA 94574 (SAN 212-6672) Tel 707-963-3117.

Historic Preservation Assn. of Bourbon County, Inc., *(Historic Pres Bourbon; 0-9601568),* 502 S. National Ave., Fort Scott, KS 66701 (SAN 211-528X) Tel 316-223-3300.

Historic Preservation Society of Durham, *(HPS Durham; 0-9615577),* 120 Morris St., Durham, NC 27701 (SAN 696-2076); Duke Univ., 341 Perkins, Durham, NC 27706 (SAN 696-2084) Tel 919-684-5637.

Historic Pubns. of Fredericksburg, *(Hist Pubns; 0-9608408),* 300 Princess Anne St., Fredericksburg, VA 22401 (SAN 240-673X) Tel 703-371-0585.

Historic Saranac Lake, *(Hist Saranac; 0-9615159),* P.O. Box 1030, Saranac Lake, NY 12983 (SAN 694-387X) Tel 518-891-0971.

Historic Savannah Foundation, Inc., *(Historic Sav; 0-9610106),* P.O. Box 1983, Savannah, GA 31402 (SAN 270-7802) Tel 912-233-7787.

Historic Seattle Preservation & Development Authority, *(Historic Seattle; 0-9616090),* 207 1/2 First Ave S., Seattle, WA 98104 (SAN 698-0791) Tel 206-622-6952.

Historical Assn. of Southern Florida, *(Hist Assn FL; 0-935761),* 101 W. Flagler St., Miami, FL 33130 (SAN 696-4737) Tel 305-375-1492.

Historical Aviation Album, *(Hist Aviation; 0-911852),* P.O. Box 33, Temple City, CA 91780 (SAN 213-5108) Tel 818-286-7655.

Historical Commission of the Southern Baptist Convention, *(Hist Comm S Baptist; 0-939804),* 901 Commerce St., Suite 400, Nashville, TN 37203-3620 (SAN 216-7352) Tel 615-244-0344.

Historical Dimensions Pr., *(Hist Dimensions; 0-9614733),* P.O. Box 12042, Washington, DC 20005 (SAN 692-7580).

Historical Pubns., *(Historical Pubns; 0-9616470),* 13 Oxford Dr., Lompoc, CA 93436 (SAN 658-8670) Tel 805-736-4160.

Historical Research Repository, Inc., *(Hist Res Reposit; 0-935319),* 19805 Greenfield No. 26, Detroit, MI 48235 (SAN 695-7803) Tel 313-899-2500.

Historical Society of Baldwin Park, The, *(Hist Soc Baldwin Pk; 0-9607306),* 13009 Amar Rd., P.O. Box 1, Baldwin Park, CA 91706 (SAN 239-2267) Tel 818-337-3285.

Historical Society of Carroll County, *(Hist Soc Carroll; 0-9614125),* 210 E. Main St., Westminster, MD 21157 (SAN 686-4724) Tel 301-848-6494.

Historical Society of Michigan, *(Historical Soc MI; 0-9614344),* 2117 Washtenaw Ave., Ann Arbor, MI 48104 (SAN 687-8008) Tel 313-769-1829.

Historical Society of Pennsylvania, *(Pa Hist Soc; 0-910732),* 1300 Locust St., Philadelphia, PA 19107 (SAN 202-8441) Tel 215-732-6200.

†Historical Society of Rockland County, The, *(Rockland County Hist; 0-911183),* 20 Zukor Rd., New City, NY 10956 (SAN 211-4488) Tel 914-634-9629; CIP.

Historical Society of Seattle & King County, *(Hist Soc Seattle; 0-939806),* 2700 24th Ave. E., Seattle, WA 98112 (SAN 216-7360) Tel 206-324-1125.

Historical Society of Western Pennsylvania, *(Hist Soc West Pa; 0-936340),* 4338 Bigelow Blvd., Pittsburgh, PA 15213 (SAN 214-0276) Tel 412-681-5537.

Historical Tales Ink, *(Hist Tales; 0-938404),* 7344 Rich St., Reynoldsburg, OH 43068 (SAN 215-7748).

Historical Times Inc., *(Historical Times; 0-918678),* 2245 Kohn Rd., Box 8200, Harrisburg, PA 17105 (SAN 685-320X) Tel 717-657-9555.

History Business Inc. The, *(Hist Bus Inc; 0-9614203),* 1421 Peachtree St. NE, Unit 410, Atlanta, GA 30309 (SAN 686-8126) Tel 404-875-0603.

History of Science Society, Inc., *(Hist Sci Soc; 0-934235),* 215 S. 34th St./D6, Philadelphia, PA 19104 (SAN 225-1930) Tel 215-898-8575; Toll free: 800-341-1522.

Hit Enterprises, *(Hit Ent; 0-935938),* 2945 Leticia Dr., Hacienda Heights, CA 91745 (SAN 213-7453).

Hitzel, Ed, *(E Hitzel; 0-9612852),* 300 Grace Ave., Mays Landing, NJ 08330 (SAN 659-2015).

†Hive Publishing Co., *(Hive Pub; 0-87960),* P.O. Box 1004, Easton, PA 18042 (SAN 202-2958) Tel 215-258-6663; CIP.

Hmong United Assn. of Pennsylvania, Inc., *(Hmong United; 0-917003),* 3944 Baring St., Phildelphia, PA 19104 (SAN 655-7279) Tel 215-387-3308.

Ho, Steve, *(S Ho; 0-9609018),* 4295 Okemos Rd., P.O. Box 99, Okemos, MI 48864 (SAN 241-5372) Tel 517-349-0795.

Ho, Van H., Assocs., *(V H Ho; 0-9602904),* P.O. Box 130, Harbor City, CA 90710 (SAN 213-5124).

Hoard, W. D., & Sons Co., *(Hoard & Sons Co; 0-932147),* 28 Milwaukee Ave., W., Ft. Atkinson, WI 53538 (SAN 686-4341) Tel 414-563-5551.

Hobar Publications, Div. of Hobar Enterprises, Inc., *(Hobar Pubns; 0-913163; 0-939381),* 1234 Tiller Lane, St. Paul, MN 55112 (SAN 283-1120) Tel 612-633-3170.

Hobart & William Smith Colleges Press, *(Hobart & Wm Smith; 0-934888),* Hobart & William Smith Colleges, Geneva, NY 14456 (SAN 213-3202) Tel 315-789-5500.

Hobbit House Press, *(Hobbit Hse; 0-9604300),* 5920 Dimmway, Richmond, CA 94805 (SAN 214-3852).

Hobby Horse Publishing, *(Hobby Horse; 0-935138),* 10091 Hobby Horse Lane, Box 54, Mentor, OH 44060 (SAN 213-5132) Tel 216-255-3434.

Hobby Hse. Pr., *(Hobby Hse; 0-87588),* 900 Frederick St., Cumberland, MD 21502 (SAN 204-059X) Tel 301-759-3770.

Hobby Publishing Service, *(Hobby Pub Serv; 0-917922),* 1318 Seventh St., NW, Albuquerque, NM 87102 (SAN 207-6330) Tel 505-242-9465.

Hochberg, Bette, *(B Hochberg; 0-9600990),* 333 Wilkes Circle, Santa Cruz, CA 95060 (SAN 281-7845) Tel 408-427-2127; Dist. by: Textile Artists Supplies, 3006 San Pablo Ave., Berkeley, CA 94702 (SAN 282-6461) Tel 415-548-9988.

Hodgson House *See* **College Kids Cookbooks**

Hoehler, Richard S., *(R S Hoehler; 0-930590),* P.O. Box 240, Conifer, CO 80433 (SAN 204-6628) Tel 303-838-4046.

Hoffman, Irwin J., Inc., *(I J Hoffman; 0-9604082),* 5734 S. Ivanhoe St., Denver, CO 80237 (SAN 214-0284).

Hoffman, J. Henry, *(J H Hoffmann; 0-9614287),* Drawer 8170, Tamuning, GU 96911 (SAN 687-4509).

Hoffman, Jane, Publishing, *(J Hoffman),* P.O. Box 16966, Irvine, CA 92713 (SAN 219-1725).

Hoffman, William N., *(W N Hoffman; 0-9612050),* 53 Claire Ave., New Rochelle, NY 10804 (SAN 286-7923) Tel 914-636-7597.

Hoffman Enterprises, *(Hoffman Enter; 0-942662),* P.O. Box 2091, Manteca, CA 95336 (SAN 241-5380) Tel 209-239-5576.

Hoffman Research Services, *(Hoffman Res; 0-910203),* P.O. Box 342, Rillton, PA 15678 (SAN 240-8597).

Hofmann, Margaret M., *(M M Hofmann; 0-937761),* P.O. Box 446, Roanoke Rapids, NC 27870 (SAN 659-2414) Tel 919-536-2888; 35 Longstreet Rd., Weldon, NC 27890 (SAN 659-2422); Dist. by: Reprint Co., 601 Hillcrest Offices, Spartanburg, SC 29304 (SAN 203-3828).

Hofmann, Margret, *(Hofmann; 0-9600166),* 2706 Nottingham Lane, Austin, TX 78704 (SAN 204-0603) Tel 512-444-8877.

Hogarth Pr., *(Hogarth; 0-911776),* P.O. Box 10606, Honolulu, HI 96816 (SAN 202-2966) Tel 808-536-4216.

Hogfiddle Press, *(Hogfiddle Pr; 0-9608842),* 46 Pleasant St., Stoneham, MA 02180 (SAN 262-0383) Tel 617-279-0744.

Hogrefe International, Affil. of C. J. Hogrefe, *(Hogrefe Intl; 0-88937),* P.O. Box 51, Lewiston, NY 14092 (SAN 293-2792) Tel 716-754-8145.

Holbrook Research Institute, *(Holbrook Res; 0-931248; 0-87623),* 57 Locust St., Oxford, MA 01540 (SAN 211-1551) Tel 617-987-0881.

Holden, Ernest, Publishing, *(E Holden Pub; 0-916261),* 1710 E. Mohave, Phoenix, AZ 85034 (SAN 294-9407) Tel 602-943-7850.

Holden-Day, Inc., *(Holden-Day; 0-8162),* 4432 Telegraph Ave., Oakland, CA 94609 (SAN 202-2990) Tel 415-428-9400.

Holden Pacific, *(Holden Pac; 0-910571),* 814-35th Ave., Seattle, WA 98122 (SAN 260-0714) Tel 206-325-4324.

Holderby and Bierce, *(Holderby & Bierce; 0-916761),* 1332 42nd Ave., Rock Island, IL 61201 (SAN 654-3979) Tel 309-788-7732.

†**Holiday Hse., Inc.,** *(Holiday; 0-8234),* 18 E. 53rd St., New York, NY 10022 (SAN 202-3008) Tel 212-688-0085; *CIP.*

Holistic Growth Pubns., *(Holistic Growth; 0-9606544),* 112 Roy St., C32, Seattle, WA 98109 (SAN 663-4613) Tel 206-283-3066.

Holland Hse. Pr., *(Holland Hse Pr; 0-913042),* Box 42, Northville, MI 48167 (SAN 204-0611) Tel 313-273-0223.

Holland Junior Welfare League, *(Holland Jr Welfare; 0-9612710),* 212 Randolph St., Douglas, MI 49406 (SAN 289-9469) Tel 616-857-4473. *Imprints:* Steketee-Van Huis, Inc. (Steketee-Van Huis).

Holland Publishing Hse., *(Holland Pub Hse; 0-9616660),* 2100 Tiebout Ave., Bronx, NY 10457 (SAN 661-3470) Tel 212-588-4670.

Hollander Co., *(Hollander Co; 0-943032),* 12320 Wayzata Blvd., Minnetonka, MN 55343 (SAN 240-3870) Tel 612-544-4111.

Hollibaugh, Hiltrud, *(Hollibaugh; 0-939114),* P.S.C. Box 6033, Blytheville, AR 72315 (SAN 219-7871).

Hollow Glen Pr., *(Hollow Glen; 0-916799),* P.O. Box 23862, Pleasant Hill, CA 94523 (SAN 654-1976) Tel 415-935-8238.

Hollow Hills Pr., *(Hollow Hills Pr; 0-9616455),* 7 Landview Dr., Dix Hills, NY 11746 (SAN 659-2430) Tel 516-271-2742.

†**Hollow Spring Press,** *(Hollow Spring Pr; 0-936198),* RD 1, Chester, MA 01011 (SAN 213-8468); *CIP.*

Holloway Historicals, *(Holloway Hist; 0-9614848),* 513 N. Pinehurst Ave., Salisbury, MD 21801 (SAN 693-1219) Tel 301-742-7432.

Holloway Hse. Publishing Co., *(Holloway; 0-87067),* 8060 Melrose Ave., Los Angeles, CA 90046 (SAN 206-8451) Tel 213-653-8060. *Imprints:* Melrose Square (Melrose Sq.).

Holly-Pix Music Publishing Co., *(Holly-Pix; 0-910736),* 4931 Alcove Ave N. Hollywood, Sherman Oaks, CA 91607 (SAN 204-062X) Tel 213-788-3668; Orders to: WIM, 2859 Holt Ave., Los Angeles, CA 90034 (SAN 204-0638).

Holly Pr., The, *(Holly Pr; 0-935968),* P.O. Box 48, Childs, MD 21916 (SAN 214-0292) Tel 301-398-2647.

Holly Society of America, *(Holly Soc; 0-939601),* 304 North Wind Road, Baltimore, MD 21204 (SAN 225-0470) Tel 301-825-8133.

HollyDay Bks., *(HollyDay; 0-943786),* 130 Ashley Rd., Hopkins, MN 55343 (SAN 241-0281) Tel 612-935-4562.

Hollym International Corp., *(Hollym Intl; 0-930878),* 18 Donald Pl., Elizabeth, NJ 07208 (SAN 211-0172) Tel 201-353-1655.

Hollywood Bowl Cookbook, The, *(Hollywood Bowl; 0-9615792),* P.O. Box 1951, Los Angeles, CA 90078 (SAN 696-8287) Tel 818-285-3688; 2301 Highland, Los Angeles, CA 90068 (SAN 696-8295); Dist. by: Collection, Inc. The, 2101 Kansas City Rd., P.O. Box 1220, Olathe, KS 66061-1220 (SAN 200-6359) Tel 913-764-1811.

Hollywood Film Archive, *(Hollywd Film Arch; 0-913616),* 8344 Melrose Ave., Hollywood, CA 90069 (SAN 206-7447) Tel 213-933-3345.

Hollywood Publishing Co., *(Hollywood Pub; 0-9617040),* 900 S. Federal Hwy., Suite B, Hollywood, FL 33020 (SAN 662-8265) Tel 305-922-7700.

†**Holman, A.J., Bible Pub.,** Div. of Baptist Sunday Schl. Bd., *(Holman; 0-87981),* 127 Ninth Ave., N. Nashville, TN 37234 (SAN 202-3016) Tel 615-251-2520; Toll free: 800-251-3225; *CIP.*

Holmes, Oakley N., *(O N Holmes; 0-9604026),* c/o Black Artists in America, Macgowan Enterprises, 39 Wilshire Dr., Spring Valley, NY 10977 (SAN 270-8000).

Holmes, Opal Laurel, Publisher, *(O L Holmes; 0-918522),* P.O. Box 2535, Boise, ID 83701 (SAN 210-1017) Tel 208-344-4517; Dist. by: Baker & Taylor Co., Midwest Div., 501 Gladiola Ave., Momence, IL 60954 (SAN 169-2100).

Holmes, Stacey, Enterprises, *(S Holmes Enter; 0-910681),* 6520 Selma Ave., Box 556, Hollywood, CA 90028 (SAN 264-0996).

Holmes & Meier Pubs., Inc., Div. of IUB, Inc., *(Holmes & Meier; 0-8419),* 30 Irving Pl., IUB Bldg., New York, NY 10003 (SAN 201-9280) Tel 212-254-4100. *Imprints:* Africana Pub. (Africana).

Holmes Book Co., *(Holmes; 0-910740),* 274 14th St., Oakland, CA 94612 (SAN 204-0654) Tel 415-893-6860.

Holmes Publishing Group, *(Holmes Pub; 0-916411),* P.O. Box 623, Edmonds, WA 98020-0623 (SAN 655-8321) Tel 206-771-2701. *Imprints:* Christian Heritage Press (Christian Heritage); Near Eastern Press (Near Eastern); Old Japan Press (Old Japan); Oriental Classics (Oriental Classics); Short Story Press (Short Story Pr).

†**Holmgangers Pr.,** *(Holmgangers; 0-914974),* 95 Carson Court Shelter Cove, Whitethorn, CA 95489 (SAN 206-5029) Tel 707-986-7700; *CIP.*

Holmgren, Gary L., Pubs., *(G L Holmgren Pubs; 0-932999),* P.O. Box 8205, Dallas, TX 75205 (SAN 689-108X) Tel 214-891-8153.

Holocaust Pubns., Inc., *(Holocaust Pubns; 0-89604),* 216 W. 18th St., New York, NY 10011 (SAN 215-0808); Dist. by: Schocken Bks., 62 Cooper Sq., New York, NY 10003 (SAN 213-7585) Tel 212-475-4900.

Holsinger, Terry Wayne, *(T W Holsinger; 0-9607966),* 150 S. Magnolia, No. 231, Anaheim, CA 92804 (SAN 239-6548) Tel 714-826-7505.

Holstein-Friesian World, Inc., *(Holstein-Friesian; 0-9614711),* P.O. Box 299, Sandy Creek, NY 13145 (SAN 692-6509); 8036 Lake St., Sandy Creek, NY 13145 (SAN 662-3018) Tel 315-387-3441.

Holt, Henry, & Co., *(H Holt & Co; 0-8050),* 521 Fifth Ave., New York, NY 10175 (SAN 200-6472) Tel 212-599-7600. Former trade-book arm of Holt, Rinehart & Winston. Acquired in 1985 by Verlagsgruppe Georg von Holtzbrinck, from CBS. *Imprints:* North-South Books (North South Bks).

Holt Associates, *(Holt Assocs; 0-913677),* 729 Boylston St., Boston, MA 02116 (SAN 286-1119) Tel 617-437-1550. *Imprints:* Pinchpenny Press (Pub. by Pinchpenny Pr).

Holt-Atherton Ctr. for Western Studies, *(Holt-Atherton; 0-931156),* Univ. of the Pacific, Stockton, CA 95211 (SAN 203-1884) Tel 209-946-2404.

Holt College Dept. *See* **Holt, Rinehart & Winston, Inc.**

Holt Elementary Bks. *See* **Holt, Rinehart & Winston, Inc.**

Holt Information Systems *See* **Holt, Rinehart & Winston, Inc.**

Holt, Rinehart & Winston, Inc., Div. of CBS College Publishing, *(HR&W; 0-03),* 383 Madison Ave., New York, NY 10017 (SAN 200-2108) Tel 212-750-1330. *Imprints:* Holt College Department (HoltC); Holt Elementary Books (HoltE); Holt Information Systems (HIS); Owl Books (Owl Bks).

Holtvluwer, Meyers, & John, Ltd., *(HMJ Ltd; 0-938431),* 1322 Edna, SE, Grand Rapids, MI 49507 (SAN 661-2938) Tel 616-243-0538.

Holtz-Carter Pubns., *(Holtz Carter; 0-9613701),* 4326 Dyes Inlet Rd., NW, Bremerton, WA 98312 (SAN 677-1297) Tel 206-377-2432.

Holtzman Press, Inc., *(Holtzman Pr; 0-941372),* 1225 Forest Ave., Evanston, IL 60202 (SAN 238-8847) Tel 312-475-5163.

†**Holy Cow! Pr.,** *(Holy Cow; 0-930100),* P.O. Box 2692, Iowa City, IA 52244 (SAN 685-3315); *CIP.*

†**Holy Cross Orthodox Press,** *(Holy Cross Orthodox; 0-917651),* 50 Goddard Ave., Brookline, MA 02146 (SAN 208-6840) Tel 617-731-3500; *CIP.*

Holy Transfiguration Monastery *See* **St. Nectarios Pr.**

Holy Trinity Episcopal Church, *(Holy Episcopal; 0-9615284),* 95 Folly Rd., Charleston, SC 29407 (SAN 694-552X) Tel 803-556-2560.

Holy Trinity Monastery, *(Holy Trinity; 0-88465),* Jordanville, NY 13361 (SAN 207-3501) Tel 315-858-0940.

Holy Trinity Orthodox Church, *(Holy Trinity Ortho; 0-930055),* P.O.Box 3707, Reston, VA 22090 (SAN 669-8557) Tel 202-287-9322.

Homana Pubns., *(Homana Pubns; 0-915563),* 3430 E. Tropicana, Suite 44, Las Vegas, NV 89121 (SAN 292-5354) Tel 702-435-8673.

Home & School Press, *(Home & Sch; 0-910742),* P.O. Box 2055, Sun City, AZ 85372 (SAN 204-0662) Tel 602-974-3063.

Home Business News, *(Home Business News; 0-933589),* 12221 Beaver Pike, Jackson, OH 45640 (SAN 692-2163) Tel 614-988-2331.

Home-Business Press, *(Home-Busn Pr; 0-939626),* 10855 S. Western Ave., Chicago, IL 60643 (SAN 216-3942).

Home Company, The, *(Home Co),* 13156 E. Dakota Ave., Aurora, CO 80012 (SAN 283-2348) Tel 303-364-3623.

Home Design Publications, Inc. *See Breland & Farmer, Designers, Inc.*

Home Economics Education Assn., *(Home Econ Educ; 0-911365),* 1201 16th St. NW, Rm. 232, Washington, DC 20036 (SAN 207-3307) Tel 202-822-7844.

Home Economist Consulting Services, *(Home Ec Consult; 0-941294),* P.O. Box 13112, Arlington, TX 76013 (SAN 238-8855).

Home Equity Co., *(Home Equity),* 600 SW Tenth St., Room 502, Portland, OR 97205 (SAN 204-0670) Tel 503-224-4522.

†**Home Mission Board of the Southern Baptist Convention,** *(Home Mission; 0-937170),* 1350 Spring St., NW, Atlanta, GA 30367 (SAN 207-5318) Tel 404-873-4041; *CIP.*

Home of Frosted Sunshine, The, *(Home Frosted; 0-937118),* R.R. 1, Box 612, Shermans Dale, PA 17090 (SAN 215-7756).

Home on Arrange, *(Home on Arrange; 0-9605758),* 2044 Paradise Dr., Tiburon, CA 94920 (SAN 216-2547).

Home Planners, Inc., *(Home Planners; 0-918894),* 23761 Research Dr., Farmington Hills, MI 48024 (SAN 201-5382) Tel 313-477-1850; Toll free: 800-521-6797; Dist. by: HP Bks., P.O. Box 5367, Tucson, AZ 85703 (SAN 201-6087) Tel 602-888-2150; Toll free: 800-528-4923.

Home Run Pr., *(Home Run Pr; 0-917125),* P.O. Box 432A, RD 1, Lake Hopatcong, NJ 07849 (SAN 655-8143) Tel 201-663-2886.

Home Schl. Headquarters Pr., *(Home Schl Headquarters; 0-9615578),* P.O. Box 366, Fremont, NE 68025 (SAN 696-2092) Tel 402-727-9642; 325 W. Eighth St., Fremont, NE 68025 (SAN 696-2106); Dist. by: Blue Bird Publishing, 1428 W. Broad St., No. 202, Columbus, OH 43222 (SAN 200-5603) Tel 614-275-6275.

Home-Science Pubs., Subs. of Mitchell & Webb Inc., *(Home-Science; 0-943440),* 839 Beacon St., Boston, MA 02215 (SAN 240-6756) Tel 617-262-6980.

Home Sweet Home Pubns., Div. of LCS Music Group, *(Home Sweet Home; 0-9616817),* P.O. Box 202406, Dallas, TX 75220 (SAN 661-1370); 6126 Meadow Rd., Dallas, TX 75230 (SAN 661-1389) Tel 214-869-2773.

Home Vision, Div. of Public Media, Inc., *(Home Vision; 0-938957),* 5547 N. Ravenswood Ave., Chicago, IL 60640 (SAN 661-7204); Toll free: 800-323-4222.

Homebuilt Pubns., *(Homebuilt Pubns; 0-9614882),* P.O. Box 4397, Glendale, CA 91202 (SAN 693-2444) Tel 818-244-5007; Dist. by: Mathew Nottonson & Co., Inc., 10945 Burbank Blvd., North Hollywood, CA 91601 (SAN 200-6812) Tel 818-985-0344; Dist. by: Motorbooks International, P.O. Box 2, Osceola, WI 54020 (SAN 169-9164) Tel 715-294-3345; Toll free: 800-826-6600.

Homefront Graphics, *(Homefront Graphics; 0-939374),* P.O. Box 4114, Santa Barbara, CA 93103 (SAN 216-4892) Tel 805-965-8841.

Homeland Pubns., *(Homeland Pubns; 0-939445),* 1808 Capri Ln., Seabrook, TX 77586 (SAN 663-3587) Tel 713-474-4730.

Homespun Pr., *(Homespun Pr; 0-915519),* 2210 Wilshire Blvd., Suite 741, Santa Monica, CA 90403 (SAN 291-1906) Tel 213-394-6518.

Homestead Book, Inc., *(Homestead Bk; 0-930180),* 6101 22nd Ave., NW, Seattle, WA 98107 (SAN 169-8796) Tel 206-782-4532; Toll free: 800-426-6777; Orders to: P.O. Box 31608, Seattle, WA 98103 (SAN 662-037X).

Homestead Books, *(Homestead NY),* Brookfield, NY 13314 (SAN 210-7422).

Homestead Pubs., *(Homestead MI; 0-913529),* 10084 Rushton Rd., South Lyon, MI 48178 (SAN 285-1679) Tel 313-437-6782.

Homestead Publishers, *(Homestead Pub; 0-913529),* P.O. Box 219, Twentynine Palms, CA 92277 (SAN 262-0391) Tel 619-367-7726.

Homestead Publishing, *(Homestead WY; 0-943972),* Box 193, Moose, WY 83012 (SAN 241-029X) Tel 307-733-6287.

Homeward Pr., *(Homeward Pr; 0-938392),* P.O. Box 2307, Berkeley, CA 94702 (SAN 220-2522).

Homosexual Information Center, Inc., Affil. of The Tangent Group, *(Homosexual Info),* 6758 Hollywood Blvd., No. 208, Hollywood, CA 90028 (SAN 210-8127) Tel 213-464-8431.

Hondale, Inc., *(Hondale; 0-942462),* 553 Auburndale Ave., Akron, OH 44313 (SAN 238-1664) Tel 216-867-9701.

Honduras Information Service, *(Honduras Info; 0-937538),* 501 Fifth Ave., Suite 1611, New York, NY 10017 (SAN 213-084X) Tel 212-490-0766.

Honey Hill Publishing Co., *(Honey Hill; 0-937642),* 1022 Bonham Terrace, Austin, TX 78704 (SAN 220-0600) Tel 512-442-4177.

Honeycomb Press, *(Honeycomb Pr; 0-9612244),* 6633 N. 8th St., Philadelphia, PA 19126 (SAN 287-7295) Tel 215-548-8453.

Honolulu He'e, *(Honolulu H; 0-9612452),* 2543 Saul Place, Honolulu, HI 96816 (SAN 289-2707) Tel 808-737-2024.

Honolulu Japanese Chamber of Commerce, *(Honolulu Japanese),* 2454 S. Beretania St., Honolulu, HI 96826 (SAN 225-6215).

Honor Books, *(Honor Bks; 0-931446),* P.O. Box 641, Rapid City, SD 57709 (SAN 208-0877).

Honor Publishing Co., *(Honor Pub),* P.O. Box 932, Greenwood, MS 38930 (SAN 693-0913); 802 W. President, Greenwood, MS 38930 (SAN 662-3123) Tel 601-453-1584.

Honor Society of Phi Kappa Phi, *(Honor Soc P K P; 0-9614651),* P.O. Box 16000 Louisiana State Univ., Baton Rouge, LA 70893 (SAN 283-9776) Tel 504-388-4917.

Hood, Alan C., Pub., *(A C Hood Pub; 0-911469),* RR 3, Box 12, Putney, VT 05346 (SAN 270-8221) Tel 802-387-4309; Dist. by: Countryman Pr., P.O. Box 175, Woodstock, VT 05091 (SAN 206-4901) Tel 802-457-1049.

Hoofnagle Graphics, *(Hoofnagle Graph; 0-9616468),* 513 E. 25th Ave., No. 3, Anchorage, AK 99503 (SAN 659-2449) Tel 907-261-0061.

Hooper, Doug, *(D Hooper; 0-9604702),* P.O. Box 792, Danville, CA 94526 (SAN 217-2402).

Hooper Publishing Co., *(Hooper Pub Co; 0-9613648),* P.O. Box 875, Lovington, NM 88260 (SAN 670-767X) Tel 505-396-3741.

Hoover, Herbert, Presidential Library & Assn., Inc., *(Hoover Lib; 0-938469),* P.O. Box 696, West Branch, IA 52358 (SAN 224-229X); Parkside Dr., West Branch, IA 52358 (SAN 658-0858) Tel 619-643-5327.

†**Hoover Institution Pr.,** Affil. of Hoover Institution, *(Hoover Inst Pr; 0-8179),* Stanford Univ., Stanford, CA 94305-2323 (SAN 202-3024) Tel 415-723-3373; Dist. by: East-West Export Bks., Univ. Pr. of Hawaii, 2840 Kolowalu St., Honolulu, HI 96822 (SAN 200-738X) Tel 808-948-8255; *CIP.*

Hope, Orville L., *(O L Hope),* 425 E. Davidson Ave., Gastonia, NC 28054 (SAN 659-9605).

Hope Enterprises of Jacksonville, Florida, Inc., *(Hope Ent Fla; 0-932650),* Box 8401, Jacksonville, FL 32211 (SAN 211-5298).

Hope Farm Press & Bookshop, *(Hope Farm; 0-910746),* Strong Rd., Cornwallville, NY 12418 (SAN 696-4807) Tel 518-239-4745.

Hope Pr., *(Hope Pr; 0-9615878),* P.O. Box 40611, Washington, DC 20016-0611 (SAN 696-835X) Tel 202-337-4507; 3923 Georgetown Ct., NW, Washington, DC 20007 (SAN 696-8368).

Hope Publishing Co., *(Hope Pub; 0-916642),* 380 S. Main Pl., Carol Stream, IL 60188 (SAN 208-3361) Tel 312-665-3200; Toll free: 800-323-1049.

Hope Publishing Hse., Subs. of S. Calif. Ecumenical Council, *(Hope Pub Hse; 0-932727),* P.O. Box 60008, Pasadena, CA 91106 (SAN 688-4849) Tel 818-792-2121.

Hopewood Press, *(Hopewood Pr; 0-936286),* P.O. Box 27541, Minneapolis, MN 55427 (SAN 215-0816).

Hopkins Syndicate, Inc., *(Hopkins; 0-910748),* Hopkins Bldg., Mellott, IN 47958 (SAN 204-0700) Tel 317-295-2253.

Hoppin, Ruth, *(R Hoppin; 0-9615957),* 15 Portola Ave., Daly City, CA 94015 (SAN 697-2985) Tel 415-992-3179.

Horatio Publishing Co., *(Horatio Pub Co; 0-915879),* Jamestown Star Rte., Boulder, CO 80302 (SAN 294-037X) Tel 303-449-1360.

Horizon Bks., *(Hor Bks MI; 0-915937),* 224 E. Front, Traverse City, MI 49684 (SAN 294-0388) Tel 616-946-7290.

Horizon Bks., *(Horizon Bks CA; 0-938840),* P.O. Box 3083, Fremont, CA 94539 (SAN 216-0390) Tel 415-657-6439.

Horizon Communications Pubs./Distributors, *(Horizon Comms; 0-913945),* 2710 San Diego, SE, Albuquerque, NM 87106 (SAN 286-7761) Tel 505-266-3431.

Horizon Pr., *(Horizon; 0-8180),* P.O. Box 402, New York, NY 10108 (SAN 202-3040) Tel 212-757-4420.

Horizon Pubs. & Distributors, Inc., *(Horizon Utah; 0-88290),* P.O. Box 490, 50 S. 500 West, Bountiful, UT 84010 (SAN 159-4885) Tel 801-295-9451; Toll free: 800-453-0812.

Horizon Trust Co., *(Horizon Trust; 0-9616335),* 1200 N. Federal Hwy., Suite 413, Boca Raton, FL 33432 (SAN 658-8689) Tel 305-394-4441.

†**Horn Bk., Inc.,** *(Horn Bk; 0-87675),* 31 St. James Ave., Park Sq. Bldg., Boston, MA 02116 (SAN 202-3059) Tel 617-482-5198; Toll free: 800-325-1170; *CIP.*

Horn of the Moon Enterprises, *(Horn Moon Ent; 0-9614070),* RRl, Box 5100, Montpelier, VT 05602 (SAN 686-0222) Tel 802-229-4220.

Hornbeam Press, Inc., *(Hornbeam Pr; 0-917496),* 6520 Courtwood Dr., Columbia, SC 29206 (SAN 209-0325) Tel 803-782-7667.

Horse & Bird Press, The, *(Horse & Bird; 0-9602214),* Pfieffer Ridge, RC1 Box 4726, Big Sur, CA 93920 (SAN 281-7888) Tel 408-667-2433; Dist. by: The Distributors, 702 S. Michigan, South Bend, IN 46618 (SAN 169-2488) Tel 219-232-8500; Dist. by: Bookpeople, 2929 Fifth St., Berkeley, CA 94710 (SAN 168-9517) Tel 415-549-3030; Dist. by: The New Leaf Distributing, 1020 White St., SW, Atlanta, GA 30310 (SAN 169-1449) Tel 404-755-2665; Dist. by: Starlite Distributors, P.O. Box 20729, Reno, NV 89515 (SAN 131-1921).

Horsesense, Inc., *(Horsesense Inc; 0-9613034),* 4760 Thatchwood Dr., Manlius, NY 13104 (SAN 294-0108) Tel 315-637-6689.

Horsethief Pubns., *(Horsethief Pubns; 0-9613777),* 334 W. Hyman, Aspen, CO 81611 (SAN 678-9730) Tel 303-925-3220.

Horticultural Books, Inc., *(Horticult FL; 0-9600046),* P.O. Box 107, Stuart, FL 33495 (SAN 204-0735) Tel 305-287-1091.

Horticultural Pubns., *(Horticult Pubns; 0-938378),* 3906 NW 31st Place, Gainesville, FL 32606 (SAN 216-1389) Tel 904-392-1753.

Horticultural Research Institute, Inc., Affil. of American Assn. Nurserymen, *(Horticult Research; 0-935336),* 1250 I St. NW, Suite 500, Washington, DC 20005 (SAN 213-3210) Tel 202-789-2900.

†**Horton, Thomas, & Daughters,** *(T Horton & Dghts; 0-913878),* 26662 S. Newtown Dr., Sun Lakes, AZ 85248 (SAN 201-5331) Tel 602-895-0480; *CIP.*

Horvath Sculpture & Graphics, Inc., *(Horvath Sculpture; 0-9616359),* 1121 Cosper Pl., Rockford, IL 61107 (SAN 658-8700) Tel 815-965-0120; Dist. by: Alan L. Horvath Memorial Pubns., 68 Marco Ln., Centerville, OH 45459 (SAN 663-3161) Tel 513-434-8573.

Hoskins, Linus A., *(L A Hoskins; 0-9613067),* 2611 Nicholson St. Apt. 2, Hyattsville, MD 20782 (SAN 294-8370) Tel 301-559-0361.

Hospital Compensation Service, Subs. of John R. Zabka Assocs., Inc., *(Hosp Compensation),* P.O. Box 321, Hawthorne, NJ 07507 (SAN 217-1090); 155 Watchung Dr., Hawthorne, NY 07507 (SAN 662-0396).

Hospital Council of Southern California, *(Hosp Council S Cal; 0-939089),* 6255 Sunset Blvd., Suite 817, Los Angeles, CA 90028 (SAN 662-9016) Tel 213-469-7311.

Names

†**Hospital Research & Educational Trust,** Affil. of American Hospital Assn., *(Hosp Res & Educ; 0-87914),* 840 N. Lake Shore Dr., Chicago, IL 60611 (SAN 206-9121) Tel 312-280-6620; Toll free: 800-AHA-2626; Orders to: AHA Services, Inc., 4444 W. Ferdinand, Chicago, IL 60626 (SAN 662-040X); *CIP.*

Hospitality Publications Inc., *(Hosp Pubns; 0-932235),* P.O. Box 448, Okemos, MI 48864 (SAN 686-5801) Tel 517-676-4030.

Host, Jim, & Associates, Inc., *(Host Assoc; 0-934554),* 120 Kentucky Ave., Suite A-1, Lexington, KY 40502 (SAN 216-1400).

Hot Chocolate Books *See* Coffee Hse. Pr., Toothpaste Pr.

Hot Hse. Pr., *(Hot House Pr; 0-9616939),* 411 W. Drew St., Houston, TX 77006 (SAN 661-8006) Tel 713-528-6288.

Hot off the Pr., *(Hot off Pr; 0-9605904; 0-933491),* 7212 S. Seven Oaks, Canby, OR 97013 (SAN 216-3977) Tel 503-266-8306.

Hot Water Publishing Co., *(Hot Water Pubs; 0-941904),* P.O. Box 773783, Eagle River, AK 99577 (SAN 239-2283) Tel 907-694-8644.

Hotchkiss House, Inc., *(Hotchkiss House; 0-912220),* 14 Shelter Creek Ln., Fairport, NY 14450 (SAN 159-5415).

Hotel Sales and Marketing Association, *(Hotel Sales Mgmt Assn),* 1400 K St., Suite 810, Washington, DC 20005 (SAN 224-7925) Tel 202-789-0089.

Hothem Hse., *(Hothem Hse; 0-9617041),* P.O. Box 458, Lancaster, OH 43130 (SAN 662-8591); 1650 Northwood Dr., Lancaster, OH 43130 (SAN 662-8605) Tel 614-653-9030.

Hotline Multi-Enterprises, *(Hotline Multi-Ent; 0-935864),* 2709 Georgetown Rd., Mechanicsville, VA 23111 (SAN 214-3860) Tel 804-746-4450.

Houghton Mifflin Co., *(HM; 0-395; 0-87466),* 1 Beacon St., Boston, MA 02108 (SAN 200-2388) Tel 617-725-5000; Toll free: 800-225-3362; Orders to: Wayside Rd., Burlington, MA 01803 (SAN 215-3793) Tel 617-272-1500. *Imprints:* Houghton Trade Books (HoughtonT); Piper Books (Piper); Riverside Editions (RivEd); Riverside Literature Series (RivLit); Riverside Reading Series (RRS); Riverside Studies in Literature (RivSL); Sandpiper Paperbacks (Sandpiper); Sentry Editions (SenEd).

Houghton Mifflin Software, Reference Div., *(HM Soft-Ref Div; 0-395),* 1 Beacon St., Boston, MA 02108 (SAN 654-9438) Tel 617-725-5000.

Houghton Trade Bks. *See* Houghton Mifflin Co.

Hour Pr., *(Hour Press; 0-939131),* P.O. Box 12743, Northgate Sta., San Rafael, CA 94913-2743 (SAN 662-4863) Tel 415-883-1539.

Hour Publishing, *(Hour Pub; 0-931343),* 24 Westminster, Venice, CA 90291 (SAN 681-8323) Tel 213-399-3901.

Hourglass Publishing, *(Hourglass Pub; 0-932479),* P.O. Box 924, Salida, CO 81201 (SAN 687-4258) Tel 303-539-2058.

Housatonuc Bookshop, *(Housatonuc; 0-910756),* Main St., Salisbury, CT 06068 (SAN 201-5447) Tel 203-435-2100.

House, Deanna, Specialties, Inc., *(Deanna Hse; 0-9610752),* Box 492, Portage, MI 49081 (SAN 264-7508) Tel 616-327-4571.

House by the Sea Publishing Co., *(Hse by the Sea),* 8610 Highway 101, Waldport, OR 97394 (SAN 212-9477).

House of Better Sales, *(Hse Better Sales; 0-9617290),* P.O. Box 2163, Ocala, FL 32678-2163 (SAN 663-5954); 818 SW Fort King St., Ocala, FL 32674 (SAN 663-5962).

House of Charles, *(Hse of Charles; 0-9605344),* 4833 NE 238th Ave., Vancouver, WA 98662 (SAN 215-8728) Tel 206-892-1589.

House of Collectibles, Inc., *(Hse of Collectibles; 0-87637),* 1904 Premier Row, Orlando, FL 32809 (SAN 202-3113) Tel 305-857-9095; Toll free: 800-327-1384.

House of Haig, *(Hse of Haig; 0-9615331),* 19 Sea Meadow Dr., Tuckerton, NJ 08087 (SAN 695-0922) Tel 609-296-8257; Orders to: House of Haig, P.O. Box 1068, Tuckerton, NJ 08087 (SAN 662-3433).

House of Peace, *(Hse of Peace; 0-936269),* P.O. Box 153, Yonkers, NY 10703 (SAN 697-8762) Tel 914-963-3197; 10 Flagg St., Yonkers, NY 10703 (SAN 698-2263).

House of Print, *(House of Print),* 322 Benzel Ave., Madelia, MN 56062 (SAN 211-0687) Tel 507-642-3298.

House of Starr, Inc., *(Hse of Starr; 0-938857),* 120 Kenmore Ave., Council Bluffs, IA 51501 (SAN 661-7042) Tel 712-328-8329.

House of Tomorrow Publishing Co., *(Hse of Tomorrow; 0-913609),* P.O. Box 931, Weaverville, CA 96093 (SAN 285-287X) Tel 916-623-6525.

House of UKE Pubns., Inc., *(Hse UKE Pubns; 0-937749),* 1610 N. Argyle Ave., Suite 109, Hollywood, CA 90078 (SAN 659-2457) Tel 213-462-7918.

House of York, *(Hse of York; 0-916660),* P.O. Box 311, Aromas, CA 95004 (SAN 208-2357) Tel 408-726-2025.

House ov Day Vid, *(Hse ov Day Vid; 0-912672),* 978 Amherst St., Apt. 6, Buffalo, NY 14216 (SAN 204-0778) Tel 716-873-8856.

Housesmith's Press, *(Housesmith's; 0-918238),* P.O. Box 157, Kittery Point, ME 03905 (SAN 210-2102) Tel 207-439-0638.

Housing Connection, The, *(Housing Connect; 0-9609586),* P.O. Box 5536, Arlington, VA 22205 (SAN 262-0405) Tel 703-243-6805.

Houston, Charles S., *(Houston C; 0-9612246),* 77 Ledge Rd., Burlington, VT 05401 (SAN 220-2727) Tel 802-863-6441.

Houston, Estelle, *(E Houston; 0-9615652),* 110 W. Gaviota Ave., San Clemente, CA 92672 (SAN 696-4710) Tel 714-492-0654.

Houston, Sam, State Univ., Institute on Contemporary Corrections & the Behavioral Sciences, *(S Houston Corrections),* Huntsville, TX 77340 (SAN 226-3726).

Houston, Sam, State Univ., National Employment Listing Service, *(S Houston Employ),* Texas Criminal Justice Ctr., Huntsville, TX 77340 (SAN 226-3688).

Houston Home, Garden Magazine Books *See* Bayland Publishing, Inc.

Houston Law Review, *(Houston Law Review; 0-913797),* 3801 Cullen Blvd., Houston, TX 77004 (SAN 226-5427) Tel 713-374-2616.

Houston Publishing, *(Houston Pub; 0-9616818),* 760 Rosewood Dr., Reno, NV 89509 (SAN 661-1192) Tel 702-826-6326.

Hover Co., The, *(Hover; 0-934414),* 14713 La Mesa Dr., La Mirada, CA 90638 (SAN 213-747X) Tel 714-521-3046.

Hovnanian, Ralph R., *(Hovnanian; 0-9607774),* 2128 Prospect Ave., Evanston, IL 60201 (SAN 241-5399).

How-To Bks., *(How-To Bks; 0-9615231),* Box 8234, Northfield, IL 60093 (SAN 695-1708) Tel 312-446-1607.

How-to Press, *(How-to Pr; 0-938356),* P.O. Box 483, Arlington, TX 76010 (SAN 215-7764).

Howard, Allen, Enterprises, Inc., *(Howard Allen; 0-914576),* P.O. Box 76, Cape Canaveral, FL 32920 (SAN 203-4662).

Howard, Barney, *(B Howard; 0-935602),* 2206 Meadowlark Ln., Harrisonville, MO 64701 (SAN 214-0314) Tel 816-884-5461.

Howard, Daniel L., *(D L Howard; 0-936144),* P.O. Box 41432, Los Angeles, CA 90041 (SAN 213-9316) Tel 213-258-2121.

Howard, Leslie, Pubns., *(L Howard Pubns; 0-937717),* 140 Duboce Ave., Suite 204, San Francisco, CA 94103 (SAN 659-2465) Tel 415-863-1238.

Howard, Marilyn Serrett, *(M Serrett Howard; 0-9616125),* 5106 Pre-Emption Rd., Geneva, NY 14456 (SAN 699-7244) Tel 315-781-0031.

Howard & Assocs., *(Howard & Assocs; 0-935801),* P.O. Box 263, Fortuna, CA 95540 (SAN 696-8384) Tel 707-725-2987; 1727 Main St., Suite C, Fortuna, CA 95540 (SAN 696-8392).

Howard Publishing, *(Howard Pub; 0-9614225),* 121 N. Fir St., Suite C, Ventura, CA 93001 (SAN 686-7618) Tel 805-648-2092.

†**Howard Univ. Pr.,** *(Howard U Pr; 0-88258),* 2900 Van Ness St. NW, Washington, DC 20008 (SAN 202-3067) Tel 202-686-6696; *CIP.*

Howarth Pr., Inc., The, *(Howarth Pr; 0-939533),* P.O. Box 2608, Falls Church, VA 22042-0608 (SAN 663-4362); 7306 Brad St., Falls Church, VA 22042 (SAN 663-4370) Tel 703-573-8521.

Howe, Shirley Swift, *(S S Howe; 0-9616538),* 39617 CR 669, Decatur, MI 49045 (SAN 659-4662).

†**Howe Brothers,** *(Howe Brothers; 0-935704),* Box 6394, Salt Lake City, UT 84106 (SAN 222-0318) Tel 801-485-7409; 1127 Wilmington Ave., Salt Lake City, UT 84106 (SAN 658-2214); *CIP.*

Howe Street Press, The, *(Howe St Pr; 0-9609666),* 212 E. Howe St., Seattle, WA 98102 (SAN 270-8507).

Howell, Will C., *(W C Howell; 0-9601140),* 185 E. Norton, Sherwood, OR 97140 (SAN 210-2110) Tel 503-625-7409.

†**Howell Bk. Hse., Inc.,** *(Howell Bk; 0-87605),* Helmsley Bldg., 230 Park Ave., New York, NY 10169 (SAN 202-3075) Tel 212-986-4488; *CIP.*

Howell-North Bks., Inc., Div. of Howell North-Darwin-Superior, *(Howell North; 0-8310),* 850 N. Hollywood Way, Burbank, CA 91505 (SAN 202-3083) Tel 818-848-0944.

Howell Pr., Subs. of Max Communications, *(Howell Pr; 0-936975),* 611 W. Main St., Louisville, KY 40202 (SAN 658-7879) Tel 508-589-7603.

Howell Pr., Inc., *(Howell Pr VA; 0-9616878),* 2000 Holiday Dr., Charlottesville, VA 22901 (SAN 661-6607) Tel 804-977-4006. Do not confuse with Howell Pr., Louisville, KY.

HOW(ever), *(HOWever; 0-933539),* 554 Jersey St., San Francisco, CA 94114 (SAN 691-8646) Tel 415-282-8873; Dist. by: Small Press Distribution, 1784 Shattuck Ave., Berkeley, CA 94702 (SAN 204-5826) Tel 415-549-3336; Dist. by: Inland Bk. Co., P.O. Box 261, 22 Hemingway Ave., East Haven, CT 06512 (SAN 200-4151) Tel 203-467-4257.

Hoyle Bks., *(Hoyle Bks; 0-937351),* HBU 27, Petrolia, CA 95558 (SAN 658-8719) Tel 415-525-0421.

HP Publishing Co., Inc., *(HP Pub Co; 0-913800),* 575 Lexington Ave., New York, NY 10022 (SAN 207-1738) Tel 212-421-7320.

HRAF Press *See* Human Relations Area Files Pr., Inc.

Hruska, Eva J. Cummings, *(Eva Hruska; 0-9614616),* Rte. 2, Schuyler, NE 68661 (SAN 691-6805) Tel 402-352-3645.

Hsin, Cheng, Pr., *(C Hsin Pr; 0-9615378),* 6601 Telegraph Ave., Oakland, CA 94609 (SAN 695-5355) Tel 415-658-0802; Dist. by: Bookpeople, 2929 Fifth St., Berkeley, CA 94710 (SAN 168-9517) Tel 415-549-3030.

HTC Publishing Co. (Hot Tub Cooks), *(HTC Pub; 0-9605582),* 10636 Main St., Suite 284, Bellevue, WA 98004 (SAN 239-8230) Tel 206-453-5569.

Hubbard, Bill, *(B Hubbard; 0-9616674),* P.O. Box 1246, Cooper Sta., New York, NY 10276 (SAN 661-180X) Tel 212-460-4673; 119-20 201st Pl., St. Albans, NY 11412 (SAN 661-1818).

Hubbard Scientific, Div. of Spectrum Industries, *(Hubbard Sci; 0-8331),* P.O. Box 104, 1946 Raymond Dr., Northbrook, IL 60062 (SAN 202-3121) Tel 312-272-7810; Toll free: 800-323-8368.

Huber/Copeland Publishing, *(Huber-Copeland Pub; 0-934293),* P.O. Box 665, Mattoon, IL 61938 (SAN 693-2657) Tel 317-872-4472.

Huddleston-Brown Pubs., Inc., *(Huddleston-Brown Pubs; 0-934355),* 18 Lewis Ln., Port Washington, NY 11050 (SAN 693-6148) Tel 516-944-3593.

†**Hudson Hills Pr., Inc.,** *(Hudson Hills; 0-933920),* 230 Fifth Ave., Suite 1308, New York, NY 10001-7704 (SAN 213-0815) Tel 212-889-3090; Dist. by: Rizzoli International Pubns., Inc., 597 Fifth Ave., New York, NY 10017 (SAN 207-7000) Tel 212-223-0100; *CIP.*

Hudson Institute, *(Hudson Inst),* Quaker Ridge Rd, Croton-on-Hudson, NY 10520 (SAN 225-7122) Tel 914-762-0700.

Hudson-Mohawk Association of Colleges & Universities, *(Hudson-Mohawk),* 91 Fiddlers Lane, Latham, NY 12110 (SAN 241-5402) Tel 518-785-3219.

Hudson Review, The, *(Hudson Rev),* 684 Park Ave., New York, NY 10021 (SAN 209-2859) Tel 212-650-0020.

Hudson River Sloop Clearwater, *(Hudson Clearwater)*, 112 Market St., Poughkeepsie, NY 12601 (SAN 225-316X) Tel 914-454-7673.

Huebner, S. S., Foundation for Insurance Education, *(Huebner Foun Insur; 0-918930)*, 3641 Locust Walk CE, Philadelphia, PA 19104 (SAN 211-6405) Tel 215-898-5644; Dist. by: Richard D. Irwin, Inc., 1818 Ridge Rd., Homewood, IL 60430 (SAN 206-8400) Tel 312-798-6000.

†**Huenefeld Co., Inc.,** *(Huenefeld Co; 0-931932)*, P.O. Box U, Bedford, MA 01730 (SAN 211-5662) Tel 617-861-9650; *CIP.*

Huffman Press, *(Huffman Pr)*, 805 N. Royal St., Alexandria, VA 22314 (SAN 208-0826) Tel 703-683-1695.

Huggy Bears Inc., *(Huggy Bears; 0-9614134)*, 28230 Orchard Lake Rd., Farmington Hills, MI 48018 (SAN 686-516X) Tel 313-626-8850.

Hughes, Clarence, *(C Hughes)*, P.O. Box 451, Annawan, IL 61234 (SAN 208-1229) Tel 309-935-6715.

Hughes, T. A., Pubns., *(TA Hughes Pubns; 0-9614866)*, 905 Aaron Dr., Columbia, SC 29203 (SAN 693-3327) Tel 803-754-4855.

Hughes Enterprises, *(Hughes Enter; 0-9608106)*, 1001 N. Calvert St., Baltimore, MD 21202 (SAN 205-3047) Tel 301-837-8271.

Hughes Press, *(Hughes Pr; 0-912560)*, 500 23rd St. NW, Box B203, Washington, DC 20037 (SAN 210-9360) Tel 202-293-2686.

Hughes Publishing Co., *(Hughes Pub; 0-9604772)*, 453 De Soto St., El Paso, TX 79912 (SAN 217-7781) Tel 915-584-0276.

Hughes Publishing Co., *(Hughes Pub Co; 0-9616112)*, 640 Church St., San Francisco, CA 94114 (SAN 699-7104) Tel 415-626-4653.

Hughley Pubns., *(Hughley Pubns; 0-9605150)*, P.O. Box 261, Springfield Gardens, NY 11413 (SAN 215-8078) Tel 718-712-5892.

Huguenot Historical Society, *(Huguenot Hist)*, P.O. Box 339, New Paltz, NY 12561 (SAN 234-4211) Tel 914-255-1660; 18 Brodhead Ave., New Paltz, NY 12561 (SAN 669-0955).

Huguley, John, Co., Inc., *(Huguley Co; 0-9605064)*, 269 King St., Charleston, SC 29401 (SAN 215-8736) Tel 803-577-2721.

Hugworks, *(Hugworks; 0-936835)*, 29161 Grove, Livonia, MI 48154 (SAN 699-8585) Tel 313-522-2092.

Huh Pubns., *(Huh Pubns; 0-938642)*, P.O. Box 30782, Santa Barbara, CA 93105 (SAN 222-9765).

Hui-Hanai, Queen Liliuokalani Childrens Center, *(Hui-Hanai-Queen)*, Dist. by: Press Pacifica, P.O. Box 47, Kailua, HI 96734 (SAN 169-1635).

Hull, Harry H., *(Hull; 0-9606118)*, 1710 Del Webb Blvd., Sun City Center, FL 33570 (SAN 281-7942) Tel 813-634-4967; c/o Albert E. Deeds Associates, 318 Martin Bldg,119 Federal St., Pittsburgh, PA 15212 (SAN 281-7950) Tel 412-323-1616.

Hull, William H., Pub., *(W H Hull; 0-939330)*, 6833 Creston Rd., Minneapolis, MN 55435 (SAN 220-1690) Tel 612-926-1327.

Hulogos'i Communications, Inc., *(Hulogos'i Inc; 0-938493)*, P.O. Box 1188, Eugene, OR 97440 (SAN 661-4132); 454 Willamette St., Eugene, OR 97401 (SAN 661-4140) Tel 503-343-0606.

Human Behavior Research Group, Inc., *(Human Behavior; 0-939552)*, P.O. Box 17122, Irvine, CA 92713 (SAN 216-6801) Tel 714-786-6946.

Human Conservancy Press, *(Human Conserv Pr; 0-9612052)*, 838 Grant St., Denver, CO 80203 (SAN 283-9164) Tel 303-830-2714.

Human Development & Educational Laboratories, Inc., *(Human Dev Educ Lab; 0-939309)*, P.O. Box 27247, Orlando, FL 32867-7274 (SAN 663-1509); Dist. by: Stackpole Bks., Cameron & Kelker Sts., Harrisburg, PA 17105 (SAN 202-5396) Tel 717-234-5041.

Human Development Press, *(Human Dev Pr; 0-938024)*, 10701 Lomas NE, 210, Albuquerque, NM 87112 (SAN 215-6555) Tel 505-292-0370.

Human Equations, Inc., *(Human Equat; 0-915159)*, World Trade Center, Suite 544, Baltimore, MD 21202 (SAN 289-9477) Tel 301-539-0344.

Human Futures, *(Human Futures; 0-932385)*, P.O. Box 893, Hermosa Beach, CA 90254-0893 (SAN 687-3871).

Human Growth & Development Assocs., *(Human Growth Dev; 0-9616626)*, 1675 Fillmore St., Denver, CO 80206 (SAN 661-1796) Tel 303-320-0991.

Human Kinetics Pubs., *(Human Kinetics; 0-931250; 0-87322)*, P.O. Box 5076, Champaign, IL 61820 (SAN 211-7088); 1607 N. Market St., Champaign, IL 61820 (SAN 658-0866) Tel 217-351-5076. *Imprints:* Life Enhancement Publications (Life Enhancement).

Human Networks Inc., *(Human Netwrks; 0-933933)*, 3517 Terhune, Ann Arbor, MI 48104 (SAN 693-0506) Tel 313-971-8342; Dist. by: Askit Co., 3517 Terhune, Ann Arbor, MI 48104 (SAN 200-7037) Tel 313-971-1034.

Human Policy Press, Div. of Center on Human Policy, Division of Special Education, Syracuse Univ., *(Human Policy Pr; 0-937540)*, P.O. Box 127, Syracuse, NY 13210 (SAN 213-8476) Tel 315-423-3851.

Human Potential Pubns., *(Human Potential; 0-939268)*, 17330 Warrington Dr., Detroit, MI 48221 (SAN 215-0832) Tel 313-341-0492.

Human Relations Area Files Pr., Inc., Affil. of Yale Univ., *(HRAFP; 0-87536)*, P.O. Box 2015, Yale Sta., New Haven, CT 06520 (SAN 200-4348); 755 Prospect St., New Haven, CT 06520 (SAN 669-0971) Tel 203-777-2334.

Human Resource Communications Group, *(Human Res Comm; 0-9609088)*, 2355 E. Stadium Blvd., Ann Arbor, MI 48104 (SAN 264-102X) Tel 313-994-9285.

Human Resource Development Pr., *(Human Res Dev Pr; 0-914234; 0-87425)*, 22 Amherst Rd., Amherst, MA 01002 (SAN 201-9213) Tel 413-253-3488; Toll free: 800-822-2801.

Human Resources Center, *(Human Res Ctr)*, Iuwillts Rd, Albertson, NY 11507 (SAN 227-0323).

Human Resources Institute, *(Human Res Inst)*, Tempe Wick Rd., Morristown, NJ 07960 (SAN 681-8234).

Human Resources Research Organization, Robotics Ctr., *(Human Resources)*, 300 N. Washington St., Alexandria, VA 22314 (SAN 207-3692) Tel 703-549-3611.

Human Rights Internet, *(Human Rights; 0-939338)*, 1338 G St. SE, Washington, DC 20003 (SAN 216-5325) Tel 202-543-9200.

†**Human Sciences Pr., Inc.,** *(Human Sci Pr; 0-87705; 0-89885)*, 72 Fifth Ave., New York, NY 10011 (SAN 200-2159) Tel 212-243-6000; Dist. by: Independent Pubs. Group, 1 Pleasant Ave., Port Washington, NY 11050 (SAN 287-2544); *CIP.*

Human Services Pr., *(Human Serv Pr; 0-9610834)*, 200 E. 24th, New York, NY 10010 (SAN 277-688X) Tel 212-679-2750.

†**Humana Pr., The,** *(Humana; 0-89603)*, P.O. Box 2148, Clifton, NJ 07015 (SAN 212-3606) Tel 201-773-4389; Crescent Manor, Clifton, NJ 07015 (SAN 658-0874); *CIP.*

Humane Society of the United States, *(Humane Soc)*, 2100 L St. NW, Washington, DC 20037 (SAN 225-8986).

†**Humanics, Ltd.,** *(Humanics Ltd; 0-89334)*, P.O. Box 7447, Atlanta, GA 30309 (SAN 208-3833) Tel 404-874-2176; Toll free: 800-874-8844; 1389 Peachtree St. NE, Suite 370, Atlanta, GA 30309 (SAN 658-0882); *CIP.*

Humanist Pr., *(Humanist Pr; 0-931779)*, 7 Harwood Dr., P.O. Box 146, Amherst, NY 14226-0146 (SAN 684-8702) Tel 716-839-5080.

Humanitarian Publishing Co., *(Humanitarian; 0-916285)*, RD 3, Clymer Rd., Quakertown, PA 18951 (SAN 295-8422) Tel 215-536-1900; Dist. by: Philosophical Pub. Co. & Humanitarian Soc., P.O. Box 220, Quakertown, PA 18951 (SAN 295-8430) Tel 215-536-5168.

Humanities & Arts Pr., *(Humanities Arts Pr; 0-9616835)*, 1 Washington Sq., English Dept., San Jose, CA 95192 (SAN 661-602X); 1761 Edgewood Rd., Redwood, CA 94062 (SAN 662-4332) Tel 415-367-1466.

Humanities Pr., International, Inc., *(Humanities; 0-391)*, 171 First Ave., Atlantic Highlands, NJ 07716-1289 (SAN 201-9272) Tel 201-872-1441; Toll free: 800-221-3845 (orders).

Humbird Enterprise, *(Humbird Ent; 0-914128)*, P.O. Box 1197, San Francisco, CA 94101 (SAN 206-9148) Tel 415-861-2333.

Humble Hills Books, *(Humble Hills; 0-935858)*, P.O. Box 7, Kalamazoo, MI 49004 (SAN 209-8466) Tel 616-343-2211.

Humble Publishing Co., *(Humble Pub Co; 0-9611756)*, 33 Ivy Trail , NE, Atlanta, GA 30342 (SAN 285-2950) Tel 404-261-3243.

Hummbird Pr., *(Hummbird Pr; 0-915161)*, 3521 Trevis Way, Carmel, CA 93923 (SAN 289-9485) Tel 408-624-0401; Dist. by: L-S Distributors, 480 Ninth St., San Francisco, CA 94103 (SAN 169-0213) Tel 415-861-6300.

Hummingbird Pr., *(Hummingbird; 0-912998)*, 2400 Hannett, NE, Albuquerque, NM 87106 (SAN 204-0794) Tel 505-268-6277.

Humphreys Academy Patrons, *(Humphreys Acad; 0-9610058)*, P.O. Box 717, Belzoni, MS 39038 (SAN 262-9070) Tel 601-247-1572.

Huna Research Inc., *(Huna Res Inc; 0-910764)*, 126 Camellia Dr., Cape Girardeau, MO 63701 (SAN 201-548X) Tel 314-334-3478; Dist. by: The Great Tradition, 750 Adrian Way, Suite 111, San Rafael, CA 94903 (SAN 200-5743) Tel 415-492-9382.

Hundred Pound Pr., The, *(Hundred Pound Pr; 0-939483)*, 4422 Whitsett Ave., No. 12A, Studio City, CA 91604 (SAN 663-2742) Tel 818-505-0472.

Hungarian Alumni Assn., *(Hungarian Alumni; 0-910539)*, P.O. Box 174, New Brunswick, NJ 08903 (SAN 260-0722) Tel 201-249-7921; Dist. by: Puski Corvin, 251 E. 82 St., New York, NY 10028 (SAN 200-7924) Tel 212-879-8893.

Hungarian Cultural Foundation, *(Hungarian Cultural; 0-914648)*, P.O. Box 364, Stone Mountain, GA 30086 (SAN 205-6240) Tel 404-377-2600.

Hungness, Carl, Publishing, *(C Hungness; 0-915088)*, P.O. Box 24308, Speedway, Indianapolis, IN 46224 (SAN 207-1193) Tel 317-638-1466; Orders to: Wilma A. Steffy, P.O. Box 24308, Speedway, IN 46224 (SAN 662-0426).

Hunt & Assocs., Consulting Engineers, *(Hunt Assocs Consult; 0-934617)*, 140 Mayhew Way, Suite 401, Pleasant Hill, CA 94523 (SAN 693-935X) Tel 415-935-3650.

Hunt Institute for Botanical Documentation, *(Hunt Inst Botanical; 0-913196)*, Carnegie-Mellon Univ., Pittsburgh, PA 15213 (SAN 206-9156) Tel 412-268-2434.

Hunter, Susan, Publishing, *(Susan Hunter; 0-932419)*, 1447 Peachtree St., NE, No. 807, Atlanta, GA 30309 (SAN 687-4126) Tel 404-874-5473.

Hunter Books, *(Hunter Bks; 0-917726)*, 201 McClellan Rd., Kingwood, TX 77339-2815 (SAN 209-2611) Tel 713-358-7575; Toll free: 800-231-3024.

Hunter Hse., Inc., *(Hunter Hse; 0-89793),* Box 1302, Claremont, CA 91711 (SAN 281-7969) Tel 714-624-2277; c/o Publisher's Services, Box 2510, Novato, CA 94948 (SAN 281-7977) Tel 415-883-3530; Dist. by: Bookpeople, 2929 Fifth St., Berkeley, CA 94710 (SAN 169-2488) Tel 415-549-3030; Dist. by: Publishers Group West, 5855 Beaudry St., Emeryville, CA 94608 (SAN 202-8522) Tel 415-658-3453; Dist. by: Distributors, The, 702 S. Michigan, South Bend, IN 46618 (SAN 212-0364) Tel 219-232-8500; Dist. by: New Leaf Distributors, The, 1020 White St., SW, Atlanta, GA 30310 (SAN 169-1449) Tel 404-658-3453; Dist. by: Quality Bks., Inc., 918 Sherwood Dr., Lake Bluff, IL 60044-2204 (SAN 169-2127) Tel 312-498-4000; Dist. by: Devorss & Co., P.O. Box 550, Marina del Rey, CA 90294 (SAN 168-9886) Tel 213-870-7478; Dist. by: Inland Bk. Co., P.O. Box 261, 22 Hemingway Ave., East Haven, CT 06512 (SAN 200-4151) Tel 203-467-4257; Dist. by: Great Tradition, The, 750 Adrian Way, Suite 111, San Rafael, CA 94903 (SAN 200-5743) Tel 415-492-9382.

Hunter Museum of Art, *(Hunter Art; 0-9615080),* 10 Bluff View, Chattanooga, TN 37403 (SAN 279-1455) Tel 615-267-0968.

Hunter Pubns., *(Hunter Pubns; 0-931019),* P.O. Box 14220, 2760-R S. Havana, Aurora, CO 80014 (SAN 678-9781) Tel 303-699-8870.

Hunter Publishing Co., *(Hunter Ariz; 0-918126),* P.O. Box 9533, Phoenix, AZ 85068 (SAN 209-2980) Tel 602-944-1022.

Hunter Publishing Co., *(Hunter Pub NC; 0-9615429),* 2505 Empire Dr., Winston-Salem, NC 27103 (SAN 696-4583) Tel 919-765-0070.

Hunter Publishing, Inc., *(Hunter Pub NY; 0-935161; 1-55650),* 300 Raritan Ctr. Pkwy., CN 94, Edison, NJ 08818 (SAN 695-3425); 155 Riverside Dr., New York, NY 10024 (SAN 663-3137) Tel 212-595-8933.

Hunter Textbooks, Inc., *(Hunter Textbks; 0-88725),* 823 Reynolds Dr., Winston-Salem, NC 27104 (SAN 209-567X) Tel 919-725-0608.

Hunterdon County Board of Agriculture, *(Hunterdon County Bd; 0-9606584),* R.D. 6, Box 48, Flemington, NJ 08822 (SAN 223-7695) Tel 201-236-2022.

Hunterdon Hse., *(Hunterdon Hse; 0-912606),* 38 Swan St., Lambertville, NJ 08530 (SAN 204-0824) Tel 609-397-2523.

Huntington, Archer M., Art Gallery, *(A M Huntington Art; 0-935213),* Univ. of Texas at Austin, 23rd & San Jacinto, Austin, TX 78712-1205 (SAN 695-7730) Tel 512-471-7324.

Huntington Hse., Inc., *(Huntington Hse Inc; 0-910311),* P.O. Box 53788, Lafayette, LA 70505 (SAN 241-5208); Toll free: 800-572-8213.

Huntington Library Pubns., *(Huntington Lib; 0-87328),* 1151 Oxford Rd., San Marino, CA 91108 (SAN 202-313X) Tel 818-405-2172.

Huntleigh House, *(Huntleigh; 0-918354),* P.O. Drawer 20602, Oklahoma City, OK 73156 (SAN 209-4487) Tel 405-751-8444.

Hurd Communications, *(Hurd Comm; 0-931021),* P.O. Box 1183, Glendale, AZ 85311 (SAN 678-979X) Tel 602-846-5853.

Hurland-Swenson Pubns., *(Hurland-Swenson; 0-9614667),* P.O. Box 283, Venice, CA 90291 (SAN 692-4778) Tel 213-827-5162; Orders to: 648 Woodlawn Ave., Venice, CA 90291 (SAN 662-2992).

Huron Shores Summer Writing Institute, *(H S S W I; 0-939345),* 445 N. Fourth St., Rogers City, MI 49779 (SAN 662-4871) Tel 517-734-3310.

Hurricane Co., The, *(Hurricane Co; 0-933272),* P.O. Box 426, Jacksonville, NC 28540 (SAN 212-7466).

Hurt, Sam, *(S Hurt; 0-9611660),* 1209 Newning Ave., Austin, TX 78704 (SAN 285-3213) Tel 512-473-2296; Dist. by: AAR/Tantalus Inc., 1600 Rio Grande, Suite 203, Austin, TX 78701 (SAN 281-2371) Tel 512-476-3225.

Hurter, Jerry, *(J Hurter; 0-9615054),* 1173 Hawkstone Dr., Cincinnati, OH 45230 (SAN 694-1370) Tel 513-231-6430.

Husher & Welch, *(Husher & Welch; 0-9603944),* 50 Nahant Rd., Nahant, MA 01908 (SAN 215-6563).

Huskey, K. W., Assocs., *(K W Huskey; 0-9604840),* P.O. Box 2715, Palm Springs, CA 92263 (SAN 659-4603).

Husky Bks. of Alaska, *(Husky Bks AK; 0-938061),* 6130 E. 12th Ave., No. C-3, Anchorage, AK 99504 (SAN 661-1834) Tel 907-337-4393.

Huston, Harvey, *(Huston; 0-9600048),* 860 Mount Pleasant St., Winnetka, IL 60093 (SAN 204-0840) Tel 312-446-1594.

Huston, John, Inc., *(J Huston; 0-9616260),* 514 Santa Monica, Corpus Christi, TX 78411 (SAN 658-344X) Tel 512-853-6512; P.O. Box 6372, Corpus Christi, TX 78411 (SAN 658-3458).

Hutar Growth Management Institute, *(Hutar; 0-918896),* 1701 E. Lake Ave. Suite 270, Glenview, IL 60025 (SAN 210-4385).

Hutchins, Jerry, Photography, *(J Hutchins; 0-9615989),* P.O. Box 84899, San Diego, CA 92138 (SAN 697-8789); 1536 E. Seventh St., National City, CA 92138 (SAN 697-8797) Tel 619-477-1320.

Hutchins Hse. See Gulf Publishing Co.

Hutchinson, Ann B., *(A B Hutchinson; 0-9615825),* 5842 S. Sheridan, Littleton, CO 80123 (SAN 696-8414) Tel 303-795-0764.

Hutchinson, Ted, *(T Hutchinson; 0-9601366),* 14 Devries Ave., N. Tarrytown, NY 10591 (SAN 209-0449) Tel 914-631-1848.

Hutchinson, William A., *(W A Hutchinson; 0-9615427),* 52 Jeffrey Ln., Amherst, MA 01002 (SAN 696-2432) Tel 413-253-7036; Dist. by: AVI Publishing Co., Inc., 250 Post Rd. E., P.O. Box 831, Westport, CT 06881 (SAN 201-4017) Tel 203-226-0738.

Hutson, Martha, Associates, *(Hutson Assoc; 0-9606126),* P.O. Box 185, Orefield, PA 18069 (SAN 215-7772) Tel 215-799-2597.

Hwong Publishing Co., *(Hwong Pub; 0-89260),* 5525 E. 7th St., Suite C, Long Beach, CA 90804 (SAN 208-2306) Tel 213-597-7743.

Hy-Teck Productions, *(Hy-Teck Prods; 0-916511),* 822 N. Ninth Ave., Wausau, WI 54401 (SAN 295-5695) Tel 715-848-2681.

Hyacinth Pr., *(Hyacinth Pr; 0-932283),* P.O. Box 15477, Santa Fe, NM 87506-0477 (SAN 696-0286).

Hybar Books, *(Hybar Bks; 0-9614345),* P.O. Box 1247, College Park, MD 20740 (SAN 687-8024) Tel 301-982-2923.

Hybrid Publishing, *(Hybrid Pub; 0-9616539),* P.O. Box 10725, Erie, PA 16510-0725 (SAN 659-4670) Tel 814-454-7833; 1520 Prospect Ave., Erie, PA 16514-0725 (SAN 659-4689).

Hyde, Arnout, *(A Hyde; 0-9604590),* 418 Lehigh Terrace, Charleston, WV 25302 (SAN 219-9750).

Hyde, Floy S., *(F S Hyde; 0-9600528),* Box 100, Owls Head, NY 12969 (SAN 205-5732).

Hyde Collection, The, *(Hyde Collect; 0-9606718),* 161 Warren St., Glens Falls, NY 12801 (SAN 219-6638) Tel 518-792-1761.

Hyde Park Press, *(Hyde Park Pr; 0-9608454),* 2302 Ellis, Boise, ID 83702 (SAN 240-4834).

Hyde School, The, *(Hyde Sch; 0-9607904),* 616 High St., Bath, ME 04530 (SAN 238-1672).

Hydraulic Institute, *(Hydraulic Inst),* 712 Lakewood Ctr. N., 14600 Detroit Ave., Cleveland, OH 44107 (SAN 224-7984) Tel 216-226-7700.

Hydronics Institute, *(Hydronics Inst),* 35 Russo Pl., Berkeley Heights, NJ 07922 (SAN 224-7887) Tel 201-464-8200.

Hyk, Doyle, Publishing Co., *(D Hyk Pub Co; 0-9615817),* P.O. Box 1021, Rochester, MI 48308-1021 (SAN 696-8430) Tel 313-375-0645.

Hykes, Susan S., *(S S Hykes; 0-9608894),* P.O. Box 713, Kilauea, HI 96754 (SAN 241-1202) Tel 808-828-1619.

Hymnary Press, The, *(Hymnary Pr; 0-942466),* P.O. Box 5782, Missoula, MT 59806-5782 (SAN 239-6564) Tel 406-721-4943.

HyperDynamics, *(HyperDynamics),* P.O. Box 392, Santa Fe, NM 87501 (SAN 208-290X) Tel 505-988-2416.

Hyperion Pr., Inc., *(Hyperion Conn; 0-88355; 0-8305),* 47 Riverside Ave., Westport, CT 06880 (SAN 202-3148) Tel 203-226-1091; P.O. Box 591, Westport, CT 06880 (SAN 658-0890).

Hypnos Press, *(Hypnos Pr; 0-939628),* 3000 Connecticut Ave. NW, Suite 308, Washington, DC 20008 (SAN 216-6283) Tel 202-462-0221.

Hyst'ry Myst'ry Hse., *(Hyst'ry Myst'ry; 0-937884),* One Brush Ct., Garnerville, NY 10923 (SAN 218-4796) Tel 914-947-3141; Dist. by: Associated Booksellers, 562 Boston Ave., Bridgeport, CT 06610 (SAN 203-5014) Tel 203-333-7268.

I A D Pubns., *(I A D Pubns; 0-912827),* P.O. Box 504, Brisbane, CA 94005 (SAN 283-362X) Tel 415-467-1700.

I & I Sports Supply Co., *(I & I Sports; 0-934489),* 3840 Crenshaw Blvd., Suite 108, Los Angeles, CA 90008 (SAN 693-8906) Tel 213-732-7212.

I & O Publishing Co., *(I & O Pub; 0-911752),* P.O. Box 906, Boulder City, NV 89005 (SAN 202-3156).

IBC Pubns., *(I B C Pubns; 0-931090),* Illinois Benedictine College, Lisle, IL 60532 (SAN 265-3877) Tel 312-960-1500.

IBM Corp., Information Systems Group, National Accounts Div., *(IBM Armonk; 0-933186),* 1133 Westchester Ave., White Plains, NY 10604 (SAN 214-1914) Tel 914-765-1900.

IBMS Inc., *(IBMS Inc; 0-933738),* P.O. Box 395, Westwood, NJ 07675 (SAN 212-9094) Tel 201-343-6855.

IBS Pr., *(IBS Press; 0-9616605),* 2339 28th St., Santa Monica, CA 90405 (SAN 661-2547) Tel 213-450-6485.

ICA Pubs., *(ICA Pubs; 0-941472),* 303 W. Pleasantview Ave., Hackensack, NJ 07601 (SAN 239-3662) Tel 201-343-8833.

ICARE Pr., Inc., *(ICARE Pr; 0-9609492),* 193-12 Nero Ave., Jamaica, NY 11423 (SAN 270-8809) Tel 718-465-2843.

ICC Publishing Corp., Affil. of International Chamber of Commerce, *(ICC Pub),* 156 Fifth Ave., Suite 820, New York, NY 10010 (SAN 297-1984) Tel 212-206-1150.

ICER Pr., *(ICER Pr; 0-914704),* P.O. Box 877, Claremont, CA 91711 (SAN 205-6267).

I.C.J. Corp., *(ICJ Corp; 0-9615943),* P.O. Box 7086, Thousand Oaks, CA 91359 (SAN 696-897X) Tel 805-496-5243; 4372 Golf Course Dr., Westlake Village, CA 91362 (SAN 696-8988).

ICS Bks., Inc., *(ICS Bks; 0-934802),* 1000 E. 80th Pl., Suite 314S, Merrillville, IN 46410 (SAN 295-3358) Tel 219-769-0585; Toll free: 800-732-3669; Dist. by: Stackpole Bks., P.O. Box 1831, Cameron & Kelker Sts., Harrisburg, PA 17105 (SAN 202-5396) Tel 717-234-5041; Toll free: 800-732-3669.

†**ICS Pr.,** Div. of Institute for Contemporary Studies, *(ICS Pr; 0-917616),* 785 Market St., Suite 750, San Francisco, CA 94103 (SAN 276-9735) Tel 415-543-6412; CIP.

ICS Pubns., Institute of Carmelite Studies, *(ICS Pubns; 0-9600876; 0-935216),* 2131 Lincoln Rd., NE, Washington, DC 20002 (SAN 201-5285) Tel 202-832-6622.

ICSU Pr., *(ICSU Pr; 0-930357),* P.O. Box 016129, Miami, FL 33101 (SAN 670-7688) Tel 305-547-6265.

ICTL Pubns., *(ICTL Pubns; 0-910733),* 3889 Ashford St., San Diego, CA 92111 (SAN 262-0413) Tel 619-279-6279.

ICU Group, The, *(ICU Group; 0-936395),* P.O. Box 5027, Cortland, NY 13045 (SAN 696-9127) Tel 716-425-2519.

I C Y Publishing Co., *(I C Y Pub; 0-9613721),* 4904 Old Court Rd., Randallstown, MD 21133 (SAN 687-6331).

I Can See Clearly Now, *(I Can See; 0-9609532),* P.O. Box 784, Coupeville, WA 98239 (SAN 260-2059) Tel 206-678-4606.

I Dare You Committee, *(I Dare You; 0-9602416),* P.O. Box 1606, St. Louis, MO 63188 (SAN 210-9034) Tel 314-982-3210.

Names

IEEE Computer Society Pr., Subs. of IEEE Computer Society, *(IEEE Comp Soc; 0-8186),* 1730 Massachusetts Ave., NW, Washington, DC 20036-1903 (SAN 264-620X) Tel 202-371-0101; Toll free: 800-272-6657 orders only; 10662 Los Vaqueros Cir., Los Alamitos, CA 90270 (SAN 264-6218) Tel 714-821-8380; Orders to: P.O. Box 80452, Worldway Postal Ctr., Los Angeles, CA 90080 (SAN 662-1988) Tel 714-821-8380; Toll free: 800-272-6657.

IFBL Pr., Subs. of Image Feedback Labs, *(IFBL Press; 0-938327),* 196 Conantville Rd., Willimantic, CT 06226 (SAN 661-3268) Tel 203-423-7758.

I. G. Group, The, *(I G Group; 0-9614951),* P.O. Box 7006, Wilton, CT 06897 (SAN 693-7578) Tel 203-762-7952.

IGJ Pubns., *(IGJ Pubns; 0-9617042),* P.O. Box 1852, Hoboken, NJ 07030 (SAN 662-8273); 1117 Park Ave., Hoboken, NJ 07030 (SAN 662-8281) Tel 201-653-2130.

I.J.E. Book Publishing, Inc., Div. of I.J.E. Inc., *(I J E Bk Pub; 0-87660),* 450 N. Park Rd., Fifth Floor, Hollywood, FL 33021 (SAN 294-040X) Tel 305-966-8520.

IJK International, *(IJK Intl; 0-9605146),* 25 Lyon Ave., Greenwich, CT 06830 (SAN 293-2903) Tel 203-661-0686; Orders to: P.O. Box 41, White Plains, NY 10605 (SAN 293-2911) Tel 203-661-0686.

I L I Press, Subs. of Infinety Limited Inc., *(ILI Pr; 0-932183),* 836 Chippewa Ave., St. Paul, MN 55107 (SAN 686-5380) Tel 612-228-0105.

ILR Pr., Div. of New York State Schl. of Industrial Relations, Cornell Univ., *(ILR Pr; 0-87546),* New York State Schl. of Industrial Relations, Cornell Univ., Ithaca, NY 14851-0952 (SAN 270-8825) Tel 607-255-3061.

I Like Me Publishing Co., the, *(I Like Me Pub; 0-9608516),* P.O. Box 43287, Chicago, IL 60628 (SAN 240-6772) Tel 312-445-6497.

IMG, Inc., *(IMG Inc; 0-936271),* 245 E. Sixth St., St. Paul, MN 55101 (SAN 697-8819) Tel 612-293-1964.

IMM/North American Pubns. Ctr., *(IMM-North Am),* Old Post Rd., Brookfield, VT 05036 (SAN 219-791X) Tel 802-276-3162.

IMS Pr., Div. of IMS Comn., Inc., *(IMS Pr; 0-910190),* 426 Pennsylvania Ave., Fort Washington, PA 19034 (SAN 204-5427) Tel 215-628-4920; Toll free: 800-523-5884.

I-Med Press, The, *(I-Med Pr; 0-933131),* 11823 E. Slauson Ave., No. 40, Santa Fe Springs, CA 90670 (SAN 689-7606) Tel 213-696-1161.

INFOH, *(INFOH; 0-939699),* Box 37745, Honolulu, HI 96837 (SAN 663-4702); 1221 Kapiolani Blvd., No. 1031, Honolulu, HI 96813 (SAN 663-4710) Tel 808-538-3111.

INFORM, *(INFORM; 0-918780),* 381 Park Ave., S., New York, NY 10016 (SAN 210-4423) Tel 212-689-4040; Dist. by: Brookfield Pr., Old Post Rd., Brookfield, VT 05036 (SAN 213-4446) Tel 617-492-0670.

I O Publishing Co., *(IO; 0-9609334),* P.O. Box 528, Graton, CA 95444 (SAN 260-2075) Tel 707-823-6433.

IOX Assessment Assocs., *(IOX Asses Assocs; 0-932166),* 11411 W. Jefferson Blvd., Culver City, CA 90230 (SAN 211-1322) Tel 213-391-6295; Orders to: P.O. Box 24095, Los Angeles, CA 90024 (SAN 669-1110) Tel 213-391-5514.

IPS Information Processing Supplies, 251 Frontage Rd., Suite 20, Burr Ridge, IL 60521 (SAN 699-0800) Tel 312-654-0110; Toll free: 800-323-5569.

IQ Foundation, The, *(IQ Found),* Box 303, Pearland, TX 77588-0303 (SAN 696-6314).

IRBN Pr., The, *(IRBN Pr; 0-936925),* 360 E. 72nd St., New York, NY 10021 (SAN 658-3490) Tel 212-340-6284.

IRL Pr., *(IRL Pr; 0-917000; 0-904147),* P.O. Box Q, McLean, VA 22101 (SAN 208-693X) Tel 703-998-2980.

IR Pubns. Ltd., *(IR Pubns; 0-931023),* 35 W. 38th St. No. 3W, New York, NY 10018 (SAN 216-2113) Tel 212-730-0518.

IR Services, *(IR Serv; 0-9616041),* Box 85508, Las Vegas, NV 89185-0508 (SAN 698-0236) Tel 702-386-0472; 1200 Chapman Dr., Las Vegas, NV 89104 (SAN 698-2417).

ISC Consultants, Inc., *(ISC Consultants; 0-935593),* 14 E. Fourth St., Suite 602, New York, NY 10012 (SAN 696-2459) Tel 212-477-8800.

I. S. C. Press, *(I S C CA; 0-912713),* P.O. Box 779, Fortuna, CA 95540 (SAN 283-0477) Tel 707-768-3284.

ISC Pubns., *(ISC Pubns; 0-942916),* P.O. Box 10857, Costa Mesa, CA 92627 (SAN 240-1169).

ISHA Enterprises, *(ISHA Enterprises; 0-936981),* 4033 W. Libby St., Glendale, AZ 85308 (SAN 658-7895) Tel 602-843-8908.

ISI Pr., Subs. of Institute for Scientific Info., *(ISI Pr; 0-89455; 0-86689; 0-946395; 0-906083),* 3501 Market St., Philadelphia, PA 19104 (SAN 209-9349) Tel 215-386-0100; Toll free: 800-523-1850.

ISS Foundation, *(ISS Found; 0-911277),* 410 Commonwealth Dr., Warrendale, PA 15086 (SAN 270-8833) Tel 412-776-1583.

I.S.S. Pubns., *(ISS Pubns; 0-915817),* 160 Washington, SE, Suite 64-R, Albuquerque, NM 87108 (SAN 294-0175) Tel 505-255-2872.

ITA Pubns., *(ITA Pubns; 0-933935),* P.O. Box 1599, Willits, CA 95490 (SAN 693-062X) Tel 707-459-6100.

IWP Publishing, Div. of Eckankar, *(IWP Pub; 0-914766; 0-88155),* P.O. Box 27200, Minneapolis, MN 55427 (SAN 203-798X); Toll free: 800-843-6666.

IAAEE *See* **Noontide Pr., The**

Iapetus Press, *(Iapetus Pr; 0-941602),* 2009 Tidewater Lane, Madison, MS 39110 (SAN 239-1023) Tel 601-987-5950.

IAQC Press, Subs. of International Assn of Quality Circles, *(IAQC Pr; 0-916429),* 801-B W. 8th St., Cincinnati, OH 45203 (SAN 295-8333) Tel 513-381-1959.

IBC *See* **McGraw-Hill Bk. Co.**

Iberian Publishing Co., *(Iberian Pub; 0-935931),* 548 Cedar Creek Dr., Athens, GA 30605-3408 (SAN 696-8473) Tel 404-546-6740.

Ibersoft, Inc., *(Ibersoft; 0-935287),* P.O. Box 3455, Trenton, NJ 08619 (SAN 695-7714) Tel 609-890-1496.

Ibis Pr. of College Station, Texas, *(Ibis Pr TX; 0-935215),* P.O. Box 1434, College Station, TX 77841 (SAN 695-7749) Tel 409-696-6257.

Ibis Publishing, Div. of Teleprint Publishing, Inc., *(Ibis Pub VA; 0-935005),* 7 Elliewood Ave., Charlottesville, VA 22903 (SAN 661-6658) Tel 804-979-3420; Toll free: 800-582-0026.

IBM Corporation - ISD, *(ISD),* New Circle Rd., Lexington, KY 40511 (SAN 651-4413). 3.

I.B.S. Internacional, *(IBS Intl; 0-89564),* 3144 Dove St., San Diego, CA 92103 (SAN 210-3001) Tel 619-298-5061.

†Icarus Publishing, *(Icarus; 0-89651),* 120 W. LaSalle St., Suite 906, South Bend, IN 46601 (SAN 211-7096) Tel 219-233-6020; Toll free: 800-242-7737; Box 1225, South Bend, IN 46601 (SAN 658-0920); Dist. by: Harper & Row, Keystone Industrial Park, Scranton, PA 18512 (SAN 215-3742); CIP.

Iced Pubns., *(ICED Pubns),* P.O. Box 217, Essex, CT 06426 (SAN 241-5429) Tel 203-767-2726; 680 Fifth Ave., New York, NY 10019 (SAN 669-0998) Tel 212-582-3970; 127 River Rd., Essex, CT 06426 (SAN 669-1005).

Ichazo, Oscar, Co., *(O Ichazo; 0-937201),* 874 Kumulani Dr., Kihei, HI 96753 (SAN 658-7321) Tel 212-362-5230.

Ichthys Bks., *(Ichthys Bks; 0-930711),* 916 Red Mountain Dr., Glenwood Springs, CO 81601 (SAN 677-2390) Tel 303-945-7052.

Icon Editions *See* **Harper & Row Pubs., Inc.**

Icon Pr., *(Icon Pr; 0-9615471),* Box 3240, Vail, CO 81658 (SAN 696-2629) Tel 303-476-1263; 1548 Spring Hill Ln., No. 2, Vail, CO 81658 (SAN 696-2637).

ICUC Pr., *(ICUC Pr; 0-910205),* P.O. Box 1447, Springfield, VA 22151 (SAN 241-5216) Tel 703-323-8065.

Ida, Yoder, *(Yoder; 0-9614083),* 180 Hall Drive, Wadsworth, OH 44281 (SAN 685-9291) Tel 216-336-0261.

Idaho First National Bank, *(Idaho First Natl Bank; 0-9600776),* c/o R. O. Beatty & Assocs., Inc., P.O. Box 763, Boise, ID 83701 (SAN 207-9909).

Idaho Museum of Natural History, *(Idaho Mus Nat Hist; 0-939696),* Campus Box 8096, Idaho State Univ., Pocatello, ID 83209 (SAN 201-5315) Tel 208-236-3168.

Idaho Press Club, The, *(Idaho Press Club; 0-9616307),* 132 W. Third St., Boise, ID 83701 (SAN 658-7348) Tel 208-733-0931; P.O. Box 2221, Boise, ID 93701 (SAN 658-7356).

Idaho. Secretary of State Office of the Secretary of State, *(Idaho Secy),* State Capitol, Rm. 203, Boise, ID 83720 (SAN 270-8965).

Idaho State Historical Society, *(Idaho State Soc; 0-931406),* 610 N. Julia Davis Dr., Boise, ID 83702-7695 (SAN 221-0827) Tel 208-334-2120.

Ide Hse., Inc., *(Ide Hse; 0-86663),* 4631 Harvey Dr., Mesquite, TX 75150-1609 (SAN 216-146X) Tel 214-681-2552; Dist. by: Liberal Pr., P.O. Box 160361, Las Colinas, TX 75016-9998 (SAN 200-5360) Tel 817-478-8564.

Ideal World Publishing Co., *(Ideal World; 0-915068),* P.O. Box 1237-EG, Melbourne, FL 32935 (SAN 201-923X) Tel 305-254-6003.

IDEALS *See* **Institute for the Development of Emotional Life Skills (IDEALS)**

Ideals Publishing Corp., Subs. of Thomas Nelson, Inc., *(Ideals; 0-89542; 0-8249),* Nelson Pl. at Elm Hill Pike, Nashville, TN 37214 (SAN 213-4403) Tel 615-889-9000; Toll free: 800-558-0740. *Imprints:* Good Friends (Good Friends).

Ideas!, Inc., *(Ideas Inc OR; 0-939447),* 3340 SW Stonebrook Dr., Portland, OR 97201 (SAN 663-3420) Tel 503-245-0018; Dist. by: Far West Book Service, 3515 NE Hassale, Portland, OR 97232 (SAN 107-6760).

†Identity Institute, The, *(Identity Inst; 0-912093),* P.O. Box 11039, Honolulu, HI 96828 (SAN 277-6898); CIP.

Idthekkethan Publishing Co., *(Idthekkethan; 0-918347),* 58 Roble Rd., Berkeley, CA 94705 (SAN 657-3533) Tel 415-644-1128.

Idylwild Books, *(Idylwild Bks; 0-9613054),* P.O. Box 246, Ojai, CA 93023 (SAN 295-3870) Tel 805-646-2646; 1465 Foothill Rd., Ojai, CA 93020 (SAN 295-3889); Dist. by: Bookpeople, 2929 Fifth St., Berkeley, CA 94710 (SAN 168-9517) Tel 415-549-3030; Toll free: 800-227-1516; Dist. by: The New Leaf Distributing, 1020 White St., SW, Atlanta, GA 30310 (SAN 169-1449) Tel 404-755-2665; Toll free: 800-241-3829; Dist. by: Starlite Distributors, P.O. Box 20729, Reno, NV 89515 (SAN 131-1921) Tel 702-359-5676.

I E C, *(I E C; 0-9611802),* 402 S. High St., Selinsgrove, PA 17870 (SAN 286-1097) Tel 717-374-2616.

If & Win Publishing, *(If & Win Pub; 0-9617025),* P.O. Box 1262, Placentia, CA 92670 (SAN 662-572X); 4711 Rapallo Plaza, Yorba Linda, CA 92686 (SAN 662-5738) Tel 714-970-8542.

IFI, Plenum *See* **Plenum Publishing Corp.**

Igaku-Shoin Medical Pubs., Subs. of Igaku-Shoin, Ltd. (Japan), *(Igaku-Shoin; 0-89640),* 1140 Ave. of the Americas, New York, NY 10036 (SAN 211-5689) Tel 212-944-7540.

Ignatius Pr., Div. of Guadalupe Assocs., Inc., *(Ignatius Pr; 0-89870),* P.O. Box 18990, San Francisco, CA 94118 (SAN 214-3887) Tel 415-387-2324; Orders to: 15 Oakland Ave., Harrison, NY 10528 (SAN 289-0127) Tel 914-835-4216.

Igram Press, *(Igram Pr; 0-911119),* 2020 16th Ave. SW, Cedar Rapids, IA 52404 (SAN 263-1709) Tel 319-366-5335.

IHI Press, *(IHI Pr),* International Homophilics Institute, 165 Marlborough St., Boston, MA 02116 (SAN 209-5688).

II Editions, *(Two Edit),* 488 Madison Ave., New York, NY 10022 (SAN 276-9417).

IIP Assocs., *(IIP Assocs; 0-916423),* Univ. of Utah, College of Health, Salt Lake City, UT 84112 (SAN 295-4281) Tel 801-582-3202.

Ike & Dudatt Pubns., *(Ike & Dudatt Pubns; 0-930297),* 9361 La Jolla Cir., P.O. Box 5762, Huntington Beach, CA 92646 (SAN 670-8412).

Ili-Cor Pubns., *(Ili-Cor Pubns),* 1460 Webster St., No. 3, San Francisco, CA 94115 (SAN 240-1525) Tel 415-567-6568.

Illini Bks. *See* **Univ. of Illinois Pr.**

Names

Illinois Baptist State Assn., *(Ill Baptist St Assn; 0-9600896),* P.O. Box 3486, Springfield, IL 62708 (SAN 208-2608).

Illinois Institute of Technology, *(IL Inst Tech),* 10 W. 32nd St., Chicago, IL 60616 (SAN 230-8304); Dist. by: Univ. of Chicago Pr., 5801 Ellis Ave., 3rd Flr., S., Chicago, IL 60637 (SAN 202-5280) Tel 312-962-7693.

Illinois Labor History Society, *(Ill Labor Hist Soc; 0-916884),* 28 E. Jackson Blvd., Chicago, IL 60604 (SAN 281-8019) Tel 312-663-4107.

Illinois Office of the Governor, *(Illinois Governor),* State Capitol, Springfield, IL 62706 (SAN 270-9082).

Illinois Secretary of State, *(Illinois Secy State),* State Capitol, Rm. 213, Springfield, IL 62706 (SAN 270-9112).

Illinois South Project, *(Illinois South; 0-943724),* 116 1/2 W. Cherry, Herrin, IL 62948 (SAN 241-0303) Tel 618-942-6613.

Illinois State Bar Assn., *(Illinois Bar),* Illinois Bar Ctr., 424 S. Second St., Springfield, IL 62701 (SAN 226-2207) Tel 217-525-1760.

Illinois State Historical Library, Div. of Illinois Historic Preservation Agency, *(Ill St Hist Lib; 0-912154),* Old State Capitol, Springfield, IL 62701 (SAN 203-7963) Tel 217-782-4836.

Illinois State Historical Society, *(Ill St Hist Soc; 0-912226),* Old State Capitol, Springfield, IL 62701 (SAN 203-7971) Tel 217-782-4836.

Illinois State Museum Society, *(Ill St Museum; 0-89792),* Spring & Edwards, Springfield, IL 62706 (SAN 201-5137) Tel 217-782-7386.

Illiterati Pr., *(Illiterati Pr; 0-937837),* 8306 Wilshire Blvd., No. 129, Beverly Hills, CA 90211 (SAN 659-4697) Tel 213-467-5232; 2142 1/2 N. Beachwood Dr., Hollywood, CA 90068 (SAN 659-4700).

Illnois Academy of Criminology, *(Ill Academy; 0-933757),* 8939 W. Emerson St., Des Plaines, IL 60016 (SAN 692-7483) Tel 312-670-2775.

†**Illuminati,** *(Illuminati; 0-89807),* P.O. Box 67E07, Los Angeles, CA 90067 (SAN 212-856X) (SAN 606-0189); *CIP.*

Illumination Engineering Society of North America, *(Illum Eng; 0-87995),* 345 E. 47th St., New York, NY 10017 (SAN 202-3180) Tel 212-705-7913.

Illuminations Pr., *(Illum Pr; 0-937088),* P.O. Box 126, St. Helena, CA 94574 (SAN 241-5445) Tel 707-963-9342.

Illuminations Pr., *(Illuminations Pr; 0-941442),* 2110 Ninth St., Apt. B, Berkeley, CA 94710 (SAN 209-8172) Tel 415-849-2102.

Ilse, Sherokee, & Associates, Div. of Wintergreen Press, *(Sherokee; 0-9609456),* 4105 Oak St., Long Lake, MN 55356 (SAN 260-0749) Tel 612-476-1303.

IM-Pr., *(IM-Pr; 0-931543),* 1412 Rosewood St., Ann Arbor, MI 48104 (SAN 682-2967) Tel 313-761-2231.

IM-Pr., *(IM-Press; 0-915727),* 1527 Virginia St., Berkeley, CA 94703 (SAN 294-0213) Tel 415-845-8409.

Image & Idea, Inc., *(Image & Idea; 0-934570),* Box 1991, Iowa City, IA 52240 (SAN 213-3229); Dist. by: Iowa State Univ. Press, 2121 S. State Ave., Ames, IA 50010 (SAN 202-7194).

Image Awareness Corp., *(Image Awareness; 0-9604592),* 1271 High St., Auburn, CA 95603 (SAN 215-1545) Tel 916-823-7092.

Image Books *See* **Doubleday & Co., Inc.**

Image Continuum Pr., *(Image Continuum; 0-9614574),* 1017 Seabright Ave., Santa Cruz, CA 95062 (SAN 691-800X) Tel 408-458-1469.

Image Gallery, *(Image Gallery; 0-918362),* 1026 SW Morrison St., Portland, OR 97205 (SAN 210-1068) Tel 503-224-9629.

Image Imprints, *(Image Imprints; 0-9615233),* P.O. Box 2764, Eugene, OR 97402 (SAN 695-1767) Tel 503-998-2612.

Image Industry Pubns., *(Image Industry; 0-933406),* 10 Bay Street Landing, Suite 7K, Staten Island, NY 10301 (SAN 212-419X) Tel 718-273-3229; Dist. by: Fairchild Bks., 7 E. 12th St., New York, NY 10003 (SAN 201-470X) Tel 212-741-4280.

Image Makers of Pittsford, *(Image Makers; 0-911705),* 6 Wood Gate, Pittsford, NY 14534 (SAN 264-1070) Tel 716-385-4567.

Image Pubns., *(Image Pubns; 0-942772),* 6409 Appalachian Way, P.O. Box 5016, Madison, WI 53705 (SAN 238-8499) Tel 608-233-5033.

Image Publishing Co., Ltd., Subs. of Roger Miller Photo, Ltd., *(Image Ltd; 0-911897),* 1411 Hollins St., Baltimore, MD 21223 (SAN 264-6781) Tel 301-566-1222.

Image West Press, *(Image West; 0-918966),* P.O. Box 5511, Eugene, OR 97405 (SAN 210-4407) Tel 503-342-3797.

Imagefax Publishing, *(Imagefax Pub; 0-939255),* P.O. Box 2032, Fairfax, VA 22031 (SAN 662-5185) Tel 703-691-1514.

Imagenes Pr., *(Imagenes; 0-939302),* P.O. Box 653, El Centro, CA 92244 (SAN 220-1712) Tel 619-352-2188; Dist. by: Charles E. Tuttle Co., P.O. Box 410, 28 S. Main St., Rutland, VT 05701-0401 (SAN 213-2621) Tel 802-773-8930.

Imagery Enterprises, *(Imagery Enter; 0-9615579),* 99 N. Fourth Ave., Suite 215, Chula Vista, CA 92010 (SAN 696-2661) Tel 619-427-8271; Dist. by: ARA Services - Magazine & Bk. Division, P.O. Box 85408, San Diego, CA 92138-5408 (SAN 200-7401); Dist. by: ARA Services, P.O. Box 2399, Yakima, WA 98907 (SAN 169-8893); Dist. by: Capital News Distribution, 19600 Washington, Boston, MA 02119 (SAN 200-8122); Dist. by: Central Wholesale, 143 S. 25th St., Pittsburgh, PA 15203 (SAN 200-6987); Dist. by: Triangle News Co., Inc., 301 Munson Ave., McKees Rocks, PA 15136 (SAN 169-7447); Dist. by: ARA Services, 3392 Bledensburg Rd., Cottage City, MD 20722 (SAN 200-8319); Dist. by: ARA Services, 16150 W. Lincoln, New Berlin, WI 53151 (SAN 200-8327).

Images Graphiques, Inc., *(Images Graphiques; 0-89545),* 37 Riverside Dr., New York, NY 10023 (SAN 210-4415) Tel 212-787-4000.

Images, Ink, Inc., *(Images Ink; 0-942088),* P.O. Box 12685, 9135 Spearhead Way, Reno, NV 89506 (SAN 238-6119) Tel 702-972-3361.

Images of Key West, *(Images Key; 0-9609272),* C/O The Langley Press 821 Georgia St., Key West, FL 33040 (SAN 260-0757) Tel 305-294-3156.

Images Unlimited, *(Images Unltd; 0-930643),* P.O. Box 305, Maryville, MO 64468 (SAN 687-6358).

Imagesmith, *(Imagesmith; 0-938700),* P.O. Box 1524, Bellevue, WA 98009 (SAN 216-0420).

Imaginart Press, *(Imaginart Pr; 0-9609464),* P.O. Box 1868, Idyllwild, CA 92349 (SAN 260-2067) Tel 714-659-5905.

Imagination Dust Publishing, *(Imagination Dust; 0-9611072),* P.O. Box 5415, Scottsdale, AZ 85261 (SAN 282-8839).

Imaginations Unlimited *See* **Drum Associates**

Imagine, Inc., *(Imagine; 0-911137),* P.O. Box 9674, Pittsburgh, PA 15226 (SAN 262-9100) Tel 412-571-1430.

Imago Imprint Inc., *(Imago Imprint Inc; 0-915829),* 150 Fifth Ave., New York, NY 10011 (SAN 294-0221) Tel 212-620-3140.

Imibooks Pubns., *(Imibooks Pubns; 0-918066),* P.O. Box 35, Greenvale, NY 11548 (SAN 209-3766) Tel 212-468-0039.

Immergut & Siolek Publishers, Inc., *(Immergut & Siolek; 0-915163),* P.O. Box 1023, Havertown, PA 19083 (SAN 289-9930) Tel 215-449-2660.

Imp Press, *(Imp Pr; 0-9603008),* P.O. Box 93, Buffalo, NY 14213 (SAN 213-0858) Tel 716-881-5391.

Impact, *(Impact IN; 0-9611220),* c/o Cornerstone Communications, Inc., 3314 Van Tassel Dr., P.O. Box 688531, Indianapolis, IN 46268 (SAN 695-4537) Tel 317-783-5098.

Impact Bks., Inc., *(Impact Bks MO; 0-89228),* 137 W. Jefferson, Kirkwood, MO 63122 (SAN 214-0330) Tel 314-833-3309.

Impact II, *(Impact II; 0-939229),* 15 E. 26th St., New York, NY 10010 (SAN 662-5932) Tel 212-340-2990.

†**Impact Press,** *(Impact Pr IL; 0-936872),* 6702 N. Sheridan Rd., Chicago, IL 60626 (SAN 213-9782) Tel 312-761-0682; *CIP.*

Impact Pubns., Div. of Baker & Bowden, *(Impact Pubns IL; 0-9607474),* P.O. Box 1896, Evanston, IL 60204-1896 (SAN 238-6127) Tel 312-475-5748.

Impact Pubns, Div. of Development Concepts, Inc., *(Impact VA; 0-942710),* 10655 Big Oak Cir., Manassas, VA 22111 (SAN 240-1142) Tel 703-361-7300.

†**Impact Pubs., Inc.,** *(Impact Pubs Cal; 0-915166),* P.O. Box 1094, San Luis Obispo, CA 93406 (SAN 202-6864) Tel 805-543-5911; *CIP.*

Impact Publishing Co., *(Impact Pub; 0-9601530),* 2110 Omega Rd., Suite A, San Ramon, CA 94583 (SAN 211-3651) Tel 415-831-1655.

Impact Publishing Co. (NY), Div. of Impact Planning Group, *(Impact Pub NY; 0-9614952),* P.O. Box 244, Katonah, NY 10536 (SAN 693-739X) Tel 212-410-3477.

Imperial Publishing Co., *(Imperial Pub Co; 0-9602960),* 190 S. Florida Ave., Bartow, FL 33830 (SAN 213-9871) Tel 813-533-4183; P.O. Box 120, Bartow, FL 33830 (SAN 658-0939).

Imperio, Leroy, *(L Imperio; 0-9609302),* Rte. 1, Box 222-C, Burlington, WV 26241 (SAN 241-5224) Tel 304-636-3434.

Impermanent Press, *(Impermanent Pr),* 218 Monclay Court, St. Louis, MO 63122 (SAN 209-0414).

Impex Publishing Co., *(Impex Pub Co; 0-9613238),* P.O. Box 5013, Greenville, SC 29606 (SAN 295-4443) Tel 803-288-6761.

Imported Pubns., Inc., *(Imported Pubns; 0-8285),* 320 W. Ohio St., Chicago, IL 60610 (SAN 169-1805) Tel 312-787-9017; Toll free: 800-345-2665.

Impresora Sahuaro, *(Impresora Sahuaro),* 7575 Sendero De Juana, Tucson, AZ 85718 (SAN 218-7760) Tel 602-297-3089.

ImPress, *(ImPress IL; 0-939535),* P.O. Box 1800, Springfield, IL 62705 (SAN 663-4400); 1547 Williams Blvd., Springfield, IL 62704 (SAN 663-4419) Tel 217-546-9017. Do not confuse with ImPress Publications in Minneapolis, MN or Morristown, TN.

Impress House, *(Impress Hse; 0-913992),* Orders to: Associated Booksellers, 147 McKinley Ave., Bridgeport, CT 06606 (SAN 206-6513).

Impress Pubns., *(Impress; 0-9614560),* 715 SE 5th St., Minneapolis, MN 55414 (SAN 691-8018) Tel 612-623-7601; P.O. Box 27246, Golden Valley, MN 55427 (SAN 662-2941).

Impressions, *(Impressions; 0-937304),* 2932 Locust Lane, Harrisburg, PA 17109 (SAN 213-2192).

Impressions, *(Impressions TX; 0-9616121),* P.O. Box 270502, Houston, TX 77277 (SAN 699-7279); 6633 W. Airport, Suite 1302, Houston, TX 77035 (SAN 699-7287) Tel 713-723-0600.

Impressions Publishing Co., *(Impress Pub; 0-913049),* P.O. Box 3286, Boise, ID 83703 (SAN 283-9784).

Imprint Editions, *(Imprint Edns),* 1520 South College, Fort Collins, CO 80524 (SAN 216-485X). *Imprints:* Capablanca (Capablanca).

Imrie/Risley Miniatures, Inc., *(Imrie-Risley; 0-912364),* P.O. Box 89, Burnt Hills, NY 12027 (SAN 206-6521) Tel 518-885-6054.

In Between Books, *(In Between; 0-935430),* Box T, Sausalito, CA 94966 (SAN 213-6236).

In Camera, *(In Camera; 0-932597),* c/o Tysh, 2371 Pulaski, Hamtramck, MI 48212 (SAN 687-5165) Tel 313-365-7913; Dist. by: Small Press Dist., 1814 San Pablo Ave., Berkeley, CA 94702 (SAN 204-5826) Tel 415-549-3336; Dist. by: Bookslinger, 213 E. 4th St., St. Paul, MN 55101 (SAN 169-4154) Tel 612-221-0429.

IN Education, Inc., *(In Educ; 0-918433),* 2000 Valley Forge Circle, Suite 624, King of Prussia, PA 19406 (SAN 657-6206) Tel 215-783-5939.

In Pursuit of Entertainment, *(In Pursuit Entertainment; 0-938489),* 1737 Frankford Rd., Suite 3403, Carrollton, TX 75007 (SAN 661-0390) Tel 214-394-1083.

In Sight Press, *(In Sight Pr NM; 0-942524),* 535 Cordova Rd., Suite 228, Santa Fe, NM 87501 (SAN 238-1680) Tel 505-471-7511.

In the Mind's Eye, Inc., *(Mind's Eye Inc; 0-9616164),* 3207-C Sutton Pl., NW, Washington, DC 20016 (SAN 699-8380) Tel 202-966-3317.

Names

In The Tradition Publishing Co., *(In Tradition Pub; 0-935369),* P.O. Box 58142, Philadelphia, PA 19102-8142 (SAN 696-667X) Tel 215-227-3154.

In-the-Valley-of-the-Wichitas House, *(In Valley Wichitas; 0-941634),* P.O. Box 6741, Lawton, OK 73506 (SAN 239-2321) Tel 405-536-7118.

IN Three D, *(IN Three D; 0-9614263),* 5841 Geary Blvd., San Francisco, CA 94121 (SAN 687-1313) Tel 415-387-7956.

Inagrams, *(Inagrams; 0-9615653),* 2 N. 551 Lawler, Lombard, IL 60148 (SAN 696-4702) Tel 312-629-0338.

Inaka/Countryside Publications, *(Inaka-Countryside Pubns; 0-9614541),* 9336 E. Lincoln, Del Rey, CA 93616 (SAN 691-7356) Tel 209-834-3648.

Incentive Pubns., Inc., *(Incentive Pubns; 0-913916; 0-86530),* 3835 Cleghorn Ave., Nashville, TN 37215 (SAN 203-8005) Tel 615-385-2934; Toll free: 800-421-2830.

Incentive Publishing, *(Incent Pub; 0-912715),* P.O. Box 15060, Sacramento, CA 95851 (SAN 283-0515) Tel 916-486-8609; Dist. by: Publishers Group West, 5855 Beaudry St., Emeryville, CA 94608 (SAN 202-8522) Tel 415-658-3453.

Incline Pr., *(Incline Pr; 0-9615161),* 456 Columbia Ave., Merced, CA 95340 (SAN 694-3853) Tel 209-723-3667.

Inco Alloys International, Div. of Inco Ltd. (New York), *(Inco Alloys Intl; 0-9615081),* P.O. Box 1958, Guyan River Rd., Huntington, WV 25720 (SAN 694-0668) Tel 304-526-5689.

Incremental Motion Control Systems Society, *(Incremental Motion; 0-931538),* P.O. Box 2772, Sta. A, Champaign, IL 61820 (SAN 211-4259) Tel 217-356-1523.

Ind-US, Inc., *(Ind-US Inc; 0-86578),* Box 56, East Glastonbury, CT 06025 (SAN 213-5809) Tel 203-663-0045.

Independence Hse. Publishing Co., Inc., Div. of Independence House, Inc., *(Independence House; 0-912551),* 15100 Birmingham Dr., Burtonsville, MD 20866 (SAN 265-2587) Tel 301-490-0112.

†Independence Press, Div. of Herald House, *(Ind Pr MO; 0-8309),* P.O. Box HH, 3225 S. Noland Rd., Independence, MO 64055 (SAN 202-6902) Tel 816-252-5010; Toll free: 800-821-7550; *CIP.*

Independent Battery Manufacturers Assn., *(IBMA Pubns; 0-912254),* 100 Larchwood Dr., Largo, FL 33540 (SAN 206-9180) Tel 813-586-1408.

Independent Christian Publications, *(Ind Christ Pubns; 0-915059),* P.O. Box 1970, Dunnellon, FL 32630 (SAN 289-9493) Tel 904-489-1982.

Independent Community Consultants, Inc., *(Ind Comm Con; 0-916721),* Research and Evaluation Office, P.O. Box 1673, West Memphis, AR 72301 (SAN 217-7838) Tel 501-735-8431.

Independent Curators Incorporated, *(Ind Curators; 0-916365),* 799 Broadway, New York, NY 10003 (SAN 295-9496) Tel 212-254-8200; Dist. by: World Wide Books, 37-39 Antwerp St., Boston, MA 02135 (SAN 287-7805) Tel 617-787-9100.

Independent Liquid Terminals Assn., *(Ind Liquid Terms),* 1133 15th St., NW, Suite 204, Washington, DC 20005 (SAN 224-9367) Tel 202-659-2301.

Independent Petroleum Association of America, *(Ind Petrol Assn),* 1101 16th St. NW, Washington, DC 20036 (SAN 224-9006) Tel 202-857-4770.

Independent Pubns., *(Ind Pubns; 0-914937),* P.O. Box 162 Park Sta., Paterson, NJ 07543 (SAN 289-2464) Tel 201-943-7299.

Independent Research Services of Irvine, *(Ind Res Servs Irvine; 0-932669),* 10 Sunfish, Irvine, CA 92714 (SAN 687-8059) Tel 714-551-0182.

Independent School District , 535, *(Independ Sch; 0-917009),* Rochester Public Schools, Edison Bldg., 615 SW 7th St., Rochester, MN 55901 (SAN 655-7376) Tel 507-285-8560.

Independent School Pr., *(Ind Sch Pr; 0-88334),* 51 River St., Wellesley Hills, MA 02181 (SAN 203-8013) Tel 617-237-2591.

Independent Sector, *(Ind Sector),* 1828 L St., NW, Washington, DC 20036 (SAN 679-1670).

Index/Citator System, Inc., *(Index-Citator; 0-936603),* 4400 Lindell Blvd., No. 19-F, St. Louis, MO 63108 (SAN 698-0481) Tel 314-652-6578.

Index Hse., *(Index Hse; 0-936697),* 7206 Farmington Way, Madison, WI 53717 (SAN 699-8682) Tel 608-833-1617.

†Index Publishing, *(Index Pub; 0-914311),* Dept. R, P.O. Box 11476, Salt Lake City, UT 84147 (SAN 287-5500); *CIP.*

Index to Jewish Periodicals, *(IJP; 0-939698),* P.O. Box 18570, Cleveland Heights, OH 44118 (SAN 204-8566) Tel 216-321-7296.

India Enterprises of the West, Inc., *(India Enterprises West; 0-933047),* P.O. Box 462, Wakefield Stn., Bronx, NY 10466 (SAN 689-7614) Tel 212-519-0709.

Indian Bk. Center, Inc., *(Indian Bk Ctr; 0-932639),* P.O. Box 2541, Edison, NJ 08818 (SAN 687-8067) Tel 201-494-8175.

Indian Crossing Bks., *(Indian Crossing Bks; 0-9616222),* 101 Seminole, DeForest, WI 53532 (SAN 658-5485) Tel 608-846-4134.

Indian Feather Publishing, *(Indian Feather; 0-937962),* 7218 SW Oak, Portland, OR 97223 (SAN 215-9996).

Indian Historian Press, Inc., *(Indian Hist Pr; 0-913436),* 1451 Masonic Ave., San Francisco, CA 94117 (SAN 202-6929) Tel 415-626-5235.

Indian Peaks Publishing Co., *(Indian Peaks Pub; 0-9616582),* Salina Star Rte., Boulder, CO 80302 (SAN 661-2008) Tel 303-440-9394; 531 Canyonside Dr., Boulder, CO 80302 (SAN 661-2016).

Indian Univ. Press, Div. of Bacone College, *(Indian U Pr OK; 0-940392),* Bacone College, Muskogee, OK 74403 (SAN 217-1821) Tel 918-683-4581. Do not confuse with Ind U Pr Indiana.

Indiana Basketball High School Record Book, *(Ind Basketball High Sch; 0-9613849),* Rt. 3 P.O. Box 570, Greencastle, IN 46135 (SAN 681-9915) Tel 317-653-6226.

Indiana Historical Society, *(Ind Hist Soc; 0-87195),* 315 W. Ohio St., Rm. 350, Indianapolis, IN 46202 (SAN 201-5234) Tel 317-232-1878.

Indiana State Univ., *(Ind St Univ; 0-940100),* Parsons Hall, Rm. 111, Terre Haute, IN 47809 (SAN 211-0202) Tel 812-232-6311.

Indiana Univ., Research Ctr. for the Language Sciences *See* Research Ctr. for Language & Semiotic Studies

Indiana University, African Studies Program, *(Indiana Africa; 0-941934),* 221 Woodburn Hall Indiana University, Bloomington, IN 47405 (SAN 238-6155) Tel 812-335-8284.

Indiana Univ. Afro-American Arts Institute, *(Ind U Afro-Amer Arts),* 109 North Jordon Ave., Bloomington, IN 47405 (SAN 209-5696).

Indiana Univ., Bureau of Business Research, *(Ind U Busn Res; 0-87925),* Bloomington, IN 47405 (SAN 202-6880) Tel 812-335-5507.

Indiana University, Dept. of Health & Safety Education, Office of Pubns. & Editorial Services, *(IN U Dept Health; 0-941636),* HPER Bldg., Rm. 116, Bloomington, IN 47405 (SAN 239-233X) Tel 812-335-7975.

Indiana Univ., Institute for Advanced Study, *(IN Univ IAS; 0-936679),* Indiana Univ., Poplars 335, Bloomington, IN 47405 (SAN 699-6728) Tel 812-335-8268.

Indiana Univ. Pr., *(Ind U Pr; 0-253),* Tenth & Morton Sts., Bloomington, IN 47405 (SAN 202-5647) Tel 812-335-7681. Do not confuse with Indian U Pr OK. *Imprints:* Midland Books (MB).

Indiana Univ. Research Institute for Inner Asian Studies, *(Ind U Res Inst; 0-933070),* Goodbody Hall 344, Bloomington, IN 47405 (SAN 215-1553) Tel 812-335-1605.

Indianapolis Museum of Art, *(Ind Mus Art; 0-936260),* 1200 W. 38th St., Indianapolis, IN 46208 (SAN 215-6571) Tel 317-925-7034.

Indigenous Pubns., *(Indigenous Pubns; 0-930740),* P.O. Box 1614, Aptos, CA 95003 (SAN 210-8801) Tel 209-529-5087.

Indigo Press, *(Indigo Pr; 0-9604060),* 5950 Fern Flat Rd., Aptos, CA 95003 (SAN 239-443X); Dist. by: Straw into Gold, 3006 San Pablo, Berkeley, CA 94702 (SAN 239-4448).

Individual Learning Systems, Inc., Div. of Southwest Offset, Inc., *(Individual Learn; 0-86589),* P.O. Box 225447, Dallas, TX 75265 (SAN 203-8021) Tel 214-630-0313.

Individual Potentials Unlimited, *(Indiv Potentials; 0-9616223),* 3540 S. 4000 W., Suite 430, West Valley City, UT 84404 (SAN 658-5493) Tel 801-968-3292.

Individualized Education Systems, *(Indiv Educ Syst; 0-938911),* P.O. Box 5136, Fresno, CA 93755 (SAN 661-8405); 134 Poppy Ln., Clovis, CA 93612 (SAN 661-8413) Tel 209-299-4639.

Indochina Curriculum Group, *(Indochina Curriculum Grp; 0-9607794),* 11 Garden St., Cambridge, MA 02138 (SAN 217-7854) Tel 617-354-6583.

Industrial Designers Society of America, *(Indus Design),* 1360 Beverly Rd., Suite 303, McLean, VA 22101-3671 (SAN 224-7941) Tel 703-556-0919.

Industrial Development Div., Institute of Science & Technology, *(Indus Dev Inst Sci; 0-938654),* Univ. of Michigan, 2200 Bonisteel Blvd., Ann Arbor, MI 48105 (SAN 204-8590) Tel 313-764-5260.

Industrial Fabrics Assn. International, *(Indus Fabrics; 0-935803),* 345 Cedar Bldg., Suite 450, St. Paul, MN 55101 (SAN 224-134X) Tel 612-222-2508.

Industrial Health Foundation, Inc., *(Indus Health Inc; 0-911890),* 34 Penn Cir. W., Pittsburgh, PA 15206 (SAN 203-803X) Tel 412-363-6600.

†Industrial Pr., Inc., *(Indus Pr; 0-8311),* 200 Madison Ave., New York, NY 10016 (SAN 202-6945) Tel 212-889-6330; Orders to: P.O. Box C-772, Brooklyn, NY 11205 (SAN 662-0434) Tel 718-852-7519; *CIP.*

Industrial Relations & Data Information Services, Inc., *(IRDIS; 0-9613923),* P.O. Box 226WOB, West Orange, NJ 07052 (SAN 683-5627) Tel 201-731-1554.

Industrial Relations Counselors, Inc., *(Indus Rel; 0-87330),* P.O. Box 1530, New York, NY 10101 (SAN 203-8048) Tel 212-541-6086; Orders to: Industrial Relations Research Assn., 7226 Social Science Bldg., Madison, WI 53706 (SAN 663-2939) Tel 608-262-2762.

Industrial Research Service, Inc., *(Indus Res Serv),* 26 Strafford Ave., Durham, NH 03824 (SAN 204-8612) Tel 603-868-2593.

Industrial Research Unit-The Wharton Schl., *(Indus Res Unit-Wharton; 0-89546),* Univ. of Pennsylvania, Vance Hall/CS, 3733 Spruce St., Philadelphia, PA 19104 (SAN 206-0744) Tel 215-898-5606.

Industrial Workers of the World, *(Indus Workers World; 0-917124),* 3435 N. Sheffield, No. 202, Chicago, IL 60657 (SAN 209-1909) Tel 312-549-5045.

Industry Book Publishing, Inc., *(Indus Bk Pub; 0-939554),* 1437 Tuttle Ave., Wallingford, CT 06492 (SAN 220-1720) Tel 203-269-9184.

Infax Corp., *(Infax Corp; 0-933937),* 5205 Hampden Ln., Bethseda, MD 20814 (SAN 693-0522) Tel 301-986-8011.

Infection Control Pubns., *(Infection Control; 0-936751),* P.O. Box 501, North Salt Lake City, UT 84054 (SAN 699-8836) Tel 801-298-0880; 421 W. 900 N., North Salt Lake City, UT 84054 (SAN 699-8844).

Infernal Artists Scribes Publishers, Div. of Apollo/Athena Enterprises, Ltd., *(Infernal Artists),* 185 Butler St., Hamden, CT 06511 (SAN 209-4495) Tel 203-787-4376; P.O. Box 4034, Hamden, CT 06514 (SAN 209-4509); Orders to: P.O. Box 4034, Hamden, CT 06514 (SAN 662-0442).

Inflation Reports, *(Inflation Reports),* P.O. Box 60148, Los Angeles, CA 90060 (SAN 291-8382) Tel 213-660-8201.

Info-All Book Co., *(Info All Bk; 0-9617218),* 5 Old Well Ln., Dallas, PA 18612 (SAN 663-4087) Tel 717-288-9375.

Info Digest, *(Info Digest; 0-939670),* 9302 Parkside Ave., Morton Grove, IL 60053 (SAN 216-9460) Tel 312-965-1456; Orders to: P.O. Box 165, Morton Grove, IL 60053 (SAN 662-7102).

Info Pr., Inc., *(Info Pr NY; 0-9692267),* 728 Center, Lewiston, NY 14092 (SAN 271-0005) Tel 716-754-4669.

Info to Go, *(Info to Go; 0-936201),* 228 Beech Rd., Newbury Park, CA 91320 (SAN 696-9011) Tel 805-498-6858.

Infobooks, *(Infobooks; 0-931137),* P.O. Box 1018, Santa Monica, CA 90406 (SAN 679-3967) Tel 213-470-6786.

Infomap, Inc., *(Infomap Inc; 0-910471),* 8255 N. Central Park Ave., Skokie, IL 60076 (SAN 262-0421) Tel 312-673-9100.

InfoMed Books, *(InfoMed Bks; 0-933295),* 100 California St., Suite 1400, San Francisco, CA 94111 (SAN 692-3178) Tel 415-956-5999.

Information Aids, Inc., *(Info Aids; 0-936474),* 1401 Windy Meadow Dr., Plano, TX 75023 (SAN 220-2557) Tel 214-422-4058.

Information Alternative, *(Info Alternative; 0-936288),* P.O. Box 5571, Chicago, IL 60680 (SAN 215-8744).

Information & Referral Federation of Los Angeles County, Inc., *(Info Referral Fed; 0-938371),* 3035 Tyler Ave., El Monte, CA 91731 (SAN 661-2709) Tel 818-350-1841.

Information Arts, *(Info Arts; 0-937665),* P.O. Box 1032, Carmel Valley, CA 933924 (SAN 659-2481) Tel 408-659-5135; 13 Via Contenta, No. 1, Carmel Valley, CA 93924 (SAN 659-249X).

†**Information Coord., Inc.,** *(Info Coord; 0-911772; 0-89990),* 1435-37 Randolph St., Detroit, MI 48226 (SAN 206-7641) Tel 313-962-9720; *CIP.*

Information Dynamics, *(Info Dynamics; 0-935437),* 111 Claybrook Dr., Silver Spring, MD 20902 (SAN 696-2688) Tel 301-593-8650.

Information Gatekeepers, Inc., *(Info Gatekeepers; 0-918435),* 214 Harvard St., Boston, MA 02134 (SAN 237-9597) Tel 617-232-3111.

Information Guides, *(Info Guides; 0-938329),* P.O. Box 0531, Hermosa Beach, CA 90254 (SAN 661-4337); 32 18th St., Hermosa Beach, CA 90254 (SAN 661-4345) Tel 213-374-1914.

Information Industry Assn., *(Info Indus; 0-942774),* 555 New Jersey Ave., NW, Washington, DC 20001 (SAN 674-5415) Tel 202-639-8262.

Information Management Press, *(Info Mgmt Pr; 0-9606408),* P.O. Box 19166, Washington, DC 20036 (SAN 218-5563) Tel 202-293-5519.

Information Pr., The, *(Info Oregon; 0-911927),* P.O. Box 957, Sisters, OR 97759 (SAN 264-1127) Tel 503-549-5181.

Information Products, *(Info Prods; 0-937978),* 30917 Rue de la Pierre, Rancho Palos Verdes, CA 90274 (SAN 214-0349) Tel 213-377-2880.

Information Pubns., *(Info Pubns; 0-931845),* P.O. Box 356, Wellesley Hills, MA 02181 (SAN 686-0214) Tel 617-235-5427.

Information Research, *(Info Res MI; 0-910085),* 10367 Paw Paw Lake Dr., Mattawan, MI 49071 (SAN 241-3159) Tel 616-668-2049.

Information Resources, Inc., *(Info Res Inc; 0-912864),* P.O. Box 417, Lexington, MA 02173 (SAN 203-1434).

Information Resources Pr., Div. of Herner & Co., *(Info Resources; 0-87815),* 1700 N. Moore St., Suite 700, Arlington, VA 22209 (SAN 202-6961) Tel 703-558-8270.

Information Services, *(Info Serv),* Suite 735, 4733 Bethesda Ave., Bethesda, MD 20814 (SAN 286-3464).

Information Store, Inc., The, *(Info Store; 0-940004),* 140 Second St., Fifth Flr., San Francisco, CA 94105 (SAN 216-8219) Tel 415-543-4636.

Information Systems Consultants, *(Info Syst Con; 0-914145),* P.O. Box 5367, Athens, GA 30604 (SAN 287-5527) Tel 404-543-4605.

Information Systems Development, *(Info Systems; 0-931738),* 1100 E. Eighth, Austin, TX 78702 (SAN 218-6244).

Information Transfer Inc., *(Info Transfer; 0-937398),* 9300 Columbia Blvd., Silver Spring, MD 20910 (SAN 213-2532) Tel 301-587-9390.

Infosource Business Pubns., *(Infosource Bus Pubns; 0-939209),* 10 E. 39th St., New York, NY 10016 (SAN 662-6122) Tel 212-889-6500.

Infosources Publishing, *(Infosources; 0-939486),* 118 W. 79th St., New York, NY 10024 (SAN 216-3985) Tel 212-595-3161.

Infosystems Publishing Co., *(Infosystems Pub; 0-935967),* 9016 Wilshire Blvd., Suite 312, Beverly Hills, CA 90211 (SAN 696-8481).

Ingham Publishing, Inc., *(Ingham Pub; 0-9611804),* P.O. Box 12642, St. Petersburg, FL 33733 (SAN 286-1127) Tel 813-343-4811.

Ingles, Andrew Lewis, & Roberta Ingles Steele, *(A L Ingles; 0-9617146),* P.O. Box 3485 FSS, Radford, VA 24143 (SAN 677-1408) Tel 703-639-6383.

Ingleside Publishing, *(Ingleside; 0-9603502),* Box 1307, Barrington, IL 60010 (SAN 213-5221) Tel 312-381-4312.

Inglewood Discoveries, *(Inglewood Dis; 0-915881),* P.O. Box 1653, Rockefeller Ctr. Sta., New York, NY 10185 (SAN 294-0418) Tel 212-362-6390.

†**Inglewood Public Library,** *(Inglewood CA; 0-913578),* 101 W. Manchester Blvd., Inglewood, CA 90301 (SAN 201-5145) Tel 213-649-7397; Orders to: Inglewood Finance Dept., P.O. Box 6500, Inglewood, CA 90301 (SAN 215-0018); *CIP.*

Ingram, Rose S., *(Ingram; 0-9606230),* P.O. Box 31895, Lafayette, LA 70503 (SAN 217-5290) Tel 318-984-3395.

Ink Arts Pubns., *(Ink Art Pubns),* P.O. Box 36070, Indianapolis, IN 46236 (SAN 213-0874) Tel 317-897-5793.

Ink Illusions Inc., *(Ink Illusions; 0-9614736),* 509 N. Horne St., Oceanside, CA 92054 (SAN 692-9087) Tel 619-722-3097.

Ink Plus, Inc., *(Ink Plus; 0-939449),* 10245 Main St., Suite 1-3, Bellevue, WA 98004 (SAN 663-3609) Tel 206-454-8473.

Ink Publishing Co., *(Ink Pub AZ),* 15 E. Calle Conquista, Tucson, AZ 85716 (SAN 663-6284); Dist. by: Donning Co. Pubs., 5659 Virginia Beach Blvd., Norfolk, VA 23502 (SAN 211-6316) Tel 804-461-8090; Toll free: 800-446-8572.

Ink Slinger Publishing Company, *(Ink Slinger Pub; 0-941956),* P.O. Box 2425, Bellingham, WA 98227 (SAN 239-7757) Tel 206-734-2123.

Ink Stain Pr., Inc., *(Ink Stain Pr; 0-9615428),* P.O. Box 940, Seaside, CA 93955 (SAN 695-779X) Tel 408-647-2237.

Inka Dinka Ink Childrens Pr., Div. of HeBo, Inc., *(I D I C P; 0-939700),* 4741 Guerley Rd., Cincinnati, OH 45238 (SAN 293-2814) Tel 513-471-0825; Dist. by: Baker & Taylor, Midwest Div., 501 Gladiola Ave., Momence, IL 60954 (SAN 169-2100) Tel 201-722-8000; Dist. by: Baker & Taylor, Southwest Div., Mt. Olive Rd., Commerce, GA 30529 (SAN 169-1503) Tel 404-335-5000; Dist. by: Baker & Taylor, Eastern Div., 50 Kirby Ave., Somerville, NJ 08876 (SAN 169-4901); Dist. by: Inka Dinka Ink Wizard Productions, 4741 Guerley Rd., Cincinnati, OH 45238 (SAN 293-2814) Tel 513-471-0825.

Inkblot Pubns., *(Inkblot Pubns; 0-934301),* 1506 Bonita, Berkeley, CA 94709 (SAN 693-4080) Tel 415-848-7510; Dist. by: Small Press Distribution, Inc., 1814 San Pablo Ave., Berkeley, CA 94702 (SAN 204-5826) Tel 415-549-3336.

Inkling Pubns., Inc., *(Inkling Pubns; 0-915521),* P.O. Box 65798, St. Paul, MN 55165-0798 (SAN 297-1801) Tel 612-221-0326.

Inkspot Press, *(Inkspot Pr; 0-9611590),* 635 Staats, Bloomington, IN 47401 (SAN 285-323X) Tel 812-336-0375.

Inkstone Books, *(Inkstone Books; 0-9604542),* P.O. Box 22172, Carmel, CA 93922 (SAN 262-043X) Tel 408-375-3296.

Inkworks Pr., *(Inkworks; 0-930712),* 4220 Telegraph Ave., Oakland, CA 94609 (SAN 281-8124) Tel 415-652-7111; Dist. by: Carrier Pigeon, 40 Plympton St., Boston, MA 02118 (SAN 169-3301) Tel 617-542-5679.

Inky Press Productions, *(Inky Pr; 0-930810),* P.O. Box 725, Urbana, IL 61801 (SAN 283-3840); Dist. by: Prairie Book Arts Center, P.O. Box 725, Urbana, IL 61801 (SAN 699-5756) Tel 217-352-6621.

Inland Coast, Ltd., *(Inland Coast; 0-936125),* P.O. Box 8632, Denver, CO 80206 (SAN 696-8503) Tel 303-377-3173; 100 S. Cherry St., Denver, CO 80206 (SAN 696-8511).

Inman, W. Richard, *(W R Inman),* 996-C Ponderoso Ave., Sunnyvale, CA 94086 (SAN 208-4198).

Inner Joy Enterprises, *(Inner Joy Ent; 0-9616187),* 4120 W. Morningside, Santa Ana, CA 92703 (SAN 658-3512) Tel 714-537-4165.

Inner Peace Publishing, *(Inner Peace Pub; 0-9615934),* P.O. Box 448, Lynden, WA 98264 (SAN 696-8996).

Inner Traditions International, Ltd., *(Inner Tradit; 0-89281),* Park St., Rochester, VT 05767 (SAN 208-6948); Orders to: Harper & Row Pubs., Inc., Keystone Industrial Pk., Scranton, PA 18512 (SAN 215-3742); Toll free: 800-C-HARPER. Imprints: Astrologer's Library (Astrologers Lib); Destiny Books (Destiny Bks); Lindisfarne Press (Lindisfarne Pr).

Inneraction *See* American Council for Voluntary International Action

Innerer Klang, *(I Klang; 0-911623),* 7 Sherman St., 2B, Charlestown, MA 02129 (SAN 264-1542) Tel 617-242-0689.

Innerlogic Circles, *(Innerlogic Cir; 0-935805),* 5666 La Jolla, La Jolla, CA 92037 (SAN 696-8635) Tel 619-456-2216.

Innersearch Publishing, *(Innersearch; 0-931029),* Rte. 2, Box 328, Clanton, AL 35045 (SAN 678-9919) Tel 205-755-9672.

InnerVision Publishing Co., *(InnerVision; 0-917483),* 1218 Eaglewood Dr., Virginia Beach, VA 23454 (SAN 656-0709) Tel 804-425-2245.

Innisfree Publishing Co., *(Innisfree; 0-918253),* 1850 N. Whitley Ave., Hollywood, CA 90028 (SAN 657-2723) Tel 213-465-1508.

Innovations Inc., *(Innovations Inc; 0-933241),* 1225 E. Ft. Union Blvd, Suite 200, Midvale, UT 84047 (SAN 692-4050) Tel 801-561-9002.

Innovations Press, *(Innovations Pr; 0-949438),* P.O. Box 13158, Pittsburgh, PA 15243 (SAN 219-967X) Tel 412-341-4863.

Innovative Communications, *(Innovative Comns; 0-936977),* 2574 N. University Dr., No. 201, Sunrise, FL 33322 (SAN 658-7313) Tel 305-742-0450.

Innovative Informations Inc., *(Innovative Inform; 0-910661),* P.O. Box 408, Greenbelt, MD 20770 (SAN 262-7302) Tel 301-345-4372.

Innovative Learning Designs, *(Innovative Learn; 0-931303),* 7811 SE 27th, Suite 104, Mercer Island, WA 98040 (SAN 685-2106) Tel 206-232-2697.

Innovative Learning Strategies, *(Innovative Lrn; 0-9616224),* 570 Pennsylvania Ave., San Francisco, CA 94107 (SAN 658-5507) Tel 415-647-1672.

Innovative Opportunity Ent., *(Innovative Opp; 0-9613924),* P.O. Box 1018, Kingston, WA 98346 (SAN 687-6366) Tel 206-842-5129.

Innovative Pr., *(Innovative AZ; 0-9615958),* P.O. Box 25582, Tempe, AZ 85282 (SAN 697-2969) Tel 602-834-1211; 114 E. Balboa, Tempe, AZ 85282 (SAN 697-2977).

Innovative Publishing Co., *(Innovative Pub; 0-9617001),* 129 Front St., Mineola, NY 11501 (SAN 662-5371) Tel 516-969-3676.

†**Innovative Sciences, Inc.,** *(Innovative Sci; 0-913804),* 300 Broad St., Stamford, CT 06901 (SAN 206-9229) Tel 203-359-1311; Orders to: Park Square Sta., P.O. Box 15129, Stamford, CT 06901 (SAN 685-3323); *CIP.*

Innovex Press, *(Innovex; 0-9609906),* 19686 Via Grande, Saratoga, CA 95070 (SAN 271-0129) Tel 415-964-3545.

Inns-Piration Guide Publishing Co., *(Inns-Piration Guide; 0-9616343),* P.O. Box 404, Newark, NY 14513 (SAN 658-7925) Tel 315-331-3904; 103 Heath St., Newark, NY 14513 (SAN 658-7933).

InPrint, *(InPrint; 0-937362),* P.O. Box 687, Farmingdale, NJ 07727 (SAN 262-0448).

Inquiry Press, *(Inquiry Pr; 0-918112),* 1880 N. Eastman, Midland, MI 48640 (SAN 208-1164) Tel 517-631-0009.

Insearch Pr., *(Insearch Pr; 0-943902),* 408 W. Main, Lexington, IL 61753 (SAN 241-1229) Tel 309-365-8746.

Inside Savannah, Inc., *(Inside Savannah; 0-937839),* P.O. Box 22307, Savannah, GA 31403 (SAN 659-4719) Tel 912-234-9090; 7 Drayton St., Savannah, GA 31403 (SAN 659-4727).

Insiders' Publishing Group, *(Insiders Pub; 0-932338),* P.O. Box 2091, Blowing Rock, NC 28605 (SAN 213-3245) Tel 704-295-3001.

Names

†**Insight Pr.,** *(Insight Pr CA; 0-935218),* 614 Vermont St., San Francisco, CA 94107 (SAN 213-0955) Tel 415-826-3488; *CIP.*

Insight Pr., *(Insight San Jose; 0-936813),* 4353 Clearpark Pl., San Jose, CA 95136 (SAN 699-8925) Tel 408-629-0570.

†**Insight Pr., Inc.,** *(Insight Pr; 0-914520),* P.O. Box 8369, New Orleans, LA 70182 (SAN 202-6988); *CIP.*

Insights Bks., *(Insights Bks; 0-910087),* P.O. Box 1784, Ann Arbor, MI 48106 (SAN 240-8252) Tel 313-663-9645; Dist. by: Alpine Enterprises, P.O. Box 766, Dearborn, MI 48121 (SAN 210-6973) Tel 313-333-3863.

Inspiration Co., *(Inspiration MI; 0-934804),* P. O. Box 17, Birmingham, MI 48012 (SAN 221-0738) Tel 313-642-4848.

Inspiration House Pubs., *(Inspiration Conn; 0-918114),* P.O. Box 1, South Windsor, CT 06074 (SAN 206-1066) Tel 203-289-7363.

Inspirational Press *See* **Arrowood Pr.**

Institute for a People's Church, *(Inst People's Church; 0-9612114),* 1051 N. Rademacher, Detroit, MI 48209 (SAN 287-7414) Tel 313-841-5885.

Institute for Advanced Studies of World Religions, The, *(Inst Adv Stud Wld; 0-915078),* 2150 Center Ave., Fort Lee, NJ 07024 (SAN 265-3885).

Institute for American Research, *(Inst Am Res; 0-911773),* 300 N. Los Carneros Rd., Goleta, CA 93117 (SAN 264-116X).

Institute For Applied Forth Research, The, *(Inst Appl Forth; 0-914593),* 478 Thurston Rd., Rochester, NY 14619 (SAN 295-3676) Tel 716-235-0168; Dist. by: Institute for Applied Forth Research, Inc., P.O. Box 27686, Rochester, NY 14627 (SAN 295-3692).

Institute for Briquetting & Agglomeration, *(Inst Briquetting),* P.O. Box 794, Erie, PA 16512 (SAN 224-8816) Tel 814-838-1133; 2615 W. Tenth St., Erie, PA 16505 (SAN 669-1064).

†**Institute for Business Planning, Inc.,** *(Inst Busn Plan; 0-87624),* B & P Marking, Route 9W, Englewood Cliffs, NJ 07632 (SAN 202-7003) Tel 201-542-2015; Orders to: Eleanor Brigida, Customer Service, 200 Old Tappan Rd., Old Tappan, NJ 07675 (SAN 685-3331) Tel 201-767-5059; *CIP.*

Institute for Byzantine & Modern Greek Studies, Inc., *(Inst Byzantine; 0-914744),* 115 Gilbert Rd., Belmont, MA 02178 (SAN 201-5110) Tel 617-484-6595.

Institute for Christian Economics, Affil. of American Bureau of Economic Research, *(Inst Christian; 0-930464),* P.O. Box 8000, Tyler, TX 75711 (SAN 297-1828) Tel 214-593-8919. *Imprints:* Reconstruction Press (Reconstruct Pr).

Institute for Christian Leadership, Div. of International Foundation, *(Inst Christ Leadership; 0-933939),* 9733 SE French Acres Dr., Portland, OR 97266 (SAN 693-0557) Tel 503-774-0111.

Institute for Computer Engineering Research, Div. of Access Conference Assocs., Inc., *(ICER; 0-937227),* 9719 Duffer Way, Gaithersburg, MD 20879 (SAN 658-7380) Tel 301-921-9424.

Institute for Contemporary Studies *See* **ICS Pr.**

Institute for Cross-Cultural Research, *(ICR; 0-911976),* 4000 Albermarle St., NW, Washington, DC 20016 (SAN 206-6505).

Institute for Cultural Progress, *(Inst Cult Prog; 0-942776),* 1710 Connecticut Ave., NW, Washington, DC 20009 (SAN 219-8398) Tel 202-387-7305; Dist. by: Publishing Center for Cultural Resources, 625 Broadway, New York, NY 10012 (SAN 274-9025) Tel 212-260-2010.

Institute for Defense & Disarmament Studies, *(Inst Def & Dis; 0-915883),* 2001 Beacon St., Brookline, MA 02146 (SAN 289-6052).

Institute For Democratic Socialism, *(Inst Dem Socialism; 0-9613009),* 145 Tremont St., Boston, MA 02111 (SAN 293-4949) Tel 617-426-9026.

Institute for Earth Education, The, *(Inst Earth; 0-917011),* P.O. Box 288, Warrenville, IL 60555 (SAN 655-7449) Tel 312-393-3096; Dist. by: Pacific Pipeline, 19215 66th Ave. S., Kent, WA 98032 (SAN 208-2128) Tel 206-872-5523; Dist. by: Bookpeople, 2929 Fifth St., Berkeley, CA 94710 (SAN 168-9517) Tel 415-549-3030.

Institute for Ecological Policies, *(Inst Ecological; 0-937786),* 9208 Christopher St., Fairfax, VA 22031 (SAN 215-6598).

†**Institute for Econometric Research,** *(Inst Econometric; 0-917604),* 3471 N. Federal Hwy., Suite 350, Ft. Lauderdale, FL 33306 (SAN 209-2174) Tel 305-563-9000; Toll free: 800-327-6720; *CIP.*

†**Institute for Economic & Financial Research,** Subs. of American Classical College, *(Inst Econ Finan; 0-86654; 0-918968),* 607 McKnight St., NW, Albuquerque, NM 87102 (SAN 662-0450); Dist. by: American Classical College Pr., P.O. Box 4526, Albuquerque, NM 87196 (SAN 201-2618) Tel 505-843-7749; *CIP.*

†**Institute for Economic & Political World Strategic Studies,** Affil. of American Classical College, *(Inst Econ Pol; 0-930008; 0-86722),* P.O. Box 4526, Sta. A, Albuquerque, NM 87106 (SAN 210-4431) Tel 505-843-7749; 607 McKnight St., Albuquerque, NM 87102 (SAN 662-0469); *CIP.*

Institute for Educational Leadership, *(Inst Educ Lead; 0-937846),* 1001 Connecticut Ave. NW, Suite 310, Washington, DC 20036 (SAN 225-7823) Tel 202-676-5900.

Institute for Educational Management, *(Inst Ed Management; 0-934222),* Harvard Graduate School of Education, 339 Gutman Library, Six Appian Way, Cambridge, MA 02138 (SAN 213-5175) Tel 617-495-2655.

Institute for Effective Management, *(Inst Effect Mgmt; 0-914804),* Chapman Rd., Fountainville, PA 18923 (SAN 206-4553) Tel 215-345-0265.

Institute for Environmental Studies, *(Inst for Environ),* 3400 Walnut St, Philadelphia, PA 19104 (SAN 226-5648).

Institute for Evolutionary Research, *(Inst Evolutionary; 0-938710),* 200 Park Ave., Suite 303 East, New York, NY 10166 (SAN 215-8760) Tel 212-687-0281; Orders to: P.O. Box 7404, Charlottesville, VA 22906 (SAN 662-0477) Tel 804-979-1270; Dist. by: DeVorss & Co., 1046 Princeton Dr., P.O. Box 550, Marina del Rey, CA 90294 (SAN 168-9886) Tel 213-870-7478; Dist. by: Samuel Weiser, Inc., P.O. Box 612, York Beach, ME 03910 (SAN 202-9588) Tel 207-363-4393; Toll free: 800-843-6666.

Institute for Family Research & Education *See* **Ed-U Pr., Inc.**

Institute for Food & Development Policy, *(Inst Food & Develop; 0-935028),* 1885 Mission St., San Francisco, CA 94103 (SAN 213-327X) Tel 415-864-8555.

Institute for Foreign Policy Analysis (IFPA) *See* **Unipub**

†**Institute for Foreign Policy Analysis, Inc.,** *(Inst Foreign Policy Anal; 0-89549),* 675 Massachusetts Ave., Central Plaza Bldg. 10th Flr., Cambridge, MA 02139 (SAN 210-444X) Tel 617-492-2116; Dist. by: Pergamon Brassey's International Defence Pubs., Maxwell House, Fairview Pk., Elmsford, NY 10523 (SAN 200-741X) Tel 914-592-7700; *CIP.*

Institute for Fund Raising *See* **Public Management Institute, Institute for Fund Raising**

Institute for Historical Review, *(Inst Hist Rev; 0-939484),* P.O. Box 1306, Torrance, CA 90505 (SAN 220-1275) Tel 213-533-8108.

Institute for Historical Review *See* **Noontide Pr., The**

Institute for Human Growth & Awareness, The, *(Inst Human Growth; 0-87852),* P.O. Box 6695, San Jose, CA 95150 (SAN 202-3636) Tel 408-275-1911.

Institute for Human Potential & Social Development, *(Inst Human Soc; 0-916843),* P.O. Box 3071, Dept. L-7, Iowa City, IA 52244 (SAN 653-8762) Tel 319-354-6910; 1530 Bladenburg Rd., Box 29, Ottumwa, IA 52501 (SAN 653-8770) Tel 515-682-4305.

Institute for Humane Studies, Inc., *(Inst Humane; 0-89617),* P.O. Box 1149, Menlo Park, CA 94025 (SAN 214-123X) Tel 415-323-2464; 1177 University Dr., Menlo Park, CA 94025 (SAN 669-1072); Orders to: P.O. Box 2256, Wichita, KS 67201 (SAN 214-1248) Tel 316-832-5604.

Institute for Independent Social Journalism, *(IISJ; 0-917654),* 33 W. 17th St., New York, NY 10011 (SAN 201-842X) Tel 212-691-0404.

Institute for Independent Study, Inc., *(Inst Indp Study; 0-938247),* 1609 Westover Hills Rd., Richmond, VA 23225 (SAN 661-4221) Tel 804-231-3451.

Institute for Information Management, *(Inst Info Mgmt; 0-931900),* Pruneyard Towers, 1901 S. Boscom Ave., Suite 230, Campbell, CA 95008 (SAN 209-0686) Tel 408-559-6911.

†**Institute for Information Studies,** *(Inst Info Stud; 0-935294),* 200 Little Falls St., Suite 104, Falls Church, VA 22046 (SAN 215-6601); *CIP.*

Institute for International Economics, *(Inst Intl Eco; 0-88132),* 11 Dupont Cir., NW, Pubns., Dept., Washington, DC 20036 (SAN 293-2865) Tel 202-328-0583.

Institute for Labor & Mental Health, *(Inst Labor & Mental; 0-935933),* 3137 Telegraph Ave., Oakland, CA 94609 (SAN 696-8643) Tel 415-482-0805.

Institute for Local Self-Reliance, *(Inst Local Self Re; 0-917582),* 2425 18th St., NW, Washington, DC 20009 (SAN 217-7919) Tel 202-232-4108.

Institute for Mathematical Philosophy Pr., *(Inst Math Philo Pr; 0-931441),* P.O. Box 3410, Annapolis, MD 21403 (SAN 683-1931) Tel 301-267-0811.

Institute for Mediterranean Affairs, *(Inst Medit Affairs),* 27 E. 62nd St, New York, NY 10028 (SAN 225-6789) Tel 212-988-1725.

Institute for Meeting and Conference Management, *(Inst Meeting Con Mgmt; 0-931273),* P.O. Box 14097, Washington, DC 20044 (SAN 681-9923) Tel 703-281-0932.

†**Institute for Palestine Studies,** *(Inst Palestine; 0-88728),* P.O. Box 25697, Georgetown Sta., Washington, DC 20007 (SAN 207-611X) Tel 202-342-3990; Toll free: 800-874-3614; Dist. by: Ubiquity Distributors, 1050 E. Fourth St., Brooklyn, NY 11230 (SAN 200-7428) Tel 718-789-3137; *CIP.*

Institute For Peace & Justice, Inc., *(Inst Peace; 0-912765),* 4144 Lindell Blvd., Suite 400, St. Louis, MO 63108 (SAN 282-7891) Tel 314-533-4445.

†**Institute for Personality & Ability Testing, Inc.,** *(Inst Personality & Ability; 0-918296),* P.O. Box 188, Champaign, IL 61820 (SAN 209-3197) Tel 217-352-4739; *CIP.*

†**Institute for Policy Studies,** *(Inst Policy Stud; 0-89758),* 1901 Q St., NW, Washington, DC 20009 (SAN 212-1026) Tel 202-234-9382; *CIP.*

Institute for Polynesian Studies, The, *(Inst Polynesian; 0-939154),* Brigham Young Univ., Hawaii Campus, Laie, HI 96762 (SAN 219-1911) Tel 508-293-3667; Brigham Young Univ., Box 1829, ; Dist. by: University of Hawaii Press, 2840 Kolowalu St., Honolulu, HI 96822 (SAN 202-5353) Tel 808-948-8697.

Institute for Product Safety, *(Inst Product; 0-938830),* P.O. Box 1931, Durham, NC 27702 (SAN 216-0439).

Institute for Public Management, Div. of Peter Warner Assocs., *(Inst Pub Mgmt; 0-935807),* 550 W. Jackson Blvd., Suite 365, Chicago, IL 60606 (SAN 238-8251) Tel 312-559-0515.

Institute for Quality in Human Life, *(Inst Qual Hum Life; 0-939630),* 6335 N. Delaware Ave., Portland, OR 97217 (SAN 206-4367) Tel 503-289-6136.

Institute for Rational-Emotive Therapy, *(Inst Rational-Emotive; 0-917476),* 45 E. 65th St., New York, NY 10021 (SAN 210-3079) Tel 212-535-0822.

Institute for Rational Living, *(Inst Rat Liv),* 1162 Beacon St., Brookline, MA 02146 (SAN 209-5068) Tel 617-739-5063.

Institute for Research in History, The, *(Inst Res Hist; 0-913865),* 1133 Broadway, Rm. 923, New York, NY 10010 (SAN 286-780X) Tel 212-691-7316.

Institute for Research of Rheumatic Diseases, *(Inst Rheumatic),* 2025 Broadway, 19C, New York, NY 10023 (SAN 271-048X) Tel 212-595-1368; P.O. Box 955, New York, NY 10023 (SAN 692-834X).

Institute for Responsive Education, *(Inst Responsive; 0-917754),* 605 Commonwealth Ave., Boston, MA 02215 (SAN 216-1451) Tel 617-353-3309.

†**Institute for Social Research Univ. of Michigan,** *(Inst Soc Res; 0-87944),* P.O. Box 1248, Ann Arbor, MI 48106-1248 (SAN 210-6035) Tel 313-764-7509; *CIP.*

†**Institute for Socioeconomic Studies,** *(Inst Socioecon; 0-915312),* Airport Rd., White Plains, NY 10604 (SAN 235-6023) Tel 914-428-7400; *CIP.*

Institute for Southern Studies, *(Inst Southern Studies),* 604 Chapel Hill St., Durham, NC 27701 (SAN 219-192X) Tel 919-688-8167; P.O. Box 531, Durham, NC 27702 (SAN 669-1080).

Institute for Studies in American Music, *(Inst Am Music; 0-914678),* Conservatory of Music, Brooklyn College, Brooklyn, NY 11210 (SAN 202-6996) Tel 718-780-5655.

Institute for Substance Abuse Research, Subs. of Security Consultant Services, Inc., *(Inst Subs Abuse Res; 0-935847),* 1717 20th St., Suite 100, Vero Beach, FL 32960 (SAN 699-7759) Tel 305-569-3121; Orders to: P.O. Box 6837, Vero Beach, FL 32961-6837 (SAN 662-4065) Tel 305-569-3121.

Institute for Technology Policy in Development, *(Inst Tech Policy; 0-9616141),* SUNY, Graduate Physics Bldg. A-134, Stony Brook, NY 11733 (SAN 699-8968) Tel 516-246-8230.

Institute for the Advancement of Health, *(Inst Advance Heal; 0-914533),* 16 E. 53rd St., New York, NY 10022 (SAN 289-2936) Tel 212-832-8282.

Institute for the Analysis, Evaluation & Design of Human Action, *(Inst Analysis; 0-938526),* 44 Clifford Ave., Pelham, NY 10803 (SAN 215-8752).

Institute for the Development of Emotional Life Skills (IDEALS), *(IDEALS PA),* Box 391, State College, PA 16801 (SAN 224-358X).

Institute for the Development of Indian Law, *(Inst Dev Indian Law),* 1104 Glydon St., SE, Vienna, VA 22180 (SAN 662-0485) Tel 703-938-7822.

Institute for the Development of the Harmonious Human Being Publishing, Inc., *(IDHHB; 0-89556),* P.O. Box 370, Nevada City, CA 95959 (SAN 211-3635) Tel 916-786-7313.

Institute for the Future, *(Inst Future),* 2740 Sand Hill Rd., Menlo Park, CA 94025 (SAN 225-1892) Tel 415-854-6322.

Institute for the Preservation of Wealth, The, *(Inst Preserv Wealth; 0-938689),* 268 Greenwood Ave., Bethel, CT 06801 (SAN 661-5708) Tel 203-748-2036; P.O. Box 60, Bethel, CT 06801 (SAN 661-5716); Dist. by: Silver & Gold Report, 268 Greenwood Ave., Bethel, CT 06801 (SAN 221-9972).

Institute for the Study of Animal Problems, *(Inst Study Animal; 0-937712),* 2100 L St., NW, Washington, DC 20037 (SAN 215-2088) Tel 202-452-1148.

Institute for the Study of Diplomacy *See* **Georgetown Univ., Schl. of Foreign Service**

Institute for the Study of Human Awareness, *(Inst Study Hum Aware; 0-937067),* P.O. Box 11068, Minneapolis, MN 55411 (SAN 658-6112) Tel 612-522-1585; 3931 Sheridan Ave., N, Minneapolis, MN 55412 (SAN 658-6120).

†**Institute for the Study of Human Issues,** *(ISHI PA; 0-89727; 0-915980),* 210 S. 13th St., Philadelphia, PA 19107 (SAN 207-6608) Tel 215-732-9729; *CIP.*

Institute for the Study of Human Knowledge, *(Ins Study Human),* P.O. Box 1062, Cambridge, MA 02238 (SAN 226-4536) Tel 617-497-4124; Toll free: 800-222-ISHK.

Institute for the Study of Man. Inc., *(Inst Study Man),* 1133 13th St., NW, Suite Comm. 2, Washington, DC 20005 (SAN 213-523X) Tel 202-789-0231.

Institute For Theory Testing, The, *(Inst Theory Test; 0-937719),* P.O. Box 635, Williamsville, NY 14221 (SAN 659-2503) Tel 716-688-5981; 60 Groton Dr., Williamsville, NY 14221 (SAN 659-2511).

Institute for Traditional Medicine, *(Inst Trad Med; 0-939163),* 2442 SE Sherman, Portland, OR 97214 (SAN 662-8346) Tel 503-233-1324.

Institute for Urban & Regional Studies, Washington Univ., *(Inst for Urban & Regional),* P.O. Box 1051, St. Louis, MO 63130 (SAN 212-2812).

Institute for Urban Design, *(Inst Urban Des; 0-942468),* Main P.O. Box 105, Purchase, NY 10577 (SAN 264-1178) Tel 914-253-9341.

Institute for Vaishnava Studies, The, *(Inst Vaishnava; 0-936979),* 42 Francis Ave., No. 3, Cambridge, MA 02138 (SAN 658-7968) Tel 617-498-4075.

Institute in Basic Youth Conflicts, *(Inst Basic Youth; 0-916888),* P.O. Box 1, Oak Brook, IL 60521 (SAN 208-6972) Tel 312-323-9800.

Institute of Arab Studies, *(Inst Arab Stud; 0-912031),* 556 Trapelo Rd., Belmont, MA 02178 (SAN 265-3583).

Institute of Behavioral Learning, *(Inst Behav; 0-910265),* 4550 Wilshire Blvd., Los Angeles, CA 90010 (SAN 240-8619).

Institute of Biblical Studies, *(Inst Biblical; 0-934743),* P.O. Box 34098, San Diego, CA 92103 (SAN 694-1672) Tel 619-291-7438.

Institute of Certified Travel Agents, *(Inst Cert Trav Agts; 0-931202),* 148 Linden St., Wellesley, MA 02181 (SAN 238-7700) Tel 617-237-0280.

Institute of Chartered Financial Analysts, *(Inst Charter Finan Analysts; 0-935015),* Box 3668, Charlottesville, VA 22901 (SAN 224-7313) Tel 804-977-6600.

Institute of Contemporary Art, *(ICA Inc; 0-910663),* 955 Boylston St., Boston, MA 02115 (SAN 279-1870).

Institute of Court Management, *(ICM Denver),* 1331 17th St., Suite 402, Denver, CO 80202 (SAN 227-0250) Tel 303-293-3063.

Institute of Creation Research *See* **Master Bk. Pubs.**

Institute of Early American History & Culture, *(Inst Early Am; 0-910776),* P.O. Box 220, Williamsburg, VA 23187 (SAN 201-5161) Tel 804-253-5118; Toll free: 800-223-2584.

Univ. of California, Institute of East Asian Studies, *(IEAS; 0-912966),* Publications Office, 2223 Fulton St., 6th Flr., Berkeley, CA 94720 (SAN 203-8730) Tel 415-643-6325.

Institute of Electrical & Electronics Engineers, *(Inst Electrical; 0-87942),* 345 E. 47th St., New York, NY 10017 (SAN 203-8064) Tel 212-705-7900; Orders to: IEEE Service Ctr., 445 Hoes Ln., Piscataway, NJ 08854 (SAN 203-8072) Tel 201-981-1393.

Institute of Environmental Sciences, *(Inst Environ Sci; 0-915414),* 940 E. Northwest Hwy., Mt. Prospect, IL 60056 (SAN 209-2077) Tel 312-255-1561.

Institute of Financial Education, Affil. of U.S. League of Savings Institutions, *(Inst Finan Educ; 0-912857),* 111 E. Wacker Dr., Chicago, IL 60601 (SAN 224-1382) Tel 312-644-3100; Dist. by: Caroline Hse., 2S, 250 Frontenac Rd., Naperville, IL 60540 (SAN 211-2280) Tel 312-983-6400.

Institute of Gas Technology, *(Inst Gas Tech; 0-910091),* 3424 S. State St., Chicago, IL 60616 (SAN 224-7631) Tel 312-567-3650.

Institute of General Semantics, *(Inst Gen Seman; 0-910780),* 163 Engle St., Englewood, NJ 07631 (SAN 203-8080) Tel 201-568-0551.

Institute of High Fidelity *See* **Electronic Industries Assn.**

Institute of Industrial Engineers, *(Inst Indus Eng; 0-89806),* 25 Technology Pk., Norcross, GA 30092 (SAN 213-2338) Tel 404-449-0460.

Institute of Internal Auditors, Inc., *(Inst Inter Aud; 0-89413),* 249 Maitland Ave., Altamonte Springs, FL 32701 (SAN 213-4411) Tel 305-830-7600. *Imprints:* Foundation for Auditability Research & Education, Incorporated (Found Audit Res).

Institute of International Education, *(Inst Intl Educ; 0-87206),* 809 United Nations Plaza, New York, NY 10017 (SAN 202-702X) Tel 212-984-5410.

Institute of Jesuit Sources, The, *(Inst Jesuit; 0-912422),* Fusz Memorial, St. Louis Univ., 3700 W. Pine Blvd., St. Louis, MO 63108 (SAN 202-7038) Tel 314-652-5737.

Institute of Judicial Administration New York University School of Law, *(IJA NYU; 0-943904),* Washington Square Village, New York, NY 10012 (SAN 227-0013).

Institute of Lesbian Studies, *(Inst Lesbian; 0-934903),* P.O. Box 60242, Palo Alto, CA 94306 (SAN 696-5059) Tel 415-941-3722; Dist. by: Inland Bk. Co., P.O. Box 261, 22 Hemingway Ave., East Haven, CT 06512 (SAN 200-4151) Tel 203-467-4257; Dist. by: Bookpeople, 2929 Fifth St., Berkeley, CA 94710 (SAN 168-9517) Tel 415-549-3030.

Institute of Logotherapy Pr., *(Inst Logo; 0-917867),* 2000 Dwight Way, Berkeley, CA 94794 (SAN 657-095X) Tel 415-845-2522.

Institute of Management & Labor Relations, *(Inst Mgmt & Labor),* Industrial Relations & Human Resources Dept., P.O Box 231, Ryders Lane, Cook Campus, New Brunswick, NJ 08903 (SAN 215-8779).

Institute of Management Sciences, The, *(Inst Mgmt Sci),* 290 Westminster St., Providence, RI 02903 (SAN 224-1390) Tel 401-274-2525.

Institute of Mathematical Statistics, *(Inst Math; 0-940600),* 3401 Investment Blvd., No.7, Hayward, CA 94545 (SAN 218-558X) Tel 415-783-8141.

Institute of Mediaeval Music, *(Inst Mediaeval Mus; 0-912024; 0-931902),* P.O. Box 295, Henryville, PA 18332 (SAN 658-0955) Tel 717-629-1278.

Institute of Mennonite Studies, *(Inst Mennonite; 0-936273),* 3003 Benham Ave., Elkhart, IN 46517 (SAN 697-8835) Tel 219-295-3726.

Institute of Middle Eastern & North African Affairs, *(Inst Mid East & North Africa; 0-934484),* P.O. Box 1674, Hyattsville, MD 20788 (SAN 213-8506).

Institute of Mind & Behavior, *(Inst Mind Behavior; 0-930195),* P.O. Box 522, Village Sta., New York, NY 10014 (SAN 691-9618) Tel 718-783-1471.

Institute of Modern Languages, Div. of Voluntad Pub., Inc., *(Inst Mod Lang; 0-88499; 0-8325),* 4255 W. Touhy, Lincolnwood, IL 60646 (SAN 662-0493) Tel 312-679-5500; Dist. by: National Textbook Co., 4255 W. Touhy Ave., Lincolnwood, IL 60646 (SAN 169-2208) Tel 312-679-5500.

Institute of Motivational Development, *(Inst Motiv Devel; 0-9616032; 0-939701),* 2200 S. Main St., Lombard, IL 60148 (SAN 697-8851) Tel 312-627-5000.

Institute of Paper Chemistry, *(Inst Paper Chem; 0-87010),* P.O. Box 1039, Appleton, WI 54912 (SAN 203-8099) Tel 414-734-9251.

Institute of Personal Image Consultants, *(Inst Pers Image),* c/o Image Industry Pubns., 10 Bay St. Landing, No. 7K, Staten Island, NY 10301-2511 (SAN 224-1412); Dist. by: Fairchild Bks., 7 E. 12th St., New York, NY 10003 (SAN 201-470X) Tel 212-741-4280.

Institute of Philosophy, *(Inst Philosophy; 0-930583),* P.O. Box 3705, Myrtle Beach, SC 29577 (SAN 677-1351).

Institute of Political Research, The, *(Inst Political Res; 0-935543),* 104 Meays Dr., Syracuse, NY 13209 (SAN 696-2505) Tel 315-635-7045.

Institute of Psychorientology, *(Inst Psych Inc; 0-913343),* P.O. Box 2249, 1110 Cedar, Laredo, TX 78044-2249 (SAN 283-118X) Tel 512-722-6391.

Institute of Public Administration, *(Inst Public Adm; 0-913824),* 55 W. 44th St., New York, NY 10036 (SAN 203-8102) Tel 212-661-2540.

Institute of Race Relations *See* **Oxford Univ. Pr., Inc.**

†**Institute of Real Estate Management,** Affil. of National Assn. of Realtors, *(Inst Real Estate; 0-912104),* 430 N. Michigan Ave., Chicago, IL 60611-4090 (SAN 202-7046) Tel 312-661-1930; 1955 Estes Ave., Elk Grove Village, IL 60007 (SAN 650-034X); *CIP.*

Institute of Recreation Research & Service, Dept. of Leisure Studies & Services, *(Inst Recreation Res; 0-943272),* University of Oregon, Rm. 133, Esslinger Hall, Eugene, OR 97403 (SAN 219-0249) Tel 503-686-3396.

Institute of Scientific Resources, *(Inst Sci Res; 0-913651),* P.O. Box 636, Hawthorne, CA 90251 (SAN 286-1135) Tel 213-973-6954.

Institute of Sino-American Research, *(Inst Sino-Amer; 0-913973),* 108 Shady Dr., Indiana, PA 15701 (SAN 241-5453) Tel 412-463-0513.

Names

Institute of Social Sciences & Arts, Inc., *(Inst Soc Sci; 0-915165),* P.O. Box 5663, Johnson City, TN 37603 (SAN 289-9507) Tel 615-282-9023.

Institute of Universal Faith, *(Inst Univ; 0-916801),* P.O. Box 3732 Rd.3, Grove City, PA 16127 (SAN 654-5432) Tel 814-786-9085.

Institute of Urban Studies, The Univ. of Texas at Arlington, *(Inst Urban Studies; 0-936440),* P.O. Box 19588, Arlington, TX 76019 (SAN 207-5253) Tel 817-273-3071.

Institute Press, *(Inst Pr; 0-931976),* 2210 Wilshire Blvd., Suite 171, Santa Monica, CA 90403 (SAN 211-321X) Tel 213-828-6541.

Institutes for Energy Development, Inc., *(Inst Energy; 0-89419),* 101 SW 25th St., Oklahoma City, OK 73107 (SAN 209-9322) Tel 405-232-2801.

Institution for Tuberculosis Research, Univ. of Illinois, Medical Ctr., *(Inst Tuberculosis; 0-915314),* 904 W. Adams St., Chicago, IL 60607 (SAN 207-1428) Tel 312-996-4688.

Institution of Electrical Engineers, *(Inst Elect Eng; 0-85296),* PPL/IEEE Service Ctr., 445 Hoes Ln., Piscataway, NJ 08854-4150 (SAN 213-0882) Tel 201-981-0060.

Institutional Development & Economic Affairs Service, Inc., *(Inst Dev & Econ),* Magnolia Star Rte., Nederland, CO 80466 (SAN 225-6681) Tel 303-443-8789.

Instituto Para El Desarrollo Del Derecho, Inc., *(Instituto Desarrollo; 0-914939),* Calle Antolin Nin 469, Hato Rey, PR 00918 (SAN 289-2502) Tel 809-790-7150.

Instructional Resources Inc., *(Instruct Res; 0-938026),* P.O. Box 3452, Tallahassee, FL 32315 (SAN 215-7799) Tel 904-385-2546.

Instructional Support Services *See I.S.S. Pubns.*

Instructional Technologies, Inc., *(Instruct Tech; 0-935115),* P.O. Box 828, Plymouth, MI 48170 (SAN 695-2666) Tel 313-565-7053.

Instructivision, Inc., *(Instructivision; 0-938797),* 3 Regent St., Livingston, NJ 07039 (SAN 661-5090) Tel 201-992-9081.

Instructo, McGraw-Hill *See McGraw-Hill Bk. Co.*

Instructor Books, *(Instructor Bks),* 545 Fifth Ave., New York, NY 10017 (SAN 669-6813); Orders to: P.O. Box 6177, Duluth, MN 55806 (SAN 699-5810).

†**Instrument Society of America,** *(Instru Soc; 0-87664; 1-55617),* P.O. Box 12277, 67 Alexander Dr., Research Triangle Park, NC 27709 (SAN 202-7054) Tel 919-549-8411; *CIP.*

Instrumentalist Co., *(Instrumental Co),* 200 Northfield Rd., Northfield, IL 60093 (SAN 203-7033) Tel 312-446-5000; Toll free: 800-323-5559.

Insurance Achievement, Inc., *(Insurance Achiev; 0-88171),* 7330 Highland Rd., Baton Rouge, LA 70808 (SAN 264-1186); Toll free: 800-535-3042.

Insurance Industries Publishing Co., *(Insur Indus; 0-918767),* 17462 Parker Dr., Tustin, CA 92680 (SAN 657-355X) Tel 714-731-3389.

Insurance Information Institute, *(Insur Info; 0-932387),* 110 William St., New York, NY 10038 (SAN 271-1192).

Insurance Institute of America, Inc., *(IIA; 0-89462),* 720 Providence Rd., Malvern, PA 19355 (SAN 210-2129) Tel 215-644-2100.

Insurance Research Service, *(Ins Res Svc; 0-942262),* 571 E. Main St., Brevard, NC 28712 (SAN 213-3288) Tel 704-883-9333.

Inswinger, Inc., *(Inswinger; 0-9608170),* 5580 La Jolla Blvd., Suite 418, La Jolla, CA 92037 (SAN 238-826X).

Intecon, Div. of International Technology Consultants, Inc., *(Intecon MA; 0-9617127),* 16 Chauncy St., Apt. G, Cambridge, MA 02138 (SAN 662-6769) Tel 617-868-0722.

†**Integral Yoga Pubns.,** *(Integral Yoga Pubns; 0-932040),* Satchidananda Ashram-Yogaville, Rte. 1, Box 172, Buckingham, VA 23921 (SAN 285-0338) Tel 804-969-4801; *CIP.*

Integrated Education Assocs., *(Integrated Ed Assoc; 0-912008),* Univ. of Massachusetts, Schl. of Education, Amherst, MA 01003 (SAN 203-8129) Tel 413-545-0327.

Integrated Energy Systems, Div. of Edith Shedd & Assocs., Inc., *(Integ Energy; 0-9608358),* Rte. 2, Box 61A1, Monroe, GA 30655 (SAN 240-6802) Tel 404-267-3534.

Integrated Excellence Pr., *(Integrated Excel Pr; 0-938383),* P.O. Box 1085, Bemidji, MN 56601 (SAN 661-4507); Rte. 2, P.O. Box 170, Becida, MN 56625 (SAN 661-4515) Tel 218-854-7300.

Integrated Press, *(Integrated Pr; 0-9610310),* 526 Comstock Dr., Tiburon, CA 94920 (SAN 263-2403) Tel 415-435-2446.

Integration Pr., *(Integ Pr; 0-9609928),* c/o H. Newton Malony, 135 N. Oakland, Pasadena, CA 91101 (SAN 271-1257) Tel 818-584-5528.

Integrity Pr., *(Integrity; 0-918048),* 3888 Morse Rd., Columbus, OH 43219 (SAN 210-2145) Tel 614-471-2759.

Integrity Times Pr., *(Integrity Times; 0-930131),* 118 Laidley St., San Francisco, CA 94131 (SAN 669-6864) Tel 415-647-3679; Dist. by: Bookpeople, 2929 Fifth St., Berkeley, CA 94710 (SAN 168-9517) Tel 415-549-3030.

Integrity Word Ministries International, Inc., *(IWM Intl; 0-938433),* Rte. 12, P.O. Box 91, Raleigh, NC 27610 (SAN 661-2946) Tel 919-266-3602; P.O. Box 19962, Raleigh, NC 27619 (SAN 661-2954).

Intel Corp., *(Intel Corp; 0-917017; 1-55512),* 3065 Bowers Ave., SC6-60, Santa Clara, CA 95051 (SAN 277-1446) Tel 408-496-7973; Toll free: 800-548-4725.

Intelligent Machine Co., *(Intel Machine; 0-937397),* 3813 N. 14th St., Arlington, VA 22201 (SAN 658-8727) Tel 703-528-9136.

Intentional Educations, Inc., *(Intent Ed Inc; 0-9607970),* 341 Mt. Auburn St., Watertown, MA 02172 (SAN 239-6610) Tel 617-923-7707.

Inter-American Development Bank, *(IADB; 0-940602),* 808 17th St. NW, Washington, DC 20577 (SAN 226-5745).

Inter-American Safety Council, *(Inter-Am Safety),* 33 Park Pl, Englewood, NJ 07631 (SAN 237-1847) Tel 201-871-0004.

Inter-American Tropical Tuna Commission, *(Inter-Am Tropical; 0-9603078),* P.O. Box 1529, La Jolla, CA 92093 (SAN 214-3143); Scripps Inst. of Oceanography, La Jolla, CA 92038 (SAN 680-0467).

†**Inter American Univ. Pr.,** *(Inter Am U Pr; 0-913480),* Call Box 5100, San German, PR 00753 (SAN 202-7062) Tel 809-892-5055; *CIP.*

Inter-Crescent Publishing Co., Inc., *(Inter-Crescent; 0-916400),* 12021 Nieta Dr., Garden Grove, CA 92640 (SAN 208-7006) Tel 714-537-1000.

Inter/Face Assocs., Inc., *(Interface Assocs; 0-938135),* 62 Washington St., Middletown, CT 06457 (SAN 661-177X) Tel 203-344-1046; Toll free: 800-433-1116.

Inter-Hemispheric Educ. Resource Ctr., *(Inter-Hem Educ; 0-911213),* P.O. Box 4506, Albuquerque, NM 87106 (SAN 275-0570) Tel 505-266-5009.

Inter-Optics Pubns., Inc., *(Inter-Optics Pubns; 0-935726),* P.O. Box 233, Ambler, PA 19002 (SAN 214-0403) Tel 215-641-0133.

Inter-Religious Task Force for Social Analysis, *(Inter-Religious Task; 0-936476),* 361 Athol Ave., Oakland, CA 94606 (SAN 216-2563).

Inter-Sellf Inc., *(Inter-Sellf; 0-932127),* P.O. Box 55759, Seattle, WA 98155 (SAN 686-5186) Tel 206-742-8244; Dist. by: Pacific Pipeline Inc., 19215 66th Ave. S., Kent, WA 98032 (SAN 208-2128) Tel 206-872-5523; Dist. by: Baker & Taylor, 50 Kirby Ave., Somerville, NJ 08876 (SAN 169-4901).

Inter-Ski Services, Inc., *(Inter-Ski; 0-931636),* P.O. Box 3635, Georgetown Sta., Washington, DC 20007 (SAN 221-0622) Tel 202-342-0886.

Inter-Travel Communications Inc., *(Inter-Travel Comms; 0-933615),* P.O. Box 12765, Jackson, MS 39211 (SAN 692-4670) Tel 601-957-3642.

Inter-University Consortium for Political & Social Research, Affil. of Univ. of Michigan Institute for Social Research, *(ICPSR; 0-89138),* P.O. Box 1248, Ann Arbor, MI 48106 (SAN 207-7450) Tel 313-763-5010.

†**Inter-Varsity Pr.,** Div. of Inter-Varsity Christian Fellowship of the USA, *(Inter-Varsity; 0-87784; 0-8308),* P.O. Box 1400, Downers Grove, IL 60515 (SAN 202-7089) Tel 312-964-5700; Toll free: 800-843-7225; *CIP.*

Interaction Bk. Co., *(Interaction Bk Co; 0-939603),* 162 Windsor Ln., New Brighton, MN 55112 (SAN 663-5970) Tel 612-631-1693.

InterActive Pubns., *(InterActive; 0-917015),* 2811 Wilshire Blvd., Suite 590, Santa Monica, CA 90403 (SAN 655-1297) Tel 213-829-0516.

Interamerican Research Corp., *(Inter Res Corp; 0-9614035),* 2030 N. 53rd St., Milwaukee, WI 53208 (SAN 683-8049) Tel 414-278-2789.

Interbook, Inc., *(Interbk Inc; 0-913456; 0-89192),* 131 Varick St., 2nd Fl., New York, NY 10013 (SAN 202-7070) Tel 212-691-7248.

Interbook Inc., Subs. of Haynes Pubns., *(Interbook; 0-946609),* 861 Lawrence Dr., Newbury Park, CA 91320 (SAN 662-3034) Tel 805-498-6703; Orders to: 14895 E. 14th St., Suite 370, San Leandro, CA 94577 (SAN 662-3042) Tel 415-352-9221.

Interchange, Inc., *(Interchange; 0-916966),* P.O. Box 16012, St. Louis Park, MN 55416 (SAN 207-2386) Tel 612-929-6669.

Intercollegiate Studies Institute, Inc., *(Intercoll Studies),* 14 S. Bryn Mawr Ave., Bryn Mawr, PA 19010 (SAN 226-577X).

Intercontinental Press, *(Intercont Press; 0-933142),* P.O. Box 565, Auburn, AL 36830 (SAN 281-8167) Tel 205-887-5297; Orders to: Intercontinental Press, Box 565, Auburn, AL 36830 (SAN 281-8175) Tel 205-887-5297.

Intercontinental Pubns., *(Intercontinental Pubns),* 25 Sylvan Rd. S., P.O. Box 5017, Westport, CT 06881 (SAN 208-9572) Tel 203-226-7463.

Intercultural Pr., Inc., *(Intercult Pr; 0-933622),* P.O. Box 768, Yarmouth, ME 04096 (SAN 212-6699) Tel 207-846-5168.

Interdependent Learning Model, *(ILM; 0-939632),* Fordham Univ. at Lincoln Ctr., 113 West 60th St., Rm. 1003, New York, NY 10023 (SAN 216-6305) Tel 212-841-5282.

Interdimensional Publishing, Div. of Interdimensional Productions, *(Inter Pub; 0-932389),* P.O. Box 41173, Nashville, TN 37204 (SAN 687-1364) Tel 615-790-2818; Dist. by: New Leaf Book Dist. Co., 1020 White St., SW, Atlanta, GA 30310 (SAN 169-1449) Tel 415-658-3453; Dist. by: Starlite Dist., P.O. Box 20729, Reno, NV 89515 (SAN 200-7789) Tel 702-359-5676.

INTEREG *See International Regulations Publishing & Distributing Organization*

Intergalactic Publishing Co., Div. of Regal Communications Corp., *(Intergalactic NJ; 0-936918),* P.O. Box 5013, Cherry Hill, NJ 08034 (SAN 213-988X) Tel 609-665-7577.

Interhouse Publishing, *(Interhouse Pub; 0-932380),* 457 Highland, Elmhurst, IL 60126 (SAN 221-0576).

Interior Design Bks., Div. of Cahners Publishing Co., *(Inter Design; 0-943370),* 475 Park Ave. S., New York, NY 10016 (SAN 240-6810) Tel 212-686-0555; Dist. by: Van Nostrand Reinhold, Co., 115 Fifth Ave., New York, NY 10003 (SAN 202-5191) Tel 212-254-3232.

Interiors by Arden, *(Interiors; 0-934892),* 1924 Swallow Ln., Carlsbad, CA 92008 (SAN 213-2540) Tel 619-931-1295.

†**Interland Publishing, Inc.,** *(Interland Pub; 0-87989),* 799 Broadway, New York, NY 10003 (SAN 203-8145) Tel 212-673-8280; *CIP.*

Interlingual Institute, *(Interlingual; 0-917848),* Box 126, Canal St. Sta., New York, NY 10013 (SAN 209-9330) Tel 212-929-0264.

Intermarket Publishing Corp., *(Intermarket; 0-937453),* 401 S. LaSalle St., No. 1100, Chicago, IL 60605 (SAN 658-8751) Tel 312-922-4300.

Intermedia, Inc., *(Intermedia; 0-910788),* 434 Woodward Rd., Nassau, NY 12123 (SAN 206-6947).

Intermedia, Inc., *(Intermedia WA; 0-937889),* 1600 Dexter Ave., N., Seattle, WA 98109 (SAN 659-4735) Tel 206-282-7262. Do not confuse with Intermedia, Nassau, NY.

Intermediate Eater Publishing Company, *(Intermed Eater; 0-914687),* Box 1281, Bellevue, WA 98009 (SAN 289-1697); Dist. by: Pacific Pipeline, 19215 66th Ave. S., Kent, WA 98032 (SAN 208-2128) Tel 206-872-5523P.O. Box 3711, Seattle, WA 98124 (SAN 289-1719).

Intermediate Technology Development Group of North America, *(Intermediate Tech; 0-942850),* P.O. Box 337, Croton-on-Hudson, NY 10520 (SAN 218-4303) Tel 914-271-6500.

Intermountain Air Press, *(Intermtn Air; 0-914680),* 171 S. Second E., Preston, ID 83263 (SAN 206-5428).

Intermountain Arts & Crafts, *(Intermntn Arts; 0-9605840),* Rte. 2, Box 2042, Burney, CA 96013 (SAN 216-5996) Tel 916-335-4330.

International Advertising Assn., *(Intl Advertising Assn),* 475 Fifth Ave., New York, NY 10017 (SAN 224-6120) Tel 212-684-1583.

International Arabian Horse Assn., *(Intl Arabian),* P.O. Box 33696, Denver, CO 80233 (SAN 224-1447) Tel 303-450-4774.

International Art Alliance, Incorporated, *(Intl Art Alliance; 0-943488),* P.O. Box 1608, Largo, FL 34294 (SAN 240-6829) Tel 813-581-7328.

International Assocs. for Life Management, Ltd., *(Intl Life Mgmt; 0-937515),* 5 Roble Rd., Suffern, NY 10901 (SAN 658-8786) Tel 914-354-7323.

International Assn. for Housing Science, *(Intl Assn Housing Sci),* P.O. Box 340254, Coral Gables, FL 33134 (SAN 271-2105) Tel 305-448-3532.

International Association for Hydrogen Energy, *(Intl Assn Hydro Energy),* Univ. of Miami, 219 McArthur Hall, Engineering Bldg., Coral Gables, FL 33146 (SAN 283-1872) Tel 305-284-4666; P.O. Box 248266, Coral Gables, FL 33124 (SAN 650-1117).

International Assn. for the Physical Sciences of the Ocean, *(Intl Assoc Phys Sci Ocean),* P.O. Box 7325, San Diego, CA 92107 (SAN 224-1463) Tel 619-222-3680.

†**International Assn. of Assessing Officers,** *(Intl Assess; 0-88329),* 1313 E. 60th St., Chicago, IL 60637-9990 (SAN 205-0277) Tel 312-947-2069; Orders to: Prepaid, P.O. Box 88874, Chicago, IL 60680-1874 (SAN 691-9529) Tel 312-947-2044; *CIP.*

International Assn. of Business Communicators, *(Intl Assn Busn Comm; 0-943372),* 870 Market St., Suite 940, San Francisco, CA 94102 (SAN 224-893X) Tel 415-433-3400.

†**International Assn. of Chiefs of Police,** *(Intl Assn Chiefs Police; 0-88269),* P.O. Box 6010, 13 Firstfield Rd., Gaithersburg, MD 20760 (SAN 211-5301) Tel 301-948-0922; *CIP.*

International Association of Counseling Services, *(Intl Counseling Svcs),* 5999 Stevenson Ave., Third Floor, Alexandria, VA 22304 (SAN 224-148X) Tel 703-820-4710.

International Association of Energy Economists, *(Intl Assn Energy Econ),* 1133 15 St., NW, No. 620, Washington, DC 20005 (SAN 224-1501) Tel 202-293-5913.

International Association of Fish & Wildlife Agencies, *(IAFWA; 0-932108),* 1412 16th St., NW, Washington, DC 20036 (SAN 213-5205) Tel 202-639-8200; Dist. by: World Wide Furbearer Conference, Inc. Book Distributor Center, 1111 E. Cold Spring Ln., Baltimore, MD 21239 (SAN 263-2217).

International Association of Law Libraries, *(Intl Law Libs),* P.O. Box 5709, Washington, DC 20016-1309 (SAN 226-5818).

International Assn. of Milk, Food, & Environmental Sanitarians, Inc., *(Intl Assn Milk),* P.O. Box 701, Ames, IA 50010 (SAN 224-7437) Tel 515-232-6699; Toll free: 800-525-5223.

International Association of Satellite Users & Suppliers, *(Intl Sat Users),* 6845 Elm St., Suite 710, P.O. Box DD, McLean, VA 22101 (SAN 224-1536) Tel 703-759-2095.

International Association of School Librarianship, *(Assn Schl Librnship; 0-9617248),* P.O. Box 1486, Kalamazoo, MI 49005 (SAN 663-5520) Tel 616-343-5728.

International Assn. of School Librarianship, *(IASL),* Box 1486, Kalamazoo, MI 49005 (SAN 233-4828); 1006 Westmorland, Kalamazoo, MI 49007 (SAN 650-0366) Tel 616-343-5728.

International Assn. of Schls. of Social Work, *(Intl Assn Schools; 0-931638),* c/o Council on Social Work Education, 111 Eighth Ave., New York, NY 10011 (SAN 692-8358).

International Assn. of Trichologists, *(Intl Assn Trichologists; 0-9614548),* 37320 22nd St., Kalamazoo, MI 49009 (SAN 224-4586) Tel 616-375-4430.

International Association of Wiping Cloth Manufacturers, *(IAWC Mfg),* 300 W. Washington St., Chicago, IL 60606 (SAN 230-5402) Tel 312-726-0050.

International Atomic Energy Agency *See* **Unipub**

International Aviation Consultants, Inc., *(Intl Av Consult; 0-9609000),* 301 SW 30th Court, Miami, FL 33135 (SAN 240-9798).

International Aviation Pubs., Inc., *(Intl Aviation Pubs; 0-89100),* P.O. Box 36, Riverton, WY 82501-0036 (SAN 209-3189); Toll free: 800-443-9250; 1000 College View Dr., Riverton, WY 82501 (SAN 658-0173) Tel 307-856-1582. *Imprints:* Big Horn Book Co. (Big Horn).

International Basement Tectonics Assn., *(Intl Basement; 0-916347),* 675 S. 400 E., Salt Lake City, UT 84111 (SAN 295-835X) Tel 518-474-5819.

International Better Life for All Movement Pr., *(Intl Better Life; 0-915935),* 3972 Dallas, Warren, MI 48091 (SAN 294-0256) Tel 313-754-8134.

International Bk. Ctr. of Atlanta, *(I B C A),* 2576 Acorn Ave., NE, Atlanta, GA 30305 (SAN 678-9064) Tel 404-261-7437.

†**International Bk. Ctr.,** *(Intl Bk Ctr; 0-917062; 0-86685),* 2007 Laurel Dr., P.O. Box 295, Troy, MI 48099 (SAN 169-4014) Tel 313-879-8436; *CIP.*

International Book Co., *(Intl Bk Co IL; 0-910790),* 332 S. Michigan Ave., Chicago, IL 60604 (SAN 205-0250) Tel 312-427-4545.

International Book Distributors, *(Intl Bk Dist; 0-86732),* P.O. Box 180, Murray Hill Sta., New York, NY 10016 (SAN 210-6337).

International Bottled Water Assn., *(Intl Bottled Water),* 113 N. Henry St., Alexandria, VA 22314 (SAN 224-649X) Tel 703-683-5213.

International Broadcasting Services, Ltd., *(Intl Broadcasting Serv; 0-914941),* 825 Cherry Ln., Penn's Park, PA 18943 (SAN 289-2553) Tel 215-598-3298; Orders to: P.O. Box 300, Penn's Park, PA 18943 (SAN 662-216X) Tel 215-794-8252.

International Business Aesthetics, *(Intl Busn Aesthetics; 0-936757),* 2082 Michelson Dr., Suite 100, Irvine, CA 92715 (SAN 699-9034) Tel 714-476-3181.

International Business & Publishing Consultants, *(I B P C Inc; 0-88115),* P.O. Box 11225, San Francisco, CA 94101 (SAN 239-5541) Tel 415-751-6876.

International Business Education & Research Program, Graduate School of Business Administration, *(Intl Busn Educ; 0-939322),* IBEAR/GSBA, Univ. of Southern California, Los Angeles, CA 90089-1421 (SAN 216-5562) Tel 213-743-2272.

International Business Information Group, Subs. of International ICS Group, *(Intl Busn Inform; 0-934493),* P.O. Box 4082, Irvine, CA 92716 (SAN 693-8922) Tel 714-552-8494.

International Center for Arid & Semi-Arid Land Studies, Div. of Texas Tech. Univ., *(Intl Ctr Arid & Semi-Arid),* P.O. Box 4620, Lubbock, TX 79409 (SAN 224-1609) Tel 806-742-2218.

International Center for Creative Thinking, *(Intl Ctr Creat Think; 0-9615400),* 56 Harrison St., New Rochelle, NY 10801 (SAN 695-5363) Tel 914-632-4492; Toll free: 800-828-8285.

International Center for Law in Development, *(Intl Ctr Law),* 777 United Nations Plaza, New York, NY 10017 (SAN 221-0592).

International Ctr. for Special Studies, *(Intl Ctr Spec Studies; 0-934495),* 400 Hobron Ln., Suite 3502, Honolulu, HI 96815-1209 (SAN 693-8930) Tel 808-947-6473.

†**International Ctr. of Photography,** *(Intl Ctr Photo; 0-933642),* 1130 Fifth Ave., New York, NY 10028 (SAN 213-3296) Tel 212-860-1777; *CIP.*

International Center of the Academy for State & Local Government, The, *(Intl Ctr Academy),* Academy for State & Local Government, 444 N. Capitol St., NW, Suite 349, Washington, DC 20001 (SAN 224-1080) Tel 202-638-1445.

†**International Childbirth Education Association,** *(Intl Childbirth; 0-934024),* P.O. Box 20048, Minneapolis, MN 55420 (SAN 224-3962) Tel 612-854-8660; *CIP.*

International Children's Festival, Inc., The, *(Intl Child Fest; 0-939029),* 322 W. 57th St., Suite 43B, New York, NY 10019 (SAN 662-8478) Tel 212-245-3463.

International Chinese Snuff Bottle Society, *(Intl Chi Snuff; 0-9609668),* 2601 N. Charles St., Baltimore, MD 21218 (SAN 271-311X); Dist. by: Paragon Book Gallery, 2130 Broadway, New York, NY 10023 (SAN 213-1986) Tel 212-496-2378.

†**International City Management Association,** *(Intl City Mgt; 0-87326),* 1120 G St., NW, Washington, DC 20005 (SAN 204-9120) Tel 202-626-4600; *CIP.*

International Co-Operative Publishing House, *(Intl Co-Op; 0-899974),* P.O. Box 245, Burtonsville, MD 20866 (SAN 213-6260).

International Commercial Service, Subs. of International ICS Group, *(Intl Comm Serv; 0-935402),* P.O. Box 4082, Irvine, CA 92716 (SAN 281-8183) Tel 714-552-8494; Dist. by: IBMI-International Commercial Services, Univ. Town Ctr., P.O. Box 4082, Irvine, CA 92716 (SAN 281-8183) Tel 714-552-8494.

†**International Commission on Radiation Units & Measurements,** *(Intl Comm Rad Meas; 0-913394),* 7910 Woodmont Ave., Suite 1016, Bethesda, MD 20814 (SAN 202-7127) Tel 301-657-2652; *CIP.*

International Communication Center, *(Intl Comm Ctr; 0-933236),* Univ. of Washington, School of Communictions DS-40, Seattle, WA 98195 (SAN 212-3614).

International Communications *See* **Watts, Franklin, Inc.**

International Communications Industries Assn., *(Internatl Comms),* 3150 Spring St., Fairfax, VA 22031 (SAN 224-6376) Tel 703-273-7200.

International Community of Christ, *(Intl Comm Christ; 0-936202),* Pub. Dept. Chancellery, 643 Ralston St., Reno, NV 89503 (SAN 214-0373).

International Computer Programs, Inc., *(Intl Computer; 0-88094),* 9100 Keystone Crossing, Indianapolis, IN 46240 (SAN 218-7949) Tel 317-844-7461; P.O. Box 40946, Indianapolis, IN 46240 (SAN 699-5373).

International Computer Recovery, *(Inter Comp Rec; 0-912247),* 7708 Briarcliff Cts., Smithfield, TX 76180 (SAN 265-1505).

International Conference of Building Officials, *(Intl Conf Bldg Off),* 5360 S. Workman Mill Rd., Whittier, CA 90601 (SAN 225-0713) Tel 213-699-0541.

International Consortium of Businesses & Services, Inc., *(ICBS Inc; 0-938197),* 44 Montgomery, 5th Flr., San Francisco, CA 94104 (SAN 661-2199) Tel 415-782-3016.

International Consumer Credit Association *See* **International Credit Assn.**

International Consumer Publishing Co., *(Intl Consumer Pub; 0-938859),* P.O. Box 300128, Arlington, TX 76010 (SAN 661-7174); 2305 Stillmeadow Dr., Arlington, TX 76014 (SAN 661-7182) Tel 817-468-1350.

International Copper Research Assn., *(Intl Copper; 0-943642),* 708 Third Ave., New York, NY 10017 (SAN 230-9858) Tel 212-697-9355.

International Council for Computers in Education, *(Intl Council Comp; 0-924667),* Univ. of Oregon, 1787 Agate St., Eugene, OR 97403 (SAN 296-7693) Tel 503-686-4414.

International Council for Traditional Music, *(Intl Coun Trad),* Dept of Music, Columbia Univ., New York, NY 10027 (SAN 223-8934) Tel 212-280-5439.

International Council of Scientific Unions, Abstracting Board of Pubns. *See* **Unipub**

International Council of Shopping Ctrs., *(Intl Coun Shop; 0-913598),* 665 Fifth Ave., New York, NY 10022 (SAN 206-7412) Tel 212-421-8181.

Names

International Court of Justice (ICJ) *See* Unipub

International Crane Foundation, *(Intl Crane)*, Rt. 1, Box 230 C, Shady Lane Rd., Baraboo, WI 53913 (SAN 224-165X) Tel 608-356-9462.

International Credit Assn., *(Intl Credit Assn)*, P.O. Box 27357, St. Louis, MO 63141-1757 (SAN 224-7003) Tel 314-991-3030; 243 N. Lindbergh Blvd., St. Louis, MO 63141-1757 (SAN 669-120X).

International Currency Analysis, Inc., *(Intl Currency; 0-917645)*, 7239 Ave. N, Brooklyn, NY 11234 (SAN 657-0968) Tel 718-531-3685.

International Defense & Aid Fund for Southern Africa, *(Intl Defense & Aid)*, P.O. Box 17, Cambridge, MA 02138 (SAN 217-796X) Tel 617-491-8343.

International Dept. *See* Harper & Row Pubs., Inc.

International Design Library *See* Stemmer Hse. Pub., Inc.

International Development Institute, *(Intl Development; 0-89249)*, Indiana University, 201 N. Indiana, Bloomington, IN 47405 (SAN 208-7030) Tel 812-335-8596.

International Dialogue Pr., *(Intl Dialogue Pr; 0-89881; 0-931364)*, P.O. Box 1257, Davis, CA 95617 (SAN 212-3827) Tel 916-758-6500.

International Downtown Executives Assn., *(Intl Downtown; 0-910473)*, 915 15th St., NW, Suite 900, Washington, DC 20005 (SAN 223-890X) Tel 202-783-4963.

International DXers Club of San Diego, *(Intl DXers)*, 1826 Cypress St., San Diego, CA 92194 (SAN 241-547X) Tel 619-429-9728.

International Education Services, *(Intl Educ Servs; 0-935439)*, 1537 Franklin St., San Francisco, CA 94109 (SAN 696-270X) Tel 415-775-2400.

International Educational Development, Inc., *(Intl Educ Dev; 0-939420)*, P.O. Box 7066, Silver Spring, MD 20910 (SAN 216-2571).

International Educational Systems, Inc., *(Intl Educ Systems; 0-934806)*, 5521 W. 110th St., Chicago, IL 60653 (SAN 210-6248) Tel 312-423-1717.

International Enlightenment, *(Intl Enlightenment; 0-9616471)*, P.O. Box 583, Fort Washington, PA 19034 (SAN 658-8808) Tel 215-885-0942; 37 Red Oak Rd., Oreland, PA 19275 (SAN 658-8816).

International Evangelism Crusade, Inc., *(Intl Evang; 0-933470)*, 14617 Victory Blvd., Suite 4, Van Nuys, CA 91411 (SAN 203-8153) Tel 818-989-5942; Orders to: P.O. Box 73, Van Nuys, CA 91408 (SAN 688-3966).

International Exhibitions Foundation, *(Intl Exhibitions; 0-88397)*, 1700 Pennsylvania Ave., NW, Suite 580, Washington, DC 20006 (SAN 204-0964) Tel 202-737-4740.

International Fanorona Association, *(Intl Fanorona; 0-932329)*, 278-A Meeting St., Charleston, SC 29401 (SAN 686-7626) Tel 803-722-2531.

International Federation of Women's Travel Organizations, *(Intl Fed Travel)*, 7432 Caminito Carlotta, San Diego, CA 92120 (SAN 691-5094) Tel 619-287-0893.

International Federation on Ageing, *(Intl Fed Ageing)*, 1909 K St. NW, Washington, DC 20049 (SAN 225-8889) Tel 202-662-4927.

International Fertilizer Development Ctr., *(Intl Fertilizer; 0-88090)*, P.O. Box 2040, Muscle Shoals, AL 35662 (SAN 240-1150) Tel 205-381-6600.

International Film Bureau, Inc., *(Intl Film; 0-8354)*, 332 S. Michigan Ave., Chicago, IL 60604 (SAN 207-4931) Tel 312-427-4545.

International Fire Service Training Association, *(Intl Fire Serv; 0-87939)*, Oklahoma State Univ., Stillwater, OK 74078 (SAN 204-1111) Tel 405-624-5723; Toll free: 800-654-4055.

International Foundation for Biosocial Development & Human Health, *(Intl Found Biosocial Dev; 0-934314)*, 6 Lomond Ave., Spring Valley, NY 10977 (SAN 214-0381).

International Foundation of Employee Benefit Plans, *(Intl Found Employ; 0-89154)*, P.O. Box 69, 18700 W. Bluemound Rd., Brookfield, WI 53008 (SAN 317-9214) Tel 414-786-6700.

International Franchise Assn., *(Intl Franchise Assn; 0-936898)*, 1350 New York Ave., NW, Suite 900, Washington, DC 20005-4709 (SAN 214-3747) Tel 202-628-8000.

International Friendship, *(Intl Friend; 0-935340)*, P.O. Box 248, Waxhaw, NC 28173 (SAN 213-5183) Tel 704-843-2185.

International Game Fish Assn., *(Intl Game Fish; 0-935217)*, 3000 E. Las Olas Blvd., Ft. Lauderdale, FL 33316-1616 (SAN 225-1876) Tel 305-467-0161.

International General, *(Intl General; 0-88477)*, P.O. Box 350, New York, NY 10013 (SAN 206-5436).

International Health Economics & Management Institute, *(IHEMI; 0-914943)*, Southern Illinois Univ. at Edwardsville, Box 1101, Edwardsville, IL 62026-1101 (SAN 289-2626) Tel 618-692-2291.

International Hse. Pubns., *(Intl Hse Pubns; 0-937127)*, 2711 LBJ Freeway, Suite 122, Dallas, TX 75234 (SAN 658-5477) Tel 214-241-9991.

†International Human Resources Development Corp., *(Intl Human Res; 0-934634; 0-88746)*, 137 Newbury St., Boston, MA 02116 (SAN 220-2549) Tel 617-536-0202; Toll free: 800-327-6756; *CIP*.

International Ideas, Inc. *See* Coronet Bks.

International Imports, *(Intl Imports; 0-943832)*, 8050 Webb Ave., North Hollywood, CA 91605-1504 (SAN 209-8202) Tel 818-768-0069.

International Information Management Congress, *(Intl Info Mgmt Con)*, P.O. Box 34404, Bethesda, MD 20817 (SAN 224-8786) Tel 301-983-0604.

International Institute for Advanced Studies, *(Intl Inst Adv Stud; 0-940604)*, 8000 Bonhomme Ave., Suite 403, Clayton, MO 63105 (SAN 218-4818).

International Institute for Environment & Development, *(Intl Inst Environment)*, 1717 Massachusetts Ave., NW, Suite 302, Washington, DC 20036 (SAN 225-1779) Tel 202-462-0900.

International Institute For Financial Research, *(Intl Inst Fin Res; 0-933001)*, 1930 Allen Dr., Jefferson City, MO 65101 (SAN 689-1519) Tel 314-636-3464.

International Institute of Garibaldian Studies, Inc., *(Intl Inst Garibaldian)*, 1025 Shadowlawn Way, Sarasota, FL 34242 (SAN 238-0037) Tel 813-349-0585.

International Institute of Natural Health Sciences, Inc., *(Intl Inst Nat Health; 0-86664)*, 7422 Mountjoy Dr., Huntington Beach, CA 92648 (SAN 216-258X).

International Institute of Rural Reconstruction, *(Intl Inst Rural)*, 1775 Broadway, New York, NY 10019 (SAN 225-9710).

International Intertrade Index Printing Consultants, Pubs., *(Intl Intertrade; 0-910794)*, P.O. Box 636, Federal Square, Newark, NJ 07101 (SAN 202-7143) Tel 201-686-2382.

International Labor Organization (ILO) *See* Unipub

International Labour Office, *(Intl Labour Office; 92-2)*, Washington Branch, 1750 New York Ave., NW, Suite 330, Washington, DC 20006 (SAN 203-817X) Tel 202-376-2137.

International Law Institute, *(Intl Law Inst; 0-935328)*, 1330 Connecticut Ave. NW, Washington, DC 20036 (SAN 224-1676) Tel 202-463-7979.

International League for Human Rights, *(Intl League Human)*, 236 E. 46th St., New York, NY 10017 (SAN 226-5850).

International Learning Institute, *(Intl Lrn Inst; 0-939311)*, P.O. Box 60, Petaluma, CA 94952 (SAN 663-1533); 22 Wooddale Dr., Petaluma, CA 94952 (SAN 663-1541) Tel 707-763-1460; Dist. by: Bookpeople, 2929 Fifth St., Berkeley, CA 94710 (SAN 168-9517) Tel 415-549-3030; Toll free: 800-227-1516.

International Learning Systems, Inc., *(Intl Learn Syst)*, 1715 Connecticut Ave., NW, Washington, DC 20009 (SAN 209-1615) Tel 202-232-4111.

International Liaison, United States Coordinating Center for Lay Missioners, Affil. of U. S. Catholic Conference, *(Intl Liaison)*, 1234 Massachusetts Ave. NW, Washington, DC 20005 (SAN 234-7407) Tel 202-638-4197; 225 S. Euclid St., St. Louis, MO 63110 (SAN 669-1226); 2451 Ridge Rd., Berkeley, CA 94709 (SAN 669-1234).

International Library Bk. Pubs., Inc., *(Intl Lib; 0-914250)*, 7315 Wisconsin Ave., Suite 229, E., Bethesda, MD 20814 (SAN 202-7151) Tel 301-961-8850.

International Life Message Inc., *(Intl Life Mess; 0-916075)*, Nine Ruth Dr., New City, NY 10956 (SAN 294-846X) Tel 914-634-8980.

International Linguistics Corp., *(Intl Linguistics; 0-939990)*, 401 W. 89th St., Kansas City, MO 64114 (SAN 220-2573) Tel 816-941-9797.

International Loss Control Institute, *(ILCI; 0-88061)*, P.O. Box 345, Loganville, GA 30249 (SAN 240-9887) Tel 404-466-2208.

International Mahayana Yoga Publishing Co., *(Intl Mahayana; 0-9615731)*, 325 Harvard St., Suite 14, Brookline, MA 02146 (SAN 696-4656) Tel 617-232-5967.

International Map Co., *(Intl Map Co; 0-937455)*, 5316 Santa Teresa, El Paso, TX 79932 (SAN 658-8824) Tel 915-833-0745.

†International Marine Publishing Co., Subs. of Diversified Communications Inc., *(Intl Marine; 0-87742; 0-8286)*, 21 Elm St., Camden, ME 04843 (SAN 202-716X) Tel 207-236-4342; Toll free: 800-328-0059 (Trade Customers Only); *CIP*.

International Marketing Institute, *(Intl Mktg; 0-942286)*, Univ. of New Orleans, New Orleans, LA 70148 (SAN 239-4464).

International Marriage Encounter, Inc., *(Intl Marriage; 0-936098)*, 955 Lake Dr., St. Paul, MN 55120 (SAN 215-6830).

International Merchandising Corp., *(Intl Merc OH; 0-9615344)*, 1 Erieview Plaza, Cleveland, OH 44114 (SAN 695-1457) Tel 216-522-1200.

†International Monetary Fund, *(Intl Monetary; 0-939934)*, Editorial Div., 700 19th St., NW, Rm. 12-510, Washington, DC 20431 (SAN 203-8188) Tel 202-623-7090; *CIP*.

International Museum of Photography at George Eastman Hse., *(Intl Mus Photo; 0-935398)*, 900 East Ave., Rochester, NY 14607 (SAN 205-0153) Tel 716-271-3361.

International Myopia Prevention Association, *(Intl Myopia; 0-9608476)*, RD 5, Box 171, Ligonier, PA 15658 (SAN 228-1848) Tel 412-238-2101.

International Oil Scouts Assn., *(Intl Oil Scouts)*, 4818 E. Ben White Blvd., Suite 301, Austin, TX 78741-7309 (SAN 231-2204) Tel 512-448-4088.

International Parents Organization, Subs. of Alexander Graham Bell Assn. for the Deaf, *(Intl Parents)*, 3417 Volta Pl., NW, Washington, DC 20007 (SAN 203-6924) Tel 202-337-5220.

International Partners Press, *(Intl Prtn Pr; 0-932895)*, Box 392, Soquel, CA 95073 (SAN 689-013X) Tel 408-475-1827.

International Peace Academy, *(Intl Peace; 0-937722)*, 777 United Nations Plaza, 4th Flr., New York, NY 10017 (SAN 225-6940) Tel 212-949-8480.

†International Personnel Management Assn., *(Intl Personnel Mgmt; 0-914945)*, 1617 Duke St., Alexandria, VA 22314 (SAN 203-8196) Tel 703-549-7100; *CIP*.

International Planned Parenthood Federation, *(Intl Plan Parent; 0-916683)*, Western Hemisphere Region 105 Madison Ave., 7th Flr., New York, NY 10016 (SAN 271-5171) Tel 212-679-2230.

International Polygonics, Ltd., *(Intl Polygonics; 0-930330)*, P.O. Box 1563, Madison Sq. Sta., New York, NY 10159 (SAN 211-0210) Tel 212-683-2914.

International Postal Marketing Corp., *(Intl Postal Mkting; 0-9606786)*, 115 Main Rd., Montville, NJ 07045 (SAN 223-1867) Tel 201-299-1500.

International Preventive Medicine Foundation, *(Intl Prev Med; 0-936553)*, 3325 W. New Haven Ave., Melbourne, FL 32904 (SAN 697-984X) Tel 305-723-5640.

Names

International Print Co., *(Intl Print),* 711 South 50th St., Philadelphia, PA 19143 (SAN 240-8627); Dist. by: Sebastian Ben Giletto, 1127 Watkins St., Philadelphia, PA 19148 (SAN 240-8635).

International Print Society, *(Intl Print Soc; 0-915169),* P.O. Box 323, New Hope, PA 18938 (SAN 289-9523) Tel 215-862-2615.

International Pro Rodeo Assn., *(Intl Rodeo),* P.O. Box 615, 106 E. McClure, Pauls Valley, OK 73075 (SAN 224-5833) Tel 405-238-6488; Dist. by: Rodeo News Publishing, P.O. Box 587, Pauls Valley, OK 73075 (SAN 669-1285).

†International Programmable Controls Inc., *(Intl Prog Controls; 0-915425),* 35 Glenlake Parkway, Suite 445, Atlanta, GA 30328 (SAN 291-2384) Tel 404-396-5064; *CIP.*

International Psychological Press, Inc., *(Intl Psych Pr; 0-915662),* 1850 Hanover Dr., Suite 69, Davis, CA 95616 (SAN 207-3722) Tel 916-756-1347.

International Pubns. Service, Div. of Taylor & Francis, Inc., *(Intl Pubns Serv; 0-8002),* 242 Cherry St., Philadelphia, PA 19106-1906 (SAN 169-5819) Tel 215-238-0939; Toll free: 800-821-8312.

International Pubs. Co., *(Intl Pubs Co; 0-7178),* 381 Park Ave. S., Suite 1301, New York, NY 10016 (SAN 202-5655) Tel 212-685-2864. *Imprints:* Little Lenin Library (LLL); Little Marx Library (LML); Little New World Paperbacks (LNW); New World Paperbacks (NW).

International Pubs. Service, Inc., *(IPS),* P.O. Box 230, Accord, MA 02018 (SAN 654-9357) Tel 617-749-2966.

International Radio Club of America, *(Intl Radio Club Am),* P.O. Box 17088, Seattle, WA 98107 (SAN 224-2133) Tel 206-522-2521.

†International Reading Assn., *(Intl Reading; 0-87207),* 800 Barksdale Rd., P.O. Box 8139, Newark, DE 19714-8139 (SAN 203-8218) Tel 302-731-1600; *CIP.*

International Regulations Publishing & Distributing Organization, *(INTEREG; 0-940394),* Dist. by: Labelmaster, 5724 N. Pulaski Rd., Chicago, IL 60646 (SAN 218-480X).

International Research & Evaluation, *(Intl Res Eval; 0-930318),* Research Pubns. Div., 21098 IRE Control Ctr., Eagan, MN 55121 (SAN 209-6668) Tel 612-888-9635.

International Research Center for Energy & Economic Development, *(Intl Res Ctr Energy; 0-918714),* Box 263, 216 Economics Bldg., Univ. of Colo., Boulder, CO 80309-0263 (SAN 211-3643).

International Research Service, Inc., *(Intl Research Serv; 0-934366),* P.O. Box 225, Blue Bell, PA 19422 (SAN 213-1935).

International Resource Development, Inc., *(Intl Res Dev; 0-924680),* 6 Prowitt St., Norwalk, CT 06855 (SAN 264-1208) Tel 203-866-7800.

International Review Service, *(Intl Review; 0-87138),* 15 Washington Pl., New York, NY 10003 (SAN 202-3539) Tel 212-751-0833; UN Bureau: Rm. 301, United Nations, New York, NY 10017 (SAN 202-3547).

International Right of Way Association, *(Intl Right Way),* 6133 Bristol Pkwy., Suite 270, Culver City, CA 90020 (SAN 232-5004) Tel 213-649-5323.

International School Psychology Association, *(Intl Schl Psych; 0-917668),* 92 S. Dawson Ave., Columbus, OH 43209 (SAN 209-2913) Tel 614-252-6687.

International Schls. Service, *(Intl School Servs; 0-913663),* P.O. Box 5910, 13 Roszel Rd., Princeton, NJ 08540 (SAN 225-8196) Tel 609-452-0990.

International Science & Technology Institute, Inc., *(Intl Sci Tech; 0-936130),* 2033 M St. NW, Suite 300, Washington, DC 20036 (SAN 212-5110) Tel 202-466-7290.

International Self-Counsel Pr., Subs. of International Self-Counsel Pr., Ltd., *(ISC Pr; 0-88908),* 1303 N. Northgate Way, Seattle, WA 98133 (SAN 240-9925) Tel 206-522-8383; Dist. by: TAB Bks., P.O. Box 40, Blue Ridge Summit, PA 17214 (SAN 202-568X) Tel 717-794-2191.

International Services Guild, *(Intl Servs Guild; 0-9616129),* 845 Lone Oak Rd., St. Paul, MN 55121 (SAN 699-7147) Tel 612-774-5980.

International Society for Animal Rights, Inc., *(Soc Animal Rights; 0-9602632),* 421 S. State St., Clarks Summit, PA 18411 (SAN 214-1418) Tel 717-586-2200.

International Society for Artificial Organs, *(Intl Soc Artifical Organs; 0-936022),* 8937 Euclid Ave., Cleveland, OH 44106 (SAN 214-039X).

International Society for General Semantics, *(Intl Gen Semantics; 0-918970),* 834 Mission St., 2nd flr., San Francisco, CA 94103 (SAN 203-8161) Tel 415-543-1747; P.O. Box 2469, San Francisco, CA 94126 (SAN 669-1315).

International Society for Intercultural Education, Training & Research, Div. of Georgetown Univ., *(Soc Intercult Ed Train & Res; 0-933934),* 1414 22nd St., NW, Washington, DC 20037 (SAN 214-1426) Tel 202-296-4710.

International Society of Certified Electronics Technicians, *(Intl Soc Cert Elect),* 2708 W. Berry, Ft. Worth, TX 76109 (SAN 271-5805) Tel 817-921-9101.

International Society of Certified Employees Benefit Specialists, *(Intl Soc Emp; 0-911731),* 18700 W. Bluemound Rd., Brookfield, WI 53008 (SAN 264-1216) Tel 414-786-8711.

International Society of Dramatists, *(Inter Soc Drama; 0-934131),* P.O. Box 1310, Miami, FL 33153 (SAN 693-2681) Tel 305-756-8313.

International Society of Fire Service Instructors, *(Intl Soc Fire Serv; 0-9615990),* 20 Main St., Ashland, MA 01721 (SAN 697-8878) Tel 617-881-5800.

International Society of Guatemala Collectors, *(Intl Guatemala),* P.O. Box 246, Troy, NY 12181 (SAN 225-5952) Tel 518-271-7629.

International Solar Energy Society (ISES) *See* Unipub

International Specialized Bk. Services, *(Intl Spec Bk; 0-89955),* 5602 NE Hassalo St., Portland, OR 97213-3640 (SAN 169-7129) Tel 503-287-3093; Toll free: 800-547-7734.

International Sport Fishing Pubns., *(Intl Sport Fish; 0-914543),* P.O. Box 873, Captiva Island, FL 33924 (SAN 289-2960) Tel 813-337-8818.

International Sport Pubns., Inc., *(Intl Sport Pubns; 0-913927),* 3030 S. Main, Salt Lake City, UT 84115 (SAN 286-7826) Tel 801-483-1777.

International Strategic Institute at Stanford, *(ISIS; 0-935371),* Stanford Univ., 320 Galvez St., Stanford, CA 94305 (SAN 696-2718) Tel 415-723-9731.

International Taekwon-Do Assn., *(Intl Taekwon-Do; 0-937314),* P.O. Box 281, Grand Blanc, MI 48439 (SAN 214-4182) Tel 313-655-6434.

International Telecommunications Satellite Organization, *(Intl Telecommunications; 0-916233),* 3400 International Dr., NW, Washington, DC 20008 (SAN 294-9431) Tel 202-944-7034.

International Test & Evaluation Assn., *(Int Test Eval),* 5641 Burke Centre Pkwy, Burke, VA 22015 (SAN 689-6898) Tel 703-425-8522.

International Training Consultants, Inc., *(Intl Training; 0-9603702),* P.O. Box 35613, Richmond, VA 23235-0613 (SAN 215-1561) Tel 804-320-2415.

International Transactional Analysis Assn., *(Intl Transactional; 0-89489),* 1772 Vallejo St., San Francisco, CA 94123 (SAN 224-4365).

International Typeface Corp., *(Intl Typeface; 0-9608034),* 2 Hammarskjold Pl. 3rd Fl., New York, NY 10017 (SAN 239-6637); c/o Robert Silver Assocs., 307 E. 37th St., New York, NY 10016 (SAN 241-5801) Tel 212-686-5630.

International Union for Conservation of Nature & Natural Resources *See* Unipub

†International Univs. Pr., *(Intl Univs Pr; 0-8236),* 59 Boston Post Rd., P.O. Box 1524, Madison, CT 06443-1524 (SAN 202-7186) Tel 203-245-4000; *CIP.*

International Univ. Pr., *(Intl Univ Pr; 0-89697),* 1301 S. Noland Rd., Independence, MO 64055 (SAN 271-6291) Tel 816-461-3633.

International Veterinary Acupuncture Society, *(Intl Vet Acup; 0-9616627),* RR. 1, Chester Springs, PA 19425 (SAN 689-6979) Tel 513-281-2162.

International Video Entertainment, Div. of NCB Entertainment, *(Intl Video; 1-55658),* 21800 Burbank Blvd., Woodland Hills, CA 91365 Tel 818-888-3040; Toll free: 800-423-7455.

International Wealth Success, Inc., *(Intl Wealth; 0-914306; 0-934311),* 24 Canterbury Rd., Rockville Centre, NY 11570 (SAN 201-5129) Tel 516-766-5850.

International Woman Center, *(Intl Woman Ctr; 0-9614609),* P.O. Box 5293, Santa Cruz, CA 95063-5293 (SAN 691-7801).

Interpersonal Communication Programs, Inc., *(Interpersonal Comm; 0-917340),* 715 Florida, Suite 209, Minneapolis, MN 55426 (SAN 208-7057) Tel 612-871-7388.

Interpharm Pr., Inc., *(Interpharm; 0-935184),* P.O. Box 530, Prairie View, IL 60069 (SAN 295-3374) Tel 312-459-8480.

Interport USA, Inc., *(Interport U S A; 0-932331),* P.O. Box 02009, Portland, OR 97202 (SAN 686-7634) Tel 503-771-6804; Toll free: 800-233-5729.

Interpretive Marketing Products, Div. of Gibco, Inc., *(Interp Mktg Prods; 0-936023),* 490 N. 31st St., Suite 108, Billings, MT 59101 (SAN 696-8651) Tel 406-248-3555; Orders to: P.O. Box 21697, Billings, MT 59104 (SAN 662-3891) Tel 406-248-3555.

Interpretive Pubns., Inc., *(Interpretive Pubns; 0-936478),* Box 1383, Flagstaff, AZ 86002-1383 (SAN 221-4830) Tel 602-525-1934.

Intersociety Committee Pathology Information, *(Intersoc Comm Path Info; 0-937888),* 4733 Bethesda Ave., Suite 735, Bethesda, MD 20814 (SAN 205-0072) Tel 301-656-2944.

Interspace Bks., *(Interspace Bks; 0-930061),* 4500 Chesapeake St., NW, Washington, DC 20016 (SAN 669-8913) Tel 202-363-9082.

Interstate Information, Inc., *(Interstate Info; 0-939451),* P.O. Box 38548, Houston, TX 77238-8548 (SAN 663-3730); 7503 Greenlawn Dr., Houston, TX 77088 (SAN 663-3749) Tel 713-847-1152.

Interstate Piano Co., *(Interstate Piano; 0-9604092),* 4001 N. Interstate Ave., Portland, OR 97227 (SAN 214-0829) Tel 503-288-2600.

Interstate Printers & Pubs., Inc., *(Inter Print Pubs; 0-8134),* 19 N. Jackson St., Danville, IL 61832 (SAN 206-6548) Tel 217-446-0500; Toll free: 800-843-4774; P.O. Box 50, Danville, IL 61834-0050 (SAN 658-0998).

Intersystems Pubns, *(Intersystems Pubns; 0-914105),* 401 Victor Way, No. 3, Salinas, CA 93907 (SAN 237-9619).

Intersystems Software, Inc., *(Intersystems; 0-924695),* 62 Bethpage Rd., Hicksville, NY 11801 (SAN 284-298X) Tel 516-367-3776.

Intertec Publishing Corp., Subs. of Macmillan, Inc., *(Intertec Pub; 0-87288),* P.O. Box 12901, Overland Park, KS 66212 (SAN 670-8463) Tel 913-888-4664; Toll free: INTERTEC OLPK.

†Intertext, *(Intertxt AK; 0-912767),* 2633 E. 17th Ave., Anchorage, AK 99508 (SAN 282-8030); *CIP.*

Interurban Pr., *(Interurban; 0-916374; 0-87046),* P.O. Box 6444, Glendale, CA 91205 (SAN 207-9593) Tel 818-240-9130.

Intervale Publishing Co., Inc., *(Intervale Pub Co; 0-932400),* Box 777, Meredith, NH 03253 (SAN 211-9633) Tel 603-284-7726.

Interweave Pr., Inc., *(Interweave; 0-934026),* 306 N. Washington Ave., Loveland, CO 80537 (SAN 214-3151) Tel 303-669-7672; Toll free: 800-272-2193.

Interwood Pr., *(Interwood Pr; 0-9610376),* 3562 Interwood Ave., Cincinnati, OH 45220 (SAN 264-1224) Tel 513-751-5239; Dist. by: National Art Education Assn., 1916 Association Dr., Reston, VA 22091 (SAN 203-7084) Tel 703-860-8000.

Intrepid Press, *(Intrepid),* P.O. Box 1423, Buffalo, NY 14214 (SAN 207-8503) Tel 716-886-7136.

Names

481

Inventors Licensing & Marketing Agency, *(Inventors Licensing),* P.O. Box 251, Tarzana, CA 91356 (SAN 223-9981) Tel 818-344-3375; 5068 Mecca Ave., Tarzana, CA 91356 (SAN 669-1366).

Inventors Workshop International Education Foundation, *(Inventor Work),* P.O. Box 251, Tarzana, CA 91356 (SAN 260-3373) Tel 818-344-3375; Dist. by: Ilma Printing & Publishing, P.O. Box 251, Tarzana, CA 91356 (SAN 260-3381) Tel 818-344-3375.

Inverted-A, Inc., *(Inverted-A; 0-938245),* 401 Forest Hill Ln., Grand Prairie, TX 75051 (SAN 661-4213) Tel 214-264-0066.

Investigations Institute, *(Investigations; 0-9607876),* 53 W. Jackson Blvd., Chicago, IL 60604 (SAN 205-0064) Tel 312-939-6050.

Investigations U.S.A., Inc., *(Invest USA; 0-9616336),* 373 N. University Dr., No. C-135, Plantation, FL 33325 (SAN 658-8840) Tel 305-476-7716.

Investment Company Institute, *(Invest Co Inst; 0-9616113),* 1600 M St. NW, Washington, DC 20036 (SAN 224-9502) Tel 202-293-7700.

Investment Evaluations Corp., *(Invest Eval; 0-9603282),* 2000 Goldenvue Dr., Golden, CO 80401 (SAN 210-9042) Tel 303-278-3464.

Investment Information Services Pr., Affil. of Investment Information Services, Inc., *(Invest Info; 0-930369),* 205 W. Wacker Dr, Chicago, IL 60606 (SAN 678-9048) Tel 312-750-9300; Dist. by: Caroline Hse., 5S 250 Frontenac Rd., Naperville, IL 60540 (SAN 211-2280) Tel 312-983-6400.

Investment Psychology Consulting, *(Invest Psych Consult; 0-935219),* 1410 E. Glenoaks Blvd., Glendale, CA 91206 (SAN 695-7757) Tel 818-241-8165.

Investor Pubns., Inc., *(Investor Pubns; 0-914230),* 219 Parkade, Cedar Falls, IA 50613 (SAN 201-5307) Tel 319-277-6341; Toll free: 800-553-1789; Sales/Marketing: 250 S. Wacker Dr., Suite 950, Chicago, IL 60606 (SAN 281-8213) Tel 312-977-0999.

Investor Relations Assocs., *(Investor Relations; 0-9614409),* 364 Lorraine, Glen Ellyn, IL 60137 (SAN 688-6019) Tel 312-858-0016.

Investor Responsibility Research Ctr., Inc., *(Investor Ctr; 0-931035),* 1755 Massachusetts Ave., NW, Suite 600, Washington, DC 20036 (SAN 271-6631) Tel 202-936-6500.

Investor's Systems, Inc., *(Investor's Syst; 0-915610),* P.O. Box 1422, Dayton, OH 45401 (SAN 207-3420) Tel 513-223-6870.

Investrek Publishing, *(Investrek; 0-9604914),* 419 Main St., No. 160, Huntington Beach, CA 92648 (SAN 216-1443); Toll free: 800-334-0854, Ext 864; Dist. by: Liberty Publishing, 50 Scott Adam Rd., Cockeysville, MD 21030 (SAN 658-1145) Tel 301-667-6680.

Invisible City/Red Hill Pr., *(Invisible-Red Hill; 0-88031),* P.O. Box 2853, San Franscisco, CA 94126 (SAN 205-6429) Tel 415-527-1018; Dist. by: Small Press Distribution, Inc., 1814 San Pablo Ave., Berkeley, CA 94702 (SAN 204-5826) Tel 415-549-3336.

Involvement Group Press, *(Involve Group Pr; 0-9610422),* 1512 N. Nicholas St., Arlington, VA 22205 (SAN 264-1240) Tel 703-241-2879.

Ion Bks., Inc., *(Ion Books; 0-938507),* 3387 Poplar, Suite 205, Memphis, TN 38111 (SAN 661-3330) Tel 401-323-8858.

Iona Foundation, *(Iona Phila; 0-941638),* P.O. Box 29136, Philadelphia, PA 19127 (SAN 239-2364) Tel 215-482-8372.

Iona Press Company, The, *(Iona Pr; 0-910789),* P.O. Box C-3181, Wooster, OH 44691 (SAN 271-6666) Tel 216-263-2470.

†**Iota Pr.,** *(Iota Pr; 0-936412),* 4302 Pickwick Circle, No. 320, Huntington Harbour, CA 92649 (SAN 214-3895) Tel 714-895-8367; CIP.

Iowa Conference Commission on Archives & History, *(IA Conf Com Arch; 0-9616298),* 1019 Chestnut St., Des Moines, IA 50309 (SAN 658-5450) Tel 712-275-4247; Orders to: Rev. Lyle Johnston, Box 416, Schaller, IA 51053 (SAN 662-412X) Tel 712-275-4247.

Iowa Natural Heritage Foundation, *(Iowa Nat Heritage; 0-943490),* 505 Fifth Ave., Des Moines, IA 50309 (SAN 240-6845) Tel 515-288-1846.

Iowa State Fair, *(Iowa St Fair; 0-930463),* State House, Des Moines, IA 50319 (SAN 670-9214).

†**Iowa State Univ. Pr.,** *(Iowa St U Pr; 0-8138),* 2121 S. State Ave., Ames, IA 50010 (SAN 202-7194) Tel 515-292-0140; CIP.

Ipse Dixit Press, Inc., *(Ipse Dixit Pr; 0-9602468),* Box 4277, St. Paul, MN 55104 (SAN 212-8098) Tel 612-690-0980.

Ipswich Pr., The, *(Ipswich Pr; 0-938864),* P.O. Box 291, Ipswich, MA 01938 (SAN 218-4826) Tel 617-426-3900.

Iran Bks., *(Iran Bks; 0-936347),* 8014 Old Georgetown Rd., Bethesda, MD 20814 (SAN 696-866X) Tel 301-986-0079.

Irego, *(Irego; 0-911732),* P.O. Box 286, Lenox Hill Sta., 221 E. 70th St., New York, NY 10021 (SAN 215-661X).

†**Ireland Educational Corp.,** *(Ireland Educ; 0-89103),* 7076 S. Alton Way, Bldg. C, Englewood, CO 80112 (SAN 207-9488); CIP.

Iridescence, *(Iridescence; 0-938331),* P.O. Box 3556, Culver City, CA 90230 (SAN 661-3144); 5925 Canterbury Dr., No. 202, Culver City, CA 90230 (SAN 661-3152) Tel 213-370-0796.

Iris I O Publishing, Subs. of Strawberry Hill Pr., *(Iris IO; 0-932987),* 316 California Ave. No.428, Reno, NV 89509 (SAN 689-0156) Tel 702-747-1638; Dist. by: Strawberry Hill Pr., 2594 15th Ave., San Francisco, CA 94127 (SAN 238-8103) Tel 415-664-8112.

†**Iris Press, Inc.,** *(Iris Pr Inc; 0-916078),* 27 Chestnut St., Binghamton, NY 13905 (SAN 219-6824) Tel 607-722-6739; CIP.

Irish American Cultural Institute, The, *(Irish Am Cult; 0-9614900),* 683 Osceola, St. Paul, MN 55105 (SAN 225-3240) Tel 612-647-5678.

Irish Bk. Ctr., *(Irish Bk Ctr),* 245 W. 104th St., New York, NY 10025 (SAN 209-1089) Tel 212-866-0309.

Irish Bks. & Media, *(Irish Bks Media; 0-937702),* 683 Osceola Ave., St. Paul, MN 55105 (SAN 215-1987) Tel 612-647-5678.

Irish Children's Fund, Inc., *(Irish Childs Fund; 0-9614331),* 5602 Hillcrest Rd., Downers Grove, IL 60516 (SAN 687-8075) Tel 312-968-6275; Dist. by: The Collection, Inc., P.O. Box 11465, Memphis, TN 38111 (SAN 289-9574) Tel 901-458-9830.

Irish Family Names Society, The, *(Irish Family Names; 0-9601868),* P.O. Box 2095, La Mesa, CA 92044-0600 (SAN 221-3567) Tel 619-466-8739.

Irish Genealogical Foundation, Div. of O'Laughlin Pr., *(Irish Genealog; 0-940134),* P.O. Box 7575, Kansas City, MO 64116 (SAN 218-4834) Tel 816-454-1463.

Iron & Steel Society, Inc., *(Iron & Steel; 0-932897),* 410 Commonwealth Dr., Warrendale, PA 15086 (SAN 224-876X) Tel 412-776-1535.

Iron Crown Enterprises, Inc., *(Iron Crown Ent Inc; 0-915795),* P.O. Box 1605, Charlottesville, VA 22902 (SAN 294-0272) Tel 804-295-3917; Toll free: 800-325-0479; 300 W. Main St., Charlottesville, VA 22901 (SAN 693-5109); Dist. by: Berkley Publishing Group, 200 Madison Ave., New York, NY 10016 (SAN 201-3991) Tel 212-686-9820.

Iron Horse Pr., *(Iron Horse Pr; 0-937219),* 20954 Pacific Coast Hwy., Malibu, CA 90265 (SAN 658-7364) Tel 213-456-8713.

†**Iron Mountain Press,** *(Iron Mtn Pr; 0-931182),* P.O. Box D, Emory, VA 24327 (SAN 217-7994); CIP.

Iron Press, The, *(Iron Pr; 0-912363),* P.O. Box 176, Franklin, MI 48025 (SAN 265-1548) Tel 313-626-1075.

†**Ironwood Press,** *(Ironwood Calif; 0-936800),* 11251 Macmurray St., Garden Grove, CA 92641 (SAN 221-9379) Tel 714-539-9830; CIP.

Ironwood Pr. (Scottsdale), *(Ironwood Scottsdale; 0-932541),* P.O. Box 8464, Scottsdale, AZ 85252 (SAN 687-4800) Tel 602-947-8872.

Iroquois Bk. Co., *(Iroquois Bk; 0-9616628),* P.O. Box 317, North Amherst, MA 01059 (SAN 661-2059); 52 Old Bay Rd., Belchertown, MA 01007 (SAN 661-2067) Tel 413-323-5589.

Irresistible Books, *(Irresistible),* P.O. Box 1059, Angleton, TX 77515 (SAN 283-3816).

Irrigation Assn., *(Irrigation; 0-935030),* 1911 N. Fort Myer Dr., Suite 1009, Arlington, VA 22209 (SAN 202-0807) Tel 703-524-1200.

Irvington Historical Society, *(Irvington Hist; 0-9611394),* 35 Clinton Terrace, Irvington, NJ 07111 (SAN 285-3280) Tel 201-994-4210.

†**Irvington Pubs.,** *(Irvington; 0-89197; 0-8290; 0-8422),* 740 Broadway, New York, NY 10003 (SAN 207-2408) Tel 212-777-4100; CIP.

Irwin, G. H., & Co., *(G H Irwin & Co; 0-936243),* P.O. Box 945, Enumclaw, WA 98022 (SAN 696-9364) Tel 206-927-4029; 41115 SE 236th, Enumclaw, WA 98022 (SAN 696-9372).

Irwin, Richard D., Inc., Subs. of Dow Jones & Co., Inc., *(Irwin; 0-256),* 1818 Ridge Rd., Homewood, IL 60430 (SAN 206-8400) Tel 312-798-6000; Toll free: 800-323-4560.

Irwinton Pubs., *(Irwinton),* 9685 Anderson Rd., Mercersburg, PA 17236 (SAN 202-7208).

Isaacs, Harold, *(H Isaacs; 0-9601406),* P.O. Box 237, Plains, GA 31780 (SAN 663-2947); Dist. by: Peanut Brigade, P.O. Box 237, Plains, GA 31780 (SAN 210-976X) Tel 912-924-8287.

Isao, Ltd., *(Isao Ltd; 0-9616819),* 235 W. Orangewood Ave., 4-D, Anaheim, CA 92802 (SAN 661-1206) Tel 714-750-5361.

Ischua Bks., *(Ischua Bks; 0-9616797),* 4611 Gile Hollow Rd., Hinsdale, NY 14743 (SAN 661-3012) Tel 716-557-2518.

Isham, *(Isham; 0-9614226),* P.O. Box 2191, Glenview, IL 60025 (SAN 686-7642) Tel 312-459-0618.

ISHI Pubns. *See* **Institute for the Study of Human Issues**

Ishiyaku EuroAmerica, Inc., Subs. of Ishiyaku Group of Cos. (Japan), *(Ishiyaku Euro; 0-912791),* 11559 Rock Island Ct., St. Louis, MO 63043 (SAN 282-8057) Tel 314-432-1933.

Isis Press, *(Isis Pr; 0-940944),* 1516 Morton Ave., Ann Arbor, MI 48104 (SAN 223-1883) Tel 313-665-4740. Do Not Confuse with an Isis Press in San Francisco, CA.

Isis Pr., *(Isis Pr CA; 0-931037),* 1827 Haight St., No. 95, San Francisco, CA 94117 (SAN 678-9943) Tel 415-346-1359.

Islamic Center of America, The, *(Islamic Ctr; 0-942776),* 15571 Joy Rd., Detroit, MI 48228 (SAN 240-2335) Tel 313-582-7442.

†**Islamic Foundation,** *(Islamic Found; 0-932815),* 300 W. High Ridge Rd., Villa Park, IL 60181 (SAN 688-6604) Tel 312-752-4575; CIP.

Islamic Productions International, *(Islamic Prods; 0-934894),* 739 E. Sixth St., Tucson, AZ 85719 (SAN 203-8625) Tel 602-791-3989. *Imprints:* Renaissance Institute (Renaissance Inst); Renaissance Productions (Renaissance Prods).

Islamic Seminary, The, *(Islamic Seminary; 0-941724),* 50-11 Queens Blvd., Woodside, NY 11377 (SAN 239-2372) Tel 718-458-0924.

Island Bed & Breakfast Hawaii, Inc., *(Island Bed & Breakfast; 0-9615970),* P.O. Box 449, Kapaa, HI 96746 (SAN 697-2926) Tel 805-822-7771; 4-1380 Kuhio Hwy., Suite 202, Kapaa, HI 96746 (SAN 697-2934) Tel 808-822-7771; Dist. by: Pacific Trade Group, P.O. Box 668, Pearl City, HI 96782-0668 (SAN 169-1635) Tel 808-671-6735; Dist. by: Pacific Pipeline, Inc., 19215 66th Ave., S., Kent, WA 98032-1171 (SAN 208-2128) Tel 206-872-5523.

Island Canoe Co., *(Island Canoe; 0-918439),* 3556 W. Blakely Ave. NE, Bainbridge Island, WA 98110 (SAN 657-6249) Tel 206-842-5997; Dist. by: Pacific Pipeline, 19215 66th Ave. S., Kent, WA 98032-1171 (SAN 208-2128); Toll free: 800-426-4727; Toll free: 800-467-4647 (in WA).

Island Heritage/Worldwide Distributors, *(Island Herit-Wrldwide Dist; 0-931548),* 1819 Kahai St., Honolulu, HI 96819-3136 (SAN 211-3392) Tel 808-531-0133.

†**Island Pr.,** Div. of Center for Resource Economics, *(Island CA; 0-933280),* Star Rte. 1, Box 38, Covelo, CA 95428 (SAN 212-5129) Tel 707-983-6432; CIP.

JMP MANUFACTURING

Island Pr., *(Island Pr; 0-87208),* 175 Bahia Via, Fort Myers Beach, FL 33931 (SAN 202-7216) Tel 813-463-9482.

Island Pubs., *(Island Pubs WA; 0-9615580),* Box 201, Anacortes, WA 98221 (SAN 696-2726) Tel 206-293-5398; 477 Section Rd., Anacortes, WA 98221 (SAN 696-2734).

Island Publishing, *(Isl Pub Lummi; 0-937391),* 3876 Centerview Rd., Lummi Island, WA 98262 (SAN 658-8867) Tel 206-758-7457.

Island Publishing House, *(Island Pub; 0-916424),* P.O. Drawer 758, Manteo, NC 27954 (SAN 208-0362) Tel 919-473-2838.

Island Resources Foundation, *(Isl Resources),* Red Hook Ctr., P.O. Box 33, St. Thomas, VI 00802 (SAN 225-4956) Tel 809-775-3225; 1718 P St., NW, Washington, DC 80036 (SAN 650-0374) Tel 202-265-9712.

Island Writers Publishing Co., *(Island Writers; 0-9604798),* P.O. Box 953, Ocean Shores, WA 98569 (SAN 220-0619) Tel 206-289-2004; Dist. by: Pacific Trade Group, Ltd., P.O. Box 668, Pearl City, HI 96782-0668 (SAN 169-1635).

Isle of Guam International Publishers, *(Isle of Guam; 0-942780),* P.O. Box 21119, Guam Main Facility, GU 96921 (SAN 240-2343) Tel 808-963-6317.

Isle Royale Natural History Assn., Inc., *(Isle Royale Hist; 0-935289),* 87 N. Ripley St., Houghton, MI 49931 (SAN 696-2513) Tel 906-482-8479.

†Ism Pr., Inc., *(Ism Pr; 0-910383),* P.O. Box 12447, San Francisco, CA 94112 (SAN 241-5496) Tel 415-333-7641; *CIP.*

Issue Action Pubns., Inc., *(Issue Action Pubns; 0-913869),* 105 Old Long Ridge Rd., Stamford, CT 06903 (SAN 286-7966) Tel 203-329-1425.

Italica Pr., *(Italica Pr; 0-934977),* 625 Main St., Suite 641, New York, NY 10044 (SAN 695-1805) Tel 212-935-4230.

Italimuse, Inc., *(Italimuse; 0-910798),* 3128 Burr St, Fairfield, CT 06430 (SAN 203-8242) Tel 203-259-5788.

ITEC, Inc., *(ITEC; 0-943908),* Box 464, Beaver, PA 15009 (SAN 241-1237) Tel 412-728-4318.

Ithaca College, *(Ithaca Coll; 0-9610556),* South Hill Campus, Ithaca, NY 14850 (SAN 264-1267) Tel 607-274-3452.

†Ithaca Hse., *(Ithaca Hse; 0-87886),* P.O. Box 6484, Ithaca, NY 14851 (SAN 202-7224) Tel 607-272-4968; *CIP.*

Ithaca Pr., *(Ithaca Pr MA; 0-915940),* P.O. Box 853, Lowell, MA 01853 (SAN 208-709X) Tel 617-453-2177.

Ivans Publishing Co., *(Ivans Pub NY; 0-9607476),* 211-10 23rd Ave., Bayside, NY 11360 (SAN 238-6143) Tel 212-423-4307.

Ivers-Saint Lloyd Pubs., *(Ivers St Lloyd; 0-938063),* P.O. Box 11245, San Francisco, CA 94101 (SAN 661-261X); 2450 Vicente, San Francisco, CA 94116 (SAN 661-2628) Tel 415-681-5267.

Ives, Dorthea S., *(D Ives; 0-9616225),* R.D. 1, Dolgeville, NY 13329 (SAN 697-1628).

Ivey Pubns., *(Ivey Pubns; 0-9600864),* 1845 Arkoe Dr., SE, Atlanta, GA 30316 (SAN 207-6799).

Ivory House, *(Ivory Hse; 0-9608896),* P.O. Box 676, 121 Randolph Rd., Freehold, NJ 07728 (SAN 241-1245) Tel 201-462-1620.

Ivory Palaces Music Publishing Co., Inc., *(Ivory Pal; 0-943644),* 3141 Spottswood Ave., Memphis, TN 38111 (SAN 238-3020) Tel 901-323-3509.

Ivory Publishing, *(Ivory Pub; 0-9614738),* P.O. Box 4595, Denver, CO 80204 (SAN 692-7440) Tel 303-572-8286; Dist. by: Publishers Group West, 5855 Beaudry St., Emeryville, CA 94608 (SAN 202-8522) Tel 415-658-3453; Toll free: 800-982-8319; Dist. by: Bookpeople, 2929 Fifth St., Berkeley, CA 94710 (SAN 168-9517) Tel 415-549-3030; Toll free: 800-227-1516; Dist. by: Samuel Weiser, Inc., P.O. Box 612, York Beach, ME 03910 (SAN 202-9588) Tel 207-363-4393; Toll free: 800-843-6666.

Ivory Scroll Books, Pubs., *(Ivory Scroll),* P.O. Box 7526, Philadelphia, PA 19101 (SAN 205-003X).

Ivory Tower Publishing Co., Inc., *(Ivory Tower Pub; 0-88032),* 125 Walnut St., Watertown, MA 02172 (SAN 658-3989) Tel 617-923-1111; Toll free: 800-322-5016; Dist. by: Contemporary Bks., Inc., 180 N. Michigan Ave., Chicago, IL 60601 (SAN 202-5493) Tel 312-782-9181.

Ivosevic, Stanley W., *(S W Ivosevic; 0-9611352),* 449 Wright St., Suite 2, Denver, CO 80228 (SAN 283-2267) Tel 303-988-6050.

Ivy Bks., Div. of Ballantine Bks., Inc., *(Ivy Books; 0-8041),* 201 E. 50th St., New York, NY 10022 (SAN 661-7832) Tel 212-572-2573.

Ivy Club, The, *(Ivy Club; 0-934756),* 43 Prospect Ave., Princeton, NJ 08540 (SAN 213-0904).

Ivy Hill Pr., Subs. of Mentors, Inc., *(Ivy Hill; 0-9601542; 0-933461),* 8817 Greenview Pl., Spring Valley, CA 92077 (SAN 212-5145) Tel 619-464-4235.

Ivy League Press, Inc, *(IVY League Pr; 0-918921),* P.O. Box 15035, Arlington, VA 22215 (SAN 670-0543) Tel 202-892-1110.

Ivystone Pubns., *(Ivystone; 0-935604),* Box 23, Ada, MI 49301 (SAN 215-3211) Tel 616-452-8376.

JAARS, Inc., Affil. of Summer Institute of Linguistics, *(JAARS Inc; 0-9615959),* Box 248, JAARS Rd., Waxhaw, NC 28173 (SAN 697-2896) Tel 704-843-2185.

JABA, *(JABA; 0-938583),* 9521 Business Ctr. Dr., Rancho Cucamonga, CA 91730 (SAN 661-1141) Tel 714-980-2722.

JACP, Inc., *(JACP Inc; 0-934609),* 414 E. Third Ave., San Mateo, CA 94401 (SAN 693-8841) Tel 415-343-9408; Orders to: P.O. Box 367, San Mateo, CA 94401 (SAN 662-3271).

J. A. Enterprises, *(J A Ent; 0-9606722),* 1447 11th St., Greeley, CO 80631 (SAN 219-6654) Tel 303-356-8630.

JAMV Publishing, *(JAMV Pub; 0-911371),* 199 Posada del Sol, Suite 219, Novato, CA 94947 (SAN 271-7166) Tel 415-883-4958; Orders to: P.O. Box 1748, Novato, CA 94948 (SAN 662-0507).

JA Micropublishing, Inc., *(JA Micropublishing; 0-912127),* 271 Main Street Box 218, Eastchester, NY 10707 (SAN 264-6730) Tel 914-793-2130; Toll free: 800-227-2477.

J&A Enterprises, *(J & A Enterprises; 0-934368),* 5522 W. Acoma Rd., Glendale, AZ 85306 (SAN 212-9116).

J & B Bks., *(J & B Bks; 0-941186),* 26 Marwood St., Albany, NY 12209 (SAN 285-0958) Tel 518-489-4009; Dist. by: Fulmont News Co., 182 Division St., Amsterdam, NY 12010 (SAN 200-7487).

J&B Pubs., *(J & B Pubs; 0-943498),* Box 2866, Taos, NM 87571 (SAN 240-6861) Tel 505-776-2355.

J & C Bks., *(J & C Bks; 0-9616091),* P.O. Box 1378, Scarborough, ME 04074-1378 (SAN 698-1267) Tel 207-883-4423.

J & F Enterprises, *(J & F Ents; 0-918441),* P.O. Box 265, Shepherdstown, WV 25443 (SAN 657-6281) Tel 304-876-3136.

J & J Books, Inc., *(J & J Bks; 0-914464),* 1004 Springhill Dr., Angola, IN 46703 (SAN 202-7232) Tel 219-665-5346.

J. & J. Distributors, *(J & J Dist),* P.O. Box 247, Raymondville, TX 78580 (SAN 213-5256) Tel 512-689-2523.

J&J Pubns., *(J&J Pubns MI; 0-9605786),* Box 1424, Traverse City, MI 49684 (SAN 216-4000).

J&L Enterprises, *(J & L Ent; 0-9613425),* 2485 Riverside Dr., Laramie, WY 82070 (SAN 656-8939) Tel 307-742-0849.

J&M Publishing Co., *(J&M Pub; 0-930630),* 11 Matthews Ave., Riverdale, NJ 07457 (SAN 211-1411) Tel 201-838-9434.

J & N Pubs., *(J & N Pubs; 0-9616042),* 121 Putnam Dr., Oroville, CA 95966 (SAN 697-8940) Tel 916-589-1487.

J&R Enterprises, *(J & R Enter; 0-9608550),* P.O. Box 140264, Anchorage, AK 99514 (SAN 240-687X) Tel 907-333-4442.

J & R Publishing Co., *(J & R Pub; 0-9616771),* P.O. Box 1514, Greenwood, SC 29646 (SAN 661-3373); Royal Oak 22, Greenwood, SC 29648 (SAN 661-3381) Tel 803-229-0154.

J&W Tex-Mex, *(J&W Tex-Mex; 0-9604842),* P.O. Box 983, Arlington, VA 22216 (SAN 215-6628).

JB & Me, *(JB & Me; 0-9616226),* P.O. Box 480311, Los Angeles, CA 90048 (SAN 658-5515) Tel 213-546-1255.

J.B. Pr., *(J B Pr; 0-9614881),* P.O. Box 4843, Duke Sta., Durham, NC 27706 (SAN 693-1227) Tel 919-493-5221.

J-B Publishing Co., *(J-B Pub; 0-916170),* 430 Ivy Ave., Crete, NE 68333 (SAN 207-2424) Tel 402-826-3356.

JCL House, *(JCL Hse; 0-9610274),* P.O. Box 1821, East Lansing, MI 48823 (SAN 264-1305) Tel 616-385-2870.

JCP Corp. of Virginia, *(JCP Corp VA; 0-938694),* P.O. Box 814, Virginia Beach, VA 23451 (SAN 220-1313) Tel 804-422-5426.

J. C. Printing Co., *(J C Print),* Dawnsonville, GA 30534-0579 (SAN 211-0245) Tel 404-265-2036.

JD McG. Pubns., *(JD McG Pubns; 0-932619),* 32 W. Glendale Ave., Alexandria, VA 22301 (SAN 687-5173) Tel 703-683-3463.

J. D. Pubs., *(JD Pubs; 0-9616688),* 13162 Miller Rd., Johnstown, OH 43031 (SAN 661-4388).

JD Publishing & Seminars, *(JD Pub & Seminars; 0-937841),* 3520-B Cadillac Ave., Costa Mesa, CA 92626 (SAN 659-4743) Tel 714-751-2787.

J. E. B. Pub. Co., *(JEB Pub; 0-940946),* Rte. 2 Box 400, Franklin, GA 30217 (SAN 281-8396); Orders to: Groover Medical Bldg., Ambulance Dr., Carrollton, GA 30117 (SAN 281-840X) Tel 404-832-6861.

JED, *(JED; 0-9602200),* P.O. Box 7143 RC, Toledo, OH 43615 (SAN 212-3622) Tel 419-885-2932.

JEF Pr., *(JEF Pr; 0-9616022),* 179 E. Third St., New York, NY 10009 (SAN 699-7589) Tel 212-505-5143.

JETS, Inc., *(Jets),* 1180 Ave. of the Americas, New York, NY 10036 (SAN 236-2570) Tel 212-705-7690; 345 E. 47th St., New York, NY 10017 (SAN 693-4919).

JFJ Assocs., *(JFJ Assocs; 0-935707),* P.O. Box 56628, Washington, DC 20011 (SAN 695-6955) Tel 202-726-5248; 1302 Floral St., NW, Washington, DC 20012 (SAN 696-0391).

JFJ Publishing, Div. of Jews for Jesus, *(JFJ Pub; 0-9616148),* 60 Haight St., San Francisco, CA 94102 (SAN 699-8240); Toll free: 800-227-3190.

†JH Pr., *(JH Pr; 0-935672),* P.O. Box 294, Village Sta., New York, NY 10014 (SAN 213-6279); *CIP.*

JJ Publishing, *(JJ Pub FL; 0-9604610),* 1312 Arthur St., Hollywood, FL 33019 (SAN 220-0090) Tel 305-929-3559; Dist. by: Milady Publishing Corporation, 3839 White Plains, Bronx, NY 10467 (SAN 202-635X).

JKL Pubs., *(JKL Pubs; 0-935757),* 8 Prince St., P.O. Box 1575, Rochester, NY 14603 (SAN 696-4753) Tel 716-624-4101.

JLA Pubns., *(JLA Pubns; 0-940374),* 50 Follen St., Suite 507, Cambridge, MA 02138 (SAN 223-1441) Tel 617-547-6382; Dist. by: Publishers Group West, 5855 Beaudry St., Emeryville, CA 94608 (SAN 202-8522) Tel 415-685-3453; Toll free: 800-982-8319.

JLC Pubns., *(J L C Pubns; 0-9613621),* 586 E. Town St., Columbus, OH 43215 (SAN 670-8846) Tel 614-464-1236.

JLJ Pubs., *(JLJ Pubs; 0-937172),* 824 Shrine Rd., Springfield, OH 45504-3999 (SAN 215-322X) Tel 513-322-4454.

JL Pr., Subs. of the Print Shoppe, *(JL Press; 0-939279),* P.O. Box 2414, Abilene, TX 79604 (SAN 662-7072); 2410 S. 14th, Abilene, TX 79605 (SAN 662-7080) Tel 915-691-0110.

J L Productions, *(J L Prods; 0-9610564),* 93 Medford St., Arlington, MA 02174 (SAN 264-1321) Tel 617-641-2852.

JMA Pr., Inc., *(JMA Pr; 0-9614742),* 9215 Ashton Ridge, Austin, TX 78750 (SAN 692-7211) Tel 512-331-9027.

JMB Pubns., *(JMB Pubns; 0-9606834),* 10810 Cherry Grove Ct., Louisville, KY 40299 (SAN 217-2410).

JMP Manufacturing Corp., *(JMP Mfg; 0-9608898),* 4467 Eaton-Gettysburg Rd., Eaton, OH 45320 (SAN 264-133X) Tel 513-456-6995.

Names

Names

JM Productions, *(J M Prods; 0-939298),* Box 1911, Brentwood, TN 37027 (SAN 216-4019) Tel 615-373-4814; Dist. by: Spring Arbor Distributors, 10885 Textile Rd., Belleville, MI 48111 (SAN 158-9016) Tel 313-481-0900; Dist. by: Ingram Book Co., 347 Reedwood Dr., Box 17266, Nashville, TN 37217 (SAN 169-7978) Tel 615-361-5000; Dist. by: East Coast Christian Distributors, 35 Readington Rd., P.O. Box 4200, Somerville, NJ 08876 (SAN 169-491X) Tel 201-722-5050; Dist. by: Quality Books, 918 Sherwood Dr., Lake Bluff, IL 60044-2204 (SAN 169-2127) Tel 312-498-4000.

JM Pubns., Inc., *(JM Pubns; 0-9615844),* P.O. Box 1408, Hendersonville, TN 37077-1408 (SAN 696-8716) Tel 615-822-0857; Walton Mall, No. 13, Hendersonville, TN 37077 (SAN 696-8724).

JMT Pubns., *(JMT Pubns; 0-942782),* P.O. Box 603, Camp Hill, PA 17011 (SAN 238-8189) Tel 717-761-6513.

J-Mar Productions, Inc., *(J-Mar Prods; 0-9615082),* 8033 Sunset Blvd., Suite 163, Los Angeles, CA 90046 (SAN 694-0676) Tel 818-500-0555.

J Mark, *(J Mark; 0-9613485),* 203 N. Cone St., Wilson, NC 27893 (SAN 657-3568) Tel 919-243-5151.

JNZ, Inc., *(JNZ; 0-913871),* 729 Windward Dr., Rodeo, CA 94572 (SAN 286-7990) Tel 415-799-1446.

JOB Pubns, *(JOB Pubns; 0-9608520),* P.O. Box 1862, Hagerstown, MD 21742 (SAN 240-6004) Tel 301-791-3250.

JOED Originals of California, Inc., *(JOED Orig; 0-916237),* P.O. Box 22439, San Diego, CA 92122-0439 (SAN 294-9520) Tel 619-453-7533.

J.O.V. Pubns., *(JOV Pubns; 0-936321),* P.O. Box 399, Needham Heights, MA 02194 (SAN 697-2861) Tel 617-367-1080; 333 Boston Rd., Chelmsford, MA 01824 (SAN 697-287X).

JP Designs, *(JP Designs; 0-9616904),* P.O. Box 6175, Kent, WA 98064-6175 (SAN 661-5155); 12916 SE 245th, Kent, WA 98064-6175 (SAN 661-5163) Tel 206-631-8910.

J P Enterprises, *(J P Enterprises; 0-9617147),* 781 Olive St., Denver, CO 80220 (SAN 663-3706) Tel 303-399-0349.

JP Pubns., *(JP Pubns WI; 0-9602978),* P.O. Box 4173, Madison, WI 53711 (SAN 214-0411) Tel 608-231-2373.

J P Pubns., *(JP Pubns CA; 0-910703),* 2952 Grinnel, Davis, CA 95616 (SAN 260-2083).

JRA, Pub., *(JRA Pub; 0-933297),* 14121 Stratford, Riverview, MI 48192 (SAN 692-3151) Tel 313-285-9265.

J.R.&G. Co., *(J R and G; 0-9608844),* 4165 Greenwood Dr., Bethlehem, PA 18017 (SAN 241-0311) Tel 215-694-0860.

JRB Publishing Co., *(JRB Pub; 0-9614289),* 2 Union St., Oneonta, NY 13820 (SAN 687-4517) Tel 607-432-7473; Orders to: Box 717, Oneonta, NY 13820 (SAN 693-5206).

J.R.C. Publishing & Minerals, *(J R C Pub; 0-916367),* 3 Roswell St., New Bedford, MA 02740 (SAN 295-852X) Tel 617-994-3403.

J.R. Pubns., *(J R Pubns; 0-913952),* 170 NE 33rd St., Ft. Lauderdale, FL 33334 (SAN 202-7283) Tel 305-563-1844.

JSL Editions, *(JSL Editions; 0-938615),* P.O. Box 503, Barrington, IL 60011 (SAN 661-5767); 418 S. Hough, Barrington, IL 60010 (SAN 661-5775) Tel 312-646-2797.

JTG of Nashville, *(JTG Nashville; 0-938971),* 1024C 18th Ave., S., Nashville, TN 37212 (SAN 661-6917) Tel 615-329-3036.

J.T. Publishing Co., *(J T Pub Co; 0-9615455),* P.O. Box 4, Manning, SC 29102 (SAN 695-7684) Tel 803-478-8407; Box 1024, Rte. 4, Manning, SC 29102 (SAN 696-0405).

JTV Enterprises, *(JTV Ent; 0-9614253),* P.O. Box 1409, Cary, NC 27511 (SAN 686-7685) Tel 919-851-8253.

JWB, *(JWB; 0-914820),* 15 E. 26th St., New York, NY 10010 (SAN 203-9060) Tel 212-532-4949.

J-Y Enterprises, *(J-Y Ent; 0-9609670),* 717 Ponce de Leon, Stockton, CA 95210 (SAN 271-7123) Tel 209-951-2341.

Jacar Pr., *(Jacar Pr; 0-936481),* 223 N. Main, Wendell, NC 27591 (SAN 698-1038) Tel 919-365-4188; P.O. Box 4, Wendell, NC 27591 (SAN 698-2530).

Jacbar Pubns., *(Jacbar Pubns; 0-9606154),* Box 103, Randolph, OH 44265 (SAN 217-1120).

Jacek Publishing Co., *(Jacek; 0-9601084),* 38 Morris Lane, Milford, CT 06460 (SAN 209-4029).

Jack Mack Paperbacks, *(Jack Mack; 0-910391),* 612 E. Manning, Apt. 3, Reedley, CA 93654 (SAN 260-0994) Tel 209-638-3392.

†**Jackpine Press,** *(Jackpine Pr; 0-917492),* 1878 Meadowbrook Dr., Winston-Salem, NC 27104 (SAN 208-273X) Tel 919-725-8828; *CIP.*

Jackrabbit Books, *(Jackrabbit; 0-9612454),* P.O. Box 1, Minneapolis, MN 55440 (SAN 289-5072) Tel 213-941-4446.

Jackson, Don, Assocs., *(Jackson Assocs; 0-913211),* 461 Park Ave. S., 9th Flr., New York, NY 10016 (SAN 283-1228) Tel 212-213-9566. *Imprints:* American Liberty Publishing (Am Liberty Pub).

Jackson, G. B., *(Jackson G B),* 1030 Edgewater Ave. W., St. Paul, MN 55112 (SAN 287-2757).

Jackson, Steve, Games, Inc., *(Jackson Games; 1-55634),* P.O. Box 18957, Austin, TX 78760 (SAN 661-3292); 2700A Metcalfe Rd., Austin, TX 78741 (SAN 661-3306) Tel 512-447-7866.

Jackson Hole Alliance for Responsible Planning, *(JHAFRP; 0-9617014),* P.O. Box 2728, Jackson, WY 83001 (SAN 662-9202); 260 E. Broadway, Jackson, WY 83001 (SAN 662-9210) Tel 307-733-9417.

Jackson Mountain Pr., *(Jackson Mtn; 0-918499),* P.O. Box 2652, Renton, WA 98056 (SAN 657-3576) Tel 206-255-6635; 1550 Union NE, Renton, WA 98056 (SAN 657-3584).

Jackson Pubns., *(Jackson Pubns; 0-937457),* Hwy. 626 & Pecan, Rm. 8, Boley, OK 74829 (SAN 658-8875) Tel 918-667-3394.

Jacksonville Art Museum, Inc., *(Jacksonville Art; 0-916235),* 4160 Blvd. Center Dr., Jacksonville, FL 32207 (SAN 294-944X) Tel 904-398-8336.

Jacobs, Mary, *(M Jacobs; 0-9612156),* 6000 E. Brundage No. 46, Bakersfield, CA 93307 (SAN 289-369X) Tel 805-366-0387.

Jacobs Ladder Pubns., *(Jacobs Ladder Pubns; 0-933647),* 5003 Cascade Ct., Culver City, CA 90230 (SAN 692-6517) Tel 213-558-1166.

Jacobs Publishing Co., *(Jacobs; 0-918272),* 3334 E. Indian School Rd., Suite C, Phoenix, AZ 85018 (SAN 209-4525) Tel 602-954-6581.

Jacobs Publishing Inc., *(Jacobs Pub; 0-9615234),* 101 E. Carmel Dr., Suite 200, Carmel, IN 46032 (SAN 692-4905) Tel 317-844-9400.

Jacobsen, Anita, *(A Jacobsen; 0-9604456),* 2896 Harbinger Lane, Dallas, TX 75252 (SAN 214-2473) Tel 214-323-0890.

Jacobsen Properties, Inc., *(Jacobsen Prop; 0-9613260),* P.O. Box 96, Westwego, LA 70094 (SAN 296-6026) Tel 504-348-2276.

Jacqueline Enterprises, Inc., *(Jacqueline Enter; 0-932446),* 4896 South El Camino Dr., Englewood, CO 80111 (SAN 221-0487) Tel 303-779-8278.

Jadd Publishing Hse., *(Jadd Pub Hse; 0-9616772),* P.O. Box 4, Melrose, WI 54642 (SAN 661-3349); 311 Washington St., Melrose, WI 54642 (SAN 661-3357) Tel 608-488-4971.

Jade House Pubns., *(Jade Hse Pubns; 0-942596),* P.O. Box 419, Bryantown, MD 20617 (SAN 239-6653) Tel 301-274-3441.

Jade Mist Pr., *(Jade Mist Pr; 0-935107),* P.O. Box 5229, Eugene, OR 97405 (SAN 695-0981) Tel 503-345-9538.

Jade Mountain Pr., *(Jade Mtn; 0-916133),* P.O. Box 72, Mountain Lakes, NJ 07046 (SAN 294-9474) Tel 203-334-1189; 11 Hillcrest Rd., Mountain Lakes, NJ 07046 (SAN 294-9482).

Jade Pubns., *(Jade Pubns; 0-937399),* P.O. Box 5567, Sherman Oaks, CA 91413 (SAN 658-8891); 8758 Sophia, Sepulveda, CA 91343 (SAN 658-8905) Tel 818-892-9433.

Jadestone Publishing Corp., *(Jadestone),* 3341 West Peoria Avenue, Phoenix, AZ 85029 (SAN 264-1348).

Jadetree Pr., Inc., *(Jadetree Pr; 0-917135),* P.O. Box 11130, Arlington, VA 22210 (SAN 655-8178) Tel 703-522-9550.

Jaeger, Julia, Mrs., *(Jaeger),* The Tenth Muse, P.O. Box 1417, Pacifica, CA 94044 (SAN 211-2957).

Jaguar Bks., *(Jaguar Bks; 0-937723),* P.O. Box 6360, Santa Fe, NM 87502 (SAN 659-2554) Tel 505-983-8068; 601 Canyon Rd., Santa Fe, NM 87501 (SAN 659-2562).

Jahan Bk. Co, *(Jahan Bk Co; 0-936665),* 116 Greenbank Ave., Piedmont, CA 94611 (SAN 699-7163) Tel 415-428-0933; Orders to: 116 Greenbank Ave., Piedmont, CA 94611 (SAN 662-4030) Tel 415-428-0933.

†**Jai Pr., Inc.,** *(Jai Pr; 0-89232),* P.O. Box 1678, Greenwich, CT 06836 (SAN 208-4082) Tel 203-661-7602; *CIP.*

Jaks Publishing Co., *(Jaks Pub Co; 0-935674),* 1106 N. Washington St., Helena, MT 59601 (SAN 214-042X).

Jakubowsky, *(Jakubowsky; 0-932588),* 1565 Madison St., Oakland, CA 94612 (SAN 212-1034) Tel 415-763-4324.

Jalamap Pubns., Inc., *(Jalamap; 0-934750; 1-55649),* 601 D St., South Charleston, WV 25303-0917 (SAN 216-1478) Tel 304-744-1353.

†**Jalmar Pr.,** Subs. of B. L. Winch & Assocs., *(Jalmar Pr; 0-915190),* 45 Hitching Post Dr., Bldg. 2, Rolling Hills Estate, CA 90274-4297 (SAN 281-8302) Tel 213-539-6430; Toll free: 800-662-9662; *CIP.*

Jama Books, *(Jama Bks; 0-934130),* 1120 Beach Dr., Flint, MI 48502 (SAN 281-8329).

Jamenair, Ltd., *(Jamenair Ltd; 0-938667),* P.O. Box 241957, Los Angeles, CA 90024 (SAN 661-6194); 10660 Wellworth Ave., Los Angeles, CA 90024 (SAN 661-6208) Tel 213-470-8105.

James, William, Pr., *(W James Pr; 0-938537),* Harvard Medical Schl., Laboratory of Neurophysiology/Mass Mental Health Ctr., 74 Fenwood Dr., Boston, MA 02115 (SAN 661-4809) Tel 617-734-1300.

James Bond 007 Fan Club, The, *(Bond Double-O Seven; 0-9605838),* P.O. Box 414, Bronxville, NY 10708 (SAN 216-5902) Tel 914-961-3440.

James, McCormick & Co., Pubs., *(James McCormick & Co; 0-934979),* 15127 NE 24th St. C-3, Suite 156, Redmond, WA 98052 (SAN 694-0323) Tel 206-643-7850.

James Pr., Inc., *(James Pr Inc; 0-9617280),* 4915 11th Ave., Brooklyn, NY 11219 (SAN 663-5229) Tel 718-853-3863.

James Pubns., *(James Pubns NY; 0-9615267),* Box 545, Guilderland, NY 12084 (SAN 695-1783) Tel 518-462-3311.

James Publishing, Inc., *(James Pub Santa Ana; 0-938065),* P.O. Box 27370, Santa Ana, CA 92799 (SAN 661-1869); 3520 Cadillac Ave., Suite A, Costa Mesa, CA 92626 (SAN 661-1877) Tel 714-556-0960. Do not confuse with James Pub. of East Irvine, CA.

Jameson, E. W., Jr., *(E W Jameson Jr; 0-9606576),* 13 Oakside, Davis, CA 95616 (SAN 207-5148) Tel 916-758-5704.

Jameson Books See Green Hill Pubs.

Jamestown Pubs., Inc., *(Jamestown Pubs; 0-89061),* P.O. Box 9168, Providence, RI 02940 (SAN 201-5196) Tel 401-351-1915; Toll free: 800-872-7323.

†**Jamieson Pr.,** Div. of Family Business Management Services, *(Jamieson Pr; 0-915607),* P.O. Box 909, 2967 Attleboro Rd., Cleveland, OH 44120 (SAN 292-5478) Tel 216-752-7970; *CIP.*

Jamison Sta. Pr., *(Jamison Stn),* 7115 Pembroke Dr., Reno, NV 89502 (SAN 277-691X).

Jan Pubns., Inc., *(Jan Pubns Inc; 0-934896),* P.O. Box 1860, Cape Coral, FL 33910 (SAN 213-2222) Tel 813-549-2093.

Janeric Press, *(Janeric Pr; 0-911373),* P.O. Box 477, Banner Elk, NC 28604 (SAN 271-7182) Tel 704-898-5500.

Janes Publishing, *(Janes Pub Eugene; 0-938333),* 28787 Gimpl Hill Rd., Eugene, OR 97402 (SAN 661-311X) Tel 503-343-2408.

Jane's Publishing, Inc., Subs. of Jane's Publishing Co., Ltd. (England), *(Jane's Pub Inc; 0-86720; 0-7106),* 115 Fifth Ave., 4th Flr., New York, NY 10003 (SAN 286-357X) Tel 212-254-9097; Orders to: 20 Park Plaza, Boston, MA 02116 (SAN 226-9791) Tel 617-542-6564.

Janevar Publishing Co., *(Janevar Pub; 0-937174),* 1303 Sunset Dr., North Manchester, IN 46962 (SAN 215-157X) Tel 219-982-8885.

JanJe Pr., *(JanJe Pr; 0-9617148),* 4843 Snowden Ave., Lakewood, CA 90713 (SAN 663-3684) Tel 213-429-9253.

Janova Press, Inc., *(Janova Pr; 0-917294),* 3833 Barker Rd., Cincinnati, OH 45229 (SAN 208-3671) Tel 513-861-0511.

Jantrex & Co., *(Jantrex & Co; 0-9615490),* Sunset Cove, Brookfield, CT 06804 (SAN 696-2807) Tel 203-775-2491.

Jantz, Virginia C., *(V C Jantz; 0-9607170),* Rte. 12 Box 450, Waco, TX 76710 (SAN 239-1031) Tel 817-848-4786.

Janus Bk. Pubs., *(Janus Bks; 0-88102; 0-915510; 0-88084),* 2501 Industrial Pkwy. W., Hayward, CA 94545 (SAN 208-0478) Tel 415-887-7070; Toll free: 800-227-2375.

Janus Pr., *(Janus Pr; 0-916172),* P.O. Box 1050, Rogue River, OR 97537 (SAN 207-5806) Tel 503-582-1520. Do not confuse with Janus Pr., Winter Springs, FL.

Janus Pr., *(Janus Pr FL; 0-9616341),* P.O. Box 3633, Winter Springs, FL 32708 (SAN 658-7461) Tel 305-671-5433; 1105 Howell Creek Dr., Casselberry, FL 32708 (SAN 658-747X).

Janus Pubns., *(Janus Pubns; 0-9613426),* Box 8705, Wichita, KS 67206 (SAN 657-0453) Tel 316-686-8320.

Japan-America Society of Washington, Inc., *(Japan-Am Soc),* 606 18th St., NW, Washington, DC 20006 (SAN 233-4356) Tel 202-289-8290.

Japan Pubns. (USA), Inc., *(Japan Pubns USA; 0-87040),* 45 Hawthorn Pl., Briarcliff Manor, NY 10510 (SAN 680-0513).

Japan Society, *(Japan Soc; 0-913304),* 333 E. 47th St., New York, NY 10017 (SAN 225-3259) Tel 212-832-1155.

Japanese American Anthology Committee, *(Japan Amer Anthlgy Com; 0-9603222),* P.O. Box 5024, San Francisco, CA 94101 (SAN 222-3643).

Japanese American Citizens League, *(Japanese Am Citizens),* 941 E. Third St., Los Angeles, CA 90013 (SAN 225-4093) Tel 213-626-6936.

Japos Study Group *See* **Journalists Authors & Poets on Stamps Study Group**

Jarchow, Michael, Publications, *(M Jarchow Pubns; 0-9608204),* P.O. Box 3238, Seal Beach, CA 90740 (SAN 238-8278); 2606 Octavia Street, San Francisco, CA 94123 (SAN 685-3390).

Jargon Society, Inc., The, *(Jargon Soc; 0-912330),* Highlands, NC 28741 (SAN 662-0515); Toll free: 800-243-0138; 1000 W. Fifth St., Winston-Salem, NC 28741 (SAN 662-0523); Dist. by: Inland Bk. Co., P.O. Box 261, 22 Hemingway Ave., East Haven, CT 06512 (SAN 200-4151) Tel 203-467-4257; Toll free: 800-243-0138.

Jarrett, Richard Buhler, *(Jarrett; 0-9606884),* P.O. Box 6007, Suite 250, Redding, CA 96099 (SAN 217-3840).

Jasmine Publishing Co., *(Jasmine Pub; 0-938861),* 1641 Third Ave., Suite 8BE, New York, NY 10128 (SAN 661-7328) Tel 212-348-8487.

Jason Publishing, *(Jason Pub; 0-9613180),* 170 Sisson Ave. 2-408, Hartford, CT 06105 (SAN 295-8570) Tel 203-232-6772.

Jason Publishing, Inc., *(Jason Pub OH; 0-938067),* 5763 Belmont Ave., Cincinnati, OH 45224 (SAN 661-1931) Tel 513-541-4346. Do not confuse with Jason Pub., Hartford, CT.

Jasper, Hazel Wright, *(H W Jasper; 0-9608106),* 6615 Mt. Vista Rd., Kingsville, MD 21087 (SAN 238-8618) Tel 301-592-5363.

Jasper Assocs., *(Jasper Assocs; 0-9613373),* P.O. Box 8971, Salt Lake City, UT 84108 (SAN 657-1476) Tel 801-277-7615.

Jasper County Abstract Co., *(Jasper County; 0-9604474),* Kellner at Van Rensselaer St., Rensselaer, IN 47978 (SAN 215-0840).

Jay & Associates, Pubs., *(Jay & Assoc; 0-939422),* P.O. Box 13898, Arlington, TX 76013 (SAN 281-837X) Tel 817-273-2876; Orders to: Marketing Department, P.O. Box 19469, Arlington, TX 76019 (SAN 281-8388).

Jay Pubns., *(Jay Pubns; 0-916666),* P.O. Box 1141, San Andreas, CA 95249 (SAN 208-3922) Tel 209-754-4520.

Jay Publishing Co., *(Jay Pub; 0-930140),* P.O. Box 454, Lakewood, CA 90714 (SAN 209-4533) Tel 714-893-0326.

Jay Ra Productions, *(Jay Ra Prods; 0-913155),* P.O. Box 785, Mill Valley, CA 94942 (SAN 283-1260) Tel 415-381-0290.

†Jayco Pub. Co., *(Jayco Pub; 0-9607728),* P.O. Box 1511, South Bend, IN 46634 (SAN 237-9627) Tel 219-291-2291; *CIP.*

Jaye, Gail C., *(G C Jaye),* 4 Chalet Dr., Bay Minette, AL 36507 (SAN 217-2941).

Jayell Enterprises Inc., *(Jayell Ent; 0-916197),* P.O. Box 2616, Dearborn, MI 48123 (SAN 294-9490) Tel 313-565-9687; Dist. by: Inland Bk. Co., P.O. Box 261, 22 Hemingway Ave., East Haven, CT 06512 (SAN 200-4151) Tel 203-467-4257; Toll free: 800-243-0138.

Jaykay Publishing Inc., *(Jaykay Pub Inc; 0-9613778),* 4930 Walnut Ave., White Bear Lake, MN 55110 (SAN 678-9951) Tel 612-372-4412; Orders to: P.O. Box 15775, Minneapolis, MN 55415 (SAN 662-2550).

†Jazz Discographies Unlimited, *(Jazz Discographies),* 337 Ellerton S., Laurel, MD 20707 (SAN 212-6710) Tel 301-776-3148; *CIP.*

Jazz Pr., *(Jazz Pr; 0-937310),* P.O. Box 2409, Aptos, CA 95001 (SAN 215-1596).

JC/DC Cartoons Ink, *(JC-DC Cartoons; 0-934574),* 5536 Fruitland Rd NE, Salem, OR 97301 (SAN 213-0963).

JCP *See* **Unipub**

Jean-Thomas, Inc., *(Jean Thomas; 0-910459),* P.O. Box 5650, Lakeland, FL 33803 (SAN 260-0277) Tel 813-644-3548.

Jeanene's Needle Arts, *(Jeanene's; 0-931716),* P.O. Box 6701, Woodland Hills, CA 91365 (SAN 211-5972) Tel 818-346-7276.

Jeanies Classics, *(Jeanies Classics; 0-9609672),* 2123 Oxford St., Rockford, IL 61103 (SAN 271-7395) Tel 815-968-4544; Dist. by: Jeanies Classics Publishing, P.O. Box 4303, Rockford, IL 61110 (SAN 271-7409).

Jeanne's Dreams, *(Jeannes Dreams; 0-9604694),* P.O. Box 211, La Farge, WI 54639 (SAN 213-6872) Tel 608-625-2425.

Jebco Books Division, *(Jebco Bks; 0-9609494),* P.O. Box 268, Harrison, OH 45030 (SAN 262-7574) Tel 513-385-5986.

Jedick, Peter, Enterprises, *(Jedick Ent; 0-9605568),* 1708 Wooster Rd., Rocky River, OH 44116 (SAN 216-0455).

Jefferson, Thomas, Equal Tax Society, *(T Jefferson Equal Tax),* 1469 Spring Vale Ave., McLean, VA 22101 (SAN 225-7254).

Jefferson, Thomas, Research Center, *(T Jefferson Res Ctr; 0-938308),* 1143 N. Lake Ave., Pasadena, CA 91104 (SAN 239-670X) Tel 818-798-0791.

Jefferson County Office of Historic Preservation & Archives, *(Jefferson County Office Hist Pres Arch; 0-9607612),* 100 Fiscal Court Building, Louisville, KY 40202 (SAN 237-9635).

Jefferson High School, *(Jefferson High; 0-9614227),* 1243 20th St. SW, Cedar Rapids, IA 52404 (SAN 686-7650) Tel 319-398-2231.

Jefferson Medical College, Dept. of Anesthesiology, *(Jefferson Med Anest),* Thomas Jefferson Univ., 1020 Walnut St., Philadelphia, PA 19107 (SAN 651-5975) Tel 215-928-6161.

Jefferson National Expansion Historical Assn., *(Jefferson Natl; 0-931056),* 11 N. 4th St., St. Louis, MO 63102 (SAN 213-0912).

Jefferson Pubns., Inc., *(Jefferson Pubns),* Monticello Bks. Div., 44 S. Old Rand Rd., Box 771, Lake Zurich, IL 60047 (SAN 207-639X) Tel 312-438-4114.

Jeffries Banknote Co., *(Jeffries Banknote),* 1330 W. Pico Blvd., Los Angeles, CA 90015 (SAN 227-2229) Tel 213-742-8888.

Jefren Pub. Co., *(Jefren Pub; 0-917244),* 1513 Auburn Ave., Rockville, MD 20850 (SAN 208-7138).

Jehara Pr., *(Jehara Pr; 0-9616227),* P.O. Box 19156, Chicago, IL 60619 (SAN 658-5612) Tel 312-873-4253; 8040 Wabash Ave., Chicago, IL 60619 (SAN 658-5620) Tel 312-873-4253.

Jei-Ai Publishing Company, Incorporated, *(Jei-Ai Pub Co),* 2101 1/2 Bush St., San Francisco, CA 94115 (SAN 293-7980) Tel 415-922-4780; Dist. by: Jei-Ai International Corp., P.O. Box 10115, Beverly Hills, CA 90213 (SAN 293-7999) Tel 213-986-4644.

†Jelm Mountain Pubns., *(Jelm Mtn; 0-936204),* c/o Green Mountain Book Co. P.O. Box 338, Markleeville, CA 96120 (SAN 216-1419) Tel 916-694-2141; *CIP.*

Jems Publishing, *(Jems Pub; 0-936174),* P.O. Box 1026, Solana Beach, CA 92075 (SAN 241-550X) Tel 619-481-1128.

Jemta Press, *(Jemta Pr; 0-9604246),* 11313 Beech Daly Rd., Redford Township, MI 48239 (SAN 209-1372) Tel 313-937-1986.

†Jen Hse. Publishing Co., *(Jen Hse Pub Co; 0-910841),* 119 Cherry Valley Rd., Reisterstown, MD 21136 (SAN 262-7604) Tel 301-833-8931; *CIP.*

Jende-Hagan, Inc., *(Jende-Hagan; 0-939650),* P.O. Box 177-A, Frederick, CO 80530 (SAN 169-0574) Tel 303-833-2030; 541 Oak St., Frederick, CO 80530 (SAN 658-1404). Imprints: Platte 'n Press (Platte n Pr); Renaissance House (Renaissance Hse).

Jenfred Pr., *(Jenfred Pr),* P.O. Box 767, Trinidad, CA 95570 (SAN 215-6644).

Jenkins, Doris, *(D Jenkins; 0-9606578),* 1201 Lincoln Mall, No. 611, Lincoln, NE 68508 (SAN 208-2624) Tel 402-477-2779.

Jenkins Publishing Co., *(Jenkins; 0-8363),* P.O. Box 2085, Austin, TX 78767 (SAN 202-7321) Tel 512-444-6616.

Jenna Pr., *(Jenna Pr; 0-941752),* 37 W. Eighth St., New York, NY 10011 (SAN 293-2881) Tel 212-477-4471; R.D. 1, Box 227, Petersburg, NY 12138 (SAN 293-289X).

Jennilee-Angel Pr., *(Jennilee-Angel Pr; 0-930217),* P.O. Box 44, Laguna Beach, CA 92652 (SAN 670-7858) Tel 714-497-7079.

Jennings Pr., Inc., *(Jennings Pr; 0-931781),* 2222 Fuller Rd. Suite 801A, Ann Arbor, MI 48105 (SAN 684-8621) Tel 313-665-7410.

Jensen, Bernard, Pub., *(B Jensen; 0-9608360; 0-932615),* Rte. One, Box 52, Escondido, CA 92025 (SAN 240-690X).

Jensen, Deana L., *(D L Jensen; 0-9615793),* Rte. 3, Box 97, Idaho Falls, ID 83401 (SAN 696-8678) Tel 208-357-3914.

Jenstan, *(Jenstan; 0-9612624),* P.O. Box 674, Franklin, MI 48025 (SAN 289-2685) Tel 313-626-1768.

Jeppesen Sanderson, Affil. of Times-Mirror Co., *(Jeppesen Sanderson; 0-88487),* 55 Inverness Dr. E., Englewood, CO 80112 (SAN 201-0224) Tel 303-779-9090.

Jepson Herbarium, *(Jepson Herbarium; 0-935628),* Univ. of California, Berkeley, Botany Dept., Berkeley, CA 94720 (SAN 214-2112) Tel 415-642-2465; Dist. by: Lubrecht & Cramer, RD 1, Box 244, Rte. 42, Forestburgh Rd., Forestburgh, NY 12777 (SAN 214-1256) Tel 914-794-8539.

Jeremy Books, *(Jeremy Bks; 0-89877),* Dist. by: Successful Living, Inc., 9905 Hamilton Road, Eden Prairie, MN 55344 (SAN 213-0939).

Jesse Bks., *(Jesse Bks; 0-9616027),* Box 339, Huntingdon Valley, PA 19006 (SAN 697-8916) Tel 215-947-5584; 960 Hunters Turn, Huntingdon Valley, PA 19006 (SAN 698-2271).

Jest 4 You Publishing, *(Jest Four You Pub; 0-9615794),* 10164 Disney Cir., Huntington Beach, CA 92646 (SAN 696-8686) Tel 714-964-4380.

Jester Press *See* **Red Hen Pr.**

Jesuit Books, *(Jesuit Bks; 0-913452),* Gonzaga University, Spokane, WA 99258 (SAN 201-0232) Tel 509-328-4220.

Jesuit Historical Institute, *(Jesuit Hist),* 3441 N. Ashland Ave., Chicago, IL 60657 (SAN 662-0531) Tel 312-281-1818; Toll free: 800-621-1008; c/o Loyola Univ. Pr., 3441 N. Ashland Ave., Chicago, IL 60657 (SAN 211-6537).

Jesuits of Holy Cross College, Inc., *(Jesuits Holy Cross; 0-9606294),* College of the Holy Cross, Worcester, MA 01610 (SAN 210-1211) Tel 617-793-3314.

Jesus-First Pubs., Inc., *(Jesus-First; 0-9602440),* 1116-4th St., NW, Ruskin, FL 33570 (SAN 212-3630) Tel 813-645-5726.

Jet'iquette, *(Jetiquette; 0-9600786),* 510 Michigan Ave., Charlevoix, MI 49720 (SAN 202-733X) Tel 616-547-6443.

Jetsand Pubs., Ltd., *(Jetsand Pubs Ltd; 0-933374),* Box 17052, West Hartford, CT 06117 (SAN 212-8349) Tel 203-658-1423.

Jewel Pr., Div. of Jewel Communications International, *(Jewel Pr; 0-937093),* P.O. Box 1833, Fort Collins, CO 80522 (SAN 658-6139) Tel 303-226-5914; 4414 E. Harmony Rd., Fort Collins, CO 80525 (SAN 658-6147); Orders to: P.O. Box 904, Fort Collins, CO 80526 (SAN 662-4146); Orders to: 4414 E. Harmony Rd., Fort Collins, CO 80526 (SAN 662-4154).

Jewel Pubns., *(Jewel Pubns; 0-917728),* 2417 Hazelwood Ave., Fort Wayne, IN 46805 (SAN 209-3049) Tel 219-483-6625.

Jewel Publishing Co., *(Jewel Pub Co; 0-9614890),* 165 Congress Run Rd., Cincinnati, OH 45215 (SAN 693-2460) Tel 513-521-1149; Dist. by: The South Bend Distributors, 702 S. Michigan, South Bend, IN 46618 (SAN 200-7134); Dist. by: Baker & Taylor (Midwest Div.), 501 Gladiola Ave., Momence, IL 60954 (SAN 169-2100).

Jewel Publishing Hse., *(Jewel Pub Hse; 0-9607000),* P.O. Box 146, New York, NY 10002 (SAN 241-5879).

Jewelers' Circular-Keystone, *(Jewelers Circular; 0-931744),* Chilton Way, Radnor, PA 19089-0140 (SAN 210-9050) Tel 215-964-4480; Orders to: Jeweler's Book Club, Chilton Way, Radnor, PA 19089-0140 (SAN 662-054X).

Jewell, Kenneth G., *(K G Jewell; 0-9615908),* R.D. 6, Bedford, PA 15522 (SAN 696-8694) Tel 814-623-8232.

Jewell-Johnson & Co. Inc., *(Jewell-Johnson; 0-930198),* 502 Benton St., Port Townsend, WA 98368 (SAN 210-9077) Tel 206-385-4342.

Jewish Board of Family & Children's Services, Library Inc., *(Jewish Bd Family),* c/o Central Library, 120 W. 57th St., New York, NY 10019 (SAN 211-9080) Tel 212-582-9100.

Jewish Combatants Pubs. House, Inc., *(Jewish Com Pub; 0-9613219),* P.O. Box 323, Brooklyn, NY 11236 (SAN 295-8821) Tel 718-763-7551.

Jewish Community Center of Greater Boston, *(Jewish Comm Ctr; 0-9605624),* 333 Nahanton St., Newton, MA 02159 (SAN 218-4842).

Jewish Council Millenium Covenant, *(JCMC Louisiana),* 1812 N. Hwy. 171, De Ridder, LA 70634 (SAN 663-6306).

Jewish Educators for Social Responsibility, Div. of Educators for Social Responsibility, *(Jewish Ed Soc Res; 0-9615897),* 90 Hanson Rd., Newton, MA 02159 (SAN 696-8708) Tel 617-738-5329.

Jewish Genealogical Society Of Illinois, *(Jewish Genealogical; 0-9613512),* 1025 Antique Ln., Northbrook, IL 60062 (SAN 657-3592) Tel 312-564-1025.

†Jewish Historical Society of New York, Inc., *(Jewish Hist; 0-916790),* 8 W. 70th St., New York, NY 10023 (SAN 208-7146) Tel 212-873-0300; *CIP.*

Jewish Hospital Auxiliary of the Jewish Hospital of St. Louis, *(Jewish Hosp Aux MO; 0-9614764),* 216 S. Kingshighway, P.O. Box 14109, St. Louis, MO 63178 (SAN 692-9109) Tel 314-454-7130.

†Jewish Pubns. Society of America, *(Jewish Pubns; 0-8276),* 1930 Chestnut St., Philadelphia, PA 19103 (SAN 201-0240) Tel 215-564-5925; *CIP.*

†Jewish Theological Seminary of America, *(Jewish Sem; 0-87334),* 3080 Broadway, New York, NY 10027 (SAN 204-9902) Tel 212-678-8000; Dist. by: Publishing Ctr. for Cultural Resources, 625 Broadway, New York, NY 10012 (SAN 274-9025) Tel 212-260-2010; *CIP.*

Jewish Welfare Board *See* JWB

Jinro Publishing Co., *(Jinro Pub; 0-940772),* 432 Board of Trade Bldg., 127 W. Tenth St., Kansas City, MO 64105 (SAN 219-6670) Tel 816-221-6640.

JML Enterprises, Inc., *(JML Enter MD; 0-938464),* P.O Box 488, Bel Air, MD 21014 (SAN 238-5279) Tel 301-879-8552.

JO-D Bks., *(JO-D Bks; 0-937791),* 81 Willard Terr., Stamford, CT 06903 (SAN 688-1203) Tel 203-322-0568.

Jo-Jo Pubns., *(Jo-Jo Pubns; 0-9602266),* 208 N. Sparrow Rd., Chesapeake, VA 23325 (SAN 212-5153) Tel 804-420-8614.

Joane Pubns., *(Joane Pubns; 0-9613925),* P.O. Box 459, Reading, MA 01867 (SAN 692-395X).

Job Data Inc., *(Job Data; 0-918443),* 105 W. Madison, Chicago, IL 60602 (SAN 657-6303) Tel 312-348-4060.

Job Hunters Forum, *(Job Hunters Forum; 0-918350),* 132 Pinecrest Dr., Annapolis, MD 21403 (SAN 209-178X) Tel 301-268-6425.

Jobeco Bks., *(Jobeco Bks; 0-9607572),* P.O. Box 3323, Humble, TX 77347-3323 (SAN 237-9651) Tel 713-358-2791.

Jobhunter's Companion, *(Jobhunter's Comp; 0-9613020),* 843 St. George Ave., Roselle, NJ 07203 (SAN 294-0558) Tel. 201-925-0080.

Joby Bks., *(Joby Bks; 0-9604284),* P.O. Box 512, Fulton, CA 95439 (SAN 209-1518); Dist. by: Bookpeople, 2929 Fifth St., Berkeley, CA 94710 (SAN 168-9517) Tel 415-549-3030.

Jochum, Helen Parker, *(Jochum; 0-9606206),* 79 Huntington Rd., Garden City, NY 11530 (SAN 215-8787); Dist. by: Skills, 24 S. Prospect St., Amherst, MA 01002 (SAN 215-8795) Tel 413-253-9500.

Johannes Pr., *(Johannes; 0-910810),* c/o Galerie St. Etienne, 24 W. 57th St., New York, NY 10019 (SAN 206-9806) Tel 212-245-6734.

Johannes Schwalm Historical Assn., Inc., *(Johannes Schwalm Hist; 0-939016),* 800-S Westbury Pl., 4807 Old Spartanburg Rd., Taylors, SC 29687 (SAN 209-5076) Tel 216-382-5711.

Johmax Bks., Inc., *(Johmax Bks Inc; 0-912095),* 48 Pine Brook Dr., Larchmont, NY 10538 (SAN 264-7559) Tel 914-834-0822.

John Clancy's Kitchen Workshop, *(Clancys Kitchen),* 324 W. 19th St., New York, NY 10011 (SAN 213-5264) Tel 212-243-0958; Orders to: Johnson Press, 49 Sheridan Ave., Albany, NY 12210 (SAN 213-5272).

John Day Co., Inc., *(John Day; 0-381),* C/O Harper & Row Pubs., 10 E. 53rd St., New York, NY 10022 (SAN 211-6960); Toll free: 800-242-7737; Dist. by: Harper & Row Pubs., Keystone Industrial Pk., Scranton, PA 18512 (SAN 215-3742); Imprints: John Day Juvenile Books (JD-J); John Day Trade Books (JD-T).

John Day Juvenile Books *See* John Day Co., Inc.

John Day Trade Books *See* John Day Co., Inc.

†John Jay Pr., *(John Jay Pr; 0-89444),* 444 W. 56th St., New York, NY 10019 (SAN 210-2196) Tel 212-489-3592; *CIP.*

Johnny Alfalfa Sprout, *(Johnny Alfalfa Sprout; 0-9616229),* P.O. Box 294, Lewisburg, PA 17837 (SAN 658-5566) Tel 717-523-7878; 606 Market St., Lewisburg, PA 17837 (SAN 658-5574).

Johnny Reads, Inc., *(Johnny Reads; 0-910812),* P.O. Box 12834, St. Petersburg, FL 33733 (SAN 201-0283) Tel 813-867-7647. *Imprints:* Educational Pubns. (Pub. by Ed Pubns).

Johns, Agnes N., *(A N Johns; 0-9612148),* P.O. Box 02026, Portland, OR 97202 (SAN 289-5846) Tel 503-238-4474.

Johns Hopkins Univ., Dept. of International Health, *(Dept Intl Health; 0-912888),* 615 N. Wolfe St., Baltimore, MD 21205 (SAN 202-3520).

†Johns Hopkins Univ. Pr., *(Johns Hopkins; 0-8018),* 701 W. 40th St., Suite 275, Baltimore, MD 21211 (SAN 202-7348) Tel 301-338-6956; *CIP.*

Johns, Johns, & Johns, *(Johns Johns & Johns; 0-939091),* 2160 Dowing St., No. 102, Denver, CO 80205 (SAN 662-8974) Tel 303-863-0043.

John's Pr., *(Johns Pr; 0-9607730),* Box 3405 CRS, Rock Hill, SC 29731 (SAN 238-7948) Tel 803-366-7392.

Johnsen, Kenneth G., *(K G Johnsen; 0-9613267),* P.O. Box 161, Renton, WA 98057 (SAN 653-7359) Tel 206-859-2111.

Johnson, Barbara Mary, *(B M Johnson),* 7381 Webb Rd., Chatsworth, CA 91311 (SAN 263-2381) Tel 818-703-1594.

Johnson, Blake, Pub., *(B Johnson Pub; 0-9615685),* 24 Oakwood Dr., N., Englewood, FL 33533 (SAN 696-303X) Tel 813-474-4708.

Johnson, Forrest Bryant, *(F B Johnson; 0-9600510),* 485 Mckellar, Suite 1, Las Vegas, NV 89119 (SAN 205-5694) Tel 702-735-1730.

Johnson, Jesse J. *See* Carver Publishing, Inc.

Johnson, Joe Donald, *(Joe D Johnson; 0-915564),* P.O. Box 6692, Napa, CA 94581 (SAN 207-3366).

Johnson, John, *(J Johnson; 0-910914),* R.D. 2, North Bennington, VT 05257 (SAN 208-4910) Tel 802-442-6738.

Johnson, Lyndon B., Schl. of Public Affairs, *(LBJ Sch Pub Aff; 0-89940),* Univ. of Texas at Austin, Drawer DY, Univ. Sta., Austin, TX 78712 (SAN 223-0410) Tel 512-471-5713.

Johnson, Mabel, Quality Paperbacks, *(M Johnson; 0-9600838),* P.O. Box 7, Boring, OR 97009 (SAN 206-1015) Tel 503-663-3428.

Johnson, Merwyn S., *(M S Johnson; 0-9601590),* P.O. Box 368, Due West, SC 29639 (SAN 212-3649) Tel 803-379-8193.

Johnson, Miriam W., *(M W Johnson; 0-9612626),* 1459 Bowman St., Clermont, FL 32711 (SAN 289-2774) Tel 904-394-2236.

Johnson, Patricia Givens, *(Pat G Johnson; 0-9614765),* Rt. 2, Box 50, Christiansburg, VA 24073 (SAN 692-915X) Tel 703-382-1251; Dist. by: Jalamap Publications, 601 "D" St., Charleston, WV 25303 (SAN 216-1478).

Johnson, Paul R., *(Paul R Johnson; 0-910097),* P.O. Box 2972, Pomona, CA 91769 (SAN 241-3973) Tel 818-338-7245.

Johnson, Rudolph, Training & Development, Inc., *(Rudolph Johnson; 0-937221),* 1004 State St., Bowling Green, KY 42101 (SAN 658-7437) Tel 502-781-1915.

Johnson, T. J., *(T J Johnson; 0-917756),* RR 2, Cabery, IL 60919 (SAN 209-2670) Tel 815-256-2260.

Johnson, Walter J., Inc., *(Walter J Johnson; 0-8472),* 355 Chestnut St., Norwood, NJ 07648 (SAN 209-1828) Tel 201-767-1303.

Johnson & Johnson Baby Products Co., *(J & J Baby Prod; 0-931562),* Grandview Rd., Skillman, NJ 08558 (SAN 211-5131).

Johnson & Simpson, *(Johnson & Simpson; 0-9615012),* 49 Bleeker St., Newark, NJ 07102 (SAN 693-9376) Tel 201-624-7788; Dist. by: Collectors Bks., P.O. Box 3009, Paducah, KY 42001 (SAN 200-7479).

Johnson Bks., Div. of Johnson Publishing Co., *(Johnson Bks; 0-933472; 1-55566),* P.O. Box 990, Boulder, CO 80301 (SAN 201-0313) Tel 303-443-1576; 1880 S. 57th Ct., Boulder, CO 80301 (SAN 658-1013).

Johnson Institute, *(Johnson Inst; 0-935908),* 510 First Ave. N., Minneapolis, MN 55403-1607 (SAN 221-4717) Tel 612-341-0435; Toll free: 800-231-5165.

Johnson, Pace, Simmons & Fennell Pubs., *(JP SF; 0-9615268),* P.O. Box 711207, Los Angeles, CA 90071 (SAN 694-6046); 515 Flower St., Los Angeles, CA 90071 (SAN 662-3417) Tel 818-352-9258.

Johnson Publishing Co., *(Johnson NC; 0-930230),* P. O. Box 217, Murfreesboro, NC 27855 (SAN 201-0291).

†Johnson Publishing Co., Inc., *(Johnson Chi; 0-87485),* 820 S. Michigan Ave., Chicago, IL 60605 (SAN 201-0305) Tel 312-322-9248; *CIP.*

Johnson Reference Bks., *(Johnson Ref Bks; 0-9600906),* P.O. Box 7152, Alexandria, VA 22307 (SAN 208-7162) Tel 703-373-9150; Toll free: 800-851-BOOK; Chatham Square Pk., Johnson-Matherly Bldg. No. 403, Fredericksburg, VA 22405 (SAN 662-0574) Tel 703-373-9150.

†Johnson Reprint Corp., Subs. of Harcourt, Brace, Jovanovich, Inc., *(Johnson Repr; 0-384),* 111 Fifth Ave., New York, NY 10003 (SAN 205-0362) Tel 212-614-3150; Toll free: 800-543-1918; *CIP.*

Johnston, A. M., Publishing Co., *(A M Johnston; 0-9612116),* 118 Herron Dr., Knoxville, TN 37919 (SAN 289-3843) Tel 615-588-2206.

Johnston Publishing Co., *(Johnston AR; 0-936853),* Rte. 2, Box 79A, Lincoln, AR 72744 (SAN 658-3555) Tel 501-846-3768.

Johnston Publishing, Inc., *(Johnston Pub; 0-942934),* Box 96, Afton, MN 55001 (SAN 240-3900) Tel 612-436-7344.

Joi Production Enterprises, *(Joi Prod Enter; 0-9616294),* 9111 Third Ave., Inglewood, CA 90305 (SAN 658-5590) Tel 213-753-1222.

Joint Border Research Institute, *(Jt Border Research; 0-937795),* New Mexico State Univ., Campus Box 3JBR, Las Cruces, NM 88003 (SAN 659-3682) Tel 505-646-3524; 1200 University Ave., Las Cruces, NM 88003 (SAN 659-3690).

†**Joint Ctr. for Political Studies,** *(Jt Ctr Pol Studies; 0-941410),* 1301 Pennsylvania Ave., NW, Suite 400, Washington, DC 20004 (SAN 233-2558) Tel 202-626-3500; Toll free: 800-323-JCPS; *CIP.*

†**Joint Commission on Accreditation of Hospitals,** *(Joint Comm Hosp; 0-86688),* Dept. of Pubns., 875 N. Michigan Ave., Chicago, IL 60611 (SAN 210-8194) Tel 312-642-6061; *CIP.*

Joint Committee on Law Study Programs, *(Jt Comm Law Study; 0-942598),* New England Schl. of Law, 154 Stuart St., Boston, MA 02116 (SAN 238-7670) Tel 617-451-0010.

Jolean Publishing Co., *(Jolean Pub Co; 0-934284),* P.O. Box 163, Arverne, NY 11692 (SAN 212-9507).

Jolex, Inc., *(Jolex; 0-89149),* P.O. Box 717, Southport, CT 06490 (SAN 662-0582) Tel 203-367-4041.

Jolley, Ginger, *(Ginger Jolley; 0-9616228),* P.O. Box 156, Rim Forest, CA 92378 (SAN 658-5523) Tel 714-337-4991; 26375 Apache Trail, Rim Forest, CA 92378 (SAN 658-5531).

Jolly, David C., *(D C Jolly; 0-911775),* P.O. Box 931, Brookline, MA 02146 (SAN 264-1380) Tel 617-232-6222.

Jomilt Pubns., *(Jomilt Pubns; 0-9616076),* 329 W. Mt. Airy Ave., Philadelphia, PA 19119 (SAN 697-9939) Tel 215-750-4173.

Jonathan David Pubs., Inc., *(Jonathan David; 0-8246),* 68-22 Eliot Ave., Middle Village, NY 11379 (SAN 169-5274) Tel 718-456-8611.

Jonathan Pubns., *(Jonathan Pubns; 0-9603348),* 660 Prospect Ave., Hartford, CT 06105 (SAN 213-330X) Tel 203-523-7587.

Jonathan Publishing, *(Jonathan LA; 0-940718),* 3604 Pinnacle Rd., Austin, TX 78746 (SAN 219-7936) Tel 512-328-2480.

Jones, Anson, Press, *(A Jones; 0-912432),* P.O. Box 65, Salado, TX 76571 (SAN 201-2014) Tel 817-947-5414.

Jones, Arnold, & Assocs., *(Arnold Jones; 0-943036),* 3400 Ben Lomand Pl. No. 123, Los Angeles, CA 90027 (SAN 240-3919) Tel 213-662-6580.

Jones, Bob, Univ. Pr., *(Bob Jones Univ Pr; 0-89084),* Bob Jones Univ., Greenville, SC 29614 (SAN 223-7512) Tel 803-242-5100; Toll free: 800-235-5731.

Jones, Edward-Lynne, & Assocs., *(Ed-Lynne Jones; 0-9602458),* 5517 17th Ave., NE, Seattle, WA 98105 (SAN 263-2195) Tel 206-524-9604.

Jones, Ernest R., *(E R Jones; 0-9600934),* 13420 Winterspoon Ln., Germantown, MD 20874 (SAN 208-0214) Tel 301-540-9107.

Jones, Gladys Powelson, *(Joseph Pub Co; 0-9612628),* 1507 E. Fox Farm Rd., Cheyenne, WY 82007 (SAN 287-7422) Tel 307-632-7568.

Jones, Hank, Publishing Co., *(H Jones Pub; 0-9613888),* P.O. Box 8341, Universal City, CA 91608 (SAN 682-2983) Tel 818-766-3567.

Jones, Harry, *(H Jones Pr; 0-9601980),* P.O. Box 10054, Austin, TX 78766-1054 (SAN 212-615X) Tel 512-451-2644.

Jones, Jesse, Productions, *(J Jones Prods; 0-9610430),* 1927 4th Ave., San Diego, CA 92101 (SAN 264-1402).

Jones, Lowell, *(L Jones; 0-9602074),* 11832 Brookmont Dr., Maryland Heights, MO 63043 (SAN 212-2847).

Jones, Marshall, Co., Div. of Golden Quill Pr., *(M Jones; 0-8338),* Francestown, NH 03043 (SAN 206-8834).

Jones, Stan, Publishing, Inc., *(Jones Pub; 0-939936),* 3421 E. Mercer St., Seattle, WA 98112 (SAN 216-8243).

Jones, Wendy, *(W Jones),* Box 7186, Canyon Lake, CA 92380 (SAN 264-1410).

Jones & Bartlett Pubs., Inc., *(Jones & Bartlett; 0-86720),* 20 Park Plaza, Boston, MA 02116 (SAN 285-0893) Tel 617-482-5243; Toll free: 800-832-0034 (Orders only). *Imprints:* Marine Science International (Marine Sci Intl).

Jones International Ltd., *(Jones Intl; 0-935910),* 9697 E. Mineral Ave., Englewood, CO 80112 (SAN 213-8530) Tel 303-792-3111.

Jones Library, *(Jones Lib; 0-9616559),* 43 Amity St., Amherst, MA 01002 (SAN 204-9872) Tel 413-256-0246.

Jones Medical Pubns., *(Jones Med; 0-930010),* 355 Los Cerros Dr., Greenbrae, CA 94904 (SAN 210-4466) Tel 415-461-3749.

Jordan, Carol, *(C Jordan; 0-9605360),* 654 Jerome St., Davis, CA 95616 (SAN 216-0463).

Jordan, Thomas F., *(T F Jordan; 0-9602762),* 2249 Dunedin Ave., Duluth, MN 55803 (SAN 240-0944).

Jordan Assn., Ltd., *(Jordan Assn; 0-9610354),* P.O. Box 814, Virginia Beach, VA 23451 (SAN 264-1437).

Jordan Enterprises, *(Jordan Enter; 0-931597),* 512 W. 35th St., Norfolk, VA 23508 (SAN 682-5079) Tel 804-627-3336.

Jordan Pr., *(Jordan Pr; 0-9613427),* 5 Amberson Ave., Yonkers, NY 10705 (SAN 657-047X) Tel 203-387-3799.

Jordan Publishing, Div. of Jordan College, *(Jordan Pub; 0-910213),* 155 Seven Mile Rd., Comstock Park, MI 49321 (SAN 240-9712) Tel 616-784-7595.

Jordan Valley Heritage Hse., *(Jordan Valley; 0-939810),* 43592 Hwy. 226, Stayton, OR 97383 (SAN 216-7425) Tel 503-859-3144.

Jordan-Volpe Gallery, The, *(Jordan-Volpe Gall; 0-942410),* 457 W. Broadway, New York, NY 10012 (SAN 214-0438) Tel 212-505-5240; Dist. by: Peregrine Smith, Inc., P.O. Box 667, Layton, UT 84041 (SAN 201-9906).

Jordon Enterprises, *(Jordon Ent; 0-9612256),* 2625 Merry Oaks Trail, Winston-Salem, NC 27103 (SAN 289-5161) Tel 919-760-0194.

Jorgensen, Richard H, *(Richard Jorgensen; 0-914306),* 302 West Redwood, Marshall, MN 56258 (SAN 693-7772).

Jorgensen Pubns., Inc., *(Jorg Pubns CA; 0-943040),* 20370 Town Center Ln., No. 245, Cupertino, CA 95014 (SAN 240-5393) Tel 408-252-1111.

Jorgenson Publishing Co., *(Jorgenson Pub; 0-938128),* 350 Cambridge Ave., Suite 300, Palo Alto, CA 94306 (SAN 219-7944) Tel 415-328-9200.

Jory Pubns., *(Jory Pubns; 0-9607732),* 12535 Sunview Dr., Creve Coeur, MO 63146 (SAN 238-0935) Tel 314-434-0066.

Joseph, Lillian, *(L Joseph; 0-9616829),* 3914 Victory Cir., No. 128, Billings, MT 59106 (SAN 658-8395).

Joseph J. Weiss, *(J J Weiss),* The Medical Plaza-Bldg D, Suite B 20317 Farmington Rd., Livonia, MI 48152 (SAN 679-1468) Tel 313-478-7860.

Joseph Newman Publishing Co., *(J Newman Pub; 0-9613835),* Rte. 1, P.O. Box 52, Lucedale, MS 39452 (SAN 682-2592); 1135 Jackson Ave., Suite 305, New Orleans, LA 70130 (SAN 658-2672).

Joseph Publishing Co., *(Joseph Pub Co; 0-915878),* P.O. Box 770, San Mateo, CA 94401 (SAN 207-8538) Tel 415-345-4100.

Josephson/Kluwer Legal Educational Ctrs., Inc., *(Josephson-Kluwer Legal Educ Ctrs; 0-940366),* 10101 W. Jefferson Blvd., Culver City, CA 90232 (SAN 209-5386) Tel 213-558-3100; Toll free: 800-421-4577.

Josey Enterprises, Inc., *(Josey Enter Inc; 0-934499),* Rte. 2, Box 235, Karnack, TX 75661 (SAN 693-8957) Tel 214-935-5358.

Joshua I Ministries, Inc., *(Joshua I Minist; 0-939313),* 50 Coe Rd., Suite 223, Belleair, FL 33516 (SAN 663-1398) Tel 813-442-5535.

Joslin Diabetes Foundation, *(Joslin Diabetes),* 1 Joslin Pl, Boston, MA 02215 (SAN 271-8200).

Joslyn Art Museum, *(Joslyn Art; 0-936364),* 2200 Dodge St., Omaha, NE 68102 (SAN 281-8442); Orders to: Joslyn Museum Shop, 2200 Dodge St., Omaha, NE 68102 (SAN 281-8450) Tel 402-342-3300; Orders to: Univ. of Nebraska Pr., 901 N. 17th, Lincoln, NE 68583 (SAN 669-1390).

†**Jossey-Bass, Inc., Pubs.,** *(Jossey Bass; 0-87589; 1-55542),* 433 California St., San Francisco, CA 94104 (SAN 201-033X) Tel 415-433-1740; Dist. by: Kampmann & Co., 9 E. 40th St., New York, NY 10016 (SAN 202-5191) Tel 212-685-2928; Toll free: 800-526-7626; *CIP.*

Jostens Pubns., *(Jostens; 0-88136),* P.O. Box 1903, Topeka, KS 66601 (SAN 241-5313) Tel 913-266-3300.

JostGIs, *(JostGIs),* 401 Science Park Rd., State College, PA 16804-0297 (SAN 655-7589).

Jotarian Productions, *(Jotarian; 0-943454),* 5353 Columbia Pike, No. 110, Arlington, VA 22204 (SAN 240-6918) Tel 703-845-1819; Orders to: P.O. Box 75683, Washington, DC 20013 (SAN 699-539X).

Journal of Chemical Education, *(Chem Educ; 0-910362),* 238 Kent Rd., Springfield, PA 19064 (SAN 203-6436); Orders to: 20th & North Hampton Sts., Easton, PA 18042 (SAN 662-0590) Tel 215-250-7264.

Journal of Irreproducible Results, *(JIR; 0-9605852),* P.O. Box 234, Chicago Hts, IL 60411 (SAN 282-7077) Tel 312-755-2080P.O. Box 234, Chicago Heights, IL 60411 (SAN 282-7085) Tel 312-755-2080.

Journal of Spanish Studies: Twentieth Century, Div. of Society of Spanish and American Studies, *(Journal Span Stud; 0-89294),* University of Colorado, Dept Spanish & Portuguese, Campus Box 278, Boulder, CO 80309-0278 (SAN 209-4541) Tel 303-492-7308; Orders to: Society of Spanish & Spanish-American Studies, University of Colorado, Dept. Spanish & Portuguese, Campus Box 278, Boulder, CO 80309-0278 (SAN 208-3221).

Journal Printing Co., *(Journal Printing; 0-9613631),* 709 N. Davis St., Kirksville, MO 63501 (SAN 670-8838) Tel 816-665-4082; Dist. by: First United Methodist Church, 300 E. Washington St., Kirksville, MO 63501 (SAN 200-7460) Tel 816-665-7712.

Journalists Authors & Poets on Stamps Study Group, *(JAPOS Study Grp),* 154 Laguna Ct., St. Augustine Shores, FL 32086 (SAN 225-5979) Tel 904-797-3513.

Journey Co., *(Journey Co; 0-9616469),* 4790 Irvine Blvd., Suite 105-112, Irvine, CA 92720 (SAN 659-2589) Tel 714-731-6173. .

†**Journey Pr.,** *(Journey Pr; 0-918572),* Box 9036, Berkeley, CA 94709 (SAN 281-8469) Tel 415-540-5500; Dist. by: Bookpeople, 2929 Fifth St., Berkeley, CA 94710 (SAN 168-9517) Tel 415-549-3030; *CIP.*

Journey Pubns., *(Journey Pubns; 0-918038),* P.O. Box 423, Woodstock, NY 12498 (SAN 209-570X) Tel 914-657-8434.

Jove Pubns., Inc., Div. of Berkley/Jove Pub. Group, *(Jove Pubns; 0-515),* 200 Madison Ave., New York, NY 10016 (SAN 215-8817) Tel 212-686-9820; Toll free: 800-223-0510; Dist. by: Kable News Co., Inc., 777 Third Ave., New York, NY 10017 (SAN 169-5835) Tel 212-371-5321.

Joy, A. F., *(A F Joy),* 64 Gardenia Ct., Orange City, FL 32763 (SAN 695-4863) Tel 904-775-2067; Orders to: Saturscent Pubns., Box 358, South Wellfleet, MA 02663 (SAN 662-3484) Tel 617-349-2921.

Joy-Co Pr., *(Joy-Co; 0-9605984),* 2636 Burgener Blvd., San Diego, CA 92110 (SAN 216-7433) Tel 619-276-9760.

Joy of Money Publishing, *(Joy Money Pub; 0-9616661),* 535 Ocean Ave., No. 7A, Santa Monica, CA 90402 (SAN 661-3608) Tel 213-393-3110.

Joy Publishing Co., *(Joy Pub Co; 0-9601758),* P.O. Box 2532, Boca Raton, FL 33427 (SAN 211-0806) Tel 305-276-5879.

Joybug Teaching Aids, Inc., *(Joybug; 0-931218),* P.O. Box 2238, 1125 E. Wayne, Salina, KS 67402-2238 (SAN 212-1050) Tel 913-825-1589; Dist. by: Publishers Group West, 5855 Beaudry St., Emeryville, CA 94608 (SAN 202-8522) Tel 415-658-3453.

Joyce Media Inc., *(Joyce Media; 0-917002),* P.O. Box 57, Action, CA 93510 (SAN 208-7197) Tel 805-269-1169.

Joydeism Pr., *(Joydeism Pr; 0-913483),* P.O. Box 14, Point Arena, CA 95468 (SAN 285-189X).

Names

Joyful Noise Productions, International, *(Joyful Noise; 0-936874),* 109 Minna St., Suite 153, San Francisco, CA 94105 (SAN 215-0883).

Joyful Woman, The, Div. of Joyful Christian Ministries, *(Joyful Woman; 0-912623),* P.O. Box 90028, Chatanooga, TN 37412 (SAN 282-8073).

Jubilee Committee *See* **Rabinowitz, Solomon, Hebrew Book Store, Inc.**

Jubilee Pr., Inc., *(Jubilee Pr; 0-9609674),* 7906 Hillside Ave., Los Angeles, CA 90046 (SAN 262-7663) Tel 213-851-5893.

Judaea Publishing Co., *(Judaea Pub Co; 0-933447),* P.O. Box 510, Hewlett, NY 11557 (SAN 691-781X) Tel 516-374-6080; P.O. Box 370773, Miami, FL 33137 (SAN 662-2917) Tel 305-576-3852; Dist. by: Sparks & Co., 979 Summer St., Stamford, CT 06905 (SAN 200-7444) Tel 203-967-3617.

Judaica Pr., Inc., *(Judaica Pr; 0-910818),* 521 Fifth Ave., New York, NY 10017 (SAN 204-9856) Tel 212-260-0520.

Judicial Administration Division *See* **American Bar Assn.**

†Judson Pr., *(Judson; 0-8170),* P.O. Box 851, Valley Forge, PA 19482-0851 (SAN 201-0348) Tel 215-768-2119; Toll free: 800-331-1053; *CIP.*

Judson Street Pr., *(Judson St Pr; 0-9617149),* 4248 Judson, Houston, TX 77005 (SAN 663-3331) Tel 713-665-5151.

Judy Publishing Co., *(Judy; 0-87702),* Main P.O., Box 5270, Chicago, IL 60680 (SAN 202-7372) Tel 312-787-7233.

Jugglebug, *(Jugglebug; 0-9615521),* 7506 J Olympic View Dr., Edmonds, WA 98020 (SAN 696-2882) Tel 206-542-2030.

Juka, S. S., *(S S Juka; 0-9613601),* 110 Terrace View Ave., New York, NY 10463 (SAN 670-7394); Dist. by: Baker & Taylor, 1515 Broadway, New York, NY 10036 (SAN 169-5606) Tel 212-730-7650.

Jukebox Collector Newsletter, *(Jukebox Coll New; 0-912789),* 2545 SE 60th Ct., Des Moines, IA 50317 (SAN 282-809X) Tel 515-265-8324.

Jukebox Pr., *(Jukebox Press; 0-930693),* 3717 Market St., Oakland, CA 94608 (SAN 678-1969) Tel 415-652-1314.

Jules' Books, *(Jules' Bks; 0-939537),* 420 Buchanan St., San Francisco, CA 94102 (SAN 663-4427) Tel 415-864-1139.

Juliahouse Pubs., *(Juliahouse Pubs; 0-9614228),* 1100 Poydras St., Suite 1800 Energy Ctr., New Orleans, LA 70163-1800 (SAN 686-7669) Tel 504-582-2223.

Julian Press *See* **Crown Pubs., Inc.**

Juliet Pr., *(Juliet Pr; 0-914426),* P.O. Box 3476, Princeton, NJ 08540-0209 (SAN 206-5479).

Junction Pr., The, *(Junction Pr; 0-935935),* P.O. Box 295, Tippah Rd., Grand Junction, TN 38039 (SAN 696-4621) Tel 901-764-6155.

JuneRose Productions, *(JuneRose Prod; 0-9617043),* 1750 E. Ridgeway Ave., Waterloo, IA 50702 (SAN 662-829X) Tel 319-234-9995.

Jung, C. G., Foundation Publications, *(C G Jung Foun; 0-913430),* 28 E. 39th St., New York, NY 10016 (SAN 207-0391) Tel 212-697-6430.

Jung, C.G., Institute of Los Angeles, Inc., *(C G Jung Inst; 0-918608),* 10349 W. Pico Blvd., Los Angeles, CA 90064 (SAN 220-6927).

Jung, C.G., Institute of San Francisco, *(C G Jung Frisco; 0-932630),* 2040 Gough St., San Francisco, CA 94109 (SAN 281-8493); Dist. by: Spring Pubs., P.O. Box 222069, Dallas, TX 75222 (SAN 282-6127).

Jungle Garden Pr., *(Jungle Garden; 0-941220),* 47 Oak Rd., Fairfax, CA 94930 (SAN 210-8216) Tel 415-456-4884.

Jungle Video, *(Jungle Video; 0-9602756),* 2013 Lincoln Apt. 3, Berkeley, CA 94709 (SAN 221-8038).

Junior Board of the Tri-City Symphony Orchestra, *(Jr Bd Tri-City Symph; 0-9606524),* P.O. Box 67, Davenport, IA 52805 (SAN 218-5601).

Junior Committee of The Cleveland Orchestra, The, *(Jr Comm Cleveland; 0-9609142),* Severance Hall, Cleveland, OH 44106 (SAN 241-5321) Tel 216-231-7300.

Junior Guild of Rocky Mount, North Carolina, The, *(Jr Guild Rocky Mt NC; 0-9616940),* P.O. Box 7912, Rocky Mount, NC 27804 (SAN 661-7972); 724 Brassie Club Dr., Rocky Mount, NC 27804 (SAN 661-7980) Tel 919-977-2607.

Junior League of Albany Pubns., *(Jr League Albany Pubns; 0-9614012),* 419 Madison Ave., Albany, NY 12210 (SAN 683-6585) Tel 518-458-8085.

Junior League of Amarillo Texas, Inc., The, *(Jr League Amarillo; 0-9604102),* P.O. Box 381, Amarillo, TX 79105 (SAN 215-0891).

Junior League of Asheville Publications, *(Jr League Asheville; 0-9608444),* P.O. Box 8723, Asheville, NC 28814 (SAN 240-6926) Tel 704-258-2098.

Junior League of Austin, Texas, *(Jr League Austin; 0-9605906),* 5416 Parkcrest, Suite 100, Austin, TX 78731 (SAN 216-6828) Tel 512-467-8982.

Junior League of Baton Rouge, Inc., *(Jr League Baton Rouge Inc; 0-9613026),* 4950-E Goverment St., Baton Rouge, LA 70806 (SAN 294-0590) Tel 504-924-0298.

Junior League of Beaumont, Inc., *(Jr League Beau; 0-9609604),* P.O. Box 7031, Beaumont, TX 77706 (SAN 260-2105) Tel 713-832-0873.

Junior League of Binghamton Publishing Company, *(Jr League Binghamton; 0-9607710; 0-9607714),* 85 Walnut St., Binghamton, NY 13905 (SAN 238-4310).

Junior League of Birmingham, Inc., *(Jr League Birm; 0-9607810),* 2212 20th Ave. S., Birmingham, AL 35223 (SAN 239-7382) Tel 205-870-5590.

Junior League of Boise, *(Jr League Boise; 0-913743),* P.O. Box 6126, Boise, ID 83707 (SAN 286-0635) Tel 208-376-6601.

Junior League of Charleston, S.C., Inc., *(Jun League Charl SC; 0-9607854),* P.O. Box 177, Charleston, SC 29402 (SAN 218-8031) Tel 803-763-5284; Dist. by: Walker, Evans & Cogswell, 5300 Rivers Ave., North Charleston, SC 29405 (SAN 265-4121) Tel 803-747-8761.

Junior League of Charleston West Virginia, Inc., *(Jr League Charleston; 0-9606232),* P.O. Box 1924, Charleston, WV 25327 (SAN 220-3359) Tel 304-343-2190.

Junior League of Charlottesville, Inc., The, *(Jr Charlottesville; 0-9615013),* P.O. Box 3603, Univ. Station, Charlottesville, VA 22903 (SAN 694-0331) Tel 804-971-2937.

Junior League of Chattanooga, Inc., *(Jr Chatta; 0-9611806),* 100 Stivers St., Chattanooga, TN 37405 (SAN 283-9628) Tel 615-265-9614.

Junior League of Chicago, Inc., The, *(JLC Inc; 0-9611622),* 1447 N. Astor St., Chicago, IL 60610 (SAN 238-8863) Tel 312-664-4462.

Junior League of Colorado Springs, Inc., The, *(Jr League Colo Spgs; 0-9609930),* P.O. Box 1058, Colorado Springs, CO 80901 (SAN 271-8332) Tel 303-632-3855.

Junior League of Columbus, Georgia, Inc., *(JL Columbus GA; 0-9606300),* 1440 Second Ave., Columbus, GA 31901 (SAN 220-1569) Tel 404-327-4207.

Junior League of Corpus Christi, Inc., *(Jr League Corpus Christi; 0-9609144),* P.O. Box 837, Corpus Christi, TX 78403 (SAN 241-533X) Tel 512-883-9351.

Junior League of Detroit, Inc., *(Jr League Detroit; 0-9613728),* 32 Lake Shore Rd., Grosse Pointe, MI 48236 (SAN 677-5136) Tel 313-886-1608.

Junior League of Durham & Orange Counties, Inc., *(Jr League Durham & Orange; 0-9615845),* 900 S. Duke St., Durham, NC 27707 (SAN 696-8740) Tel 919-682-0449.

Junior League of El Paso, Inc, *(Jr League El Paso; 0-9607974),* 520 Thunderbird, El Paso, TX 79912 (SAN 240-9518).

Junior League of Elmira, Inc., *(Jr League Elmira; 0-9609980),* P.O. Box 3150, Elmira, NY 14905 (SAN 271-8413) Tel 607-732-9846.

Junior League of Eugene Pubs., *(Jr League Eugene; 0-9607976),* 2839 Willamette St., Eugene, OR 97405 (SAN 238-5341) Tel 503-345-7370.

Junior League of Fort Lauderdale, *(Jr League Ft Lauderdale; 0-9604158),* 2510 NE 15th Ave., Fort Lauderdale, FL 33305 (SAN 214-2481) Tel 305-566-3736.

Junior League of Fresno, *(Jr League Fresno; 0-9615379),* 5384 N. Briarwood, Fresno, CA 93711 (SAN 699-8216) Tel 209-439-1401.

Junior League of Gainesville Florida, Inc., *(Jr League Gainesville; 0-9606616),* P.O. Box 422, Gainesville, FL 32602 (SAN 219-6697) Tel 904-376-3805.

Junior League of Galveston County, Inc., *(Jr League Galveston; 0-9613779),* 8620 Twelve Oaks Dr., Texas City, TX 77591 (SAN 678-996X) Tel 409-938-0607.

Junior League of Greater Alton, *(Greater Alton Jr League; 0-9615898),* P.O. Box 27, Alton, IL 62002 (SAN 696-8759) Tel 618-462-4897; 78 Fairmont Addition, Alton, IL 62002 (SAN 699-6469).

Junior League of Greensboro Pubns., *(J League Greensboro; 0-9605788),* 220 State St., Greensboro, NC 27408 (SAN 216-5333) Tel 919-275-9292.

Junior League of Greenville, Inc., *(Greenville SC Jr League; 0-9608172),* P.O. Box 8703, Sta. A, Greenville, SC 29604 (SAN 240-236X) Tel 803-288-1991.

Junior League of Indianapolis, Inc., *(Jr League Indianapolis; 0-9614447),* 3050 N. Meridian, Indianapolis, IN 46208 (SAN 689-3732) Tel 317-923-7004.

Junior League of Jackson, Mississippi, *(Jr League Jackson; 0-9606886),* P.O. Box 4553, Jackson, MS 39216 (SAN 217-3867) Tel 601-948-2357.

Junior League of Jacksonville Inc., *(Jun League Jackson; 0-9609338),* 2165 Park St., Jacksonville, FL 32204 (SAN 260-2113) Tel 904-389-5497.

Junior League of Kalamazoo, *(Jr League Kalamazoo; 0-9606506),* 309 E. Water St., Kalamazoo, MI 49007 (SAN 217-1880) Tel 616-344-9814.

Junior League of Kansas City, Missouri, Inc., *(Jr League KC; 0-9607076),* 4651 Roanoke Pkwy., Kansas City, MO 64112 (SAN 238-9959) Tel 816-531-4453.

Junior League of Lafayette, The, *(Jr League Lafayette; 0-935032),* P.O. Box 52387, Oil Ctr. Sta., Lafayette, LA 70505 (SAN 212-3657) Tel 318-988-1079; 100 Felecie, Lafayette, LA 70506 (SAN 650-0382).

Junior League of Lansing Publications, *(Jr League Lansing; 0-9611852),* P.O. Box 1782, East Lansing, MI 48823 (SAN 286-1542) Tel 517-349-9611; 4965 Chipping Camden Lane, Okemos, MI 48864 (SAN 286-1550).

Junior League of Las Vegas Pubns., Inc., Div. of J.L.L.V., *(Jr League Las Veg; 0-9614100),* 1100 E. Sarhara Ave., Suite 311, Las Vegas, NV 89104 (SAN 685-9801) Tel 702-733-1660; Orders to: P.O. Box 43419, Las Vegas, NV 89116 (SAN 662-2666) Tel 702-733-1660; Dist. by: Southwest Cookbook Distributors, Inc., 1901 South Shore Dr., Bonham, TX 75418 (SAN 200-4925) Tel 214-583-8898; Dist. by: Dot Gibson Pubns., 161 Knight Ave. Cir., Waycross, GA 31501 (SAN 200-4143) Tel 912-285-2848; Dist. by: The Collection, Inc., 2101 Kansas City Rd., Olathe, KS 66061 (SAN 200-6359) Tel 913-764-1811; Dist. by: Baker & Taylor Co., Western Div., 380 Edison Way, Reno, NV 89564 (SAN 169-4464) Tel 702-786-6700.

Junior League of Lynchburg (VA), Inc., *(Jr League Lynchburg VA; 0-9614766),* P.O. Box 3304, Lynchburg, VA 24503 (SAN 692-9125) Tel 804-846-1045.

Junior League of Memphis, Inc., The, *(Jr League Memphis; 0-9604222),* 2711 Union Ave. Extended, Memphis, TN 38112 (SAN 214-316X) Tel 901-452-2151.

Junior League of Monroe, *(Jun League Mon; 0-9602364),* P.O. Box 7138, Monroe, LA 71211-7138 (SAN 208-1822) Tel 318-322-3863.

Junior League of New Orleans, Inc., *(Jr League New Orleans; 0-9604774),* 4319 Carondelet, New Orleans, LA 70115 (SAN 215-6652) Tel 504-891-5845.

Junior League of Newport Harbor, Inc., *(Jun League NH; 0-9608306),* 170 Newport Center Dr., .Suite 100, Newport, CA 92660 (SAN 240-5407) Tel 714-720-7477.

Junior League of Norfolk-Virginia Beach, Incorporated, The, *(Jr League Norfolk; 0-9614767),* P.O. Box 956, Norfolk, VA 23510 (SAN 692-9117) Tel 804-623-7270.

Junior League of Northern Westchester, Inc., *(Jr League N Westchester; 0-9604314),* P.O. Box 214, Chappaqua, NY 10514 (SAN 265-4067) Tel 914-666-4966.

Junior League of Odessa, Inc., *(Jr League Odessa; 0-9612508),* P.O. Box 7273, Odessa, TX 79760 (SAN 289-5048).

Junior League of Ogden, Utah, *(Jr League Ogden; 0-9613453),* 5123 Aztec Dr., Ogden, UT 84403 (SAN 688-4202); Orders to: JLO Pubns., 2580 Jefferson Ave., Ogden, UT 84403 (SAN 688-4210).

Junior League of Oklahoma City, Inc., The, *(Jr League OK; 0-9613374),* P.O Box 21418, Oklahoma City, OK 73156 (SAN 657-0976).

Junior League of Owensboro, Inc. The, *(Jr League Owensboro; 0-9611770),* 2021 Frederica St., Owensboro, KY 42301 (SAN 285-3051) Tel 502-683-1430; Orders to: P.O. Box 723, Owensboro, KY 42302 (SAN 662-2062).

Junior League of Palo Alto, Inc., *(Jr League Palo Alto; 0-9606324),* 555 Ravenswood Ave., Menlo Park, CA 94025 (SAN 217-1899) Tel 415-327-3027.

Junior League of Peoria, Inc., *(Jr League Peoria; 0-9608206),* 256 NE Randolph Ave., Peoria, IL 61606 (SAN 238-8286).

Junior League of Rochester, Inc., *(Jr League Rochester; 0-9605612),* 444 E. Main St., Rochester, NY 14604 (SAN 216-1486) Tel 212-232-7040.

Junior League of Rockford, Inc., *(Rockford Lea; 0-9613563),* 4118 Pinecrest Rd., Rockford, IL 61107 (SAN 669-9596) Tel 815-399-4518.

Junior League of San Antonio, The, *(Jr League Antonio; 0-9610416),* 819 Augusta Street, San Antonio, TX 78215 (SAN 264-1461) Tel 512-225-1861.

Junior League of Shreveport, Inc., *(Jr League Shreveport; 0-9602246),* 3805 Gilbert-Madison Parish Business Ctr., Shreveport, LA 71104 (SAN 214-4297) Tel 318-868-7866; P.O. Box 4648, Shreveport, LA 71134 (SAN 669-1404).

Junior League of South Bend, Inc., *(Jr League S Bend; 0-9607120),* P.O. Box 305, South Bend, IN 46624 (SAN 662-0604) Tel 219-233-6520; c/o Nutbread & Nostalgia, P.O. Box 305, South Bend, IN 46624 (SAN 238-9967) Tel 219-233-6520.

Junior League of Spartanburg, S.C., Inc., *(Jr League Spartanburg),* P.O. Box 2881, Spartanburg, SC 29304 (SAN 212-2855) Tel 803-579-0079.

Junior League of Springfield, MO, *(Jr League MO; 0-9613307),* 2574 E. Bennett, Springfield, MO 65804 (SAN 654-2662) Tel 417-887-3563; Dist. by: Dot Gibson Publications, P.O. Box 117, Waycross, GA 31502 (SAN 660-9287); Dist. by: The Collection, Inc., 2101 Kansas City Rd., Olathe, KS 66061 (SAN 200-6359) Tel 913-764-1811.

Junior League of the Palm Beaches, Inc., The, *(JL Palm Beaches; 0-9608090),* P.O. Box 168, Palm Beach, FL 33480 (SAN 240-1177).

Junior League of Tucson, Inc., *(Jr League Tucson; 0-9616403),* 2099 E. River Rd., Tucson, AZ 85718 (SAN 658-8956) Tel 602-299-4762.

Junior League of Tulsa Pubns., *(Jr League Tulsa; 0-9604368),* 167 London Square, Tulsa, OK 74105 (SAN 219-9718) Tel 918-743-9767.

Junior League of Tyler, Inc., The, *(Jr League Tyler; 0-9607122),* 4500 S. Broadway, Suite C, Tyler, TX 75703 (SAN 238-9975) Tel 214-593-1143.

Junior League of Wichita, Inc., *(Jr League Wichita; 0-9609676),* 6402 E. 12th St., Wichita, KS 67206 (SAN 271-8340) Tel 316-682-7473.

Junior League of Winston-Salem, Inc., *(Jr League Winston-Salem; 0-9615429),* 909 S. Main St., Winston-Salem, NC 27101 (SAN 699-6329) Tel 919-748-8547; Dist. by: The Collection, Inc., 2101 Kansas City Rd., P.O. Box 1220, Olathe, KS 66061 (SAN 200-5638); Dist. by: Dot Gibson Pubns., P.O. Box 117, Waycross, GA 31502 (SAN 200-4143) Tel 912-285-2848.

Junior League Of Salt Lake City, Inc., The, *(Jr League Salt Lake City; 0-9616972),* 952 E. Ninth S., Salt Lake City, UT 84105 (SAN 661-7921) Tel 801-272-0894.

Junior Museum of Bay County, Inc., *(Jr Mus Bay; 0-9612774),* P.O. Box 977, 1731 Jenks Ave., Panama City, FL 32401 (SAN 289-5064) Tel 904-769-6128.

Junior Service League of DeLand Florida, *(Jr Serv DeLand; 0-9616689),* 2121 Hontoon Rd., DeLand, FL 32720 (SAN 661-4396) Tel 904-736-0197.

Junior Service League of Fort Walton Beach Florida, *(Jr Serv League FL; 0-9613562),* P.O. Box 24, Ft. Walton Beach, FL 32549 (SAN 669-9707) Tel 904-243-2665.

Junior Service League of Rome, Inc., *(Jr Serv Rome; 0-9615581),* P.O. Box 1003, Rome, GA 30161 (SAN 696-2823) Tel 404-232-4896; 102 Chatillon Rd., Rome, GA 30161 (SAN 696-2831).

Junior Social Workers of Chickasha, Oklahoma, *(Jr Soc Workers; 0-9613296),* 116 St. Charles Place, Chickasha, OK 73018 (SAN 654-4878) Tel 405-222-1340.

Junior Welfare League of Enid, Oklahoma, Inc., *(Jr Welfare Enid; 0-9609340),* P.O. Box 5877, Enid, OK 73702 (SAN 276-9700) Tel 405-234-2665.

Junior Welfare League of Florence, South Carolina, Inc., *(Jr Welfare SC; 0-9615863),* P.O. Box 3715, Florence, SC 29502 (SAN 696-8791) Tel 803-669-3461.

Junior Welfare League of Fort Myers, Florida Inc., *(Jr Welfare FL; 0-9613314),* Gulfshore Delights, P.O. Box 6774, Ft. Myers, FL 33911-6774 (SAN 656-8947) Tel 813-275-4336.

Juniper *See Fawcett Bk. Group*

Juniper Hse., *(Juniper Hse; 0-931870),* P.O. Box 2094, Boulder, CO 80306 (SAN 212-1891) Tel 303-449-7757.

†**Juniper Ledge Publishing Co.,** *(Juniper Ledge Pub; 0-931545),* P.O. Box 381, Sorrento, ME 04677 (SAN 682-2991) Tel 202-638-7929; 1012 14th St., NW, Suite 1101, Washington, DC 20005 (SAN 699-587X) Tel 202-638-7929; *CIP.*

Juniper Pr., *(Juniper Maine; 0-913977),* c/o Betts Bookstore, Bangor Mall, Stillwater Ave., Bangor, ME 04401 (SAN 212-1077) Tel 207-947-7052.

Juniper Pr., *(Juniper Pr WI; 0-910822),* 1310 Shorewood Dr., La Crosse, WI 54601 (SAN 207-8570) Tel 608-788-0096.

Juniper Pubs., *(Juniper Pubs; 0-9605986),* P.O. Box 11872, Lexington, KY 40511 (SAN 207-2432) Tel 606-266-4675.

Juniper Ridge Pr., *(Juniper Ridge; 0-916289),* P.O. Box 338, Ashland, OR 97520 (SAN 295-8899) Tel 503-482-9585.

Junius, Inc., *(Junius Inc; 0-9603932),* 842 Lombard St., Philadelphia, PA 19147 (SAN 214-0934) Tel 215-627-8298.

Junius-Vaughn Pr., The, *(Junius-Vaughn; 0-940198),* P.O. Box 85, Fairview, NJ 07022 (SAN 217-1139) Tel 201-868-7725.

Juno-Western Publishing Co., *(Juno-West; 0-914597),* 3086 Patricia Ave., Los Angeles, CA 90064 (SAN 289-3150) Tel 213-204-4748.

Jupiter Bks., *(Jupiter Bks; 0-935344),* 7300 Eades Ave., La Jolla, CA 92037 (SAN 213-7658).

†**Jupiter Pr.,** *(Jupiter Pr; 0-933104),* P.O. Box 101, Lake Bluff, IL 60044 (SAN 212-5161) Tel 312-234-3997; *CIP.*

Jupiter Productions, *(Jupiter Prods; 0-915981),* 2125 Dailey Ave., Latrobe, PA 15650 (SAN 294-0485) Tel 412-539-2824.

Jupiter Pubns., *(Jupiter Pubns; 0-939270),* 118 W. 74th St., New York, NY 10023 (SAN 216-5341) Tel 212-873-3132.

Jury Verdict Research Inc., *(Jury Verdict; 0-934607),* 5325-B Naiman Pkwy., Solon, OH 44139 (SAN 227-2415); Toll free: 800-321-6910.

Just Above Midtown, Inc., *(Just Above Midtown; 0-9605830),* 503 Broadway, 5th Flr., New York, NY 10012 (SAN 211-4704) Tel 212-966-7020.

Just Another Asshole, *(Just Another; 0-913803),* Eight Spring St., 4 EF, New York, NY 10012 (SAN 286-1291) Tel 212-966-0623.

Just Clare Corporation, *(Just Clare; 0-9608092),* 1850 Union St No. 379, San Francisco, CA 94123 (SAN 240-2386) Tel 415-563-6313.

Just For Fun Horse Cartoons, *(Just Fun Horse),* P.O. Box 2656, Boca Raton, FL 33427 (SAN 682-2436).

Justice Systems Pr., *(Justice Syst Pr; 0-937935),* 415 E. Vashon, Port Angeles, WA 98362 (SAN 659-5103) Tel 206-457-5320.

Justim Publishing Co., *(Justim Pub; 0-938691),* P.O. Box 1217, Lafayette, CA 94549-1217 (SAN 661-5562); 3683 Boyer Cir., Lafayette, CA 94549 (SAN 661-5570) Tel 415-283-4849.

Justin Bks., *(Justin Bks; 0-918537),* 41 Greenwich Ave., New York, NY 10014 (SAN 657-6370) Tel 212-924-1071.

†**Juul, Peter Pr., Inc.,** *(P Juul Pr; 0-915456),* P.O. Box 40605, Tucson, AZ 85717 (SAN 207-513X) Tel 602-622-3409; *CIP.*

Juvenescent Research Corp., *(Juvenescent; 0-9600148),* 807 Riverside Dr., New York, NY 10032 (SAN 206-7250) Tel 212-795-8765.

Jym Enterprises, *(Jym Ent),* P.O. Box 73, Batavia, OH 45103 (SAN 210-5373).

KASST (Ken's Automotive Savings & Safety Tips), *(K A S S T; 0-9611716),* P.O. Box 1812, 940 W. Princeton St., Ontario, CA 91762 (SAN 285-3558) Tel 714-986-8312.

K&A Pubns., *(K & A Pubns; 0-9616230),* P.O. Box 22075, San Diego, CA 92122 (SAN 658-5981) Tel 619-455-6578.

K & K Enterprises, *(K & K Enter; 0-935346),* 22311 Caminito Tecate, Laguna Hills, CA 92653 (SAN 221-4652).

K&K Pubs., *(K & K Pubs; 0-9604218),* 216 N. Batavia Ave., Batavia, IL 60510 (SAN 214-3186) Tel 312-879-6214.

K & K Publishing, *(K & K Pub MA; 0-9614689),* 34 Glenburnie Rd., Roslindale, MA 02131 (SAN 692-6037) Tel 617-323-6171; Dist. by: Airline Careers Media, Box 9200, Boston, MA 02114 (SAN 200-6839) Tel 617-323-1607.

K & K Publishing, *(K&K Pub Calif; 0-9608500),* 1161 Nogales St., Lafayette, CA 94549 (SAN 240-5431) Tel 415-934-8196.

K & R Publishing, *(K & R Pub; 0-9616178),* P.O. Box 672, Eureka Springs, AR 72632 (SAN 699-8739) Tel 501-253-9215.

KCI Communications, Inc., *(KCI Comns; 0-937583),* 1300 N. 17th St., Arlington, VA 22209 (SAN 658-8964) Tel 703-276-7100.

KC Pubns., *(KC Pubns; 0-916122; 0-88714),* P.O. Box 14883, Las Vegas, NV 89114 (SAN 201-0364) Tel 702-731-3123; Toll free: 800-626-9673; 2901 Industrial Rd., Las Vegas, NV 89109 (SAN 658-103X).

K-D Enterprises, *(K-D Enter; 0-9613877),* 14111 12th Ave. SW, Seattle, WA 98166 (SAN 681-994X) Tel 206-243-2372; Orders to: P.O. Box 66594, Seattle, WA 98166 (SAN 662-7676) Tel 206-243-2372; Dist. by: C P Publications, P.O. Box 1072, Port Angeles, WA 98362 (SAN 287-5276) Tel 206-457-7550.

KDK Pubns., *(KDK Pubns; 0-910165),* 1892 Fell St., San Francisco, CA 94117 (SAN 241-2144) Tel 415-386-9656.

K-Dimension Pubs., *(K-Dimension; 0-917595),* P.O. Box 371289, Decatur, GA 30037 (SAN 657-1484) Tel 404-241-1565; Toll free: 800-241-4702.

KEL Pubns., *(KEL Pubns; 0-9605710),* 443 Schley Rd., Annapolis, MD 21401 (SAN 216-1508) Tel 301-268-9704.

KEND Publishing, *(KEND Pub; 0-938218),* 15 Dorchester Rd., Emerson, NJ 07630 (SAN 217-2429) Tel 201-261-9281.

KET, *(KET; 0-910475),* Network Ctr., 600 Cooper Dr., Lexington, KY 40502 (SAN 264-147X); Toll free: 800-354-9067.

K Four Enterprises, Inc., *(K-Four Ent; 0-939473),* 2115 New York Ave., Whiting, IN 46394 (SAN 663-2602) Tel 219-659-2323.

KG Bks. Co., *(KG Bks Co; 0-930425),* 5912 Schaefer Rd., Edina, MN 55436 (SAN 682-0514) Tel 612-925-5134.

KGI Pr., *(KGI Pr; 0-936349),* 440 Cesano Ct., No. 306, Palo Alto, CA 94306 (SAN 697-8959) Tel 415-948-9262.

KGI Publishing, *(KGI Pub; 0-939231),* 7280 Blue Hill Dr., No. 14, San Jose, CA 95129 (SAN 662-5924) Tel 408-446-5574.

KID Broadcasting Corp., *(KID Broadcast; 0-9607304),* P.O. Box 2006, Idaho Falls, ID 83401 (SAN 240-9569).

KM Assocs., *(KM Assocs; 0-930819),* 4711 Overbook Rd., Bethesda, MD 20816 (SAN 677-6582) Tel 301-652-4536.

Names

KMG Pubns., *(KMG Pubns OR; 0-938928),* 290 E. Ashland Ln., Ashland, OR 97520 (SAN 215-9562) Tel 503-488-1302.

KMS Pr., *(KMS Pr CO; 0-9605564),* 765 Galena, Aurora, CO 80010 (SAN 215-9570) Tel 303-366-4566.

†KOSMOS, *(KOSMOS; 0-916426),* 20 Millard Road, Larkspur, CA 94939 (SAN 208-029X) Tel 415-927-1145; *CIP.*

K/P Medical Systems, *(KP Med),* P.O. Box 8900, Stockton, CA 95208 (SAN 209-5726) Tel 209-466-6761.

K-Q Assocs., Inc., *(K Q Assocs; 0-941988),* P.O. Box 2132, Cedar Rapids, IA 52406 (SAN 238-4655).

Kaaikaula, Hale Pa'I O, *(Kaaikaula; 0-914599),* P.O. Box 26448, Honolulu, HI 96825-0078 (SAN 289-3207) Tel 808-373-4430.

Kabel Pubns., *(KABEL Pubs; 0-930329),* 11225 Huntover Dr., Rockville, MD 20852 (SAN 670-8323).

Kabyn Bks., *(Kabyn; 0-940444),* 3341 Adams Ave., San Diego, CA 92116 (SAN 217-1902) Tel 619-284-0999.

Kadon, John C., *(Kadon; 0-917130),* 2538 N. Eight St., Sedona, AZ 86336 (SAN 208-4074) Tel 602-990-8346.

Kaff Publishing Group, *(Kaff Pub Group; 0-916557),* 318 Nutt St., Wilmington, NC 28401 (SAN 295-4508) Tel 919-343-1100.

Kahn, Hannah, *(H Kahn; 0-9602340),* 3301 NE Fifth Ave., Suite 318, Miami, FL 33137 (SAN 208-1342) Tel 305-576-1499.

Kahn, Joan, Bk., A *See* St. Martin's Pr., Inc.

†Kahn & Kahan Publishing Co., Inc., *(Kahn & Kahan; 0-9604286),* 31 South St., P.O. Box 661, Morristown, NJ 07960 (SAN 214-2597); *CIP.*

Kahn Publishing, *(Kahn Pub; 0-9611134),* P.O. Box 210404, San Francisco, CA 94121-0404 (SAN 283-3654) Tel 415-751-4286; Dist. by: Bookpeople, 2929 Fifth St., Berkeley, CA 94710 (SAN 168-9517) Tel 415-549-3030; Dist. by: L-S Distributors, 480 Ninth St., San Francisco, CA 94103 (SAN 169-0213) Tel 415-861-6300; Dist. by: Publisher's Group West, 5855 Beaudry St., Emeryville, CA 94608 (SAN 202-8522) Tel 415-658-3453.

Kaihong, *(Kaihong; 0-940446),* c/o P.O. Box 1706, MPK, Los Angeles, CA 91754-1706 (SAN 218-4850).

Kairos Books, Inc., *(Kairos Bks; 0-9608410),* P.O. Box 708, Libertyville, IL 60048 (SAN 240-6942) Tel 312-362-1898.

Kairos, Inc., *(Kairos Inc; 0-934501),* 2213 NW Market St., Seattle, WA 98107 (SAN 693-8965) Tel 206-789-7615; P.O. Box 71280, Seattle, WA 98107 (SAN 662-328X).

Kajfez Consulting, *(Kajfez Con; 0-930071),* P.O. Box 757, University, MS 38677 (SAN 669-9766) Tel 601-234-4287.

Kajun Pr., *(Kajun Pr; 0-9614385),* 209 Mississippi St., San Francisco, CA 94107 (SAN 658-6469) Tel 415-863-2494.

Kalamazoo Institute of Arts, *(Kalamazoo Inst Arts; 0-933742),* 314 S. Park St., Kalamazoo, MI 49007 (SAN 221-4660) Tel 616-349-7775.

Kaleidoscope in Education Co., *(Kaleid Educ; 0-914741),* P.O. Box 292, St Albans, WV 25177 (SAN 291-8196).

Kaleidoscope Pubns., *(Kaleidoscope Pubns; 0-938001),* 13000 Bel-Red Rd., Suite 101, Bellevue, WA 98005 (SAN 661-4183) Tel 206-451-1961.

Kalimat Pr., *(Kalimat; 0-933770),* 1600 Sawtelle Blvd., Suite 34, Los Angeles, CA 90025 (SAN 213-7666) Tel 213-479-5668; Toll free: 800-323-1880.

Kalium, Inc., *(Kalium; 0-9610114),* 141 Mt. Horeb Rd., Warren, NJ 07060 (SAN 271-8480) Tel 201-647-6016.

Kallman Publishing Co., *(Kallman; 0-910824),* 1614 W. University Ave., Box 14076, Gainesville, FL 32601 (SAN 203-9141) Tel 904-376-6066.

Kalmbach Publishing Co., *(Kalmbach; 0-89024),* 1027 N. Seventh St., Milwaukee, WI 53233 (SAN 201-0399) Tel 414-272-2060; Toll free: 800-558-1544.

Kalum Press, *(Kalum Pr; 0-937788),* 596 Joey Ave., El Cajon, CA 92020 (SAN 215-6660).

Kambrina, *(Kambrina; 0-9605742),* P.O. Box 16, Depoe Bay, OR 97341 (SAN 216-2601).

Kamp, Gayle O., *(G O Kamp; 0-9613163),* 7741 Lola Court, Indianapolis, IN 46219 (SAN 294-9687) Tel 317-357-6128.

Kampmann & Co., Inc., *(Kampmann),* 9 E. 40th St., New York, NY 10016 (SAN 202-5191) Tel 212-685-2928; Toll free: 800-526-7626.

Kan, Johnny, Inc., *(Kan J; 0-9608900),* 708 Grant Ave., San Francisco, CA 94108 (SAN 241-127X) Tel 415-982-2388.

Kane/Miller Bk. Pubs., *(Kane-Miller Bk; 0-916291),* P.O. Box 529, Brooklyn, NY 11231 (SAN 295-8945) Tel 718-624-5120; 310 President St., Brooklyn, NY 11231 (SAN 693-9902); Orders to: P.O. Box 12374, La Jolla, CA 92037 (SAN 685-3897) Tel 619-456-0540. *Imprints:* Cranky Nell Book, A (Cranky Nell Bk).

Kanegis, James, *(Kanegis; 0-9600226),* 3907 Madison St., Hyattsville, MD 20781 (SAN 201-0402) Tel 301-699-5064.

Kaneshiro, Hansel S., *(Kaneshiro; 0-9600670),* 1524 N. Hoyne Ave., Chicago, IL 60622 (SAN 203-915X) Tel 312-276-8024.

Kansas Arts Commission, *(Kansas Arts Com; 0-9607978),* 700 Kansas, Suite 1004, Topeka, KS 66603 (SAN 239-9393) Tel 913-296-3335.

Kansas Bar Association, Div. of CLE, *(KS Bar CLE),* Box 1037, Topeka, KS 66601 (SAN 237-7314) Tel 913-234-5696.

Kansas State Historical Society, *(Kansas St Hist; 0-87726),* Center for Historical Research, 120 W. 10th St., Topeka, KS 66612 (SAN 207-0014) Tel 913-296-4784.

Kansas State Univ., *(KSU),* Orders to: Library Publications, Kansas State Univ. Library, Manhattan, KS 66506 (SAN 210-1483).

Kansas State Univ., College of Engineering, *(College Engineering KS; 0-9609342),* Durland Hall, Manhattan, KS 66506 (SAN 260-213X) Tel 913-532-5590.

Kanthaka Press, *(Kanthaka; 0-916926),* P.O. Box 696, Brookline Village, MA 02147 (SAN 206-4375) Tel 617-734-8146.

Kanyaku Imin J.V., *(Kanyaku Imin JV; 0-9615045),* 245 Kuupua St., Kailua, HI 96734 (SAN 693-8973) Tel 808-944-5200.

Kapilian, Ralph H., Pub., *(R H Kapilian; 0-916311),* 30 Lake St., Brighton, MA 02135 (SAN 295-9232) Tel 617-254-3054.

Kapilla, Cleo, & Eleanor Simons, *(K & S; 0-9611466),* P.O. Box 4995, Ocala, FL 32678 (SAN 277-6928) Tel 904-622-4914.

Kapitan Szabo Publishers, *(Kapitan Szabo; 0-916845),* 2120 Pennsylvania Ave. NW, Washington, DC 20037 (SAN 200-4607).

Kappeler Institute Publishing, *(Kappeler Inst Pub; 0-942958),* 2019 Delaware Ave., Wilmington, DE 19806 (SAN 240-1185) Tel 302-571-9570.

Kaptur Pr., *(Kaptur Pr; 0-936987),* P.O. Box 1829, Costa Mesa, CA 92628 (SAN 658-7992) Tel 714-962-4464; 19822 Brookhurst, No. 50, Huntington Beach, CA 92646 (SAN 658-800X).

Kar-Ben Copies, Inc., *(Kar Ben; 0-930494),* 6800 Tildenwood Ln., Rockville, MD 20852 (SAN 210-7511) Tel 301-984-8733; Toll free: 800-452-7236.

Karagan, Phillip P., *(P P Karagan; 0-9612394),* 2449 Karagan Dr., Mobile, AL 36606 (SAN 289-3886) Tel 205-473-4970.

Karam, Anwar, *(A Karam; 0-9613780),* 12000 Fondren No. 11, Houston, TX 77035 (SAN 678-9587) Tel 713-728-1317.

Karan Marketing, *(Karan Mktg; 0-9616852),* 1007 Fifth Ave., Suite 1100, San Diego, CA 92101 (SAN 661-6011) Tel 619-692-9400.

Karger, S., AG, *(S Karger; 3-8055),* 79 Fifth Ave., New York, NY 10003 (SAN 281-8531) Tel 212-924-9222.

Karlin's Kitchen, *(Karlins Kitchen; 0-9615941),* 1343 Sunset Ave., Santa Monica, CA 90405 (SAN 696-8406) Tel 213-399-0261.

Karma Publishing Co., *(Karma Pub; 0-9604568),* 4404 Pennsylvania Ave., Pittsburgh, PA 15224 (SAN 238-888X).

Karmiole, Kenneth, Bookseller, Inc., *(K Karmiole; 0-931043026),* 1225 Santa Monica Mall, Santa Monica, CA 90401 (SAN 289-5188).

Karoma Pubs., Inc., *(Karoma; 0-89720),* 3400 Daleview Dr., Ann Arbor, MI 48105 (SAN 213-8131) Tel 313-665-3331.

Karp Publishing, *(Karp; 0-9612360),* 609-B Flournoy, Austin, TX 78745 (SAN 289-3908) Tel 512-479-9255.

Karpat Pub., *(Karpat; 0-918570),* 19608 Thornridge Ave., Cleveland, OH 44135 (SAN 209-939X) Tel 216-362-0316.

Karwyn Enterprises, *(Karwyn Ent; 0-939938),* 17227 17th Ave. W., Lynnwood, WA 98036 (SAN 289-0143) Tel 206-743-0722; Dist. by: Publishers' Marketing Group, 1104 Summit Ave., No. 100-B, Plainview, TX 75074 (SAN 262-0995) Tel 214-423-0312.

†Karz-Cohl Pubs., Inc., *(Karz-Cohl Pub; 0-943828),* 77 Bleecker St., Apt. PH24E, New York, NY 10012 (SAN 238-3063) Tel 212-505-2546; *CIP.*

†Karz Pubs., *(Karz Pub; 0-918294),* 320 W. 105th St., New York, NY 10025 (SAN 209-9403) Tel 212-663-9059; *CIP.*

Kashong Pubns., *(Kashong Pubns; 0-9607734),* P.O. Box 90, Bellona, NY 14415 (SAN 218-8074) Tel 315-789-9574; Dist. by: ARGS Bookstore, 6 Glen Terr., Scotia, NY 12302 (SAN 200-7967).

Katahdin Press, *(Katahdin; 0-939212),* P.O. Box 231, Campbell, CA 95009 (SAN 216-261X).

Katanya Pubns., *(Katanya Pubns; 0-912101),* P.O. Box 5355, Takoma Park, MD 20912 (SAN 264-7575) Tel 301-589-8263.

Katchadour Publishing *See* Ohanian

Katonah Gallery, *(Katonah Gal; 0-915171),* 28 Bedford Rd., Katonah, NY 10536 (SAN 279-2680) Tel 914-232-9555.

†Katydid Bks., *(Katydid Bks; 0-942668),* Oakland Univ., Dept. of English, Rochester, MI 48063 (SAN 238-7603) Tel 313-377-2250; Dist. by: Univ. of Washington Pr., P.O. Box 85569, Seattle, WA 98145 (SAN 212-2502) Tel 206-543-4050; Toll free: 800-441-4115; *CIP.*

Katydid Bks. & Records, *(Katyd Bks & Recds; 0-934573),* Box 395, Jerome, AZ 86331 (SAN 693-8981) Tel 602-634-8075; Orders to: Box 395, Jerome, AZ 86331 (SAN 693-8981) Tel 602-634-8075; Dist. by: Many Feathers, 5738 N. Central Ave., Phoenix, AZ 85012 (SAN 158-8877) Tel 602-266-1043.

Katz, Aaron L., Publishing Co., *(A L Katz Pub; 0-9615654),* 21098 Bank Mill Rd., Saratoga, CA 95070 (SAN 696-2548) Tel 408-741-1008; P.O. Box 719, Saratoga, CA 95071 (SAN 696-9658).

Kauai Museum Assn., Ltd., *(Kauai Museum; 0-940948),* Box 248, Lihue, HI 96766 (SAN 213-1013) Tel 808-245-6931; 4428 Rice St., Lihue, HI 96766 (SAN 685-3412).

Kauf Pubs., *(Kauf Pubs; 0-936804),* 715 38th St., West Des Moines, IA 50265 (SAN 218-4419) Tel 515-224-0338.

Kaufman, Alvin B., Pubs., *(Kaufman AB Pubs; 0-9607736),* 22420 Philiprimm St., Woodland Hills, CA 91367 (SAN 239-5568) Tel 818-340-8945.

Kaufman House Pubs., *(Kaufman Hse; 0-9602500),* 366 Terrace Ave., Cincinnati, OH 45220 (SAN 212-517X) Tel 513-751-6381.

†Kaufmann, William, Inc., *(W Kaufmann; 0-913232; 0-86576),* 95 First St., Los Altos, CA 94022 (SAN 202-9383) Tel 415-948-5810; Dist. by: Publishers Group West, 5855 Beaudry St., Emeryville, CA 94608 (SAN 202-8522) Tel 415-658-3453; *CIP.*

Kavanagh, Peter, Hand Press, *(Kavanagh; 0-914612),* 250 E. 30th St., New York, NY 10016 (SAN 205-6291) Tel 212-686-5099.

Kawaida Pubns., *(Kawaida Pubns; 0-943412),* 2560 West 54th St., Los Angeles, CA 90043 (SAN 219-5925).

Kay, L.E., Publishing Co., *(L E Kay; 0-9611256),* P.O. Box 333, Fogelsville, PA 18051 (SAN 283-3026); 2 Woodsbluff Run, Fogelsville, PA 18051 (SAN 283-3034) Tel 215-398-0107.

Kay Assocs., *(Kay Assocs; 0-9616188),* 16840 NE 19th Ave., North Miami Beach, FL 33162 (SAN 658-3571) Tel 305-949-3922.

Kayak, *(Kayak; 0-87711),* 325 Ocean View Ave., Santa Cruz, CA 95062 (SAN 203-9168).

Kaycee Pr., *(Kaycee Pr; 0-9614884),* 6586 Eastpointe Pines St., Palm Beach Gardens, FL 33410 (SAN 693-1960) Tel 305-626-5368.

Kaye's & Knight Pub. Co., *(K K Pub Co; 0-9612140),* P.O. Box 2065, 503 Broadway, Fargo, ND 58107 (SAN 287-2765) Tel 701-237-4525.

Kaylor, Christopher, Co., *(Kaylor Christ Co; 0-916039),* P.O. Box 737, Huntsville, AL 35804 (SAN 294-8524) Tel 205-534-6156; 706 Holmes Ave., Huntsville, AL 35801 (SAN 294-8532).

Kaypro Corp., *(Kaypro Corp),* P.O. Box N, Del Mar, CA 92014 (SAN 692-0446) Tel 619-481-3900; Toll free: 800-4KAYPRO; 533 Stevens Ave., Solana Beach, CA 92075 (SAN 697-8355) Tel 619-481-4300.

Kay's Kitchen Cookbook, *(Kay Kitchen; 0-9613781),* P.O. Box 2124, El Dorado, AR 71731-2124 (SAN 693-9953) Tel 501-862-6651.

Kazi Pubns., *(Kazi Pubns; 0-935782; 0-933511),* 1215 W. Belmont Ave., Chicago, IL 60657 (SAN 162-3397) Tel 312-327-7598.

Kearney Publishing Co., *(Kearney; 0-9604688),* 2515 Peachtree Lane, Northbrook, IL 60062 (SAN 212-7512) Tel 312-559-2985.

Keasbey, Doramay, *(D Keasbey; 0-9611136),* 5031 Alta Vista Rd., Bethesda, MD 20814 (SAN 283-9512) Tel 301-530-5031.

Keast, Winifred, *(W Keast; 0-9613847),* 740 Memorial Dr., Winthrop, ME 04364 (SAN 655-4326) Tel 207-377-8087.

†**Keats Publisher,** *(Keats Pub; 0-941962),* 12110 Webb Chaple Rd., Suite E305, Dallas, TX 75234 (SAN 238-2474) Tel 214-620-0620; CIP.

Keats Publishing, Inc., *(Keats; 0-87983),* Box 876, New Canaan, CT 06840 (SAN 201-0410) Tel 203-966-8721; 27 Pine St., New Canaan, CT 06840 (SAN 658-1048).

Kechely, Raymond O., *(R O Kechely; 0-930202),* P.O. Box 4514, Palm Springs, CA 92263 (SAN 210-752X) Tel 714-327-7779.

Kedcograph Co., *(Kedcograph; 0-936605),* 3037 Montrose Ave., Chicago, IL 60618 (SAN 698-0430) Tel 312-478-5836; P.O. Box 59118, Chicago, IL 60659 (SAN 698-245X).

Keeble Pr., The, *(Keeble Pr; 0-933144),* 3634 Winchell Rd., Shaker Heights, OH 44122 (SAN 214-249X) Tel 216-283-8245.

Keech, John, *(J Keech; 0-9607200),* P.O. Box 43, State University, AR 72467 (SAN 239-1058) Tel 501-935-2573.

Keegan Pr., *(Keegan Pr; 0-9607328),* 201 Sunnyslope Ave., Petaluma, CA 94952 (SAN 239-2445) Tel 707-763-0427; Dist. by: Inland Bk Co., P.O. Box 261, 22 Hemingway Ave., East Haven, CT 06512 (SAN 200-4151) Tel 203-467-4257.

Keeling, Inc., *(Keeling Inc; 0-9616525),* 309 Washington St., W., Charleston, WV 25302 (SAN 659-4751) Tel 304-345-0448.

Keene, J. Calvin, *(J Calvin Keene; 0-9603084),* 134 Verna Rd., Lewisburg, PA 17837 (SAN 211-9099).

Keep America Beautiful, Inc., *(Keep Am Beautiful),* 99 Park Ave., New York, NY 10016 (SAN 232-7457) Tel 212-682-4564.

Keewaydin Camp Ltd., *(Keewaydin Camp; 0-9691378),* 4242 Brookdale St., Jackson, MS 39206 (SAN 296-1245).

Keilco, Inc., *(Keilco Inc; 0-9615732),* 4504 Westward, Wichita Falls, TX 76308 (SAN 695-8494) Tel 817-691-5017.

Keim, Abe, *(A Keim; 0-9608214),* P.O. Box 18, Mt. Hope, OH 44660 (SAN 240-3161).

Keith County Historical Society, *(Keith County Hist),* P.O. Box 27, Ogallala, NE 69153 (SAN 694-0080) Tel 308-284-3544; Dist. by: Elaine Nielsen, P.O. Box 599, Ogallala, NE 69153 (SAN 200-7975).

Keithwood Publishing Co., *(Keithwood),* 6835 Greenway Ave., Philadelphia, PA 19142 (SAN 213-9324) Tel 215-727-0883.

Kelane Pubns., *(Kelane Pub; 0-9609394),* 5640 118th Ave., SE, Bellevue, WA 98006 (SAN 281-8558) Tel 206-747-9849.

Kelby Publishing, *(Kelby Pub; 0-937555),* P.O. Box 369, Los Lunas, NM 87031 (SAN 658-9022) Tel 505-299-7719.

Keller, Helen, National Ctr. for Deaf-Blind Youths & Adults, *(H Keller Natl Ctr; 0-9615138),* 111 Middle Neck Rd., Sands Point, NY 11050 (SAN 277-7150) Tel 516-944-8900.

Keller, J. J., Assocs., Inc., *(J J Keller; 0-934674),* 145 W. Wisconsin Ave., Neenah, WI 54956 (SAN 201-5056) Tel 414-722-2848; Toll free: 800-558-5011; Toll free: 800-242-6469 (WI only).

Keller, Burns & McGuirk Pub. Co., *(Keller-Burns & McGuirk; 0-9602506),* c/o James P. Gould, Colony Park Bldg., 37th & Woodland, West Des Moines, IA 50265 (SAN 213-2230) Tel 515-225-3122.

Keller International Publishing Corp., *(Keller Intl Pub; 0-937843),* 150 Great Neck Rd., Great Neck, NY 11021 (SAN 659-476X) Tel 516-829-9210.

Kelley, Augustus M., Pubs., *(Kelley; 0-678),* 1140 Broadway, Rm. 901, New York, NY 10001 (SAN 206-975X) Tel 212-685-7202; Orders to: 300 Fairfield Rd., P.O. Box 1308, Fairfield, NJ 07006 (SAN 206-9768). *Imprints:* Baker Library (Baker Library); Reference Book Publishers (Reference Bk Pubs).

Kelley, Etna M., *(E M Kelley),* 497 Fulton St., New York, NY 10038 (SAN 697-7057).

Kelley, Mary Palmer, *(M P Kelley; 0-9613313),* Garden History Assocs., P.O. Box 12606, Columbia, SC 29211 (SAN 656-8955).

Kelley, Rosemary Sue, *(R S Kelley; 0-9616905),* P.O. Box 505, HCR 69, School St., Friendship, ME 04547 (SAN 661-5171) Tel 207-832-4206.

Kelley, Sarah F., Pub., *(S F Kelley; 0-9615960),* 567 Whispering Hills Dr., Nashville, TN 37211 (SAN 697-2772) Tel 615-833-4219.

Kelley Pubns., *(Kelley Pubns; 0-9614480),* P.O. Box No.1, Seaman, OH 45679-0001 (SAN 689-3767) Tel 513-386-2375.

Kellner/McCaffery Associates, Inc., *(Kellner-McCaffery; 0-911069),* 150 Fifth Ave., Suite 322, New York, NY 10011 (SAN 271-8782) Tel 212-741-0280; Orders to: Gary Waller, Carnegie-Mellon Univ., English Dept., Pittsburgh, PA 15213 (SAN 662-0612) Tel 412-578-2850.

Kellogg, Edward P., Jr., *(Kellogg; 0-9603914),* 1755 Trinity Ave., No. 79, Walnut Creek, CA 94596 (SAN 213-6880) Tel 415-937-4841; Orders to: EHUD International Language Foundation, P.O. Box 2082, Dollar Ranch Sta., Walnut Creek, CA 94595 (SAN 214-2988) Tel 415-937-4841.

Kelly, Allan O., *(Allan Kelly),* P.O. Box 1065, Carlsbad, CA 92008 (SAN 693-7810).

Kelly, Thomas, *(Kelly; 0-910832),* 23 Prospect Terrace, Montclair, NJ 07042 (SAN 206-7242) Tel 201-746-7884.

Kelly Enterprises, *(Kelly Ent; 0-9615582),* P.O. Box 247, Holt, MI 48842-0247 (SAN 696-2815) Tel 517-694-1799; 2203 Meadowlane, Holt, MI 48842-0247 (SAN 699-6302).

Kelner, A., & Assocs., *(A Kelner; 0-939812),* 1201 First Ave., Salt Lake City, UT 84103 (SAN 213-2249) Tel 801-359-5387.

Kelsey, Mavis P., *(M P Kelsey; 0-9613308),* No. 2 Longbow Lane, Houston, TX 77024 (SAN 654-3308) Tel 713-686-3768.

Kelsey Publishing, *(Kelsey Pub; 0-9605824),* 310 E. 950 S., Springville, UT 84663 (SAN 216-5775) Tel 801-489-6666.

†**Kelsey Street Pr.,** *(Kelsey St Pr; 0-932716),* P.O. Box 9235, Berkeley, CA 94709 (SAN 212-6729) Tel 415-845-2260; CIP.

Kelso Manufacturing Co., *(Kelso; 0-942140),* Rte. 2, Box 499, Greenville, MS 38701 (SAN 210-1491).

Kemah Press, *(Kemah Pr; 0-9610806),* 91 Paradise Lane, Halifax, MA 02338 (SAN 265-0959) Tel 617-293-6655.

Kemetic Institute, *(Kemetic Inst; 0-939539),* 700 East Oakwood Blvd., Chicago, IL 60653 (SAN 663-4435) Tel 312-268-7500.

Kemnitz, Milton N., *(M N Kemnitz),* 1180 Bird Rd., P.O. Box 7390, Ann Arbor, MI 48107 (SAN 211-1586) Tel 313-668-9895.

Kempe, C. Henry, National Ctr. for Prevention & Treatment of Child Abuse & Neglect, Div. of Univ. of Colorado Health Science Ctr., Dept. of Pediatrics, *(Kempe Nat Ctr),* 1205 Oneida St., Denver, CO 80220 (SAN 240-9429) Tel 303-321-3963.

Kempfer, Lester L., *(L Kempfer),* P.O. Box 317, Marysville, OH 43040 (SAN 201-0569).

Kempler Institute, *(Kempler Inst; 0-9600808),* P.O. Box 1692, Costa Mesa, CA 92628 (SAN 207-6284) Tel 714-545-8942.

Ken-Bks., *(Ken-Bks; 0-913164),* 56 Midcrest Ave., San Francisco, CA 94131 (SAN 201-0429) Tel 415-826-6550.

Ken Kra Pubs., *(Ken Kra Pubs; 0-941522),* 1657 Thornwood Dr., Concord, CA 94521 (SAN 239-0000) Tel 415-676-9184.

Kenco Publishing Co., *(Kenco Pub Co; 0-916041),* 1224 Catalpa Lane, Naperville, IL 60540 (SAN 294-8591) Tel 312-346-5145.

Kendall Books, *(Kendall Bks; 0-935678),* 1212 N.W. 12th Ave., Gainesville, FL 32601 (SAN 221-4563) Tel 904-376-4913.

Kendall/Hunt Publishing Co., Subs. of Wm. C. Brown Co., Pubs., *(Kendall-Hunt; 0-8403),* 2460 Kerper Blvd., Dubuque, IA 52001 (SAN 203-9184) Tel 319-589-2833.

Kendall Whaling Museum, *(Kendall Whaling; 0-937854),* 27 Everett St., P.O. Box 297, Sharon, MA 02067 (SAN 204-9783) Tel 617-784-5642.

Kenedy, P. J., & Sons, Subs. of Macmillan Publishing Co., *(Kenedy),* 866 Third Ave., New York, NY 10022 (SAN 203-9192) Tel 212-935-2000; Orders to: Macmillan Co., Riverside, NJ 08075 (SAN 202-5582).

Kenilworth Press, *(Kenilworth; 0-9603876),* 421 W. Grant Ave., Eau Claire, WI 54701 (SAN 204-9775) Tel 715-832-2161.

Kennebec River Pr., Inc., The, *(Kennebec River; 0-933858),* 36 Old Mill Rd., Falmouth, ME 04105 (SAN 221-458X) Tel 207-781-3002; Dist. by: Harpswell Pr., 132 Water St., Gardiner, ME 04345 (SAN 208-1199) Tel 207-582-1899.

Kennedy, Alan, *(Kennedy Alan; 0-87940),* 344 E. 63rd St., New York, NY 10021 (SAN 693-3920).

Kennedy, Byron, & Co., *(Kennedy & Co; 0-941072),* P.O. Box 10937, St. Petersburg, FL 33733 (SAN 217-3875) Tel 813-822-3738.

Kennedy, David M., International Ctr., Brigham Young Univ., *(D M Kennedy Ctr Brigham; 0-912575),* 280 HRCB, Provo, UT 84602 (SAN 283-2895) Tel 801-378-6528.

Kennedy, M., *(M Kennedy),* 310 Franklin St., No. 285, Boston, MA 02110 (SAN 239-5576).

Kennedy Galleries, *(Kennedy Gall; 0-87920),* 40 W. 57th St., New York, NY 10019 (SAN 207-3226).

Kennedy-King College, *(Kennedy King Col; 0-938299),* 6800 S. Wentworth Ave., Chicago, IL 60621-3798 (SAN 661-1737) Tel 312-962-3707.

Kenneth Publishing Co., *(Kenneth Pub Co; 0-913451),* Box 344, Palos Heights, IL 60463 (SAN 285-1733) Tel 312-776-4648.

Kensington Historical Pr., *(Kensington Hist),* Cardinal Sta., Box 1314, Washington, DC 20064 (SAN 706-2416).

Kensington Publishing Co., *(Kensington Pub; 0-931445),* 3537 Mt. Diablo Blvd., Lafayette, CA 94549 (SAN 687-7516) Tel 415-283-1964.

Kent, Carol Miller, *(C M Kent; 0-9604886),* 929 E. 50th, Austin, TX 78751 (SAN 212-5188).

Kent, Earl, Welding Consultant, *(E Kent; 0-918782),* P.O. Box 575, Cypress, CA 90630 (SAN 210-4482) Tel 213-941-0195.

Kent, Edward, & Co., *(Kent & Co; 0-935625),* 1129 State St., Suite 20, Santa Barbara, CA 93101 (SAN 696-4095) Tel 805-966-1551.

Kent Popular Press, *(Kent Popular; 0-933522),* P.O. Box 715, Kent, OH 44240 (SAN 213-6295).

Kent Pubns., *(Kent Pubns; 0-917458),* 18301 Halstead St., Northridge, CA 91325 (SAN 209-0597) Tel 818-349-2080.

†**Kent Publishing Co.,** Div. of Wadsworth, Inc., *(Kent Pub Co; 0-534),* 20 Park Plaza, Boston, MA 02116 (SAN 215-3491) Tel 617-542-1629; Toll free: 800-343-2204; CIP.

†**Kent State Univ. Pr.,** *(Kent St U Pr; 0-87338),* Kent, OH 44242 (SAN 201-0437) Tel 216-672-7913; Toll free: 800-USA-KENT; Toll free: 800-FOR-KENT in Ohio; Orders to: 101 Franklin Hall, Kent, OH (SAN 215-3742); Dist. by: Harper & Row, Keystone Industrial Pk., Scranton, PA 18512 (SAN 215-3742); Toll free: 800-242-7737; Toll free: 800-242-7737; CIP.

Kentucky Arts Council, *(Kentucky Arts; 0-939058),* Berry Hill, Frankfort, KY 40601 (SAN 218-4869).

Kentucky Ctr. for Energy Research Laboratory, Div. of Commonwealth of Kentucky, *(KY Ctr Energy Res; 0-86607),* Iron Works Pike, Box 13015, Lexington, KY 40512 (SAN 239-4456) Tel 606-252-5535.

Kentucky Derby Museum, The, *(KY Derby Mus; 0-9617103),* P.O. Box 3513, Louisville, KY 40201 (SAN 662-488X); 704 Central Ave., Louisville, KY 40208 (SAN 662-4898) Tel 502-637-1111.

Kentucky Historical Society, *(Kentucky Hist; 0-916968),* Old-State-House, Box H, Frankfort, KY 40602 (SAN 204-9759) Tel 502-564-3016.

Kentucky Mining Institute, *(Kentucky Mining; 0-9615443),* 120 Graham Ave., Lexington, KY 40506 (SAN 695-7218) Tel 606-254-0367; P.O. Box 680, Lexington, KY 40586 (SAN 696-947X).

Kentucky Rifle Assn., *(Kentucky Rifle; 0-9615925),* 601 Madison St., Alexandria, VA 22314 (SAN 696-6667) Tel 703-836-6020.

Kentwood Publications, *(Kentwood; 0-917855),* 2515 Santa Clara Ave., No. 103, P.O. Box 2787, Alameda, CA 94501 (SAN 657-100X) Tel 415-865-4415.

Kenwood Publishing, *(Kenwood Pub; 0-9612776),* 2120 Kenwood Pkwy., Minneapolis, MN 55405 (SAN 289-7423) Tel 612-374-3337.

Kenyon Hill Pubns., Inc., *(Kenyon Hill; 0-917241),* Box 170, Hanover, NH 03755 (SAN 655-8666) Tel 603-795-4027.

Kenyon Pubns., *(Kenyon; 0-934286),* 361 Pin Oak Ln., Westbury, NY 11590 (SAN 201-5072) Tel 516-333-3236; Dist. by: G. Schirmer, Inc., 7101 Westfield Ave., Pennsauken, NJ 08110 (SAN 222-9544).

Keoki's Pubns., *(Keoki's Pubns),* 1229 W. Sixth St., Ontario, CA 91762 (SAN 295-012X).

Kepler Pr., *(Kepler Pr; 0-912938),* 84 Main St., Rockport, MA 01966 (SAN 203-9745) Tel 617-546-9614.

Kepley, Ray R., *(Kepley; 0-9604248),* Rte. 2 Box 128A, Ulysses, KS 67880 (SAN 214-3208) Tel 316-356-1568.

Kepner-Tregoe, Inc., *(Kepner-Tregoe),* 17 Research Rd., P.O. Box 704, Princeton, NJ 08540 (SAN 264-1496).

Keramos Bks., Subs. of Westwood Ceramic Supply Co., *(Keramos Bks; 0-935066),* P.O. Box 2305, Bassett, CA 91746 (SAN 207-5571) Tel 213-330-0631; 14400 Lomitas Ave., City of Industry, CA 91746 (SAN 207-558X).

Kern County Historical Society, *(Kern Historical; 0-943500),* P.O. Box 141, Bakersfield, CA 93302 (SAN 240-6969) Tel 805-322-4962.

Kerning Arts Press, The, *(Kerning Arts; 0-9606956),* 719 S. Elm Blvd., Champaign, IL 61820 (SAN 239-4472) Tel 217-359-2575.

Kerr, Charles H., Publishing, Co., *(C H Kerr; 0-88286),* 1740 W. Greenleaf Ave., Chicago, IL 60626 (SAN 207-7043) Tel 312-465-7774.

Kerr Assocs., Inc., *(Kerr Assoc; 0-937890),* 1409 Willow St., Suite 201, Minneapolis, MN 55403 (SAN 220-0635) Tel 612-871-6503.

Kersenbrock, Paul, *(Paul's Pubns; 0-9606032),* 1424 Grove, Crete, NE 68333 (SAN 216-9010) Tel 402-826-2003.

Kerth, A. L., *(A L Kerth; 0-9601188),* Jericho Run, Buckland Valley Farms, Washington Crossing, PA 18977 (SAN 207-3773) Tel 215-493-6683.

†**Kesend, Michael, Publishing, Ltd.,** *(Kesend Pub Ltd; 0-935576),* 1025 Fifth Ave., New York, NY 10028 (SAN 213-6902) Tel 212-249-5150; CIP.

Kesher Pr., *(Kesher; 0-9602394),* 1817 21st Ave., S., Nashville, TN 37212 (SAN 212-6761).

Kester, J. J., *(J J Kester; 0-9602084),* 416 Pine Grove Circle, Scotch Plains, NJ 07076 (SAN 212-8357) Tel 201-889-7077.

Ketab-E-Nemouneh, *(K E Nemouneh; 0-9616820),* P.O. Box 850029, New Orleans, LA 70185-0029 (SAN 661-4787); Carrolton Ave., New Orleans, LA 70185-0029 (SAN 661-4795) Tel 504-866-4667.

Keter Foundation, *(Keter Found; 0-933413),* P.O. Box 1312, Provo, UT 84602 (SAN 691-4993) Tel 801-378-4161.

Keturah Pr., *(Keturah Pr; 0-942546),* 350-A Quincy St., Brooklyn, NY 11216 (SAN 240-0774) Tel 718-636-1437.

Kevco Beneficial Bks., *(Kevco Ben Bks; 0-932297),* 146 Stenner St., Unit 7, San Luis Obispo, CA 93401 (SAN 686-6573) Tel 805-541-6140.

Key Book Service, Inc., *(Key Bk Serv; 0-934636),* 425 Asylum St., Bridgeport, CT 06610 (SAN 169-0671) Tel 203-334-2165; Toll free: 800-243-2790.

Key Books, *(Key Bks),* Dist. by: Associated Booksellers, 147 McKinley Ave., Bridgeport, CT 06606 (SAN 203-5014).

Key Bks. Pr., Div. of Hadady Corp., *(Key Bks Pr; 0-9611390),* P.O. Box 90490, Pasadena, CA 91109-0490 (SAN 285-290X); 61 S. Lake Ave., No. 309, Pasadena, CA 91101 (SAN 660-9511) Tel 818-793-2645.

Key Curriculum Project, *(Key Curr Proj; 0-913684),* P.O. Box 2304, Berkeley, CA 94702 (SAN 202-6538) Tel 415-548-2304; Toll free: 800-338-7638.

Key Foundation, *(Key Found; 0-911533),* 1601 Bayshore Hwy., No. 350, Burlingame, CA 94010 (SAN 293-2229) Tel 415-692-8853; Dist. by: DeVorss & Co., P.O. Box 550, Marina del Rey, CA 90291 (SAN 168-9886).

Key of David Pubns., *(Key of David; 0-943374),* 222 N. 17th, Philadelphia, PA 19103 (SAN 239-4480) Tel 215-664-4673.

Key Pubns., Div. of Corporate Computer Training Ctr., *(Key Pubns; 0-937141),* 812 Lyndon Ln., Suite 4, Louisville, KY 40222 (SAN 658-5655) Tel 502-725-2148.

Key West Women's Club, The, *(Key West Wmns Club; 0-9615035),* 319 Duval St., Key West, FL 33040 (SAN 693-7934) Tel 305-294-2039; Dist. by: Langley Pr., 821 Georgia St., Key West, FL 33040 (SAN 264-164X) Tel 305-294-3156.

Keymate Systems, *(Keymate Syst; 0-936379),* 9225 Mira Mesa Blvd., No. 212, San Diego, CA 92126 (SAN 697-2780) Tel 619-566-2283.

Keynote Series *See* **Barnes & Noble Bks.-Imports**

Keys, Elsie, *(E Keys; 0-9604750),* 1239 E. Marshall Ave., Phoenix, AZ 85014 (SAN 215-2428).

Keystone Bks. *See* **Pennsylvania State Univ. Pr.**

Keystone Pubns., Subs. of Wilfred American Educational Pubns., *(Keystone Pubns; 0-912126),* 250 W. 57th St., Suite 823, New York, NY 10019 (SAN 204-9708) Tel 212-582-2254; Toll free: 800-223-0935.

Khaneghah & Maktab of Maleknia Naseralishah, *(Khaneghah & Maktab; 0-917220),* P.O. Box 665, Palisades, NY 10964 (SAN 208-5046) Tel 914-359-7547.

KhaniQahi-Nimatullahi, Sufi Order, *(KhaniQahi-Nimatullahi-Sufi; 0-933546),* 306 W. 11th St., New York, NY 10014 (SAN 212-3673) Tel 212-924-7739; Dist. by: Samuel Weiser, Inc., P.O. Box 612, York Beach, ME 03910 (SAN 202-9588) Tel 207-363-4393; Toll free: 800-843-6666; Dist. by: The New Leaf Distributing, 1020 White St., SW, Atlanta, GA 30310 (SAN 169-1449) Tel 404-755-2665.

Khedcanron Publishing, *(Khedcanron Pub; 0-9610264),* 126 Westward Dr., Corte Madera, CA 94925 (SAN 264-150X) Tel 415-924-1944.

Khiralla, T. W., *(T W Khiralla; 0-9601752),* 12400 Rye St., Studio City, CA 91604 (SAN 211-531X) Tel 213-763-2679.

Khorassan Pr., *(Khorassan Pr; 0-9617114),* P.O. Box 9197, St. Louis, MO 63117 (SAN 662-7021); 5591 Lindell, St. Louis, MO 63112 (SAN 662-703X) Tel 314-361-0808; Dist. by: Paperback Supply Co., 4121 Forest Pk. Blvd., St. Louis, MO 63108 (SAN 169-4324) Tel 314-652-1000.

Kibler Flying Service, *(Kibler Flying; 0-9613506),* P.O. Box 823, Milford, PA 18337 (SAN 657-2774) Tel 717-296-7721.

Kibo Bks., *(Kibo Bks; 0-941266),* P.O. Box 1442, Main Post Office, Brooklyn, NY 11202 (SAN 239-5584).

Kici, Gasper, *(G Kici),* P.O. Box 1855, Washington, DC 20013 (SAN 203-4115) Tel 703-560-6467.

Kickapoo Pr., *(Kickapoo; 0-933180),* P.O. Box 1443, Peoria, IL 61655 (SAN 214-2503).

Kickapoo Tribal Pr., *(Kickapoo Tribal; 0-931045),* P.O. Box 106, Powhattan, KS 66527 (SAN 678-8998) Tel 913-474-3550.

Kid-Love Unlimited, *(Kid-Love Unltd; 0-912249),* 2036 Galaxy Dr., Newport Beach, CA 92660 (SAN 265-1572) Tel 714-642-1179.

Kid Power Enterprises, *(Kid Power Ent; 0-935441),* P.O. Box 2367, Decatur, GA 30031-2367 (SAN 696-2971); Dist. by: DeVorss & Co, P.O. Box 550, 1046 Princeton Dr., Marina del Rey, CA 30310 (SAN 168-9886) Tel 404-755-2665; Dist. by: The New Leaf Distributing, 1020 White St., SW, Atlanta, VA (SAN 169-1449); Toll free: 800-241-3829.

Kids Come in Special Flavors Co., *(Kids Special; 0-941854),* P.O. Box 292786, Kettering Sta., Kettering, OH 45429-0786 (SAN 216-2628) Tel 513-294-2797.

Kids In Distress, Inc., *(Kids In Distress; 0-9615864),* 2627 NE Ninth Ave., Fort Lauderdale, FL 33334 (SAN 696-6020) Tel 305-942-1800.

Kidsmart, *(Kidsmart; 0-936985),* P.O. Box 34066, Memphis, TN 38184-0066 (SAN 658-5639) Tel 901-372-7550; 3276 Hawksmoor Pl., Cordova, TN 38018 (SAN 658-5647).

Kiewit Computation Center, *(Kiewit Comput; 0-89580),* Dartmouth College, Hanover, NH 03755 (SAN 211-027X) Tel 603-646-2643.

Kilgore, Jack, & Assocs., *(Kilgore Assocs; 0-935809),* 5209 Thurman Dr., Sioux Falls, SD 57106 (SAN 696-6055) Tel 605-361-0711.

Kilgore, *(Kilgore; 0-9609280),* 1424 Acacia Dr., Colorado Springs, CO 80907 (SAN 260-0870) Tel 303-598-2410.

Kilkerrin Hse., *(Kilkerrin House; 0-9611728),* 740 Puente Dr., Santa Barbara, CA 93110 (SAN 285-3647) Tel 805-967-1903.

Kilmarnock Pr., The, *(Kilmarnock Pr; 0-937982),* P.O. Box 1302, South Pasadena, CA 91030 (SAN 265-3893) Tel 818-795-2170.

Kilthau-West Pubns., *(Kilthau West Pubns; 0-939347),* 13514 Rainbow Falls, Houston, TX 77083 (SAN 662-4901) Tel 713-568-3574.

Kiltie, Ordean, & Co., *(Kiltie; 0-937364),* 2445 Fairfield, A201, Ft. Wayne, IN 46807 (SAN 209-5718) Tel 219-745-9139.

Kimball, Charles, , *(C Kimball; 0-9613507),* 151 Capt. Lijah Rd., Centerville, MA 02632 (SAN 657-2634) Tel 617-775-1410.

Kimbell Art Museum, *(Kimbell Art; 0-912804),* 3333 Camp Bowie Blvd., P.O. Box 9440, Ft. Worth, TX 76107 (SAN 208-0516) Tel 817-332-8451; Dist. by: University of Washington Pr., P.O. Box C-50096, Seattle, WA 98145-5096 (SAN 212-2502) Tel 206-543-8870; Dist. by: Harry N. Abrams, Inc., 100 Fifth Ave., New York, NY 10011 (SAN 200-2434) Tel 212-206-7715.

Kimberly-Jones Publishing Co., *(Kimberly-Jones; 0-941412),* 2828 S. 94th St., P.O. Box 14213, Omaha, NE 68124 (SAN 238-8898) Tel 402-393-8121; Dist. by: International Specialized Bk., Servs., Inc., 5602 NE Hassalo St., Portland, OR 97213-3640 (SAN 169-7129) Tel 503-287-3093.

Kimberly Pr., *(Kimberly Pr; 0-9615913),* P.O. Box 632, Baldwin Place, NY 10505 (SAN 697-225X) Tel 914-628-2636.

Kimdar Books, *(Kimdar Bks; 0-939541),* P.O. Box 19542, Houston, TX 77224 (SAN 663-4389); 15455 Point NW, Blvd., No. 2101, Houston, TX 77095 (SAN 663-4397) Tel 713-550-0482.

Kincaid Pubs., *(Kincaid Pubs; 0-9616989),* 2101 Geer Rd., Suite 105A, Turlock, CA 95380 (SAN 661-731X) Tel 209-537-2447.

Kinder Read, *(Kinder Read; 0-934361),* P.O. Box 18, Ingomar, PA 15127 (SAN 693-4552); 970 Broadmeadow Dr., Pittsburgh, PA 15237 (SAN 662-3247) Tel 412-366-9761.

Kinderpress, *(Kinder Pr; 0-931047),* 2240 135th Pl. SE, Bellevue, WA 98005 (SAN 678-9005) Tel 206-643-2695; P.O. Box 5761, Bellevue, WA 98006 (SAN 662-2534).

Kindler, Leonard, *(Kindler; 0-943502),* P.O. Box 12328, Philadelphia, PA 19119 (SAN 240-6977) Tel 215-843-4487.

Kindred Joy Pubns., *(Kindred Joy; 0-911141),* 554 W. 4th, Coquille, OR 97423 (SAN 262-9275) Tel 503-396-4154.

Kindred Pr., *(Kindred Pr),* Box L, Hillsboro, KS 67063 (SAN 205-8634) Tel 316-947-3151; Orders to: 616 Walnut Ave., Scottdale, PA 15683 (SAN 202-2915) Tel 412-887-8500.

King, C. D., Ltd., *(C King; 0-9608862),* 311 12th St., Huntington Beach, CA 92648 (SAN 241-0397) Tel 714-960-5285.

King, Helen B., *(King ME; 0-9615366),* 11 Pierce St., Orono, ME 04473 (SAN 695-2240) Tel 207-866-3309.

King, Lary, Co., The, *(L King Co; 0-9611450),* P.O. Box 1247, Hollywood, CA 90078 (SAN 283-1503) Tel 818-509-3841.

King, LeRoy O., Jr., *(L O King; 0-9600938),* 4815 Allencrest, Dallas, TX 75244 (SAN 208-7243) Tel 214-239-1280.

King, Martin Luther, Pr., Subs. of Martin Luther King Fellows, Inc., *(M L King Pr; 0-937644),* 132 W. 116th St., New York, NY 10026 (SAN 658-5868) Tel 212-866-0301.

King, Phil, *(Phil King; 0-9601900),* 3005 Woodlawn Ave., Wesleyville, PA 16510 (SAN 211-9641) Tel 814-899-3532.

King & Mary, *(King & Mary; 0-9601890),* 4709 Comita, Fort Worth, TX 76132 (SAN 211-8602) Tel 817-292-1295.

King Authors Court Pr. at Vision Studios, *(King Authors Court; 0-936888),* Box 32, Route 1, Thompson Station, TN 37179 (SAN 214-4433) Tel 615-790-3138.

King Bks., *(King Bks; 0-9611532),* 817 S. 265th St., Kent, WA 98032 (SAN 285-368X) Tel 206-941-2992.

King Fisher Press, *(King Fisher Pr; 0-9612972),* 5115 E. Virginia, Phoenix, AZ 85008 (SAN 292-5567) Tel 602-840-2342.

King Freedom Pubns., *(King Freedom; 0-911435),* Box 962, Glenwood Springs, CO 81602 (SAN 271-888X) Tel 303-945-8847.

King Philip Publishing Co., *(King Philip Pub; 0-9614811),* 466 Ocean Ave., Portland, ME 04103 (SAN 692-9133) Tel 207-772-2685.

King Publishing Co., *(King Co),* 4757 Distribution Dr., Tampa, FL 33605 (SAN 260-2288) Tel 813-248-3330.

Kingdom Bks., *(Kingdom Bks; 0-9613181),* 18548 Arminta St., Reseda, CA 91335 (SAN 295-902X) Tel 818-342-8740.

Kingdom Hse., *(Kingdom Hse; 0-9609926),* 309 W. 7th St., Fulton, MO 65251 (SAN 271-8898) Tel 314-642-2150.

Kingdom of God, *(Kingdom God; 0-9607702),* P.O. Box 7123, Minneapolis, MN 55407 (SAN 238-6704) Tel 612-823-1783.

Kingdom Pr., *(Kingdom; 0-910840),* 105 Chestnut Hill Rd., Amherst, NH 03031 (SAN 201-0461) Tel 603-673-3208.

Kingman-Block Publishing, Inc., *(Kingman Pub; 0-937353),* 180 Seventh Ave., Santa Cruz, CA 95062 (SAN 658-9030) Tel 408-375-9200.

King's Court Communications, Inc., *(Kings Court; 0-89139),* 590 Pearl Rd., Box 224, Brunswick, OH 44212 (SAN 207-3730) Tel 216-273-2100.

King's Crown Paperbacks *See* Columbia Univ. Pr.

King's Farspan, Inc., *(Kings Farspan; 0-932814),* 1473 S. La Luna Ave., Ojai, CA 93023 (SAN 211-8084) Tel 805-646-2928; Dist. by: Spring Arbor Distributors, 10885 Textile Rd., Bellville, MI 48111 (SAN 158-9016) Tel 313-481-0900; Toll free: 800-521-3990; Dist. by: Living Bks., Inc., 12155 Magnolia Ave., Bldg 11-B, Riverside, CA 92503 (SAN 662-0639) Tel 714-354-7330; Toll free: 800-854-4746.

†King's Hse. Publishing Co., *(King's Hse Pub; 0-916333),* 3000 Fairfield at Kings Hwy., Shreveport, LA 71104 (SAN 295-9046) Tel 318-222-1995; *CIP.*

Kingston Ellis Pr., *(Kingston Ellis; 0-914425),* 1014 Freemason St., Knoxville, TN 37917 (SAN 291-820X) Tel 615-687-8467.

Kingston Korner, Inc., *(Kingston Korner; 0-9614594),* 50 Sunrise St., Norwich, CT 06360 (SAN 691-7828) Tel 203-889-5619; Orders to: 6 S. 230 Cohasset Rd., Naperville, IL 60540 (SAN 662-2925) Tel 312-961-3559.

†Kingston Pr., Inc., The, *(Kingston Pr; 0-940670),* P.O. Box 1456, Princeton, NJ 08542 (SAN 226-7950) Tel 609-921-0609; *CIP.*

Kinkead, Eugene, *(E Kinkead; 0-9600476),* 282 Airline Rd., Clinton, CT 06413 (SAN 203-8277) Tel 203-669-6189.

Kinko's Publishing Group, *(Kinko's Pub; 1-55577),* 4141 State St., Santa Barbara, CA 93110 (SAN 699-8852) Tel 805-967-0192.

Kinnickinnic Pr., *(Kinnickinnic Pr; 0-9615065),* 1101 W. Division St., River Falls, WI 54022 (SAN 694-1397) Tel 715-425-6897.

Kino Pubns., *(Kino Pubns; 0-9607366),* 6625 N. First Ave., Tucson, AZ 85718 (SAN 238-2547) Tel 602-297-7278.

Kinser Publishing, Inc., *(Kinser Pub; 0-9615659),* Rte. 3, Box 157A, Aurora, MO 65605 (SAN 695-9482) Tel 417-574-6961.

Kinsinger, Chris, *(C Kinsinger; 0-9615612),* 2205 N. Second St., Harrisburg, PA 17110 (SAN 696-2793) Tel 717-238-2218.

Kinucan & Brons, Pubs., *(Kinucan & Brons; 0-9615444),* 420 N. Hulen Way, Ketchum, ID 83340 (SAN 695-7234) Tel 208-263-8604; P.O. Box 765, Ketchum, ID 83340 (SAN 696-9488).

Kiowa Pr., *(Kiowa Pr; 0-9607602),* P.O. Box 555, Woodburn, OR 97071 (SAN 222-9773) Tel 503-981-3017.

Kiplinger Washington Editors, Inc., The, *(Kiplinger Wash Eds; 0-938721),* 1729 H St., NW, Washington, DC 20006 (SAN 661-6100) Tel 202-887-6434; Dist. by: Select Magazines, Inc., 8 E. 40th St., New York, NY 10016 (SAN 200-6693).

Kiracofe, Roderick, Pr., *(R K Press; 0-9613708; 0-913327),* 3242 Washington, San Francisco, CA 94115 (SAN 677-5527) Tel 415-931-6003; Dist. by: Quilt Digest Pr., 955 14th St., San Francisco, CA 94114 (SAN 293-4531) Tel 415-431-1222.

Kirban, Salem, Inc., *(Kirban; 0-912582),* 2117 Kent Rd., Huntingdon Valley, PA 19006 (SAN 201-047X) Tel 215-947-4894; Dist. by: AMG Publishers, 6815 Shallowford Rd., Chattanooga, TN 37422 (SAN 211-3074) Tel 615-894-6062; Toll free: 800-251-7206.

Kirin Books & Art, *(Kirin Bks & Art; 0-935034),* 4528 Peacock Ave., Alexandria, VA 22304 (SAN 213-5280) Tel 703-751-3141.

Kirk Fleming, Leslee, *(L F Kirk; 0-9613746),* 4913 E. 97th Ave., Crown Point, IN 46307 (SAN 677-6736) Tel 219-769-3388.

Kirk Pr., *(Kirk Pr),* 205 W. Kent Rd., Duluth, MN 55812 (SAN 211-4275).

Kirk Publishing, Div. of Kirksite Enterprises, Inc., *(Kirk Pub; 0-911821),* One E. First St., No. 1400, Reno, NV 89501 (SAN 264-1518) Tel 415-826-1005.

Kiryat Sefer, Ltd., *(K Sefer; 965-17),* c/o Ridgefield Pub. Co., 6925 Canby Ave., Suite 104, Reseda, CA 91335 (SAN 215-8035). Moved, left no forwarding address.

Kisaku, Inc., *(Kisaku; 0-934625),* 920 Prospect St., Honolulu, HI 96822 (SAN 285-6603) Tel 808-533-6753.

Kitchen Classics, *(Kitchen Classics; 0-9615522),* 539 Stonewood Dr., Stone Mountain, GA 30087 (SAN 696-2866) Tel 404-549-2593; 1220 Mason Mill Rd., Stone Mountain, GA 30087 (SAN 699-6310).

Kitchen Harvest Pr., *(Kitchen Harvest; 0-917234),* 3N 681 Bittersweet Dr., St. Charles, IL 60174 (SAN 207-2467) Tel 312-584-4084.

Kitchen Sink Pr., *(Kitchen Sink; 0-87816),* 2 Swamp Rd., Princeton, WI 54968 (SAN 212-7784) Tel 414-295-6922.

Kitchen Treasures, *(Kitchen Treas; 0-9609282),* 9939 103rd Ave. N., P.O. Box 541, Maple Grove, MN 55369 (SAN 260-0897) Tel 612-425-1309.

Kitchen Wisdom Publishing Co., *(Kitchen Wisdom; 0-937383),* 10032 SE Linwood Ave., Portland, OR 97222 (SAN 658-9065) Tel 503-771-1402.

Kitten Pubns., *(Kitten Pub; 0-9608722),* 240 Indian Hills, Corydon, IN 47112 (SAN 238-3071) Tel 812-738-8452.

Kitwardo Pubs., Inc., *(Kitwardo Pubs; 0-932641),* 115 S. Third St., Apt. No. 1108, Jacksonville Beach, FL 32250 (SAN 687-8091) Tel 904-246-2071.

†KI2 Enterprises, *(KITwo Enter; 0-9608744),* P.O. Box 13322, Portland, OR 97213 (SAN 241-1261) Tel 502-256-3486; *CIP.*

Kiyler Creations, *(Kiyler Creations; 0-936025),* 25 Maxim Southard Rd., Howell, NJ 07731 (SAN 697-2284) Tel 201-364-5481; P.O. Box 372, Howell, NJ 07731 (SAN 699-6477).

Kjellberg & Sons, Inc., *(Kjellberg & Sons; 0-912868),* 24W770 Geneva Rd., Wheaton, IL 60187 (SAN 201-5102) Tel 312-653-2244.

Kjos, Neil A., Music Co., *(Kjos; 0-910842; 0-8497),* 4380 Jutland Dr., San Diego, CA 92117-0894 (SAN 201-0488) Tel 619-270-9800; Toll free: 800-854-1592.

Klamath Pioneer Publishing, *(Klamath Pioneer Pub; 0-9605120),* 132 S. Seventh St., Klamath Falls, OR 97601 (SAN 239-8443) Tel 503-882-1821.

Klassic Advertising & Publishing Co., *(Klassic Advert & Pub; 0-9615523),* 7615 Glade Ave., Unit 101, Canoga Park, CA 91304 (SAN 696-2874) Tel 818-994-4145.

Kleberg, Caesar, Wildlife Research Institute, Subs. of Texas A & M Univ., *(CK Wildlife Res; 0-912229),* Texas A & I Univ., College of Agriculture, Campus Box 218, Kingsville, TX 78363 (SAN 265-1041) Tel 512-595-3922.

Klein, B., Pubns., *(B Klein Pubns; 0-87340),* P.O. Box 8503, Coral Springs, FL 33065 (SAN 210-7554) Tel 305-752-1708.

Klein, Elizabeth Pfahning, *(E P Klein; 0-9604250),* 11041 SW 46th St., Miami, FL 33165 (SAN 214-3216).

Klein, F., Pubns., *(F Klein Pubns; 0-913051),* 515 Magdalena, Los Altos, CA 94022 (SAN 283-1287).

Klein Post Card Service, *(Klein Post Card Serv; 0-915983),* 16 Havard Ave., Hyde Park, MA 02136 (SAN 294-8621) Tel 617-361-6324.

Kline, Charles H., & Co., Inc., *(Kline; 0-917148),* 330 Passaic Ave., Fairfield, NJ 07006 (SAN 202-6546) Tel 201-227-6262.

Kline, Nathan S., Institute, *(N S Kline Inst; 0-936934),* Information Sciences Div., Bldg. 37, Orangeburg, NY 10962 (SAN 239-6041) Tel 914-359-1050.

Klock & Klock Christian Pubs., *(Klock & Klock; 0-86524),* 2527 Girard Ave. N., Minneapolis, MN 55411 (SAN 212-0003) Tel 612-522-2244.

Klutz Pr., *(Klutz Pr; 0-932592),* P.O. Box 2992, Stanford, CA 94305 (SAN 212-7539) Tel 415-857-0888.

Kluwer Academic Pubs., Subs. of Kluwer NV, *(Kluwer Academic; 0-89838),* 101 Philip Dr., Assinippi Pk., Norwell, MA 02061 (SAN 211-481X) Tel 617-871-6600; Orders to: P.O. Box 358, Accord Sta., Hingham, MA 02018-0358 (SAN 662-0647).

Kluwer Law Bk. Pubs., Inc., Affil. of Kluwer, N.V., *(Kluwer Law Bk; 0-930273),* 36 W. 44th St., New York, NY 10036 (SAN 670-8781) Tel 212-382-2855; Toll free: 800-821-4526.

†Kluwer-Nijhoff Publishing, Div. of Kluwer Academic Pubs., *(Kluwer-Nijhoff; 0-89838; 90-247),* 101 Philip Dr., Assinipi Pk., Norwell, MA 02061 (SAN 211-481X) Tel 617-871-6600; Orders to: P.O. Box 358, Accord Sta., Hingham, MA 02018-0358 (SAN 662-0655); *CIP.*

Knapp, Susan F., *(S F Knapp; 0-9610610),* P.O. Box 140, Sewickley, PA 15143 (SAN 264-1550) Tel 412-935-0503.

Knapp Press *See* Crown Pubs., Inc.

†Knapp Pr., The, Div. of Knapp Communications Corp., *(Knapp Pr; 0-89535),* 5900 Wilshire Blvd., Los Angeles, CA 90036 (SAN 210-4490) Tel 213-937-3454; Toll free: 800-526-4264; *CIP.*

Knauff, Thomas, *(Knauff; 0-9605676),* Rural Delivery, Julian, PA 16844 (SAN 216-1524) Tel 814-355-1792.

Kneeling Santa, *(Kneeling Santa; 0-9616286),* 821 S. Bronson Ave., Los Angeles, CA 90005 (SAN 658-6155) Tel 213-933-2686.

Knees Paperback Publishing Co., *(Knees Pbk; 0-9600978),* 4115 Marshall St., Dallas, TX 75210 (SAN 208-760X) Tel 214-948-3613.

Knickerbocker Publishing Co., *(Knickerbocker; 0-911635),* Rt Box 113, 10 Summit Ave., Fiskdale, MA 01518 (SAN 264-1569) Tel 617-347-2039.

Knife World Pubns., *(Knife World; 0-940362),* P.O. Box 3395, Knoxville, TN 37917 (SAN 218-5628) Tel 615-523-3339.

Knight Gallery-Spirit Square Arts Center, *(Knight Gallery-Spirit; 0-915427),* 110 E. 7th St., Charlotte, NC 28202 (SAN 291-2414) Tel 704-372-9664.

493

Knight Media, *(Knight Media; 0-933545),* 60 Benzing Rd., Antioch, TN 37013 (SAN 691-8689) Tel 615-833-1909; Dist. by: JM Pubns., P.O. Box 837, Brentwood, TN 37027 (SAN 200-7975).

†**Knights Pr.,** *(Knights Pr; 0-915175),* P.O. Box 454, Pound Ridge, NY 10576 (SAN 289-744X) Tel 203-322-7381; *CIP.*

Knighttime Pubns., *(Knighttime Pubns; 0-942902),* P.O. Box 591, Cupertino, CA 95015 (SAN 240-317X) Tel 408-996-0668; Dist. by: Bookpeople, 2929 Fifth St., Berkeley, CA 94710 (SAN 168-9517); Dist. by: Publishers Group West, 5835 Beaudry St., Emeryville, CA 94608 (SAN 202-8522) Tel 415-658-3453; Dist. by: L-S Distributors, P.O. Box 3063, 1161 Post St., San Francisco, CA 94119 (SAN 169-0213); Dist. by: Pacific Pipeline, 19215 66th Ave., S., Kent, WA 98032 (SAN 208-2128); Dist. by: Quality Bks., 918 Sherwood Dr., Lake Bluff, IL 60044-2204 (SAN 169-2127); Dist. by: Baker & Taylor (Western Div.), 380 Edison Way, Reno, NV 89564 (SAN 169-4464) Tel 702-786-6700.

Knoedler Publishing Inc., *(Knoedler; 0-937608),* 19 E. 70th St., New York, NY 10021 (SAN 215-2177).

†**Knollwood Publishing Co.,** *(Knollwood Pub; 0-915611),* P.O. Box 735, 513 Benson Ave. E., Willmar, MN 56201 (SAN 207-5504) Tel 612-235-4950; *CIP.*

Knopf, Alfred A., Inc., Subs. of Random Hse., Inc., *(Knopf; 0-394),* 201 E. 50th St., New York, NY 10022 (SAN 202-5825) Tel 212-751-2600; Toll free: 800-638-6460; Orders to: 400 Hahn Rd., Westminster, MD 21157 (SAN 202-5833). *Imprints:* Knopf College Department (KnopfC).

Knopf College Dept. *See* Knopf, Alfred A., Inc.

Knott Communications Co., *(Knott Comm Co; 0-911701),* P.O. Box 3755, Alhambra, CA 91803 (SAN 264-1593) Tel 818-284-2949.

Know Himm Pr., *(Know Him Pr; 0-9614014),* 13425 Valna Dr., Whittier, CA 90602 (SAN 683-6542) Tel 213-693-9118; Orders to: P.O. Box 4002, Whittier, CA 90607 (SAN 662-2615) Tel 213-693-7412; Dist. by: Living Bks., Inc., 12155 Magnolia AVe., Bldg 11-B, Riverside, CA 92503 (SAN 662-2623) Tel 714-354-7330; Toll free: 800-854-4746.

Know How Pubns., *(Know How; 0-910846),* Box 7126, Landscape Sta., Berkeley, CA 94707 (SAN 207-0359) Tel 415-526-5400. Out of business.

Know, Inc., *(Know Inc; 0-912786),* P.O. Box 86031, Pittsburgh, PA 15221 (SAN 201-050X) Tel 412-241-4844.

Knowing Pr., The, *(Knowing Pr; 0-936927),* 400 Sycamore, McAllen, TX 78501 (SAN 658-361X) Tel 512-686-4033.

Knowledge Bank Pubs., Inc., *(Knowledge Bank; 0-939036),* P.O. Box 2364, Falls Church, VA 22042 (SAN 224-1765) Tel 703-938-4095.

Knowledge Builders, Inc., *(Knowledge Builders; 0-940950),* 744 E. Green Briar, Lake Forest, IL 60045 (SAN 217-3883) Tel 312-295-2099.

Knowledge Industry Pubns., Inc., Subs. of Knowledge Industry Sciences, *(Knowledge Indus; 0-914236; 0-86729),* 701 Westchester Ave., White Plains, NY 10604 (SAN 214-2082) Tel 914-328-9157; Toll free: 800-248-5474. *Imprints:* American Society for Information Science (ASIS).

Knowledge Unlimited, *(Know Unltd; 0-915291),* P.O. Box 52, Madison, WI 53701 (SAN 290-0017) Tel 608-271-2771; 1409 Greenway Cross, Madison, WI 53711 (SAN 290-0025).

Knowledge Unlimited, *(Knowledge Unltd; 0-9616043),* 1271 W. Dundee Rd., Suite 14-A, Buffalo Grove, IL 60089 (SAN 698-0201) Tel 312-358-4795.

Knowlton, Ed, *(E Knowlton; 0-9615036),* Peck, ID 83545 (SAN 693-7942) Tel 208-486-7572.

Knox, Daryl K., *(D Knox; 0-9605790),* 3533 Queensway Dr., Brownsville, TX 78521 (SAN 216-4035) Tel 512-544-2428.

†**Knox, John, Pr.,** Div. of Presbyterian Publishing Hse., *(John Knox; 0-8042),* 341 Ponce de Leon Ave., NE, Rm. 416, Atlanta, GA 30365 (SAN 201-0275) Tel 404-873-1549; Toll free: 800-334-6580; Orders to: P.O. Box 54658, Atlanta, GA 30308 (SAN 662-0566); *CIP.*

Knox, Trudy, Pub., *(T Knox Pub; 0-9611354),* 168 Wildwood Dr., Granville, OH 43023 (SAN 282-9517) Tel 614-587-3400.

Knoxville News-Sentinel Co., Inc., Subs. of Scripps Howard, *(Knoxville News-Sentinel; 0-9615656),* 208 W. Church Ave., Knoxville, TN 37901 (SAN 696-219X) Tel 615-523-3131; P.O. Box 80, Knoxville, TN 37901 (SAN 696-9615).

†**Kober Press, The,** *(Kober Pr; 0-915034),* P.O. Box 2194, San Francisco, CA 94126 (SAN 207-0758) Tel 415-362-1231; *CIP.*

Kobro Pubns., Inc., *(Kobro Pubns; 0-9604676),* 114 East 32nd Street, New York, NY 10016 (SAN 215-6695) Tel 212-689-4611.

Koch, Nora, *(N Koch; 0-9615583),* 12135 N. State, Otisville, MI 48463 (SAN 696-3390) Tel 313-631-4567.

†**Kodansha International USA, Ltd.,** Subs. of Kodansha, Ltd. (Japan), *(Kodansha; 0-87011),* c/o Harper & Row Pubs., 10 E. 53rd St., New York, NY 10022 (SAN 201-0526) Tel 212-207-7050; Toll free: 800-242-7737; Dist. by: Harper & Row Pubs., Inc., Keystone Industrial Pk., Scranton, PA 18512 (SAN 215-3742); Orders to: Mail Order Dept., P.O. Box 1531, Hagerstown, MD 21741 (SAN 662-0671); *CIP.*

†**Kodokan Iowa Publishing,** Subs. of Judomeister, *(Kodokan IA Pub; 0-933099),* 1201 Royal Dr., Cedar Falls, IA 50613 (SAN 689-5603) Tel 319-277-4707; Dist. by: U. S. Judo Assn., 19 N. Union Blvd., Colorado Springs, CO 80909 (SAN 276-3257); *CIP.*

Kokono, Div. of Front Row Experience, *(Kokono; 0-916956),* 540 Discovery Bay Blvd., Byron, CA 94514 (SAN 208-6026) Tel 415-634-5710; Dist. by: Front Row Experience, 540 Discovery Bay Blvd., Byron, CA 94514 (SAN 207-1274) Tel 415-634-5710.

Kolowalu Book *See* Univ. of Hawaii Pr., The

Komunikey Publishing Co Inc., *(Komunikey Pub; 0-931219),* 28990 Pacific Coast Highway 215, Malibu, CA 90265 (SAN 681-9958) Tel 213-457-1502.

†**Konglomerati Florida Foundation for Literature & the Book Arts, Inc.,** *(Konglomerati; 0-916906),* P.O. Box 5001, Gulfport, FL 33737 (SAN 207-8589) Tel 813-323-0386; *CIP.*

Konocit, Sipapu *See* Sipapu, Konocti Books

Koolewong, Ltd., *(Koolewong; 0-935221),* 118 S. Elmhurst Ave., Mt. Prospect, IL 60056 (SAN 695-720X) Tel 312-253-9357.

Kopec Pubns., *(Kopec Pubns; 0-9615236),* P.O. Box 157, Whitmore, CA 96096 (SAN 695-1724) Tel 916-472-3438.

Koponen, Joan, *(J Koponen; 0-9610356),* 710 Chena Ridge, Fairbanks, AK 99701 (SAN 264-1607) Tel 907-479-6782.

Korakas, Roberts & Kirby, *(Korakas-Roberts-Kirby; 0-9605744),* 600 N.W. 46th St., Oklahoma City, OK 73118 (SAN 216-1532) Tel 405-524-5985.

Korea Development Institute *See* Univ. of Hawaii Pr., The

Korea Economic Institute of America, *(Korea Eco Inst; 0-914601),* 1030 15th St. NW, Suite 662, Washington, DC 20005 (SAN 289-338X) Tel 202-376-0690.

Korean Independent Monitor, Inc., *(Korean Independent; 0-911987),* 32 W. 32nd St., No. 501, New York, NY 10001 (SAN 264-6757) Tel 212-244-0150.

Korn, Alfred, Jr., *(Korn; 0-917498),* 324 Coolidge Dr., Kennilworth, NJ 07033 (SAN 209-0589).

Kornberg, Patti, *(P Kornberg; 0-9609240),* 650 N. Atlantic Ave., Cocoa Beach, FL 32931 (SAN 241-5356) Tel 305-783-7079.

Korpalski, Adam, *(A Korpalski),* Ferry Bridge Rd., Washington, CT 06793 (SAN 211-1977) Tel 203-868-2503.

Kosciuszko Foundation, *(Kosciuszko; 0-917004),* 15 E. 65th St., New York, NY 10021 (SAN 208-7251) Tel 212-734-2130.

Kosikowski, F. V., & Assocs., *(F V Kosikowski; 0-9602322),* P.O. Box 139, Brooktondale, NY 14817 (SAN 211-6693) Tel 607-272-7779.

Kosovo Publishing Co., *(Kosovo Pub Co; 0-915887),* 1404 Norma Rd., Columbus, OH 43229 (SAN 294-0531) Tel 614-885-5977; 604 S. Hanover St., Nanticoko, PA 18634 (SAN 294-054X).

Kovak Bks., *(Kovak Bks; 0-9604704),* P.O. Box 1422, Bakersfield, CA 93302 (SAN 695-1031).

Kovar, Milo, *(Milo Kovar; 0-941208),* 2640 Greenwich, No. 403, San Francisco, CA 94123 (SAN 239-5592) Tel 415-921-1192.

Kowalkowski, Pat, *(P Kowalkowski; 0-9616583),* P.O. Box 21602, Ft. Lauderdale, FL 33335 (SAN 661-3993); 1740 SW Second St., Ft. Lauderdale, FL 33335 (SAN 661-4000) Tel 305-764-8085.

Kraken Pr., *(Kraken Pr; 0-936623),* 3035 17th Ave., S, Minneapolis, MN 55407 (SAN 699-7112) Tel 612-729-8593.

Kramer, H. J., Inc., *(H J Kramer Inc; 0-915811),* P.O. Box 1082, Tiburon, CA 94920 (SAN 294-0833); Orders to: 1474 West Ave. No. 43, Los Angeles, CA 90065 (SAN 662-2259); Toll free: 800-227-1516; Dist. by: Publishers Group West, 5855 Beaudry St., Emeryville, CA 94608 (SAN 202-8522); Toll free: 800-982-8319; Dist. by: Bookpeople, 2929 Fifth St., Berkeley, CA 94710 (SAN 168-9517).

Kramer, Justin, Inc., *(J Kramer),* 1028 W. 8th Place, Los Angeles, CA 90017 (SAN 209-1224).

Krank Pr., *(Krank Pr; 0-9612260),* P.O. Box 16271, St. Louis, MO 63105 (SAN 222-9781) Tel 314-997-5907.

Krantz Co., Pubs., Inc., The, *(Krantz Co; 0-913765),* 2210 N. Burling Ave., Chicago, IL 60614 (SAN 219-8541) Tel 312-472-4900; Dist. by: Facts on File, Inc., 460 Park Ave. S, New York, NY 10016 (SAN 201-4696) Tel 212-683-2244.

Kraus International Pubns., Div. of Kraus-Thomson Organization, Ltd., *(Kraus Intl; 0-527),* 1 Water St., White Plains, NY 10601 (SAN 210-7562) Tel 914-761-9600.

Kraus Reprint & Periodicals (KRP), *(Kraus Repr; 0-527; 3-601; 3-262; 0-8115),* Rte. 100, Millwood, NY 10546 (SAN 201-0542) Tel 914-762-2200.

Kraus Sikes, Inc., *(Kraus Sikes; 0-9616012),* 150 W. 25th St., New York, NY 10001 (SAN 697-2799) Tel 212-242-3730.

Krause Pubns., Inc., *(Krause Pubns; 0-87341),* 700 E. State St., Iola, WI 54990 (SAN 202-6554) Tel 715-445-2214.

Krebs, John E., *(J E Krebs; 0-9607026),* 711 Santa Fe Dr., Apt. 232, Weatherford, TX 76086 (SAN 239-0027) Tel 817-594-6135.

†**Kregel Pubns.,** Div. of Kregel, Inc., *(Kregel; 0-8254),* P.O. Box 2607, Grand Rapids, MI 49501-2607 (SAN 206-9792) Tel 616-451-4775; Toll free: 800-253-5465; *CIP.*

Kreider Consolidated Enterprises Publishing, *(KCE Pub; 0-940686),* 40 Cordone Dr., San Anselmo, CA 94960 (SAN 218-5636) Tel 415-951-6160.

Krejcarek, Philip, *(P Krejcarek),* 1439 N. 49th, Milwaukee, WI 53208 (SAN 212-2863) Tel 414-453-1263.

Kreysa, Francis John, *(Kreysa; 0-9611398),* 18742 Curry Powder Lane, Germantown, MD 20874 (SAN 285-3752) Tel 301-349-5001.

†**Kricket Pubns.,** Subs. of Britannia Realty, Inc., *(Kricket; 0-918785),* P.O. Box 91832, Santa Barbara, CA 93190 (SAN 657-3606) Tel 805-962-2557; *CIP.*

†**Krieger, Robert E., Publishing Co., Inc.,** *(Krieger; 0-88275; 0-89874; 0-89464),* P.O. Box 9542, Melbourne, FL 32902-9542 (SAN 202-6562) Tel 305-724-9542; *CIP.*

Kripalu Pubns., Div. of Kripalu Ctr. for Yoga & Health, *(Kripalu Pubns; 0-940258),* Rte. 183, Box 793, Lenox, MA 01240 (SAN 217-5320) Tel 413-637-3280; Dist. by: Samuel Weiser, P.O. Box 612, York Beach, ME 03910 (SAN 202-9588) Tel 207-363-4393; Toll free: 800-843-6666; Dist. by: The New Leaf Distributing, 1020 White St., SW, Atlanta, GA 30310 (SAN 169-1449) Tel 404-755-2665.

Krishna Press, Div. of Gordon Press, *(Krishna Pr),* P.O. Box 459, Bowling Green Sta., New York, NY 10004 (SAN 202-6570).

Kristana Esperantista Ligo Internacia, *(Kristana),* Dist. by: Edwin C. Harter, Jr., 47 Hardy Rd., Levittown, PA 19056 (SAN 282-633X).

Kroll, Cecelia, *(C Kroll; 0-9614913),* P.O. Box 71764, Los Angeles, CA 90071-0764 (SAN 693-4544) Tel 213-481-8086.

Kronos Pr., *(Kronos Pr; 0-917994),* P.O. Box 343, Wynnewood, PA 19096 (SAN 210-2226) Tel 609-445-6048.

KronOscope Press, *(KronOscope; 0-9608768),* 1241 Independence Ave., SE., Washington, DC 20003 (SAN 238-308X) Tel 202-543-1266.

Kronour, David R., Publishing Co., *(D R Kronour; 0-9616118),* 3939 N. Diamond Mill Rd., Dayton, OH 45426 (SAN 699-718X) Tel 513-837-4260.

Krumwiede, Grace I., *(G I Krumwiede),* 3713 S. George Mason Dr., No. 608W, Falls Church, VA 22041 (SAN 213-0998) Tel 703-998-0251.

Ktav Publishing Hse., Inc., *(Ktav; 0-87068; 0-88125),* Box 6249, Hoboken, NJ 07030 (SAN 201-0038); 900 Jefferson St., Hoboken, NJ 07030 (SAN 658-1056) Tel 201-963-9524. *Imprints:* Hebrew Union College Press (HUC Pr).

Kubi, K. Appiah, *(K Appiah Kubi; 0-9614573),* P.O. Box 7601, Bloomfield, CT 06002 (SAN 691-8298) Tel 203-242-8927.

Kudzu & Co., *(Kudzu; 0-9615015),* Box 415, Walls, MS 38680 (SAN 693-823X) Tel 601-781-0267.

Kudzu-Ivy, *(Kudzu-Ivy; 0-9605142),* P.O. Box 52743, Atlanta, GA 30355 (SAN 215-9589) Tel 404-351-4827.

Kuehn Radtke Publications & Productions, *(Kuehn Radtke; 0-916639),* P.O. Box 205, Waimanalo, HI 96795 (SAN 296-6409) Tel 808-941-5421.

Kukla Press, *(Kukla Pr),* 855 Morse Ave., Elk Grove Village, IL 60007 (SAN 213-3318); Dist. by: Common Sense Ltd., P.O. Box 353, Des Plaines, IL 60016 (SAN 213-2990).

†**Kulchur Foundation,** *(Kulchur Foun; 0-936538),* 888 Park Ave., New York, NY 10021 (SAN 207-2475) Tel 212-988-5193; *CIP.*

Kumar, Navin, *(N Kumar; 0-9611400),* 24 E. 73rd St., New York, NY 10021 (SAN 285-371X) Tel 212-734-4075.

Kumarian Pr., *(Kumarian Pr; 0-931816),* 630 Oakwood Ave., Suite 119, West Hartford, CT 06110 (SAN 212-5978) Tel 203-524-0214.

Kundalini Research Foundation, *(Kundalini Research; 0-917776),* 475 Fifth Ave., New York, NY 10017 (SAN 688-1181) Tel 212-889-3241; Dist. by: Book Dynamics, 836 Broadway, New York, NY 10003 (SAN 169-5649) Tel 212-254-7798.

Kunsman, Jack L., Jr., *(J L Kunsman; 0-914235),* 116 Lincoln St., Easton, PA 18042 (SAN 287-5578) Tel 215-253-8018.

Kuppinger, Roger, *(R Kuppinger; 0-9605616),* 77 Woodland Ln., Arcadia, CA 91006 (SAN 212-677X) Tel 213-355-1785; Dist. by: Publishers Group West, 5855 Beaudry St., Emeryville, CA 94608 (SAN 202-8522).

Kurian, George, Reference Bks., *(G Kurian; 0-914746),* P.O. Box 519, Baldwin Place, NY 10505 (SAN 203-1981) Tel 914-962-3287.

Kurios Foundation, *(Kurios Found; 0-932210),* P.O. Box 946, Bryn Mawr, PA 19010 (SAN 213-1005) Tel 215-527-4635.

†**Kurious Pr.,** *(Kurious Pr; 0-916588),* P.O. Box 946, Bryn Mawr, PA 19010 (SAN 207-7159) Tel 215-527-4635; *CIP.*

Kurtzman, Elene, *(E Kurtzman; 0-9615907),* 14918 Broadgreen, Houston, TX 77079 (SAN 661-1997) Tel 713-497-2708; Dist. by: Brewer & Brewer Pubs., 1129 Garden Gate Cir., Garland, TX 75043 (SAN 200-5913).

Kusel, George, *(Kusel; 0-9604476),* 600 Lakevue Dr., Willow Grove, PA 19090 (SAN 215-7837).

Kushner, Daniel, , Ltd., *(D Kushner Ltd; 0-9615694),* 2441 W. Sharon Ave., Phoenix, AZ 85029 (SAN 696-2203) Tel 602-263-8411; P.O. Box 26243, Phoenix, AZ 85068 (SAN 696-5598).

Kutenai Pr., The, *(Kutenai Pr; 0-937459),* 515 Stephens Ave., Missoula, MT 59801 (SAN 658-9081) Tel 406-549-6383.

Kwibidi Publisher, *(Kwibidi Pub; 0-933483),* P.O. Box 6639, Greensboro, NC 27415 (SAN 691-8867) Tel 919-275-4610.

Kwik Sew Pattern Co., Inc., *(Kwik Sew; 0-913212),* 3000 Washington Ave. N., Minneapolis, MN 55411 (SAN 209-1380) Tel 612-521-7651.

LAD Publishing, *(LAD Pub; 0-938723),* 17625 Drayton Hall Way, San Diego, CA 92128 (SAN 661-6097) Tel 619-487-4976.

LaL Pub., *(LAL Pub; 0-910737),* P.O. Box 1225, Denison, TX 75020 (SAN 238-0641) Tel 214-465-7311.

L A Wholistic Publishing, *(L A Wholistic; 0-915157),* P.O. Box 6010, Suite 421, Sherman Oaks, CA 91403 (SAN 289-9442) Tel 213-871-8054.

L. A. Writer, *(L A Writer; 0-9613661),* P.O. Box 1183, Culver City, CA 90232 (SAN 670-7726) Tel 213-837-1196.

L & J International, *(L & J Intl; 0-9615269),* 3 Northwest Ct., Little Rock, AR 72212 (SAN 695-1848) Tel 501-225-5720.

L & L Pubs., *(L & L Pubns; 0-9612778),* 19362 S. Henrici Rd., Oregon City, OR 97045 (SAN 289-7458) Tel 503-631-2480.

L & M Books, *(L & M Bks; 0-914237),* 18387 Highway 18, Apple Valley, CA 92307 (SAN 287-525X) Tel 619-242-8102.

†**L B L Publishing,** *(L B L Pub; 0-914947),* 214 Correo Fronteriza, San Ysidro, CA 92073 (SAN 289-2804) Tel 619-970-7289; *CIP.*

LB Pubns., *(LB Pubns; 0-9616746),* 8338 San Leandro, Dallas, TX 75218 (SAN 661-2776) Tel 214-327-5207.

L B S Productions, *(LBS Productions; 0-9607796),* 2389 Sherwood Rd., Columbus, OH 43209 (SAN 240-0472).

L.C.D. Pub., *(LCD; 0-941414),* 663 Calle Miramar, Redondo Beach, CA 90277 (SAN 239-0035) Tel 213-375-6336.

†**LDA Pubs.,** *(L D A Pubs; 0-935912),* 42-36 209th St., Bayside, NY 11361 (SAN 221-4423) Tel 718-224-0485; *CIP.*

LDS Pubns., *(LDS Pubns; 0-9614734),* 2901 Wilshire Blvd., Suite 435, Santa Monica, CA 90403 (SAN 692-7637) Tel 213-828-4480.

LDT Pr., *(LDT Pr; 0-9613565),* 4401 Larchmont, Dallas, TX 75205 (SAN 670-0012) Tel 214-526-1723.

LEHI Publishing Co., *(LEHI Pub Co; 0-934486),* 303 Gretna Green Way, Los Angeles, CA 90049 (SAN 213-4101) Tel 213-476-6024.

LGO Publishing, *(LGO Pub; 0-936483),* 6065 Mission Gorge Rd., Suite 235, San Diego, CA 92120 (SAN 698-102X) Tel 619-485-0822.

LISI Pr. The, Subs. of Laforest International Service Inc., *(L I S I Pr; 0-914163),* P.O. Box 1063, Palm Harbor, FL 34273 (SAN 287-5128) Tel 813-784-3628.

LISP Co., The, *(LISP Co; 0-924856),* 430 Monterey Ave., Suite 4, Los Gatos, CA 95030 (SAN 697-2551) Tel 408-354-3668.

L. I. S. Z. Pubns., *(L I S Z Pubns; 0-9611428),* P.O. Box 819, Boca Raton, FL 33429-0819 (SAN 285-3345) Tel 305-426-5232.

LJB Foundation, *(LJB Found),* 933 Overlook Rd., Whitehall, PA 18052 (SAN 210-9107) Tel 215-433-7667.

LJC Bks. Pr., *(LJC Bks Pr; 0-937461),* 421 Staten Ave., No. 301, Oakland, CA 94610 (SAN 658-9103) Tel 415-272-0672.

LJ Pubns., *(L J Pubns),* 359 San Miquel, Newport Beach, CA 92660 (SAN 264-1623).

LL Co., *(LL Co; 0-937892),* 1647 Manning Ave., Los Angeles, CA 90024 (SAN 203-0314) Tel 213-475-3664.

LMI Bks., *(LMI Books; 0-9616921),* 19 Eastbrook Bend, Peachtree City, GA 30269 (SAN 661-4841) Tel 803-862-4555.

L O M A (Life Office Management Assn.), *(LOMA; 0-915322; 0-939921),* 5770 Powers Ferry Rd., Atlanta, GA 30327 (SAN 207-2548) Tel 404-951-1770; Orders to: Professional Bk. Distributors, 200 Hembree Pk. Dr., Roswell, GA 30076 (SAN 207-2556) Tel 404-442-8631; Toll free: 800-848-0773.

LOM Pr., Inc., *(LOM Pr),* 1 Plaza Pl., Suite 1008, St. Petersburg, FL 33701 (SAN 217-2453).

LOTIC Enterprises, *(LOTIC; 0-930531),* 5301-1 Dunsmuir Rd., Bakersfield, CA 93309 (SAN 679-1328) Tel 805-325-7348.

†**L P Pubns.,** Div. of The Love Project, *(L P Pubns; 0-916192),* P.O. Box 7601, San Diego, CA 92107-0601 (SAN 207-2513) Tel 619-225-0133; 4470 Orchard Ave., San Diego, CA 92107 (SAN 650-0390); *CIP.*

L Pubns., *(L Pubns; 0-917824),* 34 Fransiscan Way, Kensington, CA 94707 (SAN 209-5734).

LUISA Productions, *(LUISA Prods; 0-939584),* P.O. Box 6836-AB, Santa Barbara, CA 93111 (SAN 216-4108).

LYFE Foundation, *(LYFE Foundation; 0-9616418),* 2131 E. Broadway Rd., Suite 19, Tempe, AZ 85282 (SAN 658-8913) Tel 602-968-1219.

LZB Publishing Co., *(LZB Pub; 0-9615899),* 102 SE 44th, Portland, OR 97215 (SAN 696-9828) Tel 503-232-0972.

L. C. Page Co. *See* Farrar, Straus & Giroux, Inc.

La Bonne Vie, Inc., *(La Bonne Vie; 0-9615991),* 234 S. Milwaukee St., Denver, CO 80209 (SAN 699-7465) Tel 303-722-5009.

La Car Publishing Co., *(La Car Pub),* 2109 Broadway, New York, NY 10023 (SAN 207-7272).

La Cassette Gourmet International, Ltd., *(La Cassette Intl; 0-935443),* 7428 E. Stetson Dr., Suite 215, Scottsdale, AZ 85251 (SAN 696-3048) Tel 602-951-2654.

La Cote Pubs., *(La Cote Pubs; 0-9615322),* 15305 La. Hwy. 16, French Settlement, LA 70733 (SAN 694-6496) Tel 504-698-6247.

La Cumbre Publishing Co., *(La Cumbre; 0-935222),* P.O. Box 30959, Santa Barbara, CA 93105 (SAN 221-4431) Tel 805-682-0904.

La Grange Pr., *(La Grange; 0-931324),* 7732 Guenivere Way, Citrus Heights, CA 95610 (SAN 211-0601) Tel 916-967-7997.

La Jolla Country Day Schl. Parents Assn., *(La Jolla Country; 0-9614176),* 9490 Genesee Ave., La Jolla, CA 92037 (SAN 686-6190) Tel 619-459-2673.

La Jolla Institute, *(La Jolla Inst; 0-943256),* P.O. Box 1434, La Jolla, CA 92038 (SAN 240-3935) Tel 619-454-8831.

†**La Jolla Museum of Contemporary Art,** *(La Jolla Mus Contemp Art; 0-934418),* 700 Prospect St., La Jolla, CA 92037 (SAN 210-8232) Tel 619-454-3541; *CIP.*

La Jolla Publishing Co., *(La Jolla Pub CA; 0-935365),* P.O. Box 99638, San Diego, CA 92109 (SAN 696-2769) Tel 619-483-2693.

La-La Ltd., *(La La Ltd; 0-937991),* P.O. Box 2060, North Babylon, NY 11703 (SAN 661-4019); 100 Grand Blvd., Wyandanch, NY 11798 (SAN 661-4027) Tel 516-491-1889.

†**La Leche League International, Inc.,** *(La Leche; 0-912500),* 9616 Minneapolis Ave., P.O. Box 1209, Franklin Park, IL 60131-8209 (SAN 201-0585) Tel 312-455-7730; *CIP.*

La Luz Press, The, *(La Luz Pr; 0-942664),* 2401 W. 15th St., Panama City, FL 32401 (SAN 219-8525) Tel 904-763-3333.

La Mariposa Pr., *(La Mariposa; 0-9613714),* P.O. Box 3519, Apache Junction, AZ 85278 (SAN 676-2670) Tel 602-981-8747.

La Pice, Margaret, *(M La Pice; 0-9604508),* 210 Montcalm, San Francisco, CA 94110 (SAN 212-1093).

LA-RAN Publishing Co., *(La-Ran Pub Co; 0-9610842),* 187 W. End Ave., Newark, NJ 07106 (SAN 265-2641) Tel 201-373-5216.

La Siesta Pr., *(La Siesta; 0-910856),* P.O. Box 406, Glendale, CA 91209 (SAN 201-0607) Tel 818-244-9305.

La Stampa Calligrafica, *(La Stampa Calligrafica; 0-9606630),* P.O. Box 209, Franklin, MI 48025 (SAN 281-8582) Tel 313-851-0796; Dist. by: Bookpeople, 2929 Fifth St., Berkeley, CA 94710 (SAN 168-9517); Dist. by: Inland Book Company, P. O. Box 261, 22 Hemingway Ave., East Haven, CT 06512 (SAN 200-4151) Tel 203-467-4257.

La Tienda El Quetzal, *(La Tienda; 0-913129),* Box 246, Troy, NY 12181 (SAN 283-1295) Tel 518-271-7629.

Laal Companies, *(Laal Co; 0-910211),* Research Group, Nine Kaufman Dr., Westwood, NJ 07675 (SAN 241-3892) Tel 201-664-6222.

Names

LaBarre, George H., Galleries, Inc., *(G H laBarre; 0-941538),* P.O. Box 746, Hollis, NH 03049 (SAN 239-1066) Tel 603-882-2411.

Labor Arts Bks., *(Labor Arts; 0-9603888),* 1064 Amherst St., Buffalo, NY 14216 (SAN 213-8158) Tel 716-873-4131.

Labor Education & Research Project, *(Labor Ed & Res; 0-914093),* P.O. Box 20001, Detroit, MI 48220 (SAN 287-5268) Tel 313-883-5580.

Labor Guild of Boston, *(Labor Guild Bost; 0-9611038),* 761 Harrison Ave., Boston, MA 02118 (SAN 282-9045) Tel 617-227-8884.

Labor Policy Assn., Inc., *(Labor Pol; 0-916603),* 1015 15th St., NW, No. 1200, Washington, DC 20005 (SAN 271-924X) Tel 202-789-8670.

Labor Relations Press, Div. of Axon Communications, Inc., P.O. Box 579, Fort Washington, PA 19034, *(Labor Relations; 0-934753),* Highland Office Center P.O. Box 579, 1035 Camphill Rd., Fort Washington, PA 19034 (SAN 237-8329) Tel 215-628-3113.

Laboratory Data Control, *(Lab Data Control; 0-9504833),* P.O. Box 10235, Interstate Industrial Pk., Riviera Beach, FL 33404 (SAN 210-9085).

Laboratory for Applied Behavioral Science, *(LABS; 0-943300),* 41 Gifford Rd., Somerset, NJ 08873 (SAN 239-4499) Tel 201-545-8269.

Labyrinth Pr., Inc., The, *(Labyrinth Pr; 0-939464),* P.O. Box 2124, Durham, NC 27702-2124 (SAN 216-6011) Tel 919-493-5051; 2814 Chapel Hill Rd., Durham, NC 27707 (SAN 281-8620).

Labyrinthos, *(Labyrinthos; 0-911437),* 6355 Green Valley Cir., Suite 213, Culver City, CA 90230 (SAN 217-3182) Tel 213-649-2612.

†Lace Pubns., *(Lace Pubns; 0-917597),* P.O. Box 10037, Denver, CO 80210-0037 (SAN 657-1506) Tel 303-778-7702; *CIP.*

Lacebark Pubns., *(Lacebark Pubns; 0-9613109),* Rte. 5, P.O. Box 174, Stillwater, OK 74074 (SAN 210-9220) Tel 405-377-3539.

Lacis Pubns., *(Lacis Pubns; 0-916896),* 2982 Adeline St., Berkeley, CA 94703 (SAN 202-9901) Tel 415-843-7178.

Lacon Pubs., *(Lacon Pubs; 0-930344),* Rte. 1, Box 15, Harrison, ID 83833 (SAN 204-9597) Tel 208-689-3467.

Lacret Publishing Co., *(Lacret Pub; 0-943144),* 601 12th St., Union City, NJ 07087 (SAN 204-3927) Tel 201-866-5257.

Lacrosse Foundation, Inc., *(Lacrosse Found; 0-9610654),* Charles & 34th St., Baltimore, MD 21218 (SAN 285-0389) Tel 301-235-6882.

Laddin Press, *(Laddin Pr; 0-913806),* 2 Park Ave., New York, NY 10016 (SAN 201-0615) Tel 212-532-4384.

Ladies Home Journal Bks., Subs. of Family Media, *(Ladies Home; 0-935639),* 3 Park Ave., New York, NY 10016 (SAN 696-1800) Tel 212-340-9605.

Ladies Philoptochos Society Chapter Four Hundred & Fifty One, *(Ladies Philo; 0-9611164),* Nativity of Christ Church 1110 Dickson Dr., Novato, CA 94948 (SAN 283-3581) Tel 415-499-1736; P.O. Box 543, Novato, CA 94948 (SAN 283-359X).

LaDow, Charles R., *(C R LaDow; 0-9617232),* 3735 Trudy Ln., San Diego, CA 92106 (SAN 663-5784) Tel 619-222-3790.

†Lady of Lake Pub., *(Lady Lake Pub; 0-931905),* P.O. Box 397, Winchester, MA 01890 (SAN 686-0184) Tel 617-729-0115; *CIP.*

Lady Raspberry Press, *(Lady Raspberry; 0-9608554),* 213 E. 49th St., New York, NY 10017 (SAN 240-6985) Tel 212-908-8100; Dist. by: Bric-A-Brac Bookwks., Box 887, Forked River, NJ 08731 (SAN 282-6364) Tel 609-693-4053.

Ladybug Pr., *(Ladybug Pr; 0-9616662),* 6474 Norway Rd., Dallas, TX 75230 (SAN 661-3594) Tel 214-368-4235.

Laframboise, Leon W., *(L W Laframboise; 0-9613855),* P.O. Box 6565, El Paso, TX 79906 (SAN 661-4418).

Lager Publishing Co., *(Lager Pub Co; 0-9615524),* 10801 Central Ave., NE, Suite 186, Albuquerque, NM 87123 (SAN 696-2890) Tel 415-956-5966.

Lahontan Images, *(Lahontan Images; 0-938373),* P.O. Box 1093, Susanville, CA 96130 (SAN 661-2687); 700-100 Wingfield Rd., Susanville, CA 96130 (SAN 661-2695) Tel 916-257-4546.

Laid-Back Pubns., *(Laid Back Pubns; 0-9615714),* 276 E. Shamrock, Rialto, CA 92376 (SAN 695-8826) Tel 714-875-1309.

Lake, A. V., & Co., *(Lake; 0-910860),* P.O. Box 1595, Beverly Hills, CA 90213 (SAN 201-0623) Tel 213-271-4386.

Lake, David S., Pubs., *(D S Lake Pubs; 0-8224),* 19 Davis Dr., Belmont, CA 94002 (SAN 212-775X) Tel 415-592-7810.

Lake Aire, Inc., *(Lake Aire; 0-936989),* 129 W. Hoover Ave., Suite 10, Mesa, AZ 85202 (SAN 658-7518) Tel 602-834-0734.

Lake Champlain Publishing Co., The, *(Lake Champlain; 0-9616412),* 176 Battery St., Burlington, VT 05401 (SAN 658-9146) Tel 802-864-7733.

Lake Erie College Pr., *(Lake Erie Col Pr; 0-935518),* Lake Erie College, Painesville, OH 44077 (SAN 204-9562) Tel 216-352-3361.

Lake Forest College Holography Workshops, *(Lake Forest; 0-910535),* Lake Forest College, Lake Forest, IL 60045 (SAN 260-0900) Tel 312-234-3100.

Lake George Historical Assn., *(Lake George Hist; 0-9613466),* P.O. Box 472, Lake George, NY 12845 (SAN 657-2782) Tel 518-668-5044.

Lake Lure Press, *(Lake Lure Pr; 0-9610172),* RR 31, Box 140, Terre Haute, IN 47803 (SAN 271-9444) Tel 812-877-2204.

Lake Michigan Federation, *(Lake Mich Fed),* 8 S. Michigan Ave., Chicago, IL 60603 (SAN 225-1787) Tel 312-263-5550.

Lake Placid Climbing Schl., Inc., *(Lake Placid Climb; 0-9615992),* Sundog Ski & Sports 90 Main St., Lake Placid, NY 12946 (SAN 696-7744).

Lake Pr., *(Lake Pr; 0-9608446),* P.O. Box 7934, Paducah, KY 42001 (SAN 240-544X) Tel 502-443-8425.

Lake View Pr., *(Lake View Pr; 0-941702),* P.O. Box 578279, Chicago, IL 60657-8279 (SAN 239-2488) Tel 312-935-2694.

Lakeside-Charter Books, *(Lakeside Chart; 0-918206),* 5466 S. Everett, Chicago, IL 60615 (SAN 210-2234) Tel 312-955-0521.

Lakeside Historical Society, The, *(Lakeside Hist; 0-9615935),* 9705 Prospect Ave., Lakeside, CA 92040 (SAN 696-8465) Tel 619-443-1267.

Lakewood Ctr. Assocs., *(Lakewood Ctr Assocs; 0-9617239),* P.O. Box 274, Lake Oswego, OR 97034 (SAN 663-5881); 368 S. State St., Lake Oswego, OR 97034 (SAN 663-589X) Tel 503-636-5935; 968 Lakeshore Rd. Lake Oswego, OR 97034 (SAN 663-5903).

Lakstun Pr., *(Lakstun Pr; 0-9603706),* P.O. Box 6483, Rockford, IL 61125-1483 (SAN 213-6309).

Lalo Pubns., *(Lalo Pubns; 0-9616941),* 9266-G Regents Rd., La Jolla, CA 92037 (SAN 661-7875) Tel 619-455-1394.

Lalonde, Larry, *(L J Lalonde; 0-9608136),* 17031 N. Eleanor, Apt 95C, Mt. Clemens, MI 48044 (SAN 238-8502) Tel 313-286-8023.

Lalvani, Haresh, *(H Lalvani),* P.O. Box 1538, New York, NY 10116 (SAN 211-3228).

Lama Foundation, *(Lama Foun),* Box 240, San Cristobal, NM 87564 (SAN 225-3178).

Lamagna, Joseph, *(J Lamagna; 0-9610464),* P.O. Box 572, Yonkers, NY 10702 (SAN 238-065X) Tel 914-963-3260.

Lamb, Howard, *(H Lamb; 0-9609150),* P.O. Box 796, Mill Valley, CA 94942 (SAN 241-3906) Tel 415-388-1163.

Lambda Christian Fellowship, *(Lambda Christian; 0-9616853),* 14060 Astoria St., Sylmar, CA 91342 (SAN 661-6003) Tel 818-362-8014.

Lambert Bk. Hse., Inc., *(Lambert Bk; 0-89315),* 133 Kings Hwy., Shreveport, LA 71104 (SAN 208-7278) Tel 318-861-3140; Box 4007, Shreveport, LA 71104 (SAN 658-1064).

Lambert-Gann Publishing Co., *(Lambert Gann Pub; 0-939093),* P.O. Box 0, Pomeroy, WA 99347 (SAN 662-8982); Rickman Gulch Rd., Pomeroy, WA 99347 (SAN 662-8990) Tel 509-843-1094.

Lambeth, James, *(Lambeth; 0-9601678),* 1591 Clark St., Fayetteville, AR 72701 (SAN 211-9102) Tel 501-521-1304.

†Lambeth Pr., *(Lambeth Pr; 0-931186),* 143 E. 37th St., New York, NY 10016 (SAN 240-0421) Tel 212-679-0163; *CIP.*

Lame Johnny Pr., *(Lame Johnny; 0-917624),* Star Rte. 3, Box 9A, Hermosa, SD 57744 (SAN 207-6136) Tel 605-255-4466.

Lamkin, Geraldine E., *(Lamkin; 0-9612632),* 8144 D. Lemon Grove Way, Lemon Grove, CA 92045 (SAN 289-2855) Tel 619-698-7255; P.O. Box 1003, Lemon Grove, CA 92045 (SAN 289-2863).

Lamm-Morada Publishing Co., Inc., *(Lamm-Morada; 0-932128),* Box 7607, Stockton, CA 95207 (SAN 212-520X) Tel 209-931-1056.

Lamont-Doherty Geological Observatory, *(Lamont-Doherty),* Columbia University, Palisades, NY 10964 (SAN 287-2609).

Lampkin, J. G., Publishing, *(Lampkin Pub; 0-9604918),* 15346 Stone Ave. N., Seattle, WA 98133 (SAN 215-6725).

Lamplighter Press, *(Lamplighter; 0-912870),* P.O. Box 258, Carlinville, IL 62626 (SAN 201-0631).

Lampus Pr., *(Lampus Pr; 0-9609002),* P.O. Box 541, Cape May, NJ 08204 (SAN 240-8643) Tel 609-884-4906.

Lancaster Horvath Productions, *(Lancaster Horvath Prods; 0-930647),* 3756 Grand Ave., Suite 302, Oakland, CA 94610 (SAN 676-2840) Tel 415-271-0701.

Lance Pubns., *(Lance Pubns; 0-934363),* P.O. Box 61189, Seattle, WA 98121 (SAN 693-5605) Tel 206-728-2821.

Lancer Militaria, *(Lancer; 0-935856),* P.O. Box 886, Mt. Ida, AR 71957 (SAN 213-7682) Tel 501-867-2232.

Land & Land Publishing Div., *(Land & Land; 0-935545),* 196 S. 14th St., Baton Rouge, LA 70802 (SAN 696-2386) Tel 504-344-1059; P.O. Box 1921, Baton Rouge, LA 70821 (SAN 696-964X).

Land Design Publishing, *(Land Design; 0-9605988),* P.O. Box 857, San Dimas, CA 91773 (SAN 216-745X) Tel 714-599-7452.

Land Development Institute, Ltd., *(Land Dev Inst),* 1401 16th St, NW, Washington, DC 20036 (SAN 237-8345) Tel 202-232-2144.

Land O' Sky Aeronautics, Inc., *(Land O' Sky Aero; 0-9616608),* P.O. Box 636, Skyland, NC 28776 (SAN 661-4108); Bishop Rd., Skyland, NC 28776 (SAN 661-4116) Tel 704-684-2092.

Land of Plenty Prods., *(Land Plenty Prods; 0-917887),* 787-22nd Ave., San Francisco, CA 94121 (SAN 657-1514) Tel 415-387-2246.

Landau Book Co., Inc., *(Landau; 0-910864),* P.O. Box 570, Long Beach, NY 11561 (SAN 201-064X).

Lander Moore Bks., *(Lander Moore Bks; 0-930751),* 6202 Olympic Overlook, Austin, TX 78746 (SAN 682-790X).

Landes, Burton R., *(B R Landes; 0-915568),* 11 College Ave., Trappe, PA 19426 (SAN 207-3625) Tel 215-489-2908.

Landfall Pr., Inc., *(Landfall Pr; 0-913428),* 5171 Chapin St., Dayton, OH 45429 (SAN 202-6627) Tel 513-298-9123.

Landgrove Pr., *(Landgrove Pr; 0-9608726),* Landgrove, VT 05148 (SAN 238-3098) Tel 802-824-5943.

Landmark Book Co., *(Landmark NY),* 260 Fifth Ave, New York, NY 10000 (SAN 216-4051) Tel 212-696-5430.

Landmark Editions Inc., *(Landmark Edns; 0-933849),* 1420 Kansas Ave., Kansas City, MO 64127 (SAN 692-6916) Tel 816-421-4919.

Landmark Enterprises, *(Landmark Ent; 0-910845),* 10324 Newton Way, Rancho Cordova, CA 95670 (SAN 157-0242) Tel 916-363-0191.

Landmark Pr., *(Landmark Pr; 0-911439),* Box 13547, St. Louis, MO 63138 (SAN 271-9568) Tel 314-355-7650; 1461 Dunn Rd., St. Louis, MO 63138 (SAN 658-1072).

Landmark Studies *See* Rowman & Littlefield, Pubs.

Landmarke Lancer Publishing Co., *(Landmarke Lancer; 0-937639),* P.O. Box 6528, Pasadena, TX 77506 (SAN 658-9170) Tel 713-472-2475; 127 E. Pasadena Freeway, Pasadena, CA 77506 (SAN 658-9189).

Landmarks Commission Village of Oak Park *See* Chicago Review Pr., Inc.

Landmarks Foundation of Montgomery Inc., *(Landmarks Found; 0-9614653),* 310 N. Hull St., Montgomery, AL 36104 (SAN 691-8700) Tel 205-263-4355.

Landmarks Preservation Commission, *(Landmarks Preserv Comm),* 20 Vesey St., New York, NY 10007 (SAN 240-0413).

Landon Pubns., *(Landon Pubns; 0-937355),* 1061-C S. High St., Harrisonburg, VA 22801 (SAN 658-9227) Tel 703-433-0919; Orders to: P.O. Box 12, Bridgewater, VA 22812 (SAN 662-4197).

Landown Hse., *(Landown Hse; 0-936562),* 5816 Esrig Way, Sacramento, CA 95841 (SAN 281-8655); Orders to: P.O. Box 176, North Highlands, CA 95660 (SAN 281-8663).

Landrum, Jeff, Publishing, *(J Landrum Pub; 0-9611894),* Box 98, Burkburnett, TX 76354 (SAN 285-3299) Tel 817-569-2580.

Landrum & Associates, *(Landrum & Assocs; 0-915286),* P.O. Box 16003, Chattanooga, TN 37416 (SAN 203-1949) Tel 615-892-3248.

Lands End Bks., *(Lands End Bks; 0-9603558),* Rte. 3, Box 998, Gloucester, VA 23061 (SAN 203-9281) Tel 804-693-4262.

Landsberry Pr., *(Landsberry Pr; 0-9616788),* 709 Massachusetts Ave., NE, Washington, DC 20002 (SAN 661-3128) Tel 202-387-3826.

Landscape Architecture Foundation, *(Landscape Architecture; 0-941236),* 1733 Connecticut Ave. NW, Washington, DC 20009 (SAN 224-1781) Tel 202-223-6229.

Landy & Assocs., *(Landy Assocs; 0-9617077),* 5311 N. Highland, Tacoma, WA 98407 (SAN 662-6211).

Lane, Joe, Publishing Co, *(Joe Lane Pub; 0-9603378),* P.O. Box 2646, Evergreen, CO 80439 (SAN 211-0784) Tel 303-674-5314.

Lane Pr., *(Lane Pr; 0-935606),* P.O. Box 7822, Stanford, CA 94305 (SAN 221-4326).

Lanfur, J., *(J Lanfur; 0-9615034),* P.O. Box 9, West Long Branch, NJ 07764 (SAN 693-7969) Tel 201-870-3075.

†**Lang, Peter, Publishing, Inc.,** Subs. of Verlag Peter Lang AG (Switzerland), *(P Lang Pubs; 0-8204),* 62 W. 45th St., New York, NY 10036-4202 (SAN 241-5534) Tel 212-302-6740; *CIP.*

Lang Pubns., *(Lang Pubns; 0-942242),* 490 N. 31st St., Suite 100, Billings, MT 59101 (SAN 238-4337); Dist. by: World Bible Publishers, Iowa Falls, IA 50126 (SAN 215-2797).

Langdon, Larry, Pubns., *(Langdon Pubns; 0-943726),* 34735 Perkins Creek Rd., Cottage Grove, OR 97424-9450 (SAN 241-0427).

Langdon & Langdon, *(Langdon & Langdon; 0-938741),* P.O. Box 633, Columbia, SC 29202 (SAN 661-7867) Tel 803-649-6679.

Langenscheidt Pubs., Inc., Subs. of Langenscheidt KG, *(Langenscheidt; 0-88729; 3-468),* 46-35 54th Rd., Maspeth, NY 11378 (SAN 276-9441).

Langley, Ray, *(Langley; 0-9605158),* 3664 Scorpio Dr., Sacramento, CA 95827 (SAN 216-6733).

Langley Pr., The, *(Langley Pr; 0-911607),* 821 Georgia St., Key West, FL 33040 (SAN 264-164X) Tel 305-294-3156.

Langley Pubns., Inc., *(Langley Pubns; 0-936991),* 1350 Beverly Rd., Suite 115-324, McLean, VA 22101 (SAN 658-7496) Tel 703-532-5388; 6609 Rosecroft Pl., Falls Church, VA 22043 (SAN 658-750X).

Langtry Pubns., *(Langtry Pubns; 0-915369),* 7838 Burnet Ave., Van Nuys, CA 91405-1051 (SAN 291-2473) Tel 818-781-9144.

Language International, *(Language Intl; 0-935655),* 21339 Velicata St., Woodland Hills, CA 91364 (SAN 696-1398); P.O. Box 26, Woodland Hills, CA 91365 (SAN 662-3662) Tel 818-716-8222.

Language Pr., *(Language Pr; 0-912386),* P.O. Box 342, Whitewater, WI 53190 (SAN 201-0674) Tel 414-473-6055.

Language Research Educational Series, *(Research Lang; 0-9609446),* P.O. Box 29512, Washington, DC 20017 (SAN 260-0927) Tel 202-635-7907.

Language Service, Inc., Pubns. Div., *(Lang Serv; 0-913942),* P.O. Box 8, Hastings-on-Hudson, NY 10706 (SAN 201-0666) Tel 914-478-3558.

Language Services, *(Lang Svcs CA; 0-9607690),* 6453 Gem Lake Ave., San Diego, CA 92119 (SAN 214-3925) Tel 619-698-7999.

Lanks, Herbert, *(H C Lanks),* Inter-American Features, Jenkintown, PA 19046 (SAN 265-3869).

Lanser Pr., *(Lanser Pr; 0-9603900),* P.O. Box 38, Plainfield, VT 05667 (SAN 214-3933).

Lantern Bks. *See* Pocket Bks., Inc.

†**Lantern Pr., Inc. Pubs.,** *(Lantern; 0-8313),* 354 Hussey Rd., Mount Vernon, NY 10552 (SAN 201-0682) Tel 914-668-9736; *CIP.*

Lantz, Walter D., *(W D Lantz; 0-9610364),* 1424 Marietta Ave., Lancaster, PA 17603 (SAN 264-1666) Tel 717-299-2943.

Lapierre Bks., *(Lapierre Bks; 0-9615846),* 49241 I-94 Service Dr., Bldg. 12, Belleville, MI 48111 (SAN 697-2209) Tel 313-699-5102.

Lapis Pr., The, *(Lapis Pr; 0-932499),* 1850 Union St., Suite 466, San Francisco, CA 94123 (SAN 687-3979) Tel 415-622-4600; Dist. by: Consortium Bk. Sales & Distribution, 213 E. Fourth St., St. Paul, MN 55101 (SAN 200-6049) Tel 612-221-9035.

Large Print Bks. *See* Hall, G. K., & Co.

Laridae Pr., *(Laridae Pr; 0-9606094),* 3012 Wesley Ave., Ocean City, NJ 08226 (SAN 216-8278) Tel 609-399-3222.

Larimi Communications, *(Larimi Comm; 0-935224),* 246 W. 38th St., New York, NY 10018 (SAN 210-8259) Tel 212-819-9310.

Lark Bks., *(Lark Bks; 0-937274),* 50 College St., Asheville, NC 28801 (SAN 219-9947) Tel 704-253-0468.

Lark Communications *See* Van Nostrand Reinhold Co., Inc.

Larkin, Larry, Pub., *(Larkin; 0-9605748),* 762 S. Lake Shore Dr., Lake Geneva, WI 53147 (SAN 240-0219) Tel 414-248-2569.

Larksdale, *(Larksdale; 0-89606),* 1706 Seamist, No. 575, Houston, TX 77008 (SAN 220-0643) Tel 713-869-9092. *Imprints:* Lindahl (Lindahl); Linolean (Linolean); Post Oak Press (Post Oak Pr).

Larksong Dayspring Pubns. of California, *(Larksong Dayspring),* P.O. Box 1667, Whittier, CA 90609 (SAN 219-0826) Tel 213-943-2320.

Larkspur Pubns., *(Larkspur; 0-939942),* P.O. Box 211, Bowmansville, NY 14026 (SAN 216-8286) Tel 716-337-2758.

†**Larlin Corp.,** *(Larlin Corp; 0-89783; 0-87797),* P.O. Box 1523, Marietta, GA 30061 (SAN 201-4432) Tel 404-424-6210; *CIP.*

Larren Pubns., *(Larren Pubs; 0-9604370),* P.O. Box 594, Nevada, MO 64772 (SAN 220-0651) Tel 417-667-3706.

Larry Smith Associates Inc., *(L Smith Assoc; 0-931741),* P.O. Box 2203, Los Gatos, CA 95031-2203 (SAN 686-273X) Tel 408-354-3406; Dist. by: Motorbooks Int., 729 Prospect Ave., Osceola, WI 54020 (SAN 169-9164) Tel 715-294-3345; Toll free: 800-826-6600; Dist. by: Automotion, 3535 Keifer, Santa Clara, CA 95051 (SAN 200-7339) Tel 408-736-9020.

Larsen, J., Publishing, *(J Larsen; 0-9602474),* P.O. Box 586, Deer Lodge, MT 59722 (SAN 212-1107) Tel 406-846-2610.

Larsen's Outdoor Publishing, *(Larsen's Outdoor; 0-936513),* 3360 Kilmer Dr., Lakeland, FL 33803 (SAN 697-8975) Tel 813-644-3381; Orders to: Atlantic Publishing Co., P.O. Box 67, Tabor City, NC 28463 (SAN 215-6237).

Larson Pubns., *(Larson Joliet; 0-9613928),* P.O. Box 2573, Joliet, IL 60434 (SAN 683-6070) Tel 815-744-6273.

Larson Pubns., Inc., *(Larson Pubns Inc; 0-943914),* 4936 Rte. 414, Burdett, NY 14818 (SAN 241-130X) Tel 607-546-9342; Dist. by: Kampmann & Co., 9 E. 40th St., New York, NY 10016 (SAN 202-5191) Tel 212-685-2928; Toll free: 800-526-7626 (excluding AK, HI, NY); Dist. by: Samuel Weiser Inc., P.O. Box 612, York Beach, ME 03910 (SAN 202-9588) Tel 207-363-4393.

Larson Publishing Co., *(Larson Pub),* P.O. Box 286, Lompoc, CA 93438 (SAN 658-8328) Tel 805-735-2095.

Las Campanas Pubns., *(Las Campanas; 0-938476),* P.O. Box 357, Bernalillo, NM 87004 (SAN 239-9369) Tel 505-867-3210.

Las Palomas De Taos, *(Las Palomas; 0-911695),* P.O. Box 3400, Taos, NM 87571 (SAN 264-1682).

Lasenda Pubs., *(Lasenda; 0-918916),* 1590 Via Chaparral, Fallbrook, CA 92028 (SAN 210-4504) Tel 619-723-1407.

Laser Institute of America, *(Laser Inst; 0-912035),* 5151 Monroe St., Suite 102 W., Toledo, OH 43623 (SAN 225-2007) Tel 419-882-8706.

LaserSet Pr., *(LaserSet Press; 0-939315),* P.O. Box 1747, Madison, WI 53701 (SAN 663-1460); 6 Sherman Terr., Rm. 6, Madison, WI 53704 (SAN 663-1479) Tel 608-241-7881.

Last Things Pr., *(Last Things; 0-9616435),* P.O. Box 22642, Alexandria, VA 22304 (SAN 663-9235) Tel 202-274-6867; 5340 Holmes Run, No. 212, Alexandria, VA 22304 (SAN 658-9243).

Laster, Jim, Publishing Co., *(J Laster Pub Co; 0-9612780),* P.O. Box 50512, Nashville, TN 37205 (SAN 289-7474) Tel 615-356-5318.

Lateiner Publishing, *(Lateiner; 0-911722),* 282 N. Washington St., Delaware, OH 43015 (SAN 201-0690) Tel 614-363-3239.

Latham Foundation Pubn., *(Latham Found Pubn),* Latham Plaza Bldg., Clement & Schiller Sts., Alameda, CA 94501 (SAN 682-7934).

Lathrop, Norman, Enterprises, *(Lathrop; 0-910868),* P.O. Box 198, Wooster, OH 44691 (SAN 285-0419) Tel 216-262-5587.

Latin, R. R., Associates, Inc., *(Latin Assoc; 0-940106),* 404 E. 55th St., New York, NY 10022 (SAN 220-2832) Tel 212-758-6389.

Latin American Jewish Studies Assn., *(Lat Am Jewish Studies; 0-916921),* 2104 Georgetown Blvd., Ann Arbor, MI 48105 (SAN 670-7300).

†**Latin American Literary Review Pr.,** *(Lat Am Lit Rev Pr; 0-935480),* P.O. Box 8385, Pittsburgh, PA 15218 (SAN 215-2142) Tel 412-351-1477; *CIP.*

Latitudes Pr., Div. of Latitudes Productions, *(Latitudes Pr),* P.O. Box 613, Mansfield, TX 76063 (SAN 202-6651) Tel 512-588-0527.

Latona Pr., *(Latona Pr; 0-932448),* Box 154, R.F.D 2, Ellsworth, ME 04605 (SAN 216-406X).

LaTour, Kathy, *(K LaTour; 0-9612870),* P.O. Box 141182, Dallas, TX 75214 (SAN 291-2511) Tel 214-827-2753.

Lattice Pr., *(Lattice Pr; 0-9616721),* P.O. Box 340, Sunset Beach, CA 90742 (SAN 661-3896); 16695 Bay View Dr., Sunset Beach, CA 90742 (SAN 661-390X) Tel 714-840-5010.

Laughing Buddha Pr., The, *(Laughing B P; 0-910913),* Sarah Lawrence College, Bronxville, NY 10708 (SAN 271-9665) Tel 914-337-0700.

Laughing Loon Pubns., *(Laughing Loon; 0-9616337),* P.O. Box 142, Glenville, MN 56036 (SAN 658-9251) Tel 507-448-2815; 111 Seventh St., SE, Glenville, MN 56036 (SAN 658-926X).

Laughing Sam's Press, *(Laughing Sams Pr; 0-9607824),* 5243 San Feliciano Dr., Woodland Hills, CA 91364 (SAN 238-0188) Tel 818-340-4175; Orders to: P.O. Box 426, Canoga Park, CA 91305 (SAN 662-068X).

Laughing Waters Pr., The, *(Laughing Waters; 0-939634),* 1416 Euclid Ave., Boulder, CO 80302 (SAN 216-6313).

Launch Pr., *(Launch Pr; 0-9613205),* P.O. Box 40174, San Francisco, CA 94140 (SAN 295-0154) Tel 415-943-7603; Dist. by: Bookpeople, 2929 Fifth St., Berkeley, CA 94710 (SAN 168-9517); Toll free: 800-277-1516; Dist. by: Inland Bk. Co., P.O. Box 261, 22 Hemingway Ave., East Haven, CT 06512 (SAN 200-4151) Tel 203-457-4257; Toll free: 800-243-0138.

Laura Bks., Inc., *(Laura Bks; 0-86540; 0-914042),* Box 918, Davenport, FL 33837 (SAN 220-7516) Tel 813-422-9135; 104 Bay St., Davenport, FL 33837 (SAN 658-1080).

Laurel Editions *See* Dell Publishing Co., Inc.

Laurel Entertainment, Inc., *(Laurel Enter; 0-930392),* 928 Broadway, New York, NY 10010 (SAN 211-0296) Tel 212-674-3800.

497

Names

Laurel Hill Press, *(Laurel Hill Pr; 0-9608688),* 107 Wildcat Creek, Chapel Hill, NC 27514 (SAN 293-2954) Tel 919-962-6945; Orders to: P.O. Box 685, Carrboro, NC 27510 (SAN 293-2962) Tel 919-962-6945; Dist. by: F.W.F. Books, P.O. Box 7125, Winter Haven, FL 33883 (SAN 293-2970) Tel 813-294-7504; c/o Nancy Barnett, .

Laurel-Howard Inc., *(Laurel-Howard; 0-933649),* 201 E. 21st St., No. 18J, New York, NY 10010 (SAN 694-017X) Tel 212-254-0853; Orders to: P.O. Box 3716, Grand Central Sta., New York, NY 10010 (SAN 662-7781).

Laurel Leaf Library See **Dell Publishing Co., Inc.**

Laurel Pr., *(Laurel Pr; 0-9613978),* P.O. Box 1553, Mill Valley, CA 94942 (SAN 682-3009) Tel 415-383-0362.

Laurel Pubns. International, *(Laurel Intl; 0-934139),* P.O. Box 704, Road Town, Tortola, (SAN 693-3777) Tel 809-494-3510.

Lauren Pubns., *(Lauren Pubns; 0-933547),* P.O. Box 815216, Dallas, TX 75381 (SAN 691-8719) Tel 214-638-4977.

Lauren Rogers Museum of Art, *(Lauren Rogers; 0-935903),* P.O. Box 1180, Laurel, MS 39441 (SAN 279-3547) Tel 601-649-6374; Fifth Ave. at Seventh St., Laurel, MS 39440 (SAN 696-6918).

Lauren Rogers Museum of Art See **Lauren Rogers Museum of Art**

Lauri, Inc., *(Lauri Inc; 0-937763),* P.O. Box F, Phillips-Avon, ME 04966 (SAN 659-2597) Tel 207-639-2000; Avon Valley Rd., Phillips-Avon, ME 04966 (SAN 659-2600).

Laurida Bk. Publishing Co., *(Laurida; 0-934810),* P.O. Box 2061, Hollywood, CA 90028 (SAN 203-9303) Tel 213-466-1707.

L'Avant Studios, *(L'Avant Studios; 0-914570),* P.O. Box 1711, Tallahassee, FL 32302 (SAN 205-6038) Tel 904-576-1327.

Laverty, J. R., *(J R Laverty),* P.O. Box 303, Jasper, AR 72641 (SAN 688-5829).

Lavin Assocs., *(Lavin Assocs; 0-941890),* 12 Promontory Dr., Cheshire, CT 06410 (SAN 239-779X) Tel 203-272-9121.

Law, Rod, *(Rod Law; 0-9601730),* P.O. Box 24025, Los Angeles, CA 90024 (SAN 222-0555).

Law & Business, Inc. See **Harcourt Brace Jovanovich, Inc.**

Law & Capital Dynamics, *(Law & Cap Dynamics; 0-9600708),* 700 S. Flower St. Suite 2600, Los Angeles, CA 90017 (SAN 213-7690) Tel 213-629-1100.

Law & Justice Pubs., *(Law & Justice),* P.O. Box 6111, San Diego, CA 92106 (SAN 212-8578).

Law & Psychology Pr., *(Law & Psych; 0-9603630),* P.O. Box 9489, Marina del Rey, CA 90295 (SAN 281-871X) Tel 213-823-4460.

Law & Technology Pr., *(Law & Tech Pr; 0-910215),* P.O. Box 3280, Manhattan Beach, CA 90266 (SAN 241-3914) Tel 213-372-1678.

Law Anthology Annuals, *(Law Anthology; 0-936607),* 18 Lewis Ln., Port Washington, NY 11050 (SAN 698-0414) Tel 516-944-3593.

†**Law-Arts Pubs.,** *(Law Arts; 0-88238),* 159 W. 53rd St., No. 14F, New York, NY 10019 (SAN 201-0712) Tel 212-586-6380; *CIP.*

Law Enforcement Ordnance Co., *(Law Enf Ord Co; 0-943850),* 2460 Peachtree Rd., NW, Suite 1411, Atlanta, GA 30305 (SAN 241-0435) Tel 404-261-1260.

Law Enforcement Reference Manual, *(Law Enforce Ref; 0-916104),* P.O. Box 7333, Trenton, NJ 08628 (SAN 206-1678) Tel 609-883-1886; Orders to: 240 Mulberry St., Newark, NJ 07101 (SAN 206-1686) Tel 201-642-0075.

†**Law of the Sea Institute,** *(Law Sea Inst; 0-911189),* Univ. of Hawaii at Manoa, William S. Richardson Schl. of Law, Honolulu, HI 96822 (SAN 226-5311) Tel 808-948-6760; *CIP.*

Law School Admission Council/Law School Admission Services, *(Law Schl Admission; 0-9610958),* Box 40, Newtown, PA 18940 (SAN 265-2676) Tel 215-968-1136.

Law Student Division See **American Bar Assn.**

Lawells Publishing, *(Lawells Pub; 0-934981),* 311 S. Gratiot Ave., Mt. Clemens, MI 48043 (SAN 694-602X) Tel 313-469-3555.

Lawhead Pr., Inc., *(Lawhead; 0-916199),* 900 E. State St., Athens, OH 45701 (SAN 294-9776) Tel 614-593-7744.

Lawkits, Inc., *(Lawkits; 0-937464),* 26339 Monte Verde, Carmel, CA 93923 (SAN 215-2282) Tel 408-373-3067; Dist. by: Publishers Group West, 5855 Beaudry St., Emeryville, CA 94608 (SAN 202-8522) Tel 415-658-3453.

Lawler, Louise, *(L Lawler; 0-931706),* 407 Greenwich St., New York, NY 10013 (SAN 211-7363).

Lawletters, Inc., *(Lawletters; 0-914239),* 332 S. Michigan Ave., Suite 1460, Chicago, IL 60604 (SAN 287-5322) Tel 312-922-0722.

Lawpress, *(Lawpress CA; 0-915544),* P.O. Box 596, Kentfield, CA 94914 (SAN 220-7524).

Lawrence, Mark A., *(M A Lawrence; 0-9616610),* 6323 Navarre Rd., SW, Navarre, OH 44662 (SAN 661-4035) Tel 216-837-4430.

Lawrence, Seymour See **Delacorte Pr.**

Lawrence & Co. Pubs., *(Lawrence & Co Pubs; 0-9607006),* P.O. Box 13167, Albuquerque, NM 87192 (SAN 238-9932) Tel 505-821-7103; Dist. by: Dow Jones-Irwin, Inc., 1818 Ridge Rd., Homewood, IL 60430 (SAN 662-0558) Tel 312-798-6000; Toll free: 800-323-4560.

Lawrence & Wishart Ltd., *(Lawrence & Wishart; 0-85315),* 39 Museum St., WC1A 1LQ.

Lawrenceville Pr., Inc., *(Lawrenceville Pr; 0-931717),* P.O. Box 6490, Lawrenceville, NJ 08648 (SAN 218-5644) Tel 609-771-6831; Dist. by: Delmar Pubs., Inc., 2 Computer Dr. W., Albany, NY 12212 (SAN 206-7544) Tel 518-459-1150; Toll free: 800-833-3350; 800-252-2550 (In New York).

Lawson's Psychological Services, *(Lawson's Psych; 0-9611668),* 2051 W. Brichta Dr., Tucson, AZ 85745 (SAN 285-3418) Tel 602-792-3181.

Lawton, Elise Timmons, *(Lawton E T; 0-9617193),* 4521 Joyce Blvd., Houston, TX 77084 (SAN 240-9615) Tel 713-463-0234.

Lawton Publishing Co., *(Lawton Pub Co; 0-9613050),* 7238 S. Garland Court, Littleton, CO 80123 (SAN 294-0949) Tel 303-973-2245.

Lawton-Teague Pubns., *(Lawton-Teague; 0-932516),* P.O. Box 12353, Oakland, CA 94604 (SAN 211-2485); Dist. by: Bookpeople, 2929 Fifth St., Berkeley, CA 94710 (SAN 168-9517); Toll free: 800-227-1516.

†**Lawyers & Judges Publishing Co.,** *(Lawyers & Judges; 0-913875),* P.O. Box 2744, Del Mar, CA 92014-5744 (SAN 202-2354) Tel 619-481-5944; *CIP.*

Lawyers Co-Operative Publishing Co., *(Lawyers Co-Op),* 1 Graves St., Rochester, NY 14694 (SAN 202-6678) Tel 716-546-5530; Toll free: 800-LCP-04301 Publishers Pkwy., Webster, NY 14580 (SAN 658-1099).

Lawyers Committee for International Human Rights, *(Lawyers Comm Intl; 0-934143),* 36 W. 44th St., Suite 914, New York, NY 10036 (SAN 693-3025) Tel 212-921-2160.

Lawyers for the Creative Arts, *(Lawyers Creative Arts; 0-936122),* 623 S. Wabash, Suite 300-N, Chicago, IL 60605 (SAN 213-7704); Dist. by: Chicago Review Pr., 814 N. Franklin, Chicago, IL 60610 (SAN 213-5744) Tel 312-337-0747.

Lawyers Pr., *(Lawyers Pr; 0-937337),* 2527 Fairmount, Dallas, TX 75201 (SAN 658-814X) Tel 214-871-7636.

Lawyers Weekly Pubns., Inc., *(Lawyers Weekly),* 30 Court Sq., Boston, MA 02108 (SAN 679-1735) Tel 617-227-6034.

Lay Counseling Institute, *(Lay Counsel Inst; 0-936709),* P.O. Box 351, Florence, MS 39073 (SAN 699-9069) Tel 601-845-2407.

Lay Leadership Institute, Inc., *(Lay Leadership; 0-88151),* 1267 Hicks Blvd., Fairfield, OH 45014 (SAN 271-9797).

Laylah Pubns., *(Laylah Pubns; 0-914157),* P.O. Box 3111, Newport Beach, CA 92663 (SAN 287-5403) Tel 714-645-5796; 1515 Santa Ana, Costa Mesa, CA 92627 (SAN 287-5411).

Lazuli Research Foundation Inc., *(Lazuli Prod; 0-9600522),* P.O. Box 19291, Portland, OR 97219 (SAN 211-738X).

Le Chateau De Chaillie, *(Le Chateau; 0-933299),* 4549 E. Montecito, Phoenix, AZ 85018 (SAN 692-3097) Tel 602-840-6576.

Le Jacq Publishing, Inc., *(Le Jacq Pub; 0-937716),* 53 Park Pl., New York, NY 10007 (SAN 658-4020) Tel 212-766-4300.

†**Lea & Febiger,** *(Lea & Febiger; 0-8121),* 600 S. Washington Sq., Philadelphia, PA 19106-4198 (SAN 201-0747) Tel 215-922-1330; Toll free: 800-433-3850; *CIP.*

Lead Industries Assn., Inc., *(Lead Indus Assn; 0-913284),* 292 Madison Ave., New York, NY 10017 (SAN 224-8735) Tel 212-578-4750.

Leader Learning Ctr., Inc., *(Leader Learn Ctr; 0-936919),* 546 Anderson Ave., Closter, NJ 07624 (SAN 658-313X) Tel 201-767-3272.

Leadership Dynamics Inc., *(Leadership Dyn; 0-911777),* 119 Longs Peak Dr., P.O. Box 320, Lyons, CO 80540 (SAN 264-1704) Tel 303-823-5146.

†**Leadership Pr.,** *(Leadership Pr; 0-936626),* Box 1144, Claremont, CA 91711 (SAN 214-3941) Tel 714-624-6242; *CIP.*

Leadership Pubns., Inc., *(Ldrshp Pubns Miami; 0-938389),* P.O. Box 651009, Miami, FL 33165 (SAN 661-3926); 16310 SW 88th Ct., Miami, FL 33157 (SAN 661-3934) Tel 305-251-6159.

Leadership Pub., Div. of Roets Pubns., *(Leadership Pub; 0-911943),* P.O. Box 51, New Sharon, IA 50207 (SAN 264-1712); 407 W. Cherry St., New Sharon, IA 50207 (SAN 658-1102) Tel 515-637-4563; Dist. by: Creative Learning Press, P.O. Box 320, Mansfield Center, CT 06250 (SAN 214-2368) Tel 203-423-8120; Dist. by: Zephyr Press, 1650 E. 18th St., Tucson, AZ 85719 (SAN 270-6830) Tel 602-623-2032.

Leagjeld, Ted, *(T Leagjeld; 0-9616127),* Rte. 1, Box 404, Pine River, MN 56474 (SAN 699-6833) Tel 218-568-4221.

League Bks., *(League Bks),* P.O. Box 91801, Cleveland, OH 44101 (SAN 209-0406).

League for Industrial Democracy, *(League Indus Demo),* 275 Seventh Ave., New York, NY 10001 (SAN 225-9494) Tel 212-989-8130.

League for International Food Education, *(League Food Ed),* 915 15th St., NW, Suite 915, Washington, DC 20005 (SAN 224-1803) Tel 202-331-1658.

League of Women Voters of TX, & League of Women Voters of TX Education Fund, *(League Women Voters TX; 0-915757),* 1212 Guadalupe, No. 107, Austin, TX 78701 (SAN 294-121X) Tel 512-472-1100.

League of Women Voters of Minnesota, *(LWV MN; 0-939816),* 555 Wabasha St., Suite 212, St. Paul, MN 55102 (SAN 216-9045) Tel 612-224-5445.

League of Women Voters of Minnesota Education Fund, Affil. of League of Women Voters of Minnesota, *(League Wmn Voters MN; 0-9613566),* 555 Wabasha, Suite 212, St. Paul, MN 55102 (SAN 670-0055) Tel 612-224-5445.

†**League of Women Voters of New York State,** *(LWV NYS; 0-938588),* 817 Broadway, New York, NY 10003 (SAN 216-1591) Tel 212-677-5050; *CIP.*

†**League of Women Voters of Pennsylvania,** *(LWVPA; 0-931370),* Strawbridge & Clothier, Eighth & Market Sts., Philadelphia, PA 19105 (SAN 207-0588) Tel 215-627-7937; *CIP.*

League of Women Voters of the City of New York, *(LWV NYC; 0-916130),* 817 Broadway, New York, NY 10003 (SAN 207-2602) Tel 212-677-5050.

League of Women Voters of the U. S., *(LWV US; 0-89959),* 1730 M. St. NW, Washington, DC 20036 (SAN 207-5288) Tel 202-429-1965.

Leahy, Barbara, *(B Leahy; 0-9610312),* 15 Missin Rd., Sedona, AZ 86336 (SAN 264-1720) Tel 602-282-3518.

Leaping Hart Pr., *(Leaping Hart Pr; 0-9615115),* 3039 N. Frederick Ave., Milwaukee, WI 53211 (SAN 694-1427) Tel 414-332-1635.

Lear Enterprises, *(Lear; 0-941990),* P.O. Box 649, Woodland Hills, CA 91365 (SAN 238-6062) Tel 818-340-8800.

Learn-N-Laugh Bks., *(Learn N Laugh; 0-9616408),* P.O. Box 4976, Boise, ID 83711-4976 (SAN 658-9316) Tel 208-939-6038; 4762 Nystrom Pl., Boise, ID 83704 (SAN 658-9324).

Learn to Flirt, *(Learn to Flirt; 0-9616376),* 3015 N. Ocean Blvd., Suite 115A, Ft. Lauderdale, FL 33308 (SAN 658-9359) Tel 305-566-1477.

Learnard, Stephen F., The Awareness Techniques Ctr., *(S F Learnard; 0-934258),* P.O. Box 338, 15 Queens Ln., Stow, MA 01775 (SAN 212-8640) Tel 617-562-2154.

Learned Information, Inc., *(Learned Info; 0-938734),* 143 Old Marlton Pike, Medford, NJ 08055 (SAN 215-8841).

Learned Pubns., Inc., *(Learned Pubns; 0-912116),* 83-53 Manton St., Jamaica, NY 11435 (SAN 201-0755) Tel 718-441-8084.

†**Learning Concepts, Inc.,** *(Learn Concepts OH; 0-934902),* 7601 Mentor Ave., Mentor, OH 44060 (SAN 213-411X) Tel 216-946-6437. Not affiliated with San Diego Learning Concepts; *CIP.*

Learning Concepts, Inc., *(Learning Concepts; 0-89384),* Orders to: Learning Concepts/Univ. Associates, 8517 Production Ave., San Diego, CA 92121 (SAN 272-006X) Tel 619-578-5900.

Learning Development Systems Pubns., *(Learn Deve; 0-936585),* 281 Walnut Grove Dr., Dayton, OH 45459 (SAN 698-083X) Tel 513-885-5957; Orders to: P.O. Box 177, Dayton, OH 45459 (SAN 662-3999) Tel 513-435-1113.

Learning Excellence, *(Learning Excell; 0-934657),* P.O. Box 1527, Redding, CA 96099 (SAN 694-0412) Tel 916-221-0440.

†**Learning Hse. Pubs.,** *(Learning Hse; 0-9602730),* 38 South St., Roslyn Heights, NY 11577 (SAN 214-3968) Tel 516-621-5755; Dist. by: Liberty Publishing Co., 50 Scott Adam Rd., Cockeysville, MD 21030 (SAN 211-030X) Tel 301-667-6680; *CIP.*

Learning House Pubns., *(Learning Hse Pubns; 0-915759),* P.O. Box 49520, Chicago, IL 60649 (SAN 295-3943) Tel 312-924-6080; 4728 S. Greenwood, Chicago, IL 60615 (SAN 295-3951).

Learning, Inc., *(Learning Inc; 0-913692),* Learning Pl., Manset, ME 04656 (SAN 201-5714) Tel 207-244-5015.

Learning International, Subs. of the Times Mirror Co., *(Learn Int; 0-935268),* P.O. Box 10211, 1600 Summer St., Stamford, CT 06904 (SAN 206-0086) Tel 203-965-8400.

Learning Line, The, *(Learning Line; 0-8449),* P.O. Box 577, Palo Alto, CA 94302 (SAN 220-018X) Tel 415-424-1400; Orders to: P.O. Box 1200, Palo Alto, CA 94302 (SAN 220-0198).

Learning Management Systems *See* **Active Learning Corp.**

Learning Process Ctr., *(Learning Proc Ctr; 0-931657),* 222 W. 24th St., National City, CA 92050 (SAN 683-5589); Toll free: 800-221-7374.

Learning Pubns., Inc., *(Learning Pubns; 0-918452; 1-55691),* 5351 Gulf Dr., Holmes Beach, FL 33510 (SAN 208-1695) Tel 813-658-5524; Toll free: 800-222-1525; Orders to: P.O. Box 1326, Holmes Beach, FL 33509 (SAN 688-3990) Tel 813-778-6818.

Learning Research & Development Center, Univ. of Pittsburgh, *(Learn Res Dev),* 3939 O'Hara St., Pittsburgh, PA 15260 (SAN 224-1811) Tel 412-624-4829.

Learning Resources in International Studies, *(LRIS; 0-936876),* 777 United Nations Plaza, Suite 9A, New York, NY 10017 (SAN 281-8752) Tel 212-972-9877; Pubns. Office, Box 337, Croton-on-Hudson, NY 10520 (SAN 658-1110).

†**Learning Resources Network,** *(LERN; 0-914951),* Box 1448, Manhattan, KS 66502 (SAN 289-2928) Tel 913-539-5376; *CIP.*

Learning Systems, Ltd. Group, *(Learning Systs Grp; 0-924893),* P.O. Box 9046, Ft. Collins, CO 80525 (SAN 293-1303) Tel 303-493-7285.

Learning Technology, Inc., *(Lrn Technology; 1-55641),* 21 Charles St., Westport, CT 06880 (SAN 661-1281) Tel 203-227-7454.

Learning Tools Co., The, *(Learn Tools; 0-938017),* 3322 McKinley St. NW, Washington, DC 20015 (SAN 692-7297) Tel 202-363-0016.

Learning Unlimited Pr., *(Lrn Unltd Pr; 0-9617078),* P.O. Box 801, Bow, WA 98232 (SAN 662-619X); 1215 Doser St., Edison, WA 98232 (SAN 662-6203) Tel 206-766-6258.

Learning Well, *(Learning Well; 0-917109; 0-936850; 1-55596),* 200 S. Service Rd., Roslyn Heights, NY 11577 (SAN 240-7027) Tel 516-621-1540; Toll free: 800-645-6564.

Learning Works, Inc., The, *(Learning Wks; 0-88160),* P.O. Box 6187, Santa Barbara, CA 93160 (SAN 272-0078) Tel 805-964-4220; Toll free: 800-235-5767.

Learntech Pubns., *(Learntech Pubns; 0-940108),* 8808 Hidden Hill Lane, Rockville, MD 20854 (SAN 220-2840) Tel 301-499-7142.

Leaseway Transportation Corp, *(Leaseway Trans Corp; 0-9610146),* 3700 Park East Dr., Cleveland, OH 44122 (SAN 272-0086) Tel 216-464-2700.

Leaven Pr., *(Leaven Pr; 0-934134),* 115 E. Armour Blvd., Kansas City, MO 64141 (SAN 686-7715) Tel 816-531-0538; Toll free: 800-821-7926. Out of business.

Leaves of Grass Pr., Inc., *(Leaves of Grass; 0-915070),* Publishers Services, P.O. Box 2510, Novato, CA 94947 (SAN 207-9321) Tel 415-833-3530.

Lebanese Cuisine, *(Lebanese Cuisine; 0-9603050),* P.O. Box 66395, Portland, OR 97266 (SAN 213-103X).

Lebhar-Friedman Bks., Subs. of Lebhar-Friedman, Inc., *(Lebhar Friedman; 0-912016; 0-86730),* 425 Park Ave, New York, NY 10022 (SAN 201-9744) Tel 212-371-9400.

Leco Publishing Co., *(Leco Pub; 0-934365),* P.O. Box 789, Middletown, CA 95461 (SAN 693-5575) Tel 707-987-3569.

Lectorum Pubns., *(Lectorum Pubns),* 137 W. 14th St., New York, NY 10011 (SAN 169-586X).

Leda Press, *(Leda Pr; 0-9605486),* 911 E. Mahanoy Ave., Mahanoy City, PA 17948 (SAN 215-2622) Tel 717-773-1586.

LedBetter, Gwenda, *(G LedBetter; 0-9617007),* 18 Woodcrest Rd., Ashville, NC 28804 (SAN 662-5525) Tel 704-254-3133.

Ledena Publishing, Div. of Ledena Corp., *(Ledena Pub; 0-9615795),* 11370 Chipmunk Dr., Boca Raton, FL 33428 (SAN 696-6004) Tel 305-487-0010 (SAN 696-9771); Orders to: P.O. Box 272887, Boca Raton, FL 33427 (SAN 662-3786).

Lederer Enterprises, *(Lederer Enterprises; 0-9608040),* P.O. Box 15750, Asheville, NC 28813 (SAN 238-0668) Tel 704-684-8094; Toll free: 800-258-7160.

†**Ledge Bks.,** *(Ledge Bks; 0-931447),* P.O. Box 19, Bernard, ME 04612 (SAN 683-1885) Tel 207-244-3464; *CIP.*

Lee, J. & L., Co., *(J & L Lee; 0-934904),* P.O. Box 5575, Lincoln, NE 68505 (SAN 213-8557) Tel 402-467-4416.

Lee, Ralph E., *(R E Lee; 0-9606268),* 5698 Hollyleaf Lane, San Jose, CA 95118 (SAN 220-3367) Tel 408-266-1440; Orders to: Publishers Group West, 5855 Beaudry St., Emeryville, CA 94608 (SAN 202-8522) Tel 415-658-3453.

Lee, Shyh-Yuan David, *(D L Shyh Yuan; 0-9611810),* P.O. Box 795759, Dallas, TX 75379 (SAN 285-3329) Tel 214-733-0015.

Lee, Terri, *(T Lee; 0-9602332),* Box 4711, Falls Church, VA 22044 (SAN 209-4568) Tel 703-370-5821.

Lee Bks., Div. of Lee S. Cole and Assocs., Inc., *(Lee Bks; 0-938676),* P.O. Box 906, Novato, CA 94948 (SAN 216-2636) Tel 415-897-3550.

Lee Enterprises, Inc., *(Lee Enterprises; 0-910847),* 130 E. Second St., Davenport, IA 52801 (SAN 262-7892) Tel 319-383-2208; Dist. by: Iowa & Illinois News Co., 8645 Northwest Blvd, Davenport, IA 52808 (SAN 693-4935) Tel 319-391-3723.

Lee Pubns., *(Lee Pubns MN; 0-9615237),* P.O. Box 331, Minneapolis, MN 55440 (SAN 695-1694) Tel 612-623-9438.

Lee Publishing, *(Lee Pub CA; 0-939171),* 1354 Miller Pl., Los Angeles, CA 90069 (SAN 662-8575) Tel 818-845-8455. Do not confuse with Lee Enterprises in Davenport, IA.

Lee Publishing Co., *(Lee Pub Co NH; 0-9616394),* 135-21 Amherst St., Amherst, NH 03031 (SAN 699-8062).

Leeco, Inc., *(Leeco; 0-941222),* 201 Benton Ave., Linthicum Heights, MD 21090 (SAN 238-0676).

Leeman, Gertrude, *(G Leeman; 0-9613628),* 7612 1/2 Eads Ave., La Jolla, CA 92037 (SAN 670-8471) Tel 619-454-4415; Dist. by: James Elko, 3590 Bayside Ln., San Diego, CA 92109 (SAN 200-7185) Tel 619-488-8471.

LeeRosa Pubs., *(LeeRosa Pubs; 0-935547),* 3602 Treachwig Rd., Humble, TX 77347 (SAN 696-2343) Tel 713-821-0185; P.O. Box 3729, Humble, TX 77347 (SAN 696-9623).

Leete's Island Bks., *(Leetes Isl; 0-918172),* P.O. Box 1131, New Haven, CT 06505 (SAN 210-2285) Tel 203-481-2536; Dist. by: Independent Pubs. Group, 1 Pleasant Ave., Pt. Washington, NY 11050 (SAN 210-2293).

Leeward Pubns., Inc. *See* **Presidio Pr.**

Lefever, Barbara Susan, *(Lefever; 0-9614690),* 1760 Alpine Rd., Dover, PA 17315 (SAN 692-6002) Tel 717-292-2827.

Lefkowicz, Edward J., *(E J Lefkowicz; 0-9617194),* 43 Fort St., P.O. Box 630, Fairhaven, MA 02719 (SAN 663-2831) Tel 617-997-6839.

Left Bank Bks., *(Left Bank; 0-939306),* 92 Pike St., Box B, Seattle, WA 98101 (SAN 216-5368) Tel 206-622-0195.

Lega Bks., Div. of Charing Cross Pub. Co., *(Lega Bks),* 658 S. Bonnie Brae St., Los Angeles, CA 90057 (SAN 212-5218) Tel 213-483-5832.

Legacy Bks., *(Legacy Bks; 0-913714),* Box 494, Hatboro, PA 19040 (SAN 202-2389) Tel 215-675-6762; 12 Meetinghouse Rd., Hatboro, PA 19040 (SAN 658-1129).

Legacy Hse., Inc., *(Legacy Hse; 0-9608008),* Box 786, Orofino, ID 83544 (SAN 238-0684) Tel 209-476-5632.

Legacy Pr., *(Legacy Pr VA; 0-9617028),* 4201 University Dr., Fairfax, VA 22030 (SAN 662-6475) Tel 703-591-9333.

Legacy Pubns., Subs. of Pace Communications, Inc., *(Legacy Pubns; 0-933101),* Rte. 4, Box 7, Burlington, NC 27215 (SAN 689-5662) Tel 919-584-6473; Orders to: P.O. Box 20630, Greensboro, NC 27420 (SAN 662-2852).

Legacy Publishing (CA), *(Legacy Publish; 0-9611902),* 1442A Walnut St., Suite 295, Berkeley, CA 94709 (SAN 286-1577) Tel 415-549-3517.

Legal Almanac Series *See* **Oceana Pubns., Inc.**

Legal Bk. Co., *(Legal Bk Co; 0-910874),* 316 W. Second St., Los Angeles, CA 90012 (SAN 201-0798) Tel 213-626-3494.

Legal Pr. Service, Inc., *(Legal Pr Serv; 0-931907),* 5010 N. Ridge Club Dr., Las Vegas, NV 89103 (SAN 686-0176) Tel 702-873-4542.

Legal Pubns., Inc., *(Legal Pubns CA; 0-940194),* P.O. Box 3723, Van Nuys, CA 91407 (SAN 210-8267) Tel 818-902-1671.

Legal Research Bureau, *(Legal Res Bureau; 0-9609346),* P.O. Box 374, Kew Gardens, NY 11415 (SAN 260-2164) Tel 718-846-4544.

Legends Pr., *(Legends Pr; 0-9608808),* 504 S. Pacific Coast Hwy., Redondo Beach, CA 90277 (SAN 238-311X) Tel 213-540-6455.

Legerete Pr., *(Legerete Pr; 0-936993),* P.O. Drawer 1410, Daphne, AL 36526 (SAN 695-1317).

Legislative Assocs., Inc., *(Legis Assocs; 0-934367),* 503 W. 14th St., Austin, TX 78701 (SAN 693-5621) Tel 512-477-5698.

Legislative Information Group Press, *(Legis Info Pr; 0-916481),* 6812 Belford Dr., Takoma Park, MD 20912 (SAN 295-1169).

Legislative Tracking Service, The, *(Legislative Track; 0-938585),* P.O. Box 844, Annapolis, MD 21404 (SAN 661-1184) Tel 301-269-7558.

Lehigh Informational Services, *(Lehigh Info; 0-913453),* P.O. Box 6055, Bethlehem, PA 18001 (SAN 285-1768) Tel 215-837-8358.

Lehigh Univ. Pr., *(Lehigh Univ Pr; 0-934223),* Dist. by: Associated University Presses, 440 Forsgate Dr., Cranbury, NJ 08512 (SAN 281-2959) Tel 609-655-4770.

Leibowitz, Herbert, *(Leibowitz),* 205 W. 89th St., New York, NY 10024 (SAN 239-4502) Tel 212-787-3569.

Leider-Harding Enterprises, *(Leider-Harding; 0-9607504),* 7101 York Ave. S., Minneapolis, MN 55435 (SAN 239-7803) Tel 612-921-3336.

Names

Names

Leihall Pubns., *(Leihall Pubns; 0-9615337),* 4710 Huntley Dr. NE, Atlanta, GA 30342 (SAN 695-1244) Tel 404-252-6742.

Leishman, Robert K., *(R Leishman; 0-9614526),* 77 W. Del Mar Blvd., Pasadena, CA 91105 (SAN 689-7665) Tel 818-792-3138.

Leisure Data Inc., *(Leisure Data; 0-913979),* 1934 Basswood Drive, Kent, OH 44240 (SAN 283-9652) Tel 216-678-0936.

Leisure-Net, Inc., *(Leisure Net; 0-9615334),* P.O. Box 2395, Livonia, MI 48151 (SAN 695-1252) Tel 313-261-6498; 33615 Wood Dr., Livonia, MI 48154 (SAN 695-1260).

†**Leisure Pr.**, Div. of Human Kinetics Pubs., Inc., *(Leisure Pr; 0-918438; 0-88011),* P.O. Box 5076, Champaign, IL 61820 (SAN 211-7088) Tel 217-351-5076; 1607 N. Market, Champaign, IL 61820 (SAN 662-0698) Tel 217-351-5076; *CIP.*

†**Leisure Science Systems International,** *(Leisure Sci Sys; 0-932057),* P.O. Box 3832, La Mesa, CA 92041 (SAN 686-2683) Tel 619-265-4451; *CIP.*

Lejon, L.J. & Associates, *(L J Lejon & Assocs; 0-9612812),* 29100 45th Ave. S., Auburn, WA 98001 (SAN 290-005X) Tel 206-839-9982.

Lekas, Danny, *(D Lekas; 0-930759),* 10 Jamaicaway, Apt 18, Boston, MA 02130 (SAN 679-193X) Tel 617-738-0736.

Leland Historical Foundation, *(Leland Hist; 0-9615430),* 301 E. Third, Leland, MS 38756 (SAN 696-1517) Tel 601-982-6371.

Leland Publishing Co., Inc., *(Leland Pub Co; 0-931306),* 81 Canal St., Boston, MA 02114 (SAN 295-0162) Tel 617-227-9314.

Lem, Dean, Associates, Inc., *(D Lem Assocs; 0-914218),* 1526 Pontius Ave., Suite C, Los Angeles, CA 90025 (SAN 201-5005) Tel 213-478-0092; Orders to: P.O. Box 25920, Los Angeles, CA 90025 (SAN 201-5013).

Lemur Musical Research Corp., *(Lemur; 0-9606888),* P.O. Box 245, Encinitas, CA 92024 (SAN 201-5706) Tel 619-942-8202.

Len Beach Press, *(Len Beach Pr),* P.O. Box 7269 R.C., Toledo, OH 43615 (SAN 213-1048).

Len Forman Publishing Co., Inc. See Golden Door, Inc.

Lena, Dan & Marie, *(D & M Lena; 0-9617032),* P.O. Box 160, Chicago, IL 60635 (SAN 662-8745); 2506 N. Newcastle, Chicago, IL 60635 (SAN 662-8753) Tel 312-745-1025.

Lenape Publishing, Ltd., *(Lenape Pub; 0-917178),* 3 Lanark Dr., Wilmington, DE 19803 (SAN 208-7324) Tel 302-479-0251.

LenChamps Publishers, *(LenChamps Pubs; 0-917230),* 607 Fourth St., S.W., Washington, DC 20024 (SAN 208-7332) Tel 202-484-3571.

Lenhart, John N., *(Lenhart; 0-9615380),* P.O. Box 20261, Cleveland, OH 44120 (SAN 695-4693) Tel 216-752-4731.

Lenjalin Publications, *(Lenjalin Pubns; 0-9614768),* P.O. Box 816, Bettendorf, IA 52722-0816 (SAN 692-7017) Tel 319-359-7220.

Lenox Bks., *(Lenox Bks; 0-9605872),* P.O. Box 104, Little Falls, NJ 07424 (SAN 216-4078).

Lenox Library Assn. See SnO Pubns.

Lenox Publishing Co., *(Lenox Pub; 0-917421),* P.O. Box 7641, Atlanta, GA 30357 (SAN 656-1373) Tel 404-881-9566.

Lent, Max, Productions, *(Max Lent; 0-932798),* 24 Wellington Ave., Rochester, NY 14611 (SAN 212-095X).

Leo Pr., *(Leo Pr; 0-931580),* Allen Park, MI 48101 (SAN 212-4300).

Leo Victor Press, *(L Victor Pr; 0-9606562),* 2203 Brandenburg Way, King of Prussia, PA 19406 (SAN 213-3970).

Leonaitis, Joseph Felix, *(Leonaitis; 0-9601272),* 3323 S. Lowe Ave., Chicago, IL 60616 (SAN 210-4547) Tel 312-376-7524.

Leonard, Cliff R. & Assocs., *(C R Leonard & Assocs; 0-9603818),* P.O. Box 43003, Jacksonville, FL 32203 (SAN 213-9804).

Leonard, Hal, Publishing Corp., *(H Leonard Pub Corp; 0-9607350; 0-88188),* 8112 W. Bluemound Rd., P.O. Box 13819, Milwaukee, WI 53213 (SAN 239-250X) Tel 414-774-3630; Toll free: 800-558-4774.

Leonardo Pr., *(Leonardo Pr; 0-914051),* P.O. Box 403, Yorktown Heights, NY 10598 (SAN 287-542X) Tel 914-962-7056.

Leonard's Assocs., *(Leonard Assoc Pr; 0-936692),* 2423 N. Second St., Harrisburg, PA 17110 (SAN 221-4318); Dist. by: Mankind Research Foundation, 1315 Apple Ave., Silver Spring, MD 20910 (SAN 208-4422).

Leone Pubns., *(Leone Pubns; 0-942786),* 2721 Lyle Ct., Santa Clara, CA 95051 (SAN 238-8510) Tel 415-948-8077.

Leonine Pr., *(Leonine Pr; 0-942228),* 2317 Outlook St., Kalamazoo, MI 49001 (SAN 240-0405) Tel 616-345-2740.

†**L'Epervier Pr.,** *(L'Epervier Pr; 0-934332),* 4522 Sunnyside N., Seattle, WA 98103 (SAN 281-8779) Tel 206-547-8306; 3635 Fremont Ave. N., Seattle, WA 98103; Dist. by: Small Press Distribution Inc., 1814 San Pablo Ave., Berkeley, CA 94712 (SAN 204-5826) Tel 415-549-3336; Dist. by: Bookslinger, 213 E. Fourth St., St. Paul, MN 55101 (SAN 169-4154) Tel 612-221-0429; *CIP.*

Lepidopterists' Society, Los Angeles County Museum of Natural History, *(Lepidopterists),* 900 Exposition Blvd, Los Angeles, CA 90007 (SAN 225-2015) Tel 213-744-3364; Orders to: C. V. Covell, Univ. of Louisville, Louisville, KY 40208 (SAN 225-2023).

Leprechaun Pr., *(Leprechaun Pr; 0-9607368),* 808 W. End Ave., No. 408, New York, NY 10025 (SAN 240-0391) Tel 212-666-3357.

Lerner Law Bk. Co., *(Lerner Law; 0-87342),* 53 E St., NW, Washington, DC 20001 (SAN 201-081X) Tel 202-628-5785.

†**Lerner Pubns. Co.,** *(Lerner Pubns; 0-8225),* 241 First Ave. N., Minneapolis, MN 55401 (SAN 201-0828) Tel 612-332-3344; Toll free: 800-328-4929; *CIP.*

Les Femmes Gourmets, *(Les Femmes Gourmets; 0-9616100),* 428 Oakview Dr., Roseburg, OR 97470 (SAN 698-1240) Tel 503-440-4600.

Leslie Press, Inc., *(Leslie Pr; 0-913816),* 161 Pittsburg, Dallas, TX 75207 (SAN 202-6708) Tel 214-748-0564.

Lesly, Philip, Co., The, *(Lesly Co; 0-9602866),* 303 E. Wacker Dr., Chicago, IL 60601 (SAN 222-2086) Tel 312-819-3590.

Lessing Society, *(Lessing Soc),* Dept. of German, M.L. 372, Univ. of Cincinnati, Cincinnati, OH 45221 (SAN 233-2094) Tel 513-475-2989; Dist. by: Wayne State Univ. Pr, 5959 Woodward Ave., Detroit, MI 48202 (SAN 202-5221) Tel 313-577-4601.

Letellier, Phyllis M., *(P M Letellier; 0-9611138),* Shell Rte. Box 23, Greybull, WY 82426 (SAN 283-2976) Tel 307-765-2109.

LeTourneau Pr., *(LeTourneau Pr; 0-935899),* 8 Stonegate Dr., Longview, TX 75601 (SAN 696-611X) Tel 214-753-0231.

Leumas Publishing, *(Leumas Pub; 0-935117),* 318 W. Hawthorne Dr., P.O. Box 7474, Round Lake Beach, IL 60073 (SAN 695-1287) Tel 312-546-7267.

Levada Services, *(Levada; 0-9605014),* P.O. Box 686, 11300 Eastside Rd., Ft. Jones, CA 96032 (SAN 215-9597).

Level Four Communications, *(Level Four Comm; 0-936995),* 3 Dallas Communications Complex, Irving, TX 75039-3510 (SAN 658-3105) Tel 214-869-7620; Box 134, 6311 N. O'Connor Rd., Irving, TX 75039-3510 (SAN 658-3113).

Levenson Pr., *(Levenson Pr; 0-914442),* P.O. Box 19606, Los Angeles, CA 90019 (SAN 202-6716).

Levi Publishing Co., Inc., *(Levi Pub; 0-910876),* P.O. Box 730, Sumter, SC 29150 (SAN 203-9338).

Levin, Hugh Lauter, Assocs., *(H L Levin; 0-88363),* 236 W. 26th St., Suite 5 NE, New York, NY 10001 (SAN 201-6109) Tel 212-242-1405; Dist. by: Macmillan Publishing Company, Front & Brown Sts., Riverside, NJ 08370 (SAN 650-0412).

Levine, Samuel P., *(S P Levine; 0-9602906),* 42367 Cosmic Dr., Temecula, CA 92309 (SAN 213-1056) Tel 714-676-3976.

†**Levinson Institute Inc.,** *(Levinson Inst; 0-9616516),* Box 95, Cambridge, MA 02138 (SAN 208-7359) Tel 617-489-3040; *CIP.*

Levko, Leo, *(Levko; 0-9614381),* P.O. Box 208 Planetarium Sta., New York, NY 10024 (SAN 688-4725) Tel 212-877-6154.

Levy, Nathan, Assocs. Inc., *(NL Assoc Inc; 0-9608240),* P.O. Box 1199, Hightstown, NJ 08520 (SAN 240-3951) Tel 201-329-6981.

Lew Originals, *(Lew Originals; 0-931249),* 3116 Vanowen St., Burbank, CA 91505 (SAN 681-9974) Tel 818-705-7778.

Lewis, A. F. & Co., Inc., *(Lewis; 0-910880),* 79 Madison Ave., New York, NY 10016 (SAN 201-0844) Tel 212-679-0770.

Lewis & Roth Pubs., Div. of Church Reform & Revitalization, Inc., *(Lewis-Roth; 0-936083),* 12431 N. Mead Way, Littleton, CO 80125-9761 (SAN 696-6454) Tel 303-794-3239.

Lewis Lee Corp., *(Lewis Lee Corp; 0-915847),* 1855 Cowper St., Palo Alto, CA 94301 (SAN 294-0566) Tel 415-853-1220.

†**Lewis Pubs, Inc.,** *(Lewis Pubs Inc; 0-87371),* 121 S. Main St., P.O. Box 519, Chelsea, MI 48118 (SAN 682-1715) Tel 313-475-8619; Toll free: 800-525-7894; *CIP.*

Lewis Publishing Hse., *(Lewis Pub Hse; 0-937225),* P.O. Box 23348, Minneapolis, MN 55423 (SAN 658-7534) Tel 612-861-8260; 6435 Farmer Trail, R.R. 4, Box 195, Northfield, MN 55057 (SAN 658-7542).

†**Lewis-Sloan Publishing Co.,** *(Lewis-Sloan; 0-915114),* 2546 Etiwan Ave., Charleston, SC 29407 (SAN 201-0852) Tel 803-766-4735; *CIP.*

Lex-Com Enterprises, Inc, *(Lex Com Enterprises Inc; 0-914691),* 548 S. Spring St.,Suite 512, Los Angeles, CA 90013 (SAN 291-8404).

Lexicon Bks., Subs. of Lexicon Music, Inc., *(Lexicon Bks; 0-937069),* P.O. Box 2222, Newbury Park, CA 91320 (SAN 658-618X) Tel 805-499-5881; 3543 Old Conejo Rd., Suite 105, Newbury Park, CA 91320 (SAN 658-6198).

Lexigrow International Corp., *(Lexigrow Intl; 0-910387),* 9202 N. Meridian St., Indianapolis, IN 46206 (SAN 262-0464) Tel 317-844-5691; P.O. Box 1491, Indianapolis, IN 46206 (SAN 658-1137).

Lexik House Pubs., *(Lexik Hse; 0-936368),* 75 Main St., P.O. Box 247, Cold Spring, NY 10516 (SAN 214-3984) Tel 914-265-2822.

Lexikos Publishing, *(Lexikos; 0-938530),* 4079 19th Ave., San Francisco, CA 94132 (SAN 219-8517) Tel 415-584-1085.

Lexington Book Co., *(Lex Bk Co CA; 0-9604372),* 4872 Old Cliffs Rd., San Diego, CA 92120 (SAN 214-3992) Tel 619-583-8348.

Lexington Bks., Div. of D. C. Heath & Co., *(Lexington Bks; 0-669),* ; Toll free: 800-235-3565; Dist. by: D. C. Heath & Co., 125 Spring St., Lexington, MA 02173 (SAN 213-7526) Tel 617-862-6650; Orders to: Phyllis McGuinness, 125 Spring St., Lexington, MA 02173 (SAN 662-0701) Tel 617-860-1204.

Lexington Data, Inc., *(Lexington Data; 0-914428; 0-88178),* Box 371, Ashland, MA 01721 (SAN 202-6724) Tel 617-881-2576.

Lexington-Fayette County Historic Commission, *(Lexington-Fayette; 0-912839),* 253 Market St., Lexington, KY 40508 (SAN 277-6936) Tel 606-255-8312.

Lexis Pr., Subs. of Diversified Academic Services, Inc., *(Lexis Pr; 0-933741),* P.O. Box 4116, Chapel Hill, NC 27515 (SAN 692-5995) Tel 919-942-1711.

Leyerle Pubns., *(Leyerle Pubns; 0-9602296),* 28 Stanley St., Mt. Morris, NY 14510 (SAN 211-5700) Tel 716-658-2193; Orders to: Box 384, Geneseo, NY 14454 (SAN 211-5719).

L5 Society, *(LFive Soc; 0-935291),* 1060 E. Elm St., Tucson, AZ 85719 (SAN 696-3633) Tel 602-622-6351.

LFL Assocs., *(LFL Assocs; 0-9613838),* 52 Condolea Ct., Lake Oswego, OR 97034 (SAN 681-9982) Tel 503-636-1559.

Li, Peter, Inc., *(Peter Li; 0-89837),* 2451 E. River Rd., Dayton, OH 45439 (SAN 238-7980) Tel 513-299-8777; Toll free: 800-531-3456.

Libera, *(Libera; 0-9614831),* 930 Alta Vista Rd., Simi Valley, CA 93063 (SAN 693-0360) Tel 818-704-9854; Orders to: Box 1920, Simi Valley, CA 93062 (SAN 662-3085).

Liberal Arts Pr. See Bobbs-Merrill Co.

Liberal Arts Pr., *(Lib Arts Pr; 0-935175),* 4800 Kelly Elliot Rd., No. 46, Arlington, TX 76017 (SAN 695-4707) Tel 817-572-7409.

Names

Lifeline, *(Lifeline)*, 3500 N. Hayden Rd., No. 1705, Scottsdale, AZ 85251 (SAN 281-8817) Tel 602-941-8094; Orders to: 1421 S. Park St., Madison, WI 53715 (SAN 281-8825). Out of business.

Lifeline Pubs., Inc., *(Lifeline Pubs; 0-930823)*, P.O. Box 1045, San Pedro, CA 90733 (SAN 677-6620) Tel 213-833-8560.

Lifesigns: Words & Images, *(Lifesigns; 0-943510)*, P.O. Box 663, El Cerrito, CA 94530 (SAN 240-7043) Tel 415-527-6722.

Lifestyle One, Inc., *(Lifestyle One; 0-9603016)*, P.O. Box 630668, Miami, FL 33163 (SAN 213-1099). Moved, left no forwarding address.

Lifestyle Pr., *(Lifestyle Pr; 0-9606860)*, P.O. Box 3025, Bellevue, WA 98009-3025 (SAN 223-1913) Tel 206-868-9000.

Lifestyle Pubns., *(Lifestyle Pubns; 0-937877)*, 24396 Pleasant View Dr., Elkhart, IN 46517 (SAN 659-4778) Tel 219-875-8618.

Lifestyle Systems, *(Lifestyle Systems; 0-9615184)*, P.O. Box 5031, Huntington Beach, CA 92615 (SAN 694-2202) Tel 714-964-3383.

†Lifetime Learning Pubns., Div. of Wadsworth Inc., *(Lifetime Learn; 0-534)*, 10 Davis Dr., Belmont, CA 94002 (SAN 211-7398) Tel 415-595-2350; Toll free: 800-354-9706; Dist. by: Van Nostrand Reinhold, 115 Fifth Ave., New York, NY 10003 (SAN 202-5183) Tel 212-254-3232; Orders to: VNR Order Dept., 7265 Empire Dr., Florence, KY 41042 (SAN 202-5191) Tel 606-525-6600; *CIP.*

Lifetime Learning Pubns. See Van Nostrand Reinhold Co., Inc.

Lifetime Pr., Subs. of Royal Publishing, *(Lifetime Pr; 0-931571)*, 137 Campbell Ave., Roanoke, VA 24011 (SAN 686-1636) Tel 703-982-1444.

Lifetouch Inc., *(Lifetouch Inc; 0-9617259)*, 400 Paramount Plaza, 7831 Glenroy Rd., Minneapolis, MN 55435 (SAN 663-480X) Tel 612-893-0500.

Light, Melvin J., *(M J Light)*, 2414 Grant Dr., Ann Arbor, MI 48104 (SAN 659-5588) Tel 313-971-2792.

Light & Life Pr. (IN), *(Light & Life; 0-89367)*, 999 College Ave., Winona Lake, IN 46590 (SAN 206-8419) Tel 219-267-7161; Toll free: 800-348-2513.

Light & Life Pub. Co., *(Light&Life Pub Co MN; 0-937032)*, 3450 Irving Ave. S., Minneapolis, MN 55408 (SAN 213-8565) Tel 612-925-3888.

Light & Sound Communications, Inc., *(Light & Sound; 1-55626)*, 279 S. Beverly Dr., No. 1188, Beverly Hills, CA 90212 (SAN 661-3691) Tel 213-275-2469.

Light Hearted Publishing Co., Div. of Montgomery's Music, *(Light Hearted Pub Co; 0-916043)*, P.O. Box 150246, Nashville, TN 37215 (SAN 294-8648) Tel 615-776-5678.

Light Impressions Corp., *(Light Impressions; 0-87992)*, 439 Monroe Ave. P.O. Box 940, Rochester, NY 14603 (SAN 169-619X) Tel 716-271-8960; Toll free: 800-828-6216.

Light Ventures, *(Light Ventures; 0-939453)*, P.O. Box 820654, Houston, TX 77282-0654 (SAN 663-3765); 3103 Misty Pk., Houston, TX 77082 (SAN 663-3773) Tel 713-496-2735.

Light Work Visual Studies, Inc., *(Light Work; 0-935445)*, 316 Waverly Ave., Syracuse, NY 13210 (SAN 696-3072) Tel 315-423-2450.

Lightbooks, *(Lightbooks; 0-934420)*, P.O. Box 1268, Twain Harte, CA 95383 (SAN 214-400X).

†Lighthouse Bks., *(Lighthouse Bks; 0-915889)*, P.O. Box 700160, San Jose, CA 95170-0160 (SAN 206-574X) Tel 408-252-6361; *CIP.*

Lighthouse Enterprises, *(Lighthouse Enterprises; 0-933549)*, P.O. Box 6361, Athens, GA 30604 (SAN 691-8727) Tel 404-549-4629.

Lighthouse Hill Publishing, *(Lighthouse Hill Pub; 0-9608690)*, 279 Edinboro Rd., Lighthouse Hill, Staten Island, NY 10306 (SAN 238-0706) Tel 718-987-7586.

Lighthouse Pr. Co., The, *(Lighthouse Pr; 0-917021)*, 1308 Lewis, La Junta, CO 81050 (SAN 655-1262) Tel 303-384-8631.

Lighthouse Pubns., *(Lighthouse Pr; 0-9610648)*, 1991 Linneal Beach Dr., Apopka, FL 32703 (SAN 695-1082) Tel 305-898-5498.

Lighthouse Pubns., *(Lighthouse Pubns; 0-914055)*, P.O. Box 2972, Mission Viejo, CA 92692 (SAN 287-508X) Tel 714-581-9184.

Lighthouse Training Institute, *(Lighthouse Trg Inst; 0-938475)*, 702 W. Chestnut St., Bloomington, IL 61701 (SAN 661-3160) Tel 309-827-6026.

Lighthouse Writers Guild, *(Lighthouse Writers; 0-935125)*, P.O. Box 51277, Pacific Grove, CA 93950 (SAN 695-1899) Tel 408-373-4998; 457 Pine St., Monterey, CA 93940 (SAN 695-1902).

Lightning Tree, *(Lightning Tree; 0-89016)*, P.O. Box 1837, Santa Fe, NM 87504 (SAN 206-555X) Tel 505-983-7434.

Lighton Pubns., *(Lighton Pubns; 0-910892)*, 73223 Sunnyvale Dr., Twentynine Palms, CA 92277 (SAN 201-0917) Tel 619-367-7386.

Lightway Pubns., International, Div. of Waldorff Corp., *(Lightway Pubns; 0-938617)*, P.O. Box 570, Big Bar, CA 96010 (SAN 661-5740) Tel 916-623-6731.

Lightyear Pr., Inc., *(Lightyear; 0-89968)*, P.O. Box 507, Laurel, NY 11948 (SAN 213-1102); Dist. by: Buccaneer Books, Inc., P.O. Box 168, Cutchogue, NY 11935 (SAN 209-1542).

Ligonier Sesquicentennial Commission, *(Ligonier Comm; 0-9615431)*, 300 S. Main St., Ligonier, IN 46767 (SAN 696-1444) Tel 219-894-3758; Dist. by: Taylor Publishing Co., 1550 Mockingbird Lnn., P.O. Box 597, Dallas, TX 75221 (SAN 202-7631) Tel 214-637-2800.

Liguori Pubns., *(Liguori Pubns; 0-89243)*, 1 Liguori Dr., Liguori, MO 63057 (SAN 202-6783) Tel 314-464-2500; Toll free: 800-325-9521 (Orders).

Lilien, M., *(M Lilien; 0-9607652)*, 68-50 Burns St., Forest Hills, NY 11375 (SAN 264-1763).

Lilmat Pr., *(Lilmat Pr; 0-935401)*, 3500 E. Fletcher Ave., Suite 509, Tampa, FL 33612 (SAN 696-3579) Tel 813-971-2781.

Lim Pr., *(LIM Press CA; 0-942714)*, P.O. Box 558, Belmont, CA 94002 (SAN 240-2424) Tel 415-591-9056.

Limberlost Pr., *(Limberlost Pr; 0-931659)*, P.O. Box 1563, Boise, ID 83701 (SAN 683-7212) Tel 208-344-2120.

†Lime Rock Press, Inc., *(Lime Rock Pr; 0-915998)*, Mount Riga Rd., Box 363, Salisbury, CT 06068 (SAN 208-2055) Tel 203-435-2236; *CIP.*

†Limelight Editions, Div. of Proscenium Pubs., *(Limelight Edns; 0-87910)*, 118 E. 30th St., New York, NY 10016 (SAN 290-0068) Tel 212-532-5525; Toll free: 800-242-7737; *CIP.*

Limerick Pubns., *(Limerick Pubns; 0-9612582)*, P.O. Box 2104, Iowa City, IA 52244 (SAN 289-2952) Tel 319-337-3712.

Limestone Pr., *(Limestone Pr; 0-919642)*, 125 Southwood Dr., Vestal, NY 13850 (SAN 209-0120) Tel 613-548-7403.

Limited Editions Press, *(Limited Ed)*, 2324 S. Highhland Ave., No. 11, Las Vegas, NV 89102 (SAN 240-9623)5055 E Charleston, F110, Las Vegas, NV 89104 (SAN 669-1471) Tel 702-459-8475.

Limitless Light Publishing Co., *(Limitless Light; 0-917913)*, 8115-1 N. 35th Ave., Phoenix, AZ 85051 (SAN 657-0518).

Linch Publishing Inc., *(Linch Pub; 0-913455)*, P.O. Box 75, Orlando, FL 32802 (SAN 285-1792) Tel 305-647-3025; Toll free: 800-327-7055 (national); Toll free: 800-434-0399 (FL); Orders to: 1950 Lee Rd., Suite 205, Winter Park, FL 32789 (SAN 693-9848); Dist. by: Ingram Industries, 347 Reedwood Dr., Nashville, TN 37217 (SAN 651-1163); Dist. by: Baker & Taylor Co., Eastern Div., 50 Kirby Ave., Somerville, NJ 08876 (SAN 169-4901); Dist. by: Baker & Taylor Co., Midwest Div., 501 Gladiola Ave., Momence, IL 60954 (SAN 169-2100); Dist. by: Baker & Taylor Co., Southeast Div., Mt. Olive Rd., Commerce, GA 30529 (SAN 169-1503); Dist. by: Baker & Taylor Co., Western Div., (SAN 169-4464).

Lincol Enterprises, *(Lincol Enter)*, Box 10541, Eugene, OR 97440 (SAN 692-6398).

Lincoln, James F., Arc Welding Foundation, *(Lincoln Arc Weld; 0-937390)*, P.O. Box 17035, Cleveland, OH 44117 (SAN 202-2443) Tel 216-481-4300.

Lincoln County Historical Society, *(Lincoln Coun Hist; 0-911443)*, 545 SW 9th St., Newport, OR 97365 (SAN 293-2989) Tel 503-265-7509.

Lincoln-Herndon Pr., The, *(Lincoln-Herndon Pr; 0-942936)*, 1 Old State Capitol Plaza, Suite 503, Springfield, IL 62701 (SAN 240-3188) Tel 217-522-2732; Dist. by: Baker & Taylor, Midwest Div., 501 Gladiola Ave., Momence, IL 60954 (SAN 169-2100); Dist. by: Distributors, The, 702 S. Michigan Ave., South Bend, IN 46618 (SAN 169-2488).

Lincoln Institute of Land Policy, *(Lincoln Inst Land)*, 26 Trowbridge St., Cambridge, MA 02138 (SAN 209-2506) Tel 617-661-3016.

Lincoln Library See Frontier Pr. Co.

Lincoln Pr., *(Lincoln Pr MI)*, 4610 Delemere Blvd., Royal Oak, MI 48073 (SAN 211-7401) Tel 313-549-1900.

Lincoln Publishing, *(Lincoln Pub; 0-918898)*, 3434 Janice Way, Palo Alto, CA 94303 (SAN 209-6730) Tel 415-494-7448.

Lincoln's Leadership Library, *(Lincoln's Leadership; 0-89764)*, 5902 E. Fourth Terrace, Tulsa, OK 74112 (SAN 215-675X).

Lind Graphics Publications, *(Lind Grap Pubns; 0-910389)*, 192 Third Ave., Westwood, NJ 07675 (SAN 260-0951) Tel 201-666-7313.

Lindahl, Judy, *(Lindahl; 0-9603032)*, 3211 NE Siskiyou, Portland, OR 97212 (SAN 210-6086) Tel 503-288-0772.

Lindahl See Larksdale

Lindberg Publishing Co., *(Lindberg Pub; 0-9615993)*, 2106 Live Oak Dr., E, Hollywood, CA 90068 (SAN 697-2837) Tel 213-856-9835.

Lindbrook Press, *(Lindbrook Pr; 0-942882)*, P.O. Box 1082, 15243 la Cruz Dr., Pacific Palisades, CA 90272 (SAN 238-0692).

Lindell Pubs., *(Lindell Pubs; 0-9604940)*, P.O. Box 28, Bucks County, Springtown, PA 18081 (SAN 215-9619).

Lindemann, Emil R., *(E R Lindemann; 0-9612192)*, P.O. Box 399, Deshler, NE 68340 (SAN 289-6001).

Linden, Millicent, *(M Linden NY; 0-912628)*, 500 E. 74th St., New York, NY 10021 (SAN 207-0596).

Linden Bks., *(Linden Bks; 0-9603288)*, Interlaken, NY 14847 (SAN 209-6692).

Linden Pubns., *(Linden Pubs; 0-89642)*, 1750 N. Sycamore, Hollywood, CA 90028 (SAN 206-7218).

Linden Publishing Co., Inc., *(Linden Pub Fresno; 0-941936)*, 3845 N. Blackstone, Fresno, CA 93726 (SAN 238-6089) Tel 209-227-2901; Toll free: 800-345-4447.

Linden Tree, The, *(Linden Tree; 0-937463)*, 1204 W. Prospect, Cloquet, MN 55720 (SAN 658-9391) Tel 218-879-5727.

Lindenhof Press, *(Lindenhof Pr; 0-9609678)*, P.O. Box 18513, Irvine, CA 92714 (SAN 262-7981) Tel 714-545-6984.

Linder, Herbert, *(H Linder; 0-917396)*, 55 Park Ave., New York, NY 10016 (SAN 206-8605) Tel 212-685-2571.

Linder, William A., Co., Pubs., *(W A Linder; 0-934844)*, P.O. Box 443, Lindsborg, KS 67456 (SAN 205-4892) Tel 913-227-2514.

Lindisfarne Press See Inner Traditions International, Ltd.

Lindner's, Al, Outdoors, Inc., *(Al Lindner's Outdoors; 0-9605254)*, P.O. Box 999, Brainerd, MN 56401 (SAN 215-8965) Tel 612-374-5581 Tel 612-341-7259.

Lindon Pubns., *(Lindon Ent; 0-939820)*, Box 1162, Southold, NY 11971 (SAN 216-9053) Tel 516-765-3584.

Lindsay Newspapers, Inc., *(Lindsay News; 0-910713)*, Postal Drawer 1719, Sarasota, FL 33578 (SAN 260-2172) Tel 813-746-2178.

Lindsay Pubns., Inc., *(Lindsay Pubns; 0-917914)*, P.O. Box 12, Bradley, IL 60915 (SAN 209-9462).

Lindy's Golf Course Guide, *(Lindys Golf; 0-9612636)*, 5511 Dunsmore Rd., Alexandria, VA 22310 (SAN 289-2979) Tel 202-676-7197.

Line Drive Publishing, *(Line Drive)*, 113 Pleasant St., Hanover, MA 02339 (SAN 663-4575) Tel 617-878-5035.

Lineal Publishing Co., *(Lineal Pub Co; 0-916628; 0-9612412)*, 2425 E. Commercial Blvd., Ft. Lauderdale, FL 33308 (SAN 208-4848) Tel 305-776-7308; Toll free: 800-222-4253.

Lingo Pubs., *(Lingo Pubs; 0-937145),* 21403 Chagrin Blvd., No. 106, Cleveland, OH 44122 (SAN 658-5760) Tel 216-991-5730.

Lingore Pr., *(Lingore Pr; 0-9607146),* 123 Mayo St., Americus, GA 31709 (SAN 239-0051) Tel 912-924-4505; Dist. by: Charles E. Tuttle Co., Inc., P.O. Box 410, 28 S. Main St., Rutland, VT 05701-0410 (SAN 213-2621) Tel 802-773-8936.

Lingua Pr., *(Lingua Pr)*, P.O. Box 3416, Iowa City, IA 52244 (SAN 215-6083) Tel 319-338-9908.

Lingual House Publishing Co., *(Lingual Hse Pub; 0-940264),* P.O. Box 3537, Tucson, AZ 85722 (SAN 220-3383) Tel 602-622-2366.

Linju-Ryu Karate Assn., Inc., *(LKA Inc; 0-917098),* Linick Bldg. 102, 7 Putter Ln., Middle Island, NY 11953-0102 (SAN 208-7375) Tel 516-924-3888.

Linmore Publishing Inc., *(Linmore Pub; 0-916591),* 409 E. South St., Barrington, IL 60010 (SAN 296-4503) Tel 312-382-7606; Orders to: P.O. Box 1545, Palatine, IL 60078 (SAN 662-2291) Tel 815-223-7499.

Linn, Jo White, *(J W Linn; 0-918470),* Box 1948, Salisbury, NC 28144 (SAN 209-9489) Tel 704-633-3575.

Linnaea Graphics, Div. of Best Printing Co., *(Linnaea; 0-912467),* 3218 Manor Rd., P.O. Box 1548, Austin, TX 78767 (SAN 265-2692) Tel 512-477-9733; Michael E. Arth, P.O. Box 13246, Austin, TX 78711 (SAN 688-4148).

Linnet *See* **Shoe String Pr., Inc.**

Linolean *See* **Larksdale**

Linscott, William D., *(W D Linscott; 0-9604920),* 40 Glen Dr., Mill Valley, CA 94941 (SAN 214-4018) Tel 415-383-2666.

Linstok Pr., Inc., *(Linstok Pr; 0-932130),* 9306 Mintwood St., Silver Spring, MD 20901 (SAN 207-6195) Tel 301-585-1939.

Lint Head Publishing Co., *(Lint Head Pub; 0-9613713),* Box 3625, Savannah, GA 31414 (SAN 677-1092) Tel 912-354-4933.

Lintel, *(Lintel; 0-931642),* P.O. Box 8609, Roanoke, VA 24014 (SAN 213-6325) Tel 703-982-2265; 100 Bleeker, Suite 17E, New York, NY 10012 (SAN 662-071X) Tel 212-674-1466.

Linwood Pr., *(Linwood Oregon; 0-9616942),* 19076 S. Midhill Dr., West Linn, OR 97068 (SAN 661-7859) Tel 503-636-3772.

†Linwood Pubs., *(Linwood Pub; 0-943512),* P.O. Box 70152, North Charleston, SC 29415 (SAN 240-7051) Tel 803-873-2719; *CIP.*

Linworth Publishing, Inc., *(Linworth Pub; 0-938865),* P.O. Box 14466, Columbus, OH 43214 (SAN 662-5800); 2950 N. High St., Columbus, OH 43214 (SAN 662-5819) Tel 614-261-6584.

†Lion Bks., *(Lion Bks; 0-87460),* Dist. by: Sayre Publishing, Inc., P.O. Box 1337, Scarsdale, NY 10583 (SAN 201-0925) Tel 914-725-2280; *CIP.*

Lion Enterprises, *(Lion Ent; 0-930962),* 8608 Old Dominion Ct., Indianapolis, IN 46231 (SAN 211-3678) Tel 317-243-8048.

Lion Hse. Pr., *(Lion House Pr; 0-914107),* P.O. Box 791, Canby, OR 97013 (SAN 287-5101) Tel 503-263-6688.

Lion/Lamb Pr., *(Lion Lamb Pr; 0-9616424),* 678 Santa Rosa Ave., Berkeley, CA 94707 (SAN 658-8557) Tel 415-528-3386; Dist. by: Bookpeople, 2929 Fifth St., Berkeley, CA 94710 (SAN 168-9517) Tel 415-549-3030; Toll free: 800-227-1516; Dist. by: Inland Book Co., 22 Hemingway Ave., East Haven, CT 06512 (SAN 200-4151).

Lion Pubs., *(Lion Pubs; 0-936635),* P.O. Box 92541, Rochester, NY 14692 (SAN 699-6841) Tel 716-385-1269; 19 Greentree, Pittsford, NY 14534 (SAN 699-685X).

†Lion Publishing, *(Lion Pub; 0-933301),* 6602 El Cajon Blvd., No. B, San Diego, CA 92115 (SAN 692-3062) Tel 619-265-8777; *CIP.*

Lion Publishing, Subs. of Lion Publishing, UK, *(Lion USA; 0-7459),* 1705 Hubbard Ave., Batavia, IL 60510 (SAN 663-611X).

Lionhart, Inc., Pub., *(Lionhart Inc Pub; 0-9617033),* 440 Canoe Hill Rd., New Canaan, CT 06840 (SAN 662-8796) Tel 203-966-7255.

Lionhead Publishing/Roar Recording, *(Lionhead Pub; 0-89018),* 2521 E. Stratford Ct., Shorewood, Milwaukee, WI 53211 (SAN 206-5568) Tel 414-332-7474.

Lions Head Pr., *(Lions Head Pr; 0-934661),* P.O. Box 5202, Klamath Falls, OR 97601 (SAN 694-0447) Tel 503-883-2101.

Lion's Head Publishing Co., *(Lion's Head),* RR2 Box 92, Albion, IN 46701 (SAN 207-2564).

Liplop Press *See* **Goodfellow Catalog Pr., Inc.**

Lippa Ph.D., M.D., Erik A., *(E A Lippa; 0-9607980),* 1045 Stevens Dr., Fort Washington, PA 19034 (SAN 238-5481) Tel 215-628-8003.

Lippincott, J. B., Co., Subs. of Harper & Row, Pubs., Inc., *(Lippincott; 0-397),* E. Washington Sq., Philadelphia, PA 19105 (SAN 201-0933) Tel 215-238-4200; Toll free: 800-523-2945. *Imprints:* Lippincott Medical (Lippincott Medical); Lippincott Nursing, Medical (Lippincott Nursing).

Lippincott, J. B., Junior Bks., Div. of Harper Junior Bks. Group, *(Lipp Jr Bks; 0-397),* 10 E. 53rd St., New York, NY 10022 (SAN 200-2086) Tel 212-207-7000; Toll free: 800-638-3030; 1700 Montgomery St., San Francisco, CA 94111 (SAN 215-3734) Tel 415-989-9000; Orders to: Keystone Industrial Pk., Scranton, PA 18512 (SAN 215-3742).

Lippincott, J. B., , Harper & Row Medical Div. *See* **Harper & Row Pubs., Inc.**

Lippincott Medical *See* **Lippincott, J. B., Co.**

Lippincott Nursing, Medical *See* **Lippincott, J. B., Co.**

LISP Machine, *(LISP Machine; 1-55530),* 1000 Massachusetts Ave., Cambridge, MA 02138 (SAN 696-2904) Tel 617-876-6819.

Liss, Alan R., Inc., *(A R Liss; 0-8451),* 150 Fifth Ave., New York, NY 10011 (SAN 207-7558) Tel 212-741-2515.

Listen & Learn, *(Listen & Learn; 0-938137),* P.O. Box 2124, Reseda, CA 91335 (SAN 661-2156); 7242 Ariel Ave., Reseda, CA 91335 (SAN 661-2164) Tel 818-705-1745.

Listen USA, *(Listen USA),* 60 Arch St., Greenwich, CT 06830 (SAN 695-4839) Tel 203-661-0101; Dist. by: Hearst Corp., International Circulation Div., 250 W. 55th St., 12th Flr., New York, NY 10019 (SAN 169-5800); Toll free: 800-223-0288.

Listner's Pr., *(Listeners Pr; 0-9616943),* 75 Old Mill Rd., Rochester, NY 14618 (SAN 661-7840) Tel 716-244-8775; Dist. by: Adler Publishing Co., Panorama Plaza, Box 25333, Rochester, NY 14625 (SAN 285-6808) Tel 716-377-5804.

Litaruan Literature, *(Litaruan Lit; 0-937557),* 12949 W. 68th Ave., Arvada, CO 80004 (SAN 658-8603) Tel 303-431-4345.

Literacy Volunteers of America, Inc., *(Lit Vol Am; 0-930713),* 5795 Widewaters Pkwy, Widewaters 1 Office Bldg., Syracuse, NY 13214 (SAN 225-3402) Tel 315-474-7039.

†Literary Classics of the U. S., Inc., *(Literary Classics; 0-940450),* 14 E. 60th St., New York, NY 10022 (SAN 217-1945) Tel 212-308-3360; Dist. by: Viking Penguin, Inc., 40 W. 23rd St., New York, NY 10010 (SAN 200-2442) Tel 212-337-5200; *CIP.*

Literary Sketches, *(Literary Sketches; 0-915588),* P.O. Box 711, Williamsburg, VA 23187 (SAN 205-6305) Tel 804-229-2901.

Literations, *(Literations; 0-943514),* P.O. Box 1845, Pittsfield, MA 01202 (SAN 240-706X) Tel 413-499-1459.

Lithuanian Information Ctr., Affil. of Lithuanian Catholic Religious Aid, *(Lith Info Ctr),* 351 Highland Blvd., Brooklyn, NY 11207 (SAN 241-5542) Tel 718-647-2434.

Lithuanian Institute of Education, Inc., *(Lith Inst Educ; 0-936694),* 5620 S. Claremont Ave., Chicago, IL 60636 (SAN 656-0512).

Lithuanian Library Press, *(Lithuanian Lib; 0-932042),* 3001 W. 59th St., Chicago, IL 60629 (SAN 213-8166) Tel 312-778-6872.

Lithuanian Scouts Assn., *(Lith Scouts; 0-9611488),* 3300 W. 63rd Place, Chicago, IL 60629 (SAN 285-3485) Tel 312-476-1739.

Litlaw Foundation, The, *(Litlaw Found; 0-9615761),* 2339 Silver Ridge Ave., Los Angeles, CA 90026 (SAN 695-8729) Tel 213-662-6669; P.O. Box 26305, Los Angeles, CA 90026 (SAN 696-9569); Dist. by: Joe Christensen Inc., 1540 Adams St., Lincoln, NE 68521 (SAN 200-8009).

Litmus, Inc., *(Litmus; 0-915214),* 350 S. Palouse, Walla Walla, WA 99362 (SAN 207-8619).

Little, Mark A., *(M A Little; 0-9613783),* 8842 N. Winding Way, Fair Oaks, CA 95628 (SAN 678-9838) Tel 916-965-0952.

Little, Ruth, *(R Little; 0-9600062),* 2255 34th St., Lubbock, TX 79411 (SAN 204-6598) Tel 806-744-5162; 2255 34th St., Lubbock, TX 79411 (SAN 694-3160).

Little Bayou Press, *(Little Bayou; 0-9609804),* 1735 First Ave. N., St. Petersburg, FL 33713 (SAN 272-085X) Tel 813-822-3278.

Little Book Publishing Co., The, *(Little Book; 0-9616080),* 10 State St., Newburyport, MA 01950 (SAN 698-1364) Tel 617-465-9359; Dist. by: Globe Pequot Pr., Inc., Old Chester Rd., Chester, CT 06412 (SAN 698-1372).

†Little Bks. & Co., *(Little Bks Co; 0-9604656),* 5892 E. Jefferson Ave., Denver, CO 80237 (SAN 217-247X) Tel 303-758-1282; *CIP.*

Little Brick House, The, *(Little Brick Hse; 0-9601648),* 621 Saint Clair St., Vandalia, IL 62471 (SAN 209-2069) Tel 618-283-0024; Dist. by: Illinois State Historical Society, Old State Capitol, Springfield, IL 62701 (SAN 662-0728) Tel 217-782-4836.

Little, Brown & Co., Div. of Time, Inc., *(Little; 0-316),* 34 Beacon St., Boston, MA 02108 (SAN 200-2205) Tel 617-227-0730; Toll free: 800-343-9204; Orders to: 200 West St., Waltham, MA 02254 (SAN 281-8892). *Imprints:* Little, Brown Medical Division (Little Med Div).

Little Cajun Bks., Subs. of Edler Bks., *(Little Cajun Bks; 0-931108),* 4182 Blecker Dr., Baton Rouge, LA 70809 (SAN 212-5250) Tel 504-292-8585.

Little Feat, *(Little Feat; 0-940112),* P.O. Box R, Mastic Beach, NY 11951 (SAN 217-0760) Tel 516-281-5661.

Little Glass Shack, *(Little Glass; 0-911508),* 3161 56th St., Sacramento, CA 95820 (SAN 201-0968) Tel 916-455-8197.

Little Gnome Delights, Div. of Artmarx, Inc., *(Little Gnome; 0-9615584),* P.O. Box 22582, Denver, CO 80222 (SAN 696-0499) Tel 303-758-7905.

Little Lady's Press, Inc., The, *(Little Lady's Pr; 0-941356),* P.O. Box 10, Park Ridge, IL 60068 (SAN 238-8928).

Little Lenin Library *See* **International Pubs. Co.**

Little London Pr., *(Little London; 0-936564),* 716 E. Washington, Colorado Springs, CO 80907 (SAN 214-0489) Tel 303-471-1322.

Little Marx Library *See* **International Pubs. Co.**

Little Nemo Pr., *(Little Nemo Pr; 0-9614451),* 198 E. Seventh St., No. 12, New York, NY 10009 (SAN 689-3848) Tel 212-254-4779.

Little New World Paperbacks *See* **International Pubs. Co.**

Little People Productions, *(Little People; 0-910219),* Kennedy Design Center, 111 S. Lincoln St., Warsaw, IN 46580 (SAN 241-3930) Tel 219-269-3823.

Little Red Hen, Inc., *(Little Red Hen; 0-933046),* P.O. Box 4260, Pocatello, ID 83201 (SAN 212-7571) Tel 208-232-1847.

Little Red Hen Press, *(Litt Red Hen Pr; 0-9612892),* Rte. 2, Box 28, Mankato, MN 56001 (SAN 291-2546) Tel 507-947-3614.

Little Texas Press, *(Little TX Pr; 0-9613381),* P.O. Box 218190, Houston, TX 77218 (SAN 670-7017) Tel 713-492-8997.

Little, Brown Medical Div. *See* **Little, Brown & Co.**

Littlebee Press, *(Littlebee; 0-940674),* 791 Boulevard E., Weehawken, NJ 07087 (SAN 239-4510) Tel 201-867-2595.

Littlebird Pubns., *(Littlebird; 0-937896),* 126 Fifth Ave., New York, NY 10011 (SAN 215-7853).

†Littlefield, Adams & Co., *(Littlefield; 0-8226),* 81 Adams Dr., Totowa, NJ 07512 (SAN 202-6791) Tel 201-256-8600; *CIP.*

Littlegreen *See* **Christopher Publishing**

Littoral Development Co., *(Littoral Develop; 0-914770),* 252 S. Van Pelt St., Philadelphia, PA 19103 (SAN 202-2427) Tel 215-546-3285.

Liturgical Conference, The, *(Liturgical Conf; 0-918208),* 806 Rhode Island Ave. NE., Washington, DC 20018 (SAN 205-6488) Tel 202-529-7400.

†Liturgical Pr., Div. of Order of St. Benedict, Inc., *(Liturgical Pr; 0-8146),* St. John's Abbey, Collegeville, MN 56321 (SAN 202-2494) Tel 612-363-2213; *CIP.*

Names

Live Free, Inc., *(Live Free; 0-942470; 0-938326)*, P.O. Box 1743, Harvey, IL 60426 (SAN 209-830X); 1125 St. Lawrence Ave., Chicago, IL 60628 (SAN 662-0736) Tel 312-928-5830.

Live Oak Media, *(Live Oak Media; 0-941078; 0-87499)*, P.O. Box 34, Ancramdale, NY 12503 (SAN 217-3921) Tel 518-329-6300; Overmountain Rd, Ancramdale, NY 12503 (SAN 669-1498).

Live-Oak Press, *(Live-Oak Pr)*, P. O. Box 99444, San Francisco, CA 94109 (SAN 214-4026).

†Live Oak Pubns., *(Live Oak Pubns; 0-911781)*, 6003 N. 51st St., P.O. Box 2193, Boulder, CO 80306 (SAN 264-1798) Tel 303-530-1087; Orders to: Liberty Publishing Co., 50 Scott Adam Rd., Cockeysville, MD 21030 (SAN 211-030X) Tel 301-667-6680; *CIP.*

Lively Hills Publishing Corp., *(Lively Hills; 0-938194)*, P.O. Box 1186, St. Charles, MO 63301 (SAN 216-1559).

Lively Mind Books, *(Lively Mind Bks; 0-9612746)*, P.O. Box 3212, Chapel Hill, NC 27514 (SAN 283-2984) Tel 919-929-2095.

†Liveright Publishing Corp., Subs. of W. W. Norton Co., Inc., *(Liveright; 0-87140)*, 500 Fifth Ave., New York, NY 10110 (SAN 201-0976) Tel 212-354-5500; Toll free: 800-233-4830; *CIP.*

Livia Pr., *(Livia Pr; 0-933949)*, 967 Neilson St., Albany, CA 94706 (SAN 692-6770) Tel 415-526-3281.

Living Bibles International, *(Liv Bibles Int'l)*, 1809C Mill St., Naperville, IL 60540 (SAN 220-1461) Tel 312-369-0100.

Living Flame Pr., *(Living Flame Pr; 0-914544)*, P.O. Box 74, Locust Valley, NY 11560 (SAN 202-6805) Tel 516-676-4265.

Living Historical Museum, *(Living Histori; 0-933960)*, 826 Goodrich Ave., St. Paul, MN 55105 (SAN 221-4199).

Living Legacies, *(Living Legacies; 0-934371)*, P.O. Box 15007, San Antonio, TX 78212-8207 (SAN 693-5648) Tel 512-231-5217.

†Living Love Pubns., *(Living Love; 0-9600688; 0-915972)*, 700 Commercial Ave., Coos Bay, OR 97420 (SAN 281-9082) Tel 503-267-4232; Dist. by: DeVorss & Co., P.O. Box 550, Marina del Rey, CA 90291 (SAN 168-9886) Tel 213-870-7478; Dist. by: Bookpeople, 2929 Fifth St., Berkeley, CA 94710 (SAN 168-9517) Tel 415-549-3030; Dist. by: Inland Bk. Co., P.O. Box 261, East Haven, CT 06512 (SAN 200-4151) Tel 203-467-4257; Dist. by: New Leaf Distributing Co., 1020 White St., SW, Atlanta, GA 30316 (SAN 169-1449); Dist. by: Publishers Group West, 5855 Beaudry, Emeryville, CA 94608 (SAN 202-8522) Tel 415-658-3453; Dist. by: The Whole Health Bk. Co., 4735 Wunder Ave, Trevose, PA 19047 (SAN 200-6073) Tel 215-322-2880; Dist. by: The Distributors, 702 S. Michigan, South Bend, IN 46618 (SAN 169-2488) Tel 219-232-8500; Dist. by: Starlite Distributors, P.O. Box 20729, Sparks, NV 89515 (SAN 131-1921) Tel 702-359-5676; *CIP.*

Living Loving Learning Ctr., *(Living Loving Learning Center; 0-9613003)*, 1239 Barry Ave., No. 14, Los Angeles, CA 90025 (SAN 292-5753) Tel 213-473-8588.

Living Poets Pr., *(Living Poets; 0-915726)*, 139 Seventh Ave., Brooklyn, NY 11217 (SAN 207-3854) Tel 718-622-4900.

Living Skills Pr., *(Living Skills; 0-941510)*, P.O. Box 83, Sebastosol, CA 93472 (SAN 239-1082) Tel 707-823-5104; Dist. by: Institute of Living Skills, P.O. Box 1461, Fallbrook, CA 92028 (SAN 239-1090) Tel 619-728-6437.

Living Spring Pubns., *(Living Spring Pubns; 0-941598)*, 389 N. Los Robles, No. 2, Pasadena, CA 91101 (SAN 239-1112) Tel 818-795-2407; 790 Metro Dr., Monterey Park, CA 91754 (SAN 699-5403) Tel 818-572-9468.

Living Stone Pubs., *(Living Stone Pubs; 0-936637)*, 15851 Eighth, NE, Seattle, WA 98155 (SAN 699-6817); P.O. Box 55324, Seattle, WA 98155 (SAN 699-6825).

Living Way Ministries, *(Living Way; 0-916847)*, c/o The Church on the Way, 14300 Sherman Way, Van Nuys, CA 91405-2499 (SAN 653-7820) Tel 818-786-7090.

Livingston County Genealogical Society, *(Livingston County; 0-9616142)*, P.O. Box 922, Brighton, MI 48116 (SAN 699-8941) Tel 313-878-3680; 9040 Farley, Pinckney, MI 48169 (SAN 699-895X).

Livingston Press, *(Livingston Pr; 0-915772)*, 30 Niantic River Rd., Waterford, CT 06385 (SAN 207-6802) Tel 203-442-3383; Orders to: Independent Pubs. Group, One Pleasant Ave., Port Washington, NY 11050 (SAN 207-6810).

†Livingston Publishing Co., *(Livingston; 0-87098; 0-915180)*, 18 Hampstead Circle, Wynnewood, PA 19096 (SAN 202-6821); Orders to: Harrowood Books, 3943 N. Providence Rd., Newtown Sq., PA 19073 (SAN 207-1622) Tel 215-353-5585; *CIP.*

LLanerch Books, *(LLanerch Bks)*, Box 711, Haverton, PA 19083 (SAN 208-4546).

†Llewellyn Pubns., Div. of Chester-Kent, Inc., *(Llewellyn Pubns; 0-87542)*, P.O. Box 64383, St. Paul, MN 55164-0383 (SAN 201-100X) Tel 612-291-1970; Toll free: 800-843-6666; 213 E. Fourth St., St. Paul, MN 55101 (SAN 658-1161); *CIP.*

Lloyd, D. K., & M. Lipow, *(Lloyd & Lipow; 0-9601504)*, c/o American Society for Quality Control, 230 W. Wells St., Milwaukee, WI 53203 (SAN 211-0318) Tel 414-272-8575.

LLoyd O'Enterprises/Publishers, *(Lloyd O'Ent Pubs; 0-9609886)*, P.O. Box 6665, Woodland Hills, CA 91365 (SAN 272-0957) Tel 818-883-4058.

Lloyd-Simone Publishing Co., *(Lloyd Simone Pub; 0-938249)*, 32 Hillside Ave., Monsey, NY 10952 (SAN 661-3683) Tel 914-356-7273; Dist. by: Library Research Assocs., Inc., P.O. Box 41, Monroe, NY 10950 (SAN 201-0887) Tel 914-783-1144.

Lloyd's of London Pr., Div. of Lloyd's of London Pr. (UK), *(Lloyds London Pr; 0-907432)*, 817 Broadway, New York, NY 10003 (SAN 679-1778) Tel 212-673-4700.

Lloylds Publishing Co., Inc., The, *(Lloylds Pub; 0-917113)*, Main St. Bldg. Drawer 544, New Milford, CT 06776 (SAN 655-7597) Tel 803-286-5555.

Lochinvar *See* Exposition Pr. of Florida, Inc.

Locke, Sue Hennigan, *(S Locke; 0-9615585)*, Box 206, Marthaville, LA 71450 (SAN 695-9067) Tel 318-472-6808.

Lockhart Pr., The, *(Lockhart Pr; 0-911783)*, Box 1207, Port Townsend, WA 98368 (SAN 264-1801) Tel 206-385-6413.

Lockman, Vic, *(V Lockman; 0-936175)*, P.O. Box 1916, Ramona, CA 92065 (SAN 697-2063) Tel 619-789-9572.

Locus, Bk. Div., Div. of T-Track Security Systems, *(Locus; 0-943812)*, 4311 Atlantic Ave., Suite 200, Long Beach, CA 90807 (SAN 238-3128) Tel 213-426-2368.

Locust Enterprises, *(Locust Ent; 0-9606730)*, W. 174 N. 9422, Devonwood Rd., Menomonee Falls, WI 53051 (SAN 219-6786) Tel 414-251-1415.

Locust Hill Pr., *(Locust Hill Pr; 0-933951)*, P.O. Box 260, West Cornwall, CT 06796 (SAN 693-0646) Tel 203-672-0060.

Lodestar Bks., Div. of E. P. Dutton, *(Lodestar Bks; 0-525)*, 2 Park Ave., New York, NY 10016 (SAN 212-5013) Tel 212-725-1818; Toll free: 800-526-0275; Dist. by: New American Library, P.O. Box 999, Bergenfield, NJ 07621 (SAN 206-8079) Tel 201-387-0600; Toll free: 800-526-0275.

Lodima Press, *(Lodima; 0-9605646)*, Revere, PA 18953 (SAN 216-1567) Tel 215-847-2005.

Loewenthal Pr., *(Loewenthal Pr; 0-914382)*, P.O. Box 1107, New York, NY 10009 (SAN 206-5576).

Loft, Barnell, Ltd., *(B Loft; 0-87965; 0-8484)*, 958 Church St., Baldwin, NY 11510 (SAN 202-3679) Tel 516-868-6064.

Log Boom Brewing, *(Log Boom; 0-9604130)*, Box 1825, Boulder, CO 80306 (SAN 214-4034).

Logan, Carolyn, *(C Logan; 0-9602804)*, Peck Slip P.O. Box 607, New York, NY 10272 (SAN 699-8186).

Logan County Kansas Historical Society, *(KS Historical Soc; 0-9617260)*, 700 W. Third, Oakley, KS 67748 (SAN 663-4818) Tel 913-672-4776. Do not confuse with Logan County Historical Society, Inc. of Guthrie, OK.

Logan Design Group, *(Logan Design; 0-9603856)*, 12344 Addison St., North Hollywood, CA 91607-3610 (SAN 213-9359) Tel 818-761-2319.

Logan Enterprises Pub Co, *(Logan Enter; 0-9613718)*, 4214 Loch Raven Blvd., Baltimore, MD 21218 (SAN 676-2905) Tel 301-433-2693.

Logan Hill Press, *(Logan Hill; 0-918610)*, 204 Fairmount Ave., Ithaca, NY 14850 (SAN 207-5520) Tel 607-273-0707.

†Logbridge-Rhodes, Inc., *(Logbridge-Rhodes; 0-937406)*, P.O. Box 3254, Durango, CO 81302 (SAN 215-0905) Tel 303-259-3053; Dist. by: Inland Book Company, P.O. Box 261, Hemingway Ave., East Haven, CT 06512 (SAN 200-4151) Tel 203-467-4257; Toll free: 800-243-0138; Dist. by: Small Press Distribution, 1814 San Pablo Ave., Berkeley, CA 94702 (SAN 204-5826) Tel 415-549-3336; *CIP.*

Logical Solutions Technology, Inc., *(Logical Solns Tech; 0-912253)*, 96 Shereen Pl., Suite 101, Campbell, CA 95008 (SAN 265-1602) Tel 408-374-3650.

Logos Bks. *See* Contemporary Bks., Inc.

Lohmann, Jeanne A., *(J A Lohmann; 0-9607688)*, 722 Tenth Ave., San Francisco, CA 94118 (SAN 209-2204) Tel 415-387-7644.

†Loiry Publishing Hse., *(Loiry Pubs Hse; 0-9607654; 0-933703)*, 226 W. Pensacola St., No. 301, Tallahassee, FL 32301 (SAN 238-7883) Tel 904-681-0019; Dist. by: Baker & Taylor Co., Eastern Div., 50 Kirby Ave., Somerville, NJ 08876 (SAN 169-4901); Dist. by: Ingram Industries, 347 Reedwood Dr., Nashville, TN 37217 (SAN 169-7978); *CIP.*

Loiselle, Emery J., *(E J Loiselle; 0-9613281)*, 361 Cambridge St., Burlington, MA 01803 (SAN 654-5386) Tel 617-272-0244.

†Loizeaux Brothers, Inc., *(Loizeaux; 0-87213)*, P.O. Box 277, Neptune, NJ 07754-0277 (SAN 202-6848); 1238 Corlies Ave., Neptune, NJ 07754-0277 (SAN 699-5411) Tel 201-774-8144; Toll free: 800-526-2796; *CIP.*

Lokman Publishing Co., Div. of Lenan Enterprises, *(Lokman Pub Co; 0-937105)*, P.O. Box 1731, Columbia, MO 65205 (SAN 658-6163) Tel 314-445-7007; Rte. 3, Box 436, Columbia, MO 65203 (SAN 658-6171).

Lola Library Collection, *(Lola Library; 0-930825)*, 10348 La Canada Way, Sunland, CA 91040 (SAN 677-6108) Tel 818-352-0402.

Lollipop Bks., *(Lollipop LA; 0-9615509)*, P.O. Box 26A41, Los Angeles, CA 90026 (SAN 696-4109) Tel 213-423-5355; P.O. Box 454, Ocean Shores, WA 98569 (SAN 662-7811).

Lollipop Power, Inc., Affil. of Cardina Wren Pr., *(Lollipop Power; 0-914996)*, P.O. Box 277, Carrboro, NC 27510 (SAN 206-9733) Tel 919-933-9679.

Loma Linda Univ. Medical Ctr.-Medical Library, *(Loma Linda U; 0-9615491)*, P.O. Box 2000, Loma Linda, CA 92354 (SAN 696-3927) Tel 714-824-0800.

Lomas Publishing Co., *(Lomas Pub; 0-932485)*, 625 Ellis St., Suite 301, Mountain View, CA 94043 (SAN 687-3987) Tel 415-965-3378.

Lomatewama, Ramson, *(Lomatewama; 0-935825)*, 1953 Plaza Dr., Hotevilla, AZ 86030 (SAN 696-5881); P.O. Box 132, Hotevilia, AZ 86030 (SAN 699-637X).

Lomond Pubns., Inc., *(Lomond; 0-912338)*, P.O. Box 88, Mt. Airy, MD 21771 (SAN 206-765X) Tel 301-829-1496; Toll free: 800-443-6299.

Lond Pubns., *(Lond Pubns)*, Pomona, NY 10970 (SAN 208-127X).

London Bookshop Ltd., *(London Bkshop; 0-939281)*, P.O. Box 10115, Ft. Dearborn Sta., Chicago, IL 60610 (SAN 662-7056); 1360 N. Lake Shore Dr., Chicago, IL 60610 (SAN 662-7064) Tel 312-642-8417.

London Hse. Pr., *(London Hse Pr; 0-930171)*, 1550 NW Highway, Park Ridge, IL 60068 (SAN 670-7262) Tel 312-298-7311.

London Publishing Co., *(London Pub;
0-9613262),* 1725 DeSales St. NW, Suite
401, Washington, DC 20036
(SAN 296-5976) Tel 202-833-3875.

†**Londonborn Pubns.,** *(Londonborn Pubns;
0-930235),* P.O. Box 42278, San Francisco,
CA 94101 (SAN 670-7297)
Tel 415-485-5433; *CIP.*

Londonderry Press, *(Londonderry Pr; 0-901869),*
15 W. Mt. Vernon Pl., Baltimore, MD 21201
(SAN 295-1010) Tel 301-837-8558.

†**Lone Eagle Publishing,** *(Lone Eagle Pub;
0-943728),* 9903 Santa Monica Blvd., No.
204, Beverly Hills, CA 90212
(SAN 293-3004) Tel 213-471-8066; Dist.
by: Quality Bks., 918 Sherwood Dr., Lake
Bluff, IL 60044-2204 (SAN 169-2127); Dist.
by: Publishers Group West, 5855 Beaudry
St., Emeryville, CA 94608 (SAN 202-8522)
Tel 415-658-3453; Toll free: 800-982-8319;
CIP.

Lone Oak Bks., *(Lone Oak; 0-936550),* 10101
Old Georgetown Rd., Bethesda, MD
20814-1857 (SAN 216-1540)
Tel 301-656-3360; Dist. by: Book Carrier,
9121 Industrial Ct., Gaithersburg, MD 20877
(SAN 200-4046) Tel 301-258-1177; Dist.
by: Publishers Group West, 5855 Beaudry St,
Emeryville, CA 94608 (SAN 202-8522)
Tel 415-658-3453; Toll free: 800-982-8319.

Lone Star Bks. *See Gulf Publishing Co.*

Lone Star Pr., *(Lone Star Pr; 0-933551),* P.O.
Box 165, Laconner, WA 98257
(SAN 691-8735) Tel 206-466-3377.

Lone Wolf Publishing Hse., *(Lone Wolf Pub;
0-933303),* 555 Sutter, Suite 305, San
Francisco, CA 94102 (SAN 692-3011)
Tel 415-626-4386.

Lonely Planet Pubns., *(Lonely Planet;
0-908086),* 1555D Park Ave., Emeryville,
CA 94608 (SAN 659-6541).

Long, Judith R., Antiquarian Bks., *(J R Long
Antiquarian; 0-9614522),* 2710 Harvest
Way, Marietta, GA 30062 (SAN 158-4944)
Tel 404-977-0794.

Long, Robert P., *(R P Long; 0-9600064),* 445
Glen Court, Cutchogue, NY 11935
(SAN 204-661X) Tel 516-734-5368; Dist.
by: Prentice-Hall, Inc., P.O. Box 500,
Englewood Cliffs, NJ 07632
(SAN 200-2175) Tel 201-592-2602.

Long Beach Island Press, *(Long Beach Isl Pr;
0-941418),* P.O. Box 151, Tempe, AZ 85281
(SAN 239-006X) Tel 602-968-1566.

Long Beach Pubns., *(Long Beach Pubns;
0-941910),* P.O. Box 14807, Long Beach,
CA 90803 (SAN 239-782X)
Tel 213-439-8962.

Long Haul Pr., *(Long Haul; 0-9602284),* P.O.
Box 592, Van Brunt Sta., Brooklyn, NY
11215 (SAN 212-5986) Tel 718-965-3639;
Dist. by: Inland Bk. Co., P.O. Box 261, 22
Hemingway Ave., East Haven, CT 06512
(SAN 200-4151) Tel 203-467-4257.

Long House, Inc., *(Long Hse; 0-912806),* P.O.
Box 3, New Canaan, CT 06840-2931
(SAN 201-4947) Tel 203-966-2931.

Long Island Library Resources Council, *(LI Lib
Resources; 0-938435),* P.O. Box 31, Bellport,
NY 11713 (SAN 661-2989); 627 N. Sunrise
Service Rd., Bellport, NY 11713
(SAN 661-2997) Tel 516-286-0400.

Long Island Univ. Confrontation Magazine Pr.,
(L I U Press; 0-913057), C.W. Post
College,English Dept., Greenvale, NY 11548
(SAN 283-1864) Tel 516-299-2391.

Long Island Univ. Pr., *(LIU Univ; 0-913252),*
Univ. Plaza, Brooklyn, NY 11201
(SAN 211-688X) Tel 718-834-6064.

Long Range Planners Pr., *(Long Range Planners;
0-9614410),* P.O. Box 60400, Pasadena, CA
91106 (SAN 688-6116) Tel 213-256-5823.

Long Shadow Bks. *See Pocket Bks., Inc.*

Longanecker Books, *(Longanecker; 0-9601126),*
P.O. Box 127, Brewster, WA 98812
(SAN 210-2323) Tel 509-689-2441.

Longfellow National Historic Site, Div. of
National Park Service, *(Longfellow;
0-9610844),* 105 Brattle St., Cambridge, MA
02138 (SAN 265-2706) Tel 617-876-4491;
Dist. by: National Park Service, 105 Brattle
St., Cambridge, MA 02138 (SAN 200-7517)
Tel 617-876-4491.

Longhorn Press, *(Longhorn Pr; 0-914208),* Box
150, Cisco, TX 76437 (SAN 206-6920)
Tel 817-442-2530.

Longleaf Pubns., *(Longleaf Pubns),* 809 Teague
Dr., Tallahassee, FL 32315 (SAN 216-4094)
Tel 904-385-0383.

**Longman Financial Services Institute,
Incorporated,** *(LFSI Minnesota; 0-943634),*
9201 E. Bloomington Freeway, Minneapolis,
MN 55420 (SAN 238-2814)
Tel 612-885-2700.

Longman Financial Services Publishing, Subs. of
Longman Group USA, Inc., *(Longman Finan;
0-88462),* 500 N. Dearborn St., Chicago, IL
60610 (SAN 201-3622) Tel 312-836-0466.
Imprints: Educational Methods (Ed
Methods); Longman Financial Services
Publishing (Longman Fin Serv Pub); Real
Estate Education Company
(Real Estate Ed).

Longman Financial Services Publishing *See
Longman Financial Services Publishing*

Longman, Inc., Subs. of Longman Group USA,
(Longman; 0-582; 0-8013), 95 Church St.,
White Plains, NY 10601 (SAN 202-6856)
Tel 914-993-5000. *Imprints:* Drumbeat
(Drumbeat).

Longone, Jan, *(J Longone),* 1207 W. Madison,
Ann Arbor, MI 48103
(SAN 238-8405).

LongRiver Bks., *(LongRiver Bks; 0-942986),*
c/o Inland Bk. Co., 22 Hemingway Ave.,
East Haven, CT 06513 (SAN 240-3986);
Toll free: 800-243-0138.

Longshanks Bk., *(Longshanks Bk; 0-9601000),*
30 Church St., Mystic, CT 06355
(SAN 208-7391)
Tel 203-536-8656.

Longview Publishing Co., *(Longview Pub;
0-940614),* P.O. Box 189, Longview, WA
98632 (SAN 218-5660)
Tel 206-577-2504.

Longwood Cottage Publishing, *(Longwood
Cottage; 0-9616338),* 101 Magnolia Oak Dr.,
Longwood, FL 32779 (SAN 658-8743)
Tel 305-869-1689.

Longwood Publishing Group, Inc., *(Longwood
Pub Group; 0-89341),* 27 S. Main St,
Wolfeboro, NH 03894-2069
(SAN 209-3170) Tel 603-569-4576; Toll
free: 800-343-9444.

Lonstein Pubns., *(Lonstein Pubns; 0-87990),* 1
Terrace Hill, Box 351, Ellenville, NY 12428
(SAN 215-0913).

Loo, C. & R., Inc., *(C & R Loo),* 1550 62nd St.,
P.O. Box 8397, Emeryville, CA 94608
(SAN 211-366X).

Look, Margaret K., *(M K Look; 0-9616922),*
P.O. Box 1173, Powell, WY 82435
(SAN 661-5074); 940 Shoshone Dr., Powell,
WY 82435 (SAN 661-5082)
Tel 307-754-4656.

Looking Glass Pubns., *(Lkng Glass Pubns;
0-936485),* 1735 Willard St. NW, Suite 5,
Washington, DC 20009 (SAN 698-0988)
Tel 202-328-3555; P.O. Box 23691, l'Enfant
Plaza Sta., Washington, DC 20026
(SAN 698-2522).

Looking Glass Pubns., *(Looking Glass;
0-937646),* P.O. Box 3604, Quincy, IL
62305 (SAN 238-8936).

Loom Pr., *(Loom Pr; 0-931507),* P.O. Box 1394,
Lowell, MA 01853 (SAN 686-2780).

Loompanics Unlimited, *(Loompanics; 0-915179),*
P.O. Box 1197, Port Townsend, WA 98368
(SAN 206-4421) Tel 206-385-5087.

Loon Press, *(Loon Pr; 0-9612638),* 10582
Barnett Valley Rd., Sebastopol, CA 95472
(SAN 289-3037) Tel 707-823-8411.

LoonBooks, *(LoonBooks; 0-910477),* P.O. Box
901, Northeast Harbor, ME 04662
(SAN 219-2098); Main St., Northeast
Harbor, ME 04662 (SAN 662-0744)
Tel 207-276-3693.

Looseleaf Law Pubns. Corp., *(Looseleaf Law;
0-930137),* P.O. Box 42, Fresh Meadows
Sta., Fresh Meadows, NY 11365
(SAN 669-6929) Tel 718-359-5559.

Lopez, Eddie, *(E Lopez; 0-9606120),* 615 S.
20th, Donna, TX 78537 (SAN 216-8316)
Tel 512-464-2658.

Lopez, Violet, *(V Lopez; 0-9615909),* 119-20
Union Tpke., Apt. E3-A3, Kew Gardens, NY
11415 (SAN 697-2233) Tel 718-544-4194.

Loras College Pr., *(Loras Coll Pr; 0-936875),*
14th & Alta Vista Sts., Dubuque, IA 52001
(SAN 699-9166) Tel 319-588-7164.

Lord, William H., *(W H Lord; 0-9606320),*
9210 N. College Ave., Indianapolis, IN
46240 (SAN 214-0497) Tel 317-846-3907.

Lord Americana & Research, Inc., *(Lord
Americana; 0-916492),* 1521 Redwood Dr.,
West Columbia, SC 29169 (SAN 207-5261)
Tel 803-794-7104.

Lord Byron Stamps, *(Lord Byron Stamps;
0-938139),* P.O. Box 4586, Portland, OR
97208 (SAN 661-2253); 808 NE 113th
Ave., Portland, OR 97220 (SAN 661-2261)
Tel 503-254-7093.

Lord John Pr., *(Lord John; 0-935716),* 19073
Los Alimos St., Northridge, CA 91326
(SAN 213-6333) Tel 818-363-6621.

Lord Publishing, Div. of R.C. Ronstadt &
Assoc., Inc., *(Lord Pub; 0-930204),* 46 Glen
St., Dover, MA 02030 (SAN 210-5403)
Tel 617-785-1575. *Imprints:* Case
Publishing (Case Pub).

Lord's Line, *(Lords Line; 0-915952),* 1734
Armour Lane, Redondo Beach, CA 90278
(SAN 207-7086) Tel 213-542-5575.

Lore Publishing, *(Lore Pub; 0-911037),* P.O.
Box 492, Times Square Sta., New York, NY
10036 (SAN 272-1058).

Lore Unlimited, Inc., *(Lore Unlim; 0-941838),*
4850 Regents Park Lane, Fremont, CA
94538 (SAN 239-2534) Tel 415-657-6331.

Loren Bks., *(Loren Bks; 0-939605),* P.O. Box
1205, Eugene, OR 97440 (SAN 659-3984);
4490 Inwood Ln., Eugene, OR 97405
(SAN 663-3196) Tel 503-343-2104.

Lorenz & Herweg Pubs., *(Lorenz & Herweg;
0-916494),* P.O. Box 7764, Long Beach, CA
90807 (SAN 208-7405) Tel 213-422-0059.
Out of business.

Lorenz Press, Inc., Div. of Lorenz Industries,
Subs. of International Entertainment Corp.,
(Lorenz Pr; 0-89328), 501 E. Third St.,
Dayton, OH 45401 (SAN 208-7413)
Tel 513-228-6118; Dist. by: Independent
Pubs. Group, 1 Pleasant Ave., Port
Washington, NY 11050 (SAN 208-7421).

Loreto, Remy A., *(R A Loreto; 0-914209),* 3459
Melony Manor Dr., Cincinnati, OH 45239
(SAN 287-640X) Tel 513-948-1300.

Lorian Pr., *(Lorian Pr; 0-936878),* P.O. Box
663, Issaquah, WA 98027 (SAN 214-4042)
Tel 206-392-3982; Dist. by: Bookpeople,
2929 Fifth St., Berkeley, CA 94710
(SAN 168-9517) Tel 415-549-3030; Dist.
by: DeVorss & Co., P.O. Box 550, Marina
del Rey, CA 90291 (SAN 168-9886)
Tel 213-870-7478; Dist. by: Inland Bk. Co.,
22 Hemingway Ave., East Haven, CT 06512
(SAN 200-4151) Tel 203-467-4257; Dist.
by: Narada Distributors (Music Only), 1804
E. North St., Milwaukee, WI 53202
(SAN 200-7649); Toll free: 800-862-7232.

Lorien Hse., *(Lorien Hse; 0-934852),* P.O. Box
1112, Black Mountain, NC 28711
(SAN 209-2999) Tel 704-669-6211.

Lorrah & Hitchcock Pubs., Inc., *(Lorrah &
Hitchcock; 0-89809),* 301 S. 15th St.,
Murray, KY 42071 (SAN 220-7915).

Loru Co., The, *(Loru Co; 0-915710),* P.O. Box
396, North Webster, IN 46555
(SAN 220-7923).

†**Los Alamos Historical Society,** *(Los Alamos
Hist Soc; 0-941232),* P.O. Box 43, Los
Alamos, NM 87544 (SAN 276-9603); Dist.
by: Univ. of New Mexico Pr., Journalism
Bldg., Rm. 220, Albuquerque, NM 87131
(SAN 213-9588) Tel 505-277-2346; *CIP.*

Los Angeles Children's Museum, *(Los Angeles;
0-914953),* 310 N. Main St., Los Angeles,
CA 90012 (SAN 289-310X)
Tel 213-687-8226; Dist. by: Publishers
Group West, 5855 Beaudry St., Emeryville,
CA 94608 (SAN 289-3118)
Tel 415-658-3453; Dist. by: Beyda &
Associates, 6943 Valjean Ave., Van Nuys,
CA 91406 (SAN 289-3126).

Los Angeles Contemporary Exhibitions, *(LA
Contemp Exhib; 0-937335),* 1804 Industrial
St., Los Angeles, CA 90021
(SAN 658-8123) Tel 213-624-5650.

†**Los Angeles County Museum of Art,** *(LA Co
Art Mus; 0-87587),* 5905 Wilshire Blvd., Los
Angeles, CA 90036 (SAN 201-0577)
Tel 213-857-6044; *CIP.*

Los Angeles Library of Architecture, *(LA Lib
Architecture; 0-86558),* P.O. Box 402,
Pasadena, CA 91102-0402 (SAN 291-8021)
Tel 818-792-5024; 99 S. Raymond Ave.,
Suite 510, Pasadena, CA 91105
(SAN 658-2478).

Names

Names

Los Angeles Municipal Art Gallery Assocs., *(LA Municipal Art; 0-936429),* 4804 Hollywood Blvd., Los Angeles, CA 90027 (SAN 699-7473) Tel 213-485-4581.

Los Angeles Museum of Contemporary Art, The, *(Los Angeles Mus Contemp; 0-914357),* 414 Boyd St., Los Angeles, CA 90013 (SAN 289-6583) Tel 213-621-2766.

Los Angeles Olympic Organizing Committee, *(L A Olympic Org; 0-9614512),* 10945 La Conte, Los Angeles, CA 90024 (SAN 691-7399). Moved, left no forwarding address.

Los Arboles, *(Los Arboles Pub; 0-941992),* 820 Calle de Arboles, Redondo Beach, CA 90277 (SAN 238-020X) Tel 213-375-0759; Orders to: P.O. Box 7000-54, Redondo Beach, CA 90277 (SAN 662-0752).

Los Ninos International Adoption & Information Ctr., *(Los Ninos; 0-935366),* 1106 Randam Cir., Austin, TX 78745 (SAN 211-9129) Tel 512-443-2833.

Lost Cemetary Pr., *(Lost Cemetery Pr; 0-9614826),* RFD Box 37, South Conway, NH 03813 (SAN 693-0034) Tel 603-447-8429.

Lost Pleiade Press, *(Lost Pleiade; 0-915270),* 4919 55th Ave. S., Seattle, WA 98118 (SAN 207-3358).

†Lost Roads Pubs., *(Lost Roads; 0-918786),* P.O. Box 5848, Weybosset Hill Sta., Providence, RI 02903 (SAN 680-0564) Tel 401-941-4188; Dist. by: Small Pr. Distribution, 1814 San Pablo Ave., Berkeley, CA 94702 (SAN 204-5826) Tel 415-549-3336; Dist. by: Spring Church Bk. Co., P.O. Box 127, Spring Church, PA 15686 (SAN 212-7075); Dist. by: Bookslinger, 213 E. Fourth St., St. Paul, MN 55101 (SAN 169-4154) Tel 612-221-0429; Dist. by: Inland Bk. Co., P.O. Box 261, 22 Hemingway Ave., East Haven, CT 06512 (SAN 200-4151) Tel 203-467-4257; *CIP.*

†Lothrop, Lee & Shepard Bks., Div. of William Morrow & Co., Inc., *(Lothrop; 0-688),* 105 Madison Ave., New York, NY 10016 (SAN 201-1034) Tel 212-889-3050; Toll free: 800-631-1199; Orders to: William Morrow & Co., Inc., Wilmor Warehouse, 6 Henderson Dr., West Caldwell, NJ 07006 (SAN 202-5779); *CIP.*

Lotsawa, Inc., *(Lotsawa; 0-932156),* 140 E. 92nd St., New York, NY 10028 (SAN 213-893X) Tel 212-534-3384; Dist. by: Book Dynamics, 836 Broadway, New York, NY 10003 (SAN 169-5649) Tel 212-254-7798; Dist. by: Bookpeople, 2929 Fifth St., Berkeley, CA 94710 (SAN 168-9517); Dist. by: Devorss & Co., P.O. Box 550, 1046 Princeton Dr., Marina del Rey, CA 90294 (SAN 168-9886).

Lotus Light Pubns., Affil. of Specialized Software, *(Lotus Light; 0-941524),* P.O. Box 2, Wilmot, WI 53192 (SAN 239-1120) Tel 414-862-2395.

Lotus Pr CA, *(Lotus Pr CA; 0-934373),* P.O. Box 800, Lotus, CA 95651 (SAN 693-5664) Tel 916-626-1510.

Lotus Pr., Inc., *(Lotus; 0-916418),* P.O. Box 21607, Detroit, MI 48221 (SAN 213-8867) Tel 313-861-1280. *Imprints:* Penway Books (Penway Bks).

Lotus Publishing, *(Lotus Publishing; 0-9617249),* 1609 1/2 S. Gramercy Pl., Los Angeles, CA 90019 (SAN 663-5628) Tel 213-731-1084.

Louis, R., Publishing, *(R Louis Pub; 0-9605410),* 940 Poplar Ave., Boulder, CO 80302 (SAN 238-7409) Tel 303-444-6030.

Louis & Corsell, Inc., *(Louis & Corsell; 0-935339),* 2049 Century Park E., Suite 1800, Los Angeles, CA 90067 (SAN 696-3056) Tel 213-277-0028.

Louisiana Historical Assn., *(LA Hist Assn),* P.O. Box 40831, Lafayette, LA 70504 (SAN 205-2504) Tel 318-231-6029; Orders to: P.O. Box 42808, Univ. of Southwest Louisiana, Lafayette, LA 70504 (SAN 669-1536).

Louisiana Museum Foundation, Affil. of Louisiana State Museum, *(L A Mus Foun; 0-916137),* P.O. Box 2458, New Orleans, LA 70176-2458 (SAN 295-0057) Tel 504-525-6552.

Louisiana State Univ., Geoscience Pubns., *(LSU Geosci Pubns; 0-938909),* Louisiana State Univ., Dept. of Geography & Anthropology, Baton Rouge, LA 70803-4105 (SAN 661-7824) Tel 504-388-6245.

Louisiana State University Law Center, *(LSU Law Center),* Baton Rouge, LA 70803 (SAN 226-3521).

Louisiana State Univ., Law Schl., Pubns. Institute, *(LSU Law Pubns; 0-940448),* Paul M. Habert Law Ctr., Baton Rouge, LA 70803 (SAN 226-9910) Tel 504-388-8491.

†Louisiana State Univ. Pr., *(La State U Pr; 0-8071),* Highland Rd., Baton Rouge, LA 70893 (SAN 202-6597) Tel 504-388-6666; *CIP.*

Louisville & Jefferson County Heritage Corporation, *(Louisville & Jefferson; 0-9603278),* One Riverfront Plaza, Louisville, KY 40202 (SAN 213-3350) Tel 502-566-5000.

Louisville Museum of History & Science, *(Louisville Mus),* 727 W. Main St., Louisville, KY 40202 (SAN 655-7619).

Loup Valley Queen, *(Loup Valley; 0-9615586),* Box 278, Kimball St., Callaway, NE 68825 (SAN 695-9245) Tel 308-836-2244.

Louvin Publishing Co., *(Louvin Pub; 0-914471),* 37 Crescent Rd., Poughkeepsie, NY 12601 (SAN 217-4996).

Love, Stephen F., , *(S F Love; 0-9613239),* P.O. Box 1069,, Lake Oswego, OR 97034 (SAN 295-5083) Tel 503-635-7239.

Love, *(Love; 0-9608692),* Box 9, Prospect Hill, NC 27314 (SAN 238-3136) Tel 919-562-3380. Do not confuse with Love Publishers of Denver, CO.

Love Agape Ministries Press, Subs. of Love Ministries, Inc., *(Love Agape Min; 0-914605),* P.O. Box 69, Worthville, KY 41098 (SAN 290-7054); 467 Sandalwood Dr., Lexington, KY 40505 (SAN 290-7062) Tel 502-732-6728.

Love in Bloom Publishing, *(Love in Bloom Pub; 0-9616630),* 23219 Collins St., Woodland Hills, CA 91367 (SAN 661-2091) Tel 818-992-8448.

Love-Jackson Pubns, *(Love-Jackson; 0-9614315),* P.O. Box 4504, Carmel, CA 93921 (SAN 687-5181) Tel 408-373-8309.

Love Pubns., *(Love Pubns; 0-9613731),* 17075 SW Johnson, Beaverton, OR 97006 (SAN 677-4962) Tel 503-649-8763.

Love Publishing, *(Love Pub LA; 0-939359),* 225 Norcross, Bossier, LA 71111 (SAN 662-6793) Tel 318-746-7940. Do not confuse with Love Pub. Co., Denver, CO.

Love Publishing Co., *(Love Pub Co; 0-89108),* 1777 S. Bellaire St., Denver, CO 80222 (SAN 205-2482) Tel 303-757-2579.

Love Song to The Messiah Assn., Inc., *(Love Song Mess Assn; 0-915775),* 1609 N. Atlantic Blvd., Ft. Lauderdale, FL 33305 (SAN 293-8871) Tel 305-563-0697; Dist. by: Spring Arbor Distributors, 10885 Textile Rd., Belleville, MI 48111 (SAN 158-9016) Tel 313-481-0900; Toll free: 800-521-3690; Dist. by: Living Books, 12155 Magnolia Ave., Bldg., 11-B, Riverside, CA 92503 (SAN 169-006X) Tel 714-354-7630; Toll free: 800-854-4746.

Love Street Bks. See Marathon International Publishing Co.

Lovejoy Press, *(Lovejoy Pr; 0-9614264),* 501 E. Main Box 36, Wellington, IL 60973 (SAN 687-1429) Tel 815-984-3996.

Lovers of the Stinking Rose, *(Lovers Stinking),* 1621 Fifth St., Berkeley, CA 94710 (SAN 235-2273) Tel 415-527-5171.

Lovett School, The (The Lovett Mothers Club), *(Lovett Sch; 0-9610846),* 4075 Paces Ferry Rd., Atlanta, GA 30327 (SAN 265-2714) Tel 404-262-3032.

Loving Pubs., *(Loving Pubs; 0-938134),* 4576 Alla Rd., Los Angeles, CA 90066 (SAN 215-6768).

Low, Jennie, *(J Low; 0-9602820),* Dist. by: Altarinda Bks., 13 Estates Dr., Orinda, CA 94563 (SAN 238-1397) Tel 415-254-3830.

Low-Tech Pr., *(Low-Tech; 0-9605626),* 30-73 47th St., Long Island City, NY 11103 (SAN 216-1583) Tel 718-721-0946.

Lowe, George L., *(G L Lowe),* 401 E. 32nd St., Chicago, IL 60616 (SAN 217-1155).

Lowe, Joseph D., Pub., *(Lowe Pub; 0-9605506),* 2537 Regent St., No. 302, Berkeley, CA 94704 (SAN 240-0227) Tel 415-843-6535.

Lowe, Thomas E., Ltd., *(T E Lowe; 0-913926),* 2 Penn Plaza, Suite 1500, New York, NY 10121 (SAN 206-5592) Tel 212-865-3269.

Lowell Conference on Industrial History, The, *(Lowell Conf Ind Hist; 0-9607478),* 800 Massachusetts Ave., North Andover, MA 01845 (SAN 238-468X) Tel 617-686-0191.

Lowell Museum Corp., *(Lowell Museum; 0-942472),* P.O. Box 8415, Lowell, MA 01853 (SAN 239-9423) Tel 617-459-1066.

†Lowell Pr., *(Lowell Pr; 0-913504; 0-932845),* 115 E. 31st St., Box 411877, Kansas City, MO 64141 (SAN 207-0774) Tel 816-753-4545; *CIP.*

Lowell Publishing Co., Inc., *(Lowell Pub; 0-943730),* P.O. Box 8515, Lowell, MA 01853 (SAN 241-0338).

Lowen Publishing, *(Lowen Pub; 0-933051),* P.O. Box 6870-12, Torrance, CA 90504 (SAN 689-7681) Tel 213-831-2770.

Lowenkamp Publishing Co., *(Lowenkamp Pub; 0-913667),* P.O. Box 878, Hazelhurst, MS 39083-0878 (SAN 286-1682) Tel 601-894-2802.

Lower Cape Publishing, *(Lower Cape; 0-936972),* P.O. Box 901, Orleans, MA 02653 (SAN 214-4050) Tel 617-255-2244.

Lowie, R. H., Museum of Anthropology, *(Lowie Mus),* 103 Kroeber Hall, Univ. of California, Berkeley, Berkeley, CA 94720 (SAN 279-4381) Tel 415-642-3681.

Lowry & Volz, Pubs., *(Lowry & Volz; 0-9601740),* 2165 Greenspring Dr., Timonium, MD 21093 (SAN 211-6219) Tel 301-252-7272.

Lowry Hill, *(Lowry Hill; 0-9606416),* 1770 Hennepin Ave., No 42, Minneapolis, MN 55403 (SAN 223-0062) Tel 612-374-1579.

Lowy Publishing, *(Lowy Pub; 0-9602940),* 5047 Wigton, Houston, TX 77096 (SAN 212-9132) Tel 713-723-3209.

Loyalty Marketing Co., The, *(Loyalty Mktg; 0-9617002),* 608 Fifth Ave., Suite 309, New York, NY 10020 (SAN 662-538X) Tel 212-794-0100.

Loyola Univ., Criminal Justice Dept., *(Loyola U Crim; 0-942854),* 820 N. Michigan Ave., Chicago, IL 60611 (SAN 693-6962) Tel 312-670-2772.

Loyola Univ. of Chicago, Ctr. for Urban Policy, Div. of Loyola Univ. of Chicago, *(Loyola U Ctr Urban; 0-911531),* 820 N. Michigan Ave., Chicago, IL 60611 (SAN 264-1836) Tel 312-670-3112.

Loyola Univ. Pr., *(Loyola; 0-8294),* 3441 N. Ashland Ave., Chicago, IL 60657 (SAN 211-6537) Tel 312-281-1818; Toll free: 800-621-1008.

Loyola Univ., Schl. of Law, *(Loyola LA Law),* 6363 St. Charles Ave., New Orleans, LA 70118 (SAN 226-3513).

LS Records, Subs. of Cristy Lane Enterprises Inc., *(L S Records; 0-9614370),* 120 Hickory St., Madison, TN 37115 (SAN 688-5950) Tel 615-868-7171.

Lu, J. L., M.D., *(J L Lu; 0-9601768),* P.O. Box 4276, Sta. A., Dallas, TX 75208 (SAN 211-9137).

Lubavitch Women's Organization, *(Lubavitch Women; 0-930178),* 770 Eastern Pkwy., Brooklyn, NY 11213 (SAN 210-6345) Tel 718-604-2785.

Lubin Press, *(Lubin Pr; 0-9612396),* 396 N. Cleveland, Memphis, TN 38104 (SAN 289-4114) Tel 901-278-0561.

Lubrecht & Cramer, Ltd., *(Lubrecht & Cramer; 0-934454),* RD 1, Box 244 Rte. 42 Forestburgh Rd., Forestburgh, NY 12777 (SAN 214-1256) Tel 914-794-8539.

Lucas, Elizabeth H., *(E H Lucas),* 518 Monrovia Ave., Long Beach, CA 90814 (SAN 272-1228).

Lucas Communications Group, Inc., *(Lucas Comns; 0-9616276),* 90 Dayton Ave., Passaic, NJ 07055 (SAN 658-6201) Tel 201-471-5980.

Lucas/Evans Bks., *(Lucas/Evans Bks; 0-937291),* 1123 Broadway, Rm. 313, New York, NY 10010 (SAN 658-7526) Tel 212-929-2583.

Lucas Pubs., *(Lucas Pubs CA; 0-9604806),* 58 Arden Way, P.O. Box 15224, Sacramento, CA 95813 (SAN 215-6776).

†Luce, Robert B., Inc., *(Luce; 0-88331),* 425 Asylum St., Bridgeport, CT 06610 (SAN 201-1069) Tel 203-334-2165; Toll free: 800-243-2790; Orders to: 540 Barnum Ave., Bridgeport, CT 06608 (SAN 201-1077) Tel 203-366-1900; *CIP.*

Luce Pubns., *(Luce Pubs; 0-930827)*, 80 Wall St., Suite 614, New York, NY 10005 (SAN 677-6167) Tel 212-422-5186; P.O. Box 483, Wall St. Sta., New York, NY 10268 (SAN 692-6339) Tel 718-622-4163. Out of business.

Lucia Gallery, *(Lucia Gallery; 0-9616961)*, 90 W. Houston St., New York, NY 10012 (SAN 661-6801) Tel 212-460-8739.

Lucian Pr., Div. of Rouetel Systems, International, *(Lucian Pr; 0-9937297)*, P.O. Box 490, Veradale, WA 99037 (SAN 658-8018) Tel 509-926-2763; E16304 Valleyway, Veradale, WA 99037 (SAN 658-8026).

Lucifer, Inc., *(Lucifer Inc; 0-935375)*, 5567 New Peachtree Rd., Atlanta, GA 30341 (SAN 696-3714) Tel 404-455-4245.

Lucis Publishing Co., Div. of Lucis Trust, *(Lucis; 0-85330)*, 113 University Pl., New York, NY 10003 (SAN 201-1085) Tel 212-982-8770.

Lucky Literature, *(Lucky Lit; 0-9611860)*, P.O. Box 21043, Woodhaven, NY 11421 (SAN 286-1402) Tel 718-296-5252.

Lucky Star *See Scholastic, Inc.*

†Lucy Mary Bks., *(Lucy Mary Bks; 0-913829)*, P.O. Box 2381, Grand Junction, CO 81502 (SAN 286-1712) Tel 303-243-3231; *CIP.*

Ludlow, Norman H., *(N H Ludlow; 0-916706)*, 516 Arnett Blvd., Rochester, NY 14619 (SAN 207-5776) Tel 716-235-0951.

Luebbers, David J., *(D Luebbers; 0-9607406)*, 78 S. Jackson, Denver, CO 80209 (SAN 209-5777) Tel 303-888-8534.

Lueth Hse. Publishing Co., *(Lueth Hse Pub; 0-937911)*, 1409 Ninth St., Aurora, NE 68818 (SAN 659-4808) Tel 402-694-3988.

Luff, Moe, *(M Luff; 0-9600162)*, 12 Greene Rd., Spring Valley, NY 10977 (SAN 205-2466) Tel 914-356-4855.

†Lukas & Sons Pubs., *(Lukas & Sons; 0-930994)*, 4179 Fairmount Ave., San Diego, CA 92105 (SAN 211-2507); *CIP.*

Luker, Vera G., *(V Luker; 0-9615733)*, 6715 Tulip Ln., Dallas, TX 75230 (SAN 695-863X) Tel 214-361-6478.

Lukman, Mphahlele, Inc., *(M Lukman; 0-9602660)*, 9110 Ave. A, Brooklyn, NY 11236 (SAN 214-1922) Tel 718-485-7009.

Lumeli Press, *(Lumeli Pr; 0-930592)*, P.O. Box 555, Gonzales, CA 93926 (SAN 211-0326).

Lumen Christi Pr., *(Lumen Christi; 0-912414)*, P.O. Box 13176, Houston, TX 77019 (SAN 201-1093) Tel 713-827-0181.

Lumen, Inc., *(Lumen Inc; 0-930829)*, 446 W. 20th St., New York, NY 10011 (SAN 219-4430) Tel 212-989-7944; Dist. by: Bookslinger, 213 E. Fourth St., Saint Paul, MN 55101 (SAN 169-4154) Tel 612-221-0429; Dist. by: Inland Bk. Co., 22 Hemingway Ave., East Haven, CT 06512 (SAN 200-4151) Tel 203-467-4257.

Lumen Series, *(Lumen Series; 0-9611722)*, 1310 Highland Glen Rd., Westwood, MA 02090 (SAN 285-3183) Tel 617-329-9388.

Luna Bisonte Productions, *(Luna Bisonte; 0-935350)*, 137 Leland Ave., Columbus, OH 43214 (SAN 209-8326) Tel 614-846-4126.

Luna Pubns., *(Luna Pubns; 0-930346)*, 655 Orchard St., Oradell, NJ 07649 (SAN 212-288X).

Lunan-Ferguson Library, Pubs., *(Lunan-Ferguson; 0-911724)*, 2219 Clement St., San Francisco, CA 94121 (SAN 203-4042) Tel 415-752-6100.

Lunar & Planetary Institute, *(Lunar & Planet Inst; 0-942862)*, 3303 Nasa Rd. One, Houston, TX 77058 (SAN 238-0730) Tel 713-486-2143.

Lunchroom Pr., The, *(Lunchroom Pr; 0-938136)*, Box 36027, Grosse Pointe, MI 48236 (SAN 215-6784).

Lund, Harry C., *(H C Lund; 0-9614818)*, 1440 Wayne St., Traverse City, MI 49684 (SAN 693-0662).

Lundberg, Eric *See Johnson, John*

Lupine Pubns., *(Lupine Pubns; 0-933743)*, 808 Avoca, No. 9, Sheridan, WY 82801 (SAN 692-5987) Tel 307-674-8059.

LuraMedia, *(LuraMedia; 0-931055)*, P.O. Box 261668, 10227 Autumnview Ln., San Diego, CA 92126 (SAN 698-9234) Tel 619-578-1948; 136 Roumfort Rd., C/O Marcia Broucek, Philadelphia, PA 19119 (SAN 662-2542) Tel 215-247-4085.

Lurie, Hannah Ross, *(H R Lurie; 0-9600728)*, Carlene Apts., B102, 2500 Belmont Ave., Philadelphia, PA 19131 (SAN 201-6079) Tel 215-472-3510.

Luso-Brazilian Bks., *(Luso-Brazilian Bks; 0-85051)*, Times Plaza Sta., Box 286, Brooklyn, NY 11213 (SAN 695-4847).

Lust, Benedict, Pubns., *(Lust; 0-87904)*, 25 Dewart Rd., Greenwich, CT 06830 (SAN 201-1107) Tel 203-661-0980; Orders to: P.O. Box 404, New York, NY 10156 (SAN 201-1115).

†Lustrum Pr., *(Lustrum Pr; 0-912810)*, 714 Broadway, New York, NY 10003 (SAN 281-9562); Dist. by: Kampmann & Co., 9 E. 40th St., New York, NY 10016 (SAN 202-5183) Tel 212-685-2928; *CIP.*

Lutheran Academy for Scholarship, *(Luth Acad; 0-913160)*, c/o Richard Jungkuntz, 6310 Hillcrest Dr., SW, Tacoma, WA 98499 (SAN 285-0451).

Lutheran Church Women, *(Lutheran Church Wmn)*, 2900 Queen Lane, Philadelphia, PA 19129 (SAN 225-4611) Tel 215-438-2200.

Lutheran Council in the U.S.A., Div. of Campus Ministries, *(Luth Coun IL; 0-9609438)*, 35 E. Wacker Dr., Suite 1847, Chicago, IL 60601 (SAN 272-135X) Tel 312-332-1387.

Lutheran Council in the U.S.A., *(Lutheran Coun US; 0-9609438)*, 360 Park Ave. S., New York, NY 10010 (SAN 225-462X) Tel 212-532-6350.

Lutheran Women's Missionary League, *(Lutheran Womens; 0-9614955)*, 3558 S. Jefferson Ave., St. Louis, MO 63118 (SAN 693-7454) Tel 314-664-7000.

Luvera, Paul N., *(P N Luvera; 0-9612848)*, 917 S. Third St., Mount Vernon, WA 98273 (SAN 290-0106) Tel 206-336-6561; Dist. by: Washington State Trial Lawyers Assn., 225 S. Washington, Seattle, WA 98125 (SAN 290-0114) Tel 206-464-1011.

Lux Natura, *(Lux Natura; 0-937727)*, 5000 Bohemian Hwy., Occidental, CA 95465 (SAN 659-2732) Tel 707-874-3147.

LWK Enterprises, *(LWK Ent; 0-931733)*, P.O. Box 1127, Newark, DE 19715 (SAN 687-6234) Tel 302-737-3698.

LYCO Publishing, *(LYCO Pub)*, 3636 Drummond, Houston, TX 77025 (SAN 240-9631) Tel 713-668-0194.

Lydette Publishing Co., *(Lydette; 0-910918)*, P.O. Box 654, Cedar Falls, IA 50613 (SAN 203-9400) Tel 319-266-7578.

Lyman County Herald, *(Lyman Co Herald)*, Presho, SD 57568 (SAN 693-7802).

Lymelite Group, Inc., *(Lymelite Group; 0-9615796)*, 105 W. 72nd St., New York, NY 10116 (SAN 696-5997) Tel 212-787-0352.

Lyn-Bar Publishing Group, *(Lyn-Bar Pub; 0-938069)*, 69 Lillie St., Princeton Junction, NJ 08550 (SAN 661-1923) Tel 609-799-1476.

Lyn-Von Enterprises, *(Lyn-Von Enter; 0-937151)*, 1515 Summit St., Suite 3, Portsmouth, OH 45662 (SAN 658-5736) Tel 614-353-0650.

Lyncean Press, *(Lyncean Pr; 0-9614229)*, 16695 NW Yorktown Dr., Beaverton, OR 97006 (SAN 686-774X) Tel 503-629-8522; Dist. by: Quality Books, 918 Sherwood Dr., Lake Bluff, IL 60044-2204 (SAN 169-2127).

Lynch, Marietta & Perry, Patricia, *(M Lynch; 0-9610962)*, 240 Atlantic Rd., Gloucester, MA 01930 (SAN 265-2722) Tel 617-283-6322.

Lynch, Ruth, *(R Lynch; 0-9617250)*, 840 Ocean Dr., Apt. 903, Juno Beach, FL 33408 (SAN 663-561X) Tel 305-622-7350.

Lynch Brothers Enterprises, Inc., *(Lynch Bros Ent; 0-9617150)*, 3224 Timmons Ln. 125, Houston, TX 77027 (SAN 663-1525) Tel 713-840-0013.

Lynch Group Publishing, *(Lynch Group Pub; 0-911671)*, P.O. Box 18012, Cleveland, OH 44118 (SAN 264-1852).

Lynes, Martha A., *(M A Lynes; 0-9616631)*, 1 Bancroft Rd., Wellesley, MA 02181 (SAN 661-2105) Tel 617-237-2450.

Lynn, Robinson, Pub., *(Rob Lynn Pub; 0-9611994)*, 100 Walnut Pl., Brookline, MA 02146 (SAN 286-8075) Tel 617-277-3562.

†Lynx House Press, *(Lynx Hse; 0-89924)*, P.O. Box 800, Amherst, MA 01002 (SAN 208-2691) Tel 413-665-3604; *CIP.*

Lyon Productions, *(Lyon Prods; 0-933953)*, 44 Monterey Blvd., Suite 39, San Francisco, CA 94131 (SAN 693-0670) Tel 415-469-0175.

Lyons, Emily Bradley, *(E B Lyons; 0-9604374)*, 19065 St. Croy Rd., Red Bluff, CA 96080 (SAN 214-4069) Tel 916-527-7386.

Lyons, Jim, *(Jim Lyons; 0-9616231)*, P.O. Box 608, Mountain View, CA 94042 (SAN 658-5728) Tel 415-494-0790.

†Lyons, Nick, Bks., *(N Lyons Bks)*, 31 W. 21st St., New York, NY 10010 (SAN 208-1881) Tel 212-620-9580; *CIP.*

Lyons, Nick, Books *See Doubleday & Co., Inc.*

Lyons Business & Professional Assn., *(Lyons Busn & Pro; 0-9615472)*, 123 Main Ave., Clinton, IA 52732 (SAN 661-5406).

Lyric Publishing Co., *(Lyric Pub Co; 0-931453)*, 7826 Crenshaw Blvd., Los Angeles, CA 90043 (SAN 683-1842) Tel 213-778-7600.

Lyrica, *(Lyrica; 0-937129)*, 90 Church St., Guilford, CT 06437 (SAN 658-571X) Tel 203-453-1503.

Lytton Publishing Co., *(Lytton Pub; 0-915728)*, Box 1212, Sandpoint, ID 83864 (SAN 207-4257) Tel 208-263-3564.

MA/AH Publishing, Div. of Sunflower Univ. Pr., *(MA-AH Pub; 0-89126)*, Kansas State Univ., Eisenhower Hall, Manhattan, KS 66506-7186 (SAN 208-0230) Tel 913-532-6733; Dist. by: Sunflower University Press, 1531 Yuma, Manhattan, KS 66502-4228 (SAN 658-1811) Tel 913-532-6733.

M.A.C. Printing & Pubns. Div., *(MAC Print; 0-910223)*, 1850 High St., Denver, CO 80218 (SAN 241-4031) Tel 303-321-2651.

M.A.D. Hse., *(MAD Hse; 0-9606732)*, P.O. Box 1716, Sanford, FL 32771 (SAN 219-6794) Tel 305-323-5159.

MAGNA Pubs., *(MAGNA Pubs; 0-9613929)*, P.O. Box 422, Warren, OH 44482 (SAN 682-5060) Tel 216-399-5300.

MAKO Publishing Co., *(MAKO Pub; 0-9616963)*, 35552 Grand River, Suite 151, Farmington Hills, MI 48024 (SAN 661-7751) Tel 313-477-6113; Dist. by: Ludington News Company, 1600 E. Grand Blvd., Detroit, MI 48211 (SAN 169-3751) Tel 313-925-7600.

M.A.R., *(M A R; 0-9611996)*, 6835 27th Ave. NE, Seattle, WA 98115 (SAN 286-813X) Tel 206-525-5583.

M & A Editions, *(M & A Edns; 0-913983)*, Rte. 5, P.O. Box 332, San Antonio, TX 78211 (SAN 286-7877) Tel 512-628-1440.

M & B Fulfillment Services, *(M & B Fulfillment)*, 540 Barnum Ave., Bridgeport, CT 06610 (SAN 282-6062) Tel 203-366-1900.

M & H Enterprises, *(M & H Enter; 0-936997)*, P.O. Box 26374, Sacramento, CA 95826 (SAN 658-3180) Tel 916-366-1053; 9230 Elmgrove Ct., Sacramento, CA 95826 (SAN 658-3199).

M & L Sales, *(M & L Sales)*, P.O. Box 467702, Atlanta, GA 30346 (SAN 693-0409) Tel 404-394-5506.

M&M Publishing Inc., Subs. of M & M Creative Group, *(M M Pub Inc; 0-915927)*, 12198 Henderson Rd., Clifton, VA 22024 (SAN 294-0582) Tel 703-830-2388.

M & R Pubns., *(M and R Pubns; 0-9607424)*, P.O. Box 2056, Turlock, CA 95381 (SAN 239-7838) Tel 209-892-6282.

M&S Enterprises, *(M & S Ent; 0-943732)*, Box 42978, Tucson, AZ 85733 (SAN 241-0346) Tel 602-746-7154. Out of business.

M&S Pr., *(M&S Pr; 0-87730)*, Box 311, Weston, MA 02193 (SAN 203-9591) Tel 617-891-5650.

M & T Publishing, Inc., *(M & T Pub Inc; 0-934375)*, 501 Galveston Dr., Redwood City, CA 94063 (SAN 210-4830) Tel 415-366-3600.

MB Bks., *(MB Books; 0-935811)*, 350 20th Ave. S., Wisconsin Rapids, WI 54494 (SAN 696-6098) Tel 715-424-1938.

MBM Bks., *(MBM Bks; 0-942144)*, P.O. Box 1087, Valley Center, CA 92082 (SAN 238-4418) Tel 619-749-2380.

MBO, Inc., *(MBO Inc; 0-9602950)*, 157 Pontoosic Rd., P.O. Box 10, Westfield, MA 01085 (SAN 213-4136).

M B Publishing, *(M B Pub; 0-932543)*, P.O. Box 12, Hugo, OK 74743 (SAN 687-4827) Tel 405-326-2677.

MCA, *(MCA)*, P.O. Box 1775, Quantico, VA 22134 (SAN 218-4923).

MC Corp., of Stillwater, The, *(MC Corp Stillwater; 0-9617195)*, 10164 Norell Ave., Stillwater, MN 55082 (SAN 663-2440) Tel 612-439-2680.

MCL Assocs., *(MCL Assocs; 0-930696)*, 6916 Rosemont Dr., McLean, VA 22101 (SAN 281-9589) Tel 703-356-5979; P.O. Box 26, McLean, VA 22101 (SAN 658-117X).

MCN Pr., Subs. of Military Collectors' News Pr., *(MCN Pr; 0-912958)*, P.O. Box 702073, Tulsa, OK 74170 (SAN 203-9915) Tel 918-743-6048; Dist. by: Baker & Taylor Co., Midwest Div., 501 S. Gladiola Ave., Momence, IL 60945 (SAN 169-2100); Dist. by: Key Bk. Service, 425 Asylum St., Bridgeport, CT 06610 (SAN 209-6404) Tel 203-334-2165; Dist. by: Baker & Taylor Co., Eastern Div., 50 Kirby Ave., Somerville, NJ 08876 (SAN 169-4901); Dist. by: Baker & Taylor Co., Southeast Div., Mt. Olive Rd., Commerce, GA 30529 (SAN 169-1503); Dist. by: Baker & Taylor Co., Western Div., 380 Edison Way, Reno, NV 89564 (SAN 169-4464) Tel 702-786-6700.

MCP Bks., *(MCP Bks; 0-9603926)*, 8818 Higdon Dr., Vienna, VA 22180 (SAN 214-1930).

M C Productions, *(MC Prods; 0-9609862)*, P.O. Box 2402, Saugatuck Sta., Westport, CT 06880 (SAN 264-1879).

M-C Pubns., *(M-C Pubns; 0-9603850)*, 449 N. Lamer St., Burbank, CA 91506 (SAN 214-0500).

MCS, *(MCS; 0-932150)*, P.O. Box 1774, Morganton, NC 28655 (SAN 239-4529).

MCS Pubns. (KY), *(MCS Pubns KY; 0-933811)*, P.O. Box 486, Murray, KY 42071 (SAN 692-7742) Tel 502-753-7750.

MDEA Pr., *(M D E A; 0-9614629)*, 79 Knollwood Dr., Newport, VA 23602 (SAN 691-8948) Tel 804-877-1172.

MDK, Inc., *(MDK Inc; 0-934580)*, P.O. Box 2831, Chapel Hill, NC 27514 (SAN 213-6341) Tel 919-929-4260.

MD Pubns., *(MD Pubns; 0-910922)*, 30 E. 60th St., New York, NY 10022 (SAN 206-7668).

M. Damien Pubs., *(M Damien Pubs; 0-930539)*, 4810 Mahalo Dr., Eugene, OR 97405 (SAN 677-0975) Tel 503-687-9055; Dist. by: Publishers Group West, 5855 Beaudry St., Emeryville, CA 94608 (SAN 202-8522) Tel 415-658-3453; Dist. by: Pacific Pipeline Inc., 19215 66th Ave. S., Kent, WA 98032 (SAN 208-2128) Tel 206-872-5523; Toll free: 800-426-4727; Dist. by: Quality Bks., Inc., 918 Sherwood Dr., Lake Bluff, IL 60044-2204 (SAN 169-2127); Toll free: 800-323-4241.

MEDA Pubns., *(MEDA Pubns; 0-9610200)*, 107 Elena Drive, Scotts Valley, CA 95066 (SAN 264-1887).

†MEP Pubns., Div. of Marxist Educational Press, *(MEP Pubns; 0-930656)*, Univ. of Minnesota, Anthropology Dept., 215 Ford Hall, 224 Church St. SE, Minneapolis, MN 55455 (SAN 276-9727) Tel 612-872-9897; CIP.

MERU Publishing, *(Meru Pub; 0-911447)*, P.O. Box 1278, Captain Cook, HI 96704 (SAN 272-1538) Tel 808-328-9656; Dist by: Bookpeople, 2929 Fifth St., Berkeley, CA 94710 (SAN 168-9517) Tel 415-549-3030; Dist. by: Publishers Group West, 5855 Beaudry St., Emeryville, CA 94608 (SAN 202-8522) Tel 415-658-3453; Dist. by: The Book Hse., 208 W. Chicago St., Jonesville, MI 49250-0125 (SAN 169-3859) Tel 517-849-2117.

META Pubns., *(META Pubns; 0-916990)*, P.O. Box 565, Cupertino, CA 95015 (SAN 208-7448) Tel 415-326-6465.

M. G. Bookgraphics, *(M G Book Graphics; 0-933484)*, Los angeles, CA 90033 (SAN 281-9600). Insufficient address, no listing in Los Angeles.

MGLS Publishing, *(M G L S Pub; 0-9601682)*, 700 S. First St., Marshall, MN 56258 (SAN 212-2170) Tel 507-532-3553.

MGM & Assocs., *(MGM Assocs; 0-9616923)*, 8118 N. 38th Ave., Phoenix, AZ 85051 (SAN 661-4590) Tel 602-841-9398.

MGM Books, *(M G M Bks; 0-9613282)*, P.O. Box 682, South St. Paul, MN 55075 (SAN 654-469X) Tel 612-455-1756; Dist. by: Bookslinger, 213 E. Fourth St., St. Paul, MN 55101 (SAN 169-4154) Tel 612-221-0429.

MGT Information Publishing, *(MGT Info; 0-9610848)*, Box 3732, Arcadia, CA 91006 (SAN 265-2730) Tel 714-594-5611.

M.H. Cap & Co., *(M H Cap; 0-911375)*, Rte. 9, Box 327A, Bakersfield, CA 93312 (SAN 272-3972) Tel 805-589-0520.

MHM Publishing, *(MHM Pub; 0-936833)*, 6105 Tilden Ln., Rockville, MD 20852 (SAN 699-9697) Tel 301-881-7337.

MH Press, *(MH Pr; 0-917882)*, 9205 Tuckerman St., Lanham, MD 20801 (SAN 219-0907).

M.I. Adventure Pubns., *(MI Adventure Pubns; 0-9616395)*, RFD 1, Box 472, West Lebanon, ME 04027 (SAN 658-8921) Tel 207-658-9053; Old Stagecoach Rd., West Lebanon, ME 04027 (SAN 658-893X).

MI Instructor Series, *(MI Instructor; 0-937371)*, 723 SW Austin Pl., Seattle, WA 98106 (SAN 658-8972) Tel 206-763-0672.

MIP Company, *(M I P Co; 0-916201)*, P.O. Box 27484, Minneapolis, MN 55427 (SAN 295-0073) Tel 612-546-7578 Tel 612-546-7578.

MIP (Multi Image Presentations) Publishing, *(MIP Pub; 0-917204)*, 1482 E. Valley Rd., No. A141, Santa Barbara, CA 93108 (SAN 663-2815) Tel 805-969-9338.

MIR, Div. of Dr. Ilija Poplasen, *(MIR PA; 0-935352)*, 845 Suismon Dr., Pittsburgh, PA 15212 (SAN 213-5825) Tel 412-322-1319; Orders to: P.O. Box 962, Pittsburgh, PA 15230 (SAN 213-5833).

MIRA Academic Press, *(MIRA; 0-917919)*, P.O. Box 4334, Civic Center Branch, San Rafael, CA 94913 (SAN 656-8963) Tel 415-472-4811.

MIT Outing Club, *(MIT Outing; 0-9601698)*, W20-461, MIT, Cambridge, MA 02139 (SAN 210-8291) Tel 617-253-2988.

MIT Pr., *(MIT Pr; 0-262)*, 28 Carleton St., Cambridge, MA 02142 (SAN 202-6414) Tel 617-253-2884.

MJB Books, *(MJB Bks; 0-9609680)*, P.O. Box 3246, Merced, CA 95344 (SAN 272-4731) Tel 209-384-0322.

MJB Pub., *(MJB Pub; 0-9605990)*, 7209 Skyway, No. 13, Paradise, CA 95969 (SAN 216-7468). Moved, left no forwarding address.

MJH Information Services, *(MJH Info Servs; 0-939289)*, 10707 Buffalo Bend, Houston, TX 77064 (SAN 662-491X) Tel 713-469-3418.

MJK Enterprises, *(MJK Ent; 0-9610996)*, P.O. Box 5571, San Antonio, TX 78201 (SAN 265-2749) Tel 512-344-4348.

MJ Pubns., *(MJ Pubns; 0-9605144)*, 6363 Lynwood Hill Rd., McLean, VA 22101 (SAN 215-790X).

M.K.L., Ltd., *(M K L Ltd; 0-9614421)*, 535 Fifth Ave., New York, NY 10017 (SAN 689-0210) Tel 212-490-0172; Dist. by: Hudson County News, 1305 Paterson Plank Rd., North Bergen, NJ 07047 (SAN 169-4782).

MLB Pub., *(MLB Pub; 0-941794)*, P.O. Box 1732, Chesapeake, VA 23320 (SAN 239-2542) Tel 804-424-5238.

M. L. Dalton Research, *(M L Dalton Res; 0-9613740)*, 6035 Aberdeen, Dallas, TX 75250 (SAN 677-7112) Tel 214-691-4925.

MLM Pubns., *(MLM Pubs; 0-939102)*, 515 S. We-Go Trail, Suite 139, Mt. Prospect, IL 60056 (SAN 216-1613) Tel 312-392-7145.

MLP Enterprises, *(MLP Ent; 0-939020)*, 236 E. Durham St., Philadelphia, PA 19119 (SAN 214-4077) Tel 215-248-3218; Orders to: P.O. Box 18918, Philadelphia, PA 19119 (SAN 650-0420).

M-L Publishing Co., Ltd., *(M-L Pub; 0-915512)*, 157 Devonshire Rd., Wilmington, DE 19803 (SAN 207-1746) Tel 302-655-2849.

MMB Music, Inc., *(MMB Music; 0-918812)*, 10370 Page Industrial Blvd., St. Louis, MO 63132 (SAN 210-4601) Tel 314-427-5660.

MM Bks., *(M M Bks; 0-9612366)*, P.O. Box 29318, Crestwood, MO 63126 (SAN 289-4149).

MMI Press, *(MMI Press; 0-936445)*, 10 Pinecrest Rd., Valley Cottage, NY 10989 (SAN 697-9017) Tel 914-268-8868.

MMO Music Group Inc., *(MMO Music; 0-935647)*, 50 S. Buckout St., Irvington, NY 10533 (SAN 696-1746) Tel 914-591-5100.

MNP Star Enterprises, *(MNP Star; 0-938880)*, P.O. Box 1552, Cupertino, CA 95015-1552 (SAN 215-9708).

M. N. Pubs., *(MN Pubs; 0-932964)*, P.O. Box 27, Bonnerdale, AR 71933 (SAN 212-291X) Tel 501-991-3815.

M.O.P. Pr., *(M O P Pr; 0-942432)*, Rte. 24, Box 53C, Ft. Myers, FL 33908 (SAN 223-0860) Tel 813-466-4690.

MPI Home Video, *(MPI Home Video; 1-55607)*, 15825 Rob Roy Dr., Oak Forest, IL 60452 (SAN 659-2953) Tel 312-687-7881.

M P Publications, *(M P Pubs; 0-932187)*, 510 W. Chestnut St., Oxford, OH 45056 (SAN 686-5860) Tel 513-523-8621.

M Pr.,The, *(M Press; 0-9617067)*, 1623 Connecticut Ave., NW, Washington, DC 20009 (SAN 662-8699) Tel 202-232-8484.

MRDC Educational Institute, *(MRDC Educ Inst; 0-9604706)*, P.O. Box 15127, Dallas, TX 75201 (SAN 214-4085). Moved, left no forwarding address.

M-R-K Publishing, *(M R K; 0-9601292)*, 448 Seavey Ln., Petaluma, CA 94952 (SAN 210-461X) Tel 707-763-0056.

MSA, Inc., *(MSA Inc; 0-9616897)*, P.O. Box 2289, Provo, UT 84603 (SAN 661-6038); 342 Wymount Terr., No. 6A, Provo, UT 84604 (SAN 661-6046) Tel 801-377-0642.

MSS Pr., *(MSS Press; 0-938621)*, SUNY at Binghamton, Binghamton, NY 13901 (SAN 219-5062) Tel 607-777-2404.

MTA Financial Services Corp., *(MTA Financial Servs)*, 1010 Hunter Court, Deerfield, IL 60015 (SAN 212-6265) Tel 312-945-3649.

MTC Publishing Co., *(M T C Pub Co; 0-9613068)*, P.O. Box A6-158, Suite O, Laguna Niguel, CA 92677 (SAN 294-6076) Tel 714-831-0456.

MTI Teleprograms Inc./A Simon & Schuster Communications Company, *(MTI Tele; 0-916070)*, 108 Wilmot Rd., Deerfield, IL 60015 (SAN 211-0350) Tel 312-940-1260; Toll free: 800-621-2131.

M/T/M Publishing Co., *(MTM Pub Co; 0-938758)*, P.O. Box 245, Washougal, WA 98671 (SAN 206-1627).

MUMPS Users Group, *(MUMPS; 0-918118)*, 4321 Hartwick Rd., Suite 510, College Park, MD 20740 (SAN 669-1633) Tel 301-779-6555.

MWS Pubns, *(MWS Pubs; 0-939640)*, 1450 Golden Gate Ave., No.204, San Francisco, CA 94115 (SAN 216-6348).

M-Z Information, *(M-Z Info; 0-937559)*, P.O. Box 2129, Wilton, NY 12866 (SAN 658-8999) Tel 518-587-7638; Hyspot Rd., Greenfield Center, NY 12833 (SAN 658-8999).

M, A Press *See* Dilithium Pr.

Ma Cherie Chienne, *(Ma Cherie Chienne; 0-9616477)*, 555 Phillips Cir., Antioch, IL 60002 (SAN 659-2902) Tel 312-395-4985.

Maat Publishing Co., *(Maat Pub; 0-917650)*, P.O. Box 281, Bronx, NY 10462 (SAN 209-2239).

Mabern & Hart, *(Mabern & Hart; 0-9616773)*, 1131 E. 28th St., Brooklyn, NY 11210 (SAN 661-4175) Tel 718-258-8866.

Macalester College, *(Mac Col MN; 0-9606844)*, Weyerhaeuser Library, St. Paul, MN 55105 (SAN 213-2567) Tel 612-696-6346.

Macalester Park Bookstore, *(Macalester; 0-910924)*, 1571 Grand Ave., St. Paul, MN 55105 (SAN 110-8077) Tel 612-698-8877.

McAlister, Marcia, Enterprises, *(M M Enter)*, P.O. Box 381704, Germantown, TN 38138 (SAN 698-1909); 1504 Wheatstone Cove, Germantown, TN 38138 (SAN 699-6523) Tel 901-755-4444; Dist. by: Wimmer Brothers Bks., 4210 BF Goodrich Blvd., Memphis, TN 38181 (SAN 209-6544) Tel 901-362-8900.

McAllister Bks., *(McAllister; 0-910930)*, 410 Lake Ct., Waukegan, IL 60085 (SAN 203-946X) Tel 312-662-1929.

MacAnna-Rose Pub. Co., *(Macanna-Rose; 0-914241)*, P.O. Box 1473, Cocoa Beach, FL 32931 (SAN 287-5179) Tel 305-784-0031.

MacArthur Memorial, *(MacArthur Memorial; 0-9606418)*, MacArthur Square, Norfolk, VA 23510 (SAN 215-8876) Tel 804-441-2965.

McArthur Pub., *(McArthur Pub; 0-9614047)*, P.O. Box 929, Ruston, LA 71273-0929 (SAN 692-6452).

McBee Sports Enterprises, Inc., *(McBee Sports; 0-9609500)*, P.O. Box 834, Burlington, NC 27216-0834 (SAN 264-1895) Tel 919-227-7684.

Names

McBogg, Bruce, *(B McBogg; 0-941400),* 3405 Alcott St., Denver, CO 80211 (SAN 237-9848).

†**McBooks Pr.,** *(McBooks Pr; 0-935526),* 106 N. Aurora, Ithaca, NY 14850 (SAN 213-8573) Tel 607-272-6602; *CIP.*

McBride, Esther, *(Esther McBride; 0-9613017),* 1460 Bramble Ct., Rio Rancho, NM 87124 (SAN 293-8928) Tel 505-892-6277.

McBride, Gisela, *(G McBride; 0-9613270),* 1443 Court St., Allentown, PA 18101 (SAN 297-0252) Tel 215-776-1824.

McBride Pub., *(McBride Pub; 0-930313),* 161 S. Whitney St., Hartford, CT 06105 (SAN 686-9300) Tel 203-523-1622.

McCabe, Donald L., *(McCabe; 0-9605856),* 3221 Greenwood Ave., Sacramento, CA 95821 (SAN 216-6054) Tel 916-334-4810.

Maccabee Publishing Co., Inc., *(Maccabee Pub; 0-942500),* 14 W. Forest Ave., Englewood, NJ 07631 (SAN 226-207X) Tel 201-569-8700.

McCafferty, Jane R., *(McCafferty; 0-9606920),* 613 Rosier Rd., Ft. Washington, MD 20744 (SAN 217-4022) Tel 301-839-5812.

McCahan Foundation & American College, *(McCahan Found Amer Coll; 0-937094),* 270 Bryn Mawr Ave., Bryn Mawr, PA 19010 (SAN 215-0921) Tel 215-896-4544.

McCain Publishing, *(McCain Pub; 0-9608314),* P.O. Box 63, Fort Recovery, OH 45846 (SAN 240-5490) Tel 419-375-4226.

McCallum, John, *(McCallum; 0-9614523),* 5926 Beechview Dr., Worthington, OH 43085 (SAN 691-7402) Tel 614-885-8416.

McCann, Lester J., *(L J McCann; 0-9616935),* 305 E. Main St., Waconia, MN 55387 (SAN 662-5711) Tel 612-442-5201.

McCarton Maritime Pub, *(McCartan Maritime; 0-935786),* 325 E. 57th St., New York, NY 10022 (SAN 214-2546) Tel 212-421-2641.

McCarty, F. M., Co., *(F M McCarty; 0-911990),* 4527 Clawson Rd., Austin, TX 78745 (SAN 205-5716) Tel 512-447-6201.

McClain Printing Co., *(McClain; 0-87012; 0-9613967),* 212 Main St., Parsons, WV 26287 (SAN 203-9478) Tel 304-478-2881.

McClanahan Publishing Hse., Inc., *(McClanahan Pub; 0-913383),* Rte. 2, P.O. Box 32, Kuttawa, KY 42055 (SAN 285-8371) Tel 502-388-9388.

McClure Press/McClure Printing Co., Inc., *(McClure Printing),* P.O. Box 936, Verona, VA 24482 (SAN 205-8065) Tel 703-248-0874.

McCombe, R. S. & Sharon Haney, *(R S Mc Combe & S Haney; 0-9611326),* P.O. Box 644, Delta Junction, AK 99737 (SAN 282-9606) Tel 907-895-4179.

McConnell, R.A., *(McConnell; 0-9610232),* 430 Kennedy Ave., Pittsburgh, PA 15214 (SAN 272-1600) Tel 412-321-1213.

McCormick, Joan, *(J McCormick; 0-9616612),* 107 Moores Creek Dr., Tabb, VA 23602 (SAN 661-4051) Tel 804-867-8034.

McCoy & Assocs., *(McCoy & Assocs; 0-930469),* 13131 W. Cedar Dr., Lakewood, CO 80228 (SAN 670-896X) Tel 303-987-0333.

McCuen, Gary E., Pubns., Inc., *(G E McCuen Pubns; 0-86596),* 411 Mallalieu Dr., Hudson, WI 54016 (SAN 691-909X) Tel 715-386-5662.

†**McCutchan Publishing Corp.,** *(McCutchan; 0-8211),* 2526 Martin Luther King Jr. Way, Berkeley, CA 94701 (SAN 203-9486) Tel 415-841-8616; Toll free: 800-227-1540; P.O. Box 774, Berkeley, CA 94701 (SAN 658-1188); *CIP.*

McDaniel Hse. Publishing, *(McDaniel House; 0-943650),* P.O. Box 13265, Portland, OR 97213 (SAN 238-3152) Tel 503-835-0230.

McDonald, Paul R., *(McDonald P R; 0-9611258),* 895 Prospect Blvd., Waterloo, IA 50701 (SAN 283-3425) Tel 319-233-0545.

McDonnell Douglas Information Systems Group, Div. of McDonnell Douglas Corp., *(McDonnell Douglas),* P.O. Box 516, St. Louis, MO 63166 (SAN 241-5585) Tel 314-232-5715; Toll free: 800-325-1087.

McDougal, Littell & Co., *(McDougal-Littell; 0-88343; 0-8123),* P.O. Box 1667, Evanston, IL 60204 (SAN 202-2532) Tel 312-967-0900.

McDougal Publishing, *(McDougal Pub TX; 0-9616143),* Rte. 2, Box 144, Abernathy, TX 79311 (SAN 699-850X) Tel 806-746-6419; Dist. by: Cookbook Publishers, The Collection, 2101 Kansas City Rd., Olathe, KS 66061 (SAN 200-6359) Tel 913-764-5900.

McDowell Publishing Co., *(McDowell Pub Co; 0-914609),* P.O. Box 128, Alief, TX 77411 (SAN 289-3533) Tel 713-772-3344.

Macduff Pr., *(Macduff Pr; 0-9606272),* 660 Market St., Rm. 205, San Francisco, CA 94104 (SAN 220-3405) Tel 415-981-0970.

Mace, Evelyn, *(E Mace; 0-9616632),* P.O. Box F, Johnson, KS 67855 (SAN 661-2113) Tel 316-492-2380.

McElderry Bk. *See* Atheneum Pubs.

McElyer Pubns., *(McElyer Pubns; 0-9615622),* 2850 W. Fairbanks Ave., Winter Park, FL 32789 (SAN 696-1258) Tel 305-644-4981.

†**McFarland & Co., Inc., Pubs.,** *(McFarland & Co; 0-89950),* Box 611, Jefferson, NC 28640 (SAN 215-093X) Tel 919-246-4460; *CIP.*

McGill Pubns., *(McGill Pubns; 0-939575),* 163 Ironia Rd., Flanders, NJ 07836 (SAN 241-5593) Tel 201-927-0993.

McGill-Queens Univ. Pr., *(McGill-Queens U Pr; 0-7735),* 33 E. Tupper St., Buffalo, NY 14203 (SAN 662-7285); Orders to: Univ. of Toronto Pr., 33 E. Tupper St., Buffalo, NY 14203 (SAN 214-2651) Tel 716-852-0342.

McGilvery, Laurence, *(McGilvery; 0-910938),* P.O. Box 852, La Jolla, CA 92038 (SAN 203-9494) Tel 619-454-4443.

†**McGinnis & Marx Music Pubs.,** *(McGinnis & Marx),* P.O. Box 229, Planetarium Sta., New York, NY 10024 (SAN 281-9627) Tel 212-243-2090; Dist. by: Pietro Deiro Music Headquarters, 123 Greenwich Ave., New York, NY 10014 (SAN 282-5880) Tel 212-675-5460; *CIP.*

McGlynn, June A., *(McGlynn; 0-9601350),* 1529 Meadowlark Dr., Great Falls, MT 59404 (SAN 210-6094) Tel 406-452-3486.

McGovern & Mulbacker, *(McGovern Mulbacker; 0-9614725),* 1225 NW Murray Rd., No. 214, Portland, OR 97229 (SAN 692-5316) Tel 503-644-6600.

McGrady, L. J., *(L J McGrady),* 5760 St. Clement Court, Toledo, OH 43613 (SAN 295-0146); Dist. by: Ye Olde Genealogie Shoppe, P.O. Box 39128, Indianapolis, IN 46239 (SAN 200-7010).

McGraw-Hill Bk. Co., Health Professions Div., PreTest Series, *(McGraw-Pretest),* Orders to: P.O. Box 400, Hightstown, NJ 08520 (SAN 207-4184).

McGraw-Hill Bk. Co., *(McGraw; 0-07; 0-914410),* 1221 Ave. of the Americas, New York, NY 10020 (SAN 200-2248) Tel 212-512-2000; Toll free: 800-628-0004; Orders to: Princeton Rd., Hightstown, NJ 08520 (SAN 200-254X) Tel 609-426-5254; Orders to: 8171 Redwood Hwy., Novato, CA 94947 (SAN 200-2566) Tel 415-897-5201; Orders to: 13955 Manchester Rd., Manchester, MO 63011 (SAN 200-2558) Tel 314-227-1600. *Imprints:* Architectural Record Books (Architectural Rec Bks); BYTE Books (BYTE Bks); C T B/McGraw-Hill (CTB McGraw Hill); Chemical Engineering (Chem Eng); I B C (IBC); Instructo/McGraw-Hill (Instructo); Pre-Test (Pre-Test); Pre-Text Series (Pre-Text Series); Professional & Reference Book Division (Prof & Ref Bk Div).

Macgregor, Scotty, Pubns., *(Macgregor; 0-912546),* 138 Antonia Dr., Jackson, NJ 08527 (SAN 206-6912) Tel 201-928-4388.

McGuffin Books *See* Gaslight Pubns.

McHenry Mansion Foundation Pr., *(McHenry Mansion; 0-9615926),* 801 11th St., Modesto, CA 95353 (SAN 696-6616) Tel 209-577-5344; P.O. Box 642, Modesto, CA 95353 (SAN 699-6418).

McHenry Museum Society Pr., *(McHenry Mus Soc; 0-930349),* 1402 I St., Modesto, CA 95354 (SAN 670-834X).

Machinery & Allied Products Institute, *(M & A Products),* 1200 18th St., NW., Washington, DC 20036 (SAN 205-8014).

MacIlo Publishing Co., *(MacIlo Pub; 0-9616512),* 2705 Vagabond Ln., Plymouth, MN 55447 (SAN 659-5111) Tel 612-473-1743.

McIlvaine, Paul, Pub., *(P McIlvaine; 0-9600410),* Sky Village, 124 Scenic Lane, Hendersonville, NC 28739 (SAN 203-7890) Tel 704-692-3971.

Maciora, Joseph G. V., *(J G V Maciora; 0-9613407),* 89 Palomino Dr., Pittsfield, MA 01201 (SAN 679-1441).

McIver, Mary, *(M McIver; 0-9613864),* 1207 Michigan St., Elizabethton, TN 37643 (SAN 685-219X) Tel 615-543-4853.

Mack Publishing Co., *(Mack Pub; 0-912734),* 20th & Northampton Sts., Easton, PA 18042 (SAN 203-9508) Tel 215-250-7241.

McKay, David, Co., Inc., Subs. of Morgan-Grampian Inc., *(McKay; 0-679),* 2 Park Ave., New York, NY 10016 (SAN 200-240X) Tel 212-340-9800; Orders to: Fodor's/McKay, O'Neill Hwy., Dunmore, PA 18512 (SAN 285-0478) Tel 717-344-2614. *Imprints:* Tarten Books (Tarten); Wyden, Peter H., Incorporated (Wyden).

McKechnie, *(McKechnie; 0-939577),* P.O. Box 2784, Fairfax, VA 22031 (SAN 663-5296); 3898 Bradwater St., Fairfax, VA 22031 (SAN 663-530X) Tel 703-323-1212.

McKee, Christian H., *(C H McKee; 0-9611046),* 210 Main St., Rm. No. One, Landisville, PA 17538 (SAN 282-9290) Tel 717-898-7109.

McKenzie, Alexander A., *(A A McKenzie; 0-9613211),* P.O. Box 38, Eaton Center, NH 03832 (SAN 295-6470) Tel 603-447-3385.

MacKenzie-Koch Associates, *(MacKenzie-Koch; 0-931094),* P.O. Box 240392, Charlotte, NC 28224 (SAN 239-4537) Tel 704-525-8194.

Mackey, Cleo, Publishing, *(C Mackey; 0-9608176),* 6435 Seco Blvd., Dallas, TX 75217 (SAN 240-2467) Tel 214-391-5597.

Mackinac Island State Park Commission, *(Mackinac Island; 0-911872),* P.O. Box 370, Mackinac Island, MI 49757 (SAN 202-5981) Tel 906-847-3328.

McKinzie Publishing Co., *(McKinzie Pub; 0-86626),* 11000 Wilshire Blvd., P.O. Box 241777, Los Angeles, CA 90024 (SAN 216-2644) Tel 213-934-7685.

McKissick Museums *See* Univ. of South Carolina, McKissick Museum

McKnight Publishing Co., *(McKnight),* 809 W. Detweiller, Peoria, IL 61615 (SAN 202-5957) Tel 309-663-1341; Toll free: 800-447-0682; Dist. by: Taplinger Publishing Co., 132 W. 22nd St.S., New York, NY 10011 (SAN 213-6821) Tel 212-741-0801.

McLaughlin, Vicki & Roger, *(V R McLaughlin; 0-9613416),* Rt. 1, P.O. Box 114G, Weston, WV 26452 (SAN 677-4997).

Maclay & Assocs., *(Maclay Assoc; 0-940776),* P.O. Box 16253, Baltimore, MD 21210 (SAN 219-6808) Tel 301-235-7985.

McLean, Dabney N., *(D N McLean; 0-9614934),* 12274 1st St., W., No. A4, Treasure Island, FL 33706 (SAN 693-3823).

McLean County Historical Society, *(McLean County; 0-943788),* 201 E. Grove St., Bloomington, IL 61701 (SAN 241-0362) Tel 309-827-0428.

McLennan Hse., Inc., *(McLennan Hse; 0-918865),* 206 S. Rogers, Waxahachie, TX 75165 (SAN 669-9243) Tel 214-937-9700.

McMallec Publishing Co., Div. of WCW Assocs., Inc., *(McMallec Pub; 0-938745),* 3609 Memorial Pkwy., SW, Huntsville, AL 35801 (SAN 661-7611); P.O. Box 4635, Huntsville, AL 35815 (SAN 661-762X) Tel 205-882-1620.

MacManiman, Inc., *(MacManiman; 0-9611998),* P.O. Box 546, 3023 362nd SE., Fall City, WA 98024 (SAN 212-0216) Tel 206-222-5587.

McMaster, Linda, Ms, *(L McMaster),* War Cycles Institute, P.O. Box 81369, Corpus Christi, TX 78412 (SAN 211-7428).

McMillan, Dennis, *(D McMillan; 0-9609986; 0-939767),* 1995 Calais Dr., No. 3, Miami Beach, FL 33141 (SAN 272-1686) Tel 305-861-9164.

Macmillan Information, Div. of Macmillan Publishing Co., Inc., *(Macmillan Info; 0-02),* 866 Third Ave., New York, NY 10022 (SAN 202-599X) Tel 212-935-2000.

McMillan Pubns., Inc., *(McMillan Pubns; 0-934228),* 3208 Halsey Dr., Woodridge, IL 60517 (SAN 213-1137) Tel 312-968-3933. Publishes railroad books only. Do not confuse with Macmillan Publishing Co., New York, NY, and Riverside NJ.

Macmillan Publishing Co., Inc., *(Macmillan;*
0-02), 866 Third Ave., New York, NY
10022 (SAN 202-5574) Tel 212-702-2000;
Toll free: 800-257-5755; Orders to: Front &
Brown Sts., Riverside, NJ 08370
(SAN 202-5582). Do not confuse with
McMillan Pubns., Woodridge, IL. *Imprints:*
Acorn Books (Acorn); Aladdin Books
(Aladdin Bks); Berlitz (Berlitz); Collier Books
(Collier); Crowell-Collier Press (CCPr); Dove
Books (Dove).

McMurry, Cathryn, *(McMurry Pub; 0-9615936),*
14845 SW Carlsbad, Beaverton, OR 97007
(SAN 696-8546) Tel 503-641-3981.

†**McNally & Loftin, Pubs.,** *(McNally & Loftin;*
0-87461), P.O. Box 1316, Santa Barbara, CA
93102 (SAN 202-5973) Tel 805-964-5117;
Orders to: 5390 Overpass Rd., Santa Barbara,
CA 93111 (SAN 281-9651)
Tel 805-964-6469; *CIP.*

McNamara Pubns., Inc., *(McNamara Pubns;*
0-932770), 741 Overlook St., P.O. Box
27277, Escondido, CA 92027
(SAN 212-2189) Tel 619-743-4942.

McNichols Publishing Co., *(McNichols Pub;*
0-935227), 731 Mulberry, Winston-Salem,
NC 27101 (SAN 695-7188)
Tel 919-724-6399.

McNulty Development, Inc., 190 Birchview Dr.,
Piscataway, NJ 08854 (SAN 698-5513)
Tel 201-356-4557.

McNutt, Randy, Pubns., *(McNutt Pubns;*
0-940152), P.O. Box 455, Fairfield, OH
45014 (SAN 217-0841) Tel 513-868-9910.

Macon Junior League Pubns., Div. of Junior
League of Macon, Inc., *(Jr League Macon),*
345 Spring St., Macon, GA 31201
(SAN 223-1697) Tel 912-743-0847.

Macor, Alida, & Sew On, *(Alida Macor;*
0-9610632), P.O. Box 71, Martinsville, NJ
08836 (SAN 264-1925) Tel 201-722-5676.

Macoupin County Homemakers, *(MCH),* 210
N. Broad St., Carlinville, IL 62626
(SAN 217-2933).

Macoy Publishing & Masonic Supply Co., Inc.,
(Macoy Pub; 0-910928; 0-88053), P.O. Box
9759, Richmond, VA 23228
(SAN 202-2265) Tel 804-262-6551.

McPhail, Arlene, *(Arlene McPhail; 0-9614596),*
1716 Bailey, Everett, WA 98203
(SAN 691-7844) Tel 206-355-6212.

McPhail, David, *(D McPhail),* 242 Trinity Ave.,
Berkeley, CA 94708 (SAN 207-6586).

McPherson & Co., *(McPherson & Co; 0-914232),*
P.O. Box 638, New Paltz, NY 12561
(SAN 203-0624) Tel 914-255-7084; 437
Springtown Rd., New Paltz, NY 12561
(SAN 658-2001).

MacPherson Pub. Co., *(MacPherson Pub;*
0-9614849), 907 Comstock Ave., Syracuse,
NY 13210 (SAN 693-1065)
Tel 315-475-0339.

McQuaid, Robert W., *(R W McQuaid;*
0-912259), 4853 Mt. Elbrus Dr., San Diego,
CA 92117 (SAN 265-1653)
Tel 619-279-5827.

McQueen & Son Publishing Co., *(McQueen &*
Son; 0-9609354), 6302 Van Maren Lane,
Citrus Heights, CA 95621 (SAN 260-2245)
Tel 916-725-3285; Orders to: Box 776,
Citrus Heights, CA 95610 (SAN 662-0760)
Tel 916-725-3285.

McQueen Publishing Co., *(McQueen; 0-917186),*
P.O. Box 198, Tiskilwa, IL 61368
(SAN 203-9516).

McQuerry Orchid Books, *(McQuerry Orchid;*
0-913928), 5700 W. Salerno Rd.,
Jacksonville, FL 32244 (SAN 203-9427)
Tel 904-387-5044.

Macra-Tack Incorporated, *(Macra-Tack Inc;*
0-9611536), P.O. Box 326, Stevensville, MT
59870 (SAN 285-3248) Tel 406-777-5408.

MacRae, Julia *See* **Watts, Franklin, Inc.**

MacRae's Blue Bk., Inc., Subs. of Business
Research Pubns., Inc., *(MacRaes Blue Bk;*
0-89910), 817 Broadway, New York, NY
10003 (SAN 241-5569) Tel 212-673-4700;
Toll free: 800-622-7237.

Macro Books, *(Macro Bks; 0-913080),* P.O. Box
26661, Tempe, AZ 85282 (SAN 207-0480)
Tel 602-991-2229.

Macrobiotics & Aids Research Project,
(Macrobiotics Aids Rsch; 0-9617097), P.O.
Box 214, Wynnewood, PA 19096
(SAN 264-4928); 945 Granite St.,
Philadelphia, PA 19124 (SAN 662-4936)
Tel 215-535-3592.

Macrobit Corp., *(Macrobit Corp; 0-939573),*
3785 NW 82nd Ave., No. 115, Miami, FL
33166 (SAN 663-5334) Tel 305-592-5354;
Dist. by: Computer Books International, 3785
NW 82nd Ave., No. 115, Miami, FL 33166
(SAN 200-8173).

Macromedia Inc., *(Macromedia Inc; 0-9601170),*
P.O. Box 1025, Lake Placid, NY 12946
(SAN 209-3790) Tel 518-523-9683.

McTaggart Publishing, Inc., *(McTaggart;*
0-9611864), 201 Gore Creek Dr., Vail, CO
81657 (SAN 286-1429) Tel 303-476-1097.

MacVeigh, Poppy E., *(MacVeigh; 0-9615594),*
335 Crestline Ave., Cincinnati, OH 45205
(SAN 695-9040) Tel 513-921-7825.

McVie Publishing Co., *(McVie Pub; 0-917487),*
17608 15th Pl., W., Lynnwood, WA 98036
(SAN 656-0733) Tel 206-743-3706.

Macy, Josiah, Jr. Foundation, *(J Macy Foun;*
0-914362), 44 E. 64th St., New York, NY
10021 (SAN 201-0151) Tel 212-486-2424;
Dist. by: Independent Publishers Group, One
Pleasant Ave., Port Washington, NY 11050
(SAN 201-2936).

Macys of Mesa, *(Macys Mesa; 0-9414691),*
8615 E. Apache Trail, No. B-39, Mesa, AZ
85207 (SAN 217-250X).

Mad Gull Pr., *(Mad Gull Pr; 0-9610330),* 5650
Riley St., San Diego, CA 92110
(SAN 264-1933) Tel 619-291-6399.

Mad River Pr., *(Mad River; 0-916422),* 141
Carter Ln., Eureka, CA 95501
(SAN 207-530X) Tel 707-443-2947.

Maddalena, Kris Louis, *(K L Maddalena;*
0-9616189), 8130 W. Indian Schl. Rd., No.
2169, Phoenix, AZ 85033 (SAN 658-3342).

Madden, Robert, *(R Madden; 0-9608256),* 5292
Rosamond Lane, Pontiac, MI 48054
(SAN 240-4028) Tel 313-681-3354.

Made Simple Books *See* **Doubleday & Co., Inc.**

Mader Enterprises, *(Mader Enter; 0-9615270),*
14 Briarwood Dr., Edgartown, MA 02539
(SAN 695-183X) Tel 617-627-9927.

Madhatter Pr., *(Madhatter; 0-941082),* 3101
12th Ave., S., Minneapolis, MN 55407
(SAN 217-3964) Tel 612-722-8951.

Madis, Valdemar, *(Madis; 0-941350),* 375
Huyler St., South Hackensack, NJ 07606
(SAN 239-4545).

Madison & Polk, *(Madison Polk; 0-910915),*
P.O. Box 8447, Asheville, NC 28814
(SAN 272-1708).

†**Madison Art Ctr., Inc.,** *(Madison Art;*
0-913883), 211 State St., Madison, WI
53703 (SAN 279-4683) Tel 608-257-0158;
CIP.

Madison Avenue Publishing Co., *(Madison Ave*
Pub; 0-9613697), P.O Box 4080, Dallas, TX
75208 (SAN 681-8269).

†**Madison County Historical Society,** *(Madison*
Cty KY Hist; 0-9615162), 515 W. Main St.,
Richmond, KY 40475 (SAN 694-3039)
Tel 606-623-1250; *CIP.*

Madison Financial Services, Inc., *(Madison*
Financial; 0-913885), 12108 Suffolk Terr.,
Gaithersburg, MD 20878 (SAN 286-7893)
Tel 301-840-2071.

Madison Park Pr., *(Madison Park Pr; 0-942178),*
3816 E. Madison St., Seattle, WA 98112
(SAN 238-7867).

Madison Pr., *(Madison Pr TX; 0-938867),* 620
King's Row, Denton, TX 76201
(SAN 662-5754) Tel 817-383-2627. Do not
confuse with Madison Pr., of Salem, OR, &
Beltsville, MD.

Madison Pr., The, *(Madison Pr; 0-9612962),*
2686 Mountain View Dr., S., Salem, OR
97302 (SAN 292-5761) Tel 503-363-0422.

Madison Publishing, *(Madison Pub;*
0-938141), 12 Concord Dr., Madison, CT
06443 (SAN 661-2237) Tel 203-421-5258.
Do not confuse with Madison Pub., New
York, NY.

Madison Square Pr., *(Madison Square;*
0-942604), 10 E. 23rd St., New York, NY
10010 (SAN 238-5384) Tel 212-505-0950;
Dist. by: Robert Silver Assocs., 307 E. 37th
St., New York, NY 10016 (SAN 241-5801)
Tel 212-686-5630.

Madrigal Publishing Co., *(Madrigal Pub;*
0-9617098), P.O. Box 1629, New Milford,
CT 06776 (SAN 662-4979); 517 Litchfield
Rd., New Milford, CT 06776
(SAN 662-4987) Tel 203-355-2694.

Madrona Pr., Inc., *(Madrona Pr; 0-89052),* P.O.
Box 3750, Austin, TX 78764
(SAN 202-6015); Toll free: 800-624-1739.

Madrona Pubs., Inc., *(Madrona Pubs; 0-914842;*
0-88089), P.O. Box 22667, Seattle, WA
98122 (SAN 212-0283); 113 Madrona Pl.,
E., Seattle, WA 98112 (SAN 281-9678)
Tel 206-325-3973; Dist. by: Interbook, 14895
E. 14th St., Suite 370, San Leandro, CA
94577 (SAN 202-5191) Tel 415-352-9221.

Maedon, *(Maedon; 0-9614549),* 825 Via Formia,
Punta Gorda, FL 33950 (SAN 687-7532)
Tel 813-639-8075.

Maelstrom Pr., *(Maelstrom; 0-917554),* 8 Farm
Hill Rd., Cape Elizabeth, ME 04107
(SAN 207-8899).

Maestro Publication *See* **Hansen, Charles,
Educational Music & Bks., Inc.**

Mafex Associates, Inc., *(Mafex; 0-87804),* 90
Cherry St., Johnstown, PA 15902
(SAN 202-2591) Tel 814-535-3597.

Magaru Enterprises, *(Magaru Enterprises;*
0-9609154), P.O. Box 10271, Waialae
Kahala Stn., Honolulu, HI 96816
(SAN 262-0472).

Magazines for Industry, Inc., Subs. of Harcourt
Brace Jovanovich, Inc., *(Mag Indus;*
0-89451), 747 Third Ave., New York, NY
10017 (SAN 205-7921) Tel 212-838-7778.

Mage-In Nation Co., Inc., *(Mage In Nation;*
0-9615749), 11716 Center Rd., Mantua, OH
44255 (SAN 695-9091) Tel 216-274-2693.

Mage Pubs., Inc., *(Mage Pubs Inc; 0-934211),*
1032-29th St. NW, Washington, DC 20007
(SAN 693-0476) Tel 202-342-1642.

Magee, John, Inc., *(Magee; 0-910944),* 103
State St., Boston, MA 02109
(SAN 206-6556).

Magee Enterprises, *(Magee Ent; 0-938167),*
6577 Peachtree Industrial Blvd., Norcross,
GA 30092-3796 (SAN 661-1958)
Tel 404-446-6611.

Magee Pubns., *(Magee Pubns; 0-937267),* P.O.
Box 26507, Prescott, AZ 86312
(SAN 658-9006) Tel 602-445-7503; 118 N.
Montezuma St., Prescott, AZ 86301
(SAN 658-9014).

Magi Bks., Inc., *(Magi Bks; 0-87343),* 33
Buckingham Dr., Albany, NY 12208
(SAN 202-6023) Tel 518-482-7781.

Magian Pr., The, *(Magian Pr; 0-917023),* P.O.
Box 117, Penn Laird, VA 22846
(SAN 655-2684) Tel 703-289-5596.

Magic By Gosh, *(Magic By Gosh; 0-9615492),*
11226 Kamloops St., Lake View Terrace, CA
91342 (SAN 696-3730) Tel 818-896-9571.

Magic Circle Press, *(Magic Cir Pr CT;*
0-913660), 10 Hyde Ridge Rd., Weston, CT
06883 (SAN 202-6031) Tel 203-226-1903;
Dist. by: Walker & Co., 720 Fifth Ave., New
York, NY 10019 (SAN 202-5213)
Tel 212-265-3632.

Magic Limited-Lloyd E. Jones, *(Magic Ltd;*
0-915926), P.O. Box 3186, San Leandro, CA
94578 (SAN 208-7480) Tel 415-352-1854;
4064 39th Ave., Oakland, CA 94619
(SAN 208-7499) Tel 415-531-5490.

Magic Ocean Pr., The, *(Magic Ocean;*
0-914317), 2711 Crooks Rd., Royal Oak, MI
48073 (SAN 287-4776) Tel 313-288-3247.

Magic Publishing *See* **CCC Pubns.**

Magic Unicorn Pubns., *(Magic Unicorn Pubns;*
0-9601836), P.O. Box 793, Yucca Valley,
CA 92286-0793 (SAN 222-0636)
Tel 619-365-0401.

Magical Rainbow Pubns., *(Magical Rainbow;*
0-911281), P.O. Box 717, Ojai, CA 93023
(SAN 272-1775) Tel 805-646-6027.

Magick Circle, The *See* **Technology Group, The**

Magickal Childe Inc., *(Magickal Childe;*
0-939708), 35 W. 19th St., New York, NY
10011 (SAN 216-4124) Tel 212-242-7182;
Toll free: 800-843-6666; Toll free:
800-243-0138.

Magister, Inc., *(Magister Inc; 0-9612312),* P.O.
Box 13646, Tallahassee, FL 32317
(SAN 289-5307) Tel 904-385-8927.

†**Magna Carta Book Co.,** *(Magna Carta Bk;*
0-910946), 5502 Magnolia Ave., Baltimore,
MD 21215 (SAN 203-9532)
Tel 301-466-8191; *CIP.*

Magna Publishing Co., *(Magna Pub Co;*
0-912150), 607 N. Sherman Ave., Madison,
WI 53704 (SAN 203-9540)
Tel 608-249-2455.

Magnaflux Corp., *(Magnaflux),* 7300 W.
Lawrence Ave., Chicago, IL 60656
(SAN 205-907X) Tel 312-867-8000.

Magnaform Corp., Div. of Beylerian, Ltd., *(Magnaform; 0-937845),* 305 E. 63rd St., 15th Flr., New York, NY 10021 (SAN 659-512X) Tel 212-755-6302.

Magnes, Judah L., Museum, *(Magnes Mus; 0-943376),* 2911 Russell St., Berkeley, CA 94705 (SAN 214-2511) Tel 415-849-2710.

Magnetic Indexes, *(Magnetic Inds; 0-918933),* 1626 N. Wilcox Ave. No. 403, Los Angeles, CA 90028 (SAN 669-9332) Tel 213-383-4734.

Magnetic Way, The, Div. of Creative Edge, Inc., *(Magnetic Way; 0-938997),* 2495 N. Forest Rd., Amherst, NY 14068 (SAN 662-5401) Tel 716-689-1657.

Magnoart Pubns., Subs. of Magnoart Culture Institute, *(Magnoart Pubns; 0-918935),* P.O. Box 2150, Van Nuys, CA 91401 (SAN 670-0993) Tel 213-780-5383; Dist. by: Wholesome Life Distributing, P.O. Box 26204, Encino, CA 91426-2204 (SAN 200-7533) Tel 818-986-7629.

Magnolia Bks., Inc., *(Magnolia Bks; 0-9612000),* 450 17th Ave., San Francisco, CA 94121 (SAN 286-8121) Tel 415-221-3519.

Magnolia Homes Tour, Inc., *(Magnolia Homes; 0-9616756),* P.O. Box 817, Columbus, TX 78934 (SAN 661-4191); 435 Spring St., Columbus, TX 78934 (SAN 661-4205) Tel 409-732-2301.

Magnolia House Publishing, *(Magnolia Hse Pub; 0-913145),* 2843 Thorndyke Ave. W., Seattle, WA 98199 (SAN 265-3915) Tel 206-283-0609.

Magnolia Laboratory, *(Magnolia Lab),* 701 Beach Blvd., Pascagoula, MS 39567 (SAN 206-2127) Tel 601-762-1643.

Magnolia Pr., *(Magnolia Pr; 0-916369),* P.O. Box 3, Swainsboro, GA 30401 (SAN 295-6233) Tel 912-237-8740.

Magnolia Pubns, *(Magnolia CO; 0-933679),* P.O. Box 6464, Colorado Springs, CO 80934 (SAN 692-7904) Tel 303-635-9163.

Magnolia Pubns., Inc., *(Magnolia Pubns Inc.; 0-943516),* 380 Lexington Ave., New York, NY 10168 (SAN 240-7116) Tel 212-682-2514.

Magnolia Street Pubs., *(Magnolia St Pub; 0-9613309),* 1250 W. Victoria, Chicago, IL 60660 (SAN 653-8843) Tel 312-561-2121.

Magnum Publishing, *(Magnum Pub; 0-937917),* 5666 La Jolla Blvd., No. 316, La Jolla, CA 92037 (SAN 659-5138) Tel 619-563-0670.

Magoo's Umbrella, *(Magoos Umbrella; 0-932904),* 18581 Devon Ave., Saratoga, CA 95070 (SAN 212-2197) Tel 408-374-7646.

Magpie Pr., *(Magpie Pr; 0-935469),* 16 Main Ave., Wallington, NJ 07057 (SAN 696-3897) Tel 201-778-2503.

Magpie Pubns., *(Magpie Pubns; 0-936480),* P.O. Box 636, Alamo, CA 94507 (SAN 221-4091) Tel 415-838-9287.

Mah-Tov Pubns., *(Mah-Tov Pubns; 0-917274),* 1680 45th St., Brooklyn, NY 11204 (SAN 208-7502) Tel 718-871-5337.

Mahanshi International Univ., Neuroscience Pr., *(MIU Neurosci Pr; 0-9616944),* Maharishi International Univ., Neuroscience Dept., Fairfield, IA 52556 (SAN 661-7794) Tel 515-472-1109.

Mahayana Sutra & Tantra Pr., Subs. of Mahayana Sutra & Tantra Center, *(Mahayana; 0-918753),* 216A W. Second St., Howell, NJ 07731 (SAN 657-6532) Tel 609-261-3458.

Maher Ventriloquist Studios, *(Maher Ventril Studio),* P.O. Box 420, Littleton, CO 80160 (SAN 208-1385) Tel 303-798-6830.

Mahler Publishing Co., *(Mahler Pub Co; 0-914431),* 24 Godwin Ave., Midland Park, NJ 07432 (SAN 289-6540) Tel 201-447-1130.

Mahoney, Eugene J., *(E J Mahoney; 0-9615994),* 5771 S. 121st St., Hales Corners, WI 53130 (SAN 699-7635) Tel 414-425-7185.

Maiden Bks., *(Maiden Bks; 0-931138),* 300 Washington St., Newark, NJ 07102 (SAN 211-2515).

Maiden Lane Pr., *(Maiden Lane; 0-9605688),* P.O. Box 3724, Charlottesville, VA 22903 (SAN 216-2652) Tel 703-456-8323.

Mail Order U.S.A., *(Mail Order; 0-914694),* Suite B-10, 3100 Wisconsin Ave. NW, Washington, DC 20016 (SAN 205-6321); Orders to: P.O. Box 19083, Washington, DC 20036 (SAN 205-633X).

Mail Trade Enterprises, *(Mail Trade; 0-931061),* 1801 S. Cardinal Ln., New Berlin, WI 53151 (SAN 678-9269) Tel 414-782-4424.

Mailbox Club, The, *(Mailbox; 0-9603752),* 404 Eager Rd., Valdosta, GA 31602 (SAN 281-9686) Tel 912-244-6812.

†**Mailman Family Press, The,** *(Mailman Family; 0-914799),* 707 Westchester Ave., White Plains, NY 10604 (SAN 289-1360) Tel 914-681-4446; Dist. by: Gryphon House, Inc., P.O. Box 275, 3706 Otis St., Mt. Rainer, MD 20712 (SAN 663-303X) Tel 301-779-6200 (SAN 669-3520); *CIP.*

Maimes, S. L., *(Maimes; 0-917246),* 42 Bellamy Rd., Dover, NH 03820 (SAN 208-1830).

Main, Zilpha P., *(Z Main; 0-9601584),* 2701 Wilshire Blvd. No. 809, Los Angeles, CA 90057 (SAN 222-0644) Tel 213-387-9762.

Main Stage Pubns., Inc., *(Main Stage Pubns; 0-936447),* P.O. Box 216, Athens, OH 45701 (SAN 697-9025) Tel 614-593-7437; 52 Depot St., Athens, OH 45701 (SAN 698-2298).

Main Street Media, *(Main St Media; 0-938143),* P.O. Box 381, Mocksville, NC 27028 (SAN 661-4434); 184 E. Maple Ave., Mocksville, NC 27028 (SAN 661-4442) Tel 704-634-3118.

Main Street Press *See* **Universe Bks., Inc.**

†**Main Street Pr., The,** *(Main Street; 0-915590; 1-55562),* William Case Hse., Pittstown, NJ 08867 (SAN 207-4443) Tel 201-735-9424; *CIP.*

Main Street Publishing, *(Main St Pub; 0-935399),* 2022 E. Edgewood, Shorewood, WI 53211 (SAN 696-3129) Tel 414-964-5757.

Main Track Pubns., Subs. of Mus-Art Corporation of America, *(Main Track; 0-933866),* 2119 Forestwood Ct., Fullerton, CA 92633-1248 (SAN 212-758X) Tel 714-441-2041.

Maine Antique Digest, Inc., *(Maine Antique; 0-917312),* P.O. Box 645, Waldoboro, ME 04572 (SAN 208-3949) Tel 207-832-7534.

Maine Appalachian Trail Club, Inc., *(ME Appalach Trail; 0-9616457),* P.O. Box 283, Augusta, ME 04330 (SAN 659-3003) Tel 207-465-3197; 85 Summer St., Oakland, ME 04963 (SAN 659-3011); Dist. by: Stephen Clark, P.O. Box 1276, Waterville, ME 04901 (SAN 200-6472).

Maine Dept. of Marine Resources, *(Maine Dept Marine; 0-89737),* Fisheries Research Sta., West Boothbay Harbor, ME 04575 (SAN 211-9145).

Maine Genealogical Society, *(ME Geneal Soc; 0-9615551),* P.O. Box 221, Farmington, ME 04938 (SAN 696-2750) Tel 207-582-4940.

Maine Historic Preservation Commission, *(ME Hist Preserv; 0-935447),* 55 Capital St. Sta., No. 65, Augusta, ME 04333 (SAN 696-3315) Tel 207-289-2132; Orders to: Maine Archaeological Society, Inc., P.O. Box 982, Augusta, ME 04330 (SAN 662-3719).

Maine Historical Society, *(Maine Hist; 0-915592),* 485 Congress St., Portland, ME 04111 (SAN 202-2605) Tel 207-774-1822.

Maine Maritime Museum, *(ME Maritime Mus; 0-937410),* 963 Washington St., Bath, ME 04530 (SAN 279-4780).

Maine State Bar Assn., *(Maine St Bar),* 124 State St., P.O. Box 788, Augusta, ME 04330 (SAN 222-0412) Tel 207-622-7523.

Main State Museum Pubns., *(Maine St Mus; 0-913764),* State Hse., Sta. 83, Augusta, ME 04333 (SAN 203-9567) Tel 207-289-2301.

Mainespring Pr., *(Mainespring; 0-9610536),* P.O. Box 905B, Stonington, ME 04681 (SAN 209-8342) Tel 207-367-2484.

Mainstream, Inc., *(Mainstream DC),* 1200 15th St. NW, Suite 403, Washington, DC 20005 (SAN 225-9400) Tel 202-833-1136.

Maisner & Mason, *(Maisner & Mason; 0-9614046),* 13219 H Fiji Way, Marina del Rey, CA 90292 (SAN 283-9709) Tel 213-827-3443; Dist. by: MBF Sports, Inc., 3940 Higuera St., Culver City, CA 90232-2505 (SAN 283-9717) Tel 213-204-1551.

Maitland Enterprises, *(Maitland Enter; 0-936759),* 8118 N. 28th Ave., Phoenix, AZ 85021 (SAN 699-8437) Tel 602-269-2213.

Maitland Public Library, *(Maitland Lib; 0-9614036),* 501 S. Maitland Avenue, Maitland, FL 32751 (SAN 683-7972).

Maize Pr., *(Maize Pr; 0-939558),* Colorado College, Box 10, Colorado Springs, CO 80903 (SAN 216-6852) Tel 303-636-3249.

Majestic Bks., *(Majestic Bks; 0-9604968),* 2338 Henderson Mill Ct., Atlanta, GA 30345 (SAN 215-6792).

Maji Bks., *(Maji Bks; 0-9615163),* 18 Ivest Dr., East Falmouth, MA 02536 (SAN 694-3047) Tel 617-564-5242.

Major Bks., *(Major Bks; 0-89041),* 21335 Roscoe Blvd., Canoga Park, CA 91304 (SAN 207-4117) Tel 213-999-4100; 18-39 128th St., College Point, NY 11356 (SAN 207-4117) Tel 212-939-1119; Orders to: Kable News, Inc., 777 Third Ave., New York, NY 10017 (SAN 207-4109) Tel 212-486-2828.

Majority Pr., The, *(Majority Pr; 0-912469),* P.O. Box 538, Dover, MA 02030 (SAN 265-2757) Tel 617-828-8450; Orders to: P.O. Box 476, Canton, MA 02021 (SAN 658-2257).

Makana Ka Koloe Publishing, *(Makana; 0-935223),* P. O. Box 55879, Seattle, WA 98155 (SAN 695-7196) Tel 206-775-6848.

Makepeace Colony Press, The, *(Makepeace Colony; 0-87741),* P.O. Box 111, Stevens Point, WI 54481 (SAN 203-9575) Tel 715-344-2636.

Makin' Do Enterprises, *(Makin Do Ent; 0-88100),* Rte. 10, Baker Pl., Lancaster, SC 29720 (SAN 277-7118) Tel 803-285-2888.

Makor Publishing, *(Makor Pub; 0-9608310),* 4910 Della Pl., San Diego, CA 92117 (SAN 240-5458) Tel 213-273-3306.

Malaga, Rose C., *(Malaga; 0-939642),* 334 Livingston Ave., Babylon, NY 11702 (SAN 216-6356) Tel 516-422-2405.

Malama Arts Inc., Div. of MAI Hawaii, *(Malama Arts; 0-931909),* P.O. Box 1761, Honolulu, HI 96806 (SAN 686-0141) Tel 808-329-5828.

Malamud-Rose Pubs., *(Malamud-Rose; 0-9610466),* 38 Stonywood Rd., Commack, NY 11725 (SAN 285-0486); P.O. Box 194, Smithtown, NY 11787 (SAN 285-0494).

Malcolm Hse., *(Malcolm Hse),* 805 Malcolm Dr., Silver Spring, MD 20901 (SAN 209-0368) Tel 301-439-4358.

Maledicta Pr., *(Maledicta; 0-916500),* 331 S. Greenfield Ave., Waukesha, WI 53186 (SAN 208-1083) Tel 414-542-5853.

Malhotra, S., *(Malhotra),* 20 Acorn Park, Cambridge, MA 02140 (SAN 203-8676); Orders to: 16 Cooke Rd., Lexington, MA 02173 (SAN 203-8684).

Malibu Publications *See* **B of A Communications Co.**

Malibu Publishing, Inc., *(Malibu Pub; 0-918937),* 31304 Via Colinas, Suite 110, Westlake Village, CA 91362 (SAN 669-8263) Tel 818-889-1495 (SAN 669-8271).

Malki Museum Pr., *(Malki Mus Pr; 0-939046),* Dept. of Linguistics, Univ. of California, Los Angeles, CA 90024 (SAN 281-9724) Tel 213-474-0169; Orders to: 11-795 Fields Rd., Morongo Indian Reservation, Banning, CA 92220 (SAN 281-9732) Tel 714-849-7289.

Mallinckrodt Communications Research, *(Mallinckrodt Comm; 0-931227),* 2937 Macomb St. NW, Washington, DC 20008 (SAN 682-8752) Tel 202-362-3381.

Maltby, Ralph, Enterprises, Inc., *(R Maltby; 0-9606792),* 4820 Jacksontown Rd., Newark, OH 43055 (SAN 217-3972) Tel 614-323-4193; Toll free: 800-848-8358; Toll free: 800-762-1831 (In Ohio).

Maltsberger, John T., *(J T Maltsberger; 0-9616355),* 30 Brimmer St., Boston, MA 02108 (SAN 658-9049) Tel 617-242-5610.

Malvaux, Ets J., *(Malvaux),* Orders to: Dillon-Donnelly Publishing, 7058 Lindell Blvd., St. Louis, MO 63130 (SAN 208-4589) Tel 314-862-6239.

Malzahn, Judith, *(Judith Malzahn; 0-9614565),* Rt. 1, Box 35-S, Clinton, MS 39056 (SAN 691-8042) Tel 601-924-8477.

Mammoth Pr., *(Mammoth Pr; 0-937902),* 40-B Grecian Garden Dr., Rochester, NY 14626 (SAN 216-4132). Moved, left no forwarding address.

Mamre Pr., Inc., *(Mamre Pr; 0-932945),* 1301 Sherwood Dr., Oxford, AL 36203 (SAN 689-1608) Tel 205-835-1973.

Man in the Northeast, *(Man NE),* Box 241, Sullivan, NH 03751 (SAN 216-3810).

Man-Root, *(Man-Root),* P.O. Box 982, Boynes, S. San Francisco, CA 94080 (SAN 207-8635); P.O. Box 762, Hot Springs, CA 95416 (SAN 693-4943).

†**Mana Publishing Co.,** *(Mana Pub; 0-935038),* P.O. Box 1855, Kailua, HI 96734 (SAN 220-1453) Tel 808-261-0050; *CIP.*

Managed Account Reports *See* **Futures Publishing Group**

Management Advisory Associates, Inc., *(Mgmt Advisory Assoc Inc),* P.O. Box 703, Bowling Green, OH 43402 (SAN 203-9907) Tel 419-352-7782.

Management Advisory Pubns., *(Management Advisory Pubns; 0-940706),* P.O. Box 151, Wellesley Hills, MA 02181 (SAN 203-8692) Tel 617-235-2895.

Management & Industrial Research Pubns., *(Mgmt & Indus Res Pubns; 0-933684),* P.O. Box 7133, Kansas City, MO 64113 (SAN 214-0535) Tel 816-444-6622.

Management & Systems Consultants, Inc., *(MSC Inc; 0-918356),* Univ. Sta., P.O. Box 40457, Tucson, AZ 85717 (SAN 209-9500); 3900 Los Portales, Tucson, AZ 85718 (SAN 662-0779) Tel 602-299-9615.

Management Club Consultants, *(Management Club),* P.O. Box 460028, Garland, TX 75046 (SAN 260-2199) Tel 214-272-9908.

Management Counselors, Inc., *(Mgmt Couns; 0-914950),* 2029 Robin Crest Lane, Glenview, IL 60025 (SAN 207-1592) Tel 312-724-1888.

Management Education Ltd., *(Management Ed; 0-943170),* 12326 Riverview Rd., Prince Georges, MD 20744 (SAN 238-8197).

Management Info Source, Inc., *(Mgmt Info Inc; 0-943518),* 1107 NW 14th St., Portland, OR 97209-2802 (SAN 240-7124) Tel 503-222-2399; Toll free: 800-626-8257 (orders only).

Management Press, Inc., *(Management Pr; 0-9607826),* P.O. Box 34965, Memphis, TN 38134 (SAN 212-1123).

Management Roundtable. Inc., *(Mgmt Roundtable; 0-932007),* 824 Boylston St., Chestnut Hill, MA 02167 (SAN 686-0974) Tel 617-232-8080.

Management Sciences for Health, *(Mgmt Sci Health; 0-913723),* c/o Learning for Life, Department BIP, 165 Allandale Rd., Boston, MA 02130 (SAN 286-1720) Tel 617-524-7799.

Management Strategies Group, The, *(Mgmt Strat Group; 0-914165),* 1342 Lost Creek Blvd., Austin, TX 78746 (SAN 287-6248) Tel 512-327-2377.

Management Telecommunications Publishing, *(Mgmt Tele Pub; 0-938303),* 1 Park Ave., New York, NY 10016 (SAN 661-3713) Tel 212-683-3899.

Manas Pubns., *(Manas; 0-911804),* Strathmore Gate E., 132 Manchineel Ct., Royal Palm Beach, FL 33411 (SAN 203-9605) Tel 305-793-0032.

Manas-Systems, *(Manas-Sys; 0-9610076),* Box 3106, Newport Beach, CA 92663 (SAN 272-2062) Tel 714-870-1064; 2901 Coronado Dr., Fullerton, CA 92635 (SAN 662-0787) Tel 714-870-1064; Dist. by: Consulting Psychologists Press Inc., 577 College Ave., Palo Alto, CA 94306 (SAN 689-8351) Tel 415-857-1444.

Manchaca Publishing Co., *(Manchaca Pub),* P.O. Box 783, Manchaca, TX 78652 (SAN 239-4553).

Manchester Group, Ltd., The, *(Manchester Group; 0-9605792),* 3501 26th Pl., W., No. 422, Seattle, WA 98199 (SAN 220-1747) Tel 206-282-2057.

Manchester Pr., *(Manchester Pr; 0-934507),* P.O. Box 5368, Playa del Rey, CA 90296 (SAN 693-8515) Tel 213-306-8052.

Manchester Pubns., *(Manchester Pubns; 0-934663),* 6085 Venice Blvd., Suite 125, Los Angeles, CA 90034 (SAN 694-051X) Tel 213-376-1630.

Manchurch, *(Manchurch; 0-935251),* P.O. Box 4114, Albany, NY 12204 (SAN 695-5037) Tel 518-434-8727; 435 Loudon Rd., Loudonville, NY 12211 (SAN 695-5045).

Mancini, Genevieve, *(G Mancini),* 176 Moffit Blvd., Islip, NY 11751 (SAN 213-1145) Tel 516-277-9547.

Mandala Bks., *(Mandala Bks; 0-9603226),* R.F.D Box 56, Vershire, VT 05079 (SAN 669-1676). Do Not Confuse with Mandala Press in MA (Mandala) or Mandala Press in NC (Mandala Pr).

Mandala Enterprises, *(Mandala Ent; 0-915891),* P.O. Box 534, Jessup, MD 20794 (SAN 294-0604) Tel 301-342-7170.

Mandala Holistic Health, *(Mandala Holistic; 0-939410),* P.O. Box 1233, Del Mar, CA 92014 (SAN 216-5783) Tel 619-481-7751.

Mandarin Press, *(Mandarin; 0-931514),* 210 Fifth Ave., New York, NY 10010 (SAN 211-514X).

Mandate Press *See* **Carey, William, Library Pubs.**

Mandekic, A.V., Enterprise, *(Mandekic; 0-9608312),* P.O. Box 649, Wrightwood, CA 92397 (SAN 240-5466) Tel 619-249-5105.

Mandel Pubns., Div. of Management Development Institute, Inc., *(Mandel Pubns; 0-941420),* P.O. Box 16432, San Antonio, TX 78216-1132 (SAN 239-0094) Tel 512-344-1991.

Manderino Bks., *(Manderino Bks; 0-9601194),* P.O. Box 291669, Los Angeles, CA 90029 (SAN 209-5793) Tel 213-665-0123.

Mandyn Co., The, *(Mandyn Co; 0-9617251),* P.O. Box 36847, Houston, TX 77236 (SAN 663-558X); 2211 Norfolk, Suite 700, Houston, TX 77098 (SAN 663-5598) Tel 713-527-0516.

†**Manet Guild,** Div. of Talco Corp., *(Manet Guild; 0-9602418),* Box 73, Babson Park, MA 02157 (SAN 293-3020) Tel 617-449-3792; 33 Morningside Rd., Needham, MA 02192 (SAN 293-3039); *CIP.*

Mangan Bks., *(Mangan Bks; 0-930208),* 6245 Snowheights Ct., El Paso, TX 79912 (SAN 209-3804) Tel 915-584-1662.

Manhattan Beach Music, *(Manhattan Beach; 0-931329),* 1595 E. 46th St., Brooklyn, NY 11234-3122 (SAN 682-000X) Tel 718-338-4137.

Manhattan Institute for Policy Research Book *See* **Universe Bks., Inc.**

Manhattan, Ltd., Pubs., *(Manhattan Ltd NC; 0-932046),* P.O. Box 18865, Raleigh, NC 27619 (SAN 211-8114) Tel 919-833-2121.

Manic D Pr., *(Manic D Pr; 0-916397),* 1853 Stockton, San Francisco, CA 94133 (SAN 670-6932).

Manifestation, Inc., *(Manifestation; 0-932947),* 708 Eighth Ave. S., Box 991, North Myrtle Beach, SC 29582 (SAN 689-0571) Tel 803-272-8183; Dist. by: Sheriar Pr., 1414 Madison St., North Myrtle Beach, SC 29582 (SAN 203-2457).

Manion Outdoors Co., Inc., *(Manion Outdoors Co; 0-9612936),* P.O. Box 188, Delafield, WI 53018 (SAN 292-3378) Tel 414-646-4196.

Manivelle Pr., *(Manivelle Pr; 0-9616106),* 7964 Jowry Terr., La Jolla, CA 92037 (SAN 699-6922).

Mankind Publishing Co., *(Mankind Pub; 0-87687),* 8060 Melrose Ave., Los Angeles, CA 90046 (SAN 208-4422) Tel 213-653-8060.

Manley, Ray, Commercial Photography, Inc., *(R Manley; 0-931418),* 238 S. Tucson Blvd., Tucson, AZ 85716 (SAN 208-7456) Tel 602-623-0307.

Mann, Al, Assocs., *(Mann Assoc; 0-9614769),* 7G Knights Bridge, Poughkeepsie, NY 12603 (SAN 693-000X) Tel 914-452-4145; Toll free: 800-437-GIMP.

Mann, Paul, Publishing Co., *(Paul Mann; 0-8184),* 1517 Rexford Pl., Las Vegas, NV 89104 (SAN 204-9341) Tel 702-385-1585.

Mann Foundation, Inc., *(Mann Found; 0-9608904),* 7111 Glass Slipper Way, Citrus Heights, CA 95610 (SAN 241-1334) Tel 916-725-4488.

Manning, James, Pub., *(James Manning; 0-9616234),* 112 Ocean Dr., Apt. 18, Miami Beach, FL 33139 (SAN 658-585X).

Manning, Lynda D., & Associates, *(L D Manning; 0-9604062),* P.O. Box 872, Temple, TX 76501 (SAN 214-0551).

Mannix Clinic, The, *(Mannix Clinic),* 2021 Pontius Ave., Los Angeles, CA 90025 (SAN 219-0893).

Manor Health Care Corp., *(Manor Health; 0-917025),* 10720 Columbia Pike, Silver Spring, MD 20901 (SAN 655-4059); Toll free: 800-637-1400.

Manor of Grace, *(Manor of Grace; 0-9616513),* 3816 Fannin, Houston, TX 77004 (SAN 659-5154) Tel 713-523-6277.

Manor Publishing Co., *(Manor Pub Co; 0-937312),* 2896 Haribinger Ln., Dallas, TX 75252 (SAN 217-2488).

†**Mansell,** *(Mansell; 0-7201),* 950 University Ave., Bronx, NY 10452 (SAN 209-5807) Tel 212-685-8149; Toll free: 800-367-6770; *CIP.*

Manufacturers' News Inc., *(Manufacturers),* 4 E. Huron St., Chicago, IL 60611 (SAN 670-7270) Tel 312-337-1084.

Manufacturers Technologies, Inc., *(Manu Technologies; 0-9614980),* 27 Capital Dr., West Springfield, MA 01089 (SAN 693-6342) Tel 413-733-1972.

Manufacturing Confectioner, *(Manufacturing Confectioner),* 175 Rock Rd., Glen Rock, NJ 07452 (SAN 205-8979) Tel 201-652-2655.

†**Manuscript Pr.,** *(Man Pr TN; 0-910159),* P.O. Box 40206, Nashville, TN 37204 (SAN 240-8651) Tel 615-298-5180; *CIP.*

†**Manuscript Pr.,** *(Manuscript Pr; 0-936414),* Box 1762, Wayne, NJ 07470 (SAN 214-3224) Tel 201-628-1259; Dist. by: PDA Enterprises, Box 1762, Wayne, NJ 07470 (SAN 222-0989) Tel 201-628-1259; *CIP.*

Manyland Bks., Inc., *(Manyland; 0-87141),* 84-39 90th St., Woodhaven, NY 11421 (SAN 203-963X) Tel 718-441-6768.

Manzanas Pr., Div. of Leona Marie Ltd., *(Manzanas Press; 0-930831),* 2641 N. Arcadia, Tucson, AZ 85712 (SAN 677-7163) Tel 602-326-9040.

Manzanita Pr., *(Manzanita Pr; 0-931644),* P.O. Box 4027, San Rafael, CA 94903 (SAN 211-0342) Tel 415-479-9636.

Map Factory, The, *(Map Factory; 0-9611538),* Box 3484, Los Angeles, CA 90078-3484 (SAN 285-3302) Tel 818-989-7890.

Map World Pubns., *(Map World; 0-89414),* Box 2818, Dublin, CA 94568 (SAN 209-6714) Tel 415-829-2728.

Maple Hill Pr., Ltd., *(Maple Hill Pr; 0-930545),* 174 Maple Hill Rd., Huntington, NY 11743 (SAN 677-105X) Tel 516-549-3748.

†**Maple Terrace Enterprises, Inc.,** *(Maple Terrace; 0-9613738),* 1217 W. Market St., Orrville, OH 44667 (SAN 679-1336) Tel 216-682-1443; *CIP.*

Maple Tree Publishing Co., *(Maple Tree Pub Co; 0-915387),* P.O. Box 479, General P.O., New York, NY 10116 (SAN 291-266X) Tel 516-536-6280.

Maplegrove & Montgrove Pr., *(Maple Mont),* 4055 N. Keystone Ave., Chicago, IL 60641 (SAN 202-2303) Tel 312-286-2655.

Maplewood Pr., *(Maplewood; 0-914048),* P.O. Box 90, Meadville, PA 16335 (SAN 203-9648) Tel 814-336-1768.

Mar Lor Pr., *(Mar Lor Pr; 0-943400),* 4304 Brigadoon Dr., St. Paul, MN 55126 (SAN 240-7140) Tel 612-483-1588; Dist. by: Contemporary Bks., Inc., 180 N. Michigan Ave., Chicago, IL 60601 (SAN 202-5493) Tel 312-782-9181.

Mar Vista Publishing Co., *(Mar Vista; 0-9604064),* 11917 Westminster Pl., Los Angeles, CA 90066 (SAN 215-255X).

Maran Publishing Co., *(Maran Pub; 0-916526),* 320 N. Eutaw St., Baltimore, MD 21201-1886 (SAN 208-7545) Tel 301-837-3634.

Maranatha Baptist Pr., *(Maranatha Baptist; 0-937136),* Maranatha Baptist Bible College, 745 W. Main St., Watertown, WI 53094 (SAN 220-2581).

Marathon Bks. *See* **Marathon International Publishing Co.**

Marathon International Publishing Co., *(Marathon Intl Pub Co; 0-915216),* P.O. Box 33008, Louisville, KY 40232 (SAN 206-443X) Tel 812-284-4163. *Imprints:* Love Street Books (Love St Bks); Marathon Books (Marathon Bks).

Marathon Pr., Subs. of Marathon Pr., International, *(Marathon Pr CA; 0-937309),* 407 W. Santa Clara Ave., Santa Ana, CA 92706 (SAN 658-8034) Tel 213-484-8420; Dist. by: Paladin Pr., P.O. Box 1307, Boulder, CO 80302 (SAN 212-0305).

Maravelas, Paul, *(P Maravelas),* Box 637, Watertown, MN 55388 (SAN 659-4034).

Names

Marber Pubns., *(Marber Pubns; 0-931239),* P.O. Box 66251, Los Angeles, CA 90066 (SAN 682-8965).

Marburger Pubns., *(Marburger; 0-915730),* P.O. Box 422, Manhasset, NY 11030 (SAN 208-0443).

MARC *See* **Media Action Research Center, Inc.**

Marcat Enterprises, *(Marcat Ent; 0-9612172),* 3050 E. Fifth St., No. 9, Long Beach, CA 90814 (SAN 289-4181). Moved, left no forwarding address.

Marcella Pr., *(Marcella; 0-938468),* P.O. Box 1185, La Quinta, CA 92253 (SAN 215-8884).

March, David, *(D March; 0-9615493),* 200 W. 54th St., New York, NY 10019 (SAN 696-3765) Tel 212-581-9150.

March Hare Publishing, *(March Hare; 0-918295),* 1251 Dolores St., San Francisco, CA 94110 (SAN 657-2812) Tel 415-552-6058.

Marco & Johnson *See* **Johnson, Paul R.**

Marco Polo Pubs., *(Marco Polo; 0-932820),* 8024 Valley Dr., N. Richland Hills, TX 76180 (SAN 212-2898) Tel 817-485-8307.

Marcon & Worthington Inc., *(M & W Inc; 0-911529),* P.O. Box 760, Locust Grove, VA 22508 (SAN 264-5076) Tel 703-972-2951.

Marconi Press, *(Marconi Pr; 0-9605434),* 7710 31st NW, Seattle, WA 98117 (SAN 218-4893) Tel 206-784-8813.

Marcor Pub., *(Marcor Pub; 0-932248),* P.O. Box 1072, Port Hueneme, CA 93041 (SAN 220-8237).

Marcourt Press, *(Marcourt Pr; 0-9608748),* 7465 Beverly Blvd., Los Angeles, CA 90036 (SAN 241-0354) Tel 213-852-2025.

Marcroft Productions, *(Marcroft Prods; 0-935849),* P.O. Box 16405, Salt Lake City, UT 84116-0405 (SAN 695-9776) Tel 801-596-3127.

Mardi Pr., *(Mardi Pr),* P.O. Box 4173, Arlington, VA 22204 (SAN 240-0952).

Marduk Manumit, Subs. of Anderson Enterprises, *(Marduk Manumit; 0-940452),* P.O. Box 9202, Birmingham, AL 35213 (SAN 217-1961) Tel 205-879-5383.

Marell Enterprise, *(Marell Ent; 0-9617088),* P.O. Box 21062, Columbus Cir. Sta., New York, NY 10023 (SAN 662-6378); 250 W. 57th St., Suite 1527, New York, NY 10019 (SAN 662-6386) Tel 212-532-8447.

Margaret Media, Inc., *(Margaret Media; 0-9616377),* 421 Manasses Pl., New Orleans, LA 70119 (SAN 695-5770) Tel 504-822-9305.

Margaretdaughters, Inc., *(Margaretdaughters; 0-931911),* P.O. Box 70, Buffalo, NY 14222 (SAN 686-0133) Tel 716-885-5850; Dist. by: Inland Bk. Co., P.O. Box 261, 22 Hemingway Ave., East Haven, CT 06512 (SAN 200-4151) Tel 203-467-4257.

Marginal Media, *(Marginal Med; 0-942788),* P.O. Box 241, Fredonia, NY 14063 (SAN 240-2475) Tel 716-679-0462.

Margoe Jane Pubns., *(Margoe Jane; 0-9602330),* Hollywood Ave. Rt. 1 Box 115, North Bangor, NY 12966 (SAN 212-2200) Tel 518-483-2020.

Mari-Lyn Publishing, *(Mari-Lyn; 0-912719),* 71 Wyndham Ave., Providence, RI 02908 (SAN 283-0787) Tel 401-272-3606.

Maria Pr., *(Maria Pr; 0-9610850),* P.O. Box 887, Plandome, NY 11030 (SAN 265-2765) Tel 516-869-8173.

†Mariana Bks., *(Mariana Books; 0-913783),* 1028 E. Pontiac Way, Fresno, CA 93704 (SAN 286-1488) Tel 209-225-0942; *CIP.*

Marianist Communication Center, *(Marianist Com Ctr; 0-9608124),* 1223 Maryhurst Dr., St. Louis, MO 63137 (SAN 240-2483) Tel 314-965-5634.

Marianna Junior Woman's Club Inc., *(Marianna Jr; 0-939114),* P.O. Box 6, Marianna, FL 32446 (SAN 264-1968).

Marin Pubns., *(Marin Pubns; 0-934377),* 4 Highland Ave., San Rafael, CA 94901 (SAN 693-7985) Tel 415-459-3817.

Marin Publishing Co., *(Marin Pub; 0-9607482),* P.O. Box 436, San Rafael, CA 94901 (SAN 238-4701) Tel 415-883-4219.

Marine Biological Laboratory, *(Marine Bio; 0-912544),* Marine Resoures Dept., Woods Hole, MA 02543 (SAN 203-9664) Tel 617-548-3705.

Marine Corps Assn., *(Marine Corps; 0-940328),* Box 1775, M.C.B., Quantico, VA 22134 (SAN 205-8952) Tel 703-640-6161.

Marine Corps League, *(Marine Corps League),* 933 N. Kenmore St., Arlington, VA 22201 (SAN 225-106X).

Marine Education Textbooks, *(Marine Educ; 0-934114),* 124 N. Van Ave., Houma, LA 70363-5895 (SAN 215-9651) Tel 504-879-3866.

Marine Endeavors Pr., *(Marine Endeavors; 0-935181),* 2607 Woolsey St., Berkeley, CA 94705 (SAN 695-4677) Tel 415-849-0932.

Marine Environmental Sciences Consortium, *(Marine Environ; 0-938917),* P.O. Box 369, Dauphin Island, AL 36528 (SAN 661-7727); Bienville Ave., at Fort Gaines, Dauphin Island, AL 36528 (SAN 661-7735) Tel 205-460-6331.

Marine Science International *See* **Jones & Bartlett Pubs., Inc.**

Marine Technology Society, *(Marine Tech Soc; 0-933957),* 2000 Florida Ave., NW., Suite 500, Washington, DC 20009 (SAN 205-8936) Tel 202-462-7557.

Mariner Press, *(Mariner Pr; 0-911920),* P.O. Box 99, Somerset, NJ 08873 (SAN 206-6904).

†Mariner Publishing Co., Inc., *(Mariner Pub; 0-936166),* 4835 W. Cypress St., Tampa, FL 33607 (SAN 221-4059) Tel 813-879-8032; *CIP.*

Mariners Pr., Inc., The, *(Mariners Boston; 0-913352),* P.O. Box 540, Boston, MA 02117-0540 (SAN 203-9680). Moved, left no forwarding address.

Mariological Society of America, *(Mariological Soc),* Marian Library, Univ. of Dayton, Dayton, OH 45469-0001 (SAN 225-4255) Tel 513-229-4214.

Marion County Library, *(Marion Cnty Lib; 0-9603086),* 101 E. Court St., Marion, SC 29571 (SAN 211-2973) Tel 803-423-2244.

Mariposa Arts, *(Mariposa Arts; 0-9617172),* 5878 Abernathy Dr., Los Angeles, CA 90045 Tel 213-391-3386.

Mariposa Printing & Publishing Inc., *(Mariposa Print Pub; 0-933553),* 922 Baca St., Santa Fe, NM 87501 (SAN 691-8743) Tel 505-988-5582.

Mariposa Publishing, Co., *(Mariposa Pub; 0-9615709),* 2201 N. Lexington, Suite 400, St. Paul, MN 55113 (SAN 695-8877) Tel 612-488-0305.

Maris & Assocs., *(Maris & Assocs; 0-937517),* 912 Williamsburg Dr., Charleston, IL 61920 (SAN 658-9057) Tel 217-348-0093.

Marist Institute for Public Opinion, *(Marist Inst; 0-939319),* Marist College, 82 North Rd., Poughkeepsie, NY 12601 (SAN 663-1487) Tel 914-471-3240.

Maritime, Pubns., *(Maritime Pubns; 0-916269),* P.O. Box 527, Everson, WA 98247 (SAN 295-0081) Tel 206-966-5805.

Mark, J, Press, *(J Mark Pr; 0-912658),* Box 33, Islip, NY 11751 (SAN 208-7553) Tel 516-666-0043.

Mark-Age Inc., *(Mark-Age; 0-912322),* P.O. Box 290368, Fort Lauderdale, FL 33329 (SAN 202-6090) Tel 305-587-5555.

Mark-Corbett, Harry, *(H Mark-Corbett; 0-9608152),* 34 Janet Dr., North Haven, CT 06473 (SAN 240-1487).

Mark Foster Music Co., *(Mark Foster Mus; 0-916656),* P.O. Box 4012, Champaign, IL 61820 (SAN 208-2861) Tel 217-398-2760.

Mark III Productions, *(Mark III Prods; 0-9609982),* P.O. Box 586, Yuba City, CA 95992 (SAN 272-2461) Tel 916-674-7377.

Mark of Excellence Publishing Co., *(Mark Excell Pub; 0-933415),* 4620 Northridge Dr., Los Angeles, CA 90043 (SAN 691-5019) Tel 213-294-2136.

Mark Publishing Co., *(Mark Pub; 0-9614039),* P.O. Box 40668, Portland, OR 97240 (SAN 684-7668) Tel 503-223-9634; Dist. by: Univ. of Wash. Pr., P.O. Box C50096, Seattle, WA 98145 (SAN 212-2502) Tel 206-543-8870.

Mark Victor Publishing Co., *(M Victor Pub; 0-9606258),* 10855 Whipple St., No. 207, N. Hollywood, CA 91602 (SAN 217-572X).

Markay Enterprises, *(Markay Enter; 0-9616055),* 2301 S. Jefferson Davis Hwy., No. 927, Arlington, VA 22202 (SAN 697-9033) Tel 703-892-6664.

Market Bk. Pubns., *(Mkt Bk Pubns; 0-9616994),* 3015 105th SE, Bellevue, WA 98004 (SAN 661-678X) Tel 206-455-5835.

Market Data Retrieval, Inc., *(Market Data Ret; 0-89770; 0-914608),* 16 Progress Dr., Shelton, CT 06484 (SAN 681-6312) Tel 203-926-4800; Toll free: 800-624-5669. Purchased Curriculum Information Ctr. in 1979.

Market Dynamics, *(Market Dyn; 0-913761),* 27 E. 22nd St., 9th Fl., New York, NY 10010 (SAN 285-337X) Tel 212-674-6888; Toll free: 800-262-7353.

Market Ed Inc., *(Market Ed; 0-937470),* P.O. Box 45181, Westlake, OH 44145 (SAN 215-3246) Tel 216-779-4689.

Market Intelligence Research Company, *(Market Res Co; 0-916483),* 4000 Middlefield Rd., Palo Alto, CA 94303 (SAN 295-1150) Tel 415-856-8200.

Market Timing Report, *(Market Timing; 0-9611670),* P.O. Box 225, Tucson, AZ 85702 (SAN 285-2985) Tel 602-624-6364; 2755 No. C W. Anklam Rd., Tucson, AZ 85745 (SAN 285-2993).

Marketforce Pubns., *(Marketforce Pubns; 0-934065),* 3650 Ashford Dunwoody Rd. 8-H, Atlanta, GA 30319 (SAN 693-1308).

Marketing Alliance, Inc., *(Marketing Alliance; 0-934985),* 3323 Old Hickory Blvd., Old Hickory, TN 37138 (SAN 695-1910) Tel 615-847-2324.

Marketing & Management Institute, Inc., *(Mktg Mgnt Inst; 0-9616722),* 3182 Davcliff, Portage, MT 49002 (SAN 661-3888) Tel 616-323-1531.

Marketing Consultants International, Inc., *(Mktg Consult Intl; 0-937195),* 100 W. Washington St., Suite 214, Hagerstown, MD 21740 (SAN 658-5817) Tel 301-791-0290.

Marketing Economics Institute, Ltd., *(Marketing Econs; 0-914078),* 108 W. 39th St., New York, NY 10018 (SAN 202-6104) Tel 212-869-8260.

Marketing Effectiveness, Advisory Publishing Service, *(Marketing Effect; 0-910797),* P.O. Box 1786, Lafayette, CA 94549 (SAN 272-2550) Tel 916-525-7951.

Marketing for Profit, Inc., *(Marketing for Profit; 0-9603370),* Box 624, St. Charles, IL 60174 (SAN 221-7457).

Marketing Intelligence, *(Market Intell; 0-9615978),* 10675 S. De Anza Blvd., Suite 2-108, Cupertino, CA 95014 (SAN 697-2888) Tel 408-446-3040.

Marketing International, Inc., *(Marketing Intl; 0-912257),* 940 Bender Bldg., 1120 Court Ave. NW, Washington, DC 20036 (SAN 265-1637) Tel 301-977-2905.

Marketscope Bks., *(Marketscope Bks; 0-934061),* 119 Richard Ct., Aptos, CA 95003 (SAN 692-9095) Tel 408-688-7535.

Markewich, Reese, *(Markewich; 0-9600160),* Bacon Hill Rd., Pleasantville, NY 10570 (SAN 203-9699) Tel 212-674-2979.

Markim, Greg, Pubs., *(G Markim; 0-938251),* P.O. Box 183, Appleton, WI 54912 (SAN 661-3659); 1916 N. Drew St., Appleton, WI 54912 (SAN 661-3667) Tel 414-734-9678.

Markins Enterprises, *(Markins Enter; 0-937729),* P.O. Box 06907, Portland, OR 97206 (SAN 659-3224) Tel 503-235-1036; 2039 SE 45th Ave., Portland, OR 97215 (SAN 659-3232).

Markow, Herbert L., *(H L Markow; 0-934108),* P.O. Box 011451, Miami, FL 33101 (SAN 281-9759) Tel 305-858-0200; Dist. by: William W Gaunt & Sons, Inc., 3011 Gulf Dr., Holmes Beach, FL 33510-2199 (SAN 202-9413) Tel 813-778-5211.

Marks, Clear, *(Clear Marks; 0-9602388),* 2408 McKinley, Berkeley, CA 94703 (SAN 212-5285).

Markus, A. F., *(A F Markus),* 758 NE St. Lucie Blvd., Jensen Beach, FL 33457 (SAN 687-6439) Tel 305-334-7099.

Marlance Bks. for Cooks, *(Marlance Bks; 0-9613733),* 1070 Barry Ln., Cincinnati, OH 45229 (SAN 677-4903) Tel 513-281-0050.

Marlboro Pr., The, *(Marlboro Pr; 0-910395),* P.O. 157, Marlboro, VT 05344 (SAN 281-9813) Tel 802-257-0781.

Marlborough Pubns., *(Marlborough Pubns; 0-9604594),* P.O. Box 16406, San Diego, CA 92116 (SAN 220-0104) Tel 619-280-8310.

Marlin Pr., *(Marlin Pr; 0-932949),* Geneva Pk., Boulder, CO 80302 (SAN 690-0062) Tel 303-443-6868.

Names

Marlin Pubns. International, Inc., *(Marlin; 0-930624),* P.O. Box 649, Plandomen, NY 11030 (SAN 210-9824) Tel 516-365-3788.

Marling Assocs., *(Marling; 0-912818),* Orders to: Altarinda Books, 13 Estates Dr., Orinda, CA 94563 (SAN 238-1397) Tel 415-254-3830.

Marlor Productions, *(Marlor Prod; 0-9616973),* P.O. Box 156, Hicksville, NY (SAN 661-7697); 17 Eva Ln., Plainview, NY 11802 (SAN 661-7700) Tel 516-935-9419; Dist. by: Arthur L. Newman, 10355 Slater Ave, No. 105, Fountain Valley, CA 92708 (SAN 200-6723); Dist. by: Oaklawn Bks., P.O. Box 2663, Providence, RI 02907 (SAN 200-6715).

Marmac Publishing Co, Inc., *(Marmac Pub; 0-939944),* 3423 Piedmont Rd., Suite 212, Atlanta, GA 30305 (SAN 669-1714) Tel 404-231-1153.

Marna Pr., *(Marna Pr; 0-9617151),* P.O. Box 1154, West Bethesda, MD 20817 (SAN 663-3315); 7009 Amy Ln., Bethesda, MD 20817 (SAN 663-3323) Tel 301-229-5763.

Marnik Pubs., *(Marnik; 0-9611760),* 17161 New Jersey, Southfield, MI 48075 (SAN 285-3396) Tel 313-557-9033.

Maron Pubns., *(Maron Pubns; 0-941944),* 7900 Old Branch Ave., No. 106, Clinton, MD 20735 (SAN 264-1976) Tel 301-868-5700.

Marquette County Historical Soc., Inc., *(Marquette Cnty; 0-938746),* 213 N. Front St., Marquette, MI 49855 (SAN 205-8871) Tel 906-226-3571.

Marquette Univ. Pr., *(Marquette; 0-87462),* 1324 W. Wisconsin Ave., Rm. 409, Milwaukee, WI 53233 (SAN 203-9702) Tel 414-224-1564.

Marquis Who's Who/Macmillan Directory Division, Subs. of MacMillan, Inc., *(Marquis; 0-8379),* 200 E. Ohio St., Chicago, IL 60611 (SAN 202-6120) Tel 312-787-2008; Toll free: 800-621-9669.

Marr, Jack, Publishing Co., *(J Marr; 0-9605854),* 350 Ridgefield Rd., Hauppauge, NY 11787 (SAN 216-6046) Tel 516-234-4927.

Marr Pubns., *(Marr Pubns; 0-938712),* P.O. Box 1421, New York, NY 10101 (SAN 213-1242) Tel 516-822-7744.

Mars Hill Pubns., Inc., *(Mars Hill Pubns; 0-9614230),* P.O. Box 362, Loma Linda, CA 92354 (SAN 686-7766).

Mars Pubns., *(Mars Pubns; 0-910759),* 1211 East Altadena Dr., Altadena, CA 91001 (SAN 264-1984) Tel 818-798-8110.

Marsh Creek Pr., *(Marsh Creek; 0-88100),* P.O. Box 432, Clayton, CA 94517 (SAN 289-5293).

Marshall, Alice, Collection, *(A Marshall Collection; 0-9616387),* 211 N. 17th St., Camp Hill, PA 17011 (SAN 658-9073) Tel 717-737-5672.

Marshall, D. C., & Sons, *(D C Marshall; 0-933815),* P.O. Box 590780, San Francisco, CA 94159-0780 (SAN 692-901X).

Marshall, John, Publishing Co., *(J Marshall Pub Co; 0-916081),* 2211 Norfolk, Suite 420, Houston, TX 77098-4096 (SAN 685-3846) Tel 713-528-3803.

Marshall, Walter H., *(W H Marshall),* 931 Knight, Helena, MT 59601 (SAN 264-1992).

Marshall Pubs., *(Marshall Pubs; 0-9615206),* 2990 Watson St., Memphis, TN 38118 (SAN 694-2989) Tel 901-363-9738.

Marshland Publishing Co., *(Marshland Pub; 0-941512),* P.O. Box 3241, Stony Creek, CT 06405 (SAN 239-1139).

Marshwinds Advisory Co., *(Marshwinds Advisory; 0-9614496),* P.O. Box 563, Midway, GA 31320 (SAN 689-3953) Tel 904-386-6555.

Marston Press *See* Forum Pr., Inc.

Maritime Assn. of the Port of New York/New Jersey, The, *(Maritime Assn; 0-9616995),* 17 Battery Pl., New York, NY 10004 (SAN 662-6424) Tel 212-425-5704.

Martin, Ben, Pubs., *(B Martin Pubs; 0-936449),* P.O. Box 4912, Shreveport, LA 71104 (SAN 697-9041) Tel 318-798-1022.

Martin, Dan C., *(D C Martin; 0-9616747),* 910 Madison, Suite 805, Memphis, TN 38103 (SAN 661-2784) Tel 901-529-0674.

Martin, Edward A., *(E A Martin),* 550 North Ave., Grand Junction, CO 81501 (SAN 210-6108) Tel 303-243-1538.

Martin, Quinn, Public Relation, *(Q Martin Public; 0-9613492),* 425 N. Lumpkin St., Ste. 205, Athens, GA 30601 (SAN 693-4315); P.O. Box 6004, Athens, GA 30603 (SAN 693-4323); Dist. by: Baker & Taylor Co., Eastern Div., 50 Kirby Ave., Somerville, NJ 08876 (SAN 169-4901).

Martin Consultants, Inc., *(Martin Consult; 0-9609060),* P.O. Box 1076, Golden, CO 80402 (SAN 241-3353) Tel 303-278-0965.

Martin Creatics, *(Martin Creatics; 0-914247),* P.O. Box 626, Fairfax, CA 94930 (SAN 287-6353) Tel 415-453-8129.

Martin Genealogical Services, *(Martin Genealog; 0-9611862),* P.O. Box Drawer 2147, Warner Robins, GA 31099 (SAN 286-1771) Tel 912-923-1261.

Martin Gordon, Inc., *(Martin Gordon; 0-931036),* 1000 Park Ave., New York, NY 10028 (SAN 211-1608) Tel 212-249-7350.

Martin Management Books, Div. of Dr. Doris Martin, Management Consultant, *(Martin Mgmt; 0-9615541),* Box 121, R.R. No. 1, Wailuku, Maui, HI 96793 (SAN 695-5789) Tel 808-244-4187.

Martin-Marrero Productions, *(Martin-Marrero; 0-9613430),* P.O. Box 30081, Indianapolis, IN 46230 (SAN 657-0526) Tel 317-251-4212.

Martin Motorsports Publishing, *(Martin Motorsports; 0-9605068),* P.O. Box 12654, Fort Wayne, IN 46864 (SAN 215-7861).

Martin Pr., *(Martin Press; 0-9617044),* P.O. Box 2109, San Anselmo, CA 94960 (SAN 662-8702); 63 Durham Rd., San Anselmo, CA 94960 (SAN 662-8710) Tel 415-454-7985. Do not confuse with Martin Pr., Los Angeles, CA, or Martin Pr., Torrance, CA.

Martin Pr., The, *(Martin Pr CA; 0-941018),* 20600 Grammercy Pl., Suite 205, Torrance, CA 90501 (SAN 217-4014); Toll free: 800-421-1212. *Imprints:* Hanson, Paul (P Hanson).

Martin Pubns., *(Martin Pubns; 0-9610182),* P.O. Box 480672, Los Angeles, CA 90048 (SAN 272-2658) Tel 213-272-4440.

Martin Publishing Co., *(Martin Pub; 0-9612640),* 4924 Comanche Dr., La Mesa, CA 92041 (SAN 289-5331) Tel 619-461-3704; Dist. by: Frank Mailing Services, P.O. Box 3038, La Mesa, CA 92041 (SAN 200-4259).

Martindale Pr., The, *(Martindale Pr; 0-914959),* P.O. Box F, Stanford, CA 94305 (SAN 289-3274).

Martingale Manuscripts, *(Martingale; 0-9603088),* Box 17, North Pitcher, NY 13124 (SAN 212-8020) Tel 315-653-4401.

Martinus, Johannes, Foundation, *(J Martinus Found; 0-9616854),* 373 Lyons Rd., Basking Ridge, NJ 07920 (SAN 661-5996) Tel 201-647-2222.

Martinus Nijhoff Publishing *See* Kluwer-Nijhoff Publishing

Marty-Nagy Bookworks, *(Marty-Nagy; 0-917296),* 624 Rhode Island St., San Francisco, CA 94107 (SAN 208-757X) Tel 415-550-2613.

Marvanco Enterprises, *(Marvanco; 0-9604336),* Box 21, Peekskill, NY 10566 (SAN 214-4093)

Marvel Comics Group, *(Marvel Comics; 0-9604146; 0-87135),* 387 Park Ave. S., New York, NY 10016 (SAN 216-9088) Tel 212-696-0808.

Marvelous Muffin Co., The, *(Marvelous Muffin; 0-9613785),* 441 Apricot Ln., Mountain View, CA 94040 (SAN 678-982X).

Marvett, Michael E., Publishing Co., *(Marvett Pub; 0-9615734),* 7804 Fourth Ave. W., Bradenton, FL 33529 (SAN 695-8516) Tel 813-792-7419.

Marwolf Publishing, *(Marwolf Pub; 0-9615847),* P.O. Box 23045, Minneapolis, MN 55423 (SAN 696-6039) Tel 612-869-4579.

Marxist-Leninist Pubns., *(Marxist-Leninist; 0-86714),* Orders to: P.O. Box 11972, Ontario St. Sta., Chicago, IL 60611 (SAN 295-3382).

Mary & Leigh Block Gallery, Northwestern Univ., *(M&L Block; 0-941680),* 1967 Sheridan Rd., Evanston, IL 60201 (SAN 239-1643) Tel 312-491-4000; Dist. by: University of Washington Press, P.O. Box C50096, Seattle, WA 98145 (SAN 212-2502) Tel 206-543-8810; Toll free: 800-441-4115.

Mary Ellen Books, *(Mary Ellen Bks.; 0-9606602),* P.O. Box 7589-Rincon Annex, San Francisco, CA 94120 (SAN 210-6388).

Mary Ellen Enterprises, *(Mary Ellen Ent; 0-941298),* 6250 Excelsior Blvd., St. Louis Park, MN 55416 (SAN 212-0429) Tel 612-925-5112.

Mary, Inc., *(Mary Inc; 0-915872),* 72 Waterman St., Providence, RI 02906 (SAN 207-5938) Tel 401-751-0566.

Mary, Queen of Apostles Formation Center, Inc., *(Mary Queen Apostles; 0-935488; 0-9615381),* Box 355, Somers, CT 06071 (SAN 215-6199) Tel 203-749-4895.

Maryben Bks., *(Maryben Bks; 0-913184),* 619 Warfield Dr., Rockville, MD 20850 (SAN 205-6313) Tel 301-762-5291.

Maryland Bk. Exchange, *(Md Bk Exch),* 4500 College Ave., College Park, MD 20740 (SAN 140-7635) Tel 301-927-2510.

Maryland Dept. of Natural Resources, *(MD Dept Natural Res; 0-9614473),* Fiscal & Supportive Services Office, Tawes State Offices Bldg. (B-4), Annapolis, MD 21401-9914 (SAN 694-3942).

Maryland Family Pr., *(MD Family Pr; 0-9614519),* 11065 Swansfield Rd., Columbus, MD 21044 (SAN 689-5700) Tel 301-730-9346.

Maryland Hall of Records Commission, *(MD Hall Records; 0-942070),* P.O. Box 828, Annapolis, MD 21404 (SAN 205-8855) Tel 301-269-3915.

Maryland Historical Pr., *(Maryland Hist Pr; 0-917882),* 9205 Tuckerman St., Lanham, MD 20706 (SAN 202-6147) Tel 301-577-5308.

†**Maryland Historical Society,** *(MD Hist; 0-938420),* 201 W. Monument St., Baltimore, MD 21201 (SAN 203-9788); *CIP.*

Maryland Locale, Ltd., *(Maryland Locale; 0-9616584),* 8090 Main St., Ellicott City, MD 21043 (SAN 661-4043) Tel 301-461-1714.

Maryland Publishing Co., *(Maryland Pub; 0-911071),* 10 Jack Frost Ln., Baltimore, MD 21204 (SAN 272-2690) Tel 301-823-3460.

Maryland Publishing Co., *(MD Pub Co; 0-9615995),* P.O. Box 19910, Baltimore, MD 21211 (SAN 699-7481) Tel 301-243-8558; 3431 Roland Ave., Baltimore, MD 21211 (SAN 699-749X).

Maryland Token & Medal Society, Inc., *(MD Token Medal Soc; 0-9616945),* P.O. Box 3273, Baltimore, MD 21228 (SAN 661-7654); 1404 Harberson Rd., Baltimore, MD 21228 (SAN 661-7662) Tel 301-744-2631.

Maryland Veterinary Medical Assn., *(MD Vet Med Assn; 0-9615658),* Box 439, Fallston, MD 21047 (SAN 695-9563) Tel 301-879-9108.

M.A.S. de Reinis, *(M.A.S. De Reinis; 0-937370),* Box 1500, Grand Central Sta., New York, NY 10163 (SAN 220-0708) Tel 718-625-4336.

MAS-Press, *(MAS Pr; 0-9607984),* P.O. Box 57374, Washington, DC 20037 (SAN 238-5392) Tel 202-659-9580; Dist. by: Borden Publishing Company, 1855 W. Main St., Alhambra, CA 91801 (SAN 201-419X) Tel 818-283-5031; Dist. by: Book Dynamics, Inc., 836 Broadway, New York, NY 10003 (SAN 169-5649) Tel 212-254-7798.

Mascot Pubs., *(Mascot Pubs; 0-9615345),* P.O. Box 1476, Theodore, AL 36590 (SAN 695-1341) Tel 205-957-2277.

Masda Publishing Co., *(Masda),* 31 Milk St., Boston, MA 02109 (SAN 202-6155).

Mason, James H., *(J H Mason; 0-9609032),* 116 N. Belmont St., Glendale, CA 91206 (SAN 240-9704).

†**Mason Clinic, The,** *(Mason Clinic; 0-9601944),* 1100 Ninth Ave., P.O. Box 900, Seattle, WA 98111 (SAN 213-8972) Tel 206-223-6985; *CIP.*

Mason County Historical Society, *(Mason Cty Hist; 0-935693),* E. 2370 Hwy. 3, Shelton, WA 98584 (SAN 696-2475) Tel 206-426-4203.

Masonic Lodge Software, *(Masonic Lodge Soft; 0-939321),* 106 Busch Hill Rd., Wetumpka, AL 36092 (SAN 663-1754) Tel 205-567-2763.

Massachusetts Bar Assn., *(Mass Bar Assn),* 20 West St., Boston, MA 02111 (SAN 226-9473) Tel 617-542-3602.

Massachusetts Coalition for Occupational Safety & Health, *(Mass Coalition; 0-9608416),* 718 Huntington Ave., Boston, MA 02115 (SAN 240-7159) Tel 617-277-0097.

Massachusetts Continuing Legal Education-New England Law Institute Inc., *(Mass CLE),* 44 School St., Boston, MA 02108 (SAN 226-3033) Tel 617-720-3606.

Massachusetts Historical Society, *(Mass Hist Soc; 0-934909),* 1154 Boylston St., Boston, MA 02215 (SAN 202-2133) Tel 617-536-1608; Dist. by: Northeastern Univ. Pr., P.O.Box 250, Ithaca, NY 14851 (SAN 205-3764) Tel 607-277-2211; Dist. by: University Microfilms International, 300 North Zeeb Rd., Ann Arbor, MI 48106 (SAN 212-2464) Tel 313-761-4700; Toll free: 800-423-6108.

Massachusetts History Workshop, *(Mass Hist Work; 0-9615588),* 46 Pleasant St., Cambridge, MA 02139 (SAN 695-9202) Tel 617-354-8807.

Massachusetts Institute of Technology, Ctr. for Advanced Engineering Study, *(MIT CAES; 0-911379),* 77 Massachusetts Ave., Rm. 9-234, Cambridge, MA 02139 (SAN 272-2771) Tel 617-253-7444.

Massachusetts Institute of Technology, Committee on the Visual Arts, *(MIT Comm Visual Arts; 0-938437),* MIT E15-109, 20 Ames St., Cambridge, MA 02139 (SAN 661-3004) Tel 617-253-4400.

Massachusetts Institute of Technology Pr. *See* **MIT Pr.**

Massachusetts Medical Society, The, *(MA Med Soc; 0-9608238),* 1440 Main St., Waltham, MA 02254 (SAN 240-4044) Tel 617-893-3800; c/o Kathy Bosworth,

Massachusetts State Council Knights of Columbus, *(Mass State; 0-9608258),* 10 Kearney Rd., Needham, MA 02194 (SAN 240-4060) Tel 617-793-2011.

Massenet Society American Branch, *(Massenet Soc; 0-9615735),* 9 Drury Ln., Fort Lee, NJ 07024 (SAN 695-8656) Tel 201-224-4526.

Massey, Alyne Queener, Law Library, *(Massey Law; 0-935449),* Vanderbilt Univ., Nashville, TN 37240 (SAN 696-4915) Tel 615-322-2726.

MassMarket Bks., *(MassMkt Bks; 0-939211),* 872 Massachusetts Ave., Rm. 1011, Cambridge, MA 02139 (SAN 662-6114) Tel 617-864-2126.

†**Masson Publishing U.S.A., Inc.,** *(Masson Pub; 0-89352),* 211 E. 43rd St., New York, NY 10017 (SAN 211-1764); Dist. by: Year Bk. Medical Pubs., 35 E. Wacker Dr., Chicago, IL 60601 (SAN 205-5600); *CIP.*

Masspac Publishing Co., *(Masspac Pub; 0-918020),* 48855 N. Gratiot, Mt. Clemens, MI 48045 (SAN 209-2948) Tel 313-949-9222.

Mast, C. L., Jr. & Associates, *(C L Mast),* 2041 Vardon Lane, Flossmoor, IL 60422 (SAN 205-8804) Tel 312-798-1817.

Master Bk. Pubs., Subs. of Creation-Life Pubs., Inc., *(Master Bks; 0-89051),* P.O. Box 1606, El Cajon, CA 92022 (SAN 205-6119) Tel 619-448-1121; Toll free: 800-621-0852 ext. 134. *Imprints:* Institute of Creation Research (Inst Creation).

Master Designer, *(Master Design),* 343 S. Dearborn St., Chicago, IL 60604 (SAN 205-8782) Tel 312-922-9075.

Master Link Publishing Co., *(Master Link; 0-9615209),* P.O. Box 30520, Long Beach, CA 90853-0520 (SAN 694-2997) Tel 213-438-3185; Dist. by: Action Distributing, P.O. Box 3811, Huntington Beach, CA 92605 (SAN 200-6782) Tel 714-840-8712.

Master Mind Publishing Co., *(Master Mind; 0-88152),* P.O. Box 1830, Warren, MI 48090 (SAN 272-2828) Tel 313-756-7050.

Master Pr., *(Master Pr; 0-9600818),* P.O. Box 432, Dayton, OR 97114 (SAN 209-8369) Tel 503-864-2987.

Master Teacher, Inc., The, *(Master Tchr; 0-914607),* Leadership Ln., P.O. Box 1207, Manhattan, KS 66502 (SAN 289-3495) Tel 913-539-0555.

Masterco Press, Inc., *(Masterco Pr; 0-912164),* P.O. Box 7382, Ann Arbor, MI 48107 (SAN 205-8774) Tel 313-428-8300; Toll free: 800-443-0100.

Masterpiece Publishing Co., Subs. of Masterpiece Productions Inc., *(Masterpiece Pub; 0-935699),* 14505 NE 29th Pl., Bellevue, WA 98007 (SAN 696-2599) Tel 206-883-4483.

Masters Pubns., *(Masters Pubns; 0-89808),* 215 Hillcrest Rd., Berkeley, CA 94705 (SAN 226-2959) Tel 415-540-0943.

MasterSon Publishing, *(MasterSon Pub; 0-9608418),* P.O. Box 3040, Peoria, IL 61614 (SAN 240-7175) Tel 309-682-9222.

Masterwork Pr., *(Masterwork Pr; 0-912156),* P.O. Box 302, Pottersville, NJ 07979 (SAN 206-720X) Tel 201-439-3816.

Masterworks Art Pubns., *(Masterworks Art; 0-9615194),* 932 Larson Dr., Altamonte Springs, FL 32714 (SAN 694-2288) Tel 305-682-5171.

Masterworks, Inc., Pubs., *(Masterwrks Inc; 0-931317),* P.O. Box 1847, Friday Harbor, WA 98250 (SAN 685-2610) Tel 206-378-4816; Toll free: 800-445-1313.

Mastery Development, *(Mastery Dev; 0-937153),* 1029 W. Second St., Mesa, AZ 85201 (SAN 658-5779) Tel 602-962-0207.

Mastery Education Corp., *(Mastery Ed; 0-935508; 0-88106),* 85 Main St., Watertown, MA 02172 (SAN 240-5474) Tel 617-926-0329; Toll free: 800-225-3214.

Mastiff Club of America, Inc., *(Mastiff Club Am; 0-9610468),* Irish Hill Rd., RD 1, P.O. Box 319A, Nassau, NY 12123 (SAN 264-200X) Tel 518-766-2336.

†**Matacia, Louis J.,** *(Matacia),* P.O. Box 32, Oakton, VA 22124 (SAN 206-8486) Tel 703-560-8993; *CIP.*

Matagiri Sri Aurobindo Ctr., Inc., *(Matagiri; 0-89071),* P.O. Box 372, High Falls, NY 12440 (SAN 214-2058) Tel 914-687-9222.

Mater Dei Provincialate, *(Mater Dei Provincialate; 0-9605784),* 9400 New Harmony Rd., Evansville, IN 47712 (SAN 216-2679).

Material Handling Institute, Inc., *(Material Handling),* 8720 Red Oak Blvd., Suite 201, Charlotte, NC 28210 (SAN 224-7992) Tel 704-522-8644; Toll free: 722-6832.

Material Development Ctr., Div. of Stout Vocational Rehabilitation Institute, *(Material Dev; 0-916671),* Stout Vocational Rehabilitation Institute, Univ. of Wisconsin-Stout, Menomonie, WI 54751 (SAN 297-1917) Tel 715-232-1342.

Materials Research Society, *(Materials Res; 0-931837),* 9800 McKnight Rd., Suite 327, Pittsburgh, PA 15237 (SAN 686-0125) Tel 412-367-3003.

Maternity Ctr. Assn., *(Maternity Ctr; 0-912758),* 48 E. 92nd St., New York, NY 10128 (SAN 203-9729) Tel 212-369-7300.

Math Counseling Institute Press, *(Math Counsel Inst; 0-9605756),* 4518 Corliss Ave. N., Seattle, WA 98103 (SAN 216-1605).

Math Hse., Div. of Mosaic Media, Inc., *(Math Hse; 0-917792),* 999 Main, Suite 200, Glen Ellyn, IL 60137 (SAN 209-2956) Tel 312-790-1117; Toll free: 800-222-3547.

†**Math-Sci Pr.,** *(Math Sci Pr; 0-915692),* 53 Jordan Rd., Brookline, MA 02146 (SAN 207-415X) Tel 617-738-0307; *CIP.*

Mathematical Alternatives, Inc., *(Math Alternatives; 0-916060),* 101 Park Ave., New York, NY 10178 (SAN 207-6578) Tel 212-486-1775.

Mathematical Assn. of America, *(Math Assn; 0-88385),* 1529 18th St., NW, Washington, DC 20036 (SAN 203-9737) Tel 202-387-5200.

Mathesis Pubns., Inc., *(Mathesis Pubns; 0-935225),* 528 Loretto Rd., Pittsburgh, PA 15217 (SAN 695-717X) Tel 412-521-8104; Orders to: Duquesne University, Department of Philosophy, Pittsburgh, PA 15282 (SAN 662-3557).

Mathews, Diane L., *(D L Mathews; 0-917247),* P.O. Box 134, Salisbury Center, NY 13454 (SAN 656-1187) Tel 315-429-3409.

Mathhart Pubs., *(Mathhart Pubs; 0-9615589),* 2424 L'Enfant Sq., Washington, DC 20020 (SAN 696-0960) Tel 202-347-2497.

Mathis, Jack, Advertising, *(J Mathis Adv),* Forum Sq., 1117 S. Milwaukee Ave., Libertyville, IL 60048 (SAN 207-6411) Tel 312-367-1826.

Mathis, Nathaniel, *(N Mathis; 0-9616389),* 1900 Bladensburg Rd., NE, Washington, DC 20002 (SAN 658-909X) Tel 202-832-3700.

Mathis Pubs. Inc., *(Mathis Pubs; 0-935491),* 1960 Plantation, Atlanta, GA 30341 (SAN 696-3951) Tel 404-457-4007; Dist. by: American Home Libraries Inc., 5405 Country Dr., Nashville, TN 37211 (SAN 200-8017).

Mathom Pr. Enterprises, *(Mathom; 0-930000),* P.O. Box 362, Oswego, NY 13126 (SAN 285-0508) Tel 315-343-4851. *Imprints:* Peaceweed (Peaceweed).

Matiasz, George Z., Editor & Pub., *(Matiasz),* 445 Mariposa, Ventura, CA 93001 (SAN 207-6047) Tel 805-643-3661.

Matilija Pr., *(Matilija Pr; 0-9612642),* 323 E. Matilija St., Suite 112, Box 123, Ojai, CA 93023 (SAN 289-3282) Tel 805-646-2346.

Matrika Pubns., Ltd., *(Matrika Pubns; 0-943648),* 10 E. End Ave., Suite 1-K, New York, NY 10021 (SAN 238-3144) Tel 212-988-5592.

Matrix Design Consortium, *(Matrix Des Con; 0-9612368),* Rte. 5, Box 802E, Canyon Lake, TX 78713 (SAN 289-4211) Tel 512-899-7575.

Matrix Design Pubns., *(Matrix Design Pubns; 0-914743),* 808 McCarthy Ct., El Segundo, CA 90245 (SAN 291-8870).

Matrix Press, *(Matrix Pr MA; 0-9610964),* P.O. Box 740, Cambridge, MA 02238 (SAN 265-2773) Tel 617-491-5800; Dist. by: Inland Book Co., P.O. Box 261, 2 Hemingway Ave., E. Haven, CT 06512 (SAN 669-3113) Tel 203-467-4257.

Matrix Pubs., Inc., *(Matrix Pubs Inc; 0-916460),* 8437 Mayfield Rd., Chesterland, OH 44026 (SAN 216-0757) Tel 216-729-2808; Toll free: 800-851-6018.

Matrix Software, *(Matrix Soft; 0-925182),* 315 Marion Ave., Big Rapids, MI 49307 (SAN 265-6108) Tel 616-796-2483; Toll free: 800-622-4070; Toll free: 800-942-7317 (IL).

Mattanawcook Observer, The, *(Mattanawcook Obs),* 14 Adelbert St., South Portland, ME 04106 (SAN 692-9028).

Mattcraft, *(Mattcraft; 0-9612080),* P.O. Box 406, La Jolla, CA 92038 (SAN 286-8156) Tel 619-459-8333.

Matthaus Pubs., *(Matthaus Pubs; 0-931065),* P.O. Box 1361, Dallas, TX 75221 (SAN 678-9293) Tel 214-341-4196.

Matthew Pubs., *(Matthew Pubs; 0-941366),* P.O. Box 18152, Lansing, MI 48901 (SAN 238-8960) Tel 616-367-4455.

Mattole Press, *(Mattole Pr; 0-916854),* P.O. Box 22324, San Francisco, CA 94122 (SAN 208-7626) Tel 707-525-1794.

Mattox, S. E., Corp., *(S E Mattox; 0-918070),* P.O. Box 431, San Pedro, CA 90733 (SAN 209-6722) Tel 213-832-0306.

Matvest Media, Inc., *(Matvest Media; 0-9616155),* 6800 France Ave., S., Suite 115, Minneapolis, MN 55435 (SAN 699-9239) Tel 612-927-6707; Toll free: 800-547-5570.

Mauer, George J., *(G J Mauer; 0-9616803),* 351 Brassie Dr., Longwood, FL 32750 (SAN 661-289X) Tel 305-834-5842.

Mauldin, Douglas J., *(D C Mauldin),* P.O. Box 411, Lyon, MS 38645 (SAN 659-4875) Tel 601-627-9563.

Maureen Points, *(Maureen Points),* 2905 Van Ness Ave., No. 101, San Francisco, CA 94109 (SAN 211-3236).

Maurer, Diane, Hand-Marbled Papers, *(D Maurer; 0-9616863),* RD 1, P.O. Box 11, Centre Hall, PA 16828 (SAN 661-1699); Brush Valley Rd., Centre Hall, PA 16828 (SAN 661-1702) Tel 814-364-9618.

Maurer & Co. Printing & Pubn., *(Maurer Print Pubn; 0-9614956),* P.O. Box Box 94743, Schaumburg, IL 60194 (SAN 693-7241) Tel 312-885-4432.

Maverick Bks. (TX), *(Maverick Bks; 0-9608612; 0-916941),* Box 549, Perryton, TX 79070 (SAN 240-7183) Tel 806-435-7611.

Maverick Prints, *(Maverick Prints; 0-9612932),* 5890 E. Sedgwick Ct., Jackson, MS 39211 (SAN 292-580X) Tel 601-956-2286.

Maverick Pubns., *(Maverick; 0-89288),* Drawer 5007, Bend, OR 97708 (SAN 208-7634) Tel 503-382-6978.

Maverick Publishing Co., *(Maverick Pub Co; 0-930077),* P.O. Box 777, New London, MO 63459 (SAN 670-0888) Tel 314-985-4902.

Maxim Publishing, *(Maxim Pub; 0-936696),* P.O. Box 42126, Los Angeles, CA 90042 (SAN 215-1626).

Maxima Communications, Inc., *(Maxima; 0-918612),* 5029 Sherborne Dr., St Louis, MO 63128 (SAN 210-122X) Tel 314-894-0370.

Maxim's Books, *(Maxims Bks),* P.O. Box 480451, Los Angeles, CA 90048 (SAN 213-5353) Tel 213-391-8538.

Maximum Marketing Systems, *(Maximum Mktg; 0-931067),* P.O. Box 6321, Alderwood Sta., Lynnwood, WA 98036 (SAN 678-9307) Tel 206-743-2520.

Maxivation Marketing, *(Maxivation Mktg; 0-937731),* P.O. Box 21175, Indianapolis, IN 46221 (SAN 659-3283) Tel 317-745-2295; 4897 Ridge Hill Way, Plainfield, IN 46168 (SAN 659-3291).

Maxrom Pr., Inc., *(Maxrom Pr; 0-930339),* 11 E. Fayette St., Baltimore, MD 21202 (SAN 670-6800) Tel 301-539-2370.

Maxwell, Harvey C., *(H C Maxwell; 0-9600068),* P.O. Box 824, Laguna Beach, CA 92652 (SAN 217-2518) Tel 714-494-2606.

Maxwell, S.E., Publishing Co., *(Maxwell Pub Co; 0-914961),* 6022 Wilshire Blvd., Los Angeles, CA 90036 (SAN 289-3290) Tel 213-930-1410.

Maxwell Museum of Anthropology, Univ. of New Mexico, *(Max Mus; 0-912535),* Corner of University & Roma, NE, Albuquerque, NM 87131 (SAN 279-5256) Tel 505-277-4404.

Maxwell Music Evaluations Bks., *(Maxwell Mus Eval; 0-912531),* 1245 Kalmia, Boulder, CO 80302 (SAN 265-2781) Tel 303-443-1603.

May, George W., *(G W May; 0-9605566),* Rte. 1 Box 117, Metropolis, IL 62960 (SAN 216-0471) Tel 618-524-4029.

May, Michael, Enterprises, *(M May Ent; 0-9612074),* P.O. Box 127, Billings, MT 59103 (SAN 286-8164) Tel 406-248-4973.

May, William E., *(W E May; 0-9616086),* 380 Hospital Dr., Suite 460, Macon, GA 31201 (SAN 661-2024) Tel 912-742-0833.

May Day Pr., *(May Day Pr; 0-9602420),* P.O. Box 1351, Bellflower, CA 90706 (SAN 212-1131) Tel 213-439-8423.

May-Murdock, *(May Murdock; 0-932916),* Drawer 1346, 90 Glenwood Ave., Ross, CA 94957 (SAN 212-7628) Tel 415-454-1771.

Maya Pr., The, *(Maya Pr; 0-910997),* 1716 Ocean Ave., Box 181, San Francisco, CA 94112 (SAN 272-2933); Dist. by: Bookpeople, 2929 Fifth St., Berkeley, CA 94710 (SAN 168-9517).

Maya Pubns., *(Maya Pubns; 0-938693),* P.O. Box 234, Bay Ridge Sta., Brooklyn, NY 11220 (SAN 661-5589); 672 51st St., Brooklyn, NY 11220 (SAN 661-5597) Tel 718-435-2672.

Maya Publishing Co. *See* Univ. Pr. of Virginia

Mayapple Pr., *(Mayapple Pr; 0-932412),* P.O. Box 3185, Kent, OH 44240 (SAN 212-1913) Tel 216-678-2775.

Mayer Assocs., International, *(Mayer Assocs; 0-9609092),* 6009 Walnut St., Pittsburgh, PA 15206 (SAN 241-399X).

Mayer-Johnson, *(Mayer-Johnson; 0-9609160),* P.O. Box AD, Solana Beach, CA 92075 (SAN 241-4007) Tel 619-481-2489.

Mayers, Joseph, & Co., Inc., *(Mayers-Joseph; 0-9604860),* 50 Park Pl., Suite H, Newark, NJ 07102 (SAN 214-4115) Tel 201-622-7854.

Mayfair Press, The, *(Mayfair Pr; 0-9607426),* 1102 Mayfair Rd., Champaign, IL 61821 (SAN 239-4588) Tel 217-351-8409. Out of business.

Mayfield Bks., *(Mayfield Bks; 0-9613682),* 10 Ridge Rd., Gloversville, NY 12078 (SAN 670-8986) Tel 518-725-7056.

Mayfield Printing and Office Equipment,Pubs., *(Mayfield Printing; 0-910513),* 810 Keyser, Natchitoches, LA 71457 (SAN 260-1028) Tel 318-357-0054.

Mayfield Publishing Co., *(Mayfield Pub; 0-87484),* 285 Hamilton Ave., Palo Alto, CA 94301 (SAN 202-8972) Tel 415-326-1640.

Mayflower Bks. *See* Dell Publishing Co., Inc.
Mayflower Bks. *See* Smith, W. H., Pubs., Inc.
Mayflower Institute, *(Mayflower Inst; 0-941370),* P.O. Box 50218, Santa Barbara, CA 93150 (SAN 238-9800) Tel 805-565-1474.

Maynard-Thomas Publishing, *(Maynard-Thomas; 0-935253),* P.O. Box 14753, Orlando, FL 32857-4753 (SAN 697-1725) Tel 305-658-1539.

Maywood Publishing, *(Maywood Pub; 0-9609004),* 2620 N. Norris Ave., Tuscon, AZ 85719 (SAN 241-3388) Tel 602-327-0823.

Mazda Pubs., *(Mazda Pubs; 0-939214),* P.O. Box 2603, Costa Mesa, CA 92626 (SAN 285-0524) Tel 714-751-5252; 2991 Grace Ln., Costa Mesa, CA 92626 (SAN 658-120X).

Maznaim Publishing Corp., *(Maznaim; 0-940118),* 4304 12th Ave., Brooklyn, NY 11219 (SAN 214-4123) Tel 718-438-7680.

Mazyx Pr., The, *(Mazyx Pr; 0-9613515),* P.O. Box 36145, San Jose, CA 95158 (SAN 657-6259) Tel 408-578-4485.

Mazzulla, Fred & Jo, *(F&J Mazzulla),* 2060 Dunes Cir., Reno, NV 89509 (SAN 205-8723).

MBPI Inc., *(MBPI; 0-918233),* 215 W. 98th St., Suite 12-B, New York, NY 10025 (SAN 657-2820) Tel 212-663-5170.

M C I Publishing, *(M C I Pub; 0-911445),* P.O. Box 162, Winfield, IL 60190 (SAN 272-2968) Tel 312-858-7004.

MCSA-Medical Communications & Services Assn., *(Med Communications; 0-917054),* 10223 NE 58th St., Kirkland, WA 98033 (SAN 203-9796) Tel 206-828-4263.

Me & My Inner Self, Inc., *(Me & My Inner Self; 0-9617045),* P.O. Box 1396, La Canada, CA 91011 (SAN 662-8176); 357 Knight Way, La Canada, CA 91011 (SAN 662-8184) Tel 818-790-4858; Dist. by: Social Studies Schl. Servs., 10000 Culver Blvd., Culver City, CA 90230 (SAN 168-9592) Tel 213-839-2436; Dist. by: Zephyr Pr., 430 S. Essex Ln., Tucson, AZ 85711 (SAN 270-6830) Tel 602-623-2022.

Mead Publishing Corp., *(Mead Pub Corp; 0-934422),* 21176 S. Alameda St., Long Beach, CA 90810 (SAN 213-1153).

Meadow Lane Pubns., *(Meadow Lane; 0-934826),* 211 N. Citrus Ave., Unit 277, Escondido, CA 92027 (SAN 213-5361) Tel 619-747-0258.

Meadow Press, *(Meadow Pr; 0-931058),* P.O. Box 35, Port Jefferson, NY 11777 (SAN 211-917X) Tel 516-473-1370.

†**Meadowbrook, Inc.,** *(Meadowbrook; 0-915658; 0-88166),* 18318 Minnetonka Blvd., Deephaven, MN 55391 (SAN 207-3404) Tel 612-473-5400; Dist. by: Simon & Schuster, 1230 Ave. of the Americas, New York, NY 10020 (SAN 200-2450) Tel 212-698-7000; Toll free: 800-223-2336 (continental U. S.); Toll free: 800-442-7070 (in NY); *CIP.*

Meadowlark Pr., *(Meadowlark; 0-941126),* P.O. Box 8172, Prairie Village, KS 66208 (SAN 238-8979) Tel 913-341-9031.

Meadowlark Pubns., *(Meadowlark Pubns; 0-9615590),* 177 Mira del Oeste, San Clemente, CA 92672 (SAN 695-9180) Tel 714-492-8226.

Meadowsweet Pr., *(Mdwsweet Pr; 0-9617297),* 1067 Meadowsweet Dr., Corte Madera, CA 94925 (SAN 663-4559) Tel 415-924-1310.

Meagher, Walter L., Subs. of Leo Books, Ltd., *(W L Meagher; 0-913115),* P.O. Box 4365, Ann Arbor, MI 48106 (SAN 283-2011).

Meals for Millions/Freedom from Hunger Foundation, *(Meals for Millions; 0-9607124),* 815 Second Ave., Suite 1001, New York, NY 10017 (SAN 239-0108).

Means, R. S., Co., Subs. of McCorquodale Holdings, Inc., *(R S Means; 0-911950; 0-87629),* 100 Construction Plaza, Kingston, MA 02364 (SAN 202-6163) Tel 617-747-1270.

†**Meckler Publishing Corp.,** *(Meckler Pub; 0-930466; 0-913672),* 11 Ferry Ln. W., Westport, CT 06880 (SAN 211-0334) Tel 203-226-6967; *CIP.*

Med/Av Publishing Co., *(Med/Av Pub; 0-939135),* 521 Lafayette Ave., Hawthorne, NJ 07506 (SAN 662-4960) Tel 201-423-3330.

Med-Ed, Inc., *(Med-Ed; 0-9609222),* P.O. Box 738, Atlanta, GA 30301 (SAN 241-4015) Tel 404-351-3253.

Medallion Bks. *See* Berkley Publishing Group

Medallion Bks., Inc., *(Medallion Bks CA; 1-55627),* 5455 Wilshire Blvd., Suite 1700, Los Angeles, CA 90036 (SAN 661-3705) Tel 213-933-2665.

Medallion Press, *(Medallion Pr; 0-9610620),* 906 Shadowlawn Dr., Tallahassee, FL 32312 (SAN 265-3591) Tel 904-385-6097.

Medcards, Inc., *(Medcards; 0-9612166),* 10012 N. Dale Marby, Suite 223, Tampa, FL 33618 (SAN 289-422X) Tel 813-961-3864.

Medea Publishing Co., *(Medea Pub Co; 0-9615432),* 4716 Old Dominion Dr., Arlington, VA 22207 (SAN 696-1061) Tel 703-527-3546.

Medi Comp Press, *(Medi-Comp; 0-9600704),* 41 Tunnel Rd., Berkeley, CA 94705 (SAN 207-2610) Tel 415-548-1188.

Medi-Ed Pr., *(Medi-Ed Pr; 0-936741),* P.O. Box 957, East Lansing, MI 48823 (SAN 699-9530) Tel 517-627-3653; 511 Sherman Rd., Lansing, MI 48917 (SAN 699-9549).

Media Action Research Center, Inc., *(Media Action; 0-918084),* 475 Riverside Dr., Rm. 1370, New York, NY 10115 (SAN 210-2366) Tel 212-865-6690.

Media Alliance, Inc., *(Media All; 0-915339),* c/o WNET, 356 W. 58th St., New York, NY 10019 (SAN 290-0130) Tel 212-560-2919.

Media & Travel Pubns., *(Media & Travel Pubns; 0-937367),* P.O. Box 8415, San Diego, CA 92102 (SAN 659-0306) Tel 619-235-6003; 1220 23rd St., No. 3, San Diego, CA 92102 (SAN 659-0314).

Media Arts Productions, *(Media Arts; 0-9614642),* 140-9D Bellamy Loop, New York, NY 10475 (SAN 691-9197) Tel 212-562-9426; Orders to: P.O. Box 48, New York, NY 10475 (SAN 662-2968).

Media Awards Handbook, *(Media Awards; 0-910744),* 621 Sheri Lane, Danville, CA 94526 (SAN 205-8707) Tel 415-837-7562.

Media Concepts Press, *(Media Concepts; 0-935608),* 331 N. Broad St., Philadelphia, PA 19107 (SAN 215-3254) Tel 215-923-2545.

Media Forum Books *See* Media Forum International, Ltd.

Media Forum International, Ltd., *(Media Forum; 0-912460),* P.O. Box 8, Fleetwood, Mt. Vernon, NY 10552 (SAN 204-5559) Tel 914-667-6575; R.F.D. 1, Box 107, West Danville, VT 05873 (SAN 694-9460) Tel 802-592-3444. *Imprints:* Media Forum Books (Media Forum Bks).

Media Horizons Inc., *(Media Horizons; 0-915616),* 50 W. 23rd St., New York, NY 10010 (SAN 211-1012) Tel 212-645-1000.

Media Institute, The, *(Media Inst; 0-937790),* 3017 M St., NW, Washington, DC 20007 (SAN 215-966X) Tel 202-298-7512.

Media International Promotions, Inc., *(Media Intl Promo),* 114 E. 32nd St. Rm 1306, New York, NY 10016 (SAN 291-9346) Tel 212-889-7447; Orders to: P.O. Box 292 Murray Hill Sta., New York, NY 10156 (SAN 691-9596) Tel 212-889-7447.

Media Materials, Inc., *(Media Materials; 0-912974; 0-89539; 0-86601),* 2936 Remington Ave., Baltimore, MD 21211 (SAN 206-9989) Tel 301-235-1722; Toll free: 800-638-1010.

Media Pr., Subs. of Woodland-Media, Inc., *(Media Pr; 0-917181),* 21540 Prairie St., Suite C, Chatsworth, CA 91311 (SAN 656-1772) Tel 818-341-3156; Toll free: 800-262-7367 (Continental U. S.); Toll free: 800-272-7367 (inside CA); Dist. by: Media Products, 21540 Prairie St., Unit C, Chatsworth, CA 91311 (SAN 659-9346) Tel 818-341-3156.

Media Productions & Marketing, Inc., *(Media Prods & Mktg; 0-939644),* 2440 "O" St., Suite 202, Lincoln, NE 68510-1125 (SAN 216-6372) Tel 402-474-2676.

Media Referral Service, *(Media Ref; 0-911125),* P.O. Box 3586, Minneapolis, MN 55403 (SAN 272-3123) Tel 612-933-2819.

Media Services, *(Media Servs; 0-9616262),* 213 Sam Bass Rd., Willow Park, TX 76086 (SAN 658-3431) Tel 817-441-8309; Orders to: Boston Music Company, 9 Airport Dr., Hopedale, MA 01747 (SAN 201-7326) Tel 617-478-4813.

Media Unlimited Inc., *(Media Unltd; 0-930394),* P.O. Box I, Alameda, CA 94501 (SAN 216-0124); Toll free: 800-428-0902.

†**Media Ventures, Inc.,** *(Media Ventures; 0-89645),* P.O. Box 41359, Cincinnati, OH 45241 (SAN 212-114X) Tel 513-771-1220; *CIP.*

Media Weavers, *(Media Weavers; 0-936085),* P.O. Box 19755, Portland, OR 97219 (SAN 696-6446) Tel 503-244-0406.

Media West, *(Media West; 0-939216),* 527 N. Prospect Ave., Redondo Beach, CA 90277 (SAN 281-9880) Tel 213-376-7087.

Mediac Pr., *(Mediac Pr; 0-9616446),* P.O. Box 3315, Van Nuys, CA 91407 (SAN 658-9111); 6504 Murietta Ave., Van Nuys, CA 91401 (SAN 658-912X) Tel 818-904-0515.

MediaHealth Pubns., *(MediaHlth Pubns; 0-938669),* P.O. Box 541, St. Helena, CA 94574 (SAN 661-6178); 660 Sanitarium Rd., St. Helena, CA 94574 (SAN 661-6186) Tel 707-963-1493.

Mediamix Assocs., *(Mediamix; 0-915893),* 3960 Laurel Canyon Blvd., Suite 340, Studio City, CA 91604 (SAN 294-0612) Tel 213-654-2603; Dist. by: Bookpeople, 2929 Fifth Ave., Berkeley, CA 94710 (SAN 168-9517); Toll free: 800-227-1516; Dist. by: Publishers Group West, 5855 Beaudry St., Emeryville, CA 94608 (SAN 202-8522) Tel 415-658-3453; Toll free: 800-982-8319.

Mediaor Co., *(Mediaor Co; 0-942206),* Box 631, Prineville, OR 97754 (SAN 238-7859).

Mediax Interactive Technologies, *(Mediax Inter Tech; 0-912056),* 3029 Fairfield Ave., Black Rock Office Bldg., Black Rock, CT 06605 (SAN 205-8685) Tel 203-332-5800.

Medic Pub. Co., *(Medic Pub; 0-934230),* P.O. Box 89, Redmond, WA 98073 (SAN 210-8313) Tel 206-881-2883.

Medical Accounts Services, Inc., *(Medical Accts Serv; 0-9612564),* 406 Evans Ave., Rm. 6, Fort Meyer, FL 33901 (SAN 289-3304) Tel 813-939-2299.

Medical Aesthetics, Div. of Michael Elam, M.D., Inc., *(Med Aesthetics; 0-937465),* 2082 Michelson Dr., Suite 100, Irvine, CA 92715 (SAN 658-9138) Tel 714-752-1339.

Medical Alternatives Pr., *(Med Alt Press; 0-935813),* 832 Havenwood Ln. S., Ft. Worth, TX 76112 (SAN 696-6101) Tel 817-457-9830.

Medical Arts Publishing Co., *(Medical Arts; 0-913092),* P.O. Box 36600, Grosse Pointe, MI 48236 (SAN 202-2184) Tel 313-886-5160.

Medical/Behavioral Associates, Inc., *(Med-Behavior; 0-936514),* 666 Park Ave. W., Mansfield, OH 44906 (SAN 214-4131).

Medical Consumers Publishing Co., *(Med Consumers; 0-936401),* 2515 Santa Clara Ave., No. 103, Alameda, CA 94501 (SAN 699-7503) Tel 209-723-3505.

†**Medical Economics Bks.,** Div. of Medical Economics Co., Inc., *(Med Economics; 0-87489),* 680 Kinderkamack Rd., Oradell, NJ 07649-9066 (SAN 202-2613) Tel 201-262-3030; Toll free: 800-223-0581; Orders to: P.O. Box C-779, Pratt Sta., Brooklyn, NY 11205 (SAN 202-2621); *CIP.*

Medical Education Consultants, *(Med Educ; 0-937142),* Box 67159, Century City, Los Angeles, CA 90067 (SAN 209-2891) Tel 213-475-5141.

†**Medical Examination Publishing Co., Inc.,** Div. of Elsevier Science Publishing Co., Inc., *(Med Exam; 0-87488),* 52 Vanderbilt Ave., New York, NY 10017 (SAN 206-7897) Tel 212-916-1204; *CIP.*

Medical Group Management Assn., *(Med Group Mgmt; 0-933948),* 1355 S. Colorado Blvd., Suite 900, Denver, CO 80222 (SAN 221-3982) Tel 303-753-1111.

Medical History Publishing Assocs., *(Med Hist Pub; 0-9616748),* 1 Claremont Ct., Arlington, MA 02174 (SAN 661-2768) Tel 617-646-6762.

Medical-Info Bks., *(Med-Info Bks; 0-916093),* P.O. Box 1A182, Lackawaxen, PA 18435 (SAN 294-6114).

Medical Letter, *(Med Letter),* 56 Harrison St., New Rochelle, NY 10801 (SAN 223-7938) Tel 914-235-0500.

Medical Library Assn., Inc., *(Med Lib Assn; 0-912176),* 919 N. Michigan Ave., Suite 3208, Chicago, IL 60611 (SAN 203-980X) Tel 312-266-2456.

Medical Locations & Permits, *(Media Loc; 0-935657),* 650 N. Bronson Ave., No. 106, Los Angeles, CA 90004 (SAN 696-1908) Tel 213-464-2177; Dist. by: Publishers Group West, 5855 Beaudry St., Emeryville, CA 94608 (SAN 202-8522) Tel 415-658-3453.

Medical Manor Bks., Subs. of Manor House Pubns., Inc., *(Med Manor Bks; 0-934232),* 3501 Newberry Rd., Philadelphia, PA 19154 (SAN 217-2526) Tel 215-824-1476; Toll free: 800-343-8464; Dist. by: Baker & Taylor Co., Eastern Div., 50 Kirby Ave., Somerville, NJ 08876 (SAN 169-4901); Dist. by: Ingram Industries, 347 Reedowood Dr., Nashville, TN 37217 (SAN 169-7978); Toll free: 800-251-5902.

Medical Media Pubs., *(Med Media Pubs; 0-939498),* 4320 Centre Ave., Pittsburgh, PA 15213 (SAN 216-4159).

Medical Productions Inc., Subs. of Metro Publishing, *(Med Prod; 0-933745),* 5308-C Elm, Houston, TX 77081 (SAN 692-5979) Tel 713-666-4269; P.O. Box 270776, Houston, TX 77277-0776 (SAN 692-8544).

Medical Research Assocs. Pubns., *(Med Res Assocs; 0-930835),* P.O. Box 1247, Ballwin, MO 63022 (SAN 677-685X) Tel 314-569-7763.

Medical Software Co., *(Med Software; 0-88672),* Box 1272, 333 Main St., Center Moriches, NY 11934 (SAN 265-1661) Tel 516-878-4840. Out of business.

Medicaldisc Reporter, *(Medicaldisc; 0-936999),* 6471 Merritt Ct., Alexandria, VA 22312 (SAN 658-7445) Tel 703-354-8155.

Medicanto, Inc., *(Medicanto; 0-931210),* 283 Greenwich Ave., Greenwich, CT 06830 (SAN 211-2574) Tel 203-869-5732.

Medicina Biologica, *(Medicina Bio),* 4830 NE 32nd Ave., Portland, OR 97211 (SAN 659-557X).

Medicine River Publishing Co., *(Med River Pub; 0-9616479),* 1425 First Ave., N., Great Falls, MT 59401 (SAN 659-3321) Tel 406-453-3593.

Medieval Academy of America, *(Medieval Acad; 0-910956),* 1430 Massachusetts Ave., Cambridge, MA 02138 (SAN 203-9826) Tel 617-491-1622.

Medieval & Renaissance Society, *(Medieval; 0-913904),* P.O. Box 13348, N. Texas State Univ., Denton, TX 76203 (SAN 202-2257) Tel 817-565-2101.

Medieval & Renaissance Texts & Studies, *(Medieval & Renaissance NY; 0-86698),* Univ. Ctr. at Binghamton, Binghamton, NY 13901 (SAN 216-6119) Tel 607-777-6758.

†**Medieval Institute Pubns.,** *(Medieval Inst; 0-918720),* Western Michigan Univ., Kalamazoo, MI 49008 (SAN 212-2928) Tel 616-383-6096; *CIP.*

Medieval Latin Press, *(Medieval Latin; 0-916760),* P.O. Box 7847, St. Matthews Sta., Louisville, KY 40207 (SAN 208-7642) Tel 502-897-1241.

Medilex Co., The, Subs. of Robert Stephan Jr. PC, *(Medilex Co; 0-916763),* 3300 N. Central Ave., Suite 1400, Phoenix, AZ 85012 (SAN 654-3340) Tel 602-241-1400.

Medina Univ., Press International, *(Medina Pr; 0-914456),* P.O. Box 614, Wilmette, IL 60091 (SAN 206-5932) Tel 312-328-7890.

MediScience Pubs., *(MediSci Pubs; 0-938869),* P.O. Box 256, Deerfield, IL 60015 (SAN 662-5304); 2501 Riverwoods Rd., Deerfield, IL 60015 (SAN 662-5312) Tel 312-945-7071.

MedMaster, Inc., *(MedMaster; 0-940780),* 17500 NE Ninth Ave., North Miami Beach, FL 33162 (SAN 219-7960) Tel 305-653-3480.

Medusa, *(Medusa; 0-9601714),* 4112 Emery Place, NW, Washington, DC 20016 (SAN 215-9678) Tel 202-244-1239.

Meeker Publishing Co., *(Meeker Pub; 0-935068),* 2605 Virginia St., NE, Albuquerque, NM 87110 (SAN 205-8650) Tel 505-299-6406.

Mega Corp., *(Mega Corp; 0-9616170),* P.O. Box 10876, Jacksonville, FL 32247 (SAN 699-9468); 4812 Cherwell Ln., Jacksonville, FL 32217 (SAN 699-9476) Tel 904-733-2051.

Megabooks, Inc., *(Megabooks; 0-935157),* 4300 NW 23rd Ave., Suite 192, P.O. Box 1702, Gainesville, FL 32602 (SAN 695-345X) Tel 904-371-6342.

Megan Pubns., *(Megan Pubns; 0-9616663),* 17128 S. Angeline NE, Suquamish, WA 98392 (SAN 661-3586) Tel 206-598-4474.

Megan's World, *(Megans Wld; 0-9610150),* 124 W. Wilshire, P.O. Box 3399, Fullerton, CA 92634 (SAN 272-3239) Tel 714-871-1369.

MegaSoft, *(MegaSoft; 0-939095),* P.O. Box 991, Jennings, LA 70546 (SAN 662-6068); 915 Granger St., Apt. 3, Jennings, LA 70546 (SAN 662-6076). Do not confuse with other companies with the same name in Battleground, WA, San Jose, CA.

Megden Publishing, *(Megden Pub; 0-9603676),* P.O. Box 217, Huntington Beach, CA 92648 (SAN 214-414X) Tel 714-960-2182.

Meher Baba Information, *(Meher Baba Info; 0-940700),* Box 1101, Berkeley, CA 94701 (SAN 202-618X) Tel 415-562-1101; Dist. by: Bookpeople, 2929 Fifth St., Berkeley, CA 94710 (SAN 168-9517).

Mehetabel & Co., *(Mehetabel & Co; 0-936094),* P.O. Box 151, Tiburon, CA 94920-0151 (SAN 281-9902) Tel 415-381-0828.

Meier & Associates, Inc., Subs. of Meier Associates, *(Meier & Assocs; 0-917489),* P.O. Box 986, 335 College Ave., Dekalb, IL 60115 (SAN 656-0741) Tel 815-758-3808.

†**Meiklejohn Civil Liberties Institute,** *(Meiklejohn Civ Lib; 0-913876),* 1715 Francisco St., Berkeley, CA 94703 (SAN 203-9834) Tel 415-848-0599; *CIP.*

Meissner Bks., *(Meissner Bks; 0-9613755),* P.O. Box 5296, Bend, OR 97708 (SAN 687-6242); Dist. by: Pacific Pipeline, P.O. Box 3711, Seattle, WA 98124 (SAN 169-8834).

Melcher Software, *(Melcher Software; 0-935977),* 412 Hollybrook Dr., Midland, MI 48640 (SAN 696-6047) Tel 517-631-7607.

Mele Loke Publishing Co., *(M Loke; 0-930932),* P.O. Box 7142, Honolulu, HI 96821 (SAN 211-1330) Tel 808-734-8611; Dist. by: Pacific Trade Group, P.O. Box 668, Pearl City, HI 96782-0668 (SAN 169-1635) Tel 808-261-6954.

Melek, Jacques, *(J Melek; 0-942330),* P.O. Box 901, Upland, CA 91786 (SAN 241-5607) Tel 714-946-6942. *Imprints:* Sunbright Books (Sunbright Bks); Sunrise Publications (Sunrise Pubns).

Melior Pubns., Div. of Futurepast: The History Co., *(Melior Pubns; 0-9616441),* P.O. Box 1905, Spokane, WA 99210 (SAN 658-9154) Tel 509-838-5242; N. 10th Post St., Suite 550, Spokane, WA 99210 (SAN 658-9162).

Melissa Data Co., *(Melissa Data; 0-937467),* 12 Balboa Coves, Newport Beach, CA 92663 (SAN 658-9197) Tel 714-650-1000.

Melkonian, Norman, *(N Melkonian; 0-9616320),* 207 W. Garfield, No. 5, Glendale, CA 91204 (SAN 658-7399) Tel 818-247-6809.

†**Mellen, Edwin, Pr.,** *(E Mellen; 0-88946),* P.O. Box 450, Lewiston, NY 14092 (SAN 207-110X); 450 Ridge St., Lewiston, NY 14092 (SAN 658-1218) Tel 716-754-2266; *CIP.*

Melrose Bk. Co., *(Melrose Bk Co; 0-934972),* 384 North San Vicente Blvd., Los Angeles, CA 90048 (SAN 211-7436) Tel 213-655-5177.

Melrose Historical Society, *(Melrose Hist; 0-9615451),* Trinity Church, 131 W. Emerson St., Melrose, MA 02176 (SAN 695-7242) Tel 617-665-7569.

Melrose Publishing Co., Inc., *(Melrose Pub Inc; 0-932735),* 9021 Melrose Ave., Suite 301, Los Angeles, CA 90069 (SAN 240-4141) Tel 213-275-3076.

Melrose Square *See* Holloway Hse. Publishing Co.

Melton-Giardini Bk. Co., *(Melton-Giardini Bk; 0-9614901),* Rte. 2, Box 34, Hull, GA 30646 (SAN 693-3092) Tel 404-543-8795.

Membrane Press, *(Membrane Pr; 0-87924),* P.O. Box 11601, Shorewood, Milwaukee, WI 53211 (SAN 202-621X).

Memento Pubns., Inc., *(Memento; 0-89436),* P.O. Box 58646, Dallas, TX 75258 (SAN 210-1246) Tel 817-387-9286.

Memorial Sloan-Kettering Cancer Ctr., Alumni Office, *(Memorial Sloan-Kettering; 0-911315),* 1275 York Ave., New York, NY 10021 (SAN 272-3271) Tel 212-207-3511.

Memorial Union Corporation, *(Memorial Union; 0-934068),* Emporia State Univ., 1200 Commercial St., Emporia, KS 66801 (SAN 264-2050).

Memory Bks., *(Memory Bks)*, P.O. Box 85, New York, NY 10113 (SAN 699-783X).

Memory Impact Publishing, *(Memory Impact Pub; 0-9616664)*, 520 La Honda Dr., Aptos, CA 95003 (SAN 661-3578) Tel 408-688-0270.

Memphis Musicraft Publications, *(Memphis Musicraft; 0-934017)*, 3149 Southern Ave., Memphis, TN 38111 (SAN 692-7696) Tel 901-452-5265.

†Memphis State Univ. Pr., *(Memphis St Univ; 0-87870)*, Memphis State Univ., Memphis, TN 38152 (SAN 202-6228) Tel 901-454-2752; *CIP.*

Men of the North, *(Men North; 0-939703)*, P.O. Box 46706, Bedford, OH 44146 (SAN 663-513X); 4713 Dalebridge Rd., No. F-36, Warrensville Heights, OH 44128 (SAN 663-5148) Tel 216-831-2698.

Menasha Ridge Pr., Inc., *(Menasha Ridge; 0-940752; 0-89732)*, P.O. Box 59257, Birmingham, AL 35259 (SAN 219-7294) Tel 205-991-0373; Dist. by: Simon & Schuster, 1230 Ave. of the Americas, New York, NY 10020 (SAN 200-2450) Tel 212-245-6400. *Imprints:* Book Arts (Book Arts).

Mendel, Carol, *(Carol Mendel; 0-9607696; 0-935179)*, P.O. Box 6022, San Diego, CA 92106 (SAN 219-3329) Tel 619-226-1406.

Mendham Public Library, Publisher, *(Mendham Publ Lib; 0-931661)*, 10 Hilltop Rd., Mendham, NJ 07945 (SAN 683-7824) Tel 201-543-4152.

Mendocino Foundation for Health Education, The, *(Mendocino Found Health; 0-9615167)*, P.O. Box 1377, Mendocino, CA 95460 (SAN 694-308X) Tel 707-964-0425.

Mendoza, Carlos R., *(C Mendoza; 0-9608420)*, 613 Point Caiman Ct., Chula Vista, CA 92011 (SAN 240-7205) Tel 619-421-8848.

Menil Foundation, *(Menil Found; 0-939594)*, c/o Harvard Univ. Pr., 79 Garden St., Cambridge, MA 02138 (SAN 200-2043).

Menlo Pr., *(Menlo Pr; 0-939607)*, 1259 El Camino Real, Suite 191, Menlo Park, CA 94025 (SAN 663-5989) Tel 415-854-6553.

Menorah Medical Center Auxilary, *(Menorah Med; 0-9614735)*, 4949 Rockhhill Rd., Kansas City, MO 64110 (SAN 692-7114) Tel 816-276-8133.

Menorah Publishing Co., Inc., *(Menorah Pub; 0-932232)*, 15 W. 84th St., New York, NY 10024 (SAN 212-1158) Tel 212-787-2248.

Menses, *(Menses; 0-9605700)*, Box 192, Croton-on-Hudson, NY 10520 (SAN 204-2466).

Menta Pubns., *(Menta Pubns; 0-935688)*, P.O. Box 7542, Shawnee Mission, KS 66207 (SAN 213-6945) Tel 913-648-2911.

Mentor Bks. *See New American Library*

Mentors, Inc., *(Mentors; 0-9601542)*, 8817 Greenview Pl., Spring Valley, CA 92077 (SAN 241-5615) Tel 714-464-4235.

Menus from the Pacific North West, *(Menus Pacific NW; 0-9615525)*, P.O. Box 532, West Linn, OR 97068 (SAN 696-2920) Tel 503-657-7659.

Meola, Edward A., *(Meola; 0-9606008)*, 5806 Circle H Place, Tucson, AZ 85713 (SAN 216-4175).

Mercadante, J. L., *(J L Mercadante)*, P.O. Box 1028, New Hyde Park, NY 11040 (SAN 211-0830).

Mercedes-Benz of North America, Inc., *(Mercedes-Benz; 0-936573)*, 1 Mercedes Dr., Montvale, NJ 07645 (SAN 698-0678) Tel 201-573-2238.

Mercer House Press, *(Mercer Hse; 0-89080)*, Clover Leaf Farm, Old Rte. 9, Rfd No. 1, Biddeford, ME 04005 (SAN 207-1754) Tel 207-282-7116; Orders to: P.O. Box 681, Kennebunkport, ME 04046 Tel 207-1762).

Mercer Island Piccolo Pr., *(Mercer Island; 0-9614231)*, 7441 W. Mercer Way, Mercer Island, WA 98040 (SAN 686-7790) Tel 206-232-7320.

Mercer Island Preschool Assn., *(Mercer Isl Preschl; 0-936353)*, P.O. Box 464, Mercer Island, WA 98040 (SAN 697-905X) Tel 206-232-6855; 7500 86th Ave. SE, Mercer Island, WA 98040 (SAN 698-2301); Orders to: Pacific Pipeline, 19215 66th Ave. S., Kent, WA 98032-1171 (SAN 169-8834) Tel 206-872-5523.

Mercer Pr., *(Mercer Pr; 0-9615033)*, P.O. Box 525, Bluefield, WV 24701 (SAN 693-8027) Tel 304-327-0379.

†Mercer Univ. Pr., *(Mercer Univ Pr; 0-86554)*, Macon, GA 31207 (SAN 220-0716) Tel 912-744-2880; *CIP.*

Merchandising Concepts Specialists, *(Merchandising; 0-943038)*, 132 S. Bedford Dr. No 206, Beverly Hills, CA 90212 (SAN 240-4087) Tel 213-276-9813.

Merchants Publishing Co., *(Merchants Pub Co; 0-89484)*, 20 Mills St., Kalamazoo, MI 49001 (SAN 209-9586) Tel 616-345-1175.

†Merck & Co., Inc., *(Merck; 0-911910)*, P.O. Box 2000, Rahway, NJ 07065 (SAN 202-6236) Tel 201-574-5403; *CIP.*

Merck Sharp & Dohme International, *(Merck-Sharp-Dohme; 0-911910)*, Professional Communications Dept., West Point, PA 19486 (SAN 212-1921).

Mercury Books, *(Mercury Bks; 0-910963)*, P.O. Box 442, Yardley, PA 19067 (SAN 272-3492) Tel 215-482-8404.

Mercury Hse., Inc., *(Mercury Hse Inc; 0-916515)*, 300 Montgomery St., Suite 700, San Francisco, CA 94104 (SAN 295-4656) Tel 415-433-7042; P.O. Box 640, Forest Knolls, CA 94933 (SAN 662-2283); Orders to: Kampmann & Co., Inc., 9 E. 40th St., New York, NY 10016 (SAN 202-5191) Tel 212-685-2928.

Mercury Media Inc., *(Mercury Media; 0-932487)*, P.O. Box 54, Wake, VA 23176 (SAN 687-4282) Tel 804-776-7717.

†Mercury Press (MO), *(Mercury Pr; 0-912393)*, P.O. Box 8884, Munger Station, Witchita, KS 67208 (SAN 264-2069); *CIP.*

Mercury Publishing, *(Mercury Pub; 0-935717)*, 4115 Flora Pl., St. Louis, MO 63110 (SAN 695-9288) Tel 314-664-6722.

Mercy Ambulance & Saint Mary's Hospital, *(Mercy Ambulance; 0-9615819)*, 357 Jefferson SE, Grand Rapids, MI 49503 (SAN 696-6152) Tel 616-459-8197.

Mercy & Truth Pubs., *(Mercy & Truth; 0-9615494)*, Rte 1, P.O. Box 503, Osceola, WI 54020 (SAN 696-379X) Tel 715-294-2052.

Mercy Oceans Pubns., *(Mercy Oceans; 0-937847)*, C/O Helen Johnson, 108 Graymoor Ln., Olympia Fields, IL 60461 (SAN 659-5162) Tel 312-748-4981; Dist. by: Bookpeople, 2929 Fifth St., Berkeley, CA 94710 (SAN 168-9517); Dist. by: New Leaf Distributing, The, 1020 White St., SW, Atlanta, GA 30310 (SAN 169-1449) Tel 404-755-2665.

Merdyne Pubs., Inc., *(Merdyne Pubs; 0-934299)*, 184 Fifth Ave., New York, NY 10010 (SAN 693-3793) Tel 212-255-8448.

Meredith, H. V., *(H V Meredith; 0-9603120)*, Orders to: The State Printing Company, P.O. Box 1388, Columbia, SC 29202 (SAN 204-6334) Tel 803-799-9550.

Merganzer Press, *(Merganzer Pr; 0-9602648)*, 659 Northmoor Rd., Lake Forest, IL 60045 (SAN 212-7636).

Merging Media, *(Merging Media; 0-934536)*, 516 Gallows Hill Rd., Cranford, NJ 07016 (SAN 206-3662) Tel 201-276-9479.

Meridian Bks. *See New American Library*

Meridian Editions, *(Meridian Ed)*, 9905 Lorain Ave., Silver Spring, MD 20901 (SAN 209-5831).

Meridian Education Corp., *(Meridian Educ; 0-936007)*, 608 E. Locust St., Bloomington, IL 61701 (SAN 696-6012) Tel 309-827-5455.

Meridian Hill Pubns., *(Meridian Hill; 0-940206)*, 2435 Vance St., Lakewood, CO 80215 (SAN 220-3413) Tel 303-237-0755; Orders to: Johnson Books, 1880 S. 57th Ct., Boulder, CO 80301 (SAN 658-1013) Tel 303-443-1576.

Meridian Press, Subs. of Center for Help for Agoraphobia/Anxiety Through New Growth Experiences, *(Meridian; 0-9609462)*, 2915 Providence Rd., Charlotte, NC 28211 (SAN 260-2253) Tel 704-365-0140.

Meridian Pr., *(Meridian Oklahoma; 0-9615776)*, P.O. Box 21567, Oklahoma City, OK 73156-1567 (SAN 696-6144) Tel 405-751-2343.

Meridian Publishing, *(Meridian Pub; 0-86610)*, 2643 Edgewood Rd., Utica, NY 13501 (SAN 215-2568).

Meridional Pubns., *(Meridional Pubns; 0-939710)*, 7101 Winding Way, Wake Forest, NC 27587 (SAN 216-7484) Tel 919-556-2940.

Merit Bks., Div. of Merit Media Intl., *(Merit Bks; 0-915929)*, P.O. Box 3319, Laguna Hills, CA 92654 (SAN 294-0620) Tel 714-768-5777.

Merit Pubs., *(Merit Calif; 0-910962)*, P.O. Box 1344, Beverly Hills, CA 90213 (SAN 203-9869) Tel 213-474-1888.

Meriwether Publishing, Ltd., *(Meriwether Pub; 0-916260)*, Box 7710, Colorado Springs, CO 80933 (SAN 208-4716); 885 Elkton Dr., Colorado Springs, CO 80907 (SAN 658-2877) Tel 303-574-4422.

Merk, *(Merk)*, 377 Merk Rd., Watsonville, CA 95076 (SAN 215-8892).

Merlin Engine Works, *(Merlin Engine Wks)*, 548 Elm, San Bruno, CA 94066 (SAN 217-8915).

†Merlin Pr., *(Merlin Pr; 0-930142)*, P.O. Box 5602, San Jose, CA 95150 (SAN 209-584X); *CIP.*

Mermaid Bks., *(Mermaid Bks; 0-9617196)*, 2160 S. Holly, Suite 107, Denver, CO 80222 (SAN 663-2459) Tel 303-759-4294.

Mermelstein, Mel, *(M Mermelstein; 0-9606534)*, c/o Auschwitz Study Foundation, 7422 Cedar St., P.O. Box 2232, Huntington Beach, CA 92647 (SAN 214-4158) Tel 213-848-1101.

Merriam, Robert L., *(R L Merriam; 0-918507)*, Newhall Rd., Conway, MA 01341 (SAN 163-4070) Tel 413-369-4052.

Merriam-Eddy Co., Inc., *(Merriam-Eddy; 0-914562)*, P.O. Box 25, South Waterford, ME 04081 (SAN 202-6252).

†Merriam-Webster, Inc., Subs. of Encyclopaedia Britannica, Inc., *(Merriam-Webster Inc; 0-87779)*, P.O. Box 281, Springfield, MA 01102 (SAN 202-6244) Tel 413-734-3134; Toll free: 800-828-1880; 47 Federal St., Springfield, MA 01102 (SAN 658-1226) Tel 413-734-3134; *CIP.*

Merrifield Co., The, *(Merrifield Co)*, 890 Edwards Lane, Sebastopol, CA 95472 (SAN 687-7524).

Merril Pr., *(Merril Pr; 0-936783)*, 12500 NE Tenth Pl., Bellevue, WA 98005 (SAN 699-9387) Tel 206-454-7009.

Merrill, Madeline O., *(M O Merrill; 0-9601332)*, 109 Water St., Saugus, MA 01906 (SAN 209-035X) Tel 617-233-5442.

Merrill, Perry H., *(P H Merrill; 0-9605806)*, 200 Elm St., Montpelier, VT 05602 (SAN 220-1755) Tel 802-223-2697.

Merrill Publishing Co., Div. of Bell & Howell Co., *(Merrill; 0-675)*, 1300 Alum Creek Dr., Columbus, OH 43216 (SAN 200-2116) Tel 614-890-1111; Toll free: 800-848-6205.

Merrimack Pubs. Circle, Div. of Salem Hse., Ltd., *(Merrimack Pub Cir; 0-941938)*, 462 Boston St., Topsfield, MA 01983 (SAN 212-193X) Tel 617-887-2440. Do not confuse with Merrimack Publishing Corp., Bridgeport, CT.

Merrimack Publishing Corp., Affil. of Associated Booksellers, *(Merrimack; 0-87497)*, 562 Boston Ave., Bridgeport, CT 06610 (SAN 203-5014) Tel 203-333-7268; Toll free: 800-232-2224; Dist. by: Associated Booksellers, 562 Boston Ave., Bridgeport, CT 06610 (SAN 203-5014). Do not confuse with Merrimack Publishers Circle, Salem, NH.

Merritt Co., *(Merritt Co; 0-930868)*, 1661 Ninth St., Santa Monica, CA 90406 (SAN 203-8110).

Merritt Pubs., *(Merritt Pubs Texas; 0-930238)*, 718 Westwood, Richardson, TX 75080 (SAN 210-6132) Tel 214-644-5765.

Merriwell, Frank, Inc., Subs. of National Learning Corp., *(F Merriwell; 0-8373)*, 212 Michael Dr., Syosset, NY 11791 (SAN 209-259X) Tel 516-921-8888; Toll free: 800-645-6337.

Merry Bears, *(Merry Bears; 0-933103)*, 27122 Ayamonte, Mission Viejo, CA 92692 (SAN 689-5778) Tel 714-495-0510.

Merry Thoughts, *(Merry Thoughts; 0-88230)*, 380 Adams St., Bedford Hills, NY 10507 (SAN 206-6882) Tel 914-241-0447.

Merton Hse. Travel & Tourism Pubs., Inc., *(Merton Hse; 0-916032)*, 2100 Manchester Rd., Suite 507, Wheaton, IL 60187 (SAN 207-9739) Tel 312-668-7410.

Merz Productions, *(Merz Prod; 0-937001),* 24142 El Rond, Lake Forest, CA 92630 (SAN 698-1844) Tel 714-855-9455.

Mesa Press, *(Mesa Pr IL),* 5835 Kimbark Ave., Chicago, IL 60637 (SAN 215-3270) Tel 312-962-1596.

†**Mesa Productions,** *(Mesa Prods; 0-914963),* 714 Westmount Ave., Dallas, TX 75211 (SAN 289-534X) Tel 214-620-9355; *CIP.*

Mesa Pubns., Div. of Mesa International, Inc., *(Mesa Pubns; 0-931984),* 6266 N. Swan Rd., Tucson, AZ 85718 (SAN 211-8629).

Mesa Verde Museum Assocs. Inc., *(Mesa Verde Museum; 0-937062),* P.O. Box 38, Verde National Park, CO 81330 (SAN 295-0456).

Mesa Verde Press, *(Mesa Verde; 0-9607220),* P.O. Box 6415, Santa Fe, NM 87502 (SAN 239-1163). Moved, left no forwarding address.

Mesorah Pubns., Ltd., *(Mesorah Pubns; 0-89906),* 1969 Coney Island Ave., Brooklyn, NY 11223 (SAN 213-1269) Tel 718-339-1700; Toll free: 800-Mesorah.

Messenger, J. R., Pub., *(J R Messenger; 0-914695),* P.O. Box 217, Piscataway, NJ 08854 (SAN 296-1199) Tel 201-356-0679.

Messenger Communications, *(Messenger Comm; 0-939336),* 18706 25th Ave. SE, Bothell, WA 98011 (SAN 216-5392) Tel 206-481-9399.

Messing, Simon D., Pub., *(Messing Pub; 0-9615946),* 58 Shepard's Knoll Dr., Hamden, CT 06514 (SAN 696-8171) Tel 203-397-4477.

†**Messner, Julian,** A Simon & Schuster Co., Div. of Gulf & Western Corp., *(Messner; 0-671),* 1230 Ave. of the Americas, New York, NY 10020 (SAN 202-6260) Tel 212-245-6400; Toll free: 800-223-2336; *CIP.*

Metacom Press, *(Metacom Pr; 0-911381),* 1 Tahanto Rd., Worcester, MA 01602 (SAN 272-3581) Tel 617-757-1683.

Metagraphics, Inc., *(Metagraphics; 0-934030),* 12381 E. Cornell Ave, Aurora, CO 80014 (SAN 679-1352).

Metal Building Manufacturers Assn., Inc., *(Metal Bldg; 0-9615996),* 1230 Keith Bldg., Cleveland, OH 44115 (SAN 699-7538) Tel 216-241-7333.

Metal Bulletin Inc., Subs. of Metal Bulletin PLC (UK), *(Metal Bulletin; 0-913333),* 708 Third Ave., New York, NY 10017 (SAN 283-2070) Tel 212-490-0791.

Metal Powder Industries Federation, *(Metal Powder; 0-918404),* 105 College Rd. E., Princeton, NJ 08540 (SAN 209-6250) Tel 609-452-7700.

Metal Properties Council, Inc., The, *(Metal Prop Coun),* 345 E. 47th St., New York, NY 10017 (SAN 225-2120) Tel 212-705-7693.

Metallurgical Society, Inc., The, *(Metal Soc; 0-87339),* 420 Commonwealth Dr., Warrendale, PA 15086 (SAN 680-0572) Tel 412-776-9000.

Metamorphic Pr., *(Metamorphic Pr; 0-9615848),* P.O. Box 1841, Santa Rosa, CA 95402 (SAN 696-6489) Tel 707-874-2606; Dist. by: Rodale Press, Incorporated, 33 E. Minor St., Emmaus, PA 18049 (SAN 200-2477) Tel 215-967-5171; Toll free: 800-527-8200.

Metamorphous Pr., Subs. of Metamorphosis, Inc., *(Metamorphous Pr; 0-943920; 1-55552),* P.O. Box 1712, Lake Oswego, OR 97034 (SAN 264-2077) Tel 503-635-6709.

Metascience Foun., *(Metascience; 0-935436),* Box 747, Franklin, NC 28734 (SAN 213-4179) Tel 704-524-5103.

Metatron Press, *(Metatron Pr; 0-931412),* P.O. Box 10333, Milwaukee, WI 53210 (SAN 211-142X) Tel 414-444-2442.

Metcut Research Associates, Inc., *(Metcut Res Assocs; 0-936974),* 3980 Rosslyn Dr., Cincinnati, OH 45209 (SAN 214-4166).

Meteora Press, *(Meteora; 0-9613347),* 58 Morningside Dr., Lowell, MA 01852 (SAN 656-1748) Tel 617-452-0116.

Methodius Press, *(Methodius Pr; 0-9611866),* 7878 Twin Pines Lane, Sebastopol, CA 95472 (SAN 286-1437) Tel 707-823-0978.

Methuen, Inc., *(Methuen Inc; 0-416; 0-7100),* 29 W. 35th St., New York, NY 10001 (SAN 213-196X) Tel 212-244-3336. Do not confuse Tavistock Publications (UK), an imprint of Methuen, Inc., with Tavistock Poetry Pr., San Diego, CA. Acquired U. S. branch of Routledge & Kegan Paul, Ltd. in 1986. *Imprints:* Ark Paperbacks (Ark Paperbks).

Methuselah Books, *(Methuselah Bks; 0-937092),* Rt. 1 Spindle Rd., Ellsworth, ME 04605 (SAN 214-4174).

Metier, *(Metier; 0-936087),* P.O. Box 51204, San Jose, CA 95151 (SAN 696-642X) Tel 408-286-9992.

Metis Pr., *(Metis Pr Inc; 0-934816),* P.O. Box 25187, Chicago, IL 60625 (SAN 213-2575).

Metric Media Book Pubs., Div. of Abbey Books, *(Metric Media Bk),* P.O. Box 266, Somers, NY 10589 (SAN 209-147X) Tel 914-248-5522.

Metrics Pr., *(Metrics Pr; 0-9607126),* P.O. Box 9248, Boston, MA 02114 (SAN 293-3047); Orders to: P.O. Box 9248, Boston, MA 02114 (SAN 293-3055).

Metrics Research Corp., *(Metrics Res Corp; 0-932393),* 130 W. Wieuca Rd., Suite 208, Atlanta, GA 30342 (SAN 686-6786) Tel 404-255-1976.

Metro Book Co., *(Metro Bk Co; 0-915371),* 3208 Cahuenga Blvd. W., Los Angeles, CA 90068 (SAN 291-2805) Tel 818-508-0884.

Metro Books, Inc., *(Metro Bks; 0-8411),* 3110 N. Arlington Heights Rd., Arlington Heights, IL 60004 (SAN 203-9893) Tel 312-253-9720.

Metro Deaf Senior Citizens, Inc., *(Metro Deaf Senior; 0-9613623),* 1298 N. Pascal St., St. Paul, MN 55108 (SAN 670-8757) Tel 612-647-9565.

Metro Pubns., *(Metro WI; 0-936537),* 1815 N. Shore Dr., Delavan, WI 53115 (SAN 697-9106) Tel 414-728-3800.

Metro Publishing, *(Metro Pub; 0-933745),* Box 270776, Houston, TX 77277 (SAN 694-3934) Tel 713-666-7841.

Metron Press, *(Metron Pr; 0-941862),* St. Anthony Falls Sta., Box 4202, Minneapolis, MN 55414 (SAN 220-259X).

Metron Pubns., *(Metron Pubns; 0-940268),* P.O. Box 1213, Princeton, NJ 08542 (SAN 217-5401) Tel 609-396-7947.

Metropol Press, *(Metropol Press),* 3323 Catturagus Ave., P.O. Box 2547, Culver City, CA 90230 (SAN 292-3351).

Metropolitan Ctr. for Educational Research, Development & Training, *(Metro Ctr Educ; 0-935405),* 32 Washington Pl. Rm. 72, New York, NY 10003 (SAN 696-3595) Tel 212-598-7729.

Metropolitan Foundation, The, *(Metro Found; 0-9615016),* 201 E. Franklin St., Richmond, VA 23219 (SAN 694-0374) Tel 804-648-1234.

Metropolitan Futures, Inc., *(Metro Futures; 0-915218),* P.O. Box 1151, New York, NY 10017 (SAN 207-1444).

Metropolitan Mothers at Work, *(Metro Mothers Work; 0-9615017),* 6917 Arlington Rd., Suite 303, Bethesda, MD 20814 (SAN 694-0382) Tel 301-986-0725; Dist. by: Andrik Associates, P.O. Box 5029, 311 Ashby St., Alexandria, VA 22305 (SAN 221-895X).

†**Metropolitan Museum of Art,** *(Metro Mus Art; 0-87099),* Fifth Ave. & 82nd St., New York, NY 10028 (SAN 202-6279) Tel 212-879-5500; Dist. by: Univ. of Chicago Pr., 5801 Ellis Ave. S., 3rd Flr., Chicago, IL 60637 (SAN 202-5280) Tel 312-962-7693; *CIP.*

Metropolitan Washington Library Council, Div. of Metropolitan Washington Council of Governments, *(Metro Wash Lib; 0-914095),* 1875 Eye St. NW, No. 200, Washington, DC 20006 (SAN 287-6043) Tel 202-223-6800.

Metrosource Pubns., Inc., *(Metrosource Pubns; 0-9608012),* 1006 Olive St., Denver, CO 80220 (SAN 293-440X) Tel 303-321-3607; Dist. by: Gordons Books, Inc., 5450 N. Valley Hwy., Denver, CO 80216 (SAN 169-0531) Tel 303-296-1830.

Mettler Studios, Inc., *(Mettler Studios; 0-912536),* Tucson Creative Dance Ctr., 3131 N. Cherry Ave., Tucson, AZ 85719 (SAN 206-1589) Tel 602-327-7453.

Metzger Press, *(Metzger Pr; 0-9608750),* 303 W. Glenoaks Blvd., Suite 208, Glendale, CA 91202 (SAN 241-0370) Tel 818-244-0365.

Mexican American Cultural Ctr., *(Mex Am Cult; 0-932545),* 3019 W. French Pl., San Antonio, TX 78228 (SAN 687-4835) Tel 512-732-2156; Toll free: 800-531-6222.

Mexican American Legal Defense & Educational Fund, *(Mex Am Legal),* 28 Geary, San Francisco, CA 94108 (SAN 232-3362).

Mexican Museum, The, *(Mexican Museum; 0-905194),* Fort Mason Ctr., Bldg. D, Laguna & Marina Blvd., San Francisco, CA 94123 (SAN 238-7832) Tel 415-441-0404.

Mey-House Books, *(Mey-Hse Bks; 0-9611140),* P.O. Box 794, Stroudsburg, PA 18360 (SAN 285-6670).

Meyer, Herbert W. H., *(H W H Meyer; 0-9616723),* 184 N. Burnet Dr., Baytown, TX 77520 (SAN 661-3861) Tel 713-424-5266.

Meyer, Leo A., Associates, Inc., *(L A Meyer; 0-88069),* 23850 Clawiter Rd., Hayward, CA 94545 (SAN 238-0951) Tel 415-785-1091.

Meyer, Sandy, & Assocs., *(S Meyer Assocs; 0-9613431),* P.O. Box 13652, Roanoke, VA 24036 (SAN 657-0143) Tel 703-344-7903; 400 S. Beverly Dr., Suite 214, Beverly Hills, CA 90212 (SAN 662-2348); Dist. by: Bookpeople, 2929 Fifth St., Berkeley, CA 94710 (SAN 168-9517) Tel 415-549-3030; Toll free: 800-227-1516.

Meyerbooks, *(Meyerbooks; 0-916638),* P.O. Box 427, Glenwood, IL 60425 (SAN 208-998X) Tel 312-757-4950; 235 W Main St., Glenwood, IL 60425 (SAN 658-1234) Tel 312-757-4950.

Mezquita Editorial, *(Mezquita Edit; 0-930174),* 20 W. 22nd St., Rm 1000, New York, NY 10010 (SAN 210-640X) Tel 201-865-4067.

M H Enterprises, *(M H Enterprises; 0-9611044),* 420 W. 4th St., Hominy, OK 74035 (SAN 282-924X) Tel 918-885-2913; Dist. by: Centennial Distributors, P.O. Box 424, Deadwood, SD 57732 (SAN 200-4321).

Mho & Mho Works, *(Mho & Mho; 0-917320),* 1259 El Camino Real, Suite 108, Menlo Park, CA 94025 (SAN 238-7999) Tel 415-327-6121; Orders to: Inland Bk. Co., 22 Hemingway Ave., East Haven, CT 06512 (SAN 200-4151) Tel 203-467-4257; Orders to: Bookpeople, 2929 Fifth Ave., Berkeley, CA 94710 (SAN 168-9517); Toll free: 800-227-1516; Dist. by: New Leaf Distributing Co., 1020 White St. SW, Atlanta, GA 30310 (SAN 169-1449) Tel 404-755-2665; Dist. by: The Great Tradition, 750 Adrian Way, Suite 111, San Rafael, CA 94903 (SAN 200-5743) Tel 415-492-9382.

Miami-Dade Community College Environmental Ctr., *(Miami Dade Environ; 0-936487),* 11011 SW 104 St., Miami, FL 33176 (SAN 698-0953) Tel 305-596-4113.

Miami Univ. Art Museum, *(Miami Univ Art; 0-940784),* Patterson Ave., Oxford, OH 45056 (SAN 219-6042) Tel 513-529-2232.

Mica Publishing Co., *(Mica Pub Co; 0-931321),* P.O. Box 14931, Portland, OR 97214 (SAN 685-2637) Tel 503-230-2903.

†**Micah Pubns.,** *(Micah Pubns; 2-916288),* 255 Humphrey St., Marblehead, MA 01945 (SAN 209-1577) Tel 617-631-7601; *CIP.*

Micamar Publishing, *(Micamar Pub; 0-937373),* P.O. Box 56, Barneveld, WI 53507 (SAN 658-9200) Tel 608-924-2101; Rte. 1, Lakeview Rd., Barneveld, WI 53507 (SAN 658-9219).

Micelle Press, Inc., *(Micelle Pr; 0-9608752),* P.O. Box 653, Cranford, NJ 07016 (SAN 241-0443).

Michael, Pansy D., *(P D Michael; 0-9602460),* R.R. 2, Box 221, South Whitley, IN 46787 (SAN 212-8624) Tel 219-839-3135.

Michael, Prudence Groff, *(P G Michael; 0-9600932),* 64472 U.S.H 31, Lakeville, IN 46536 (SAN 208-7669) Tel 219-291-0454.

Michael Anthony Pubns., *(M Anthony Pubns; 0-9615979),* 11365 SW Ironwood Loop, Tigard, OR 97223 (SAN 698-1704) Tel 503-620-0872.

Michaels, M. C., Enterprises, *(M C Michaels; 0-9616182),* 1720 Elm St., Fairfield, CA 94533 (SAN 699-9786) Tel 707-422-0758.

Michaud, Carole & Susan, *(C & S Michaud; 0-9617264),* 30 Plaza Rd., Garden City, NY 11530 (SAN 663-4885) Tel 516-437-8798.

Michelin Guides & Maps, Div. of Michelin Tire Corp., *(Michelin),* P.O. Box 3305, Spartanburg, SC 29304-3305 (SAN 202-6309) Tel 803-599-0850; Orders to: Bibendum Rd., at New Cut Rd., Spartanburg, SC 29303 (SAN 693-9651).

Michelman, Herbert, Bks. *See* **Crown Pubs., Inc.**

519

Michie Co., The, Subs. of Macmillan Publishing, *(Michie Co; 0-87215; 0-672; 0-87473),* P.O. Box 7587, Charlottesville, VA 22906 (SAN 202-6317) Tel 804-972-7600; Toll free: 800-446-3410; 609 E. Market St., Charlottesville, VA 22901 (SAN 699-5438). Acquired law div. of Bobbs-Merrill Co. 1981. Acquired Allen Smith Co. 1985. *Imprints:* Smith, Allen, Co. (A Smith Co).

Michigan Assn. of Middle Schl. Educators, *(MI Middle Educ; 0-918449),* c/o Michigan State Univ., College of Education, Erickson 419, East Lansing, MI 48824 (SAN 657-6672) Tel 517-353-5461.

Michigan City Historical Society Inc., *(MI City Hist; 0-935549),* P.O. Box 512, Michigan City, IN 46360 (SAN 696-2335) Tel 219-872-6133.

Michigan Dept. of State, *(MI Dept Hist; 0-935719),* Bureau of History, 208 N. Capitol Ave., Lansing, MI 48933 (SAN 695-9415) Tel 517-373-3703.

Michigan Municipal League, *(MI Municipal),* 1675 Green Rd., Box 1487, Ann Arbor, MI 48106 (SAN 226-3157) Tel 313-662-3246.

Michigan Natural Resources Magazine, *(Mich Nat Res; 0-941912),* Box 30034, Lansing, MI 48909 (SAN 239-4596).

Michigan Orchid Society, *(Mich Orchid Soc; 0-9610332),* 920 Southdown Rd., Bloomfield Hills, MI 48013 (SAN 264-2093) Tel 313-644-2183; Orders to: 14800 Harrison, Livonia, MI 48154 (SAN 662-0809) Tel 313-421-0082.

Michigan Publications on East Asia *See* Univ. of Michigan, Ctr. for Chinese Studies

Michigan Romance Studies, *(Mich Romance; 0-939730),* Dept. of Romance Languages, Univ. of Michigan, Ann Arbor, MI 48109 (SAN 216-7654) Tel 313-764-5386.

†**Michigan Slavic Pubns.,** *(Mich Slavic Pubns; 0-930042),* Dept. of Slavic Languages & Literatures, Univ. of Michigan, Ann Arbor, MI 48109-1275 (SAN 210-4636) Tel 313-763-4496; *CIP.*

Michigan State Univ., African Studies Ctr., *(Mich St Univ; 0-939323),* 100 International Center, East Lansing, MI 48824 (SAN 663-1762) Tel 517-353-1700.

Michigan State Univ., Community Development Programs, *(MSU Comm Dev; 0-941872),* Michigan State Univ., 43 Kellogg Ctr., East Lansing, MI 48824-1022 (SAN 202-2583) Tel 517-355-0100.

†**Michigan State Univ. Pr.,** *(Mich St U Pr; 0-87013),* 1405 S. Harrison Rd., 25 Manly Miles Bldg., East Lansing, MI 48824 (SAN 202-6295) Tel 517-355-9543; Dist. by: Wayne State Univ. Pr., Leonard N. Simons Bldg., 5959 Woodward Ave., Detroit, MI 48202 (SAN 202-5221) Tel 313-577-4601; *CIP.*

Michigan United Conservation Clubs, *(Mich United Conserv; 0-933112),* P.O. Box 30235, Lansing, MI 48909 (SAN 208-1091) Tel 517-371-1041.

Michilander Industries, *(Michilander Indust; 0-941640),* 1100 State St., St. Joseph, MI 49085 (SAN 238-7816) Tel 616-983-4972.

Micka, Mary Virginia, & Assocs., *(M V Micka; 0-9617046),* 1420 Randoloh Ave., St. Paul, MN 55105 (SAN 662-8141) Tel 612-690-6559; Dist. by: Bookslinger, 213 E. 4th St., St. Paul, MN 55101 (SAN 169-4154) Tel 612-221-0429.

Mickler Hse. Pubs., The, *(Mickler Hse; 0-913122),* P.O. Box 38, Chuluota, FL 32766 (SAN 206-6874) Tel 305-365-3636.

Micro Analysis & Design, Inc., *(Micro Analysis; 0-937197),* 9132 Thunderhead Dr., Boulder, CO 80302 (SAN 658-5825) Tel 303-442-6947.

Micro Data Management, Inc., *(Micro Data Mgmt; 0-938623),* P.O. Box 1230, Cerritos, CA 90701 (SAN 661-5724); 18944 Vickie Ave., No. 92, Cerritos, CA 90701 (SAN 661-5732) Tel 213-594-6282.

Micro db Systems, *(Micro db Sys; 0-930627),* P.O. Box 2380 3713 Lawndale Drive, Midland, MI 48640 (SAN 687-7338).

Micro Demographics, Inc., *(Micro Demo; 0-935965),* P.O. Box 10070, Anaheim, CA 92802-8070 (SAN 696-6128) Tel 714-535-5456.

Micro Information Publishing, *(Micro Info; 0-912603),* 4730 Dakota St. SE, Prior Lake, MN 55372 (SAN 282-7867) Tel 612-447-6959; Toll free: 800-328-0196.

Micro Magic Cooking Co., *(Micro Magic; 0-9606096),* 145 N. 46th St., Lincoln, NE 68503 (SAN 216-8367) Tel 402-475-4536.

Micro Pro Litera Pr., *(Micro Pro Litera Pr; 0-939477),* P.O. Box 14045, San Francisco, CA 94114 (SAN 663-3900); 109 Douglass St., No. 2, San Francisco, CA 94114 (SAN 663-3919) Tel 415-863-3037.

Micro-Tech Index, The, *(Micro Tech; 0-9617152),* 20005 Graves Run Rd., Hampstead, MD 21074 (SAN 663-3617) Tel 301-374-5810.

Micro Text Pubns., Inc., *(Micro Text Pubns; 0-942412),* One Lincoln Plaza, Suite 27C, New York, NY 10023 (SAN 238-1753) Tel 212-877-8539.

Micro-Wave Foods Inc., *(Micro-Wave Foods; 0-9614957),* P.O. Box 53, Malibu, CA 90265 (SAN 693-7462) Tel 213-456-5686; Dist. by: Club Products, 1100 Redmond Rd., Jacksonville, AR 72076 (SAN 200-7509) Tel 501-982-0555; Toll free: 800-643-8259.

Micro Works, Inc., The, *(Micro Works),* 1942 S. El Camino Real, Encinitas, CA 92024 (SAN 277-6049) Tel 619-942-2400.

Microbim, *(Microbim; 0-914394),* 16 Tain Dr., Great Neck, NY 11021 (SAN 202-697X) Tel 516-466-2498.

Microcomputer Applications, *(Microcomputer Appns; 0-935230),* P.O. Box E, Suisun City, CA 94585 (SAN 285-0540).

Microconsulting Northwest, *(Microconsulting NW; 0-916241),* P.O. Box 15075, Portland, OR 97214 (SAN 294-9695) Tel 503-227-5150.

MicroDesigns, *(MicroDesigns; 0-938799),* 2954 Orlando, Oklahoma City, OK 73120 (SAN 661-5104) Tel 405-755-9806.

Microfilming Corp. of America, *(Microfilming Corp; 0-88455; 0-667),* 200 Park Ave., New York, NY 10166 (SAN 202-6325) Tel 212-972-1070. Microforms of newspapers, periodicals, books, curriculum materials, documents & archival materials for research.

Microlit Pubs., *(Microlit; 0-931145),* 17857 Aguacate Way, San Diego, CA 92127 (SAN 687-8679) Tel 619-485-1773; Dist. by: Micro-Pace, 1510 N. Neil, Champaign, IL 61820 (SAN 200-7762) Tel 217-356-1884; Toll free: 800-362-9653; Dist. by: The Distributors, 702 S. Michigan St., South Bend, IN 46618 (SAN 169-2488) Tel 219-232-8500; Toll free: 800-348-5200; Dist. by: Slawson Communications, Inc., 3719 Sixth Ave., San Diego, CA 92103-4316 (SAN 200-6901) Tel 619-291-9126.

Micronesian Productions, *(Micronesian; 0-930839),* P.O. Box 6608, Tammuning, GU 96911 (SAN 677-6906).

Microphys Programs, *(Microphys Prog; 0-925534),* 1737 W. Second St., Brooklyn, NY 11223 (SAN 265-6906) Tel 718-375-5151.

Microprints, *(Microprints; 0-935193),* 2423 S. Spencer St., Seattle, WA 98108 (SAN 695-5061) Tel 206-723-3988.

Microrim, Inc., *(Microrim; 0-916937),* 3925 159th Ave. NE, Box 97022, Redmond, WA 98073-9722 (SAN 287-7171) Tel 206-885-2000.

MicroScope, *(MicroScope TX; 0-9607740),* P.O. Box 97762, Houston, TX 77279 (SAN 292-3386) Tel 713-468-8455.

Microscope Pubns., Div. of McCrone Research Institute, *(Microscope Pubns; 0-904962),* 2508 S. Michigan Ave., Chicago, IL 60616 (SAN 209-9594) Tel 312-842-7100.

Microsignal, *(Microsignal; 0-912911; 0-927775),* P.O. Box 60312, Santa Barbara, CA 93160 (SAN 265-881X) Tel 805-964-2227.

†**Microsoft Pr.,** Div. of Microsoft Corp., *(Microsoft; 0-914845),* 16011 NE 36th Way, Box 97017, Redmond, WA 98073-9717 (SAN 264-9969) Tel 206-882-8080; Toll free: 800-223-2336; Dist. by: Harper & Row, 10 E. 53rd St., New York, NY 10022 (SAN 200-2086) Tel 212-207-7099; *CIP.*

Microtraining Associates, Inc., *(Microtraining Assocs; 0-917276),* P.O. Box 641, North Amherst, MA 01059 (SAN 208-7677) Tel 413-549-2630.

MicroUse Information, *(MicroUse Info; 0-931555),* 1400 Commonwealth Ave., West Newton, MA 02165 (SAN 682-1901) Tel 617-527-3431.

Microwave Cuisine, *(Microwave Cuisine; 0-932243),* 32 Harvard St., Garden City, NY 11530 (SAN 686-5887) Tel 516-437-8160.

Microwave Helps, *(Microwave Helps; 0-9602930),* P.O. Box 32223, Minneapolis, MN 55432 (SAN 212-9531) Tel 612-571-6091.

Microwave Kitchen Press, *(Microwave Kitch; 0-912471),* P.O. Box 17466, Pittsburgh, PA 15235 (SAN 265-2803) Tel 412-824-8817.

Microwave News, *(Microwave; 0-9610580),* P.O. Box 1799, Grand Central Sta., New York, NY 10163 (SAN 264-2107) Tel 212-517-2802.

Microwave Touch, *(Microwave Touch; 0-9614205),* 942 Greenwood Dr., Greensboro, NC 27410 (SAN 686-788X) Tel 919-294-0767.

Mid-America Press, *(Mid Am Pr; 0-9604672),* P.O. Box 21241, Columbia Heights, MN 55421 (SAN 220-0724) Tel 612-781-5166.

Mid America Publishing Company, *(Mid Am Pub; 0-89991),* 1808 Washington Ave., St. Louis, MO 63103 (SAN 220-8660) Tel 515-282-8220.

Mid-America Publishing Hse., *(Mid-Amer Pub Hse KS; 0-939543),* 2420 NE 39th St., Topeka, KS 66617 (SAN 663-3307) Tel 913-286-1423. Do not confuse with Mid-America Pub Co of St. Louis, MO.

Mid-Atlantic Solar Energy Assn., *(MASEA; 0-9601884),* P.O. Box 541, Brattleboro, VT 05301 (SAN 220-2603).

Mid East Publishing Co., *(Mid East Pub Co),* P.O. Box A 3777, Chicago, IL 60690 (SAN 212-7644) Tel 312-545-0478.

Mid-Hudson Library System, *(Mid-Hudson Lib; 0-936213),* 103 Market St., Poughkeepsie, NY 12601 (SAN 696-849X) Tel 914-471-6060.

Mid-Lifelines, *(Mid-Life; 0-9609806),* 267 Firestone Dr., Walnut Creek, CA 94598 (SAN 272-4103) Tel 415-933-5481.

Mid-Peninsula Library Cooperative, *(Mid-Peninsula Lib; 0-933249),* 424 Stephenson Ave., Iron Mountain, MI 49801-3455 (SAN 692-3836) Tel 906-774-3005.

Mid-South Scientific Pubs., *(Mid South Sci Pubs; 0-935974),* Box FM, Hwy. 82 E., Mississippi State Univ., Mississippi State, MS 39762 (SAN 213-7771).

Midcoast Pubns., *(MidCoast Pubns; 0-910025),* 1982 Karlin Dr., Suite 200, St. Louis, MO 63131 (SAN 285-0613) Tel 314-966-3023; Dist. by: Quality Books Inc., 918 Sherwood Dr., Lake Bluff, IL 60044-2204 (SAN 169-2127); Orders to: Stafford Enterprises, 201 S. Central, Suite 300, St. Louis, MO 63105 (SAN 285-0648) Tel 314-863-5060; Orders to: P.O. Box 16880, St. Louis, MO 63105 (SAN 285-0656); Dist. by: Terschluse M., 727 Westbourne Dr., Suite 112, West Hollywood, CA 90069 (SAN 212-0364) Tel 213-659-9083; Dist. by: Baker & Taylor/Midwestern Division, 501 Gladiola Ave., Momence, IL 60954 (SAN 169-2100); Dist. by: Baker & Taylor/Eastern Division, 50 Kirby Ave., Somerville, NJ 08876 (SAN 169-4901); Dist. by: Baker & Taylor/Western Division, 380 Edison Way, Reno, NV 89564 (SAN 169-4464) Tel 702-786-6700.

†**Middle Atlantic Pr.,** *(Mid Atlantic; 0-912608),* P.O. Box 263, Wallingford, PA 19086 (SAN 202-6341) Tel 215-565-2445; *CIP.*

Middle Atlantic Regional Pr. of the Apostolic Faith Churches of God, Div. of Apostolic Faith Churches of God, *(Mid Atl Reg Pr; 0-9616056),* 1619 13th St., NW, Washington, DC 20009 (SAN 698-0635) Tel 202-265-7609; Orders to: P.O. Box 6021, Washington, DC 20005 (SAN 662-3972).

Middle Coast Publishing, *(Mid Coast Pub; 0-934523),* P.O. Box 2522, Iowa City, IA 52244 (SAN 693-9031) Tel 319-353-3432.

Middle East Assessments Group, *(Mid East Assess; 0-937783),* 2400 Virginia Ave., NW, Suite C916, Washington, DC 20037 (SAN 659-3402) Tel 202-822-0955.

†**Middle East Editorial Assocs.,** *(Middle East Edit; 0-918992),* 1100 17th St., NW, Suite 300, Washington, DC 20036 (SAN 210-4644) Tel 202-785-0022; *CIP.*

Middle East Executive Reports, Ltd., *(Mid East Exec Reports Ltd; 0-915797),* 717 D St. NW, Suite 300, Washington, DC 20004-2807 (SAN 293-8936) Tel 202-628-6900.

Middle East Institute, *(Mid East Inst; 0-916808),* 1761 N St., NW, Washington, DC 20036 (SAN 202-2168) Tel 202-785-1141.

Middle East Review *See* **American Academic Assn. for Peace in the Middle East**

Middle States Assn. of Colleges & Schools, *(Mid St Coll & Schl),* 3624 Market St., Philadelphia, PA 19104 (SAN 225-7653) Tel 215-662-5600.

†**Middleburg Pr., The,** *(Middleburg Pr; 0-931940),* Box 166, Orange City, IA 51041 (SAN 212-9183); *CIP.*

Middlewood Pr., *(Middlewood Pr; 0-935961),* 5737 Middlewood Ave., Salt Lake City, UT 84118 (SAN 696-6136) Tel 801-966-8034.

Midgard Pr., *(Midgard Pr; 0-9615948),* 4214 Midway Ave., Grants Pass, OR 97527 (SAN 696-8538) Tel 503-476-3603.

Midland Bks. *See* **Indiana Univ. Pr.**

Midlothian Mirror, *(Midlothian),* Box 1140, Midlothian, TX 76065 (SAN 205-8464).

Midmarch Arts/Women Artists News, *(Midmarch Arts-WAN; 0-9602476),* Box 3304, Grand Central Sta., New York, NY 10163 (SAN 213-3393) Tel 212-666-6990.

Midnight Call, *(Midnight Call; 0-937422),* P.O. Box 4389, West Columbia, SC 29171 (SAN 211-8130).

Midnight Express, *(Midnight Express; 0-917915),* Box 26941, Austin, TX 78755 (SAN 657-0534) Tel 512-267-5535.

Midnight Oil Pr., *(Midnight Oil Pr; 0-937269),* 266 Morris St., Stirling, NJ 07980 (SAN 658-9278) Tel 201-580-0656; Dist. by: Baker & Taylor, Eastern Div., 50 Kirby Ave., Somerville, NJ 08876 (SAN 169-4901); Dist. by: Book Dynamics, Inc., 836 Broadway, New York, NY 10003 (SAN 169-5649) Tel 212-254-7798.

Midnight Pr., *(Midnight Pr; 0-9616400),* Box 902, Westhampton Beach, NY 11978 (SAN 658-9286) Tel 516-288-3831; 401 Montauk Hwy., Westhampton Beach, NY 11978 (SAN 658-9294).

Midnight Sun, *(Midnight Sun; 0-935292),* 223 E. 28th St., 1RE, New York, NY 10016 (SAN 213-537X).

Midtown Stationery & Supply Co., 2658 Pittman Dr., Silver Spring, MD 20910 (SAN 699-4105) Tel 301-588-6777.

Midway Pubs., *(Midway Pubs; 0-938300),* 588 Charlton Ct., NW, Marietta, GA 30064 (SAN 217-2534) Tel 404-422-4169.

Midway Reprint *See* **Univ. of Chicago Pr.**

†**Midwest Alliance in Nursing, Inc.,** *(Midwest Alliance Nursing; 0-942146),* Indiana Univ., 1226 W. Michigan St., Rm. 108 BR, Indianapolis, IN 46223 (SAN 238-0226) Tel 313-655-6434; *CIP.*

Midwest Financial Pubns., Inc., Div. of The Beckley Group, Inc., *(Midwest Finan Pubns; 0-933623),* P.O. Box 992, Fairfield, IA 52556 (SAN 692-4697); 607 W. Broadway, Fairfield, IA 52556 (SAN 662-7765) Tel 515-472-0333; Dist. by: Publishers Group West, 5855 Beaudry St., Emeryville, CA 94608 (SAN 202-8522) Tel 415-658-3453; Toll free: 800-982-8319.

Midwest Heritage Publishing Co., *(Midwest Heritage; 0-934582),* 108 Pearl St., Iowa City, IA 52240 (SAN 213-1161) Tel 319-351-2364.

Midwest Institute for Design Research, Inc., *(Midwest Inst Design; 0-937169),* 616 E. Lake View Ave., Milwaukee, WI 53217 (SAN 658-5787) Tel 414-961-0769.

Midwest Media Assocs., *(Midwest Media; 0-9616013),* P.O. Box 10684, Midwest City, OK 73140 (SAN 697-290X); 10020 NE Fourth St., Midwest City, OK 73130 (SAN 697-2918) Tel 405-677-0334.

Midwest Motor Mart, *(Midwest Motor Mart; 0-9617015),* 506 Prior Ave. N., St. Paul, MN 55104 (SAN 662-6602) Tel 612-646-8968; Dist. by: ARA Services, P.O. Box 448, Brainerd, MN 56401 (SAN 169-4049).

Midwest Old Settlers & Threshers Assn., *(Midwest Old Settlers),* Mount Pleasant, IA 52641 (SAN 233-6480).

†**Midwest Plan Service,** *(Midwest Plan Serv; 0-89373),* Iowa State Univ., 122 Davidson Hall, Ames, IA 50011 (SAN 209-0295) Tel 515-294-4337; *CIP.*

Midwest Political Pubns., Div. of Martin Hauan Agency, *(Midwest Pol Pubns; 0-9612830),* 2809 NW Expressway, No. 450, Oklahoma City, OK 73112 (SAN 210-9271) Tel 405-843-7351.

Midwest Pubns. Co., Inc., *(Midwest Pubns; 0-910974; 0-89455),* P.O. Box 448, Pacific Grove, CA 93950 (SAN 207-0510) Tel 408-375-2455.

Midwest Research, *(Midwest Research; 0-915987),* 343 S. Dearborn St., Suite 1505, Chicago, IL 60604 (SAN 294-6130) Tel 312-663-5623.

Midwest Sci-Tech Pubs., Inc., *(Midwest Sci-Tech; 0-910853),* 17385 Conant, Detroit, MI 48212 (SAN 272-4219) Tel 313-892-8110.

Midwest Villages & Voices Pubns., *(Midwest Villages; 0-935697),* 3220 Tenth Ave. S., Minneapolis, MN 55407 (SAN 696-2653) Tel 612-224-7687.

Midwestern State Univ. Pr., *(Midwestern St U Pr; 0-915323),* 3400 Taft, Wichita Falls, TX 76308-2099 (SAN 290-0149) Tel 817-692-6611.

Midwife Pr., *(Midwife Pr; 0-9614513),* 2749 N. Weil, Milwaukee, WI 53212 (SAN 691-7313) Tel 414-562-1927; Orders to: Midwife Press, P.O. Box 92482, Milwaukee, WI 53212 (SAN 662-2887).

Migrations Ltd., *(Migrations Ltd; 0-9613519),* 1385 Pine St., Suite 16, San Francisco, CA 94109 (SAN 657-6699) Tel 415-771-1388; 1347 Divisadero St., Suite 217, San Francisco, CA 94117 (SAN 699-5802) Tel 415-931-6973; Orders to: Gaston's Guide, 1347 Divisadero St. Suite 217, San Francisco, CA 94117 (SAN 662-2380).

Mih Pubns., *(Mih),* 15 Arnold Place, New Bedford, MA 02740 (SAN 207-8651) Tel 617-993-0156.

Mike Nicholes, Subs. of Damascus Publishing Co., *(Mike Nicholes; 0-932149),* P.O. Box 727 655 NE Hood St., Gresham, OR 97030 (SAN 686-4244) Tel 503-666-7478.

Milady Publishing Corp., Div. of John Wiley & Sons, *(Milady; 0-87350),* 3839 White Plains Rd., Bronx, NY 10467 (SAN 202-635X) Tel 212-881-3000; Toll free: 800-223-8055.

Milagro Pr., Inc., *(Milagro Pr Inc; 0-9608504),* P.O. Box 1804, Santa Fe, NM 87501 (SAN 240-7221) Tel 505-988-1166.

Milbeck Pr., Div. of Lew Miller Advertising, *(Milbeck Pr; 0-9615752),* 1614 Dundee Way, Louisville, KY 40205 (SAN 695-9881) Tel 502-458-1752.

Mile Square Pub., *(Mile Sq Pub; 0-9616759),* P.O. Box 44185, Indianapolis, IN 46244 (SAN 661-4469); 445 N. Pennsylvania, Suite 709, Indianapolis, IN 46204 (SAN 661-4477) Tel 317-632-1984.

Milener, Eugene D., III, *(E D Milener; 0-9610682),* 6 Suncrest Terr., Oneonta, NY 13820 (SAN 264-763X) Tel 607-432-2174.

Miles, James F., *(J F Miles; 0-9600480),* P.O. Box 1041, Clemson, SC 29631 (SAN 203-8978) Tel 803-654-2410.

Miles, R & E, *(R&E Miles; 0-936810),* P.O. Box 1916, San Pedro, CA 90733 (SAN 221-3834) Tel 213-833-8856; 1252 W. 23 St., San Pedro, CA 90731 (SAN 691-9537).

Miles River Pr., *(Miles River; 0-917917),* 1009 Duke St., Alexandria, VA 22314 (SAN 657-0550) Tel 703-683-1500.

Milestext Pr., *(Milestext Pr; 0-910525),* 884 Whitney Dr., St. Paul, MN 55124 (SAN 260-2261) Tel 612-432-2273.

Milestone Pr., *(Milestone Pr; 0-936091),* 2173 Folwell St., St. Paul, MN 55112 (SAN 696-6403) Tel 612-631-8333.

Milestone Pr., *(Milestone Pr; 0-9615736),* 2302 40th St., Snyder, TX 79549 (SAN 695-8540) Tel 915-573-9708.

Milestones, Unlimited, *(Milestones Unltd; 0-9616833),* 24931 Woodridge Dr., Farmington Hills, MI 48018 (SAN 661-4752) Tel 313-477-2927.

Milford Historical Society, *(Milford Hist Soc; 0-9607742),* 124 E. Commerce, Milford, MI 48042 (SAN 238-7905) Tel 313-684-0845.

Milford House, Div. of Longwood Pub. Group, *(Milford Hse; 0-87821),* 51 Washington St., Dover, NH 03820 (SAN 202-6368); Toll free: 800-343-9444.

Milford Null Modem, *(Milford Null),* Phoenixville Pike & Charlestown Rd., Malvern, PA 19355 (SAN 654-598X); Toll free: 800-345-2121.

Military Marketing Services, Inc., *(Military Marketing; 0-914862),* P.O. Box 4010, Arlington, VA 22204 (SAN 207-365X) Tel 703-237-0203.

Military Operations Research Society, Inc., *(Military Opera Res; 0-930473),* Landmark Towers, Ste 202, 101 S. Whiting St., Alexandria, VA 22304 (SAN 670-8943) Tel 703-751-7290.

Milkovich, John, *(J Milkovich; 0-9613467),* 548 Dalzell, Shreveport, LA 71104 (SAN 295-6357) Tel 318-226-6605.

Milkweed Editions, Subs. of Milkweed Chronicle, Journal of Poetry & Graphics, *(Milkweed Ed; 0-915943),* P.O. Box 24303, Minneapolis, MN 55424 (SAN 294-0663) Tel 612-332-3192; 528 Hennepin Ave., Minneapolis, MN 55403 (SAN 294-0671); Dist. by: Consortium Bk. Sales & Distribution, 213 E. Fourth St., St. Paul, MN 55101 (SAN 200-6049) Tel 612-221-9035; Dist. by: Small Press Distribution, 1814 San Pablo Ave., Berkeley, CA 94709 (SAN 204-5826) Tel 415-549-3336.

Mill Books, *(Mill Bks),* Mill & Main St., Darby, PA 19023 (SAN 210-6140).

Mill Creek Pubns., *(Mill Creek Pubns; 0-933251),* P.O. Box 404, Lakeside, AZ 85929 (SAN 655-7635) Tel 714-792-8643.

Mill Town Graphics, Div. of Higgins & Ross, *(Mill Town Graph; 0-914613),* 281 Princeton St., North Chelmsford, MA 01863 (SAN 289-3800) Tel 617-454-4248.

Millenium House Pubs., Affil. of Millenium Foundation, *(Millenium Hse; 0-916538),* P.O. Box 85, Agoura, CA 91301 (SAN 203-9923) Tel 213-889-3711.

Millennial Productions, *(Millennial Prods; 0-9602626),* 2455 Calle Roble, Thousand Oaks, CA 91360 (SAN 213-3407).

Miller, Edmund, *(Edmund Miller; 0-9600486),* 61-07 Woodside Ave., Apt. 5J, Woodside, NY 11377 (SAN 203-8374) Tel 718-424-0480.

Miller, Herman, Inc., *(Herman Miller; 0-925614; 0-87911),* 8500 Byron Rd., Zeeland, MI 49464 (SAN 296-2357) Tel 616-531-8860.

Miller, Herman, Research Corp., Subs. of Herman Miller, Inc., *(H Miller Res; 0-936658),* 3971 S. Research Park Dr., Ann Arbor, MI 48104 (SAN 221-3842) Tel 313-994-0200.

Miller, Janus R., Publishing Co., *(Miller Pub Co; 0-9606160),* P.O. Box 21634, 20017 Monica Ave., Detroit, MI 48221 (SAN 217-1163).

Miller, Joan, Ph. D, P.C., *(J Miller; 0-9613786),* c/o Windy Hill Therapy Associates, 2550 Windy Hill Rd., Suite 104, Marietta, GA 30067 (SAN 678-9986) Tel 404-952-3308.

Miller, Joe, Publishing, *(Joe Miller Pub; 0-9616542),* 5905-D Clark Rd., Suite 183, Paradise, CA 95969 (SAN 659-5227) Tel 916-877-1649.

Miller, Lawrence, Publishing, *(L Miller Pub; 0-914021),* 3 Lisa Dr., Thorndale, PA 19372 (SAN 286-8296) Tel 215-384-8944.

Miller, M. Dolly, *(M D Miller; 0-9613120),* P.O. Box 26610, Tempe, AZ 85282 (SAN 294-6157) Tel 602-968-6629.

Miller, Merl, & Assocs., *(Merl Miller Assoc; 0-933557),* 480 SW Fifth St., Lake Oswego, OR 97034 (SAN 691-876X) Tel 503-636-2023; P.O. Box 367, Lake Oswego, OR 97034 (SAN 658-2737) Tel 503-636-0552.

Miller, Neil, *(N Miller; 0-9601444),* 747 Bruce Dr., East Meadow, NY 11554 (SAN 211-0393) Tel 516-292-9569.

Miller, Oscar R., *(O R Miller; 0-9600552),* P.O. Box 229, Berlin, OH 44610 (SAN 203-7556) Tel 216-893-2870.

Miller, Sandra Lake, *(S L Miller; 0-9609448),* 69 River Dr., Ormond Beach, FL 32075-2851 (SAN 262-8236) Tel 904-441-8987.

Miller Books, *(Miller Bks; 0-912472),* 2908 W. Valley Blvd., Alhambra, CA 91803 (SAN 203-9931) Tel 818-284-7607.

Names

Names

Miller Enterprises, *(Miller Ent; 0-89566),* P.O. Box 395, Boulder Creek, CA 95006 (SAN 210-6426) Tel 408-338-9633.

Miller Enterprises, *(Miller OH; 0-9607658),* P.O. Box 353, Athens, OH 45701 (SAN 241-5631).

Miller Freeman Pubns., Inc., Subs. of United Newspapers, *(Miller Freeman; 0-87930),* 500 Howard St., San Francisco, CA 94105 (SAN 213-6511) Tel 415-397-1881.

Miller Money Management Inc., *(Miller Money Mgmt; 0-933203),* 304 Safety Building, Rock Island, IL 61201-8019 (SAN 692-3194) Tel 309-793-0387.

Millerhill Pr., *(Mill Press; 0-9614177),* Rte. 1, Box 280, Bryan, TX 77803 (SAN 686-659X) Tel 409-823-0828.

Miller's Design Studio, *(Miller Des; 0-934155),* 555 Brush St., Suite 805, Detroit, MI 48226 (SAN 692-9036) Tel 313-222-1706.

Millers Graphics, *(Millers Graphics; 0-931831),* 1475 W. Cypress Ave., San Dimas, CA 91773 (SAN 687-6277) Tel 714-599-1431.

Millers River Publishing Co, *(Millers River Pub Co; 0-912395),* Box 159, Athol, MA 01331 (SAN 265-3605) Tel 617-249-7612; Dist. by: Inland Book Co., P.O. Box 261, 22 Hemingway Ave., East Haven, CT 06512 (SAN 200-4151) Tel 203-467-4257; Toll free: 800-243-0138.

Millien, Oneal, Publishing Co., *(O Millien; 0-9617055),* 306 Gardenia Dr., Donaldsonville, LA 70346 (SAN 662-8397) Tel 504-473-8880.

Mills, Charles P., *(C P Mills),* 952 Old Huntingdon Pike, Huntingdon Valley, PA 19006 (SAN 201-8640).

Mills & Sanderson, Pubs., Affil. of Huenefeld Co., Inc., *(Mills Sanderson; 0-938179),* P.O. Box U, Bedford, MA 01730 (SAN 661-1982); 10 Muzzey St., Lexington, MA 02173 (SAN 661-1990) Tel 617-861-9650.

Mills Historical Pr., *(Mills Historical; 0-931069),* 107 Woodridge, Tuscaloosa, AL 35406 (SAN 678-9315) Tel 205-752-4031.

Mills Publishing Co., *(Mills Pub Co; 0-935356),* King Sta., P.O. Box 6158, Santa Ana, CA 92706 (SAN 272-2464) Tel 714-541-5750.

Milting, Martha, *(M Milting; 0-9614455),* 1980 McDade, Conroe, TX 77304 (SAN 689-3902) Tel 409-756-5810.

Milton Bradley Co., *(Milton Bradley Co; 0-88049),* 443 Shaker Rd., East Longmeadow, MA 01028 (SAN 238-7891) Tel 413-525-6411.

Milwaukee Academy of Medicine Pr., *(Milw Acad Med; 0-9617070),* P.O. Box 26509, Milwaukee, WI 53226 (SAN 662-8923); 8701 Watertown Plank Rd., Milwaukee, WI 53226 (SAN 662-8931) Tel 414-464-4460.

Milwaukee Books, *(Milwaukee Bks; 0-942608),* 2147 N. 56th St., Milwaukee, WI 53208 (SAN 238-5422) Tel 414-257-3750.

Milwaukee County Historical Society, *(Milwaukee County; 0-938076),* 910 N. Third St., Milwaukee, WI 53203 (SAN 205-8383) Tel 414-273-8288.

†**Milwaukee Public Museum,** *(Milwaukee Pub Mus; 0-89326),* 800 W. Wells St., Milwaukee, WI 53233 (SAN 202-229X) Tel 414-278-2787; *CIP.*

Milwaukee Sentinel, The, *(Milwaukee Sentinel),* 918 N. 4th St., P.O. Box 371, Milwaukee, WI 53201 (SAN 215-2827) Tel 414-224-2120.

Mimir Pubs., Inc., *(Mimir; 0-912084),* P.O. Box 5011, Madison, WI 53705 (SAN 202-6376) Tel 608-231-1667.

Mimosa Pubns, *(Mimosa Pubns; 0-916335),* 135 Old Suffolk St., Monroeville, PA 15146 (SAN 295-6969) Tel 412-856-9324.

Mina Pr. Publishing, Inc., *(Mina Pr; 0-942610),* P.O. Box 854, Sebastopol, CA 95472 (SAN 238-5430) Tel 707-829-0854.

Mind Communication, Inc., *(Mind Comn; 0-938871; 1-55667),* 945 Burton SW, Grand Rapids, MI 49509 Tel 616-241-6095.

Mind-Dog Bks., *(Mind-Dog; 0-9613432),* 64 Windell, Cambridge, MA 02138 (SAN 657-0542) Tel 617-876-1750.

Mind Matter Motion, *(Mind-Matter-Motion; 0-9608910),* P.O. Box 1091, Tiburon, CA 94920 (SAN 262-0790) Tel 415-331-6142.

Mind Productions & Assocs., *(Mind Prods Assocs; 0-935257),* 1411 Eleanor Dr., P.O. Box 11221, Tallahassee, FL 32302 (SAN 695-5304) Tel 904-644-2491; Dist. by: New Mind Productions, P.O. Box 11221, Tallahassee, FL 32302 (SAN 200-5565).

Mindbody, Inc., *(Mindbody Inc),* 50 Maple Pl., Manhasset, NY 11030 (SAN 214-0365) Tel 516-365-7722.

Mindbody Pr., *(Mindbody; 0-939508),* 1427 Milvia St., Berkeley, CA 94709 (SAN 216-4183) Tel 415-527-4980; Dist. by: Bookpeople, 2929 Fifth St., Berkeley, CA 94710 (SAN 168-9517) Tel 415-549-3030.

Mindlifter Pr., *(Mindlifter Pr; 0-931959),* P.O. Box 571, Boston, MA 02215 (SAN 686-0087) Tel 617-236-1758.

Mind's Eye Publishing Co., The, *(Minds Eye Illinois; 0-939249),* 100 Crabtree Rd., E. Dundee, IL 60118 (SAN 662-586X) Tel 312-426-9205.

Mineralogical Society of America, *(Mineralogical Soc; 0-939950),* 1625 I St., NW, Suite 414, Washington, DC 20006 (SAN 232-8739) Tel 202-775-4344.

Mineralogical Society of Arizona, *(Mineral Soc Ari; 0-910011),* P.O. Box 902, Phoenix, AZ 85001 (SAN 241-2241) Tel 602-995-0633.

†**Mini-World Pubns.,** *(Mini-World Pubns; 0-931323),* 9965 Quaker Ln., Maple Grove, MN 55369 (SAN 685-2645) Tel 612-424-5440; *CIP.*

Minibooks *See* Bantam Bks., Inc.

Ministering Angel, *(Ministering Angel; 0-9617005),* 6995 Applegate Dr., Helena, MT 59601 (SAN 662-5487) Tel 406-458-9339.

Ministries, Inc., *(Ministries; 0-9607986),* P.O. Box 4038, 319 Fleming, Montgomery, AL 36105 (SAN 238-5449) Tel 205-284-5645.

Ministry Pubns., *(Ministry Pubns; 0-938234),* P.O. Box 276, Redlands, CA 92373 (SAN 215-787X).

Minkow, Barry, *(B Minkow; 0-9615900),* 7040 Darby Ave. No. 207-208, Reseda, CA 91335 (SAN 696-6381) Tel 818-344-7615.

Minkus Pubns., Inc., *(Minkus; 0-912236),* c/o Minkus Stamp Journal, 41 W. 25th St., New York, NY 10010 (SAN 207-6233).

Minne HA! HA!, *(Minne HA HA; 0-937706),* P.O. Box 14009, Minneapolis, MN 55414 (SAN 215-6814).

Minneapolis College of Art & Design, Library & Media Center, *(Minneapolis Coll Art; 0-9611672),* 133 E. 25th St., Minneapolis, MN 55404 (SAN 279-604X).

Minneapolis Institute of Arts, *(Minneapolis Inst Arts; 0-912964),* 2400 Third Ave., S., Minneapolis, MN 55404 (SAN 202-2567) Tel 612-870-3029.

†**Minneapolis Public Library & Information Center,** *(Mpls Publ Lib; 0-9613716),* 300 Nicollet Mall, Minneapolis, MN 55401 (SAN 279-6066) Tel 612-372-6606; *CIP.*

Minneapolis Riverfront Development Coordination Board, *(Minneapolis Riverfront; 0-9604360),* 235 City Hall, Minneapolis, MN 55415 (SAN 215-0956).

†**Minneapolis Star & Tribune Co., The,** *(Minneapolis Tribune; 0-932272),* 425 Portland Ave., Minneapolis, MN 55488 (SAN 220-2611) Tel 612-372-4420; Dist. by: The Bookmen, Inc., 525 N. Third St., Minneapolis, MN 55401 (SAN 169-409X); *CIP.*

Minnesota Council of Foundations, *(MN Coun Found; 0-9616378),* 1216 Foshay Tower, Minneapolis, MN 55402 (SAN 658-9332) Tel 612-338-1989.

Minnesota Geological Survey, Div. of University of Minnesota, *(Minn Geol Surv; 0-934938),* 2642 University Ave., St. Paul, MN 55114 (SAN 203-994X) Tel 612-373-3372.

†**Minnesota Historical Society Pr.,** *(Minn Hist; 0-87351),* 690 Cedar St., St. Paul, MN 55101 (SAN 202-6384) Tel 612-297-3243; Toll free: 800-647-7827 (In Midwest); Orders to: 1500 Mississippi St., St. Paul, MN 55101 (SAN 202-6392); *CIP.*

Minnesota Library Assn., *(Minn Library; 0-939098),* 1315 Lowry Ave. N., North Regional Library, Minneapolis, MN 55411 (SAN 239-6947) Tel 612-521-1735.

Minnesota Medical Alley Publishing Co., *(Minn Med Alley; 0-931833),* P.O. Box 24796, Edina, MN 55424 (SAN 686-0079) Tel 612-935-0162.

Minnesota Medical Foundation, Inc., *(Minn Med Found; 0-940210),* Univ. of Minn, P.O. Box 73 Mayo Bldg., 420 Delaware St. SE, Minneapolis, MN 55455 (SAN 217-541X) Tel 612-373-7933.

Minnesota North Country Pr., *(MN North; 0-9613489),* 3514 Cedarlane, Bemidji, MN 56601 (SAN 657-3649) Tel 218-751-1041.

Minnesota Poetry for the People Press, *(Minn Poetry People; 0-916079),* P.O. Box 3818, Loring Park Sta., Minneapolis, MN 55403 (SAN 294-6289) Tel 612-488-4896; 1034 N. Victoria, St. Paul, MN 55103 (SAN 294-6297).

Minnesota Public Radio, Inc., *(Minn Publ Radio; 0-942110),* 45 E. Eighth St., St. Paul, MN 55101 (SAN 238-6771) Tel 612-221-1531; Dist. by: Bookmen, Inc., 525 N. Third St., Minneapolis, MN 55401 (SAN 168-9517).

Minnesota Scholarly Pr., Inc., *(Minn Scholarly; 0-933474),* P.O. Box 224, Mankato, MN 56001 (SAN 214-2554) Tel 507-387-4964.

Minnesota Society for the Prevention of Blindness & Preservation of Hearing, *(Minn Soc Prev Blind; 0-9612370),* 1208 Pioneer Bldg., P.O. Box 1528, St. Paul, MN 55101-0528 (SAN 289-5358) Tel 612-227-8808.

Mino Pubns., *(Mino Pubns; 0-931719),* 9009 Paddock Ln., Potomac, MD 20854 (SAN 683-5511) Tel 301-294-9514.

Minobras Mining Services & Research, *(Minobras; 0-942218),* P.O. Box 1620, Fallbrook, CA 92028 (SAN 215-9694) Tel 619-726-5678.

Minor Heron Pr., Subs. of Society of the Muse of the Southwest, *(Minor Heron; 0-9615914),* P.O. Box 2615, Taos, NM 87571 (SAN 697-2020) Tel 505-758-0081.

Minority Rights Group (New York), *(Minority Rights),* P.O. Box 4S, 35 Claremont, New York, NY 10027 (SAN 283-1902) Tel 212-864-7986.

Minotaur Press *See* Penthouse Press, Limited

MINSA, *(Minsa; 0-914833),* 1435 State St., Suite No.609, Santa Barbara, CA 93101 (SAN 289-3339) Tel 805-964-5454.

Minuscule University Press Inc., *(Minuscule Univ Pr; 0-931805),* 66358 Buena Vista Avenue, Desert Hot Springs, CA 92240 (SAN 684-7072) Tel 619-329-8463.

Minuteware, *(Minuteware; 0-913131),* Wilde Lake Village Green, Suite 245, Columbia, MD 21045 (SAN 283-2127) Tel 301-995-1166.

Miracle Months, The, *(Miracle Months; 0-936515),* P.O. Box 20787, Oklahoma City, OK 73156 (SAN 697-9122) Tel 405-842-7628; 1830 Coventry Ln., Oklahoma City, OK 73120 (SAN 697-9130).

Mirage Bks., Subs. of Dephi-Pacific, *(Mirage Bks; 0-939137),* P.O. Box 1213, Agana Facilty, Agana, GU 96910 (SAN 662-6327).

Mirage Pr., Ltd., *(Mirage Pr; 0-88358),* P.O. Box 28, Manchester, MD 21102 (SAN 202-6406) Tel 301-239-8999.

Miriam Hospital Women's Assn., The, Affil. of The Miriam Hospital, *(Miriam Hosp; 0-9608666),* 164 Summit Ave., Providence, RI 02906 (SAN 240-723X) Tel 401-274-3700; Dist. by: Wimmer Brothers Books, 4210 B.F. Goodrich Blvd., Memphis, TN 38181 (SAN 209-6544) Tel 901-362-8900.

Miriam Pr., The, *(Miriam Press; 0-939409),* P.O. Box 798, Highland, NY 12528 (SAN 663-1681); 439 Upper North Rd., Highland, NY 12528 (SAN 663-169X) Tel 914-691-7271.

Mirth, Karlo, *(K Mirth; 0-9615737),* Box 1767, Grand Central Sta., New York, NY 10017 (SAN 226-3289); 37-60 88th St., Jackson Heights, NY 11372 (SAN 699-5446) Tel 718-458-8556.

Miskar Publishing Co., *(Miskar Pub; 0-936681),* 102 Rebecca Way, Folsom, CA 95630 (SAN 699-6779) Tel 916-985-2320.

Miss Jackie Music, *(Miss Jackie; 0-939514),* 10001 El Monte, Overland Park, KS 66207 (SAN 216-4191).

Missing Diagnosis, Inc., *(Missing Diag; 0-9615758),* 2614 Highland Ave., Birmingham, AL 35205 (SAN 695-8966) Tel 205-326-0642; Orders to: P.O. Box 26508, Birmingham, AL 35226 (SAN 662-359X) Tel 205-328-6483.

Missing Link Products, *(Missing Link),* 210 N. Union Blvd., Colorado Springs, CO 80909 (SAN 655-1653) Tel 303-473-8909.

Mission Dolores, *(Dolores SF; 0-912748),* 16th & Dolores Sts., San Francisco, CA 94103 (SAN 696-6349).

Mission Pr., *(Mission Pr CA; 0-918418),* 124 Treehaven Ct., Suite B-330, Kenwood, CA 95452 (SAN 209-9624) Tel 707-833-4683; Box 614, Kenwood, CA 95452 (SAN 658-1242).

Mission Project Service, *(Mission Proj Serv; 0-913671),* 1 Haven Plaza, Apt. 25A, New York, NY 10009 (SAN 286-1461) Tel 212-533-6286.

Mission Publishing Co., *(Mission Pub; 0-916910),* Woodstone Oaks, Suite 609; 11865 IH Ten W., San Antonio, TX 78230 (SAN 209-1836) Tel 512-692-3552.

Missionaries of Africa, *(Missionaries Africa),* 1624 21st St. NW, Washington, DC 20009 (SAN 223-7997) Tel 202-232-5154.

Missionary Internship, *(Missionary Intern; 0-942726),* 36200 Freedom Rd., P.O. Box 457, Farmington, MI 48024 (SAN 240-253X) Tel 313-474-9110.

Missions Advanced Research & Communication Ctr., Div. of World Vision International, *(Missions Adv Res Com Ctr; 0-912552),* 919 W. Huntington Dr., Monrovia, CA 91016 (SAN 240-0529) Tel 818-303-8811.

Mississippi Dept. of Archives & History, Div. of State of Mississippi, *(Mississippi Archives; 0-938896),* P.O. Box 571, Jackson, MS 39205 (SAN 279-618X) Tel 601-359-1424.

Mississippi Ornithological Society, *(Mississippi Orni; 0-912265),* Box Z, Mississippi State, MS 39762 (SAN 262-0499).

Mississippi Research & Development Center, *(MS Res & Dev Ctr; 0-940786),* Computer Service, 3825 Ridgewood Rd., Jackson, MS 39211 (SAN 202-2109) Tel 601-982-6466.

Missouri Archaeological Society, *(MO Arch Soc; 0-943414),* P.O. Box 958, Columbia, MO 65205 (SAN 238-8316).

Missouri Bar Assn., *(MO Bar Assn),* P.O. Box 119, Jefferson City, MO 65102 (SAN 227-0404) Tel 314-635-4128.

Missouri Basketball, *(MO Basketball; 0-9605092),* 364 Hearnes Bldg., Columbia, MO 65211 (SAN 215-7888).

Missouri Botanical Garden, *(Miss Botan; 0-915279),* P.O. Box 299, St. Louis, MO 63166 (SAN 290-0157) Tel 314-577-5164.

Missouri Political Science Assn., *(MO Poli Sci),* Univ. of Missouri, 118 Middlebush Hall, Columbia, MO 65201 (SAN 226-3335).

Mistaire Laboratories, *(Mistaire; 0-9602490),* 152 Glen Ave., Millburn, NJ 07041 (SAN 204-2762) Tel 201-376-0915.

Mr. Coach, Inc., *(Mr Coach; 0-9607324),* P.O. Box 9171, Downers Grove, IL 60515 (SAN 239-2631) Tel 312-964-3090.

Mr. Cogito Pr., *(Mr Cogito Pr; 0-932191; 0-7401205),* P.O. Box 66124, Portland, OR 97266 (SAN 212-9191) Tel 503-233-8151; Pacific Univ., UC Box 627, Forest Grove, OR 97116 (SAN 662-0825) Tel 503-357-6151.

Mr. D's the Poetic Experience Publishing Co., *(MrD's Poetic Exp; 0-9607748),* 3208 Cahuenga Blvd., West Hollywood, CA 90068 (SAN 240-1274).

Mr. Information, *(Mr Info; 0-88635),* 2515 Rainier Ave. S., Seattle, WA 98144 (SAN 692-9044) Tel 604-653-9260.

Mr. Maurice Collection, *(Maurice Collection; 0-935721),* 4232 Redledge Dr., Scottsdale, AZ 85253 (SAN 695-9326) Tel 602-994-1166.

Mr. Padco Pubns., *(Mr Padco Pubns; 0-9615147),* 16850 Alcross St., Covina, CA 91722 (SAN 692-9052) Tel 818-966-3439; Orders to: P.O. Box 2111, Irwindale, CA 91706 (SAN 662-3069) Tel 818-966-3439.

Mist'er Rain, Inc., *(Mist'er Rain; 0-916970),* 8411 Pacific Hwy E., Tacoma, WA 98424 (SAN 208-7685) Tel 206-927-7333.

Misty Hill Pr., *(Misty Hill Pr; 0-930079),* 5024 Turner Rd., Sebastopol, CA 95472 (SAN 670-0942) Tel 707-823-7437; Dist. by: Bookpeople, 2929 Fifth St., Berkeley, CA 94710 (SAN 168-9517) Tel 415-549-3030; Toll free: 800-227-1516.

Mitchell Publishing, Inc., *(Mitchell Pub; 0-938188),* 915 River St., Santa Cruz, CA 95060 (SAN 215-7896) Tel 408-425-3851; Toll free: 800-435-2665.

Mittman, Edward A., & Associates, *(E A Mittman; 0-942940),* 311 Ruby, Balboa Island, CA 92662 (SAN 238-8200) Tel 714-673-0188.

Mitzi Bks., Div. of Sinai-Christian Pubns., *(Mitzi Bks; 0-940958),* P.O. Box 160452, Mobile, AL 36616 (SAN 223-1948) Tel 404-834-4044.

Mizan Pr., *(Mizan Pr; 0-933782),* P.O. Box 4065, Berkeley, CA 94704 (SAN 213-117X) Tel 415-549-1634.

Mize, An E., *(A E Mize; 0-9617087),* 2151 Old Oakland Rd., No. 287, San Jose, CA 95131 (SAN 662-5894) Tel 408-263-3706.

Mnemosyne Publishing Co., Inc., *(Mnemosyne),* 410 Alcazar Ave., Coral Gables, FL 33134 (SAN 203-9966) Tel 305-444-8908.

Mobile Junior League Pubns., Div. of The Junior League of Mobile, Inc., *(Mobile Jr League Pubns; 0-9603054),* 179 Bayshore Ave., Mobile, AL 36607 (SAN 212-1069) Tel 205-479-5133.

Mobile Post Office Society, *(Mobile PO),* RFD 1, Box 91, Contoocook, NH 03229 (SAN 225-5995).

Mockingbird Bks., *(Mockingbird Bks; 0-89176),* Box 624, St. Simons Island, GA 31522 (SAN 207-6470) Tel 912-638-7212.

Mockingbooks, *(Mockingbooks; 0-9615626),* P.O. Box 2122, La Mesa, CA 92041 (SAN 696-1096) Tel 619-461-1055.

Modal Logic Corp., *(Modal Logic; 0-937003),* 341 San Fernando Dr., San Francisco, CA 94127 (SAN 658-7402) Tel 619-481-5707; P.O. Box 1382, Solana Beach, CA 92075 (SAN 658-7410).

Model A Ford Club of America, *(Model A),* 250 S. Cypress, La Habra, CA 90631 (SAN 225-5138) Tel 213-697-2712; 2222 Loma Vista, Pasadena, CA 91104 (SAN 662-0833) Tel 818-794-9841.

Model Agency Pr., The, *(Model Agency; 0-942794),* 7021 Vicky Ave., Canoga Park, CA 91307 (SAN 240-2548) Tel 818-340-7268.

Model Cities Research Institute, *(Model Cities; 0-941496),* 11126 National Blvd., Los Angeles, CA 90064 (SAN 208-1296) Tel 213-479-7394.

Modell, Tod, *(Modell T; 0-9608292),* P.O. Box 3047, San Jose, CA 95156 (SAN 240-4095) Tel 408-258-4931.

Moderation Pr., *(Moderation Pr),* P.O. Box 741955, Dallas, TX 75374-1955 (SAN 292-336X).

Modern Bks. & Crafts, Inc., *(Modern Bks; 0-913274),* Dist. by: Associated Booksellers, 562 Boston Ave., Bridgeport, CT 06610 (SAN 203-5014).

Modern Communication Assocs., *(Modern Comm Assocs; 0-9613854),* P.O. Box 670085, Dallas, TX 75367-0085 (SAN 685-2157) Tel 214-239-2183; Dist. by: Book Dynamics, 836 Broadway, New York, NY 10003 (SAN 169-5649) Tel 212-254-7798; Dist. by: Distributors, The, 702 S. Michigan, South Bend, IN 46618 (SAN 169-2488) Tel 219-232-8500.

†Modern Curriculum Pr., Div. of Esquire, Inc., *(Modern Curr; 0-87895; 0-8136),* 13900 Prospect Rd., Cleveland, OH 44136 (SAN 206-6572); Toll free: 800-321-3106; CIP.

Modern Guides Co., *(Modern Guides; 0-940788),* P.O. Box 1340, Old San Juan, PR 00902 (SAN 219-6069) Tel 809-723-9105.

Modern Handcraft, Inc., *(Mod Handcraft; 0-86675),* 4251 Pennsylvania Ave., Kansas City, MO 64111 (SAN 216-1621) Tel 816-531-5730. *Imprints:* Aunt Ellen's (Aunt Ellen's); Flower & Garden (Flower & Garden); Workbasket (Workbasket); Workbench (Workbench).

Modern Humanities Research Association, *(Modern Humanities Res),* George Washington University, Washington, DC 20006 (SAN 225-3186) Tel 202-676-6130.

†Modern Language Assn. of America, *(Modern Lang; 0-87352),* 10 Astor Pl., New York, NY 10003 (SAN 202-6422) Tel 212-614-6314; CIP.

Modern Library College Department *See* **Modern Library, Inc.**

Modern Library, Inc., *(Modern Lib; 0-394),* 201 E. 50th St., New York, NY 10022 (SAN 204-5605) Tel 212-751-2600; Orders to: Order Dept., 400 Hahn Rd., Westminster, MD 21157 (SAN 204-5613). *Imprints:* Modern Library College Department (Mod LibC).

Modern Liturgy *See* **Resource Pubns., Inc.**

Modern Media Institute *See* **Poynter Institute**

Modern Signs Pr., Inc., *(Modern Signs; 0-916708),* 10443 Los Alamitos Blvd., Los Alamitos, CA 90720 (SAN 282-0048) Tel 213-596-6858; Orders to: P.O. Box 1181, Los Alamitos, CA 90720 (SAN 282-0056) Tel 213-493-4168.

Modern Studies Group *See* **Heroica Bks.**

Modern Words, *(Modern Wrds; 0-9614055),* P.O. Box 1093, Hermosa Beach, CA 90254 (SAN 684-720X) Tel 213-461-9909.

Modern World Publishing Co., *(Modern World; 0-910978),* P.O. Box 65766, Los Angeles, CA 90065 (SAN 203-9982) Tel 213-221-8044.

Modular Information Systems, *(Modular Info Syst; 0-939325),* 431 Ashbury St., San Francisco, CA 94117 (SAN 663-1290) Tel 415-552-8648.

Moe-Tavation, *(Moe-Tavation; 0-9615797),* 1230 Caroline, Port Angeles, WA 98362 (SAN 696-5954) Tel 206-457-5052.

Moen, R. E., *(R E Moen; 0-9614819),* 3152 S. 27th St., La Crosse, WI 54601 (SAN 693-0794) Tel 608-788-8753.

Moffat Publishing Co., Inc., *(Moffat Pub; 0-86670),* Box 236, Nutley, NJ 07110 (SAN 217-2569) Tel 201-235-9444.

Moffett Publishing Co., *(Moffett; 0-9605650),* Rte. 3, Box 175A, Cushing, OK 74023 (SAN 215-6822).

Mogul Book & FilmWorks, *(Mogul Bk; 0-9610404),* P.O. Box 2773, Pittsburgh, PA 15230 (SAN 264-2131) Tel 412-461-0705.

Mohs Seaplane Corp., *(Mohs Seaplane Co; 0-931279),* 2355 University Ave., Madison, WI 53705 (SAN 682-0026) Tel 608-233-1627.

Mohsena Memorial Trust, *(Mohsena Memorial; 0-9617273),* 40 Tar Hees Rd., Mercerville, NJ 08619 (SAN 663-5075) Tel 609-587-4414.

Moir, George E., *(G E Moir; 0-9616974),* 1341 Holbrook St., Wenatchee, WA 98801 (SAN 661-7603) Tel 509-662-6004.

Moira Books, *(Moira; 0-900204),* 1460 Heights Blvd., Winona, MN 55987 (SAN 203-9990).

Mojave Bks., *(Mojave Bks; 0-87881),* 7118 Canby Ave., Reseda, CA 91335 (SAN 202-6430) Tel 818-342-3403.

Moldeven, Meyer, *(M Moldeven; 0-9615092),* 2106 Valleydale Lane, Encinatas, CA 92024 (SAN 694-1761) Tel 619-942-4188.

Mole Publishing Co., *(Mole Pub Co; 0-9604464),* Route 4, Box 618, Bonners Ferry, ID 83805 (SAN 212-8608) Tel 208-267-7349.

Molinoff, Henry C., *(H C Molinoff; 0-9616983),* 234 Edgewood Ave., Smithtown, NY 11787 (SAN 661-759X) Tel 516-277-9708; Dist. by: New Era Pr., P.O. Box 29, Farmingdale, NY 11735 (SAN 264-2441) Tel 516-277-9708.

Mollica Stained Glass Press, *(Mollica Stained Glass; 0-9601306),* 10033 Broadway Terr., Oakland, CA 94611 (SAN 209-2220) Tel 415-655-5736.

Molly Yes Pr., *(Molly Yes; 0-931308),* P.O. Box 292322, Ft. Lauderdale, FL 33329 (SAN 217-9075) Tel 305-474-5010.

Molakai Book Pubs., *(Molokai Bk Pubs; 0-930081),* P.O. Box 1239, Kaunakakai, HI 96748 (SAN 670-1000) Tel 808-553-3376.

Mom & Pop Publishing Co., *(Mom & Pop Pub; 0-937469),* 1035 Browning Dr., Tallahassee, FL 32308 (SAN 658-9340) Tel 904-877-1436.

†Momo's Pr., *(Momos; 0-917672),* 45 Sheridan St., San Francisco, CA 94103 (SAN 206-1619) Tel 415-863-3009; CIP.

Mona Pubns., Div. of Mona & McGrath Public Relations, *(Mona Pubns; 0-937849),* 8400 Normandale Lake Blvd., Suite 1220, Bloomington, MN 55437 (SAN 659-5235) Tel 612-831-8515.

Monarch *See* **Monarch Pr.**

Monarch Pr., Div. of Simon & Schuster, Inc., *(Monarch Pr; 0-671),* 215 Park Ave. S., New York, NY 10003 (SAN 204-5621) Tel 212-777-6300. *Imprints:* Monarch (Monarch).

523

Monarch Trails Pubns., *(Monarch Trails Pubns;
0-9616665)*, P.O. Box 05272, Detroit, MI
48205 (SAN 661-3543); 12180 Flanders St.,
Detroit, MI 48205 (SAN 661-3551)
Tel 313-521-8011.

Monday Bks., *(Monday Bks; 0-918510)*, 8450
W. Dry Creek Rd., Healdsburg, CA 95448
(SAN 209-6552) Tel 707-433-3188.

Mondiello, Anthony S., *(Mondiello; 0-939658)*,
20008 N. 28th St., Phoenix, AZ 85024
(SAN 218-4931).

Monet, Maurice, Publishing Co., *(Maurice
Monet; 0-9616235)*, 633 Post St., Suite 540,
San Francisco, CA 94109 (SAN 658-5876)
Tel 415-673-4450.

Money Advocate, The, *(Money Advoc;
0-913725)*, 4180 W. Broadway, Robbinsdale,
MN 55422 (SAN 286-1283)
Tel 612-533-3664.

Money & Success Program, *(Money Success
Prog; 0-9616879)*, P.O. Box 39600,
Charleston, SC 29407 (SAN 661-6615); 114
Rutledge Ave., Charleston, SC 29403
(SAN 661-6623) Tel 803-723-2026.

Money-Maker Publishing Co., *(Money-Maker;
0-910481)*, 311 Gruenther Ave., Rockville,
MD 20851 (SAN 260-1060)
Tel 301-762-1385.

Money Making Methods, *(Money Methods;
0-9605094)*, 5556 Bloch St., San Diego, CA
92122 (SAN 276-9697) Tel 619-453-6033.

Money Market Directories, Inc., Subs. of
McGraw-Hill, Inc., *(Money Mkt; 0-939712)*,
300 E. Market St., Charlottesville, VA 22901
(SAN 216-7492) Tel 804-977-1450; Toll
free: 800-446-2810.

Money Mastery Publishing, *(Money Mastery
Pub; 0-9613663)*, P.O. Box 336, Piermont,
NY 10968 (SAN 670-8935).

Money Publishing, *(Money Pub; 0-9616077)*,
519 S. G St., Tacoma, WA 98405
(SAN 698-0880) Tel 206-627-6010.

Moneymatters Publishing, *(Moneymatters;
0-912913)*, 2616 Juniper Ave. Suite 5,
Boulder, CO 80302 (SAN 283-3050)
Tel 303-449-6689.

Mongolia Society, Inc., The, *(Mongolia;
0-910980)*, 321-322 Goodbody Hall, Indiana
Univ., Bloomington, IN 47405
(SAN 204-000X) Tel 812-335-4078.

†Monitor Bk. Co., Inc., *(Monitor; 0-9600252)*,
9441 Wilshire Blvd., Beverly Hills, CA 90212
(SAN 204-0018); Orders to: P.O. Box 3668,
Beverly Hills, CA 90212 (SAN 689-2426)
Tel 213-271-5558; CIP.

Monkey Joe Enterprises, Inc., *(Monkey Joe Ent;
0-933208)*, 3310 Lebanon Rd., Suite 104,
Hermitage, TN 37076 (SAN 212-4319).

Monkey Man Pr., *(Monkey Man; 0-9605594)*,
3895 Fredonia Dr., Los Angeles, CA 90068
(SAN 216-1648) Tel 213-876-2299.

†Monkey Sisters Inc., the, *(Monkey Sisters;
0-933606)*, 22971 Via Cruz, Laguna Niguel,
CA 92677 (SAN 212-7660)
Tel 714-859-5014; CIP.

Monkfish Publishing Corp., *(Monkfish Pub;
0-9615623)*, 10740 Pine Bluff, Whitmore
Lake, MI 48189 (SAN 696-1207)
Tel 313-662-1353.

Monks of New Skete, *(Monks of New Skete;
0-9607924; 0-935129)*, New Skete Rd.,
Cambridge, NY 12816 (SAN 240-0553)
Tel 518-677-3928.

Monna Lisa Precision, *(M Lisa Precision;
0-87643)*, Dist. by: Barclay Bridge Supplies,
Eight Bush Ave., Port Chester, NY 10573
(SAN 202-3768) Tel 914-937-4200.

Mono Lake Committee, The, *(Mono Lake
Comm; 0-933916)*, Box 29, Lee Vining, CA
93541 (SAN 282-0064) Tel 619-647-6386;
Dist. by: Bookpeople, 2929 Fifth St.,
Berkeley, CA 94710 (SAN 168-9517)
Tel 415-549-3030; Dist. by: Publishers
Group West, 5855 Beaudry St., Emeryville,
CA 94608 (SAN 202-8522)
Tel 415-658-3453.

Monocacy Bk. Co., *(Monocacy; 0-913186)*, P.O.
Box 765, Redwood City, CA 94064
(SAN 202-6473) Tel 415-369-8934.

Monogram Aviation Pubns., *(Monogram
Aviation; 0-914144)*, 625 Edgebrook Dr.,
Boylston, MA 01505 (SAN 206-5983)
Tel 617-869-6836.

Monogram Pr., Inc., *(Monogram Pr; 0-938107)*,
12720 Hillcrest Rd., Suite 305, Dallas, TX
75230 (SAN 661-406X) Tel 214-991-9800.

Monongahela Publishing Co., Inc.,
(Monongahela Pub), 106 Morningside Dr.,
New York, NY 10027 (SAN 209-3545)
Tel 212-666-5187; Orders to: 78 B Stony
Rd., Fairmont, WV 26554 (SAN 209-3553).

Monroe, Lynn Lewis, *(L L Monroe; 0-9615125)*,
46 Pine Hill Dr., Alfred, NY 14802
(SAN 694-177X) Tel 607-587-8240.

Monroe County Library System, *(Monroe
County Lib; 0-940696)*, 3700 S. Custer Rd.,
Monroe, MI 48161 (SAN 213-5396)
Tel 313-241-5277.

Monroe Pr., *(Monroe Pr; 0-936781)*, 16107
Gledhill St., Sepulveda, CA 91343
(SAN 699-9883) Tel 818-891-6464; Dist.
by: Baker & Taylor Co., 6 Kirby Ave.,
Somerville, NJ 08876 (SAN 169-4901)
Tel 201-526-8000; Dist. by: Quality Books,
Inc., 918 Sherwood Dr., Lake Bluff, IL
60044-2204 (SAN 169-2127); Toll free:
800-323-4241; Dist. by: Bookpeople, 2929
Fifth St., Berkeley, CA 94710
(SAN 168-9517); Toll free: 800-624-4466.

Monson Productions, *(Monson Product;
0-942796)*, P.O. Box 5324, Madison, WI
53705 (SAN 240-2556) Tel 608-271-2016.

Monson Trading, Ltd., *(Monson Trading;
0-937667)*, 210 Main St., Suite 4, Kirkland,
WA 98033 (SAN 659-350X)
Tel 206-822-1883.

Montaigne Publishing, Inc., *(Montaigne;
0-917430)*, 99 El Toyonal, Orinda, CA
94563 (SAN 208-9602).

Montana Bankers Assn., *(Montana Bankers;
0-9612006)*, No. One N. Last Chance
Gulch, Helena, MT 59601 (SAN 286-830X)
Tel 406-443-4121.

Montana Historical Society Pr., *(MT Hist Soc;
0-917298)*, 225 N. Roberts St., Helena, MT
59620 (SAN 208-7693) Tel 406-444-4708;
Dist. by: Univ. of Washington Pr., P.O. Box
C-50096, Seattle, WA 98105
(SAN 212-2502) Tel 206-543-4050.

Montana Magazine, Inc., *(MT Mag; 0-938314)*,
Box 5630, Helena, MT 59604
(SAN 220-0732) Tel 406-443-2842; Toll
free: 800-821-3874 (MT).

Montana Reconnaissance Project, *(MRP;
0-939872)*, P.O. Box 8507, Missoula, MT
59807 (SAN 216-9118) Tel 406-543-7357.

Montana Tech Foundation, *(Montana Tech;
0-930609)*, W. Park St., Butte, MT 59701
(SAN 679-1867).

Montclair State College, *(Montclair State;
0-933559)*, Upper Montclair, NJ 07043
(SAN 691-8778) Tel 201-893-7215; Dist.
by: Hispamerica, 5 Pueblo Ct., Gaithersburg,
MD 20878 (SAN 213-9200).

Monte Publishing Co., *(Monte Pub; 0-9606942)*,
P.O. Box 361, Underwood, WA 98651
(SAN 238-8987) Tel 509-493-2396.

Montecito Pr., *(Montecito Pr; 0-935377)*, 100
Oceangate, Suite 1010, Long Beach, CA
90802 (SAN 696-3277) Tel 213-432-8929.

Monterey Peninsula Audubon Society,
(Monterey Audubon; 0-9615798), P.O. Box
5656, Carmel, CA 93921 (SAN 696-5970)
Tel 408-373-6658.

Montevista Pr, *(Montevista Pr; 0-931551)*, 5041
Meridian Rd., Bellingham, WA 98226
(SAN 682-191X) Tel 206-734-4279; Dist.
by: Pacific Pipeline, 19215 66th Ave. S.,
Kent, WA 98032 (SAN 208-2128)
Tel 206-872-5523; Toll free: 800-562-4647
(In Washington); Dist. by: Robert Hale &
Co., 1840 130th Ave. NE, Suite 10, Bellevue,
WA 98005 (SAN 200-6995)
Tel 206-881-5212; Dist. by: Baker & Taylor,
Eastern Div., 50 Kirby Ave., Somerville, NJ
08876 (SAN 169-4901).

Montezuma Micro, *(Montezuma Micro;
0-928295)*, Redbird Airport, Hangar No. 8,
P.O. Box 763009, Dallas, TX 75376-3009
(SAN 657-5390); Toll free: 800-527-0347
Tel 214-339-5105; Toll free: 800-442-1310
(TX).

Montfort Pubns., Div. of Montfort Missionaries,
(Montfort Pubns; 0-910984), 26 S. Saxon
Ave., Bay Shore, NY 11706
(SAN 169-5053) Tel 516-665-0726.

Montgomery, Barbara, *(B Montgomery;
0-9615738)*, 2481 Morton St., Oak park, MI
48237 (SAN 695-8613) Tel 313-399-0824.

Montgomery , Richard H. & Assocs., *(R H Mont
Assocs; 0-915991)*, 913 Helen St., Midland,
MI 48640 (SAN 294-6319)
Tel 517-631-9334.

Montgomery County Historical Society,
(Montgomery Co Hist; 0-9601094), 103 W.
Montgomery Ave., Rockville, MD 20850
(SAN 210-1262) Tel 301-762-1492.

Montgomery County Historical Society,
(Montgomery Hist; 0-9608694), Fort
Johnson, NY 12070 (SAN 238-3179)
Tel 518-843-0300.

Montgomery Museum of Fine Arts,
(Montgomery Mus; 0-89280), 440 S.
McDonough St., Montgomery, AL 36104
(SAN 208-3299) Tel 205-832-2976.

Montgomery Scientific Pubns., *(Mont Sci Pubns;
0-935643)*, 4180 Poinciana Ave., Miami, FL
33133 (SAN 696-1614) Tel 305-326-6633.

Monthly Review Pr., Div. of Monthly Review
Foundation, Inc., *(Monthly Rev; 0-85345)*,
155 W. 23rd St., New York, NY 10011
(SAN 202-6481) Tel 212-691-2555.

Monument Pr., *(Monument Pr; 0-930383)*, P.
O. Box 160361, Las Colinas, TX 75016
(SAN 670-7742) Tel 214-948-7001; Dist.
by: Publishers Assocs., P.O. Box 160361, Las
Colinas, TX 75016-9998 (SAN 662-2488)
Tel 817-478-8564.

Monza Fels See Plantin Pr.

Moody Colportage Library See Moody Pr.

Moody Giant See Moody Pr.

Moody Pr., Div. of Moody Bible Institute,
(Moody; 0-8024), 820 N. LaSalle Dr.,
Chicago, IL 60610 (SAN 202-5604)
Tel 312-973-7800; Toll free: 800-621-5111;
Toll free: 800-621-4323 (In Illinois).
Imprints: Moody Colportage Library (MCL);
Moody Giant (MG); Moody Youth Library
(MYL).

Moody Youth Library See Moody Pr.

Moon of New Ferns, *(Moon New Ferns;
0-9612784)*, Rte. 9, Box 820, Tucson, AZ
85743 (SAN 289-7660); Dist. by: New
Woman Press, 2000 King Mountain Trail,
Sunny Valley, OR 97497-9799
(SAN 209-8474).

Moon Over the Mountain Publishing Co.,
(Moon Over Mntn; 0-9602970), 6700 W.
44th Ave., Wheatridge, CO 80033
(SAN 213-3415) Tel 303-420-4272.

Moon Pubns., *(Moon Pubns CA; 0-9603322;
0-918373)*, P.O. Box 1696, Chico, CA 95927
(SAN 221-7406); 133 W. Lindo, Chico, CA
95927-1696 (SAN 658-1250)
Tel 916-345-5473.

Mooney, Alfred J., *(A J Mooney; 0-9616946)*,
2111 Evanston, Wichita, KS 67219
(SAN 661-7581) Tel 316-744-3358.

Mooney, Tom, *(Mooney; 0-9601240)*, 3410
Balt-Som Rd., Millersport, OH 43046
(SAN 210-1270) Tel 614-862-8159.

Moonlight Editions See Schocken Bks., Inc.

Moonlight Pr., *(Moonlight FL; 0-913545)*, 3407
Crystal Lake Dr., Orlando, FL 32806
(SAN 293-3063) Tel 305-857-1113.

Moonlight Pr., *(Moonlight Pr IL; 0-9616493)*,
202 N. Brighton Pl., Arlington Heights, IL
60004 (SAN 659-3542) Tel 312-392-8438.
Do not confuse with other companies with
same name in Orlando, FL, Austin, TX,
Troy, NY, Menominie, WI.

Moonlight Pr., *(Moonlight Press; 0-9612002)*,
1402 Mathews St., Menomonie, WI 54751
(SAN 286-8334) Tel 715-235-7465. Do not
confuse with other companies with same
name in Orlando, FL, Austin, TX, Troy, NY,
Arlington Heights, IL.

Moonlight Pr., The, *(Moonlight Pr; 0-941818)*,
611 Pawling Ave., Troy, NY 12180
(SAN 239-2607).

Moonlight Pubns., *(Moonlight Pubns; 0-931350)*,
Box 671, La Jolla, CA 92038
(SAN 211-2566).

Moonmad Pr., *(Moonmad Pr; 0-917918)*, P.O.
Box 757, Terre Haute, IN 47808
(SAN 209-3537).

Moonowl Creations, *(Moonowl Creat; 0-932009)*,
P.O. Box 488, Pagosa Springs, CO 81147
(SAN 686-0958) Tel 303-264-5655.

Moonraker Pubns., *(Moonraker; 0-940620)*,
24452B Alta Vista, Dana Point, CA 92629
(SAN 222-9862) Tel 714-661-9172.

Moonsquilt Pr., *(MoonsQuilt Pr; 0-943216)*,
16401 NE 4th Ave., N., Miami, FL 33162
(SAN 240-5512) Tel 305-947-9534.

Names

Moonstone Pr., *(Moonstone; 0-940410),* P.O. Box 142, Beverly Hills, CA 90213 (SAN 282-017X) Tel 714-956-2246; Dist. by: Ingram Industries, 347 Reedwood Dr., Nashville, TN 37217 (SAN 169-7978); Dist. by: Last Gasp, 2180 Bryant St., San Francisco, CA 94110 (SAN 216-8294) Tel 415-824-6636; Dist. by: Quality Bks., 918 Sherwood Dr., Lake Bluff, IL 60044-2204 (SAN 203-610X); Dist. by: Baker & Taylor Co., Midwest Div., 501 Gladiola Ave., Momence, IL 60954 (SAN 169-2100); Orders to: P.O. Box 661, Anaheim, CA 92805 (SAN 662-0841). *Imprints:* Disharmony Books (Disharmony Bks).

Moontree Pr., *(Moontree Pr),* 3719 4th St., NW, Albuquerque, NM 87107 (SAN 241-5666).

Moore, Diane M., *(D M Moore; 0-9604030),* P.O. Box 1073, New Iberia, LA 70560 (SAN 214-0608) Tel 318-364-6730.

Moore, Donna J., Pub., *(Moore D; 0-9605466),* P.O. Box 723, Bainbridge Island, WA 98110 (SAN 240-0243) Tel 206-842-2170.

Moore, Louis C., *(L C Moore; 0-9616361),* P.O. Box 243, Carmel Valley, CA 93924 (SAN 658-9375); Professional Bldg., Village Dr., Carmel Valley, CA 93924 (SAN 658-9383) Tel 408-659-2901.

Moore, Milton T., Jr., *(M T Moore; 0-9608138),* P.O. Box 140280, Dallas, TX 75214 (SAN 240-2564) Tel 214-821-0407.

Moore, Wendell, Pub., *(W Moore Pub; 0-934281),* 3085 W. Hwy. 89A, Sedona, AZ 86336 (SAN 693-3114) Tel 602-282-3419; Dist. by: EPM Pubns., 3085 W. Hwy. 89A, Sedona, AZ (SAN 200-8025).

Moore & Quinn, *(Moore & Quinn; 0-9614483),* Rt. No.3, Camden, NY 13316 (SAN 689-3996); Dist. by: North Country Books, 18 Irving Pl., Utica, NY 13501 (SAN 287-0231).

Moore Data Management Services, *(Moore Data; 0-918451),* 1660 South Hwy 100, Minneapolis, MN 55416 (SAN 693-5508) Tel 612-588-7205.

Moore Historical Foundation, *(Moore Hist; 0-914167),* 300 E. State St., No. 506, Redlands, CA 92373 (SAN 287-6191) Tel 714-798-2403.

Moore Memorial Hospital Auxiliary, *(Moore Memorial),* P.O. Box 704, Pinehurst, NC 28374 (SAN 217-2909) Tel 919-281-3388.

Moore Pubns, *(Moore Pubns; 0-9602616),* 9216 220th SW, Edmonds, WA 98020 (SAN 238-4396).

Moore Publishing Co., Inc. (Il), *(Moore Pub IL; 0-935610),* P.O. Box 709, Oak Park, IL 60303 (SAN 222-643X) Tel 312-848-7401; 136 S. Wesley Ave., Oak Park, IL 60302 (SAN 669-1803).

Moorefields Pr., *(Moorefields Pr; 0-9615920),* Rte. 6, Box 743, Hillsborough, NC 27278 (SAN 697-2276) Tel 919-732-5941.

Moosehead Products, *(Moosehead Prods; 0-9609208),* Rte. 1-4710, Corinna, ME 04928 (SAN 241-4090) Tel 207-278-3556.

Mor-Mac Publishing Co., *(Mor-Mac; 0-912178),* P.O. Box 985, Daytona Beach, FL 32015 (SAN 204-0042) Tel 904-255-4427.

Morales Pubns, *(Morales Pubns; 0-934157),* 1524 Independence, No. J, Plano, TX 75075 (SAN 693-2010) Tel 214-596-1203.

Moran/Andrews, Inc., *(Moran Andrews; 0-912286),* 211 E. Ohio St., Chicago, IL 60611 (SAN 202-6503) Tel 312-644-2793.

Moran Publishing Co., *(Moran Pub FL),* 9125 Bachman Rd., Orlando, FL 32859 (SAN 264-2166).

Moran Publishing Corp., *(Moran Pub Corp; 0-86518),* 5425 Florida Blvd., P.O. Box 66538, Baton Rouge, LA 70896 (SAN 214-0616) Tel 504-923-2550; Dist. by: Aviation Book Co., 1640 Victory Blvd., Glendale, CA 91201 (SAN 212-0259) Tel 213-240-1771.

Moravian Music Foundation, *(Moravian Music; 0-8078),* 20 Cascade Ave., Winston-Salem, NC 27107 (SAN 225-3569) Tel 919-725-0651.

Moravian Music Foundation Pr., *(Morav Music Found; 0-941642),* Dist. by: Associated University Presses, 440 Forsgate Dr., Cranbury, NJ 08512 (SAN 281-2959) Tel 609-655-4770.

More, Thomas, Pr., Subs. of Thomas More Assn., *(Thomas More; 0-88347),* 223 W. Erie St., Chicago, IL 60611 (SAN 203-0675) Tel 312-951-2100; Toll free: 800-835-8965.

More Information, *(More Info; 0-936355),* 4717 12th Ave, S., Minneapolis, MN 55407 (SAN 697-9149) Tel 612-822-6167.

Moreau, Xavier, Inc., *(Xavier Moreau; 0-937950),* 437 Madison Ave., New York, NY 10022 (SAN 264-2174) Tel 212-355-1410.

Morehouse-Barlow Co., *(Morehouse; 0-8192),* 78 Danbury Rd., Wilton, CT 06897 (SAN 202-6511) Tel 203-762-0721.

†Moretus Pr., Inc., The, *(Moretus Pr; 0-89679),* P.O. Box 867, Ossining, NY 10562-0867 (SAN 211-2523) Tel 914-941-0409; CIP.

Morford, Wanda L., *(W L Morford; 0-9616543),* 3310 Queen City Ave., Apt. 6, Cincinnati, OH 45238 (SAN 659-5243) Tel 513-632-3126; Orders to: P.O. Box 118734, Cincinnati, OH 45211 (SAN 662-4278) Tel 513-481-0982.

†Morgan, Pierpont, Library, *(Pierpont Morgan; 0-87598),* 29 E. 36th St., New York, NY 10016 (SAN 204-8957) Tel 212-685-0008; CIP.

Morgan & Morgan, Inc., Affil. of Morgan Pr., Inc., *(Morgan; 0-87100),* 145 Palisade St., Dobbs Ferry, NY 10522 (SAN 202-5620) Tel 914-693-0023.

Morgan Aviation Bks. *See Arco Publishing, Inc.*

Morgan Kaufmann Pubs., Inc., *(Morgan Kaufmann; 0-934613),* 95 First St., Suite 120, Los Altos, CA 94022 (SAN 693-918X) Tel 415-941-4960; Orders to: P.O. Box 50490, Palo Alto, CA 94303 (SAN 200-2272) Tel 415-965-4081.

Morgan Pr., *(Morgan Pr TX),* P.O. Box 580355, Houston, TX 77258-0355 (SAN 659-560X). Do not confuse with Morgan Pr., Milwaukee, WI.

Morgan-Rand Pubns., Inc., *(Morgan-Rand; 0-913061),* 2200 Sansom St., Philadelphia, PA 19103 (SAN 283-2135) Tel 215-557-8200; Toll free: 800-354-8673.

†Morgan State Univ., *(Morgan State; 0-9610324),* Cold Spring Ln., Baltimore, MD 21239 (SAN 264-2182) Tel 301-444-3165; CIP.

Morgantown Printing & Binding Co., *(Morgantown Print & Bind; 0-930284),* P.O. Box 850, Morgantown, WV 26505 (SAN 213-1188) Tel 304-292-3368.

Moriarty, Dan, Associates, *(D Moriarty; 0-933968),* 1410 Second Ave., Newport, MN 55055 (SAN 211-6448) Tel 612-459-1857.

Morishima, Michael, *(M Morishima; 0-9616866),* 20707 Crawford Dr., Sunnyvale, CA 94087 (SAN 661-1605) Tel 408-732-7381.

Morning Coffee Chapbooks *See Coffee Hse. Pr., Toothpaste Pr.*

†Morning Glory Pr., Inc., *(Morning Glory; 0-930934),* 6595 San Haroldo Way, Buena Park, CA 90620 (SAN 211-2558) Tel 714-828-1998; CIP.

Morning Star Gallery, *(Morning Star Gal; 0-9617085),* 513 Canyon Rd., Santa Fe, NM 87501 (SAN 662-5916) Tel 505-982-8187.

Morning Star Pr., *(Mrng Star SF; 0-937937),* 16 California St., Suite 205, San Francisco, CA 94111 (SAN 659-5294) Tel 415-751-0904.

Morningland Pubns., Inc., *(Morningland; 0-935146),* 2600 E. Seventh St., Long Beach, CA 90804 (SAN 213-6368) Tel 213-433-9906.

Morningsun Pubns., *(Morningsun Pubns; 0-9603424),* 692 Edna Way, San Mateo, CA 94402 (SAN 211-6235) Tel 415-341-4491.

Morris, John, *(J Morris; 0-9602278),* 3333 Nutmeg Ln., Walnut Creek, CA 94598 (SAN 200-4011) Tel 415-933-3365.

Morris, Robert, Assocs., *(Robt Morris Assocs; 0-936742),* 1616 Philadelphia National Bank Bldg., Philadelphia, PA 19107 (SAN 224-6472).

Morris, Victoria S., Bks., *(V S Morris; 0-914318),* 39 Gleneden Ave., Oakland, CA 94611 (SAN 202-2125) Tel 415-652-2013.

Morris, William, Society, *(Wm Morris Soc; 0-931332),* 420 Riverside Dr., 12G, New York, NY 10025 (SAN 225-2899).

Morris-Burt Press, *(Morris-Burt Pr; 0-9600890),* 10 Gary Way, Alamo, CA 94507 (SAN 222-0857) Tel 415-837-4426.

Morris County Historical Society, *(M C H S; 0-910301),* P.O. Box 170 M, Morristown, NJ 07960 (SAN 241-4104) Tel 201-267-3465.

Morris Genealogical Library, *(Morris Genealog Lib),* P.O. Box 63, Allenhurst, NJ 07711 (SAN 207-6012).

Morris Museum of Arts & Sciences, *(Morris Museum Art Science),* 6 Normandy Heights Rd., Morristown, NJ 07960 (SAN 279-6678).

Morris Publishing Co., Subs. of Face Metier, Inc., *(Morris Pub; 0-9606890; 0-9615396),* 3 Blue Ridge Rd., Plymouth Meeting, PA 19462 (SAN 282-0234) Tel 215-828-4865; Orders to: Box 124, Plymouth Meeting, PA 19462 (SAN 282-0242) Tel 215-828-4865.

Morris Publishing Co. of San Francisco, Div. of Images by Suzie, *(Morris Pub CA; 0-9616472),* 1958 Vallejo, Suite 3, San Francisco, CA 94123 (SAN 658-9413) Tel 415-331-6021.

Morrison Peterson Publishing, Inc., *(Morrison Peterson Pub; 0-936062),* P.O. Box 1870, Kailua, HI 96734 (SAN 238-8944) Tel 808-262-2533; Toll free: 800-528-3665.

Morrison Publishing Co., *(Morrison Pub Co; 0-911593),* 14 Brown St., Warren, RI 02885 (SAN 264-2190).

Morrison, Raven-Hill Co., *(Morrison Rav; 0-912189),* 9466 Hidden Valley Pl., Beverly Hills, CA 90210 (SAN 277-6952).

Morrissette, *(Morrissette; 0-9615627),* 140 Russell St., Lewiston, ME 04240 (SAN 696-1177) Tel 207-784-1618.

Morristown Historical Society, *(Morristown Hist Soc; 0-9607288),* c/o Sargent & White, Morrisville, VT 05661 (SAN 293-308X).

Morrow, Felix, Pub, *(F Morrow; 0-9615659),* 13 Welwyn Rd., Great Neck, NY 11021 (SAN 696-1029) Tel 516-482-1044; Orders to: The Talman Company, Distributor, 150 Fifth Ave., Rm. 514B, New York, NY 10011 (SAN 662-3654) Tel 212-620-3182.

Morrow, William, & Co., Inc., Subs. of Hearst Corp., *(Morrow; 0-688),* 105 Madison Ave., New York, NY 10016 (SAN 202-5760) Tel 212-889-3050; Toll free: 800-631-1199; Orders to: Wilmor Warehouse, 6 Henderson Dr., West Caldwell, NJ 07006 (SAN 202-5779). *Imprints:* Quill Paperbacks (Quill); Reynal (Reynal).

Morse, Albert L., *(A L Morse; 0-918320),* 320 Miller Ave., Mill Valley, CA 94941 (SAN 209-4614) Tel 415-332-3571.

Morse Pr., Inc., *(Morse Pr; 0-933350),* 3441 Thorndyke Ave. W., Seattle, WA 98119 (SAN 211-8165) Tel 206-282-9988.

Mortal Press, *(Mortal Pr; 0-9604152),* 1516 Muldoon Dr., Rockford, IL 61103-1639 (SAN 211-254X) Tel 815-654-7943.

Morten Publishing Co., Inc., *(Morten Pub; 0-9607848),* 605 N. Bittersweet, Muncie, IN 47304 (SAN 238-1788).

Mortensen Educational Products, Inc., *(Mortensen Educ Prods; 0-937005),* 9757 Eton Ave., Chatsworth, CA 91311 (SAN 658-7429) Tel 818-341-1031.

Mortgage Bankers Assn. of America, *(Mortgage Bankers),* 1125 15th St., NW, Washington, DC 20005 (SAN 224-8212) Tel 202-861-6500.

Mortgage Techniques, *(Mortgage Tech; 0-9615886),* 8469 Farrah Ln., Memphis, TN 38138 (SAN 696-639X) Tel 901-755-8578; Toll free: 800-468-1255; Toll free: 800-523-1307 (In Tennessee); Orders to: Mortgage Techniques, P.O. Box 17214, Memphis, TN 38127-0214 (SAN 662-3794) Tel 901-755-8728; Toll free: 800-468-1255; 800-523-1307 (In Tennessee).

Morton, Julia F., *(J F Morton; 0-9610184),* 20534 SW 92nd Ct., Miami, FL 33189 (SAN 272-5185) Tel 305-284-3741.

Morton Falls Pub. Co., Div. of Douglas Kirk's Animals of the Performing Arts, *(Morton Falls Pub; 0-934279),* Rt. 9, Box 810S, Canyon Lake, TX 78130 (SAN 693-3149) Tel 512-899-3290.

Morton Lane Pr., *(Morton Ln Pr; 0-938695),* P.O. Box 4264, Athens, GA 30602 (SAN 661-5686); 320 Morton Farm Ln., Athens, GA 30605 (SAN 661-5694) Tel 404-543-8786.

Morton Publishing Co., *(Morton Pub; 0-89582),* 925 West Kenyon Ave., Unit 4, Englewood, CO 80110 (SAN 210-9174) Tel 303-761-4805.

Names

525

Mosadot Pubns., Inc., *(Mosadot Pubns; 0-913185)*, 71 Broadway, New York, NY 10006 (SAN 290-6961) Tel 212-425-3466.

Mosaic Bks., *(Mosaic Bks; 0-914255)*, 3923 Partridge Ln., Baton Rouge, LA 70809 (SAN 287-5594) Tel 504-292-1029; Dist. by: New Leaf Distributors, The, 1020 White St., SW, Atlanta, GA 30310 (SAN 169-1449) Tel 404-755-2665.

Mosaic Media, Inc., *(Mosaic Media; 0-917792)*, P.O. Box 711, Glen Ellyn, IL 60137 (SAN 209-2956) Tel 312-790-1117.

Mosaic Press, *(Mosaic Pr OH; 0-88014)*, 358 Oliver Rd., Cincinnati, OH 45215 (SAN 219-6077) Tel 513-761-5977.

Mosaic Pr., the, *(Mosaic Pr; 0-934696)*, 158 Kachina Trail, No. 1, Flagstaff, AZ 86001 (SAN 213-4187).

Mosby, C.V., Co., Subs. of The Times Mirror Co., *(Mosby; 0-8016)*, 11830 Westline Industrial Dr., St. Louis, MO 63146 (SAN 200-2280) Tel 314-872-8370; Toll free: 800-325-4177.

†Mosby/Multi-Media, Div. of Mosby/Times Mirror, *(Multi Media CO; 0-940122; 0-8016)*, 11830 Westline Industrial Dr., Saint Louis, MO 63146 (SAN 220-2913) Tel 303-778-1404; Toll free: 800-325-4177; *CIP.*

Moschetta, Paul & Evelyn, Drs., *(P & E Moschetta)*, 28 Shore Ln., Bay Shore, NY 11706 (SAN 663-0731) Tel 516-666-1155.

Moses Poetry Collection & Bk. Publishing Co., Inc., *(Moses Pub Pubns; 0-932324)*, P.O. Box 701 Plaza, Hudson, NY 12534-0701 (SAN 219-3779) Tel 518-828-7335.

Mosley, Marilyn C., *(M C Mosley; 0-9614850)*, Rt. 1 Box 862, Vashon, WA 98070 (SAN 693-0972) Tel 206-567-4751.

Mosley, P, & Co., *(P Mosley; 0-917661)*, 810 N. Arthur, Fresno, CA 93728 (SAN 657-1573) Tel 209-268-7512.

Moss, David L., Publications, *(D L Moss Pubns; 0-914509)*, 7986 Daggett St., San Diego, CA 92111 (SAN 289-6575) Tel 619-571-0506.

Moss Pubns., *(Moss Pubns VA; 0-943522)*, Box 729, Orange, VA 22960 (SAN 214-4220) Tel 703-672-5921.

Mossart, *(Mossart; 0-9606162)*, Box 929, Weaverville, CA 96093 (SAN 217-1171) Tel 916-623-5406.

Mostly Microwave, *(Mostly Micro; 0-9614072)*, c/o Janice Martin, Rt. 1, Box 78A, Gibbon, NE 68840 (SAN 686-0060) Tel 308-468-6115.

Mostly Movement Ltd., *(Mostly Movement; 0-934848)*, 58-15 211th St.,, Bayside, NY 11364 (SAN 222-6456).

Motamed Medical Pub., Inc., *(Motamed Med Pub; 0-910161)*, 7141 N. Kedzie Ave. Suite 1504, Chicago, IL 60645 (SAN 241-2276) Tel 312-761-6667.

Moth House Pubns., *(Moth Hse; 0-936718)*, 3967 S. 2200 W., Salt Lake City, UT 84119 (SAN 222-6375).

Mother Courage Pr., *(Mother Courage; 0-941300)*, 1533 Illinois St., Racine, WI 53405 (SAN 239-4618) Tel 414-634-1047.

Mother Duck Press, *(Mother Duck Pr; 0-934600)*, Rte. 1, Box 25A, McNeal, AZ 85617 (SAN 213-1196).

Mother Earth News, The, *(Mother Earth; 0-938432)*, P.O. Box 70, Hendersonville, NC 28791 (SAN 215-7918); Toll free: 800-438-0238.

Mothering Publications, Inc., *(Mothering Pubns; 0-914257)*, P.O. Box 8410, Santa Fe, NM 87504 (SAN 287-5616) Tel 505-984-8116.

Motheroot Pubns., *(Motheroot; 0-934238)*, P.O. Box 8306, Pittsburgh, PA 15218-0306 (SAN 216-4205) Tel 412-731-4453.

Motivational Aids, *(Motiv Aids; 0-9607372)*, 524 Dickson St., Endicott, NY 13760 (SAN 239-4626) Tel 607-785-7032.

Motivational Methods, Inc., *(Motiv Methods; 0-933664)*, 8569 Ramblewood Dr., Coral Springs, FL 33065 (SAN 212-7687) Tel 305-753-3579.

Motivators Unlimited, *(Motiv Unltd; 0-9609084)*, P.O. Box 35922, Tucson, AZ 85740-5922 (SAN 241-4112) Tel 602-887-9404.

Motor Cities Publishing Co., *(Motor Cities; 0-911383)*, 10405 Rushton Rd., South Lyon, MI 48178 (SAN 205-8146).

Motor Transportation Association of South Carolina, *(MTASC; 0-9608140)*, P.O. Box 50166, Columbia, SC 29205 (SAN 240-2580) Tel 803-799-4306.

Motor Vehicle Manufacturers Assn. of the United States, *(Motor Veh Man; 0-943350)*, Orders to: Comm. Dept., 300 New Ctr. Bldg., Detroit, MI 48202 (SAN 272-5312) Tel 313-872-4311.

Motorbooks International, Pubs. & Wholesalers, Inc., Subs. of Motorbooks Zenith Aviation, *(Motorbooks Intl; 0-87938)*, 729 Prospect Ave., Osceola, WI 54020 (SAN 169-9164) Tel 715-294-3345; Toll free: 800-826-6600; Orders to: Box 2, Osceola, WI 54020 (SAN 699-5462).

Motorcycle Safety Foundation, *(Motorcycle Safety)*, P.O. Box 5044, Costa Mesa, CA 92628 (SAN 224-9413); Rte. 1, Chadds Ford W. Complex, Chadds Ford, PA 19317 (SAN 669-182X) Tel 215-388-1555.

Motormatics Pubns., Div. of Motormatics, Inc., *(Motormatics; 0-930968)*, c/o Beach Cities Enterprises, P.O. Box 91051, Long Beach, CA 90809 (SAN 211-1349) Tel 213-434-6701.

†Mott Media, *(Mott Media; 0-915134; 0-88062)*, 1000 E. Huron, Milford, MI 48042 (SAN 207-1460) Tel 313-685-8773; *CIP.*

Mount Angel Abbey Pubns., *(Mt Angel Abbey; 0-918941)*, Saint Benedict, OR 97373 (SAN 669-8530) Tel 503-845-3380.

Mt. Eden Historical Pubs., *(Mt Eden Hist; 0-936193)*, 22237 Main St., Hayward, CA 94541 (SAN 696-6624) Tel 415-582-3969.

Mount Hood Publishing Co., *(Mt Hood Pub; 0-938071)*, 4135 Cunningham Dr., Mount Hood, OR 97041-9726 (SAN 661-1915) Tel 503-352-7465.

Mount St. Mary's College, *(Mount St Marys; 0-9606972)*, Emmitsburg, MD 21727 (SAN 223-1964) Tel 301-447-6122.

Mount Shasta Pubns., *(Mt Shasta Pubns; 0-9616478)*, P.O. Box 436, Mount Shasta, CA 96067 (SAN 659-2805) Tel 916-926-5653; 200 Sheldon, No. 6, Mount Shasta, CA 96067 (SAN 659-2813).

†Mt. Vernon Ladies Assn. of the Union, Library, *(Mt Vernon Ladies; 0-931917)*, Museum Shop, Mount Vernon, VA 22121 (SAN 225-3976) Tel 703-780-2000; *CIP.*

†Mount Vernon Pr., *(Mount Vernon Pr; 0-931213)*, 1121 112th NE, Bellevue, WA 98004 (SAN 682-0034) Tel 206-454-6982; *CIP.*

Mountain, *(Mountain Calif; 0-9605992)*, Box 1408, Lower Lake, CA 95457 (SAN 216-7522).

Mountain & Sea Publishing, *(Mountain Sea; 0-911449)*, P.O. Box 126, Redondo Beach, CA 90277 (SAN 272-5371) Tel 213-379-9321.

Mountain Automation Corp., *(Mntn Automation; 0-936206)*, P.O. Box 6020, Woodland Park, CO 80866 (SAN 221-4148).

Mountain Brook Pubns., *(Mntn Brook Pubns; 0-938747)*, P.O. Box 7474, Mountain Brook, AL 35253 (SAN 661-7549); 2652 Alta Glen Dr., Birmingham, AL 35243 (SAN 661-7557) Tel 205-867-6517.

Mountain Elegance, *(Mntn Elegance)*, P.O. Box 8723, Asheville, NC 28814 (SAN 240-964X).

Mountain Grizzly Pubns., *(Mntn Grizzly Pubns; 0-9616480)*, 133 E. 1600 N., Orem, UT 84057 (SAN 659-2775) Tel 801-226-8741.

Mountain House Publishing, Inc., *(Mntn Hse Pub; 0-939274)*, Rte. 1 Box 433 A, Waitsfield, VT 05673 (SAN 216-4213).

Mountain Lamp Pubns., *(Mtn Lamp Pubns; 0-9615265)*, Rt. 6, Box 185B, Morgantown, WV 26505 (SAN 696-2963) Tel 304-292-1108.

Mountain Laurel Publications, *(Mountain Laurel; 0-911687)*, P.O. Box 1621, Harrisburg, PA 17105 (SAN 264-2239).

Mountain Memories Bks., *(Mntn Memories Bks; 0-938985)*, 216 Sutherland Dr., South Charleston, WV 25303 (SAN 661-6771) Tel 304-744-5772.

Mountain Missionary Pr., Div. of Mountain Missionary Institute, Inc., *(MMI Pr; 0-912145)*, Aldworth Rd., P.O. Box 279, Harrisville, NH 03450 (SAN 264-7664) Tel 603-827-3914; Toll free: 800-367-1888.

Mountain Movers Ministry, Affil. of Mountain Movers Publishers, *(Mountain Movers; 0-9616309)*, 1231 Dewey, Wauwatosa, WI 53213 (SAN 658-7453) Tel 414-257-1259.

Mountain Pr., *(Mountain Pr CA; 0-9616070)*, 30951 Tinkerbell Ln., Shingletown, CA 96088 (SAN 697-9157) Tel 916-474-5660.

†Mountain Pr., Publishing Co., Inc., *(Mountain Pr; 0-87842)*, P.O. Box 2399, Missoula, MT 59806 (SAN 202-8832) Tel 406-728-1900; Toll free: 800-732-3669; 2016 Strand, Missoula, MT 59801 (SAN 662-0868); *CIP.*

Mountain States Telephone & Telegraph Co., Regulatory Matters Division, *(Mountain St Tel; 0-9602580)*, 931-14th St., Rm. 1010, Denver, CO 80202 (SAN 213-120X).

Mountain Valley Publishing Hse., *(Mtn Valley Pub; 0-9615415)*, Box 25432, Prescott Valley, AZ 86312 (SAN 695-5266) Tel 602-772-8838.

Mountain View Pr., Inc., *(Mntn View Pr; 0-914699)*, P.O. Box 4656, Mountain View, CA 94040 (SAN 287-3141) Tel 415-961-4103.

Mountain West Publishing Co., *(Mountain West; 0-9610968)*, P.O. Box 1841, Grand Junction, CO 81502 (SAN 265-2838) Tel 303-242-5035.

Mountaineers Bks., The, Div. of Mountaineers, The, *(Mountaineers; 0-916890; 0-89886)*, 306 Second Ave. W., Seattle, WA 98119 (SAN 212-8756) Tel 206-285-2665.

Mountcastle Corp., The, *(Mountcastle; 0-913063)*, P.O. Box 1688, Redondo Beach, CA 90278 (SAN 285-6689).

Mouse Pr., *(Mouse Pr; 0-913968)*, 3118 17th St., Santa Monica, CA 90405 (SAN 203-1795) Tel 213-452-3259; Dist. by: Light Impressions Corp., P.O. Box 940, 439 Monroe Ave., Rochester, NY 14603 (SAN 169-619X) Tel 716-271-8960.

Mouton De Gruyter, Div. of Walter De Gruyter, Inc., *(Mouton; 90-279)*, 200 Saw Mill River Rd., Hawthorne, NY 10532 (SAN 210-9239) Tel 914-747-0110.

Mouvement Pubns., *(Mouvement Pubns; 0-932392)*, 109 E. State St., Ithaca, NY 14850 (SAN 211-7460) Tel 607-272-2157.

Moveable Feast Pr., *(Moveable Feast Pr; 0-943430)*, P.O. Box 5057, El Dorado Hills, CA 95630 (SAN 240-7256) Tel 916-933-2375.

Moving Parts Pr., *(Moving Parts; 0-939952)*, 419-A Maple St., Santa Cruz, CA 95060 (SAN 216-8383) Tel 408-427-2271.

Moving Picture Co., Inc., The, *(Moving Picture Co; 1-55565)*, 2507 Thornwood Ave., Wilmette, IL 60091 (SAN 658-5795) Tel 312-256-1111.

Mowbray, *(Mowbray; 0-9614233)*, 108 Laguna Blvd., Jacksonville Beach, FL 32250 (SAN 686-7936) Tel 904-249-4936.

Mowry Pr., *(Mowry Pr; 0-9605368)*, Box 405, Wayland, MA 01778 (SAN 215-9724) Tel 617-358-4555.

Moyer Bell, Ltd., *(Moyer Bell Limited; 0-918825)*, Colonial Hill, RFD 1, Mt. Kisco, NY 10549 (SAN 669-6961) Tel 914-666-0084; Dist. by: Kampmann & Co., 9 E. 40th St., New York, NY 10016 (SAN 202-5191) Tel 212-685-2928; Toll free: 800-526-7626.

Ms. Leroy Pr., *(Ms Leroy Pr; 0-9616758)*, 3511 S. 172nd, Seattle, WA 98188 (SAN 238-9150) Tel 206-243-3687.

MSC, Inc. See Management & Systems Consultants, Inc.

M.T.O. Shahmaghsoudi, *(M T O Shahmag; 0-910735)*, P.O. Box 1135, San Rafael, CA 94915 (SAN 271-6852) Tel 415-454-1555.

Mu Alpha Theta, National High School Mathematics Club, *(Mu Alpha Theta; 0-940790)*, 601 Elm Ave., Rm. 423, Norman, OK 73019 (SAN 204-0077) Tel 405-325-4489.

Mu Phi Epsilon, *(Mu Phi Ep)*, 833 Laurel Ave., Highland Park, IL 60035 (SAN 224-5191) Tel 312-940-1222.

Mudra, *(Mudra; 0-914726)*, Dist. by: Bookpeople, 2929 Fifth St., Berkeley, CA 94710 (SAN 168-9517) Tel 415-549-3030.

Names

Muhammad, Mustafa M., Pubns., *(M M Muhammad; 0-9616801),* P.O. Box 1423, Santa Barbara, CA 93101 (SAN 661-2652); 1125 Garden Ln., Montecito, CA 93108 (SAN 661-2660) Tel 805-969-7520.

Muhlbut Pr., *(Muhlbut Pr; 0-88100),* P.O. Box 165, Dunmor, KY 42339 (SAN 655-167X).

†Muir, John, Pubns., *(John Muir; 0-912528),* P.O. Box 613, Santa Fe, NM 87504-0613 (SAN 203-9079) Tel 505-982-4078; Dist. by: W.W. Norton & Co., 500 Fifth Ave., New York, NY 10110 (SAN 202-5795) Tel 212-354-5500; Toll free: 800-223-2584; *CIP.*

Mul-T-Rul Pr., Div. of Mul-T-Rul Co., *(Mul-T-Rul; 0-9606556),* P.O. Box 250, Ft. Morgan, CO 80701 (SAN 223-0097) Tel 303-867-6201.

Mulberry Avenue Bks., *(Mulberry Ave Bks; 0-938036),* 2609 A&M Circle, San Angelo, TX 76904 (SAN 240-0510).

Mulberry Tree Press, The, *(Mulberry Tree; 0-9610684),* 327 N. Loudoun St, Winchester, VA 22601 (SAN 264-7672) Tel 703-665-0683.

†Mulch Press, *(Mulch Pr; 0-913142),* 1648 Waller St., San Francisco, CA 94117 (SAN 206-5061); Dist. by: Small Press Distribution, Inc., 1814 San Pablo Ave., Berkeley, CA 94702 (SAN 204-5826) Tel 415-549-3336; *CIP.*

Mule Mountain Pr., *(Mule Mt Pr; 0-932645),* 108 La Cholla, Bisbee, AZ 85603 (SAN 687-8245) Tel 602-432-3160.

Mulford Colebrook Publishing Co., *(Mulford Colebrook; 0-930144),* Box 289, Mifflinburg, PA 17844 (SAN 210-6434) Tel 217-344-1024.

Multi Dimensional Communications, Inc., *(Multi Dimen; 0-89507),* P.O. Box 427, Bedford Hills, NY 10507 (SAN 209-9632).

Multi Media Arts, *(Multi Media TX; 0-86617),* Box 14486, Austin, TX 78761 (SAN 214-4239) Tel 512-837-5503.

Multi Media Resource Ctr., *(MMRC; 0-9603968; 0-914684),* 1525 Franklin St., San Francisco, CA 94109 (SAN 206-6017) Tel 415-673-5100.

Multi-Spectral Pr., *(Multi Spectral; 0-918210),* 4948 Meadowbrook Rd., Buffalo, NY 14221 (SAN 210-2412) Tel 716-632-0921.

Multi-Strategy Pubs., Inc., *(Multi Strategy Pubs; 0-9616896),* P.O. Box 23, Grand Central Sta., New York, NY 10163 (SAN 661-6143); 72-10 112th St., Suite 1D, Forest Hills, NY 11375 (SAN 661-6151) Tel 718-793-9417.

Multilingual Typesetting, *(Multilingual; 0-9616413),* 56 Rockland Lake Pk., Valley Cottage, NY 10989 (SAN 658-9421) Tel 914-268-3782.

Multiple Breath Music Co., *(Multiple Breath Music; 0-939407),* 10 Leonard St., New York, NY 10013 (SAN 663-1401) Tel 212-226-6718.

Multiple Pr., *(Multiple Pr; 0-934911),* P.O. Box 1817, New York, NY 10009 (SAN 695-0078) Tel 212-614-0710.

Multiscience Publications Ltd. *See* Brookfield Pub. Co.

Multistate Tax Commission, *(Multistate Tax),* 1790 30th St., Suite 314, Boulder, CO 80301 (SAN 272-5509).

†Multnomah Pr., Div. of Multnomah Schl. of the Bible, *(Multnomah; 0-930014; 0-88070),* 10209 SE Division St., Portland, OR 97266 (SAN 210-4679) Tel 503-257-0526; Toll free: 800-547-5890; *CIP.*

Muncy Manuscripts, Inc., *(Muncy Manuscripts; 0-9617231),* P.O. Box 1561, Grapevine, TX 76051 (SAN 663-4788); 2960 Trail Lake Dr., Grapevine, TX 76051 (SAN 663-4796) Tel 817-481-7659.

Mundo Trade International Inc., *(Mundo Trade Intl; 0-931919),* 720 N. Barbara Ave., Solana Beach, CA 92075 (SAN 686-0052) Tel 619-755-1132.

Mundus Artium Pr., *(Mundus Artium; 0-939378),* P.O. Box 830688, Richardson, TX 75083-0688 (SAN 206-6866) Tel 214-690-2092.

Munger Oil Information Service, *(Munger Oil),* 9800 S. Sepulveda Blvd., Suite 723, Los Angeles, CA 90045 (SAN 205-7867) Tel 213-776-3990.

Municipal Analysis Services, Inc., *(Municipal Analysis; 1-55507),* P.O. Box 13453, Austin, TX 78711 (SAN 694-2148) Tel 512-327-3328.

Municipal Art Society of New York, The, *(Municipal Art Soc; 0-9606892),* 457 Madison Ave., New York, NY 10022 (SAN 217-4065) Tel 212-935-3960.

Municipal Finance Officers Assn. of the U. S. & Canada, *(Municipal; 0-89125),* 180 N. Michigan Ave., Suite 800, Chicago, IL 60601 (SAN 202-2540) Tel 312-977-9700.

Municipal Research & Services Ctr. of Washington, *(Muni Res WA),* 4719 Brooklyn Ave. NE, Seattle, WA 98105 (SAN 226-630X).

Munro, J Alex, *(J Alex Munro; 0-9601670),* 304 Saxon Dr., Springfield, IL 62704 (SAN 212-1174) Tel 217-787-6621.

Munro, John A., Assocs., Inc., *(Munro Assocs; 0-911553),* 16 E. 41st St., New York, NY 10017 (SAN 272-555X) Tel 212-689-8787.

Muns, J. B., Bks., *(J B Muns),* 1162 Shattuck Ave., Berkeley, CA 94707 (SAN 213-8786) Tel 415-525-2420.

Munson Books, *(Munson Bks),* 3436 Willow Dr., Mattoon, IL 61938 (SAN 209-1593) Tel 217-234-8465.

†Munson-Williams-Proctor Institute, *(Munson Williams; 0-915895),* 310 Genesee St., Utica, NY 13502 (SAN 272-5568) Tel 315-797-0000; *CIP.*

Muntu Bks., *(Muntu Bks; 0-9614140),* 2439 Jefferson Ave., Apt. B, Berkeley, CA 94703 (SAN 686-2225) Tel 415-548-6476; P.O. Box 3952, Berkeley, CA 94703 (SAN 649-4553) Tel 415-548-6476; Dist. by: Bookpeople, 2929 Fifth St., Berkeley, CA 94710 (SAN 168-9517) Tel 415-549-3030; Toll free: 800-227-1516.

Murach, Mike, & Assocs., Inc., *(M Murach & Assoc; 0-911625),* 4697 W. Jacquelyn, Fresno, CA 93711 (SAN 264-2255) Tel 209-275-3335; Toll free: 800-221-5528; Toll free: 800-221-5527 (In California).

Murat, Felix, Co., *(F Murat; 0-9600356),* 2132 NW 11th Ave., Miami, FL 33127 (SAN 205-5724).

Muratore Agency, Inc., *(Muratore),* 766 W. Shore Rd., P.O. Box 486, Warwick, RI 02889 (SAN 205-6356) Tel 401-737-6460.

Murdock, Maureen, *(M Murdock; 0-9616379),* 121 Wavecrest Ave., Venice, CA 90291 (SAN 658-943X) Tel 213-392-3111; Dist. by: Greater Spiral, The, P.O. Box 12515, Portland, OR 12515 (SAN 200-6383).

Murdock, Mike, Evangelistic Assn., *(Mike Murdock; 0-937427),* P.O. Box 47684, Dallas, TX 75247 (SAN 658-9634) Tel 214-438-1600; 1100 E. Airport Freeway, No. 132, Irving, TX 75062 (SAN 658-9642).

Murphy, Eileen M., Div. of Eileen's Beautique, *(E M Murphy; 0-9609792),* 16901 S. Jonesville Rd., Columbus, IN 47201 (SAN 269-8684) Tel 812-522-4079.

Murphy, John M., *(J M Murphy; 0-9616425),* 1135 La Jolla Rancho Rd., La Jolla, CA 92037 (SAN 658-9405) Tel 619-459-1056.

Murphy & Broad Publishing Co., *(Murphy & Broad; 0-940792),* 425 30th St., Suite 8, P.O. Box 3208, Newport Beach, CA 92663 (SAN 219-6085) Tel 714-673-3348.

Murphy Publishing Co., *(Murphy Pub Co),* P.O. Box 64, Timonium, MD 21093 (SAN 205-7840) Tel 301-377-5083.

Murray & Garig Tool Works, *(Murray & Garig; 0-9611896),* 220 E. Texas Ave., Baytown, TX 77520 (SAN 285-3477) Tel 713-427-5923.

Murrayhollow Pubs., *(Murrayhollow; 0-9610242),* Murrayhollow Rd., Shushan, NY 12873 (SAN 264-2263) Tel 518-854-3305.

Murton Pr., The, *(Murton Pr; 0-9608042),* 26 Anderson Rd., Greenwich, CT 06830 (SAN 240-0960) Tel 203-869-4434.

Murvin, H. L., Publisher, *(H L Murvin; 0-9608498),* 500 Vernon St., Oakland, CA 94610 (SAN 240-7264) Tel 415-658-7517.

Muse-Ed Co., *(Muse-Ed Comp; 0-9604434),* 14141 Margate St., Van Nuys, CA 91401 (SAN 283-3514) Tel 818-501-3854.

Muse Federation Ink, *(Mus Fed Ink; 0-9614084),* P.O. Box 642 St. Albans Sta., Jamaica, NY 11412 (SAN 686-0044) Tel 718-723-9880.

Museum Bks., Inc., *(Museum Bks; 0-87544),* 6 W. 37th St., New York, NY 10018 (SAN 204-0131) Tel 212-563-2770.

Museum Computer Network, Inc., *(Museum Comp Network),* 2018 Empire State Plaza Sta., Albany, NY 12220 (SAN 223-8012) Tel 518-473-1746.

Museum Graphics, *(Mus Graphics; 0-913832),* P.O. Box 2368, Menlo Park, CA 94025 (SAN 201-8454) Tel 415-368-5531; Orders to: Little, Brown & Co., 200 West St., Waltham, MA 02154 (SAN 201-8462).

Museum of African Art, Smithsonian Institution, *(Mus African Art),* 316-332 A St., NE, Washington, DC 20002 (SAN 213-1250) Tel 202-287-3490.

Museum of American Textile History, *(Museum America; 0-937474),* 800 Massachusetts Ave., North Andover, MA 01845 (SAN 205-8537) Tel 617-686-0191.

Museum of Art, Carnegie Institute, *(Mus Art Carnegie; 0-88039),* 4400 Forbes Ave., Pittsburgh, PA 15213 (SAN 239-1171) Tel 412-622-3228.

Museum of Art Rhode Island School of Design, *(Mus of Art RI; 0-940794),* 224 Benefit St., Providence, RI 02903 (SAN 204-0107) Tel 401-331-3511; Toll free: 800-343-9444; Dist. by: Milford House, Inc., 51 Washington St., Dover, MA 03820 (SAN 202-6368).

Museum of Arts & Sciences, *(Museum Art Sciences; 0-933053),* 1040 Museum Blvd., Daytona Beach, FL 32014 (SAN 279-7127) Tel 904-255-0285.

Museum of Arts & Sciences, Macon, Georgia, *(Museum Art GA; 0-916769),* 4182 Forsyth Rd., Macon, GA 31210 (SAN 653-8851) Tel 912-477-3232.

Museum of Fine Arts, Boston, *(Mus Fine Arts Boston; 0-87846),* 465 Huntington Ave., Boston, MA 02115 (SAN 202-2230) Tel 617-267-9300.

Museum of Holography, *(Mus Holography; 0-936210),* 11 Mercer St., New York, NY 10013 (SAN 222-6324) Tel 212-925-0581.

Museum of Modern Art, *(Museum Mod Art; 0-87070),* 11 W. 53rd St., New York, NY 10019 (SAN 202-5809) Tel 212-708-9733; Toll free: 800-343-9204.

†Museum of New Mexico Pr., *(Museum NM Pr; 0-89013),* P.O. Box 2087, Santa Fe, NM 87503 (SAN 202-2575) Tel 505-827-6455; *CIP.*

Museum of Northern Arizona, *(Mus Northern Ariz; 0-89734),* Rte. 4, Box 720, Flagstaff, AZ 86001 (SAN 204-0093) Tel 602-774-5211.

Museum of Science & History, The, *(Mus Sci & Hist; 0-9604642),* MacArthur Park, Little Rock, AR 72202 (SAN 215-7926).

Museum of the American China Trade, *(Mus Am China Trade; 0-937650),* Peabody Museum of Salem, East India Sq., Salem, MA 01970 (SAN 204-1030) Tel 617-745-1876.

Museum of the American Indian, *(Mus Am Ind; 0-934490),* Broadway at 155th St., New York, NY 10032 (SAN 204-0085) Tel 212-283-2420.

Museum of the City of Mobile, *(Museum Mobile; 0-914334),* 355 Government St., Mobile, AL 36602 (SAN 213-1218) Tel 205-438-7569.

Museum of the City of New York, *(Mus City NY; 0-910961),* Fifth Ave. at 103rd St., New York, NY 10029 (SAN 279-7461) Tel 212-534-1672.

Museum of the Great Plains, Pubns. Dept., *(Mus Great Plains; 0-911728),* 601 Ferris, P.O. Box 68, Lawton, OK 73502 (SAN 205-7794) Tel 405-353-5675.

Museum of the Rockies, *(Museum Rockies; 0-933819),* Montana State Univ., Bozeman, MT 59717-0001 (SAN 692-8870) Tel 406-994-2251.

Museum of Western Art, *(Mus W Art; 0-914965),* 1727 Tremont Pl., Denver, CO 80202 (SAN 289-3355) Tel 303-292-6776; Toll free: 800-525-5047.

Museum Systems, *(Mus Sys; 0-941094),* 760 N. La Cienaga Blvd., Los Angeles, CA 90069 (SAN 204-0123) Tel 213-657-5811.

Museums at Stony Brook, *(Mus Stony Brook; 0-943924),* 1208 Rte. 25A, Stony Brook, NY 11790 (SAN 279-7623) Tel 516-751-0066; Dist. by: Univ. of Wash. Pr., P.O. Box C50096, Seattle, WA 98145 (SAN 212-2502) Tel 206-543-8870.

Names

Museums Collaborative, Inc., *(Mus Collaborative),* 15 Grammercy Park S., New York, NY 10003 (SAN 219-7987) Tel 212-674-0030.

Museums Council of New Jersey, The, *(Museums Council; 0-9616363),* Old Barracks Museum, Barrack St., Trenton, NJ 08608 (SAN 658-9669) Tel 609-396-1776.

Mushroom Cave, Inc., The, *(Mushroom Cave; 0-9601516),* P.O. Box 894, Battle Creek, MI 49016 (SAN 211-6723) Tel 616-962-3497.

Mushroom Technology Corp., *(Mushroom Tech),* P.O. Box 2612, Naperville, IL 60565 (SAN 670-705X) Tel 312-961-3286.

Mushrooms, Etc., *(Mushrooms Etc; 0-9606236),* 2610 Vivian St., Lakewood, CO 80215 (SAN 220-343X) Tel 303-233-6238.

Music Education Pubns., *(Music Educ Pubns; 0-943988),* P.O. Box 3402, Fullerton, CA 92634 (SAN 241-5674) Tel 714-525-1397.

Music Educators National Conference, *(Music Ed Natl; 0-940796),* 1902 Association Dr., Reston, VA 22090 (SAN 676-8733) Tel 703-860-4000.

Music for Children Pr., *(Music Child Pr; 0-9616737),* 96 County St., Norwalk, CT 06851 (SAN 661-4329) Tel 203-866-3298.

Music In Action, *(Music In Action; 0-939139),* P.O. Box 204, East Stroudsburg, PA 18301 (SAN 662-4944); Meadow Lake Rd., Sciota, PA 18354 (SAN 662-4952) Tel 717-992-7953.

†**Music Library Assn.,** *(Music Library Assn),* P.O. Box 487, Canton, MA 02021 (SAN 233-4909) Tel 617-828-8450; *CIP.*

Music Pr., *(Music Pr; 0-918318),* 155 W. 68th St., New York, NY 10023 (SAN 209-0899) Tel 212-877-3175.

Music Sales Corp., *(Music Sales; 0-8256),* 24 E. 22nd St., New York, NY 10010 (SAN 282-0277) Tel 212-254-2100; Toll free: 800-431-7187; Orders to: Music Sales Distribution Ctr., 5 Bellvale Rd., P.O. Box 572, Chester, NY 10918 (SAN 662-0876) Tel 914-469-2271. *Imprints:* Acorn Music Press (Acorn); Amsco Music (Amsco Music); Hidden House (Hidden Hse); Oak Pubns. (Oak).

Music Study Services, *(Music Study; 0-936245),* 259 S. Madison Ave., Louisville, CO 80027 (SAN 696-852X) Tel 303-666-7836; Dist. by: Publishers Group West, 5855 Beaudry St., Emeryville, CA 94608 (SAN 202-8522) Tel 415-658-3453; Toll free: 800-982-8319.

Music Teachers National Association, *(Music Tchrs),* 2113 Carew Tower, Cincinnati, OH 45202 (SAN 225-8528) Tel 513-421-1420.

Music Treasure Pubns., *(Music Treasure; 0-912028),* 620 Fort Washington Ave., 1-F, New York, NY 10040 (SAN 204-0158).

Music Works, *(Music Works; 0-9617272),* 1250 Ollie St., Stephanville, TX 76401 (SAN 663-4877) Tel 512-454-0147.

Musica para Ninos *See* Hansen, Charles, Educational Music & Bks., Inc.

†**Musica Publishing Co.,** *(Musica; 0-9600964),* Box 1266, Edison, NJ 08818 (SAN 208-9696); *CIP.*

Musical Alternatives, *(Musical Alternatives; 0-9616599),* 11 Spring St., Oneonta, NY 13820 (SAN 659-5146) Tel 607-432-0570.

Musical Box Society International, The, *(Musical Box Soc; 0-915000),* 1300 E. Third St., St. Paul, MN 55106 (SAN 215-9732) Tel 612-774-2590.

Musical Scope Pubns., *(Musical Scope; 0-913000),* P.O. Box 125, Audubon Sta., New York, NY 10032 (SAN 202-8867).

Musicbiz Publishing Co., *(Musicbiz Pub; 0-937965),* P.O. Box 97008, Bellevue, WA 98009 (SAN 659-5170) Tel 206-453-0764; 10900 NE Eighth, Suite 169, Bellevue, WA 98004 (SAN 659-5189); Dist. by: Columbia Pictures Pubns., 15800 NW 48th Ave., Miami, FL 33014 (SAN 203-042X) Tel 305-620-1500.

†**Musicdata, Inc.,** *(Musicdata; 0-88478),* P.O. Box 48010, Philadelphia, PA 19144-8010 (SAN 203-1566) Tel 215-842-0555; *CIP.*

Musicgraphics, *(Musicgraphics; 0-941814),* 124 Atlantic Ave., Lynbrook, NY 11563 (SAN 239-264X) Tel 516-599-5990.

Muskingum County Footprints, *(Muskingum; 0-917033),* 2740 Adamsville Rd., Zanesville, OH 43701 (SAN 655-2536) Tel 614-453-8231.

Muso Pr., *(Muso Pr; 0-9614614),* 180 4th Ave., Apt. 12, San Francisco, CA 94118 (SAN 691-7852) Tel 415-221-5212; Orders to: P.O. Box 590232, San Francisco, CA 94159-0232 (SAN 663-3129) Tel 415-221-5212.

Mustang Publishing, *(Mustang Pub; 0-914457),* P.O. Box 9327, New Haven, CT 06533 (SAN 289-6702) Tel 203-624-5485; Dist. by: Kampmann & Co., Inc., 9 E. 40th St., New York, NY 10016 (SAN 202-5191) Tel 212-685-2928; Toll free: 800-526-7626.

Mustardseed Press, Subs. of Interuniverse, *(Mustardseed; 0-917920),* 707 N. Carolina Ave., Cocoa, FL 32922 (SAN 209-9659) Tel 305-632-2769.

Muste, A. J., Memorial Institute, *(Muste; 0-9608096),* 339 Lafayette St., New York, NY 10012 (SAN 240-2599) Tel 212-533-4335.

Mutual Pr., *(Mutual Pr IL; 0-9605628),* 664 N. Michigan, Suite 1010, Chicago, IL 60611 (SAN 216-2717) Tel 312-478-4030.

Mutual Publishing of Honolulu, *(Mutual Pub HI; 0-935180),* 2055 N. King St., Honolulu, HI 96819 (SAN 222-6359).

Mutualist Press, The, *(Mutualist Pr),* GPO Box 2009, Brooklyn, NY 11202 (SAN 213-1226).

Mutzal Me'esh Institute, *(Mutzal Me'esh Inst; 0-914787),* 2311 Ave J., Brooklyn, NY 11210 (SAN 683-4248).

MVR Books, *(MVR Bks),* 3020 E Ave., Berwyn, IL 60402 (SAN 210-4709) Tel 312-749-7697.

Myco Publishing House, *(Myco Pub Hse; 0-936634),* P.O. Box 1237, Arcadia, CA 91006 (SAN 214-2538) Tel 714-661-4957.

Mycological Society of San Francisco, Inc., *(Mycological; 0-918942),* Box 11321, San Francisco, CA 94101 (SAN 210-3621) Tel 415-839-4263.

Mycotaxon, Ltd., *(Mycotaxon Ltd; 0-930845),* P.O. Box 264, Ithaca, NY 14851 (SAN 677-6051) Tel 607-273-4357.

Mycroft & Moran *See* Arkham Hse. Pubs.

Myers, Albert E., *(A E Myers; 0-9602156),* 5341 Windsor Rd., Harrisburg, PA 17112 (SAN 213-1234).

Myers, S. D., Inc., *(Myers Inc; 0-939320),* P.O. Box 4724, Akron, OH 44310 (SAN 216-2725); Toll free: 800-321-9580.

Mykro Pub, Subs. of Santa Cruz EDP Mgmt., *(Mykro; 0-931281),* 2506 Charlene Ln., Santa Cruz, CA 95062 (SAN 682-0042) Tel 408-475-5346; P.O. Box 2383, Los Gatos, CA 95031-2383 (SAN 692-6355).

Myleen Press, *(Myleen Pr),* 614 Lyndhurst Ave., Roseville, CA 95678 (SAN 213-9405).

Myles, Ralph, Pub., Inc., *(R Myles; 0-87926),* P.O. Box 1533, Colorado Springs, CO 80901 (SAN 204-6601).

Mynabird Publishing, *(Mynabird Pub; 0-917758),* 20 Shoshone Place, Portola Valley, CA 94025 (SAN 209-1550) Tel 415-851-8554.

Myriad Moods, *(Myriad; 0-911843),* 313 Joliet, San Antonio, TX 78209 (SAN 264-2271) Tel 512-824-9554.

†**Myriade Pr.,** *(Myriade; 0-918142),* 7 Stony Run, New Rochelle, NY 10804 (SAN 210-2439) Tel 914-235-8470; *CIP.*

Myrin Institute, Inc., *(Myrin Institute; 0-913098),* 136 E. 64th St., New York, NY 10021 (SAN 204-0182) Tel 212-758-6475.

Myrtle Bank Pr., *(Myrtle Bank; 0-9606978),* 408 N. Pearl St., Natchez, MS 39120 (SAN 238-8995).

Myrtle Tree Pubns., *(Myrtle Tree Pubns; 0-9614422),* 7522 44th Pl., Seattle, WA 98136 (SAN 689-0245) Tel 206-938-1463.

Mysiewicz, Deborah, Pubs., Inc., *(D Mysiewicz; 0-936451),* Box 1210, Port Angeles, WA 98362 (SAN 697-9165) Tel 206-928-3176.

Mysterious Pr., Subs. of Penzler Bks., *(Mysterious Pr; 0-89296),* 129 W. 56th St., New York, NY 10019 (SAN 208-2152) Tel 212-765-0901; Dist. by: Farrar, Straus & Giroux, 19 Union Sq. W., New York, NY 10003 (SAN 206-782X) Tel 212-741-6900. *Imprints:* Penzler Books (Penzler Bks).

Mystic Bay Books, *(Mystic Bay Bk; 0-9608974),* Box 525, Mystic, CT 06355 (SAN 689-0539).

Mystic Jhamom Pubs., *(Mystic Jhamom; 0-933961),* 1650 Rocky Pl., Arroyo Grande, CA 93420 (SAN 693-0689) Tel 805-922-8802; P.O. Box 904, Santa Maria, CA 93456 (SAN 694-972X).

Mystic Light Society, The, *(Mystic Soc; 0-910433),* P.O. Box 53134, Philadelphia, PA 19105 (SAN 260-1494) Tel 215-925-7527.

Mystic Seaport Museum, Inc., *(Mystic Seaport; 0-913372),* Green Manville, Mystic, CT 06355 (SAN 213-7550) Tel 203-572-0711.

NAMAC, *(NAMAC; 0-936916),* P.O. Box 963, Ingleside, TX 78362 (SAN 216-0498) Tel 512-776-2305; Dist. by: Astrology & Spiritual Ctr., 4535 Hohman Ave., Hammond, IN 46327 (SAN 159-0456) Tel 219-931-8050; Dist. by: Devorss & Co., Box 550, 1046 Princeton Dr., Marina del Rey, CA 90291 (SAN 168-9886); Dist. by: Starlite, Box 20729, Reno, NV 89515 (SAN 169-0299); Dist. by: Parapsychology Education Ctr., P.O. Box 6240, Little Rock, AR 72216 (SAN 200-4186); Dist. by: Waldenbook Co., 201 High Ridge Rd., Stamford, CT 06905 (SAN 203-1752); Dist. by: The Distributors, 702 S. Michigan, South Bend, IN 46618 (SAN 212-0364) Tel 219-232-8500; Dist. by: Macoy Publishing, Box 9759, Richmond, VA 23228 (SAN 200-4194) Tel 804-262-6551.

N. A. Orchestra, *(N A Orchestra; 0-9613672),* John F. Kennedy Center for the Performing Arts, Washington, DC 20566 (SAN 682-0530) Tel 202-785-8100.

NASSTRAC, *(NASSTRAC; 0-9616271),* 1750 Pennsylvania Ave. NW, Suite 1105, Washington, DC 20006 (SAN 272-5967) Tel 202-393-5505.

NAVA, The International Communications Industries Assn., *(NAVA Intl Comm),* 3150 Spring St., Fairfax, VA 22031-2399 (SAN 225-7807) Tel 703-273-7200.

N & D Publishing Co., *(N & D Pub Co; 0-9616044),* 806 Ewing Blvd., Murfreesboro, TN 37130 (SAN 696-0596) Tel 615-898-2386.

N&N Publishing Co., Inc., *(N & N Pub Co; 0-9606036),* 10 Lydia Dr., Wappinger, NY 12590 (SAN 216-4221) Tel 914-297-6389; Orders to: 44 Wisner Ave., Middletown, NY 10940 (SAN 662-0884) Tel 914-342-1677.

N & N Resources, *(N & N Resources),* P.O. Box 332, Troy, ID 83871 (SAN 209-0376) Tel 208-835-2012.

NBM, *(NBM; 0-918348),* 156 E. 39th St., New York, NY 10016 (SAN 210-0835) Tel 212-661-8129; Dist. by: Publishers Group West, 5855 Beaudry St., Emeryville, CA 94608 (SAN 202-8522) Tel 415-658-3453; Toll free: 800-982-8319.

NB Marketing, *(NB Mktg; 0-939417),* 9420 Reseda Blvd., Suite 442, Northridge, CA 91324 (SAN 663-1614) Tel 818-993-9161.

NCEMMH, *(NCEMMH; 0-936882),* 356 Arps Hall, 1945 N. High St., Columbus, OH 43210 (SAN 262-1118) Tel 614-422-8787.

†**NCHE Pr.,** Div. of National Ctr. for Health Education, *(NCHE Press; 0-914617),* 30 E. 29th St., New York, NY 10016 (SAN 289-3959) Tel 212-689-1866; *CIP.*

NCJW, Inc., *(NCJW; 0-941840),* 15 E. 26th St., New York, NY 10010 (SAN 239-2658) Tel 212-532-1740.

NEC Home Electronics USA, Inc., Subs. of NEC America, Inc., *(NEC Home Elect; 0-925739),* 1255 Michael Dr., Wood Dale, IL 60191-1094 (SAN 277-1861) Tel 312-860-9500; Toll free: 800-632-7638.

NET Pr., *(Net Pr; 0-937462),* 5001 Ave. N, Lubbock, TX 79412 (SAN 291-8005) Tel 806-762-8094; Toll free: 800-NEA-GROW; Toll free: 800-TXA-GROW (in TX).

NHI Pr., *(NHI Press; 0-9617115),* P.O. Box 825, Concord, NH 03301 (SAN 662-6874); 9 Tahanto St., Concord, NH 03301 (SAN 662-6882) Tel 603-224-3420.

NIA Techniques, Inc., *(NIA Techniques; 0-939529),* 491 Lovell Ave., Mill Valley, CA 94941 (SAN 663-379X) Tel 415-381-8506.

NILS Publishing Co., Subs. of Capital Cities/ABC, *(NILS Pub; 0-89246),* 21625 Prairie St., Chatsworth, CA 91311 (SAN 695-6246) Tel 818-998-8830; Toll free: 800-423-5910.

N. J. International, Inc., *(NJ Intl Inc; 0-934088),* 77 W. Nicholai St., Hicksville, NY 11801 (SAN 220-9276) Tel 516-433-8720.

N. L. Endeavors, *(N L Endeavors; 0-936803),* 4111 Lincoln Blvd., Suite 603, Los Angeles, CA 90045 (SAN 699-9905).

NMSEA, *(NMSEA; 0-942372),* P.O. Box 2004, Santa Fe, NM 87504 (SAN 240-0502).

NOK Pubs., Intl., *(NOK Pubs; 0-88357),* 150 Fifth Ave., New York, NY 10011 (SAN 205-7522) Tel 212-675-5785.

NPA, *(NPA; 0-88806),* 1606 New Hampshire Ave. NW, Washington, DC 20009 (SAN 239-538X).

NPC Publishing Co., *(NPC Pub Co; 0-932634),* 17237 Hiawatha St., Granada Hills, CA 91344 (SAN 212-7814) Tel 213-363-8458.

N.P.D. Corp., *(NPD Corp; 0-937230),* 939 Driver Cir., El Paso, TX 79903 (SAN 282-0676); 7701 N. Lamar Blvd., Austin, TX 78752 (SAN 282-0684) Tel 915-565-3001.

NPP Books, *(NPP Bks; 0-916182),* P.O. Box 1491, Ann Arbor, MI 48106-1491 (SAN 208-1067) Tel 313-971-7363.

N W R Pubns., *(NWR Pubns; 0-916972),* 104-07 102nd St., Ozone Park, NY 11417 (SAN 208-4686).

Na Pali Publishing Co., *(Na Pali Pub; 0-917132),* P.O. Box 88082, Honolulu, HI 96830-0810 (SAN 208-3876).

Nadeau Publishing Co., *(Nadeau Pub; 0-9613891),* 10607 Ainsworth Ave. S., Tacoma, WA 98444 (SAN 682-3025) Tel 206-535-2259.

Nader, Ralph, *(R Nader; 0-936486),* P.O. Box 19367, Washington, DC 20036 (SAN 282-0285) Tel 202-387-8030; Dist. by: Learning Research Project, P.O. Box 19312, Washington, DC 20036 (SAN 282-5961).

Naftaolh Pubns., *(Naftaolh Pubns; 0-9616130),* P.O. Box 2503, Columbus, MS 39704 (SAN 699-7368) Tel 601-325-4879; 323 Rebecca Ln., Columbus, MS 39704 (SAN 699-7376).

Nags Head Art, *(Nags Head Art; 0-9616344),* P.O. Box 88, Nags Head, NC 27959 (SAN 658-8093); 7734 Virginia Dare Trail, Nags Head, NC 27959 (SAN 658-8107) Tel 919-441-7480.

Nahass, Rick, Publishing, *(R Nahass; 0-9608422),* P.O. Box 27630, San Francisco, CA 94127 (SAN 240-7299) Tel 415-334-7191.

Naiad Pr., *(Naiad Pr; 0-930044),* P.O. Box 10543, Tallahassee, FL 32302 (SAN 206-801X) Tel 904-539-9322. *Imprints:* Volute Books (Volute Bks).

Naire, Bill O., Enterprises, *(Naire Ent; 0-9615799),* 1041 Adason Dr., San Leandro, CA 94578 (SAN 696-5989) Tel 415-895-1773.

Nakii, D., Enterprises, *(Nakii Ent; 0-9615195),* P.O. Box 7639, Albuquerque, NM 87194 (SAN 694-2946) Tel 505-344-3843; Dist. by: Publishers Marketing Group, 1104 Summit Ave., Plainview, TX 75074 (SAN 262-0995) Tel 214-423-0312.

Nalini International Pubns., *(Nalini Intl Pubs; 0-9614416),* P.O. Box 40, Livingston, NJ 07039 (SAN 688-9050) Tel 201-325-6444.

Namaste Pr., *(Namaste Pr; 0-916727),* P.O. Box 4435, Albuquerque, NM 87196 (SAN 653-886X) Tel 505-268-4231.

Namaste Pubns., *(Namaste Pubns; 0-938147),* P.O. Box 262, Marshfield, MO 65706 (SAN 661-3438); 324 Banning, Marshfield, MO 65706 (SAN 661-3446) Tel 417-468-5053.

Namuk International, Inc., *(Namuk Intl Inc; 0-933057),* P.O. Box 4543, Silver Spring, MD 20904 (SAN 689-7738); 1011 Brantford Ave., Silver Spring, MD 20904 Tel 301-622-4744.

Nance, Frank, Co., *(Frank Nance Co; 0-9615739),* 2700 Pierce Ave., El Paso, TX 79930 (SAN 695-8567) Tel 915-565-6450.

Nancy's Notions, Ltd., *(Nancys Notions; 0-931071),* 1010 DeClark, P.O. Box 683, Beaver Dam, WI 53916 (SAN 678-9323) Tel 414-885-9175.

Nanny Goat Productions, *(Nanny Goat; 0-918440),* P. O. Box 845, Laguna Beach, CA 92652 (SAN 209-9675) Tel 714-494-7930.

Nantucket Historical Assn., *(Nantucket Hist Assn; 0-9607340),* Box 1016, Nantucket, MA 02554 (SAN 239-2666) Tel 617-228-1894.

Nantucket Nautical Pubs., *(Nantucket Nautical; 0-9604436),* 5 New Mill St., Nantucket, MA 02554 (SAN 215-8914).

Napa Landmarks, *(Napa Landmarks; 0-935360),* P.O. Box 702, Napa, CA 94558 (SAN 213-5418) Tel 707-255-1836.

Napoleonic Heritage Bks., Div. of Robert Sherower Group, Ltd., *(Napoleonic Heritage; 0-937811),* 521 Fifth Ave., 17th Flr., New York, NY 10175 (SAN 659-381X) Tel 212-355-5633.

Napsac Reproductions, *(Napsac Reprods; 0-934426),* Rte. 1 Box 646, Marble Hill, MO 63764 (SAN 222-4607) Tel 314-238-2010.

Narcotics Education, Inc., *(Narc Ed),* 6830 Laurel St., NW, Washington, DC 20012 (SAN 205-7727) Tel 202-722-6740.

†**Naris Pubns.,** *(Naris Pubns; 0-916263),* P.O. Box 30805, Santa Barbara, CA 93130 (SAN 294-9741); Dist. by: John Daniel Publisher, P.O. Box 21922, Santa Barbara, CA 93121 (SAN 215-1995) Tel 805-962-1780; CIP.

Nash, James H., *(J H Nash; 0-9612498),* 16740 Obispo Lane, San Diego, CA 92128 (SAN 655-7538).

Nash Group, The, *(Nash Group; 0-934569),* P.O. Box 16200-361, Mesa, AZ 85201 (SAN 693-8566) Tel 602-838-6208.

Nass, Sylvan & Ulla, *(Nass; 0-9606468),* 220 Sunnybrook Rd., Flourtown, PA 19031 (SAN 215-9740) Tel 215-836-4884.

Nassau County Assn. of Mathematics Supervisors, *(Nassau Co Assn Mathematics Supv; 0-9612940),* Forest Rd. School, Valley Stream, NY 11582 (SAN 292-5850) Tel 516-791-2220.

Nassau Pr., *(Nassau Pr; 0-911491),* 228 Alexander St., Princeton, NJ 08540 (SAN 272-5959) Tel 609-921-1058; Toll free: 800-526-0275.

Nataraj Bks., *(Nataraj Bks),* P.O. Box 5076, Springfield, VA 22150 (SAN 696-6527) Tel 703-455-4996.

Natchez Trace Genealogical Society, *(Natchez Trace; 0-933253),* P.O. Box 420, Florence, AL 35631-0420 (SAN 692-3933) Tel 205-764-4749.

Nathan, Isaac, Institute, *(N Isaac Inst; 0-914615),* 22711 Cass Ave., Woodland Hills, CA 91364 (SAN 289-3924) Tel 818-346-9631.

Nation, Edna, *(Edna Nation; 0-9614669),* 61 Mediation Way, Florissant, MO 63031 (SAN 692-4700) Tel 314-921-0349.

National Academy of Gallaudet College, The, *(Natl Acad Gallaudet Coll; 0-934336),* 800 Florida Ave. NE, Washington, DC 20002 (SAN 213-3423) Tel 202-651-5595.

National Academy of Songwriters, *(Natl Academy Songwriters; 0-916641),* P.O. Box 421411, San Francisco, CA 94142 (SAN 200-4526).

†**National Academy Pr.,** Div. of National Academy of Sciences, *(Natl Acad Pr; 0-309),* 2101 Constitution Ave., NW, Washington, DC 20418 (SAN 202-8891) Tel 202-334-3313; CIP.

National Action Research Military Industrial Complex, *(Natl Act Res MIC),* 1501 Cherry St., Philadelphia, PA 19102 (SAN 225-6959) Tel 215-241-7175.

National Addiction Research Foundation, *(National Addiction; 0-937119),* 3002 E. Sylvia, Tucson, AZ 85716 (SAN 658-5965) Tel 602-881-6101.

National Aeronautic Assn., *(Natl Aero),* 1400 Eye St., NW, Suite 550, Washington, DC 20005 (SAN 210-6167) Tel 202-898-1313.

National Alliance, *(Natl Alliance; 0-937944),* Box 3535, Washington, DC 20007 (SAN 220-0759) Tel 703-979-1886.

National Alumni Association of the College of Education & Home Economics, *(Natl Alumni Assn Ed Home Econ; 0-9602480),* Alumni Publications (Loc. No. 24), Univ. of Cincinnati, Cincinnati, OH 45221 (SAN 212-7709) Tel 513-475-4641.

National Archery Assn. of the U. S., *(Natl Archery),* 1750 E. Boulder St., Colorado Springs, CO 80909 (SAN 224-537X) Tel 303-578-4576.

†**National Archives & Records Administration,** *(Natl Archives & Records; 0-911333),* Pubns. Div., Seventh St. & Pennsylvania Ave., Washington, DC 20408 (SAN 210-363X) Tel 202-523-5611. Official records of the federal government on microfilm; facsimiles & reproductions of important historical documents, census records from 1790 to 1910 on microfilm. Catalog of National Archives Microfilm Publications, Black Studies, Indian Studies, immigration, and genealogical records. Catalogs of Federal Population Census, 1790 to 1910. Books and guides on the preservation and use of federal records; CIP.

National Art Education Assn., *(Natl Art Ed; 0-937652),* 1916 Association Dr., Reston, VA 22091 (SAN 203-7084) Tel 703-860-8000.

National Art Services, Inc. See World-Wide Pubns.

National Asphalt Pavement Assn., *(Natl Asphalt Pavement; 0-914313),* 6811 Kenilworth Ave., Riverdale, MD 20840 (SAN 225-4417).

National Assessment of Educational Progress, Div. of Educational Testing Service, *(Natl Assessment; 0-89398),* CN 6710, P.O. Box 2923, Princeton, NJ 08541-6710 (SAN 272-653X); Toll free: 800-223-0267.

National Assn. for Retarded Citizens See Association for Retarded Citizens of the U. S.

National Assn. for Armenian Studies & Research, *(Natl Assn Arm; 0-935411),* 175 Mt. Auburn St., Cambridge, MA 02138 (SAN 272-6645) Tel 617-876-7630.

National Association for Female Executives, *(Natl Assn Female Execs),* 160 E. 56th St., New York, NY 10022 (SAN 224-6724).

National Assn. for Foreign Student Affairs, *(NAFSA Washington; 0-912207),* 1860 19th St., NW, Washington, DC 20009 (SAN 272-6742) Tel 202-462-4811.

National Assn. for Gifted Children, *(Nat Assn Gift Child; 0-912723),* 4175 Lovell Rd., Suite 140, Circle Pines, MN 55014 (SAN 225-8005) Tel 612-784-3475.

National Association for Hispanic Elderly See Asociacion nacional pro personas mayores

National Assn. for Irish Freedom, *(Natl Assn Irish Free),* 799 Broadway, Rm. 422, New York, NY 10003 (SAN 224-1951) Tel 212-254-1757.

National Association for Law Placement, *(NALP),* Tulane Law Schl., 6325 Freret St., New Orleans, LA 70118 (SAN 260-3330) Tel 504-865-5945.

National Assn. for Public Continuing & Adult Education, *(NAPCAE; 0-912782),* 1201 16th St., NW, Washington, DC 20036 (SAN 207-0286) Tel 202-833-5486.

National Assn. for State Educational, Media Professionals (NASTEMP), Div. of Publications, *(Natl Assn Media; 0-9614484),* 605 S. O St., Indianola, IA 50125 (SAN 677-8976) Tel 515-961-3012.

National Assn. for Stock Car Auto Racing, *(Nat Assn Stock),* 1801 Speedway Blvd., Daytona Beach, FL 32015 (SAN 272-6882) Tel 904-253-0611; P.O. Box K, Daytona Beach, FL 32015 (SAN 669-1862).

National Assn. for the Advancement of Humane Education, Div. of Humane Society of the U. S., *(NAAHE; 0-941246),* P.O. Box 362, East Haddam, CT 06423 (SAN 285-0680) Tel 203-488-3923.

National Assn. for the Education of Young Children, *(Natl Assn Child Ed; 0-912674; 0-935989),* 1834 Connecticut Ave., NW, Washington, DC 20009-5786 (SAN 202-8905) Tel 202-232-8777; Toll free: 800-424-2460.

National Assn. for the Preservation & Perpetuation of Storytelling, *(Natl Assn Preserv & Perpet Storytelling),* P.O. Box 309, Slemons Hse., Fox St., Jonesboro, TN 37659 (SAN 224-1978) Tel 615-753-2171.

National Assn. for Women Deans, Administrators & Counselors, *(Natl Assn Women; 0-943302),* 1325 18th St. NW, Suite 210, Washington, DC 20036 (SAN 202-1080) Tel 202-659-9330.

National Assn. of Accountants, *(Natl Assn Accts),* 10 Paragon Dr., P.O. Box 433, Montvale, NJ 07645-0433 (SAN 207-2637) Tel 201-573-6268.

Names

National Assn. of Advisors for the Health Professions, Inc., *(NAAHP Inc; 0-911899)*, P.O. Box 5017 Sta. A, Champaign, IL 61820-9017 (SAN 264-679X) Tel 217-344-6013.

National Assn. of Attorneys General, *(Natl Attys General)*, Hall of States, 444 N. Capitol St., Washington, DC 20001 (SAN 225-090X) Tel 202-624-5450.

National Assn. of Baptist Professors of Religion, *(NABPR; 0-932180; 0-86554)*, Mercer Univ., Macon, GA 31207 (SAN 211-2175) Tel 912-744-2880; Dist. by: Mercer University Press, Macon, GA 31207 (SAN 220-0716).

National Assn. of Biology Teachers, Inc., *(Natl Assn Bio Tchrs; 0-941212)*, 11250 Roger Bacon Dr., Reston, VA 22090 (SAN 217-4073) Tel 703-471-1134.

National Assn. of Bond Lawyers, *(Nat Assn Bond)*, Box 397, Hinsdale, IL 60521 (SAN 688-7457) Tel 312-920-0160.

National Assn. of Broadcasters, *(Natl Assn Broadcasters; 0-89324)*, 1771 N St. NW, Washington, DC 20036 (SAN 224-1986) Tel 202-293-3579.

†National Assn. of College & Univ. Business Officers, *(NACUBO; 0-915164)*, 1 Dupont Cir., Suite 500, Washington, DC 20036-1178 (SAN 207-1479) Tel 202-861-2534; *CIP.*

National Assn. of Community Health Ctrs., *(Natl Assn Comm Health Ctrs)*, 1625 I St. NW, Suite 420, Washington, DC 20006 (SAN 224-3253) Tel 202-833-9280.

National Assn. of Concessionaires, *(Nat Assoc Concession)*, 35 E. Wacker Dr., Chicago, IL 60601 (SAN 224-9766) Tel 312-236-3858.

†National Assn. of Conservation Districts, *(NACD; 0-9614178)*, 1025 Vermont Ave., NW, Suite 730, Washington, DC 20005 (SAN 272-7536); Orders to: P.O. Box 855, League City, TX 77573 (SAN 693-9678) Tel 713-332-3402; *CIP.*

National Assn. of Corrosion Engineers, *(Natl Corrosion Eng; 0-915567)*, P.O. Box 218340, Houston, TX 77218 (SAN 224-2001) Tel 713-492-0535.

National Assn. of Counties, *(Natl Assn Counties; 0-911754)*, 440 First St., NW, Washington, DC 20001 (SAN 205-7565) Tel 202-393-6226.

†National Assn. of Credit Management, *(NACM; 0-934914)*, 520 Eighth Ave., New York, NY 10018-6571 (SAN 205-7573) Tel 212-947-5070; *CIP.*

National Assn. of Educational Broadcasters, *(NAEB; 0-8105)*, 5807 Massachusetts Ave., NW, Bethesda, MD 20816 (SAN 220-0112) Tel 301-657-8420.

National Assn. of Electrical Distributors, *(Natl Assn Elect Dist)*, 600 Summer St., Stamford, CT 06901 (SAN 272-7889) Tel 203-327-1290.

National Assn. of Elementary Schl. Principals, *(NAES Alexandria; 0-939327)*, 1615 Duke St., Alexandria, VA 22314 (SAN 663-155X) Tel 703-684-3345.

National Assn. of Environmental Professionals, *(Natl Environment Pros)*, Box 9400, Washington, DC 20016 (SAN 232-7473) Tel 301-229-7171.

National Assn. of Exposition Managers, *(Nat Assn Expo Mgrs)*, 334 E. Garfield Rd., P.O. Box 377, Aurora, OH 44202 (SAN 272-801X).

†National Assn. of Home Builders, Div. of The National Assn. of Home Manufacturers, *(Nat Assn H Build; 0-86718)*, 15th & M Sts., NW, Washington, DC 20005 (SAN 207-7035); Toll free: 800-368-5242; *CIP.*

National Assn. of Housing & Redevelopment Officials, *(NAHRO)*, 2600 Virginia Ave., NW, Washington, DC 20037 (SAN 680-0610) Tel 202-333-2020.

†National Assn. of Independent Schls., *(NAIS; 0-934338)*, 18 Tremont St., Boston, MA 02108 (SAN 202-0920) Tel 617-723-6900; *CIP.*

National Assn. of Insurance Commissioners, *(Nat Assn Insu Comm; 0-89382)*, 1125 Grand Ave., Kansas City, MO 64106 (SAN 225-0780) Tel 816-842-3600; 67 Wall St., New York, NY 10005 (SAN 669-1927).

National Assn. of Intercollegiate Athletics, *(NAIA Pubns)*, 1221 Baltimore St., Kansas City, MO 64105 (SAN 201-9574) Tel 816-842-5050.

National Assn. of Legal Secretaries, *(Natl Assn Legal Secys)*, 3005 E. Skelly Dr., Suite 120, Tulsa, OK 74105 (SAN 225-0918) Tel 918-749-6423; Dist. by: West Publishing Co., P.O. Box 64526, St. Paul, MN 55164-0526 (SAN 202-9618).

National Assn. of Parents & Professionals for Safe Alternatives in Childbirth, International, *(NAPSAC; 0-917314; 0-934426)*, P.O. Box 646, Marble Hill, MO 63764 (SAN 208-7766) Tel 314-238-2010; Dist. by: Napsac Reproductions, Rte. 1, Box 646, Marble Hill, MO 63764 (SAN 222-4607).

National Assn. of Personnel Consultants, *(NAPC; 0-9611608)*, 1432 Duke St., Alexandria, VA 22314 (SAN 285-2926) Tel 703-684-0180.

National Assn. of Pool Owners, *(Natl Assn Pool Owners)*, 280 Hillside Ave., Needham, MA 02194 (SAN 224-5965).

National Association of Printers & Lithographers, *(NAPL)*, 780 Palisade Ave., Teaneck, NJ 07666 (SAN 224-8298) Tel 201-342-0700.

National Assn. of Printing Ink Manufacturers, *(NAPIM)*, 47 Halstead Ave., Harrison, NY 10528 (SAN 230-4376) Tel 914-835-5650.

National Assn. of Private Schls. for Exceptional Children, *(Natl Assoc Priv Sch)*, 2021 K St. NW, Suite 315, Washington, DC 20006 (SAN 223-8977) Tel 202-296-1800.

National Assn. of Professional Baseball Leagues, *(Natl Assn Pro)*, P.O. Box A, St. Petersburg, FL 33731 (SAN 272-913X) Tel 813-822-6937.

National Assn. of Professional Upholsterers, *(Nat Assn Pro Upholsterers)*, P.O. Box 2754, High Point, NC 27261 (SAN 699-7740).

National Assn. of Real Estate Appraisers, *(Natl Assn Real Estate)*, 8715 Via DeCommercio, Scottsdale, AZ 85258 (SAN 225-4395) Tel 602-948-8000.

National Assn. of Real Estate Investment Trusts, *(NAREIT)*, 1101 17th St., NW, Suite 700, Washington, DC 20036 (SAN 231-3707) Tel 202-785-8717.

National Assn. of Realtors, *(Natl Assoc Realtors; 0-938785)*, 430 N. Michigan Ave., Chicago, IL 60611 (SAN 224-9294) Tel 312-329-8292.

National Association of Recycling Industries, *(Natl Recycling; 0-941096)*, 330 Madison Ave., New York, NY 10017 (SAN 205-7603) Tel 212-867-7330.

National Assn. of Regulatory Utility Commissioners, *(NARUC)*, 1102 ICC Bldg., P.O. Box 684, Washington, DC 20044 (SAN 260-339X) Tel 202-628-7324.

National Assn. of Schl. Psychologists, *(Nat Assn Sch Psych)*, 10 Overland Dr., Stratford, CT 06497 (SAN 223-9000) Tel 203-337-4249.

National Association of School Psychologists, *(Natl Assn Psych; 0-932955)*, 14605 Granger Rd, Maple Hts, OH 44137 (SAN 688-9077) Tel 419-734-1748.

National Assn. of Secondary School Principals, *(Natl Assn Principals; 0-88210)*, 1904 Association Dr., Reston, VA 22091 (SAN 676-8776) Tel 703-860-0200.

†National Assn. of Social Workers, *(Natl Assn Soc Wkrs; 0-87101)*, 7981 Eastern Ave., Silver Spring, MD (SAN 202-893X); Toll free: 800-638-8799; *CIP.*

National Assn. of State Boards of Education, *(NASBE)*, 701 N. Fairfax St., Suite 340, Alexandria, VA 22314 (SAN 236-1205) Tel 703-684-4000.

National Assn. of Student Councils, Div. of Student Activities of the National Assn. of Secondary School Principals, *(Natl Assn Student; 0-88210)*, 1904 Association Dr., Reston, VA 22091 (SAN 260-3888) Tel 703-860-8550.

National Assn. of the Deaf, *(Natl Assn Deaf; 0-913072)*, 814 Thayer Ave., Silver Spring, MD 20910 (SAN 203-7092) Tel 301-587-1788.

National Assn. of Theatre Owners, *(Natl Assn Theatre Owners)*, 1560 Broadway, Suite 714, New York, NY 10036 (SAN 231-0546).

National Assn. of Trade & Technical Schls., *(Natl Assn Trade Tech Schl; 0-942426)*, 2251 Wisconsin Ave. NW, Suite 200, Washington, DC 20007 (SAN 238-406X) Tel 202-333-1021.

National Assn. of Underwater Instructors, *(NAUI; 0-916974)*, P.O. Box 14650, Montclair, CA 91763 (SAN 208-1024) Tel 714-824-5440.

National Assn. of Watch & Clock Collectors, *(Natl Assn Watch & Clock; 0-9614984)*, 514 Poplar St., Columbia, PA 17512 (SAN 223-9035) Tel 717-684-5544.

National Assn. of Wholesale Distributors, *(Natl Assn Wholesale Dists)*, 1725 K St., NW, Washington, DC 20006 (SAN 224-9820) Tel 202-872-0885.

National Attorney's Pubns., Inc., *(Natl Attorneys Pubns; 0-936855)*, 1401 Main St., Port Jefferson, NY 11777 (SAN 658-3660) Tel 516-928-0295; P.O. Box 150, East Setauket, NY 11733 (SAN 658-3679).

†National Audubon Society, *(Natl Audubon; 0-930698)*, 950 Third Ave., New York, NY 10022 (SAN 282-0307) Tel 212-546-9122; *CIP.*

National Bed & Breakfast Assn., *(Natl Bed; 0-9611298)*, P.O. Box 23, Norwalk, CT 06852 (SAN 282-9355); 148 E. Rocks Rd., Norwalk, CT 06851 (SAN 669-3180) Tel 203-847-6196; 147 Mc Kinley Ave., Bridgeport, CT 06606 (SAN 669-3199).

National Behavior Systems, *(Natl Behavior; 0-937654)*, 805 N. Howard St., No. 232, Alexandria, VA 22304 (SAN 282-0323) Tel 703-370-2568; Dist. by: Baker & Taylor, Eastern Div., 50 Kirby Ave., Somerville, NJ 08876 (SAN 169-4901).

National Bellamy Award, *(Natl Bellamy)*, Three Oaks Court, Albany, NY 12203 (SAN 208-337X); Orders to: Frank P. Di Berardino, Three Oaks Court, Albany, NY 12203 (SAN 669-2001) Tel 518-456-0964.

National Bestseller Corp., *(Natl Bestseller; 0-931073)*, 400 Federation Pl., Elgin, IL 60120 (SAN 678-9331) Tel 312-695-1122.

National Biomedical Research Foundation, *(Natl Biomedical; 0-912466)*, Georgetown Univ. Medical Ctr, 3900 Reservoir Rd., NW, Washington, DC 20007 (SAN 203-7106) Tel 202-625-2121.

National Bk. Co., Div. of Educational Research Assocs., *(Natl Book; 0-89420)*, 333 SW Park Ave., Portland, OR 97205-3784 (SAN 212-4661) Tel 503-228-6345. *Imprints:* Halcyon House (Halcyon).

National Braille Pr., *(Natl Braille Pr; 0-939173)*, 88 St. Stephen St., Boston, MA 02115 (SAN 273-0952).

National Buffalo Assn., *(Natl Buffalo Assn; 0-9601792)*, 10 Main St., Ft. Pierre, SD 57532 (SAN 224-9863) Tel 605-223-2829; P.O. Box 565, Ft. Pierre, SD 57532 (SAN 699-5470) Tel 605-223-2829.

†National Bureau of Economic Research, Incorporated, *(Natl Bur Econ Res; 0-87014)*, 1050 Massachusetts Ave., Cambridge, MA 02138 (SAN 203-7114); Toll free: 800-621-2736; Dist. by: Ballinger Publishing Co., 54 Church St., Harvard Sq., Cambridge, MA 02138 (SAN 201-4084) Tel 617-492-0670; Dist. by: Columbia Univ. Pr., 136 S. Broadway, Irvington-on-Hudson, New York, NY 10533 (SAN 212-2472) Tel 914-591-9111; Dist. by: Harvard Univ. Pr., 79 Garden St., Cambridge, MA 02138 (SAN 281-7721) Tel 617-495-2600; Dist. by: The M.I.T. Pr., 28 Carleton St., Cambridge, MA 02142 (SAN 202-6414) Tel 617-253-2884; Dist. by: Princeton Univ. Pr., 41 William St., Princeton, NJ 08540 (SAN 202-0254) Tel 609-452-4913; Dist. by: Univ. of Chicago Pr., Order Dept., 11030 S. Langley Ave., Chicago, IL 60628 (SAN 202-5299) Tel 312-568-1550; *CIP.*

National Bus Trader, Inc., *(Natl Bus Trader; 0-933449)*, Rte. 3, Box 349B, Theater Rd., Delavan, WI 53115-9566 (SAN 691-7879) Tel 414-728-2691.

National Business & Education Collaborative, Inc., *(NBECI; 0-938697)*, 97 Hulst Rd., Amherst, MA 01002 (SAN 661-5333) Tel 413-253-5096; Rte. 1, Amherst, MA 01002 (SAN 661-5341).

National Business Clearinghouse, *(NBC; 0-941176)*, Box 327, Croton Plaza, Croton, NY 10520 (SAN 238-9010).

National Business Education Assn., *(Natl Busn Ed Assoc)*, 1906 Association Dr., Reston, VA 22091 (SAN 225-7610).

National Business Institute, *(Natl Busn Inst; 0-925761)*, P.O. Box 1626, Eau Claire, WI 54702 (SAN 286-9691) Tel 715-835-8525.

National Cable Television Assn., *(Natl Cable; 0-940272)*, 1724 Massachusetts Ave., NW, Washington, DC 20036 (SAN 215-7934) Tel 202-775-3550.

National Cable Television Institute, *(Natl CTV Inst; 0-88683)*, P O Box 27277, Denver, CO 80227 (SAN 224-6597) Tel 303-761-8554; Orders to: 3301 W. Hampden Ave., Englewood, CO 80110 (SAN 662-0892).

National Cartoonists Society, *(Natl Cartoonists)*, 9 Ebony Ct., Brooklyn, NY 11229 (SAN 225-2694) Tel 718-743-6510.

National Catholic Development Conference, *(Natl Cath Dev; 0-9603196)*, 86 Front St., Hempstead, NY 11550 (SAN 209-0872) Tel 516-481-6000.

National Catholic Educational Assn., *(Natl Cath Educ)*, 1077 30th St. NW, Suite 100, Washington, DC 20007-3852 (SAN 676-8636) Tel 202-337-6232.

National Catholic Office for the Deaf, *(Natl Cath Off Deaf)*, 814 Thayer Ave., Silver Spring, MD 20910 (SAN 225-4271) Tel 301-587-7992.

National Catholic Pharmacists Guild of the United States, *(Natl Cath Pharm)*, 1012 Surrey Hills Dr., St. Louis, MO 63117 (SAN 224-4209) Tel 314-645-0085.

National Ctr. for Appropriate Technology, *(NCAT; 1-55579)*, Box 3838, Butte, MT 59702 (SAN 260-342X) Tel 406-494-4572.

National Ctr. for Computer Crime Data, *(Natl Ctr Computer Crime; 0-933561)*, 2700 N. Cahuenga Blvd., Los Angeles, CA 90068 (SAN 691-8956) Tel 213-850-0509.

National Ctr. for Constitutional Studies, *(Natl Ctr Constitutional; 0-88080)*, 3740 W. 1987 S., Salt Lake City, UT 84104 (SAN 237-7055) Tel 801-973-1776; Orders to: P.O. Box 37110, Washington, DC 20013 (SAN 693-9570); Toll free: 800-522-6227.

National Ctr. for Educ. Brokering, *(Natl Ctr Educ Broker; 0-935612)*, 325 Ninth St., San Francisco, CA 94103 (SAN 211-7479).

National Center for Experiential Sales Training, *(Natl Ctr Exper Sales; 0-933343)*, 2122 Coronado SE, Grand Rapids, MI 49506 (SAN 692-3267) Tel 616-243-4343.

National Ctr. for Faculty Dev., *(Natl Ctr Faculty; 0-938540)*, 1320 S. Dixie Hwy., No. 900A, Coral Gables, FL 33146 (SAN 216-423X). Out of business.

National Ctr. for Financial Education, Inc., *(Natl Ctr Fin Ed; 0-935451)*, 25 Van Ness Ave., Suite 5600, San Francisco, CA 94102 (SAN 693-2061) Tel 415-621-6961.

†National Ctr. for Health Statistics, Div. of Dept. of Health & Human Service, *(Natl Ctr Health Stats; 0-8406)*, Federal Ctr. Bldg., Rm. 1-57, 3700 East-West Hwy., Hyattsville, MD 20782 (SAN 206-6033) Tel 301-436-8500; *CIP.*

National Ctr. for Job-Market Studies, *(Natl Ctr Job Mkt; 0-935234)*, P.O. Box 3651 BN, Washington, DC 20007 (SAN 213-5841) Tel 202-229-4885.

National Center for Paralegal Training, *(Natl Ctr PT)*, 1271 Ave. of the Americas, Rm. 777, New York, NY 10020 (SAN 227-0005) Tel 212-581-6844.

National Ctr. for Policy Alternatives, *(NCPA Washington; 0-89788)*, 2000 Florida Ave., NW, Washington, DC 20009 (SAN 235-8255) Tel 202-387-6030.

National Ctr. for Policy Analysis, *(Natl Ctr Pol; 0-943802)*, 7701 N. Stemmons, Suite 717, Dallas, TX 75247 (SAN 241-0869) Tel 214-951-0306.

National Ctr. for Public Productivity, *(Natl Ctr Public Prod; 0-942942)*, 445 W. 59th St., New York, NY 10019 (SAN 210-7929) Tel 212-489-5030.

National Ctr. for Research in Vocational Education, *(Natl Ctr Res Voc Ed)*, 1960 Kenny Rd., Columbus, OH 43210 (SAN 225-882X) Tel 614-486-3655.

†National Ctr. for State Courts, *(Natl Ctr St Courts; 0-89656)*, 300 Newport Ave., Williamsburg, VA 23187-8798 (SAN 210-928X) Tel 804-253-2000; Toll free: 800-446-8952; *CIP.*

National Ctr. for the Diaconate, *(Natl Ctr Diaconate; 0-9605790)*, 14 Beacon St., Rm. 103, Boston, MA 02108 (SAN 220-1763) Tel 617-742-1460.

National Chamber Foundation, *(Natl Chamber Foun; 0-89834)*, 1615 H St., NW, Washington, DC 20062 (SAN 238-0757).

National Christian Pr., Inc., *(Natl Christian Pr; 0-934916)*, P.O. Box 472, Seagoville, OK 73153 (SAN 212-1182) Tel 214-287-7179; P.O. Box 1001, Jonesboro, AR 72401 (SAN 693-496X); Orders to: National Christian Press, Inc., P.O. Box 6709, Moore, Tel 405-794-8298.

National Citizens Coalition for Nursing Home Reform, *(Natl Citizen's Coalition; 0-939611)*, 1424 16th St., NW, Suite L2, Washington, DC 20036 (SAN 235-5817) Tel 202-797-0657.

National Clearinghouse for Bilingual Education, *(Natl Clearinghse Bilingual Ed; 0-89763)*, 1555 Wilson Blvd., Suite 605, Arlington, VA 22209 (SAN 212-839X); Toll free: 800-336-4560.

National Clearinghouse for Legal Services Incorporated, *(NCLS Inc)*, 500 N. Michigan Ave., Rm. 1940, Chicago, IL 60611 (SAN 226-2169) Tel 312-353-2566.

National Coalition Against Censorship, *(NCAC; 0-9611430)*, 132 W. 43rd St., New York, NY 10036 (SAN 260-373X) Tel 212-944-9899.

National Coalition to Ban Handguns, *(Natl Coal Ban Handguns)*, 100 Maryland Ave. NE, Washington, DC 20002 (SAN 235-6317) Tel 202-544-7190.

National College of Chiropractic, *(Natl Coll Chiro; 0-9615849)*, 200 E. Roosevelt Rd., Lombard, IL 60148 (SAN 696-6470) Tel 312-629-2000; Dist. by: Williams & Wilkins, 428 E. Preston St., Baltimore, MD 21202 (SAN 202-5175) Tel 301-528-8521.

National College of District Attorneys, *(Natl Coll DA)*, Univ. of Houston, Bates College of Law, Houston, TX 77004 (SAN 225-0934) Tel 713-749-1571.

National Color Graphics, Inc., *(Natl Color Graphics; 0-9616045)*, E. 502 Fifth Ave., Spokane, WA 99202 (SAN 698-2409); Orders to: Pacific Pipeline, Inc., 19215 66th Ave. S., Kent, WA 98031 (SAN 169-8834).

National Commission on Resources for Youth, Subs. of Institute for Responsive Education, *(Natl Comm Res Youth; 0-912041)*, 605 Commonwealth Ave., Boston, MA 02215 (SAN 225-7785) Tel 617-353-3309.

National Committee for Adoption, *(Natl Adoption; 0-9615820)*, 326 Connecticut Ave. NW, Washington, DC 20036 (SAN 696-6160) Tel 202-463-7559.

†National Committee for Citizens in Education, *(NCCE; 0-934460)*, 10840 Little Patuxent Pkwy., Suite 301, Columbia, MD 21044 (SAN 206-1023) Tel 301-997-9300; *CIP.*

National Committee for Clinical Laboratory Standards, *(Natl Comm Clin Lab Stds)*, 771 E. Lancaster Ave., Villanova, PA 19085 (SAN 224-344X) Tel 215-525-2435.

National Committee to Repeal the Federal Reserve Act, *(Natl Comm Repeal)*, P.O. Box A-H, Bunker Hill, IL 62014 (SAN 273-222X) Tel 618-585-4700.

National Computer Dealers Association Publishing Co., *(Natl Computer; 0-933325)*, 5420 Hwy 6 N., Houston, TX 77084 (SAN 691-926X) Tel 713-859-14191343 Columbia Suite 405, Richardson, TX 75081 (SAN 691-9278).

National Computer Graphics Assn., *(Natl Comp Graphics; 0-941514)*, 2722 Merrilee Dr., Suite 200, Fairfax, VA 22031 (SAN 654-1755) Tel 703-698-9600.

National Conference of Appellate Court Clerks, *(Natl Conf Appellate; 0-934730)*, 300 Newport Ave., Williamsburg, VA 23187-8798 (SAN 213-1285) Tel 804-253-2000.

National Conference of State Legislatures, *(Natl Conf State Legis; 0-941336; 1-55516)*, 1050 17th St., Suite 2100, Denver, CO 80265-2101 (SAN 225-1000) Tel 303-623-7800.

National Conference on Social Welfare, *(Natl Conf Soc Welfare; 0-933597)*, 1730 M. St., NW, Suite 911, Washington, DC 20036 (SAN 225-9958) Tel 202-785-0817.

National Consumer Cooperative Bank, *(Natl Con Coopera Bank; 0-918943)*, 1630 Connecticut Ave., NW, Washington, DC 20009 (SAN 669-8514) Tel 202-745-4753.

National Consumer Law Ctr., Inc., *(Nat Consumer Law; 0-943116)*, 11 Beacon St., Boston, MA 02108 (SAN 226-6520) Tel 617-523-8010.

National Contract Management Assn., *(Natl Contract Mgmt)*, 6728 Old McLean Village Dr., McLean, VA 22101 (SAN 224-7755) Tel 703-442-0137.

National Cooperative Business Assn., *(NCBA; 0-910440)*, National Cooperative Business Ctr., 1401 New York Ave., NW, Suite 1100, Washington, DC 20005 (SAN 269-3747) Tel 202-638-6222; Orders to: P.O. Box 8293, Ann Arbor, MI 48107 (SAN 661-9827) Tel 313-665-2667.

National Corprate Cash Management Assn., *(Natl Corp Cash Mgmt; 0-9614799)*, P.O. Box 7001, Newtown, CT 06470 (SAN 692-6789) Tel 203-426-3007.

National Council for International Visitors, *(Natl Coun Intl Visitors)*, Meridian Hse., 1630 Crescent Pl. NW, Washington, DC 20009 (SAN 223-9094) Tel 202-332-1028; Toll free: 800-523-8101.

National Council for the Social Studies, *(Nat Coun Soc Studies; 0-87986)*, 3501 Newark St., NW, Washington, DC 20016 (SAN 202-1900) Tel 202-966-7840.

National Council for Urban Economic Development, *(Natl Coun Econ Dev)*, 1730 K St. NW, Washington, DC 20006 (SAN 225-6541) Tel 202-223-4735.

National Council for US-China Trade, *(Natl Coun US-China; 0-935614)*, 1818 N St. NW, Suite 500, Washington, DC 20036 (SAN 222-4631) Tel 202-429-0340.

National Council of Architectural Registration Boards, *(NCARB; 0-9607310)*, 1735 New York Ave., NW, Suite 700, Washington, DC 20006 (SAN 240-1282) Tel 202-783-6500.

National Council Of Jewish Women, Omaha Section, *(Omaha Sec Nat; 0-9612406)*, 1720 S. 86 Ave., Omaha, NE 68124 (SAN 283-3484).

National Council of Juvenile & Family Court Judges, *(Natl Juv & Family Ct Judges)*, Univ. of Nevada, Box 8970, Reno, NV 89507 (SAN 225-0942).

†National Council of Teachers of English, *(NCTE; 0-8141)*, 1111 Kenyon Rd., Urbana, IL 61801 (SAN 202-9049) Tel 217-328-3870; *CIP.*

†National Council of Teachers of Mathematics, *(NCTM; 0-87353)*, 1906 Association Dr., Reston, VA 22091 (SAN 202-9057) Tel 703-620-9840; *CIP.*

National Council on Alcoholism, *(Natl Coun Alcoholism)*, 12 W. 21st St., New York, NY 10010 (SAN 236-7653) Tel 212-206-6770.

National Council on Compensation Insurance, *(Natl Comp Ins)*, 1 Penn Plaza, New York, NY 10001 (SAN 224-8360) Tel 212-560-1829.

National Council on Crime & Delinquency, *(Natl Coun Crime)*, 77 Maiden Ln., 4th Flr., San Francisco, CA 94108 (SAN 236-9095) Tel 415-956-5651.

†National Council on Radiation Protection & Measurements, *(NCRP Pubns; 0-913392)*, 7910 Woodmont Ave., Suite 1016, Bethesda, MD 20814 (SAN 677-1254) Tel 301-657-2652; *CIP.*

National Council on Teachers Retirement, *(Natl Coun Teach)*, P.O. Box 1882, Austin, TX 78767 (SAN 273-348X) Tel 512-397-6401.

†National Council on the Aging, The, *(Natl Coun Aging; 0-910883)*, 600 Maryland Ave., SW, Washington, DC 20024 (SAN 675-3361) Tel 202-479-1200; *CIP.*

National Council on the Handicapped, *(Nat Coun Handicapped; 0-936825)*, 800 Independence Ave., SW, No. 814, Washington, DC 20591 (SAN 699-9662) Tel 202-453-3846.

National Council on U.S.-Arab Relations, *(Natl Coun Arab; 0-916729)*, 1625 I St. NW, Suite 625, Washington, DC 20006 (SAN 653-9025) Tel 202-293-0801.

National Cowboy Hall of Fame & Western Heritage Ctr., *(Natl Cowboy Hall of Fame; 0-932154)*, 1700 NE 63rd St., Oklahoma City, OK 73111 (SAN 225-3895) Tel 405-478-2250; Dist. by: Lowell Pr., 115 E. 31st St., P.O. Box 1877, Kansas City, MO 64141 (SAN 207-0774) Tel 816-753-4545.

National Crime Prevention Council, *(Natl Crime DC; 0-934513)*, 733 15th St., NW, Suite 540, Washington, DC 20005 (SAN 693-8574) Tel 202-393-7141. No Relationship to the Natl. Crime Prevention Assn., also in Washington, D.C.

Names

National Dairy Council, *(Natl Dairy Coun; 1-55647),* 6300 N. River Rd., Rosemont, IL 60018 (SAN 224-702X) Tel 312-696-1020.

National Dance Association, *(Natl Dance Assn),* 1900 Association Dr., Reston, VA 22091 (SAN 225-3046) Tel 703-476-3436.

National Data Service for Higher Education, Div. of John Minter Assocs., Inc., *(Nat Data Service; 0-937767),* 2400 Central Ave., Suite B-2, Boulder, CO 80301 (SAN 659-3798) Tel 303-449-5569.

National Decision Systems, Inc., *(Natl Decision; 0-911871),* 539 Encinitas Blvd., Encinitas, CA 92024 (SAN 264-2336) Tel 619-942-7000.

National Defense Council Foundation, *(NDCF; 0-936277),* 108 S. Columbus St., Suite 101, Alexandria, VA 22314 (SAN 699-7546) Tel 703-836-3443.

National Directions, *(Natl Directions; 0-9615168),* 4330 N. Franklin Ave., Loveland, CO 80537 (SAN 694-3020) Tel 303-669-6719; Orders to: 500 26th St., Greeley, CO 80631 (SAN 662-3360) Tel 303-353-0662.

National Dissemination Ctr., *(Natl Dissem Ctr; 0-89857),* 417 Rock St., Fall River, MA 02720 (SAN 699-6701) Tel 617-678-5696.

National District Attorneys Assn., *(Natl Dist Atty),* 1033 N. Fairfax St., Suite 200, Alexandria, VA 22314 (SAN 282-0404) Tel 703-549-9222; Dist. by: National College of District Attorneys, Univ. of Houston, Bates College of Law, Houston, TX 77004 (SAN 225-0934) Tel 713-749-1571.

National Easter Seal Society, *(Natl Easter Seal; 0-933851),* 2023 W. Ogden Ave., Chicago, IL 60612 (SAN 225-9419) Tel 312-243-8400.

†**National Education Assn.,** *(NEA; 0-8106),* 1201 16th St., NW, Washington, DC 20036 (SAN 203-7262) Tel 202-822-7250; Orders to: P.O. Box 509, West Haven, CT 06516 (SAN 203-7270) Tel 203-934-2669; *CIP.*

National Education Standards, *(Natl Ed Stand; 0-918192),* One Wilshire Bldg., Suite 1210, 624 S. Grand Ave., Los Angeles, CA 90017 (SAN 210-3141) Tel 213-623-9135.

National Electric Sign Assn., *(Natl Elec Sign),* 801 N. Fairfax St., Suite 205, Alexandria, VA 22314 (SAN 224-7151) Tel 703-836-4012.

National Electrical Manufacturers Assn., *(Natl Elec Mfrs),* 2101 L St., NW, Washington, DC 20037 (SAN 224-716X) Tel 202-457-8400.

National Encyclopedia Corp., *(Natl Encyclopedia; 0-938171),* 1585 Peachtree Battle Ave., NW, Atlanta, GA 30327 (SAN 661-194X) Tel 404-351-7125.

National Entertainment Research & Advisory Services *See* NERAS Systems

National Farm & Power Equipment Dealers Assn., *(Natl Farm & Power),* 10877 Watson Rd., St Louis, MO 63127 (SAN 224-7275).

National Federation of Abstracting & Information Services, *(NFAIS; 0-942308),* 112 S. 16th St., 12th Fl., Philadelphia, PA 19102 (SAN 203-7394) Tel 215-563-2406.

National Federation of Christian Life Communities, *(NFCLC; 0-913605),* 3721 Westminster Pl., St. Louis, MO 63108 (SAN 276-4555) Tel 314-533-3185.

National Federation of State High School Assns., *(Natl Fed High Schl Assns),* P.O. Box 20626, Kansas City, MO 64195 (SAN 224-540X) Tel 816-464-5400.

National Film Society, *(Natl Film Soc),* 8340 Mission Rd., Suite 106, Shawnee Mission, KS 66206 (SAN 225-3437) Tel 913-341-1919.

National Fire Protection Assn., *(Natl Fire Prot; 0-87765),* Batterymarch Park, Quincy, MA 02269 (SAN 202-8948) Tel 617-770-3000; Toll free: 800-344-3555.

National Flag Foundation, *(Natl Flag Foun),* Flag Plaza, Pittsburgh, PA 15219 (SAN 225-3097) Tel 412-261-1776.

National Flightshops, *(Flightshops; 0-939158),* St. Petersburg-Clearwater Airport, Clearwater, FL 33520 (SAN 240-9127).

National Fluid Power Assn., *(Natl Fluid Power; 0-942220),* 3333 N. Mayfair Rd., Milwaukee, WI 53222 (SAN 224-800X) Tel 414-778-3344.

National Forensic Ctr., Div. of Forensic Services Directory, Inc., *(Natl Forensic; 0-9602962),* 17 Temple Terr., Lawrenceville, NJ 08648 (SAN 212-7792) Tel 609-883-0550; Toll free: 800-526-5177.

National Forum of Educational Administration & Supervision Journal, *(Nat Forum Ed Admin & Supervision; 0-934989),* 1705 Plantation Dr., Alexandria, LA 71301 (SAN 695-1864) Tel 318-442-6976.

National Foundation for Ileitis & Colitis, Inc., *(Natl Found Ileitis; 0-9615495),* 444 Park Ave. S., New York, NY 10016 (SAN 224-3393) Tel 212-685-3440.

National Foundation for Infectious Diseases, The, *(Nat Found Infect Diseases; 0-9614520),* P.O. Box 42022, Washington, DC 20015 (SAN 689-7762) Tel 301-656-0003.

National Foundation for the Study of Equal Employment Policy, *(NFSEEP; 0-916559),* 1015 15th St. NW, Suite 1200, Washington, DC 20005 (SAN 295-5245) Tel 202-789-8685.

†**National Foundation March of Dimes,** *(March of Dimes; 0-86525),* 1275 Mamaroneck Ave., White Plains, NY 10605 (SAN 205-7441) Tel 914-428-7100; *CIP.*

National Fuchsia Society, *(Natl Fuchsia),* c/o George Ghiotto, 702 Sunrise Blvd., Long Beach, CA 90806 (SAN 210-1289).

†**National Gallery of Art,** *(Natl Gallery Art; 0-89468),* Fourth St. & Constitution Ave., NW, Washington, DC 20565 (SAN 203-5545) Tel 202-842-6207; Dist. by: Univ.of Chicago Pr., 5801 Ellis Ave., 3rd Flr., S., Chicago, IL 60637 (SAN 202-5280) Tel 312-962-7693; Dist. by: Univ. Pr. of New England, 3 Lebanon St., Hanover, NH 03755 (SAN 203-3283) Tel 603-646-3349; Dist. by: Univ. of Wash. Pr., P.O. Box C50096, Seattle, WA 98145 (SAN 212-2502) Tel 206-543-8870; *CIP.*

National Gardening Assn., Inc., *(Natl Gardening Assn; 0-915873),* 180 Flynn Ave., Burlington, VT 05401 (SAN 294-0086) Tel 802-863-1308; Dist. by: Inland Book, P.O. Box 261, 22 Hemingway Ave., East Haven, CT 06512 (SAN 200-4151) Tel 203-467-4257.

†**National Genealogical Society,** *(Natl Genealogical; 0-915156),* 4527 17th St. N., Arlington, VA 22207-2363 (SAN 202-1056) Tel 703-525-0050; *CIP.*

†**National Geographic Society,** *(Natl Geog; 0-87044),* 17th & M Sts., NW, Washington, DC 20036 (SAN 202-8956) Tel 202-857-7000; *CIP.*

National Graves Assn. of Ireland, Div. of National Graves Assn., *(Natl Graves Assn; 0-9616291),* P.O. Box 630134, Bronx, NY 10463-9992 (SAN 658-5884); 34-C Edgewater Pk., Bronx, NY 10465 (SAN 658-5892); Orders to: The Last Post, P.O. Box 630134, Bronx, NY 10463-9992 (SAN 200-755X).

National Grocers Assn., *(Nat Grocers Assn),* 1825 Samuel Morse Dr., Reston, VA 22090 (SAN 224-7410) Tel 703-437-5300.

National Guild of Community Schools of the Arts, Inc., *(NGCSA),* P.O. Box 8018, Englewood, NJ 07631 (SAN 218-4966) Tel 201-871-3337.

National Health Federation, *(Natl Health Fed),* Box 688, Monrovia, CA 91016 (SAN 227-9266) Tel 818-357-2181.

National Health Insurance, *(NHI),* 1740 N St NW, Washington, DC 20036 (SAN 226-6008).

National Heritage, *(Natl Heritage; 0-913188),* P.O. Box 84, Saint James, Beaver Island, MI 49782 (SAN 205-7425) Tel 616-448-2299.

National Heritage Map Co., *(Heritage Map Co; 0-934827),* 20121 Ventura Blvd., Suite 125, Woodland Hills, CA 91364 (SAN 694-2296) Tel 818-347-8151.

National Hispanic University, The, *(Natl His Univ),* 255 E. 14th St., Oakland, CA 94606 (SAN 670-7211).

National Home Planning Service, *(Nat Home Planning; 0-933133),* 37 Mountain Ave., Springfield, NJ 07081 (SAN 689-7754) Tel 201-376-3200.

National Home Study Council, *(Natl Home Study; 0-937471),* 1601 18th St., NW, Washington, DC 20009 (SAN 225-7696) Tel 202-234-5100.

National Homecaring Council, *(Natl Homecaring; 0-88154),* 235 Park Ave. S., New York, NY 10003 (SAN 223-811X) Tel 212-674-4990.

National Housing Law Project, *(Natl Housing Law; 0-9606098),* 1950 Addison St., Berkeley, CA 94704 (SAN 216-8391) Tel 415-548-2600.

National Humanities Institute, *(Natl Human Inst; 0-932783),* 426 C St. NE, Washington, DC 20002 (SAN 688-5640) Tel 202-544-3158.

National Industrial Conference Board, *(Natl Indus Conf),* 845 Third Ave., New York, NY 10022 (SAN 227-1168).

National Information Ctr. for Educational Media, Div. of Access Innovations, Inc., *(Natl Info Ctr NM; 0-89320),* P.O. Box 40130, Albuquerque, NM 87196 (SAN 208-4570) Tel 505-265-3591; Toll free: 800-421-8711.

National Institute for Burn Medicine, *(Natl Inst Burn; 0-917478),* 909 E. Ann St., Ann Arbor, MI 48104 (SAN 209-0570) Tel 313-769-9000.

†**National Institute for the Food Service Industry,** *(Natl Inst Food Service; 0-915452),* 20 N. Wacker Dr., Chicago, IL 60606 (SAN 224-747X) Tel 312-782-1703; *CIP.*

National Institute for Trial Advocacy, *(Natl Inst Trial Ad; 1-55681),* 1507 Energy Park Dr., St. Paul, MN 55108 (SAN 286-6927) Tel 612-644-0323; Toll free: 800-225-6482.

National Institute for Urban Wildlife, *(Natl Inst Urban Wildlife),* 10921 Trotting Ridge Way, Columbia, MD 21044 (SAN 225-1841) Tel 301-596-3311.

National Institute for Work & Learning, *(Nat'l Inst Work; 0-86510),* 1200 18th St. NW, Suite 316, Washington, DC 20036 (SAN 241-5704) Tel 202-887-6800.

National Institue of Career Planning, Inc., *(Natl Inst Career; 0-917592),* 577 College Ave., Palo Alto, CA 94306 (SAN 208-0206) Tel 415-857-1444; P.O. Box 60070, Palo Alto, CA 94306 (SAN 658-1277).

National Institute of Judicial Dynamics, *(NIJD Colorado),* 411 Lakewood Cir., Suite B711, Colorado Springs, CO 80910 (SAN 224-2311) Tel 303-574-2082.

National Institute of Philanthropy, *(Natl Inst Phil; 0-9614316),* 1092 E. Mendocino St., Altadena, CA 91001 (SAN 687-522X) Tel 818-797-5606.

National Institute on Mental Retardation, *(NIMR),* Kinsmen Bldg., York Univ. Campus, 4700 Keele St., Downsview, ON M3J 1P3, (SAN 273-5733) Tel 416-661-9611.

National Insurance Law Service Codes & Regulations, Inc. *See* NILS Publishing Co.

National Intelligence Study Ctr., *(NISC; 0-938450),* 1800 K St. NW, Suite 1102, Washington, DC 20036 (SAN 216-0005).

National Interreligious Service Board for Conscientious Objectors, *(NISBCO),* 800 18th St., NW, Suite 600, Washington, DC 20006 (SAN 218-8589) Tel 202-293-5962.

National Jewish Information Service, *(Natl Jewish Info),* 5174 W. Eighth St., Los Angeles, CA 90036 (SAN 225-4581) Tel 213-936-6033.

National Judicial College, *(Natl Judicial Coll),* Judicial College Bldg., Univ. of Nevada, Reno, NV 89557 (SAN 211-3708) Tel 702-784-6747.

National Juvenile Law Center, *(Natl Juv Law),* 3701 Lindell Blvd., P.O. 14200, St. Louis, MO 63178 (SAN 226-6059) Tel 314-652-5555.

National Kidney Foundation of Georgia, Inc., Affil. of National Kidney Foundation, *(Nat Kidney GA; 0-9615527),* 1627 Peachtree Rd., Suite 306, Atlanta, GA 30309 (SAN 696-3447) Tel 404-872-7540.

National Kitchen Cabinet Assn., *(Natl Kitchen Cabinet),* P.O. Box 6830, Falls Church, VA 22046 (SAN 224-8417) Tel 703-237-7580.

National law Publishing Corp., *(Natl Law; 0-932500),* 99 Painters Mill Rd., Owings Mills, MD 21117 (SAN 226-1634) Tel 301-363-6400.

†**National Lawyers Guild,** *(Natl Lawyers Guild; 0-9602188),* 853 Broadway, Rm. 1705, New York, NY 10003 (SAN 212-5307) Tel 212-260-1360; Dist. by: National Lawyers Guild Report, P.O. Box 14023, Washington, DC 20044 (SAN 212-5315) Tel 202-223-3111; *CIP.*

National League for Nursing, *(Natl League Nurse; 0-88737),* 10 Columbus Cir., New York, NY 10019 (SAN 203-7130) Tel 212-582-1022; Toll free: 800-847-8480 (Outside NY State); Toll free: 800-442-4546 (NY State).

National League of Cities, *(Natl League Cities; 0-933729),* 1301 Pennsylvania Ave. NW, Washington, DC 20004 (SAN 225-0721) Tel 202-626-3150.

National Learning Corp., *(Natl Learning; 0-8373; 0-8293),* 212 Michael Dr., Syosset, NY 11791 (SAN 206-8869) Tel 516-921-8888; Toll free: 800-645-6337. Educational, commercial, industrial and government sales.

National Legal Aid & Defender Assn., *(Natl Legal Aid & Defender),* 1625 K St., NW, Suite 800, Washington, DC 20006 (SAN 225-0977) Tel 202-452-0620.

National Legal Ctr. for the Public Interest, *(Nat Legal Ctr Pub Interest; 0-937299),* 1000 16th St., NW, Suite 301, Washington, DC 20036 (SAN 658-8115) Tel 202-296-1683.

National Lilac Publishing Co., *(Natl Lilac Pub; 0-9614126),* 2310 17th, Anacortes, WA 98221 (SAN 686-4716).

National Literary Guild, *(Natl Lit Guild; 0-86666),* 210 N. Pass Ave., Suite 204, Burbank, CA 91505 (SAN 220-2492) Tel 818-845-2687.

National Live Stock & Meat Board, *(Natl Live Stock; 0-88700),* 444 N. Michigan Ave., Chicago, IL 60611 (SAN 273-6276) Tel 312-467-5520.

National LP-Gas Assn., *(Natl LP Gas; 0-88466),* 1301 W. 22nd St., Oak Brook, IL 60521 (SAN 203-5472) Tel 312-986-4808.

National Lubricating Grease Institute, *(Natl Lubrica Grease; 0-9613935),* 4635 Wyandotte St., Kansas City, MO 64112 (SAN 273-6314) Tel 816-931-9480.

National Marfan Foundation, The, *(Natl Marfan Foun; 0-918335),* 54 Irma Ave., Port Washington, NY 11050 (SAN 657-2855) Tel 516-883-8712.

National Marine Manufacturers Assn., *(Natl Marine Mfrs),* 401 N. Michigan Ave., Chicago, IL 60611 (SAN 223-9140) Tel 312-836-4747; 353 Lexington Ave., New York, NY 60611 (SAN 693-4994) Tel 212-684-6622.

National Marine Representatives Assn., *(Natl Marine Reps),* 16-2 St. Thomas Colony, Fox Lake, IL 60020 (SAN 224-859X) Tel 312-587-1253.

National Maritime Museum Assn., *(Natl Maritime; 0-9605182),* Presidio of San Francisco Building 275, Crissy Field, San Francisco, CA 94129 (SAN 239-9385) Tel 415-921-0202; Orders to: Barbara Gatou, Suite 330, 680 Beach St., San Francisco, CA 94109 (SAN 685-3501).

National Materials Development Center for French, *(Natl Mat Dev; 0-911409),* Dept. of Media Services, Dimond Library, UNH, Durham, NH 03824 (SAN 264-2344).

National Mental Health Assn., *(Natl Mental Health),* 1021 Prince St., Alexandria, VA 22314-2971 (SAN 223-9159) Tel 703-684-7722.

National Middle Schl. Assn., *(Natl Middle Schl),* P.O. Box 14882, Columbus, OH 43214 (SAN 225-8455) Tel 614-263-5407.

National Minority Business, *(Natl Minority Bus),* 65 22nd Ave., NE, Minneapolis, MN 55418 (SAN 225-9605) Tel 612-781-6819.

National Minority Campus Chronicle, *(Nat Minority; 0-935483),* P.O. Box 9869, Madison, WI 53715 (SAN 695-9989) Tel 608-244-5633.

National Museum of American Art, Smithsonian Institute, *(Natl Mus Amer Art; 0-937311),* Eighth & Good Sts., NW, Washington, DC 20560 (SAN 658-8158) Tel 202-357-1812; Dist. by: Smithsonian Institute Press, 955 L'Enfant Plaza, Suite 2100, Washington, DC 20560 (SAN 206-8044) Tel 202-287-3765.

National Native American Co-Operative, *(Natl Native; 0-9610334),* P.O. Box 5000, San Carlos, AZ 85550-0301 (SAN 264-2352) Tel 602-244-8244.

National Neighbors, *(Natl Neighbors),* Bowen Bldg., 815 15th St., NW, Suite 611, Washington, DC 20005 (SAN 223-9175) Tel 202-347-6501.

†**National Notary Assn.,** *(Natl Notary; 0-9600158; 0-933134),* 23012 Ventura Blvd., P.O. Box 4625, Woodland Hills, CA 91365-4625 (SAN 202-8964) Tel 818-347-2035; *CIP.*

National Nursing Review, Inc., *(Natl Nursing; 0-917010),* P.O. Box 806, 342 State St., No. 6, Los Altos, CA 94022 (SAN 208-7804) Tel 415-941-5784; Toll free: 800-221-4093.

National Nutrition Consortium, *(NNC),* 24 Third St., NE, Suite 200, Washington, DC 20002 (SAN 260-2903) Tel 202-547-4819.

National Obscenity Law Center, Div. of Morality In Media Inc., *(Natl Obscenity; 0-9614159),* 475 Riverside Dr., Rm. 239, New York, NY 10115 (SAN 686-5437) Tel 212-870-3232.

National Office Products Assn., *(Natl Office Products),* 301 N. Fairfax St., Alexandria, VA 22314 (SAN 223-8152) Tel 703-549-9040.

National Opera Assn., *(Natl Opera Assn; 0-938178),* Rte. 2, Box 93, Commerce, TX 75428 (SAN 218-8600) Tel 214-886-3830.

National Opinion Research Ctr., *(NORC; 0-932132),* 6030 S. Ellis Ave., Chicago, IL 60637 (SAN 205-7735) Tel 312-962-1213.

National Organization on Legal Problems of Education, *(NOLPE),* 3601 SW 29th St., Suite 223, Topeka, KS 66614 (SAN 226-6105) Tel 913-273-3550.

National PTA, *(Natl PTA; 0-88109),* 700 N. Rush St., Chicago, IL 60611 (SAN 225-8560) Tel 312-787-0977.

National Paperback Bks., Inc., *(Natl Paperback; 0-89826),* Orders to: P.O. Box 146, Knoxville, TN 37901 (SAN 211-5344) Tel 615-588-6293.

National Paragon Corp., Div. of Reiss Games, Inc., *(Natl Paragon; 0-89515),* 230 Fifth Ave., New York, NY 10001 (SAN 209-9969) Tel 212-679-2440; Dist. by: E. P. Dutton Co., 2 Park Ave., New York, NY 10016 (SAN 201-0070) Tel 212-725-1818.

†**National Park Service Div. of Pubns.,** *(Natl Park Serv; 0-912627),* Harpers Ferry Ctr., Harpers Ferry, WV 25425 (SAN 282-7980) Tel 304-535-6371; *CIP.*

National Parks & Conservation Assn., *(Natl Parks & Cons; 0-940091),* 1015 31st St., NW, Washington, DC 20007 (SAN 225-1124) Tel 202-265-2717.

National Pecan Marketing Council, *(Natl Pecan; 0-9613698),* 219 N. Main, Suite 513, Bryan, TX 77803 (SAN 677-0916) Tel 409-775-4009.

National Planning Assn., *(Natl Planning; 0-89068),* 1616 P St., NW, Suite 400, Washington, DC 20036 (SAN 207-0030) Tel 202-265-7685.

National Poetry Foundation, *(Natl Poet Foun; 0-915032),* Univ. of Maine, 305 Neville Hall, Orono, ME 04469 (SAN 206-5088) Tel 207-581-3814.

National Potato Council, *(Natl Potato Coun),* 4685 Peoria St., Suite 101, Denver, CO 80239 (SAN 225-0640) Tel 303-373-5639.

National Practice Institute, *(Natl Prac Inst),* 510 First Ave. N., Suite 205, Minneapolis, MN 55403 (SAN 217-2577); Toll free: 800-328-4444.

National Pr., Inc., *(Natl Pr Inc; 0-915765),* 7508 Wisconsin Ave., Bethesda, MD 20814 (SAN 293-8839) Tel 301-657-1616.

National Pubs., Div. of Krastman & Assocs., *(Nat Pubs CA; 0-935551),* P.O. Box 8042, Van Nuys, CA 91409 (SAN 696-2238) Tel 818-705-8865; 5941 Texhoma, Encino, CA 91316 (SAN 696-5245) Tel 818-909-2016.

National Pubs. of the Black Hills, Inc., *(Natl Pub Black Hills; 0-935920),* 137 E. Main St., Elmsford, NY 10523 (SAN 222-6227) Tel 914-592-6006; Orders to: 521 Kansas City St., Rapid City, SD 57701 (SAN 685-351X) Tel 605-394-4482.

National Radio Club, *(Natl Radio Club),* P.O. Box 118, Poquonock, CT 06064 (SAN 223-9221); P.O. Box 24, Cambridge, WI 53523 (SAN 669-2087).

National Railway Historical Society, Inc., Atlanta Chapter, *(National Railway Hist Soc; 0-939037),* P.O. Box 13132, Atlanta, GA 30324-0132 (SAN 663-4982); 3966 US Hwy. 23, Duluth, GA 30136-4135 (SAN 663-4990) Tel 404-266-9566.

†**National Railway Historical Society, Intermountain Chapter,** *(Natl Railway Hist; 0-917884),* P.O. Box 5181, Terminal Annex, Denver, CO 80217 (SAN 206-1643) Tel 303-623-6747; *CIP.*

National Railway Historical Society, Rio Grande Chapter, *(Natl Rail Rio Grande; 0-939646),* Box 3381, Grand Junction, CO 81502 (SAN 220-1771) Tel 303-242-3304.

National Railway Historical Society, Rochester Chapter, *(Natl Rail Rochester; 0-9605296),* P.O. Box 664, Rochester, NY 14602 (SAN 282-0447) Tel 716-244-6438; Orders to: P.O. Box 664, Rochester, NY 14602 (SAN 282-0455).

†**National Railway Historical Society, Washington D.C. Chapter,** *(Natl Rail Hist Soc DC Chap; 0-933954),* P.O. Box 487, Washington, DC 20044 (SAN 212-8403); *CIP.*

National Real Estate Institute (NREI), *(Natl Real Estate Inst; 0-915799),* 12860 NE 15th Place, Bellevue, WA 98005 (SAN 293-8855) Tel 206-454-5251.

National Register Publishing Co., Subs. of Macmillan Inc., *(Natl Register; 0-87217),* 3004 Glenview Rd., Wilmette, IL 60091 (SAN 207-5180) Tel 312-256-6067; Toll free: 800-323-6772.

National Reproduction Corp., *(Natl Repro Corp; 0-932335),* 433 E. Larned, Detroit, MI 48226 (SAN 686-7960) Tel 313-761-6870.

National Research and Information Center, *(Nat Res Info; 0-9608220),* 1614 Central St., Evanston, IL 60201 (SAN 240-4125) Tel 312-328-6545.

National Research Bureau, Div. of Automated Marketing Systems, *(Natl Res Bur; 0-912610),* 310 S. Michigan Ave., Suite 1150, Chicago, IL 60604 (SAN 205-7336) Tel 312-663-5580; Orders to: 424 N. Third St., Burlington, IA 52601 (SAN 205-7344) Tel 319-752-5415.

†**National Research Council,** *(Natl Res Coun; 0-309),* 2101 Constitution Ave., Washington, DC 20418 (SAN 223-923X) Tel 202-334-2000; *CIP.*

National Research Group, *(Natl Res Group),* P.O. Box 93, Valdosta, GA 31601 (SAN 262-0510).

National Resource Ctr. for Consumers of Legal Services, *(NRCCLS; 0-937271),* 3254 Jones Ct., NW, Washington, DC 20007 (SAN 226-1677) Tel 202-338-0714.

†**National Restaurant Assn.,** *(Natl Restaurant Assn; 0-914528),* 311 First St., NW, Washington, DC 20001 (SAN 224-7496) Tel 202-638-6100; *CIP.*

National Retail Hardware Assn., *(Natl Retail Hardware; 0-9609048),* 770 N. High School Rd., Indianapolis, IN 46224 (SAN 224-7879) Tel 317-248-1261.

National Retail Merchants Assn., *(Natl Ret Merch; 0-87102),* 100 W. 31st St., New York, NY 10001 (SAN 654-178X) Tel 212-244-8780.

National Reunion Assn., *(Natl Reunion Assn; 0-9610470),* P.O. Box 295, Nevada City, CA 95959 (SAN 264-2360) Tel 916-265-6028.

National Rifle Assn., *(Natl Rifle Assn; 0-935998),* 1600 Rhode Island Ave. NW, Washington, DC 20036 (SAN 213-859X) Tel 202-828-6000; Dist. by: A B & C Sales, 2010 Eisenhower Ave., Alexandria, VA 22314 (SAN 282-6607) Tel 703-960-6600.

National Roofing Contractors Assn., *(Natl Roofing Cont; 0-934809),* 8600 Bryn Mawr Ave., Chicago, IL 60631 (SAN 229-9283) Tel 312-693-0700.

National Rural Electric Cooperative Assn., *(Natl Rural; 0-917599),* 1800 Massachusetts Ave., NW, Washington, DC 20036 (SAN 205-7328) Tel 202-857-9550; Orders to: Bermont Bks., P.O. Box 309, Glenelg, MD 21737 (SAN 211-1705).

National Safety Council, *(Natl Safety Coun; 0-87912),* 444 N. Michigan Ave., Chicago, IL 60611 (SAN 203-7157) Tel 312-527-4800.

Names

National Sanitation Foundation, *(Natl Sanit Foun; 0-940006),* P.O. Box 1468, 3475 Plymouth Rd., Ann Arbor, MI 48106 (SAN 216-8413) Tel 313-769-8010.

†**National School Boards Assns.,** *(Natl Sch Boards; 0-88364),* 1680 Duke St., Alexandria, VA 22314 (SAN 676-8288) Tel 703-838-6711; *CIP.*

National School Public Relations Assn., *(Natl Sch PR; 0-87545),* 1501 Lee Hwy., Dept. 5, Arlington, VA 22209 (SAN 203-7165) Tel 703-528-5840.

National Schl. Services, *(Natl School; 0-932957),* 250 N. Wolf Rd., Wheeling, IL 60090 (SAN 689-9986) Tel 312-541-2768.

National Science Foundation, *(NSF),* 1800 G St., NW, Rm. 527, Washington, DC 20550 (SAN 233-0113) Tel 202-257-9498.

National Science Supervisors Assn., Affil. of National Science Teachers Assn., *(Natl Sci Super Assn),* P.O. Box AL, Amagansett, NY 11930 (SAN 226-8132) Tel 516-267-3692.

†**National Science Teachers Assn.,** Affil. of the American Assn. for the Advancement of Science, *(Natl Sci Tchrs; 0-87355),* 1742 Connecticut Ave., NW, Washington, DC 20009 (SAN 203-7173) Tel 202-328-5800; *CIP.*

National Seafood Educators, *(Nat Seafood Educ; 0-9616426),* P.O. Box 60006, Richmond Beach, WA 98160 (SAN 658-9685) Tel 206-546-6410; 20103 23rd, NW, Seattle, WA 98177 (SAN 658-9693).

National Senior Citizens Law Center, *(Natl Sen Citizens; 0-932605),* 2025 M Street NW, Suite 400, Washington, DC 20036 (SAN 687-5238) Tel 202-887-5280.

National Sharegraphics *See* **Curtis Media Corp.**

National Shorthand Reporters Assn., *(Natl Shorthand Rptr; 0-933305),* 118 Park St. SE, Vienna, VA 22180 (SAN 224-9588) Tel 703-281-4677.

National Skeet Shooting Assn., *(Natl Skeet Shoot),* Box 28188, San Antonio, TX 78228 (SAN 224-5620).

National Society for Internships & Experiential Education, *(NSIEE; 0-937883),* 122 St. Mary's St., Raleigh, NC 27605 (SAN 659-5251) Tel 919-834-7536.

National Society of Professional Engineers, *(Natl Soc Prof Engrs; 0-915409),* 2029 K St., NW, Washington, DC 20006 (SAN 225-168X) Tel 202-463-2300.

National Society of the Sons of the American Revolution, The, *(Nat Soc of Sons; 0-9607188),* 1000 S. Fourth St., Louisville, KY 40203 (SAN 239-121X).

National Society to Prevent Blindness, *(Natl Soc Prevent Blindness; 0-916102),* 79 Madison Ave., New York, NY 10016 (SAN 224-2745) Tel 212-684-3505; Toll free: 800-221-3004.

National Speakers Assn., *(Natl Speakers),* 4747 N. Seventh St., Suite 310, Phoenix, AZ 85014 (SAN 225-3771) Tel 602-265-1001.

National Speleological Society, Inc., *(Natl Speleological; 0-9615093),* 2813 Cave Ave., Huntsville, AL 35810 (SAN 273-8619) Tel 205-852-1300.

National Square Dance Directory, *(Natl Sq Dance; 0-9605494),* P.O. Box 54055, Jackson, MS 39208 (SAN 215-2576) Tel 601-825-6831.

National Standards Association, *(Natl Standards Assn),* 5161 River Rd., Bethesda, MD 20816 (SAN 223-9272) Tel 301-951-1389.

National State Leadership Training Institute on Gifted & Talented, *(NSLTIGT),* One Wilshire Bldg., 624 S. Grand Ave., Suite 1007, Los Angeles, CA 90017-3311 (SAN 226-3837) Tel 213-489-7470; Orders to: LTI Publications, 535 E. Main St., Ventura, CA 93009 (SAN 662-0906) Tel 805-652-7345.

National States Rowing Association, *(Nat States Rowing),* 251 N. Illinois St., Suite 980, Indianapolis, IN 46204 (SAN 224-585X) Tel 317-237-2769.

National Steeplechase & Hunt Assn., *(Natl Steeplechase),* Box 308, Elmont, NY 11003 (SAN 224-5809).

National Student Educational Fund, *(Natl Stud Ed; 0-940624),* 2000 P St. NW, Suite 305, Washington, DC 20036 (SAN 218-5199) Tel 202-785-1856.

National Support Ctr. for Families of the Aging, *(Natl Support Ctr; 0-910227),* Box 245, Swarthmore, PA 19081 (SAN 241-4147) Tel 215-544-5933.

National Tax Assn.-Tax Institute of America, *(Natl Tax; 0-934729),* 21 E. State St., Columbus, OH 43215 (SAN 225-1299) Tel 614-224-8352.

National Technical Information Service, U. S. Dept. of Commerce, *(Natl Tech Info; 0-934213),* 5285 Port Royal Rd., Springfield, VA 22161 (SAN 205-7255) Tel 703-487-4838.

National Textbook Co., *(Natl Textbk; 0-8442; 0-8325),* 4255 W. Touhy Ave., Chicago, IL 60646 (SAN 169-2208) Tel 312-679-5500; Toll free: 800-854-4014. *Imprints:* Passport Books (Passport Bks).

National Tinnitus Fund, *(Natl Tinn Fund; 0-9612648),* P.O. Box 5081, Springfield, MO 65801 (SAN 289-3428) Tel 417-831-0436.

National Tooling & Machining Assn., *(Natl Tool & Mach),* 9300 Livingston Rd., Ft. Washington, MD 20744 (SAN 224-232X) Tel 301-248-6200.

National Tour Assn., *(Natl Tour Assn; 0-910399),* P.O. Box 3071, Lexington, KY 40596 (SAN 224-974X); Toll-free: 800-NTA-8886; 546 E. Main St., Lexington, KY 40508 (SAN 662-0914) Tel 606-253-1036; Toll-free: 800-828-6999 (In Canada).

National Translations Ctr., *(Nat Transl Ctr; 0-935599),* Univ. of Chicago, John Crerar Library, 5730 S. Ellis Ave., Chicago, IL 60637 (SAN 204-2592) Tel 312-962-7060.

National Trust for Historic Preservation *See* **Preservation Pr., The**

National Underwriter Co., *(Natl Underwriter; 0-87218),* 420 E. Fourth St., Cincinnati, OH 45202 (SAN 205-7247) Tel 513-721-2140; Toll free: 800-543-0874.

National Unity Equality Leadership Fraternity Pr., *(NELF Pr),* 78 Maplevale Dr., Woodbridge, CT 06525 (SAN 203-7297) Tel 203-393-3913.

National Univ. Pubns. *See* **Associated Faculty Pr.**

National Urban League, *(Natl Urban; 0-914758),* 500 E. 62nd St., New York, NY 10021 (SAN 215-2290).

National Video Clearinghouse, Inc., The, *(Natl Video; 0-935478),* 100 Lafayette Dr., Syosset, NY 11791 (SAN 213-4209) Tel 516-364-3686.

National Water Well Association, *(Natl Water Well),* 500 W Wilson Bridge Rd, Worthington, OH 43085 (SAN 231-7273) Tel 614-846-9355.

National Waterways Conference, Inc., *(Natl Waterways; 0-934292),* 1130 17th St. N.W., No. 200, Washington, DC 20036 (SAN 203-719X) Tel 202-296-4415.

National Wild Turkey Federation, Inc., *(Natl Wild Turkey),* 770 Augusta Rd., Edgefield, SC 29824 (SAN 225-0098) Tel 803-637-3106; Box 530, Edgefield, SC 29824 (SAN 225-0922).

†**National Wildlife Federation,** Div. of Books and Special Publications, *(Natl Wildlife; 0-912186),* 8925 Leesburg Pike, Vienna, VA 22180 (SAN 202-8980) Tel 703-790-4227; *CIP.*

National Woman's Christian Temperance Union, *(WCTU),* 1730 Chicago Ave., Evanston, IL 60201 (SAN 225-8935).

National Women's Hall of Fame, *(Natl Wmns Hall Fame; 0-9610622),* 76 Falls St. P.O. Box 335, Seneca Falls, NY 13148 (SAN 223-9299) Tel 315-568-8060.

National Women's History Project, *(Natl Womens Hist; 0-938625),* 2321 Coddingtown Ctr., Santa Rosa, CA 95401 (SAN 661-6275) Tel 707-526-5974.

National Wood Carvers Association, *(Natl Wood Carver),* 7424 Miami Ave., Cincinnati, OH 45243 (SAN 225-5510) Tel 513-561-9051.

National Writers Club, The, Subs. of Association Headquarters, Inc., *(Natl Writers Club),* 1450 S. Havana, Suite 620, Aurora, CO 80012 (SAN 225-3992) Tel 303-751-7844; Dist. by: National Writers Pr., 1450 S. Havana, Suite 620, Aurora, CO 80012 (SAN 240-320X).

National Writers Pr., The, Div. of National Writers Club, Subs. of Association Headquarters, Inc., *(Natl Writ Pr; 0-88100),* 1450 S. Havana, Suite 620, Aurora, CO 80012 (SAN 240-320X) Tel 303-751-7844.

Native American Pub. Co., *(Native Am Pub; 0-9614958),* P.O. Box 6338, Incline Village, NV 89450 (SAN 693-725X) Tel 702-831-7726.

Native Nevadan Pubns., *(Native Nevadan Pubns; 0-930083),* 145 W. Plumb Lane, Reno, NV 89509 (SAN 670-106X) Tel 702-329-7557.

Natter Publishing Co., *(Natter Pub; 0-936143),* 36 Durham Rd., White Plains, NY 10605 (SAN 696-6373) Tel 914-428-5404.

Natural Designs, *(Natural Designs; 0-9616179),* 61 Atherton Ave., Atherton, CA 94025 (SAN 699-9735) Tel 415-326-8003; Dist. by: Publishers Group West, 5855 Beaudry St., Emeryville, CA 94608 (SAN 202-8522) Tel 415-658-3453; Toll free: 800-982-8319.

Natural History Museum of Los Angeles County, *(Nat Hist Mus; 0-938644),* 900 Exposition Blvd., Los Angeles, CA 90007 (SAN 238-6925) Tel 213-744-3330.

Natural History Pr., *(Natural Hist),* ; Toll free: 800-645-6156; Dist. by: Doubleday & Co., Inc., 501 Franklin Ave., Garden City, NY 11530 (SAN 281-6083) Tel 516-873-4561. *Imprints:* American Museum Science Books (AMS); American Museum Sourcebooks in Anthropology (AMSA).

Natural History Publishing Co., *(Nat Hist Pub Co; 0-9603144),* P.O. Box 962, La Jolla, CA 92038 (SAN 207-7515) Tel 619-459-0835.

Natural Hygiene Pr., Div. of American Natural Hygiene Society, *(Natural Hygiene; 0-914532),* 12816 Race Track Rd., Tampa, FL 33625 (SAN 202-4314) Tel 813-855-6607.

Natural Pr., Div. of Natural Enterprises, *(Natural Pr; 0-939956),* P.O. 2107, Manitowoc, WI 54220 (SAN 287-0215) Tel 414-682-0738; Dist. by: Nutri Books, P.O. Box 5793, Denver, CO 80323 (SAN 169-054X).

Natural Products Co., *(Natural Prod; 0-9614234),* P.O. Box 273, Vashon, WA 98070 (SAN 686-7952) Tel 206-567-4788; Dist. by: Bookpeople, 2929 Fifth St., Berkeley, CA 94710 (SAN 168-9517) Tel 415-549-3030; Dist. by: Pacific Pipeline, 19215 66th Ave. S., Kent, WA 98032 (SAN 208-2128) Tel 206-872-5523.

Natural Resources Defense Council, *(Natl Resources Defense Coun),* 122 E. 42nd St., New York, NY 10168 (SAN 273-9615).

Natural Resources Enterprises, Inc., *(Natural Res Ent; 0-939870),* P.O. Box 4523, Lincoln, NE 68504 (SAN 216-9150) Tel 402-472-1519.

Natural Resources Unlimited Inc., *(Natl Res Unltd; 0-912475),* 3531 Roesner Dr., Markham, IL 60426 (SAN 265-2846) Tel 312-331-7964.

Natural Science for Youth Foundation, *(Natural Sci Youth; 0-916544),* 763 Silvermine Rd., New Canaan, CT 06840 (SAN 208-2039) Tel 203-966-5643.

Natural Selection, The, *(Nat Select; 0-9610722),* 2560 Harris St., Eugene, OR 97405 (SAN 264-7680) Tel 503-485-3915.

Natural Therapy Foundation Press, The, *(Nat Therapy; 0-937792),* 5 Greenleaf, Irvine, CA 92714 (SAN 215-6849) Tel 714-551-0381.

Natural World Pr., *(Natural World; 0-939560),* 607 Chiltern Rd., Hillsborough, CA 94010 (SAN 216-6879) Tel 415-344-5014.

Naturally Beautiful You, *(Naturally Beaut You; 0-9616880),* 1226 E. St. George Ave., Linden, NJ 07036 (SAN 661-6550) Tel 201-486-9105.

Nature Bks. Pubs., *(Nature Bks Pubs; 0-912542),* P.O. Box 12157, Jackson, MS 39211 (SAN 203-7211) Tel 601-956-5686.

Nature Conservancy, The, *(Nature Conservancy),* Box 338, 122 Main St., Topsham, ME 04036 (SAN 273-964X).

Nature Life, Div. of McGill-Jensen, *(Nature Life; 0-918134),* 655 Fairview Ave. N., St. Paul, MN 55104 (SAN 209-3596) Tel 612-645-3129.

Nature Study Guild, *(Nature Study; 0-912550),* P.O. Box 972, Berkeley, CA 94701 (SAN 203-722X).

Nature Trails Pr., *(Nature Trails; 0-937794),* 933 Calle Loro, Palm Springs, CA 92262 (SAN 207-3609) Tel 619-323-9420.

Naturegraph Pubs., Inc., *(Naturegraph; 0-911010; 0-87961),* P.O. Box 1075, Happy Camp, CA 96039 (SAN 202-8999) Tel 916-493-5353.

Naturetrek Communications, *(Naturetrek Comn; 0-9616236),* Box 775, Corvallis, OR 97339 (SAN 658-5949) Tel 503-757-3142; 8130 Oak Ck. Dr., Corvallis, OR 97330 (SAN 658-5957).

Nauful, Eli S., *(Nauful),* P.O. Box 1260, Lynchburg, VA 24502 (SAN 209-6269).

†**Nautical & Aviation Publishing Co., of America, Inc.,** *(Nautical & Aviation; 0-933852),* 101 W. Read St., Suite 314, Baltimore, MD 21201 (SAN 213-3431) Tel 301-659-0220; *CIP.*

Nautical Research Guild, Inc., *(Nautical Res; 0-9603456),* 6413 Dahlonega Rd., Bethesda, MD 20816 (SAN 221-7260).

Nautilus Bks., Div. of Nautilus Communications, Inc., *(Nautilus Bks; 0-941476),* 375 Fifth Ave., New York, NY 10016 (SAN 239-1228) Tel 212-685-7007.

Nautilus Bks., Inc., *(Nautilus Inc; 0-935055),* 496 LaGuardia Pl., New York, NY 10012 (SAN 694-6054) Tel 212-243-7050.

†**Navajo Community College Pr.,** *(Navajo Coll Pr; 0-912586),* Navajo Community College, Tsaile, AZ 86556 (SAN 201-9582); *CIP.*

Navajo Curriculum Ctr. Pr., *(Navajo Curr; 0-936008),* Rough Rock Demonstration Schl., Star Rte. 1, Rough Rock, AZ 86503 (SAN 203-1604) Tel 602-728-3311.

Navajo Tribal Museum, Div. of Navajo Tribe, *(Navajo),* Box 308, Window Rock, AZ 85615 (SAN 279-8131) Tel 602-871-6673.

Naval Fighters, *(Naval Fighters; 0-942612),* 1754 Warfield Cir., Simi Valley, CA 93063 (SAN 238-5457) Tel 805-584-9732.

†**Naval Institute Pr.,** *(Naval Inst Pr; 0-87021),* U. S. Naval Institute, Annapolis, MD 21402 (SAN 202-9006) Tel 301-268-6110; Orders to: Customer Service, U.S. Naval Institute Operations Ctr., 2062 Generals Hwy., Annapolis, MD 21401 (SAN 662-0930) Tel 301-224-3378; *CIP.*

Navarro Pubs., *(Navarro Pubs; 0-932079),* 1752 S. Dayton Pl., Kennewick, WA 99337 (SAN 686-2632) Tel 509-582-6720.

Navpress, A Ministry of The Navigators, *(NavPress; 0-89109),* P.O. Box 6000, Colorado Springs, CO 80934 (SAN 211-5352) Tel 303-598-1212; Toll free: 800-525-7151.

Navy League of the United States, *(Navy League US; 0-9610724),* 2300 Wilson Blvd., Arlington, VA 22201-3308 (SAN 264-7699) Tel 703-631-0571; Dist. by: Almanac of Seapower, The, P.O. Box 11455, Alexandria, VA 22312 (SAN 200-8033) Tel 703-354-7094.

NAWDAC *See* **National Assn. for Women Deans, Administrators & Counselors**

Nazareth Group, Inc., The, *(Nazareth Group),* Box 448, Waynesboro, PA 17265 (SAN 656-8971) Tel 717-762-9716.

Neahtawanta Pr., *(Neahtawanta Pr; 0-943806),* 309 E. Front St., Traverse City, MI 49684 (SAN 239-3689) Tel 616-947-2462.

Neal, Richard, Assocs., *(Neal Assoc; 0-9605018),* Box 23, Manassas, VA 22110 (SAN 215-6857).

Neal Pubns., Inc., *(Neal Pubns Inc; 0-9609006),* P.O. Box 451, Perrysburg, OH 43551 (SAN 240-8198) Tel 419-874-7422.

†**Neal-Schuman Pubs., Inc.,** *(Neal-Schuman; 0-918212; 1-55570),* 23 Leonard St., New York, NY 10013 (SAN 210-2455) Tel 212-925-8650; *CIP.*

Near, Jean, *(J Near; 0-9609166),* 14909 Tomki Road, Redwood Valley, CA 95470 (SAN 264-2409) Tel 707-485-8598.

Near Eastern Press *See* **Holmes Publishing Group**

†**Nebraska Art Assn.,** *(Nebraska Art; 0-9602018),* Univ. of Nebraska-Lincoln, Sheldon Memorial Art Gallery, Lincoln, NE 68588-0300 (SAN 212-1972) Tel 402-472-2461; *CIP.*

Nebraska Review, *(Nebraska Review; 0-937796),* Southeast Community College, 924 K St., Fairbury, NE 68352 (SAN 220-262X).

†**Nebraska State Historical Society,** *(Nebraska Hist; 0-933307),* 1500 R St., P.O. Box 82554, Lincoln, NE 68501 (SAN 209-4630) Tel 402-471-4747; *CIP.*

Necronomicon Pr., *(Necronomicon; 0-940884),* 101 Lockwood St., West Warwick, RI 02893 (SAN 210-315X) Tel 401-828-5319.

Neechee Associates, Inc., *(Neechee Assoc; 0-9602582),* 6664 Paseo Dorado, Tucson, AZ 85715 (SAN 215-6865).

Needlemania, Inc., *(Needlemania),* P.O. Box 123, Franklin, MI 48025 (SAN 240-9208).

Neely Publishing Co., Div. of Neely Assocs., Inc., *(Neely Pub; 0-9616947),* 528 E. Boulevard, Charlotte, NC 28203 (SAN 661-7530) Tel 704-373-0051.

Neff-Kane *See* **Presidio Pr.**

Negative Capability Pr., *(Negative Capability Pr; 0-942544),* 6116 Timberly Rd. N, Mobile, AL 36609 (SAN 238-5465) Tel 205-661-9114.

Nehmer, Wilford, *(W Nehmer; 0-9616386),* 5362 Cedardale Dr., West Bend, WI 53095 (SAN 658-9782) Tel 414-644-8175.

Neighbors Publishing, *(Neighbors Pub; 0-933387),* P.O. Box 15071, Minneapolis, MN 55415 (SAN 691-6821) Tel 612-372-4489.

Neild/Kuvet Publishing Co., *(Neild-Kuvet; 0-912945),* P.O. Box 9184, Berkeley, CA 94709 (SAN 283-1015) Tel 415-527-9640.

Neiman, Michele, *(Neiman; 0-9615461),* 75 Juniper, Sierra Vista, AZ 85635 (SAN 695-7226) Tel 602-378-6894.

Neither/Nor Pr., The, *(Neither-Nor Pr; 0-911627),* P.O. Box 8043, Ann Arbor, MI 48107 (SAN 264-2417) Tel 313-434-6172.

Nel-Mar Enterprises, *(Nel Mar Enter; 0-9615760),* P.O. Box 1138, Wimberley, TX 78676 (SAN 695-8699) Tel 512-847-9415.

Nelson, Alice Jean, *(A J Nelson; 0-9614497),* 1233 Panama Dr., Sarasota, FL 33580 (SAN 689-3716) Tel 813-953-3656.

Nelson, G. L., Publishing, Inc., *(Nelson G L; 0-937416),* 1505 McCormick Pl., Wheaton, IL 60187 (SAN 287-2714).

Nelson, Irene J., *(I J Nelson; 0-9601464),* P.O. Box 28, Tuskegee Institute, AL 36088 (SAN 211-0725).

Nelson, Scott H., *(S H Nelson; 0-9616436),* 270 Spanglers Mill Rd., New Cumberland, PA 17070 (SAN 658-9855) Tel 717-774-6019.

Nelson, Ted, Pub., *(T Nelson; 0-89347),* Box 3, Schooleys Mountain, NJ 07870 (SAN 208-7820) Tel 312-352-8796; Dist. by: The Distributors, 702 S. Michigan, South Bend, IN 46618 (SAN 212-0364) Tel 219-232-8500.

Nelson, Thomas, Pubs., *(Nelson; 0-8407),* P.O. Box 141000, Nelson Pl. at Elm Hill Pike, Nashville, TN 37214 (SAN 209-3820) Tel 615-889-9000; Toll free: 800-872-4445; Toll free: 800-821-4370 (TN).

Nelson, Vera Joyce, *(V J Nelson),* 1969 SW Park, No. 310, Portland, OR 97201 (SAN 207-6829).

Nelson-Atkins Museum of Art, The, *(Nelson-Atkins; 0-942614),* 4525 Oak St., Kansas City, MO 64111 (SAN 238-5473) Tel 816-561-4000.

Nelson Communications, Subs. of Thomas Nelson Pubs., *(Nelson Comm; 0-8407),* Nelson Pl. at Elm Hill Pike, Nashville, TN 37214 (SAN 692-0543) Tel 615-889-9000; Toll free: 800-872-4445.

Nelson Graphics, *(Nelson Graphics; 0-936881),* 201 Weed St., New Canaan, CT 06840 (SAN 658-3733) Tel 203-966-8230.

†**Nelson-Hall, Inc.,** *(Nelson-Hall; 0-911012; 0-88229; 0-8304),* 111 N. Canal St., Chicago, IL 60606 (SAN 202-9065) Tel 312-930-9446; *CIP.*

Newmarket Publishing Co., *(Newmarket Pub; 0-918315),* P.O. Box 1624, Hoboken, NJ 07030 (SAN 657-2944) Tel 212-473-3652.

Nembutsu Pr., *(Nembutsu Pr; 0-912624),* 6257 Golden West Ave., Temple City, CA 91780 (SAN 208-0060).

Nemeth, Doris I., *(Nemeth; 0-932192),* 2314 W. Sixth St., Mishawaka, IN 46544 (SAN 217-118X).

Neo-Medical Publishing, *(Neo Med Pub; 0-9611870),* Moose River Rd., RD 3, Boonville, NY 13309 (SAN 286-1356) Tel 315-942-4253.

Neo Pr., *(Neo Pr; 0-911014),* P.O. Box 32, Peaks Island, ME 04108 (SAN 203-7300).

Neolog Publishing, *(Neolog; 0-9613477),* 422 High St., No. 17, Medford, MA 02156 (SAN 657-3673) Tel 617-391-7894.

Neptune Books *See* **Tail Feather**

Neptune Historical Society, *(Neptune His Soc),* 25 Neptune Blvd., Neptune, NJ 07754 (SAN 676-2093).

NERAS Systems, *(NERAS Syst),* 425 N. Doheny Dr., Suite 8, Beverly Hills, CA 90210 (SAN 211-1616) Tel 213-278-8584. Deceased.

Neri & Assocs., *(Neri & Assocs; 0-9615528),* 15720 Ventura Blvd. No. 502, Encino, CA 91436 (SAN 696-348X) Tel 818-906-0111.

Nesbit, Martha, *(M Nesbit; 0-9617126),* 25 E. 44th St., Savannah, GA 31405 (SAN 662-6777) Tel 912-232-7052.

Nesbit, Norman L., *(Nesbit; 0-911746),* 2104 Goddard Pl., Boulder, CO 80303 (SAN 206-1651) Tel 303-494-6206.

Nesbitt Enterprises, *(Nesbitt Ent),* 5220 NE Roselawn, Portland, OR 97218 (SAN 219-8029) Tel 503-287-0306.

Ness Pr., *(Ness Press; 0-938749),* 1650 President St., Apt. 1E, Brooklyn, NY 11213 (SAN 661-7522) Tel 718-778-0747.

Netherton, H. Eugene, *(Netherton),* 1035 Park Blvd., West Sacramento, CA 95691 (SAN 238-9029).

Nettleton House, *(Nettleton Hse),* 737 Fifth Ave., San Francisco, CA 94118 (SAN 214-4263).

Network Against Psychiatric Assault, *(NAPA),* 2054 University Ave., Rm. 406, Berkeley, CA 94704 (SAN 260-3748) Tel 415-548-2980.

Network Bks., *(Network GA Pubns; 0-915281),* Roundtree Bridge Rd., Sparks, GA 31647 (SAN 656-8998) Tel 912-549-7119.

Network Communications, Inc., Div. of Miranontes & Assocs., Inc., *(Network CA Comm; 0-934913),* 9880 Via Pasar, San Diego, CA 92126 (SAN 693-2053) Tel 619-549-3333.

Network for Ani-Males & Females, Inc., *(Network Ani-Males & Females; 0-938073),* 18707 Curry Powder Ln., Germantown, MD 20874 (SAN 661-2725) Tel 301-428-3675.

Network Media, Inc., *(Network Media; 0-939455),* 2812 W. Ramada Dr., Mobile, AL 36609 (SAN 663-3781) Tel 205-666-5170.

Network Project, *(Network Project),* Columbia Univ., 101 Earl Hall, New York, NY 10027 (SAN 206-166X) Tel 212-923-3900.

Network Pubns., Div. of ETR Assocs., Inc., *(Network Pubns; 0-941816),* P.O. Box 1830, Santa Cruz, CA 95061-1830 (SAN 216-2881) Tel 408-429-9822.

Neubauer Pr., *(Neubauer Pr; 0-9617265),* 268 Russell Rd., Princeton, NJ 08540 (SAN 663-4893) Tel 609-924-9629.

Neuberger, Phyllis J., *(P J Neuberger; 0-9610050),* 5855 Sheridan Rd., Chicago, IL 60660 (SAN 262-9607) Tel 312-334-7744; c/o Ten Plus, Inc., Thomas Graphics, Inc., 547 S. Clark St., Chicago, IL 60605 (SAN 262-9615) Tel 312-922-1301.

Neuffer, Claude Henry, *(C H Neuffer),* 4532 Meadowood Rd., Columbia, SC 29206 (SAN 207-2076) Tel 803-787-3823.

Neuropsychology Pr., *(Neuropsych Pr; 0-934515),* 1338 E. Edison St., Tucson, AZ 85719 (SAN 693-8256) Tel 602-795-3717.

Neuse Pr., *(Neuse Pr; 0-9613763),* P.O. Box 71, New Bern, NC 28560 (SAN 683-2938) Tel 919-637-4267.

Nev Multimedia Pubs., *(NEV Multimedia Pubs; 0-9606426),* 19 Summit Rd, Wellesley, MA 02181 (SAN 218-5709) Tel 617-237-7493.

Nevada County Historical Society, *(Nevada County Hist Society; 0-915641),* P.O. Box 1300, Nevada City, CA 95959 (SAN 291-8218) Tel 916-273-2909.

Nevada Families Project, *(NV Families Proj; 0-9616633),* 1916 Maryland Pkwy., Las Vegas, NV 89104-3106 (SAN 661-2121) Tel 702-878-1742.

Nevada League of Cities, *(NV League Cities),* Box 2307, Carson City, NV 89701 (SAN 226-1782).

Nevada Pubns., *(Nevada Pubns; 0-913814),* 4135 Badger Cir., Reno, NV 89509 (SAN 203-7319) Tel 702-747-0800.

Nevertheless Pr., *(Nevertheless; 0-9612532),* Box 9779, Berkeley, CA 94709 (SAN 679-1832).

Nevin, Mark, *(M Nevin; 0-9613132),* 1860 Ala Moana Apt. 704, Honolulu, HI 96815 (SAN 285-6751) Tel 808-941-6088.

Names

Nevins Publishing Co.,Inc., *(Nevins Pub Co; 0-914359),* 508-1A Auten Rd., Somerville, NJ 08876 (SAN 289-6613) Tel 201-874-5939.

New Age Action Group, *(New Age Action),* 910 Crescent Dr., Alexandria, VA 22302 (SAN 213-1293) Tel 703-836-4930.

New Age Bible & Philosophy Ctr., *(New Age Bible; 0-933963),* 1139 Lincoln Blvd., Santa Monica, CA 90403 (SAN 693-0697); Dist. by: DeVorss & Co., P.O. Box, 1046 Princeton Dr., Marina del Rey, CA 90294 (SAN 168-9886) Tel 213-870-7478.

New Age Business Books, *(New Age Bus Bks; 0-911201),* P.O. Box 423, Boulder City, NV 89005 (SAN 263-1687) Tel 702-293-6590.

New Age Ministries Spiritualist Church in Christ on Earth, *(New Age Min Spiritualist),* P.O. Box 129, Lake Helen, FL 32744 (SAN 211-7967).

New Age Pr., Inc., *(New Age; 0-87613),* P.O. Box 1216, Black Mountain, NC 28711 (SAN 203-7327) Tel 704-669-6214.

New Age Pub. Co., *(New Age FL Pub; 0-934619),* P.O. Box 011549, Miami, FL 33101 (SAN 694-0226) Tel 305-534-8437.

New Age Study of Humanity's Purpose, *(New Age Study Human; 0-9615287),* P.O. Box 41883, Tucson, AZ 85717 (SAN 694-4094) Tel 602-298-2222.

New American Library, *(NAL; 0-451; 0-452; 0-453),* 1633 Broadway, New York, NY 10019 (SAN 206-8079) Tel 212-397-8000; Orders to: P.O. Box 999, Bergenfield, NJ 07621 (SAN 206-8087) Tel 201-387-0600; Toll free: 800-526-0275. *Imprints:* Mentor Books (Ment); Meridian Books (Mer); Onyx (Onyx); Plume Books (Plume); Signet Books (Sig); Signet Classics (Sig Classics); Signette (Sgnt).

New American Library *See Norton, W. W., & Co., Inc.*

New Atlantis Pr., *(New Atlantis; 0-9615480),* 473 Pavonia Ave., Jersey City, NJ 07306 (SAN 695-9083) Tel 201-653-8221.

New Bedford Pr., *(New Bedford; 0-931656),* 5800 W. Century Blvd., Dept. 91502, Los Angeles, CA 90009 (SAN 219-9688) Tel 213-837-2961. *Imprints:* Bedpress Books (Bedpress).

New Beginnings Co., *(New Begin Co; 0-932489),* 711 E. Walnut St. Suite 401, Pasadena, CA 91101 (SAN 687-4304) Tel 818-793-3612.

New Benjamin Franklin Hse., The, *(New Benjamin; 0-933488),* 304 W. 58th St., 5th Flr., New York, NY 10019 (SAN 212-6168) Tel 212-247-7484. *Imprints:* University Editions (Univ Edns).

New Books, Inc. *See Berg, R. J., & Co.*

New Boundary Design Inc., *(New Boundary Design; 0-913703),* 1453 Park Rd., Chanhassen, MN 55317 (SAN 286-0899) Tel 612-474-0924; Toll free: 800-328-6795.

New Breed Pr., *Div. of Light Mgmt., (New Breed Pr; 0-9617166),* 10664 Bluffside Dr., Studio City, CA 91604 (SAN 662-9482) Tel 213-826-4433.

New Canaan Historical Society, *(New Canaan; 0-939958),* 13 Oenoke Ridge, New Canaan, CT 06840 (SAN 216-843X) Tel 203-966-1776.

New Capernaum Works, *Div. of Universal Spiritual Action, (New Capernaum; 0-938792),* 4615 NE Emerson St., Portland, OR 97218 (SAN 215-8922) Tel 503-281-1307.

New Century Pubns., Inc., *Div. of New Century Education Corp., (New Century; 0-8329),* 220 Old New Brunswick Rd., Piscataway, NJ 08854 (SAN 217-1201) Tel 201-981-0820.

New Choices Pr., *(New Choices; 0-934297),* 610 West End Ave., New York, NY 10024 (SAN 693-3165) Tel 212-362-6808.

New City Pr., *(New City; 0-911782),* 206 Skillman Ave., Brooklyn, NY 11211 (SAN 203-7335) Tel 718-782-2844.

New Classics Library, Inc., *(New Classics Lib; 0-932750),* P.O. Box 1618, Gainesville, GA 30503 (SAN 212-1190) Tel 404-536-0309; Toll free: 800-336-1618.

New Collage Press, *(New Collage; 0-936814),* 5700 N. Tamiami Trail, Sarasota, FL 33580 (SAN 210-6159) Tel 813-355-7671; Dist. by: Faxon Co., The, 15 SW Park, Westwood, MA 02090 (SAN 159-8619) Tel 617-329-3350; Toll free: 800-225-6055.

New Collectors Group, *(New Collectors; 0-9616634),* 259 S. Teller St., Apt. 311, Lakewood, CO 80226-7338 (SAN 661-214X) Tel 303-238-5805.

New College & Univ. Pr., The, *(New Coll U Pr; 0-8084),* P.O. Box 1392, Schenectady, NY 12301 (SAN 203-6223) Tel 518-346-2649. *Imprints:* Twayne's U. S. Author Series (Twayne).

New Cometerra Press, *(New Comet; 0-914701),* P.O. Box 1026, Palatine, IL 60078 (SAN 289-6982) Tel 312-397-8005.

New Concepts Publishing, Inc., *(New Concepts Pub; 0-941136),* 475 Fifth Ave., New York, NY 10017 (SAN 217-4081) Tel 212-889-3241.

New Dawn Pubns., *(New Dawn; 0-934271),* 1605 Edith Ln., Colorado Springs, CO 80909 (SAN 693-3181) Tel 303-591-9556.

New Day Pr., *(New Day Pr; 0-913678),* c/o Karamu Hse., 2355 E. 89th St., Cleveland, OH 44106 (SAN 279-2664).

New Day Pubns, Inc., *(New Day Pubns; 0-9605994; 0-9612328),* P.O. Box 70161, Washington, DC 20088 (SAN 216-7530) Tel 301-439-0271; 910 Newhall St., Silver Spring, MD 20901 (SAN 293-4841).

New Dimension Studio, *(New Dimen Studio; 0-916928),* 3872 Augusta Dr., Rm. 1, Nashville, TN 37209 (SAN 208-385X) Tel 615-876-6371; Orders to: P.O. Box 90492, Nashville, TN 37209 (SAN 208-3868).

New Directions for Young Women, Inc., *(New Dir Young Women; 0-9608696),* 2356 E. Hampton St., Tucson, AZ 85719 (SAN 240-7337) Tel 602-327-4022.

New Directions Press, *(New Dir Pr; 0-9609616),* 80 Eighth Ave., New York, NY 10011 (SAN 260-2326) Tel 212-255-0230.

New Directions Publishing, *(New Dir Salem; 0-938393),* 4743 Nighthawk Ct., NE, Salem, OR 97301 (SAN 661-3853) Tel 503-362-4415.

†New Directions Publishing Corp., *(New Directions; 0-8112),* 80 Eighth Ave., New York, NY 10011 (SAN 202-9081) Tel 212-255-0230; Toll free: 800-223-2584; Dist. by: W. W. Norton Co., 500 Fifth Ave., New York, NY 10110 (SAN 202-5795) Tel 212-354-5500; *CIP.*

New England & Regional Allergy Proceedings, *Affil. of New England Society of Allergy, (New Eng & Reg All; 0-936587),* 95 Pitman St., Providence, RI 02906 (SAN 698-0856) Tel 401-331-2510.

New England Gerontology Ctr., *(New Eng GE; 0-89634),* Dist. by: Systems Planning Assocs., Pub. Div., 3 Aliber Pl., Keene, NH 03431 (SAN 287-3028) Tel 603-357-4005.

New England Historic Genealogical Society, *(New Eng Hist; 0-88082),* 101 Newbury St., Boston, MA 02116 (SAN 274-0117) Tel 617-536-5740.

New England History Pr., *Subs. of NH Publishing Co., Inc., (NE History; 0-89725),* P.O. Box 70, Somersworth, NH 03878 (SAN 264-2433).

New England Old Newspaper Index, *(New Eng Old News),* P.O. Box 152, Danville, ME 04223 (SAN 295-0502).

New England Pr., *(New England Pr; 0-931060),* 45 Tudor City, No. 1903, New York, NY 10017 (SAN 211-9196).

New England Pr., Inc., The, *(New Eng Pr VT; 0-933050),* P.O. Box 575, Shelburne, VT 05482 (SAN 213-6376) Tel 802-863-2520.

New England Pub. Co., *(New Eng Pub MA; 0-914265),* 728 Hampden St., Holyoke, MA 01040 (SAN 287-5837) Tel 413-533-4231.

New England Science Fiction Assn., *(New Eng SF Assoc; 0-915368),* Box G, MIT Branch P.O., Cambridge, MA 02139 (SAN 223-8187).

New Era Pr., *(New Era Pr; 0-937590),* P.O. Box 124, Weaverville, CA 96093 (SAN 215-8930) Tel 916-623-5966. Do no confuse with New Era Pubns., Happy Camp, CA, or New Era Pr., Of Farmingdale, NY.

New Era Pubns., Inc., *(New Era Pubns MI; 0-939830),* P.O. Box 8139, Ann Arbor, MI 48107 (SAN 220-1941) Tel 313-663-1929.

New Era Pubns. *See World Merchandise-Import Center*

New Expressions Unltd., *(New Expressions),* 30886 Sutherland Dr., Redlands, CA 92373 (SAN 209-4053) Tel 714-794-4868.

New Fortress Pubns., *(New Fortress Pub; 0-937799),* 2332 S. Peck Rd., Suite 268, Whittier, CA 90601 (SAN 659-3801) Tel 213-699-3443.

New Forums Pr., Inc., *(New Forums; 0-913507),* P.O. Box 876, Stillwater, OK 74076 (SAN 285-8673) Tel 405-372-6158.

New Hampshire Publishing Co., *(NH Pub Co; 0-912274; 0-89725),* P.O. Box 70, Somersworth, NH 03878 (SAN 202-9189) Tel 603-692-3727.

New Harbinger Pubns., *(New Harbinger; 0-934986),* 2200 Adeline, Suite 305, Oakland, CA 94607 (SAN 205-0587).

New Haven Pubs., *Subs. of New Haven Publishers, (New Haven Pubs; 0-918313),* 1703 N. Tyland Blvd., New Haven, IN 46774 (SAN 657-2928) Tel 219-749-2646.

New Hope, *(New Hope AL; 0-936625),* P.O. Box 11657, Birmingham, AL 35202-1657 (SAN 699-7015) Tel 205-991-8100; 100 Missionary Ridge, Birmingham, AL 35202-1657 (SAN 699-7023).

New Hope Books *See Revell, Fleming H., Co.*

†New Horizon Pr. Pubs., Inc., *(New Horizon NJ; 0-88282),* P.O. Box 669, Far Hills, NJ 07931 (SAN 677-119X) Tel 201-234-9546; Toll free: 800-257-5755; Orders to: Charles Scribner & Sons, Front & Brown Sts., Riverside, NJ 08075 (SAN 663-3099); *CIP.*

New Horizons Bk. Publishing Co., *(New Hor Bk; 0-932279),* P.O. Box 10904, Marina del Rey, CA 90295 (SAN 686-547X) Tel 213-827-4940.

†New Horizons Pr., *(New Horizons; 0-914914),* P.O. Box 1758, Chico, CA 95927 (SAN 206-7927) Tel 916-895-6227; *CIP.*

New Horizons Publishing, *(New Horizons Pub; 0-9613807),* P.O. Box 23416, Santa Barbara, CA 93121 (SAN 679-4017).

New Horizons Pubs., *(New Hor Pubs; 0-915325),* 737 Tenth Ave., E., Seattle, WA 98102 (SAN 290-0238) Tel 206-323-1102; Dist. by: Pacific Pipeline, Inc., 19215 66th Ave. S., Kent, WA 98032 (SAN 208-2128) Tel 206-872-5523; Toll free: 800-426-4727.

New Idea Pr., Inc., *(New Idea Pr; 0-9617099),* P.O. Box 13683, Boulder, CO 80308-3683 (SAN 662-5002); 1736 36th St., Boulder, CO 80308-3683 (SAN 662-5010) Tel 303-494-4488.

New Image, *(New Image; 0-9609168),* 310 Colima Ct., La Jolla, CA 92037 (SAN 241-4163) Tel 619-456-2122.

New Impressions, *(New Impressions; 0-9611606),* Box 558, 118 Middle St., Lancaster, NH 03584 (SAN 285-2942) Tel 603-788-4492.

New In Chess, *(New Chess),* 2423 Noble Station, Bridgeport, CT 06608 (SAN 683-2946).

New Issues, Inc., *(New Issues; 0-9616275),* P.O. Box 11564, Milwaukee, WI 53211 (SAN 658-5922) Tel 414-962-6990; 2720 N. Frederick Ave., Suite 232, Milwaukee, WI 53211 (SAN 658-5930).

New Jersey Assocs., *(NJ Assocs; 0-911273),* Box 505, Montclair, NJ 07042 (SAN 285-0702) Tel 201-746-2000.

New Jersey Dept. of Education, *(NJ DOE; 0-916855),* 225 W. State St., CN 500, Trenton, NJ 08625 (SAN 654-3138) Tel 609-292-5850.

†New Jersey Historical Society, *(NJ Hist Soc; 0-911020),* 230 Broadway, Newark, NJ 07104 (SAN 205-7131) Tel 201-483-3939; *CIP.*

New Jersey Institute for Continuing Legal Education, *(NJ Inst CLE; 0-939457),* 15 Washington St., Suite 1400, Newark, NJ 07101 (SAN 226-997X) Tel 201-648-5571.

New Jersey Schl. Board Assn., *(NJ Schl Bds; 0-912337),* P.O. Box 909, Trenton, NJ 08605 (SAN 226-1847) Tel 609-695-7600.

New Jersey State Museum, *(NJ State Mus; 0-938766),* 205 W. State St., Trenton, NJ 08625 (SAN 220-2638) Tel 609-292-6300.

New Jersey Veterinary Medical Assn., *(New Jersey Vet; 0-9614059),* P.O. Box 320, Rockaway, NJ 07866 (SAN 686-0036) Tel 201-379-1100.

New Leaf Pr., *(New Leaf; 0-89221),* P.O. Box 311, Green Forest, AR 72638 (SAN 207-9518) Tel 501-438-5288; Toll free: 800-643-9535.

New Letters Bks., *(New Letters MO; 0-938652),* 5310 Harrison, Kansas City, MO 64110 (SAN 209-8458) Tel 816-276-1168.

New Life Pubns., *(New Life Pubns; 0-935379),* 2730 Lapey, Rockford, IL 61109 (SAN 696-3234) Tel 815-397-4563.

New Life Pubs., Subs. of Creative New Life Ministries, *(New Life Pubs; 0-9616016),* 1797 S. Monrovia, Costa Mesa, CA 92627 (SAN 697-2942) Tel 714-642-4053.

New Life Thru Faith Pubns., *(New Life Faith; 0-934285),* P.O. Box 598, Mesa, AZ 85201 (SAN 693-3173) Tel 602-898-8513.

New Lifestyle Publishing, *(New Lifestyle; 0-941256),* P.O. Box 4419, Los Angeles, CA 90051 (SAN 239-4642) Tel 213-660-8201.

New London County Historical Society, *(New London County; 0-9607744),* 11 Blinman St., New London, CT 06320 (SAN 207-0049) Tel 203-443-1209.

New London Pr., *(New London Pr; 0-89683),* Box 7458, Dallas, TX 75209 (SAN 211-4402) Tel 214-742-9037.

New Meridian Pr., *(New Meridian Pr; 0-914882),* P.O. Box 229, Clifton Park, NY 12065 (SAN 206-5045) Tel 518-877-5845.

New Mexico Magazine, *(New Mexico Mag; 0-937206),* Bataan Memorial Building, Santa Fe, NM 87503 (SAN 677-072X).

†New Mexico State Univ., Ctr. for Latin American Studies, *(NMSU CLAS; 0-937793),* Campus Box 3JBR, Las Cruces, NM 88003 (SAN 659-3607) Tel 505-646-3254; 1200 University Ave., Las Cruces, NM 88003 (SAN 659-3615); *CIP.*

New Mexico State Univ., Center for Real Estate & Land Resource Research, Div. of New Mexico State Univ., *(NM St U Ctr Real Est; 0-934471),* New Mexico State Univ., Box 3 Rea, Las Cruces, NM 88001 (SAN 693-7640) Tel 505-646-5176.

New Mexico State Univ. - Studies in Latin American Popular Culture, *(New Mexico St Univ; 0-9608664),* Dept. of Foreign Languages, Box 3L, Las Cruces, NM 88003 (SAN 239-5428) Tel 505-646-2942.

New Mind Prods., *(New Mind Prod; 0-933821),* P.O. Box 5185, Jersey City, NJ 07305 (SAN 200-5565) Tel 201-434-1939.

New Mississippi, Inc., *(New Mississippi; 0-9616362),* P.O. Box 3568, Jackson, MS 39207 (SAN 658-9863) Tel 601-352-3398.

New Museum of Contemporary Art, The, *(New Mus Contemp Art; 0-915557),* 583 Broadway, New York, NY 10012 (SAN 291-3070) Tel 212-219-1222; Dist. by: Contemporary Arts Press, P.O. Box 3123, Rincon Annex, San Francisco, CA 94119 (SAN 213-3016) Tel 415-431-7672.

New Music Times, Inc., The, *(New Music Times; 0-9606830),* P.O. Box 8573, Albany, NY 12208 (SAN 219-6115) Tel 518-438-4815.

New Nativity Pr., *(New Nativity; 0-940128),* P.O. Box 6223, Leawood, KS 66206 (SAN 217-0779) Tel 913-341-8369.

New Nurse, Pub., The, *(New Nurse; 0-914698),* P.O. Box 803, Plattsburgh, NY 12901 (SAN 206-6041). Name Formerly Hanton.

New Options Publishing, *(New Options Pub; 0-9614635),* 1939 Park Ave., Denver, CO 80218 (SAN 692-3968) Tel 303-830-7718; Dist. by: Bookpeople, 2929 Fifth St., Berkeley, CA 94710 (SAN 168-9517) Tel 415-549-3030; Toll free: 800-227-1516; Dist. by: Inland Bk. Co., P.O. Box 261, 22 Hemingway Ave., East Haven, CT 06512 (SAN 200-4151) Tel 203-467-4257.

†New Orleans Museum of Art, *(New Orleans Mus Art; 0-89494),* P.O. Box 19123, New Orleans, LA 70179-0123 (SAN 209-9713) Tel 504-488-2631; Dist. by: Univ. of Wash. Pr., P.O. Box C50096, Seattle, WA 98145 (SAN 212-2502) Tel 206-543-8870; *CIP.*

New Orleans Poetry Journal Pr., The, *(New Orleans Poetry; 0-938498),* 2131 General Pershing St., New Orleans, LA 70115 (SAN 215-8949).

New Orleans Urban Folklife Society, *(New Orleans Urban; 0-9613133),* 1210 Short St., New Orleans, LA 70118 (SAN 658-2524) Tel 504-866-8940.

†New Outlook Pubs. & Distributors, The, *(New Outlook; 0-87898),* 235 W. 23rd St., New York, NY 10011 (SAN 202-9111); *CIP.*

New Pacific Pubns., Inc., *(New Pacific Pubns; 0-932737),* 21650 Burbank Blvd., No. 103, Woodland Hills, CA 91367 (SAN 688-5659) Tel 818-884-3987.

New Pages Pr., *(New Pages Pr; 0-941644),* P.O. Box 438, Grand Blanc, MI 48439 (SAN 239-2682) Tel 313-743-8055.

New Paradise Bks., *(New Paradise Bks; 0-943654),* Suite 206, 3000 N. Atlantic, Cocoa Beach, FL 32931 (SAN 238-0765) Tel 305-783-5655.

New Past Pr., Inc., The, *(New Past Pr; 0-938627),* RR 2, 2098 18th Ave., Friendship, WI 53934 (SAN 661-6283) Tel 608-339-3907.

New Pen Publishing Co., *(New Pen Pub Co; 0-9609808),* P.O. Box 1690, Newark, NJ 07101 (SAN 264-2476).

New Pittsburgh Pubns., *(New Pittsburgh; 0-9608484),* P.O. Box 81875, Pittsburgh, PA 15217 (SAN 240-7345) Tel 412-681-8528.

New Place Pr., *(New Place Pr; 0-9617167),* P.O. Box 2902, Taunton, MA 02780 (SAN 662-9490); 50 Prospect St., Taunton, MA 02780 (SAN 662-9504) Tel 617-823-0305.

New Plays-Bks., Inc., *(New Plays Bks; 0-932720),* Box 273, Rowayton, CT 06853 (SAN 220-9411).

New Poets Series, *(New Poets; 0-932616),* 541 Piccadilly Rd., Baltimore, MD 21204 (SAN 209-4622) Tel 301-321-2863.

New Product Development Newsletter Co., *(New Prod Develop; 0-911909),* P.O. Box 1309, Point Pleasant, NJ 08742 (SAN 265-4083).

New Puritan Library, Inc., *(New Puritan; 0-932050),* 91 Lytle Rd., Fletcher, NC 28732 (SAN 213-4217).

New Ray Pr., *(New Ray Pr; 0-936303),* 27835 Troublesome Gulch Rd., Kittredge, CO 80457 (SAN 697-2993) Tel 303-674-0534; P.O. Box 549, Kittredge, CO 80457 (SAN 697-3000).

New Readers Pr., Div. of Laubach Literacy International, *(New Readers; 0-88336),* Box 131, Syracuse, NY 13210 (SAN 202-1064) Tel 315-422-9121; Toll free: 800-448-8878. *Imprints:* Sundown (Sundown).

New Research Pubns., *(New Research; 0-910891),* P.O. Box 231, Greenvale, NY 11548 (SAN 274-0389) Tel 516-293-1171.

New Riders Publishing, *(New Riders Pubn; 0-934035),* P.O. Box 4846, Thousand Oaks, CA 91360 (SAN 692-9575) Tel 818-991-5392.

New Rivers Pr., *(New Rivers Pr; 0-912284; 0-89823),* 1602 Selby Ave., St. Paul, MN 55104 (SAN 202-9138) Tel 612-645-6324; Dist. by: Bookslinger, 213 E. Fourth St., Saint Paul, MN 55101 (SAN 169-4154) Tel 612-221-0429; Dist. by: Small Press Distribution, Inc., 1814 San Pablo Ave., Berkeley, CA 94702 (SAN 204-5826) Tel 415-549-3336.

New Santander Pr., Subs. of Omni-Media, Inc., *(New Santander; 0-935071),* 721 W. Sprague, P.O. Box 306, Edinburg, TX 78540 (SAN 694-6534) Tel 512-383-2567.

New Schl. for Music Study Pr., *(New Schl Mus Study; 0-913277),* P.O. Box 407, Princeton, NJ 08540 (SAN 285-8266) Tel 609-921-2900.

New Science Pr., *(New Sci Pr; 0-9616114),* 106 Henry St., Greenwich, CT 06830 (SAN 699-7341) Tel 203-531-5312.

New Seed Pr., *(New Seed; 0-938678),* P.O. Box 9488, Berkeley, CA 94709 (SAN 282-0501); Dist. by: Bookpeople, 2929 Fifth St., Berkeley, CA 94710 (SAN 168-9517); Dist. by: Childrens Small Press Collection, The, 719 N Fourth Ave., Ann Arbor, MI 48104 (SAN 200-6081); Dist. by: Inland Book Co., Inc., P.O. Box 261, 22 Hemingway Ave., E. Haven, CT 06512 (SAN 200-4151) Tel 203-467-4257.

New Sibylline Bks., Inc., *(New Sibylline; 0-9603352),* Box 266, Village Sta., New York, NY 10014 (SAN 214-4271).

New Society Pubs., Div. of New Society Education Foundation, Inc., *(New Soc Pubs; 0-86571),* 4722 Baltimore Ave., Philadelphia, PA 19143 (SAN 213-540X) Tel 215-726-6543.

New South Co., The, *(New South Co; 0-917990),* P.O. Box 24918, Los Angeles, CA 90024-0918 (SAN 209-3340) Tel 714-548-9279.

New South Moulton Pr., *(South Moulton Pr; 0-939731),* 96 Rumsey Rd., Buffalo, NY 14209 (SAN 663-5873) Tel 716-881-3626.

New Start Pubns., Inc., *(New Start Pubns; 0-915451),* P.O. Box 139, Sterling, VA 22170 (SAN 291-3119) Tel 703-450-5983.

New Testament Christian Pr., *(New Testament Christ Pr; 0-931247),* P.O. Box 1694, Media, PA 19063 (SAN 682-0050) Tel 215-544-5065.

New Tide MTL Pubs., *(New Tide; 0-88100),* Box 21 Contra Station Six, 1525 Sherman St., Denver, CO 80203 (SAN 264-2492).

New Univ. Pr., *(New Univ Pr; 0-89044),* 737 N. LaSalle St., Chicago, IL 60610 (SAN 680-0661) Tel 312-944-2525; Orders to: Daphnean Press, 737 N. LaSalle St., Chicago, IL 60610 (SAN 657-1344) Tel 312-944-2525.

New Venture Research Institute, Subs. of Berk Enterprises, Inc., *(New Venture; 0-916735),* 84 Slater Ave., Providence, RI 02906 (SAN 653-8983) Tel 401-438-1324.

New Victora Pubs., Inc., *(New Victoria Pubs; 0-934678),* P.O. Box 27, Norwich, VT 05055 (SAN 212-1204) Tel 802-649-5297.

New Virginia Review, Inc., *(New VA),* 1306 E. Cary St., 2A, Richmond, VA 23219 (SAN 656-898X) Tel 804-782-1043.

New Vision Pubns., *(New Vision; 0-916337),* 1438 Ridge Rd., Homewood, IL 60430 (SAN 295-7299) Tel 312-957-5856.

New Visions Pr., *(New Visions Pr; 0-934340),* P.O. Box 2025, Gaithersburg, MD 20760 (SAN 212-9213) Tel 301-869-1888.

New Vista Pr., *(New Vista; 0-936544),* 10 Oak Tree Dr.,, Santa Rosa, CA 95401 (SAN 293-3098).

New Vistas Publishing, *(New Vistas Pub; 0-9616881),* P.O. Box 44, Simi Valley, CA 93062 (SAN 661-6569); 6676 Charing St., Simi Valley, CA 93063 (SAN 661-6577) Tel 805-583-4228.

New Voices *See Noontide Pr., The*

New Wave Consultants, *(New Wave; 0-943172),* P.O. Box 2203, La Jolla, CA 92038 (SAN 240-415X) Tel 619-274-2030.

New Ways Ministry, *(New Ways Min; 0-935877),* 4012 29th St., Mount Rainier, MD 20712 (SAN 695-877X) Tel 301-277-5674.

New Ways to Work, *(New Ways Work),* 149 Ninth St., San Francisco, CA 94103 (SAN 663-4664).

New West Hse. Pubs., The, *(New West Hse; 0-9614974),* Box 175, Bruneau, ID 83604 (SAN 693-5591) Tel 208-845-2502.

New Woman Pr., *(New Woman),* 2000 King Mountain Trail, Sunny Valley, OR 97497-9799 (SAN 209-8474).

†New World Bks., *(New World Bks; 0-917480),* 4515 Saul Rd., Kensington, MD 20895 (SAN 208-3388); *CIP.*

†New World Bks., *(New World NY; 0-917601),* P.O. Box 117, East Elmhurst, NY 11369 (SAN 657-1530) Tel 718-545-6434; *CIP.*

New World Bks., *(New World OH; 0-9615748),* 336 Ludlow Ave., Cincinnati, OH 45220 (SAN 695-913X) Tel 513-861-6100.

New World Cup Press, *(New World Cup CA; 0-9604636),* 9061 Madison Ave., Westminster, CA 92683 (SAN 215-1634).

New World Paperbacks *See International Pubs. Co.*

†New World Press, *(New World Press NY; 0-911026),* P.O. Box 416, New York, NY 10017 (SAN 203-736X) Tel 212-972-0460; *CIP.*

New World Pubns., *(New World Pubns; 0-916933),* P.O. Box 244, Highlands, NJ 07732 (SAN 655-7643) Tel 201-741-6109.

New Worlds Unlimited, *(New Worlds; 0-917398),* 3-42 26th St., Fair Lawn, NJ 07410 (SAN 207-267X); Orders to: P.O. Box 556, Saddle Brook, NJ 07662 (SAN 207-2688).

New Writers Guild Pr., *(New Writers Guild; 0-913459),* 6323 Rimpau Blvd., Los Angeles, CA 90043 (SAN 277-6960) Tel 213-293-1281.

New Year Pubns., *(New Year Pubns; 0-935341),* 316 Fifth Ave., New York, NY 10001 (SAN 696-3013) Tel 212-868-3330.

†New York Academy of Sciences, *(NY Acad Sci; 0-89072; 0-89766),* Pubns. Dept., 2 E. 63rd St., New York, NY 10021 (SAN 203-753X) Tel 212-838-0230; Toll free: 800-843-6927; *CIP.*

Names

†**New York Botanical Garden,** *(NY Botanical; 0-89327),* Scientific Pubns. Dept., Bronx, NY 10458 (SAN 205-7085) Tel 212-220-8721; *CIP.*

†**New York Bound,** *(NY Bound; 0-9608788),* 43 W. 54th St., New York, NY 10019 (SAN 238-3195) Tel 212-245-8503; *CIP.*

New York Chamber of Commerce and Industry, *(NY Chamber; 0-9613808),* 200 Madison Ave., New York, NY 10016 (SAN 679-405X) Tel 212-561-2176; 65 Liberty St., New York, NY 10005 (SAN 692-820X)

New York Chiropractic College, *(NY Chiro Coll; 0-938470),* P.O. Box 167, Glen Head, NY 11545 (SAN 216-1680).

New York Circus Pubns., Inc., *(NY Circus Pubns),* P.O. Box 37, Times Sq. Sta., New York, NY 10108 (SAN 661-440X).

New York City Coalition for Women's Mental Health, *(NYCCWMH; 0-9616908),* 320 W. 86th St., No 2B, New York, NY 10024 (SAN 697-9203) Tel 212-787-1766.

New York City Commission on the Status of Women, *(NYC Comm Women; 0-9610688),* 52 Chambers St., Suite 207, New York, NY 10007 (SAN 240-9224) Tel 212-566-3830; Dist. by: Golden Lee, 1000 Dean St., Brooklyn, NY 11238 (SAN 282-5805) Tel 718-857-6333; Dist. by: Inland Bk. Co., P.O. Box 261, 22 Hemingway Ave., East Haven, CT 06512 (SAN 200-4151) Tel 203-467-4257.

New York City Publishing Co., *(NYC Pub Co; 0-9614772),* 37 W. 37th St. 4th Flr., New York, NY 10018 (SAN 696-0758).

New York Graphic Society Bks., Div. of Little, Brown & Co., *(NYGS; 0-8212),* 34 Beacon St., Boston, MA 02106 (SAN 202-5841) Tel 617-227-0730; Toll free: 800-343-9204; Dist. by: Little, Brown & Co., 200 W. St., Waltham, MA 02254 (SAN 281-8892). *Imprints:* Philadelphia Maritime Museum (Phila Maritime Mus)

New York Graphic Society in Greenwich, *(NYGS CT),* P.O. Box 1469, Greenwich, CT 06836 (SAN 209-2492) Tel 203-661-2400.

†**New York Institute of Finance,** *(NY Inst Finance),* 70 Pine St., New York, NY 10270-0003 (SAN 239-3697) Tel 212-344-2900; *CIP.*

New York Labor News, *(NY Labor News; 0-935534),* 914 Industrial Ave., Palo Alto, CA 94303 (SAN 202-0947) Tel 415-494-1532.

New York Law Journal, *(NY Law Journ),* 111 Eighth Ave., New York, NY 10011 (SAN 287-7023) Tel 212-741-8300. Microfilm & Microfiche.

New York Law Publishing Co., *(NY Law Pub),* 111 Eighth Ave., New York, NY 10011 (SAN 226-2800) Tel 212-741-8300.

New York Library Assn., *(NY Lib Assn; 0-931658),* 15 Park Row, Suite 434, New York, NY 10038 (SAN 211-6758) Tel 212-227-8032.

†**New York Literary Forum,** *(NY Lit Forum; 0-931196),* 21 E. 79th St., New York, NY 10021 (SAN 212-9221); *CIP.*

†**New York Literary Press,** *(NY Lit Pr; 0-930910),* 417 W. 56th St., New York, NY 10019 (SAN 211-5379); *CIP.*

New York-New Jersey Trail Conference, Inc., *(NY-NJ Trail Confer; 0-9603966),* 232 Madison Ave., New York, NY 10016 (SAN 213-9421).

New York Outdoor Guide, Inc., *(NY Outdoor Guide; 0-937328),* 328 E. Main, Rm. 300, Rochester, NY 14604 (SAN 215-6873) Tel 716-325-1636.

New York Party Directory Publishing Assocs., The, *(NY Party Pub Ass; 0-933255),* 123 E. 54th St., Suite 6C, New York, NY 10022 (SAN 692-3984) Tel 212-486-0410.

New York Production Manual, Inc., *(NY Prod Manual; 0-935744),* 611 Broadway, Suite 807, New York, NY 10012-2608 (SAN 213-6384) Tel 212-777-4002.

New York Public Library, *(NY Pub Lib; 0-87104),* Publications Office, Fifth Ave. & 42nd St., New York, NY 10018 (SAN 202-926X) Tel 212-512-0203; Orders to: Publishing Ctr. for Cultural Resources, 625 Broadway, New York, NY 10012 (SAN 209-9926) Tel 212-260-2010; Orders to: New York Public Library, Branch Libraries, 455 Fifth Ave., New York, NY 10016 (SAN 695-6254) Tel 212-340-0897. *Imprints:* Branch Libraries (Branch Libraries).

New York Review of Books, Inc., The, *(NY Rev Bks; 0-940322),* 250 W. 57th St., New York, NY 10019 (SAN 220-3448) Tel 212-757-8070.

New York State Bar Assn., *(NYS Bar; 0-942954),* 1 Elk St., Albany, NY 12207 (SAN 226-1952) Tel 518-463-3200.

New York State College of Agriculture & Life Sciences, *(NY St Coll Ag; 0-9605314; 0-9609010),* Media Services, 1152 Comstock Hall, Cornell Univ., Ithaca, NY 14853 (SAN 282-0536) Tel 607-255-3126; Orders to: 7 Research Park, Cornell Univ., Ithaca, NY 14850 (SAN 282-0544) Tel 607-255-2080.

New York State Council on the Arts, *(NYSCA),* 915 Broadway, New York, NY 10010 (SAN 220-0767) Tel 212-614-2903.

New York State Dept. of Environmental Conservation, *(NYS Dept Environ Conserv; 0-9615433),* 50 Wolf Rd., Rm. 522, Albany, NY 12233-4753 (SAN 696-2777) Tel 518-457-8174.

New York State Education Dept., *(NYS Ed Dept),* State Univ. of New York, State Education Bldg., Albany, NY 12234 (SAN 280-6215).

New York State English Council, *(NY St Eng Coun; 0-930348),* P.O. Box 2397, Liverpool, NY 13089 (SAN 211-0377) Tel 315-487-4566.

New York State Institute For Glaze Research, *(NYS Inst Glaze; 0-914267),* 511 N. Hamilton St., Painted Post, NY 14870 (SAN 287-5861) Tel 607-962-1671.

New York State Library, *(NYS Library),* CEC, ESP, Albany, NY 12230 (SAN 205-7034) Tel 418-474-5953.

New York State Museum, *(NYS Museum; 1-55557),* Univ. of the State of New York, 3140 Cultural Education Ctr., Albany, NY 12230 (SAN 205-7026) Tel 518-474-3505.

New York State School of Industrial & Labor Relations, Cornell Extension, *(NY Ind Labor; 0-9615917),* 15 E. 26th St., New York, NY 10010 (SAN 696-6586) Tel 212-340-2800.

New York Times, *(NY Times),* 229 W. 43rd St., New York, NY 10036 (SAN 208-3027) Tel 212-556-7291.

New York Univ. Pr., *(NYU Pr; 0-8147),* 70 Washington Sq., S., New York, NY 10012 (SAN 658-1293) Tel 212-598-2886; Dist. by: Columbia Univ. Pr., 562 W. 113th St., New York, NY 10025 (SAN 212-2472) Tel 212-316-7100.

New York Zoetrope, *(NY Zoetrope; 0-918432),* 80 E. 11th St., New York, NY 10003 (SAN 209-6293) Tel 212-420-0590; Toll free: 800-242-7546.

New You Publishing Co., *(New You Pub; 0-917762),* 609 Santa Cruz Ave., Menlo Park, CA 94025 (SAN 209-0317) Tel 415-322-9959.

Newark Beth Israel Medical Ctr., *(Newark Beth; 0-937714),* 201 Lyons Ave., Newark, NJ 07112 (SAN 215-3297).

†**Newark Museum Assn., The,** *(Newark Mus; 0-932828),* 49 Washington St., P.O. Box 540, Newark, NJ 07101 (SAN 205-700X) Tel 201-396-6550; *CIP.*

Newaves Publishing, *(Newaves Pub; 0-930946),* P.O. Box 5169, Santa Monica, CA 90405 (SAN 211-3422).

Newberry Library, *(Newberry; 0-911028),* 60 W. Walton St., Chicago, IL 60610 (SAN 203-7378) Tel 312-943-9090; Toll free: 800-621-2736.

Newbold Enterprises, *(Newbold Ent; 0-9616906),* 860 Paiute Ln., Susanville, CA 96130 (SAN 661-518X) Tel 916-257-2009.

Newbold Publishing Inc., *(Newbold Pub; 0-910945),* 142-20 Franklin Ave., Flushing, NY 11355 (SAN 264-2514) Tel 718-463-2862.

Newbury Bks., *(Newbury Bks; 0-912728; 0-912729),* P.O. Box 29, Topsfield, MA 01983 (SAN 203-7386) Tel 617-887-5082.

†**Newbury Hse. Pubs.,** *(Newbury Hse; 0-88377; 0-912066),* 54 Church St., Cambridge, MA 02138 (SAN 202-9146) Tel 617-492-0670; Toll free: 800-343-1240; *CIP.*

Newcastle Publishing Co., Inc., *(Newcastle Pub; 0-87877),* 13419 Saticoy St., North Hollywood, CA 91605 (SAN 202-9154) Tel 818-873-3191; Orders to: P.O. Box 7589, Van Nuys, CA 91409 (SAN 202-9162).

Newconcept Pr., Inc., *(Newconcept Pr; 0-931231),* P.O. Box 124, Emerson, NJ 07630 (SAN 689-1705) Tel 201-666-4225.

Newell, M., Co. Builders, Pub., Subs. of M. Newell Company Builders, *(M Newell Co; 0-9615901),* 16731 74th NE, Bothell, WA 98011 (SAN 696-6640) Tel 206-488-2844.

Newhouse Pr., *(Newhouse Pr; 0-918050),* 146 N. Rampart Blvd., Los Angeles, CA 90026 (SAN 209-2689) Tel 213-383-1089; Orders to: P.O. Box 76145, Los Angeles, CA 90076 (SAN 209-2697).

Newlight Bks., *(Newlight Bks; 0-9615740),* 911 Elden St., Herndon, VA 22070 (SAN 695-8575) Tel 703-471-7220.

Newman, Albert M., Enterprises, *(A M Newman),* P.O. Box 88196, Honolulu, HI 96830-8196 (SAN 209-0864) Tel 808-923-4489.

Newman, Isadore, *(I Newman; 0-917180),* Univ. of Akron, Dept. of Educational Foundations, Akron, OH 44325 (SAN 208-7863) Tel 216-867-7519.

Newman, S. B., Printing Co., *(S B Newman; 0-942268),* 104 Commerce Ave., Knoxville, TN 37902 (SAN 238-8081).

Newman, Evelyn E., Group, *(E E Newman; 0-9616356),* 40 N. Kingshighway, St. Louis, MO 63108 (SAN 658-9898) Tel 314-361-1616.

Newmark Management Insitute, *(Newmark Mgmt Inst; 0-932767),* 18345 Ventura Blvd., Suite 314, Tarzana, CA 91356 (SAN 688-5977) Tel 818-708-1244.

Newmark Publishing Co., *(Newmark Pub; 0-938539),* P.O. Box 603, South Windsor, CT 06074 (SAN 661-4760); 729 Ellington Rd., South Windsor, CT 06074 (SAN 661-4779) Tel 203-282-7265.

†**Newmarket Pr.,** Div. of Newmarket Publishing Co., *(Newmarket; 0-937858),* 3 E. 48th St., New York, NY 10017 (SAN 217-2585) Tel 212-832-3575; Toll free: 800-257-7577; Dist. by: Harper & Row, Pubs., Inc., Keystone Industrial Pk., Scranton, PA 18512 (SAN 201-002X); *CIP.*

Newnes-Butterworth *See* Butterworth's (Scientific, Technical, Medical)

Newport Beach Pubs, *(Newport Beach; 0-9602980),* 4001 Westerly Pl., Suite 106, Newport Beach, CA 92660 (SAN 213-1730) Tel 714-833-0512.

Newport Beach Rentals/Tours Inc., *(Newport Bch Rent; 0-933796),* P.O. Box 7223, Newport Beach, CA 92660 (SAN 222-402X).

Newport-Mesa Unified Schl. District, *(Newport Mesa Sch; 0-9614891),* 600 Irvine Ave., Newport Harbor HS Library, Newport Beach, CA 92663 (SAN 693-1901) Tel 714-760-3328.

News & Features Press *See* Berg, R. J, & Co.

News & Letters Committees, *(News & Letters; 0-914441),* 59 E. Van Buren St., Suite 707, Chicago, IL 60605 (SAN 217-989X) Tel 312-663-0839.

News and Observer, The, *(News & Observer; 0-935400),* 215 S. McDowell St., Raleigh, NC 27602 (SAN 222-6189).

News Bks., International Inc., *(News Bks Intl; 0-89730),* 6100 N. Keystone, Indianapolis, IN 46220 (SAN 676-8350) Tel 317-259-0569.

News Media Information Service, *(News Media Info; 0-932685),* 1325 E. Franklin Ave., Pomona, CA 91766 (SAN 687-8261) Tel 714-623-2402.

News Review Publishing Co., *(News Rev Pub; 0-9607506),* 409 S. Jackson, P.O. Box 8187, Moscow, ID 83843 (SAN 239-7854) Tel 208-882-5561.

News-Tribune, The, *(News-Tribune; 0-939348),* P.O. Box 1116, Fort Worth, TX 76101 (SAN 220-178X) Tel 817-338-1055.

NewSage Pr., *(NewSage Press; 0-939165),* P.O. Box 41038, Pasadena, CA 91104 (SAN 662-8370); 1250 N. Wilson, Pasadena, CA 91104 (SAN 662-8389) Tel 818-791-4122.

Newsgraphics of Delmar, Inc., *(Newsgraphics Delmar Inc),* 125 Adams St., Delmar, NY 12054 (SAN 687-7478).

Newsletter Assn. of America, *(Newsletter Assn; 0-9610222),* Colorado Bldg., 1341 G St. NW, Suite 700, Washington, DC 20005 (SAN 274-0826) Tel 202-347-5220.

Newsletter Inago, *(Newsletter Inago; 0-917835),* P.O. Box 7541, Tucson, AZ 85725 (SAN 657-1549) Tel 602-294-7031.

Newspaper Agency, Inc., The, *(Newspaper Agcy; 0-9607254),* 39 Burchell Blvd., Bay Shore, NY 11706 (SAN 239-2690).

Newspaper Enterprise Assn., Inc., *(Newspaper Ent; 0-915106),* 200 Park Ave., New York, NY 10166 (SAN 212-0615) Tel 212-692-3824. Imprints: Enterprise Publications (Enterprise Pubns).

Newspaper Guild, *(Newspaper Guild),* 1125 15th St., NW, Suite 550, Washington, DC 20005 (SAN 223-9353) Tel 202-296-2990.

Newspaper Services, *(Newspaper Serv; 0-918488),* P.O. Box 38, Storden, MN 56174 (SAN 209-6757) Tel 507-445-3210.

Newspaper Syndication Specialists, *(Newspaper Syn; 0-9615800),* P.O. Box 19654, Irvine, CA 92720 (SAN 696-5490).

NewTEK Industries, Subs. of Coastar Publishing Co., *(NewTEK Indust; 0-930437),* P.O. Box 46116, Hollywood, CA 90046 (SAN 670-9613) Tel 213-874-6669.

Newton, Fred P., *(Newton),* 319 E. California, Gainesville, TX 76240 (SAN 217-2593).

Newton Publishing, *(Newton Pub; 0-930721),* Box 181, Middlebury, VT 05753 (SAN 677-2730) Tel 802-655-4621.

Newtowne Publishing, *(Newtowne Pub; 0-9615705),* P.O. Box 1882, Cambridge, MA 02238 (SAN 696-2645) Tel 617-354-0539.

Next Question Please, *(Next Question; 0-938527),* Rte. 2, P.O. Box 690, Metaline Falls, WA 99153 (SAN 661-1451) Tel 509-446-3255.

Nexus Press, Div. of Nexus Contemporary Art Ctr., *(Nexus Pr; 0-932526),* 608 Ralph McGill Blvd., Atlanta, GA 30312 (SAN 213-2265) Tel 404-577-3579.

Nexus Press (Wa), *(Nexus WA; 0-936666),* P.O. Box 911, Kirkland, WA 98083 (SAN 218-4621) Tel 206-822-5240; Dist. by: Pacific Pipeline, 19215 66th Ave. S., Kent, WA 98032 (SAN 208-2128) Tel 206-872-5523; Toll free: 800-426-4727.

NFS Pr., *(NFS Pr; 0-917986),* 243 Grand View Ave., San Francisco, CA 94114 (SAN 210-1831) Tel 415-282-5372.

Nguyen, Nam Ngoc, *(N N Nguyen; 0-9614634),* 104 W. 35th St., Reading, PA 19606 (SAN 694-3950).

Niagara Univ. Pr., *(Niagara U Pr; 0-937656),* Niagara Univ., Niagara, NY 14109 (SAN 214-2139) Tel 716-285-1212.

Nichols, Joseph, Pub., *(Joseph Nichols; 0-912484),* 100 Center Plaza, No. 303, P.O. Box 2394, Tulsa, OK 74101 (SAN 203-901X) Tel 918-583-3390; P.O. Box 2394, Tulsa, OK 74119 (SAN 658-1021).

Nichols, M. Q., *(M Q Nichols; 0-9612516),* 1815 Texas Ave., Bridge City, TX 77611 (SAN 291-8226).

Nichols' Music, *(Nichols Music; 0-932447),* 7625 E. Camelback Rd., Suite 418 B, Scottsdale, AZ 85251 (SAN 686-7979) Tel 602-945-2771; Dist. by: Baker & Taylor Co., Eastern Div., 50 Kirby Ave., Somerville, NJ 08876 (SAN 169-4901).

Nichols Publishing Co., *(Nichols Pub; 0-89397),* P.O. Box 96, New York, NY 10024 (SAN 212-0291) Tel 212-580-8079.

Nicholson, Mary John, *(M J Nicholson; 0-9607574),* P.O. Box 1351, Skokie, IL 60076 (SAN 281-9848).

Nickens, T. R., *(T R Nickens; 0-9613285),* 4017 16th St. NW, Washington, DC 20011 (SAN 654-472X) Tel 202-829-3347.

†**Nicolas-Hays, Inc.,** *(Nicolas-Hays; 0-89254),* P.O. Box 612, York Beach, ME 03910 (SAN 662-0949) Tel 207-363-4393; Dist. by: Samuel Weiser, Inc., P.O. Box 612, York Beach, ME 03910 (SAN 202-9588) Tel 207-363-4393; *CIP.*

Nicolaysen Art Museum, *(Nicolaysen Art Mus),* 596 N. Poplar, Casper, WY 82601 (SAN 279-8808) Tel 307-235-5247; Dist. by: University of Nebraska Press, 901 N. 17th St.,318 Nebraska Hall, Lincoln, NE 68588 (SAN 202-5337).

Nielsen, Peter N., Enterprises, Ltd., *(P N Nielsen; 0-9616855),* 6689 Orchard Lake Rd., West Bloomfield, MI 48033 (SAN 661-5988) Tel 313-851-5021.

Niemi, Helena Ruth, *(H R Niemi; 0-9607800),* P.O. Box 155, Oakridge, OR 97463 (SAN 240-0537) Tel 503-782-3165.

Nienstedt, Vermadel P. & Lynn Smith, Pubs., *(Nienstedt VP & L Smith; 0-9613010),* 2429 Rigby Dr., Columbia, SC 29204 (SAN 292-5869) Tel 803-787-2536.

Nierenberg & Zeif Pubs., *(Nierenberg-Zeif; 0-936305),* 230 Park Ave., New York, NY 10169 (SAN 697-3027) Tel 212-986-5555.

Nieves Press, *(Nieves Pr; 0-9612008),* P.O. Box 2205, Sta. One, Kingsville, TX 78363 (SAN 286-8385) Tel 512-477-3910.

Night Horn Books, *(Night Horn Books; 0-941842),* 495 Ellis St., Box 1156, San Francisco, CA 94102 (SAN 239-2704) Tel 415-431-6198.

Night Owl Press, *(Night Owl Pr; 0-9612902),* 1758 Hewitt Ave., St. Paul, MN 55104 (SAN 291-3127) Tel 612-646-8746.

Night Owl Publishing, Div. of Night Owl, Inc., *(Night Owl Pub; 0-9616237),* P.O. Box 1776, Groton, CT 06340-0402 (SAN 658-5906); 33A Elderkin Ave., No. 2, Groton, CT 06340 (SAN 658-5914) Tel 203-445-4063.

Night Tree Pr., *(Night Tree Pr; 0-935939),* 414 W. Thomas St., Rome, NY 13440 (SAN 661-4159) Tel 315-337-4142.

Nightbird CA, *(Nightbird CA; 0-9613435),* 110 Bucareli Dr., San Francisco, CA 94132 (SAN 656-9919) Tel 415-239-5262; Dist. by: Alchemy Books, 717 Market St., Suite 514, San Francisco, CA 94101 (SAN 211-304X) Tel 415-777-2197.

Nightbird Pr., *(Nightbird Pr; 0-916023),* 208 W. 23rd St., P.O. Box 918, New York, NY 10011 (SAN 294-0744) Tel 212-255-6269.

Nighthawk Press, *(Nighthawk Pr; 0-936518),* Box 42265, Portland, OR 97242 (SAN 214-428X).

Nightingale Press,The, *(Nightingale Pr; 0-910705),* P.O. Box 6586, Gulfport, MS 39501 (SAN 260-2350) Tel 601-896-6819.

Nightingale Resources, *(Nightingale Res; 0-911389),* P.O. Box322, Cold Spring, NY 10516 (SAN 274-1016) Tel 914-265-3282.

Nightjar Pr., *(Nightjar Pr; 0-938751),* New Mexico State Univ., Box 3E, Las Cruces, NM 88003 (SAN 661-549X) Tel 505-522-2590.

Nightmare Alley Productions, *(Nightmare Alley),* P.O. Box 10806, South Lake Tahoe, CA 95731 (SAN 207-642X).

Nightphlyte Creations, *(Nightphlyte; 0-9616514),* 2270 Madison Rd., Apt. 4C, Cincinnati, OH 45208 (SAN 659-526X) Tel 513-871-4160.

Nightsun Books *See* Adler Publishing Co.

Nike Pr., *(Nike Pr; 0-9613960),* P.O. Box 9089, Fountain Valley, CA 92728 (SAN 682-305X) Tel 714-895-4689.

Nikki Press, *(Nikki Pr; 0-943148),* 6 Heath St., Eatontown, NJ 07724 (SAN 240-7361) Tel 201-222-9343.

Nikmal Publishing, *(Nikmal Pub),* 698 River St., Mattapan, MA 02126 (SAN 219-2241) Tel 617-361-2101; 698 River St., Mattapan, MA 02126 (SAN 662-0957); Orders to: 20 Park Plaza, Rm. 480, Boston, MA 02116 (SAN 200-710X) Tel 617-542-8689.

†**Nilgiri Pr.,** *(Nilgiri Pr; 0-915132),* P.O. Box 477, Petaluma, CA 94953 (SAN 207-6853) Tel 707-878-2369; *CIP.*

Nilles, Mary E., *(M E Nilles; 0-9616845),* P.O. Box 155, Rollingstone, MN 55969 (SAN 661-129X); 300 Jay St., Brooklyn, NY 11201 (SAN 661-1303) Tel 718-643-4900.

Nilles Publishing, *(Nilles Pub; 0-9613683),* 303 N. Main, Newberg, OR 97132 (SAN 687-746X).

†**Nimrod Pr.,** *(Nimrod Pr),* 170 Brookline Ave., Boston, MA 02215 (SAN 237-8973); *CIP.*

Nin-Ra Enterprises, *(Nin-Ra Ent; 0-933276),* 1721 La Barranca Rd., La Canada, CA 91011 (SAN 214-1957) Tel 818-790-7137.

Nina & Zelik, Inc., *(Nina & Zelik; 0-9616558),* 4222 Ethel Ave., Suite 24, Studio City, CA 91604 (SAN 659-5278) Tel 818-981-5263.

910 Press, *(Nine Hundred-Ten Pr; 0-9606736),* P.O. Box 22361, San Francisco, CA 94122 (SAN 219-659X) Tel 415-752-6684.

Nineteenth Century Club, *(Nineteenth Cent),* 1433 Union, Memphis, TN 38104 (SAN 217-2925) Tel 901-274-4174.

Nineteenth Hole International, *(Nineteenth Hole),* 2620 Senate Dr., Lansing, MI 48912 (SAN 223-9388).

Ninja Pr., *(Ninja Pr; 0-9614597),* 14429 Greenleaf St., Sherman Oaks, CA 91423 (SAN 691-7887) Tel 818-906-9972.

Ninth Sign Pubns., *(Ninth Sign; 0-930840),* M-525, Hoboken, NJ 07030 (SAN 210-9301).

Ninth Street Ctr., Inc., *(Ninth St Ctr; 0-932961),* 319 E. Ninth St., New York, NY 10003 (SAN 695-6777).

Niota Pr., *(Niota Pr; 0-9614973),* 1633 Pullan Ave., Cincinnati, OH 45223 (SAN 693-5567) Tel 513-542-4645.

Nippon Shuppan Hanbai U.S.A., Inc., *(Nippon),* 1123 Dominguez St., Unit K, Carson, CA 90746 (SAN 670-6797).

Nishan Grey Inc., *(N Grey Inc; 0-9605652),* P.O. Box 8368, Salt Lake City, UT 84108 (SAN 238-1303) Tel 801-466-9578.

Nittany Pr., *(Nittany Press; 0-9613823),* Box 702, State College, PA 16804 (SAN 679-1824).

†**Nitty Gritty Productions,** *(Nitty Gritty; 0-911954),* P.O. Box 2088, Benicia, CA 94510 (SAN 202-9197) Tel 707-746-0800; *CIP.*

Nixdorf/Bert, *(B Nixdorf),* 9 Randolph Drive, Mt. Holly, NJ 08060 (SAN 264-2530).

No Dead Lines, *(No Dead Lines; 0-931832),* 261 Hamilton, No. 320D, Palo Alto, CA 94301 (SAN 211-6103) Tel 415-321-0842.

No Secrets Pr., *(No Secrets Pr; 0-936779),* 1020 Bush St., No. 10, San Francisco, CA 94109 (SAN 696-3404) Tel 415-775-9979; Dist. by: The New Leaf Distributing, 1020 White St., SW, Atlanta, GA 30310 (SAN 662-3727) Tel 404-755-2665; Toll free: 800-241-3829.

Noble, Gilbert W., *(G W Noble; 0-911036),* P.O. Box 931, Winter Park, FL 32789 (SAN 206-4472) Tel 305-647-2431.

Noble, Robert, *(R Noble),* 5431 N. 12th St., Philadelphia, PA 19141 (SAN 277-7029) Tel 215-329-4502.

Noble, T., *(T Noble; 0-9607144),* 1650 Argonne Pl., NW, Washington, DC 20009 (SAN 239-0132) Tel 202-483-8713.

Noble & Noble Pubs., Inc. *See* Bowmar, Noble Pubs.

Noble House Publishing, *(Noble Hse; 0-9603490),* 256 S. Robertson, Beverly Hills, CA 90211 (SAN 213-4225) Tel 213-659-4210.

NobleVison, Inc., *(Noblevision Inc; 0-918525),* P.O. Box 452, Mays Landing, NJ 08330 (SAN 657-2146) Tel 609-625-3246.

Nodin Pr., *(Nodin Pr; 0-931714),* c/o The Bookmen, Inc., 525 N. Third St., Minneapolis, MN 55401 (SAN 204-398X) Tel 612-333-6300.

Noe, Fay, Estate of, *(Noe; 0-9600208),* Orders to: Vivian Kirkwood, HCRI Box 155, Ellis Prairie, MO 65444 (SAN 662-0965) Tel 417-967-2125.

Noell's Ark Pub., *(Noells Ark; 0-9602422),* P.O. Box 396, Tarpon Springs, FL 35589 (SAN 213-7801) Tel 813-937-8683.

Noise Control Foundation, *(Noise Control; 0-931784),* P.O. Box 2469, Arlington Branch, Poughkeepsie, NY 12603 (SAN 215-2193) Tel 914-462-6719.

Noit Amrofer Publishing Co., *(Noit Amrofer; 0-932998),* 5706 30th Ave. NE, Seattle, WA 98105 (SAN 212-3738).

Noles, BJ, *(BJ Noles; 0-9613684),* 11859 SW Riverwood Rd., Portland, OR 97219 (SAN 671-0115) Tel 503-636-6896; Dist. by: Pacific Pipeline Inc., 19215 66th Ave. S, Kent, WA 98031 (SAN 208-2128); Dist. by: Pacific Trade Group, P.O. Box 668, Pearl City, HI 96782-0668 (SAN 169-1635).

Nolo Pr., *(Nolo Pr; 0-87337),* 950 Parker St., Berkeley, CA 94710 (SAN 206-7935) Tel 415-549-1976.

Names

Names

Non-Fiction Pubns. Corp., *(Non Fiction Pubns; 0-913279),* P.O. Box 129, Island Park, NY 11558 (SAN 285-9106) Tel 516-431-2933; Dist. by: Icea Bk. Center, P.O. Box 20048, Minneapolis, MN 55420 (SAN 285-9114) Tel 612-854-8660; Dist. by: The Baker & Taylor Co., Western Div., 380 Edison Way, Reno, NV 89564 (SAN 169-4464) Tel 702-786-6700; Dist. by: Baker & Taylor Co., Midwest Div., 501 Gladiola Ave., Momence, IL 60954 (SAN 169-2100); Dist. by: Baker & Taylor Co., Eastern Div., 50 Kirby Ave., Somerville, NJ 08876 (SAN 169-4901); Dist. by: Baker & Taylor CO., Southeast Div., Mt. Olive Rd., Commerce, GA 30529 (SAN 669-3369); Dist. by: Taylor-Carlisle Booksellers, 245 Seventh Ave, New York, NY 10001 (SAN 285-9564) Tel 212-255-8702.

†Non-Stop Bks., *(Non-Stop Bks; 0-936816),* 105 Imperial Ave., Bennington, VT 05201 (SAN 214-4298); *CIP.*

Noname Pr., *(Noname Pr; 0-9617328),* 5200 Klingle St. NW, Washington, DC 20016 (SAN 203-1639) Tel 202-244-6243.

Nonpareil Bks. *See Godine, David R., Pub., Inc.*

Nook Pubs., The, *(Nook Pubs; 0-938339),* P.O. Box 4282, Shreveport, LA 71134 (SAN 661-2830); 937 College St., Shreveport, LA 71104 (SAN 661-2849) Tel 318-222-3029.

Noon Rock, *(Noon Rock; 0-9602934),* Station Hill Rd., Barrytown, NY 12507 (SAN 213-8611) Tel 914-758-1221.

Noontide Pr., The, *(Noontide; 0-911038; 0-939482),* P.O. Box 1248, Torrance, CA 90505 (SAN 213-1307). *Imprints:* Christian Book Club of America (Chr Bk Club); I A A E E (IAAEE); Institute for Historical Review (Inst Hist Rev); New Voices (New Voices); Northern League (N League); Samisdat Publishers Ltd. (Samisdat); Uriel Publications (Uriel Pubns); Vanguard Books (Vanguard).

Norawell Pubs., *(Norawell Pubs; 0-9602118),* 1229 Golden Gate Blvd., Cleveland, OH 44124 (SAN 212-3754).

Norbeck Research, *(Norbeck Res),* 117 Ruch St., Coplay, PA 18037 (SAN 692-7343) Tel 215-262-8779.

Norblo Co., *(Norblo Co; 0-933509),* The Arcade, 9th Flr. No. 3, Euclid Ave., Cleveland, OH 44114 (SAN 692-3992) Tel 216-566-1414.

Nordbook, *(Nordbook; 0-9616967),* 3644 34th Ave., S., Minneapolis, MN 55406 (SAN 661-7514) Tel 612-729-6346.

Nordic Bks., *(Nordic Bks; 0-933748),* P.O. Box 1941, Philadelphia, PA 19105 (SAN 212-5323) Tel 215-464-4186.

Nordic Ski Press, *(Nordic Ski; 0-9610410),* Box 36, Norden, CA 95724 (SAN 239-4650).

Nordic Translators, *(Nordic Trans; 0-938500),* 1747 Holton St., St. Paul, MN 55113 (SAN 239-9199) Tel 612-645-8352.

Nordland Heritage Foundation, *(Nordland Her Found; 0-9604816),* Humanities Box 2170, Augustana College, Sioux Falls, SD 57197 (SAN 276-9662).

Noreascon Two *See New England Science Fiction Assn.*

Norfolk Port & Industrial Authority, *(Norfolk Port; 0-9605682),* P. O. Box 249, Wayne, PA 19087 (SAN 216-2741); Dist. by: International Society for General Semantics, 834 Mission St., 2nd Flr., San Francisco, CA 94103 (SAN 203-8161) Tel 415-543-1747.

Norm Burleson, Bookseller, *(N Burleson; 0-930577),* 104 First Ave., P.O. Box 15007, Spartanburg, SC 29302 (SAN 677-587X) Tel 803-583-8845.

Norman, Albert, *(A Norman),* Three Alpine Dr., Northfield, VT 05663 (SAN 295-1053).

Norman & Sandra, *(Norman & Sandra; 0-936520),* 1010 Village Lane, Orient, NY 11957-0218 (SAN 220-0252) Tel 516-323-3602.

Norman Publishing Co., *(Norman Pub; 0-9601788),* 52 Toms Point Lane, Lincoln Park, NJ 07035 (SAN 212-2944) Tel 201-696-2256.

Normandie Publishing Co., The, *(Normandie; 0-9602986),* 225 W. 86th St., Suite 805, New York, NY 10024 (SAN 213-1315) Tel 212-873-5433.

Normandy Square Pubns., *(Normandy Pubns; 0-916399),* 1125 Grand, Suite 500, Kansas City, MO 64106 (SAN 295-7337) Tel 816-471-1060.

Normark Corp., *(Normark Corp),* 1710 E. 78th St., Minneapolis, MN 55423 (SAN 209-3006) Tel 612-869-3293.

Norns Publishing Co./Green Turtle Pubns., *(Norns Pub Co; 0-939960),* P.O. Box 17925, Plantation, FL 33318 (SAN 216-8456) Tel 305-474-1318; Orders to: Green Turtle Pubns., P.O. Box 17925, Plantation, FL 33318 (SAN 693-9694).

Norris Assocs. Pr., *(Norris Assocs Pr; 0-931569),* 215 Palisades Dr., Santa Barbara, CA 93109-1943 (SAN 682-1774) Tel 805-962-7703.

Norse Press, *(Norse Pr; 0-9602692; 0-9613274),* 909 E. 35th St, Sioux Falls, SD 57105 (SAN 221-7686) Tel 605-336-6055; Toll free: 800-843-1300.

Norseman Publishing Co., *(Norseman Pub; 0-9613202),* P.O Box 6617, Lubbock, TX 79493-6617 (SAN 295-7507) Tel 806-795-9875.

North, Christina Bolt, *(C B North; 0-9609008),* 41-06 12th St., Long Island City, NY 11101 (SAN 239-5487) Tel 718-784-7705.

North, Gloria, *(G North; 0-931758),* 15 Estelle Ave., Larkspur, CA 94939 (SAN 211-5115).

North American Archives, *(N American Archives; 0-915431),* P.O. Box 9685, N. Hollywood, CA 91609 (SAN 291-3143) Tel 818-786-6069.

North American Association of Christians in Social Work, *(N American Assn),* P.O. Box 90, Saint Davids, PA 19087 (SAN 225-994X).

†North American Congress on Latin America, *(NA Cong Lat Am; 0-916024),* 151 W. 19th St., 9th Fl., New York, NY 10011 (SAN 218-0022) Tel 212-989-8890; *CIP.*

North American Editions, *(North Am Edit; 0-933967),* 101 Phillips Rd., Holden, MA 01520 (SAN 693-0719) Tel 617-829-2330.

North American Falconry & Hunting Hawks, *(North Am Fal Hunt; 0-912510),* P.O. Box 1484, Denver, CO 80201 (SAN 203-7440) Tel 303-797-0442.

North American Hunting Club, Inc., *(N Amer Hunt Club; 0-914697),* 7901 Flying Cloud Dr., No. 210, Minneapolis, MN 55435 (SAN 661-2636); P.O. Box 35557, Minneapolis, MN 55435 (SAN 661-2644).

†North American, Inc., *(North American Inc; 0-930244),* P.O. Box 65, New Brunswick, NJ 08903 (SAN 210-6469) Tel 201-246-8546; *CIP.*

North American International, *(North Am Intl; 0-88265),* P.O. Box 21012, Washington, DC 20009 (SAN 202-9200) Tel 202-462-1776.

North American Man/Boy Love Assn., *(N Am Man-Boy; 0-9615497),* P.O. Box 174 Midtown Sta., New York, NY 10018 (SAN 696-382X) Tel 212-807-8578; Dist. by: Glad Day Books, 43 Winter St., Boston, MA 02108 (SAN 221-282X) Tel 617-542-0144.

North American Manufacturing Company, *(North Am Mfg Co; 0-9601596),* 4455 E. 71st St., Cleveland, OH 44105 (SAN 222-0946).

North American Pubs., Inc., *(N Amer Pubs; 0-9617079),* P.O. Box 1231, Bloomington, IN 47402 (SAN 662-5878); 1113 S. High St., Bloomington, IN 47401 (SAN 662-5886) Tel 812-336-5611.

†North American Publishing Co., *(North Am Pub Co; 0-912920),* 401 N. Broad St., Philadelphia, PA 19108 (SAN 203-1647) Tel 215-238-5300; *CIP.*

North American Review Pr., *(North Am Rev; 0-915996),* Univ. of Iowa, Cedar Falls, IA 50614 (SAN 206-0760) Tel 319-273-2681.

North American Students of Cooperation, *(NASCO; 0-931062),* P.O. Box 7715, Ann Arbor, MI 48107 (SAN 260-3810) Tel 313-663-0889; 530 S. State St., Rm. 4312, Ann Arbor, MI 48109 (SAN 669-2192).

North American Technology, *(N Amer Tech; 0-911261),* 174 Concord St., Peterborough, NH 03458 (SAN 274-158X) Tel 603-924-7136.

North American Trackless Trolley Association, Inc., *(NA Trackless Trolley; 0-939875),* 1042 Bradstown Rd. No. 2, Louisville, KY 40204-1318 (SAN 287-6566) Tel 502-459-5261.

North American Vegetarian Society, *(North Amer Veg; 0-9615401),* Sweet Hill Rd., P.O. Box 72, Dolgeville, NY 13329 (SAN 695-4685) Tel 518-568-7970.

North American Youth Sport Institute, *(No Amer Youth; 0-937412),* 4985 Oak Garden Dr., Kernersville, NC 27284 (SAN 692-9435) Tel 919-784-4926.

†North Atlantic Bks., Div. of Society of the Study of Native Arts & Science, *(North Atlantic; 0-938190; 0-913028; 1-55643),* 2320 Blake St., Berkeley, CA 94704 (SAN 203-1655) Tel 415-540-7934; *CIP.*

North Beach Pr., *(North Beach Pr; 0-935093),* 524 Union St., San Francisco, CA 94133 (SAN 695-0019) Tel 415-982-8432.

North Bks., *(North Bks; 0-939495),* P.O. Box 337, Peace Dale, RI 02883 (SAN 663-4052); 39 North Road, Peace Dale, RI 02883 (SAN 663-4060) Tel 401-783-4320.

North Carolina Bar Foundation, *(NC Bar Found),* 1025 Wade Ave., Raleigh, NC 27605 (SAN 237-8981) Tel 919-828-0561.

North Carolina Central Univ., Dept. of Political Science, *(NC Central Pol Sci),* Durham, NC 27707 (SAN 206-1708).

North Carolina Div. of Archives & History, *(NC Archives; 0-86526),* Historical Pubns. Section, 109 E. Jones St., Raleigh, NC 27611 (SAN 203-7246) Tel 919-733-7442.

North Carolina Genealogical Society, Inc., *(N C Genealogical; 0-936370),* P.O. Box 1492, Raleigh, NC 27602 (SAN 222-4003); Orders to: Reprint Co., Pubs., P.O. Box 5401, Spartanburg, SC 29304 (SAN 203-3828) Tel 803-582-0732.

North Carolina Haiku Society Pr., The, *(NC Haiku Soc; 0-9614161),* 326 Golf Course Dr., Raleigh, NC 27610 (SAN 686-5496) Tel 919-828-5551; Orders to: P.O. Box 14247, Raleigh, NC 27620 (SAN 662-2712).

†North Carolina Museum of Art, *(NCMA; 0-88259),* 2110 Blue Ridge Blvd., Raleigh, NC 27607 (SAN 202-9030) Tel 919-833-1935; *CIP.*

†North Carolina State Museum of Natural History, Div. of N.C. Dept. of Agriculture, *(NC Natl Hist; 0-917134),* 102 N. Salisbury St., P.O. Box 27647, Raleigh, NC 27611 (SAN 208-788X) Tel 919-733-7450; P.O. Box 27647, Raleigh, NC 27611 (SAN 662-0973); *CIP.*

North Carolina State Univ., Dept. of Plant Pathology, *(NC Path Intl Dev; 0-931901),* North Carolina State Univ., Dept. of Plant Pathology, Box 7616, Raleigh, NC 27695-7616 (SAN 686-0206) Tel 919-737-2721.

North Carolina Wesleyan College, Friends of the Library, *(NC Wesleyan Friends Lib; 0-933598),* 3400 Wesleyan Blvd., Rocky Mount, NC 27801 (SAN 238-6364).

†North Castle Bks., Inc., *(North Castle; 0-911040),* 212 Bedford Rd., Greenwich, CT 06831 (SAN 202-9219) Tel 203-869-7766; *CIP.*

North Central Assn. of Colleges & Schools, *(NCACS Boulder),* P.O. Box 18, Boulder, CO 80306 (SAN 225-7661) Tel 303-497-0261.

North Central Publishing Co., *(North Central; 0-935476),* Riverview Industrial Park, 274 Fillmore Ave. East, St. Paul, MN 55107 (SAN 203-7459) Tel 612-224-5455. *Imprints:* Society for German-American Studies (Soc German-Amer Studies).

North Central Regional Ctr. for Rural Development, *(NCRCRD; 0-936913),* Iowa State Univ., No. 578 Heady Hall, Ames, IA 50010 (SAN 658-3636) Tel 515-294-1184.

North Central Section Wildlife Society The, *(N Central Sect Wildlife; 0-932547),* 300 W. First St., Bloomington, IN 47401 (SAN 687-4924) Tel 812-334-1137.

North Coast Publishing, *(North Coast Pubs; 0-912269),* 18428 Parkland Dr., Shaker Heights, OH 44122 (SAN 265-0703) Tel 216-561-1763.

North Country Book Express, Inc./Solstice Press, *(NC Bk Express; 0-932722),* 112 W. Fourth St., P.O. Box 9223, Moscow, ID 83843 (SAN 169-1686) Tel 208-882-0888.

North Country Bks., Inc., *(North Country; 0-932052),* P.O. Box 506, Sylvan Beach, NY 13157 (SAN 287-0231) Tel 315-762-5140; 18 Irving Pl., Utica, NY 13501 (SAN 287-024X) Tel 315-735-4877.

†North Country Community College Press, *(No Country Comm Coll; 0-940280),* 20 Winona Ave., Box 89, Saranac Lake, NY 12983 (SAN 217-5479) Tel 518-891-2915; *CIP.*

North Dakota Council On The Arts, *(N Dak Coun Arts; 0-911205),* Black Bldg., Suite 606, Fargo, ND 58102 (SAN 293-311X) Tel 701-237-8959; Dist. by: Germans From Russia Heritage Society, P.O. Box 1671, Bismarck, ND 58502 (SAN 293-3128).

North Dakota Institute for Regional Studies, *(N Dak Inst; 0-911042),* State Univ. Sta., Fargo, ND 58105 (SAN 203-1574) Tel 701-237-8655.

North Foster Baptist Church, *(N Foster Baptist),* R.R. 1 Box 282 E. Killingly Rd., Foster, RI 02825 (SAN 282-0595) Tel 401-647-5805; Dist. by: Rhode Island Publications Society, 189 Wickenden St., Providence, RI 02903 (SAN 219-9696) Tel 401-272-1776.

North Frontier Pr., *(North Frontier Pr; 0-933309),* P.O. Box 11450, Chicago, IL 60611 (SAN 692-297X) Tel 312-472-8051; Dist. by: Puett Electronics, P.O. Box 28572, Dallas, TX 75228 (SAN 205-4035) Tel 214-321-0927.

North Gull Publishing, *(North Gull Pub; 0-936753),* 3 Lamson Pl., Cambridge, MA 02139 (SAN 699-9816) Tel 617-492-3148.

North-Holland *See* Elsevier Science Publishing Co., Inc.

North Lake Productions, *(North Lake Prod; 0-9601722),* 9732 Boucher Dr., Otter Lake, MI 48464 (SAN 212-1980) Tel 517-795-2250.

North Light Bks., Div. of F & W Pubns., Inc., *(North Light Bks; 0-89134),* 9933 Alliance Rd., Cincinnati, OH 45242 (SAN 287-0274) Tel 513-984-0717; Toll free: 800-543-4644.

North Pacific Pubs., *(North Pacific; 0-913138),* P.O. Box 13255, Portland, OR 97213 (SAN 203-7467) Tel 503-236-9343.

North Plains Pr., Div. of Dakota North Plains Corp., *(North Plains; 0-87970),* P.O. Box 1830, Aberdeen, SD 57402-1830 (SAN 202-9243); 1216 S. Main St., Aberdeen, SD 57401 (SAN 660-9392) Tel 605-225-5360.

North Point Historical Society, *(N Point Hist Soc; 0-9606072),* Box 557, Milwaukee, WI 53201 (SAN 216-9177) Tel 414-271-2395.

†North Point Pr., *(N Point Pr; 0-86547),* 850 Talbot Ave., Berkeley, CA 94706 (SAN 220-133X) Tel 415-527-6260; Dist. by: Farrar Straus Giroux, Inc, 19 Union Sq., W., New York, NY 10003 (SAN 206-782X) Tel 212-741-6900; *CIP.*

North Publishing, *(North Pub; 0-9613355),* 3030 14th Ave. West, Suite 205, Seattle, WA 98119 (SAN 656-1616) Tel 206-624-6271.

North Ridge Bks., *(North Ridge Bks; 0-937813),* P.O. Box 13401, Akron, OH 44313-8801 (SAN 659-3828) Tel 216-864-8786; 84 Sand Run Rd., Akron, OH 44313 (SAN 659-3836).

†North River Pr., Inc., *(North River; 0-88427),* P.O. Box 241, Croton-on-Hudson, NY 10520 (SAN 202-1048) Tel 914-941-7175; *CIP.*

North Scale Institute Publishing Co., *(North Scale Co; 0-916299),* P.O. Box 27555, San Francisco, CA 94127 (SAN 295-7418) Tel 415-731-5819; 2440 15th Ave., San Francisco, CA 94116 (SAN 295-7426).

North-South Books *See* Holt, Henry, & Co.

North-South Publishing Co., Inc., The, *(NS Pub Co Inc; 0-913897),* P.O. Box 610, Lanham, MD 20706 (SAN 286-8423) Tel 301-552-1098; 7011 Ren Lane, Lanham, MD 20706 (SAN 286-8431).

†North Star Pr., *(North Star; 0-87839),* P.O. Box 451, St. Cloud, MN 56302-0451 (SAN 203-7491) Tel 612-253-1636; *CIP.*

†North Stonington Pr., *(N Stonington; 0-938538),* P.O. Box 501, Greenwich, CT 06836 (SAN 282-0633) Tel 203-622-0878; *CIP.*

North Texas State Univ., Professional Development Institute, *(N Texas St U Pro Devel Inst; 0-940966),* P.O. Box 13288, Denton, TX 76203 (SAN 223-1980) Tel 817-565-2483.

North Valley Diver Publications, *(North Valley; 0-911615),* 585 Royal Oak Dr., Redding, CA 96001 (SAN 264-2557) Tel 916-246-2009; Orders to: P.O. Box 6007, Suite 166, Redding, CA 96099 (SAN 662-0981).

North West Bk. Arts, *(North West Bk; 0-937631),* 18215 Ballinger Way, NE, Seattle, WA 98155 (SAN 658-9928) Tel 206-365-2907.

North West International Trading, Inc., *(NW Intl),* P.O. Box 11483, Eugene, OR 97440 (SAN 264-2565) Tel 503-484-7060.

Northcountry Publishing Co., *(Northcountry Pub; 0-930366),* 50 S. Cretin Ave., St. Paul, MN 55105 (SAN 211-061X) Tel 612-699-3102; Orders to: 1509 Fillmore St., Alexandria, MN 56308 (SAN 662-099X) Tel 612-763-3874.

Northcross Hse., *(Northcross Hse; 0-9617256),* Rte. 1, Box 12-A, Elliston, VA 24087 (SAN 663-5725) Tel 703-268-5005.

Northeast Academic Services, Inc., *(Northeast A S; 0-913811),* 10 Lydia Dr., Wappingers, NY 12590 (SAN 286-1372) Tel 914-297-6389.

Northeast Bks., Div. of Cultural Society of Northeastern Pennsylvania, *(NE Bks; 0-937374),* 401 Clark St., Clarks Green, PA 18411 (SAN 215-2665) Tel 717-586-0077.

Northeast Conference on the Teaching of Foreign Languages, *(NE Conf Teach Foreign; 0-915432),* P.O. Box 623, Middlebury, VT 05753 (SAN 207-5113) Tel 802-388-2598.

Northeast Marine Advisory Council, *(NE Marine Advisory; 0-9616907),* Univ. of New Hampshire, NEC Administration Bldg., Durham, NH 03824 (SAN 661-5198) Tel 603-862-3460.

Northeast Outdoors, Inc., *(NE Outdoors; 0-936216),* P.O. Box 2180, Waterbury, CT 06722-2180 (SAN 214-0691).

Northeast Regional Agricultural Engineering Service, *(NE Agri Engineer; 0-935817),* Cornell Univ., Riley Robb Hall, Ithaca, NY 14853 (SAN 696-6543) Tel 607-255-7654.

Northeast Regional Ctr. for Rural Development, *(NE Regional Ctr; 0-9609010),* Pennsylvania State Univ., 104 Weaver Bldg., University Park, PA 16802 (SAN 241-3418) Tel 814-863-4656.

†Northeast Sportsman's Pr., *(Northeast Sportsmans; 0-942990),* P.O. Box 188, Tarrytown, NY 10591 (SAN 238-8219); *CIP.*

Northeastern Political Science Association, *(NE Poli Sci),* 426 Thompson Hall, Univ. of Massachusetts, Amherst, MA 01003 (SAN 226-9279) Tel 413-545-1354.

Northeastern Publishing Co., Inc., *(Northeastern Pub; 0-933389),* 1378 President St., Brooklyn, NY 11213 (SAN 691-683X) Tel 718-756-1708.

Northeastern State Univ., Div. of Arts & Letters, *(NE St U Arts & Letters; 0-9615355),* The Phoenix SH 218, Northeastern State Univ., Tahlequah, OK 74464 (SAN 695-1821) Tel 918-456-5511.

†Northeastern Univ. Pr., *(NE U Pr; 0-930350; 1-55553),* 360 Huntington Ave., Huntington Plaza, Suite 272, Northeastern Univ., Boston, MA 02115 (SAN 205-3764) Tel 617-437-5480; Orders to: P.O. Box 250, Ithaca, NY 14851 (SAN 282-0668); *CIP.*

Northern Arizona Univ., Dept. of Anthropology, *(N Arizona U; 0-910953),* Box 15200, Flagstaff, AZ 86011 (SAN 264-2573) Tel 602-523-3180; Dist. by: Northern Arizona Univ. Bookstore, P.O. Box 6044, Flagstaff, AZ 86011 (SAN 200-7541) Tel 602-523-4041.

Northern California Grantmakers, *(Northern Cal),* 334 Kearny St., San Francisco, CA 94108 (SAN 287-2706) Tel 415-788-2982.

Northern Cartographic Inc., *(N Cartographic; 0-9606738),* P.O. Box 133, Burlington, VT 05402 (SAN 219-6131) Tel 802-655-4321.

Northern Illinois Univ. Ctr. for Governmental Studies, *(NIU Ctr Govmt),* 143 N. Third St., DeKalb, IL 60115 (SAN 227-0439) Tel 815-753-1901.

†Northern Illinois Univ. Pr., *(N Ill U Pr; 0-87580),* Williston, 320A, DeKalb, IL 60115 (SAN 202-8875) Tel 815-753-1826; *CIP.*

Northern League *See* Noontide Pr., The

Northern Michigan Univ. Pr., *(Northern Mich; 0-918616),* 607 Cohodas Administrative Ctr., Marquette, MI 49855 (SAN 205-3748) Tel 906-227-2720; Orders to: NMU Bookstore, Don H. Bottum University Ctr., Marquette, MI 49855 (SAN 205-3756) Tel 906-227-2480.

Northern Nut Growers Assn., *(N Nut Growers; 0-9602248),* 13 Broken Arrow Rd., Hamden, CT 06518 (SAN 206-9695) Tel 203-288-1026; 4518 Holston Hills Rd., Knoxville, TN 37914 (SAN 650-0455) Tel 615-524-0416.

Northern Press, *(Northern Pr),* 18 Cedar St., Potsdam, NY 13676 (SAN 211-7495).

†Northern Trails Pr., *(N Trails; 0-914269),* P.O. Box 964, Alamosa, CO 81101 (SAN 287-5918) Tel 303-274-4162; *CIP.*

†Northland Pr., Div. of Justin Industries, *(Northland; 0-87358),* P.O. Box N, Flagstaff, AZ 86002 (SAN 202-9251) Tel 602-774-5251; Toll free: 800-FINE-BKS; Toll free: 800-46-BOOKS (AZ); *CIP.*

Northland Pubns., *(Northland Pubns WA),* P.O. Box 12157, Seattle, WA 98102 (SAN 210-931X).

Northland Publishing Co., *(Northland WI; 0-939834),* Rte. 4, Box 110, Menomonie, WI 54751 (SAN 216-9193) Tel 715-235-9434.

Northlands Press, *(Northlands MI; 0-918808),* 2723 Lake Lansing Rd., East Lansing, MI 48823 (SAN 210-3176) Tel 517-332-4274.

Northstar Maschek A.G., *(Northstar-Maschek; 0-910667),* P.O. Box 810, Lakeville, MN 55044-0810 (SAN 274-1911) Tel 612-469-5433; Dist. by: Northstar Commemoratives, Inc., P.O. Box 803, Lakeville, MN 55044-0803 (SAN 200-6545).

Northstar Publishing Co., *(Northstar Pub; 0-938255),* P.O. Box 9151, San Jose, CA 95157 (SAN 661-3632); 5676 McKellar Dr., San Jose, CA 95129 (SAN 661-3640) Tel 408-257-1925.

Northumberland Pr., *(Northumberland Pr; 0-934565),* 1717 Blvd. of the Allies, Pittsburgh, PA 15219 (SAN 693-854X) Tel 412-281-6179.

Northwest Christian Pubns., Inc., *(NW Christian Pubns; 0-914271),* P.O. Box 31133, Seattle, WA 98103 (SAN 287-5926) Tel 206-523-9911.

Northwest Denver Bks., *(Northwest Denver; 0-9616057),* 2800 Vrain St., Denver, CO 80212 (SAN 698-1100) Tel 303-455-9042.

Northwest Historical Consultants, *(NW Hist Cons; 0-9609562),* 2780 26th St., Clarkston, WA 99403 (SAN 274-1989) Tel 509-758-5773; Dist. by: Pacific Pipeline, Inc., 19215 66th Ave. S., Kent, WA 98032 (SAN 208-2128) Tel 206-872-5523; Toll free: 800-426-4727; Dist. by: Servatius News Agency, 601 2nd St., Clarkson, WA 99403 (SAN 169-8737).

Northwest Home Designing, Inc., *(Northwest Home; 0-936909),* 10901 Bridgeport Way, SW, Tacoma, WA 98499 (SAN 658-3725) Tel 206-584-6309.

Northwest Illustrated *See* Hippocrene Bks., Inc.

†Northwest Learning Associates, Inc., *(Northwest Learn; 0-931836),* 5728 N. Via Umbrosa, Tucson, AZ 85715 (SAN 211-6251) Tel 602-299-8435; *CIP.*

Northwest Panorama Publishing, Inc., *(Northwest Panorama; 0-9613787),* Box 1858, Bozeman, MT 59715 (SAN 678-9846); Toll free: 800-547-2525.

Northwest Perfection Pubs., *(NW Perfection Pub; 0-9616757),* 911 North L St., Tacoma, WA 98403 (SAN 661-3721) Tel 206-627-6506.

Northwest Regional Educational Laboratory, *(Northwest Regional; 0-89354),* 300 SW Sixth Ave., Portland, OR 97204 (SAN 208-9998) Tel 503-248-6800.

Northwest Resources, *(Northwest Res; 0-9614579),* 1617 E. Bay Dr., Olympia, WA 98506 (SAN 692-3488) Tel 206-943-5048.

†Northwest Review Bks., *(NW Review Bks; 0-918402),* 369 PLC, Univ. of Oregon, Eugene, OR 97403 (SAN 209-9721) Tel 503-686-3957; *CIP.*

Names

Northwest Silver Pr., *(NW Silver Pr; 0-9610202),* 88 Cascade Key, Bellevue, WA 98006 (SAN 264-2581) Tel 206-643-0143.

Northwestern Institute of Unquestionable Taste, *(NW Inst Taste),* P.O. Box 264, Bend, OR 97709 (SAN 694-5406).

Northwestern Memorial Hospital, *(Northwest Memorial; 0-9605996),* 215 E. Chicago Ave Rm 1206, Chicago, IL 60611 (SAN 216-7549) Tel 312-649-7432.

Northwestern Mutual Life Insurance Co., *(NW Mutual Life; 0-9612010),* 720 E. Wisconsin Ave., Milwaukee, WI 53202 (SAN 286-844X) Tel 414-271-1444.

Northwestern Publishing House, *(Northwest Pub; 0-8100),* 3624 W. North Ave., Milwaukee, WI 53208 (SAN 206-7943) Tel 414-442-1810.

Northwestern State Univ. of Louisiana Press, *(NSU Pr LA; 0-917898),* P.O. Box 5305, Natchitoches, LA 71497 (SAN 209-973X) Tel 318-357-4586.

†**Northwestern Univ. Dept. of Astronomy,** *(NWU Astro; 0-939160),* Dept. of Astronomy, Evanston, IL 60201 (SAN 217-2305); *CIP.*

Northwestern Univ. Pr., *(Northwestern U Pr; 0-8101),* P.O. Box 1093, Evanston, IL 60201 (SAN 202-5787); Orders to: 1735 Benson Ave., Evanston, IL 60201 (SAN 669-2222) Tel 312-491-5313. *Imprints:* Transportation Center Publications (Trans).

Northwestern Univ. Traffic Institute, *(Traffic Inst; 0-912642),* 405 Church St., P.O. Box 1409, Evanston, IL 60204-1409 (SAN 202-7909) Tel 312-492-5408; Toll free: 800-323-4011.

†**Northwood Institute Pr.,** *(Northwood Inst Pr; 0-87359),* 110 W. Signet, Midland, MI 48640 (SAN 202-098X) Tel 517-631-1600; *CIP.*

Northwoods Country Collection, *(Northwoods IL; 0-936847),* 24435 W. Blvd. de John, Plainfield, IL 60544 (SAN 658-3709) Tel 815-436-9234.

†**Northword,** *(Northword; 0-942802),* P.O. Box 5634, Madison, WI 53705 (SAN 240-4842) Tel 608-231-2355; Dist. by: Hazel Rice, 1206 Dartmouth Rd., Madison, WI 53705 (SAN 200-6928) Tel 608-233-6543; *CIP.*

Norton, Jeffrey, Pubs., Inc., *(J Norton Pubs; 0-88432),* Suite A2, On-The-Green, Guilford, CT 06437 (SAN 213-957X) Tel 203-453-9794; Toll free: 800-243-1234. *Imprints:* Audio-Forum Division (Audio-Forum); Speechphone Institute (Speechphone).

†**Norton, R. W., Art Gallery,** *(Norton Art; 0-913060; 0-9600182),* 4747 Creswell Ave., Shreveport, LA 71106 (SAN 213-7569) Tel 318-865-4201; *CIP.*

Norton, W. W., & Co., Inc., *(Norton; 0-393),* 500 Fifth Ave., New York, NY 10110 (SAN 202-5795) Tel 212-354-5500; Toll free: 800-223-2584. *Imprints:* New American Library (NAL); Norton College Division (NortonC); Norton Library (Norton Lib).

Norton College Div. *See* **Norton, W. W., & Co., Inc.**

Norton Gallery & School of Art, *(Norton Gal Art),* 1451 S. Olive Ave., West Palm Beach, FL 33401 (SAN 279-926X); Dist. by: Publishing Center for Cultural Resources, 625 Broadway, New York, NY 10012 (SAN 692-8188).

Norton Library *See* **Norton, W. W., & Co., Inc.**
Norwalk Press *See* **O'Sullivan, Woodside & Co.**
Norway Books, *(Norway Bks; 0-939648),* P.O. Box 2010, Sparks, NV 89431 (SAN 216-4248).

Norwegian-American Historical Assn., *(Norwegian-Am Hist Assn; 0-87732),* St. Olaf College, Northfield, MN 55057 (SAN 203-1086) Tel 507-663-3221.

Nor'Westing Inc., *(Nor'Westing; 0-931923),* P.O. Box 375, Edmonds, WA 98020 (SAN 686-0028) Tel 206-776-3138.

†**Norwood Editions,** *(Norwood Edns; 0-88305; 0-8482),* P.O. Box 38, Norwood, PA 19074 (SAN 206-8613) Tel 215-583-4550; *CIP.*

Norwood/Fontbone Home & School Assn., *(Norwood-Fontbone; 0-9614938),* 8891 Germantown Ave., Dept "C", Philadelphia, PA 19118 (SAN 689-0520) Tel 215-242-3199.

Nosbooks, *(Nosbooks; 0-911046),* 42 W. 88th St., New York, NY 10024 (SAN 203-7513).

Nostos Bks., *(Nostos Bks; 0-932963),* Box 19086, Minneapolis, MN 55419 (SAN 689-1500) Tel 612-825-0387.

Nottingham Press, *(Nottingham Pr; 0-913958),* 1448 Page St., Alameda, CA 94501 (SAN 203-7521) Tel 415-522-4547.

Nourishing Thoughts Enterprises, *(Nourishing Thoughts; 0-9601198),* 1837 Beech St., Stow, OH 44224 (SAN 210-9298).

Nova, Inc., *(Nova; 0-9612264),* 1560 Broadway, Rm. 807, New York, NY 10036 (SAN 289-5374) Tel 212-869-3050.

Nova Univ. Press, *(Nova-NYIT U Pr; 0-917736),* College Ave., Fort Lauderdale, FL 33314 (SAN 211-6111) Tel 305-475-7300.

Nova Publishing Co., *(Nova Pub IL; 0-935755),* P.O. Box 101, Wheaton, IL 60189-0101 (SAN 695-8117) Tel 618-392-2406.

Novak, Anita A., *(A A Novak; 0-9614803),* 222 E. Chestnut St., No. 2D, Chicago, IL 60611 (SAN 692-7734) Tel 312-664-7712.

Novel Ideas, Inc., *(Novel Ideas; 0-914059),* 3499 Bunker Ave., Wantagh, NY 11793 (SAN 277-6979) Tel 516-783-8833.

November Books, *(November Bks; 0-941098),* P.O. Box 1074, Santa Barbara, CA 93111 (SAN 217-409X) Tel 805-967-3185.

Novick, Dorothy Dina, *(D D Novick; 0-9617274),* 1749 N. Highland Ave., Tucson, AZ 85719 (SAN 663-5067) Tel 602-324-4513.

Nowell, Eppler, *(E Nowell; 0-9611454),* 46 Cragmont Ave., San Francisco, CA 94116 (SAN 283-9229); Dist. by: Bookpeople, 2929 Fifth St., Berkeley, CA 94710 (SAN 168-9517) Tel 415-549-3030.

Nowfel Pubns., *(Nowfel),* Dist. by: Intercontinental Enterprises Co., 69 Stewart Ave., Eastchester, NY 10707 (SAN 218-7914). Moved, left no forwarding address.

Noyes Art Bks. *See* **Noyes Data Corp., Noyes Pubns.**

Noyes Data Corp./Noyes Pubns., *(Noyes; 0-8155),* Mill Rd. at Grand Ave., Park Ridge, NJ 07656 (SAN 209-2840) Tel 201-391-8484. *Imprints:* Noyes Art Books (NAB); Noyes Press (NP); Noyes Publications (Noyes Pubns).

Noyes Pr. *See* **Noyes Data Corp., Noyes Pubns.**
Noyes Pubns. *See* **Noyes Data Corp., Noyes Pubns.**

NTL Institute, *(NTL Inst; 0-9610392),* P.O. Box 9155, Rosslyn Sta., Arlington, VA 22209 (SAN 223-9485) Tel 703-527-1500; 1501 Wilson Blvd., Suite 1000, Arlington, VA 22209 (SAN 669-2249).

Nu-Diet Enterprises, *(Nu-Diet; 0-9609896),* 1739 Blue Ash Place, P.O. Box 29250, Columbus, OH 43229 (SAN 274-2101) Tel 614-846-1423.

Nuance Pr. Intl., *(Nuance Pr; 0-917924),* 32 E. Swan St., Columbus, OH 43215 (SAN 209-9748) Tel 614-221-1032.

Nuclear Information & Resource Service, *(Nuclear Info Res; 0-9615323),* 1616 P St., NW, Suite 160, Washington, DC 20036 (SAN 695-0140) Tel 202-328-0002.

Nuclear Negotiation Project, *(Nuclear Project; 0-9613615),* Harvard Law School, Pound Hall 513, Cambridge, MA 02138 (SAN 677-0630).

Nugget Enterprises, *(Nugget Ent; 0-931461),* 43930 228th Ave. SE, P.O. Box 184, Enumclaw, WA 98022 (SAN 683-1648) Tel 206-825-3855.

Numarc Bk. Corp., *(Numarc Bk Corp; 0-88471),* 50 Alcona Ave., Buffalo, NY 14226 (SAN 268-8702) Tel 716-834-1390.

Numard Bks., *(Numard Bks; 0-9612266),* 6005 Midnight Pass Rd., Sarasota, FL 34242 (SAN 289-4807) Tel 813-346-1396.

Numen Chapbooks, *(Numen Chapbks; 0-939162),* 3202 Ellerslie Ave., Baltimore, MD 21218 (SAN 216-4256).

Numerical Algorithms Group, Inc., *(Numer Algorithms; 1-85206),* 1101 31st St., Suite 100, Downers Grove, IL 60515 (SAN 679-2693) Tel 312-971-2337.

Numismatic Fine Arts, Inc., *(Numismatic Fine Arts),* 342 N. Rodeo Dr., Beverly Hills, CA 90212 (SAN 205-9029) Tel 213-278-1535; Orders to: P.O. Box 3788, Beverly Hills, CA 90212 (SAN 205-9037).

Nunciata Publishing, *(Nunciata),* P.O. Box 570122, Houston, TX 77257 (SAN 285-6883); Dist. by: Associated Advertisers Services, .

Nunes, Leslie K., *(Nunes; 0-9604190),* 613 Kaimalino Place, Kailua, HI 96734 (SAN 219-9769) Tel 808-254-1242.

Nur-I-Alam Pubns., *(Nur Pubns; 0-9608440),* 2331 N. Dunn St., Bloomington, IN 47401 (SAN 663-2963) Tel 812-339-5615; Dist. by: Worldwide Evangelization Crusade, 709 Pennsylvania Ave., Fort Washington, PA 19034 (SAN 276-8577) Tel 215-646-2322.

Nurseco, Inc. *See* **Admates**

Nurseline Assocs., Inc., *(Nurseline Assocs; 0-9616339),* P.O. Box 66682, Seattle, WA 98166 (SAN 658-9979) Tel 206-242-9797; 2819 SW 169th St., Seattle, WA 98166 (SAN 658-9987).

Nurtury Family School, The, *(Nurtury Fam; 0-9610612),* 374 W. Baltimore, Larkspur, CA 94939 (SAN 264-262X) Tel 415-924-9675.

Nutri-Kinetic Dynamics Inc., *(Nutri-Kinetic; 0-938478),* 850 Kam Hwy., Pearl City, HI 96782 (SAN 216-2768).

Nutrition Education Center, Subs. of C.L. Gerwick & Associates, Inc., *(Nutrition Ed; 0-915187),* 9500 Nall Ave., Suite 304, Overland Park, KS 66207 (SAN 289-7776) Tel 913-383-3464.

Nutrition Foundation, Inc., *(Nutrition Found; 0-935368),* Office of Education, 888 17th St., NW, Washington, DC 20017 (SAN 224-3911).

Nutshell Enterprises, Ltd., *(Nutshell Enterprises; 0-930723),* 3327 Charles St., Fallston, MD 20147 (SAN 677-6043) Tel 301-557-7583; Dist. by: Metra, P.O. Box 7130 University Station, Provo, UT (SAN 221-3885).

Nuttall Ornithological Club, *(Nuttall Ornith),* Harvard Univ., Museum of Comparative Zoology, Cambridge, MA 02138 (SAN 232-9123) Tel 617-495-2471.

Nuzum, David G., *(D G Nuzum; 0-9609538),* 201 D. St., Keyser, WV 26726 (SAN 260-2377) Tel 304-788-3549.

Nyerges, Anton N., *(Nyerges; 0-9600954),* 201 Langford Court, Richmond, KY 40475 (SAN 208-791X) Tel 606-623-7153.

O. ARS, *(O ARS; 0-942030),* P.O. Box 179, Cambridge, MA 02238 (SAN 238-6011) Tel 603-883-3536.

O & B Bks., Inc., *(O & B Bks; 0-9601586),* 1215 NW Kline Pl., Corvallis, OR 97330 (SAN 210-9328) Tel 503-752-2178.

†**OCLC Online Computer Library Ctr., Inc.,** *(OCLC Online Comp; 0-933418; 1-55653),* 6565 Frantz Rd., Dublin, OH 43017-0702 (SAN 694-597X); *CIP.*

ODS Pubns., Inc., *(ODS Pubns; 0-9602516),* 6415 N. Lemai Ave., Chicago, IL 60646 (SAN 212-842X) Tel 312-774-6550.

OES Pubns., *(OES Pubns; 0-89779),* Univ. of Kentucky, College of Engineering, Lexington, KY 40506-0046 (SAN 212-1255) Tel 606-257-3343.

OGAB Publishing, Subs. of Midwest Pub., *(Ogab Pubs; 0-912477),* 49 Grandview Dr., S. Zanesville, OH 43701 (SAN 265-3109) Tel 614-453-5574; Dist. by: Mark Wieder c/o Midwest Pub. & Dist. Service, P.O. Box 239, Portage, WI 53901 (SAN 200-805X).

OK Publishing, *(OK Pub; 0-9616615),* 8151 Mary Ellen Ave., North Hollywood, CA 91605 (SAN 661-4078) Tel 818-901-7903.

OLW Editions, *(OLW Editions; 0-934995),* Rte. 4, Box 9375, Barre, VT 05641 (SAN 694-6585) Tel 802-476-4618; Dist. by: Daily Bread, Richford, VT 05476 (SAN 200-5506); Dist. by: Ravengate Pr., The, P.O. Box 103, Cambridge, MA 02238 (SAN 203-090X) Tel 617-456-8181.

OMF Bks., Div. of Overseas Missionary Fellowship, *(OMF Bks; 0-85363),* 404 S. Church St., Robesonia, PA 19551 (SAN 211-8351).

†**OOLP Out of London Pr., Inc.,** *(Oolp Pr; 0-915570),* 1 Washington Sg. Village, New York, NY 10003 (SAN 202-8263) Tel 212-598-7860; *CIP.*

O R Publishing, *(OR Pub; 0-9614162),* 1481 Lafayette Rd., Claremont, CA 91711 (SAN 686-5518) Tel 714-624-1792.

OSI Pubns., Ltd., Div. of On-Line Software, *(OSI Pubns; 0-918317),* Ft. Lee Executive Pk., 2 Executive Dr., Ft. Lee, NJ 07024 (SAN 657-2952) Tel 201-592-5450.

Names

OTO (Society Ordo Templi Orientis in America), *(O T O; 0-913735),* P.O. Box 90144, Nashville, TN 37209 (SAN 219-9610); Dist. by: Bookpeople, 2929 Fifth St., Berkeley, CA 94710 (SAN 168-9517); Dist. by: The Distributors, 702 S. Michigan, South Bend, IN 46618 (SAN 169-2488) Tel 219-232-8500.

OVN Pubns., *(O V N Pubns; 0-9610188),* P.O. Box 491432, Los Angeles, CA 90049 (SAN 274-2632) Tel 213-820-6178.

O.E.G. Foundation *See* Exposition Pr. of Florida, Inc.

Oak Grove Pubns., *(Oak Grove Pubns; 0-9607162),* P.O. Box 521, Menlo Park, CA 94026 (SAN 239-0140) Tel 415-854-2059.

Oak Hill Bks., *(Oak Hill Bks; 0-9616701),* P.O. Box 576, Arroyo Grande, CA 93420 (SAN 661-3020) Tel 805-773-1977; 966 Printz Rd., Arroyo Grande, CA 93420 (SAN 661-3039) Tel 805-773-4369.

Oak Hill Pub., *(Oak Hill UT; 0-911391),* P.O. Box 520765 Brickyard Corporate Plaza, Salt Lake City, UT 84152 (SAN 274-2357) Tel 801-278-4042; 4456 Covecrest, Salt Lake City, UT 84214 (SAN 662-1007).

Oak House, The, *(Oak Hse; 0-931335),* P.O. Box 7809, Fresno, CA 93747 (SAN 682-7543).

†Oak Knoll Books, *(Oak Knoll; 0-938768),* 214 Delaware St., New Castle, DE 19720 (SAN 216-2776) Tel 302-328-7232; *CIP.*

Oak Lodge Publishing, *(Oak Lodge Pub; 0-9615661),* P.O. Box 68403, Oak Grove, OR 97268 (SAN 695-8680) Tel 503-654-2058; Dist. by: Western States Bk. Service, P.O. Box 855, Clackamas, OR 97015 (SAN 200-5662).

Oak Opening Pr., *(Oak Opening Pr; 0-9613850),* P.O. Box 811, Kalamazoo, MI 49005 (SAN 682-0077) Tel 616-388-5722.

Oak Park Michigan, *(Oak Park; 0-938968),* 24443 Roanoke, Oak Park, MI 48237 (SAN 216-1427).

Oak Pr., *(Oak Pr; 0-9615242),* 904 Broadway Ave., Wausau, WI 54401 (SAN 695-1643) Tel 715-842-7369.

Oak Pubns. *See* Music Sales Corp.

†Oak Ridge Associated Univs., *(Oak Ridge; 0-930780),* P.O. Box 117, Oak Ridge, TN 37831-0117 (SAN 211-3716) Tel 615-576-3365; *CIP.*

Oak Tree Pubns., Inc., Div. of Lakeside Industries, Inc., *(Oak Tree Pubns; 0-916392; 0-86679),* 9601 Aero Dr., Suite 202, San Diego, CA 92123 (SAN 211-4828) Tel 619-560-5163.

Oak Valley Pr., The, *(Oak Valley; 0-9609170),* 228 Virginia Ave., San Mateo, CA 94402 (SAN 241-418X) Tel 415-343-3397.

Oak Woods Media, Inc., *(Oak Woods Media; 0-88196),* 8701 West F Ave., P.O. Box 527, Oshtemo, MI 49077-0527 (SAN 264-6285) Tel 616-375-5621.

Oakland-PR, Div. of Project Review Inc., *(Oakland-PR; 0-9614236),* P.O. Box 1214, Oakland, CA 94604-1214 (SAN 686-6883) Tel 415-839-2767; Dist. by: Bookpeople, 2929 Fifth St., Berkeley, CA 94710 (SAN 168-9517) Tel 415-549-3030; Toll free: 800-227-1516.

†Oaklawn Press, Inc., *(Oaklawn Pr; 0-916198),* 1318 Fair Oaks Ave., S. Pasadena, CA 91030 (SAN 208-0621) Tel 213-799-0880; *CIP.*

Oakton Hills Pubns., *(Oakton Hills Pubns; 0-939047),* P.O. Box 557, Oakton, VA 22124 (SAN 661-681X); 2535 Oak Valley Dr., Vienna, VA 22180 (SAN 662-7870) Tel 703-255-1270.

Oakview Book Press, *(Oakview; 0-9601104),* P.O. Box 990, Adelphi, MD 20783 (SAN 210-0088) Tel 301-434-8106.

Oakwood Pr. (CA), *(Oakwood Pr CA; 0-934247),* 2168 Feliz Dr., Novata, CA 94947 (SAN 693-191X) Tel 415-892-7149.

Oasis Bks., *(Oasis Bks; 0-939213),* P.O. Box 37021, Denver, CO 80237 (SAN 662-6092); 10700 E. Dartmouth, Suite NN 312, Aurora, CO 80014 (SAN 662-6106) Tel 303-368-8545. Do not confuse with Oasis Bks. of Covina, CA.

Oasis International Communications, Inc., *(Oasis Intl; 0-938341),* P.O. Box 17510, San Diego, CA 92117 (SAN 661-2873); 5331 Mt. Alifan, San Diego, CA 92111 (SAN 661-2881) Tel 619-277-4991.

Oasis Press *See* PSI Research

Oates, Joan, *(J Oates; 0-9617047),* 5912 Kingsfield Dr., W. Bloomfield, MI 48033 (SAN 662-8133) Tel 313-661-2335; Dist. by: Green Gate Bks., P.O. Box 934, Lima, OH 45802 (SAN 169-6785).

Oatman, Russell Swinton, *(R S Oatman; 0-9616593),* 132 Mirick Rd., Princeton, MA 01541 (SAN 659-5197) Tel 617-464-5530.

Oaxacado Publishing Co., The, *(Oaxacado Pub Co; 0-915311),* 7333 Conestoga Ct., San Diego, CA 92120 (SAN 290-0262) Tel 619-286-9149.

OBAhouse, *(OBAhouse; 0-933653),* 108 College Ave., Columbia, MO 65201 (SAN 692-6754) Tel 314-874-0368; Orders to: P.O. Box 6024, Chicago, IL 60680-6024 (SAN 699-5934).

Ober Publishing, *(Ober Pub; 0-911785),* 9514-9 Reseda Blvd., No. 478, Northridge, CA 91324 (SAN 264-2654) Tel 818-701-6237.

†Oberlin College, Allen Memorial Art Museum, *(Ober Coll Allen; 0-942946),* Oberlin College, Main & Lorain Sts., Oberlin, OH 44074 (SAN 240-3226) Tel 216-775-8665; Dist. by: Indiana Universtiy Pr., Tenth & Morton Sts., Bloomington, IN 47405 (SAN 202-5647); *CIP.*

Oberlin College Conservatory Library, *(Oberlin Con Lib; 0-9611434),* Oberlin College, Oberlin, OH 44074 (SAN 283-3042) Tel 216-775-8280.

Oberlin College Pr., *(Oberlin Coll Pr; 0-932440),* Rice Hall, Oberlin College, Oberlin, OH 44074 (SAN 212-1883) Tel 216-775-8407. *Imprints:* Field Translation Series (Field Translat Ser).

Oberlin Pr. of the Times, *(Oberlin Pr Times),* 60 S. Pleasant St., Oberlin, OH 44074 (SAN 659-5634).

Oberling, Grace, *(G Oberling; 0-9616924),* 6732 Berneil Dr., Paradise Valley, AZ 85253 (SAN 661-485X) Tel 602-951-4310; Orders to: LUVType, 7707 N. 27th Ave., Phoenix, AZ 85051 (SAN 661-4868).

Oblate Fathers, *(Oblate),* P.O. Box 96, San Antonio, TX 78291 (SAN 209-5890) Tel 512-736-1685.

Oblong Pr., *(Oblong Pr; 0-9616635),* 1675 Broderson, Los Osos, CA 93402 (SAN 661-2148) Tel 805-528-4942.

Oboe Bks., *(Oboe Bks; 0-935659),* P.O. Box 0204, Oberlin, OH 44074 (SAN 695-8702) Tel 216-774-1576; Main P.O. Box 0204, Oberlin, OH 44074 (SAN 695-8710).

Obol International, Div. of Unigraphics, Inc., *(Obol Intl; 0-916710; 0-86723),* 4747 N. Spaulding, Chicago, IL 60625 (SAN 282-0692) Tel 312-267-3662.

Obolensky, Helene, Enterprises, Inc., *(Helene Obolensky Ent; 0-9609736),* P.O. Box 87, 909 Third Ave., New York, NY 10150 (SAN 274-2381) Tel 212-838-4722.

Obranoel Press, *(Obranoel Pr),* 63 Franklin Sq., New York, NY 11010 (SAN 208-4473).

O'Brien, F. M., Bookseller, *(O'Brien),* 34 & 36 High St., Portland, ME 04101 (SAN 203-7580).

O'Brien's Auto Racing Pubns., *(OBriens Auto Racing Pubns; 0-9616916),* 5618 Windsor Ave., Sioux City, IA 51106 (SAN 661-5392) Tel 712-274-1541.

Observational Research Pubns. Co., *(Observational; 0-942884),* 16 Polo Cir., Colorado Springs, CO 80906 (SAN 240-2629) Tel 303-632-2434.

Occam Press, *(Occam Pr; 0-9614238),* 1070 Queensbrook Dr., San Jose, CA 95129 (SAN 686-6891) Tel 415-857-7978.

Occasional Papers/Reprints Series in Contemporary Asian Studies, Inc., *(Occasional Papers; 0-942182),* 500 W. Baltimore St., Univ. of Maryland, School of Law, Baltimore, MD 21201 (SAN 226-2894) Tel 301-528-3870.

Occasional Productions, *(Occasional Prods; 0-933264),* 593 Vasona Avenue., Los Gatos, CA 95030 (SAN 211-6863).

Occidental Press, *(Occidental; 0-911050),* P.O. Box 1005, Washington, DC 20013 (SAN 203-7599).

Ocean Allen Publishing, *(Ocean Allen Pub; 0-917071),* 13130 Sundance Ave., San Diego, CA 92129 (SAN 655-2382) Tel 619-484-5401; Rte. 4, Box 369, Spokane, WA 99204 (SAN 691-4276) Tel 509-466-7095.

Ocean East Publishing Co., *(Ocean East; 0-9607028),* 1655 71st Ct., Vero Beach, FL 32960 (SAN 239-0159) Tel 305-567-0960.

Ocean Publishing, *(Ocean Pub; 0-936867),* P.O. Box 1673, Key West, FL 33041 (SAN 699-9107) Tel 305-296-6001; 425 Frances St., Key West, FL 33040 (SAN 699-9115) Tel 305-296-6001.

Ocean Tree Bks., *(Ocean Tree Bks; 0-943734),* P.O. Box 1295, Santa Fe, NM 87504 (SAN 241-0478) Tel 505-983-1412; Dist. by: Bookpeople, 2929 Fifth St., Berkeley, CA 94710 (SAN 168-9517); Toll free: 800-227-1516; Dist. by: DeVorss & Co., P.O. Box 550, 1046 Princeton Dr., Marina del Rey, CA 90294 (SAN 168-9886) Tel 213-870-7478; Dist. by: New Leaf Distributors, 1020 White St., SW, Atlanta, GA 30310 (SAN 169-1449) Tel 404-755-2665; Toll free: 800-241-3829.

Ocean View Pr., *(Ocean View Pr; 0-938075),* P.O. Box 4148, Mountain View, CA 94900 (SAN 661-1893); 1645 Mercy St., Mountain View, CA 94040 (SAN 661-1907) Tel 415-965-3721.

Oceana Pubns., Inc., *(Oceana; 0-379),* 75 Main St., Dobbs Ferry, NY 10522 (SAN 202-5744) Tel 914-693-1733. *Imprints:* Docket Series (D); Legal Almanac Series (LA).

Oceanic Institute, The, *(Oceanic Inst; 0-9617016),* Makapuu Point, Waimanalo, HI 96705 (SAN 662-8818) Tel 808-259-7951.

Oceanic Publishing Co., *(Oceanic Pub Co; 0-916467),* P.O. Box 156, Na'Alehu, HI 96772 (SAN 295-1517) Tel 808-929-9101.

Oceanic Society, *(Oceanic Soc Stamford),* 185 Magee Ave., Stamford, CT 06902 (SAN 225-2236) Tel 203-327-9786; Orders to: Fort Mason, Bldg. E, San Francisco, CA 94123 (SAN 669-2273).

Oceanus Institute, Inc., *(Oceanus; 0-915189),* Learning Place, Manset, ME 04656 (SAN 289-7784) Tel 207-244-5015.

Ocelot Press, *(Ocelot Pr; 0-912434),* P.O. Box 504, Claremont, CA 91711 (SAN 203-7602) Tel 714-621-2200.

Ochlocknee Community Civic Club, Inc., *(Ochlocknee),* Ochlocknee, GA 31773 (SAN 694-5414).

O'Connor Hse-Pubs., Inc., *(O'Connor Hse-Pubs; 0-913243),* P.O. Box 64098, Virginia Beach, VA 23464 (SAN 679-1492) Tel 804-420-2551.

O'Connor Publishing Co., *(O'Connor Pub.; 0-9615466),* 587 Greenwood Ave., Glencoe, IL 60022 (SAN 695-8753) Tel 312-835-1040.

Ocorr Press, The, *(Ocorr Pr; 0-937478),* P.O. Box 64322, Los Angeles, CA 90064 (SAN 214-2147) Tel 213-839-3155.

†Ocotillo Press, *(Ocotillo; 0-918380),* 215 N. 51st St., Seattle, WA 98103 (SAN 209-4061); *CIP.*

†Octameron Assocs., *(Octameron Assocs; 0-917760),* P.O. Box 3437, Alexandria, VA 22314 (SAN 282-0714) Tel 703-823-1882; 4805A Eisenhower Ave., Alexandria, VA 22304 (SAN 658-1307); Orders to: P.O. Box 3437, Alexandria, VA 22302 (SAN 282-0722); *CIP.*

Octavia Press, *(Octavia Pr; 0-9605882),* 2611 Octavia St., San Francisco, CA 94123 (SAN 282-0730) Tel 415-922-4127; Orders to: P.O. Box 42493, San Francisco, CA 94101 (SAN 282-0749) Tel 415-922-4127.

October House, *(October; 0-8079),* P.O. Box 454, Stonington, CT 06378 (SAN 203-7610) Tel 203-535-3725.

October Press, Inc., The, *(October Pr; 0-935440),* 105 Blue Lake Ct., Austin, TX 78734 (SAN 220-1216).

Octopus Bks., *(Octopus Bks; 1-55580),* One Madison Ave., New York, NY 10010 (SAN 661-4582).

Oda, James, *(Oda),* 7054 Vanscoy Ave., N. Hollywood, CA 91605 (SAN 216-4264).

Oddo Publishing, Inc., *(Oddo; 0-87783),* Storybook Acres, Box 68, Fayetteville, GA 30214 (SAN 202-7857) Tel 404-461-7627.

Odens, Peter R., *(P R Odens; 0-9609484),* P.O. Box 222,, El Centro, CA 92244 (SAN 274-2438) Tel 619-356-1243.

Odin Pr., *(Odin Pr; 0-930500),* P.O. Box 536, New York, NY 10021 (SAN 211-3244) Tel 212-744-2538.

Odin Publishing Co., *(Odin Pub Co; 0-9610210),* 95 Eldridge Ave., Mill Valley, CA 94941 (SAN 274-2454) Tel 415-381-1807.

Odium, *(Odium),* P.O. Box 65594, Los Angeles, CA 90065 (SAN 218-4982) Tel 213-794-1959.

O'Donnell, Chuck Publishing, *(C O'Donnell Pub; 0-9613166),* 216 N. Chester, Park Ridge, IL 60068 (SAN 294-9873) Tel 312-698-4560.

O'Donnell, Hugh Roe, Guild, The, *(H R O'Donnell Guild; 0-9617208),* ST. Paul's Church, c/o Father Gerald McCarthy, Tappen, ND 58487 (SAN 663-2785) Tel 701-845-0432; Dist. by: Irish Books & Media, 683 Osceola Ave., St. Paul, MN 55105 (SAN 215-1987) Tel 612-647-5678.

O'Dwyer, J.R., Co., Inc., *(J R O'Dwyer; 0-941424),* 271 Madison Ave., New York, NY 10016 (SAN 226-3386).

Odyssey Enterprise, Ltd., *(Odyssey Ent; 0-939006),* P.O. Box 1686, Norman, OK 73070 (SAN 216-2784) Tel 405-364-9811.

Odyssey Press, *(Odyssey Pr; 0-672; 0-8399),* Dist. by: Bobbs-Merrill Co., 4300 W. 62nd St., Indianapolis, IN 46468 (SAN 201-3959).

Odyssey Pubns., Inc., *(Odyssey MA; 0-933752),* 334 E. Squantum St., Quincy, MA 02171 (SAN 214-4301) Tel 617-328-9460; Orders to: P.O. Box G-148, Greenwood, MA 01880 (SAN 662-1015).

Oelgeschlager, Gunn & Hain, Inc., *(Oelgeschlager; 0-89946),* 131 Clarendon St., Boston, MA 02116 (SAN 213-6937) Tel 617-437-9620.

Of Course Pubns., Inc., *(Of Course Pubns; 0-935255),* P.O. Box 70732, Houston, TX 77270-0732 (SAN 695-507X) Tel 713-863-0250; 607 W. 14th St., Houston, TX 77008 (SAN 695-5088).

†**Office of Air Force History,** *(Off Air Force; 0-912799),* Building 5681, Bolling Air Force Base, Washington, DC 20332 (SAN 218-8821) Tel 202-767-4548; *CIP.*

Office of Management Studies, Div. of Association of Research Libraries, *(OMS),* 1527 New Hampshire Ave. NW, Washington, DC 20036 (SAN 260-3853) Tel 202-232-8656.

Office of Public Instruction, *(Office Pub Instruct; 0-9614692),* State Capitol, Helena, MT 59620 (SAN 670-7327).

Office of the Federal Register, Div. of National Archives and Records Administration, *(Office Fed Register),* 1100 L St., NW, Rm. 8401, Washington, DC 20408 (SAN 226-5168) Tel 202-523-5240; Orders to: Superintendent of Documents, U.S. Government Printing Office, Washington, DC 20402 (SAN 691-4195) Tel 202-783-3238.

Office Publications, Inc., *(Office Pubns; 0-911054),* 1600 Summer St., P.O. Box 1231, Stamford, CT 06904 (SAN 203-7637) Tel 203-327-9670.

Office Research Institute, *(Office Res; 0-911056),* 1517 Sparrow St., Longwood, FL 32750 (SAN 203-7645) Tel 305-339-8527.

Officers Christian Fellowship, *(Off Christian Fellowship),* P.O. Box 36200, Denver, CO 80236 (SAN 291-8439).

Official Corp., The, *(Official Corp; 0-9605074),* 240 Newport Center Drive Suite 200, Newport Beach, CA 92660 (SAN 216-2792).

Official Shit Co., *(Official Shit Co; 0-9616172),* 105B S. Witchduck Rd., No. 225, Virginia Beach, VA 23462 (SAN 699-9875) Tel 804-467-8845.

Offset Hse., *(Offset Hse),* South Burlington, VT 05401 (SAN 698-1496); Dist. by: Creative Expression, P.O. Box 456, Colchester, VT 05446 (SAN 200-5816).

Offshoot Pubns., *(Offshoot Pub; 0-910013),* 1280 Goodpasture Island Rd., Eugene, OR 97401 (SAN 241-3426) Tel 503-686-8266.

Ogden Shepard Publishing Co., *(Ogden Shepard Pub; 0-937313),* 2305 Canyon Blvd., Boulder, CO 80302 (SAN 658-8166) Tel 303-444-2381.

Ogham House, Inc., *(Ogham Hse; 0-916590),* 6 Sherri Lane, Spring Valley, NY 10977 (SAN 208-0486).

Ohanian, *(Ohanian; 0-9613618),* El Capitan Assocs., P.O. Box 5025, San Diego, CA 92105 (SAN 670-8625) Tel 619-283-5994; 3911 Dove St., No. 105, San Diego, CA 92103 (SAN 663-3080) Tel 619-260-0218.

O'Hara, Betsy, *(B O'Hara; 0-9604188),* 2562 26th Ave., San Francisco, CA 94116 (SAN 219-9777) Tel 415-731-1472. Not to be confused with O'Hara Publications in Burbank, CA.

O'Hara, J. Philip, Inc., Pubs., *(O'Hara; 0-87955),* c/o Scroll Press, Inc., 2858 Valerie Court, Merrick, NY 11566 (SAN 202-5868) Tel 516-379-4283. *Imprints:* Potato Press (Potato Pr).

Ohara Pubns., Inc., *(Ohara Pubns; 0-89750),* 1813 Victory Pl., Burbank, CA 91504 (SAN 205-3632) Tel 818-843-4444; Toll free: 800-423-2874; P.O. Box 7728, Burbank, CA 91510 (SAN 658-1315). Do not confuse with Betsy O'Hara, San Francisco, CA.

O'Hayre Publishing Co., *(O'Hayre Pub; 0-9613183),* 3123 O'Hayre Ct., Lakewood, CO 80215 (SAN 295-7647) Tel 303-233-7227.

†**Ohio Academy of Science, The,** *(Ohio Acad Sci; 0-933128),* 445 King Ave., Columbus, OH 43201 (SAN 212-3762) Tel 614-424-6045; *CIP.*

Ohio Antique Review, Inc., *(Ohio Antique Rev; 0-9603290),* P.O. Box 538, Worthington, OH 43085 (SAN 213-344X) Tel 614-885-9757.

Ohio Arts Council, *(OH Arts Council; 0-913335),* 727 E. Main St., Columbus, OH 43205 (SAN 283-2232) Tel 614-466-2613.

Ohio Biological Survey, Subs. of Ohio State University, *(Ohio Bio Survey; 0-86727),* Ohio State Univ., 980 Biological Sciences Bldg., 484 W. 12th Ave., Columbus, OH 43210 (SAN 217-0787) Tel 614-422-9645.

Ohio Dept. of Natural Resources, *(Ohio Nat Res; 0-931079),* Fountain Sq., Columbus, OH 43224 (SAN 678-9366) Tel 614-265-6807.

Ohio Genealogical Society, *(OH Genealogical; 0-935057),* 419 W. Third., P.O. Box 2625, Mansfield, OH 44906 (SAN 218-8848) Tel 419-522-9077.

Ohio Historical Society, *(Ohio Hist Soc; 0-87758),* Ohio Historical Ctr., 1985 Velma Ave., Columbus, OH 43211 (SAN 202-1331) Tel 614-466-1500.

Ohio Library Assn., *(Ohio Lib Assn; 0-911060),* 40 S. 3rd St., Suite 230, Columbus, OH 43215 (SAN 203-7653) Tel 614-221-9057.

Ohio Magazine, *(Ohio Mag; 0-938040),* 40 S. Third St., Columbus, OH 43215 (SAN 215-7969).

Ohio Psychology Publishing Co., *(Ohio Psych Pub; 0-910707),* 5 E. Long St., Suite 610, Columbus, OH 43215 (SAN 260-2385) Tel 614-224-0034.

Ohio Regional Art Directory, *(OH Regional Art; 0-912669),* 2803 Bridge Ave., Cleveland, OH 44113 (SAN 282-7875) Tel 216-861-0347.

†**Ohio Review, The,** *(Ohio Review; 0-942148),* Ohio Univ., Ellis Hall, Athens, OH 45701-2979 (SAN 239-9687) Tel 614-593-1900; *CIP.*

Ohio Savings Assn., *(Ohio Savings),* 13109 Shaker Square, Cleveland, OH 44120 (SAN 211-0555) Tel 216-752-7000.

Ohio State Univ. College of Administrative Science, *(Ohio St U Admin Sci; 0-87776),* 220 W. 12th Ave., Columbus, OH 43210 (SAN 203-7661) Tel 614-422-2061; Orders to: O.S.U. Pr., The Ohio State Univ., 2070 Neil Ave., Columbus, OH 43210 (SAN 202-8158).

Ohio State Univ. Pr., *(Ohio St U Pr; 0-8142),* 1050 Carmack Rd., Columbus, OH 43210-1002 (SAN 202-8158) Tel 614-422-6930. *Imprints:* Sandstone Books (Sandstone Bks).

Ohio Univ. Ctr. for Afro-American Studies, *(Ctr Afro Stud Ohio; 0-911393),* Ohio Univ., Athens, OH 45701 (SAN 274-2586) Tel 614-594-5477.

Ohio Univ. Pr., *(Ohio U Pr; 0-8214),* Scott Quadrangle, Rm. 223, Athens, OH 45701 (SAN 282-0773) Tel 614-594-5852; Toll free: 800-242-7737; Orders to: Harper & Row Pubs., Inc., Keystone Industrial Pk., Scranton, PA 18512 (SAN 282-0781).

Ohio Veterinary Medical Association, *(Ohio Vet; 0-9613273),* 1350 W. Fifth Ave., Columbus, OH 43212 (SAN 297-0449) Tel 614-486-7253.

Ohsawa, George, Macrobiotic Foundation, *(G Ohsawa; 0-918860),* 1511 Robinson St., Oroville, CA 95965 (SAN 207-7663) Tel 916-533-7702.

Oil & Gas Consultants International, Inc., *(Oil & Gas; 0-930972),* 4554 S. Harvard, Tulsa, OK 74135 (SAN 221-9484).

†**Oil Daily,** *(Oil Daily; 0-918216),* 1401 New York Ave., NW, Suite 500, Washington, DC 20005 (SAN 210-2498) Tel 202-662-0700; Toll free: 800-368-5803; *CIP.*

Ojai Printing & Publishing, *(Ojai; 0-943134),* 111 N. Blanche, Ojai, CA 93023 (SAN 240-9216).

Ojar Pub., *(Ojar Pub; 0-9615075),* 24 Warrenton St., Springfield, MA 01109 (SAN 694-0455) Tel 413-783-7372.

O'Keefe Press, *(O'Keefe Pr; 0-915191),* P.O. Box 3723, Stanford, CA 94305 (SAN 289-7806); Dist. by: Shapolsky/Steimatzky, 56 E. 11th St., New York, NY 10003 (SAN 200-8068).

Okefenokee Press, *(Okefenokee Pr; 0-9601606),* Rte. 3, Box 142-C, Folkston, GA 31537 (SAN 208-3752) Tel 912-496-7401.

Okie Doke Pr., *(Okie Doke Pr; 0-9614329),* P.O. Box 290, Snoqualmie, WA 98065 (SAN 687-7869) Tel 206-888-0504.

Oklahoma Bankers Association, *(OK Bankers; 0-916937),* P.O. Box 18246, Oklahoma City, OK 73154 (SAN 654-4703) Tel 405-424-5252.

Oklahoma Museum of Art, *(Okla Mus Art; 0-911919),* 7316 Nichols Rd., Oklahoma, OK 73120 (SAN 279-957X) Tel 405-840-2759.

Oklahoma State University Press, *(Okla State Univ Pr; 0-914956),* N. Monroe St., Stillwater, OK 74078 (SAN 221-9514); Dist. by: Will Rogers Memorial, P.O. Box 157, Claremore, OK 74018 (SAN 280-3003) Tel 918-341-0719.

Oklahoma Wildlife Federation, *(OK Wildlife Fed; 0-937733),* 4545 N. Lincoln, Suite 171, Oklahoma City, OK 73105 (SAN 659-3844) Tel 405-524-7009.

Okolo, Anthony, *(A Okolo; 0-9616272),* 1100 Grand Concourse, No. 5E, Bronx, NY 10456 (SAN 658-6015) Tel 212-538-1263; P.O. Box 50, Bronx, NY 10462-0050 (SAN 658-6023).

Ol' Attic Books, *(Ol'Attic Bks; 0-9611264),* RTE 1, Box 137A, Pennsboro, WV 26415 (SAN 282-9398) Tel 304-659-2212.

Olam Pubns., *(OLAM; 0-916222),* 2101 N. Court Hse. Rd., Arlington, VA 22201 (SAN 207-933X) Tel 703-527-7688.

Old Adobe Press, *(Old Adobe Pr),* P.O. Box 115, Penngrove, CA 94251 (SAN 203-7696).

Old Army Pr., *(Old Army; 0-88342),* P.O. Box 2243, Fort Collins, CO 80521 (SAN 202-1307) Tel 303-484-5535.

Old Betsy Bks., *(Old Betsy Bks; 0-9616636),* 4940 Golfview Ct., Charlotte, NC 28212 (SAN 661-1788) Tel 704-545-9172.

Old Bk. Shop Pubn., *(Old Bk Shop Pubn; 0-938673),* P.O. Box 447, Palm Beach, FL 33480 (SAN 661-4817); 1028 N. L St., Lake Worth, FL 33460 (SAN 661-4825) Tel 305-588-5129; Dist. by: FEC News Distributing Co., 2601 Mercer Ave., West Palm Beach, FL 33402 (SAN 200-6677).

Old Cookbooks, *(Old Cookbooks HT Hicks; 0-932965),* P.O. Box 462, Haddonfield, NJ 08033 (SAN 689-9935) Tel 609-854-2844.

Old Dominion Pr., *(Old Dominion Pr; 0-913513),* P.O. Box 10423, Alexandria, VA 22310-0423 (SAN 285-6735) Tel 703-922-8741.

Old Farm Kennels, *(Old Farm Ken),* NE 5451 Eastside Hwy., Florence, MT 59833 (SAN 285-6727) Tel 406-273-6837.

Old Fields Pubs., *(Old Fields Pubs; 0-942434),* P.O. Box 6154, Tallahassee, FL 32301 (SAN 239-5398).

Old Golf Shop, Inc., *(Old Golf Shop; 0-936557),* 325 W. Fifth St., Cincinnati, OH 45202 (SAN 698-1046) Tel 513-241-7789; Toll free: 800-227-8700.

Old Harbor Pr., *(Old Harbor Pr; 0-9615529),* P.O. Box 97, Sitka, AK 99835 (SAN 695-880X) Tel 907-747-3584; Orders to: P.O. Box 97, Sitka, AK 99835 (SAN 699-6116).

Old Hickory Pubs., *(Old Hickory; 0-9613193),* 100 Lake Vista Dr., Hendersonville, TN 37075 (SAN 295-754X) Tel 615-824-3546.

Old Hse. Journal Corp., The, *(Old Hse Journ Corp; 0-942202),* 69A Seventh Ave., Brooklyn, NY 11217 (SAN 238-6801) Tel 718-636-4515.

Old Iron Book Company, *(Old Iron Bk Co; 0-942804),* R.R. 1, Box 28-A, Atkins, IA 52206 (SAN 238-8324).

Old Japan Press *See* **Holmes Publishing Group**

Old Main Bks., *(Old Main Bks; 0-940166),* 74 W. Main St., Mechanicsburg, PA 17055 (SAN 238-3586); Dist. by: Berkshire Traveller Pr., Pine St., Stockbridge, MA 01262 (SAN 201-4424) Tel 413-298-3636.

Old Man Pr., The, *(Old Man Pr; 0-934435),* P.O. Box 31463, San Francisco, CA 94131 (SAN 693-5699) Tel 415-333-7785.

Old Maps, *(Old Maps; 0-911653),* P.O. Box 54, West Chesterfield, NH 03466 (SAN 264-2689) Tel 603-256-6519.

Old Master Gallery Press, *(Old Master Gallery Pr; 0-9610970),* 15438 Hawthorne Blvd., Lawndale, CA 90260 (SAN 265-3117) Tel 213-679-2525.

Old New York Book Shop Press, *(Old NY Bk Shop; 0-937036),* 1069 Juniper St., NE, Atlanta, GA 30309 (SAN 215-6903); Dist. by: Norman S. Berg, P.O. Box 15232, Atlanta, GA 30333 (SAN 226-8086).

Old Oaktree Motor Co., *(Old Oaktree; 0-9603194),* 2012 Hyperion Ave., Los Angeles, CA 90027 (SAN 213-2273).

Old Plate Press *See* **From Here Pr.**

Old Sparta Press, *(Old Sparta Pr; 0-9608344),* P.O. Box 6363, Raleigh, NC 27628 (SAN 239-5401) Tel 919-832-1358.

Old Stone Presbyterian Church, *(Old Stone Pres Church; 0-9611706),* 200 Church St., Lewisburg, WV 24901 (SAN 285-2756).

Old Sturbridge, Inc., *(Old Sturbridge; 0-913387),* Old Sturbridge Village, Sturbridge, MA 01566 (SAN 203-0004) Tel 617-347-3362.

Old Suffolk Square Pr, *(Old Suffolk; 0-932247),* 476 Main St., Malden, MA 02148 (SAN 686-6220) Tel 617-324-0440.

Old Theology Book House, *(Old Theology Bk Hse; 0-9612964),* P.O. Box 12232, Minneapolis, MN 55412 (SAN 293-4965).

Old Time Bottle Publishing Co., *(Old Time; 0-911068),* 611 Lancaster Dr., NE, Salem, OR 97301 (SAN 203-7718) Tel 503-362-1446.

Old Town Pr., *(Old Town Pr; 0-9610140),* 833 S. Main, St. Charles, MO 63301 (SAN 274-2764).

Old Violin-Art Publishing, *(Old Violin; 0-918554),* Box 500, 225 S. Cooke, Helena, MT 59624 (SAN 209-9756).

Old Warren Road Press, *(Old Warren; 0-9610858),* 141 W. 17th St., 5th Fl., New York, NY 10011 (SAN 264-2697) Tel 212-242-5762; Dist. by: Book Dynamics, Inc., 836 Broadway, New York, NY 10003 (SAN 169-5649) Tel 212-254-7798.

Old West Publishing Co., *(Old West; 0-912094),* 1228 E. Colfax Ave., Denver, CO 80218 (SAN 202-8174) Tel 303-832-7190.

Oleander Pr., *(Oleander Pr; 0-902675; 0-900891; 0-906672),* 210 Fifth Ave., New York, NY 10010 (SAN 206-1031).

†**Olearius Editions,** *(Olearius Edns; 0-917526),* Drawer H, Kemblesville, PA 19347 (SAN 207-2696) Tel 215-255-4335; *CIP.*

Olimpo Publishing Hse., *(Olimpo Pub Hse; 0-938873),* 101 SW 33rd Ave., Miami, FL 33135 (SAN 662-5762) Tel 305-444-8451.

Olin Ski Co., Inc., Subs. of Olin Corp., *(Olin Ski Co; 0-9606740),* 475 Smith St., Middletown, CT 06457 (SAN 219-6158) Tel 203-632-2000.

Olio Publishers, *(Olio Pubs; 0-934381),* P.O. Box 78, Glen Echo, MD 20812-0078 (SAN 693-8043) Tel 301-229-6916.

†**Olive Pr. Pubns.,** *(Olive Pr Pubns; 0-933380),* P.O. Box 99, Los Olivos, CA 93441 (SAN 212-5331) Tel 805-688-2445; *CIP.*

Olive Pr., The, *(Olive Pr; 0-9612150),* 17709 Sierra Trail, P.O. Box 194, Lake Hughes, CA 93532 (SAN 289-4823) Tel 805-724-1870.

Oliver, Lawrence, Book, *(L Oliver Bk; 0-9606432),* 815 Armada Terrace, San Diego, CA 92106 (SAN 206-7226).

†**Oliver-Nelson,** *(Oliver-Nelson; 0-8407),* Nelson Pl. at Elm Hill Pike, Nashville, TN 37214 (SAN 689-1470); Toll free: 800-872-4445 (Sales); Toll free: 800-821-4370 (Sales TN); *CIP.*

Olivet College Press, *(Olivet; 0-911070),* Dist. by: Bill Whitney, P.O. Box 20, Mott Academic Ctr., Olivet, MI 49076 (SAN 282-6801).

Olivia & Hill Press Inc., The, *(Olivia & Hill; 0-934034),* P.O. Box 7396, Ann Arbor, MI 48107 (SAN 212-923X) Tel 313-663-0235.

Olivo, C. Thomas, Assocs., *(C T Olivo; 0-938561),* 169 Rosemont St., Albany, NY 12206 (SAN 661-4744) Tel 518-459-4653; Dist. by: Delmar Pubs., Inc., 2 Computer Dr., W, Albany, NY 12212 (SAN 206-7544) Tel 518-459-1150.

Olken Pubns., *(Olken Pubns; 0-934818),* 2830 Kennedy St., Livermore, CA 94550 (SAN 203-7939) Tel 415-447-5177.

Oll Korrect Pr., *(Oll Korrect),* 6553 Bellaire Ave., N. Hollywood, CA 91606 (SAN 209-8512) Tel 818-762-3375.

Ololon Pubns., *(Ololon Pubns; 0-9607332),* P.O. Box 569, Lumberton, NC 28359 (SAN 239-2712) Tel 919-738-9396.

Olson, David V., Q M D, Book & Insignia Exchange, *(Olson QMD; 0-9609690),* 1740 Stanbridge, St. Paul, MN 55113 (SAN 282-079X) Tel 612-633-2914; Dist. by: 4540 Morningside Ave., Vadnais Heights, MN 55110 (SAN 663-2971) Tel 612-426-9768.

Olswanger, Anna, *(Anna Olswanger; 0-9614598),* 177 N. Highland, No. 909, Memphis, TN 38111 (SAN 691-7593) Tel 901-327-4341.

Olympian King Co., *(Olympian King Co; 0-9615662),* 14184 Penrod Rd., Detroit, MI 48223 (SAN 695-8842) Tel 313-272-7956; Dist. by: Multi-Media Education, P.O. Box 35396, Detroit, MI 48235 (SAN 200-7126) Tel 313-342-1261.

Olympic Media Information, *(Olympic Media; 0-88367),* 550 First St., Hoboken, NJ 07030-6553 (SAN 202-8190) Tel 201-963-1600.

Olympics Made Easy, *(Olympics Made; 0-910935),* 54 Cottonwood Cir., Rolling Hills Estates, CA 90274 (SAN 274-2810) Tel 213-541-2842.

†**Olympus Publishing Co.,** *(Olympus Pub Co; 0-913420),* 1670 E. 13th, S., Salt Lake City, UT 84105 (SAN 202-8204) Tel 801-583-3666; *CIP.*

Omaha Printing Company, *(Omaha Print; 0-9609116),* 4700 F. Street, Omaha, NE 68117 (SAN 264-2700).

O'Malley, Martin J., *(M J O'Malley; 0-9606610),* 222 Paulison Ave., Passaic, NJ 07055 (SAN 207-4702) Tel 201-473-4643.

Oman, Robert, Publishing, *(R Oman Pub; 0-931660),* 204 Fair Oaks Park, Needham, MA 02192 (SAN 211-7599).

Oman Enterprises, *(Oman Ent; 0-917346),* P.O. Box 222357, Carmel, CA 93922 (SAN 208-7936) Tel 408-624-4386.

Ombudsman Pr., *(Omb; 0-930175),* 470 W. Highland Ave., Sierra Madre, CA 91024 (SAN 210-3184) Tel 818-355-1325.

Omdega Pr., *(Omdega Pr; 0-9614611),* P.O. Box 1546, Provincetown, MA 02657 (SAN 691-8182) Tel 617-487-1117.

Omega Books (Los Angeles), *(Omega LA; 0-9613094),* 5648 Heatherdale Dr., Los Angeles, CA 90043 (SAN 294-6386) Tel 213-293-9608.

Omega Center, *(Omega Ctr; 0-938726),* 137 W. Station St., Barrington, IL 60010 (SAN 219-8061).

Omega Pr., Div. of Sufi Order in the West, *(Omega Pr NM; 0-930872),* P.O. Box 574, Lebanon Springs, NY 12114 (SAN 214-1493) Tel 518-794-8181; Dist. by: New Leaf Distributing, 1020 White St., SW, Atlanta, GA 30310 (SAN 169-1449) Tel 404-755-2665; Toll free: 800-241-3829; Dist. by: Omega Pr., P.O. Box 574, Lebanon Springs, NY 12114 (SAN 214-1493) Tel 518-794-8181.

Omega Pubns., Div. of Omega Corporation, *(Omega Pubns OR; 0-86694),* P.O. Box 4130, Medford, OR 97501 (SAN 220-1534) Tel 503-826-1030.

Omega-Three Project, Inc., *(Omega Three Project; 0-9616775),* 10615-G Tierrasanta Blvd., Suite 347, San Diego, CA 92124 (SAN 661-4450) Tel 619-278-9578.

Omenana, *(Omenana; 0-943324),* 116 Howland St., Roxbury, MA 02121 (SAN 240-5571) Tel 617-445-0161.

Omicron Pr., *(Omicron Pr),* 8475 La Jolla Scenic Dr. N., La Jolla, CA 92037 (SAN 297-1992) Tel 619-453-0133; Orders to: P.O. Box 694, La Jolla, CA 92038 (SAN 685-3927) Tel 619-453-0133.

Omkara Press, *(Omkara Pr; 0-934094),* 912 Beaver St., Santa Rosa, CA 95404 (SAN 212-9558) Tel 707-575-1736.

Ommation Pr., *(Ommation Pr; 0-941240),* 5548 N. Sawyer Ave., Chicago, IL 60625 (SAN 216-2997) Tel 312-539-5745.

Omni Learning Systems, Inc., *(Omni Lrn Syst; 0-938257),* 2508 Fifth Ave., Suite 110, Seattle, WA 98121 (SAN 661-3616) Tel 206-682-9469; 8306 N. Point Rd., Hansville, WA 98340 (SAN 661-3624) Tel 206-638-2414.

Omni Worldwide Corp., *(Omni Worldwide; 0-938259),* P.O. Box 4427, Clearwater, FL 33518 (SAN 661-4353); 1100 Cleveland, Suite 900, Clearwater, FL 33515 (SAN 661-4361) Tel 813-442-1197.

Omnibook, Co. *See* **Bible Study, Pr.**

Omnibus Pr., *(Omnibus Pr; 0-939383),* 339 Naymut, Menasha, WI 54952 (SAN 662-9458) Tel 414-722-4034.

Omnicom, Inc., *(Omnicom; 0-937375),* 501 Church St., NE, Suite 304, Vienna, VA 22180 (SAN 659-0055) Tel 703-281-1135.

Omnimaven Bks., *(Omnimaven Bks; 0-9614514),* P.O. Box 2015, Princeton, NJ 08540 (SAN 691-7305) Tel 609-737-9421.

On Our Way, Inc., *(On Our Way; 0-9614773),* P.O. Box 1972, Sedona, AZ 86336 (SAN 692-9974) Tel 602-282-5427.

On the Road Publishing, *(On the Road Pub; 0-9616316),* 2870-1 Twin Brooks Rd., NE, Atlanta, GA 30319 (SAN 658-7488) Tel 404-261-8396.

Onager Publishing, *(Onager Pub; 0-936491),* 1420 Fifth St., Berkeley, CA 94710-1234 (SAN 698-1348) Tel 415-526-0383.

Onami Publications, *(Onami Pubns; 0-911929),* P.O. Box 25466, Rochester, NY 14625-0466 (SAN 264-2727) Tel 716-385-5718.

Onaway Pubns., *(Onaway; 0-918900),* 28 Lucky Dr., San Rafael, CA 94904 (SAN 210-4768) Tel 415-924-0884.

Once Upon Some Stories Publishing Co., *(Once Upon Stories; 0-9617219),* 2581 NE 31st Ave., Portland, OR 97212 (SAN 663-4206) Tel 503-282-1319.

Onchiota Books, *(Onchiota Bks; 0-934820),* Rte. 99, Loon Lake, NY 12968 (SAN 213-1366) Tel 518-891-3249.

Ondine Press, *(Ondine Pr; 0-910795),* 6318 Vesper Ave., Van Nuys, CA 91411-2378 (SAN 262-8449) Tel 818-781-4360.

One Candle Pr., *(One Candle; 0-914032),* P.O. Box 888681, Atlanta, GA 30356 (SAN 658-1331) Tel 404-394-6870.

One Eight, Inc., *(One Eight Inc; 0-935081),* P.O. Box 2075, Forks, WA 98331-0822 (SAN 695-0132) Tel 206-374-6500.

One-Horse Pr., *(One-Horse Pr; 0-935941),* P.O. Box 15016, Springfield, MA 01115 (SAN 696-8805) Tel 413-568-4569; 1500 Main St., Springfield, MA 01115 (SAN 696-8813).

†**101 Productions,** *(One Hund One Prods; 0-912238; 0-89286),* 834 Mission St., San Francisco, CA 94103 (SAN 202-8220) Tel 415-495-6040; Toll free: 800-621-0851 Ext. 300; Dist. by: Macmillan, Front & Brown Sts., Riverside, NJ 08075 (SAN 202-5582); *CIP.*

101st Airborne Division Assn., *(One Hund First Air),* 2677 Willakenzie Rd., Eugene, OR 97401 (SAN 210-1297) Tel 503-345-2236.

132nd Infantry Assn. of World War II, *(One Hund Thirty-Second Infantry; 0-9615127),* P.O. Box 56189, Chicago, IL 60656-0189 (SAN 694-1796); 4935 Frank Pkwy., Norridge, IL 60656 (SAN 662-3344) Tel 312-457-0453.

120 Creative Corner, *(One Hund Twenty Creat; 0-912773),* 4175 Lovell Rd., Box 18, Circle Pines, MN 55014 (SAN 283-1252) Tel 612-784-8375.

Names

Oregon State Fair & Exposition Ctr., *(Oreg St Fair Expo Cntr; 0-9612966)*, 2330 17th St, NE, Salem, OR 97310 (SAN 292-5885) Tel 503-378-3247.

Oregon State Univ. Book Stores, Inc., *(Oreg St U Bkstrs; 0-88246)*, P.O. Box 489, Corvallis, OR 97339 (SAN 100-5189) Tel 503-754-4323.

†Oregon State Univ. Pr., *(Oreg St U Pr; 0-87071)*, Oregon State Univ., 101 Waldo Hall, Corvallis, OR 97331 (SAN 202-8328) Tel 503-754-3166; *CIP.*

Oregon Street Pr., *(Oreg Street Pr; 0-9613331)*, 2145 Oregon St., Berkeley, CA 94705 (SAN 655-7651) Tel 415-841-2008.

Oregon Students Writing & Art Foundation, *(OR Students Writing; 0-9616058)*, P.O. Box 2100, Portland, OR 97208-2100 (SAN 698-0546) Tel 503-280-6333; 1826 SE 54th Ave., Portland, OR 97206 (SAN 698-2468) Tel 503-232-7737.

O'Reilly & Assocs., Inc., *(O'Reilly & Assocs; 0-937175)*, 171 Jackson St., Newton, MA 02159 (SAN 658-5973) Tel 617-527-4210.

Organ Literature Foundation, The, *(Organ Lit; 0-913746)*, 45 Norfolk Rd, Braintree, MA 02184 (SAN 203-7769) Tel 617-848-1388.

Organic Agriculture Research Institute, *(Organic Agri; 0-9610726)*, P.O. Box 475, Graton, CA 95444 (SAN 264-7737) Tel 707-823-5106.

Organica Pr., *(Organica Pr; 0-939157)*, 4419 N. Manhattan Ave., Tampa, FL 33614 (SAN 662-9334) Tel 813-877-4186.

Organization Development Services, Inc. *See* ODS Pubns., Inc.

Organization for Economic Cooperation & Development, *(OECD)*, 1750 Pennsylvania Ave., NW, Suite 1207, Washington, DC 20006 (SAN 202-1277) Tel 202-724-1857.

Organization for Equal Education of the Sexes, *(Org Equal Educ Sexes; 0-9616645)*, 438 Fourth St., Brooklyn, NY 11215 (SAN 661-4086) Tel 718-788-3478.

Organization of American States, *(OAS; 0-8270)*, 17th St. & Constitution Ave., NW, Washington, DC 20006 (SAN 206-8877) Tel 202-789-3533.

Organization Resources Pr., Ltd., *(Org Resources Pr; 0-938180)*, P.O. Box 977, Indianapolis, IN 46206 (SAN 692-7467).

†Organizational Analysis & Practice, Inc., *(Organizational; 0-930475)*, 120 E. Buffalo St., Ithaca, NY 14850 (SAN 670-8927) Tel 607-273-3033; *CIP.*

Organizational Measurement Systems Press, *(Organizat Meas; 0-917926)*, Box 81, Atlanta, GA 30301 (SAN 209-9764) Tel 404-355-9472.

Oriel Pr., *(Oriel Pr; 0-938628)*, 2020 SW Kanan, Portland, OR 97201 (SAN 282-0870) Tel 503-245-6696; Dist. by: Childrens Small Press Collection, The, 719 N. 4th Ave., Ann Arbor, MI 48104 (SAN 200-514X).

Orient Bk. Distributors, *(Orient Bk Dist; 0-89684)*, P.O. Box 100, Livingston, NJ 07039 (SAN 211-819X) Tel 201-992-6992.

Oriental Bk. Store, The, *(Oriental Bk Store)*, P.O. Box 177, South Pasadena, CA 91030-0177 (SAN 285-0818) Tel 818-577-2413; 630 E. Colorado Blvd., Pasadena, CA 91101 (SAN 285-0826) Tel 213-577-2413.

Oriental Classics *See* Holmes Publishing Group

Oriental Insects, *(Oriental Insects)*, P.O. Box 13148, Gainesville, FL 32604-1148 (SAN 295-0170) Tel 904-392-9279.

Oriental Research Partners, *(Orient Res Partners; 0-89250)*, P.O. Box 158, Newtonville, MA 02160-0158 (SAN 208-2764) Tel 617-964-1638.

Orientalia Art, Ltd., *(Orientalia; 0-87902)*, P.O. Box 597, New York, NY 10003 (SAN 282-0919); 61 Fourth Ave., New York, NY 10003 (SAN 282-0927).

Original Kleptonian Neo-American Church, The, *(Neo-Am Church)*, Box 97, Bethel, VT 05032 (SAN 266-0008) Tel 512-443-8464.

Original Music, *(Original Music; 0-9614458)*, Rd. 1 Box 190, Lasher Rd., Tivoli, NY 12583 (SAN 689-4054) Tel 914-756-2767.

Original Music *See* Riverrun Pr.

Original Pubns., Subs. of Jamil Prods. Corp., *(Original Pubns; 0-942272)*, 2486 Webster Ave., Bronx, NY 10458 (SAN 238-1001) Tel 212-367-9589.

Orinda Art Council, *(Orinda Art Coun; 0-9613069)*, P.O. Box 121, Orinda, CA 94563 (SAN 294-6408) Tel 415-254-6744.

Orinda Pr., *(Orinda Pr CA; 0-9611094)*, P.O. Box 244, Orinda, CA 94563 (SAN 282-9428) Tel 415-254-2895.

Oriole Bks., *(Oriole Bks; 0-9612652)*, 5 Cliff St., Orleans, VT 05860 (SAN 289-3541) Tel 802-754-8503. Do not confuse with Oriole Editions.

Oriole Editions, *(Oriole Edns; 0-88211)*, 120 E 81st St, New York, NY 10028 (SAN 227-2598).

Orion *See* Signature Bks., Inc.

Orion Pr., *(Orion Pr GA; 0-936639)*, 1529 Druid Valley Dr., Suite A, Atlanta, GA 30329 (SAN 699-7058) Tel 404-894-4522; Dist. by: Datazine Pubns., P.O. Box 19413, Denver, CO 80219 (SAN 200-5980).

Orion Pr., *(Orion Press FL; 0-938629)*, 4375 SW 60th Ave., Ft. Lauderdale, FL 33314 (SAN 661-5791) Tel 305-581-9050.

Orion Research, *(Orion Res; 0-932089)*, 1315 Main Ave., Suite 230, Durango, CO 81301 (SAN 295-0189) Tel 303-247-8855.

Orirana Pr., *(Orirana Pr; 0-938364)*, 19737 Covello St., Canoga Park, CA 91306 (SAN 214-0713) Tel 818-341-7079.

Orlando Pubns., *(Orlando Pubns; 0-913065)*, P.O. Box 15352, Pittsburgh, PA 15237 (SAN 283-233X) Tel 412-366-4112.

Orleans County Historical Society, *(Orleans; 0-9610860)*, Old Stone Hse. Museum, Browningtoon, VT 05680 (SAN 265-1297) Tel 802-754-2022.

Ormsby, John R., Jr., *(Ormsby; 0-943736)*, Drawer 2429, Greenville, NC 27834 (SAN 240-9232).

Ornis Pr., *(Ornis Pr; 0-930477)*, P.O. Box 385, Kingston, RI 02881 (SAN 670-8919).

Orovan Bks., Div. of Orovan Associates, *(Orovan Bks; 0-913748)*, P.O. Box 6082, Honolulu, HI 96818 (SAN 203-7793) Tel 808-841-7992.

Orpheus Press, *(Orpheus Pr; 0-915648)*, P.O. Box 48423, Los Angeles, CA 90048 (SAN 207-3714) Tel 213-653-5800.

†Orr, Ken, & Assocs., Inc., *(Orr & Assocs; 0-9605884)*, 1725 Gage Blvd., Topeka, KS 66604 (SAN 216-4280) Tel 913-273-0653; Toll free: 800-255-2459; *CIP.*

Orr, Leonard, *(L Orr)*, Orders to: Inspiration University, P.O. Box 234, Sierraville, CA 96126 (SAN 207-2505) Tel 916-994-8984.

Orr, William N. & Elizabeth, *(W&E Orr; 0-9606502)*, P.O. Box 5286, Eugene, OR 97405 (SAN 226-2053).

Ortalda & Assocs., *(Ortalda & Assocs; 0-9616101)*, 1202 Delaware St., Berkeley, CA 94702 (SAN 698-0945) Tel 415-524-2040; Dist. by: Bookpeople, 2929 Fifth St., Berkeley, CA 94710 (SAN 168-9517); Toll free: 800-674-4466 (domestic U. S.); Toll free: 800-674-4466 (within CA).

Ortho Bks., Div. of Chevron Chemical Co., Subs. of Standard Oil Co. of CA, *(Ortho; 0-917102; 0-89721)*, 575 Market St., Rm. 3188, San Francisco, CA 94105 (SAN 662-7293) Tel 415-894-0277; Dist. by: Chevron Chemical Co., Consumer Products Div., Ortho Information Services, 1728 Montreal Circle, Tucker, GA 30084 (SAN 218-6780) Tel 404-934-0494; Dist. by: Chevron Chemical Co., Consumer Products Div., Ortho Information Services, One Crossroads of Commerce, Suite 1000, Rolling Meadows, IL 60008 (SAN 662-7307) Tel 312-870-3430; Dist. by: Chevron Chemical Co., Consumer Products Div., Ortho Information Services, 1200 State St., Perth Amboy, NJ 08861 (SAN 662-7315) Tel 201-738-2187; Dist. by: Chevron Chemical Co., Consumer Products Div., Ortho Information Services, 3260 Blume Dr., Suite 300, Richmond, CA 94806 (SAN 662-7323) Tel 415-222-9700.

Ortho Diagnostic Systems, Inc., *(Ortho Diag; 0-910771)*, Room B-50, Raritan, NJ 08869 (SAN 260-2393) Tel 201-524-2181.

Ortho Information Services, Div. of Chevron Chemical Co., *(Ortho Info; 0-917102; 0-89721)*, 575 Market St., San Francisco, CA 94105 (SAN 699-7856) Tel 415-894-0277.

Orthodox Christian Educational Society, *(Orthodox Chr; 0-938366)*, 1916 W. Warner Ave., Chicago, IL 60613 (SAN 215-1642) Tel 312-549-0584.

Orton Dyslexia Society, Inc., *(Orton Dyslexia; 0-89214)*, 724 York Rd., Baltimore, MD 21204 (SAN 224-3121) Tel 301-296-0232.

†Oryn Pubns., Inc., *(Oryn Pubns Inc; 0-916207)*, P.O. Box 18225, Washington, DC 20036 (SAN 294-989X) Tel 301-441-4645; *CIP.*

Oryx Pr., *(Oryx Pr; 0-912700; 0-89774)*, 2214 N. Central Ave., Phoenix, AZ 85004-1483 (SAN 220-0201) Tel 602-254-6156; Toll free: 800-457-6799.

Orzano Publishing Co., *(Orzano Pub Co; 0-936668)*, P.O. Box 394, Islip, NY 11751 (SAN 214-2155) Tel 516-666-1950.

Osage Publishing, *(Osage Pub; 0-9616666)*, P.O. Box 151, Osage, MN 56570 (SAN 661-3527) Tel 612-573-3463.

Osborne, *(Osborne Dr; 0-915631)*, 6108 Centinella St., Simi Valley, CA 93063 (SAN 292-5893) Tel 805-527-1314; Orders to: Jean Osborne, 1409 Kuehner Dr., Suite 113, Simi Valley, CA 93063 (SAN 662-2240).

Osborne Enterprises, *(Osborne Ent; 0-932117)*, P.O. Box 28312, Tempe, AZ 85282 (SAN 686-4694) Tel 602-437-3461; Orders to: Jellyroll Productions, P.O. Box 24092, Tempe, AZ 85282 (SAN 663-3110) Tel 602-437-3461.

Osborne/McGraw-Hill, Div. of McGraw-Hill, *(Osborne-McGraw; 0-07)*, 2600 Tenth St., Berkeley, CA 94710 (SAN 274-3450) Tel 415-548-2805; Toll free: 800-227-0900.

Osgood, Merle, Productions, *(M Osgood; 0-913067)*, 720 Eleventh St., Bellingham, WA 98225 (SAN 283-975X); Dist. by: Pacific Pipeline, Inc., 19215 66th Ave. S., Kent, WA 98032 (SAN 208-2128) Tel 206-872-5523.

Osprey Bks., *(Osprey Bks; 0-943738)*, P.O. Box 965, Huntington, NY 11743 (SAN 241-0508) Tel 516-549-0143. Do not confuse with Osprey Bks., San Diego, CA.

Osprey Bks., *(Osprey CA; 0-9614239)*, 1958 Sunset Cliffs Blvd., Suite 109, San Diego, CA 92107 (SAN 686-6905) Tel 619-223-2715. Do not confuse with Osprey Bks., Huntington, NY.

Ossi Pubns., *(Ossi Pubns; 0-930912)*, 195 Lake Destiny Trail, Altamonte, FL 32714 (SAN 211-0415) Tel 305-862-2392 (SAN 699-5497).

Osteen, Ike, *(I Osteen; 0-9602724)*, 380 Kansas St., Springfield, CO 81073 (SAN 212-9248) Tel 303-523-6580.

Osteen, John, Pubns., *(J O Pubns; 0-912631)*, P.O. Box 23117, Houston, TX 77228 (SAN 282-8049) Tel 713-635-4154.

Ostendor, Virginia A., Inc., *(V A Ostendorf; 0-937007)*, P.O. Box 2896, Littleton, CO 80161-2896 (SAN 696-2564); 7085 S. Pennsylvania St., Littleton, CO 80161 (SAN 658-2923) Tel 303-797-3131.

Osthoff-Thalden & Assocs., *(Osthoff-Thalden; 0-9614346)*, 7 N. Taylor, St. Louis, MO 63108 (SAN 687-830X) Tel 314-367-5677.

O'Sullivan, Woodside & Co., *(O'Sullivan Woodside; 0-89019)*, 2218 E. Magnolia, Phoenix, AZ 85034 (SAN 207-4052) Tel 602-244-1000; Dist. by: Caroline House Pubs., Inc., 236 Forest Park Place, Ottawa, IL 61350 (SAN 207-6705) Tel 815-434-7905. *Imprints:* Norwalk Press (Norwalk Pr).

Otafra Pr., *(Otafra; 0-9605220)*, P.O. Box 814, Mesilla, NM 88046 (SAN 220-1224) Tel 505-522-6757.

Other Alligator Creek Co. The, *(Other Alligator; 0-931083)*, 1195 Oakhaven Dr., Roswell, GA 30075 (SAN 678-9382) Tel 404-993-8128.

Other Bks., *(Other Bks)*, 1412 Spruce St., Berkeley, CA 94709 (SAN 209-0813) Tel 415-841-6359.

Otis Art Institute of Parsons Schl of Design, Div. of New School for Social Research, *(Otis Art; 0-930209)*, 2410 Wilshire Blvd., Los Angeles, CA 90057 (SAN 280-0144) Tel 213-251-0500.

Otstot, Charles M., *(C M Otstot; 0-9603808)*, 5124 N. 33rd St., Arlington, VA 22207 (SAN 206-9539) Tel 703-538-5446.

Names

Ottawa County Historical Society, *(Ottawa Co Hist),* P.O. Box 385, Port Clinton, OH 43452 (SAN 692-719X); Dist. by: Waterfront Books, 18330 Brim Rd., No. 321, Bowling Green, OH 43402 (SAN 213-0610).

Otter Nonsense, *(Otter Nonsense; 0-9616238),* P.O. Box 2843, Santa Rosa, CA 95405 (SAN 658-599X) Tel 707-539-9598; 5815 Melita Rd., Santa Rosa, CA 95405 (SAN 658-6007).

Otter Veterinary Services Inc., *(Otter Veterinary; 0-9614459),* 22764 Desoto St., Grand Terrace, CA 92324 (SAN 689-4127) Tel 714-783-2067.

Otterden Press, *(Otterden; 0-918868),* 111 Plymouth Rd., Hillsdale, NJ 07642 (SAN 210-4792) Tel 201-664-2583.

Otto Pubs., *(Otto Pubs; 0-9615548),* 3730 Southview Dr., Suite 423, San Diego, CA 92117 (SAN 696-3218) Tel 619-272-5391.

Ouabache Pr., *(Ouabache Pr; 0-9609026),* Box 2076, West Lafayette, IN 47906 (SAN 240-9240) Tel 317-463-9857.

Oubre, Edward Paul, *(E P Oubre; 0-9613873),* P.O. Box 503, Amarillo, TX 79105 (SAN 681-980X) Tel 806-372-9998.

Ouimette, Helen, *(H Ouimette; 0-9617116),* 1706 Pitcher St., Neillsville, WI 54456 (SAN 662-7048) Tel 715-743-3422.

Our Baby's First Seven Years, *(Our Baby's; 0-937909),* 5841 Maryland Ave., Chicago, IL 60637 (SAN 287-2951) Tel 312-667-5184; Dist. by: Caroline Hse., Inc., 5 S. 250 Frontenac Rd., Naperville, IL 60540 (SAN 211-2280) Tel 312-983-6400.

†Our Child Pr., *(Our Child Pr; 0-9611872),* 800 Maple Glen Ln., Wayne, PA 19087 (SAN 682-272X) Tel 215-964-1837; CIP.

Our Sunday Visitor, Publishing Div., *(Our Sunday Visitor; 0-87973),* 200 Noll Plaza, Huntington, IN 46750 (SAN 202-8344) Tel 219-356-8400; Toll free: 800-348-2440 except Indiana.

†Out & Out Bks., *(Out & Out; 0-918314),* 476 Second St., Brooklyn, NY 11215 (SAN 209-4665) Tel 718-499-9227; CIP.

Out of Harm's Way, Inc., *(Out of Harm's; 0-9616239),* P.O. Box 63, Brooklyn, NY 11230 (SAN 658-6031) Tel 718-252-1664; 1205 Glenwood Rd., Brooklyn, NY 11230 (SAN 658-604X).

Out of Mouths Pr., *(Out Mouths Pr; 0-9616776),* 1448 Oakley Dr., Baton Rouge, LA 70806 (SAN 661-4167) Tel 504-924-2510.

Out of the Ashes Pr., *(Out of the Ashes; 0-912874),* P.O. Box 42384, Portland, OR 97242 (SAN 202-8352).

Outbooks, Inc., *(Outbooks; 0-89646),* 217 Kimball Ave., Golden, CO 80401 (SAN 211-0849); Orders to: Vistabooks, Inc., 217 Kimball Ave., Golden, CO 80401 (SAN 662-1031) Tel 303-279-4070.

Outdoor Assocs., *(Outdoor Assocs; 0-9605556),* 1279 Dean St., Schenectady, NY 12309 (SAN 207-270X) Tel 518-372-4585.

Outdoor Books, Nature Series, Inc., *(Outdoor Bks; 0-942806),* 3813 Fenchurch Rd., Baltimore, MD 21218 (SAN 238-8561) Tel 301-243-1179.

Outdoor Circle, The, *(Outdoor Circle; 0-9069082),* 200 N. Vineyard Blvd., Suite 502, Honolulu, HI 96817 (SAN 241-4228) Tel 808-521-0074.

Outdoor Communications, *(Outdoor Comm; 0-932753),* 8942 Creekford Dr., Lakeside, CA 92040 (SAN 688-6000) Tel 619-443-6648.

†Outdoor Empire Publishing, Inc., *(Outdoor Empire),* 511 Eastlake Ave., P.O. Box C-19000, Seattle, WA 98109 (SAN 207-1312) Tel 206-624-3845; CIP.

Outdoor Life Bks. See Crown Pubs., Inc.

Outdoor Pictures, *(Outdoor Pict; 0-911080),* P.O. Box 277, Anacortes, WA 98221 (SAN 203-7815) Tel 206-293-3200.

Outdoor Pubns., *(Outdoor Pubns; 0-939166),* P.O. Box 355, Ithaca, NY 14851 (SAN 202-1250) Tel 607-273-0061.

Outdoor Skills Bookshelf, *(Outdoor Skills; 0-940022),* P.O. Box 13, Louisville, AL 36048 (SAN 216-8472) Tel 205-266-5062.

Outer Ring Publishing, *(Outer Ring Pub; 0-936235),* 500 Promontory Dr. W., Newport Beach, CA 92660 (SAN 696-8767) Tel 818-349-0616; Dist. by: Halley's Comet Watch '86, Inc., 158 W. Boston Post Rd., Box AB, Mamaroneck, NY 10543 (SAN 200-5840).

Outer Straubville Pr., *(Outer Straubville),* Box 470, Occidental, CA 95465 (SAN 203-7823); Dist. by: Bookpeople, 2929 Fifth St., Berkeley, CA 94710 (SAN 168-9509).

Outermost Pr., *(Outermost Pr; 0-940282),* Box 183, St. Johnsbury Ctr., VT 05863 (SAN 217-5509) Tel 802-748-5034.

Outlet Bk. Co., Affil. of Crowns Pubs., Inc., *(Outlet Bk Co; 0-87000),* 225 Park Ave., S., New York, NY 10003 (SAN 200-2620) Tel 212-254-1600; Toll free: 800-526-4264. Promotional books of all kinds; remainders, reprints, imports, original publications. *Imprints:* Avenel (Avenel); Bell (Bell); Bonanza (Bonanza); Chatham River Press (Chatham River Pr); Greenwich House (Greenwich Hse); Greenwich House/Chatham River Press (Greenwich Hse-Chatham River Pr).

Outlook Bk. Service, Inc., *(Outlook; 0-911082),* 512 E. Main St., Richmond, VA 23219 (SAN 206-684X).

Outre Hse., *(Outre House; 0-9605404),* 1622 N. St., No. 302, Sacramento, CA 95814 (SAN 238-7093)

Tel 916-442-6354.

Outreach Press, *(Outreach Press; 0-9613699),* 198 Yerba Buena Ave., San Francisco, CA 94127 (SAN 677-5969) Tel 415-661-5969.

Outside Enterprise Pr., *(Outside Ent; 0-937232),* P.O. Box 2650, College Sta., Pullman, WA 99165 (SAN 215-0972) Tel 509-335-2691.

Ovation Pubns., *(Ovation Pubns; 0-910723),* 750 Joranollo, Tracy, CA 95376 (SAN 269-6088) Tel 209-835-3279.

Over Easy Publishing, *(Over Easy Pub; 0-913975),* 11101 N. 21st St., Tampa, FL 33612 (SAN 286-7834) Tel 813-972-3461.

Overbrook Hse., *(Overbrook Hse; 0-910773),* P.O. Box 7688, Mountain Brook, AL 35253 (SAN 260-2407) Tel 205-879-8222.

Overcomer Pr., Inc., *(Overcomer Pr; 0-942504),* 7300 SW Ninth Ct., P.O. Box 14363, Ft. Lauderdale, FL 33302 (SAN 238-1834) Tel 305-797-8989.

Overland Pr., Inc., *(Overland Pr; 0-930851),* P.O. Box 7386, Shawnee Mission, KS 66207 (SAN 670-8900); 9853 Rosewood, Shawnee Mission, KS 66207 (SAN 662-2496) Tel 913-383-2068.

Overlook Hospital Auxiliary, *(Overlook Hosp; 0-9604560),* 99 Beauvoir Pl., Summit, NJ 07901 (SAN 215-0980) Tel 201-522-2004.

†Overlook Pr., *(Overlook Pr; 0-87951),* 12 W. 21st St., 12th Flr., New York, NY 10010 (SAN 202-8360) Tel 212-337-5472; Toll free: 800-631-3577; Orders to: RR 1 Box 496, Woodstock, NY 12498; Dist. by: Viking-Penguin, Inc., 40 W. 23rd St., New York, NY 10010 (SAN 200-2442) Tel 212-337-5200; Toll free: 800-631-3577; CIP.

Overman, Marjorie, Publishing, *(Overman Pub; 0-9614853),* 323 E. Cavenaugh St., Wallace, NC 28466 (SAN 693-1936) Tel 919-285-3375.

Overmountain Pr., *(Overmountain Pr; 0-932807),* P.O. Box 1261, Johnson City, TN 37605 (SAN 687-6641) Tel 615-926-2691.

†Overseas Crudades, Inc., Div. of Global Church Growth, *(Overseas Crusade),* 25 Corning Ave., Milpitas, CA 95035 (SAN 223-7822) Tel 408-263-1101; CIP.

Overseas Development Council, *(Overseas Dev Council),* 1717 Massachusetts Ave., NW, Washington, DC 20036 (SAN 215-2711) Tel 202-234-8701.

Overseas Development Network, *(Overseas Net; 0-935747),* P.O. Box 1430, Cambridge, MA 02238 (SAN 695-8885) Tel 617-868-3002; 16 Longfellow Pk., Cambridge, MA 02138 (SAN 695-8893).

Overseas Education Fund, *(Overseas Ed; 0-912917),* 2101 L St. NW, Suite 916, Washington, DC 20037 (SAN 283-2356) Tel 202-466-3430.

Overstreet Pubns., Inc., *(Overstreet; 0-911903),* 780 Hunt Cliff Dr. NW, Cleveland, TN 37311 (SAN 216-4302) Tel 615-472-4135.

Overthrow, *(Overthrow),* P.O. Box 392 Canal St. Sta., New York, NY 10012 (SAN 289-1433) Tel 212-533-5027.

Overture Publishing, *(Overture Pub; 0-932763),* P.O. Box 99, Newton, MA 02162 (SAN 688-5993) Tel 617-924-4484.

Overview Pr., Inc., *(Overview Pr; 0-932403),* 5004 Orleans Ct., Kensington, MD 20895 (SAN 686-6913) Tel 301-942-0655.

Oviedo Publishing Co., *(Oviedo Pub Co; 0-9603034),* P.O. Box 837, Oviedo, FL 32765 (SAN 213-1331).

Ovulation Method Teachers Assn., *(OMT Assn; 0-9616481),* P.O. Box 101780, Anchorage, AK 99510 (SAN 659-3852) Tel 907-277-3189; 510 L St., Anchorage, AK 99501 (SAN 659-3860).

Owen, Stephen, Pub., *(S Owen Pub; 0-9614830),* 5520 20th Ave., Meridian, MS 39301 (SAN 693-059X) Tel 601-483-7643; Dist. by: Southeastern Printing Co., 215 22nd Ave., Meridian, MS 39301 (SAN 200-5484).

Owen, William M, *(W M Owen; 0-9613247),* 885 Heather Rd., Deerfield, IL 60015 (SAN 295-4370) Tel 312-945-9290.

Owen County Historical Society, *(Owen Cty Hist Soc; 0-9617100),* Main St., Owenton, KY 40359 (SAN 662-5770) Tel 502-484-3087.

Owen Publishing Co., Div. of Owen Communications Corp., *(Owen Pub; 0-939349),* P.O. Box 771, Battle Ground, WA 98604 (SAN 662-5029); 1605 NE 249th St., Ridgefield, WA 98642 (SAN 662-5037) Tel 206-887-8646.

Owen's Publishing Company (OD) See Unipub a

Owl Bks. See Holt, Rinehart & Winston, Inc.

Owl Creek Pr., *(Owl Creek Pr; 0-937669),* 1620 N. 45th St., Seattle, WA 98103 (SAN 694-3926) Tel 206-633-5929.

Owl Press, Inc., *(Owl Pr NV),* 312 Almond Tree Ln., Las Vegas, NV 89104 (SAN 219-0915).

Owl Publishing Co., *(Owl Pub Co; 0-9613143),* P.O. Box 5, Bodega, CA 94922 (SAN 294-992X) Tel 707-874-2736.

Owlswick Pr., *(Owlswick Pr; 0-913896),* P.O. Box 8243, Philadelphia, PA 19101 (SAN 202-8387) Tel 215-382-5415.

Owner-Builder Pubns., *(Owner-Builder; 0-910225),* P.O. Box 817, North Fork, CA 93643 (SAN 207-1894).

Ox Bow Pr., *(Ox Bow; 0-918024),* P.O. Box 4045, Woodbridge, CT 06525 (SAN 210-2501) Tel 203-387-5900.

Oxbridge Communications, Inc., *(Oxbridge Comm; 0-917460),* 150 Fifth Ave., Suite 301, New York, NY 10011 (SAN 209-0724) Tel 212-741-0231.

Oxfam Americs, *(Oxfam Am; 0-910281),* 115 Broadway, Boston, MA 02116 (SAN 213-7828) Tel 617-247-3304.

Oxford Joint College & Medical Div. See Oxford Univ. Pr., Inc.

Oxford Paperback Univ. Series See Oxford Univ. Pr., Inc.

Oxford Paperbacks See Oxford Univ. Pr., Inc.

Oxford Univ. Pr., Inc., *(Oxford U Pr; 0-19),* 200 Madison Ave., New York, NY 10016 (SAN 202-5884) Tel 212-679-7300; Toll free: 800-458-5833; Orders to: 16-00 Pollitt Dr., Fair Lawn, NJ 07410 (SAN 202-5892) Tel 201-564-6680. *Imprints:* Hesperides Paperbacks (HS); Institute of Race Relations (IRR); Oxford Joint College & Medical Division (OxC&M); Oxford Paperback University Series (OPUS); Oxford Paperbacks (OPB).

Oxmoor Hse., Inc., *(Oxmoor Hse; 0-8487),* P.O. Box 2262, Birmingham, AL 35201 (SAN 205-3462) Tel 205-877-6534; Toll free: 800-242-7737; Dist. by: Little, Brown, 200 West St., Waltham, MA 02254 (SAN 215-3742).

Oxxi, Inc., *(Oxxi Inc; 0-938385),* 3428 Falcon Ave., Long Beach, CA 90807 (SAN 661-4523) Tel 213-427-2080.

Oxymora Book Press, *(Oxymora Bk Pr; 0-911109),* P.O. Box 429, Venice, CA 90294 (SAN 262-9755) Tel 213-822-6524.

Oyez, *(Oyez; 0-911088),* 212 Colgate Ave., Kensington, CA 94707 (SAN 206-877X).

Oyster Bay Historical Society, *(Oyster Bay Hist; 0-9615929)*, P.O. Box 297, Oyster Bay, NY 11771-0297 (SAN 696-8821) Tel 516-922-5032; 20 Summit St., Oyster Bay, NY 11771 (SAN 696-883X).

Oyster Press, *(Oyster Pr; 0-933114)*, 103 S. Soledad St., Santa Barbara, CA 93103 (SAN 212-7849).

†Oz Pr., The, *(Oz Pr; 0-916049)*, P.O. Box 33088, Seattle, WA 98133 (SAN 294-6432) Tel 206-367-6849; 12722 Lake City Way NE, Seattle, WA 98125 (SAN 294-6440); *CIP.*

Ozark Mountain Fly Fishers, *(Ozark Mtn Fishers; 0-9614599)*, 1 Johnson St., Rolla, MO 65401 (SAN 691-8190) Tel 314-364-5509.

Ozark Mountain Pubs., *(Ozark Mtn Pubs; 0-915394)*, P.O. Box 4718 G.S., Springfield, MO 65808-4718 (SAN 207-3595) Tel 417-881-3060.

Ozark Society Foundation, *(Ozark Soc Bks; 0-912456)*, P.O. Box 3503, Little Rock, AR 72203 (SAN 282-096X) Tel 501-847-3738; 16 Shobe Rd., Alexander, AR 72002 (SAN 680-0726).

†Ozer, Jerome S., Pub., Inc., *(Ozer; 0-89198)*, 340 Tenafly Rd., Englewood, NJ 07631 (SAN 202-8395) Tel 201-567-7040; *CIP.*

PAGL Press, *(P A G L; 0-913105)*, 2854 N. Santiago Blvd. No. 100, Orange, CA 92667 (SAN 283-2372) Tel 714-974-9471; Dist. by: Hunter House Inc., Box 3914, San Rafael, CA 94901 (SAN 281-7977) Tel 415-883-3530.

PAJ Pubns., Div. of Performing Arts Journal, Inc., *(PAJ Pubns; 0-933826; 1-55554)*, 325 Spring St., Suite 318, New York, NY 10013 (SAN 220-2670) Tel 212-243-3885; Dist. by: Farrar, Straus & Giroux, Inc., 19 Union Sq., W., New York, NY 10003 (SAN 206-782X) Tel 212-741-6900.

†P.A.R., Inc., Subs. of Abbott Park Associates, *(PAR Inc; 0-913310; 0-89702)*, 290 Westminster St., Providence, RI 02903-3416 (SAN 203-0209) Tel 401-331-0130; Toll free: 800-556-7277. Do not confuse with PAR, Inc., FL; *CIP.*

PASE Inc., *(PASE)*, P.O. Box 1299, Highland Park, NJ 08904 (SAN 264-2808) Tel 201-545-0100.

PAX Tapes, Inc., *(PAX Tapes)*, 611 Rosetta, Florissant, MO 63031 (SAN 265-3923).

P & D Publishing Co., *(P&D Pub; 0-9616614)*, 588 Audubon Ave. NE, Palm Bay, FL 32907 (SAN 659-7483) Tel 305-725-7243.

P & H Enterprises, *(P & H Ent; 0-9615690)*, Box 495, Stillwater, MN 55082 (SAN 696-0456) Tel 612-439-9051; 13565 116th St. N, Stillwater, MN 55082 (SAN 696-0464).

P & K Enterprises, *(P & K Ent; 0-918176)*, 306 Columbus Cir., Wildwood, FL 32785 (SAN 210-251X) Tel 904-748-2302.

P & L Resources, *(P & L Res; 0-9613376)*, 2496 S. Leyden, Denver, CO 80222 (SAN 657-1069) Tel 303-758-8793.

PBC International Inc., *(PBC Intl Inc; 0-86636)*, One School St., Glen Cove, NY 11542 (SAN 223-1476) Tel 516-676-2727.

P.C.A. Enterprises, *(PCA Enterp; 0-916765)*, 2843 Alhambra Ave., Martinez, CA 94553 (SAN 682-806X).

PC Art, *(PC Art; 0-925999)*, 3101 Oak St., Terre Haute, IN 47803 (SAN 654-5416) Tel 812-235-4185.

PC Ctr., Inc., The, *(PC Ctr NC; 0-939215)*, P.O. Box 1184, Cary, NC 27511 (SAN 662-6734); 154 E. Cedar St., Cary, NC 27511 (SAN 662-6742) Tel 919-467-3911.

PC Software Interest Group, *(PC Software; 0-915835)*, 1030 E. Duane Suite D, Sunnyvale, CA 94086 (SAN 293-8952) Tel 408-730-9291; Toll free: 800-222-2996; Dist. by: Publishers Group West, 5855 Beaudry St., Emeryville, CA 94608 (SAN 693-9872) Tel 415-658-3453.

PDA Pubs. Corp., *(PDA Pubs; 0-914886)*, 1725 East Fountain, Mesa, AZ 85203 (SAN 207-0340) Tel 602-835-9161.

PDQ Printers, *(PDQ Printers)*, 11725 N. 19th Ave., Phoenix, AZ 85027 (SAN 289-5382).

†PEM Press, Div. of Pathescope Educational Media, Inc., *(PEM Pr)*, 71 Weyman Ave., P.O. Box 719, New Rochelle, NY 10802 (SAN 214-0721) Tel 914-235-0800; *CIP.*

PEN American Ctr., *(PEN Am Ctr; 0-934638)*, 568 Broadway, New York, NY 10012 (SAN 675-4112) Tel 212-334-1660.

PFC Publishing Co., *(PFC; 0-9603830)*, 133 Everett Pl., Englewood, NJ 07631 (SAN 206-8338) Tel 201-567-1979.

P.I. Industries Publishing Co., *(P I Industries; 0-916976)*, 330 S. Loomis Ave., Fort Collins, CO 80521 (SAN 208-7995) Tel 303-224-9381; P.O. Box 2285, Fort Collins, CO 80521.

P.I. Pubns., *(PI Pubns; 0-935383)*, 25829 Mission Blvd., No. 122, Hayward, CA 94544 (SAN 695-9571) Tel 415-889-9668.

PJD Pubns., Ltd., *(PJD Pubns; 0-9600290; 0-915340)*, P.O. Box 966, Westbury, NY 11590 (SAN 202-0068) Tel 516-626-0650.

PMA Inc., *(PMA; 0-941562)*, 180 Township Line Rd., Belle Mead, NJ 08502 (SAN 264-2824) Tel 201-359-5200.

P-M Enterprises, *(PM Ent; 0-9601846)*, P.O. Box 23104, Euclid, OH 44123 (SAN 210-3192) Tel 216-289-7663.

PMF Research Co., *(PMF Research; 0-934036)*, P.O. Box 424, Kenilworth, IL 60043 (SAN 212-9574).

PMS Industries, Div. of Proto Systems of Atlanta, *(PMS Indus; 0-931463)*, 1790 Hembree Rd., Alpharetta, GA 30201 (SAN 683-1486) Tel 404-475-1818.

PMS Self Help Ctr., *(PMS Self Help; 0-936614)*, 170 State St., Suite 222, Los Altos, CA 94022 (SAN 216-776X) Tel 415-941-1540; Dist. by: Ingram Distribution Group, Inc., 347 Reedwood Dr., Nashville, TN 37217 (SAN 169-7978); Toll free: 800-251-5900; Dist. by: Bookpeople, 2929 Fifth St., Berkeley, CA 94710 (SAN 168-9517); Toll free: 800-227-1516; Toll free: 800-624-4466 (CA).

P/P Pubns., *(P-P Pubns; 0-9608316)*, 500 N. Dearborn, Suite 900, Chicago, IL 60610 (SAN 240-4850); Dist. by: Dianco, P.O. Box 39100, Chicago, IL 60639 (SAN 200-8084).

PRESCOB Publishing Co., *(PRESCOB; 0-933257)*, 10421 E. 44 St., Tulsa, OK 74146 (SAN 211-612X) Tel 918-664-6717.

PR Publishing Co., Inc., *(P R Pub Co)*, P.O. Box 600, Exeter, NH 03833 (SAN 205-3438) Tel 603-778-0514.

PSG Publishing Co., Inc., *(PSG Pub Co; 0-88416; 0-7236; 0-931890)*, P.O. Box 6, Littleton, MA 01460 (SAN 201-8934) Tel 617-486-8971; Toll free: 800-225-5020; 545 Great Rd., Littleton, MA 01460 (SAN 658-2230). *Imprints:* PSG/Biomedical (Biomed Pubns).

PSI & Assocs., *(PSI Assocs MD; 0-938261)*, 2700 Maurleen Ct., Baltimore, MD 21209 (SAN 659-834X) Tel 301-653-1913.

PSI Research, Subs. of Publishing Services, Inc., *(PSI Res; 0-916378; 1-55571)*, 720 S. Hillview Dr., Milpitas, CA 95035 (SAN 218-9240) Tel 408-263-9671; Toll free: 800-228-2275; Toll free: 800-221-4089 (In California); Dist. by: Publishers Group West, 5855 Beaudry St., Emeryville, CA 94608 (SAN 202-8522) Tel 415-658-3453; Toll free: 800-982-8319. *Imprints:* Oasis Press (Oasis).

P.S.I. Rhythms, Inc., *(PSI Rhythms; 0-918882)*, P.O. Box 1838, Ormond Beach, FL 32074 (SAN 210-4806); 2085 S. Halifax, Daytona Beach, FL 32018 (SAN 210-4814).

PTL Pubns., *(PTL Pubns; 0-915420)*, Box 1277, Tustin, CA 92680 (SAN 211-8203) Tel 714-838-7715.

PWBBA Productions, *(PWBBA Prod; 0-9610972)*, 696 Stone Canyon Rd., Los Angeles, CA 90077 (SAN 265-3125) Tel 213-472-3681.

PWS Pubs., Div. of Wadsworth, Inc., *(PWS Pubs; 0-87150; 0-534)*, 20 Park Plaza, Boston, MA 02116 (SAN 200-2264) Tel 617-482-2344; Toll free: 800-354-9706; Dist. by: Wadsworth., Inc., 7625 Empire Dr., Florence, KY 41042 (SAN 202-3369); Toll free: 800-354-9706. *Imprints:* Duxbury Press (Duxbury Pr); Prindle, Weber & Schmidt (Prindle); PWS Computer Science (PWS Computer Sci).

Pac-Co Publishing Co., *(Pac-Co Pub; 0-935141)*, P.O. Box 2148, Hawthorne, CA 90250 (SAN 695-2151) Tel 213-337-0326; 11509 E. 216 St., Suite 116, Lakewood, CA 90715 (SAN 695-216X).

Pace Educational Systems, Inc., *(Pace Educ Systems; 0-935385)*, 61 Kingsley Rd., Kendall Park, NJ 08824 (SAN 695-8915) Tel 201-297-2525.

†Pace Gallery, *(Pace Gallery Pubns; 0-938608)*, 32 E. 57th St., New York, NY 10022 (SAN 220-2646); *CIP.*

PACE Grace Lutheran School, *(PACE Grace; 0-9612728)*, P.O. Box 9265, Winter Haven, FL 33880 (SAN 289-7873) Tel 813-299-6905; 227 Lake Link Rd., SE, Winter Haven, FL 33880 (SAN 289-7881); Dist. by: Dot Gibson Pubns., 161 Knight Ave. Cir., Waycross, GA 31501 (SAN 289-789X); Dist. by: Collection Inc., The, 1012 Locust St., P.O. Box 15624, Kansas City, MO 64106 (SAN 689-8467).

Pace International Research Inc., *(Pace Intl Res; 0-89209)*, P.O. Box 51, Arch Cape, OR 97102 (SAN 670-7041).

Pace Publishing Co., *(Pace Pub Co; 0-936683)*, 2545 B Ridgeway Dr., National City, CA 92050 (SAN 699-7317) Tel 619-267-2236.

†Pacesetter Pub. Hse., Div. of Pacesetter Enterprises, Inc., *(Pacesetter Pub Hse OH; 0-9603826)*, P.O. Box 33430, Cleveland, OH 44133-0430 (SAN 218-4990) Tel 216-447-9130; *CIP.*

†Pachart Publishing Hse., Div. of Pachart Foundation, *(Pachart Pub Hse; 0-88126; 0-912918)*, P.O. Box 35549, Tucson, AZ 85740 (SAN 204-9139) Tel 602-297-4797; 1130 San Lucas Cir., Tucson, AZ 85704 (SAN 662-1058) Tel 602-297-6760; *CIP.*

†Pacific/Asian American Mental Health Research Ctr., *(Pacific-Asian; 0-934584)*, 1033 W. Van Buren St., Suite 7N, Chicago, IL 60607 (SAN 214-4336) Tel 312-996-2964; *CIP.*

Pacific Book Supply Co., *(Pacific Bk Supply; 0-911090)*, 1238 N. Rose Ave., Farmersville, CA 93223 (SAN 202-1366) Tel 209-594-4155.

†Pacific Bks., Pubs., *(Pacific Bks; 0-87015)*, P.O. Box 558, Palo Alto, CA 94302-0558 (SAN 202-8468) Tel 415-856-0550; *CIP.*

Pacific District Mennonite Brethren Churches, Family Commission, *(Pacific Dist Mennonite; 0-9606436)*, 4812 E. Butler, Fresno, CA 93727 (SAN 219-807X) Tel 209-251-8681.

Pacific Editions, *(Pacific Edns; 0-938226)*, 350 Arballo Dr., No. 5D, San Francisco, CA 94132 (SAN 220-0813) Tel 415-334-5716.

Pacific Gallery Pubs., *(Pacific Gallery; 0-938942)*, P.O. Box 19494, Portland, OR 97219 (SAN 220-2654) Tel 503-244-2300.

Pacific Horizons Pubns., *(Pac Horizons Pubns; 0-938375)*, E. 300 Dana Dr., Shelton, WA 98584 (SAN 661-0358) Tel 206-426-0752.

Pacific Information, Inc., *(Pacific Info; 0-913203)*, 11684 Ventura Blvd., No. 295, Studio City, CA 91604 (SAN 283-0272) Tel 818-797-7654.

Pacific Institute, *(Pacific Inst; 0-9609174)*, P.O. Box 33111, San Diego, CA 92103 (SAN 241-4236) Tel 619-279-9682.

Pacific Institute for Public Policy Research, *(PIPPR; 0-936488; 0-88410)*, 177 Post St., San Francisco, CA 94108 (SAN 283-345X) Tel 415-989-0833.

Pacific International Publishing Co., *(Pacific Intl; 0-918074)*, P.O. Box 850, Friday Harbor, WA 98250 (SAN 210-2528) Tel 206-378-2393.

Pacific Isle Publishers, *(Pacific Isle Pub; 0-9614775)*, P.O. Box 223, Kihei, HI 96753 (SAN 692-9966) Tel 808-879-7068.

Pacific Medical Pr., *(Pacific Med Pr; 0-9608102)*, P.O. Box 590238, San Francisco, CA 94159 (SAN 238-8332) Tel 415-921-4868.

Pacific Meridian Publishing Co., *(Pacific Mer; 0-911092)*, 13540 Lake City Way, NE, Seattle, WA 98125 (SAN 206-832X) Tel 206-362-0900.

Pacific Northwest Labor History Assn., *(Pacific NW Labor; 0-932942)*, P.O. Box 25048, Northgate Sta., Seattle, WA 98125 (SAN 216-1710).

Pacific Northwest National Parks & Forests Assn., *(Pacif NW Natl Pks; 0-914019)*, 83S. King St., Suite 212, Seattle, WA 98104 (SAN 286-8504) Tel 206-442-7958.

Names

Pacific Pipeline, Inc., *(Pacific Pipeline),* 19215 66th Ave. S., Kent, WA 98032 (SAN 208-2128) Tel 206-872-5523; Toll free: 800-562-4647 (WA); P.O. Box 3711, Seattle, WA 98124 (SAN 169-8834); Toll free: 800-426-4727 (OR,ID,MT,NV, & Northern CA).

†**Pacific Pr. Publishing Assn.,** *(Pacific Pr Pub Assn; 0-8163),* P.O. Box 7000, Boise, ID 83707-1000 (SAN 202-8409) Tel 208-465-2500; Toll free: 800-447-7377; CIP.

Pacific Pr. Santa Barbara, *(Pacific Santa Barbara; 0-911094),* P.O. Box 219, Pierce City, MO 65723 (SAN 202-1161) Tel 417-476-2034.

Pacific Pubs., *(Pacific Pubs; 0-936521),* Box 272, Tiburon, CA 94920 (SAN 697-9335) Tel 415-868-2909; 35 Brighton, Bolinas, CA 94937 (SAN 698-2328); Orders to: Pacific Pipeline, 19215 66th Ave. S., Kent, WA 98032 (SAN 169-8834) Tel 206-872-5523.

Pacific Publishing, Div. of Pacific Productions Inc., *(Pacific Pub HI; 0-934997),* 1750 Kalakaua Ave., Suite 3901, Honolulu, HI 96826 (SAN 695-1996) Tel 808-946-8833; Dist. by: Worldwide Dist., Ltd., 550 N. Nimitz Hwy., Honolulu, HI 96817-5030 (SAN 169-1627).

Pacific Publishing Hse., *(Pacif Pub Hawaii; 0-918872),* 2430 Kirkham St., San Francisco, CA 94122 (SAN 210-3214) Tel 415-566-2988.

Pacific Radiation Corp., *(Pacific Rad; 0-916339),* 2945 Stonehill Dr., Altadena, CA 91001 (SAN 295-7698) Tel 818-798-8100.

Pacific Rim Research, *(Pacific Rim Res; 0-9613954),* P.O. Box 4538, North Hollywood, CA 91607 (SAN 282-0986) Tel 818-995-7042.

Pacific Science Ctr., *(Pacific Sci Ctr; 0-935051),* 200 Second Ave., N, Seattle, WA 98109 (SAN 694-5244) Tel 206-443-2001.

Pacific Scientific Press, Inc., *(Pacific Scientific; 0-943792),* 3506 Pennsylvania Sta., Long View, WA 98632 (SAN 241-0532) Tel 206-425-8592.

Pacific Search Pr., *(Pacific Search; 0-914718; 0-931397),* 222 Dexter Ave. N., Seattle, WA 98109 (SAN 202-8476) Tel 206-682-5044; Toll free: 800-858-0628.

Pacific Shoreline Pr., *(Pacific Shoreline; 0-932967),* P.O. Box 217, Temple City, CA 91780 (SAN 689-9897) Tel 818-287-4767.

Pacific Sports Actualities, *(Pacific Sports; 0-910405),* Box 2443, Berkeley, CA 94702 (SAN 260-1141) Tel 415-848-5423.

Pacific Sun Pr., *(Pacific Sun; 0-9602908),* 3785 Arroyo Sorrento Dr., San Diego, CA 92130 (SAN 214-073X) Tel 714-755-4422.

Pacific Technical Group, Inc., Publications Division, *(Pacific Tech; 0-913727),* 19329 Via Crecente Ct. P.O. Box 2115, Saratoga, CA 95070 (SAN 286-102X) Tel 408-867-0666.

Pacific Telecommunications Council *See* Univ. of Hawaii Pr., The

Pacific Western Publishing Co., *(Pacific-West; 0-911096),* P.O. Box 604, Bakersfield, CA 93302 (SAN 220-9772).

Pacific Whale Foundation Pr., *(Pac Whale Found Pr; 0-938725),* P.O. Box 1038, Kihei, HI 96753 (SAN 661-6070); Azeka Pl., Suite 303, Kihei, HI 96753 (SAN 661-6089) Tel 808-879-8811.

Pacifica House, Inc., Pubs., *(Pacifica; 0-911098),* c/o Borden Publishing Co., 1855 W. Main St., Alhambra, CA 91801 (SAN 201-419X).

Pacifica Pr., *(Pacifica Pr; 0-935553),* 1149 Grand Teton Dr., Pacifica, CA 94044 (SAN 695-8958) Tel 415-355-6678.

Pacifica Publishing, *(Pacifica Lodi CA; 0-935109),* 1732 LeBec Ct., Lodi, CA 95240 (SAN 695-2135) Tel 209-369-2368.

Pack Publishing, *(Pack Pub; 0-9616304),* P.O. Box 16163, Panama City, FL 32406 (SAN 693-8752) Tel 904-235-0794.

Package Publicity Service, Inc., *(Package Publ; 0-911100),* 27 W. 24 St., New York, NY 10010 (SAN 206-8621) Tel 212-255-2872.

Packard, Rosa Covington, *(R C Packard),* 208 W. Old Mill Rd., Greenwich, CT 06830 (SAN 211-089X) Tel 203-661-8946.

Packard Pr., Financial Pubns. Div., *(Packard Pr Fin; 0-936093),* 10th & Spring Garden Sts., Philadelphia, PA 19123 (SAN 696-8856) Tel 215-236-2000.

Packard Publishing, *(Packard; 0-941710),* P.O. Box 10372, Beverly Hills, CA 90213 (SAN 239-2895) Tel 818-716-7306.

†**Packrat Pr.,** *(Packrat WA; 0-915433),* 4366 N. Diana Ln., Oak Harbor, WA 98277 (SAN 291-3232); CIP.

Packrat Press Books, *(Packrat Pr; 0-9607554),* P.O. Box 4904 Glenstone Sta., Springfield, MO 65804 (SAN 211-7525) Tel 417-865-1113.

PacTel Publishing, *(Pactel Pub; 0-934315),* P.O. Box 8124, Walnut Creek, CA 94596 (SAN 693-3564) Tel 415-932-6300; Orders to: Redbook Subscription Ctr., P.O. Box 2044, Marion, OH 43305 (SAN 662-3182).

Paddlewheel Pr., *(Paddlewheel; 0-938274),* 15100 SW 109th, Tigard, OR 97224 (SAN 215-8973) Tel 503-639-5637.

Padilla, Francisco, *(Padilla; 0-9605292),* P.O. Box 11468, Denver, CO 80211 (SAN 216-2814) Tel 303-629-2425.

Padma Press, *(Padma; 0-917960),* P.O. Box 56, Oatman, AZ 86433 (SAN 209-4088).

Padre Pio Pubs., *(Padre Pio Pubs; 0-9615916),* P.O. Box 468, Patagonia, AZ 85624 (SAN 696-8864) Tel 602-394-2018; 223 Duquesne Ave., Patagonia, AZ 85624 (SAN 696-8872).

Padre Productions, *(Padre Prods; 0-914598),* P.O. Box 1275, San Luis Obispo, CA 93406 (SAN 202-8484) Tel 805-543-5404.

Paduano, Joseph, *(J Paduano; 0-9615590),* 14 Heidl Ave., West Long Branch, NJ 07764 (SAN 289-355X) Tel 201-222-7620.

†**Pagan Pr.,** *(Pagan Pr; 0-943742),* 26 St. Marks Pl., New York, NY 10003 (SAN 241-0540) Tel 212-674-3321; CIP.

Paganiniana Pubns., Inc., Div. of T.F.H. Pubns., Inc., *(Paganiniana Pubns; 0-87666),* P.O. Box 427, Neptune, NJ 07753 (SAN 209-309X) Tel 201-988-8400; Toll free: 800-631-2188.

Page One Pubns., *(Page One; 0-9607274),* P.O. Box 2674, La Mesa, CA 92041 (SAN 239-3700) Tel 619-697-1584.

Page Publishing Co., *(Page Pub WI; 0-89769),* Box 432, Brookfield, WI 53005 (SAN 239-3719).

Page/Wand Pr., *(Page Wand; 0-9615663),* 2124 Kittredge St., No. 99, Berkeley, CA 94704 (SAN 695-8974) Tel 415-841-6500.

Pageant Publishing Co., *(Pageant Pub Co; 0-914623),* P.O. Box 4455, Seattle, WA 98104 (SAN 287-296X) Tel 206-883-3202; Orders to: Shelley Marketing Services, P.O. Box 1288, Champlain, NY 12919-1288 (SAN 662-2119) Tel 514-678-5774.

Pages to Go!!, *(Pages to Go; 0-943102),* 2140 N. Iris Ln., Escondido, CA 92026 (SAN 240-4206) Tel 619-747-8644.

Paget Pr., *(Paget Pr; 0-920348),* P.O. Box 3993, Santa Barbara, CA 93130 (SAN 692-9648).

Paideia House, Pubs. (CA), *(Paideia Hse; 0-914027),* 22704 Ventura Blvd. Suite 435, Woodland Hills, CA 91364 (SAN 286-8547) Tel 818-888-7834.

†**Paideia Pubs.,** *(Paideia MA; 0-913993),* P.O. Box 343, Ashfield, MA 01330 (SAN 287-7511) Tel 413-628-3838; CIP.

Paige Pubns., *(Paige Pubns; 0-938699),* P.O. Box 1384, Rancho Mirage, CA 92270 (SAN 661-535X); 2 Lincoln Pl., Rancho Mirage, CA 92270 (SAN 661-5368) Tel 619-328-7898.

Paine, Tom, Institute *See* Tom Paine Institute
PaineWebber Mortgage Finance, *(PaineWebber Mortgage; 0-9603790),* P.O. Box 905, Columbia, MD 21044 (SAN 213-8174) Tel 301-964-8933.

Paint Box Studio, The, *(Paint Box; 0-9613287),* 145 Ashley Rd., Hopkins, MN 55343 (SAN 695-8118) Tel 612-935-3283.

Pair-O'-Dice Press, *(Pair O Dice; 0-943446),* 525 SE 16th Ave., Portland, OR 97214 (SAN 240-740X) Tel 503-236-2931.

Pajarito Pubns., *(Pajarito Pubns; 0-918358),* 2633 Granite NW, Albuquerque, NM 87104 (SAN 209-8555) Tel 505-242-8075.

Pakin, Sandra & Associates, Inc., *(Pakin Assocs; 0-9608178),* 6007 N. Sheridan Rd., Chicago, IL 60660 (SAN 240-2637) Tel 312-271-2848.

Pal, J. B., & Co., Inc., *(J B Pal; 0-916836),* 904 W. Castlewood Terr., Chicago, IL 60640 (SAN 208-0567) Tel 312-271-0123.

P.A.L. Pr., *(PAL Pr; 0-938034),* P.O. Box 487, San Anselmo, CA 94960 (SAN 220-0791) Tel 415-453-8547.

Pal Publishing, *(Pal Pub; 0-918104),* 10755 Bachelor Valley Rd., Witter Springs, CA 95493 (SAN 282-1001) Tel 707-275-2777; P.O. Box 807, Northridge, CA 91328 (SAN 282-101X)95493.

Pal Publishing Co., *(Pal Pub MA; 0-914765),* P.O. Box 2325, Fitchburg, MA 01420 (SAN 291-8455).

Palace Mission, Inc., *(Palace Mission; 0-9609078),* 1622 Spring Mill Rd., Gladwyne, PA 19035 (SAN 238-0773) Tel 215-525-5598; Dist. by: ADFD Pubns., 20 S. 36th St., Suite 104, Philadelphia, PA 19104 (SAN 282-6615) Tel 215-387-4857.

Paladin House Pubs., *(Paladin Hse; 0-88252),* P.O. Box 387, 2623 Kaneville Rd., Geneva, IL 60134 (SAN 203-7041) Tel 312-232-2711.

Paladin Pr., *(Paladin Pr; 0-87364),* P.O. Box 1307, Boulder, CO 80306 (SAN 212-0305); Toll free: 800-824-7888; 2523 Broadway Ave., Boulder, CO 80302 (SAN 662-1066) Tel 303-443-7250. *Imprints:* Sycamore Island Books (Sycamore Island).

Paladin Software Corp., *(Paladin; 0-912213),* 3255 Scott Blvd., Suite 7E, Santa Clara, CA 95054 (SAN 264-9837) Tel 408-970-0566. Formerly known as VisiCorp Personal Software, Inc.

Palasam Pubs., *(Palasam Pub; 0-9607430),* 6808 Bowling Dr., Sacramento, CA 95823 (SAN 239-7889).

Palatine Pubns., Inc., *(Palatine Pubns; 0-936638),* P.O. Drawer 1265, Ruston, LA 71273-1265 (SAN 214-0748).

Pale Horse Press, *(Pale Horse; 0-914720),* 433 Fair Ave., NE, New Philadelphia, OH 44663 (SAN 206-6092) Tel 216-364-3715.

Paleontological Research Institution, *(Paleo Res; 0-87710),* 1259 Trumansburg Rd., Ithaca, NY 14850 (SAN 204-918X) Tel 607-273-6623.

Palestine Focus Pubns., *(Palestine Focus; 0-935177),* 1885 Mission St., San Francisco, CA 94103-3584 (SAN 695-460X) Tel 415-861-1552.

†**Palisades Pubs.,** *(Palisades Pub; 0-913530),* P.O. Box 744, Pacific Palisades, CA 90272 (SAN 204-9198) Tel 213-454-0826; CIP.

Palladium Bks., *(Palladium Bks; 0-916211),* 5924-26 Lonyo, Detroit, MI 48210 (SAN 294-9504) Tel 313-843-1275.

†**Palladium Pubns., Inc.,** *(Palladium Pubns),* P.O. Box 58672, Seattle, WA 98188 (SAN 295-0197) Tel 206-251-5477; CIP.

Palm Books, *(Palm Bks; 0-9608036),* 2055 Foxway, Dept. 17,, Concord, CA 94518 (SAN 239-3727) Tel 415-674-8440.

Palm Pubns., *(Palm Pubns; 0-9613110),* 2654 Gough St., No. 102, San Francisco, CA 94123 (SAN 294-0760) Tel 415-928-3369.

Palm Publishing Co., *(Palm Pub Co; 0-936187),* P.O. Box 8091, Laguna Hills, CA 92654-8091 (SAN 696-8902) Tel 714-458-5708; 25181 Woolwich, Laguna Hills, CA 92653 (SAN 696-8910).

Palm Springs Media, Inc., *(PS Media Inc; 0-939271),* P.O. Box 2740, Palm Springs, CA 92263 (SAN 662-815X); 555 Commercial Rd., Suite 13, Palm Springs, CA 92262 (SAN 662-8168) Tel 619-322-3050.

Palm Springs Publishing, *(Palm Springs Pub; 0-914445),* 1380 Tamarisk Rd., Palm Springs, CA 92262 (SAN 289-663X) Tel 619-323-9968.

Palm Tree Library, *(Palm Tree Lib; 0-933266),* P.O. Box 84268, Los Angeles, CA 90073 (SAN 212-3789).

Palm Tree Publishing, Inc., *(Palm Tree Pub; 0-935627),* P.O. Box 292227, Ft. Lauderdale, FL 33329 (SAN 695-9008) Tel 305-584-0303; 4375 60th Ave., SW, Davie, FL 33314.

Palmen Institute, The, *(Palmen Inst; 0-9617213),* P.O. Box 671, Edmonds, WA 98020 (SAN 663-4214); 4620 200th St. SW, Suite D, Lynnwood, WA 98036 (SAN 663-4222) Tel 206-672-4750.

Palmer, A. N., Co., The, *(A N Palmer; 0-914268; 0-913941),* 1720 W. Irving Park Rd., Schaumburg, IL 60193 (SAN 202-1374) Tel 312-894-4300; Toll free: 800-323-9563.

Palmer, Birch, *(R H Palmer; 0-9610168),* 1729 Grant Ave., Ogden, UT 84404 (SAN 264-2840) Tel 801-394-6864.

Palmer, J., Pub., *(J Palmer),* 155 W. Clark St., No. 5, Manchester, NH 03104 (SAN 206-2097) Tel 603-625-5103.

Palmer Enterprises, *(Palmer Ent; 0-912479),* P.O. Box 966, Orangevale, CA 95662 (SAN 215-1650) Tel 916-988-8435.

Palmer Memorial Episcopal Church, *(Palmer Memorial; 0-9617291),* 6221 S. Main St., Houston, TX 77005 (SAN 663-608X) Tel 713-529-6196.

Palmer-Pletsch Associates, *(Palmer-Pletsch; 0-935278),* P.O. Box 12046, Portland, OR 97212 (SAN 209-1933) Tel 503-231-4908.

Palmer Pubns. at Amherst, *(Palmer Pubns WI),* Amherst, WI 54406 (SAN 295-3609) (SAN 295-3617).

Palmetto Pr., Inc., *(Palmetto Pr; 0-9615619),* P.O. Box 660-445, Miami Springs, FL 33266 (SAN 695-8559) Tel 305-887-7157; 88 Glendale Dr., Miami Springs, FL 33314 (SAN 696-0421).

Palmetto Publishing Co., *(Palmetto Pub; 0-9613853),* 1318 Geiger Ave., Columbia, SC 29201 (SAN 685-2173) Tel 803-252-4867.

†**Palomar Books,** *(Palomar Bks; 0-932882),* P.O. Box 222, San Marcos, CA 92069 (SAN 212-2952) Tel 805-931-1755; *CIP.*

Palomar Publishing Co., *(Palomar),* P.O. Box 4444, Whittier, CA 90607 (SAN 204-9201).

Palomares & Associates, *(Palomares & Assoc; 0-86584),* P.O. Box 1577, Spring Valley, CA 92077 (SAN 669-0963) Tel 619-698-6654.

Palomino Pr., *(Palomino Pr; 0-9610036),* 86-07 144th St., Briarwood, NY 11435 (SAN 241-5739) Tel 718-297-5053; Dist. by: Quality Bks., 918 Sherwood Dr., Lake Bluff, IL 60044-2204 (SAN 169-2127); Dist. by: Baker & Taylor Co., 50 Kirby Ave., Somerville, NJ 08876 (SAN 169-4901).

Palos Verdes Bk. Co., *(Palos Verdes; 0-936848),* P.O. Box 456, Lomita, CA 90717 (SAN 218-4532) Tel 904-383-8727.

Pambili Books, *(Pambili Bks; 0-917336),* 105 Gates St., San Francisco, CA 94110 (SAN 208-8010) Tel 415-821-9717.

Pamela Pubns., Subs. of Pamela, Inc., *(Pamela Pubns; 0-938003),* 1117 Marquette Ave., Suite 1601, Minneapolis, MN 55403 (SAN 659-7491) Tel 612-339-8139.

Pan-Am Books *See* **Pan-American Publishing Co.**

Pan Am Pubns., *(Pan Am Pubns; 0-87582),* Pan Am Bldg., New York, NY 10166 (SAN 204-9228).

Pan American Commmite/International Ozone, *(Pan Am Intl Ozone; 0-918650),* 83 Oakwood Ave., Norwalk, CT 06850 (SAN 271-5082) Tel 203-847-8169.

Pan American Navigation Service, Inc., *(Pan Am Nav; 0-87219),* P.O. Box 90406, Van Nuys, CA 91409 (SAN 202-8506) Tel 818-345-2744; Toll free: 800-423-5932.

Pan-American Publishing Co., *(Pan-Am Publishing Co; 0-932906),* P.O. Box 1505, Las Vegas, NM 87701 (SAN 212-5366).

Pan/Ishtar Unlimited, *(Pan Ishtar; 0-941698),* P.O. Box 216, Edgewood, TX 75117 (SAN 239-2747) Tel 214-896-1700.

Pan Productions, *(Pan Prods; 0-9606100),* Box 72, Coronado, CA 92118 (SAN 216-8480) Tel 619-435-6042.

Pana Pr., *(Pana Pr; 0-9615244),* 4559 Fran Way, Richmond, CA 94803 (SAN 695-166X) Tel 415-222-4672.

Panache Productions, *(Panache Prods; 0-9610596),* 1388 Moorpark Rd., Thousand Oaks, CA 91360 (SAN 264-2859) Tel 805-495-6608.

Pancake Pr., *(Pancake Pr; 0-942908),* 163 Galewood Circle, San Francisco, CA 94131 (SAN 218-0448) Tel 415-665-9215.

Panda Bks., Pubs., *(Panda Bks Pubs; 0-937541),* P.O. Box 90488, San Diego, CA 92109-0860 (SAN 658-974X) Tel 619-461-5169. *Imprints:* Silk Butterfly Press (Silk Butterfly Pr).

Panda Pr., *(Panda Press VA; 0-9616700),* 4111 Watkins Trail, Annandale, VA 22003 (SAN 659-6711) Tel 703-256-2461.

Panda Programs, *(Panda Programs; 0-942476),* 1872 W. Lotus Pl., Brea, CA 92621 (SAN 219-2403).

Pandora's Treasures, *(Pandora's Treasures; 0-9605236),* 1609 Eastover Terrace, Boise, ID 83706 (SAN 282-1036) Tel 208-342-4002.

†**Panel Pubs.,** Affil. of Worldwide Walter Samsom Group, *(Panel Pubs; 0-916592),* 14 Plaza Rd., Greenvale, NY 11548 (SAN 204-921X) Tel 516-484-0006; *CIP.*

Panhandle-Plains Historical Society Museum, *(Panhandle; 0-913463),* P.O. Box 967, W.T. Sta., Canyon, TX 79016 (SAN 280-0446) Tel 806-655-7191.

†**Panjandrum Bks. ,** *(Panjandrum; 0-915572),* 11321 Iowa Ave., Suite 1, Los Angeles, CA 90025 (SAN 282-1257) Tel 213-477-8771; Dist. by: Baker & Taylor (Western Div.), 380 Edison Way, Reno, NV 89564 (SAN 169-4464) Tel 702-786-6700; Dist. by: Talman Co., Inc., 150 Fifth Ave., Rm. 514, New York, NY 10011 (SAN 200-5204) Tel 212-620-3182; Dist. by: Blackwell North America, 6024 SW. Jean Rd., Bldg. G, Lake Oswego, OR 97034 (SAN 656-4917) Tel 503-684-1140; Dist. by: Bookpeople, 2929 Fifth St., Berkeley, CA 94710 (SAN 168-9517); Dist. by: Shakti Distributors, Inc., 1020 White St, SW, Atlanta, GA 30310 (SAN 200-7258); Dist. by: Coutts Library Services, 736-738 Cayugo St., Lewiston, NY 14092 (SAN 169-5401); *CIP.*

Panoply Press, Inc., *(Panoply Pr; 0-9615067),* P.O. Box 1885, Lake Oswego, OR 97034 (SAN 693-9279) Tel 503-620-7239.

Panoptic Enterprises, *(Panoptic Ent; 0-912481),* P.O. Box 1099, Woodbridge, VA 22193-0099 (SAN 265-3141) Tel 703-670-2812.

Panorama Publishing Co., *(Panorama Van Nuys; 0-937671),* 14640 Victory Blvd., No. 210, Van Nuys, CA 91411 (SAN 659-2627) Tel 818-988-4690.

Panorama West Bks., *(Panorama West; 0-914330),* 2002 N. Gateway Suite 102, Fresno, CA 93727 (SAN 216-0501) Tel 209-251-7801.

Panoramic Pr., *(Panoramic Pr CA; 0-937879),* 340 Panoromic Hwy., Mill Valley, CA 94941 (SAN 659-5529) Tel 415-454-1892; Dist. by: Ancient Future, P.O. Box 264, Kentfield, CA 94914 (SAN 200-6499).

Panozzo, Joseph Guido, *(J G Panozzo; 0-9615974),* 609 Dennis St., Rochelle, IL 61068 (SAN 696-8945) Tel 815-562-2571.

Pantagraph Books *See* **Evergreen Communications, Inc.**

Pantheon Bks., Div. of Random Hse., Inc., *(Pantheon; 0-394),* 201 E. 50th St., New York, NY 10022 (SAN 202-862X) Tel 212-751-2600; Toll free: 800-638-6460; Orders to: Random Hse., Inc., 400 Hahn Rd., Westminster, MD 21157 (SAN 202-5515). *Imprints:* Pantheon Books for Young Readers (Pant Bks Young).

Pantheon Books for Young Readers *See* **Pantheon Bks.**

Pants Pr., *(Pants Pr; 0-9614241),* 4628 Drew Ave. South, Minneapolis, MN 55410 (SAN 686-693X) Tel 612-372-3998.

Paolino, Adele, *(A Paolino; 0-9611448),* 50 Bedford Ave., Breezy Point, NY 11697 (SAN 277-6995) Tel 718-634-5552.

Papaloa Pr., *(Papaloa Pr; 0-9615498),* 362 Selby Ln., Atherton, CA 94025 (SAN 695-5487) Tel 415-369-9994; Dist. by: Baker & Taylor, 1515 Broadway, New York, NY 10036 (SAN 169-5606) Tel 212-730-7650; Dist. by: Quality Bks., 918 Sherwood Dr., Lake Bluff, IL 60044-2204 (SAN 169-2127); Dist. by: Western States Book Service, P.O. Box 855, Clackamas, OR 97015 (SAN 200-5662); Dist. by: Pacific Pipeline, 19215 66th Ave., S., Kent, WA 98032 (SAN 208-2128) Tel 206-872-5523.

Papa's Pr., *(Papa's Pr; 0-9601968),* P.O. Box 81555, San Diego, CA 92138-1555 (SAN 207-6292) Tel 619-582-6294.

Paper Bag Players, *(Paper Bag; 0-9606662),* 50 Riverside Dr., New York, NY 10024 (SAN 212-9566); Orders to: Walter Baker Co., 100 Chauncey St., Boston, MA 02111 (SAN 662-1074); Orders to: Eeyore Bookstore, 82nd & Madison Ave., New York, NY 10028 (SAN 662-1082).

Paper Birch Pr., Inc., *(Paper Birch Pr; 0-9613961; 0-939687),* P.O. Box 128, Ashland, WI 54806 (SAN 682-3076) Tel 715-682-9418; Toll free: 800-336-5666; Dist. by: Bookman, 519 N. Third St., Minneapolis, MN 55401 (SAN 282-7352) Tel 612-341-3333; Dist. by: Baker & Taylor, Midwest Div., 501 Gladiola Ave., Momence, IL 60954 (SAN 169-2100); Dist. by: The Distribtuors, 702 S. Michigan, South Bend, IN 46618 (SAN 169-2488) Tel 219-232-8500.

Paper Cloud Pr., The, *(Paper Cloud Pr; 0-9615850),* P.O. Box 2178, Santa Barbara, CA 93120 (SAN 696-8929) Tel 805-969-0863; 72 Canyon View Rd., Santa Barbara, CA 93108 (SAN 696-8937).

Paper Corp. of America, *(Paper Corp Am; 0-936239),* c/o Baldwin Paper Co., 161 Sixth Ave., New York, NY 10013 (SAN 696-8775) Tel 212-255-1600.

Paper Dreams, *(Paper Dreams; 0-937149),* 1511 Forest Way, Del Mar, CA 92014 (SAN 658-4810) Tel 619-755-3289; P.O. Box 2951, Del Mar, CA 92014 (SAN 658-4829).

†**Paper Mill Pr.,** *(Paper Mill Pr; 0-9612304),* 8650 Lords Manor Way, Rohnert Park, CA 94928 (SAN 287-7546) Tel 707-795-4132; *CIP.*

Paper Pile Pr. of San Anselmo, *(Paper Pile; 0-915195),* P.O. Box 337, San Anselmo, CA 94960 (SAN 287-3087) Tel 415-454-5552.

Paper Tiger Paperbacks, Inc., *(Paper Tiger Pap; 0-933334),* 1512 NW Seventh Pl., Gainesville, FL 32603 (SAN 212-5374) Tel 904-371-7771; Dist. by: Hippocrene Bks., Inc., 171 Madison Ave., New York, NY 10016 (SAN 213-2060) Tel 718-454-2366.

Paper Vision Press *See* **Western Tanger Pr.**

Paperback Quarterly Pubns., *(Paperback Quarterly; 0-941858),* 1710 Vincent St., Brownwood, TX 76801 (SAN 239-4669); Dist. by: Borgo Press, P.O. Box 2845, San Bernardino, CA 92406-2845 (SAN 208-9459) Tel 714-884-5813.

Paperback Video, Inc., *(Paperback Video; 0-937621),* 448 Ignacio Blvd., Suite 254, Novato, CA 94947 (SAN 658-9790) Tel 415-382-1560.

Paperbacks Plus Pr., *(Paperbacks Plus; 0-942186),* 108 E. Davis, Mesquite, TX 75149 (SAN 262-0545).

Papermac Bks. *See* **St. Martin's Pr., Inc.**

†**Paperweight Pr.,** *(Paperweight Pr; 0-933756),* 761 Chestnut St., Santa Cruz, CA 95060 (SAN 212-5390); Dist. by: Charles Tuttle Publishing Co., 49 Central Ave., Rutland, VT 05701 (SAN 169-6629) Tel 513-381-3881; *CIP.*

Papier-Mache Pr., *(Papier-Mache Press; 0-918949),* 34 Malaga Place E., Manhattan Beach, CA 90266 (SAN 669-8336) Tel 213-545-3812.

Papillon Pr., *(Papillon Pr; 0-9608826),* 1232 Vallecito Rd., Carpinteria, CA 93013 (SAN 213-1447) Tel 805-684-5038.

Papillon Pubns., *(Papillon Pubns; 0-938750),* 101 First St., Suite 284, Los Altos, CA 94022 (SAN 238-7468) Tel 415-948-5320.

Papp Historical Pubns., *(Papp Hist Pubns; 0-937735),* 58 Woodlawn St., Schenectady, NY 12306 (SAN 659-266X) Tel 518-387-7727.

Pappani, Debra Ann, *(Pappani; 0-9606062),* 1990 Hurst Ave., San Jose, CA 95125 (SAN 216-9207) Tel 408-264-9907.

Papyrus Pubs., *(Papyrus Pubs; 0-943698),* P.O. Box 466, Yonkers, NY 10704 (SAN 238-079X) Tel 914-664-0840.

Paquin, Larue, Publishing, *(L Paquin Pub; 0-9615547),* Box 61, West Tremont, ME 04690 (SAN 695-9830) Tel 207-244-5132.

Para-Bk-Pr., *(Para-Bk-Pr; 0-9612120),* P.O. Box 647, N. Hollywood, CA 91603 (SAN 287-7554) Tel 818-896-1630.

†**Para Publishing,** *(Para Pub; 0-915516),* P.O. Box 4232-R, Santa Barbara, CA 93140-4232 (SAN 215-8981) Tel 805-968-7277; Dist. by: Baker & Taylor, Eastern Div., 50 Kirby Ave., Somerville, NJ 08876 (SAN 169-4901); Dist. by: Bookpeople, 2929 Fifth St., Berkeley, CA 94710 (SAN 168-9517); Dist. by: Publishers Group West, 5855 Beaudry St., Emeryville, CA 94608 (SAN 202-8522) Tel 415-658-3453; *CIP.*

Para Research, Inc., *(Para Res; 0-914918),* 85 Eastern Ave., P.O. Box 61, Gloucester, MA 01930 (SAN 213-4438) Tel 617-283-3438.

Parable, *(Parable),* 38 N. Austin Blvd., Oak Park, IL 60302 (SAN 283-9792) Tel 312-848-0025.

†**Parable Pr.,** *(Parable Pr; 0-917250),* 136 Gray St., Amherst, MA 01002 (SAN 208-4449) Tel 413-253-5634; *CIP.*

Parables, Subs. of Bentley Enterprises, *(Parables; 0-9614960),* P.O. Box 73, Ludlow, MA 01056 (SAN 693-7535) Tel 413-543-5809.

Names

Parabolic Press, Inc., *(Parabolic Pr; 0-915760),* P.O. Box 3032, Stanford, CA 94305 (SAN 207-5814) Tel 415-328-1084.

Paracelsus College, *(Paracelsus; 0-915939),* 3555 S. 700 E., Utah Institute of Parachemistry, Salt Lake City, UT 84106 (SAN 294-0779) Tel 801-486-6730.

Parachute Pr., Inc., *(Parachute Pr; 0-938753),* 200 Fifth Ave., Room 461, New York, NY 10010 (SAN 661-5554) Tel 212-691-1421. Do not confuse with Parachute Pr., Tempe, AZ.

†**Parachuting Resources,** *(Parachuting Res; 0-933382),* MC P.O. Box 1291, Dayton, OH 45402 (SAN 212-5404) Tel 513-258-1777; *CIP.*

Paraclete Pr., Div. of Creative Joys, Inc., *(Paraclete Pr; 0-941478),* Box 1568, Orleans, MA 02653 (SAN 282-1508) Tel 617-255-4685; Toll free: 800-451-5006.

Paradesa Editions, *(Paradesa Edit; 0-937943),* 9 Nebraska St., San Francisco, CA 94110 (SAN 659-7505) Tel 415-824-0259.

Paradigm Co., The, *(Paradigm ID; 0-914981),* P.O. Box 45161, Boise, ID 83711 (SAN 682-8019) Tel 208-322-4440.

Paradigm Corp., *(Paradigm Corp)* 2546 W. Main St., Littleton, CO 80120 (SAN 658-8271).

Paradigm Pr., *(Paradigm Pr; 0-937572),* 127 Greenbrae Boardwalk, Greenbrae, CA 94904 (SAN 220-0821) Tel 415-461-5457; Dist. by: Bookpeople, 2929 Fifth St., Berkeley, CA 94710 (SAN 168-9517).

†**Paradigm Pubns.,** *(Paradigm Pubns; 0-912111),* 44 Linden St., Brookline, MA 02146 (SAN 264-7745); Dist. by: Redwing Book Co., 44 Linden St., Brookline, MA 02146 (SAN 159-9348) Tel 617-738-4664; *CIP.*

Paradise House, Inc., *(Paradise Hse; 0-87358),* 10231 N. Scottsdale Rd. B-1, Scottsdale, AZ 85253 (SAN 693-3580); Dist. by: Northland Press, P.O. Box N, Flagstaff, AZ 86002 (SAN 202-9251).

Paradise Place, *(Paradise Pl; 0-9616821),* 7064 Nicholas St., Omaha, NE 68132 (SAN 661-4736) Tel 402-556-6262.

Paradise Plus, *(Paradise; 0-9616059),* 929 SW Salmon, 112, Portland, OR 97205 (SAN 698-0848) Tel 503-228-2316; Dist. by: Pacific Pipeline, Inc., 19215 66th Ave. S., Kent, WA 98032 (SAN 208-2128) Tel 805-543-5404; Toll free: 800-426-4727; Dist. by: Booklink Distributors, P.O. Box 1275, San Luis Obispo, CA 93406 (SAN 159-0782).

Paradise Press, *(Paradise Press; 0-940806),* P.O. Box 5306, Santa Monica, CA 90405 (SAN 219-6190) Tel 213-392-4098. Do not confuse with Paradise Pr., Corte Madera, CA.

Paradise Pubns., *(Paradise Pubns; 0-9614113),* 8110 SW Wareham Cir., Portland, OR 97223 (SAN 685-9976) Tel 503-246-1555.

Paragon Assocs./Benson Co., Inc., *(Paragon Benson; 0-89477),* 365 Great Circle Road, Nashville, TN 37228 (SAN 209-9780) Tel 615-259-9111; Dist. by: Alexandria Hse., P.O. Box 23618, Alexandria, IN 46001 (SAN 209-9799).

Paragon Group, Inc., The, *(Paragon Group; 0-9615902),* 19417 SE 425, Enumclaw, WA 98022 (SAN 696-7876) Tel 206-825-2832.

Paragon Hse., Pubs., *(Paragon Hse; 0-913729; 0-88702; 0-89226; 0-943852; 0-913757),* 2 Hammarskjold Plaza, New York, NY 10017 (SAN 286-1704) Tel 212-223-6433.

Paragon Pr./Dynapress, *(Paragon-Dynapress; 0-942910),* P.O. Box 866, Fern Park, FL 32730 (SAN 240-3234) Tel 305-331-5550.

Paragon Productions, *(Paragon Prods; 0-9602184),* 817 Pearl St., Denver, CO 80203 (SAN 213-2702) Tel 303-832-7687.

Paragon Publishing, *(Paragon Pub CA; 0-914809),* P.O. Box 53, Santa Rosa, CA 95402 (SAN 289-3592) Tel 707-527-8185.

†**Paragon-Reiss,** Div. of National Paragon Corp., *(Paragon-Reiss; 0-910199),* 57-07 31st Ave., Woodside, NY 11377 (SAN 241-4244) Tel 718-728-5300; *CIP.*

Paragraph Press, *(Paragraph Pr; 0-915462),* 204 Circle Dr., P.O. Box 1107, Felton, CA 95018 (SAN 207-4974) Tel 408-335-4406.

Paragraphics, *(Paragraphics; 0-9616637),* 427 Third St., Brooklyn, NY 11215 (SAN 659-672X) Tel 718-965-2231.

Paragraphics Pr., Div. of Mercury Typographers, Inc., *(Paragraphics Pr; 0-939175),* 133 Fifth Ave., Third Flr., New York, NY 10003 (SAN 662-9075) Tel 201-332-5917. Do not confuse with Paragraphics of Brooklyn, NY.

Parallax Pr., *(Parallax Pr; 0-938077),* P.O. Box 7355, Berkeley, CA 94707 (SAN 663-4494) Tel 415-525-0101. Do not confuse with Parallax Pr., Middletown, CT.

Parallel Integration, *(Parallel Integ; 0-9617281),* P.O. Box 6001, Lincoln, NE 68506 (SAN 663-5237); 2640 Lake Condominium "D", Lincoln, NE 68502 (SAN 663-5245) Tel 402-474-2727.

Parallel Lines, Inc., *(Parallel Lines; 0-9616882),* RD 2, P.O. Box 673, Howell, NJ 07731 (SAN 661-6585) Tel 201-370-2095.

Paramount Bks., *(Paramount Bks; 0-9616024),* 1200 N. Terr., Suite 229, Provo, UT 84604 (SAN 697-936X) Tel 801-375-1053.

†**Paramount Publishing,** *(Paramount; 0-918668),* 800 Roosevelt Rd., Suite 413, Bldg. B, Glen Ellyn, IL 60137 (SAN 212-6796) Tel 312-790-2483; *CIP.*

Paramount Publishing, *(Paramount TX; 0-942376),* P.O. Box 3730, Amarillo, TX 79116-3730 (SAN 238-1028) Tel 806-355-1040.

Paranoid Pubns., *(Paranoid Pubns; 0-9602716),* P.O. Box 614, 631/2 S. Main, Manteno, IL 60950 (SAN 212-7857) Tel 815-468-3778.

Parapsych Press, *(Parapsych Pr; 0-911106),* P.O. Box 6847, College Sta., Durham, NC 27708 (SAN 204-9252) Tel 919-688-8241.

Parapsychology Foundation, Inc., *(Parapsych Foun; 0-912328),* 228 E. 71st St., New York, NY 10021 (SAN 203-6851) Tel 212-628-1550.

Parchment Press, *(Parchment Pr; 0-88428),* 5345 Atlanta Hwy., Montgomery, AL 36193 (SAN 202-8670) Tel 205-272-5820.

Pardo Press, The, *(Pardo Pr; 0-9609204),* 702 Polk Avenue, Lawrenceville, NJ 08648 (SAN 241-4252) Tel 609-396-7214.

Parent-Child Pr., *(Parent-Child Pr; 0-9601016; 0-939195),* P.O. Box 767, Altoona, PA 16603 (SAN 208-4333); 4201 Second Ave., Altoona, PA 16602 (SAN 662-7331) Tel 814-946-5213.

Parent Scene, *(Parent Scene; 0-910529),* P.O. Box 2222, 1280 E. San Bernardino Ave., Redlands, CA 92373 (SAN 260-244X) Tel 714-792-2412.

Parenteral Drug Association, Inc., *(PDA; 0-939459),* Avenue of the Arts Bldg., 1346 Chestnut St., Philadelphia, PA 19107 (SAN 260-3233) Tel 215-735-9752.

Parenthesis Press, *(Parenthesis Pr; 0-9601580),* P.O. Box 114, Bridgewater College, Bridgewater, VA 22812 (SAN 202-8689) Tel 703-828-6656.

†**Parenting Pr.,** *(Parenting Pr; 0-9602862; 0-943990),* P.O. Box 15163, Seattle, WA 98115 (SAN 215-6938); Toll free: 800-99B-OOKS; 7744 31st Ave. NE, Seattle, WA 98115 (SAN 699-5500); *CIP.*

Parents Anonymous, *(Parents Anon),* 7120 Franklin Ave., Los Angeles, CA 90046 (SAN 217-2607) Tel 213-876-9642; Toll free: 800-421-0353.

Parents as Teachers, *(Parents as Tchrs; 0-9616691),* P.O. Box 44093, Tacoma, WA 98444 (SAN 659-817X); 701 Violet Meadow S., Tacoma, WA 98444 (SAN 659-8188) Tel 206-531-0312.

†**Parents Magazine Pr.,** Div. of Gruner & Jahr, USA, Publishing, *(Parents; 0-8193),* 685 Third Ave., New York, NY 10017 (SAN 202-8697) Tel 212-878-8700; Toll free: 800-526-0275; Dist. by: New American Library, P.O. Box 999, Bergenfield, NJ 07621 (SAN 282-6348) Tel 201-387-0600; Dist. by: E. P. Dutton, 2 Park Ave., New York, NY 10016 (SAN 201-0070) Tel 212-725-1818; Toll free: 800-526-0275; *CIP.*

Parents' Pointers Pubns., *(Parents Pointers; 0-9608756),* Route 1, Box 238, Lawrenceburg, TN 38464 (SAN 241-063X) Tel 615-762-2663.

Parents Pr., *(Parents Pr KY; 0-935111),* P.O. Box 2180, Bowling Green, KY 42102-2180 (SAN 695-1422) Tel 502-843-1245; Dist. by: Baker & Taylor (Midwest Div.), 501 Gladiola Ave., Momence, IL 60954 (SAN 169-2100) Tel 815-472-2444; Toll free: 800-435-5111.

Parey, Paul, Scientific Pubs., *(Parey Sci Pubs; 3-489),* 35 W. 38th St., No. 3W, New York, NY 10018 (SAN 216-0021) Tel 212-730-0518.

Pargh, B. A., Co., Inc., 1283 Murfreesboro Rd., Nashville, TN 37217 (SAN 285-712X) Tel 615-366-3000; Toll free: 800-227-1000.

Park, S. H., *(S H Park; 0-9604440),* P.O. Box 7474, Trenton, NJ 08628 (SAN 215-1685) Tel 609-883-3551.

Park Avenue Pubns., *(Park Ave Pubns; 0-938149),* P.O. Box 303, Canandaigua, NY 14424 (SAN 659-8951); 132 Park Ave., Canandaigua, NY 14424 (SAN 659-896X) Tel 716-394-8632.

Park City Press, Div. of Sunflower Publishing, Inc., *(Park City Pr),* P.O. Box 25, Glenwood Landing, NY 11457 (SAN 287-2838).

Park Lane Enterprises, *(Park Lane Ent; 0-9609362),* 24 Park Ln., Minneapolis, MN 55416 (SAN 260-2458) Tel 612-922-1888.

Park Maitland School, The, *(Park Maitland; 0-9613532),* 1450 S.Onado Ave., Maitland, FL 32751 (SAN 657-369X) Tel 305-647-3038.

Park Pr. Co., *(Park Pr Co; 0-941226),* 2612 N. Mattis Ave., Champaign, IL 61821 (SAN 239-4685).

Park Publishing, Inc., *(Park Pub; 0-9603294),* 1999 Shepard Rd., St. Paul, MN 55116 (SAN 204-9260) Tel 612-698-1667.

Park Row Pr., *(Park Row Pr; 0-935749),* 1418 Park Row, San Diego, CA 92037 (SAN 695-9105) Tel 619-459-2121.

Park View Press, Inc., *(Park View; 0-87813),* 1066 Chicago Ave., Harrisonburg, VA 22801 (SAN 204-9279) Tel 703-434-0765.

Park West, *(Park West; 0-9610480),* P.O. Box 1502, Sausalito, CA 94966 (SAN 264-2875); Dist. by: Bookpeople, 2929 Fifth St., Berkeley, CA 94710 (SAN 168-9517); Dist. by: Distributors, The, 702 S. Michigan, South Bend, IN 46618 (SAN 212-0364) Tel 219-232-8500; Dist. by: Publishers Group West, 5855 Beaudry St., Emeryville, CA 94608 (SAN 696-0200) Tel 415-658-3453; Dist. by: Quality Books, 918 Sherwood Dr., Lake Bluff, IL 60044-2204 (SAN 169-2127).

Parker, Clayton A., Publications, *(C A Parker Pubns; 0-9604438),* 450 Wendell Dr., Salt Lake City, UT 84115 (SAN 218-5768) Tel 801-266-2292.

Parker, Gertrude M., *(G M Parker; 0-89279),* Southview, Apt. 4, Stanhope, IA 50246 (SAN 286-3480).

Parker, Oliver, Pub., *(O Parker Pub; 0-937155),* Frenchman's Hill, Bar Harbor, ME 04609 (SAN 658-4756); P.O. Box 429, Bar Harbor, ME 04609 (SAN 658-4764).

Parker & Son Pubns., Inc., *(Parker & Son; 0-911110),* Box 60001, Los Angeles, CA 90060 (SAN 202-8719) Tel 213-727-1088.

Parker Brothers Publishing, Div. of Parker Brothers, *(Parker Bro; 0-910313; 0-87372; 0-926088),* 50 Dunham Rd., Beverly, MA 01915 (SAN 241-4260); Toll free: 800-225-0540.

Parker Chiropractic Research Foundation, Inc., *(Parker Chiro; 0-9609606),* P.O. Box 40444, Fort Worth, TX 76140 (SAN 260-2466) Tel 816-293-6444.

Parker Engineering Publishing, *(Parker Engine Pub; 0-9611048),* 1510 Eisenhower, No. 331, Boulder, CO 80303 (SAN 283-3417) Tel 303-443-1286.

Parker Press, The, *(Parker Pr; 0-939562),* 31 Marlboro St., Newburyport, MA 01950 (SAN 216-4310) Tel 617-462-3427.

Parker Publishing Co. See **Prentice-Hall, Inc.**

Parkhurst Brook Pubs., *(Parkhurst Br; 0-9615664),* Perrin Rd., RD 3, Potsdam, NY 13676 (SAN 695-9121) Tel 315-265-9037.

Parkhurst Press, *(Parkhurst; 0-939500),* P.O. Box 143, Laguna Beach, CA 92652 (SAN 216-4329).

Parkrail, *(Parkrail; 0-9616240),* 1025 Oxford, Apt. L-138, Fort Collins, CO 80525 (SAN 658-4691) Tel 303-226-1233.

Parks & Nature Centers, Inc., *(Parks & Nature; 0-9613492),* P.O. Box 1791, Athens, GA 30603 (SAN 657-3703) Tel 404-548-3811.

Parkside Press, *(Parkside; 0-941180),* 2026 Parkside Court, West Linn, OR 97068 (SAN 239-3735).

Parkside Press Publishing Co., *(Parkside Pub Co; 0-911585),* P.O. Box 11585, Santa Ana, CA 92711 (SAN 264-2883) Tel 714-838-1888.

Parkside Pubns. Ltd., *(Park Pubns Ltd; 0-9617266),* 999 Third Ave., Suite 3210, Seattle, WA 98104 (SAN 663-4907) Tel 206-621-1818.

Parkway Pr., *(Parkway; 0-9610176),* P.O. Box 161, Roslyn Heights, NY 11577 (SAN 695-7099).

Parkway Press, Inc., *(Parkway Pr; 0-930408),* 3347 E. Calhoun Pkwy., Minneapolis, MN 55408 (SAN 211-0474) Tel 612-827-3347.

Parkway Press Ltd., *(Parkway Pr Ltd; 0-938270),* Box 174, West Tisbury, MA 02575 (SAN 239-4693) Tel 617-693-4596; Orders to: Box 8158, Shawnee Mission, KS 66208. Do not confuse with Parkway in Minneapolis & Parkway in Roslyn Heights NY.

Parkway Pubns., *(Parkway Pubns; 0-9608398),* P.O. Box 19845, 5616 W. Rita Drive, West Allis, WI 53219 (SAN 238-0803) Tel 414-321-5454.

Parkwest Pubns., *(Parkwest Pubns; 0-88186),* P.O. Caller Box A-10, Cathedral Sta., New York, NY 10025 (SAN 264-6846) Tel 212-222-6100. *Imprints:* Tarquin (Tarquin).

Parliamentarians International, *(Parliamentarians; 0-942302),* 50 Redwood Ave., No. 303, Redwood City, CA 94061-3002 (SAN 238-0811) Tel 415-367-1962.

Parmadale Childrens Village, *(Parmadale; 0-9615123),* 6753 State Rd., Parma, OH 44134 (SAN 694-180X) Tel 216-845-7700.

Parmly Billings Library, *(Parmly Lib; 0-9613224),* 510 N. Broadway, Billings, MT 59101 (SAN 295-1347) Tel 406-657-8294.

Parnassus Imprints, *(Parnassus Imprints; 0-940160),* Box 335, Orleans, MA 02653 (SAN 217-0809) Tel 617-225-2932; 21 Canal Rd., Orleans, MA 02653 (SAN 658-1366) Tel 617-225-2932.

Parpaglion & Co., *(Parpaglion; 0-9604252),* 413 Woodland Ave., Cherry Hill, NJ 08002 (SAN 214-4360) Tel 609-488-4494.

Parr, V., Publishing, *(V Parr Pub; 0-9613991),* P.O. Box 727, Santa Paula, CA 93060 (SAN 682-1626) Tel 805-646-0063.

Parr Publishing Co., Inc., *(Parr Pub; 0-89473),* 1200 S. Post Oak Rd., Suite 428, Houston, TX 77056 (SAN 209-6315) Tel 713-626-7830.

Parrish, Vernon, Publishing, *(V Parrish Pub; 0-9615774),* 1900 S. Eads St., Arlington, VA 22202 (SAN 696-6306) Tel 703-892-1993.

†Parrish Art Museum, The, *(Parrish Art; 0-943526),* 25 Jobs Ln., Southampton, NY 11968 (SAN 240-7418) Tel 516-283-2118; *CIP.*

Parrott Pr., *(Parrott Pr; 0-9616749),* 18 Otis St., Watertown, MA 02172 (SAN 661-0439) Tel 617-926-9668.

Parsonage Pr., The, *(Parsonage Pr; 0-9615872),* 4620-29th Ave. S., Minneapolis, MN 55406 (SAN 696-6179) Tel 612-729-1798.

Parson's Pr., *(Parsons Pr; 0-931085),* 140 Garden Ave., Roselle, IL 60172 (SAN 678-9390) Tel 312-529-1307.

Part-Ease, *(Part-Ease; 0-9607664),* P.O. Box 144, New Milford, NJ 07646 (SAN 238-082X).

Parthenon Pubns., *(Parthenon Pubns),* 139 Santa Fe Ave., El Cerrito, CA 94530 (SAN 214-4379) Tel 415-527-1374.

Partington, Paul G., *(P G Partington; 0-9602538),* 7320 S. Gretna Ave., Whittier, CA 90606 (SAN 212-3797).

Partisan Press, Inc., *(Partisan Pr; 0-935150),* P.O. Box 31387, Seattle, WA 98103 (SAN 215-6946).

Partner Press, *(Partner Pr; 0-933212),* Box 124, Livonia, MI 48152 (SAN 212-7865) Tel 313-651-8997; Dist. by: Gryphon House, Inc., 3706 Otis St., Mount Rainier, MD 20712 (SAN 169-3190) Tel 301-779-6200; Toll free: 800-638-0928.

†Partners for Livable Places, *(Partners Livable; 0-941182),* 1429 21st St., NW, Washington, DC 20036 (SAN 200-402X) Tel 202-887-5990; *CIP.*

Partners in Publishing, *(PIP; 0-937660),* P.O. Box 50347, Tulsa, OK 74150-0347 (SAN 209-6323) Tel 918-584-5906.

Partners Pr., *(Partners Pr NJ; 0-942676),* 301 N. Harrison St., Bldg. B, Suite 279, Princeton, NJ 08540 (SAN 239-8656) Tel 609-924-4438.

Partnership Foundation, the, *(Partnership Foundation; 0-934538),* C/O Capon Springs & Farms, Capon Springs, WV 26823 (SAN 220-9918).

Partridge Pair, Inc., The, *(Partridge Pair; 0-9606440),* P.O. Box 61, Sandy Springs, SC 29677 (SAN 218-5776) Tel 803-261-8430.

Partyline Enterprises, *(Partyline Enter; 0-9616680),* 1517 W. Lake St., Minneapolis, MN 55403 (SAN 659-6746) Tel 612-339-0103.

Pasadena Art Alliance, *(Pasadena Art; 0-937042),* 314 S. Mentor Ave., Pasadena, CA 91106 (SAN 213-5434) Tel 818-795-9276.

Pasadena Pr., *(Pasadena Pr; 0-930227),* 267 S. Madison, No. 204, Pasadena, CA 91106 (SAN 694-6410) Tel 818-796-3840; P.O. Box 60184, Pasadena, CA 91106 (SAN 699-6035).

Pascal Pubs., *(Pascal Pubs; 0-938836),* 21 Sunnyside Ave., Wellesley, MA 02181 (SAN 215-3319).

Pasha Pubns., Inc., *(Pasha Pubns; 0-935453),* 1401 Wilson Blvd., No. 910, Arlington, VA 22209 (SAN 695-9148) Tel 703-528-1244; Toll free: 800-424-2908.

Pass Press, *(Pass; 0-9601870),* 170 2nd Ave., 2A, New York, NY 10003 (SAN 210-5411).

Pass the Plate, Inc., *(Pass the Plate),* P.O. Box 836, New Bern, NC 28560 (SAN 217-295X).

Passages, Inc., *(Passages; 0-9614334),* P.O. Box 1565, Fayetteville, AR 72702 (SAN 687-6625) Tel 501-442-7662.

Passepartout Travel Pub., Subs. of Three T Group, *(Passepartout; 0-935981),* 540 University Ave., No. 120, Palo Alto, CA 94301-1954 (SAN 696-6268) Tel 415-327-1756.

Passive Solar Institute, *(Passive Solar; 0-933490),* 1625 Curtis St., Berkeley, CA 94702 (SAN 282-1516) Tel 415-526-1549; Orders to: Solar Usage Now, P.O. Box 306, Bascom, OH 44809 (SAN 282-1524) Tel 419-937-2226.

Passport Books *See* **National Textbook Co.**

Passport Pr., *(Passport Pr; 0-930016),* Box 1346, Champlain, NY 12919-1346 (SAN 211-7533) Tel 514-937-8155.

Passport to New York Restaurants, *(Passport NY Rest; 0-937413),* 967 Lexington Ave., Suite 115, New York, NY 10021 (SAN 658-9812) Tel 212-772-3942.

Past in Glass, *(Past in Glass; 0-9600212),* 515 Northridge Dr., Boulder City, NV 89005 (SAN 204-9317) Tel 702-293-3114.

Pastoral & Matrimonial Renewal Center, *(Past & Mat Rene Ctr; 0-911905),* 67 Prince St., Elizabeth, NJ 07208 (SAN 264-6854) Tel 201-353-8640.

Pastoral Press, *(Pastoral Pr; 0-9602378; 0-912405),* 225 Sheridan St. NW, Washington, DC 20011 (SAN 272-8966).

Pastore Press, *(Pastore),* Seven Shetland Lane, Stony Brook, NY 11790 (SAN 209-4703) Tel 516-751-2254.

Pat Publishing Co., *(Pat Pub Co; 0-9613323),* P.O. Box 180454, Austin, TX 78718-0454 (SAN 655-766X) Tel 512-478-4987.

Pat Tung's International Gourmet Inc., *(P Tungs Intl G; 0-9614469),* P.O. Box 16141, Rocky River, OH 44116 (SAN 689-4690) Tel 216-356-1987.

Pataki, Eva, *(E Pataki; 0-9615932),* 84-47 Kendrick Pl., Jamaica Estates, NY 11432 (SAN 696-7884) Tel 718-291-4354.

Patch & Frazzle Press *See* **Boyd Co., The**

Patch As Patch Can, *(Patch As Patch; 0-9601896),* P.O. Box 843, Port Washington, NY 11050 (SAN 239-8575) Tel 516-671-7342.

Patchwork Pubns., *(Patchwork Pubns; 0-930628),* 2961 Industrial Rd., Las Vegas, NV 89109 (SAN 211-3430) Tel 702-732-4541; Toll free: 800-634-6268.

Patelson, Joseph, Music House , Ltd., *(J Patelson Mus; 0-915282),* 160 W. 56th St., New York, NY 10019 (SAN 203-9028) Tel 212-757-5587.

Patent Data Pubns., Inc., *(Patent Data; 0-935714),* 901 N. President St., Wheaton, IL 60187 (SAN 213-9448).

Patent Educational Pubns., *(Patent Ed; 0-913995),* P.O. Box 857, Troy, OH 45373 (SAN 286-8563) Tel 513-339-3172.

Pateo Publishing Co., *(Pateo Pub; 0-936797),* 480 Naples St., W, Chula Vista, CA 92011 (SAN 699-8402) Tel 619-420-5126.

Pathfinder Bks. *See* **Bantam Bks., Inc.**

†Pathfinder Fund, *(Pathfinder Fund; 0-933853),* 1330 Boylston St, Chestnut Hill, MA 02167 (SAN 225-9664) Tel 617-731-1700; *CIP.*

Pathfinder Pr., *(Path Pr NY; 0-87348),* 410 West St., New York, NY 10014 (SAN 202-5906) Tel 212-741-0690.

Pathfinder Pubns., *(Pathfinder HI),* Hamakua Ctr., 150 Hamakua Dr., Suite 401, Kailua, HI 96734 (SAN 696-7922) Tel 808-261-4557.

Pathfinder Pubns., Inc., *(Path Pubns NJ; 0-939888),* 210 Central Ave., Madison, NJ 07940 (SAN 216-9215) Tel 201-822-2395.

Pathfinder Publications (MS), *(Pathfinders Pubns MS; 0-9612012),* Rte. One, P.O. Box 115, Tillatoba, MS 38961 (SAN 286-8466) Tel 601-647-5927.

Pathfinder Publishing, *(Pathfinder CA; 0-934793),* 458 Dorothy Ave., Ventura, CA 93003 (SAN 694-2571) Tel 805-642-9278.

Pathfinder Tour Consultants, *(Pathfinder Tour Con; 0-9613819),* P.O. Box 318, Olney, MD 20832 (SAN 686-2772).

Pathfinders, *(Pathfinders; 0-937260),* P.O. Box 11950, Reno, NV 89510 (SAN 205-9487) Tel 714-489-0590.

Pathfound Pubs., *(Pathfound Pubs; 0-930725),* 910 Florin Rd., Suite 104, Sacramento, CA 95831 (SAN 677-4784) Tel 916-422-7133.

Pathway Bks., *(Pathway Bks; 0-935538),* 700 Parkview Terrace, Golden Valley, MN 55416 (SAN 213-4241) Tel 612-377-1521; Dist. by: Publishers Group West, 5855 Beaudry Ave., Emeryville, CA 94608 (SAN 202-8522) Tel 415-658-3453; Toll free: 800-982-8319; Dist. by: Quality Books, 918 Sherwood Dr., Lake Bluff, IL 60044-2204 (SAN 169-2127) Tel 312-295-2010; Toll free: 800-323-4241 (Libraries only).

Pathway Press, Div. of Pittenger & Associates, *(Pathway AL; 0-912919),* c/o Pittenger & Associates, 5568 Surrey Ln., Birmingham, AL 35243 (SAN 283-2399) Tel 205-991-7075.

Pathway Pr., *(Pathway Pr; 0-87148),* 1080 Montgomery Ave., Cleveland, TN 37311 (SAN 202-8727) Tel 615-476-4512; Toll free: 800-251-7216.

Pathway Pubns., Inc., *(Pathway Pubns; 0-9606442),* 1632 Seventh Ave. W., Birmingham, AL 35208 (SAN 218-5784) Tel 205-785-9584.

Pathway Publishers, *(Pathway Pubs; 0-915197),* P.O. Box 5021, Esmond, RI 02917 (SAN 289-7911) Tel 401-231-8225.

Pathways Press, *(Pathwys Pr CA; 0-9605022),* P.O. Box 60196-A, Palo Alto, CA 94306 (SAN 283-4367).

Pathwork Pr., *(Pathwork Pr; 0-9614777),* Box 66, Phoenicia, NY 12464 (SAN 692-7009) Tel 914-688-2211; Orders to: Stillpoint Publishing, Box 640, Meeting House Rd., Walpole, NH 03608 (SAN 662-3026) Tel 603-756-3508; Toll free: 800-847-4014.

Patio Pubns., *(Patio Pubns; 0-9696040),* 850 Woodhollow Lane, Buffalo Grove, IL 60090 (SAN 216-9223) Tel 312-259-8500.

†Patmos Pr., *(Patmos Pr; 0-915762),* P.O. Box V, Shepherdstown, WV 25443 (SAN 207-4192) Tel 304-876-2086; *CIP.*

†Patrice Pr., *(Patrice Pr; 0-935284),* Box 42, Gerald, MO 63037 (SAN 203-1019) Tel 314-764-2801; *CIP.*

†Patrick's Pr., *(Patricks Pr; 0-9609412),* P.O. Box 5189, Columbus, GA 31906 (SAN 274-466X) Tel 404-322-1584; *CIP.*

Patriotic Publishers, *(Patriotic Pubs; 0-9608188),* 159 Woodland Ave., Verona, NJ 07044 (SAN 240-124X).

Patron Books *See* **Don Bosco Multimedia**

Pattarozzi, Michelle M., *(M M Pattarozzi),* 105 Iron Bark Ct., East Peoria, IL 61611 (SAN 682-2541) Tel 309-671-2700.

Pattern Pubns., *(Pattern Pubns; 0-911986),* 2627 Seabrook Island Rd., Johns Island, SC 29455 (SAN 204-9333).

Patterns Ltd., *(Patterns Ltd; 0-9609874),* P.O. Box 1924, Redondo Beach, CA 90278 (SAN 274-4708) Tel 213-379-9417.

Names

Patterson, Eleanora, Pr., *(E Patterson Pr; 0-9607432)*, P.O. Box 343, Putney, VT 05346 (SAN 239-5355).

Patterson, Richard, *(R Patterson; 0-936004)*, 3829 William Penn Blvd., Virginia Beach, VA 23452 (SAN 213-8638).

Patterson, W. B., *(W B Patterson; 0-9606968)*, 3080 Alaneo Pl., Wailuku, Maui, HI 96793 (SAN 205-4914) Tel 808-244-5437.

Pattie Properties, Inc., *(Pattie Prop Inc; 0-911789)*, 1403 Springdale Rd., Zephyrhills, FL 34248 (SAN 264-2891) Tel 813-782-9187.

Patton Creative Associates, *(Patton Creative; 0-911003)*, 21 Tulip Circle, Salinas, CA 93905 (SAN 274-4716) Tel 408-422-4192.

Patton Pacific Pr., *(Patton Pac Pr; 0-9614074)*, P.O. Box 5888, Chula Vista, CA 92012-5888 (SAN 679-1794).

Pau Hana Press, *(Pau Hana Pr; 0-912921)*, 1750 Kalakaua Ave., Suite 3-577, Honolulu, HI 96826 (SAN 283-9245).

Paul, Michael, *(Michael Paul; 0-9616367)*, 528 S. Church St., Apt. 1N, Decatur, IL 62522 (SAN 658-9847) Tel 217-423-4802.

Paul, Reginald F., Pub., *(R Paul Pub; 0-9616241)*, 2415 Morena Blvd., San Diego, CA 92110 (SAN 658-4993) Tel 619-276-4222.

Paula Di Educational Enterprises, *(Paula Di Ed; 0-9613130; 0-936543)*, 181-21 Aberdeen Rd., Jamaica, NY 11432 (SAN 294-6467) Tel 718-969-3320.

Paulette Publishing Co., *(Paulette Pub)*, 523 Worcester Dr., Cambria, CA 93428 (SAN 217-1228) Tel 805-927-3715.

Paulist Pr., *(Paulist Pr; 0-8091)*, 997 MacArthur Blvd., Mahwah, NJ 07430 (SAN 202-5159) Tel 201-825-7300; Toll free: 800-325-9521. *Imprints:* Deus Books (Deus).

Paumalu Press, *(Paumalu Pr; 0-9602354)*, P.O. Box 3788, San Clemente, CA 92672 (SAN 212-7873) Tel 714-496-5922.

Paunch, *(Paunch; 0-9602478)*, 123 Woodward Ave., Buffalo, NY 14214 (SAN 209-1461).

Pauper Press, Inc., *(Pauper Pr; 0-9601144)*, Box 303, Two Rivers, WI 54241 (SAN 210-2560) Tel 414-794-8817.

Pavan Pubs., *(Pavan Pubs; 0-915944)*, P.O. Box 1661, Palo Alto, CA 94302 (SAN 207-5695) Tel 415-327-3960.

Pavillion of Fashion, *(Pavillion Fashion; 0-9614714)*, 4144 Maritime Rd., Palos Verdes, CA 90274 (SAN 211-299X).

Paw-Print Press, *(Paw-Print; 0-9608958)*, 9012 Spring Hill Lane, Chevy Chase, MD 20815 (SAN 241-3469) Tel 301-656-5793.

Pawnee Publishing Co., Inc., *(Pawnee Pub; 0-913688)*, P.O. Box 630, Higginsville, MO 64037 (SAN 207-4036) Tel 816-394-2424.

Pawpaw Pr., *(Pawpaw Pr; 0-9614563)*, P.O. Box 9191, Moscow, ID 83843 (SAN 691-8050) Tel 208-882-3366.

Paws IV Press, *(Paws Four Pub; 0-934007)*, P.O. Box 87-1444, Wasilla, AK 99687 (SAN 692-7890) Tel 907-376-7572.

Pawson, John R., *(Pawson; 0-9602080)*, Box 411, Willow Grove, PA 19090 (SAN 213-229X).

Pax Publishing, *(Pax Pub; 0-9614914)*, 231 Arballo Dr., San Francisco, CA 94132 (SAN 693-4188) Tel 415-585-1072; Dist. by: Nutri Books Corp., 790 W. Tennessee Ave., Denver, CO 80223 (SAN 693-4196).

Paycock Pr., *(Paycock Pr; 0-9602424; 0-931181)*, P.O. Box 3567, Washington, DC 20007 (SAN 212-5420) Tel 202-333-1544.

Pazmany Aircraft Corp., *(Pazmany Aircraft; 0-9616777)*, 927 Runnymead Ln., San Diego, CA 92106 (SAN 661-0293) Tel 619-224-7330.

Peabody, Robert S., Foundation for Archaeology, *(Peabody Found; 0-939312)*, Phillips Academy, Andover, MA 01810 (SAN 207-0006) Tel 617-475-0248.

†Peabody Museum of Archaeology & Ethnology, Harvard Univ., Pubns. Dept., *(Peabody Harvard; 0-87365)*, 11 Divinity Ave., Cambridge, MA 02138 (SAN 203-1426) Tel 617-495-3938; Dist. by: Harvard Univ. Pr., 79 Garden St., Cambridge, MA 02138 (SAN 200-2043) Tel 617-495-2600; *CIP*.

†Peabody Museum of Salem, *(Peabody Mus Salem; 0-87577)*, E. India Sq., Salem, MA 01970 (SAN 289-1786); *CIP*.

†Peabody Publishing Co., Inc., *(Peabody Pub; 0-930559)*, P.O. Box 1867, Brockton, MA 02403 (SAN 295-3412) Tel 617-586-3969; Orders to: P.O. Box 180, Plymouth, NH 03264 (SAN 295-3420) Tel 603-726-3976; *CIP*.

Peace & Pieces Books *See* San Francisco Arts & Letters Foundation

Peace Research Laboratory, *(Peace Res Lab; 0-933061)*, 6251 San Bonita, St. Louis, MO 63105 (SAN 225-6975) Tel 314-721-8219; 865 Virginia, 102, Dunedin, FL 33528 (SAN 669-2354) Tel 813-734-7608; 1115 Magnet, St. Louis, MO 63132 (SAN 669-2362) Tel 314-993-2464.

Peace Ways Pubns., *(Peace Ways; 0-912730)*, 11261 Alger St., Warren, MI 48093 (SAN 206-6610).

Peaceable Kingdom Pr., *(Peaceable Kingdom; 0-936001)*, P.O. Box 5337, Bloomington, IN 47402-5337 (SAN 696-6241) Tel 812-336-8396; 4725 E. Bethal Ln., Bloomington, IN 47401 (SAN 696-9801).

Peacehaven Pubns., *(Peacehaven; 0-917610)*, P.O. Box 45, Deer, AR 72628 (SAN 209-3065) Tel 501-446-5793.

Peaceweed *See* Mathom Pr. Enterprises

†Peach Mountain Pr., Ltd., *(Peach Mount Pr; 0-931850)*, Rte. 2 Box 195, Charlevoix, MI 49720 (SAN 220-9942) Tel 616-547-4883; *CIP*.

Peach Pubns., *(Peach; 0-918240)*, 45 Cottage St., New Haven, CT 06511 (SAN 209-472X) Tel 203-777-3337.

Peach Publishing Co., *(Peach Pub Co; 0-9615999)*, 1945 Bayside Dr., Corona del Mar, CA 92625 (SAN 697-9378) Tel 714-673-5096.

Peachpit Pr., *(Peachpit Pr; 0-938151)*, 2110 Marin Ave., Berkeley, CA 94707 (SAN 659-8978) Tel 415-524-0184.

†Peachtree Pubns., Ltd., *(Peachtree Pubs; 0-931948)*, 494 Armour Cir., NE, Atlanta, GA 30324 (SAN 212-1999) Tel 404-876-8761; Toll free: 800-241-0113; Toll free: 800-282-0225 (In Georgia); *CIP*.

Peacock, F. E., Publishers, Incorporated, *(Peacock Pubs; 0-87581)*, 115 N. Prospect Ave., Itasca, IL 60143 (SAN 202-876X) Tel 312-773-1155.

Peacock *See* Bantam Bks., Inc.

Peacock Bks. *See* Penguin Bks., Inc.

Peacock Enterprises, *(Peacock Ent; 0-926113)*, 8501 Sextant Dr., Baldwinsville, NY 13027 (SAN 652-9712).

Peacock Enterprises, *(Peacock Glenview; 0-937673)*, P.O. Box 2341, Glenview, IL 60025 (SAN 659-2694) Tel 312-724-0350.

Peak Skill Publishing, *(Peak Skill; 0-917879)*, P.O. Box 5489, Playa del Rey, CA 90296 (SAN 656-9943) Tel 213-306-6403; Dist. by: Ingram Bk. Co., 347 Reedwood Dr., Nashville, TN 37217 (SAN 169-7978); Toll free: 800-251-5900; Dist. by: Bookpeople, 2929 Fifth St., Berkeley, CA 94710 (SAN 168-9517) Tel 415-549-3030; Toll free: 800-227-1516.

Peanut Butter Publishing, Subs. of McGraw Mountain, Inc., *(Peanut Butter; 0-89716)*, 911 Western Ave., Suite 401, Maritime Bldg., Seattle, WA 98104 (SAN 212-7881) Tel 206-628-6200; Dist. by: Pacific Pipeline, 19215 66th Ave., S., Kent, WA 98032 (SAN 662-1090) Tel 206-872-5523; Toll free: 800-426-4727.

Pearce-Evetts Publishing, *(Pearce Evetts; 0-936823)*, 241 Morrison Dr., Pittsburgh, PA 15216 (SAN 699-9271) Tel 412-344-5451.

Pearl, R. M., Bks., *(R M Pearl Bks; 0-940566)*, 16 Valley Pl., Colorado Springs, CO 80903 (SAN 206-6440) Tel 303-634-7345.

Pearl Pr., *(Pearl Pr; 0-914566)*, 238 Ave. U, Brooklyn, NY 11223 (SAN 202-8778) Tel 718-449-2464.

Pearl-Win Publishing Co., *(Pearl-Win)*, Rte. 1, Box 300, Hancock, WI 54943 (SAN 217-1236).

Pearse, John, Music Publishing, *(J Pearse Mus Pub; 0-9617175)*, P.O. Box 295, Center Valley, PA 18034 (SAN 663-1711) Tel 215-282-3319.

Pearson, Bob, Enterprises, Inc., *(B Pearson; 0-9608378)*, Box 9901, Birmingham, AL 35220-0901 (SAN 240-4249) Tel 205-833-6944.

Pearson, J. Michael, *(J M Pearson; 0-916528)*, P.O. Box 402844, Ocean View Sta., Miami Beach, FL 33140 (SAN 202-1536) Tel 305-538-0346.

Pearson Consulting, *(Pearson Consul; 0-938265)*, 5910 Flower St., Arvada, CO 80004 (SAN 659-8196) Tel 303-421-2164.

Pearson Museum, The, *(Pearson Museum)*, Southern Illinois University School of Medicine, P.O. Box 3926, Springfield, IL 62708 (SAN 241-5755) Tel 217-782-4261.

Peartree, *(Peartree; 0-935343)*, P.O. Box 14533, Clearwater, FL 34279 (SAN 695-6335) Tel 813-531-4973; 1448 Rosetree Ct., Clearwater, FL 33546 (SAN 699-6086) Tel 813-531-4973; Dist. by: Baker & Taylor (SE Div.), MT. Olive Rd., Commerce, GA 30529 (SAN 169-1503); Toll free: 800-241-6000; Dist. by: Baker & Taylor (Midwest Div.), 501 Gladiola Ave., Momence, IL 60954 (SAN 662-3514); Toll free: 800-435-5111.

Peasant Cottage Press, *(Peasant Cottage Pr; 0-9602698)*, P.O. Box 276, Cambria, CA 93428 (SAN 222-237X).

Peat Marwick Mitchell & Co., *(Peat Marwick)*, 345 Park Ave., New York, NY 10022 (SAN 226-7071).

Pebble & The Best Cellar Press, *(Pebble Cellar; 0-916891)*, Dept. of English, Univ. of Nebraska, Lincoln, NE 68588-0333 (SAN 656-1233) Tel 402-472-1802.

Pecalhen Co., *(Pecalhen; 0-938910)*, 14401 SW 85th Ave., Miami, FL 33158 (SAN 216-0048) Tel 305-235-3858.

Pecan Tree Pr., *(Pecan Tree Pr; 0-938169)*, 315 Fairway, Bryan, TX 77801 (SAN 659-7203) Tel 409-822-7070.

Peccary Pr., *(Peccary Pr; 0-932337)*, Box 3547 Univ. Sta., Tucson, AZ 85722 (SAN 686-7227) Tel 602-327-1845.

Pecci Educational Pubs., *(Pecci Educ Pubs; 0-943220)*, 440 Davis Court, No. 405, San Francisco, CA 94111 (SAN 240-558X) Tel 415-391-8579.

Pech Publishing, *(Pech Pub; 0-9613851)*, 14584 SE Bonnie Way, Milwaukie, OR 97267 (SAN 682-0093) Tel 503-655-6250.

Peck, Herbert Books, *(H Peck Bks; 0-9617153)*, 174-4550 N. Flowing Wells Rd., Tucson, AZ 85705 (SAN 663-3676) Tel 602-887-9734.

Pedaro, Inc., *(Pedaro; 0-933113)*, 32606 Seventh Ave., SW, Federal Way, WA 98003 (SAN 689-9854) Tel 206-874-2555.

Peddlers Wagon, *(Peddlers Wagon; 0-9601048)*, 610 Spruce St., Dowagiac, MI 49047 (SAN 204-9309) Tel 616-782-3270.

†Pediatric Projects, Inc., *(Pediatric Projects; 0-912599)*, P.O. Box 1880, Santa Monica, CA 90406 (SAN 282-8146) Tel 213-828-8963; *CIP*.

Pediatric Therapies, Inc., *(Pediatric Therapies; 0-937977)*, 14042 NE Eighth, Suite 201, Bellevue, WA 98007 (SAN 659-5308) Tel 206-746-7959.

†Pedipress, Inc., *(Pedipress; 0-914625)*, 125 Red Gate Ln., Amherst, MA 01002 (SAN 287-7570) Tel 413-549-6151; *CIP*.

Peek, T. H., Pub., *(T H Peek; 0-917962)*, 897 Independence, Suite 2F, Mountain View, CA 94043 (SAN 202-1382) Tel 415-962-1010; Orders to: P.O. Box 50123, Palo Alto, CA 94303 (SAN 693-9708).

Peel Productions, Inc., *(Peel Prod; 0-939217)*, 15 Cedar Chase Pl., The Woodlands, TX 77381 (SAN 662-6726) Tel 713-368-0822; Dist. by: Baker & Taylor, Eastern Div., 50 Kirby St., Somerville, NJ 08876 (SAN 169-4901); Toll free: 800-345-2282.

Peeples, Edwin A., *(Peeples; 0-9600080)*, Vixen Hill, R.D. 2, Phoenixville, PA 19460 (SAN 204-9368) Tel 215-827-7241.

Peer-Southern Pubns., *(Peer-Southern)*, 1740 Broadway, New York, NY 10019 (SAN 206-3034) Tel 212-265-3910; Dist. by: The Theodore Presser Co., Presser Pl., Bryn Mawr, PA 19010 (SAN 203-5553) Tel 215-525-3636; Dist. by: Columbia Pictures Pubns., 15800 NW, 48th Ave., Miami, FL 33014 (SAN 662-1104) Tel 305-620-1500; Toll free: 800-327-7643.

Peerless Publishing Co., *(Peerless; 0-930234)*, 2745 Lafitte Ave., New Orleans, LA 70119 (SAN 210-3222) Tel 504-486-6225.

Pegasus, Affil. of Bobbs-Merrill Co., Inc., *(Pegasus)*, 4300 W. 62nd St., P.O. Box 7080, Indianapolis, IN 46206 (SAN 201-3959); Toll free: 800-428-3750.

Names

Pegasus Company, *(Pegasus Co SC; 0-9602144),* Rt. 1, Rambling Path, Anderson, SC 29621 (SAN 221-7562).

Pegasus Prose, *(Pegasus Prose; 0-9617240),* 6423 13th Ave. NW, Rochester, MN 55901 (SAN 663-5407) Tel 507-288-0779.

Pegasus Pubns., *(Pegasus Pubns; 0-936552),* P.O. Box 1060, Pt. Reyes Station, CA 94956 (SAN 222-1101).

Pegasus Rex *See* **Fell, Frederick, Pubs., Inc.**

Pegasus Rex Press, Inc., The, *(Pegasus Rex NJ; 0-937484),* 695 Bloomfield Ave., Montclair, NJ 07042 (SAN 215-2061). Moved, left no forwarding address.

Pegma Bks. *See* **Green Hill Pubs.**

Pegus Press, *(Pegus Pr; 0-941218),* 648 W. Sierra Ave., Box 429, Clovis, CA 93612 (SAN 241-5763) Tel 209-299-3263.

Pejepscot Press, *(Pejepscot; 0-917638),* 10 Mason St., Brunswick, ME 04011 (SAN 202-1447) Tel 207-729-3442.

Pelican Bks. *See* **Penguin Bks., Inc.**

Pelican Pr., *(Pelican Pr; 0-938937),* 3463 State St., Suite 342, Santa Barbara, CA 93105 (SAN 661-7506) Tel 805-569-2269.

Pelican Publishing Co., Inc., *(Pelican; 0-911116; 0-88289),* 1101 Monroe St., Gretna, LA 70053 (SAN 212-0623) Tel 504-368-1175; P.O. Box 189, Gretna, LA 70053 (SAN 658-1374) Tel 504-368-1175.

Pelion Pr. *See* **Rosen Pub. Group**

Pella Publishing Co., Inc., *(Pella Pub; 0-918618; 0-933824),* 337 W. 36th St., New York, NY 10018 (SAN 210-6183) Tel 212-279-9586.

Pellegrini, Mary, *(M Pellegrini; 0-9612938),* 2944 Washington Blvd., Cleveland Heights, OH 44118 (SAN 292-4447) Tel 216-371-9252.

Pelton, Charles L. *See* **Family Health Media**

Pember Library & Museum, *(Pember Lib Mus; 0-9616427),* 33 W. Main St., Granville, NY 12832 (SAN 658-9901) Tel 518-642-1515.

Pembridge Press (England) *See* **Shoe String Pr., Inc.**

Pembroke Pr., *(Pembroke CT; 0-938563),* 99 Cross Hwy., Westport, CT 06880 (SAN 661-4728) Tel 203-226-8784. Do not confuse with Pembroke Pr., New York, NY.

Pen & Booth, *(Pen & Booth; 0-9605686),* 1608 "R" St. NW, Washington, DC 20009 (SAN 213-1439).

Pen & Ink Pr., *(Pen & Ink; 0-9607544),* c/o Banyan Books, Inc., P.O. Box 431160, Miami, FL 33143 (SAN 208-340X) Tel 305-665-6011.

Pen & Podium, Inc., *(Pen & Podium; 0-9603982),* 40 Central Park S., New York, NY 10019 (SAN 214-0756) Tel 212-759-8454.

Pen-Art Pubs., *(Pen-Art; 0-941242),* 402 Fairview Ave., Westwood, NJ 07675 (SAN 211-3287) Tel 201-664-8412; Dist. by: New York Poetry Forum, Inc, 3064 Albany Crescent, Apt. 54, Bronx, NY 10463 (SAN 200-8092) Tel 212-796-5948.

Pen-Dec Pr., *(Pen-Dec; 0-915199),* 1724 Georgia St., Marysville, MI 48040 (SAN 289-792X) Tel 313-364-8024.

Pen Notes Inc., *(Pen Notes; 0-939564),* 134 Westside Ave., Freeport, NY 11520 (SAN 216-4337) Tel 516-868-5753.

Pena, Lydia, *(Pena Lydia; 0-9612982),* 3001 S. Federal Blvd., Denver, CO 80236 (SAN 292-594X) Tel 303-936-8441.

Pencil Pr., *(Pencil Pr; 0-9615665),* 109 Orange St., San Rafael, CA 94901 (SAN 695-9164) Tel 415-456-7469; P.O.Box 9011, San Rafael, CA 94912 (SAN 658-2893); Dist. by: Bookpeople, 2929 Fifth St., Berkeley, CA 94710 (SAN 662-362X); Toll free: 800-227-1516 800-624-4466 (CA).

Pencraft of Chris Jennings, The, *(Pencraft C Jennings; 0-9616295),* 22 Flagg St., Cambridge, MA 02238 (SAN 658-4837) Tel 617-497-6502; P.O. Box 411, Cambridge, MA 02238 (SAN 658-4845).

Pencraft Pr., Inc., *(Pencraft Pr; 0-936771),* P.O. Box 1789, West Palm Beach, FL 33402-1789 (SAN 699-9212); 1603 Northbridge Tower, 515 N., Flagler Dr., West Palm Beach, FL 33401 (SAN 699-9220) Tel 305-659-2060.

Pendell Publishing Co., *(Pendell Pub; 0-87812),* 1700 James Savage Rd., P.O. Box 2066 Bip, Midland, MI 48640 (SAN 202-8786) Tel 517-496-3333.

Pendelton Lane Publishing, Subs. of Flint, Inc., *(Pendelton Lane; 0-937851),* 3676 Collin Dr., Suite 20, West Palm Beach, FL 33406 (SAN 659-5537) Tel 305-968-7708.

Pendle Hill Pubns., *(Pendle Hill; 0-87574),* Pendle Hill, 338 Plush Mill Rd., Wallingford, PA 19086 (SAN 202-8794) Tel 215-566-4507.

Pendleton Hse., Inc., *(Pendleton Hse; 0-934919),* Rte. 2, Butler, KY 41006 (SAN 694-423X) Tel 606-472-2721.

Pendleton Pubns., *(Pendleton Pubns; 0-9616609),* P.O. Box 471, Franklin, WV 26807 (SAN 659-7521); Rte. 4, Smith Creek Rd., Franklin, WV 26807 (SAN 659-753X) Tel 304-358-2822.

Pendragon Pr., Subs. of Camelot Publishing Co., Inc., *(Pendragon NY; 0-918728),* R.R. 1, Box 159, Stuyvesant, NY 12173-9720 (SAN 213-1463) Tel 518-828-3008.

Pendragon Press, *(Pendragon Oregon; 0-914010),* P.O. Box 14834, Portland, OR 97214 (SAN 204-9376) Tel 503-232-0869.

Pendulum Books, *(Pendulum Bks; 0-941760),* P.O. Box 3627, 615 Garnet St., Redondo Beach, CA 90277 (SAN 239-2771) Tel 213-372-0925.

Pendulum Pr., Inc., *(Pendulum Pr; 0-88301),* Academic Bldg., Saw Mill Rd., West Haven, CT 06516 (SAN 202-8808) Tel 203-933-2551.

Penfield Pr., *(Penfield; 0-9603858; 0-941016),* 215 Brown St., Iowa City, IA 52240 (SAN 221-6671) Tel 319-337-9998; Toll free: 800-255-2255 Ext. 9998.

Penguin Bks., Inc., *(Penguin; 0-14),* 40 W. 23rd St., New York, NY 10010 (SAN 202-5914) Tel 212-807-7300; Toll free: 800-631-3577. *Imprints:* Peacock Books (Peacock); Pelican Books (Pelican); Peregrine Books (Peregrine); Puffin Books (Puffin).

Penguin Communications Group, *(Penguin Comns; 0-938269),* P.O. Box 984, Yakima, WA 98907 (SAN 659-8307); 336 N. 23rd Ave., Yakima, WA 98907 (SAN 659-8315) Tel 509-575-8386.

Peninsula Press, *(Peninsula NY; 0-9609012),* Water's Edge, Fishers Island, NY 06390 (SAN 241-3485) Tel 516-788-7868.

Peninsula Publishing, *(Peninsula CA; 0-932146),* P.O. Box 867, Los Altos, CA 94023 (SAN 212-257X) Tel 415-948-2511.

Peninsula Publishing, Inc., *(Peninsula WA; 0-918146),* P.O. Box 412, Port Angeles, WA 98362 (SAN 210-1300) Tel 206-457-7550; Dist. by: Pacific Pipeline, 19215 66th Ave. S., Kent, WA 98032 (SAN 208-2128) Tel 206-872-5523; Toll free: 800-562-4647 (In Washington).

Peninsula Pubns., *(Peninsula Pubns; 0-914372),* 26030 New Bridge Dr., Los Altos Hills, CA 94022 (SAN 202-8816) Tel 415-948-1405.

Peninsula United Methodist Homes, Inc., *(Peninsula United Homes),* P.O. Box 1127, Newark, DE 19715 (SAN 687-6234) Tel 302-737-3698.

Peninsular Publishing Co., *(Peninsular Pub Co; 0-9616000),* 2503 Jackson Bluff Rd., Tallahassee, FL 32314 (SAN 697-9386) Tel 904-576-4151.

Penisula Press of Texas, *(Penisula TX; 0-9614885),* P.O. Box 1742, Crystal Beach, TX 77650 (SAN 693-1871) Tel 713-729-7355; Orders to: P.O. Box 694, Houston, TX 77001 (SAN 694-0218).

Penkevill Publishing Co., The, *(Penkevill; 0-913283),* P.O. Box 212, Greenwood, FL 32443 (SAN 285-8304).

Penmaen Pr., *(Penmaen Pr; 0-915778),* R.D. 2, P.O. Box 145, Great Barrington, MA 01230 (SAN 208-1113) Tel 413-528-2749.

†Pennant Books, *(Pennant Bks; 0-915201),* 3463 State St., Suite 238, Santa Barbara, CA 93105 (SAN 289-7938) Tel 805-683-1079; Dist. by: Quality Bks., Inc., 918 Sherman Dr., Lake Bluff, IL 60044-2204 (SAN 169-2127); Dist. by: Baker & Taylor Co., Eastern Div., 50 Kirby Ave., Somerville, NJ 08876 (SAN 169-4901); Dist. by: Baker & Taylor Co., Midwest Div., 501 Gladiola Ave., Momence, IL 60954 (SAN 169-2100); Dist. by: Baker & Taylor Co., Southest Div., Mt. Olive Rd., Commerce, GA 30529 (SAN 169-1503); Dist. by: Baker & Taylor Co., Western Div., 380 Edison Way, Reno, NV 89564 (SAN 169-4464) Tel 702-786-6700; *CIP.*

Pennant Pr., *(Pennant Pr; 0-913458),* 7620 Miramar Rd., No. 4100, San Diego, CA 92126 (SAN 201-9884) Tel 619-695-1810.

Pennington Publishing, *(Pennington Pub; 0-936599),* 2710 North Ave., Bridgeport, CT 06604 (SAN 698-0368) Tel 203-366-4155.

Pennington Trading Post, *(Pennington; 0-911120),* c/o Eunice Pennington, Fremont, MO 63941 (SAN 204-9392).

Pennon Pr., *(Pennon Pr; 0-937941),* P.O. Box 206, Carlisle, PA 17013 (SAN 659-7513) Tel 717-243-4739.

†Penns Valley Pubs., *(Penns Valley; 0-931992),* 1298 S. 28th St., Harrisburg, PA 17111 (SAN 202-1455) Tel 717-232-5844; *CIP.*

Pennsylvania Academy of Fine Arts, *(Penn Acad Art; 0-943836),* Broad & Cherry St., Philadelphia, PA 19102 (SAN 280-0748).

Pennsylvania Academy of Fine Arts, The *See* **Art Bks. International, Ltd.**

Pennsylvania Academy of Science, *(Penn Science; 0-9606670),* Dept. of Biology, Lafayette College, Easton, PA 18042 (SAN 219-6220) Tel 215-250-5464.

Pennsylvania Association of Notaries, *(Penn Assoc Not; 0-9610862),* 14 Wood St., Pittsburgh, PA 15222 (SAN 264-2921) Tel 412-281-0678.

Pennsylvania Bar Institute, *(PA Bar Inst),* P.O. Box 1027, Harrisburg, PA 17108 (SAN 226-8329).

Pennsylvania Economy League, Eastern Div., *(PA Econ League),* 215 S. Broad St., Philadelphia, PA 19107 (SAN 226-8337).

Pennsylvania German Society, *(Penn German Soc; 0-911122),* 55 Kohler School Rd., New Oxford, PA 17350 (SAN 205-1958) Tel 717-624-4106; Orders to: P.O. Box 397, Birdsboro, PA 19508 (SAN 205-1966) Tel 215-582-1441.

Pennsylvania Historical & Museum Commission, *(Pa Hist & Mus; 0-911124; 0-89271),* Box 1026, Harrisburg, PA (SAN 282-1532) Tel 717-783-1991; Orders to: Pubn. Sales Program, Dept. PL. P.O. Box 11466, Harrisburg, 17108-1466 Tel 717-787-2407.

Pennsylvania Paperbooks *See* **Univ. of Pennsylvania Pr.**

Pennsylvania Pubs. Grunwald, Inc., *(Penn Pubs),* 5049 Admiral Wright Rd., Suite 344, Virginia Beach, VA 23462 (SAN 699-7708) Tel 804-490-1132; Orders to: Pennsylvanis Pubs., 45 N. Duke St., Lancaster, PA 17602 (SAN 662-4057) Tel 717-299-4600.

Pennsylvania. Secretary of State, Dept. of State, *(Penna Secy),* North Office Bldg., Rm. 302, Harrisburg, PA 17120 (SAN 274-4937).

Pennsylvania State University, Department of Art History, *(Penn St Univ Dept Art Hist; 0-915773),* 227 Arts Bldg., University Park, PA 16802 (SAN 293-8995) Tel 814-865-6326; Orders to: Susan S. Munshower, 221 Arts Building, University Park, PA 16802 (SAN 685-3811).

Pennsylvania State Univ., Dept. of Food Science, *(Penn State Food; 0-9616407),* 116 Borland Laboratory, University Park, PA 16802 (SAN 658-9995) Tel 814-863-2962.

Pennsylvania State Univ., Dept. of Mineral Economics, *(Penn St Min Econ; 0-9613333),* 221 Walker Bldg., University Park, PA 16802 (SAN 655-7678) Tel 814-865-0691.

Pennsylvania State Univ., Museum of Art, *(Penn St Art; 0-911209),* Pennsylvania State Univ., University Park, PA 16802 (SAN 213-9014) Tel 814-863-0111.

Pennsylvania State Univ. Pr., *(Pa St U Pr; 0-271),* 215 Wagner Bldg., University Park, PA 16802 (SAN 213-5760) Tel 814-865-1327. *Imprints:* Keystone Books (Keystone Bks).

PennWell Bks., Div. of PennWell Publishing Co., *(PennWell Bks; 0-87814),* P.O. Box 1260, Tulsa, OK 74101 (SAN 282-1559) Tel 918-835-3161; Orders to: P.O. Box 21288, Tulsa, OK 74121 (SAN 282-1567) Tel 918-831-9421. *Imprints:* SCIDATA (SCIDATA).

Names

Penny Dreadful Publishers, *(Penny Dreadful Pubs; 0-911793),* 315 S. Bowen St., Jackson, MI 49204 (SAN 264-293X) Tel 517-782-4775; P.O. Box 364, Jackson, MI 49204 (SAN 699-5527); Dist. by: The Distributors, 702 S. Michigan Ave, South Bend, IN 46618 (SAN 169-2488) Tel 219-232-8500; Dist. by: Baker & Taylor (Midwest Div.), 501 Gladiola Ave., Momence, IL 60954 (SAN 169-2100); Toll free: 800-435-5111.

Penny Lane Pubns., Inc., *(Penny Lane Pubns; 0-911211),* P.O. Box 425, Lenox Hill Sta., New York, NY 10021 (SAN 274-4961) Tel 212-570-2970.

PennyByte Pubs., *(PennyByte Pubs; 0-9616594),* 2791 McBride Ln., No. 168, Santa Rosa, CA 95401 (SAN 659-5316) Tel 707-578-7465.

Pennypress Inc, *(Pennypress; 0-937604),* 1100 23rd Ave. E., Seattle, WA 98112 (SAN 215-6954) Tel 206-325-1419.

Pennywhistle Pr., The, *(Pennywhistle Pr; 0-938631),* 22244 Pacific Coast Hwy., Malibu, CA 90265 (SAN 661-5783) Tel 213-456-8373.

Pennywise Pr., *(Pennywise Pr; 0-918953),* P.O. Box 596, Arlington, VA 22216 (SAN 669-8301) Tel 703-525-8316.

Penobscot Bay Press, Inc., *(Penobscot Bay; 0-941238),* Box 36, Stonington, ME 04681 (SAN 212-2960).

Penokie Press, *(Penokie Pr; 0-9611052),* 404 Neipsic Rd., Glastonbury, CT 06033 (SAN 282-8332) Tel 203-633-6996.

PenOwl Press, *(PenOwl Pr; 0-9610680),* P.O. Box 1011, Jamaica, NY 11431 (SAN 283-9253).

†**Penrith Publishing Co.,** *(Penrith; 0-936522),* P.O. Box 18070, Cleveland Heights, OH 44118 (SAN 214-2163); *CIP.*

Penrod/Hiawatha Co., *(Penrod-Hiawatha; 0-942618),* Rte. 1, Box 256 M140, Berrien Center, MI 49102 (SAN 238-5546) Tel 616-461-6993.

Pensacola Historical Society, *(Pensacola Hist; 0-939566),* 405 S. Adams St., Pensacola, FL 32501 (SAN 216-6909) Tel 904-433-1559.

Penseur Press, *(Penseur Pr; 0-9604044),* P.O. Box 659, El Cerrito, CA 94530 (SAN 214-0764).

Penso Pubns., Inc., *(Penso Pubns; 0-943796),* 4815 Apollo Dr., Houston, TX 77018 (SAN 241-0656) Tel 713-861-9785.

Penstemon Pr., *(Penstemon Pr; 0-9613938),* 1218 18th Ave., Apt.4, San Francisco, CA 94122 (SAN 679-176X) Tel 415-661-9314.

Pentagram, *(Pentagram; 0-915316; 0-937596),* Box 379, Markesan, WI 53946 (SAN 207-1789) Tel 414-398-2161.

Pentalic *See* Taplinger Publishing Co., Inc.

Penthouse Press, Limited, Div. of Penthouse Magazine, *(Penthouse Pr; 0-89110),* 1965 Broadway, New York, NY 10023 (SAN 207-4133) Tel 212-496-6100. *Imprints:* Minotaur Press (Minotaur Pr).

Penton Overseas, Inc., *(Penton Overseas; 0-939001),* 850 Winthrop Rd., San Marino, CA 91108 Tel 818-799-6050.

Penton Publishing, Inc., Div. of Pittway Corp., *(Penton Pub; 0-932905),* 1100 Superior Ave., Cleveland, OH 44114 (SAN 689-982X) Tel 216-696-7000.

Penumbra, Inc., *(Penumbra Inc; 0-9602030),* 302 Termino Ave., Long Beach, CA 90814 (SAN 282-1575); Orders to: 3001 W. Big Beaver Rd., Ste. 620, Troy, MI 48084 (SAN 282-1583).

Penumbra Press, The, *(Penumbra Press),* 920 S. 38th St., Omaha, NE 68105 (SAN 209-858X) Tel 402-346-7344.

Penway Books *See* Lotus Pr., Inc.

Penworthy Publishing Co., *(Penworthy Pub; 0-87617),* 219 N. Milwaukee St., Milwaukee, WI 53202 (SAN 693-2746) Tel 414-272-4889.

Penzler Books *See* Mysterious Pr.

Peony Pr., *(Peony Pr; 0-917139),* Box 553, Cutchogue, NY 11935 (SAN 655-8232) Tel 516-734-7030.

People for Life, Inc., *(People for Life; 0-938755),* 3937 N. 46th St., Milwaukee, WI 53216 (SAN 661-7492) Tel 414-784-1022.

People for Open Space, *(PFOS; 0-9605262),* 512 Second St., San Francisco, CA 94107 (SAN 215-899X).

People-Media, Inc., *(People Media; 0-9615591),* 327 Morgantown Rd., Reading, PA 19603 (SAN 695-8583) Tel 215-376-0500; Dist. by: Raylon Corp., 345 Morgantown Rd., P.O. Box 91, Reading, PA 19603 (SAN 200-6529); Toll free: 800-523-8213 MD,DE,NY,NJ.

People Patch, Inc., *(People Patch; 0-936535),* P.O. Box 3485, Federal Way, WA 98003 (SAN 697-9394) Tel 206-946-0820.

People Places, Inc., *(People Places; 0-9604068),* 24 West Beverley Street, Staunton, VA 24401 (SAN 214-0772).

Peopleism Pubns., *(Peopleism Pubns; 0-937009),* 3661 W Laredo St., Chandler, AZ 85226 (SAN 658-6783) Tel 602-899-1228.

People's Computer Co., *(People Computer; 0-918790),* 2682 Bishop Dr., Suite 107, San Ramon, CA 94583 (SAN 674-8929) Tel 415-833-8604.

People's Yellow Pages Press, The, *(People's Yellow Pages; 0-942278),* P.O. Box 31291, San Francisco, CA 94131 (SAN 216-4345) Tel 415-821-1015.

PeopleTalk Assocs., Inc., *(PeopleTalk; 0-915907),* 3020 Dartmouth, Plano, TX 75075-7610 (SAN 294-0787) Tel 214-931-2240; Orders to: P.O. Box 863652, Plano, TX 75086 (SAN 685-382X) Tel 214-423-4634.

Peoria Medical Society Auxilary, Inc., *(Peoria Med Soc; 0-9615434),* P.O. Box 9094, Peoria, IL 61614 (SAN 695-927X) Tel 309-387-6336.

Pepper Jones Martinez, Inc., *(P J Martinez; 0-935759),* 4640 Harry Haines Blvd., Dallas, TX 75235 (SAN 695-930X) Tel 214-630-7460; Dist. by: Lone Star Schl. Bk. Depository, 4640 Harry Haines Blvd., Dallas, TX 75235 (SAN 200-5697).

Pepper Publishing, Div. of Arran Enterprises, Ltd., *(Pepper Pub; 0-914468),* 2901 E. Mabel, Tucson, AZ 85716 (SAN 201-8780) Tel 602-881-0783.

Pepperbox, *(Pepperbox; 0-9614625),* P.O. Box 7304, Suite 245, North Hollywood, CA 91603 (SAN 691-9030) Tel 818-763-5691.

Peppercorn *See* Putnam Publishing Group, The

Pepperdine Univ. Pr., *(Pepperdine U Pr; 0-932612),* c/o Pepperdine Univ. Bookstore, 1121 W. 79th St., Los Angeles, CA 90044 (SAN 295-3439) Tel 213-971-1884.

Peppertree Publishing, *(Peppertree; 0-936822),* Box 1712, Newport Beach, CA 92663 (SAN 214-4387) Tel 714-642-3669.

Pepys Pr., The, *(Pepys Pr; 0-9602270),* 1270 Fifth Ave., Apt. 5G, New York, NY 10029 (SAN 212-4343) Tel 212-348-6847.

Pequod Press, *(Pequod Press; 0-937912),* P.O. Box 122, Northridge, CA 91328 (SAN 262-0553).

Per, *(PER),* Suite 918, 818 Olive St., St. Louis, MO 63101 (SAN 239-5843) Tel 314-241-1445.

Per Ardua Pr., *(Per Ardua; 0-917252),* 6216 Ellenview Ave., Canoga Park, CA 91307 (SAN 208-8053) Tel 818-888-1421.

Per, Inc., *(Per Inc; 0-9602446),* P.O. Box 11465, Memphis, TN 38111 (SAN 282-7107).

Perception Development Techniques, *(Percept Dev Tech; 0-918316),* P.O. Box 1068, Cathedral Sta., New York, NY 10025 (SAN 209-9810) Tel 212-662-2916.

Perception Pubns., *(Perception Pubns; 0-940406),* 1814 W. Seldon Ln., Phoenix, AZ 85021 (SAN 265-3931) Tel 602-997-2292.

Perceptual Learning Systems Pubs., Inc., *(Perceptual Learn Sys; 0-9612654),* P.O. Box 864, Dearborn, MI 48121 (SAN 289-3703).

†**Perci Books,** *(Perci Bks; 0-914657),* P.O. Box 528224, Chicago, IL 60652 (SAN 289-4386); *CIP.*

†**Perdido Bay Pr., The,** *(Perdido Bay; 0-933776),* Rte. 2 Box 323, Pensacola, FL 32506 (SAN 215-1693); *CIP.*

Pere Marquette Press, *(Pere Marquette; 0-934640),* P.O. Box 495, Alton, IL 62002 (SAN 206-3042) Tel 618-462-5415.

Peregrine Assocs., *(Peregrine Assoc; 0-9609176),* P.O. Box 22292, Fort Lauderdale, FL 33316 (SAN 239-5851) Tel 305-987-2423.

Peregrine Bks. *See* Penguin Bks., Inc.

Peregrine Falcon Co., *(Peregrine CA; 0-939649),* 2330 Marinship Way, Suite 307, Sausalito, CA 94965 (SAN 663-5423) Tel 415-331-8131.

Peregrine Pr., *(Peregrine Pr; 0-933614),* Box 751, Old Saybrook, CT 06475 (SAN 213-3474) Tel 203-388-0285.

Peregrine Smith Books *See* Smith, Gibbs M., Inc.

Perennial Editions, *(Perennial Editions; 0-9615414),* P.O. Box 590717, San Francisco, CA 94159-0717 (SAN 695-4944) Tel 415-668-0968.

Perennial Fiction Library *See* Harper & Row Pubs., Inc.

Perennial Library *See* Harper & Row Pubs., Inc.

Perennial Mystery Library *See* Harper & Row Pubs., Inc.

Perennial Pubns., *(Perennial Pubns; 0-9612234),* P.O. Box 32, Gainesville, GA 30503 (SAN 289-2588) Tel 404-536-3611; Dist. by: Dot Gibson Distributors, 161 Knight Ave. Cir, Waycross, GA 31501 (SAN 200-4143); Dist. by: The Collection, Inc., 2101 Kansas City Rd., Olathe, KS 66061 (SAN 200-6359) Tel 913-764-1811; Toll free: 800-821-5745.

Perfas, Inc., *(Perfas; 0-9604302),* P.O. Box 1010, Sharon, CT 06069 (SAN 296-1032).

Perfect Graphic Arts, *(Perfect Graphic; 0-911126),* 14 Dearborn Dr., Old Tappan, NJ 07675 (SAN 204-9430) Tel 201-767-8575.

Perfect Productions, *(Perfect Prods; 0-941648),* P.O. Box 396, Larkspur, CA 94939 (SAN 239-278X) Tel 415-924-0850.

Performance Dynamics, Inc., *(Perf Dynamics; 0-912940),* 6 Becker Farm Rd., Roseland, NJ 07068 (SAN 201-9914) Tel 201-992-6007.

Performance Management Pub. Inc., *(Perf Manage; 0-937100),* 3531 Habersham at Northlake, Tucker, GA 30084 (SAN 262-0561).

Performance Pr., *(Perf Pr; 0-9613575),* P.O. Box 7307, Everett, WA 98201 (SAN 670-1523) Tel 206-252-7660.

Performance Programs Company, *(Perf Progs TX; 0-915777),* 9208 Meadow Vale, Austin, TX 78758 (SAN 296-1237).

Performance Resource Press, Inc., *(Perf Resource Pr; 0-9610026),* 2145 Crooks Rd. No. 103, Troy, MI 48084 (SAN 274-5127) Tel 313-528-1252.

Performance Systems Pr., *(Perf Syst Pr; 0-938757),* P.O. Box 431, Granville, OH 43023 (SAN 661-7476); 1753 Louden St., Granville, OH 43023 (SAN 661-7484) Tel 614-587-3983.

Performing Arts Network, *(Perf Arts Network; 0-942230),* 9025 Wilshire Blvd., Beverly Hills, CA 90211 (SAN 240-9259).

Performing Arts Referral Service, *(Performing Arts; 0-9616927),* 9582 Hamilton Ave., Huntington Beach, CA 92646 (SAN 661-5325) Tel 714-964-6041.

Pergamon Pr., Inc., *(Pergamon; 0-08),* Maxwell Hse., Fairview Pk., Elmsford, NY 10523 (SAN 213-9022) Tel 914-592-7700.

Pergot Pr., *(Pergot Pr; 0-936865),* 1001 J Bridgeway, Suite 227, Sausalito, CA 94965 (SAN 699-9441) Tel 415-332-0279; Dist. by: L-S Distributors, 460 9th St., San Francisco, CA 94103 (SAN 169-0213) Tel 415-861-6300; Dist. by: Bookpeople, 2929 Fifth St., Berkeley, CA 94710 (SAN 168-9517); Toll free: 800-227-1516; Dist. by: Quality Books, 918 Sherwood Dr., Lake Bluff, IL 60044-2204 (SAN 169-2127).

Periday Co., *(Periday; 0-9605586),* Box 583, Woodland Hills, CA 91365 (SAN 216-051X).

Perigee Pr., The, *(Perigee Pr; 0-9615171),* Box 639, Colonial Dr., Walpole, NH 03608 (SAN 694-2849) Tel 603-756-3084.

Perigree Bks. *See* Putnam Publishing Group, The

Perilous Press, *(Perilous Pr; 0-9609502),* P.O. Box 17914, Tampa, FL 33612 (SAN 262-057X).

Perimeter Pr., Ltd., *(Perimeter Pr; 0-937486),* 4041 N. Main St., Racine, WI 53402 (SAN 264-2964) Tel 414-631-4121; P.O. Box 1919, Racine, WI 53401 (SAN 658-1382).

Perinatal Loss, Div. of OHSU, *(Perinatal Loss; 0-9615197),* 2116 NE 18th Ave., Portland, OR 97212 (SAN 694-2911) Tel 503-284-7426.

Perinatology Pr., Subs. of Promethean Press, *(Perinatology; 0-916859),* P.O. Box 6827, Ithaca, NY 14851 (SAN 656-0520) Tel 607-257-3278.

Perinton Pr., *(Perinton Press; 0-931157),* P.O. Box 1105, Fairport, NY 14450 (SAN 679-3789) Tel 716-223-2319.

Peripatetic Press, The, *(Peripatetic; 0-9602870),* P.O. Box 68, Grinnell, IA 50112 (SAN 213-425X) Tel 515-236-5861.

Periscope Press, *(Periscope Pr; 0-914083),* P.O. Box 6926, Santa Barbara, CA 93160 (SAN 286-8652).

Perish Press, *(Perish Pr; 0-934038),* P.O. Box 75, Mystic, CT 06355 (SAN 212-789X) Tel 203-536-2304.

†Perishable Pr., Ltd., The, *(Perishable Pr),* P.O. Box 7, Mt. Horeb, WI 53572 (SAN 210-8437) Tel 608-523-4473; *CIP.*

Perivale Pr., *(Perivale Pr; 0-912288),* 13830 Erwin St., Van Nuys, CA 91401 (SAN 201-9922) Tel 818-785-4671; Dist. by: Small Pr. Distribution, Inc., 1814 San Pablo Ave., Berkeley, CA 94702 (SAN 204-5826) Tel 415-549-3336; Dist. by: Anton Mikofsky, 57 W. 84th St., Apt.1-C, New York, NY 10024 (SAN 219-5747).

Periwinkle Pr., *(Periwinkle; 0-9615666),* 317 Ave. B, Snohomish, WA 98290 (SAN 695-9369) Tel 206-568-2508.

Periwinkle Pubns, *(Periwinkle Pubns; 0-942886),* 6015 SW 187th Dr., Aloha, OR 97006 (SAN 240-2653) Tel 503-642-5009.

Perkins, Dorothy J., *(D J Perkins; 0-9604742),* Box 194, Moylan, PA 19065 (SAN 215-6970).

Perkins, E. Stuart, & Associates, *(Perkins & Assoc; 0-9606444),* Box 362, Wellington, OH 44090 (SAN 219-810X).

Perkins, George P., *(G P Perkins; 0-9613144),* Box 910, South Lake Tahoe, CA 95705 (SAN 294-9512) Tel 916-544-2100. Summer: 916-565-3260.

Perkins, Percy H. Jr., *(P H Perkins Jr; 0-9603090),* 1300 Shawnee Dr., Waycross, GA 31501 (SAN 212-2987) Tel 912-283-2803.

Perkiomen Pubns. Co., Inc., *(Perkiomen; 0-9605598),* P.O. Box 36, Schwenksville, PA 19473 (SAN 218-5008).

Perma Bound Bks., Subs. of Hertzberg-New Method, *(Perma Bound; 0-916056; 0-8479),* 617 E. Vandalia Rd., Jacksonville, IL 62650 (SAN 169-2003) Tel 217-243-5451; Toll free: 800-637-6581.

Permanent Pr., Inc., *(Perm Pr; 0-915393),* 1614 Calle San Mateo, Santurce, PR 00912 (SAN 291-3267).

Permanent Pr., The, *(Permanent Pr; 0-932966),* RD 2 Noyac Rd., Sag Harbor, NY 11963 (SAN 212-2995) Tel 516-725-1101; Toll free: 800-221-0960.

Perrin, Thomas W., Inc., *(Perrin Inc; 0-933825),* P.O. Box 190, 5 Allen Rd., Rutherford, NJ 07070 (SAN 200-6510) Tel 201-460-7912; Toll free: 800-321-7912.

Perry, Charles, Pub., *(C Perry Pub; 0-9615139),* 2790 Flora, Memphis, TN 38114 (SAN 694-2482) Tel 901-528-4571.

Perry, Warner, *(W Perry; 0-9603962),* 23 Knickerbocker Dr., Newark, DE 19713 (SAN 213-5450).

Perry Enterprises, *(Perry Enterprises; 0-941518),* 2666 N. 650 E, Provo, UT 84604 (SAN 239-0175) Tel 801-375-9529.

Perry-Omega Pub., Inc., *(Perry Omega; 0-9602586),* P.O. Box 27097, Escondido, CA 92027 (SAN 213-1420).

Perry Publishing, *(Perry Pub),* 1252-20th Place, Yuma, AZ 85364 (SAN 213-2303).

Persea Bks., Inc., *(Persea Bks; 0-89255),* 225 Lafayette St., New York, NY 10012 (SAN 212-8233) Tel 212-431-5270.

Persepolis Pr., *(Persepolis Pr; 0-9615741),* P.O. Box 4552, Greenville, SC 29608 (SAN 695-9490) Tel 803-834-8463; McElhaney Rd., Rte. 3, Greenville, SC 29611 (SAN 695-9504).

Perseus Pr., *(Perseus Pr; 0-918026),* P.O. Box 1221, Pacific Palisades, CA 90272 (SAN 207-2726) Tel 213-208-7991. Orders & checks for audiotapes produced by Carl Faber should be made out in his name, not Perseus Pr. *Imprints:* Faber, Carl, Audiotapes (C Faber Audiotapes).

†Perseverance Pr., *(Perseverance Pr; 0-9602676),* P.O. Box 384, Menlo Park, CA 94026 (SAN 212-9272) Tel 415-323-5572; Dist. by: Capra Pr., P.O. Box 2068, Santa Barbara, CA 93120 (SAN 201-9620) Tel 805-966-4590; *CIP.*

Persian Rug Ctr., *(Persian Rug Ctr; 0-9615592),* 2121 S. Ninth St., Springfield, IL 62703 (SAN 692-9664) Tel 217-544-3418.

Persimmon Pr., *(Persimmon NY; 0-9615462),* 118 Tillinghast Pl., Buffalo, NY 14216 (SAN 695-7056) Tel 716-838-3633.

Person to Person Network, *(Person Person Network; 0-937993),* 7250 Auburn Blvd., Suite 222, Citrus Heights, CA 95610 (SAN 659-7548) Tel 916-723-1000.

Persona Pr., *(Persona LA; 0-940142),* 522 Dumaine, Apt. 3, New Orleans, LA 70116 (SAN 293-3136) Tel 504-561-0221.

Persona Press, *(Persona Pr; 0-931906),* P.O. Box 14022, San Francisco, CA 94114 (SAN 212-3002) Tel 415-775-6143.

Personabooks, *(Personabks; 0-932456),* 434-66th St., Oakland, CA 94609 (SAN 215-1707) Tel 415-658-2482; Dist. by: The Talman Co., 150 Fifth Ave., Rm. 514, New York, NY 10011 (SAN 200-5204) Tel 212-620-3182.

Personal Achievement Institute, *(Personal Achievement; 0-906744),* 535 Ocean Ave., Suite 8C, P.O. Box 1542, Santa Monica, CA 90406 (SAN 219-6247) Tel 213-393-3230.

Personal Achievement Library *See* **Telecom Library, The**

Personal Assocs., *(Personal Assocs; 0-9613749),* P.O. Box 311, Pine Beach, NJ 08741 (SAN 677-7473) Tel 201-240-4957.

Personal Christianity, *(Personal Christianity; 0-938148),* Box 549, Baldwin Park, CA 91706 (SAN 211-8211) Tel 818-338-7333.

Personal Development Ctr., *(Personal Dev Ctr; 0-917828),* P.O. Box 251, Windham Center, CT 06280 (SAN 209-164X) Tel 203-423-4785.

Personal Growth Resources, *(Personal Growth; 0-937477),* P.O. Box 6265, Champaign, IL 61821 (SAN 659-0101) Tel 217-359-7669; 2416 Morrissey Pk., Champaign, IL 61821 (SAN 659-011X).

Personal Planning Programs, Inc., *(Personal Planning),* 7550 France Ave. S. Suite 214, Minneapolis, MN 55435 (SAN 217-2615) Tel 612-893-0403.

Personal Power Potential, *(Personal Power; 0-9607312),* 300 N. Martingale Rd., Suite 500, Schaumburg, IL 60194 (SAN 239-2798) Tel 312-426-6979.

Personal Power Pr., *(Prsnl Power Pr; 0-9616046),* 611 Schuring Rd., No. 3, Portage, MI 49081 (SAN 698-0155) Tel 616-327-2761.

Personal Pr., *(Personal Press; 0-9605634),* 1515 Riebl Rd., Santa Rosa, CA 95404 (SAN 219-9807) Tel 707-525-1338; Dist. by: Inland Book Co., P.O. Box 261. 22 Hemingway Ave., East Haven, CT 06512 (SAN 200-4151) Tel 203-467-4257; Dist. by: Bookpeople, 2929 Fifth St., Berkeley, CA 94710 (SAN 662-1120) Tel 415-549-3030.

Personal Responsibility, *(Personal Resp; 0-9610488),* 314 Eighth St. SE, Washington, DC 20003 (SAN 264-2972) Tel 202-546-0492.

Personal Security Systems, *(Personal Security; 0-918384),* P.O. Box 152, River Forest, IL 60305 (SAN 207-2793) Tel 312-336-7330.

Personal Selling Power, *(Personal Selling; 0-939613),* 1127 International Pkwy., Fredericksburg, VA 22405 (SAN 663-5059) Tel 703-752-7000.

Personal Systems Pubns., *(Personal Sys Pubns; 0-915097),* 1802 N. Carson, Suite 214-240, Carson City, NV 89701 (SAN 289-7970) Tel 702-883-2116.

Personal Touch, A, *(Personal Touch; 0-9616317),* P.O. Box 68392, Oak Grove, OR 97268 (SAN 658-6821) Tel 503-659-8156; 15510 SE Hugh Ave., Milwaukie, OR 97267 (SAN 658-683X).

Personnel Decisions, Inc., *(Personnel Decisions; 0-938529),* 821 Marquette St., Foshay Tower, Suite 2300, Minneapolis, MN 55402 (SAN 661-1443) Tel 612-339-0927.

Perspective Press, *(Perspective Chicago; 0-9603382),* 629 Deming Place, Rm. 401, Chicago, IL 60614 (SAN 208-3191) Tel 312-871-4820.

Perspectives Pr., *(Perspect Indiana; 0-9609504),* 905 West Wildwood Ave., Fort Wayne, IN 46807 (SAN 262-5059) Tel 219-456-8411.

Perspicilli Press, *(Perspicilli Pr; 0-936064),* 1916 Oak Knoll Dr., Belmont, CA 94002 (SAN 213-8646).

Persson, R. J., Enterprises, Incorporated, *(R J Persson Ent; 0-9608486),* P.O. Box 2069, Montrose, CO 81402-2069 (SAN 240-7426) Tel 303-249-6000.

Persun & Berlin, Pubs., *(Persun & Berlin; 0-936111),* P.O. Box 623, Media, PA 19063-0623 (SAN 661-6682).

Perth, J. M., Publishing, Inc., *(Perth Pub; 0-9606546),* P.O. Box 82, Delaplane, VA 22025 (SAN 218-5806) Tel 703-347-3620.

Pescar Nelson Langley West Publishing Group, Inc., *(PNLW; 0-932457),* 3817 Atlantic Ave., Suite 227, Long Beach, CA 90807 (SAN 686-7243) Tel 213-595-8559.

Pet Protector Co., The, *(Pet Pro Co; 0-931573),* 146-01 Jamaica Ave., Jamaica, NY 11435 (SAN 682-1928) Tel 718-523-2211.

Peter Pan Industries, *(Peter Pan; 0-88149),* 145 Komorn St., Newark, NJ 07105 (SAN 287-7589).

Peter Pauper Pr., Inc., *(Peter Pauper; 0-88088),* 202 Mamaroneck Ave., White Plains, NY 10601 (SAN 204-9449) Tel 914-681-0144; Dist. by: Kampmann & Co., Inc., 9 E. 40th St., New York, NY 10016 (SAN 202-5191) Tel 212-685-2928; Toll free: 800-526-7626.

Petereins Pr., The, *(Petereins Pr; 0-9606102),* P.O. Box 10446, Glendale, CA 91209 (SAN 215-9007).

Peters, Ferguson E., Co., *(F E Peters; 0-918214),* P.O. Box 3527, Vero Beach, FL 32964 (SAN 210-2579) Tel 305-231-6285.

Peters, Paul, Studio, *(P Peters Studio; 0-9607030),* 2305 Park Ave., Bay City, TX 77414 (SAN 239-0183) Tel 409-245-7527.

Peters Corp., *(Peters Corp NM; 0-935037),* P.O. Box 2524, Santa Fe, NM 87504-2524 (SAN 697-2462) Tel 505-988-8961; Toll free: 800-621-5884.

Peters, Ted H., *(T H Peters; 0-9601466),* Box 1299, Greenville, TX 75401 (SAN 222-1144) Tel 214-455-1240.

Peters Wright Creative Dance, Inc, *(Peters Wright; 0-916645),* 2695 Sacramento St., San Francisco, CA 94115 (SAN 296-6883) Tel 415-931-0365.

Petersburg Pr., *(Petersburg Pr; 0-902825),* 380 Lafayette St., New York, NY 10003 (SAN 240-1819) Tel 212-420-0890.

Petersen Publishing Co., Bk. Div., *(Petersen Pub; 0-8227),* 8490 Sunset Blvd., Los Angeles, CA 90069 (SAN 201-9949) Tel 213-657-5100.

Peterson, Arthur G., *(A G Peterson; 0-9605664),* P.O. Box 252, DeBary, FL 32713 (SAN 214-0780) Tel 305-668-6587.

Peterson, Carrol P., *(C P Peterson),* P.O. Box 244, Lewiston, MN 55952 (SAN 678-920X).

Peterson, E. R., *(E R Peterson; 0-9616442),* 3267 B Sutton Pl., NW, Washington, DC 20016 (SAN 659-0136) Tel 202-363-9275.

Peterson, John C. & Doris M., *(J & D Peterson; 0-9604376),* R R 1, Box 25, Delphi, IN 46923 (SAN 216-0056) Tel 317-564-2855.

Peterson Publishing, *(Peterson Pub; 0-9613986),* 159 McBoal, St. Paul, MN 55102 (SAN 682-1731) Tel 612-297-9630.

Peterson Publishing Co. (CO), *(Peterson Pub CO; 0-9614806),* 211 S. Main St., Gunnison, CO 81230 (SAN 692-7831) Tel 303-641-3910.

†Peterson's Guides, Inc., *(Petersons Guides; 0-87866),* P.O. Box 2123, Princeton, NJ 08543-2123 (SAN 200-2167) Tel 609-924-5338; Toll free: 800-225-0261; *CIP.*

Petervin Pr., The, *(Petervin Pr; 0-943932),* P.O. Box 280, Davis, CA 95617 (SAN 238-0838) Tel 916-756-1105.

Petit Appetit, *(Petit Appetit; 0-9616883),* 9215 Ensley Ln., Leawood, KS 66206 (SAN 661-6496) Tel 913-383-3610.

Petit Pr., *(Petit Press; 0-9610174),* 1661 E. Lakeshore Dr., Baton Rouge, LA 70808 (SAN 274-5321) Tel 504-383-3270; P.O. Box 4053, Baton Rouge, LA 70821 (SAN 695-6262).

Petras Press *See* **Riverrun Pr.**

Names

Names

Petras Press Inc., *(Petras Pr; 0-9614568),* 70 Greenwich Ave., Room 561, New York, NY 10011 (SAN 691-8204) Tel 212-267-8448; Dist. by: Flatiron Book Distributors Inc., 1170 Broadway, Suite 80, New York, NY 10001 (SAN 240-9917) Tel 211-206-1118.

Petrie Hse. Pubns., *(Petrie Hse; 0-936824),* 2140 W. Olympic Blvd., Los Angeles, CA 90006 (SAN 218-4540) Tel 213-487-2666.

Petro-Media Inc., *(Petro-Media; 0-916647),* 1729 Rose Rd., Tyler, TX 75701 (SAN 296-6573) Tel 214-592-8348.

†**Petrocelli Bks.,** *(Petrocelli; 0-89433),* Research Pk., 251 Wall St., Princeton, NJ 08540 (SAN 211-3848) Tel 609-924-5851; Dist. by: TAB Bks., P.O. Box 40, Blue Ridge Summit, PA 17214 (SAN 202-568X) Tel 717-794-2191; *CIP.*

Petroglyph Press Ltd., *(Petroglyph; 0-912180),* 201 Kinoole St., Hilo, HI 96720 (SAN 204-9457) Tel 808-935-6006; Dist. by: Pacific Trade Group, P.O. Box 668, Pearl City, HI 96782 (SAN 169-1635) Tel 808-671-6735; Dist. by: Mid-Pacific Book Distributors, 150 Haili St., Hilo, HI 96720 (SAN 169-1597) Tel 808-935-5622.

Petroleum Extension Service (PETEX), *(PETEX; 0-88698),* Div. of Continuing Ed., Univ. of Texas at Austin, Balcones Research Ctr.-2,10100 Burnet Rd., Austin, TX 78758 (SAN 208-3892).

Petroleum Marketing Education Foundation, *(Petro Mktg Ed Found; 0-937273),* 101 N. Alfred St., Suite 200, Alexandria, VA 22314 (SAN 224-9014) Tel 703-684-0000.

Petronium Press, *(Petronium Pr; 0-932136),* 1255 Nuuanu Ave., 1813, Honolulu, HI 96817 (SAN 211-7541).

Petruska-Petruska Pubn., *(Petruska-Petruska; 0-936189),* 435 Water St., Excelsior, MN 55331 (SAN 696-799X) Tel 612-474-3117.

Pettengill, Pryor, *(Pryor Pettengill; 0-933462),* Box 7074, Ann Arbor, MI 48107 (SAN 213-8697).

Pettway & Kipp Publishing Co., *(Pettway Kipp Pub; 0-937561),* P.O. Box 720944, Houston, TX 77272-0944 (SAN 659-0195) Tel 713-498-4070; 8811 Boone Rd., Houston, TX 77099 (SAN 659-0209).

Pex Publishing Co., *(Pex Pub; 0-933767),* 117 Kingsley Way, Freehold, NJ 07728 (SAN 692-7645) Tel 201-780-4455.

Peyton Hse. Pr., *(Peyton Hse Pr; 0-939097),* P.O. Box 1092, Pacific Palisades, CA 90272 (SAN 662-6041); 18203 Coastline Dr., No. 2, Malibu, CA 90265 (SAN 662-605X) Tel 213-459-0512.

Peyton's, *(Peyton's),* P.O. Box 5756, Virginia Beach, VA 23455 (SAN 682-2444).

Pfeiffer, Philip A., *(Pfeiffer; 0-9601038),* 1617 N. Baylen St., Pensacola, FL 32501 (SAN 208-3205) Tel 904-433-2906.

Pflaum-Standard *See* **CEBCO Standard Publishing**

Pflueger Architects, *(Pflueger Architects; 0-9614133),* 165 Tenth St., San Francisco, CA 94103 (SAN 686-2209) Tel 415-431-5630.

Phaedrus, *(Phaedrus WI; 0-9616380),* N61, WI5263, Wigwam Dr., Menomonee Falls, WI 53051 (SAN 659-0233) Tel 414-252-3135.

Phaedrus, Ltd., *(Phaedrus; 0-9614048),* 2301 Walnut St., Harrisburg, PA 17103 (SAN 684-8230) Tel 717-238-4544.

Phaeton Press, Inc., *(Phaeton; 0-87753),* Orders to: Gordian Press, 85 Tompkins St., P.O. Box 304, Staten Island, NY 10304 (SAN 201-6389) Tel 212-273-4700.

Phaidon *See* **Dutton, E. P.**

Phanes Pr., *(Phanes Pr; 0-933999),* P.O. Box 6114, Grand Rapids, MI 49516 (SAN 692-879X) Tel 616-949-5678.

Phantasia Pr., *(Phantasia Pr; 0-932096),* 5536 Crispin Way, West Bloomfield, MI 48033 (SAN 211-755X) Tel 313-855-3737.

†**Pharmacotherapy Pubns., Inc.,** *(Pharm Pubns; 0-931591),* New England Medical Ctr., Box 806, Boston, MA 02111 (SAN 682-5052) Tel 617-956-5390; *CIP.*

Pharos Bks., Div. of Newspaper Enterprise Assn., *(Pharos Bks NY; 0-911818),* 200 Park Ave., New York, NY 10166 (SAN 211-7703) Tel 212-692-3824.

Ph.D. Publishing Co., *(PhD Pub; 0-932010),* 3958 Bentley Ave., No. 1, Culver City, CA 90230 (SAN 210-9565) Tel 213-204-1604.

Pheasant Run Pubns., Subs. of International Press, *(Pheasant Run; 0-936978),* 2601 Natural Bridge Rd., St. Louis, MO 63107 (SAN 215-1715) Tel 314-534-1752.

Phelan, Helene C., *(Phelan; 0-9605836),* 114 S. Main St., Almond, NY 14804 (SAN 216-4922) Tel 607-276-6166.

Phelon, Sheldon & Marsar, Inc., *(P S & M Inc),* 15 Industrial Ave., Fairview, NJ 07022 (SAN 205-1869) Tel 201-941-8804.

Phenix Pubns., Div. of Phenix Technology, Inc., *(Phenix Pub; 0-910105),* 1504 Ave. De La Estrella, Suite A, San Clemente, CA 92672 (SAN 241-4279) Tel 714-492-3324.

Phi Delta Kappa Educational Foundation, *(Phi Delta Kappa; 0-87367),* Eighth & Union, Box 789, Bloomington, IN 47402 (SAN 289-1859) Tel 812-339-1156.

Phian Bks. Co., *(Phian Bks; 0-9615097),* 7001 Ridge Blvd., Brooklyn, NY 11209 (SAN 694-2601) Tel 718-748-4586.

Phiebig, Albert J. *See* **Karger, S., AG**

Philadelphia Maritime Museum, *(Phila Maritime Mus; 0-913346),* 321 Chestnut St., Philadelphia, PA 19106 (SAN 203-6975) Tel 215-925-5439.

Philadelphia Maritime Museum *See* **New York Graphic Society Bks.**

†**Philadelphia Museum of Art,** *(Phila Mus Art; 0-87633),* 26th & Pkwy P.O. Box 7646, Philadelphia, PA 19101 (SAN 203-0969) Tel 215-763-8100; *CIP.*

Philadelphia Patristic Foundation, Ltd., *(Phila Patristic; 0-915646),* 99 Brattle St., Cambridge, MA 02138 (SAN 208-3507) Tel 617-868-3450.

†**Philadelphia Society for Promoting Agriculture,** *(Phila Soc Prom; 0-9614267),* 325 Walnut St., Philadelphia, PA 19106 (SAN 687-1496) Tel 215-483-3200; *CIP.*

Philadelphia Yearly Meeting, Religious Society of Friends, Book Services, *(Religious Soc Friends; 0-941308),* 1515 Cherry St., Philadelphia, PA 19102 (SAN 239-3778).

Philam Bk. Distributors, *(Philam Bk),* 828 Morse Ave., Sunnyvale, CA 94086 (SAN 210-6191).

Philatelic Foundation, *(Philatelic Found; 0-911989),* 270 Madison Ave., New York, NY 10016 (SAN 235-3253) Tel 212-889-6483.

Philbrook Art Ctr., *(Philbrook Art; 0-86659),* 2727 S. Rockford Rd., P.O. Box 52510, Tulsa, OK 74152 (SAN 280-106X) Tel 918-749-7941.

Philgor Publishing, *(Philgor Pub),* 1555 Winona Court, Denver, CO 80204 (SAN 240-107X); P.O. Box 2505, Denver, CO 80201 (SAN 226-8442).

Philippine Ancestors, *(Philippine Anc; 0-9608528),* P.O. Box 1104, Provo, UT 84603-1104 (SAN 240-7434) Tel 801-374-1123; Dist. by: Stevenson's Genealogical Center, 230 W. 1230N., Provo., UT 84604-2534 (SAN 200-8106).

Phillie Dee Enterprises, Inc., *(Phillie Dee Ent; 0-9612058),* 515-12 High St., Port Jefferson, NY 11777 (SAN 286-8482) Tel 516-928-5876.

Phillipps, John, *(John Philipps; 0-9611412),* 1111 Belair Dr., Fallbrook, CA 92028 (SAN 285-6743) Tel 619-723-9126.

Phillips, Bradley Ray & Kyle Lee Helmick, *(B R Phillips; 0-9613513),* Rte. 3 Box 333, Buckhannon, WV 26201 (SAN 679-2049).

†**Phillips, S. G., Inc.,** *(S G Phillips; 0-87599),* P.O. Box 83, Chatham, NY 12037 (SAN 293-3152) Tel 518-392-3068; c/o M & B Fulfillment Service, Inc., 540 Barnum Ave., Bridgeport, CT 06608 (SAN 293-3160) Tel 203-366-1900; *CIP.*

Phillips Collection, *(Phillips Coll; 0-943044),* 1600-1612 21st St. NW, Washington, DC 20009 (SAN 321-2297) Tel 202-387-2151.

Phillips Exeter Academy Pr., The, *(Phillips Exeter Academy; 0-939618),* Exeter, NH 03833 (SAN 216-4353); Orders to: Exeter Bookstore, 13 Spring St., Exeter, NH 03833 (SAN 662-1139).

Phillips Friends Co., Inc., *(P Friends Co Inc; 0-911305),* R.R. 2, Box 135, West Liberty, IA 52776 (SAN 274-5968) Tel 319-627-4556.

Phillips-Neuman, *(Phillips Neuman; 0-910107),* 8320 Woodhaven Blvd., Bethesda, MD 20817 (SAN 240-8244).

Phillips Pubns., Inc., *(Phillips Pubns; 0-932572),* P.O. Box 168, Williamstown, NJ 08094 (SAN 208-3523) Tel 609-567-0695.

Phillips Publishing Inc., *(Phillips Pub Inc; 0-934960),* 7811 Montrose Rd., Potomac, MD 20854 (SAN 201-9981).

Phillips Publishing, Inc., *(Phillips Pub; 0-938657),* 367 Cypress St., Broomfield, CO 80020 (SAN 661-1338) Tel 303-466-2714.

Philmar Publishers, *(Philmar Pub; 0-88100),* P.O. Box 402, Diablo, CA 94528 (SAN 262-0596) Tel 415-837-3490.

Philmer Enterprises, *(Philmer; 0-918836),* No. 4 Hunter's Run, Spring House, PA 19477 (SAN 209-4746) Tel 215-643-2976.

Philomel Bks. *See* **Putnam Publishing Group, The**

Philomod Corp., *(Philomod Corp; 0-938545),* 4356 Yacht Club Rd., Jacksonville, FL 32210 (SAN 663-0839); Dist. by: Publishers Group West, 5855 Beaudry St., Emeryville, CA 94608 Tel 415-658-3453.

Philosopher Pr., *(Philosopher Pr; 0-9617048),* P.O. Box 8282, Green Bay, WI 54308 (SAN 662-8117); 4012 Champeau Rd., New Franken, WI 54229 (SAN 662-8125) Tel 414-468-4098.

Philosophia Pr., *(Philosophia Pr; 3-88405),* P.O. Box 4194, Hamden, CT 06514 (SAN 699-7449) Tel 203-785-8688.

†**Philosophical Library, Inc.,** *(Philos Lib; 0-8022),* 200 W. 57th St., Suite 510, New York, NY 10019 (SAN 201-999X) Tel 212-265-6050; Dist. by: Kampmann & Co., Inc., 9 E. 40th St., New York, NY 10016 (SAN 202-5191) Tel 212-685-2928; *CIP.*

Philosophical Publishing Co., *(Philos Pub; 0-932785),* R. D. 3, Clymeir Road, Quakertown, PA 18951 (SAN 295-8430) Tel 215-536-5168.

†**Philosophical Research Society, Inc.,** *(Philos Res; 0-89314),* 3910 Los Feliz Blvd., Los Angeles, CA 90027 (SAN 205-3829) Tel 213-663-2167; *CIP.*

Philosophy of Education Society, *(Phil Ed Soc),* Syracuse Univ., Cultural Foundations of Education, Syracuse, NY 13210 (SAN 225-8587) Tel 606-257-3993.

Philosophy of Science Assn., *(Philos Sci Assn; 0-917586),* Michigan State Univ., Philosophy Dept., 18 Morrill Hall, East Lansing, MI 48824 (SAN 650-048X) Tel 517-353-9392.

Phil's Photo Inc., *(Phils Photo; 0-933107),* 2380 Champlain St., NW, Washington, DC 20009 (SAN 689-5867) Tel 202-293-2214.

Phipps Publishing Co., Subs. of New England Manufacturing Co., *(Phipps Pub; 0-918442),* 66 Bridge St., Norwell, MA 02061 (SAN 209-9829) Tel 617-659-7504.

Phobia Society of America, *(Phobia Soc Am; 0-935943),* 5820 Hubbard Dr., Rockville, MD 20852 (SAN 696-8015) Tel 301-231-9350.

Phoenix Art Museum, *(Phoenix Art; 0-910407),* 1625 N. Central Ave., Phoenix, AZ 85004-1685 (SAN 280-1140) Tel 602-257-1880.

Phoenix Assocs., Inc., Div. of Omega Group, Ltd., *(Phoenix Assocs; 0-915222),* P.O. Box 693, Boulder, CO 80306 (SAN 211-4429) Tel 303-449-3750.

Phoenix Book Shop, *(Phoenix Bk Shop; 0-916228),* 22 Jones St., New York, NY 10014 (SAN 211-3724) Tel 212-675-2795.

Phoenix Bks., Pubs., *(Phoenix Bks; 0-914778),* P.O. Box 32008, Phoenix, AZ 85064 (SAN 282-1613) Tel 602-952-0163.

Phoenix Medical Communication, *(Phoenix Med Comn; 0-938633),* 1909 E. Camino de los Ranchos, Phoenix, AZ 85022 (SAN 661-5821) Tel 602-971-3960.

Phoenix Pr., *(Phoenix Pr FL; 0-9616898),* 2787 E. Oakland Pk. Blvd., Suite 211, Ft. Lauderdale, FL 33306 (SAN 661-6062) Tel 305-565-1429.

Phoenix Press & Distributing Co., *(Phoenix Press & Dist),* 4352 Grow Rd, NW, Stanton, MI 48888 (SAN 212-9590).

Phoenix Pr. Services, Inc., *(Phoenix Pr NJ; 0-936671),* P.O. Box 172, South River, NJ 08882 (SAN 699-6868) Tel 201-390-0883; 22 Deerfield Rd., East Brunswick, NJ 08816 (SAN 699-6876).

Phoenix Projects, The, *(Phoenix Projects; 0-910109),* 1819 Eaton Rd., Terre Haute, IN 47802 (SAN 241-4295) Tel 812-234-3607.

Phoenix Pubns., Inc., *(Phoen Pubns; 0-9615021),* P.O. Box 128, Cedarburg, WI 53012 (SAN 694-0390) Tel 414-377-7888.

†**Phoenix Publishing,** *(Phoenix Pub; 0-914016; 0-914659),* Canaan, NH 03741 (SAN 201-8810) Tel 603-523-9901; Sugar Hill, NH 03585 (SAN 691-4209); *CIP.*

Phoenix Publishing Co., The, *(Phoenix FL; 0-940810),* P.O. Box 430733, Miami, FL 33143 (SAN 219-8428) Tel 305-552-6388.

Phoenix Publishing, Inc., *(Phoenix WA; 0-919345),* P.O. Box 10, Custer, WA 98240 (SAN 695-5517) Tel 206-467-8219.

Phoenix Rising, *(Phoenix Rising; 0-9610314),* 601 Dale Dr., Silver Spring, MD 20910 (SAN 264-3014) Tel 703-847-2434.

Phoenix Society, The, *(Phoenix Soc),* 11 Rust Hill Rd., Levittown, PA 19056 (SAN 225-9796) Tel 215-946-4788.

Phoenix Systems, Inc., *(Phoenix Syst GA; 0-936019),* 3300 NE Expressway, Atlanta, GA 30341 (SAN 696-8031) Tel 404-458-6445.

Phoenix with Children, *(Phoenix Children; 0-9616482),* 1107 W. Palm Ln., Phoenix, AZ 85007 (SAN 659-2783) Tel 602-253-7328; Dist. by: Evans Distributing, 3128 W. Clarendon, Phoenix, AZ 85017 (SAN 200-6448).

Pholiota Pr., Inc., *(Pholiota; 0-910231),* 6421 Antrim Cir., Huntington Beach, CA 92647 (SAN 240-8783) Tel 714-898-4129.

Photo-Go Pr., *(Photo-Go Pr; 0-931662),* P.O. Box 522562, El Paso, TX 79552-0014 (SAN 211-7576) Tel 915-581-6218.

Photo/Graphics Unlimited, *(Photo Graphics; 0-9613638),* P.O. Box 126342, San Diego, CA 92101 (SAN 677-5063).

Photo Survey, *(Photo Survey; 0-9609812),* Box 9157, Akron, OH 44305 (SAN 262-5075).

Photoglass Pr., *(Photoglass Pr; 0-9616724),* 1203 Searle Dr., Normal, IL 61761 (SAN 659-8536) Tel 309-452-3837.

Photographic Arts Ctr., The, Div. of Photograph Collectors Newsletter, Ltd., *(Photo Arts Ctr; 0-940926; 0-913069),* 127 E. 59th St., New York, NY 10022 (SAN 217-3603) Tel 212-838-8640.

Photographic Memorabila, *(Photo Memorabila; 0-9604352),* P.O. Box 351, Lexington, MA 02173 (SAN 282-163X) Tel 617-646-0775.

Photographic Research Pubns., *(Photo Res; 0-934918),* P.O. Box 333, Seven Oaks, Detroit, MI 48235 (SAN 213-9456) Tel 313-493-3503.

Photographic Resource Ctr., *(Photo Res Ctr; 0-9615801),* 1019 Commonwealth Ave., Boston, MA 02215 (SAN 696-6217) Tel 617-783-9333.

Photographit, *(Photographit; 0-9605168),* 12 S. Gallatin Ave., Uniontown, PA 15401 (SAN 215-7985).

Photography Media Institute, Inc., *(PMI Inc; 0-936524),* P.O. Box 78, Staten Island, NY 10304 (SAN 216-1729) Tel 718-447-3280.

Photography Research Institute/Carson Endowment, *(Photo Res Inst Carson Endowment; 0-915827),* 21237 S. Moneta Ave., Carson, CA 90745 (SAN 293-9002) Tel 213-328-9272.

Photography West Graphics, Inc., *(Photog West Graphics; 0-9616515),* P.O. Box 7116, Carmel, CA 93921 (SAN 659-5553) Tel 408-625-1719.

Photopia Press, *(Photopia Pr; 0-942478),* P.O. Box 1844, Corvallis, OR 97339 (SAN 238-5562) Tel 503-757-8761.

Phrygian Pr., *(Phrygian Pr; 0-932155),* 58-09 205th St., Bayside, NY 11364 (SAN 686-4317) Tel 718-428-9368.

Phunn Pubs., *(Phunn Pubs; 0-931762),* P.O. Box 201, Wild Rose, WI 54984 (SAN 212-128X) Tel 414-622-3251.

Physical Studies Institute, *(Physical Stud; 0-914447),* 80 Cuesta Vista Dr., Monterey, CA 93940 (SAN 287-7597) Tel 408-373-5447.

Physicians' Record Co., *(Physicians Rec; 0-917036),* 3000 S. Ridgeland Ave., Berwyn, IL 60402 (SAN 205-3853) Tel 312-749-3111; Toll free: 800-323-9268.

Physsardt Pubs., *(Physsardt; 0-916062),* Dist. by: Bloomington Distribution Group, P.O. Box 841, Bloomington, IN 47402 (SAN 282-6828).

Pi Pr., Inc., *(Pi Pr; 0-931420),* Box 23371, Honolulu, HI 96822 (SAN 669-2400); 3169-A Alika Ave., Honolulu, HI 96817 Tel 808-595-3426.

Pi Rho Press, *(Pi Rho; 0-9607376),* 11365 Quartz Dr. 64, Auburn, CA 95603 (SAN 239-4731).

†**Pi Yee Press,** *(Pi Yee Pr; 0-935926),* 7910 Ivanhoe Ave., No. 34, La Jolla, CA 92037 (SAN 214-0799); *CIP.*

Piarist Fathers, Inc., *(Piarist Father; 0-9614908),* 512 Ave. 20, S., Los Angeles, CA 90031 (SAN 693-5362) Tel 213-223-4153.

Pic-Gramics Pubns., *(Pic Gramics Pubns; 0-937914),* 7505 Fannin, Suite 214, Houston, TX 77054-1913 (SAN 659-2090) Tel 713-797-1345.

Pica Press *See* Universe Bks., Inc.

Pica Special Studies *See* Universe Bks., Inc.

Picayune Publishing, Inc, *(Picayune Pr; 0-937430),* 920 Frenchman St., New Orleans, LA 70116 (SAN 215-1723).

Picchione, Richard, *(R Picchione; 0-9602840),* P.O. Box 5534, Reno, NV 89513 (SAN 213-1471).

Pick Pubns., Inc., *(Pick Pub MI; 0-936526),* 28715 Greenfield Rd., Southfield, MI 48076 (SAN 282-1648) Tel 313-443-1799; Toll free: 800-247-1559.

Pickens County Publishing, *(Pickens County Pub; 0-937229),* P.O. Box 476, Pickens, SC 29671 (SAN 658-6554) Tel 803-878-2453; 117 W. Main St., Pickens, SC 29671 (SAN 658-6562).

Pickle Pr., *(Pickle Pr; 0-9615499),* 400 Missouri St., San Francisco, CA 94107 (SAN 695-9601) Tel 415-826-0747.

Pickleweed Press, *(Pickleweed; 0-9607890),* 212 Del Casa Dr., Mill Valley, CA 94941 (SAN 238-1885) Tel 415-388-6002.

†**Pickwick Pubns.,** *(Pickwick; 0-915138; 1-55635),* 4137 Timberlane Dr., Allison Park, PA 15101 (SAN 210-1319) Tel 412-487-2159; *CIP.*

Pictorial Histories Publishing Co., *(Pictorial Hist; 0-933126),* 713 S. Third W., Missoula, MT 59801 (SAN 212-4351) Tel 406-549-8488.

Pictorial Legends, Subs. of Event Co., *(Pictorial Legends; 0-939031),* 435 Holland Ave., Los Angeles, CA 90042 (SAN 642-8486) Tel 213-254-4416; Dist. by: Publishers Group West, 5855 Beaudry St., Emeryville, CA 94608 (SAN 202-8522) Tel 415-658-3453; Toll free: 800-982-8319.

Pictorial Publishers Inc., *(Pictorial Pubs),* 8081 Zionsville Rd., Indianapolis, IN 46268 (SAN 205-1338) Tel 317-872-7220.

Picturama Pubns., *(Picturama; 0-918506),* Box 50, 1033 Grand Ave., Arroyo Grande, CA 93420 (SAN 209-9837) Tel 805-481-0550.

Picture Bk. Studio, USA, *(Picture Bk Studio USA; 0-88708; 0-907234),* 60 N. Main St., Natick, MA 01760 (SAN 293-8227) Tel 617-655-9696; Toll free: 800-462-1252; Dist. by: Alphabet Pr., 60 N. Main St., Natick, MA 01760 (SAN 217-1449) Tel 617-655-9696.

Picture Postcard Productions, Inc., *(Pic Postcard; 0-934813),* 110 Buchanan Dr., Sausalito, CA 94965 (SAN 694-2768) Tel 415-331-3400.

Pidcock Pr., *(Pidcock Pr; 0-9616111),* Box 1, Gardenville, PA 18926 (SAN 699-7406) Tel 215-794-8187; 5579 Lower Mountain Rd., R.D. 2, New Hope, PA 18938 (SAN 699-7414).

Pie Light Publishing, *(Pie Light Pub; 0-9616725),* 2 Riverview Heights, Rochester, NY 14623 (SAN 659-8617) Tel 716-235-3301.

Piece Of The Rainbow, *(Rainbow; 0-933477),* 166 Second Ave., Brooklyn, NY 11215 (SAN 692-4018) Tel 718-807-8603.

Pieceful Pleasures, *(Pieceful Pleasures; 0-933758),* 566 30th Ave., San Mateo, CA 94403 (SAN 212-7954) Tel 415-573-9243.

Piedmont Pr., *(Piedmont Pr OH; 0-9616908),* 4080 Porter Rd., Westlake, OH 44145 (SAN 661-5201) Tel 216-871-2077.

†**Piedmont Press, Inc.,** *(Piedmont; 0-912680),* P.O. Box 3605, Georgetown, Washington, DC 20007 (SAN 205-3861) Tel 703-549-3980; *CIP.*

Piequet Pr., *(Piequet Pr; 0-914275),* 196 S. Euclid Ave., Upland, CA 91786 (SAN 286-6889) Tel 714-985-5302.

Pier Press, *(Pier Pr; 0-943306),* 190 Riverdell Dr., Saunderstown, RI 02874 (SAN 240-7442) Tel 401-295-5767.

Pierce, Clayton C., *(C C Pierce; 0-9601564),* 325 Carol Dr., Ventura, CA 93003 (SAN 210-9336) Tel 805-653-5979.

Pierce, Ken, Inc., *(K Pierce Inc; 0-912277),* Box 322, Park Forest, IL 60466 (SAN 265-0835) Tel 312-672-4457.

Pierce, Olive, *(Olive Pierce; 0-9617101),* 165 Upland Rd., Cambridge, MA 02140 (SAN 662-5045) Tel 617-864-2438.

Pierce-Ellis Enterprises, *(Pierce Ellis Ent; 0-938701),* 607 S. Park View St., 4th Flr., Los Angeles, CA 90057 (SAN 661-5376) Tel 213-388-8488. *Imprints:* Ear-Literature (Ear-Lit).

Pierian Pr., *(Pierian; 0-87650),* P.O. Box 1808, Ann Arbor, MI 48106 (SAN 204-8949) Tel 313-434-5530. *Imprints:* Greenfield Books (Greenfield Bks).

Piermont Co., *(Piermont Co; 0-9613685),* P.O. Box 888, West Chester, PA 19381-0888 (SAN 295-799X) Tel 215-696-1218.

Pierremont Press, *(Pierremont Press; 0-930883),* P.O. Box 33932, Shreveport, LA 71130 (SAN 677-8151) Tel 318-674-6240.

Pig Iron Pr., *(Pig Iron Pr; 0-917530),* P.O. Box 237, Youngstown, OH 44501 (SAN 209-0937) Tel 216-783-1269.

Pigeon River Country Assn., Inc., *(Pigeon River; 0-9615851),* 110 W. Fifth, Gaylord, MI 49735 (SAN 696-6225) Tel 517-732-2607; P.O. Box 122, Gaylord, MI 49735 (SAN 696-978X).

Pigeon Roost Press, *(Pigeon Roost Pr),* 739 Clematis Dr., Nashville, TN 37205 (SAN 211-8661).

Pig's Whisker Music, *(Pigs Whisker; 0-9602874),* P.O. Box 27522, Los Angeles, CA 90027 (SAN 218-4583).

Piirisild & Treumut Partnership, *(Piirisild & Treumut; 0-9609364),* P.O. Box 2562, Van Nuys, CA 91404 (SAN 216-2857) Tel 818-765-2587.

Pika Press, *(Pika Pr; 0-935160),* P.O. Box C-9, Mammoth Lakes, CA 93546 (SAN 213-4268).

Pike & Fischer, Inc., Subs. of Bureau of National Affairs, *(Pike Fischer; 0-937275),* 4550 Montgomery Ave., Suite 433N, Bethesda, MD 20814 (SAN 659-0411) Tel 301-654-6262.

Pikestaff Press, The, Div. of Pikestaff Publications, Inc., *(Pikestaff Pr; 0-936044),* P.O. Box 127, Normal, IL 61761 (SAN 213-8654) Tel 309-452-4831.

Pilbat, Frank, *(F Pilbat; 0-9614411),* 41-07 Bowne St., Flushing, NY 11355 (SAN 688-6035) Tel 718-445-0368.

Pilgram Hse. Publishing Co., *(Pilgram Hse; 0-916213),* 801 Easy St., Simi Valley, CA 63065 (SAN 294-9539) Tel 805-526-0813; Dist. by: Bookpeople, 2929 Fifth St., Berkeley, CA 94710 (SAN 168-9517).

Pilgrim Bks., *(Pilgrim Bks OK; 0-937664),* P.O. Box 2399, Norman, OK 73070 (SAN 215-6989) Tel 405-360-5658.

Pilgrim Books, *(Pilgrim NJ; 0-9610624),* 26 Georgia, Medford, NJ 08055 (SAN 265-4097) Tel 609-953-0404.

Pilgrim Hse., *(Pilgrim Hse; 0-932131),* 1637 Westhaven Ave. NW, Salem, OR 97304 (SAN 686-2195) Tel 503-362-4030.

Pilgrim Press Corp., *(Pilgrim Pr Corp NY; 0-932256),* 36-01 43rd Ave., Long Island City, NY 11101 (SAN 211-9226).

†**Pilgrim Pr., The,** *(Pilgrim Pr; 0-933476),* 39 University Pl., Princeton, NJ 08540 (SAN 211-2647) Tel 609-924-9095; *CIP.*

Pilgrim Pr., The United Church Pr., Div. of United Church Board for Homeland Ministries, *(Pilgrim NY; 0-8298),* 132 W. 31st St., New York, NY 10001 (SAN 212-601X) Tel 212-239-8700; Dist. by: Publishers Distribution Ctr., 25 Branca Rd., Rutherford, NJ 07073 (SAN 200-5018) Tel 201-939-6064. *Imprints:* Gemini Music Division (Gemini Music).

Pilgrim Pubns., *(Pilgrim Pubns),* P.O. Box 66, Pasadena, TX 77501 (SAN 206-3069) Tel 713-477-2329.

Pilgrim Society, *(Pilgrim Soc; 0-940628),* 75 Court St., Plymouth, MA 02360 (SAN 280-1221) Tel 617-746-1620.

Names

Pilgrimage, Inc., *Div. of Anderson Publishing Co., (Pilgrimage Inc; 0-932930),* Rte. 11, Box 553, Jonesboro, TN 37659 (SAN 285-0834) Tel 615-735-4887; Toll free: 800-582-7295; 646 Main St., P.O. Box 2676, Cincinnati, OH 45201 (SAN 285-0842).

Pilgrimage Press, *(Pilgrimage; 0-918550),* 2398 Telegraph Ave., Berkeley, CA 94704 (SAN 210-1327) Tel 415-548-2626.

Pilgrimage Publishing, Inc., *(Pilgrimage Pub; 0-935819),* 104 Central Ave., Tarrytown, NY 10591 (SAN 696-6276) Tel 914-631-0488.

Pill Enterprises, *(Pill Enter; 0-9616021),* N. 22790 Hwy. 101, Shelton, WA 98584 (SAN 697-9416) Tel 206-877-5825; Dist. by: Pacific Pipeline, 19215 66th Ave., S., Kent, WA 98032 (SAN 208-2128) Tel 206-872-5523.

Pillar Point Pr., *(Pillar Point Pr; 0-9614114),* P.O. Box 20041, Denver, CO 80220 (SAN 685-3056) Tel 303-377-9259; Dist. by: Pacific Pipeline, Inc., 19215 66th Ave, S., Kent, WA 98032 (SAN 208-2128) Tel 206-872-5523.

Pillar Press, *(Pillar Pr; 0-9611190),* 636 Tarryton Isle, Alameda, CA 94501 (SAN 282-8499) Tel 415-522-4187; Dist. by: Bookpeople, 2929 Fifth St., Berkeley, CA 94710 (SAN 168-9517); Toll free: 800-227-1516 (USA); Toll free: 800-624-4466 (CA).

Pillman, K., Pubs., *(K Pillman; 0-9608620),* 3039 SW 116th Pl., Seattle, WA 98146 (SAN 238-339X) Tel 206-244-1266.

Pillsbury Baptist Bible College Pr., *(PBBC Pr; 0-9606952),* 315 S. Grove St., Owatonna, MN 55060 (SAN 207-2734) Tel 507-451-2710.

†Pilot Bks., *(Pilot Bks; 0-87576),* 103 Cooper St., Babylon, NY 11702 (SAN 202-0017) Tel 516-422-2225; *CIP.*

Pilot Light, *(Pilot Light; 0-9608376),* 3510 Cloudland Dr., Stone Mountain, GA 30083 (SAN 240-8791) Tel 404-296-3294; Orders to: P.O. Box 305, Stone Mountain, GA 30086-0305 (SAN 662-734X) Tel 404-296-3296.

Pilot Pubns., *(Pilot Pubns; 0-938923),* P.O. Box 3190, Ocala, FL 32678 (SAN 215-0999) Tel 904-351-5900; Toll free: 800-521-2120; 1601 SW, 18th Ave., Ocala, FL 32674 (SAN 660-9414); Dist. by: Aviation Bk. Co., 1640 Victory Blvd., Glendale, CA 91201 (SAN 212-0259) Tel 213-240-1771.

Pilots Pubs., Inc., *(Pilots Pubs Inc; 0-939426),* P.O. Box 661, Redwood City, CA 94064 (SAN 216-5813) Tel 415-594-9300.

Pimmit Press, *(Pimmit Pr; 0-9606042),* Box 4815, Washington, DC 20008 (SAN 216-9231).

Pimteoui Pubns., *(Pimiteoui Pubns; 0-934253),* P.O. Box 48, Rodney, MI 49343-0048 (SAN 693-2142) Tel 616-972-2178.

Pin High Pubns., *(Pin High Pubns; 0-937479),* 306 SE Eighth, Portland, OR 97214 (SAN 659-0438) Tel 503-231-7121.

Pin Prick Pr., The, *(Pin Prick; 0-936424),* 2664 S. Green Rd., Shaker Heights, OH 44122 (SAN 214-1965) Tel 216-932-2173.

Pinal County Schl. Office, *(Pinal Cnty Schl Ofc; 0-9616993),* P.O. Box 769, Florence, AZ 85232 (SAN 661-6879); 1301 N. Pinal, Florence, AZ 85232 (SAN 661-6887) Tel 602-868-5801.

Pinata Pubns., *(Pinata Pubns; 0-934925),* 427 Grand Ave., Oakland, CA 94610 (SAN 694-6062) Tel 415-893-6682.

Pinchpenny Press *See Holt Associates*

Pindar Press, *(Pindar Pr; 0-918223),* 30 Rockefeller Plaza, New York, NY 10112 (SAN 669-6996).

Pine Barrens Pr. *See Barnegat Light Pr.*

Pine Hall Pr., *(Pine Hall; 0-9615022),* P.O. Box 150657, Nashville, TN 37215-0657 (SAN 694-0536) Tel 615-373-2657.

Pine Hill Press, *(Pine Hill Pr)* Freeman, SD 57029 (SAN 211-0873).

Pine Mountain Pr., Inc, *(Pine Mntn; 0-89769),* 2440 O St., Suite 202, Lincoln, NE 68510-1125 (SAN 282-1664) Tel 402-474-2676; Dist. by: Media Productions & Mktg., Inc., 2440 "O" St., Suite 202, Lincoln, NE 68510-1125 (SAN 216-6372) Tel 402-474-2676.

†Pine Pr., *(Pine Pr; 0-930502),* Box 530, RD 1, Landisburg, PA 17040 (SAN 211-2655) Tel 717-789-4466; *CIP.*

Pine Ridge Publishing Co., *(Pine Ridge; 0-9607480),* P.O. Box 234, Amesbury, MA 01913 (SAN 238-4698) Tel 617-388-0969.

Pine Row Pubns., *(Pine Row; 0-935238),* P.O. Box 428, Washington Crossing, PA 18977 (SAN 214-0810) Tel 215-493-4259.

Pine Tree Press, *(Pine Tree Pr; 0-932196),* P.O. Box 2353, Orange, CA 92669 (SAN 208-4937) Tel 714-639-0706; Dist. by: Rampart Institute, Box 4, Fullerton, CA 92704 (SAN 282-6410).

Pine Tree Pubns., Inc., *(Pine Tree Inc; 0-943974),* 711 Woodgate Court, Suite C-1, Augusta, GA 30909 (SAN 241-0672) Tel 404-738-3610.

†Pineapple Pr., Inc., *(Pineapple Pr; 0-910923),* 202 Pineapple St., Englewood, FL 33533 (SAN 285-0850); Orders to: P.O. Box 314, Englewood, FL 33533 (SAN 285-0869) Tel 813-475-2238; *CIP.*

Pinebrook Press, *Div. of Pinebrook Educational Group, Inc., (Pinebrook Pr; 0-910859),* 2 East Ave., Larchmont, NY 10538 (SAN 262-0618).

†Pinecrest Fund, The, *(Pinecrest Fund; 0-9601858),* 616 E. 63rd St., Suite 204, Kansas City, MO 64110 (SAN 212-3010) Tel 816-444-9400; *CIP.*

Pinecrest Publishing Co., *(Pinecrest Pub Co; 0-913287),* 3505 Pinecrest Dr., Kilgore, TX 75662 (SAN 283-9288) Tel 214-984-5695.

Pineridge Publishing House, *(Pineridge Pub; 0-9610490),* P.O. Box 289 Gedney, White Plains, NY 10605 (SAN 264-3057) Tel 914-761-8962.

Pinerolo Publishing Co., *(Pinerolo Pub; 0-9616692),* 1275 Fourth St., No. 203, Santa Rosa, CA 95404 (SAN 659-8404) Tel 707-578-8890.

Pinewood Press, *(Pinewood; 0-9604498),* P.O. Box 79104, Houston, TX 77279 (SAN 215-9058).

Pink House Publishing Co., *(Pink Hse Pub; 0-915946),* 410 Magellan Ave., Penthouse 1002, Honolulu, HI 96813 (SAN 204-8965) Tel 808-537-1875.

Pinnaroo Publishing, *(Pinnaroo; 0-939705),* P.O. Box 7525, Bend, OR 97708 (SAN 663-5156); 17560 Cascade Estate Dr., Bend, OR 97701 (SAN 663-5164) Tel 503-382-4657.

†Pinon Productions, *(Pinon Productions; 0-930855),* 781 McCarthy Blvd., Pueblo, CO 81005 (SAN 677-7813) Tel 303-564-2210; *CIP.*

Pintores Pr., *(Pintores Pr; 0-934116),* Box 1597, Roswell, NM 88201 (SAN 213-1412).

Pinus Strobus Pr., *(Pinus; 0-9615771),* 615 Kerry Dr., Bloomington, IN 47401 (SAN 695-9660) Tel 812-339-3809.

Pinwheel Pubs., Inc., *(Pinwheel Pubs; 0-914771),* 910 Stuart Ave., Mamaroneck, NY 10543 (SAN 289-5420); Orders to: Box 777, Berryville, VA 22611 (SAN 662-2178) Tel 705-955-4171.

Pinyon Pr., *(Pinyon Pr; 0-936323),* P.O. Box 4197, Sparks, NV 89432 (SAN 697-2845) Tel 702-355-7535; 875 E. York Way, Sparks, NV 89431 (SAN 697-2853).

Pioneer Balloon Co., *(Pioneer Balloon; 0-9616600),* 555 N. Woodlawn Ave., Wichita, KS 67208 (SAN 659-5324) Tel 316-685-2266.

Pioneer Book Pubs., *(Pioneer Bk TX; 0-933512),* Box 426, Seagraves, TX 79359 (SAN 209-4762) Tel 806-546-2498.

Pioneer Farm, *(Pioneer Farm; 0-9614899),* Ohop Valley Rd., Eatonville, WA 98328 (SAN 693-2738) Tel 206-832-6923.

Pioneer Graphics, *(Pioneer Graph; 0-936711),* 426 First St., Eureka, CA 95501 (SAN 699-9328) Tel 707-443-9735.

Pioneer Pr. Bks., *(Pioneer Pr Bks; 0-936546),* 37 S. Palouse St., Walla Walla, WA 99362 (SAN 222-1209).

†Pioneer Press, Inc., *Div. of Dixie Gun Works, Inc., (Pioneer Pr; 0-913150),* P.O. Box 684, Union City, TN 38261 (SAN 204-8973) Tel 901-885-0374; *CIP.*

Pioneer Publishing & Distributing, *(Pioneer Englewood; 0-937881),* 5555 DTC Pkwy., Suite 1005, Englewood, CO 80111 (SAN 659-5685) Tel 303-337-6433.

Pioneer Ventures, Inc., *(Pioneer Vent; 0-915321),* 4027 Lanark, Houston, TX 77025 (SAN 290-0351) Tel 713-666-0051; Toll free: 800-521-3690; Toll free: 800-482-3653 (In Michigan); Dist. by: Spring Arbor Distributors, 10885 Textile Rd., Belleville, MI 48111 (SAN 158-9016) Tel 313-481-0900.

Pip Productions, *(Pip Prods; 0-936151),* 9204 NE 52nd St., Vancouver, WA 98662 (SAN 696-8090) Tel 206-254-2156.

Pipeline Pubns., *(Pipeline Pubns; 0-938189),* 1800 S. Robertson Blvd., No. 239, Los Angeles, CA 90035 (SAN 659-7343); 3436 Vinton Ave., No. 8, Los Angeles, CA 90034 (SAN 659-7351).

Piper Bks. *See Houghton Mifflin Co.*

†Piper Publishing, Inc., *(Piper; 0-87832),* Box 1, Blue Earth, MN 56013 (SAN 202-005X) Tel 507-526-5448; *CIP.*

Piping Industry Progress & Education Trust Fund, *(Piping Indust Prog & Ed; 0-936387),* 501 Shatto Pl., Suite 405, Los Angeles, CA 90020 (SAN 697-2829) Tel 213-382-5255.

Pipsqueak Pr, *(Pipsqueak Pr; 0-9614601),* RFD 3, Box 1035, Dexter, ME 04930 (SAN 691-8220) Tel 207-277-5163.

Piraeus Publishers *See Forum Pr., Inc.*

Pisang Press, *(Pisang Pr; 0-9612826),* 1721 Las Canoas Rd., Santa Barbara, CA 93105 (SAN 291-350X) Tel 805-962-0596.

Pisapia, John, Associates, *(J Pisapia Assocs; 0-917964),* 210- Kanawha Blvd., Charleston, WV 25311 (SAN 209-9845) Tel 304-345-4868.

Pisces Pr., *(Pisces Pr AZ; 0-9616565),* 10923 Meade Dr., Sun City, AZ 85351 (SAN 659-5693) Tel 602-977-2264.

Pisces Pr., *(Pisces Pr TX; 0-938328),* 3209 26th St., Lubbock, TX 79410 (SAN 215-7993) Tel 806-799-5220.

Pison River House, *(Pison River Hse; 0-931925),* P.O. Box 1103, South Miami, FL 33143 (SAN 685-995X) Tel 305-666-9674; 900 N. Federal Hwy., Suite160-60, Boca Raton, FL 33432 (SAN 699-5896).

Pitcairn Press, Inc., *(Pitcairn Pr; 0-914874),* 388 Franklin St., Cambridge, MA 02139 (SAN 207-4087).

Pittenbruach Pr., *(Pittenbruach Pr; 0-938875),* P.O. Box 553, Northhampton, MA 01060 (SAN 662-6688); 15 Walnut, Northhampton, MA 01060 (SAN 662-6696) Tel 413-584-8547.

Pittore Euforico, *(Pittore Euforico; 0-934376),* P.O. Box 1132, Peter Stuyvesant Sta., New York, NY 10009 (SAN 213-5469) Tel 212-673-2705.

Pittsburgh History & Landmarks Foundation, *(Pitt Hist & Landmks Found; 0-916670),* 450 The Landmarks Bldg., One Station Square, Pittsburgh, PA 15219 (SAN 205-129X) Tel 412-471-5808; Dist. by: Central Wholesale, 143 S. 25th St., Pittsburgh, PA 15203 (SAN 200-6987) Tel 412-488-2800.

Pittsburgh Jewish Pubn. & Education Foundation, *(Pitt Jewish Foun)* 315 S. Bellefield Ave., Pittsburgh, PA 15213 (SAN 206-3077).

Pittsburgh Theological Seminary, Clifford E. Barbour Library, *(Pitts Theolog; 0-931222),* 616 N. Highland Ave., Pittsburgh, PA 15206 (SAN 240-981X) Tel 412-362-5610.

Pivot *See Taplinger Publishing Co., Inc.*

Pixel Products & Pubns., *(Pixel Prods Pubns; 0-935163),* R.D. 2, Box C110, Lock Haven, PA 17745 (SAN 695-3557) Tel 717-748-7064.

†Pixie Press, *(Pixie Pr AZ; 0-9607128),* P.O. Box 13383, Phoenix, AZ 85002 (SAN 239-0205) Tel 602-253-7259; *CIP.*

Pizzazz Press, *(Pizzazz Pr; 0-939390),* 5114 Chicago, Omaha, NE 68132 (SAN 220-1801) Tel 402-556-1371.

PKR Foundation, *(PKR Foundation; 0-9614567),* 20 W. Ninth St., Kansas City, MO 64105 (SAN 691-8433) Tel 816-421-1869.

Place in the Woods, *(Place in the Woods; 0-932991),* 3900 Glenwood Ave., Golden Valley, MN 55422-5302 (SAN 689-058X) Tel 612-374-2120; Dist. by: Bacon's, Box 228B, East Chatham, NY 12060 (SAN 200-5573); Dist. by: Walnut Pr., LTO Enterprises, 6036 N. Tenth Way, Phoenix, AZ 85014 (SAN 285-113X); Dist. by: Midwest Library Service, 11443 St. Charles Rock Rd., Bridgeton, MO 63044 (SAN 169-4243); Dist. by: BookFare, 5609-2A Fishers Ln., Rockville, MD 20852 (SAN 200-5581).

†**Place of Herons Press,** *(Place Herons; 0-916908),* P.O. Box 1952, Austin, TX 78767-1952 (SAN 208-8088) Tel 512-478-5870; *CIP.*

Plaid Pony Pubns., *(Plaid Pony Pubns; 0-935195),* P.O. Box 68502, Seattle, WA 98168 (SAN 695-510X) Tel 206-242-8376; 3220 S. 166th St., Seattle, WA 98188 (SAN 695-5118).

Plain View Pr., *(Plain View; 0-911051),* 1509 Dexter, Austin, TX 78704 (SAN 264-3073) Tel 512-441-2452.

Plains Pr., *(Plains Press; 0-918461),* Southwest State Univ., Marshall, MN 56258 (SAN 677-0185) Tel 507-537-6463.

Plamen Publishing Co., *(Plamen Pub; 0-9602138),* P.O. Box 3088, Steinway Sta., Astoria, NY 11103 (SAN 212-3029).

Planet Bks., *(Planet Bks; 0-88009),* 65-42 Fresh Meadow Lane, Fresh Meadows, NY 11365 (SAN 282-5759) Tel 718-961-9240.

Planet/Drum Foundation, *(Planet Drum Books; 0-937102),* P.O. Box 31251, San Francisco, CA 94131 (SAN 216-437X) Tel 415-285-6556.

Planet Press, *(Planet CA; 0-931671),* 115 29th St., Newport Beach, CA 92663-3418 (SAN 686-9203) Tel 714-675-5994.

Planet Watch Pubns., *(Planet Watch Pubns; 0-9617168),* P.O. Box 515. Old Chelsea Sta., New York, NY 10113 (SAN 663-1258) Tel 212-242-1958.

Planned Parenthood Assn. of Idaho, Inc., *(PP Idaho; 0-9611762),* 4301 Franklin Rd., Boise, ID 83705-0839 (SAN 285-3574) Tel 208-345-0839.

†**Planned Parenthood Federation of America, Inc.,** *(Plan Parent; 0-934586),* 810 Seventh Ave., New York, NY 10019 (SAN 205-1281) Tel 212-541-7800; *CIP.*

Planned Parenthood of Central California, *(Plan Par Ctrl CA; 0-9610122),* 633 N. Van Ness Ave., Fresno, CA 93728 (SAN 274-6662) Tel 209-486-2411.

Planned Parenthood of Northwest New Jersey, Inc., Affil. of Planned Parenthood Federation of America, *(NW Plan Parent; 0-9609366),* 196 Speedwell Ave., Morristown, NJ 07960-3889 (SAN 260-2482) Tel 201-539-9580.

Planned Parenthood of Westchester, Inc., *(Planned Parenthood; 0-9614179),* 88 East Post Rd., White Plains, NY 10601 (SAN 686-6611) Tel 914-428-7876.

Planners Pr., Div. of American Planning Association, *(Planners Pr; 0-918286),* 1313 E. 60th St., Chicago, IL 60637 (SAN 209-3928) Tel 312-955-9100.

Planning Retirement, *(Planning Retire; 0-9614180),* 8321 Westlawn Ave., Los Angeles, CA 90045 (SAN 686-6263) Tel 213-932-6225.

Planning Forum, The, *(Planning Forum; 0-912841),* P.O. Box 70, Oxford, OH 45056 (SAN 230-8673) Tel 513-523-4185; 5500 College Corner Pike, Oxford, OH 45056 (SAN 669-2435).

Plant, W.E.C., Enterprises, *(W E C Plant Ent; 0-913611),* P.O. Box 030096, Ft. Lauderdale, FL 33303 (SAN 285-3612) Tel 305-467-3512; Dist. by: W. E. C. Plant Enterprises, P.O. Box 030096, Ft. Lauderdale, FL 33303 (SAN 285-3612).

Plant Press, The, *(Plant Pr MA; 0-940960),* P.O. Box 133, Halifax, MA 02338 (SAN 217-4162) Tel 617-293-3163.

Plantagenet House, Inc., *(Plantagenet Hse; 0-940812),* P.O. Box 271, Blackshear, GA 31516 (SAN 219-6271) Tel 912-449-6601.

Plantation Pr., *(Plantation; 0-911150),* 9140 Davies Plantation Rd., Brunswick, Memphis, TN 38134 (SAN 205-1273) Tel 901-386-2015.

Plantin Pr., *(Plantin Pr; 0-9612546),* P.O. Box 905, Minneapolis, MN 55440 (SAN 205-1265) Tel 612-566-6795.

Platen Publishing Co., *(Platen Pub Co; 0-932607),* 14240 Bledsoe St., Sylmar, CA 91342 (SAN 687-5246) Tel 818-367-9613.

Platform Studio, *(Platform Studio; 0-942812),* 636 Beacon St., Boston, MA 02215 (SAN 240-4885).

Platinum Pen Publishers, Inc., *(Platinum Pen Pubs; 0-912815),* P.O. Box 11127, 4810 NE Vivion Rd., Kansas City, MO 64119 (SAN 265-394X) Tel 816-741-2894.

Platonic Academy Pr., The, *(Platonic Acad Pr; 0-937011),* Box 409, Santa Cruz, CA 95061 (SAN 658-6767) Tel 408-423-7923; 129 Spring St., Santa Cruz, CA 95060 (SAN 658-6775).

†**Platt & Munk Pubs.,** Div. of Grosset & Dunlap, *(Platt; 0-448),* 200 Madison Ave., New York, NY 10010 (SAN 211-9668) Tel 212-576-8900; *CIP.*

Platte 'n Press *See Jende-Hagan, Inc.*

Platte River Whooping Crane Trust, Inc., *(PRWCT; 0-938441),* 2550 N. Diers Ave., Suite H, Grand Island, NE 68803 (SAN 661-0455) Tel 308-384-4633.

†**Platypus Bks., Ltd.,** *(Platypus Bks; 0-930905),* P.O. Box 492, Pittsford, NY 14534 (SAN 679-1727) Tel 716-248-8636; Dist. by: Writers & Books, 740 University Ave., Rochester, NY 14607 (SAN 156-9678) Tel 716-473-2590; *CIP.*

Play Schools Assn., *(Play Schs; 0-936426),* 19 W. 44th St., New York, NY 10017 (SAN 202-0076) Tel 212-921-2940.

Playboy Paperbacks, Div. of P.E.I. Bks., Inc., *(Playboy Pbks; 0-87216; 0-86721),* 200 Madison Ave., New York, NY 10019 (SAN 213-2672) Tel 212-686-9820; Dist. by: ICD, 250 W. 55th St., New York, NY 10019 (SAN 270-885X) Tel 212-262-7444.

Players Pr., Inc., *(Players Pr; 0-941426; 0-88734),* P.O. Box 1132, Studio City, Los Angeles, CA 91604 (SAN 239-0213) Tel 818-789-4980.

Playette Corp., *(Playette Corp; 0-940630),* 85 Longview Rd., Port Washington, NY 11050 (SAN 203-1000) Tel 516-883-7460.

†**Plays, Inc.,** *(Plays; 0-8238),* 120 Boylston St., Boston, MA 02116 (SAN 202-0084) Tel 617-423-3157; *CIP.*

Playspaces-International, *(Playspaces; 0-85953),* 31D Union Ave., Sudbury, MA 01776 (SAN 216-2121) Tel 617-443-7146.

Playwrights Pr., *(Playwrights Pr; 0-9617282),* c/o Amherst Writers & Artists, P.O. Box 1076, Amherst, MA 01004 (SAN 663-5180) Tel 413-584-7729; c/o Amherst Writers & Artists, 77 McClellan, Amherst, MA 01002 (SAN 663-5199).

Plaza Pubs., *(Plaza Pubs),* 2010 Empire Blvd., Webster, NY 14580 (SAN 202-1544) Tel 716-671-1533.

Pleasant Co., *(Pleasant Co; 0-937295),* 7 N. Pinckney St., Madison, WI 53703 (SAN 658-7755) Tel 608-251-2222.

Pleasant Hill Press *(Pleasant Hill),* 2600 Pleasant Hill Rd., Sebastopol, CA 95472 (SAN 207-1630) Tel 701-823-6583.

Pleasantry Pr., Inc., *(Pleasantry Pr; 0-932407),* 7 N. Pinckney St., Madison, WI 53703 (SAN 686-6948) Tel 608-251-2222.

Please Pr., Ltd., *(Please Pr; 0-938580),* Box 3036, Flint, MI 48502 (SAN 215-8000) Tel 313-239-3110.

†**Pleasure Dome Press,** Div. of L.I. Poetry Collective, Inc., *(Pleasure Dome; 0-918870),* Box 773, Huntington, NY 11743 (SAN 210-4849) Tel 516-421-2376; *CIP.*

Pleasure Trove Books, *(Pleasure Trove; 0-930400),* 2156 Merokee Dr., Merrick, NY 11566 (SAN 207-2742) Tel 516-379-2501; Dist. by: Light House Hill Pub., 279 Edinboro Rd., Staten Island, NY 10306 (SAN 238-0706) Tel 718-987-7586; Dist. by: Quality Books, 918 Sherwood Dr., Lake Bluff, IL 60044-2204 (SAN 169-2127) Tel 312-498-4000.

Pleiades Press/Studio Graphics Workshop, *(Pleiades Pr; 0-9616152),* 310 Old Main St., W., Bradenton, FL 33505 (SAN 699-9417) Tel 813-748-8638.

Pleiades Publishing, *(Pleiades Pub; 0-9613722),* P.O. Box 2133, Sandy, UT 84091 (SAN 683-2822).

Pleneurethic International, *(Pleneurethic Intl),* Earth Light Bookstore, 113 E. Main, Walla Walla, WA 99362 (SAN 209-116X) Tel 509-525-4983.

Plenum Medical Bk. Co. *See* **Plenum Publishing Corp.**

Plenum Pr. *See* **Plenum Publishing Corp.**

Plenum Publishing Corp., *(Plenum Pub; 0-306),* 233 Spring St., New York, NY 10013 (SAN 201-9248) Tel 212-620-8000; Toll free: 800-221-9369; 170 Le Grand Ave., Northvale, NJ 07647 (SAN 658-1412). *Imprints:* Consultants Bureau (Consultants); I F I/Plenum (IFI-Plenum); Plenum Medical Book Company (Plenum Med Bk); Plenum Press (Plenum Pr); Plenum Rosetta (Rosetta).

Plenum Rosetta *See* **Plenum Publishing Corp.**

Pletsch & Associates, *(Pletsch Assocs; 0-917927),* P.O. Box 1409, Albany, GA 31702-1409 (SAN 656-9978) Tel 912-432-7705.

Plexus Publishing, Inc., *(Plexus Pub; 0-937548),* 143 Old Marlton Pike, Medford, NJ 08055 (SAN 212-436X) Tel 609-654-6500.

Plezia, Valerie, *(V Plezia; 0-9609368),* 14009 Mohawk Trail, Cleveland, OH 44130 (SAN 260-2490) Tel 216-842-4581.

Ploof Stuff, *(Ploof Stuff; 0-9611740),* 123 W. Main, Melrose, MN 56352 (SAN 285-3655).

Ploss, Douglas A., *(D A Ploss; 0-9603632),* 38764 N. Gratton Rd., Lake Villa, IL 60046 (SAN 213-7852) Tel 312-356-5944.

Ploss, Thomas H., *(T H Ploss; 0-9613788),* 1016 E. Hyde Park Blvd., Chicago, IL 60615 (SAN 678-9889) Tel 312-373-4308.

Plossl, George, Educational Services, Inc., *(G P Ed Serv; 0-926219),* 1850 Parkway Pl., Suite 335, Marietta, GA 30067 (SAN 294-457X) Tel 404-423-7620.

Plough Publishing House, The, Subs. of Woodcrest Service Committee, *(Plough; 0-87486),* Hutterian Brethren, Rte. 213, Rifton, NY 12471 (SAN 202-0092) Tel 914-658-3141.

Ploughshare Press, *(Ploughshare Pr; 0-912396),* P.O. Box 123, Sea Bright, NJ 07760 (SAN 205-6380) Tel 201-842-0336.

Ploughshares Bks., Subs. of Ploughshares Inc., *(Ploughshares Bks; 0-933277),* 214A Waverley Ave., Watertown, MA 02172 (SAN 691-8069) Tel 617-926-9875.

Plover Pr., *(Plover Pr; 0-917635),* P.O. Box R, Kaneohe, HI 96744 (SAN 656-9005) Tel 808-254-5725; Dist. by: Talman Co., Inc., 150 Fifth Ave., New York, NY 10011 (SAN 200-5204) Tel 212-620-3182.

Plowshare Press, Inc., *(Plowshare; 0-87368),* P.O. Box 2252, Boston, MA 02107 (SAN 204-899X).

Plucked String, Inc., *(Plucked; 0-9614120),* P.O. Box 11125, Arlington, VA 22210 (SAN 669-7003) Tel 301-622-1069.

Plum Apple Publishing, *(Plum Apple Pub; 0-9616794),* 1401 Tower Rd., Winnetka, IL 60093 (SAN 659-9400) Tel 312-446-2079.

Plum Grove Bks., *(Plum Grove Bks; 0-9616856),* 314 S. Benton St., Palatine, IL 60067 (SAN 661-5961) Tel 312-358-0408.

Plum Hall Inc., *(Plum Hall; 0-911537),* 1 Spruce Ave., Cardiff, NJ 08232 (SAN 264-3103) Tel 609-927-3770.

Plum Nelly Shop, Inc., The, *(Plum Nelly),* 1201 Hixson Pike, Chattanooga, TN 37405 (SAN 216-1745) Tel 615-266-0585.

Plum Publishing Co., *(Plum Pub; 0-9613789),* 25115 DeSalle St., Laguna Hills, CA 92653 (SAN 678-9854) Tel 714-770-4104.

Plumbers Ink Books, *(Plumbers Ink Bks; 0-935684),* P.O. Box 233, Cerrillos, NM 87010 (SAN 213-8662).

Plumbing Pubns., *(Plumbing Pubns; 0-9603462),* 1700 N. H St., Midland, TX 79701 (SAN 213-3148) Tel 915-683-5574; Orders to: P.O. Box 5461, Midland, TX 79701 (SAN 213-3156) Tel 915-682-3249.

Plume Bks. *See* **New American Library**

Plunkett Lake Pr., *(Plunkett Lake Pr; 0-9614696),* 551 Franklin St., Cambridge, MA 02139 (SAN 692-655X) Tel 617-576-2738.

Pluribus Pr., Inc., Div. of Teach'em, Inc., *(Pluribus Pr; 0-931028),* 160 E. Illinois St., Chicago, IL 60611 (SAN 238-8413) Tel 312-467-0424.

Plus One Publishing, Inc, *(Plus One Pub; 0-934822),* 625 N. Mansfield Ave., Hollywood, CA 90036 (SAN 213-1404) Tel 213-936-1783.

Plus Seven Books, *(Plus Seven Bks; 0-943416),* SR Box 13, Brandy Station, VA 22714 (SAN 240-7469) Tel 703-825-9163.

Plutarch Press *See Advent Bks., Inc*

Plycon Pr., Div. of Plycon Industries, *(Plycon Pr; 0-916434),* P.O. Box 220, Redondo Beach, CA 90277 (SAN 201-8829) Tel 213-379-9725; Orders to: 10612 Collett, Granada Hills, CA 91344 (SAN 693-9716) Tel 213-379-9725.

Plymouth Colony Research Group, *(Plymouth Col),* 128 Massasoit Dr., Warwick, RI 02888 (SAN 241-4376) Tel 401-781-6759.

Plymouth Press, Subs. of International Language Institute, *(Plymouth Pr; 0-935540),* P.O. Box 390205, Miami, FL 33119 (SAN 212-9612) Tel 305-538-5022.

Plymouth Rock Foundation, *(Plymouth Rock Found; 0-942516),* 14 McKinley Cir., Marlborough, NH 03455 (SAN 239-8583) Tel 603-876-4658.

PM, Inc., *(PM Inc; 0-9608846),* No. 106, 14545 Friar, Van Nuys, CA 91411 (SAN 241-0524) Tel 818-873-4399.

PMnet, *(PMnet; 0-935293),* 580 College Ave., Palo Alto, CA 94306 (SAN 695-9679) Tel 415-856-0135.

P'Nye Press, *(P'Nye Pr; 0-9602402),* The Printers Shop, 4047 Transport, Palo Alto, CA 94303 (SAN 212-5463) Tel 415-494-6802.

Pocahontas Pr., Inc., *(Pocahontas Pr; 0-936015),* 2805 Wellesley Ct., Blacksburg, VA 24060 (SAN 696-6195) Tel 703-951-0467.

Pocket Bks., Inc., Div. of Simon & Schuster, Inc., *(PB; 0-671),* 1230 Ave. of the Americas, New York, NY 10020 (SAN 202-5922) Tel 212-246-2121; Toll free: 800-223-2336; Orders to: 200 Old Tappan, Old Tappan, NJ 07675 (SAN 662-1147) Tel 201-767-5000. *Imprints:* Gallen, Richard (Gallen); Lantern Books (Lantern); Long Shadow Books (Long Shadow Bks); Poseidon Press (Poseidon); Timescape (Timescape); Wallaby (Wallaby).

Pocket Pal Publishing Co., *(Pocket Pal Pub; 0-938079),* P.O. Box 23391, Baltimore, MD 21203 (SAN 659-6916); 2101 Callow Ave., Baltimore, MD 21217 (SAN 659-6924) Tel 301-523-6113.

Pocket Pro, *(Pocket Pro; 0-9615593),* 5627 University Way, NE, Seattle, WA 98105 (SAN 695-9695) Tel 206-527-4822.

Pocket Testament League, Inc, *(Pocket Testament),* 117 Main St., Lincoln Park, NJ 07035 (SAN 225-4204) Tel 201-696-1900; P.O. Box 368, Lincoln Park, NJ 07035 (SAN 669-2443).

Pocumtuck Valley Memorial Assn., *(Pocumtuck Valley Mem; 0-9612876),* Memorial Hall Museum, Deerfield, MA 01342 (SAN 211-2663) Tel 413-774-7476.

Podesta Fishing Co., Pubs., *(Podesta Fishing),* 140 S. Peter Dr., Campbell, CA 95008 (SAN 211-0881) Tel 408-377-7700.

Podiatric Educational Pubns., *(Podiatric Educ; 0-9600302),* 28 Prospect St., Waltham, MA 02154 (SAN 204-9007) Tel 617-894-1985.

Poe, Edgar Allan, Society of Baltimore, The, *(Poe Soc Baltimore; 0-9616449),* 402 E. Gittings Ave., Baltimore, MD 21212 (SAN 659-0535) Tel 301-234-4821.

Poet Papers, *(Poet Papers; 0-9600288),* P.O. Box 528, Topanga, CA 90290 (SAN 209-4770).

Poet Tree Pr., The, *(Poet Tree Pr; 0-916922),* Box 97, Antrim, NH 03440 (SAN 202-3172) Tel 603-588-2730.

Poetasumanos Press, *(Poetasumanos; 0-938254),* 949 Capp St., No. 10, San Francisco, CA 94110 (SAN 215-6997).

Poetica Pr., Div. of Denehen, Inc., *(Poetica Pr; 0-9613534),* 4316 Marvin Dr., Fort Wayne, IN 46806-2596 (SAN 669-7011) Tel 219-744-4798.

Poetry Eastwest, *(Poetry Eastwest; 0-912206),* P.O. Box 391, Sumter, SC 29150 (SAN 202-0106) Tel 803-773-5170.

Poetry Publicatons *See Quill Bks.*

Poets Alive Pr., *(Poets Alive Pr; 0-936641),* P.O. Box 999, Harrisburg, NC 28075 (SAN 699-6949); 631 Louise Ave., Charlotte, NC 28204 (SAN 699-6957) Tel 704-332-5955.

Poets & Playwrights, Inc., The, *(Poets Playwrights; 0-9615306),* 322 W. 52nd St., P.O. Box 136, Radio City Sta., New York, NY 10019 (SAN 694-6003) Tel 212-582-7898.

†Poets & Writers, *(Poets & Writers; 0-913734),* 201 W. 54th St., New York, NY 10019 (SAN 204-8981) Tel 212-757-1766; *CIP.*

Poet's Mark, *(Poets Mark; 0-9614820),* 19311 Orleans Ave., Detroit, MI 48203 (SAN 693-0778) Tel 313-892-4536.

Pogment Pr., The, *(Pogment Pr; 0-938823),* 4609 Village Dr., Fairfax, VA 22030 (SAN 661-7468) Tel 703-273-2934.

Pohl, J., Assocs., *(J Pohl Assocs; 0-939332),* 461 Spring Run Rd., Coraopolis, PA 15108 (SAN 220-181X) Tel 412-457-6300.

Poiletman Publishing Co., *(Poiletman Pub; 0-937519),* 196 Sweet Wood Cir., Columbia, SC 29210 (SAN 659-0551) Tel 803-781-1417; Orders to: P.O. Box 210726, Columbia, SC 29221-0726 (SAN 662-4200).

Point *See Scholastic, Inc.*

Point Foundation/Whole Earth Review, *(Point Calif),* 27 Gate 5 Rd., Sausalito, CA 94965 (SAN 210-7139) Tel 415-332-4335; Dist. by: Random Hse., 400 Hahn Rd., Westminster, MD 21157 (SAN 202-5515); Toll free: 800-638-6460.

Point Loma Pubns., Inc., *(Point Loma Pub; 0-913004),* P.O. Box 6507, San Diego, CA 92106 (SAN 204-9023); 3727 Charles St., San Diego, CA 92106 (SAN 662-1155) Tel 619-222-3291.

Point Park College, *(Point Park; 0-9615172),* 201 Wood St., Pittsburgh, PA 15222 (SAN 694-2881) Tel 412-392-3860.

Point Reyes Pr., *(Point Reyes Pr; 0-9613145),* P.O. Box 332, Point Reyes, CA 94956 (SAN 294-6505) Tel 415-663-1612; 39 Drake's Summit, Point Reyes, CA 94956 (SAN 294-6513); Dist. by: Bookpeople, 2929 Fifth St., Berkeley, CA 94710 (SAN 168-9517) Tel 415-549-3030.

Point Two Pubns., *(Point Two; 0-911073),* P.O. Box 725, R.C.U., New York, NY 10185 (SAN 274-6948) Tel 212-719-9045.

Pointe Pubs., Inc., *(Pointe Pubs; 0-935897),* P.O. Box 3078, Centerline, MI 48015-0078 (SAN 696-6292) Tel 313-778-0404; 22317 Kelly Rd., East Detroit, MI 48021 (SAN 696-981X) Tel 313-445-6724; Toll free: 800-852-7409; Dist. by: Spring Arbor, 10885 Textile Rd., Belleville, MI 48111-2398 (SAN 158-9016) Tel 313-481-0900; Toll free: 800-443-5524; Dist. by: Growth Publishing, 201 Davis Dr., Suite U, Sterling Industrial Pk., Sterling, VA 22170 (SAN 682-9112) Tel 703-450-6460; Toll free: 800-426-8095.

Pokeberry Publications, *(Pokeberry Pubns; 0-911111),* P.O. Box 421, Luquillo, PR 00673 (SAN 274-6956).

Poko Pr., *(Poko Press; 0-9616929),* P.O. Box 14766, Columbus, OH 43214 (SAN 661-5252); 300 Oakland Pk., Columbus, OH 43214 (SAN 661-5260) Tel 614-262-3865.

Poky Nose Pr., *(Poky Nose Pr; 0-9613576),* P.O. Box 232E, Star Rte., Albrightsville, PA 18210 (SAN 670-168X) Tel 717-646-8748.

Polamerica Press, *(Polamerica Pr; 0-914310),* P.O. Box 36415, Los Angeles, CA 90036 (SAN 206-8672).

Polanie Publishing Co., *(Polanie; 0-911154),* 643 Madison St., N.E., Minneapolis, MN 55413 (SAN 204-9031) Tel 612-379-9134.

Polar Palm Productions, Inc., *(Polar Palm; 0-918792),* 1238 G St., Anchorage, AK 99501 (SAN 282-1702) Tel 907-279-1859; Orders to: Box 4-907, Anchorage, AK 99509-0907 (SAN 282-1710).

Polaris Press, *(Polaris Pr; 0-930504),* 16540 Camellia Terrace, Los Gatos, CA 95030 (SAN 204-904X).

Polaroid Corp., *(Polaroid Corp; 0-9616459),* 575 Technology Sq., No. 9P, Cambridge, MA 02139 (SAN 659-2759) Tel 617-577-3096.

Polestar Nexus Publishing, Inc., *(Polestar Nexus; 0-931087),* 8333 Corbin Ave., Canoga Park, CA 91306 (SAN 678-9404) Tel 818-765-7827.

Polestar Pubns., *(Polestar; 0-942044),* 620 S. Minnesota Ave., Sioux Falls, SD 57104 (SAN 239-474X) Tel 605-338-2888.

Police Beat Press, *(Police Beat Pr; 0-942724),* 723 N. 53rd St., Milwaukee, WI 53208 (SAN 240-1231).

Police Bookshelf, *(Police Bkshelf; 0-936279),* P.O. Box 122, Concord, NH 03301 (SAN 697-9424) Tel 603-224-6814; 72 Broadway, Concord, NH 03301 (SAN 698-2336).

Police Executive Research Forum, *(Police Exec Res),* 2300 M St. NW, Suite 910, Washington, DC 20037 (SAN 274-7014).

Police Foundation, *(Police Found),* 1001 22 ST. NW, Suite 200, Washington, DC 20037 (SAN 237-8280).

Police Press, *(Police Pr; 0-89415),* P.O. Box 2818, Dublin, CA 94568-0818 (SAN 209-9853) Tel 415-829-2728.

Police Training Foundation, *(Police Train),* 3412 Ruby St., Franklin Park, IL 60131 (SAN 262-0626) Tel 312-678-4009.

†Policy Studies Assocs., *(PS Assocs Croton; 0-936826),* P.O. Box 337, Croton-on-Hudson, NY 10520 (SAN 214-4417) Tel 914-271-6500; *CIP.*

Policy Studies Organization, *(Policy Studies; 0-918592),* Univ. of Illinois at Urbana-Champaign, 361 Lincoln Hall, 702 S. Wright St., Urbana, IL 61801 (SAN 210-1343) Tel 217-359-8541.

Polish American Historical Assn., *(Polish American; 0-940962),* 984 Milwaukee Ave., Chicago, IL 60622 (SAN 212-3037).

Polish Genealogical Society, *(Polish Genealog; 0-9602162),* 984 N. Milwaukee Ave., Chicago, IL 60622 (SAN 224-4934).

Polish Institute of Arts & Sciences, *(Polish Inst Art & Sci),* 59 E. 66th St., New York, NY 10021 (SAN 225-3747) Tel 212-988-4338.

Polish Museum of America, *(Polish Museum Am; 0-9602162),* 984 N. Milwaukee Ave., Chicago, IL 60622 (SAN 274-7103) Tel 312-384-3352.

†Political Research, Inc., *(Political Re; 0-915140),* 16850 Dallas Pkwy., Dallas, TX 75248 (SAN 218-9097) Tel 214-931-8831; *CIP.*

Polk, James K., Memorial Auxilary, *(James K Polk; 0-9607668),* Box 741, Columbia, TN 38401 (SAN 239-5908) Tel 615-388-2354.

Polk's Bluebooks of Hobbies, *(Polk; 0-911399),* 314 Fifth Ave., New York, NY 10001 (SAN 274-7227) Tel 212-279-9034.

Polley Pubs., *(Polley Pubs),* 93156 Marcola Rd., Marcola, OR 97454 (SAN 677-010X).

Pollnow, James L., *(J L Pollnow; 0-9603708),* 1310 Aldersgate Rd., Little Rock, AR 72205 (SAN 213-8670).

Pollux Press, *(Pollux Pr; 0-913933),* P.O. Box 12, Victor, CO 80860 (SAN 286-8687) Tel 303-689-3000.

Polonia Bookstore & Pubs., Co., *(Polonia Bkstore & Pubs; 0-935455),* 2886 N. Milwaukee Ave., Chicago, IL 60618 (SAN 695-9717) Tel 312-489-2554.

Poltergeist Press, *(Poltergeist; 0-9603918),* 706 S. Morain St., Kennewick, WA 99336 (SAN 213-5477) Tel 509-735-4078.

†Poltroon Pr., *(Poltroon Pr; 0-918395),* 2315 Carleton St., Berkeley, CA 94704 (SAN 218-2475) Tel 415-845-8097; Dist. by: Anacapa Bks., 3090 Claremont Ave., Berkeley, CA 94705 (SAN 200-724X) Tel 415-654-3517; *CIP.*

Poly Concepts Publishing Co., *(Poly Concepts; 0-915203),* 2948 N. Terrace Dr., Wichita, KS 67220 (SAN 289-8012) Tel 316-684-8297.

Poly Tone Pr., *(Poly Tone; 0-933830),* 16027 Sunburst St., Sepulveda, CA 91343 (SAN 210-6515) Tel 818-892-0044.

Polyconomics, Inc., *(Polyconomics; 0-938081),* 86 Maple Ave., Morristown, NJ 07960 (SAN 659-6975) Tel 201-267-4641.

Polycrystal Book Service, *(Polycrystal Bk Serv; 0-9601304),* P.O. Box 27, Western Springs, IL 60558 (SAN 212-6753) Tel 312-246-3818.

Polyglot Productions, *(Polyglot Prods; 0-917381),* 136 Brattle St., Cambridge, MA 02138 (SAN 294-1546) Tel 617-491-3541. No longer produces software.

†Polygonal Publishing Hse., *(Polygonal Pub; 0-936428),* 210 Broad St., Washington, NJ 07882 (SAN 218-4559) Tel 201-689-3894; *CIP.*

Polymers & Plastics Technical Publishing House, *(Polymers & Plastics Tech Pub Hse; 0-942378),* 373 Bush Hill Ct., Lake Mary, FL 32746 (SAN 239-8591).

Polymus Publishing Co., *(Polymus Pub; 0-931379),* 20734 Schoolcraft St., Canoga Park, CA 91306 (SAN 682-613X) Tel 818-887-1297.

PolyScience Corp., *(PolyScience; 0-913106),* 7800 Merrimac Ave., Niles, IL 60648 (SAN 209-0740) Tel 312-965-0611.

Pomegranate Artbooks, Inc., *(Pomegranate Calif; 0-917556; 0-87654),* P.O. Box 980, Corte Madera, CA 94925 (SAN 211-0857); Toll free: 800-227-1428 Tel 415-924-8141.

Pomegranate Pr., Ltd., *(Pomegranate Pr; 0-938817),* 3236 Bennett Dr., Los Angeles, CA 90068 (SAN 661-745X) Tel 213-850-6719.

Pomme le Terre, *(Pomme le Terre; 0-939964),* P.O. Box 357, Heber City, UT 84032 (SAN 216-8499) Tel 801-583-9870; Dist. by: Green River Forge, Ltd., Box 257, Fulton, CA 95439 (SAN 200-8114).

Pomona Valley Writers Assn., *(Pomona Val Writers; 0-939503),* P.O. Box 3428, Ontario, CA 91761 (SAN 663-396X); 1541 North Baker Ave., Ontario, CA 91764 (SAN 663-3978) Tel 714-981-8339.

Ponce Pr., *(Ponce Pr; 0-933829),* P.O. Box 73, 1081 Alameda, Belmont, CA 94002 (SAN 692-8757) Tel 415-591-9802.

Ponchie & Co., *(Ponchie; 0-9604418),* W.V.U., Dept of Foreign Languages, Morgantown, WV 26506 (SAN 214-4425).

Pond Woods Pr., *(Pond Woods; 0-9604334),* P.O. Box 82, Stony Brook, NY 11790 (SAN 212-4378) Tel 516-751-3232.

Ponderosa Pr., *(Ponderosa Pr; 0-933393),* P.O. Box 10225, Colorado Springs, CO 80932 (SAN 691-5051) Tel 303-471-3637.

Ponderosa Pubs., *(Ponderosa; 0-913162),* Rte. 1, Box 68, Saint Ignatius, MT 59865 (SAN 204-9058) Tel 406-745-4455.

Pong, Ted, *(Pong; 0-939966),* P.O. Box 321, Freeland, WA 98249 (SAN 216-0544).

Pong Yui, *(Pong Yui),* 2976 Vincent Rd., Cuyhoga Falls, OH 44224 (SAN 692-6800).

Ponicsan, Darryl, *(D Ponicsan),* P.O. Box 1596, Ojai, CA 93023 (SAN 206-8192) Tel 805-646-4215.

Pontine Pr., *(Pontine Pr),* 1153 N. Orange, Hollywood, CA 90038 (SAN 201-8845).

Pony Pr., *(Pony Pr; 0-9616501),* 3981 Fort Jim Rd., Placerville, CA 95667 (SAN 659-283X) Tel 916-644-6853.

Pony X Press, *(Pony X Pr; 0-939428),* 915 Shorepoint Ct. E303, Alameda, CA 94501 (SAN 220-1828) Tel 415-522-4928.

Pool Pubns., *(Pool Pubns; 0-9609588),* Box 3362, Enfield, CT 06082 (SAN 274-7332) Tel 203-745-9162.

Poopsie's, Inc., *(Poopsies; 0-9616060),* P.O. Box 4009, Appleton, WI 54915 (SAN 698-0503) Tel 414-735-9181; 1283 Valley Fair Mall, Appleton, WI 54915 (SAN 698-0511).

Poor Richard's Pr., Affil. of Men's Rights Assoc., *(Poor Richards; 0-917212),* 17854 Lyons, Forest Lake, MN 55025 (SAN 208-2519) Tel 612-464-7663.

Poor Souls Pr./Scaramouche Bks., *(Poor Souls Pr; 0-916296),* P.O. Box 236, Millbrae, CA 94030 (SAN 209-679X) Tel 415-588-4163.

Poorhouse Pr., *(Poorhouse Pr; 0-9614728),* 8333 W. McNab Rd., Tamarac, FL 33321 (SAN 692-5057) Tel 305-726-4343.

Pop Hits Publishing, *(Pop Hits Pub; 0-934019),* 3149 Southern Ave, Memphis, TN 38111 (SAN 692-7815) Tel 901-452-5265.

†**Popcorn Pubs,** *(Popcorn Pubs; 0-930506),* P.O. Box 1308, Pittsfield, MA 01202 (SAN 211-044X) Tel 413-443-5601; *CIP.*

†**Pope John Center,** *(Pope John Ctr; 0-935372),* 186 Forbes Rd., Braintree, MA 02184 (SAN 282-1729) Tel 617-848-6965; *CIP.*

Pope John XXIII Medical-Moral Research & Education Center *See* Pope John Center

Poplar Books, *(Poplar Bks; 0-915045),* P.O. Box 62, Shiloh, TN 38376 (SAN 287-2595) Tel 901-632-1289.

Poppy Pr., *(Poppy Pr; 0-9616145),* 913 Hampton Rd., Sacramento, CA 95864 (SAN 699-9336) Tel 916-487-9507.

Popular Medical Pubns., Inc., *(Pop Med Pubns; 0-9614618),* 3907 Pinewood Ln., Hollywood, FL 33021 (SAN 691-6856) Tel 305-989-4183.

Popular Medicine Pr., *(Popular Med Pr; 0-936575),* P.O. Box 12607, Toledo, OH 43606 (SAN 658-828X) Tel 419-472-8701.

Popular Pubns., *(Popular Pubns; 0-9615362),* P.O. Box 1558, Oroville, WA 98844-1558 (SAN 694-4108).

†**Population Council Office of Communications,** *(Population Coun; 0-87834),* 1 Dag Hammarskjold Plaza, New York, NY 10017 (SAN 225-1582) Tel 212-644-1300; *CIP.*

Population Reference Bureau, *(Population Ref; 0-917136),* 777 14th St.,NW, Washington, DC 20005 (SAN 205-1230) Tel 202-639-8040.

Population Review Pubn., *(Popl Rev CA; 0-9609080),* 8976 Cliffridge Ave., La Jolla, CA 92037 (SAN 241-4341) Tel 619-455-6093.

Porcella Studios, *(Porcella Studios; 0-936589),* 3619 Shoemake Ave., Modesto, CA 95351 (SAN 698-1313) Tel 209-524-1134.

Porch Swing Press, Inc., *(Porch Swing; 0-9606550),* P.O. Box 15014, Nashville, TN 37215 (SAN 219-8118).

Porcupine Pr., Inc., *(Porcupine Pr; 0-87991),* 310 S. Juniper St., Philadelphia, PA 19107 (SAN 202-0122) Tel 215-735-0101. *Imprints:* Basil Blackwell (England) (Basil Blackwell).

Porkyspine Press, *(Porkyspine; 0-9612014),* 99 Crosman Terrace, Rochester, NY 14620 (SAN 286-8520) Tel 716-473-2949.

Porphyrion Press, *(Porphyrion Pr; 0-913884),* RR 2, Box 439, Middle Grove, NY 12850 (SAN 206-6823) Tel 518-587-9809.

Port Love International Publishing Co., *(Port Love Intl),* P.O. Box 423, Amazonia, MO 64421 (SAN 686-2764).

Port Orchard Specialties, *(Pt Orchard Spec; 0-9616198),* 7775 SE Blakeview Dr., Port Orchard, WA 98366 (SAN 699-9581) Tel 206-871-5535.

Port Press, *(Port Pr; 0-9606104),* 16 Ridge Dr., Port Washington, NY 11050 (SAN 216-8502).

Portack Pr., *(Portack Pr; 0-938163),* P.O. Box 10, Springfield, MA 01103 (SAN 659-6959); 55 State St., Springfield, MA 01103 (SAN 659-6967) Tel 413-781-6005.

Portals Pr., *(Portals Pr; 0-916620),* P.O. Box 1048, Tuscaloosa, AL 35403 (SAN 208-8126) Tel 205-758-1874.

Porter, Bern, *(Bern Porter; 0-911156),* 22 Salmond Rd., Belfast, ME 04915 (SAN 202-0130). Do not confuse with Porter Publishing Co., Center City, MN.

Porter, Janice, Bks., *(J Porter Bks; 0-9607670),* P.O. Box 2367, Reston, VA 22090 (SAN 240-0979).

Porter Co., The, Div. of Kepner-Tregoe, *(Porter Co PA; 0-936095),* P.O. Box 816, Easton, PA 18044-0816 (SAN 696-8104) Tel 215-258-9948; 705 Reeder St., Easton, PA 18042 (SAN 696-8112).

Porter Publishing Co., *(Porter Pub Co; 0-933565),* P.O. Box 134, Center City, MN 55012 (SAN 691-9006) Tel 612-257-5232. Do not confuse with Bern Porter, Belfast, ME.

Porter Sargent Pubs., Inc., *(Porter Sargent; 0-87558),* 11 Beacon St., Boston, MA 02108 (SAN 208-8142) Tel 617-523-1670.

Portfolio Pr., *(Portfolio Pr; 0-942620),* RD 1, Huntington, NY 11743 (SAN 238-5554) Tel 212-989-8700.

Porthole Pr., *(Porthole Fla; 0-932907),* P.O. Box 15, Oldsmar, FL 33557 (SAN 689-9803) Tel 813-855-4590.

†**Portland Cement Assn.,** *(Portland Cement; 0-89312),* 5420 Old Orchard Rd., Skokie, IL 60077-4321 (SAN 207-6004) Tel 312-966-6200; *CIP.*

Portland Litho, *(Portland Litho; 0-9615157),* 1600 Congress St., Portland, ME 04101 (SAN 659-2082).

Portland Symphony Orchestra Women's Committee, *(Portland Symphony Cookbook; 0-9601266),* 30 Myrtle St., Portland, ME 04112 (SAN 206-9881) Tel 207-773-8191.

Portner, Hal, *(Portner; 0-913149),* 67 Westhampton Rd., Northampton, MA 01060 (SAN 283-4162) Tel 413-584-1285.

Portola Pr., *(Portola CA; 0-936559),* 470 Cervantes Rd., Portola Valley, CA 94025 (SAN 698-1003) Tel 415-851-8953; P.O. Box 620361, Woodside, CA 94062 (SAN 698-1011).

Portola Pr., *(Portola Pr; 0-9605998),* P.O. Box 1225, Santa Barbara, CA 93102 (SAN 216-7573) Tel 805-682-7974.

Portolan Press, *(Portolan; 0-916762),* 825 Rathjen Rd., Brielle, NJ 08730 (SAN 208-8134) Tel 201-528-8264.

Portrayal Pr., *(Portrayal; 0-938242),* P.O. Box 1913, Bloomfield, NJ 07003 (SAN 215-9066) Tel 201-743-1851.

Portriga Pubns., *(Portriga Pubns; 0-9602274),* 823 N. Edinburg Ave., Los Angeles, CA 90046 (SAN 212-4386).

†**Portsmouth Marine Society, The,** *(Portsmouth Marine Soc; 0-915819),* P.O. Box 147, Portsmouth, NH 03801 (SAN 293-9029) Tel 603-431-5667; *CIP.*

Poseidon Press *See* Pocket Bks., Inc.

Poseidon Pubns., *(Poseidon Pubns; 0-937378),* 1340 N. Alameda, Las Cruces, NM 88001 (SAN 215-1731).

Posey International, *(Posey Intl; 0-940348),* P.O. Box 338, Orem, UT 84057 (SAN 220-2700) Tel 801-377-5504.

Positive Attitude Pr., *(Positive Attitude; 0-936383),* 3790 El Camino Real, Suite 2002, Palo Alto, CA 94306 (SAN 697-2802) Tel 415-964-7587; 1965 San Ramon, No. 4, Mountain View, CA 94043 (SAN 697-2810).

Positive Images, Inc., *(Positive Images; 0-9615271),* 1203 Carver St., P.O. Box 483, Myrtle Beach, SC 29578-0483 (SAN 695-2682) Tel 803-448-5361.

Positive Notes Pubns., *(Positive Notes; 0-9612786),* P.O. Box 193, Hubbard, OH 44425 (SAN 289-8071) Tel 216-568-7306.

Post-Apollo Pr., The, *(Post Apollo Pr; 0-942996),* 35 Marie St., Sausalito, CA 94965 (SAN 240-429X) Tel 415-332-1458.

Post-Era Books, *(Post-Era; 0-911160),* Box 150, 119 S. First Ave., Arcadia, CA 91006 (SAN 205-1672) Tel 818-446-5000.

Post Horn Pr., Inc., *(Post Horn Pr; 0-935311),* 1288 Lenox Cir., NE, Atlanta, GA 30306 (SAN 695-5525) Tel 404-876-0518.

Post Oak Press *See* Larksdale

Post Parade Pubs., *(Post Parade; 0-943808),* 6828-3 Quebec Court, San Diego, CA 92139 (SAN 238-3411) Tel 619-470-1035.

Post-Tribune Publishing Co., Subs. of Knight-Rider Newspapers, Inc., *(Post-Tribune; 0-917495),* 1065 Broadway, Gary, IN 46402 (SAN 656-0792) Tel 219-881-3000.

Postilion Pubns., Div. of Roger Koerber Inc., *(Postilion Pubns; 0-941480),* 15565 Northland Dr., Suite 605W, Southfield, MI 48075 (SAN 239-1260) Tel 313-569-1411.

Postroad Press Inc, *(Postroad Pr Inc; 0-912691),* P.O. Box 1212, Roanoke, VA 24006 (SAN 283-9318); 635 Day Ave., SW Roanoke, VA 24016 (SAN 283-9326).

Posy Pubns., *(Posy Pubns; 0-9616061),* P.O. Box 1624, Independence, MO 64055 (SAN 698-0465) Tel 816-373-2967; 3948 Sherman Dr., Independence, MO 64055 (SAN 698-0473).

Posy Pubns., *(Posy Va; 0-9603526),* 115 Shasta Ct., Charlottesville, VA 22903 (SAN 213-3490) Tel 804-293-8506.

Pot of Gold Pubns., *(Pot of Gold; 0-9605542),* 435 10th St., Manhattan Beach, CA 90266 (SAN 216-0552).

Potala Corp., *(Potala; 0-9611474),* 107 E. 31st St., Fourth flr., New York, NY 10016 (SAN 283-1570) Tel 212-213-5011.

Potato Press *See* O'Hara, J. Philip, Inc., Pubs.

Potboiler Pr., *(Potboiler Pr; 0-939329),* 521 W. Point Ave., St. Louis, MO 63130 (SAN 663-1649) Tel 314-727-6050.

Potentials Development, Inc., *(Potentials Development; 0-932910),* 775 Main St., Suite 321, Buffalo, NY 14203 (SAN 239-5916) Tel 716-842-2658.

Potes & Poets Pr., Inc., *(Potes Poets; 0-937013),* 181 Edgemont Ave., Elmwood, CT 06110 (SAN 658-6759) Tel 203-233-2023.

Potomac Appalachian Trail Club, *(Potomac Appalach; 0-915746),* 1718 N St., NW, Washington, DC 20036 (SAN 208-1121) Tel 202-638-5307.

Names

Potomac Area Council, American Youth Hostels Inc., *(Potomac Area; 0-9614892),* 1332 I St. NW, Suite 451, Washington, DC 20005 (SAN 693-188X) Tel 202-783-4943; 1017 K St., Second flr., Washington, DC 20001 (SAN 662-3158) Tel 202-783-4943; Orders to: PAC-AYH, P.O. Box 28607-Central Sta., Washington, DC 20038-8607 (SAN 662-3166) Tel 202-783-4943.

Potomac Bks., Inc., Pubs., *(Potomac; 0-87107),* P.O. Box 40604, Palisades Sta., Washington, DC 20016 (SAN 202-0149) Tel 703-592-3225.

Potomac Enterprises, *(Potomac Ent; 0-939836),* Box 146, Fort Branch, IN 47648 (SAN 216-924X) Tel 812-753-4977; Dist. by: Sanford J. Durst, 29-28-41st Ave., Long Island City, NY 11101 (SAN 211-6987) Tel 718-706-0303.

Potomac Pr., *(Potomac Pr; 0-917262),* P.O. Box 31086, Washington, DC 20031 (SAN 208-8150) Tel 202-582-4064.

Potomac Valley Pr., *(Potomac Val Pr),* 1424 16th St., NW, Washington, DC 20036 (SAN 659-8161).

Potpourri Ventures, *(Potpourri; 0-9611150),* Box 303, North Chelmsford, MA 01863 (SAN 283-8893) Tel 617-256-4602.

Potshot Pr., Subs. of Epsilon Pr., Inc., *(Potshot Pr; 0-932373),* P.O. Box 1117, Pacific Palisades, CA 90272 (SAN 687-3804) Tel 213-454-9393.

Potter, Clarkson N., Bks. *See* Crown Pubs., Inc.

Potter Pubns., *(Potter Pubns; 0-9613087),* 3108 S. Oakhurst Ave., Los Angeles, CA 90034 (SAN 283-9830) Tel 213-838-8425.

Pottle, Ralph R., *(Pottle; 0-911162),* 1101 N. Gen. Pershing, Hammond, LA 70401 (SAN 204-9066) Tel 504-345-6133.

Poudre Pr., Div. of Poudre Publishing Co., *(Poudre Pr; 0-935240),* P.O. Box 181, La Porte, CO 80535 (SAN 213-3504) Tel 303-482-0758.

Pound Publishing, *(Pound; 0-9613486),* Love Rd., Underwood, WA 98651 (SAN 657-372X) Tel 509-493-3514.

Pourboire Press, *(Pourboire),* P.O. Box 6881, Providence, RI 02940 (SAN 209-8628) Tel 401-331-9800; Dist. by: Woods Hole Press, P.O. Box 305, Woods Hole, MA 02543 (SAN 210-332X) Tel 617-548-9600.

Poverty Bay Publishing Co., *(Poverty Bay; 0-936528),* 529 SW 294, Federal Way, WA 98003 (SAN 214-1973).

Poverty Hill Press, *(Poverty Hill Pr; 0-88083),* P.O. Box 519, Leavenworth, WA 98826 (SAN 238-5570) Tel 509-548-7551.

Poway Historical & Memorial Society, *(Poway Hist; 0-914137),* 17105 Tam O'Shanter Dr., Poway, CA 92064 (SAN 293-4736) Tel 619-487-7199; Orders to: Poway Historical & Memorial Society, 12916 Community Rd., Poway, CA 92064 (SAN 293-4744) Tel 619-748-5004; Dist. by: Poway Historical and Memorial Society, P.O. Box 19, Poway, CA 92064 (SAN 293-4752); Dist. by: Poway Chamber of Commerce, 13505 Midland Rd., Poway, CA 92064 (SAN 293-4779) Tel 619-748-0016; Dist. by: Iverson Book Center, 13446 Poway Rd., Poway, CA 92064 (SAN 293-4787) Tel 619-486-2665.

Powder River Publishing Co., *(Powder River; 0-9614237),* P.O. Box 721, Gillette, WY 82716 (SAN 209-0082) Tel 307-686-0023.

Powell, Dan, *(Dan Powell),* 2515 Olive St., Cedar Falls, IA 50613 (SAN 695-8435).

Powell, Robert Blake, *(R B Powell; 0-9600680),* P.O. Box 833, Hurst, TX 76053 (SAN 203-3968) Tel 817-284-8145.

Powell, Samuel, Pub. Co., *(Samuel P Co; 0-910021),* 2201 I St., Sacramento, CA 95816 (SAN 219-2756) Tel 916-443-1161.

Power & Systems Training, Inc., *(Power & Sys; 0-910411),* P.O. Box 388, Prudential Sta., Boston, MA 02199 (SAN 260-1184) Tel 617-437-1640.

Power Books *See* Revell, Fleming H., Co.

Power Dynamics, Inc., *(Power Dynamics Inc; 0-936643),* 8715 Jackson Ave., Manassas, VA 22110 (SAN 699-6981) Tel 703-361-7458.

Powers, M. J., & Co. Pubs., *(M J Powers & Co; 0-913323),* 374 Millburn Ave., Millburn, NJ 07041 (SAN 283-9660) Tel 201-467-4556.

Powers, Nancy, & Co. Pubs., Inc., *(N Powers; 0-941684),* 241 Central Park W., New York, NY 10024 (SAN 239-281X) Tel 212-877-3262.

Powley, Mark, Assocs., Inc., *(M Powley; 0-943378),* 15 Meigs Ave., Madison, CT 06443 (SAN 240-7485) Tel 203-245-8561.

Powner, Charles T., Co., Inc., *(Powner; 0-911164),* 7056 W. Higgins Rd., Chicago, IL 60656 (SAN 204-9082) Tel 312-939-7360.

Poynter Institute, *(Poynter Inst; 0-935742),* 801 Third St. S., St. Petersburg, FL 33701 (SAN 214-0586) Tel 813-821-9494.

Poyser, T. & A. D. , Ltd., *(T & A D Poyser; 0-85661),* Dist. by: Buteo Books, P.O. Box 481, Vermillion, SD 57069 (SAN 212-0054) Tel 605-624-4343.

Practical Allergy Research Foundation, *(Practical Allergy; 0-9616318),* 1421 Colvin Blvd., Buffalo, NY 14223 (SAN 658-6813) Tel 716-875-5578.

Practical Archivists, Inc., *(Practical Arch; 0-938019),* 536 Emerson St., Palo Alto, CA 94301 (SAN 659-7556) Tel 415-323-7822.

Practical Cookbooks, *(Practical Cookbks; 0-9614556),* 145 Malcolm Ave. SE, Minneapolis, MN 55414 (SAN 691-8131) Tel 612-378-9697; Dist. by: Baker & Taylor Co., Midwest Div., 501 Gladiola Ave., Momence, IL 60954 (SAN 169-2100); Dist. by: Spring Arbor Distributors, 10885 Textile Rd., Belleville, MI 48111 (SAN 158-9016) Tel 313-481-0900; Toll free: 800-521-3990.

Practical Pubns., *(Practical Pubns; 0-912914),* 6272 W. North Ave., Chicago, IL 60639 (SAN 204-9090) Tel 312-237-2986.

Practical Publishing Corp., *(Pract Pub NY; 0-9613662),* P.O. Box 1020, Lenox Hill Sta., New York, NY 10021 (SAN 670-8870).

Practical Technology, Inc., *(Practical Tech; 0-938877),* 30485 Oakview Way, Birmingham, MI 48010 (SAN 662-5290) Tel 313-258-5684.

Practice Management Assocs., Ltd., *(Practice Mgmt; 1-55538),* 126 Harvard St., Brookline, MA 02146 (SAN 695-975X) Tel 617-731-1913.

Practising Law Institute, *(PLI; 0-87224),* 810 Seventh Ave., New York, NY 10019 (SAN 203-0136) Tel 212-765-5700.

Prader-Willi Syndrome Assn., *(Prader-Willi),* 5515 Malibu Dr., Edina, MN 55436 (SAN 224-4292) Tel 612-933-0113.

†**Praeger Pubs.,** Div. of Greenwood Pr., *(Praeger; 0-275),* P.O. Box 5007, Westport, CT 06881 (SAN 202-022X) Tel 203-226-3571; 88 Post Rd., W., Westport, CT 06881 (SAN 658-1439); 521 Fifth Ave., New York, NY 10175 (SAN 658-1447); *CIP.*

†**Praestant Pr.,** *(Praestant; 0-930112),* P.O. Box 43, Delaware, OH 43015-0043 (SAN 210-6523) Tel 614-363-1458; *CIP.*

Praetorius Books, *(Praetorius Bks),* P.O. Box 167, Valhalla, NY 10595 (SAN 217-1244).

Pragmatic Publications, *(Pragmatic Pubns; 0-939962),* P.O. Box 75082, St. Paul, MN 55175 (SAN 216-8464) Tel 612-457-8600.

Prairie Bk. Arts Ctr., *(Prairie Bk Ctr; 0-935983),* 41 E. University Ave., Champaign, IL 61820 (SAN 696-625X) Tel 217-352-6621; P.O. Box 725, Urbana, IL 61801 (SAN 696-6396).

Prairie Craftsman, *(Prairie Craft; 0-9603788),* Box 424, Hoopeston, IL 60942 (SAN 224-6701).

Prairie du Chien Year of the French Committee, *(PDC French Comm; 0-9615831),* P.O. Box 326, Prairie du Chien, WI 53821 (SAN 697-2764) Tel 608-326-8555; Orders to:

Prairie Hse., Inc., *(Prairie Hse; 0-911007),* P.O. Box 9199, Fargo, ND 58109 (SAN 262-9844) Tel 701-235-0210.

Prairie Imprints, *(Prairie Imp; 0-9615098),* P.O. Box 481, Stillwater, OK 74076 (SAN 692-9672) Tel 405-377-3750.

Prairie Lark Pr., *(Prairie Lark; 0-918533),* P.O. Box 699, Springfield, IL 62705 (SAN 657-7113) Tel 217-546-4399.

Prairie Pr., *(Prairie Pr; 0-9613939),* P.O. Box 305, Prairie du Chien, WI 53841 (SAN 682-3084) Tel 608-326-2576.

Prairie Publishing, *(Prairie Pub),* RR 1, Rushville, NE 69360 (SAN 207-7442).

Prairie Rambler Press, *(Prairie Ramb; 0-912279),* P.O. Box 505, Claremont, CA 91711-0505 (SAN 265-0843) Tel 714-621-8109.

Prairie School Pr., *(Prairie Sch; 0-87370),* c/o Prairie Avenue Bookshop, 711 S. Dearborn, Chicago, IL 60605 (SAN 274-7723) Tel 312-922-8311.

Prairie Wind Bks., *(Prairie Wind Bks; 0-9616585),* 1006 N. 64th St., Omaha, NE 68132 (SAN 659-7564) Tel 402-556-5872.

Prakken Pubns., Inc., *(Prakken; 0-911168),* P.O. Box 8623, Ann Arbor, MI 48105 (SAN 204-9112) Tel 313-769-1211.

Prather, DeWitt G., *(D G Prather; 0-9616836),* 1623 Lansdale Dr., Charlotte, NC 28205 (SAN 662-5703) Tel 704-537-3962; Dist. by: BNR Press, 132 E. Second St., Port Clinton, OH 43452 (SAN 211-5948) Tel 419-734-2422.

Pratt, Collin B., *(C B Pratt; 0-9617049),* P.O. Box 18401-7K, Las Vegas, NV 89114 (SAN 662-8877); 2600 Arville, F 14, Las Vegas, NV 89102 (SAN 662-8885) Tel 702-871-9764.

Pratt Pr., *(Pratt Press; 0-930557),* c/o Robins, 83 Wooster St., New York, NY 10012 (SAN 677-5101) Tel 212-925-3714.

Pratt Publishing Co., *(Pratt Pub Co; 0-9615750),* P.O. Box 253, Austell, GA 30001 (SAN 695-9954) Tel 404-941-5514.

Prayer Book Pr., Inc., Subs. of Media Judaica, Inc., *(Prayer Bk; 0-87677),* 304 E. 49th St., New York, NY 10017 (SAN 282-1788) Tel 212-319-6666; Orders to: Media Judaica, Inc., 1363 Fairfield Ave., Bridgeport, CT 06605 (SAN 207-0022) Tel 203-384-2284.

Pre-Columbian Art Research Institute, *(Pre-Columbian Art; 0-934051),* 1100 Sacramento St., San Francisco, CA 94108 (SAN 693-0786) Tel 415-776-0606.

Pre-School Learning Corp., *(Pre-School Learn),* P.O. Box 6244, 10206 Rosewood, Overland Park, KS 66207 (SAN 207-6241).

Pre-Test *See* McGraw-Hill Bk. Co.

Pre-Text Series *See* McGraw-Hill Bk. Co.

†**Precedent Publishing, Inc.,** *(Precedent Pub; 0-913750),* 737 N. LaSalle St., Chicago, IL 60610 (SAN 205-1583) Tel 312-944-2525; Toll free: 800-392-5448; *CIP.*

Precious Resources, *(Precious Res; 0-937836),* Box 14463, Parkville, MO 64152 (SAN 213-3512) Tel 816-386-2946.

Precision Models, Inc., *(Precision Mod; 0-9605414),* 3000 Sand Hill Rd., No. 4-170, Menlo Park, CA 94025 (SAN 240-8805) Tel 415-854-9553.

Precision Publishing Co., *(Precision Pub Co; 0-937916),* P.O. Box 172, Fort Myers, FL 33902 (SAN 215-3343).

Predicasts, *(Predicasts),* 11001 Cedar Ave., Cleveland, OH 44106 (SAN 695-5746) Tel 216-795-3000.

Preferred Press, *(Preferred Pr; 0-914759),* 5702 Research Dr., Huntington Beach, CA 92649 (SAN 291-8463) Tel 714-895-1083; Toll free: 800-762-6937.

Prelude Pr., *(Prelude Press; 0-931580),* P.O. Box 69773, Los Angeles, CA 69872 (SAN 262-0642).

Prema Bks., *(Prema Bks; 0-941122),* 310 West End Ave., New York, NY 10023 (SAN 217-4170) Tel 212-874-7692.

Premier Bks. *See* Fawcett Bk. Group

Premier Pr., *(Prem Press; 0-912722),* 2914 Domingo Ave., Berkeley, CA 94705 (SAN 282-180X) Tel 415-841-2091; Orders to: P.O. Box 4428, Berkeley, CA 94704 (SAN 282-1818).

Premier Pubns., *(Premier Pubns; 0-9617080),* 567 17th Ave., San Francisco, CA 94121 (SAN 663-4966) Tel 415-668-7108.

Premier Pubs., Inc., *(Premier Publishers; 0-915665),* P.O. Box 16254, Fort Worth, TX 76133 (SAN 292-5966) Tel 817-293-7030.

Premier Publishing Co., *(Premier Pub; 0-942622),* 1200 Pillsbury Center, Minneapolis, MN 55402 (SAN 282-1826) Tel 612-339-8551.

Prentice-Hall, Inc., *(P-H; 0-13),* Rte. 9W, Englewood Cliffs, NJ 07632 (SAN 200-2175) Tel 201-592-2000; Orders to: 200 Old Tappan Rd., Old Tappan, NJ 07675 (SAN 215-3939) Tel 201-767-5049. *Imprints:* Appleton-Century-Crofts (Appleton-Century-Crofts); Business & Professional Division (Busn); Parker Publishing Company (Parker); Prism Books (Prism); Reward Books (Reward); Spectrum Books (Spec).

Prentice-Hall Media, *(Prentice-Media; 0-926276),* 90 S. Bedford Rd., Mt. Kisco, NY 10549 (SAN 656-2272) Tel 914-631-8300.

Presbyterian & Reformed Publishing Co., *(Presby & Reformed; 0-87552),* P.O. Box 817, Phillipsburg, NJ 08865 (SAN 205-3918); Toll free: 800-631-0094; Marble Hill Rd., Phillipsburg, NJ 08865 (SAN 658-1463) Tel 201-454-0505.

Presbyterian & Reformed Renewal Ministries International, *(Presby Ref Ren; 0-934421),* 2245 NW 39th St., Oklahoma City, OK 73112 (SAN 274-7804) Tel 405-525-2552.

Presbyterian Historical Society, *(Presby Hist; 0-912686),* 425 Lombard St., Philadelphia, PA 19147 (SAN 205-1575) Tel 215-627-1852.

Presbyterian Homes, Inc., *(Presbyterian Homes; 0-9616428),* 1217 Slate Hill Rd., Camp Hill, PA 17011 (SAN 659-056X) Tel 717-737-9700.

Prescott, Joseph, *(J Prescott),* 79-31 257th St., Floral Park, NY 11004-1228 (SAN 695-9784).

Prescott/Durrell, & Co., *(Prescott Durrell & Co; 0-9609506),* Box C-32000, Richmond, VA 23261-2000 (SAN 274-7855) Tel 804-321-3467.

Prescott Pr., Inc., *(Prescott Pr; 0-933451),* P.O. Box 53777, Lafayette, LA 70505 (SAN 691-8247) Tel 318-235-5127.

†**Prescott St. Pr.,** *(Prescott St Pr; 0-915986),* P.O. Box 40312, Portland, OR 97240-0312 (SAN 207-4729) Tel 503-254-2922; *CIP.*

Presence Inc., *(Presence Inc; 0-937296),* P.O. Box 1867, Easley, SC 29641 (SAN 240-8813) Tel 803-878-7239.

Preservation Ink, *(Preserv Ink; 0-9605294),* P.O. Box 92314, Milwaukee, WI 53202 (SAN 239-9962) Tel 414-272-1193.

Preservation League of New York State, *(Pres League NYS; 0-942000),* 307 Hamilton St., Albany, NY 12210 (SAN 238-5945) Tel 518-462-5658.

†**Preservation Pr., The,** Div. of National Trust for Historic Preservation, *(Preservation Pr; 0-89133),* 1785 Massachusetts Ave., NW, Washington, DC 20036 (SAN 209-3146) Tel 202-673-4058; *CIP.*

Preservation Publishing Co., *(Preserv Pub Co; 0-911515),* P.O. Box 567, 719 State St., Grinnell, IA 50112-0567 (SAN 264-3162) Tel 515-236-5575.

Preservation Society of Asheville & Buncombe County, Inc., *(Pres Soc Asheville; 0-937481),* P.O. Box 2806, Asheville, NC 28802 (SAN 659-0365) Tel 704-254-2343.

Preservation Society of Newport County, The, *(Preserv Soc Newport),* Dist. by: Rhode Island Pubns. Society, 189 Wickenden St., Providence, RI 02903 (SAN 219-9696) Tel 401-272-1776.

Preservation Trust of Vermont, *(Preser Trust; 0-9615706),* P.O. Box 1777, Windsor, VT 05089-0021 (SAN 695-9806) Tel 802-658-6647; Windsor Hse., Main St., Windsor, VT 05089-0021 (SAN 695-9814).

President & Trustees of Bowdoin College, *(Bowdoin Coll; 0-916606),* Bowdoin College, Getchell Hse., Brunswick, ME 04011 (SAN 695-6394) Tel 207-725-8731.

Presidential Accountability Group, *(Presidential Acct; 0-936400),* Box 19312, Washington, DC 20036 (SAN 239-5924).

Presidents Assn., Div. of American Management Assns., *(Presidents Assn; 0-8144),* 135 W. 50th St., New York, NY 10020 (SAN 219-385X) Tel 212-903-7945.

Presidial Press, *(Presidial; 0-935978),* P.O. Box 5248, Austin, TX 78763 (SAN 209-4789) Tel 512-472-6653.

Presidio Pr., *(Presidio Pr; 0-89141),* 31 Pamaron Way, Novato, CA 94947 (SAN 214-2759) Tel 415-883-1373. *Imprints:* Leeward Publications, Inc. (Leeward Pubns).(Neff-Kane).

---

†**Press Associates, Inc.,** *(Pr Assocs; 0-919763),* 806 15th St. NW, Suite 632, Washington, DC 20005 (SAN 657-3738) Tel 202-638-0444; *CIP.*

Press at California State Univ., Fresno, The, *(Cal State Pr; 0-912201),* Shaw & Maple, Fresno, CA 93740 (SAN 264-6307) Tel 209-294-3056.

Press De LaPlantz, *(Press LaPlantz; 0-942002),* 899 Bayside Cutoff, Bayside, CA 95524 (SAN 282-1842) Tel 707-822-6009.

Press, Duck, *(Pr Duck; 0-918961),* 3308 W. Juneau, Milwaukee, WI 53208 (SAN 670-0551) Tel 414-344-2308.

†**Press for Peace,** Div. of Penichet Publishing Co., *(Press for Peace; 0-9614103),* 2514 S. Grand Ave., Los Angeles, CA 90007 (SAN 685-9771) Tel 213-749-6213; *CIP.*

Press 451, *(Press Four Fifty One; 0-917796),* 2600 S.16th St., No. 729, Arlington, VA 22204 (SAN 262-0707) Tel 202-857-7764.

Press in Tuscany Alley, *(Pr Tuscany; 0-915918),* One Tuscany Alley, San Francisco, CA 94133 (SAN 208-8185) Tel 415-986-0641.

Press North America, *(Press N Amer; 0-938271),* 835 Lakechime Dr., Sunnyvale, CA 94089 (SAN 659-8285) Tel 408-734-1680.

Press of A Colish, *(Pr of A Colish),* 40 Hartford Ave., Mount Vernon, NY 10550 (SAN 209-6528) Tel 914-664-4668.

Press of Appletree Alley, The, *(Press Alley; 0-916375),* P.O. Box 608, 138 S. Third St., Lewisburg, PA 17837 (SAN 295-9747) Tel 717-524-7064.

Press of Arden Park, *(Pr Arden Park; 0-936300),* 861 Los Molinos Way, Sacramento, CA 95864 (SAN 209-8644) Tel 916-481-7881.

Press of Morningside Bookshop, *(Pr of Morningside; 0-89029),* P.O. Box 1087, Dayton, OH 45401 (SAN 202-0211) Tel 513-461-6736.

Press of Peachtree Presbyterian Church, Inc., The, *(Pr Peachtree; 0-9616001),* 3434 Roswell Rd., Atlanta, GA 30363 (SAN 697-9777) Tel 404-261-7651.

Press of the Langdon Assocs., The, *(Langdon Assoc; 0-916704),* 41 Langdon St., Cambridge, MA 02138 (SAN 209-2379) Tel 617-864-4518.

Press of the Nightowl, *(Nightowl; 0-912960),* 320 Snapfinger Dr., Athens, GA 30605 (SAN 205-6364) Tel 404-353-7719.

Press of the Nova Scotia College of Art & Design, *(Pr of Nova Scotia),* Dist. by: Jaap Rietman, Inc., 157 Spring St., New York, NY 11012 (SAN 205-2105).

Press-on-Press, *(Press on Pr; 0-917043),* P.O. Box 135, La Jolla, CA 92038 (SAN 655-2870) Tel 619-454-0573.

Press on Press, *(Press on SF; 0-9616792),* P.O. Box 640203, San Francisco, CA 94109 (SAN 661-0692); 49 Cumberland, San Francisco, CA 94110 (SAN 661-0706) Tel 415-285-0260. Do not confuse with Press on Pr., La Jolla, CA.

†**Press Pacifica,** *(Pr Pacifica; 0-916630),* 1230 Kainui Dr., Kailua, HI 96734 (SAN 169-1635) Tel 808-261-6594; *CIP.*

Press West, *(Press West; 0-914592),* 4947 E. Tanqueray, St. Louis, MO 63129 (SAN 202-988X) Tel 314-982-2616.

Presser Le Pas, *(Presser Le Pas; 0-9616726),* 554 W. 50th St., 6th Flr., New York, NY 10019 (SAN 659-8773) Tel 212-757-1189.

Pressure Applications, *(Pressure Appli; 0-9614857),* 1621 Tiffany Way, San Jose, CA 95125 (SAN 693-1898) Tel 408-280-7420.

Pressure Vessel Handbook Publishing, Inc., *(Pressure; 0-914458),* P.O. Box 35365, Tulsa, OK 74153-0365 (SAN 206-6149) Tel 918-742-9637.

Pressworks Publishing, Inc., *(Pressworks; 0-939722),* P.O. Box 12606, Dallas, TX 75225 (SAN 216-7581) Tel 214-369-3113; 6140 Deloache St., Dallas, TX 75225 (SAN 658-1471).

Prestegord Pubs., *(Prestegord Pubs; 0-912751),* 2210A Naudain St., Philadelphia, PA 19146 (SAN 282-8251) Tel 215-568-1112; Dist. by: Koen Book Distributors, 514 N. Read Ave., Cinnaminson, NJ 08077 (SAN 169-4642).

†**Prestige Educational,** *(Prestige Educ; 0-9613577),* 100-11 67 Rd., Forest Hills, NY 11375 (SAN 670-0462); *CIP.*

Prestige Enterprise, *(Prestige Ent; 0-915455),* P.O. Box 723, Columbia, SC 29202 (SAN 291-3763) Tel 803-798-4792; 1041C Barmettler Place, Columbia, SC 29210 (SAN 291-3771).

Prestige Pubns., *(Prestige Pubns; 0-911009),* P.O. Box 2157, Princeton, NJ 08540 (SAN 274-791X); 100 Hamilton Ave., Princeton, NJ 08540 (SAN 662-7366) Tel 609-921-7403.

Prestige Video, *(Prestige Video; 1-55533),* 2400 N. Sixth St., Burbank, CA 91504 (SAN 695-9822) Tel 818-841-9697; Dist. by: Vantage Sales & Marketing Inc., 27 Bucknell Dr., Hazlet, NJ 07730 (SAN 200-5719).

Presto Bks., *(Presto Bks; 0-943224),* 3435 NW 54th Terr., Gainesville, FL 32606 (SAN 240-4893).

Preston, France, *(F Preston; 0-939222),* 1800 S. Robertson Blvd., Suite 281, Los Angeles, CA 90035 (SAN 216-5090).

Preston, J. A., Corp., *(Preston Corp),* 60 Page Rd., Clifton, NJ 07012 (SAN 274-7928) Tel 201-777-2700.

Preston-Hill, Inc., *(Preston-Hill; 0-914616),* P.O. Box 572, Chapel Hill, NC 27514 (SAN 201-8861) Tel 919-967-7904.

Preston Publications, Inc., *(Preston Pubns; 0-912474),* P.O. Box 48312, Niles, IL 60648 (SAN 205-3926) Tel 312-965-0566.

Preston Street Press, *(Preston St Pr; 0-939382),* 6 Preston St., Rye, NY 10580 (SAN 220-1232) Tel 914-765-2178.

Prestressed Concrete Institute, *(Prestressed Concrete; 0-937040),* 201 N. Wells St., Suite 1410, Chicago, IL 60606 (SAN 202-1528) Tel 312-346-4071.

Prestwick Poetry Publishing Co., *(Prestwick Pub; 0-9607812),* P.O. Box 90277, San Diego, CA 92109-0780 (SAN 239-5932) Tel 619-456-2366.

Presznick, Rose M., *(R M Presznick; 0-912000),* RD 1, 7810 Avon Lake Rd., Lodi, OH 44254 (SAN 205-1524).

Pretty Good Publishing, *(Pretty Good TX; 0-9130020),* P.O. Box 40, Lindale, TX 75771-0040 (SAN 663-1940).

Pretty Penny Pr., Inc., *(Pretty Penny Pr; 0-938509),* P.O. Box 3890, Santa Monica, CA 90403 (SAN 661-0226) Dist. by: Panjandrum Bks., 11321 Iowa Ave., Suite 1, Los Angeles, CA 90025 (SAN 282-1257) Tel 213-477-8771.

Pricare Inc., *(Pricare; 0-9613095),* 3838 E. Phillips Circle, Littleton, CO 80122 (SAN 294-6521) Tel 303-740-8136.

Price, Christine, *(C Price; 0-9603654),* c/o Esalen Institute, Big Sur, CA 93920 (SAN 221-7252).

Price, David L., *(D L Price; 0-9604482),* 1954 Old Hickory Blvd., Brentwood, TN 37027 (SAN 215-3351) Tel 615-373-0946.

Price, Polly S., *(P S Price; 0-9604012),* 3102 Eisenhauer B-16, San Antonio, TX 78209 (SAN 221-6639) Tel 512-824-6523.

Price Guide Pubs., *(Price Guide; 0-911182),* P.O. Box 525, Kenmore, WA 98028-0525 (SAN 205-3934) Tel 206-362-6670.

Price-Pottenger Nutrition Foundation, *(Price-Pottenger; 0-916764),* 5871 El Cajon Blvd., San Diego, CA 92115 (SAN 208-1849) Tel 619-583-7450.

†**Price, Stern, Sloan, Pubs., Inc.,** *(Price Stern; 0-8431),* 410 N. La Cienega Blvd., Los Angeles, CA 90048 (SAN 202-0246) Tel 213-657-6100; Toll free: 800-421-0892; 1900 Sacramento St., Los Angeles, CA 90021 (SAN 658-148X); Toll free: 800-227-8801 (In California); *CIP.*

Price Waterhouse, *(Price Waterhouse),* National Office Distribution Dept., 1251 Ave. of the Americas, New York, NY 10020 (SAN 237-8094).

Prichard, Arthur C., *(A C Prichard; 0-9612788),* 214 Pleasant St., Mannington, WV 26583 (SAN 289-8063) Tel 304-986-1521.

Prickly Pear Pr., *(Prickly CA; 0-9605794),* 150 Midcrest Way, San Francisco, CA 94131 (SAN 216-5449); Dist. by: Bookpeople, 2929 Fifth St., Berkeley, CA 94710 (SAN 691-4217); Dist. by: Inland Bk. Co., 22 Hemingway Ave., P.O. Box 261, East Haven, CT 06512 (SAN 691-4225) Tel 203-467-4257.

Names

Prickly Pear Pr., *(Prickly Pear; 0-933384)*, 2132 Edwin St., Fort Worth, TX 76110 (SAN 212-4394).

Pride In America Co., The, *(Pride in Am; 0-9614917)*, 176 Warwick Dr., Pittsburgh, PA 15241 (SAN 223-9566) Tel 412-833-1717.

Pride Products Co., Inc., *(Pride Prods; 0-934383)*, P.O. Box 1639, Sun City, AZ 85372 (SAN 693-8051) Tel 602-972-4925.

Prima Agua Press, *(Prima Agua Pr; 0-939652)*, 302 Union, Las Cruces, NM 88001 (SAN 216-6429).

Prima Materia Bks., *(Prima Materia; 0-9615315)*, P.O. Box 1399, Quoque, NY 11959 (SAN 694-650X) Tel 516-653-5627; Dist. by: Bookpeople, 2929 Fifth St., Berkeley, CA 94710 (SAN 168-9517); Toll free: 800-227-1516; Dist. by: Baker & Taylor Co., Eastern Div., 50 Kirby Ave., Somerville, NJ 08876 (SAN 169-4901); Dist. by: Baker & Taylor Co., Midwest Div., 501 Gladiola Ave,, Momence, IL 60954 (SAN 169-2100); Dist. by: Baker & Taylor Co., Southeast Div,, Mt. Olive Rd., Commerce, GA 30529 (SAN 169-1503); Dist. by: Baker & Taylor Co., Western Div., 380 Edison Way, Reno, NV 89564 (SAN 169-4464) Tel 702-786-6700; Toll free: 800-648-3540.

Prima Publishing & Communication, Div. of Cal Co Am, Inc., *(Prima Pub Comm; 0-914629)*, P.O. Box 1260, Rocklin, CA 95677-1260 (SAN 289-5609) Tel 916-624-1260; Dist. by: Interbook, Inc., 14895 E. 147th St., Suite 370, San Leandro, CA 94577 (SAN 692-7564) Tel 415-352-9221.

Prima Vera Publications, *(Prima Vera Pubns; 0-934485)*, 2307 Oakdale Rd., Bldg. 4, Suite 3, Modesto, CA 95355 (SAN 693-806X) Tel 209-524-4351; P.O. Box 6958, Modesto, CA 95355 (SAN 699-5985).

Primary Pr., *(Primary Pr; 0-934982)*, Box 105a, Parker Ford, PA 19457 (SAN 216-1753) Tel 215-495-7529.

Primary Programs, *(Primary Progs; 0-9612060)*, 409 Crescent Gardens Dr., Pittsburgh, PA 15235 (SAN 286-8555) Tel 412-795-7487.

Primary Pubblishing Co., *(Primary Pub; 0-9616563)*, 883 S. Marengo, Pasadena, CA 91106 (SAN 659-574X) Tel 818-449-5733.

Primary Sources, *(Primary; 0-911184)*, P.O. Box 472, Cooper Sta., New York, NY 10003 (SAN 205-3942).

Primate Publishing, *(Primate Pub; 0-9615289)*, 1710 Baker St., San Francisco, CA 94115 (SAN 694-4191) Tel 415-563-5160.

Primavera, *(Primavera; 0-916980)*, Ida Noyes Hall, Univ. of Chicago, 1212 E. 59th St., Chicago, IL 60637 (SAN 208-2527) Tel 312-684-2742.

Primavera Productions, *(Primavera Prods; 0-9607990)*, 1063 N. Cove, Union, OR 97883 (SAN 238-5597) Tel 503-562-5091.

Prime National Publishing Co., *(Prime Natl Pub; 0-932834)*, 470 Boston Post Rd., Weston, MA 02193 (SAN 212-3053) Tel 617-899-2702.

Prime Press, Ltd., *(Prime Pr AZ; 0-911539)*, 3003 W. Northern, No. 1, Phoenix, AZ 85021 (SAN 264-3197) Tel 602-995-8803; Orders to: Prime Press, Ltd., P.O. Box 17073, Mesa, AZ 85212 (SAN 662-1163) Tel 602-831-5823.

Prime Pubns., Inc., *(Prime Pubns; 0-932053)*, 1111 W. 22nd St., Suite 200, Minneapolis, MN 55408 (SAN 686-2659) Tel 612-377-9200.

Prime Pubs., *(Prime Pubs; 0-937514)*, 1460 Boulder Ave., Cresent City, CA 95531 (SAN 209-6307) Tel 707-464-1081.

Prime Time Aerobics, *(Prime Time Aerobics; 0-9610234)*, 3089C Clairmont Dr., No. 130, San Diego, CA 92117 (SAN 264-3456) Tel 619-268-0684.

Primer Pr., *(Primer Pr MA; 0-910617)*, 12 Sherman Bridge Rd., Wayland, MA 01778 (SAN 260-2512) Tel 617-358-2660.

Primer Pubs., *(Primer Pubs; 0-935810)*, 5738 N. Central, Phoenix, AZ 85012 (SAN 220-0864) Tel 602-266-1043; Dist. by: Many Feathers, 5738 N. Central, Phoenix, AZ 85012 (SAN 220-0864).

Primipara, *(Primipara; 0-9613790)*, Box 371, Oconto, WI 54153 (SAN 218-2629) Tel 414-834-3860.

Primo Productions, *(Primo Prod; 0-936357)*, 633 Battery St., Suite 910, San Francisco, CA 94111 (SAN 697-9432) Tel 415-788-7977.

Primrose Press, *(Primrose Pr)*, 2131 S. Primrose Ave., Alhambra, CA 91803 (SAN 212-9620) Tel 213-283-5468.

Prince, Derek, Ministries Pubns., *(Derek Prince; 0-934920)*, P.O. Box 300, Fort Lauderdale, FL 33302 (SAN 211-822X) Tel 305-763-5202.

Prince, Thelma F., *(T F Prince; 0-9614020)*, 44 Clemson Rd., Parlin, NJ 08859 (SAN 683-6305) Tel 201-721-1342.

Prince George's County Genealogical Society, *(Prince Georges County Gen Soc; 0-916805)*, Box 819, Bowie, MD 20715 (SAN 218-9135).

Prince of Peace Publishing Inc., *(Prince Peace Pub; 0-933173)*, 13801 Fairview Dr., Burnsville, MN 55337 (SAN 692-3305) Tel 612-435-8102.

Prince Paperback *See* Crown Pubs., Inc.

Prince Street Editions, *(Prince St Ed; 0-943998)*, 8 Prince St., New York, NY 10012 (SAN 241-2152) Tel 212-226-7086.

Princeton Architectural Pr., *(Princeton Arch; 0-910413)*, 40 Witherspoon St., Princeton, NJ 08540 (SAN 260-1176) Tel 609-924-7911; Toll free: 800-334-0854.

Princeton Bk. Co., *(Princeton Bk Co; 0-916622; 0-903102; 0-87127; 0-932582)*, P.O. Box 109, Princeton, NJ 08540 (SAN 208-404X) Tel 609-737-8178; 12 W. Delaware Ave., Pennington, NJ 08534 (SAN 658-1498).

Princeton Hightech Group Inc., *(Princeton Hightech; 0-934603)*, 73 Maplestream Rd., E. Windsor, NJ 08520 (SAN 693-921X) Tel 609-443-4114; Orders to: Order Service, P.O. Box 231, Princeton Junction, NJ 08850 (SAN 662-3298) Tel 609-443-3470.

Princeton Opinion Press, *(Princeton Opinion)*, 53 Bank St., Princeton, NJ 08542 (SAN 295-3447) Tel 609-924-9600.

Princeton Publishing, *(Princeton Pub; 0-915038)*, 221 Nassau St., Princeton, NJ 08540 (SAN 663-1789) Tel 609-924-7555.

Princeton Research Institute, *(Princeton Res Inst; 0-913354)*, P.O. Box 363, Princeton, NJ 08540 (SAN 207-4478) Tel 609-396-0305.

Princeton Research Pr., *(Princet Res Pr; 0-936231)*, P.O. Box 704, Princeton, NJ 08540 (SAN 696-8155) Tel 609-921-2806; 11 Research Rd., Princeton, NJ 08540 (SAN 696-8163).

Princeton Scientific Publishing Co., Inc., *(Princeton Sci Pubs; 0-911131)*, P.O. Box 2155, Princeton, NJ 08543 (SAN 274-7995) Tel 609-683-4750.

Princeton Univ., Dept. of History, *(Princeton Dept Hist; 0-938495)*, 129 Dickinson Hall, Princeton, NJ 08544 (SAN 661-0471) Tel 609-452-5550.

Princeton Univ., Industrial Relations Section, *(PU Indust Rel)*, Firestone Bldg., P.O. Box 248, Princeton, NJ 08540 (SAN 205-1494) Tel 609-452-4040.

†Princeton Univ. International Finance Section, Dept. of Economics, *(Princeton U Int Finan Econ; 0-88165)*, Princeton Univ., Dickinson Hall, Princeton, NJ 08544 (SAN 205-1109) Tel 609-452-4048. Do not confuse with Princeton Univ. Pr; *CIP*.

Princeton Univ. Library, *(Princeton Lib; 0-87811)*, Nassau St., Princeton, NJ 08544 (SAN 205-3950) Tel 609-452-3184.

†Princeton Univ. Pr., *(Princeton U Pr; 0-691)*, 41 William St., Princeton, NJ 08540 (SAN 202-0254) Tel 609-452-4900; Orders to: Marge Weiland, 3175 Princeton Pike, Lawrenceville, NJ 08648 (SAN 662-1171) Tel 609-896-1344; *CIP*.

Princeton Urban & Regional Research Center, *(PURRC; 0-938882)*, Woodrow Wilson School, Princeton University, Princeton, NJ 08544 (SAN 282-1869) Tel 609-452-5662; Orders to: Transaction Books, Rutgers University, New Brunswick, NJ 08903 (SAN 282-1877) Tel 201-932-2280.

Principal's Library, The, *(Principals Lib; 0-9617117)*, P.O. Box 1342, Massapequa, NY 11758 (SAN 662-8095); 41 Sheppard Ln., Huntington, NY 11743 (SAN 662-8109) Tel 516-326-4687.

Principia Press, *(Principia Pr; 0-911188)*, 5743 Kimbark Ave., Chicago, IL 60637 (SAN 205-3888) Tel 312-643-8295.

Prindle, Weber & Schmidt *See* PWS Pubs.

Prinit Pr., *(Prinit Pr; 0-932970)*, Box 65, Dublin, IN 47335 (SAN 212-680X).

Prinroad Pubs., *(Prinroad Pubs; 0-911629)*, 5717 E. Thomas Rd., Scottsdale, AZ 85251 (SAN 264-3200) Tel 602-941-5760.

Print Media Services, Ltd., *(Print Med Serv Ltd; 0-942398)*, 1310 Jarvis Ave., Elk Grove, IL 60007 (SAN 238-1109) Tel 312-981-0100; Toll free: 800-323-8899.

†Printed Editions, *(Printed Edns; 0-914162)*, P.O. Box 27, Sta. Hill Rd., Barrytown, NY 12507 (SAN 206-5851) Tel 914-758-6488; Dist. by: Writers & Books, 740 University Ave., Rochester, NY 14607 (SAN 156-9678) Tel 716-473-2590; Dist. by: Small Pr. Distribution, 1814 San Pablo Ave., Berkeley, CA 94702 (SAN 204-5826) Tel 415-549-3336; *CIP*.

Printed Horse, The, *(Printed Horse; 0-912830)*, P.O. Box 1908, Fort Collins, CO 80522 (SAN 210-4377) Tel 303-482-2286.

Printed Matter, Inc., *(Printed Matter; 0-89439)*, 7 Lispenard St., New York, NY 10013 (SAN 169-5924) Tel 212-925-0325.

Printed Word Publishing, *(Printed Word)*, c/o Barber, 23561 Vaughn Rd., Veneta, OR 97487 (SAN 295-3463) Tel 503-935-7701.

Printek, *(Printek; 0-938042)*, 6989 Oxford St., Minneapolis, MN 55426 (SAN 215-7012).

Printing Industries of America, Inc., *(Print Indus Am; 0-89740)*, 1730 N. Lynn St., Arlington, VA 22209 (SAN 224-7828) Tel 703-841-8100; 1731 N. Moore St., Arlington, VA 22209 (SAN 669-2486).

Printing, Mailing Services, Inc., *(Print Mail Serv)*, 126 N. Ontario St., Toledo, OH 43624 (SAN 216-0064) Tel 419-241-4266.

Printwheel Pr., *(Printwheel; 0-916401)*, 2674 E. Main St., Suite C-124, Ventura, CA 93003 (SAN 295-9208) Tel 805-643-0965.

Printworld, Inc., *(Printworld; 0-943606)*, P.O. Box 785, Bala Cynwyd, PA 19004 (SAN 240-7515) Tel 215-649-5140.

Priorities Inc., *(Priorities; 0-932043)*, 1430 Massachusetts Ave., Suite 306-85, Cambridge, MA 02138 (SAN 685-298X) Tel 718-788-7214.

Priority Pr., *(Priority GA; 0-9615772)*, P.O. Box 431, Riverdale, GA 30274 (SAN 695-9865) Tel 404-478-7498; 8381 Willows Way, Riverdale, GA 30274 (SAN 695-9873).

Priority Press, *(Priority Pr; 0-913815)*, P.O. Box 670152, Dallas, TX 75367-0152 (SAN 289-5447) Tel 214-368-0135.

†Priority Pr. Pubns./Twentieth Century Fund, Subs. of Twentieth Century Fund, Inc., *(Priority Pr Pubns; 0-87078)*, 41 E. 70th St., New York, NY 10021 (SAN 205-4647) Tel 212-535-4441; *CIP*.

Priority Pubs., Inc., *(Priority Pubs; 0-930229)*, P.O. Box 1585, Bellevue, WA 98009 (SAN 682-8272).

Priory Bks., *(Priory Bks)*, 1200 Kenwood Ave., Duluth, MN 55811 (SAN 206-1309) Tel 218-723-6555. Do not confuse with Priory Pr., Chicago, IL.

Priory Pr., The, *(Priory Pr IL; 0-8296)*, 1111 N Richmond St., Chicago, IL 60622 (SAN 658-6341) Tel 218-723-6582. Do not confuse with Priory Pr., Duluth, MN.

Priory Productions, *(Priory Prods; 0-936161)*, 840 S. Main St., Mt. Angel, OR 97362 (SAN 696-821X) Tel 503-845-6773.

Priscilla's Pubns., & Products, Subs. of Martin Instrument Co., *(Priscillas Pubns; 0-917119)*, P.O. Box 16270, Philadelphia, PA 19114 (SAN 655-7686) Tel 215-677-5600.

Prism Bks. *See* Prentice-Hall, Inc.

Prism Entertainment Corp., *(Prism Enter Corp; 1-55668)*, 1875 Century Pk., E., Suite 1010, Los Angeles, CA 90067 Tel 213-277-3270.

†Prism Press, *(Prism Pr; 0-938774)*, 11706 Longleaf Lane, Houston, TX 77024 (SAN 216-4388) Tel 713-782-5189; *CIP*.

Prisma Bks., Inc., *(Prisma Bks; 0-910235)*, 2501 Irving Ave. S., Minneapolis, MN 55405 (SAN 241-4384) Tel 612-377-0133. *Imprints:* Prisma Institute (Prisma Inst).

Prisma Institute *See* Prisma Bks., Inc.

Prismatique Pubns., *(Prismatique; 0-9614150)*, P.O. Box 1059, Daly City, CA 94015 (SAN 686-6115) Tel 415-756-1834.

Pritchard, Anita, *(A Prichard CA; 0-9612560)*, 915B Biloxi Dr., Norman, OK 73071 (SAN 289-3819) Tel 405-360-8115.

Names

†Pritchett & Hull Assocs., Inc., *(Pritchett & Hull; 0-939838),* 3440 Oakcliff Rd., NE, Suite 110, Atlanta, GA 30340 (SAN 216-9258) Tel 404-451-0602; Toll free: 800-241-4925; *CIP.*

Privacy Journal, *(Privacy Journal; 0-930072),* Box 15300, Washington, DC 20003 (SAN 210-6531) Tel 202-547-2865.

Private Adjudication Ctr., Inc., *(Private Adjudication; 0-933329),* Duke Univ., Schl. of Law, Durham, NC 27706 (SAN 691-9359) Tel 919-684-2253.

Private Books, *(Private Bks; 0-9606112),* 500 19th Ave., San Francisco, CA 94121 (SAN 216-8510) Tel 415-751-2338.

Private Carrier Conference, Inc., *(Private Carrier),* 2200 Mill Rd., Alexandria, VA 22314 (SAN 217-264X).

Private Doctors of America, *(Private Doctors),* 3422 Bienville St., New Orleans, LA 70119 (SAN 224-4241) Tel 504-486-5891.

Privateer Publishing Co, *(Privateer Pub Co; 0-931339),* 512-Viewmont St., Benicia, CA 94510 (SAN 682-0123) Tel 707-745-1627.

P.R.N. Corp., *(P R N Corp; 0-910757),* 330 First St. SE, Cedar Rapids, IA 52401 (SAN 260-2415).

Pro-Action Publishing, Div. of Pro-Action Sports, Inc., *(Pro Action Pub; 0-9615126),* 1717 N. Glendale Blvd., Los Angeles, CA 90026 (SAN 694-1826) Tel 213-666-7789.

Pro Canto Pr., *(Pro Canto; 0-935751),* 37 Phelps St., Marlboro, MA 01752 (SAN 695-989X) Tel 617-481-2322; Dist. by: Support Services, 221 Milk St., Westboro, MA 01581 (SAN 200-5700).

†Pro-Ed, *(Pro Ed; 0-936104),* 5341 Industrial Oaks Blvd., Austin, TX 78735 (SAN 222-1349) Tel 512-892-3142; *CIP.*

Pro Libris Press, *(Pro Libris Pr; 0-943530),* 10 Third St., Bangor, ME 04401 (SAN 240-7523) Tel 207-942-3019.

†Pro Lingua Assocs., *(Pro Lingua; 0-86647),* 15 Elm St., Brattleboro, VT 05301 (SAN 216-0579) Tel 802-257-7779; *CIP.*

Pro-Motion Music, *(Pro-Motion Music; 0-939141),* 3737 NE 112th St., Portland, OR 97220 (SAN 662-5053) Tel 503-257-8185.

Pro Pacific, Inc., *(Pro Pacific; 0-9616429),* 7117 40th St., No. 14, Tacoma, WA 98466 (SAN 659-0586) Tel 206-565-9480.

Pro-Se Law Project, Inc., *(Pro-Se Law; 0-937945),* P.O. Box 164, Palmerton, PA 18071 (SAN 659-7572) Tel 215-826-2000.

Pro Se Pubns., *(Pro Se Pubns; 0-9617267),* Box 3082, Denton, TX 76202 (SAN 663-4915); 601 Jupiter St., Denton, TX 76201 (SAN 663-4923) Tel 817-387-1878.

Pro-Search, *(Pro-Search; 0-9602540),* 3256 Ridge Rd., P.O. Box 24, Lansing, IL 60438 (SAN 213-148X) Tel 312-895-8800.

Pro Serve Corp. of Sarasota, Inc., *(Pro Serve Corp; 0-936177),* 1938 Ringling Blvd., Sarasota, FL 33577 (SAN 696-8279) Tel 813-366-9024; Toll free: 800-237-9222.

Pro West, *(Pro West; 0-9606746),* 7355 Citrus Way E., Scottsdale, AZ 85253 (SAN 215-1758) Tel 602-991-3183; Dist. by: Motorbooks International, 729 Prospect Ave., Osceola, WI 54020 (SAN 212-3304) Tel 715-294-3345.

ProActive Pr., *(ProActive Pr; 0-914158),* 64 Vian La Cumbre, Greenbrae, CA 94904 (SAN 201-8888) Tel 415-461-7854.

Probata Pr., *(Probata Pr; 0-933109),* P.O. Box 10522, Marina del Rey, CA 90292 (SAN 689-5905) Tel 213-827-5477.

Probe Company, *(Probe Co; 0-9614050),* 1830 North Grand River Ave., Lansing, MI 48906 (SAN 684-8958) Tel 517-372-8440.

†Probus Publishing Co., Inc., *(Probus Pub Co; 0-917253),* 118 N. Clinton, Chicago, IL 60606 (SAN 655-8615) Tel 312-346-7985; *CIP.*

Procedural Aspects of International Law Institute, *(Proced Aspects Intl; 0-9615124),* 910 17th St., NW, Washington, DC 20006 (SAN 604-1699) Tel 202-293-5670.

Procedures Unlimited, Inc, *(Procedures),* P.O. Box 66, Palos Park, IL 60464 (SAN 287-2811) Tel 312-448-8695.

†Process Pr., *(Process Pr; 0-9605378),* 2322 Haste, No. 31, Berkeley, CA 94704 (SAN 215-9074) Tel 415-548-6510; *CIP.*

Procter & Gamble Educational Services, *(Procter Gamble Educ; 0-938973),* 1 Procter & Gamble Plaza, Cincinnati, OH 45202 (SAN 661-6844) Tel 513-983-3152.

Proctor, Jones Publishing Co., *(Proctor Jones; 0-9608860),* 3401 Sacramento St., San Francisco, CA 94118 (SAN 293-3179) Tel 415-922-9222; Dist. by: Publishers Group West, 5855 Beaudry St., Emeryville, CA 94608 (SAN 202-8522) Tel 415-658-3453.

ProDesign, Inc., *(ProDesign; 0-931141),* 58 Bank St., New York, NY 10014 (SAN 659-8153) Tel 212-929-0416.

Prodigal Publishing Co., *(Prodigal Publishing; 0-9617285),* 1288 Kika St., Kailua, HI 96734 (SAN 663-6071) Tel 808-262-7229; Dist. by: Pacific Trade Group, P.O. Box 668, Pearl City, HI 96782-0668 (SAN 169-1635).

Prodist *See Watson, Neale, Academic Pubns.*

Produce Marketing Assn., *(Produce Mktg Assn),* 700 Barksdale Plaza, Newark, DE 19711 (SAN 224-8646) Tel 302-738-7100.

Product Crafters Inc., *(Prod Craftrs Inc; 0-931673),* 646 Hwy. 18, E. Brunswick, NJ 08816 (SAN 683-7700) Tel 201-238-1470.

Product Structuring Enterprises, *(PSE; 0-940964),* P.O. Box 17723, San Diego, CA 92117 (SAN 217-4197) Tel 619-451-1427.

Production House Corp., *(Prod Hse; 0-932638),* P.O. Box 8408, La Jolla, CA 92038 (SAN 201-1018) Tel 619-287-2560.

Productivity Pr., Div. of Productivity, Inc., *(Prod Press; 0-915299),* P.O. Box 814, Cambridge, MA 02238 (SAN 290-036X) Tel 617-497-5146.

Productivity Research International, Inc., *(Productivity Rsch; 0-9616778),* P.O. Box 1171, Melrose, MA 02176-0018 (SAN 661-0595); 61 W. Hill Ave., Melrose, MA 02176 (SAN 661-0609) Tel 617-665-5777.

Professional & Reference Bk. Div. *See McGraw-Hill Bk. Co.*

Professional Assocs., *(Prof Assocs; 0-931802),* Box 6254, Harrisburg, PA 17112 (SAN 6693-1332).

†Professional Bk. Ctr., Inc., *(Prof Bk Ctr Inc; 0-943226),* 5600 NE Hassalo St., Portland, OR 97213 (SAN 240-5601) Tel 503-288-1255; Orders to: International Specialized Book Services, 5602 NE Hassalo St., Portland, OR 97213-3640 (SAN 169-7129) Tel 503-287-3093; Toll free: 800-547-7734; *CIP.*

Professional Bks./Future Health, Inc., *(Prof Bks Future Health; 0-933478),* P.O. Box 3494, Jackson, TN 38301 (SAN 205-3977); 681 Skyline Dr., Jackson, TN 38301 (SAN 662-7374) Tel 901-423-5100; Orders to: P.O. Box 846, Jackson, TN 38302 (SAN 695-6270).

Professional Books Service, *(Prof Bks Serv; 0-9601052),* Box 366, Dayton, OH 45401-0366 (SAN 165-6309) Tel 513-223-3734.

Professional Communications, Div. of Kirkland Investment Management, Inc., *(Pro Communications; 0-9614654),* P.O. Box 7585, Phoenix, AZ 85011 (SAN 691-9014) Tel 602-274-2128; Dist. by: Baker & Taylor Co., Eastern Div., 50 Kirby Rd., Somerville, NJ 08876 (SAN 169-4901) Tel 201-526-8000.

Professional Communications, Inc., *(Prof Comn Inc; 0-937211),* 5799 Tall Oaks Rd., Madison, WI 53715 (SAN 658-6791) Tel 608-271-5791; P.O. Box 9036, Madison, WI 53715 (SAN 658-6805).

Professional Desk References, Inc., *(Prof Desk Ref; 0-939735),* 2246 Maiden Ln., Altadena, CA 91001 (SAN 663-1924).

Professional Development Services, *(Prof Dev Serv; 0-941944),* 7900 Old Branch Ave. No.106, Clinton, MD 20735 (SAN 239-4758).

Professional Driver Products Corp., *(Prof Driver Prods; 0-935879),* P.O. Box 1385, Palatine, IL 60078-1385 (SAN 695-9903) Tel 312-359-2662; 706 Deer Run Dr., Palatine, IL 60067 (SAN 695-9911).

Professional Editorial Service, Inc., *(Pro Edit Serv; 0-9615276),* 62 Floyd St., Winthrop, MA 02152 (SAN 694-4086) Tel 617-846-5639.

Professional Education Systems, Inc., *(PES Inc WI),* 3410 Sky Park Blvd., P.O. Box 1208, Eau Claire, WI 54702; Toll free: 800-826-7155.

Professional Engineering Registration Program, *(Prof Engine; 0-932276),* P.O. Box 911, San Carlos, CA 94070 (SAN 282-1915) Tel 415-593-9731; c/o Professional Pubns., Inc., P.O. Box 199, San Carlos, CA 94070 (SAN 282-1923) Tel 415-593-9119.

Professional Engineers in Private Practice, *(Prof Engr Priv Prac),* 2029 K St., NW, Washington, DC 20006 (SAN 689-9641) Tel 202-652-7767.

Professional Golfers Assn. of America, *(Pro Golfers; 0-9614856),* 100 Ave. of the Champions, Palm Beach Gardens, FL 33410 (SAN 224-5655) Tel 305-626-3600.

Professional Insurance Agents, *(Prof Ins Agents),* 400 N. Washington St., Alexandria, VA 22314 (SAN 274-8304) Tel 703-836-9340.

Professional Insurance Publications, *(Pro Insure Pubns; 0-931811),* 2495 Campus Dr., Irvine, CA 92715 (SAN 685-9887) Tel 714-955-2267.

Professional Photographers of America, *(Prof Photog),* 1090 Executive Way, Des Plaines, IL 60018 (SAN 224-9111) Tel 312-299-8161.

Professional Picture Framers Assn., *(Prof Picture Frame),* 4305 Sarellen Rd., Richmond, VA 23231 (SAN 225-2708) Tel 804-226-0430.

Professional Pr., Subs. of M. Systems Inc., *(Prof Press PA; 0-9614729),* P.O. Box 503, Spring House, PA 19477-0503 (SAN 692-6924) Tel 215-542-7008.

Professional Pr. Bks., Inc., Div. of Fairchild Books & Visuals, *(Prof Pr Bks NYC; 0-87873),* 7 E. 12th St., New York, NY 10003 (SAN 205-3985) Tel 212-741-6640.

Professional Pubns., Inc., *(Prof Pub Inc; 0-912045; 0-932276),* P.O. Box 199, San Carlos, CA 94070 (SAN 264-6315) Tel 415-593-9119.

Professional Publishing Co., *(Prof Pub Radford; 0-937419),* 1301 Madison St., Radford, VA 24141 (SAN 659-0667) Tel 703-731-5310.

Professional Pubns., Div. of Harris & Walsh Management Consultants, Inc., *(Prof Pubns; 0-9605954),* P.O. Box 698, c/o Harris & Walsh, New Rochelle, NY 10802-0698 (SAN 216-4396) Tel 914-576-0820.

Professional Pubns., Div. of MetaData, Inc., *(Prof Pubns NY; 0-932836),* 310 E. 44th St., New York, NY 10017 (SAN 213-3539); Orders to: P.O. Box 319, Huntington, NY 11743 (SAN 213-3547).

Professional Pubns. & Education, Inc., *(Prof Pubns & Educ),* 1150 Delaware St., Denver, CO 80204 (SAN 237-8299).

Professional Pubns., Inc., *(Prof Pubns Ohio; 0-934706),* 1609 Northwest Blvd., Columbus, OH 43212 (SAN 203-0942) Tel 614-488-8236.

Professional Reading Services Inc., *(Prof Reading Serv; 0-9614374),* P.O. Box 7281, Roanoke, VA 24019 (SAN 688-5985) Tel 703-563-0634.

Professional Real Estate Pubs., *(Prof Real Estate; 0-89764),* Orders to: Lincoln's Leadership Library, 5902 E. Fourth Terrace, Suite 100, Tulsa, OK 74112 (SAN 214-4476) Tel 918-622-7737.

Professional Resource Exchange, Inc., *(Pro Resource; 0-943158),* P.O. Box 15560, Sarasota, FL 34277-1560 (SAN 240-1223) Tel 813-366-7913; Toll free: 800-443-3364; Toll free: 800-366-7913.

Professional Services Publishing, *(Pro Servs Pub),* P.O. Box 327, Redding Ridge, CT 06876 (SAN 265-9794) Tel 203-938-9548.

Professionals Unlimited, *(Profs Unltd; 0-915039),* 3951 Lantern Dr., Silver Spring, MD 20902 (SAN 289-8098) Tel 301-933-5569.

Professor Jones Professional Handicapping Systems, *(Prof Jones; 1-55604),* 1940 W. State St., Boise, ID 83702 (SAN 697-2497) Tel 208-342-6939.

Profiles Publishing, Inc., *(Profiles Pub; 0-912733),* 49 Wethersield Ave., Hartford, CT 06114 (SAN 283-1406) Tel 203-522-2528.

Profit Ideas, *(Profit Ideas; 0-940398),* 8361 Vickers St., Suite 304, San Diego, CA 92111 (SAN 219-8436) Tel 619-560-6922.

567

Profit Sharing Research Foundation, *(Profit Sharing; 0-911192),* 1718 Sherman Ave., Evanston, IL 60201 (SAN 205-3993) Tel 312-869-8787.

Progenesys Pr., *(Progenesys Pr; 0-917255),* P.O. Box 2623, Christiansburg, VA 24068 (SAN 656-0318) Tel 703-382-5493.

Progenitor Genealogical Society, Inc., *(Progenitor Soc; 0-9616381),* Box 16422, Salt Lake City, UT 84116 (SAN 659-1817) Tel 801-328-8128.

Progeny Press, Inc., *(Progeny Pr; 0-934168),* P.O. Box 206, Villanova, PA 19085 (SAN 213-6740) Tel 215-525-5446.

Program Counsel, *(Program Counsel; 0-9601096),* 4900 Marine Dr., Suite 811, Chicago, IL 60640 (SAN 206-3093) Tel 312-784-3636.

Program for Cincinnati, the, *(Prog Cincinnati; 0-9608200),* 230 E. 9th St., Cincinnati, OH 45202 (SAN 238-8588) Tel 513-721-5522.

Program in Ethnomusicology, *(Progm Ethnom; 0-88287),* UCLA Dept. of Music, Los Angeles, CA 90024 (SAN 682-8108) Tel 213-825-5947.

Program Information Assocs., *(Program Assocs; 0-935555),* 7920 Makaaoa Pl., Honolulu, HI 96825 (SAN 695-8524) Tel 808-395-0197; P.O. Box 26300, Honolulu, HI 96825 (SAN 696-9550).

Programmed Pr., *(Prog Pr; 0-916106),* 2301 Baylis Ave., Elmont, NY 11003 (SAN 203-0993) Tel 516-775-0933.

†**Programmed Studies, Inc.,** *(Prog Studies; 0-917194),* P.O. Box 113, Stow, MA 01775 (SAN 207-7434) Tel 617-897-2130; *CIP.*

Programs & Pubns., *(Progs & Pubns; 0-934382),* 321 Queen St., Philadelphia, PA 19147 (SAN 213-3555) Tel 215-467-5291.

Programs for Education, Inc., *(Programs Educ; 0-935493),* 82 Park Ave., Flemington, NJ 08822 (SAN 695-9962).

Programs in Communication Press, *(Programs Comm; 0-937104),* P.O. Box 970, Monument, CO 80132 (SAN 218-9186) Tel 303-594-4711.

Programs on Change, *(Progs on Change; 0-9606012; 0-916471),* 784 Columbus Ave., Suite 1C, New York, NY 10025 (SAN 216-759X) Tel 212-222-4606.

Progresiv Publishr, *(Progresiv Pub; 0-89670),* 401 E. 32nd St., No. 1002, Chicago, IL 60616 (SAN 212-6818) Tel 312-225-9181.

†**Progressive Baptist Publishing House,** *(Prog Bapt Pub; 0-89191),* 850 N. Grove Ave., Elgin, IL 60120 (SAN 277-7010); *CIP.*

Progressive Concepts, Inc., *(Prog Concepts; 0-940010),* 2541 Lakewood Lane, Chesapeake, VA 23321 (SAN 285-0877) Tel 804-465-0646; Dist. by: Career Management Concepts, Inc., 2541 Lakewood Lane, Chesapeake, VA 23321 (SAN 285-0877) Tel 804-465-0646.

Progressive Education, *(Prog Educ; 0-935396),* P.O. Box 120574, Nashville, TN 37212 (SAN 239-4766).

Progressive Found., *(Prog Found; 0-942046),* 315 W. Gorham St., Madison, WI 53703 (SAN 238-5961) Tel 608-256-4146.

Progressive Grocer, *(Prog Grocer; 0-911790),* 1351 Washington Blvd., Stamford, CT 06902 (SAN 202-0270) Tel 203-325-3500.

Progressive Pilot Seminars *See* **Aviation Bk. Co.**

Progressive Pubns., *(Progressive Pubns; 0-937157),* 5719 Templar Crossing, West Bloomfield, MI 48033 (SAN 658-4721) Tel 313-661-1511; P.O. Box 307, Walled Lake, MI 48088 (SAN 658-473X).

Progressive Science Institute, *(Progressive Sci Inst; 0-917929),* P.O. Box 5335, Berkeley, CA 94705-0335 (SAN 657-0038) Tel 415-654-1619.

Proguides, *(Proguides; 0-9613657),* 320 Lake Crest Dr., Roswell, GA 30075 (SAN 670-7769) Tel 404-993-2298; Orders to: Proguides, P.O. Box 2738, Knoxville, TN 37901 (SAN 688-4237) Tel 615-933-3348.

Project Planning Associates, *(Project Plan; 0-9613322),* 157 Polsin Dr., Schenectady, NY 12303 (SAN 655-7694) Tel 518-356-1528.

Project Share, *(Project Share; 0-936597),* P.O. Box 2309, Rockville, MD 20852 (SAN 296-502X) Tel 301-251-5170.

Projections Enterprises, Inc., *(Projections Ent; 0-9612318),* Box 1032, 1100 Huener Lane, Jacksonville, OR 97530 (SAN 289-4882) Tel 503-899-7347.

Proletarian Pubs, *(Proletarian Pubs; 0-89380),* P.O. Box 3925, Chicago, IL 60654 (SAN 209-2158); Orders to: Vanguard Books, P.O. Box 3566, Chicago, IL 60654 (SAN 213-8212) Tel 312-342-3425.

ProLogo, *(ProLogo; 0-9616884),* P.O. Box 147, Quincy, MA 02170 (SAN 661-650X); 14 Sachem St., Quincy, MA 02170 (SAN 661-6518) Tel 617-471-8427.

Prologue Pr., *(Prologue Pr; 0-911711),* P.O. Box 640, Menlo Park, CA 94026 (SAN 264-4037) Tel 415-321-9110.

Prologue Pubns., *(Prologue; 0-930048),* P.O. Box 7119, Menlo Park, CA 94026 (SAN 210-1351) Tel 415-322-1663.

Promark Asociates, *(Promark Assocs; 0-9607930),* Box 222, High Falls, NY 12440 (SAN 238-5619) Tel 914-687-7230.

Promenade Publishing, Div. of Promenade, *(Promenade Pub; 0-932255),* P.O. Box 2092, Boulder, CO 80306 (SAN 686-628X) Tel 303-440-4807; 835 39th St., Boulder, CO 80302 (SAN 697-7103) Tel 303-440-4807.

Promethean Arts, *(Promethean Arts; 0-942624),* P.O. Box 2619, Toledo, OH 43606 (SAN 238-5627) Tel 419-536-4257.

†**Prometheus Bks.,** *(Prometheus Bks; 0-87975),* 700 E. Amherst St., Buffalo, NY 14215 (SAN 202-0289) Tel 716-837-2475; Toll free: 800-421-0351; *CIP.*

Prometheus Bound, *(Prometheus Bound; 0-9616867),* P.O. Box 9611, New Haven, CT 06535 (SAN 661-1354); 1423 Chapel St., New Haven, CT 06511 (SAN 661-1362) Tel 203-865-7443.

Prometheus Enterprises, *(Prometheus Ent; 0-9617155),* 4320 Stevens Creek Blvd., Suite 175, San Jose, CA 95129 (SAN 663-3668) Tel 408-985-9885.

Prometheus Nemesis Book Co., Inc., *(Prometheus Nemesis; 0-9606954),* P.O. Box 2748, Del Mar, CA 92014 (SAN 215-7020) Tel 619-755-5980.

Promise Corp., *(Promise Corp; 0-936982),* P.O. Box 1534, Pawtucket, RI 02862 (SAN 214-4484).

Promise Publishing, Inc., *(Promise Pub CA; 0-939497),* P.O. Box 6289, Orange, CA 92613-6289 (SAN 663-4141); 876 N. Batavia St., Orange, CA 92668 (SAN 663-415X) Tel 714-751-4080.

Promised Land Publications, Inc., Div. of Eagle Systems International, *(Promised Land; 0-911712),* 5600 N. University Ave., Provo, UT 84601 (SAN 204-3130) Tel 801-225-2293.

Promontory Publishing, Inc., *(Promontory Pub; 0-938703),* P.O. Box 117213, Carrollton, TX 75011-7213 (SAN 661-5627); 1015 Ridgeview Cir., Carrollton, TX 75007 (SAN 661-5635) Tel 214-492-0886.

Promotions Ltd. Publishing, *(Promotions Ltd; 0-913679),* 6069 Bonnie Bern Court, Burke, VA 22015 (SAN 286-178X) Tel 703-451-0884.

Promotions Unlimited, *(Promotions Unlimit; 0-914749),* P.O. Box 10081, Lynchburg, VA 24506 (SAN 659-2074).

Proof Press, *(Proof Pr; 0-935070),* P.O. Box 1256, Berkeley, CA 94701 (SAN 209-8687) Tel 415-521-8741.

Prophecy Pressworks *See* **Sufi Islamia, Prophecy Pubns.**

Proprietary Assn., *(Proprietary Assn; 0-939060),* 1700 Pennsylvania Ave., NW, Washington, DC 20006 (SAN 209-2034) Tel 202-393-1700.

Proscenium Pr., *(Proscenium; 0-912262),* P.O. Box 361, Newark, DE 19711 (SAN 203-0950) Tel 215-255-4083.

Prosody Publishers, *(Prosody Pubs; 0-933977),* 96 Dickerson Ave., Newbury Park, CA 91320 (SAN 692-6797) Tel 805-499-8190.

Prospect Hill, *(Prospect Hill; 0-941526),* 216 Wendover Rd., Baltimore, MD 21218 (SAN 239-3743).

Prospect Press, *(Prospect Pr; 0-937562),* 14427 Pebble Hill Lane, Gaithersburg, MD 20878 (SAN 282-194X); Orders to: Box 3069, Gaithersburg, MD 20878 (SAN 282-1958) Tel 301-251-4746.

Prospector's Advertising Service, *(Prospectors Ad Serv; 0-9616047),* 5785 Hermosillo, Atascadero, CA 93422 (SAN 698-0120) Tel 805-466-9759.

Prosperity & Profits Unlimited, Distribution Services, *(Prosperity & Profits),* Box 570213, Houston, TX 77257-0213 (SAN 200-4682).

Prosveta, USA, *(Prosveta USA; 0-911857),* P.O. Box 49614, Los Angeles, CA 90049-0614 (SAN 264-3235) Tel 213-820-7478.

Protecto Enterprises, *(Protecto Ent),* P.O. Box 550, Barrington, IL 60010 (SAN 285-7448) Tel 312-382-5244.

Proteus Press, Subs. of Proteus Design, Inc., *(Proteus; 0-918150),* 9217 Baltimore Blvd., College Park, MD 20740 (SAN 210-2617) Tel 301-441-2928.

Proteus Press, The, *(Proteus Calif; 0-932864),* 250 Thunderbird Dr., Aptos, CA 95003 (SAN 212-3800).

Proteus Publishing Co., Inc., *(Proteus Pub NY; 0-86276),* P.O. Box 20398, Dag Hammarskjold Ctr., New York, NY 10017-0004 (SAN 215-2363).

Proton Editora Ltd., *(Proton Edit Ltd),* 18 E. 23rd St. Basement, New York, NY 10010 (SAN 689-1454) Tel 212-864-6249.

Proton Publishing Hse., Inc., *(Proton Pub Hse; 0-939019),* 233 Valentine Ln., Yonkers, NY 10705 (SAN 662-5827).

Proven Performances, *(Proven Perf; 0-9615869),* 3321 Ridgeway Dr., Metairie, LA 70002 (SAN 696-7434) Tel 504-835-2706; Orders to: Proven Performances, 5660 S. Lakeshore Dr., No. 506, Shreveport, LA 71119 (SAN 662-3840) Tel 318-631-6507.

Providence Journal Co., *(Providence Journ; 0-937550),* 75 Fountain St., Providence, RI 02902 (SAN 264-3243) Tel 401-277-7461.

Providential Press, *(Providential Pr),* P.O. Box 218026, Houston, TX 77218 (SAN 276-9794) Tel 713-578-7837.

Province, C. M., *(C M Province; 0-932348),* 11307 Vela Dr., San Diego, CA 92126 (SAN 211-4445) Tel 619-271-6517.

Provinicial Pr., *(Provincial NC; 0-936179),* P.O. Box 2311, Chapel Hill, NC 27514 (SAN 205-1079) Tel 919-942-6412. Do not confuse with Provincial Pr., Ashland, OR.

Provincial Press (OR), *(Provincial Pr OR; 0-9614779),* P.O. Box 3051, Ashland, OR 97520 (SAN 692-7823) Tel 503-488-2043.

Provost, C. Antonio, *(Provost),* 4474 Sunburst Dr., Oceanside, CA 92056-3540 (SAN 239-3751).

Prow Bks./Franciscan Marytown Pr., *(Prow Bks-Franciscan; 0-913382),* 1600 W. Park Ave., Libertyville, IL 60048 (SAN 205-1060).

Proximity Technology, Inc., *(Proximity Tech; 0-926390),* 3511 NE 22nd Ave., Fort Lauderdale, FL 33308 (SAN 294-5827) Tel 305-566-3511.

Prudent Pubs., *(Prudent Pubs; 0-915499),* 1335 Madison St., NW, Washington, DC 20011 (SAN 291-3860).

Prudential Publishing Company, *(Prudential Pub Co; 0-934432),* 7089 Crystal Blvd., Diamond Springs, CA 95619 (SAN 213-1498) Tel 916-622-8928.

†**Pruett Pub. Co.,** *(Pruett; 0-87108),* 2928 Pearl St., Boulder, CO 80301 (SAN 205-4035) Tel 303-449-4919; *CIP.*

Prytaneum Press, *(Prytaneum Pr; 0-907152),* P.O. Box 7161, Amarillo, TX 79114 (SAN 214-4506).

P. S. Ltd. Publishing, *(P S Publishing; 0-912727),* P.O. Box 16-A, Newport Beach, CA 92662 (SAN 283-3093) Tel 714-675-5253.

PS Pubns., *(PS Pubns; 0-910115),* P.O. Box 2512, Fairfield, CA 94533 (SAN 241-435X) Tel 707-864-2010.

PSG, Biomedical *See* **PSG Publishing Co., Inc.**

PSR Pubns., Subs. of Fisher Investments, *(PSR Pubns; 0-931133),* 433 Airport Blvd. Suite 106, Burlingame, CA 94010-2095 (SAN 678-9196) Tel 415-342-4994.

Psych Graphic Pubs., *(Psych Graphic; 0-932382),* 470 Nautilus St., Suite 303, La Jolla, CA 92037 (SAN 210-6213) Tel 619-459-3484.

Psychegenics Pr., Subs. of MCM Inc., *(Psychegenics; 0-931865),* P.O. Box 332, Gaithersburg, MD 20877 (SAN 686-0567) Tel 301-948-1122.

Psychiatric Bks., *(Psych Bks; 0-9615865),* 13305 Cleveland Dr., Rockville, MD 20850 (SAN 696-6233) Tel 301-762-0334; Box 10578, Rockville, MD 20850 (SAN 696-9798).

Psychiatric Genocide Research Institute, *(Psych Genocide Res; 0-9614961),* P.O. Box 80071, Springfield, MA 01108 (SAN 693-7527) Tel 413-788-9523.

Psychic Bks., *(Psychic Bks; 0-930984),* 440 Avalon Pl., Oxnard, CA 93033 (SAN 219-2586) Tel 805-488-8670.

Psycho Dynamics Pr., *(Psycho Dynamics Pr; 0-937605),* 9348 Santa Monica Blvd., Beverly Hills, CA 90210 (SAN 659-0691) Tel 213-550-6250; Dist. by: DeVorss & Co., Inc., P.O. Box 550, 1046 Princeton Dr., Marina del Rey, CA 90294 (SAN 168-9886).

Psychoanalytic Quarterly, Inc., *(Psych Qtly; 0-911194),* 175 Fifth Ave., New York, NY 10010 (SAN 205-4043).

Psychogenic Disease Publishing Co., *(Psychogenic Disease; 0-87312),* P.O. Box 19098, Sacramento, CA 95819 (SAN 203-4239) Tel 916-677-1610.

†**Psychohistory Pr.,** Div. of Atcom, Inc., Pubs., *(Psychohistory Pr),* 2315 Broadway, New York, NY 10024 (SAN 201-8926) Tel 212-873-5900; Toll free: 800-521-7004; CIP.

†**Psychological Assessment Resources (PAR), Incorporated,** *(Psych Assess; 0-911907),* 16102 N. Florida Ave., Lutz, FL 33549 (SAN 264-6897) Tel 813-968-3003; Toll free: 800-331-8378; CIP.

Psychological Corp. See Harcourt Brace Jovanovich, Inc.

Psychological Development Pubns., *(Psych Dev Pubns; 0-912397),* P.O. Box 3198, Aspen, CO 81612 (SAN 265-1904) Tel 303-925-9272.

†**Psychological Dimensions, Inc.,** *(Psych Dimensions; 0-88437),* 10 W. 66th St., Suite 4H, New York, NY 10023 (SAN 204-3866) Tel 212-877-2313; CIP.

Psychological Pr., *(Psych Pr WA; 0-937668),* Box 45435, Seattle, WA 98145-0435 (SAN 215-1766) Tel 206-323-5753.

Psychological Processes, Inc., *(Psych Processes Inc; 0-912149),* P.O. Box 3914, San Rafael, CA 94901 (SAN 264-7788) Tel 415-883-3530.

Psychology & Consulting Assocs. Pr., *(Psych & Consul Assocs; 0-930626),* P.O. Box 1837, La Jolla, CA 92038 (SAN 211-3856) Tel 619-457-3900.

Psychomet Research, *(Psychomet Res; 0-9604710),* 3330 NE 135th Ave., Portland, OR 97230 (SAN 214-4492) Tel 503-256-4705.

Psychometric Affiliates, *(Psychometric; 0-9606044),* 1620 E. Main St., Murfreesboro, TN 37130 (SAN 203-1205) Tel 219-836-1661.

Pterodactyl Pr., The, *(Pterodactyl Pr; 0-931757),* Main St., Cumberland, IA 50843 (SAN 684-7722) Tel 712-774-2244.

P T L Enterprises, *(PTL Enterprises; 0-912275),* Charlotte, NC 28279 (SAN 283-3085) Tel 704-542-6000.

PTL Reproductions, *(PTL Repro; 0-910709),* 115 S. First St., Broken Arrow, OK 74012 (SAN 260-2423) Tel 918-251-3787.

Ptolemy Pr., Ltd., *(Ptolemy Pr; 0-933550),* P.O. Box 243, Grove City, PA 16127-0243 (SAN 211-2671) Tel 412-458-5145.

Ptolemy/The Browns Mills Review Press, *(Ptolemy Brown; 0-911851),* P.O. Box 905, Browns Mills, NJ 08015 (SAN 217-3123).

Public Administration Service, *(Pub Admin Serv; 0-87151),* 1313 E. 60th St., Chicago, IL 60637 (SAN 237-8183).

Public Affairs Clearinghouse See California Institute of Public Affairs

Public Affairs Committee, Inc., *(Pub Affr Comm; 0-88291),* 381 Park Ave. S., New York, NY 10016 (SAN 205-4027) Tel 212-683-4331.

Public Affairs Information Service, Inc., *(Pub Aff Info),* 11 W. 40th St., New York, NY 10018 (SAN 225-3372) Tel 212-736-6629.

Public Affairs Pr., *(Pub Aff Pr; 0-8183),* 419 New Jersey Ave., Washington, DC 20003 (SAN 202-1471) Tel 202-544-3024.

Public Affairs Research Communications, Inc., *(Pub Aff Res; 0-930331),* 3103 South St. NW, Washington, DC 20007 (SAN 670-8366) Tel 202-337-0855.

Public Affairs Research Council of Louisiana, *(Pub Aff LA),* Box 3118, 300 Louisiana Ave., Baton Rouge, LA 70821 (SAN 237-8191).

Public Citizen, Inc., *(Pub Citizen Inc; 0-937188),* 2000 P St. NW, No. 605, Washington, DC 20036 (SAN 239-4774).

Public Info. Pr., Inc., *(Public Info Pr; 0-934954),* P.O. Box 402611, Miami Beach, FL 33140 (SAN 213-1390) Tel 305-538-5308.

Public Insights Pr., *(Public Insights; 0-9608776),* Box 242, Drexel Hill, PA 19026 (SAN 238-3438).

Public Interest Clearinghouse, Inc., *(Public Int Clear; 0-915999),* 17 Murray St., New York, NY 10007 (SAN 294-653X) Tel 212-349-8155.

Public Interest Economics Foundation, *(Public Int Econ),* 1525 New Hampshire Ave., NW, Washington, DC 20036 (SAN 218-9232) Tel 202-872-0313.

Public Interest Research Group, *(PIRG),* 1346 Connecticut Ave. NW, Suite 419A, Washington, DC 20036 (SAN 225-0993) Tel 202-833-3934.

Public Management Associates, *(Pub Mgmt Assoc; 0-939968),* 2014 Siegle Dr., Lemon Grove, CA 92045 (SAN 216-8537) Tel 714-575-2395.

Public Management Institute, Institute for Fund Raising, *(Public Management; 0-916664),* 358 Brannan St., San Francisco, CA 94107 (SAN 208-6964) Tel 415-896-1900.

Public Media, Inc., Subs. of Public Media, Inc., *(Public Media Inc; 0-913349),* 5547 N. Ravenswood Ave., Chicago, IL 60640 (SAN 283-3786) Tel 312-878-2600; Toll free: 800-323-4222.

Public Pr., *(Public Pr; 0-9611738),* Orders to: Mary Clark, 646 Ninth Ave., New York, NY 10036 (SAN 219-4546) Tel 212-333-7538.

Public Relations Publishing Co., Inc., *(Public Relations; 0-913046),* 888 Seventh Ave., New York, NY 10106 (SAN 202-957X) Tel 212-315-8250.

Public Safety Automation, *(Public Safety; 0-939257),* P.O. Box 957, Buellton, CA 93427 (SAN 662-5193); 391 Freear Dr., Buellton, CA 93427 (SAN 662-5207) Tel 805-736-2155.

Public Sector Labor Relations Conference Board, *(Pub Sect Lab Rel; 0-913400),* Univ. of Maryland, Division of Behavorial and Social Sciences, College Park, MD 20742 (SAN 205-4051).

Public Securities Assn., *(Pub Securities; 0-9605198),* 40 Broad St., 12th flr., New York, NY 10004-2373 (SAN 216-2903) Tel 212-809-7000.

Public Service Materials Center, *(Public Serv Materials; 0-914977),* 111 N. Central Ave., Hartsdale, NY 10530 (SAN 211-9676) Tel 914-949-2242.

Public Service Pubns., Inc., *(Public Serv Pubns; 0-936656),* 1523 W. Eighth St., Los Angeles, CA 90017 (SAN 212-1328) Tel 213-484-1088.

Public Technology, Inc., *(Pub Tech Inc),* 1301 Pennsylvania Ave., NW, Washington, DC 20004 (SAN 225-1256) Tel 202-626-2400.

Public Utilities Reports, Inc., *(Public Util; 0-910325),* 1700 N. Moore St., Suite 2100, Rosslyn Ctr. Bldg., Arlington, VA 22209 (SAN 241-4392) Tel 703-243-7000; Toll free: 800-368-5001.

Pub. Arts, *(Pubn Arts NJ; 0-942190),* 579 Goffle Road, Ridgewood, NJ 07450 (SAN 239-9717) Tel 201-652-9393.

Publication Board of the American Society of Landscape Architects, *(Am Soc Landscape; 0-911241),* 1190 E. Broadway, Louisville, KY 40204 (SAN 274-8975) Tel 502-589-1167.

Pubns. Development Co., *(Pubns Devl Co; 0-936431),* P.O. Box 1075, Crockett, TX 75835 (SAN 211-0490) Tel 409-544-5137; Hwy. 287 N., Crockett, TX 75835 (SAN 699-5543).

Publications of the Pennsylvania-Yale Expedition to Egypt, *(Penn-Yale Expedit),* Yale Univ., 102 Hall of Graduate Studies, New Haven, CT 06520 (SAN 662-118X) Tel 203-436-8779; c/o Peabody Museum of Natural History, Pubns. Office, 170 Whitney Ave., P.O. Box 6666, New Haven, CT 06511 (SAN 205-177X) Tel 203-436-1131.

Publicity in Print, *(Publicity; 0-915716),* 935 Thornton Way, San Jose, CA 95128 (SAN 207-2750) Tel 408-293-3997.

Publish or Perish, Inc., *(Publish or Perish; 0-914098),* 3701 W. Alabama, Suite 450-130, Houston, TX 77027 (SAN 202-0319) Tel 713-524-5515; P.O. Box 27703-130, Houston, TX 77027 (SAN 660-9422).

Publisher Vaidava, *(Pub Vaidava; 0-936302),* 1621 S. 21st St., Lincoln, NE 68502 (SAN 214-2198).

Pubs. Assocs., Inc., *(Publishers Assocs; 0-915911),* 3601 West Devon Ave., Suite 108, Chicago, IL 60659 (SAN 294-0957) Tel 312-463-2030.

Publishers Consultants, *(Publishers Consult; 0-88310),* Box 1908, Ft. Collins, CO 80522 (SAN 203-2449) Tel 303-482-2286. Formerly Shields Publishing Co., Inc.

Publishers Group West, *(Publishers Group),* 5855 Beaudry St., Emeryville, CA 94608 (SAN 202-8522) Tel 415-658-3453; Toll free: 800-982-8319.

Publishers Guild, *(Publishers Guild),* P.O. Box 754, Palatine, IL 60067 (SAN 212-7180) Tel 312-991-0255.

Pubs. Guild of California, *(Pubs Guild CA; 0-9612016),* P.O. Box 90906, San Diego, CA 92109 (SAN 286-8571) Tel 619-272-8366.

Publishers, Inc., *(Pubs Inc; 0-89163),* Drawer P, Del Mar, CA 92014 (SAN 207-4222) Tel 714-481-8133.

Publishers Mark, The, *(Pub Mark; 0-9614636),* 255 B Bluff Ct., Barrington, IL 60010 (SAN 691-9154) Tel 312-381-6451; Dist. by: Paperback Supply, 4121 Forest Park Ave., St. Louis, MO 63108 (SAN 169-4324); Dist. by: Richardson's Education, 2014 Low Ellen Ln., Houston, TX 77018 (SAN 691-9170); Dist. by: The Publishers Mark, P.O. Box 267, Cary, IL 60013 (SAN 694-0153); Dist. by: Baker & Taylor, Eastern Div., 50 Kirby Ave., Somerville, NJ 08876 (SAN 169-4901).

Publishers Marketing Corp., *(Pubs Mktg Corp; 0-937593),* 35 Cedar Hills, Weston, CT 06883 (SAN 659-073X) Tel 203-454-0400.

Publishers Media, *(Publishers Media; 0-934064),* 5507 Morella Ave., N. Hollywood, CA 91607 (SAN 213-5493).

Publisher's Pr., *(Publishers Pr; 0-943592),* 1935 SE 59th Ave., Portland, OR 97215 (SAN 240-7558) Tel 503-232-9293.

Pubs. Press, *(Pubs Pr UT; 0-916095),* 1900 W. 2300 S., Salt Lake City, UT 84119 (SAN 219-3884) Tel 801-972-6600.

Publishers Services, *(Pub Service; 0-937602),* P.O. Box 2510, Novato, CA 94948 (SAN 201-3037) Tel 415-883-3530; 11A Commercial Blvd., Novato, CA 94947 (SAN 200-7223) Tel 415-883-3140.

Publishers Services, *(Pubs Servs; 0-916145),* 6318 Vesper Ave., Van Nuys, CA 91411 (SAN 294-961X) Tel 818-785-8038.

Publishing Ctr. for Cultural Resources, Inc., *(Pub Ctr Cult Res; 0-89062),* 625 Broadway, New York, NY 10012 (SAN 274-9025) Tel 212-260-2010.

Publishing Division of J C S, *(Pub Div JCS; 0-932411),* 3998 W. Akron Rd., Akron, MI 48701 (SAN 687-4053) Tel 517-691-5484.

Publishing Domain Exchange, *(Pub Domain; 0-9614731),* 673 Hermitage Pl., San Jose, CA 95134 (SAN 692-5952) Tel 408-942-0309; Dist. by: Publishers Group West, 5855 Beaudry Ave., Emeryville, CA 94608 (SAN 662-300X) Tel 415-658-3453; Toll free: 800-982-8319.

Publishing Enterprises, Inc., *(Pub Enterprises; 0-941368),* P.O. Box 66344, Seattle, WA 98166 (SAN 239-0248) Tel 206-838-2997.

Publishing Horizops, Inc., *(Pub Horizons; 0-942280),* 2950 N. High St., P.O. Box 02190, Columbus, OH 43202 (SAN 239-7439) Tel 614-261-6565.

Publishing Services Center, *(Pub Serv Ctr),* 95 First St., Los Altos, CA 94022 (SAN 662-1198) Tel 415-965-4081; Dist. by: William Kaufmann, Inc., 95 First St., Los Altos, CA 94022 (SAN 202-9383) Tel 415-948-5810.

Publishing Ward, Inc., The, *(Pub Ward Inc; 0-911631),* 700 E. Drake Rd., Q-6, Fort Collins, CO 80525 (SAN 264-3308) Tel 303-493-7556.

Names

569

Names

†**Publitec Editions,** *(Publitec; 0-913581),* 271-A Lower Cliff Dr., P.O. Box 4342, Laguna Beach, CA 92652 (SAN 285-3663) Tel 714-497-6100; *CIP.*

Publitek *See* **Unipub a**

Publitex International Corp., *(Publitex Intl; 0-938083),* P.O. Box 6657, Lakeland, FL 33807 (SAN 659-7009); 5295 Misty Lake Rd., Mulberry, FL 33860 (SAN 659-7017) Tel 813-425-5035.

Publius Pr., *(Publius Pr; 0-9614135),* 3100 Philamena Pl., Tucson, AZ 85730 (SAN 686-4686) Tel 602-886-4380.

Publius Publishing, *(Publius Pub; 0-937947),* P.O. Box 411, Pacific Palisades, CA 90272 (SAN 659-7580); 16015 Northfield, Pacific Palisades, CA 90272 (SAN 659-7599) Tel 714-851-9411.

Puckerbrush Pr., *(Puckerbrush; 0-913006),* 76 Main St., Orono, ME 04473 (SAN 202-0327) Tel 207-581-3832; Dist. by: Inland Book Co., P.O. Box 261, 22 Hemingway Ave., East Haven, CT 06512 (SAN 200-4151) Tel 203-467-4257; Dist. by: Maine Writers & Pubs., Alliance, 25A Forest Ave., Portland, ME 04101 (SAN 224-2303) Tel 207-775-6260.

Puddin' Head Pr., *(Puddin Head Pr; 0-9615879),* P.O. Box 1443, North Riverside, IL 60546 (SAN 696-8317) Tel 312-248-6767; 1339 S. 57th Ave., Cicero, IL 60650 (SAN 696-8325).

Pudding Magazine, *(Pudding),* 2384 Hardesty Dr. S., Columbus, OH 43204 (SAN 693-1324).

Pudding Pubns., Affil. of Ohio Poetry Therapy Center and Library, *(Pudding Pubns),* 2384 Hardesty Dr. S., Columbus, OH 43204 (SAN 677-881X) Tel 614-279-4188.

Puddingstone Press, *(Puddingston),* P.O. Box 67, Banner Elk, NC 28604 (SAN 205-4019).

Pudvan Publishing Company, *(Pudvan Pub; 0-934165),* 1935 Shermer Rd., Northbrook, IL 60062 (SAN 693-1928) Tel 312-498-9840.

Pueblo County Historical Society, *(Pueblo Co Hist Soc; 0-915617),* 33550 Hwy. 96E, No. 190, Pueblo, CO 81001 (SAN 292-630X) Tel 303-948-3290.

Pueblo of Acoma Press, *(Pueblo Acoma Pr; 0-915347),* P.O. Box 449, Acomita, NM 87034 (SAN 290-0386) Tel 505-552-9833.

Pueblo Publishing Co., Inc., *(Pueblo Pub Co; 0-916134),* 100 W. 32nd St., New York, NY 10001-3210 (SAN 211-7606) Tel 212-695-4282.

Pueblo Publishing Pr., *(Pueblo Pub Pr; 0-942316),* 401 Vandamet Ave., Yukon, OK 73099 (SAN 239-5940) Tel 405-354-7825; Dist. by: ARA Services, 909 W. 23rd St., Tulsa, OK 74107 (SAN 169-7013); Dist. by: Baker & Taylor Co., 1515 Broadway, New York, NY 10036 (SAN 169-5606) Tel 212-730-7650.

Pueo Press, *(Pueo Pr; 0-917850),* P.O. Box 2066, San Rafael, CA 94912 (SAN 209-6331).

Puerto Rico Almanacs, Inc., *(Puerto Rico Almanacs; 0-934642),* P.O. Box 9582, Santurce, PR 00908 (SAN 213-1382) Tel 809-724-2402.

Puffin Bks. *See* **Penguin Bks., Inc.**

Pugh-Killeen Assocs., *(Pugh Killeen; 0-937853),* 1 Bowdoin Dr., Newton, MA 02161 (SAN 659-5731) Tel 617-964-9045.

Puissance Pubns., Inc., *(Puissance Pubns; 0-940634),* 2802 N. Patton St., Arlington Heights, IL 60004 (SAN 218-5229) Tel 314-870-1840.

Pul-Star Publishing, *(Pul-Star Pub; 0-931471),* 1239 Bernal Ave., Burlingame, CA 94010 (SAN 683-1443) Tel 415-344-2349.

Pull/Press, *(Pull-Pr; 0-914705),* 1800 Market St., Suite 65, San Francisco, CA 94102 (SAN 289-548X).

Pullen Memorial Baptist Church, *(Pullen Mem Baptist; 0-9614485),* 1801 Hillsborough St., Raleigh, NC 27605 (SAN 689-4216) Tel 919-828-0897.

Pulp, *(Pulp; 0-9603092),* c/o Howard Sage, 720 Greenwich St., New York, NY 10014 (SAN 218-3404) Tel 212-989-0190.

Pulsante Assn. News, *(Pulsante Assn News; 0-940774),* P.O. Box 80639, San Marino, CA 91108 (SAN 219-6778) Tel 818-446-0870.

Pulsar Pubns., *(Pulsar Pub; 0-9609442),* 120 Village Sq. Suite 117, Orinda, CA 94563 (SAN 260-1206) Tel 415-254-7535; Orders to: Divack Assocs., 195 25th Ave., Suite 301, San Francisco, CA 94121 (SAN 238-8103) Tel 415-474-0323.

†**Pulse-Finger Press,** *(Pulse-Finger; 0-912282),* P.O. Box 488, Yellow Springs, OH 45387 (SAN 206-6785) Tel 513-376-9033; *CIP.*

Pumpkin Guides, *(Pumpkin Guides; 0-938011),* 906 Third St., Snohomish, WA 98290 (SAN 659-7602) Tel 206-568-5973; Dist. by: King of the Road Maps, P.O. Box 55758, Seattle, WA 98155 (SAN 200-6553).

Pumpkin Hse. Pr., *(Pumpkin Hse Pr; 0-937499),* 878 Jackman St., Suite 132, El Cajon, CA 92020 (SAN 659-0810) Tel 619-447-1278.

Pumpkin Ltd., *(Pumpkin Ltd; 0-9617017),* 201 S. Franklin St., Denver, CO 80209 (SAN 662-8613) Tel 303-744-3631.

Punch Poster, Inc., *(Punch Poster Inc; 0-941714),* 7540 Little River Tpk., Annandale, VA 22003 (SAN 239-2860) Tel 703-642-8490.

Punster's Pr., *(Punster's Pr; 0-9601402),* 3834 Joanne Dr., Glennview, IL 60025 (SAN 211-3449) Tel 312-564-4342.

Puppet Masters, The, *(Puppet Masters; 0-941764),* P.O. Box 60162, Palo Alto, CA 94306 (SAN 218-9259) Tel 415-493-3339.

Purcell, Royal, Pub., *(Purcell Pub; 0-933189),* 806 W. Second St., Bloomington, IN 47401 (SAN 691-7224) Tel 812-336-4195.

Purcell Productions, Inc., *(Purcell Prods; 0-9610742),* 484 W. 43rd St., 23M, New York, NY 10036 (SAN 264-780X) Tel 212-279-0795.

Purcells, Inc., *(Purcells; 0-931068),* 305 S. 10th, Box 190, Broken Bow, NE 68822 (SAN 211-1357) Tel 308-872-2471.

Purchase Press, The, *(Purchase Pr; 0-938266),* P.O. Box 5,, Harrison, NY 10528 (SAN 215-9090) Tel 212-645-4442.

Purdue Univ. Calumet, Regional Studies Institute, The, *(Regional Study; 0-943766),* Purdue Univ., Hammond, IN 46323 (SAN 238-3454) Tel 219-838-7275.

†**Purdue Univ., Dept. of International Programs in Agriculture,** *(Intl Prog Agricult; 0-9614109),* Purdue Univ., AGAD Bldg., West Lafayette, IN 47907 (SAN 685-3005) Tel 317-494-5962; Orders to: ACS Mailing Rm., 301 S. Second St., Lafayette, IN 47901 (SAN 662-264X) Tel 317-494-6794; *CIP.*

Purdue Univ., Modern Fiction Studies, *(Purdue U Fiction; 0-9615802),* Purdue Univ., English Dept., West Lafayette, IN 47907 (SAN 696-6209) Tel 317-494-3760.

Purdue Univ., Office of Pubns., *(Purdue U Pubns; 0-931682),* South Campus Courts, Bldg. D, West Lafayette, IN 47907 (SAN 215-2649) Tel 317-494-2035. Do not confuse with Purdue U Pr, same address. Use ISBN to determine publisher.

†**Purdue Univ. Pr.,** *(Purdue U Pr; 0-911198),* South Campus Cts., Bldg. D, West Lafayette, IN 47907 (SAN 203-4026) Tel 317-494-2035; Dist. by: Indiana Univ. Pr., Tenth & Morton Sts., Bloomington, IN 47405 (SAN 202-5647) Tel 812-335-7681; Dist. by: Feffer & Simon, Inc., 100 Park Ave., New York, NY 10017 (SAN 200-6804) Tel 212-686-0888. Do not confuse with Purdue U Pubns, same address. Use ISBN to determine publisher; *CIP.*

Puritan Publishing Co. The, *(Puritan Pub Co; 0-930517),* 1359 Phelps Ave., No.1, San Jose, CA 95117 (SAN 677-5195) Tel 408-296-6951.

Purple Mouth Press, *(Purple Mouth; 0-9603300),* 713 Paul St., Newport News, VA 23605 (SAN 209-8709) Tel 804-380-6595.

Purple Unicorn Books, *(Purple Unicorn; 0-931998),* 4532 London Rd., Duluth, MN 55804 (SAN 212-3061) Tel 218-525-4781.

Purpose Bks., *(Purpose Bks; 0-916739),* P.O. Box 1752, Wenatchee, WA 98801-0015 (SAN 654-4436) Tel 509-884-6198.

Pursifull, Carmen M., *(C M Pursifull; 0-9607856),* 809 W. Maple, Champaign, IL 61820 (SAN 237-9880) Tel 217-359-5056.

Push the Button Enterprises, *(Push the Button Enter; 0-934389),* P.O. Box 592, Crystal Lake, IL 60014 (SAN 693-8086) Tel 815-455-7277.

Pushcart Pr., The, *(Pushcart Pr; 0-916366),* P.O. Box 380, Wainscott, NY 11975 (SAN 202-9871) Tel 516-324-9300; Toll free: 800-223-2584; Dist. by: W. W. Norton Co., 500 Fifth Ave., New York, NY 10110 (SAN 202-5795) Tel 212-354-5500.

Pushkin Press, the, *(Pushkin Pr; 0-943046),* 1930 Columbia Rd. NW, Washington, DC 20009 (SAN 240-4338) Tel 202-265-1871.

Puski-Corvin, *(Puski-Corvin; 0-930888),* 251 E. 82nd St., New York, NY 10028 (SAN 682-8485).

Pussy Willow Pr., *(Pussy Willow; 0-9615763),* 209 W. Pine St., Alexandria, VA 22305 (SAN 695-9997) Tel 703-836-4986.

Pussywillow Publishing Hse., Inc., *(Pussywillow Pub; 0-934739),* 500 E. Encinas Ave., P.O. Box 1806, Gilbert, AZ 85234 (SAN 694-1702) Tel 602-892-1316; Dist. by: Baker & Taylor Co., Eastern Div., 50 Kirby Ave., Somerville, NJ 08876 (SAN 169-4901); Dist. by: New Leaf Distributing Co., 1020 White St., SW, Atlanta, GA 30310 (SAN 169-1449) Tel 404-755-2665; Dist. by: Roadrunner Library Serv., 1221 E. Washington St., Phoenix, AZ 85034 (SAN 168-9339); Dist. by: Many Feathers SW Bks., 5738 N. Central, Phoenix, AZ 85012 (SAN 158-8877).

Putnam Publishing Group, The, *(Putnam Pub Group; 0-399),* 200 Madison Ave., New York, NY 10016 (SAN 202-5531); Toll free: 800-631-8571. *Imprints:* Coward, McCann & Geoghegan (Coward); Grossett & Dunlap, Inc. (G&D); Peppercorn (Peppercorn); Perigee Books (Perigee); Philomel Books (Philomel); Putnam's, G. P., Sons (Putnam); Seaview (Seaview); Wideview (Wideview).

Putnam's, G. P., Sons *See* **Putnam Publishing Group, The**

Putney, R. Q., *(R Q Putney; 0-9616443),* P.O. Box 81903, Lincoln, NE 68501-9605 (SAN 659-0861) Tel 402-475-2389; 2954 Ryons, Lincoln, NE 68502 (SAN 659-087X).

Putterin Pr., *(Putterin; 0-938946),* P.O. Box 72, Burlingame, CA 94010 (SAN 238-7212) Tel 415-343-8426.

P V C Co., *(PVC Co),* Box 129, Chimney Rock, NC 28720 (SAN 212-226X) Tel 704-245-3934.

PWS Computer Science *See* **PWS Pubs.**

Pygmalion Press, *(Pygmalion Pr; 0-915242),* 609 El Centro, South Pasadena, CA 91030 (SAN 206-8206); 2104 Holly Dr., Hollywood, CA 90028 (SAN 206-8214) Tel 213-461-2557.

Pym-Randall Press, *(Pym-Rand Pr; 0-913219),* 73 Cohasset St., Roslindale, MA 02131 (SAN 238-2793) Tel 617-547-5602.

Pyquag Books, Pubs., *(Pyquag; 0-912492),* P.O. Box 328, Wethersfield, CT 06109 (SAN 205-4086).

Pyramid Designs Pr., Div. of Pyramid Designs, Ltd., *(Pyramid Designs Pr; 0-937071),* Investment Bldg., Suite 1017, Pittsburgh, PA 15222 (SAN 658-4314) Tel 412-642-6698; Seventh & Grant St., Pittsburgh, PA 15230 (SAN 658-4322); Dist. by: The Distributors, 702 S. Michigan, South Bend, IN 46618 (SAN 169-2488) Tel 219-232-8500; Toll free: 800-348-5200; Dist. by: Central Wholesale, Inc., 143 S. 25th St., Pittsburgh, PA 15203 (SAN 200-6987) Tel 412-988-2800.

Pyramid House *See* **Pyramid Pubns., Inc.**

Pyramid Press Publishing Co., *(Pyramid WV),* 1686 Marshall St., Benwood, WV 26031 (SAN 207-6683).

Pyramid Pubns., Inc., *(Pyramid Pubns; 0-515),* 9 Garden St., Moonachie, NJ 07074 (SAN 202-5523) Tel 201-641-3311. *Imprints:* Arena (Arena); Pyramid House (Pyramid Hse); Royal Books (Royal); Worlds of Science Books (WS).

Pyramid Publishing Co., *(Pyramid Pub Co; 0-914279),* 815 E St., Box 12176, San Diego, CA 92112 (SAN 287-5098) Tel 619-573-0168.

Pyramid Systems, *(Pyramid Systems; 0-942888),* 2800 Corona Dr., Davis, CA 95616 (SAN 240-4907) Tel 916-756-2242.

Pyxidium Pr., *(Pyxidium Pr; 0-936568),* Box 462, Old Chelsea Sta., New York, NY 10011 (SAN 214-4514) Tel 212-242-5224.

PZA Enterprises, *(PZA Enterp; 0-943304),* One Anders Tower, Box 12852, Dallas, TX 75225 (SAN 240-7396) Tel 214-696-5291.

QBLH Pubns., *(QBLH Pubns; 0-9603680),* Box 1166, Ramona, CA 92065 (SAN 214-1310).

QDP Inc., *(QDP Inc; 0-9610044),* 701 Erie St., Muskegon, MI 49441 (SAN 262-9887) Tel 616-726-6229.

QED Information Sciences, Inc., *(QED Info Sci; 0-89435),* 170 Linden St., Wellesley, MA 02181 (SAN 210-136X) Tel 617-237-5656; Toll free: 800-343-4848.

Q.E.D. Pr., *(QED Press; 0-9615997),* 1012 Hill St., Suite 6, Ann Arbor, MI 48104 (SAN 699-752X) Tel 313-994-0371.

QSKY Publishing, *(QSKY Pub; 0-931387),* P.O. Box 3042, Springfield, IL 62708 (SAN 679-7830).

Q V Publishing, Inc., *(QV Pub; 0-910767),* 250 E. Hartsdale Ave., Hartsdale, NY 10530 (SAN 260-2520) Tel 914-472-7060.

Quackenbush, Robert, Studios, *(R Quackenbush; 0-9612518),* 460 E. 79th St., New York, NY 10021 (SAN 656-0458) Tel 212-744-3822.

Quad Corp., *(Quad Data Corp),* P.O. Box 2097, Tallahassee, FL 32316 (SAN 687-7486) Tel 904-539-5759.

Quade, Vicki, *(V Quade; 0-9602604),* 3000 N. Sheridon Rd., Apt 5-E, Chicago, IL 60657 (SAN 213-151X) Tel 312-528-2569.

Quadrant Press, *(Quadrant Pr; 0-915276),* 19 W. 44th St., New York, NY 10036 (SAN 211-5727).

Quail Productions, *(Quail Prods; 0-9610764),* Box 312, Roseland, NJ 07068 (SAN 264-6323); 37 Belmont Dr., Livingston, NJ 07039 (SAN 264-6331) Tel 201-992-5865.

Quail Ridge Pr., Inc., *(Quail Ridge; 0-937552),* P.O. Box 123, Brandon, MS 39042 (SAN 214-2201); Dist. by: Dot Gibson Pubns., 161 Knight Ave. Cir., Waycross, GA 31501 (SAN 241-3760) Tel 912-285-2848; Dist. by: Southwest Cookbook Distributors, 1901 S. Shore Dr., Bonham, TX 75418 (SAN 200-4925) Tel 214-583-8898; Dist. by: Quail Ridge Pr., P.O. Box 123, Brandon, MS 39042 (SAN 214-2201).

Quail Run Pubns., Inc., *(Quail Run; 0-930380),* 2705 E. Indian School Rd., Phoenix, AZ 85016 (SAN 210-9476) Tel 602-955-5953.

Quail Valley Pubns., *(Quail Valley; 0-934249),* 19234 Vanowen St., Reseda, CA 91335 (SAN 693-1944) Tel 818-705-1157.

Quaker City Books, *(Quaker City; 0-917931),* Mill & Main Sts., Darby, PA 19023 (SAN 209-1178) Tel 215-583-4550.

Quaker Pr., *(Quaker; 0-911200),* 3218 O St. NW, Washington, DC 20007 (SAN 204-6547) Tel 202-338-3391.

Quality Assurance Institute, *(Quality Assurance),* 9222 Bay Point Dr., Orlando, FL 32819 (SAN 241-5798) Tel 305-856-4292.

Quality Bks., *(Quality Bks OH; 0-9616274),* Box 264 Hilda Cir., Bloomingdale, OH 43910 (SAN 658-4349) Tel 614-264-4643.

Quality Books, Inc., *(Quality Bks IL; 0-89196),* 918 Sherwood Dr., Lake Bluff, IL 60044-2204 (SAN 169-2127); Toll free: 800-323-4241 (Libraries Only). Warehouse open for walk-through buyers. Imprints: Book Value International (Bk Value Intl); Domus Books (Domus Bks).

Quality Books of Kansas City, Missouri, *(Quality MO; 0-9606586),* P.O. Box 8487, Kansas City, MO 64114 (SAN 219-0923) Tel 913-383-2160.

Quality Circle Institute, *(Quality Circle; 0-937670),* 1425 Vista Way, Airport Industrial Park, P.O. Box 1503, Red Bluff, CA 96080-1335 (SAN 220-0880) Tel 916-527-6970.

Quality Communication, *(Quality Comn; 0-939143),* 337 Empire Blvd., Rochester, NY 14609 (SAN 662-9032) Tel 716-624-2772.

Quality Education Data, Inc., Subs. of Peterson's Guides, *(Quality Ed Data; 0-88747),* 1580 Logan St., 3rd. Fl., Denver, CO 80203 (SAN 291-3941) Tel 303-572-8692; Toll free: 800-525-5811.

Quality Educators, Ltd., *(Quality Educ),* 1236 SE Fourth Ave., Ft. Lauderdale, FL 33316 (SAN 212-9280) Tel 305-522-2249.

†**Quality Groups Publishing,** *(Quality Groups Pub; 0-930733),* 5850 Thille St., Suite 107, Ventura, CA 93003 (SAN 676-5688) Tel 805-642-6691; *CIP.*

Quality Hill Books, *(Quality Hill; 0-9605044),* 674 Church St., San Luis Obispo, CA 93401 (SAN 216-0595).

Quality Library Editions, *(Quality Lib),* P.O. Box 148, Darby, PA 19023 (SAN 209-1186).

Quality Pr., *(Quality Pr MI; 0-9616002),* 5930 Salabelle, Jackson, MI 49201 (SAN 697-9467) Tel 517-788-2060.

Quality Pubns., Div. of Quality Printing Co., Inc., *(Quality Pubns; 0-89137),* P.O. Box 1060, Abilene, TX 79604 (SAN 203-0071) Tel 915-677-6262.

Quality Pubns. Inc., *(Quality Ohio; 0-934040),* P.O. Box 2633, Lakewood, OH 44107 (SAN 216-2911); Orders to: Gary S. Skeens, 1483 Winchester Ave., Lakewood, OH 44107 (SAN 662-7382).

Quality Services, Inc., *(Quality Serv; 0-9608966),* P.O. Box 2848, Gillette, WY 82716 (SAN 240-9801) Tel 307-686-2428.

Quality Software, *(Quality Soft; 0-912985),* 21610 Lassen, No. 7, Chatsworth, CA 91311 (SAN 265-7759) Tel 818-709-1721.

Quality Time Video, *(Quality Time; 0-937095),* 274 Funston Ave., San Francisco, CA 94118 (SAN 658-4705) Tel 415-386-5061.

Quam, Martin, Press, *(Quam Pr; 0-9601600),* 1515 Columbia Dr., Cedar Falls, IA 50613 (SAN 213-3571) Tel 319-266-6242; Orders to: 201 Rio St., Rio, WI 53960 (SAN 213-358X).

Quantal Publishing Co., Div. of Quetzal Investing, *(Quantal; 0-936596),* P.O. Box 1598, Goleta, CA 93116 (SAN 215-1014) Tel 805-964-7293.

Quantum Communications, *(Quantum Comns; 0-938939),* 3301 W. Hampden Ave., Suite N, Englewood, CO 80110 (SAN 661-7441) Tel 303-781-0679. Do not confuse with Quantum Communications, Berkeley, CA, & Falls Church, VA.

Quantum Press *See* **Doubleday & Co., Inc.**

Quantum Publications Enterprises, Inc., *(Quantum Pubns; 0-9611548),* P.O. Box 1039, Orange, CT 06477-7039 (SAN 285-2578) Tel 203-934-3945; 88 Canton St., W. Haven, CT 06516 (SAN 285-2586).

Quark Publishing Co., *(Quark Pub; 0-937949),* 4709 Rockbluff Dr., Rolling Hills Estates, CA 90274 (SAN 659-7610) Tel 213-375-6431.

†**Quarterdeck Pr.,** Affil. of Yoga Transformations, *(Quarterdeck; 0-918546),* P.O. Box 134, Pacific Palisades, CA 90272 (SAN 209-990X) Tel 213-454-5392; Dist. by: Bookpeople, 2929 Fifth St., Berkeley, CA 94710 (SAN 168-9517) Tel 415-549-3030; Toll free: 800-227-1516; *CIP.*

Quarterly Review of Literature Q R L Poetry Series, *(Quarterly Rev),* 26 Haslet Ave., Princeton, NJ 08540 (SAN 282-1982) Tel 609-921-6976; Dist. by: B. Deboer, 113 E. Centre St., Nutley, NJ 07110 (SAN 282-1990) Tel 201-667-9300.

Quarterman Pubns., Inc., *(Quarterman; 0-88000),* P.O. Box 156, Lincoln, MA 01773 (SAN 203-3992) Tel 617-259-8047.

Quartuccio, Anthony, *(A Quartuccio; 0-9606934),* 4819 Kingdale Dr., San Jose, CA 95124 (SAN 239-5460).

Quartus Bks., Div. of Quartus Foundation, *(Quartus Bks; 0-942082),* P.O. Box 26683, Austin, TX 78755 (SAN 238-0080) Tel 512-335-8346; Dist. by: Quartus Books, P.O. Box 26683, Austin, TX 78755 (SAN 238-0080) Tel 512-335-8346; Dist. by: New Leaf Distributing Co., 1020 White St., Sw, Atlanta, GA 30310 (SAN 169-1449) Tel 404-755-2665.

Quartz Press, The, *(Quartz Pr; 0-911455),* P.O. Box 465, Ashland, OR 97520 (SAN 274-9246) Tel 503-482-8119.

Quartzite Bks., *(Quartzite Bks; 0-931849),* P.O. Box 1931, Mount Vernon, WA 98273 (SAN 685-4346) Tel 206-336-3345; Dist. by: Pacific Pipeline, 19215 66th Ave. S., Kent, WA 98032 (SAN 208-2128) Tel 206-872-5523.

Quasem, M. Adul, *(Quasem),* Dist. by: Habibur Rahman, 502 N. Elm St., Centralia, IL 62801 (SAN 209-5939).

Quay Assocs., *(Quay Assocs; 0-9616062),* P.O. Box 18052, Columbus, OH 43218 (SAN 698-0929) Tel 614-261-1990; 247 E. Beck St., Columbus, OH 43206 (SAN 698-0937).

Que Corp., Div. of Macmillan, *(Que Corp; 0-88022),* 7999 Knue Rd., Indianapolis, IN 46250 (SAN 219-6298) Tel 317-842-7162; Toll free: 800-428-5331.

Queen Anne Press, The, Div. of Wye Institute, Inc., *(Queen Anne Pr; 0-937692),* Cheston-on-Wye, Queenstown, MD 21658 (SAN 215-272X) Tel 301-827-7401; Orders to: P.O. Box 50, Queenstown, MD 21658 (SAN 215-2738).

Queen of the Missions Publishing Co., *(Queen Missions; 0-941428),* 1503 la Coronilla Dr., Santa Barbara, CA 93109 (SAN 239-376X).

†**Queens College Pr.,** *(Queens Coll Pr; 0-930146),* Editorial Services, Flushing, NY 11367 (SAN 203-1973) Tel 718-520-7599; *CIP.*

†**Queens House/Focus Service,** *(Queens Hse-Focus Serv; 0-89244),* P.O. Box 145, Dana Point, CA 92629 (SAN 208-2802) Tel 714-240-3242; *CIP.*

Queequeg Enterprises, *(Queequeg; 0-915947),* P.O. Box 277, Ludlow, VT 05149 (SAN 294-1015) Tel 802-824-6004.

Quest Books *See* **Theosophical Publishing Hse.**

Quest Editions, *(Quest Edns),* P.O. Box 67, Sharon Hill, PA 19079 (SAN 209-1194).

Quest National Ctr., Inc., *(Quest Natl Center; 0-933419),* 6655 Sharon Woods Blvd., Columbus, OH 43229 (SAN 691-506X) Tel 614-882-6400.

Quest Northwest Publishing Co., *(Quest NW Pub; 1-55585),* P.O. Box 240, Salkum, WA 98582 (SAN 658-4861) Tel 206-985-2999.

Quest Products, Inc., *(Quest Prods; 0-9608002),* 11920 Cragwood Way, Potomac, MD 20854 (SAN 264-3332) Tel 301-299-7837.

Quest Publishing, *(Quest Pub IL; 0-940286),* 2018 29th St., Rock Island, IL 61201 (SAN 217-5584) Tel 309-786-2342.

Quest Publishing Co., *(Quest Pub; 0-930844),* 1351 Titan Way, Brea, CA 92621 (SAN 211-3740) Tel 714-738-6400.

Quest Publishing Inc., *(Quest Utah; 0-938662),* P.O. Box 27317, Salt Lake City, UT 84127-0317 (SAN 215-9775).

Quester Pr. *See* **Rapid System Development, Inc.**

Questpress, *(Questpr; 0-914631),* 103 Briar Rd., Oak Ridge, TN 37830 (SAN 289-5625) Tel 615-483-1183; Orders to: The Fayette Fellowship, 101 Carriage Ln., Peachtree City, GA 30269 (SAN 662-2186) Tel 404-487-5683.

Queue, Inc., *(Queue Inc; 0-87200; 0-87492),* 798 North Ave., Bridgeport, CT 06606 (SAN 265-3397) Tel 203-335-0908; Toll free: 800-232-2224.

Queue Pubns., Inc., *(Queue Pubns; 0-9615691),* 24825 Shiloh Ln., Conifer, CO 80433 (SAN 695-8508) Tel 303-838-4391; P.O. Box 1010, Conifer, CO 80433 (SAN 696-9542).

Quick American Publishing Co., *(Quick Am Pub; 0-932551),* P.O. Box 477, San Francisco, CA 94101 (SAN 687-4843) Tel 415-843-6449; Toll free: 800-428-7825.

Quicksilver Productions, *(Quicksilver Prod; 0-930356),* P.O. Box 340, Ashland, OR 97520 (SAN 211-9684) Tel 503-482-5343; 559 S Mountain Ave., Ashland, OR 97520 (SAN 658-151X).

Quietude Productions, *(Quietude Prod; 0-936775),* P.O. Box 1011, Glendale, CA 91209 (SAN 699-9344) Tel 818-578-0177; 328 W. Bellevue Dr., Pasadena, CA 91105 (SAN 699-9352).

Quigley Publishing Co. Inc., *(Quigley Pub Co; 0-900610),* 159 W. 53rd. St., New York, NY 10019 (SAN 205-1141) Tel 212-247-3100.

Quill, Div. of william Morrow & CO., Inc., *(Quill NY; 0-688),* 105 Madison Ave., New York, NY 10016 (SAN 239-4790) Tel 212-889-3050; Orders to: Wilmor Warehouse, 6 Henderson Dr., West Caldwell, NJ 07006 (SAN 662-7390).

Quill and Brush Press, *(Quill and Brush Pr; 0-9610494),* 7649 Old Georgetown Rd., Bethesda Square, Bethesda, MD 20814 (SAN 264-3340) Tel 301-951-0290.

Quill & Scroll Society, *(Quill & Scroll),* School of Journalism & Mass Communication, University of Iowa, Iowa City, IA 52242 (SAN 224-5051) Tel 319-353-4475.

Quill Bks., *(Quill Bks; 0-943536),* Box 728, Minot, ND 58701 (SAN 274-9300) Tel 701-839-7232. *Imprints:* Poetry Publicatons (Peotry Pubns).

Quill Paperbacks *See* Morrow, William, & Co., Inc.

Quill Publications GA, *(Quill Pubns GA; 0-932281),* P.O. Box 8193, Columbus, GA 31908 (SAN 686-6123) Tel 404-323-9313.

Quilt Digest Pr., The, *(Quilt Digest Pr; 0-913327),* 955 14th St., San Francisco, CA 94114 (SAN 293-4531) Tel 415-431-1222; Dist. by: Publishers Group West, 5855 Beaudry St., Emeryville, CA 94608 (SAN 202-8522) Tel 415-658-3453; Toll free: 800-982-8319.

Quiltwork Pubns., *(Quiltwork Pubns; 0-914455),* 2600 Oak Valley Dr., Vienna, VA 22180 (SAN 287-7619) Tel 703-938-6175.

Quince Mill Bks, *(Quince Mill Bks; 0-914757),* 21 Quince Mill Court, Gaithersburg, MD 20878 (SAN 291-7996).

Quincunx, *(Quincunx; 0-942626),* 235 S. 15th St. 3B, Philadelphia, PA 19102 (SAN 238-5643) Tel 215-732-0593.

Quinlan Pr., Subs. of Quinlan Publishing & AC Getchell, *(Quinlan Pr; 0-9611268; 0-933341),* 131 Beverly St., Boston, MA 02114 (SAN 226-4641) Tel 617-227-4870; Toll free: 800-551-2500.

Quinlin Campbell Pubs., *(Quinlin C Pubs; 0-934665),* P.O. Box 651, Boston, MA 02134 (SAN 694-0544) Tel 617-296-4306.

Quinn-Gallagher Press, *(Quinn-Gallagher; 0-935282),* 6372 Forward Ave., Pittsburgh, PA 15217 (SAN 213-3598) Tel 412-521-1863.

Quinn Pubns., *(Quinn Pubns),* 612 Cougar Loop, NE, Albuquerque, NM 87122 (SAN 663-0847) Tel 818-358-1846; Dist. by: Eye Communications, 870 S. Myrtle Ave., Monrovia, CA 91016 (SAN 663-3250).

†**Quintessence Pubns.,** *(Quintessence; 0-918466),* 356 Bunker Hill Mine Rd., Amador City, CA 95601 (SAN 209-5947) Tel 209-267-5470; *CIP.*

†**Quintessence Publishing Co., Inc.,** *(Quint Pub Co; 0-931386; 0-86715),* 870 Oak Creek Dr., Lombard, IL 60148-6405 (SAN 215-9783) Tel 312-620-4443; Toll free: 800-621-0387; *CIP.*

Quintilone Enterprises, *(Quintilone Ent; 0-9616980),* 29 Merrimac St., Buffalo, NY 14214 (SAN 661-7433) Tel 716-836-0945.

Quissett Corporation, *(Quissett Corp; 0-938602),* P.O. Box 484, Cambridge, MA 02138 (SAN 216-2458) Tel 617-864-7970.

Quixote Pr., Div. of Anticapitalist Wordslingers Collective, *(Quixote; 0-9600306),* 1810 Marshall, Houston, TX 77098 (SAN 202-1463) Tel 713-529-7944; Dist. by: Inland Bk. Co., 22 Hemingway Ave., East Haven, CT 06512 (SAN 200-4151) Tel 203-467-4257.

Quixsilver Pr., *(Quixsilver Pr; 0-9615768),* Box 7635, Baltimore, MD 21207 (SAN 696-0014) Tel 301-944-0661.

Quod Publishing Co., *(Quod Pub Co; 0-933137),* P.O. Box 3309, Ann Arbor, MI 48106 (SAN 689-7827) Tel 313-973-7386.

Quonochontaug Pr., The, *(Quonochontaug; 0-937245),* P.O. Box 2478, Waterbury, CT 06722 (SAN 658-6856) Tel 203-758-1637; 6 Southview Ave., Middlebury, CT 06762 (SAN 658-6864).

Quorum Bks. *See* Greenwood Pr.

Quotamus Press, *(Quotamus Pr; 0-932621),* 721 S. Catalina Ave., P.O. Box 86, Redondo Beach, CA 90274 (SAN 687-5254) Tel 213-378-3446.

Quotidian, Inc., *(Quotidian; 0-934391),* 394 Franklin Ave., Rockaway, NJ 07866 (SAN 693-8094) Tel 201-625-4788; Dist. by: Thomas W. Perrin, Inc., P.O. Box 190, 5 Glen Rd., Rutherford, NJ 07070 (SAN 200-6510) Tel 201-460-7912.

Qwint Systems, Inc., *(Qwint Systems),* 625 Barclay, Lincolnshire, IL 60069 (SAN 210-8305) Tel 312-634-6700.

RAK Publishing Co., *(RAK Pub; 0-9616948),* 4625 Hope Valley Rd., No. D, Durham, NC 27707-5615 (SAN 661-7425) Tel 919-489-8693.

RAMCO Pubns., *(RAMCO Pubns; 0-939844),* 224 Harding Ave., Libertyville, IL 60048 (SAN 216-9282) Tel 312-362-4948.

RAPCOM Enterprises, *(RAPCOM Enter),* 2109 Wilkinson Pl., Alexandria, VA 22306 (SAN 689-0563).

R & D Pr., *(R & D Pr; 0-88274),* 885 N. San Antonio Rd., Los Altos, CA 94022 (SAN 203-0896) Tel 415-948-0370.

R & D Pubns., Inc., *(R & D Pubns; 0-938152),* Box 351, Spring Valley, NY 10977 (SAN 282-2008).

R&D Pubs., *(R&D Pubs),* P.O. Box 1584, Los Gatos, CA 95031 (SAN 223-1689).

R & D Publishing, Inc., *(R D Pub; 0-937483),* 2251 Grand Ave., Ft. Myers, FL 33901 (SAN 659-0926) Tel 813-332-5510.

R & D Services, *(R & D Serv; 0-89511),* P.O. Box 644, Des Moines, IA 50303 (SAN 209-6765) Tel 515-288-8391.

R & E Pubs., *(R & E Pubs; 0-88247),* P.O. Box 2008, Saratoga, CA 95070 (SAN 293-3195) Tel 408-866-6303.

R & H Publishers, *(R & H Pubs; 0-935246),* Box 3587, Georgetown Sta., Washington, DC 20007 (SAN 210-5691) Tel 703-524-4226.

R&M Publishing Co., *(R&M Pub Co; 0-936026),* P.O. Box 1276, Holly Hill, SC 29059 (SAN 213-6392) Tel 804-732-4094.

R & M Publishing, Inc., *(R & M Pub NV; 0-9616779),* 4230 Fairbanks Cir., Las Vegas, NV 89103 (SAN 661-0501) Tel 702-876-9632.

R & W Enterprises, *(R W Enterprises; 0-9616382),* 3011 White Oak Ln., Oak Brook, IL 60521 (SAN 659-0969) Tel 312-887-2738.

R. B. H. Publishing Enterprises, Div. of Advertising Unlimited Ltd., *(RBH Pub; 0-939842),* 4528 W. Charleston Blvd., Las Vegas, NV 89102 (SAN 282-2024) Tel 702-878-8534; Orders to: 4263 Powell Ave, Las Vegas, NV 89121 (SAN 282-2032) Tel 702-878-8534.

RBMU International, *(RBMU Intl),* 8102 Elberon Ave., Philadelphia, PA 19111 (SAN 225-4689) Tel 215-745-0680.

RB Pubns., *(RB Pubns CA; 0-9616727),* 240 Tamal Vista Blvd., Corte Madera, CA 94925 (SAN 659-8765) Tel 415-924-6820.

RBR (Religious Bks. for Russia), *(RBR; 0-934927),* P.O. Box 631, Lenox Hill Sta., New York, NY 10021 (SAN 695-0167) Tel 914-478-2151; Dist. by: MCA Pr., 575 Scarsdale Rd., Crestwood, NY 10707 (SAN 200-5514).

RCA Distributor & Special Products, *(RCA Dist Spec Prods; 0-913970),* Deptford, NJ 08096 (SAN 208-1210).

RCA Solid State Div., *(RCA Solid State; 0-913972),* P.O. Box 3200, Somerville, NJ 08876 (SAN 205-115X).

R.C. Law & Co., Inc., *(R C Law & Co; 0-939925),* 579 S. State College Blvd., Fullerton, CA 92631 (SAN 200-609X) Tel 714-871-0940.

RCM Pubns., *(RCM Pubns; 0-938154),* P.O. Box 33565, San Diego, CA 92103 (SAN 215-2584).

†**RCP Pubns.,** *(RCP Pubns; 0-89851),* P.O. Box 3486, Merchandise Mart, Chicago, IL 60654 (SAN 212-4408) Tel 312-663-5920; *CIP.*

R. C. Press, *(R C Pr; 0-943854),* 7140 Madison Ave. W., Golden Valley, MN 55427 (SAN 241-0613) Tel 612-537-4065.

R C Pubns., *(R C Pubns; 0-915734),* 6400 Goldsboro Rd., Bethesda, MD 20817 (SAN 209-1119) Tel 301-229-9040; Toll free: 800-222-2654; 355 Lexington Ave., New York, NY 10017 (SAN 662-7404) Tel 212-682-0830.

R. C. Pubns., *(R C Pubns OR; 0-942152),* 1828 NE Stanton, Portland, OR 97212 (SAN 239-5967) Tel 503-287-1009.

R-C Publications, *(R-c Pubns; 0-933311),* P.O. Box 35425, Phoenix, AZ 85069 (SAN 692-6061) Tel 602-242-9276.

RCS Assocs., Inc., *(RCS Assocs; 0-930293),* 1603 Danbury Dr., Claremont, CA 91711 (SAN 292-7195) Tel 714-624-1801.

RCS Co., *(RCS Co; 0-938153),* 9445 Bay Colony, 2N, Des Plaines, IL 60016 (SAN 659-8986) Tel 312-824-4181.

RDC Pubs., *(RDC Pubs; 0-9600576),* 4741 School St., Yorba Linda, CA 92686 (SAN 207-0154) Tel 714-777-3376.

R.E.F. Typesetting & Publishing, Inc., *(R E F Typesetting Pub; 0-9612862),* 9400 Fairview Ave., Manassas, VA 22110 (SAN 291-3976) Tel 703-631-1115.

R.E.P. Pubs., *(REP Pubs; 0-9604876),* 12703 Red Fox Court, Maryland Hgts., MO 63043 (SAN 239-3786).

RE Pubns., *(RE Pubns; 0-9615272),* 246 Campbell St., Harrisonburg, VA 22801 (SAN 695-2747) Tel 703-433-0382.

RFF Assocs., *(RFF Assocs; 0-9611414),* 808 Francis Pl., St. Louis, MO 63105 (SAN 283-4324) Tel 314-863-0625.

RF Productions, *(RF Prod; 0-936523),* Box 310, Langley, OK 74350 (SAN 697-9491) Tel 918-782-3029.

RFTS Productions, *(RFTS Prod; 0-939401),* 739 Falls Ave., Box 414, Cuyahoga Falls, OH 44222 Tel 216-928-3606.

R. G. Enterprises, *(R G Enterprises; 0-910575),* 2000 Center St., No. 1067, Berkeley, CA 94704 (SAN 274-9327).

RGK Pubns., *(RGK Pubns; 0-9616383),* 10560 NE Madison St., Blaine, MN 55434 (SAN 659-1116) Tel 612-786-1442.

RGM Pubns., *(RGM Pubns; 0-942436),* H-28 Miriam St., Key West, FL 33040 (SAN 238-1931) Tel 305-294-5710; Dist. by: Publishers Group West, 5855 Beaudry St., Emeryville, CA 94608 (SAN 202-8522) Tel 415-658-3453; Toll free: 800-982-8319; Dist. by: Comics Unlimited, 6833 Amboy Rd., Staten Island, NY 10309 (SAN 200-7029) Tel 212-948-2223.

RHM & Assocs., *(RHM & Assocs; 0-9616949),* 10839 S. Houston, Jenks, OK 74037 (SAN 661-7417) Tel 918-495-6006.

†**R. H. M. Pr.,** *(R H M Pr; 0-89058),* 172 Forest Ave., Glen Cove, NY 11542 (SAN 206-9873) Tel 516-759-2904; *CIP.*

R.H.O.P.A.R. Corp., The, *(RHOPAR Corp; 0-937015),* 3 Malaga Cove Plaza, No. 844, Palos Verdes Estates, CA 90274 (SAN 658-7917) Tel 213-377-0647.

RICO Law Reporter, *(RICO Law),* 1519 Connecticut Ave., NW, Washington, DC 20036 (SAN 663-0812) Tel 202-462-5755.

RIF Marketing, *(RIF Mktg; 0-9606000),* 912 Five Points Rd., P.O. Box 3055, Virginia Beach, VA 23454 (SAN 216-7611) Tel 804-857-0512.

R in R Ink, *(R in R; 0-941530),* 203 Joaquin Dr., San Ramon, CA 94583 (SAN 239-1279) Tel 415-820-8477.

R/J Associates, *(RJ Assocs; 0-9602090),* 564 Tyler Ave., Livermore, CA 94550 (SAN 212-1352) Tel 415-443-7140.

RK Editions, *(RK Edns; 0-932360),* P.O. Box 73, Canal St. Sta., New York, NY 10013 (SAN 211-447X).

RKM Publishing Co., Div. of RKM Enterprises, Inc., *(RKM Pub Co; 0-87500),* P.O. Box 23042, Euclid, OH 44123 (SAN 689-4321) Tel 216-261-2610; Dist. by: Starlite Distributors, 395 Freeport Blvd., No. 10, Sparks, NV 89431 (SAN 131-1921) Tel 702-359-5676; Dist. by: New Leaf Distributing Co., 1020 White St., SW, Atlanta, GA 30310 (SAN 169-1449) Tel 404-755-2665.

RKO Homevideo, Div. of RKO Pictures, *(RKO Homevideo; 1-55545),* 1900 Ave. of the Stars, Los Angeles, CA 90067 (SAN 696-575X) Tel 818-906-1722.

RKT Publishing, *(R K T Pub; 0-931715),* 2215 Starr, Royal Oak, MI 48073 (SAN 683-5562) Tel 313-549-3199.

RMI Corp., *(RMI; 0-910117),* 341 Broadway, Cambridge, MA 02139 (SAN 240-835X).

RMK Publishing, Div. of R. Martin Krol & Assocs., Ltd., *(RMK Pub; 0-938879),* 2025 Fox's Lair Trail, Norfolk, VA 23518 (SAN 661-7395) Tel 804-853-6358.

RMP Financial Consultants, *(RMP Finan Consul; 0-931664),* 10 Petit Bayou Lane, New Orleans, LA 70129 (SAN 211-9692) Tel 504-241-1171.

RND Publishing, *(RND Pub; 0-9615416),* 721 Fairway Dr., Broderick, CA 95605 (SAN 695-5711) Tel 916-371-3779; P.O. Box 781, West Sacramento, CA 95691 (SAN 695-572X).

ROMARC, Inc., *(ROMARC Inc; 0-940522),* 3738 14 Mile Rd., Stockton, CA 95209 (SAN 219-8150).

Names

R.P.W. Publishing Corp., Affil. of Shepard's/McGraw-Hill, *(R P W Pub; 0-9608450; 0-932725)*, P.O. Box 729, Lexington, SC 29072 (SAN 240-561X) Tel 803-359-9941; Toll free: 800-334-5971; Orders to: Shepards/McGraw-Hill, P.O. box 1235, Colorado Springs, CO 80901 (SAN 662-1317) Tel 303-475-7230; Toll free: 800-525-2474.

RRN Bks., Div. of Rural Radio Network, Inc., *(RRN Bks; 0-9611416)*, P.O. Box 415, New Palestine, IN 46163 (SAN 283-9849) Tel 317-861-4394.

R.R.P. Pubs., *(RRP Pub; 0-9607034)*, 12 W. 17th St., New York, NY 10011 (SAN 239-0264) Tel 212-924-4127.

RSC Pubs., Div. of Research Services Corp., *(RSC Pubs; 0-915074)*, 3863 SW Loop 820, Suite 100, P.O. Drawer 16489, Ft. Worth, TX 76133-2076 (SAN 238-8294) Tel 817-292-4272.

RSG Publishing, *(RSG Pub; 0-9614858)*, P.O. Box 441, Sidney, NY 13838 (SAN 693-0573) Tel 607-563-9000; RD. 3, Box 146A, Bainbridge, NY 13733 (SAN 662-3093) Tel 607-563-9000; Orders to: P.O. Box 441, Sidney, NY 13838-0441 (SAN 662-3107) Tel 607-563-9000.

RS Publishing Co., *(RS Pub Co; 0-9614293)*, P.O. Box 129, Portland, OR 97207 (SAN 687-4568) Tel 503-223-0123.

RSVP Pr., *(RSVP Press; 0-930865)*, P.O. Box 394, Society Hill, SC 29593 (SAN 657-6346).

RWS Books, *(RWS Bks; 0-939400)*, 4296 Mulholland St., Salt Lake City, UT 84124 (SAN 220-1593) Tel 801-272-7835.

RWU Parachuting Pubns., *(RWU Parachuting Pubns)*, 1656 Beechwood Ave., Fullerton, CA 92635 (SAN 209-1879) Tel 714-990-0369.

R. H. Lowrie Museum of Anthropology *See* Lowie, R. H., Museum of Anthropology

Rabin, Barry, *(B Rabin; 0-9603968)*, 5595 E. Seventh St., Suite 353, Long Beach, CA 90804 (SAN 658-8433) Tel 213-494-5604.

Rabinowitz, Solomon, Hebrew Book Store, Inc., *(Rabinowitz Hebrew Book; 0-87374)*, 30 Canal St., New York, NY 10002 (SAN 205-1176) Tel 212-267-2406.

Raccoon Bks., Inc., Div. of Ion Bks., Inc., *(Raccoon Memphis; 0-938507)*, 3387 Poplar Ave., Suite 205, Memphis, TN 38111 (SAN 659-6142).

Racer's Edge Publishing Co., *(Racer's Edge Pub Co; 0-9612062)*, 3336 Glenmore Dr., P.O. Box 1607, Falls Church, VA 22041 (SAN 291-8579) Tel 703-578-0853.

Racila, John, Assocs., *(J R Assocs; 0-916655)*, 2820 Oak Brook Rd., Oak Brook, IL 60521 (SAN 296-6905) Tel 312-655-1444.

Racquet Sports Information Service, *(Racquet Sports)*, P.O. Box 1710, Easton, MD 21601 (SAN 207-0308). Out of business.

Racz Publishing Co., *(Racz Pub; 0-916546)*, P.O. Box 287, Oxnard, CA 93032 (SAN 208-0265) Tel 805-642-1186.

Rada Pr., *(Rada Pr; 0-9604212)*, 2297 Folwell Ave., St. Paul, MN 55108 (SAN 214-4522) Tel 612-559-2306.

Radcliffe College, Bunting Institute, *(Radcliffe Coll; 0-9601774)*, 10 Garden St., Cambridge, MA 02138 (SAN 221-3419) Tel 617-495-8212.

Radiance Assocs., *(Radiance Assocs; 0-933267)*, P.O. Box 86188, St. Petersburg, FL 33738 (SAN 692-4735); Dist. by: New Leaf Distributing, 1020 White St., SW, Atlanta, GA 30310 (SAN 169-1449) Tel 404-755-2665; Toll free: 800-241-3829.

Radiation and Medical Research Foundation of the Southwest, *(Radiation Med Found SW; 0-9614550)*, 1450 Eighth Ave., Fort Worth, TX 76104 (SAN 691-8077) Tel 817-923-7393.

Radicus Communications, *(Radicus Comm; 0-941564)*, 9356 Home Circle, Des Plaines, IL 60016 (SAN 239-2917) Tel 312-299-0912.

Radio City Bk. Store, *(Radio City; 0-911202)*, 324 W. 47th St., New York, NY 10036 (SAN 204-6644) Tel 212-245-5754.

Radio Free Europe Radio Liberty, *(Radio Free Eur)*, 1775 Broadway, New York, NY 10019 (SAN 274-9505) Tel 212-397-5318.

Radio Pubns., Inc., *(Radio Pubns; 0-933616)*, P.O. Box 149, Wilton, CT 06897 (SAN 215-336X) Tel 603-428-7707.

Radio Resource Co., *(Radio Resource; 0-943382)*, 301 Hillcrest Dr., Fort Atkinson, WI 53538 (SAN 287-7651) Tel 414-563-5050.

Radio Shack, Div. of Tandy Corp., *(Radio Shack; 1-55508)*, 1800 One Tandy Ctr., Fort Worth, TX 76102 (SAN 692-3356) Tel 817-390-3011.

Radiofile, *(Radiofile)*, c/o Tagliabue, 10 West 66th St., New York, NY 10023 (SAN 204-6652).

Radiological Management Communications, Ltd., *(Radiol Mgmt Comm; 0-938705)*, 10342 Wilkins Ave., Los Angeles, CA 90024 (SAN 661-5643) Tel 213-552-9921.

Radius Pr., *(Radius Pr; 0-942154)*, P.O. Box 1271, FDR Sta., New York, NY 10150 (SAN 239-5975) Tel 212-988-4715.

Radix Bks., Inc., *(Radix Bks)*, 11 Knickerbocker Ln., Orinda, CA 94563 (SAN 209-1364) Tel 415-254-3039.

Radke, George E., *(G E Radke; 0-9607994)*, 41 Harvard Rd., Havertown, PA 19083 (SAN 238-8308) Tel 215-446-0786.

Rae John Pubs., *(Rae John; 0-9605226; 0-939438)*, Box 660068, Sacramento, CA 95866-0068 (SAN 220-1739) Tel 916-925-0420.

Ragan, Lawrence, Communications, Inc., *(Ragan Comm; 0-931368)*, 407 S. Dearborn St., Chicago, IL 60605 (SAN 212-2243) Tel 312-922-8245.

Ragusan Press, *(Ragusan Pr; 0-918660)*, 2527 San Carlos Ave., San Carlos, CA 94070 (SAN 212-0445) Tel 415-592-1190.

Raheb, Barbara J., *(B J Raheb; 0-938759)*, 4166 Ellenita Ave., Tarzana, CA 91356 (SAN 661-7379) Tel 818-344-9640.

Rahija Associates, *(Rahija; 0-942670)*, Dist. by: ACLD, 4156 Library Rd., Pittsburgh, PA 15234 (SAN 282-6741).

Raiko Corp., *(Raiko; 0-910263)*, P.O. Box 597, New York, NY 10003 (SAN 240-9542) Tel 212-783-2597.

Rail-Europe/Baxter Guides, *(Rail-Europe-Baxter; 0-913384)*, P.O. Box 3255, Alexandria, VA 22302 (SAN 203-3933).

†Railhead Pubns., *(Railhead Pubns; 0-912113)*, P.O. Box 526, Canton, OH 44701 (SAN 264-7826) Tel 216-454-7519; *CIP.*

Railroadians of America, Inc., *(Railroadians; 0-941652)*, 18 Okner Pkwy., Livingston, NJ 07039 (SAN 239-2925) Tel 201-487-3719.

Railway & Locomotive Historical Society, Inc., *(Railway Loco Hist; 0-9616102)*, P.O. Box 112, East Boothbay, ME 04544 (SAN 287-6333-4333; Church & Main Sts., East Boothbay, ME 04544 (SAN 698-259X).

Railways Atlas, *(Railways; 0-9615046)*, P.O. Box 297, Short Hills, NJ 07078 (SAN 654-5475) Tel 201-376-8976.

Raima Corp., *(Raima Corp; 0-928469)*, 12201 SE Tenth St., Bellevue, WA 98005 (SAN 269-6589) Tel 206-747-5570; Toll free: 800-843-3313.

Raimi, Ralph A., *(Raimi; 0-9609370)*, Dept. of Mathematics, University of Rochester, Rochester, NY 14627 (SAN 240-8295) Tel 716-275-4411.

Rain Belt Pubns., Inc., *(Rain Belt; 0-938428)*, 18806-40th Ave. W., Lynnwood, WA 98036 (SAN 216-180X) Tel 206-778-5449.

Rainbow Assocs., *(Rainbow Assocs; 0-9615830)*, 5026 Chesterfield Rd., Arlington, VA 22206 (SAN 696-5652) Tel 202-363-0234; P.O. Box 1928, Bailey's Crossroads, VA 22041-0928 (SAN 696-9739).

Rainbow Bks., *(Rainbow Bks; 0-935834)*, Dept. 1-H, P.O. Box 1069, Moore Haven, FL 33471 (SAN 213-5515) Tel 813-946-0293; Dist. by: Quality Bks. (Library orders only), 918 Sherwood Dr., Lake Bluff, IL 60044-2204 (SAN 169-2127); Toll free: 800-232-4241.

Rainbow Books, Inc., *(Rainbow Bks; 0-89508)*, 725 Dell Rd., Carlstadt, NJ 07072 (SAN 209-9918) Tel 201-935-3369.

Rainbow Children's Books, *(Rainbow Child; 0-9608784)*, Box 513, 311 E. Madison, Goshen, IN 46526 (SAN 238-3470) Tel 219-533-4232.

†Rainbow Collection, *(Rainbow Collect; 0-935448)*, P.O. Box 75, Akron, OH 44309 (SAN 213-7860); *CIP.*

Rainbow Disc, *(Rainbow Disc; 0-9616048)*, P.O. Box 3077, Pontiac, MI 48059 (SAN 698-0104) Tel 313-338-7241; 18 N. Glenwood, Pontiac, MI 48058 (SAN 698-2395).

Rainbow Enterprises, *(Rainbow Ent)*, P.O. Box 267, West Friendship, MD 21794 (SAN 239-5983).

Rainbow Heaven, Inc., *(Rainbow Heaven; 0-938881)*, P.O. Box 554, Union City, NJ 07087 (SAN 662-6645); 9 Ridgely Pl., Weehawken, NJ 07087 (SAN 662-6653) Tel 201-392-8777.

Rainbow Medical Clinic, Inc., *(Rainbow Med Clinic; 0-914135)*, P.O. Box 2986, La Jolla, CA 92038 (SAN 287-5225) Tel 619-454-0539; 626 A Arenas St., La Jolla, CA 92037 (SAN 287-5233); Dist. by: DeVorss & Co., P.O. Box 550, 1046 Princeton Dr., Marina del Rey, CA 90294 (SAN 287-5241).

Rainbow Morning Music Alternatives, *(Rainbow Morn; 0-9615696)*, 2121 Fairland Rd., Silver Spring, MD 20904 (SAN 218-2963) Tel 301-384-9207.

Rainbow Press, *(Rainbow Pr NY; 0-943156)*, 222 Edwards Dr., Fayetteville, NY 13066 (SAN 240-4354).

Rainbow Pubns., *(Rainbow Pubns; 0-9613765)*, 6836 Walmore Rd., Niagara Falls, NY 14304 (SAN 679-3851) Tel 716-731-3581.

Rainbow Pubns., *(Rainbow WA; 0-940364)*, 9520 N.E. 120th, A-2, Kirkland, WA 98034-8915 (SAN 217-1279) Tel 206-821-2814.

Rainbow Publishing Co., *(Rainbow Pub Co; 0-936218)*, P.O. Box 397, Chesterland, OH 44026 (SAN 219-9912).

Rainbow Publishing Co., First United Nursery Schl., *(Rainbow Nursery; 0-9616693)*, 848 W. Lake St., Oak Park, IL 60301 (SAN 659-8412) Tel 312-848-4910.

Rainey, Al, Pubns., *(Al Rainey Pubns; 0-932971)*, 1015 N. El Centro Ave., Los Angeles, CA 90038 (SAN 690-0488) Tel 213-463-7876.

Rainey, Ralph, *(Rainey R; 0-9615061)*, Box 296, Carlyle, IL 62231 (SAN 694-1575) Tel 615-594-3559.

Rainforest Publishing, *(Rainforest Pub; 0-937017)*, P.O. Box 101251, Anchorage, AK 99510 (SAN 658-7941) Tel 907-345-0190; 2420 Dennis Way, Anchorage, AK 99510 (SAN 658-795X).

Rainshadow Pubns., *(Rainshadow Pubns; 0-9614129)*, P.O. Box 1393, Gig Harbor, WA 98335 (SAN 686-5216) Tel 206-857-6274.

Raintree Pubs., Inc., *(Raintree Pubs; 0-8172; 0-8393; 0-940742; 0-86514)*, 310 W. Wisconsin Ave., Mezzanine Level, Milwaukee, WI 53203 (SAN 207-9607) Tel 414-273-0873; Toll free: 800-558-7264.

Rainy Day Pr., *(Rainy Day Fl; 0-9615290)*, P.O. Box 65-3441, Miami, FL 33265-3441 (SAN 694-4183) Tel 305-821-5407.

Rainy Day Pr., *(Rainy Day Oreg; 0-931742)*, 1147 E. 26th St., Eugene, OR 97403 (SAN 211-397X) Tel 503-484-4626.

Rainy Day Press, *(Rainy Day Pr; 0-918796)*, Box 471, Sausalito, CA 94965 (SAN 209-102X); Dist. by: Bookpeople, 2929 Fifth St., Berkeley, CA 94710 (SAN 168-9517).

Rajah Pr., *(Rajah; 0-911204)*, P.O. Box 23, Summit, NJ 07901 (SAN 204-6679).

Rajneesh Neo-Sannyas International Commune, *(Rajneesh Neo-Sannyas Intl; 0-918963)*, P.O. Box 1, Rajneeshpuram, OR 97741 (SAN 669-8786) Tel 503-489-3411; Dist. by: Rajneesh Pubns., Inc., P.O. Box 1510, Boulder, CO 80306 (SAN 240-0987) Tel 303-665-6611.

†Rajneesh Pubns., Inc., Div. of Rajneesh Foundation International, *(Rajneesh Pubns; 0-88050)*, P.O. Box 1510, Boulder, CO 80306 (SAN 240-0987) Tel 303-665-6611; *CIP.*

Rakhamin Pubns., *(Rakhamin Pubns; 0-9612500)*, 3094 Fortune Way, Oakland, CA 94609 (SAN 291-848X); Dist. by: Bookpeople, 2929 Fifth St., Berkeley, CA 94710 (SAN 168-9517); Dist. by: Inland Bk. Co., 22 Hemingway Ave., P.O. Box 261, East Haven, CT 06512 (SAN 669-3571) Tel 203-467-4257.

Names

Raleigh Little Theatre, Inc., *(Raleigh Little; 0-9615689),* 301 Pogue St., Raleigh, NC 27607 (SAN 696-0898) Tel 919-836-7882; P.O. Box 5637, Raleigh, NC 27607 (SAN 699-623X).

Raleigh Publishing Co., *(Raleigh Pub; 0-9615775),* P.O. Box 898, Wayzata, MN 55391 (SAN 696-5660) Tel 612-473-3027.

Ralston-Pilot, Inc., Pubs., *(Ralston-Pilot; 0-931116),* P.O. Box 1357, Cedar City, UT 84720 (SAN 282-2067) Tel 801-586-7395.

RAM Assocs., *(RAM Assocs WI; 0-9617209),* 1319 Oakwood Ave., Menomonie, WI 54751 (SAN 663-3846) Tel 715-235-5174. Do not confuse with RAM Assoc. of Poquoson, VA.

Ram Associates, Ltd., *(Ram Assoc; 0-943308),* Box 2277, Poquoson, VA 23662 (SAN 240-1118) Tel 804-868-8970.

†Ram Publishing Co., *(Ram Pub; 0-915920),* P.O. Drawer 38649, Dallas, TX 75238 (SAN 203-0837) Tel 214-278-8439; *CIP.*

Rama Publishing Co., *(Rama Pub Co; 0-913071),* P.O. Box 793, Carthage, MO 64836 (SAN 283-3875) Tel 417-358-1093.

Ramadan Pr., *(Ramadan Pr; 0-935387),* 5001 W. 80th St., Suite 885, Bloomington, MN 55437 (SAN 695-9296) Tel 612-835-2245.

Ramakrishna-Vivekananda Ctr., *(Ramakrishna; 0-911206),* 17 E. 94th St., New York, NY 10128 (SAN 204-6687) Tel 212-534-9445.

Ramapo Pr., *(Ramapo Pr; 0-915071),* 363 Seventh Ave., 10th Flr., New York, NY 10001 (SAN 289-811X) Tel 212-564-1877.

Rambler Bks., *(Rambler Bks; 0-9614963),* 1430 Park Ave., Baltimore, MD 21217 (SAN 693-4242) Tel 301-669-6694.

Rambler Pr., *(Rambler Pr; 0-9609754),* P.O. Box 184, Weiser, ID 83672 (SAN 264-3375) Tel 503-889-9409.

Ramey, Fredric D., *(F D Ramey; 0-910889),* 126 W. 119th St., New York, NY 10026 (SAN 274-9734).

Ramfre Press, *(Ramfre; 0-911208),* 1206 N. Henderson, Cape Girardeau, MO 63701 (SAN 204-6695) Tel 314-335-6582.

Ramico Pubns., *(Ramico Pubns; 0-9607272),* P.O. Box 5218, N. Hollywood, CA 91607 (SAN 239-2933) Tel 818-998-6196.

Ramifications, Unlimited, *(Ramif Julian; 0-936789),* P.O. Box 619, Julian, CA 92036 (SAN 658-8174) Tel 619-765-2525. Do not confuse with Ramifications Publishing, Limited, Tiburon, CA.

Ramira Publishing, *(Ramira Pub; 0-9612720),* P.O. Box 1707, Aptos, CA 95001 (SAN 289-8128) Tel 408-688-6666; Dist. by: Bookpeople, 2929 Fifth Ave., Berkeley, CA 94710 (SAN 168-9517); Dist. by: New Leaf Distributing, 1020 White St, NW, Atlanta, GA 30310 (SAN 169-1449) Tel 404-755-2665; Toll free: 800-241-3829.

Rampant Lion Pubs, *(Rampant Lion Pubs; 0-942872),* 8344 Melrose Ave., 23, Los Angeles, CA 90069 (SAN 240-1215); Orders to: 216 S. Fourth St., Las Vegas, NV 89101 (SAN 662-7412).

†Ramparts Pr., *(Ramparts; 0-87867),* P.O. Box 50128, Palo Alto, CA 94303 (SAN 203-3925) Tel 415-325-7861; *CIP.*

Ramsay, Roger, Gallery, Inc., *(R Ramsay Gallery; 0-9613449),* 212 W. Superior, Chicago, IL 60610 (SAN 669-7038) Tel 312-337-4678.

Ramsco Publishing Co., Div. of RAM Assocs., Ltd., *(Ramsco Pub; 0-943596),* P.O. Box N, Laurel, MD 20707 (SAN 240-7582) Tel 301-953-3699.

Ramsey, Sylvia, *(S Ramsey),* 6614 Whitewing, Corpus Christi, TX 78413 (SAN 696-2262).

Ramshorn Publishing Co., *(Ramshorn Pub; 0-9615478),* P.O. Box 263, Fremont, MI 49412 (SAN 696-0766) Tel 616-924-3325.

Rana Hse., *(Rana Hse; 0-930172),* Box 2997, St. Louis, MO 63130 (SAN 210-542X).

Ranch House Press, *(Ranch House Pr; 0-88100),* Rte. 2, Box 296, Pagosa Springs, CO 81147 (SAN 240-1126) Tel 303-264-2647.

Rancho Bernardo Junior Woman's Club, Inc., *(Rancho Bern; 0-9608548),* 12652 Gibraltar Dr., San Diego, CA 92128 (SAN 240-7590) Tel 619-485-0210.

Rancho Santa Ana Botanic Garden, *(Rancho Santa Ana; 0-9605808),* 1500 N. College, Claremont, CA 91711 (SAN 220-1836) Tel 714-626-3489.

Ranck, Joyce H., *(Ranck; 0-9606006),* 1103 Fairacres Rd., Richmond, IN 47374 (SAN 216-4426) Tel 317-966-2370.

†Rand Corp., The, *(Rand Corp; 0-8330),* P.O. Box 2138, Santa Monica, CA 90406-2138 (SAN 218-9291) Tel 213-318-3766; *CIP.*

Rand Editions/Tofua Pr., *(Rand-Tofua; 0-914488),* P.O. Box 2610, Leucadia, CA 92024 (SAN 206-8001) Tel 619-753-2500.

†Rand McNally & Co., *(Rand McNally; 0-528),* P.O. Box 7600, Chicago, IL 60680 (SAN 203-3917) Tel 312-673-9100; Toll free: 800-323-4070; *CIP.*

Randale Resources, *(Randale Resources; 0-9616728),* 2155 Verdugo Blvd., Suite 202, Montrose, CA 91020 (SAN 659-8749) Tel 818-957-1487.

†Randall, Peter E., *(P E Randall Pub; 0-914339),* Nobles Island Market St., P.O. Box 4726, Portsmouth, NH 03801 (SAN 223-0496) Tel 603-431-5667; *CIP.*

Randall Bk., Co., *(Randall Bk Co; 0-934126; 1-55517),* 9500 S. 500 W., Suite 108, Sandy, UT 84070 (SAN 214-1329) Tel 801-562-5481; Toll free: 800-453-1356; Dist. by: Publishers Marketing Group, 1104 Summit Ave., Plainview, TX 75074 (SAN 262-0995) Tel 214-423-0312.

Randall Hse. Pubns., *(Randall Hse; 0-89265),* 114 Bush Rd., P.O. Box 17306, Nashville, TN 37217 (SAN 207-5040) Tel 615-361-1221; Toll free: 800-251-5762; Toll free: 800-624-6538 (in Tennessee).

Randelle Pubns., *(Randelle Pubns; 0-910445),* 1527 First Ave., Charleston, WV 25312 (SAN 260-1222) Tel 304-344-4494.

Randolph Research, *(Randolph Res),* P.O. Box 146, Nebo, NC 28761 (SAN 211-092X) Tel 704-652-8150.

Random, *(Random Hse., Inc.; 0-394; 0-676),* Random Hse. Publicity, (11-6), 201 E. 50th St., New York, NY 10022 (SAN 202-5507) Tel 212-751-2600; TOLL FREE: 800-638-6460; Orders to: 400 Hahn Rd., Westminster, MD 21157 (SAN 202-5515)

Random House School Div., *(Random Sch Div; 0-394; 0-676),* 201 E. 50th St., New York, NY 10022 (SAN 669-2524); Orders to: 400 Hahn Rd., Westminster, MD 21157

Random Lengths Pubns., Inc., *(Random Lgths Pubns; 0-9614042),* P.O. Box 867, Eugene, OR 97440-0867 (SAN 684-7978) Tel 503-686-9925.

Random Motion, *(Random Motion; 0-933457),* 159 Western Ave. W, No.484, Seattle, WA 98119 (SAN 691-6864) Tel 206-284-8052.

Ranger Assocs., Inc., *(Ranger Assocs; 0-934588),* 600 Washington Court, Guilderland, NY 12084 (SAN 213-5523) Tel 518-456-6401.

Ranieri, Helene, *(H Ranieri),* 2760 Devonshire Place, NW, Washington, DC 20008

Ranney Pubns., *(Ranney Pubns),* 5395 Industrial Dr., Unit C,, Huntington Beach, CA 92649 (SAN 211-867X) Tel 714-891-2145.

Rano, Dennis W., *(D W Rano; 0-9612510),* P.O. Box 7842, South Lake Tahoe, CA 95705

Ransom Distributing Co., *(Ransom Dist Co),* P.O. Box 2010, Sparks, NV 89432

Ransom Hill Pr., *(Ransom Hill; 0-9604342),* 3601 Main St., Ramona, CA 92065 (SAN 215-9104) Tel 619-789-0620.

†Ransom Press, *(Ransom ID; 0-912737),* 125 E. Third St., Moscow, ID 83843 (SAN 283-2216) Tel 208-883-1464; *CIP.*

Ransom Pr., *(Ransom Pr; 0-931221),* P.O. Box 1456, Bernsville, MN 55337 (SAN 682-0166) Tel 612-588-8707.

Rape and Abuse Crisis Center of Fargo Moorhead, *(Rape Abuse Crisis; 0-914633),* P.O. Box 2984, Fargo, ND 58108 (SAN 289-5684) Tel 701-293-7273.

Rape Crisis Ctr., *(Rape Crisis Ctr),* P.O. Box 21005, Washington, DC 20009

Raphael, Morris, Books, *(M Raphael; 0-9608866),* 1404 Bayou Side Dr., New Iberia, LA 70560 (SAN 241-0737) Tel 318-369-3220.

Rapid System Development, Inc., *(Rapid Syst Dev; 0-914751),* 211 W. 56th St., Suite 36H, New York, NY 10019-4323 Tel 212-245-8870.

Rapides Symphony Guild, *(Rapides Symphony; 0-9603758),* P.O. Box 4172, Alexandria, LA 71301-0172 (SAN 293-3691) Tel 318-442-9707; Dist. by: Dot Gibson Publications, 161 Knight Ave. Circle, Waycross, GA 31501 (SAN 293-3705) Tel 912-285-2848; Dist. by: Express Publishing Co., 305 Decatur St., New Orleans, LA 70130 (SAN 293-3713) Tel 504-524-6963; Dist. by: South Louisiana News Agency, 102 Industrial Dr. Crowley-Rayne Industrial Park, Rayne, LA 70578 (SAN 169-2917); Dist. by: The Collection, 2101 Kansas City Rd., Olathe, KS 66061 (SAN 293-373X) Tel 913-764-1811; Dist. by: Wimmer Brothers Books, 4210 BF Goodrich Blvd., Memphis, TN 38118 (SAN 293-3748) Tel 901-362-8900; Dist. by: Forest Sales & Distributing Co., 2616 Spain St., New Orleans, LA 70117 (SAN 293-3756) Tel 504-947-2106; Dist. by: Bayou News Agency, P.O. Box 15639, Baton Rouge, LA 70815 (SAN 169-2895) Tel 504-275-5670; Dist. by: Red River News, 950 Frontage Rd., Monroe, LA (SAN 159-9321).

Rapids Christian Press, Inc., *(Rapids Christian; 0-915374),* P.O. Box 487, 810 4th Ave. N., Wisconsin Rapids, WI 54494 (SAN 205-0986) Tel 715-423-4670.

Rapier, Regina C., *(R C Rapier; 0-9600584),* 292 S. Cherokee Rd., Social Circle, GA 30279 (SAN 204-6571) Tel 404-464-2582.

Rapollo Books, *(Rapollo Bks; 0-9603670),* 1362 Banyan Dr., Fallbrook, CA 92028 (SAN 213-6066); Dist. by: Caroline Hse. Pubs., 2 Ellis Pl., Ossining, NY 10562 (SAN 211-2299).

Rapple Prod Production, Subs. of Ding A Ling Press, *(Rapple Prod; 0-932784),* 2039 Civic Ctr. Dr., Suite 320, North Las Vegas, NV 89030 (SAN 212-1484) Tel 702-649-1018.

Rapport Unlimited Pubns., *(Rapport Unltd Pubns; 0-9616729),* 3 Maple Grove St., Battle Creek, MI 49017 (SAN 659-8730) Tel 616-964-1389.

Raquette Press, *(Raquette Pr; 0-916136),* Box 1, Star Route, Canton, NY 13617 (SAN 207-6187) Tel 315-386-8354.

Rare Publishing, *(Rare Pub; 0-939024),* 23352 Erwin St., Woodland Hills, CA 91367 (SAN 238-1311) Tel 805-526-7616.

Raspberry Recordings, Div. of Raconteur Records, *(Raspberry Rec; 0-934721),* P.O. Box 11247 Dr., Capitol Sta., Columbia, SC 29211 (SAN 694-1605) Tel 803-254-9120.

Rasselas Press, *(Rasselas Pr; 0-9609180),* 13505 Lucca Dr., Pacific Palisades, CA 90272 (SAN 241-4422) Tel 213-937-6250.

Rateavers, *(Rateavers; 0-9600698; 0-915966),* 9049 Covina St., San Diego, CA 92126 (SAN 205-6402) Tel 619-566-8994.

Rather Press, *(Rather Pr),* 3200 Guido St., Oakland, CA 94602 (SAN 293-3772) Tel 415-531-2938; Dist. by: The Printers' Shop, 4047 Transport, Palo Alto, CA 94303 (SAN 293-3780) Tel 415-494-6802.

Rational Island Pubs., *(Rational Isl; 0-911214; 0-913937),* P.O. Box 2081, Main Office Sta., Seattle, WA 98111 (SAN 204-6725); 719 Second Ave. N., Seattle, WA 98109 (SAN 662-1201) Tel 206-284-0311.

Rau, Diantha Christine, *(D C Rau; 0-935557),* P. O. Box 515, Yellow Springs, OH 45387 (SAN 695-9741) Tel 513-767-1561.

Rauch Assocs., Inc., *(Rauch Assocs; 0-932157),* P.O. Box 6802, Bridgewater, NJ 08807 (SAN 686-4325) Tel 201-231-9548.

Rave Reviews Publications, Div. of Junior League of North Little Rock, *(Rave Reviews; 0-9611224),* P.O. Box 15753, N. Little Rock, AR 72231 (SAN 283-3069) Tel 501-372-1436.

†Raven Pr., Pubs., Subs. of Wolters Samson Group, *(Raven; 0-89004; 0-88167),* 1140 Ave. of the Americas, New York, NY 10036 (SAN 203-3909) Tel 212-575-0335; *CIP.*

Raven Rocks Pr., *(Raven Rocks Pr; 0-9615779),* Rte. 1, Beallsville, OH 43716 (SAN 696-5679) Tel 614-926-1481.

Ravenel Books, *(Ravenel Bks; 0-916427),* P.O. Box 3318, Alexandria, VA 22302 (SAN 295-4958) Tel 703-751-5256.

†Ravengate Press, *(Ravengate Pr; 0-911218),* P.O. Box 103, Cambridge, MA 02238 (SAN 203-090X) Tel 617-456-8181; *CIP.*

Raving Festival Assn. Women's Board, *(Raving Fest; 0-9615803),* 22 W. Monroe St., Chicago, IL 60603 (SAN 696-5687) Tel 312-782-9696.

Raw Bks. & Graphics, *(Raw Bks & Graph; 0-915043),* 27 Greene St., New York, NY 10013 (SAN 289-8136) Tel 212-226-0146. *Imprints:* A Raw One Shot (A Raw One Shot).

Rawson Assocs., Div. of Scribner Bk. Co., Inc, *(Rawson Assocs; 0-89256),* 115 Fifth Ave., New York, NY 10003 (SAN 209-3154) Tel 212-614-1300; Toll free: 800-257-5755; Dist. by: The Scribner Bk. Co., Inc., Front & Brown Sts., Riverside, NJ 08075 (SAN 209-3162).

Ray/Foster, Publishers, *(Ray-Foster; 0-9612346),* 3756 Decade St., Las Vegas, NV 89121 (SAN 289-2294) Tel 702-454-0199; Orders to: P.O. Box 12807, E Las Vegas, NV 89112 (SAN 669-3547) Tel 702-454-0199.

Rayburn Pr., The, *(Rayburn Pr; 0-9615942),* 644 Montclair Dr., Lexington, KY 40502 (SAN 696-8139) Tel 606-266-8590.

Raycol Products, *(Raycol Prods; 0-9605176),* 5346 E. 9th St., Tucson, AZ 85711 (SAN 215-8019) Tel 602-745-1033.

Raye's Eclectic Craft Yarns, Inc., *(Rayes Eclec; 0-9601282),* P.O. Box 2356, 8240 Parkway Drive, Suite 105, La Mesa, CA 92041 (SAN 210-3672) Tel 619-460-0721.

Rayid Model Pubns., *(Rayid Pubns; 0-917197),* 3905 NE 38th, Portland, OR 97212 (SAN 655-8720) Tel 503-288-3617.

Rayline Company, *(Rayline),* 1413 Edinger, Santa Ana, CA 92705 (SAN 210-6566).

RayMark Publishing, Inc., *(Raymark Pub; 0-9617275),* P.O. Box 0286, College Grove Sta., San Diego, CA 92115 (SAN 663-5253); 6970 Central Ave., Lemon Grove, CA 92045 (SAN 663-5261) Tel 619-589-4024.

Raymond's Quiet Pr., *(Raymonds Quiet Pr; 0-943228),* 6336 Leslie NE, Albuquerque, NM 87109 (SAN 240-7604) Tel 505-821-3627.

Raynor Pr., The, *(Raynor Pr; 0-9615069),* 1 Raynor Rd., West Orange, NJ 07052 (SAN 693-9236) Tel 201-731-5925.

Rays Energy Consultants, *(Rays Energy; 0-936561),* 701 S. MacArthur Blvd., Springfield, IL 62704 (SAN 698-0961) Tel 217-544-2434.

RB Pubns., *(R B Pubns; 0-9613579),* P.O. Box 11452, Memphis, TN 38111 (SAN 669-9286) Tel 901-767-4669.

Re, Frank M., *(F M Re),* 68 Palm Club, Pompano Beach, FL 33062 (SAN 208-0818) Tel 305-946-1234.

Re-Entry From Military Service To Civilian Employment, *(Re-Entry; 0-9605826),* P.O. Box 13535, Portland, OR 97213 (SAN 216-5821) Tel 503-285-6560.

Re-Geniusing Project, The, *(Re-Geniusing; 0-941386),* 1432 Spruce St., Berkeley, CA 94709 (SAN 239-0272) Tel 415-841-4903.

Re/Search Pubns., *(Re Search Pubns; 0-940642),* 20 Romolo, No. B, San Francisco, CA 94133 (SAN 218-5849) Tel 415-362-1465; Dist. by: The Subterranean Company, 1327 W. Second St., Eugene, OR 97402 (SAN 662-7420) Tel 503-343-6324P.O. Box 10233, Eugene, OR 97440 (SAN 662-7439).

Read, Elizabeth, R. D., *(E Read; 0-9600996),* 4429 E. 46th Pl., Tulsa, OK 74135 (SAN 208-8274) Tel 918-627-0213.

Read-A-Bol Group, The, *(Read A Bol; 0-938155),* 301 Village Run E., Encinitas, CA 92024 (SAN 659-8994) Tel 619-753-0663.

Read Bks. Pubs., *(Read Bks Pubs; 0-937869),* P.O. Box 776, South Lancaster, MA 01561 (SAN 659-5758); 64 Albright Rd., Sterling, MA 01564 (SAN 659-5766) Tel 617-422-6303.

Read Me Publishing Co., *(Read Me Pub; 0-9602842),* 514 Anneslie Rd., Baltimore, MD 21212 (SAN 222-2248).

Read Publishing Group, Div. of Roland Read Assocs., *(Read Pub Group; 0-9614299),* 811 S. Broadway, Baltimore, MD 21231 (SAN 687-4851) Tel 301-522-4000.

Readel, Fred W., *(F W Readel; 0-9616822),* 2970 N. Victoria, St. Paul, MN 55113 (SAN 661-1214) Tel 612-484-1408.

†Reader's Digest Assn., Inc., *(RD Assn; 0-89577),* 750 Third Ave., New York, NY 10017-2797 (SAN 240-9720) Tel 212-850-7007; Toll free: 800-431-1726; Orders to: Customer Service, Pleasantville, NY 10570 (SAN 282-2091) Tel 914-769-7000; Dist. by: Random House, Inc., 400 Hahn Rd., Westminster, MD 21157 (SAN 202-5515); Toll free: 800-638-6460. Publisher. Not a true association; *CIP.*

†Reader's Digest Pr., *(Readers Digest Pr; 0-88349),* 200 Park Ave., New York, NY 10166 (SAN 203-3887); Dist. by: McGraw-Hill Bk. Co., 1221 Ave. of the Americas, New York, NY 10020 (SAN 293-3802) Tel 212-512-2000; Dist. by: Random Hse. Inc., 201 E. 50th St., New York, NY 10022 (SAN 293-3810) Tel 212-872-8036; *CIP.*

Readers Enrichment Series *See* Washington Square Pr., Inc.

Readers International, *(Readers Intl; 0-930523),* Subscription Service Dept., P.O. Box 959, Columbia, LA 71418 (SAN 677-5403) Tel 318-649-7288; Dist. by: Persea Books, 225 Lafayette St., New York, NY 10012 (SAN 212-8233) Tel 212-431-5270.

†Readex Bks., *(Readex Bks; 0-918414),* 58 Pine St., New Canaan, CT 06840 (SAN 209-9926) Tel 203-966-5906. Conventional reference works in reduced size (compact editions), research & reference collections in microprint (opaque), microfiche & reel microfilm; *CIP.*

Reading Fun, *(Reading Fun; 0-9616296),* 9210 Westwind Ct., Dallas, TX 75231 (SAN 658-5000) Tel 214-340-2064.

Reading Gems, *(Reading Gems; 0-915988),* P.O. Box 806, Madison, WI 53701 (SAN 207-6934).

Reading Hse., The, *(Reading Hse; 0-9604388),* Box 2975, Seal Beach, CA 90740 (SAN 282-2105) Tel 213-598-2289; Orders to: Box 2748, Mission Viejo, CA 92692 (SAN 168-9886) Tel 714-770-1511; Dist. by: DeVorss & Co., P.O. Box 550, 1046 Princeton Dr, Marina Del Rey, CA 90294 (SAN 662-121X).

Reading Matters, *(Reading Matters; 0-9614780),* P.O. Box 300309, Denver, CO 80203 (SAN 692-6827) Tel 303-388-4211; Dist. by: Quality Bks., Inc., 918 Sherwood DR., Lake Bluff, IL 60044-2204 (SAN 169-2127); Toll free: 800-323-4241; Dist. by: Bookpeople, 2929 Fifth St., Berkeley, CA 94710 (SAN 168-9517).

Reading Readiness *See* Word Play

Reading Reform Foundation, *(Reading Reform Found),* 7054 E. Indian School Rd., Scottsdale, AZ 85251 (SAN 225-8668).

Reading Research *See* ARO Publishing Co.

Readon Publishing, *(Readon Pub; 0-9604638),* 5016 Barranca Lora, Pensacola, FL 32514 (SAN 215-2843) Tel 904-477-1882.

†Ready Reference Press, *(Ready Ref Pr; 0-916270),* P.O. Box 5249, Santa Monica, CA 90405 (SAN 218-9305); *CIP.*

Real Comet Pr., The, Div. of Such A Deal Corp., *(Real Comet; 0-941104),* 500 E. Pike St., Seattle, WA 98112-3618 (SAN 217-4227) Tel 206-328-1801; Dist. by: Publishers Group West, 5855 Beaudry St., Emeryville, CA 94608 (SAN 202-8522).

Real Computers & Intelligence, *(Real Comp & Int; 0-934190),* P.O. Box 74, Santa Clara, CA 95050 (SAN 212-9639).

Real Estate Education Company *See* Longman Financial Services Publishing

Real Estate Futures, *(Real Est Futures; 0-9600488),* P.O. Box 2580, Vail, CO 81658 (SAN 203-4123) Tel 303-949-4858.

Real Estate Investment Assocs., *(Real Estate Invest; 0-9616730),* 2715 Elizabeth, Zion, IL 60099 (SAN 659-8706) Tel 312-872-2681.

Real Estate Publishing Co., *(Real Estate Pub; 0-914256),* P.O. Box 41177, Sacramento, CA 95841 (SAN 202-9782) Tel 916-677-3864.

Real Estate Solutions, Inc., *(Real Est Sol; 0-917935),* 2609 Klingle Rd., NW, Washington, DC 20008 (SAN 657-0100) Tel 202-362-9854.

Real Food, *(Real Food; 0-9611550),* P.O. Box 721, Colfax, CA 95713 (SAN 284-9496) Tel 916-346-2450.

†Real People Pr., *(Real People; 0-911226),* P.O. Box F, Moab, UT 84532 (SAN 203-3879) Tel 801-259-7578; *CIP.*

Realities Library, *(Realities; 0-916982),* 2745 Monterey Rd., No. 76, San Jose, CA 95111 (SAN 208-0761).

Reality Bks., *(Reality Bks; 0-9616930),* P.O. Box 824, Lansdale, PA 19446 (SAN 661-5295); 41950 Main St., Sellersville, PA 18960 (SAN 661-5309) Tel 215-257-1940.

Reality Productions, *(Reality Prods; 0-9608622),* 9978 Holder St., Buena Park, CA 90620 (SAN 238-3497) Tel 714-828-2199.

Realm Books, Ltd., *(Realm Bks; 0-941654),* P.O. Box 2831, Phoenix, AZ 85002 (SAN 239-2941).

RealSoft, Inc., *(RealSoft NC; 0-939259),* P.O. Drawer 160, Atlantic Beach, NC 28512 (SAN 662-5215) Tel 919-726-2865. Do not confuse with Realsoft, Inc., of Ft. Myers, FL.

†Realtors National Marketing Institute, *(Realtors Natl; 0-913652),* 430 N. Michigan Ave., Suite 500, Chicago, IL 60611-4092 (SAN 202-0963) Tel 312-670-3780; Toll free: 800-621-7035; *CIP.*

Reavco Publishing, *(Reavco Pub; 0-935695),* 7646 Hayvenhurst Ave., Van Nuys, CA 91406 (SAN 696-0863) Tel 818-780-3939.

Rebel Montgomery Temple, *(Rebel Mont Tem; 0-89279),* 302 W. Main No. 3 SE, Kasson, MN 55944 (SAN 265-3680).

Rebel Publishing Co., Inc., *(Rebel Pub; 0-9605666),* Rte. 5 Box 347-M, Texarkana, TX 75501 (SAN 239-4804) Tel 214-832-4726.

Rebound Pubns., *(Rebound Pubns; 0-9615024),* Box 21866, Waco, TX 76750 (SAN 694-0560) Tel 314-546-2773.

Recess Pr., *(Recess Press; 0-9616784),* P.O. Box 310, Dixon, CA 95620 (SAN 660-9716); 353 E. B St., Dixon, CA 95620 (SAN 660-9724) Tel 916-678-4664.

Rechs Pubns., *(Rechs Pubns; 0-937568),* 8157 Madison Ave., South Gate, CA 90280 (SAN 215-2274).

Recipes for Life, Inc., *(Recipes Life; 0-9614347),* P.O. Box 4718, Lafayette, LA 70502 (SAN 679-1646) Tel 318-234-1295.

Recipes Unlimited, Inc., *(Recipes Unltd; 0-918620),* P.O. Box 1271, Burnsville, MN 55337 (SAN 209-0058) Tel 612-890-6655.

Recognition Technologies Users Assn., *(Recog Tech; 0-943072),* P.O. Box 2016, Colburn House, Manchester Center, VT 05255 (SAN 240-4362) Tel 802-362-4151.

Recon Pubns., *(Recon Pubns; 0-916894),* P.O. Box 14602, Philadelphia, PA 19134 (SAN 207-8880).

Reconstruction Press *See* ICE

Reconstructionist Pr., Div. of Federation of Reconstructionist Congregations & Havurot, *(Reconstructionist Pr; 0-935457),* 270 W. 89th St., New York, NY 10024 (SAN 695-8745) Tel 212-496-2960; Dist. by: Hebrew Publishing Co., 100 Water St., Brooklyn, NY 11201 (SAN 200-6774).

Reconstructionist Rabbinical College Pr., *(RRCP; 0-938945),* Church Rd., & Greenwood Ave., Wyncote, PA 19095 (SAN 661-7360) Tel 215-576-0800.

Record-Rama (Sound Archives), *(Record-Rama; 0-910925),* 4981 McKnight Rd., Pittsburgh, PA 15237 (SAN 264-3391) Tel 412-367-7330.

Record Research, Inc., *(Record Research; 0-89820),* P.O. Box 200, Menomonee Falls, WI 53051 (SAN 212-9655) Tel 414-251-5408.

Record Stockman & Coyote Cowboy Co., *(R Stockman & Coyote; 0-939343),* P.O. Box 190, Brighton, CO 80601 (SAN 663-0820); 755 S. Eighth Ave., Brighton, CO 80601 Tel 303-654-1474.

Recovery Pubns., *(Recovery Pubns; 0-9613185),* Box 7631, Amarillo, TX 79114-7631 (SAN 295-9372) Tel 806-372-5865.

Recreation Consultants, *(Recreat Consult; 0-9614086),* P.O. Box 842, Seattle, WA 98111 (SAN 686-0788) Tel 206-329-7894.

Recreation Pub., *(Recreat Pub; 0-932413),* P.O. Box 168, Wakefield, RI 02880 (SAN 686-6824) Tel 401-789-3041.

Recreation Vehicle Industry Assn., *(RV Indus Assn),* P.O. Box 2999, 1896 Preston White Dr., Reston, VA 22090 (SAN 231-3928) Tel 703-620-6003.

Recro Products Corp., *(Recro Products; 0-911275),* 565 Fifth Ave., Suite 702, New York, NY 10017 (SAN 274-9904) Tel 212-687-1228.

Rector, L. T., Publishing, *(Rector Pub; 0-9606170),* 310 E. 25th St., Minneapolis, MN 55404 (SAN 223-0704).
Rector Prs., Ltd., *(Rector Pr; 0-934393),* P.O. Box 301, Leverett, MA 01054-9740 (SAN 693-8108) Tel 413-548-9253; 511 Long Plain Rd., Leverett, MA 01054-9740 (SAN 658-2788).
Red Alder Books, *(Red Alder; 0-914906),* P.O. Box 2992, Santa Cruz, CA 95063 (SAN 206-6181) Tel 408-426-7082.
Red Cedar Press, *(Red Cedar; 0-937190),* English Dept., Michigan State Univ., East Lansing, MI 48824 (SAN 216-6812) Tel 517-351-4313; Dist. by: Stone Press, 1790 Grand River, Okemos, MI 48864 (SAN 207-902X).
Red Dragon Pr., *(Red Dragon; 0-942384),* P.O. Box 2, Wilmot, WI 53192 (SAN 239-6009) Tel 414-862-2395; Dist. by: Lotus Light, P.O. Box 2, Wilmot, WI 53192 (SAN 239-1120) Tel 414-862-2395.
†Red Dust, Inc., *(Red Dust; 0-87376),* P.O. Box 630, Gracie Sta., New York, NY 10028 (SAN 203-3860) Tel 212-348-4388; *CIP.*
Red Feather Publishing Co., *(Red Feather; 0-936430),* P.O. Drawer 2007, Lubbock, TX 79408 (SAN 215-1030) Tel 806-795-7272; Dist. by: Baker & Taylor, Eastern Div., 50 Kirby Ave., Somerville, NJ 08876 (SAN 169-4901).
Red Hen Pr., *(Red Hen Pr; 0-931093),* P.O. Box 3774, Santa Barbara, CA 93130 (SAN 678-9420) Tel 805-682-1278.
 Imprints: Jester Press (Jester Pr).
Red Herring Press, *(Red Herring; 0-932884),* 1209 W. Oregon, Urbana, IL 61801 (SAN 212-2251) Tel 217-359-0067.
Red Key Press, *(Red Key Pr; 0-943696),* P.O. Box 551, Port St. Joe, FL 32456 (SAN 240-8848).
Red Lake Bks., *(Red Lake Bks; 0-9611678),* P.O. Box 1315, Flagstaff, AZ 86002 (SAN 284-9526).
Red Leopard Pr., *(Red Leopard; 0-916939),* 1602 Lincoln St., Berkeley, CA 94703 (SAN 655-7716); Orders to: P.O. Box 167, Berkeley, CA 94701 (SAN 689-8491).
Red Lion Bks., *(Red Lion; 0-940162),* 12 Ryder Ct., Dixville, NY 11746 (SAN 217-4898) Tel 516-586-1072.
Red Lyon Pubns., *(Red Lyon Pubns; 0-941894),* 1975 Minda Dr., Eugene, OR 97401 (SAN 239-295X) Tel 503-345-5536.
Red Mountain Editions, *(Red Mtn; 0-911234),* P.O. Box 95, Burnsville, NC 28714 (SAN 204-675X) Tel 704-682-3735.
Red Mountain Museum, *(Red Mountain Mus; 0-936359),* 1421 22nd St. S., Birmingham, AL 35205 (SAN 697-9475) Tel 205-933-4104.
Red River Publishing Co., *(Red River Pub Co; 0-938794),* P.O. Box 3055, Wichita Falls, TX 76309 (SAN 240-8856) Tel 817-855-4335.
Red Rose Pr., *(Red Rose Pr; 0-9609888),* P.O. Box 24, Encino, CA 91426 (SAN 282-2121) Tel 818-981-7638; Dist. by: Bookpeople, 2929 Fifth St., Berkeley, CA 94710 (SAN 168-9517); Dist. by: Holistic Health, 1214 Tenth Ave., Seattle, WA 98122 (SAN 200-6286) Tel 206-325-9077; Orders to: DeVorss & Co., 1046 Princeton Dr., P.O. Box 550, Marina del Rey, CA 90294 (SAN 168-9886); Dist. by: Baker & Taylor, Midwest Div., 501 Gladiola Ave., Momence, IL 60954 (SAN 169-2100); Dist. by: Inland Bk. Co., 22 Hemingway Ave., P.O. Box 261, East Haven, CT 06512 (SAN 200-4151); Dist. by: New Leaf Distributing Co., 1020 White St. SW, Atlanta, GA 30310 (SAN 169-1449) Tel 404-755-2665; Dist. by: Starlight Distributors, 395 Freeport Blvd., Sparks, NV 89431 (SAN 200-6502) Tel 702-359-5676; Dist. by: Ingram Distribution Group, Inc., 347 Reedwood Dr., Nashville, TN 37217 (SAN 285-760X) Tel 615-360-2819.
Red Rose Studio, *(Red Rose Studio; 0-932514),* 358 Flintlock Dr., Willow Street, PA 17584 (SAN 212-162X).
Red Sea Pr., Affil. of Africa World Press, Inc., *(Red Sea Pr; 0-932415),* 556 Bellevue Ave., Trenton, NJ 08618 (SAN 686-6964) Tel 609-695-3402.
Red Sun Pr., *(Red Sun Pr; 0-932728),* 94 Green St., Jamaica Plain, MA 02130 (SAN 212-3819) Tel 617-524-6822.

Red-Tape Publication, *(Red Tape; 0-9608154),* P.O. Box 1236, Ft. Collins, CO 80522 (SAN 240-2718) Tel 303-484-1007.
Redbird Press, *(Redbird; 0-9606046),* 3838 Poplar Ave., Memphis, TN 38111 (SAN 216-9304) Tel 901-323-2233.
Redbird Productions, *(Redbird Prods; 0-9613437),* P.O. Box 363, Hastings, MN 55033 (SAN 657-0119) Tel 612-437-3179.
Redbud, *(Redbud; 0-938763),* P.O. Box 352, Culver, IN 46511 (SAN 661-5600); 310 White St., Culver, IN 46511 (SAN 661-5619) Tel 219-842-3751. Do not confuse with Redbud Pr., Bloomington, IN.
Redcor Book Publishing Co., *(Redcor Bk; 0-939588),* 501 W. Port Royale Lane, Phoenix, AZ 85023 (SAN 216-4434) Tel 602-863-1415.
Redd, Charles, Center for Western Studies, *(C Redd Ctr),* 4069 Harold B. Lee Library, Brigham Young Univ., Provo, UT 84602 (SAN 287-2900) Tel 801-378-4048; Dist. by: Signature Books, 3503 4th East, Suite G4, Salt Lake City, UT 84111 (SAN 217-4391) Tel 801-531-1483.
Redding, Thomas, & Assocs., *(T Redding; 0-939099),* P.O. Box 9039, Incline Village, NV 89450 (SAN 662-6025); 640 14th Green Dr., Incline Village, NV 89450 (SAN 662-6033) Tel 702-831-7799.
Reddy Communications, Inc., *(Reddy Comm; 0-9603716),* P.O. Box 3209, Albuquerque, NM 87109 (SAN 213-6406) Tel 505-884-7500.
Redencion Viva, *(Redencion Viva; 0-9607576),* Box 141167, Dallas, TX 75214 (SAN 239-6017); Orders to: Box 141167, Dallas, TX 75214 (SAN 669-2559) Tel 214-821-5357.
†Redgrave Publishing Co., *(Redgrave Pub Co; 0-913178),* 380 Adams St., Bedford Hills, NY 10507 (SAN 212-9663) Tel 914-241-7100; *CIP.*
Redpath Pr., Div. of Redpath Assocs., Inc., *(Redpath Pr; 1-55628),* 3137 Holmes Ave., S., Minneapolis, MN 55408 (SAN 659-9303) Tel 612-825-9154.
Redrock Enterprises, *(Redrock Ent; 0-936821),* P.O. Box 553, Woodinville, WA 98072 (SAN 696-7752) Tel 206-371-2681.
Redwood City Seed Co., *(Redwood Seed; 0-933421),* P.O. Box 361, Redwood City, CA 94064 (SAN 691-5078) Tel 415-325-7333.
Redwood Pr., *(Redwood Press; 0-939061),* P.O. Box 776, Inverness, CA 94937 (SAN 662-8443); 388 Drakes View Dr., Inverness, CA 94937 (SAN 662-8451) Tel 415-663-8384. Do not confuse with Redwood Pr., Burlingame, CA.
Redwood Pr., The, Div. of Syntax Associates, *(Redwood Pr; 0-941196),* P.O. Box 412, Burlingame, CA 94011-0412 (SAN 239-4812) Tel 415-342-4411.
Redwood Pubs., *(Redwood; 0-917928),* P.O. Box 7424, Menlo Park, CA 94025 (SAN 209-4827) Tel 415-854-3723. Do Not Confuse with Redwood Publishing Co. in San Luis Obispo, CA.
Redwood Publishing Co., *(Redwood Pub Co; 0-937316),* 3860 S. Higuera, Space 105, San Luis Obispo, CA 93401 (SAN 213-4314). Do Not Confuse with Redwood Publishers in Menlo Park, CA.
Redwood Records, *(Redwood Records; 0-9608774),* 476 W. MacArthur Blvd., Oakland, CA 94609 (SAN 218-3080) Tel 415-428-9191; Toll free: 800-227-2400.
Reebie Associates, Inc., *(Reebie Assoc; 0-9604776),* P.O. Box 1278, Greenwich, CT 06836 (SAN 220-0899) Tel 203-661-8661.
Reed, Ishmael, & Al Young's Quilt, *(Reed & Youngs Quilt; 0-931676),* 1446 Sixth St. Suite D, Berkeley, CA 94710 (SAN 282-2334) Tel 415-527-1586; Dist. by: Bookpeople, 2929 Fifth St., Berkeley, CA 94710 (SAN 168-9517); Dist. by: Small Press Distribution, Inc., 1814 San Pablo Ave., Berkeley, CA 94702 (SAN 204-5826) Tel 415-549-3336; Dist. by: Bookslinger, 213 E. Fourth St., St. Paul, MN 55101 (SAN 169-4154) Tel 612-221-0429; Dist. by: Inland Bk. Co., P.O. Box 261, 22 Hemingway Ave., E. Haven, CT 06512 (SAN 282-2385) Tel 203-467-4257.
Reed, James H., *(J H Reed; 0-9601314),* 1315 Melrose, Richardson, TX 75080 (SAN 209-0031) Tel 214-826-8835.

Reed, R., *(R Reed),* P.O. Box 1106, Laguna Beach, CA 92652 (SAN 207-5644).
Reed, Robert D., *(R D Reed),* 18581 McFarland Ave., Saratoga, CA 95070 (SAN 212-8632).
Reed & Cannon Co., *(Reed & Cannon; 0-918408),* 1446 Sixth St. No. D, Berkeley, CA 94710 (SAN 282-2393) Tel 415-527-1586; Dist. by: Bookpeople, 2929 Fifth St., Berkeley, CA 94710 (SAN 168-9517); Dist. by: Bookslinger, 213 E. Fourth St., St. Paul, MN 55101 (SAN 169-4154) Tel 612-221-0429; Dist. by: Inland Book Co., P.O. Box 261, 22 Hemingway Ave., East Haven, CT 06512 (SAN 200-4151) Tel 203-467-4257; Dist. by: Small Press Distribution, 1814 San Pablo Ave., Berkeley, CA 94702 (SAN 204-5826) Tel 415-549-3336.
†Reed Pubs., *(Reed Pubs HI; 0-917064),* P.O. Box 10667, Honolulu, HI 96816 (SAN 208-483X) Tel 808-732-1515; *CIP.*
Reed Publishing, *(Reed Pub; 0-939224),* 342 Bryan Dr., Danville, CA 94526 (SAN 220-1844) Tel 415-820-6292; Orders to: Publishers Business Services, P.O. Box 643, Cambridge, MA 02159 (SAN 202-8522) Tel 617-491-6562; Dist. by: Publishers Group West, 5855 Beaudry St., Emeryville, CA 94608 (SAN 662-1228) Tel 415-658-3453; Toll free: 800-982-8315.
Reeder, Robert L., Pub., *(R L Reeder; 0-9616667),* 1400 S. Andrews Ave., Fort Lauderdale, FL 33316 (SAN 659-9273) Tel 305-764-8911.
Reef Dwellers Press, *(Reef Dwellers; 0-9602530),* One Pitcairn Pl., Jenkintown, PA 19046 (SAN 213-1528) Tel 215-887-6700; Orders to: Reef Dwellers Press, P.O. Box 582, Bryn Athyn, PA 19009 (SAN 213-1536) Tel 215-675-2305.
Reeks, Lindsay S., *(L S Reeks; 0-9616950),* 2013 Westover Dr., Pleasant Hill, CA 94523 (SAN 661-7352) Tel 415-934-9416.
Reel Research, *(Reel Res),* P.O. Box 6037, Albany, CA 94706 (SAN 209-0066) Tel 415-549-0923.
Reep, James W., *(James Reep; 0-9614602),* 3511 55th Ave., Hyattsville, MD 20784 (SAN 691-8255) Tel 301-927-7241.
Reeves, Emma B., *(E B Reeves; 0-911013),* 1614 Redbud St., Nacogdoches, TX 75961 (SAN 274-9971) Tel 409-564-0130.
Reference & Guide Books Pub. Co., *(Ref Guide Bks; 0-9607942),* 4963 Elmhurst, Box 3581, Ventura, CA 93006 (SAN 240-0650) Tel 805-644-8672.
Reference & Research Services, *(Ref Rsch Serv; 0-937855),* 511 Lincoln St., Santa Cruz, CA 95060 (SAN 659-5774) Tel 408-426-4479.
Reference Bk. Pubs. See Kelley, Augustus M., Pubs.
Reference Guides, *(Ref Guides; 0-939228),* Rte. 2, Box 162, Detroit, TX 75436 (SAN 220-1402) Tel 214-674-5403.
†Reference Pubns., Inc., *(Ref Pubns; 0-917256),* 218 St. Clair River Dr., P.O. Box 344, Algonac, MI 48001 (SAN 208-4392) Tel 313-794-5722; *CIP.*
Reference Service Pr., *(Ref Serv Pr; 0-918276),* 3540 Wilshire Blvd., Suite 310, Los Angeles, CA 90010 (SAN 210-2633) Tel 213-251-3743.
Referral Service, The, *(Referral Serv; 0-9616300),* 80 E. San Francisco, No. 14, Santa Fe, NM 87501 (SAN 658-4926) Tel 505-984-0878.
Reflecting Pond Pubns., *(Reflecting Pond; 0-915395),* P.O. Box 292, Port Ludlow, WA 98365 (SAN 291-400X) Tel 206-437-2681; Dist. by: DeVorss & Co., P.O. Box 550, 1046 Princeton Dr., Marina del Rey, CA 90294 (SAN 168-9886); Dist. by: New Leaf Distributing, 1020 White St. SW, Atlanta, GA 30310 (SAN 169-1449) Tel 415-658-3453; Dist. by: Bookpeople, 2929 Fifth St., Berkeley, CA 94710 (SAN 168-9517); Dist. by: Pacific Pipeline, 19215 66th Ave. S., Kent, WA 98032 (SAN 208-2128) Tel 206-872-5523; Dist. by: Inland Bk. Co., P.O. Box 261, 22 Hemingway Ave., East Haven, CT 06512 (SAN 200-4151) Tel 203-467-4257; Dist. by: Samuel Weiser, Inc., P.O. Box 612, York Beacon, ME 03910 (SAN 200-9588) Tel 207-363-4393; Dist. by: Starlite Distributers, P.O. Box 20729, Reno, NV (SAN 131-1921).

Reflection Publishing, (*Reflection Pub;
0-9616564*), P.O. Box 52146, Livonia, MI
48152 (SAN 659-5782); 19505 Angling Rd.,
Livonia, MI 48152 (SAN 659-5790)
Tel 313-476-7829.

Reflection Publishing (CA), (*Reflection CA;
0-939725*), P.O. Box 1630, Guerneville, CA
95446 (SAN 663-6055); 11840 Mays
Canyon Rd., Guerneville, CA 95446
(SAN 663-6063) Tel 707-869-3503. Do not
confuse with Reflection Publishing in
Livonia, MI.

Reflex Bks., (*Reflex Bks; 0-9616430*), 2050
Grape St., Denver, CO 80207
(SAN 659-1132) Tel 303-393-0446.

Reflex Management Publishing, (*Reflex Mgmt
Pub; 0-935459*), Box 331, Rte. 2,
Rogersville, MO 65742 (SAN 695-8761)
Tel 417-882-9408.

†**Reformation Research Press, Inc.,** (*Reformation
Res; 0-936592*), P.O. Box 1886, Decatur,
GA 30031-1886 (SAN 214-1981); *CIP.*

**Reformed Church Press, Reformed Church in
America,** (*Reformed Church; 0-916466*),
475 Riverside Dr., 18th Fl., New York, NY
10027 (SAN 207-4508) Tel 212-870-3020.

Reformed Presbyterian Theological Seminary,
(*Ref Presby Theo; 0-9616417*), 7418 Penn
Ave., Pittsburgh, PA 15208
(SAN 659-1159) Tel 412-731-8690; Dist.
by: Crown & Covenant Pubns., 7418 Penn
Ave., Pittsburgh, PA 15208
(SAN 200-6766) Tel 412-731-8690.

Refsnes, Rauscher Pierce, Inc., Public Finance,
(*R P Refsnes Inc; 0-9611718*), One
California St. No. 2630, San Francisco, CA
94111 (SAN 285-2616) Tel 415-989-2300.

Regal American Marketing Corp., (*Regal Am
Mktg; 0-940814*), 1901 Walnut Plaza,
Carrollton, TX 75006 (SAN 216-4442)
Tel 214-242-7541.

†**Regal Bks.,** Div. of Gospel Light Pubns.,
(*Regal; 0-8307*), 2300 Knoll Dr., Ventura,
CA 93003 (SAN 203-3852)
Tel 805-644-6869; Toll free: 800-235-3415
(outside CA); Box 3875, Ventura, CA 93006
(SAN 658-1528); *CIP.*

Regal Rebel Rouser Creations, (*Regal Rebel
Rouser; 0-9616909*), 47 Eldora Dr.,
Mountain View, CA 94041 (SAN 661-5244)
Tel 415-967-8022.

Regan, Pat, (*P Regan; 0-9615826*), 120 W.
Brainard, Pensacola, FL 32592
(SAN 696-5695) Tel 904-434-5374; P.O.
Box 363, Pensacola, FL 32592
(SAN 696-9755).

Regehr, Margaret, (*M Regehr; 0-9614486*),
HCR 85, Box 64, Bonners Ferry, ID 83805
(SAN 689-3929) Tel 208-267-2801.

Regenbogen-Verlag, (*Regenbogen-Verlag;
0-940816*), Box 6214, Silver Spring, MD
20906 (SAN 216-0072) Tel 301-933-8521.

Regency Bks., Div. of Investment & Tax Pubns.,
Inc., (*Regency Bks; 0-910019*), P.O. Box
27368, Tempe, AZ 85282 (SAN 696-2424)
Tel 602-967-6923; 1600 W. Broadway, Suite
385, Tempe, AZ 85282 (SAN 697-712X);
Dist. by: Kampmann & Co., 9 E. 40th St.,
New York, NY 10016 (SAN 202-5191)
Tel 212-685-2928.

Regency Pr. *See* **Scholarly Pr., Inc.**

Regency Press, (*Regency Pr; 0-933324*), 32
Ridge Dr., Port Washington, NY 11050
(SAN 211-8688) Tel 516-935-1143.

Regent Graphic Services, (*Regent Graphic Serv;
0-912710*), P.O. Box 8372, Swissvale, PA
15218 (SAN 204-6768) Tel 412-371-7128.

Regent House *See* **B of A Communications Co.**

Regent Street Books, (*Regent St Bks; 0-916147*),
2747 Regent St., Berkeley, CA 94705
(SAN 294-9717) Tel 415-548-8459.

Regents Publishing Co., Inc., Subs. of Hachette,
(*Regents Pub; 0-88345*), 2 Park Ave., New
York, NY 10016 (SAN 203-3844)
Tel 212-889-2780; Toll free: 800-822-8202
(outside NY).

Reggie The Retiree Co., (*Reggie the Retiree;
0-9609960*), 6946 Myerlee Country Club
Blvd., Fort Myers, FL 33907
(SAN 262-9925) Tel 207-646-2767.

†**Regina Bks.,** (*Regina Bks; 0-941690*), P.O. Box
280, Claremont, CA 91711 (SAN 239-2968)
Tel 714-624-8466; *CIP.*

**Regional Institute of Social Welfare Research,
Inc.,** (*Regional Inst Social Welfare*), P.O.
Box 152, Athens, GA 30603
(SAN 225-9966) Tel 404-542-7614.

†**Regional Plan Assn.,** (*Regional Plan Assn*),
1040 Ave. of the Americas, New York, NY
10011 (SAN 225-1159) Tel 212-398-1140;
CIP.

†**Regional Publishing Co.,** Affil. of Genealogical
Publishing Co., (*Regional; 0-8063*), 1001 N.
Calvert St., Baltimore, MD 21202
(SAN 206-8842) Tel 301-837-8271; *CIP.*

Regional Science Research Institute, (*Regional
Sci Res Inst*), P.O. Box 833, Amherst, MA
01004 (SAN 239-3794) Tel 413-256-8525.

†**Regional Young Adult Project,** (*Regional
Young; 0-9606198*), 330 Elis St., Rm. 518,
San Francisco, CA 94102 (SAN 220-3049)
Tel 415-771-8375; *CIP.*

Register Press, (*Register Pr; 0-911242*),
Yarmouth Port, MA 02675
(SAN 205-2237) Tel 617-362-2111.

Registry of Intrepreters for the Deaf, Inc., (*RID
Pubns; 0-9602220; 0-916883*), 814 Thayer
Ave., Silver Spring, MD 20910
(SAN 216-1796) Tel 301-588-2406.

Registry Pubns., Ltd., (*Registry Pubns;
0-940640*), 425 Huehl Rd., No. 6B,
Northbrook, IL 60062 (SAN 204-2932)
Tel 312-498-4010.

Regmar Publishing Co., Inc., (*Regmar Pub;
0-914338*), P.O. Box 11358, Memphis, TN
38111 (SAN 203-2015) Tel 901-323-7442.

Regnery Bks., Div. of Regnery Gateway, Inc.,
(*Regnery Bks; 0-89526*), 700 E St., SE,
Washington, DC 20003 (SAN 210-5578);
Dist. by: Independent Pubs. Group, 1
Pleasant Ave., Port Washington, NY 11050
(SAN 287-2544). *Imprints:* Gateway
Editions (Gateway Editions).

Regnier, Susan L., (*Regnier; 0-9606266*), 5011
Turtle Lane W., Shoreview, MN 55112
(SAN 220-3480) Tel 612-483-0390.

Regs Enterprises, (*Regs Ent; 0-9614859*), 14659
Dexter Ct., Dale City, VA 22193
(SAN 693-2029) Tel 703-670-4415.

†**Regular Baptist Press,** Div. of General
Association of Regular Baptist Churches,
(*Reg Baptist; 0-87227*), 1300 N. Meacham
Rd., Schaumburg, IL 60173
(SAN 205-2229) Tel 312-843-1600; *CIP.*

Rehab Publications, (*Rehab Pubns; 0-9614877*),
P.O. Box 22606, San Francisco, CA 94122
(SAN 693-0549).

Rehabilitation International, (*Rehab Intl;
0-9605554*), 25 E. 21st St., New York, NY
10106 (SAN 216-0080) Tel 212-420-1500.

Rehi Bks., (*Rehi Bks; 0-938273*), 734 McGill
Dr., Rochester, MI 48063 (SAN 659-8331)
Tel 313-370-0629.

Rehmel, Judy, Quilt Books, (*J Rehmel;
0-913731*), P.O. Box 1002, Richmond, IN
47375 (SAN 286-116X) Tel 317-935-1127.

Rehnborg, C. F., Literary Foundation, The, (*C F
Rehnborg; 0-9606564*), 5600 Beach Blvd.,
Buena Park, CA 90622-5940
(SAN 218-5857); 7412 E. Bonita Dr.,
Scottsdale, AZ 85253 (SAN 693-9759).

Reichner, Herbert, (*H Reichner; 0-9601520*),
Shaker Hill, Enfield, NH 03748
(SAN 205-2210) Tel 603-632-7725.

Reid, Hazel E., (*H E Reid; 0-9601892*), P.O.
Box 317, Manhattanville, New York, NY
10027 (SAN 211-0148) Tel 212-490-0077.

Reid, Hugh B., (*H B Reid; 0-911244*), 2500 S.
State St., Ann Arbor, MI 48104
(SAN 694-3195); Dist. by: Reid Publishing,
1255 Buckingham, Grosse Pointe, MI 48230
(SAN 238-566X) Tel 313-882-0532.

Reiff Press, (*Reiff Pr; 0-911246*), 120 S. Eighth
St., Apt 3, Indiana, PA 15701
(SAN 207-3552) Tel 412-349-3347.

Reignbow, (*Reignbow; 0-942334*), P.O. Box
26174, Phoenix, AZ 85068
(SAN 239-8605).

Reiman Assocs., (*Reiman Assocs; 0-89821*),
5400 S. 60th St., Greendale, WI 53129
(SAN 208-4368) Tel 414-423-0100; Orders
to: Country Store, P.O. Box 572, Milwaukee,
WI 53201 (SAN 208-4376); Toll free:
800-558-1013 800-248-6065 (WI).

Reinecke Assocs., (*Reinecke Assocs; 0-9617064*),
P.O. Box 3112, West Chester, PA 19380
(SAN 662-8524); 940 Harmony Hill Rd.,
West Chester, PA 19380 (SAN 662-8532)
Tel 215-269-1288.

Reiner Pubns., (*Reiner; 0-87377*), Box 25,
Sterling, VA 22170 (SAN 204-6784)
Tel 703-430-2813.

Reinforced Concrete Research Council,
(*Reinforced Res*), 5420 Old Orchard Rd.,
Skokie, IL 60077 (SAN 669-2575)
Tel 312-966-6200; Orders to: American
Society of Civil Engineers, 345 E. 47th St.,
New York, NY 10017 (SAN 662-1236).

Reinforcement Learning, Inc., (*Reinforcement
Lrn; 0-937901*), P.O. Box 563, Upper Saddle
River, NJ 07458 (SAN 659-5804); 87
Dimmig Rd., Upper Saddle River, NJ 07458
(SAN 659-5812) Tel 201-825-2244.

Reis Network, (*Reis Network; 0-9616384*), 4111
Lincoln Blvd., No. 634, Marina del Rey, CA
90292 (SAN 659-1094) Tel 213-395-4078;
1636 Palm Ct., Santa Monica, CA 90401
(SAN 659-1108).

Reisner Publishing, (*Reisner Pub; 0-9611680*),
20 Los Altos Square, Los Altos, CA 94022
(SAN 284-9542) Tel 415-948-6427.

Rejected Works Publishing Hse., Ltd., (*Rejected
Works; 0-932493*), N600 Wolf Lodge Creek
Rd., Coeur d'Alene, ID 83814
(SAN 687-4312).

Rekalb Press, (*Rekalb Pr; 0-9604614*), 6203
Jane Lane, Columbus, GA 31909
(SAN 282-2415) Tel 404-561-3497.

Rel-Psych, Inc., (*Rel Psych; 0-9611682*), 201
Husson Ave., Apt. T1, Bangor, ME 04401
(SAN 285-1415) Tel 207-945-5997.

Relationship & Family Communications,
(*Relation Family Comns; 0-937905*), 1120
Conneticut Ave., NW, 940 Bender Bldg.,
Washington, DC 20036 (SAN 659-5669)
Tel 202-526-5505; Orders to: Rafcom Books,
P.O. Box 1554, Washington, DC 20013-1554
(SAN 662-4308) Tel 202-526-5505.

Relationship Training Institute, (*RTI; 0-935559*),
2036 Pauoa Rd., Honolulu, HI 96813
(SAN 696-0650) Tel 808-523-1752; P.O.
Box 27373, Honolulu, HI 96827
(SAN 696-9585).

Relevant Pubns., Ltd., (*Relevant Pub;
0-9606750*), 14241 Mango Dr., Del Mar,
CA 92014 (SAN 202-974X)
Tel 619-755-7522.

Reliance Health Systems, (*Reliance Health;
0-9615436*), 10341 N. Scottsdale Rd.,
Scottsdale, AZ 85254 (SAN 696-0820)
Tel 602-948-9533.

Reliance Publishing Co., (*Reliance Pub;
0-937740*), 380 Steinwehr Ave., Gettysburg,
PA 17325 (SAN 220-0910)
Tel 717-334-1103.

Reliant Publishing, (*Reliant Pub; 0-9613987*),
P.O. Box 17456, Portland, OR 97217
(SAN 682-1944) Tel 503-281-3586.

Religion & Ethics Institute, (*Religion & ethics;
0-914384*), P.O. Box 664, Evanston, IL
60204 (SAN 202-9731) Tel 312-328-4049.

Religious Activities Press, (*Religious Activ*),
413 S. Main St., Goodlettsville, TN 37072
(SAN 212-7911) Tel 615-859-5519.

Religious Education Pr., Inc., (*Religious Educ;
0-89135*), 1531 Wellington Rd.,
Birmingham, AL 35209 (SAN 207-3951)
Tel 205-879-4040. *Imprints:* REP Books
(REP Bks).

Relmo Pubs., (*Relmo Pubs; 0-9613940*), P.O.
Box 1606, Apache Junction, AZ 85220
(SAN 686-1725).

Relocation/Realty Consultants, Inc., (*Relocation
Realty; 0-939361*), 607 W. 58th Terr.,
Kansas City, KS 64113 (SAN 662-6920)
Tel 816-444-4646.

Rember Publishing, (*Rember Pub; 0-939101*),
7786 S. Elizabeth Ct., Littleton, CO 80122
(SAN 662-6017) Tel 303-770-1548.

Rembrandt Pr., (*Rembrandt Pr; 0-9617169*),
9601 Wilshire Blvd., Suite 728, Beverly Hills,
CA 90210 (SAN 663-141X)
Tel 213-271-9171.

Remcon Publishing, Inc., (*Remcon Pub;
0-937183*), 800 W. Deleon St., Tampa, FL
33606 (SAN 658-4950) Tel 813-253-0176.

Rememberbooks, (*Rememberbooks; 0-935231*),
P.O. Box 2501, Virginia Beach, VA 23450
(SAN 695-7161).

Remembrance Pr., The, Div. of Rosemary
House, Inc., (*Remembrance Pr; 0-9617210*),
120 S. Market St., Mechanicsburg, PA 17055
(SAN 663-2777) Tel 717-697-5111.

Remi Bks., (*Remi Bks; 0-943362*), 205 E. 78th
St., New York, NY 10021 (SAN 240-9267)
Tel 212-570-6265; Dist. by: Kampmann &
Co., 9 E. 40th St., New York, NY 10016
(SAN 663-298X) Tel 212-685-2928.

Names

Names

Renaissance Artists & Writers Asssociation,
Subs. of Ananda Marga Pubns., *(Renaissance
Art Writ Assn; 0-9611360),* 854 Pearl St.,
Denver, CO 80203 (SAN 282-9975)
Tel 303-832-6465.

Renaissance Books, *(Renaissance Bks;
0-932476),* 834 N. Plankinton Ave.,
Milwaukee, WI 53203 (SAN 211-9722)
Tel 414-271-6850.

Renaissance House *See* **Jende-Hagan, Inc.**

Renaissance Institute *See* **Islamic Productions
International**

Renaissance Pr., Inc., *(Renn Pr NOLA;
0-9616289),* P.O. Box 30808, New Orleans,
LA 70190 (SAN 658-4357)
Tel 504-899-8801; 805 Marengo, New
Orleans, LA 70190 (SAN 658-4365).

Renaissance Productions *See* **Islamic
Productions International**

Renaissance Pubns., *(Renaissance OH;
0-936645),* 4782 Brodribb Ct., Box D,
Columbus, OH 43220 (SAN 699-7295)
Tel 614-459-9279.

†Renaissance Pubs., *(Renaissance Pubs;
0-916560),* 2485 NE 214th St., Miami, FL
33180 (SAN 207-5091) Tel 305-931-3392;
CIP.

Renaissance Society of America, *(Renaissance
Soc Am; 0-9602696),* 1161 Amsterdam
Ave., New York, NY 10027
(SAN 209-4835) Tel 212-280-2318.

Rendezvous Pubns., *(Rendezvous Pubns;
0-938447),* 701 Northview Dr., Jupiter, FL
33458 (SAN 660-9929) Tel 305-744-6149;
P.O. Box 4269, Jupiter, FL 33469-4269
(SAN 660-9937).

Rendina, Dave, Publishing Co., *(D Rendina),* 1
Lake Rd., Newfield, NJ 08344
(SAN 212-0461).

Renfrew Group, The, *(Renfrew Group;
0-935601),* 985 High St., Bath, ME 04530
(SAN 696-0928) Tel 207-443-6070; Orders
to: The Renfrew Group, P.O. Box 617,
Freeport, ME 04032 (SAN 662-3646)
Tel 207-443-1587.

Renfro, Nancy, Studios, *(Renfro Studios;
0-931044),* 1117 W. Ninth St., Austin, TX
78703 (SAN 211-9730) Tel 512-472-2140.

Renino, Marjorie C. H., *(M Renino; 0-9615866),*
14 Ogden Ave., White Plains, NY 10605
(SAN 696-5709) Tel 914-946-2702.

Renovare Company, *(Renovare Co; 0-913986),*
8033 Sunset Blvd., No. 31, Los Angeles, CA
90046 (SAN 202-246X) Tel 213-656-4420;
Dist. by: Historical Films, P.O. Box 46505,
Los Angeles, CA 90046 (SAN 200-7274)
Tel 213-656-4420.

**Rensselaer Polytechnic Institute, Schl. of
Architecture,** *(RPI Schl Arch; 0-937919),*
Rensselaer Polytechnic Institute, Troy, NY
12180-3590 (SAN 659-5332)
Tel 518-266-6862.

REP Books *See* **Religious Education Pr., Inc.**

†Report Store, Div. of Ergosyst Assocs., Inc.,
(Report; 0-916313), 910 Massachusetts St.,
Suite 503, Lawrence, KS 66044
(SAN 130-1314) Tel 913-842-7348; *CIP.*

†Reprint Co., *(Reprint; 0-87152),* P.O. Box
5401, 601 Hillcrest Offices, Spartanburg, SC
29304 (SAN 203-3828) Tel 803-582-0732;
CIP.

Republican Co., *(Republican Co; 0-9615852),*
1860 Main St., Springfield, MA 01101
(SAN 696-771X) Tel 413-788-1212.

Republican National Committee, *(Rep Natl
Com),* 310 First St. SE, Washington, DC
20003 (SAN 235-8875) Tel 202-863-8700.

Rescan Assocs., Inc., *(Rescan Assocs Inc;
0-937737),* 401 Boyden Ave., Maplewood,
NJ 07040 (SAN 659-2856)
Tel 201-763-7534.

Research Advisory Services, Pubns., Inc., *(Res
Adv Serv; 0-931602),* P.O. Box 8151, 286
N. McCarrons Blvd., St. Paul, MN 55113
(SAN 211-3759).

Research & Education Assn., *(Res & Educ;
0-87891),* 505 Eighth Ave., New York, NY
10018 (SAN 204-6814) Tel 212-695-9487.

Research & Service Institute, Inc., *(Res & Serv
Inst; 0-942660),* Two Maryland Farms, Suite
233, Brentwood, TN 37027
(SAN 238-5678) Tel 615-377-3217; Orders
to: Harry Randles, Peabody College, Box
514, Nashville, TN 37203 (SAN 662-1244)
Tel 615-322-8000.

Research Assocs., Inc., *(Res Assocs; 0-943938),*
425 W. Broadway, Suite D, North Little
Rock, AR 72114 (SAN 241-144X).

Research Ctr. for Language & Semiotic Studies,
(Res Ctr Lang Semiotic; 0-87750), Dist. by:
Humanities Pr. International, Inc., 171 First
Ave., Atlantic Highlands, NJ 07716
(SAN 201-9272) Tel 201-872-1441.

†Research Centre of Kabbalah, *(Res Ctr
Kabbalah; 0-943688),* 200 Park Ave., Suite
303 E., New York, NY 10017
(SAN 210-9484) Tel 212-986-2515; Orders
to: 83-15 124th Pl., Kew Gardens, NY 11415
(SAN 662-7447) Tel 718-805-9122; *CIP.*

**Research Council on Diagnostic & Prescriptive
Mathematics, Inc.,** *(R C D P M; 0-940466),*
Univ. of North Carolina at Wilmington, 601
S. College Rd., Wilmington, NC 28403-3297
(SAN 217-2046) Tel 919-395-3363; Orders
to: Kent State Univ., 404 White Hall,
Teacher Dev., Ctr., Kent, OH 44242
(SAN 662-1252) Tel 216-672-2293.

Research Enterprises, Pubs., *(Res Ent Pubs;
0-915025),* P.O. Box 7569, Washington, DC
20044 (SAN 289-825X); 4701 Kenmore
Ave., Suite 905, Alexandria, VA 22304
(SAN 289-8268) Tel 703-370-4044.

Research Institute for Studies in Education,
(Res Inst Stud; 0-943206), The Quadrangle,
Iowa State University, Ames, IA 50011
(SAN 240-9275) Tel 515-294-7009.

Research Institute Management Reports, Inc.,
(Res Inst Man Rep), 589 Fifth Avenue,
New York, NY 10017 (SAN 265-4091).

Research Institute of America, *(Res Inst Am),*
589 Fifth Ave., New York, NY 10017
(SAN 227-0064) Tel 212-755-8900.

Research Materials Corp., *(Res Materials;
0-934631),* Box 243, College Park, MD
20740 (SAN 693-9228) Tel 301-552-2622.

Research Planning Institute, Inc., *(Res Plan
Inst; 0-931531),* 925 Gervais St., Columbia,
SC 29201 (SAN 682-3092)
Tel 803-256-7322.

†Research Pr. Co., *(Res Press; 0-87822),* 2612
N. Mattis Ave., Champaign, IL 61821
(SAN 282-2482) Tel 217-352-3273; Orders
to: Box 3177, Champaign, IL 61821
(SAN 282-2490). Do not confuse with
Research Pr., Prairie Village, KS. Do not
confuse with Resolute Pr., Edison, NJ; *CIP.*

Research Pubns., *(Res Pubns AZ; 0-914981),*
11855 N. 19th Ave., Phoenix, AZ 85029
(SAN 289-3894) Tel 602-252-4477; Toll
free: 800-528-0559.

Research Pubns., *(Research Pubns; 0-9600478),*
P.O. Box 801, Glen Rock, NJ 07452
(SAN 204-6830).

†Research Pubns., Inc., Subs. of International
Thomson Organization, Inc., *(Res Pubns CT;
0-89235),* 12 Lunar Dr., Drawer AB,
Woodbridge, CT 06525 (SAN 238-2717)
Tel 203-397-2600; Toll free: 800-732-2477; J.
Dick Publishing, 801 Green Bay Rd., Lake
Bluff, IL 60044 (SAN 661-9924)
Tel 312-234-1220; *CIP.*

Research Pubns., Inc., *(Res Pubns NC;
0-935233),* 92 Fairway Dr., Asheville, NC
28815 (SAN 695-5479) Tel 704-298-8291;
P.O. Box 9267, Asheville, NC 28815
(SAN 699-606X).

Research Pubs., *(Res Publs; 0-911252),* 108 S.
Patton, Arlington Heights, IL 60005
(SAN 206-6645) Tel 312-255-1961.

Research Publishing, *(Research Pub; 0-933833),*
2113 S St. NW, Washington, DC 20008
(SAN 692-8730) Tel 202-234-7069.

Research Services Unlimited, *(Res Serv Unltd;
0-912177),* P.O. Box 562, Toms River, NJ
08754 (SAN 265-4105) Tel 201-349-2799;
Dist. by: Gamblers Book Club, 630 S. 11th
St., P.O. Box 4115, Las Vegas, NV 89127
(SAN 200-7282) Tel 702-382-7555; Dist.
by: Casino Distributors, P.O. Box 849,
Pleasantville, NJ 08232 (SAN 200-7290)
Tel 609-646-4165.

Resolute Press, *(Resolute Pr; 0-9604382),* 13
Regent Ct., Edison, NJ 08817
(SAN 216-0099) Tel 201-287-0640. Do not
confuse with Research Pr. Co., Champaign,
IL.

Resource Applications Inc., *(Res Appl Inc;
0-932491),* 720 Light St., P.O. Box 6397,
Baltimore, MD 21230-3895
(SAN 687-4061) Tel 301-962-0250; Toll
free: 800-826-1877.

Resource Directories, *(Resource Direct;
0-937521),* 3103 Executive Pkwy., Suite
212, Toledo, OH 43606 (SAN 659-1183)
Tel 419-536-5353.

Resource Pr., *(Resource Texas; 0-9609182),*
P.O. Box 774, 433 Belle Grove, Richardson,
TX 75080 (SAN 241-4457)
Tel 214-458-1466.

Resource Publications, Inc. (Utah), *(Resource
UT; 0-936348),* P.O. Box 1515, Provo, UT
84603 (SAN 221-9883) Tel 801-756-6360.

Resource Pubns., Inc., *(Resource Pubns;
0-89390),* 160 E. Virginia St., No. 290, San
Jose, CA 95112 (SAN 209-3081)
Tel 408-286-8505; Toll free: 800-228-2028.

Resource Publishing Group, Inc., *(Resource Pub
Grp; 0-915619),* P.O. Box 390, Arlington,
VA 22210 (SAN 293-4981)
Tel 703-524-0815; 1401 Wilson Blvd., Ste.
101, Arlington, VA 22209
(SAN 293-499X).

Resources, *(Resources; 0-933342),* P.O. Box
1067 Harvard Square, Cambridge, MA 02238
(SAN 209-0457).

Resources for Children in Hospitals, *(Resources
Children; 0-9608150),* P.O. Box 10,
Belmont, MA 02178 (SAN 240-2734)
Tel 617-492-6220.

†Resources for the Future, Inc., *(Resources
Future; 0-915707),* 1616 P St., NW, Rm.
532, Washington, DC 20036
(SAN 213-1544) Tel 202-328-5086; Dist.
by: Resources for the Future Customer
Services, P.O. Box 4852, Hampden Sta.,
Baltimore, MD 21211 (SAN 200-5166)
Tel 301-338-6953; *CIP.*

Responsive Logic, *(Respons Logic; 0-928459),*
156 Donald St., Oregon City, OR 97045
(SAN 669-5108) Tel 503-655-4980.

Responsive Systems Assocs., Inc., *(Responsive
Syst; 0-9616483),* P.O. Box 846, Clinton,
OK 73601 (SAN 695-1023)
Tel 518-439-3838; 90-100 N. 31st St.,
Clinton, OK 73601 (SAN 658-2869).

Restaurant Recipes, *(Rest Recipes; 0-9613112),*
P.O. Box 4618, San Luis Obispo, CA 93403
(SAN 294-0868) Tel 805-528-3142.

Restauration Bks., *(Res Bks; 0-934263),* 150 S.
Glenoaks, No. 9176, Burbank, CA 91510
(SAN 693-2770) Tel 818-841-6479.

Reston Publishing Co., Inc., A Prentice-Hall Co.,
(Reston; 0-87909; 0-8359), Englewood
Cliffs, NJ 07632 (SAN 699-556X)
Tel 201-592-2427; Orders to: P.O. Box 500,
Englewood Cliffs, NJ 07632
(SAN 215-3939) Tel 201-767-5049.
Imprints: Reward Edition (Reward Edn).

Restoration Research, *(Restoration Re;
0-942284),* P.O. Box 547, Bountiful, UT
84010 (SAN 238-1133) Tel 801-298-4058.

Results Enterprises, *(Results Ent; 0-934713),*
2600 NE 21st. St., Fort Lauderdale, FL
33305 (SAN 694-1621) Tel 305-566-7739.

Resurge Pr., *(Resurge Pr),* 910 Madison, Suite
805, Memphis, TN 38103 (SAN 661-4612)
Tel 901-529-0874.

Resurgens Pubns., Inc., *(Resurgens Pubns;
0-89583),* P.O. Box 49321, Atlanta, GA
30329 (SAN 211-0539) Tel 404-834-1343.

Retail Reporting Bureau, *(Retail Report;
0-934590),* 101 Fifth Ave., New York, NY
10003 (SAN 213-1552) Tel 212-255-9595;
Toll free: 800-251-4545.

Retirement Research, *(Retirement Res;
0-9602938),* Box 401, Appleton, WI 54912
(SAN 204-6849) Tel 414-734-6610.

Retriever Bks., *(Retriever; 0-9604628),* 250 W.
87th St., New York, NY 10024
(SAN 213-5531) Tel 212-874-5579.

Reunion Pr., *(Reunion Pr; 0-935616),* P.O. Box
1738, Twain Harte, CA 95383
(SAN 657-7148) Tel 209-928-4800.

Reunion Publishing Hse., *(Reunion Pub Hse;
0-938173),* 140 Mayhew Way, Suite 700,
Pleasant Hill, CA 94523 (SAN 659-7211)
Tel 415-938-7444.

Reunions, Joseph & Mary Ray, *(J & M R
Reunions),* 8416 Forest Hills Blvd., Dallas,
TX 75218 (SAN 203-8250)
Tel 214-321-1302.

Rev Pubns, *(Rev Pubns),* P.O. Box 4787-B,
Santa Barbara, CA 93103 (SAN 239-6025)
Tel 805-964-0458.

Reveal Pubns., *(Reveal Pubns; 0-9602536),* 2208
Woodlawn St., Kannapolis, NC 28081
(SAN 212-6826) Tel 704-932-3476.

Revelation Hse. Pubs., Inc., *(Revelation Hse;
0-9604852),* P.O. Box 73175, Metairie, LA
70033 (SAN 217-1295).

Revelation Press, *(Revelation Pr; 0-913681),* P.O. Box 80141, Baton Rouge, LA 70898-0141 (SAN 286-1828) Tel 504-766-7746; 353 Stanford Ave., Baton Rouge, LA 70808 (SAN 286-1836).

Revelation 2/24, *(Revelation),* P.O. Box 7700, Pasadena, TX 77508 (SAN 692-221X).

Revell, Fleming H., Co., Subs. of Zondervan Corp., *(Revell; 0-8007),* 184 Central Ave., Old Tappan, NJ 07675 (SAN 203-3801) Tel 201-768-8060; Toll free: 800-631-1970. *Imprints:* New Hope Books (New Hope); Power Books (Power Bks); Spire Books (Spire Bks).

Reverchon Press, *(Reverchon Pr; 0-9601902),* 3520 Routh St., Dallas, TX 75219 (SAN 212-9671) Tel 214-528-6540.

†**Review & Herald Pub. Assn.,** *(Review & Herald; 0-8280),* 55 W. Oak Ridge Dr., Hagerstown, MD 21740 (SAN 203-3798) Tel 301-791-7000; Toll free: 800-582-5600; *CIP.*

Review of Existential Psychology & Psychiatry, *(Rev Exist Psych; 0-914857),* P.O. Box 23220, Seattle, WA 98102 (SAN 289-3940) Tel 206-328-2024.

Reviewer, The, *(Reviewer; 0-9606796),* 2197 Berkeley, Salt Lake City, UT 84109 (SAN 207-2815) Tel 801-487-4274.

†**Revisionist Pr.,** *(Revisionist Pr; 0-87700),* P.O. Box 2009, Brooklyn, NY 11202 (SAN 203-378X); *CIP.*

Revival Pr., Inc., *(Revival Press; 0-938612),* P.O. Box 130, Bedford, TX 76021 (SAN 240-8228) Tel 817-283-2873.

Revival Teaching, *(Revival Teach; 0-9616360),* 21 County Rd., Chatham, IL 62629 (SAN 659-1205) Tel 217-483-4109.

Reward Bks. *See* Prentice-Hall, Inc.

Reward Edition *See* Reston Publishing Co., Inc.

Reward Systems Services, Inc., *(Reward Systs Servs; 0-938115),* 245 E. 63rd St., New York, NY 10021 (SAN 659-6932) Tel 212-832-0590.

†**Reymont Associates,** *(Reymont; 0-918734),* 6556 Sweet Maple Lane, Boca Raton, FL 33433 (SAN 204-6857) Tel 305-483-4343; *CIP.*

Reynal *See* Morrow, William, & Co., Inc.

Reynard House, *(Reynard Hse; 0-932998),* 5706 30th NE, Seattle, WA 98105 (SAN 216-2954).

Reynolds, Bryan P., *(B P Reynolds; 0-9606448),* P.O. Box 186, Palos Park, IL 60464 (SAN 215-8027) Tel 312-257-7757.

Reynolds, Jane, *(J Reynolds; 0-930114),* 2135 Encinitas Blvd., Encinitas, CA 92024 (SAN 210-6604) Tel 619-942-1025.

Reynolds Morse Foundation, *(Reynolds Morse; 0-934236),* 10395 Stafford Rd., Chagrin Falls, OH 44022 (SAN 282-2520); Dist. by: J.D.S. Bks., P.O. Box 67, MCS, Dayton, OH 45402 (SAN 282-5864).

Reynolds Publishing Co., *(Reynolds Pub; 0-938343),* P.O. Box 51, White Oak, TX 75693 (SAN 659-9427); 304 Mockingbird St., White Oak, TX 75693 (SAN 659-9435) Tel 214-758-8114.

Rhapis Gardens, *(Rhapis Gardens; 0-9612130),* P.O. Box 287, Hwy. 181, Gregory, TX 78359 (SAN 286-8628) Tel 512-643-2061.

Rhema Bible Church *See* Hagin, Kenneth, Ministries, Inc.

Rhema, Inc. Pubs., *(Rhema Inc Pub; 0-935945),* 1220 Three Mile Rd., Grosse Point Park, MI 48230 (SAN 696-7531) Tel 313-881-3299.

Rheumatoid Disease Foundation, The, *(Rheumatoid; 0-9615437),* Rte. 4, Box 137, Franklin, TN 37064 (SAN 696-0677) Tel 615-646-1030.

Rhino Books, *(Rhino Books; 0-930589),* 1201 Olympic Blvd., Santa Monica, CA 90404 (SAN 677-5454) Tel 213-450-6323.

Rhino's Press, The, *(Rhinos Pr; 0-937382),* P.O. Box 3520, Laguna Hills, CA 92654 (SAN 214-4565) Tel 714-997-3217.

Rho-Delta Press, *(Rho-Delta Pr; 0-913770),* P.O. Box 69540, Los Angeles, CA 90069 (SAN 204-6881) Tel 213-651-1925.

Rhode Island Bicentennial Foundation *See* Rhode Island Pubns. Society

Rhode Island College Alumni Assn., *(RI Coll Alumni; 0-9616171),* 600 Mt. Pleasant Ave., Providence, RI 02908 (SAN 699-9247) Tel 401-456-8086.

Rhode Island Genealogical Society, *(RI Genealogical; 0-9604144),* 128 Massasoit Dr., Warwick, RI 02888 (SAN 216-4450) Tel 401-781-6759.

Rhode Island Historical Preservation Commission, *(RI Hist Preserv; 0-939261),* 150 Benefit St., Providence, RI 02903 (SAN 662-5223) Tel 401-277-2678.

Rhode Island Historical Society, *(RI Hist Soc; 0-932840),* 110 Benevolent St., Providence, RI 02906 (SAN 203-0829) Tel 401-331-8575.

Rhode Island Mayflower Society, *(RI Mayflower; 0-930272),* 128 Massasoit Dr., Warwick, RI 02888 (SAN 209-4843) Tel 401-781-6759.

Rhode Island Pubns. Society, *(RI Pubns Soc; 0-917012),* 189 Wickenden St., Providence, RI 02903 (SAN 219-9696) Tel 401-272-1776. *Imprints:* Rhode Island Bicentennial Foundation (RI Bicent Found).

Rhode Island Special Olympics, *(RI Spec Olym; 0-9615853),* 1 Commerce Way, Suite 200, Johnston, RI 02919 (SAN 696-7574) Tel 401-421-6037.

Rhodes Geographic Library, Inc., *(Rhodes Geo Lib; 0-933768),* 3225 Rum Row, Naples, FL 33940 (SAN 212-792X) Tel 813-262-6713.

Rhombus Publishing Co., *(Rhombus Pub; 0-936455),* P.O. Box 806, Corrales, NM 87048 (SAN 698-0287); Lot 4, Rincon de Corrales, Corrales, NM 87048 (SAN 698-2425) Tel 505-897-3700.

RHS Enterprises, *(RHS Ent; 0-914503),* 11368 Matinicus Ct., Cypress, CA 90630 (SAN 289-6699) Tel 714-892-9012.

Ribe, *(Ribe; 0-9616049),* P.O. Box 1256, Cambridge, MA 02238 (SAN 698-0082) Tel 617-576-3923; 13A Ware St., No. 8, Cambridge, MA 02138 (SAN 698-2387).

Ricard, Virginia B., *(V B Ricard; 0-9613508),* 1826 Indian Meadows Ln., Fort Collins, CO 80525 (SAN 657-3096) Tel 303-493-1922.

Ricci, Joan, *(Ricci; 0-9614699),* 2535 NW 41st. St., Boca Raton, FL 33434 (SAN 692-6088) Tel 305-994-4853; Toll free: 800-523-6504 (U. S.); Toll free: 800-331-1262 (FL); Dist. by: Baker & Taylor, Eastern Div., 50 Kirby Ave., Somerville, NJ 08876 (SAN 169-4901).

Rice, A. K., Institute, *(Rice Inst; 0-9615099),* P.O. Box 30912, Washington, DC 20016 (SAN 694-2024) Tel 202-857-8447.

Rice Univ., Institute for the Arts, *(Inst for the arts; 0-914412),* P.O. Box 1892, Houston, TX 77251 (SAN 218-933X) Tel 713-527-4858; Orders to: Menil Foundation, Institute for the Arts Catalogue Orders, 1427 Branard, Houston, TX 77006 (SAN 662-1260).

†**Rice Univ. Pr.,** *(Rice Univ; 0-89263; 0-911216),* Rice Univ. P.O. Box 1892, Houston, TX 77251 (SAN 204-689X) Tel 713-527-6035; Dist. by: Texas A & M Univ. Pr., Drawer C, College Station, TX 77843 (SAN 207-5237) Tel 409-845-1436; *CIP.*

Rich, Will B., *(W B Rich; 0-9612468),* 606 W. Barry St. 166, Chicago, IL 60657 (SAN 289-5714).

Rich Pubs., *(Rich SC; 0-9607832),* P.O. Box 1185, Clemson, SC 29633 (SAN 207-5857) Tel 803-654-2507.

Rich Publishing Co., Subs. of Dobson & Assocs., Inc., *(Rich Pub Co; 0-9607256),* 10611 Creektree, Houston, TX 77070 (SAN 239-300X) Tel 713-469-9165.

Rich Publishing, Inc., *(Rich Pub; 0-9607256),* P.O. Box 555, Temecula, CA 92390 (SAN 206-9660) Tel 714-676-5712.

Richards, David R., *(D R Richards; 0-9614431),* 480 W. Ash St., Zionsville, IN 46077 (SAN 688-5802) Tel 317-929-8517.

Richards, John Thomas, *(J T Richards; 0-9605980),* 309 W. Ninth St., Rolla, MO 65401 (SAN 220-1917) Tel 314-364-5723; Orders to: New Frontiers Foundation, Inc., Fellowship Farm, Route 1, Oregon, WI 53575 (SAN 214-0659) Tel 608-835-3795.

Richards, Peter, Co., The, *(Richards Co),* 3 Parkview Plaza, Morristown, NJ 07960 (SAN 239-4820).

Richards, S. P., *(S P Richards; 0-9608224),* Box 501, New Providence, NJ 07974 (SAN 240-1193).

Richards Hse.-FACTS, *(Richards Hse; 0-930702),* P.O. Box 208, Wellesley Hills, MA 02181 (SAN 211-0547) Tel 617-235-1142.

Richards Publishing, *(Richards Pub OK; 0-9616017),* 4338 E. 67th St., Tulsa, OK 74136 (SAN 699-7554) Tel 918-493-7353.

Richards Publishing Co., *(Richards Pub; 0-88323),* P.O. Box 66, Phoenix, NY 13135 (SAN 203-0861) Tel 315-695-7261.

Richardson & Snyder, *(Rich & Snyder; 0-943940),* 25 Broad St., New York, NY 10004 (SAN 241-1458) Tel 212-344-1200; Toll free: 800-526-0275; Dist. by: New American Library, P.O. Box 999, Bergenfield, NJ 07621 (SAN 200-6758) Tel 201-387-0600.

Richardson & Steirman, *(Richardson & Steirman; 0-931933),* 246 Fifth Ave., New York, NY 10001 (SAN 685-9852) Tel 212-213-1203.

Richardsons' Marine Publishing, Inc., *(Richardsons Marine; 0-932647),* P.O. Box 23, Streamwood, IL 60103 (SAN 687-8342) Tel 312-741-4239.

†**Richboro Press,** *(Richboro Pr; 0-89713),* Box 1, Richboro, PA 18954 (SAN 214-1353) Tel 215-355-6084; *CIP.*

Richcraft Engineering Ltd., *(Richcraft Eng; 0-940972),* Drawer 1065, No. 1 Wahmeda Industrial Park, Chautauqua, NY 14722 (SAN 219-0931) Tel 716-753-2654.

Richelieu Court Pubns., Inc., *(Richelieu Court; 0-911519),* P.O. Box 388 Aspen Heights, Slingerlands, NY 12159 (SAN 264-3480) Tel 518-439-7942.

Richman Publishing, Div. of Richman Communications, *(Richman Pub; 0-941846),* P.O. Box 11307, Salt Lake City, UT 84147 (SAN 239-3018) Tel 801-964-0378.

Richmond County Historical Society, *(Richmond Cty Hist Soc; 0-937044),* Reese Library, Augusta College, 2500 Walton Way, Augusta, GA 30910 (SAN 662-7455) Tel 404-737-1745.

Richmond Hse., *(Richmond Hse; 0-939505),* 573 North Mountain Ave., Suite 263, Upland, CA 91786 (SAN 663-4001) Tel 714-945-3112.

Richter Library of the Desert Botanical Garden *See* Desert Botanical Garden

Richwood Pr., *(Richwood Pr; 0-9613310),* 107 Konnarock Cir., Greenville, SC 29611 (SAN 653-8835) Tel 803-246-6690.

†**Richwood Pub., Co.,** *(Richwood Pub; 0-915172),* P.O. Box 381, Scarsdale, NY 10583 (SAN 207-3250) Tel 914-723-1286; *CIP.*

Rischer Publishing, Ltd., Subs. of Ricsher Enterprises, Inc., *(Ricsher Pub Ltd; 0-931347),* P.O. Box 34828, Bethesda, MD 20817 (SAN 682-6237) Tel 301-469-6481.

Ricwalt Publishing Co., *(Ricwalt Pub Co; 0-933054),* C-3 Bldg., Rm. 110, Fishermen's Terminal, Seattle, WA 98119 (SAN 213-1587) Tel 206-282-7545.

Rider, John F. *See* Hayden Bk. Co.

Ridge Row Pr., *(Ridge Row; 0-940866),* Univ. of Scranton, Dept. of Theology & Religious Studies, Scranton, PA 18510 (SAN 688-4067) Tel 717-961-7449; Dist. by: Montrose Publishing Co., 10-20 S. Main St., Montrose, PA 18801 (SAN 200-6898) Tel 717-278-1141.

Ridge Soaring, Inc., *(Ridge Soaring),* R.D., Julian, PA 16844 (SAN 695-2569) Tel 814-355-1792.

Ridge Times Pr., The, *(Ridge Times Pr; 0-934203),* Box 90, 1020 1/2 Main St., Mendocino, CA 95460 (SAN 693-0565) Tel 707-937-1188.

Ridgefield Bicentennial Commission, *(Ridgefield Bicen Com; 0-9601114),* 400 Main St., Ridgefield, CT 06877 (SAN 209-9985) Tel 203-438-7218.

Ridgeline Pr., *(Ridgeline Pr; 0-918967),* 1136 Orchard Rd., Lafayette, CA 94549 (SAN 669-9685) Tel 415-283-5836.

Ridgeview Junior High Press, *(Ridgeview Jr High Pr; 0-936920),* 9424 Highlander Court, Walkersville, MD 21793 (SAN 214-4573).

Ridgeview Publishing Co., *(Ridgeview; 0-917930),* Box 686, Atascadero, CA 93423 (SAN 209-9993) Tel 805-466-7252.

Ridgeway Books, *(Ridgeway Bks),* P.O. Box 6431, Philadelphia, PA 19145 (SAN 207-7485).

Ridgeway Pr., *(Ridgeway Pr; 0-943230),* 12032 Montecito Rd., Los Alamitos, CA 90720 (SAN 240-4915) Tel 213-596-8851.

Names

Names

Rieker Communications, *(Rieker Communications; 0-941656),* 48 Groveland Terr., Suite 410, Minneapolis, MN 55403 (SAN 239-3026) Tel 612-377-4770.

†**Rienner, Lynne, Pubs., Inc.,** *(Lynne Rienner; 0-931477; 1-55587),* 948 North St., No. 8, Boulder, CO 80302 (SAN 683-1869) Tel 303-444-6684; CIP.

Rietman, Jaap, *(Jaap Rietman; 0-930034),* 167 Spring St., New York, NY 10012 (SAN 205-2105) Tel 212-966-7044.

Rigelle Pubns., *(Rigelle Pubns; 0-9614389),* P.O. Box 1055, Cortez, CO 81321 (SAN 688-6485) Tel 303-565-7157.

Riggers Bible, Inc., *(Riggers Bible; 0-9600992),* P.O. Box 3302, Glenstone Sta., Springfield, MO 65804 (SAN 207-2823) Tel 417-869-9236.

Riggs, Karen B., *(Riggs),* Rte. 12, Box 1559, Mechanicsville, VA 23111 (SAN 275-0899) Tel 804-779-3557.

Right Brain Publishing, *(Right Brain Pub; 0-935295),* 7812 NW Hampton Rd., Kansas City, MO 64152 (SAN 695-9350) Tel 816-587-8687.

Right to Life League of Southern California, *(Right to Life; 0-9613809),* 1616 W. Ninth St., Suite 220, Los Angeles, CA 90015 (SAN 219-8142) Tel 213-380-8750.

Rigsbee, Ken, *(Rigsbee K; 0-9615296),* 3402 Water Locust Dr., Sugar Land, TX 77479 (SAN 694-4310) Tel 713-980-1755; Dist. by: Cuerno Largo Pubns., 3402 Water Locust Dr., Sugar Land, TX 77479 (SAN 200-5476).

Riley, Maurice W., *(M W Riley; 0-9603150),* 512 Roosevelt Blvd., Ypsilanti, MI 48197 (SAN 213-3628).

Riling, Ray, Arms Bks. Co., *(Ray Riling; 0-9603096),* P.O. Box 18925, 6844 Gorsten St., Philadelphia, PA 19119 (SAN 205-2385) Tel 215-438-2456.

RIM Classroom Plays *See* **Stevens & Shea Pubs.**

Rima Pr., *(Rima Pr; 0-9613941),* 1420 Mound St., Alameda, CA 94501 (SAN 689-1713).

Rinehart, Roberts, Inc. Pubs., *(R Rinehart Inc; 0-911797),* P.O. Box 3161, Boulder, CO 80303 (SAN 264-3510) Tel 303-449-3221.

Ringa Press, *(Ringa Pr; 0-88100),* 6833 W. Grand Avenue, Chicago, IL 60635 (SAN 264-3529).

Ringling, John & Mabel, Museum of Art Foundation, *(Ringling Mus Art; 0-916758),* 5401 Bayshore Rd., Sarasota, FL 33578 (SAN 208-7154) Tel 813-355-5101.

†**Rio Grande Pr., Inc., The,** *(Rio Grande; 0-87380),* P.O. Box 33, Glorieta, NM 87535 (SAN 203-3763) Tel 505-757-6275; La Casa Escuela, Glorieta, NM (SAN 662-7463); CIP.

Rip Off Pr., Inc., *(Rip off; 0-89620),* P.O. Box 14158, San Francisco, CA 94114 (SAN 207-7671) Tel 415-469-5800.

Risale i Nur Institute of America, *(Risale i Nur Inst; 0-933552),* 2506 Shattuck Ave., Berkeley, CA 94704 (SAN 212-6192) Tel 415-845-4355.

Rising Publishing, *(Rising Pub; 0-917047),* P.O. Box 72478, Los Angeles, CA 90002 (SAN 655-3060) Tel 213-677-5599.

Rising Star Press, *(Rising Star; 0-933670),* 557 Wellington Ave., San Carlos, CA 94070 (SAN 213-3636) Tel 415-592-2459.

Risk Analysis & Research Corp., *(Risk Analysis; 0-932056),* P.O. Drawer DPFC, Monterey, CA 93942 (SAN 211-6464).

Risk Enterprises, *(Risk Ent),* 1133 Curtis, Laramie, WY 82070 (SAN 213-1560).

Risk Management Pr., *(Risk Mgmt Pr; 0-9614860),* P.O. Box 670, Inverness, CA 94937 (SAN 693-2045) Tel 415-669-1501.

Risk Management Society Publishing, Inc., *(Risk Management; 0-937802),* 205 E. 42nd St., New York, NY 10017 (SAN 215-8043) Tel 212-286-9292.

Ritchie, George F., *(G F Ritchie; 0-9604392),* 1840 Clay St., No. 203, San Francisco, CA 94109 (SAN 212-6834) Tel 415-441-7126.

Rite Bks. Publishing, *(Rite Bks Pub; 0-9614423),* P.O. Box 3439, Warren, OH 44485 (SAN 689-027X) Tel 216-399-4949.

Ritner, George, *(G Ritner),* 411 Broadway, Suite 203, San Diego, CA 92101 (SAN 211-268X).

Rittenhouse Bk. Distributors, *(Rittenhouse; 0-87381),* 511 Feheley Dr., King of Prussia, PA 19406 (SAN 213-4454) Tel 215-277-1414; Toll free: 800-345-6425.

Riva Press, *(Riva; 0-9613194),* 8408 Paseo Del Ocaso, La Jolla, CA 92037 (SAN 295-8996) Tel 619-454-8529.

Rival Pubs., *(Rival Pubs; 0-9607100),* P.O. Box 5628, Everett, WA 98206 (SAN 239-0302) Tel 206-334-3965.

River Basin Publishing Co., *(River Basin; 0-936106),* P.O. Box 75573, St. Paul, MN 55175 (SAN 213-7887) Tel 612-291-0980; Dist. by: The Distributors, 702 S. Michigan, South Bend, IN 46618 (SAN 169-2488) Tel 219-232-8500; Dist. by: Baker & Taylor, Eastern Div., 50 Kirby Ave., Somerville, NJ 08876 (SAN 662-1279).

River Bend Club, Inc., *(River Bend Club; 0-9615100),* P.O. Box 23021, Ft. Lauderdale, FL 33307 (SAN 694-2636) Tel 305-391-9162.

River Bend Publishing, *(River Bend; 0-9605162),* 1222 Vista Court, No. 2, Muscatine, IA 52761 (SAN 275-9112).

River City Pubs., Ltd., *(River City MO; 0-933150),* P.O. Box 28665, St. Louis, MO 63141 (SAN 222-982X) Tel 314-724-7160.

River Falls Univ. Press, *(River Falls),* 113 E. Hathorn, River Falls, WI 54022 (SAN 203-6983) Tel 715-425-3100.

River Forest Community Center, *(River Forest C C; 0-9606314),* 414 Jackson, River Forest, IL 60305 (SAN 239-8613) Tel 312-771-6159.

River House, *(River Hse; 0-940644),* 2213 Pennington Bend, Nashville, TN 37214 (SAN 216-2962) Tel 615-889-2968.

River Press, *(River Pr; 0-915535),* P.O. Box 2006, Florissant, MO 63032 (SAN 291-4042) Tel 618-345-4731; 11 Kimberly Ct., Collinsville, IL 62034 (SAN 291-4050).

River Road Pr., *(River Road Pr),* P.O. Box 1130, Conway, AR 72032 (SAN 695-5452).

River Valley Publishing, *(River Valley Pub; 0-9615070),* P.O. Box 99752, Jeffersontown, KY 40299 (SAN 692-722X).

River West Bks., *(River W Bks; 0-9607192),* 663 S. 11th St., Coos Bay, OR 97420 (SAN 239-1287) Tel 503-269-1363.

Riverdale Co., Inc., The, *(Riverdale Co; 0-913215),* 5506 Kenilworth Ave., No. 102, Riverdale, MD 20737 (SAN 283-3905) Tel 301-864-2029.

Riverdale Systems Design, Inc., *(Riverdale Systs; 0-939545),* 3333 Henry Hudson Pkwy., Riverdale, NY 10463 (SAN 697-4309) Tel 212-549-1692; Toll free: 800-622-4070.

Riverrun Pr., Affil. of John Calder Pubs. (London, UK), *(Riverrun NY; 0-7145; 0-86676),* 1170 Broadway, Rm. 807, New York, NY 10001 (SAN 240-9917) Tel 212-889-6850; Dist. by: Kampmann & Co., Inc., 9 E. 40th St., New York, NY 10016 (SAN 202-5191) Tel 212-685-2928; Toll free: 800-526-7626. *Imprints:* Breachwood Publications (Breachwood Pubns); Original Music (Original Music); Petras Press (Petras Press).

Riverrun Pr., *(Riverrun Piermont; 0-936415),* 500 Piermont Ave., Piermont, NY 10968 (SAN 699-7511) Tel 914-359-2629.

RiversEdge Press, *(RiversEdge Pr; 0-938884),* P.O. Box 1547, Edinburg, TX 78539 (SAN 239-8931) Tel 512-381-3335.

Riverside Bks., *(Riverside Bks; 0-938777),* 24 Riverside Dr., New York, NY 10023 (SAN 661-6399) Tel 212-874-1817.

Riverside Editions *See* **Houghton Mifflin Co.**

Riverside Literature Series *See* **Houghton Mifflin Co.**

Riverside Museum Pr., *(Riverside Mus Pr; 0-935661),* 3720 Orange St., Riverside, CA 92501 (SAN 280-2740) Tel 714-787-7273.

Riverside Reading Series *See* **Houghton Mifflin Co.**

Riverside Studies in Literature *See* **Houghton Mifflin Co.**

Riverstone Pr., *(Riverstone; 0-9601130),* P.O. Box 148006, Chicago, IL 60614 (SAN 210-2641).

Riverstone Pr., *(Riverstone Pr; 0-9617206),* 795 River Heights Dr., Meridian, ID 83642 (SAN 663-2548) Tel 208-888-6290. Do not confuse with Riverstone Press of Portland, OR, and Chicago, IL.

Riverstone Press of the Foothills Art Center, *(Riverstone Foothills; 0-936600),* 809 15th St., Golden, CO 80401 (SAN 214-0144).

Rizzo, Tony, *(T Rizzo; 0-9611330),* Rte. 4, Box 154, Culpeper, VA 22701 (SAN 283-0019) Tel 703-971-8920; 4600 Duke St., No. 514, Alexandria, VA 22304 (SAN 693-5087) Tel 703-370-4587.

†**Rizzoli International Pubns., Inc.,** *(Rizzoli Intl; 0-8478),* 597 Fifth Ave., New York, NY 10017 (SAN 207-7000) Tel 212-223-0100; Toll free: 800-433-1238; CIP.

Ro-Lyn Industries, *(Ro-Lyn Ind; 0-9615141),* P.O. Box 162931, Sacramento, CA 95816-2931 (SAN 694-2598).

Ro-Mar Publishing Co., *(Ro-Mar; 0-9609566),* 11325 Valley Oak Dr., Oakdale, CA 95361 (SAN 275-102X).

Road-Runner Pr., *(Road Runner Pr; 0-9615668),* 2294 Baskerville Ave., Bishop, CA 93514 (SAN 696-0871) Tel 619-872-1706.

Road Street Press, The, *(Road St Pr; 0-9609536),* P.O. Box 9605, Washington, DC 20016 (SAN 275-1062); Dist. by: Mary Mitchell, 2810 R St. NW, Washington, DC 20007 (SAN 200-4100) Tel 202-333-2401.

Roadrunner Pubns., Inc., *(Roadrunner Pubns; 0-914635),* P.O. Box 13548, Austin, TX 78711 (SAN 289-5749) Tel 512-454-5391. Out of Business.

Roadrunner-Technical Pubns., Inc., Div. of Desert Laboratories, Inc., *(Roadrunner Tech; 0-89741),* 3136 E. Columbia St., Tucson, AZ 85714 (SAN 204-2169) Tel 602-294-3431.

Roan Horse Pr., *(Roan Horse; 0-933234),* 2509 N. Campbell Ave., Suite 277, Tucson, AZ 85719 (SAN 215-9120).

Robbie's Creations, Inc., *(Robbies Creations; 0-9616639),* P.O. Box 7997, Berkeley, CA 94707 (SAN 659-6878); 935 Filmore St., Albany, CA 94706 (SAN 659-6886) Tel 415-524-1607.

Robert Crown Center, The, *(R Crown Ctr; 0-9613700),* 21 Salt Creek Lane, Hinsdale, IL 60521 (SAN 677-4237) Tel 312-325-1773.

Roberta Pr., *(Roberta Pr; 0-9615742),* 6311 Sanford St., Houston, TX 77096 (SAN 696-0987) Tel 713-771-6053.

Roberts, A., *(A Roberts),* 714 Andover Ln., Albany, GA 31705 (SAN 239-4839).

Roberts, F. M., Enterprises, *(F M Roberts; 0-912746),* P.O. Box 608, Dana Point, CA 92629-0608 (SAN 201-4688) Tel 714-493-1977.

Roberts, Ken, Publishing Co., *(K Roberts; 0-913602),* P.O. Box 151, Fitzwilliam, NH 03447 (SAN 203-0888) Tel 603-585-6612.

Roberts, Mervin F., *(Roberts M; 0-9615047),* 1 Duck River Ln., Old Lyme, CT 06371 (SAN 693-8590) Tel 203-434-5178.

Roberts, Richard Owen, Publishers, *(R O Roberts),* 5N740 Dunham Rd., Wayne, IL 60184 (SAN 239-4847) Tel 312-584-8069.

Roberts, Sam, & Assocs., *(S Roberts & Assocs; 0-9615473),* 12243 Shorewood Dr., SW, Seattle, WA 98146 (SAN 696-2211) Tel 206-243-1234.

Roberts Enterprises, *(Roberts Ent; 0-9604184),* 7350 N. Montero Dr., No. 1406, Tucson, AZ 85741 (SAN 214-4603) Tel 602-247-7467.

Roberts Publishing, *(Roberts CA; 0-9616192),* 5048 J Pkwy., Sacramento, CA 95823 (SAN 699-9263) Tel 916-421-8332.

Roberts Publishing Corp., *(Roberts Pub; 0-936492),* 45 John St., New York, NY 10038 (SAN 203-0772) Tel 212-233-3768.

Robertson, Donald W., *(Robertson),* 3811 Marquette Pl., No. 2 G, San Diego, CA 92106 (SAN 211-0911) Tel 619-225-8060.

Robertson, James E., *(J E Robertson; 0-9600756),* 5213 Don Pio Dr., Woodland Hills, CA 91364 (SAN 202-7267) Tel 818-884-9008.

Robertson Pr., *(Robertson Pr; 0-9614317),* 27 Wexford Rd., Delmar, NY 12054 (SAN 687-5262) Tel 518-439-3681.

Robin, Eddie, Publishing, *(E Robin Pub; 0-936362),* P.O. Box 70688, Las Vegas, NV 89170-0688 (SAN 214-4611) Tel 702-798-5029.

Robin & Russ Handweavers, *(Robin & Russ; 0-936563),* 533 N. Adams St., McMinnville, OR 97128 (SAN 207-284X) Tel 503-472-5760.

Robinson, Alma, *(A Robinson),* 196 Dover Rd., Warrenton, VA 22186 (SAN 211-6308).

Robinson, Nelson B., Bookseller, *(Nelson B Robinson; 0-930352),* 51 Main St., Rockport, MA 01966 (SAN 209-004X) Tel 617-546-7323.

Robinson, Peggy, *(P Robinson),* 1326 Fell St., San Francisco, CA 94117 (SAN 215-2223) Tel 415-387-9339; Dist. by: Far West Book Service, 3515 NE Hassalo, Portland, OR 97232 (SAN 282-6429) Tel 503-234-7664.

Robinson, Ruth E., Bks., *(Robinson Bks; 0-9603556),* Rte. 7, Box 162A, Morgantown, WV 26505 (SAN 213-4322) Tel 304-594-3140.

Robinson, Sue, *(Sue Robinson; 0-9617332),* P.O. Box 31186, Phoenix, AZ 85046 (SAN 663-1886); 12601 N. 34th Pl., Phoenix, AZ 85032 Tel 602-992-6613.

Robinson & Assocs., *(Robinson Assocs; 0-9615804),* 746 N. Eucalyptus 18, Inglewood, CA 90302 (SAN 696-253X); P.O. Box 4245, Inglewood, CA 90302 (SAN 699-6299).

Robinson & Robinson, Ltd., *(Robinson & Robinson; 0-932587),* 5829 Wynkoop Rd., Lockport, NY 14094 (SAN 687-5009) Tel 716-434-7338.

Robinson Newspapers, *(Robinson News),* 207 SW 150th St., Burien, WA 98166 (SAN 263-2268) Tel 206-242-0100.

Robinson Press, Inc., *(Robinson Pr; 0-913730),* 1137 Riverside Dr., Fort Collins, CO 80524 (SAN 205-2369) Tel 303-482-5393.

Robinson Publishing Co. Inc., *(Robinson Pub),* P.O. Box 48119, Seattle, WA 98148 (SAN 283-4316).

Robinson Typographics, *(Robinson Typos; 0-918837),* 1614 S. Clementine St., Anaheim, CA 92802 (SAN 679-1271) Tel 714-533-2610.

Roblin Enterprises Inc., *(Roblin Enterprises; 0-934968),* 23 Rosedale Rd., Yonkers, NY 10710 (SAN 264-3561) Tel 914-337-4576.

Robot Institute of America *See Robotic Industries Assn.*

Robotic Industries Assn., *(Robot Inst Am; 0-933747),* P.O. Box 3724, Ann Arbor, MI 48106 (SAN 275-1119) Tel 313-994-6088.

Robotics Age Inc., *(Robotics Age; 0-916863),* 174 Concord St., Peterborough, NH 03458 (SAN 296-1709) Tel 603-924-7136.

†Robotics Pr., *(Robotics Pr; 0-89661),* 8285 SW Nimbus, Suite 151, Beaverton, OR 97005 (SAN 282-2563) Tel 503-646-2713; Toll free: 800-457-1842; Orders to: P.O. Box 606, Beaverton, OR 97075 (SAN 282-2571); *CIP.*

Roca Publishing, Inc., *(Roca Pub; 0-88025),* P.O. Box 176, Saint Davids, PA 19087 (SAN 217-4243) Tel 215-337-0576.

Rochester Folk Art Guild, *(Rochester Folk Art),* Rte. 1, Box 10, Middlesex, NY 14507 (SAN 210-9492) Tel 716-554-3539.

Rochester Philharmonic League, *(Rochester Philharmonic; 0-9612176),* 108 E. Ave., Rochester, NY 14604 (SAN 289-4912) Tel 716-454-2620.

Rocin Pr., Div. of Rocin Laboratories, Inc., *(Rocin; 0-9608304),* 8 E. 62 St., New York, NY 10021 (SAN 240-9550) Tel 212-355-0109.

Rock Foundation, *(Rock Found; 0-937691),* 222 Central Pk. S., New York, NY 10019 (SAN 659-1248) Tel 212-757-9110.

Rock Harbor Press, *(Rock Harbor; 0-932260),* P.O. Box 1206, Hyannis, MA 02601 (SAN 214-199X).

Rock Tech Pubns., *(Rock Tech Pubns; 0-914283),* 171 W. Putnam Ferry Rd., Woodstock, GA 30188 (SAN 287-5357) Tel 404-926-1311.

Rockabilia Pr., *(Rockabilia Pr; 0-9616805),* 107 N. Arbor, Savannah, MO 64485 (SAN 661-0277) Tel 816-232-1567.

Rockcom Publishing, *(Rockcom Pub; 0-933246),* 225 South Blvd., Nyack, NY 10960 (SAN 211-7223) Tel 914-358-3631.

†Rockdale Ridge Pr., *(Rockdale Ridge; 0-9602338),* 8501 Ridge Rd., Cincinnati, OH 45236 (SAN 212-4459) Tel 513-891-9900; *CIP.*

†Rockefeller Univ. Pr., *(Rockefeller; 0-87470),* 1230 York Ave., New York, NY 10021 (SAN 203-3747) Tel 212-570-8571; Box 291, New York, NY 10021 (SAN 658-1536) Tel 212-570-8572; Orders to: Rockefeller Press, P.O. Box 5483, Church St., Sta., New York, NY 10249 (SAN 662-1295); *CIP.*

Rocket Publishing Co., *(Rocket Pub Co),* P.O. Box 412, Normangee, TX 77871 (SAN 204-5699) Tel 713-828-4265.

Rockfall Press, *(Rockfall Pr; 0-9601502),* Cider Mill Rd., Rockfall, CT 06481 (SAN 212-1638).

Rockin Enterprises, Inc., *(Rockin Enter; 0-9616081),* 1503 W. Greenleaf Ave., Chicago, IL 60626 (SAN 698-0759) Tel 312-761-4893.

Rocking Chair Press, Inc., *(Rocking Chair Pr; 0-913562),* 2109 Queenswood Dr., Tallahassee, FL 32303 (SAN 204-6938) Tel 904-562-1207.

Rocking Horse Pr., *(Rocking Horse; 0-932306),* 32 Ellise Rd., Storrs, CT 06268 (SAN 212-4467) Tel 203-429-1474.

Rockport Art Assn., Inc., *(Rockport Art Assn; 0-9616560),* P.O. Box 987, Rockport, TX 78382 (SAN 659-5820) Tel 512-729-5519.

†Rockport Pubns., *(Rockport Pubns; 0-936220),* P.O. Box 2787, Newport Beach, CA 92663 (SAN 214-462X) Tel 714-646-9481; *CIP.*

Rockport Pubs., *(Rockport Pubs; 0-935603),* 5 Smith St., Rockport, MA 09166 (SAN 696-236X) Tel 617-546-9590; P.O. Box 396, Rockport, MA 01966 (SAN 696-9631); Dist. by: Robert Silver Assocs., 307 E. 37th St., New York, NY 10016 (SAN 241-5801) Tel 212-686-5630.

Rockway Hse. Publishing Co., Inc., *(Rockway Hse; 0-932285),* 130 W. Main St., P.O. Box 1, Little Chute, WI 54301 (SAN 686-6131) Tel 414-788-4310.

Rockwell, Norman, Museum at Stockbridge, *(Rockwell Museum; 0-9615273),* P.O. Box 308, Stockbridge, MA 01262 (SAN 695-2712) Tel 413-298-3869.

Rocky Mountain Books, *(Rocky Mtn Bks; 0-9605648),* P.O. Box 10663, Denver, CO 80210 (SAN 215-7047).

Rocky Mountain Books, Inc., *(Rocky Mount CO; 0-914459),* 928 13th St. Suite Two, Greeley, CO 80631 (SAN 289-6729) Tel 303-353-9481.

Rocky Mountain Nature Assn., *(Rocky Mtn Nature Assn; 0-930487),* Rocky Mountain National Park, Estes Park, CO 80517 (SAN 670-9036) Tel 303-586-2371.

Rocky Mountain Research Center, *(Rocky Mtn Res; 0-915207),* P.O. Box 4694, Missoula, MT 59806 (SAN 289-8276) Tel 406-549-6330.

Rocky Mountain Writers Guild Pubns., *(Rocky Mtn Writer; 0-915091),* 837 15th St., Boulder, CO 80302 (SAN 240-9658) Tel 303-444-4100.

Rocky Point Pr., *(Rocky Point Pr; 0-930093),* P.O. Box 4814, North Hollywood, CA 91607 (SAN 670-1736) Tel 818-761-3386.

Rocky Top Pubns., *(Rocky Top Pubns; 0-937317),* P.O. Box 33, Stamford, NY 12167 (SAN 658-7763) Tel 607-652-2567.

RoCoCo, *(RoCoCo; 0-938275),* 204 Main St., Ellsworth, ME 04605 (SAN 659-8242) Tel 207-667-9353.

Rod & Staff Pubs., Inc., *(Rod & Staff),* Hwy. 172, Crockett, KY 41413 (SAN 206-7633) Tel 606-522-4348.

Rodale Institute, *(Rodale Inst; 0-935641),* 222 Main St., Emmaus, PA 18049 (SAN 695-9466) Tel 215-967-5171.

†Rodale Pr., Inc., *(Rodale Pr Inc; 0-87857),* 33 E. Minor St., Emmaus, PA 18049 (SAN 200-2477) Tel 215-967-5171; Toll free: 800-527-8200; *CIP.*

Rodeo Studio, *(Rodeo Studio; 0-9614570),* P.O. Box 1016, Pine Bluffs, WY 82082 (SAN 691-8271) Tel 307-245-3884.

Rodney Pubns., Inc., *(Rodney; 0-913830),* 349 E. 49th St., New York, NY 10017 (SAN 204-6954) Tel 212-421-5444.

RoDonn Publishing Co., *(RoDonn Pub; 0-932058),* P.O. Box 6976, Colorado Springs, CO 80904 (SAN 692-1116) Tel 303-632-4832.

Roehrs Co., *(Roehrs; 0-911266),* P.O. Box 125, 136 Park Ave., East Rutherford, NJ 07073 (SAN 204-6962); 24 High St., East Rutherford, NJ 07073 (SAN 662-1309) Tel 201-933-0090.

Roerick Music Co., *(Roerick Music; 0-9612684),* 4046 Davana Rd., Sherman Oaks, CA 91423 (SAN 239-8621) Tel 818-783-2496.

Rogers, Gay Ann, *(G A Rogers),* Box 181, Claremont, CA 91711 (SAN 287-301X).

Rogers, Helga M., *(H M Rogers; 0-9602294),* 4975 59th Ave., S., St. Petersburg, FL 33715 (SAN 207-0316) Tel 813-864-3292.

Rogers, Millicent, Museum, *(M Rogers Mus; 0-9609818),* P.O. Box A, Taos, NM 87571 (SAN 264-3588) Tel 505-758-2462.

Rogers Historical Museum, *(Rogers Hist Mus; 0-9616640),* 322 S. Second St., Rogers, AR 72756 (SAN 659-6894) Tel 501-636-0162.

Rogers Hse. Museum Gallery, *(Rogers Hse Mus; 0-9600686),* 102 E. Main So., Ellsworth, KS 67439 (SAN 204-6989) Tel 913-472-3255.

Rogue Wave Publishing Co., *(Rogue Wave Pub; 0-938005),* P.O. Box 7921, Berkeley, CA 94707 (SAN 659-7629) Tel 415-763-1264; 1732 Sixth Ave., No. 12, Oakland, CA 94606 (SAN 659-7637).

Rohn, Jim, Productions, Inc., *(Jim Rohn Prod; 0-939490),* 22951 Mill Creek Dr. Dr., No. 100, Laguna Hills, CA 92653 (SAN 216-5945) Tel 714-951-5740.

Rohrich Corporation, *(Rohrich Corp; 0-9611500),* 903 Tallmadge Ave., Akron, OH 44310-3592 (SAN 226-8965).

Role Training Associates of California, *(Role Train Assocs),* 6304 Marina Pacifica Dr. S., Long Beach, CA 90803 (SAN 208-0931) Tel 213-493-3400.

Rolf's Gallery, *(Rolfs Gall; 0-910579),* P.O. Box 9, Montevideo, MN 56265 (SAN 260-2571) Tel 612-269-8409.

Rolling Block Press, *(Rolling Block; 0-940028),* P.O. Box 5357, Buena Park, CA 90622 (SAN 217-0817).

Rolling Hills Pr., *(Rolling Hills Pr; 0-943978),* 40 Pilgrim Park, San Rafael, CA 94903 (SAN 282-2601) Tel 415-499-8135.

Rolling Hse. Pubns., *(Rolling Hse; 0-934169),* 174 Santa Clara Ave., Oakland, CA 94610 (SAN 693-3629) Tel 415-654-5920; Orders to: Rolling House Pubns., P.O. Box 3865, Berkeley, CA 94703 (SAN 662-3190); Orders to: Shirley Fontoura, 1625 Woolsey St., Suite 7, Berkeley, CA 94703 (SAN 662-3204) Tel 415-548-4228.

Rolling Meadows Library, *(Rolling Meadows; 0-9602782),* 3110 Martin Lane, Rolling Meadows, IL 60008 (SAN 213-7895) Tel 312-259-6050.

Rollins College, George D. & Harriet W. Cornell Fine Arts Ctr., *(Rollins Coll; 0-9615828),* 601 Holt Ave., Winter Park, FL 32789-4496 (SAN 280-3054) Tel 305-646-2526.

Romaine Pierson Pubns., Inc., *(Pierson Pubs; 0-935466),* 80 Shore Rd., Port Washington, NY 11050 (SAN 213-3660) Tel 516-883-6350.

Roman Catholic Archbishop of Boston, *(Roman Catholic Arch; 0-9614384),* 2121 Commonwealth Ave., Brighton, MA 02135 (SAN 688-6078) Tel 617-254-0100.

Roman Enterprises, *(Roman Enter; 0-9606642),* 16548 Linch Path, Lakeville, MN 55044 (SAN 217-426X) Tel 612-435-5024.

Roman, Inc., *(Roman Inc; 0-937739),* 4850 N. Harlem, Harwood Heights, IL 60656-3581 (SAN 659-2899) Tel 312-867-6660.

†Romance Monographs, Inc., *(Romance),* P.O. Box 7553, University, MS 38677 (SAN 209-4878) Tel 601-234-0001; *CIP.*

Romanian Historical Studies, *(Romanian Hist; 0-937019),* 1029 Euclid Ave., Miami Beach, FL 33139 (SAN 658-4942) Tel 305-534-0120.

Romantic Tidings Bks., *(Romantic Tidings; 0-935235),* Rte. 2, Box 142, Watson, IL 62473 (SAN 695-7129) Tel 217-536-6848.

Romantic Times, Inc., *(Romantic Times; 0-9604338),* 163 Joralemon St., Brooklyn Heights, NY 11201 (SAN 218-5032).

Romney Press, *(Romney Pr; 0-9604640),* 308 Fourth Ave., Iowa City, IA 52240 (SAN 215-7055); Dist. by: Eble Music Co., P.O. Box 2570, Iowa City, IA 52244 (SAN 282-6275).

Ronald, George, Pub., Ltd., *(G Ronald Pub; 0-85398),* P.O. Box 447, St. Louis, MO 63166 (SAN 679-1859).

Roncorp, Inc., *(Roncorp; 0-939103),* P.O. Box 724, Cherry Hill, NJ 08003 (SAN 662-5991); 506 Morris Dr., Cherry Hill, NJ 08003 (SAN 662-6009) Tel 609-428-3492.

Rondy Pubns., *(Rondy Pubns; 0-9616638),* 6704 Cheyenne Trail, Edina, MN 55435 (SAN 659-6800) Tel 612-941-2292.

Names

Ronin Publishing, Inc., Affil. of And/Or Press, Inc., *(Ronin Pub; 0-914171),* P.O. Box 1035, Main P.O., Berkeley, CA 94701 (SAN 287-5365) Tel 415-540-6278; Dist. by: Baker & Taylor Co., Midwest Div., 501 Gladiola Ave., Momence, IL 60954 (SAN 169-2100); Dist. by: Baker & Taylor Co., Southeast Div., Mt. Olive Rd., Commerce, GA 30529 (SAN 169-1503); Dist. by: Baker & Taylor Co., Eastern Div., 50 Kirby Ave., Somerville, NJ 08876 (SAN 169-4901); Dist. by: Baker & Taylor Co., Western Div., 380 Edison Way, Reno, NV 89564 (SAN 169-4464) Tel 702-786-6700; Dist. by: Ingram Book Company, 347 Reedwood Dr., Nashville, TN 37217 (SAN 651-1163); Dist. by: Publishers Group West, 5855 Beaudry St., Emeryville, CA 94608 (SAN 202-8522) Tel 415-658-3453; Dist. by: Pacific Pipeline, Inc., 19215 66th Ave., S., Kent, WA 98032 (SAN 208-2128) Tel 206-872-5523.

Room to Write, *(Room to Write; 0-938449),* 7851 Lori Dr., Huntington Beach, CA 92648 (SAN 660-9902) Tel 714-841-5315.

Rooney Pubns., *(Rooney Pubns; 0-9604600),* P.O. Box 44146, Panorama City, CA 91412 (SAN 215-1790) Tel 213-894-2585.

Roosevelt Univ., *(Roosevelt U),* 430 S. Michigan Ave., Chicago, IL 60605 (SAN 210-3265) Tel 312-341-3808.

Root, A. I., Co., *(A I Root; 0-936028),* Box 706, Medina, OH 44258 (SAN 205-230X) Tel 216-725-6677.

Roots International, *(Roots Intl; 0-932019),* 3239 N. 58th St., Milwaukee, WI 53216 (SAN 686-0869) Tel 414-871-7421.

Roper Center/International Survey Library Association, *(Roper Ctr User),* University of Connecticut, Box U-164, Storrs, CT 06268 (SAN 287-2617) Tel 203-486-4440; P.O. Box 440, Storrs, CT 06268-0440 (SAN 680-103X).

Rorge Publishing Co., *(Rorge Pub Co; 0-914920),* 824 Laramie Ave., Alliance, NE 69301 (SAN 202-9715).

Rosallen Pubns, *(Rosallen Pubns; 0-9607486),* P.O. Box 927, North Hollywood, CA 91603 (SAN 239-605X) Tel 818-766-6045.

Rosario Productions, *(Rosario Prod; 0-9614970),* P.O. Box 563, Eastsound, WA 98245 (SAN 693-4234) Tel 206-376-4787.

Roscoe Pound-American Trial Lawyers Assn., Subs. of Association of Trial Lawyers of America, *(R Pound-Am Trial Lawyers; 0-933067),* 1050 31st. St., NW, Washington, DC 20007 (SAN 689-7894) Tel 202-965-3500; Toll free: 800-424-2725.

Rose, Gena, Pr., *(G Rose Pr; 0-9604178),* 2424 Franklin, Denver, CO 80205 (SAN 215-0751).

Rose Deeprose Press, *(Rose Deeprose; 0-937738),* 1661 Oak St., San Francisco, CA 94117 (SAN 215-3408) Tel 415-552-0991; Dist. by Subterranean Co., P.O. Box 10233, 1327 W. 2nd, Eugene, OR 97440 (SAN 169-7102) Tel 503-343-6324.

Rose Hill Press, *(Rose Hill; 0-917264),* 12368 Old Pen Mar Rd., Waynesboro, PA 17268 (SAN 208-8312) Tel 717-762-7072.

Rose of Sharon Press, Inc., *(Rose Sharon Pr; 0-932502),* G.P.O. Box 2432, New York, NY 10116 (SAN 212-3207) Tel 914-736-2521.

Rose Petal Creations of California, *(Rose Petal Creat CA; 0-9613996),* 2033 Norris Dr. W., Fresno, CA 93703 (SAN 682-4811) Tel 209-266-1671.

Rose Press, *(Rose Pr),* 1442A Walnut, No. 373, Berkeley, CA 94709 (SAN 240-8767).

Rose Pr., *(Rose Pr NJ; 0-9616603),* 39 Hamilton Ave., Hasbrouck Heights, NJ 07604 (SAN 659-7661) Tel 201-288-5184.

Rose Pr., *(Rose Pr OR; 0-9615248),* 6531 SE Ivon St., Portland, OR 97206 (SAN 695-1627) Tel 503-777-1337; Dist. by: Pacific Pipeline, Inc., 19215 66th Ave. S., Kent, WA 98032 (SAN 208-2128) Tel 206-872-5523; Toll free: 800-426-4727; Dist. by: Far West Bk. Serv., 3515 NE Hassal, Portland, OR 97232 (SAN 107-6760) Tel 503-234-7664.

Rose Pubns., *(Rose Pubns),* 3828 Ben Lomond Ct., Toledo, OH 43607 (SAN 209-5963).

Rose Publications, *(Rose Pubns AZ; 0-914817),* P.O. Box 35033, Tucson, AZ 85740 (SAN 289-3975) Tel 602-297-3606.

Rose Publishing Co., *(Rose Pub Co CA; 0-9603356),* 124 Anderson St., San Francisco, CA 94110 (SAN 207-3188) Tel 415-285-7403; Dist. by: Bookpeople, 2929 Fifth St., Berkeley, CA 94710 (SAN 168-9517).

†Rose Publishing Co., *(Rose Pub MI; 0-937320),* 4676 Morningside Dr., SE, Grand Rapids, MI 49508 (SAN 211-8378) Tel 616-698-8282; *CIP.*

Rose Publishing Co., Inc., *(Rose Pub; 0-914546),* 301 Louisiana, Little Rock, AR 72201 (SAN 203-3739) Tel 501-372-1666.

Rose Star Creations, *(Rose Star; 0-936719),* 177 Webster St., Monterey, CA 93946 (SAN 699-8453) Tel 408-646-1288; Box 361, Monterey, CA 93946 (SAN 699-8461).

Rose-Strandtmann Joint Venture, *(Rose Strandtmann; 0-9617102),* 3403 Canyon Rd., Lubbock, TX 79403 (SAN 662-5061) Tel 806-742-2726.

Rosecott Publishing, *(Rosecott Pub; 0-9615940),* 3140 Ave. A, Suite 19, Riviera Beach, FL 33404 (SAN 696-690X) Tel 305-842-7170; Orders to: P.O. Box 9876, Riviera Beach, FL 33404 (SAN 662-3824) Tel 305-842-7170.

Rosegarden Press, *(Rosegarden Pr; 0-9610340),* Box 49084, Austin, TX 78765 (SAN 264-3596) Tel 512-453-7919.

Rosejoy Pubns., *(Rosejoy Pubns; 0-933453),* P.O. Box 668, Kalamazoo, MI 49005-0668 (SAN 691-828X) Tel 616-344-4016; Orders to: Spring Arbor Distributors, 10885 Textile Rd., Belleville, MI 48111-2398 (SAN 263-5222) Tel 313-483-8462.

Rosemary House Press, *(Rosemary Hse; 0-9613275),* Durrell's Bridge Rd., Kennebunk, ME 04043 (SAN 656-0393) Tel 207-985-4878; Orders to: G. Robert Butler, 109 Main St., Saco, ME 04072 (SAN 662-2321) Tel 207-284-6781.

Rosen, Pauline, *(P Rosen; 0-9600214),* 658 Main St., Placerville, CA 95667 (SAN 206-8303).

Rosen Pub. Group, *(Rosen Group; 0-8239),* 29 E. 21st St., New York, NY 10010 (SAN 203-3720) Tel 212-777-3017.
Imprints: Pelion Press (Pelion Pr).

Rosenbach Museum & Library, The, *(Rosenbach Mus & Lib; 0-939084),* 2010 De Lancey Pl., Philadelphia, PA 19103 (SAN 211-9749) Tel 215-732-1600.

Rosenbaum, Arthur, *(Rosenbaum; 0-9615408),* 17 E. Thompson Ave., Springfield, PA 19064 (SAN 695-5134) Tel 215-544-3206.

Rosenberg, Marilyn R., *(M Rosenberg; 0-913615),* 101 Lakeview Ave. W., Peekskill, NY 10566 (SAN 285-3728) Tel 914-737-2052.

Rosenberg, Mary S., Inc., *(M S Rosenberg; 0-917324),* 17 W. 60th St., New York, NY 10023 (SAN 205-2296) Tel 212-362-4873.

Rosenberg, Vivian Graff, *(V G Rosenberg),* R.D. 2 Box 274, Walkers Mill Rd., Germantown, NY 12526 (SAN 212-1360) Tel 518-537-6159.

Rosenblatt, Emil, *(E Rosenblatt; 0-9610060),* 64 Sunset Dr., Croton-on-Hudson, NY 10520 (SAN 275-1267) Tel 914-271-3211.

†Rosenthal, Bernard M., Inc., Booksellers, *(B M Rosenthal Inc; 0-9600094),* 251 Post St., San Francisco, CA 94108 (SAN 209-0465) Tel 415-982-2219; *CIP.*

Rosenthal, Daniel, & Assocs., Inc., *(Rosenthal Assocs; 0-9615814),* 251 Lafayette Cir., Suite 310, Lafayette, CA 94549 (SAN 696-5814) Tel 415-283-7051; Orders to: Daniel Rosenthal & Assocs., 268 Greenwood Ave., Bethel, CT 06801 (SAN 662-376X) Tel 203-748-2036.

Roserich Designs, Ltd., *(Roserich Ltd; 0-913289),* P.O. Box 1030, Carpinteria, CA 93013 (SAN 285-8401) Tel 805-684-6977.

Rosey-Royce Publishing Co., *(Rosey-Royce; 0-934138),* 436 W. Ostrander Ave., Syracuse, NY 13205 (SAN 217-2666).

Rosholt Hse., *(Rosholt Hse; 0-910417),* Box 104, Rosholt, WI 54473 (SAN 260-1249) Tel 715-677-4722.

Rosicrucian Order See AMORC

Ross, Betsy, Pubns., *(Betsy Ross Pubns; 0-943232),* 3057 Betsy Ross Dr., Bloomfield Hills, MI 48013 (SAN 240-7612) Tel 313-646-5357.

Ross, Sidney Scott, *(Sidney Scott Ross; 0-9602028),* 1020 Meridian Ave., Suite 405, Miami Beach, FL 33139 (SAN 212-1379) Tel 305-538-1442.

Ross & Haines Old Books Co., *(Ross; 0-87018),* 167 N. Snelling Ave., St. Paul, MN 55104 (SAN 204-7004) Tel 612-647-1471.

Ross/Back Rds. Pr., *(Ross-Back Roads; 0-931272),* P.O. Box 4340, Berkeley, CA 94704 (SAN 211-2000).

†Ross Bks., *(Ross Bks; 0-89496),* P.O. Box 4340, Berkeley, CA 94704 (SAN 209-5912) Tel 415-841-2474; *CIP.*

Ross Enterprises, *(Ross Ent; 0-9613186),* P.O. Box 491308, Los Angeles, CA 90049 (SAN 295-9089) Tel 213-826-7512.

Ross-Erikson, Inc., *(Ross-Erikson; 0-915520),* 223 Via Sevilla, Santa Barbara, CA 93105 (SAN 208-0494) Tel 805-965-5367.

Ross-Hargreaves, Div. of L & M Equipment Co., Inc., *(Ross-Hargreaves; 0-910690),* P.O. Box 11897, Lahaina, HI 96761 (SAN 204-0247) Tel 808-667-9097.

Ross Publishing Co., *(Ross Pub Co; 0-9615202),* Rte. 3, 188A-1 Forrester Rd., Slippery Rock, PA 16057 (SAN 694-2903) Tel 412-794-2837.

Ross Street Pr., *(Ross St; 0-9615463),* 1310 Ross St., Plymouth, MI 48170 (SAN 695-7137) Tel 313-453-2394.

Ross Valley Book Co., Inc., The, *(Ross Valley; 0-937106),* 1407 Solano Ave., Albany, CA 94706 (SAN 216-4868) Tel 415-526-6400.

Rossel Bks., Div. of Seymour Rossel Co., Inc., *(Rossel Bks; 0-940646),* 15512 Golden Creek, Dallas, TX 75248 (SAN 213-6414) Tel 214-458-1004.

Rossi Pubns., *(Rossi Pubns; 0-935618),* P.O. Box 2001, Beverly Hills, CA 90213 (SAN 213-6414) Tel 213-556-0337.

Rostrum Books, *(Rostrum Bks),* P.O. Box 1191, Miami, FL 33101 (SAN 205-227X) Tel 305-573-5900.

Roswell Historical Society, Inc., *(Roswell Hist; 0-9615854),* 227 S. Atlanta St., Roswell, GA 30075 (SAN 696-7566) Tel 404-922-1665.

Roswell Museum & Art Ctr., *(Roswell Mus; 0-914983),* 100 W.11th St., Roswell, NM 88201 (SAN 280-3143) Tel 505-622-4700.

Roswell Symphony Guild Pubns., *(Roswell Symphony Guild; 0-9612466),* P.O. Box 3078, Roswell, NM 88201 (SAN 291-8501).

Rosycross Pr., Div. of The Spiritual School of the Golden Rosycross--The Lectorium Rosicrucianum, *(Rosycross Pr; 0-9070196),* 709 A St., C-21, Bakersfield, CA 93304-1917 (SAN 659-2104) Tel 805-328-0707; Orders to: P.O. Box 9246, Bakersfield, CA 93389-9246 (SAN 662-4235) Tel 805-327-2827.

Rosywick Press, *(Rosywick Pr; 0-9608712),* 175 W. 12th St., New York, NY 10011 (SAN 238-356X).

Rotary Club of Marquette, Michigan, *(Rotary Club; 0-9609764),* c/o Marquette Area Chamber of Commerce, 501 S. Front Street, Marquette, MI 49855 (SAN 264-3618); Dist. by: Marquette County Historical Society, 213 N. Front St., Marquette, MI 49855 (SAN 205-8871) Tel 906-226-3571.

Rotary International, *(Rotary Intl; 0-915062),* 1600 Ridge Ave., Evanston, IL 60201 (SAN 207-9585) Tel 312-328-0100.

Roth, Lora, *(L Roth; 0-9616242),* 5965 Crestwood, West Bloomfield, MI 48033 (SAN 658-4969) Tel 313-661-4966.

Roth Publishing, *(Roth Pub; 0-87957),* 125 Mineola Ave., Roslyn Hts., NY 11577 (SAN 203-0810) Tel 516-621-7242.

Roth Publishing, Inc., *(Roth Pub Inc; 0-89609; 0-8486),* 11 Middle Neck Rd., Great Neck, NY 11021 (SAN 210-9735) Tel 516-466-3676; Toll free: 800-327-0295 (For orders). Acquired Granger Bks., and Core Collection.

Rothbart, Janet, *(Rothbart; 0-9612952),* 2605 S. Seventh St., Minneapolis, MN 55407 (SAN 291-4077) Tel 612-370-0516; P.O. Box 9722, Minneapolis, MN 55440 (SAN 695-6300).

Rothenberg, Edward, *(E Rothenberg; 0-9613865),* 2718 Hampshire, Cincinnati, OH 45208 (SAN 682-8124) Tel 513-321-1150.

Rothman, Fred B., & Co., *(Rothman; 0-8377),* 10368 W. Centennial Rd., Littleton, CO 80127 (SAN 159-9437) Tel 303-979-5657; Toll free: 800-457-1986. Acquired Rothman Reprints.

Rotunda Bks., *(Rotunda Bks; 0-9613164),* P.O. Box 1475, Cambridge, MA 02238 (SAN 294-9784) Tel 617-354-2932.

Rotz, Anna Overcash, *(Rotz; 0-9605108),* Box 266, 12182 Main St., Fort Loudon, PA 17224 (SAN 215-9139).

Rough Notes Co., Inc., The, *(Rough Notes; 0-942326),* 1200 N. Meridial St., P.O. Box 564, Indianapolis, IN 46206 (SAN 203-5588) Tel 317-634-1541.

Rough Rock Demonstration School Board, Inc., *(Rough Rock Demonst),* Star Rte. 1, Rough Rock, AZ 86503 (SAN 686-1644).

Round Oak Co., *(Round Oak; 0-9616910),* P.O. Box 54, Wayne, MI 48184 (SAN 661-5236) Tel 313-595-1126.

Round River Publishing Co., *(Round River Pub; 0-933437),* P.O. Box 3324, Madison, WI 53704 (SAN 691-5116) Tel 608-241-4289.

Roundtable Pr., *(Roundtable Pr; 0-934512),* 4 Linden Sq., Wellesley, MA 02181-4709 (SAN 282-2628) Tel 617-235-5320. Do not confuse with Roundtable Pub., Santa Monica, CA.

Roundtable Publishing, *(Roundtable Pub; 0-9605662; 0-915677),* 933 W. Pico Blvd., Santa Monica, CA 90405 (SAN 237-9260) Tel 213-450-9777. Do not confuse with Roundtable Pr., Wellesley, MA.

Rountree Publishing, *(Rountree Pub NC; 0-934073),* P.O. Box 87, Stokes, NC 27884 (SAN 693-7780) Tel 919-746-2524.

Roush, John H., Jr., *(J H Roush; 0-9600830),* 27 Terrace Ave., Kentfield, CA 94904 (SAN 207-1827) Tel 415-453-7130.

Roush Bks., *(Roush Bks; 0-934044),* P.O. Box 4203, Valley Village, North Hollywood, CA 91607 (SAN 219-2705).

Rovan Productions Co., *(Rovan Prod Co; 0-9615500),* 14878 Espinosa Ave., Visalia, CA 93291 (SAN 695-9253) Tel 209-798-1028.

Rovern Pr., *(Rovern Pr; 0-943150),* 185 Birch St., Willimantic, CT 06226 (SAN 240-7620) Tel 203-423-6387.

Rovi Pubs., Inc., *(Rovi; 0-911282),* P.O. Box 259, Belvedere, CA 94920 (SAN 204-7020) Tel 415-435-3174.

Roving Pr. Pubns., *(Roving Pr Pub; 0-910449),* Rte. 5, Box 310, Livingston, TX 77351 (SAN 260-1257) Tel 409-327-8873.

Rowan Tree Pr., Ltd., *(Rowan Tree; 0-937672),* 124 Chestnut St., Boston, MA 02108 (SAN 214-4638) Tel 617-523-7627; Dist. by: Bookslinger, 213 E. Fourth St., St. Paul, MN 55101 (SAN 169-4154) Tel 612-221-0429; Dist. by: Small Pr. Distribution, 1814 San Pablo Ave., Berkeley, CA 94702 (SAN 204-5826) Tel 415-549-3336; Dist. by: Bookpeople, 2929 Fifth St., Berkeley, CA 94710 (SAN 168-9517); Toll free: 800-227-1516; Dist. by: Inland Bk. Co., P.O. Box 261, 22 Hemingway Ave., East Haven, CT 06512 (SAN 200-4151) Tel 203-467-4257; Toll free: 800-243-0138.

Rowillan Publishing Co., *(Rowillan Pub; 0-935237),* 890 W. 20th Ave, Box 2824, Oshkosh, WI 54903 (SAN 695-7110) Tel 414-233-4917.

Rowland, C., Pub., *(C Rowland; 0-9601426),* Rte. 2, Box 131-J, Berkeley Springs, WV 25411 (SAN 210-9832) Tel 304-258-1835. Out of business.

Rowland, Ralph & Star, *(R & S Rowland; 0-9605746),* 4209 San Juan Dr., Fairfax, VA 22030 (SAN 209-4800) Tel 703-273-4891.

Rowman & Allanheld *See* **Rowman & Littlefield, Pubs.**

Rowman & Littlefield, Pubs., Div. of Littlefield, Adams, & Co., *(Rowman; 0-87471; 0-8476),* 81 Adams Dr., Totowa, NJ 07512 (SAN 203-3704) Tel 201-256-8600. *Imprints:* Allanheld & Schram (Allanheld & Schram); Helix Books (Helix Bks); Landmark Studies (Landmark Studies); Rowman & Allanheld (Rowman & Allanheld).

Roxbury Data Interface, *(Roxbury Data; 0-89902),* Box 1100, Verdi, NV 89439 (SAN 212-8659) Tel 702-345-7374.

Roxbury Publishing Co., *(Roxbury Pub Co; 0-935732),* P.O. Box 491044, Los Angeles, CA 90049 (SAN 213-6422) Tel 213-458-3493.

Royal Books *See* **Pyramid Pubns., Inc.**

Royal C. B. S. Publishing, *(Royal CBS; 0-934344),* 18825 Hicrest Rd., P.O. Box 1120, Glendora, CA 91740 (SAN 692-2465).

Royal Court Reports, Pubs., *(Royal Court; 0-941354),* 3720 NE 28 Ter., Ocala, FL 32670 (SAN 219-8177) Tel 904-351-1855.

Royal Hse. Publishing Co., Div. of Recipes-of-the-Month Club, *(Royal Hse; 0-930440),* 9465 Wilshire Blvd., Suite 410, Beverly Hills, CA 90212 (SAN 210-9190) Tel 213-550-7170; Toll free: 800-222-3360; P.O. Box 5027, Beverly Hills, CA 90210 (SAN 215-7071).

Royal Literary Publications, *(Royal Lit; 0-918329),* P.O. Box 6794, Laguna Niguel, CA 92677 (SAN 657-3002) Tel 714-495-5049.

Royal Pr., *(Royal Pr; 0-9616641),* 221 Westminster Rd., Rochester, NY 14607 (SAN 659-6908) Tel 716-473-4816.

Royal Publishing Co., Inc., *(Royal Pub Co),* P.O. Box 2241, Palm Beach, FL 33480 (SAN 226-8299) Tel 305-588-9773.

Royale Pubs., *(Royale Pubs; 0-9601378),* 9119 Blair River Circle, Fountain Valley, CA 92708 (SAN 211-9757) Tel 714-963-4419.

Royale Publishing Co., *(Royale LA; 0-9614929),* 444 Fairway Dr., New Orleans, LA 70124 (SAN 693-3610) Tel 504-486-4414.

Royall Pr., *(Royall Pr; 0-914735),* P.O. Box 9022, San Rafael, CA 94912 (SAN 291-7890) Tel 415-885-1484.

Royalty Publishing Co., *(Royalty Pub; 0-910487),* P.O. Box 2016, Manassas, VA 22110 (SAN 260-1265) Tel 703-368-9878; Dist. by: Spring Arbor Distributors, 10885 Textile Rd., Belleville, MI 48111 (SAN 158-9016) Tel 313-481-0900; Dist. by: Whitaker House, Pittsburgh & Colfax Sts., Springdale, PA 15144 (SAN 203-2104) Tel 412-274-4440; Toll free: 800-245-2422.

R P I Pubns., Inc., *(RPI Pubns; 0-943424),* 521 Fifth Ave., New York, NY 10175 (SAN 240-7566) Tel 212-986-7510.

R2uSK, Inc., *(RtwouSk Inc; 0-9616894),* P.O. Box 2504, University, AL 35486 (SAN 661-5910); 165 N. 22nd St., Tuscaloosa, AL 35406 (SAN 661-5929) Tel 205-348-1526.

Rube, Ned J., Publisher, *(N J Rube; 0-930562),* 68 Marion Dr., New Rochelle, NY 10804 (SAN 211-0385).

Ruben Publishing, *(Ruben Pub; 0-917434),* P.O. Box 414, Avon, CT 06001 (SAN 208-9645) Tel 203-673-0740.

Rubes Pubns., *(Rubes Pubns; 0-943384; 0-941364),* 14447 Titus St., Panorama City, CA 91402 (SAN 240-7647) Tel 818-782-0800; Dist. by: Alfred Publishing Co., Inc., 15335 Morrison St., Sherman Oaks, CA 91413 (SAN 201-243X) Tel 818-995-8811; Toll free: 800-292-6122; 800-821-6083 (In California).

Rubicon, *(Rubicon; 0-938124),* 5 Old Chimney Rd., Huntsville, AL 35801 (SAN 215-658X) Tel 205-534-6844.

Rubicon Bks., *(Rubicon Bks; 0-913791),* P.O. Box 37103, Phoenix, AZ 85069 (SAN 286-1895) Tel 602-978-0546.

Rubio-Boitel, Fr. Fernando, *(Rubio-Boitel),* Our Lady of Belen Church,10th and Church Sts., Belen, NM 87002 (SAN 212-5528) Tel 505-865-4455.

Rucker, Edward W., Enterprises, *(Edw Rucker Ent; 0-9614352),* P.O. Box 25674, Oklahoma City, OK 73125 (SAN 687-8350) Tel 405-478-3299.

Rucker, Ellie, & Carole Rylander, *(Rucker & Rylander; 0-9615692),* 166 E. Riverside, Austin, TX 78704 (SAN 696-0472) Tel 512-445-3695.

Rucker, John, *(J Rucker; 0-9613658),* P.O. Box 9432, Greensboro, NC 27429 (SAN 670-7696) Tel 919-621-9775. Summer address only.

Rucks, Meta A., *(M A Rucks; 0-9613402),* Rte. 3 Box 115, S. Haven, MN 55382 (SAN 670-7203).

Rudolf Dreikurs Institute of Colorado Pubns., *(RDIC Pubns; 0-933450),* P.O. Box 3118, Boulder, CO 80307 (SAN 213-5566) Tel 303-499-4500.

Rudra Pr., *(Rudra Pr; 0-915801),* P.O. Box 1973, Cambridge, MA 02238 (SAN 294-1260) Tel 617-576-3394.

Rue Morgue Pr., *(Rue Morgue; 0-915230),* P.O. Box 4119, Boulder, CO 80306 (SAN 207-737X) Tel 303-443-8346.

†Ruffled Feathers Publishing Co., *(Ruffled Feathers; 0-9603582),* 2725 Juniper St., Boulder, CO 80302-2464 (SAN 213-7917); *CIP.*

Ruffner, Tacey, *(T Ruffner; 0-9610424),* 8626 No. Lower Sacramento Rd. Suite 18-7083, Stockton, CA 95210 (SAN 264-3634) Tel 209-952-1271.

Rufio Enterprises, *(Rufio Ent; 0-9612658),* 7 E. 14th St., New York, NY 10003 (SAN 289-3983) Tel 212-929-7498.

Rugged, B., *(B Rugged; 0-9612018),* 11 S. Adelaide Ave., Highland Park, NJ 08904 (SAN 277-6561) Tel 201-828-6098.

Rugging Room, The, *(Rugging Rm; 0-9611554),* Ten Sawmill Dr., Westford, MA 01886 (SAN 284-9372) Tel 617-692-8600.

Ruggles Publishing Co., *(Ruggles Pub; 0-915909),* 960 Pomelo Ave., Sarasota, FL 33577 (SAN 294-0841) Tel 813-951-0493.

Ruhge, Justin M., *(J M Ruhge; 0-9614807),* P.O. Box 2216, Goleta, CA 93118 (SAN 292-3394) Tel 805-961-5453.

Rules Service Co., *(Rules Serv Co),* 7658 Standish Pl., Suite 106, Rockville, MD 20855 (SAN 227-0455) Tel 301-424-9402.

Rulorca Press, *(Rulorca; 0-917613),* P.O. Box 235, Half Moon Bay, CA 94019-0235 (SAN 657-1603) Tel 415-726-4214.

Rumar Enterprises, *(Rumar Ent; 0-913907),* 18700 Sherman Way No. 203, Reseda, CA 91335 (SAN 286-8717) Tel 818-609-1987.

Rumbleseat Pr., Inc., Affil. of Green Valley World, Inc., *(Rumbleseat; 0-913444),* 41 S. Ocean Blvd., Cayucos, CA 93430 (SAN 205-6437) Tel 805-995-1378.

Runaway Pubns., *(Runaway Pubns; 0-943662),* P.O. Box 1172, Ashland, OR 97520-0040 (SAN 238-3608) Tel 503-482-2578.

Runnels, Tom, Pubns., *(T Runnels Pubns; 0-9603710),* Marble Hill, MO 63764 (SAN 213-8719) Tel 314-238-2824.

Runner's Log, *(Runner's Log; 0-933872),* 10-50 Jackson Ave., Long Island City, NY 11101 (SAN 216-2970).

Running Pr. Bk. Pubs., *(Running Pr; 0-89471),* 125 S. 22nd St., Philadelphia, PA 19103 (SAN 204-5702) Tel 215-567-5080; Toll free: 800-428-1111.

Runyon Publishing Co., Div. of Runyon Institute, *(Runyon Pub; 0-936699),* 15 Alden Ave., Warrensburg, NY 12885 (SAN 699-9301) Tel 518-623-3930.

Rural America, *(Rural America),* 1312 18th St. NW, Washington, DC 20036 (SAN 225-946X) Tel 202-659-2800.

Rural Development Committee, Ctr. for International Studies, *(RDC Ctr Intl Stud; 0-86731),* 170 Uris Hall, Ithaca, NY 14853 (SAN 217-510X) Tel 607-256-6370.

Rural Education Assn., *(Rural Educ),* Colorado State Univ., 300 Education Bldg., Ft. Collins, CO 80523 (SAN 207-3269) Tel 303-491-7022.

Rural Life, *(Rural Life),* Rte. 1, Box 183-C, Whitewater, WI 53190 (SAN 206-6769).

Rusch, Shari, *(S Rusch; 0-9615922),* 15421 61st Pl. NE, Bothell, WA 98011 (SAN 696-7582) Tel 206-488-7842; P.O. Box 82627, Kenmore, WA 98028 (SAN 699-6434).

†Rush, James E., Assoc., Inc., *(Rush Assoc; 0-912803),* 2223 Carriage Rd., Powell, OH 43065-9703 (SAN 200-2744); *CIP.*

Rush-Presbyterian-St. Luke's Medical Center, Dept. of Preventive Medicine, *(Rush-Presby-St Lukes; 0-941516),* 1743 W. Harrison St., Tenth Floor, Chicago, IL 60612 (SAN 219-094X).

Rushlight Club, *(Rushlight Club; 0-917422),* Old Academy Library, 150 Main St., Wethersfield, CT 06109 (SAN 207-4958) Tel 203-529-7656.

Russel & King, *(Russel & King; 0-9615280),* P.O. Box 18227, Cleveland Heights, OH 44118 (SAN 694-4051) Tel 216-932-0817.

Russell, E. W., Publications, *(E W Russell; 0-918467),* 2305 Bunker Ave., El Monte, CA 91732 (SAN 657-6125) Tel 818-579-7031.

Russell, John, *(J Russell),* 19 Doughty Lane, Fair Haven, NJ 07701 (SAN 262-0731) Tel 201-747-6722.

Russell, Martin, Publisher, *(M Russell NY; 0-912209),* 61 Kincaid Dr., Yonkers, NY 10710 (SAN 265-0967) Tel 914-793-5296.

Russell & Russell Pubs., Div. of Atheneum Pubs., *(Russell; 0-8462),* 115 Fifth Ave., New York, NY 10003 (SAN 282-2644) Tel 212-614-1315; Orders to: Scribner Book Co., Front & Brown Sts., Burlington County, Riverside, NJ 08075 (SAN 201-002X).

Russell Pr., *(Russell Pr; 0-918377),* P.O. Box 67, Sharon Hill, PA 19079 (SAN 657-3762) Tel 215-583-4550.

Russell Pubns., *(Russell Pubns; 0-933558),* P.O. Box 2461, Tampa, FL 33601 (SAN 210-5764) Tel 813-879-8580. Do Not Confuse with Russell & Russell in NY (Russell).

Russell Sage Foundation, *(Russell Sage; 0-87154),* 112 E. 64th St., New York, NY 10021 (SAN 203-3674) Tel 212-750-6000; Toll free: 800-242-7737; Orders to: Basic Bks., Inc., 10 E. 53rd St., New York, NY 10022 (SAN 201-4521).

Russian Hill Hse. Bks., *(Russian Hill; 0-9608968),* P.O. Box 157, San Francisco, CA 94101 (SAN 282-2709) Tel 415-931-7249; Dist. by: Publishers Group West, 5855 Beaudry St., Emeryville, CA 94608 (SAN 202-8522) Tel 415-658-3453; Dist. by: Bookpeople, 2929 Flfth St., Berkeley, CA 94710 (SAN 168-9517); Dist. by: L-S, 480 Ninth St., San Francisco, CA 94103 (SAN 169-0213) Tel 415-771-0330.

Russian Numismatic Society, *(Russian Numis; 0-912671),* P.O. Box 3013, Alexandria, VA 22302 (SAN 277-7053) Tel 703-920-2043.

Russian Orthodox Church of The Nativity of Christ, *(Russian Orthodox Ch; 0-9617062),* 251 E. Front St., Erie, PA 16507 (SAN 662-9423) Tel 814-454-8618.

Russian Review, *(Russian Rev; 0-918444),* 1737 Cambridge St., Cambridge, MA 02138 (SAN 210-0002) Tel 617-495-4007.

†**Russian River Writers' Guild,** *(Russian River; 0-930489),* 378 Grand Ave., Suite 304, Oakland, CA 94610 (SAN 670-8978) Tel 415-444-6063; CIP.

Russica Pubs., *(Russica Pubs; 0-89830),* c/o Russica Book & Art Co., 799 Broadway, New York, NY 10003 (SAN 212-310X).

Rustler Printing & Publishing, *(Rustler Print & Pub; 0-930535),* 2420 Shevidan Ave, Cody, WY 82414 (SAN 682-8647).

Rutgers Ctr. of Alcohol Studies Pubns., *(Rutgers Ctr Alcohol; 0-911290),* Smithers Hall, Rutgers Univ., New Brunswick, NJ 08903 (SAN 203-3658) Tel 201-932-3510; Orders to: Rutgers Ctr. of Alcohol Studies, Business Office, P.O. Box 969, Piscataway, NJ 08854 (SAN 203-3666) Tel 201-932-2190.

†**Rutgers Univ. Pr.,** *(Rutgers U Pr; 0-8135),* 109 Church St., New Brunswick, NJ 08901 (SAN 203-364X) Tel 201-932-7764; Orders to: R.U.P. Distribution Ctr., P.O. Box 4869, Baltimore, MD 21211 (SAN 662-1325) Tel 303-338-6974; CIP.

Rutgers Univ., Puerto Rican Studies, *(Rutgers PR Studies; 0-9615805),* Rutgers Univ., Newark College of Arts & Sciences, Newark, NJ 07102 (SAN 696-6284) Tel 201-648-5538.

Rutgers Univ., Schl. of Information, Communication & Library Studies, *(Rutgers U SICLS),* 4 Huntington St., New Brunswick, NJ 08903 (SAN 205-9738) Tel 201-932-7362.

†**Rutledge Hill Pr.,** *(Rutledge Hill Pr; 0-934395),* P.O. Box 140483, Nashville, TN 37214 (SAN 693-8116) Tel 615-292-7322; CIP.

Rutledge Pr. *See* Smith, W. H., Pubs., Inc.

Ruud, David A., Publishing, *(D A Ruud; 0-939145),* Rte. 1, P.O. Box 146, Fordland, MO 65652 (SAN 662-507X) Tel 314-875-4414.

Ruwanga Trading, *(Ruwanga Trad; 0-9615102),* P.O. Box 1027, Puunene, HI 96784 (SAN 694-2776) Tel 808-572-8115; Dist. by: Pacific Trade Group, P.O. Box 668, Pearl City, HI 96782-0668 (SAN 169-1635) Tel 808-261-6594.

RVer Annie & Co., *(RVer Annie; 0-9613607),* 150 E. 93 St., New York, NY 10128 (SAN 670-7009) Tel 212-831-4159; Orders to: RVer Annie, Wolcott, VT 05680 (SAN 662-2461) Tel 802-888-2880.

Ryan Co., *(Ryan Co; 0-914202),* 2188 Latimer Lane, Los Angeles, CA 90024 (SAN 202-9707) Tel 213-474-4175.

Ryan Research Intl., *(Ryan Research; 0-942158),* 1593 Filbert Ave., Chico, CA 95926 (SAN 239-9776) Tel 916-343-2373.

Rydal Pr., The, Div. of Great Southwest Bks., The, *(Rydal; 0-911292),* 960 Camino Santander, Santa Fe, NM 87501 (SAN 204-7098) Tel 505-983-1680.

Ryder, Beverly, *(B Ryder; 0-9614390),* 2428 Lisa Ln., Madison, WI 53711 (SAN 688-6558) Tel 608-271-3452.

Ryder Geosystems, *(Ryder Geo; 0-941784),* 6061 South Willow Dr., Suite 330, Englewood, CO 80111 (SAN 239-3042) Tel 303-740-8824; Toll free: 800-LANDSAT.

Ryder Press, *(Ryder Pr; 0-916816),* 3307 Chadbourne Rd., Shaker Heights, OH 44120 (SAN 208-8339) Tel 216-921-7975.

Ryder Publishing Co., *(Ryder Pub Co; 0-935973),* 1914 N. Little Rib Cir., Wausau, WI 54401 (SAN 696-5822) Tel 715-675-6568.

Rye Historical Society, *(Rye Hist Soc; 0-9615327),* 1 Purchase St., Rye, NY 10580 (SAN 695-0663) Tel 914-967-7588.

Rymer Bks., *(Rymer Bks; 0-9600792; 0-934723),* P.O. Box 104, Tollhouse, CA 93667 (SAN 207-1010) Tel 209-298-0761; 22249 E. Tollhouse, Clovis, CA 93612 (SAN 699-5586).

Rynd Communications, *(Rynd Comm; 0-932500),* 99 Painters Mill Rd., Owings Mills, MD 21117 (SAN 699-766X) Tel 301-363-6400; Toll free: 800-446-2221.

Ryter, A. E., *(Canaveral),* 315 Montana Ave., No. 203, Santa Monica, CA 90403 (SAN 281-3777) Tel 213-394-0514.

Ryukyu Philatelic Specialist Society, Ltd., *(Ryukyu Philatelic),* P.O. Box 15368, Plantation, FL 33318-5368 (SAN 225-6037).

SAA Publishing, *(SAA Pub; 0-937922),* P.O. Box 117, Northport, MI 49670 (SAN 240-9194).

S-A Design Books, *(S-A Design Bks),* 515 W. Lambert, Bldg. E, Brea, CA 92621-3991 (SAN 670-736X).

SAG Pubns., *(SAG Pubns; 0-9616105),* 662 Granville Dr., Winter Park, FL 32789 (SAN 698-1194) Tel 305-647-4292; P.O. Box 2186, Winter Park, FL 32790 (SAN 698-2581).

SAS Institute, Inc., *(SAS Inst; 0-917382; 1-55544),* Box 8000, SAS Cir., Cary, NC 27511 (SAN 208-8347) Tel 919-467-8000.

S & A Pubns., *(S&A Pubns Inc; 0-9600768),* P.O. Box 2660, Sta. "A", Champaign, IL 61820 (SAN 204-7101) Tel 217-359-4222.

S & J Bks., *(S&J Books; 0-9609608),* 387 Ocean Pkwy., Brooklyn, NY 11218 (SAN 260-2598) Tel 718-941-1833.

S&S Pr., *(TX S & S Pr; 0-934646),* P.O. Box 5931, Austin, TX 78763 (SAN 212-6885). Do Not Confuse with (S&S) Simon & Schuster.

S & S Pub. Co. *See* Scharff Assocs.

S & S Publishing, Inc., *(S & S Pubs Inc; 0-9614426),* P.O. Box 998, Greenville, NC 27834 (SAN 689-0822) Tel 919-758-4093.

SBS Publishing, Inc., *(SBS Pub; 0-89961),* 50 Railroad Ave., Closter, NJ 07624 (SAN 213-3695) Tel 201-767-9450; Toll free: 800-631-2564.

SCOAL Press, *(SCOAL Pr; 0-933556),* 53 Pondview Circle, Brockton, MA 02401 (SAN 213-3717) Tel 617-587-4275.

†**SCOP Pubns., Inc.,** *(SCOP Pubns),* P.O. Box 376, College Park, MD 20740 (SAN 211-2035); CIP.

SDH Co., *(SDH Co; 0-9613866),* P.O. Box 923, Spokane, WA 99210 (SAN 685-2211) Tel 509-838-2265.

S.E.E. Publishing Co., *(SEE Pub Co; 0-937147),* 1556 Halford Ave., Suite 288, Santa Clara, CA 95051 (SAN 658-5035) Tel 408-248-8244; 1201 Sycamore Terr., Suite 40, Sunnyvale, CA 94086 (SAN 658-5043); Dist. by: Bookpeople, 2929 Fifth St., Berkeley, CA 94710 (SAN 168-9517); Toll free: 800-227-1516.

SERA Presents, *(SERA Presents; 0-938883),* 4226 Longbranch Ct., Atlanta, GA 30319 (SAN 662-6661) Tel 404-455-0389.

S. E. Ward, *(S E Ward; 0-9613595),* 45-180-39, Mahalani Place, Kaneohe, HI 96744 (SAN 677-1475) Tel 808-247-3874.

SFO Pr., *(SFO Pr; 0-937741),* 55 New Montgomery St., San Francisco, CA 94105 (SAN 659-2929) Tel 415-543-6234.

SFP Designs, Inc., *(SFP Designs; 0-936361),* 369 Redwood Ave., Corte Madera, CA 94925 (SAN 699-7562) Tel 415-331-8828.

SH Pr., Div. of Sports Hotline, Inc., *(SH Press; 0-938157),* 2872 Heathercrest Dr., Yorktown Heights, NY 10528 (SAN 659-7157) Tel 914-835-0900.

SIR Inc., *(SIR Inc; 1-55534),* 5215 Old Orchard, Suite 800, Skokie, IL 60077 (SAN 695-8605) Tel 312-470-9770.

SJB Publishing Co., *(SJB Pub Co; 0-912287),* 26632 Valpariso Rd., Mission Viejo, CA 92691 (SAN 265-0975) Tel 714-768-7238.

SJF Co, *(S J F Co; 0-9614185),* 1471 Treasure Ln., Santa Ana, CA 92705 (SAN 676-9411) Tel 714-669-8034.

SKO Studios, *(Sko Studios; 0-9615546),* 482 15th Ave., San Francisco, CA 94118 (SAN 695-9172) Tel 415-752-5053.

SLUSA, *(SLUSA; 0-917129; 0-9606758),* 88 Eastern Ave., Somerville, NJ 08876 (SAN 216-1931) Tel 201-725-6789.

SMARTCO, *(SMARTCO; 0-917619),* Drawer C, Rocheport, MO 65279 (SAN 657-1654) Tel 314-698-4535.

SMC Corp., *(SMC Corp; 0-939547),* 3475 Washington Dr., No. 201, Eagan, MN 55122 (SAN 663-3412) Tel 612-452-9270.

SMS Publishing Corp., *(S M S Pub; 0-914985),* P.O. Box 2276, Glenview, IL 60025 (SAN 289-4025) Tel 312-724-1427.

SNB Publishing, *(SNB Pub; 0-932909),* 10603 Glen Forest Trail, Brecksville, OH 44141 (SAN 688-9093) Tel 216-526-6552.

SNF Financial, *(S N F Fin; 0-9614300),* P.O. Box 82275, San Diego, CA 92138 (SAN 687-486X) Tel 619-295-2490.

SNM Publishing Co., *(SNM Pub; 0-9614613),* 102 W. Sixth St., Box 29, Larned, KS 67550 (SAN 691-8336) Tel 316-285-3177.

S.O.C.O. Pubns., *(SOCO Pubns; 0-910119),* Box 733, Herkimer, NY 13350 (SAN 241-5720).

SO Metro, *(SO Metro; 0-9616398),* P.O. Box 44089, Indianapolis, IN 46204 (SAN 659-1272) Tel 317-924-3663; 118 E. 33rd St., Indianapolis, IN 46205 (SAN 659-1280).

SOS Ministries Pr., Div. of Shama Sound Ministries, *(SOS Minist Pr; 0-938573),* P.O. Box 27054, San Francisco, CA 94127 (SAN 661-4701); 78 Sycamore St., San Francisco, CA 94110 (SAN 661-471X) Tel 415-552-2300.

SOS Pubns., *(SOS Pubns CA; 0-938422),* 4223 W. Jefferson Blvd., Los Angeles, CA 90016-4112 (SAN 238-5317) Tel 213-730-1815; Toll free: 800-325-7953 (Orders).

S.O.S. Pubs., *(S O S Pubs; 0-930867),* 21777 Ventura Blvd., Suite 210, Woodland Hills, CA 91364 (SAN 677-8097) Tel 818-704-0145.

SOS Publishing, *(SOS Pub OR; 0-931689),* P.O. Box 68290, Oak Grove, OR 97268 (SAN 686-1814) Tel 503-654-9123.

SPA Creek Co., Div. of Spa Creek Instruments, *(SPA Creek; 0-911551),* 612 Third St., Annapolis, MD 21401 (SAN 264-3650) Tel 301-267-6565; Orders to: Spa Creek Inc., 616 Third St., Annapolis, MD 21403 (SAN 685-3587) Tel 301-267-6565.

SPAR, *(SPAR),* 1123 Broadway, New York, NY 10010 (SAN 694-5325).

SPIE-International Society for Optical Engineering, *(SPIE; 0-89252),* 1022 19th St., Bellingham, WA 98225 (SAN 224-1706) Tel 206-676-3290; P.O. Box 10, Bellingham, WA 98227 (SAN 669-1323).

†**SP Medical & Scientific Bks.,** Div. of Spectrum Pubns., Inc., *(SP Med & Sci Bks; 0-89335),* 175-20 Wexford Terr., Jamaica, NY 11432 (SAN 213-5574) Tel 718-658-0888; CIP.

SP Pr., International, *(SP Press Intl; 0-9617129),* 7806 Honeybee Ct., Bethesda, MD 20817 (SAN 662-6939) Tel 301-365-2739.

SPSS, Inc., *(SPSS Inc; 0-926673; 0-918469),* 444 N. Michigan Ave., Suite 3000, Chicago, IL 60611 (SAN 653-8975) Tel 312-329-3600.

SRL Publishing Co., *(SRL Pub Co; 0-918152),* P.O. Box 2277, Sta. A, Champaign, IL 61820 (SAN 209-3871) Tel 217-356-1523.

SRS Co., *(S R S Co; 0-9610766),* No. 160, 2554 Lincoln Blvd., Marina del Rey, CA 90291 (SAN 264-634X) Tel 213-397-2600; Dist. by: Hal Leonard Pub. Corp., 8112 W. Bluemound Rd., Milwaukee, WI 53212 (SAN 239-250X) Tel 414-774-3630; Toll free: 800-558-4774.

S S J Publications, *(S S J Pubns; 0-914465),* P.O. Box 3165 Arlington Sta., Poughkeepsie, NY 12603 (SAN 289-6753) Tel 914-433-3652.

STL International Inc., *(STL Intl; 0-936215),* 12101 E. 51st St., No. 107, Tulsa, OK 74146 (SAN 696-8783) Tel 918-250-1488; Dist. by: International Cassette Corp., P.O. Box 1928, Greenville, TX 75401 (SAN 200-5824).

STO Pubns., *(STO Pub; 0-9614540),* 6224 N. 13th St., Philadelphia, PA 19141 (SAN 691-7240) Tel 215-927-3392.

STTU, Specialized Training Unit, *(STTU Spc Unit; 0-939235),* P.O. Box 491261, Los Angeles, CA 90049 (SAN 662-6890); 1440 Princeton Ave., Santa Monica, CA 90404 (SAN 662-6904) Tel 213-829-1738.

ST2, *(ST Two; 0-943542),* 203 Si Town Rd., Castle Rock, WA 98611 (SAN 238-3810) Tel 206-636-2645.

SWAC Pr., Div. of Swac, Inc., *(SWAC Pr),* Box 236, South Elgin, IL 60177 (SAN 699-7848) Tel 312-741-0500.

SYDA Foundation, Div. of Sushila Blackman, *(SYDA Found; 0-914602),* P.O. Box 600, South Fallsburg, NY 12779 (SAN 206-5649) Tel 914-434-2000.

SYNTEC Inc, *(SYNTEC Inc; 0-943494),* P.O. Box 1402, Bowie, MD 20716 (SAN 240-6780) Tel 301-249-9265.

S. H. C. *See* Steinlitz-Hammacher Co.

Sabayt Pubns., *(Sabayt Pubns; 0-9616649),* 5441 S. Kenwood Ave., Chicago, IL 60615 (SAN 659-6940) Tel 312-667-2227.

Sabbagh Management Corp., *(Sabbagh Manage; 0-912369),* 3310 45th St., NW, Washington, DC 20016 (SAN 265-0991) Tel 202-966-2651.

Sabbot, Rudolph William, Natural History Bks., *(Sabbot-Natural Hist Bks),* 5239 Tendilla Ave., Woodland Hills, CA 91364 (SAN 213-2583) Tel 818-346-7164.

Sabio Publishing Co., *(Sabio Pub; 0-9617050),* P.O. Box 9296, Santa Fe, NM 87501 (SAN 662-6408); 38 Vuelta Sabio, La Tierra, Santa Fe, NM 87501 (SAN 662-6416) Tel 505-988-4300.

Sachem Pr., *(Sachem Pr; 0-937584),* P.O. Box 9, Old Chatham, NY 12136 (SAN 215-6075) Tel 518-794-8327.

Saco River Publishing Co., *(Saco River Pub; 0-9607522),* P.O. Box 685, North Conway, NH 03860 (SAN 238-6178) Tel 603-356-5091.

Sacred Dance Guild, *(Sacred Dance Guild),* Pacific Schl. of Religion, 1798 Scenic Ave., Berkeley, CA 94709 (SAN 225-3054); Dist. by: Sharing Co., P.O. Box 2224, Austin, TX 78768-2224 (SAN 211-0563) Tel 512-452-4366.

Sacred Heart Convent of Houston, Texas, *(Sacred Heart Convent; 0-9617026),* 6501 Almeda Rd., Houston, TX 77021 (SAN 662-6564) Tel 713-747-3310.

Sacred Lands Project of the Christic Institute, *(SLPOTCI; 0-9616823),* 1831 Belmont Rd., NW, Washington, DC 20009 (SAN 661-1249) Tel 202-234-1856.

Sacred Music Press, The, *(Sacred Music Pr; 0-937021),* 501 E. Third St., Dayton, OH 45401 (SAN 692-7475) Tel 513-228-6118.

Sacrum Pr., *(Sacrum Pr; 0-937543),* P.O. Box 3044, W. Durham Sta., Durham, NC 27705 (SAN 659-1329) Tel 919-684-3325; 8 Chancery Pl., Durham, NC 27707 (SAN 659-1337).

Saddle River Day School Parents Guild, *(Saddle River Day; 0-9612374),* 147 Chestnut Ridge Rd., Saddle River, NJ 07458 (SAN 289-551X) Tel 201-327-4050.

Saddle Sore Pubns., *(Saddle Sore; 0-9612660),* 2381 S. 2000 W., Syracuse, UT 84041 (SAN 289-405X) Tel 801-825-9303.

Saddlebag Bks., *(Saddlebag Bks; 0-936457),* 210 S. Fourth St., Basin, WY 82410 (SAN 698-0295) Tel 307-568-3800; Box 48, Basin, WY 82410 (SAN 698-2433).

†Sadler, John M., & Co., *(J M Sadler; 0-930250),* 215 Commonwealth Ave., Massapequa, NY 11758 (SAN 210-6620) Tel 516-798-9059; *CIP.*

Sadlier, William H., Inc., *(Sadlier; 0-8215),* 11 Park Place, New York, NY 10007 (SAN 204-0948) Tel 212-227-2120; Toll free: 800-221-5175.

Sadtler Research Laboratories, Inc., *(Sadtler Res; 0-8456),* 3316 Spring Garden St., Philadelphia, PA 19104 (SAN 203-0063) Tel 215-382-7800.

Saeta Ediciones, *(Saeta; 0-917049),* 7642 SW 96th Ct., Miami, FL 33173 (SAN 655-2226) Tel 305-596-4097; Orders to: Saeta Ediciones, P.O. Box 440156, Miami, FL 33144-0156 (SAN 662-2305) Tel 305-596-4097.

Safari Museum Pr., *(Safari Museum Pr),* 16 S. Grant Ave., Chanute, KS 66720 (SAN 218-9364) Tel 314-431-2730.

Safe Harbor Press, *(Safe Harbor Pr; 0-913221),* West Ave. J, P.O. Box 4345, Lancaster, CA 93534 (SAN 283-9040).

Safety Now Co., Inc., *(Safety Now; 0-917066),* P.O. Box 567, Jenkintown, PA 19046 (SAN 208-8355) Tel 215-884-0210.

Sagamore Bks., Inc., *(Sagamore Bks MI),* P.O. Box 195, Grand Rapids, MI 49588 (SAN 699-8038) Tel 616-455-8530.

Sagamore Institute, *(Sagamore; 0-913393),* Sagamore Rd., Raquette Lake, NY 13436 (SAN 285-8444) Tel 315-354-5311.

†Sagapress, Inc., *(Sagapr; 0-89831),* Rte. 100, Millwood, NY 10546 (SAN 295-9100) Tel 914-762-2200; Dist. by: Kraus Reprint, Route 100, Millwood, NY 10546 (SAN 217-4979) Tel 914-762-2200; *CIP.*

Sage Pr., *(Sage Pr; 0-9615725),* 1450 E. Peoria Ave., Phoenix, AZ 85020 (SAN 696-1487) Tel 602-943-9875.

Sage Pubns., Inc., *(Sage; 0-8039),* 275 S. Beverly Dr., Beverly Hills, CA 90212 (SAN 204-7217) Tel 213-274-8003.

Sage Publishing Co., Inc., *(Sage Oregon; 0-937485),* 9510 Butte Falls Hwy., Eagle Point, OR 97524 (SAN 659-1353) Tel 503-772-9973; P.O. Box 2349, White City, OR 97503 (SAN 659-1361).

Sagebrush Pr., *(Sagebrush Pr; 0-930704),* P.O. Box 87, Morongo Valley, CA 92256 (SAN 211-4496).

Sagittarius Rising, *(Sag Rising; 0-933620),* P.O. Box 252, Arlington, MA 02174 (SAN 282-2741) Tel 617-646-2692.

Saguaro Pr., *(Saguaro Pr; 0-935561),* 9270 E. Mission Ln., Suite 101, Scottsdale, AZ 85258 (SAN 696-1851) Tel 602-998-0824.

Saguaro Publishing, *(Saguaro; 0-9608864),* 1302 E. Becker Lane, Phoenix, AZ 85020 (SAN 241-0761).

Sai Systems, *(Sai Systems; 0-930869),* 4000 Albermarle St., Suite 310, Washington, DC 20016 (SAN 677-8054) Tel 202-363-1903.

Saifer, Albert, Pub., *(Saifer; 0-87556),* P.O. Box 239 W.O.B., West Orange, NJ 07052 (SAN 204-1723).

Saiga Publishing Co., Ltd., *(Saiga; 0-86230),* 51 Washington St., Dover, NH 03820 (SAN 656-8777); Dist. by: Longwood Publishing Group, 21 Washington St., Dover, NH 03820 (SAN 209-3170).

†Sail Bks., Inc., *(Sail Bks; 0-914814),* 34 Commercial Wharf, Boston, MA 02110 (SAN 207-0820); *CIP.*

Sail Sales Publishing, *(Sail Sale Pub; 0-943798),* P.O. Box 1028, Aptos, CA 95001 (SAN 241-077X) Tel 408-662-2456.

St. Alban Press, *(St Alban Pr; 0-918980),* 10606 Parrot Ave. Apt. A., Downey, CA 90241 (SAN 210-492X) Tel 213-861-7569; Orders to: Gene/Smith, P.O. Box 598, Ojai, CA 93023 (SAN 210-4938) Tel 805-646-6790.

St. Alban Pr., San Diego, Subs. of Liberal Catholic Church, *(St Alban Pr CA; 0-935461),* 741 Cerro Gordo Ave., San Diego, CA 92102 (SAN 695-8664) Tel 619-239-0637.

St. Andrew Pr., *(St Andrew Pr; 0-939485),* Rt. 1, Box 283, Big Island, VA 24526 (SAN 663-3951) Tel 804-299-5956. Do not confuse with St. Andrews Press in Laurinburg, NC or in New York, NY.

St. Andrews Press, *(St Andrews NC; 0-932662),* St. Andrews Presbyterian College, Laurinburg, NC 28352 (SAN 207-8902) Tel 919-276-3652.

St. Anthony Messenger Pr., *(St Anthony Mess Pr; 0-912228; 0-86716),* 1615 Republic St., Cincinnati, OH 45210 (SAN 204-6237) Tel 513-241-5616; Toll free: 800-325-9521.

St. Anthony of Padua Schl., *(St Anthony Northport; 0-9616243),* 6 Fifth Ave., East Northport, NY 11731 (SAN 658-6880) Tel 516-261-5130.

Saint Anthony Orthodox Pubns., Div. of Kellion of St. Anthony the Great, *(St Anthony Orthodox; 0-936649),* P.O. Box 1432, Alamogordo, NM 88311-1432 (SAN 699-7031).

St. Augeo Publishing Co., *(St Augeo Pub; 0-9606900),* P.O. Box 567, Cross Keys Rd., R.D. 1, Glassboro, NJ 08028 (SAN 217-4308) Tel 609-881-4958.

Saint Augustine Historical Society, *(St Augustine Hist; 0-9612744; 0-917553),* 271 Charlotte St., St. Augustine, FL 32084 (SAN 289-8306) Tel 904-824-2872.

St. Basil Press, *(St Basil Pr; 0-9604278),* 4106 N. Ozark Ave., Norridge, IL 60634 (SAN 215-1057).

†St. Bede's Pubns., *(St Bedes Pubns; 0-932506),* P.O. Box 545, Petersham, MA 01366-0545 (SAN 222-9692) Tel 617-724-3407; *CIP.*

St. Clair Publishing, *(St Clair Pub; 0-9616319),* Rte. 1, Box 371A, Cottontown, TN 37048 (SAN 658-6635) Tel 615-672-4844.

St. Cuthbert's Treasury Press, *(St Cuthberts; 0-914724),* 1290 Maricopa Dr., Oshkosh, WI 54901 (SAN 206-1287) Tel 414-235-2057.

St. David's Bks., *(St David's Bks; 0-9613616),* 537 Hilaire Rd., Saint Davids, PA 19087 (SAN 677-0053).

St. David's Society of Wyoming Valley, *(St David's Soc of WY Val),* 205 Maple St., Trucksville, PA 18708 (SAN 663-1916).

Saint Edward's Univ., *(St Edwards Univ; 0-938472),* 3001 S. Congress Ave., Austin, TX 78704 (SAN 215-9155).

St. Francis Hospital, Dr. William G. Eckert Laboratory, *(St Francis Hosp),* Wichita, KS 67214 (SAN 226-7403).

St. Genesius Press, Ltd., *(St Genesius Pr Ltd; 0-911673),* 519 Seventh St., Rapid City, SD 57701 (SAN 264-3669) Tel 605-348-5465.

St. George Book Service, Inc., *(St George Bk Serv; 0-916786),* P.O. Box 225, Spring Valley, NY 10977 (SAN 208-8371) Tel 914-623-7852.

St. George Pr., *(St George Pr; 0-932104),* 3500 N. Coltrane Rd., Oklahoma City, OK 73121 (SAN 209-6773) Tel 405-427-5005.

Saint George Pr., The, *(St George IA; 0-939846),* 2814 Summit St., Sioux City, IA 51104-3743 (SAN 216-2989) Tel 309-676-4799.

St. George's Episcopal Church, *(St Georges Episcopal; 0-9613533),* 8250 Hwy. 72, P.O. Box 38447, Germantown, TN 38138-0447 (SAN 657-3819) Tel 901-525-2494.

Saint Giles Pr., *(St Giles; 0-9607382),* Box 1416, Lafayette, CA 94549 (SAN 239-4901) Tel 415-939-3485.

St. Herman of Alaska Brotherhood, *(St Herman AK; 0-938635),* P.O. Box 70, Platina, CA 96076 (SAN 661-583X); Beegum Gorge Rd., Platina, CA 96076 (SAN 661-5848).

St. James Pr., *(St James Pr; 0-912289),* 425 N. Michigan Ave., Chicago, IL 60611 (SAN 205-9258) Tel 312-329-0806.

St. Joan's Pr., *(St Joans Pr; 0-942160),* 215 E. 80th St., New York, NY 10021 (SAN 226-2797).

St. John, John, Gallery, *(St John Gallery; 0-9605946),* 1683 Copenhagen Dr., Solvang, CA 93463 (SAN 216-6445).

St. John the Evangelist Church, *(St John Evang; 0-9616134),* 126 W. Georgia St., Indianapolis, IN 46225 (SAN 699-959X) Tel 317-635-2021.

St. John's Publishing, *(St Johns Pub; 0-938577),* 6824 Oaklawn Ave., Edina, MN 55435 (SAN 661-1125) Tel 612-920-9044.

St. John's Univ., Christian Humanism Project, *(St Johns Univ Christ Hum; 0-9613867),* P.O. Box 5766, Collegeville, MN 56321 (SAN 685-2246) Tel 612-363-2417.

St. Joseph Hospital, Div. of St. Joseph Health System, *(St Joseph Hosp; 0-9616857),* 1100 W. Stewart, Orange, CA 92668 (SAN 661-597X) Tel 714-771-8040.

St. Joseph's Univ. Pr., *(St Joseph; 0-916101),* 5600 City Ave., Philadelphia, PA 19131 (SAN 240-8368) Tel 215-879-7325.

St. Louis Humanities Forum, *(St Louis Human; 0-9616369),* 711 N. 11th St., St. Louis, MO 63101 (SAN 659-0012) Tel 314-241-5109.

St. Louis Public Library, Pubns. Dept, *(St Louis Pub Lib; 0-937322),* 1301 Olive St., St. Louis, MO 63103 (SAN 205-9215) Tel 314-241-2288.

†St. Luke's Pr., *(St Luke TN; 0-918518),* Mid-Memphis Tower, 1407 Union Ave., Suite 401, Memphis, TN 38104 (SAN 210-0029) Tel 901-357-5441; Toll free: 800-524-5554 (dial 4617, orders); *CIP.*

St. Luke's Publishing Co., Subs. of St. Luke's Pr./Fine Arts Productions, *(St Luke Pub; 0-939502),* P.O. Box 1378, South Bend, IN 46624 (SAN 216-6925) Tel 219-234-5115.

St. Margaret's Hospital, *(St Margaret's),* Administrator's Office, 90 Cushing Ave., Boston, MA 02125 (SAN 207-5156).

St. Margaret's Hse. & hospital for Babies, *(St Marg Hse Hosp; 0-9611828),* 27 Hackett Blvd., Albany, NY 12208 (SAN 286-1941) Tel 518-465-2461.

St. Mark Coptic Orthodox Church, *(St Mark Coptic Orthodox),* P.O. Box 692, Troy, MI 48094 (SAN 240-1533) Tel 313-764-0350.

St. Martin's Pr., Inc., Subs. of Macmillan Pubs., *(St Martin; 0-312; 0-9603648),* 175 Fifth Ave., New York, NY 10010 (SAN 200-2132) Tel 212-674-5151; Toll free: 800-221-7945; 165 Marlborough St., Boston, MA 02116 (SAN 650-0560). *Imprints:* Kahn, Joann, Book, A (J Kahn); Papermac Books (Papermac).

St. Mary's Pr., Subs. of Christian Brothers of Minnesota, *(St Mary's; 0-88489),* Terrace Heights, Winona, MN 55987 (SAN 203-073X) Tel 507-452-9090; Toll free: 800-533-8095.

Saint Matthew's Episcopal Church, *(St Matthew's),* 1401 W. Broad St., Savannah, GA 31401 (SAN 219-0966).

St. Maurice Church, *(St Maurice Church; 0-9615563),* 32 Hebron Rd., Bolton, CT 06040 (SAN 696-7272); Dist. by: Kathleen J. Callahan, 53 Burnt Hill Rd., Hebron, CT 06248 (SAN 200-8203) Tel 203-228-0873.

St. Michaels Historical Museum, *(St Michaels),* St. Michaels Mission, Drawer D, St. Michaels, AZ 86511 (SAN 239-5290) Tel 602-871-4172.

St. Michael's Pr., *(St Michael VA; 0-910581),* P.O. Box 6009, Portsmouth, VA 23703 (SAN 260-2601) Tel 804-484-3690.

St. Nectarios Pr., *(St Nectarios; 0-913026),* 10300 Ashworth Ave. N., Seattle, WA 98133-9410 (SAN 203-3542) Tel 206-522-4471. *Imprints:* Holy Transfiguration Monastery (Holy Transfiguration).

Saint Paul the Apostle Church, *(St Paul the Apostle; 0-9602352),* 202 E. Washington St., Greencastle, IN 46135 (SAN 212-6206).

St. Peter's Pr., *(St Peters Pr),* Kaduna/Dept. of State, Washington, DC 20520 (SAN 240-8376).

St. Sophia Religious Assn. of Ukrainian Catholics, *(St Sophia Religious),* 7911 Whitewood Rd., Philadelphia, PA 19117 (SAN 204-949X) Tel 215-635-1555.

St. Thomas Academy, *(St Thomas Aca; 0-9615710),* 949 Mendota Heights Rd., Mendota Heights, MN 55120 (SAN 695-9385) Tel 612-454-0090.

St. Thomas Pr., *(St Thomas; 0-940648),* P.O. Box 1036 SMS, Fairfield, CT 06430 (SAN 204-6288) Tel 713-666-3111.

St. Thomas Pubs., *(St Thomas Pub; 0-9615048),* 4831 SE Powell Blvd., Suite 1043, Portland, OR 97206 (SAN 693-8612) Tel 503-231-9080.

St. Vincent Hospital, *(St Vincent Hosp),* Dept. D., P.O. Box 2107, Santa Fe, NM 87501 (SAN 211-4003).

†St. Vladimir's Seminary Pr., *(St Vladimirs; 0-913836; 0-88141),* 575 Scarsdale Rd., Crestwood, NY 10707 (SAN 204-6296) Tel 914-961-8313; *CIP.*

Sakura/Dragon Corp., *(Sakura-Dragon Corp; 0-86568),* c/o Unique Publications, 4201 W. Vanowen Pl., Burbank, CA 91505 (SAN 214-3313) Tel 818-845-2656.

Sakura Pr., *(Sakura Press; 0-936845),* 36787 Sakura Ln., Pleasant Hill, OR 97455 (SAN 658-3350) Tel 503-747-5817.

Sal Magundi Enterprises, *(Sal Magundi Ent; 0-9609024),* 12960 SW Carmel St., Portland, OR 97224 (SAN 241-2470) Tel 503-684-3972; Dist. by: Douglas County Museum, P.O. Box 1559, Roseburg, OR 97470 (SAN 200-819X); Toll free: 800-452-0991.

Salaam, Yusef A., *(Y A Salaam; 0-9613032),* 167 W. 136th, Suite 5, New York, NY 10030 (SAN 287-3001).

Salamander Press, *(Salamander Pr; 0-912708),* P.O. Box 153, Carmel, CA 93921 (SAN 204-7233).

Salant, Michael Alan, *(M A Salant; 0-9609288),* 2412 19th St. NW Apt. 9, Washington, DC 20009-1552 (SAN 260-129X) Tel 202-332-2368; Orders to: P.O. Box 33421, Farragut Sta., Washington, DC 20033-0421 (SAN 200-2760).

†Salem Pr., Inc., *(Salem Pr; 0-89356),* P.O. Box 1097, Englewood Cliffs, NJ 07632 (SAN 208-838X) Tel 201-871-3700; Toll free: 800-221-1592; *CIP.*

Salem Publishing Co., *(Salem Pub; 0-939475),* P.O. Box 25448, Winston Salem, NC 27114 (SAN 663-2467); 514 S. Stratford Rd., Winston Salem, NC 27103 (SAN 663-2475) Tel 919-724-2778.

Sales, Billee, *(B Sales; 0-9605244),* 2638 NW 59th Ave., Margate, FL 33063 (SAN 215-8051).

Sales Executives Club of New York, The, *(Sales Execs Club),* 114 E. 32nd St., Suite 1301, New York, NY 10016 (SAN 224-9472) Tel 212-683-9755.

Sales Success Press, *(Sales Success; 0-9613319),* 425 Vista Flora Suite 777, Newport Beach, CA 92660 (SAN 656-1721) Tel 714-542-7777; Toll free: 800-772-1172.

Salesiana Publishers *See* **Don Bosco Multimedia**

Salesman's Guide, Inc., *(Salesmans; 0-87228),* 1140 Broadway, New York, NY 10001 (SAN 203-3593) Tel 212-684-2985; Toll free: 800-223-1797.

Salitore, Edward V., & Evelyn D., *(E V Salitore),* P.O. Box 500, Temecula, CA 92390 (SAN 201-2847) Tel 714-676-6355.

Sallyforth, Inc., *(Sallyforth; 0-939413),* 2611 Garden Rd., Monterey, CA 93940 Tel 408-375-4474.

Salt Resources, Inc., *(Salt Resc; 0-9616562),* 427 Lynn Ave., Winston-Salem, NC 27104 (SAN 659-5839) Tel 919-725-1750.

Salt Warrior Pr., *(Salt Warrior Pr; 0-9611028; 0-931857),* 3800 S. Tamiami Trail, Sarasota, FL 33579 (SAN 289-5536) Tel 813-951-0473.

Salt-Works Pr., *(Salt-Works Pr; 0-938535),* RFD 1, P.O. Box 141, Grenada, MS 38901 (SAN 209-7672); Rte. 404, Hardin Rd., Grenada, MS 38901 (SAN 660-9430); Dist. by: Small Pr. Distribution, 1814 San Pablo Ave., Berkeley, CA 94702 (SAN 204-5826) Tel 415-549-3336.

Saltillo Press, *(Saltillo Pr; 0-913473),* 607 Gregory, El Paso, TX 79902 (SAN 285-1865) Tel 915-532-3564.

Salvation Army, *(Salvation Army; 0-89216),* 120 W. 14th St., New York, NY 10011 (SAN 237-2649) Tel 212-337-7435; Orders to: 145 W. 15th St., New York, NY 10011 (SAN 662-1341).

Salvation Army Supplies, Southern, *(Salv Army Suppl South; 0-86544),* 1424 NE Expressway, Atlanta, GA 30329 (SAN 211-9765) Tel 404-321-7870.

Salyer Publishing Co., *(Salyer; 0-911298),* 3111 19th St., NW, Oklahoma City, OK 73107 (SAN 204-725X).

Sam Houston State Univ., Criminal Justice Ctr., National Employment Listing Service, *(Natl Employment; 0-935530),* Huntsville, TX 77341 (SAN 222-6278) Tel 409-294-1692.

Samara Pubns., *(Samara Pubns; 0-935513),* 15505 SE Arista Dr., Milwaukie, OR 97267 (SAN 695-8923) Tel 503-659-1067; Dist. by: Western States Bk. Service, P.O. Box 855, Clackamas, OR 97015 (SAN 200-5662).

†SamHar Pr., Div. of Story House Corp., *(SamHar Pr; 0-85157),* Bindery Ln., Charlotteville, NY 12036 (SAN 203-3585) Tel 607-397-8725; *CIP.*

Samisdat, *(Samisdat),* Box 129, Richford, VT 05476 (SAN 207-8929) Tel 514-263-4439.

Samisdat Pubs. Ltd. *See* **Noontide Pr., The**

Samizdat, *(Samizdat; 0-9613814),* 700 New Hampshire Ave., NW, Suite 701, Washington, DC 20027 (SAN 682-0298).

†Sammis Publishing, *(Sammis Pub; 0-87469),* 122 E. 25th St., New York, NY 10010 (SAN 208-4503) Tel 212-598-6976; Dist. by: M.A.G.I.C., Inc., 1950 Craig Rd., St. Louis, MO 63146 (SAN 202-5191); Dist. by: Kampmann & Co., 9 E. 40th St., New York, NY 10016 (SAN 200-2639) Tel 212-685-2928; Toll free: 800-526-7676; Dist. by: Crown Publishers, 225 Park Ave., S., New York, NY 10003 (SAN 662-1333) Tel 212-254-1600; *CIP.*

Sams, Howard W., & Co., Div. of Macmillan, Inc., *(Sams; 0-672),* 4300 W. 62nd St., Indianapolis, IN 46268 (SAN 203-3577) Tel 317-298-5400; Toll free: 800-428-3602.

Samson Pubs., Div. of Light Pubns., *(Samson Pubs; 0-935985),* 1437 40th St., Brooklyn, NY 11218 (SAN 695-5533) Tel 718-871-7265; P.O.Box 719, Midwood Sta., Brooklyn, NY 11230 (SAN 699-6078) Tel 718-435-1434.

San Anselmo Publishing Co., *(San Anselmo Pub; 0-943264),* P.O. Box 2299, Norman, OK 73070 (SAN 240-5644) Tel 405-275-2415.

San Antonio Art Institute, *(San Antonio Art; 0-9614862),* 6000 N. New Braunfels, P.O. Box 6092, San Antonio, TX 78209 (SAN 693-2819) Tel 512-824-0531.

San Antonio Junior Forum Pubns., *(San Antonio Jr Forum; 0-9616917),* 418 W. French, San Antonio, TX 78212 (SAN 661-5414) Tel 512-735-8345; P.O. Box 16372, San Antonio, TX 78216 (SAN 661-5422).

San Diego Art Ctr., *(San Diego Art Ctr; 0-939003),* P.O. Box 126458, San Diego, CA 92112 (SAN 662-5428) Tel 619-232-5722.

San Diego Historical Society, *(San Diego Hist; 0-918740),* P.O. Box 81825, San Diego, CA 92138 (SAN 210-5438) Tel 619-297-3258.

San Diego Publishing Co., *(San Diego Pub Co; 0-912495),* P.O. Box 9222, San Diego, CA 92109-0060 (SAN 265-1971) Tel 619-295-9190.

San Diego Society of Natural History, *(San Diego Soc Nat Hist; 0-918969),* P.O. Box 1390, San Diego, CA 92112 (SAN 669-9618) Tel 619-232-3821.

San Diego State Univ., Pr., *(SDSU Press; 0-916304),* 5189 College Ave., San Diego, CA 92182 (SAN 202-0637) Tel 619-265-6220. *Imprints:* Campanile Press (Campanile).

San Diego State Univ., University Art Gallery, *(SDSU Univ Art; 0-937097),* 5402 College Ave., San Diego, CA 92182-0214 (SAN 280-3941) Tel 619-265-4941.

San Diego's Cooking, *(San Die Cooking; 0-9617211),* P.O. Box 86244, San Diego, CA 92138 (SAN 663-2750); 219 Chesterfield Dr. Ste. A, Cardiff, CA 92007 (SAN 663-2769) Tel 619-753-6069.

San Francisciana, *(San Francisciana; 0-934715),* P.O. Box 590955, San Francisco, CA 94159 (SAN 694-1613) Tel 916-363-3547.

San Francisco Arts & Letters Foundation, *(SF Arts & Letters; 0-914024),* P.O. Box 640394, San Francisco, CA 94164 (SAN 202-8751) Tel 415-771-3431. *Imprints:* Peace & Pieces Books (Peace & Pieces).

San Francisco Bay Area Dance Coalition, *(SF Dance Coalition; 0-9616244),* Ft. Mason Ctr., Bldg. C, San Francisco, CA 94123 (SAN 658-3601) Tel 415-673-8172.

San Francisco Bay Guardian, *(SF Bay Guardian; 0-913192),* 2700 19th St., San Francisco, CA 94110 (SAN 215-2746) Tel 415-824-7660.

San Francisco Ctr. for Visual Studies, *(SF Center Vis Stud; 0-930976),* 49 Rivoli St., San Francisco, CA 94117 (SAN 209-5106) Tel 415-664-4699.

San Francisco Historic Records, *(SF Hist Records; 0-911792),* 1204 Nimitz Dr., Colma, CA 94014 (SAN 204-5885) Tel 415-755-2204.

San Francisco Mime Troupe, Inc., *(SF Mime; 0-9606902),* 855 Treat, San Francisco, CA 94110 (SAN 217-4316) Tel 415-285-1717.

†San Francisco Museum of Modern Art, *(San Fran MOMA; 0-928471),* 401 Van Ness Ave., San Francisco, CA 94102-4582 (SAN 218-9445) Tel 415-863-8800; *CIP.*

San Francisco Press, Inc., *(San Francisco Pr; 0-911302),* Box 6800, San Francisco, CA 94101-6800 (SAN 207-4990) Tel 415-524-1000.

San Francisco Study Ctr., *(SF Study Ctr; 0-936434),* P.O. Box 5646, San Francisco, CA 94101 (SAN 214-4654) Tel 415-626-1650.

San Francisco Yesterday, *(SF Yesterday),* P.O. Box 4343, San Rafael, CA 94903 (SAN 209-4886) Tel 415-479-1550.

San Francisco Zoological Society, *(SF Zoological; 0-933155),* Sloat Blvd. at the Pacific Ocean, San Francisco, CA 94132 (SAN 689-8513) Tel 415-661-2023.

San Jacinto Publishing Co., *(San Jacinto; 0-911982),* P.O. Box. 66254, Houston, TX 77006 (SAN 694-3209) Tel 713-845-1436; c/o Texas A&M Univ. Pr., Drawer "C", College Station, TX 77843 (SAN 207-5237) Tel 409-845-1436.

San Jose Face, *(San Jose Face; 0-932161),* 475 S. 12th St., San Jose, CA 95112 (SAN 686-4678).

San Jose Historical Museum Assn., *(San Jose His Mus Assn; 0-914139),* 635 Phelan Ave., San Jose, CA 95112 (SAN 287-5470) Tel 408-287-2290.

San Juan County Bk. Co., *(San Juan County; 0-9608000),* P.O. Box 1, Silverton, CO 81433 (SAN 238-5775) Tel 303-387-5477.

†San Luis Quest Pr., *(San Luis Quest; 0-935320),* Box 998, San Luis Obispo, CA 93406 (SAN 213-4306) Tel 805-543-8500; CIP.

San Marco Bookstore, *(San Marcos Bk; 0-935259),* 1971 San Marco Blvd., Jacksonville, FL 32207 (SAN 693-3734) Tel 904-396-7597; Dist. by: Morningside Bookshop, P.O. Box 1087, Dayton, OH 45401 (SAN 202-2206) Tel 513-461-6738.

San Marcos Pr., *(San Marcos; 0-88235),* 4705 Marquette NE, Albuquerque, NM 87108 (SAN 206-3751) Tel 505-266-4412. Out of business.

San Pedro Bay Historical Society, *(San Pedro Hist; 0-9611556),* P.O. Box 1568, San Pedro, CA 90733 (SAN 285-1377) Tel 213-548-3208; 1159 Amar St., San Pedro, CA 90732 (SAN 285-1385) Tel 213-833-2872.

Sanatana Publishing Society, *(Sanatana; 0-933116),* 503 Pope St., Menlo Park, CA 94025 (SAN 212-7946) Tel 415-326-4232.

Sanchez, Jacqueline, *(J Sanchez; 0-910863),* 2076 Vinewood, Detroit, MI 48216 (SAN 275-2042).

Sanchin Publishing Co., *(Sanchin Pub; 0-934999),* 7210 Shawnee Way, Colorado Springs, CO 80915 (SAN 695-6033) Tel 303-596-7552.

Sanctuary Pr., *(Sanctuary Pr; 0-935971),* P.O. Box 90159, San Jose, CA 95112 (SAN 696-5830) Tel 408-287-8210; 85 S. 12th St., San Jose, CA 95112 (SAN 699-6353).

Sand, George, , Books, *(George Sand; 0-942498),* 9011 Melrose Ave., Los Angeles, CA 90069 (SAN 239-6084) Tel 213-858-1648.

Sand Dollar Press, *(Sand Dollar),* Landscape Station, P. O. Box 7400, Berkeley, CA 94707 (SAN 203-2686) Tel 415-527-1931.

Sand Pond Pubs., *(Sand Pond; 0-915209),* P.O. Box 405, Shady Ln., Hancock, NH 03449 (SAN 203-0713) Tel 603-525-6615.

Sandbar Willow Pr., *(Sandbar; 0-9615711),* 123 Sewall Ave., 1E, Brookline, MA 02146 (SAN 695-8419) Tel 617-739-2890; P.O. Box 883, Brookline, MA 02146 (SAN 696-9534).

Sandbird Publishing Group, The, *(Sandbird Pub; 0-9615111),* P.O. Box 1257, Shalimar, FL 32579 (SAN 694-1540) Tel 904-862-3746.

Sandcrab Press, *(Sandcrab; 0-9609870),* P.O. Box 1479, Corpus Cristi, TX 78403 (SAN 264-3685) Tel 512-852-5359; Dist. by: Publishers' Marketing Group, 1104 Summit Ave., Plainview, TX 75074 (SAN 262-0995) Tel 214-423-0312.

Sanderson, T. K., Organization, *(T K Sanderson; 0-911304),* 200 E. 25th St., Baltimore, MD 21218 (SAN 202-0785) Tel 301-235-3383.

Sandhills Pr., Inc., *(Sandhills Pr; 0-911015),* 219 S. 19th St., Ord, NE 68862 (SAN 275-2050).

†Sandlapper Publishing Co., Inc., *(Sandlapper Pub Co; 0-87844),* P.O. Box 1932, Orangeburg, SC 29116 (SAN 203-2678) Tel 803-531-1658; CIP.

Sandness, Robert C., *(Sandness; 0-9614076),* 321 Beaumont, Las Vegas, NV 89106 (SAN 685-9712) Tel 702-382-3796.

Sandollar Press, *(Sandollar Pr),* P.O. Box 4157, Santa Barbara, CA 93140-4157 (SAN 202-9952) Tel 805-963-7077.

Sandpiper Paperbacks *See* **Houghton Mifflin Co.**

Sandpiper Press, *(Sandpiper CA; 0-940356),* P.O.Box 128, Solana Beach, CA 92075 (SAN 217-5657) Tel 619-481-5259.

Sandpiper Pr., *(Sandpiper MI; 0-9614518),* 22023 Trombly, St. Clair Shores, MI 48080 (SAN 689-5921) Tel 313-773-3427.

Sandpiper Pr., *(Sandpiper OR; 0-9603748),* P.O. Box 286, Brookings, OR 97415 (SAN 213-5582) Tel 503-469-5588.

Sandrock & Foster, *(Sandrock & Foster),* Memorial Foundation, Box 841, Winona, MN 55987 (SAN 210-9514) Tel 507-452-1859.

Sandscape Pr., *(Sandscape Pr; 0-936721),* 1647 Willow Pass Rd., Suite 300, Concord, CA 94520 (SAN 699-8445) Tel 415-682-5327.

Sandspur Pr., *(Sandspur Pr; 0-932837),* P.O. Box 6011, Gulf Breeze, FL 32561 (SAN 688-606X) Tel 904-932-4725.

Sandstone Books *See* **Ohio State Univ. Pr.**

Sandstone Press *See* **Beil, Frederic C., Publishing Co.**

Sangamon State Univ., *(Sangamon St U),* Shepherd Rd., Springfield, IL 62708 (SAN 226-2215) Tel 217-786-6600.

Sangamon State Univ., Office of Public Affairs Communication, *(Sangamon Pub Aff; 0-938943),* Sangamon State Univ., Springfield, IL 62708 (SAN 661-7344) Tel 217-786-6502.

Sanguinaria Publishing, *(Sanguinaria; 0-9605210),* 85 Ferris St., Bridgeport, CT 06605 (SAN 215-806X) Tel 203-576-9168.

Sangwyne, *(Sangwyne; 0-938387),* 4548 Commonwealth, Detroit, MI 48208 (SAN 659-8781) Tel 313-832-5490.

Sankaty Head Press, *(Sankaty Head; 0-9606626),* Box 18, Siasconset, MA 02564 (SAN 223-114X).

Sansper, *(Sansper; 0-916865),* 134 Broadway, Costa Mesa, CA 92627 (SAN 654-5297) Tel 714-631-7273.

Sant Bani Ashram, Inc., *(Sant Bani Ash; 0-89142),* Franklin, NH 03235 (SAN 209-5114) Tel 603-934-2948.

Santa Barbara Botanic Garden, *(Santa Barb Botanic; 0-916436),* 1212 Mission Canyon Rd., Santa Barbara, CA 93105 (SAN 208-8398) Tel 805-682-4726.

Santa Barbara Museum of Art, *(Santa Barb Mus Art; 0-89951),* 1130 State St., Santa Barbara, CA 93101 (SAN 130-8165) Tel 805-963-4364; Dist. by: Univ. of Wash. Pr., P.O. Box C50096, Seattle, WA 98145 (SAN 212-2502) Tel 206-543-8870.

†Santa Barbara Pr., *(Santa Barb Pr; 0-915643),* 1129 State St., Suite H, Santa Barbara, CA 93101 (SAN 292-6431) Tel 805-966-2060; Dist. by: Publishers Group West, 5855 Beaudry St., Emeryville, CA 94608 (SAN 202-8522) Tel 415-658-3453; CIP.

Santa Barbara Pro Life Education, *(Santa Barb Life Ed; 0-9609902),* P.O. Box 30815, Santa Barbara, CA 93130 (SAN 262-9992).

Santa Catalina Publishing, *(Santa Catalina; 0-9612300),* Santa Catalina Schl., Mark Thomas Dr., Monterey, CA 93940 (SAN 289-5552) Tel 408-649-1432.

Santa Fe Botanical Research & Education Project, *(Santa Fe Botanical; 0-9616460),* P.O. Box 9459, Santa Fe, NM 87504-9459 (SAN 659-2961) Tel 505-988-4723; 825 Calle Mejia, Apt. 134, Santa Fe, NM 87504 (SAN 659-297X).

Santa Fe Ctr. For Photography, *(Santa Fe Photo; 0-9615298),* 104 W. San Francisco St., Santa Fe, NM 87501 (SAN 694-4663) Tel 505-988-4363.

Santa Fe Community School, *(Santa Fe Comm Sch),* P.O. Box 87504-2241, Santa Fe, NM 87501 (SAN 211-5743) Tel 505-471-6928.

Santa Fe East Gallery Pubns., *(Santa Fe E Gallery; 0-86534),* 200 Old Santa Fe Trail, Santa Fe, NM 87501 (SAN 239-3824) Tel 505-988-3103.

Santa Monica Publishing Co., *(Santa Monica Pub; 0-917640),* 414 Camino de las Animas, Santa Fe, NM 87501 (SAN 209-3855) Tel 505-983-4138.

Santa Susana Press *See* **California State Univ., Northridge Library**

†Santarasa Pubns., *(Santarasa Pubns; 0-935548),* P.O. Box 825, Manford, OK 74044 (SAN 213-7925); CIP.

Santiago Press, Inc., *(Santiago Pr; 0-940470),* 3616 Hyde Park, Midland, TX 79703 (SAN 219-0958).

Santiam Books, *(Santiam Bks; 0-9609936),* 744 Mader Ave. SE, Salem, OR 97302 (SAN 263-0001) Tel 503-362-7471.

Santillana Publishing Co., *(Santillana; 0-88272),* 257 Union St., Northvale, NJ 07647 (SAN 205-1133) Tel 201-767-6961; Toll free: 800-526-0107.

Santilli, Al, Jr., *(A Santilli; 0-9604394),* P.O. Box 2492, Dept.-5M, La Habra, CA 90631 (SAN 213-585X).

Santo Tomas Pr., The, *(Santo Tomas Pr; 0-930541),* P.O. Box 8, Sahuarita, AZ 85629 (SAN 687-6285).

Santos-Santos Pubns., *(Santos Santos Pubns; 0-9616484),* 4815 E. River Rd., Tucson, AZ 85718 (SAN 659-3399) Tel 602-577-2078.

Saphrograph Corp., *(Saphrograph; 0-87557),* 4910 Ft. Hamilton Pkwy., Brooklyn, NY 11219 (SAN 204-7276) Tel 718-331-1233.

Sara Publications, *(Sara Pubns; 0-9613096),* 603 SE Third St., Cochran, GA 31014 (SAN 294-6572) Tel 912-934-4794.

Sarasota Opera Society, The, Subs. of Sarasota Opera Association, Inc., *(Sarasota Opera; 0-9605844),* 4573 Northlake Dr., Sarasota, FL 33582 (SAN 216-3012) Tel 813-371-2408; 61 N. Pineapple St., Sarasota, FL 33582 (SAN 650-0579).

Sarasota Scientific Pr., *(Sarasota Sci; 0-9614464),* P.O. Box 25604, Sarasota, FL 34277 (SAN 689-433X) Tel 813-922-0604.

Sarasvati, *(Sarasvati; 0-9615026),* P.O. Box 306, Brookline, MA 02146 (SAN 694-0595) Tel 617-734-2939.

Sarcastic Toys, Div. of Massen's Fabrics, *(Sarcastic; 0-916437),* P.O. Box 2448, Yountville, CA 94599 (SAN 295-9143) Tel 707-253-1100.

Sarmen Book Co., *(Sarmen Bk Co; 0-9610394),* 87 Eileen St., Yarmouth Port, MA 02675 (SAN 283-2550) Tel 617-362-3518.

Sarsaparilla, *(Sarsaparilla; 0-930281),* 62 W. Huron, Chicago, IL 60610 (SAN 676-9810).

SarSan Pub Co, *(SarSan Pub; 0-940336),* Box 984, Brawley, CA 92227 (SAN 217-5665) Tel 714-344-9593.

Saru, *(Saru; 0-935086),* P.O. Box 1067, Sedona, AZ 86336 (SAN 687-6293).

Sasco Associates, *(Sasco; 0-912980),* P.O. Box 335, Southport, CT 06490 (SAN 204-7284).

Sasquatch Publishing Co., *(Sasquatch Pub; 0-912365),* 1931 Second Ave., Seattle, WA 98101 (SAN 289-0208) Tel 206-441-5555; Dist. by: Pacific Pipeline, 19215 66th Ave. S., Kent, WA 98032 (SAN 208-2128) Tel 206-872-5523.

Sassafras Pr., *(Sassafras Pr; 0-930528),* P.O. Box 1366, Evanston, IL 60204 (SAN 214-4662) Tel 312-670-5000.

Sassafras Pr., The, *(Sassafras MS; 0-9609692),* C/O Mijo Lithographing Co., Inc., P.O. Box 1104, Yazoo City, MS 39194 (SAN 662-135X) Tel 601-746-4693; c/o Mijo Lithographing Co., Inc., P.O. Box 1104, Yazoo City, MS 39194 (SAN 282-275X) Tel 601-746-4693.

Sassy Sayings Co., *(Sassy Sayings; 0-9615347),* P.O. Box 1851, North Little Rock, AR 72115 (SAN 695-1481) Tel 501-753-4971; 4019 Mellene, North Little Rock, AR 72118 (SAN 695-149X); Dist. by: PMG International, 1343 Columbia, No. 405, Richardson, TX 75081 (SAN 200-4739).

Satchell's Publishing, *(Satchells Pub; 0-931841),* 3124 Fifth Ave., Richmond, VA 23222 (SAN 685-9704) Tel 804-329-2130; Orders to: Adam Pr., 30 W. Washington St., Chicago, IL 60602 (SAN 662-2658) Tel 312-676-3426.

Satellite Continuing Education Inc., *(Satellite Cont; 0-9609184),* 706 Second Ave., Charles City, IA 50616 (SAN 241-4503) Tel 515-228-5558.

Satellite World, *(Satellite; 0-910419),* P.O. Box 74874, Los Angeles, CA 90004 (SAN 260-1303) Tel 213-669-1984.

Satori Pr., *(Satori Pr; 0-9617268),* 904 Silver Spur Rd., No. 324, Rolling Hills Estates, CA 90274 (SAN 663-5377); 2668 Via Olivera P. V., Rolling Hills Estates, CA 90274 (SAN 663-5385) Tel 213-377-7810.

Satori Pubns., *(Satori Pubns; 0-931937),* P.O. Box 1019, San Rafael, CA 94915-1019 (SAN 685-9690) Tel 415-955-6317.

Satori Resources, *(Satori Resources; 0-937277),* 732 Hamlin Way, San Leandro, CA 94578 (SAN 659-140X) Tel 415-895-8614; Dist. by: New Leaf Distributing, The, 1020 White St., SW, Atlanta, GA 30310 (SAN 169-1449); Dist. by: Bookpeople, 2929 Fifth St., Berkeley, CA 94710 (SAN 168-9517).

Names

Satterfield, Phillip Michael, *(P M Satterfield; 0-9616014),* 16702 Sampan Cir., Cerritos, CA 90701 (SAN 697-3132) Tel 213-865-7844; P.O. Box 447, Cypress, CA 90630 (SAN 697-3140).

†Saturday Pr., Inc., *(Saturday Pr; 0-938158),* P.O. Box 884, Upper Montclair, NJ 07043 (SAN 207-5792) Tel 201-256-1731; *CIP.*

Saturscent Pubns., *(Saturscent Pubns; 0-934703),* Box 358, South Wellfleet, MA 02663 (SAN 694-2687) Tel 617-349-2921.

†Saugus Historical Society, *(Saugus Hist; 0-936363),* 59 Water St., Saugus, MA 01906 (SAN 698-0317) Tel 617-242-5680; *CIP.*

Sauk Valley, *(Sauk),* Irish Hills, Brooklyn, MI 49230 (SAN 209-5122) Tel 517-467-2061.

Sauna Society of America, *(Sauna Soc),* 1001 Connecticut Ave., Washington, DC 20036 (SAN 224-6333) Tel 202-331-1365; Dist. by: Commercial Assocs., Inc., 1001 Connecticut Ave., Washington, DC 20036 (SAN 224-6341) Tel 202-331-1363.

Saunders, H. Duane, *(H D Saunders; 0-9616461),* 9840 Purgatory Rd., Eden Prairie, MN 55344 (SAN 659-3046) Tel 612-944-1656.

Saunders, W. B., Co., Subs. of Columbia Broadcasting System, *(Saunders; 0-7216),* W. Washington Sq., Philadelphia, PA 19105 (SAN 203-266X) Tel 215-574-4808. *Imprints:* Baillaire-Tindall (Bailliere-Tindall).

†Saunders College Publishing, Div. of CBS College Publishing, *(SCP; 0-03),* 383 Madison Ave., New York, NY 10017 (SAN 282-2768) Tel 212-872-2244; Orders to: CBS College Publishing, 383 Madison Ave., New York, NY 10017 (SAN 282-2776) Tel 212-750-1330; *CIP.*

Saur, K. G., Inc., Subs. of K. G. Saur Verlag, *(K G Saur; 0-89664),* 175 Fifth Ave., New York, NY 10010 (SAN 214-1264) Tel 212-982-1302.

Saurian Press, *(Saurian Pr; 0-936830),* New Mexico Tech, Socorro, NM 87801 (SAN 215-1065) Tel 505-835-5445.

Sauvie Island Press, *(Sauvie Island; 0-9606752),* 14745 NW Gillihan Rd., Portland, OR 97231 (SAN 219-6344) Tel 503-621-3357.

Savadove Productions, Inc., *(Savadove Prod; 0-938707),* 7420 Franklin Ave., Los Angeles, CA 90046 (SAN 661-5651) Tel 213-851-8400.

Savannah Junior Auxiliary, The, *(Savannah Jr Aux; 0-939114),* P.O. Box 434, Savannah, TN 38372 (SAN 262-0758).

Save on Shopping, *(S O S Pubns),* P.O. Box 10482, Jacksonville, FL 32207 (SAN 204-7160) Tel 904-733-8877; Dist. by: Random House, 201 E. 50th St., New York, NY 10022 (SAN 202-554X) Tel 212-872-8036.

Save Our Schools Research & Education Foundation, *(SOSREF; 0-938159),* 777 14th St., NW, Washington, DC 20005 (SAN 659-9001) Tel 703-356-0440.

Savoyard Bks. *See* **Wayne State Univ. Pr.**

Sawan Kirpal Pubns., *(Sawan Kirpal Pubns; 0-918224),* 115 S. "O" St., Lake Worth, FL 33460 (SAN 211-0571) Tel 804-633-5789; Orders to: Rte. 1, Box 24, Bowling Green, VA 22427 (SAN 211-058X).

Say When Pr., *(Say When Pr; 0-9615174),* P.O. Box 942, Greenbelt, MD 20770 (SAN 694-2873) Tel 301-474-0352.

Saybrook Pr., The, *(Saybrook Pr; 0-917941),* 146 Elm St., P.O. Box 629, Old Saybrook, CT 06475 (SAN 657-0186) Tel 203-388-5737.

Saybrook Publishing Co., Inc., *(Saybrook Pub Co; 0-933071),* 4223 Cole Ave., Suite 4, Dallas, TX 75205 (SAN 689-7924) Tel 214-521-2375; Dist. by: W. W. Norton Co., 500 Fifth Ave., New York, NY 10110 (SAN 202-5795) Tel 212-354-5500; Toll free: 800-223-2584.

Saylor, Lee, Inc., *(Saylor; 0-931708),* 1855 Olympic Blvd., Walnut Creek, CA 94596 (SAN 211-5751).

S.C. Toof & Co., *(S C Toof),* P.O. Box 14607, Memphis, TN 38114 (SAN 289-5498).

Scala Bks., *(Scala Books; 0-935748),* 1035 Fifth Ave., New York, NY 10028 (SAN 282-2784) Tel 212-737-0242; Toll free: 800-242-7737; Orders to: Harper & Row Pubs., Inc., Keystone Industrial Pk., Scranton, PA 18512 (SAN 215-3742).

Scale Manufacturers Association, *(Scale Mfrs),* 152 Rollins Ave., Suite 208, Rockville, MD 20852 (SAN 224-9812) Tel 301-984-9080.

Scandia Pubs., *(Scandia Pubs; 0-937242),* 5921 Niwot Rd., Longmont, CO 80501 (SAN 282-2806) Tel 303-530-0824.

Scandinavian Philatelic Foundation, *(Scand Philatelic; 0-936493),* 292 Green Moor Pl., Thousand Oaks, CA 91359 (SAN 698-0783) Tel 805-496-9993; Box 6716, Thousand Oaks, CA 91359 (SAN 698-2514).

Scanner Master Publishing Co., *(Scanner Master; 0-939430),* 13 Pond St., Natick, MA 01760 (SAN 216-583X) Tel 617-653-4016.

Scanning Electron Microscopy, Inc., *(Scanning Electron; 0-931284),* P.O. Box 66507, AMF O'Hare, Chicago, IL 60666 (SAN 213-5868) Tel 312-529-6677.

Scarab Press, *(Scarab Pr; 0-912962),* 63 Bates Blvd., Orinda, CA 94563 (SAN 204-7306).

†Scarecrow Pr., Inc., Subs. of Grolier Educational Corp., *(Scarecrow; 0-8108),* 52 Liberty St., Box 4167, Metuchen, NJ 08840 (SAN 203-2651) Tel 201-548-8600; *CIP.*

Scarf Press, *(Scarf Pr; 0-934386),* 58 E. 83rd St., New York, NY 10028 (SAN 212-9698) Tel 212-744-3901.

SCB Photographics, *(SCB Photos; 0-940468),* P.O. Box 491114, Brentwood, CA 94513 (SAN 223-1581) Tel 213-826-8341.

Scenographic Media, *(Scenographic; 0-913868),* Box 2122, Norwalk, CT 06851 (SAN 205-1443).

Scepter Pubs., *(Scepter Pubs; 0-933932),* 481 Main St., New Rochelle, NY 10801 (SAN 207-2858) Tel 914-636-3377.

Sceptre Publishing Co., *(Sceptre Pub; 0-9615855),* 12584 Cresta Ct., San Diego, CA 92128 (SAN 696-7558) Tel 619-485-9355; Orders to: Sceptre Pub. Co., P.O. Box 28531, San Diego, CA 92128 (SAN 662-3867) Tel 619-485-9355.

Schaefer Studios, *(Schaefer Studios; 0-9614928),* Shorewood Dr., Madison Lake, MN 56063 (SAN 693-3645) Tel 507-243-3300.

Schaffer, Frank, Pubns., Inc., *(Schaffer Pubns; 0-86734),* 19771 Magellan Dr., Torrance, CA 90502 (SAN 217-5827) Tel 213-532-5420.

Schafler Enterprises, *(Schafler Ent; 0-9603154),* 257 Ricardo Rd., Mill Valley, CA 94941 (SAN 212-5536) Tel 415-383-0830.

Schalaco Publishing Co., *(Schalaco Pub; 0-9608560),* 5123 E. McDonald Dr., Paradise Valley, AZ 85253 (SAN 240-768X) Tel 602-279-2885.

Schalit, Michael, *(M Schalit; 0-9604630),* 451 Bell Ave., Livermore, CA 94550 (SAN 213-7933) Tel 415-443-2456.

Schalkenbach, Robert, Foundation, *(Schalkenbach; 0-911312),* 5 E. 44th St., New York, NY 10017 (SAN 206-1317) Tel 212-986-8684.

Schar Publishing Co., *(Schar Pub Co; 0-9611830),* 2541 W. Ainslie St., Chicago, IL 60625 (SAN 240-8279) Tel 312-784-2186; Dist. by: K. V. Schar, 2541 W. Ainslie St., Chicago, IL 60625 (SAN 240-8287).

Scharf & Silverman Pubs., Ltd., *(Scharf & Sil Publishers; 0-916523),* 50 E. 42nd St., Suite 1007, New York, NY 10017 (SAN 295-4966) Tel 212-697-4026.

Scharff Assocs., *(Scharff Assocs; 0-937558),* R.D. 1, Box 276, New Ringgold, PA 17960 (SAN 697-1822) Tel 717-943-2216.

†Schaumburg Pubns., Inc., *(Schaumburg Pubns; 0-935690),* 1432 S. Mohawk, Roselle, IL 60172 (SAN 214-221X); *CIP.*

Scheid, Margaret M., Author Pub., *(M Scheid; 0-9616115),* P.O. Box 1167, Southwest Harbor, ME 04679 (SAN 699-7201) Tel 207-244-3870.

†Schenkman Bks., Inc., *(Schenkman Bks Inc; 0-87073; 0-87047),* 190 Concord Ave., Cambridge, MA 02138 (SAN 203-2643) Tel 617-492-4952; Orders to: P.O. Box 1570, Cambridge, MA 02138 (SAN 662-1368); *CIP.*

Scherer, John L., Jr., *(J L Scherer; 0-9607258),* 4900 18th Ave. S., Minneapolis, MN 55417 (SAN 209-1429) Tel 612-722-2947.

Schiedt, Duncan P., *(D Schiedt; 0-9603528),* R.R.1, Box 217A, Pittsboro, IN 46167 (SAN 211-3996) Tel 317-852-8528.

Schiffer Publishing, Ltd., *(Schiffer; 0-916838; 0-88740),* 1469 Morstein Rd., West Chester, PA 19380 (SAN 208-8428) Tel 215-696-1001.

Schiffli Lace & Embroidery Manufacturers Assn., Inc., *(Schiffli Lace),* 512 23rd St., Union City, NJ 07087 (SAN 224-6228) Tel 201-863-7300.

Schildge Publishing Co., *(Schildge Pub; 0-9615595),* R.D. 2, Box 336, Plattsburgh, NY 12901 (SAN 696-1770) Tel 518-561-4752.

Schiller, Alexandra, *(A Schiller),* 911 E. 420 S., Provo, UT 85601 (SAN 696-7264) Tel 801-375-2938.

Schirmer, E. C., Music Co., Inc., *(E C Schirmer; 0-911318),* 138 Ipswich St., Boston, MA 02215 (SAN 201-3517) Tel 617-236-1935.

Schirmer Bks., Div. of Macmillan Publishing Co., Inc., *(Schirmer Bks; 0-911320),* 866 Third Ave., New York, NY 10022 (SAN 222-9544); Toll free: 800-257-5755.

Schmidt, Terry L., Inc., *(T L Schmidt Inc; 0-9612066),* 8950 Villa La Jolla Dr., Suite 1200, La Jolla, CA 92037 (SAN 286-8709) Tel 619-457-3444.

Schmul Publishing Co. Inc., *(Schmul Pub Co; 0-88019),* P.O. Box 4068, Salem, OH 44460 (SAN 211-8246).

Schmutz, Ervin M., *(E M Schmutz; 0-9617156),* 1811 N. Highland Ave., Tucson, AZ 85719 (SAN 663-1665) Tel 602-326-9479; Dist. by: Northland Press, P.O. Box N, Flagstaff, AZ 86002 (SAN 202-9251) Tel 602-774-5251; Dist. by: Univ Of Az Press, 1615 E. Speedway, Tucson, AZ 85719 (SAN 205-468X) Tel 602-795-0583.

Schnatz, G, Pubns., *(G Schnatz Pubns; 0-9614145),* 192 Woodside Ave., Lodi, NJ 07644 (SAN 686-2276) Tel 201-471-2624.

Schneeberger, Tilly, & Assoc., *(Schneeberger),* P.O. Box 623, 578 El Sol St., Ojai, CA 93023 (SAN 213-3709) Tel 805-646-0208.

Schneider, Bennett, Bookseller, *(B Schneider; 0-918797),* 300 Ward Parkway, Kansas City, MO 64112 (SAN 657-3266) Tel 816-531-8484.

Schneider, Coleman, *(C Schneider; 0-9601662),* P.O. Box 762, Tenafly, NJ 07670 (SAN 211-4186) Tel 201-567-9157.

Schneider, J. G., *(J G Schneider; 0-9613335),* Box 165 1402 S. Cage, Pharr, TX 78577 (SAN 655-7503) Tel 512-781-0045.

Schneider, Le Roy, *(Schneider; 0-9614482),* 27515 Baretta Dr., Bonita Springs, FL 33923 (SAN 212-6214) Tel 813-992-0531.

Schneider, R., Pubs., *(Schneider Pubs; 0-936984),* 312 Linwood Ave., Stevens Point, WI 54481 (SAN 217-1317) Tel 715-341-0020.

Schnell Publishing Co., Inc., *(Schnell Pub; 0-9606454),* 100 Church St., New York, NY 10007-2694 (SAN 205-1435) Tel 212-732-9820.

Schocken, Wolfgang A., *(W Schocken; 0-9615883),* 18 Traill St., Cambridge, MA 02138 (SAN 696-7698) Tel 617-354-6192.

Schocken Bks., Inc., *(Schocken; 0-8052),* 62 Cooper Sq., New York, NY 10003 (SAN 213-7585) Tel 212-475-4900. *Imprints:* Moonlight Editions (Moonlight Edns).

Schoenhof's Foreign Books, Inc., Subs. of Editions Gallimard, *(Schoenhof; 0-87774),* 76A Mount Auburn St., Cambridge, MA 02138 (SAN 212-0062) Tel 617-547-8855.

Schoepfer, G. R., *(G R Schoepfer; 0-931436),* 786 Hudson Pkwy., Whiting, NJ 08759 (SAN 211-1659) Tel 201-849-0689.

Schofield Publishing Co., *(Schofield Pub; 0-9608720),* 29928 Lilac Rd., Valley Ctr., CA 92082 (SAN 238-3659) Tel 714-749-1325.

Schola Press, *(Schola Pr TX; 0-931016),* P.O. Box 294, Lorena, TX 76655 (SAN 216-4469) Tel 817-857-3566.

Scholarly Pr., Inc., *(Scholarly; 0-403),* P.O. Box 160, St. Clair Shores, MI 48080 (SAN 209-0473). *Imprints:* Regency Press (Regency).

Scholarly Pubns., *(Scholarly Pubns; 0-88065; 1-55528),* 7310 El Cresta Dr., Houston, TX 77083 (SAN 650-0587) Tel 713-879-8319.

†Scholarly Resources, Inc., (Scholarly Res Inc; 0-8420), 104 Greenhill Ave., Wilmington, DE 19805 (SAN 203-2619) Tel 302-654-7713; Toll free: 800-772-8937. Source materials on 35mm microfilm, monographs, reference books & microfiche. Subjects: ethnic studies, genealogy, history, law, military studies & political science. Government documents, journals, manuscript collections & newspapers; CIP.

†Scholars Book Co., (Scholars Bk; 0-914348), 4431 Mt. Vernon, Houston, TX 77006-5889 (SAN 205-1419) Tel 713-528-4395; CIP.

Scholars Bks., (Scholars Bks; 0-938659), P.O. Box 160361, Irving, TX 75016 (SAN 661-1346) Tel 214-686-5332.

†Scholars' Facsimiles & Reprints, (Schol Facsimiles; 0-8201), P.O. Box 344, Delmar, NY 12054 (SAN 203-2627) Tel 518-439-5978; CIP.

Scholars Portable Pubns., (Scholars Portable; 0-9604778), 1459 Southfield Rd., Evansville, IN 47715 (SAN 211-3465) Tel 812-476-6697.

Scholars Pr., (Scholars Pr GA; 0-89130; 1-55540), P.O. Box 1608, Decatur, GA 30031-1608 (SAN 293-3896) Tel 404-636-4757; Dist. by: Johns Hopkins Univ. Pr., P.O. Box 4869, Hampden Sta., Baltimore, MD 21211 (SAN 202-7348) Tel 301-338-6946.

Scholars' Press, Ltd., (Scholars Pr Ltd; 0-914044), P.O. Box 7231, Roanoke, VA 24019 (SAN 203-2600).

Scholar's Reference Library, (Scholars Ref Lib), P.O. Box 148, Darby, PA 19023 (SAN 205-1400).

Scholars Studies Press, (Scholars Studies; 0-89177), 109 E. Ninth St., New York, NY 10003 (SAN 208-3795) Tel 212-674-5296.

Scholastic Hardcover See Scholastic, Inc.

Scholastic, Inc., (Scholastic Inc; 0-590), 730 Broadway, New York, NY 10003 (SAN 202-5442) Tel 212-505-3000; Toll free: 800-392-2179; Orders to: P.O. Box 7502, 2931 E. McCarty St., Jefferson City, MO 65102 (SAN 202-5450). Imprints: Apple Paperbacks (Apple Paperbacks); Blue Ribbon Books (Blue Ribbon Bks); Citation Press (Citation); Hello Reader (Hello Reader); Lucky Star (Lucky Star); Point (Point); Scholastic Hardcover (Scholastic Hardcover); Seesaw Books (Seesaw Bks); Starline (Starline); Sunfire (Sunfire); Vagabond (Vagabond); Wildfire Press (Wildfire); Windswept Books (Windswept Bks); Wishing Star Books (Wishing Star Bks).

Scholastic Testing Service, Inc., (Schol Test; 0-936224), 480 Meyer Rd., P.O. Box 1056, Bensenville, IL 60106-8056 (SAN 200-2183) Tel 312-766-7150.

†Scholasticus Pub., (Scholasticus; 0-9606754), P.O. Box 2727, Springfield, VA 22152 (SAN 211-450X); CIP.

Scholium International, Inc., (Scholium Intl; 0-87936), 265 Great Neck Rd., Great Neck, NY 11021 (SAN 169-5282) Tel 516-466-5181.

Scholl Communications, Inc., (Scholl; 0-912519), P.O. Box 560, Deerfield, IL 60015 (SAN 265-296X) Tel 312-945-1891.

Schon, Kurt E., Ltd., (K E Schon; 0-9603880), 510 Saint Louis St., New Orleans, LA 70130 (SAN 214-1361) Tel 504-524-5462.

School Administrators' Bookstore, (Schl Admin Bkst; 0-939136), P.O. Box 1767, Tustin, CA 92681 (SAN 239-6823) Tel 714-720-0773.

†School Age Notes, (School Age; 0-917505), P.O. Box 120674, Nashville, TN 37212 (SAN 656-1004) Tel 615-292-4957; CIP.

School Aid Co., (Sch Aid; 0-87385), 911 Colfax Dr., P.O. Box 123, Danville, IL 61832 (SAN 158-3719); Toll free: 800-447-2665.

School & Home CourseWare, Inc., (Sch Home CourseWare; 0-918123), 301 W. Mesa, Fresno, CA 93704 (SAN 650-9169) Tel 209-431-8300.

School Dept. See Harper & Row Pubs., Inc.

†School of American Research Pr., (School Am Res; 0-933452), P.O. Box 2188, Santa Fe, NM 87504 (SAN 212-6222) Tel 505-984-0741; CIP.

School of Architecture & Interior Design, (Sch Arch Interior Des; 0-939592), Univ. of Cincinnati, Cincinnati, OH 45221 (SAN 216-650X) Tel 513-475-6485.

School of Foreign Service See Georgetown Univ., Schl. of Foreign Service

School of Library and Information Management Emporia State Univ., (Sch Lib Sci), 1200 Commercial, Emporia, KS 66801 (SAN 209-598X) Tel 316-343-1200.

School of Living Adult Education, (School Living; 0-87663; 0-87983), RD 7, Box 388, York, PA 17402 (SAN 275-2271) Tel 717-755-2666.

School Projectionist Club of America, (Sch Proj Club; 0-911328), P.O. Box 44, State College, PA 16801 (SAN 204-7322).

School Science & Mathematics Assn., Inc., (Sch Sci Math; 0-912047), Bowling Green State Univ., 126 Life Science Bldg., Bowling Green, OH 43403-0256 (SAN 275-228X) Tel 419-372-7393.

School Street Pr., (Schl St Pr; 0-939105), P.O. Box 558, Hastings-On-Hudson, NY 10706 (SAN 662-5975); 28 School St., Hastings-on-Hudson, NY 10706 (SAN 662-5983) Tel 914-478-4490.

School Zone Publishing Co., (Sch Zone Pub Co; 0-938256; 0-88743), 1819 Industrial Dr., P.O. Box 703, Grand Haven, MI 49417 (SAN 289-8314) Tel 616-846-5030; Toll free: 800-253-0564.

Schoolhouse Pr., (Schoolhouse Pr; 0-9615669), 46 Mountain View Dr., Peterborough, NH 03458-1325 (SAN 696-1312) Tel 603-924-7849. Do not confuse with either of two other companies with the same name: Schoolhouse Pr., Pittsville, WI, or Independence, OH.

Schoolhouse Pr., (Schoolhouse WI; 0-942018), 6899 Cary Bluff, Pittsville, WI 54466 (SAN 239-8044) Tel 715-884-2799. Do not confuse with either of two other companies with the same name: Schoolhouse Pr., Peterborough, NH, or Independence, OH.

Schpitfeir Publishing, Subs. of Schpitfeir Enterprises, (Schpitfeir; 0-9607330), P.O. Box 4253, Seattle, WA 98104-0253 (SAN 293-387X) Tel 206-622-7222; Dist. by: Cogan Bks., 4332 W. Artesia Ave., Fullerton, CA 92633 (SAN 168-9649); Dist. by: The Distributors, 702 S. Michigan, South Bend, IN 46618 (SAN 212-0364) Tel 219-232-8500; Dist. by: Pacific Pipeline, 19215 66th Ave. S., Kent, WA 98032 (SAN 208-2128) Tel 206-872-5523; Dist. by: C & M Pubns., 6110 Highway 290, West Austin, TX 78735 (SAN 216-227X) Tel 512-892-5234; Dist. by: EZ Cookin Book' Co., 9925 Currant Ave., Fountain Valley, CA 92708 (SAN 240-9364) Tel 714-968-9102; Dist. by: Quality Bks., 918 Sherwood Dr., Lake Bluff, IL 60044-2204 (SAN 169-2127).

Schrello Direct Marketing, (Schrello Market; 0-935823), 555 E. Ocean Blvd., Long Beach, CA 90801 (SAN 696-5849) Tel 213-437-2230; P.O. Box 1610, Long Beach, CA 90801 (SAN 699-6361).

Schroder Music Co., (Schroder Music; 0-915620), 1450-6th St., Berkeley, CA 94710 (SAN 207-3935) Tel 415-524-5804; Dist. by: The Childrens Small Pr. Collection, 719 N. Fourth Ave., Ann Arbor, MI 48104 (SAN 200-514X).

†Schroeder Prints, Inc., (Schroeder Prints; 0-931766), Green Shed, 33 W. St., Annapolis, MD 21401 (SAN 211-6472) Tel 301-269-1812; CIP.

Schroeppel, Tom, (Schroeppel; 0-9603718), 4705 Bay View Ave., Tampa, FL 33611 (SAN 213-7941).

Schubert Club, The, (Schubert; 0-912373), 302 Landmark Center, St. Paul, MN 55102 (SAN 265-1998) Tel 612-292-3267.

Schuchman-Falk, (Schuchman; 0-9615049), 4135 Washburn Ave. N., Minneapolis, MN 55412 (SAN 693-8620) Tel 612-521-4328.

Schueler Communications, (Schueler Comm; 0-9614965), 208 N. Townsend St., Syracuse, NY 13203 (SAN 693-7500) Tel 315-472-6948.

Schulak, Bernard, & Assoc. Architects, Pub., (Schulak & Assoc; 0-9602186), 6889 W. Maple Rd., West Bloomfield, MI 48033 (SAN 212-2278).

Schultz, Elva, (E Schultz; 0-9616431), 300 Country Rd. 9, SE, Brainerd, MN 56401 (SAN 659-1507) Tel 218-829-3449.

Schumacher Pubns, (Schumacher Pubns; 0-917378), 28 Holly Ln., Zenith Terr., Proctor, MN 55810 (SAN 208-8436) Tel 218-624-7728.

Schwab, Henry R., /Doberman Bks., (H R Schwab; 0-939681), 290 York St., New Haven, CT 06511 (SAN 663-4842) Tel 203-777-8954; Dist. by: Inland Book Co., P.O. Box 261, 22 Hemingway Ave., East Haven, CT 06512 (SAN 200-4151) Tel 203-467-4257.

Schwartz, Barbara, (Barbara Schwartz; 0-936627), 3835 Sedgwick Ave., 9-B, Bronx, NY 10463 (SAN 699-6930) Tel 212-365-2611.

Schweitzer, Albert, Fellowship, (Albert Schweitzer), 866 United Nations Plaza, New York, NY 10017 (SAN 225-3968) Tel 212-725-1760.

Schwenkfelder Library, (Schwenkfelder Lib; 0-935980), 1 Seminary St., Pennsburg, PA 18073 (SAN 213-795X) Tel 215-679-3103.

Sci-Tech Pubns., (Sci-Tech Pubns; 0-914469), P.O. Box 5201, San Jose, CA 95150 (SAN 289-7113) Tel 408-266-5706.

SCIDATA See PennWell Bks.

Science & Behavior Bks., Inc., (Sci & Behavior; 0-8314), P.O. Box 60519, Palo Alto, CA 94306 (SAN 204-7349) Tel 415-326-6465.

Science & Technology Pr., (Sci & Tech Pr; 0-912291), P.O. Box 614, Latham, NY 12110 (SAN 203-2597) Tel 518-785-8517.

†Science Associates/International, Inc., (Sci Assoc Intl; 0-87837), 1841 Broadway, New York, NY 10023 (SAN 204-7357) Tel 212-265-4995; CIP.

Science Enterprises, Inc., (Sci Ent; 0-930116), Box 88443, Indianapolis, IN 46208 (SAN 210-6639) Tel 317-259-1054.

Science Fiction & Fantasy Productions, Inc., (Sci Fict & Fant Prodns; 0-931683), 21111 Mapleridge, Southfield, MI 48075-5704 (SAN 683-759X) Tel 313-355-9827.

Science for Citizens Ctr., (Sci Citizens; 0-931123), Western Michigan Univ., Kalamazoo, MI 49008 (SAN 655-1335).

Science for the People, (Sci People; 0-9607314), 897 Main St., Cambridge, MA 02139 (SAN 218-3544) Tel 617-547-0370.

Science History Publications See Watson, Neale, Academic Pubns.

Science Man Pr., Div. of TSM Marketing, Inc., (Science Man Pr; 0-936046), 4738 N. Harlem Ave., Harwood Heights, IL 60656 (SAN 213-7968).

Science-Med Pr., (Sci Med Pr; 0-9617051), 617 Grant, No. 4, Santa Monica, CA 90405 (SAN 662-8850) Tel 213-396-5136.

Science Museum of Minnesota, (Sci Museum; 0-911338), 30 E. Tenth St., St. Paul, MN 55101 (SAN 204-7365) Tel 612-221-9488.

Science of Identity Foundation, (Science Identity; 0-88187), P.O. Box 27450, Honolulu, HI 96827 (SAN 264-6900) Tel 808-488-4798.

Science of Mind Pubns., Div. of United Church of Religious Science, (Sci of Mind; 0-917849), P.O. Box 75127, Los Angeles, CA 90075 (SAN 203-2570) Tel 213-388-2181; Dist. by: Devorss & Co., P.O. Box 550, 1046 Princeton Dr., Marina del Rey, CA 90294 (SAN 168-9886); Dist. by: New Leaf Distributors, The, 1020 White St., SW, Altanta, GA 30310 (SAN 169-1449) Tel 404-755-2665.

Science Paperbacks See Barnes & Noble Bks.-Imports

†Science Pr., (Sci Pr; 0-89500), 8 Brookstone Dr., Princeton, NJ 08540 (SAN 210-0053) Tel 609-921-3405; CIP.

†Science Research Assocs., Subs. of IBM, (SRA; 0-574), 155 N. Wacker Dr. Chicago, IL 60606 (SAN 295-3498) Tel 312-984-7226; Toll free: 800-621-0476; CIP.

Science Research Assocs., Inc., College Div., Subs. of IBM, (Sci Res Assoc Coll), 155 N. Wacker Dr., Chicago, IL 60606-1780 (SAN 215-207X) Tel 312-984-7000.

Science Software Systems, Inc., (Science Software; 0-937292), 11899 W. Pico Blvd., West Los Angeles, CA 90064 (SAN 240-155X) Tel 213-477-8541.

†Science Tech, Inc., (Sci Tech Inc; 0-910239), 701 Ridge St., Madison, WI 53705 (SAN 241-4511) Tel 608-238-8664; CIP.

Science, Technology, & Human Values, (STHV; 0-932564), Massachusetts Institute of Technology, Bldg. 14, Cambridge, MA 02139 (SAN 212-2286) Tel 617-253-4010.

Names

589

Names

Science-Thru-Media, Inc., *(Sci-Thru-Media; 0-918473),* 303 Fifth Ave., Suite 803, New York, NY 10016 (SAN 657-7156) Tel 212-684-5366.

Scienspot Pubns., *(Scienspot; 0-937926),* 39 Brunswick Ave., Troy, NY 12180 (SAN 216-1850).

†**Scientific American Bks.,** *(Sci Am Bks),* 41 Madison Ave., New York, NY 10010 (SAN 291-9311) Tel 212-532-7660; Orders to: 44 19 W. 1980 S., Salt Lake City, UT 84104 (SAN 291-932X); *CIP.*

Scientific American, Inc., Subs. of W. H. Freeman & Co., *(Scientific Am Inc; 0-89454),* 415 Madison Ave., New York, NY 10017 Tel 212-754-0476.

Scientific Communication International, *(Sci Comm Intl; 0-936097),* 745 High, Pullman, WA 99163 (SAN 696-7523) Tel 509-335-4300.

Scientific Manpower Commission, *(Sci Manpower),* 1500 Massachusetts Ave., NW, Suite 831, Washington, DC 20005 (SAN 225-2058) Tel 202-223-6995.

Scientific Medical Pubns. of France, *(S M P F Inc),* 16 E. 34th St., 7th Flr., New York, NY 10016 (SAN 689-8998) Tel 212-683-4441.

Scientific Newsletter Enterprises, Inc., *(Sci Newsletters; 0-930914),* P.O. Box 3205, Mission Viejo, CA 92690-1205 (SAN 212-2294) Tel 714-240-3579.

Scientific Peace Builders Foundation, *(Sci Peace Builders),* P.O. Box 3037, Santa Monica, CA 90403 (SAN 204-7373) Tel 213-394-4111.

Scientific Pr., The, *(Scientific Pr; 0-89426; 0-928763),* 540 University Ave., Palo Alto, CA 94301 (SAN 687-8520) Tel 415-322-5221.

†**Scientific Software, Inc.,** *(Sci Ware; 0-89498),* P.O. Box 536, Mooresville, IN 46158 (SAN 209-9691) Tel 317-831-6296; *CIP.*

Scientific Software Products, Inc., *(Sci Soft Prods; 0-918127),* 5720 W. 71st St., Indianapolis, IN 46278 (SAN 296-7065) Tel 317-293-9270.

Scientific Therapeutics Information, *(Sci Therapeutics Info; 0-936871),* 2050 Center Ave., Suite 200, Fort Lee, NJ 07024 (SAN 699-931X) Tel 201-461-4969.

Scion Information Services, *(Scion Info Servs; 0-936495),* 332 S. Division, No. 4, Ann Arbor, MI 48104 (SAN 698-0708) Tel 313-761-4842; P.O. Box 13, Ann Arbor, MI 48107 (SAN 698-2506).

Scolar Pr., *(Scolar; 0-85967),* 2430 Bancroft Way, Berkeley, CA 94704 (SAN 679-1719).

Scop & Gleeman, *(Scop & Gleeman; 0-9616986),* RR 4, P.O. Box 400, Putnam Valley, NY 10579 (SAN 661-7298) Tel 914-528-7385; Bell Hollow Rd., Putnam Valley, NY 10579 (SAN 661-7301).

Scoper, Vincent, Jr., *(V Scoper; 0-9600514),* P.O. Box 2366, Laurel, MS 39440 (SAN 205-4736).

Scorpio Pr., The, Div. of Peralta Shipping Corp., *(Scorpio Pr; 0-938727),* 50 Broadway, New York, NY 10004 (SAN 661-6135) Tel 212-509-2835.

Scorpio Pubns., *(Scorpio Pubns; 0-936099),* 2 E. Butler Ave., Chalfont, PA 18914 (SAN 696-7515) Tel 215-822-3987.

Scorpion Pr., *(Scorpion Pr; 0-9609290),* 20125 S.W. TV Hwy. 21, Aloha, OR 97006 (SAN 240-8759).

Scot, Bret, Pr., Div. of College Marketing Group, Inc., *(Bret Scot Pr; 0-936443),* 50 Cross St., Winchester, MA 01890 (SAN 699-7597) Tel 617-729-4813.

Scotpress, Div. of Unicorn Ltd., *(ScotPr; 0-912951),* P.O. Box 778, Morgantown, WV 26505 (SAN 283-3670) Tel 304-599-1877.

†**Scott, Amanda, Publishing Co.,** *(A Scott Pub Co; 0-916525),* 6117 Squirrelwood Lane, Cincinnati, OH 45247 (SAN 295-5261) Tel 513-741-7272; *CIP.*

Scott, Beverly A., Pub., *(B A Scott),* P.O. Box 114, Chandler, AZ 85224 (SAN 207-6101) Tel 602-963-5787.

Scott, Jack, *(Jack Scott; 0-9616029),* 26 Township Line Rd., Apt. C48, Elkins Park, MD 19117 (SAN 699-7600) Tel 215-379-2898.

Scott, M. L., & Associates, Pubs., *(Scott & Assocs; 0-9602726),* P.O. Box 816, Ithaca, NY 14850 (SAN 669-2621) Tel 607-387-9560; Dist. by: R. J. Young, P.O. Box 816, Ithaca, NY 14850 (SAN 669-263X) Tel 607-387-9560.

Scott & Craft Pubs., *(Scott Craft Pubs; 0-9614538),* P.O. Box 1312, Kingsport, TN 37662 (SAN 692-3364) Tel 615-247-7535; Orders to: Albury Press, P.O. Box 55388, Tulsa, OK 74155 (SAN 662-2984).

Scott & Daughters Publishing, Inc., *(Scott & Daughters; 0-911113),* 940 N. Highland Ave., Los Angeles, CA 90038 (SAN 275-2395) Tel 213-856-0008; Toll free: 800-547-2688.

†**Scott, Foresman & Co.,** Subs. of SFN Co., *(Scott F; 0-673),* 1900 E. Lake Ave., Glenview, IL 60025 (SAN 200-2140) Tel 312-729-3000; *CIP.*

†**Scott Pubns.,** *(Scott Pubns MI),* 30595 W. Eight Mile Rd., Livonia, MI 48152 (SAN 240-8872) Tel 313-477-6650; Toll free: 800-458-8237; *CIP.*

Scott Publishing Co., Subs. of Amos Pr., Inc., *(Scott Pub Co; 0-89487),* P.O. Box 828, Sidney, OH 45365 (SAN 205-9770) Tel 513-498-0802; Toll free: 800-848-4406; 911 Vandemark Rd., Sidney, OH 45365 (SAN 658-1579).

Scott-Wesley Publishing, *(Scott-Wesley; 0-936137),* 20155 Keswick St., Suite 210, Canoga Park, CA 91306 (SAN 697-1644); P.O. Box 2253, Canoga Park, CA 91306 (SAN 697-1652).

Scottwall Assocs., *(Scottwall Assocs; 0-9612790),* 95 Scott St., San Francisco, CA 94117 (SAN 289-8322) Tel 415-861-1956.

Scout Creek Pr., *(Scout Creek Pr; 0-930219),* P.O. Box 3, 3467 Chippewa Court, West Linn, OR 97068 (SAN 670-8404) Tel 503-635-1333; Orders to: Pacific Northwest Books, Inc., P.O. Box 314, Medford, OR 97501 (SAN 660-9546).

Scream Pr., *(Scream Pr; 0-910489),* P.O. Box 8531, Santa Cruz, CA 95061 (SAN 260-132X) Tel 408-425-0233.

Screaming Suicide Pr., *(Screaming Suicide; 0-936365),* 140 E. Magnolia, San Antonio, TX 78212 (SAN 698-0325) Tel 512-737-2137.

Scribblers Inc., *(Scribblers; 0-943386),* 411 N. Akard, Suite 810, Dallas, TX 75201 (SAN 240-7698) Tel 214-954-0189.

Scribe, B. C., Pubns., *(B C Scribe; 0-930548),* P.O. Box 2453, Providence, RI 02906-0453 (SAN 212-1727) Tel 401-245-6478.

Scribe Write, *(Scribe Write; 0-939909),* P.O. Box 9263, Missoula, MT 59807 (SAN 661-454X).

Scribner's, Charles, Sons, Div. of Macmillan Publishing Co., *(Scribner; 0-684),* 115 Fifth Ave., New York, NY 10003 (SAN 200-2191) Tel 212-614-1300; Toll free: 800-257-5755; Orders to: Order Dept., Front & Brown Sts., Riverside, NJ 08075 (SAN 282-6550); Toll free: 800-257-5755.

†**Scrimshaw Pr.,** *(Scrimshaw; 0-87155),* P.O. Box 10, Centerville, MA 02632 (SAN 206-9253); *CIP.*

Scripps Institution of Oceanography, Univ of California, San Diego, *(Scripps Inst Ocean; 0-9603078),* A007, La Jolla, CA 92093 (SAN 213-1625).

Scripps Ranch Pubns., *(Scripps Ranch Pubns; 0-9614489),* 10743 Brookview Ln., San Diego, CA 92131 (SAN 689-4542) Tel 619-271-9749.

†**Scripta Humanistica,** *(Scripta; 0-916379),* 1383 Kersey Lane, Potomac, MD 20854 (SAN 295-8562) Tel 301-340-1095; *CIP.*

Scriptorium Pr., The, *(Scriptorium Pr; 0-931485),* 71 S. Main St., Alfred, NY 14802 (SAN 683-1354) Tel 607-587-9371.

Scriptorium, The, *(Scriptorium),* c/o The Gryphon Bookshop, 216 W. 89 St., New York, NY 10024 (SAN 293-3918) Tel 212-362-0706.

Scripture Press Pubns., Inc., *(SP Pubns; 0-88207; 0-89693),* 1825 College Ave., Wheaton, IL 60187 (SAN 222-9471) Tel 312-668-6000; Toll free: 800-323-9409. *Imprints:* Sonflower Books (Sonflower Bks).

Scripture Union Publishing, *(Scripture U Pub; 0-913585),* 1716 Spruce St., Philadelphia, PA 19103 (SAN 285-3817) Tel 215-732-2079.

ScriptWriters-Filmmakers Publishing Co., *(Script Writers; 0-910665),* 8033 Sunset Blvd., Suite 306, West Hollywood, CA 90046 (SAN 262-7639) Tel 213-650-0600 Tel 714-892-2562.

†**Scroll Pr., Inc.,** *(Scroll Pr; 0-87592),* 2858 Valerie Ct., Merrick, NY 11566 (SAN 206-796X) Tel 516-379-4283; *CIP.*

Sculpt-Nouveau, *(Sculpt-Nouveau; 0-9603744),* 21 Redwood Dr., San Rafael, CA 94901 (SAN 213-9634).

Sea Challengers, *(Sea Chall; 0-930118),* 4 Sommerset Rise, Skyline Forest, Monterey, CA 93940 (SAN 210-5446) Tel 408-373-6306; Dist. by: Padre Productions, P.O. Box 1275, San Luis Ospispo, CA 93406 (SAN 202-8484) Tel 805-543-5404; Dist. by: Chartguide Ltd., Anaheim, CA 92801 (SAN 215-7373) Tel 714-533-1423; Dist. by: Harrowood Bks., 3943 N. Providence Rd., Newton Square, PA 19073 (SAN 207-1622) Tel 215-353-5585.

Sea Fog Pr., Inc., *(Sea Fog Pr; 0-917507),* P.O. Box 210056, San Francisco, CA 94121-0056 (SAN 656-1012) Tel 415-221-8527.

Sea History Pr., Div. of National Maritime Historical Society, *(Sea Hist Pr; 0-930248),* 132 Maple St., Croton-on-Hudson, NY 10520 (SAN 210-6647) Tel 914-271-2177.

†**Sea Horse Pr., Ltd., The,** *(Sea Horse; 0-933322),* 307 W. 11th St., New York, NY 10014 (SAN 212-4505) Tel 212-691-9066; *CIP.*

Sea Lion Publishing Co., *(Sea Lion Pub; 0-9616266),* 2853 N. Griggs, St. Paul, MN 55113 (SAN 658-3741) Tel 612-484-1659.

Sea-Mount Publishing Co., *(Sea-Mount Pub Co; 0-915539),* 1545 N.E. 104 St., Miami, FL 33138 (SAN 291-4212) Tel 305-754-1027.

Sea Shore Pubns., *(Sea Shore Pubn; 0-9611342),* 211 S. Sea Shore Ave., Long Beach, MS 39560 (SAN 283-3107) Tel 312-864-4573.

Sea Sports Pubns., *(Sea Sports Pubns; 0-9616399),* P.O. Box 647, Belden Sta., Norwalk, CT 06850 (SAN 659-1485) Tel 203-866-5376; 10 Buckingham Pl., Norwalk, CT 06851 (SAN 659-1493).

Sea Studios, *(Sea Studios; 0-9616824),* 886 Cannery Row, Monterey, CA 93940 (SAN 661-1257) Tel 408-649-5152; Dist. by: Publishers Group West, 5855 Beaudry St., Emeryville, CA 94608 (SAN 202-8522) Tel 415-658-3453.

Sea Urchin Pr., *(Sea Urchin; 0-9605208),* P.O. Box 10503, Oakland, CA 94610 (SAN 215-8086).

Sea-Wind Pr., *(Sea-Wind Pr; 0-9607436),* P.O. Box 222964, Carmel, CA 93922 (SAN 239-8036) Tel 408-372-8386.

Seabird Imprint, Subs. of Stagecoach Road Press, *(Seabird; 0-933499),* 4838 Rivervale Dr., Soquel, CA 95073 (SAN 691-8859) Tel 408-475-6445; Orders to: P.O. Box 1087, Soquel, CA 95073 (SAN 694-0129) Tel 408-475-6445.

Seabird Publishing, *(Seabird Pub; 0-938105),* P.O. Box 624, Broken Arrow, OK 74013 (SAN 659-767X); 1605 N. Hickory Ct., Broken Arrow, OK 74013 (SAN 659-7688) Tel 918-258-6209.

Seablom Design, *(Seablom; 0-918800),* 2106 2nd Ave. N., Seattle, WA 98109 (SAN 210-4962) Tel 206-285-2308.

Seaborn, Evan D., *(E D Seaborn; 0-9616393),* 4 Framar Rd., Wellesley, MA 02181 (SAN 659-2112); 273 Concord St., Framingham, MA 01701 (SAN 663-3188).

Seabright, *(Seabright; 0-9613824),* Rte. 1, Box 135, Nags Head, NC 27959 (SAN 679-9973) Tel 703-434-8553; Dist. by: Storie /McOwen Publishers, P.O. Box 308, Manteo, NC 27954 (SAN 265-0940).

Seacliffe, Ltd., *(Seacliffe; 0-911017),* 6338 Otis, Detroit, MI 48210 (SAN 263-0028) Tel 313-859-7158.

Seacoast Poets, *(Seacoast Poets; 0-936367),* P.O. Box 8638, La Jolla, CA 92038 (SAN 698-0015) Tel 619-753-5784.

Seagram, Joseph E., & Sons, Inc., *(J E Seagram; 0-916745),* 375 Park Ave., New York, NY 10152 (SAN 654-2077) Tel 212-572-7379.

Seagull Publishing Co., *(Seagull Pub Co; 0-9612698),* 2915 Stanford Ave., Suite 7, Marina del Rey, CA 90291 (SAN 209-0235).

Seahawk Pr., *(Seahawk Pr; 0-913008),* 6840 SW 92nd St., Miami, FL 33156 (SAN 204-7411) Tel 305-667-4051.

Seahorse Pr., The, *(Seahorse Pr; 0-938787),* 350 Ward Ave., Suite 106, Honolulu, HI 96814 (SAN 661-5481) Tel 808-988-7517; Dist. by: Pacific Trade Group, P.O. Box 668, Pearl City, HI 96782-0668 (SAN 169-1635).

SEAI Technical Pubns., *(SEAI Tech Pubns; 0-89671),* P.O. Box 590, Madison, GA 30650 (SAN 212-6915).

Seajay Pr, The, *(Seajay Pr; 0-935239),* P.O. Box 5174, Columbia, SC 29250 (SAN 695-7080) Tel 803-256-9489.

Seajay Pubns., *(Seajay; 0-9609014),* P.O. Box 2176, Dearborn, MI 48123 (SAN 241-2489) Tel 313-274-9731.

†Seal Pr., *(Seal Pr; 0-930364),* 500 E. Pike St., Seattle, WA 98122 (SAN 210-9522) Tel 206-329-7106; *CIP.*

Seal Pr.-Feminist, *(Seal Pr Feminist; 0-931188),* 500 E. Pike, Seattle, WA 98122 (SAN 215-3416) Tel 206-329-7160; Dist. by: Bookpeople, 2929 Fifth St., Berkeley, CA 94710 (SAN 168-9517) Tel 415-549-3030; Dist. by: Inland Bk. Co., P.O. Box 261, 22 Hemingway Ave., East Haven, CT 06512 (SAN 204-4151) Tel 203-467-4257; Dist. by: Pacific Pipeline, Inc., 19215 66th Ave., S., Kent, WA 98032 (SAN 208-2128) Tel 206-872-5523; Dist. by: Bookslinger, 213 E. Fourth St., St. Paul, MN 55101 (SAN 169-4154) Tel 612-221-0429; Orders to: Consortium Bk. Sales & Distribution, Inc., 213 E. Fourth St., St. Paul, MN 55101 (SAN 200-6049) Tel 612-221-9035.

Seals, Evelyn Johnson, *(E J Seals; 0-9608268),* N. 7th St., Middlesboro, KY 40965 (SAN 240-4397) Tel 606-248-5939.

Seals, Howard E., *(H E Seals; 0-9600232),* 3831 S. Michigan Ave., Rear Bldg., Chicago, IL 60653 (SAN 203-4697) Tel 312-285-3256.

Seamount Pubns., *(Seamount Pubns; 0-9614294),* P.O. Box 362, Pacific Palisades, CA 90272 (SAN 687-4576) Tel 213-454-8061.

Seaport Poets & Writers Pr., *(Seaport Poets & Writers; 0-942856),* 94 Fulton St. 4th Flr., New York, NY 10038 (SAN 240-1568).

Search, *(Search; 0-930871),* 106 Sterling Ave., Mt. Sterling, KY 40353 (SAN 677-8038) Tel 606-498-0661.

Search & Rescue Magazine, *(Search & Rescue; 0-9603392),* P.O. Box 641, Lompoc, CA 93438 (SAN 204-5745) Tel 805-733-3986.

Search Books *See* **Andrews, McMeel & Parker**

Search Group, Inc., *(SEARCH Grp),* 925 Secret River Dr., Suite H, Sacramento, CA 95831 (SAN 225-9257) Tel 916-392-2550; Dist. by: National Criminal Ref. Serv., Box 6000, Rockville, MD 20850 (SAN 200-7320); Toll free: 800-851-3420.

Search-One Productions, *(Search-One; 0-9616694),* P.O. Box 98, McKenzie, TN 38201-0098 (SAN 659-8455); Bethel College, East Hall, Rm. 39, Box 117C, McKenzie, TN 38201-0098 (SAN 659-8463) Tel 901-352-9935.

Search Pubns., *(Search Public; 0-910715),* 2000 Old Stage Rd., Florissant, CO 80816 (SAN 262-0766) Tel 303-748-3341.

SEARCH Technical Services, *(SEARCH Tech Servs; 0-932975),* HCR 11-Box 17, Davenport, WA 99122 (SAN 689-0873) Tel 509-725-6666.

Search The (CA), *(Search CA; 0-9613723),* 5634 Caminito Isla, La Jolla, CA 92037 (SAN 682-2487).

Searchers Pubns., *(Searchers Pubns),* 4314 Island Crest Way, Mercer Island, WA 98040 (SAN 212-5579).

Seas Pubns., *(Seas Pubns; 0-937677),* P.O. Box 8804, Atlanta, GA 30306-0804 (SAN 659-3097).

Seascape Enterprises, *(Seascape Enters; 0-931595),* P.O. Box 176, Colonial Heights, VA 23834 (SAN 682-4765) Tel 804-520-3628.

Seattle Airplane Pr., *(Seattle Air; 0-917196),* 6727 Glen Echo Ln., Tacoma, WA 98499 (SAN 209-0775) Tel 206-584-7307.

†Seattle Art Museum, *(Seattle Art; 0-932216),* 14th E. & E. Prospect, Seattle, WA 98112 (SAN 205-9762) Tel 206-443-4673; Dist. by: Univ. of Washington Pr., Seattle, WA 98105 (SAN 212-2502) Tel 206-543-4050; *CIP.*

Seattle Audubon Society, *(Seattle Audubon Soc; 0-914516),* 619 Joshua Green Bldg., 1425 Fourth Ave., Seattle, WA 98101 (SAN 203-2562) Tel 206-622-6695; Dist. by: Pacific Search Pr., 222 Dexter Ave. N., Seattle, WA 98109 (SAN 202-8476) Tel 206-682-5044.

Seattle Bk. Co., *(Seattle Bk; 0-915112),* P.O. Box 9254, Seattle, WA 98109 (SAN 207-1835) Tel 206-285-1226. *Imprints:* Slick Books (Slick).

Seattle Publishing Co., Inc., *(Seattle Pub Co),* RR One Box 1035, Johnson, VT 05656 (SAN 212-8667) Tel 902-635-7440.

Seattle's Child Publishing, *(Seattle Child Pub; 0-9614626),* P.O. Box 22578, Seattle, WA 98122 (SAN 691-8999) Tel 206-322-2594; Dist. by: Pacific Pipeline, Inc., 19215-66th Ave. S., Kent, WA 98032 (SAN 694-0137) Tel 206-872-5523.

Seaver Bks., *(Seaver Bks; 0-394),* 333 Central Park W., New York, NY 10025 (SAN 214-4719) Tel 212-866-9278; Orders to: Grove Pr., Inc., 196 W. Houston St., New York, NY 10014 (SAN 201-4890) Tel 212-242-4900; Dist. by: Arbor Hse. Publishing Co., 235 E. 45th St., New York, NY 10017 (SAN 201-1522) Tel 212-599-3131.

Seaview *See* **Putnam Publishing Group, The**

Seaview Press, *(Seaview Pr; 0-9606048),* P.O. Box 32, El Cerrito, CA 94530 (SAN 216-4477) Tel 415-525-5495.

Seaweeds & Constructions *See* **Univ. of Hawaii Pr., The**

Seawinds Pr., *(Seawinds Pr; 0-9616375),* P.O. Box 5469, Macon, GA 31208 (SAN 658-9308) Tel 912-743-1016.

Sebago Publishing, Div. of Sebago Inc., *(Sebago Pub; 0-9614880),* 800 Heinz St., Berkeley, CA 94701 (SAN 693-1146) Tel 415-658-3326.

Sebastian Publishing Co., *(Sebastian Pub Co; 0-913347),* 1109 Royal Ln., San Carlos, CA 94070 (SAN 287-4466) Tel 415-598-0310; Dist. by: Pacific Pipeline, Inc., 19215 66th Ave., S., Kent, WA 98032 (SAN 287-4466) Tel 206-872-5523; Dist. by: Sebastian Publishing Co., 1109 Royal Ln., San Carlos, CA 94070 (SAN 287-4466) Tel 415-598-0310; Dist. by: Baker & Taylor, Western Div., 380 Edison Way, Reno, NV 89564 (SAN 169-4464) Tel 702-786-6700.

Sebastian Publishing Co., *(Sebastian LI; 0-9616731),* P.O. Box 471, Port Jefferson Station, NY 11776 (SAN 659-865X); Dark Hollow Rd., Port Jefferson, NY 11777 (SAN 659-8668) Tel 516-928-6745.

Second Amendment Foundation, *(Second Amend; 0-911475),* 12500 NE Tenth Pl., Bellevue, WA 98005 (SAN 275-2654) Tel 206-454-7012.

Second Chance Pr., *(Second Chance; 0-933256),* RD2, Noyac Rd., Sag Harbor, NY 11963 (SAN 213-1633) Tel 516-725-1101; Toll free: 800-221-0960; Dist. by: Golden Lee Bk. Dstb., 1000 Dean St., Brooklyn, NY 11238 (SAN 169-5126) Tel 718-857-6333; Toll free: 800-221-0960.

Second City Software, *(Second City Soft; 0-937023),* P.O. Box 442, Mount Prospect, IL 60056 (SAN 697-533X) Tel 312-577-7680.

Second Coming Pr., *(Second Coming; 0-915016),* P.O. Box 31249, San Francisco, CA 94131 (SAN 206-376X) Tel 415-647-3679.

Second Hand, The, *(Second Hand; 0-9605858),* P.O. Box 204, Plymouth, WI 53073 (SAN 220-1879) Tel 414-893-5226.

Second Language Pubns., *(Second Lang),* P.O. Box 1700, Blaine, WA 98230 (SAN 206-3778).

Second Society Foundation, *(Second Soc Foun),* 333 N. Michigan Ave., Suite 707, Chicago, IL 60601 (SAN 203-204X).

Second Thoughts, *(Second Thoughts; 0-9601286),* 88 W. Schiller, Suite 704, Chicago, IL 60610 (SAN 210-4970) Tel 312-337-6044.

Second Thoughts Press, *(Sec Thoughts OR; 0-9607036),* P.O. Box 10741, Eugene, OR 97440 (SAN 239-3832) Tel 503-344-3491.

Second Thoughts Publishing, *(Second T Pub; 0-913587),* 153 Halsted, Chicago Heights, IL 60411 (SAN 285-3825) Tel 312-756-7500.

Secret Garden, *(Secret Garden; 0-939263),* 1713 Grove, Berkeley, CA 94709 (SAN 662-5231) Tel 415-540-5454.

Secret Library, The, *(Secret Library; 0-917115),* 2757 State St., San Diego, CA 92103 (SAN 655-7767) Tel 619-542-0902; Dist. by: DeVorss & Co., P.O. Box 550, 1046 Princeton Dr., Marina del Rey, CA 90294 (SAN 168-9886).

Secretarial Pubns., *(Secretarial Pubns; 0-943544),* P.O. Box 672, Santa Barbara, CA 93102 (SAN 238-3667) Tel 805-682-5706.

Section of Administrative Law *See* **American Bar Assn.**

Section of Antitrust Law *See* **American Bar Assn.**

Section of Bar Activities *See* **American Bar Assn.**

Section of Corporation Banking & Business Law *See* **American Bar Assn.**

Section of Criminal Justice *See* **American Bar Assn.**

Section of Economics of Law Practice *See* **American Bar Assn.**

Section of General Practice *See* **American Bar Assn.**

Section of Individual Rights & Responsibilities *See* **American Bar Assn.**

Section of Insurance Negligence & Compensation Law *See* **American Bar Assn.**

Section of International Law *See* **American Bar Assn.**

Section of Labor Relations Law *See* **American Bar Assn.**

Section of Legal Education and Admissions to the Bar *See* **American Bar Assn.**

Section of Litigation *See* **American Bar Assn.**

Section of Natural Resources Law *See* **American Bar Assn.**

Section of Patent, Trademark, & Copyright Law *See* **American Bar Assn.**

Section of Public Contract Law *See* **American Bar Assn.**

Section of Public Utility Law *See* **American Bar Assn.**

Section of Real Property Probate & Trust Law *See* **American Bar Assn.**

Section of Science & Technology *See* **American Bar Assn.**

Section of Taxation *See* **American Bar Assn.**

Section of Tort & Insurance Practice Law *See* **American Bar Assn.**

Section of Urban, State, & Local Government Law *See* **American Bar Assn.**

Securities Industry Assn., *(Securities Industry),* 120 Broadway, New York, NY 10271 (SAN 212-608-1500.

Security Dupont Pr., *(Security Dupont; 0-9611422),* 617 Sibley Tower Building, Rochester, NY 14604 (SAN 284-9275) Tel 716-494-1466; Orders to: 10 Gates St., Bergen, NY 14416 (SAN 662-2046) Tel 716-404-1466.

Security Letter, Inc., *(Security Let; 0-9609820),* 166 E. 96th St., New York, NY 10128 (SAN 262-1134); Dist. by: Butterworths, 80 Montvale Ave, Stoneham, MA 02180 (SAN 206-3964).

Security Press, Inc., *(Security Pr; 0-939568),* Box 854, McLean, VA 22101 (SAN 216-6933) Tel 703-734-1326.

Security Seminars Pr., *(Security Seminars; 0-936101),* 1204 SE 28th Ave., Ocala, FL 32671 (SAN 696-7507) Tel 904-694-6185; Orders to: Security Seminars Press, P.O. Box 70162, Ocala, FL 32670 (SAN 662-3859) Tel 904-694-6185.

See-Do Press, *(See Do Pr; 0-9607836),* P.O. Box 815, Lower Lake, CA 95457 (SAN 238-1974) Tel 707-994-5204.

See-Saw Pr., *(See-Saw Pr; 0-9614144),* 744 Newark-Pompton Turnpike, Pompton Plains, NJ 07444 (SAN 686-2268) Tel 201-835-4647.

See Sharp Pr., *(See Sharp Pr; 0-9613289),* P.O. Box 6118, San Francisco, CA 94101 (SAN 653-8134) Tel 415-647-2710.

Seed Ctr., *(Seed Center; 0-916108),* Box 1700, Redway, CA 95560 (SAN 203-2554) Tel 707-923-2524.

Seed of Life Pubns., *(Seed Life Pubns; 0-930875),* P.O. Box 33961, Phoenix, AZ 85067 (SAN 677-7945) Tel 602-842-9102.

Seed Saver Pubns., *(Seed Saver Pubns; 0-9613977),* Box 70, Decorah, IA 52101 (SAN 682-3114) Tel 319-382-3949.

Seek-It Pubns., *(Seek-It Pubns; 0-930706),* P.O. Box 1074, Birmingham, MI 48012 (SAN 215-3424) Tel 313-642-9262.

Names

Seeker Press, *(Seeker Pr; 0-917615),* 1020 Carol Dr., Los Angeles, CA 90069 (SAN 657-162X) Tel 213-858-1182.

†**Seemann, E. A., Publishing, Inc.,** *(E A Seemann; 0-912458; 0-89530),* P.O. Box K, Miami, FL 33156 (SAN 201-3495) Tel 305-233-5852; *CIP.*

Seer Ox, *(Seer Ox; 0-916064),* 807 Prospect Ave. No. 107, South Pasadena, CA 91030 (SAN 207-8945).

Seesaw Books *See* **Scholastic, Inc.**

Seesaw Music Corp., *(Seesaw Music; 0-937205),* 2067 Broadway, New York, NY 10023 (SAN 658-6899) Tel 212-874-1200.

Segal, Berty, Inc., *(B Segal; 0-938395),* 1749 Eucalyptus St., Brea, CA 92621 (SAN 660-9759) Tel 714-529-5359.

Segue, *(Segue NYC; 0-937804),* 300 Bowery, New York, NY 10012 (SAN 699-8003).

Seguin, Mary A., *(M A Seguin; 0-9616951),* 145 S. First Ave., Alpena, MI 49707 (SAN 661-7336) Tel 517-356-1481.

Seibels, Gren, *(G Seibels; 0-9613056),* 2400 Heyward St., Columbia, SC 24205 (SAN 294-1287) Tel 803-799-1838; Dist. by: Morris Aviation Ltd., P.O. Box 718, Statesboro, GA 30458 (SAN 652-0286) Tel 912-489-8161.

Seibert Assocs., *(Seibert Assocs; 0-939461),* 3455 Spring Hill Dr., Janesville, WI 53545 (SAN 663-3374) Tel 608-755-0300.

Seiler-Doar Bks., Inc., *(Seiler-Doar; 0-916001),* 3449 Ramona, Palo Alto, CA 94306 (SAN 294-6580) Tel 415-857-0280.

Seismograph Pubns., *(Seismograph Pubns; 0-932977),* P.O. Box 882664, San Francisco, CA 94188 (SAN 689-9781) Tel 415-621-4450; Dist. by: The Subterranean Co., P.O. Box 10233, 1327 W. Second St., Eugene, OR 97440 (SAN 169-7102) Tel 503-343-6324.

Sekan Pubns. Co., *(Sekan Pubns; 0-931365),* 2210 S. Main St., Fort Scott, KS 66701 (SAN 686-9173).

Sekoni Pubs., *(Sekoni Pubs; 0-9606958),* P.O. Box 15007, Durham, NC 27704 (SAN 217-4367) Tel 919-688-5983.

Selbstverlag Pr., *(Selbstverlag; 0-911706),* P.O. Drawer 606, Bloomington, IN 47402-0606 (SAN 204-5761) Tel 812-334-2166.

Select Bks., *(Select Bks; 0-910458),* Rte. 2, Box 109, Willow Springs, MO 65793 (SAN 202-0602) Tel 417-934-6775.

Selective Pubs., Inc., *(Selective; 0-912584),* P.O. Box 1140, Clearwater, FL 33517 (SAN 204-577X) Tel 813-442-5440.

Selena Pr., *(Selena Pr; 0-938451),* P.O. Box 7082, Fargo, ND 58103 (SAN 660-9880); 1010 Southwood Pl., Fargo, ND 58103 (SAN 660-9899) Tel 701-235-2890.

Selene Bks., *(Selene Bks; 0-9609866),* P.O. Box 136, Kew Gardens, NY 11415 (SAN 275-276X) Tel 718-847-5184.

Self-Help Distributors, Inc., *(Self Help Dist; 0-937487),* 725 W. 18th St., No. 2, Merced, CA 95340 (SAN 659-1515) Tel 209-722-7559; Dist. by: Carlton Pr., 11 W. 32nd St., New York, NY 10001 (SAN 201-9655).

Self Help for Hard of Hearing People, Inc., *(SHHH; 0-935473),* 7800 Wisconsin Ave., Bethesda, MD 20814 (SAN 695-9024) Tel 301-657-2473.

Self-Motivated Careers, *(Self-Motiv Careers; 0-381),* 3589 Hermitage Plantation, Duluth, GA 30136 (SAN 220-2743).

Self-Programmed Control Pr., *(Self-Prog Control; 0-9601926),* P.O. Box 49939, Los Angeles, CA 90049 (SAN 212-2308) Tel 213-826-1959.

Self Realization Fellowship, *(Self Realization; 0-87612),* 3880 San Rafael Ave., Los Angeles, CA 90065 (SAN 204-5788) Tel 213-225-2471.

Self Reliance Foundation, *(Self Reliance; 0-941580),* P.O. Box 1, Las Trampas, NM 87576 (SAN 239-3085) Tel 505-689-2250.

Self Rich Bks., *(Self Rich Bks; 0-914365),* 36 Midland Dr., Tolland, CT 06084 (SAN 289-6788) Tel 203-872-3419.

Self-Sufficiency Assn., *(Self-Sufficiency; 0-9616968),* 1912 Avenida Estudiante, San Pedro, CA 90732 (SAN 661-7387) Tel 213-519-0097; Dist. by: Nutri-Books Corp., 790 W. Tennessee Ave., Denver, CO 80223 (SAN 169-054X) Tel 303-778-8383; Dist. by: Periodical Services, Inc., P.O. Box 367, Stockton, NJ 08559 (SAN 200-6707).

Sellens, *(Sellens; 0-9612068),* 134 Clark St., Augusta, KS 67010 (SAN 212-3843) Tel 316-775-5540.

Sellers Pubns, *(Sellers Pubns; 0-9608122),* Crane Brook Rd., Alstead, NH 03602 (SAN 238-8383).

Seltzer, Rozie, *(R Seltzer; 0-9615365),* 8535 Casa del Lago, Apt. 37F, Boca Raton, FL 33433 (SAN 695-5428).

Seluzicki, Charles, Fine Books, *(Seluzicki Fine Bks; 0-931356),* 3733 NE 24th Ave., Portland, OR 97212 (SAN 211-9773).

Semiconductor Services, *(Semiconductor; 0-9613880),* 1145 Glenn Ave., Suite 213, San Jose, CA 95125 (SAN 692-7572).

Seminal Publishing Hse., *(Sem Pub Hse),* P.O. Box 213, Northampton, MA 01060 (SAN 209-2018).

Seminar on the Acquisition of Latin American Library Materials, *(SALALM; 0-917617),* Univ. of Wisconsin Madison, Memorial Library, Madison, WI 53706 (SAN 657-1638) Tel 608-262-3240.

Seminary Co-Operative Bookstore, Inc., *(Seminary Co-Op; 0-912182),* 5757 S. University Ave., Chicago, IL 60637 (SAN 204-5818) Tel 312-752-4381.

Seminary Pr., *(Seminary Pr; 0-912832),* P.O. Box 2218, Univ. Sta., Enid, OK 73702 (SAN 203-2546) Tel 405-237-4433.

Seminole Publishing Co., *(Seminole Pub Co; 0-9612302),* P.O. Box 3315, High Mar Sta., Boulder, CO 80307 (SAN 287-752X) Tel 303-492-7901.

Senda Nueva De Ediciones, Inc., *(Senda Nueva; 0-918454),* 640 W. 231st St., Apt. 3-B, Mail Box 139, Bronx, NY 10463 (SAN 210-0061) Tel 212-548-5288; Orders to: P.O. Box 488, Montclair, NJ 07042 (SAN 662-1392).

Seneca Bks., Inc., *(Seneca Bks; 0-89092),* Rte. 6, Box 81-B, Morgantown, WV 26505 (SAN 213-4322) Tel 304-594-1324.

Seneca Park Publishing, *(Seneca Pk Pub; 0-9616447),* P.O. Box 315, Lynn Haven, FL 32444 (SAN 659-1604) Tel 904-265-2314; 303 Florida Ave., Lynn Haven, FL 32444 (SAN 659-1612).

Seneca Pr., *(Seneca Pr MD; 0-9605908),* 503 Bonifant St., Silver Spring, MD 20910 (SAN 216-6941) Tel 301-588-2688.

Senior Pubns., *(Senior Pubns; 0-931685),* 20 South Broadway, Yonkers, NY 10701 (SAN 683-7573) Tel 914-423-0112.

Senkers' Whim Enterprises, *(Senkers Whim Ent; 0-9610506),* P.O. Box 797, Devon, PA 19333 (SAN 264-3820) Tel 215-293-1044.

Sense Pubns., Inc., *(Sense Pubns Inc; 0-932673),* 7910 W. Blvd. Dr., Alexandria, VA 22308 (SAN 687-8369) Tel 703-768-6892.

Senseman, Lawrence A., *(L A Senseman; 0-9614413),* 1365 Pine Ave., Carlsbad, CA 92008 (SAN 688-6086) Tel 619-729-7284.

Sensible Solutions, Inc., *(Sensible Sol),* 14 E. 75th St., New York, NY 10016 (SAN 664-4574).

Sensitive Man Project, The, *(Sensitive Man; 0-938582),* 33 Oakwood Dr., Fairfield, CT 06430 (SAN 685-3560) Tel 203-368-2316.

Senterprises Pubns., Inc., *(Senterprises; 0-9613189),* 3610 Avenue Q, Suite 221, Lubbock, TX 79412 (SAN 295-8783) Tel 806-744-2844.

Sentinel Pr., *(Sentinel Pub; 0-931097),* 4845 50th St., Lubbock, TX 79414 (SAN 678-9447) Tel 806-792-3801; Toll free: 800-858-4602.

Sentry Books, Inc., *(Sentry; 0-913194),* 10781 White Oak Ave., Granada Hills, CA 91344 (SAN 205-9460) Tel 213-368-2012; Dist. by: Aviation Book Co., 1640 Victory Blvd., Glendale, CA 91201 (SAN 212-0259) Tel 213-240-1771.

Sentry Editions *See* **Houghton Mifflin Co.**

Separate Reality, Inc., *(Separate Real; 0-932163),* P.O. Box 398057, Miami Beach, FL 33139 (SAN 686-5224) Tel 305-531-4835.

Sepher-Hermon Pr., Inc., *(Hermon; 0-87203),* 1265 46th St., Brooklyn, NY 11219 (SAN 169-5959) Tel 718-972-9010.

September Pr., Inc., *(September Pr; 0-937159),* P.O. Box 584, Jamestown, RI 02835 (SAN 658-506X) Tel 401-423-0455.

Sequatchie County Board of Education, *(Sequatchie; 0-930739),* P.O. Box 488, Dunlap, TN 37327 (SAN 677-5349) Tel 615-949-3617.

Sequoia Audubon Society Inc., *(Sequoia Aud Soc; 0-9614301),* 720 El Camino Real Suite 403, Belmont, CA 94002 (SAN 687-4878) Tel 415-593-7368.

Sequoia Pr., Inc., *(Sequoia NYC; 0-939033),* 150 Fifth Ave., New York, NY 10011 (SAN 662-8494) Tel 212-362-5230.

Seraphim Pr., *(Seraphim Pr; 0-942632),* Suite 263, 7439 La Palma Ave., Buena Park, CA 90620 (SAN 238-5791) Tel 714-527-4475.

Sercolab, *(Sercolab; 0-918332),* 244 Sesuit Neck Rd., Box 957, East Dennis, MA 02641 (SAN 209-5165).

Serconia Pr., *(Serconia Pr; 0-934933),* P.O. Box 1786, Seattle, WA 98111 (SAN 695-006X) Tel 206-633-2375.

Serenade-Saga *See* **Zondervan Publishing Hse.**

Serendipity, *(Serendip Illinois; 0-9616864),* P.O. Box 293, Kenilworth, IL 60043 (SAN 661-1613); 1418 10th St., Wilmette, IL 60091 (SAN 661-1621) Tel 312-256-3185.

†**Serenity Hse. Publishing,** *(Serenity Hse; 0-914789),* P.O. Box 462, Port Washington, NY 11050 (SAN 670-6983); *CIP.*

Sergio Publishing, Inc., *(Sergio Pub; 0-936003),* 132 W. 24th St., Suite 747, New York, NY 10011 (SAN 696-5857) Tel 305-858-1591.

Serif Pr., Inc., *(Serif Pr; 0-914125),* 1331 H. St. NW, Suite 110 LL, Washington, DC 20005 (SAN 287-5519) Tel 202-737-4650.

Serina Pr., *(Serina; 0-911952),* 70 Kennedy St., Alexandria, VA 22305 (SAN 204-5834) Tel 703-548-4080.

Serpent Publishing Co. *See* **Artex Pr.**

Serrell & Simons, Pubs., *(Serrell-Simons; 0-943104),* P.O. Box 64, Winnebago, WI 54985 (SAN 240-4400) Tel 414-231-1939; Dist. by: Baker & Taylor, Southeast Div., Mt. Oliver Rd., Commerce, GA 30599 (SAN 169-1503); Dist. by: Baker & Taylor, Midwest Div., 501 S. Gladiola Ave., Momence, IL 60954 (SAN 169-2100); Dist. by: Baker & Taylor, Western Div., 380 Edison Way, Reno, NV 89564 (SAN 169-4464) Tel 702-786-6700; Dist. by: Baker & Taylor, Eastern Div., 50 Kirby Ave., Somerville, NJ 08876 (SAN 169-4901); Dist. by: The Distributors, 702 S. Michigan, South Bend, IN 46618 (SAN 212-0364) Tel 219-232-8500; Dist. by: Wisconsin Authors & Pubs. Alliance, 34 S. Pontiac Dr., Janesville, WI 53545 (SAN 200-6057); Dist. by: Conkey's Bk. Store, 226 E. College Ave., Appleton, WI 54911 (SAN 200-6294) Tel 414-739-1223.

Servant Pubns., *(Servant; 0-89283),* 840 Airport Blvd., Ann Arbor, MI 48107 (SAN 208-9238) Tel 313-761-8505; Orders to: Customer Service Dept., Box 8617, Ann Arbor, MI 48107 (SAN 208-9246) Tel 313-761-8505; Dist. by: Spring Arbor, 10885 Textile Rd., Belleville, MI 48111 (SAN 662-1406) Tel 313-481-0900; Toll free: 800-521-3690; Dist. by: East Coast Christian Dist., P.O. Box 4200, 35 Readington Rd., Somerville, NJ 08876 (SAN 662-1414). Formerly Named Word of Life.

Service League of Natchitoches, Inc., *(Service League; 0-9607674),* P.O. Box 2206, Natchitoches, LA 71457 (SAN 226-7993) Tel 318-352-6723.

Service Pr., *(Service Press NE; 0-9617063),* 1021 N. Main St., Box 606, Henderson, NE 68371 (SAN 662-9431); 125 Coventry Ln., No. 12, Grand Island, NE 68801 (SAN 662-944X) Tel 308-384-6386. Do not confuse with Service Pr., of Haslett, MI.

Service Publishing Co., *(Service Pub; 0-913104),* Park Lane Bldg., 2025 I St. NW, Suite 722, Washington, DC 20006 (SAN 204-5842) Tel 202-872-0082.

Servnet Corp., *(Servnet Corp; 0-933073),* 4886 54th St., San Diego, CA 92115 (SAN 689-7959) Tel 619-265-8328.

SES Development Corporation, *(SES Development; 0-943982),* Dist. by: The Book Carrier, Inc., 9121 Industrial Court, Gaithersburg, MD 20877 (SAN 200-4046) Tel 301-258-1177.

Sesnon, Mary P., Art Gallery, *(Sesnon Art Gall; 0-939982),* College V, Univ. of California, Santa Cruz, CA 95064 (SAN 216-8669) Tel 408-429-2314.

Sessions Pubs., *(Sessions; 0-911366),* 48 Nassau Dr., New Hyde Park, NY 11040 (SAN 204-5850) Tel 516-747-3144.

†**Seton Medical Ctr.,** Div. of Mission Services Corp., *(Seton Med Ctr; 0-9616516),* 1900 Sullivan Ave., Daly City, CA 94015 (SAN 659-5847) Tel 415-991-6733; *CIP.*

Seton Pr., The, *(Seton Pr; 0-934397),* Box 1476, Tacoma, WA 98402 (SAN 693-8124) Tel 206-564-6062.

Settles Books, *(Settles Bks),* Box 1121, Aurora, IL 60507 (SAN 240-1576).

†**Seven Arts Press, Inc.,** *(Seven Arts; 0-911370),* 6253 Hollywood Blvd., No. 1100, Hollywood, CA 90028 (SAN 203-2538) Tel 213-469-1095; *CIP.*

Seven Hills Bks., Div. of Books for the Decorative Arts, Inc., *(Seven Hills Bks; 0-911403),* 49 Central Ave., Cincinnati, OH 45202 (SAN 169-6629) Tel 513-381-3881.

†**Seven Locks Pr.,** *(Seven Locks Pr; 0-932020),* 5125 MacArthur Blvd., NW, Washington, DC 20016 (SAN 211-9781) Tel 202-362-4714; P.O. Box 27, Cabin John, MD 20818 (SAN 658-1587); *CIP.*

7-M Publishing Co., *(Seven-M Pub Co; 0-916527),* P.O. Box 136, Chriesman, TX 77838 (SAN 295-5482) Tel 409-567-7266.

Seven Oaks Press, *(Seven Oaks; 0-932508),* 405 S. 7th St., St. Charles, IL 60174 (SAN 212-1735) Tel 312-584-0187.

Seven Palms Pr., *(Seven Palms; 0-912593),* Box 3371, Tucson, AZ 85722 (SAN 283-3115) Tel 602-621-3791.

†**Seven Seas Pr., Inc.,** *(Seven Seas; 0-915160),* 2 Dean Ave., Newport, RI 02840 (SAN 206-8737) Tel 401-849-9610; Toll free: 800-723-7323; Dist. by: Simon & Schuster, 1230 Ave. of Americas, New York, NY 10020 (SAN 200-2450) Tel 212-245-6400; *CIP.*

Seven Seasons Service Co., *(Seven Seasons Serv Co; 0-9610868),* 8187 Westmore Rd., San Diego, CA 92126 (SAN 283-9105).

Seven Seven Search Pubns., *(Seven Seven Search; 0-934726),* P.O. Box 252, Solana Beach, CA 92075 (SAN 213-5892) Tel 714-436-4843.

Seven Shadows Pr., *(Seven Shadows; 0-916225),* P.O. Box 1118, Shaker Heights, OH 44120 (SAN 294-9989) Tel 216-283-5578.

Seven Springs Center, *(Seven Springs; 0-943006),* RD 3, Oregon Rd., Mount Kisco, NY 10549 (SAN 240-3269) Tel 914-241-1880.

Seven Suns Pubns., *(Seven Suns; 0-931783),* P.O. Box 773, Rte. 1, Castle Estate, Fairfield, IA 52556 (SAN 684-846X) Tel 515-472-8613; Dist. by: New Leaf Distributing, The, 1020 White St., SW, Atlanta, GA 30310 (SAN 169-1449) Tel 404-755-2665; Toll free: 800-241-3829.

†**Seven Woods Press,** *(Seven Woods Pr; 0-913282),* P.O. Box 32 Village Sta., New York, NY 10014 (SAN 203-2503); *CIP.*

Seven Worlds Pr., *(Seven Worlds Pr; 0-936497),* 7312 Badgett Rd., Knoxville, TN 37919 (SAN 698-066X) Tel 615-522-3548.

Seventh Son Pr., *(Seventh Son Pr; 0-933837),* P.O. Box 13224, Baltimore, MD 21203 (SAN 692-6851) Tel 301-276-3073.

Seventh Trumpet Publishing Company, *(Seventh Trumpet; 0-9610268),* P.O. Box 18, Schiller Park, IL 60176 (SAN 264-3847).

Severino, Roberto, *(R Severino; 0-937389),* 4949 Quebec St., NW, Washington, DC 20016 (SAN 659-168X) Tel 202-363-5279.

Sevier County Cookbook Committee, *(Sevier County Cookbk; 0-9614182),* P.O. Box 66, Lockesburg, AR 71846 (SAN 686-6298) Tel 501-289-3401.

Seville Publishing Co., *(Seville Pub; 0-930990),* 6740 Kester Ave., Second Floor, Van Nuys, CA 91405 (SAN 222-9323) Tel 818-501-5200.

Sew/Fit Pub. Co., *(Sew-Fit; 0-933956),* 23 Calendar Ct., No. 207, La Grange, IL 60525 (SAN 212-1387) Tel 312-579-3222; Orders to: Sew-Fit Publishing Co., P.O. Box 565, La Grange, IL 60525 (SAN 212-1387) Tel 312-579-3222.

Sewing Knits Inc., *(Sewing Knits; 0-9605860),* 634 W. Huntington Dr., No.12, Arcadia, CA 91006 (SAN 216-6089) Tel 818-435-8069.

Sewing Machine Man, *(Sewing Machine Man; 0-9614713),* RD 1, Box 430, Glen Rock, PA 17327 (SAN 692-6576) Tel 717-235-1215.

Sewing Sampler Productions, *(Sewing Sampler; 0-937679),* P.O. Box 39, Springfield, MN 56087 (SAN 659-3135) Tel 507-723-6547; 502 N. Van Buren, Springfield, MN 56087 (SAN 659-3143).

Sex Information & Education Council of the U. S., *(SIECUS; 0-9609212),* 80 Fifth Ave., Suite 801, New York, NY 10011 (SAN 224-2435) Tel 212-929-2300; Library, 715 Broadway, 2nd Flr., New York, NY 10003 (SAN 693-501X) Tel 212-673-3850.

Sexauer, Charles F., Publishing Co., *(C F Sexauer; 0-9607148),* 13909 Old Harbor Ln., No. 102, Marina del Rey, CA 90291 (SAN 239-0337) Tel 213-821-2164.

Sexson, Jeanne E., *(J E Sexson; 0-9613817),* 1906 Polster, Evansville, IN 47715 (SAN 682-2630).

Sextant *See* **Childrens Pr.**

Seybold Pubns., Inc., *(Seybold; 0-918514),* Box 644, Media, PA 19063 (SAN 210-007X) Tel 215-565-2480.

SF Design, Inc. /Owlswood Productions, *(SF Design; 0-915942),* 287 Harborway South, S. San Francisco, CA 94080 (SAN 207-7264) Tel 415-583-8050.

Sgovio, Sgovio; 0-9614127), 24 Villa Ave., Buffalo, NY 14216 (SAN 686-466X) Tel 716-873-4383.

Shadduck & Sullivan, *(Shadduck-Sullivan; 0-935975),* 3508 45th Ave. S., Minneapolis, MN 55406-2927 (SAN 696-5865) Tel 612-729-1292.

Shade Tree Books, *(Shade Tree; 0-930742),* P.O. Box 2268, Huntington Beach, CA 92647 (SAN 211-0954) Tel 714-846-3869.

Shades of Blue Pubns., *(Shades Blue Pubns; 0-9616669),* 286 S. Batavia, Apt. 9, Orange, CA 92666 (SAN 659-9060) Tel 714-997-2328.

Shades of Mother Nature, *(Shades Mother Nat; 0-9614021),* 206 Buckingham Dr., Glen Burnie, MD 21061 (SAN 683-6283) Tel 301-768-0648.

Shadow Pr., U.S.A., *(Shadow Pr; 0-937724),* P.O. Box 8803, Minneapolis, MN 55408 (SAN 218-3617) Tel 612-822-3488; Dist. by: Midwest Distributors, P.O. Box 4642, Kansas City, MO 64109 (SAN 219-5038).

Shadowood Pubns., *(Shadowood Pubns; 0-937025),* 7134 Fifth Ave., N, St. Petersburg, FL 33710 (SAN 658-7097) Tel 813-384-4723.

Shadrach Productions, *(Shadrach; 0-9613356),* P.O. Box 712, Moorestown, NJ 08057 (SAN 656-1330) Tel 609-234-5892.

Shadwold Press, *(Shadwold; 0-9603024),* P.O. Box 706, Kennebunkport, ME 04046 (SAN 212-5587) Tel 207-967-4400.

Shady Side Peninsula Assn. Inc., *(Shady Side Pen; 0-9614295),* P.O. Box 114, Shady Side, MD 20764 (SAN 687-4584) Tel 301-867-7028.

Shadyside Presbyterian Church, The, *(Shadyside Presby; 0-9615554),* 5121 Westminster Pl., Pittsburgh, PA 15232 (SAN 696-0502) Tel 412-456-3520.

Shadyside Press, *(Shadyside),* 320 Brooks Ave., Venice, CA 90291 (SAN 265-9808); Dist. by: Bookpeople, 2929 Fifth St., Berkeley, CA 94710 (SAN 168-9517); Dist. by: The Distributors, 702 S. Michigan, South Bend, IN 46618 (SAN 695-6920) Tel 219-232-8500.

Shaeffer, R. E., *(R Shaeffer; 0-9611418),* 3623 SW Nevada St., Portland, OR 97219 (SAN 284-9399) Tel 503-245-1018.

Shafer Bks., Inc., *(Shafer Bks; 0-931687),* 139 Grand St., P.O. Box 40, Croton-On-Hudson, NY 10520 (SAN 695-6939) Tel 914-271-6919.

Shaffer, Dale E., *(D E Shaffer; 0-915060),* 437 Jennings Ave., Salem, OH 44460 (SAN 206-9067) Tel 216-337-3348.

Shah, Kirit N., *(K N Shah; 0-9609614),* 980 Moraga Ave., Piedmont, CA 94611 (SAN 260-2628) Tel 415-653-2076.

Shain, Fayga, *(Shain F; 0-9614920),* P.O. Box 7 Rte. 524, Adelphia, NJ 07710 (SAN 693-4307) Tel 201-431-4107.

Shaker Heritage Society, *(Shaker Her Soc; 0-89062),* Albany Shaker Rd., Albany, NY 12211 (SAN 289-0410) Tel 518-456-7890.

Shaker Museum Foundation Inc., *(Shaker Mus; 0-937942),* Shaker Museum Rd., Old Chatham, NY 12136 (SAN 206-7684) Tel 518-794-9100.

Shaker Prairie Publication, *(Shaker Prairie),* R.R. One, Oaktown, IN 47561 (SAN 209-5173) Tel 812-745-3153.

Shaker Pr., The, *(Shaker Pr ME; 0-915836),* Sabbathday Lake, Poland Spring, ME 04274 (SAN 214-1388) Tel 207-926-4597.

Shakti Pr., *(Shakti Pr; 0-933211),* 2929 Fifth St., Berkeley, CA 94710 (SAN 682-8655) Tel 415-843-7869; Dist. by: Bookpeople, 2929 Fifth St., Berkeley, CA 94710 (SAN 168-9517) Tel 415-549-3030.

Shale Bks., *(Shale Bks; 0-930237),* P.O. Box 7000-477, Redondo Beach, CA 90277 (SAN 676-973X).

Shalit Literary Service, *(Shalit Liter),* 38 Sherman Place, Morristown, NJ 07960 (SAN 297-195X) Tel 201-538-6118.

Shallway Foundation, *(Shallway Foun; 0-934392),* 125 S. Fourth St., Connellsville, PA 15425 (SAN 213-1641).

Shalom, P., Pubns., Inc., *(Shalom; 0-87559),* 5409 18th Ave., Brooklyn, NY 11204 (SAN 204-5893).

Shamal Books, Inc., *(Shamal Bks; 0-917886),* G.P.O. Box 16, New York, NY 10116 (SAN 209-3618) Tel 212-622-4426.

†**Shaman Books,** *(Shaman Bks; 0-9611274),* 1033 W. Loyola Ave., No. 1007, Chicago, IL 60626 (SAN 283-1627) Tel 312-262-4888; *CIP.*

Shamar Book, A, *(Shamar Bk; 0-9607058),* 9215 N. Concho Lane, Phoenix, AZ 85028 (SAN 239-3840).

Shambala Pubns., *(Shambala Pubns; 0-9614632),* 1049 Cresewood, E. Lansing, MI 48823 (SAN 691-8875) Tel 517-332-1623.

Shambhala Pubns., Inc., *(Shambhala Pubns; 0-87773; 0-394),* 314 Dartmouth St., Boston, MA 02116 (SAN 203-2481); Toll free: 800-638-6460 Tel 617-424-0030; Dist. by: Random Hse., Inc., 400 Hahn Rd., Westminster, MD 21157 (SAN 202-5515). *Imprints:* Great Eastern Books (Great Eastern); Hermes House (Hermes Hse).

Shameless Hussy Pr., *(Shameless Hussy; 0-915382),* Box 3092, Berkeley, CA 94703 (SAN 282-3071) Tel 415-547-1062; Dist. by: Bookpeople, 2929 Fifth St., Berkeley, CA 94710 (SAN 168-9517) Tel 415-549-3030; Dist. by: Bookslinger, 213 E. Fourth St., St. Paul, MN 55101 (SAN 169-4154) Tel 612-221-0429; Dist. by: The Distributors, 702 S. Michigan, South Bend, IN 46618 (SAN 212-0364) Tel 219-232-8500; Dist. by: Inland Book Company, P.O. Box 261, 22 Hemingway Ave., East Haven, CT 06512 (SAN 200-4151) Tel 203-467-4257.

Shamro Creative Productions, *(Shamro Creative Prod; 0-939711),* 9560 Black Mountain Rd., San Diego, CA 90404 (SAN 663-6047) Tel 619-695-0099.

Shamrock Press & Publishing Co., *(Shamrock Pr; 0-910583),* P.O. Box 7256, Alexandria, VA 22307 (SAN 260-2636) Tel 703-683-3114.

Shamrock Pubns., *(Shamrock Pubns; 0-9608142),* 406 Rising Hill Dr., Fairborn, OH 45324 (SAN 240-1584).

Shane Publishing, *(Shane Pub; 0-86632),* P.O. Box 1615, Baltimore, MD 21203 (SAN 656-9021).

Shanelle, Sally, *(S Shanelle; 0-9616642),* 3636 Camino del Rio N., Suite 110, San Diego, CA 92108 (SAN 659-6797) Tel 619-282-8864; Dist. by: Publishers West, 4535 30th St., No. 212, San Diego, CA 92116 (SAN 200-674X).

Shank, Jack, *(Jack Shank; 0-9616123),* 3633 48th St., Meridian, MS 39305 (SAN 699-7139) Tel 601-483-1681.

Shanken, M., Communications, Inc., *(M Shanken Comm; 0-918076),* 400 E. 51st St., New York, NY 10022 (SAN 210-2773) Tel 212-751-6500; Toll free: 800-227-1617.

Shanks, Hershel, Pub., *(Hershel Shanks Pubs; 0-9607092),* 3111 Rittenhouse St. NW, Washington, DC 20015 (SAN 237-9570) Tel 202-244-9011.

Shano Pubs., Affil. of Grace Nash Publications, *(Shano Pubs; 0-914778),* P.O. Box 1753-N, Scottsdale, AZ 85252 (SAN 692-2392) Tel 602-945-8821.

Names

†**Shanty Pr.,** *(Shanty Pr; 0-916403),* 3236 Dupont S., Minneapolis, MN 55408 (SAN 295-5113) Tel 612-822-2375; *CIP.*

Shapian/Morrell Productions, *(Shapian-Morrell; 0-9610992),* 9110 Sunset Blvd., No. 240, Los Angeles, CA 90069 (SAN 265-2056) Tel 213-276-1005.

Shapiro, Leonard, *(Shapiro; 0-9607318),* 1567 N. Prospect Ave., Apt. 416, Milwaukee, WI 53202 (SAN 239-3093) Tel 414-272-8683.

Shapolsky Bks. *See* Shapolsky, Steimatzky

Shapolsky/Steimatzky, *(Shapolsky Steimatzky; 0-933503),* 56 E. 11th St., New York, NY 10003 (SAN 200-8068) Tel 212-505-2505. *Imprints:* Shapolsky Bks. (Shapolsky Bks).

Share Publishing Co., *(Share Pub Co; 0-933344),* P.O. Box 3453, Annapolis, MD 21403 (SAN 212-5595).

Shared Care, *(Shared Care; 0-9608702),* 6102 N. 14th St., Phoenix, AZ 85014 (SAN 238-3683) Tel 602-279-2619.

Sharing Co., The, *(Sharing Co; 0-941500),* P.O. Box 2224, Austin, TX 78768-2224 (SAN 211-0563) Tel 512-452-4366.

Sharon Hill Books, *(Sharon Hill; 0-932062),* P.O. Box 67, Sharon Hill, PA 19079 (SAN 210-5632).

Sharon Kimberly Damon Publishing Co., *(SKD Publishing; 0-937875),* 4201 Via Marina, No. 160, Marina del Rey, CA 90292 (SAN 659-5855); 624 S. Central Expressway, Richardson, TX 75080 (SAN 663-320X).

Sharon Pubns., *(Sharon Pubns NYC; 0-915697),* 270 West End Ave., New York, NY 10023 (SAN 292-6601) Tel 212-362-3141.

Sharon Pubns., Inc., Subs. of Edrei Communications Corp., *(Sharon Pubns; 0-89531),* 1086 Teaneck Rd., Teaneck, NJ 07666 (SAN 210-4989) Tel 201-833-1133; Orders to: New American Library, 1633 Broadway, New York, NY 10019 (SAN 206-8079) Tel 212-397-8126; Toll free: 800-526-0275.

Sharp, Vera, Publishing Co., *(V Sharp Pub; 0-9616987),* 204C Edgewater Towers, 17350 Sunset Blvd., Pacific Palisades, CA 90272 (SAN 658-8360) Tel 213-454-2111.

†**Sharp & Dunningan,** *(Sharp & Dunn; 0-918495),* P.O. Box 660, Forest Ranch, CA 95942 (SAN 657-3029) Tel 916-891-6602; Dist. by: Baker & Taylor, Eastern Div., 50 Kirby Ave., Somerville, NJ 08876 (SAN 169-4901); Dist. by: Ingram Book Company, 347 Reedwood Dr., Nashville, TN 37217 (SAN 651-1163); Dist. by: Quality Books, 918 Sherwood Dr., Lake Bluff, IL 60044-2204 (SAN 169-2127); Toll free: 800-323-4241; *CIP.*

Sharpe, John K., Incorporated, *(J K Sharpe Inc),* Box 442, Wilmette, IL 60091 (SAN 276-9395) Tel 312-295-1024.

Sharpe, M. E., Inc., *(M E Sharpe; 0-87332),* 80 Business Pk. Dr., Armonk, NY 10504 (SAN 202-7100) Tel 914-273-1800; Toll free: 800-638-6460; 39 Westmoreland Ave., White Plains, NY 10603 (SAN 658-1595).

Sharratt & Company, *(Sharratt & Co; 0-912295),* 3713 E. Easter Circle N., Littleton, CO 80122 (SAN 277-7061) Tel 303-773-3967.

Shasta Abbey Pr., *(Shasta Abbey; 0-930066),* P.O. Box 199, Mt. Shasta, CA 96067 (SAN 210-6655) Tel 916-926-4208; Dist. by: Bookpeople, 2929 Fifth St., Berkeley, CA 94710 (SAN 168-9517).

Shasta Pubns., *(Shasta FL; 0-9615596),* 201 N. Federal Hwy., Suite 215, Deerfield Beach, FL 33441 (SAN 696-1665) Tel 305-426-8503.

Shasta Pubns., *(Shasta Pubns; 0-9608202),* 1062 Tahoe Terr., Cincinnati, OH 45238 (SAN 240-2793) Tel 513-451-2774.

Shattinger International *See* Hansen, Charles, Educational Music & Bks., Inc.

ShaunTar Enterprises, *(ShaunTar Ent; 0-910241),* P.O. Box 11784, Santa Rosa, CA 95406 (SAN 241-4546) Tel 707-544-1478; Dist. by: The Distributors, 702 S. Michigan, South Bend, IN 46618 (SAN 169-2488) Tel 219-232-8500.

†**Shaw, Harold, Pubs.,** *(Shaw Pubs; 0-87788),* P.O. Box 567, 388 Gundersen Dr., Wheaton, IL 60189 (SAN 203-2473) Tel 312-665-6700; Toll free: 800-SHAW-PUB; *CIP.*

Shaw, Li Kung, Pubs., *(Li Kung Shaw; 0-9607806),* 2530 33rd Ave., San Francisco, CA 94116 (SAN 240-0480) Tel 415-731-0829.

Shaw, Rufus, Publishing, *(R S Publishing; 0-936436),* P.O. Box 15568, Dallas, TX 75215 (SAN 221-9948).

†**Shaw, Lloyd, Foundation Inc., The,** *(L Shaw Found; 0-915213),* 5421 Easley Rd., Golden, CO 80403 (SAN 289-8381); Orders to: Sales Div., P.O. Box 1148, Salida, CO 81201 (SAN 650-9967); *CIP.*

Shaw Pubs., Inc., *(Shaw Pub; 0-9615773),* Box 63, Marissa, IL 62257 (SAN 696-5873) Tel 618-295-2241.

†**Shawme Enterprises,** *(Shawme Ent; 0-914151),* 36 Rte. 6A, R.F.D. 1, Sandwich, MA 02563 (SAN 287-556X) Tel 617-888-2519; *CIP.*

Shawnee County Historical Society, *(Shawnee County Hist; 0-916934),* 1205 W. 29th St., Rm. 430, Topeka, KS 66611 (SAN 282-3136) Tel 913-267-0309; P.O. Box 56, Topeka, KS 66601 (SAN 282-4359).

Shawnee Press, Inc., *(Shawnee Pr; 0-9603394),* Waring Dr., Delaware Water Gap, PA 18327 (SAN 202-084X) Tel 717-476-0550.

Shawnee Printing Co., *(Shawnee Print; 0-9604662; 0-939371),* P.O. Box 426, Shawnee, OK 74801 (SAN 662-7978); Toll free: 800-654-4166; 132 S. Union, Shawnee, OK 74801 (SAN 662-7986) Tel 405-275-4750.

Shayna Ltd., *(Shayna Ltd; 0-9604208),* 100 Andrew St., Newton, MA 02161 (SAN 214-4727) Tel 617-244-1870.

Shaynew Pr., *(Shaynew Pr; 0-936705),* 2029 Stockton St., San Francisco, CA 94133 (SAN 699-945X) Tel 415-391-9295; Orders to: P.O. Box 11719, San Francisco, CA 94101 (SAN 662-7854).

Shea, Ralph A., *(R A Shea; 0-930409),* 489 Oak St., Ridgefield, NJ 07657 (SAN 670-8374) Tel 201-945-5150.

†**Shearer Publishing,** *(Shearer Pub; 0-940672),* 406 Post Oak Rd., Fredericksburg, TX 78624 (SAN 218-5989) Tel 512-997-6529; *CIP.*

Shearwater Press, *(Shearwater; 0-938050),* Box 417, Wellfleet, MA 02667 (SAN 216-1923).

Sheba Review, Inc., *(Sheba Rev; 0-9610626),* P.O. Box 1623, Jefferson City, MO 65102 (SAN 264-6927) Tel 314-893-5834; Dist. by: Paperback Supply, 4121 Forest Park Blvd., St. Louis, MO 63108 (SAN 169-4324); Dist. by: Cowley Distributing, Inc., 732 Heisinger Rd., Jefferson City, MO 65101 (SAN 169-426X) Tel 314-636-6511.

Shedd Aquarium Society, *(Shedd Aquarium; 0-9611074),* 1200 S. Lake Shore Dr., Chicago, IL 60605 (SAN 283-4359).

Sheed & Ward, Div. of National Catholic Reporter Publishing Co., Inc., *(Sheed & Ward MO; 0-934134; 1-55612),* P.O. Box 414292, Kansas City, MO 64141-0281 (SAN 207-7396); Toll free: 800-821-7926; 115 E. Armour Blvd., Kansas City, MO 61414-0281 (SAN 658-1269) Tel 816-531-0538; Toll free: 800-821-7296.

Sheed & Ward, Ltd., *(Sheed & Ward; 0-7220),* 2 Creechurch Ln., London EC3A 5AQ,

Sheehan Industries, *(Sheehan Indust; 0-9617018),* P.O. Box 801, Lake Stevens, WA 98258 (SAN 662-8621); 11918 24th PL., NE, Lake Stevens, WA 98258 (SAN 662-863X) Tel 206-377-3466.

†**Sheep Meadow Pr., The,** *(Sheep Meadow; 0-935296),* 5247 Independence Ave., Riverdale-on-Hudson, NY 10471 (SAN 669-2648) Tel 212-549-3321; Dist. by: Persea Bks., Inc., 225 Lafayette St., New York, NY 10012 (SAN 293-3926) Tel 212-431-5270; *CIP.*

Sheephead Books, *(Sheephead Bks; 0-9604644),* P.O. Box 562, Vidalia, GA 30474 (SAN 215-8094) Tel 912-537-2852.

Sheer Press, *(Sheer Pr; 0-9601254),* P.O. Box 4071, Walnut Creek, CA 94596 (SAN 210-4997) Tel 415-932-1144; 3601 Valley Vista Rd., Walnut Creek, CA 94598 (SAN 210-5004).

Sheets & Associates, *(Sheets & Assocs; 0-9613266),* P.O. Box 1853, Salt Lake City, UT 84110 (SAN 297-1933); 324 S. State St., No. 500, 84111 (SAN 297-1941).

Sheffield Bks., *(Sheffield Bks; 0-934831),* P.O. Box 578099, Chicago, IL 60657 (SAN 694-292X) Tel 312-935-3689.

Sheffield Publishing Co., Subs. of Waveland Pr., Prospect Heights, IL, *(Sheffield Wisc; 0-917974; 0-88133),* P.O. Box 359, Salem, WI 53168 (SAN 658-4519); 9009 Antioch Rd., Salem, WI 53168 (SAN 658-4527) Tel 414-843-2281.

Shelburne Museum, Inc., *(Shelburne; 0-939384),* Shelburne, VT 05482 (SAN 205-941X) Tel 802-985-3346.

Shelburne Publishing Co., *(Shelburne Pub; 0-930873),* P.O. Box 6162, Shawnee Mission, KS 66206 (SAN 677-7996) Tel 816-333-9700.

Shelcor Publishing, Inc., *(Shelcor Pub; 0-937107),* 4634 Van Nuys Blvd., Sherman Oaks, CA 91403 (SAN 658-4411) Tel 818-789-5700.

Sheldon, Bill, Pub., *(B Sheldon; 0-9616668),* 5478 Mary Jo Way, San Jose, CA 95124 (SAN 659-9079) Tel 408-264-2728.

Sheldon, Marc, Publishing, *(M Sheldon Pub; 0-932262),* P.O. Box 272, 777 N. Loren Ave., Azusa, CA 91702 (SAN 211-9234) Tel 818-969-1866.

Shell Cabinet, *(Shell Cab; 0-913792),* P.O. Box 29, Falls Church, VA 22046 (SAN 122-8455) Tel 703-256-0707.

Shell Hse., Inc., *(Shell House; 0-9615700),* P.O. Box 1027, Lake Junaluska, NC 28745 (SAN 696-1215) Tel 704-456-3960; 71 Lakeshore Dr., Lake Junaluska, NC 28745 (SAN 696-9593).

Shellback Pr., *(Shellback Pr; 0-931099),* P.O. Box 2442, Ventnor, NJ 08406 (SAN 678-9455) Tel 609-823-4549.

Shelley Bks., *(Shelley Bks; 0-9615188),* P.O. Box 17184, NorthHills, Raleigh, NC 27619 (SAN 694-2660) Tel 919-782-1254.

Shellie Press, *(Shellie Pr; 0-9607038),* 420 Wisteria Rd., Venice, FL 33595 (SAN 239-3859).

†**Shelter Pubns., Inc.,** *(Shelter Pubns; 0-936070),* P.O. Box 279, Bolinas, CA 94924 (SAN 212-4521) Tel 415-868-0280; Dist. by: Random Hse., 400 Hahn Rd., Westminster, MD 21157 (SAN 202-5515); Toll free: 800-638-6460; Dist. by: HP Books, P.O. Box 5367, Tucson, AZ 85703 (SAN 201-6087) Tel 602-888-2150; Toll free: 800-528-4923; *CIP.*

Shelton Pubns., *(Shelton; 0-918742),* P.O. Box 391, Sausalito, CA 94966 (SAN 210-4733) Tel 415-332-1165; Dist. by: Publishers Group West, 5855 Beaudry St., Emeryville, CA 94608 (SAN 202-8522) Tel 415-444-3570; Toll free: 800-982-8317; Dist. by: Bookpeople, 2929 Fifth St., Berkeley, CA 94710 (SAN 168-9517) Tel 415-549-3030; Toll free: 800-227-1516; Dist. by: Cal-West Periodicals, 2400 Filbert St., Oakland, CA 94607 (SAN 168-9983); Dist. by: Milligan News Co., Inc., 150 N. Autumn, San Jose, CA 95110 (SAN 169-0272) Tel 408-298-3322; Dist. by: L-S Distributors, 480 Ninth St., San Francisco, CA 94103 (SAN 169-0213) Tel 415-861-6300.

Shemco, Div. of Shemco Copr., The, *(Shemco; 0-937057),* 729 Washington Rd., Pittsburgh, PA 15228 (SAN 658-3520) Tel 412-341-1223.

Shenandoah History, *(Shenandoah Hist; 0-917968),* P.O. Box 98, Edinburg, VA 22824 (SAN 210-0118) Tel 703-459-4598.

Shenandoah Natural History Assn., Inc., *(Shenandoah Nat Assn; 0-931606),* Shenandoah National Park, Rte. 4, Box 292, Luray, VA 22835 (SAN 222-9250) Tel 703-999-2243.

Shengold Pubns., Inc., *(Shengold; 0-88400),* 23 W. 45th St., New York, NY 10036 (SAN 203-2465) Tel 212-944-2555.

Shenson, Howard L., Inc., *(H L Shenson; 0-910549),* 20121 Ventura Blvd., No. 245, Woodland Hills, CA 91354 (SAN 260-1346) Tel 818-703-1415.

Shep, R. L., *(R L Shep; 0-914046),* P.O. Box C-20, Lopez Island, WA 98261 (SAN 215-3432).

Shepard, Joyce, *(Shepard J),* 13 Sixpence Way, Coronado, CA 92118 (SAN 219-3167).

Shepard Poorman Communications Corp., *(Shepard Poorman; 0-9607968),* P.O. Box 68110, Indianapolis, IN 46268 (SAN 238-0463) Tel 317-293-1500.

594

†**Shepard's/McGraw-Hill,** Div. of McGraw-Hill Bk. Co., *(Shepards-McGraw; 0-07),* 402 N. Cascade Ave., Colorado Springs, CO 80901 (SAN 205-9886) Tel 303-633-5521; Toll free: 800-525-2474; P.O. Box 1235, Colorado Springs, CO 80901 (SAN 658-1609); *CIP.*

Shepherd-Moore, Marie, Educational Foundation, *(Shepherd-Moore Ed Foun; 0-9603948),* 692 E. 40th St., Brooklyn, NY 11210 (SAN 221-6582).

Shepherd News Trust, *(Shepherd News Trust; 0-933663),* 174 Pierce St., W. Boylston, MA 01583 (SAN 692-5383) Tel 617-835-6663.

Shepherd Pubs., *(Shepherd Pubs VA; 0-9607308),* 118 Pinepoint Rd., Williamsburg, VA 23185 (SAN 240-1622) Tel 804-229-0661.

Sheppard, W. L., *(W L Sheppard; 0-9607610),* 923 Old Manoa Rd., Havertown, PA 19083 (SAN 216-3225) Tel 215-449-2167.

Sher Music Co., *(Sher Music; 0-9614701),* P.O. Box 40742, San Francisco, CA 94140 (SAN 692-610X) Tel 415-552-3172.

Sheriar Pr., Inc., *(Sheriar Pr; 0-913078),* 1414 Madison St., S., North Myrtle Beach, SC 29582 (SAN 203-2457) Tel 803-272-5333.

Sheridan Hse., Inc., *(Sheridan; 0-911378),* 145 Palisade St., Dobbs Ferry, NY 10522 (SAN 204-5915) Tel 914-693-2410.

Sheridan Medical Bks., Div. of Sheridan Hse., Inc., *(Sheridan Med Bks; 0-911378),* 145 Palisade St., Dobbs Ferry, NY 10522 (SAN 204-5915).

†**Sheridan Square Pubns., Inc.,** *(Sheridan Square Pubns),* P.O. Box 677, New York, NY 10013 (SAN 678-903X) Tel 212-254-1061; *CIP.*

Sherlock, *(Sherlock; 0-9616268),* 2627 Buckeye, Newport Beach, CA 92669 (SAN 658-3717) Tel 714-760-3636.

Sherlock's Bookshop, *(Sherlocks Book; 0-934935),* 492 S. First Ave., Des Plaines, IL 60016 (SAN 694-4167) Tel 312-297-8288.

Sherman, Faith, *(F Sherman; 0-9607286),* 159 S. Lakewood Rd., Tygh Valley, OR 97063 (SAN 239-3107) Tel 503-544-3392.

Sherman, Harvey, *(Sherman),* 4011 Garden Ave., Los Angeles, CA 90039 (SAN 210-3680).

Sherman, Robert T., *(R T Sherman; 0-9613031),* 3516 Lawson Rd., Glenview, IL 60025 (SAN 294-1309) Tel 312-498-9826; Orders to: Robert T. Sherman, Box 444, Glenview, IL 60025 (SAN 669-3644) Tel 312-498-9826.

Sherman Pr., *(Sherman Pr; 0-9614031),* 14755 Ventura Bl. 1-626, Sherman Oaks, CA 91403 (SAN 686-2756).

Sherrod, Paul, *(P Sherrod),* 4410 Olsen, Amarillo, TX 79106 (SAN 212-1395).

†**Sherway Publishing Co.,** *(Sherway Pub; 0-912641),* P.O. Box 3096, Chatsworth, CA 91313-3096 (SAN 282-7905) Tel 818-700-9049; *CIP.*

Sherwood Communications, *(Sherwood Comns; 0-914877),* P.O. Box 535, Southampton, PA 18966 (SAN 289-0682) Tel 215-357-9065.

Sherwood Co., The, *(Sherwood Co; 0-933056),* P.O. Box 21645, Denver, CO 80221 (SAN 212-8136) Tel 303-422-7900.

Sherwood Pr., *(Sherwood Pr; 0-9613290),* 17 High St., Woodbury, NJ 08096 (SAN 653-8355) Tel 609-848-8231.

Shetal Enterprises, *(Shetal Ent; 0-932888),* 1787-B. W. Touhy, Chicago, IL 60626 (SAN 213-9553) Tel 312-262-1133.

Shieldalloy Corp.-Metallurg Alloy Corp., *(Shieldalloy; 0-9606196),* N. West Blvd., Newfield, NJ 08344 (SAN 220-3065) Tel 609-692-4200.

Shields Pubns., *(Shields; 0-9600102; 0-914116),* P.O. Box 669, Eagle River, WI 54521 (SAN 204-5923) Tel 715-479-4810.

Shift Publishing Co., *(Shift Pub; 0-931533),* P.O. Box 2242, Novato, CA 94948 (SAN 682-3122) Tel 415-892-4390.

Shikar Publishing Co., *(Shikar Pub; 0-938199),* P.O. Box 9296, Santa Fe, NM 87501 (SAN 659-6606); Rte. 10, P.O. Box 1045, Santa Fe, NM 87501 (SAN 659-6614) Tel 505-988-4300.

Shillea, Thomas John, *(T J Shillea; 0-9616925),* 1921 Chestnut St., Philadelphia, PA 19103 (SAN 661-4884) Tel 215-561-3141.

Shillelagh Books, Inc., *(Shillelagh; 0-9607838),* 8104 Wisner St., Niles, IL 60648 (SAN 238-1982) Tel 312-937-4257.

Shilo Publishing House, Inc., *(Shilo Pub Hse; 0-88328),* 73 Canal St., New York, NY 10002 (SAN 205-9894) Tel 212-925-3468.

Shim, Sang Kyu, Publisher, *(S K Shim Pub; 0-942062),* 17625 W. 7 Mile, Detroit, MI 48235 (SAN 238-5929).

†**Shining Star Press,** *(Shining Star; 0-9613073),* P.O. Box 206, Goleta, CA 93116 (SAN 294-6599) Tel 805-968-1868; Dist. by: Bookpeople, 2929 Fifth St., Berkeley, CA 94710 (SAN 168-9517) Tel 415-549-3030; Dist. by: Inland Bk. Co., P.O. Box 261, 22 Hemingway Ave., East Haven, CT 06512 (SAN 200-4151) Tel 203-467-4257; *CIP.*

Shinn, Duane, Pubns., *(Duane Shinn; 0-912732),* Box 700, Medford, OR 97501 (SAN 204-5931) Tel 503-664-2317.

Shintaido of America, *(Shintaido; 0-942634),* 145 Judah, No. 6, San Francisco, CA 94122 (SAN 238-5805) Tel 415-731-9364.

Ship, Inc., Pubns., *(Ship Inc),* 6206 S. First Avenue, Phoenix, AZ 85041 (SAN 208-1636) Tel 602-276-9654.

Ship to Shore, Div. of Robinson Yacht Co., Inc., *(Ship-Shore; 0-9612686),* 10500 Mt. Holly Rd., Charlotte, NC 28214 (SAN 289-419X) Tel 704-392-4740.

Shipley, Alice M., *(A M Shipley; 0-9610918),* 217 W. Roma Ave., Phoenix, AZ 85013 (SAN 265-1076) Tel 602-265-5894.

Shipley Assocs., *(Shipley; 0-933427),* P.O. Box 40, Bountiful, UT 84010 (SAN 691-5175) Tel 801-295-2386; Toll free: 800-343-0009.

Shippers National Freight Claim Council, Inc., *(Shippers Natl),* 120 Main St., Box Z, Huntington, NY 11743 (SAN 224-9553) Tel 516-549-8984.

Shire Pr., *(Shire Pr; 0-918828),* P.O. Box 1728, Santa Cruz, CA 95061 (SAN 293-3942) Tel 408-425-0842; Dist. by: Bookpeople, 2929 Fifth St., Berkeley, CA 94710 (SAN 168-9517) Tel 415-549-3030.

Shirjieh Pubs., *(Shirjieh Pubs; 0-912496),* P.O. Box 259, Menlo Park, CA 94025 (SAN 204-594X).

Shirk-Heath, Sandra J., *(Shirk-Heath; 0-9615104),* 1935-42nd St. NW, Rochester, MN 55901 (SAN 694-2784) Tel 507-289-0711.

Shirlee Pubns., *(Shirlee; 0-9613476),* P.O. Box 22122, Carmel, CA 93922 (SAN 657-3789) Tel 408-646-0600.

Shirley's Publishing, Ltd., *(Shirleys Pub; 0-9609868),* 1608 Shenstone Ct., Virginia Beach, VA 23455 (SAN 275-3197) Tel 804-460-3668.

Shiver Mountain Press, Inc., *(Shiver Mntn; 0-89488),* Rte. 47, Washington Depot, CT 06794 (SAN 210-0134) Tel 203-868-0533.

Shoaf, Mary Jo Davis, *(M J D Shoaf; 0-9602520),* 5140 Hackney Ln., SW, Roanoke, VA 24018 (SAN 212-6893) Tel 703-774-2667.

†**Shoal Creek Pubs.,** *(Shoal Creek Pub; 0-88319),* 406 Post Oak Rd., Fredericksburg, TX 78624 (SAN 203-2430) Tel 512-997-6529; Orders to: Shearer Publishing, 406 Post Oak Rd., Fredericksburg, TX 78624 (SAN 662-1449) Tel 512-447-6529; *CIP.*

Shoalwater Kitchen, *(Shoalwater Kitch; 0-9613895),* P.O. Box 624, Oysterville, WA 98641 (SAN 682-3130) Tel 206-665-4949; Dist. by: Pacific Pipeline, 19215 66th Ave., S., Kent, WA 98032 (SAN 208-2128) Tel 206-872-5523.

Shockley Pr., *(Shockley Pr; 0-942048),* P.O. Box 36012, Los Angeles, CA 90036 (SAN 238-5937) Tel 213-933-4198.

Shoe Service Institute of America, *(Shoe Serv Inst; 0-931424),* 112 Calendar Court Mall, Lagrange, IL 60525 (SAN 211-5018) Tel 312-482-8010.

Shoe String Pr., Inc., *(Shoe String; 0-208),* P.O. Box 4327, Hamden, CT 06514 (SAN 213-2079) Tel 203-248-6307; 925 Sherman Ave., Hamden, CT 06514 (SAN 696-9410). *Imprints:* Archon Books (Archon Bks), Bingley, Clive, Limited (England) (Pub. by Bingley England); Cooper (Cooper); CT Academy (CT Academy); Library Professional Publications (Lib Prof Pubns); Linnet (Linnet); Pembridge Press (England) (Pub. by Pembridge Pr UK); Tompson & Rutter, Incorporated (Pub. by Thompson & Rutter, Inc.).

Shoe Tree Pr., *(Shoe Tree Pr; 0-936915),* P.O. Box 356, Belvidere, NJ 07823 (SAN 658-375X) Tel 201-475-4751; 26 Parker St., Belvidere, NJ 07823 (SAN 658-3768).

Shoemaker, Rhoda, *(R Shoemaker; 0-9600474),* 1141 Orange Ave., Menlo Park, CA 94025 (SAN 204-6636) Tel 415-854-5768.

Shoerue Pr., *(Sheorue Pr; 0-9616292),* P.O. Box 3221, Santa Barbara, CA 93110 (SAN 658-442X) Tel 805-964-5841; 4025 State St., No. 35, Santa Barbara, CA 93110 (SAN 658-4438).

Shofar Pubns., Inc., *(Shofar Pubns; 0-936685),* P.O. Box 88711, Carol Stream, IL 60188 (SAN 699-7325) Tel 312-665-2150; 26 W 021 Astor Pl., Wheaton, IL 60187 (SAN 658-3024).

Sholars, Robert E., *(Sholars; 0-9611178),* P.O. Box 2340, Mendocino, CA 95460 (SAN 283-4308).

Shopen, Sylvia Ames, *(S A Shopen),* Norwich, VT 05055 (SAN 212-7024).

Shopping Experience, The, *(Shopping Experience; 0-934758),* 2 Grace Ct., Brooklyn, NY 11201 (SAN 213-9472) Tel 718-625-2772.

†**Shopsmith, Inc.,** *(Shopsmith; 0-936611),* 6640 Poe Ave., Dayton, OH 45414 (SAN 686-2748) Tel 513-898-6070; Dist. by: Rodale Press Inc., 33 E. Minor St., Emmaus, PA 18049 (SAN 200-2477); *CIP.*

Shopware Educational Systems, *(Shopware Educ; 1-55669),* Rte. 1 Box 330-E, Aberdeen, WA 98520 (SAN 663-3838) Tel 206-532-3392.

Shore, C., Pr., *(C Shore Pr; 0-9612136),* P.O. Box 14008, Bradenton, FL 34280 (SAN 286-8733) Tel 813-792-4535.

Shore, Michael, Assocs., *(M Shore Assocs; 0-910243),* 24 Westfield Rd., Milford, CT 06460 (SAN 241-4554) Tel 203-877-9218.

Shore/Campbell Publishing, *(Shore-Campbell; 0-938297),* 1437 Lucile Ave., Los Angeles, CA 90026 (SAN 659-6592) Tel 213-666-6967; Dist. by: Baker & Taylor, Eastern Div., 50 Kirby Ave., Somerville, NJ 08876 (SAN 169-4901).

Shorewood Fine Art Books, Inc., *(Shorewood Fine Art; 0-87230),* 27 Glen Rd., Sandy Hook, CT 06482 (SAN 219-9637) Tel 203-426-8100. *Imprints:* Woodbine Books, Inc. (Woodbine Bks).

Shorey Pubns., *(Shorey; 0-8466),* 110 Union St., Seattle, WA 98101 (SAN 204-5958) Tel 206-624-0221.

Short Methods & Systems, *(Short Methods; 0-915800),* 1212 Hillsdale Dr., Claremont, CA 91711 (SAN 207-4842) Tel 714-626-3213.

Short Story Press *See* Holmes Publishing Group

Showcase Charbo-Miles, *(Showcase; 0-938201),* 3612 Stratford Rd., Topeka, KS 66604 (SAN 659-6622) Tel 913-272-5605.

†**Showcase Pubns.,** *(Showcase Pubns; 0-917800),* P.O. Box 40165, Pasadena, CA 91104 (SAN 213-5906) Tel 818-794-7782; *CIP.*

Showcase Publishing Co., *(Showcase Fairfield; 0-88205),* 1125 Missouri St., Fairfield, CA 94533 (SAN 213-6430) Tel 707-427-3130; Toll free: 800-526-0275.

Shreveport Publishing Co., *(Shreveport Pub; 0-939042),* P.O. Box 31110, Shreveport, LA 71130 (SAN 216-1842).

Shrewd Pubns., Subs. of SourceWorks International, *(Shrewd Pubns; 0-936103),* 2487 Samia Dr., Duluth, GA 30136 (SAN 696-7728) Tel 404-497-1100; P.O. Box 956277, Duluth, GA 30136 (SAN 699-6442).

Shrine of the Eternal Breath of Tao, The, *(SEBT; 0-937064),* 117 Stonehaven Way, Los Angeles, CA 90049 (SAN 217-2704).

Shroud of Turin Research Project, Inc., *(Shroud of Turin; 0-9605516),* P.O. Box 7, Amston, CT 06231 (SAN 216-1834).

Shrout, Beatrice Lentz, *(B L Shrout; 0-9609070),* 513 Riverside Dr., Welch, WV 24801 (SAN 241-2500) Tel 304-436-3411.

Shrubsole, S. J., Corp., *(S J Shrubsole; 0-9616646),* 104 E. 57th St., New York, NY 10022 (SAN 659-770X) Tel 212-753-8920.

Shu Publishing Co., *(Shu Pub; 0-938885),* 218 Dewey St., Worcester, MA 01610 (SAN 661-7158) Tel 617-756-6962.

Shubin, Daniel H., *(D H Shubin),* 5865 Crown Dr., Mira Loma, CA 91752 (SAN 659-4026).

Names

Names

Shulman, Joel J., *(J J Shulman; 0-9616302),* 6 Linda Ln., Plainview, NY 11803 (SAN 698-1712) Tel 516-681-3677.

Shulsinger Sales, Inc., *(Shulsinger Sales; 0-914080),* 50 Washington St., Brooklyn, NY 11201 (SAN 205-9851) Tel 718-852-0042.

†**Shumway, George, Pub.,** *(Shumway; 0-87387),* RD 7, Box 388B, York, PA 17402 (SAN 203-2422) Tel 717-755-1196; *CIP.*

Shumway Family History Services, *(Shumway Family Hist; 0-938717),* 1308 Cozy Terr., Anaheim, CA 92806 (SAN 661-616X) Tel 714-778-6199.

Shutts Ministries, *(Shutts Minist; 0-9614077),* P.O. Box 28, Marysville, OH 43040 (SAN 686-0648) Tel 513-644-9785.

Si-sa-yong-o-sa, Inc., *(Si-sa-yong-o-sa; 0-87296),* 115 W. 29th St., 5th Flr., New York, NY 10001 (SAN 673-1252) Tel 212-736-5092.

Siamese Imports Co., Inc., *(Siamese Imports; 0-940202),* 148 Plandome Rd., Manhasset, NY 11030 (SAN 220-3545) Tel 516-365-8867.

Sibyl Jarvis Pischke, *(Sibyl; 0-9608532),* 1401 NE 35th St., Ft. Lauderdale, FL 33334 (SAN 240-7736) Tel 305-566-5078.

Siegel, Kenneth L., Publishing, *(Siegel; 0-939848),* 19780 Ventura Blvd., Woodland Hills, CA 91364 (SAN 216-762X) Tel 818-999-6903.

Siegmond, W. E., Enterprises, *(W E Siegmond; 0-916610),* 382 Central Park West, New York, NY 10025 (SAN 208-225X).

Siemens Communication Graphics, *(Siemens Com Graphics; 0-936226),* 1501 Greenleaf, Evanston, IL 60602 (SAN 221-9956).

Siepierski, Gerald E., *(G E Siepierski; 0-9611278),* 20257 Ecorse Rd., Taylor, MI 48180 (SAN 283-1643) Tel 313-382-4816.

Sierra Bks., Subs. of Sierra Records, *(Sierra Bks; 0-916003),* P.O. Box 5853, Pasadena, CA 91107-0853 (SAN 294-6602) Tel 818-355-0181.

†**Sierra Club Bks.,** *(Sierra; 0-87156),* 730 Polk St., San Francisco, CA 94109 (SAN 203-2406) Tel 415-776-2211; Toll free: 800-638-6460; Dist. by: Random Hse., Inc., 400 Hahn Rd., Westminster, MD 21157 (SAN 202-5515); *CIP.*

Sierra Club, Santa Fe Group, *(Sierra Santa Fe; 0-9616458),* 1301 Luisa St., Santa Fe, NM 87501 (SAN 659-302X) Tel 505-983-2703.

Sierra Nevada Chapter, *(Sierra NV Chapter),* Special Libraries Assn., P.O. Box 8159, Reno, NV 89507 (SAN 676-9659).

Sierra Pacific Press, *(Sierra Pr; 0-943238),* 1722 J St., Suite 19, Sacramento, CA 95814 (SAN 240-7744) Tel 916-444-9133.

Sierra Pr., The, *(Sierra Press; 0-939365),* P.O. Box 102, Yosemite National Park, CA 95389 (SAN 662-6955); Lot 60 El Portal Administrative Site, Yosemite National Park, CA 95389 (SAN 662-6963) Tel 209-379-2330. Do not confuse with Sierra Press, Phoenix, AZ.

Sierra Pubns., *(Sierra Pubns CA; 0-932848),* 70 Valley View Ave., San Jose, CA 95127 (SAN 211-6154) Tel 408-251-3799.

Sierra Publishing Co., *(Sierra Pub Co; 0-918493),* P.O. Box 213, Jackson, CA 95642 (SAN 676-9578) Tel 209-223-4238.

Sierra Publishing (San Francisco), *(Sierra Pub CA; 0-932417),* 55 Sutter St., Suite 6, San Francisco, CA 94104 (SAN 686-7006) Tel 415-621-3652; Dist. by: Alchemy Bks., 717 Market St., Suite 514, San Francisco, CA 94101 (SAN 211-304X) Tel 415-777-2197.

Sierra Trading Post, *(Sierra Trading; 0-9605890),* P.O. Box 2497, San Francisco, CA 94126 (SAN 216-6097) Tel 415-456-9378.

Siftsoft, *(Siftsoft; 0-936687),* 100 Valencia, San Francisco, CA 94103 (SAN 699-914X) Tel 415-824-0731; P.O. Box 260, San Francisco, CA 94103 (SAN 699-9158).

†**Sigga Press,** *(Sigga Pr; 0-916348),* P.O. Box 25, Nottingham, NH 03290 (SAN 211-2698); *CIP.*

Sightseer Pubns., *(Sightseer; 0-937928),* 7400 N. Kendall Dr., Miami, FL 33156 (SAN 220-1240).

Sigma Delta Chi *See* **Society of Professional Journalists, Sigma Delta Chi**

Sigma Press, *(Sigma Pr NY),* P.O. Box 264, Manhasset, NY 11030 (SAN 240-9577).

Sigma Press Inc., *(Sigma Pr; 0-9604516),* P.O. Box 379, South Bound Brook, NJ 08880 (SAN 215-8116).

Sigma Publishing Co., Inc., *(Sigma Pub; 0-937027),* 1316 Broad St., Syracuse, NY 13224 (SAN 658-3474) Tel 315-446-0781.

Sigma Scientific, Inc., *(Sigma Sci Inc; 0-915313),* 903 Myers Place, Blacksburg, VA 24060 (SAN 290-0416) Tel 703-951-0258.

Sigma Tau Gamma, *(Sigma Tau Gamma),* Box 54, Warrensburg, MO 64093 (SAN 224-5337) Tel 816-747-2222.

Signal Bks., Subs. Of Compute Textual Services, *(Signal Bks; 0-930095),* 201-C E. Main St., Carrboro, NC 27510 (SAN 670-1795) Tel 919-929-5985.

Signal Environmental Systems, Inc., Johnson Division, *(SES Johnson Div; 0-9616456),* 1950 Old Highway 8, New Brighton, MN 55112 (SAN 659-2570) Tel 612-636-3900.

Signal Media Corp., *(Signal Media; 0-9616677),* 14951 Dallas Pkwy., Suite 1030, Dallas, TX 75240 (SAN 659-6789) Tel 214-458-8400.

Signals Publishing Co., *(Signals Pub; 0-9615962),* P.O. Box 5071, Beverly Hills, CA 90210 (SAN 696-7760) Tel 213-650-0701; 2121 Kress St., Los Angeles, CA 90046 (SAN 697-3086).

Signature Bks., Inc., *(Signature Bks; 0-941214),* 350 S. 400 E., Salt Lake City, UT 84111 (SAN 217-4391) Tel 801-531-1483. Imprints: Eden Hill Publishing (Eden Hill Pub); Orion (Orion).

Signature Publishing Corp., *(Signature Pub; 0-939147),* 1155 Watson Way, No. 5, Sparks, NV 89431 (SAN 662-9059) Tel 702-331-1211.

Signet Bks. *See* **New American Library**
Signet Classics *See* **New American Library**
Signette *See* **New American Library**

Signmaker Press, *(Signmaker; 0-9605774),* Box 967, Ashland, OR 97520 (SAN 216-549X).

Signpost Bk. Pub. Co., *(Signpost Bk Pub; 0-913140),* 8912 192nd St. SW, Edmonds, WA 98020 (SAN 204-5966) Tel 206-776-0370.

Signpost Pr., *(Signpost Pr; 0-9609592),* N 56 W21414 Silver Spring Rd., Menomonee Falls, WI 53051 (SAN 275-3596) Tel 414-252-3219.

Signpost Pr., Inc., The, *(Signpost; 0-936563),* 412 N. State St., Bellingham, WA 98225 (SAN 698-097X) Tel 206-734-9781.

Signs of the Times Publishing Co., *(Signs of Times; 0-911380),* 407 Gilbert Ave., Cincinnati, OH 45202 (SAN 204-5974) Tel 513-421-2050; Toll free: 800-543-1925.

Signum Books Limited, *(Signum Bks; 0-9612034),* P.O. Box 5057, Oregon City, OR 97045-8057 (SAN 286-8768) Tel 503-657-3567.

Sigo Pr., *(Sigo Pr; 0-938434),* 77 N. Washington St., No. 201, Boston, MA 02114 (SAN 216-3020) Tel 617-523-2321.

Silbert & Bress Pubns., *(Silbert Bress; 0-89544),* P.O. Box 68, Mahopac, NY 10541 (SAN 210-5020) Tel 914-628-7910.

Silicon Pr., *(Silicon Pr; 0-9615336),* 25 Beverly Rd., Summit, NJ 07901 (SAN 695-1538) Tel 201-273-2272.

†**Siliconix Inc.,** *(Siliconix Inc; 0-930519),* 2201 Laurelwood Rd., Santa Clara, CA 95054 (SAN 692-7750) Tel 408-970-4066; Toll free: 800-554-5564; *CIP.*

Silk Butterfly Pr. *See* **Panda Bks., Pubs.**

Sill, Stephen P., Publishing Co., *(S P Sill Pub; 0-9615806),* P.O. Box 1334, San Andreas, CA 95249 (SAN 696-589X) Tel 802-885-3671; Dist. by: Bible & Bk. Room, 100 River St., Springfield, VT 05156 (SAN 200-593X).

Sillars, Mal, Weather Consultants, Inc., *(M Sillars; 0-9616885),* P.O. Box 36733, Grosse Pointe, MI 48236 (SAN 661-6526); 316 McKinley, Grosse Pointe Farms, MI 48236 (SAN 661-6534) Tel 313-881-3244.

Silo Pubs., The, *(Silo Pubs; 0-937109),* P.O. Box 3662, Hesperia, CA 92345 (SAN 658-439X) Tel 619-244-1674; 18019 Danbury Ave., Hesperia, CA 92345 (SAN 658-4403).

Silver, David E. (A/P), *(D E Silver; 0-9612792),* 8523 Mt. Whitney Dr., El Paso, TX 79904 (SAN 289-8403) Tel 915-751-1850.

Silver, Robert, Assocs., *(R Silver; 0-937414),* 307 E. 37th St., New York, NY 10016 (SAN 241-5801) Tel 212-686-5630.

Silver Age Publishing, *(Silver Age Pub; 0-940294),* P.O. Box 384, Rego Park, NY 11374 (SAN 217-5835) Tel 718-897-6938.

Silver & Gold Report, *(Silver & Gold; 0-935754; 0-916373),* P.O. Box 40, Bethel, CT 06801 (SAN 221-9972).

Silver Apples Press, *(Silver App Pr; 0-943710),* P.O. Box 292, Hainesport, NJ 08036 (SAN 238-3721).

†**Silver Buckle Pr.,** *(Silver Buckle Pr; 0-931101),* Memorial Library, Rm. 443, University of Wisconsin, 728 State St., Madison, WI 53706 (SAN 676-9497); *CIP.*

†**Silver Burdett Co.,** Subs. of SFN Cos, Inc., *(Silver; 0-382),* 250 James St., Morristown, NJ 07960-1918 (SAN 204-5982) Tel 201-285-7700; Toll free: 800-631-8081; *CIP.*

Silver D. Investments, Inc., *(Silver D Invest Inc; 0-912497),* P.O. Box 833038, Richardson, TX 75083 (SAN 265-315X) Tel 214-699-0439.

Silver Dollar City, Inc., *(Silver Dollar),* Silver Dollar City, MO 65616 (SAN 210-3699) Tel 417-388-2611.

Silver Dollar Pr., *(Silv Dollar Pr; 0-9615146),* 5021 Arlington Dr., North Little Rock, AR 72116 (SAN 694-2725) Tel 501-753-4181.

Silver Fox Connections, *(Silver Fox; 0-9605910),* 1244 SW 301st St., Federal Way, WA 98003 (SAN 216-4485) Tel 206-839-3784.

Silver Sea Pr., *(Silver Sea; 0-916005),* 820 Pacific Coast Hwy., Suite 103, Hermosa Beach, CA 90254 (SAN 294-6610) Tel 213-379-8959.

Silver Seal Books, *(Silver Seal Bks; 0-910867),* P.O. Box 106, Fox Island, WA 98333 (SAN 264-3871).

Silver Skates Publishing Co., *(Silver Skates; 0-936105),* 1020 Santa Fe Ave., Albany, CA 94706 (SAN 696-7493) Tel 415-528-1302.

Silver Spring Press, *(Silver Sg Pr; 0-931953),* 15721 New Hampshire Ave, Silver Spring, MD 20904 (SAN 685-9674) Tel 301-384-9385.

Silverado Publishing Co., *(Silverado; 0-87938),* St. Helena, CA 94574 (SAN 213-3725); Dist. by Motorbooks International, Pubs. & Wholesalers, 729 Prospect Ave., Osceola, WI 54020 (SAN 212-3304) Tel 715-294-3345.

Silverback Books, *(Silverback; 0-916747),* 323 Franklin Bldg. S., Suite 804/Department S-199, Chicago, IL 60606-7096 (SAN 654-4495) Tel 219-736-2112; Dist. by: The Distributors, 702 S. Michigan, South Bend, IN 46618 (SAN 169-2488) Tel 219-232-8500.

Silverbell Pr., *(Silverbell Pr; 0-937489),* 25 Glenhaven, DeRidder, LA 70634 (SAN 659-1698) Tel 318-462-5105.

Silverfish Review Press, *(Silverfish Rev Pr; 0-9610508),* P.O. Box 3541, Eugene, OR 97403 (SAN 264-388X).

†**Silvergirl, Inc.,** *(Silvergirl Inc),* P.O. Box 4858, Austin, TX 78765 (SAN 239-3875) Tel 512-473-2478; *CIP.*

†**Silverleaf Press,** *(Silverleaf Pr; 0-915591),* 19 Harding Lane, Westport, CT 06880 (SAN 292-6660) Tel 203-227-5727; *CIP.*

Silvermine Pubs., *(Silvermine; 0-87231),* Comstock Hill, Silvermine, Norwalk, CT 06850 (SAN 209-6005) Tel 203-847-4732.

Simile II, *(Simile II),* 218 Twelfth St., P.O. Box 910, Del Mar, CA 92014 (SAN 208-8525) Tel 619-755-0272.

Simjac Press, Subs. of Danforth Publishing, Inc., *(Simjac Pr; 0-9615076),* 75 Russell St., Hamden, CT 06514 (SAN 694-048X) Tel 203-734-3331.

Simmons, Carol Lynn, *(C L Simmons; 0-9615885),* 220 Hedgewood Terr., Greer, SC 29651 (SAN 696-7485) Tel 803-244-4511.

Simmons-Boardman Bks., Inc., Subs. of Simmons-Boardman Publishing Corporation, New York, *(Simmons Boardman; 0-911382),* 1809 Capitol Ave., Omaha, NE 68102 (SAN 213-2605) Tel 402-346-4300; Toll free: 800-228-9670.

Simon, Jeffrey R., Publishing Co., *(J R Simon; 0-916343),* P.O. Box 13390, Pittsburgh, PA 15243 (SAN 295-9801) Tel 412-279-6525.

†**Simon, Joseph,** Div. of Pangloss Press, *(J Simon; 0-934710),* Box 4071, Malibu, CA 90265 (SAN 213-9669); 29500 Heathercliff Rd., No. 161, Malibu, CA 90265 (SAN 662-1457) Tel 213-457-3293; *CIP.*

Simonetta Pr., *(Simonetta Pr; 0-941594),* 15 W. Locust St., Bethlehem, PA 18018 (SAN 239-3883) Tel 215-867-5479.

Simons & Meredith, *(Simons Meredith; 0-938277),* P.O. Box 554, Hasbrouck Heights, NJ 07604 (SAN 659-9141); 300 Speedwell Ave., Morris Plains, NJ 07950 (SAN 659-915X) Tel 201-538-1000.

Simons Bks., Inc., *(Simons Bks; 0-937812),* P.O. Box 2145, Oceanside, CA 92054 (SAN 216-4493).

Simontsits, Attila L., *(Simontsits; 0-920004),* 4118 Ridge Rd., Apt. 6, Brooklyn, OH 44144 (SAN 283-409X) Tel 216-661-4319.

Simple Productions, *(Simple Prod; 0-938497),* 12 E. 15th St., No. 3, Arcata, CA 95521 (SAN 661-0536) Tel 707-822-3148.

Simple Soft Computer Services, *(Simp Soft Computer; 0-939463),* 3208 Cahuenga Blvd. W., Suite 121, Los Angeles, CA 90068 (SAN 663-3382) Tel 818-505-9832.

Simplex Communications, Inc., *(Simplex Comm; 0-935248),* P.O. Box 9133, Fort Wayne, IN 46783 (SAN 213-3741) Tel 219-672-3702. Moved, left no forwarding address.

Simplicity Pattern Co., Inc., *(Simplicity; 0-918178),* 200 Madison Ave., New York, NY 10016 (SAN 282-3179) Tel 212-576-0533; Orders to: Simplicity Educational Div., 901 Wayne St., Niles, MI 49121 (SAN 282-3187).

Simplified Regulations, *(Simplified Reg; 0-9607866),* W. 137 N. 8235 Parkview Dr., Menomonee Falls, WI 53051 (SAN 238-1990) Tel 414-255-2204.

Simply Delightful Merchandising, *(Simply Delight; 0-9614249),* 316 California Ave., Suite 304, Reno, NV 89509 (SAN 686-7308) Tel 702-673-0907.

Simply Elegant Co., *(Simply Elegant; 0-9600492),* 3801 N. Mission Hills Rd., Northbrook, IL 60062 (SAN 204-5990) Tel 312-564-2221; Orders to: P.O. Box 74, Winnetka, IL 60093 (SAN 204-6008).

Simpson, Jeanne R., Gallery of Fine Art Ltd., *(J R Simpson; 0-9611558),* 2811 W. 67 Terrace, Shawnee Mission, KS 66208 (SAN 284-9127) Tel 913-831-1902.

Simpson, Ruth M. Rasey, *(R M R Simpson; 0-9604048),* 286 Goundry St., North Tonawanda, NY 14120 (SAN 212-971X) Tel 716-692-1830.

Simpson, J. B. & Associates, *(J B Simpson; 0-9603882),* 2345 Oglesby Bridge Rd., Conyers, GA 30208 (SAN 221-6590) Tel 404-922-6256.

Simpson Publishing Co., *(Simpson Pub),* 1115 S. Franklin St., Kirksville, MO 63501 (SAN 202-9928) Tel 816-665-7251.

Sims Publishing, *(Sims Pub; 0-930795),* P.O. Box 9576, Sacramento, CA 95823 (SAN 693-3726).

Simtek, *(Simtek; 0-933836),* P.O. Box 105, Carlisle, MA 01741-0105 (SAN 212-6907) Tel 617-369-5538.

Simulation Learning Institute, Inc., *(Simul Learn; 0-918640),* 1 Adams Ct., Oyster Bay, NY 11771 (SAN 210-3702) Tel 516-922-6490.

†**Sinauer Assocs., Inc.,** *(Sinauer Assocs; 0-87893),* N. Main St., Sunderland, MA 01375 (SAN 203-2392) Tel 413-665-3722; CIP.

Sinclair, Dorothy, Enterprises, *(Sinclair Ent; 0-9615311),* P.O. Box 782, Bellaire, TX 77401-0782 (SAN 694-5996) Tel 713-664-9809.

Sinclaire Pr., *(Sinclaire Pr; 0-9616886),* 42 Bay View Rd., Wellesley, MA 02181 (SAN 661-6542) Tel 617-237-0140.

Sindwilf Ltd. Pr., *(Sindowilf Ltd; 0-939580),* 110 La Bolsa Rd., Walnut Creek, CA 94598 (SAN 216-695X) Tel 415-932-7612.

Singer Press, *(Singer Pr; 0-9610922),* 1540 Rollins Dr., Los Angeles, CA 90063 (SAN 265-1106) Tel 213-263-2640.

Singh, Kirpal, Publishing, *(K Singh Pub; 0-9615501),* 147-47 Jasmine Ave., Flushing, NY 11355 (SAN 696-4060) Tel 718-359-0307.

Singh, Swayam, *(S Singh; 0-935380),* 2311 Meadow Croft Dr., Lansing, MI 48912 (SAN 213-5914).

Singing Bone Pr., *(Singing Bone Pr; 0-933439),* 2318 Albion Pl., St. Louis, MO 63104 (SAN 691-5221) Tel 314-865-2789.

Singing Horse Pr., *(Singing Horse; 0-935162),* P.O. Box 40034, Philadelphia, PA 19106 (SAN 219-2810) Tel 215-844-7429.

Singing River Pubns., *(Singing River),* 4310 Twin Oaks Ave., Pascagoula, MS 39567 (SAN 239-4855).

Singing Stars Pr., *(Singing Stars Pr; 0-936319),* P.O. Box 217, Rosemont, NJ 08556 (SAN 697-3159) Tel 609-397-8311.

Single Action Productions, Div. of Images, *(Single Action Prod; 0-938887),* 60 E. 135th St., Suite 7C, New York, NY 10037 (SAN 662-6572) Tel 212-690-2472.

Single Graphics, *(Single Graph; 0-914067),* 5043 N. 20th Ave., Phoenix, AZ 85015 (SAN 287-5535) Tel 602-246-7499.

Single Impressions, *(Single Impressions; 0-938562),* 1240 W. Eureka, Tucson, AZ 85704 (SAN 215-8132).

Single Vision Pubns., *(Single Vision; 0-9608960),* Box No. 804, Lebanon, OR 97355 (SAN 241-2519) Tel 503-258-5888.

Singlejack Bks., of Miles & Weir, Ltd., Div. of Miles & Weir Ltd., *(Singlejack Bks; 0-917300),* P.O. Box 1906, San Pedro, CA 90733 (SAN 208-8541) Tel 213-548-5964; 839 S. Beacon St., Suite 308, San Pedro, CA 90733 (SAN 662-1465); Dist. by: Baker & Taylor Co., Eastern Div., 50 Kirby Ave., Somerville, NJ 08876 (SAN 169-4901); Dist. by: Baker & Taylor Co., Southeast Div., Mt. Olive Rd., Commerce, GA 30529 (SAN 169-1503); Dist. by: Baker & Taylor Co., Western Div., 380 Edison Way, Reno, NV 89564 (SAN 169-4464) Tel 206-872-5523; Dist. by: Baker & Taylor Co., Midwest Div., 501 Gladiola Ave., Momence, IL 60954 (SAN 169-2100); Dist. by: The Distributors, 702 S. Michigan, South Bend, IN 46618 (SAN 169-2488) Tel 219-232-8500.

Singles World Publishing Co., *(Singles World; 0-936890),* 1094 Cudahy, No. 102, San Diego, CA 92110 (SAN 214-4735); Dist. by: Communication Creativity, P.O. Box 213, Saguache, CO 81149 (SAN 210-3478) Tel 303-655-2502.

Singular Hse. Pr., *(Singular Hse Pr; 0-9616388),* 1302 Meridene Dr., Baltimore, MD 21239 (SAN 6509-1736) Tel 301-435-0392.

Singular Speech Press, *(Singular Speech Pr; 0-9607756),* 507 Dowd Ave., Canton, CT 06019 (SAN 238-115X) Tel 203-693-6059.

Sinister Wisdom Bks., *(Sinister Wisdom Bks; 0-931103),* P.O. Box 1308, Montpelier, VT 05602 (SAN 694-2199) Tel 802-229-9104.

†**Sipapu/Konocti Books,** Subs. of Konocti Books, *(Sipapu-Konocti Bks; 0-914134),* Rte. 1, Box 216, Winters, CA 95694 (SAN 206-5517) Tel 916-662-3364; CIP.

SIPRI *See* Taylor & Francis, Inc.

Siren Publisher, *(Siren; 0-9613395),* 1034 Valota Rd., Redwood City, CA 94061 (SAN 657-114X) Tel 415-367-7755.

Sirius Books, *(Sirius Bks; 0-917108),* 4745 Anderson Ln., Eureka, CA 95501 (SAN 275-3766) Tel 707-442-8481.

Sirius League, The, *(Sirius Leag; 0-9610762),* P.O. Box 40507, Albuquerque, NM 87196 (SAN 264-6366) Tel 505-262-0720.

Sirius Pubns., *(Sirius Pubns),* P.O. Box 1201, Agoura Hills, CA 91301 (SAN 282-3195) Tel 818-706-8838 (SAN 282-3209).

Siriusware, *(Siriusware; 0-926848),* 6 Turning Mill Rd., Lexington, MA 02173 (SAN 653-8606) Tel 617-862-9570.

SirS *See* Social Issues Resources Series, Inc.

Sister Kenny Institute, *(Sis Kenny Inst; 0-88440),* Pubns. Office, 800 E. 28th St., Minneapolis, MN 55407 (SAN 203-0705) Tel 612-874-4175.

Sisters, *(Sisters; 0-9610930),* P.O. Box 14593, Minneapolis, MN 55414 (SAN 265-2080) Tel 612-729-5383.

Sisters' Choice Press, *(Sisters Choice; 0-932164),* 1450-Sixth St., Berkeley, CA 94710 (SAN 211-7126) Tel 415-524-5804; Dist. by: Childrens Small Pr. Collection, 719 N. Fourth Ave., Ann Arbor, MI 48104 (SAN 200-514X).

Sisters Grim Pr., The, *(Sisters Grim Pr; 0-9614371),* 140 Wylie Dr., No. 12, Baton Rouge, LA 70808 (SAN 688-6124) Tel 504-891-3458.

Sisters of Christian Charity, *(Sisters Christ Charity; 0-9616887),* 1041 Ridge Rd., Wilmette, IL 60091-1560 (SAN 661-6402) Tel 312-256-1060.

Sisters of St. Mary of Oregon, *(Sisters St Mary OR; 0-9616750),* 4440 SW, 148th Ave., Beaverton, OR 97007 (SAN 661-0420) Tel 503-644-9181.

Sisters of the Divine Savior, *(Sisters Divine; 0-9616092),* 4311 N. 100th St., Milwaukee, WI 53222 (SAN 698-1232) Tel 414-466-0810.

Sisyphus Editions *See* Slow Loris Pr.

Sitare, Inc., *(Sitare Inc; 0-940178),* 1888 Century Park E., No. 10, Los Angeles, CA 90067 (SAN 217-0833).

SITES, *(SITES; 0-86528),* P.O. Box 1949, Washington, DC 20013 (SAN 692-7513) Tel 202-357-3168; Dist. by: Smithsonian Institution Traveling Exhibition Service, 1100 Jefferson Dr., SW, Suite 3147, Washington, DC 20560 (SAN 206-8044) Tel 202-357-3168.

†**Sitnalta Press,** *(Sitnalta Pr; 0-931826),* P.O. Box 2730, San Francisco, CA 94126 (SAN 211-5026); CIP.

Six Lights, *(Six Lights; 0-938919),* P.O. Box 357, Cutler, ME 04626 (SAN 661-7409) Tel 207-259-4424.

6 Press, *(Six Pr; 0-943310),* 11889 Dogwood Ave., Fountain Valley, CA 92708 (SAN 240-7752) Tel 714-839-1857.

Sixteenth Century Journal Pubs., Inc., *(Sixteenth Cent; 0-940474),* NE Missouri State Univ., Laughlin Bldg., No. 115, Kirksville, MO 63501 (SAN 223-159X) Tel 816-785-4665.

Sixth House Press, Inc., The, *(Sixth House Pr Inc; 0-913911),* P.O. Box 10458, St. Petersburg, FL 33733 (SAN 286-8741) Tel 813-864-1630.

SK Pubns., *(SK Pubns; 0-936306),* 7149 Natalie Blvd., Northfield, OH 44067 (SAN 214-1396).

Skagit County Historical Society, *(Skagit Cnty Hist; 0-914989),* P.O. Box 424, Mount Vernon, WA 98273 (SAN 289-4297) Tel 206-424-1328.

Skandia America Group, *(Skandia; 0-9609050),* 280 Park Ave., New York, NY 10017 (SAN 240-9062).

Skandisk, Inc., *(Skandisk; 0-9615394),* 3424 19th Ave. S., Minneapolis, MN 55407 (SAN 695-4405) Tel 612-724-6561.

SKE Publishing, Subs. of Sherman Keene Pubns., *(SKE Pub; 0-942080),* P.O. Box 2519, Sedona, AZ 86336 (SAN 238-6046) Tel 602-282-1258.

Skelton, Dorothy Geneva Simmons, *(D G S Skelton; 0-9616290),* Lotos Lakes, Brightwood, VA 22715 (SAN 658-4500) Tel 703-547-2140.

Skies Call, *(Skies Call; 0-9503341),* 6339 31st Pl., NW, Washington, DC 20015 (SAN 207-5385) Tel 202-966-5186; Orders to: P.O. Box 57238, Washington, DC 20037 (SAN 207-5393).

Skill Builders, Inc., *(Skill Builders; 0-915625),* 1800 Penfield Rd., Penfield, NY 14526 (SAN 292-6695).

Skillcorp Pubs, *(Skillcorp; 0-88085),* 203 Eighth St., Honesdale, PA 18431 (SAN 240-2807) Tel 717-253-4558; Orders to: 2300 W. Fifth Ave., P.O. Box 712, Columbus, OH 43216 (SAN 669-2656) Tel 614-486-0631.

Skillman, Penny, *(P Skillman; 0-9603396),* 149 Anderson St., San Francisco, CA 94110 (SAN 212-0488).

Skills Improvement, *(Skills Improvement; 0-939570),* P.O. Box 595, Aurora, CO 80040 (SAN 216-6968) Tel 303-695-6187.

Skinner House Books *See* Unitarian Universalist Assn.

Skinny Books, *(Skinny Bks; 0-912499),* Box A 94, New York, NY 10272 (SAN 265-2110) Tel 212-732-0358.

Skokie Valley Pr., *(Skokie Valley Pr; 0-9614516),* 4250 N. Marine Dr., Chicago, IL 60613 (SAN 689-8106) Tel 312-549-1412.

Skribent Press, *(Skribent; 0-9609374),* 9700 SW Lakeside Dr., Tigard, OR 97223 (SAN 283-2542) Tel 503-620-0471; Dist. by: Pacific Pipeline Distributors, 19215 66th ave., S, Kent, WA 98032 (SAN 208-2128) Tel 206-872-5523.

Sky Bks., *(Sky Bks; 0-9612274),* 2352 Ogden, No. Two, Denver, CO 80205 (SAN 289-5692) Tel 303-837-9235.

Sky Pubns., *(Sky Pubns NJ; 0-941566),* 210 Skylands Rd., Ringwood, NJ 07456 (SAN 239-3123) Tel 201-962-6606. Not to be confused with Sky Publishing Corp. in Cambridge, MA.

†Sky Publishing Corp., *(Sky Pub; 0-933346),* 49 Bay State Ave., Cambridge, MA 02238 (SAN 212-4556) Tel 617-864-7360. Not to be confused with Sky Publications in Ringwood, NJ; *CIP.*

Sky River Pr., *(Sky River Pr; 0-918475),* 236 E. Main St., Ashland, OR 97520 (SAN 657-7164) Tel 503-488-0645.

Sky Road Pr., *(Sky Road Pr; 0-9616544),* 940 Mathews Dr., Chico, CA 95926 (SAN 659-5340) Tel 916-343-6719.

Skybridge Publishing, Inc., *(Skybridge Pub Inc; 0-911675),* 238 Smith Ridge Rd., New Canaan, CT 06840 (SAN 264-391X) Tel 203-966-8585.

Skydog, *(Skydog OR),* 6735 SE 78th St., Portland, OR 97206 (SAN 226-8019).

Skye Terrier Club of America, Affil. of American Kennel Club, *(Skye Terrier; 0-9600722),* 2222 S. 12th St., St. Louis, MO 63104 (SAN 206-5681) Tel 314-773-4444.

Skyer Consultation Ctr., *(Skyer Consul; 0-943106),* P.O. Box 121, Rockaway Park, NY 11694 (SAN 240-4427) Tel 718-634-7206.

Skylark *See Bantam Bks., Inc.*

Skylight Pr., Inc., *(Skylight; 0-910423),* 3603 Hamilton St., Philadelphia, PA 19104 (SAN 240-9070).

Skylight Productions, *(Skylight Prod; 0-938111),* P.O. Box 6129, San Rafael, CA 94903 (SAN 659-7726); 617 Wakerobin Ln., San Rafael, CA 94983 (SAN 659-7734) Tel 415-499-1023.

Skyline Pr., Div. of David White, Inc., *(Skyline Press),* 1 Pleasant Ave., Port Washington, NY 11050 (SAN 678-9021) Tel 516-944-9325.

Skyline Publishing, *(Skyline Pub; 0-918981),* P.O. Box 1880, Columbia Falls, MT 59912 (SAN 669-8662) Tel 406-892-5560.

Skyline West Pr., Affil. of Calendars Unlimited, *(Skyline West Pr; 0-914767),* 4311 Woodland Park Ave. N., Seattle, WA 98103 (SAN 295-0472) Tel 206-633-2485; Dist. by: Medicine Bow Post, P.O. Box 56, Medicine Bow, WY 82329 (SAN 200-7053) Tel 307-379-2255; Dist. by: Calendars Unlimited, 4930 Everglade Dr., Santa Rosa, CA 95405 (SAN 200-7061) Tel 707-538-2503; Dist. by: Pacific Pipeline, Inc., 19215 66th Ave., S., Kent, WA 98032 (SAN 208-2128) Tel 206-872-5523; Toll free: 800-426-4727.

Skyview Publishing, *(Skyview Pub; 0-934618),* Drawer L, Bellmore, NY 11710 (SAN 214-2015) Tel 212-255-5550.

Skyward Bound Publishing, *(Skyward Bound Pub; 0-9617212),* 6000 California St., San Francisco, CA 94121 (SAN 663-4230) Tel 415-751-4962.

Slack, Inc., *(Slack Inc; 0-913590; 0-943432; 1-55642),* 6900 Grove Rd., Thorofare, NJ 08086 (SAN 201-8632) Tel 609-848-1000; Toll free: 800-257-8290.

Slash & Burn Pr., *(Slash Burn Pr; 0-938345),* 1016 N. Fifth St., Philadelphia, PA 19123 (SAN 660-9643) Tel 215-625-0570.

Slate Pr., *(Slate Pr; 0-9616193),* Box 1421 Cooper Station, New York, NY 10276 (SAN 699-9409) Tel 212-475-8067.

Slate Services, *(Slate Servs; 0-913448),* P.O. Box 80, Westminster, CA 92684 (SAN 203-2384) Tel 714-892-0889.

Slater, Jaye, Publisher, *(Slater Pub; 0-9607454),* 12911 Newhope St., Garden Grove, CA 92640 (SAN 239-801X) Tel 714-530-8825.

Slavia Library, *(Slavia Lib; 0-918884),* 418 W. Nittany Ave., State College, PA 16801 (SAN 211-0598).

Slavica Pubs., Inc., *(Slavica; 0-89357),* P.O. Box 14388, Columbus, OH 43214 (SAN 208-8576) Tel 614-268-4002.

Slawenski, J. W., Computer Keyboard Co., 616 Ninth St., Union City, NJ 07087 (SAN 677-6523) Tel 201-863-0999.

Slawson Communications, Inc., *(Slawson Comm; 0-915391),* 3719 Sixth Ave., San Diego, CA 92103-4316 (SAN 200-6901) Tel 619-291-9126.

Slaybaugh, C. S., & Assocs., *(Slaybaugh & Assocs; 0-917509),* 285 Manning Rd., Mogadore, OH 44260 (SAN 656-1047) Tel 216-699-4578.

S.L.E. Pubns., *(SLE; 0-9608230),* P.O. Box 52, Kingston, RI 02881 (SAN 240-3250) Tel 401-783-4503.

Sleeping Bird Pr., *(Sleeping Bird; 0-9611424),* R.R. 1, Box 67, Wingdale, NY 12594-9801 (SAN 284-9143) Tel 914-832-6019.

†Sleepy Hollow Pr., *(Sleepy Hollow; 0-912882),* 150 White Plains Rd., Tarrytown, NY 10591 (SAN 202-0750) Tel 914-631-8200; Dist. by: Independent Pubs. Group, 1 Pleasant Ave., Pt. Washington, NY 11050 (SAN 202-0769); *CIP.*

Sliabhair, *(Sliabhair; 0-937785),* P.O. Box 34096, Bethesda, MD 20817 (SAN 659-3151) Tel 202-475-2297; 9011 Lindale Dr., Bethesda, MD 20817 (SAN 659-316X).

Slick Books *See Seattle Bk. Co.*

Slideways Pubns., *(Slideways Pubns; 0-931105),* P.O. Box 188, Marne, MI 49435 (SAN 678-9463) Tel 616-784-2571.

Slingerland-Comstock Co., *(Slingerland; 0-9613097),* 5881 Cold Brook Rd., Homer, NY 13077 (SAN 293-4485) Tel 607-749-3655.

Sloan, M. Ismail, Pubs., *(M Ismail Sloan Pubs; 0-9609190),* 917 Old Trents Ferry Rd., Lynchburg, VA 24503 (SAN 240-1592) Tel 718-230-9736; Toll free: 800-221-5724.

Sloane, Mark, & Co., *(M Sloane; 0-938347),* P.O. Drawer 571, Coraopolis, PA 15108 (SAN 659-9443); 104 Great Oaks Dr., Coraopolis, PA 15108 (SAN 659-9451) Tel 412-269-1490; Dist. by: Tab Bks., P.O. Box 40, Blue Ridge Summit, PA 17214 (SAN 202-568X); Dist. by: David J. Gingery, 2045 Boonville, Springfield, IL 65803 (SAN 214-3771); Dist. by: Lindsay Pubns., P.O. Box 12, Bradley, IL 60915 (SAN 209-9462).

Slohm, Natalie, Assocs., Inc., *(Slohm Assoc; 0-916840),* 49 W. Main St., Cambridge, NY 12816 (SAN 282-3217) Tel 518-677-3040; P.O. Box 273, Cambridge, NY 12816 (SAN 282-3225).

Slough Pr., Subs. of Slough Productions, *(Slough Pr TX; 0-941720),* Box 1385, Austin, TX 78767 (SAN 239-3131) Tel 512-474-5488.

Slovak Institute of Cleveland, Ohio, *(Slov Ins; 0-9610908),* 2900 E. Blvd., Cleveland, OH 44107 (SAN 265-1122) Tel 216-721-5300.

Slow Loris Pr., *(Slow Loris; 0-918366),* 923 Highview St., Pittsburgh, PA 15206 (SAN 209-6803).

Slumbering Giant Publishing Co., *(Slumbering; 0-9614702),* 2812 Fogarty Ave., Key West, FL 33040 (SAN 692-6118) Tel 305-294-3985.

Slurry Technology, *(Slurry Tech; 0-932066),* 1800 Connecticut Ave., NW, Suite 300, Washington, DC 20009 (SAN 211-7134) Tel 202-332-5751.

Small, A. G., Pubns., *(A G Small Pubns; 0-915457),* P.O. Box 6222, San Rafael, CA 94903 (SAN 291-4409) Tel 415-479-6625.

Small Business Success Press *See First International Publishing Corp.*

Small Businessman's Clinic, *(Sm Busn Clinic; 0-914285),* 113 Vista Del Lago, Scotts Valley, CA 95066 (SAN 287-5608) Tel 408-438-1411.

Small Helm Pr., *(Small Helm Pr; 0-938453),* 622 Baker St., Petaluma, CA 94952 (SAN 660-9805) Tel 707-763-5757.

Small Pr. Distribution, Inc., *(Small Pr Dist; 0-914068),* 1814 San Pablo Ave, Berkeley, CA 94702 (SAN 204-5826) Tel 415-549-3336.

Small-Scale Master Builder, The, *(Small Master; 0-911215),* P.O. Box 5, San Luis Obispo, CA 93406 (SAN 283-3395).

Small-Small Pr., *(Small-Small Pr; 0-9616143),* 226 Linden St., Rumford, ME 04276 (SAN 699-9506) Tel 207-364-7237; Orders to: Maine Writers & Pubs., Alliance, 19D Mason St., Brunswick, ME 04011 (SAN 662-4081) Tel 207-729-6333.

Smart, *(Smart; 0-942912),* Central Missouri State Univ., Dept. of English, Warrensburg, MO 64093 (SAN 240-3242).

Smedley, W. P., Co., *(W P Smedley; 0-938279),* 60 W. Vaughn St., Kingston, PA 18704 (SAN 659-820X) Tel 717-288-8386.

Smile Pubns., *(Smile Pubns; 0-9616018),* 612 W. Michigan Ave., Paw Paw, MI 49079 (SAN 699-7619) Tel 616-657-3121.

Smith, Allen, Co. *See Michie Co., The*

Smith, Alma A., *(Alma Smith; 0-9614863),* 554 Anna May Dr., Cincinnati, OH 45244 (SAN 693-2320) Tel 513-528-1840.

Smith, Carolyn A., *(C A Smith; 0-9606292),* 12901 Twisted Oak Rd., Oklahoma City, OK 73120 (SAN 214-140X) Tel 405-751-3166.

Smith, Cortland Gray, *(C G Smith),* 248 Circle Dr., Plandome, NY 11030 (SAN 209-1771) Tel 516-627-5856.

Smith, Dean Lance, P.E., *(D L Smith; 0-918699),* P.O. Box 31245, Houston, TX 77231-1245 (SAN 294-4804) Tel 713-721-5499.

Smith, Donald F., *(D F Smith; 0-9613357),* 1405 No. C St., Aberdeen, WA 98520 (SAN 656-1357) Tel 206-532-4978.

Smith, Doug, *(D Smith; 0-9602728),* P.O. Box 260, Corvallis, OR 97330 (SAN 212-8144) Tel 503-754-3434; Dist. by: Bookpeople, 2929 Fifth St., Berkeley, CA 94710 (SAN 168-9517) Tel 415-549-3030; Toll free: 800-227-1516.

Smith, Fred T., *(F T Smith; 0-9611210),* P.O. Box 120, Lathrup Village, MI 48076 (SAN 282-8731) Tel 313-258-5411; Dist. by: Merle Distributing Co., 27222 Plymouth Rd., Detroit, MI 48239 (SAN 169-3778) Tel 313-937-8400; Toll free: 800-233-9380 (Orders).

Smith, Gary E., *(G E Smith; 0-9613113),* P.O. Box 463, Azusa, CA 91702-0463 (SAN 294-0876) Tel 818-969-2492.

Smith, Gibbs M., Inc., *(Gibbs M Smith; 0-87905),* P.O. Box 667, Layton, UT 84041 (SAN 201-9906) Tel 801-554-9800; Toll free: 800-421-8714. *Imprints:* Falcon Books (Falcon Bks); Peregrine Smith Books (Peregrine Smith).

Smith, Harley, Investments, Inc., *(Harley Smith Invest; 0-916350),* 740 West Willow, Stockton, CA 95203 (SAN 208-1679) Tel 209-943-1650.

Smith, Jedediah, Society, The, *(J Smith Soc; 0-9612094),* c/o University of the Pacific, Stockton, CA 95211 (SAN 286-8776) Tel 209-946-2404.

Smith, Joe C., Jr., Affil. of Bit/s Software, *(Smith J C; 0-9615176),* P.O. Box B-36085, Phoenix, AZ 85232 (SAN 694-2822); Orders to: BIT/S Software, 3202 W. Fillmore, Florence, AZ 85009 (SAN 662-3352) Tel 602-269-8234.

Smith, John V., *(J V Smith),* 974 Hancock Ave., Akron, OH 44314 (SAN 289-503X) Tel 216-848-3474.

Smith, Johnson C., Univ., *(J C Smith Univ; 0-9614603),* 100 Beatties Ford Rd., Charlotte, NC 28216 (SAN 691-8328) Tel 704-378-1019.

Smith, Leonard H., Jr., *(L H Smith),* P.O. Box 6745, Clearwater, FL 33518 (SAN 205-9819) Tel 813-581-4444.

Smith, Malcolm L., *(M L Smith),* P.O. Box 6712, Washington, DC 20020 (SAN 213-1668).

Smith, Michael T., *(M T Smith; 0-9616494),* 504 Sharon Rd., Chapel Hill, NC 27514 (SAN 659-3275) Tel 919-929-9429.

Smith, Nicholas T., *(N T Smith; 0-935164),* P.O. Box 66, Bronxville, NY 10708 (SAN 213-6457) Tel 914-793-0610.

†Smith, Patterson, Publishing Corp., *(Patterson Smith; 0-87585),* 23 Prospect Terr., Montclair, NJ 07042 (SAN 202-8735) Tel 201-744-3291 (SAN 658-1617); *CIP.*

Smith, Peter, Pub., Inc., *(Peter Smith; 0-8446),* 6 Lexington Ave., Magnolia, MA 01930 (SAN 206-8885) Tel 617-525-3562.

Smith, Philip D., *(P D Smith; 0-9616643),* 1207 Cavalier Ln., West Chester, PA 19380 (SAN 659-6681) Tel 215-692-6240.

Smith, Phoebe, *(P Smith; 0-9602976),* 764 North Ave., Hapeville, GA 30354 (SAN 213-1676).

Smith, Ruth, *(R Smith; 0-9601182),* Box 327, Cooper Sta., New York, NY 10003 (SAN 210-0177) Tel 212-260-4374.

Smith, Toby, *(T Smith; 0-9608762),* First Presbyterian Church, 215 Locust NE., Albuquerque, NM 87102 (SAN 241-0710) Tel 505-247-9594.

Smith, W. H., Pubs., Inc., Subs. of W. H. Smith & Son, Ltd., *(Smith Pubs; 0-8317),* 112 Madison Ave., New York, NY 10016 (SAN 216-3241) Tel 212-532-6600; Toll free: 800-932-0070; 80 Distribution Blvd., Edison, NJ 08817 (SAN 658-1625). *Imprints:* Mayflower Books (Mayflower Bks); Rutledge Press (Rutledge Pr); Sunflower Books (Sunflower Bks).

Smith, W. R. C., Publishing Co., *(W R C Smith; 0-912476),* 1760 Peachtree Rd., N.W., Atlanta, GA 30357 (SAN 202-9391) Tel 404-874-4462.

Smith, Warren Hunting, Library, *(Smith Lib; 0-939624),* Hobart & William Smith Colleges, Geneva, NY 14456 (SAN 216-6275) Tel 315-789-5500.

Smith & Associates, *(Smith & Assoc; 0-938260),* Box 61648, Houston, TX 77208 (SAN 215-8140) Tel 713-932-0518.

Smith & Smith Publishing Co., *(Smith & Smith Pub; 0-9609230),* 119 N. Fourth St., Suite 411, Minneapolis, MN 55401 (SAN 241-4570) Tel 612-338-8235.

Smith College Museum of Art, *(Smith Coll Mus Art),* Elm at Bedford Terr., Northampton, MA 01063 (SAN 282-3233) Tel 413-584-2700; Toll free: 800-621-2736; Dist. by: Univ. of Chicago Pr., 5801 Ellis Ave., 3rd flr. S., Chicago, IL 60637 (SAN 202-5280) Tel 312-568-1550.

†Smith College, Pubns., *(Smith Coll; 0-87391),* Office of the Director of Technical Services, Northampton, MA 01063 (SAN 204-6032) Tel 413-584-2700; Dist. by: Neilson Library, Office of the Director of Technical Services, Northampton, MA 01063 (SAN 204-6040) Tel 413-584-2700; *CIP.*

Smith, Frank E., Inc., *(Smith F E; 0-9602288),* 12846 Ironwood Cir., Beacon Woods, Hudson, FL 33567 (SAN 222-2791).

Smith Productions, Affil. of Hatha Yoga Center, *(Smith Prod; 0-9616545),* 4550 11th Ave., NE, Seattle, WA 98105 (SAN 659-5359) Tel 206-632-1706; Orders to: Smith Productios, 2116 N. 122, Seattle, WA 98133 (SAN 662-4286) Tel 206-363-1051.

Smith, Smith & Smith Publishing Co., *(S S S Pub Co; 0-913626),* 17515 SW Blue Heron Rd., Lake Oswego, OR 97034 (SAN 203-3607) Tel 503-636-2979.

Smith, The, Subs. of The Generalist Assoc., Inc., *(The Smith; 0-912292),* 5 Beekman St., New York, NY 10038 (SAN 202-7747) Tel 212-732-4821.

Smith's Slogans & Sayings, *(Smith Slogans; 0-939403),* 3014 Melina Ct., Bensalem, PA 19020 (SAN 663-138X) Tel 215-757-0844.

†Smithsonian Bks., *(Smithsonian Bks; 0-89599),* 955 L'Enfant Plaza, Rm. 2100, Washington, DC 20560 (SAN 216-1974) Tel 202-287-3388; Toll free: 800-223-2584; Dist. by: W. W. Norton & Co., 500 Fifth Ave., New York, NY 10110 (SAN 202-5795) Tel 212-354-5500; Dist. by: Harmony Bks., 1 Park Ave., New York, NY 10016 (SAN 282-7360) Tel 212-532-9200; Dist. by: Harry N. Abrams, 100 Fifth Ave., New York, NY 10011 (SAN 200-2434) Tel 212-206-7715; Dist. by: Cambridge Univ. Pr., 32 E. 57th St., New York, NY 10022 (SAN 281-3750) Tel 212-688-8888; *CIP.*

Smithsonian Institution Pr., *(Smithsonian; 0-87474),* 955 L'Enfant Plaza, Suite 2100, Washington, DC 20560 (SAN 206-8044) Tel 202-287-3765; Orders to: Customer Services, P.O. Box 4866, Hampden Sta., Baltimore, MD 21211 (SAN 206-8052) Tel 301-338-6963.

Smoky Hill River Pr., *(Smoky Hill; 0-932199),* P.O. Box 2181, Salina, KS 67402-2181 (SAN 686-595X) Tel 913-827-4640.

†Smoky Valley Historical Pubns., Subs. of Smoky Valley Historical Assn., Inc., *(Smoky Valley Hist; 0-918331),* P.O. Box 255, Lindsborg, KS 67456-0255 (SAN 657-3037) Tel 913-227-2302; *CIP.*

Smoley, C. K., & Sons, Div. of Lewis Pubs., Inc., *(Smoley; 0-911390),* P.O. Box 531, Chelsea, MI 48118 (SAN 204-6059) Tel 313-475-8610.

Smoloskyp Pubs., Inc., *(Smoloskyp; 0-914834),* P.O. Box 561, Ellicott City, MD 21043 (SAN 206-1260) Tel 301-461-1764.

Smugglers Cove Pub., *(Smugglers; 0-918484),* Ben Dennis & Assoc., 107 W. John St., Seattle, WA 98119 (SAN 209-8857) Tel 206-285-3171. Out of business.

Smyres Pubns., *(Smyres Pubns; 0-9616952),* P.O. Box 4796, Ithaca, NY 14852 (SAN 661-7565); 818 Hanshaw Rd., Ithaca, NY 14850 (SAN 661-7573) Tel 607-257-7517.

Smyrna Pr., *(Smyrna; 0-918266),* P.O. Box 1803, GPO, Brooklyn, NY 11202 (SAN 207-897X) Tel 718-638-8939.

Sneek-A-Peek Books, *(Sneak-A-Peek Bks; 0-943944),* Fontenelle Dam, Kemmerer, WY 83101 (SAN 241-1512) Tel 307-877-9615.

Snipe International, *(Snipe; 0-938740),* 210 Crystal Park Rd., Manitou Springs, CO 80829 (SAN 238-7514) Tel 303-685-9044.

Snipe Publishing Co., The, *(Snipe Pub; 0-9617027),* P.O. Box 1280, Friendswood, TX 77546 (SAN 662-6459); 2 Narnia Way, Friendswood, TX 77546 (SAN 662-6467) Tel 713-482-0669.

SnO Pubns., *(SnO Pubns; 0-937814),* Stockbridge, MA 01262 (SAN 217-1325). *Imprints:* Lenox Library Assn. (Lenox Lib Assn).

Snohomish Publishing, *(Snohomish Pub),* P.O. Box 2188, Soldotna, AK 99669 (SAN 262-0804).

Snow, Helen F., *(H F Snow; 0-911392),* 148 Mungertown Rd., Madison, CT 06443 (SAN 206-3131) Tel 203-245-9714.

Snow Lion Graphics, *(Snow Lion Graphics; 0-9617066),* P.O. Box 9465, Berkeley, CA 94709 (SAN 662-8729); 1526 Walnut, Berkeley, CA 94709 (SAN 662-8737) Tel 415-841-5525.

Snow Lion Pubns., *(Snow Lion; 0-937938),* P.O. Box 6483, Ithaca, NY 14851 (SAN 281-7292) Tel 607-273-8506; Dist. by: Bookpeople, 2929 Fifth St., Berkeley, CA 94710 (SAN 168-9517) Tel 415-549-3030; Dist. by: Inland Bk. Co., Inc., P.O. Box 261, 22 Hemingway Ave., East Haven, CT 06512 (SAN 200-4151) Tel 203-467-4257; Dist. by: Samuel Weiser, Inc., P.O. Box 612, York Beach, ME 03910 (SAN 202-9588) Tel 207-363-4393; Dist. by: The Great Tradition, 750 Adrian Way, Suite 111, San Rafael, CA 94903 (SAN 200-5743) Tel 415-492-9382; Dist. by: New Leaf Distributors, The, 1020 White St. SW, Atlanta, GA 30310 (SAN 169-1449) Tel 404-755-2665; Dist. by: Book Dynamics, 836 Broadway, New York, NY 10003 (SAN 169-5649) Tel 212-254-7798; Dist. by: Distributors, The, 702 S. Michigan, South Bend, IN 46618 (SAN 169-2488) Tel 219-232-8500.

Snow Pr., *(Snow Pr; 0-9601148),* 9300 Home Court, Des Plaines, IL 60016 (SAN 210-3729) Tel 312-299-7605.

Snowco-Publishing, *(SNOWCO; 0-939230),* 266 N. El Camino Real, Suite D-12, Oceanside, CA 92054 (SAN 216-5112).

Snowstorm Pubns., *(Snowstorm; 0-9605366),* Box 2310, Breckenridge, CO 80424 (SAN 216-194X).

†Snug Harbor Cultural Ctr., *(Snug Harbor NY; 0-9604254),* 914 Richmond Terr., Staten Island, NY 10301 (SAN 214-4751) Tel 718-448-2500; *CIP.*

Snuggle & Read *See* **Avon Bks.**

Snyder, Walter, Printer, Inc., *(Snyder Inc; 0-9601556),* Troy, NY 12180 (SAN 239-5789).

Snyder Institute of Research, *(Snyder Inst Res; 0-940714),* 508 N. Pacific Coast Hwy., Redondo Beach, CA 90277 (SAN 204-9694) Tel 213-372-4469.

Snyder Publishing Co., *(Snyder Pub Co; 0-9609526),* No. 250, 1275 Fourth St., Santa Rosa, CA 95404 (SAN 260-2660) Tel 707-829-1388.

So & So Pr., *(So&So Pr; 0-918842),* 1003 Kieth Ave., Berkeley, CA 94708 (SAN 210-3893) Tel 415-525-2781.

Soap & Detergent Assn., *(Soap & Detergent; 0-9601394),* 475 Park Ave. S., New York, NY 10016 (SAN 224-7089) Tel 212-725-1262.

Soaring Society of America, *(Soaring Soc),* 3200 Airport Ave., No. 12, Santa Monica, CA 90405 (SAN 229-2742) Tel 213-390-4447; P.O. Box 66071, Los Angeles, CA 90066 (SAN 669-2664).

Sobell Assocs., *(Sobell Assocs; 0-937613),* 521 Ross Ct., Palo Alto, CA 94303 (SAN 659-1760) Tel 415-856-3460.

Sobredo, Sergio, Technical Services, *(S Sobredo Tech Serv; 0-9616888),* 11507 SW 34th Ln., Miami, FL 33165 (SAN 661-6410) Tel 305-221-1271.

†Soccer Book Co., The, *(Soccer Bk Co; 0-916019),* 32 W. Anapanu St., Suite 285, Santa Barbara, CA 93101 (SAN 294-0892) Tel 805-969-5051; *CIP.*

Soccer Education, *(Soccer Ed; 0-9616953),* 509 Laurel Dr., Thiensville, WI 53092 (SAN 661-7638) Tel 414-242-3137.

Soccer for Americans, *(Soccer for Am; 0-916802),* P.O. Box 836, Manhattan Beach, CA 90266 (SAN 208-3787) Tel 213-372-9000. Do Not Confuse with Sport-Shelf.

Soccer Publications, Inc., *(Soccer Pubns Inc; 0-943752),* 3530 Greer Rd., Palo Alto, CA 94303 (SAN 216-3217) Tel 415-494-6338.

Social Change Pr., *(Soc Change Pr; 0-9609376),* Box 2212, Sun City, AZ 85372 (SAN 260-1370) Tel 602-972-8346.

†Social Issues Resources Series, Inc., *(Soc Issues; 0-89777),* P.O. Box 2348, Boca Raton, FL 33427 (SAN 222-8920) Tel 305-994-0079; Toll free: 800-327-0513; *CIP.*

†Social Matrix Research, Inc., *(Social Matrix; 0-89995),* P.O. Box 9128, Boston, MA 02114 (SAN 213-5922) Tel 617-247-2181; *CIP.*

Social Science & Sociological Resources, *(Soc Sci & Soc Res; 0-915574),* P.O. Box 241, Aurora, IL 60507 (SAN 203-235X).

†Social Science Education Consortium, Inc., *(Soc Sci Ed; 0-89994),* 855 Broadway, Boulder, CO 80302 (SAN 213-1684) Tel 303-492-8154; *CIP.*

Social Science Institute, *(Soc Sci Inst; 0-911394),* Harborside, ME 04642 (SAN 206-3158).

Social Science Paperbacks *See* **Barnes & Noble Bks.-Imports**

Social Science Press, Inc., *(Soc Sci Pr; 0-911396),* 100 Oakdale Rd., Athens, GA 30606 (SAN 204-6083) Tel 404-542-4581.

Social Science Research Council, *(Soc Sci Res; 0-911400),* 605 Third Ave., New York, NY 10016 (SAN 204-6091).

Social Systems Pr., *(Social Sys Pr; 0-935563),* P.O. Box 1091, Jeffersonville, IN 47131 (SAN 696-060X) Tel 502-423-8006.

Society For A World Service Federation, *(Soc Wld Serv; 0-9614149),* P.O. Box 1362, Dunedin, FL 34296-1362 (SAN 686-2101); 2058 Alpine Rd., No. 20, Clearwater, FL 33515 (SAN 662-2674) Tel 813-447-5673.

Society for American Archaeology, *(Soc Am Arch; 0-932839),* 1511 K St. NW, Washington, DC 20005 (SAN 275-5211) Tel 202-638-6079; Dist. by: Kraus Reprint & Periodicals, Rte. 100, Millwood, NY 10546 (SAN 227-3233) Tel 914-762-2200.

Society for American Baseball Research, *(Soc Am Baseball Res; 0-910137),* P.O. Box 1010, Cooperstown, NY 13326 (SAN 224-5434) Tel 607-547-9160.

Society for Commo Insights Pr., Inc., *(Soc Common Insights; 0-940888),* 481 Eighth Ave., Suite 926, New York, NY 10001 (SAN 223-2158) Tel 212-947-1657.

Society for Computer Applications in Engineering, Planning & Architecture, Inc., *(Soc Comp Eng; 0-933007),* 15713 Crabbs Branch Way, Rockville, MD 20855 (SAN 654-9802) Tel 301-926-7070.

Society for Computer Simulation, *(Soc Computer Sim; 0-911801),* P.O. Box 17900, San Diego, CA 92117 (SAN 225-1973) Tel 619-277-3888.

Society for Ethnomusicology, Inc., *(Soc Ethnomusicology),* P.O. Box 2984, Ann Arbor, MI 48106 (SAN 225-3615) Tel 313-665-9400.

Society for German-American Studies *See* **North Central Publishing Co.**

Society for Humanistic Judaism, *(Soc Humanistic; 0-912645),* 28611 W. Twelve Mile Rd., Farmington Hills, MI 48018 (SAN 275-4576) Tel 313-478-7610.

Society for Individual Liberty of the Genesee Valley, *(Society Indiv Lib; 0-9608490),* P.O. Box 10224, Rochester, NY 14610 (SAN 240-7760) Tel 716-671-2077.

Names

Society for Industrial & Applied Mathematics, *(Soc Indus-Appl Math; 0-89871),* 117 S. 17th St., Suite 1400, Philadelphia, PA 19103-5052 (SAN 206-5207) Tel 215-564-2929.

Society for Industrial Microbiology, *(Soc Indus Micro),* P.O. Box 12534, Arlington, VA 22209-8534 (SAN 223-8306) Tel 703-941-5373.

Society for Information Display, *(SID),* 8055 W. Manchester Ave., No. 615, Playa Del Rey, CA 90293 (SAN 260-3446) Tel 213-305-1502.

Society for Libertarian Life, *(Soc Libertarian Life),* Box 4, Fullerton, CA 92632 (SAN 225-6770) Tel 714-962-6491.

Society for Mad Poets Pr., *(Soc Mad Poets; 0-9615250),* P.O. Box 14095, Chicago, IL 60614 (SAN 694-6070) Tel 312-975-1547; Dist. by: Bookslinger, 213 E. Fourth St., ST. Paul, MN 55101 (SAN 169-4154) Tel 612-221-0429.

Society for New Language Study, Inc., *(Soc New Lang Study; 0-9502699; 0-936072),* P.O. Box 10596, Denver, CO 80210 (SAN 203-2368) Tel 303-777-6115.

Society for Nutrition Education, *(Soc Nutrition Ed; 0-910869),* 1736 Franklin St., Oakland, CA 94612 (SAN 225-8552) Tel 415-444-7133.

Society for Range Management, *(Soc Range Mgmt; 0-9603692),* 2760 W. Fifth Ave., Denver, CO 80204 (SAN 225-0586) Tel 303-571-0174.

Society for Scholarly Publishing, *(Soc Schol Pub),* 2000 Florida Ave., NW, Washington, DC 20009 (SAN 225-1949) Tel 202-328-3555.

Society for Slovene Studies, *(Soc Slovene Studies),* 420 W. 118th St., New York, NY 10027 (SAN 225-8706).

Society for Teachers of Family Medicine, *(Soc Tchrs Fam Med),* 1740 W. 92nd St., Kansas City, MO 64114 (SAN 224-3199) Tel 816-333-9700; Toll free: 800-821-2512.

Society for Technical Communication, *(Soc Tech Comm; 0-914548),* 815 15th St., NW, Washington, DC 20005 (SAN 206-569X) Tel 202-737-0035; Orders to: Univelt, Inc., P.O. Box 28130, San Diego, CA 92128 (SAN 204-8868) Tel 619-746-4005.

Society for the Advancement of Continuing Education for Ministry, *(Soc Adv Cont Ed; 0-918983),* 855 Locust St., Collegeville, PA 19426 (SAN 224-2184) Tel 215-489-6358.

Society for the Advancement of Materials & Process Engineering, *(Soc Adv Material; 0-938994),* 843 W. Glentana, Covina, CA 91722 (SAN 295-3528); P.O. Box 2459, Covina, CA 91722 (SAN 295-3536) Tel 818-331-0616.

Society for the Improvement of Stray Animals, *(SICSA; 0-9615105),* 2600 Wilmington Pike, Dayton, OH 45419 (SAN 694-2709) Tel 513-294-6505; Box 82, Dayton, OH 45405 (SAN 694-2717).

†**Society for the Preservation of Old Mills,** *(Soc Preservation; 0-930497),* 604 Ensley Dr. Rte. 29, Knoxville, TN 37920 (SAN 670-9621) Tel 615-577-7757; *CIP.*

Society for the Promotion of Science & Scholarship, Inc., *(SPOSS; 0-930664),* 4139 El Camino Way, Palo Alto, CA 94306 (SAN 211-3473) Tel 415-325-3958; Dist. by: Arcata Graphics, P.O. Box 711, Kingsport, TN 37662 (SAN 200-7304) Tel 615-246-7131.

Society for the Right to Die, Inc., *(Soc Right to Die; 0-9613825),* 250 W. 57th St., New York, NY 10107 (SAN 225-9354) Tel 212-246-6973.

Society for the Scientific Study of Religion, *(Soc Sci Stud Rel; 0-932566),* Catholic Univ. of America, Marist Hall, Rm. 108, Storrs, CT 06268 (SAN 212-1670).

†**Society For Vascular Surgery, The,** *(Society Vascular Surgery; 0-9612978),* 13 Elm St., Manchester, MA 01944 (SAN 292-6741) Tel 617-927-8330; *CIP.*

Society for Visual Education, Inc., *(Soc for Visual; 0-89290),* 1345 Diversey Pkwy., Chicago, IL 60614 (SAN 208-3930) Tel 312-525-1500; Toll free: 800-621-1900.

Society of Actuaries, *(Soc Actuaries; 0-938959),* 500 Park Blvd., Itasca, IL 60143 (SAN 224-8387) Tel 312-773-3010.

†**Society of American Archivists,** *(Soc Am Archivists; 0-931828),* 600 S. Federal, Suite 504, Chicago, IL 60605 (SAN 211-7614) Tel 312-922-0140; *CIP.*

Society of American Foresters, *(Soc Am Foresters; 0-939970),* 5400 Grosvenor Ln., Bethesda, MD 20814 (SAN 216-8561) Tel 301-897-8720.

Society of American Military Engineers, *(Soc Am Mil Eng),* 607 Prince St., Alexandria, VA 22314 (SAN 669-2680) Tel 703-549-3800.

Society of American Travel Writers, *(Soc Am Travel Writers),* 1120 Connecticut Ave. NW,, Washington, DC 20036 (SAN 224-9758) Tel 202-785-5567.

Society of American Value Engineers, *(Soc Am Value E),* 220 N. Story Rd., Suite 114, Irving, TX 75061 (SAN 223-968X) Tel 214-253-5171.

†**Society of Automotive Engineers,** *(Soc Auto Engineers; 0-89883),* 400 Commonwealth Dr., Warrendale, PA 15096 (SAN 232-5721) Tel 412-776-4841; *CIP.*

Society of Chartered Property & Casualty Underwriters, *(Soc Charter Prop Underwriters),* Kahler Hall, CB No. 9, Malvern, PA 19355 (SAN 682-9287) Tel 215-251-2728.

Society of Christian Ethics, *(Soc Christian Ethics),* Vancouver Schl. of Theology, 6000 Iona Dr., Vancouver, BC V6T 1L4, (SAN 223-9701).

Society of Economic Paleontologists & Mineralogists, *(SEPM; 0-918985),* P.O. Box 4756, Tulsa, OK 74159 (SAN 260-3462) Tel 918-743-9765.

Society of Exploration Geophysicists, *(Soc Expl Geophys; 0-931830),* P.O. Box 702740, Tulsa, OK 74170-2740 (SAN 206-2844) Tel 918-493-3516.

Society of Fire Protection Engineers, *(Society Fire Protect),* 60 Batterymarch St., Boston, MA 02110 (SAN 209-3863) Tel 617-482-0686.

Society of Industrial Realtors Educational Fund, *(Soc Industrial Realtors),* 777 14th St., NW, Washington, DC 20005-3271 (SAN 202-0718) Tel 202-383-1150.

Society of Inter-Celtic Arts & Culture, *(Soc Inter Celtic; 0-936651),* 96 Marguerite Ave., Waltham, MA 02154 (SAN 699-7120) Tel 617-899-2204.

Society of Logistics Engineers, *(Soc Logistics Engrs),* 303 Williams Ave., Park Plaza, Suite 922, Huntsville, AL 35801 (SAN 223-8314) Tel 205-539-3800 Tel 205-539-3833; Dist. by: Prentice Hall, Inc., Rte. 9W, Englewood Cliffs, NJ 07632 (SAN 200-2175) Tel 201-592-2352.

Society of Manufacturing Engineers, *(SME; 0-87263),* P.O. Box 930, 1 SME Dr., Dearborn, MI 48121 (SAN 203-2376) Tel 313-271-1500.

Society of Mining Engineers, Inc., *(Soc Mining Eng; 0-87335),* 8307 Shaffer Pkwy., Caller No. D., Littleton, CO 80127 (SAN 225-2163) Tel 303-973-9550.

Society of Motion Picture & Television Engineers, *(Soc Motion Pic & TV Engrs; 0-940690),* 862 Scarsdale Ave., Scarsdale, NY 10583 (SAN 224-0173) Tel 914-472-6600.

Society of Naval Architects & Marine Engineers, *(Soc Naval Arch; 0-9603048; 0-939773),* 1 World Trade Ctr., Suite 1369, New York, NY 10048 (SAN 202-0572) Tel 212-432-0310.

Society of Neuroscience, *(Soc Neuroscience),* 9650 Rockville Pike, Bethesda, MD 20014 (SAN 224-0165) Tel 301-530-8955.

Society of North American Goldsmiths, *(SNAG; 0-9604446),* 6707 N. Santa Monica Blvd.,, Milwaukee, WI 53217 (SAN 215-1081).

†**Society of Nuclear Medicine, Inc.,** *(Soc Nuclear Med; 0-932004),* 136 Madison Ave., New York, NY 10016 (SAN 212-5625) Tel 212-889-0717; *CIP.*

Society of Nursing Professionals, The, *(Soc Nursing Prof),* P.O. Box 50822, Washington, DC 20004 (SAN 661-4558).

Society of Photo-Optical Instrumentation Engineers *See* SPIE-International Society for Optical Engineering

Society of Professional Journalists, Sigma Delta Chi, *(Soc Pro; 0-9613340),* 840 N. Lake Shore Dr., Suite 801W, Chicago, IL 60611 (SAN 275-6072) Tel 312-649-0224.

Society of Professors of Education, *(Soc Profs Ed; 0-933669),* Portland State Univ., P.O. Box 751, Portland, OR 97207 (SAN 224-0181) Tel 503-229-4750.

Society of Real Estate Appraisers, *(Soc Real Estate Appraisers; 0-934737),* 645 N. Michigan Ave., Chicago, IL 60611 (SAN 682-9430) Tel 312-346-7422; Toll free: 800-331-7732.

Society of Spanish & Spanish-American Studies, *(Society Sp & Sp-Am; 0-89295),* Univ. of Colorado, Dept. of Spanish and Portuguese, Boulder, CO 80309-0278 (SAN 208-3221) Tel 303-492-7308.

Society of the Alumni of the College of William & Mary in Virginia, Inc., *(Soc Alu Wm; 0-9615670),* 500 Richmond Rd., Williamsburg, VA 23187 (SAN 695-9652) Tel 804-229-1693; P.O. Box GO, Williamsburg, VA 23187 (SAN 699-6167).

Society of the Descendants of Washington's Army at Valley Forge, *(Soc Descend Wash Army; 0-9606828),* P.O. Box 915, Valley Forge, PA 19482 (SAN 224-4896) Tel 617-335-7670.

Society of the Plastic Industry, Inc, *(Soc Plastic Ind),* 355 Lexington Ave., New York, NY 10017 (SAN 224-9162) Tel 212-573-9400.

Society of Vertebrate Paleontology, *(Soc Vertebrate; 0-918799),* University of California, Museum of Paleontology, c/o Joseph T. Gregory, Berkeley, CA 94720 (SAN 669-7062) Tel 415-642-1730; Orders to: Society of Vertebrate Paleontology, LACM of Natural History, 900 Exposition Blvd., Los Angeles, CA 90007 (SAN 662-2410) Tel 213-744-3445.

Society of Wine Educators, *(Soc Wine Educators; 0-935347),* 132 Shaker Rd., Suite 14, East Longmeadow, MA 01028 (SAN 225-8846) Tel 413-567-8282.

Society of Wood Science & Technology, *(Soc Wood),* P.O. Box 5062, Madison, WI 53705 (SAN 260-3470) Tel 608-264-5747.

Sociology Pr., *(Sociology Pr),* P.O. Box 400, Mill Valley, CA 94942 (SAN 212-7962).

Soda-Licious, *(Soda-Licious; 0-9616340),* 8625 NE Weidler, Portland, OR 97220 (SAN 659-1930) Tel 503-254-6132.

Soft Tech, Inc., *(Soft Tech MI; 0-938087),* 18505 W. Eight Mile Rd., Suite 104, Detroit, MI 48219 (SAN 659-7025) Tel 313-544-8544.

SoftCorp, Inc., *(SoftCorp FL; 0-937701),* 2340 State Rd. 580, Suite 244, Clearwater, FL 33575 (SAN 697-5356) Tel 813-799-3984; Toll free: 800-255-7526.

†**Softext Pubishing Corp.,** *(Softext Pub; 0-934577),* 17 E. 45th St., 6th Flr., New York, NY 10017 (SAN 693-9023) Tel 212-986-5985; *CIP.*

Softlaw Publishing Co., *(Softlaw Pub; 0-9616328),* 2136 Matthews Ave., Bronx, NY 10462 (SAN 658-3628) Tel 212-597-3746.

Software Development Corp., Div. of City Software Development Corp., *(Software Dev; 0-937333),* 735 W. Wisconsin Ave., Milwaukee, WI 53233 (SAN 658-8131) Tel 414-291-5466.

Software Digest, Inc., *(Software Inc; 0-916543),* One Winding Rd., Philadelphia, PA 19131 (SAN 295-1185) Tel 215-878-9300.

Software Directions, Inc., *(Soft Direct; 0-936517),* 1572 Sussex Tpk., Randolph, NJ 07869 (SAN 697-8126) Tel 201-584-8466; Toll free: 800-346-7638.

Software Hse., *(Software Hse; 0-912055),* 1105 Massachusetts Ave., Cambridge, MA 02138 (SAN 264-6374) Tel 617-661-7023.

Software Institute of America Inc., *(Software Inst Am),* 8 Windsor St., Andover, MA 01810 (SAN 291-851X) Tel 617-470-3870.

Software Shop Pr., The, *(Soft Shop Pr; 0-937405),* 4977 Livernois, Troy, MI 48098 (SAN 659-1779) Tel 313-524-1581.

Software Source, *(Soft Source; 0-930241),* 2701-C W. 15th St., Suite 109, Plano, TX 75075 (SAN 653-4341) Tel 214-424-0758.

Softwriters Development Corp., *(Softwriters Dev; 0-9616781; 0-939673),* 4718 Harford Rd., Baltimore, MD 21214 (SAN 660-9678) Tel 301-426-4466.

Sohn, Mark F., Pubns., *(M F Sohn Pubns; 0-9616911),* 508 Sixth St., Pikeville, KY 41501 (SAN 661-5228) Tel 606-437-6467.

Soho Pr., Inc., The, *(Soho Press; 0-939149),* One Union Sq., New York, NY 10003 (SAN 662-5088) Tel 212-243-1527; Dist. by: Farrar, Straus & Giroux, 19 Union Sq., W., New York, NY 10003 (SAN 206-782X) Tel 212-741-6900.

†Soil Conservation Society of America, *(Soil Conservation; 0-935734),* 7515 NE. Ankeny Rd., Ankeny, IA 50021-9764 (SAN 213-6961) Tel 515-289-2331; *CIP.*

Soil Science Society of America, Affil. of American Society of Agronomy Crop Science Society of America, *(Soil Sci Soc Am; 0-89118),* 677 S. Segoe Rd., Madison, WI 53711 (SAN 206-2879) Tel 608-273-8080.

Sojourners Press, Ltd., *(Sojourners Pr Ltd; 0-936768),* 601 W. Tonopah, Suite 5, Phoenix, AZ 85027 (SAN 221-8933) Tel 602-582-1439.

Sokoloff, Valentin A., *(Sokoloff; 0-9607438),* 773 Cypress Ave., San Bruno, CA 94066 (SAN 239-4863) Tel 415-589-4511.

Sol Press *See Wisconsin Bks.*

Solano Pr., *(Solano Pr; 0-9614657),* P.O. Box 7629, Berkeley, CA 94707-0629 (SAN 692-2236) Tel 415-527-8668.

Solar Age Pr., *(Solar Age Pr; 0-914304),* Indian Mills, WV 24949 (SAN 208-8630).

Solar Energy Institute of North America, *(SEINAM),* 1110 Sixth St., NW, Washington, DC 20001 (SAN 211-3015).

Solar Pr., *(Solar Pr; 0-9616785),* 1120 Frontenac Rd., Naperville, IL 60566 (SAN 660-9708) Tel 312-983-1400.

Solar Studio, The, *(Solar Studio; 0-932320),* 178 Cowles Rd., Woodbury, CT 06798 (SAN 222-8823) Tel 203-263-3147.

Solar Training Pubns., *(Solar Training; 0-940894),* 10921 W. Exposition Dr. P.O. Box 26241, Lakewood, CO 80226 (SAN 219-6360) Tel 303-989-1611.

SOLARC - Solar Energy in Architecture, *(SOLARC),* 2300 Cliff Dr., Newport Beach, CA 92663 (SAN 209-1283) Tel 714-631-3182.

†Solaris Pr., Inc., *(Solaris Pr; 0-933760),* P.O. Box 1009, Rochester, MI 48063 (SAN 262-0820) Tel 313-656-0667; *CIP.*

Solarium Analytika, *(Solarium Analy; 0-935861),* P.O. Box 3594, West Sedona, AZ 86336 (SAN 696-0529); 105 Mountain Shadows Dr., Sedonax, AZ 86336 (SAN 699-6205) Tel 602-282-1903.

SolarVision, Inc., *(SolarVision; 0-918984),* 7 Church Hill, Harrisville, NH 03450 (SAN 210-508X) Tel 603-827-3347.

†Soldier Creek Pr., *(Soldier Creek; 0-936996),* Drawer U, Lake Crystal, MN 56055 (SAN 215-9171) Tel 507-726-2985; 642 S Hunt St., Lake Crystal, MN 56055 (SAN 658-1633); *CIP.*

S.O.L.E. Pubns., *(S O L E Pubns; 0-9608626),* P.O. Box 2063, Beaverton, OR 97075 (SAN 238-3624).

Solidarity Pubns., *(Solidarity; 0-942638),* P.O. Box 40874, San Francisco, CA 94140 (SAN 238-5724) Tel 415-626-6626.

Solipaz Publishing Co., *(Solipaz Pub Co; 0-913999),* P.O. Box 366, Lodi, CA 95241 (SAN 286-8814) Tel 209-368-1595.

Solitaire Publishing, *(Solitaire Pub; 0-933143),* 216 S. Bungalow , P.O. Box 14508, Tampa, FL 33690 (SAN 670-6975) Tel 813-876-0286.

Solo Music, Inc., *(Solo; 0-913754),* P.O. Box 1333, Sedona, AZ 86336 (SAN 206-7692) Tel 602-282-4023.

Solo Pr., *(Solo Pr),* 7975 San Marcos, Atascadero, CA 93422 (SAN 206-3794) Tel 805-466-3083.

Solo Pr., *(Solo Press MA; 0-941866),* 1009 Mass. Ave., Lexington, MA 02173 (SAN 239-3158) Tel 617-861-1340.

Solomon Assocs., *(Solomon Assocs; 0-9617198),* 9240 Broken Timber Way, Columbia, MD 21045 (SAN 663-2483) Tel 301-596-4433.

Solomon Intl Pub. Co., *(Solomon Intl; 0-946155),* P.O. Box 7164, Huntington Beach, CA 92615-7164 (SAN 655-1327).

Solpub Co., *(Solpub; 0-931912),* 16311 Heatherdale Dr., Houston, TX 77059 (SAN 212-7970) Tel 713-280-0454.

Solson Pubns., *(Solson Pubns; 0-9615671),* P.O. Box 274, Brooklyn, NY 11235 (SAN 696-057X) Tel 718-846-6553; 2362 E. 13th St., Brooklyn, NY 11229 (SAN 699-6213).

Solus Impress, *(Solus Impress),* Porthill, ID 83853 (SAN 262-0839).

Soma Pr., *(Soma Pr; 0-932510),* P.O. Box 416, Yellow Springs, OH 45387 (SAN 222-8858) Tel 513-767-1573.

Soma Pr. of California, *(Soma Pr Cal; 0-943564),* P.O. Box 3682, Pinedale, CA 93650 (SAN 238-3772) Tel 209-439-4829.

Somerset Hse. Corp., *(Somerset Hse; 0-938941),* 515 Post Oak Blvd., No. 600, Houston, TX 77027 (SAN 661-7646) Tel 713-963-0300.

Somerset Pr., Div. of Hope Publishing Co., *(Somerset Pr IL; 0-916642),* Executive Dr., Carol Stream, IL 60188 (SAN 214-3267) Tel 312-665-3200; Toll free: 800-323-1049.

Somerset Pubs., *(Somerset Pub),* 200 Park Ave., Suite 303 E., New York, NY 10017 (SAN 204-6105) Tel 313-884-0400.

Somerton Pr., *(Somerton Pr; 0-934129),* P.O. Box 1746, Somerton, AZ 85350 (SAN 693-2665).

Sometime Pr., Inc., *(Sometime Pr; 0-936230),* 216 Pleasant St., Marblehead, MA 01945 (SAN 214-1442).

Somm, *(Somm; 0-9615807),* 3017 Santa Monica Blvd., No. 155, Santa Monica, CA 90404 (SAN 696-5911) Tel 213-839-9691.

Somrie Pr., *(Somrie Pr; 0-9603950; 0-933749),* Ryder St. Sta. Box 328, Brooklyn, NY 11234-0328 (SAN 214-1450) Tel 718-251-3690; 1134 E. 72nd St., Brooklyn, NY 11234 (SAN 692-6304).

Son-Rise Pubns., *(Son-Rise Pubns; 0-936369),* Rte. 3, Box 202, New Wilmington, PA 16142 (SAN 698-0031) Tel 412-946-8334; Dist. by: Spring Arbor, 10885 Textile, Belleville, MI 48111 (SAN 158-9016) Tel 717-234-5041; Dist. by: Whitaker Hse., Pittsburgh & Colfax Sts., Springdale, PA 15144 (SAN 203-2104) Tel 412-274-4440.

Son Rise Pubns., *(Son Rise Williston; 0-938355),* 119 Industrial Pkwy., Williston, VT 05495 (SAN 659-8358) Tel 802-864-0724.

Son/West Pubs., *(Son West Pubs; 0-9616546),* P.O. Box 2122, Clovis, NM 88101 (SAN 659-5367) Tel 505-762-4020; 204 W. Christopher, Clovis, NM 88101 (SAN 659-5375).

Soncino Pr., *(Soncino Pr),* 5 Essex St., New York, NY 10002 (SAN 681-2740).

Sonenschein, David, *(D Sonenschein; 0-915289),* P.O. Box 15744, San Antonio, TX 78212-8944 (SAN 290-0432) Tel 512-829-0048.

Sonflower Books *See Scripture Press Pubns., Inc.*

Songa Pubns., Div. of Songa Braids, *(Songa Pubns; 0-936017),* 2053 McGraw Ave., Apt. 1H, Bronx, NY 10462 (SAN 696-592X) Tel 212-409-2132; Orders to: Professional Secrets, P.O. Box 1566, GPO, Bronx, NY 10451 (SAN 662-3778) Tel 212-409-2132.

Songs & Stories Children Love, *(Songs & Stories; 0-934591),* 4243 Carpenter Ave., Bronx, NY 10466 (SAN 694-0609) Tel 212-325-9004.

Sonica Press, *(Sonica Pr),* P.O. Box 42720, Los Angeles, CA 90042 (SAN 216-1966) Tel 213-666-7197.

Sonoma County Bike Trails, *(Sonoma County),* 50 Crest Way, Penngrove, CA 94951 (SAN 215-7098) Tel 707-795-8911.

Sonoma League for Historic Preservation, *(Sonoma Lea Hist; 0-9616547),* P.O. Box 766, Sonoma, CA 95476 (SAN 659-5383) Tel 707-938-2996; 465 E. MacArthur, Sonoma, CA 95476 (SAN 659-5391).

Sonoran Pr., *(Sonoran; 0-943332),* Box 423, Youngtown, AZ 85363 (SAN 240-5687) Tel 602-974-0720.

Sons of Liberty, Div. of New Christian Crusade Church, *(Sons Lib; 0-89562),* Box 214, Metairie, LA 70004 (SAN 210-6663) Tel 504-887-3217.

Sons of the Prophets Pr., *(Sons Prophets Pr; 0-915315),* 12359 Falling Leaves Ct., St. Louis, MO 63141 (SAN 290-0440) Tel 314-878-9270.

Sooty-Face Publishing Co., *(Sooty-Face; 0-9602366),* P.O. Box 26, Clairton, PA 15025 (SAN 212-5633) Tel 412-233-6141.

Sophia Bks., *(Sophia Bks; 0-933981),* 191 W. Rosslynn Ave., Columbus, OH 43214-1445 (SAN 693-0824) Tel 614-885-0823.

†Sophia Institute Pr., *(Sophia Inst Pr; 0-918477),* P.O. Box 5284, Manchester, NH 03108 (SAN 657-7172); *CIP.*

Sophia Press, *(Sophia Pr; 0-9609378),* P.O. Box 533, Durham, NH 03824 (SAN 260-1397) Tel 603-868-2318.

Soque Publishers, Div. of Mark of the Potter, *(Soque; 0-9608770),* Rte. 3, Box 83, Clarkesville, GA 30523 (SAN 238-3780) Tel 404-947-3440.

Sore Dove Pubs., *(Sore Dove Pubs; 0-9611976),* P.O. Box 6332, San Mateo, CA 94403 (SAN 286-7737) Tel 415-571-1632.

Sorger Assocs., Inc., *(Sorger Assocs; 0-9604072),* 229 Humphrey St., Marblehead, MA 01945 (SAN 214-1469).

SOS, *(S O S),* Box 7100, Warwick, RI 02887 (SAN 655-1424) Tel 401-739-1269.

Sotheby Pubns., *(Sotheby Pubns),* 1035 Fifth Ave., New York, NY 10028 (SAN 678-9188) Tel 212-737-0242; Orders to: Scala Bks., Keystone Industrial Pk., Scranton, PA 18512 (SAN 215-3742).

Soul Pubns., *(Soul Pubns; 0-937327),* 6041 Cleveland Ave., Columbus, OH 43227 (SAN 658-8050) Tel 614-497-8536.

Soulbook, *(Soulbook),* P.O. Box 61213, Los Angeles, CA 90061 (SAN 218-401X); c/o Community Resources Inc., 927 15th st., Suite 605 NW, Washington, DC 20005 (SAN 692-8412).

Soules, Gordon, Economic Marketing Research, *(Gordon Soules Econ; 0-919574),* 507 Third Ave., Suite 1240, Seattle, WA 98104 (SAN 208-2845).

Sound Advice Enterprises, *(Sound Advice; 0-943668),* 40 Holly Lane, Roslyn Heights, NY 11577 (SAN 238-3799) Tel 516-621-2445.

Sound Approach, Inc., *(Sound Approach; 0-939265),* 109 Caernarvon Ct., Exton, PA 19341 (SAN 662-524X) Tel 215-363-2900.

Sound Enterprises Publishing Co., *(Sound Ent; 0-935565),* 970 Cornwallis Dr., West Chester, PA 19380 (SAN 696-1886) Tel 215-431-4512.

Sound Feelings Publishing, *(Sound Feelings; 0-9615963),* 24266 Walnut St., Newhall, CA 91321 (SAN 697-3167) Tel 805-254-4938.

Sound Food Co., *(Sound Food Co; 0-9615672),* Rte. 2, Box 298, Vashon, WA 98070 (SAN 696-1371) Tel 206-463-3842.

Sound Nutrition, *(Sound Nut; 0-9609226),* 2560 N. 560 E., Provo, UT 84604 (SAN 241-4597) Tel 801-375-8227; Dist. by: Nutri-Books, P.O. Box 5793, Denver, CO 80223 (SAN 169-054X) Tel 303-778-8383.

Sound Publishing Co., *(Sound Pub),* P.O. Box 920, Great Neck, NY 10022 (SAN 206-2909) Tel 516-466-5750.

Sound View Pr., Div. of P. Hastings Falk, Inc., *(Sound View Pr; 0-932087),* 20 Wall St., Suite 150, Madison, CT 06443 (SAN 686-5240) Tel 203-245-2246.

Soundprint, *(Soundprint; 0-9611938),* 2250 N. 800 E., Provo, UT 84604 (SAN 286-0554) Tel 801-377-0553.

Sounds of Kansas, *(Sounds Kansas; 0-9615597),* Rte. 1, Inman, KS 67546 (SAN 696-1657) Tel 316-585-2389.

Soup to Nuts Press, *(Soup to Nuts; 0-9604780),* 582 Fernando Dr., Novato, CA 94947 (SAN 215-918X).

Source Productions, *(Source Prods; 0-9614966),* 10415 Sarah St., Toluca Lake, CA 91602 (SAN 693-7470) Tel 818-506-0236.

Source Pubns., *(Source Pubns; 0-937589),* P.O. Box 1543, Colorado Springs, CO 80901 (SAN 659-1787) Tel 303-632-1419; 515 N. Custer, Colorado Springs, CO 80903 (SAN 659-1795).

Source Publishing, *(Source Pub; 0-9615719),* 1812 NW Flanders, Apt. 41, Portland, OR 97209 (SAN 696-1282) Tel 503-224-5529.

Sourcebook Project, The, *(Sourcebook; 0-9600712; 0-915554),* P.O. Box 107, Glen Arm, MD 21057 (SAN 201-7652) Tel 301-668-6047.

†SourceFinders Information Corp., *(SourceFinders; 0-917097),* 68 Sandra Rd., Voorhees, NJ 08043 (SAN 655-1157) Tel 609-772-2355; *CIP.*

SourceNet, *(SourceNet; 0-915051),* P.O. Box 6767, Santa Barbara, CA 93160 (SAN 289-0224) Tel 805-964-6066.

Sources, *(Sources; 0-9603232),* 26 Hart Ave., Hopewell, NJ 08525 (SAN 211-5182) Tel 609-466-0051.

SourceView Software International, Subs. of SourceView Corp., *(SourceView; 0-87007; 0-87017),* 835 Castro St., Martinez, CA 94553 (SAN 654-3073) Tel 415-228-6228; Toll free: 800-443-0100.

Sourdough Enterprises, *(Sourdough; 0-911803),* 16401 3rd Ave. SW, Seattle, WA 98166 (SAN 264-3987)

Tel 206-244-8115.

South Asia Bks., *(South Asia Bks; 0-88386; 0-8364),* P.O. Box 502, Columbia, MO 65205 (SAN 207-4044)

Tel 314-449-1359.

South Carolina Bar Continuing Legal Education Committee, *(SC Bar CLE; 0-943856),* P.O. Box 11039, Columbia, SC 29211 (SAN 226-4137)

Tel 803-799-6653.

South Carolina Magazine of Ancestral Research, *(SCMAR; 0-913363),* P.O. Box 21766, Columbia, SC 29221 (SAN 285-8525)

Tel 803-772-6919.

South Carolina Sea Grant Consortium, *(SC Sea Grant; 0-933005),* 287 Meeting St., Charleston, SC 29401 (SAN 689-1535)

Tel 803-727-2078.

South Dakota Peace Officers Assn., *(SD Peace Officers; 0-9608456),* 3102 Pine Tree Trail, Sturgis, SD 57785 (SAN 240-5695)

Tel 605-677-5242.

†**South End Pr.,** *(South End Pr; 0-89608),* 116 St. Botolph St., Boston, MA 02115 (SAN 211-979X) Tel 617-266-0629; Orders to: 300 Raritan Ctr. Pkwy., CN-3137, Edison, NJ 08818 (SAN 695-4502) Tel 201-225-1900; *CIP.*

South Forty Publishing, *(South Forty; 0-9615291),* 20626 Whitewing Ct., P.O. Box 7735, Bend, OR 97708 (SAN 694-4175) Tel 503-382-3866.

South Georgia College, *(South Georgia Coll),* William S Smith Library, Douglas, GA 31533 (SAN 682-2479).

South Group Pubs., Ltd., *(South Group; 0-940842),* 30 Main St., Port Washington, NY 11050 (SAN 219-6379)

Tel 516-944-6161.

South Jersey Dining Guide, *(S Jersey Dining; 0-9612852),* 300 Grace Ave., Mays Landing, NJ 08330 (SAN 290-0491)

Tel 609-625-7433.

South Mountain Pr., Inc., *(South Mtn Pr; 0-937339),* 17 W. Pomfret St., Suite 7, Carlisle, PA 17013 (SAN 659-1809)

Tel 717-245-2933.

South Pasadena Public Library, *(Pasadena Public Lib; 0-9617293),* 1100 Oxley St., South Pasadena, CA 91030

(SAN 663-6039)

Tel 818-799-9109.

South Platte Pr., *(South Platte; 0-9609568),* P.O. Box 163, David City, NE 68632 (SAN 262-0855) Tel 402-367-4734.

South Salem News, *(S Salem News; 0-9610326),* 5330 Commercial SE, Salem, OR 97306 (SAN 264-4002) Tel 503-363-1539.

South Star Publishing Co., *(South Star Pub; 0-938637),* P.O. Box 821, Gainesville, FL 32604 (SAN 661-6313); 1130 NW Third Ave., Gainesville, FL 32601 (SAN 661-6321) Tel 305-294-3156; Dist. by: Langley Pr., 821 Georgia St., Key West, FL 33040 (SAN 264-164X).

South Street Seaport Museum, *(South St Sea Mus; 0-913344),* 203 Front St., New York, NY 10038 (SAN 282-3322)

Tel 212-766-9020.

South-Western Publishing Co., Subs. of SFN Cos INC., *(SW Pub; 0-538),* 5101 Madison Rd., Cincinnati, OH 45227 (SAN 202-7518) Tel 513-271-8811; Toll free: 800-543-0487.

SouthArt, Inc., *(SouthArt Inc; 0-9610698),* P.O. Box 5304, Hilton Head Island, SC 29938 (SAN 264-7931) Tel 803-671-2576.

Southco, *(Southco; 0-9614058),* 1724 Wildcat Ln., Ogden, UT 84403-3238 (SAN 685-9631) Tel 801-621-5520.

Southeastern Regional Council of the National Assn. of Housing & Redevelopment Officials, *(SERC NAHRO; 0-939647),* 201 Granby Mall, P.O. Box 968, Norfolk, VA 23501 (SAN 663-5474) Tel 804-623-1111.

Southern Association on Children Under Six, *(So Assn Child Six; 0-942388),* P.O. Box 5403, Brady Sta., Little Rock, AR 72215 (SAN 236-8560) Tel 501-227-6404.

Southern California Committee for the Olympic Games, *(S CA Committee; 0-9606628),* 515 Lillian Way, Los Angeles, CA 90004 (SAN 219-6387) Tel 213-465-1669; John C. Argue, 801 S. Flower St., Los Angeles, CA 90017-4699 (SAN 685-3609)

Tel 213-622-3100.

Southern Center for International Studies, Inc., *(Southern Ctr Intl Stud; 0-935082),* 320 W. Paces Ferry Rd., NW, Atlanta, GA 30305 (SAN 213-375X) Tel 404-261-5763.

Southern Exposure, *(Southern Exposure; 0-943810),* c/o Institute for Southern Studies, P.O. Box 531, Durham, NC 27702 (SAN 275-6994) Tel 919-688-8167.

Southern Historical Pr., Inc., *(Southern Hist Pr; 0-89308),* P.O. Box 738, Easley, SC 29641-0738 (SAN 208-8657)

Tel 803-859-2346.

Southern Ill. Univ. at Carbondale, Ctr. for Arch. Investigations, *(Center Archaeo; 0-88104),* Carbondale, IL 62901 (SAN 240-5709)

Tel 618-536-5529.

Southern Illinois Univ. at Edwardsville, *(Southern Ill U; 0-933991),* P.O. Box 74, Dept. of Art & Design, Edwardsville, IL 62026 (SAN 692-8919) Tel 618-692-3071.

†**Southern Illinois Univ. Pr.,** *(S Ill U Pr; 0-8093),* P.O. Box 3697, Carbondale, IL 62901-3697 (SAN 203-3623)

Tel 618-453-2281; *CIP.*

Southern Illinois Univ., Schl. of Medicine, *(Southern IL Univ Sch; 0-931369),* P.O. Box 3926, Springfield, IL 62708

Tel 217-782-4055.

Southern Institute Pr., *(Southern Inst Pr; 0-9615502),* P.O. Box 533, Indian Rocks Beach, FL 33535 (SAN 695-9237)

Tel 904-262-1883.

†**Southern Methodist Univ. Pr.,** *(SMU Press; 0-87074),* P.O. Box 415, Dallas, TX 75275 (SAN 203-3615); 6410 Airline Dr., Dallas, TX 75205 (SAN 658-1641)

Tel 214-739-5959; *CIP.*

Southern Ohio Genealogical Society, *(S Ohio Genealog; 0-941000),* P.O. Box 414, Hillsboro, OH 45133 (SAN 219-6395)

Tel 513-393-2452.

Southern Oregon Historical Society, *(South Oregon; 0-943388),* P.O. Box 480, 206 N. Fifth St., Jacksonville, OR 97530 (SAN 240-7779) Tel 503-899-1847.

Southern Pines Centennial Committee, *(Southern Pines; 0-9617019),* P.O. Box 870, Southern Pines, NC 28387 (SAN 662-9369); 500 W. Morganton Rd., Southern Pines, NC 28387 (SAN 662-9377) Tel 919-692-7021.

Southern Pubns., *(Southern Pubns; 0-9617083),* P.O. Box 750, Fairhope, AL 36532 (SAN 662-6262); 159 S. School St., Fairhope, AL 36532 (SAN 662-6270) Tel 205-928-7681.

Southern Publishing Assn., Div. of Review & Herald Pub. Assn., *(South Pub Assn; 0-8127),* 6856 Eastern Ave., Washington, DC 20012 (SAN 658-6473)

Tel 202-723-3700.

Southern Publishing Co., *(Southern Pub; 0-9616517),* 954 W. Tropical Way, Plantation, FL 33063 (SAN 659-5863) Tel 305-974-2029.

Southern Regional Education Board, *(S Regional Ed),* 1340 Spring St. NW, Atlanta, GA 30309 (SAN 206-1783) Tel 404-875-9211.

Southern Research Institute, *(S Res Inst; 0-940824),* 2000 Ninth Ave. S., Birmingham, AL 35255 (SAN 206-1791) Tel 205-323-6592.

Southern Resources Unlimited, *(Southern Resources; 0-915575),* P.O. Box 29, Nashville, TN 37221 (SAN 292-6776) Tel 615-646-0199.

Southern Univ. Pr., *(Southern U Pr; 0-87651),* 130 S. 19th St., Birmingham, AL 35233 (SAN 204-6148).

Southern Utah State College Library, *(South Utah St; 0-935615),* 351 W. Center, Cedar City, UT 84720 (SAN 696-0642)

Tel 801-586-7939.

Southfarm Pr., The, Subs. of Haan Graphi Pub. Services, Ltd., *(Southfarm; 0-913337),* P.O. Box 1296, Middletown, CT 06457 (SAN 283-4146) Tel 203-344-9137; Dist. by: Stackpole Books, P.O. Box 1831, Cameron & Kelker Sts., Harrisburg, PA 17105 (SAN 202-5396) Tel 717-234-5041.

Southland Specialty Publications Companies, *(Southland Spec; 0-911041),* 2170 W. Broadway, No. 202, Anaheim, CA 92804 (SAN 263-0087) Tel 714-999-0299.

Southwest American Publishing Co., *(SW Amer Pub Co; 0-911217),* 5720 North 1-35 Industrial Blvd., Edmond, OK 73034 (SAN 264-4010).

Southwest Educational Enterprises, *(SW Educ Ent; 0-937029),* 10711 Auldine, San Antonio, TX 78230 (SAN 658-7089)

Tel 512-342-2297.

Southwest Missouri State Univ., Dept. of English, *(S M S U; 0-913785),* 901 S. National, Springfield, MO 65804 (SAN 286-1992) Tel 417-836-5107.

†**Southwest Museum,** *(Southwest Mus; 0-916561),* P.O. Box 128, Highland Park Sta., Los Angeles, CA 90042 (SAN 203-0683) Tel 213-221-2164; *CIP.*

Southwest Natural History Association, The, *(SW Nat Hist Assn; 0-9610126),* P.O. Box 35141, Phoenix, AZ 85069 (SAN 275-7214) Tel 602-973-0591.

Southwest Parks & Monuments Assn., *(SW Pks Mnmts; 0-911408),* 221 N. Court, Tucson, AZ 85701 (SAN 202-750X)

Tel 602-622-1999.

Southwest Publishing Co., *(Southwest Pub; 0-9615438),* 1814 Leisure World, Mesa, AZ 85206 (SAN 696-107X) Tel 602-981-2843.

Southwest Scientific Publishing, *(SW Sci Pub; 0-9606246),* P.O. Drawer 3 AM, University Park, NM 88003 (SAN 220-3553)

Tel 505-525-1370.

Southwest Univ. Pr., Div. of Southwest Univ., *(SW Univ Press; 0-937681),* 4532 W. Napoleon Ave., Metairie, LA 70001 (SAN 659-3305) Tel 504-455-2900; 1021 N. Carrollton Ave., New Orleans, LA 70119 (SAN 659-3313).

Southwestern Legal Foundation, *(SW Legal Found),* P.O. Box 830707, Richardson, TX 75083 (SAN 232-380X) Tel 214-690-2377; 2601 N. Floyd Rd., Richardson, TX 75080 (SAN 669-2702).

Southwestern Mission Research Ctr., *(SW Mission; 0-915076),* Arizona State Museum, Tucson, AZ 85721 (SAN 215-8167) Tel 602-621-4898.

Sovereign Bks., *(Sovereign VA; 0-9614715),* 2272 Pimmit Run La., No. 104, Falls Church, VA 22043 (SAN 692-6606) Tel 703-356-5377.

Sovereign Pr., *(Sovereign Pr; 0-914752),* 326 Harris Rd., Rochester, WA 98579 (SAN 206-1279) Tel 206-273-5109.

Sovereignty, Inc., *(Sovereignty; 0-932201),* P.O. Box 909, Eastsound, WA 98245-0483 (SAN 686-5968) Tel 206-376-2177.

Soviet Studies, *(Soviet Studies; 0-930232),* P.O. Box 16, Hayward, CA 94543 (SAN 210-6671).

Sowa Books, *(Sowa Bks; 0-9605638),* 9637 Huntress Ln., San Antonio, TX 78255 (SAN 216-1826) Tel 512-695-2411.

Soyfoods Center, *(Soyfoods Center; 0-933332),* P.O. Box 234, Lafayette, CA 94549 (SAN 212-8411); 1021 Dolores Dr., Lafayette, CA 94549 (SAN 658-165X) Tel 415-283-2991.

Soza, Shari, Enterprises, *(S Soza Enters; 0-931711),* 349 N. Oregon St., P.O. Box 81, Yreka, CA 96097 (SAN 682-627X) Tel 916-842-2367.

Sozo Pub. Co., *(Sozo Pub Co; 0-9614465),* P.O. Box 23541, Nashville, TN 37202-3541 (SAN 678-917X) Tel 615-885-0198.

†**Space & Time,** *(Space And; 0-917053),* 138 W. 70th St., Apt. 4B, New York, NY 10023-4432 (SAN 218-4095)

Tel 212-595-0894; *CIP.*

Space News Publishing Co., *(Space News Pub; 0-936591),* P.O. Box 66521, Baton Rouge, LA 70896 (SAN 698-1259).

Space-Time Assocs., *(Space-Time; 0-918159),* 2039 Country Club Dr., Manchester, NH 03102 (SAN 296-8258) Tel 603-625-1094. Do not confuse with Space/Time Designs, Inc., Redmond, WA.

Space/Time Designs, Inc., *(Space-Time WA; 0-9603570),* P.O. Box 2286, Redmond, WA 98073 (SAN 213-3776) Tel 206-392-9879. Do not confuse with Space-Time Assocs., Manchester, NH.

Space Travel & Astronautic Research Society, *(Space Travel & Astron Res; 0-935313),* P.O. Box 92254, Pasadena, CA 91109-2254 (SAN 695-7153) Tel 818-795-8133; 2384 E. Orange Grove Blvd., Pasadena, CA 91104 (SAN 699-6108).

Spad Systems, Ltd., *(Spad Sys; 0-913913),* P.O. Box 571, Williamsville, NY 14221 (SAN 286-8873) Tel 716-688-4259.

Spadra Pr., *(Spadra Pr; 0-937161),* 126 Heritage Ln., Denton, TX 76201 (SAN 658-5019) Tel 817-382-5334; P.O. Box 23434, Denton, TX 76204 (SAN 658-5027).

Span, Inc., *(Span Inc; 0-938281),* 2805 W. Seventh St., Little Rock, AR 72205 (SAN 659-8269) Tel 501-562-4307.

Spanish Barb Breeders Association, *(Sp Barb Breeders),* 2888 Bluff St., P.O. Box 487, Boulder, CO 80301 (SAN 225-039X) Tel 303-452-5951.

Spanish Literature Pubns. Co., Inc., *(Spanish Lit Pubns; 0-938972),* P.O. Box 707, York, SC 29745 (SAN 216-3039) Tel 803-323-2231.

Sparhawk Books, Inc., Div. of Pawprints, Inc., *(Sparhawk; 0-9605776),* Pierce Crossing Rd., Jaffrey, NH 03452 (SAN 216-5538) Tel 603-532-9337; Toll free: 633-2900; Orders to: Box 446, Jaffrey, NH 03452 (SAN 699-5608).

Sparkiestuff, *(Sparkiestuff; 0-9616616),* P.O. Box 1005, Augusta, ME 04330 (SAN 659-7750) Tel 207-623-2101; Worster Hse., Apt. 17, Hallowell, ME 04347 (SAN 659-7769).

Sparks Press, *(Sparks Pr; 0-916822),* 900 W. Morgan St., P.O. Box 26747, Raleigh, NC 27611 (SAN 208-8673) Tel 919-834-8283.

Sparrow Pr., *(Sparrow Pr; 0-935552),* 103 Waldron St., West Lafayette, IN 47906 (SAN 205-0730) Tel 317-743-1991.

Sparrow Press of California, Subs. of Sparrow Corporation, *(Sparrow Pr CA; 0-917143),* 9255 Deering Ave., Chatsworth, CA 91311 (SAN 655-8844) Tel 818-703-6599.

Sparrow Pubns., *(Sparrow Pub NY; 0-9611460),* 799 Sixth Ave., New York, NY 10001 (SAN 285-1296) Tel 212-741-0254.

Sparrow Publishing, *(Sparrow Pub; 0-942818),* W. 308 S. 7144 Hwy I, Mukwonago, WI 53149 (SAN 238-8634) Tel 414-968-2803.

Spartan Bks., Inc. *See* **Hayden Bk. Co.**

Spartan Press, *(Spartan Pr; 0-912924),* P.O. Box 221, East Lansing, MI 48823 (SAN 204-6172).

Spaulding Hse. Pubns., *(Spaulding Hse Pubns; 0-9613692),* 3217 Potterton Dr., Falls Church, VA 22044 (SAN 670-977X) Tel 703-241-7870.

Spectrum Pubns., Ltd., *(Spectrum Pubns; 0-9616287),* P.O. Box 3006, Laurel, MD 20708 (SAN 658-4381) Tel 301-490-3590.

Speak for Yourself, Inc., *(Speak Yourself; 0-9614864),* 2925 Lindaloa Lane, Pasadena, CA 91107 (SAN 693-0603) Tel 818-791-5150.

Spears, W. H., Jr., *(Spears; 0-9600106),* 426 N. Kennicott, Arlington Heights, IL 60004 (SAN 204-6180).

†**Special Additions, Inc.,** *(Spec Addns; 0-9613439),* 23 Boulder Brook Rd., Greenwich, CT 06830 (SAN 657-0216) Tel 203-661-7759; *CIP.*

Special Aviation Pubns., *(Spec Aviation; 0-915376),* Rte. One, Box 730, China Spring, TX 76633 (SAN 208-8681) Tel 817-836-4269.

Special Bks., *(Special Bks; 0-939641),* 101 William St., South Dartmouth, MA 02748 (SAN 663-5288) Tel 617-999-5441.

Special Child Pubns., *(Spec Child; 0-87562),* P.O. Box 33548, Seattle, WA 98133 (SAN 203-2317) Tel 206-771-5711.

Special Children's Friends, Inc, *(Spec Child Friends; 0-939331),* RD 1, Box 84, Surry, ME 04684 (SAN 663-1428); Newbury Neck Rd., Surry, ME 04684 (SAN 663-1436) Tel 207-667-8331.

Special Committee on Environmental Law *See* **American Bar Assn. a**

†**Special Libraries Assn.,** *(SLA; 0-9613358),* 1700 18th St., NW, Washington, DC 20009 (SAN 680-0882) Tel 202-234-4700; *CIP.*

Special Literature Pr., *(Spec Lit Pr; 0-938594),* P.O. Box 4397, Benson Sta., Omaha, NE 68104 (SAN 215-8175).

Special Places, Inc., *(Special Places; 0-936777),* 391 SE Sycamore Creek Ln., Issaquah, WA 98027 (SAN 699-9573) Tel 206-392-0451.

Special Project Researchers, *(Special Project; 0-916257),* P.O. Box 384, Devon, PA 19333 (SAN 295-0049) Tel 215-964-9534.

Special Resource Pubns., *(Special Resc Pubns; 0-938639),* 11 Wethersfield Rd., Natick, MA 01760 (SAN 661-5864) Tel 617-651-3806.

Specialist Publishing Co., The, *(Specialist; 0-911416),* 109 La Mesa Dr., Burlingame, CA 94010 (SAN 204-6199) Tel 415-344-4958.

Specialized Information Products, *(Special Info Prod; 0-937563),* Mohawk Terr., Suite 513, Clifton Park, NY 12065 (SAN 659-1825) Tel 518-371-6900.

Specialized International Bibliographies, *(Specialized Intl Biblio; 0-916409),* 2006 Reagan Blvd., Carrollton, TX 75006 (SAN 295-4907) Tel 214-245-8687.

Specialized Studies, Inc., *(Spec Studies MD; 0-914547),* P.O. Box 854, Frederick, MD 21701 (SAN 289-5889) Tel 301-694-5530; 8605 Pinecliff Dr., Frederick, MD 21701 (SAN 289-5897).

Specialized Systems Consultants, Inc., *(Specialized Sys; 0-916151),* P.O. Box 55549, Seattle, WA 98155 (SAN 294-6696) Tel 206-367-8649.

Specialized Training & Education Programs, Inc., *(STEP; 0-934937),* 20 Golf Rd., P.O. Box 7414, Springfield, IL 62704 (SAN 694-2954) Tel 217-546-7493.

Specialties of the Hse., *(Spec Hse NY; 0-9615769),* Box 527, Manhasset, NY 11030 (SAN 669-8194) Tel 516-365-9832; 29 Shelter Rock Rd., Manhasset, NY 11030 (SAN 699-8208).

Specialty Bks., International, *(Specialty Bks Intl; 0-89445),* P.O. Box 1785, Ann Arbor, MI 48106 (SAN 210-2714) Tel 517-456-4764.

Specialty Press, Inc., *(Spec Pr NJ; 0-913556),* P.O. Box 2187, Ocean, NJ 07712 (SAN 202-0831) Tel 201-774-8447.

Specialty Press Pubs. & Wholesalers, Inc., *(Specialty Pr; 0-933424),* 16155 Quality Trail, Scandia, MN 55073 (SAN 212-6230) Tel 612-433-3813.

Specialty Publishing Co., *(Spec Pub; 0-939850),* P.O. Box 1355, La Crosse, WI 54602-1355 (SAN 216-9339) Tel 608-783-6470.

Specific Action Corp., *(Specific Action; 0-932569),* 8700 Concord Church Rd., Lewisville, NC 27023 (SAN 687-4894) Tel 919-945-5252.

Specific Pr., *(Specific Pr; 0-930846),* 1523 Franklin St., San Francisco, CA 94109 (SAN 222-8556) Tel 415-928-1133.

Speck, J. B. Pr., *(Speck Press; 0-9613736),* 6345 Alexander Dr., St. Louis, MO 63105 (SAN 676-4711) Tel 314-727-1297; Orders to: Stop Struggling with your Teen, P.O. Box 9138, Richmond Heights, MO 63117 (SAN 169-4901) Tel 314-576-1014; Dist. by: Baker & Taylor, 50 Kirby Ave., Somerville, NJ 08876 (SAN 202-8522); Dist. by: Publishers Group West, 5855 Beaury Ave., Emeryville, CA 94608 (SAN 169-7978) Tel 415-658-3453; Toll free: 800-982-8319; Dist. by: Ingram Bk. Co., P.O. Box 17266, Nashville, TN 37217 (SAN 169-2127); Toll free: 800-251-5900; Dist. by: Quality Bks., 918 Sherwood Dr., Lake Bluff, IL 60044-2204 (SAN 662-2518).

Spectator Pubns., *(Spectator Publ; 0-9614785),* P.O. Box 12887, Raleigh, NC 27605 (SAN 692-9915) Tel 919-828-7393.

Spectra *See* **Bantam Bks., Inc.**

Spectra Publishing Co., Inc., *(Spectra Pub Co; 0-915667),* P.O. Box 1403, Dillon, CO 80435 (SAN 292-6814) Tel 303-468-6439.

Spectracolor-Reynolds Pubs., Div. of Reynolds Publishers, *(Spectracolor-Reynolds; 0-914715),* 458 Third Ave., Cherry Hill, NJ 08002 (SAN 291-7920).

Spectromini, *(Spectromini; 0-943946),* P.O. Box 177, 168 Genesee St., Utica, NY 13503 (SAN 241-1520) Tel 315-735-2406.

Spectrum Bks. *See* **Prentice-Hall, Inc.**

Spectrum Business Systems, Inc., *(Spectrum Bus Syst; 0-936499),* 9 College Ave., Roanoke, VA 24153 (SAN 698-0643) Tel 703-389-4157; P.O. Box 847, Roanoke, VA 24153 (SAN 698-2492).

Spectrum Music Pr., *(Spectrum Music; 0-938555),* 845 Via de la Paz, Pacific Palisades, CA 90272 (SAN 661-4698) Tel 213-454-6197.

Spectrum Productions, *(Spectrum Prods; 0-914502),* 979 Casiano Rd., Los Angeles, CA 90049 (SAN 202-9898) Tel 213-476-4543. Do Not Confuse with Spectrum Publications or Spectrum Books.

Speculum Orbis Pr., *(Speculum Orbis; 0-932757),* 207 W. Superior, Chicago, IL 60610 (SAN 688-6213) Tel 312-663-1717.

Spedco Assoc., Inc., *(Spedco Assocs; 0-9615856),* 9 Pleasant Pl., Farmingville, NY 11738 (SAN 696-754X) Tel 516-798-9481; P.O. Box 120, Farmingville, NY 11738 (SAN 699-6426).

Speech Bin, The, *(Speech Bin; 0-937857),* 8 Beechtree Ln., Plainsboro, NJ 08536 (SAN 659-5871) Tel 609-799-3935.

Speech Foundation of America, *(Speech Found Am; 0-933388),* P.O. Box 11749, Memphis, TN 38111 (SAN 282-3330); 5139 Klingle St., Washington, DC 20016 (SAN 282-3349).

Speech Science Pubns., *(Speech Science; 0-88161),* P.O. Box 24428, Apple Valley, MN 55124 (SAN 262-0863) Tel 612-431-2460.

Speechphone Institute *See* **Norton, Jeffrey, Pubs., Inc.**

Speedx, *(Speedx; 0-934705),* 1510-E Portabella Trail, Mt. Pleasant, MI 48858-4035 (SAN 694-2733) Tel 517-773-9612; Orders to: 7738 E. Hampton St., Tucson, AZ 85715-4212 (SAN 694-2741) Tel 602-296-4773.

Speer Books, *(Speer Bks; 0-917832),* 333 Ash St., Red Bluff, CA 96080 (SAN 208-3566).

Speleo Press, *(Speleo Pr; 0-914092),* P.O. Box 7037, Austin, TX 78712 (SAN 206-5754) Tel 512-847-2709.

Spell, Leonard, & Assocs., *(Spell Assoc; 0-9615439),* 723 S. Mansfield Ave., Los Angeles, CA 90036 (SAN 696-1118) Tel 213-935-2186.

†**Speller, Robert, & Sons, Pubs., Inc.,** *(Speller; 0-8315),* 30 E. 23rd St., New York, NY 10010 (SAN 203-2295) Tel 212-477-5524; Orders to: P.O. Box 461, Times Sq. Sta., New York, NY 10108 (SAN 203-2309); *CIP.*

Speltz, Robert G., *(R G Speltz; 0-932299),* 505 Albert Lea St., Albert Lea, MN 56007 (SAN 686-2721) Tel 507-373-2145; Orders to: Real Runabouts, The, 505 Albert Lea St., Albert Lea, MN 56007 (SAN 662-2682) Tel 507-373-2145.

Spencer Butte Pr., *(S Butte Pr; 0-9609420),* 84889 Harry Taylor Rd., Eugene, OR 97405 (SAN 262-916X) Tel 503-345-3962.

Spencer Institute, The, *(Spencer Inst; 0-932270),* 8 Burnside Rd., Newton, MA 02161 (SAN 205-5651) Tel 617-965-8388.

Spencer Judd, Pubs., *(S Judd Pubs; 0-911805),* Six University Ave., Sewanee, TN 37375 (SAN 264-4045) Tel 615-598-5353.

Spencer Museum of Art, *(Spencer Muse Art; 0-913689),* Univ. of Kansas, Lawrence, KS 66045 (SAN 280-5944) Tel 913-864-4710.

Spencer's International Enterprises, *(Spencers Intl; 0-937771),* P.O. Box 43822, Los Angeles, CA 90043 (SAN 659-333X) Tel 213-484-6707; 3111 W. Slauson Ave./6227 S. Wilton Pl., Los Angeles, CA 90043 (SAN 659-3348).

Sperry Information Systems, *(Sperry Info Syst),* P.O. Box 2191, Princeton, NJ 08540 (SAN 677-8992).

Spevack, Jerome M., Inc., *(Spevack; 0-9604480),* 1219 N. 20th Ave., Hollywood, FL 33020 (SAN 215-1103).

Speyer, Edward, *(E Speyer; 0-9613359),* 19501 Sierra Santo, Irvine, CA 92715 (SAN 656-1470) Tel 714-854-8426.

†**Sphinx Pr.,** Affil. of International Universities Pr., Inc., *(Sphinx Pr; 0-8236),* 59 Boston Post Rd., P.O. Box 1524, Madison, CT 06443-1524 (SAN 669-2729) Tel 203-245-4000; Dist. by: International Universities Pr., Inc., 59 Boston Post Rd., P.O. Box 1524, Madison, CT 06443-1524 (SAN 202-7186) Tel 203-245-4000; *CIP.*

Sphinx Publishing, Inc., *(Sphinx Pub; 0-932729),* 4234 E. University Dr., Phoenix, AZ 85034 (SAN 688-5691) Tel 602-437-0201.

Spice West Co., *(Spice West; 0-9602812),* P.O. Box 2044, Pocatello, ID 83201 (SAN 214-476X).

Names

Names

Spill Control Association of America, *(Spill Control Assn),* 17117 W. Nine Mile Rd. 1040, Southfield, MI 48075 (SAN 224-9561) Tel 313-552-0500.

Spilman Press, Subs. of Spilman Printing Co., *(Spilman Pr; 0-918180),* 1801 9th St., Sacramento, CA 95814 (SAN 210-2722) Tel 916-444-0411.

Spin-A-Test Publishing Co., *(Spin-A-Test Pub; 0-915048),* 3177 Hogarth Dr., Sacramento, CA 95827 (SAN 282-3500) Tel 916-369-2032; Dist. by: J.R. Holcomb Co., 3000 Quigley Rd., Cleveland, OH 44113 (SAN 282-5856) Tel 216-621-6580; Dist. by: Baker & Taylor Co., Eastern Div., 50 Kirby Ave., Somerville, NJ 08876 (SAN 169-4901); Dist. by: Educational Exchange, 600 35th Ave., San Francisco, CA 94101 (SAN 282-3535) Tel 415-752-3302; Dist. by: Teachers Exchange, 6916A Sunrise Blvd., Citrus Heights, CA 95610 (SAN 200-8254) Tel 916-723-4711.

Spina Bifida Assn. of America, *(Spina Bifida),* 343 S. Dearborn Ave., No. 310, Chicago, IL 60604 (SAN 224-4632) Tel 312-663-1562.

Spindrift Press, *(Spindrift; 0-914864),* P.O. Box 2222, Cocoa, FL 32923-2222 (SAN 206-3808) Tel 305-639-3162.

Spinner Pubns., Inc., *(Spinner Pubns; 0-932027),* 63 Mechanics Lane, New Bedford, MA 02740 (SAN 686-0826) Tel 617-994-4564.

Spinning Spool, *(Spinning Spool),* P.O. Box 1425, East Lansing, MI 48823 (SAN 207-2890) Tel 517-332-3739.

Spinsters/Aunt Lute Bk. Co., *(Spinsters Aunt Lute; 0-933216),* Box 410687, San Francisco, CA 94141 (SAN 212-6923); 223 Mississippi St., San Francisco, CA 94107 (SAN 658-1676) Tel 415-558-9655.

Spiral Galaxy Publishing, *(Spiral Galaxy; 0-9617056),* P.O. Box 6316, North Plymouth, MA 02360 (SAN 662-9245); 7 Surrey Ln., Kingston, MA 02364 (SAN 662-9253) Tel 617-585-8965.

Spiraling Bks., *(Spiraling Bks; 0-9613585),* 12431 Camilla St., Whittier, CA 90601 (SAN 669-9235) Tel 213-692-2198.

Spire Books *See* Revell, Fleming H., Co.

Spiricult Publishing, *(Spiricult Pub; 0-938803),* 118 S. Main St., Spring Valley, NY 10977 (SAN 661-5503) Tel 914-425-3269; P.O. Box 65, Thiells, NY 10984 (SAN 661-5511).

Spirit Mountain Press, *(Spirit Mount Pr; 0-910871),* P.O. Box 1214, Fairbanks, AK 99707 (SAN 283-9156).

Spirit of America Day, The, *(Spirit Am Day),* P.O. Box 3333, Jackson, MS 39207 (SAN 225-6320) Tel 601-373-4400; Dist. by: Barrett & Co., P.O. Box 6700, Jackson, MS 39212 (SAN 240-8732) Tel 601-373-4400.

Spirit of Christ Ministries, *(Spirit Christ; 0-9615536),* Box 10952, Suite 194, Houston, TX 77292 (SAN 696-1002) Tel 713-757-3509.

Spirit of Faith Ministries, *(Spirit Faith; 0-936371),* 7040 SW 47th St., Miami, FL 33155 (SAN 698-0147) Tel 305-662-5778.

Spirit of Prophecy Ministries, *(Spirit Prophecy; 0-930351),* 1350 E. Flamingo, Las Vegas, NV 89132 (SAN 670-7661) Tel 702-737-0040; P.O. Box 19020-277, Las Vegas, NV 89132 (SAN 658-2591).

Spirit Press *See* Golz, J.L., Co.

Spirit Speaks, *(Spirit Speaks; 0-938283),* P.O. Box 84304, Los Angeles, CA 90073 (SAN 663-1908).

†**Spirit that Moves Us Pr., The,** *(Spirit That Moves; 0-930370),* P.O. Box 1585, Iowa City, IA 52244 (SAN 210-8585) Tel 319-338-7502; *CIP.*

Spiritual Fiction Pubns. *See* Garber Communications, Inc.

Spiritual Frontiers Fellowship, *(Spirit Front Fellow; 0-914071),* 3310 Baring St., Philadelphia, PA 19104 (SAN 287-0282) Tel 215-222-0619; 10819 Winner Rd., Independence, MO 64052 (SAN 287-0290); Dist. by: Samuel Weiser, Inc., P.O. Box 612, York Beach, ME 03910 (SAN 202-9588) Tel 207-363-4393.

Spiritual Growth Resources, Div. of Organization Resoures Press Ltd., *(Spiritual Growth; 0-938180),* P.O. Box 977, Indianapolis, IN 46206 (SAN 692-8951).

Spiritual Renaissance Press, Affil. of Highreach Press, *(Spiritual Renaissance; 0-938380),* 315 Harvard Ln., Boulder, CO 80303 (SAN 220-1259) Tel 303-494-7577; Dist. by: Bookpeople, 2929 Fifth St., Berkeley, CA 94710 (SAN 168-9517) Tel 415-549-3030; Dist. by: DeVorss & Co., P.O. Box 550, 1046 Princeton Dr., Marina Del Rey, CA 90291 (SAN 168-9886) Tel 213-870-7478.

Spiritual Science Library *See* Garber Communications, Inc.

Spiritual Union, *(Spiritual; 0-9614275),* 237 Rivoli St., San Francisco, CA 94117 (SAN 687-407X) Tel 415-564-1826; Dist. by: Bookpeople, 2929 Fifth St., Berkeley, CA 94710 (SAN 168-9517) Tel 415-549-3030.

Spiritual Warfare Ministries, *(Spiritual Warfare; 0-9615445),* P.O. Box 6515, Lakeland, FL 33807 (SAN 695-7064); Toll free: 800-282-8490; 730 Creative Dr., No. 1, Lakeland, FL 33803 (SAN 699-6094) Tel 813-644-7506; Dist. by: Spring Arbor, 10885 Textile Rd., Belleville, MI 48111 (SAN 158-9016) Tel 313-481-0900; Orders to: Whitaker House, Pittsburg & Colfax Sts., Springdale, PA 15144 (SAN 662-3549) Tel 412-274-4440; Toll free: 800-245-2422.

Spiritwarrior Publishing Co., *(Spiritwarrior Pub; 0-940298),* 306 Cecil St., Waynoka, OK 73880 (SAN 217-5851).

Spiritwood Publishers, *(Spiritwood Pub; 0-9611928),* 421 Queen N., Minneapolis, MN 55405 (SAN 283-3409) Tel 612-377-4259.

Spizzirri Pub. Co., Inc., *(Spizzirri; 0-86545),* P.O. Box 664, Medinah, IL 60157 (SAN 215-2851) Tel 312-529-1181; Toll free: 800-325-9819.

Splittgerber, *(Splittgerber; 0-9614321),* 333 Old Mill Rd., No. 118, Santa Barbara, CA 93110 (SAN 687-5300) Tel 805-964-6161.

Spohler, Albert A., *(A A Spohler; 0-9606580),* P.O. Box 2322, Palos Verdes, CA 90274 (SAN 207-1983); 5417 Littlebow Rd., Palos Verdes, CA 90274 (SAN 207-1991).

†**Spoken Language Services, Inc.,** *(Spoken Lang Serv; 0-87950),* P.O. Box 783, Ithaca, NY 14851 (SAN 203-2279) Tel 607-257-0500; *CIP.*

Spoon River Poetry Pr., *(Spoon Riv Poetry; 0-933180),* P.O. Box 1443, Peoria, IL 61655 (SAN 210-8593) Tel 507-537-6463. Do Not Confuse with the Spoon River Press.

Spoon River Pr., The, *(Spoon River; 0-930358),* P.O. Box 3635, Peoria, IL 61614 (SAN 211-5190) Tel 309-673-2266. Do not confuse with Spoon River Poetry Pr.

Spoonwood Press, *(Spoonwood Pr; 0-939026),* 99 Pratt St., Suite 408, Hartford, CT 06103 (SAN 219-855X) Tel 203-246-7200; Orders to: Publishers Business Service, P.O. Box 643, Cambridge, MA 02139 (SAN 693-9767) Tel 617-481-6562.

Spore Prints, *(Spore Prints; 0-9612020),* 2985 Sacramento Dr., Redding, CA 96001 (SAN 283-3433) Tel 916-246-4834.

Sporting News Publishing Co., Subs. of Times Mirror Co., *(Sporting News; 0-89204),* P.O. Box 56, St. Louis, MO 63166 (SAN 203-2260); 1212 N. Lindbergh Blvd., St. Louis, MO 63132 (SAN 699-5616); Orders to: P.O. Box 44, St. Louis, MO 63166 (SAN 662-1481).

Sportnet, Inc., *(Sportnet; 0-9616011),* 1680 38th St., Suite 100, Boulder, CO 80303 (SAN 699-3175) Tel 303-442-5565; P.O. Box 4064, Boulder, CO 80306 (SAN 699-6507).

Sports Fishing Institute, *(Sport Fishing; 0-9602382),* 1010 Massachusetts Ave., NW Suite 100, Washington, DC 20001 (SAN 210-9719) Tel 202-898-0770.

Sports Hall of Oblivion, *(Sports Hall Oblivion; 0-938455),* P.O. Box 69025, Pleasant Ridge, MI 48069-0025 (SAN 660-9732); 959 W. Drayton, Ferndale, MI 48220 (SAN 660-9740) Tel 313-543-9412.

Sports Information Press, *(Sports Info Pr; 0-916533),* 2240 Harlan St., Denver, CO 80214 (SAN 295-4745) Tel 303-237-8613.

Sports Information Service, *(Sports Info Serv; 0-936301),* 471 W. Longlake Dr., Harrison, MI 48625 (SAN 696-8333) Tel 517-539-2611; Dist. by: Balfour Inc., 22 County Rd., Attleboro, MA 02703 (SAN 200-8246).

Sports Marketing, Inc., *(Sports Market; 0-936169),* 2734 Hunters Forest, Germantown, TN 38138 (SAN 696-7590) Tel 901-755-7297.

Sports Medicine Bks., Inc., *(Sports Med Bks Inc.; 0-914363),* 22-1B Mulford Pl., Hempstead, NY 11550 (SAN 289-6818) Tel 516-481-8688.

Sports Psychology Pubns., *(Sports Psych Pubns; 0-9616954),* P.O. Box 80632-2387, Greeley, CO 80631 (SAN 661-7670); 2623 17th Ave., Greeley, CO 80631 (SAN 661-7689) Tel 303-352-8947.

Sports Records Bureau, *(Sports Rec; 0-934175),* 528 Turf Ln., Wheaton, IL 60187 (SAN 693-367X) Tel 312-668-2484.

Sports Vision, Inc., *(Sports Vision; 0-9614895),* 3114 NE 125th, Seattle, WA 98125 (SAN 693-2088) Tel 206-363-9111.

Sportsbooks, *(Sportsbks; 0-939468),* P.O. Box 494, Bolivar, NY 14715 (SAN 220-1887) Tel 716-928-2825.

Sportsguide, Inc., *(Sportsguide; 0-935644),* P.O. Box 1417, Princeton, NJ 08542 (SAN 213-5590) Tel 609-921-8599.

Sportsminded Pubns., *(Sportsminded Pubns; 0-9601912),* 2000 Center St., Suite 1330, Berkeley, CA 94704 (SAN 211-9803).

SportSoft, Inc., *(SportSoft; 0-939267),* P.O Drawer 160, Atlantic Beach, NC 28512 (SAN 662-6300) Tel 919-726-2865.

Sportsrite Publishing Co. Ltd, *(Sportsrite Pub Co; 0-930097),* 2601 Elliott Ave. Suite 5139, Seattle, WA 98121 (SAN 670-1841) Tel 206-448-4448.

SportsWare, *(SportsWare; 0-938709),* P.O. Box 18734, Washington, DC 20036-8734 (SAN 661-566X); 139 D St. SE, Washington, DC 20036 (SAN 661-5678) Tel 202-543-2114.

Sposato, Kenneth A., *(K A Sposato; 0-9612832),* 46 Gedney Park Dr., White Plains, NY 10605 (SAN 290-0475) Tel 914-948-4995.

SPOSS, Inc. *See* Society for the Promotion of Science & Scholarship, Inc.

Spraysaver Pubns., *(Spraysaver Pubns; 0-9616523),* P.O. Box 392, Rockport, ME 04856 (SAN 659-588X); 7 Summer St., Rockport, ME 04856 (SAN 659-5898) Tel 207-236-3656.

Spriggle, Howard, *(H Spriggle; 0-938686),* Box 550, Ocean View, DE 19970 (SAN 211-271X) Tel 302-539-2816.

Spring Harbor Pr., Div. of Spring Harbor, Ltd., *(Spring Harbor; 0-935891),* P.O. Box 346, Delmar, NY 12054 (SAN 695-9768); 29 Bennett Terr., Delmar, NY 12054 (SAN 699-6175) Tel 518-439-5978.

Spring Hill Center, *(Spring Hill; 0-932676),* P.O. Box 288, Wayzata, MN 55391 (SAN 212-2332); Dist. by: Publishing Center for Cultural Resources, 625 Broadway, New York, NY 10012 (SAN 685-3617) Tel 212-260-2010.

Spring Manufacturers Institute, *(Spring Manufac; 0-9604120),* 380 W. Palatine Rd., Wheeling, IL 60090 (SAN 691-3326) Tel 312-520-3290.

Spring Pubns., Inc., *(Spring Pubns; 0-88214),* P.O. Box 222069, Dallas, TX 75222 (SAN 203-2244); 408 N. Bishop, Suite 108, Dallas, TX 75208 (SAN 658-1692) Tel 214-943-4093.

†**Spring Street Pr.,** *(Spring St Pr; 0-931691),* 104 Spring St., Amherst, MA 01002 (SAN 682-4722) Tel 413-253-7748; *CIP.*

Springer, Miloslav, *(M Springer; 0-9616955),* 2955 Cortina Dr., Colorado Springs, CO 80918 (SAN 661-7719) Tel 303-599-8407.

†**Springer Publishing Co., Inc.,** *(Springer Pub; 0-8261),* 536 Broadway, New York, NY 10012 (SAN 203-2236) Tel 212-431-4370; *CIP.*

†**Springer-Verlag New York, Inc.,** Subs. of Springer-Verlag GmbH & Co. KG, *(Springer-Verlag; 0-387),* 175 Fifth Ave., New York, NY 10010 (SAN 203-2228) Tel 212-460-1500; Toll free: 800-526-7254; *CIP.*

Springfield Art Museum, *(Springfield; 0-934306),* 1111 E. Brookside Dr., Springfield, MO 65807 (SAN 213-5957) Tel 417-866-2716.

Springfield Historical Commission, *(Spring Historical; 0-943572),* Planning Dept., Springfield City Hall, Springfield, OR 97477 (SAN 240-7787) Tel 503-686-9961.

Springfield Library & Museum Assn., (Springfield Lib & Mus; 0-916746), 49 Chestnut St., Springfield, MA 01103 (SAN 214-2228).

Springfield Publishing Co., (Springfield Pub Co; 0-937500), 9041 Newcastle Ave., Northridge, CA 91325 (SAN 220-0937) Tel 818-701-6821.

Springfield Research Service, (Springfield Res Serv; 0-9603306), P.O. Box 4181, Silver Spring, MD 20904 (SAN 221-7058); 724 Springloch Rd., Silver Spring, MD 20904 (SAN 662-149X) Tel 301-622-2247.

†Springhouse Publishing Co., (Springhouse Pub; 0-916730; 0-87434), 1111 Bethlehem Pike, Springhouse, PA 19477 (SAN 208-1202) Tel 215-646-8700; Toll free: 800-346-7844; 711 E. Union, West Chester, PA 19380 (SAN 658-0971); CIP.

Springmeadow Pubs., (Springmeadow Pub; 0-9614703), P.O. Box 31038, Seattle, WA 98103 (SAN 692-6126) Tel 206-633-1087.

Springtide Books, (Springtide; 0-910873), 30 Watkins Rd., Brick, NJ 08724 (SAN 262-4230) Tel 201-458-1543.

Springtime Interprises, Inc., (Springtime Inter; 0-9606462), 11832 Timmy Ln., Garden Grove, CA 92640 (SAN 218-5067) Tel 714-971-7833.

Sproing Books, (Sproing; 0-916176), 10612 Altman St., Tampa, FL 33612 (SAN 206-3816).

Sprout Pubns. Inc., (Sprout Pubns; 0-932972), P.O. Box 4064, Sarasota, FL 33578 (SAN 212-6931) Tel 813-349-1714; Dist. by: Nutri Bks., P.O. Box 5793, Denver, CO 80223 (SAN 169-054X) Tel 303-778-8383; Dist. by: Bookpeople, 2929 Fifth St., Berkeley, CA 94710 (SAN 662-1503) Tel 415-549-3030; Toll free: 800-227-1516.

Spur Pubs., (Spur Pubs; 0-9615503), P.O. Box 5895, Columbia, SC 29250 (SAN 695-9229) Tel 803-799-4540.

Sputz, David, (Sputz; 0-9604312), 611 Bedford Ave., Brooklyn, NY 11211 (SAN 215-1847).

Spuyten Duyvil, (S Duyvil), 817 West End Ave., No. 4-A, New York, NY 10025 (SAN 237-9481) Tel 212-666-3648.

Spyglass Productions, (Spyglass Pro; 0-913487), 6 Thelma Ave., Glen Burnie, MD 21061 (SAN 285-1938) Tel 301-768-3157.

Squadron Signal Pubns., (Squad Sig Pubns; 0-89747), 1115 Crowley Dr., Carrollton, TX 75006 (SAN 400-3748) Tel 214-242-1485; Toll free: 800-527-7427.

Squalor Productions, (Squalor Prod; 0-9611426), 2711 W. Adams St., Chicago, IL 60612 (SAN 284-9208) Tel 312-826-5126.

Squantum Press, (Squantum Pr; 0-9607532), 92 Old Colony Ave., Quincy, MA 02170 (SAN 238-4817) Tel 617-471-8380.

Square Circle Press, (Square Circle; 0-930159), 137 Granada Dr., Corte Madera, CA 94925 (SAN 669-7054) Tel 415-924-6045.

Square One Pubs., Inc., (Sq One Pubs; 0-938961), P.O. Box 4385, Madison, WI 53711 (SAN 661-7271); 501 S. Prospect, Madison, WI 53711 (SAN 662-4340) Tel 608-255-8425. Imprints: Stamp Out Sheep Press (Stamp Out Sheep Pr).

Squarebooks, (Squarebooks; 0-916290), P.O. Box 1000, Mill Valley, CA 94942 (SAN 209-1062) Tel 415-383-0202.

Squeezer Press, (Squeezer; 0-9608270), 311 Lake, San Francisco, CA 94118 (SAN 240-4451) Tel 415-751-7373.

Squire, Ron, (Squire), Orders to: Shirley Squire, 174 Calle Cuervo, San Clemente, CA 92672 (SAN 204-8728) Tel 714-492-7068.

Sri Aurobindo Universal, (Sri Aurobindo; 0-935075), 331 E. 14th St., Apt 6C, New York, NY 10003 (SAN 695-0000) Tel 212-254-3321.

Sri Rama Publishing, (Sri Rama; 0-918100), 161 Robles Dr., Santa Cruz, CA 95060 (SAN 282-3578) Tel 408-426-5098; Orders to: P.O. Box 2550, Santa Cruz, CA 95063 (SAN 282-3586) Tel 408-426-5098.

Sri Shirdi Sai Pubns., (Sri Shirdi Sai; 0-938924), 251 Wilbur Ave., Pittsburgh, PA 15145 (SAN 220-2751) Tel 412-823-1296.

Sroda, George, (G Sroda; 0-9604486), P.O. Box 97, Amherst Junction, WI 54407 (SAN 210-8607) Tel 715-824-3868.

Sroge, Maxwell, Publishing, Inc., (Sroge M; 0-942674), 731 N. Cascade, The Sroge Bldg., Colorado Springs, CO 80903-3205 (SAN 238-5732) Tel 303-633-5556.

ST Pubns. See Signs of the Times Publishing Co.

Stabell, Brenda B., (B B Stabell; 0-9610872), 10827 Overbrook, Houston, TX 77042 (SAN 264-407X).

Stack the Deck, Inc., (Stack the Deck; 0-933282), 9126 Sandpiper Ct., Orland Park, IL 60462 (SAN 212-5668) Tel 312-349-8345.

Stackpole Bks., Inc., (Stackpole; 0-8117), P.O. Box 1831, Cameron & Kelker Sts., Harrisburg, PA 17105 (SAN 202-5396) Tel 717-234-5041; Toll free: 800-READ-NOW. Imprints: Giniger, K. S., Books (K S Giniger).

Stafford, Joseph, Pub., (J Stafford; 0-9617123), P.O. box 07011, Detroit, MI 48207 (SAN 662-684X); 8200 E. Jefferson, Apt. 403, Detroit, MI 48214 (SAN 662-6858) Tel 313-331-5680; Dist. by: Baker & Taylor, Eastern Div., 50 Kirby Ave., Somerville, NJ 08876 (SAN 169-4901); Toll free: 800-345-2282.

Stafford, Shirley, (S Stafford; 0-9607580), 4231 Casa De Machado, La Mesa, CA 92041 (SAN 239-9806).

Stafford Publishing Co., Inc., (Stafford Co; 0-9612954), 2876 Putting Green, Memphis, TN 38115 (SAN 292-6830) Tel 901-794-9682.

Staffort Hart Publishing Co., (Staffort Hart; 0-932301), 70 E. Sixth Ave., Denver, CO 80206 (SAN 686-6646) Tel 303-781-7883.

Stage Guild, (Stage Guild; 0-9612330), 820 E. Genesee St., Syracuse, NY 13210 (SAN 289-4998) Tel 315-423-4008.

Staging & Stuff, (Staging & Stuff; 0-935723), P.O. Box 158545, Nashville, TN 37215 (SAN 695-961X) Tel 615-297-7883; 1806 Primrose Ave., Nashville, TN 37212 (SAN 699-6159) Tel 615-251-2544; Dist. by: Broadman-Holman, 127 Ninth Ave. N, Nashville, TN 37234 (SAN 281-3440).

Stained Glass Images, Inc., (Stained Glass; 0-936459), 135 Dolton Ave., San Carlos, CA 94070 (SAN 698-0163) Tel 415-592-4858.

Staked Plains Press, (Staked Plains; 0-918028), P.O. Box 779, Canyon, TX 79015 (SAN 209-360X) Tel 806-655-7121.

Stalcup's Unlimited, (Stalcup; 0-933501), 413 W. Gaston Ave., Bessemer City, NC 28016 (SAN 691-8840) Tel 704-629-3940.

Stallard, Bernard, (B Stallard; 0-9606908), 73 Woodsdale, Cincinnati, OH 45216 (SAN 282-3616); Orders to: Rte. 1, Box 60, Morningview, KY 41063 (SAN 662-1511) Tel 606-356-3990.

Stallcup, Richard W., (Stallcup R; 0-9615073), P.O. Box 36, Inverness, CA 94937 (SAN 693-9244) Tel 415-669-1568.

Stalsby/Wilson Pr., (Stalsby-Wilson; 0-911299), P.O. Box 19976, Houston, TX 77224 (SAN 693-3750).

Stamberger Publishing Co., (Stamberger Pub; 0-9614372), 2330 Severn St., Baltimore, MD 21230 (SAN 688-6264) Tel 301-752-6035.

Stamlyn Publishing Co., Div. of Stamlyn Corp., (Stamlyn Pub Co; 0-9614339), 3 West End Ave., P.O. Box 402, Old Greenwich, CT 06870-0402 (SAN 687-8385) Tel 203-637-9470.

Stamp Journals Index Co., The, (Stamp Journal; 0-9608004), 177 Columbia Heights, Brooklyn, NY 11201 (SAN 238-5740).

Stamp Out Sheep Press See Square One Pubs., Inc.

Standard & Poor's Corp., Subs. of McGraw-Hill Inc., (Standard Poors; 0-927201), 25 Broadway, New York, NY 10004 (SAN 205-0900) Tel 212-208-8000.

Standard Arts Pr., (Standard Arts; 0-911426), 2324 Butler Rd., Butler, MD 21023 (SAN 204-6318) Tel 301-472-4698.

†Standard Educational Corp., (Standard Ed; 0-87392), 200 W. Monroe, Chicago, IL 60606 (SAN 204-6326) Tel 312-346-7440; CIP.

Standard Publishing Co., Div. of Standex International, (Standard Pub; 0-87239; 0-87403), 8121 Hamilton Ave., Cincinnati, OH 45231 (SAN 220-0147) Tel 513-931-4050; Toll free: 800-543-1353; Toll free: 800-582-1385 in Ohio.

Standards Engineering Society, (Standards Eng; 0-9616825), 6700 Penn Ave. S., Minneapolis, MN 55423 (SAN 661-1265) Tel 612-861-4990.

Standing Committee on Lawyers Title Guaranty Funds See American Bar Assn. a

Standing Committee on Legal Assistance for Military Personnel See American Bar Assn. a

Standing Committee on Unauthorized Practice of Law See American Bar Assn. a

Standish See Dell Publishing Co., Inc.

Stanford Alumni Assn., (Stanford Alumni Assn; 0-916318), Bowman Alumni House, Stanford, CA 94305 (SAN 222-8513).

Stanford Environmental Law Society, (Stanford Enviro), Stanford, CA 94305 (SAN 226-3483).

Stanford Univ., Dept. of Mechanical Engineering, (Dept Mech E CA; 0-9607348), Stanford Univ., Stanford, CA 94305 (SAN 265-9778).

†Stanford Univ. Pr., (Stanford U Pr; 0-8047), Stanford, CA 94305 (SAN 203-3526) Tel 415-723-9434; CIP.

Stanger, Robert A., Co., (R A Stanger; 0-943570), 1129 Broad St., P.O. Box 7490, Shrewsbury, NJ 07701 (SAN 262-0898) Tel 201-389-3600; Toll free: 800-631-2291.

Stanhope, Lacy, Jr., (L Stanhope; 0-9612362), 5201 E. Sunset Rd., Knoxville, TN 37914 (SAN 289-3991) Tel 615-522-0887.

Stanley Foundation, The, (Stanley Found; 0-9603112), 420 E. Third St., Muscatine, IA 52761 (SAN 221-7066).

Stanley Publishing Co., The, (Stanley Pub Co; 0-9613291), P.O. Box 689, Westboro, MA 01581 (SAN 653-8444) Tel 617-366-9442.

Stanoff, Jerrold G., (J G Stanoff), P.O. Box 1599, Aptos, CA 95001 (SAN 213-1706) Tel 408-724-4911.

Stanton, Allaben, Production, (Stanton Production; 0-913109), 70 Little Pond Rd., Londonderry, VT 05148 (SAN 283-3441).

Stanton & Lee Pubs., Subs. of Carley Capital Group, (Stanton & Lee; 0-88361), 44 E. Mifflin St., Madison, WI 53703 (SAN 211-2744) Tel 608-255-3254; Toll free: 800-356-4600; Toll free: 800-362-5464 (WI).

StanzaPress, (StanzaPr), 706 Fifth St., Steilacoom, WA 98388 (SAN 295-6381).

Staples, Walter D., (W D Staples; 0-9616385), 12 Country Meadow, Rolling Hills Estates, CA 90274 (SAN 659-1833) Tel 213-541-3497.

Star & Elephant Books See Green Tiger Pr., The

Star Athlete, (Star Athlete; 0-937565), P.O. Box 1815, Laredo, TX 78044-1815 (SAN 659-1841) Tel 512-722-6391; 910 Cedar, No. 16, Laredo, TX 78040 (SAN 659-185X).

Star Bks., Inc., (Star Bks Inc; 0-915541), 408 Pearson St., Wilson, NC 27893 (SAN 291-4468) Tel 919-237-1591.

Star Pubns., (Star City Pubns; 0-9615937), 1735 S. 20th St., Lincoln, NE 68502 (SAN 696-8244) Tel 402-477-5025; Orders to: Star City Publications, P.O. Box 2914, Lincoln, NE 68502 (SAN 662-3883).

Star-Gate Enterprises, (Star-Gate; 0-911167), P.O. Box 1006, Orinda, CA 94563 (SAN 281-5125) Tel 415-945-1210; Toll free: 800-824-2222 Ext. 35; Dist. by: Bookpeople, 2929 Fifth St., Berkeley, CA 94710 (SAN 168-9517) Tel 415-549-3030; Dist. by: U.S. Game Systems, 38 E. 32nd St., New York, NY 10016 (SAN 282-7336) Tel 212-685-4300; Dist. by: DeVorss & Co., P.O. Box 550, 1046 Princeton Dr., Marina del Rey, CA 90294 (SAN 692-6266); Dist. by: Publishers Group West, 5855 Beaudry St., Emeryville, CA 94608 (SAN 692-6274) Tel 415-658-3453.

Star Power Productions, (Star Power Prod; 0-938641), 636 Hermosa, Chaparral, NM 88021 (SAN 661-5856) Tel 505-824-4213.

Star Pr., (Star Pr; 0-937038), P.O. Box 835, Friday Harbor, WA 98250 (SAN 226-8035) Tel 206-378-5871.

Star Pubns., (Star Pubns MO; 0-932356), 1211 W. 60th Terrace, Kansas City, MO 64113 (SAN 212-4564) Tel 816-523-8228.

Star Publishing, (Star Pub TX; 0-935103), P.O. Box 3537-168, Austin, TX 78764 (SAN 695-1775) Tel 512-327-8310.

Star Publishing Co., Inc., *(Star Pub Fla),* 609 N. Railroad, P.O. Drawer BB, Boynton Beach, FL 33435 (SAN 207-2904).

Star Publishing Co., *(Star Pub CA; 0-89863),* 940 Emmett Ave., Belmont, CA 94002 (SAN 212-6958) Tel 415-591-3505.

Star Rover Hse. at Jack London Heritage Hse., *(Star Rover; 0-932458),* 1914 Foothill Blvd., Oakland, CA 94606 (SAN 212-4572) Tel 415-532-8408.

Star System Press, *(Star System; 0-932890),* P.O. Box 15202, Wedgwood Sta., Seattle, WA 98115 (SAN 207-5059) Tel 206-522-2589.

Star Tree Pr., *(Star Tree; 0-940506),* 114 Honeyspot Rd., Stratford, CT 06497 (SAN 219-0982).

Star Valley Pubns., *(Star Valley; 0-911223),* P.O. Box 421, Noti, OR 97461 (SAN 287-7562) Tel 503-935-2974.

Starblaze *See* Donning Co. Pubs.

Starbright Bks., *(Starbright; 0-9606248),* P.O. Box 353, Freeland, WA 98249 (SAN 282-3632) Tel 206-321-6138; Orders to: 1611 E. Dow Rd., Freeland, WA 98249 (SAN 282-3640) Tel 206-321-6138.

Starchand Press, *(Starchand Pr; 0-910425),* P.O. Box 468, Wainscott, NY 11975 (SAN 260-1419) Tel 516-324-2632.

Starfield Pr., *(Starfield Pr; 0-9616826),* P.O. Box 3247, Shawnee, KS 66203 (SAN 661-4671); 5930 Barton, Shawnee, KS 66203 (SAN 661-468X) Tel 913-631-6060.

Starfire *See* Bantam Bks., Inc.

Starfire Books, *(Starfire Bks; 0-9608006),* 9502 Indian Hills Dr., Sun City, AZ 85351 (SAN 238-5759) Tel 602-972-0547.

Starhaven, *(Starhaven; 0-936315),* P.O. Box 3045, La Jolla, CA 92038 (SAN 697-3191).

Starkey Laboratories, Inc., *(Starkey Labs; 0-9601970),* 6700 Washington Ave. S., Eden Prairie, MN 55344 (SAN 215-1111); Toll free: 800-328-8602.

Starlight Pr., *(Starlight Pr; 0-9605438),* P.O. Box 3102, Long Island City, NY 11103 (SAN 216-0633).

Starlight Pubns., *(Starlight Pubns; 0-9615667),* 1438 Epping Forest Dr., Atlanta, GA 30319 (SAN 695-9644) Tel 404-237-7125.

Starlight Publishing Co., *(Starlight Houston; 0-9616401),* P.O. Box 41275, Houston, TX 77241-1275 (SAN 659-1868) Tel 713-937-7465; 7850 Greenedge Dr., Houston, TX 77040 (SAN 659-1876).

Starline *See* Scholastic, Inc.

Starlite Distributors, *(Starlite; 0-931941),* P.O. Box 20729, Reno, NV 89515 (SAN 200-7789).

Starlog Pr., Div. of Starlog Group, *(Starlog Group; 0-931064; 0-934551),* 475 Park Ave. South, New York, NY 10016 (SAN 212-1247) Tel 212-689-2830.

Starmark Publishing, Div. of Starmark, Inc., *(Starmark; 0-936572),* 706 N. Dearborn St., Chicago, IL 60610 (SAN 214-2236) Tel 312-922-3388.

†**Starmont Hse.,** *(Starmont Hse; 0-916732; 0-930261),* P.O. Box 851, Mercer Island, WA 98040 (SAN 208-8703) Tel 206-232-8484; *CIP.*

Starogubski Pr., *(Starogubski; 0-9603234),* Westbeth, 55 Bethune St., Suite H658, New York, NY 10025 (SAN 207-2912) Tel 212-255-3322.

Starosciak, Kenneth, Bookseller, *(K Starosciak; 0-9613150),* 117 Wilmot, San Francisco, CA 94115 (SAN 201-0372).

†**Starpath School of Navigation,** *(Starpath; 0-914025),* 2101 N. 34th St., Seattle, WA 98103 (SAN 286-889X) Tel 206-632-1293; *CIP.*

Starports Publishing, *(Starports Pub; 0-9616977),* 13624 Crestway Dr., Brook Park, OH 44142 (SAN 661-7743) Tel 216-362-0122.

Starr, Arnold, & Co., *(Starr TX; 0-9607194),* 1334 Country Place Cir., Houston, TX 77079 (SAN 239-1317) Tel 713-497-0004; Dist. by: Richardson's Educators, 2014 Lou Ellen Ln., Houston, TX 77018 (SAN 169-829X) Tel 713-688-2244; Toll free: 800-231-0588; 800-392-8562 (In Texas).

Starr Pubns., *(Starr Pubns; 0-9613292),* 4015 SE Franklin St., Portland, OR 97202 (SAN 653-8487) Tel 503-234-4185.

Starr Studios, *(Starr Studios; 0-9612548),* P.O. Box 5604, Missoula, MT 59806 (SAN 287-7643) Tel 406-543-4638; Dist. by: Publisher's Group West, 5855 Beaudry St., Emeryville, CA 94608 (SAN 202-8522) Tel 415-658-3453.

Starrett Publishing Co., *(Starrett Pub Co; 0-911983),* 550 Hilbar Lane, Palo Alto, CA 94303 (SAN 276-9409) Tel 415-327-1472.

Starry Messenger Books, Inc., Div. of National Toxicology Monitor Inc., *(Starry Messenger Bks; 0-930179),* 262 Kalmia Ave., No. 12, Lexington, KY 40508 (SAN 670-6916).

Starseed Pubns., Inc., *(Starseed Pubns; 0-915763),* P.O. Box 2258, Gearhart, OR 97138 (SAN 293-8863) Tel 503-738-3659.

Start Now Press, *(Start Now Pr; 0-913819),* 4811 Lomitas Dr., San Diego, CA 92116 (SAN 286-0589) Tel 619-294-2239.

Stasiuk Enterprises, *(Stasiuk Ent; 0-932421),* 3150 NE 30th Ave., Portland, OR 97212 (SAN 687-4088) Tel 503-284-6887.

Stat Medical Publishing Co., *(Stat Med Pub; 0-935463),* 1527 Pine St., Philadelphia, PA 19102 (SAN 695-8648) Tel 215-735-5175.

State Bar of Arizona, *(AZ St Bar; 0-88726),* 363 N. First Ave., Phoenix, AZ 85003 (SAN 227-1400) Tel 602-252-4804.

State Bar of Texas, *(State Bar TX; 0-938160),* P.O. Box 12487, Capitol Sta., Austin, TX 78711 (SAN 216-4531) Tel 512-463-1481.

†**State Historical Society of Iowa,** *(State Hist Iowa; 0-89033),* 402 Iowa Ave., Iowa City, IA 52240 (SAN 206-5770) Tel 319-353-6689; *CIP.*

†**State Historical Society of Wisconsin,** *(State Hist Soc Wis; 0-87020),* 816 State St., Madison, WI 53706 (SAN 203-350X) Tel 608-262-1368; *CIP.*

State Hse. Pr., *(State House Pr; 0-938349),* P.O. Drawer 15247, Austin, TX 78761 (SAN 660-9651); 1604 S. Congress, Austin, TX 78704 (SAN 660-966X) Tel 512-448-0770.

State, Local, & Intergovernmental Center, Div. of Harvard University, *(St Local Inter; 0-943142),* 53 Church St., Cambridge, MA 02138 (SAN 240-5385) Tel 617-495-7908.

State Mutual Bk. & Periodical Service, Ltd., *(State Mutual Bk; 0-89771),* 521 Fifth Ave., 17th Flr., New York, NY 10017 (SAN 658-3849) Tel 212-682-5844.

State of Alaska, Dept. of Natural Resources, *(State AK Nat Res; 0-9616003),* Div. of Parks, Pouch 7-001, Anchorage, AK 99510 (SAN 699-7627) Tel 907-762-4530.

State Revenue Society, *(State Revenue Soc; 0-934939),* 51 Westchester Ave., Thornwood, NY 10594 (SAN 225-6053) Tel 914-747-0882.

State Street Pr., *(State Street Pr; 0-933581),* P.O. Box 252, Pittsford, NY 14534 (SAN 692-2252) Tel 716-244-4850.

State Univ. of New York at Albany, Univ. Art Gallery, *(SUNY Albany U Art; 0-910763),* 1400 Washington Ave., Albany, NY 12222 (SAN 260-2679) Tel 518-457-3375.

State University of New York at Buffalo, *(SUNY Buffalo),* Capen Hall, Amherst Campus, Buffalo, NY 14260 (SAN 227-0234).

State Univ. of New York at Buffalo, Comparative Education Ctr., *(SUNY Compar Educ Ctr; 0-937033),* SUNY Buffalo, Faculty of Educational Studies, Comparative Education Ctr., 428 Baldy Hall, Amherst, NY 14260 (SAN 659-4573).

State Univ. of New York at Buffalo Music Department, *(State U NY Buffalo; 0-931111),* 222 Baird Hall, Buffalo, NY 14260 (SAN 678-9498) Tel 716-636-2765.

State Univ. of New York at Buffalo, Univ. Libraries, *(SUNY Buffalo Univ Lib; 0-915769),* Amherst Campus, Capen Hall, Rm. 410, Buffalo, NY 14260 (SAN 294-1317) Tel 716-636-2818.

†**State Univ. of New York at Potsdam, Brainerd Art Gallery,** *(SUNYP Brainerd; 0-942746),* State Univ. College of Arts & Sciences, Potsdam, NY 13676 (SAN 240-1959) Tel 315-267-2254; *CIP.*

State Univ. of New York, College of Environmental Science & Forestry at Syracuse Univ., *(SUNY Environ),* Bray Hall, Rm. 123, Syracuse, NY 13210 (SAN 205-0633) Tel 315-470-6647.

†**State Univ. of New York Pr.,** *(State U NY Pr; 0-87395; 0-88706),* State Univ. Plaza, Albany, NY 12246 (SAN 658-1730) Tel 518-472-5000; Orders to: P.O. Box 6525, Ithaca, NY 14850 (SAN 203-3496) Tel 607-277-2211; *CIP.*

Statelaw Guides, Inc., *(Statelaw Guides; 0-934055),* P.O. Box 28962, St. Louis, MO 63132 (SAN 693-0867) Tel 314-993-2610.

Staten Island Continuum of Education, Inc., *(SI Cont Ed Inc; 0-914639),* 130 Stuyvesant Pl., Staten Island, NY 10301 (SAN 289-6028) Tel 718-447-2600.

Staten Island Historical Society, *(Staten Island; 0-9606756),* 441 Clarke Ave., Richmondtown, NY 10306 (SAN 205-0641) Tel 212-351-1611.

Station Hill Pr., *(Station Hill Pr; 0-930794),* Station Hill Rd., Barrytown, NY 12507 (SAN 214-1485); Dist. by: Small Press Dist., 1814 San Pablo Ave., Berkeley, CA 94702 (SAN 204-5826) Tel 415-549-3336; Dist. by: Inland Bk. Co., P.O. Box 261, 22 Hemingway St., East Haven, CT 06512 (SAN 200-4151) Tel 203-467-4257; Dist. by: Station Hill Pr., Sta. Hill Rd., Barrytown, NY 12507 (SAN 214-1485); Dist. by: Writers & Bks., 740 University Ave., Rochester, NY 14607 (SAN 662-152X) Tel 716-473-2590.

Station Representatives Assn., Inc., *(Station Reps Assn),* 230 Park Ave., New York, NY 10017 (SAN 224-6600) Tel 212-687-2484.

Statistical Pr., *(Statistical Pr; 0-9610700),* P.O. Box 11019, San Francisco, CA 94101 (SAN 264-7958) Tel 415-922-1267.

Statistikon Corp., The, *(Statistikon Corp),* P.O. Box 246, East Norwich, NY 11732 (SAN 696-6721) Tel 516-922-0882.

Stay Away Joe Pubs., *(Stay Away; 0-911436),* P.O. Box 2054, Great Falls, MT 59403 (SAN 204-6350).

Steam Pr., *(Steam Pr MA; 0-942820),* 15 Warwick Rd., Watertown, MA 02172 (SAN 238-8642) Tel 617-923-1046; Dist. by: Kampmann & Company, 9 E. 40th St., New York, NY 10016 (SAN 202-5191) Tel 212-685-2928.

Steamship Historical Society of America, Inc., *(Steamship Hist Soc; 0-913423),* 414 Pelton Ave., Staten Island, NY 10310 (SAN 285-0915) Tel 718-727-9583; Orders to: Steamship Hist. Soc, HC Hall Bldg., 345 Blackstone Blvd., Providence, RI 02906 (SAN 285-0923) Tel 401-274-0805.

Stearn Publishers Ltd., *(Stearn Pubs; 0-9612186),* 500 E. 77th St., New York, NY 10162 (SAN 289-5005) Tel 212-737-9304.

Steaven Research & Publishing, *(Steaven Res & Pub; 0-932609),* 9860 SW Davies Rd., Beaverton, OR 97005 (SAN 687-5319) Tel 503-626-3693.

Steel Founders' Society of America, *(Steel Founders; 0-9604674),* 455 State St., Des Plaines, IL 60016 (SAN 215-2002) Tel 312-299-9160.

Steel Joist Institute, *(Steel Joist Inst),* 1205 48th Ave. N., Suite A, Myrtle Beach, SC 29577 (SAN 229-7841) Tel 803-449-0487.

Steel Structures Painting Council, *(SSPC),* 4400 Fifth Ave., Pittsburgh, PA 15213 (SAN 260-3187) Tel 412-578-3327; Orders to: Publications Department, SSPC-4400 Fifth Ave., Pittsburgh, PA 15213 (SAN 662-1538) Tel 412-268-3455.

SteelDragon Pr., *(SteelDragon Pr; 0-916595),* P.O. Box 7253, Powderhorn Sta., Minneapolis, MN 55407 (SAN 296-6727) Tel 612-721-6076.

Steelstone Pr., *(Steelstone; 0-9605678),* 4607 Claussen Lane, Valparaiso, IN 46383 (SAN 216-1877) Tel 219-464-1792.

Steffanides, George F., *(Steffanides; 0-9600114),* 66 Lourdes Dr., Fitchburg, MA 01420 (SAN 204-6369) Tel 617-342-1997.

Steffen Publishing Co., *(Steffen Pub Co; 0-911913),* Main St., Holland Patent, NY 13354 (SAN 283-9199) Tel 315-865-4132.

Stehsel, Donald, *(Stehsel; 0-9606582),* 2600 S. Third Ave., Arcadia, CA 91006 (SAN 206-3824) Tel 818-446-3679.

Stein, Shifra, Productions/Stein Pr., *(S Stein Prods; 0-9609752),* 3733 Pennsylvania; P.O. Box 5862, Kansas City, MO 64111 (SAN 263-2284).

†**Stein & Day,** *(Stein & Day; 0-8128),* Scarborough Hse., Briarcliff Manor, NY 10510 (SAN 203-3461) Tel 914-762-2151; *CIP.*

Stein & Kolber Assocs., *(S&K Assocs; 0-936565),* 633 Edison Dr., East Windsor, NJ 08520 (SAN 697-7561) Tel 609-443-4513.

Stein Collectors International, *(Stein Coll Intl),* P.O. Box 463, Kingston, NJ 08528 (SAN 225-5456) Tel 201-329-2567.

Steiner, Ralph, Incorporated, *(Steiner R; 0-9615132),* Thetford, VT 05074 (SAN 694-2644) Tel 802-785-2476; Dist. by: Univ. of New Mexico Pr., Journalism Bldg., Rm. 220, Albuquerque, NM 87131 (SAN 213-9588) Tel 505-277-2346.

Steiner, Rudolf, Institute, *(Steiner Inst; 0-9615304),* RD 2, Box 199, Phoenixville, PA 19460 (SAN 694-5422) Tel 215-495-5406.

Steiner, Rudolf, Pubns. *See Garber Communications, Inc.*

Steinerbooks *See Garber Communications, Inc.*

Steinlage Products, *(Steinlage; 0-914754),* 4766 Kremer Hoying Rd., St. Henry, OH 45883 (SAN 206-1295) Tel 419-678-4125.

Steinlitz-Hammacher Co., *(Steinlitz-Hammacher; 0-917208),* P.O. Box 187, Hasbrouck Heights, NJ 07604 (SAN 293-3985) Tel 201-667-1429; Dist. by: Nacscorp, 528 E. Lorain St., Oberlin, OH 44074 (SAN 293-3993) Tel 216-775-8084; Dist. by: The Distributors, 702 S. Michigan, South Bend, IN 46618 (SAN 169-2488) Tel 219-232-8500.

Steinway & Sons, Subs. of Steinway Musical Properties, Inc., *(Steinway; 0-9607196),* Steinway Place, Long Island City, NY 11105 (SAN 239-1325) Tel 718-721-2600; Toll free: 800-223-6017.

Steketee-Van Huis, Inc. *See Holland Junior Welfare League*

Stel-Mar, *(Stel-Mar; 0-935456),* 329 Rhoda Dr., Lancaster, PA 17601 (SAN 215-1855).

Stella, Albert A. M., *(A Stella),* 220 Exchange St., Susquehanna, PA 18847 (SAN 212-1417); Orders to: Deinotation-7 Press, P.O. Box 204, Susquehanna, PA 18847 (SAN 212-1425); Dist. by: Brodart, 500 Arch St., Williamsport, PA 17705 (SAN 203-6711) Tel 717-326-2461.

Stella, Joseph G., *(J G Stella; 0-9600908; 0-8390),* P.O. Box 2158, Ft. Lauderdale, FL 33303 (SAN 208-8746) Tel 305-561-2487; Dist. by: Abner Schram, 36 Park St., Montclair, NJ 07042 (SAN 169-4766).

Stella Maris Books, *(Stella Maris Bks; 0-912103),* P.O. Box 11483, Ft. Worth, TX 76110 (SAN 264-7613) Tel 817-924-7221.

Stelle Group, *(Stelle; 0-9600308),* P.O. Box 75, Quinlan, TX 75474 (SAN 204-6385) Tel 214-864-0799.

Stemmer Hse. Pub., Inc., *(Stemmer; 0-916144; 0-88045),* 2627 Caves Rd., Owings Mills, MD 21117 (SAN 207-9623) Tel 301-363-3690. *Imprints:* International Design Library (Intl Design); Story-to-Color (Story-to-Color).

Stempien, G., Publishing Co., *(G Stempien; 0-930472),* 1213 Edgehill Ave., Joliet, IL 60432 (SAN 210-9840) Tel 815-722-4216.

Stenotype Educational Products, Inc., *(Stenotype Educ; 0-938643),* P.O. Box 959, Melrose, FL 32666 (SAN 661-6356); Rte. 1, P.O. Box 1235, Melrose, FL 32666 (SAN 661-6364) Tel 904-475-3332.

Stensrud, Mary, *(M Stensrud; 0-9616956),* 1102 S. 41st Ave., Yakima, WA 98908 (SAN 661-776X) Tel 509-965-0459.

Step Ahead Pr., Affil. of Heartlite, Inc., *(Step Ahead Pr; 0-934941),* 6509 Breckville Rd., P.O. Box 31360, Cleveland, OH 44131 (SAN 695-0159) Tel 216-526-6727.

Step By Step Pubns., *(Step By Step Pubns; 0-9615611),* 2209 Madison, Norfolk, NE 68701 (SAN 695-8818) Tel 402-371-5023.

Stephanus, Isidore, Sons Publishing, *(I Stephanus Pub; 0-9615964),* P.O. Box 6772, Ithaca, NY 14851 (SAN 697-2950) Tel 607-272-0056.

Stephens Engineering Associates, Inc., *(Stephens Eng Assocs; 0-911677),* 7030 220th SW., Mountlake Terrace, WA 98043 (SAN 264-4126) Tel 206-771-2182.

Stephens Press, *(Stephens Pr),* Drawer 1441, Spokane, WA 99210 (SAN 210-9573) Tel 509-838-8222.

Stepping Stones Pr., *(Step Stones Pr; 0-9616502),* P.O. Box 4585, McAllen, TX 78502 (SAN 659-3429) Tel 512-686-6829; 221 N. Main St., McAllen, TX 78502 (SAN 659-3437).

Steppingstone Enterprises, Inc., *(Steppingstone Ent; 0-939728),* 2108 S. University Dr., Park Place Plaza, Suite 103, Fargo, ND 58103 (SAN 216-7646) Tel 701-237-4742.

Steppingstones Pr., *(Stpngstns Pr NY; 0-935821),* P.O. Box 1856, New York, NY 10027 (SAN 695-992X) Tel 718-474-5063; 247 Beach 122nd St., Belle Harbor, NY 11694 (SAN 699-6191).

Stereopticon Press, *(Stereopticon Pr; 0-9608824),* 534 Wahlmont Dr., Webster, NY 14580 (SAN 238-3829) Tel 716-671-2342.

Sterling, A. James, Jr., Architect Photographer, *(A J Sterling; 0-9607042),* 2500 N. Lakeview Ave., Chicago, IL 60614 (SAN 241-5828) Tel 312-528-6648.

Sterling Heights Genealogical & Historical Society, *(Sterling Hgts Geneal; 0-9616495),* 40255 Dodge Pk. Rd., Sterling Heights, MI 48078 (SAN 659-3380) Tel 313-731-3778.

Sterling Instrument, *(Sterling Instru),* 2101 Jericho Tpke., New Hyde Park, NY 11040 (SAN 207-2920).

Sterling Life Insurance Co., *(Sterling Life Ins; 0-9617162),* One S. Limestone St., Springfield, OH 45502 (SAN 662-8087) Tel 602-953-1564.

Sterling Magic Creations, Inc., *(Sterling Magic; 0-941658),* P.O. Box 251, San Bruno, CA 94066 (SAN 239-3174) Tel 415-871-8626.

Sterling Publishing Co., Inc., *(Sterling; 0-8069),* 2 Park Ave., New York, NY 10016 (SAN 211-6324) Tel 212-532-7160; 900 Magnolia Ave., Elizabeth, NJ 07201 (SAN 658-1773). *Imprints:* Davis Publications (Davis Pubns).

Sterling Travel Pubns., *(Sterling Travel Pubn; 0-913303),* 12616-12th Ave. S., Seattle, WA 98168 (SAN 285-8592) Tel 206-246-4092.

Stern, Clarence Ames, *(Stern; 0-9600116),* P.O. Box 2294, Oshkosh, WI 54903 (SAN 204-6393) Tel 414-231-6786.

Stery, William, Co., *(W Stery; 0-937913),* P.O. Box 371595, Decatur, GA 30037-1595 (SAN 659-5901); 2897 Bradmoor Ct., Decatur, GA 30034 (SAN 659-591X) Tel 404-241-5003.

Stevens, Gareth, Publishing, *(Stevens Pub; 0-918831; 1-55532),* 7221 W. Green Tree Rd., Milwaukee, WI 53223 (SAN 696-1592) Tel 414-466-7550.

Stevens, Hat, Pub., *(Hat Stevens; 0-9605690),* 5718 Dorsett Dr., Madison, WI 53711 (SAN 239-698X) Tel 608-271-2689.

Stevens, J. P., & Co., Inc., *(J P Stevens & Co; 0-935605),* 1 Cottage St., Easthampton, MA 01027 (SAN 696-1819) Tel 413-527-0700.

Stevens & Shea Pubns., *(Stevens & Shea; 0-89550),* P.O. Box 794, Stockton, CA 95201 (SAN 206-3670) Tel 209-465-1880.

Stevens & Sons Ltd., *(Stevens & Sons UK; 0-420),* 11 New Fetter Ln., London EC4P 4EE, .

Stevens Bk., Pr., Div. of Stevens Book Shop, *(Stevens Bk Pr; 0-913029),* P.O. Box 71, Wake Forest, NC 27587 (SAN 159-1126) Tel 919-556-3830.

Stevenson, Robert Louis, Schl., The *See Univ. of Texas Pr.*

Stevenson International, *(Stevenson Intl; 0-9606252),* 525 Princeton Circle W., Fullerton, CA 92631 (SAN 217-5878).

Stevenson Language Skills, Inc., *(Stevenson Lang Skills; 0-941112),* 85 Upland Rd., Attleboro, MA 02703 (SAN 217-4413) Tel 617-222-1133.

†**Stevenson Pr.,** *(Stevenson Pr; 0-89482),* P.O. Box 10021, Austin, TX 78766 (SAN 209-8873); *CIP.*

Steves Wide World Studios, *(Steves Wide World),* 111 Fourth Ave. N., Edmonds, WA 98020 (SAN 214-2244). Deceased.

Steward & Sons, *(Steward & Sons; 0-917144),* P.O. Box 24-8583, Coral Gables, FL 33124 (SAN 208-8789).

Stewardship Enterprises, *(Stewardship Enters; 0-9611282),* P.O. Box 29403, Richmond, VA 23229 (SAN 283-3468) Tel 804-740-2608.

Stewart, B. M., *(B M Stewart),* 4494 Wausau Rd., Okemos, MI 48864 (SAN 202-0548) Tel 517-349-0297.

Stewart, Lois, *(L Stewart; 0-9609512),* 3657 W. Nichols, Springfield, MO 65803 (SAN 262-088X) Tel 417-831-6140.

Stewart, William J., *(W J Stewart; 0-9615440),* P.O. Box 793, Mill Valley, CA 94942 (SAN 696-1169) Tel 415-456-8415.

†**Stewart, Tabori & Chang, Pubs.,** *(Stewart Tabori & Chang; 0-941434; 1-55670),* 740 Broadway, New York, NY 10003 (SAN 293-4000) Tel 212-460-5000; Dist. by: Workman Publishing Co., Inc., One W. 39th St., New York, NY 10018 (SAN 203-2821) Tel 212-398-9160; Dist. by: Random House, Inc., 201 E. 50th St., New York, NY 10022 (SAN 202-5507) Tel 212-572-8030; *CIP.*

Stice, Will, *(W Stice; 0-9610512),* P.O. Box 12886, Salem, OR 97309 (SAN 264-4142) Tel 503-588-0344.

Stickley, George F., Co., *(G F Stickley Co; 0-89313),* 210 W. Washington Sq., Philadelphia, PA 19106 (SAN 209-0783) Tel 215-922-7126.

Still News Pubns., *(Still News; 0-940828),* P.O. Box 353, Port Ludlow, WA 98365 (SAN 219-6417).

Still Point Pr., *(Still Point TX; 0-933841),* 4222 Willow Grove Rd., Dallas, TX 75220 (SAN 692-6746) Tel 214-352-8282.

Stillgate Pubs., *(Stillgate; 0-938286),* P.O. Box 67, Alstead, NH 03602 (SAN 216-1885).

Stillpoint Publishing, *(Stillpoint; 0-913299),* P.O. Box 640, Walpole, NH 03608 (SAN 285-8630) Tel 603-756-3508; Toll free: 800-526-0275; Orders to: Dutton-NAL, 34 Engelhard Dr., Cranbury, NJ 08512 (SAN 694-9622); Dist. by: New American Library, P.O. Box 999, Bergenfield, NJ 07621 (SAN 206-8087) Tel 201-387-0600.

Stilwell Studio, The, *(Stilwell Studio; 0-9605862),* P.O. Box 50, Carmel, CA 93921 (SAN 220-1895) Tel 408-624-0340.

Stimler Associates, *(Stimler Assoc; 0-9600770),* 33 W. Second St., Moorestown, NJ 08057 (SAN 206-7994).

Stindt Bks., *(Stindt Bks; 0-9615465),* 3363 Riviera West Dr., Kelseyville, CA 95451 (SAN 695-7145) Tel 707-279-8581.

Stinson Beach Press, *(Stinson Beach; 0-918540),* P.O. Box 475, Stinson Beach, CA 94970 (SAN 209-8881) Tel 415-868-1424.

Stipes Publishing Co., *(Stipes; 0-87563),* P.O. Box 526, 10-12 Chester St., Champaign, IL 61820 (SAN 206-8664) Tel 217-356-8391.

Stirrup Associates, Inc., *(Stirrup Assoc; 0-937420),* 115 Church St., Decatur, GA 30030 (SAN 215-1863) Tel 404-378-4372.

Stivers, Stephen N., *(Stivers; 0-9615274),* 4725 SE 49th St., Portland, OR 97206 (SAN 695-2194) Tel 503-775-2816; Dist. by: Stinna Co., 4725 SE 49th St., Portland, OR 97206 (SAN 200-5778).

Stock & Breznau Publishing Co., *(Stock-Breznau; 0-936525),* 12335 Santa Monica Blvd., Suite 207, Los Angeles, CA 90025 (SAN 698-018X).

Stock Drive Products, *(Stock Drive; 0-9609878),* 2101 Jericho Turnpike, New Hyde Park, NY 11040 (SAN 204-6415).

†**Stockton Pr.,** Div. of Grove's Dictionaries of Music, Inc., *(Stockton Pr; 0-935859; 0-943818),* 15 E. 26th St., New York, NY 10010 (SAN 696-0545) Tel 212-481-1334; Toll free: 800-221-2123; *CIP.*

Stockton Press *See Groves Dictionaries of Music, Inc.*

Stockton Unified School District, The, *(Stockton Unified Schl Dist; 0-9607134),* 701 N. Madison St., Stockton, CA 95203 (SAN 239-037X).

†**Stoeger Publishing Co.,** Subs. of Stoeger Industries, *(Stoeger Pub Co; 0-88317),* 55 Ruta Ct., South Hackensack, NJ 07606 (SAN 206-118X) Tel 201-440-2700; Toll free: 800-631-0723; *CIP.*

Stokes Publishing Co., *(Stokes; 0-914534),* 1125 Robin Way, Suite E, Sunnyvale, CA 94087 (SAN 206-5789) Tel 408-736-4637.

Stokesville Publishing Co., *(Stokesville Pub; 0-936030),* P.O. Box 14401, Atlanta, GA 30324 (SAN 211-3333) Tel 404-261-5316.

Names

Names

Stoma Pr., Inc., *(Stoma Pr; 0-89939),* 13231 42nd Ave., NE., Seattle, WA 98125 (SAN 222-8432).

Stone, Martha Jane, *(Martha J Stone; 0-9617084),* 810 Cramer Ave., Lexington, KY 40502 (SAN 662-6335) Tel 606-266-5030.

Stone, Michael B., *(M B Stone; 0-9603448),* 8434 55th Ave., S., Seattle, WA 98118 (SAN 213-5973).

Stone, Robert H., *(R H Stone; 0-9609192),* 1439 S. Kansas, Springfield, MO 65807 (SAN 264-4169).

Stone, Sarah Howard, Inc., *(S H Stone; 0-937773),* Rte. 2, Box 315, Old Selma Rd., Montgomery, AL 36108 (SAN 659-3445) Tel 205-262-7154.

Stone Age Pr. of Alaska, *(Stone Age Pr; 0-9615808),* 1649 Bannister Dr., Anchorage, AK 99508 (SAN 696-5938) Tel 907-279-3740.

Stone Canyon Pr., *(Stone Canyon Pr; 0-937641),* 10635 Stone Canyon Rd., Dallas, TX 75230 (SAN 659-1884) Tel 214-360-9848.

Stone Country Pr., *(Stone Country; 0-930020),* P.O. Box 132, Menemsha, MA 02522 (SAN 209-7788) Tel 617-693-5832.

Stone Hse. Pr., *(Stone Hse Pr; 0-937035),* P.O. Box 196, Roslyn, NY 11576 (SAN 658-7062) Tel 516-621-7145; 35 Post Dr., Roslyn Harbor, NY 11576 (SAN 658-7070). Do not confuse with with Stone House Pr., Fairfax VT.

Stone Man Pr., *(Stone Man Pr; 0-914473),* Lubec, ME 04652 (SAN 289-6826) Tel 207-733-2194.

Stone-Marrow Press, *(Stone-Marrow Pr),* P.O. Box 1157, Anacortes, WA 98221 (SAN 203-3429).

Stone Pr., *(Stone Pr CA; 0-916889),* 6800 Pacific View Dr., Los Angeles, CA 90068 (SAN 656-0377) Tel 213-876-3054.

Stone St. Pr., The, *(Stone St Pr; 0-943984),* 1 Stone St., Staten Island, NY 10304 (SAN 219-8185) Tel 718-447-1436.

Stone Trail Pr., *(Stone Trail Pr; 0-932123),* P.O. Box 34320, Bethesda, MD 20817 (SAN 686-5259) Tel 301-365-2238.

†**Stone Wall Pr., Inc.,** *(Stone Wall Pr; 0-913276),* 1241 30th St. NW, Washington, DC 20007 (SAN 203-3402) Tel 202-333-1860; Dist. by: Independent Pubs. Group, 1 Pleasant Ave., Port Washington, NY 11050 (SAN 287-2544); *CIP.*

Stoneback, Jean, Publishing Co., *(Stoneback Pub; 0-931440),* 588 Franklin St., Alburtis, PA 18011 (SAN 222-8440).

Stonecrest Pr., *(Stonecrest Pr; 0-9616004),* P.O. Box 5927, Napa, CA 94558 (SAN 699-7643) Tel 707-255-8702.

Stonegate Publishing, *(Stonegate Pub),* P.O. Box 4853, Topeka, KS 66604 (SAN 291-8528).

Stoneground Publishing, *(Stoneground Pub; 0-933145),* 127 Piedra Loop, Los Alamos, NM 87544 (SAN 692-3380) Tel 505-672-9310.

Stonehaven Pubs., *(Stonehaven Pubs; 0-937775),* Box 367, Lena, IL 61048 (SAN 659-347X); 602 Oak St., Lena, IL 61048 (SAN 659-3488) Tel 815-369-2823.

Stonehill Pr., *(Stonehill Pr; 0-937167),* 24-B Bigelow St., Cambridge, MA 02139 (SAN 658-5108) Tel 617-723-8300; Orders to: Stonehill Press, P.O. Box 1362, Boston, MA 02104 (SAN 662-4103) Tel 617-497-9577.

Stonehouse Pubns., *(Stonehouse; 0-9603236),* Sweet, ID 83670 (SAN 206-1058).

Stoneridge Institute of Politico-Socio-Economics Press, *(Stoneridge Inst; 0-937300),* 7703 Baltimore National Pike, Frederick, MD 21701 (SAN 215-112X) Tel 301-473-8287.

Stoneridge Publishing, *(Stoneridge Pub; 0-938767),* P.O. Box 1495, Pleasanton, CA 94566 (SAN 661-7778); 6000 Stoneridge Mall Rd., Suite 390, Pleasanton, CA 94566 (SAN 661-7786) Tel 415-462-3470.

Stoney Brook Publishing Co., *(Stoney Brook; 0-912928),* 186 Main St. W., Chelmsford, MA 01863 (SAN 204-6423).

Stoneydale Pr. Publishing Co., *(Stoneydale Pr Pub; 0-912299),* 304 Main St., P.O. Drawer B, Stevensville, MT 59870 (SAN 265-3168) Tel 406-777-2729.

Stony Brook Press, *(Stony Brook Pr; 0-9603726),* Box 158A, St. James, NY 11780 (SAN 209-5955) Tel 516-862-9296.

Stony Point Pubns., *(Stony Point Pubns; 0-931293),* P.O. Box 4467, Petaluma, CA 94953 (SAN 682-0220) Tel 707-778-8754.

Storey Communications, Inc., *(Storey Comm Inc; 0-88266),* Schoolhouse Rd., Pownal, VT 05261 (SAN 203-4158) Tel 802-823-5811; Toll free: 800-441-5700; Dist. by: Harper & Row Pubs., 10 E. 53rd St., New York, NY 10022 (SAN 200-2086) Tel 212-207-7099. *Imprints:* Garden Way Publishing (Garden Way Pub); Storey Publishing (Storey Pub).

Storey Publishing *See* **Storey Communications, Inc.**

Storie/McOwen Pubs., Inc., *(Storie McOwen; 0-912367),* P.O. Box 308, Manteo, NC 27954 (SAN 265-0940) Tel 919-473-5881.

Stories from Westport's Past, Div. of Joanna Foster Assocs., *(Stories Westports Past; 0-9615410),* 32 Narrow Rocks Rd., Westport, CT 06880 (SAN 695-5142) Tel 203-226-0397.

Storm King Pr., *(Storm King Pr; 0-935166),* P.O. Box 3566, Washington, DC 20007 (SAN 213-6988) Tel 202-944-4224.

Storm Mountain Pubs., Subs. of LTM Design, *(Storm Mtn Pubs; 0-939167),* 8791 Wolff Ct., Suite 200, Westminister, CO 80030 (SAN 662-8540) Tel 303-426-1671.

Stormline Pr., Inc., *(Stormline Pr; 0-935153),* P.O. Box 593, Urbana, IL 61801 (SAN 695-3506); 403 E. Washington St., Urbana, IL 61801 (SAN 662-3476) Tel 217-328-2665.

†**Story Hse. Corp.,** *(Story Hse Corp; 0-87157),* Bindery Ln., Charlotteville, NY 12036 (SAN 169-5193) Tel 607-397-8725; Toll free: 800-428-1008 (NY State); Toll free: 800-847-2105 (Outside NY); *CIP.*

Story Line Pr., *(Story Line; 0-934257),* c/o The Reaper, 325 Ocean View Ave., Santa Cruz, CA 95062 (SAN 693-3289) Tel 408-426-5539.

†**Story Press,** *(Story Pr; 0-931704),* P.O. Box 10040, Chicago, IL 60610 (SAN 212-6982) Tel 312-246-1064; *CIP.*

Story-to-Color *See* **Stemmer Hse. Pub., Inc.**

Storypole Pr., *(Storypole; 0-9609940),* 11015 Bingham Ave., E., Tacoma, WA 98446 (SAN 275-8199) Tel 206-531-2032.

Storyviews Publishing Co., *(Storyviews Pub; 0-9617057),* 136 E. 55th St., New York, NY 10022 (SAN 662-8354) Tel 212-751-7307; Dist. by: Bookazine Co., 303 W. 10th St., New York, NY 10014 (SAN 169-5665) Tel 212-675-8877.

Stough Institute, Inc., The, *(Stough Inst; 0-940830),* 54 W. 16th St., New York, NY 10011 (SAN 219-8193).

†**Stowe-Day Foundation,** *(Stowe-Day; 0-917482),* 77 Forest St., Hartford, CT 06105 (SAN 209-052X) Tel 203-522-9258; *CIP.*

Strafford Pubns., Inc., *(Strafford Pubns; 0-9616858),* 1375 Peachtree St., NE, No. 260, Atlanta, GA 30367 (SAN 661-5953) Tel 404-881-1141.

Stragetic Moves, Div. of Strategic Corporation, The, *(Strategic Moves; 0-915375),* 2188 SW Park Place, Portland, OR 97205 (SAN 291-4476) Tel 503-222-9028; Toll free: 800-992-2911 (Oregon only); Toll free: Y.

Strahm, Virgil, *(Strahm; 0-9606050),* P.O. Box 900, Branson, MO 65616 (SAN 216-9347) Tel 417-334-4381.

Straight Arrow Pubs., *(Straight Pubs; 0-9613653),* P.O. Box 1236, Los Altos, CA 94023 (SAN 670-7785) Tel 415-949-5243; Dist. by: Mustang Publishing, P.O. Box 9327, New Haven, CT 06533 (SAN 289-6702) Tel 203-624-5485.

Straight Street Publishing, Inc., *(Straight St Pub; 0-936309),* 1500 NW Seventh Ct., Miami, FL 33136 (SAN 697-3221) Tel 305-326-8966.

Strain, Robert W., Publishing, Inc., *(R W Strain; 0-939727),* P.O. Box 1000, Wingdale, NY 12594 (SAN 663-4540) Tel 914-832-9384.

Strang Communications Co., *(Strang Comms Co; 0-930525),* 190 N. Westmonte Dr., Altamonte Springs, FL 32714 (SAN 677-5640) Tel 305-869-5005.

Strategic Assessments, Inc., *(Strategic Assessments; 0-915669),* P.O. Box 8005-265, Boulder, CO 80306 (SAN 292-6873) Tel 303-444-1343.

Strategic Learning Systems, *(Strategic Systs; 0-937037),* 18-15 215th St., Suite 2S, Bayside, NY 11360 (SAN 658-5094) Tel 718-631-1453.

Stratford Hse. Publishing Co., *(Stratford Hse; 0-938614),* 5761 Whitnall Highway, Suite 202, North Hollywood, CA 91601 (SAN 216-1893); Orders to: P.O. Box 7077, Burbank, CA 91510 (SAN 669-2753) Tel 818-761-5752.

Stratford Pubns., Inc., *(Stratford Pubns; 0-941568),* 8614 Camden St., Alexandria, VA 22308 (SAN 239-3204) Tel 703-780-4104.

Strathcona Publishing Co., *(Strathcona; 0-931554),* 77 Bleecker St., New York, NY 10012 (SAN 211-4550) Tel 212-505-2546.

Stratmar Educational Systems, Inc., *(Stratmar Ed Sys; 0-935465),* 109 Willett Ave., Port Chester, NY 10573 (SAN 695-8621) Tel 914-937-7171.

Straub Printing & Publishing, *(Straub Printing; 0-9609036),* 4535 Union Bay Place NE, Seattle, WA 98105 (SAN 676-9977).

Straughan's Book Shop, Inc., *(Straughan; 0-911452),* 2168 Lawndale Dr., Greensboro, NC 27408 (SAN 206-9555) Tel 919-273-1214.

Strauss, Daniel, *(D Strauss; 0-9608338),* 2870 Grand Concourse, Bronx, NY 10458 (SAN 240-4478) Tel 212-369-0500.

Strauss, Mary Miller, *(M M Strauss; 0-9616837),* P.O. Box 145, Accident, MD 21520 (SAN 661-4663) Tel 301-826-8183.

†**Stravon Educational Pr.,** Subs. of Stravon Pubs., Inc., *(Stravon; 0-87396),* 845 Third Ave., New York, NY 10022 (SAN 202-7402) Tel 212-371-2880; *CIP.*

Strawberry Hill Pr., *(Strawberry Hill; 0-89407),* 2594 15th Ave., San Francisco, CA 94127 (SAN 238-8103) Tel 415-664-8112.

Strawberry Patchworks, *(Straw Patchwork; 0-9608428),* 11597 Southington Ln., Herndon, VA 22070 (SAN 240-7809) Tel 703-481-1225.

Strawberry Pr., *(Strawberry Pr NY; 0-936574),* P.O. Box 451, Bowling Green Sta., New York, NY 10004 (SAN 215-9198).

Strawberry Valley Press, *(Strawberry Valley; 0-913612),* P.O. Box 157, Idyllwild, CA 92349 (SAN 202-7410) Tel 714-659-2145.

Stream Stalker Publishing Co., Div. of Stream Stalker, Inc., *(Stream Stalker; 0-9614704),* Box 1010, Aspen, CO 81612 (SAN 692-6134) Tel 303-925-3474.

Streamline Publishing Co., *(Streamline Pub; 0-938457),* 822 N. Court St., Ottumwa, IA 52501 (SAN 660-9813) Tel 515-683-3553.

Streamline Software Systems, Inc., *(Streamline Soft; 0-939333),* 14 Perimeter Ctr. E., Suite 1406, Atlanta, GA 30346 (SAN 662-7919) Tel 404-392-9500.

Street Editions, *(St Edns; 0-935694),* 20 Desbrosses St., New York, NY 10013 (SAN 282-373X).

Street Pr., *(Street Pr; 0-935252; 0-913433),* Box 555, Port Jefferson, NY 11777 (SAN 207-9046) Tel 516-821-0678. *Imprints:* Everett Press (Everett Pr).

Street Sense Pubns., *(Street Sense Pubns; 0-9616712),* 69 Lakewood Dr., Mineral City, OH 44656 (SAN 659-8919) Tel 216-343-4335.

StressPress, *(StressPress; 0-9613102),* P.O. Box 474, Putney, VT 05346 (SAN 294-1058) Tel 802-257-9468.

Stretching Inc., *(Stretching Inc; 0-9601066),* P.O. Box 767, Palmer Lake, CO 80133 (SAN 208-1334) Tel 714-525-5004.

Strether & Swann, *(Strether & Swann; 0-931522),* 1309 Seventh St., New Orleans, LA 70115 (SAN 211-9811).

Strider Software, *(Str Software; 0-936921),* Beecher Lake Rd., Pembine, WI 54156 (SAN 658-3776) Tel 715-324-5487.

Strine Publishing Co., *(Strine Pub Co; 0-9613972),* I-83 Industrial Park, P.O. Box 149, York, PA 17405 (SAN 683-4396).

Strode Communications, Inc., *(Strode Comm; 0-942894),* 300 W. Wieuca Rd. NE, Suite 215, Atlanta, GA 30342 (SAN 240-8260) Tel 404-256-6401.

Strode Pubs., *(Strode; 0-87397),* P.O. Box 626, Tomball, TX 77375 (SAN 202-7429) Tel 713-320-9141.

Stroker Press, *(Stroker; 0-918154),* 129 Second Ave., No. 3, New York, NY 10003 (SAN 209-6811).

Stronghold Press, *(Stronghold Pr; 0-910429),* Box 2337, Bismarck, ND 58502 (SAN 260-1435) Tel 701-258-6201.

Stroock, Paul A., *(P A Stroock; 0-9601138),* 35 Middle Lane, P.O. Box 126, Jericho, NY 11753 (SAN 210-2765) Tel 516-433-9018.

Stropes Editions, Ltd., *(Stropes Editions; 0-9608512),* Dist. by: Thoth Corp., P.O. Box 92413, Milwaukee, WI 53202 (SAN 275-8245).

Strunk, J. H., *(J H Strunk; 0-9613943),* 100 Wakefield Terr, RD 2, Box 262, Mansfield, PA 16933 (SAN 687-7508).

Stryker, William Norman, *(W N Stryker; 0-9602936),* 3804 Adrienne Dr., Alexandria, VA 22309 (SAN 212-7989).

Stryker-Post Pubns., *(Stryker-Post; 0-943448),* 888 17th St., NW, Washington, DC 20006 (SAN 204-6431) Tel 202-298-9233.

Stuart, C. E., Gnathological Instruments, *(C E Stuart; 0-9613441),* P.O. Box 1298, Ventura, CA 93001 (SAN 657-0771) Tel 805-647-1478.

Stuart, J., Publishing Co., *(Stuart Pub; 0-939232),* 14342 Rutherford Ave., Detroit, MI 48227 (SAN 216-4574).

†**Stuart, Lyle, Inc.,** Div. of Citadel, *(Lyle Stuart; 0-8184),* 120 Enterprise Ave., Secaucus, NJ 07094 (SAN 201-1131) Tel 201-866-0490; Toll free: 800-LS-BOOKS; *CIP.*

Stuart & Day Publishing Co., Inc., *(Stuart & Day Pub; 0-941436),* P.O. Box 25001, Colorado Springs, CO 80936 (SAN 239-0388) Tel 303-598-8322.

Stuart Books, *(Stuart Bks; 0-9608716),* P.O. Box 460081, Garland, TX 75046 (SAN 241-1547).

Stubs Pubns., *(Stubs; 0-911458),* 234 W. 44th St., New York, NY 10036 (SAN 202-7445) Tel 212-398-8370; Toll free: 800-223-7565; Dist. by: Hagstrom Co., 46-35 54th Rd., Maspeth, NY 11378 (SAN 203-543X) Tel 718-784-0055.

Student Assn. Pr., *(Student Assn; 0-931118),* 1000 Chervy Rd., Memphis, TN 38117 (SAN 212-5676) Tel 901-761-1353.

Student College Aid, *(Student Coll; 0-932495),* 3641 Deal St., Houston, TX 77025 (SAN 687-4320) Tel 713-668-7899.

Student Editors Association, *(Student Ed Assoc; 0-910127),* 504 S. Wheaton Ave., Wheaton, IL 60187 (SAN 241-4813) Tel 312-668-8690.

Student Press Law Center Incorporated, *(Student Pr Law),* 1033 30th St., NW, Washington, DC 20007 (SAN 226-3831).

Student Success, *(Student Success; 0-9615809),* 16798 Woodridge Cir., Fountain Valley, CA 92708 (SAN 696-5946) Tel 714-964-8845.

Studeophile Pubs., *(Studeophile Pub; 0-933569),* P.O. Box 2863, Des Plaines, IL 60018 (SAN 691-9049) Tel 312-694-2700.

Studia Hispanica Editors, *(Studia Hispanica; 0-934840),* P.O. Box 7304, University Sta., Austin, TX 78713 (SAN 214-1639) Tel 512-471-9113.

Studia Slovenica, Inc., *(Studia Slovenica; 0-938616),* P.O. Box 232, New York, NY 10032 (SAN 213-6996).

Studio Bks. *See* Viking-Penguin, Inc.

Studio J Publishing, Inc., *(Studio J Pub; 0-940002),* 274 North St., Ridgefield, CT 06877 (SAN 216-7808) Tel 203-438-7826.

Studio Pr., Ltd., *(Studio Pr; 0-9615598),* 901 Warburton Rd., Elkton, MD 21921 (SAN 696-1738).

Studio Workshop Pr., *(Studio Workshop Pr; 0-9616269),* 66 Noah's Path, Rocky Point, NY 11778 (SAN 658-3164).

Studios West Pubns., *(Studios West; 0-939656),* 167 Saxony Rd., Encinitas, CA 92024 (SAN 216-6461) Tel 619-753-8186.

Study Buddy Books *See* Dahlstrom & Co., Inc.

Stugallz, *(Stugallz; 0-9610702),* 339 N. Virgil Ave., Los Angeles, CA 90004 (SAN 264-7982) Tel 213-661-8968.

Stump, William C., *(W C Stump; 0-9613487),* 108 Mapother St., Loyall, KY 40854 (SAN 657-3894) Tel 606-573-6868.

Stureck Educational Services, *(Stureck Ed Serv; 0-933471),* P.O. Box 12165, Boulder, CO 80302 (SAN 691-8794) Tel 303-442-5585.

Sturge, Judi, *(J Sturge),* 18 Lodge Pole Rd., Pittsford, NY 14534 (SAN 211-7622).

Sturges Publishing Co., *(Sturges Pub; 0-936373),* 300 Alexander Pk., Princeton, NJ 08540 (SAN 698-0228) Tel 609-452-7333.

Sturzebecker, R. L., *(Sturzebecker; 0-9600466),* 503 Owen Rd., West Chester, PA 19380 (SAN 206-1228) Tel 215-696-4590.

Stuttman, H. S., Inc., *(Stuttman; 0-87475),* 333 Post Rd. W., Westport, CT 06889 (SAN 202-7453) Tel 203-226-7841.

Style Pubns., *(Style Pubns; 0-9616246),* 808 Post St., Suite 615, San Francisco, CA 94109 (SAN 658-6910) Tel 415-357-0148.

StyleWare, Inc., *(StyleWare; 0-939677),* 5250 Gulfton, Suite 2E, Houston, TX 77081 (SAN 663-0650) Tel 713-668-1360.

Subar Pubns., *(Subar Pubns; 0-939411),* 2118 Payton Cir., Colorado Springs, CO 80915 (SAN 663-1673) Tel 303-597-8781.

Subs. of Amer. Econo-Clad Services *See* **Crawford Press**

Substance of Faith Ministries, *(Substance Faith; 0-937357),* 221 W. North Ave., Flora, IL 62839 (SAN 659-1892) Tel 618-662-7711.

Success Advertising & Publishing, *(Success Ad; 0-931113),* 10258 Riverside Dr., Palm Beach Gardens, FL 33410 (SAN 678-9501) Tel 305-626-4643.

Success Foundation, Inc., The, *(Success Found; 0-913200),* P.O. Box 6302, Louisville, KY 40206 (SAN 208-1261) Tel 502-893-3038.

Success Now, Inc., *(Success Now; 0-912545),* P.O. Box 32578, Tucson, AZ 85751 (SAN 265-220X) Tel 602-298-9129.

Success Press, *(Success Pr; 0-9607858),* 3700 First Ave. NE, Cedar Rapids, IA 52402 (SAN 238-1176) Tel 319-366-0767.

Success Unlimited, *(Success Unltd; 0-918448),* 401 N. Wabash, Chicago, IL 60611 (SAN 209-2867) Tel 312-828-9500.

Successful Living Pr., *(Successful Living; 0-937743),* P.O. Box 163482, Sacramento, CA 95818 (SAN 659-3526) Tel 916-927-7942; 727 56th St., Sacramento, CA 95818 (SAN 659-3534).

Sudden Jungle Pr., *(Sudden Jungle Pr; 0-937567),* P.O. Box 310, Colorado Springs, CO 80901 (SAN 659-1906) Tel 303-632-6199; 1615 N. Nevada Ave., Colorado Springs, CO 80947 (SAN 659-1914).

Sue Ann, *(Sue Ann; 0-9604172),* Box 2, North Haven, CT 06473 (SAN 215-1138) Tel 203-288-1913.

Suffolk County Historical Society, *(Suffolk Cnty Hist Soc; 0-938769),* 300 W. Main St., Riverhead, NY 11901 (SAN 661-552X) Tel 516-727-2881.

Suffolk House, *(Suffolk Hse; 0-936066),* 155 E. Main St., Smithtown, NY 11787 (SAN 216-4582).

Sufi Islamia/Prophecy Pubns., *(Sufi Islamia-Prophecy; 0-915424),* 65 Norwich St., San Francisco, CA 94110 (SAN 282-3748) Tel 415-285-0562. *Imprints:* Prophecy Pressworks (Prophecy Pressworks).

Sugar Marbel Press, *(Sugar Marbel Pr; 0-9608320),* 1547 Shenandoah Ave., Cincinnati, OH 45237 (SAN 240-1002) Tel 513-761-8000.

Sugarfree Center, Inc., *(Sugarfree),* 13715 Burbank Blvd., P.O. Box 114, Van Nuys, CA 91408 (SAN 241-5836) Tel 818-994-1093.

Sugden, Sherwood, & Co., *(Sugden; 0-89385),* 1117 Eighth St., La Salle, IL 61301 (SAN 210-5659) Tel 815-223-1231; Dist. by: Open Court Publishing Co., 315 Fifth St., Box 599, Peru, IL 61354 (SAN 202-5876) Tel 815-223-2520. *Imprints:* A M D G Press (AMDG Pr).

Suhrkamp/Insel Pubs. Boston,Inc., *(Suhrkamp; 3-458; 3-518),* 380 Green St., Cambridge, MA 02139 (SAN 215-2762) Tel 617-876-2327.

Sukenick, Ronald, *(R Sukenick),* Box 188, Cooper Sta., New York, NY 10003 (SAN 226-4323).

Sullen Art Pr., *(Sullen Art Pr; 0-9616752),* 68 Lowell St., Waltham, MA 02154 (SAN 659-879X) Tel 617-891-8496.

Sullivan, Dorothy, Production, *(Sullivan Prod; 0-9604928),* P.O. Box 7045, St. Petersburg, FL 33734 (SAN 215-9201).

Sullivan, E. M., *(Sullivan; 0-911460),* P.O. Box 5823, Orange, CA 92667 (SAN 204-6458).

Sullivan, Phyllis R., *(P R Sullivan; 0-9615470),* 401 Flinn Ave., Apt. 22, Ravenswood, WV 26164 (SAN 696-1843) Tel 304-273-3692.

Sullwold, William S., Publishing, Inc., *(W S Sullwold; 0-88492),* 18 Pearl St., Taunton, MA 02780 (SAN 203-1744) Tel 617-823-0924.

Sultan of Swat/S.O.S. Books, *(S O S Books; 0-911809),* 1821 Kalorama Rd., NW, Washington, DC 20009 (SAN 264-4193) Tel 202-638-1956.

Sulveri, *(Sulveri; 0-9615545),* Mountain Rte., Box 36, Jemez Springs, NM 87025 (SAN 695-9075) Tel 505-829-3738.

Sumac Press, *(Sumac Mich; 0-912090),* P.O. Box 39, Fremont, MI 49412 (SAN 206-1236) Tel 616-924-3464.

Summa Pubns., *(Summa Pubns; 0-917786),* 3601 Westbury Rd., Birmingham, AL 35223 (SAN 212-0925) Tel 205-967-5724; Orders to: P.O. Box 20725, Birmingham, AL 35216 (SAN 662-0124) Tel 205-822-0463.

Summa Publishing Bureau, Div. of Computer Communications Corp., *(Summa Pub Bur; 0-943960),* 6133 Blue Circle Dr., Minnetonka, MN 55343 (SAN 241-1636).

Summa Publishing Co., *(Summa Pub; 0-932423),* 240 Lombard St., Suite 102, Thousand Oaks, CA 91360 (SAN 687-4096) Tel 805-495-3237.

Summer Institute of Linguistics, Academic Pubns, *(Summer Inst Ling; 0-88312; 1-55671),* 7500 W. Camp Wisdom Rd., Dallas, TX 75236 (SAN 204-6466) Tel 214-298-3331 Tel 214-298-3331.

Summer Stream Pr., *(Summer Stream; 0-932460),* P.O. Box 6056, Santa Barbara, CA 93160 (SAN 212-6990) Tel 805-964-1727; 359 Fort Washington Ave., Suite 4H, New York, NY 10033 (SAN 699-5659) Tel 212-795-3262.

Summertime Press, *(Summertime Pr),* P.O. Box 1555, Murray Hill Sta., New York, NY 10156 (SAN 297-1798).

Summertown Texts, Subs. of Summertown Co., Inc., *(Summertown; 0-9614303),* P.O. Box 453, Signal Mountain, TN 37377-0453 (SAN 687-4908) Tel 615-886-1660.

†**Summit Bks.,** Subs. of Simon & Schuster, *(Summit Bks; 0-671),* 1230 Ave. of the Americas, New York, NY 10020 (SAN 206-1244) Tel 212-246-2471; Toll free: 800-223-2336; *CIP.*

Summit County Chapter O G S, *(Summit Cnty OH),* 410 Bonshire Rd., Akron, OH 44319 (SAN 219-9823) Tel 216-644-8660.

Summit Enterprises, Inc., *(Summit Ent; 0-934174),* 4500 N. 32nd St., Suite 201, Phoenix, AZ 85018 (SAN 213-6465); Toll free: 800-321-5378.

Summit Junior Fortnightly Club, *(Summit Jr Fort; 0-9608052),* 214 Springfield Ave., Summit, NJ 07901 (SAN 238-8650) Tel 201-665-1796.

Summit Lighthouse, The, *(Summit),* Box A, Colorado Springs, CO 80901 (SAN 209-6455).

Summit Pr., *(Summit Pr CO; 0-936163),* P.O. Box 207, Manitou Springs, CO 80829 (SAN 696-7620) Tel 303-685-9103.

Summit Publishing Co., *(Ohio-Summit Pub; 0-9609310),* 1800 Stoney Hill Dr., P.O. Box 303, Hudson, OH 44236 (SAN 241-5844) Tel 216-650-4321.

Summit Univ. Pr., *(Summit Univ; 0-916766),* Box A, Malibu, CA 90265 (SAN 208-4120) Tel 818-991-4751.

Summy-Birchard Music, Div. of Birch Tree Group, Ltd., *(Summy-Birchard; 0-87487),* 180 Alexander Rd., Box 2072, Princeton, NJ 08540 (SAN 202-7461) Tel 609-683-0090. *Imprints:* Suzuki Method International (Suzuki Method).

Sun, H. C., *(H C Sun),* 114 South Fox Road, Sterling, VA 22170 (SAN 210-1386) Tel 703-430-7040.

SUN, *(SUN; 0-915342),* 347 W. 39th St., New York, NY 10018 (SAN 206-3832) Tel 212-594-8428.

Sun & Moon Pr., *(Sun & Moon CA; 0-940650),* P.O. Box 481170, Los Angeles, CA 90048 (SAN 216-3063) Tel 213-653-6711; 6363 Wilshire Blvd., Suite 115, Los Angeles, CA 90048 (SAN 658-179X).

Sun Dance Books, *(Sun Dance Bks; 0-913330),* 1520 N. Crescent Heights, Hollywood, CA 90046 (SAN 204-6474) Tel 213-654-2383; Dist. by: The Borgo Press, P.O. Box 2845, San Bernardino, CA 92406-2845 (SAN 208-9459) Tel 714-884-5813.

Names

Sun Designs, Subs. of Rexstrom Co., Inc., *(Sun Designs; 0-912355),* P.O. Box 206, Delafield, WI 53018 (SAN 265-1181); 36802 Genesee Lake Rd., Oconomowoc, WI 53066 (SAN 265-119X) Tel 414-567-4255; Dist. by: Sterling Publishing Co., Two Park Ave., New York, NY 10016 (SAN 669-3083) Tel 212-532-7160.

Sun Features, Inc., *(Sun Features; 0-937238),* Suite 2C, 7720 El Camino Real, Rancho La Costa, CA 92008 (SAN 282-3764) Tel 619-753-3489; Orders to: Box 368-P, Cardiff, CA 92007 (SAN 282-3772) Tel 619-753-3489.

SUN/Gemini Pr., *(Sun-Gemini Pr; 0-933313),* P.O. Box 42170, Tucson, AZ 85733 (SAN 692-3747) Tel 602-299-1097.

Sun Life, *(Sun Life; 0-937930),* Greystone, Thaxton, VA 24174 (SAN 240-8333) Tel 703-586-4898.

Sun Litho-Print/Frazetta Prints, *(Sun Litho Frazetta; 0-9607060),* P.O. Box R, Marshall Creek, PA 18335 (SAN 239-0396) Tel 717-424-2692.

Sun, Man, Moon, Inc., *(Sun Man Moon; 0-917738),* 4891 Pearce St. No. 1, Huntington Beach, CA 92649 (SAN 210-3745) Tel 714-840-9192; Orders to: P.O. Box 5084, Huntington Beach, CA 92646 (SAN 662-1554).

Sun Pr. of Florida, *(Sun Pr FL; 0-937039),* 35 Trotters Cir., Kissimmee, FL 32743 (SAN 658-702X) Tel 305-933-1586.

Sun Publishing Co., *(Sun Pub; 0-914172; 0-89540),* P.O. Box 5588, Santa Fe, NM 87502-5588 (SAN 206-1325) Tel 505-988-2033.

Sun Publishing, Inc., *(Sun Pub GA; 0-942970),* P.O. Box 450776, Atlanta, GA 30345 (SAN 238-8669).

Sun Ray Publishing Co., *(Sun Ray Pub; 0-9614244),* 27885 SE Sun Ray Dr., Boring, OR 97009 (SAN 686-7014) Tel 503-663-3228.

Sun-Scape Pubns., *(Sun-Scape Pubns; 0-919842),* P.O. Box 42725, Tucson, AZ 85733 (SAN 211-870X) Tel 602-744-0257.

Sun Scope Publishing Co., *(Sun Scope; 0-9609188),* 9 Sunrise Rd., Danbury, CT 06810 (SAN 241-4635) Tel 203-743-6943.

Sun Seeker Bks., *(Sun Seeker Bks; 0-9614662),* P.O. Box 4246, Clearlake, CA 95422 (SAN 692-4751) Tel 707-994-9161.

Sun Star Pubns., *(Sun Star Pubns; 0-937787),* P.O. Box 519, Phoenix, AZ 85016 (SAN 659-3550) Tel 602-948-4346; 3104 E. Camelback Rd., Phoenix, AZ 85016 (SAN 659-3569).

Sun Tracks, *(Sun Tracks; 0-936350),* Univ. of Arizona, Dept. of English, Tucson, AZ 85721 (SAN 214-2007).

Sun Valley Book, *(Sun Valley; 0-9605212),* P.O. Box 1688, Sun Valley, ID 83353 (SAN 240-8406).

Sun Valley Publishing, *(Sun Valley Pub; 0-915803),* P.O. Box 1081, Ketchum, ID 83340 (SAN 294-1333) Tel 208-726-9685.

Sunbank Publishing Co., *(Sunbank Pub Co; 0-9616190),* 3100 Damon Way, Burbank, CA 91504 (SAN 699-928X) Tel 213-849-1191.

Sunbeam Books, *(Sunbeam Bks; 0-916433),* 23650 Old Owen Rd., Monroe, WA 98272 (SAN 296-0036).

Sunbeam Pubns., *(Sunbeam; 0-9609514),* 780 N. 2250 W., Provo, UT 84601 (SAN 262-0928) Tel 801-374-6987.

†**Sunbelt Pubns.,** *(Sunbelt Pubns; 0-932653),* P.O. Box 191126, San Diego, CA 92119 (SAN 687-8407) Tel 619-697-4811; *CIP.*

Sunbelt Publishing Co., *(Sunbelt Pub Co; 0-9616247),* 6833 Lemon Rd., McLean, VA 22101 (SAN 658-6953) Tel 703-821-3195.

Sunberry Books, *(Sunberry Bks; 0-9613151),* P.O. Box 697, West Acton, MA 01720 (SAN 283-4294).

Sunbow Pubns., *(Sunbow Pubns; 0-9615610),* P.O. Box 8936, Detroit, MI 48224 (SAN 695-8869) Tel 313-882-2269; 10718 Marne, Detroit, MI 48224 (SAN 699-6124).

†**SunBox Press,** *(SunBox; 0-930052),* 750 Alta Vista Way, Laguna Beach, CA 92651 (SAN 210-511X) Tel 714-494-2203; *CIP.*

Sunbright Books *See* **Melek, Jacques**

Sunburst, *(Sunburst; 0-9609618),* P.O. Box 1433, Tacoma, WA 98401 (SAN 275-8571) Tel 206-565-2041.

Sunburst *See* **Sunburst Publishing**

Sunburst Bks. *See* **Farrar, Straus & Giroux, Inc.**

Sunburst Communications, Inc., *(Sunburst Comm; 0-911831; 1-55636),* 39 Washington Ave., Pleasantville, NY 10570 (SAN 213-5620) Tel 914-769-5030; Toll free: 800-431-1934.

Sunburst Pr., *(Sunburst Pr; 0-934648),* P.O. Box 14205, Portland, OR 97214 (SAN 206-3840).

Sunburst Pr., *(Sunburst Pr CA; 0-9615673),* P.O. Box 3129, Pacoima, CA 91333-3129 (SAN 695-9512); 13024 Sunburst St., Pacoima, CA 91331 (SAN 699-6140) Tel 818-899-0818.

Sunburst Publishing, *(Sunburst Pub; 0-9614865),* P.O. Box 11671, Zephyr Cove, NV 89448 (SAN 693-286X) Tel 916-544-1346; Dist. by: Bookpeople, 2929 Fifth St., Berkeley, CA 94710 (SAN 168-9517) Tel 415-549-3030; Toll free: 800-227-1516. *Imprints:* Sunburst (Sunburst).

Suncoast Professional Publishing Corp., *(Suncoast Prof Pub; 0-937569),* 8800 49th St., N., Suite 102, Pinellas Park, FL 33565 (SAN 659-1922) Tel 813-545-1327.

Sundance Books *See* **Sundance Pubns., Ltd.**

Sundance Pubns., Ltd., *(Sundance; 0-913582),* 250 Broadway, Denver, CO 80203 (SAN 203-0721) Tel 303-777-2880.

Sundance Publishing Co., *(Sundance OR; 0-942822),* P.O. Box 604, Salem, OR 97308 (SAN 240-2858) Tel 503-378-0465.

Sundance/Venture Resources, Div. of Sundance West, Inc., *(Sundance Vent; 0-935389),* 7515 Cabrillo Ave., La Jolla, CA 92037 (SAN 696-1045); P.O. Box 1396, La Jolla, CA 92038 (SAN 699-6248) Tel 619-454-4700.

Sunday Edition, The, *(Sunday Edition; 0-932655),* P.O. Box 312, Tiburon, CA 94920 (SAN 687-8415) Tel 415-388-1298.

Sunday Paper, The, *(Sunday Paper; 0-9614022),* 188 Willow St., New Haven, CT 06511 (SAN 683-6259) Tel 203-624-2520.

Sunday Pubns., Inc., *(Sunday Pubns; 0-941850),* 1937 10th Ave. N., Lake Worth, FL 33461 (SAN 239-3220) Tel 305-533-0990.

Sunday School Publishing Board, *(Sunday School; 0-910683),* 330 Charlotte Ave., Nashville, TN 37201 (SAN 275-8598) Tel 615-256-0856.

Sundial Books *See* **Sunstone Pr., The**

Sundog Pr., *(Sundog Pr; 0-9603640),* P. O. Box 111022, Anchorage, AK 99511 (SAN 221-699X).

Sundown *See* **New Readers Pr.**

Sundowner Services, *(Sundowner Serv; 0-932241),* 2559-47th Ave., San Francisco, CA 94116 (SAN 215-9228) Tel 415-564-0068.

Sundstrom, Jessie Y., *(J Y Sundstrom; 0-936281),* P.O. Box 528, Custer, SD 57730 (SAN 699-7651) Tel 605-673-4377.

Sunfire *See* **Scholastic, Inc.**

Sunfisher Books, *(Sunfisher Bks; 0-915413),* 105 Upper Sunset, Sonora, CA 95370 (SAN 683-4361); Dist. by: Baker & Taylor Co., Western Div., 380 Edison Way, Reno, NV 89502 (SAN 169-4464) Tel 206-872-5523.

Sunflower Bks. *See* **Smith, W. H., Pubs., Inc.**

Sunflower Ink, *(Sunflower Ink; 0-931104),* Palo Colorado Canyon, Carmel, CA 93923 (SAN 212-9728) Tel 408-625-0588.

Sunflower Univ. Pr., *(Sunflower U Pr; 0-89745),* 1531 Yuma, Manhattan, KS 66502-4228 (SAN 218-5075); 1531 Yuma, Manhattan, KS 66502-4228 (SAN 658-1811) Tel 913-532-6733.

Sunkist House, *(Sunkist Hse; 0-9614705),* 196 Sunkist, Los Altos, CA 94022 (SAN 692-6142) Tel 415-948-3594.

Sunlakes Publishing Co., *(Sunlakes Pub; 0-9615884),* 4153 Bayard Rd., South Euclid, OH 44121 (SAN 696-7663) Tel 216-951-9100.

Sunland Publishing, *(Sunland Pub; 0-915621),* Rancho Don Carmel, P.O. Box 27552, Rancho Bernardo, CA 92128 (SAN 292-6903) Tel 619-746-5800.

SunMoon Press, *(SunMoon Pr; 0-942064),* P.O. Box 1516, Eugene, OR 97440 (SAN 238-4825) Tel 503-343-9544.

Sunnycrest Publishing, *(Sunnycrest Pub; 0-9610012),* Rte. 1, Box 1, Clements, MN 56224 (SAN 264-424X) Tel 507-692-2246.

Sunnyside Publishing Co., *(Sunnyside; 0-934650),* Box 29, 51 Willow St., Lynn, MA 01903 (SAN 213-1757) Tel 617-595-4742.

Sunnyvale Marketing, *(Sunnyvale Mkting; 0-941662),* 2627 19th St., Rockford, IL 61109 (SAN 239-3239) Tel 815-397-3344.

Sunnyvale Psychotherapy, *(Sunnyvale Psy; 0-9615762),* 783 Steuben Dr., Sunnyvale, CA 94087 (SAN 695-9687) Tel 408-245-2677.

Sunrise Artistries, Inc., *(Sunrise Artistries; 0-936519),* 64-24 Grand Ave., Maspeth, NY 11378 (SAN 698-0252) Tel 718-894-7683; Orders to: Sunrise Artistries, Inc., Box 125, Maspeth, NY 11378 (SAN 662-3964).

Sunrise Christian Bks., *(Sunrise Chr Bks; 0-940652),* c/o One Way, Ltd., 1707 "E" St., Eureka, CA 95501 (SAN 211-8254) Tel 707-442-4004.

SunRise House, *(SunRise Hse; 0-915764),* P.O. Box 217, Longwood, FL 32750 (SAN 216-6529) Tel 305-830-7333.

Sunrise Museums, Inc., *(Sunrise Museums; 0-9607962),* 746 Myrtle Rd., Charleston, WV 25314 (SAN 241-5852) Tel 304-344-8035.

Sunrise Press, *(Sunrise Pr; 0-9606896),* 4984 Arboleda Dr., Fair Oaks, CA 95628 (SAN 237-9953) Tel 916-961-5551.

Sunrise Press, *(Sunrise Pr IL; 0-935800),* 2004 Grant St., Evanston, IL 60201 (SAN 215-286X) Tel 312-475-3651.

Sunrise Pubns., *(Sunrise Texas; 0-937789),* P.O. Box 34512, San Antonio, TX 78265 (SAN 659-3585) Tel 512-656-2055; 14502 Waddesdon Bluff, San Antonio, TX 78233 (SAN 659-3593).

Sunrise Publications *See* **Melek, Jacques**

Sunrise Publications (CO), *(Sunrise Publ; 0-9614786),* P.O. Box 5075, Littleton, CO 80123 (SAN 692-9907) Tel 303-979-6096.

Sunrise Publishing, *(Sunrise Pub OR; 0-9604344),* P.O. Box 38, Lincoln City, OR 97367 (SAN 215-1871) Tel 503-994-6723.

Sunrise Publishing Co. Inc., *(Sunrise Pub NY; 0-934401),* P.O. Box 408, New York, NY 10019 (SAN 693-4269) Tel 212-541-7143; Orders to: Sunrise Pub., 170 NE 33rd St., Ft. Lauderdale, FL 33334 (SAN 662-3220) Tel 305-563-1844.

Sunrise Publishing House, *(Sunrise Pub Hse; 0-9607672),* 12021 Wilshire Blvd., Suite 225, Los Angeles, CA 90025 (SAN 240-1010).

Sunrise Tortoise Books, *(Sunrise Tortoise; 0-932222),* Box 61, Sandpoint, ID 83864 (SAN 212-5684).

Sunrise Ventures, *(Sunrise Vent; 0-9615674),* 708 Parkman Dr., Bloomfield Hills, MI 48013 (SAN 696-1428) Tel 313-645-6741.

Sunset Bks./Lane Publishing Co., *(Sunset-Lane; 0-376),* 80 Willow Rd., Menlo Park, CA 94025 (SAN 201-0658) Tel 415-321-3600; Toll free: 800-227-7346; 1320 Willow Rd., Menlo Park, CA 94025 (SAN 658-182X).

Sunset Pubns., *(Sunset Pubns HI; 0-9601256; 0-941244),* 1655 Makaloa St., Suite 906, Honolulu, HI 96814 (SAN 215-1146).

Sunset Video, Inc., *(Sunset Video; 0-936155),* 2210 Wilshire Blvd., Suite 542, Santa Monica, CA 90403 (SAN 696-7639) Tel 213-459-5826.

SunShine, *(SunShine; 0-937710),* Box 4351, Austin, TX 78765 (SAN 220-0945) Tel 512-453-2334.

Sunshine Academic Press, Inc., *(Sunshine Acad; 0-933064),* 304 27th St., West Palm Beach, FL 33407 (SAN 212-4602).

Sunshine Arts, *(Sunshine Arts WA; 0-938244),* W. 1018 Shannon, Spokane, WA 99205 (SAN 215-8183).

Sunshine Computer Software Co., *(Sunshine; 0-927286),* 1101 Post Oak Blvd., Suite 9-493, Houston, TX 77056 (SAN 277-6359) Tel 713-552-0949.

Sunshine Pr., *(Sunshine Pr; 0-936223),* 3830 N. Oakland St., Arlington, VA 22207 (SAN 696-8252) Tel 703-243-8768.

Sunshine Pr., *(Sunshine TX; 0-9615743),* P.O. Box 851, Comfort, TX 78013 (SAN 696-0510) Tel 512-995-2599; Dist. by: Quality Books, Inc., 918 Sherwood Dr., Lake Bluff, IL 60044-2204 (SAN 169-2127); Toll free: 800-323-4241 (Libraries only); Dist. by: The Distributors, 702 South Michigan, South Bend, IN 46618 (SAN 213-9502) Tel 219-232-8500.

Sunshine Services Corp., Div. of Sunshine News Services, *(Sunshine Serv; 0-942236),* 325 Pennsylvania Ave. SE, Washington, DC 20003 (SAN 239-9830) Tel 202-544-3647.

Sunstone Foundation, *(Sunstone Found; 0-9606760),* 59 West First South, Salt Lake City, UT 84101 (SAN 213-9693) Tel 801-355-5926.

Sunstone Pr., The, Subs. of Sunstone Corp., *(Sunstone Pr; 0-913270; 0-86534),* P.O. Box 2321, Santa Fe, NM 87504-2321 (SAN 214-2090) Tel 505-988-4418. *Imprints:* Sundial Books (Sundial Bks).

Sunstone Publications, Div. of Sunstone, Inc., *(Sunstone Pubns; 0-913319),* R.D. 3, Box 100A, Cooperstown, NY 13326 (SAN 283-4227) Tel 607-547-8207.

Sunwise Turn, Ltd., *(Sunwise Turn; 0-88004),* P.O. Box 117, New York, NY 10003 (SAN 222-9838) Tel 718-230-8479.

Superior Pubns., *(Superior WI),* 5510 Tower Ave., Superior, WI 54880 (SAN 209-682X) Tel 715-392-8060.

†**Superior Publishing,** *(Superior Pub; 0-87564),* 708 Sixth Ave. N., Box 1710, Seattle, WA 98111 (SAN 202-747X) Tel 206-282-4310; Dist. by: Harbor Hse. Pubs., 221 Water St., Boyne City, MI 49712 (SAN 200-5751) Tel 616-582-2814; *CIP.*

Superlove, *(Superlove; 0-9602334),* 4245 Ladoga Ave., Lakewood, CA 90713 (SAN 211-982X) Tel 213-429-6447.

Supnick, Mark, *(M Supnick; 0-9611446),* 8524 NW Second St., Coral Springs, FL 33065 (SAN 283-1694) Tel 305-755-3448.

Supplies & Services, Government of Canada *See* Unipub

Suratao, Incorporated, *(Suratao; 0-932286),* 4763 W. 12th St., Los Angeles, CA 90019 (SAN 212-1441) Tel 213-931-0371.

Sure Fire Press, Subs. of Holmes Publishing Group, *(Sure Fire; 0-916411),* c/o Holmes Publishing Group, P.O. Box 623, Edmonds, WA 98020 (SAN 656-9102) Tel 206-771-2701.

Sure Foundation, *(Sure Found; 0-936595),* Rte. 2, Box 74, Cloverdale, IN 46120 (SAN 698-1054) Tel 317-795-3136.

Surevelation, *(Surevelation; 0-917302),* P.O. Box 2193, Concord, CA 94521 (SAN 208-8800) Tel 415-687-2703.

Surface Checking Gage Co., *(Surf Chek; 0-911464),* P.O. Box 1912, Prescott, AZ 86302 (SAN 204-6482) Tel 602-778-3160.

Surface Travel Pubns. Co., *(Surf Trav Pubns; 0-915821),* 385 Brighton Ave., Long Branch, NJ 07740 (SAN 294-1341) Tel 201-222-9196; Orders to: P.O. Box 616, Long Branch, NJ 07740 (SAN 663-3056) Tel 609-853-7940.

Surfer Pubns., Inc., Div. of For Better Living, Inc., *(Surfer Pubns; 0-939337),* 33046 Calle Aviador, San Juan Capistrano, CA 92675 (SAN 662-5096) Tel 714-496-5922; P.O. Box 1028, Dana Point, CA 92629 (SAN 662-510X); Dist. by: Select Magazine, 8 E. 40th St., New York, NY 10016 (SAN 200-7436).

Surincik, Don, *(Don Surincik; 0-9613231),* P.O. Box 127, Andrews Rd. RD 2, Edinburg, PA 16116 (SAN 295-1614).

†**Surrey Bks., Inc.,** *(Surrey Bks; 0-9609516),* 500 N. Michigan Ave., Suite 1940, Chicago, IL 60611 (SAN 275-8857) Tel 312-661-0050; Dist. by: Publishers Group West, 5855 Beaudry St., Emeryville, CA 94608 (SAN 202-8522) Tel 415-658-3453; *CIP.*

Surrey Press, *(Surrey Pr; 0-9610652),* 224 Surrey Rd., Warminster, PA 18974 (SAN 264-696X) Tel 215-675-4569.

Survival, *(Survival CT; 0-9604256),* Turkey Hills, Haddam, CT 06438 (SAN 213-9480).

Survival Education Assn., *(Survival Ed Assoc; 0-913724),* 9035 Golden Givens Rd., Tacoma, WA 98445 (SAN 204-6490) Tel 206-531-3156.

Susedik Method, Inc. The, *(Susedik Meth; 0-914717),* P.O. Box 997, Cambridge, OH 43725 (SAN 287-766X) Tel 614-432-5204.

Susquehanna Publisning Co., *(Susquehanna; 0-9609382),* 709 Apache Dr., Independence, MO 64056 (SAN 260-2695) Tel 816-257-0280.

Susquehanna Univ. Pr., *(Susquehanna U Pr; 0-941664),* Dist. by: Associated University Presses, 440 Forsgate Dr., Cranbury, NJ 08512 (SAN 281-2959) Tel 609-655-4770.

Sussex Prints, Inc., *(Sussex Prints; 0-911145),* P.O. Box 469, Georgetown, DE 19947 (SAN 275-8873) Tel 302-856-0026.

Sustaining Systems, *(Sustaining Syst; 0-939335),* 4300 4th Ave., NE, Seattle, WA 98105 (SAN 662-8893) Tel 206-547-7104.

Sutherland, Ruth, *(R Sutherland; 0-9616133),* 815 Carson Ave., Painesville, OH 44077-1114 (SAN 699-9425) Tel 216-354-9331.

Sutherland Learning Assocs., Inc., *(Sutherland Learn Assocs; 0-934100),* 8700 Reseda Blvd., No. 108, Northridge, CA 91324 (SAN 212-8152) Tel 818-701-1344.

Sutherland Publishing, Div. of Sutherland Printing Company, Inc., *(Sutherland FL; 0-930942),* 16956-6 McGregor Blvd., Ft. Myers, FL 33908 (SAN 222-8335) Tel 813-466-1626; Orders to: P.O. Box 426, Grinnell, IA 50112 (SAN 662-1570) Tel 515-236-6589.

†**Sutter House,** *(Sutter House; 0-915010),* 77 Main St., P.O. Box 212, Lititz, PA 17543 (SAN 207-1207) Tel 717-626-0800; *CIP.*

Sutton, Polly Rachel McGaughey, *(Mc Gaughey Sutton; 0-9613693),* 2700 NW 61st St., Oklahoma City, OK 73112 (SAN 670-9710).

Sutton, Weldon L., Publisher, *(W Sutton; 0-9607388),* 5481 Kingsly Ave., Apt.A, Montclair, CA 91763 (SAN 239-7994) Tel 714-626-8600.

Sutton Aviation Press, *(Sutton Avn Pr; 0-940300),* 3631-22nd Ave. S., Minneapolis, MN 55407 (SAN 217-1333) Tel 612-729-1175.

Sutton Pubns., *(Sutton Pubns; 0-9617199),* 13 Thicket, Irvine, CA 92714 (SAN 663-2610) Tel 914-786-8054.

Suwannee Poetry, *(Suwannee Poetry; 0-938285),* P.O. Box 2902, Florence, AL 35630 (SAN 659-882X); Rte. 9, Florence, AL 35630 (SAN 659-8838) Tel 615-722-5404.

Suzuki Method International, Div. of Birch Tree Group Ltd., *(Suzuki Intl; 0-87487),* 180 Alexander Rd., Box 2072, Princeton, NJ 08540 (SAN 693-3718) Tel 609-683-0090.

Suzuki Method International *See* Summy-Birchard Music

Sverge-Haus Pubs., Div. of Sverge Rijks Haus, *(Sverge-Haus; 0-933348),* 11 Indian Spring Rd., Milton, MA 02186 (SAN 212-4610) Tel 617-773-2709.

Swain, Thomas B., & Son, *(T B Swain & Son; 0-938915),* 8269 Lodgepole Trail, Littleton, CO 80124 (SAN 661-7883) Tel 303-790-1489.

Swallow Publications, *(Swallow Pubns; 0-9614245),* P.O. Drawer 10, Ville Platte, LA 70536 (SAN 686-7030) Tel 318-363-2139.

Swallow's Tale Pr., *(Swallows Tale Pr; 0-930501),* P.O. Box 930040, Norcross, GA 30093 (SAN 670-9206) Tel 404-493-4932.

Swampgas Press, *(Swampgas; 0-933838),* 3201 St. Charles Ave., No. 313, New Orleans, LA 70115 (SAN 212-7008) Tel 504-897-3413.

Swan, Frances M., *(F M Swan; 0-9602126),* 11533 Old St. Charles Rd., Bridgeton, MO 63044 (SAN 212-3835).

†**Swan Bks.,** *(Swan Books; 0-934048),* P.O. Box 332, Fair Oaks, CA 95628 (SAN 212-7016) Tel 916-961-8778; *CIP.*

Swan Pr., *(Swan Pr; 0-9615530),* 10443 N. Cave Creek Rd., Suite 211, Phoenix, AZ 85020 (SAN 659-8990) Tel 602-943-5492; P.O.Box 33517, Phoenix, AZ 85067 (SAN 699-6132).

Swansea Publishing Co., Inc., *(Swansea Pr),* P.O. Box 27785, Philadelphia, PA 19118 (SAN 292-4757) Tel 215-836-1400; Toll free: 800-276-6732; 803 E. Willow Grove Ave., Philadelphia, PA 19118 (SAN 658-2494).

Swansea Publishing Co., *(Swansea; 0-916315),* 45 Tamarack Dr., Windsor, CT 06095 (SAN 295-8325) Tel 203-242-0254.

Swanson, Evadene, *(E Swanson; 0-9600862),* Park Ctr., No. 35, 1020 E. 17th St., Minneapolis, MN 55404 (SAN 208-1156) Tel 612-338-1839.

Swanson Publishing Co., *(Swanson; 0-911466),* P.O. Box 334, Moline, IL 61265 (SAN 204-6520).

†**Swedenborg Foundation, Inc.,** *(Swedenborg; 0-87785),* 139 E. 23rd St., New York, NY 10010 (SAN 202-7526) Tel 212-673-7310; *CIP.*

Swedenborg Scientific Association, *(Swedenborg Sci Assn; 0-915221),* 654 Dale Rd., P.O. Box 11, Bryn Athyn, PA 19009 (SAN 289-8454) Tel 215-947-4200.

Swedish-American Historical Society, *(Swedish-Am; 0-914819),* 5125 N. Spaulding Ave., Chicago, IL 60625 (SAN 225-3828) Tel 312-583-5722.

Swedish Council of America, *(Swedish Council; 0-9609620),* c/o American Swedish Institute, 2600 Park Ave., Minneapolis, MN 55407 (SAN 277-9668) Tel 612-871-4907.

Sweet CH'I Pr., *(Sweet Ch'I Pr; 0-912059),* 662 Union St., Brooklyn, NY 11215 (SAN 264-6382) Tel 718-857-0449.

†**Sweet Publishing,** *(Sweet; 0-8344),* 3934 Sandshell, Ft. Worth, TX 76137 (SAN 206-8958) Tel 817-232-5661; Toll free: 800-531-5220; Toll free: 800-252-9213 (in Texas); *CIP.*

Sweetbrier Pr., *(Sweetbrier; 0-936736),* 536 Emerson St., Palo Alto, CA 94301 (SAN 216-1915) Tel 415-323-7822.

Sweeter Than Honey, *(Sweeter Than Honey; 0-934244),* P.O. Box 7110, Tyler, TX 75711 (SAN 685-3625) Tel 214-561-6415.

Sweetlight Bks., *(Sweetlight; 0-9604462),* P.O. Box 307, Arcata, CA 95521 (SAN 215-1154) Tel 707-786-9328; Dist. by: Bookpeople, 2929 Fifth St., Berkeley, CA 94710 (SAN 168-9517) Tel 415-549-3030; Toll free: 800-624-4466; Dist. by: Naturegraph Publishers, P.O. Box 1075, Happy Camp, CA 96039 (SAN 202-8999) Tel 916-493-5353.

Sweetman, Leonard, *(L Sweetman; 0-9600518),* 1712 Fisherville Rd., Coatesville, PA 19320 (SAN 203-9265).

Sweets Corners Press, *(Sweets Corners; 0-9611284),* 1321 Sweets Corners Rd., Penfield, NY 14526 (SAN 283-3476) Tel 716-377-2962.

Sweetser, Albert G., *(A G Sweetser; 0-9605500),* 17 Broadleaf Dr., Clifton Park, NY 12065 (SAN 206-1864) Tel 518-371-7674.

Sweetwater Pr., *(Sweetwater Pr; 0-9615504),* 1071 Duna Dr., Laramie, WY 82070 (SAN 695-9199) Tel 307-742-3082.

Sweetwater River Press, *(Sweetwater River Pr; 0-931950),* P.O. Box 985, National City, CA 92050 (SAN 222-8289).

Swenson, Albert W., *(A W Swenson; 0-9616131),* 4582 Madison Ave., Trumbull, CT 06611 (SAN 699-9492) Tel 203-261-5966.

Swenson & Pinckney, *(Swenson Pinckney; 0-9610190),* 2850 Mesa Verde Dr. E., Costa Mesa, CA 92626 (SAN 289-7121) Tel 714-979-8073; Dist. by: Publishers Marketing Group, 1104 Summit Ave., Plainview, TX 75074 (SAN 289-713X) Tel 214-423-0312.

Swenson Publishing, *(Swenson Pub; 0-9615688),* 430 Magnolia Ln., N., Plymouth, MN 55441 (SAN 696-4427) Tel 612-545-6659.

Swets North America, *(Swets North Am),* P.O. Box 517, Berwyn, PA 19312 (SAN 295-3544); Dist. by: C. J. Hogrefe Inc., P.O. Box 51, Lewiston, NY 14092 (SAN 295-5532) Tel 716-754-4944.

Swift, Sterling *See* Heath, D. C., Co.

Swiger, Elizabeth D., *(E D Swiger; 0-9616245),* 1599 Hillcrest Rd., Fairmont, WV 26554 (SAN 658-6988) Tel 804-366-0033.

Swim Safe, *(Swim Safe; 0-939627),* P.O. Box 1017, Longwood, FL 32750 (SAN 663-6012); 1350 Hobson St., Longwood, FL 32750 (SAN 663-6020) Tel 305-339-1003.

Swimfants, *(Swimfants; 0-9604096),* 1517 Lenox Dr., Modesto, CA 95350 (SAN 213-3105) Tel 209-526-2820.

Swimming World, *(Swimming; 0-911822),* 116 W. Hazel, Inglewood, CA 90302-2905 (SAN 204-6539) Tel 213-674-2120.

Swiss Village Bk. Store, *(Swiss Village; 0-9615744),* 907 Main St., Highland, IL 62249 (SAN 126-9925) Tel 618-654-2521; Box 412, Highland, IL 62249 (SAN 699-6183).

Switz Press, The, *(Switz Pr; 0-930333),* RR 3, P.O. Box 311, Vevay, IN 47043 (SAN 670-8439) Tel 812-427-2529.

Swollen Magpie Pr., *(Swollen Magpie; 0-9609090),* Rte. 2, Box 499, Putnam Valley, NY 10579 (SAN 240-933X) Tel 914-526-3392.

Names

Sword & Shield Release, *(Sword Shield Release; 0-938471),* P.O. Box 128, Fairmont, WV 26554 (SAN 661-0641); 109 Linda Ln., Fairmont, WV 26554 (SAN 661-065X) Tel 304-363-6925.

Sword & Stone Press, *(Sword & Stone; 0-939086),* 4330 Windward Circle, Dallas, TX 75252 (SAN 216-3071) Tel 214-380-1433.

Sword of the Lord Pubs., *(Sword of Lord; 0-87398),* P.O. Box 1099, 224 Bridge Ave., Murfreesboro, TN 37130 (SAN 203-5642) Tel 615-893-6700.

Swordsman Pr., Inc., *(Swordsman Pr; 0-940018),* 15445 Ventura Blvd., No. 10, Sherman Oaks, CA 91413 (SAN 216-860X) Tel 818-888-2688; Box 5973, Sherman Oaks, CA 91413 (SAN 658-1838); Dist. by: Contemporary Bks., 180 N. Michigan Ave., Chicago, IL 60601 (SAN 202-5493) Tel 312-782-9181; Dist. by: Warner Bros. Pubns., 9000 Sunset Blvd., Penthouse, Los Angeles, CA 90069 (SAN 200-7347) Tel 213-273-3323.

Swordsman Pubns., *(Swordsman Pubns; 0-913493),* P.O. Box 111, Burnt Hills, NY 12027 (SAN 285-869X) Tel 518-399-0677.

Sybar Publishing, *(Sybar Pub; 0-936791),* 2344 Sixth St., Berkeley, CA 94710 (SAN 690-260X) Tel 415-848-8233. Do not confuse with Sybex, Inc., same address.

Sybex Computer Bks. *See* Sybex, Inc.

Sybex, Inc., *(Sybex; 0-89588),* 2344 Sixth St., Berkeley, CA 94710 (SAN 211-1667) Tel 415-848-8233; Toll free: 800-227-2346; Interstate 80 at Maple Ave., Pine Brook, NJ 07058 (SAN 658-1846). *Imprints:* Sybex Computer Bks. (Sybex Computer Bks).

Sycamore Island Bks. *See* Paladin Pr.

Sycamore Pr., Inc., *(Sycamore Pr; 0-916768),* P.O. Box 552, Terre Haute, IN 47808 (SAN 208-8827) Tel 812-299-2784.

Syder Press, *(Syder Pr; 0-939470),* 5893 Kahara Court, Sacramento, CA 95822 (SAN 216-4590).

Sydon, Inc, *(Sydon),* 3725 Monitor Circle N., Stockton, CA 95209 (SAN 202-070X).

Syentek Books Co., Inc., *(Syentek Bks; 0-914082),* P.O. Box 26588, San Francisco, CA 94126 (SAN 202-7534) Tel 415-928-0471.

Sylvan Bks., *(Sylvan Bks; 0-916317),* P.O. Box 481, Syracuse, IN 46567 (SAN 295-8457) Tel 219-457-5647.

Sylvan Institute of Mental Health, *(Sylvan Inst; 0-918428),* 7104 NE Hazel Dell Ave., Vancouver, WA 98665 (SAN 209-6838) Tel 206-694-0911.

Sylvan Pubns., *(Sylvan Pubns; 0-9606678),* 42185 Baintree Circle, Northville, MI 48167 (SAN 219-6433) Tel 313-349-4827.

Syman, A., Pubns., *(A Syman Pubns; 0-941704),* P.O. Box 8245, Scottsdale, AZ 85252 (SAN 239-541X) Tel 602-990-1890; Dist. by: Publishers Group West, 5855 Beaudry St., Emeryville, CA 94608 (SAN 202-8522); Dist. by: Many Feathers SW Books and Maps, 5738 N. Central Ave., Phoenix, AZ 85012 (SAN 158-8877).

Symbiosis Bks., *(Symbiosis Bks; 0-9615903),* 8 Midhill Dr., Mill Valley, CA 94941 (SAN 696-8457) Tel 415-383-7722.

Symbol of Excellence Publishers, Inc., *(Symbol Exc Pubs; 0-932437),* 3169 Cahaba Heights Rd., Birmingham, AL 35243 (SAN 686-7316) Tel 205-967-8402; Toll free: 800-231-0503.

Symbols & Signs, *(Sym & Sign; 0-912504),* P.O. Box 4536, North Hollywood, CA 91607 (SAN 205-4094).

Symmes Systems, *(Symmes Syst; 0-916352),* P.O. Box 8101, Atlanta, GA 30306 (SAN 169-1465) Tel 404-876-7260.

Sympatico Pr., *(Sympatico Pr; 0-9612666),* 17 Rising Pl., Rochester, NY 14607 (SAN 289-4408) Tel 716-442-7851.

Symphony League of Jackson, Mississippi, *(Sym League; 0-9608552),* P.O. Box 9402, Jackson, MS 39206 (SAN 240-7833) Tel 601-960-1565.

Symphony Pr., Inc., *(Symphony),* P.O. Box 515, Tenafly, NJ 07670 (SAN 210-6310).

Symposia Press, *(Symposia Pr; 0-918542),* P.O. Box 418, Moorestown, NJ 08057 (SAN 209-892X) Tel 609-235-8439.

Symposium Pr., *(Symposium Pr; 0-936576),* 1620 Greenfield, Los Angeles, CA 90025 (SAN 213-1943) Tel 213-473-1758.

Synaptic Pr., *(Synaptic Pr; 0-9616988),* 220 S. Rose, No. 13, Los Angeles, CA 90012 (SAN 661-728X) Tel 213-687-4172.

Synaxis Pr., *(Synaxis Pr; 0-911523),* P.O. Box 689, Lynden, WA 98264 (SAN 685-4338).

Syncline, *(Syncline; 0-9603794),* 7825 S. Ridgeway, Chicago, IL 60652 (SAN 214-1515).

Syncretic Productions, Inc., *(Syncretic Prod; 0-935863),* 1821 Hyde St., San Francisco, CA 94109 (SAN 695-9792) Tel 415-474-6366; P.O. Box 16012, San Francisco, CA 94116 (SAN 696-5172).

Syndactics, Inc., *(Syndactics; 0-9614322),* 8900 N. Central, No. 212, Phoenix, AZ 85020 (SAN 670-7084) Tel 602-944-4976; Orders to: P.O. Box 10004, Phoenix, AZ 85064 (SAN 699-5829) Tel 602-944-4976.

Syndicate Books, *(Syndicate; 0-911474),* 551 Fifth Ave., Rm 1600, New York, NY 10176 (SAN 205-4108) Tel 212-682-0546.

Synergetics, *(Synergetics; 0-936501),* 65 Meetinghouse Ridge, Meriden, CT 06450 (SAN 698-0627) Tel 203-235-3452; Dist. by: Roland Corp, 7200 Dominion Cir., Los Angeles, CA 90040 (SAN 200-5956).

Synergetics Pr., The, *(Synergetics WV; 0-910217),* Box 2091, Parkersburg, WV 26101 (SAN 241-4643) Tel 304-485-0460.

†Synergistic Pr., Inc., *(Synergistic Pr; 0-912184),* 3965 Sacramento St., San Francisco, CA 94118 (SAN 205-4116) Tel 415-387-8180; *CIP.*

Synergy Books *See* Walsh, Patrick, Pr.

Synergy Group, Inc., *(Synergy Group; 0-916899),* 4766 Park Granada, Suite 106, Calabasas, CA 91302 (SAN 691-8786) Tel 818-887-9100.

Synergy House, *(Synergy Hse; 0-934962),* P.O. Box 1827, Costa Mesa, CA 92626 (SAN 213-3792) Tel 714-549-4484.

Synergy Pr., *(Synergy Pr; 0-9616548),* 3420 Holly Rd., Annandale, VA 22003 (SAN 659-5405) Tel 703-573-0909.

Synergy Pubs., *(Synergy Pubs; 0-915223),* P.O. Box 18268, Denver, CO 80218 (SAN 289-8489).

Synod of North Carolina, Presbyterian Church (U.S.A.), *(Synod NC Church),* 1015 Wade Ave. P.O. Box 10785, Raleigh, NC 27605 (SAN 206-2356) Tel 919-834-4379.

Syntax Pubns., *(Syntax Pubns; 0-910687),* 340 Norton St., Boulder, CO 80303 (SAN 240-9879).

†Synthesis Pubns., *(Synthesis Pubns; 0-89935),* P.O. Box 40099, San Francisco, CA 94140 (SAN 282-3888) Tel 415-824-1465; *CIP.*

Synthetix, *(Synthetix; 0-9612174; 0-937637),* P.O. Box 1080, Berkeley, CA 94701 (SAN 291-8536) Tel 415-339-0601; 20 Villanova Dr., Oakland, CA 94611 (SAN 658-2486).

Syntony Publishing, Inc., *(Syntony Inc Pub; 0-9613172; 0-933347),* 1450 Bryon St., Palo Alto, CA 94301 (SAN 294-9997) Tel 415-326-5615; Dist. by: Publishers Group West, 5855 Beaudry St., Emeryville, CA 94698 (SAN 202-8522) Tel 415-658-3453; Toll free: 800-982-8319.

Sypher, Francis, *(F Sypher),* 220 E. 50th St., New York, NY 10022 (SAN 215-0492).

Syracuse Cultural Workers, *(Syracuse Cultural; 0-935155),* 601 Allen St., Syracuse, NY 13210 (SAN 695-3484) Tel 315-474-1132; Box 6367, Syracuse, NY 13217 (SAN 695-3492); Orders to: Syracuse Cultural Workers, P.O. Box 6367, Syracuse, NY 13217 (SAN 662-3468) Tel 315-474-1132.

Syracuse Univ., Foreign & Comparative Studies Program, *(Syracuse U Foreign Comp; 0-915984),* 724 Comstock Ave., Syracuse, NY 13244 (SAN 220-0082) Tel 315-423-2552.

Syracuse Univ. Pr., *(Syracuse U Pr; 0-8156),* 1600 Jamesville Ave., Syracuse, NY 13244-5160 (SAN 206-9776) Tel 315-423-2596.

Syracuse Univ. Pubns. in Continuing Education, *(Syracuse U Cont Ed; 0-87060),* Syracuse, NY 13210 (SAN 202-7577) Tel 315-423-3421.

System Development Corp., *(System Dev CA; 0-916368),* 2525 Colorado Pl., Santa Monica, CA 90406 (SAN 222-8246) Tel 213-820-4111.

System Logistics, Inc., *(System Logistics; 0-9602362),* P.O. Box 25776, 507 Kawaihae St., Honolulu, HI 96825 (SAN 212-5692) Tel 808-396-9650.

Systematic Development, Inc., *(Systematic Dev),* P.O. Box 52, Pasadena, CA 91102 (SAN 218-981X).

Systems Co., *(Systems Co; 0-937041),* P.O. Box DE, Panorama City, CA 91412 (SAN 699-7880) Tel 818-892-4190; 15056 Rayen St., Sepulveda, CA 91343 (SAN 658-3040) Tel 818-354-4031.

Systems Impact, Inc., *(Syst Impact; 0-934403),* 4400 MacArthur Blvd., NW, No. 203, Washington, DC 20007 (SAN 693-7349) Tel 202-342-9369; Toll free: 800-822-INFO.

Systems Modeling Corp., *(Syst Modeling; 0-928791),* Calder Sq. P.O. Box 10074, State College, PA 16805 (SAN 670-6533); 248 Calder Way, state College, PA 16801 (SAN 662-2453) Tel 814-238-5919.

Systems Planning Associates, Pubns. Div., *(Systems Planning),* 3 Aliber Place, Keene, NH 03431 (SAN 287-3028) Tel 603-357-4005.

Systems Pubns., Inc., Div. of Armond Dalton Publishers, Inc., *(Systems Pubns; 0-912503),* P.O. Box 318, Haslett, MI 48840 (SAN 265-2234) Tel 517-349-4695.

Systems Publishing Corp., *(Systems Pub; 0-938974),* P.O. Box 2161, West Lafayette, IN 47906 (SAN 216-308X).

Systems Research Institute, *(Systems Res; 0-912352),* Publications Dept., P.O. Box 4568, Los Angeles, CA 90051-2568 (SAN 202-7585).

Systemsware Corp., The, *(Systemsware; 0-938801),* 9612 Culver St., Kensington, MD 20895 (SAN 661-5112) Tel 202-728-8600.

Sytek Press, *(Sytek Pr; 0-9613248),* 1225 Charleston Rd., Mountain View, CA 94043 (SAN 295-5016) Tel 415-966-7300.

Syzygy, *(Syzygy; 0-943108),* P.O. Box 428, Rush, NY 14543 (SAN 240-1541) Tel 716-226-2127.

Syzygy Press, *(Syzygy Pr; 0-9608372),* P.O. Box 183, Mill Valley, CA 94942 (SAN 240-4508) Tel 415-824-3452; Dist. by: Subterranean Co., The, P.O. Box 10233, 1327 W. Second, Eugene, OR 97440 (SAN 169-7102) Tel 503-343-6324.

Szoke, John, Graphics, Inc., *(J Szoke Graphics; 0-936598),* 164-166 Mercer St., New York, NY 10012 (SAN 222-1748).

Szwede Slavic Books, *(Szwede Slavic),* P.O. Box 1214, Palo Alto, CA 94302 (SAN 202-053X).

TA Assocs., *(TA Assocs; 0-9617020),* 815 Indian Rd., Glenview, IL 60025 (SAN 662-8648) Tel 312-729-5133.

TAB Bks., Inc., *(TAB Bks; 0-8306; 0-8168),* P.O. Box 40, Blue Ridge Summit, PA 17214 (SAN 202-568X) Tel 717-794-2191; Toll free: 800-233-1128. Acquired Windcrest Software. *Imprints:* Gernshack Library (Gernshack); T A B/T P R (TAB/TPR); TAB-Aero (TAB-Aero).

T A B, T P R *See* TAB Bks., Inc.

T.A.C.L., *(TACL),* 641 Towle Way, Palo Alto, CA 94306 (SAN 211-5778) Tel 415-493-3628.

TAM Assocs., *(TAM Assoc; 0-913005),* 911 Chicago, Oak Park, IL 60302 (SAN 283-4235) Tel 312-848-6760.

TAN Bks. & Pubs., Inc., *(TAN Bks Pubs; 0-89555),* 2135 N. Central Ave., Rockford, IL 61103 (SAN 282-390X) Tel 815-962-2662; Orders to: P.O. Box 424, Rockford, IL 61105 (SAN 282-3918).

T.A.P., *(T A P; 0-9612878),* P.O. Box 3028, Apopka, FL 32703-0028 (SAN 291-4492) Tel 305-886-1343.

†TA Pr., Div. of International Transactional Analysis Assn., *(TA Press; 0-89489),* 1772 Vallejo St., San Francisco, CA 94123 (SAN 209-6846) Tel 415-885-5992; *CIP.*

TAU Pr., *(TAU Pr; 0-916453),* P.O. Box 2283, Rolling Hills, CA 90274 (SAN 209-3022).

T & E Enterprises, *(T & E Ent; 0-9609942),* P.O. Box 14324, Albuquerque, NM 87191 (SAN 275-9101) Tel 505-299-7502.

T & J Sports Cards, *(T & J Sports Cards; 0-937903),* P.O. Box 191, Richland Center, WI 53581 (SAN 659-5928); 1055 W. Kinder St., Richland Center, WI 53581 (SAN 659-5936) Tel 608-647-6687.

T & M Publishing Co., *(T & M; 0-9607062),* 1493 Granada Dr., New Orleans, LA 70122 (SAN 239-0477) Tel 504-283-6800.

T & R Pubs., *(T & R Pubs; 0-936809),* 11844 Rancho Bernardo Rd., Suite 120-31, San Diego, CA 92128 (SAN 699-9778) Tel 619-451-2680.

TBJ Pubns., *(T B J Pubns; 0-935855),* 10 Brookfield Rd., Methuen, MA 01844 (SAN 695-8907) Tel 617-686-3145 (SAN 662-7803).

†TBN Enterprises, *(TBN Ent; 0-935554),* Box 55, Alexandria, VA 22313 (SAN 206-2380) Tel 703-684-6111; *CIP.*

TBW Bks., *(TBW Bks; 0-931474),* 36 Old Mill Rd., Falmouth, ME 04105 (SAN 224-2303) Tel 207-781-3002; Orders to: Harpswell Press, 132 Water St., Gardiner, ME 04345 (SAN 208-1199) Tel 207-582-1899.

T/C Pubns., Div. of Technology Conferences, *(T-C Pubns CA; 0-938648),* P.O. Box 842, El Segundo, CA 90245 (SAN 239-491X) Tel 213-938-6923.

TDM Audio, *(TDM Audio; 0-88749),* 560 S. State College Blvd., Fullerton, CA 92631 (SAN 292-6970) Tel 714-441-0782.

TEC Pubns., *(TEC Pubns; 0-937533),* 1410 Robertson Way, Sacramento, CA 95818 (SAN 659-0322) Tel 916-443-3315.

T.E.D. Assocs., *(T E D Assocs; 0-916598),* 42 Lowell Rd., Brookline, MA 02146 (SAN 208-8835) Tel 617-277-8446.

T. E. L. L. Pubns., *(TELL Pubns; 0-939028),* P.O. Box 9044, Hampton, VA 23670 (SAN 217-2712).

TEL Pr., *(TEL Pr; 0-9613839),* 245 N. Oakland Ave., Indianapolis, IN 46201 (SAN 682-0239) Tel 317-638-1641.

TEL Pubs., Ltd., *(TEL Pubs; 1-55588),* 2516 S. Alpine, Rockford, IL 61125 (SAN 658-5116) Tel 815-398-6730; Toll free: 800-835-5835; P.O. Box 5471, Rockford, IL 61125 (SAN 658-5124).

TES Publishing Co., *(TES Pub; 0-9616432),* 447 Hillside, Rossford, OH 43460 (SAN 659-0357) Tel 419-666-4835.

†TFH Publishing, Inc., *(TFH Pubns; 0-87666; 0-86622),* 211 W. Sylvania Ave., Neptune, NJ 07753 (SAN 202-7720) Tel 201-988-8400; Toll free: 800-631-2188; Box 427, Neptune, NJ 07753 (SAN 658-1862); *CIP.*

T.I.S., Inc., Div. of T.I.S. Enterprises, *(TIS Inc; 0-89917),* P.O. Box 669, 1928 Arlington Rd., Bloomington, IN 47402 (SAN 169-2313) Tel 812-332-3307; Toll free: 800-367-4002.

T.J. Designs, *(T J Designs; 0-939287),* 5905 Ironwood, Rancho Palos Verdes, CA 90274 (SAN 659-4565) Tel 213-598-1423.

T.J. Enterprises, *(TJ Enter IL; 0-936503),* 8000 S. Archer Rd., A106, Willow Springs, IL 60480 (SAN 698-0619) Tel 312-839-2611; P.O. Box 255, Chicago Ridge, IL 60415-0255 (SAN 698-2484).

T.J. Pubs., Inc., *(T J Pubs; 0-932666),* 817 Silver Spring Ave., 206, Silver Spring, MD 20910 (SAN 656-903X) Tel 301-585-4440.

T. K. Publishers, *(TK Pubs; 0-9614023),* P.O. Box 779, Cocoa, FL 32922 (SAN 683-6232) Tel 305-636-1952.

TLC Bks., *(TLC Bks; 0-9617081),* 416 N. Byrkit St., Mishawaka, IN 46544 (SAN 662-6165) Tel 219-959-1775; P.O. Box 1391, Mishawaka, IN 46544 (SAN 662-6173).

TLC Enterprises, *(TLC Enterprises; 0-9614922),* P.O. Box 3372, Englewood, CO 80112 (SAN 693-1278) Tel 303-799-5424.

T L C Publishing Co., *(T L C; 0-918365),* P.O. Box 21508, Oklahoma City, OK 73156 (SAN 657-3835) Tel 405-840-5511; Toll free: 800-654-9121.

TL Enterprises, Inc., *(TL Enterprises; 0-934798),* 29901 Agoura Rd., Agoura, CA 91301 (SAN 213-1803) Tel 818-991-4980.

TLT Pubns., *(TLT; 0-943314),* 202 S. Fifth St., Goshen, IN 46526 (SAN 240-7841) Tel 616-361-8013.

TMH Publishing Co., *(T M H Pub Co; 0-933987),* 4000 Hawthorne, No. 5, Dallas, TX 75219 (SAN 693-0883) Tel 214-526-3524.

TMH Publishing, Ltd., *(TMH Pub; 0-939386),* P.O. Box 6344, Santa Barbara, CA 93160-6344 (SAN 216-3047).

TOWERS Club, U. S. A., *(Towers Club; 0-930668),* P.O. Box 2038, Vancouver, WA 98668-2038 (SAN 209-6072); 9107 NW 11th St., Vancouver, WA 98665 (SAN 699-5683) Tel 206-574-3084.

TPA Publishing Ltd., *(TPA Pub; 0-9609996),* 540 W. 112th St., Los Angeles, CA 90044 (SAN 263-2349).

TP Assocs./TP Pr., *(TP Assocs; 0-913939),* P.O. Box 3226, Newport Beach, CA 92663 (SAN 286-8962) Tel 714-963-4482; 22181 Wood Island Ln., Huntington Beach, CA 92646 (SAN 286-8970) Tel 714-963-4482.

T.P. Publishing, *(T P Pub; 0-914281),* 483 W. 23rd, Eugene, OR 97405 (SAN 287-5667) Tel 503-687-9053; Dist. by: Pacific Pipeline, 19215 66th Ave. S., Kent, WA 98032 (SAN 287-5675) Tel 206-872-5523.

TPR Publishing Co., Inc., *(TPR Pub Inc; 0-918000),* 81 Montgomery St., Scarsdale, NY 10583 (SAN 210-282X) Tel 914-472-0366.

TPW Publishing Co., *(TPW Pub Co; 0-914475),* P.O. Box 4467, Mountain View, CA 94040-0467 (SAN 289-6834) Tel 408-243-1300.

TSL Pr. (Time & Space, Ltd.), *(T S L Pr; 0-939858),* 139 W. 22nd St., New York, NY 10011 (SAN 216-938X) Tel 212-741-1032.

TSM Bks., Inc., *(TSM Books; 0-941316),* 555 Broad Hollow Rd., Suite 271, Melville, NY 11747 (SAN 239-040X) Tel 516-420-0961.

TSR, Inc., *(TSR Inc; 0-935696; 0-88038),* Box 756, Lake Geneva, WI 53147 (SAN 222-0091) Tel 414-248-3625; Toll free: 800-372-4667; Dist. by: Random Hse., Inc., 400 Hahn Rd., Westminster, MD 21157 (SAN 202-5515); Toll free: 800-638-6460 (except Alaska); Toll free: 800-492-0782 (Maryland).

TTR Publishing, *(TTR Pub; 0-938771),* 513 W. Florence, Tucson, AZ 85705 (SAN 661-7891) Tel 602-622-5718.

TV Guide, Div. of Triangle Publications, Inc., *(TV Guide; 0-9603684),* 4 Radnor Corporate Ctr., Radnor, PA 19088 (SAN 214-4808) Tel 215-293-8947.

TVR Publishing Co., *(TVR Pub Co; 0-9614079),* 5682 Oak Dr., La Palma, CA 90623 (SAN 693-3769) Tel 714-739-2125.

TVRT, *(TVRT; 0-931106),* 25 E. Fourth St., New York, NY 10003 (SAN 206-1341) Tel 212-260-4254; Dist. by: Printed Matter, 7 Lispenard St., New York, NY 10013 (SAN 169-5924) Tel 212-925-0325.

TWG Publishing, *(TWG Pub; 0-937077),* P.O. Box 2359, Daly City, CA 94017 (SAN 658-4470) Tel 415-333-9966.

TW Pubs, *(T W Pubs),* P.O. Box 152, River Forest, IL 60305 (SAN 205-4124).

TY Publishing, Ltd., *(TY Pub Ltd; 0-930613),* P.O. Box 2589, Littleton, CO 80161-2589 (SAN 686-2691).

TAB-Aero *See* TAB Bks., Inc.

Tabard Pr., Div. of W. S. Konecky Assocs., *(Tabard Pr; 0-914427),* 27 W. 20th St., New York, NY 10011 (SAN 663-2432) Tel 212-807-8230; Dist. by: Marboro Bks., 205 Moonachie Rd., Moonachie, NJ 07074 (SAN 150-8059).

Tabb, Jeanne J., & Margaret Ann Thetford, Pubs., *(Tabb Thetford Pubs; 0-9616931),* 3725 Mockingbird Ln., Dallas, TX 75205-2124 (SAN 661-6674) Tel 214-522-3806.

Taber, Thomas T., *(T T Taber; 0-9603398),* Muncy, PA 17756 (SAN 211-9838).

Table Talk Bridge Club, *(Table Talk Bridge; 0-9616705),* 404 Lamar Dr., Macon, GA 31204 (SAN 659-8943) Tel 912-474-0586.

Tabor Sarah Bks., *(Tabor Sarah Bks; 0-935079),* 2419 Jefferson Ave., Berkeley, CA 94703 (SAN 695-0353) Tel 415-845-2540.

Tadpole, *(Tadpole; 0-9615253),* 6030 Autumn Arbor, Houston, TX 77092 (SAN 695-0965) Tel 713-681-8377.

Tafnews Pr., Div. of Track & Field News, Inc., *(Tafnews; 0-911520; 0-911521),* P.O. Box 296, Los Altos, CA 94022 (SAN 202-7593) Tel 415-948-8188.

Taft Group, The, *(Taft Group; 0-914756),* 5130 MacArthur Blvd., NW, Washington, DC 20016 (SAN 206-5215) Tel 202-966-7086; Toll free: 800-424-3761.

Taft Museum, The, *(Taft Museum; 0-915577),* 316 Pike St., Cincinnati, OH 45202 (SAN 292-6946) Tel 513-241-0343.

Tahoma Pubns., *(Tahoma Pubns; 0-9616969),* P.O. Box 44306, Tacoma, WA 98444 (SAN 661-7905); 9609 S. Sheridan, Tacoma, WA 98444 (SAN 661-7913) Tel 206-537-7877.

Tahrike Tarsile Quran, *(Tahrike Tarsile Quran; 0-940368),* P.O. Box 1115, Elmhurst, NY 11373 (SAN 217-1341) Tel 718-779-6505; 80-10 51 Ave., Elmhurst, NY 11373 (SAN 658-1870).

Tai Chi Chuan Ctr. of New York, *(Tai Chi Ctr NY; 0-9616586),* 1117 Ave. of the Americas, New York, NY 10036 (SAN 659-7785) Tel 212-221-6110.

Tail Feather, *(Tail Feather; 0-911756),* c/o Card Lake Services, 3600 S. Harbor Blvd., No. 178, Oxnard, CA 93030 (SAN 205-4132) Tel 805-483-0689. *Imprints:* Neptune Books (Neptune Bks).

Take Five Pubs., *(Take Five Pubs; 0-930099),* P.O. Box 1094, Arlington, IL 60006 (SAN 670-1884) Tel 312-577-2966.

Talbert, Robert, *(R Talbert),* 260 W. 72nd St., Suite 5D, New York, NY 10023 (SAN 211-9846) Tel 212-724-9246.

Talent-Ed, *(Talent-Ed; 0-935003),* P.O. Box 455, Manlius, NY 13104-0455 (SAN 694-6577) Tel 315-682-7872.

Tales of the Mojave Road Pub., Co., *(Tales Mojave Rd; 0-914224),* P.O. Box 307, Norco, CA 91760 (SAN 202-7607) Tel 714-737-3150.

Talisman Literary Research, Inc., *(Talisman Research; 0-934614),* P.O. Box 455, Georgetown, CA 95634 (SAN 206-9547) Tel 916-333-4486.

Talisman Pr., *(Talisman; 0-934612),* P.O. Box 455, Georgetown, CA 95634 (SAN 205-4140) Tel 916-333-4486.

Talk of the Town, *(Talk Town; 0-9612668),* 1313 Sunset Rd., Colorado Springs, CO 80909 (SAN 289-4416) Tel 303-633-2724.

Talking Leaves Publishing Co., *(Talking Leaves Pub; 0-932077),* P.O. Box 84, Urbana, IL 61801 (SAN 686-2624) Tel 217-564-2462.

Talking Seal Pr., *(Talking Seal; 0-9606322),* P.O. Box 4301, Flint, MI 48504 (SAN 218-5083).

Talking Tree Pr., *(Talking Tree Pr; 0-9616957),* 19288 Galen Rd., Bend, OR 97702 (SAN 661-793X) Tel 503-389-0604.

Talking Your Roots, *(Talking Roots; 0-9614867),* P.O. Box 3452, Washington, DC 20010 (SAN 693-3238) Tel 202-232-7892.

Tall Oaks Publishing, Inc., *(Tall Oaks Pub; 0-927188),* 1507 Evesham Rd., Voorhees, NJ 08043 (SAN 294-8583) Tel 609-795-1454.

Talley Assocs. Corp., *(Talley Assoc; 0-932059),* 4107 Spice Wood Springs Rd., Austin, TX 78759 (SAN 686-2594) Tel 512-573-2128.

Talley Productions, *(Talley Prods; 0-9606588),* 1626 N. Wilcox, Suite 200, Hollywood, CA 90028 (SAN 219-8207).

Tallstone Publishing, *(Tallstone Pub; 0-936191),* 10 Vine Ave., Sharon, PA 16146 (SAN 696-7604) Tel 412-347-5857.

Talmis, Inc., Subs. of Link Resources, *(Talmis),* 215 Park Ave. S., New York, NY 10003 (SAN 654-4487) Tel 212-473-5600.

Talmud Pr., *(Talmud Pr; 0-9604554),* P.O. Box 3453, San Mateo, CA 94403 (SAN 213-9081) Tel 415-347-5751.

Talsorian, R., Inc., *(R Talsorian; 0-937279),* P.O. Box 2288, Aptos, CA 95001-2288 (SAN 658-6600) Tel 408-462-0261; 750 Bay Ave., No. 114, Capitola, CA 95010 (SAN 658-6619).

Tamal Land Pr., *(Tamal Land; 0-912908),* 39 Merwin Ave., Fairfax, CA 94930 (SAN 207-0162) Tel 415-456-4705.

Tamal Vista Pubns., *(Tamal Vista; 0-917436),* 222 Madrone Ave., Larkspur, CA 94939 (SAN 218-9844) Tel 415-924-7289.

Tamalpais Press, *(Tamalpais Pr; 0-916596),* 601 Van Ness Ave., No. 708, San Francisco, CA 94102 (SAN 209-2573) Tel 415-885-6613.

Tamara Pr., *(Tamara Pr; 0-914991),* c/o Cannon, 440 E. 75th St., New York, NY 10021 (SAN 289-4424) Tel 516-625-0549.

Tamarack Editions, *(Tamarack Edns; 0-918092),* P.O. Box 6773, Ithaca, NY 14851 (SAN 210-170X).

†Tamarack Pr., *(Tamarack Pr; 0-915024),* P.O. Box 5650, Madison, WI 53705 (SAN 209-2425) Tel 608-231-2444; *CIP.*

Tamas & Brownson Pubs., Subs. of Tamas & Assocs., Inc., *(Tamas & Brownson; 0-915403),* 18251 McDurmott St., Suite A, Irvine, CA 92714 (SAN 291-4506) Tel 714-660-8822.

Tambra Publishing, *(Tambra Pub; 0-9615698),* P.O. Box3355, Covina, CA 91722 (SAN 200-562X) Tel 818-332-1983; Dist. by: Baker & Taylor, Eastern Div., 50 Kirby Ave., Somerville, NJ 08876 (SAN 169-4901); Toll free: 800-345-2282.

Tamburitza Pr., *(Tamburitza; 0-936922),* 1801 Blvd. of the Allies, Pittsburgh, PA 15219 (SAN 216-065X).

Tamerlane Press *See* **Underwood, Miller**

Tamm, Edward, *(Ed Tamm; 0-9616793),* P.O. Box 498, North Amherst, MA 01059 (SAN 661-048X); 83 Spring St., North Amherst, MA 01059 (SAN 661-0498) Tel 413-253-5070.

Tam's Books, Inc., *(Tam's Bks; 0-89179),* 3333 S. Hoover St., Los Angeles, CA 90007 (SAN 207-6497) Tel 213-746-1141.

Tan Pr., *(Tan Pr; 0-9615754),* P.O. Box 3721, Washington, DC 20007 (SAN 695-894X) Tel 202-333-6501.

Tanadgusix Corp., *(Tanadgusix Corp; 0-9601948),* St. Paul, AK 99660 (SAN 211-7630).

Tanam Pr., *(Tanam Pr; 0-934378),* 40 White St., New York, NY 10013 (SAN 215-3467) Tel 212-431-9183.

†Tandem Pr. Pubs., *(Tandem Pr; 0-913024),* P.O. Box 237, Tannersville, PA 18372 (SAN 202-7615) Tel 717-629-0940; *CIP.*

Tandem Pubs., *(Tandem Pubs VA; 0-9606244),* 5821 Banning Place, Burke, VA 22015 (SAN 218-5091).

Tangelwuld Pr., *(Tangelwuld; 0-934667),* P.O. Box 160361, Las Colinas, TX 75016 (SAN 695-8982) Tel 214-686-5332.

Tangent Pr., Subs. of Tangent Toy Co., *(Tangent Pr; 0-932165),* 140 Carl St., Suite 146, San Francisco, CA 94117 (SAN 687-6307); Dist. by: Bookpeople, 2929 Fifth St., Berkeley, CA 94710 (SAN 168-9517) Tel 219-232-8500; Dist. by: Publishers Group West, 5855 Beaudry St., Emeryville, CA 94608 (SAN 202-8522).

Tangents, *(Tangents; 0-9611742),* 328 W. Mulberry, Kankakee, IL 60901 (SAN 285-3809) Tel 815-932-5130.

Tanglewood Pr., *(Tanglewood Press; 0-9614553),* 5012 Tanglewood Dr., Raleigh, NC 27612 (SAN 678-9153) Tel 919-787-2287.

Tanner, Ralph, Assocs., Inc., *(R Tanner Assocs Inc; 0-942078),* Suite 102, Great Western Bank Bldg., 122 N. Cortez St., Prescott, AZ 86301 (SAN 239-9857) Tel 602-778-4162.

Tanner Trust Fund *See* **Univ. of Utah Pr.**

Tanro Co., *(Tanro Co; 0-9617220),* 1020 Rilma Ln., Los Altos, CA 94022 (SAN 663-4176) Tel 415-941-2623.

Tanstaafl, *(Tanstaafl; 0-931358),* P.O. Box 60026, Sunnyvale, CA 94086 (SAN 211-3805) Tel 408-280-1776.

Tao of Wing Chun Do, *(Tao of Wing; 0-918642),* 11023 NE. 131st, Kirkland, WA 98034 (SAN 211-9854) Tel 206-821-1487.

Tao Pub., *(Tao Pub; 0-942196),* 2700 Ocean Ave., San Francisco, CA 94132 (SAN 239-9865) Tel 415-771-7181.

Taoist Pubs., *(Taoist Pubs; 0-9608030),* Dist. by: EDT, Inc., P.O. Box 979, Royal Oak, MI 48068 (SAN 239-4928) Tel 313-399-4926; Dist. by: New Leaf Distributing Co., 1020 White St., SW, Atlanta, GA 30310 (SAN 169-1449) Tel 404-755-2665; Toll free: 800-241-3829.

Taos Heritage Publishing Co., *(Taos Heritage; 0-9615177),* P.O. Box NNN, Taos, NM 87571 (SAN 694-2830) Tel 505-758-2450.

Taosedon Pr., *(Taosedon Pr; 0-9615915),* P.O. Box 2252, Taos, NM 87571 (SAN 696-7787) Tel 505-758-1029.

Tapley, Lance, Pub., *(L Tapley; 0-912769),* 86 Winthrop St., P.O. Box 2439, Augusta, ME 04330 (SAN 216-2539) Tel 207-622-1179.

Taplinger Publishing Co., Inc., *(Taplinger; 0-8008),* 132 W. 22nd St., New York, NY 10011 (SAN 213-6821) Tel 212-741-0801. *Imprints:* Crescendo (Crescendo); Pentalic (Pentalic); Pivot (Pivot).

Tara Ctr., The, Subs. of Share International Magazine (Amsterdam, Netherlands), *(Tara Ctr; 0-936604),* P.O. Box 6001, North Hollywood, CA 91603 (SAN 282-3950) Tel 818-785-6300; Dist. by: DeVorss & Co., P.O. Box 550, 1046 Princeton Dr., Marina del Rey, CA 90294 (SAN 168-9886).

Taran Hse. Publishing, *(Taran House Pub; 0-933315),* 3703 E. Cornell Woods Dr., Suite C, Dayton, OH 45406 (SAN 692-3704) Tel 513-274-2942.

Tarantula Pr., *(Tarantula Pr; 0-935737),* 1359 Conalea, Tucson, AZ 85748 (SAN 695-9032) Tel 602-296-5332; Orders to: Tara-Press, P.O. Box 17211, Tucson, AZ 85731 (SAN 662-3611).

Taraxacum, *(Taraxacum; 0-9602822),* 1227 30th St. NW, Washington, DC 20007 (SAN 213-8255) Tel 202-357-2681.

†Tarcher, Jeremy P., Inc, *(J P Tarcher; 0-87477),* 9110 Sunset Blvd., Suite 250, Los Angeles, CA 90069 (SAN 202-0424) Tel 213-273-3274; Toll free: 800-225-3362; Dist. by: St. Martin's Pr., 175 Fifth Ave., New York, NY 10010 (SAN 200-2132) Tel 212-674-5151; Toll free: 800-221-7945; *CIP.*

Target Communications Corp., *(Target Comm; 0-913305),* 7626 W. Donges Bay Rd., P.O. Box 188, Mequon, WI 53092 (SAN 289-1913) Tel 414-242-3990.

Targeted Communications, *(Targeted Comm; 0-933117),* P.O. Box 1148, Cleveland, OH 44120-0868 (SAN 689-4674); 3644 Rolliston Rd., Cleveland, OH 44120-5137 (SAN 662-7730) Tel 216-921-8074.

Tari Bk. Pubs., *(Tari Bk Pubs; 0-9604258),* 146 E. 34th St., Eugene, OR 97405 (SAN 214-1523).

Tarnhelm Pr. *See* **CSA Pr.**

TarPar, Ltd., *(TarPar; 0-933193),* P.O. Box 3, Kernersville, NC 27284 (SAN 207-494X) Tel 919-523-5369.

Tarquin *See* **Parkwest Pubns.**

Tarrant, Patrick, *(Tarrant; 0-9608850),* 1907 Castle Ave., Bloomington, IL 61701 (SAN 241-080X).

Tartan Tiger, *(Tartan Tiger; 0-935827),* 2320 144th SE, Bellevue, WA 98007 (SAN 696-6535) Tel 206-747-7655.

Tarten Bks. *See* **McKay, David, Co., Inc.**

Tartt, Gene, *(G Tartt; 0-934746),* The Vineyard Almanac, P.O. Box 2641, Saratoga, CA 95070 (SAN 220-2778) Tel 408-867-1614.

Tartu Pubns., *(Tartu Pubns; 0-9614357),* P.O. Box 85208, Seattle, WA 98145 (SAN 687-7427) Tel 206-547-7678.

Tasa Publishing Co., *(Tasa Pub Co; 0-935698),* P.O. Box 35053, Edina, MN 55435 (SAN 216-0668).

Tashmoo Pr., *(Tashmoo; 0-932384),* RFD Box 590, Vineyard Haven, MA 02568 (SAN 212-5706) Tel 617-693-3199.

Tastes of Tahoe, *(Tastes of Tahoe; 0-934181),* P.O. Box 6114, Incline Village, NV 89450 (SAN 693-3807) Tel 702-831-5182.

Tatnic Pr., The, *(Tatnic Pr; 0-9615599),* R. D. 1, Box 528, South Berwick, ME 03908 (SAN 695-9938) Tel 207-676-2276.

Tatsch Assocs., *(Tatsch; 0-912890),* P.O. Box 622, Fredericksburg, TX 78624 (SAN 202-7623) Tel 512-997-8785.

Tatum, Larry, *(L Tatum; 0-9616249),* 664 S. Oak Knoll Ave., Pasadena, CA 91106 (SAN 697-3183); Dist. by: Unique Pubns., 4201 W. Vanowen Pl., Burbank, CA 91505 (SAN 214-3313) Tel 818-845-2656.

Taunton Pr., Inc., *(Taunton; 0-918804),* Box 355, Newtown, CT 06470 (SAN 210-5144) Tel 203-426-8171; Toll free: 800-243-7252; Dist. by: W.W. Norton & Co. Inc., 500 Fifth Ave., New York, NY 10110 (SAN 202-5795) Tel 212-354-5500.

Taurus Editions, *(Taurus Ed; 0-913925),* 96 Grand St., New York, NY 10013 (SAN 286-0597) Tel 212-966-1222.

Taurus Publishing Co., *(Taurus Pub Co; 0-913495),* 56 Doris Rd., Box 492, Halifax, MA 02338 (SAN 283-8753) Tel 617-293-9110.

Taven-Lourveney Publishing Co., Subs. of Taven-Lourveney Enterprises, *(Taven-Lourveney; 0-932167),* 105 Lawrence St., Hackensack, NJ 07601 (SAN 686-421X) Tel 201-343-5674.

Taverly-Churchill, *(Taverly-Churchill; 0-9616595),* P.O. Box 2097, Wawona, CA 95389 (SAN 659-5413) Tel 209-375-6300.

Tavistock Poetry Pr., *(Tavistock Poetry; 0-9613117),* 5475 Pire Ave., San Diego, CA 92122 (SAN 655-1378) Tel 619-450-0120. Do not confuse with Tavistock Publications (UK), an imprint of Methuen, Inc.

Tax Analysts, *(Tax Analysts; 0-918255),* 6830 N. Fairfax Dr., Arlington, VA 22213 (SAN 226-4781) Tel 703-532-1850; Toll free: 800-336-0439.

Tax Foundation, Inc., *(Tax Found; 0-9606762),* 1 Thomas Cir., NW, Suite 500, Washington, DC 20005 (SAN 225-1302) Tel 202-822-9050.

†Tax Management Inc., *(Tax Mgmt),* 1231 25th St., NW, Washington, DC 20037 (SAN 240-1630); *CIP.*

Tax Reform Research Group, *(Tax Reform Res),* 215 Pennsylvania Ave., SE, Washington, DC 20003 (SAN 225-7246) Tel 202-546-4996.

Taxpayers' Foundation, *(Taxpayers Found; 0-911415),* 325 Pennsylvania Ave. SE, Washington, DC 20003 (SAN 265-3648) Tel 202-543-3070.

Taylor, Carl B., *(C B Taylor; 0-9605948),* 773 Augusta, Morgantown, WV 26505 (SAN 216-6488) Tel 304-292-8190.

Taylor, Dorothy Loring, *(D L Taylor; 0-9610640),* R. R. 2, Box 152, Virginia, IL 62691 (SAN 265-3567) Tel 217-458-2506.

Taylor, Henry T., *(H T Taylor; 0-938956),* P.O. Box 111, Eggertville, NY 14226 (SAN 264-5149).

Taylor, J. A., *(J A Taylor; 0-9615675),* Box 147 B Cohasset Stage, Chico, CA 95926 (SAN 696-3005) Tel 916-342-1675.

Taylor, James, Ltd., *(J Taylor CA; 0-943950),* P.O. Box 12502, La Crescenta, CA 91214 (SAN 241-5860).

Taylor, James R., Pub., *(J R Taylor; 0-9616670),* 2811 Zinnia Ct., Union City, CA 94587 (SAN 659-9044) Tel 415-487-4628.

Taylor, Joanna, Bks., *(J Taylor Bks),* 2461 el Pavo Way, Rancho Cordova, CA 95670 (SAN 238-8227).

Taylor, Pat, *(P Taylor; 0-9611404),* 719 Gales Ave., Winston Salem, NC 27103 (SAN 283-8796) Tel 919-722-2810.

Taylor, Robert H., , *(R H Taylor; 0-9613586),* Box 46, Lumberville, PA 18933 (SAN 282-5767).

Taylor, Sally, & Friends, *(S Taylor & Friends; 0-9604904; 0-934101),* 1442 Willard St., San Francisco, CA 94117 (SAN 216-1990) Tel 415-824-1563; Dist. by: Bookpeople, 2929 Fifth St., Berkeley, CA 94710 (SAN 168-9517) Tel 415-549-3030; Dist. by: Publishers Group West, 5855 Beaudry St., Emeryville, CA 94608 (SAN 202-8522) Tel 415-658-3453; Dist. by: The Wine Appreciation Guild, 1377 Ninth Ave., San Francisco, CA 94107 (SAN 282-5546).

Taylor, W. Thomas, Bookseller, *(W T Taylor; 0-935072),* 708 Colorado, Suite 704, Austin, TX 78701 (SAN 211-1454) Tel 512-478-7628.

Taylor, William M., *(W M Taylor),* 412 Red Hill Ave., San Anselmo, CA 94960 (SAN 212-9736) Tel 415-457-2214.

Taylor & Francis, Inc., *(Taylor & Francis; 0-85066; 0-905273; 1-85000; 0-335-; 0-86353; 0-903796),* 242 Cherry St., Philadelphia, PA 19106-1906 (SAN 286-2182) Tel 215-238-0939; Toll free: 800-821-8312. *Imprints:* Falmer Press (Falmer Pr); Open University Press (Open Univ Pr); S I P R I (SIPRI).

Taylor & Ng, Subs. of Environmental Ceramics, Inc., *(Taylor & Ng; 0-912738),* 271 Sutter St., San Francisco, CA 94108 (SAN 208-3396) Tel 415-398-8548; Toll free: 800-227-4090; Box 8888, Fairfield, CA 94533 (SAN 658-1889); 2700 Maxwell Way, Fairfield, CA 94533 (SAN 658-1897).

Taylor-Carlisle, *(Taylor-Carlisle),* 451 Greenwich St., New York, NY 10013 (SAN 169-6017) Tel 212-226-0707.

Taylor County & Historical Society, *(Taylor Cty Hist Soc; 0-9617105),* Grafton, WV 26354 (SAN 662-5118) Tel 304-265-5015.

Taylor Museum of the Colorado Springs Fine Arts Ctr. *See* **Colorado Springs Fine Arts Ctr.**

Taylor Pubns., *(Taylor Pubns; 0-935881),* P.O. Box 464, Ripley, TN 38063 (SAN 695-9970) Tel 901-635-0263.

Taylor Pubs., *(Taylor Pubs; 0-935947),* 2336 Market St., Suite 41, San Francisco, CA 94114 (SAN 696-7779) Tel 415-392-8822.

Names

Taylor Publishing, *(Taylor Pub WA; 0-9609056)*, 1525 Lincoln St., Bellingham, WA 98226 (SAN 240-9860) Tel 206-734-6073.

†Taylor Publishing Co., Subs. of Insilco, *(Taylor Pub; 0-87833)*, 1550 Mockingbird Ln., Dallas, TX 75235 (SAN 202-7631) Tel 214-637-2800; *CIP.*

Taylor Street Pr., *(Taylor Street; 0-911407)*, 60 Taylor Dr., Fairfax, CA 94930 (SAN 275-9403) Tel 415-453-2765.

Taylor, Taylor & Taylor, *(Taylor Taylor; 0-9616149)*, 6644 Hellman Ave., Alta Loma, CA 91701 (SAN 699-9727) Tel 714-987-2769.

Tayu Pr., Div. of Tayu Center for Gay Spirituality, *(Tayu Pr; 0-934350)*, P.O. Box 11554, Santa Rosa, CA 95406 (SAN 213-1773) Tel 707-887-2490.

Tazelaar, *(Tazelaar; 0-9613792)*, P.O. Box 68603, Seattle, WA 98168 (SAN 678-9897) Tel 206-246-6753.

Te-Cum-Tom Enterprises, *(Te Cum Tom; 0-913508)*, 5770 Franson Ct., North Bend, OR 97459 (SAN 205-4183) Tel 503-756-5757.

Teach Me Tapes, Inc., *(Teach Me; 0-934633)*, 6024 Walnut Dr., Edina, MN 55436 (SAN 693-9309) Tel 612-938-8583.

Teach'em, Inc., *(Teach'em; 0-931028)*, 160 E. Illinois St., Chicago, IL 60611 (SAN 211-2787) Tel 312-467-0424.

Teacher Update, Inc., *(Teacher Update; 0-89780)*, P.O. Box 205, Saddle River, NJ 07458 (SAN 212-3878) Tel 201-342-9024.

Teachers & Writers Collaborative, *(Tchrs & Writers Coll; 0-915924)*, 5 Union Sq. W., New York, NY 10003 (SAN 206-3859) Tel 212-691-6590.

†Teachers Insurance & Annuity Assn., *(Tchrs Insurance; 0-9613704)*, 730 Third Ave., New York, NY 10017 (SAN 677-5705) Tel 212-490-9000; *CIP.*

Teacher's Load Pr., *(Teachers Load; 0-9603750)*, 2631 Farber Dr., St. Louis, MO 63136 (SAN 213-8735) Tel 314-653-0761.

Teachers of English to Speakers of Other Languages, *(Tchrs Eng Spkrs; 0-939791)*, Tesol Suite 205 1118 22nd St. NW, Washington, DC 20037 (SAN 225-7858) Tel 202-625-4569.

Teacher's Practical Press *See* Lieber-Atherton, Inc.

Teacher's Tax Service, *(Teachers Tax; 0-912772)*, 1303 E. Balboa Blvd., Newport Beach, CA 92661 (SAN 202-0394) Tel 714-675-9891.

Teak Wood Pr., *(Teak Wood Pr; 0-937281)*, 160 Fiesta Dr., Kissimmee, FL 32743 (SAN 659-0640) Tel 305-348-7330.

Teal Pr., *(Teal Pr; 0-913793)*, P.O. Box 4346, Portsmouth, NH 03801 (SAN 286-2042); 40 Pleasant St., Portsmouth, NH 03801 (SAN 662-2097) Tel 603-431-2319.

Teaparty Bks., *(Teaparty Bks; 0-9610602)*, 10 Loring Ave., Box 232, Kingston, MA 02364 (SAN 265-3656) Tel 617-585-4666.

Tech Data Pubns., *(Tech Data; 0-937816)*, 6324 W. Fond Du Lac Ave., Milwaukee, WI 53218 (SAN 216-0129).

Tech Ed Publishing, *(Tech Ed Pub; 0-933554)*, P.O. Box 28262, Tempe, AZ 85282 (SAN 212-6842) Tel 602-838-3974; Toll free: 800-323-3133.

Tech Tran Consultants, Inc., *(Tech Tran Consult)*, P.O. Box 206, Lake Geneva, WI 53147 (SAN 296-0656) Tel 414-248-9510.

Techkits, Inc., *(Techkits; 0-918662)*, P.O. Box 105, Demarest, NJ 07627 (SAN 210-3753) Tel 201-768-7334.

Technical Analysis, Inc., *(Tech Analysis; 0-938773)*, 9131 California Ave., SW, Seattle, WA 98146 (SAN 661-5317) Tel 206-938-0570.

Technical & Education Center of the Graphic Arts, Rochester Institute of Technology (T&E Center), *(Tech & Ed Ctr Graph Arts RIT; 0-89938)*, 1 Lomb Memorial Dr., Rochester, NY 14623 (SAN 205-2334) Tel 716-475-2761.

Technical Assn. of the Graphic Arts, *(Tech Assn Graphic)*, Rochester Institute of Technology, T & E Ctr., 1 Lomb Memorial Dr., P.O. Box 9887, Rochester, NY 14623-0887 (SAN 224-7836) Tel 716-272-0557.

Technical Assn. of the Pulp & Paper Industry, *(TAPPI; 0-89852)*, P.O. Box 105113, Atlanta, GA 30348 (SAN 676-5629) Tel 404-446-1400.

Technical Communications Assocs., Inc., *(Tech Comm Assoc; 0-9611694)*, 1250 Oakmead Pkwy, Suite 210, Sunnyvale, CA 94086 (SAN 284-9097).

Technical Data Corp., *(Tech Data Corp; 0-927469)*, 330 Congress St., Boston, MA 02210 (SAN 286-5378) Tel 617-482-3341; Toll free: 800-343-7745.

Technical Database Corp., *(Tech Data TX; 0-910747)*, P.O. Box 720, Conroe, TX 77305 (SAN 262-4281) Tel 713-439-1687.

Technical Dictionaries Co., *(Tech Dict; 0-911484)*, Box 2130, Mt. Vernon, ME 04352 (SAN 205-4191).

Technical Directions, Inc., *(Tech Direct; 0-918876)*, P.O. Box 2221, West Lafayette, IN 47906 (SAN 207-1924) Tel 317-494-3888.

Technical Education Pr., *(Tech Ed Pr; 0-911908)*, P.O. Box 342, Seal Beach, CA 90740 (SAN 205-4205) Tel 213-431-8515.

Technical Education Services, *(Tech Ed Serv; 0-930552)*, Univ. of Missouri, School of Journalism, Kappa Alpha Mu, Box 838, Columbia, MO 65201 (SAN 213-3849) Tel 314-442-3161; Dist. by: Running Press, 125 S. 22nd St., Philadelphia, PA 19103 (SAN 204-5702) Tel 215-567-5080.

Technical Educational Consultants, *(Tech Educ Conslt; 0-939247)*, 76 N. Broadway, Hicksville, NY 11801 (SAN 662-6343) Tel 516-681-1773; Dist. by: Bio Learning Systems, Inc., Rte. 106, Jericho, NY 11753 (SAN 200-8262) Tel 516-433-2992.

Technical Information Project, Inc., *(Tech Info Proj; 0-939578)*, P.O. Box 39185, Washington, DC 20016 (SAN 214-2619) Tel 202-363-1133.

Technical Information Pubn. Service, *(Tech Info Pubn; 0-930747)*, 707 Ellis St., Ridgecrest, CA 93555 (SAN 679-1484).

Technical Insights, Inc., *(Tech Insights; 0-914993)*, P.O. Box 1304, Fort Lee, NJ 07024 (SAN 289-4459) Tel 201-568-4744.

Technicon Pubns., *(Technicon Pubs; 0-915428)*, P.O. Box 1413, Novato, CA 94947 (SAN 207-3560) Tel 415-897-7638.

Technics Pubns., Inc., *(Technics Pubns; 0-935159)*, 75-19 Vleigh Pl., Flushing, NY 11367 (SAN 696-1290).

Technipubs, Inc., *(Technipubs; 0-936743)*, 7002 Boulevard E., Suite 360, Guttenberg, NJ 07093 (SAN 699-9603) Tel 201-869-4452.

Technique Assocs., *(Technique Assoc; 0-9614034)*, P.O. Box 25330, Milwaukee, WI 53225 (SAN 683-5201) Tel 414-771-1450.

Technocracy, Inc., *(Technocracy; 0-9606470)*, P.O. Box 238, Savannah, OH 44874 (SAN 209-7842) Tel 419-962-4712.

TechnoLiteracy Assocs., Inc., *(TechnoLiteracy Assocs; 0-9614335)*, 1001 Connecticut Ave. NW, Suite 628, Washington, DC 20036 (SAN 687-8423) Tel 202-293-0909.

Technology & Business Communications, Inc., *(TBC Inc; 0-914849)*, 730 Boston Post Rd., Order Dept., P.O. Box 915, Sudbury, MA 01776 (SAN 289-4491) Tel 617-443-4671.

Technology Group, The, *(Tech Group; 0-939856)*, P.O. Box 93124, Pasadena, CA 91109 (SAN 220-195X) Tel 818-794-6013. *Imprints:* Magick Circle, The (Magick Circle).

Technology Marketing Corp., *(Tech Marketing; 0-936840)*, One Technology Plaza, Norwalk, CT 06854-1924 (SAN 212-4629) Tel 203-852-6800; Toll free: 800-243-6002.

†Technology Press, Inc., The, *(Tech Pr Inc; 0-89321)*, P.O. Box 380, Fairfax Station, VA 22039-0380 (SAN 208-8851) Tel 703-978-5299; *CIP.*

Technology Search International, Inc., *(Tech Search Int; 0-943420)*, 500 East Higgins Rd., Elk Grove Village, IL 60007 (SAN 240-7868) Tel 312-593-2111.

Technology Transfer Institute, *(Tech Trans Inst; 0-942948)*, 741 10th St., Santa Monica, CA 90402 (SAN 240-4516) Tel 213-394-8305.

†Technomic Publishing Co., *(Technomic; 0-87762)*, 851 New Holland Ave., Box 3535, Lancaster, PA 17604 (SAN 202-764X) Tel 717-291-5609; Toll free: 800-233-9936 (For orders); *CIP.*

Techscience, Inc., *(Techscience Inc; 0-918910)*, P.O. Box 1100, Hawthorne, CA 90250 (SAN 208-1733) Tel 503-926-5739.

Techsonic Industries, Inc., *(Techsonic Ind; 0-9616859)*, 1 Hummingbird Ln., Eufaula, AL 36027 (SAN 661-5945) Tel 205-687-6613.

Tecohio Publishing Co., *(Tecohio Pub Co; 0-9616116)*, 27900 Fairmount Blvd., Cleveland, OH 44124 (SAN 699-7309) Tel 216-831-1884.

Tecolote Pubns., *(Tecolote Pubns; 0-938711)*, 4978 Coronado Ave., San Diego, CA 92107 (SAN 661-5058) Tel 619-222-6066.

Tee Loftin Pubs., Inc., *(Tee Loftin; 0-934812)*, 3100 R St., NW, Washington, DC 20007 (SAN 215-9635).

Teen Round-Up, Inc., *(Teen Round-Up; 0-9614268)*, Rte. 1, Box 226A, Duncan, OK 73533 (SAN 687-1534) Tel 405-255-5207.

Teitan Pr., Inc., The, *(Teitan Pr; 0-933429)*, 339 W. Barry, Suite 16B, Chicago, IL 60657 (SAN 200-8211) Tel 312-929-7892.

Tekakwitha Institute of Ancient Man, *(Tekakwitha Ins; 0-935569)*, 1812 Warren Dr., Woodbridge, VA 22191-2421 (SAN 696-1363) Tel 703-841-2569.

Teknek, *(Teknek; 0-930363)*, 19936 Lorne St., Canoga Park, CA 91306 (SAN 670-7793) Tel 818-882-7122; Dist. by: Baker & Taylor Co., Eastern Div., 50 Kirby Ave., Somerville, NJ 08876 (SAN 169-4901).

Tele-Sell Research Institute *See* C. & R. Anthony, Inc.

Tele-Viewer Pubns. *See* Garber Communications, Inc.

Telecom Library, The, *(Telecom Lib; 0-936648)*, 12 W. 21st St., New York, NY 10010 (SAN 211-9862) Tel 212-691-8215; Toll free: 800-542-279. *Imprints:* Personal Achievement Library (Personal Achievement).

Telecommunications Research & Action Ctr., *(T R A C; 0-9603466; 0-943444)*, 1530 P St., NW, P.O. Box 12038, Washington, DC 20005 (SAN 210-9182) Tel 202-462-2520.

Teleflite Corp., The, *(Teleflite Corp; 0-930387)*, 11620 Kitching St., Sunnymead, CA 92388 (SAN 255-7973) Tel 714-242-0500.

Telegraph Bks., *(Telegraph Bks; 0-89760)*, Box 38, Norwood, PA 19074 (SAN 213-8042) Tel 215-583-4550.

Telegraphic Cable & Radio Registrations, Inc., *(Tele Cable; 0-916446)*, P.O. Box 14, Larchmont, NY 10538 (SAN 208-886X); 2076 Boston Post Rd., Larchmont, NY 10538 (SAN 662-1589) Tel 914-834-7888.

Teleometrics International, Inc., *(Teleometrics; 0-937932)*, 1755 Woodstead Court, The Woodlands, TX 77380 (SAN 220-0953) Tel 713-367-0060; Toll free: 800-527-0406.

†Telephone Bks. Pr., *(Telephone Bks; 0-916382)*, 109 Dunk Rock Rd., Guilford, CT 06437 (SAN 208-2462) Tel 203-453-1921; Dist. by: Inland Book Co., P.O. Box 261, 22 Hemingway Ave., East Haven, CT 06512 (SAN 200-4151) Tel 203-467-4257; Dist. by: Small Press Traffic, 3841-B 24th St., San Francisco, CA 94114 (SAN 200-7371); *CIP.*

Telephony Publishing Corp., *(Telephony; 0-917845)*, 55 E. Jackson Blvd., Chicago, IL 60604 (SAN 657-1174) Tel 312-922-2435.

Television Digest, Inc., *(TV Digest; 0-911486)*, 1836 Jefferson Place, NW, Washington, DC 20036 (SAN 207-2955) Tel 202-872-9200.

Television Information Office, *(TV Info Off; 0-937361)*, 745 Fifth Ave., New York, NY 10151 (SAN 275-9624) Tel 212-759-6800.

Television Music Archives Pr., *(TV Music Arch; 0-9615965)*, 3000 Bronx Pk., E., Bronx, NY 10467 (SAN 697-3019) Tel 212-882-5989.

Televisionary Press, *(Televisionary Pr; 0-915857)*, 32 Union Sq., Room 805, New York, NY 10003 (SAN 670-7130).

Telex-Russian Educational Bks., Inc., *(Telex Russian Educ Bks; 0-938181)*, 730 Newark Ave., Jersey City, NJ 07306 (SAN 659-7238) Tel 201-332-3807.

Telford Pr., The, *(Telford Pr; 0-936923)*, 285 Bloomfield Ave., Caldwell, NJ 07006 (SAN 658-3652) Tel 201-228-1487.

Telos Press Ltd., *(Telos Pr; 0-914386)*, 431 E. 12th St., New York, NY 10009 (SAN 282-4027) Tel 212-228-6479.

†Telshare Publishing Co., Inc., *(TelShare Pub Co; 0-910287)*, P.O. Box 679, Marshfield, MA 02050 (SAN 241-4651); Toll free: 800-343-9707; *CIP.*

Telstar Inc., *(Telstar Inc; 0-943000),* 366 N. Prior Ave., St. Paul, MN 55104 (SAN 240-4524) Tel 612-644-4726.

Tembo Productions, Inc., *(Tembo Prod; 0-938177),* 15 Oakland Ave., Harrison, NY 10528 (SAN 659-722X) Tel 914-825-0900.

Tembrook Pr., *(Tembrook Pr; 0-9614080),* 23 Copper Beech Dr., Lafayette Hill, PA 19444 (SAN 685-9445) Tel 215-825-9333.

Temescal Bks., *(Temescal Bks; 0-914289),* P.O. Box 20067, Oakland, CA 94620-0067 (SAN 293-4795) Tel 415-655-5240.

Temmer, Stephen F., Publishing Co., *(S F Temmer; 0-9617200),* 767 Greenwich St., New York, NY 10014-2111 (SAN 663-3986) Tel 212-741-7418.

Tempest Bks., *(Tempest Brookline),* P.O. Box 492, Brookline, MA 02146 Tel 617-629-2397.

Templar Pr., *(Templar Pr OH; 0-939039),* 187 E. Duncan St., Columbus, OH 43202-2675 (SAN 662-6556) Tel 614-261-7241. Do not confuse with Templar Pr. of New York, NY.

Temple, Ellen C., *(E C Temple; 0-936650),* 32 Sundown Pkwy., Austin, TX 78746 (SAN 215-1162) Tel 512-327-4961.

Temple Genealogical Society, *(Temple Geneal; 0-9616195),* 101 Main St., Temple, TX 76501 (SAN 699-8291) Tel 817-774-8435.

Temple of Kriya Yoga, The, *(Temple Kriya Yoga; 0-9613099),* 2414 N. Kedzie Ave., Chicago, IL 60647 (SAN 240-9348) Tel 312-795-0031.

Temple Pubns., Inc., *(Temple Pubns; 0-918341),* 3327 SW Dosch Rd., Portland, OR 97201 (SAN 657-3045) Tel 503-223-8863; Dist. by: New Leaf Distr. Co., 1020 White St., SW, Atlanta, GA 30310 (SAN 169-1449) Tel 404-755-2665.

†**Temple Univ. Pr.,** *(Temple U Pr; 0-87722),* Broad & Oxford Sts., University Services Bldg., Philadelphia, PA 19122 (SAN 202-7666) Tel 215-787-8787; CIP.

Temple Univ., Temple Gallery, The, *(Temple Univ Gallery; 0-939351),* 1619 Walnut St., Philadelphia, PA 19103 (SAN 662-5126) Tel 215-787-5041.

Templegate Pubs., *(Templegate; 0-87243),* 302 E. Adams St., P.O. Box 5152, Springfield, IL 62705 (SAN 213-1994) Tel 217-522-3361.

Templeman, Eleanor Lee, *(Templeman; 0-911044),* 3001 N. Pollard St., Arlington, VA 22207 (SAN 207-0189) Tel 703-528-1112.

Templeton, Larry D., *(Templeton; 0-9608914),* 320 W. Algre Dr., Litchfield Park, AZ 85340 (SAN 241-1571) Tel 602-935-4346.

Templeton Pubns., Div. of Templeton Investment Counsel, *(Templeton Pubs; 0-934405),* 1 Financial Plaza, Suite 2202, Ft. Lauderdale, FL 33394 (SAN 693-8272) Tel 305-764-7390.

Temporal Acuity Products, Inc., *(Temporal; 0-911723),* 300-120th Ave. NE, Bldg. No.1, Bellevue, WA 98005 (SAN 264-4274) Tel 206-462-1007; Toll free: 800-426-2673.

Ten Penny Players, Inc., *(Ten Penny; 0-934830),* 799 Greenwich St., New York, NY 10014 (SAN 213-8743) Tel 212-929-3169; Dist. by: Waterways Project, 799 Greenwich St., New York, NY 10014 (SAN 219-5402).

Ten Pound Island Bk. Co., *(Ten Pound Isl Bk; 0-938459),* 108 Main St., Gloucester, MA 01930 (SAN 660-9821) Tel 617-283-5299.

†**Ten Speed Pr.,** *(Ten Speed Pr; 0-913668; 0-89815),* P.O. Box 7123, Berkeley, CA 94707 (SAN 202-7674) Tel 415-845-8414; Toll free: 800-841-BOOK; CIP.

Ten Talents, *(Ten Talents; 0-9603532),* P.O. Box 86A, Rte. 1, Chisholm, MN 55719 (SAN 207-9364) Tel 218-254-5357.

Ten-Thirty Pr., The, Div. of Ten-Thirty Corp., *(Ten-Thirty Pr; 0-916153),* 77-12 35th Ave., Suite 56A, Jackson Heights, NY 11372 (SAN 295-0022) Tel 718-476-8881.

Tenameca, Inc., *(Tenameca; 0-918582),* P.O. Box 44436, Indianapolis, IN 46244 (SAN 210-3761) Tel 317-631-6304.

Tenderfoot Pr., *(Tenderfoot Pr; 0-915397),* P.O. Box 780, Narberth, PA 19072 (SAN 695-4669) Tel 215-667-4769.

Tendril, *(Tendril; 0-937504),* P.O. Box 512, Green Harbor, MA 02041 (SAN 215-188X).

Tennessee Amer. Soc. of Interior Designers, *(ASID),* P.O. Box 15391, Nashville, TN 37215 (SAN 217-2992).

Tennessee Arts Commission, *(Tenn Arts),* 320 Sixth Ave. N., Nashville, TN 37219 (SAN 239-4936).

Tennessee Bar Assn., *(Tenn Bar Assn),* 3622 West End Ave., Nashville, TN 37205 (SAN 226-9694) Tel 615-383-7421.

Tennessee Federation of Garden Clubs, *(Tenn Fed Garden; 0-939114),* 3325 Lakewood Dr., Memphis, TN 38128 (SAN 219-8215).

Tennessee Municipal League, *(Tenn Muni League),* 226 Capitol Blvd, Nashville, TN 37219 (SAN 226-4862).

Tennis Manual, *(Tennis Manual; 0-9606066),* 9241 W. Broward Blvd., Plantation, FL 33324 (SAN 216-4620) Tel 305-474-6642.

Tensleep Pubns., Div. of Video Resources, Inc., *(Tensleep; 0-9610130; 0-937603),* P.O. Box 925, Aberdeen, SD 57401 (SAN 262-7477) Tel 605-226-0488; 202 S. Main, Citizen Bldg., Suite 524, Aberdeen, SD 57401 (SAN 658-1900).

Tent of Meeting, The, *(Tent Meeting; 0-9615531),* P.O. Box 8518, Santa Fe, NM 87504 (SAN 696-1479) Tel 505-988-8084.

Tenth Avenue Editions, Inc., *(Tenth Ave Edit; 0-932169),* 885 Tenth Ave., New York, NY 10019 (SAN 686-4201) Tel 212-307-6780.

Tenth House Enterprises, Inc., *(Tenth Hse Ent; 0-9603310),* P.O. Box 810, Gracie Sta., New York, NY 10028 (SAN 239-4944) Tel 212-737-7536.

Terhell Bks., *(Terhell Bks; 0-9614165),* 5302 Kenwood Ave., Baltimore, MD 21206 (SAN 686-6670) Tel 301-668-0174.

Terra View Pubns., *(Terra View; 0-9608474),* 2929 Campus Dr., Suite 430, San Mateo, CA 94403 (SAN 240-9089) Tel 415-574-5154; Dist. by: Business Media Resources, 150 Shoreline Hwy., Bldg. B, Suite 27, Mill Valley, CA 94941 (SAN 200-8270) Tel 415-331-6021.

Terraspace Inc., *(Terraspace; 0-918990),* 1823 Greenplace Terr., Rockville, MD 20850 (SAN 210-5152) Tel 301-340-2687.

Terrell, Bob, *(B Terrell),* P.O. Box 66, Asheville, NC 28802 (SAN 209-1941) Tel 704-255-8435.

Terrell, Judy, *(J Terrell; 0-9616780),* 2405 Clublake Trail, McKinney, TX 75069 (SAN 661-0579) Tel 214-542-1530.

Terrenate Assocs., *(Terrenate Assocs; 0-938479),* P.O. Box 5112, Bisbee, AZ 85603 (SAN 659-7815) Tel 602-432-2135.

Terripam Pubs., Inc., *(Terripam Pubs; 0-9617270),* 4616 Cahuenga, No. 3, Toluca Lake, CA 91602 (SAN 663-527X) Tel 818-508-8804.

Terry, Keith C., Assocs., *(K C Terry; 0-937043),* 26 Drakes Bay Dr., Corona del Mar, CA 92625 (SAN 658-7143) Tel 714-759-1421.

Teruko, Inc., *(Teruko Inc; 0-938789),* P.O. Box 1116, La Mirada, CA 90637-1116 (SAN 662-5657); 2254 Rosecrans Ave., Fullerton, CA 92633 (SAN 662-5665) Tel 714-773-5437.

Tesla Book Co., *(Tesla Bk Co; 0-9603536; 0-914119),* 1580 Magnolia Ave., Millbrae, CA 94030 (SAN 213-7011) Tel 415-697-4903.

Tesseneer, Laura F., Publishing Co., *(L F Tesseneer; 0-9613793),* 18 Linden Hill Dr., Crescent Springs, KY 41017 (SAN 679-0011) Tel 606-341-2145.

Test Corporation of America See **Westport Pubs., Inc.**

Test Master, Inc. See **Softwriters Development Corp.**

Testament See **Exposition Pr. of Florida, Inc.**

Tested Recipe Pubs., Inc., Div. of American Printers & Lithographers, *(Test Recipe; 0-88351),* 6701 Oakton St., Chicago, IL 60648 (SAN 202-0467) Tel 312-966-6500.

Tethys Press, *(Tethys Pr; 0-941446),* 9407 Old Redwood Hwy., Penngrove, CA 94951 (SAN 239-0418) Tel 707-795-8345.

Teton Bookshop Publishing Co., *(Teton Bkshop; 0-933160),* Box 1903, Jackson, WY 83001 (SAN 213-1781) Tel 307-733-9220.

Teton Publishing House, *(Teton Pub Hse; 0-9606622),* P.O. Box 2870, Jackson, WY 83001 (SAN 219-6476) Tel 307-733-4470.

Tetra Tech, Inc., *(Tetra Tech; 0-916646),* 1911 Ft. Myer Dr., Suite 601, Arlington, VA 22209 (SAN 208-3345).

Tetragrammaton Press, *(Tetragrammaton; 0-937326),* 1015 Gayley, No. 288, LA, CA 90024 (SAN 214-4778) Tel 213-281-7533.

Tetrahedron, Inc., *(Tetrahedron; 0-9609386),* P.O. Box 402, Rockport, MA 01966 (SAN 260-2717) Tel 617-546-6586.

Teutsch, Joel & Champion, *(Teutsch),* 2049 Century Park E., Suite 2730, Los Angeles, CA 90067 (SAN 206-3867) Tel 213-277-8773.

Tex-Mex Books Publishers International Texas, *(Tex-Mex; 0-918268),* Box 186, 820 San Antonio Ave., San Juan, TX 78589 (SAN 208-0079) Tel 512-781-2186.

Texana Heritage Services, *(Texana Herit Serv; 0-9614104),* Rte. 2, Box 162, Dayton, TX 77535 (SAN 685-9763) Tel 713-576-2378.

TexArt Services, Inc., *(Texart; 0-935857),* P.O. Box 15440, San Antonio, TX 78212-8640 (SAN 696-0022) Tel 512-826-2889.

Texas A & I University, *(Texas Univ),* Campus Box 127, Kingsville, TX 78363 (SAN 283-4340) Tel 512-854-6857.

†**Texas A & M Univ. Pr.,** *(Tex A&M Univ Pr; 0-89096),* Drawer "C", College Station, TX 77843 (SAN 207-5237) Tel 409-845-1436; Lewis St., Univ. Campus, College Station, TX 77843 (SAN 658-1919); CIP.

†**Texas Assn. of Museums,** *(Tex Assn Mus; 0-935260),* P.O. Box 13353, Capitol Sta., Austin, TX 78711 (SAN 213-3873) Tel 512-472-0641; CIP.

Texas Cedar Pr., *(Texas Cedar Pr; 0-9613869),* 6008 N. Lamar, No. 209, Austin, TX 78752 (SAN 685-2548) Tel 512-459-3024.

Texas Ctr. for Writers Pr., *(Tex Ctr Writers),* P.O. Box 428, Montrose, AL 36559 (SAN 208-0257) Tel 205-928-9325; 1100 Glendon Ave., PH4, Los Angeles, CA 90024 (SAN 662-7471) Tel 213-470-7173.

†**Texas Christian Univ. Pr.,** *(Tex Christian; 0-912646; 0-87565),* Box 30783, Fort Worth, TX 76129 (SAN 202-7690) Tel 817-921-7822; Dist. by: Texas A & M Univ. Pr., Drawer C, College Sta., TX 77843 (SAN 207-5237) Tel 409-845-1436; CIP.

Texas Congress of Parents & Teachers, *(Tex Congr Parent & Teach),* 408 W. 11th St., Austin, TX 78701 (SAN 210-959X) Tel 512-476-6769.

Texas Consumer Assn., *(Tex Consumer; 0-937606),* 314 W. 11th St., Austin, TX 78701 (SAN 220-0961) Tel 512-479-0278.

Texas Foundation for Women's Resources, *(Tex Foun Womens Res; 0-9606256),* P.O. Box 50224, Austin, TX 78763 (SAN 220-3510) Tel 512-476-6112; Dist. by: E-Heart Pr., 3700 Mockingbird Ln., Dallas, TX 75205 (SAN 216-3691) Tel 214-528-2655.

Texas Gardener Pr., Div. of Suntex Communications, Inc., *(TX Gardener Pr; 0-914641),* P.O. Box 9005, Waco, TX 76714-9005 (SAN 289-615X); Dist. by: Texas Monthly Pr., P.O. Box 1569, Austin, TX 78767 (SAN 200-2531); Toll free: 800-252-4437 (Texas).

Texas Geographic Interests, *(Texas Geograph; 0-915101),* P.O. Box 9932, Austin, TX 78766 (SAN 289-8519) Tel 512-453-1885.

Texas Government Newsletter, *(Tex Gov; 0-916813),* P.O. Box 13274, Austin, TX 78711 (SAN 654-5092) Tel 512-474-2110.

Texas Inroads Corp., *(Tex Inroads; 0-915483),* P.O. Box 3803, Bryan, TX 77805 (SAN 291-4522) Tel 409-846-4888.

Texas Instruments, Inc., *(Tex Instr Inc; 0-89512),* P.O. Box 655012 MS54, Dallas, TX 75265 (SAN 209-6854) Tel 214-995-4258.

Texas Medical Pr., Inc., *(Tex Med Pr; 0-9615085),* P.O. Box 1409, Texarkana, TX 75504 (SAN 694-0641) Tel 214-792-7151; 21 Northridge Cir., Texarkana, TX 75504 (SAN 699-5993) Tel 214-792-1315; Dist. by: PMG International, 1343 Columbia, No. 405, Richardson, TX 75081 (SAN 200-4739).

†**Texas Monthly Pr.,** Subs. of Mediatex Communication Corp., *(Texas Month Pr; 0-932012; 0-87719),* P.O. Box 1569, Austin, TX 78767 (SAN 200-2531); Toll free: 800-252-4437 (TX only); 3900-D Drossett Dr., Austin, TX 78744 (SAN 658-1927) Tel 512-476-7085; CIP.

Texas State Historical Assn., *(Tex St Hist Assn; 0-87611),* 2-306 Richardson Hall, Univ. Sta., Austin, TX 78712 (SAN 202-7704) Tel 512-471-1525; Dist. by: Texas A & M Univ. Pr., Drawer "C", College Station, TX 77843-4354 (SAN 207-5237) Tel 409-845-1436.

†**Texas Tech Pr.,** Affil. of Texas Tech Univ., *(Tex Tech Pr; 0-89672),* P.O. Box 4240, Lubbock, TX 79409 (SAN 218-5989) Tel 806-742-2768; Orders to: Sales Office, Texas Tech Univ., P.O. Box 4240, Lubbock, TX 79409 (SAN 208-1717) Tel 806-742-1569; *CIP.*

Texas Water Utilities Assn., *(Texas Water; 0-933317),* 6521 Burnet Ln., Austin, TX 78757 (SAN 692-2953) Tel 512-459-3124.

Texas Western Pr., *(Tex Western; 0-87404),* Univ. of Texas at El Paso, El Paso, TX 79968 (SAN 202-7712) Tel 915-747-5688.

†**Texas Woman's University Press,** *(TX Womans U Pr; 0-9607488),* P.O. Box 23866, Denton, TX 76204 (SAN 238-4833) Tel 817-382-1531; *CIP.*

Texas World Bks., *(Texas World Bks; 0-940672),* 406 Post Oak Rd., Fredericksburg, TX 78624 (SAN 693-0328) Tel 512-997-6529; Dist. by: Shearer Publishing, 406 Post Oak Rd., Fredericksburg, TX 78624 (SAN 218-5989).

Texian Press, *(Texian; 0-87244),* P.O. Box 1684, Waco, TX 76703 (SAN 205-4256) Tel 817-754-5636.

Texsoft Corp., *(Texsoft Corp; 0-938589),* P.O. Box 1804, Lexington, SC 29072 (SAN 661-1583); 16-D Harborside, Lexington, SC 29072 (SAN 661-1591) Tel 803-532-6839.

Text-Fiche Pr., The, *(Text-Fiche; 0-89969),* 15 Watsons Ln., Hampton, NH 03842 (SAN 220-097X) Tel 603-926-5682; Orders to: Box 382, Glencoe, IL 60022 (SAN 220-0988).

Textbook Specifications, *(Textbk Specif),* P.O. Box 368, Ridgefield, CT 06877 (SAN 226-8043).

Textile Bridge Pr., Div. of Moody Street Irregulars, Inc., *(Textile Bridge; 0-938838),* P.O. Box 157, Clarence Center, NY 14032 (SAN 216-0676) Tel 716-741-3393.

Textile Museum, *(Textile Mus; 0-87405),* 2320 S St., NW, Washington, DC 20008 (SAN 205-4264) Tel 202-667-0441.

Thalassa Press, *(Thalassa Pr; 0-939472),* Box 2098, Astoria, NY 11102 (SAN 216-4647).

Thalia Bks., *(Thalia Bks; 0-9614706),* P.O. Box 1804, Stone Mountain, GA 30086-1804 (SAN 692-6150) Tel 404-294-7198.

Thames & Hudson, *(Thames Hudson; 0-500),* Dist. by: W. W. Norton & Co., Inc., 500 Fifth Ave., New York, NY 10110 (SAN 202-5795) Tel 212-354-5500; Toll free: 800-233-4830.

That New Publishing Co., *(That New Pub; 0-918270),* 1525 Eielson St., Fairbanks, AK 99701 (SAN 209-6862) Tel 907-452-3007.

That Patchwork Place, Inc., *(That Patchwork; 0-943574),* P.O. Box 118, Bothell, WA 98041 (SAN 240-7876); Toll free: 800-426-3126 Tel 206-483-3313.

Thayer & Assocs., *(Thayer Assocs; 0-9611000),* 522 Wilcox St., Fort Atkinson, WI 53538 (SAN 283-4278).

Thayer-Jacoby, *(Thayer-Jacoby; 0-9606472),* 1432 E. Ninth St., Brooklyn, NY 11230 (SAN 213-9685) Tel 718-339-3278.

Thayse Management, Inc., *(Thayse Mgmt; 0-9616462),* 801 N. Elmwood, Sioux Falls, SD 57104 (SAN 659-3623) Tel 605-338-3599.

The Garden, *(The Garden; 0-9602790),* 6605 Rowland Rd., Eden Prairie, MN 55344 (SAN 212-9752) Tel 612-944-2404.

The Plan, *(The Plan; 0-9612188),* P.O. Box 872, Santa Cruz, CA 95061 (SAN 289-4858) Tel 408-458-3365.

Theatre Arts Bks., *(Theatre Arts; 0-87830),* 153 Waverly Pl., New York, NY 10014 (SAN 202-7763) Tel 212-675-1815.

Theatre Bay Area, *(Theatre Bay Area; 0-9605896),* 2940 16th St., Suite 102, San Francisco, CA 94103 (SAN 216-4655).

Theatre Communications Group, Inc., *(Theatre Comm; 0-930452),* 355 Lexington Ave., New York, NY 10017 (SAN 210-9387) Tel 212-697-5230.

Theatre Crafts Magazine, *(Theatre Crfts Mag; 0-916477),* 135 Fifth Ave., New York, NY 10010 (SAN 295-1096) Tel 212-677-5997; Dist. by: Drama Bk. Pubs., 821 Broadway, New York, NY 10003 (SAN 295-110X) Tel 212-228-3400.

Theatre Guild, Inc., *(Theatre Guild; 0-9614424),* 765 Roslyn Rd., Winston-Salem, NC 27104 (SAN 689-0954) Tel 919-723-7596.

Theatre Library Assn., *(Theatre Lib; 0-932610),* 111 Amsterdam Ave., New York, NY 10023 (SAN 225-3380) Tel 212-870-1670.

Theatrical Ink Pr., *(Theatrical Ink Pr; 0-937283),* 39 Tompkins St., Staten Island, NY 10304 (SAN 659-0489) Tel 718-448-5621; Dist. by: Three Presses Agency, 39 Tompkins St., Staten Island, NY 10304 (SAN 200-6391).

†**Thelema Pubns.,** *(Thelema Pubns; 0-913576),* P.O. Box 1393, Kings Beach, CA 95719 (SAN 205-4272) Tel 916-546-2160; Dist. by: Teitan Press, Inc., The, 339 W. Barry Ave., Suite 16B, Chicago, IL 60657 (SAN 200-8211) Tel 312-929-7892; *CIP.*

Thelpini Press, *(Thelpini Pr; 0-915017),* 1218 Forest Rd., New Haven, CT 06515 (SAN 289-6273) Tel 203-387-1788.

Theobald, Paul, & Co., *(Theobald; 0-911498),* 5 N. Wabash Ave., Rm. 1406, Chicago, IL 60602 (SAN 205-4280) Tel 312-236-3994.

†**Theophrastus,** *(Theophrastus; 0-913728),* P.O. Box 458, Little Compton, RI 02837 (SAN 202-7771) Tel 401-635-4348; *CIP.*

†**Theorex,** *(Theorex; 0-916004),* 8327 La Jolla Scenic Dr., La Jolla, CA 92037 (SAN 207-6632) Tel 619-453-6988; *CIP.*

Theoscience Foundation Pub., *(Theoscience Found; 0-917802),* 193 Los Robles Dr., Burlingame, CA 94010 (SAN 209-0260).

Theosophical Publishing Hse., Div. of Theosophical Society in America., *(Theos Pub Hse; 0-8356),* 306 W. Geneva Rd., Wheaton, IL 60187-0270 (SAN 202-5698) Tel 312-665-0123; P.O. Box 270, Wheaton, IL 60189-0270 (SAN 699-5667). Imprints: Quest Books (Quest).

Theosophical Univ. Pr., *(Theos U Pr; 0-911500),* P.O. Bin C, Pasadena, CA 91109 (SAN 205-4299) Tel 818-798-3378.

Theosophy Co., *(Theosophy; 0-938998),* 245 W. 33rd St., Los Angeles, CA 90007 (SAN 295-3560) Tel 213-748-7244; 347 E. 72nd St., New York, NY 10021 (SAN 295-3579).

Theotes-Logos Research, Inc., *(Theotes; 0-911806),* 4318 York Ave. S., Minneapolis, MN 55410 (SAN 205-4310) Tel 612-922-3202.

These Are the Jokes Folks, *(These Jokes; 0-9613443),* P.O. Box 1806, Ross, CA 94957 (SAN 657-1182) Tel 415-924-1665.

Thevenin, Tine, *(T Thevenin; 0-9602010),* P.O. Box 16004, Minneapolis, MN 55416 (SAN 210-9603) Tel 612-922-4024.

Thibodaux Service League, *(Thibodaux; 0-9608800),* P.O. Box 305, Thibodaux, LA 70302 (SAN 241-0818) Tel 504-446-9818.

†**Thieme, Inc.,** Subs. of Georg Thieme Verlag, *(Thieme Inc; 0-913258; 0-86577),* 381 Park Ave., S., New York, NY 10016 (SAN 169-5983) Tel 212-683-5088; *CIP.*

Thieme-Stratton, Inc. See Thieme, Inc.

Thigpen, S. G., *(Thigpen; 0-911892),* P.O. Box 819, Picayune, MS 39466 (SAN 205-4329).

Think Network, Inc., *(Think Net Inc; 0-936673),* P.O. Box 6124, New York, NY 10128 (SAN 699-6892) Tel 212-348-3894; 171 E. 89th St., New York, NY 10128 (SAN 699-6906).

Think Shop, Inc., *(Think Shop; 0-937871),* P.O. Box 114, Gallina, NM 87017 (SAN 659-5944) Tel 505-638-5678.

Thinking Caps, Inc., *(Thinking Caps; 0-9610876),* P.O. Box 7239, Phoenix, AZ 85011 (SAN 239-4960) Tel 602-956-1515.

Thinking Gnomes Pr., *(Thinking Gnomes; 0-931945),* 1724 Sacramento St., Suite 49, San Francisco, CA 94109 (SAN 685-9410) Tel 415-673-1079.

Thinking Kids' Pr., *(Thinking Kids Pr; 0-939707),* 1921 Alta Vista Dr., Alhambra, CA 91803 (SAN 663-5172) Tel 818-282-7339.

Thinking Pubns., *(Thinking Pubns; 0-9610370; 0-930599),* 10 Platt St., P.O. Box 163, Eau Claire, WI 54702-0163 (SAN 264-4320) Tel 715-832-2488; Toll free: 800-225-GROW; P.O. Box 163, Eau Claire, WI 54702-0163 (SAN 658-1935); Toll free: 800-362-GROW (In Wisconsin).

Third National Corp., *(Third Natl Corp; 0-9615676),* 201 Fourth Ave. N., Nashville, TN 37244 (SAN 696-1568) Tel 615-748-5317.

Third Party Pub. Co., Div. of Third Party Assocs., Inc., *(Third Party Pub; 0-89914),* P.O. Box 13306, Montclair Sta., Oakland, CA 94661-0306 (SAN 127-7294) Tel 415-339-2323.

Third Pyramid, Inc., *(Third Pyramid; 0-916479),* P.O. Box 260, Watertown, WI 53094 (SAN 296-0052); Dist. by: Third Pyramid Corporation, P.O. Box 260, Watertown, WI 53094-0260 (SAN 296-0052) Tel 414-699-2441.

Third Sector Pr., *(Third Sector; 0-939120),* P.O. Box 18044, Cleveland, OH 44118 (SAN 217-2720) Tel 216-831-9300.

Third World Bk. Shop, *(Third World Bk; 0-9616005),* 3001 Hickory St., Alexandria, VA 22305 (SAN 697-967X) Tel 703-548-0387.

Third World Press, *(Third World; 0-88378),* 7524 S. Cottage Grove, Chicago, IL 60019 (SAN 202-778X) Tel 312-651-0700.

Thirteen Colonies Pr., *(Thirteen Colonies Pr; 0-934943),* 710 S. Henry St., Williamsburg, VA 23185 (SAN 695-0361) Tel 804-229-1775.

Thirteenth House, *(Thirteenth Hse; 0-935458),* 71 Vondran St., Huntington Station, NY 11746 (SAN 213-5639).

13th Moon, Inc., *(Thirteenth Moon; 0-9601224),* Box 309 Cathedral Station, New York, NY 10025 (SAN 208-9831) Tel 212-678-1074.

Thirty-Three Press, *(Thirty-three Pr; 0-9611912),* P.O. Box 456, Topsham, ME 04086 (SAN 286-2069) Tel 207-725-5263.

This 'N That Press, *(This N That; 0-941900),* 334 Crescent Dr., Galt, CA 95632 (SAN 239-8001) Tel 209-745-1000.

Thistlerose Pubns., *(Thistlerose; 0-9605630),* 1007 Greenbrier St., St. Paul, MN 55106 (SAN 216-3098).

Thoburn Pr., *(Thoburn Pr; 0-932029),* P.O. Box 6941, Tyler, TX 75711 (SAN 686-0818) Tel 214-581-0677.

†**Thomas, Charles C., Pub.,** *(C C Thomas; 0-398),* 2600 S. First St., Springfield, IL 62794-9265 (SAN 201-9485) Tel 217-789-8980; *CIP.*

Thomas, James Blake, *(J B Thomas; 0-9616285),* 2946 Mt. Hope, Okemos, MI 48864 (SAN 658-4462) Tel 517-351-3447.

Thomas, Robert C., *(R C Thomas; 0-9616250),* 18 Monte Vista Ave., Vallejo, CA 94590 (SAN 658-7100) Tel 707-644-0680.

Thomas, Susan K., *(S K Thomas; 0-9613660),* P.O. Box 58202, Renton, WA 98057 (SAN 670-7777) Tel 206-235-0899.

Thomas Brothers Maps, *(Thomas Bros Maps; 0-88130),* 17731 Cowan, Irvine, CA 92714 (SAN 158-8192) Tel 714-863-1984; Toll free: 800-432-8430 (CA Only).

Thomas Co., The, *(Thomas Co),* 1669 Maple, No. 6, Box 718, Solvang, CA 93463 (SAN 696-7175) Tel 805-688-7026.

Thomas County Historical Society, *(Thomas County His; 0-9615822),* 725 N. Dawson St., Thomasville, GA 31792 (SAN 696-6675) Tel 912-226-7664.

Thomas Enterprises International, *(Thomas Ent; 0-935243),* 6580 W. 49th St., Mission, KS 66202 (SAN 695-7269) Tel 913-362-0405.

Thomas Geale Pubns., Inc., *(Thomas Geale; 0-912781),* Drawer C.P. 223, 1142 Manhattan Ave., Manhattan Beach, CA 90226 (SAN 283-3735) Tel 213-379-4405.

Thomas Henry Publishing Co., *(T Henry Pub; 0-910078),* 606 Yale Ave. N., Seattle, WA 98109 (SAN 262-0979).

Thomas International, *(Thomas Intl DC; 0-9612128),* P.O. Box 6376, Washington, DC 20015 (SAN 277-7088) Tel 301-657-2910.

Thomas International Publishing Co., Inc., Subs. of Thomas Publishing Co., *(Thomas Intl Pub; 0-937200),* 1 Penn Plaza, New York, NY 10001 (SAN 213-8263) Tel 212-695-0500.

Thomas-Newell, *(Thomas-Newell; 0-9600690),* 1201 Monroe St., P.O. Box 329, Endicott, NY 13760 (SAN 205-4337) Tel 607-754-0410.

Thomas Paine Press, *(Thomas Paine Pr; 0-934162),* 9528 Miramar Rd., Suite 130, San Diego, CA 92126 (SAN 212-9760) Tel 619-484-4798.

Thomas Partners Advertising, Inc., *(Thomas Partners; 0-9616602),* 3255 Wilshire Blvd., Suite 1034, Los Angeles, CA 90010 (SAN 659-7793) Tel 213-385-6285.

Names

617

Thomas Pr., Inc., *(Thomas Pr; 0-911487)*, 2030 Ferdon Rd., Ann Arbor, MI 48104 (SAN 692-8706) Tel 313-662-1275.

Thomas Pubns., *(Thomas Merritt Island; 0-9616889)*, P.O. Box 1736, Merritt Island, FL 32952 (SAN 661-6429); 60 Parnell St., Merritt Island, FL 32952 (SAN 661-6437) Tel 305-452-1979.

Thomas Pubns., *(Thomas Pubns TX; 0-918487)*, 8200 Cameron Rd., No. D, Suite 100B, Austin, TX 78753 (SAN 657-6990); P.O. Box 33244, Austin, TX 78764 (SAN 662-2399).

Thomassen, T. B., *(T B Thomassen; 0-913741)*, 4704 Jean Dr., San Diego, CA 92115 (SAN 286-0627) Tel 619-287-5364.

Thomasson-Grant, Inc., *(Thomasson-Grant; 0-934738)*, 505 Faulconer Dr., Suite 1-C, Charlottesville, VA 22901 (SAN 239-3948) Tel 804-977-1780.

Thomond Pr. *See* Elsevier Science Publishing Co., Inc.

Thompson, Joseph M., Pub., *(J Thompson Pub; 0-9616281)*, 5154 Mountain View Dr., Boise, ID 83704 (SAN 658-5213) Tel 208-322-0672.

Thompson, Paul J., *(P J Thompson; 0-9601288)*, 2200 Prospect Ave., Rm. 437, Cleveland, OH 44115 (SAN 210-5160).

†Thompson & Co., Inc., *(Thompson Co Inc; 0-918351)*, 1313 Fifth St., SE, Suite 301, Minneapolis, MN 55414-1524 (SAN 657-3843) Tel 612-331-3963; *CIP.*

Thompson & Forbes Company, *(Thompson Forbes Co; 0-9613694)*, P.O. Box 2405, Duxbury, MA 02331 (SAN 670-9850) Tel 617-477-9208.

Thompson Pr., *(Thompson Pr; 0-931947)*, P.O. Box 263, Conway, NH 03818 (SAN 685-9399) Tel 603-447-5569.

Thompson Pubs., *(Thompson; 0-933479)*, 2555 N. 19th St., Milwaukee, WI 53206 (SAN 691-8972) Tel 414-264-9241.

Thompson Publishing Group, *(Thompson Pub Group)*, 1725 K St., Suite 200 NW, Washington, DC 20006 (SAN 287-2986) Tel 202-872-1766.

Thompson, Roberts & Clare, Pubs., *(T R & C Pubs)*, 12640 N. 70th St., Scottsdale, AZ 85254 (SAN 695-9156).

Thompson's, *(Thompson's)*, P.O. Box 550, Albertville, AL 35950 (SAN 207-4656) Tel 205-878-2021.

Thomson, Phillip, *(Thomson; 0-911504)*, 836 Georgia St., Williamston, MI 48895 (SAN 202-7798) Tel 517-655-2930.

Thomson Pubns., *(Thomson Pubns; 0-913702)*, P.O. Box 9335, Fresno, CA 93791 (SAN 210-377X) Tel 209-435-2163.

Thomson-Shore, Inc., *(Thomson-Shore)*, 7300 W. Joy Rd., Dexter, MI 48130 (SAN 262-0952) Tel 313-426-3939; Dist. by: D. B. Stiles, P.O. Box 812, Gautier, MS 39553 (SAN 262-0960).

†Thor Publishing Co., *(Thor; 0-87407)*, P.O. Box 1782, Ventura, CA 93002 (SAN 202-7801) Tel 805-648-4560; *CIP.*

Thoreau Foundation, Inc., Subs. of Thoreau Society, Inc., *(Thoreau Found; 0-912130)*, 156 Belknap St., Concord, MA 01742 (SAN 205-4353) Tel 617-369-5912.

Thorn Creek Press, *(Thorn Creek Pr; 0-915664)*, Rte. 2, Box 160, Genesee, ID 83832 (SAN 264-4339) Tel 208-224-6924.

Thorn Hse. Pr., *(Thorn Hse Pr; 0-937385)*, 5764 Morley St., Los Angeles, CA 90045 (SAN 659-0500) Tel 818-347-5446; P.O. Box 45264, Los Angeles, CA 90045 (SAN 659-0519); Dist. by: White-Hatch Group, 6625 Springpark, Suite 14, Los Angeles, CA 90056 (SAN 200-6405).

†Thorndike Pr., *(Thorndike Pr; 0-89621)*, P.O. Box 159, Thorndike, ME 04986 (SAN 212-2375) Tel 207-948-2962; Toll free: 800-223-6121; *CIP.*

Thornfield Pr., *(Thornfield Pr; 0-9613075)*, P.O. Box 192, Castleton, VT 05735 (SAN 294-6815) Tel 802-468-5812; Dist. by: Baker & Taylor Co., Eastern Div., 50 Kirby Ave., Somerville, NJ 08876 (SAN 169-4901).

Thornton Pubns., *(Thornton Pubns; 0-9613035)*, 407 Levering Mill Rd., Bala Cynwyd, PA 19004 (SAN 294-1376) Tel 215-667-0887.

Thorntree Pr., *(Thorntree Pr; 0-939395)*, 547 Hawthorn Ln., Winnetka, IL 60093 (SAN 663-1371) Tel 312-446-8099.

Thornwood Book Publishers, *(Thornwood Bk; 0-943054)*, P.O. Box 1442, Florence, AL 35631 (SAN 240-4540) Tel 205-766-4100.

Thoro Press, *(Thoro; 0-9613455)*, 7454 Warrior Ct., Dayton, OH 45415 (SAN 657-3053) Tel 513-836-1386; Orders to: 3936 Salem Ave., Suite 275, Dayton, OH 45406 (SAN 662-2364).

†Thorp Springs Pr., *(Thorp Springs; 0-914476)*, 803 Red River St., Austin, TX 78701 (SAN 202-781X); 1002 Lorrain, Austin, TX 78703 (SAN 694-6348) Tel 804-476-8078; *CIP.*

†Thorsons Pubs., Inc., Subs. of Thorsons Publishing Group (Great Britain), *(Thorsons Pubs; 0-7225)*, 1 Park St., Rochester, VT 05767 (SAN 277-7398) Tel 802-767-3174; Dist. by: Inner Traditions, Park St., Rochester, VT 05767 (SAN 208-6948); Orders to: Harper & Row Pubs., Inc., Keystone Industrial Pk., Scranton, PA 18512 (SAN 215-3742); Toll free: 800-C-HARPER; *CIP.*

Thoughts by Bonnie, *(Thoughts by Bonnie; 0-9616611)*, Rte. 2, Oslo, MN 56744 (SAN 659-7963) Tel 218-695-5111.

Thrash, *(Thrash Pubns; 0-942658)*, Rte. 1, Box 273, Seale, AL 36875 (SAN 277-7096).

Thrasher Balloons, *(Thrasher; 0-9601514)*, P.O. Box 1111, Homestead, FL 33030 (SAN 211-5425) Tel 305-247-8412.

Three Continents Pr., *(Three Continents; 0-89410; 0-914478)*, 1636 Connecticut Ave., NW, Suite 501, Washington, DC 20009 (SAN 212-0070) Tel 202-332-3885.

Three Crowns Industries, Inc., *(Three Crowns Indus; 0-9613100)*, 7831 Temple Rd., Philadelphia, PA 19150 (SAN 294-6793) Tel 215-549-4497.

3-D Pubs., *(Three D Pubs; 0-9600500)*, P.O. Box 428, Edgerton, OH 43517 (SAN 205-4361).

Three Dimensional Thinking, *(Three Dimensional; 0-9613613)*, 1420 Iroquois Ave., Long Beach, CA 90815 (SAN 669-8212) Tel 213-423-1441.

Three L Press, *(Three L Pr; 0-9601938)*, 3142 La Mesa Dr., San Carlos, CA 94070 (SAN 212-0518).

Three Meadows Press, *(Three Meadows Pr; 0-942892)*, 861 Oak Knoll Dr., Perrysburg, OH 43551 (SAN 240-1649) Tel 419-874-8489.

Three Mountains Pr., *(Three Mtn Pr; 0-930986)*, P.O. Box 50, Cooper Sta., New York, NY 10003 (SAN 209-7885) Tel 212-989-2737.

Three River Ctr., *(Three River Ctr; 0-9615677)*, 607 Menlo Ave., Menlo Park, CA 94025 (SAN 696-1622) Tel 415-328-2013.

Three Rivers Pr., *(Three Rivers Pr; 0-915606)*, P.O. Box 21, Carnegie Mellon Univ., Pittsburgh, PA 15213 (SAN 207-9097).

Three Squares Corp., *(Three Squares; 0-9615678)*, 217 S. Orange St., Suite No. 4, Glendale, CA 91204 (SAN 696-1681) Tel 213-661-0420.

Three Star Enterprises, *(Three Star Ent; 0-912507)*, 9709 Raymond Dr., Belleville, IL 62235 (SAN 265-2293) Tel 618-397-1155.

Three-Stones Pubns., Ltd., *(Three-Stones Pubns; 0-933673)*, P.O. Box 69143, Seattle, WA 98168 (SAN 692-5421) Tel 206-431-0195.

Threshold Bks., *(Threshold VT; 0-939660)*, RFD 3, Box 1350, Putney, VT 05346 (SAN 216-6496) Tel 802-254-8300; Dist. by: Great Tradition, The, 750 Adrian Way, Suite 111, San Rafael, CA 94903 (SAN 200-5743) Tel 415-492-9382; Toll free: 800-654-3333; Dist. by: Bookpeople, 2929 Fifth St., Berkeley, CA 94710 (SAN 168-9517); Toll free: 800-227-1516.

Thrift, Richard, *(R Thrift; 0-9604520)*, 108 Clarke Court, Charlottesville, VA 22903 (SAN 211-5433).

Through Thick & Thin, *(Through Thick & Thin; 0-9608638)*, 6216 Hills Dr., Birmingham, MI 48010 (SAN 239-5649) Tel 313-642-4252.

Throwkoff, G., *(G Throwkoff; 0-942004)*, 223 Arballo Dr., San Francisco, CA 94132 (SAN 238-4841) Tel 415-585-9996.

Thrown to the Winds Pr., *(Thrown Winds Pr; 0-9616301)*, 171 Jackson St., Newton, MA 02159 (SAN 658-5140) Tel 617-964-7448.

Thueson, James D., *(Thueson; 0-911506)*, P.O. Box 14474, University Sta., Minneapolis, MN 55414 (SAN 239-4979).

Thum Printing, *(Thum Print; 0-932920)*, 116 W. Pierce St., Elburn, IL 60119 (SAN 212-3150).

Thunder River Press, *(Thunder River; 0-9604274)*, P.O. Box 10935, Aspen, CO 81611 (SAN 214-4786).

Thunderbird Circle Pubs. Co., *(Thunderbird; 0-9615140)*, OS350 Winfield Rd., Winfield, IL 60190 (SAN 694-2091) Tel 312-462-1768.

Thunderbolt Publications, *(Thunderbolt Pubns; 0-9612538)*, Box 70427, 141 S. Taaffe, Sunnyvale, CA 94086 (SAN 289-5722) Tel 415-960-0146.

Thunderchief Corp., *(Thunderchief)*, P.O. Box 85, Troutdale, OR 97060 (SAN 212-8683).

†Thunder's Mouth Pr., *(Thunder's Mouth; 0-938410)*, P.O. Box 780, New York, NY 10025 (SAN 216-4663) Tel 212-595-2025; *CIP.*

Thurau Pr., Div. of Wild International Corp., *(Thurau Pr; 0-914291)*, P.O. Box 8482, Asheville, NC 28814 (SAN 287-5780) Tel 704-254-5000.

Thurnbriar Pr., *(Thurnbriar Pr; 0-937163)*, Robinhood, SR 2, Box 420, Bath, ME 04530 (SAN 658-5167).

Thursday Pubs., *(Thursday Pubs; 0-934502)*, 1846N Pine Bluff Rd., Stevens Point, WI 54481-8905 (SAN 212-9779) Tel 715-344-6441.

Tia Mia, Inc., *(Tia Mia; 0-9612880)*, 720 N. Walnut St., El Paso, TX 79903 (SAN 291-4581) Tel 915-533-0464.

Tiare Pubns., *(Tiare Pubns; 0-936653)*, P.O. Box 493, Lake Geneva, WI 53147 (SAN 699-7066) Tel 414-248-4845; Rte. 4, Box 110, Lake Geneva, WI 53147 (SAN 699-7074).

Tiberias Institute, The, *(Tiberias Inst; 0-917873)*, 1212 LaSombra Ct., El Cajon, CA 92020 (SAN 657-0240) Tel 619-444-8200.

Tichenor Publishing, Div. of T.I.S., Inc., *(Tichenor Pub; 0-89917)*, 1928 Arlington Rd., Bloomington, IN 47402 (SAN 283-8818) Tel 812-332-3307; Toll free: 367-4002.

Ticknor & Fields, Affil. of Houghton Mifflin Co., *(Ticknor & Fields; 0-89919)*, 52 Vanderbilt Ave., New York, NY 10017 (SAN 282-4043) Tel 212-687-8996; Toll free: 800-225-3362; Dist. by: Houghton Mifflin Co., 1 Beacon St., Boston, MA 02108 (SAN 200-2388) Tel 617-725-5000. *Imprints:* Clarion Books (Pub. by Clarion).

Tidal Pr., The, *(Tidal Pr; 0-930954)*, P.O. Box 150, Portsmouth, NH 03801 (SAN 211-3783) Tel 603-430-9475.

†Tide Bk. Publishing Co., *(Tide Bk Pub Co; 0-9602786)*, P.O. Box 101, York Harbor, ME 03911-0101 (SAN 282-406X) Tel 207-363-4534; Orders to: The Distributors, Inc., 702 S. Michigan, South Bend, IN 46618 (SAN 282-4078) Tel 219-232-8500; *CIP.*

Tide-Mark Pr., Ltd, *(Tide-Mark; 0-936846)*, P.O. Box 813, Hartford, CT 06142 (SAN 222-1802) Tel 203-289-0363.

Tide Pr., *(Tide Pr; 0-912931)*, P.O. Box 4224, Linden, NJ 07036 (SAN 283-3158) Tel 201-862-0762.

†Tidewater Pubs., Div. of Cornell Maritime Pr., Inc., *(Tidewater; 0-87033)*, P.O. Box 456, Centreville, MD 21617 (SAN 202-0459) Tel 301-758-1075; Toll free: 800-638-7641; *CIP.*

Tieck, W. A., *(W A Tieck; 0-9600398)*, 3930 Bailey Ave., Bronx, NY 10463 (SAN 205-4906) Tel 212-549-5566.

Tiffany, Jennifer, *(J Tiffany)*, 525 S. Danby Rd., Spencer, NY 14883 (SAN 287-2943).

Tiffany Press, *(Tiffany; 0-914800)*, P.O. Box 304, Newton, MA 02158 (SAN 206-5819) Tel 617-527-9395.

Tiffany Publishing Co., *(Tiffany Pub; 0-9616079)*, 98 Puritan Ave., Worcester, MA 01604 (SAN 698-1321) Tel 617-756-1911.

Tiger Pubns., *(Tiger Pubn; 0-9611318)*, 32 Friendship Ct., Red Bank, NJ 07701 (SAN 283-3506) Tel 201-747-9042.

Tiger Stream Pr., *(Tiger Stream Pr; 0-935829)*, P.O. Box 96, Pismo Beach, CA 93449 (SAN 696-6519) Tel 805-541-6969.

Tigereyes Pr., *(Tigereyes Pr; 0-931763)*, P.O. Box 172, Lemoyne, PA 17043 (SAN 683-7921) Tel 717-774-6352.

Names

Tigertail Enterprises, *(Tigertail Ent; 0-938921),* P.O. Box 1914, Santa Monica, CA 90402 (SAN 661-6690) Tel 805-683-2938.

Tilden Pr., *(Tilden Pr; 0-9605750),* 1001 Connecticut Ave, NW, Suite 310, Washington, DC 20036 (SAN 217-135X) Tel 202-659-5855.

Till Press, *(Till Pr; 0-931208),* P.O. Box 27816, Los Angeles, CA 90027 (SAN 211-4569).

Tiller Publishing, *(Tiller Pub NJ; 0-9616671),* P.O. Box 4014, Dunellen, NJ 08812 (SAN 659-9109) Tel 201-968-2672.

Tillotson, Ira M., *(I M Tillotson),* P.O. Box 3019, Missoula, MT 59801 (SAN 212-9299).

Tilman Pubns., *(Tillman Pubns; 0-9605752),* P.O. Box 488, Arverne, NY 11692 (SAN 239-8125).

†Tilted Planet Pr., *(Tilted Planet; 0-912973),* P.O. Box 8646, Austin, TX 78173 (SAN 283-3808) Tel 512-447-7619; *CIP.*

Tilth, *(Tilth; 0-931380),* 4649 Sunnyside No., Seattle, WA 98103 (SAN 220-4096).

†Timber Pr., *(Timber; 0-917304; 0-88192),* 9999 SW Wilshire, Portland, OR 97225 (SAN 216-082X) Tel 503-287-3093; Dist. by: International Specialized Bk. Services, Inc., 5602 NE Hassalo, Portland, OR 97213-3640 (SAN 169-7129) Tel 503-287-3093; *CIP.*

Timberline Books, *(Timberline Bks; 0-913488),* 25890 Weld Rd. 53, Kersey, CO 80644-8802 (SAN 202-0416) Tel 303-353-3785.

Timberline Pr.(CO), *(Timberline Pr; 0-9608284),* Box 70011, Eugene, OR 97401 (SAN 240-4559) Tel 503-345-1771.

Timberline Pr., Inc., *(Timberline CO; 0-931235),* 7207 Lipan St., Denver, CO 80221 (SAN 693-7713) Tel 303-429-4053. Do not confuse with Timberline Pr., Fulton, MO.

Timbertrails *See* **Capstan Pubns.**

Timberwind Publishing, *(Timberwind; 0-912849),* 7073 Maplewood Ave., Englewood, CO 80110 (SAN 283-3832) Tel 303-781-6366.

Timberwood Industries, Inc., Div. of Books on Music Div., *(Timberwood; 0-9602298),* P.O. Box 82, South Salem, NY 10590 (SAN 212-6079) Tel 914-533-2020.

Timco International, *(Timco Intl; 0-915624),* P.O. Box 431, Berkeley, CA 94701 (SAN 207-3331).

Timco Manufacturing., Inc., *(Timco Mfg; 0-9611060),* 851 15th St., Prairie du Sac, WI 53578 (SAN 282-8901) Tel 608-643-8534.

Time & Space, Ltd. *See* **TSL Pr. (Time & Space, Ltd.)**

†Time-Life Bks., Div. of Time, Inc., *(Time-Life; 0-8094),* 777 Duke St., Alexandria, VA 22314 (SAN 202-7836) Tel 703-960-5421; Toll free: 800-621-7026; 4200 N Industrial Blvd., Indianapolis, IN 46254 (SAN 658-1951); Toll free: 800-631-8081; Toll free: 800-543-9204; Dist. by: Little, Brown & Co., 34 Beacon St., Boston, MA 02106 (SAN 281-8892) Tel 617-227-0730; Dist. by: Morgan & Morgan Co., 145 Palisades St., Dobbs Ferry, NY 10522 (SAN 202-5620); Orders to: Silver Burdett Co., 250 James St., Morristown, NJ 07960 (SAN 204-5982). Lib. & School Orders to: Silver Burdett Co; *CIP.*

Time Manager International USA, Inc., *(Time Mgr Intl; 0-937079),* 3727 Buchanan St., San Francisco, CA 94123 (SAN 658-5256) Tel 415-931-1100.

Time Museum, The, Div. of United Realty Corp., *(Time Museum; 0-912947),* 7801 E. State St., P.O. Box 5285, Rockford, IL 61125 (SAN 283-3522) Tel 815-398-6000.

Time Out to Enjoy, Inc., *(Time Out; 0-9608010),* 715 Lake St., Suite 100, Oak Park, IL 60301 (SAN 238-5864) Tel 312-383-9017.

Time Share Corp., Subs. of Houghton-Mifflin, *(Time Share Corp; 0-89466),* 3 Lebanon St., Hanover, NH 03755 (SAN 658-3830) Tel 603-643-3640.

Time Table Bks., *(Time Table Bks; 0-9614208),* 1015 Cadillac Way, Suite 106, Burlingame, CA 94010 (SAN 686-7359) Tel 415-579-5632.

Time Warp Publishing, *(Time Warp Pub; 0-938889),* 7956 White Oak Ave., Northridge, CA 91325 (SAN 661-7948) Tel 818-344-2286.

Time-Wise Pubns., *(Time-Wise; 0-918826),* P.O. Box 597, Yucca Valley, CA 92284 (SAN 208-2543) Tel 619-365-5888.

†Timeless Bks., Div. of Association for the Development of Human Potential, *(Timeless Bks; 0-931454),* P.O. Box 160, Porthill, ID 83853 (SAN 211-6502) Tel 604-227-9224; *CIP.*

Timely Bks., *(Timely Bks; 0-931328),* P.O. Box 267, New Milford, CT 06776 (SAN 211-3791) Tel 203-744-4719.

Times Bks., Subs. of Random Hse., Inc., *(Times Bks; 0-8129),* 201 E. 50th St., New York, NY 10022 (SAN 202-5558) Tel 212-751-2600; Toll free: 800-242-7737; Orders to: Random Hse., 400 Hahn Rd., Westminster, MD 21157 (SAN 200-2086). *Imprints:* Demeter Press (Demeter); Encounter Books (Enctr).

†Times Change Pr., *(Times Change; 0-87810),* Publishers Services, P.O. Box 2510, Novato, CA 94948 (SAN 202-7860) Tel 415-883-3530; *CIP.*

Times Mirror Pr., *(Times Mirror; 0-911510),* P.O. Box 23951, Los Angeles, CA 90023 (SAN 207-3765) Tel 213-265-6767.

Times Press, The, *(Times Pr; 0-9606608),* 11661 San Vicente Blvd., No. 901, Los Angeles, CA 90049 (SAN 219-8223) Tel 213-820-8767.

Times Publishing Group, Inc., Affil. of Celebrity Service, International, Inc., *(Times Pub; 0-9615476),* 305 Washington Ave., Towson, MD 21204 (SAN 696-1754) Tel 301-337-2640; Toll free: 800-223-1796; C/O Celebrity Service, Inc., 1780 Broadway, Suite 300, New York, NY 10019 (SAN 662-3670) Tel 212-245-1460.

Timescape *See* **Pocket Bks., Inc.**

Timetable Pr., *(Timetable Pr; 0-87974),* 50 Sagamore Dr., Syosset, NY 11791 (SAN 205-440X) Tel 516-921-2137.

Timpanogos Pubs., *(Timpanogos Pub; 0-935329),* 683 South 1040 West, Orem, UT 84058 (SAN 695-7285) Tel 801-225-5898; P.O. Box 776, Orem, UT 84058 (SAN 696-5148).

Tin Man, *(Tin Man CT; 0-9610604),* 194 North St., Willimantic, CT 06226 (SAN 264-4363) Tel 203-423-7370; Dist. by: Holos Gallery, 194 North St., Willimantic, CT 06226 (SAN 264-4363) Tel 203-423-7370.

Tin Man Pr., *(Tin Man Pr; 0-936110),* Box 219, Stanwood, WA 98292 (SAN 222-0156).

Tin Penny Pubs., *(Tin Penny Pubs; 0-937285),* 407 Magnolia, Garden, KS 67846 (SAN 659-0578) Tel 316-276-4265.

Tinkers Dam Pr., *(Tinkers Dam Pr; 0-943608),* 1703 E. Michigan Ave., Jackson, MI 49202 (SAN 240-7884) Tel 517-784-6158.

Tinnon-Brown Publishing Co., *(Tinnon-Brown; 0-87252),* Orders to: Borden Publishing Co., 1855 W. Main St., Alhambra, CA 91801 (SAN 201-419X).

Tiny's Self Help Bks. for Children, *(Tinys Self Help Bks; 0-9616596),* 174 Main St., Apt. 108W, Bangor, ME 04401 (SAN 659-5421) Tel 207-947-2279; Orders to: Paperback Book Stores, Airport Mall, Bangor, ME 04401 (SAN 662-4294) Tel 207-942-9191.

Tioga Pubns., *(Tioga Pubns; 0-9616890),* 101 N. Fenton Rd., Chenango Forks, NY 13746 (SAN 661-6445) Tel 607-648-8578.

†Tioga Pub. Co., *(Tioga Pub Co; 0-935382),* P.O. Box 98, Palo Alto, CA 94302 (SAN 669-280X) Tel 415-854-2445; Dist. by: William Kaufmann, Inc., 95 First St., Los Altos, CA 94022 (SAN 202-9383) Tel 415-948-5810; *CIP.*

Tip Pubns., Subs. of Hunter Enterprises, *(Tip Pubns; 0-935567),* P.O. Box 514, El Segundo, CA 90245 (SAN 696-1762) Tel 213-322-8437; 305 Richmond, El Segundo, CA 90245 (SAN 662-3689).

Tip-top, *(Tip-top; 0-9610000),* Box 442, New York, NY 10025 (SAN 263-2306).

Tipi Workshop Bks., *(Tipi Wkshp Bks; 0-942914),* 1377 Quaker, Golden, CO 80401 (SAN 240-3277) Tel 303-278-7777; Orders to: P.O. Box 84, Allenspark, CO 80510 (SAN 693-9775).

†Tippers International, Ltd., *(Tippers Intl; 0-9612552),* P.O. Box 1934, Wausau, WI 54401 (SAN 225-6460) Tel 715-842-4616; *CIP.*

Tiptoe Publishing, *(Tiptoe Pub; 0-937953),* P.O. Box 206, Naselle, WA 98638-0206 (SAN 659-7971) Tel 206-484-7722; 110 Wildwood Dr., Naselle, WA 98638 (SAN 659-798X).

Tire Management Consultants, Ltd., *(Tire Mgmt; 0-937377),* P.O. Box 1069, Eugene, OR 97440 (SAN 659-0608) Tel 503-683-0163; 1277 SE Reservoir, Roseburg, OR 97470 (SAN 659-0616).

Tiresias Pr., Inc., *(Tiresias Pr; 0-913292),* 116 Pinehurst Ave., New York, NY 10033 (SAN 202-7879) Tel 212-568-9570.

Tirtha, Ranjit, *(R Tirtha),* Eastern Michigan University, Dept. of Geography, Ypsilanti, MI 48197 (SAN 214-3283) Tel 313-487-0218.

Tisdale Publishing Co., *(Tisdale Pub; 0-9616672),* P.O. Box 888, Mars Hill, NC 28754 (SAN 659-9087); Brook St., Mars Hill, NC 28754 (SAN 659-9095) Tel 704-689-2934.

TISSA, Inc., *(Tissa Inc; 0-9616162),* Rte. 1, Box 349A, Culpepper, VA 22701 (SAN 699-8313) Tel 703-547-2989.

Tissue Culture Assn., *(Tissue Culture Assn; 0-931767),* 19110 Montgomery Village Ave., Suite 300, Gaithersburg, MD 20879 (SAN 225-2546) Tel 301-869-2900.

Titan Publishing Co., *(Titan Pub Co; 0-9603314),* P.O. Box 506, Mesilla, NM 88046 (SAN 211-7142).

Titanium Development Assn., *(Titanium; 0-935297),* 11 W. Monument Ave., Suite 510, Dayton, OH 45402 (SAN 696-1827) Tel 513-223-8432; P.O. Box 2307, Dayton, OH 45401 (SAN 696-1835).

Title Bks., Inc., *(Title Books),* P.O. Box 31170, Birmingham, AL 35233 (SAN 168-9207) Tel 205-324-2596.

Titus Publishing Co., *(Titus Pub Co; 0-9610792),* 433 Sunbelt Dr., Suite E, P.O. Box 6788, Corpus Christi, TX 78411-0788 (SAN 265-1432) Tel 512-289-8282.

Tivoli Publishing Co., *(Tivoli Pub; 0-9614788),* P.O. Box 19164, Kansas City, MO 64141 (SAN 692-9893) Tel 816-923-2546.

Tixcacalcupul Pr., *(Tixcacalcupul; 0-938531),* P.O. Box 709, Summerland, CA 93067 (SAN 661-1427); 200 Greenwell Ave., Summerland, CA 93067 (SAN 661-1435) Tel 805-969-0525; Dist. by: Printed Matter, Inc., 7 Lispenard St., New York, NY 10013 (SAN 169-5924) Tel 212-925-0325.

TKM Publications, *(TKM Pubns; 0-915301),* Rte. 6, Box 143-A, Abingdon, VA 24210 (SAN 290-0483) Tel 703-628-4887.

TM Productions, *(TM Prods; 0-937522),* Box 189, Wilmette, IL 60091 (SAN 215-2096) Tel 312-869-9242.

To Begin With, *(To Begin With; 0-9606764),* 1142 Hornell Dr., Silver Spring, MD 20904 (SAN 662-1597) Tel 301-421-9406; c/o Gordon Pledger, 1142 Hornell Dr., Silver Spring, MD 20904 (SAN 219-645X) Tel 301-421-9406.

To-the-Point Press, *(To-the-Point; 0-9606476),* Drawer 546, Dana Point, CA 92629 (SAN 223-0127) Tel 714-496-6677.

Toadwood Publishers, *(Toadwood Pubs; 0-9610878),* R.R.6, Box 63, Edwardsville, IL 62025 (SAN 282-5775) Tel 618-656-0531; Dist. by: Southwestern Stringed Instruments & Accessories, 1228 E. Prince Rd., Tucson, AZ 85719 (SAN 200-4003); Dist. by: Ability Development, Inc., Box 4260, Athens, OH 45701-4260 (SAN 111-9125) Tel 614-954-3547; Toll free: 800-221-9254.

Today in Bible Prophecy, Inc., *(Today Bible; 0-937682),* 113 S. Delano St. No. 1, Anaheim, CA 92804 (SAN 293-4566) Tel 714-995-1869; Orders to: P.O. Box 5700, Huntington Beach, CA 92615 (SAN 293-4574) Tel 714-963-7766.

Today News Service, Inc., *(Today News; 0-932746),* National Press Bldg., Washington, DC 20045 (SAN 202-7887) Tel 202-628-6999.

Today, the Bible, and You, *(Today Bible & You; 0-9617286),* P.O. Box 1722, Broken Arrow, OK 74013 (SAN 663-5997); 13422 E. 131st St., Broken Arrow, OK 74011 (SAN 663-6004) Tel 918-455-2047.

Todd, Richard E., *(R E Todd; 0-9605324),* 8055 N. Marion Dr., Clovis, CA 93612 (SAN 215-9805).

Todd & Honeywell, Inc., *(Todd & Honeywell; 0-89962),* 10 Cuttermill Rd., Great Neck, NY 11021 (SAN 213-179X) Tel 516-487-9777; Toll free: 800-233-3361.

Todd Pubns., *(Todd Pubns; 0-915344),* 10 Rapids Rd., Stamford, CT 06905 (SAN 207-0804) Tel 203-322-5488.

Names

Todd Publications, *(Todd Pubns NY),* P.O. Box 92, Lenox Hill Station, New York, NY 10021 (SAN 226-3599).

Todd Publishing, Inc., *(Todd Pub; 0-935988),* P.O. Box 5837, Scottsdale, AZ 85261 (SAN 222-0172) Tel 602-998-3000.

Todd Tarbox Bks., *(Todd Tarbox; 0-89297),* 2424 Lancelot Dr., Baton Rouge, LA 70816 (SAN 208-2012) Tel 504-293-6308.

Toe Run Pr., *(Toe Run Pr; 0-9615857),* P.O. Box 271606, Houston, TX 77277 (SAN 696-186X) Tel 713-961-7681; 4040 San Felipe, No. 108, Houston, TX 77027 (SAN 699-6264).

Toggitt, Joan, Ltd., *(Toggitt; 0-911514),* 35 Fairfield Pl., West Caldwell, NJ 07006 (SAN 205-4418); Toll free: 800-922-0808.

Token & Medal Society, Inc., *(TAMS; 0-918492),* P.O. Box 366, Bryantown, MD 20617 (SAN 685-3641) Tel 301-274-3441; Orders to: Dorothy Baver, 611 Oakwood Way, El Cajon, CA 92021 (SAN 200-8238).

Toledo Blade Co., The, *(Toledo Blade; 0-9614554),* 541 Superior St., Toledo, OH 43660 (SAN 691-8115) Tel 419-245-6280.

Toledo Museum of Art, The, *(Toledo Mus Art; 0-935172),* Box 1013, Toledo, OH 43697 (SAN 213-8980) Tel 419-255-8000; Dist. by: Pennsylvania State Univ. Press, 215 Wagner Bldg., University Park, PA 16802 (SAN 213-5760) Tel 814-865-1327.

Tolemac, Inc., *(Tolemac; 0-9609520),* P.O. Box 418, Ashland, OR 97520 (SAN 263-2314) Tel 503-482-2720.

Tolff Pubs., Div. of Trinity of Light Fellowship Foundation., *(Tolff; 0-916498),* 5750 Via Real, No. 230, Carpinteria, CA 93013 (SAN 208-8916) Tel 805-684-6363.

Tolle Pubns., *(Tolle Pubns; 0-915378),* P.O. Box 6243, Beaumont, TX 77705 (SAN 211-0970) Tel 713-860-5628; 7920 Wilcox Lane, Beaumont, TX 77706 (SAN 211-0989).

Tolstoy Foundation, Inc., *(Tolstoy Found),* 200 Park Ave. S., Rm. 1612, New York, NY 10003 (SAN 209-2778) Tel 212-677-7770.

Tolteca Pubns., Div. of Centro Cultural de la Raza, *(Tolteca Pubns; 0-938461),* P.O. Box 8251, San Diego, CA 92102 (SAN 660-983X); 2004 Park Blvd., San Diego, CA 92101 (SAN 660-9848) Tel 619-235-6135.

Tolvan Co., *(Tolvan Co; 0-916774),* P.O. Box 1933, Appleton, WI 54911 (SAN 208-8924) Tel 414-766-1828.

†**Tom Paine Institute,** *(T Paine Inst; 0-931803),* 1155 S. Dora St., Ukiah, CA 95482 (SAN 696-0278) Tel 707-462-5648; *CIP.*

Tom Sawyer Bks., *(T Sawyer Bks; 0-937573),* 2801 New Mexico Ave., NW, Penthouse No. 4, Washington, DC 20007 (SAN 659-1442) Tel 202-965-5686.

Tomart Pubns., *(Tomart Pubns; 0-914293),* P.O. Box 2102, Dayton, OH 45429 (SAN 287-5810) Tel 513-299-3785.

Tomash Pubs., *(Tomash Pubs; 0-938228),* P.O. Box 49613, Los Angeles, CA 90049 (SAN 239-4987).

Tombouctou Bks., *(Tombouctou; 0-939180),* P.O. Box 265, Bolinas, CA 94924 (SAN 282-4647) Tel 415-868-2738; Dist. by: Subterranean Bk. Co., P.O. Box 10233, 1327 W. Second, Eugene, OR 97440 (SAN 200-4917) Tel 503-343-6324; Dist. by: Bookpeople, 2929 Fifth St., Berkeley, CA 94710 (SAN 168-9517); Toll free: 800-227-1516; Dist. by: Inland Book Co., P.O. Box 261, 22 Hemingway Ave., East Haven, CT 06512 (SAN 200-4151) Tel 203-467-4257; Toll free: 800-243-0138; Dist. by: Small Press, 1814 San Pablo Ave., Berkeley, CA 94702 (SAN 204-5826) Tel 415-549-3336.

Tompkins, Iverna, Ministry, *(I Tompkins; 0-9611260),* 7036 E. Thunderbird Rd., Scottsdale, AZ 85254 (SAN 283-2240) Tel 602-991-8803.

†**Tompson & Rutter, Inc.,** *(Tompson Rutter Inc; 0-936988),* P.O. Box 297, Grantham, NH 03753 (SAN 220-1380); Dunbar Hill Rd., Grantham, NH 03753-0297 (SAN 655-196X) Tel 603-863-4392; Dist. by: Shoe String Pr., Inc., P.O. Box 4327, Hamden, CT 06514 (SAN 213-2079) Tel 203-248-6307925 Sherman Ave., Hamden, CT 06514 (SAN 699-5675); *CIP.*

Tompson & Rutter, Inc. *See* Shoe String Pr., Inc.

*Tom's Guide,** Div. of Martom Investments, Inc., *(Toms Guide; 0-938557),* P.O. Box 669, Pearl River, LA 70452-0669 (SAN 661-4647); 292 Oak St., Pearl River, LA 70452 (SAN 661-4655) Tel 504-863-2570.

Tonatiuh/Quinto Sol International, Inc., *(Tonatiuh-Quinto Sol Intl; 0-88412; 0-89229),* P.O. Box 9275, Berkeley, CA 94709 (SAN 203-3984) Tel 415-655-8036.

†**Tonnis Productions Inc.,** *(Tonnis; 0-917057),* P.O. Box 311, Harleyville, PA 19438 (SAN 655-1319) Tel 215-256-9633; *CIP.*

Tony Press/Tony B. Enterprises, *(Tony Pr-Ent),* 2168 Candelero, Santa Fe, NM 87505 (SAN 239-507X).

Too Young to Retire, *(Too Young; 0-935703),* 321 W. 78th St., New York, NY 10024 (SAN 696-1916) Tel 212-496-8151.

Toolbox, The, *(Toolbox; 0-9606548),* 8219 Old Petersburg Rd., Evansville, IN 47711 (SAN 223-0135).

Tools & Bks., Ltd., *(Tools Bks; 0-938089),* Old Potter Hill Rd., Westerly, RI 02891 (SAN 659-7998) Tel 401-377-8270.

Tools & Techniques, Inc., *(Tools Techniques; 0-939283),* 1620 W. 12th St., Austin, TX 78703-3945 (SAN 662-5134) Tel 512-482-0824.

†**Tools for Inner Growth,** *(Tools for Inner; 0-914073),* P.O. Box 520, Chiloquin, OR 97624 (SAN 287-5829); *CIP.*

Tooth of Time Bks., *(Tooth of Time; 0-940510),* 634 Garcia St., Santa Fe, NM 87501 (SAN 219-8231); Dist. by: Bookpeople, 2929 Fifth St., Berkeley, CA 94710 (SAN 168-9517) (SAN 200-4151); Dist. by: Bookslinger, 213 E. Forth St., St. Paul, MN 55101 (SAN 169-4154) Tel 612-221-0429; Dist. by: S.D.P., 1784 Shattuck, Berkeley, CA 94709 (SAN 292-823X).

Top-Ecol Press, *(Top-Ecol Pr),* 3025 Highridge Rd., La Crescenta, CA 91214 (SAN 218-9976) Tel 818-248-6369.

Top Stories, Inc., *(Top Stories; 0-917061),* 228 Seventh Ave., New York, NY 10011 (SAN 655-3419) Tel 212-989-3869.

Topaz Press, *(Topaz Pr; 0-915767),* P.O. Box 5066, Billerica, MA 01821 (SAN 294-1392) Tel 617-663-7173.

Topaz Pr., *(Topaz Pr LA; 0-9616733),* 3855 Partridge Ln., Baton Rouge, LA 70809 (SAN 659-8900) Tel 504-924-0983.

Topeka Genealogical Society, The, *(Topeka Geneal Soc),* P.O. Box 4048, Topeka, KS 66604-0048 (SAN 218-9984) Tel 913-233-5762.

†**Topgallant Publishing Co., Ltd.,** *(Topgallant; 0-914916),* 547 Halekauwila St., Suite 101, Honolulu, HI 96813 (SAN 209-4932) Tel 808-524-0884; *CIP.*

Topix Press, *(Topix Pr; 0-911269),* 420 S. Harbor Dr.s, Venice, FL 33595 (SAN 670-7114); Dist. by: Dracula Press, 29 Washington Sq. W., New York, NY 10011 (SAN 219-4228).

Topping International Institute, *(Topping Inst; 0-935299),* 4278 King Ave., Bellingham, WA 98226 (SAN 696-1932) Tel 206-647-2703; Orders to: 4291 Rural Ave., Bellingham, WA 98226 (SAN 662-3697) Tel 206-647-2703.

Tops Learning Systems, *(Tops Learning; 0-941008),* 10970 S. Mulino Rd., Canby, OR 97013 (SAN 217-4456) Tel 503-266-8550.

Topside Pubs., *(Topside Pubs; 0-9617157),* P.O. Box 129, Dillard, GA 30537 (SAN 663-1568); Betty's Creek Rd., Dillard, GA 30537 (SAN 663-1576) Tel 404-746-2134.

Tor Bks., Div. of Tom Doherty Assocs., Inc., *(Tor Bks; 0-8125),* 49 W. 24th St., New York, NY 10010 (SAN 239-3956) Tel 212-741-3100; Dist. by: St. Martin's Pr., 175 Fifth Ave., New York, NY 10010 (SAN 200-2132) Tel 212-674-5151; Dist. by: Warner Pub. Services, 75 Rockefeller Plaza, 9th Flr., New York, NY 10019 (SAN 200-5522).

Torah Aura Productions, *(Torah Aura; 0-933873),* 4423 Fruitland Ave., Los Angeles, CA 90058 (SAN 692-7025) Tel 213-585-7312; Toll free: 800-238-6724.

†**Torah Resources,** *(Torah Res; 0-9603100),* 951-56th St., Brooklyn, NY 11219 (SAN 213-702X); *CIP.*

Torah Umesorah Pubns., *(Torah Umesorah; 0-914131),* 160 Broadway, New York, NY 10003 (SAN 218-9992) Tel 212-227-1000.

Torchbooks *See* Harper & Row Pubs., Inc.

Torchbooks Library Binding *See* Harper & Row Pubs., Inc.

Torey Press, *(Torey Pr; 0-941318),* P.O. Box 2114, Glen Ellyn, IL 60137 (SAN 239-0426) Tel 312-620-5641.

Torres, Angel, *(A Torres; 0-9614110),* 6111 Dennison St., Los Angeles, CA 90022 (SAN 685-3021) Tel 213-722-1133.

Torres, Eliseo, & Sons, *(E Torres & Sons; 0-88303),* Box 2, Eastchester, NY 10709 (SAN 207-0235).

Tosaw Publishing Co., *(Tosaw; 0-9609016),* 7305 Delcielo Way, P.O. Box 939, Ceres, CA 95307 (SAN 240-9097).

Tosefos Media, Inc., *(Tosefos; 0-936617),* 824 Eastern Pkwy., Brooklyn, NY 11213 (SAN 696-7167) Tel 718-756-1498.

Total Commitment Ministries, *(Total Comm Ministries),* Box 242, Harrisburg, OR 97446 (SAN 689-6499).

Total Communications, *(Total Comm; 0-932801),* 16408 Brandsford Pl., Chesterfield, MO 63017 (SAN 688-6167) Tel 314-537-1100.

†**Total Concepts,** *(Total Concepts; 0-915805),* P.O. Box 90607, Honolulu, HI 96835-0607 (SAN 294-1406) Tel 808-595-4410; *CIP.*

Total Graphics, *(Total Graphics; 0-912860),* 1251 Rowena Ave., San Marcos, CA 92069 (SAN 207-0243) Tel 619-744-6599.

Total Publishing, *(Total Pub; 0-914997),* 657 W. Milford Ave., Unit 19, Glendale, CA 91203 (SAN 289-453X) Tel 818-244-2758.

Total Training, *(Total Train; 0-9613123),* 657 W. Milford Ave., Glendale, CA 91203 (SAN 294-6823) Tel 818-244-2758.

Total Trial System, The, *(Total Trial; 0-9605222),* P.O. Box 3663, St. Paul, MN 55165 (SAN 215-8191).

Touch Productions, Inc., *(Touch Prods Inc; 0-9615810),* P.O. Box 505, Lincolnton, NC 28092 (SAN 696-6462) Tel 704-735-4316; Rte. 1, Box 410, Iron Station, NC 28080 (SAN 699-640X).

Touch the Heart Press, Div. of Louis Foundation Pubs., *(Touch Heart; 0-9605492),* Box 210, Eastsound, WA 98245 (SAN 216-1575) Tel 206-376-2250.

Touche Ross & Co., *(Touche Co; 0-942640),* 1633 Broadway, 9th Flr., New York, NY 10019 (SAN 239-5657) Tel 212-489-1600.

Touchstone Art Magic, Inc., *(Touch Art Magic; 0-9616550),* 1106 Paradise Ln., Ashland, OR 97520 (SAN 659-543X) Tel 503-488-0001.

Touchstone Ctr. for Children, Inc., The, *(Touchstone Ctr Child),* 141 E. 88th St., New York, NY 10028 (SAN 265-3664) Tel 212-831-7717; Dist. by: Publishing Ctr. for Cultural Resources, 625 Broadway, New York, NY 10012 (SAN 685-3692) Tel 212-260-2010.

Touchstone Pr., *(Touchstone Oregon; 0-911518),* P.O. Box 81, Beaverton, OR 97075 (SAN 205-4442) Tel 503-646-8081.

Touchstone Programs, *(Touchstone Prog; 0-939467),* P.O. Box 3446, Granada Hills, CA 91344; 10550 Encino Ave., Granada Hills, CA 91344 Tel 213-829-2102.

Tough Dove Bks., *(Tough Dove; 0-9615129),* P.O. Box 548, Little River, CA 95456 (SAN 694-1818).

Tout De Suite A la Microwave, Inc., *(Tout De Suite; 0-9605362),* P.O. Box 30121, 305 Wood Bluff, Lafayette, LA 70503 (SAN 238-7565) Tel 318-984-2903.

Tout Press, *(Tout Pr; 0-932412),* 420 E. College St., Kent, OH 44240 (SAN 693-7799); Dist. by: Mayapple Press, P.O. Box 3185, Kent, OH 44240 (SAN 212-1913).

Tower Enterprises, *(Tower Ent; 0-910431),* 3380 S. Fourth Ave., No. 18, Yuma, AZ 85365 (SAN 260-1478) Tel 602-726-0471.

Tower Hill Press, *(Tower Hill Pr; 0-941668),* P.O. Box 1132, 301 S. Main St., Doylestown, PA 18901 (SAN 239-3298) Tel 215-345-1856.

Tower Pr., *(Tower Pr PA; 0-932153),* 410 Penn St., Hollidaysburg, PA 16648 (SAN 686-4333) Tel 814-946-7310.

Tower Publishing Co., *(Tower Pub Co; 0-89442),* 34 Diamond St., P.O. Box 7220, Portland, ME 04112 (SAN 210-2811) Tel 207-774-9813.

Town of Andover, MA, *(Town of Andover MA; 0-9603160),* Town Clerk, 20 Main St., Andover, MA 01810 (SAN 211-4836) Tel 617-475-3205.

Town of Concord, Massachusetts, *(Town Concord Mass; 0-9614575),* P.O. Box 535, Concord, MA 01742 (SAN 691-8352) Tel 617-371-0350; 46 Kenney Ln., Concord, MA 01742 (SAN 662-295X) Tel 617-369-8352.

Town of Islip, *(Town Islip; 0-9615532),* Islip Town Hall, Islip, NY 11751 (SAN 696-1967) Tel 516-224-5500.

Towncourt Enterprises, Inc., *(Towncourt Ent; 0-9608928),* P.O. Box 9151, Coral Springs, FL 33075 (SAN 281-8671).

Towne, Holly H., *(H H Towne; 0-9613947),* Rte. 7, P.O. Box 378, Sevierville, TN 37862 (SAN 686-2713).

Townhouse Publishing, *(Townhouse Pub; 0-939219),* 301 N. Harrison St., Bldg. B, Suite 115, Princeton, NJ 08540 (SAN 662-6254) Tel 609-585-5539.

Townsend Harbor Pr., *(Townsend Harbor; 0-9613629),* P.O. Box 119, Townsend, MA 01469 (SAN 670-8676) Tel 617-597-6396.

Toy Works Pr., Div. of The Toy Works, *(Toy Works Pr; 0-938715),* 902 Broadway, Penthouse, New York, NY 10010 (SAN 661-6216) Tel 212-982-2269.

Toys 'n Things Pr., Div. of Resources for Child Caring, Inc., *(Toys 'n Things; 0-934140),* 906 N. Dale St., St. Paul, MN 55103 (SAN 212-8691) Tel 612-488-7284.

Trabuco Creek Pr., *(Trabuco Creek Pr; 0-939107),* 109 E. Ave., San Clemente, CA 92672 (SAN 662-5967) Tel 714-498-3783.

Traces Institute Pubns., *(Traces Inst; 0-934185),* 705 Park Ave., No. 203, Plainfield, NJ 07060 (SAN 693-3874) Tel 201-755-5070.

Trackaday, *(Trackaday; 0-9606522),* Rte. 1, Box 330, New Market, VA 22844 (SAN 201-8624).

Tract, Sam, Advertising, *(S Tract Advert; 0-930579),* 505 Worcester Rd., Framingham, MA 01701 (SAN 694-5368).

Traction Slides International, Div. of Graphic Concepts, *(Traction Slides; 0-9610414),* 2160 Washington St., Merrick, NY 11566 (SAN 264-438X) Tel 516-221-3629.

Tracy, John, Clinic Bulletin, *(John Tracy Clinic; 0-9606312),* 806 W. Adams Blvd., Los Angeles, CA 90007 (SAN 203-056X) Tel 213-748-5481.

Tracy Publishing, *(Tracy Pub; 0-933984),* 1627 Boathouse Circle, Suite No. H-228, Sarasota, FL 33581 (SAN 209-5750) Tel 813-966-3797.

Tradd Street Pr., *(Tradd St Pr; 0-937684),* 1042B Hwy. 17 Bypass, Mt. Pleasant, SC 29464 (SAN 205-4469) Tel 803-881-3016.

Trade House Publishing Co., *(Trade House; 0-943600),* P.O. Box 17845, Denver, CO 80217 (SAN 240-7906) Tel 303-469-7200.

Trade Routes Antiques, *(Trade Rte Antiq),* 8462 San Fernando Way, Dallas, TX 75218 (SAN 696-7221) Tel 214-559-4440.

Trade Service Publications, Inc., Div. of Trade Service Publications, Inc., *(Trade Srv Pubns; 0-915955),* 10996 Torreyana, San Diego, CA 92121 (SAN 293-9533) Tel 619-457-5920; Toll free: 800-542-6421.

Trade Wind Impressions, *(Trade Wind; 0-9616251),* 865 Hao St., Honolulu, HI 96821 (SAN 658-7127) Tel 808-373-1141.

Trademark Register, *(Trademark Reg; 0-911522),* 300 Washington Sq., Washington, DC 20036 (SAN 205-4477); 1050 Connecticut Ave., NW, Washington, DC 20036 (SAN 658-1978) Tel 202-429-6668.

Traders Pr, Inc., *(Traders Pr; 0-934380),* P.O. Box 10344, Greenville, SC 29603 (SAN 212-9795) Tel 803-288-3900.

Tradeship Publishing Co., *(Tradeship Pub Co; 0-934592),* 60 State St., 34th Fl. Tower, Boston, MA 02109 (SAN 213-876X).

Tradesman Publishing, *(Tradesman Pub; 0-935831),* 5363 Estrade Dr., San Jose, CA 95118 (SAN 696-6500) Tel 408-269-1176; Orders to: Tradesman Publishing, P.O. Box 7654, San Jose, CA 95150 (SAN 662-3808).

Tradewhims, *(Tradewhims; 0-936701),* 1741 20th St., Kingsburg, CA 93631 (SAN 699-9654) Tel 209-897-3286.

Tradewinds Publishing, *(Tradewinds Pub; 0-938379),* 1441 Woodland Dr., Deerfield, IL 60015 (SAN 661-0331) Tel 312-945-4101.

Tradex Pubns., *(Tradex Pubns; 0-931528),* P.O. Box 27561, Houston, TX 77027 (SAN 212-1743) Tel 713-961-4432.

Traditional Acupuncture Foundation, Inc., The, *(Trad Acupuncture; 0-912381),* American City Bldg., Suite 100, Columbia, MD 21044 (SAN 265-2366) Tel 301-997-4888.

Traditional Pr., Inc., *(Traditional Pr; 0-933711),* 1022 51st St., Brooklyn, NY 11219 (SAN 692-4980).

Traditional Publishing, *(Trad Pub; 0-915377),* 1354 Bel Nor Rd., McKinleyville, CA 95521 (SAN 291-459X) Tel 707-839-1162.

Traditional Studies Pr., *(Traditional Stud; 0-919608),* 423 E. 84th St., New York, NY 10028 (SAN 215-2592).

Traditionalist Press, *(Trad Pr; 0-9610736),* P.O. Box 1611, Louisville, KY 40201 (SAN 265-4148) Tel 502-636-0959.

Traditions Pr., *(Traditions Pr; 0-937745),* P.O. Box 1296, Lexington, SC 29073 (SAN 659-364X) Tel 803-359-0045; Rte. 6, Box 261, Shirway Rd., Lexington, SC 29072 (SAN 659-3658).

†Trado-Medic Bks., Div. of Conch Magazine, Ltd., Pubs., *(Trado-Medic; 0-932426),* 102 Normal Ave., Buffalo, NY 14213 (SAN 212-5722); CIP.

Traffic Service Corp., *(Traffic Serv; 0-87408),* 1325 G St., NW, Suite 900, Washington, DC 20005 (SAN 202-7917) Tel 202-626-4540.

Trailer Visions, *(Trailer Vis; 0-914483),* 1326 Santa Anita Ave., S. El Monte, CA 91733 (SAN 289-6877) Tel 213-575-3224.

Trails End Bks., *(Trails End; 0-9614896),* 3232 S. Clifton, Suite 134, Wichita, KS 67216 (SAN 693-2118) Tel 316-686-9311.

Trainex Pr., *(Trainex Pr; 0-8463),* P.O. Box 116, Garden Grove, CA 92641 (SAN 205-4515); Toll free: 800-854-2485.

Training in Abuse Prevention Project, *(Trg Abuse Prevention; 0-9616782),* P.O. Box 5340, Charleston, WV 25361-0340 (SAN 661-0552); 1614 Washington St., E., Charleston, WV 25361-0340 (SAN 661-0560) Tel 304-340-3695.

Training Resource Corporation, *(Train Res Corp; 0-933794),* Five S. Miller Rd., Harrisburg, PA 17109 (SAN 216-0684) Tel 717-652-6300; Toll free: 800-222-9909.

Tramway Pr., Inc., *(Tramway Pr; 0-932497),* 3611 Newton St., Denver, CO 80211 (SAN 687-4134) Tel 303-238-5614.

Tranquility Pr., *(Tranquil Pr; 0-9614923),* 200 Leslie Dr., Box 516, Hallandale, FL 33009 (SAN 693-465X) Tel 305-454-8082.

†Trans-Anglo Bks., *(Trans-Anglo; 0-87046),* P.O. Box 38, Corona del Mar, CA 92625 (SAN 276-0851) Tel 714-645-7393; CIP.

Trans-Atlantic Pubns., Inc., *(Trans-Atl Phila),* 311 Bainbridge St., Philadelphia, PA 19147 (SAN 464-0234) Tel 215-925-5083. Do not confuse with Transatlantic Arts, Inc., Albuquerque, NM.

Trans-Cal Publishing, *(Trans-Cal Pub; 0-936567),* P.O. Box 377, North Palm Springs, CA 92258 (SAN 698-0902) Tel 619-329-2221; 70-200 Dillon Rd., Desert Hot Springs, CA 92240 (SAN 698-0910).

Trans-Galactic Pubns., *(Trans Gala Pubns; 0-9616078),* 20 Sunnyside Ave., Suite A134, Mill Valley, CA 94941 (SAN 698-0899) Tel 415-388-7554.

Trans Tech Management Press, *(Trans Tech Mgmt; 0-938398),* P.O. Box 23032, Sacramento, CA 95823 (SAN 216-0692).

Trans Tech Pubns., *(Trans Tech; 0-87849),* 16 Bear Skin Neck, Rockport, MA 01966 (SAN 202-7933) Tel 617-546-6426.

Transaction Bks., *(Transaction Bks; 0-87855; 0-88738),* Rutgers Univ., New Brunswick, NJ 08903 (SAN 202-7941) Tel 201-932-2280.

Transatlantic Arts, Inc., *(Transatl Arts; 0-693),* P.O. Box 6086, Albuquerque, NM 87197 (SAN 202-7968) Tel 505-898-2289. Do not confuse with Trans-Atlantic Pubns., Inc., Philadelphia, PA.

Transculture, Inc., *(Transculture Inc; 0-935862),* Village Box 104, New York, NY 10014 (SAN 213-8050).

Transemantics, Inc., *(Transemantics; 0-930124),* 1601 Connecticut Ave., NW, Suite 500, Washington, DC 20009 (SAN 293-4043) Tel 202-659-9640; 5151 Wisconsin Ave., NW, Washington, DC 20016 (SAN 662-1600) Tel 202-362-2505.

Transformations, Inc., *(Transform Inc; 0-9604856),* 2728 N. Prospect Ave., Milwaukee, WI 53211 (SAN 215-8906) Tel 414-962-0213; Orders to: 4200 W. Good Hope Rd., Milwaukee, WI 53209 (SAN 662-085X) Tel 414-351-5770.

Transformations Press, *(Transform Berkeley; 0-930162),* 1625 Jaynes St., Berkeley, CA 94703 (SAN 210-6744) Tel 415-524-8391.

Transitions, *(Transitions),* P.O. Box 478, Peoria, AZ 85345 (SAN 287-282X) Tel 602-972-7504.

Translation & Interpretation Service, *(Trans Inter Serv; 0-9615505),* 355 W. Fourth St., Winona, MN 55987 (SAN 695-2089) Tel 507-452-1038.

Translation Pr., *(Translation Pr; 0-931556),* 2901 Heatherway, Ann Arbor, MI 48104 (SAN 211-4739).

Transmediacom, Inc., *(Transmediacom; 0-942696),* 300 Corporate Court, P.O. Box 408, South Plainfield, NJ 07080 (SAN 239-944X) Tel 201-756-6868.

TransMedica, Div. of CBS, Inc., *(TransMedica; 0-88137),* 41 Madison Ave., New York, NY 10010 (SAN 241-466X) Tel 212-951-8900.

Transnational Data Reporting Service, Inc., *(Trans Data Rep; 0-936107),* P.O. Box 2039, Springfield, VA 22152 (SAN 696-7701) Tel 202-488-3434.

Transnational Pubs., Inc., *(Transnatl Pubs; 0-941320),* P.O. Box 7282, Ardsley-on-Hudson, NY 10503 (SAN 226-2967) Tel 914-693-0089; 22 Myrtle Ave., Dobbs Ferry, NY 10522 (SAN 658-1986).

Transnational Publishing Co., *(Transnational Pub; 0-935949),* P.O. Box 19908, Los Angeles, CA 90019 (SAN 696-6551) Tel 213-731-3127; 3841 W. Washington Blvd., Los Angeles, CA 90018 (SAN 696-656X).

Transport Environment, The, *(Transport Env; 0-9608112),* SR 285 Old Squaw Dr., Kitty Hawk, NC 27949 (SAN 240-1657) Tel 919-261-2267.

Transport for Christ International, *(Transport Chr),* 3200 Gilichrist Rd., Mogadore, OH 44260 (SAN 225-4697) Tel 216-794-0587; P.O. Box 6242, Akron, OH 44312 (SAN 658-1994).

Transportation Ctr. Pubns. See **Northwestern Univ. Pr.**

Transportation Research Board, *(Transport Res Bd; 0-309),* 2101 Constitution Ave., NW, Washington, DC 20418 (SAN 225-2554).

Transportation Systems Group, *(Trans Syst Group; 0-9615600),* 1850 K St., NW, Suite 950, Washington, DC 20006 (SAN 696-1975) Tel 202-862-1105.

Transrep/Bibliographics, *(Transrep; 0-918370),* P.O. Box 22678, Denver, CO 80222 (SAN 209-8997).

TransWorld Productions, *(TransWorld; 0-917517),* Orders to: Box 1842, Orange, CA 92668-0842 (SAN 656-108X).

Transylvania Publications Inc., *(Transylvania; 0-911959),* 2 Stewart Ave., Eastchester, NY 10707 (SAN 672-3985).

Trask House Books, Inc., *(Trask Hse Bks; 0-932264),* 2754 SE 27th Ave., Portland, OR 97202 (SAN 211-9889) Tel 503-235-1898.

Traumwald Press, *(Traumwald Pr; 0-913676),* 3550 N. Lake Shore Dr., Suite 10, Chicago, IL 60657 (SAN 205-454X) Tel 312-525-5303.

Travel & Tourism Press, *(Travel & Tourism; 0-935638),* P.O. Box 1188, Santa Cruz, CA 95061 (SAN 213-7038) Tel 408-429-1709.

Travel & Tourism Research Assn., *(Travel & Tour Res),* P.O. Box 8066, Foothill Sta., Salt Lake City, UT 84108 (SAN 224-0254) Tel 801-581-6333.

Travel Digests, Div. of Paul Richmond & Co., Pubs., *(Travel Digests; 0-912640),* 73-465 Ironwood St., Palm Desert, CA 92260 (SAN 202-7976) Tel 619-346-4792.

†Travel Discoveries, *(Travel Discover; 0-930570),* 10 Fenway N., Milford, CT 06460 (SAN 211-0067); CIP.

Names

Travel Fit, Inc., *(Travel Fit; 0-935753),* 225 E. 86th St., Suite 902, New York, NY 10028 (SAN 696-2017) Tel 212-369-5627.

†Travel Guides Publishing, *(Travel Guides Pub; 0-930103),* P.O. Box 430, Redondo Beach, CA 90277 (SAN 670-2147) Tel 213-534-1536; *CIP.*

Travel Information Bureau, *(Travel Info; 0-914072),* 44 County Line Rd., Farmingdale, NY 11735 (SAN 202-7992) Tel 516-454-0880.

Travel Interludes, *(Travel Inter; 0-9609388),* P.O. Box 4276, Carmel, CA 93921 (SAN 260-2725) Tel 408-624-0928.

†Travel Keys, *(Travel Keys; 0-931367),* P.O. Box 160691, Sacramento, CA 95816 (SAN 682-2452) Tel 916-452-5200; *CIP.*

Travel Photography Pubns., *(Travel Photo; 0-9616197),* P.O. Box 1251, Los Altos, CA 94023-1251 (SAN 699-8305) Tel 415-969-4375.

Travel Pr, Affil. of MacMillan Publishing Co., *(Travel Pr; 0-930328),* P.O. Box 70 16 E. Third Ave., Suite 1A, San Mateo, CA 94401 (SAN 210-6760) Tel 415-342-9117; Dist. by: Charles Scribner's & Sons, Front & Brown Sts., Riverside, NJ 08075 (SAN 201-002X); Toll free: 800-257-5755; Dist. by: MacMillan Publishing Company, Incorporated, 866 Third Ave., New York, NY 10022 (SAN 202-5574) Tel 212-702-2000; Toll free: 800-257-5755.

Travel Text Assocs., *(Travel Text; 0-917063),* 12605 E. State Fair, Detroit, MI 48205 (SAN 297-1704) Tel 313-527-6971.

Travel World Pubns., *(Travel World; 0-89416),* Box 2818, Dublin, CA 94568 (SAN 210-5462) Tel 415-829-2728.

Traveler's Pr., *(Travelers Pr; 0-9617158),* Drawer L, Red Lodge, MT 59068 (SAN 663-3633); Lazy S L Estates, Red Lodge, MT 59068 (SAN 663-3641) Tel 406-446-3026.

Traveling Right, *(Travel Right; 0-936109),* P.O. Box 805, New York, NY 10002 (SAN 696-768X) Tel 212-228-2517.

Travellers' Bed & Breakfast, *(Travellers Bed; 0-9613481),* P.O. Box 492, Mercer Island, WA 98040 (SAN 657-3851) Tel 206-232-2345.

Travfunish Publishing, *(Trafunish Pub; 0-9612022),* P.O. Box 1018, Decatur, AL 35602 (SAN 286-8865) Tel 205-355-2603.

Travis Piano Service, *(Travis; 0-9600394),* P.O. Box 5359-0359, 8012 Carroll Ave., Takoma Park, MD 20912 (SAN 205-4558) Tel 301-439-4111.

Travis Publishing Co., *(Travis Pub Co; 0-917065),* Orders to: 19528 Ventura Blvd., Suite 336, Tarzana, CA 91356 (SAN 685-3951) Tel 818-995-3329.

Treadle Pr., Div. of Binding & Printing Co., *(Treadle Pr; 0-935143),* Box D, Sheperdstown, WV 25443 (SAN 695-2070) Tel 304-876-2557.

Treasure Chest Enterprises, Inc., *(Treas Chest Ent; 0-939161),* 1710 Carrie Hills Ln., La Habra Heights, CA 90631 (SAN 662-9385) Tel 213-694-4486; Dist. by: Santillana, 942 Gerhart, Los Angeles, CA 90022 (SAN 200-7606).

Treasure Chest Pubns., *(Treasure Chest; 0-918080),* 1850 W. Grant Rd., Suite 101, Tucson, AZ 85745 (SAN 209-3243) Tel 602-623-9558; Toll free: 800-223-5369 EXT 239; Orders to: P.O. Box 5250, Tucson, AZ 85703 (SAN 209-3251).

Treasure Guide Publishing Co., *(Treasure Guide Pub),* P.O. Box 368, Mesilla Park, NM 88047 (SAN 209-1747).

Treasure Hunt Pubns., *(Treasure Hunt Pubns; 0-937111),* P.O. Box 1710, Temple City, CA 91780 (SAN 658-4446) Tel 818-285-5905; 5816 N. Rowland Ave., Temple City, CA 91780 (SAN 658-4454).

Treasure Pubns., *(Treasure Publications; 0-912119),* P.O. Box 3300, Roanoke, VA 24015-1300 (SAN 264-8016) Tel 703-774-5144.

Treasured Receipts Co., *(Treasured Co; 0-918489),* P.O. Box 381097, Germantown, TN 38183-1097 (SAN 657-7288) Tel 901-362-8900.

Tree Bks., *(Tree Bks),* Box 9005, Berkeley, CA 94709 (SAN 203-6576).

Tree Communications, Inc., *(Tree Comm; 0-934504),* 250 Fifth Ave., New York, NY 10001 (SAN 282-714X) Tel 212-213-9670; Toll free: 800-242-7737.

Tree Hse. Enterprises, *(Tree House; 0-935571),* 34316 Thornbrook Dr., Farmington Hills, MI 48018 (SAN 699-6025) Tel 313-474-8467; Orders to: 9739 Calgary Dr., Stanwood, MI 49346 (SAN 699-6272) Tel 313-474-8467. Do not confuse with Tree House Pr., of Shelter Island, NY & Treehouse Pr., of Chagrin Falls, OH.

Tree Hse. Pr., *(Tree Hse Pr; 0-9615628),* P.O. Box 1032, Shelter Island Heights, NY 11965 (SAN 696-2041) Tel 516-749-2394. Do not confuse with Tree House Enterprises of Farmington Hills, MI & Treehouse Pr., of Chagrin Falls, OH.

Tree of Life Pubns., *(Tree Life Pubns; 0-930852),* P.O. Box 5688, Santa Monica, CA 90405 (SAN 222-5395) Tel 213-393-0350; Toll free: 800-628-2828, ext. 628.

Tree of Life Publishing Co., *(Tree of Life; 0-9615679),* P.O. Box 1851, Eagle River, WI 54521 (SAN 696-2068); 3975 Columbus Rd., Eagle River, WI 54521 (SAN 699-6280) Tel 715-479-6030.

Treehouse Pr., *(Treehouse Pr; 0-9614789),* 369 N. Main St., Chagrin Falls, OH 44022 (SAN 692-9850) Tel 216-247-8554. Do not confuse with Tree House Pr., of Shelter Island, NY & Tree House Enterprises of Farmington, MI.

Treeroots Pr., *(Treeroots; 0-9604450),* P.O. Box 2302, Los Angeles, CA 90078 (SAN 215-1170); Dist. by: Bookpeople, 2929 Fifth St., Berkeley, CA 94710 (SAN 168-9517) Tel 415-549-3030.

Trees Co. Pr., *(Trees Co Pr; 0-937401),* 49 Van Buren Way, San Francisco, CA 94131 (SAN 659-0659) Tel 415-334-8352.

Trejos Literary Agency, *(Trejos Lit Agy; 0-939551),* 18235 Avalon Blvd., Carson, CA 90746 (SAN 663-3471) Tel 213-538-2945.

TREK-CIR Pubns., *(Trek-CIR; 0-932464),* Box 898, Valley Forge, PA 19481 (SAN 212-2383) Tel 215-337-3110.

Tremaine Graphic & Publishing, *(Tremaine Graph & Pub; 0-939860),* 2727 Front St., Klamath Falls, OR 97601 (SAN 216-9398) Tel 503-884-4193.

Tremar Productions, *(Tremar Prod; 0-9616587),* 2306 Seminary Rd., Silver Spring, MD 20910 (SAN 659-8005) Tel 301-588-3107.

Tremont Pr., The, *(Tremont Pr; 0-943954),* P.O. Box 2307, Silver Spring, MD 20902 (SAN 241-1601) Tel 301-649-6666.

Trempealeau Press, *(Trempealeau; 0-912540),* 800 Hillcrest Dr., Santa Fe, NM 87501 (SAN 211-9897) Tel 505-983-1947.

Tremper, W.J., *(Tremper; 0-9604166),* 340 Fairmount Ave., Jersey City, NJ 07306 (SAN 214-4794).

Trends & Customs, Inc., *(Trends & Custom; 0-910879),* P.O. Box 170008, Overland Plaza, Arlington, TX 76017 (SAN 262-0987); Dist. by: Publishers Marketing Group, 1104 Summit Ave., Plainview, TX 75074 (SAN 262-0995) Tel 214-423-0312.

Trends & Events, Inc., *(Trends & Events; 0-942698),* P.O. Box 158, Fayette, IA 52142 (SAN 240-2882) Tel 319-425-4411.

Trends Publishing Co., *(Trends Pub; 0-9602426),* 31733 Northwestern Hwy., Suite 258, Farmington Hills, MI 48018 (SAN 206-2445) Tel 313-851-7726.

Trenna Productions, Div. of One to Grow On!, *(Trenna Prods; 0-918519),* P.O. Box 2484, Malibu, CA 90265 (SAN 657-730X) Tel 213-457-2583.

Tres Amigos Pubns., *(Tres Amigos Pubns; 0-930277),* 26535 Carmelo, Carmel, CA 93923 (SAN 670-8668) Tel 408-625-1579.

Trestleetree Pubns., *(Trestleetree Pubns; 0-939109),* P.O. Box 295, Albany, NY 12201 (SAN 662-5940); 445 Broadway, Albany, NY 12201 (SAN 662-5959) Tel 518-456-7028.

Trevor Hill Pr., *(Trevor Hill Pr; 0-9616695),* P.O. Box 1851, Davis, CA 95616 (SAN 659-8498); 2163 Bella Casa, Davis, CA 95616 (SAN 659-8501) Tel 916-752-1272.

Tri-Color Pr, *(Tri-Color Pr; 0-9614604),* P.O. Box 36851, Los Angeles, CA 90036-0851 (SAN 691-8387) Tel 805-393-5902.

Tri-County Special Services, *(Tri-County; 0-943390),* P.O. Box 145, St. Anthony, ID 83445 (SAN 241-5887) Tel 208-624-3146.

Tri-Med Press, *(Tri-Med),* 65 Christopher St., Montclair, NJ 07042 (SAN 216-0706) Tel 201-746-9132.

Tri-Oak Education, *(Tri-Oak; 0-9609732),* 24663 Dry Canyon Colocrk, Calabasas, CA 91302 (SAN 262-1002).

Tri State Promotions, *(Tri State Prom; 0-9607868),* P.O. Box 30926, Amarillo, TX 79120 (SAN 239-5665) Tel 806-372-6614.

Tri-State Railway Historical Society Inc., *(Tri-State Rail; 0-9607444),* P.O. Box 2243, Clifton, NJ 07015-2243 (SAN 239-3301) Tel 201-488-5429.

Triad III Publishing Co., *(Triad III Pub; 0-938891),* P.O. Box 535, Desert Hot Springs, CA 92240 (SAN 662-6580).

†Triad Press, *(Triad Pr TX),* P.O. Box 42006-K, Houston, TX 77242 (SAN 214-2023) Tel 713-789-0424; *CIP.*

Triad Pubs., *(Triad Pubs; 0-935673),* 1 S. Pinckeny St., Suite 313, Madison, WI 53703 (SAN 696-2114) Tel 608-255-0659.

†Triad Publishing Co., Inc., Subs. of Triad Communications, Inc., *(Triad Pub FL; 0-9600472; 0-937404),* 1110 NW Eighth Ave., Gainesville, FL 32601 (SAN 205-4574) Tel 904-373-5800; Toll free: 800-874-7777 (SAN 658-201X); Orders to: P.O. Box 13096, Gainesville, FL 32604 (SAN 662-1619); *CIP.*

Triad Publishing Co., The, *(Triad Pub; 0-936703),* 128 Brookmoor Rd., West Hartford, CT 06107 (SAN 699-9794) Tel 203-521-3390.

Triadoption Library, Inc., *(Triadoption Lib; 0-941770),* P.O. Box 638, Westminster, CA 92684 (SAN 239-331X) Tel 714-892-4098.

Triadvocates Associated, *(Triadvocates Assoc; 0-9616806),* P.O. Box 336, Springfield, PA 19064 (SAN 661-4639) Tel 215-544-6927.

TriAm Press, Inc., *(TriAm Pr; 0-914075),* 5015 McKean Ave., Philadelphia, PA 19144 (SAN 287-5853) Tel 215-849-2286.

Triangle Pr., *(Triangle Pr; 0-937144),* 211 North La Salle St., Suite 2026, Chicago, IL 60601 (SAN 216-2016) Tel 312-346-3265.

Triang Pr., The, *(Triang Pr; 0-931513),* 5850 Hubbard Dr., Rockville, MD 20852 (SAN 682-3149) Tel 301-984-5730; Dist. by: W. W. Norton Co., Inc., 500 Fifth Ave,, New York, NY 10110 (SAN 202-5795) Tel 212-354-5500.

Tribal Pr., *(Tribal Pr; 0-9607044),* c/o Lowell Jensen, Rte. 2 Box 599, Cable, WI 54821 (SAN 239-0442) Tel 715-794-2247.

Tribeca Communications, Inc., *(Tribeca Comm; 0-943392),* 401 Broadway, Suite 1907, New York, NY 10013 (SAN 240-7922) Tel 212-226-6047; 44 W 74th St., New York, NY 10023 (SAN 658-2028) Tel 212-496-1923. *Imprints:* Tripro Books (Tripro Bks).

Tribune Publishing Co., Inc., *(Tribune Pub; 0-940654),* 18 Okner Pkwy., Livingston, NJ 07039 (SAN 219-8258) Tel 201-992-1060.

Trice, Bernie A., *(B A Trice; 0-9616006),* 19840 SW 242nd Terr., Homestead, FL 33031 (SAN 697-9696) Tel 305-245-3395.

Trico Pr., *(Trico Pr; 0-916751),* 97 Franklin St., Stamford, CT 06902 (SAN 654-4002) Tel 203-324-5441.

Tricore Associates, Inc., *(Tricore Assoc; 0-9607132),* 170 Kinnelon Rd., Suite 5, Kinnelon, NJ 07405 (SAN 239-0469) Tel 201-492-2798.

Trifecta Charley, Ltd., *(Trifecta Charley),* P.O. Box 0215, Roseville, MI 48066 (SAN 659-2120).

Trike Pub., *(Trike; 0-917588),* 201 Martin, Novato, CA 94947 (SAN 210-3273) Tel 415-382-1591; Dist. by: Small Press Distribution, Incorporated, 1814 San Pablo Ave., Berkeley, CA 94702 (SAN 204-5826) Tel 415-549-3336.

†Trilateral Commission, *(Trilateral Comm; 0-930503),* 345 E. 46th St., New York, NY 10017 (SAN 225-6703); *CIP.*

Trill Press, *(Trill Pr; 0-914485),* 2523 V St., Sacramento, CA 95818 (SAN 240-1673) Tel 916-736-2339.

Trillium Pr., *(Trillium Pr; 0-89824),* P.O. Box 921, New York, NY 10159 (SAN 212-4637) Tel 212-684-7399; Orders to: P.O. Box 209, Monroe, NY 10950 (SAN 662-1627) Tel 914-783-2999.

Names

Trilogy Pubs., *(Trilogy Pubs; 0-931558)*, 2901 Heatherway, Ann Arbor, MI 48104 (SAN 211-4747).

Trimark Publishing Co., Inc, *(Trimark Pub Co; 0-914663)*, 184 Quigley Blvd., New Castle, DE 19720 (SAN 287-7686) Tel 302-322-2143; Toll free: 800-TRIMARK.

†Trine Books, *(Trine Bks; 0-912361)*, P.O. Box 446, Wallingford, CT 06492 (SAN 265-1459) Tel 203-269-6262; *CIP.*

Trinet, Inc., Subs. of Control Data Corporation, *(Trinet; 0-86692)*, Nine Campus Dr., Parsippany, NJ 07054 (SAN 216-3721) Tel 201-267-3600; Toll free: 800-Trinet-1.

Tringa Pr., *(Tringa Pr; 0-9615255)*, 217 N. Ashley St., Ann Arbor, MI 48104 (SAN 694-4027) Tel 313-665-6792.

Trinity Communications, *(Trinity Comns; 0-937495)*, P.O. Box 3610, Manassas, VA 22110 (SAN 659-0675) Tel 703-369-2429; 9380 C1 Forestwood Ln., Manassas, VA 22110 (SAN 659-0683).

Trinity County of Office of Education, *(Trinity County; 0-961243)*, P.O. Box AH-201, Memorial Dr., Weaverville, CA 96093 (SAN 295-4478) Tel 916-623-2861.

Trinity Enterprises, *(Trinity Ent; 0-9617233)*, 7590 Stanwick Ct., Dublin, OH 43017 (SAN 663-5806) Tel 614-766-4887.

Trinity House, Inc., *(Trinity House; 0-913309)*, P.O. Box 104, Crestwood, KY 40014 (SAN 283-3182) Tel 502-241-1492.

Trinity Lutheran Pr., *(Trinity Luth Pr; 0-9616252)*, P.O. Box Z, Brewster, MA 02631 (SAN 658-4489) Tel 617-896-3396.

Trinity Pubns., *(Trinity Pubns; 0-9610132)*, P.O. Box 15608, Cincinnati, OH 45215 (SAN 226-8051) Tel 513-821-9770.

Trinity Publishing House, Inc., *(Trinity Pub Hse; 0-933656)*, 107 Lafayette, Winona, MN 55987 (SAN 215-1189).

Trinity Trail Pubns., *(Trinity Trail Pubns; 0-934409)*, P.O. Box 267, Delores, CO 81323 (SAN 693-8299) Tel 303-882-4979.

†Trinity Univ. Pr., *(Trinity U Pr; 0-911536; 0-939980)*, 715 Stadium Dr., San Antonio, TX 78284 (SAN 205-4590) Tel 512-736-7619; *CIP.*

Triple B Sales, *(Triple B)*, 44 Butternut Dr., Pittsford, NY 14534 (SAN 210-3788) Tel 716-381-7767.

Triple Play Pubns., *(Triple Play Pubns; 0-934289)*, 177-F Riverside Dr., Newport Beach, CA 92663 (SAN 693-2894) Tel 714-548-2045.

Triple Press, *(Triple Pr; 0-941264)*, 33 N. Main St., Medford, NJ 08055 (SAN 239-3964).

Triple S Publishing Co., *(Triple Pub; 0-9615539)*, 426 Felix Ln., West St. Paul, MN 55118 (SAN 696-2122) Tel 612-457-9321.

Triple Seven International, *(Triple Seven; 0-9614870)*, R2, Box 221, Gaston, IN 47342 (SAN 693-2134) Tel 317-358-3713.

Triplett Enterprises, Ltd., *(Triplett Ents)*, Munday-Brohard Rd., Macfarlan, WV 26148 (SAN 207-2947) Tel 304-477-3246.

Trippensee Corp., *(Trippensee Pub; 0-943956)*, 301 Cass St., Saginaw, MI 48602 (SAN 206-2518) Tel 517-799-8102.

Trippon Fashion Center, *(Trippon Fash; 0-935245)*, 5656 Carlton Way, Hollywood, CA 90028 (SAN 696-2149) Tel 213-463-3471.

Tripro Books *See* Tribeca Communications, Inc.

TriQuarterly Books, *(TriQuarterly; 0-916384)*, Northwestern Univ., 1735 Benson Ave., Evanston, IL 60201 (SAN 208-8959) Tel 312-492-3490.

Triton Books, *(Triton Bks; 0-943958)*, P.O. Box 27934, Los Angeles, CA 90027 (SAN 241-161X) Tel 213-247-4177.

Triton College Press, English Dept., *(Triton Coll; 0-931672)*, 2000 Fifth Ave., River Grove, IL 60171 (SAN 211-2779).

Tritone Music, *(Tritone Music; 0-9603470)*, 155 Montclair Ave., Montclair, NJ 07042 (SAN 213-6023) Tel 201-746-7946.

Triumph Pr., Inc., *(Triumph Pr; 0-931515)*, 1062 Edison NW, Grand Rapids, MI 49504 (SAN 682-3157) Tel 616-453-6891.

Triumph Publishing Co., *(Triumph Pub; 0-917182)*, P.O. Box 292, Altadena, CA 91001 (SAN 207-3927).

Triune Bks., *(Triune Bks; 0-9613602)*, 8 Ullman Terrace, Monsey, NY 10952 (SAN 669-7100) Tel 914-352-6950.

Trogon Pubns., *(Trogon Pubns; 0-9600578)*, 1210 Loucks Ave., Scottdale, PA 15683 (SAN 205-4604) Tel 412-887-9436.

Troisi, Ralph E., *(R E Troisi; 0-9615474)*, 15471 S. Bigrock Hoop, Mulino, OR 97042 (SAN 696-2130) Tel 503-829-5511.

Trojan Books, *(Trojan Bks; 0-9610986)*, 1330 Cleveland Ave., Wyomissing, PA 19610 (SAN 265-3176) Tel 215-372-4692.

Trojan Press, Inc., *(Trojan Pr; 0-913914)*, 310 E. 18th St., North Kansas City, MO 64116 (SAN 202-8069) Tel 816-421-3858.

Troll Assocs., Subs. of Educational Reading Services, *(Troll Assocs; 0-89375; 0-8167)*, 320 State Hwy. 17, Mahwah, NJ 07430 (SAN 169-4758) Tel 201-529-4000; Toll free: 800-526-5289.

Trolley Talk, *(Trolley Talk; 0-914196)*, 59 Euclid Ave., Cincinnati, OH 45215 (SAN 205-4612).

Trollpost Greetings, *(Trollpost)*, 2285 Norwegian Dr. No. 57, Clearwarter, FL 33575 (SAN 262-1010).

Troostwyk Pr., *(Troostwyk Pr; 0-914487)*, Box 22292, Denton, TX 76204 (SAN 289-5757).

Trophy *See* Harper & Row Junior Bks.

Tropic Isle Pubs., Inc., *(Tropic Isle Pub; 0-937379)*, P.O. Box 343, Rumson, NJ 07760 (SAN 659-0713); 130 Maple Ave., Suite 3H, Red Bank, NJ 07701 (SAN 659-0721) Tel 201-842-6004; Orders to: P.O. Box 610935, North Miami, FL 33261-0935 (SAN 662-4219) Tel 305-893-4277.

Trossbach, J. E., *(J E Trossbach; 0-9608936)*, 2608 W. Columbine Rd., Phoenix, AZ 85029 (SAN 241-1628) Tel 602-997-2882.

Trotevale, Inc., *(Trotevale; 0-915333)*, P.O. Box 58, Lander, WY 82520 (SAN 294-2895) Tel 307-332-6532.

†Troubador Pr., *(Troubador Pr; 0-912300; 0-89844)*, 410 N. La Cienega Blvd., Los Angeles, CA 90048 (SAN 285-0931) Tel 415-397-3716; One Sutter St., San Francisco, CA 94104 (SAN 658-2044); Dist. by: Price/Stern/Sloan Pubs., 410 N. La Cienega Blvd., Los Angeles, CA 90048 (SAN 202-0246) Tel 213-657-6100; *CIP.*

Trout Creek Pr., *(Trout Creek; 0-916155)*, 5976 Billings Rd., Parkdale, OR 97041 (SAN 294-9881) Tel 503-352-6494.

Trout Gulch Pr., *(Trout Gulch Pr; 0-9614605)*, P.O. Box 20904, Castro Valley, CA 94546 (SAN 691-8379) Tel 415-581-0789.

†Troy State University Press, *(Troy State Univ; 0-916624)*, Wallace Hall, Troy, AL 36082 (SAN 208-8967) Tel 205-566-3000; *CIP.*

Troyanovich, Steve, *(S Troyanovich)*, Dist. by: Spring Church Book Co., P.O. Box 127, Spring Church, PA 15686 (SAN 212-7075).

Tru-Faith Publishing Co., *(Tru-Faith; 0-937498)*, P.O. Box 2283, Gainesville, GA 30503 (SAN 216-3101).

Truchinski, L. E., *(L E Truchinski; 0-913059)*, 1010 E. Griffith Ave., Wisconsin Rapids, WI 54494 (SAN 283-1937) Tel 715-421-2220.

Truck Press, *(Truck Pr; 0-916562)*, P.O. Box 2204, Short Beach, CT 06405 (SAN 208-3531) Tel 203-467-4257; Orders to: Inland Book Co., 22 Hemingway Ave., E. Haven, CT 06512 (SAN 204-1871); Toll free: 800-243-0138.

Truck Trailer Manufacturers Assn., *(Truck Trailer Mfrs)*, 1020 Princess St., Alexandria, VA 22314 (SAN 224-8867).

Trudco Publishing, *(Trudco Pub; 0-937571)*, 12155B Nottingham Ln., St. Louis, MO 63044 (SAN 659-0756) Tel 314-291-4402.

True Enterprises, *(True Ent; 0-9613360)*, 9324 McFall Dr., El Paso, TX 79925 (SAN 656-1519) Tel 915-591-8385.

True Grid Editions, *(True Grid; 0-9610880)*, 2600 S. 16th St., No. 729, Arlington, VA 22204 (SAN 265-2870) Tel 703-979-2432.

True Heitz-Thelma Yes Press, *(True Heitz)*, 1400 McAndrew Rd., Ojai, CA 93023 (SAN 262-1029).

True Life Foundation, The, *(True Life Found; 0-912753)*, 14510 Cordary Ave., Hawthorne, CA 90250 (SAN 283-3557) Tel 213-676-7567.

True Vine Pubns., *(True Vine Pubns; 0-939269)*, 140 S. Volusia Ave., Arcadia, FL 33821 (SAN 662-5258) Tel 813-993-0630.

†Trudog Pr., *(Truedog; 0-937212)*, 216 W. Academy St., Loanoke, AR 72086 (SAN 215-3475); *CIP.*

Trust for Hidden Villa, The, *(Trust Hidden Villa)*, 26870 Moody Rd., Los Altos, CA 94022 (SAN 661-4566).

Trustees for the Complete Writings of Herbert W. Eustace, C.S.B. *See* Eustace, Herbert W., C.S.B.

Truth Consciousness, *(Truth Consciousness; 0-933572)*, Gold Hill, Salina Star Rte., Boulder, CO 80302 (SAN 212-7083) Tel 303-447-1637.

Truth in Money, Inc., *(Truth in Money; 0-9606938)*, P.O. Box 30, Chagrin Falls, OH 44022 (SAN 219-8266) Tel 216-247-8772.

Truth Missions, *(Truth Missions; 0-910607)*, P.O. Box 3849, Manhattan Beach, CA 90266 (SAN 264-1909) Tel 213-546-3689.

Truth or Consequences Publishing Co., *(Truth Cons Pub; 0-937409)*, P.O. Box 1643, Truth or Consequences, NM 87901 (SAN 659-0772) Tel 505-523-8856; 501 Main St., Truth or Consequences, NM 87901 (SAN 659-0780).

Truth Publishers, Inc. (Orange, CA, *(Truth CA; 0-913621)*, 146 S. Trevor Ave., Anaheim, CA 92806 (SAN 285-3841) Tel 714-632-9554; Dist. by: Living Books, 12155 Magnolia Ave., Bldg. 11-B, Riverside, CA 92503 (SAN 669-330X) Tel 714-354-7330.

Truth Publishing, Inc., *(Truth Pub MN)*, 3802 W. Malapi Dr., Phoenix, AZ 85021 (SAN 214-1558) Tel 602-938-9019.

Truth Seeker Company Inc., *(Truth Seeker; 0-939040)*, P.O. Box 2832, San Diego, CA 92112 (SAN 226-3645) Tel 619-574-7600.

TSink Publishing, *(TSink Pub; 0-9613949)*, P.O. Box 2402, Norcross, GA 30091 (SAN 686-2705).

Tube Toys, *(Tube Toys; 0-9616305)*, 929 Moana Dr., San Diego, CA 92106 (SAN 658-5183) Tel 619-223-4182; P.O. Box 60451, San Diego, CA 92106 (SAN 658-5191).

Tubular Exchange Manufacturers Assn., *(Tubular Exch; 0-9609214)*, 25 N. Broadway, Tarrytown, NY 10591 (SAN 224-8042) Tel 914-332-0040.

Tucker, Grayson L., *(G L Tucker; 0-9610706)*, 2310 Tyler Ln., Louisville, KY 40205 (SAN 264-8024) Tel 502-458-2234.

Tucker Pubns., *(Tucker Pubns)*, 409 Hill St., Fayetteville, TN 37334 (SAN 213-6031).

Tucson Creative Dance Center *See* Mettler Studios, Inc.

Tucson Museum of Art, *(Tucson Mus Art; 0-911611)*, 140 N. Main, Tucson, AZ 85705 (SAN 280-798X) Tel 602-624-2333.

Tudor Pubs., Inc., *(Tudor Pubs; 0-936389)*, P.O. Box 3443, Greensboro, NC 27402 (SAN 697-3035); 3712 Old Battleground Rd., Greensboro, NC 27408 (SAN 697-3043) Tel 919-282-5907.

Tuffy Bks., Inc., *(Tuffy Bks; 0-89828)*, 84 Calvert St., P.O. Box 838, Harrison, NY 10528 (SAN 213-3903) Tel 914-835-5603.

Tulane Studies in Romance Languages & Literature, *(Tulane Romance Lang; 0-912788)*, Newcomb Coll., Tulane Univ., New Orleans, LA 70118 (SAN 206-1333) Tel 504-865-5115.

Tulane Univ., *(Tulane Univ; 0-87409)*, Dist. by: Tulane University, Howard-Tilton Memorial Library, Special Collections Division, New Orleans, LA 70118 (SAN 207-5458).

Tulane Univ. Library/Southeastern Architectural Archive, *(Tulane SE Arch)*, 7001 Freret St., New Orleans, LA 70118 (SAN 697-2446).

Tulane University, Louisiana Conference on Hispanic Languages & Literatures, *(Tulane U Conf Hispanic Lit; 0-9607798)*, 300C Newcomb Hall Tulane Univ., New Orleans, LA 70118 (SAN 226-2118) Tel 504-865-5524.

Tulane University, Tulane Studies in Political Science, *(Tulane Stud Pol; 0-930598)*, Tulane Univ., College of Arts & Sciences, Dept. of Political Science, New Orleans, LA 70118 (SAN 276-1246) Tel 504-865-6191.

Tulip Pr., *(Tulip Pr; 0-941800)*, P.O. Box J, Truckee, CA 95734 (SAN 239-3328) Tel 916-587-2995.

Tulip Press, *(Tulip Pr MN; 0-9608766)*, 1018 Chester Park Dr., Duluth, MN 55812 (SAN 241-0826) Tel 312-864-6747.

Tullis Productions, *(Tullis Prods)*, 4310 Normal Ave., Hollywood, CA 90029 (SAN 209-195X); Orders to: P.O. Box 54119, Los Angeles, CA 90054 (SAN 209-1968).

Names

†Tullos Books, *(Tullous; 0-916913),* P.O. Box 6322, Macon, GA 31208 (SAN 656-0369) Tel 912-742-0833; *CIP.*

Tumbleweed Pr., *(Tumbleweed Pr; 0-938091),* 11503 Carrollwood Dr., Tampa, FL 33618 (SAN 659-705X) Tel 813-932-8487.

Tumbleweed Productions, Inc., *(Tumble Prods; 0-9611004),* 101 E. Park Blvd., Plano, TX 75074 (SAN 282-8979) Tel 214-881-1505.

Tumbleweed Publishing Co., *(Tumbleweed Pub Co; 0-9612160),* 3112 Van Ave., Eugene, OR 97401 (SAN 289-5102) Tel 503-345-7770.

Tundra Bks. of Northern New York, Affil. of Tundra Books (Canada), *(Tundra Bks; 0-912766; 0-88776),* P.O. Box 1030, Plattsburgh, NY 12901 (SAN 202-8085); Dist. by: Univ. of Toronto Pr., 33 E. Tupper St., Buffalo, NY 14203 (SAN 200-4224) Tel 716-852-0342.

Tundra Pubns., *(Tundra Pubns; 0-9606768),* Moraine Rte., Estes Park, CO 80517 (SAN 219-6492) Tel 303-586-5794.

Tung's Publishing Co., Affil. of Asia Food Co., *(Tungs Pub; 0-9616253),* 5224-28 York Rd., Baltimore, MD 21212 (SAN 658-7119) Tel 301-823-3738.

Tunick, David, Inc., *(Tunick Inc; 0-9605298),* 12 E. 81st St., New York, NY 10028 (SAN 216-311X).

Tunnel Press, Incorporated, *(Tunnel Pr; 0-916597),* 2888 Bluff St. Suite 184, Boulder, CO 80302 (SAN 296-6786) Tel 213-874-3816.

Tunstede, *(Tunstede; 0-9616526),* 212 Vaughn's Gap Rd., Nashville, TN 37205 (SAN 292-3416) Tel 615-352-0971.

Tuppence, Inc., *(Tuppence; 0-939662),* 2701 S. 35th, Lincoln, NE 68506 (SAN 220-1607) Tel 402-488-3655.

†Turbomachinery International Publications, Div. of Business Journals, Inc., *(Turbo Intl Pubn; 0-937506),* P.O. Box 5550, Norwalk, CT 06856 (SAN 205-3055) Tel 203-853-6015; *CIP.*

Turbomachinery Maintenance Institute, Inc., *(Turbomachinery; 0-9615256),* P.O. Box 5550, Norwalk, CT 06850 (SAN 695-1619) Tel 203-853-6015.

Tureen, Richard M., Publishing Co., *(Tureen R M; 0-9613113),* 8566 NW 19th Dr., Coral Springs, FL 33065 (SAN 294-1074) Tel 305-753-9733.

Turkey Hill Press, *(Turkey Hill Pr; 0-9608050),* 3 Turkey Hill Ln., Westport, CT 06880 (SAN 240-4966); Dist. by: Inland Book Co., P.O. Box 261, 22 Hemingway Ave., East Haven, CT 06512 (SAN 200-4151) Tel 203-467-4257.

Turkey Pr., *(Turkey Pr; 0-918824),* 6746 Sueno Rd., Isla Vista, CA 93117 (SAN 210-5195) Tel 805-685-3603.

Turn of the Century Editions, *(Turn of Cent; 0-940326),* 250 W. Broadway, New York, NY 10013 (SAN 220-3529) Tel 212-925-6587.

Turn the Page Pr., *(Turn the Page; 0-931540; 0-931793),* 203 Baldwin Ave., Roseville, CA 95678 (SAN 281-3629) Tel 916-444-7933.

Turnaround Pr., *(Turnaround Pr; 0-936203),* 384 Everett Ave., Palo Alto, CA 94301 (SAN 696-8554) Tel 415-325-9348.

Turnbull & Company, *(Turnbull & Co; 0-914999),* 19 Mt. Auburn St., Cambridge, MA 02138 (SAN 289-4602) Tel 617-864-1110.

Turnbull & Willoughby Pubs., Inc., *(Turnbull & Willoughby; 0-943084),* 1151 W. Webster, Chicago, IL 60614 (SAN 240-4311) Tel 312-348-3181; Orders to: Contemporary Bk., Inc., 180 N. Michigan Ave., Chicago, IL 60601 (SAN 669-2478) Tel 312-782-9181.

Turner, M. F., Publishing, *(M F Turner Pub; 0-9616007),* 2963 N. 52nd Pkwy., Phoenix, AZ 85031 (SAN 697-9734) Tel 602-247-5322.

Turner Publishing, *(Turner Pub NY; 0-9615464),* 124 Highview Ave., Eastchester, NY 10709 (SAN 695-7277) Tel 914-337-9387; P.O. Box 261, Eastchester, NY 10709 (SAN 696-513X).

Turner Publishing Co., *(Turner Pub KY; 0-938021),* 555 Jefferson, Suite 201, Paducah, KY 42001 (SAN 659-803X) Tel 502-443-0121.

Turning Point Pubns., *(Turning Pubns; 0-934947),* 1122 M St., Eureka, CA 95501 (SAN 694-4272) Tel 707-445-2290.

Turning Wheel Pr., *(Turning Wheel Pr; 0-9602590),* 4 Washington Sq. Village 17-0, New York, NY 10012 (SAN 214-1566).

Turpin, John C., & Assocs., *(Turpin & Assocs; 0-939506),* 1825 E. Faunsdale Dr., Sandy, UT 84092-3817 (SAN 216-700X) Tel 801-572-0999.

Turquoise Books, *(Turquoise Bks; 0-917834),* 1202 Austin Bluffs Pkwy., Colorado Springs, CO 80907 (SAN 206-5223) Tel 303-634-1556.

Turquoise Mountain Pubns., *(Turquoise Mount; 0-917947),* P.O. Box 10153, Berkeley, CA 94709 (SAN 657-0267) Tel 415-525-7853.

Turret Publishing, *(Turret; 0-931952),* 5346 N. Enid Ave., Azusa, CA 91702 (SAN 211-4577) Tel 818-334-9534.

Turtle Bks., *(Turtle Bks; 0-937693),* 2540 S. Zephyr Ct., Lakewood, CO 80227 (SAN 659-3704) Tel 303-989-7459; Orders to: Turtle Bks., P.O. Box 27799, Denver, CO 80227 (SAN 662-4251) Tel 303-989-7459.

Turtle Island Foundation, Netzahaulcoyotl Historical Society, *(Turtle Isl Foun; 0-913666),* 2845 Buena Vista Way, Berkeley, CA 94708 (SAN 205-4639) Tel 415-654-7020.

Turtle Lodge Pr., *(Turtle Lodge; 0-934182),* 10628 Arabian Park Dr., Scottsdale, AZ 85259 (SAN 213-1811).

Turtle Pr., *(Turtle Pr; 0-916844),* 333 E. 49th St., New York, NY 10017 (SAN 208-8975) Tel 212-753-7945.

Turtles Quill Scriptorium, *(Turtles Quill; 0-937686),* P.O. Box 643, Mendocino, CA 95460 (SAN 206-8966) Tel 707-937-4328.

Tusayan Gospel Ministries, Inc., *(Tusayan Gospel; 0-9601124),* P.O. Box 9861, Phoenix, AZ 85068 (SAN 209-3391) Tel 602-878-2838; Dist. by: Living Books, Inc., 12155 Magnolia Ave. 11-B, Riverside, CA 92503 (SAN 169-006X) Tel 714-354-7330.

Tusker Pr., *(Tusker Pr; 0-937633),* P.O. Box 597004, San Francisco, CA 94159 (SAN 659-0799) Tel 415-931-7877; 1405-1/2 Lyon St., San Francisco, CA 94115 (SAN 659-0802).

Tustin Institute of Technology, Inc., *(Tustin Inst; 0-918247),* 22 E. Los Olivos St., Santa Barbara, CA 93105 (SAN 670-7092) Tel 805-682-7171.

Tuszynski, Carole, *(C Tuszynski; 0-9617170),* 6 Bronze Ct., Huntington, NY 11743 (SAN 662-9512) Tel 516-427-2454.

Tutorial Pr., *(Tutorial IL; 0-9613076),* 323 S. Franklin Bldg., Suite T-206, Chicago, IL 60606-7096 (SAN 294-6858).

Tutorial Pr., The, *(Tutorial Press; 0-912329),* 711-A Encino Pl. NE, Albuquerque, NM 87123 (SAN 265-1467) Tel 505-296-8636.

Tuttle, Charles E., Co., Inc., *(C E Tuttle; 0-8048),* P.O. Box 410, 28 S. Main St., Rutland, VT 05701-0410 (SAN 213-2621) Tel 802-773-8930.

Tuttle, Tom, & Associates, *(Tom Tuttle; 0-930556),* P.O. Box 91529, Santa Barbara, CA 93190 (SAN 208-2551) Tel 805-683-2812.

T.V. Music Co., *(T V Music; 0-918806),* 1650 Broadway, New York, NY 10019 (SAN 210-5136) Tel 212-246-3126.

Twain Publishing, *(Twain Pub; 0-9609194),* 35 E St., NW, Washington, DC 20001 (SAN 241-4678) Tel 202-382-3802.

Twayne's U. S. Author Series *See* New College & Univ. Pr., The

Twelvetrees Pr., *(Twelvetrees Pr; 0-942642),* P.O. Box 188, Pasadena, CA 91102 (SAN 239-9458) Tel 818-798-5207.

†Twenty-First Century Pr., *(Twen Fir Pr; 0-918357),* P.O. Box 5010, Madison, WI 53705 (SAN 657-3878) Tel 608-231-2765; *CIP.*

21st Century Pubns., *(Pubns Twenty First; 0-9610708),* 190 Old Stafford Rd., Tolland, CT 06084 (SAN 264-8032) Tel 203-872-4083.

Twenty First Century Pubns., *(Twen Fir Cent; 0-933278),* P.O. Box 702, 401 N. 4th St., Fairfield, IA 52556 (SAN 211-8181) Tel 515-472-5105.

Twenty-Third Pubns., *(Twenty-Third; 0-89622),* P.O. Box 180, Mystic, CT 06355 (SAN 210-9204); Toll free: 800-321-0411; 185 Willow St., Mystic, CT 06355 (SAN 658-2052); Toll free: 800-321-0411.

Twesten, Gary, Publisher, *(G Twesten; 0-9602428),* Fox Run, Millstadt, IL 62260 (SAN 209-1402) Tel 618-233-5070.

†Twickenham Pr., *(Twickenham Pr; 0-936726),* 31 Jane St., Suite 17B, New York, NY 10014 (SAN 214-3291); Dist. by: Daedalus Bk., 2260 25th Pl., NE, Washington, DC 20018 (SAN 158-9202) Tel 202-526-0558; *CIP.*

Twiggs Communications, *(Twiggs Comm; 0-914003),* 5366 Breeze Hill, Troy, MI 48098 (SAN 286-9039) Tel 313-641-8248.

Twin Circle Publishing Co., *(Twin Cir; 0-937045),* 6404 Wilshire Blvd., Suite 900, Los Angeles, CA 90048 (SAN 658-7135) Tel 213-653-2200.

Twin Cities Natural Family Planning Ctr., Inc., *(TCNFPC; 0-9616827),* 2414 S. Seventh St., Minneapolis, MN 55454 (SAN 661-1273) Tel 612-340-9830.

Twin City Printery, *(Twin City; 0-9609914),* Box 890, Lewiston, ME 04240 (SAN 206-2577) Tel 207-784-9181.

Twin Oaks Books, *(Twin Oaks Bks; 0-9608918),* 4343 Causeway Dr., Lowell, MI 49331 (SAN 238-0862).

Twin Peaks Pr., *(Twin Peaks Pr; 0-933261),* P.O. Box 8097, Portland, OR 97207 (SAN 692-4034) Tel 206-256-1670; 8608 NE Mason Dr., Suite 10, Vancouver, WA 98662 (SAN 697-6018).

Twin Pines Press, *(Twin Pines Pr; 0-9609840),* 851 Rivervale Rd., River Vale, NJ 07675 (SAN 264-4428) Tel 201-391-6860.

Twining Pr., The, *(Twining Pr; 0-936877),* 319 Lovell Ave., Mill Valley, CA 94941 (SAN 699-9700) Tel 415-383-7464.

Twitchell, Bob, *(B Twitchell; 0-9616798),* 207 W. Holly, Bellingham, WA 98225 (SAN 661-0366) Tel 206-676-1222.

Twitty, Conway, Enterprises, *(Conway Twitty; 0-9616438),* 1 Music Village Blvd., Hendersonville, TN 37075 (SAN 659-1477) Tel 615-822-3210.

2AM Pubns., Div. of Anderson & McCombs Advertising & Marketing, *(TwoAM Pubns; 0-937491),* P.O. Box 50444, Chicago, IL 60650 (SAN 659-0837) Tel 312-652-0013; 1406 S. 51st Ct., Chicago, IL 60650 (SAN 659-0845).

Two A's Industries, Inc., *(Two A's; 0-915001),* 285 S. Dr., Mt. View, CA 94040 (SAN 289-4564) Tel 415-968-3111.

Two-Eighteen Press, *(Two Eighteen; 0-938690),* P.O. Box 218, Village Sta., New York, NY 10014 (SAN 207-9127) Tel 212-966-5877.

Two Ems, Inc., *(Two Ems; 0-936652),* 18 Harkness Dr., Madison, CT 06443 (SAN 222-1853); P.O.Box 1083, Madison, CT 06443 (SAN 658-2060).

Two Riders Pr., *(Two Riders; 0-915860),* P.O. Box 31, Chestnut Hill, MA 02167 (SAN 207-6179) Tel 617-232-8819.

Two Rivers Press, *(Two Rivers; 0-89756),* 28070 S. Meridan Rd., Aurora, OR 97002 (SAN 211-6510).

Two Trees Pr., *(Two Trees Pr; 0-935725),* P.O. Box 8190-18, Fargo, ND 58102 (SAN 696-2181) Tel 701-235-1120.

Two Trees Publishing, *(Two Trees Pub; 0-938183),* 1272 Bear Mountain Ct., Boulder, CO 80303 (SAN 659-7262) Tel 303-494-5192.

Two Zee's Enterprises, Ltd., *(Two Zees; 0-9606054),* 2010 Jones Rd., Fort Lee, NJ 07024 (SAN 216-9401) Tel 212-988-7813.

TwoPeninsula Pr., *(TwoPeninsula Pr; 0-941912),* Box 30034, Lansing, MI 48909 (SAN 676-990X).

Two's Co./Cookbooks, *(Twos Co-Cookbks),* P.O. Box 977, Pebble Beach, CA 93953 (SAN 689-6464) Tel 408-624-7600.

Twowindows Pr., *(Twowindows Pr; 0-912136),* 2644 Fulton St., Berkeley, CA 94704 (SAN 205-4671).

Tycooly Publishing *See* Unipub a

Tycooly Publishing USA, Affil. of Tycooly Int'l, *(Tycooly Pub),* P.O. Box C-166, Riverton, NJ 08077 (SAN 659-4557) Tel 609-829-6830.

Tyler-Gibson Pubs., *(Tyler-Gibson; 0-9605520),* P.O. Box 1266, Boston, MA 02205 (SAN 220-1437) Tel 617-734-7049.

Tyndale, William, College Pr., *(William Tyndale Col Pr; 0-912407),* 35700 W. 12 Mile Rd., Farmington Hills, MI 48018 (SAN 265-3702) Tel 313-553-7200.

Tyndale Hse. Pubs., *(Tyndale; 0-8423),* 336 Gundersen Dr., P.O. Box 80, Wheaton, IL 60189 (SAN 206-7749) Tel 312-668-8300; Toll free: 800-323-9400.

Typographeum Bookshop, The, *(Typographeum; 0-930126),* The Stone Cottage, Bennington Rd., Francestown, NH 03043 (SAN 211-3031).

Typrofile Pr., *(Typrofile Pr; 0-943316),* Church Rd., Box 223, Wernersville, PA 19565 (SAN 240-7930) Tel 215-678-3886.

UAH Press, *(UAH Pr; 0-933958),* P.O. Box 1247, Huntsville, AL 35807 (SAN 212-8160).

U & K Publishing Co., *(U & K Pub; 0-9616357),* 806 Carter Rd., Rockville, MD 20852 (SAN 659-090X) Tel 301-762-8980.

U&U Pubns., Inc., *(U & U Pubns; 0-912163),* 3435 Ridgewood Rd., NW, Atlanta, GA 30327 (SAN 264-8040) Tel 404-921-7814.

U Assocs., Inc., *(U Assocs; 0-9615393),* 1160 N. Federal Hwy., Suite 721, Ft. Lauderdale, FL 33304 (SAN 695-3530) Tel 305-763-5991.

U-Bild Enterprises, Div. of U-B Newspaper Syndicate, *(U-Bild; 0-910495),* Box 2383, 15233 Stagg St., Van Nuys, CA 91409 (SAN 260-1508) Tel 818-785-6368.

U Bks. *See* Barnes & Noble Bks.-Imports

UCLA Tissue Typing Laboratory, *(UCLA Tissue; 0-9604606),* UCLA School of Medicine, Los Angeles, CA 90024 (SAN 282-4752); Orders to: 1000 Veteran Ave., Los Angeles, CA 90024 (SAN 282-4760) Tel 213-825-7651.

UFO Schools, Inc., *(UFO Schools; 0-933938),* 31800 Schoenherr, Apt. H9, Warren, MI 48093 (SAN 213-182X) Tel 313-293-5867.

UMI Pubns., Inc., *(UMI Charlotte; 0-943860),* P.O. Box 30036, Charlotte, NC 28230 (SAN 241-0834) Tel 704-374-0420. Do not confuse with UMI Research Pr., Ann Arbor, MI.

UMI Research Pr., Div. of University Microfilms, International, *(UMI Res Pr; 0-8357),* 300 N. Zeeb Rd., Ann Arbor, MI 48106 (SAN 212-2464) Tel 313-761-4700; Toll free: 800-521-0600. Do not confuse with UMI Publications, Inc., Charlotte, NC.

UNIFO Pubns., Ltd., *(UNIFO Pubs; 0-89111),* P.O. Box 37, Pleasantville, NY 10570 (SAN 219-8290); 28 Lower Main St., Ossining, NY 10562 (SAN 658-2079) Tel 914-941-1330.

UOI Co., *(UOI Co; 0-913929),* 15445 Ventura Blvd., Sherman Oaks, CA 91403 (SAN 286-9047) Tel 818-785-5050.

U-Read Pubns., *(U-Read Pubns; 0-938925),* 389 Marin Ave., Mill Valley, CA 94941 (SAN 661-7956) Tel 415-383-5638; Dist. by: Publishers Group West, 5855 Beaudry St., Emeryville, CA 94608 (SAN 202-8522) Tel 415-658-3453.

USA Pubs., *(USA Pubs; 0-936577),* 500 Gatlin Ave., Orlando, FL 32806 (SAN 698-1119) Tel 305-851-7334.

USA Publishing Co., *(USA Pub CA; 0-938446),* 2929 Castro, San Pablo, CA 94806 (SAN 658-4306) Tel 415-236-4960.

USA Research, *(USA Res; 0-917191),* 24 Hancock Street, Boston, MA 02114-4109 (SAN 656-9064) Tel 617-720-0082.

U. S./ICOMOS (United States National Committee, International Council on Monuments & Sites), *(US ICOMOS; 0-911697),* 1600 "H" St. NW, Washington, DC 20006 (SAN 264-4525) Tel 202-673-4211.

USR Group, *(USR Group; 0-936593),* 4655 Old Ironsides Dr., Suite 200, Santa Clara, CA 95054 (SAN 698-1305) Tel 408-986-8840.

UTA Pr., The, Affil. of Univ. of Texas at Arlington, *(UTA Pr; 0-932408),* Box 19929, Univ. of Texas at Arlington, Arlington, TX 76019-0929 (SAN 212-0542) Tel 817-273-3391; Orders to: Univ. of Texas at Arlington, Univ. Bookstore, Box 19075, Arlington, TX 76019 (SAN 662-1767) Tel 817-273-2785.

Ubu Repertory Theater Pubns., *(Ubu Repertory; 0-913745),* 149 Mercer St., New York, NY 10012 (SAN 286-2077) Tel 212-925-0999; Dist. by: Publishing Ctr. for Cultural Resources, 625 Broadway, New York, NY 10012 (SAN 274-9025) Tel 212-260-2010.

Uchill, Ida Libert, *(Uchill; 0-9604468),* 795 S. Jersey St., Denver, CO 80224 (SAN 214-3305) Tel 303-355-9829; Dist. by: L & B Enterprises, 1205 S. Ivy Way, Denver, CO 80224 (SAN 200-7681) Tel 303-756-4563.

UCLA, Grad, School of Management, GSM Pubns. Services, *(UCLA Mgmt; 0-911798),* 405 Hilgard Ave., Los Angeles, CA 90024 (SAN 203-0179) Tel 213-206-8197.

Ucross Bks., *(Ucross Bks; 0-9614024),* P.O. Box 764, Los Alamos, NM 87544 (SAN 683-7344) Tel 505-662-6591.

UFO Photo Archives, *(UFO Photo; 0-9608558; 0-934269),* P.O. Box 17206, Tuscon, AZ 85710 (SAN 240-7949) Tel 602-296-6753.

UHL's Publishing Co. (U-L), *(UHLs Pub; 0-943240),* RD 1, Box 119, Spencer, NY 14883 (SAN 240-7957) Tel 607-589-6594.

UIE *See* Unipub

SI, *(Ujjaini Pubs; 0-9610134),* 8911 Leamont, Houston, TX 77099 (SAN 276-1432) Tel 713-495-5849.

Ukiyo-e Society of America, Inc., *(Ukiyo-e Soc; 0-9610398),* 1692 Second Ave., New York, NY 10028 (SAN 264-4479).

Ukrainian Academic Press, Div. of Libraries Unlimited, Inc., *(Ukrainian Acad; 0-87287),* P.O. Box 263, Littleton, CO 80160 (SAN 203-3305) Tel 303-770-1220.

Ukrainian Academy of Arts & Sciences in the U.S., The, *(Ukrainian Arts Sci; 0-916381),* 206 W. 100 St., New York, NY 10025 (SAN 206-2607) Tel 212-222-1866.

Ukrainian Cultural Institute, *(Ukrainian Cult Inst),* Dickinson State College, Dickinson, ND 58601 (SAN 287-2366).

Ukrainian Education Assn. of Maryland, Inc., *(Ukrainian Ed Assn; 0-9606178),* 518 S. Wolfe St., Baltimore, MD 21231 (SAN 220-3537) Tel 301-252-3051.

Ukrainian Heritage Co., *(Ukrainian Her Co; 0-936113),* 8444 Kraay, Munster, IN 46321 (SAN 696-7671) Tel 219-972-3108.

Ukrainian National Women's League of America, *(UNWLA; 0-9610788),* 108 Second Ave., New York, NY 10003 (SAN 234-1298) Tel 212-533-4646.

Ukrainian News, Inc., *(Ukrainian News; 0-912601),* 19411 W. Warren Ave., Detroit, MI 48228 (SAN 282-8413).

Ukrainian Political Science Assn. in the U. S., *(Ukrainian Pol),* P.O. Box 12963, Philadelphia, PA 19108 (SAN 236-5537).

Ukrainian Research Foundation, *(Ukrainian Res; 0-934760),* 6931 S. Yosemite St., Englewood, CO 80112 (SAN 213-5647).

Ullrich, Marion Chambers, Pub., *(M C Ullrich; 0-9617091),* 3340 Ingelow St., San Diego, CA 92106 (SAN 662-6319) Tel 619-224-1425.

Ulrich's Bks., Inc., *(Ulrich; 0-914004),* 549 E. University Ave., Ann Arbor, MI 48107-8607 (SAN 100-2945) Tel 313-662-3201.

Ultima Thule Publishing Co., *(Ultima Thule Pub; 0-938203),* P.O. Box 100731, Anchorage, AK 99510 (SAN 659-6657); 524 W. Fourth Ave., Suite 204C, Anchorage, AK 99510 (SAN 659-6665) Tel 907-277-0875.

Ultra Nutrimol Technical Pubs., *(Ultra-Nutri; 0-9612386),* 19 Westglow St., A2, Boston, MA 02122 (SAN 287-7694) Tel 617-825-0595.

Ultralight Pubns., *(Ultralight Pubns; 0-938716),* P.O. Box 234, Hummelstown, PA 17036 (SAN 220-2786) Tel 717-566-0468; Toll free: 800-441-7527. *Imprints:* AViation Publishers (AViation Pubs).

Ultramarine Publishing Co., Inc., *(Ultramarine Pub; 0-89366),* P.O. Box 303, Hastings-on-Hudson, NY 10706 (SAN 208-8762) Tel 914-478-2522.

Ulysses Pr., *(Ulysses Pr; 0-915233),* Box 4000 H, Berkeley, CA 94704 (SAN 289-8764) Tel 415-644-0915; 309 Deakin St., Berkeley, CA 94705 (SAN 289-8772); Dist. by: Publishers Group West, 5855 Beaudry St., Emeryville, CA 94608 (SAN 202-8522) Tel 415-658-3453.

UNABASHED Librarian, *(UNABASHED Lib; 0-916444),* G.P.O. Box 2631, New York, NY 10116-2631 (SAN 208-8983).

Unarius Pubns., *(Unarius Pubns; 0-932642; 0-935097),* 145 S. Magnolia Ave., El Cajon, CA 92020 (SAN 168-9614) Tel 619-447-4170.

Undena Pubns., *(Undena Pubns; 0-89003),* P.O. Box 97, Malibu, CA 90265 (SAN 293-406X) Tel 818-366-1744; Dist. by: Eisenbrauns, P.O. Box 275, Winona Lake, IN 46590-0278 (SAN 293-4078) Tel 219-269-2011.

C. S. Underhill, *(Underhill; 0-9600268),* P.O. Box 127, East Aurora, NY 14052 (SAN 206-670X) Tel 716-652-0185.

Underhill Enterprises, *(Underhill Enter; 0-9616734),* 1815 Russell Ave., Cheyenne, WY 82001 (SAN 659-8889) Tel 307-632-5197.

Underwater Specialists, Ltd., *(Underwater Spec Ltd; 0-936655),* 5700 Sheridan St., Hollywood, FL 33021 (SAN 699-7236).

Underwood, Barry, *(Underwood B; 0-9614790),* 5504 Dobbs St., No. 77, Los Angeles, CA 90032 (SAN 692-9869) Tel 213-225-9352.

Underwood/Miller, *(Underwood-Miller; 0-934438; 0-88733),* 651 Chestnut St., Columbia, PA 17512 (SAN 282-4795) Tel 717-684-7335. *Imprints:* Tamerlane Press (Tamerlane).

Undiscovered Denver Dining, *(Undiscovered; 0-9610064),* 940 Emerson, Denver, CO 80218 (SAN 285-1008); Dist. by: Gordon's, 5450 Valley Hwy., Denver, CO 80216 (SAN 285-1016) Tel 303-296-1830; Dist. by: Dillon's, P.O. Drawer J, Boulder, CO 80306 (SAN 285-1024) Tel 303-442-5323.

Une Publishing, *(Une Pub),* 9 Moss Ave., Danbury, CT 06810 (SAN 217-1368).

Uneeda Pr., *(Uneeda Pr; 0-9617283),* 701 Howe Ave., Suite G-48, Sacramento, CA 95825 (SAN 663-5202) Tel 916-922-2066.

Unesco Records *See* Unipub a

UNESCO Regional Office for Education in Asia & the Pacific (Bangkok) *See* Unipub a

Unesco Slides *See* Unipub a

Ungar Publishing Co., *(Ungar; 0-8044),* 370 Lexington Ave., New York, NY 10017 (SAN 202-5256) Tel 212-532-3650; Orders to: Harper & Row, Keystone Industrial Park, Scranton, PA 18512 (SAN 662-1635); Toll free: 800-242-7737.

UNI-SUN, *(Uni-Sun; 0-912949),* P.O. Box 25421, 4005 NE 49th Terrace, Kansas City, MO 64119 (SAN 283-4332) Tel 816-454-8705.

Unibra Publishing Co., *(Unibra Pub Co; 0-933077),* P.O. Box 901079, Memphis, TN 38109 (SAN 689-8122) Tel 901-785-1902; Orders to: Robert Lee, Book Order Dept. - A, P.O. Box 901079, Memphis, TN 38109 (SAN 662-2860) Tel 901-785-4589.

Unicon Enterprises, *(Unicon Ent; 0-912327),* 3602 W. Glen Branch, Peoria, IL 61614 (SAN 265-1475) Tel 309-688-3772.

Unicorn Bookshop, *(Unicorn Bkshop; 0-9615275),* P.O. Box 154, Trappe, MD 21673 (SAN 695-2178) Tel 301-476-3838.

Unicorn Communications, *(Unicorn Comm; 0-913311),* P.O. Box 2507, Billings, MT 59103 (SAN 287-7708) Tel 406-657-1200.

Unicorn Enterprises, *(Unicorn Ent; 0-87884),* 1620 Collinsdale Ave., Cincinnati, OH 45230 (SAN 206-6696).

Unicorn Pr., *(Unicorn NJ; 0-937004),* P.O. Box 138, Monmouth Junction, NJ 08852 (SAN 213-4772) Tel 215-968-0155.

†Unicorn Pr., *(Unicorn Pr; 0-87775),* P.O. Box 3307, Greensboro, NC 27402 (SAN 203-3313) Tel 919-852-0281; *CIP.*

Unicorn Publishing Hse., Inc., The, *(Unicorn Pub; 0-88101),* 1148 Parsippany Blvd., Parsippany, NJ 07054 (SAN 240-4567) Tel 201-334-0353; 300 Raritan Ctr. Pkwy., Edison, NJ 08818 (SAN 658-2087).

Unicorn Rising Ltd., *(Unicorn Rising; 0-913313),* Rte. 2, P.O. Box 360, Sheridan, OR 97378 (SAN 285-8924) Tel 503-843-3902.

Unification Church Pubns., *(Unification Church),* 4 W. 43rd St., New York, NY 10036 (SAN 211-8270).

Unification Theological Seminary, *(Unif Theol Seminary; 0-932894),* G.P.O. Box 2432, New York, NY 10116 (SAN 212-3193) Tel 914-758-6881; Dist. by: Rose of Sharon Press Inc., G.P.O. Box 2432, New York, NY 10116 (SAN 212-3207) Tel 914-758-6881.

Unikorn Magik, *(Unikorn Magik; 0-9604016),* Three Gregg St., Beverly, MA 01915-2913 (SAN 214-1582) Tel 617-927-9388.

Unilaw *See* Donning Co. Pubs.

Uniline Division John Klein &Assoc. Inc., *(Uniline Div; 0-912904),* John Klein Assocs., Inc., 20700 Miles Ave., Cleveland, OH 44128 (SAN 203-0497) Tel 216-587-3070.

Union & Confederacy Inc., *(Union & Confed Inc.; 0-911679),* Route 1, Box 267, College Grove, TN 37046 (SAN 276-9425) Tel 615-368-7175.

†Union College Press, *(Union Coll; 0-912756),* Orders to: Union College Press, College Grounds, Schenectady, NY 12308 (SAN 206-9776) Tel 518-370-6096; *CIP.*

Union Congregational Church, *(Union Cong Church; 0-9610366),* 176 Cooper Ave., Upper Montclair, NJ 07043 (SAN 264-4509).

Union League of Philadelphia, *(Union League PA; 0-915810),* 140 S. Broad St., Philadelphia, PA 19102 (SAN 207-687X) Tel 215-563-6500.

†Union of American Hebrew Congregations, *(UAHC; 0-8074),* 838 Fifth Ave., New York, NY 10021 (SAN 203-3291) Tel 212-249-0100; *CIP.*

Union of Concerned Scientists, *(Union Conc Sci),* 26 Church St., Cambridge, MA 02238 (SAN 225-6894) Tel 617-547-5552; 1346 Connecticut Ave., NW, Washington, DC 20036 (SAN 650-0633).

Union of Messianic Jewish Congregations Publishing, *(Union Messianic Jew Pub; 0-9614555),* 2208 Rockland Ave., Rockville, MD 20851 (SAN 691-8123) Tel 301-770-2494.

Union Park Press, *(Union Park; 0-9601570),* P.O. Box 2737, Boston, MA 02208 (SAN 211-5808) Tel 617-754-0708.

Union Press, *(Union Pr; 0-9603384),* 3009 Hillegass Ave., Berkeley, CA 94705 (SAN 212-3088) Tel 415-845-9658.

Union Printers Historical Society, *(Union Printers Hist Soc),* 1726 West Jarvis Ave., Chicago, IL 60626 (SAN 240-4990).

Union Representative, *(Union Rep; 0-918515),* 430 S. Michigan Ave., Chicago, IL 60605 (SAN 657-7334) Tel 312-798-1660.

Union Square Books *See* Crittenden Publishing, Inc.

Union Station, The, *(Union Sta; 0-9615257),* 785 Murrah Rd., North Augusta, SC 29841 (SAN 694-3810) Tel 803-279-5975.

Unipub, Div. of Kraus-Thomson Organization, Ltd., *(Unipub; 0-89059; 0-400; 0-527),* 9730E George Palmer Hwy., Lanham, MD 20706 (SAN 210-7562) Tel 301-459-7666; Toll free: 800-521-8110. *Imprints:* Asian Productivity Organization (APO); D U O (DUO); Editions Delta (Edns Delta); Fishing News Books, Limited (FNB); Food & Agriculture Organization (FAO); Fund for Multinational Management Education (FMME); Fund for Multinational Management Education - Council of the Americas (FMME-COA); General Agreement on Tariffs & Trade (GATT); International Atomic Energy Agency (IAEA); International Council of Scientific Unions, Abstracting Board of Publications (ICSU); International Union for Conservation of Nature & Natural Resources (IUCN); O R D I N A (ORDINA); Supplies & Services, Government of Canada (SSC); U I E (UIE); United Nations Educational, Scientific & Cultural Organization (UNESCO); United Nations Industrial Development Organization (UNIDO); World Intellectual Property Organization (WIPO).

Capital Publishing Corporation (CPC) (Capital Pub Corp); Centre for Agricultural Publishing & Documentation (PDC); Commonwealth Agricultural Bureau (CAB) (CAB); International Labor Organization (ILO) (ILO); Owen's Publishing Company (OD) (Owen's Pub Co); Publitek (PUB); Tycooly Publishing (TYP); Unesco Records (UR); Unesco Slides (US); United Nations Center for Regional Development (CRD) (CRD); United Nations University, The (TUNU) (TUNU); UNESCO Regional Office for Education in Asia & the Pacific (Bangkok) (UB); Who's Who in the International Red Series (WWIR) (WWIR); Worldwide Furbearer Conference Inc. (Worldwide Furbearer). American Productivity Center (AMPC); Editions Delta (ED); Europa (EUR); F U J I (FUJI); Institute for Foreign Policy Analysis (IFPA) (IFPA); International Court of Justice (ICJ) (ICJ); International Solar Energy Society (ISES) (ISES); JCP (JCP); Venture Economics (Venture Econo).

Unique Golf Resorts of The World Inc., *(Unique Golf Res; 0-9612294),* 4501 Camden Dr., Corona Del Mar, CA 92625 (SAN 289-5137) Tel 714-760-0208.

Unique Pubns., Subs. of CFW Enterprises,INC., *(Unique Pubns; 0-86568),* 4201 W. Vanowen Pl., Burbank, CA 91505 (SAN 214-3313) Tel 818-845-2656; Toll free: 800-332-3330.

Unique Pubs., *(Unique Pubs; 0-936811),* 11901 Andrew St., Wheaton, MD 20902 (SAN 699-9514) Tel 202-755-6961.

Unique Publishing Co., *(Unique Pub CA; 0-934189),* 1825 Clinton Ave., Suite D, Alameda, CA 94501 (SAN 693-403X) Tel 415-865-1987; 7941 La Riviera Dr., Sacramento, CA 95826 (SAN 662-3212) Tel 916-381-4783.

Unitarian Universalist Assn., *(Unitarian Univ; 0-933840),* 25 Beacon St, Boston, MA 02108 (SAN 225-4840) Tel 617-742-2100. *Imprints:* Skinner House Books (Skinner Hse Bks).

Unitarian Universalist Church, The, *(Unitarian),* E. Main St., Canton, NY 13617 (SAN 213-1838).

†United Bible Societies, *(United Bible; 0-8267),* 1865 Broadway, New York, NY 10023 (SAN 204-8787) Tel 212-581-7400; Orders to: American Bible Society, P.O. Box 5656, Grand Central Station, New York, NY 10163 (SAN 662-1643); Toll free: 800-543-8000; *CIP.*

United Cerebral Palsy Assn. of the North Bay, *(UCPANB; 0-9616891),* 1057 College Ave., No. 104, Santa Rosa, CA 95404 (SAN 661-6453) Tel 707-544-3448.

United Cerebral Palsy Assns., Inc., *(United CP),* 66 E. 34th St., New York, NY 10016 (SAN 224-2869).

United Cerebral Palsy of New York City, Inc., *(UCP NYC; 0-9616554),* 122 E. 23rd St., New York, NY 10010 (SAN 659-6061) Tel 212-677-7400.

United Communications of America, Inc., *(United Comns; 0-937047),* 2445 Hartrey Ave., Evanston, IL 60201 (SAN 658-6627) Tel 312-869-9888; Dist. by: Kampmann & Co., 9 E. 40th St., New York, NY 10016 (SAN 202-5191) Tel 212-685-2928.

United Educators, Inc., *(United Ed; 0-87566),* 900 Armour Dr., Lake Bluff, IL 60044 (SAN 204-8795) Tel 312-234-3700.

United Electrical Radio & Machine Workers of America, *(United Elec R&M; 0-916180),* 11 E. 51st St., New York, NY 10022 (SAN 208-3973) Tel 212-753-1960.

United Galactic Publishing Foundation Press *See* First International Publishing Corp.

United Health Resource, Inc., *(United Health),* 2082 Michelson Dr., Irvine, CA 92715 (SAN 670-6789) Tel 714-476-2167.

United Learning Corp., *(United Learn; 0-915671),* P.O. Box 5441, Eugene, OR 97405 (SAN 207-298X) Tel 503-683-3383.

United Methodist Board of Higher Education & Ministry, *(United Meth Educ; 0-938162),* Box 871, Nashville, TN 37202 (SAN 216-3136) Tel 615-327-2700.

United Methodist Church, Commission on Archives & History, *(United Meth Archives; 0-915466),* P.O. Box 127, Madison, NJ 07940 (SAN 203-0578) Tel 201-822-2787.

United Methodist Church of the Dunes, *(UMCD; 0-9608642),* 943 Lake Ave., Grand Haven, MI 49417 (SAN 238-3993) Tel 616-846-5429.

United Nations, *(UN; 0-680),* Sales Section, Publishing Div., Rm. DC2-853, New York, NY 10017 (SAN 206-6718) Tel 212-754-8302.

†United Nations Assn. of the United States of America, Inc., *(UNA-USA; 0-934654),* 300 E. 42nd St, New York, NY 10017 (SAN 204-8892) Tel 212-697-3232; *CIP.*

United Nations Center for Regional Development (CRD) *See* Unipub a

United Nations Educational, Scientific & Cultural Organization *See* Unipub

United Nations Industrial Development Organization *See* Unipub

United Nations Institute for Training & Research, *(UNITAR),* 801 UN Plaza, New York, NY 10017 (SAN 227-1214).

United Nations Univ., The (TUNU) *See* Unipub a

United Ostomy Assn., *(United Ostomy),* 2001 W. Beverly Blvd., Los Angeles, CA 90057 (SAN 224-408X) Tel 213-413-5510.

United Piece Dye Works, *(United Piece; 0-911546),* 111 W. 40th St., New York, NY 10018 (SAN 204-8809) Tel 212-840-0400.

United Publishers International, Ltd., *(United Pubs Intl; 0-939499),* 252 W. 47th St., Suite 6, New York, NY 10036 (SAN 663-4044) Tel 212-921-7664.

United Publishing Co., *(United Pub Co; 0-937323),* 11 Elm Pl., Albany, NY 12203 (SAN 658-8077) Tel 518-456-1321.

United Research, *(United Res; 0-915235),* P.O. Box 1146, Black Mountain, NC 28711 (SAN 289-8780) Tel 704-669-6845.

United Research, Div. of Solar Products, Inc., *(United Res CA; 0-9614924),* 2816 Atadero Ct., Carlsbad, CA 92008 (SAN 693-5834) Tel 619-942-0335.

United Resources Publishing, *(United Res Pub; 0-932307),* 1100 Quail St., Suite 100, Newport Beach, CA 92660-2701 (SAN 686-726X) Tel 714-851-2717.

United Seminars of America, Inc., *(United Seminars Amer; 0-938093),* P.O. Box 19324, San Diego, CA 92119 (SAN 659-7068); 7290 Navajo Rd., No. 212, San Diego, CA 92119 (SAN 659-7076) Tel 619-463-6405.

United Spiritual Temple, *(United Spirit; 0-935611),* 249412 Sumner Ave., Brooklyn, NY 11206 (SAN 695-7978) Tel 718-424-5275; P.O. Box 249, Metro Sta., Brooklyn, NY 11206 (SAN 696-0413).

U.S.A. Publishing Co., *(U S A Pub Co; 0-9612124),* c/o Northwest Title & Escrow, Inc., 165 Cook St., No. 202, Denver, CO 80206 (SAN 289-5110).

U. S. Air Force Auxiliary, Oklahoma Wing, *(USAF Aux; 0-938893),* P.O. Box 10659, Attn. DOH, Midwest City, OK 73140-1659 (SAN 662-6610); Bldg. 240, Rm. 304, Tinker AFB, OK 73145 (SAN 662-6629) Tel 918-747-2282.

U. S. Assn. for the Club of Rome, *(US Assn Club Rome; 0-942718),* 1325 G St. NW, Suite 1003, Washington, DC 20005 (SAN 240-2939) Tel 202-879-3038.

U. S. Capitol Historical Society, *(US Capitol Hist; 0-916200),* 200 Maryland Ave., NE, Washington, DC 20002 (SAN 226-6601) Tel 202-543-8919.

U. S. Catholic Conference, *(US Catholic; 1-55586),* Pubns. Office, 1312 Massachusetts Ave., NW, Washington, DC 20005 (SAN 207-5350) Tel 202-659-6860; Toll free: 800-235-USCC.

U. S. Catholic Historical Society, *(US Cath Hist; 0-930060),* P.O. Box 97, Eltingville Sta., Staten Island, NY 10312 (SAN 210-5470) Tel 718-624-8022.

U. S. Central Intelligence Agency, *(US CIA),* Washington, DC 20505 (SAN 226-2320); Dist. by: Document Expediting DOCEX Project, Library of Congress, Washington, DC 20540 (SAN 282-6216).

United States-China Peoples Friendship Association, *(US-China Peoples Friendship),* 2025 Eye St., NW, Suite 715, Washington, DC 20006 (SAN 224-0262); Toll free: 800-368-5883; c/o Robert Mendel, 720 Massachusetts Ave., Cambridge, MA 02139 (SAN 669-2869).

U. S. Coast Guard Auxiliary National Board, Inc., *(US Coast Guard; 0-930028),* 69 Palm Club, 1431 S. Ocean Blvd., Pompano Beach, FL 33062-7302 (SAN 210-5217) Tel 305-964-6969.

U. S. Committee for Refugees, *(US Comm Refugees; 0-936548),* 815 15th St., NW, Suite 610, Washington, DC 20005 (SAN 214-1590).

U. S. Committee for UNICEF, *(US Comm Unicef; 0-935738),* 331 E. 38th St., New York, NY 10016 (SAN 202-9286) Tel 212-686-5522.

U. S. Committee on Irrigation & Drainage, *(US Comm Irrigation),* Box 15326, Denver, CO 80215 (SAN 225-0411) Tel 303-236-6960.

United States Court Tennis Assn., *(US Court Tennis; 0-9615695),* 215 S. 16th St., Philadelphia, PA 19102 (SAN 695-8370) Tel 212-512-2928.

†U. S. Dept. of Commerce, Bureau of the Census, *(US Dept Com-Bureau Census),* Superintendent of Documents, U.S. Government Printing Office, Washington, DC 20402 (SAN 240-1053) Tel 202-783-3238; *CIP.*

U. S. Dept. of Energy, *(DOE; 0-87079),* DOE Office of Scientific & Technical Information, Oak Ridge, TN 37831 (SAN 210-7996) Tel 615-576-1541; Dist. by: National Technical Information Service (NTIS), U. S. Dept. of Commerce, 5285 Port Royal Rd., Springfield, VA 22161 (SAN 205-7263) Tel 703-487-4838.

U. S. Department of Health and Human Services, *(US HHS; 1-55672),* 200 Independence Ave. SW, Rm. 356-G, Washington, DC 20201 (SAN 663-4346) Tel 202-472-5543.

U. S. Directory Service, Inc., *(US Direct Serv; 0-916524),* P.O. Box 68-1700, Miami, FL 33168 (SAN 282-4825); 655 NW 128th St., Miami, FL 33168 (SAN 662-1651) Tel 305-769-1700; Orders to: USD Bldg., 655 NW 128th St., Miami, FL 33168 (SAN 282-4833).

U. S. Dressage Federation, Inc., *(US Dressage Fed),* P.O. Box 80668, Lincoln, NE 68501 (SAN 224-5817) Tel 402-474-7632.

U.S. Eighteen Sixty Nine Pictorial Research Associates,Inc., *(US Pict Res; 0-9610384),* 720-17 Tramway Lane NE, Albuquerque, NM 87122 (SAN 264-4533) Tel 415-846-7083.

U. S. Federal Judicial Ctr., *(Fed Judicial Ctr),* 1520 H St., NW, Washington, DC 20005 (SAN 226-2541).

U. S. Field Hockey Assn., Inc., *(US Field Hockey),* 1750 E. Boulder St., Colorado Springs, CO 80909 (SAN 224-5604) Tel 303-578-4567.

U. S. Games Systems, Inc., *(US Games Syst; 0-913866; 0-88079),* 38 E. 32nd St., New York, NY 10016 (SAN 158-6483) Tel 212-685-4300.

United States General Accounting Office, *(US GAO),* 441 G St., NW, Washington, DC 20548 (SAN 276-3141).

U. S. Golf Assn., *(US Golf Assn; 0-941774),* Golf House, Far Hills, NJ 07931 (SAN 224-5663) Tel 201-234-2300.

†U. S. Government Printing Office, *(Gov Printing Office),* USGPO Stop SSMR, Washington, DC 20401 (SAN 206-152X) Tel 202-783-3238; Orders to: Superintendent of Documents, Washington, DC 20402-9325 (SAN 658-0785) Tel 202-783-3238; *CIP.*

United States Holocaust Memorial Council, *(US Holocaust Mem; 0-9616518),* 2000 L St., NW, Washington, DC 20036 (SAN 659-5952) Tel 202-653-9220.

U. S. Information Moscow, *(US Info Moscow; 0-934192),* 3220 Sacramento St., San Francisco, CA 94115 (SAN 218-4753) Tel 415-922-2422.

United States LST Assn., *(US LST Assn; 0-9616588),* P.O. Box 8769, Toledo, OH 43623 (SAN 659-8048); 1347 Sylvania Ave., Toledo, OH 43612 (SAN 659-8056) Tel 419-882-7868.

U. S. League of Savings Institutions, *(US League Savi Inst),* 111 E. Wacker Dr., Chicago, IL 60601 (SAN 223-8497) Tel 312-644-3100; 1709 New York Ave., NW, Suite 801, Washington, DC 20006 (SAN 669-2885) Tel 202-637-8900.

U. S. Lifesaving Assn., *(US Lifesaving),* P.O. Box 366, Huntington Beach, CA 92648 (SAN 223-8500) Tel 714-226-6868.

United States Pharmacopeial Convention, Inc., *(USPC; 0-913595),* USPC, Inc., Order Processing Dept. P.O. Box 2248, Rockville, MD 20852 (SAN 220-2794) Tel 301-881-0666.

U. S. Philatelic Classics Society, Inc., *(US Phil Classics; 0-9603548),* P.O. Box 1011, Falls Church, VA 22041 (SAN 223-8519).

United States Postal Service, Philatelic Marketing Division, *(USPS; 0-9604756),* 475 L'Enfant Plaza, Washington, DC 20260-6355 (SAN 219-8304) Tel 202-268-2350.

US Pubs. Assn., *(US Pubs; 0-911548),* 46 Lafayette Ave., New Rochelle, NY 10801 (SAN 204-8922) Tel 914-576-1121.

U. S. School of Professional Paperhanging, Inc., *(US School Prof; 0-9608506),* 16 Chaplin Ave., Rutland, VT 05701 (SAN 240-9852).

U S Screen Print Ind., Inc., *(US Screen; 0-9603530),* 7740 E. Redfield Rd., No. 106, Scottsdale, AZ 85260 (SAN 213-8727).

U.S. Ski Assn., *(US Ski; 0-9604162),* U.S. Olympic Complex, 1750 E. Boulder St., Colorado Springs, CO 80909 (SAN 214-2252) Tel 303-578-4600.

U. S. Soccer Federation, *(US Soccer Fed),* 350 Fifth Ave., New York, NY 10118 (SAN 224-5922) Tel 212-736-0915.

United States Space Foundation, *(US Space Found; 0-9616962),* 1525 Vapor Trail, Colorado Springs, CO 80916 (SAN 661-7999) Tel 303-550-1000; Dist. by: Univelt, Inc., P.O. Box 28130, San Diego, CA 92128 (SAN 204-8868) Tel 619-746-4005.

U.S. Standard, Inc., *(U S Standard Inc; 0-915229),* 309 Garden Ct., Sycamore, IL 60178 (SAN 289-8667) Tel 815-895-2646; P.O. Box 131, Sycamore, IL 60178 (SAN 658-246X); Dist. by: Pan American Navigation, P.O. Box 9046, Van Nuys, CA 91409 (SAN 202-8506) Tel 213-345-2744; Dist. by: Sportsman's Market, Clermont County Airport, Batavia, OH 41503 (SAN 205-0803) Tel 513-732-2411; Dist. by: Aviation Bk. Co., 1640 Victory Blvd., Glendale, CA 91201 (SAN 289-8691) Tel 818-240-1771.

U. S. Strategic Institute, *(U S Strat Inst; 0-913187),* 265 Winter St., Waltham, MA 02154 (SAN 287-7759) Tel 617-890-5030.

US Synchronized Swimming, *(US Synch Swim; 0-911543),* 901 W. New York St., Indianapolis, IN 46223 (SAN 276-3702) Tel 317-633-2000; Orders to: Synchro - USA Merchandising, P.O. Box 5447, Indianapolis, IN 46255 (SAN 662-166X) Tel 317-630-3336.

U. S. Tennis Assn./Ctr. for Education & Recreational Tennis, *(USTA-CERT; 0-938822),* 729 Alexander Rd., Princeton, NJ 08540 (SAN 207-6551) Tel 609-452-2580.

U. S. Trademark Assn., *(US Trademark; 0-939190),* 6 E. 45th St., New York, NY 10017 (SAN 203-0527) Tel 212-986-5880.

U. S. Trotting Assn., *(US Trotting),* 750 Michigan Ave., Columbus, OH 43215 (SAN 206-1554) Tel 614-224-2291.

United States Book Service, Subs. of United Synagogue of America, *(United Syn Bk; 0-8381),* 155 Fifth Ave., New York, NY 10010 (SAN 203-0551) Tel 212-533-7800.

United Synagogue Commission on Jewish Education, *(United Synagogue; 0-8381),* 155 Fifth Ave., New York, NY 10010 (SAN 236-4174).

United Thoroughbred Trainers of America, Inc., *(United Thoroughbred Trnrs),* 19363 James Couzens Hwy., Detroit, MI 48235 (SAN 224-5728).

United West Pr., *(United West Pr; 0-9612488),* 611 Dell St., P.O. Box 337, Solana Beach, CA 92075 (SAN 291-8609) Tel 619-481-1990.

Unity Church of Denver, *(Unity Church Denver; 0-942482),* 3021 S. University, Denver, CO 80210 (SAN 161-4541) Tel 303-758-5664.

Unity Pr., *(Unity Pr; 0-9615041),* P.O. Box 5500 Jasmine Ct., Castro Valley, CA 94552 (SAN 693-8302) Tel 415-538-5291.

Unity School of Christianity, *(Unity School; 0-87159),* Unity School of Christianity, Unity Village, MO 64065 (SAN 204-8817) Tel 816-524-3550.

Univ. Bks. *See* Hall, G. K., & Co.

Univ. of Texas, Austin Institute of Public Affairs *See* Johnson, Lyndon B., Schl. of Public Affairs

Univ. Paperbacks *See* Barnes & Noble Bks.-Imports

Univelt, Inc., *(Univelt Inc; 0-912183; 0-87703; 0-914548),* P.O. Box 28130, San Diego, CA 92128 (SAN 204-8868) Tel 619-746-4005; 740 Metcalf St., Suite 13, Escondido, CA 92025 (SAN 658-2095).

Universal Autograph Collectors Club, *(Univ Autograph; 0-9608816),* P.O. Box 467, Rockville Centre, NY 11571 (SAN 260-3675) Tel 516-766-0093.

Universal Black Writer Pr., The, *(Univ Black Pr; 0-930569),* P.O. Box 5, Radio City Station, New York, NY 10101 (SAN 219-5658) Tel 212-622-5996.

Universal Bk. Co., The, *(Universal Book Co),* P.O. Box 60943, Terminal Annex, Los Angeles, CA 90060 (SAN 219-8983) Tel 213-723-1776.

Universal Books, Inc., *(Universal Bks; 0-9608856),* 526 Silver Leaf Dr., Oroville, CA 95965 (SAN 241-0850) Tel 916-589-3171.

Universal Coterie of Pipe Smokers, *(Univ Coterie Pipe),* 20-37 120th St., College Point, NY 11356 (SAN 223-8543).

Universal Developments Publishing, *(Universal Develop; 0-935624),* 2855 Velasco Lane, Costa Mesa, CA 92626 (SAN 205-9835) Tel 714-641-0188; Orders to: P.O. Box 5253, Orange, CA 92667 (SAN 662-1678).

Universal Electronics Inc., *(Universal Elect; 0-916661),* 4555 Grove Rd., Suite 3, Columbus, OH 43232 (SAN 296-6859) Tel 614-866-4605.

Universal Goddess Center Inc., *(Univ Goddess; 0-937946),* P.O. Box 671, Malibu, CA 90265 (SAN 220-0996) Tel 213-457-7119; Dist. by: The Distributors, 702 S. Michigan, South Bend, IN 46618 (SAN 212-0364) Tel 219-232-8500.

Universal Great Brotherhood, Inc., *(Univ Great Brother; 0-915594),* P.O. Box 9154, St. Louis, MO 63117 (SAN 207-3447).

Universal Intelligence Data Bank of America, *(U Intel Data Bank; 0-9610740),* P.O. Box 865, Railroad RT No. 2, Independence, MO 64050 (SAN 264-8067) Tel 816-249-3374; 866 Twyman Rd., Independence, MO 64050 (SAN 693-5079) Tel 816-249-5933.

Universal Life & Science Foundation, *(Univ Life Sci; 0-914295),* Foundation Book Store, 2980 E. Bay Dr., Largo, FL 33541 (SAN 287-590X) Tel 813-531-1670.

Universal Ministries, Inc., Publishing House, *(Universal Ministries; 0-942428),* P.O. Box 9017, Pittsburgh, PA 15224 (SAN 238-2032) Tel 301-622-9238.

Universal Pr., *(Universal Pr; 0-918950),* 6609 Cherrywood Ave., Bakersfield, CA 93308 (SAN 210-5225) Tel 805-393-0381.

Universal Pubns., *(Univ Pubns; 0-941116),* P.O. Box 117, Fawnskin, CA 92333 (SAN 217-4480) Tel 714-585-9636.

Universal Publishing, *(Univ Pub CA; 0-9617022),* 15760 Ventura Blvd., Suite 1700, Encino, CA 91436 (SAN 662-5568) Tel 818-783-2934. Do not confuse with other companies with the same name in Maitland, FL, Oak Park, IL, Stoughton, MA.

Universal Publishing Co., Massachusetts, *(Univ Pub MA; 0-932427),* 264 Tosca Dr., Stoughton, MA 02072 (SAN 687-4347) Tel 617-821-0398.

Universal Science Pr., Inc., Div. of Universal Science Centers, Inc., *(Univ Sci Ctrs; 0-934669),* 10604 Santa Monica Blvd., Los Angeles, CA 90025 (SAN 694-0765) Tel 805-581-3244; Orders to: Sam Sonders, P.O. Box 420, Simi Valley, CA 93062 (SAN 662-3301) Tel 805-581-3244.

Universal Scientific Pubns. Co., Inc., The, *(TUSPCO; 0-88078),* P.O. Box 60943, Terminal Annex, Los Angeles, CA 90060 (SAN 220-309X) Tel 213-723-1776.

Universal Technology Corp., *(Univ Tech; 0-912426),* Corporate Headquaters, 1616 Mardon Dr., Dayton, OH 45432 (SAN 204-885X) Tel 513-426-8530; Orders to: Technology & Audiovisual Complex, 2700 N. Fairfield Rd., Dayton, OH 45432 (SAN 650-0641) Tel 513-426-2808.

Universe Bks., Inc., Div. of South Park Pr., *(Universe; 0-87663; 1-55550),* 381 Park Ave. S., New York, NY 10016 (SAN 202-537X) Tel 212-685-7400. *Imprints:* Free Life Editions (Free Life); Main Street Press (Main St); Manhattan Institute for Policy Research Book (Man Inst Pol Res); Pica Press (Pica Pr); Pica Special Studies (Pica Spec Stud).

Universe Publishing Co., *(Universe Pub Co; 0-935484),* 185 W. Demarest Ave., Englewood, NJ 07631 (SAN 214-3321) Tel 201-567-4296.

Universities Field Staff International, Inc., *(U Field Staff Intl; 0-910116; 0-88333),* P.O. Box 150, Hanover, NH 03755 (SAN 202-4764) Tel 603-448-5741.

University *See* **Exposition Pr. of Florida, Inc.**

University Art Museum, California State University, Long Beach, *(CA St U LB Art; 0-936270),* 1250 Bellflower Blvd., Long Beach, CA 90840 (SAN 223-3827) Tel 213-498-5761.

University Assocs., *(Univ Assocs; 0-88390),* 8517 Production Ave., San Diego, CA 92121 (SAN 203-333X) Tel 619-578-5900; 8535 Production Ave., San Diego, CA 92121 (SAN 658-2109).

Univ. Bk. Hse., *(Univ Book Hse; 0-936461),* 112 Russell Woods Dr., Lynchburg, VA 24502 (SAN 697-9742) Tel 804-237-1486.

Univ. Bk. Service, *(Univ Bk Serv; 0-942644),* 2162 Gerritsen Ave., Brooklyn, NY 11229 (SAN 206-4014) Tel 718-280-5066.

University Books, Inc., Div. of Lyle Stuart, Inc., *(Univ Bks; 0-8216),* 120 Enterprise Ave., Secaucus, NJ 07094 (SAN 203-3348) Tel 201-866-0490; Toll free: 800-572-6657.

University Classics, Ltd., Publishers, *(Univ Class; 0-914127),* 1 Bryan Rd., Briarwood, Athens, OH 45701 (SAN 287-5934) Tel 614-592-4543. *Imprints:* University Classics, Limited (Univ Classics Ltd).

University Classics, Limited *See* **University Classics, Ltd., Publishers**

University Co-Operative Society, *(Univ Co-Op Soc; 0-916048),* P.O. Box 7520, Austin, TX 78712 (SAN 207-5083) Tel 512-476-7211.

University Editions, Subs. of Aegina Press, *(Univ Edns; 0-916383),* 4937 Humphrey Rd., Huntington, WV 25704 (SAN 295-8287) Tel 304-736-1027.

University Editions *See* **New Benjamin Franklin Hse., The**

University Extension Pubns, Univ. of California, Berkeley, *(Univ Extension Pubns; 0-917936),* 2223 Fulton St., Berkeley, CA 94720 (SAN 208-0311) Tel 415-642-3112.

University Games, *(Univ Games; 0-935145),* 4055 Bohannon Dr., Menlo Park, CA 94025 (SAN 695-2321) Tel 415-322-3953.

University Lions Club Foundation of Seattle, The, *(Univ Lions Club; 0-9617052),* 4312 NE 85th St., Seattle, WA 98115 (SAN 662-8842) Tel 206-523-1557.

University Microfilms, Inc., Div. of Bell & Howell, *(Univ Microfilms; 0-8357),* 300 N. Zeeb Rd., Ann Arbor, MI 48106 (SAN 212-2464) Tel 313-761-4700; Toll free: 800-521-0600; Toll free: 800-343-5299 (Canada). Serials and newspapers in microform, reprints of articles and issues, dissertations published and available on demand. Imprints: Books on Demand, reprinting of out-of-print books, and UMI Research Press, scholarly and professional book publishing.

University Monographs, Subs. of Wright State Univ., *(Univ Monographs; 0-932429),* Wright State Univ., Rm. 442 Millett, Dayton, OH 45435 (SAN 687-4355) Tel 513-873-3023.

University of Alabama, Center for Business & Economic Research, *(U of Ala Ctr Bus; 0-943394),* P.O. Box AK, University, AL 35486 (SAN 206-1074) Tel 205-348-6191.

University of Alabama in Huntsville, Department of Mechanical Engineering, *(U AL Dept Mech Eng; 0-942166),* Huntsville, AL 35899 (SAN 239-989X) Tel 205-895-6154.

Univ. of Alabama Pr., *(U of Ala Pr; 0-8173),* P.O. Box 2877, University, AL 35486 (SAN 202-5272) Tel 205-348-5180.

University of Alabama School of Law, *(U AL Law),* P.O. Box 1976, University, AL 35486 (SAN 226-8949).

University of Alaska, *(Univ Alaska; 0-943712),* Museum, Fairbanks, AK 99501 (SAN 200-4240).

University of Alaska, Elmer E. Rasmuson Library, *(U Alaska Rasmuson Lib; 0-935792),* Fairbanks, AK 99701 (SAN 206-1082) Tel 907-479-7224.

Univ. of Alaska, Institute of Marine Science, *(U of AK Inst Marine; 0-914500),* Publications Office, Fairbanks, AK 99775-1080 (SAN 208-1032) Tel 907-474-7843.

Univ. of Alaska, Institute of Social & Economic Research, Div. of Univ. of Alaska, *(U Alaska Inst Res; 0-88353),* 3211 Providence Dr., Anchorage, AK 99508 (SAN 203-0144) Tel 907-786-7710.

Univ. of Alaska Pr., *(U of Alaska Pr; 0-912006),* Univ. of Alaska, Vice Chancellor of Research & Advanced Study, Signer's Hall, Fairbanks, AK 99775-1580 (SAN 203-3011) Tel 907-474-6389.

Univ. of Alberta Pr., *(U Alta Pr; 0-88864),* 123 Administration Bldgs., Edmonton, AB T6G 2E2, .

Univ. of Arizona, Arizona Educational Materials Ctr., *(U of AZ Ed Mat; 0-940870),* College of Education, P.O. Box 601, Tucson, AZ 85721 (SAN 219-6514) Tel 602-621-3724.

Univ. of Arizona, Ctr. for Creative Photograhy, *(U Ariz Ctr Photog; 0-938262),* 843 E. University, Tucson, AZ 85719 (SAN 285-1032) Tel 602-621-7968; Dist. by: Univ. of Arizona Pr., 1615 E. Speedway, Tucson, AZ 85719 (SAN 285-1040) Tel 602-795-0583.

Univ. of Arizona, College of Agriculture, *(Univ AZ Agriculture; 0-932913),* Univ. of Arizona, Tucson, AZ 85721 (SAN 689-9706) Tel 602-621-7180.

Univ. of Arizona, Mexican American Studies & Research Ctr., *(Univ AZ Mex Amer Studies; 0-939363),* 1625 E. Speedway, No. 8, Tucson, AZ 85719 (SAN 662-6971) Tcl 602-621-5121.

†**Univ. of Arizona Pr.,** *(U of Ariz Pr; 0-8165),* 1615 E. Speedway, Tucson, AZ 85719 (SAN 205-468X) Tel 602-795-0583; 250 E Valencia, Tucson, AZ 85706 (SAN 658-2125); *CIP.*

Univ. of Arkansas, Accounting Dept. Foundation, *(U AR Acc Dept; 0-935951),* Business Administration, Rm. 204, Fayetteville, AR 72701 (SAN 696-7817) Tel 501-575-6123.

†**Univ. of Arkansas Pr.,** *(U of Ark Pr; 0-938626),* Univ. of Arkansas, Fayetteville, AR 72701 (SAN 239-3972) Tel 501-575-3246; Toll free: 800-242-7737; Dist. by: Texas A & M Univ. Pr., Drawer C, College Station, TX 77843 (SAN 207-5237) Tel 409-845-1436; *CIP.*

Univ. of California, Div. of Library Automation, *(UCDLA; 0-913248),* 186 University Hall, Berkeley, CA 94720 (SAN 207-3617) Tel 415-642-9485.

Univ. of California, American Indian Studies Ctr., *(U Cal AISC; 0-935626),* 3220 Campbell Hall, Los Angeles, CA 90024 (SAN 220-1283) Tel 213-825-7315.

University of California at Berkeley, Center for Real Estate & Urban Economics, *(UCB Real Estate),* 156 Barrows Hall, Berkeley, CA 94720 (SAN 237-6482).

Univ. of California at Los Angeles, Schl. of Law, *(UCLA Law),* Rm. 2125C, Los Angeles, CA 90024 (SAN 226-3637).

Univ. of California at Riverside, Boyd Deep Canyon Desert Research Ctr., *(Boyd Deep Canyon; 0-942290),* Univ. of California, Riverside, Dept. of Biology, Riverside, CA 92521 (SAN 210-8852) Tel 714-787-5917.

Univ. of California, Berkeley, Ctr. for Labor Research & Education, *(UCal Berk CLRE; 0-937817),* 2521 Channing Way, Berkeley, CA 94720 (SAN 659-4336) Tel 415-642-0323.

†**Univ. of California, Berkeley, Chicano Studies Library,** *(UC Chicano; 0-918520),* 3404 Dwinelle Hall, Berkeley, CA 94720 (SAN 209-9039) Tel 415-642-3859; *CIP.*

Univ. of California, Dutch Studies Program, *(Univ CA Dutch Studies; 0-9616744),* Dept. of German, 5317 Dwinelle Hall, Berkeley, CA 94720 (SAN 661-0447) Tel 415-642-2941.

†**Univ. of California, Institute of Governmental Studies,** *(Inst Gov Stud Berk; 0-87772),* 109 Moses Hall, Berkeley, CA 94720 (SAN 202-7011) Tel 415-642-1428; Orders to: Univ. of California, Publications Office, 119 Moses Hall, Berkeley, CA 94720 (SAN 662-1686) Tel 415-642-5537; *CIP.*

Univ. of California, Institute of Industrial Relations, *(U Cal LA Indus Rel; 0-89215),* 405 Hilgard Ave., Los Angeles, CA 90024 (SAN 205-4698) Tel 213-825-9191.

†**Univ. of California, Institute of International Studies,** *(U of Cal Intl St; 0-87725),* 215 Moses Hall, Berkeley, CA 94720 (SAN 203-3038) Tel 415-642-7189; *CIP.*

Univ. of California, Institute on Global Conflict and Cooperation, *(U of CA Inst Global; 0-934637),* Univ. of Cal., San Diego, IGCC Central Office, Q-60, La Jolla, CA 92093 (SAN 693-9163) Tel 619-452-3352.

Univ. of California, Latin American Ctr., *(UCLA Lat Am Ctr; 0-87903),* 405 Hilgard Ave., Los Angeles, CA 90024 (SAN 201-0704) Tel 213-825-6634.

University of California, Los Angeles, Business Forecasting Project, *(UCLA Busn Forecasting; 0-913404),* Graduate School of Management, Rm. 4371-C, Los Angeles, CA 90024 (SAN 203-0160) Tel 213-825-1623.

Univ. of California, Los Angeles, Chicano Studies Research Ctr., Pubns. Unit, *(UCLA Chicano Stud; 0-89551),* 3126 Campbell Hall, 405 Hilgard Ave., Los Angeles, CA 90024 (SAN 209-097X) Tel 213-825-2642.

†**Univ. of California, Los Angeles, Institute of Archaeology,** *(UCLA Arch; 0-917956),* 405 Hilgard Ave., Los Angeles, CA 90024 (SAN 210-3281) Tel 213-825-7411; *CIP.*

Univ. of California Los Angeles, Museum of Cultural History, *(UCLA Mus Hist; 0-930741),* 405 Hilgard Ave., 55A Haines Hall, Los Angeles, CA 90024 (SAN 280-8501) Tel 213-825-4361.

Univ. of California, Office for History of Science & Technology, *(U Cal Hist Sci Tech; 0-918102),* 470 Stephens Hall, Univ. of California, Berkeley, CA 94720 (SAN 210-1394) Tel 415-642-4581.

†**Univ. of California Pr.,** *(U of Cal Pr; 0-520),* 2120 Berkeley Way, Berkeley, CA 94720 (SAN 203-3046) Tel 415-642-6683; Toll free: 800-822-6657 (For orders); 1095 Essex St., Richmond, CA 94801 (SAN 658-2133). Do not confuse U of Cal Pr, Berkeley, CA, with the Univ. of Calgary Pr., Calgary, AB, Canada; *CIP.*

University of California, School of Law, *(U of Cal Sch Law; 0-935076),* Davis, CA 95616 (SAN 206-7374); Dist. by: Fred B. Rothman & Co., 10368 W. Centennial Rd., Littleton, CO 80127 (SAN 159-9437) Tel 303-979-5657.

University of California, Wm. Andrews Clark Memorial Library, *(UC-Wm Andrews Clark; 0-88330),* 2520 Cimarron St., Los Angeles, CA 90018 (SAN 206-1104) Tel 213-731-8529.

Univ. of Central Arkansas Pr., *(Univ Central AR Pr; 0-9615143),* Box S, UCA, Conway, AR 72032 (SAN 694-2083) Tel 501-450-3180.

Univ. of Chicago, Ctr. for Health Administration Studies, *(Univ Chi Ctr Hlth; 0-9616519),* 1101 E. 58th St., Chicago, IL 60637 (SAN 659-5960) Tel 312-962-7104.

University of Chicago, Center for Policy Study, *(U Chi Ctr Policy),* 5801 S. Ellis Ave., Rm. 200, Chicago, IL 60637 (SAN 220-102X) Tel 312-962-8352.

Univ. of Chicago, Community & Family Study Ctr., *(Comm & Family; 0-89836),* 1411 E. 60th St., Chicago, IL 60637 (SAN 276-4164) Tel 312-753-2974.

Univ. of Chicago, Dept. of Anthropology, *(U Chi Dept Anthro; 0-916256),* 1126 E. 59th St., Chicago, IL 60637 (SAN 208-0583) Tel 312-962-7314.

Univ. of Chicago, Dept. of Education, *(U Chi Dept Educ; 0-936745),* 5835 S. Kimbark Ave., Chicago, IL 60637 (SAN 699-9719) Tel 312-962-9457.

†Univ. of Chicago, Department of Geography, Research Papers, (U Chicago Dept Geog; 0-89065), 5828 S. University Ave., Chicago, IL 60637 (SAN 203-3003) Tel 312-962-8314; CIP.

University of Chicago, Graduate School of Business, (U Chicago Grad Sch Busn; 0-918584), 1101 E. 58th St., Chicago, IL 60637 (SAN 211-4585) Tel 312-962-7431.

University of Chicago, Midwest Administration Center, (U Chicago Midwest Admin; 0-931080), 5835 S. Kimbark Ave., Chicago, IL 60637 (SAN 206-0906) Tel 312-962-1565.

Univ. of Chicago, Oriental Institute, (Oriental Inst; 0-918986), 1155 E. 58th St., Chicago, IL 60637 (SAN 276-430X) Tel 312-962-9508.

Univ. of Chicago Pr., Div. of Univ. of Chicago, (U of Chicago Pr; 0-226), 5801 Ellis Ave., 3rd Flr., S., Chicago, IL 60637 (SAN 202-5280) Tel 312-962-7693; Toll free: 800-621-2736; Orders to: 11030 S. Langley Ave., Chicago, IL 60628 (SAN 202-5299) Tel 312-568-1550. Imprints: Chicago Original Paperback (Chicago Original Paperback); Chicago Visual Library (Chicago Visual Lib); Midway Reprint (Midway Reprint).

Univ. of Cincinnati, (Univ of Cincinnati; 0-9611212), Dept. of Geography, Mail Location 131, Cincinnati, OH 45221 (SAN 283-8842).

Univ. of Cincinnati, College of Educ., (Univ Cinn Coll Ed; 0-915645), Office Of The Dean, Cincinnati, OH 45221 (SAN 292-7187).

University of Colorado, Bureau of Governmental, Research & Science, (UCO BGR), 125 Ketchum Bldg., Boulder, CO 80302 (SAN 226-9163).

Univ. of Colorado, Business Research Div., Div. of College of Business, (U CO Busn Res Div; 0-89478), Box 420, Univ. of Colorado, Boulder, CO 80309 (SAN 209-9047) Tel 303-492-8227.

Univ. of Colorado-Denver, Dept. of History, (Univ CO Dept Hist; 0-937859), P.O. Box 105, Denver, CO 80202 (SAN 659-5979); 1100 14th St., Denver, CO 80202 (SAN 659-5987) Tel 303-556-3442.

University of Colorado, Colorado Associated University Press See Colorado Associated Univ. Pr., Univ. of Colorado

†Univ. of Connecticut Library Business Services, U-5B, (Univ Conn Lib; 0-917590), Fairfield Ave., Box U-5BO, Storrs, CT 06268 (SAN 209-3901) Tel 203-486-2520; CIP.

University of Connecticut, School of Law Press, (U Conn Sch Law; 0-939328), 35 Elizabeth St., Hartford, CT 06105 (SAN 216-5554) Tel 203-241-4609.

Univ. of Dallas Pr., (U of Dallas Pr; 0-918306), 1845 E. Northgate, Irving, TX 75062 (SAN 209-4940) Tel 214-721-5226.

†Univ. of Delaware Pr., (U Delaware Pr; 0-87413), c/o Associated Univ. Presses, Inc., 440 Forsgate Dr., Cranbury, NJ 08512 (SAN 203-4476) Tel 609-655-4770; CIP.

Univ. of Denver, Ctr. for Teaching, International Relations Pubns., (U of Denver Teach; 0-943804), GSIS, Univ. of Denver, Denver, CO 80208 (SAN 241-0877) Tel 303-871-2426.

†Univ. of Denver, Graduate Schl. of International Studies, Monograph Series in World Affairs, (Monograph Series; 0-87940), Univ. of Denver, Denver, CO 80208 (SAN 205-4701) Tel 303-871-2555; CIP.

Univ. of Detroit Pr., (U of Detroit Pr; 0-911550), 4001 W. McNichols, Detroit, MI 48221 (SAN 205-471X).

Univ. of Evansville Pr., (U of Evansville Pr; 0-930982), 1800 Lincoln Ave., Evansville, IN 47722 (SAN 265-413X) Tel 812-479-2488.

Univ. of Flordia Ctr. for African Studies, (U of FL African Studies; 0-935833), 470 Grinter Hall, Gainesville, FL 32611 (SAN 695-8796) Tel 904-392-2187.

University of Florida, College of Law, (U Fla Law), Law Ctr., Gainesville, FL 32611 (SAN 227-0536).

Univ. of Florida, Institute of Food & Agricultural Sciences, (Univ Fla Food; 0-916287), Bldg. 459 Shealy Dr., Gainesville, FL 32611 (SAN 295-6055) Tel 904-392-2186.

University of Florida, University Gallery See Univ. Presses of Florida

†Univ. of Georgia, Carl Vinson Institute of Government, (U of GA Inst Govt; 0-89854), Terrell Hall, Athens, GA 30602 (SAN 212-8012); CIP.

Univ. of Georgia, Institute of Community & Area Development, The, Div. of UGA, (Inst Community; 0-911847), 300 Old College, Athens, GA 30602 (SAN 264-4541) Tel 404-542-7103.

Univ. of Georgia Institute of Natural Resources, (Univ GA Nat Res; 0-935835), Univ. of Georgia, Athens, GA 30602 (SAN 696-6497) Tel 404-542-1555.

†Univ. of Georgia Pr., (U of Ga Pr; 0-8203), Terrell Hall, Athens, GA 30602 (SAN 203-3054) Tel 404-542-2830; CIP.

Univ. of Hawaii at Manoa, Curriculum Research & Development Group, (UH CRDG; 0-937049), 1776 University Ave., CM 103, Honolulu, HI 96822 (SAN 658-6597) Tel 808-948-6823; Dist. by: Educational Merchandising & Consulting, 8912 Mineral King Ct., Elk Grove, CA 95624 (SAN 200-6308).

Univ. of Hawaii at Manoa, Industrial Relations Ctr., (U Hawaii), 2425 Campus Rd., Honolulu, HI 96822 (SAN 280-8773).

Univ. of Hawaii Pr., The, (UH Pr; 0-8248), 2840 Kolowalu St., Honolulu, HI 96822 (SAN 202-5353) Tel 808-948-8697; 1330 Lower Campus Rd., Honolulu, HI 96822 (SAN 658-215X). Imprints: Consortium for Pacific Arts & Cultures (Consort Pac Arts); Eastwest Center Press (Eastwest Ctr); Kolowalu Book (Kolowalu Bk); Korea Development Institute (Korea Devel Inst); Pacific Telecommunications Council (Pac Telecomm); Seaweeds & Constructions (Seaweeds & Cons).

Univ. of Healing Pr., (U of Healing; 0-940480), 32750 Hwy. 94, Campo, CA 92006 (SAN 211-7983) Tel 619-478-5111; 1101 Far Valley Rd., Campo, CA 92006 (SAN 693-9783) Tel 619-478-5111.

Univ. of Houston, Mexican American Studies Program, (Univ Houston Mex Amer; 0-939709), 4800 Calhoun Rd., Houston, TX 77004 (SAN 663-0766).

Univ. of Idaho, Ctr. for Business Development & Research, (U ID Ctr Busn; 0-940982), Moscow, ID 83843 (SAN 205-9673) Tel 208-885-6611.

Univ. of Idaho Pr., Div. of Idaho Research Foundation, Inc., (U of Idaho Pr; 0-89301), University Sta., Box 3368, Moscow, ID 83843 (SAN 208-905X) Tel 208-885-6245.

†Univ. of Illinois, at Urbana-Champaign, Archaeological Survey, Inc., (U IL-Archaeological; 0-942704), 109 Davenport Hall, 607 S. Mathews Ave., Urbana, IL 61801 (SAN 240-1037); CIP.

Univ. of Illinois at Urbana-Champaign, College of Law, (UI Law Urbana), 209 Law Bldg., Champaign, IL 61820 (SAN 226-8779).

Univ. of Illinois at Urbana-Champaign, Graduate Schl. of Library & Information Science, (U of Ill Lib Info Sci; 0-87845), Pubns. Office, 249 Armory Bldg, 505 E. Armory St., Champaign, IL 61820 (SAN 277-4917) Tel 217-333-1359.

Univ. of Illinois Pr., (U of Ill Pr; 0-252), 54 E. Gregory Dr., Champaign, IL 61820 (SAN 202-5310) Tel 217-333-0950; Toll free: 800-242-7737; Orders to: Harper & Row, Inc., Keystone Industrial Pk., Scranton, PA 18512 (SAN 215-3742); Orders to: Univ. of Illinois Pr., P.O. Box 1650, Hagerstown, MD 21741. Imprints: Illini Books (IB).

University of Illinois, School of Music, (U IL Sch Music), University of Illinois, Urbana, IL 61801 Tel 217-333-1027; 1114 W. Nevada, Urbana, IL 61801 (SAN 662-1708).

Univ. of Iowa, Audiovisual Ctr., (U IA Audiovisual), C215 Seashore Hall, Iowa City, IA 52242 (SAN 241-5909) Tel 319-353-7368.

Univ. of Iowa, Ctr. for Educational Experimentation, Development & Evaluation, (U IA Ctr Ed Experiment; 0-939984; 0-88670), N345 Oakdale Hall, Oakdale, IA 52319 (SAN 216-8677) Tel 319-353-4200.

Univ. of Iowa, College of Law, (U Iowa Law), Iowa City, IA 52240 (SAN 226-9155).

Univ. of Iowa, Institute of Public Affairs, Div. of Continuing Education, (U Iowa IPA), 507 N. Clinton, Iowa City, IA 52242 (SAN 262-1231) Tel 319-353-3270.

†Univ. of Iowa Pr., (U of Iowa Pr; 0-87745), Univ. of Iowa, Iowa City, IA 52242 (SAN 282-4868) Tel 319-353-3181; Orders to: Graphic Services Bldg., Iowa City, IA 52242 (SAN 282-4876) Tel 319-353-4171; CIP.

Univ. of Iowa, Schl. of Social Work, (U of Iowa Sch Soc Wk; 0-934936), Iowa City, IA 52242 (SAN 214-1612).

Univ. of Kansas, Dept. of Art & Music Education & Music Therapy, (U KS Dept Art Music; 0-936117), 311 Bailey Hall, Lawrence, KS 66045-4322 (SAN 696-7655) Tel 913-864-4784.

University of Kansas, Division of Continuing Education, (U of KS Cont Ed; 0-936352), Continuing Education Bldg., Lawrence, KS 66045 (SAN 214-1620).

Univ. of Kansas, Museum of Natural History, (U of KS Mus Nat Hist; 0-89338), 602 Dyche Hall, Lawrence, KS 66045 (SAN 206-0957) Tel 913-864-4540.

Univ. of Kansas Pubns., (U of KS Pubns), Exchange & Gift Dept., Watson Library, Univ. of Kansas, Lawrence, KS 66045 (SAN 215-7101).

Univ. of Kentucky Libraries, (U of KY Libs; 0-917519), Department of Special Collections & Archives, Lexington, KY 40506-0059 (SAN 656-1098) Tel 606-257-1466.

University of Kentucky, Library Associates, (U Ky Lib Assocs; 0-919123), Lexington, KY 40506 (SAN 241-4686) Tel 606-257-9401.

Univ. of Maine, at Orono Pr., (U Maine Orono; 0-89101), PICS Bldg., Univ. of Maine at Orono, Orono, ME 04469 (SAN 207-2971) Tel 207-581-1700.

Univ. of Mary Hardin-Baylor Pr., (UMHB Pr; 0-9616297), 11th & College St., Belton, TX 76513 (SAN 658-5310) Tel 817-939-5811; P.O. Box 431, UMHB Sta., Belton, TX 76513 (SAN 658-5329).

Univ. of Maryland, College of Library & Information Services, (U of Md Lib Serv; 0-911808), 3116 Hornbake Library Bldg., College Park, MD 20742 (SAN 203-3097) Tel 301-454-2590; Orders to: University of Maryland, Univ. Bk. Ctr., College Park, MD 20742 (SAN 203-3100).

Univ. of Maryland, College Park, Institute for Urban Studies, (U MD Inst; 0-913749), 1113 Lefrak Hall, Univ. of Maryland, College Park, MD 20742 (SAN 286-2107) Tel 301-454-2662.

Univ. of Maryland, Dept. of Geography, (U MD Geography; 0-918512), 1113 Lefrak Hall, College Park, MD 20742 (SAN 209-9055) Tel 301-454-2241.

Univ. of Maryland, Schl. of Law, (U MD Law), 500 W. Baltimore St., Baltimore, MD 21201 (SAN 226-9260).

University of Maryland, School of Medicine-Anatomy Department, (Univ Maryland; 0-9608786), 655 W. Baltimore St., Baltimore, MD 21201 (SAN 238-4019) Tel 301-528-3532.

University of Maryland, Sea Grant Program, (MD Sea Grant Col; 0-943676), H. J. Patterson, Rm. 1224, College Park, MD 20742 (SAN 238-4035) Tel 301-454-6054.

Univ. of Massachusetts, Ctr. for International Education, Div. of School of Ed., (Ctr Intl Ed U of MA; 0-932288), 285 Hills Hse., S., Amherst, MA 01003 (SAN 212-9329) Tel 413-545-0465.

University of Massachusetts, Graduate School, (Univ Mass Grad; 0-9604712), Amherst, MA 01003 (SAN 240-9836); Dist. by: Department of Geology & Geography, Univ. of Massachusetts, Amherst, MA 01003 (SAN 282-6143).

†Univ. of Massachusetts Pr., (U of Mass Pr; 0-87023), P.O. Box 429, Amherst, MA 01004 (SAN 203-3089) Tel 413-545-2217; CIP.

Univ. of Miami, Comparative Sedimentology Laboratory, Div. of Marine Geology and Geophysics (MGG-RSMAS), (Univ Miami CSL; 0-932981), Fisher Island Sta., Miami Beach, FL 33139 (SAN 219-0141) Tel 305-672-1840.

Names

University of Miami, Law & Economics Center, *(Law & Econ U Miami; 0-916770),* P.O. Box 248000, Coral Gables, FL 33124 (SAN 208-9017) Tel 305-284-6174.

Univ. of Miami North/South Ctr., Graduate Schl. of International Studies, *(U Miami N-S Ctr; 0-935501),* P.O. Box 248123, Coral Gables, FL 33124 (SAN 695-8834) Tel 305-284-4303.

†**Univ. of Michigan Pr.,** *(U of Miami Pr; 0-87024),* P.O. Box 4836, Hampden Sta., Baltimore, MD 21211 (SAN 203-3119) Tel 301-338-6952; *CIP.*

Univ. of Miami, Rosenstiel School of Marine & Atmospheric Science, *(U Miami Marine; 0-930050),* Orders to: Publications-STO Sales, 4600 Rickenbacker Causeway, Miami, FL 33149 (SAN 276-4210) Tel 305-361-4616.

Univ. of Michigan Alumnae Council, Subs. of Alumni Assn. of the Univ. of Michigan, *(U of Mich Alumnae; 0-9613460),* 200 Fletcher St., Ann Arbor, MI 48109 (SAN 657-307X) Tel 313-763-9708.

Univ. of Michigan, Ctr. for Chinese Studies, *(U of Mich Ctr Chinese; 0-89264),* 104 Lane Hall, Ann Arbor, MI 48109 (SAN 208-2772) Tel 313-763-7181.

†**Univ. of Michigan, Ctr. for Japanese Studies,** *(U MI Japan; 0-939512),* 108 Lane Hall, Ann Arbor, MI 48109 (SAN 216-7018) Tel 313-763-7265; *CIP.*

Univ. of Michigan, Ctr. for Near Eastern & North African Studies, *(UM Ctr NENAS; 0-932098),* 144 Lane Hall, Ann Arbor, MI 48109-1290 (SAN 211-7150) Tel 313-764-0350; Orders to: Univ. of Michigan Resources Ctr., 204 S. Fourth St., Ann Arbor, MI 48103 (SAN 653-483X) Tel 313-764-8288; Dist. by: Univ. of Michigan Pr., Pubns. Distribution Ctr., 839 Greene St., Ann Arbor, MI 48106 (SAN 285-1075) Tel 313-764-4394; Dist. by: Cambridge Univ. Pr., 510 North Ave., New Rochelle, NY 10801 (SAN 285-1083) Tel 914-235-0300; Dist. by: International Bk. Ctr., P.O. Box 295, Troy, MI 48099 (SAN 208-7022) Tel 313-879-8436. Do not confuse with Univ. of Michigan, Dept. of Near Eastern Studies.

Univ. of Michigan, Ctr. for South & Southeast Asian Studies, *(Ctr S&SE Asian; 0-89148),* 130 Lane Hall, Ann Arbor, MI 48109 (SAN 206-491X) Tel 313-764-0352.

Univ. of Michigan, College of Architecture & Urban Planning, *(U Mich Arch; 0-9614792),* 292 Harmon St., Birmingham, MI 48009 (SAN 693-0182) Tel 313-644-0604.

Univ. of Michigan-Dearborn, Branch of Univ. of Michigan, *(U Mich-Dearborn; 0-933691),* 4901 Evergreen Rd., Dearborn, MI 48128-1491 (SAN 291-3615) Tel 313-593-5075; Orders to: Follett's Bookstore, 4901 Evergreen Rd., Dearborn, MI 48128-1491 (SAN 662-2224) Tel 313-593-5530.

Univ. of Michigan, Dept. of Near Eastern Studies, Div. of Univ. of Michigan, *(UM Dept NES; 0-916798),* 3074 Frieze Bldg., Ann Arbor, MI 48109 (SAN 285-1059) Tel 313-764-0314; Dist. by: Eisenbrauns, P.O. Box 275, Winona Lake, IN 46590 (SAN 285-1067) Tel 219-269-2011. Do not confuse with Univ. of Michigan, Ctr. for Near Eastern & North African Studies.

†**Univ. of Michigan, Div. of Research, Graduate Schl. of Business Administration,** *(U Mich Busn Div Res; 0-87712),* Ann Arbor, MI 48109 (SAN 204-8736) Tel 313-764-1366; *CIP.*

Univ. of Michigan, Institute of Labor & Industrial Relations, *(U of Mich Inst Labor; 0-87736),* University of Michigan, Victor Vaughn Bldg., 1111 E. Catherine, Ann Arbor, MI 48109 (SAN 662-1716) Tel 313-747-0699; Dist. by: ILIR Pubns., Univ. of Michigan, Victor Vaughn Bldg., 1111 E. Catherine, Ann Arbor, MI 48109-2054 (SAN 203-3127) Tel 313-763-1187.

Univ. of Michigan, Law Schl., Institute of Continuing Legal Education, *(U MI Law CLE; 0-88288),* 625 S. State, Ann Arbor, MI 48104 (SAN 226-9295).

Univ. of Michigan, Museum of Anthropology, *(UMI Mus Anthro; 0-915703),* 4009 Museums, Ann Arbor, MI 48109 (SAN 280-901X).

Univ. of Michigan, Museum of Anthropology, Pubns. Dept., *(U Mich Mus Anthro; 0-932206),* 4009 Museums Bldg., 1109 Geddes, Ann Arbor, MI 48109 (SAN 203-0489) Tel 313-764-6867.

†**Univ. of Michigan, Museum of Art, Alumni Memorial Hall,** *(Michigan Mus),* 525 S. State St., Ann Arbor, MI 48109 (SAN 280-9028); *CIP.*

Univ. of Michigan Pr., *(U of Mich Pr; 0-472),* P.O. Box 1104, Ann Arbor, MI 48106 (SAN 282-4884) Tel 313-764-4330; Orders to: 839 Greene St., Ann Arbor, MI 48106 (SAN 282-4892) Tel 313-764-4392. *Imprints:* Ann Arbor Books (AA).

Univ. of Michigan Program in Dental Public Health, *(Univ MI Dental; 0-935837),* 109 Observatory, Ann Arbor, MI 48109 (SAN 696-6632) Tel 313-764-5477.

Univ. of Minnesota, Div. of Pediatric Nephrology & the Minnesota Medical Foundation, *(U Minn Pediatric; 0-940210),* P.O. Box 73, Mayo Bldg., Minneapolis, MN 55455 (SAN 262-1037); 420 Delaware St., SE, Minneapolis, MN 55455 (SAN 658-2168).

Univ. of Minnesota, Bell Institute of Pathology, *(U of Minn Bell; 0-912922),* P.O. Box 302, Mayo Memorial Bldg., Minneapolis, MN 55455 (SAN 204-8744).

Univ. of Minnesota, College of Liberal Arts, Ctr. for Humanistic Studies, *(U of MN College Lib Arts; 0-9607884),* 117 Pleasant St., SE, Minneapolis, MN 55118 (SAN 238-4027) Tel 612-624-0003.

Univ. of Minnesota, Computer Ctr., *(U of Minn Comp Ctr; 0-936992),* Univ. of Minnesota, Duluth, MN 55812 (SAN 215-1200).

Univ. of Minnesota, Dept. of Anthropology, *(Dept Anthro U Minn; 0-911599),* 215 Ford Hall, 224 Church St. SE, Minneapolis, MN 55455 (SAN 264-4576) Tel 612-373-4614.

Univ. of Minnesota Hospital & Clinic, Consultation/Education Div., Div. of Univ. of Minnesota, *(U M H & C; 0-937423),* Box 603, Harvard St. at East River Rd., Minneapolis, MN 55455 (SAN 659-0934) Tel 612-626-6356; Orders to: Pritchett & Hall Assocs., Inc., 3440 Oakcliff Rd., NE, Suite 110, Atlanta, GA 30340 (SAN 662-4227) Tel 404-451-0602.

Univ. of Minnesota, Immigration History Research Center, *(Immig His Res; 0-932833),* 826 Berry St., St. Paul, MN 55114 (SAN 219-0184) Tel 612-373-5581.

Univ. of Minnesota, Law Schl., *(U Minn Law),* Minneapolis, MN 55455 (SAN 227-3276).

Univ. of Minnesota Pr., *(U of Minn Pr; 0-8166),* 2037 University Ave., SE, Minneapolis, MN 55414 (SAN 213-2648) Tel 612-624-6055.

Univ. of Minnesota, Schl. of Architecture, *(Univ Minn Sch; 0-943352),* Dist. by: Univ. of Minnesota Press, 2037 University Ave. SE, Minneapolis, MN 55414 (SAN 213-2648) Tel 612-376-2972.

Univ. of Minnesota, Univ. Art Museum, *(Univ MN Art Mus; 0-938713),* 84 Church St., SE, Minneapolis, MN 55455 (SAN 661-5066) Tel 612-624-9052.

Univ. of Mississippi, Bureau of Business & Economic Research, *(UM Bus Econ; 0-938004),* 300 LaBauve A, University, MS 38677 (SAN 206-0841) Tel 601-232-7481.

Univ. of Mississippi, Law Ctr., *(U MS Law Ctr; 0-8377),* University, MS 38677 (SAN 213-3938); Dist. by: Fred B. Rothman & Co., 10368 W. Centennial Rd., Littleton, CO 80123 (SAN 159-9437) Tel 303-979-5657.

Univ. of Mississippi Schl. of Engineering, The, *(Univ MS Schl Engin; 0-937099),* Univ. of Mississippi, University, MS 38677 (SAN 658-4373) Tel 601-232-5374.

University of Missouri-Columbia, Interdisciplinary Plant Biochemistry & Physiology Group, *(U MO Plant Bio; 0-936463),* Univ. of Missouri-Columbia, 322 Chemistry Bldg., Columbia, MO 65203 (SAN 697-9769) Tel 314-882-7606.

Univ. of Missouri-Kansas City, Gallery of Art, *(Univ Miss-KS Art; 0-914489),* Dept. of Art & Art History, Kansas City, MO 64110 (SAN 289-6893) Tel 816-276-1502.

University of Missouri, Museum of Anthropology, *(Mus Anthro MO; 0-913134),* 104 Swallow Hall, Columbia, MO 65211 (SAN 203-0195) Tel 314-882-3764.

Univ. of Missouri, Museum of Art & Archaeology, *(U of Missouri Mus Art Arch; 0-910501),* 1 Pickard Hall, Univ. Of Missouri, Columbia, MO 65211 (SAN 260-2733) Tel 314-882-3591.

†**Univ. of Missouri Pr.,** *(U of Mo Pr; 0-8262),* 200 Lewis, Columbia, MO 65211 (SAN 203-3143) Tel 314-882-7641; Toll free: 800-242-7737; Dist. by: Harper & Row Pubs., Inc., 10 E. 53rd St., New York, NY 10022 (SAN 215-3742) Tel 212-207-7099; *CIP.*

University of Missouri-Saint Louis, *(U MO-St Louis; 0-9601616),* 8001 Natural Bridge Rd., St. Louis, MO 63121 (SAN 211-8726) Tel 314-553-5168.

Univ. of Montana Pubns. in History, *(U of MT Pubns Hist; 0-934054),* Missoula, MT 59812 (SAN 208-080X) Tel 406-243-2231.

Univ. of Montana, School of Fine Arts, *(U of MT Sch Arts; 0-9615029),* Univ. of Montana, Missoula, MT 59812 (SAN 693-7853) Tel 406-243-4970.

Univ. of Nebraska, Dept. of Human Development & the Family, Ctr. for Family Strengths, *(U Nebr Dept Human; 0-934949),* Univ. of Nebraska, Center for Family Strengths, Lincoln, NE 68583-0830 (SAN 695-071X) Tel 402-472-1672.

Univ. of Nebraska, Institute of Agriculture & Natural Resources, *(U Nebr IANR; 0-9616828),* Univ. of Nebraska, 108 ACB, Lincoln, NE 68583-0918 (SAN 661-1672) Tel 402-472-3007.

Univ. of Nebraska-Lincoln, Bureau of Business Research, Div. of Univ. of Nebraska, *(Bur Busn Res U Nebr; 0-917810),* Univ. of Nebraska, 200 CBA Bldg., Lincoln, NE 68588-0406 (SAN 209-262X) Tel 402-472-2334.

Univ. of Nebraska Pr., *(U of Nebr Pr; 0-8032),* 901 N. 17th St., Lincoln, NE 68588-0520 (SAN 202-5337) Tel 402-472-3581. *Imprints:* Bison Books (Bison).

†**Univ. of Nevada Pr.,** *(U of Nev Pr; 0-87417),* Reno, NV 89557 (SAN 203-316X) Tel 702-784-6573; *CIP.*

Univ. of Nevada, Reno Bureau of Business & Economic Research, *(U of Nev Bur Busn; 0-942828),* Reno, NV 89557 (SAN 240-1711) Tel 702-784-6877.

Univ. of New Haven Pr., *(U New Haven Pr; 0-936285),* 300 Orange Ave., West Haven, CT 06516 (SAN 697-9785) Tel 203-932-7118.

Univ. of New Mexico, Native American Studies, *(U of NM Nat Am Std; 0-934090),* 1812 Las Lomas NE, Albuquerque, NM 87131 (SAN 212-8446).

Univ. of New Mexico Pr., *(U of NM Pr; 0-8263),* Journalism Bldg., Rm. 220, Albuquerque, NM 87131 (SAN 213-9588) Tel 505-277-2346.

Univ. of New Mexico, Schl. of Law, *(U NM Law),* 1117 Stanford NE, Albuquerque, NM 87131 (SAN 227-3357).

†**Univ. of North Carolina at Chapel Hill, Carolina Population Ctr.,** *(Carolina Pop Ctr; 0-89055),* Population Pubns., University Sq. 300A, Chapel Hill, NC 27514-3997 (SAN 201-7687) Tel 919-966-2152; *CIP.*

Univ. of North Carolina at Chapel Hill, Dept. of Health Administration, Schl. of Public Health, Div. of Univ. of Michigan, *(U of NC Dept Health; 0-89055),* 263 Rosenau 201H, Chapel Hill, NC 27514 (SAN 207-7574) Tel 919-966-4091.

Univ. of North Carolina at Chapel Hill, Dept. of Statistics, *(U NC Dept Statistics),* 322 Phillips Hall, Chapel Hill, NC 27514 (SAN 239-5673).

Univ. of North Carolina, Institute for Research in Social Science, *(U NC Inst Res Soc Sci; 0-89143),* IRSS Pubns., Manning Hall 026A, Chapel Hill, NC 27514 (SAN 206-0795) Tel 919-966-3204.

Univ. of North Carolina, Institute of Government, *(U of NC Inst Gov),* Knapp Bldg. 059A, Chapel Hill, NC 27514 (SAN 204-8752) Tel 919-966-4119.

†**Univ. of North Carolina Pr.,** *(U of NC Pr; 0-8078),* P.O. Box 2288, Chapel Hill, NC 27514 (SAN 203-3151) Tel 919-966-3561; *CIP.*

Univ. of North Dakota Pr., *(U ND Pr),* P.O. Box 8006, Grand Forks, ND 58202 (SAN 206-0787) Tel 701-777-2544.

Univ. of Northern Iowa, Dept. of Art, *(U of NI Dept Art; 0-932660),* Cedar Falls, IA 50614-0362 (SAN 212-2391) Tel 319-273-2077.

Univ. of Notre Dame Pr., *(U of Notre Dame Pr; 0-268),* P.O. Box L, Notre Dame, IN 46556 (SAN 203-3178) Tel 219-239-6346; Toll free: 800-242-7737; Dist. by: Harper & Row Pubs., Keystone Industrial Pk., Scranton, PA 18512 (SAN 215-3742).

Univ. of Oklahoma, Bureau of Government Research, *(Univ OK Gov Res; 0-942646),* 455 West Lindsey, Rm. 304, Norman, OK 73019 (SAN 209-6102) Tel 405-325-6621.

Univ. of Oklahoma, Ctr. for Economic & Management Research, *(U OK Ctr Econ; 0-931880),* College of Business Administration, 307 W. Brooks St., Rm. 4, Norman, OK 73019 (SAN 212-3916) Tel 405-325-2931.

Univ. of Oklahoma Health/Science Ctr., Department of Family Medicine, *(Univ Health Ctr; 0-9617230),* P.O. Box 26901, Oklahoma City, OK 73190 (SAN 663-6322); 800 NE 15th St., Oklahoma City, OK 73190 (SAN 663-6330) Tel 405-271-6388; Dist. by: Society for Teachers of Family Medicine, 1740 W. 92nd St., Kansas City, MO 64114 (SAN 224-3199).

Univ. of Oklahoma Pr., *(U of Okla Pr; 0-8061),* 1005 Asp Ave., Norman, OK 73019 (SAN 203-3194) Tel 405-325-5111; Toll free: 800-242-7737; Dist. by: Harper & Row, Inc., Keystone Industrial Pk., Scranton, PA 18512 (SAN 215-3742); Orders to: Univ. of Oklahoma Pr., P.O. Box 1657, Hagerstown, MD 21741 (SAN 203-3194); Toll free: 800-638-3030.

Univ. of Oregon Bks., *(U of Oreg Bks; 0-87114),* Univ. Pubns., 101 Chapman Hall, Univ. of Oregon, Eugene, OR 97403 (SAN 206-7757) Tel 503-686-5396.

Univ. of Oregon, Bureau of Governmental Research & Service, *(U OR BGR),* P.O. Box 3177, Eugene, OR 97403 (SAN 227-339X) Tel 503-686-5232.

Univ. of Oregon, Ctr. for Educational Policy & Management, *(Ctr Educ Policy Mgmt; 0-936276),* College of Education, Eugene, OR 97403 (SAN 211-223X) Tel 503-686-5077.

Univ. of Oregon ERIC Clearinghouse on Educational Management, Div. of U. S. Dept. of Education, *(U of Oreg ERIC; 0-86552),* University of Oregon, 1787 Agate St., Eugene, OR 97403 (SAN 226-806X) Tel 503-686-5043.

Univ. of Pennsylvania, Dept. of South Asia Regional Studies, *(U Penn South Asia; 0-936115),* Univ. of Pennsylvania, 820 Williams Hall/CU, Philadelphia, PA 19104 (SAN 697-001X) Tel 215-898-7475.

Univ. of Pennsylvania, Institute of Contemporary Art, *(U of Pa Contemp Art; 0-88454),* 34th & Walnut Sts., Philadelphia, PA 19104 (SAN 203-3208) Tel 215-898-7108.

Univ. of Pennsylvania, Law School, *(U Penn Law),* 3400 Chestnut St., Philadelphia, PA 19174 (SAN 227-3411).

Univ. of Pennsylvania Pr., *(U of Pa Pr; 0-8122),* 418 Service Dr., Blockley Hall, 13th Flr., Philadelphia, PA 19104 (SAN 202-5345) Tel 215-898-6261. *Imprints:* Pennsylvania Paperbooks (Pa Paperbks).

Univ. of Pennsylvania, Univ. Museum, *(Univ Mus of U PA; 0-934718),* 33rd & Spruce Sts., Philadelphia, PA 19104 (SAN 207-9283) Tel 215-898-4090.

Univ. of Pittsburgh Pr., *(U of Pittsburgh Pr; 0-8229),* 127 N. Bellefield Ave., Pittsburgh, PA 15260 (SAN 203-3216) Tel 412-624-4110; Toll free: 800-242-7737; Dist. by: Harper & Row Pubs., Inc., Keystone Industrial Pk., Scranton, PA 18512 (SAN 215-3742); Toll free: 800-242-7737; 800-982-4377 (In Pennsylvania).

†**Univ. of Puerto Rico Pr.,** *(U of PR Pr; 0-8477),* P.O. Box X, U.P.R. Sta., Rio Piedras, PR 00931 (SAN 208-1245) Tel 809-763-0812; *CIP.*

†**Univ. of Queensland Pr.,** *(U of Queensland Pr; 0-7022),* P.O. Box 1365, New York, NY 10023 (SAN 206-8540) Tel 212-799-3854; Orders to: Publishers Distribution Services, Inc., 250 Commercial St., Manchester, NH 03101 (SAN 206-8559) Tel 603-623-0305; *CIP.*

Univ. of Rhode Island, Ctr. for Ocean Management Studies, *(Univ RI Ocean Mgt; 0-938095),* 19 Upper College Rd., Kingston, RI 02881 (SAN 659-7084) Tel 401-792-2145.

Univ. of Rochester Policy Center Pubns., *(U Rochester Policy; 0-932468),* 105 Dewey Hall, Univ. of Rochester, Rochester, NY 14627 (SAN 212-3924) Tel 716-275-3218.

Univ. of St. Thomas, *(U of St Thomas),* 3812 Montrose Blvd., Houston, TX 77006 (SAN 206-0701) Tel 713-522-7911.

†**Univ. of St. Thomas, Ctr. for Thomistic Studies,** *(Ctr Thomistic; 0-9605456),* University of Notre Dame, Notre Dame, IN 46544 (SAN 662-1732) Tel 219-239-6346; Dist. by: Univ. of Notre Dame Pr., P.O. Box L, Notre Dame, IN 46556 (SAN 203-3178) Tel 219-239-6346; Dist. by: Harper & Row, 1 Baker Dr., Conklin, NY 13748 (SAN 200-688X) Tel 607-775-4142; *CIP.*

Univ. of Scranton, Ethnic Studies Program, *(U Scranton Ethnic; 0-9607870),* Univ. of Scranton, Dept. of Hist. & Political Sci., Scranton, PA 18510 (SAN 239-7498) Tel 717-961-7443.

Univ. of South Carolina, McKissick Museum, *(McKissick; 0-938983),* Columbia, SC 29208 (SAN 280-946X) Tel 803-777-7251.

†**Univ. of South Carolina Pr.,** *(U of SC Pr; 0-87249),* Columbia, SC 29208 (SAN 203-3224) Tel 803-777-5243; *CIP.*

Univ. of South Dakota, Governmental Research Bureau, *(U of SD Gov Res Bur; 1-55614),* 233 Dakota Hall, Vermillion, SD 57069 (SAN 206-0698) Tel 605-677-5242.

Univ. of Southern California, Fisher Gallery, *(USC Fisher Gallery; 0-9602974),* University Pk, Los Angeles, CA 90007-0292 (SAN 222-2469).

Univ. of Southern California Press, *(U of S Cal Pr; 0-88474),* Student Union 400, Univ. of Southern California, Los Angeles, CA 90007 (SAN 203-1892).

Univ. of Southern Maine, College of Education, *(Univ South ME; 0-939561),* University of Southern Maine, College of Education, Bailey Hall 400, Gorham, ME 04038 (SAN 663-4281) Tel 207-780-5316.

Univ. of Southwestern Louisiana Ctr. Louisiana Studies, *(U of SW LA Ctr LA Studies; 0-940984),* P.O. Box 40831, USL, Lafayette, LA 70504 (SAN 217-4502) Tel 318-231-6027.

Univ. of Southwestern Louisiana, Univ. Art Museum, *(USL Art Museum; 0-936819),* USL Drawer 42571, Lafayette, LA 70504 (SAN 280-9532).

Univ. of Temecula Pr., *(U Temecula Pr; 0-936283),* 29860 Camino del Sol, Temecula, CA 92390 (SAN 697-9793) Tel 714-676-5234; P.O. Box 1239, Temecula, CA 92390 (SAN 698-2352).

Univ. of Tennessee, Bureau of Public Administration, Div. of Univ. of Tennessee, *(Bureau Pub Admin U Tenn; 0-914079),* 1001 McClung Tower, Knoxville, TN 37996-0410 (SAN 291-9192) Tel 615-974-5278.

Univ. of Tennessee, College of Social Work, Office of Research & Public Service, *(U Tenn CSW; 0-89695),* 1838 Terrace Ave., Knoxville, TN 37996-3920 (SAN 287-2994) Tel 615-974-6015.

Univ. of Tennessee, Dept. of Geological Sciences, Div. of University of Tennessee, Knoxville, *(U of Tenn Geo; 0-910249),* Rm 306, Geography & Geology Bldg., Knoxville, TN 37996-1410 (SAN 241-4694) Tel 615-974-2366.

Univ. of Tennessee National Alumni Assn., The, *(Univ TN Alumni; 0-9616311),* Univ. of Tennessee, 600 Andy Holt Tower, Knoxville, TN 37996 (SAN 658-716X) Tel 615-974-6071.

Univ. of Tennessee Pr., Div. of Univ. of Tennessee & Member of Assn. of American University Presses, *(U of Tenn Pr; 0-87049),* 293 Communications Bldg., Knoxville, TN 37996-0325 (SAN 212-9930) Tel 615-974-3321; Orders to: P.O. Box 6525, Ithaca, NY 14850 (SAN 662-1740) Tel 607-277-2211.

Univ. of Texas at Arlington Pr., The, *(U of Tex Arlington Pr; 0-87706),* Box 19075, Arlington, TX 76019 (SAN 213-9707); Orders to: English Dept., Box 19035, Arlington, TX 76019 (SAN 213-9715).

University of Texas At Arlington, Texas Humanities Resource Center, *(U TX Arl TX Hum; 0-942484),* Library, P.O. Box 19497, Arlington, TX 76019 (SAN 238-5880) Tel 817-273-2767.

Univ. of Texas at Austin, Ctr. for the Study of American Architechture, *(UTX CSAA; 0-934951),* Univ. of Texas at Austin, Schl. of Architecture, Austin, TX 78712 (SAN 695-0671) Tel 512-471-1922.

Univ. of Texas at Austin Film Library, *(U Tex Austin Film Lib; 0-913648),* Drawer W, University Sta., Austin, TX 78713-7448 (SAN 203-0446) Tel 512-471-3572.

Univ. of Texas at Austin, General Libraries, *(U TX Austin Gen Libs; 0-930214),* Univ. of Texas at Austin, P.O. Box P, Austin, TX 78713-7330 (SAN 210-6795) Tel 512-471-3811; Orders to: University of Texas at Austin, General Libraries, Publications, P.O. Box P, Austin, TX 78713-7330 (SAN 662-1759) Tel 512-471-3811.

Univ. of Texas at Austin, Graduate Schl. of Business, Institute for Constructive Capitalism, *(Inst Constructive Cap),* Univ. of Texas at Austin, Austin, TX 78712 (SAN 211-3198).

Univ. of Texas at Austin, Graduate Schl. of Library & Information Science, *(UTX SLIS; 0-938729),* Austin, TX 78712-1276 (SAN 661-5872) Tel 512-471-3821.

Univ. of Texas at Austin, Institute of Latin American Studies, *(U TX Inst Lat Am Stud; 0-86728),* Sid Richardson Hall 1-310, Austin, TX 78712 (SAN 220-3103) Tel 512-471-5551.

University of Texas at Austin, Bureau of Business Research *See* Univ. of Texas, Bureau of Business Research

Univ. of Texas, Dept. of Astronomy, *(U of Tex Dept Astron; 0-9603796),* RLM 15.308, Austin, TX 78712 (SAN 214-1647) Tel 512-471-4461.

Univ. of Texas, Harry Ransom Humanities Research Ctr., Div. of Univ. of Texas at Austin, *(U of Tex H Ransom Ctr; 0-87959),* P.O. Box 7219, Austin, TX 78713 (SAN 203-1906) Tel 512-471-9113.

†**Univ. of Texas, Institute of Texan Cultures,** *(U of Tex Inst Tex Culture; 0-933164; 0-86701),* P.O. Box 1226, San Antonio, TX 78294 (SAN 213-8778) Tel 512-226-7651; *CIP.*

Univ. of Texas Pr., *(U of Tex Pr; 0-292),* P.O. Box 7819, Austin, TX 78713-7819 (SAN 212-9876) Tel 512-471-7233; Toll free: 800-252-3206 (Orders Only). *Imprints:* Stevenson, Robert Louis, School, The (Stevenson Sch).

Univ. of Texas, Tarlton Law Library, *(U of Tex Tarlton Law Lib; 0-935630),* 727 E. 26th St., Austin, TX 78705-5799 (SAN 214-1655) Tel 512-471-7726.

Univ. of the South, The, *(Univ South; 0-918769),* SPO 1145, Sewanee, TN 37375 (SAN 287-2676).

†**Univ. of the Trees Pr.,** *(Univ of Trees; 0-916438),* P.O. Box 66, Boulder Creek, CA 95006 (SAN 212-9965); 13165 Pine St., Boulder Creek, CA 95006 (SAN 658-2176) Tel 408-338-2161 (SAN 264-2441); *CIP.*

Univ. of Toronto Pr., *(U of Toronto Pr; 0-8020),* 33 E. Tupper St., Buffalo, NY 14203 (SAN 214-2651) Tel 716-852-0342.

Univ. of Tulsa, Information Services Div., *(U Tulsa Info Serv; 0-932602),* 600 S. College Ave., Tulsa, OK 74104 (SAN 206-0671) Tel 918-939-6351.

University of Utah, Bureau of Economic & Business Research, *(Univ Utah; 0-942486),* 401 Kendall D. Garff Bldg., Salt Lake City, UT 84112 (SAN 238-5899) Tel 801-581-7274.

Names

Univ. of Utah Pr., *(U of Utah Pr; 0-87480),* 101 University Services Bldg., Salt Lake City, UT 84112 (SAN 220-0023) Tel 801-581-6771; Toll free: 800-662-0062 Ext. 6771. *Imprints:* Tanner Trust Fund (Tanner).

Univ. of Utah, State Arboretum of Utah, *(State Arbor; 0-942830),* Univ. of Utah, Bldg. 436, Salt Lake City, UT 84112 (SAN 240-2971) Tel 801-581-5322.

Univ. of Vermont, Dept. of History, *(U of VT Dept Hist; 0-9614365),* 442 Main St., Burlington, VT 05405 (SAN 688-5721) Tel 802-656-3180.

Univ. of Vermont, Dept. of Psychiatry, *(U of VT Psych; 0-9611898; 0-938685),* One S. Prospect St., Burlington, VT 05401 (SAN 286-2123) Tel 802-656-4563.

University of Virginia Committee on Continuing Legal Education School of Law, *(U VA CLE Law),* Charlottesville, VA 22901 (SAN 226-2819) Tel 804-924-3416.

University of Virginia Institute of Government, *(U VA Inst Gov),* 207 Minor Hall, Charlottesville, VA 22903 (SAN 227-1001) Tel 804-924-3396.

Univ. of Washington, Ctr. for Social Welfare Research, *(U WA Ctr Soc Welfare; 0-935035),* Univ. of Washington, Schl. of Social Work, 4101 15th Ave. NE, Box JH-30, Seattle, WA 98195 (SAN 694-5252) Tel 206-545-1632.

Univ. of Washington, Graduate School of Business, *(U of Wash Grad Sch Busn),* Mackenzie Hall, DJ-10, Seattle, WA 98195 (SAN 203-0187) Tel 206-543-4598.

Univ. of Washington Pr., *(U of Wash Pr; 0-295),* P.O. Box 50096, Seattle, WA 98105 (SAN 212-2502) Tel 206-543-4050; Toll free: 800-441-4115 (not in Alaska, Hawaii, Washington.

Univ. of West Florida, Gulf Coast History & Humanities Conference, *(U of W Fla; 0-940836),* Univ. of West Florida, Bldg. 32, Pensacola, FL 32514 (SAN 219-6522) Tel 904-474-2492.

Univ. of Wisconsin, Graduate Schl. of Business, Bureau of Business Research, *(Bur Busn Wis; 0-866303),* 1155 Observatory Dr., Rm. 110, Commerce Bldg., Madison, WI 53706 (SAN 669-0319) Tel 608-262-1550.

Univ. of Wisconsin, Industrial Relations Research Assn., *(Indus Relations Res; 0-913447),* 7226 Social Science Bldg., Madison, WI 53706 (SAN 224-8077) Tel 608-262-2762.

†**Univ. of Wisconsin-Madison, Land Tenure Ctr.,** *(U of Wis Land; 0-934519),* Univ. of Wisconsin, 1300 University Ave., Madison, WI 53706 (SAN 693-4927) Tel 608-262-3657; *CIP.*

Univ. of Wisconsin-Madison Law Schl., *(U Wisc Law Madison; 0-933431),* 975 Bascom Mall, Madison, WI 53706 (SAN 237-8876) Tel 608-262-2240.

University of Wisconsin-Madison Law School, Disputes Processing Research Center, *(Univ Wis-Mad Law; 0-915305),* Room 209 Law School, Madison, WI 53706 (SAN 290-0521) Tel 608-263-2545.

Univ. of Wisconsin-Madison, Schl. of Library & Information Studies, *(U Wis Sch Lib; 0-936442),* 600 N. Park St., Madison, WI 53706 (SAN 219-9874).

Univ. of Wisconsin-Milwaukee, Center for Architecture & Urban Planning Research, Subs. of School of Architecture and Urban Planning, UW-Milwaukee, *(U of Wis Ctr Arch-Urban; 0-938744),* P.O. Box 413, Milwaukee, WI 53201 (SAN 211-9900) Tel 414-963-4014.

Univ. of Wisconsin-Milwaukee, Ctr. for Consumer Affairs, *(UWIM CCA),* 929 N. Sixth St., Milwaukee, WI 53203 (SAN 235-5671) Tel 414-224-4177.

Univ. of Wisconsin-Milwaukee, Ctr. for Latin America, *(U Wis-Mil Ctr Latin Am; 0-930450),* Univ. of Wisconsin-Milwaukee, P.O. Box 413, Milwaukee, WI 53201 (SAN 224-0939) Tel 414-963-4401; 3243 N. Downer Ave., Milwaukee, WI 53211 (SAN 669-036X).

†**Univ. of Wisconsin Pr.,** *(U of Wis Pr; 0-299),* 114 N. Murray St., Madison, WI 53715 (SAN 203-3259) Tel 608-262-8782; *CIP.*

Univ. of Wisconsin Sea Grant Institute, Div. of Univ. of Wisconsin, *(U WI Sea Grant; 0-936287),* 1800 University Ave., Madison, WI 53705 (SAN 697-9831) Tel 608-263-3259.

Univ. of Wisconsin-Stevens Point Foundation Pr., *(U of Wis-Stevens Point; 0-932310),* 428 COPS Bldg., Stevens Point, WI 54481 (SAN 212-2405) Tel 715-346-4496.

Univ. of Wisconsin-Superior Ctr. for Lake Superior Environmental Studies, *(UWIS CLSES; 0-9614968),* Univ. of Wisconsin-Superior, Superior, WI 54880 (SAN 693-7306) Tel 715-394-8422.

Univ. of Wisconsin System American Ethnic Studies Coordinating Committee (AESCC), *(U of Wis Sys Ethnic; 0-942672),* c/o UW-Milwaukee - SHP-304, P.O. Box 413, Milwaukee, WI 53201 (SAN 282-4922) Tel 414-963-4700.

Univ. of Wisconsin, Univ. Ctr. for Cooperatives, *(U WI Ctr Coop; 0-942288),* 514 Lowell Hall, 610 Langdon St., Madison, WI 53703 (SAN 240-1681) Tel 608-262-3251.

Univ. of Wyoming, *(U of Wyoming; 0-941570),* P.O. Box 3315, University Sta., Laramie, WY 82071 (SAN 206-0620) Tel 307-766-2379.

University Place Book Shop, *(Univ Place; 0-911556),* 821 Broadway, New York, NY 10003 (SAN 204-8841) Tel 212-254-5998.

University Pr., *(Univ Pr San Francisco; 0-9616978),* 6521 California St., San Francisco, CA 94121 (SAN 661-8014) Tel 415-731-1702.

University Pr., *(University Pr; 0-8418),* Drawer N, Wolfe City, TX 75496 (SAN 203-3356) Tel 214-496-2226.

University Pr. Bks., *(UPB; 0-8295),* Box 460, Middletown, NY 10940 (SAN 207-4907) Tel 914-343-5323.

University Pr. of America, *(U Pr of Amer; 0-8191),* 4720 Boston Way, Lanham, MD 20706 (SAN 200-2256) Tel 301-459-3366.

Univ. Press of California, *(U Pr of Cal; 0-935048),* 1000 N. Coast Hwy., No. 3, Laguna Beach, CA 92651 (SAN 212-3215) Tel 714-497-4861.

†**Univ. Pr. of Kansas,** *(U Pr of KS; 0-7006),* 329 Carruth, Lawrence, KS 66045 (SAN 203-3267) Tel 913-864-4154; *CIP.*

†**Univ. Pr. of Kentucky,** *(U Pr of Ky; 0-8131),* Univ. of Kentucky, 102 Lafferty Hall, Lexington, KY 40506-0024 (SAN 203-3275) Tel 606-257-2951; Dist. by: Harper & Row Pubs., Inc., Keystone Industrial Pk., Scranton, PA 18512 (SAN 215-3742); Toll free: 800-242-7737; *CIP.*

†**Univ. Pr. of Mississippi,** *(U Pr of Miss; 0-87805),* 3825 Ridgewood Rd., Jackson, MS 39211 (SAN 203-1914) Tel 601-982-6205; *CIP.*

†**Univ. Pr. of New England,** *(U Pr of New Eng; 0-87451),* 3 Lebanon St., Hanover, NH 03755 (SAN 203-3283) Tel 603-646-3349.

Univ. Pr. of Virginia, *(U Pr of Va; 0-8139),* P.O. Box 3608, Univ. Sta., Charlottesville, VA 22903 (SAN 202-5361) Tel 804-924-3468. *Imprints:* Bird & Bull Press, The (Bird & Bull Pr); Colonial Society of Massachusetts (Colonial Soc MA); Friends of the University of Rochester Libraries (Friends U Rochester); Maya Publishing Company (Maya Pub Co).

†**Univ. Press of Washington, D.C.,** *(U Pr of Wash; 0-87419),* University Press Bldg., Delbrook Campus C.A.S., Riverton, VA 22651 (SAN 204-8760) Tel 703-635-4029; Dist. by: Coronet Press, The, 41 Morton St., New York, NY 10014 (SAN 241-2934) Tel 212-924-3986; *CIP.*

Univ. Press, Univ. of Wisconsin-River Falls, *(U Pr Wisc River Falls),* 118 N. Hall, River Falls, WI 54022 (SAN 214-1663).

Univ. Presses of Florida, *(U Presses Fla; 0-8130),* 15 NW 15th St., Gainesville, FL 32603 (SAN 207-9275) Tel 904-392-1351. *Imprints:* University of Florida, University Gallery (Univ Gallery U of FL).

University Pubns., *(Univ Pubs NY; 0-911463),* P.O. Box 219, Sayville, NY 11782 (SAN 264-4592).

University Pubns. of America, Inc., *(U Pubns Amer; 0-89093; 1-55655),* 44 N. Market St., Frederick, MD 21701 (SAN 210-5802) Tel 301-694-0100; Toll free: 800-692-6300. *Imprints:* Aletheia Books (Aletheia Bks).

Univ. Pubs., *(Univ Pub; 0-931117),* P.O. Box 3571, Chattanooga, TN 37404 (SAN 678-9528) Tel 615-624-3784.

University Publishing Assocs., Inc., Subs. of University Pr. of America, *(Univ Pub Assocs; 0-8026),* 4720 Boston Way, Lanham, MD 20706 (SAN 662-6394) Tel 301-459-3366.

University Publishing Group, *(Univ Pub Group; 1-55572),* 107 E. Church St., Frederick, MD 21701 (SAN 699-7171) Tel 301-694-8531.

Univ. Publishing Hse., *(Univ Pub Hse; 0-9614194),* 6319 St. Henry Dr., Nashville, TN 37205 (SAN 686-7367) Tel 615-352-7192.

University Publishing, Inc., *(Univ Pub Inc; 0-938381),* 2400 Broadway, Beaumont, TX 77702 (SAN 661-0323) Tel 713-748-8690; Dist. by: Lone Star College Bk., P.O. Box 19569, Austin, TX 78760 (SAN 200-6626).

University Science Bks., *(Univ Sci Bks; 0-935702),* 20 Edgehill Rd., Mill Valley, CA 94941 (SAN 213-8085) Tel 415-383-1430.

University Services, *(Univ Servs Inc; 0-913535),* 1159 Second Ave., Salt Lake City, UT 84103 (SAN 285-2012).

University Statistical Tracts, *(Univ Stat Tracts; 0-931316),* 75-19 171st St., Flushing, NY 11366 (SAN 211-3341) Tel 718-969-7553.

†**Universiy of Nebraska, Cooperative Extension Service,** Div. of University of Nebraska, *(Coop Ext Serv Univ Nebraska; 0-9613015),* 202 Natural Resources Hall, Lincoln, NE 68583-0819 (SAN 294-2909) Tel 402-472-6822; *CIP.*

†**Univ. of Texas, Bureau of Business Research,** *(Bureau Busn UT; 0-87755),* P.O. Box 7459, Austin, TX 78713-7459 (SAN 203-3232) Tel 512-471-1616; *CIP.*

Unlimited Golden Opportunities Pr., *(Unlimited Golden Pr; 0-934521),* P.O. Box 27218, Oakland, CA 94602 (SAN 693-8434) Tel 415-534-6472.

Unlimited Marketing Pubns., Div. of Unlimited Marketing & Research Services, Inc., *(Unltd. Mktg. Pubns.; 0-912305),* 190 Angell St., P.O. Box 944 Annex Sta., Providence, RI 02901 (SAN 265-2897) Tel 401-421-7080.

Unmuzzled Ox Pr., *(Unmuzzled Ox; 0-934450),* 105 Hudson St., New York, NY 10013 (SAN 207-9151) Tel 212-226-7170.

Unnameable Pr., *(Unnameable Pr; 0-934227),* P.O. Box 11689, Atlanta, GA 30355-1689 (SAN 693-1170); 594 Wimbledon Rd., NE Apt. G-3, Atlanta, GA 30324 (SAN 662-314X) Tel 404-892-2424.

Unsinn Pubns., Inc., *(Unsinn Pubns; 0-9615386),* P.O. Box 672, Drexel Hill, PA 19026 (SAN 695-3522) Tel 215-543-0999.

Unspeakable Visions of the Individual, *(TUVOTI; 0-934660),* P.O. Box 439, California, PA 15419 (SAN 207-916X) Tel 412-938-8956; Dist. by: Bookslinger, 213 E. Fourth St., St. Paul, MN 55101 (SAN 669-2893) Tel 612-221-0429; Dist. by: Bookpeople, 2929 Fifth St., Berkeley, CA 94710 (SAN 669-2907).

Updegraff Pr., The, *(Updcgraff; 0-9613203),* 2564 Cherosen Rd., Louisville, KY 40205 (SAN 283-3530) Tel 502-454-3206.

†**Upjohn, W. E., Institute for Employment Research,** *(W E Upjohn; 0-911558),* 300 S. Westnedge Ave., Kalamazoo, MI 49007 (SAN 236-9486) Tel 616-343-5541; *CIP.*

Uplift Books, *(Uplift Bks; 0-88005),* 760-C N. Golden Springs Dr., Diamond Bar, CA 91765 (SAN 219-8312) Tel 714-595-8409.

Upper Country People Probe, *(Upper Country),* 204 Andrews Ave., Hartsville, TN 37074 (SAN 239-5002).

Upper Crust Cookbook, The, *(Upper Crust; 0-9613757),* P.O. Box 5363, Scottsdale, AZ 85261 (SAN 692-7599) Tel 602-483-0755.

Upper Room Publishing Co., *(Upper Rm Pub; 0-938645),* P.O. Box 629, Alamo, GA 30411 (SAN 661-633X); Pine St., Alamo, GA 30311 (SAN 661-6348) Tel 912-568-7249.

Upper Room, The, *(Upper Room; 0-8358; 0-941478),* 1908 Grand Ave., P.O. Box 189, Nashville, TN 37202 (SAN 203-3364) Tel 615-327-2700; Dist. by: Abingdon Pr., 201 Eighth Ave., S., Nashville, TN 37202 (SAN 201-0054) Tel 615-749-6290.

Names

Upper Strata Ink, Inc., *(Upper Strata; 0-9616589),* P.O. Box 250, Bernalillo, NM 87004 (SAN 659-8064); 500 Beehive Ln., Bernalillo, NM 87004 (SAN 659-8072) Tel 505-867-5812.

Uprisings Publishing Co., *(Uprisings Pub Co; 0-9611600),* P.O. Box 2755, Ann Harbor, MI 48106 (SAN 283-8869).

Upsala College, College Relations Office, *(Upsala Coll; 0-9601668),* Prospect St., East Orange, NJ 07019 (SAN 211-545X).

†**Upstat Publishing Co.,** *(Upstat; 0-87916),* 2291 University Ave., No. 114, Riverside, CA 92507 (SAN 203-3372) Tel 714-638-4576; *CIP.*

Upton & Sons, *(Upton Sons; 0-912783),* 917 Hillcrest St., El Segundo, CA 90245 (SAN 160-5216) Tel 213-322-7202.

Uptown Books, *(Uptown Bks),* Box 11146, Glendale, CA 91206 (SAN 240-9828).

Uranian Consultants, *(Uranian Consult; 0-9609700),* P.O. Box 40024, Washington, DC 20016 (SAN 264-4614) Tel 301-229-2858.

Uranian Pubns., Inc., *(Uranian Pubns; 0-89159),* P.O. Box 114, Franksville, WI 53126-0114 (SAN 210-5705) Tel 414-632-2892.

Urantia Foundation, *(Urantia Foun; 0-911560),* 533 Diversey Pkwy., Chicago, IL 60614 (SAN 204-8906) Tel 312-525-3319.

Uranus Publishing Co., *(Uranus Pub; 0-9601080),* 5050 Calatrana Dr., Woodland Hills, CA 91364 (SAN 207-3544) Tel 818-347-8499.

Urban & Schwarzenberg, *(Urban & S; 0-8067),* 7 E. Redwood St., Baltimore, MD 21202 (SAN 209-6897) Tel 301-539-2550.

Urban Books, *(Urban Bks),* 295 Grizzly Peak Blvd., Berkeley, CA 94708 (SAN 204-8914) Tel 415-524-3315.

Urban Information Interpreters, Inc., *(Urban Info Interp),* P.O. Box AH, College Park, MD 20740 (SAN 218-1452).

†**Urban Institute Pr.,** *(Urban Inst; 0-87766),* 2100 M St., NW, Washington, DC 20037 (SAN 203-3380) Tel 202-857-8724; Orders to: P.O. Box 19958, Hampden Sta., Baltimore, MD 21211 (SAN 685-3676) Tel 301-338-6951; *CIP.*

Urban Land Institute, *(Urban Land; 0-87420),* 1090 Vermont Ave. NW, Washington, DC 20005 (SAN 203-3399) Tel 202-289-8500.

Urban Research Institute, Inc., *(Urban Res Inst; 0-941484),* 840 E. 87th St., Chicago, IL 60619 (SAN 239-0515) Tel 312-994-7200.

Urbanek, Mae, *(Urbanek; 0-940514),* Lusk, WY 82225 (SAN 213-9006) Tel 307-334-2473.

Ure Pr., *(Ure Pr; 0-933571),* 316 Summit Rd., Danville, VA 24540 (SAN 691-9057) Tel 804-793-7075.

Urfer, Bill, *(Urfer; 0-9604306),* Box 155, Libby Rte., Heber Springs, AR 72543 (SAN 216-3144) Tel 501-362-5209.

Urie, Sherry, *(Sherry Urie; 0-9603324),* RFD No. 3, Box 63, Barton, VT 05822 (SAN 211-4526).

Uriel Pubns *See* **Noontide Pr., The**

†**Urion Press,** *(Urion Pr CA; 0-913522),* P.O. Box 10085 Westgate Station, San Jose, CA 95157 (SAN 282-4949) Tel 408-867-7695; *CIP.*

Urquhart, Edward F., *(E Urquhart; 0-9611618),* Box 75092, Northgate Sta., Seattle, WA 98125 (SAN 284-902X) Tel 206-523-3200.

Ursuline Convent Cookbook, *(Ursuline; 0-9604718),* P.O. Box 7491, Metairie, LA 70010 (SAN 215-7977).

Ursus Pr., *(Ursus Pr NY; 0-9615441),* P.O. Box 1261, New York, NY 10113 (SAN 695-8273) Tel 212-989-7020. Do not confuse with Ursus Pr., Chicago, IL.

Urthkin, *(Urthkin; 0-933456),* 537 Jones St., Suite 172, San Francisco, CA 94102 (SAN 213-3962).

USAMERICA, Subs. of USAMERICA Inc., *(Usamerica; 0-934763),* 2351 SW 92nd. Pl., Miami, FL 33165 (SAN 694-1850) Tel 305-552-8301.

Usborne-Hayes *See* **EDC Publishing**

Used Car Pubns., Subs. of J. L. Sales, *(Used Car Pubns; 0-932675),* 5502 Englishman Place, Rockville, MD 20852 (SAN 687-844X) Tel 301-493-5686.

Usonia Pr., *(Usonia Pr; 0-9615348),* P.O. 19440 Diamond Lake Sta., Minneapolis, MN 55419 (SAN 695-1007) Tel 612-824-7258.

USS North Carolina, Battleship Commission, *(USS North Car; 0-9608538),* P.O. Box 417, Wilmington, NC 28402 (SAN 240-7973) Tel 919-762-1829.

Utah Arts Festival Foundation, Inc., *(UT Arts Festival; 0-939011),* 168 W. 500 N., Salt Lake City, UT 84103 (SAN 662-5835) Tel 801-322-2428.

Utah Division of State History *See* **Utah State Historical Society**

Utah Folklife Center, Subs. of Utah Arts Council, *(Utah Folklife Ctr; 0-9614561),* 617 E. South Temple, Salt Lake City, UT 84102 (SAN 691-814X) Tel 801-533-5760.

Utah Geographic Series, *(Utah Geo Series; 0-936331),* Box 8325, Salt Lake City, UT 84108 (SAN 697-9866) Tel 801-583-2333; 1308 S. 1700 E., No. 207, Salt Lake City, UT 84105 (SAN 698-2360).

Utah Museum of Natural History, *(Utah Mus Natural Hist; 0-940378),* University of Utah, Salt Lake City, UT 84112 (SAN 213-5663).

Utah State Historical Society, *(Utah St Hist Soc; 0-913730),* 300 Rio Grande, Salt Lake City, UT 84101 (SAN 204-8930) Tel 801-533-6024.

†**Utah State Univ. Pr.,** *(Utah St U Pr; 0-87421),* Logan, UT 84322-9515 (SAN 202-9294) Tel 801-750-1362; *CIP.*

Utama Pubns., Inc., *(Utama Pubns Inc; 0-911527),* Tano Rd., Box 236, Santa Fe, NM 87501 (SAN 282-4779) Tel 505-988-7321.

Utica House Publishing Co., *(Utica Hse; 0-9609296),* RR No. 1, Utica, IL 61373 (SAN 260-1532) Tel 815-223-3200.

Utopia Press, *(Utopia Pr; 0-911947),* 4480 Annie Oakley Dr., Las Vegas, NV 89121 (SAN 264-4622).

Utopian Universe Publishing Co., *(Utopian Universe),* P.O. Box 26, East Elmhurst, NY 11369 (SAN 207-4923) Tel 718-478-3291.

Uxor Pr., Inc., *(Uxor Pr; 0-932555),* 425 E. 51st St., New York, NY 10022 (SAN 687-4916) Tel 212-688-9199.

Uzzano Pr., *(Uzzano Pr; 0-930600),* 511 Sunset Dr., Menomonie, WI 54751 (SAN 211-1020).

V & M World Wide Bks., Corp., *(V & M World Wide; 0-933517),* 22 Sunset Ave., Lynbrook, NY 11563 (SAN 691-9235).

VCH Pubs., Inc., *(VCH Pubs; 0-89573),* 220 E. 23rd St., Suite 109, New York, NY 10010 (SAN 212-2421); Orders to: 303 NW 12th Ave., Deerfield Beach, FL 33442-1705 (SAN 662-1783) Tel 305-426-5566.

VC Publishing, *(VC Pub; 0-935333),* 7506 New Jersey Ave., Hudson, FL 33567 (SAN 695-8044) Tel 813-863-2738; Toll free: 800-472-9336; Dist. by: Veronica Cass, Inc., P.O. Box 5519, Hudson, FL 33567 (SAN 200-5808).

VEATU Press, *(VEATU; 0-9610276),* 7126 Morgan Ave. S, Richfield, MN 55423 (SAN 264-4649) Tel 612-869-8324.

VHW Publishing, *(V H Pub; 0-9610912),* 3780 Hope Terr., Santa Barbara, CA 93110 (SAN 265-153X) Tel 805-687-4087.

VIEW, Inc., *(VIEW Inc; 0-8030),* 34 E. 23rd St., New York, NY 10010 Tel 212-674-5550.

VIP Directory, The, Div. of Ads Agency, Inc., *(VIP Directory; 0-937955),* P.O. Box 6030, Stateline, NV 89449 (SAN 659-8080); 200 Kingsbury Grade, Suite A, Stateline, NV 89449 (SAN 659-8099) Tel 702-588-6445.

VIP International, Inc., *(VIP Int; 0-9615601),* 6342 SW Macadam Ave., Portland, OR 97201 (SAN 695-8109) Tel 503-245-3390; Orders to: P.O. Box 383, Marylhurst, OR 97036 (SAN 662-3581).

†**V.I. Pr., Inc.,** *(V I Pr; 0-916945),* P.O. Box 1403, Pompano Beach, FL 33061 (SAN 655-7813) Tel 305-785-5588; *CIP.*

VJP Enterprises, *(V J P Enter; 0-9615924),* 636 Cleveland, Missoula, MT 59801 (SAN 696-7825) Tel 406-728-6968; Dist. by: Pacific Pipeline, 19215 66th Ave. S., Kent, WA 98032-1171 (SAN 208-2128) Tel 206-762-5523; Dist. by: Pictorial Histories Publishing Co., 713 South Third W., Missoula, MT 59801 (SAN 212-4351) Tel 406-549-8488.

VLE, Ltd., *(VLE Ltd; 0-912693),* P.O. Box 547, Tenafly, NJ 07670 (SAN 282-8472) Tel 201-567-5536.

VTR Publishing Co., *(VTR Pub; 0-915146),* 23 Eaton Rd., Syosset, NY 11791 (SAN 207-0979) Tel 516-938-0878.

Vadare Publishing Co., *(Vadare; 0-9610782; 0-933725),* 4 Burnham Ln., Dix Hills, NY 11746 (SAN 265-1491) Tel 516-661-3855; Toll free: 800-645-1112.

Vagabond *See* **Scholastic, Inc.**

†**Vagabond Press,** *(Vagabond Pr; 0-912824),* 1610 N. Water St., Ellensburg, WA 98926 (SAN 203-0535) Tel 509-925-5634; *CIP.*

Vail-Ballou Press, Inc., *(Vail Ballou; 0-9600868),* 187 Clinton St., Binghamton, NY 13902 (SAN 239-5681).

Vail Publishing, *(Vail Pub; 0-9607872),* 8285 SW Brookridge, Portland, OR 97225 (SAN 240-0766) Tel 503-292-9964.

Vaishnava Research Institute, *(Vaishnava; 0-935485),* 5825 Telegraph Ave., No. 21, Oakland, CA 94609 (SAN 695-7927) Tel 415-540-7665; Dist. by: New Leaf Distributing, 1020 White St., SW, Atlanta, GA 30310 (SAN 169-1449) Tel 404-755-2665.

Val-House Publishing, *(Val-Hse Pub; 0-936354),* 2903 Carriage Lane, P.O. Box 490443, College Park, GA 30349 (SAN 214-4816) Tel 404-957-9802.

Valaske Publishing, *(Valaske Pub; 0-9616601),* 6118 Fourth Ave., Kenosha, WI 53142 (SAN 659-5448) Tel 414-654-6007.

Vale Pr., *(Vale Pr; 0-916475),* P.O. Box 6519, Newport News, VA 23606 (SAN 295-1320) Tel 804-599-4256.

Valee Studios, *(Valee Studios; 0-9615939),* 4103 Scripps Ave., Palo Alto, CA 94306 (SAN 696-8589) Tel 415-493-1617.

Valen Publishing, *(Valen Pub; 0-9613897),* 23243 Spires St., Canoga Park, CA 91304 (SAN 682-3203) Tel 818-348-9034.

Valencia, Jerry, *(Valencia; 0-9604784),* 7525 Raytheon Rd., San Diego, CA 92111 (SAN 220-1038); Orders to: P.O. Box 758, La Jolla, CA 92038 (SAN 220-1046) Tel 619-729-3344.

Valentine Publishing & Drama Co., *(Valentine Pub; 0-941672),* P.O. Box 1378, Ashland, OR 97520 (SAN 239-3379) Tel 503-773-7035. *Imprints:* Bardavon Books (Bardavon Bks).

Valhalla Press, *(Valhalla Pr; 0-9607070),* Box 301, Chicago, IL 60690 (SAN 282-4981) Tel 312-761-1888.

Valhalla Rehabilitation Pubns., Ltd., *(Valhalla Rehab; 0-911681),* P.O. Box 195, Valhalla, NY 10595 (SAN 262-1053) Tel 914-948-1004.

Valiant Pubns., *(Valiant Pubns; 0-9608244),* 1200 Beneficial Life Tower, Salt Lake City, UT 84111 (SAN 240-4656) Tel 801-538-2000.

Valkyrie Publishing Hse., Subs. of Freedom Press, *(Valkyrie Pub Hse; 0-912760; 0-934616; 0-912589),* 8245 26th Ave. N., St. Petersburg, FL 33710 (SAN 203-1671) Tel 813-345-8864.

Valley Bk. Co., *(Valley Bk; 0-9616255),* 502 Cranwell Cir., Blacksburg, VA 24060 (SAN 658-5280) Tel 703-951-7984; P.O. Box 884, Blacksburg, VA 24060 (SAN 658-5299).

Valley Geological Pubns., *(Val Geol Pubns; 0-9616520),* 36 Plantation Cir., Greenfield, MA 01301 (SAN 659-5995) Tel 413-774-4827.

Valley Guild, The, Non Profit Organization of The Steinbeck House of Salinas, *(Valley Guild; 0-9612742),* 132 Central Ave., Salinas, CA 93901 (SAN 289-8802) Tel 408-424-7672; Orders to: Steinbeck House, 132 Central Ave., Salinas, CA 93901 (SAN 289-5498).

Valley Lights Pubns., *(Valley Lights; 0-9606482),* P.O. Box 1537, Ojai, CA 93023 (SAN 219-8320) Tel 805-646-9888.

Valley of the Sun Publishing Co., Div. of Sutphen Corp., *(Valley Sun; 0-911842; 0-87554),* P.O. Box 38, Malibu, CA 90265 (SAN 206-8974) Tel 818-889-1575; Toll free: 800-421-6603; Dist. by: Pocket Bks., 1230 Ave. of the Americas, New York, NY 10020 (SAN 202-5922) Tel 212-246-2121; Toll free: 800-223-2336; Orders to: Box 2010, Malibu, CA 90265; Toll free: 800-421-6603; 800-225-4717 (In California).

Valley Presbyterian Hospital, *(Valley Presbyterian; 0-9605718)*, 15107 Vanowen St., Van Nuys, CA 91405 (SAN 216-4701) Tel 818-981-1300.

†Valley Publishing, *(Valley Publishing; 0-9612990)*, P.O. Box 2223, Lower Burrell, PA 15068 (SAN 292-7209) Tel 412-337-0635; *CIP.*

Valley Pubs. *See* Western Tanger Pr.

Valley View Blueberry Press, *(Valley View; 0-9608432)*, 21717 N.E. 68th St., Vancouver, WA 98662 (SAN 240-7981) Tel 206-892-2839.

Valor Publishing Co., Affil. of Game Marketing, *(Valor Pub; 0-941052)*, 3355 Birch Cir., Allentown, PA 18103-4512 (SAN 217-3662) Tel 215-437-3622.

Valuation Pr., Inc., *(Valuation; 0-930458)*, 131-60 Mindanao Way, Suite 270, Marina del Rey, CA 90292 (SAN 210-6809); Orders to: P.O. Box 1080, Marina del Rey, CA 90291 (SAN 210-6817) Tel 213-822-3691.

†Value Communications, Subs. of Oak Tree Pubns., Inc., *(Value Comm; 0-916392)*, 9601 Aero Dr., San Diego, CA 92123 (SAN 208-0990) Tel 619-560-5163; *CIP.*

Valuwrite Pubns., *(ValuWrite; 0-940986)*, P.O. Box E, Provo, UT 84603 (SAN 223-2022) Tel 801-373-1111.

Van Arsdales Video Travel Guides, *(Van Arsdale Video; 0-939005)*, P.O. Box 3175, Naples, FL 33939 (SAN 662-5436); 281 11th Ave. S., Naples, FL 33940 (SAN 662-5444) Tel 813-649-5828.

Van Dean Educators Inc, *(Van Dean)*, Box 1422, Malvern, PA 19355 (SAN 240-8996).

Van der Marck, Alfred, Editions, *(Van der Marck; 0-912383)*, 1133 Broadway, Suite 301, New York, NY 10033 (SAN 265-2919) Tel 212-645-5150; Orders to: Harper & Row Pubs., Inc., Keystone Industrial Park, Scranton, PA 18512 (SAN 693-9821); Dist. by: Harper & Row Pubs., Inc., 10 E. 53rd St., New York, NY 10022 (SAN 200-2086) Tel 212-207-7099.

Van Diver, Bradford B., *(Van Diver; 0-9601106)*, The State University College of Arts & Science at Potsdam, Dept. of Geology, Potsdam, NY 13676 (SAN 209-908X) Tel 315-267-2288.

Van Dyk Pubns., *(Van Dyk)*, 816 W. White Oak, Independence, MO 64050 (SAN 209-6129) Tel 816-836-3290.

Van Horn Office Supply, P.O. Box 1060, Van Horn, TX 79855 (SAN 287-6485) Tel 915-283-2920.

Van Impe, Jack, Ministries, *(J Van Impe; 0-934803)*, 800 N. Crooks, Clawson, MI 48017 (SAN 697-3620).

Van Ness LOTCO, *(Van Ness LOTCO; 0-9608648)*, 2309 Newmarket Dr., Louisville, KY 40222 (SAN 238-4094) Tel 502-425-5118.

Van Nostrand Reinhold Co., Inc., Div. of International Thomson Organisation, Inc., *(Van Nos Reinhold; 0-442; 0-8436)*, 115 Fifth Ave., New York, NY 10003 (SAN 202-5183) Tel 212-254-3232; Orders to: VNR Order Processing, 7625 Empire Dr., Florence, KY 41042 (SAN 202-5191) Tel 606-525-6600. *Imprints:* Lark Communications (Lark Comms); Lifetime Learning Pubns. (Lifetime Pubns.).

Van Pelt, Harold & Erica, *(H & E Van Pelt; 0-9616785)*, 752 Seward St., Los Angeles, CA 90038 (SAN 659-3712) Tel 213-462-6604.

Van Siclen Bks., *(Van Siclen Bks; 0-933175)*, 111 Winnetka Rd., San Antonio, TX 78229 (SAN 692-3399) Tel 512-349-2913.

Van Trees, Robert V., *(R Van Trees; 0-9616282)*, 804 N. Central Ave., Fairborn, OH 45324-5216 (SAN 658-5272) Tel 513-878-3588; Orders to: Robert V. Van Trees, P.O. Box 2062, Fairborn, OH 45324-8062 (SAN 662-4111).

†Van Vactor & Goodheart, *(Van Vactor & Goodheart; 0-941324)*, 24 Lee St., Cambridge, MA 02139 (SAN 282-5007) Tel 617-497-5277; *CIP.*

Van Veer Nursery *See* Binford & Mort Publishing; Metropolitan Pr.

Van Vliet, Sherrie, *(S Van Vliet)*, E.C.S. P.O. Box 7000-37, Palos Verdes, CA 90274 (SAN 697-0141).

Van Wariebey, Glean, *(G Van Wariebey; 0-916829)*, 2 E. River St., Susquehanna, PA 18847 (SAN 699-8283).

Van Winkle Pub. Co., Inc., *(Van Winkle; 0-918664)*, Box 2000, 140 River Ave., Holland, MI 49423 (SAN 210-6833) Tel 616-396-1546.

Vance Bibliographies, *(Vance Biblios; 0-88066; 0-89028; 1-55590)*, P.O. Box 229, 112 N. Charter St., Monticello, IL 61856 (SAN 212-6273) Tel 217-762-3831.

Vance Pubns., *(Vance Pubns; 0-938595)*, P.O. Box 2158, Mansfield, OH 44905 (SAN 661-1400); Toll free: 800-423-9074; 1016 N. Stewart Rd., Mansfield, OH 44905 (SAN 661-1419) Tel 419-589-8401; Dist. by: Publishers Marketing Group, 1104 Summit Ave., Plainview, TX 75074 (SAN 262-0995) Tel 214-423-0312.

Vancento Pub. Co., *(Vancento Pub; 0-934142)*, 62 Court St., Reno, NV 89501 (SAN 238-7697).

Vanderbilt Press Inc., *(Vanderbilt Pr; 0-916815)*, 65 N.W. 21st St., Miami, FL 33127 (SAN 654-2603) Tel 305-573-0906.

†Vanderbilt Univ. Pr., *(Vanderbilt U Pr; 0-8265)*, 1211 18th Ave. S., Nashville, TN 37212 (SAN 202-9308) Tel 615-322-3585; Dist. by: Univ. of Illinois Pr., c/o Harper & Row Pubs., Inc., Keystone Industrial Pk., Scranton, PA 18512 (SAN 202-5310) Tel 217-333-0950; Toll free: 800-242-7737; Orders to: Univ. of Illinois Pr., P.O. Box 1650, Hagerstown, MD 21741; Toll free: 800-638-3030; *CIP.*

Vanderbilt Univ. Pubns. in Anthropolgy, *(Vanderbilt Pubns; 0-935462)*, Box 1532 Sta. B, Vanderbilt Univ., Nashville, TN 37235 (SAN 695-7986) Tel 615-322-7522.

Vanderkolk Publishing, *(Vanderkolk; 0-9617269)*, 4555 Acacia, La Mesa, CA 92041 (SAN 663-5083) Tel 619-589-6201.

Vanderstoel, Graeme, *(G Vanderstoel)*, P.O. Box 599, El Cerrito, CA 94530 (SAN 263-239X) Tel 415-527-2882.

Vanessa-Ann Collection, The, *(Vanessa-Ann Collec; 0-913921)*, P.O. Box 9113, Ogden, UT 84409 (SAN 286-6897) Tel 801-621-2777.

Vanessapress, *(Vanessapress)*, P.O. Box 81335, Fairbanks, AK 99708 (SAN 696-5040); 1560 Farmer's Loop, Fairbanks, AK 99708 Tel 907-479-0172.

†Vanguard Books, *(Vanguard Bks; 0-917702)*, P.O. Box 3566, Chicago, IL 60654 (SAN 213-8212) Tel 312-342-3425; *CIP.*

Vanguard Books *See* Noontide Pr., The

Vanguard Institutional Pubs., *(Vanguard Inst; 0-934725)*, 1011 4th St., Suite 305, Santa Monica, CA 90403 (SAN 694-1508) Tel 213-394-1284.

Vanguard Pr., Inc., *(Vanguard; 0-8149)*, 424 Madison Ave., New York, NY 10017 (SAN 202-9316) Tel 212-753-3906; Dist. by: Columbia Publishing Co., Inc., Drawer A, Frenchtown, NJ 08825 (SAN 202-9316) Tel 201-996-2141.

VanMeer Pubns., Inc., *(VanMeer Pubns; 0-937826)*, P.O. Box 1289, Clearwater, FL 33517 (SAN 220-1054) Tel 813-531-6047.

Vanni, S. F., *(S F Vanni; 0-913298)*, 30 W. 12th St., New York, NY 10011 (SAN 220-0031) Tel 212-675-6336.

Vanous, Arthur, Co., *(Vanous; 0-89918)*, P.O. Box 650279, Vero Beach, FL 32965 (SAN 169-4871) Tel 305-562-9186.

Vantage Information, *(Vantage Info; 0-914791)*, P.O. Box 22684, Lexington, KY 40522 (SAN 655-1459).

Vantage Pr., Inc., *(Vantage; 0-533)*, 516 W. 34th St., New York, NY 10001 (SAN 206-8893) Tel 212-736-1767.

Vantage Printing Company, *(Vantage Printing; 0-943110)*, 2003 Broadway, Houston, TX 77012 (SAN 240-4672) Tel 713-644-1994.

Vardaman Press, *(Vardaman Pr; 0-942648)*, 2720 E. 176th St., Tacoma, WA 98445 (SAN 239-9482).

Varfley, Edwin B., *(Varfley; 0-9609570)*, P.O. Box 2916, Providence, RI 02908 (SAN 276-4806).

Vargas, Glenn, *(Glenn Vargas; 0-917646)*, 85-159 Ave. 66, Thermal, CA 92274 (SAN 203-4301) Tel 619-397-4264.

Variena Publishing, *(Variena Publishing; 0-939225)*, 6796 Lowell Blvd., Denver, CO 80221 (SAN 663-4974) Tel 303-650-0910.

Varietal Fair, *(Varietal Fair; 0-9614025)*, 4022 Harrison Grade Rd., Sebastopol, CA 95472 (SAN 683-6216) Tel 707-874-3105.

Variety Artists Bks., *(Variety Artists Bks; 0-939639)*, 4232 Herschel Ave., Suite 209, Dallas, TX 75219 (SAN 663-5792) Tel 214-521-7177.

Varner, Nick, *(Nick Varner; 0-9607536)*, P.O. Box 1309, Owensboro, KY 42302 (SAN 239-569X).

Varnes Pubs., *(Varnes Pubs; 0-943584)*, 9404 Genesee Ave., No. 284, La Jolla, CA 92037 (SAN 240-8007) Tel 619-453-3081; Orders to: P.O. Box 9655, Marina del Rey, CA 90295 (SAN 662-1775).

Varsity Publishing, *(Varsity Pubs; 0-9614872)*, RD 1, Box 326, Valatie, NY 12184 (SAN 693-2266) Tel 518-784-3025.

Vashon Point Productions, *(Vashon Pt Prod; 0-9616103)*, Rte. 1, P.O. Box 432, Vashon, WA 98070 (SAN 659-5642).

Vassilion, Harry J., *(Vassilion; 0-9606180)*, 5519 N. Hills Dr., Raleigh, NC 27612 (SAN 216-471X).

Vaughan, Edwards, Pubs., *(Vaughan Edwards; 0-911237)*, Box 2015, Dusty Bend Sta., Camden, SC 29020 (SAN 275-8903) Tel 803-432-3849.

Vaughan Pubns., *(Vaughan Pubns; 0-9613951)*, P.O. Box 1527, Chandler Heights, AZ 85224 (SAN 686-1628) Tel 602-838-1924.

Vaughn, Greene M., *(V Greene)*, 548 Elm Ave., San Bruno, CA 94066 (SAN 683-2784) Tel 415-589-4224.

Vaughn Pubs., *(Vaughn Pub KY)*, P.O. Box 97, London, KY 40741 (SAN 693-1006).

Vector Associates, *(Vector Assocs; 0-930808)*, P.O. Box 6215, Bellevue, WA 98007 (SAN 211-1039) Tel 206-747-5881.

Vector Counseling Institute, *(Vector Counsel; 0-913596)*, P.O. Box 1271, Mt. Vernon, WA 98273 (SAN 205-4752) Tel 206-855-0630.

Vector Golf, Inc., *(Vector Golf; 0-9613027)*, 6608 Genoa Rd., Fort Worth, TX 76116 (SAN 293-9053) Tel 817-731-0424.

Vector Intercontinental, *(Vector Inter; 0-937907)*, P.O. Box 20820, Cleveland, OH 44120 (SAN 659-6002); 13221 Shaker Sq., Cleveland, OH 44120 (SAN 659-6010) Tel 216-561-3677.

Vedanta Centre Pubs., Div. of Vedanta Centre, Inc., *(Vedanta Ctr; 0-911564)*, 130 Beechwood St., Cohasset, MA 02025 (SAN 206-7781) Tel 617-383-0940.

Vedanta Pr., Div. of Vedanta Society, *(Vedanta Pr; 0-87481)*, 1946 Vedanta Pl., Hollywood, CA 90068-3996 (SAN 202-9340) Tel 213-465-7114.

Vedanta Society of St. Louis, *(Vedanta Soc St Louis; 0-916356)*, 205 S. Skinker Blvd., St. Louis, MO 63105 (SAN 208-1180) Tel 314-721-5118.

Vedette Printing Co., *(Vedette Print)*, Greenfield, MO 65661 (SAN 239-5703).

VEEP, Incorporated, *(Veep; 0-9614166)*, P.O. Box 882, Norristown, PA 19404 (SAN 686-6719) Tel 215-277-3778.

Vega, Carlos B., Pub., *(C B Vega; 0-88174)*, P.O. Box 4195, West New York, NJ 07093 (SAN 287-7724) Tel 201-869-6916.

Vehicle Editions, *(Vehicle Edns; 0-931428)*, 238 Mott St., New York, NY 10012 (SAN 212-5773) Tel 212-226-1769; Dist. by: Talman Company, The, 150 Fifth Ave., Rm. 514, New York, NY 10011 (SAN 200-5204) Tel 212-620-3182.

Veilleux, Eugene D., *(E D Veilleux; 0-9610248)*, 137 Haggetts Pond Rd., Andover, MA 01810 (SAN 264-4703) Tel 617-475-2611.

Vel-or Co., *(Vel-or Co; 0-9615906)*, 2141 Lakeview Rd., Vista, CA 92084 (SAN 696-7612) Tel 619-727-2230.

Veldt Protea Institute, *(Veldt Protea Inst; 0-917538)*, 3207 Las Palmas St., Houston, TX 77027 (SAN 209-3626); Dist. by: British Market Inc., 2366 Rice Blvd., Houston, TX 77005 (SAN 200-8289) Tel 713-529-9889.

Velo-News, *(Velo-News; 0-941950)*, Box 1257, Brattleboro, VT 05301 (SAN 239-5711) Tel 802-254-2305; Dist. by: Countryman Press, Inc., P.O. Box 175, Woodstock, VT 05091 (SAN 206-4901) Tel 802-457-1049.

Velocities, *(Velocities; 0-930231)*, 2740 College, No. 302, Berkeley, CA 94705 (SAN 679-1522).

VeNard Pubs., *(VeNard Pubs; 0-9610342),* 4812 Folson Blvd. No. H, Sacramento, CA 95819 (SAN 264-469X) Tel 916-739-8343.

†**Vendome Pr., The,** *(Vendome; 0-86565),* 515 Madison Ave., Suite 1906, New York, NY 10022 (SAN 215-2347) Tel 212-838-8991; Dist. by: Rizzoli International Pubns., 597 Fifth Ave., New York, NY 10017 (SAN 207-7000) Tel 212-223-0100; Toll free: 800-433-1238; *CIP.*

Venice West Pubs., *(Venice West),* 319 North Cordova St., Burbank, CA 91505 (SAN 210-2986) Tel 818-843-5515; Dist. by: Capra Press, P.O. Box 2068, Santa Barbara, CA 93120 (SAN 208-0494) Tel 805-966-4590.

Venti Amati, *(V Amati; 0-9614119),* 202 Park, Marshall, MN 56258 (SAN 656-9072) Tel 507-532-3647.

Ventnor Pubs., *(Ventnor; 0-911566),* Drawer G, Ventnor Post Office,, Ventnor, NJ 08406-0078 (SAN 205-4760).

Ventura Pr., *(Ventura Pr; 0-917438),* P.O. Box 1076, Guerneville, CA 95446 (SAN 205-4779).

Venture Assocs., Inc., *(Venture Assocs; 0-9616346),* P.O. Box 140165, Nashville, TN 37214 (SAN 658-7976) Tel 615-758-0430; 704 Valley Brook Dr., Mt. Juliet, TN 37122 (SAN 658-7984).

Venture Books, *(Venture Bks; 0-9600432),* P.O. Box 131, Coopersburg, PA 18036 (SAN 205-4787) Tel 215-965-2891.

Venture Concepts Press, *(Venture Con Pr; 0-9611214),* 806 15th St. NW Suite 421, Washington, DC 20005 (SAN 282-9304) Tel 212-783-1166.

Venture Economics *See* **Unipub b**

Venture Economics Inc., *(Venture Econ Inc; 0-914470),* P.O. Box 348, 16 Laurel Ave., Wellesley Hills, MA 02181 (SAN 206-2240) Tel 617-431-8100; Toll free: 800-521-8110.

Venture Industries, Inc., *(Venture Indus; 0-937051),* P.O. Box 393, St. Augustine, FL 32085 (SAN 658-6678) Tel 904-829-0221; 117A King St., St. Augustine, FL 32085 (SAN 658-6686).

Venture Perspective Pr., *(Venture Persp Pr; 0-932309),* 4300 Stevens Creek Blvd., Suite 155, San Jose, CA 95129 (SAN 686-7375) Tel 408-247-1325.

Venture Pr., *(Venture Pr AZ; 0-936465),* 1626 Ventura Dr., Tempe, AZ 85281 (SAN 697-9904) Tel 602-966-2116.

Venture Pubns., *(Venture CA; 0-9612478),* 2687 Montrose Pl., Santa Barbara, CA 93105 (SAN 289-6427) Tel 805-682-5074.

Venture Publishing, *(Venture Pub PA; 0-910251),* 1640 Oxford Cir., State College, PA 16801 (SAN 240-897X) Tel 814-234-4561.

Venturecraft Kits Co., *(Venturecraft Co; 0-941326),* 47 Great River Dr., Sound Beach, NY 11789 (SAN 239-5738) Tel 516-744-4395.

Ventures International, *(Ventures Intl; 0-917437),* P.O. Box 6539, San Diego, CA 92106 (SAN 656-1381) Tel 619-223-6787.

Venus Bks., *(Venus Bks; 0-939352),* 9655 Chimney Hill, Suite 2118, Dallas, TX 75243 (SAN 216-4728) Tel 214-644-7482.

Verbatim, *(Verbatim Bks; 0-930454),* Box 668, Essex, CT 06426 (SAN 211-1047) Tel 203-767-8248.

VerDugo Pr., *(VerDugo Pr; 0-941140),* 6715 Sunset Blvd., Hollywood, CA 90028 (SAN 239-572X); Dist. by: Hollywood Reporter, 6715 Sunset Blvd., Hollywood, CA 90028 (SAN 217-3824) Tel 213-464-7411.

Vergin Pr., *(Vergin Pr; 0-935839),* 1101 Avalon Dr., Apt. J, El Paso, TX 79925 (SAN 696-6411) Tel 915-779-8678.

Veridon Editions, *(Veridon Edns; 0-912061),* P.O. Box 65, New Rochelle, NY 10804 (SAN 264-7028).

Veritas Foundation, *(Veritas; 0-911568),* P.O. Box 111, West Sayville, NY 11796 (SAN 206-3107). Formerly Named Probe.

Veritas Press, *(Veritas Pr; 0-932208),* 3310 Rochambeau Ave., New York, NY 10467 (SAN 212-2413) Tel 212-655-7566.

†**Veritat Foundation, Inc.,** *(Veritat Found; 0-938760),* 3910 Los Feliz Blvd., Los Angeles, CA 90027 (SAN 205-6348); *CIP.*

Veritie Press, Inc., *(Veritie Pr; 0-915964),* P.O. Box 222, Novelty, OH 44072 (SAN 207-6977) Tel 216-338-3374.

Vermont Bks., Inc., Div. of TL. Vermont Book Shop, *(Vermont Bks; 0-911570),* 38 Main St., Middlebury, VT 05753 (SAN 205-4817) Tel 802-388-2061.

Vermont Council on the Arts, Inc., *(VT Council Arts; 0-916718),* 136 State St., Montpelier, VT 05602 (SAN 208-9092) Tel 802-828-3291.

Vermont Heritage Press, *(Vermont Herit Pr; 0-911853),* 124 Elm St., Bennington, VT 05201 (SAN 264-472X) Tel 802-442-6873.

†**Vermont Historical Society,** *(VT Hist Soc; 0-934720),* 109 State St., Montpelier, VT 05602 (SAN 206-0442) Tel 802-828-2291; *CIP.*

†**Vermont Life Magazine,** *(VT Life Mag; 0-936896),* 61 Elm St., Montpelier, VT 05602 (SAN 215-8213); *CIP.*

Vernal Equinox Pr., *(Vernal Equinox; 0-942380),* P.O. Box 581, San Anselmo, CA 94960 (SAN 240-1762).

Verry, Lawrence, Inc., *(Verry; 0-8426),* P.O. Box 215, Mystic, CT 06355 (SAN 202-5205) Tel 203-536-3104.

Versailles, Elizabeth Starr, *(Versailles; 0-9606002),* 42 Nash Hill Rd., Williamsburg, MA 01096 (SAN 203-0330) Tel 413-268-7056.

Vert Milon Pr., *(Vert Milon Pr; 0-9613980),* P.O. Box 332, Alexandria, VA 22313 (SAN 682-2061) Tel 703-549-8330.

Vertex Co., *(Vertex),* 4438 Manzanita Dr., San Jose, CA 95129 (SAN 209-4096) Tel 408-252-2592.

Verve Pr., *(Verve Pr; 0-937363),* P.O. Box 1997, Huntington Beach, CA 92647 (SAN 659-0985) Tel 714-846-9640; 17171 Sims, Huntington Beach, CA 92649 (SAN 659-0993).

Vervir, Inc., *(Vervir; 0-935247),* 251 Willows Dr., Laguna Hills, CA 92653 (SAN 695-832X) Tel 714-458-6442.

Very Best Publishers, The, *(Very Best; 0-911729),* Cranehill, 194 Maple Ave., Great Barrington, MA 01230 (SAN 293-4086) Tel 617-262-3477.

Very Healthy Enterprises, *(Very Healthy Ent; 0-9615452),* P.O. Box 4728, Inglewood, CA 90309 (SAN 696-2254) Tel 213-672-3269.

Very Idea, The, *(Very Idea; 0-9615130),* 1604 Ave J, Box 53, Abernathy, TX 79311 (SAN 694-1869) Tel 806-298-4252.

Very Serious Business Enterprises, *(VSBE; 0-9605304),* P.O. Box 356, Newark, NJ 07101 (SAN 215-8221).

Very Vera, *(Very Vera; 0-937747),* P.O. Box 2311, Honolulu, HI 96804 (SAN 659-3739) Tel 808-988-3395; 2804 Manoa Rd., Honolulu, HI 96822 (SAN 659-3747); Dist. by: Mediatech, 737 Bishop St., Suite 2790, Honolulu, HI 96813 (SAN 200-6456).

†**Vestal Pr., Ltd.,** *(Vestal; 0-911572),* P.O. Box 97, 320 N. Jensen Rd., Vestal, NY 13850 (SAN 205-4825) Tel 607-797-4872; *CIP.*

Vestron Video Blvd., *(Vestron Video; 0-8051),* 1011 High Ridge Rd., Stamford, CT 06907 (SAN 658-6430) Tel 203-968-0000; P.O. Box 4000, Stamford, CT 06907.

Vetco Printing & Publishing, *(Vetco Printing; 0-9616448),* 4217 N. Main St., Suite 110, Dayton, OH 45405 (SAN 659-1000) Tel 513-275-2837.

Veterans Education Project, Inc., *(Vets Ed Proj; 0-941486),* P.O. Box 42130, Washington, DC 20015 (SAN 239-054X) Tel 202-686-2741.

Veterans Information Service, *(Veterans Info),* P.O. Box 111, East Moline, IL 61244 (SAN 205-4833) Tel 309-797-1868.

Veterinary Medicine Publishing Co., Subs. of Medical Economics Co., *(Veterinary Med; 0-935078),* 9073 Lenexa Dr., Lenexa, KS 66215 (SAN 209-0074) Tel 913-492-4300; Toll free: 800-255-6864.

Veterinary Textbooks, *(Veterinary Textbks; 0-9601152),* 36 Woodcrest Ave., Ithaca, NY 14850 (SAN 207-2998) Tel 607-272-1860.

Veterinarians Professional Management Co., *(Vets Prof Mgmt; 0-936233),* 5722 San Miguel Rd., Bonita, CA 92002 (SAN 696-8562) Tel 619-479-5555.

Vibrante Pr., *(Vibrante Pr; 0-935301),* 2430 Juan Tabo, NE, Suite 110, Albuquerque, NM 87112 (SAN 696-2351) Tel 505-298-4793.

Vichitra Pr., *(Vichitra Pr; 0-941582),* 10582 Cheviot Dr., Los Angeles, CA 90064 (SAN 239-3387) Tel 213-839-8547; Dist. by: Asian Humanities Pr., 3204 Adeline St., P.O. Box 3056, Berkeley, CA 94703 (SAN 213-6503).

Vicious Circle Pr., *(Vicious Cir Pr; 0-936393),* Box 18244, Louisville, KY 40218 (SAN 697-3051) Tel 502-538-7222; Rte. 2, Armstrong Ln. Box 158, Mt. Washington, KY 40047 (SAN 699-6493).

Vicksburg Junior Auxiliary, *(Vicksburg Jr Aux; 0-9614988),* No. 5 Lakewood, Vicksburg, MS 39180 (SAN 693-7691) Tel 601-638-8562.

Vicris Pubn., *(Vicris Pubn; 0-9616644),* 4502 W. Ashlan Ave., Fresno, CA 93711 (SAN 659-669X) Tel 209-276-0345.

Victimology Inc., *(Victimology; 0-916818; 0-943242),* 2333 N. Vernon St., Arlington, VA 22207 (SAN 208-3728) Tel 703-528-8872.

Victim's Pr., *(Victims Pr; 0-935261),* 640 Turk St., Suite 46, San Francisco, CA 94102 (SAN 695-5274) Tel 415-673-5460.

Victor Bks., Div. of Scripture Pr. Pubns., Inc., *(Victor Bks; 0-88207; 0-89693),* P.O. Box 1825, Wheaton, IL 60187 (SAN 207-7302) Tel 312-668-6000; Toll free: 800-323-9409 (For orders); Orders to: 1825 College Ave., Wheaton, IL 60187 (SAN 207-7310).

†**Victoria House, Pubs.,** *(Victoria Hse; 0-918480),* 2218 N.E. 8th Ave., Portland, OR 97212 (SAN 209-9101) Tel 503-284-4801; *CIP.*

Victoria Pr., The, *(Victoria Pr; 0-9613204),* 39865 Cedar Blvd., Suite 240, Newark, CA 94560 (SAN 295-6128).

Victorian Design Pr., *(Victorian Design; 0-913693),* P.O. Box 5186, Mill Valley, CA 94942 (SAN 286-2158); 382 Throckmorton Ave., Mill Valley, CA 94941 (SAN 286-2166) Tel 415-388-4990.

Victorian Video Productions, *(Victorian Video; 0-936225),* P.O. Box 1328, Port Townsend, WA 98368 (SAN 696-8570) Tel 916-961-9359.

Victorious Ministry Through Christ, Inc., *(Victorious Ministry; 0-9605178),* P.O. Box 1804, Winter Park, FL 32790 (SAN 215-823X); Dist. by: Impact Books, 137 W. Jefferson, Kirkwood, MO 63122 (SAN 214-0330) Tel 314-833-3309.

Victory Hse., Inc., *(Victory Hse; 0-932081),* P.O. Box 700238, Tulsa, OK 74170 (SAN 686-2667) Tel 918-747-5009.

Victory Publishing, *(Victory Pub; 0-935303),* 1068 Del Norte Ave., Menlo, CA 94025 (SAN 696-2408) Tel 415-322-4402.

Vidano, Carl L., Publishing Co., *(C L Vidano Pub; 0-9616606),* P.O. Box 5446, Huntington Beach, CA 92615 (SAN 659-8102); 9601 Gleneagles Cr., Westminster, CA 92683 (SAN 659-8110) Tel 714-895-4563.

Video Assocs., Inc., *(Video Assocs; 1-55593),* 5419 Sunset Blvd., Los Angeles, CA 90028 (SAN 658-7151) Tel 213-463-3255.

Video Athlete Corp., *(Video Athlete; 0-915659),* 120 W. Mifflin, Madison, WI 53703 (SAN 287-2358).

Video Award Motion Pictures, Inc., *(Video Award; 0-936311),* 1585 Broadway, New York, NY 10036 (SAN 697-3094) Tel 212-315-2600.

Video-Forum, Div. of Jeffrey Norton Pubs., *(Video-Forum; 0-88432),* 96 Broad St., Guilford, CT 06437 (SAN 217-4707) Tel 203-453-9794; Toll free: 800-243-1234.

Video-Info Pubns., *(Video-Info; 0-931294),* P.O. Box 2685, Santa Fe, NM 87501 (SAN 212-5781) Tel 505-983-6422.

Video International Entertainment World *See* **VIEW, Inc.**

Video Pubns., Ltd., *(Video Pubns Ltd; 0-935667),* 915 Oliver St., St. Louis, MO 63101 (SAN 696-2467) Tel 314-231-9550.

Video Travel, Inc., *(Video Travel; 1-55629),* 153 W. Fourth St., Williamsport, PA 17701 (SAN 659-9311) Tel 717-326-6525; Toll free: 800-828-6888.

Video Treasures, *(Video Treas; 1-55529),* 200 Robbins Ln., Jericho, NY 11753 (SAN 696-2521) Tel 201-778-0877.

Video Wizard Co., *(Video Wizard; 0-943320),* 134 St. Charles Ave., San Francisco, CA 94132 (SAN 240-8023) Tel 415-952-4990.

Vienna Hse, Inc., *(Vienna Hse; 0-8443),* 342 Madison Ave., New York, NY 10017 (SAN 202-9367) Tel 212-986-7724.

Vietnam Marine Pubns., *(Viet Nam Mar; 0-9611880),* P.O. Box 201, Lancaster, TX 75146 (SAN 286-0694) Tel 214-227-3365; Dist. by: Presidio Pr., 31 Pamaron Way, Novato, CA 94947 (SAN 214-2759) Tel 415-883-1373.

Viewpoint Pr., *(Viewpoint Pr; 0-943962),* P.O. Box P, Tehachapi, CA 93561 (SAN 241-1644) Tel 213-318-3645.

Vigilantero Pr., *(Vigilantero Pr; 0-9616829),* P.O. Box 7513, Boulder, CO 80306 (SAN 661-1656); 1627 Columbine, Boulder, CO 80306 (SAN 661-1664) Tel 303-440-0713.

Viking Import House, Inc., *(Viking Import; 0-911576),* 412 SE Sixth St., Ft. Lauderdale, FL 33301 (SAN 205-485X).

Viking Kestrel *See* **Viking-Penguin, Inc.**

Viking-Penguin, Inc., *(Viking; 0-670),* 40 W. 23rd St., New York, NY 10010 (SAN 200-2442) Tel 212-337-5200; Toll free: 800-631-3577; Orders to: 299 Murray Hill Pkwy., East Rutherford, NJ 07073 (SAN 282-5074). *Imprints:* Compass Books (Comp); Elisabeth Sifton Books (E Sifton Bks); Explorer Books (Exp); Studio Books (Studio); Viking Kestrel (Viking Kestrel).

Vilips, Kathryn L, Studios, Inc., *(K L Vilips; 0-938473),* P.O. Drawer G, Wofford Heights, CA 93285 (SAN 660-9686); 237 Split Mountain Way, Wofford Heights, CA 93285 (SAN 660-9694) Tel 619-376-3634.

Villa Pr., Affil. of Schoolhouse Software, *(Villa Pr; 0-913472),* 69-10 164th St., Fresh Meadows, NY 11365 (SAN 203-0322) Tel 718-591-0894.

Villa Pr., *(Villa Pr AZ; 0-933843),* 4506 W. Citrus Way, Glendale, AZ 85301 (SAN 692-6878) Tel 602-934-3607.

Village Hse. Pubs., *(Village Hse Pubs; 0-9617255),* 3541 Brookwood Rd., Birmingham, AL 35223 (SAN 663-5466) Tel 205-967-2284.

Village of Oak Park, *(Vil Oak Pk; 0-9616915),* 1 Village Hall Plaza, Oak Park, IL 60302 (SAN 661-6593) Tel 312-383-6400; Dist. by: Chicago Review Pr., 814 N. Franklin, Chicago, IL 60610 (SAN 213-5744) Tel 312-337-0747.

Village Press (AL), The, *(Village AL; 0-9613152),* P.O. Box 787, Daphne, AL 36526 (SAN 294-9911) Tel 205-626-3505.

Village Pr., The, *(Village Pr; 0-940310),* P.O. Box 174, Unionville, CT 06085 (SAN 217-5770) Tel 203-673-9827.

Village Voice, *(Village Voice; 0-934465),* 842 Broadway, New York, NY 10003 (SAN 205-4868) Tel 212-475-3300.

Villanova Univ., Athletic Dept., *(Villanova U Ath; 0-9615910),* Field Hse., Villanova, PA 19085 (SAN 696-7647) Tel 215-647-9590.

Villanova Univ. Law Schl., *(Villanova Law),* Villanova Univ., Villanova, PA 19085 (SAN 226-7810).

Vimach Associates, *(Vimach Assocs; 0-917949),* 3039 Indianola Ave., Columbus, OH 43202 (SAN 657-0283) Tel 614-262-0471.

Vincente Bks., *(Vincente Bks; 0-915241),* P.O. Box 7388, Berkeley, CA 94707-0388 (SAN 289-8829) Tel 415-528-5648.

Vincentian Evangelization, *(Vincentian; 0-9608630),* 1025 Napoleon Ave., New Orleans, LA 70115 (SAN 219-0974) Tel 504-899-1130.

Vinco Pr., *(Vinco Pr; 0-9603836),* 1553 Woodward, Detroit, MI 48226 (SAN 213-8093).

VinMar Agency, Inc., *(VinMar Agency; 0-943964),* P.O. Box 1329, Avon Park, FL 33825 (SAN 241-1652) Tel 813-453-7412.

Vintage America Publishing Co., *(Vintage Am; 0-932330),* P.O. Box 57361, Washington, DC 20037 (SAN 212-1689). Do Not Confuse with Vintage Trade Books, Imprint of Random.

Vintage '45 Pr., *(Vintage Forty-Five; 0-9614375),* P.O. Box 266, Orinda, CA 94563 (SAN 688-6302) Tel 415-254-7266; Dist. by: Bookpeople, 2929 Fifth St., Berkeley, CA 94710 (SAN 168-9517); Toll free: 800-227-1516; 800-624-4466 (In California); Dist. by: Inland Book Company, P.O. Box 261, 22 Hemingway Ave., East Haven, CT 06512 (SAN 200-4151) Tel 203-467-4257; Toll free: 800-243-0138.

†**Vintage Image,** *(Vin Image; 0-918666),* 1335 Main St., St. Helena, CA 94574 (SAN 210-329X) Tel 707-963-3883; *CIP.*

Vintage Pr., *(Vintage Press; 0-9615324),* 40 Christine Dr., East Hanover, NJ 07936 (SAN 695-0493) Tel 201-887-5020. Do not confuse with 'Vintage' imprints of Random House, New York, NY.

Vintage Pubns., *(Vintage Pubns; 0-931973),* 806 Adobe Dr., Santa Rosa, CA 95404 (SAN 686-0761) Tel 707-539-1699.

Vintage Radio Co., *(Vintage Radio; 0-914126),* 26451 Dunwood Rd., P.O. Box 2045, Rolling Hills Estates, CA 90274 (SAN 282-5104) Tel 213-375-4272; Dist. by: McMahon Vintage Radio, P.O. Box 1331,, N. Highlands, CA 95660 (SAN 282-6356) Tel 916-332-8262.

Vinton Publishing, *(Vinton),* 1244 Wyoming St., Boulder City, NV 89005 (SAN 277-710X).

Violet Pr., *(Violet Pr; 0-912968),* P.O. Box 398, New York, NY 10009 (SAN 203-1701).

Violetta Bks., *(Violetta Bks; 0-915913),* 76 Byers St., Springfield, MA 01105 (SAN 294-1090) Tel 413-737-8118; Orders to: Box 15151, Springfield, MA 01115 (SAN 693-5117).

Vip Aero Publishers Inc., *(Vip Aero Pubs; 0-934575),* P.O. Box 16103, Colorado Springs, CO 80935 (SAN 693-8442) Tel 303-596-4172.

Virago *See* **Doubleday & Co., Inc.**

Vireo Press, *(Vireo Pr; 0-9612144),* Box 898, Waycross, GA 31501 (SAN 287-7783).

Virgin Islands Commission on Youth, *(VICY; 0-937421),* P.O. Box 580, Charlotte Amalie, St. Thomas, VI 00801 (SAN 659-1019) Tel 809-774-6012.

Virginia Army National Guard Foundation, *(VA Army Natl Guard; 0-9616860),* 501 E. Franklin St., Richmond, VA 23219 (SAN 661-5937) Tel 804-344-4103.

Virginia Book Co., *(VA Bk; 0-911578),* Box 431, Berryville, VA 22611 (SAN 206-7773) Tel 703-955-1428.

Virginia Cardinal Pubns, Inc., *(VA Cardinal Pubns; 0-938951),* P.O. Box 1177, Vienna, VA 22180 (SAN 661-7220); 135 Park St., NE, Vienna, VA 22180 (SAN 661-7239) Tel 703-938-0666.

Virginia Ctr. for Creative Arts, *(VA Ctr Creative Arts),* Dist. by: Associated University Presses, 440 Forsgate Dr., Cranbury, NJ 08512 (SAN 281-2959) Tel 609-655-4770.

Virginia Chamber of Commerce, Publishing Div., *(VA Chamber Com; 0-918529),* 9 S. Fifth St., Richmond, VA 23219 (SAN 219-0354) Tel 804-644-1607.

Virginia City Restoration Corp., *(VA City Rest; 0-9604560),* P.O. Box 221691, Carmel, CA 93922 (SAN 215-1901).

Virginia Community Action Re-Entry Systems, Inc., *(Va CARES; 0-9613647),* P.O. Box 2868, Roanoke, VA 24001 (SAN 670-7807) Tel 703-342-1880.

Virginia Municipal League, *(VA Muni League; 0-932993),* P.O. Box 12203, Richmond, VA 23241 (SAN 226-787X) Tel 804-649-8471.

†**Virginia Museum of Fine Arts,** *(Va Mus Arts; 0-917046),* Blvd. & Grove, Richmond, VA 23221 (SAN 281-0204) Tel 804-257-0818; Blvd. & Grove Ave., Office of Publications, Richmond, VA 23221 (SAN 661-9282) Tel 804-257-0534; Dist. by: University of Washington Press, P.O. Box C50096, Seattle, WA 98145-0096 (SAN 212-2502) Tel 206-543-8870; *CIP.*

Virginia Office of the Attorney General, *(VA Atty Genl),* Supreme Court Bldg., 101 N. Eighth St., Richmond, VA 23219 (SAN 226-7888).

Virginia State Bar, *(Virginia Bar),* 801 E. Main St., Ross Bldg., 10th Flr., Richmond, VA 23219 (SAN 226-7829) Tel 804-293-6618.

†**Virginia State Library,** *(VA State Lib; 0-88490),* 11th St. at Capitol Sq., Richmond, VA 23219 (SAN 203-0543) Tel 804-786-2312; *CIP.*

Virginia Surveyors Foundation, *(VA Surveyors; 0-9604076),* 6001 Lakeside Ave., Richmond, VA 23228 (SAN 282-5120) Tel 804-262-1351.

Virgo Press, *(Virgo Pr; 0-930558),* 975 Arthur Godfrey Rd., Suite 401, Miami Beach, FL 33140 (SAN 211-1063) Tel 305-538-6324.

Virtue Notagraph Editions, *(Virtue Notagraph; 0-914596),* 4940 Beaumont Dr., La Mesa, CA 92041 (SAN 206-1376) Tel 619-469-6634.

Virtuoso Pubns., Inc., *(Virtuoso; 0-918624),* 206 SE 46th Lane, Cape Coral, FL 33904 (SAN 210-153X) Tel 813-549-1802.

Visa Publishing Corp., *(Visa Pub; 0-9606802),* 50 E. 42nd St., New York, NY 10017 (SAN 217-2739); Dist. by: Bookazine Co., Inc., 303 W. Tenth St., New York, NY 10014 (SAN 169-5665) Tel 212-675-8877.

Vishwa Dharma Pubns., *(Vishwa; 0-942508),* 174 Santa Clara Ave., Oakland, CA 94610 (SAN 238-2075) Tel 415-654-4683.

Visibility Enterprises, *(Visibility Ent; 0-9603740),* 450 West End Ave., New York, NY 10024 (SAN 214-4832) Tel 212-787-9239.

Visible Difference International, A, *(Visible Diff; 0-933675),* P.O. Box 175, Selden, NY 11784-0175 (SAN 692-543X) Tel 516-924-1786.

Vision Bks. *See* **Farrar, Straus & Giroux, Inc.**

Vision Books, *(Vision Bks; 0-942024),* 790 Commercial Ave., Coos Bay, OR 97420 (SAN 293-4256) Tel 503-267-4232 (SAN 168-9886) (SAN 212-0364); Dist. by: Vision Books, 790 Commercial Ave., Coos Bay, OR 97420 (SAN 293-4264) Tel 503-267-4232; Dist. by: DeVorss & Co.,Inc., P.O. Box 550, 1046 Princeton Dr., Marina del Rey, CA 90294 (SAN 168-9886); Dist. by: Bookpeople, 2929 Fifth St., Berkeley, CA 94710 (SAN 168-9517); Toll free: 800-227-1516; Dist. by: Publishers Group West, 5855 Beaudry St., Emeryville, CA 94608 (SAN 202-8522); Dist. by: New Leaf Distributing, 1020 White St. SW, Atlanta, GA 30310 (SAN 169-1449) Tel 404-755-2665; Dist. by: Ingram Book Co., 347 Reedwood Dr., Nashville, TN 37217 (SAN 169-7978).

Vision Foundation, Incorporated, *(Vision Found; 0-9606836),* 818 Mt. Auburn St., Watertown, MA 02172 (SAN 217-1376) Tel 617-926-4232; Toll free: 800-852-3029 Massachusetts only.

Vision Hse., *(Vision Hse; 0-88449),* 2300 Knoll Dr., Ventura, CA 93003 (SAN 282-5155) Tel 805-644-9721; Orders to: Gospel Light Publications, P.O. Box 6309, Oxnard, CA 93031 (SAN 282-5163).

Vision Pubns., *(Vision Pubns; 0-912063),* P.O. Box 8555, St. Louis, MO 63126 (SAN 289-0267) Tel 314-962-7600; 951 Briarton, Crestwood, MO 63126 (SAN 289-0275).

Vision Ventures, Inc., Div. of Vision Services-An Agency for the Visually Impaired, *(Vision Ventures; 0-9616958),* 1401 Madison St., Suite 284, Seattle, WA 98104 (SAN 661-8049) Tel 206-386-6666.

Visionaide Pr., *(Visionaide Pr; 0-9612134),* 3 White Oak Rd., Roseland, NJ 07068 (SAN 286-8881) Tel 201-226-0958.

Visionary Publishing, Inc., *(Visionary Pub; 0-937223),* P.O. Box 2440, San Anselmo, CA 94960 (SAN 658-7178) Tel 415-461-4784; 500 V. F. Vista Grande, Greenbrae, CA 94904 (SAN 658-7186).

Visions for Success, Inc., *(Visions Success; 0-9616406),* P.O. Box 1616, Richmond, VA 23214 (SAN 659-1027) Tel 804-740-9178; 1223A Gaskins Rd., Richmond, VA 23214 (SAN 659-1035).

Vismar Publishing Co., *(Vismar; 0-9602206),* P.O. Box 29034, Parma, OH 44129 (SAN 212-3932).

Vista Pubns., *(Vista Pubns; 0-930938),* 1108 McAdams Ave., Dallas, TX 75224 (SAN 211-2817). Do Not Confuse with Vista Pubns. in California.

Vistara Pubns., *(Vistara Pubns; 0-930551; 0-935384),* P.O. Box 30577, Phoenix, AZ 85032 (SAN 677-4180).

Visual Attraction, *(Visual Attraction; 0-9617201),* 114 Holly Way, Pismo Beach, CA 93449 (SAN 663-267X) Tel 805-546-8836.

Visual Communication Books *See* **Hastings Hse. Pubs.**

Visual Communications, Inc., *(Visual Comm; 0-9615759),* 1518 Fifth Ave. Suite 305, Moline, IL 61265 (SAN 695-8095) Tel 309-762-9076; Orders to: Peoria Historical Society, 942 NE, Glen Oak Ave., Peoria, IL 61603 (SAN 662-3573) Tel 309-674-1921.

Visual Education Assn., Div. of Graphic Paper Products Corp., *(Visual Educ Assn; 1-55637),* P.O. Box 1666, Springfield, OH 45501 (SAN 660-9775); Toll free: 800-543-5947; 581 W. Leffel Ln., Springfield, OH 45501 (SAN 660-9783); Dist. by: Southern California Bk. Co., 2219 S. Union Ave., Los Angeles, CA 90007 (SAN 168-9827); Dist. by: Marshall/Mangold, 4805 Nelson Ave., Baltimore, MD 21215 (SAN 169-3115).

Visual Evangels Publishing Co., *(Visual Evangels; 0-915398),* 1401 Ohio St., Michigan City, IN 46360 (SAN 212-002X) Tel 219-874-3902.

Visual Impact Pubs., Communicators, *(Visual Impact; 0-913426),* 723 S. Wells St., Chicago, IL 60607 (SAN 206-8591) Tel 312-922-2083.

Visual Purple, *(Visual Purple; 0-917198),* Box 996, Berkeley, CA 94701 (SAN 208-9114); Dist. by: Bookpeople, 2929 Fifth St., Berkeley, CA 94710 (SAN 168-9517) Tel 415-549-3030.

Visual Resources Assn., *(Visual Resources Assn; 0-938852),* 20 W. 31st Ave., Eugene, OR 97405-3326 (SAN 215-9686) Tel 503-686-3052; Orders to: Visual Resources Assn., Christina Updike, Treas., c/o James Madison Univ., Art Dept., Harrisonburg, VA 22807 (SAN 662-0817).

†**Visual Studies Workshop,** *(Visual Studies; 0-89822),* 31 Prince St., Rochester, NY 14607 (SAN 218-1606); CIP.

Visually Handicapped Inspiration Library, *(Brians Pub; 0-9608650; 0-914009; 1-55677),* 8010 Petaluma Hill Rd., Penngrove, CA 94951 (SAN 213-3679) Tel 707-795-4875.

Vita Pr., *(Vita Pr TN),* 2143 Poplar Ave., Memphis, TN 38104 (SAN 214-4840) Tel 901-725-4072.

Vita-Sign, Subs. of Copy Write, *(Vita Sign; 0-939389),* 3412 Dodge St., Omaha, NE 68131 (SAN 663-1274) Tel 402-341-1647.

Vital Pr., *(Vital Pr; 0-915660),* Box 38341, Sacramento, CA 95838 (SAN 213-1846).

Vitality Assocs., *(Vitality Assocs; 0-930918),* P.O. Box 2154, Saratoga, CA 95070 (SAN 211-2809); 14600 Wild Oak Way, Saratoga, CA 95070 (SAN 669-294X) Tel 408-867-1241.

Vitality House International, Inc., *(Vitality Hse Int Inc; 0-912547),* 3707 N. Canyon Rd.,No. 8C, Provo, UT 84604-4568 (SAN 265-2935) Tel 801-224-9214.

Vitriol Pubns., *(Vitriol Pubns; 0-930635),* 110 E. 23rd St., Suite 801, New York, NY 10010 (SAN 676-3200) Tel 212-254-4538.

Viv-Poo, *(Viv-Poo; 0-9611952),* P.O. Box 32327, Washington, DC 20007 (SAN 286-0791) Tel 703-524-0627.

Vivekananda Vedanta Society, *(Vivekananda; 0-9600826),* 5423 S. Hyde Park Blvd., Chicago, IL 60615 (SAN 222-190X).

Voc-Offers, *(Voc-Offers; 0-918995),* P.O. Box 4273, Hayward, CA 94540 (SAN 669-8247) Tel 408-255-6579.

Vocal Power, Div. of Voice Works Institude., *(Vocal Power; 0-934419),* 17200 Burbank Blvd., Encino, CA 91316 (SAN 693-4471) Tel 818-994-1060; Dist. by: Cherry Lane Bks., P.O. Box 430, Port Chester, NY 10573-0430 (SAN 219-0788).

Vocational & Career Assessment, *(Voc Career Assess; 0-940150),* P.O. Box 1566, Lakeside, CA 92040 (SAN 220-3111) Tel 619-561-2092.

Vocational Industrial Clubs of America, Inc., *(Voc Indus Clubs; 0-933263),* P.O. Box 3000, Leesburg, VA 22075 (SAN 225-8137) Tel 703-777-8810.

Vocational Publishing, *(Voc Pub; 0-934635),* 10620 Fillmore St., Blaine, MN 55434 (SAN 693-9317) Tel 612-784-1846.

Vogt, Helen, *(H Vogt; 0-9602542),* 121 Blaine Ave., Brownsville, PA 15417 (SAN 212-579X) Tel 412-785-3804.

Voice of Liberty Pubns., *(Voice of Liberty; 0-934762),* 3 Borger Place, Pearl River, NY 10965 (SAN 213-568X) Tel 914-735-8140.

Voigt, Tracy, *(T Voigt),* P.O. Box 76382, Los Angeles, CA 90076 (SAN 239-5746).

Voland, Gerard A., *(G A Voland; 0-9615603),* 522 Callet St., Palmdale, CA 93550 (SAN 696-2556) Tel 805-947-2781.

Volaphon Bks., Div. of Woodbine Press, *(Volaphon Bks; 0-916258),* 73 Fox Ridge Crescent, Warwick, RI 02886 (SAN 208-0559) Tel 401-738-2638.

Volare Books, *(Volare Bks; 0-915243),* 781 S. Stillwater Lane, Anaheim, CA 92807 (SAN 289-8845) Tel 714-998-7901.

Volcanda Educational Pubns., *(Volcanda Educ),* 211 Deerfoot Rd., DeLand, FL 32720 (SAN 211-3368).

Volcano Press, Incorporated, *(Volcano Pr; 0-912078),* 330 Ellis St., San Francisco, CA 94102 (SAN 220-0015) Tel 415-664-5600.

Voldstad Enterprise, *(Voldstad Ent; 0-9603906),* 688 S. Hobart Blvd., Los Angeles, CA 90005 (SAN 209-0791).

Volin, Stan, *(S Volin; 0-9600922),* 19 Steven St., Plainview, NY 11803 (SAN 207-7469) Tel 516-681-6040; Orders to: Box 571-B, Hicksville, NY 11802 (SAN 207-7477).

Volunteer Council of the Tulsa Philharmonic Society, Inc., *(Volunteer Council; 0-9617004),* 8177 S. Harvard, Suite 431, Tulsa, OK 74137 (SAN 662-5479) Tel 918-663-2226.

Volunteer Lawyers for the Arts, *(Vol Lawyers Arts; 0-917103),* 1285 Ave. of the Americas, 3rd Flr., New York, NY 10019 (SAN 227-0617) Tel 212-575-1150.

Volunteer Management Assocs., *(Volunteer Mgmt; 0-9603362),* 279 S. Cedar Brook Rd., Boulder, CO 80302 (SAN 221-6914).

Volunteer Pubns., *(Volunteer Pubns; 0-938310),* P.O. Box 240786, Memphis, TN 38124-0786 (SAN 215-9287) Tel 901-685-9577.

Volunteer The National Center, *(VTNC Arlington; 0-939239),* 1111 N. 19th St., Suite 500, Arlington, VA 22209 (SAN 276-5330) Tel 703-276-0542.

Volunteers in Technical Assistance, *(Vols Tech Asst; 0-86619),* 1815 N. Lynn St., Suite 200, Arlington, VA 22209 (SAN 225-6711) Tel 703-276-1800.

Volute Books *See* Naiad Pr.

Von-Bogckmann Jones, Printers, *(Von-Bogckmann),* Austin, TX 78742 (SAN 262-1061).

Von Gehr Pr., The, *(Von Gehr; 0-9601470),* P.O. Box 7654, Menlo Park, CA 94026 (SAN 211-3376) Tel 415-342-2631.

Von Palisaden Publications, Incorporated, *(Von Palisaden Pubns; 0-932375),* 195 Spring Valley Rd., Paramus, NJ 07652 (SAN 687-3812) Tel 201-262-4919.

Vongrutnorv Og Press, *(Vongrutnorv Og; 0-9603504),* Randall Flat Rd. P.O. Box 411, Troy, ID 83871 (SAN 211-7169) Tel 208-835-4902.

Voter Education Project, *(Voter Ed Proj),* 52 Fairlie St. NW, Atlanta, GA 30303 (SAN 235-8336).

Voters Service Education Fund of the League of Women Voters of the Cincinnati Area, The, *(Voters Serv Educ; 0-9608724),* 103 Wm. Howard Taft Rd., Cincinnati, OH 45219 (SAN 238-4108) Tel 513-281-8683.

Voyager Bks. *See* Harcourt Brace Jovanovich, Inc.

Voyager Pubns., Inc., *(Voyager Pubns; 0-9603020),* 2604 First National Bank Tower, Atlanta, GA 30303 (SAN 213-1854) Tel 404-658-1228; Orders to: P.O. Box 229, Lansing, NY 14882 (SAN 213-1862) Tel 607-257-1648.

Voyager Publishing Hse., *(Voyager Pub Hse; 0-9616751),* 23131 State Rte. 2, Monroe, WA 98272 (SAN 659-9419) Tel 206-794-7453.

Voyager Publishing, Inc., *(Voyager Pub FL; 0-938161),* 1950 Lee Rd., Suite 223, Winter Park, FL 32789 (SAN 659-9036) Tel 305-740-8348.

Voyageur Pr., Inc., *(Voyageur Pr Inc; 0-89658),* 7225 Wash Ave., Edina, MN 55435 (SAN 287-2668).

Voyaging Pr., *(Voyaging Pr; 0-910711),* 669 N. 400 W., West Lafayette, IN 47906 (SAN 260-275X) Tel 317-743-2042.

Vu-Point Pubs., *(Vu-Point Pubs; 0-9614557),* P.O. Box 3006, West Chester, PA 19381 (SAN 691-8158) Tel 215-696-8461.

Vulcan Bks., Inc., *(Vulcan Bks; 0-914350),* 12722 Lake City Way, NE, Seattle, WA 98125 (SAN 203-1728) Tel 206-362-2606; Orders to: P.O. Box 25616, Seattle, WA 98125 (SAN 203-1736).

VUV Associates, *(VUV Assocs),* 1600 Regency Dr., Lincoln, NE 68506 (SAN 282-583X).

Vydex Management Group, Inc., *(Vydex Mgmt; 0-935663),* 125 Worth Ave., Suite 112, Palm Beach, FL 33480 (SAN 695-8400) Tel 305-659-3288.

W&M Press, *(W & M Pr; 0-942240),* 6301 Colby, Des Moines, IA 50311 (SAN 241-5925) Tel 515-277-4354.

W & W Publishers, *(W & W Pubs; 0-9614026),* P.O. Box 905, Fort Valley, GA 31030 (SAN 683-616X) Tel 912-825-5850.

WB&A Pubns., Div. of William Bloomfield & Associates, Inc., *(WB&A Pubns; 0-942834),* 456 Pond St., Boston, MA 02130 (SAN 240-298X) Tel 617-524-3938.

W B T *See* Washington Book Trading Co.

WCF Pubns., *(WCF Pubns; 0-9615904),* Box 568, Waterloo, IA 50704 (SAN 696-7833) Tel 319-233-1267.

WCP Pubns., *(WCP Pubns; 0-937365),* 9528 Miramar Rd., Suite 106, San Diego, CA 92126 (SAN 659-1043) Tel 619-271-9445; 8767 Covina St., San Diego, CA 92126 (SAN 659-1051).

WD Pr., *(WD Pr; 0-9614272),* P.O. Box 24115, St. Louis, MO 63130 (SAN 687-4142) Tel 314-727-8554.

WELS Board for Parish Education, *(WELS Board; 0-938272),* 2929 N. Mayfair Rd., Milwaukee, WI 53222 (SAN 216-3160) Tel 414-771-9357.

WFI Publishing Co., Div. of WFI Corporation, *(WFI Pub Co; 0-933560),* 2049 Century Park E., Suite 3330, Los Angeles, CA 90067 (SAN 212-9817) Tel 213-553-8700.

WFMT, Inc., Affil. of Chicago Magazine, *(W F M T Inc; 0-9613952),* 303 E. Wacker Dr., Chicago, IL 60601 (SAN 682-1642) Tel 312-565-5139; Dist. by: Charles Levy Circ. Co., 1200 N. Branch, Chicago, IL 60622 (SAN 159-835X) Tel 312-440-4400.

W.G.M. Publishing Co., *(W G M Pub; 0-934439),* P.O. Box 312, Maplewood, NJ 07040 (SAN 694-5295) Tel 201-761-6667.

WICC Books, Inc., Div. of Worth Intl Communications Corp., *(WICC Bks; 0-918878),* P.O. Box 69-3780, Miami, FL 33169 (SAN 210-5292) Tel 305-653-0123.

WIM, *(WIM Oakland; 0-938842),* 6000 Contra Costa Rd., Oakland, CA 94618 (SAN 216-2059) Tel 415-547-0193.

WIM Pubns., *(WIM Pubns; 0-934172),* 2215-R Market St., Box 15, San Franscisco, CA 94114 (SAN 282-5198) Tel 415-776-0470.

WPL Assocs., Inc., Affil. of Construction Industry Press, *(WPL Assocs; 0-9605442),* 1105-G Spring St., Silver Spring, MD 20910 (SAN 662-4375) Tel 301-589-8588.

WPS Publishing Co., *(W P S Pub Co; 0-935841),* 7655 Redfield, Suite 5, Scottsdale, AZ 85260 (SAN 696-6438) Tel 602-951-4001.

WRITE, *(W R I T E; 0-915441),* 160 S. Springer Rd., Los Altos, CA 94022 (SAN 276-8623) Tel 415-964-8923; Orders to: Roberta Speer, 4665 Shady Ln., Colorado Springs, CO 80908 (SAN 662-1929) Tel 303-495-3875.

WRK Productions, Subs. of Sutherland Productions, Inc., *(WRK Prods; 0-939579),* P.O. Box 7127, Eugene, OR 97401 (SAN 663-4826); 2175 Debra Dr., Springfield, OR 97477 (SAN 663-4834) Tel 503-343-3771.

WWF Bks., Div. of Titan Sports, Inc., *(WWF Bks; 0-9616263),* P.O. Box 4520, Greenwich, CT 06830 (SAN 658-3687); 81 Holly Hill Ln., Greenwich, CT 06830 (SAN 658-3695) Tel 203-869-4100.

WWH Press, *(WWH Pr; 0-939240),* 41 Hampton Rd., Scarsdale, NY 10583 (SAN 216-5163) Tel 914-725-3632.

WWW Pubs., *(WWW Pubs; 0-9613654),* 4501 Camino Del Obispo, Tucson, AZ 85718 (SAN 670-7815) Tel 602-299-6105; P.O. Box 42224, Tucson, AZ 85733 (SAN 670-7823).

WWWWW Information Services, *(WWWWW Info Serv; 0-912688),* P.O. Box 10046, Rochester, NY 14610 (SAN 203-2783) Tel 716-482-2022.

Names

W.A. Fisher Co., *(Fisher Co; 0-933287),* 123 Chestnut St., Virginia, MN 55792 (SAN 692-3518) Tel 218-741-9544.

Waconia Heritage Assn., *(Waconia Heritage; 0-9615181),* 119 Cherry St., Waconia, MN 55387 (SAN 694-3500) Tel 612-442-4234; Orders to: P.O. Box 241, Waconia, MN 55387 (SAN 662-3379) Tel 612-442-4234.

Waddell, Ward, Jr., *(Waddell; 0-9600130),* 495 San Fernando St., San Diego, CA 92106 (SAN 205-4973).

Wade Books, *(Wade Bks)* P.O. Box 847, Kentfield, CA 94914 (SAN 241-5933).

†Wadley Institutes of Molecular Medicine, *(Wadley Inst Molecular Med; 0-935994),* 9000 Harry Hines, Dallas, TX 75235 (SAN 213-8794); CIP.

Wadsworth Atheneum, *(Wadsworth Atheneum; 0-918333),* 600 Main St., Hartford, CT 06103 (SAN 205-4981) Tel 203-278-2670.

Wadsworth Publishing Co., Subs. of International Thomson Organization, Ltd., *(Wadsworth Pub; 0-534; 0-927794; 0-7150),* 10 Davis Dr., Belmont, CA 94002 (SAN 200-2213) Tel 415-595-2350; Toll free: 800-831-6996. *Imprints:* Continuing Education Division (Continuing Ed).

Wag On The Wall, *(Wag On Wall; 0-9609628),* 2005 Valle Vista, National City, CA 92050 (SAN 262-4419).

Wagapaw Pr., The, *(Wagapaw Pr; 0-918999),* P.O. Box 1381, San Luis Obispo, CA 93406 (SAN 669-7968) Tel 805-544-5339.

Waggoner Centennial '86 Committee, *(Waggoner Cent; 0-9616552),* Box 46, Waggoner, IL 62572 (SAN 659-5456) Tel 217-227-3321; 251 E. Main St., Waggoner, IL 62572 (SAN 659-5464).

Wagner, D. M., Enterprises, *(D M Wagner; 0-937053),* P.O. Box 559, Alva, OK 73717 (SAN 658-6716) Tel 405-327-1883; 318 College Ave., Alva, OK 73717 (SAN 658-6724).

Wagner, Eileen Elizabeth, *(E E Wagner; 0-9613484),* 1025 W. Hazelhurst St., Ferndale, MI 48220 (SAN 657-3371) Tel 313-542-1025; P.O. Box 20087, Ferndale, MI 48220 (SAN 663-3072).

Wagon & Star Pubs., *(Wagon & Star),* 4032 W. Century Blvd., Inglewood, CA 90304 (SAN 202-9421).

Wahr, George, Publishing Co., *(Wahr; 0-911586),* 304 1/2 S. State St., Ann Arbor, MI 48104 (SAN 205-5015) Tel 313-668-6097.

Wainwright, *(Wainwright; 0-934553),* c/o Ostrics, P.O. Box 11309, West Park, OH 44111 (SAN 693-8310).

Wait, N. S., *(N S Wait; 0-911588),* Box 407, Valparaiso, IN 46384 (SAN 206-6491). Formerly H. H. Wait Pub.

Waite, Benjamin & Martha, Press, Ltd., *(B & M Waite Pr; 0-934528),* 1126 E. 59th St., Chicago, IL 60637 (SAN 213-3989).

Wake, Harry S., *(H S Wake; 0-9607048),* 4171 Stettler Way, San Diego, CA 92122 (SAN 293-4302) Tel 619-455-1370; Dist. by: Metropolitan Music Co., Mountain Rd., Stowe, VT 05672 (SAN 293-4310); Dist. by: International Violin Co., 4026 W. Belvedere Ave., Baltimore, MD 21215 (SAN 293-4329); Dist. by: International Luthier Supply, Inc., P.O. Box 15444, Tulsa, OK 74112 (SAN 293-4337); Dist. by: Vitali Import Co., P.O. Box 249, Maywood, CA 90270 (SAN 293-4345); Dist. by: Howard Core & Co., Rte. No. 1 "The Cedars", Munford, AL 36268 (SAN 293-4353); Dist. by: Buck Musical Instruments Products, 40 Sand Rd., New Britain, PA 18901 (SAN 293-4361); Dist. by: Luthier's Mercantile, 412 Moore Lane, Healdsburg, CA 95448 (SAN 293-437X); Dist. by: Elderly Instruments, 1100 N. Washington, Lansing, MI 48906 (SAN 293-4388).

Wake-Brook Hse., *(Wake-Brook; 0-87482),* 990 NW 53rd St., Ft. Lauderdale, FL 33309 (SAN 205-5023) Tel 305-776-5884; P.O. Box 153, Hyannis, MA 02601 (SAN 694-4744) Tel 617-775-5860.

Wake Forest Univ., *(U Wake Forest; 0-918401),* 7227 Reynolda Sta., Winston-Salem, NC 27109 (SAN 657-3908) Tel 919-761-5769.

Wake Forest Univ. Pr., *(Wake Forest; 0-916390),* Box 7333, Winston-Salem, NC 27109 (SAN 658-2206) Tel 919-761-5448; Dist. by: Univ. of North Carolina Pr., Box 2288, Chapel Hill, NC 27514 (SAN 203-3151) Tel 919-966-3561.

Wake Forest Univ., Schl. of Law, Continuing Legal Education, *(Wake Forest Law),* P.O. Box 7206, Reynolda Sta., Winston-Salem, NC 27109 (SAN 237-9074) Tel 919-761-5560.

Wakestone Bks., *(Wakestone Bks; 0-9613859),* 405 Clifton Heights, Newport, TN 37821 (SAN 683-2199) Tel 615-623-7394.

Walch, J. Weston, Pub., *(J W Walch; 0-8251),* P.O. Box 658, Portland, ME 04104 (SAN 669-6562) Tel 207-772-2846; Toll free: 800-341-6094.

†Walck, Henry Z., Inc., Div. of David McKay Co. Inc., *(Walck; 0-8098),* 2 Park Ave., New York, NY 10016 (SAN 285-1121) Tel 212-340-9800; Toll free: 800-327-4801 (Orders); CIP.

Walden Press, *(Walden Pr; 0-911938),* 423 S. Franklin Ave., Flint, MI 48503 (SAN 205-5031).

†Waldman Hse. Pr., *(Waldman Hse Pr; 0-931674),* 525 N. Third St., Minneapolis, MN 55401 (SAN 295-0243); Dist. by: Bookmen, Inc., 525 N. Third St., Minneapolis, MN 55401 (SAN 169-409X); CIP.

Waldo Bruce Pubs., *(Waldo Bruce Pubns; 0-9607338),* P.O. Box 140906, Dallas, TX 75214 (SAN 239-3409) Tel 214-368-2614.

Waldos Pr., *(Waldos Pr; 0-9613882),* 309 North 36th 12A, Seattle, WA 98103 (SAN 682-6350).

Waldron, A. James, Enterprises, *(Waldron; 0-911590),* 371 Kings Hwy., W., Haddonfield, NJ 08033 (SAN 205-504X) Tel 609-428-3742.

Walker, David, Pr., Inc., *(D Walker Pr; 0-912135),* P.O. Box 741, Brooklyn, NY 11207 (SAN 264-8075) Tel 718-788-2044; 670 Carroll St., Brooklyn, NY 11215 (SAN 264-8083).

Walker, Frank R., Co., *(F R Walker; 0-911592),* 5030 N. Harlem Ave., Chicago, IL 60656 (SAN 206-4022) Tel 312-867-7070; Toll free: 800-631-7795.

Walker, Rebecca J., *(R J Walker; 0-9612284),* P.O. Box 5892, Austin, TX 78763 (SAN 289-5250) Tel 512-443-7950; Dist. by: Wimmer Brothers Books, BF Goodrich Blvd., Memphis, TN 38118 (SAN 209-6544) Tel 901-362-8900.

Walker & Co., Div. of Walker Publishing Co., Inc., *(Walker & Co; 0-8027),* 720 Fifth Ave., New York, NY 10019 (SAN 202-5213) Tel 212-265-3632.

Walker Educational Bk. Corp., Affil. of Walker & Co., *(Walker Educ; 0-8027),* 720 Fifth Ave., New York, NY 10019 (SAN 206-1899) Tel 212-265-3632.

Walker, Evans & Cogswell Co., *(Walker Evans & Cogswell),* 5300 Rivers Ave., North Charleston, SC 29405 (SAN 265-4121) Tel 803-747-8761.

Walkers Manual, Inc., *(Walkers Manual; 0-916234),* C/O National Standards Assn., Inc., 5161 River Rd., Bethesda, MD 20816 (SAN 211-2833).

Walking Bird Publishing, *(Walking Bird OR; 0-9615387),* 340 N. Grand St., Eugene, OR 97402 (SAN 695-4642) Tel 503-485-6312.

Walking News, Inc., *(Walking News Inc; 0-915850),* P.O. Box 352 - Canal St. Sta., New York, NY 10013 (SAN 239-5436) Tel 212-925-2632.

Wall, R. A. Investments, Inc., *(R A Wall; 0-916522),* 9465 Wilshire Blvd., Suite 525, Beverly Hills, CA 90212 (SAN 208-032X).

Wallaby *See* Pocket Bks., Inc.

Wallace-Homestead Bk. Co., Subs. of Capital Cities/ABC, Inc., *(Wallace-Homestead; 0-87069),* 580 WatersEdge Rd., Lombard, IL 60148 (SAN 205-5058) Tel 312-953-1100; Toll free: 800-323-2596.

Wallace Publishing, *(Wallace Pub; 0-9606804),* 2307 Shoreland Ave., Toledo, OH 43611 (SAN 217-4529) Tel 419-729-9065.

Wallcur, Inc., *(Wallcur Inc; 0-918082),* 3287 F St., Suite G, San Diego, CA 92102 (SAN 209-3642) Tel 619-233-9628.

Wallingford Pr., *(Wallingford NJ; 0-930988),* 500 Grand Ave., Englewood, NJ 07631 (SAN 211-3821) Tel 201-568-5111.

Wallis, Joe, *(J Wallis; 0-9605950),* P.O. Box 2294, Washington, DC 20013 (SAN 216-4752).

Walloon Press, *(Walloon Pr),* 4260 Ridgecrest Dr., El Paso, TX 79902 (SAN 207-5539) Tel 915-533-3166.

Walmyr Publishing Co., *(Walmyr; 0-942390),* P.O. Box 3554, Leon Sta., Tallahassee, FL 32303 (SAN 238-1249) Tel 904-386-5796.

†Walnut Pr., *(Walnut AZ; 0-931318),* 12010 Hillcrest Dr., Sun City, AZ 85351 (SAN 285-113X) Tel 602-972-5814; Orders to: LTO Enterprises, 6036 N. 10th Way, Phoenix, AZ 85014 (SAN 662-1805) Tel 602-265-7765; CIP.

†Walnut Pr., *(Walnut Pr),* Tully, NY 13159 (SAN 207-9992) Tel 607-842-6668; CIP.

Walrus Pr., *(Walrus Pr; 0-932033),* 73 Pine St., Haworth, NJ 07641 (SAN 686-0796) Tel 201-385-0364.

Walsh, Patrick, Pr., *(P Walsh Pr; 0-86700),* 2017 S. Ventura, Tempe, AZ 85282 (SAN 216-6135) Tel 602-968-1549. *Imprints:* Synergy Books (Synergy Bks).

Walsh Publishing Hse., *(Walsh Pub Hse; 0-9610254),* P.O. Box 120, Kew Gardens, NY 11415 (SAN 264-4789) Tel 718-544-8692.

Walsworth Publishing Co., Inc., *(Walsworth's),* Marceline, MO 64658 (SAN 295-0251).

Walter, Russ, Pub., *(R Walter; 0-939151),* 22 Ashland St., Somerville, MA 02144 (SAN 662-8206) Tel 617-666-2666.

Walter & Colleen Spivey, *(Walter & Colleen; 0-87418),* Rte. 2, Box 58, New Market, VA 22844 (SAN 693-4293); Dist. by: Coleman Publishing, Inc., 99 Milbar Blvd., Farmingdale, NY 11735 (SAN 238-1508) Tel 516-293-0383.

Walterick Pubs., Inc., *(Walterick Pubs; 0-937396),* Box 2216, Kansas City, KS 66110-0216 (SAN 211-9366) Tel 913-371-3273; Toll free: 800-255-4097.

Walters Art Gallery, *(Walters Art; 0-911886),* 600 N. Charles St., Baltimore, MD 21201 (SAN 202-9448) Tel 301-547-9000.

Walters Publishing Co., *(Walters Pub; 0-940412),* 90 Abbotsford Rd., Brookline, MA 02146 (SAN 211-1136).

Walther, Lou, *(Walther; 0-9612672),* 210 W. Sixth Ave., Broomfield, CO 80020 (SAN 289-4580) Tel 303-466-7757.

Walthers, William K., Inc., *(W K Walthers; 0-941952),* 5601 W. Florist Ave., P.O. Box 18676, Milwaukee, WI 53218 (SAN 238-4868) Tel 414-527-0770; Toll free: 800-558-5478.

Waltman & Buckner Pubs. Inc, *(Waltman & Buckner Pub; 0-934191),* 3651 Lancaster, P.O. Box 41478, Plymouth, MN 55441 (SAN 693-4390) Tel 612-544-1762.

Wampeter Pr., *(Wampeter Pr; 0-931694),* P.O. Box 512, Green Harbor, MA 02041 (SAN 212-3231) Tel 305-296-4244.

Wampler, Joseph Carson, *(J Wampler; 0-935080),* Box 45, Berkeley, CA 94701 (SAN 206-1910).

†Wanderer Bks., Div. of Simon & Schuster, *(Wanderer Bks; 0-671),* 1230 Ave. of the Americas, New York, NY 10020 (SAN 212-5803) Tel 212-245-6400; Toll free: 800-223-2336; CIP.

Wanderer Pr., The, Subs. of The Wanderer Printing Co., *(Wanderer Pr; 0-915245),* 201 Ohio St., St. Paul, MN 55107-9984 (SAN 240-8961) Tel 612-224-5733.

Wandering You Pr., Subs. of Creative Resources, Inc., *(Wandering You Pr; 0-9617104),* P.O. Box 20, Lodi, NJ 07644-0020 (SAN 662-5142); 70 Outwater Ln., Garfield, NJ 07026 (SAN 662-5150) Tel 201-772-1052.

Wang, Joan Chi Chin, *(J C C Wang; 0-9617295),* 4328 Muscatel, Rosemead, CA 91770 (SAN 663-4605); Dist. by: Evergreen Publishing Co., 136 S. Atlantic Blvd., Monterey Park, CA 91754-2727 (SAN 662-9113) Tel 818-281-3622.

Want Publishing Co., *(Want Pub; 0-942008),* 1511 K St., NW, Washington, DC 20005 (SAN 238-7727) Tel 202-783-1887.

War Eagle Cooks, *(War Eagle Cooks; 0-9616521),* Rte. 6, P.O. Box 127A, Rogers, AR 72756 (SAN 659-6029) Tel 501-789-5343.

Ward, Baldwin H., Pubns., *(B H Ward Pubns; 0-913482),* 1364 N. McDowell Blvd., Petaluma, CA 94952 (SAN 203-025X) Tel 707-762-0737; 11 Davis Dr., Belmont, CA 94002 (SAN 695-4529).

Ward, H. M., Memorial Laboratory, Inc., *(H M Ward Lab; 0-9615506),* P.O. Box 207, Valley Home, CA 95384 (SAN 696-2939) Tel 209-847-2509; Lab Building, 13906 Valley Home Rd., Oakdale, CA 95801 (SAN 696-2947).

Ward, Marcia, *(M Ward; 0-9613444),* P.O. Box 96, Johnson City, NY 13790 (SAN 657-1050) Tel 607-729-1675.

Ward, S. Alexander, *(S A Ward; 0-939189),* 2801 NE 183rd St., No. 1416, North Miami Beach, FL 33160 (SAN 662-5282) Tel 305-935-5583.

Ward Pr., The, *(Ward Pr; 0-932142),* P.O. Box 1712, Rochester, NY 14603 (SAN 212-6281) Tel 716-467-8400.

Wards Communications, Inc., *(Wards Comm; 0-910589),* 28 W. Adams, Detroit, MI 48226 (SAN 206-3905) Tel 313-962-4433.

Ward's Natural Science Establishment, Inc., *(Ward's Natl Sci; 0-89873),* P.O. Box 92912, Rochester, NY 14692-9012 (SAN 658-8409) Tel 716-359-2502.

Warehouse Publishing Co., *(Warehouse Pub; 0-9616841),* 1456 E. Philadelphia St., No. 22, Ontario, CA 91761 (SAN 661-4604) Tel 714-947-3210.

Waring & Associates, *(Waring & Assocs; 0-912307),* 845 Heathermoor Lane, Perrysburg, OH 43551 (SAN 265-2978) Tel 419-874-6044.

Warman Publishing Co., Inc., *(Warman; 0-911594),* P.O. Box 1112, Willow Grove, PA 19090 (SAN 202-9464) Tel 215-657-1812; Dist. by: Kampmann & Co., 9 E. 40th St., New York, NY 10016 (SAN 202-5191) Tel 212-685-2928; Toll free: 800-526-7626.

Warne, Frederick, & Co., Inc., *(Warne; 0-7232),* 40 W. 23rd. St., New York, NY 10010 (SAN 212-9884) Tel 212-337-5200.

Warner, Elizabeth Hall, *(E H Warner; 0-9615972),* 51 Elm St., Milford, NH 03055 (SAN 697-3108) Tel 603-673-2233.

Warner, John W., Inc., Pubs., *(J W Warner; 0-938097),* 4800 Bayview Dr., Ft. Lauderdale, FL 33308 (SAN 659-7106) Tel 305-771-6881.

Warner Bks., Inc., Div. of Warner Communications, *(Warner Bks; 0-446),* 666 Fifth Ave., New York, NY 10103 (SAN 282-5368) Tel 212-484-2900; Toll free: 800-638-6460; Dist. by: Ballantine Bks., Inc., 201 E. 50th St., New York, NY 10022 (SAN 214-1183) Tel 212-751-2600.

†**Warner Pr. Pubs.,** *(Warner Pr; 0-87162),* 1200 E. Fifth St., Anderson, IN 46012 (SAN 202-9472) Tel 317-644-7721; Toll free: 800-428-6409; Orders to: P.O. Box 2499, Anderson, IN 46018 (SAN 691-4241); *CIP.*

Warrbek Video Productions, *(Warrbek Video; 0-937403),* Rte. 6, Box 806, Cleburne, TX 76031 (SAN 659-1086) Tel 817-645-6961.

Warren, M., Bks., *(Warren Bks; 0-9615183),* 707 Dixmyth Ave., Suite 212E, Cincinnati, OH 45220 (SAN 694-3535) Tel 513-559-1487.

Warren, M. E., *(M E Warren; 0-9606060),* P.O. Box 1508, Annapolis, MD 21404 (SAN 216-7670).

Warren Bk. Publishing Co., *(Warren Bk Pub; 0-938287),* P.O. Box 1376, Warren, MI 48090-1376 (SAN 659-8846) Tel 313-756-7886; 7515 Yacht St., Warren, MI 48091 (SAN 659-8854) Tel 313-756-7886.

†**Warren, Gorham & Lamont, Inc.,** Subs. of International Thomson Organisation, Ltd. (London), *(Warren; 0-88262; 0-88712),* 210 South St., Boston, MA 02111 (SAN 202-9480); Toll free: 800-922-0066; *CIP.*

Warren, McVeigh & Griffin, Inc., *(Warren Mac; 0-941360),* 1420 Bristol St. N., Suite 220, Newport Beach, CA 92660 (SAN 239-0566) Tel 714-752-1058.

Warren Publishing Co., *(Warren Pub; 0-9606004),* 2240 Galahad Dr., Indianapolis, IN 46208 (SAN 213-5698) Tel 317-253-2830.

Warren Publishing House, Incorporated, *(Warren Pub Hse; 0-911019),* P.O. Box 2255, Everett, WA 98203 (SAN 264-4800); 1004 Harborview Ln., Everett, WA 98203 (SAN 660-9465) Tel 206-252-3546; Dist. by: Gryphon House, Inc., P.O. Box 275, 3706 Otis St., Mt. Rainier, MD 20712 (SAN 169-3190) Tel 301-779-6200.

Warrior, Betsy, *(B Warrior; 0-9601544),* 46 Pleasant St., Cambridge, MA 02139 (SAN 210-993X)Box E-94, Earlham College, Richmond, IN 47374 (SAN 662-1813) Tel 317-962-6561.

Warrior Publishing, *(Warrior Pub WI; 0-9616735),* P.O. Box 637, Chippewa Falls, WI 54729 (SAN 659-8862); 1023 Gerald St., Chippewa Falls, WI 54729 (SAN 659-8870) Tel 715-723-9276.

Warrior Publishing, Inc., *(Warrior Pub; 0-9615507),* 1630 Welton St., Suite 300, Denver, CO 80202 (SAN 695-7951) Tel 303-589-8223.

Warthog Pr., *(Warthog Pr; 0-942292),* 29 South Valley Rd., West Orange, NJ 07052 (SAN 219-5399) Tel 201-731-9269.

Warwick Pr. See Watts, Franklin, Inc.

Wary Canary Pr., *(Wary Canary; 0-9616126),* P.O. Box 8820, Ft. Collins, CO 80525 (SAN 699-699X) Tel 303-223-8816; 2608 Avocet Rd., Ft. Collins, CO 80526 (SAN 699-7007).

Wasatch Education Systems, *(Wasatch Educ Syst; 0-938897),* 1214 Wilmington Ave., Suite 205, Salt Lake City, UT 84106 (SAN 661-6968); Toll free: 800-624-1732.

Wasatch Pubs., Inc., *(Wasatch Pubs; 0-915272),* 4647 Idlewild Rd., Salt Lake City, UT 84124-4726 (SAN 207-1576) Tel 801-278-3174.

Wash Launderan Pr., *(Wash Launderan; 0-9605326),* 5804 Ingersoll Ave., Des Moines, IA 50312 (SAN 215-9295) Tel 515-279-7774.

Washington, Eliza, *(E Washington; 0-939354),* 614 Wilshire Ave., Waterloo, ID 50701 (SAN 216-4957) Tel 319-234-1460.

Washington Book Trading Co., *(Wash Bk Trad; 0-915168),* P.O. Box 1676, Arlington, VA 22210 (SAN 216-7115) Tel 703-525-6873. *Imprints:* W B T (WBT).

Washington Business Information, Inc., *(Wash Busn Info; 0-914176),* 1117 N. 19th St., No. 200, Arlington, VA 22209-1798 (SAN 201-890X) Tel 703-247-3434.

Washington County Historical Society, *(WA County Hist; 0-9608434),* Box 456, Chatom, AL 36518 (SAN 240-8058).

Washington County Museum of Fine Arts, *(WA Museum Arts; 0-914495),* P.O. Box 423, Hagerstown, MD 21741 (SAN 281-0565) Tel 301-739-5727.

Washington Crossing Card Collectors Club, *(Wash Cross Card; 0-9610608),* P.O. Box 39, Washington Crossing, PA 18977 (SAN 264-7052) Tel 215-598-7534.

Washington Dolls' Hse. & Toy Museum, *(Wash Dolls Hse),* 5236 44th St., NW, Washington, DC 20015 (SAN 217-2747) Tel 202-363-6400.

Washington Emergency Squad, *(Wash Emerg Squad; 0-9604020),* 19 W. Washington Ave., Washington, NJ 07882 (SAN 221-6477).

Washington History Committee, *(Wash Hist Comm),* Box 75, Washington, NH 03280 (SAN 210-9670) Tel 603-495-3566.

Washington Independent Writers, *(Wash In Writers; 0-912521),* 205 Colorado Building, 1341 G Street NW, Washington, DC 20005 (SAN 265-2986) Tel 202-347-4973.

†**Washington International Arts Letter,** *(Wash Intl Arts; 0-912072),* 325 Pennsylvania Ave., SE, Washington, DC 20003 (SAN 205-5066) Tel 202-328-1900; Orders to: P.O. Box 15240, Washington, DC 20003 (SAN 205-5074); *CIP.*

Washington International Assocs., *(Wash Intl Assocs),* P.O. Box N, Accokeek, MD 20607 (SAN 663-0774).

Washington National Monument Assn., *(Wash Natl Monument),* 740 Jackson Pl. NW, Washington, DC 20506 (SAN 206-2925) Tel 202-842-0806.

Washington Office on Latin America, *(WOLA; 0-9613249),* 110 Maryland Ave. NE, Suite 40404, Washington, DC 20002 (SAN 225-6630) Tel 202-544-8045.

Washington Opera, The, *(Wash Opera; 0-9610542),* The Kennedy Center, Washington, DC 20566 (SAN 264-4835) Tel 202-337-5533; Orders to: The Washington Cookbook, P.O. Box 40897, Washington, DC 20016 (SAN 693-9791).

Washington Park Pr., *(Wash Park; 0-9605460),* 7 Englewood Pl., Albany, NY 12203 (SAN 215-9309) Tel 518-465-0169.

Washington Project for the Arts, *(Wash Proj Arts; 0-937237),* 400 Seventh St., NW, Washington, DC 20004 (SAN 658-6694) Tel 202-347-4813.

Washington Research Assocs., *(Wash Res Assocs; 0-937801),* 2103 N. Lincoln St., Arlington, VA 22207 (SAN 659-378X) Tel 703-276-8260.

Washington Researchers Publishing, Div. of Washington Researchers, Ltd., *(Wash Res Pubn; 0-934940),* 2612 P St. NW, Washington, DC 20007 (SAN 211-6286) Tel 202-333-3533.

†**Washington Sea Grant Program,** *(Wash Sea Grant; 0-934539),* c/o Univ. of Washington, 3716 Brooklyn Ave. NE, Seattle, WA 98105-6795 (SAN 693-7861) Tel 206-543-6600; Dist. by: Univ. of Washington Pr., P.O. Box C50096, Seattle, WA 98145 (SAN 212-2502) Tel 206-543-4050; *CIP.*

Washington Square Pr., Inc., Div. of Simon & Schuster, Inc., *(WSP; 0-671),* 1230 Ave. of the Americas, New York, NY 10020 (SAN 206-9784) Tel 212-246-2121; Toll free: 800-223-2336; Orders to: 200 Old Tappan Rd., Old Tappan, NJ 07675 (SAN 662-1821) Tel 201-767-5000. *Imprints:* A N T A Series of Distinguished Plays (ANTA); Collateral Classics Series (CC); Readers Enrichment Series (RE).

Washington State Bar Assn., *(Wash St Bar; 0-88129),* 505 Madison St., Seattle, WA 98104 (SAN 241-2365) Tel 206-622-6021.

Washington State Bar Association, Continuing Legal Education, *(Wash Bar CLE; 0-88129),* 505 Madison St., Seattle, WA 98104 (SAN 237-9155) Tel 206-622-6021.

Washington State Historical Society, *(Wash St Hist Soc; 0-917048),* 315 N. Stadium Way, Tacoma, WA 98403 (SAN 203-2155) Tel 206-593-2830; Dist. by: Pacific Northwest Books, P.O. Box 314, Medford, OR 97501 (SAN 200-5263) Tel 503-664-4442.

†**Washington State Univ. Pr.,** *(Wash St U Pr; 0-87422),* Publications Bldg., Rm. 40, Pullman, WA 99164-5910 (SAN 206-6688) Tel 509-335-3518; *CIP.*

Washington State Univ., Dept. of Veterinary Microbiology & Pathology, *(WA State U Vet; 0-936375),* Washington State Univ., Pullman, WA 99164-7040 (SAN 697-9912) Tel 509-335-6850.

Washington Trails Assn., *(Wash Trail Assn; 0-936289),* 16812 36th Ave. W., Lynnwood, WA 98036 (SAN 697-9955) Tel 206-743-3947.

Washington Univ., Gallery of Art, Div. of Washington University, *(Wash U Gallery; 0-936316),* Campus Box 1214, St. Louis, MO 63130 (SAN 214-4859) Tel 314-889-5490.

Washington University School of Law Library, *(Wash U Law Lib),* Campus Box 1120, St. Louis, MO 63130 (SAN 237-9171) Tel 314-889-6459.

Washington Univ. School of Medicine Library, *(Wash U Med Lib; 0-912260),* 4580 Scott Ave., St. Louis, MO 63110 (SAN 203-2163) Tel 314-362-2786.

Washington Writers Publishing House, *(Wash Writers Pub; 0-931846),* P.O. Box 50068, Washington, DC 20004 (SAN 211-9250) Tel 202-546-1020.

Washoe Pr., *(Washoe; 0-89376),* P.O. Box 91922, Los Angeles, CA 90009 (SAN 209-0694).

Washout Pub. Co., *(Washout; 0-918310),* P.O. Box 9252, Schenectady, NY 12309 (SAN 209-9128).

Water Information Center, Inc., Subs. of Geraghty & Miller, Inc., *(Water Info; 0-912394),* 125 Bethpage Rd., Planview, NY 11803 (SAN 202-9510) Tel 516-249-7634.

Water Lane Publishing Co., *(Water Lane Pub; 0-9614800),* P.O. Box 10321, Marina del Rey, CA 90295 (SAN 692-6886) Tel 213-257-5837.

Names

Water Mark Pr., *(Water Mark; 0-931956)*, 138 Duane St., New York, NY 10013 (SAN 212-5811) Tel 212-285-1609.

Water Pollution Control Federation, *(Water Pollution; 0-943244)*, 601 Wythe St., Alexandria, VA 22314-1994 (SAN 217-1406) Tel 202-337-2500; Toll free: 556 8700.

Water Resources Pubns., *(WRP; 0-918334)*, P.O. Box 2841, Littleton, CO 80161 (SAN 209-9136) Tel 303-790-1836.

Water Row Pr., Div. of Water Row Books, Inc., *(Water Row Pr; 0-934953)*, P.O. Box 438, Sudbury, MA 01776 (SAN 694-6011) Tel 617-443-8910.

Water Street Pubs., *(Water St Missouri; 0-9616799)*, 6125 Marwinette Ave., St. Louis, MO 63116 (SAN 661-0382) Tel 314-351-2427.

Watercress Pr., Subs. of Evett & Assocs., *(Watercress Pr; 0-934955)*, 111 Grotto, San Antonio, TX 78216 (SAN 694-4116) Tel 512-344-5338; Dist. by: Texas Publishers Association, 2315 Briarwood, San Antonio, TX 78029 (SAN 676-5947) Tel 512-828-1605.

Waterfall Pr., The, *(Waterfall LA; 0-930684)*, 916 Moss St., New Orleans, LA 70119 (SAN 697-1156) Tel 504-865-7040.

Waterford Pr., *(Waterford Pr; 0-9608706)*, P.O. Box 1176, Freehold, NJ 07728 (SAN 238-4124); 38-19 52nd St., Long Island City, NY 11104 (SAN 662-183X) Tel 718-639-6773; c/o Unicorn Music Co., Inc. The, 170 NE 33rd St., Ft. Lauderdale, FL 33334 (SAN 200-8297) Tel 305-563-1844.

Waterfront Bks., *(Waterfront Bks; 0-914525)*, 98 Brookes Ave., Burlington, VT 05401 (SAN 289-6923) Tel 802-658-7477; Dist. by: Bookpeople, 2929 Fifth St., Berkeley, CA 94710 (SAN 168-9517) Tel 415-549-3030; Toll free: 800-227-1516; Dist. by: DeVorss & Co., P.O. Box 550, Marina Del Rey, CA 90294 (SAN 168-9886) Tel 213-870-7478; Toll free: 800-241-3829; Dist. by: New Leaf Distributing Co., 1020 White St., SW, Atlanta, GA 30310 (SAN 169-1449) Tel 404-755-2665.

Waterfront Pr., *(Waterfront NJ; 0-943862)*, 52 Maple Ave., Maplewood, NJ 07040 (SAN 241-5941) Tel 201-762-1565.

Waterfront Press Co., *(Waterfront Pr; 0-937288)*, 1115 46th, N.W., Seattle, WA 98107 (SAN 215-191X).

Waterfront Pr., The, *(Waterfront DC; 0-935957)*, 1536 44th St. NW, Washington, DC 20007 (SAN 696-740X) Tel 202-337-0356.

Watermill Pubs., *(Watermill Pubs; 0-88370)*, 4 Crescent Dr., Albertson, NY 11507 (SAN 206-2941) Tel 516-484-2391.

Water's Edge Publishing Co., *(Waters Edge; 0-9615609)*, 2318 Alki Ave. SW, No. 8, Seattle, WA 98116 (SAN 695-8532) Tel 206-935-6912.

Waters Information Services, Inc., *(Waters Info; 0-916817)*, Suite 322 Security Mutual Bldg., Binghamton, NY 13901 (SAN 654-2646) Tel 607-770-1945.

Waters Publishing, *(Waters Pub; 0-930107)*, P.O. Box 442, Brevard, NC 28712 (SAN 670-2309) Tel 704-884-4495.

Waterside Press, *(Waterside; 0-936628)*, Box 1298, Stuyvesant Sta., New York, NY 10009 (SAN 214-4867).

Waterway Pr., *(Waterway Pr; 0-936689)*, Rte. 2, Box 145, Supply, NC 28462 (SAN 699-6736) Tel 919-842-2320; Stone Chimney Rd., Supply, NC 28462 (SAN 699-6744).

Watosh Publishing, *(Watosh Pub; 0-9611954)*, P.O. Box 11231, Las Vegas, NV 89111 (SAN 286-1976) Tel 702-361-3734.

Watson, Neale, Academic Pubns., *(Watson Pub Intl; 0-88202)*, P.O. Box 493, Canton, MA 02021 (SAN 689-8386) Tel 617-828-8450. *Imprints:* Prodist (Prodist); Science History Publications (Sci Hist).

Watson-Guptill Pubns., Inc., Div. of Billboard Pubns., Inc., *(Watson-Guptill; 0-8230; 0-8174; 0-87165)*, 1 Astor Plaza, 1515 Broadway, New York, NY 10036 (SAN 282-5384) Tel 212-764-7518; Toll free: 800-526-3641 (Orders & Customer Service); Orders to: 1695 Oak St., Lakewood, NJ 08701 (SAN 282-5392). *Imprints:* Art & Antique Books (Art & Antique); Billboard Books (Billboard Bks); Whitney Library (Whitney Lib).

Watson Publishing Hse., *(Watson Pub Hse; 0-939035)*, P.O. Box 32762, Oklahoma City, OK 73123 (SAN 662-9261); 7324 Crown Point Rd., Oklahoma City, OK 73132 (SAN 662-927X) Tel 405-722-3075.

Wattles, Gurdon H., Pubns., *(Wattles Pubns; 0-9606962)*, c/o J. F. Rems Assoc., 1442 Irvine Blvd., Suite 120, Tustin, CA 92680 (SAN 219-8347) Tel 714-832-5711; P.O. Box 5702, Orange, CA 92667 (SAN 694-9614).

Watts, Franklin, Inc., Subs. of Grolier, Inc., *(Watts; 0-531)*, Shermann Tpke., Danbury, CT 06816 (SAN 285-1156) Tel 212-686-7070; Toll free: 800-672-6672. *Imprints:* Business Travelers, Incorporated (Busn Travel); College Division (College Div); Fontana Paperbacks (Fontana Pap); Gloucester Press (Gloucester Pr); International Communications (Intl Communications); MacRae, Julia (MacRae); Warwick Press (Warwick).

Waukesha County Historical Society, *(Waukesha; 0-9613624)*, 101 W. Main St., Waukesha, WI 53186 (SAN 281-0700) Tel 414-548-7186.

Waumbek Books, *(Waumbek; 0-9603106)*, P.O. Box 573, Ashland, NH 03217 (SAN 213-5701) Tel 603-968-7959.

Waveland Pr., Inc., *(Waveland Pr; 0-917974; 0-88133)*, P.O. Box 400, Prospect Heights, IL 60070 (SAN 209-0961) Tel 312-634-0081.

Waverly Community Hse., Inc., *(Waverly Comm Hse; 0-9616433)*, Main St., Waverly, PA 18471 (SAN 659-1124) Tel 717-587-5811.

Waverly Pubs., *(Waverly Pub; 0-9615681)*, 235 West End Ave., New York, NY 10023 (SAN 695-8184) Tel 212-873-8571.

Way of Seeing, Inc., A, *(Way of Seeing)*, 2869 Grant Dr., Ann Arbor, MI 48104 (SAN 216-3152) Tel 313-973-7717.

Way Up, Firm & High Tail It Bright Out of Town Detective Agency Poetry Press, The, *(Way Up Firm; 0-933326)*, 2620 F St., No. 5, Sacramento, CA 95816 (SAN 212-5846). Moved, left no forwarding address.

Wayfarer Pubns., *(Wayfarer Pubns; 0-935099)*, P.O. Box 26156, Los Angeles, CA 90026 (SAN 695-054X) Tel 213-665-7773.

Wayfinder Pr., *(Wayfinder Pr; 0-9608764)*, Box 1877, Ouray, CO 81427 (SAN 241-0796) Tel 303-325-4150; Dist. by: Johnson Books, 1880 S. 57th Ct., Boulder, CO 80301 (SAN 658-1013) Tel 415-658-3453.

Wayland Pr., *(Wayland Pr; 0-933573)*, 2640 E. 12th Ave., Box 715, Denver, CO 80206 (SAN 691-9065) Tel 303-233-5453.

Waymark Bks. *See* Doubleday & Co., Inc.

Wayne-Omari Educational Game Co., *(Wayne Omari Ed Game; 0-9616325)*, 25 Eastern Pkwy., Brooklyn, NY 11238 (SAN 658-7909) Tel 718-638-1617.

Wayne State University, Bureau of Business Research, Schl. of Business Admin., *(WSU Bur Bus Res; 0-942650)*, Wayne State Univ., Schl of Business Admin., Prentis Bldg. 209, Detroit, MI 48202 (SAN 239-9512) Tel 313-577-4213.

Wayne State Univ. Pr., *(Wayne St U Pr; 0-8143)*, Leonard N. Simons Bldg., 5959 Woodward Ave., Detroit, MI 48202 (SAN 202-5221) Tel 313-577-4601. *Imprints:* Savoyard Books (Savoyard).

Waynor Publishing Co., *(Waynor; 0-917070)*, P.O. Box 699, Goshen, NH 03752 (SAN 208-9165) Tel 603-863-1364.

Weather Workbook Co., *(Weather Wkbk; 0-931778)*, 827 N.W. 31st St., Corvallis, OR 97330 (SAN 206-393X).

Weatherby, Thomas, Pub., *(T Weatherby)*, 115 Billings St., Sharon, MA 02067 (SAN 212-582X).

Weatherford, R.M., Press, *(Weatherford; 0-9604078)*, 10902 Woods Creek Rd., Monroe, WA 98272 (SAN 126-4206) Tel 206-794-4318.

†**Weatherhill, John, Inc.**, *(Weatherhill; 0-8348)*, 6 E. 39th St., New York, NY 10016 (SAN 202-9529) Tel 212-686-2857; Dist. by: Charles E. Tuttle, Co., Inc., 28 S. Main St., P.O. Box 410, Rutland, VT 05701-0410 (SAN 213-2621) Tel 802-773-8930; *CIP.*

Weatherly Pr., *(Weatherly Pr; 0-935727)*, 1840-130th Ave. NE, Suite 10, Bellevue, WA 98005 (SAN 695-8230) Tel 206-881-5212.

Weatherman, Hazel Marie, *(Weatherman; 0-913074)*, c/o Glassbooks, Inc., Rte. 1, Box 357A, Ozark, MO 65721 (SAN 237-9554) Tel 417-485-7812.

†**Weathervane Bks.**, *(Weathervane CA; 0-943246)*, P.O. Box 2157, Walnut Creek, CA 94595 (SAN 240-5040); *CIP.*

Weaver, Marilyn, *(M Weaver; 0-9615682)*, 715 21th Ave. N, Estherville, IA 51334 (SAN 696-2696) Tel 712-362-7002.

Weaver, Ruth C., *(R C Weaver; 0-9607168)*, RD 2 Box 218, Canonsburg, PA 15317 (SAN 239-1376) Tel 412-745-8907.

Webb, Helen, *(H Webb; 0-9615859)*, Rte. 1, Box 635, South Point, OH 45680 (SAN 698-1836).

Webb Country Kennel, Div. of Webb Country Farms, *(Webb Country)*, Rte. 2, Box 201, Mocksville, NC 27028 (SAN 663-6098) Tel 919-998-3908.

Webb-Newcomb Co., Inc., *(Webb-Newcomb; 0-935054)*, 308 N.E. Vance St., Wilson, NC 27893 (SAN 213-4004) Tel 919-291-7231.

Weber, John, Gallery, *(J Weber Gall; 0-9608288)*, 142 Greene St., New York, NY 10012 (SAN 240-4575).

Weber, Martin F., Co., Subs. of Martin Instrument Co., *(M F Weber Co; 0-917121)*, P.O. Box 16270, Philadelphia, PA 19114 (SAN 655-7627) Tel 215-677-5600.

Weber Oil Co., *(Weber Oil; 0-9616358)*, 700 Main St., Bangor, ME 04401 (SAN 659-1140) Tel 207-942-5501.

†**Weber Systems, Inc.**, *(Weber Systems; 0-938862)*, 8437 Mayfield Rd., No. 102, Chesterland, OH 44026 (SAN 240-8201) Tel 216-729-2858; Toll free: 800-851-6018; *CIP.*

Webfoot, Inc., *(Webfoot Inc; 0-9610358)*, Box 248, Wendell, NC 27591 (SAN 264-4851) Tel 919-365-5088.

Webster Publishing Co., *(Webster Pub Co FL; 0-930814)*, 2108 S. Crystal Lake Dr., Lakeland, FL 33801 (SAN 683-2326) Tel 813-665-1024.

Weckstein, Joyce R., *(J R Weckstein; 0-9600980)*, 28290 Tavistock Trail, Southfield, MI 48034 (SAN 208-9173) Tel 313-353-6221.

Wedge Publishing, *(Wedge Pub)*, c/o Radix Books, Inc., 11 Knickerbocker Ln., Orindand, CA 94563 (SAN 209-1364) Tel 415-254-3039.

†**Wedgestone Pr.**, *(Wedgestone Pr; 0-911459)*, P.O. Box 175, Winfield, KS 67156 (SAN 276-5888) Tel 316-221-2779; *CIP.*

Wee Smile Books, *(Wee Smile; 0-9605444)*, P.O. Box 1329, Sparks, NV 89431 (SAN 215-983X) Tel 702-356-0216.

Weed Science Society of America, *(Weed Sci Soc; 0-911733)*, 309 W. Clark St., Champaign, IL 61820 (SAN 276-5918).

Weedy Rail Bks. *See* David & Charles, Inc.

Weeg Computing Center, *(Weeg Comp; 0-937114)*, Univ. of Iowa, 120 LC, Iowa City, IA 52242 (SAN 215-2630).

Weeks Enterprises, *(Weeks Ent; 0-9615604)*, 9408 Thomas Rd., Bloomington, MN 55431 (SAN 695-8125) Tel 612-881-5145.

Weeks Pubs., *(Weeks Pubs; 0-9614492)*, P.O. Box 10282, Arlington, VA 22210 (SAN 689-4720) Tel 703-528-2304.

Wegeleben, Eilene, Enterprises, *(E Wegeleben; 0-9616861)*, P.O. Box 58154, Renton, WA 98058 (SAN 661-6054) Tel 206-255-7755.

Weger, William G., *(W G Weger; 0-9617058)*, P.O. Box 976, Ottumwa, IA 52501 (SAN 662-8400); 425 N. Green, Apt. 5, Ottumwa, IA 52501 (SAN 662-8419) Tel 515-683-3014.

Wegferd Pubns., *(Wegferd Pubns; 0-937861)*, 2021 Sherman Ave., North Bend, OR 97459 (SAN 659-6037) Tel 503-756-7401.

Wehawken Book Co., *(Wehawken Bk; 0-916386)*, 4221 45th St., NW, Washington, DC 20016 (SAN 207-5512) Tel 202-362-3185.

Names

Wehman Brothers, Inc., *(Wehman; 0-911604),* Ridgedale Ave., Morris County Mall, Cedar Knolls, NJ 07927 (SAN 206-779X) Tel 201-539-6300.

Wehmeyer Printing Co., *(Wehmeyer Print),* Ste. Genevieve, MO 63670 (SAN 239-5444).

Wei-Chuan's Cooking, *(Wei-Chuan's Cooking; 0-941676),* 1455 Monterey Pass Rd., No. 110B, Monterey Park, CA 91754 (SAN 239-5096) Tel 213-261-3880.

Weidenfeld & Nicolson, *(Weidenfeld; 1-55584),* 10 E. 53rd St., 14th Flr., New York, NY 10022 (SAN 658-4497) Tel 212-207-6900.

Weinberg, Alyce T., *(A T Weinberg; 0-9604552),* Box 16, Braddock Heights, MD 21714 (SAN 215-1928).

Weinberg, Michael Aron, *(Weinberg; 0-9601014),* P.O. Box 27957, Los Angeles, CA 90027 (SAN 208-2314) Tel 213-661-9844.

Weinberg Bks., *(Weinberg Bks; 0-907053),* P.O. Box 438, Sudbury, MA 01776 (SAN 695-5444).

Weinstock, Beatrice C., *(Weinstock; 0-9600568),* 1971 San Marco Blvd., Jacksonville, FL 32207 (SAN 205-5139) Tel 904-396-7597.

Weisberg, Harold, *(Weisberg; 0-911606),* 7627 Old Receiver Rd., Frederick, MD 21701 (SAN 205-5147) Tel 301-473-8186.

†**Weiser, Samuel, Inc.,** *(Weiser; 0-87728),* P.O. Box 612, York Beach, ME 03910 (SAN 202-9588) Tel 207-363-4393; Toll free: 800-843-6666; Toll free: 800-423-7087 orders; *CIP.*

Weiss, Martin D., Publishing, Div. of Martin D. Weiss Research, Inc., *(M D Weiss Pub; 0-9613048),* 5656 Corporate Way, West Palm Beach, FL 33407 (SAN 294-2925) Tel 305-684-8100.

Weiss, Sigmund, *(Weiss S & D),* 11 Lancaster Place, Stony Brook, NY 11790 (SAN 219-3035).

Weiss Publishing Co., Inc., *(Weiss Pub; 0-916720),* 5309 W. Grace St., Richmond, VA 23226 (SAN 208-4775) Tel 804-282-4641.

Weisser, Thomas, *(Tom Weisser; 0-9610710),* Box 53, Monmouth, OR 97361 (SAN 264-8105) Tel 503-838-6051.

Weist Publishing Co., The, *(Weist Pub OH; 0-938166),* P.O. Box 164, Englewood, OH 45322 (SAN 215-8256).

Welch, Julia Conway, *(J C Welch; 0-9615535),* 204 S. Florida, Caldwell, ID 83605 (SAN 695-9113) Tel 208-454-9125.

Welcome Pr., *(Welcome Pr; 0-916871),* 2701 Queen Anne Ave. N., Seattle, WA 98109 (SAN 654-5114) Tel 206-282-5336.

Welcome Publishing, *(Welcome Pub; 0-932849),* P.O. Box 549, Santa Ynez, CA 93460-0574 (SAN 691-2966) Tel 805-688-3574.

Welding Research Council, *(Welding Res Coun),* 345 E. 47th St., New York, NY 10017 (SAN 225-2562) Tel 212-705-7956.

Welding Specialist, *(Welding Spec; 0-9613213),* 3101 Ensign Ave.N, New Hope, MN 55427 (SAN 295-6659) Tel 612-545-7681.

Welkin Bks., *(Welkin Bks; 0-9614873),* 28 Watkins Ave., Oneonta, NY 13820 (SAN 693-2908) Tel 607-432-1915.

Well Aware About Health, *(Well Aware; 0-943562),* P.O. Box 43338, Tuscon, AZ 85733 (SAN 238-4140) Tel 602-297-2960.

Well-Made Products, *(Well-Made Prod),* 832 N.E. 104th, Seattle, WA 98125 (SAN 238-7719).

Wellbeing Bks., Tapes, Seminars, Div. of Open Marketing Group, *(Wellbeing Bks; 0-943450),* P.O. Box 396, 17 Omar Tr., Newtonville, MA 02160 (SAN 240-4680) Tel 617-332-7845.

Weller Institute for the Cure of Design, Inc., *(Weller Inst; 0-916873),* 2427 Park Oak Dr., Los Angeles, CA 90068 (SAN 654-5149) Tel 213-467-4576.

Wellesley-Cambridge Pr., *(Wellesley-Cambridge Pr; 0-9614088),* Rm. 2-240, Massachusetts Inst. of Technology, Cambridge, MA 02139 (SAN 686-0699) Tel 617-253-4383; P.O. Box 157, Wellesley, MA 02181 (SAN 686-0702) Tel 617-235-9537.

Wellingham-Jones, Patricia, *(Wellingham-Jones; 0-939221),* P.O. Box 238, Tehama, CA 96090 (SAN 662-670X); 8619 Sherwood Blvd., Los Molinos, CA 96055 (SAN 662-6718) Tel 916-384-1341.

Wellington Pr., *(Wellington Pr; 0-910959),* P.O. Box 13504, Tallahassee, FL 32317 (SAN 264-4878) Tel 904-878-6500; Dist. by: The Baker & Taylor Co., 1515 Broadway, New York, NY 10036 (SAN 169-5606) Tel 212-730-7650; Dist. by: Book Dynamics, 836 Broadway, New York, NY 10003 (SAN 169-5649) Tel 212-254-7798; Dist. by: Distributors The, 702 S. Michigan, South Bend, IN 46618 (SAN 212-0364) Tel 219-232-8500; Dist. by: Bookpeople, 2929 Fifth St., Berkeley, CA 94710 (SAN 168-9517) Tel 415-549-3030; Dist. by: The New Leaf Distributors, 1020 White St., SW, Atlanta, GA 30310 (SAN 169-1449) Tel 404-755-2665; Dist. by: Inland Book Co., P.O. Box 261, 22 Hemingway Ave., East Haven, CT 06512 (SAN 200-4151) Tel 203-467-4257.

Wellington Pubns., *(Wellington Pubns; 0-915915),* P.O. Box 223159, Carmel, CA 93923 (SAN 294-1104) Tel 408-624-7871.

Wellness and Health Activation Networks, *(Health Activ),* P.O. Box 923, Vienna, VA 22180 (SAN 224-3237) Tel 703-281-3830.

Wellness Institute, Inc., *(Wellness Inst; 0-9617202),* 2901 General DeGaulle St., Ste. 106B, New Orleans, LA 70114 (SAN 663-382X) Tel 504-361-1845.

Wellness Pubns., *(Wellness Pubns; 0-934957),* 225 W. 30th, P.O. Box 3021, Holland, MI 49423 (SAN 694-468X) Tel 616-396-5477.

Wellpower Pubns., *(Wellpower; 0-917073),* 11346 W. Jefferson, River Rouge, MI 48229 (SAN 655-5659) Tel 313-841-4849.

Wells, L. A., Co., *(L A Wells; 0-9616256),* 2025 Chatsworth Blvd., San Diego, CA 92107 (SAN 658-7275) Tel 619-224-8286.

Wells & West Pubs., *(Wells & West Pubs; 0-917545),* 1166 Winsor, North Bend, OR 97459 (SAN 669-7119).

Wells of Salvation, *(WOS),* 6821 SR 366, Huntsville, OH 43324 (SAN 217-1414).

Wellspring Bks., *(Wellspring Bks; 0-9614712),* Rte. 1, Box 27, Groton, VT 05046 (SAN 692-6614) Tel 802-584-3674. Do not confuse wit Wellspring Bks., Ukiah, CA.

Wellspring Bks., *(Wellspring Ukiah; 0-9616568),* 144 Clara Ave., Ukiah, CA 95482 (SAN 659-5472) Tel 707-463-0165. Do not confuse with Wellspring Bks., Groton, CT.

Wellspring Enterprises, *(Wellspring Ent; 0-937575),* 9921 Carmel Mountain Rd., Suite 188, San Diego, CA 92129 (SAN 659-1167) Tel 619-484-4479; 9008 Sundance Ct., San Diego, CA 92129 (SAN 659-1175).

Wellspring Press, *(Wellspring Pr; 0-914688),* Page Rd., Lincoln, MA 01773 (SAN 203-2171).

Wellspring Publishing, *(Wellspring Utah; 0-9608658),* P.O. Box 1113, Sandy, UT 84091 (SAN 239-5800) Tel 415-571-8662.

Wellton Bks., *(Wellton Bks; 0-943678),* P.O. Box 989, Citrus Heights, CA 95610 (SAN 238-4159) Tel 916-783-8536.

Welsh Society of Philadelphia, *(Welsh Soc Phila),* 450 Broadway, Camden, NJ 08103 (SAN 225-4158).

Welstar Pubns., Div. of Occupational Hygiene Center of NY, Inc., *(Welstar Pubns; 0-938503),* 20 Colonel Robert Magaw Pl., New York, NY 10033 (SAN 660-9791) Tel 212-928-7528.

Werner, J. Paul, *(J P Werner; 0-9601368),* 4643 N. Front St., Philadelphia, PA 19140 (SAN 209-6013) Tel 215-457-4081.

Werner Pubns., *(Werner Pubn; 0-933147),* 2020 18th Ave., Greeley, CO 80631 (SAN 692-3429) Tel 303-352-8566.

Wertz Pubns., *(Wertz Pubns; 0-9609196),* 6007 Lockport Rd., Niagara Falls, NY 14305 (SAN 240-9003) Tel 716-297-0455.

Wescott Cove Publishing Co., *(Wescott Cove; 0-918752),* Box 130, Stamford, CT 06904 (SAN 210-5810) Tel 203-322-0998.

Wesis Pubns., *(Wesis Pubns),* 29 Meadowbrook Lane, Cedar Grove, NJ 07009 (SAN 209-6153) Tel 201-256-7997.

Weslee Publishing, *(Weslee Pub; 0-933319),* 808 Fourth & Battery Bldg., Seattle, WA 98121 (SAN 692-2937) Tel 206-789-4931.

Wesley Foundation, The, *(Wesley Found; 0-9606652),* 211 N. School St., Normal, IL 61761 (SAN 219-6557) Tel 309-452-1435.

Wesley Institute Inc., *(Wesley Inst; 0-9614501),* 243 Johnston Rd., Pittsburgh, PA 15241 (SAN 689-9625) Tel 412-831-9390; Orders to: Wesley Institute, P.O. Box 113445, Pittsburgh, PA 15241 (SAN 662-2879) Tel 412-831-9390.

†**Wesleyan Univ. Pr.,** *(Wesleyan U Pr; 0-8195),* 110 Mt. Vernon St., Middletown, CT 06457 (SAN 282-5414) Tel 203-344-7918; Toll free: 800-242-7737; Orders to: Harper & Row Pubs., Inc., Keystone Industrial Pk., Scranton, PA 18512 (SAN 215-3742) Tel 717-343-4761; Toll free: 800-242-7737; *CIP.*

Wesolowski, Zdzislaw P., *(Z P Wesolowski; 0-937527),* 3702 NE 171st St., Apt. 13, North Miami Beach, FL 33160 (SAN 659-1191) Tel 305-945-5087; Dist. by: Printing Services, Inc., 3249 NW 38th St., Miami, FL 33142 (SAN 200-7096) Tel 305-633-2571.

West, Bill, *(B West; 0-911614),* 536 E. Ada Ave., Glendora, CA 91740 (SAN 202-3687) Tel 818-335-7060.

West, Mark, Pubs., *(M West Pubs),* P.O. Box 1914, Sandpoint, ID 83864 (SAN 215-711X) Tel 708-263-0969.

†**West, Richard,** *(R West; 0-8492; 0-8274),* Box 6404, Philadelphia, PA 19145 (SAN 206-8907); *CIP.*

West Anglia, *(W Anglia Pubns; 0-942424),* c/o Ben Sen Pr., P.O. Box 2683, La Jolla, CA 92038 (SAN 238-2091) Tel 714-453-0706.

West-Art, *(West-Art; 0-914301),* P.O. Box 279, Clarence, NY 14031 (SAN 287-6124) Tel 716-634-8805; 8555 Main St., Williamsville, NY 14221 (SAN 287-6132).

West Atlantic Pubns., *(West Atlantic; 0-935262),* 426 Columbia Ave., Mount Joy, PA 17552 (SAN 213-4012) Tel 717-653-2296; Orders to: P.O. Box 273, Mount Joy, PA 17552 (SAN 213-4020) Tel 717-653-5619.

West-Central Kentucky Family Research Assn., *(West Cent KY Family Re Assoc),* P.O. Box 1932, Owensboro, KY 42302 (SAN 219-0508) Tel 502-684-4150.

West Coast Poetry Review, *(West Coast; 0-915596),* 1335 Dartmouth Dr., Reno, NV 89509 (SAN 207-3684) Tel 702-322-4467.

West End Pr., *(West End; 0-931122),* Box 291477, Los Angeles, CA 90029 (SAN 211-3406); Box 27334, Albuquerque, NM 87125 (SAN 662-1864) Tel 505-242-9762; Orders to: Publishers Services, P.O. Box 3914, San Rafael, CA 94902 (SAN 201-3037).

West Fourth Street Block Assn., *(W Fourth St Block),* 285 W. Fourth St., New York, NY 10014 (SAN 208-077X) Tel 212-929-1452.

West Gate Press, *(West Gate Pr; 0-942836),* P.O. Box 961, Portland, ME 04104-0961 (SAN 240-5059).

West of Boston, *(West Boston; 0-911155),* 14 Bayfield Rd., Wayland, MA 01778 (SAN 284-978X) Tel 617-653-7241; Orders to: P.O. Box 2 Cochituate Station, Wayland, MA 01778 (SAN 689-8289).

West Pasco Genealogical Society, *(West Pasco Genealogical; 0-9614369),* 1016 Club House Dr., New Port Richey, FL 33552 (SAN 688-6310) Tel 813-847-7513; Orders to: Ethel Sweitzer, 122 E. Brentwood Dr., Port Richey, FL 33568 (SAN 662-2801) Tel 813-848-4795.

West Philadelphia Women's Committee for the Philadelphia Orchestra, The, *(W Phila Womens Comm; 0-9607586),* P.O. Box 685, Bryn Mawr, PA 19010 (SAN 217-2887) Tel 215-688-4930.

West Pr., *(West Press; 0-930743),* P.O. Box 99717, San Diego, CA 92109 (SAN 676-5580) Tel 619-270-9096.

West Pubns., *(West Pubns CA; 0-930109),* P.O. Box 487, Anaheim, CA 92805 (SAN 669-7127) Tel 714-772-0227.

West Publishing Co., *(West Pub; 0-8299; 0-314),* P.O. Box 64526, 50 W. Kellogg Blvd., St. Paul, MN 55102-1611 (SAN 202-9618) Tel 612-228-2500; Toll free: 800-328-9352.

West River Press, *(West River; 0-9602190),* 3530 W. Huron River Dr., Ann Arbor, MI 48103 (SAN 212-324X) Tel 313-668-8170.

West Side Pr., Div. of Eagle Eye Maps, *(West Side Pr; 0-935073),* P.O. Box 1457, Glenwood Springs, CO 81602 (SAN 694-6933); 8261/2 Grand Ave. No. 29, Glenwood Springs, CO 81601 (SAN 694-6941) Tel 303-945-8857.

West Southwest Publishing Co., *(West SW Pub Co; 0-938658),* 2755 Irwin Rd., Redding, CA 96002 (SAN 214-4883) Tel 916-221-4421.

West Summit Pr., *(West Summit; 0-9601356),* 26400 George Zeiger Drive, Suite 216, Beachwood, OH 44122 (SAN 295-3587) Tel 216-765-1028; Summit Pl., Suite C-206, 500 Old Highway 441, Mt. Dora, FL 32757 (SAN 295-3595) Tel 904-383-1708. Second address: alternate winter contact.

West Texas Museum Assn., *(West Tex Mus; 0-911618),* P.O. Box 4499, Lubbock, TX 79409 (SAN 206-667X) Tel 806-742-2443.

West Village Publishing Co., *(West Village; 0-933308),* 2904 E. Vanowen Ave., Orange, CA 92667 (SAN 213-1870) Tel 714-633-1420.

West Virginia Business Publishing Corp., *(WV Business Pub; 0-937683),* P.O. Box 5173, Charleston, WV 25361 (SAN 659-3666) Tel 304-345-8283; 1614 Washington St. E., Charleston, WV 25361 (SAN 659-3674).

West Virginia Highlands Conservancy, *(WV Highlands; 0-9616553),* 1206 Virginia St., E, Suite 201, Charleston, WV 25301 (SAN 659-5480) Tel 304-645-6028.

West Virginia University, Center for Extension & Continuing Education, *(W Va U Ctr Exten),* 308 Knapp Hall, Morgantown, WV 26506 (SAN 213-4039).

West Virginia Univ. Cooperative Extension Service, Div. of West Virginia Univ. Pr., *(WV Univ Coop Ext; 0-9616194),* 506 Knapp Hall, Morgantown, WV 26506-6031 (SAN 699-9522) Tel 304-293-4221.

West Virginia Univ., Perley Isaac Reed Schl. of Journalism, *(Sch Journal WVU; 0-930362),* West Virginia Univ., 112 Martin Hall, Morgantown, WV 26506-6010 (SAN 219-4104) Tel 304-293-3505.

West Virginia Univ. Pr., *(West Va U Pr; 0-937058),* Main Library, P.O. Box 6069, Morgantown, WV 26506 (SAN 205-5163) Tel 304-293-4040.

West Virginia Wesleyan College, *(W VA Wesleyan),* Department of English, West Virginia Wesleyan College, Buckhannon, WV 26201 (SAN 239-5762) Tel 304-473-8000.

West Virginia Women's Foundation, *(WV Womens Found; 0-9617031),* P.O. Box 5069, Charleston, WV 25311 (SAN 662-8761); WB-9 Capitol Complex, Charleston, WV 25305 (SAN 662-877X) Tel 304-348-0070.

West Washington State College, Programme in East Asian Studies *See* Western Washington Univ., Ctr. for East Asian Studies

West Winds Productions, Inc., *(West Wind Prod; 0-935969),* P.O. Box 3532, Boulder, CO 80307 (SAN 696-6594) Tel 303-443-2800; 855 Broadway, Boulder, CO 80307 (SAN 696-6608).

Westbourne Enterprises, *(Westbourne Ent; 0-9613885),* P.O. Box 3623, Hollywood, CA 90028 (SAN 682-6393) Tel 213-876-1338.

Westbrook Publications, *(Westbrook Pubns; 0-9614247),* P.O. Box 869, Millbrook, AL 36054 (SAN 686-6778) Tel 205-285-5407.

Westburg Assocs., Pubs., *(Westburg; 0-87423),* 1745 Madison St., Fennimore, WI 53809 (SAN 205-5171) Tel 608-822-6237.

Westbury Hse. *See* Butterworth's (Scientific, Technical, Medical)

Westcliff Pubns., *(Westcliff Pubns; 0-932896),* 1441 Avocado, No. 408, Newport Beach, CA 92660 (SAN 212-2448).

Westcliffe Pubs., Inc., *(Westcliffe Pubs Inc; 0-942394),* P.O. Box 1261, Englewood, CO 80150 (SAN 239-7528) Tel 303-935-0900; Toll free: 800-523-3692; 2650 S. Zuni St., Englewood, CO 80110 (SAN 660-9473).

Westcoast Publishing Co., *(Westcoast Pub; 0-937957),* P.O. Box 1046, Port Richey, FL 34288 (SAN 659-5499) Tel 813-847-3066; 105 Royal Palm Ave., New Port Richey, FL 33553 (SAN 659-5502).

Westcott Pubs., *(Westcott; 0-911620),* P.O. Box 803, Springfield, MO 65801 (SAN 205-518X) Tel 417-466-7455.

Westerfield, Scott, *(Westerfield; 0-9615537),* 7418 Nottoway Cir., Louisville, KY 40214 (SAN 695-8079) Tel 502-361-3998.

Westergaard, Marjorie, *(M Westergaard; 0-9609578),* 31246 Wagner, Warren, MI 48093 (SAN 260-2768) Tel 313-977-8942.

†Western Assn. of Map Libraries, *(Western Assn Map; 0-939112),* Univ. of California Library, C-075-P, c/o Larry Cruse, La Jolla, CA 92093 (SAN 216-3179) Tel 619-452-3338; Orders to: Western Assn. of Map Libraries, Univ. of California Library, c/o Stanley D. Stevens, Santa Cruz, CA 95064 (SAN 662-1872) Tel 408-429-2364; *CIP.*

Western Bk. Journal Pr., *(Western Bk Journ; 0-936029),* 1470 Woodberry Ave., San Mateo, CA 94403 (SAN 206-2305) Tel 415-573-8877.

Western Bks., *(Western Bks; 0-938463),* P.O. Box 1, Woodston, KS 67675 (SAN 660-9856) Tel 913-994-6253.

Western Educational Services, *(Western Educ Serv; 0-916236),* 168 N. Main St., P.O., 596, Centerville, UT 84014 (SAN 207-7426).

Western Enterprises, *(Western Enter; 0-9613461),* 3538 Oak Cliff Dr., Fallbrook, CA 92028 (SAN 679-1611) Tel 619-728-6465.

Western Epics Publishing Co., *(Western Epics; 0-914740),* 254 S. Main St., Salt Lake City, UT 84101 (SAN 206-1384) Tel 801-328-2586.

Western Fisherman's Pr., *(Western Fish Pr; 0-9617059),* P.O. Box 23943, Portland, OR 97223 (SAN 662-8508); 14355 SW Pacific Hwy., Tigard, OR 97223 (SAN 662-8516) Tel 503-639-4848.

Western Guideways, Ltd., *(Western Guideways; 0-931788),* P.O. Box 15532, Lakewood, CO 80215 (SAN 210-6264) Tel 303-237-0583.

Western Gull Publishing, Book Div. of the Daily News, Subs. of Longview Pub Co., *(Western Gull Pub; 0-9610910),* P.O. Box 1330, 305 W. First St., Port Angeles, WA 98362 (SAN 265-1556) Tel 206-452-2345.

Western Horizons Bks., *(Western Horizons Bks; 0-934959),* P.O. Box 4068, Helena, MT 59604 (SAN 692-7262) Tel 406-442-7795; Dist. by: Pacific Pipeline, Inc., 19215 66th Ave. S., Kent, WA 98032 (SAN 699-5942) Tel 206-872-5523; Toll free: 800-426-4727; 800-562-4647 (In Washington).

Western Horseman, Inc., The, *(Western Horseman; 0-911647),* P.O. Box 7980, Colorado Springs, CO 80933 (SAN 264-4894) Tel 303-633-5525.

Western Illinois Univ. Essays in Literature, *(WIU Essays Lit; 0-934312),* 114 Simpkins Hall, Macomb, IL 61455 (SAN 215-7128) Tel 309-298-2212.

Western Imprints *See* Western Imprints, Pr. of the Oregon Historical Society, The

Western Imprints, Pr. of the Oregon Historical Society, The, *(Western Imprints; 0-87595),* 1230 SW Park Ave., Portland, OR 97205-2483 (SAN 202-8301) Tel 503-222-1741. *Imprints:* Western Imprints (Western Imprints).

Western Islands, *(Western Islands; 0-88279),* 395 Concord Ave., Belmont, MA 02178 (SAN 206-8435) Tel 617-489-0606.

†Western Marine Enterprises Inc., *(Western Marine Ent; 0-930030),* Box Q, Ventura, CA 93002 (SAN 210-525X) Tel 805-644-6043; *CIP.*

Western Massachusetts Pubs., *(Western MA Pubs; 0-9616486),* 101 Caseland St., Springfield, MA 01107 (SAN 659-3720) Tel 413-787-6050.

Western Michigan News, *(Western Michigan),* P.O. Box 7264, Seymour Sq. Sta., Grand Rapids, MI 49508 (SAN 169-3875); P.O. Box 10, 301 S. Rath Ave., Ludington, MI 49431 (SAN 169-3905).

Western Michigan Univ., New Issues Pr., *(New Issues MI; 0-932826),* Kalamazoo, MI 49008 (SAN 276-6299) Tel 616-383-1886.

Western Mountain Press, *(Western Mtn; 0-911265),* 524C Cardenas S. E., Albuquerque, NM 87108 (SAN 275-1143) Tel 505-268-8776.

Western North Carolina Pr., Inc., Affil. of Books of Distinction, *(Western NC Pr; 0-915948),* 16 Tahquitz Ct., Camarillo, CA 93010 (SAN 208-9181) Tel 805-987-5760.

Western Profiles Publishing Co., *(Western Prof; 0-937231),* 1616 Champa St., Suite 210, Denver, CO 80202 (SAN 658-7232) Tel 303-623-2828; Orders to: P.O. Box 1026, Denver, CO 80201-1026 (SAN 662-4162).

Western Psychological Services, Div. of Manson Western Corp., *(Western Psych; 0-87424),* 12031 Wilshire Blvd., Los Angeles, CA 90025 (SAN 202-9634) Tel 213-478-2061.

Western Pubs., *(Western Pubs FL; 0-9602218),* 1711 S. Lakeside Dr., Lake Worth, FL 33460 (SAN 212-8039) Tel 305-588-6848. Not to be confused with Western Publishing, New York, NY.

Western Pub. Co., Inc., *(Western Pub; 0-307),* 850 Third Ave., New York, NY 10022 (SAN 202-523X) Tel 212-753-8500; 1220 Mound Ave., Racine, WI 53401 (SAN 669-2982) Tel 414-633-2431; Orders to: Dept. M, P.O. Box 700, Racine, WI 53401; Toll free: 800-558-3291; Dist. by: Childrens Pr., 1224 W. Van Buren St., Chicago, IL 60607 (SAN 201-9264) Tel 312-666-4200; Toll free: 800-621-1115. Do not confuse with Western Publisher, Lake Worth, FL. *Imprints:* Golden Press (Golden Pr).

Western Reserve Pr., The, *(Western Res Pr; 0-912400),* P.O. Box 675, Ashtabula, OH 44004 (SAN 205-5201) Tel 216-997-5851.

Western Son Academy, *(Western Son Acad; 0-938647),* P.O. Box 4080, Irvine, CA 92716 (SAN 661-6119); 2 Hopkins, Irvine, CA 92715 (SAN 661-6127) Tel 714-786-9585.

Western States Arts Foundation, *(Western States; 0-9611710),* 207 Shelby St., Sante Fe, NM 87501 (SAN 285-3531) Tel 505-988-1166.

Western States Historical Pubs., Inc., *(W States Historical; 0-912506),* 4020 W. 77th Pl., Westminster, CO 80030 (SAN 203-0217) Tel 303-429-1927.

Western States Shelter/Western Ctr. on Domestic Violence, *(W States Shelter; 0-912309),* 870 Market St., Suite 1058, San Francisco, CA 94102 (SAN 265-3001) Tel 415-362-0454.

Western Sun Pubns., *(Western Sun Pubns; 0-9608146),* P.O. Box 1470, Yuma, AZ 85364 (SAN 240-5067) Tel 602-726-6239.

Western Tanger Pr., *(Western Tanager; 0-934136),* 1111 Pacific Ave., Santa Cruz, CA 95060 (SAN 220-0155) Tel 408-425-1111. *Imprints:* Paper Vision Press (Paper Vision); Valley Publishers (Valley Calif).

Western Union Corp., *(Western Union),* 1 Lake St., Upper Saddle River, NJ 07458 (SAN 694-6968) Tel 201-825-6246.

Western Washington State College, Bureau of Faculty Research, *(Bur Faculty Res Wash; 0-930216),* Western Washington State College, Bellingham, WA 98225 (SAN 210-6841) Tel 206-676-3234.

Western Washington Univ., Ctr. for East Asian Studies, *(WWUCEAS; 0-914584),* Bellingham, WA 98225 (SAN 203-218X) Tel 206-676-3041.

Western Wood Products Association, *(Western Wood; 0-9600912),* Portland, OR 97204 (SAN 276-6426).

Western World Pr., *(West World Pr; 0-88189),* Box 366, Sun City, CA 92381 (SAN 290-6945); 980 N. State, D-6, Hemet, CA 92343 (SAN 290-6953) Tel 714-652-8288.

Western World Pubs., *(Western World; 0-931864),* P.O. Box 23785, Pleasant Hill, CA 94523 (SAN 207-6616) Tel 415-825-1042.

Westerners International, *(Westerners Intl),* Box 3485, Tucson, AZ 85722 (SAN 233-7797).

Westernlore Pubns., *(Westernlore; 0-87026),* 609 No. 4th Ave., Tucson, AZ 85705 (SAN 202-9642) Tel 602-297-5491; Orders to: Westernlore Press, P.O. Box 35305, Tucson, AZ 85740 (SAN 202-9650) Tel 602-297-5491.

Westfield Ctr. for Early Keyboard Studies, Inc., *(Westfield Ctr Early Keyboard; 0-9616755),* 1 Cottage St., Easthampton, MA 01027 (SAN 659-8374) Tel 413-527-7664.

Westgard, Gilbert, K. II, *(G K Westgard; 0-916061),* 1001 SW Fifth Ct., Boynton Beach, FL 33435 (SAN 240-5032).

Westgate Hse., *(Westgate Hse; 0-9607320),* 56 Westgate Dr., San Francisco, CA 94127 (SAN 239-5819) Tel 415-584-8338.

Westgate Pr., Div. of Westgate Group, Ltd., *(Westgate Pr),* 8 Bernstein Blvd., Center Moriches, NY 11934 (SAN 687-6579) Tel 516-878-2901.

Westgate Pr. (Oregon), *(Westgate OR Pr; 0-9614926)*, 225 Westgate Sq., 3800 SW Cedar Hills Blvd., Beaverton, OR 97005 (SAN 693-5869) Tel 503-646-0820; Dist. by: Pacific Pipeline, 19215 66th Ave., S., Kent, WA 98032 (SAN 208-2128) Tel 206-872-5523.

†Westin Communications, *(Westin Comm; 0-86620)*, 5760 Owensmouth Ave., Suite 31, Woodland Hills, CA 91367 (SAN 297-1968); Toll free: 800-421-1893; Orders to: Westin Communications, Jonathan Industrial Ctr., Chaska, MN 55318 (SAN 212-3681) Tel 612-448-5773; Orders to: NACSCORP, Oberlin, OH 44074 (SAN 209-2824) Tel 216-775-8048; Orders to: Wybel Distribution Co., Inc., 101 S. Hough St., Barrington, IL 60010 (SAN 159-3668); *CIP.*

Westlake Publishing Co., *(Westlake Pub; 0-935709)*, 11601 Wilshire Blvd., Suite 720, Los Angeles, CA 90025 (SAN 695-8346) Tel 213-824-0330.

Westland Pubns., *(Westland Pubns; 0-915162)*, P.O. Box 117, McNeal, AZ 85617-0117 (SAN 207-1169).

Westloch Pubns., *(Westloch Pubns; 0-9616964)*, 2440 NW 57th St., No. 2, Seattle, WA 98107 (SAN 661-8073) Tel 206-783-5671.

Westmail Pr., *(Westmail Pr)*, 179 Westmoreland Ave., White Plains, NY 10606 (SAN 207-5326) Tel 914-948-1116.

†Westminster Pr., *(Westminster; 0-664)*, 925 Chestnut St., Philadelphia, PA 19107 (SAN 202-9669) Tel 215-928-2700; Toll free: 800-523-1631; Toll free: 800-462-0405 (In Pennsylvania); Orders to: P.O. Box 718, William Penn Annex, Philadelphia, PA 19105 (SAN 202-9677) Tel 215-928-2760; *CIP.*

Westminster Trading Corp., The, *(Westminster Trading; 0-938953)*, 5 Northern Blvd., Amherst, NH 03031 (SAN 661-7212) Tel 603-886-5041.

Westmoreland Museum of Art, *(Westmoreland; 0-931241)*, 221 N. Main St., Greensburg, PA 15601 (SAN 264-4916); Toll free: 800-242-7737; Dist. by: Univ. of Pittsburgh Pr., 127 N. Bellefield Ave., Pittsburgh, PA 15260 (SAN 203-3216).

Westover Press, *(Westover Pr; 0-9612836)*, P.O. Box 1667, Murray Hill Sta., New York, NY 10156 (SAN 290-0602) Tel 212-889-3591; Seven Park Ave., New York, NY 10016 (SAN 290-0610).

Westover Pub Co. *See* Barre Publishing Co.

Westpark Bks., *(Westpark Bks; 0-936205)*, 1819 Birdseye Creek Rd., Gold Hill, OR 97525 (SAN 696-8600) Tel 503-582-1234; Dist. by: Quality Bks., Inc., 918 Sherwood Dr., Lake Bluff, IL 60044-2204 (SAN 169-2127); Dist. by: Southwest Parks & Monuments Assn., 221 N. Court St., Tucson, AZ 85701 (SAN 202-750X) Tel 602-622-1999.

Westphal Publishing, *(Westphal Pub; 0-9610520)*, P.O. Box 19542, Irvine, CA 92713 (SAN 262-1088) Tel 714-660-0727.

Westphalia Pr., The, *(Westphalia Pr; 0-915637)*, Rte. 1, P.O. Box 96, Loose Creek, MO 65054 (SAN 292-7284) Tel 314-897-3526; Dist. by: Paperback Supply Co., 4121 Forest Park Ave., St. Louis, MO 63108 (SAN 169-426X); Toll free: 800-325-8404; Dist. by: Cowley Distributing Co., 732 Heisenger Rd., Jefferson City, MO 65101 (SAN 169-426X).

Westport Pubs., Inc., Subs. of Test Corporation of America, *(Westport Pubs; 0-9611286; 0-933701)*, 330 W. 47th St., Suite 205, Kansas City, MO 64112 (SAN 283-3492) Tel 816-756-1490. *Imprints:* Test Corporation of America (Test Corp America).

Westrail Pubns., *(Westrail Pubns; 0-9602466)*, Box 300, Glendora, CA 91740 (SAN 212-7091).

Westridge Pr., Ltd., *(Westridge; 0-918832)*, 1090 Southridge Pl., S., Salem, OR 97302 (SAN 210-5268) Tel 503-363-2422.

Westrom Co., The, *(Westrom; 0-938230)*, P.O. Box 85527, Los Angeles, CA 90072 (SAN 215-8264).

Westroots, *(Westroots; 0-936580)*, 3131a Via Alicante, La Jolla, CA 92037 (SAN 222-0296).

WestSea Pub. Co., Inc., *(WestSea Pub; 0-937820)*, 149D Allen Blvd., Farmingdale, NY 11735 (SAN 215-7144) Tel 516-420-1110.

Westview Pr., *(Westview; 0-89158; 0-86531; 0-8133)*, 5500 Central Ave., Boulder, CO 80301 (SAN 219-970X) Tel 303-444-3541.

WestView Publishing Co., *(WestView Pub; 0-937535)*, 6065 Mission Gorge Rd., Suite 425, San Diego, CA 92120 (SAN 619-123X) Tel 619-444-6807.

Westville Pub. Co. Ltd., *(Westville Pub Co; 0-938860)*, P.O. Box 81, Old Westbury, NY 11568 (SAN 240-0359).

Westwater Bks., Div. of Belknap Photographic Services, Inc., *(Westwater; 0-916370)*, P.O. Box 365, Boulder City, NV 89005 (SAN 208-3698) Tel 702-293-1406.

Westwind Pr., *(Westwind Pr; 0-9602342)*, Rte. 1, Box 208, Farmington, WV 26571 (SAN 215-7152).

Westwind Pubns., *(Westwind Pubns; 0-9613379)*, 89 Kearney St., S. San Francisco, CA 94080 (SAN 657-1204) Tel 415-588-6493.

Westwood Enterprises, *(Westwood Ent; 0-9617118)*, 5302 N. 79th Pl., Scottsdale, AZ 85253 (SAN 662-8028) Tel 602-994-8244.

Westwood Pr., Inc., *(Westwood Pr; 0-936159)*, 251 Park Ave. S., New York, NY 10010 (SAN 696-7183) Tel 212-420-8008.

Westwood Publishing Co., *(Westwood Pub Co; 0-930298)*, 312 Riverdale Dr., Glendale, CA 91204 (SAN 211-8769) Tel 818-242-3497.

Wetherbee, Martha, Basket Shop, *(M Wetherbee; 0-9609384)*, Star Rte. 35, Sanbornton, NH 03269 (SAN 260-2709) Tel 603-286-8927.

Wettenstein, Raphael, *(R Wettenstein; 0-9617252)*, 59 Lawrence Ave., Staten Island, NY 10310 (SAN 663-5636) Tel 718-720-8320.

Weybridge Publishing Co., *(Weybridge; 0-939356)*, 16911 Brushfield Dr., Dallas, TX 75248 (SAN 216-4965) Tel 214-931-7770.

Wff'n Proof Pubs., *(Wffn Proof; 0-911624)*, 1490 South Blvd., Ann Arbor, MI 48104 (SAN 205-521X) Tel 313-665-2269.

Whale Museum/Moclips Cetological Society, The, *(Whale Museum; 0-933331)*, P.O. Box 945, Friday Harbor, WA 98250 (SAN 692-2864) Tel 206-378-4710.

Whale Pubns., *(Whale Pubns; 0-9615448)*, 526 W. 123rd St., New York, NY 10027 (SAN 695-7528) Tel 212-316-3862.

Whale Publishing, *(Whale Pub; 0-9616487)*, P.O. Box 21696, St. Louis, MO 63109 (SAN 659-3755); 6015 Potomac, St. Louis, MO 63139 (SAN 659-3763) Tel 314-832-5734.

What to Do County Pubns., Inc., Div. of Hardscrabble Pubns., Inc., *(What to Do; 0-930520)*, P.O. Box 396, Pleasantville, NY 10570 (SAN 213-5728).

Whatcom County Opportunity Council, *(Whatcom Cty Opp; 0-934671)*, 314 E. Holly St., Bellingham, WA 98225 (SAN 694-0781) Tel 206-734-5121.

†Whatever Publishing Inc., *(Whatever Pub; 0-931432)*, P.O. Box 137, Mill Valley, CA 94942 (SAN 211-8777) Tel 415-388-2100; Toll free: 800-227-3900 (Retail orders only); Dist. by: Publishers Group West, 5855 Beaudry, Emeryville, CA 94608 (SAN 202-8522) Tel 415-658-3453; Toll free: 800-982-8319; Dist. by: Bookpeople, 2929 Fifth St., Berkeley, CA 94710 (SAN 168-9517) Tel 415-549-3030; Toll free: 800-227-1516; *CIP.*

What's Cooking Pubns., *(Whats Cooking; 0-9614250)*, 226 Birchwood Rd., P.O. Box 323, Hinsdale, IL 60521 (SAN 686-7391) Tel 312-986-1595.

Wheal-Grace Inc., *(Wheal Grace; 0-933433)*, 420 Valley Brook Ave., Lyndhurst, NJ 07071 (SAN 691-5310) Tel 201-933-7092.

Wheat Forder's Press, *(Wheat Forders; 0-917888)*, P.O. Box 6317, Washington, DC 20015 (SAN 209-9187) Tel 202-362-1588.

Wheatherstone Press, *(Wheatherstone Pr; 0-9613011)*, 20 Wheatherstone, Lake Oswego, OR 97034 (SAN 292-7292) Tel 503-635-2646.

Wheat'N Flower Designs, *(Wheat'N Flower; 0-9613993)*, P.O. Box 2433, Springfield, IL 62705 (SAN 683-129X) Tel 217-546-5096.

Wheaton Resource Corp., *(Wheaton Resource; 0-936657)*, 1800 N. Main St., Wheaton, IL 60187 (SAN 699-7090) Tel 312-665-6200; Dist. by: Chicago Review Press, 814 N. Franklin St., Chicago, IL 60610 (SAN 213-5744) Tel 312-337-0747.

Wheedle, Inc., *(Wheedle Inc; 0-936873)*, P.O. Box 4053, Wenatchee, WA 98801 (SAN 699-9638) Tel 509-662-8737; 23 S. Wenatchee Ave., Suite 115, Wenatchee, WA 98801 (SAN 699-9646).

Wheel Pr., Inc., *(Wheel Pr; 0-936747)*, P.O. Box 23233, Tigard, OR 97223 (SAN 697-2594); 9203 SE Mitchell, Portland, OR 97266 (SAN 699-6485).

Wheeler, Carol Jean, *(C J Wheeler; 0-9608448)*, 420 Carolwood Ln., NE, Atlanta, GA 30342 (SAN 240-5733) Tel 404-252-9157; Dist. by: Dot Gibson's Publications, P.O. Box 117, Waycross, GA 31502 (SAN 241-3760) Tel 912-285-2848; Dist. by: Southwest Cookbook Distributors, 1901 S. Shore Dr., Bonham, TX 75418 (SAN 200-4925) Tel 214-583-8898; Dist. by: Quik Cook Inc., 439 Central Ave., Rochester, NY 14605 (SAN 200-5115) Tel 716-546-7663; Dist. by: Collection, The, 2101 Kansas City Rd., Olathe, KS 66061 (SAN 689-8467) Tel 913-764-1811.

Wheeler, Eva Floy, *(E F Wheeler; 0-9613197)*, 1199 Margarita Ave., Grover City, CA 93433 (SAN 264-4940).

Wheeler, Harris E., Pub., *(H E Wheeler; 0-9616830)*, P.O. Box 245, Bradford, NH 03221 (SAN 661-163X); Water St., Bradford, NH 02331 (SAN 661-1648).

Wheeler Productions, *(Wheeler Prods; 0-9614362)*, 2183 Payne Ave., St. Paul, MN 55117 (SAN 688-573X) Tel 612-774-3057.

Wheelgun Pr., Div. of FR3 Enterprises, *(Wheelgun Pr; 0-937289)*, P.O. Box 2022, Simi Valley, CA 93065 (SAN 659-1256) Tel 805-527-7835; 2046 Sheridan Ct., Simi Valley, CA 93065 (SAN 659-1264).

Wheelock Whitney & Company, *(W Whitney; 0-917105)*, 123 E. 62nd St., New York, NY 10021 (SAN 655-3648) Tel 212-688-4474.

Wheelwright Press, *(Wheelwright Pr; 0-935706)*, 300 Page St., San Francisco, CA 94102 (SAN 222-0326) Tel 415-863-3136.

Wheelwright Press, Ltd., *(Wheelwright UT; 0-937512)*, 1836 Sunnyside Ave., Salt Lake City, UT 84108 (SAN 205-9533) Tel 801-582-8158.

Where to Find The Oregon in Oregon, *(Where to Find OR in OR; 0-9616696)*, 7277 SW Barnes Rd., Portland, OR 97225 (SAN 659-8382) Tel 503-292-4549; Dist. by: Bay News Co., 3155 NW Yeon Ave., Portland, OR 97210 (SAN 169-7153)19215 66th Ave., S., Kent, WA 98032 (SAN 208-2128).

Where To Go, Inc., *(Where To Go; 0-912785)*, P.O. Box 204, Excelsior, MN 55331 (SAN 282-8219) Tel 612-474-7000.

Whimsie Pr., *(Whimsie Pr; 0-916178)*, P.O. Box 70, Mill Creek Rd., Otego, NY 13825 (SAN 239-5770).

Whipporwill, *(Whipporwill; 0-917012)*, c/o R. I. Pubns. Society, 189 Wickenden St., Providence, RI 02903 (SAN 239-4006).

Whirling Vortices, *(Whirling Vortices; 0-9616147)*, 408 Sixth Ave., Clarence, IA 52216 (SAN 699-976X) Tel 319-452-3293.

Whirlpool Corp., *(Whirlpool; 0-938336)*, Home Study Department, La Porte, IN 46350 (SAN 215-8272) Tel 219-325-2345.

Whispering Sands Pubns., *(Whispering Sands Pubns; 0-9608718)*, P.O. Box 181t., P.O. Box 181, Santa Fe, NM 87501 (SAN 238-0870).

Whispers Pr., *(Whispers; 0-918372)*, 70 Highland Ave., Binghamtom, NY 13905 (SAN 210-6272) Tel 607-729-6920.

Whitaker Hse., *(Whitaker Hse; 0-88368)*, Pittsburgh & Colfax Sts., Springdale, PA 15144 (SAN 203-2104) Tel 412-274-4440; Toll free: 800-245-2422.

White, A., Publishing Co., *(A White Pub; 0-9613812)*, c/o Linn 19 Essex St., New York, NY 10002 (SAN 679-3878) Tel 212-673-5080; Dist. by: Printed Matter Inc, 7 Lispenard St., New York, NY 10013 (SAN 169-5924) Tel 212-925-0325.

White, Carter, *(C White; 0-9613384)*, Box 708, Hale Center, TX 79041 (SAN 657-078X) Tel 806-839-2666.

†White, David, Co., *(D White; 0-87250)*, One Pleasant Ave., Port Washington, NY 11050 (SAN 201-2936) Tel 516-944-9325; *CIP.*

White, Eugene V., *(E V White; 0-9602034)*, 1 W. Main St., Berryville, VA 22611-0286 (SAN 212-5838) Tel 703-955-2280.

Names

White, Glenn E. F., *(White G E F; 0-9611926),* 101 Buckingham St., Meriden, CT 06450 (SAN 286-1011) Tel 203-235-7462.
White, John A., *(J A White; 0-9603242),* 1200 Toyon Dr, Millbrae, CA 94030 (SAN 207-1932) Tel 415-697-1187.
White, Laurie A., & Steven L. Spencer, *(White & Spencer; 0-9612024),* 4340 Tamarac Trail, Harbor Springs, MI 49740 (SAN 287-7791) Tel 616-347-6701.
White, Stewart W., *(White S W; 0-9614794),* 105 Shore Acres SW, Tacoma, WA 98498 (SAN 693-0018) Tel 206-584-7893.
White Consultants Inc., *(White Consult; 0-932263),* State Rd. 625, P.O. Box D, Gainesville, VA 22065 (SAN 686-6328) Tel 703-347-0030.
White Crane Pubns., *(White Crane Pubns; 0-9604880),* P.O. Box 3081, Eugene, OR 97403 (SAN 237-9708) Tel 503-342-2759.
White Cross Press, *(White Cross; 0-918186),* Route One, Box 592, Granger, TX 76530 (SAN 210-2862) Tel 512-859-2814.
White Deer Bks., *(White Deer Bks; 0-931567),* 80 Beekman St., New York, NY 10038 (SAN 687-6560).
White Dove Pr., *(White Dove Pr; 0-9614576),* 2120 Haskell Ave., Lawrence, KS 66046 (SAN 691-8395) Tel 913-842-1937.
White Dove Publishing Co., *(White Dove Pub Co; 0-914541),* 4640 Jewell St., Suite 104, San Diego, CA 92109 (SAN 289-6443) Tel 619-581-2266; Toll free: 800-621-0852.
White Eagle Pub., The, *(White Eagle Pub; 0-941804),* P.O. Box 1332, Dept. BP-0111, Lowell, MA 01853 (SAN 239-3441); Dist. by: Baker & Taylor Co., Eastern Div., 50 Kirby Ave., Somerville, NJ 08876 (SAN 169-4901).
White Ewe Press, *(White Ewe; 0-917976),* P.O. Box 1614, Baltimore, MD 21203 (SAN 209-410X).
White Hall Books See Betterway Pubns., Inc.
White Horse Productions, Inc., *(White Horse; 0-940376),* 286 Cabot St., Beverly, MA 01915 (SAN 219-8355) Tel 617-927-3677.
White House Historical Assn., *(White House Hist; 0-912308),* 740 Jackson Pl. NW, Washington, DC 20506 (SAN 226-8108) Tel 202-737-8292.
White Hse. Theater, The, *(White Hse; 0-9615860),* 3017 Brighton Sixth St., Brooklyn, NY 11235 (SAN 696-7795) Tel 718-769-1013; P.O. Box 245, New York, NY 10013 (SAN 660-9570). *Imprints:* Double Trouble Day (Double Trouble Day).
White Lion Pr., *(White Lion Pr; 0-9615707),* 225 E. Fifth St. No. 4-D, New York, NY 10003 (SAN 695-7919) Tel 212-260-1677.
White Meadow Pr., *(White Meadow; 0-933855),* P.O. Box 582, Rockaway, NJ 07866 (SAN 692-7408) Tel 201-696-1666.
White Peony Pr., *(White Peony; 0-917951),* Rte. 1, Box 90, Cairnbrook, PA 15924 (SAN 657-0305) Tel 814-754-4944.
White Pine Pr., *(White Pine; 0-934834),* 76 Center St., Fredonia, NY 14063 (SAN 209-8067) Tel 716-672-5743.
White Pine Pr., *(White Pine OR; 0-9610988),* 505 SW Long Farm Rd., West Linn, OR 97068 (SAN 265-301X) Tel 503-638-0500; Dist. by: International Specialized Bk. Services, Inc., 5602 NE Hassalo St., Portland, OR 97213-3640 (SAN 169-7129) Tel 503-287-3093; Toll free: 800-547-7734.
White Rhinoceros Pr., The, *(White Rhino Pr; 0-9616760),* 804 Gracelyn Ct., Blacksburg, VA 24060 (SAN 659-851X) Tel 703-552-2976; Dist. by: Pocahontas Press, Inc., 2805 Wellesley Dr., Blacksburg, VA 24060 (SAN 696-6195); Dist. by: Virginia Polytechnic Institute & State Univ. Bookstore, Blacksburg, VA 24061 (SAN 291-6134).
†White River Pr., Inc., *(White River; 0-932431),* 1857 N. Pennsylvania St., Indianapolis, IN 46202 (SAN 687-4150) Tel 317-925-6668; CIP.
White Rose Marketing, *(White Rose; 0-9605128),* 23101 Moulton Pkwy., Suite 110, Laguna Hills, CA 92653 (SAN 216-3233).
White Saddle Bks., *(White S Bks; 0-912142),* 9144 Knauf Rd., Canfield, OH 44406 (SAN 205-5236).
White Sound Pr., *(White Sound; 0-932265),* 1615 W. Harrison Ave., Decatur, IL 62526 (SAN 686-6336) Tel 217-423-0511.

White Wing Publishing Hse. & Pr., *(White Wing Pub; 0-934942),* P.O. Box 3000, Cleveland, TN 37311 (SAN 203-2198) Tel 615-476-8536.
Whitebrook Bks., *(Whitebrook Bks; 0-9608934),* P.O. Box 746, Easthampton, MA 01027 (SAN 237-9694).
Whitefield, George, Publishing Co., *(G Whitefield Pub; 0-9614323),* P.O. Box 243, Gladstone, OR 97027 (SAN 687-5343) Tel 503-653-2249.
Whiteford International Enterprise See Wheat Forder's Press
Whitehall Co., *(Whitehall Co; 0-87655),* 1200 S. Willis Ave., Wheeling, IL 60090 (SAN 696-737X) Tel 312-541-9290.
Whitehall Pr.-Budget Pubns., *(Whitehall Pr; 0-916565),* Whitehall, Rt. 1, Box 603, Sandersville, GA 31082 (SAN 295-5512) Tel 912-552-7455.
Whitehaven Publishing, *(Whitehaven Pub; 0-936291),* 2924 Brakley, Suite B-6, Baton Rouge, LA 70816 (SAN 697-9971) Tel 504-291-7942.
Whitehead Photography, *(Whitehead Photo; 0-9603486),* 13 S. Foushee St., Richmond, VA 23220 (SAN 213-7054) Tel 804-648-3219.
Whitehorse, *(Whitehorse; 0-937591),* 4154 Ticonderoga Way, Boise, ID 83706 (SAN 659-1299) Tel 208-336-8650.
Whitenwife Pubns., *(Whitenwife Pubns; 0-9603656),* 149 Magellan St., Capitola, CA 95010 (SAN 213-8816) Tel 408-476-2730.
Whites Creek Pr., *(Whites Creek Pr; 0-9616918),* P.O. Box 266, Whites Creek, TN 37189 (SAN 661-5430); 4772 Lickton Pike, Whites Creek, TN 37189 (SAN 661-5449) Tel 615-876-2622.
Whiteside, Dora M., Pub., *(D M Whiteside; 0-938353),* 501 Juniper Dr., Prescott, AZ 86301 (SAN 659-9133) Tel 602-445-7245; Dist. by: Magee Bk. Store, 118 N. Montezuma St., Prescott, AZ 86301 (SAN 200-6588).
Whitewater, *(Whitewater; 0-9612286),* 509 E. 73rd St., No. 18, New York, NY 10021 (SAN 289-5765).
Whitfield, *(Whitfield; 0-930920),* 1841 Pleasant Hill Rd., Pleasant Hill, CA 94523 (SAN 210-6280) Tel 415-938-6759.
Whitfield Publishing Co., *(Whitfield Pub; 0-938649),* P.O. Box 53617, San Jose, CA 95153 (SAN 661-6372); 5343 Birch Grove Dr., San Jose, CA 95153 (SAN 661-6380) Tel 408-282-9991.
Whitinsville Bk. Co., *(Whitinsville Bk; 0-915949),* 20 Steele St., Worcester, MA 01607 (SAN 294-1120) Tel 617-754-1115.
Whitlaker Marketing, *(Whitlaker; 0-914303),* P.O. Box 661, Whitmore Lake, MI 48189 (SAN 287-6175) Tel 313-552-3764; 10329 Cedar Crest, Whitmore Lake, MI 48189 (SAN 287-6183).
Whitley, Joe F., Pub., *(J F Whitley; 0-937577),* 1414 Spokane Ave., Coeur d' Alene, ID 83814 (SAN 659-1345) Tel 208-664-2329.
†Whitman, Albert, & Co., *(A Whitman; 0-8075),* 5747 W. Howard St., Niles, IL 60648 (SAN 201-2049) Tel 312-647-1355; CIP.
Whitman, Walt Ctr. for the Atrs & humanities, *(Walt Whitman; 0-9615683),* Second & Cooper Sts., Camden, NJ 08102 (SAN 695-8303) Tel 609-757-7276.
Whitman-Walker Clinic, Inc., the, *(Whitman-Walker),* 2335 18th St., NW, Washington, DC 20009 (SAN 237-9775).
†Whitmore Publishing Co., *(Whitmore; 0-87426),* 35 Cricket Terrace, Ardmore, PA 19003 (SAN 203-2112) Tel 215-896-6116; CIP.
Whitney, Harvey, Bks., *(H W Bks; 0-9606488),* P.O. Box 42696, Cincinnati, OH 45242 (SAN 217-2143) Tel 513-793-3555.
Whitney, Philip B., *(Whitney PB; 0-9612992),* Rte. 2, Stephens City, VA 22655 (SAN 292-7349) Tel 703-869-1713.
Whitney Library See Watson-Guptill Pubns., Inc.
Whitston Pub. Co., Inc., *(Whitston Pub; 0-87875),* P.O. Box 958, Troy, NY 12181 (SAN 203-2120) Tel 518-283-4363.
Whitt, Jane Chapman, *(Whitt; 0-9615446),* 3332 Glenmore Dr., Falls Church, VA 22041 (SAN 695-7307) Tel 703-578-1861.
Whittell, George, Memorial Pr., *(G Whittell Mem; 0-910781),* 3722 S. Ave., Youngstown, OH 44502 (SAN 260-2776) Tel 216-783-0645.

Whitten Publishing Co., *(Whitten Pub Co; 0-9602766),* P.O. Box 513, Flatonia, TX 78941 (SAN 213-1889).
Whitt's Three Enterprises, *(Whitts Three Ent; 0-9617082),* RR 1, Box 301, North Liberty, IN 46554 (SAN 662-6432); 59105 Crumstown Hwy., North Liberty, IN 46554 (SAN 662-6440).
Whole Person Assocs., Inc./Whole Person Pr., *(Whole Person; 0-938586),* P.O. Box 3151, Duluth, MN 55803 (SAN 282-5430) Tel 218-728-6807; Dist. by: Bookpeople, 2929 Fifth St., Berkeley, CA 94710 (SAN 168-9517) Tel 415-549-3030; Orders to: Whole Person Pr., P.O. Box 3249, Duluth, MN 55803 (SAN 282-5457) Tel 218-728-4077.
Whole World Publishing, Inc., *(Whole World; 0-938184),* 400 Lake Cook Rd., No. 207, Deerfield, IL 60015 (SAN 217-1422) Tel 312-945-8050; Toll free: 800-323-4305.
Wholeo Bks., *(Wholeo Bks; 0-942488),* 565 Willow Rd., No. 26, Menlo Park, CA 94025 (SAN 239-9547) Tel 415-324-3462.
Who's What and Where, *(Who's What Where; 0-9614418),* P.O. Box 921, Detroit, MI 48231 (SAN 689-0512) Tel 313-886-5611.
Who's Who Among Black Americans, Inc., *(Who's Who Black Am),* 721 N. McKinley, Lake Forest, IL 60045 (SAN 207-9968) Tel 312-295-6650.
Who's Who Historical Society, *(Who's Who Hist Soc; 0-9603166),* P.O. Box 4240, San Clemente, CA 92672 (SAN 213-7062) Tel 714-498-0600.
Who's Who in America's Restaurants, Div. of Who's Who in Restaurants, *(Whos Who Rest; 0-910297),* 1841 Broadway, Suite 808, New York, NY 10023 (SAN 241-4775) Tel 212-581-0360.
Who's Who in Artificial Intelligence, *(WWAI; 0-937287),* P.O. Box 620098, Woodside, CA 94062 (SAN 659-106X) Tel 415-493-7905; 275 Ventura Blvd., Apt. 31, Palo Alto, CA 94305 (SAN 659-1078).
Who's Who in Chiropractic International Publishing Co., *(Chiropractic; 0-918336),* P.O. Box 2615, Littleton, CO 80161 (SAN 209-9209) Tel 303-798-5128.
Who's Who in Consumer Electronics, Inc., Div. of Martin Porter Associate Publications, *(Who's Who Electro; 0-935305),* 76 Court St., Brooklyn, NY 11201 (SAN 695-8443) Tel 718-875-7616.
Who's Who in the International Red Series (WWIR) See Unipub a
Who's Who of Black Millionaires, Inc., *(Who's Black Mill; 0-915021),* P.O. Box 12092, Fresno, CA 93776 (SAN 289-4661) Tel 209-266-5438.
Wibat Pubns., *(Wibat Pubns; 0-935996),* P.O. Box 60, Forestville, CA 95436 (SAN 214-1698).
Wichita Art Museum, Div. of City of Whichita, *(Wichita Art Mus; 0-939324),* 619 Stackman Dr., Wichita, KS 67203 (SAN 205-5260) Tel 316-268-4921.
Wicker Park Pr., *(Wicker Park; 0-911595),* Box 5597, Chicago, IL 60680 (SAN 264-4967) Tel 312-486-2191.
Wicker Pubns., *(Wicker Pubns; 0-930111),* 28833 SE Amisted Lane, Eagle Creek, OR 97022 (SAN 670-2570) Tel 503-637-3412.
Wickstrom Pubs., Inc., *(Wickstrom; 0-936240),* 5901 SW 74th St., Suite 310, Miami, FL 33143 (SAN 206-0345) Tel 305-661-4222; Dist. by: Banyan Books, Inc., P.O. Box 431160, Miami, FL 33243 (SAN 208-340X) Tel 305-665-6011.
Wickwire Pr., *(Wickwire Pr; 0-9612556),* Rd. 1, Sutton, VT 05867 (SAN 289-467X) Tel 802-467-3218; Dist. by: Countryman Press, Inc., Maxham Meadows, Box 175, VT 05091 (SAN 206-4901) Tel 802-457-1049.
Widdy Publishing, *(Widdy Pub; 0-9614981),* 731 Cascade Dr., Woodburn, OR 97071 (SAN 693-6792) Tel 503-981-3378.
Wide Horizons Pr., *(Wide Horiz Pr; 0-938109),* 13 Meadowsweet, Irvine, CA 92715 (SAN 659-8137) Tel 714-786-7922.
Wide Skies Pr., *(Wide Skies),* P.O. Box 7, Rte. 1, Polk, NE 68654 (SAN 205-5279) Tel 402-765-3798.

Wide World Publishing/Tetra, *(Wide World-Tetra; 0-933174),* P.O. Box 476, San Carlos, CA 94070 (SAN 211-1462) Tel 415-593-2839; Dist. by: Bookpeople, 2929 Fifth St., Berkeley, CA 94710 (SAN 168-9517) Tel 415-549-3030; Toll free: 800-624-4466; Dist. by: Publishers Group West, 5855 Beaudry St., Emeryville, CA 94608 (SAN 202-8522) Tel 415-658-3453.

Widening Horizons, Inc., *(Widening Horizons; 0-9616310),* 9582 Hamilton Ave., Suite 241, Huntington Beach, CA 92646 (SAN 658-7208) Tel 714-964-2363; 9622 Chevy Chase Dr., Huntington Beach, CA 92646 (SAN 658-7216).

Wider Opportunities for Women, *(WOW Inc; 0-934966),* 1325 G St., NW, Lower Level, Washington, DC 20005 (SAN 213-4047) Tel 202-638-3143.

Wideview *See Putnam Publishing Group, The*

Wiener, Markus, Publishing, *(Wiener Pub Inc; 0-910129),* 2901 Broadway, Suite 107, New York, NY 10025 (SAN 282-5465) Tel 212-678-7138; Dist. by: Schocken Bks. (Masterworks of Jewish Writing Ser. only), 62 Cooper Sq., New York, NY 10003 (SAN 213-7585) Tel 212-475-4900; Dist. by: M & B Fulfillment Services, 540 Barnum Ave., Bridgeport, CT 06610 (SAN 282-6062) Tel 203-366-1900.

Wiener, Moshe, *(M Wiener; 0-9605406),* 854 Newburg Ave., North Woodmere, NY 11581 (SAN 215-9856).

Wiese, Michael, Film Production, *(M Wiese Film Prod; 0-941188),* P.O. Box 406, Westport, CT 06881 (SAN 237-9716) Tel 203-226-6979.

Wieser & Wieser, Inc., *(Wieser & Wieser; 0-914373),* 118 E 25th St., New York, NY 10010 (SAN 289-6958) Tel 212-260-0860.

Wigan Pier Press, *(Wigan Pier; 0-934594),* 1283 Page St., San Francisco, CA 94117 (SAN 213-1897) Tel 415-863-6664.

Wiggins, John H., *(J H Wiggins; 0-9600346),* 1650 S. Pacific Coast Hwy., Suite 206, Redondo Beach, CA 90277 (SAN 205-5287).

Wight, Oliver, Ltd., Pubns., Inc., Subs. of The Oliver Wright Cos., *(Oliver Wight; 0-939246),* 5 Oliver Wight Dr., Essex Junction, VT 05452 (SAN 216-5198) Tel 802-878-8161; Toll free: 800-343-0625.

Wiide Pubns., Co., *(Wiide Pubns Co; 0-933151),* 1100 Center Point., Stevens Point, WI 54481 (SAN 200-4771) Tel 715-344-9600.

Wikenhauser, Betty, *(B Wikenhauser; 0-9613796),* 15212 Harvest Ave., Norwalk, CA 90650 (SAN 678-9609) Tel 213-868-7039.

Wilcord Pubns., Ltd., *(Wilcord Pubns; 0-920986),* c/o Robert Silver Assocs., 307 E. 37th St., New York, NY 10016 (SAN 241-5801) Tel 212-686-5630.

Wild Clover Bks., *(Wild Clover Bks; 0-9616008),* Rte. 2, Inavale, NE 68952 (SAN 697-9998) Tel 402-746-3589.

Wild Duck Press, *(Wild Duck Pr; 0-9612542),* Porterville Rd., East Aurora, NY 14052 (SAN 289-7075) Tel 716-652-8246.

Wild Geese Publishing Co., The, *(Wild Geese; 0-918379),* 116 Elessa Dr., Hendersonville, TN 37075 (SAN 657-3916) Tel 615-822-7177.

Wild Horses Publishing Co., *(Wild Horses; 0-9601088; 0-937148),* 12310 Concepcion Rd., Los Altos Hills, CA 94022 (SAN 211-8289) Tel 415-941-3396.

Wild Rose, *(Wild Rose; 0-915507),* P.O. Box 29234, Los Angeles, CA 90029 (SAN 291-4654) Tel 213-241-0284; 1355 Cedar Court Rd., Glendale, CA 91207 (SAN 291-4662).

Wild Skies Press *See Entheos Communications*

Wild Trees Pr., *(Wild Trees Press; 0-931125),* P.O. Box 378, Navarro, CA 95463 (SAN 678-9552); Dist. by: Bookpeople, 2929 Fifth St., Berkeley, CA 94710 (SAN 168-9517) Tel 415-549-3030; Dist. by: Publishers Group West, 5855 Beaudry St., Emeryville, CA 94608 (SAN 202-8522) Tel 415-658-3453; Dist. by: Inland Bk. Co., P.O. Box 261, 22 Hemingway, East Haven, CT 06512 (SAN 200-4151) Tel 203-467-4257.

Wild Willow Pr., *(Wild Willow; 0-9614795),* P.O. Box 438, Baraboo, WI 53913 (SAN 693-0301); 700 Second St., Baraboo, WI 53913 (SAN 662-3077) Tel 608-356-9048.

Wilderness Adventure Books, *(Wilder Advent Bks; 0-9611596),* 320 Garden Ln., P.O. Box 968, Fowlerville, MI 48836 (SAN 285-6662) Tel 517-223-9581.

Wilderness House, *(Wilderness Hse; 0-931798),* 11129 Caves Hwy., Cave Junction, OR 97523 (SAN 208-0907) Tel 503-592-2106.

†**Wilderness Pr.,** *(Wilderness Pr; 0-89997; 0-911824),* 2440 Bancroft Way, Berkeley, CA 94704-1676 (SAN 203-2139) Tel 415-843-8080; *CIP.*

Wilderness Society, The, *(Wilderness Soc)* 1400 Eye St. NW, 10th Flr., Washington, DC 20005 (SAN 225-0128) Tel 202-842-3400.

Wildfire Press *See Scholastic, Inc.*

Wildfire Publishing Co., *(Wildfire Pub; 0-938444),* 5797 Honors Drive, San Diego, CA 92122 (SAN 216-2040) Tel 619-458-1728.

Wildflower Pr., *(Wildflower; 0-938370),* P.O. Box 1027, Woodland Hills, CA 91365 (SAN 215-8280).

Wildlife & Preservation Trust International, Inc., Affil. of Jersey Wildlife Preservation Trust, *(WPTI),* 34th St. & Girard Ave., Philadelphia, PA 19104 (SAN 260-3306) Tel 215-222-3636.

Wildlife Education, Ltd., *(Wildlife Educ; 0-937934),* 930 W. Washington, Suite 14, San Diego, CA 92103 (SAN 215-8299) Tel 619-299-5034.

Wildlife Management Institute, *(Wildlife Mgmt),* Suite 725, 1101 14th St., NW, Washington, DC 20005 (SAN 225-0136) Tel 202-347-1774.

†**Wildlife Society, Inc. The,** *(Wildlife Soc; 0-933564),* 5410 Grosvenor Ln., Bethesda, MD 20814 (SAN 203-0225) Tel 301-897-9770; *CIP.*

Wildlife-Wildlands Institute, *(Wildlife-Wildlands; 0-910439),* 5200 Upper Miller Creek Rd., Missoula, MT 59803 (SAN 260-1575) Tel 406-251-3867.

Wildwater Designs Ltd., *(Wildwater Designs),* 230 Penllyn Pike, Penllyn, PA 19422 (SAN 219-8371).

Wildwood Pr., *(Wildwood; 0-918944),* 2110 Wood Ave., Colorado Springs, CO 80907 (SAN 210-5284) Tel 303-634-8078.

Wildwood Pr., *(Wildwood Pr; 0-9607260),* 209 SW Wildwood, Grants Pass, OR 97526 (SAN 239-345X) Tel 503-479-3434.

Wildwood Pubns., Div. of Live Stream, Inc., *(Wildwood Pubns MI; 0-914104),* P.O. Box 629, Traverse City, MI 49684 (SAN 206-5916) Tel 616-941-7160; Toll free: 800-447-7367.

Wildwood Publishing Co., *(Wildwood Pub Co; 0-915251),* 6851 Ream's Rd., Alanson, MI 49706 (SAN 289-8926).

Wiley, John, & Sons, Inc., *(Wiley; 0-471; 0-8260),* 605 Third Ave., New York, NY 10158 (SAN 200-2272) Tel 212-850-6418. *Imprints:* Harwal Publishing Company (Harwal Pub Co).

Wiley, Leonard, *(L Wiley; 0-911742),* 2927 SE 75th Ave., Portland, OR 97206 (SAN 203-9273) Tel 503-777-3645.

Wilk Publishing Co., *(Wilk Pub),* P.O. Box 320, Park Ridge, IL 60068 (SAN 203-221X) Tel 312-725-4878.

Wilkerson J. L.Publishing Co., *(Wilkerson Pub Co; 0-915253),* 731 Franklin St., Westbury, NY 11590 (SAN 289-8950) Tel 516-334-6297.

Wilkinson, Paul H., *(Wilkinson; 0-911710),* 5900 Kingswood Rd., NW, Washington, DC 20014 (SAN 205-5295) Tel 301-530-0888.

Wilks, Karl Glyn, *(K G Wilks; 0-9616912),* 528 N. Main St., McGregor, TX 76657 (SAN 661-521X) Tel 817-840-4503.

Willamette Kayak & Canoe Club, *(Willamette Kayak Canoe Club; 0-9616257),* P.O. Box 1062, Corvallis, OR 97339 (SAN 658-3784) Tel 503-754-4323; 218 NW 28th, Corvallis, OR 97330 (SAN 658-3792).

Willamette Pr., *(Willamette; 0-913695),* P.O. Box 2065, Beaverton, OR 97075 (SAN 286-2174) Tel 503-643-1357.

Willamette River Press, *(Willamette River; 0-915443),* P.O. Box 317, W. Linn, OR 97068 (SAN 291-4697) Tel 503-656-6300.

Willard, John A., *(J A Willard; 0-9612398),* 3119 Country Club Circle, Billings, MT 59102 (SAN 289-5323) Tel 406-259-1966.

Willard/Bower, *(Willard-Bower; 0-9606810),* 100 Marilyn Ave., Roseville, CA 95678 (SAN 211-9943) Tel 916-786-2632.

Willard Pr., *(Willard Pr; 0-9615349),* P.O. Box 1254, Summit, NJ 07901 (SAN 695-099X) Tel 201-273-5143.

Willco Publishing, *(Willco Pub; 0-937579),* 325 N. 33rd Ave., Suite 104, St. Cloud, MN 56301 (SAN 658-8352) Tel 612-393-2829.

Willcox, P. J., *(P J Willcox; 0-9608436),* P.O. Box 39, Huntington, IN 46750 (SAN 240-8066).

Willcraft Pubs., *(Willcraft; 0-910585),* 5093 Williamsport Dr., Norcross, GA 30092 (SAN 260-2784) Tel 404-449-4758.

Willer, Ed, *(Willer; 0-9614931),* 2606 Lewis Farm Rd., Raleigh, NC 27608 (SAN 693-4463) Tel 919-832-8881; Orders to: Village Book and Stationery, Inc., P.O. Box 10485, Raleigh, NC 27605 (SAN 662-3239) Tel 919-834-6234.

Willert, James, *(J Willert; 0-930798),* 12804 S. Graff Dr., La Mirada, CA 90638 (SAN 212-2456) Tel 213-691-5641.

Willett Publishing Co., *(Willett Pub Co; 0-915005),* 388 Berkeley Ave., Winnetka, IL 60093 (SAN 289-4688) Tel 312-441-8818.

William & Allen, *(William & Allen; 0-9614403),* P.O. Box 6147, Olympia, WA 98502 (SAN 688-7058) Tel 206-866-7417.

William & Dana Co., *(William Dana; 0-9616258),* 518 N. Nevada, Suite 210, Colorado Springs, CO 80903 (SAN 658-7305) Tel 303-632-2213.

†**William & Richards, Pubs.,** *(William & Rich; 0-9600202),* P.O. Box 2546, San Francisco, CA 94126 (SAN 282-5481) Tel 415-461-2835; *CIP.*

William Bloomfield & Associates *See WB&A Pubns.*

William Hammond Mathers Museum, *(W H Mathers Mus; 0-9605982),* 601 E. Eighth St., Indiana University, Bloomington, IN 47405 (SAN 216-7379) Tel 812-335-6873.

William Henry Thomas Family, *(Wm H T Fam; 0-9614787),* 8 Central Highlands, Tuscaloosa, AL 35404 (SAN 692-7610) Tel 205-556-9330.

William of Orange Publications, *(William of Orange),* N84 W16033 Menomonee Ave., No. 109, Menomonee Falls, WI 53051 (SAN 264-4983) Tel 414-255-4309; Orders to: Gerry Max or Carole Rahn, 1450 Vallejo St., No. 205, San Francisco, CA 54109 (SAN 662-748X) Tel 415-771-2364.

Williams, Edward, Publishing, *(Williams Pub Co; 0-934411),* P.O. Box 33280, No. 231, Austin, TX 78764 (SAN 693-8345) Tel 512-528-5884. *Imprints:* Banned Books (Banned Bks).

Williams, H. J., *(H J WIlliams; 0-9616843),* P.O. Box 203, Sausalito, CA 94966 (SAN 661-101X); 191 Santa Rosa Ave., Sausalito, CA 94965 (SAN 661-1028) Tel 415-332-8635; Dist. by: Publishers Group West, 5855 Beaudry St., Emeryville, CA 94608 (SAN 202-8522) Tel 415-658-3453.

Williams, Howard D., *(H Williams; 0-9615684),* 60 Broad St., Hamilton, NY 13346 (SAN 695-8176) Tel 315-824-0974.

Williams, Ken J., Pubns., *(K J Williams Pubns; 0-9603742),* 881 Tenth Ave., Suite 4C, New York, NY 10019 (SAN 214-4891) Tel 212-247-3374.

Williams, Russell I., *(R I Williams; 0-9613013),* 414 E. 23rd St., Cheyenne, WY 82001 (SAN 294-2941) Tel 303-634-7905.

Williams & Assocs., Subs. of South Seas Visuals, *(Wms & Assocs IA; 0-938185),* 4068 Tanglefoot Terr., Bettendorf, IA 52722 (SAN 659-7335) Tel 319-355-7142.

†**Williams & Wilkins Co.,** Div. of Waverly Pr., Inc., *(Williams & Wilkins; 0-683),* 428 E. Preston St., Baltimore, MD 21202 (SAN 202-5175) Tel 301-528-8521; Toll free: 800-638-0672; *CIP.*

Williams College, *(Williams Coll; 0-915081),* P.O. Box 676, Williamstown, MA 01267 (SAN 289-8993) Tel 413-597-2278; 75 Park St., Williamstown, MA 01267 (SAN 289-9000).

Williams Communications, Inc., *(Williams Com; 0-9612296),* P.O. Box 1849, Orangeburg, SC 29115 (SAN 263-2365).

Williams Foundation *See* **Historic New Orleans Collection, The**

Williams Press, *(Williams Pr),* 417 Commerce St., Nashville, TN 37219 (SAN 211-1438).

Williams/Wright Pubs., *(Williams-Wright Pub; 0-937961),* 18402 SW 89th Pl., Miami, FL 33157 (SAN 659-5510) Tel 305-251-2756.

Williamson & Assocs. Advertising Agency, *(Williamson Ad Agcy; 0-934033),* 3004 16th Street, Suite 304, San Francisco, CA 94108 (SAN 692-9710) Tel 415-981-0911.

†**Williamson Publishing Co.,** *(Williamson Pub Co; 0-913589),* Church Hill Rd., P.O. Box 185, Charlotte, VT 05445 (SAN 285-3884) Tel 802-425-2102; *CIP.*

Williamson School of Horsemanship, *(Williamson Sch; 0-9600144),* P.O. Box 506, Hamilton, MT 59840 (SAN 205-5317) Tel 406-363-2874.

Willie, Ralph G., D.D.S., *(R G Willie DDS),* 30317 16th Ave. S., Federal Way, WA 98003 (SAN 212-7113) Tel 206-839-7270.

Willis, Harold L., *(H L Willis; 0-912311),* 623 Vine St., Wisconsin Dells, WI 53965 (SAN 277-6871).

Willis, Locker & Owens Publishing, *(Willis Locker & Owens; 0-930279),* 71 Thompson St., New York, NY 10012 (SAN 670-8641) Tel 212-966-4629.

Willmann-Bell, Inc., *(Willmann-Bell; 0-943396),* P.O. Box 35025, Richmond, VA 23235 (SAN 240-8074) Tel 804-320-7016.

Willoughby Books, *(Willoughby),* 14 Hamburg Turnpike, Hamburg, NJ 07419 (SAN 205-5341).

Willoughby Wessington Publishing Co., *(Willoughby Wessington; 0-911227),* P.O. Box 911, Mercer Island, WA 98040 (SAN 276-6795) Tel 206-232-1867.

Willow Creek Pr., Div. of Wisconsin Sportsman, *(Willow Creek Pr; 0-932558),* P.O. Box 2266, Oshkosh, WI 54903 (SAN 211-2825) Tel 414-233-4143; Toll free: 800-341-7770; Orders to: 2663 Oregon St., Oshkosh, WI 54901 (SAN 662-1880) Tel 414-233-4143; Toll free: 800-341-7770.

Willow Pr., *(Willow Pr; 0-9617159),* 19630 166th Ave., NE, Woodinville, WA 98072 (SAN 663-253X) Tel 206-483-9198.

Willow Publishing Co., *(Willow Pub; 0-9606948),* P.O. Box 6636-AH Sta., San Antonio, TX 78209 (SAN 205-9401) Tel 512-822-5263.

Willow Run Publishing, *(Willow Run Pub; 0-9614700),* 2655 Tompkins Pl., Dayton, OH 45430 (SAN 692-6096) Tel 513-429-3545.

Willow Tree Pr., *(Willow Tree NY; 0-9606960),* 124 Willow Tree Rd., Monsey, NY 10952 (SAN 217-4588) Tel 914-354-9139.

Willowdale Pr., *(Willowdale Pr; 0-9613955),* P.O. Box 3655, Cherry Hill, NJ 08034 (SAN 697-1857).

†**Willowisp Pr., Inc.,** *(Willowisp Pr; 0-87406),* 401 E. Wilson Bridge Rd., Worthington, OH 43085 (SAN 687-4592) Tel 614-431-2203; Dist. by: Sterling Publishing Co., 2 Park Ave., New York, NY 10016 (SAN 211-6324) Tel 212-532-7160; *CIP.*

Willowood Pr., *(Willowood Pr; 0-938376),* P.O. Box 22321, Lexington, KY 40522 (SAN 215-8302).

Willyshe Publishing Co., Inc., *(Willyshe Pub; 0-936112),* 112 Mountain Rd., Linthicum Heights, MD 21090 (SAN 213-9499) Tel 301-789-0241.

Wilmar Pubs., *(Wilmar Pubs),* P.O. Box 5295, Sherman Oaks, CA 91413 (SAN 210-9697) Tel 818-762-1234.

Wilmer Graphics, Inc., *(Wilmer Graph; 0-9615967),* P.O. Box 140, Huntington, NY 11743 (SAN 697-3116).

Wilmington Press, *(Wilmington Pr; 0-936654),* Orders to: 13315 Wilmington Dr., Dallas, TX 75234 (SAN 282-549X) Tel 214-620-8431.

Wilmot Publishing Co., *(Wilmot Pub Co; 0-916405),* P.O. Box 27836, Orlando, FL 32867-7836 (SAN 295-5555) Tel 305-273-4775.

Wilshire Bk. Co., *(Wilshire; 0-87980),* 12015 Sherman Rd., North Hollywood, CA 91605-3781 (SAN 205-5368) Tel 213-875-1711.

Wilson, Barbara Juarez, *(B J Wilson; 0-9610712),* 15 Ledyard St., San Francisco, CA 94124 (SAN 264-813X) Tel 619-454-3746.

Wilson, Billy, *(B Wilson KY; 0-9617160),* Rte. 5, Box 222, Irvine, KY 40336 (SAN 662-9520) Tel 606-723-5889. Do not confuse with B. Wilson of Sheridan, WY.

Wilson, Bob, *(B Wilson; 0-9608192),* 1542 Big Horn Ave., Sheridan, WY 82801 (SAN 240-3021) Tel 307-674-8422.

Wilson, Charles A., *(C A Wilson; 0-9616261),* P.O. Box 278, Story, WY 82842 (SAN 658-3806) Tel 307-683-2188.

Wilson, H. W., *(Wilson; 0-8242),* 950 University Ave., Bronx, NY 10452 (SAN 203-2961) Tel 212-588-8400; Toll free: 800-367-6770.

Wilson, J. B., Pr., Inc., *(J B Wilson; 0-933458),* 1730 Columbia Dr. E., Fresno, CA 93727 (SAN 211-769X) Tel 209-251-8751.

Wilson, John, *(Wilson J; 0-9608494),* Rt. Four, 111 Cravens Terrace, Chattanooga, TN 37409 (SAN 240-8082) Tel 615-821-2087.

Wilson, P., Services, *(P Wilson Serv),* 4441 McPherson Ave., St. Louis, MO 63108 (SAN 209-3847).

Wilson, Pierre, Publishing Co., *(P Wilson Pub; 0-9616033),* 3900 Martin Luther King Way, Oakland, CA 94609 (SAN 697-9408) Tel 415-653-6666.

Wilson, *(Wilson OK; 0-9615259),* 1409 Lowry Ln., Atoka, OK 74525 (SAN 695-1597) Tel 405-889-5859.

Wilson & Crewe, *(Wilson Crewe; 0-9616673),* 1845 Anaheim St., No. 3C, Costa Mesa, CA 92627 (SAN 659-9249) Tel 714-631-1132.

Wilson Brothers Pubns., *(Wilson Bros; 0-934944),* P.O. Box 712, Yakima, WA 98907 (SAN 212-2014) Tel 509-457-8275.

Wilson Ornithological Society, *(Wilson Ornithological),* Museum of Zoology, Ann Arbor, MI 48109 (SAN 225-2287) Tel 313-764-0457; Winthrop College, Dept. of Biology, Keith L. Bildstein (Ed.), Rock Hill, SC 29733 (SAN 662-1899); Orders to: Ornithological Societies of North America, Ohio State Univ., 1735 Neil Ave., Dept. of Zoology, Columbus, OH 43210 (SAN 662-1902).

Wilson Publishing, Inc., *(Wilson Pub Inc; 0-9616299),* P.O. Box 2190, Glenwood Springs, CO 81602 (SAN 695-8036); 1512 Grand Ave., Glenwood Springs, CO 81602 (SAN 658-2885) Tel 303-945-5600.

†**Wilton Enterprises, Bk. Div.,** *(Wilton; 0-912696),* 1603 S. Michigan Ave., Chicago, IL 60616 (SAN 206-0248) Tel 312-663-5096; Toll free: 800-772-711; *CIP.*

Wilton Place Communications, *(Wilton Place; 0-914499),* P.O. Box 2020, Burbank, CA 91507 (SAN 282-5503) Tel 818-841-7286.

Wimbledon Music Inc., *(Wimbledon Music; 0-938170),* 1888 Century Park E., Century City, CA 90067 (SAN 219-8444) Tel 213-556-3000.

Wimer, Margaret R., *(M R Wimer; 0-9617069),* P.O. Box 782, Franklin, WV 26807 (SAN 662-9024) Tel 304-358-7675.

Wimmer Brothers Bks., *(Wimmer Bks),* 4210 BF Goodrich Blvd., Memphis, TN 38181 (SAN 209-6544) Tel 901-362-8900.

Wimsey Hse., *(Wimsey Hse; 0-915919),* 17743 San Fernando Mission Blvd., Grenada Hills, CA 91344 (SAN 294-1139) Tel 213-363-6652.

Winans, Chip, Productions, *(Winans; 0-9613234),* 21 Quason Lane, Harwichport, MA 02646 (SAN 295-1371) Tel 617-432-2728; Dist. by: Caroline Hse., Inc., 5S 250 Frontenac Rd., Naperville, IL 60540 (SAN 211-2280) Tel 312-983-6400; Toll free: 900-245-2665.

Winch, B. L., & Assocs./Jalmar Pr., *(B L Winch; 0-935266),* 45 Hitching Post Dr., Bldg. 2, Rolling Hills Estates, CA 90274-4297 (SAN 214-1728) Tel 213-539-6430; Toll free: 800-662-9662.

Winchell, Jane Neely, , *(J N Winchell; 0-9610978),* P.O. Box 5336, Waco, TX 76708 (SAN 265-3478) Tel 817-772-2262.

Winchester, M. C., Publishing, *(M C Winchester; 0-9616703),* P.O. Box 817, Hermosa Beach, CA 90254 (SAN 659-9354) Tel 213-212-6580; Dist. by: Nuth Bks., P.O. Box 5793, Denver, CO 80217 (SAN 200-6596).

Wind & Sea Pr., *(Wind & Sea Pr; 0-9616009),* P.O. Box 2311, Carlsbad, CA 92008 (SAN 697-9645) Tel 619-434-6648; 2955 Ocean St., No. 6, Carlsbad, CA 92008 (SAN 697-9653).

Wind Chimes, *(Wind Chimes; 0-941190),* P.O. Box 601, Glen Burnie, MD 21061 (SAN 237-9724).

Wind River Bks., *(Wind River Bks; 0-938023),* 1310 W. Fourth Ave., Suite 302, Broomfield, CO 80020 (SAN 661-4094) Tel 303-465-2672.

Wind River Press, *(Wind River Pr; 0-932119; 0-932119),* 3403 Andtree, Austin, TX 78724 (SAN 686-161X) Tel 512-928-1664.

Wind River Scribes, The, *(Wind River Scri; 0-942652),* 460 Lindale Dr., No. 81, Springfield, OR 97477 (SAN 238-5902) Tel 503-726-0759.

WindBooks, Div. of A Wind Publishing Corp., *(WindBks; 0-88016),* P.O. Box 4008, St. Johnsbury, VT 59819-4008 (SAN 282-552X) Tel 802-748-3360.

Windemede Publishing, *(Windemede Pub; 0-931517),* P.O. Box 417, Amherst, OH 44001 (SAN 682-3181); 854 South Lake St., Amherst, OH 44001 (SAN 662-7684) Tel 216-984-3522.

Windemere Pr., Inc., Subs. of Motivational Dynamics, Inc., *(Windemere Pr; 0-930115),* 360 SW Breeze Ct., P.O. Box 25104, Portland, OR 97225 (SAN 670-2686) Tel 503-292-8314; Dist. by: Far West Book Service, 3515 NE Hassalo, Portland, OR 97232 (SAN 107-6760) Tel 503-234-7664.

Windfall *See* **Doubleday & Co., Inc.**

Windfall Publishing Co., Inc., *(Windfall Pub; 0-9613604),* P.O. Box 469, Annapolis, MD 21401 (SAN 683-2334); 400 Ridyely Ave., Annapolis, MD 21401 (SAN 662-2607) Tel 301-268-3654.

†**Windflower Pr.,** *(Windflower Pr; 0-931534),* Rte. 1, Box 10, Garland, NE 68360 (SAN 208-9211) Tel 402-588-2272; *CIP.*

Windgate Pr., *(Windgate Pr; 0-915269),* 532 Sausalito Blvd., Sausalito, CA 94965 (SAN 289-9027) Tel 415-332-0912; Box 1715, Sausalito, CA 94965 (SAN 660-9538).

Windham Bay Pr., *(Windham Bay),* P.O. Box 1332, Juneau, AK 99802 (SAN 214-4905).

Windhover *See* **Berkley Publishing Group**

Windless Orchard Series, *(Windless Orchard; 0-87883),* Indiana Univ., English Dept., Fort Wayne, IN 46805 (SAN 206-023X) Tel 219-482-5583.

Windmill Bks. *See* **Dutton, E. P.**

†**Windmill Bks., Inc.,** Div. of Intext, *(Windmill Bks; 0-87807; 0-671),* 1230 Ave. of the Americas, New York, NY 10020 (SAN 205-5376) Tel 212-245-6400; *CIP.*

Windmill Publishing Co., *(Windmill Pub Co; 0-933846),* 2147 Windmill View Rd., El Cajon, CA 92020 (SAN 212-8047) Tel 619-448-5390.

Window Editions, *(Window Edns; 0-939290),* 350 Old Roaring Brook Rd., Mount Kisco, NY 10549 (SAN 216-5201) Tel 914-241-2813.

Windrose Pubns., *(Windrose Pub; 0-9615508),* P.O. Box 619, Port Townsend, WA 98368 (SAN 695-7943) Tel 206-385-5053.

Winds of the World Pr., *(Winds World Pr; 0-938338),* 35 Whittemore Rd., Framingham, MA 01701 (SAN 215-8310).

Windsinger Enterprises, Inc., *(Windsinger; 0-942224),* 1256 E. 1980, N, Logan, UT 84321 (SAN 213-8115) Tel 801-753-3344.

†**Windsong Books International,** *(Windsong; 0-934604),* P.O. Box 867, Huntington Beach, CA 92648 (SAN 213-7143) Tel 714-963-0324; *CIP.*

Windsor, Janna H., *(J H Windsor; 0-9600400),* 225 E. Laurel Ave., Arcadia, CA 91006 (SAN 221-5438).

Windsor Bks. Div., Div. of Windsor Marketing Corp., *(Windsor),* P.O. Box 280, Brightwaters, NY 11718 (SAN 203-2945).

Windsor Hse., *(Windsor Hse; 0-911321),* 3308 Midway Dr., Suite 145, San Diego, CA 92110 (SAN 276-6906).

Windsor Locks Historical Society, *(Wndsr Locks Hist Soc),* Noden-Reed Pk., 58 West St., Windsor Locks, CT 06096 (SAN 663-4583).

Windsor Pr., The, *(Windsor Pr; 0-9608260),* P.O. Box 786, Binghamton, NY 13902-0786 (SAN 240-1703).

Windsor Press, Inc., The *See* **Gamliel's Pub**

Windsor Pubns., Inc., *(Windsor Pubns Inc; 0-89781),* 8910 Quartz Ave., P.O. Box 9071, Northridge, CA 91328 (SAN 265-3699) Tel 818-700-0200; Toll free: 800-423-5761.

Windstar Bks., *(Windstar Bks; 0-9616306),* 1017 Abingdon Rd., Virginia Beach, VA 23451 (SAN 658-5353) Tel 804-422-2945; P.O. Box 1643, Virginia Beach, VA 23451 (SAN 658-5361).

Windstone *See* **Bantam Bks., Inc.**

Windswept Books *See* **Scholastic, Inc.**

Windswept Hse. Pubs., *(Windswept Hse; 0-932433),* P.O. Box 159, Mt. Desert, ME 04660 (SAN 687-4363) Tel 207-244-7149.

Windwalker Pr., *(Windwalker Pr; 0-938025),* 555 S. State, Orem, UT 84057 (SAN 659-8129) Tel 801-224-9933.

Windward Publishing Inc., *(Windward Pub; 0-89317),* 105 NE 25th St., P.O. Box 371005, Miami, FL 33137 (SAN 208-3663) Tel 305-576-6232.

Windyridge Pr., *(Windyridge; 0-913366),* P.O. Box 327, Medford, OR 97501 (SAN 206-3948) Tel 503-772-5399; Orders to: Northwest Textbook Depository, P.O. Box 5608, Portland, OR 97228 (SAN 206-3956) Tel 503-772-5399.

Wine, J. F., *(J F Wine; 0-9604350),* 924 Woodland Ave., Winchester, VA 22601 (SAN 206-0221) Tel 703-662-5735.

Wine Appreciation Guild, The, *(Wine Appreciation; 0-932664),* 155 Connecticut St., San Francisco, CA 94107 (SAN 201-9515) Tel 415-864-1202; Toll free: 800-242-9462 (Orders only).

Wine Books, *(Wine Bks; 0-9604488),* P.O. Box 1015, San Marcos, CA 92069 (SAN 215-1936).

Wine Consultants of California, *(Wine Consul Calif; 0-916040),* P.O. Box 27187, San Francisco, CA 94127 (SAN 207-4214) Tel 415-681-8989.

Wine Country Pubs., *(Wine Country; 0-9612674),* 706 Mariano Dr., Sonoma, CA 95476 (SAN 289-470X) Tel 707-938-0485.

Wine Pubns., *(Wine Pubns; 0-913840),* 96 Parnassus Rd., Berkeley, CA 94708 (SAN 205-5392) Tel 415-843-4209.

Wineberry Pr., The, *(Wineberry Pr; 0-9612158),* 3207 Macomb St. NW, Washington, DC 20008 (SAN 289-5412) Tel 202-363-8036.

Winecellar Pr., The, *(Winecellar; 0-9613446),* 197 North Rd., Kingston, RI 02881 (SAN 657-1212) Tel 401-789-7338.

Winequest, *(Winequest; 0-9615063),* 31 Belford Ave., Bay Shore, NY 11706 (SAN 694-1516) Tel 516-666-4216.

Winfoto, *(Winfoto; 0-9605522),* 1790 Kearney St., Denver, CO 80220 (SAN 216-2067).

Wingate High School Pr., *(Wingate HS Pr; 0-9613681),* 600 Kingston Ave., Brooklyn, NY 11203 (SAN 692-7505).

Wingbow Pr., *(Wingbow Pr; 0-914640),* Dist. by: Bookpeople, 2929 Fifth St., Berkeley, CA 94710 (SAN 168-9517) Tel 415-549-3030; Toll free: 800-227-1516.

Winged Lion Publishing Ltd., *(Winged Lion; 0-915922),* 414 S. Western Ave., P.O. Box 75936, Los Angeles, CA 90075 (SAN 208-0346).

Wings of Faith Publishing Hse., *(Wings Faith Pub; 0-930555),* 500 Bruns Ave., Charlotte, NC 28208 (SAN 677-4687) Tel 704-332-8923.

Wings Pr., *(Wings ME; 0-939736),* R.F.D 2, P.O. Box 730, Belfast, ME 04915 (SAN 216-7689) Tel 207-338-2005.

Wings Pr., *(Wings Pr; 0-930324),* P.O. Box 25296, Houston, TX 77005 (SAN 209-4975) Tel 713-668-7953.

Wings Publishing & Production Co., *(Wings Pub Prod; 0-9616010),* P.O. Box 683, Severna Park, MD 21146 (SAN 696-7205) Tel 301-987-6244; 732 Benfield Rd., Severna Park, MD 21146 (SAN 698-2158).

Winicorp, *(Winicorp; 0-9610634),* P.O. Box 3314, San Leandro, CA 94578 (SAN 276-9476) Tel 415-483-3029.

Winkleman, Babe, Productions, Inc., *(B Winkelman Prods; 0-915405),* P.O. Box 407, 213 NW Fourth St., Brainerd, MN 56401 (SAN 291-4700) Tel 218-829-1144.

Winkler, Charles R., Ltd., *(C R Winkler Ltd; 0-9615613),* 7222 W. Cermak Rd., North Riverside, IL 60546 (SAN 696-3145) Tel 312-447-3800.

Winkler, Marion R., *(M R Winkler; 0-9610344),* 5225 N. 20th St., Phoenix, AZ 85016 (SAN 264-4991) Tel 602-957-2922.

Winmar Pr., *(Winmar Pr; 0-9613253),* 5800 W. Century Blvd., P.O. Box 91157-1157, Los Angeles, CA 90009 (SAN 686-1601) Tel 213-672-0735.

Winmark Pr., *(Winmark Pr; 0-9608278),* P.O. Box 148, Stratford, CT 06497 (SAN 240-5083).

Winn Bks., Div. of The Winn Corporation, *(Winn Bks; 0-916947),* P.O. Box 80157, Seattle, WA 98108 (SAN 655-7864) Tel 206-763-9544; Toll free: 800-426-5589; Dist. by: Ingram, 1125 Heil Quaker Blvd., LaVergne, TN 37086 (SAN 169-7978) Tel 615-793-5000; Dist. by: Publishers Group West, 5855 Beaudry St., Emeryville, CA 94608 (SAN 202-8522) Tel 415-658-3453; Dist. by: Bookpeople, 2929 Fifth St., Berkeley, CA 94710 (SAN 168-9517) Tel 415-549-3030; Dist. by: Pacific Pipeline, 19215 66th Ave. S., Kent, WA 98032 (SAN 208-2128) Tel 206-872-5523; Dist. by: Pacific Trade Group, P.O. Box 668, Pearl City, HI 96782-0668 (SAN 169-1635).

Winnen, Jo, *(J Winnen; 0-9603404),* 624 S. Fancher Rd., Racine, WI 53406 (SAN 207-2416).

Winners Publishing Co., *(Winners Pub; 0-938099),* P.O. Box 1335, Coronado, CA 92118 (SAN 659-7114); 842 H Ave., Coronado, CA 92118 (SAN 659-7122) Tel 619-435-6407.

Winnetka Pr., *(Winnetka Pr; 0-938901),* 5101 Suffield Ct., Skokie, IL 60077 (SAN 662-6548) Tel 312-966-2730.

Winning Pubns., *(Winning St Paul; 0-9617124),* 1439 Arcade St., Suite 120, St. Paul, MN 55106 (SAN 662-6831) Tel 612-774-0678. Do not confuse with Winning Pubns., Oakland, CA.

Winning Ways Pr., *(Winning Ways Pr; 0-931501),* 2888 Bluff, Suite 433, Boulder, CO 80301 (SAN 683-1230) Tel 303-447-8483.

Winrock International, *(Winrock Intl; 0-933595),* Rte. 3, Morrilton, AR 72110-9537 (SAN 692-7165) Tel 501-727-5435; Dist. by: Agribookstore/Winrock, Rosslyn Plaza, 1611 N. Kent St., Suite 600, Arlington, VA 22209 (SAN 200-6693) Tel 703-525-9455.

Winship Pr., *(Winship Pr; 0-915430),* 2324 Clayton St., Macon, GA 31204 (SAN 207-3005) Tel 912-743-0029.

Winski, Joseph Anthony, *(J A Winski; 0-9616976),* 13815 S. Normandie Ave., No. 48, Gardena, CA 90249 (SAN 661-8103) Tel 213-327-8000.

Winslow Wolverton & Kornegay, Div. of Triad Publications, *(Winslow Wolverton; 0-9614874),* P.O. Box 283, Herford, NC 27944 (SAN 693-2304) Tel 919-426-7665; Dist. by: Wimmer Brothers Books, 4210 BF Goodrich Blvd., Memphis, TN 38181 (SAN 662-3174) Tel 901-362-8900.

Winston, Harry, Inc., *(H Winston Inc; 0-87311),* 718 Fifth Ave., New York, NY 10019 (SAN 695-1058) Tel 212-245-2000; Toll free: 800-223-2305.

Winston & Beck, *(Winston & Beck; 0-9615921),* 3504 Chaucer Pl., Raleigh, NC 27609 (SAN 696-7736) Tel 919-782-4615.

Winston-Derek Pubs.,Inc., *(Winston-Derek; 0-938232; 1-55523),* P.O. Box 90883, Nashville, TN 37209 (SAN 216-4760) Tel 615-321-0535; Toll free: 800-826-1888; Dist. by: Baker & Taylor Co., Midwest Div., 5 Gladiola Ave., Momence, IL 60954 (SAN 169-2100).

Winston Pr., Inc., Div. of Harper & Row, Inc., *(Winston Pr; 0-86683),* c/o Harper & Row Pubs., Inc., 1700 Montgomery St., San Francisco, CA 94111 (SAN 215-3734) Tel 415-989-9000; Toll free: 800-242-7737 (Bookstores & schools); Toll free: 800-638-3030 (Individuals); Orders to: Harper & Row Pubs., Inc., Keystone Industrial Pk., Scranton, PA 18512 (SAN 215-3742). Harper & Row acquired Winston-Seabury from CBS Educational Publishing. Now considered an 'imprint' of Harper & Row. Please use San Francisco address for editorial inquiries.

Winter Brook Publishing Co., *(Winter Brook; 0-9602204),* P.O. Box 1106, Covina, CA 91722 (SAN 212-7121) Tel 714-585-7101.

Winter Publishing Co., *(Winter Pub Co; 0-938372),* P.O. Box 36536, Tucson, AZ 85740 (SAN 220-1100); 6632 N. Willowbrook Dr., Tucson, AZ 85704 (SAN 220-1119) Tel 602-742-4104.

Winterbourne Pr., *(Winterbourne Pr; 0-9609172),* 1407 Gilman St., Berkeley, CA 94706 (SAN 241-4201) Tel 415-527-9885.

†**Wintergreen & Advance Pubs.,** *(Wintergreen; 0-933460),* 1131 Tellem Drive, Pacific Palisades, CA 90272 (SAN 212-713X) Tel 213-459-1341; *CIP.*

Wintergreen Pr., *(Wintergreen P),* 4105 Oak St., Long Lake, MN 55356 (SAN 694-101X) Tel 612-476-1303.

Winters, David/Music, *(D Winters; 0-9616283),* 103 Van Ness St., Santa Cruz, CA 95060 (SAN 277-6707) Tel 408-426-0198.

Winters' Pubns., *(Winters Pubns; 0-935011),* P.O. Box 156, North Adams, MI 49262 (SAN 695-1929) Tel 517-287-5712.

WinterSpring Pr., *(WinterSpring Pr; 0-938651),* 406 Second St., Davis, CA 95616 (SAN 661-6305) Tel 916-753-2262.

Winterthur Museum & Gardens, *(Winterthur; 0-912724),* Rte. 52, Winterthur, DE 19735 (SAN 205-5406) Tel 302-656-8591; Dist. by: W. W. Norton & Co., 500 Fifth Ave., New York, NY 10110 (SAN 202-5795) Tel 212-354-5500; Toll free: 800-223-2584; Dist. by: Harry N. Abrams, 100 Fifth Ave., New York, NY 10011 (SAN 200-2434) Tel 212-206-7715; Toll free: 800-345-1359; Dist. by: Garland Press, 1611 Hilton Ave., Columbia, GA 31906 (SAN 223-1840); Dist. by: University Press of Virginia, P.O. Box 3608, University Station, Charlottesville, VA 22903 (SAN 202-5361) Tel 804-924-3468.

Wire Association International, *(Wire Assn Intl),* 1570 Boston Post Rd., Guilford, CT 06437 (SAN 224-8778) Tel 203-453-2777; P.O. Box H, Guilford, CT 06510 (SAN 669-3008).

Wires, Ltd., *(Wires Ltd; 0-9616173),* 1717 K St. NW, Suite 706, Washington, DC 20006 (SAN 699-9913) Tel 202-293-5540.

Wirth, Diane E., *(D E Wirth; 0-9602096),* 16804 E. Peakview Ave., Aurora, CO 80016 (SAN 212-3940) Tel 303-693-5653.

Wisconsin Annual Conference of the United Methodist Church, The, *(WI Conf United Meth Ch; 0-938779),* 750 Windsor St., Sun Prairie, WI 53590 (SAN 661-647X) Tel 608-837-3367; P.O. Box 220, Sun Prairie, WI 53590 (SAN 661-6488).

Wisconsin Bks., *(Wisconsin Bks; 0-913370),* 2769 Marshall Pkwy., Madison, WI 53713 (SAN 213-8875) Tel 608-257-4126. *Imprints:* Allison, R. B., Co. (R B Allison Co); Sol Press (Sol Press).

Wisconsin Education Fund, *(Wis Ed Fund; 0-9600358),* P.O. Box 321, Port Washington, WI 53074 (SAN 205-5414) Tel 414-284-9066.

Wisconsin Institute on Drug Abuse, Div. of Tellurian Community, Inc., *(Wis Inst Drug Abuse; 0-9615363),* 300 Femrite Dr., Madison, WI 53716 (SAN 695-2690) Tel 608-222-7311.

Wisconsin Sportsman, *(Wisconsin Sptmn; 0-932558),* P.O. Box 2266, Oshkosh, WI 54903 (SAN 207-3013) Tel 414-233-1327.

Wisconsin State Genealogical Society, Inc., *(Wisconsin Gen; 0-910255),* 5049 LaCrosse Ln., Madison, WI 53705 (SAN 223-0623) Tel 608-233-8018; c/o Hedberg, P.O. Box 685, Madison, WI 53701 (SAN 662-7498).

Wiscott Enterprises, *(Wiscott Ent; 0-938533),* 401 S. Kingsley Dr., Suite 126, Los Angeles, CA 90020 (SAN 661-1540) Tel 213-387-2283.

Wisdom Bk. Pubs., Inc., *(Wisdom Bk Pubs; 0-930509),* 2854 Angelo Dr., Los Angeles, CA 90077 (SAN 670-9702) Tel 213-271-1380.

Wisdom Garden Bks., *(Wisdom Garden; 0-914794),* P.O. Box 29448, Los Angeles, CA 90029 (SAN 206-5584) Tel 213-380-1968.

Wisdom Hse. Pr., *(Wisdom House; 0-932560),* 43222 SE Tapp Rd., Sandy, OR 97055 (SAN 212-2022) Tel 503-668-3119.

Wisdom Pr., *(Wisdom Pr; 0-915050),* P.O. Box 28031, Las Vegas, NV 89126 (SAN 693-8469) Tel 702-382-3009.

Wisdom Pubns. *See* **Great Traditions**

Names

Wise Publishing Co., *(Wise Pub; 0-915766),* 5625 Wilhelmina Ave., Woodland Hills, CA 91367 (SAN 203-1876) Tel 818-883-7527.

Wish Booklets, *(Wish Bklets; 0-913786),* 3807 Meredith Dr., Greensboro, NC 27408 (SAN 205-5430) Tel 919-282-2122.

WISH Pubns., *(Wish Pubns; 0-917392),* 113 W. 60th St., New York, NY 10023 (SAN 276-7090) Tel 212-841-5514.

Wishing Room, Inc., The, *(Wishing Rm; 0-931563),* P.O. Box 337, Mechanicsville, VA 23111 (SAN 682-207X) Tel 804-746-0375.

Wishing Star Books *See* Scholastic, Inc.

Wisla Pubs., *(Wisla Pubs; 0-9614274),* 1404 Twisted Oak Ln., Baton Rouge, LA 70810 (SAN 687-4169) Tel 504-766-6036; Orders to: P.O. Box 65042, Baton Rouge, LA 70896-5042 (SAN 662-2763).

Wismer, Romaine, *(R Wismer; 0-9617021),* 501 Sable Palm N., Ellenton, FL 33532 (SAN 662-8826) Tel 813-729-1027; Dist. by: Gulf Coast Periodicala, 1954 Whitfield Ave., Sarasota, FL 33580 (SAN 200-7568).

Wistaria Pr., *(Wistaria Pr; 0-916930),* 4373 NE Wistaria Dr., Portland, OR 97213 (SAN 237-9732) Tel 503-281-5945.

With Kids, *(With Kids; 0-9611292),* P.O. Box 353, West Sand Lake, NY 12196 (SAN 283-9903).

With Love Foundation, Inc., *(With Love Foun; 0-9614082),* 535 Cordova Rd., Suite 182, Santa Fe, NM 87501 (SAN 685-9321) Tel 505-983-1809.

Witkower Pr., Inc., *(Witkower; 0-911638),* P.O. Box 2296, Bishop's Corner, West Hartford, CT 06117 (SAN 205-5449) Tel 203-232-1127.

Witness to the Holocaust Project, *(Witness Holocaust; 0-912313),* Emory University, Atlanta, GA 30322 (SAN 264-5025) Tel 404-727-7525.

Witt, Bud, *(B Witt; 0-9604932),* P.O. Box 2527, 4212 W. Olive, Fullerton, CA 92633 (SAN 215-7160).

Wittenborn, George, Inc., *(Wittenborn; 0-8150),* 1018 Madison Ave., New York, NY 10021 (SAN 125-0957) Tel 212-288-1558.

Wittman Pubns., Inc., *(Wittman Pubns),* P.O. Box 3689, Baltimore, MD 21214 (SAN 210-9905) Tel 301-254-0273.

Wizard Productions *See* Inka Dinka Ink Childrens Pr.

Wizards Bookshelf, *(Wizards; 0-913510),* P.O. Box 6600, San Diego, CA 92106 (SAN 203-2872) Tel 619-235-0340; Dist. by: DeVorss & Co., P.O. Box 550, 1046 Princeton Dr., Marina del Rey, CA 90291 (SAN 282-6151); Dist. by: New Leaf Distributing, 1020 White St., SW, Atlanta, GA 30310 (SAN 294-1449).

WMC Service Corp., Subs. of Wisconsin Manufacturers & Commerce, *(WMC Serv; 0-942198),* P.O. Box 352, Madison, WI 53701 (SAN 687-6544); 501 E. Washington Ave., Madison, WI 53703 (SAN 662-278X) Tel 608-258-3400.

Wofsy, Alan, Fine Arts, *(A Wofsy Fine Arts; 0-915346; 1-55660),* P.O. Box 2210, San Francisco, CA 94126 (SAN 207-6438); 401 China Basin St., San Francisco, CA 94107 (SAN 662-7501) Tel 415-986-3030.

Wolcotts, Inc., *(Wolcotts; 0-910531),* 15124 Downey Ave., Paramount, CA 90723 (SAN 260-2792); Toll free: 800-421-2220; Toll free: 800-262-1538 (In California).

Wolf, George, *(G Wolf; 0-9616503),* 2323 Delanoy Ave., Bronx, NY 10469 (SAN 659-3577) Tel 212-519-0256.

Wolf Creek Pr., *(Wolf Creek Pr; 0-9611886),* P.O. Box 327, Canyondam, CA 95923 (SAN 286-0848) Tel 916-596-3412.

†**Wolf Hse. Bks.,** *(Wolf Hse; 0-915046),* P.O. Box 6657, Grand Rapids, MI 49506 (SAN 203-2856) Tel 616-245-8812; *CIP.*

Wolf Run Bks., *(Wolf Run Bks; 0-942296),* P.O. Box 9620, Minneapolis, MN 55440 (SAN 206-9571).

Wolfdog Pubns., *(Wolfdog Pubns; 0-9616191),* P.O. Box 142506, Anchorage, AK 99514-2506 (SAN 699-9824); 4938 Mills Dr., Anchorage, AK 99508 (SAN 699-9832) Tel 907-333-1481.

Wolfe, Ernest, Pubns., *(E Wolfe Pubns; 0-9603660),* 1655 Sawtelle Blvd., Los Angeles, CA 90025 (SAN 213-6481) Tel 213-478-2960.

Wolfe, Howard H., *(H H Wolfe; 0-9600850),* 12405 Davis Blvd., SE, Fort Myers, FL 33905 (SAN 206-0167) Tel 813-694-1825.

Wolfe Publishing Co., Inc., *(Wolfe Pub Co; 0-935632),* 6471 Airpark Dr., Prescott, AZ 86301 (SAN 289-7083) Tel 602-445-7810.

Wolfenbarger Publishing, *(Wolfenbarger; 0-913127),* P.O. Box 277, Phoenix City, AL 36867 (SAN 283-3344).

Wolfson Publishing Co., *(Wolfson; 0-916114),* Seven Wood St., Conestoga Bldg., Pittsburgh, PA 15222 (SAN 208-922X) Tel 412-391-6190.

Wolk & Rais, *(Wolk & Rais; 0-947647),* 1 Longford St., Philadelphia, PA 19136 (SAN 695-2437).

Woltz, Raymond K., *(R K Woltz; 0-9613447),* 1355 Hermes Ave., Leucadia, CA 92024 (SAN 657-1115) Tel 619-753-0055.

Wolverine Pr., *(Wolverine Pr; 0-9615395),* Box 962, Hellgate Sta., New York, NY 10029 (SAN 695-4626) Tel 212-369-4394; 430 E. 105th St., Apt. 2C, New York, NY 10029 (SAN 695-4634).

Womack Associates, *(Womack Assoc; 0-9605530),* 512 Westwood Dr., Prescott, AZ 86301 (SAN 215-9864).

Womack Educational Pubns., Div. of Womack Machine Supply Co., *(Womack Educ Pubns; 0-9605644),* 2010 Shea Rd., P.O. Box 35027, Dallas, TX 75235 (SAN 205-9657) Tel 214-357-3871.

Woman Activist, Inc., *(Woman Activist; 0-917560),* 2310 Barbour Rd., Falls Church, VA 22043 (SAN 209-617X) Tel 703-573-8716.

Woman Time Management, *(Woman Time Mgmt; 0-9610530),* 4719 Taft, Wichita Falls, TX 76308 (SAN 264-5033) Tel 817-691-1196; Dist. by: Baker & Taylor Co., Midwest Div., 501 Gladiola Ave., Momence, IL 60954 (SAN 169-2100); Dist. by: Baker & Taylor Co., Southeast Div., Mt. Olive Rd., Commerce, GA 30529 (SAN 169-1503); Dist. by: Dot Gibson, 161 Knight Ave. Cir., Waycross, GA 31501 (SAN 200-4143) Tel 912-285-2848; Dist. by: Southwest Cookbook Distributors, 1901 S. Shore Dr., Bonham, TX 75418 (SAN 200-4925) Tel 214-583-8898.

Woman's Club of Denton, Inc., The, *(W Club Denton; 0-9612076),* P.O. Box 35, Denton, MD 21629 (SAN 286-8938) Tel 301-479-1186.

Woman's Institute for Continuing Jewish Education, *(Womans Inst-Cont Jewish Ed; 0-9608054),* 4079 54th St., San Diego, CA 92105 (SAN 240-1061).

Woman's Pr., The, *(Woman's Pr; 0-9614878),* 245 W. 107th St., Apt. 12B, New York, NY 10029 (SAN 659-3631) Tel 212-427-1816; Orders to: P. B. S., P.O. Box 643, Cambridge, MA 02139 (SAN 662-4243) Tel 617-491-6562; Toll free: 800-544-1016.

Wombat Enterprises, Unlimited, *(Wombat Ent; 0-9605722),* P.O. Box 428, Latham, NY 12110 (SAN 239-5029).

Women for Sobriety, Inc., *(WFS),* P.O. Box 618, Quakertown, PA 18951 (SAN 216-4779) Tel 215-536-8026.

Women-in-Literature, Inc., *(Women-in-Lit; 0-935634),* P.O. Box 60550, Reno, NV 89506 (SAN 213-8824) Tel 702-972-1671.

Women in the Arts Foundation, Inc, *(Women Arts Found),* 325 Spring St., New York, NY 10013 (SAN 225-3941) Tel 212-691-0988.

Women on Words & Images, *(Women on Words; 0-9600724),* 30 Valley Rd., Princeton, NJ 08540 (SAN 206-622X) Tel 609-921-8653; Orders to: P.O. Box 2163, Princeton, NJ 08540 (SAN 206-6238).

Women Writers Alliance, *(Women Writers Alliance; 0-9615675),* P.O. Box 1083, Springfield, MA 01101 (SAN 292-7381) Tel 413-737-4888.

†**Women's Action Alliance, Inc.,** *(Women's Action; 0-9605828),* 370 Lexington Ave., New York, NY 10017 (SAN 207-6950) Tel 212-532-8330; *CIP.*

Women's Auxiliary of the American Cancer Society, Affil. of American Cancer Society, *(Womens Auxiliary Cancer; 0-9607282),* 241 Fourth Ave., Pittsburgh, PA 15222 (SAN 239-3506) Tel 412-261-4352; Orders to: WAACS Cookbook, 838 Goldview Dr., McKeasport, PA 15135 (SAN 662-1910) Tel 412-751-3535.

Women's Committee of the Buffalo Philharmonic Orchestra Society, Inc., *(Womens Com Buffalo; 0-9607538),* 26 Richmond Ave., Buffalo, NY 14222 (SAN 239-7986) Tel 716-839-1482.

Women's Committee of the Richmond Symphony, *(Womens Com Rich; 0-9613752),* 211 W. Franklin St., Richmond, VA 23220 (SAN 677-8224) Tel 804-740-8180.

Women's History Research Center, Inc., *(Women's Hist; 0-912374),* 2325 Oak St., Berkeley, CA 94708 (SAN 207-7175) Tel 415-548-1770.

Women's Institute for Freedom of the Press, *(Womens Inst Free Press; 0-930470),* 3306 Ross Pl., NW, Washington, DC 20008 (SAN 225-7114) Tel 202-966-7783.

Women's International Bowling Congress, *(WIBC),* 5301 S. 76th St., Greendale, WI 53129 (SAN 216-4787) Tel 414-421-9000.

Women's International League for Peace & Freedom, *(WILPF),* 1213 Race St., Philadelphia, PA 19107 (SAN 208-9858) Tel 215-563-7110.

Women's International Network News Quarterly, *(WINNEWS; 0-942096),* 187 Grant St., Lexington, MA 02173 (SAN 237-9740) Tel 617-862-9430.

Women's League for Conservative Judaism, *(WLCJ; 0-936293),* 48 E. 74th St., New York, NY 10021 (SAN 697-9661) Tel 212-628-1600.

Women's Legal Defense Fund, *(Women's Legal Defense; 0-932689),* Box 6189, Santa Barbara, CA 93160 (SAN 212-9892) Tel 805-965-7039.

Women's Referral Service, Inc., *(Womens Referral Serv; 0-937121),* P.O. Box 3093, Van Nuys, CA 91407 (SAN 658-5337) Tel 818-995-6646.

Women's Research Action Project, *(Womens Research Act; 0-930522),* 72 Cornell St., Roslindale, MA 02131 (SAN 209-6900) Tel 617-327-5016.

Women's Service League of West Feliciana Parish, *(Womens Serv; 0-9609422),* P.O. Box 904, 205 Pine St., St. Francisville, LA 70775 (SAN 276-7589) Tel 504-635-6162.

Women's Times Publishing, *(Womens Times; 0-910259),* Box 215, Grand Marais, MN 55604 (SAN 240-8945) Tel 218-387-2509.

Women's Yellow Pages, *(Womens Yellow Pgs; 0-9610748),* P.O. Box 66093, Los Angeles, CA 90066 (SAN 282-5562) Tel 213-398-5761.

Women's Yellow Pages, Inc., *(Women Yellow CO; 0-932439),* 1758 Emersen, Denver, CO 80218 (SAN 686-7405) Tel 303-861-2568.

Wonder-Treasure Bks., Inc., Div. of Price-Stern-Sloan, *(Wonder; 0-448),* Price/Stern/Sloan Publishers, 410 N. La Cienega Blvd., Los Angeles, CA 90048 (SAN 205-5457) Tel 213-657-6100; Toll free: 800-421-0892; Toll free: 800-227-8801 (In California).

Wonder View Pr., *(Wonder View Pr; 0-930117),* P.O. Box 3301, Mililani, HI 96789 (SAN 670-2813) Tel 808-623-5337.

Wood, Bob, Assocs., *(B Wood Assocs; 0-937863),* 6916 E. Fourth Plain Blvd., Vancouver, WA 98668 (SAN 659-6045) Tel 206-694-0628; Dist. by: Pacific Pipeline, 19215 66th Ave. S., Kent, WA 98032 (SAN 208-2128) Tel 206-872-5523; Toll free: 800-426-4727; Dist. by: All Sports Book Distributors, Box 5793, Denver, CO 80217 (SAN 200-7398); Toll free: 800-525-9030.

Wood, Curtis, Pubns., *(Curtis Wood Pubs; 0-9614875),* 4416 Eaton's Creek Rd., Nashville, TN 37218 (SAN 693-2312) Tel 615-876-1729.

Wood, Debby, *(D Wood; 0-9607490),* Box 1737, Cape Coral, FL 33910 (SAN 239-961X) Tel 813-481-6297; 3689 Liberty Square, Fort Myers, FL 33908 (SAN 693-5060).

Wood, Fern Morrow, *(F M Wood; 0-9606922),* Rte. 2, Cherryvale, KS 67335 (SAN 217-460X).

Wood, James Madison, Research Institute, The, *(J M Wood Res; 0-916767),* Box 2134, Stephens College, Columbia, MO 65215 (SAN 285-676X) Tel 314-876-7277.

Wood, R. S., & Co., *(R S Wood; 0-937635),* Star Rte. 81, Box 430, Liberty, ME 04949 (SAN 659-137X).

Wood, R. V., *(R V Wood),* 230 Payson Rd., Belmont, MA 02178 (SAN 217-4715).

Wood, Richard D., *(R D Wood; 0-9603898),* 76 Stonehenge Rd., Kingston, RI 02881 (SAN 207-5873) Tel 401-783-2135.

Wood & Jones Pubs., *(Wood & Jones; 0-9606114),* 139 W. Colorado Blvd., Pasadena, CA 91105 (SAN 216-8707) Tel 818-449-1144.

Wood Fire Ashes Pr., *(Wood Fire; 0-9613338),* 9230 E. Shore, Big Fork, MT 59911 (SAN 655-7872) Tel 406-837-5134.

Wood Lake Pr., *(Wood Lake Pr; 0-919599),* Dist. by: Friendship Pr., 475 Riverside Dr., Rm. 772, New York, NY 10027 (SAN 682-2754) Tel 212-870-2497.

Wood Library-Museum of Anesthesiology, Subs. of American Society of Anesthesiologists, *(Wood Lib-Mus; 0-9614932),* 515 Busse Hwy., Park Ridge, IL 60068 (SAN 693-4048) Tel 312-825-5586.

Wood Machinery Manufacturers of America, *(Wood Machinery),* 1900 Arch St., Philadelphia, PA 19103 (SAN 224-8514).

Wood Moor Enterprises, *(Wood Moor Ent; 0-936307),* Box 100, Nelson Rd., Brighton, IN 38011 (SAN 696-8619) Tel 901-476-5618. Out of Business.

Wood Pond Pr., *(Wood Pond; 0-934260),* 365 Ridgewood Rd., West Hartford, CT 06107 (SAN 217-1112) Tel 203-521-0389.

Wood Pubns., Inc., *(Wood Pubns),* P.O. Box 963, Rancho Santa Fe, CA 92067 (SAN 670-7254) Tel 619-756-3382.

Woodall Publishing Co., *(Woodall; 0-912082),* 11 N. Skokie Hwy., Suite 205, Lake Bluff, IL 60044 (SAN 205-5465) Tel 312-295-7799; Dist. by: Simon & Schuster, Inc., 1230 Ave. of the Americas, New York, NY 10020 (SAN 200-2450) Tel 212-245-6400; Toll free: 800-223-2348.

Woodbine Books, Inc. See **Shorewood Fine Art Books, Inc.**

Woodbine Hse., *(Woodbine House; 0-933149),* 10400 Connecticut Ave., Suite 512, Kensington, MD 20895 (SAN 692-3445) Tel 301-949-3590.

Woodbridge Pr. Publishing Co., *(Woodbridge Pr; 0-912800; 0-88007),* P.O. Box 6189, Santa Barbara, CA 93160 (SAN 212-9892) Tel 805-965-7039.

Woodburn Press, *(Woodburn Pr; 0-9612798),* P.O. Box 5653, Duke Sta., Durham, NC 27706 (SAN 289-906X) Tel 919-493-2655.

Woodbury Pr., *(Woodbury Pr; 0-912123),* Whippoorwill Rd., P.O. Box 700, R.F.D No. 1, Litchfield, ME 04350 (SAN 264-6463) Tel 207-268-4604; Dist. by: Portland News, 270 Western Ave., S. Portland, ME 04106 (SAN 688-413X) Tel 207-774-2633; Dist. by: Maine Writers & Pubs. Alliance, 25A Forest Ave., Portland, ME 04101 (SAN 693-9805) Tel 207-775-6260.

Woodcock Press, *(Woodcock Pr; 0-941674),* P.O. Box 4744, Santa Rosa, CA 95402 (SAN 239-3514) Tel 707-542-6326.

Woodcock Pubns., *(Woodcock; 0-9605352),* P. O. Box 985, Pacific Grove, CA 93950 (SAN 217-1430).

Woodcraft Supply Corp., *(Woodcraft Supply; 0-918036),* 41 Atlantic Ave., P.O. Box 4000, Woburn, MA 01888 (SAN 210-2900) Tel 617-935-5860; Toll free: 800-225-1153.

Wooden Nutmeg Press, *(Wooden Nutmeg; 0-918164),* 74 Waller Rd., Bridgeport, CT 06606 (SAN 210-2919) Tel 203-372-8806.

Wooden Shoe, *(Wooden Shoe),* P.O. Box 174, Pleasantville, NY 10570 (SAN 207-3021) Tel 914-769-5580.

Woodford Memorial Editions, Inc., *(Woodford Mem; 0-9601574),* P.O. Box 55085, Seattle, WA 98155 (SAN 210-9727) Tel 206-364-4167.

Woodgreene Pr., *(Woodgreene Pr; 0-910257),* 6915 Greenfield Way, Salt Lake City, UT 84121 (SAN 241-4791) Tel 801-942-0761.

Woodhill Pr., Inc., *(Woodhill; 0-532),* 300 W. 43rd St., New York, NY 10036 (SAN 202-6066) Tel 212-397-5200.

Woodland Pr., The, *(Woodland ID; 0-9615031),* Box 3524 Univ., Sta., Moscow, ID 83843 (SAN 693-8833) Tel 208-882-6668.

†**Woodland Publishing Co., Inc.,** *(Woodland; 0-934104),* 230 Manitoba Ave., Wayzata, MN 55391 (SAN 213-1900) Tel 612-473-2725; *CIP.*

Woodlands Pr., *(Woodlands Pr; 0-917627),* 79 San Marino Dr., San Rafael, CA 94901 (SAN 657-1697) Tel 415-258-0729.

Woodlawn Plantation-Wright Hse. Council, *(Woodlawn Plant; 0-9608708),* P.O. Box 37, Mt. Vernon, VA 22121 (SAN 281-1863).

Woodlawn Pubns., Inc., *(Woodlawn Pubs; 0-914111),* P.O. Box 2334, Wichita, KS 67201 (SAN 287-623X) Tel 316-788-3293.

Woodley, Bob, Memorial Pr., The, Div. of Bob Woodley Memorial Foundation, *(B Woodley Pr; 0-939391),* Washburn Univ., Topeka, KS 66621 (SAN 663-1266) Tel 913-295-6448.

Woodley Pubns., *(Woodley Pubns; 0-937623),* 4620 DeRussey Pkwy., Chevy Chase, MD 20815 (SAN 659-1418) Tel 301-986-9276.

Woodmere Pr., *(Woodmere Press),* P.O. Box 20190, Cathedral Finance Sta., New York, NY 10025 (SAN 678-3058) Tel 212-678-7839.

Woodmont Pr., The, *(Woodmont Pr; 0-9607762),* P.O. Box 108, Green Village, NJ 07935 (SAN 217-2755) Tel 201-377-6243.

Woodpile Pubs., *(Woodpile Pubs; 0-9608118),* 1046 N. Herbert Ave., Tuscon, AZ 85705 (SAN 240-303X) Tel 602-628-1260.

Woodrow, Ralph, Evangelistic Assn., Inc., *(R Woodrow; 0-916938),* P.O. Box 124, Riverside, CA 92502 (SAN 206-3700) Tel 714-686-5467.

Woodruff Publishing Co., *(Woodruff Pub; 0-9616165),* 4153 Kennesaw Dr., Birmingham, AL 35213 (SAN 699-9891) Tel 205-879-8102.

Woods, Alfred L., *(A L Woods; 0-9811160),* 1525 E. 53rd St., Suite 621, Chicago, IL 60615 (SAN 283-0485) Tel 312-955-1486.

Woods, Jo, Pubns., *(J Woods Pubns),* 2701 Ozark Drive, North Little Rock, AR 72116 (SAN 213-8832) Tel 501-835-0795.

Woods Colt Pr., *(Woods Colt Pr),* 5900 Ward Pkwy., Kansas City, MO 64113 (SAN 663-0790).

Woods Creek Pr., *(Woods Creek Pr; 0-916541),* P.O. Box 339, Ridgecrest, CA 93555 (SAN 295-5571) Tel 619-375-1988.

Woods End Agricultural Institute, *(Woods End; 0-9603554),* Orchard Hill Rd., Temple, ME 04982 (SAN 239-5037).

Woods Hole Historical Collection, *(Woods Hole Hist; 0-9611374),* P.O. Box 185, Woods Hole, MA 02543 (SAN 283-1791) Tel 617-548-2768.

Woods Hole Pr., Subs. of Job Shop, *(Woods Hole Pr; 0-915176),* 3 Water St. P.O. Box 305, Woods Hole, MA 02543 (SAN 210-332X) Tel 617-548-9600.

Woods Library Publishing Co., *(Woods Lib Pub; 0-912304),* 9159 Clifton Park, Evergreen Park, IL 60642 (SAN 205-5473) Tel 312-423-5986.

Woods Music & Bks. Publishing, *(Woods Mus Bks Pub; 0-9602990; 0-936661),* P.O. Box 29521, Los Angeles, CA 90029 (SAN 213-1919) Tel 818-247-4177.

Woods Pubns., *(Woods Pubns; 0-943168),* 2200 Guadalupe, Austin, TX 78705 (SAN 240-5105).

Woodside-Atherton Auxiliary to Stanford Children's Hospital, *(Woodside-Atherton; 0-9615260),* 75 Arbor Rd., Menlo Park, CA 94025 (SAN 694-4124) Tel 415-326-0880.

Woodside Pr., Div. of Applied Human Development, Inc., *(Woodside Pr; 0-9615870),* 105 South Dr., Mountain View, CA 94040 (SAN 696-7078) Tel 415-989-8226; Dist. by: Publishers Group West, 5855 Beaudry St., Emeryville, CA 94608 (SAN 662-3816) Tel 415-658-3453.

Woodside Pr., *(Woodside Pr ID; 0-938191),* P.O. Box 1935, Sun Valley, ID 83353 (SAN 659-7181); 1018 Baldy View Dr., Hailey, ID 83333 (SAN 659-719X) Tel 208-788-2346.

Woodsong Graphics, Inc., *(Woodsong Graph; 0-912661),* P.O. Box 238, New Hope, PA 18938-0238 (SAN 282-8235) Tel 215-794-8321; Orders to: P M G International, 1104 Summit Ave., 100B, Plano, TX 75074 (SAN 662-202X) Tel 214-423-0312.

Woodstone Bks., *(Woodstone Bks; 0-939866),* 3217-Villanova St., Dallas, TX 75225 (SAN 216-9436) Tel 214-824-0527.

Woodward, Claire, *(C Woodward; 0-9606812),* 10806 Fairway Ct. W., Sun City, AZ 85351 (SAN 202-4618) Tel 602-974-6919.

Woodward Centennial Committee, *(Woodward Centennial),* Woodward, IA 50276 (SAN 291-8722).

Woodworker's Index, *(Woodworkers Index; 0-9616050),* P.O. Box 2376, West Lafayette, IN 47906 (SAN 698-0074) Tel 317-463-9883; 1833 Summit Dr., West Lafayette, IN 47906 (SAN 698-2379).

Woodworth-Barnes, E. L., *(Woodworth-Barnes; 0-9613798),* 150 Downs Blvd., Clemson Downs Apts., B-209, Clemson, SC 29631 (SAN 678-965X) Tel 803-654-5454.

Wooley, Rebecca Smith, *(R S Wooley; 0-9601654),* 1250 S. Fairfield, Chicago, IL 60608 (SAN 211-4453).

Woolf, Eugene T., Utah System of High Education, *(Woolf UT Sys; 0-910153),* 355 W. North Temple, 3 Triad Ctr., Suite 550, Salt Lake City, UT 84180-1205 (SAN 669-2788); Orders to: Tanner Ctr. for Human Values, Southern Utah State College, Cedar City, UT 84720 (SAN 280-5782) Tel 801-533-5617.

†**Woolmer/Brotherson, Ltd.,** *(Woolmer-Brotherson; 0-913506),* Revere, PA 18953 (SAN 205-5481) Tel 215-847-5074; *CIP.*

Worcester Art Museum, *(Worcest Art; 0-936042),* 55 Salisbury St., Worcester, MA 01609-3196 (SAN 281-1936) Tel 617-799-4406; Dist. by: University of Massachusetts Press, P.O. Box 429, Amherst, MA 01004 (SAN 203-3089) Tel 413-545-2217.

Worcester County Newspapers, *(Worcester County; 0-917523),* 25 Elm St., Southbridge, MA 01550 (SAN 656-111X) Tel 617-764-4325.

Word Aflame Pr., Subs. of Pentecostal Publishing House, *(Word Aflame; 0-912315),* 8855 Dunn Rd., Hazelwood, MO 63042 (SAN 220-0046) Tel 314-837-7300.

Word Among Us Pr., *(Word Among Us; 0-932085),* P.O. Box 3646, Washington, DC 20007 (SAN 686-4651) Tel 301-977-2500; Toll free: 800-638-8539.

Word Beat Pr., *(Word Beat; 0-912527),* P.O. Box 22310, Flagstaff, AZ 86002 (SAN 265-3060).

Word Doctor Publications, *(Word Doctor; 0-918248),* P.O. Box 9761, 6516 Ben Ave., N. Hollywood, CA 91609 (SAN 207-5865) Tel 818-980-3316.

Word Dynamics Concept, *(Word Dynamics; 0-939023),* P.O. Box 5256, Sacramento, CA 95817-0256 (SAN 662-5541); 6115 Ctr. Mall Way, Sacramento, CA 95823 (SAN 662-555X) Tel 916-427-6836.

Word Enterprise, *(Word Ent; 0-938722),* 574 Auten Rd., Suite 3F, South Somerville, NJ 08876 (SAN 215-9325) Tel 201-874-5323.

Word Factory, *(Word Factory; 0-936854),* 2029-F Cerrissa Ct., San Diego, CA 92154 (SAN 214-4913).

Word for Today, The, *(Word for Today; 0-936728),* P.O. Box 8000, Costa Mesa, CA 92628 (SAN 214-2260) Tel 714-979-0706; Dist. by: Living Books, 12155 Magnolia Ave., Bldg. 11-B, Riverside, CA 92503 (SAN 169-0067X) Tel 714-354-7330; Toll free: 800-922-0047 (In California).

Word Foundation, Inc., The, *(Word Foun; 0-911650),* P. O. Box 18235, Dallas, TX 75218 (SAN 205-549X) Tel 214-348-5006.

Word-Fraction Math Aid Co., *(Word-Fraction; 0-911642),* P.O. Box 475, Woodland Hills, CA 91366 (SAN 205-5503).

Word In Rhyme Publishing Co., The, *(Word In Rhyme; 0-936377),* 320 Lithia, St. Louis, MO 63119 (SAN 697-9688) Tel 314-968-0177.

†**Word, Inc.,** Subs. of Capital Cities/American Broadcasting Co., *(Word Bks; 0-87680; 0-8499),* 4800 W. Waco Dr., Waco, TX 76796 (SAN 203-283X) Tel 817-772-7650; Orders to: Customer Service, P.O. Box 1790, Waco, TX 76796; Toll free: 800-433-3340; *CIP.*

Word Lab Inc., *(Word Lab; 0-916579),* P.O. Box 53462, Houston, TX 77052 (SAN 289-7091) Tel 713-621-4984.

Word Merchant Press, *(Word Merchant Pr; 0-931482),* 40 Clinton St., No. 6C, Brooklyn, NY 11201 (SAN 265-4113).

Word Ministries Inc., *(Word Ministries Inc; 0-9613051),* P.O. Box 145, Greenville, SC 29602 (SAN 294-295X) Tel 912-746-3223; Dist. by: First Presbyterian Church, 682 Mulberry St., Macon, GA 31201 (SAN 200-4550).

Names

Word of Faith, *(Word Faith; 0-914307),* P.O. Box 819000, Dallas, TX 75381 (SAN 287-6272) Tel 214-620-1586.

Word of Mouth Pr., *(Word of Mouth; 0-910027),* Box 824, Yonkers, NY 10701 (SAN 240-8937) Tel 212-519-6325; Dist. by: Baker & Taylor Co., Eastern Div., 50 Kirby Ave., Somerville, NJ 08876 (SAN 169-4901); Toll free: 800-526-3825; Dist. by: Quality Books, 918 Sherwood Dr., Lake Bluff, IL 60044-2204 (SAN 169-2127).

Word Picture Productions, *(Word Picture Prod; 0-937865),* 5859 Brighton Pl., New Orleans, LA 70114 (SAN 659-6053) Tel 504-393-2761.

Word Play, *(Word Play DC; 0-938761),* P.O. Box 5810, Washington, DC 20016 (SAN 661-6739) Tel 202-244-6631; 4537 44th St., NW, Washington, DC 20016 (SAN 661-6747).

Word Power, Inc., *(Word Power; 0-934832),* Lockbox 17034, Seattle, WA 98107 (SAN 213-3881) Tel 206-782-1437.

Word Services & Pied Pubns. Publishing Co., *(Word Serv; 0-918626),* 1927 S. 26th St., Lincoln, NE 68502 (SAN 210-5519).

Word Store, Div. of Legal Education Ltd., *(Word Store; 0-934961),* 1047 Emmet St., Charlottesville, VA 22905 (SAN 695-0515) Tel 804-971-4741.

Word Weavers, *(Word Weavers; 0-9615605),* P.O. Box 8742, Minneapolis, MN 55408 (SAN 695-2305) Tel 612-824-9243.

Word Wheel Books, Inc., *(Word Wheel; 0-913700),* 181 Stanford Ave., Menlo Park, CA 94025 (SAN 203-1868) Tel 415-854-2496.

Word Works, Inc., *(Word Works; 0-915380),* P.O. Box 42164, Washington, DC 20015 (SAN 293-4426) Tel 202-554-3014.

Wordcrafter Pubns., *(Wordcraft MD; 0-941448),* 15804 White Rock Rd., Gaithersburg, MD 20878 (SAN 239-0590) Tel 301-948-2539.

Worden Pr., *(Worden Pr; 0-914821),* Main St., Brookfield, NY 13314-0010 (SAN 289-4718) Tel 315-899-3366.

Wordpix Services, *(Wordpix Serv; 0-9615971),* 1379 Biscayne Way, Haslett, MI 48840 (SAN 697-2616) Tel 517-339-9357.

Wordpower, *(Wordpower; 0-915257),* 637-C Shalimar Dr., Costa Mesa, CA 92627 (SAN 290-0629) Tel 714-642-2142.

Words for Living Ministries Inc., *(Words Living Minis; 0-934527),* 102 W. Carlisle St., Marion, KY 42064 (SAN 693-8477) Tel 502-965-5060.

Words Press, *(Words Pr; 0-9607390),* P.O. Box 1935, Beaverton, OR 97075 (SAN 239-7951).

Wordscope, Inc., *(Wordscope Inc; 0-930121),* 8040 Floral Ave., Suite 304, Skokie, IL 60077 (SAN 670-3194) Tel 312-677-0506; Orders to: P.O Box 1594, Skokie, IL 60076 (SAN 214-204X) Tel 312-677-0506; Dist. by: Bloch Pub. Co., 19 W. 21st St., New York, NY 10010 (SAN 169-5274) Tel 212-989-9104; Dist. by: Jonathan David Co., 68-22 Eliot Ave., Middle Village, NY 11379 (SAN 662-2445) Tel 718-456-8611.

WordSmith, Inc., *(WordSmith Inc; 0-936295),* 806 Mullins Hill Dr., Huntsville, AL 35802 (SAN 697-970X) Tel 205-535-4033P.O. Box 16021, Huntsville, AL 35802 (SAN 662-3956).

Wordsmith Pubns., *(Wordsmith Pubns),* 3317 Mayfield Ave., San Bernardino, CA 92405 (SAN 219-1032). Do not confuse with Wordsmith Pubns., Charlotte, NC.

Wordsmith Pubns., *(Wrdsmith Pubns; 0-9615608),* 1600 La Salle St., Charlotte, NC 28216 (SAN 695-8257) Tel 704-536-6558. Do not confuse with Wordsmith Pubns., San Bernardino, CA.

Wordsmiths, The, *(Wordsmiths; 0-9606108),* P.O. Box 2231, Evergreen, CO 80439 (SAN 216-8715) Tel 303-674-8017.

Wordspinner Pr., *(Wordspinner Pr; 0-939043),* 752 E. 1700 S., Salt Lake City, UT 84105 (SAN 662-6483) Tel 801-484-0863; Dist. by: Sounds of Zion, 5180 S. 300 W, Unit U, Murray, UT 84107 (SAN 200-7525).

†**Wordtree, The,** *(Wordtree; 0-936312),* 10876 Bradshaw, Overland Park, KS 66210-1148 (SAN 214-1752) Tel 913-469-1010; *CIP.*

Wordware Publishing, Inc., *(Wordware Pub; 0-915381; 1-55622),* 1506 Capitol Ave., Suite 101, Plano, TX 75074 (SAN 291-4786) Tel 214-423-0090; Toll free: 800-231-7467.

Wordworks, *(Wordworks; 0-933314),* 2901 Mirante Court, Richmond, CA 94803 (SAN 211-187X) Tel 415-222-6363.

Work at Home Pr., *(Work at Home; 0-917525),* P.O. Box 5520, Ocala, FL 32678 (SAN 656-1128) Tel 904-629-1220.

†**Work in America Institute Inc.,** *(Work in Amer; 0-89361),* 700 White Plains Rd., Scarsdale, NY 10583 (SAN 208-9262) Tel 914-472-9600; Dist. by: Pergamon Pr. Inc., Maxwell House, Fairview Park, Elmsford, NY 10523 (SAN 213-9022) Tel 914-592-7700; Dist. by: Van Nostrand Reinhold, 115 Fifth Ave., New York, NY 10003 (SAN 202-5183) Tel 212-254-3232; Dist. by: Moffat Publishing Co., Box 400, Nutley, NJ 07110 (SAN 217-2569); *CIP.*

Work Saving International, *(Work Saving Intl; 0-914501),* 1638 19th St. NW, Washington, DC 20009 (SAN 289-6966) Tel 202-234-0103.

Workbasket *See* **Modern Handcraft, Inc.**

Workbench *See* **Modern Handcraft, Inc.**

Workbooks Pr., *(Workbks Pr; 0-915849),* P.O. Box 8504, Atlanta, GA 30306 (SAN 294-1147) Tel 404-874-1044.

Workers Compensation Research Institute, *(Workers Comp Res Inst; 0-935149),* 245 First St., Suite 402, Cambridge, MA 02141 (SAN 695-2291) Tel 617-494-1240.

Workers of Our Lady of Mt. Carmel, Inc., the, *(Workers Lady Mt Carmel; 0-9604310),* Box 606, Lindenhurst, NY 11757 (SAN 237-9783).

†**Workers Pr.,** *(Workers Pr; 0-917348),* P.O. Box 3705, Chicago, IL 60654 (SAN 208-9270); Dist. by: Vanguard Press, P.O. Box 3566, Chicago, IL 60654 (SAN 213-8212) Tel 312-342-3425; *CIP.*

Working Directory of Philadelphia Artists, The, *(Working Dir PA Artists),* 737 E. Passyunk Ave., Philadelphia, PA 19147 (SAN 212-3258) Tel 215-625-9367.

Working Peoples Artists, *(Working Peoples Art),* P.O. Box 2307, Berkeley, CA 94702 (SAN 209-0023).

Working Women Education Fund, *(Work Women Educ; 0-912663),* 614 Superior Ave., NW, Cleveland, OH 44113 (SAN 283-992X) Tel 216-566-9308.

Workingmans Pr., *(Workingmans Pr; 0-935388),* P.O. Box 12486, Seattle, WA 98111 (SAN 209-2298); Dist. by: Small Pr. Distribution, 1814 San Pablo Ave., Berkeley, CA 94702 (SAN 688-4121) Tel 415-549-3336.

†**Workman Publishing Co., Inc.,** *(Workman Pub; 0-911104; 0-89480),* 1 W. 39th St., New York, NY 10018 (SAN 203-2821) Tel 212-398-9160; Toll free: 800-722-7202; *CIP.*

Workmen's Circle Education Department, *(Workmen's Circle),* 45 E. 33rd St., New York, NY 10016 (SAN 216-2075).

Workshop Pubns., *(Workshop Pubns; 0-939223),* P.O. Box 120, Acme, MI 49610 (SAN 662-667X) Tel 616-946-3712.

Workshop, The, *(Workshop; 0-9614534),* P.O. Box 265, Petersburg, AK 99833 (SAN 692-3453) Tel 907-772-4809; Dist. by: Pacific Pipeline, Inc., 19215 66th Ave. S., Kent, WA 98032 (SAN 208-2128) Tel 206-872-5523; Dist. by: Creative Communications, 529 Dayton St., Edmonds, WA 98020 (SAN 239-684X) Tel 206-775-5877.

Workshops for Innovative Teaching, *(Wkshops Innovative Teach; 0-9604042),* 191 Edgewood Ave., San Francisco, CA 94117 (SAN 214-1744) Tel 415-665-4932.

Workshops Unlimited, *(Workshops Unltd; 0-9616926),* 1700 Glenwood, Fort Collins, CO 80526 (SAN 661-4876) Tel 303-221-0629.

World Action Pubs., *(World Action; 0-932742),* 135 Ridge Rd., Wethersfield, CT 06109 (SAN 212-1468).

†**World Bank, The, Pubns. Dept.,** *(World Bank; 0-8213),* 1818 H St., NW, Washington, DC 20433 (SAN 219-0648) Tel 202-477-1234; Toll free: 800-482-0831 (In Boston); Toll free: 800-226-5315 (In New York); *CIP.*

World Bible Pubs., Inc., Subs. of Riverside Bk. & Bible, *(World Bible; 0-529; 0-8326),* 795 Sharon Dr., Westlake, OH 44145 (SAN 215-2793) Tel 216-221-4370; Toll free: 800-247-5195; Orders to: P.O. Box 370, Iowa Falls, IA 50126 (SAN 215-2797) Tel 800-247-5111.

World Bk., Inc., A Scott Fetzer Co., *(World Bk; 0-7166),* Merchandise Mart Plaza, Rm. 510, Chicago, IL 60654 (SAN 201-4815) Tel 312-245-3456; Toll free: 800-621-8202.

World Books *See* **Bahm, Archie J.**

World Christian Bookshelf *See* **Carey, William, Library Pubs.**

World Class Enterprises, Inc., *(World Class Enterprises; 0-933079),* 2002 Skylane Dr., Albany, GA 31705 (SAN 689-8149) Tel 912-436-7434.

World Class Ski Tuning, *(World Class Ski; 0-9615712),* P.O. Box 1045, Portland, OR 97207 (SAN 695-829X); Dist. by: Pacific Pipeline, Inc., 19215 66th Ave. S., Kent, WA 98083 (SAN 208-2128); Toll free: 800-426-4727.

World Conference on Religion & Peace, *(World Confer Rel & Peace; 0-932934),* 777 United Nations Plaza, New York, NY 10017 (SAN 213-8840).

World Council of Churches, *(Wrld Coun Churches),* 475 Riverside Dr., Rm. 1062, New York, NY 10115 (SAN 234-3207) Tel 212-870-2533.

World Eagle, Inc., *(World Eagle; 0-9608014; 0-930141),* 64 Washburn Ave., Wellesley, MA 02181 (SAN 239-9555) Tel 617-235-1415.

World Education Project, *(I N Thut World Educ Ctr; 0-918153),* Univ. of Connecticut, Schl. of Education, Box U-32, Storrs, CT 06268 (SAN 209-6358) Tel 203-486-3321.

World Environment Ctr., *(World Enviro; 0-910499),* 605 Third Ave., 17th Flr., New York, NY 10158 (SAN 260-2806) Tel 212-986-7200.

World Evangelical Fellowship, *(World Evang Fellow; 0-936444),* P.O. Box WEF, Wheaton, IL 60189 (SAN 214-1760) Tel 312-668-0404.

World Evangelism, Inc., *(World Evangelism),* 144-25 Roosevelt Ave, Flushing, NY 11354 (SAN 225-4476).

World Exonumia, *(World Exo; 0-912317),* P.O. Box 4143 WY, Rockford, IL 61110-0643 (SAN 265-3079) Tel 815-226-0771.

World Federation of Free Latvians, *(World Fed Free Latvians),* Box 16, Rockville, MD 20850 (SAN 225-6290).

World Federation of Health Agencies for the Advancement of Voluntary Surgical Contraception, *(WFHAAVSC; 0-935955),* 122 E. 42nd St., New York, NY 10168 (SAN 696-7809) Tel 212-573-8338.

World Food Pr., *(World Food; 0-930922),* 10 Myrtle St., Jamaica Plain, MA 02130 (SAN 211-1098); Dist. by: Bookland, Inc., 56 Suffolk St., Holyoke, MA 01040 (SAN 211-1101) Tel 413-533-8475.

World Free Flight Press, *(World Free Flight Review; 0-933066),* 7513 Sausalito Ave., Canoga Park, CA 91307 (SAN 213-6783) Tel 818-340-1704.

†**World Future Society,** *(World Future; 0-930242),* 4916 St. Elmo Ave., Bethesda, MD 20814-5089 (SAN 210-6892) Tel 301-656-8274; Dist. by: Transaction Bks., Rutgers Univ., New Brunswick, NJ 08903 (SAN 202-7941) Tel 201-932-2280; Dist. by: Westview Press, 5500 Central Ave., Boulder, CO 80301 (SAN 219-970X) Tel 303-444-3541; *CIP.*

World Guide Corp., *(World Guide; 0-939491),* 163 Saratoga Ave., Ballston Spa, NY 12020 (SAN 663-3579) Tel 518-885-1281.

World Health Organization, *(World Health),* Dist. by: Q Corp., 49 Sheridan Ave., Albany, NY 12210 (SAN 221-6310).

World Information Corp., The, *(Wrld Info NY; 0-916006),* 1 World Trade Ctr., Suite 7800, New York, NY 10048 (SAN 208-1903) Tel 212-432-8072.

World Intellectual Property Organization *See* **Unipub**

World Leisure Corp., *(World Leis Corp; 0-915009),* 177 Paris St., Boston, MA 02128 (SAN 289-4742) Tel 617-569-1966; Dist. by: Kampmann & Company, 9 E. 40th St., New York, NY 10016 (SAN 202-5191) Tel 212-685-2928.

Names

World Light Pubns., *(World Light; 0-916940),* 1518 Poplar Level Rd., Louisville, KY 40217 (SAN 208-9300) Tel 502-634-4185.

World Link Bks., *(Wrld Link Bks; 0-932093),* 919 N. 19th St., Colorado Springs, CO 80904 (SAN 686-4643) Tel 303-633-7525.

World Marketing Systems, Publishing Co., Inc., *(World Mktg Systems; 0-937284),* 256 Robertson Blvd., Beverly Hills, CA 90211 (SAN 212-5994) Tel 213-657-1575.

World Medical Assn., *(World Med),* c/o AMA, 535 N. Dearborn, Chicago, IL 60610 (SAN 206-8516) Tel 312-645-4385.

World Merchandise-Import Center, Div. of Prime Publishers, *(World Merch Import; 0-937514),* 1460 Boulder Ave., Crescent City, CA 95531 (SAN 220-0171) Tel 707-464-1081. *Imprints:* New Era Publications (New Era).

World Mission Crusade, *(Wrld Mission Crusade; 0-938351),* 5930 18th St., NE, St. Petersburg, FL 33703-1739 (SAN 661-0676) Tel 813-527-5205.

World Missionary Assistance Plan, *(World Mission; 0-9615442),* 900 N. Glenoaks Blvd., Burbank, CA 91502 (SAN 695-8281) Tel 818-843-7233.

World Modeling Assn., Div. of World of Modeling, Inc., *(World Modeling; 0-941330),* P.O. Box 100, Croton-on-Hudson, NY 10520 (SAN 324-5187); 35 Lakeview Ave. W., Peekskill, NY 10566 (SAN 669-3024).

World Music Pr., *(World Music Pr; 0-937203),* P.O. Box 2565, Danbury, CT 06813 (SAN 658-733X) Tel 203-748-1131.

World Neighbors, *(World Neigh; 0-942716),* 5116 N. Portland Ave., Oklahoma City, OK 73112 (SAN 276-8283) Tel 405-946-3333.

World of Modeling, Inc., *(World Model; 0-941330),* P.O. Box 100, Croton-on-Hudson, NY 10520 (SAN 239-0604) Tel 914-737-8512.

World of Nature Productions & Publications, *(World Nature; 0-915261),* P.O. Box 21134, Indianapolis, IN 46221 (SAN 289-9140) Tel 317-634-0874.

World of Poetry Press, *(World Poetry Pr; 0-910147),* 2431 Stockton Blvd., Sacramento, CA 95817 (SAN 241-2403) Tel 916-455-4128.

World of Yesterday, The, *(World Yesterday; 0-936505),* Rte. 3, Box 263H, Waynesville, NC 28786 (SAN 698-0597) Tel 704-648-5647.

World Peace Univ., *(World Peace Univ; 0-939169),* 3829 NE Tillamook St., Portland, OR 97212 (SAN 662-8567) Tel 503-282-0280.

World Policy Journal, *(World Policy; 0-911646),* 777 United Nations Plaza, New York, NY 10017 (SAN 205-5511) Tel 212-490-0010.

World Prayer Band Ministries, *(World Prayer; 0-933495),* 3939 E. Admiral Place, Tulsa, OK 74115-8305 (SAN 692-753X) Tel 918-836-6644.

World Pr., Ltd., Div. of World News Syndicate, Ltd., *(World Pr Ltd; 0-912171),* 6223 Selma Ave., Suite 201, Los Angeles, CA 90028 (SAN 276-9581) Tel 213-469-2333.

World Print Council, *(World Print Coun; 0-9602496),* Ft. Mason Ctr., Laguna & Marina, San Francisco, CA 94123 (SAN 225-2724) Tel 415-776-9200.

World Priorities, *(World Prior; 0-918281),* P.O. Box 25140, Washington, DC 20007 (SAN 679-1433) Tel 202-965-1661.

World Purpose Foundation, *(World Purpose Found; 0-915485),* P.O. Box 3710, Beverly Hills, CA 90212-0710 (SAN 291-4794) Tel 213-855-7057; Dist. by: Bookpeople, 2929 Fifth St., Berkeley, CA 94710 (SAN 168-9517) Tel 415-549-3030; Toll free: 800-227-1516.

World Record Pubns., Ltd., *(World Rec Pubns; 0-930804),* P.O. Box 41, Williston Park, NY 11596 (SAN 211-0059) Tel 516-248-8965.

World Rehabilitation Assn. for the Psycho-Socially Disabled, *(World Rehab),* P.O. Box 898, Ansonia Sta., New York, NY 10023 (SAN 223-8713); 1990 Broadway, New York, NY 10023 (SAN 223-8721).

World Rehabilitation Fund, Inc., *(World Rehab Fund; 0-939986),* 400 E. 34th St., New York, NY 10016 (SAN 216-8723) Tel 212-679-2934.

World Relations Pr., *(World Relations Pr; 0-9615032),* P.O. Box 67 E 33, Century City, CA 90067 (SAN 693-787X) Tel 213-657-0246.

World Resources Institute, *(World Resources Inst; 0-915825),* Pubns. Dept., 1750 New York Ave., NW, Washington, DC 20006 (SAN 294-2968) Tel 202-393-4055; Exec. Hdqtrs., 1735 New York Ave., NW, Washington, DC 20006 (SAN 693-9880) Tel 202-683-6300; Orders to: WRI Pubns., P.O. Box 620, Holmes, PA 19043 (SAN 693-9899).

World Trade Academy Pr., *(World Trade; 0-8360),* 50 E. 42nd St., New York, NY 10017 (SAN 203-2813) Tel 212-697-4999.

World Tribune Pr., *(World Tribune Pr; 0-915678),* 525 Wilshire Blvd., Santa Monica, CA 90406 (SAN 683-230X).

World University, *(World Univ AZ; 0-941902),* P.O. Box 2470, Benson, AZ 85602 (SAN 239-7943) Tel 602-586-2985.

World Univ. of America, *(World Univ Amer; 0-939375),* 107 N. Ventura St., Ojai, CA 93023 (SAN 662-8907) Tel 805-646-1444.

World Univ. Press, *(World Univ Pr; 0-938340),* 1425 Bedford St., Suite 1A, Stamford, CT 06905 (SAN 215-8329).

World View Press, *(World View Pr; 0-931610),* P.O. Box 15, Fort Lee, NJ 07024 (SAN 686-1598).

†**World View Pubs.,** *(World View Pubs; 0-89567),* 46 W. 21st St., New York, NY 10010 (SAN 223-8764) Tel 212-255-0352; *CIP.*

World Vision International, *(World Vision Intl; 0-918261),* 919 W. Huntington Dr., Monrovia, CA 91016 (SAN 225-4719) Tel 818-303-8811.

World-Wide Bks., *(Wrld-Wide Bks; 0-9614296),* 2027 Grand Canal Blvd. 20, Stockton, CA 95207 (SAN 687-4606) Tel 209-957-9601.

World Wide Ministry of Deliverance, Inc., *(World Wide Mini; 0-9612676),* 104 S. Main, Hersey, MI 49639 (SAN 289-4769) Tel 616-796-5958.

World Wide Products, *(World Wide Prods; 0-934062),* 740 Pine St., San Francisco, CA 94108 (SAN 212-8721) Tel 415-391-6324.

World Wide Publications, *(World Wide Pubs; 0-89066),* 1303 Hennepin Ave., Minneapolis, MN 55403 (SAN 203-185X) Tel 612-333-0940.

World-Wide Pubns., *(World-Wide Tampa; 0-911977),* P.O. Box 24339, Tampa, FL 33623 (SAN 276-9492) Tel 813-858-6034.

World Wide Publishing Corp., *(World Wide OR; 0-930294),* P.O. Box 105, Ashland, OR 97520 (SAN 207-4818) Tel 503-482-3800.

World Wide Trade Service, *(Wrld Wide Trade; 0-911652),* P.O. Box 283, Medina, WA 98039 (SAN 204-9953).

World Wisdom Books, *(Wrld Wisdom Bks; 0-941532),* P.O. Box 2682, Bloomington, IN 47402-2682 (SAN 239-1406) Tel 812-332-1663; Dist. by: Bookpeople, 2929 Fifth St., Berkeley, CA 94710 (SAN 168-9517) Tel 415-549-3030; Toll free: 800-227-1516; Dist. by: New Leaf, 1020 White St., SW, Atlanta, GA 30310 (SAN 169-1449) Tel 404-755-2665; Toll free: 800-241-3829; Dist. by: Great Tradition, The, 750 Adrian Way, Suite 111, San Rafael, CA 94903 (SAN 200-5743) Tel 415-492-9382; Toll free: 800-634-2665.

World Without War Council, *(World Without War Pubns; 0-912018),* 421 S. Wabash, Chicago, IL 60605 (SAN 203-2805) Tel 312-663-4250.

Worlds of Science Books *See* **Pyramid Pubns., Inc.**

Worlds of Wonder, *(Worlds Wonder; 1-55578),* 4209 Technology Dr., Fremont, CA 94538 (SAN 699-993X) Tel 415-659-4300.

Worldwatch Institute, *(Worldwatch Inst; 0-916468),* 1776 Massachusetts Ave., NW, Washington, DC 20036 (SAN 209-2727) Tel 202-452-1999.

Worldwide Furbearer Conference Inc. *See* **Unipub a**

Worldpide Investment & Tax Management Service, Inc., *(Worldwest Invest; 0-930891),* P.O. Box 18414-123, Las Vegas, NV 89114 (SAN 677-8240) Tel 702-735-3658.

Worldwide Travel & Tourism Ctr., *(Worldwide Travel; 0-9690625),* 3 Roosevelt Terr., Plattsburgh, NY 12901 (SAN 696-5601). Do not confuse with Worldwide Travel Series, Santa Barbara, CA.

Worldwide Travel Series, *(Wrldwide Trav SB; 0-938653),* 133 E. de la Guerra, Santa Barbara, CA 93101 (SAN 661-6291) Tel 805-963-3180. Do not confuse with Worldwide Travel & Tourism Ctr., Plattsburgh, NY.

Wormhoudt, Arthur, *(Wormhoudt; 0-916358),* William Penn College, Oskaloosa, IA 52577 (SAN 207-5547) Tel 515-673-3091.

Wormwood Pr., *(Wormwood Pr; 0-937523),* P.O. Box 8125, Calabasas, CA 91302-8125 (SAN 659-1434) Tel 213-455-1791.

Wormwood Review Pr., *(Wormwood Rev; 0-935390),* P.O. Box 8840, Stockton, CA 95208-0840 (SAN 209-8113) Tel 209-466-8231.

Worth, H. S., Co., *(H S Worth; 0-939248),* P.O. Box 601, Oakridge, OR 97463 (SAN 220-1615) Tel 503-782-2703; Dist. by: Louise Loehr, 163 W. Main St., Kutztown, PA 19530 (SAN 200-8300).

Worth Pubs., Inc., *(Worth; 0-87901),* 33 Irving Pl., New York, NY 10003 (SAN 205-5546) Tel 212-475-6000.

Worthprinting Pubs., *(Worthprinting; 0-9609734),* 1791 D Rolling Hills Dr., Twinsburg, OH 44087 (SAN 670-6762) Tel 216-425-9571.

Wounded Coot Greetings, *(Wounded Coot; 0-935583),* 1825 15th Ave. SE No., 205, St. Cloud, MN 56301 (SAN 695-796X) Tel 612-363-5771; P.O. Box 418, St. Cloud, MN 56374 (SAN 696-5156).

Wredco Pr., Div. of Writing & Editing Consultants, *(Wredco Pr; 0-931705),* P.O. Box 3387, Flagstaff, AZ 86003 (SAN 683-7476) Tel 602-526-4941; Toll free: 800-423-5819 (Arizona only).

Wrede, Mary M., *(M M Wrede; 0-9615969),* P.O. Box 364, Hillsboro, IN 47949 (SAN 696-8627); 203 N. Cross St., Hillsboro, IN 47949 (SAN 699-6450) Tel 317-798-3200.

Wreden, William P., *(Wreden; 0-9600574),* P.O. Box 56, Palo Alto, CA 94302 (SAN 123-4048) Tel 415-325-6851.

Wright, Curtis, Publications, *(Wright Pub; 0-935249),* 1019 University Ave., Honolulu, HI 96826 (SAN 695-8060) Tel 808-942-2928.

Wright, Deonne Beasley, *(D B Wright),* 10925 S. Union Ave., Chicago, IL 60628 (SAN 663-1932).

Wright, Mildred S., G.R.S., *(M S Wright; 0-917016),* 140 Briggs, Beaumont, TX 77707-2329 (SAN 208-9335) Tel 409-832-2308.

Wright, Richard E., *(Wright R E; 0-9604210),* Dist. by: Caucasian Rugs, 5666 Northcumberland St., Pittsburgh, PA 15217 (SAN 276-8615) Tel 412-422-0300.

Wright, Stephen, Press, *(Stephen Wright; 0-9601904),* Box 1341, F.D.R. Post Office Sta., New York, NY 10150 (SAN 211-8785) Tel 212-927-2869.

Wright, Stuart, Pub./Palaemon Pr., Ltd., *(S Wright; 0-913773),* P.O. Box 7527, Reynolda Sta., Winston-Salem, NC 27109 (SAN 293-4582); 2100 Faculty Dr., Winston-Salem, NC 27106 (SAN 293-4590) Tel 919-725-5985; Dist. by: Small Press Distribution, Inc., 1814 San Pablo Ave., Berkeley, CA 94702 (SAN 204-5826) Tel 415-549-3336.

Wright, Zelma H., Jr., *(Z H Wright),* 140 Briggs, Beaumont, TX 77707-2329 (SAN 209-133X) Tel 409-832-2308.

Wright-Armstead, *(Wright-Armstead; 0-931505),* 2410 Barker Ave., Suite 14-G, Bronx, NY 10467 (SAN 686-158X) Tel 212-654-9445.

Wright Group, The, Div. of Thomas C. Wright, Inc., *(Wright Group; 0-940156; 1-55624),* 10949 Technology Pl., San Diego, CA 92127 (SAN 201-9884) Tel 619-487-8820; Toll free: 800-523-2371; Toll free: 800-331-4524 (In California).

Wright Hand Book Keeping, *(Wright Hand; 0-9616960),* 15640 Alum Rock Ave., San Jose, CA 95127 (SAN 661-8138) Tel 408-258-0841.

Wright Pr., The, *(Wright Pr; 0-915263),* P.O. Box 94, Paris, TX 75460 (SAN 289-9159) Tel 214-785-4060.

651

Names

Yates Ventures, *(Yates Vent; 0-917195),* 3350 W. Bayshore Rd. Suite 201, Palo Alto, CA 94303 (SAN 655-9190) Tel 415-424-8844.

†**Ye Galleon Pr.,** *(Ye Galleon; 0-87770),* P.O. Box 287, Fairfield, WA 99012 (SAN 205-5597) Tel 509-283-2422; *CIP.*

Ye Olde Printery, *(Ye Olde Print; 0-932606),* 5815 Cherokee Dr., Cincinnati, OH 45243 (SAN 213-408X) Tel 513-561-4338.

Yeamans, George Thomas, *(G T Yeamans; 0-9601006),* 4507 W. Burton Dr., Muncie, IN 47304 (SAN 208-9351) Tel 317-288-4345; Orders to: Ball State Bookstore, Muncie, IN 47306 (SAN 209-1623) Tel 317-285-8080.

†**Year Bk. Medical Pubs., Inc.,** Subs. of Times Mirror, *(Year Bk Med; 0-8151),* 35 E. Wacker Dr., Chicago, IL 60601 (SAN 205-5600) Tel 312-726-9733; Toll free: 800-621-9262; *CIP.*

Yearling Bks. *See* Dell Publishing Co., Inc.

Yearround Pr., Div. of Mary Ann Trombold Enterprises, *(Yearround Pr; 0-9615262),* P.O. Box 371, Mercer Island, WA 98040 (SAN 695-0485) Tel 206-232-7023.

Yellow Book of Pennsylvania, Inc., *(Yellow Bk PA; 0-9604612),* 1 Fairway Plaza, P.O. Box 315, Huntingdon Valley, PA 19006 (SAN 219-9858) Tel 215-938-0600.

Yellow Jacket Pr., *(Yellow Jacket; 0-915626),* 1101 N. Lewis, Stillwater, OK 74075 (SAN 207-3048) Tel 405-743-2566.

Yellow Moon Pr., *(Yellow Moon; 0-938756),* P. O. Box 1316, Cambridge, MA 02238 (SAN 216-4809) Tel 617-628-7894.

†**Yellow Press,** *(Yellow Pr; 0-916328),* 2394 Blue Island Ave., Chicago, IL 60608 (SAN 207-9631); Dist. by: Small Press Dist., Inc., 1814 San Pablo Ave., Berkeley, CA 94702 (SAN 204-5826) Tel 415-549-3336; *CIP.*

Yellow Rose Financial Corp., *(Yellow Rose Fin; 0-930631),* 221 N. Monroe St., San Angelo, TX 76901 (SAN 683-4280).

Yellow Rose Pr., *(Yellow Rose Pr; 0-912854),* P.O. Box 160221, Irving, TX 75016 (SAN 203-4271) Tel 214-233-6610.

Yellow Springs Computer Camp, Inc., *(Yellow Springs; 0-912529),* P.O. Box 292, Yellow Springs, OH 45387 (SAN 265-3087) Tel 513-767-7717.

Yellow Umbrella Press, *(Yellow Umb Pr; 0-942654),* 501 Main St., Chatham, MA 02633 (SAN 223-1018).

Yellowstone Library & Museum Assn., The, *(Yellowstone Lib; 0-934948),* Yellowstone Park, WY 82190 (SAN 214-4921).

Yellowstone Pr., Div. of Dan Bailey, *(Yellow Stone Pr; 0-9617253),* P.O. Box 1019, Livingston, MT 59047 (SAN 663-5733); 209 W. Park St., Livingston, MT 59047 (SAN 663-5741) Tel 406-222-1673.

YES Books *See* Youth Education Systems, Inc.

Yes! Inc., *(Yes Inc; 0-936119),* 1035 31st St., NW, Washington, DC 20007 (SAN 223-064X) Tel 202-338-6969; Dist. by: Random Hse., Inc., 201 E. 50th St., New York, NY 10022 (SAN 202-5507) Tel 212-872-8036.

Yes International, *(Yes Intl; 0-936663),* 449 Portland Ave., St. Paul, MN 55102 (SAN 699-6787) Tel 612-224-0503.

Yes Press *See* Down There Pr.

Yesnaby Inc., *(Yesnaby Inc; 0-9606262),* P.O. Box 213, RD 8, Danville, PA 17821 (SAN 220-3499) Tel 717-437-3488.

Yesod Pubs., *(Yesod Pubs),* 75 Prospect Park W., Brooklyn, NY 11215 (SAN 211-8300) Tel 718-768-5591.

Yiddish Archivist Press, *(Yiddish Arch Pr; 0-942656),* 27 Halls Point Rd., Stonycreek, CT 06450 (SAN 239-9571) Tel 203-481-0888.

Yivo Institute for Jewish Research, *(Yivo Inst; 0-914512),* 1048 Fifth Ave., New York, NY 10028 (SAN 207-1614) Tel 212-535-6700.

Yo-Mark Production Co., *(Yo-Mark Prodn; 0-9604607),* P.O. Box 765, Gettysburg, PA 17325 (SAN 691-8409) Tel 717-334-0751.

Yoga Pubn. Society, *(Yoga; 0-911662),* P.O. Box 8885, Jacksonville, FL 32239-8885 (SAN 203-2724); Dist. by: Landau Bk. Co., Inc., 272 W. Park Ave., Long Beach, NY 11561 (SAN 201-064X); Dist. by: De Vorss & Company, P.O. Box 550, 1046 Princeton Dr., Marina del Rey, CA 90294 (SAN 200-4321).

Yoga Research Foundation, *(Yoga Res Foun; 0-934664),* 6111 SW 74th Ave., Miami, FL 33143 (SAN 209-0279) Tel 305-666-2006.

Yogi Gupta New York Center, *(Yogi Gupta; 0-911664),* 90-16 51st Ave., Elmhurst, NY 11373 (SAN 205-5619).

Yokefellow Press, *(Yokefellow Pr; 0-932970; 0-914005),* 230 College Ave., Richmond, IN 47374 (SAN 276-9336) Tel 317-962-6810.

Yoknapatawpha Pr., *(Yoknapatawpha; 0-916242),* Box 248, Oxford, MS 38655 (SAN 213-7593) Tel 601-234-0909.

Yonay, Shahar, *(S Yonay; 0-9616783),* 126 Dover St., Brooklyn, NY 11235 (SAN 661-0544) Tel 718-615-0027.

Yoon, F. T., Co., *(F T Yoon; 0-931168),* P.O. Box 470, Pebble Beach, CA 93953 (SAN 212-873X) Tel 408-646-9499.

York, C. C., *(C C York),* 9000 E. Jefferson Ave., Apt. 1511, Detroit, MI 48214 (SAN 264-5165) Tel 313-824-9506.

York Hse., *(York Hse; 0-9615389),* 148 York Ave., Kensington, CA 94708 (SAN 276-9468) Tel 415-525-7167.

†**York Press, Inc.,** *(York Pr; 0-912752),* 2712 Mt. Carmel Rd., Parkton, MD 21120 (SAN 203-2708) Tel 301-343-1417; *CIP.*

Yorke, Harvey, *(Harvey Yorke; 0-9607598),* 495 Rowland Blvd., Novato, CA 94947 (SAN 200-2612) Tel 415-897-4050; P.O. Box 252, Novato, CA 94948 (SAN 237-9767).

†**Yorke Medical Bks.,** Div. of Technical Publishing, *(Yorke Med; 0-914316),* 875 Third Ave., New York, NY 10022 (SAN 207-155X) Tel 212-605-9620; Orders to: Box C-757, Brooklyn, NY 11205 (SAN 662-1961); *CIP.*

Yosef, Aish, Pubs., *(Aish Yosef Pub; 0-942694),* 2 W. 46th St., Rm. 402, New York, NY 10036 (SAN 239-9598) Tel 212-921-0544.

Yosemite-Di-Maggio, *(Yosemite D; 0-911819),* 618 Grand Ave., Oakland, CA 94610 (SAN 264-5173) Tel 415-839-9780; Dist. by: Bookpeople, 2929 Fifth Ave., Berkeley, CA 94710 (SAN 168-9517) Tel 415-549-3030; Toll free: 800-227-1516; Dist. by: L & S Distributors, 480 Ninth St., San Francisco, CA 94103 (SAN 169-0213) Tel 415-861-6300.

Yosemite Natural History Assn., *(Yosemite Natl Hist; 0-939666),* Box 545, Yosemite National Park, CA 95389 (SAN 225-2201) Tel 209-379-2646; Orders to: P.O. Box 230, El Portal, CA 95318 (SAN 662-197X) Tel 209-379-2646.

You Are a Winner, *(You Are Winner; 0-9615778),* 74 Basinside Way, Alameda, CA 94501 (SAN 696-6659) Tel 415-534-4109.

You Can Be a Classic, Inc., *(Y C B A C; 0-939285),* P.O. Box 5369, Louisville, KY 40205 (SAN 662-5169); 1701 Sulgrave Rd., Louisville, KY 40205 (SAN 662-5177) Tel 502-454-6699.

You Can Make It Enterprises, *(You Can Make It Ent; 0-9606328),* 121 Bank St., Grass Valley, CA 95945 (SAN 219-1040) Tel 415-947-1767.

You Can Publishing, *(You Can Pub; 0-916819),* 3219 Fourth St., N., Minneapolis, MN 55412 (SAN 654-505X) Tel 612-823-9044.

†**Young, Brigham, Univ. Pr.,** *(Brigham; 0-8425),* P.O. Box 140, Tanner Bldg., Provo, UT 84602 (SAN 201-9337) Tel 801-378-6599; Toll free: 800-453-3235; Orders to: 205 University Press Bldg., Provo, UT 84602 (SAN 201-9345) Tel 801-378-2809; *CIP.*

Young, Ione, *(I Young; 0-9605660),* 4107 Wildwood Rd., Austin, TX 78722 (SAN 207-6268).

Young, Jean, Bks., *(J Young Bks),* P.O. Box 8, Woodstock, NY 12498 (SAN 670-6967).

Young, Katherine, *(K Young),* 140 East 40th St., New York, NY 10016 (SAN 237-9791) Tel 212-684-0999.

Young, Robert G., *(R G Young; 0-9611010),* P.O. Box 40743, Grand Junction, CO 81504-0743 (SAN 277-7037) Tel 303-242-1707.

Young, Robert Stephan, *(R S Young; 0-9607068),* 820 Second St. NW, Albuquerque, NM 87102 (SAN 241-5968) Tel 505-243-4043.

Young, Thomas, *(Young; 0-9614151),* P.O. Box 550, Bellaire, TX 77401 (SAN 686-418X) Tel 713-667-3356.

Young, Victor A., *(V Young; 0-9603694),* 548 S. Main St., Red Lion, PA 17356 (SAN 213-5736) Tel 717-244-6816.

Young Ideas, *(Young Ideas; 0-9616786),* 2928 Hill Dr., Troy, MI 48098 (SAN 660-9767) Tel 313-689-3618.

Young Lawyers Section *See* American Bar Assn. a

Young Life National Services, *(Young Life; 0-932856),* Box 520, Colorado Springs, CO 80901 (SAN 211-8319) Tel 303-473-4262.

Young People's Pr., *(Yng Peoples Pr; 0-9606964),* Box 1005, Avon, CT 06001 (SAN 239-4022) Tel 203-677-6409.

Young Pine Pr., *(Young Pine Pr; 0-9608280),* c/o Asian Multi-Media, 6036 Upland Terrace S., Seattle, WA 98118 (SAN 200-433X) Tel 206-344-7580.

Young Pr., *(Young Pr Idaho; 0-9616273),* Rte. 4, Box 76, St. Maries, ID 83861 (SAN 658-4330) Tel 208-245-3645.

Young Woman's Auxiliary of the Woman's Club of Evanston, The, *(Y W A W C E; 0-9613115),* 1702 Chicago Ave., Evanston, IL 60201 (SAN 294-1198); 1204 Milford St., Evanston, IL 60202 (SAN 294-1201) Tel 312-475-0932.

Young Women's Christian Assn., National Board, *(YWCA),* 726 Broadway, New York, NY 10003 (SAN 207-9674) Tel 212-614-2700.

Young Womens Christian Assn. of Seattle, *(YWCA WA; 0-9615533),* 1118 Fifth Ave., Seattle, WA 98101 (SAN 695-8249) Tel 206-447-4855.

Young Women's Christian Organization (YWCO), *(YWCO; 0-9608282),* 201 St. Charles St., Baton Rouge, LA 70802 (SAN 240-4613).

Younique Pr., *(Younique Pr; 0-9601920),* 2550 Long Lake Rd., St. Paul, MN 55112 (SAN 221-296X).

Your New Beginning, *(Your New Beginning; 0-9616892),* 10312 E. Freer St., Temple City, CA 91780 (SAN 661-6461) Tel 818-443-2637.

†**Yourdon Pr.,** *(Yourdon; 0-917072),* 1501 Broadway, New York, NY 10036 (SAN 208-2136) Tel 212-391-2828; Toll free: 800-223-2452; *CIP.*

Yours Truly, Inc., Div. of Burdett Pubns., *(Yours Truly; 0-932946),* 5455 Garden Grove Blvd., Westminster, CA 92683 (SAN 295-1045); Toll free: 800-845-7076.

Youth Challenge Pub., *(Youth Challenge; 0-9606116),* P.O. Box 4567, Topeka, KS 66604 (SAN 216-4817) Tel 913-478-3300.

Youth Education Systems, Inc., *(Youth Ed; 0-87738),* Box 223, Scarborough Sta., Scarborough, NY 10510 (SAN 205-5635) Tel 212-599-8417. *Imprints:* YES Books (YES Bks).

Youth Specialties, *(Youth Special; 0-910125),* 1224 Greenfield Dr., El Cajon, CA 92021 (SAN 211-8327) Tel 619-440-2333.

Youth with a Mission International, *(Youth Mission; 0-9615534),* P.O. Box 4407, Kailua Kona, HI 96745 (SAN 695-8265) Tel 808-329-1621.

Yuchi Pines Institute, *(Yuchi Pines),* P.O. Box 319, Fort Mitchell, AL 36856 (SAN 239-5053).

Yuen, Jim J., *(J J Yuen; 0-9613077),* 3655 Oso St., San Mateo, CA 94403 (SAN 294-6971) Tel 415-572-9123; Dist. by: Ten Speed Press, P.O. Box 7123, Berkeley, CA 94707 (SAN 202-7674) Tel 415-845-8414; Toll free: 800-841-BOOK.

Yuganta Pr., *(Yuganta Pr; 0-938999),* 85 Midland Ave., Stamford, CT 06906 (SAN 662-541X) Tel 203-323-7160.

Yuletide International, *(Yuletide Intl; 0-911049),* 9665 Malad St., Boise, ID 83709 (SAN 264-5181) Tel 208-322-1260.

Yummy Designs, *(Yummy Designs; 0-936467),* P.O. Box 2033, Chino, CA 91708 (SAN 697-9718) Tel 714-591-5256; 12836 12th St., No. 44, Chino, CA 91710 (SAN 697-9726); Orders to: Character Medical Co., 390 Swift, South San Francisco, CA 94080 (SAN 698-2344).

Z-Graphic Pubns., *(Z Graphic Pubns; 0-941572),* 833 Joost Ave., San Francisco, CA 94127 (SAN 239-3522) Tel 415-584-4048.

ZON International Publishing Co., Div. of Zon International Design Inc., *(Zon Intl Pub; 0-939549),* 50 Overlook Rd., Ossining, NY 10562 (SAN 663-3439) Tel 914-941-1836.

Names

Z Pr., Inc., *(Z Pr; 0-915990),* Calais, VT 05648 (SAN 289-0240); Dist. by: Inland Bks. Co., P.O. Box 261, 22 Hemingway Ave., East Haven, CT 06512 (SAN 200-4151) Tel 203-467-4257.

ZZYZX Publishing Co., Inc., *(ZZYZX Pub; 0-938103),* 2460 S. University Blvd., Denver, CO 80210 (SAN 659-7149) Tel 303-778-1796.

Zachry Pubns., *(Zachry Pubns),* 502 E. N. 16th, Abilene, TX 79601 (SAN 203-1825) Tel 915-673-2356.

Zalo Pubns. & Services, Inc., *(Zalo; 0-931200),* Dist. by: Frangipani Press, Div. of T.I.S. Enterprises, P.O. Box 669, 1928 Arlington Rd., Bloomington, IN 47402 (SAN 169-2313) Tel 812-332-3307.

Zalozba Prometej, *(Zalozba Prometej; 0-934158),* P.O. Box 8391, New Orleans, LA 70182 (SAN 212-8462) Tel 504-283-7177.

Zamisdat Pr., *(Zamisdat Pr; 0-934727),* P.O. Box 1255, Gracie Sta., New York, NY 10028 (SAN 694-1524) Tel 212-473-4888.

Zanel Pubns., *(Zanel Pubns; 0-936914),* P.O. Box 255867, Sacramento, CA 95865-5867 (SAN 212-985X) Tel 916-973-8050.

Zaner-Bloser, Inc., Subs. of Highlights for Children, *(Zaner-Bloser; 0-88309),* 2300 W. Fifth Ave., P.O. Box 16764, Columbus, OH 43216-6764 (SAN 282-5678) Tel 614-486-0221.

Zapffe, Carl A., *(C A Zapffe; 0-9601448),* 6410 Murray Hill Rd., Baltimore, MD 21212 (SAN 221-2978).

ZapoDel Inc., *(ZapoDel Inc; 0-934545),* P.O. Box 1049, Del Mar, CA 92014 (SAN 693-8361) Tel 619-481-7337; Dist. by: Quality Books, Inc., 918 Sherwood Dr., Lake Bluff, IL 60044-2204 (SAN 169-2127) Tel 312-498-4000; Dist. by: Publishers Group West, 5855 Beaudry St., Emeryville, CA 94608 (SAN 202-8522) Tel 415-658-3453; Toll free: 800-982-8319.

Zaram Promotional Concepts, *(Zaram Promo; 0-935395),* 1400 N. Lake Shore Dr., Chicago, IL 60610 (SAN 659-815X) Tel 312-943-2277.

Zarathustrotemo Pr., The, *(Zarathustrotemo Pr; 0-937581),* 601-2 Harwood Rd., Suite 172, Bedford, TX 76021 (SAN 658-8301) Tel 817-831-2586; 2900 Haltom Rd., Ft. Worth, TX 76117 (SAN 658-831X) Tel 817-831-2586.

Zarcon Pr., *(Zarcon Pr; 0-9604916),* 2000 Allston Way, Berkeley, CA 94701 (SAN 658-8336); P.O. Box 428, Berkeley, CA 94701 (SAN 658-8344).

Zartscorp, Inc. Books, *(Zartscorp; 0-9605610),* 333 West End Ave., New York, NY 10023 (SAN 209-5017) Tel 212-724-5071.

Zebra Bks. *See* Grove Pr.

Zebra Bks., *(Zebra; 0-89083; 0-8217),* 475 Park Ave. S., New York, NY 10016 (SAN 207-9860) Tel 212-889-2299; Toll free: 800-221-2649; Dist. by: Simon & Schuster Mass Merchandise Sales Co., 1230 Ave. of the Americas, New York, NY 10020 (SAN 169-5835) Tel 212-245-6400.

Zen Center, The, *(Zen Ctr; 0-940306),* 7 Arnold Park, Rochester, NY 14607 (SAN 217-569X) Tel 716-473-9180.

Zen Ctr. of Los Angeles, Inc. *See* Center Pubns.

Zenanko, Tom, Outdoors, *(Zenanko Outdoors; 0-9610296),* 5420 71st Circle, Brooklyn Center, MN 55429 (SAN 276-9352).

†**Zenger Publishing Co., Inc.,** *(Zenger Pub; 0-89201),* P.O. Box 42026, Washington, DC 20015 (SAN 208-0427) Tel 301-881-1470; CIP.

Zenith Books *See* Doubleday & Co., Inc.

Zentner Pubns., *(Zentner Pubns; 0-934950),* 2407 Larkspur Ln., No. 231, Sacramento, CA 95825 (SAN 213-4098) Tel 916-972-0182. Out of Business.

Zephyr *See* Doubleday & Co., Inc.
Zephyr-BFYR *See* Doubleday & Co., Inc.
Zephyr Pr., Subs. of Aspect, Inc., *(Zephyr Pr; 0-939010),* 13 Robinson St., Somerville, MA 02145 (SAN 239-7668) Tel 617-623-2799; Dist. by: Publishers Group West, 5855 Beaudry St., Emeryville, CA 94608 (SAN 202-8522) Tel 415-658-3453; Dist. by: Baker & Taylor Co., Eastern Div., 50 Kirby Ave., Somerville, NJ 08876 (SAN 169-4901); Dist. by: Inland Bk. Co., P.O. Box 261, 22 Hemingway Ave., East Haven, CT 06512 (SAN 200-4151) Tel 203-467-4257; Dist. by: Small Pr. Distribution, Inc., 1814 San Pablo Ave., Berkeley, CA 94702 (SAN 204-5826) Tel 415-549-3336; Dist. by: Bookpeople, 2929 Fifth St., Berkeley, CA 94710 (SAN 168-9517); Dist. by: Bookslinger, 213 E. Fourth Ave., Saint Paul, MN 55101 (SAN 169-4154) Tel 612-221-0429.

Zephyr Pr. AZ, *(Zephyr Pr AZ; 0-913705),* 430 S. Essex Ln., Tucson, AZ 85711 (SAN 270-6830) Tel 602-623-2022.

Zephyr Pr. (CA), *(Zephyr CA; 0-913751),* P.O. Box 3066, Berkeley, CA 94703 (SAN 286-0937) Tel 415-763-3627.

Zephyr Pubs., *(Zephyr; 0-931782),* P.O. Box 43-1275, South Miami, FL 33143 (SAN 205-5678) Tel 305-279-7817.

Zeppelin Pub. Co., *(Zeppelin; 0-915628),* P.O. Box 22252, Louisiana State Univ. Sta., Baton Rouge, LA 70893 (SAN 204-6776) Tel 504-272-6600; Pelican Office Ctr., 11628 S. Choctaw Dr., Baton Rouge, LA 70815 (SAN 200-4208) Tel 504-272-6600.

Zero Publishing Co., *(Zero Pub; 0-9615716),* P.O. Box 1385, Mountain View, CA 94042 (SAN 695-8397) Tel 415-968-7439; 56 Centre St., Apt. 5, Mountain View, CA 94041 (SAN 696-9526).

Zest Publishing Co., *(Zest Pub; 0-933245),* P.O. Box 3068, Southfield, MI 48037-3068 (SAN 692-3615).

Zeus Pubs., Div. of Warren H. Green, Inc., *(Zeus Pubs; 0-931743),* 8356 Olive Blvd., St. Louis, MO 63132 (SAN 687-6382) Tel 314-991-1335.

Zia Enterprises, *(Zia Enter; 0-9615404),* 343 Turf Ln., Castlerock, CO 80104 (SAN 695-4952).

Zieleks Co., *(Zielcks Co; 0-936675),* 11215 Sageland Dr., Houston, TX 77089 (SAN 699-6965) Tel 713-481-3783.

Ziesing, Mark, *(Mark Ziesing; 0-9612970),* P.O. Box 806, Willimantic, CT 06226 (SAN 292-7446) Tel 203-423-5836; 768 Main St., Willimantic, CT 06226 (SAN 658-2508).

Ziesing Brothers Book Emporium, *(Ziesing Bros; 0-917488),* 768 Main St., Willimantic, CT 06226 (SAN 209-6935) Tel 203-423-5836.

Zig Zag Papers, The, *(Zig Zag Paper; 0-9614498),* 70796 Barlow Trail, Zig Zag, OR 97049 (SAN 689-4763) Tel 503-622-3425; Orders to: Box 247, Zig Zag, OR 97049 (SAN 662-2844) Tel 503-622-3425.

Zilzal Pr., *(Zilzal Pr; 0-938397),* 132 N. Milpas St., Santa Barbara, CA 93103 (SAN 659-8528) Tel 805-966-5570.

Zimmer, Elizabeth A., *(E A Zimmer; 0-9615968),* 355 E. Woodward Ave., Roger City, MI 49779 (SAN 697-3124).

Zimmerman, Al, Publishing, *(A Zimmerman; 0-914081),* 843 Van Nest Ave., Bronx, NY 10462 (SAN 276-9387) Tel 212-822-7333.

Zimmerman, Gary, *(Zimmerman; 0-916202),* 2701 Ave. J, Brooklyn, NY 11210 (SAN 208-0982) Tel 718-338-8720.

Zimmermann, A. M., & Co., *(A M Zimmermann; 0-912125),* 2210 Jackson St., Suite 404, San Francisco, CA 94115 (SAN 238-0897) Tel 415-929-7577; Dist. by: Publishers Group West, 5855 Beaudry St., Emeryville, CA 94608 (SAN 202-8522) Tel 415-658-3453; Dist. by: Bookpeople, 2929 Fifth St., Berkeley, CA 94710 (SAN 168-9517) Tel 415-549-3030.

Zinc Institute Inc., *(Zinc Inst),* 292 Madison Ave., New York, NY 10017

Zincs Career Guidance, *(Zincs Career Guide; 0-939469),* P.O. Box 13110, Las Vegas, NV 89112 (SAN 663-334X); 3969 Maryland Ave., Las Vegas, NV 89121 (SAN 663-3358) Tel 702-451-0718.

Zink, J., Inc., *(J Zink; 0-942490),* P.O. Box 3279, Manhattan Beach, CA 90266 (SAN 239-9601) Tel 213-545-1031.

Zinman's Rapid Writing, *(Zinmans; 0-911672),* 55 Inwood Ave., Dept. Z, Point Lookout, NY 11569 (SAN 205-5686).

Zion Natural History Assn., *(Zion; 0-915630),* Zion National Park, Springdale, UT 84767 (SAN 205-9959) Tel 801-772-3256.

Zo Publishing, *(Zo Pub; 0-938465),* P.O. Box 61335, Honolulu, HI 96839 (SAN 660-9864); 3081-H Paty Dr., Honolulu, HI 96839 Tel 808-988-7111.

Zoe Pubns., *(Zoe Pubns; 0-89841),* P.O. Box 1361, Clemmons, NC 27012

Zomeworks Corp., *(Zomeworks Corp),* P.O. Box 25805, Albuquerque, NM 87125 (SAN 210-8771) Tel 505-242-5354.

Zondervan Publishing Hse., Div. of Zondervan Corp., *(Zondervan; 0-310),* 1415 Lake Dr. SE, Grand Rapids, MI 49506 (SAN 203-2694) Tel 616-698-6900; Toll free: 800-253-1309 (wholesale orders, bookstores); Toll free: 800-253-4475 (retail orders). *Imprints:* Clarion Classics (Clarion Class); Serenade-Saga (Serenade-Saga).

Zone Pr., Affil. of Zone Press, Inc., *(Zone Pr; 0-936469),* Box 1881, Cambridge, MA 02238 (SAN 697-9750) Tel 617-492-3687; Dist. by: Baker & Taylor Co., Eastern Div., 50 Kirby Ave., Somerville, NJ 08876 (SAN 169-4901); Dist. by: NASCORP, Inc., 528 E. Lorain St., Oberlin, OH 44074 (SAN 169-6823) Tel 216-775-7777; Toll free: 800-321-3883.

Zoo Pr., *(Zoo Pr; 0-911969),* 805 Homestead St., Baltimore, MD 21218 Tel 301-366-2950.

Zoological Society of San Diego, *(Zoological Soc; 0-911461),* P.O. Box 551, San Diego, CA 92112 (SAN 276-931X) Tel 619-265-8171.

Zoom Publishing, *(Zoom; 0-9602964),* P.O. Box 730, El Toro, CA 92630 (SAN 264-5238).

Zubal, John T., Inc., *(Zubal Inc; 0-939738),* 2969 W. 25th St., Cleveland, OH 44113 (SAN 165-5841) Tel 216-241-7640.

Zucchini Patch, *(Zucchini Patch; 0-940158),* P.O. Box 1100, Nipomo, CA 93444 (SAN 220-3146) Tel 805-929-1718.

Zucker, Marjorie B., *(M B Zucker; 0-9604260),* 333 Central Park W., New York, NY 10025 (SAN 211-335X).

Zybert, Richard, *(Zybert),* 1169 Folsom St., San Francisco, CA 94103 (SAN 214-2279) Tel 415-863-7229.

Zyga Multimedia Research, *(ZYGA; 0-9608438),* P.O. Box 7452, Oakland, CA 94601 (SAN 240-8112) Tel 415-261-6837.

Zygote Pr., *(Zygote Pr; 0-939358),* 1712 Mount Curve Ave., Minneapolis, MN 55403 (SAN 216-4973) Tel 612-377-8035.

Zymark Corp., *(Zymark Corp; 0-931565),* Zymark Ctr., Hopkinton, MA 01748 (SAN 682-2096) Tel 617-435-9501.

Zytech Western Publishing, *(Zytech Western Pub; 0-936749),* 716 E. Valley Pkwy., Escondido, CA 92025 (SAN 699-9867) Tel 619-789-8822.

Names

PUBLISHERS' AND DISTRIBUTORS' TOLL-FREE NUMBERS

The *Publishers and Distributors' Toll Free Numbers* index is arranged alphabetically by company name, and includes the following elements (in the same sequence as listed) where applicable: company name, ISBN prefix(es), city, state, toll-free telephone number(s), and the toll-free telephone number of the company's distributor(s). Distributors' names appear in parentheses, following the toll-free telephone number.

ABC-Clio Information Services
(0-87436; 0-903450; 1-85109)
Santa Barbara, CA
800-422-2546

ACS Pubns., Inc.
(0-917086; 0-935127)
San Diego, CA
800-826-1085
800-525-1786 (in California)

AFCEA International Pr.
(0-916159)
Burke, VA
800-336-4583

APL Pr.
(0-917326)
Rockville, MD
800-592-0050

A.R.E. Pr.
(0-87604)
Virginia Beach, VA
800-368-2727

ASQC Quality Pr.
(0-87389)
Milwaukee, WI
800-952-6587

A Thomas Publishing Co.
(0-937329; 0-9613884)
Southfield, MI
800-331-6871

A.C.A.T. Pr.
(0-9616025)
Santa Rosa, CA
800-227-1516 (Bookpeople)

Aames-Allen Publishing Co.
(0-936930)
Huntington Beach, CA
800-547-7734 (I.S.B.S.)

Aaron Blake Pubs.
(0-937609)
Los Angeles, CA
800-227-1516 (Bookpeople)

Abbeville Pr., Inc.
(0-89659)
New York, NY
800-227-7210

Abilene Christian Univ. Pr.
(0-89112; 0-915547)
Abilene, TX
800-527-0575
800-592-1404 (TX)

Abingdon Pr.
(0-687)
Nashville, TN
800-251-3320

Abrams, Harry N., Inc.
(0-8109)
New York, NY
800-345-1359

Academic Guild Publishers
(0-938550; 0-938552)
Cambridge, MA
800-428-4825
800-428-4824 in CA

Academic Pr., Inc.
(0-12)
Orlando, FL
800-321-5068

Academy Pubns.
(0-931560)
Sherman Oaks, CA
800-227-1516 (Bookpeople)

Accent Bks.
(0-89636; 0-916406)
Denver, CO
800-525-5550

Accent Pubns.
(0-9613104)
Scituate, MA
800-525-5550

Access Pr., Ltd.
(0-915461; 0-9604858)
New York, NY
800-222-3774 (Orders)

Accura Music, Inc.
(0-918194)
Athens, OH
800-221-9254

Achievement Hse.
(0-9615629)
Danbury, CT
800-551-1133

Acropolis Bks.
(0-87491)
Washington, DC
800-621-5199

Actor Training & Research Institute Pr.
(0-9616087)
Chicago, IL
800-257-7341 (Blackwell N. America)
800-248-1146 (The Book House)

Ad-Lib Pubns.
(0-912411)
Fairfield, IA
800-624-5893

Adama Pubs., Inc.
(0-915361)
New York, NY
800-672-6672

Adler & Adler Pubs., Inc.
(0-917561)
Bethesda, MD
800-253-3677 (Harper & Row Pubs., Inc.)

Adler's Foreign Bks., Inc.
(0-8417)
Evanston, IL
800-235-3771

Advocacy Pr.
(0-911655)
Santa Barbara, CA
800-251-5900 (Ingram Book Co.)

Agape
(0-916642)
Carol Stream, IL
800-323-1049

Agency for Instructional Technology
(0-9603244)
Bloomington, IN
800-457-4509

AgriData Resources, Inc.
(0-910939)
Milwaukee, WI
800-558-9044

Agrinde Pubns., Ltd.
(0-9601068)
New York, NY
800-251-4000

Alemany Pr., Inc.
(0-88084)
Hayward, CA
800-227-2375

Alexandrian Pr.
(0-916485)
Palo Alto, CA
800-227-8324

Alfred Publishing Co., Inc.
(0-88284)
Sherman Oaks, CA
800-821-6083

Allen & Unwin, Inc.
(0-04; 0-86861)
Winchester, MA
800-547-8889

Allyn & Bacon, Inc.
(0-205)
Newton, MA
800-526-4799

Almaas Pubns.
(0-936713)
Richmond, CA
800-227-1516 (Bookpeople)

Alpha Pubs.
(0-9615632)
Minneapolis, MN
800-521-3990 (Spring Arbor Distributors)

Alphabet Pr.
(0-940032)
Natick, MA
800-462-1252

Alternate Source, The
(0-915363)
Lansing, MI
800-253-3200 ext 700

American Assn. for Medical Transcription
(0-935229)
Modesto, CA
800-982-2182

American Assn. of University Women
(0-9611476)
Washington, DC
800-424-9717

American Assn. on Mental Deficiency
(0-940898)
Washington, DC
800-424-3688

American Bible Society
(0-8267)
New York, NY
800-543-8000

American Board of Medical Specialties
(0-934277)
Evanston, IL
800-621-4249 (Login Brothers Bk. Co.)

American Cancer Society, Minnesota Div., Inc.
(0-9602796)
Minneapolis, MN
800-582-5152

American Chemical Society
(0-8412)
Washington, DC
800-424-6747

**American College of Laboratory Animal
Medicine**
Hershey, PA
800-321-5068 (Academic Press, Inc.)

American Correctional Assn.
(0-942974)
College Park, MD
800-222-5646

American Council on Education
(0-8268)
Washington, DC
800-257-5755

American Educational Trust, The
(0-937165)
Washington, DC
800-368-5788

**American Enterprise Institute for Public Policy
Research**
(0-8447)
Washington, DC
800-424-2873

American Geological Institute
(0-913312)
Alexandria, VA
800-336-4764

American Geophysical Union
(0-87590)
Washington, DC
800-424-2488

American Guidance Service, Inc.
(0-88671; 0-913476)
Circle Pines, MN
800-328-2560

American Health & Nutrition, Inc.
(0-914851)
Larkspur, CA
800-241-3829 (New Leaf Distributing, The)

American Health Consultants, Inc.
(0-9603332)
Atlanta, GA
800-559-1032

American Hospital Assn.
(0-87258)
Chicago, IL
800-242-2626

American Hospital Publishing, Inc.
(0-939450; 1-55648)
Chicago, IL
800-242-2626

American Institute of Physics
(0-88318)
New York, NY
800-247-7497

American Institute of Small Business
(0-939069)
Minneapolis, MN
800-328-2906

American Language Academy
(0-934270)
New York, NY
800-822-8202

American Law Institute
(0-8318)
Philadelphia, PA
800-253-6387

American Mathematical Society
(0-8218)
Providence, RI
800-556-7774

American Numismatic Assn.
(0-89637)
Colorado Springs, CO
800-367-9723

American Nurses Assn.
Kansas City, MO
800-368-5643

American Phytopathological Society
(0-89054)
St. Paul, MN
800-328-7560

American Polygraph Assn.
Severna Park, MD
800-272-8037

American Psychiatric Pr., Inc.
(0-88048; 0-89042)
Washington, DC
800-368-5777

American Society for Information Science
(0-87715)
Washington, DC
800-248-5474

American Society of Civil Engineers
(0-87262)
New York, NY
800-548-2723

American Society of Clinical Pathologists Pr.
(0-89189)
Chicago, IL
800-621-4142

American Technical Pubs., Inc.
(0-8269)
Homewood, IL
800-323-3471

American Travel Pubns., Inc.
(0-936929)
Carlsbad, CA
800-227-7346 (Sunset Books)

American Veterinary Pubns., Inc.
(0-939674)
Santa Barbara, CA
800-235-6947

Amnesty International of the USA, Inc.
(0-939994)
New York, NY
800-251-4000

**Anaheim Publishing Company, a Division of
Wadsworth, Incorporated**
(0-88236)
Belmont, CA
800-831-6996

Ancestry Inc.
(0-916489)
Salt Lake City, UT
800-531-1790

And Bks.
(0-89708)
South Bend, IN
800-348-5200 (The Distributors)

Anderson, John MacKenzie
(0-9615813)
Cincinnati, OH
800-732-2663

Anderson, Robert D., Publishing Co.
(0-942028)
Sacramento, CA
800-222-3030

Anderson Publishing Co.
(0-87084)
Cincinnati, OH
800-543-0883

Anderson World, Inc.
(0-89037)
Mountain View, CA
800-257-5755

Andrews, McMeel & Parker
(0-8362)
Kansas City, MO
800-826-4216

Annual Reviews, Inc.
(0-8243)
Palo Alto, CA
800-523-8635

Answers Period, Inc.
(0-917875)
Corpus Christi, TX
800-251-5902 (Ingram Industries)

Antarctic Pr.
(0-930655)
Bellevue, WA
800-426-4727 (Pacific Pipeline, Inc.)

Antioch Publishing Co.
(0-89954)
Yellow Springs, OH
800-543-2397

Aperture Foundation, Inc.
(0-89381; 0-912334)
New York, NY
800-631-3577

Apollo Bk.
(0-938290)
Poughkeepsie, NY
800-431-5003

Apollo Books, Inc. (MN)
(0-916829)
Winona, MN
800-328-8963

Apollo Editions
(0-8152)
New York, NY
800-242-7737

Applause Theater Bk. Pubs.
(0-936839)
New York, NY
800-242-7737 (Harper & Row)

Appleton & Lange
(0-8385)
East Norwalk, CT
800-826-2618

Arbit Bks., Inc.
(0-930038)
Milwaukee, WI
800-558-6908

Architectural Bk. Publishing Co., Inc.
(0-8038)
Stamford, CT
800-526-7626 (Kampmann & Co.)

Archway Paperbacks
(0-671)
800-223-2336

Argus Communications
(0-89505; 0-913592)
Allen, TX
800-527-4748

Ariel Pr.
(0-89804)
Columbus, OH
800-336-7769
800-336-7768 (OH)

Arista Corp.
(0-8073; 0-89796; 0-914876)
New York, NY
800-227-1606

Arizona Daily Star
(0-9607758)
Tucson, AZ
800-362-4890

Arnold, Edward, Pubs., Ltd.
(0-7131)
Baltimore, MD
800-638-7511

Arrowood Bks., Inc.
(0-934847)
Corvallis, OR
800-426-4727 (Pacific Pipeline, Inc.)

Art Institute of Chicago
(0-86559)
Chicago, IL
800-621-2736

Ash-Kar Pr.
(0-9605308)
San Francisco, CA
800-227-1516

Ashton-Tate Publishing Group
(0-912677)
Torrance, CA
800-437-4329

Aspen Pubs., Inc.
(0-87189; 0-89443; 0-912654; 0-912862)
Rockville, MD
800-638-8437

Associated Booksellers
(0-87497)
Bridgeport, CT
800-232-2224

Association for Library Service to Children
Chicago, IL
800-545-2433

Association of College & Research Libraries
(0-8389)
Chicago, IL
800-545-2433
800-545-2445 (in IL)

Astrolabe
(0-87199; 0-913637)
Orleans, MA
800-826-1085 (ACS Pubns., Inc.)
800-525-1786 (in CA)

Atheneum Pubs.
(0-689)
New York, NY
800-257-5755

Atlantic Monthly Pr.
(0-87113)
Boston, MA
800-343-9204

Auerbach Pubs., Inc.
(0-87769)
New York, NY
800-257-8162

Augsburg Publishing Hse.
(0-8066)
Minneapolis, MN
800-328-4648

Aura Books
(0-937736)
Los Angeles, CA
800-843-6666 (Samuel Weiser, Inc.)

Auromere, Inc.
(0-89744)
Pomona, CA
800-243-0138

Aurora Pr.
(0-943358)
New York, NY
800-241-3829 (New Leaf Distributing, The)
800-227-1516 (Bookpeople)

Automobile Quarterly Pubns.
(0-911968)
Princeton, NJ
800-523-0236

Avant-Garde Publishing Corp.
(0-87275; 0-930182)
Novato, CA
800-874-6544

Aviation Bk. Co.
(0-911720; 0-911721; 0-916413)
Glendale, CA
800-423-2708

Aviation Bk. Co.
(0-911720; 0-911721)
Glendale, CA
800-423-2708
800-542-6657 (in California)

Avon Bks.
(0-380)
New York, NY
800-247-5470

Axcess Software, Inc.
(0-938929)
Tempe, AZ
800-292-3687

Axiom Pr. Pubs.
(0-933800)
Burlingame, CA
800-421-7149; (J. A. Majors Co. California)
800-352-7277 (in California)

BE Pubs.
(0-9617074)
Bridgeport, CT
800-826-8692

BLOC Development Corp.
(0-938843)
Miami Beach, FL
800-231-1149

BMH Bks.
(0-88469)
Winona Lake, IN
800-348-2756

BNA Bks.
(0-87179)
Washington, DC
800-372-6033
800-3521400

BUC International Corp.
(0-911778)
Fort Lauderdale, FL
800-327-6929

Backcountry Pubns., Inc.
(0-942440)
Woodstock, VT
800-635-5009

Baha'i Publishing Trust
(0-87743)
Wilmette, IL
800-323-1880

Baja Bks.
(0-9602838; 0-9615829)
Santa Barbara, CA
800-251-5900 (Ingram Bk. Co.)

Ballantine Bks., Inc.
(0-345)
New York, NY
800-638-6460

Ballinger Publishing Co.
(0-88410; 0-88730)
Cambridge, MA
800-638-3030

Balsam Pr., Inc.
(0-917439)
New York, NY
800-526-7626 (Kampmann & Co., Inc.)

Baltimore Vegetarians
(0-931411)
Baltimore, MD
800-241-3829 (New Leaf Distributing, The)

Bamberger Bks.
(0-917453)
Flint, MI
800-243-0138 (Inland Bk. Co.)

Banks-Baldwin Law Publishing Co.
(0-8322)
Cleveland, OH
800-362-4500

Bantam Bks., Inc.
(0-553)
New York, NY
800-323-9872

Banyan Tree Bks.
(0-9604320)
Berkeley, CA
800-227-1516 (Bookpeople)

Barbacoa Pr.
(0-933579)
Kansas City, MO
800-255-0513
800-9828319 (Publishers Group West)

Barbour & Co., Inc.
(0-916441)
Westwood, NJ
800-221-2648

Barre Publishing Co.
800-526-4264

Basic Bks., Inc.
(0-465)
New York, NY
800-242-7737

Battelle Pr.
(0-935470)
Columbus, OH
800-526-7254

Beacon Pr., Inc.
(0-8070)
Boston, MA
800-242-7737 (Harper & Row Pubs., Inc.)

Bear & Co., Inc.
(0-939680)
Santa Fe, NM
800-932-3277

Beau Bayou Publishing Co.
(0-935619)
Lafayette, LA
800-624-0466

Beaufort Bks., Inc.
(0-8253)
New York, NY
800-526-7626

Bedrick, Peter, Bks.
(0-87226; 0-911745)
New York, NY
800-242-7737 (Harper & Row Pubs., Inc.)

Beginner Books
(0-394)
New York, NY
800-638-6460

Beginning Pr.
(0-9615514)
Seattle, WA
800-426-3711 (Pacific Pipeline, Inc.)

Behrman Hse., Inc.
(0-87441)
West Orange, NJ
800-221-2755

Bender, Matthew, & Co., Inc.
(0-87571)
800-821-2232

Bentley, Robert, Inc.
(0-8376)
Cambridge, MA
800-423-4595

Bergwall Educational Software, Inc.
(0-8064; 0-943008)
Uniondale, NY
800-645-1737

Bergwall Productions, Inc.
(0-8064; 0-943008)
Garden City, NY
800-645-1737

Berkley Publishing Group
(0-425; 0-515)
New York, NY
800-223-0510

Berkshire Hse. Pubs.
(0-936397)
Great Barrington, MA
800-251-5902 (Ingram Industries)

Berry Patch Pr.
(0-9609912)
Portland, OR
800-562-4647 (Pacific Pipeline, Inc.)

Bethany Hse. Pubs.
(0-87123; 1-55661)
Minneapolis, MN
800-328-6109

Bethel Publishing Co.
(0-934998)
Elkhart, IN
800-348-7657

Bethsheva's Concern
(0-9610802)
Clifton, NJ
800-241-3829 (New Leaf Distributing, The)

Betzina, Sandra
(0-9615614)
San Francisco, CA
800-227-1516 (Bookpeople)

Bhaktivedanta Bk. Trust
(0-912776)
Los Angeles, CA
800-356-3000

Bibli O'Phile Publishing Co.
(0-942104)
New York, NY
800-255-1660

Bicycle Bks., Inc.
(0-933201)
San Francisco, CA
800-526-7627 (Kampmann & Co., Inc.)

Bilingual Bks., Inc.
(0-916682)
Seattle, WA
800-228-4078

Billner & Rouse, Inc.
(0-932755)
New York, NY
800-343-9444 (Longwood Publishing Group, Inc.)

Binns, Joseph J.
(0-89674)
Bethesda, MD
800-243-2790

Bisel, George T., Co.
Philadelphia, PA
800-247-3526 in Pennsylvania

Bishop Graphics, Inc.
(0-938009; 0-9601748)
Westlake Village, CA
800-222-5808

BkMk Pr., (Univ., of Missouri-Kansas City)
(0-933532)
Kansas City, MO
800-257-7341 (Blackwell North America)

Blacksmith Corp.
(0-941540)
Southport, CT
800-531-2665

Blackwell, Basil, Inc.
(0-233; 0-423; 0-631; 0-7456; 0-85520;
0-900186; 0-904679)
New York, NY
*800-242-7737 (Harper & Row Pubs., Inc.
(Trade orders)*

Blackwell North America
(0-946344)
Blackwood, NJ
800-257-7341
800-547-6426

Blackwell Scientific Pubns., Inc.
(0-86542)
Boston, MA
800-325-4177

Blair, John F., Pub.
(0-89587; 0-910244)
Winston-Salem, NC
800-222-9796

Blake Printing & Publishing, Inc.
(0-918303)
San Luis Obispo, CA
800-792-6946

Blood-Horse, Inc.
(0-936032; 0-939049)
Lexington, KY
800-354-9207

Blue Bird Publishing
(0-933025)
Columbus, OH
800-255-2665

Blue Heron Pr.
(0-935317)
Bellingham, WA
800-426-4727 (Pacific Pipeline, Inc.)

Blue Moon, Pr., Inc.
(0-933188)
800-526-7626 (Kampmann & Co., Inc.)

Blue Mountain Pr., Inc.
(0-88396)
Boulder, CO
800-525-0642
Blue Whale Pr.
(0-9615303)
Glendale, CA
800-227-1516 (Bookpeople)
800-426-4727 (Pacific Pipeline, Inc.)
Bluejay Bks.
(0-312)
New York, NY
800-221-7945 (St. Martin's Pr.)
Board of Pubn., LCA
(0-8006)
Philadelphia, PA
800-367-8737
Boardman, Clark, Co., Ltd.
(0-87632)
New York, NY
800-221-9428
Bobbeh Meisehs Pr.
(0-9616933)
Cambridge, MA
800-227-1516 (Bookpeople)
Boehm, Edward Marshall, Inc.
(0-918096)
Trenton, NJ
800-257-9410
Book Express
(0-9612322)
Bellflower, CA
800-251-5900 (Ingram Book Co.)
800-648-3540 (Baker & Taylor (Western Div.))
Bkhaus
(0-931613)
East Detroit, MI
800-323-4241 (Quality Books, Inc.)
800-982-8319 (Publishers Group West)
Booklegger Pr.
(0-912932)
San Francisco, CA
800-227-1516 (Bookpeople)
Bookman Publishing
(0-934780)
Baltimore, MD
800-826-6600 (Motorbooks International, Pubs. & Wholesalers, Inc.)
Books on Demand
(0-8357)
Ann Arbor, MI
800-521-0600
Books on Tape, Inc.
(0-913369)
Newport Beach, CA
800-626-3333
Borderline Pr.
(0-9614941)
New York, NY
800-241-3829 (New Leaf Distributing, The)
Bowker, R. R., Co.
(0-8352; 0-911255)
New York, NY
800-521-8110 US
800-537-8416 Canada
Boyars, Marion, Pubs., Inc.
(0-7145; 0-905223; 0-906890)
New York, NY
800-526-7626 (Kampmann & Co., Inc.)
Bradbury Pr.
(0-87888)
New York, NY
800-257-5755
Brady Communications Co., Inc.
(0-87618; 0-87619; 0-89303)
Englewood Cliffs, NJ
800-638-0220
Branchemco, Inc.
(0-9610178)
Jacksonville, FL
800-874-5990
800-342-1259 (In Florida)
Breakthrough Pubns., Inc.
(0-914327)
Briarcliff, NY
800-824-5000
Brentwood Communications Group
(0-916573; 1-55630)
Columbus, GA
800-334-8861
Brethren Pr.
(0-87178)
Elgin, IL
800-323-8039

Breton Pubs.
(0-534)
Boston, MA
800-343-2204
800-354-9706
800-833-3350 (Delmar Publishers, Inc.)
Bridge Pubns. Inc.
(0-88404)
Los Angeles, CA
800-722-1733
800-843-7389 (in California)
Bridge Publisnting, Inc.
(0-88270)
South Plainfield, NJ
800-631-5802
Bright Ring Publishing
(0-935607)
Bellingham, WA
800-426-4727 (Pacific Pipeline, Inc.)
Broadman Pr.
(0-8054)
Nashville, TN
800-251-3225
Broadway Play Publishing
(0-88145)
New York, NY
800-752-9782 (except NY, HI, AK)
Brodart Co.
(0-87272)
Williamsport, PA
800-233-8467
Brookes, Paul H., Pubs.
(0-933716)
Baltimore, MD
800-638-3775
Broude Brothers Ltd., Music
(0-8450)
New York, NY
800-225-3197
Brown, Jerald R.
(0-9614679)
Occidental, CA
800-227-1516 (Bookpeople)
Brownlow Publishing Co., Inc.
(0-915720)
Fort Worth, TX
800-433-7610
Bryce-Waterton Pubns.
(0-913339)
Portage, IN
800-323-4241 (Quality Bks.)
Buckeye Pr.
(0-9615559)
Columbus, GA
800-241-8981
Buckley-Little Bk. Catalogue Co., Inc.
(0-916667)
New York, NY
800-242-7546 (New York Zoetrope)
Buffalo Fine Arts Academy
(0-914782)
Buffalo, NY
800-441-4115 (Univ. of Washington Pr.)
Builders Publishing Co., The
(0-941000)
Salt Lake City, UT
800-241-3829 (New Leaf Distributing, The)
800-227-1516 (Bookpeople)
Bull Publishing, Co.
(0-915950)
Palo Alto, CA
800-526-7626 (Kampmann & Co., Inc.)
Buryn, Ed, Pub.
(0-916804)
San Francisco, CA
800-227-1516 (Bookpeople)
Business Pubns., Inc.
(0-256)
Plano, TX
800-323-4560 (Richard D. Irwin, Inc.)
Business Research Services Inc.
(0-933527)
Lombard, IL
800-325-8720
Butterfly Publishing Co.
(0-9614637)
Santa Monica, CA
800-241-3829 (New Leaf Distributing, The)
800-648-3540 (Baker & Taylor Co., Western Div.)
800-634-2665 (Great Tradition, The)
Butterworth Legal Pubs.
Redmond, WA
800-544-1013
Butterworth's (Scientific, Technical, Medical)
(0-250; 0-407; 0-408; 0-409)
Stoneham, MA
800-544-1013

CBP Pr.
(0-8272)
St. Louis, MO
800-351-2665
CBS Educational & Professional Publishing
(0-03)
New York, NY
800-227-2754
CEO Pubns.
(0-937415)
Healdsburg, CA
800-982-8319 (Publishers Group West)
CIBA Medical Education Div.
(0-914168)
West Caldwell, NJ
800-631-1181
800-631-1162 (Editorial)
CPI Publishing, Inc.
(0-675)
New York, NY
800-321-3106 (Modern Curriculum Pr.)
CRC Pr., Inc.
(0-8493; 0-87819)
Boca Raton, FL
800-272-7737
C.C. Pubns., Inc.
(0-88120)
Tigard, OR
800-547-4800
C.S.S. of Ohio
(0-89536; 1-55673)
Lima, OH
800-537-1030
Caedmon
(0-89845; 0-9601156)
New York, NY
800-223-0420
Cajun Pubs.
(0-933727)
New Iberia, LA
800-551-3076
Calbre Pr., Inc.
(0-935878)
Northbrook, IL
800-323-0037
California College Pr.
(0-933195)
National City, CA
800-221-7374
Callaghan & Co.
(0-8366)
Wilmette, IL
800-323-1336
800-323-8067 (Editorial)
Cambridge Bk. Co.
(0-8428)
New York, NY
800-221-4764
Cambridge Univ. Pr.
(0-521)
New York, NY
800-431-1580
Campbell's List
(0-933089)
Maitland, FL
800-624-2232
Canter & Assocs.
(0-939007; 0-9608978)
Santa Monica, CA
800-262-4347
Canterbury Pr.
(0-933753)
Berkeley, CA
800-243-0138 (Inland Bk Co.)
Capitol Pubns., Ltd., Education Research Group
(0-937925)
Alexandria, VA
800-827-7204
Carcanet Pr.
(0-85635; 0-902145)
New York, NY
800-242-7737
Cardinal Point, Inc.
(0-932065)
Ellettsville, IN
800-628-2828
Career Publishing Corp.
(0-934829)
New York, NY
800-835-2246
Career Publishing, Inc.
(0-89262)
Orange, CA
800-854-4014
CareerTrack Pubns., Inc.
(0-943066)
Boulder, CO
800-334-1018

Carolina Biological Supply Co.
(0-89278)
Burlington, NC
800-334-5551
Caroline Hse., Inc.
Naperville, IL
800-245-2665
Carolrhoda Bks., Inc.
(0-87614)
Minneapolis, MN
800-328-4929
Carroll & Graf Pubs.
(0-88184)
New York, NY
800-982-8319
Casenotes Publishing Co., Inc.
(0-87457)
Beverly Hills, CA
800-421-1893 (Law Distributors, Inc.)
Cassell Communications Inc.
(0-942980)
Fort Lauderdale, FL
800-351-9278
800-851-3392 (FL)
Cavendish, Marshall, Corp.
(0-85685; 0-86307)
Freeport, NY
800-821-9881
Caxton Printers, Ltd.
(0-87004)
Caldwell, ID
800-451-8791 (Idaho only)
Celestial Arts Pub. Co.
(0-89087; 0-912310)
Berkeley, CA
800-841-2665
Centennial Pr.
(0-8220)
Lincoln, NE
800-228-4078
Ceres Pr.
(0-9606138)
Woodstock, NY
800-227-1516 (Bookpeople)
800-241-3829 (New Leaf Ditributing, The)
800-525-9030 (Nutri-Books Corp.)
Chaco Pr.
(0-9616019)
La Canada-Flintridge, CA
800-223-5369 (Treasure Chest)
Chalmers, Irena, Cookbooks, Inc.
(0-941034)
New York, NY
800-334-8128
Charismatic Renewal Services
(0-943780)
South Bend, IN
800-348-2227
Chartcrafters Pubs.
(0-930151)
Baltimore, MD
800-258-5327 (Yankee Inc.)
Chase Pubns.
(0-914779)
San Francisco, CA
800-227-1516 (Bookpeople)
800-982-8319 (Publishers Group West)
Chatsworth Pr.
(0-917181)
Chatsworth, CA
800-262-7367
800-982-8319 (Publishers Group West)
Chatterbox Voice Learning Systems
(0-939557)
Boulder, CO
800-531-5314
Chelsea Hse. Pubs.
(0-87754; 1-55546)
Edgemont, PA
800-523-0458
Cherry Lane Bks.
(0-89524)
Port Chester, NY
800-354-4004
Chicago Historical Society
(0-913820)
Chicago, IL
800-621-2736
Child Safe Products, Inc., Publishing Div.
(0-917461)
Plantation, FL
800-334-0090
Children's Defense Fund
(0-938008)
Washington, DC
800-424-9602

Childrens Pr.
(0-516)
Chicago, IL
800-621-1115
Children's Ventures, Inc.
(0-9615985)
Grants Pass, OR
800-426-4727 (Pacific Pipeline, Inc.)
Chiron Publications
(0-933029)
Wilmette, IL
800-435-6850 (Open Court Publishing Co.)
Christian Bks. Pub. Hse.
(0-940232)
Gardiner, ME
800-228-2665
Christian Pubns., Inc.
(0-87509)
Camp Hill, PA
800-932-0382
Christian Publishing Services, Inc.
(0-88144)
Tulsa, OK
800-826-5992
Chronicle Bks.
(0-87701)
San Francisco, CA
800-652-1657
CineBooks, Inc.
(0-933997)
Chicago, IL
800-521-8110 (R. R. Bowker Co. selected titles)
Citadel Pr.
(0-8065)
Secaucus, NJ
800-572-6657
Civic-Data Corp.
(0-937628)
Newport Beach, CA
800-824-9896 (Southern California Business Directory)
Civilized Pubns.
(0-933405)
Philadelphia, PA
800-241-3829 (New Leaf Distributing, The)
Cliff's Notes, Inc.
(0-8220)
Lincoln, NE
800-228-4078
Close Up Foundation
(0-932765)
Arlington, VA
800-336-5479
800-336-5479 (Close Up Foundation)
Coastline Publishing, Co.
(0-932927)
Carmel, CA
800-227-1516 (Bookpeople)
800-243-0138 (Inland Book Co.)
Cohen, Alan
(0-910367)
New Brunswick, NJ
800-241-3829 (New Leaf Distributing)
Cold Spring Harbor Laboratory
(0-87969)
Cold Spring Harbor, NY
800-843-4388
Coleman Publishing, Inc.
(0-87418; 0-942494)
Farmingdale, NY
800-227-3489
Collector Bks.
(0-89145)
Paducah, KY
800-626-5420
College-Hill Pr., Inc.
(0-316)
San Diego, CA
800-854-2541
College Pr. Publishing Co., Inc.
(0-89900)
Joplin, MO
800-641-7148
College Skills Ctr.
(0-89026)
Baltimore, MD
800-638-1010
College Survival, Inc.
(0-942456)
Rapid City, SD
800-528-8323
Colon Health Ctr. Publishing Co.
(0-9616184)
Larkspur, CA
800-525-9030 (Nutri-books Corp.)
800-227-1516 (Bookpeople)

Colorado Schl. of Mines
(0-918062)
Golden, CO
800-446-9488
Columbia Pictures Pubns.
(0-913650)
Miami, FL
800-327-7643
Columbia Univ., Teachers College, Teachers College Pr.
(0-8077)
New York, NY
800-242-7737 (Harper & Row)
Colwell Systems, Inc.
(0-940012)
Champaign, IL
800-248-7000
800-233-7777
Comedy Ctr., The
Wilmington, DE
800-441-7098
Communication Channels, Inc.
(0-915962; 0-916164)
Atlanta, GA
800-241-9834
Communication Networks, Inc.
(0-935419)
Richmond, VA
800-882-4800
CompCare Pubns.
(0-89638)
Minneapolis, MN
800-328-3330
COMPress
(0-88720; 0-933694)
Wentworth, NH
800-221-0419
CompuSoft Publishing
(0-932760)
San Diego, CA
800-854-6505
Computer Information Ltd.
(0-9614906)
San Diego, CA
800-528-3665
Computing!
(0-913733)
San Francisco, CA
800-428-7824
Concept Development Assocs., Inc.
(0-935745)
Bethesda, MD
800-828-7250 (Ingram Software Distribution Services)
Concordia Publishing Hse.
(0-570)
St. Louis, MO
800-325-3040
Conference Board, Inc., The
(0-8237)
New York, NY
800-872-6273
Congdon & Weed
(0-86553)
New York, NY
800-221-7945
Consumer Guide Bks./Pubns. Intl., Ltd.
(0-88176)
Skokie, IL
800-526-4264
Context Pubns.
(0-932654)
Rohnert Park, CA
800-227-1516 (Bookpeople)
Continuum Pub. Co.
(0-8264)
New York, NY
800-242-7737 (Harper & Row)
Cook, David C., Publishing Co.
(0-89191; 0-912692; 1-55513)
Elgin, IL
800-323-7543
Cornell Maritime Pr., Inc.
(0-87033)
Centreville, MD
800-638-7641
Cornerstone Library, Inc.
(0-346)
800-223-2336
Cosmoenergetics Pubns.
(0-938954)
San Diego, CA
800-241-3829 (New Leaf)
Council Oak Bks., Ltd.
(0-933031)
Tulsa, OK
800-526-7626

Toll-Free Numbers

Countryman Pr., Inc.
(0-88150; 0-914378)
Woodstock, VT
800-635-5009

Covenant Pr.
(0-910452)
Chicago, IL
800-621-1290

Crain Bks.
(0-87251)
Chicago, IL
800-621-6877

Crawford Press
(0-8085; 0-88103)
Topeka, KS
800-255-3502

Creative Cataylist
(1-55663)
Oakland, CA
800-227-1516 (Bookpeople)

Creative Computing Pr.
(0-87194; 0-916688)
New York, NY
800-631-8112

Creative Homeowner Pr.
(0-932944)
Upper Saddle River, NJ
800-631-7795

Creative Programming, Inc.
(0-912079)
Malibu, CA
800-323-6354

Creative Teaching Pr., Inc.
(0-916119)
Huntington Beach, CA
800-732-1548

Crestwood Hse., Inc.
(0-89686; 0-913940)
Mankato, MN
800-535-4393

Crittenden Publishing, Inc.
(0-913153)
Novato, CA
800-421-3483

Crossroad Pub. Co.
(0-8245)
New York, NY
800-242-7737 (Harper & Row Pubs., Inc.)

Crowell, Thomas Y., Co.
(0-690)
New York, NY
800-242-7737

Crowell, Thomas Y., Junior Bks.
(0-690)
New York, NY
800-638-3030

Crown Pubs., Inc.
(0-517)
New York, NY
800-526-4264

Cy De Cosse, Inc.
(0-86573)
Minnetonka, MN
800-328-3895

DAW Bks.
(0-8099)
800-526-0275

D & S Pubs.
Clearwater, FL
800-237-9707
800-282-8118 in Florida

DOK Pubs., Inc.
(0-914634)
East Aurora, NY
800-458-7900

Da Capo Pr., Inc.
(0-306)
New York, NY
800-221-9369

Dalkey Archive Pr., The
(0-916583)
Elmwood Park, IL
800-243-0138 (Inland Book Co.)

Dance Magazine, Inc.
(0-930036)
New York, NY
800-331-1750

Danceways Books
(0-937180)
New York, NY
800-221-2154 (Variety Arts, Inc.)

Dartnell Corp.
(0-85013)
Chicago, IL
800-621-5463

Datacom Computer Sales & Supplies
Medina, OH
800-604-5553

Datamost, Inc.
(0-88190)
Chatsworth, CA
800-692-1649

Datar Publishing Co.
(0-931572)
Crestwood, MO
800-633-8378

David & Charles, Inc.
(0-7153)
North Pomfret, VT
800-423-4525

Davis, F. A., Co.
(0-8036)
Philadelphia, PA
800-523-4049

Dawn Horse Pr.
(0-913922; 0-918801)
San Rafael, CA
800-521-4785

Dealer's Choice Bks., Inc.
Tampa, FL
800-238-8288

Decker Pr., Inc.
(0-933724)
Grand Junction, CO
800-525-3454

Dekker, Marcel, Inc.
(0-8247)
New York, NY
800-228-1160

Delacorte Pr.
(0-87459)
New York, NY
800-221-4676

Delgren Bks.
(0-943472)
Tuscon, AZ
800-528-4923

Delilah Bks.
(0-933328)
New York, NY
800-847-5515

Dell Publishing Co., Inc.
(0-440)
New York, NY
800-932-0070

Delmar Co., The
(0-912081)
Charlotte, NC
800-438-1504

Delmar Pubs., Inc.
(0-8273)
Albany, NY
800-833-3350

Delorme Publishing Co.
(0-89933)
Freeport, ME
800-227-1656

Dembner Bks.
(0-934878)
New York, NY
800-233-4830 (W. W. Norton & Co., Inc.)

Denison, T. S., & Co., Inc.
(0-513)
Minneapolis, MN
800-328-3831

Denoyer-Geppert Co.
(0-87453)
Chicago, IL
800-323-1887

Deseret Bk. Co.
(0-87579; 0-87747)
Salt Lake City, UT
800-453-3876

Deutsch, Andre
(0-233)
800-526-0275 (E. P. Dutton)
800-526-0275 (New American Library)

DeVore & Sons, Inc.
(1-55665)
Wichita, KS
800-835-1051

Dial Bks. for Young Readers
New York, NY
800-526-0275

Dialogue Hse. Library
(0-87941)
New York, NY
800-221-5844

Digital Pr./Digital Equipment Corp.
(0-932376; 1-55558)
Bedford, MA
800-343-8322

Dilithium Pr.
(0-88056; 0-918398; 0-930206)
Beaverton, OR
800-547-1842

Dillon Pr., Inc.
(0-87518)
Minneapolis, MN
800-328-8322

Dimedia, Inc.
(0-89300)
Newark, NJ
800-982-8319 (Publishers Group West)

Directories Publishing Co., Inc.
(0-937020)
Clemson, SC
800-222-4531

Distributors, The
(0-942520)
South Bend, IN
800-348-5200

Dodd, Mead & Co.
(0-396; 0-89696)
New York, NY
800-251-4000

Dog-Eared Pubns.
(0-941042)
Corvallis, OR
800-426-4727 (Pacific Pipeline, Inc.)

Dog-Master Systems
Agoura Hills, CA
800-824-7888

Donning Co. Pubs.
(0-89865; 0-915442)
Norfolk, VA
800-446-8572

Dormac, Inc.
(0-86575)
Beaverton, OR
800-547-8032

Dorset Hse. Publishing Co., Inc.
(0-932633)
New York, NY
800-342-6657

Dorsey Pr., The
(0-256)
Chicago, IL
800-323-4560

Double Helix Press
(0-930578)
Los Angeles, CA
800-631-3577

Doubleday & Co., Inc.
(0-385)
New York, NY
800-645-6156
800-457-7605 (Sales Service)

Dover Pubns., Inc.
(0-486)
New York, NY
800-223-3130

Dow Jones-Irwin, Inc.
(0-256; 0-87094; 1-55623)
Homewood, IL
800-323-4566

Down East Bks.
(0-89272)
Camden, ME
800-432-1670 (In ME only)

Drakes View Publishing
(0-939123)
Inverness, CA
800-227-1516 (Bookpeople)

Drawing Board, Computer Supplies Div., The
Hartford, CT
800-243-3207

Dream Research
(0-9607172)
Tacoma, WA
800-426-4727 (Pacific Pipeline, Inc.)
800-241-3829 (New Leaf Distributing, The)

Drivers License Guide Co.
(0-938964)
Redwood City, CA
800-227-8827

Drollery Pr.
(0-940920)
Alameda, CA
800-982-8319 (Publishers Group West)

Dryden Pr.
(0-8498)
Hinsdale, IL
800-323-7437

Duco, Joyce
(0-9612896)
Nashville, TN
800-521-3990 (Spring Arbor Distributors)

Dun's Marketing Services
(0-918257)
Mountain Lakes, NJ
800-526-0651

Duquesne Univ. Pr.
(0-8207)
Pittsburgh, PA
800-221-3845

Dushkin Publishing Group, Inc.
(0-87967)
Guilford, CT
800-243-6532

Dutton, E. P.
(0-525)
New York, NY
800-221-4676

Dynamic Pubns., Inc.
(0-915569)
Silver Spring, MD
800-255-1777

EBSCO Industries, Inc.
(0-913956)
Birmingham, AL
800-633-6088

EDC Publishing
(0-88110)
Tulsa, OK
800-331-4418

EIC/Intelligence, Inc.
(0-89947)
New York, NY
800-223-6275

EMC Publishing
(0-8219; 0-88436; 0-912022)
St. Paul, MN
800-328-1452

ERA/CCR Corp.
(0-913935)
Nyack, NY
800-845-8402

ESP, Inc.
(0-8209)
Jonesboro, AR
800-643-0280

Early Educators Pr.
(0-9604390)
Lake Alfred, FL
800-638-0928 (Gryphon Hse., Inc.)

Earth Heart
(0-934747)
Point Reyes Station, CA
800-227-1516 (Bookpeople)

East Woods Pr./Fast & McMillan Pubs.
(0-88742; 0-914788)
Charlotte, NC
800-438-1242

Easter Seal Rehabilitation Center of Eastern Fairfield County, Inc.
(0-9613209)
Bridgeport, CT
800-223-1718 (Dot Gibson Pubns.)

Eastman Kodak Co.
(0-87985)
Rochester, NY
800-242-7737

Ecco Pr.
(0-88001; 0-912946)
New York, NY
800-223-2584

Economics Pr., Inc.
(0-910187)
Fairfield, NJ
800-526-2554
800-526-1128 (NJ)

Editorial Caribe
(0-89922)
Miami, FL
800-222-5342

Educational Activities, Inc.
(0-89525; 0-914296)
Baldwin, NY
800-645-3739

Educational Design, Inc.
(0-87694)
New York, NY
800-221-9372

Educational Development Corp.
(0-89403; 0-913332)
Tulsa, OK
800-331-4418

Educational Ministries, Inc.
(0-940754)
Brea, CA
800-221-0910

Educational Service, Inc.
(0-89273)
Stevensville, MI
800-253-0763

Eerdmans, William B., Publishing Co.
(0-8028)
Grand Rapids, MI
800-253-7521

Eighth Mountain Pr.
(0-933377)
Portland, OR
800-227-1516 (Bookpeople)
800-243-0138 (Inland Bk. Co)

Eldan Pr.
(0-9615128)
Menlo Park, CA
800-982-8319 (Publishers Group West)

Elek-Tek, Inc.
Chicago, IL
800-621-1269

Elrod, Bruce C.
(0-9614805)
White Rock, SC
800-722-8690

Empire Books
(0-88015)
New York, NY
800-242-7737

Employee Benefit Research Institute
(0-86643)
Washington, DC
800-354-5425

Encyclopaedia Britannica Educational Corp.
(0-8347; 0-87827)
Chicago, IL
800-554-9862

Encyclopaedia Britannica, Inc.
(0-85229)
Chicago, IL
800-554-9862

Enrich
(0-86582; 0-933358)
San Jose, CA
800-367-4241

Entwood Publishing, Inc.
(0-9605978)
Wausau, WI
800-245-2665 (Caroline Hse., Inc.)

Episcopal Churchwoman of All Saints, Inc.
(0-9606880)
River Ridge, LA
800-982-8319 (Publishers Group West)

Eurasia Pr.
(0-932030)
Teaneck, NJ
800-242-7737

Evans, M., & Co., Inc.
(0-87131)
New York, NY
800-526-0275

Everest, F. Alton
(0-9608352)
Whittier, CA
800-233-9604 (Mix Pubns., Inc.)

Excel Fitness, Pubs.
(0-916915)
Seattle, WA
800-562-4647 (Pacific Pipeline)
800-426-4727 (in OR, ID, MT, NV, & Northern CA)

Executive Enterprises, Inc.
(0-88057; 0-917386)
New York, NY
800-645-7880

Facts on File, Inc.
(0-8160; 0-87196)
New York, NY
800-322-8755

Fainshaw Pr.
(0-943290)
Westmoreland, NH
800-634-2665 (Great Tradition, The)

Family Circle Bks.
(0-933585)
New York, NY
800-247-2904

Family Process Pr.
(0-9615519)
New York, NY
800-223-2584 (W. W. Norton & Co.)

Family Skills, Inc.
(0-934275)
Dallas, TX
800-543-7545

Farm Journal, Inc.
(0-89795)
Philadelphia, PA
800-237-1212

Farmer, W. D., Residence Designer, Inc.
(0-931518)
Atlanta, GA
800-225-7526
800-221-7526 (In Georgia)

Farragut Publishing Co.
(0-918535)
Washington, DC
800-243-0138 (Inland Bk. Co.)

Farrar, Straus & Giroux, Inc.
(0-374)
New York, NY
800-242-7737

Fawcett Bk. Group
(0-449)
New York, NY
800-638-6460

Faxon Co., The
(0-87305)
Westwood, MA
800-225-6055

Federal Document Retrieval Inc.
(0-932929)
Washington, DC
800-368-1009

Fell, Frederick, Pubs., Inc.
(0-8119)
Hollywood, FL
800-526-7626

Feminist Pr. at the City Univ. of New York, The
(0-912670; 0-935312)
New York, NY
800-242-7737 (Harper & Row, Pubs., Inc.)

Field Publications
(0-8374)
Middletown, CT
800-852-5000

Fifth Avenue Brides, Inc.
(0-9615882)
La Crosse, WI
800-527-5807 (Howard Gardiner, Inc.)

Film Communicators
(0-9606702)
N. Hollywood, CA
800-423-2400

FIND-SVP Information Clearing Hse.
(0-931634)
New York, NY
800-346-3787

Fine Line Productions
(0-936413)
San Francisco, CA
800-227-1516 (Bookpeople)
800-241-3829 (New Leaf Distributing, The)

Fins Pubns.
(0-9615221)
Roseville, MN
800-328-8411 (Bookman, Inc.)

Fire Engineering Bk. Service
(0-912212)
New York, NY
800-992-4447 (Fire Engineering Bk. Service)

Fireside Bks.
(0-87527)
St. Louis, MO
800-223-2336

FlipTrack Learning Systems
(0-917792)
Glen Ellyn, IL
800-222-3547

Florida Bar Continuing Legal Education Pubns., The
(0-910373)
Tallahassee, FL
800-874-0005

Foghorn Pr.
(0-935701)
San Francisco, CA
800-227-1516 (Bookpeople)

Forest Publishing
(0-9605118)
Lake Forest, IL
800-323-9442

Forster, Reginald Bishop, Assocs., Inc.
Sacramento, CA
800-328-5091;
800-321-9789 in California

Fortress Pr.
(0-8006)
Philadelphia, PA
800-367-8737

Forum for Scriptural Christianity, Inc.
(0-917851)
Wilmore, KY
800-672-1789 (Cokesbury)

Forum Quorum
(0-9606778)
Waldwick, NJ
800-821-5745 (The Collection)

Forward Movement Pubns.
(0-88028)
Cincinnati, OH
800-543-1813

Foundation Ctr., The
(0-87954)
New York, NY
800-424-9836

Foundation for Life Action
(1-55531)
Los Angeles, CA
800-367-2246
800-732-5489 (In California)

Four Trees Pubns.
(0-936329)
San Francisco, CA
800-227-1516 (Bookpeople)

Franklin, Burt, Pub.
(0-89102)
New York, NY
800-223-0766

Franklin, Charles, Pr., The
(0-932091; 0-9603516)
Edmonds, WA
800-992-6657

Free Pr.
(0-02)
New York, NY
800-257-5755

Freundlich Bks.
(0-88191)
New York, NY
800-526-7626 (Kampmann & Co., Inc.)

Friends' Pr.
(0-9615090)
Weston, CT
800-227-1516 (Bookpeople)
800-241-3829 (New Leaf Distributing)

Frost & Sullivan, Inc.
(0-86621)
New York, NY
800-242-7737

Fulcrum, Inc.
(1-55591)
Golden, CO
800-992-2908

Funk & Wagnalls Co.
(0-308)
New York, NY
800-242-7737

GFI Assocs.
(0-915309)
Arlington, VA
800-526-7626 (Frederick Fell Pubs.)

G-Jo Institute/Falkynor Bks., The
(0-916878)
Davie, FL
800-843-6666 (Samuel Weiser)

GP Courseware
(0-87683)
Columbia, MD
800-638-3838

Gale Research Co.
(0-8103)
Detroit, MI
800-223-4253

Gallaudet College Pr.
(0-913580; 0-930323)
Washington, DC
800-672-6720 (ext. 5595)

Galley Press
(0-9604800)
Portland, OR
800-932-0070

Gannett Bks.
(0-930096)
Portland, ME
800-442-6036

Garner, Clifford S.
(0-9612808)
Santa Clara, CA
800-826-0364 (Enterprises Store, The)

Gateway Pr.
(0-936533)
Mill Valley, CA
800-277-1516 (Bookpeople)

Gay Sunshine Pr.
(0-917342)
San Francisco, CA
800-243-0138 (Inland Bk. Co.)

Geneva Pr., The
(0-664)
Philadelphia, PA
800-523-1631

Genova, Inc.
(0-9616509)
Davison, MI
800-521-7488

Gentle World, Inc.
(0-9614248)
Umatilla, FL
800-241-3829 (New Leaf)

George Washington Univ. National Law Ctr., Government Contracts Program
(0-935165)
Washington, DC
800-446-2221

Gibson, C. R., Co.
(0-8378)
Norwalk, CT
800-243-6004

Ginn Pr.
(0-536)
Lexington, MA
800-848-9500

Glastonbury Pr.
(0-932145)
Whittier, CA
800-982-8319 (Publishers Group West)

Glencoe Publishing Co.
(0-02)
Encino, CA
800-257-5755

Glenn, Peter, Pubns., Inc.
(0-87314)
New York, NY
800-223-1254

Global Engineering Documents
(0-912702)
Santa Ana, CA
800-854-7179

Globe Pequot Pr.
(0-87106)
Chester, CT
800-243-0495
800-962-0973 (CT only)

Godine, David R., Pub., Inc.
(0-87923)
Boston, MA
800-242-7737 (Harper & Row Pubs., Inc.)

Golden-Lee Bk.
(0-912331)
Brooklyn, NY
800-221-0960

Golden Sceptre Publishing
(0-9615117)
Berkeley, CA
800-227-1516 (Bookpeople)
800-624-4466 in California (New Leaf Distributing)

Gollehon Pr., Inc.
(0-914839)
Grand Rapids, MI
800-262-4947

Good Apple, Inc.
(0-86653; 0-916456)
Carthage, IL
800-435-7234

Good Bks.
(0-934672)
Intercourse, PA
800-762-7171

Good Money Pubns., Inc.
(0-933609)
Worcester, VT
800-535-3551

Good News Pubs.
(0-89107)
Westchester, IL
800-323-3890 Sales only

Good Old Spot Pr.
(0-9616718)
Seattle, WA
800-562-4647 (WA)

Goodheart-Willcox Co.
(0-87006)
South Holland, IL
800-323-0440

Gospel Advocate Co., Inc.
(0-89225)
Nashville, TN
800-251-8446
800-242-8006 in Tennessee
800-342-8006 in Tennessee

Gospel Publishing Hse.
(0-88243)
Springfield, MO
800-641-4310
800-492-7625 in Missouri

Granite Pr.
(0-9614886)
Penobscot, ME
800-243-0138 (Inland Bk. Co.)

Graphic Arts Ctr. Publishing Co.
(0-912856; 0-932575)
Portland, OR
800-452-3032

Gravity Publishing
(0-936067)
Oakland, CA
800-227-1516 (Bookpeople)

Great Game Products
(0-935307)
Bethesda, MD
800-426-3748

Great Outdoors Publishing Co.
(0-8200)
St. Petersburg, FL
800-433-5560 (Florida only)

Great Plains National Instructional Television Library
(0-9614949)
Lincoln, NE
800-228-4630

Great Plains Software
(0-924261)
Fargo, ND
800-345-3276

Greene, Stephen, Pr.
(0-8289; 0-86616)
Lexington, MA
800-631-3577 (Viking Penguin, Inc.)

Greenhaven Pr.
(0-89908; 0-912616)
St. Paul, MN
800-231-5163

Greensward Pr.
(0-930165)
San Francisco, CA
800-525-9030 (Nutri Books)

Greenwich Pr., Ltd.
(0-86713)
Trumbull, CT
800-243-4246

Greenwillow Bks.
(0-688)
New York, NY
800-631-1199

Grove Pr.
(0-394; 0-8021)
New York, NY
800-638-6460

Groves Dictionaries of Music, Inc.
(0-943818)
New York, NY
800-221-2123

Grumbacher, M., Inc.
New York, NY
800-346-3278

Grune & Stratton, Inc.
(0-8089)
800-321-5068

Gryphon Hse., Inc.
(0-87659)
Mount Rainier, MD
800-638-0928

Guilford Pr., The
(0-89862)
New York, NY
800-221-3966

HP Bks.
(0-89586; 0-912656)
Tucson, AZ
800-528-4923

Hafner Pr.
(0-02)
New York, NY
800-257-5755

Hall, G. K., & Co.
(0-8161)
Boston, MA
800-343-2806

Halsted Pr.
(0-470)
New York, NY
800-526-5368

Hammond Inc.
(0-8437)
Maplewood, NJ
800-526-4953

Hansen, Charles, Educational Music & Bks., Inc.
(0-8494)
Miami Beach, FL
800-327-8202 (Hansen Hse.)
Happiness Unlimited Pubns.
(0-939372)
Virginia Beach, VA
800-525-5018, Ext 552
Harcourt Brace Jovanovich, Inc.
(0-15)
San Diego, CA
800-543-1918
Harper & Row Pubs., Inc.
(0-06)
New York, NY
800-242-7737
Harris Publishing Company
(0-916512)
Twinsburg, OH
800-321-9136
Harrison Co.
(0-910694)
Norcross, GA
800-241-3561
800-282-9867 (In Georgia)
Harrison Hse., Inc.
(0-89274)
Tulsa, OK
800-331-3647
Harvard Business Schl. Pr.
(0-87584)
Boston, MA
800-638-3030 (Harper & Row Pubs., Inc.)
Harvest Hse. Pubs., Inc.
(0-89081)
Eugene, OR
800-547-8979
Harvey Woman's Club
(0-9611654)
Palestine, TX
800-821-5745 (The Collection)
Hastings Hse. Pubs.
(0-8038)
New York, NY
800-52607626
Hayden Bk. Co.
(0-8104)
Hasbrouck Heights, NJ
800-631-0856
Hays, Rolfes & Assocs.
(0-9602448)
Memphis, TN
800-223-1781 (The Collection, Inc.)
Hazelden Foundation
(0-89486)
Center City, MN
800-328-9000
Health Communications, Inc.
(0-932194)
Pompano Beach, FL
800-857-9100
HealthProInk Publishing
(0-933803)
Farmington Hills, MI
800-802-4966 in Michigan
Heath, D. C., Co.
(0-278; 0-669; 0-88408)
Lexington, MA
800-428-8071
Hegeler Institute, The
(0-914417)
Los Angeles, CA
800-435-6850 (The Monist)
Hein, William S., & Co., Inc.
(0-89941; 0-930342)
Buffalo, NY
800-828-7571
Heinle & Heinle Pubs., Inc.
(0-8384)
Boston, MA
800-225-3782
Hemisphere Publishing Corp.
(0-89116)
New York, NY
800-242-7737
Herald Hse.
(0-8309)
Independence, MO
800-821-7550
Herald Pr.
(0-8361)
Scottdale, PA
800-245-7894
Hermetician Pr.
(0-935895)
North Miami, FL
800-241-3829 (New Leaf Distributing)

Hero Games
(0-915795; 0-917481)
Charlottesville, VA
800-325-0479
Heron Pr.
(0-935999)
San Francisco, CA
800-251-5700 (Ingram Bk. Co.)
Hewlett-Packard Co.
(0-9612030)
Santa Clara, CA
800-367-4772
Hi-Time Publishing Corp.
(0-937997)
Milwaukee, WI
800-558-2292
Hideaways International
(0-933613)
Littleton, MA
800-843-4433
Higley Publishing Corp.
(0-9614116)
Jacksonville, FL
800-521-4340 (Spring Arbor)
Hill & Wang, Inc.
(0-8090)
New York, NY
800-242-7737
Hilltop Publishing Co.
(0-912133)
Sonoma, CA
800-227-1516 (Bookpeople)
Hinds, Norman C., Jr., Publishing Co.
(0-935541)
Newburyport, MA
800-241-3829 (New Leaf Distributing, The)
History of Science Society, Inc.
(0-934235)
Philadelphia, PA
800-341-1522
Holman, A.J., Bible Pub.
(0-87981)
Nashville, TN
800-251-3225
Home Planners, Inc.
(0-918894)
Farmington Hills, MI
800-521-6797
Home Vision
(0-938957)
Chicago, IL
800-323-4222
Homebuilt Pubns.
(0-9614882)
Glendale, CA
800-826-6600 (Motorbooks International)
Homestead Book, Inc.
(0-930180)
Seattle, WA
800-426-6777
Hope Publishing Co.
(0-916642)
Carol Stream, IL
800-323-1049
Horizon Pubs. & Distributors, Inc.
(0-88290)
Bountiful, UT
800-453-0812
Horn Bk., Inc.
(0-87675)
Boston, MA
800-325-1170
Hospital Research & Educational Trust
(0-87914)
Chicago, IL
800-242-2626
Houghton Mifflin Co.
(0-395; 0-87466)
Boston, MA
800-225-3362
House of Collectibles, Inc.
(0-87637)
Orlando, FL
800-327-1384
Hubbard Scientific
(0-8331)
Northbrook, IL
800-323-8368
Human Resource Development Pr.
(0-87425; 0-914234)
Amherst, MA
800-822-2801
Humanics, Ltd.
(0-89334)
Atlanta, GA
800-874-8844

Humanities Pr. International, Inc.
(0-391)
Atlantic Highlands, NJ
800-221-3845
Hunter Books
(0-917726)
Kingwood, TX
800-231-3024
Huntington Hse., Inc.
(0-910311)
Lafayette, LA
800-572-8213
ICS Bks., Inc.
(0-934802)
Merrillville, IN
800-732-3669
IEEE Computer Society Pr.
(0-8186)
Washington, DC
800-272-6657
IMS Pr.
(0-910190)
Fort Washington, PA
800-523-5884
IPS Information Processing Supplies
Burr Ridge, IL
800-323-5569
ISI Pr.
(0-86689; 0-89495; 0-906083; 0-946395)
Philadelphia, PA
800-523-1850
IWP Publishing
(0-88155; 0-914766)
Minneapolis, MN
800-843-6666
Ibis Publishing
(0-935005)
Charlottesville, VA
800-582-0026
Icarus Pr., Inc.
(0-89651)
South Bend, IN
800-242-7737
Ideals Publishing Corp.
(0-8249; 0-89542)
Nashville, TN
800-558-0740
Idylwild Books
(0-9613054)
Ojai, CA
800-227-1516 (Bookpeople)
800-241-3829 (The New Leaf Distributing)
Imported Pubns., Inc.
(0-8285)
Chicago, IL
800-345-2665
Incentive Pubns., Inc.
(0-86530; 0-913916)
Nashville, TN
800-421-2830
Independence Press
(0-8309)
Independence, MO
800-821-7550
Ink Publishing Co.
Tucson, AZ
800-446-8572 (Donning Co. Pubs.)
Inner Traditions International, Ltd.
(0-89281)
Rochester, VT
800-242-7737 (Harper & Row Pubs., Inc.)
Institute for Econometric Research
(0-917604)
Ft. Lauderdale, FL
800-327-6720
Institute for Evolutionary Research
(0-938710)
New York, NY
800-843-6666 (Samuel Weiser, Inc.)
Institute for Palestine Studies
(0-88728)
Washington, DC
800-874-3614
Institute for the Study of Human Knowledge
Cambridge, MA
800-222-4745
Institute of Early American History & Culture
(0-910776)
Williamsburg, VA
800-223-2584
Instrumentalist Co.
Northfield, IL
800-323-5559

Toll-Free Numbers

Insurance Achievement, Inc.
(0-88171)
Baton Rouge, LA
800-535-3042

Intel Corp.
(0-917017; 1-55512)
Santa Clara, CA
800-548-4725

Inter/Face Assocs., Inc.
(0-938135)
Middletown, CT
800-433-1116

Inter-Varsity Pr.
(0-8308; 0-87784)
Downers Grove, IL
800-843-7225

International Assn. of Milk, Food, & Environmental Sanitarians, Inc.
Ames, IA
800-525-5223

International Aviation Pubs., Inc.
(0-89100)
Riverton, WY
800-443-9250

International Center for Creative Thinking
(0-9615400)
New Rochelle, NY
800-828-8285

International Fire Service Training Association
(0-87939)
Stillwater, OK
800-654-4055

International Human Resources Development Corp.
(0-88746; 0-934634)
Boston, MA
800-327-6756

International Learning Institute
(0-939311)
Petaluma, CA
800-227-1516 (Bookpeople)

International Marine Publishing Co.
(0-8286; 0-87742)
Camden, ME
800-328-0059 (Trade Customers Only)

International Pubns. Service
(0-8002)
Philadelphia, PA
800-821-8312

International Specialized Bk. Services
(0-89955)
Portland, OR
800-547-7734

International Video Entertainment
(1-55658)
Woodland Hills, CA
800-423-7455

Interport USA, Inc.
(0-932331)
Portland, OR
800-233-5729

Interstate Printers & Pubs., Inc.
(0-8134)
Danville, IL
800-843-4774

Interweave Pr., Inc.
(0-934026)
Loveland, CO
800-272-2193

Investor Pubns., Inc.
(0-914230)
Cedar Falls, IA
800-553-1789

Investrek Publishing
(0-9604914)
Huntington Beach, CA
800-334-0854, Ext 864

Iron Crown Enterprises, Inc.
(0-915795)
Charlottesville, VA
800-325-0479

Irwin, Richard D., Inc.
(0-256)
Homewood, IL
800-323-4560

Island Canoe Co.
(0-918439)
Bainbridge Island, WA
800-426-4727 (Pacific Pipeline)
800-467-4647 (in WA)

Ivory Publishing
(0-9614738)
Denver, CO
800-982-8319 (Publishers Group West)
800-227-1516 (Bookpeople)
800-843-6666 (Samuel Weiser, Inc.)

Ivory Tower Publishing Co., Inc.
(0-88032)
Watertown, MA
800-322-5016

JA Micropublishing, Inc.
(0-912127)
Eastchester, NY
800-227-2477

JFJ Publishing
(0-9616148)
San Francisco, CA
800-227-3190

JLA Pubns.
(0-940374)
Cambridge, MA
800-982-8319 (Publishers Group West)

Jalmar Pr.
(0-915190)
Rolling Hills Estate, CA
800-662-9662

Jamestown Pubs., Inc.
(0-89061)
Providence, RI
800-872-7323

Janus Bk. Pubs.
(0-88084; 0-88102; 0-915510)
Hayward, CA
800-227-2375

Jargon Society, Inc., The
(0-912330)
Highlands, NC
800-243-0138

Jayell Enterprises Inc.
(0-916197)
Dearborn, MI
800-243-0138 (Inland Bk. Co.)

Jesuit Historical Institute
Chicago, IL
800-621-1008

John Day Co., Inc.
(0-381)
New York, NY
800-242-7737

Johnson Institute
(0-935908)
Minneapolis, MN
800-231-5165

Johnson Reference Bks.
(0-9600906)
Alexandria, VA
800-851-2665

Johnson Reprint Corp.
(0-384)
New York, NY
800-543-1918

Joint Ctr. for Political Studies
(0-941410)
Washington, DC
800-323-5277

Jones, Bob, Univ. Pr.
(0-89084)
Greenville, SC
800-235-5731

Jones & Bartlett Pubs., Inc.
(0-86720)
Boston, MA
800-832-0034

Josephson/Kluwer Legal Educational Ctrs., Inc.
(0-940366)
Culver City, CA
800-421-4577

Jossey-Bass, Inc., Pubs.
(0-87589; 1-55542)
San Francisco, CA
800-526-7626 (Kampmann & Co.)

Jove Pubns., Inc.
(0-515)
New York, NY
800-223-0510

Judson Pr.
(0-8170)
Valley Forge, PA
800-331-1053

Jury Verdict Research Inc.
(0-934607)
Solon, OH
800-321-6910

KC Pubns.
(0-88714; 0-916122)
Las Vegas, NV
800-626-9673

K-Dimension Pubs.
(0-917595)
Decatur, GA
800-241-4702

KET
(0-910475)
Lexington, KY
800-354-9067

Kalimat Pr.
(0-933770)
Los Angeles, CA
800-323-1880

Kalmbach Publishing Co.
(0-89024)
Milwaukee, WI
800-558-1544

Kampmann & Co., Inc.
New York, NY
800-526-7626

Kar-Ben Copies, Inc.
(0-930494)
Rockville, MD
800-452-7236

Katydid Bks.
(0-942668)
Rochester, MI
800-441-4115 (Univ. of Washington Pr.)

Kaypro Corp.
Del Mar, CA
800-452-9776

Keller, J. J., Assocs., Inc.
(0-934674)
Neenah, WI
800-558-5011
800-242-6469 (WI only)

Kent Publishing Co.
(0-534)
Boston, MA
800-343-2204

Kent State Univ. Pr.
(0-87338)
Kent, OH
800-872-5368
800-367-5368 Ohio
800-242-7737 (Harper & Row)

Key Book Service, Inc.
(0-934636)
Bridgeport, CT
800-243-2790

Key Curriculum Project
(0-913684)
Berkeley, CA
800-338-7638

Keystone Pubns.
(0-912126)
New York, NY
800-223-0935

KhaniQahi-Nimatullahi, Sufi Order
(0-933546)
New York, NY
800-843-6666 (Samuel Weiser, Inc.)

Kid Power Enterprises
(0-935441)
Decatur, GA
800-241-3829 (The New Leaf Distributing)

King's Farspan, Inc.
(0-932814)
Ojai, CA
800-521-3990 (Spring Arbor Distributors)
800-854-4746 (Living Bks., Inc.)

Kirban, Salem, Inc.
(0-912582)
Huntingdon Valley, PA
800-251-7206 (AMG Publishers)

Kjos, Neil A., Music Co.
(0-8497; 0-910842)
San Diego, CA
800-854-1592

Kluwer Law Bk. Pubs., Inc.
(0-930273)
New York, NY
800-821-4526

Knapp Pr., The
(0-89535)
Los Angeles, CA
800-526-4264

Knopf, Alfred A., Inc.
(0-394)
New York, NY
800-638-6460

Know Himm Pr.
(0-9614014)
Whittier, CA
800-854-4746 (Living Bks., Inc.)

Knowledge Industry Pubns., Inc.
(0-86729; 0-914236)
White Plains, NY
800-248-5474

Knox, John, Pr.
(0-8042)
Atlanta, GA
800-334-6580
800-822-1917 (in GA)

Kodansha International USA, Ltd.
(0-87011)
New York, NY
800-242-7737

Kramer, H. J., Inc.
(0-915811)
Tiburon, CA
800-227-1516
800-982-8319 (Publishers Group West)

Kregel Pubns.
(0-8254)
Grand Rapids, MI
800-253-5465

Kripalu Pubns.
(0-940258)
Lenox, MA
800-843-6666 (Samuel Weiser)

L O M A (Life Office Management Assn.)
(0-915322; 0-939921)
Atlanta, GA
800-848-0773 (Professional Bk. Distributors)

Larry Smith Associates Inc.
(0-931741)
Los Gatos, CA
800-826-6600 (Motorbooks Int.)

Larson Pubns., Inc.
(0-943914)
Burdett, NY
800-526-7626
(Kampmann & Co.)

Launch Pr.
(0-9613205)
San Francisco, CA
800-277-1516 (Bookpeople)
800-243-0138 (Inland Bk. Co.)

Lawrence & Co. Pubs.
(0-9607096)
Albuquerque, NM
800-323-4560 (Dow Jones-Irwin, Inc.)

Lawrenceville Pr., Inc.
(0-931717)
Lawrenceville, NJ
800-833-3350; (Delmar Pubs., Inc.)
800-252-2550 (In New York)

Lawton-Teague Pubns.
(0-932516)
Oakland, CA
800-227-1516 (Bookpeople)

Lawyers Co-Operative Publishing Co.
Rochester, NY
800-527-0430

Lea & Febiger
(0-8121)
Philadelphia, PA
800-433-3850

Learning Process Ctr.
(0-931657)
National City, CA
800-221-7374

Learning Pubns., Inc.
(0-918452; 1-55691)
Holmes Beach, FL
800-222-1525

Learning Well
(0-917109; 0-936850; 1-55596)
Roslyn Heights, NY
800-645-6564

Learning Works, Inc., The
(0-88160)
Santa Barbara, CA
800-235-5767

Leaven Pr.
(0-934134)
Kansas City, MO
800-821-7926

Lederer Enterprises
(0-9608040)
Asheville, NC
800-258-7160

Leonard, Hal, Publishing Corp.
(0-88188; 0-9607350)
Milwaukee, WI
800-558-4774

Lerner Pubns. Co.
(0-8225)
Minneapolis, MN
800-328-4929

Lewis Pubs, Inc.
(0-87371)
Chelsea, MI
800-525-7894

Lexington Bks.
(0-669)
800-235-3565

Li, Peter, Inc.
(0-89837)
Dayton, OH
800-531-3456

Library of America, The
(0-940450)
New York, NY
800-631-3577

Lifecircle Pubns.
(0-935815)
Kent, OH
800-241-3892 (New Leaf Distributing)

Lifetime Learning Pubns.
(0-534)
Belmont, CA
800-354-9706

Light & Life Pr. (IN)
(0-89367)
Winona Lake, IN
800-348-2513

Light Impressions Corp.
(0-87992)
Rochester, NY
800-828-6216

Liguori Pubns.
(0-89243)
Liguori, MO
800-325-9521

Limelight Editions
(0-87910)
New York, NY
800-242-7737

Linch Publishing Inc.
(0-913455)
Orlando, FL
800-327-7055
800-434-0399 (FL)

Linden Publishing Co., Inc.
(0-941936)
Fresno, CA
800-345-4447

Lineal Publishing Co.
(0-916628; 0-9612412)
Ft. Lauderdale, FL
800-222-4253

Lion/Lamb Pr.
(0-9616424)
Berkeley, CA
800-227-1516 (Bookpeople)

Lippincott, J. B., Co.
(0-397)
Philadelphia, PA
800-523-2945

Lippincott, J. B., Junior Bks.
(0-397)
New York, NY
800-638-3030

Listen USA
Greenwich, CT
800-223-0288 (Hearst Corp., International Circulation Div.)

Little, Brown & Co.
(0-316)
Boston, MA
800-343-9204

Liveright Publishing Corp.
(0-87140)
New York, NY
800-233-4830

Llewellyn Pubns.
(0-87542)
St. Paul, MN
800-843-6666

Lodestar Bks.
(0-525)
New York, NY
800-526-0275

Logbridge-Rhodes, Inc.
(0-937606)
Durango, CO
800-243-0138 (Inland Book Company)

Lomond Pubns., Inc.
(0-912338)
Mt. Airy, MD
800-443-6299

Lone Eagle Publishing
(0-943728)
Beverly Hills, CA
800-982-8319 (Publishers Group West)

Lone Oak Bks.
(0-936550)
Bethesda, MD
800-982-8319 (Publishers Group West)

LongRiver Bks.
(0-942986)
800-243-0138 (Inland Bk. Co.)

Longwood Publishing Group, Inc.
(0-89341)
Wolfeboro, NH
800-343-9444

Lorian Pr.
(0-936878)
Issaquah, WA
800-862-7232 (Narada Distributors (Music Only))

Lothrop, Lee & Shepard Bks.
(0-688)
New York, NY
800-631-1199

Love Song to The Messiah Assn., Inc.
(0-915775)
Ft. Lauderdale, FL
800-521-3690 (Spring Arbor Distributors)
800-854-4746 (Living Books)

Loyola Univ. Pr.
(0-8294)
Chicago, IL
800-621-1008

Luce, Robert B., Inc.
(0-88331)
Bridgeport, CT
800-243-2790

MTI Teleprograms Inc./A Simon & Schuster Communications Company
(0-916070)
Deerfield, IL
800-621-2131

M. Damien Pubs.
(0-930539)
Eugene, OR
800-426-4727 (Pacific Pipeline Inc.)
800-323-4241 (Quality Bks., Inc.)

McCutchan Publishing Corp.
(0-8211)
Berkeley, CA
800-227-1540

McDonnell Douglas Information Systems Group
St. Louis, MO
800-325-1087

McGraw-Hill Bk. Co.
(0-07; 0-914410)
New York, NY
800-628-0004

McKnight Publishing Co.
Peoria, IL
800-447-0682

Macmillan Publishing Co., Inc.
(0-02)
New York, NY
800-257-5755

MacRae's Blue Bk., Inc.
(0-89910)
New York, NY
800-622-7237

Madrona Pr., Inc.
(0-89052)
Austin, TX
800-624-1739

Magickal Childe Inc.
(0-939708)
New York, NY
800-843-6666

Maltby, Ralph, Enterprises, Inc.
(0-9606792)
Newark, OH
800-848-8358
800-762-1831 (In Ohio)

Management Information Source, Inc.
(0-943518)
Portland, OR
800-626-8257

Mann, Al, Assocs.
(0-9614769)
Poughkeepsie, NY
800-437-4467

Manor Health Care Corp.
(0-917025)
Silver Spring, MD
800-637-1400

Mansell
(0-7201)
Bronx, NY
800-367-6770

Market Data Retrieval, Inc.
(0-89770; 0-914608)
Shelton, CT
800-624-5669

Market Dynamics
(0-913761)
New York, NY
800-262-7353

Marquis Who's Who/Macmillan Directory Division
(0-8379)
Chicago, IL
800-621-9669

Martin Pr., The
(0-941018)
Torrance, CA
800-421-1212

Mary & Leigh Block Gallery, Northwestern Univ.
(0-941680)
Evanston, IL
800-441-4115 (University of Washington Press)

Massachusetts Historical Society
(0-934909)
Boston, MA
800-423-6108 (University Microfilms International)

Master Bk. Pubs.
(0-89051)
El Cajon, CA
800-621-0852 ext. 134

Masterco Press, Inc.
(0-912164)
Ann Arbor, MI
800-443-0100

Masterworks, Inc., Pubs.
(0-931317)
Friday Harbor, WA
800-445-1313

Mastery Education Corp.
(0-88106; 0-935508)
Watertown, MA
800-225-3214

Math Hse.
(0-917792)
Glen Ellyn, IL
800-222-3547

Matrix Pubs., Inc.
(0-916460)
Chesterland, OH
800-851-6018

Matrix Software
(0-925182)
Big Rapids, MI
800-622-4070
800-942-7317 (IL)

Matvest Media, Inc.
(0-9616155)
Minneapolis, MN
800-547-5570

Meadowbrook, Inc.
(0-88166; 0-915658)
Deephaven, MN
800-223-2336
(Simon & Schuster)
800-442-7070 (in NY)

Media Materials, Inc.
(0-86601; 0-89539; 0-912974)
Baltimore, MD
800-638-1010

Media Pr.
(0-917181)
Chatsworth, CA
800-262-7367
800-272-7367 (inside CA)

Media Unlimited Inc.
(0-930394)
Alameda, CA
800-428-0902

Mediamix Assocs.
(0-915893)
Studio City, CA
800-227-1516 (Bookpeople)
800-982-8319 (Publishers Group West)

Medical Economics Bks.
(0-87489)
Oradell, NJ
800-223-0581

Medical Manor Bks.
(0-934232)
Philadelphia, PA
800-343-8464
800-251-5902 (Ingram Industries)

Merriam-Webster, Inc.
(0-87779)
Springfield, MA
800-828-1880

Merrill Publishing Co.
(0-675)
Columbus, OH
800-848-6205

Merrimack Publishing Corp.
(0-87497)
Bridgeport, CT
800-232-2224

Merriwell, Frank, Inc.
(0-8373)
Syosset, NY
800-645-6337

Mesorah Pubns., Ltd.
(0-89906)
Brooklyn, NY
800-637-6724

Messner, Julian
(0-671)
New York, NY
800-223-2336

Metamorphic Pr.
(0-9615848)
Santa Rosa, CA
800-527-8200 (Rodale Press, Incorporated)

Mexican American Cultural Ctr.
(0-932545)
San Antonio, TX
800-531-6222

Meyer, Sandy, & Assocs.
(0-9613431)
Roanoke, VA
800-227-1516 (Bookpeople)

Mho & Mho Works
(0-917320)
Menlo Park, CA
800-227-1516 (Bookpeople)

Michie Co., The
(0-672; 0-87215; 0-87473)
Charlottesville, VA
800-446-3410

Micro Information Publishing
(0-912603)
Prior Lake, MN
800-328-0196

Micro-Wave Foods Inc.
(0-9614957)
Malibu, CA
800-643-8259 (Club Products)

Microlit Pubs.
(0-931145)
San Diego, CA
800-362-9653 (Micro-Pace)
800-348-5200 (The Distributors)

Microsoft Pr.
(0-914845)
Redmond, WA
800-223-2336

Midwest Financial Pubns., Inc.
(0-933623)
Fairfield, IA
800-982-8319 (Publishers Group West)

Milady Publishing Corp.
(0-87350)
Bronx, NY
800-223-8055

Milford House
(0-87821)
Dover, NH
800-343-9444

Milford Null Modem
Malvern, PA
800-345-2121

Millers River Publishing Co
(0-912395)
Athol, MA
800-243-0138 (Inland Book Co.)

Minnesota Historical Society Pr.
(0-87351)
St. Paul, MN
800-647-7827 (In Midwest)

Misty Hill Pr.
(0-930079)
Sebastopol, CA
800-227-1516 (Bookpeople)

Mitchell Publishing, Inc.
(0-938188)
Santa Cruz, CA
800-435-2665

Modern Curriculum Pr.
(0-8136; 0-87895)
Cleveland, OH
800-321-3106

Money Market Directories, Inc.
(0-939712)
Charlottesville, VA
800-446-2810

Monroe Pr.
(0-936781)
Sepulveda, CA
800-323-4241 (Quality Books, Inc.)
800-624-4466 (Bookpeople)

Montana Magazine, Inc.
(0-938314)
Helena, MT
800-821-3874 (MT)

Montevista Pr
(0-931551)
Bellingham, WA
800-562-4647
(Pacific Pipeline)

Montezuma Micro
(0-928295)
Dallas, TX
800-527-0347
800-442-1310 (TX)

Moody Pr.
(0-8024)
Chicago, IL
800-621-5111
800-621-4323 (In Illinois)

More, Thomas, Pr.
(0-88347)
Chicago, IL
800-835-8965

Morgan-Rand Pubns., Inc.
(0-913061)
Philadelphia, PA
800-354-8673

Morrison Peterson Publishing, Inc.
(0-936062)
Kailua, HI
800-528-3665

Morrow, William, & Co., Inc.
(0-688)
New York, NY
800-631-1199

Mortgage Techniques
(0-9615886)
Memphis, TN
800-468-1255
800-523-1307 (In Tennessee)

Mosby, C.V., Co.
(0-8016)
St. Louis, MO
800-325-4177

Mosby/Multi-Media
(0-8016; 0-940122)
Saint Louis, MO
800-325-4177

Mother Earth News, The
(0-938432)
Hendersonville, NC
800-438-0238

Motorbooks International, Pubs. & Wholesalers, Inc.
(0-87938)
Osceola, WI
800-826-6600

Mountain Missionary Pr.
(0-912145)
Harrisville, NH
800-367-1888

Mountain Pr., Publishing Co., Inc.
(0-87842)
Missoula, MT
800-732-3669

Moyer Bell, Ltd.
(0-918825)
Mt. Kisco, NY
800-526-7626 (Kampmann & Co.)

Muir, John, Pubns.
(0-912528)
Santa Fe, NM
800-223-2584 (W.W. Norton & Co.)

Multnomah Pr.
(0-88070; 0-930014)
Portland, OR
800-547-5890

Muntu Bks.
(0-9614140)
Berkeley, CA
800-227-1516 (Bookpeople)
Murach, Mike, & Assocs., Inc.
(0-911625)
Fresno, CA
800-221-5528
800-221-5527 (In California)
Museum of Art Rhode Island School of Design
(0-940794)
Providence, RI
800-343-9444
Museum of Modern Art
(0-87070)
New York, NY
800-343-9204
Museum of Western Art
(0-914965)
Denver, CO
800-525-7047
Music Sales Corp.
(0-8256)
New York, NY
800-431-7187
Music Study Services
(0-936245)
Louisville, CO
800-982-8319 (Publishers Group West)
Mustang Publishing
(0-914457)
New Haven, CT
800-526-7626 (Kampmann & Co., Inc.)
Myers, S. D., Inc.
(0-939320)
Akron, OH
800-321-9580
NBM
(0-918348)
New York, NY
800-982-8319 (Publishers Group West)
NEC Home Electronics USA, Inc.
(0-925739)
Wood Dale, IL
800-632-7638
NET Pr.
(0-937462)
Lubbock, TX
800-632-4769
800-892-4769   (in TX)
NILS Publishing Co.
(0-89246)
Chatsworth, CA
800-423-5910
Nassau Pr.
(0-911491)
Princeton, NJ
800-526-0275
National Assessment of Educational Progress
(0-89398)
Princeton, NJ
800-223-0267
National Assn. for the Education of Young Children
(0-912674; 0-935989)
Washington, DC
800-424-2460
National Assn. of Home Builders
(0-86718)
Washington, DC
800-368-5242
National Assn. of Social Workers
(0-87101)
Silver Spring, MD
800-638-8799
National Bureau of Economic Research, Incorporated
(0-87014)
Cambridge, MA
800-621-2736
Natl. Ctr. for Constitutional Studies
(0-88080)
Salt Lake City, UT
800-522-6227
National Ctr. for State Courts
(0-89656)
Williamsburg, VA
800-446-8952
National Clearinghouse for Bilingual Education
(0-89763)
Arlington, VA
800-336-4560
National Council for International Visitors
Washington, DC
800-523-8101

National Fire Protection Assn.
(0-87765)
Quincy, MA
800-344-3555
National Forensic Ctr.
(0-9602962)
Lawrenceville, NJ
800-526-5177
National Information Ctr. for Educational Media
(0-89320)
Albuquerque, NM
800-421-8711
National Institute for Trial Advocacy
(1-55681)
St. Paul, MN
800-225-6482
National League for Nursing
(0-88737)
New York, NY
800-847-8480
800-442-4546 (NY State)
National Learning Corp.
(0-8293; 0-8373)
Syosset, NY
800-645-6337
National Nursing Review, Inc.
(0-917010)
Los Altos, CA
800-221-4093
National Practice Institute
Minneapolis, MN
800-328-4444
National Register Publishing Co.
(0-87217)
Wilmette, IL
800-323-6772
National Society to Prevent Blindness
(0-916102)
New York, NY
800-221-3004
National Textbook Co.
(0-8325; 0-8442)
Chicago, IL
800-854-4014
National Tour Assn.
(0-910399)
Lexington, KY
800-682-8886
800-828-6999 (In Canada)
National Underwriter Co.
(0-87218)
Cincinnati, OH
800-543-0874
Natural Designs
(0-9616179)
Atherton, CA
800-982-8319 (Publishers Group West)
Natural History Pr.
800-645-6156
Navpress, A Ministry of The Navigators
(0-89109)
Colorado Springs, CO
800-525-7151
Nelson, Thomas, Pubs.
(0-8407)
Nashville, TN
800-872-4445
800-821-4370 (TN)
Nelson Communications
(0-8407)
Nashville, TN
800-872-4445
New American Library
(0-451; 0-452; 0-453)
New York, NY
800-526-0275
New Boundary Design Inc.
(0-913703)
Chanhassen, MN
800-328-6795
New Classics Library, Inc.
(0-932750)
Gainesville, GA
800-336-1618
New Collage Press
(0-936814)
Sarasota, FL
800-225-6055 (Faxon Co., The)
New Directions Publishing Corp.
(0-8112)
New York, NY
800-223-2584
New Horizon Pr. Pubs., Inc.
(0-88282)
Far Hills, NJ
800-257-5755

New Horizons Pubs.
(0-915325)
Seattle, WA
800-426-4727 (Pacific Pipeline, Inc.)
New Leaf Pr.
(0-89221)
Green Forest, AR
800-643-9535
New Options Publishing
(0-9614635)
Denver, CO
800-227-1516 (Bookpeople)
New Readers Pr.
(0-88336)
Syracuse, NY
800-448-8878
New York Academy of Sciences
(0-89072; 0-89766)
New York, NY
800-843-6927
New York Graphic Society Bks.
(0-8212)
Boston, MA
800-343-9204
New York Zoetrope
(0-918432)
New York, NY
800-242-7546
Newberry Library
(0-911028)
Chicago, IL
800-621-2736
Newbury Hse. Pubs.
(0-88377; 0-912066)
Cambridge, MA
800-343-1240
Newmarket Pr.
(0-937858)
New York, NY
800-257-7577
Nexus Press (Wa)
(0-936666)
Kirkland, WA
800-426-4727 (Pacific Pipeline)
No Secrets Pr.
(0-936779)
San Francisco, CA
800-241-3829 (The New Leaf Distributing)
Norse Press
(0-9602692; 0-9613274)
Sioux Falls, SD
800-843-1300
North Light Bks.
(0-89134)
Cincinnati, OH
800-543-4644
Northland Pr.
(0-87358)
Flagstaff, AZ
800-346-3257
800-462-6657 (AZ)
Northwest Historical Consultants
(0-9609562)
Clarkston, WA
800-426-4727 (Pacific Pipeline, Inc.)
Northwest Panorama Publishing, Inc.
(0-9613787)
Bozeman, MT
800-547-2525
Northwestern Univ. Traffic Institute
(0-912642)
Evanston, IL
800-323-4011
Norton, Jeffrey, Pubs., Inc.
(0-88432)
Guilford, CT
800-243-1234
Norton, W. W., & Co., Inc.
(0-393)
New York, NY
800-223-2584
Oakland-PR
(0-9614236)
Oakland, CA
800-227-1516 (Bookpeople)
Ocean Tree Bks.
(0-943734)
Santa Fe, NM
800-227-1516 (Bookpeople)
800-241-3829 (New Leaf Distributors)
Ohara Pubns., Inc.
(0-89750)
Burbank, CA
800-423-2874
Ohio Univ. Pr.
(0-8214)
Athens, OH
800-242-7737

Oil Daily
(0-918216)
Washington, DC
800-368-5803
Old Golf Shop, Inc.
(0-936557)
Cincinnati, OH
800-227-8700
Oliver-Nelson
(0-8407)
Nashville, TN
800-872-4445 (Sales)
800-821-4370 (Sales TN)
Omega Pr.
(0-930872)
Lebanon Springs, NY
800-241-3829 (New Leaf Distributing)
101 Productions
(0-89286; 0-912238)
San Francisco, CA
800-621-0851 Ext. 300
Open Court Publishing Co.
(0-8126; 0-87548; 0-89688; 9-12050)
Peru, IL
800-435-6850
800-892-6831
Optimus Productions
New York, NY
800-241-3829 (New Leaf Distributing)
Orbis Bks.
(0-88344)
Maryknoll, NY
800-258-5838
Oregon State Bar Assn.
Portland, OR
800-452-1639
Orr, Ken, & Assocs., Inc.
(0-9605884)
Topeka, KS
800-255-2459
Ortalda & Assocs.
(0-9616101)
Berkeley, CA
800-674-4466
(Bookpeople)
Oryx Pr.
(0-89774; 0-912700)
Phoenix, AZ
800-457-6799
Osborne/McGraw-Hill
(0-07)
Berkeley, CA
800-227-0900
Our Sunday Visitor, Publishing Div.
(0-87973)
Huntington, IN
800-348-2440 except Indiana
Outlet Bk. Co.
(0-87000)
New York, NY
800-526-4264
Overlook Pr.
(0-87951)
New York, NY
800-631-3577
(Viking-Penguin, Inc.)
Oxford Univ. Pr., Inc.
(0-19)
New York, NY
800-458-5833
Oxmoor Hse., Inc.
(0-8487)
Birmingham, AL
800-242-7737
PC Software Interest Group
(0-915835)
Sunnyvale, CA
800-222-2996
PMS Self Help Ctr.
(0-936614)
Los Altos, CA
800-251-5900 (Ingram Distribution Group, Inc.)
800-227-1516 (Bookpeople)
800-624-4466 (CA)
PSG Publishing Co., Inc.
(0-7236; 0-88416; 0-931890)
Littleton, MA
800-225-5020
PSI Research
(0-916378; 1-55571)
Milpitas, CA
800-228-2275
800-221-4089 (In California)
PWS Pubs.
(0-534; 0-87150)
Boston, MA
800-354-9706

P.A.R., Inc.
(0-89702; 0-913310)
Providence, RI
800-556-7277
Pacific Pipeline, Inc.
Kent, WA
800-562-4647 (WA)
800-426-4727 (OR,ID,MT,NV, & Northern CA)
Pacific Pr. Publishing Assn.
(0-8163)
Boise, ID
800-447-7377
Pacific Search Pr.
(0-914718; 0-931397)
Seattle, WA
800-858-0628
Paganiniana Pubns., Inc.
(0-87666)
Neptune, NJ
800-631-2188
Paladin Pr.
(0-87364)
Boulder, CO
800-824-7888
Palmer, A. N., Co., The
(0-913941; 0-914268)
Schaumburg, IL
800-323-9563
Pan American Navigation Service, Inc.
(0-87219)
Van Nuys, CA
800-423-5932
Pantheon Bks.
(0-394)
New York, NY
800-638-6460
Paper Birch Pr., Inc.
(0-939687; 0-9613961)
Ashland, WI
800-336-5666
Paraclete Pr.
(0-941478)
Orleans, MA
800-451-5006
Paradise Plus
(0-9616059)
Portland, OR
800-426-4727 (Pacific Pipeline, Inc.)
Parenting Pr.
(0-943990; 0-9602862)
Seattle, WA
800-992-6657
Parents Anonymous
Los Angeles, CA
800-421-0353
Parents Magazine Pr.
(0-8193)
New York, NY
800-526-0275
(E. P. Dutton)
Parents Pr.
(0-935111)
Bowling Green, KY
800-435-5111 (Baker & Taylor Midwest Div.)
Pargh, B. A., Co., Inc.
Nashville, TN
800-227-1000
Parker Brothers Publishing
(0-87372; 0-910313; 0-926088)
Beverly, MA
800-225-0540
Partner Press
(0-933212)
Livonia, MI
800-638-0928 (Gryphon House, Inc.)
Pasha Pubns., Inc.
(0-935453)
Arlington, VA
800-424-2908
Patchwork Pubns.
(0-930628)
Las Vegas, NV
800-634-6268
Pathway Bks.
(0-935538)
Golden Valley, MN
800-982-8319 (Publishers Group West)
800-323-4241 (Quality Books)
Pathway Pr.
(0-87148)
Cleveland, TN
800-251-7216
Pathwork Pr.
(0-9614777)
Phoenicia, NY
800-847-4014 (Stillpoint Publishing)

Paulist Pr.
(0-8091)
Mahwah, NJ
800-325-9521
Peachtree Pubs., Ltd.
(0-931948)
Atlanta, GA
800-241-0113
800-282-0225 (In Georgia)
Peak Skill Publishing
(0-917879)
Playa del Rey, CA
800-251-5900 (Ingram Bk. Co.)
800-227-1516 (Bookpeople)
Peanut Butter Publishing
(0-89716)
Seattle, WA
800-426-4727 (Pacific Pipeline)
Peartree
(0-935343)
Clearwater, FL
800-241-6000 (Baker & Taylor SE Div.)
800-435-5111 (Baker & Taylor Midwest Div.)
Peel Productions, Inc.
(0-939217)
The Woodlands, TX
800-345-2282 (Baker & Taylor, Eastern Div.)
Peer-Southern Pubns.
New York, NY
800-327-7643 (Columbia Pictures Pubns.)
Pegasus
Indianapolis, IN
800-428-3750
Pencil Pr.
(0-9615665)
San Rafael, CA
800-227-1516 (Bookpeople)
800-624-4466 (CA)
Penfield Pr.
(0-941016; 0-9603858)
Iowa City, IA
800-255-2255 Ext. 9998
Penguin Bks., Inc.
(0-14)
New York, NY
800-631-3577
Peninsula Publishing, Inc.
(0-918146)
Port Angeles, WA
800-562-4647
(Pacific Pipeline)
Penny Dreadful Publishers
(0-911793)
Jackson, MI
800-435-5111 (Baker & Taylor (Midwest Div.))
People-Media, Inc.
(0-9615591)
Reading, PA
800-523-8213 (MD,DE,NY,NJ)
Perennial Pubns.
(0-9612234)
Gainesville, GA
800-821-5745 (The Collection, Inc.)
Pergot Pr.
(0-936865)
Sausalito, CA
800-227-1516 (Bookpeople)
Perma Bound Bks.
(0-8479; 0-916056)
Jacksonville, IL
800-637-6581
Permanent Pr., The
(0-932966)
Sag Harbor, NY
800-221-0960
Perrin, Thomas W., Inc.
(0-933825)
Rutherford, NJ
800-321-7912
Peter Pauper Pr., Inc.
(0-88088)
White Plains, NY
800-526-7626 (Kampmann & Co., Inc.)
Peters Corp.
(0-935037)
Santa Fe, NM
800-621-5884
Peterson's Guides, Inc.
(0-87866)
Princeton, NJ
800-225-0261
Physicians' Record Co.
(0-917036)
Berwyn, IL
800-323-9268

Pick Pubns., Inc.
(0-936526)
Southfield, MI
800-247-1559

Pictorial Legends
(0-939031)
Los Angeles, CA
800-982-8319 (Publishers Group West)

Picture Bk. Studio, USA
(0-88708; 0-907234)
Natick, MA
800-462-1252

Pilgrimage, Inc.
(0-932930)
Jonesboro, TN
800-582-7295

Pillar Press
(0-9611190)
Alameda, CA
800-227-1516 (Bookpeople)
800-624-4466 (CA)

Pilot Pubns.
(0-938923)
Ocala, FL
800-521-2120

Pioneer Ventures, Inc.
(0-915321)
Houston, TX
800-521-3690
800-482-3653 (In Michigan)

Plenum Publishing Corp.
(0-306)
New York, NY
800-221-9369

Pocket Bks., Inc.
(0-671)
New York, NY
800-223-2336

Point Foundation/Whole Earth Review
Sausalito, CA
800-638-6460 (Random Hse.)

Pointe Pubs., Inc.
(0-935897)
Centerline, MI
800-852-7409
800-426-8095 (Growth Publishing)

Pomegranate Artbooks, Inc.
(0-87654; 0-917556)
Corte Madera, CA
800-227-1428

Practical Cookbooks
(0-9614556)
Minneapolis, MN
800-521-3990 (Spring Arbor Distributors)

Precedent Publishing, Inc.
(0-913750)
Chicago, IL
800-392-5448

Preferred Press
(0-914759)
Huntington Beach, CA
800-762-6937

Presbyterian & Reformed Publishing Co.
(0-87552)
Phillipsburg, NJ
800-631-0094

Price, Stern, Sloan, Pubs., Inc.
(0-8431)
Los Angeles, CA
800-421-0892
800-227-8801 (In California)

Prima Materia Bks.
(0-9615315)
Quoque, NY
800-227-1516 (Bookpeople)
800-648-3540 (Baker & Taylor Co., Western Div.)

Princeton Architectural Pr.
(0-910413)
Princeton, NJ
800-334-0854

Print Media Services, Ltd.
(0-942398)
Elk Grove, IL
800-323-8899

Pritchett & Hull Assocs., Inc.
(0-939838)
Atlanta, GA
800-241-4925

Pro Serve Corp. of Sarasota, Inc.
(0-936177)
Sarasota, FL
800-237-9222

Professional Bk. Ctr., Inc.
(0-943226)
Portland, OR
800-547-7734 (International Specialized Book Services)

Professional Education Systems, Inc.
Eau Claire, WI
800-826-7155

Professional Resource Exchange, Inc.
(0-943158)
Sarasota, FL
800-443-3364
800-366-7913

Prometheus Bks.
(0-87975)
Buffalo, NY
800-421-0351

Psychohistory Pr.
New York, NY
800-521-7004

Psychological Assessment Resources (PAR), Incorporated
(0-911907)
Lutz, FL
800-331-8378

Public Media, Inc.
(0-913349)
Chicago, IL
800-323-4222

Public Utilities Reports, Inc.
(0-910325)
Arlington, VA
800-368-5001

Publishers Group West
Emeryville, CA
800-982-8319

Publishing Domain Exchange
(0-9614731)
San Jose, CA
800-982-8319 (Publishers Group West)

Pushcart Pr., The
(0-916366)
Wainscott, NY
800-223-2584

Putnam Publishing Group, The
(0-399)
New York, NY
800-631-8571

Pyramid Designs Pr.
(0-937071)
Pittsburgh, PA
800-348-5200 (The Distributors)

QED Information Sciences, Inc.
(0-89435)
Wellesley, MA
800-343-4848

Quality Books, Inc.
(0-89196)
Lake Bluff, IL
800-323-4241 (Libraries Only)

Quality Education Data, Inc.
(0-88747)
Denver, CO
800-525-5811

Quarterdeck Pr.
(0-918546)
Pacific Palisades, CA
800-227-1516 (Bookpeople)

Que Corp.
(0-88022)
Indianapolis, IN
800-428-5331

Queue, Inc.
(0-87200; 0-87492)
Bridgeport, CT
800-232-2224

Quick American Publishing Co.
(0-932551)
San Francisco, CA
800-445-7825

Quilt Digest Pr., The
(0-913327)
San Francisco, CA
800-982-8319 (Publishers Group West)

Quinlan Pr.
(0-933341; 0-9611268)
Boston, MA
800-551-2500

Quintessence Publishing Co., Inc.
(0-86715; 0-931386)
Lombard, IL
800-621-0387

R C Pubns.
(0-915734)
Bethesda, MD
800-222-2654

RGM Pubns.
(0-942436)
Key West, FL
800-982-8319 (Publishers Group West)

R.P.W. Publishing Corp.
(0-932725; 0-9608450)
Lexington, SC
800-334-5971

Radiance Assocs.
(0-933267)
St. Petersburg, FL
800-241-3829 (New Leaf Distributing)

Raima Corp.
(0-928469)
Bellevue, WA
800-843-3313

Rainbow Bks.
(0-935834)
Moore Haven, FL
800-232-4241 (Quality Bks. Library orders only)

Raintree Pubs., Inc.
(0-8172; 0-8393; 0-86514; 0-940742)
Milwaukee, WI
800-558-7264

Ramira Publishing
(0-9612720)
Aptos, CA
800-241-3829 (New Leaf Distributing)

Rand McNally & Co.
(0-528)
Chicago, IL
800-323-4070

Randall Bk., Co.
(0-934126; 1-55517)
Sandy, UT
800-453-1356

Randall Hse. Pubns.
(0-89265)
Nashville, TN
800-251-5762
800-624-6538 (in Tennessee)

Rawson Assocs.
(0-89256)
New York, NY
800-257-5755

Reader's Digest Assn., Inc.
(0-89577)
New York, NY
800-431-1726
800-638-6460 (Random House, Inc.)

Reading Matters
(0-9614780)
Denver, CO
800-323-4241 (Quality Bks., Inc.)

Realtors National Marketing Institute
(0-913652)
Chicago, IL
800-621-7035

Redwood Records
(0-9608774)
Oakland, CA
800-227-2400

Reed Publishing
(0-939224)
Danville, CA
800-982-8315 (Publishers Group West)

Regal Bks.
(0-8307)
Ventura, CA
800-235-3415

Regents Publishing Co., Inc.
(0-88345)
New York, NY
800-822-8202 (outside NY)

Reiman Assocs.
(0-89821)
Greendale, WI
800-558-1013 (Country Store)
800-248-6065 (WI)

Research Pubns.
(0-914981)
Phoenix, AZ
800-528-0559

Research Pubns., Inc.
(0-89235)
Woodbridge, CT
800-732-2477

Resource Applications Inc.
(0-932491)
Baltimore, MD
800-826-1877

Resource Pubns., Inc.
(0-89390)
San Jose, CA
800-228-2028

Retail Reporting Bureau
(0-934590)
New York, NY
800-251-4545

Toll-Free Numbers

Revell, Fleming H., Co.
(0-8007)
Old Tappan, NJ
800-631-1970
Review & Herald Pub. Assn.
(0-8280)
Hagerstown, MD
800-582-5600
Ricci, Joan
(0-9614699)
Boca Raton, FL
800-523-6504 (U. S.)
800-331-1262 (FL)
Richardson & Snyder
(0-943940)
New York, NY
800-526-0275
Rittenhouse Bk. Distributors
(0-87381)
King of Prussia, PA
800-345-6425
Riverdale Systems Design, Inc.
(0-939545)
Riverdale, NY
800-622-4070
Riverrun Pr.
(0-7145; 0-86676)
New York, NY
800-526-7626 (Kampmann & Co., Inc.)
Rizzoli International Pubns., Inc.
(0-8478)
New York, NY
800-433-1238
Robotics Pr.
(0-89661)
Beaverton, OR
800-457-1842
Rodale Pr., Inc.
(0-87857)
Emmaus, PA
800-527-8200
Roscoe Pound-American Trial Lawyers Assn.
(0-933067)
Washington, DC
800-424-2725
Rose Pr.
(0-9615248)
Portland, OR
800-426-4727 (Pacific Pipeline, Inc.)
Roth Publishing, Inc.
(0-8486; 0-89609)
Great Neck, NY
800-327-0295
Rothman, Fred B., & Co.
(0-8377)
Littleton, CO
800-457-1986
Rowan Tree Pr., Ltd.
(0-937672)
Boston, MA
800-227-1516 (Bookpeople)
800-243-0138 (Inland Bk. Co.)
Royal Hse. Publishing Co.
(0-930440)
Beverly Hills, CA
800-222-3360
Royalty Publishing Co.
(0-910487)
Manassas, VA
800-245-2422 (Whitaker House)
Rubes Pubns.
(0-941364; 0-943384)
Panorama City, CA
800-292-6122; (Alfred Publishing Co., Inc.)
800-821-6083 (In California)
Running Pr. Bk. Pubs.
(0-89471)
Philadelphia, PA
800-428-1111
Russell Sage Foundation
(0-87154)
New York, NY
800-242-7737
Ryder Geosystems
(0-941784)
Englewood, CO
800-526-3752
Rynd Communications
(0-932500)
Owings Mills, MD
800-446-2221
SBS Publishing, Inc.
(0-89961)
Closter, NJ
800-631-2564

SOS Pubns.
(0-938422)
Los Angeles, CA
800-325-7953
SRS Co.
(0-9610766)
Marina del Rey, CA
800-558-4774 (Hal Leonard Pub. Corp.)
S.E.E. Publishing Co.
(0-937147)
Santa Clara, CA
800-227-1516 (Bookpeople)
Sadlier, William H., Inc.
(0-8215)
New York, NY
800-221-5175
St. Luke's Pr.
(0-918518)
Memphis, TN
800-524-5554 Ext 4617
St. Martin's Pr., Inc.
(0-312; 0-9603648)
New York, NY
800-221-7945
Sal Magundi Enterprises
(0-9609024)
Portland, OR
800-452-0991 (Douglas County Museum)
Salem Pr., Inc.
(0-89356)
Englewood Cliffs, NJ
800-221-1592
Sales Success Press
(0-9613319)
Newport Beach, CA
800-772-1172
Salesman's Guide, Inc.
(0-87228)
New York, NY
800-223-1797
Sammis Publishing
(0-87469)
New York, NY
800-526-7676 (Kampmann & Co.)
Sams, Howard W., & Co.
(0-672)
Indianapolis, IN
800-428-3602
Santillana Publishing Co.
(0-88272)
Northvale, NJ
800-526-0107
Saybrook Publishing Co., Inc.
(0-933071)
Dallas, TX
800-223-2584 (W. W. Norton Co.)
Scala Bks.
(0-935748)
New York, NY
800-242-7737
Schirmer Bks.
(0-911320)
New York, NY
800-257-5755
Scholarly Resources, Inc.
(0-8420)
Wilmington, DE
800-772-8937
Scholastic, Inc.
(0-590)
New York, NY
800-392-2179
School Aid Co.
(0-87385)
Danville, IL
800-447-2665
School Zone Publishing Co.
(0-88743; 0-938256)
Grand Haven, MI
800-253-0564
Science Research Assocs.
(0-574)
Chicago, IL
800-621-0476
Scott & Daughters Publishing, Inc.
(0-911113)
Los Angeles, CA
800-547-2688
Scott Pubns.
Livonia, MI
800-458-8237
Scott Publishing Co.
(0-89487)
Sidney, OH
800-848-4406

Scribner's, Charles, Sons
(0-684)
New York, NY
800-257-5755
Scripture Press Pubns., Inc.
(0-88207; 0-89693)
Wheaton, IL
800-323-9409
Search Group, Inc.
Sacramento, CA
800-851-3420 (National Criminal Ref. Serv.)
Second Chance Pr.
(0-933256)
Sag Harbor, NY
800-221-0960
Sentinel Publishing Co.
(0-931097)
Lubbock, TX
800-858-4602
Servant Pubns.
(0-89283)
Ann Arbor, MI
800-521-3690 (Spring Arbor)
Seven Seas Pr., Inc.
(0-915160)
Newport, RI
800-723-7323
Seven Suns Pubns.
(0-931783)
Fairfield, IA
800-241-3829 (New Leaf Distributing, The)
Shambhala Pubns., Inc.
(0-394; 0-87773)
Boston, MA
800-638-6460
Shanken, M., Communications, Inc.
(0-918076)
New York, NY
800-227-1617
Sharon Pubns., Inc.
(0-89531)
Teaneck, NJ
800-526-0275 (New American Library)
Sharp & Dunningan
(0-918495)
Forest Ranch, CA
800-323-4241 (Quality Books)
Sharpe, M. E., Inc.
(0-87332)
Armonk, NY
800-638-6460
Shaw, Harold, Pubs.
(0-87788)
Wheaton, IL
800-742-9782
Shawnee Printing Co.
(0-939371; 0-9604662)
Shawnee, OK
800-654-4166
Sheed & Ward
(0-934134; 1-55612)
Kansas City, MO
800-821-7926
Shelter Pubns., Inc.
(0-936070)
Bolinas, CA
800-638-6460 (Random Hse.)
800-528-4923 (HP Books)
Shelton Pubns.
(0-918742)
Sausalito, CA
800-982-8317 (Publishers Group West)
800-227-1516 (Bookpeople)
Shepard's/McGraw-Hill
(0-07)
Colorado Springs, CO
800-525-2474
Shipley Assocs.
(0-933427)
Bountiful, UT
800-343-0009
Showcase Publishing Co.
(0-88205)
Fairfield, CA
800-526-0275
Sierra Club Bks.
(0-87156)
San Francisco, CA
800-638-6460
Signs of the Times Publishing Co.
(0-911380)
Cincinnati, OH
800-543-1925
Siliconix Inc.
(0-930519)
Santa Clara, CA
800-554-5564

Silver Burdett Co.
(0-382)
Morristown, NJ
800-631-8081

Simmons-Boardman Bks., Inc.
(0-911382)
Omaha, NE
800-228-9670

Skyline West Pr.
(0-914767)
Seattle, WA
800-426-4727

Slack, Inc.
(0-913590; 0-943432; 1-55642)
Thorofare, NJ
800-257-8290

Sloan, M. Ismail, Pubs.
(0-9609190)
Lynchburg, VA
800-221-5724

Smith, Doug
(0-9602728)
Corvallis, OR
800-227-1516 (Bookpeople)

Smith, Fred T.
(0-9611210)
Lathrup Village, MI
800-233-9380 (Merle Distributing
Co.)

Smith, Gibbs M., Inc.
(0-87905)
Layton, UT
800-421-8714

Smith, W. H., Pubs., Inc.
(0-8317)
New York, NY
800-932-0070

Smith College Museum of Art
Northampton, MA
800-621-2736

Smithsonian Bks.
(0-89599)
Washington, DC
800-223-2584

Social Issues Resources Series, Inc.
(0-89777)
Boca Raton, FL
800-327-0513

Society for Teachers of Family Medicine
Kansas City, MO
800-821-2512

Society for Visual Education, Inc.
(0-89290)
Chicago, IL
800-621-1900

Society of Real Estate Appraisers
(0-934737)
Chicago, IL
800-331-7732

SoftCorp, Inc.
(0-937701)
Clearwater, FL
800-255-7526

Software Directions, Inc.
(0-936517)
Randolph, NJ
800-346-7638

Somerset Pr.
(0-916642)
Carol Stream, IL
800-323-1049

SourceView Software International
(0-87007; 0-87017)
Martinez, CA
800-443-0100

South-Western Publishing Co.
(0-538)
Cincinnati, OH
800-543-0487

Speck, J. B. Pr.
(0-9613736)
St. Louis, MO
800-982-8319 (Publishers Group West)
800-251-5900 (Ingram Bk. Co.)

Spiritual Warfare Ministries
(0-9615445)
Lakeland, FL
800-282-8490
800-245-2422 (Whitaker House)

Spizzirri Pub. Co., Inc.
(0-86545)
Medinah, IL
800-325-9819

Springer-Verlag New York, Inc.
(0-387)
New York, NY
800-526-7254

Springhouse Publishing Co.
(0-87434; 0-916730)
Springhouse, PA
800-346-7844

Sprout Pubns. Inc.
(0-932972)
Sarasota, FL
800-227-1516 (Bookpeople)

Squadron Signal Pubns.
(0-89747)
Carrollton, TX
800-527-7427

St. Anthony Messenger Pr.
(0-86716; 0-912228)
Cincinnati, OH
800-325-9521

St. Mary's Pr.
(0-88489)
Winona, MN
800-533-8095

Stackpole Bks., Inc.
(0-8117)
Harrisburg, PA
800-732-3669

Stafford, Joseph, Pub.
(0-9617123)
Detroit, MI
800-345-2282 (Baker & Taylor, Eastern Div.)

Standard Publishing Co.
(0-87239; 0-87403)
Cincinnati, OH
800-543-1353
800-582-1385 in Ohio

Stanger, Robert A., Co.
(0-943570)
Shrewsbury, NJ
800-631-2291

Stanton & Lee Pubs., Inc.
(0-88361)
Madison, WI
800-356-4600
800-362-5464 (WI)

Star-Gate Enterprises
(0-911167)
Orinda, CA
800-824-2222 Ext. 35

Starkey Laboratories, Inc.
(0-9601970)
Eden Prairie, MN
800-328-8602

Starr, Arnold, & Co.
(0-9607194)
Houston, TX
800-231-0588; (Richardson's Educators)
800-392-8562 (In Texas)

Steinway & Sons
(0-9607196)
Long Island City, NY
800-223-6017

Stillpoint Publishing
(0-913299)
Walpole, NH
800-526-0275

Stockton Pr.
(0-935859; 0-943818)
New York, NY
800-221-2123

Stoeger Publishing Co.
(0-88317)
South Hackensack, NJ
800-631-0723

Storey Communications, Inc.
(0-88266)
Pownal, VT
800-441-5700

Story Hse. Corp.
(0-87157)
Charlotteville, NY
800-428-1008 (NY State)
800-847-2105 (Outside NY)

Stragetic Moves
(0-915375)
Portland, OR
800-992-2911 (Oregon only)

Stuart, Lyle, Inc.
(0-8184)
Secaucus, NJ
800-572-6657

Stubs Pubns.
(0-911458)
New York, NY
800-223-7565

Summit Bks.
(0-671)
New York, NY
800-223-2336

Summit Enterprises, Inc.
(0-934174)
Phoenix, AZ
800-321-5378

Sunburst Communications, Inc.
(0-911831; 1-55636)
Pleasantville, NY
800-431-1934

Sunburst Publishing
(0-9614865)
Zephyr Cove, NV
800-227-1516 (Bookpeople)

Sunset Bks./Lane Publishing Co.
(0-376)
Menlo Park, CA
800-227-7346

Sunshine Pr.
(0-9615743)
Comfort, TX
800-323-4241 (Quality Books,
Inc.)

Swansea Pr., Inc.
Philadelphia, PA
800-792-6732

Sweet Publishing
(0-8344)
Ft. Worth, TX
800-531-5220
800-252-9213 (in Texas)

Sweetlight Bks.
(0-9604462)
Arcata, CA
800-624-4466 (Bookpeople)

Sybex, Inc.
(0-89588)
Berkeley, CA
800-227-2346

Symbol of Excellence Publishers, Inc.
(0-932437)
Birmingham, AL
800-231-0503

Syntony Publishing, Inc.
(0-933347; 0-9613172)
Palo Alto, CA
800-982-8319 (Publishers Group West)

Systems Impact, Inc.
(0-934403)
Washington, DC
800-822-4636

TAB Bks., Inc.
(0-8168; 0-8306)
Blue Ridge Summit, PA
800-233-1128

TEL Pubs., Ltd.
(1-55588)
Rockford, IL
800-835-5835

T L C Publishing Co.
(0-918365)
Oklahoma City, OK
800-654-9121

TSR, Inc.
(0-88038; 0-935696)
Lake Geneva, WI
800-372-4667
800-492-0782 (Maryland)

TFH Pubns., Inc.
(0-86622; 0-87666)
Neptune, NJ
800-631-2188

T.I.S., Inc.
(0-89917)
Bloomington, IN
800-367-4002

Taft Group, The
(0-914756)
Washington, DC
800-424-3761

Tambra Publishing
(0-9615698)
Covina, CA
800-345-2282 (Baker & Taylor, Eastern Div.)

Taoist Pubs.
(0-9608030)
800-241-3829 (New Leaf Distributing Co.)

Tarcher, Jeremy P., Inc
(0-87477)
Los Angeles, CA
800-225-3362

Taunton Pr., Inc.
(0-918804)
Newtown, CT
800-243-7252

Toll-Free Numbers

Tax Analysts
(0-918255)
Arlington, VA
800-336-0439

Taylor & Francis, Inc.
(0-335-; 0-85066; 0-86353; 0-903796;
0-905273; 1-85000)
Philadelphia, PA
800-821-8312

Taylor & Ng
(0-912738)
San Francisco, CA
800-227-4090

Tech Ed Publishing
(0-933554)
Tempe, AZ
800-323-3133

Technical Data Corp.
(0-927469)
Boston, MA
800-343-7745

Technology Marketing Corp.
(0-936840)
Norwalk, CT
800-243-6002

Technomic Publishing Co.
(0-87762)
Lancaster, PA
800-233-9936

Telecom Library, The
(0-936648)
New York, NY
800-542-279

Teleometrics International, Inc.
(0-937932)
The Woodlands, TX
800-527-0406

Telshare Publishing Co., Inc.
(0-910287)
Marshfield, MA
800-343-9707

Temporal Acuity Products, Inc.
(0-911723)
Bellevue, WA
800-426-2673

Ten Speed Pr.
(0-89815; 0-913668)
Berkeley, CA
800-841-2665

Texas Gardener Pr.
(0-914641)
Waco, TX
800-252-4437 (Texas Monthly Pr.)

Texas Monthly Pr.
(0-87719; 0-932012)
Austin, TX
800-252-4437 (TX only)

Thames & Hudson
(0-500)
800-233-4830 (W. W. Norton & Co., Inc.)

That Patchwork Place, Inc.
(0-943574)
Bothell, WA
800-426-3126

Thinking Pubns.
(0-930599; 0-9610370)
Eau Claire, WI
800-225-4709
800-362-4709 (In Wisconsin)

Thomas Brothers Maps
(0-88130)
Irvine, CA
800-432-8430 (CA Only)

Thorndike Pr.
(0-89621)
Thorndike, ME
800-223-6121

Thorsons Pubs., Inc.
(0-7225)
Rochester, VT
800-242-7737 (Harper & Row Pubs., Inc.)

Threshold Bks.
(0-939660)
Putney, VT
800-634-2665 (Great Tradition, The)
800-227-1516 (Bookpeople)

Ticknor & Fields
(0-89919)
New York, NY
800-225-3362

Tidewater Pubs.
(0-87033)
Centreville, MD
800-638-7641

Time-Life Bks.
(0-8094)
Alexandria, VA
800-621-7026
800-631-8081
800-343-9204

Times Bks.
(0-8129)
New York, NY
800-242-7737

Times Publishing Group, Inc.
(0-9615476)
Towson, MD
800-223-1796

Toadwood Publishers
(0-9610878)
Edwardsville, IL
800-221-9254 (Ability Development, Inc.)

Todd & Honeywell, Inc.
(0-89962)
Great Neck, NY
800-233-3361

Toggitt, Joan, Ltd.
(0-911514)
West Caldwell, NJ
800-922-0808

Tombouctou Bks.
(0-939180)
Bolinas, CA
800-227-1516 (Bookpeople)
800-243-0138 (Inland Book Co.)

Torah Aura Productions
(0-933873)
Los Angeles, CA
800-238-6724

Trade Service Publications, Inc.
(0-915955)
San Diego, CA
800-542-6421

Trainex Pr.
(0-8463)
Garden Grove, CA
800-854-2485

Training Resource Corporation
(0-933794)
Harrisburg, PA
800-222-9909

Travel Pr
(0-930328)
San Mateo, CA
800-257-5755 (Charles Scribner's & Sons)
*800-257-5755 (MacMillan Publishing
Company, Incorporated)*

Treasure Chest Pubns.
(0-918080)
Tucson, AZ
800-223-5369 EXT 239

Tree Communications, Inc.
(0-934504)
New York, NY
800-242-7737

Tree of Life Pubns.
(0-930852)
Santa Monica, CA
800-628-2828, ext. 628

Triad Publishing Co., Inc.
(0-937404; 0-9600472)
Gainesville, FL
800-874-7777

Trimark Publishing Co., Inc
(0-914663)
New Castle, DE
800-874-6275

Trinet, Inc.
(0-86692)
Parsippany, NJ
800-874-6381

Troll Assocs.
(0-8167; 0-89375)
Mahwah, NJ
800-526-5289

Truck Press
(0-916562)
Short Beach, CT
800-243-0138 (Inland Book Co.)

Twenty-Third Pubns.
(0-89622)
Mystic, CT
800-321-0411

Tyndale Hse. Pubs.
(0-8423)
Wheaton, IL
800-323-9400

UMI Research Pr.
(0-8357)
Ann Arbor, MI
800-521-0600

Ultralight Pubns.
(0-938716)
Hummelstown, PA
800-441-7527

Ungar Publishing Co.
(0-8044)
New York, NY
800-242-7737 (Harper & Row)

Unipub
(0-400; 0-527; 0-89059)
Lanham, MD
800-521-8110

Unique Pubns.
(0-86568)
Burbank, CA
800-332-3330

United Bible Societies
(0-8267)
New York, NY
800-543-8000 (American Bible Society)

U. S. Catholic Conference
(1-55586)
Washington, DC
800-235-8722

**United States-China Peoples Friendship
Association**
Washington, DC
800-368-5883

University Books, Inc.
(0-8216)
Secaucus, NJ
800-572-6657

University Microfilms, Inc.
(0-8357)
Ann Arbor, MI
800-521-0600
800-343-5299 (Canada)

Univ. of Arkansas Pr.
(0-938626)
Fayetteville, AR
800-242-7737

Univ. of California Pr.
(0-520)
Berkeley, CA
800-822-6657

Univ. of Chicago Pr.
(0-226)
Chicago, IL
800-621-2736

Univ. of Illinois Pr.
(0-252)
Champaign, IL
800-242-7737

Univ. of Missouri Pr.
(0-8262)
Columbia, MO
800-242-7737

Univ. of Notre Dame Pr.
(0-268)
Notre Dame, IN
800-242-7737

Univ. of Oklahoma Pr.
(0-8061)
Norman, OK
800-242-7737
800-638-3030 (Univ. of Oklahoma Pr.)

Univ. of Pittsburgh Pr.
(0-8229)
Pittsburgh, PA
800-242-7737

Univ. of Texas Pr.
(0-292)
Austin, TX
800-252-3206

Univ. of Utah Pr.
(0-87480)
Salt Lake City, UT
800-662-0062 Ext. 6771

Univ. of Washington Pr.
(0-295)
Seattle, WA
*800-441-4115 (not in Alaska, Hawaii,
Washington*

Univ. Pr. of Kentucky
(0-8131)
Lexington, KY
800-242-7737 (Harper & Row Pubs., Inc.)

University Pubns. of America, Inc.
(0-89093; 1-55655)
Frederick, MD
800-692-6300

VC Publishing
(0-935333)
Hudson, FL
800-472-9336

Vadare Publishing Co.
(0-933725; 0-9610782)
Dix Hills, NY
800-645-1112

Valley of the Sun Publishing Co.
(0-87554; 0-911842)
Malibu, CA
800-421-6603
800-421-6603; 800-225-4717 (In California)

Vance Pubns.
(0-938595)
Mansfield, OH
800-423-9074

Vanderbilt Univ. Pr.
(0-8265)
Nashville, TN
800-242-7737 (Univ. of Illinois Pr.)
800-638-3030 (Univ. of Illinois Pr.)

Vendome Pr., The
(0-86565)
New York, NY
800-433-1238 (Rizzoli International Pubns.)

Venture Economics Inc.
(0-914470)
Wellesley Hills, MA
800-521-8110

Veterinary Medicine Publishing Co.
(0-935078)
Lenexa, KS
800-255-6864

Victor Bks.
(0-88207; 0-89693)
Wheaton, IL
800-323-9409

Video-Forum
(0-88432)
Guilford, CT
800-243-1234

Video Travel, Inc.
(1-55629)
Williamsport, PA
800-828-6888

Viking-Penguin, Inc.
(0-670)
New York, NY
800-631-3577

Vintage '45 Pr.
(0-9614375)
Orinda, CA
800-227-1516; (Bookpeople)
800-624-4466 (In California)
800-243-0138 (Inland Book Company)

Vision Books
(0-942024)
Coos Bay, OR
800-227-1516 (Bookpeople)

Vision Foundation, Incorporated
(0-9606836)
Watertown, MA
800-852-3029 Massachusetts only

Visual Education Assn.
(1-55637)
Springfield, OH
800-543-5947

Wadsworth Publishing Co.
(0-534; 0-7150; 0-927794)
Belmont, CA
800-831-6996

Walch, J. Weston, Pub.
(0-8251)
Portland, ME
800-341-6094

Walck, Henry Z., Inc.
(0-8098)
New York, NY
800-327-4801

Walker, Frank R., Co.
(0-911592)
Chicago, IL
800-631-7795

Wallace-Homestead Bk. Co.
(0-87069)
Lombard, IL
800-323-2596

Walterick Pubs., Inc.
(0-937396)
Kansas City, KS
800-255-4097

Walthers, William K., Inc.
(0-941952)
Milwaukee, WI
800-558-5478

Wanderer Bks.
(0-671)
New York, NY
800-223-2336

Warman Publishing Co., Inc.
(0-911594)
Willow Grove, PA
800-526-7626 (Kampmann & Co.)

Warner Bks., Inc.
(0-446)
New York, NY
800-638-6460

Warner Pr. Pubs.
(0-87162)
Anderson, IN
800-428-6409

Warren, Gorham & Lamont, Inc.
(0-88262; 0-88712)
Boston, MA
800-922-0066

Wasatch Education Systems
(0-938897)
Salt Lake City, UT
800-624-1732

Washington Square Pr., Inc.
(0-671)
New York, NY
800-223-2336

Waterfront Bks.
(0-914525)
Burlington, VT
800-227-1516 (Bookpeople)
800-241-3829 (DeVorss & Co.)

Watson-Guptill Pubns., Inc.
(0-8174; 0-8230; 0-87165)
New York, NY
800-526-3641 (Orders & Customer Service)

Watts, Franklin, Inc.
(0-531)
Danbury, CT
800-672-6672

Weber Systems, Inc.
(0-938862)
Chesterland, OH
800-851-6018

Weiser, Samuel, Inc.
(0-87728)
York Beach, ME
800-843-6666
800-423-7087

Wesleyan Univ. Pr.
(0-8195)
Middletown, CT
800-242-7737

West Publishing Co.
(0-314; 0-8299)
St. Paul, MN
800-328-9352

Westcliffe Pubs., Inc.
(0-942394)
Englewood, CO
800-523-3692

Western Horizons Bks.
(0-934959)
Helena, MT
800-426-4727; (Pacific Pipeline, Inc.)
800-562-4647 (In Washington)

Western Pub. Co., Inc.
(0-307)
New York, NY
800-558-3291
800-621-1115 (Childrens Pr.)

Westin Communications
(0-86620)
Woodland Hills, CA
800-421-1893

Westminster Pr.
(0-664)
Philadelphia, PA
800-523-1631
800-462-0405 (In Pennsylvania)

Westmoreland Museum of Art
(0-931241)
Greensburg, PA
800-242-7737

Westphalia Pr., The
(0-915637)
Loose Creek, MO
800-325-8404 (Paperback Supply Co.)

Whatever Publishing Inc.
(0-931432)
Mill Valley, CA
800-227-3900 (Retail orders only)
800-227-1516 (Bookpeople)

Whitaker Hse.
(0-88368)
Springdale, PA
800-245-2422

White Dove Publishing Co.
(0-914541)
San Diego, CA
800-621-0852

White Pine Pr.
(0-9610988)
West Linn, OR
*800-547-7734 (International Specialized Bk.
Services, Inc.)*

Whole World Publishing, Inc.
(0-938184)
Deerfield, IL
800-323-4305

Wide World Publishing/Tetra
(0-933174)
San Carlos, CA
800-624-4466 (Bookpeople)

Wight, Oliver, Ltd., Pubns., Inc.
(0-939246)
Essex Junction, VT
800-343-0625

Wildwood Pubns.
(0-914104)
Traverse City, MI
800-447-7367

Williams & Wilkins Co.
(0-683)
Baltimore, MD
800-638-0672

Willow Creek Pr.
(0-932558)
Oshkosh, WI
800-341-7770

Wilson, H. W.
(0-8242)
Bronx, NY
800-367-6770

Wilton Enterprises, Bk. Div.
(0-912696)
Chicago, IL
800-772-711

Winans, Chip, Productions
(0-9613234)
Harwichport, MA
900-245-2665 (Caroline Hse., Inc.)

Winch, B. L., & Assocs./Jalmar Pr.
(0-935266)
Rolling Hills Estates, CA
800-662-9662

Windsor Pubns., Inc.
(0-89781)
Northridge, CA
800-423-5761

Wine Appreciation Guild, The
(0-932664)
San Francisco, CA
800-242-9462 (Orders only)

Wingbow Pr.
(0-914640)
800-227-1516 (Bookpeople)

Winn Bks.
(0-916947)
Seattle, WA
800-426-5589

Winston, Harry, Inc.
(0-87311)
New York, NY
800-223-2305

Winston-Derek Pubs.,Inc.
(0-938232; 1-55523)
Nashville, TN
800-826-1888

Winston Pr., Inc.
(0-86683)
San Francisco, CA
800-242-7737 (Bookstores & schools)
800-638-3030 (Individuals)

Winterthur Museum & Gardens
(0-912724)
Winterthur, DE
800-223-2584 (W. W. Norton & Co.)
800-345-1359 (Harry N. Abrams)

Wolcotts, Inc.
(0-910531)
Paramount, CA
800-421-2220
800-262-1538 (In California)

Woman's Pr., The
(0-9614878)
New York, NY
800-544-1016 (P. B. S.)

Wonder-Treasure Bks., Inc.
(0-448)
Los Angeles, CA
800-421-0892
800-227-8801 (In California)
Wood, Bob, Assocs.
(0-937863)
Vancouver, WA
800-426-4727 (Pacific Pipeline)
800-525-9030 (All Sports Book Distributors)
Woodall Publishing Co.
(0-912082)
Lake Bluff, IL
800-223-2348 (Simon & Schuster, Inc.)
Woodcraft Supply Corp.
(0-918036)
Woburn, MA
800-225-1153
Word Among Us Pr.
(0-932085)
Washington, DC
800-638-8539
Word for Today, The
(0-936728)
Costa Mesa, CA
800-922-0047 (In California)
(Living Books)·
Word of Mouth Pr.
(0-910027)
Yonkers, NY
800-526-3825 (Baker & Taylor Co., Eastern Div.)
Word, Inc.
(0-8499; 0-87680)
Waco, TX
800-433-3340 (Customer Service)
Wordware Publishing, Inc.
(0-915381; 1-55622)
Plano, TX
800-231-7467
Workman Publishing Co., Inc.
(0-89480; 0-911104)
New York, NY
800-722-7202

World Bank, The, Pubns. Dept.
(0-8213)
Washington, DC
800-482-0831 (In Boston)
800-226-5315 (In New York)
World Bible Pubs., Inc.
(0-529; 0-8326)
Westlake, OH
800-247-5195
World Bk., Inc.
(0-7166)
Chicago, IL
800-621-8202
World Class Ski Tuning
(0-9615712)
Portland, OR
800-426-4727 (Pacific Pipeline, Inc.)
World Purpose Foundation
(0-915485)
Beverly Hills, CA
800-227-1516 (Bookpeople)
World Wisdom Books
(0-941532)
Bloomington, IN
800-227-1516 (Bookpeople)
800-241-3829 (New Leaf)
800-634-2665 (Great Tradition, The)
Wredco Pr.
(0-931705)
Flagstaff, AZ
800-423-5819 (Arizona only)
Wright Group, The
(0-940156; 1-55624)
San Diego, CA
800-523-2371
800-331-4524 (In California)
Writers Digest Bks.
(0-89879; 0-911654)
Cincinnati, OH
800-543-4644
Writing Consultants
(0-931295)
East Rochester, NY
800-828-6293

Yankee Bks.
(0-89909; 0-911658)
Dublin, NH
800-258-5327
Year Bk. Medical Pubs., Inc.
(0-8151)
Chicago, IL
800-621-9262
Yosemite-Di-Maggio
Oakland, CA
800-227-1516 (Bookpeople)
Young, Brigham, Univ. Pr.
(0-8425)
Provo, UT
800-453-3235
Yourdon Pr.
(0-917072)
New York, NY
800-223-2452
Yours Truly, Inc.
(0-932946)
Westminster, CA
800-845-7076
Yuen, Jim J.
(0-9613077)
San Mateo, CA
800-841-BOOK (Ten Speed Press)
ZapoDel Inc.
(0-934545)
Del Mar, CA
800-982-8319 (Publishers Group West)
Zebra Bks.
(0-8217; 0-89083)
New York, NY
800-221-2649
Zondervan Publishing Hse.
(0-310)
Grand Rapids, MI
800-253-1309 (wholesale orders, bookstores)
800-253-4475 (retail orders)
Zone Pr.
(0-936469)
Cambridge, MA
800-321-3883 (NASCORP, Inc.)

The *Wholesalers' and Distributors' Index* is arranged alphabetically by company name, and contains full address and ordering information, SAN(S), and, where applicable, ISBN prefix(es) and toll-free telephone numbers.

A B & C Sales, 2010 Eisenhower Ave., Alexandria, VA 22314 (SAN 282-6607).
ABC Book Distributors, SE. Court Warehouse, San Francisco International Airport, San Francisco, CA 94128 (SAN 159-8007).
ABC School Supply Inc., 240 Ninth St. N., St. Petersburg, FL 33705 (SAN 169-1279).
ACEF pubns., P.O. Box 261, Great Falls, VA 22066-0261 (SAN 282-6666).
A C L D, 4156 Library Rd., Pittsburgh, PA 15234 (SAN 282-6674).
ACS Pubns., Inc., *(A C S Pubns Inc; 0-917086; 0-935127),* P.O. Box 16430, San Diego, CA 92116-0430 (SAN 208-5380) Tel 619-297-9203; Toll free: 800-826-1085; Toll free: 800-525-1786 (in California).
A D F D Pubns., Suite 104, 20 S. 36th St., Philadephia, PA 19104 (SAN 282-6615) Tel 215-387-4857.
AHA, Inc., *(0-918545),* P.O. Box 8405, Santa Cruz, CA 95061-8405 (SAN 295-5059) Tel 408-458-9119.
AIMS Media, *(AIMS Media; 0-8068),* 6901 Woodley Ave., Van Nuys, CA 91406-4878 (SAN 687-3464) Tel 818-785-4111; Toll free: 800-367-2467.
AKA Periodicals Distribution Group, Eastern Region, P.O Box 1805, Washington, DC 20013 (SAN 169-0906).
A-K News Co., P.O. Box 24067, 121 E. Hill, Oklahoma City, OK 73124 (SAN 169-6971); P.O. Box 1193, Liberal, KS 67901 (SAN 281-2401).
ANCO Management Services, 202 N. Court St., Florence, AL 35630 (SAN 663-3269) Tel 205-766-3824.
ANSCO, 1243 W. 134th St., Gardena, CA 90247 (SAN 689-1268) Tel 213-532-7780; Toll free: 800-421-1270.
ARA Magazines & Book Divisions, P.O. Box 963, Bridgeton, MO 63044 (SAN 169-4049) Tel 314-291-7775; Toll free: 800-291-7775 (SAN 169-4235).
A R A Services, P.O. Box 448, Brainerd, MN 56401 (SAN 169-4049).
ARA Services, 7000 N. Robinson, Oklahoma City, OK 73125 (SAN 281-2827) Tel 405-843-9383; Toll free: 800-522-9207; 909 W 23rd St., Tulsa, OK 74107 (SAN 169-7013); P.O. Box 2399, Yakima, WA 98907 (SAN 169-8893); P.O. Box 25489, Oklahoma City, OK 73125 (SAN 661-9460).
ARA Services, 3392 Bledensburg Rd., Cottage City, MD 20722 (SAN 200-8319).
ARA Services, 16150 W. Lincoln, New Berlin, WI 53151 (SAN 200-8327).

ARA Services, Magazine & Bk. Div., P.O. Box 85408, San Diego, CA 92138-5408 (SAN 200-7401) Tel 619-275-3090.
ARA Services, Magazine & Bk. Div., 2340 S. Fairfax Ave., Los Angeles, CA 90016 (SAN 200-4968) Tel 213-661-3708; P.O. Box 78003, Los Angeles, CA 90016 (SAN 662-7641).
ARGS Bookstore, 6 Glen Terr., Scotia, NY 12302 (SAN 200-7967).
ARHE, Inc., 1206 Calle 16, SE., Caparra Terrace, PR 00921 (SAN 169-930X).
ASI Distributors, 63 W 38th St., Suite 505, New York, NY 10018 (SAN 156-5737) Tel 212-719-2919.
AVI Publishing Co., Inc., *(AVI; 0-87055),* 250 Post Rd. E., P.O. Box 831, Westport, CT 06881 (SAN 201-4017) Tel 203-226-0738.
Aardvark Industries, *(Aardvark Indus; 0-928388),* 1690 Bolton St., Walled Lake, MI 48088 (SAN 277-3457) Tel 313-669-3110.
Ability Development, Inc., Box 4260, Athens, OH 45701-4260 (SAN 111-9125) Tel 614-594-3547; Toll free: 800-221-9254.
Abingdon Pr., Div. of United Methodist Publishing Hse., *(Abingdon; 0-687),* 201 Eighth Ave., S., Nashville, TN 37202 (SAN 201-0054) Tel 615-749-6290; Toll free: 800-251-3320; 1015 Visco Dr., Nashville, TN 37210 (SAN 699-9956). *Imprints:* Apex Books (Apex); Festival Books (Festival).
About Time Publishing Co., The, Affil. of Friends of Freedom, *(About Time MA; 0-913683),* P.O. Box 836, Northampton, MA 01061 (SAN 286-1186) Tel 413-545-2145; P.O. Box 1060, Amherst, MA 01004 (SAN 662-2070) Tel 413-545-2148; Orders to: P.O. Box 160, Hadley, MA 01035 (SAN 200-7304) Tel 413-586-5487; Dist. by: Richard Rawe, P.O. Box 443, Soap Lake, WA 98851 (SAN 290-7054) Tel 509-246-1559; Dist. by: Love Ministries, Inc., P.O. Box 69, Worthville, KY 41098 (SAN 662-2089).
Abramovic Associates, 140 S. Jefferson St., Kittanning, PA 16201 (SAN 169-7404).
Abrams, Harry N., Inc., Subs. of Times Mirror Co., *(Abrams; 0-8109),* 100 Fifth Ave., New York, NY 10011 (SAN 200-2434) Tel 212-206-7715; Toll free: 800-345-1359; Orders to: Wayne Public Warehouse, 150 Parish Dr., Wayne, NJ 07470 (SAN 699-9964).

Academy Chicago Pubs., *(Academy Chi Pubs; 0-915864; 0-89733),* 425 N. Michigan Ave., Chicago, IL 60611 (SAN 213-2001) Tel 312-644-1723.
Acorn Bks. *See* Macmillan Publishing Co., Inc.
Acorn Music Press *See* Music Sales Corp.
Acropolis Bks., Subs. of Colortone Pr., Inc., *(Acropolis; 0-87491),* 2400 17th St. NW, Washington, DC 20009 (SAN 201-2227) Tel 202-387-6805; Toll free: 800-621-5199.
Action Business Services, 704 Airport Blvd., Suite 4, Ann Arbor, MI 48104 (SAN 200-7142).
Action Distributing, P.O. Box 3811, Huntington Beach, CA 92605 (SAN 200-6782) Tel 714-840-8712.
Activity Resources Co., Inc., *(Activity Resources; 0-918932),* P.O. Box 4875, 20655 Hathaway Ave., Hayward, CA 94541 (SAN 209-0201) Tel 415-782-1300.
Actuarial Bookstore, The, P.O. Box 318, Abington, CT 06230 (SAN 200-5867) Tel 203-975-3540.
Adair Distributors Inc., 208 S. Mulanix St., Kirksville, MO 63501 (SAN 169-4286) Tel 816-665-4662.
Adams News, 1555 W. Galer St., Seattle, WA 98119 (SAN 169-8842) Tel 206-284-7617.
Adams Periodical Service, 415 Mississippi St., Vallejo, CA 94590 (SAN 169-0418).
Adco International Co., 80-00 Cooper Ave., Bldg. No.3, Glendale, NY 11227 (SAN 285-8010).
Addison-Wesley Pub. Co., Inc., Health Sciences Div. *See* Addison-Wesley Publishing Co., Inc.
Addison-Wesley Publishing Co., Inc., *(Addison-Wesley; 0-201),* 1 Jacob Way, Reading, MA 01867 (SAN 200-2000) Tel 617-944-3700; Toll free: 800-447-2226. *Imprints:* Addison-Wesley Publishing Company, Incorporated, Health Sciences Division (Health Sci).
Addman, Joe, 217-17 82nd Ave., Jamaica, NY 11427 (SAN 285-8002).
Addor Assocs., Inc., *(Addor),* P.O. Box 2128, Westport, CT 06880 (SAN 200-5948) Tel 203-226-9791; 115 Roseville Rd., Westport, CT 06880 (SAN 658-2982).
Adirondack Mountain Club, Inc., *(ADK Mtn Club; 0-935272),* 174 Glen St., Glens Falls, NY 12801 (SAN 204-7691) Tel 518-793-7737.
Adler, Leo, 2305 Main St., Baker, OR 97814 (SAN 169-7021).

Wholesalers & Distributors

Adler Publishing Co., *(Adler Pub Co; 0-913623),* Panorama Plaza, Box 25333, Rochester, NY 14625 (SAN 285-6808) Tel 716-377-5804; Dist. by: Writers & Bks., 740 University Ave., Rochester, NY 14607 (SAN 156-9678) Tel 716-473-2590. Do not confuse with Adler's Foreign Bks., Inc., New York, NY. *Imprints:* Nightsun Books (Nightsun Bks).

Advance Research Press, 2120 Smithtown Ave., Ronkonkoma, NY 11779 (SAN 200-4860).

Advanced Business Systems, Inc., 811 N. Nowell St., Orlando, FL 32808 (SAN 695-5975).

Advanced Professional Development, Inc., *(Adv Prof Dev; 0-912907),* 5519 Carpenter Ave., North Hollywood, CA 91607 (SAN 282-9576) Tel 818-506-7765.

Advanced Systems, Inc., *(0-922152),* 155 E. Algonquin Rd., Arlington Heights, IL 60005 (SAN 655-0703) Tel 312-981-1500; Toll free: 800-323-0377; Toll free: 800-593-0377.

Advertising Trade Pubns., Inc., 10 E. 39th St., 6th Flr., New York, NY 10016 (SAN 282-6704) Tel 212-889-6500.

Affiliated Book Distributor, 415 N. Wolf Rd., Wheeling, IL 60090 (SAN 169-2267).

Affiliated Medical Book Corp., 1355 Nostrand Ave., Brooklyn, NY 11226 (SAN 169-5096).

Africa Agency, P.O. Box 1118, Concord, MA 01742 (SAN 169-3417).

Afro-American Book Distributor, 2537 Prospect, Houston, TX 77004 (SAN 169-8257).

Agencia de Publicaciones de Puerto Rico, GPO Box 4903, San Juan, PR 00936 (SAN 169-9296).

Agribookstore/Winrock, Affil. of Winrock International, *(Agribookstore),* Rosslyn Plaza, 1611 N. Kent St., Suite 600, Arlington, VA 22209 (SAN 200-6693) Tel 703-525-9455.

Air Science Co., *(Air Sci Co; 0-903608),* P.O. Box 143, Corning, NY 14830 (SAN 210-7791) Tel 607-962-5591.

Airline Careers Media, P.O. Box 9200, Boston, MA 92114 (SAN 200-6839) Tel 617-323-1607.

Airways Supply, P.O. Box 810469, Dallas, TX 75381 (SAN 200-5182).

Akiba Pr., *(Akiba Pr; 0-934764),* Box 13086, Oakland, CA 94661 (SAN 212-0666) Tel 415-339-1283.

Alabama Bk. Store, P.O. Box 1279, Tuscaloosa, AL 35403-1279 (SAN 111-851X) Tel 205-758-4532.

Aladdin Bks. *See* Atheneum Pubs.

Aladdin Bks. *See* Macmillan Publishing Co., Inc.

Alaska News Agency Inc., Book Dept., 325 W. Potter Dr., Anchorage, AK 99502 (SAN 168-9274).

Alaska Pacific Univ. Pr., *(Alaska Pacific; 0-935094),* A.P.U., 4101 University Dr., Anchorage, AK 99508 (SAN 215-2908) Tel 907-564-8291.

Alchemy Bks., *(Alchemy Bks; 0-931290),* 717 Market, Suite 514, San Francisco, CA 94103 (SAN 211-304X) Tel 415-777-2197.

Aleutian Pribilof Islands Assn., Inc. (AANG ANGAGIN), *(Aleutian; 0-9609308),* 1689 C St., Anchorage, AK 99501 (SAN 260-0102) Tel 907-276-2700.

Alexander News Co., Box 1091, Asheville, NC 28802 (SAN 169-6335).

Alexandria House, P.O. Box 23618, Alexandria, IN 46011 (SAN 209-9799).

Alfonsi Enterprises, 1446 Ashby Rd., Saint Louis, MO 63132 (SAN 169-4227).

Alfonsi News-Book Service Inc., P.O. Box 100, Taylorville, IL 62568 (SAN 169-2240).

Alfred Publishing Co., Inc., *(Alfred Pub; 0-88284),* 15335 Morrison St., Sherman Oaks, CA 91413 (SAN 201-243X) Tel 818-995-8811; Toll free: 800-821-6083.

Alico International, Inc., 990 Greentree Rd., Pittsburgh, PA 15220 (SAN 157-874X).

All America Distributors, 8431 Melrose Place, Los Angeles, CA 90069 (SAN 168-972X).

All Sports Bk. Distributors, P.O. Box 5793, Denver, CO 80217 (SAN 200-7398).

Allen Pr., Inc., *(Allen Pr; 0-935868),* P.O. Box 368, Lawrence, KS 66044 (SAN 213-7186).

Allenson, Alec R., Inc., *(A R Allenson; 0-8401),* P.O. Box 447, Geneva, AL 36340 (SAN 162-4903).

Allentown News Agency, Inc., 721-723 Liberty St., P.O. Box 446, Allentown, PA 18105 (SAN 169-7226).

Allied Book & Education Resources, 933 Tewa Loop, Los Alamos, NM 87544 (SAN 169-4995) Tel 505-662-9705.

Almanac of Seapower, The, 2300 Wilson Blvd., Arlington, VA 22210 (SAN 200-8033) Tel 703-528-1775.

Alpha & Omega Distributor, 5970 W. 60th Ave., Arvada, CO 80003 (SAN 169-0515) Tel 303-431-1772.

Alphabet Pr., *(Alphabet MA; 0-940032),* 60 N. Main St., Natick, MA 01760 (SAN 217-1449) Tel 617-655-9696; Toll free: 800-462-1252.

Alpic Library Co., 424 Edwin Dr., Virginia Beach, VA 23462 (SAN 169-8710); 2211 Church St., Greensboro, NC 27405 (SAN 169-6408).

Alta News, 37401 Paris St., Denver, CO 80239 (SAN 111-6347).

Altarinda Books, *(Altarinda Bks; 0-9607896),* 13 Estates Dr., Orinda, CA 94563 (SAN 238-1397) Tel 415-254-3830.

Alternate Source, The, *(Alter Source; 0-915363),* 704 N. Pennsylvania Ave., Lansing, MI 48906 (SAN 265-6833) Tel 517-482-8270; Toll free: 800-253-3200 ext 700.

Altweger, Nicholas H., Co., 19935 Butternut, Southfield, MI 48076 (SAN 287-2587) Tel 313-553-7678.

Amarillo Periodical Distributors, P.O. Box 31985, Amarillo, TX 79120 (SAN 156-4986) Tel 806-372-5035.

Amart Bk., & Catalog Distributing Co., Inc., 100 E. Ohio St., Rm. B-20, Chicago, IL 60611 (SAN 276-9778).

Amateur Computer Society of Central Ohio, P.O. Box 28606, Columbus, OH 43228-0606 (SAN 671-6989).

Amatix, Inc., 9670 S. La Cienaga Blvd., Inglewood, CA 90301 (SAN 678-5786) Tel 213-417-8989; Toll free: 800-953-7772.

Amber West Corp., *(0-922233),* 1000 Ortega Way, Placentia, CA 92670 (SAN 285-6980) Tel 714-632-9560; Toll free: 800-325-7157.

Amereon, Ltd., *(Amereon Ltd; 0-88411; 0-89190; 0-8488),* P.O. Box 1200, Mattituck, NY 11952 (SAN 201-2413) Tel 516-298-5100.

America Ado, Inc., 357 Van Ness Way, Suite 180, Torrance, CA 90501 (SAN 686-5046) Tel 213-212-5332.

American Alliance for Health, Physical Education, Recreation & Dance, Affil. of National Education Assn., *(AAHPERD; 0-88314),* 1900 Association Dr., Reston, VA 22091 (SAN 202-3237) Tel 703-476-3400.

American Assn. of Petroleum Geologists, *(AAPG; 0-89181),* P.O. Box 979, Tulsa, OK 74101 (SAN 204-7950) Tel 918-584-2555.

American Casting Association, 2341 Fifth Ave., San Rafael, CA 94901 (SAN 282-7247).

American Chiropractic Academic Press, *(Am Chiro Acad; 0-936948),* 6840 NW 16th, Suite 146, Oklahoma City, OK 73127 (SAN 215-6180); Dist. by: American Chiropratic Assn., 1916 Wilson Blvd., Arlington, VA 22201 (SAN 215-6180) Tel 703-276-8800.

American Chiropractic Assn., *(Am Chiro Assn; 0-9606618),* 1916 Wilson Blvd., Suite 300, Arlington, VA 22201 (SAN 215-6180) Tel 703-276-8800.

American Classical College Pr., *(Am Classical Coll Pr; 0-913314; 0-89266),* P.O. Box 4526, Albuquerque, NM 87196 (SAN 201-2618) Tel 505-843-7749.

American Council on Education, *(ACE; 0-8268),* 1 Dupont Cir., Washington, DC 20036 (SAN 201-2170) Tel 202-939-9380; Toll free: 800-257-5755; Dist. by: Macmillan Publishing Co., Inc., 866 Third Ave., New York, NY 10022 (SAN 202-5574) Tel 212-702-2000.

American Econo-Clad Service, Div. of American Companies Inc., P.O. Box 1777, Topeka, KS 66608 (SAN 169-2763).

American Home Libraries, Inc., 1960 Plantation Dr., Nashville, TN 37211 (SAN 200-8017).

American Hospital Publishing, Inc., Subs. of American Hospital Assn., *(AHPI; 0-939450; 1-55648),* 211 E. Chicago Ave., Chicago, IL 60611 (SAN 216-5872) Tel 312-440-6800; Toll free: 800-242-2626; Orders to: AHA Services, Inc., P.O. Box 99376, 4444 W. Ferdinande, Chicago, IL 60624 (SAN 661-9363) Tel 312-280-6020.

American Institute of Physics, *(Am Inst Physics; 0-88318),* 335 E. 45th St., New York, NY 10017 (SAN 201-162X) Tel 212-661-9404; Toll free: 800-247-7497. Publisher of scholarly journals, books and databases in physics and related sciences in hardcopy, 16mm and 35mm microfilm, reel and cartridge, and microfiche. North American distributor of journals from the Institute of Physics (UK), Annals of the Israel Physical Society, Physics Briefs from the Fachinformationszentrum (West Germany), and Physica Scripta (Royal Swedish Academy of Sciences).

American Legacy Press *See* Crown Pubs., Inc.

American Library Assn., *(ALA; 0-8389),* 50 E. Huron St., Chicago, IL 60611 (SAN 201-0062) Tel 312-944-6780; Toll free: 800-545-2433; Toll free: 800-545-2444 in Illinois; Toll free: 800-545-2455 in Canada. *Imprints:* Bootlegger Press (Pub by Bootlegger Pr).

American Magazine Service, 914 Jefferson, Topeka, KS 66607 (SAN 285-8037); Toll free: 800-225-3220.

American Media Corp., 219 N. Milwaukee St., Milwaukee, WI 53202 (SAN 695-698X) Tel 414-272-3355. Specializes in juveniles.

American National Supply Corporation *See* ANSCO

American Overseas Book Co., Inc., 550 Walnut St., Norwood, NJ 07648 (SAN 169-4863).

American Printing House for the Blind, *(Am Printing Hse),* 1839 Frankfort Ave., Box 6085, Louisville, KY 40206 (SAN 203-5235) Tel 502-895-2405.

American Scotch Highland Breeder's Assn., Member of National Society of Livestock Record Assns., *(Am Scotch Highland),* P.O. Box 81, Remer, MN 56672 (SAN 689-2574) Tel 218-566-1321.

American Small Business Computers, Inc., *(Am Small Busn Comp; 0-922264),* 118 S. Mill St., Pryor, OK 74361 (SAN 287-5551) Tel 918-825-4844.

American Society for Information Science, *(Am Soc Info Sci; 0-87715),* 1424 16th St., NW, Suite 404, Washington, DC 20036 (SAN 202-4748) Tel 202-462-1000; Toll free: 800-248-5474.

American Society for Information Science *See* Knowledge Industry Pubns., Inc.

American Used Computer, P.O. Box 68, Kenmore Sta., Boston, MA 02215 (SAN 265-5128) Tel 617-437-1100.

Americana *See* Crown Pubs., Inc.

Ames News Agency Inc., 2110 E. 13th St., Ames, IA 50010 (SAN 169-2550).

Amoskeag News Agency, 375 Canal St., Manchester, NH 03101 (SAN 169-4537).

Amsco Music *See* Music Sales Corp.

Anacapa Bks., 3090 Claremont Ave., Berkeley, CA 94705 (SAN 200-724X) Tel 415-654-3517.

Anchor Books *See* Doubleday & Co., Inc.

Anchor Press *See* Doubleday & Co., Inc.

Ancient Future, P.O. Box 264, Kentfield, CA 94914 (SAN 200-6499).

Anderson News Co., P.O. Box 219, Helton Dr., Florence, AL 35630 (SAN 168-9223) Tel 205-766-3789; 3669 E. Lasalle, Pensacola, FL 32503 (SAN 168-9363) Tel 904-477-0920; P.O. Box 22998, Knoxville, TN 37933 (SAN 169-7927) Tel 615-966-7575; 3945 Volunteer Dr., Chattanooga, TN 37416 (SAN 169-7862) Tel 615-894-3945; 6301 Forbing Rd., Caller No. 4, Little Rock, AR 72219 (SAN 106-956X) Tel 501-562-7360; 1818 S. Monroe, Tallahassee, FL 32301 (SAN 169-1309) Tel 904-222-2323; 1857 W. Grant, P.O. Box 5465, Tucson, AZ 85703 (SAN 168-9401) Tel 602-622-2831.

Andich Brothers News Co., 2115 Fourth Ave., Rock Island, IL 61201 (SAN 169-2186).

Andrik Associates, *(0-936856),* P.O. Box 5029, 311 Ashby St., Alexandria, VA 22305 (SAN 221-895X).

Andrzejewski's Church & Religious Goods, 1304 Kosciuszko Ave., Bay City, MI 48708 (SAN 157-0145).

Angel Book Distribution Center, 561 Tyler St., Monterey, CA 93940 (SAN 200-5042).

Angelina Periodicals, P.O. Box 1465, Lufkin, TX 75901 (SAN 169-8346).

Answers Period, Inc., *(Answers Period; 0-917875),* P.O. Box 72666, Corpus Christi, TX 78472 (SAN 656-9617) Tel 512-852-8927; Dist. by: Baker & Taylor Co., Midwest Div., 501 Gladiola Ave., Momence, IL 60954 (SAN 169-2100) Tel 815-472-2444; Dist. by: Ingram Industries, 347 Reedwood Dr., Nashville, TN 37217 (SAN 169-7978) Tel 615-360-2819.

Anthracite News Co., P.O. Box 1123, Scranton, PA 18501 (SAN 169-7625).

Antique Phonograph Monthly, 502 E. 17th St., Brooklyn, NY 11226 (SAN 200-5123).

Aperture Foundation, Inc., *(Aperture; 0-89381; 0-912334),* 20 E. 23rd St., New York, NY 10010 (SAN 201-1832) Tel 212-505-5555; Toll free: 800-631-3577; Dist. by: Farrar Straus & Giroux, 19 Union Sq. W., New York, NY 10003 (SAN 206-782X) Tel 212-741-6900.

Apex Books *See Abingdon Pr.*

Apogee Software Distributors, *(0-922319),* P.O. Box 71, Morton Grove, IL 60053 (SAN 285-7073).

Apollo Library Book Supplier, 672 Artwood Dr., Philadelphia, PA 19115 (SAN 159-8031).

Apothecary Shop, The, 2230 Hillside Ct., Walnut Creek, CA 94596 (SAN 200-660X).

Appalachian Bible Co. & Christian Bks., 604 Rolling Hills Dr., Johnson City, TN 37601 (SAN 169-7889) Tel 615-926-0128; Toll free: 800-251-7032; P.O. Box 1573, Johnson City, TN 37601 (SAN 661-9452).

Appalachian Mountain Club Bks., *(Appalach Mtn; 0-910146),* 5 Joy St., Boston, MA 02108 (SAN 203-4808) Tel 617-523-0636.

Apple Country Ltd., P.O. Box 1099, Julian, CA 92036 (SAN 287-3192).

Apple Paperbacks *See Scholastic, Inc.*

Apple Puget Sound Program Library Exchange Co-op, *(Apple Coop; 0-927988; 0-928503),* 290 SW 43rd St., Renton, WA 98055 (SAN 657-4319) Tel 206-251-5222; Toll free: 800-426-3667.

Apple-Wood Bks., *(Apple Wood; 0-918222),* Box 2870, Cambridge, MA 02139 (SAN 210-3419) Tel 617-350-0311; Dist. by: Arbor House Publishing Co., 235 E. 45th St., New York, NY 10017 (SAN 201-1522) Tel 212-599-3131.

Applecart Programs for Education, *(Applecart; 0-928504),* 515 N. Franklin St., Juneau, AK 99801 (SAN 200-7754) Tel 907-586-3689.

Appleton & Lange, Subs. of Simon & Schuster, A Gulf & Western Co., *(Appleton & Lange; 0-8385),* 25 Van Zant St., East Norwalk, CT 06855 (SAN 209-1488) Tel 203-838-4400; Toll free: 800-826-2618; Drawer L, Los Altos, CA 94022 (SAN 663-2866); Orders to: Appleton & Lange, 25 Van Zant St., East Norwalk, CT 06855 (SAN 209-1488); Dist. by: Prentice-Hall, Inc., Englewood Cliffs, NJ 07632 (SAN 200-2175) Tel 201-592-2000.

Appleton-Century-Crofts *See Prentice-Hall, Inc.*

Appleton News Agency, 512 S. Lyndale Dr., Appleton, WI 54911 (SAN 159-804X).

Applied Educational Systems, *(Appl Educ Systs; 0-917079),* P.O. Box 2220, Concord, NH 03301 (SAN 284-8104) Tel 603-225-5511.

Apt Bks., Inc., *(Apt Bks; 0-86590),* 141 E. 44th St., Suite 511, New York, NY 10017 (SAN 215-7209) Tel 212-697-0887.

Aqua-Craft II, 7992 Miramar Rd., San Diego, CA 92126 (SAN 200-7363) Tel 619-271-7000; Toll free: 800-854-2110.

Aquarian Age Book Distributor, Box 3383, St. Paul, MN 55165 (SAN 159-8058); Toll free: 800-843-6666.

ARA Periodical Services, P.O. Box 29323, 924 Kenner Ave., Kenner, LA 70063 (SAN 169-2941).

Ara Periodicals Distribution Group, Eastern Region, P.O. Box 1805, Washington, DC 20013 (SAN 169-0906).

Arbit Bks., Inc., *(Arbit; 0-930038),* 8050 N. Pt. Washington Rd., Milwaukee, WI 53217 (SAN 210-4695) Tel 414-352-4404; Toll free: 800-558-6908.

Arbor Hse. Pub. Co., Div. of Hearst Corp., *(Arbor Hse; 0-87795),* 235 E. 45th St., New York, NY 10017 (SAN 201-1522) Tel 212-599-3131.

Arcane Books, U.S. Rte. 1A, York Harbor, ME 03911 (SAN 282-6798).

Arcata Graphics, P.O. Box 711, Kingsport, TN 37662 (SAN 200-7304) Tel 615-246-7131.

Architectural Record Bks. *See McGraw-Hill Bk. Co.*

Archon Bks. *See Shoe String Pr., Inc.*

Argo Bks. *See Atheneum Pubs.*

Arkansas News Co., Box 1405, Fort Smith, AR 72902 (SAN 168-9444).

Arlington Bk. Co., *(Arlington Bk; 0-930163),* P.O. Box 327, Arlington, VA 22210-0327 (SAN 200-786X) Tel 202-296-6750.

Arlington Hse. *See Crown Pubs., Inc.*

Armchair Sailor Bookstore, Lee's Wharf, Newport, RI 02840 (SAN 127-2853) Tel 401-847-4252. Retail, wholesale & mail order marine books, including professional & college texts.

Armor Books, Div. of Reynolds Bindery, 1703 Lister, Kansas City, MO 64127 (SAN 159-8066).

Armstrong, D., Co., Inc., *(D Armstrong),* 2000-B Governor's Cir., Houston, TX 77092 (SAN 210-0320) Tel 713-688-1441.

Armstrong, J.B., News Agency, 2750 Griffith Rd., Winston-Salem, NC 27103 (SAN 169-6513).

Armstrong Systems & Consulting, 5101 Tremont, Davenport, IA 52809 (SAN 695-5835) Tel 319-386-9090.

Arrowhead Magazine Co., Inc., Box 5947, San Bernardino, CA 92412 (SAN 169-0094).

Arrowhead News Co., 1200 Elm St., Antigo, WI 54409 (SAN 169-9016).

Art & Antique Bks. *See Watson-Guptill Pubns., Inc.*

Arwyn Map Co., *(Arwyn Map; 0-936039),* 9090 W. 74th Ave., Arvada, CO 80005 (SAN 696-9917) Tel 303-428-2864.

ASHO Pubns. *See Bridge Pubns. Inc.*

Ashton-Tate Publishing Group, *(Ashton-Tate Pub; 0-912677),* 20101 Hamilton Ave., Torrance, CA 90502 (SAN 265-4628) Tel 213-329-8000; Toll free: 800-437-4329. Now handles all Multimate Products.

Asian Humanities Pr., *(Asian Human Pr; 0-89581; 0-87573),* 2512 Ninth St., Suite 8, Berkeley, CA 94710 (SAN 213-6503) Tel 415-485-8065; Dist. by: Great Tradition, The, 750 Adrian Way, Suite 11, San Rafael, CA 94903 (SAN 200-5743) Tel 415-492-9382.

Askit Co., 3517 Terhune, Ann Arbor, MI 48104 (SAN 200-7037) Tel 313-971-1034.

Aspen West Publishing, *(Aspen West Pub; 0-9615390),* P.O. Box 1245, Sandy, UT 84091 (SAN 694-2318) Tel 801-571-7435; Orders to: 9267 S. Tortellini Dr., Sandy, UT 84902 (SAN 699-6019).

Associated Booksellers, Affil. of Merrimack Publishing Corp., *(Assoc Bk; 0-87497),* 562 Boston Ave., Bridgeport, CT 06610 (SAN 203-5014) Tel 203-333-7268; Toll free: 800-232-2224.

Associated Libraries Inc., 229-33 N. 63rd St., Philadelphia, PA 19139 (SAN 169-7528).

Associated News, 914 Winbern, Houston, TX 77002 (SAN 157-5457).

Associated University Presses, *(Assoc Univ Prs; 0-8453),* 440 Forsgate Dr., Cranbury, NJ 08512 (SAN 281-2959) Tel 609-655-4770. *Imprints:* Cornwall Books (Cornwall Bks).

Astran, Inc., 7965 NW 64th St., Miami, FL 33166 (SAN 169-1082) Tel 305-591-8766.

Astro Analytics Pubns., 16440 Haynes St., Van Nuys, CA 91406 (SAN 200-6189).

Astrologer's Library *See Inner Traditions International, Inc.*

Atheneum Pubs., Subs. of Scribner Bk. Cos., Inc., *(Atheneum; 0-689),* 115 Fifth Ave., New York, NY 10003 (SAN 200-0011) Tel 212-614-1300; Toll free: 800-257-5755; Dist. by: Riverside Distribution Ctr., Front & Brown Sts., Riverside, NJ 08075 (SAN 200-5018). *Imprints:* Aladdin Books (Aladdin); Argo Books (Argo); Children's Books (Childrens Bk); McElderry Book (McElderry Bk).

Atlanta News Agency Inc., 4070 Shirley Dr., SW, Atlanta, GA 30336 (SAN 169-1384).

Atlantic Books, 33 Commerce Dr., Montgomery, PA 18936 (SAN 159-8090).

Atlas News Co., 50 Shrewsbury St., Boylston, MA 01505 (SAN 169-3360).

Audubon Prints & Bks., 499 S. Capitol St., Suite 520, Washington, DC 20003 (SAN 111-820X).

Augsburg Publishing Hse., *(Augsburg; 0-8066),* 426 S. Fifth St., P.O. Box 1209, Minneapolis, MN 55440 (SAN 169-4081) Tel 612-330-3300; Toll free: 800-328-4648; Orders to: 57 E. Main St., Columbus, OH 43215 (SAN 146-3365) Tel 604-221-7411; Orders to: 5210 N. Lamar, P.O. Box 49337, Austin, TX 78765 (SAN 661-9495) Tel 512-459-1112; Orders to: 3224 Beverly Blvd., Box 57974, Los Angeles, CA 90057 (SAN 661-9509) Tel 213-386-3722.

Augusta News Co., 569 Riverside Dr., Augusta, ME 04330 (SAN 169-3026).

Aurobindo Books, 1291 Weber St., Pomona, CA 91768 (SAN 169-0043).

Auromere, Inc., *(Auromere; 0-89744),* 1291 Weber St., Pomona, CA 91768 (SAN 169-0043) Tel 714-629-8255; Toll free: 800-243-0138; Dist. by: Bookpeople, 2929 Fifth St., Berkeley, CA 94710 (SAN 168-9517) Tel 415-549-3030; Dist. by: Devorss & Co., Bk. Pubs. & Distributors, P.O. Box 550, 1040 Princeton Dr., Marina del Rey, CA 90294 (SAN 168-9886) Tel 213-870-7478; Dist. by: New Leaf Distributing Co., 1020 White St. SW, Atlanta, GA 30310 (SAN 169-1449) Tel 404-755-2665; Dist. by: Samuel Weiser, P.O. Box 612, York Beach, ME 03910 (SAN 202-9588) Tel 207-363-4393; Dist. by: Inland Bk. Co., P.O. Box 261, 22 Hemingway Ave., East Haven, CT 06512 (SAN 200-4151) Tel 203-467-4257; Dist. by: Distributors, 702 S. Michigan St., South Bend, IN 46618 (SAN 212-0364) Tel 219-232-8500; Dist. by: Starlite Distributors, P.O. Box 20729, Reno, NV 89515 (SAN 131-1921).

Aurora News Register Publishing Co., *(Aurora News Reg; 0-8300),* 1320 K, Aurora, NE 68818 (SAN 281-2991); Dist. by: Shirley Lueth, 1409 9th St., Aurora, NE 68818 (SAN 282-5910) Tel 402-694-3988.

Austin Agency, The, P.O. Box 9812, 425 E. 63rd St., Savannah, GA 31412 (SAN 285-8126).

Austin News Agency Inc., P.O. Box 2133, Austin, TX 78768 (SAN 169-8036).

Austin Periodical Service, 701 E. Princeton, P.O. Box 31, Springfield, IL 62705 (SAN 169-2216).

Austin Periodical Services, 54 Lawrence Switch Rd., Jackson, TN 38301 (SAN 169-7870).

Austin Periodical Services, Route Four, Fayetteville Hwy., Shelbyville, TN 37160 (SAN 169-8001).

Austin Pr., Div. of Lone Star Pubs. Inc., *(Austin Pr; 0-914872),* P.O. Box 9774, Austin, TX 78766 (SAN 206-7870) Tel 512-453-8611.

Australian Book Center, P.O. Box 634, New Rochelle, NY 10802 (SAN 169-5576).

Avery BookStores Inc., 308 Livingston St., Brooklyn, NY 11217 (SAN 169-510X).

Aviation Bk. Co., *(Aviation; 0-911720; 0-911721; 0-916413),* 1640 Victory Blvd., Glendale, CA 91201 (SAN 212-0259) Tel 818-240-1771; Toll free: 800-423-2708. Toll free: 800-542-6657 (in California). *Imprints:* Bomber Books (Pub. by Bomber). Progressive Pilot Seminars (Progressive Pilot Sem).

Avnet Computer Technologies, Inc., Subs. of Hamilton Avnet, 10000 W. 76th St., Minneapolis, MN 55344 (SAN 678-2310) Tel 612-944-1114; Toll free: 800-328-4028.

Avonlea Bks., P.O. Box 74, Main Sta., White Plains, NY 10602 (SAN 680-4446) Tel 914-946-5923. Worldwide mail order search service for out-of-print books of all categories. Phone requests accepted. Serves individuals, corporations, libraries, and many bookstores.

Awareness & Health, Unlimited, 3110 N. High St., Columbus, OH 43202 (SAN 200-6537).

Axlon, Inc., *(Axlon Inc; 0-934571),* 1287 Lawrence Station Rd., Sunnyvale, CA 94089 (SAN 694-4353) Tel 408-747-1900.

Aztec Copy Inc., 881 E. 3900 S., Salt Lake City, UT 84105 (SAN 283-2933).

B. Alexander Gallery, 20 W. 57th St., New York, NY 10019 (SAN 661-9436).

B & H Books, 330 Paloma Ave., San Rafael, CA 94901 (SAN 282-6070).

Wholesalers & Distributors

B. Dalton, General Office Distribution Ctr., 9340 James Ave. S., Minneapolis, MN 55431 (SAN 147-099X) Tel 612-893-7000; Pillsbury Ctr., 200 S. Sixth St., Minneapolis, MN 55402 (SAN 147-6025).

B.G. Enterprises, Inc., 5 BG 8483 E. Chaparral, Scottsdale, AZ 85251 (SAN 653-9955).

BGS Enterprises, BG Sound Division, 60 E. Ninth St., New York, NY 10003 (SAN 680-7100).

BMC International, Inc., (BCM Intl Inc; 0-86508), 237 Fairfield Ave., Upper Darby, PA 19082 (SAN 211-7762) Tel 215-352-7177.

BMI Educational Computing Services, Div. of IBM Educational Services, (0-922443), Hay Press Rd., Dayton, NJ 08810 (SAN 294-7064) Tel 201-329-6991; Toll free: 800-222-8100.

BNR Pr., (BNR Pr; 0-931960), 132 E. Second St., Port Clinton, OH 43452 (SAN 211-5948) Tel 419-734-2422.

Back-to-Basics Books, P.O. Box 70, Hendersonville, NC 28793 (SAN 169-6440) Tel 704-693-0211; Toll free: 800-438-0238 (Orders).

Backcountry Pubns., Inc., (Backcountry Pubns; 0-942440), P.O. Box 175, Woodstock, VT 05091 (SAN 238-1427) Tel 802-457-1049; Toll free: 800-635-5009; Dist. by: Countryman Pr., P.O. Box 175, Woodstock, VT 05091 (SAN 206-4901) Tel 802-457-1049.

Bacon's, P.O. Box 2288, East Chatham, NY 12060 (SAN 200-5573).

Badger Periodicals Distributors, 2420 W. 4th, Appleton, WI 54911 (SAN 169-9024).

Baggins Books, 115 Unity, Bellingham, WA 98225 (SAN 156-501X).

Baja Trail Pubns., Inc., (Baja Trail; 0-914622), P.O. Box 6088, Huntington Beach, CA 92615 (SAN 206-3301) Tel 714-847-2252.

Baker & Taylor Co., Eastern Div., 50 Kirby Ave., Somerville, NJ 08876 (SAN 169-4901).

Baker & Taylor Co., Midwest Div., 501 Gladiola Ave., Momence, IL 60954 (SAN 169-2100).

Baker & Taylor Co., Southeast Div., Mt. Olive Rd., Commerce, GA 30529 (SAN 169-1503).

Baker & Taylor Co., Western Div., 380 Edison Way, Reno, NV 89564 (SAN 169-4464) Tel 702-786-6700; Toll free: 800-648-3540.

Baker & Taylor Cos., The, (0-8480), 1515 Broadway, New York, NY 10036 (SAN 169-5606) Tel 201-218-0400.

Balfour, Inc., 22 County Rd., Attleboro, MA 02703 (SAN 200-8246).

Balick, Lillian R., (L R Balick; 0-9615834), 15 Clermont Rd., Wilmington, DE 19803 (SAN 200-5875) Tel 302-571-5340.

Ballantine Bks., Inc., Div. of Random Hse., Inc., (Ballantine; 0-345), 201 E. 50th St., New York, NY 10022 (SAN 214-1175) Tel 212-751-2600; Toll free: 800-638-6460; Orders to: 400 Hahn Rd., Westminster, MD 21157 (SAN 214-1183). Imprints: Del Rey Books (Del Rey).

Ballard & Tighe, Inc., (Ballard & Tighe; 0-937270; 1-55501), 480 Atlas St., Brea, CA 92621 (SAN 200-7991) Tel 714-990-4332; Toll free: 800-321-4332.

Ballen Booksellers International, Main Office, 66 Austin Blvd., Commack, NY 11725 (SAN 169-5207) Tel 516-543-5600; West Coast Office, 349 Topeka, 337 N San Pedro Rd., Irvine, CA 92714 (SAN 156-5370) Tel 714-559-1742; West Coast Office, 70 Chalda Court, San Rafael, CA 94903 (SAN 650-0099) Tel 415-492-9033; Southeast Office, P.O. Box 95361 Executive Park, Sta., Atlanta, GA 30347 (SAN 650-0102); Midwest Office, P.O. Box 472 Downtown Sta., Glenellyn, IL 60138 (SAN 156-5990) Tel 312-653-9062; Mid-Atlantic Office, 32 Hampton Court, Woodbury, NY 11797 (SAN 650-0129) Tel 516-496-9810; East Coast Office, 270 Riverside Dr., New York, NY 10025 (SAN 156-8523) Tel 212-316-6382.

Ballin, M. H., Publ., 111-45 76th Ave., Forest Hills, NY 11375 (SAN 285-8312).

Ballinger Publishing Co., Subs. of Harper & Row, Inc., (Ballinger Pub; 0-88410; 0-88730), 54 Church St., Harvard Sq., Cambridge, MA 02138 (SAN 201-4084) Tel 617-492-0670; Toll free: 800-638-3030.

Banbury See **Dell Publishing Co., Inc.**

Banner of Truth, The, (Banner of Truth; 0-85151), P.O. Box 621, Carlisle, PA 17013 (SAN 211-7738) Tel 717-249-5747.

Banyan Books, (Banyan Bks; 0-916224), P.O. Box 431160, Miami, FL 33243 (SAN 208-340X) Tel 305-665-6011.

Barbary Coast Bks., (Barbary Coast Bks; 0-936041), P.O. Box 3645, Oakland, CA 94609 (SAN 697-0060) Tel 415-653-8048; 5362 Miles Ave., Oakland, CA 94618 (SAN 697-0079).

Barclay Bridge Supplies, Inc., (Barclay Bridge; 0-87643), 8 Bush Ave., Port Chester, NY 10573 (SAN 202-3768) Tel 914-937-4200.

Barnes & Noble Books See **Harper & Row Pubs., Inc.**

Barnes & Noble Wholesale Division, 600 Fifth Ave., New York, NY 10003 (SAN 169-5614).

Barnhart's Computer Ctr., Div. of Barhart Stores, Inc., P.O. Box 110, 548 N. Main St., Urbana, OH 43078 (SAN 690-9469) Tel 513-653-7257; Toll free: 800-762-9810.

Barrett & Co., Pubs., (Barrett; 0-9609396), P.O. Box 6700, Jackson, MS 39212 (SAN 240-8732) Tel 601-373-4400; P.O. Box 1182, Houston, TX 77251 (SAN 685-3161) Tel 713-641-6335.

Barrett Bk. Co., (Barrett Bk; 0-932684), 1123 High Ridge Rd., Stamford, CT 06905 (SAN 211-5883).

Bartley Subscription Agency, 1254 Ranchland Dr., Cleveland, OH 44124 (SAN 285-8045).

Basic Bks., Inc., Subs. of Harper & Row Pubs., Inc., (Basic; 0-465), 10 E. 53rd St., New York, NY 10022 (SAN 201-4521) Tel 212-207-7292; Toll free: 800-242-7737.

Basic Crafts Co., 1201 Broadway, New York, NY 10001 (SAN 169-5622).

Basic Educational Products, (Basic Educ Prods; 0-933891), P.O. Box 81, South Westerlo, NY 12163 (SAN 200-7703).

Basin Distributing Co., 1900 Fawcett Court, Farmington, NM 87401 (SAN 169-0558).

Basin News Agency Inc., P.O. Box 3429, Midland, TX 79702 (SAN 169-8362).

Basin News Co., 1051 Husband Rd., Paducah, KY 42001 (SAN 169-2860).

Baver, Dorothy, 611 Oakwood Way, El Cajon, CA 92021 (SAN 200-8238).

Bay News Co., 3155 N.W. Yeon Ave., Portland, OR 97210 (SAN 169-7153).

Bayor, Ronald, Georgia Institute of Technology, Atlanta, GA 30332 (SAN 200-7932).

Bayou Bks., 1005 Monroe St., Gretna, LA 70053 (SAN 159-8120) Tel 504-368-1171.

Bayou News Agency, 10641 N. Dual, Box 15639, Baton Rouge, LA 70815 (SAN 169-2895); 200 Harbor Circle, New Orleans, LA 70124 (SAN 159-7213).

Beach & Co., Pubs., P.O. Box 303, Cherry Valley, NY 13320 (SAN 200-6847).

Beagle Brothers, (Beagle Bros; 0-917085), 3990 Old Town Ave., Suite 102C, San Diego, CA 92110 (SAN 264-8326) Tel 619-296-6400; Toll free: 800-227-3800.

Beal's News Agency, P.O. Box 509, Olney, IL 62450 (SAN 169-2135).

Bear & Co., Inc., (Bear & Co; 0-939680), P.O. Drawer 2860, Santa Fe, NM 87504-2860 (SAN 216-7174) Tel 505-983-5968; Toll free: 800-932-3277; Dist. by: Bookpeople, 2929 Fifth St., Berkeley, CA 94710 (SAN 168-9517) Tel 415-549-3030; Dist. by: Spring Arbor Distributors, 10885 Textile Rd., Belleville, MI 48111 (SAN 158-9016) Tel 313-481-0900; Dist. by: New Leaf Distributing, 1020 White St., SW, Atlanta, GA 30310 (SAN 169-1449) Tel 404-755-3454; Dist. by: Distributors, The, 702 S. Michigan, South Bend, IN 46618 (SAN 212-0364) Tel 404-755-3454; Dist. by: Inland Bk. Co., 22 Hemingway Ave., East Haven, CT 06512 (SAN 200-4151) Tel 203-467-4257; Dist. by: Quality Bks., 400 Anthony Trail, Northbrook, IL 60062 (SAN 169-2127).

Beaver News Co., Inc., 230 W. Washington St., Rensselaer, IN 47978 (SAN 159-8139).

Beck News Agency, Box 1340, Albuquerque, NM 87103 (SAN 169-4960).

Beck's Book Store, 1120 W. Wilson, Chicago, IL 60640 (SAN 159-8139).

Beekman Publishers, Inc., (Beekman Pubs; 0-8464), P.O. Box 888, Woodstock, NY 12498 (SAN 201-4467) Tel 914-679-2300.

Before Columbus Foundation, 1446 Sixth St., Suite D, Berkeley, CA 94710 (SAN 159-2955).

Behavioral Publications, Inc. See **Human Sciences Pr., Inc.**

Beijing Book, 701 E. Linden Ave., Linden, NJ 07036-2495 (SAN 169-5673).

Bell Bks. See **Farrar, Straus & Giroux, Inc.**

Bell Controls, 270 Prospect Dr., San Rafael, CA 94901 (SAN 200-4658).

Bell Magazine, 17 Metz Rd., Seaside, CA 93955 (SAN 169-0353); P.O. Box 1957, Monterey, CA 93940 (SAN 159-7221).

Berg, Norman S. , Publisher, Ltd., (Berg; 0-910220), P.O. Box 15232, Atlanta, GA 30333 (SAN 226-8086).

Berkeley Educational Paperbacks, 2480 Bancroft Way, Berkeley, CA 94704 (SAN 168-9509).

Berkley Publishing Group, Affil. of G.P. Putnam's Sons, (Berkley Pub; 0-425; 0-515), 200 Madison Ave., New York, NY 10016 (SAN 201-3991) Tel 212-686-9820; Toll free: 800-223-0510; Dist. by: ICD, 250 W. 55th St., New York, NY 10019 (SAN 169-5800) Tel 212-262-7444. Imprints: Highland Books (Highland); Medallion Books (Medallion); Windhover (Windhover).

Berkshire News, Inc., Third Ave. & Cherry St., West Reading, PA 19602 (SAN 169-7668).

Berkshire Traveller, Pr., (Berkshire Traveller; 0-912944), Pine St., Stockbridge, MA 01262 (SAN 201-4424) Tel 413-298-3636.

Berlitz See **Macmillan Publishing Co., Inc.**

Bernan Assocs., Inc., (Bernan Assocs), 9730-E George Palmer Hwy., Lanham, MD 20706 (SAN 169-3182) Tel 301-459-7666.

Berry, P. D., Box 68, Louisa, KY 41230 (SAN 223-1042).

Bertel Distributing Co., 604 N. Foothill Rd., Beverly Hills, CA 90210 (SAN 159-8155).

Bethlehem News Agency, Box E, 902 Wyandotte St., Bethlehem, PA 18015 (SAN 169-7250).

Better Book Fairs, 6821 SW 81st St., South Miami, FL 33143 (SAN 169-1295).

Beverly Books Inc., International Subscription Agency, 36 E. Price St., Linden, NJ 07036 (SAN 169-474X).

Beyda & Associates Inc., 6943 Valjean Ave., Van Nuys, CA 91406 (SAN 169-0426).

BFP (Bks. for Professionals) See **Harcourt Brace Jovanovich, Inc.**

Bible & Bk. Room, 100 River St., Springfield, VT 05156 (SAN 200-593X).

Bible Gift Shop, 7545 NE Glisan St., Portland, OR 97213 (SAN 206-1961) Tel 503-253-9020.

Biblio Distribution Ctr., Div. of Littlefield, Adams & Co., (Biblio Dist), 81 Adams Dr., Totowa, NJ 07512 (SAN 211-724X) Tel 201-256-8600. Do not confuse with Biblio Pr. in Fresh Meadows, NY.

Bickel Agency, 949 Via Rasita, Santa Barbara, CA 93110 (SAN 285-8479).

Biddy Books, Rte. 2, P.O. Box 2775, 16th Model Rd., Manchester, TN 37353 (SAN 157-8561).

Big Country Bks., Inc., 1431 Harrison Ave., Blaine, WA 98230 (SAN 200-7215) Tel 604-538-1114.

Bilingual Educ. Servs., Inc., (Bilingual Ed Serv; 0-86624), 2514 S. Grand Ave., Los Angeles, CA 90007 (SAN 218-4680) Tel 213-749-6213.

Bilingual Pubns., Co., (Bilingual Company), 1966 Broadway, New York, NY 10023 (SAN 212-3975) Tel 212-873-2067.

Billboard Bks. See **Watson-Guptill Pubns., Inc.**

Billings News Inc., 711 Fourth Ave. N., Billings, MT 59101 (SAN 169-4340); Toll free: 800-332-7294.

Bingley, Clive, Ltd. (England) See **Shoe String Pr., Inc.**

Bio Learning Systems, Inc., (Bio Learning Syst; 0-922533), Route 106, Jericho, NY 11753 (SAN 655-9379) Tel 516-433-2992 (SAN 200-8262).

Biofeedback & Stress Management Services, P.O. Box 95, Schererville, IN 46375 (SAN 200-5271).

Bird & Bull Press, The See **Univ. Pr. of Virginia**

Bison Books See **Univ. of Nebraska Pr.**

Bks. for Young Readers See **Random Hse., Inc.**

Black, Samuel, Co., 104 Memorial Ave., West Springfield, MA 01089 (SAN 169-3611).

Black Box Corp., Subs. of Micom Systems, *(Black Box),* Mayview Rd. at Park Dr., P.O. Box 12800, Pittsburgh, PA 15241 (SAN 277-1985) Tel 412-746-5530.

Black Cat Bks. *See* Grove Pr.

Black Magazine Agency, Box 342, Logansport, IN 46947 (SAN 285-838X).

Blackburn News Agency, P.O. Box 1039, Kingsport, TN 37662 (SAN 169-7900).

Blackwell North America, *(NA Blackwell; 0-946344),* 1001 Fries Mill Rd., Blackwood, NJ 08012 (SAN 169-4596) Tel 609-629-0700; Toll free: 800-257-7341; 6024 SW. Jean Rd., Bldg. G, Lake Oswego, OR 97034 (SAN 169-7048) Tel 503-684-1140; Toll free: 800-547-6426.

Blackwells, 2210 S. Main St., Tulsa, OK 74114 (SAN 282-681X) Tel 918-583-8716.

Blaine, O. B., Brokerage Agency, 3032 Terry Rd., Jackson, MS 39212 (SAN 285-8649).

Block & Company, Inc., 1111 S. Wheeling Rd., Wheeling, IL 60090 (SAN 277-3376).

Bloomington Distribution Group, P.O. Box 841, Bloomington, IN 47402 (SAN 282-6828).

Bloomington News Agency, 304 S. Mason St., Bloomington, IL 61701 (SAN 169-1732).

Blue Bird Publishing, *(Blue Bird Pub; 0-933025),* 1428 W. Broad, No. 202, Columbus, OH 43222 (SAN 200-5603) Tel 614-275-6275; Toll free: 800-255-2665.

Blue Cat, *(Blue Cat; 0-936200; 0-932679),* 349 Paseo Tesoro, Walnut, CA 91789 (SAN 214-0322) Tel 714-594-3317; Dist. by: Ingram Industries, 347 Reedwood Dr., Nashville, TN 37217 (SAN 169-7978); Dist. by: Baker & Taylor Co., Eastern Div., 50 Kirby Ave., Somerville, NJ 08876 (SAN 169-4901); Dist. by: Baker & Taylor Co., Midwest Div., 501 Gladiola Ave., Momence, IL 60954 (SAN 169-2100); Dist. by: Baker & Taylor Co., Southeast Div., Mt. Olive Rd., Commerce, GA 30529 (SAN 169-1503).

Blue Mountain Pr., Inc., *(Blue Mtn Pr CO; 0-88396),* P.O. Box 4549, Boulder, CO 80306 (SAN 169-0477) Tel 303-449-0536; Toll free: 800-525-0642.

Blue Ribbon Books *See* Scholastic, Inc.

Blue Ridge News Inc., 101 E. Patrick St., Frederick, MD 21701 (SAN 169-3158).

Blue Wind Press, *(Blue Wind; 0-912652),* P.O. Box 7175, Berkeley, CA 94707 (SAN 206-7099) Tel 415-525-2098.

Bluefield News Agency Inc., P.O. Box 947, Bluefield, WV 24701 (SAN 169-8915).

Bluestem Productions, *(Bluestem Prod; 0-9609064),* Box 334, 2327 Lafayette Rd., Wayzata, MN 55391 (SAN 240-9742); Dist. by: Bluestem & the Bookmen, Inc., 525 N. Third St., Minneapolis, MN 55401 (SAN 169-409X) Tel 612-471-7795; Dist. by: Badger Periodicals Distributors, Inc., 2420 W. Fourth St., Appleton, WI 54914 (SAN 169-9024) Tel 414-731-9521; Dist. by: Voelz Educational Services, 1528 Vista Ave., Janesville, WI 53545 (SAN 200-4291) Tel 608-752-0211; Dist. by: The Distributors, 702 South Michigan, South Bend, IN 46618 (SAN 169-2488) Tel 219-232-8500.

Bluff City News Co., Inc., P.O. Box 22246, Memphis, TN 38122 (SAN 169-7943).

Bobbie Holladay, 413 E. Dobbins Rd., Phoenix, AZ 85040 (SAN 200-5654).

Bobbs-Merrill Co., Subs. of Macmillan Publishing Co., Inc., *(Bobbs; 0-672),* 866 Third Ave., New York, NY 10022 (SAN 201-3959) Tel 212-702-2000. *Imprints:* Charter Books (Chart); Liberal Arts Press (Lib).

Bomber Bks. *See* Aviation Bk. Co.

Bon-Jay Sales, 6325 Erdman Ave., Baltimore, MD 21205 (SAN 158-9814); Toll free: 800-622-5656 (Orders).

Bonanza Industries, 110 E. 9th St., Los Angeles, CA 90015 (SAN 168-9738).

Bonneville News Co., 965 Beardsley Place, Salt Lake City, UT 84119 (SAN 169-8516).

Book Arts *See* Menasha Ridge Pr., Inc.

Book Caboose, 94 Compark Rd., Centerville, OH 45459 (SAN 124-1095).

Book Co., The, 2140 S. Klamath, Denver, CO 80223 (SAN 200-2809).

Bk. Distribution Ctr., *(Book Dist Ctr; 0-941722),* P.O. Box 31669, Houston, TX 77235 (SAN 226-2770) Tel 713-721-1980.

Book Dynamics Inc., *(0-9612440),* 836 Broadway, New York, NY 10003 (SAN 169-5649) Tel 212-254-7798.

Book Fare, 12-J Wendy Court, P.O. Box 18006, Greensboro, NC 27419 (SAN 158-5096).

Book Home, The, 228 E. Monument St., Colorado Springs, CO 80903 (SAN 285-8169).

Book Inventory Systems, 719 Ellsworth Rd., Bldg. 6, Ann Arbor, MI 48104 (SAN 169-3662).

Book Mark, P.O. Box 18006, 12-J Wendy Court, Greensboro, NC 27409 (SAN 158-5096).

Book Mart, The, 1153 E. Hyde Park, Inglewood, CA 90302 (SAN 168-969X).

Book Sales, Inc., 110 Enterprise Ave., Secaucus, NJ 07094 (SAN 169-488X) Tel 201-864-6341; Toll free: 800-526-7257.

Book Service of Puerto Rico, 102 De Diego, Santurce, PR 00907 (SAN 169-9326).

Book Service Unlimited, 15030 Hwy. 99 S., Lynnwood, WA 98037 (SAN 169-877X).

Book Services International, 425 Asylum St., Bridgeport, CT 06610-9990 (SAN 157-9541) Tel 203-334-2165; Toll free: 800-243-2337. All available titles from any publisher, government agency or nonprofit organization from any country; out-of-print book search; paperbacks converted to hardbound; rush, continuation & standing orders; online order capability via UTLAS.

Book Value International *See* Quality Books, Inc.

Book World Promotions, 87-93 Christie St., Newark, NJ 07105 (SAN 158-0442) Tel 201-589-7877; 200 Fifth Ave., New York, NY 10010 (SAN 696-5539) Tel 212-243-7360. Specializes in academic & scholarly textbooks, & university press titles. Drop ships.

Bookazine Co., Inc., 303 W. Tenth St., New York, NY 10014 (SAN 169-5665) Tel 212-675-8877.

Bookbinders Store, The, Box 1777, Topeka, KS 66608 (SAN 159-8201).

Bookcraft, 1848 W. 2300 S., Salt Lake City, UT 84119 (SAN 169-8532).

Bookfare, 5609-2A Fishers Ln., Rockville, MD 20852 (SAN 200-5581).

Bookland Inc., 56 Suffolk St., Holyoke, MA 01040 (SAN 211-1101) Tel 413-533-8475.

Booklegger, The, *(Bklegger CA; 0-936421),* 12693 Oak Dr., Grass Valley, CA 95945 (SAN 120-6125) Tel 916-272-1556; P.O. Box 1855, Grass Valley, CA 95945 (SAN 697-9548).

Bookline, 2232 S. 11th St., Niles, MI 49120 (SAN 169-877X).

Booklink Distributors, Box 1275, 3430-B Sacramento Dr., San Luis Obispo, CA 93401 (SAN 159-0782) Tel 805-543-5404.

Bookman Publishing, Subs. of Bookman Dan!, Inc., *(Bookman Pub; 0-934780),* 1601 St. Paul St., Baltimore, MD 21202 (SAN 238-6453) Tel 301-625-0067; P.O. Box 13492, Baltimore, MD 21203 (SAN 658-0203); Orders to: Motorbooks International, Pubs. & Wholesalers, Inc., P.O. Box 2, Osceola, WI 54020 (SAN 169-9164) Tel 715-294-3345. Do not confuse with Bookman Publishing Co., Waianae, HI.

Bookmark, The, 2206 W. 39th Ave., Kansas City, KS 66103 (SAN 131-4017) Tel 913-384-1288; P.O. Box 16059, Shawnee Mission, KS 66203 (SAN 662-4405).

Bookmen, Inc., 525 N. Third St., Minneapolis, MN 55401 (SAN 169-409X) Tel 612-341-3333; Toll free: 800-3288411.

Bookpeople, *(Bookpeople),* 2929 Fifth St., Berkeley, CA 94710 (SAN 168-9517) Tel 415-549-3030; Toll free: 800-227-1516.

Books A Go Go, Box 670, Laramie, WY 82070 (SAN 169-9253).

Books in Print, 9 W. Main St., Middletown, NY 10940 (SAN 289-9558) Tel 914-343-1616. Retail book sales, university presses.

Booksellers of Bethlehem, P.O.Box 3095, Bethlehem, PA 18017 (SAN 169-7269).

Bookslinger, *(Bookslinger),* 213 E. Fourth St., Saint Paul, MN 55101 (SAN 169-4154) Tel 612-221-0429.

Booksmith, Inc., 432 Park Ave. S., New York, NY 10016 (SAN 169-5681) Tel 718-782-0405. Remainders & promotional assortments to trade & institutional markets. Specializes in art, juveniles, quality paperbacks, textbooks, psychology & general nonfiction titles.

Bookworm Bookfairs, 968 Farmington Ave. W., West Hartford, CT 06107 (SAN 156-5621); P.O. Box 3934, San Rafael, CA 94901 (SAN 169-0310).

Bootlegger Pr. *See* American Library Assn.

Borchardt, G., Inc., 136 E. 57th St., New York, NY 10022 (SAN 285-8614).

Borden Publishing Co., *(Borden; 0-87505),* 1855 W. Main St., Alhambra, CA 91801 (SAN 201-419X) Tel 818-283-5031.

Borgo Pr., *(Borgo Pr; 0-89370; 0-8095),* P.O. Box 2845, San Bernardino, CA 92406-2845 (SAN 208-9459) Tel 714-884-5813.

Boston Computer Society, *(0-928524),* 1 Center Plaza, Boston, MA 02108 (SAN 650-809X) Tel 617-367-8080.

Boston Univ. Bookstore, 660 Beacon St., Boston, MA 02215 (SAN 295-1835).

Boswell, S.R., Co., 871 S. Westchester Place, Los Angeles, CA 90005 (SAN 159-821X).

Bound to Stay Bound Book, W. Morton Rd., Jacksonville, IL 62650 (SAN 169-1996).

Bradshaw, Bob, P.O. Box 195, Sudona, AZ 86336 (SAN 282-6836) Tel 602-282-7385.

Bradt Enterprises Pubns., *(Bradt Ent; 0-9339822; 0-9505797),* 93 Harvey St., Apt. 8, Cambridge, MA 02140 (SAN 169-328X) Tel 617-492-8776.

Branden Publishing Co., *(Branden Pub Co; 0-8283),* Box 843, Brookline Village, Boston, MA 02147 (SAN 201-4106) Tel 617-734-2045.

Brass Pr., *(Brass Pr; 0-914282),* 136 Eighth Ave., N., Nashville, TN 37203-3798 (SAN 201-8608) Tel 615-254-8969.

Brauninger News Co., P.O. Box 438, Trenton, NJ 08603 (SAN 169-4936).

Brazos Peridocal Distributors, Box 4131, Bryan, TX 77805 (SAN 169-8060).

Breachwood Publications *See* Riverrun Pr.

Breton Pubs., Div. of Wadsworth Publishing Co., Inc., *(Breton Pubs; 0-534),* Statler Office Bldg., 20 Park Plaza, Boston, MA 02116 (SAN 213-4691) Tel 617-482-2344; Toll free: 800-343-2204; Toll free: 800-354-9706 (Orders); Dist. by: Wadsworth Publishing Co., Inc., 10 Davis Dr., Belmont, CA 94002 (SAN 200-2213) Tel 415-595-2350; Dist. by: Delmar Publishers, Inc., 2 Computer Dr., W., Albany, NY 11212 (SAN 206-7544).

Brewer & Brewer Pubs., 1129 Garden Gate Cir., Garland, TX 75043 (SAN 200-5913).

Brewmaster, 1330 Davis St., San Leandro, CA 94577 (SAN 200-7916) Tel 415-278-5486.

Bric-a-Brac Bookworks, *(Bric-A-Brac),* Box 887, Forked River, NJ 08731 (SAN 282-6364) Tel 609-693-4053.

Bridge Pubns. Inc., *(Bridge Pubns Inc; 0-88404),* 1414 N. Catalina St., Los Angeles, CA 90027 (SAN 208-3884) Tel 213-382-0382; Toll free: 800-722-1733; Toll free: 800-843-7389 (in California). *Imprints:* ASHO Pubns. (ASHO).

Bright Horizons, 138 Springside Rd., Ashville, NC 28803 (SAN 200-7193) Tel 704-684-8840.

British Book Center, *(British Bk Ctr; 0-8277),* Fairview Park, Elmsford, NY 10523 (SAN 201-9361) Tel 914-592-7700.

British Market, Inc., 2366 Rice Blvd., Houston, TX 77005 (SAN 200-8289).

Broadman Pr., Div. of Southern Baptist Convention, Sunday School Board, *(Broadman; 0-8054),* 127 Ninth Ave. N., Nashville, TN 37234 (SAN 201-937X) Tel 615-251-2544; Toll free: 800-251-3225.

Brodart Co., *(Brodart; 0-87272),* 500 Arch St., Williamsport, PA 17705 (SAN 203-6711) Tel 717-326-2461; Toll free: 800-233-8467.

Bronx County News Corp., 47-25 34th, Long Island City, NY 11101 (SAN 159-8244).

Brooklyn News Co., 1 Ave. M, Brooklyn, NY 11230 (SAN 169-5118).

Brotherhood of Life, Inc., *(Bro Life Inc; 0-914732),* 110 Dartmouth, SE, Albuquerque, NM 87106 (SAN 202-4233) Tel 505-255-8980.

Brown & Connolly, 2 Keith Way, Hingham, MA 02043 (SAN 169-3298); Toll free: 800-225-8233; Toll free: 800-232-1902 (MA only).

Browser, The, 133 Louiselle St., Mobile, AL 36690 (SAN 120-8020).

Brunner News Agency, 217 Flanders Ave., P.O. Box 598, Lima, OH 45801 (SAN 169-6777).

Bryans *See* Dell Publishing Co., Inc.

Buccaneer Bks., *(Buccaneer Bks; 0-89966),* P.O. Box 168, Cutchogue, NY 11935 (SAN 209-1542).

Buck Hill Assocs., *(Buck Hill; 0-917420),* 129 Garnet Lake Rd., Johnsburg, NY 12843 (SAN 202-4403) Tel 518-251-2743.

Buck Musical Instruments Products, 40 Sand Rd., New Britain, PA 18901 (SAN 293-4361).

Buckeye News Co., Box 1012, Toledo, OH 43697 (SAN 169-6874).

Buckley Pubns., Inc., *(Buckley Pubns; 0-915388),* 4848 N. Clark St., Chicago, IL 60640-4711 (SAN 208-1954) Tel 312-271-0202.

Bud Plant, Inc., 12555 Loma Rica Dr., No. 10, Grass Valley, CA 95945 (SAN 268-5086) Tel 916-273-9588; Toll free: 800-824-8532; 13393 Grass Valley Dr., Suite 7, P.O. Box 1886, Grass Valley, CA 95945 (SAN 168-9673).

Bud Plant Number Two, 22378 Thunderbird Ave., Hayward, CA 94545 (SAN 157-1044).

Budget Marketing Service, P.O. Box 1805, Des Moines, IA 50306 (SAN 285-8754).

Budget Reading Service, Div. of Periodicals Pub., 1 N. Superior, Sandusky, OH 44870 (SAN 285-8770).

Burgess International Group, Inc., *(Burgess MN Intl; 0-8087),* 7110 Ohms Ln., Edina, MN 55435 (SAN 212-6001) Tel 612-831-1344. Imprints: Continuing Education Pubn., Co. (CEPCO); Feffer & Simons (Feffer & Simons).

Burlington News Agency, 257 Pine St., Burlington, VT 05402 (SAN 169-8583).

Burns News Agency, P.O. Box 505, Glens Falls, NY 12801 (SAN 169-5320).

Business & Professional Div. See Prentice-Hall, Inc.

Business Computer Systems, 1550 Spring Rd., Oak Brook, IL 60521 (SAN 672-9487) Tel 312-530-7700.

Business Media Resources, *(Busn Media Res; 0-938545),* 150 Shoreline Hwy., Bldg. B, Suite 27, Mill Valley, CA 94941 (SAN 661-2806) Tel 415-331-6021.

Business/Technology Information Service, *(Busn Tech Info Serv; 0-930978; 0-89934),* P.O. Box 574, Orinda, CA 94563 (SAN 282-5902) Tel 415-254-2913; Orders to: Manufacturing Productivity Ctr., IIT Ctr., 10 W. 35th St., Chicago, IL 60616 (SAN 694-9606) Tel 312-567-4808.

Business Travelers, Inc. See Watts, Franklin, Inc.

Buteo Bks., *(Buteo; 0-931130),* P.O. Box 481, Vermillion, SD 57069 (SAN 212-0054).

Butler Associates, Inc., 82 Winchester, Newton Highlands, MA 02162 (SAN 678-1365) Tel 617-964-5270; Toll free: 800-232-1120.

Butterworths U. S., Legal Pubs., Inc., New England Div., *(Butterworth Legal Pubs; 0-88063; 0-86673; 0-406; 0-409),* 84 Montvale Ave., Stoneham, MA 02180-2471 (SAN 238-1451) Tel 617-438-8464.

By Hand & Foot, Ltd., Div. of Green River Tools, Inc., *(By Hand & Foot; 0-938670),* 5 Cotton Mill-Hill, P.O. Box 611, Brattleboro, VT 05301 (SAN 215-8493).

Byrrd Enterprises, Inc., 1126 Cedardale, Alexandria, VA 22308 (SAN 169-8605).

BYTE Bks. See McGraw-Hill Bk. Co.

C & B Book House, 21 Oak Ridge Rd., Monroe, CT 06468 (SAN 159-8279).

C & H News Co., 402 N. T St., Harlingen, TX 78550 (SAN 169-8249).

C & M Enterprises, P.O. Box 130, Camden, TN 38320 (SAN 157-8758).

C&M Pubns., *(C&M Pubns; 0-938934),* 6110 Hwy. 290 W., Austin, TX 78735 (SAN 216-227X).

C & S News Agency, 114 S. Lucas, Waxahachie, TX 75165 (SAN 169-8478).

C & W Zabel Co., P.O. Box 41, Palisades Park, NJ 07605 (SAN 169-4731).

CBS Computers, Inc., 7233 Whipple NW, North Canton, OH 44720 (SAN 677-9212) Tel 216-499-0753.

CDI Information Systems, Inc., *(CDI Info Sys; 0-917281),* 1309 114th Ave. SE, Suite 202, Bellevue, WA 98004 (SAN 285-7219) Tel 206-455-5117.

C.J. Jung Institute, 10349 W. Pico Blvd., Los Angeles, CA 90064 (SAN 200-464X).

CP Pubns., *(0-914195),* P.O. Box 1072, Port Angeles, WA 98362 (SAN 287-5276) Tel 206-457-7550.

CRS/Communication Ctr., 107 N. Michigan, South Bend, IN 46606 (SAN 200-6421).

C-Spec Corp., *(C-Spec Corp),* 20 Marco Lane, Dayton, OH 45459 (SAN 686-4856) Tel 513-439-2882.

CW Communications, Inc., P.O. Box 880, 375 Cochituate Rd., Framingham, MA 01701 (SAN 285-7359) Tel 617-879-0700; Toll free: 800-343-6474.

Cain & Bultman Distributors, 2145 Dennis St., Jacksonville, FL 32203 (SAN 657-7547) Tel 904-356-4812; Toll free: 800-342-3051.

Cal-West Periodicals, 2400 Filbert St., Oakland, CA 94607 (SAN 168-9983).

Calendars Unlimited, 4930 Everglade Dr., Santa Rosa, CA 95405 (SAN 200-7061) Tel 707-538-2503.

Calico Subscription Co., P.O. Box 11, Milpitas, CA 95035 (SAN 285-9173).

Callahan, Kathleen J., Affil. of St. Maurice Church, *(K J Callahan; 0-9615563),* 53 Burnt Hill Rd., Hebron, CT 06248 (SAN 200-8203) Tel 203-228-0873.

Cambridge Bk. Co., Div. of Simon & Schuster (Gulf & Western), *(Cambridge Bk; 0-8428),* 888 Seventh Ave., New York, NY 10106 (SAN 169-5703) Tel 212-957-5300; Toll free: 800-221-4764.

Cambridge Univ. Pr., *(Cambridge U Pr; 0-521),* 32 E. 57th St., New York, NY 10022 (SAN 200-206X) Tel 212-688-8888; Toll free: 800-431-1580; Orders to: 510 North Ave., New Rochelle, NY 10801 (SAN 281-3769) Tel 914-235-0300.

Camden Hse., Inc., P.O. Box 4836, Hampden Sta., Baltimore, MD 21211 (SAN 200-7665) Tel 301-338-6950.

Campus Subscription, Inc., 382 Channel Dr., Port Washington, NY 11050 (SAN 285-886X).

Candence Subscription Agency, 841 Chestnut St., Philadelphia, PA 19401 (SAN 285-8835).

Canfield Pr. See Harper & Row Pubs., Inc.

Cape News Co., 700 Clearlake Rd., P.O. Box 3466, Cocoa, FL 32922 (SAN 169-0949); 49 Potomska St., Box H-3051, New Bedford, MA 02741 (SAN 169-3506).

Capital City, 2827 Perry St., Madison, WI 53713 (SAN 200-5328).

Capital Distributing Co., Charlton Bldg., Derby, CT 06418 (SAN 169-068X); Toll free: 800-243-6684.

Capital News Co., P.O. Box 3169, Jackson, MS 39207 (SAN 169-4219); 499 Merritt Ave., Nashville, TN 37203 (SAN 169-796X).

Capital News Distribution, 19600 Washington, Boston, MA 02119 (SAN 200-8122).

Capitol News Agency, Box 7771, Richmond, VA 22331 (SAN 169-8699).

Capper, F., Publications, Sixth & Jefferson Sts., Topeka, KS 66607 (SAN 285-8886).

Capra Pr., *(Capra Pr; 0-88496; 0-912264),* P.O. Box 2068, Santa Barbara, CA 93120 (SAN 201-9620) Tel 805-966-4590.

Captain MegaByte, 5195 NE 12 Ave., Fort Lauderdale, FL 33334 (SAN 679-9922) Tel 305-491-2300; Toll free: 800-327-1013.

Caravan Bks., Subs. of Scholar's Facsimiles & Reprints, *(Caravan Bks; 0-88206),* P.O. Box 344, Delmar, NY 12054 (SAN 206-7323) Tel 518-439-5978.

Cards Books N Things, 716 Lincolnway W., La Porte, IN 46350 (SAN 159-8295).

Career Management Concepts, Inc., 2541 Lakewood Ln., Chesapeake, VA 23321 (SAN 200-4348) Tel 804-640-1400.

Carla Books, Box 10276, Caparra Heights Sta., San Gerardo, PR 00922 (SAN 159-8309).

Carlton Pr., *(Carlton; 0-8062),* 11 W. 32nd St., New York, NY 10001 (SAN 201-9655) Tel 212-714-0300.

Carolina News Co., P.O. Drawer Ten, Fayetteville, NC 28302 (SAN 169-6394).

Caroline Hse., Inc., *(Caroline Hse),* 5S 250 Frontenac Rd., Naperville, IL 60540 (SAN 211-2280) Tel 312-983-6400; Toll free: 800-245-2665.

Casa Escobar, 721 W. Roosevelt Rd., Chicago, IL 60607 (SAN 158-9482).

Cascade News Co., 1055 Commerce Ave., Longview, WA 98632 (SAN 169-8761).

Casino Distributors, P.O. Box 849, Pleasantville, NJ 08232 (SAN 200-7290) Tel 609-646-4165.

Casio, Inc., Personal Computer Div., Subs. of Casio Computer Pro. Ltd., Toyko, *(Casio Inc),* 15 Gardner Rd., Fairfield, NJ 07006 (SAN 277-0520) Tel 201-575-7400.

Casper Magazine Agency, Box 2979, Casper, WY 82601 (SAN 159-8325).

Cass, Veronica, Inc., P.O. Box 5519, Hudson, FL 33567 (SAN 200-5808).

Catholic Book & Supply Co., 1234 Milwaukee Ave., South Milwaukee, WI 53172 (SAN 169-9199); Toll free: 800-323-6041.

Catholic Bookrack Service, 194 Akenside Rd., P.O. Box 145, Riverside, IL 60546 (SAN 169-2178).

Catholic Literary Guild, Ltd., 225 Central Ave., White Plains, NY 10606 (SAN 285-8908).

Caucasian Rugs, 5666 Northcumberland St., Pittsburgh, PA 15217 (SAN 276-8615) Tel 412-422-0300.

Causa International, *(Causa Intl; 0-933901),* 401 Fifth Ave., New York, NY 10016 (SAN 692-7793) Tel 212-684-6122.

Causa USA, *(Causa USA; 0-916501),* 4301 Harewood Rd., Washington, DC 20017 (SAN 295-2548) Tel 202-529-7700; Dist. by: Causa International, 401 Fifth Ave., New York, NY 10016 (SAN 295-2556).

Caxton Printers, Ltd., *(Caxton; 0-87004),* P.O. Box 700, Caldwell, ID 83605 (SAN 201-9698) Tel 208-459-7421; Toll free: 800-451-8791 (Idaho only).

Cecchi News Agency Inc., P.O. Box 564, Olean, NY 14760 (SAN 169-6114).

Celestial Arts Pub. Co., Subs. of Ten Speed Press, *(Celestial Arts; 0-912310; 0-89087),* P.O. Box 7327, Berkeley, CA 94707 (SAN 159-8333) Tel 415-524-1801; Toll free: 800-841-2665.

Cellar Bk. Shop, *(Cellar),* 18090 Wyoming, Detroit, MI 48221 (SAN 213-4330) Tel 313-861-1776.

Celo Pr., *(Celo Pr; 0-914064),* 1901 Hannah Branch Rd., Burnsville, NC 28714 (SAN 201-971X) Tel 704-675-4925.

Centennial Distributors, P.O. Box 424, Deadwood, SD 57732 (SAN 287-2625).

Center for Applications of Psychological Type, Inc., *(Ctr Applications Psych; 0-935652),* 2720 NW Sixth St., Gainesville, FL 32609 (SAN 213-9162) Tel 904-375-0160.

Center for Assn. Pubns., Dept. T, P.O. Box 2410, Falls Church, VA 22042 (SAN 650-9290) Tel 703-698-6968. Erroneously listed as a publisher in 1984 (Computer Books, Center for Assn. Pubns.). Former symbol: Comp Bks Assn.

Central Arizona Distributing, 4932 W. Pasadena Ave., Glendale, AZ 85301 (SAN 200-7630).

Central Kentucky Books, Box 500, Mayking, KY 41837 (SAN 158-6688); Toll free: 800-633-9138 (KY Only).

Central Kentucky News Co., 1236 Versailles Rd., Lexington, KY 40508 (SAN 169-2836).

Central News Co., Box 1783, Columbia, SC 29202 (SAN 169-7765); 111 E. Voris St., Akron, OH 44311 (SAN 169-6572).

Central News of Sandusky, 2115 George St., Sandusky, OH 44870 (SAN 169-684X).

Central Wholesale, 143 S. 25th St., Pittsburgh, PA 15203 (SAN 200-6987) Tel 412-488-2800.

Centralia News Co., 119 E. Broadway, Centralia, IL 62801 (SAN 159-8341).

Ceramic Book & Literature Service, 44 Wisner Ave., Middletown, NY 10940 (SAN 169-5517).

Champaign-Urbana News Agency, 501 Kenyon Rd., Champaign, IL 61820 (SAN 169-1759).

Chapel Bks. See Dell Publishing Co., Inc.

Chapter & Cask, P.Q. Box 113, Glenshaw, PA 15116 (SAN 219-0877).

Chariot Books See Cook, David C., Publishing Co.

Charleston News Co., P.O. Drawer 40, Charleston Heights, SC 29402 (SAN 169-7757).

Charter Bks. See Bobbs-Merrill Co.

ChartGuide Ltd., *(ChartGuide Ltd; 0-938206),* 300 N. Wilshire Ave., Suite 5, Anaheim, CA 92801 (SAN 215-7373) Tel 714-533-1423.

Chas Levy Circulating, 1200 N. North Branch St., Chicago, IL 60622 (SAN 159-835X).

Chattanooga Magazine Co., 1220 McCallie Ave., Chattanooga, TN 37404 (SAN 169-7862).

Checkmark See Facts on File, Inc.

Chemical Engineering See McGraw-Hill Bk. Co.

Chemical Publishing Co., Inc., *(Chem Pub; 0-8206)*, 80 Eighth Ave., New York, NY 10011 (SAN 203-6444) Tel 212-255-1950.

Cheng & Tsui Co., *(Cheng & Tsui; 0-917056; 0-88727)*, 25-31 West St., Boston, MA 02111 (SAN 169-3387) Tel 617-426-6074.

Cherry Lane Bks., Div. of Cherry Lane Music Co., Inc., *(Cherry Lane; 0-89524)*, 110 Midland Ave., Port Chester, NY 10573 (SAN 219-0788) Tel 914-937-8601; Toll free: 800-354-4004; P.O. Box 430, Port Chester, NY 10573.

Chicago Original Paperback See Univ. of Chicago Pr.

Chicago Review Pr., Inc., *(Chicago Review; 0-914090; 1-55652)*, 814 N. Franklin St., Chicago, IL 60610 (SAN 213-5744) Tel 312-337-0747. Imprints: Landmarks Commission Village of Oak Park (Landmarks Comm Village Oak Pk).

Chicago Visual Library See Univ. of Chicago Pr.

Chico News Agency, P.O. Box 690, Chico, CA 95927 (SAN 168-9533).

Child Study Clinic, 611 S.W. Campus Dr., Portland, OR 97201 (SAN 218-5121).

Children's Books See Atheneum Pubs.

Childrens Pr., Div. of Regensteiner Publishing Enterprises, Inc., *(Childrens; 0-516)*, 1224 W. Van Buren St., Chicago, IL 60607 (SAN 201-9264) Tel 312-666-4200; Toll free: 800-621-1115. Imprints: Elk Grove Books (Elk Grove Bks); Golden Gate (Golden Gate); Sextant (Sextant).

Children's Small Press Collection, The, 719 N. Fourth Ave., Ann Arbor, MI 48104 (SAN 200-514X).

Chili Coin-Stamp & Supply, 1356 Buffalo Rd., Rochester, NY 14624 (SAN 157-5430); Toll free: 800-325-7495.

China Books & Periodicals, 125 Fifth Ave., New York, NY 10003 (SAN 169-5711); 174 Randolph St., Chicago, IL 60601 (SAN 169-1775); 2929 24th St., San Francisco, CA 94110 (SAN 169-0167).

Chinese American Co., 83 Harrison Ave., Boston, MA 02111 (SAN 169-331X); 79 Kneeland St., Boston, MA 02111 (SAN 159-7248).

Choice Books, 1251 Edon Rd., Box 1252, Harrisonburg, VA 22801 (SAN 156-4897).

Christensen, Joe, Inc., 1540 Adams St., Lincoln, NE 68521 (SAN 200-8009).

Christian Book Distributors, 2042 A Gladwick St., Compton, CA 90220-6293 (SAN 168-955X).

Christian Communications, P.O. Box 150, Nashville, TN 37202 (SAN 200-7207); Toll free: 800-251-8446; Toll free: 800-342-8006 in Tennessee.

Christian Literature Crusade, Inc., *(Chr Lit; 0-87508)*, P.O. Box 1449, Fort Washington, PA 19034-8449 (SAN 169-7358) Tel 215-542-1240.

Chrome Yellow Private Pr./Nords Studio, *(Chrome Yellow; 0-935656)*, 125 Central Ave., Crescent City, FL 32012 (SAN 200-7614) Tel 904-698-2430; Dist. by: Educational Trade Publishing, 124 Central Ave., Crescent City, FL 32012 (SAN 200-7606).

Church of Scientology·Information Service-Pubns., *(Church of Scient Info; 0-915598)*, c/o Bridge Pubns., Inc., 4833 Fountain Ave., Los Angeles, CA 90029 (SAN 268-9774).

Church Richards Co., 10001 Roosevelt Rd., Westchester, IL 60153 (SAN 285-8975).

Cicero Bible Pr., 1901 Airport Rd., Harrison, AR 72601 (SAN 200-7231) Tel 501-741-3400; Toll free: 800-643-9780.

Ciener Enterprises, 2901 H Whittington Ave., Baltimore, MD 21230 (SAN 157-5406); 980 Lake Harvey Rd., Oviedo, FL 32765 (SAN 158-2747).

Circle Book Service, P.O. Box 73265, 22819 Commercial Ln, Tomball, TX 77090 (SAN 158-2526).

Circular Ltd., *(Circular Ltd; 0-916067)*, One Public Square, Cleveland, OH 44113 (SAN 294-7153) Tel 216-241-2600.

Citation Press See Scholastic, Inc.

City News, 630 W. 25th Ave., Sault Sainte Mari, MI 49783 (SAN 127-2055).

City News Agency, Box 2587, Spartanburg, SC 29304 (SAN 169-782X); P.O. Box 2069, Newark, OH 43055 (SAN 169-6947); 220 Cherry Ave. NE, Canton, OH 44702-1198 (SAN 169-6602); 303 E. LasalleSt., S. Bend, IN 46617 (SAN 159-9992); 417 S. McKinnley, Harrisburg, IL 62946 (SAN 169-1961).

City News, Inc., 435 N. Rose St., Kalamazoo, MI 49006 (SAN 169-3867); 103 Wendover Ln., Charlottesville, VA 22901 (SAN 159-7256).

City Wide Book & Premium, Box 211 WMBS Sta., Brooklyn, NY 11211-0211 (SAN 164-6346).

Clarion Classics See Zondervan Publishing Hse.

Clark, Arthur H., Co., *(A H Clark; 0-87062)*, P.O. Box 230, Glendale, CA 91209 (SAN 201-2006) Tel 213-254-1600.

Clark, Stephen, P.O. Box 1276, Waterville, ME 04901 (SAN 200-6472).

Clarks Out of Town News, 318 S. Andrews Ave., Ft. Lauderdale, FL 33301 (SAN 159-8384).

Class Publications, 2074 Park St, Hartford, CT 06106 (SAN 670-4174).

Classroom Reading Service, *(Classroom Read)*, 720-B S. Vail Ave., Montebello, CA 90640 (SAN 680-7267) Tel 213-721-5011; Toll free: 800-422-6657.

Clayton Publishing House, Inc., *(Clayton Pub Hse; 0-915644)*, 3438 Russell Blvd., Suite 203, St. Louis, MO 63104 (SAN 158-6807) Tel 314-772-5757; Dist. by: People Lovers Bks, 27 N. Gore, Webster Groves, MO 63117 (SAN 200-6138).

Clergy Book Service, 12855 W. Silver Spring Dr., Butler, WI 53007 (SAN 169-9032); Toll free: 800-558-0580.

Cliff Notes, Inc., P.O. Box 80728, Lincoln, NE 68501 (SAN 200-4275) Tel 402-477-6971; Toll free: 800-228-4078.

Club Products, 1100 Redmond Rd., Jacksonville, AZ 72076 (SAN 200-7509) Tel 501-982-0555; Toll free: 800-643-8259.

CNS Judaica, 111 Lakeview Ave., Clifton, NJ 07011 (SAN 158-6254).

Cochran News Agency Inc., P.O. Box 1110, Wichita Falls, TX 76307 (SAN 169-8486).

Cogan News Agency, 4332 W. Artesia Ave., Fullerton, CA 92633 (SAN 168-9649); Toll free: 800-556-2665 (Orders Only, Outside CA); Box 765, La Mirada, CA 90637 (SAN 159-7264); Toll free: 800-262-2665 (CA Only(.

Cohn News Agency, 209 E. Third St., Muscatine, IA 52761 (SAN 169-2682).

Cokesbury, 201 Eighth Ave. S., Nashville, TN 37203 (SAN 200-6863); Toll free: 800-672-1789.

Cole, David M./Outreach Books, *(Cole-Outreach)*, P.O. Box 425, Corona, CA 91718 (SAN 214-2589).

Coleman Publishing, Inc., *(Coleman Pub; 0-942494; 0-87418)*, 99 Milbar Blvd., Farmingdale, NY 11735 (SAN 238-1508) Tel 516-293-0383; Toll free: 800-227-3489.

Coleman School Supply Inc., 1830 W. Mason, Green Bay, WI 54303 (SAN 159-8392).

Collection Inc. The, Subs. of Cookbook Publishers, Inc., *(Collection Inc)*, 2101 Kansas City Rd., Olathe, KS 66061 (SAN 200-6359) Tel 913-764-1811; Toll free: 800-223-1781; P.O. Box 1220, Olathe, KS 66061 (SAN 658-277X) Tel 913-764-5900; Toll free: 800-821-5745.

Collection The, P.O. Box 11465, Memphis, TN 30111 (SAN 670-1205); Toll free: 800-223-1781.

Collector Bks., Div. of Schroeder Publishing Co., Inc., *(Collector Bks; 0-89145)*, 5801 Kentucky Dam Rd., Paducah, KY 42001 (SAN 157-5368) Tel 502-898-6211; Toll free: 800-626-5420; P.O. Box 3009, Paducah, KY 42001 (SAN 200-7479).

College Book Co. of California Inc., 12100 Knot Ave., Garden Grove, CA 92641 (SAN 269-0802).

College Course Guides See Doubleday & Co., Inc.

College Div. See Watts, Franklin, Inc.

Collegedale Distributors, 6101 Mountain View Rd., Ooltewah, TN 37363 (SAN 169-7994); Toll free: 800-251-6258; Box 626, Collegedale, 37315.

Collier Bks. See Macmillan Publishing Co., Inc.

Colonial Society of Massachusetts See Univ. Pr. of Virginia

Colophon Bks. See Harper & Row Pubs., Inc.

Colorado Periodical Distributor Inc., P.O. Box 2925, Grand Junction, CO 81502 (SAN 169-0582).

Colorado Springs Fine Arts Ctr., *(CO Springs Fine Arts; 0-916537)*, 30 W. Dale St., Colorado Springs, CO 80903 (SAN 240-9372) Tel 303-634-5581. Imprints: Taylor Museum of the Colorado Springs Fine Arts Ctr. (Taylor Museum).

Columbia County News, 135 Warren St., Hudson, NY 12534 (SAN 169-5339).

Columbia Pictures Pubns., *(Columbia Pictures; 0-913650)*, 15800 NW 48th Ave., Miami, FL 33014 (SAN 203-042X) Tel 305-620-1500; Toll free: 800-327-7643 (outside FL).

Columbia Publishing Co., Inc., *(Columbia Pub; 0-914366)*, Drawer AA, Frenchtown, NJ 08825 (SAN 201-8977) Tel 201-996-2141; Dist. by: Vanguard Pr., Inc., 424 Madison Ave., New York, NY 10017 (SAN 202-9316) Tel 212-753-3906.

Columbia Univ. Pr., *(Columbia U Pr; 0-231)*, 562 W. 113th St., New York, NY 10025 (SAN 212-2472) Tel 212-316-7100; Orders to: 136 S. Broadway, Irvington-on-Hudson, NY 10533 (SAN 212-2480) Tel 914-591-9111. Imprints: King's Crown Paperbacks (King's Crown Paperbacks).

Columbine Distributing Co., 1671 Valtec Lane, P.O. Box 9050, Boulder, CO 80302 (SAN 169-0485); Drawer E, Boulder, CO 80301 (SAN 159-7272).

Com-Pute Services, P.O. Box 3361, Oak Park, IL 60303 (SAN 680-7135).

Comics Unlimited, 6833 Amboy Rd., Staten Island, NY 10309 (SAN 200-7029) Tel 718-948-2223.

Commercial Associates Inc., 1001 Connecticut Ave., Washington, DC 20036 (SAN 224-6341) Tel 202-331-1363.

Commission of the European Communities, *(Comm Europe Comm)*, 2100 M St. NW, Suite 707, Washington, DC 20037 (SAN 680-0297) Tel 202-862-9500.

Common Sense Ltd., *(Com Sense Ltd)*, 8060 W. Catherine, Norwood Park, IL 60656 (SAN 285-0028) Tel 312-457-0811; P.O. Box 353, Des Plaines, IL 60016 (SAN 285-0036).

Communication Creativity, *(Comm Creat; 0-918880)*, P.O. Box 213, Saguache, CO 81149 (SAN 210-3478) Tel 303-589-8223.

Communication Line, *(Comm Line)*, 3938 Smith St., Union City, CA 94587 (SAN 652-8775).

Communications Technology, Inc., *(Comm Tech; 0-918232)*, Main St., Greenville, NH 03048 (SAN 159-8198) Tel 603-878-1441.

Como Sales Co., Inc., 799 Broadway, New York, NY 10003 (SAN 202-8549) Tel 212-677-1720.

Compass Bks. See Viking-Penguin, Inc.

CompCare Pubns., Div. of Comprehensive Care Corp., *(CompCare; 0-89638)*, 2415 Annapolis Ln., Minneapolis, MN 55441 (SAN 211-464X) Tel 612-559-4800; Toll free: 800-328-3330.

Complete Book Service, 22 Caroline Dr., Dix Hills, NY 11746 (SAN 159-8406).

COMPress, Div. of Wadsworth, Inc., *(COMPress; 0-933694; 0-88720)*, P.O. Box 102, Wentworth, NH 03282 (SAN 284-9887); Toll free: 800-221-0419 Tel 603-764-5831.

Compumart, 65 Bent St., Dept. 7502, Cambridge, MA 02139 (SAN 295-771X) Tel 617-577-1720; Toll free: 800-343-5504.

Computer Book Service, 4201 Raymond Dr., Hillside, IL 60162 (SAN 169-197X).

Computer Discount, *(Comp Discount)*, West Milford Mall, West Milford, NJ 07480 (SAN 287-5241) Tel 201-728-8080; Toll free: 800-526-5313.

Computer Generated Data, Subs. of Wagener Enterprises, 5541 Parliament Dr., Suite 208, Virginia Beach, VA 23462 (SAN 284-1630).

Computer Library, 3225 Danny Park, New Orleans, LA 70002 (SAN 679-7393) Tel 504-455-5300.

Computer Masters International Corp., *(Computer Masters; 0-917735)*, 1170 Broadway, Suite 1213, New York, NY 10001 (SAN 295-8120) Tel 212-685-1318.

Wholesalers & Distributors

Computer Mat, P.O. Box 1664-J, Lake Haven City, AZ 86403 (SAN 680-7186) Tel 602-855-3357.

Computer Software/Books R Us, P.O. Box 16501, Irvine, CA 92714 (SAN 157-5376) Tel 714-786-7857.

Computercraft Inc., *(Computercraft),* 4211 S. Lemar, Austin, TX 78704 (SAN 654-0015) Tel 512-443-4183.

Computerized Management Systems, Incorporated, 1314 Bedford Ave., Baltimore, MD 21208 (SAN 686-4872) Tel 301-653-3394.

Computime, Inc., 11684 Lilburn Park Rd., St. Louis, MO 63146 (SAN 285-7286) Tel 314-428-1428.

Conch Magazine Ltd. Pubs., Div. of Conch Communications Co., *(Conch Mag; 0-914970),* 102 Normal Ave., Buffalo, NY 14213 (SAN 206-4855) Tel 716-885-3686.

Concord Bks., *(Concord Bks),* P.O. Box 2707, Seal Beach, CA 90740 (SAN 158-0337) Tel 808-326-2514.

Conde Nast Publishers, Inc., The, 304 E. 45th St., New York, NY 10017 (SAN 285-905X).

Conkey's Bookstore, 226 E. College Ave., Appleton, WI 54911 (SAN 200-6294) Tel 414-739-1223.

Connemara Trading Co., 409 W. Rosemary St., Chapel Hill, NC 27514 (SAN 169-6343).

Consortium Bk. Sales & Distribution, 213 E. Fourth St., St. Paul, MN 55101 (SAN 200-6049) Tel 612-221-9035.

Construction Publishing Co., Inc., Box 88, Darien, CT 06820 (SAN 169-4390).

Consultants Bureau *See* **Plenum Publishing Corp.**

Consulting Psychologists Pr., Inc., *(Consulting Psychol; 0-89106),* 577 College Ave., Palo Alto, CA 94306 (SAN 201-7849) Tel 415-857-1444.

Contemporary Arts Pr., Div. of La Mamelle, Inc., *(Contemporary Arts; 0-931818),* P.O. Box 3123, Rincon Annex, San Francisco, CA 94119 (SAN 213-3016).

Contemporary Bks., Inc., *(Contemp Bks; 0-8092),* 180 N. Michigan Ave., Chicago, IL 60601 (SAN 202-5493) Tel 312-782-9181. Formerly: Henry Regnery Co. *Imprints:* Gateway Editions (Gate); Great Debate Series (GrDeb); Logos Books (Logos)

Continental Bk. Co., 80-00 Cooper Ave., Bldg. No. 20, Glendale, NY 11385 (SAN 169-5436) Tel 718-326-0560.

Continuing Education Div. *See* **Wadsworth Publishing Co.**

Continuing Education Pubn., Co. *See* **Burgess International Group, Inc.**

Controlled-C Software Inc., *(Controlled-C; 0-924763),* 6441 SW Canyon Ct., Portland, OR 97221 (SAN 284-3013) Tel 503-292-6330.

Cook, David C., Publishing Co., *(Cook; 0-89191; 0-912692; 1-55513),* 850 N. Grove Ave., Elgin, IL 60120 (SAN 206-0981) Tel 312-741-2400; Toll free: 800-323-7543. *Imprints:* Chariot Books (Chariot Bks).

Cooper *See* **Shoe String Pr., Inc.**

Cooper Island News Inc., 632 Quincy St., Hancock, MI 49930 (SAN 169-3824).

Coos Bay Distributors, 131 N. Schoneman St., Coos Bay, OR 97420 (SAN 169-7064).

Cop, W. T., Rte. 6, 411 Marcia Dr., Goldsboro, NC 27530 (SAN 285-9084).

Copper Island News, 632 Quincy St., Hancock, MI 49930 (SAN 169-3824).

Copple Hse. Bks., *(Copple Hse; 0-932298),* Roads' End, Lakemont, GA 30552 (SAN 658-0378) Tel 404-782-2134.

Core, Howard, & Co., Rte. 1, "The Cedars", Munford, AL 36268 (SAN 169-3395).

Cornelia & Michael Bessie Books *See* **Harper & Row Pubs., Inc.**

Cornell Univ. Pr., *(Cornell U Pr; 0-8014),* 124 Roberts Pl., P.O. Box 250, Ithaca, NY 14851 (SAN 202-1862) Tel 607-257-7000; Orders to: 714 Cascadilla St., Ithaca, NY 14851 (SAN 281-5680) Tel 607-277-2211.

Cornwall Books *See* **Associated University Presses**

Cortina Learning International, Inc., *(Cortina; 0-8327),* 17 Riverside Ave., Westport, CT 06880 (SAN 204-2711) Tel 203-227-8471; Orders to: 327 Main Ave., Norwalk, CT 06851 (SAN 658-0386).

Country Furniture, Old Gardner Mill, 1050 W. 7800 S., West Jordan, UT 84084 (SAN 204-4100).

Country News Distributor, Putney Rd., P.O. Box 807, Brattleboro, VT 05301 (SAN 169-8575).

Country Scholar Inc, The, Rte. 127, Contoocook, NH 03229 (SAN 169-4545).

Countryman Pr., Inc., *(Countryman; 0-914378; 0-88150),* Box 175, Woodstock, VT 05091 (SAN 206-4901) Tel 802-457-1049; Toll free: 800-635-5009 (orders only). *Imprints:* Foul Play Press (Foul Play).

County News Agency, Inc., 221 N. Queen St., Lancaster, PA 17603 (SAN 169-7412).

Coutts Library Service, 736 Cayuga St., Lewiston, NY 14092 (SAN 169-5401).

Covenant Recordings, *(Covenant Record; 1-55503),* P.O. Box 26817, Salt Lake City, UT 84126 (SAN 169-8540) Tel 801-487-1096; Dist. by: Metacom, 1401 B. West River Rd., Minneapolis, MN 55411 (SAN 265-279X) Tel 612-588-2781; Dist. by: Telebooks Co., One Lincoln Plaza, Suite 39A, New York, NY 10023 (SAN 240-2866) Tel 212-787-5125; Dist. by: Liberty Press, 500 W. 12003, Orem, UT 84057 (SAN 264-1747).

Coward, McCann & Geoghegan *See* **Putnam Publishing Group, The**

Cowley Distributing Agency, 732 Heisinger Rd., Jefferson City, MO 65101 (SAN 169-426X).

Cox, Betty, Assocs., 232 E. University Pkwy., Baltimore, MD 21218 (SAN 695-7412).

Cox, Dorris, 2910 Bruce Lane, Sebring, FL 33870 (SAN 285-9122).

Coyote Love Pr., *(Coyote Love; 0-913341),* 87 State St., No. 2, Portland, ME 04101 (SAN 283-040X) Tel 207-774-8451; Dist. by: Small Press Distribution, 1814 San Pablo Ave., Berkeley, CA 94702 (SAN 204-5826) Tel 415-549-3336.

Creative Associates, Efficient Seeing Pubns., 7510 Soquel Dr., Aptos, CA 95003 (SAN 159-8430).

Creative Communications, *(Creative Comm; 0-939116),* 529 Dayton St., Edmonds, WA 98020 (SAN 239-684X) Tel 206-775-5877.

Creative Expressions, P.O. Box 456, Colchester, VT 05446 (SAN 200-5816).

Creative Learning Pr., Inc., *(Creative Learning; 0-936386),* P.O. Box 320, Mansfield Center, CT 06250 (SAN 214-2368) Tel 203-281-4036.

Credit Lyonnais, 95 Wall St., New York, NY 10005 (SAN 285-9165).

Crescendo *See* **Taplinger Publishing Co., Inc.**

Crescent News Distributor Inc., Box 123, New Hyde Park, NY 11040 (SAN 159-8449).

Crest Challenge Books, *(Crest Challenge; 0-913776),* 42 Dart St., Loma Linda, CA 92354 (SAN 203-6142) Tel 714-796-1536; Orders to: P.O. Box 993, Loma Linda, CA 92354 (SAN 203-6150).

Crosroad/Continuum, 370 Lexington Ave., New York, NY 10017 (SAN 282-602X) Tel 212-532-3650; Toll free: 800-257-5755.

Cross-Life Expressions, 1455 Ammons St., Lakewood, CO 80215 (SAN 169-0590).

Crossing Pr., The, *(Crossing Pr; 0-89594; 0-912278),* Box 640, Trumansburg, NY 14886 (SAN 202-2060) Tel 607-387-6217.

Crowell-Collier Pr. *See* **Macmillan Publishing Co., Inc.**

Crowley, Inc., 330 E. 204 St., Bronx, NY 10467 (SAN 285-9130).

Crown Agents Ser. Ltd., 3100 Massachusetts Ave. N.W., Washington, DC 20008 (SAN 285-919X).

Crown & Covenant Pubns., 7418 Penn Ave., Pittsburgh, PA 15208 (SAN 200-6766) Tel 412-241-0436.

Crown Pubs., Inc., *(Crown; 0-517),* 225 Park Ave., S, New York, NY 10003 (SAN 200-2639) Tel 212-254-1600; Toll free: 800-526-4264. *Imprints:* American Legacy Press (AM Legacy Pr.); Americana (Americana); Arlington House (Arlington Hse); Harmony Books (Harmony); Julian Press (Julian Pr.); Knapp Press (Knapp Pr.); Michelman, Herbert, Books (Michelman Books); Outdoor Life Books (Outdoor Life); Potter, Clarkson N., Books (C N Potter Bks); Prince Paperback (Prince Paper).

CT Academy *See* **Shoe String Pr., Inc.**

CTB, McGraw-Hill *See* **McGraw-Hill Bk. Co.**

Cuban Boy's Spanish Books, 1225 W 18th St., Chicago, IL 60608 (SAN 162-3087).

Cucumber Information Systems, 5611 Kraft Dr., Rockville, MD 20852 (SAN 123-5125) Tel 301-881-2722.

Cuisenaire Co. of America, Inc., *(Cuisenaire; 0-914040; 0-938587),* 12 Church St., New Rochelle, NY 10805 (SAN 201-7806) Tel 914-235-0900.

Cultural Hispana, 1413 Crestridge Dr., Silver Spring, MD 20910 (SAN 159-2823).

Cultural Survival, Inc., *(Cultural Survival; 0-939521),* 11 Divinity Avenue, Cambridge, MA 02138 (SAN 200-5034); Dist. by: Red Sea Press, 556 Bellevue Ave., Trenton, NJ 08618 (SAN 686-6964) Tel 609-695-3402.

Cummins News Co., P.O. Box 1273, Bloomington, IN 47401 (SAN 169-2305); Box 114, Danville, IL 61832 (SAN 169-1910).

Cuson News Agency, 1118 Union St., Monroe, MI 48161 (SAN 169-3913).

Custom Computer Technology, 1 CCT Plaza, P.O. Box 4160, West Sedona, AZ 86340 (SAN 654-0058) Tel 602-282-6299; Toll free: 800-222-8686.

Cypress Book Company, Inc., Subs. of China International Bk. Trading Corp., *(Cypress Co; 0-934643),* Paramus Pl., 205 Robin Rd., Suite 225, Paramus, NJ 07652 (SAN 694-0285) Tel 201-967-7820.

D & H News Co., 79 Albany Post Rd., Montrose, NY 10548 (SAN 169-5533).

D & J Enterprises, 5 McLeod Terr., New City, NY 10956 (SAN 200-6650).

DELTAK, Inc., Subs. of Prentice-Hall, Inc., *(DELTAK Inc; 0-13),* East-West Technological Ctr., 1751 W. Diehl Rd., Naperville, IL 60566 (SAN 294-281X) Tel 312-369-3000; Toll free: 800-323-3682 (Orders only).

DEMCO Period Bound Books, Inc.., P.O. Box 7488, Madison, WI 53707 (SAN 111-1167).

DISC, 2139 Pontus Ave., Los Angeles, CA 90025 (SAN 686-0451) Tel 213-478-0891; Toll free: 800-523-3485.

DMR Distributors South, 5748 Commerce La., Miami, FL 33143 (SAN 159-3781).

DSI Micro, Inc., Div. of Dialogue Systems, Inc., *(0-928415),* 519 Dutchess Tpke., Poughkeepsie, NY 12603 (SAN 669-5957) Tel 914-471-0131.

Dade County Newsdealers Supply Co., Box 155, Miami, FL 33152 (SAN 159-8457).

Daedalus Bk., 2260 25th Pl., NE, Washington, DC 20018 (SAN 158-9202) Tel 202-526-0558. Trade & scholarly remainders.

Daily Bread, Richford, VT 05476 (SAN 200-5506).

Dakota News Inc., 828 N. Main Ave., Sioux Falls, SD 57102 (SAN 169-7854).

Dalcon Computer Center, 1222 16th Ave., South, Nashville, TN 37212 (SAN 654-0074) Tel 615-321-9000.

Dallas SIL Bookstore, 7500 W. Camp Wisdom Rd., Dallas, TX 75236 (SAN 200-5425) Tel 214-298-3331.

Damascus Hse., *(Damascus Hse),* Dist. by: Doubleday, 501 Franklin Ave., Garden City, NY 11530 (SAN 201-3231).

Dame, Nathaniel, & Co., Inc., 133 Walden St., Cambridge, MA 02140 (SAN 169-3395).

Daniel, John, Pub., *(J Daniel; 0-936784),* P.O. Box 21922, Santa Barbara, CA 93121 (SAN 215-1995) Tel 805-962-1780.

Danville News Agency, P.O. Box 2145, Danville, VA 24541 (SAN 169-863X); 421 N. Gilbert, Danville, IL 61832 (SAN 169-1929).

Darr Subscription Agency, Centralia, KS 66415 (SAN 285-9149).

Wholesalers & Distributors

Data Base Co., 9778 Katella Ave., 106, Anaheim, CA 92804 (SAN 679-9930) Tel 714-534-8140.

Datacom Computer Sales & Supplies, 144 D Canterbury Lane, Medina, OH 44256-2563 (SAN 287-5896) Tel 216-225-0600; Toll free: 800-604-5553.

Datamed Research, Inc., *(Datamed Res; 0-923620),* 1433 Rosecomore Rd., Los Angeles, CA 90077 (SAN 287-2625) Tel 213-472-8825.

DataSource, 7450 Washington Ave. S., Minneapolis, MN 55344 (SAN 655-1041); Toll free: 800-328-2260.

Datazine Pubns., P.O. Box 19413, Denver, CO 80219 (SAN 200-5980).

David, Jonathan, Inc., 68-22 Elliot Ave., Middle Village, Flushing, NY 11379 (SAN 169-5274).

David & Charles, Inc., *(David & Charles; 0-7153),* P.O. Box 257, North Pomfret, VT 05053 (SAN 213-8859) Tel 802-457-1911; Toll free: 800-423-4525. *Imprints:* Weedy Rail Books (Weddy Rail Bks).

Davis Publications *See* **Sterling Publishing Co., Inc.**

Dawn Horse Pr., Div. of Advaitayana Buddhist Communion, *(Dawn Horse Pr; 0-913922; 0-918801),* 750 Adrian Way, San Rafael, CA 94903 (SAN 201-3029) Tel 415-492-0922; Toll free: 800-521-4785.

Day School Magazine Service, P.O. Box 262, Blythebourne Sta., Brooklyn, NY 11219 (SAN 285-9157).

Daytona News Inc., 1840 Mason Ave., Daytona Beach, FL 32020 (SAN 169-099X).

De Fremery & Co., 74 Tehama St., San Francisco, CA 94106 (SAN 282-6097).

De Sales Literature, 11210 Montgomery Rd., Cincinnati, OH 45242 (SAN 159-8465).

De Vorss & Co., *(De Vorss; 0-87516),* P.O. Box 550, Marina del Rey, CA 90292 (SAN 168-9886) Tel 213-870-7478.

Dean, Bill, 48 E 50th St., New York, NY 10022 (SAN 169-572X); 151-49 7th Ave., Whitestone, NY 11357 (SAN 169-6327).

Debeor, B., 113 E. Centre St., Nutley, NJ 07110 (SAN 282-1990) Tel 201-667-9300.

Defiance Wholesale News, 500 Fifth St., Defiance, OH 43512 (SAN 159-8481).

Del Rey Bks. *See* **Ballantine Bks., Inc.**

Delcon Corp., *(Delcon; 0-934856),* P.O. Box 323, Harlan St. Rte., Eddyville, OR 97343 (SAN 213-4853).

Dell Publishing Co., Inc., Subs. of Doubleday & Co., Inc., *(Dell; 0-440),* 1 Dag Hammarskjold Plaza, 245 E. 47th St., New York, NY 10017 (SAN 201-0097) Tel 212-605-3000; Toll free: 800-932-0070. *Imprints:* Banbury (Banbury); Bryans (Bryans); Chapel Books (Chapel); Dell Trade Paperbacks (Dell Trade Pbks); Delta Books (Delta); Emerald (Emerald); Laurel Editions (LE); Laurel Leaf Library (LFL); Mayflower Books (MB); Standish (Standish); Yearling Books (YB).

Dell Trade Paperbacks *See* **Dell Publishing Co., Inc.**

Delmar News Agency Inc., 848 Church St.,Box 945, Wilmington, DE 19899 (SAN 169-0892); Toll free: 800-441-7025.

Delmar Pubs., Inc., Div. of International Thomson Educational Pub., Inc., *(Delmar; 0-8273),* 2 Computer Dr. W., Albany, NY 12212 (SAN 206-7544) Tel 518-459-1150; Toll free: 800-833-3350; P.O. Box 15-015, Albany, NY 12212 (SAN 658-0440).

DeLong Subscription Agency, 308 N. Fourth St., Lafayette, IN 47902 (SAN 285-9246).

Delta Bks. *See* **Dell Publishing Co., Inc.**

DemoNet, Inc., *(DemoNet; 0-933337),* 7310 C Adams, Paramount, CA 90723 (SAN 107-9476) Tel 213-408-1966.

Denver News Co., 3601 E. 46th Ave., Denver, CO 80216 (SAN 169-0523).

Des Moines News Agency, 3301 McKinley Ave., Des Moines, IA 50310 (SAN 169-2615).

Deseret Bk. Co., Div. of Deseret Management Corp., *(Deseret Bk; 0-87747; 0-87579),* P.O. Box 30178, Salt Lake City, UT 84130 (SAN 201-3185) Tel 801-534-1515; Toll free: 800-453-3876.

Desert News Co., P.O. Box 2197, Lancaster, CA 93539 (SAN 168-9711).

Destiny Books *See* **Inner Traditions International, Ltd.**

Determined Productions, Inc., *(Determined Prods; 0-915696),* 315 Pacific Ave. at Battery, P.O. Box 2150, San Francisco, CA 94126 (SAN 212-7385) Tel 415-433-0660.

Deus Bks. *See* **Paulist Pr.**

Devin-Adair Pubs., Inc., *(Devin; 0-8159),* 6 N. Water St., Greenwich, CT 06830 (SAN 213-750X) Tel 203-531-7755.

Devoke Co., P.O. Box 58051, Santa Clara, CA 95052-8051 (SAN 277-3384) Tel 408-980-1366.

Devore, Bert, P.O. Box 10276 Caparra, Heights Sta., Rio Piedras, PR 00926 (SAN 169-927X).

Dewolfe & Fiske Co., 300 Turnpike, Canton, MA 02021 (SAN 169-3409).

Dhahran School Library, Box 101 Bookmart, Gardener, NY 12525 (SAN 285-8703).

Dial/Delacorte Sales, Dag Hammarskjold Plaza, 245 E. 47th St., New York, NY 10017 (SAN 282-6178) Tel 212-605-3000; Toll free: 800-626-3355; Toll free: 800-847-4239 (Orders only).

Dial Pr. *See* **Doubleday & Co., Inc.**

Diamond Farm Bk. Pubs., Div. of Diamond Enterprises, *(Diamond Farm Bk; 0-9506932),* P.O. Box 537, Alexandria Bay, NY 13607 (SAN 674-9054) Tel 613-475-1771.

Dianco, P.O. Box 39100, Chicago, IL 60639 (SAN 200-8084).

Dicmar Trading Co., Inc., 4057 Highwood Ct., NW, Washington, DC 20007 (SAN 200-5298).

Digital Marketing Corp., *(Digital Market; 0-917773),* 1136 Saranap Ave., Suite P, P.O. Box 2012, Walnut Creek, CA 94595 (SAN 265-3303) Tel 415-947-1000; Toll free: 800-862-2222 (Orders only).

Dillon Book, Subs. of Harold Dillon, Inc., Drawer J, 3640 Walnut, Boulder, CO 80306 (SAN 169-0493) Tel 303-442-5323; Toll free: 800-525-0842.

Dimension Systems, 605 E. Safari Pkwy., Suite C4, Grand Prairie, TX 75050 (SAN 287-0789) Tel 214-262-8201.

Dinosaur Discounts, 5068-B W. Chester Pike, Edgemont, PA 19028 (SAN 159-5369).

Discipleship Resources, Subs. of Board of Discipleship of the United Methodist Church, *(Discipleship Res; 0-88177),* P.O. Box 840, 1908 Grand Ave., Nashville, TN 37202 (SAN 264-0074) Tel 615-327-2700; Orders to: P.O. Box 189, Nashville, TN 37202 (SAN 661-9932).

Distribuidora Escolar Inc., Box 650871, Miami, FL 33165 (SAN 169-1104).

Distributors, 1441 S. Main St., Gardena, CA 90248 (SAN 200-531X) Tel 213-321-3275; Toll free: 800-421-1893.

Distributors International, Div. of Dennis-Landman Publishers, 1150 18th St., Santa Monica, CA 90403 (SAN 129-8089) Tel 213-453-4643.

Distributors, The, *(distributors; 0-942520),* 702 S. Michigan, South Bend, IN 46618 (SAN 169-2488) Tel 219-232-8500; Toll free: 800-348-5200.

District News Co., Inc., Box 1805, Washington, DC 20013 (SAN 169-314X).

District of Columbia Assn. of Educational Data Systems, *(DC Assn Ed),* 1201 16th St., NW, Washington, DC 20036 (SAN 674-9003) Tel 202-822-7845.

Diversified Marketing Serv. Co., 921 E. 86th St., P.O. Box 40212, Suite 205, Indianapolis, IN 46240 (SAN 285-9289).

Dixie News Co., P.O. Box 21066, Charlotte, NC 28206 (SAN 169-636X).

Doctor of Northbrook Court, The, 1186 Northbrook Ct., Northbrook, IL 60062 (SAN 200-5220) Tel 312-272-7272.

Document Expediting DOCEX Project, Library of Congress, Washington, DC 20540 (SAN 282-6216).

Dodd, Mead & Co., *(Dodd; 0-396; 0-89696),* 79 Madison Ave., New York, NY 10016 (SAN 201-3339) Tel 212-685-6464; Toll free: 800-251-4000; Orders to: P.O. Box 141000, Nashville, TN 37214 (SAN 287-0177).

Dolphin Books *See* **Doubleday & Co., Inc.**

Dominion News Co., Box 954, Newport News, VA 23607 (SAN 169-8664).

Domus Books *See* **Quality Books, Inc.**

Don & Linda's Suitcase of Books, 603 12th St., Oregon City, OR 97045 (SAN 158-8036).

Donnelley, R. H., Co., 1515 Bummer St., Stamford, CT 06905 (SAN 285-9297).

Doubleday & Co., Inc., *(Doubleday; 0-385),* 245 Park Ave., New York, NY 10017 (SAN 201-0089) Tel 212-953-4561; Toll free: 800-645-6156 (Orders); Toll free: 800-457-7605 (Sales Service); Orders to: 501 Franklin Ave., Garden City, NY 11530 (SAN 281-6083) Tel 516-873-4561. *Imprints:* Anchor Books (Anch); Anchor Press (Anchor Pr); College Course Guides (CCG); Dial Press (Dial); Dolphin Books (Dolp); Echo Books (Echo); Galilee (Galilee); Image Books (Image Bks); Lyons, Nick, Books (NLB); Made Simple Books (Made); Quantum Press (Quantum Pr); Virago (Virago); Waymark Books (Waymark); Windfall (Windfall); Zenith Books (Zenith); Zephyr (Zephyr); Zephyr-BFYR (Zephyr-BFYR).

Douglas County Museum, P.O. Box 1559, Roseburg, OR 97470 (SAN 200-819X).

Dove Bks. *See* **Macmillan Publishing Co., Inc.**

Dow Jones-Irwin, Inc., Div. of Richard D. Irwin, Inc., *(Dow Jones-Irwin; 0-87094; 0-256; 1-55623),* 1818 Ridge Rd., Homewood, IL 60430 (SAN 220-0236) Tel 312-798-6000; Toll free: 800-323-4566.

Downtown Bk. Ctr., Inc., *(Downtown Bk; 0-941010),* 245 SE First St., Suites 236-237, Miami, FL 33131 (SAN 169-1112) Tel 305-377-9941.

Dracula Pr., Subs. of Dracula, Unlimited, *(Dracula Pr; 0-9611944),* 29 Washington Sq. W., Penthouse, New York, NY 10011 (SAN 219-4228) Tel 212-533-5018.

Drama Bk. Pubs., *(Drama Bk; 0-910482; 0-89676),* 821 Broadway, New York, NY 10003 (SAN 213-5752) Tel 212-627-2158.

Drawing Board, Computer Supplies Div., The, Div. of Pitney Bowes, Greenwoods Industrial Pk., P.O. Box 2995, Hartford, CT 06104 (SAN 695-2933); Toll free: 800-243-3207.

Drown News Agency, 15172 Golden West Circle, Westminster, CA 92683 (SAN 169-0450).

Drumbeat *See* **Longman, Inc.**

Duke Univ. Pr., *(Duke; 0-8223),* Box 6697 College Sta., Durham, NC 27708 (SAN 201-3436) Tel 919-684-2173.

Dumbarton Oaks, *(Dumbarton Oaks; 0-88402),* 1703 32nd St., NW, Washington, DC 20007 (SAN 293-2547) Tel 202-342-3259; Dist. by: Dumbarton Oaks Publishing Service, P.O. Box 4866, Hampden Sta., Baltimore, MD 21211 (SAN 293-2555) Tel 301-338-6954.

Durst, Sanford J., *(S J Durst; 0-915262; 0-942666),* 29-28 41st Ave., Long Island City, NY 11101 (SAN 211-6987) Tel 718-706-0303.

Dutton, E. P., *(Dutton; 0-525),* 2 Park Ave., New York, NY 10016 (SAN 201-0070) Tel 212-725-1818; Toll free: 800-221-4676. *Imprints:* Elsevier-Phaidon (Elsevier-Phaidon); Gingerbread House (Gingerbread); Hawthorn Books (Hawthorn); Phaidon (Pub. by Phaidon); Windmill Books (Windmill).

Duval-Bibb Publishing Co., *(Duval Bibb Pub; 0-937713),* P.O. Box 23704, Tampa, FL 33623 (SAN 659-3119) Tel 813-870-1970; 200 N. Westshore Blvd., Tampa, FL 33609 (SAN 659-3127).

EAL Enterprises, Inc., 22700 Shore Center Dr., Cleveland, OH 44123 (SAN 169-6645).

E & R Development Co., Vandalia Rd., Jacksonville, IL 62650 (SAN 159-8503).

EBSCO Industries, Inc., *(EBSCO Ind; 0-913956),* P.O. Box 1943, Birmingham, AL 35201 (SAN 201-3584) Tel 205-991-6600; Toll free: 800-633-6088.

EBS Inc. Book Service, 290 Broadway, Lynbrook, NY 11563 (SAN 169-5487).

ECA Assocs., *(ECA Assoc; 0-938818),* P.O. Box 15004, Great Bridge Sta., Chesapeake, VA 23320 (SAN 215-9503) Tel 804-547-5542; P.O. Box 20186, Cathedral Finance Sta., New York, NY 10025 (SAN 215-9511) Tel 212-866-8694.

EDT, Inc., P.O. Box 979, Royal Oak, MI 48068 (SAN 239-4928) Tel 313-399-4926.

E-Heart Pr., Inc., *(E-Heart Pr; 0-935014),* 3700 Mockingbird Ln., Dallas, TX 75205 (SAN 216-3691) Tel 214-528-2655.

EMC Publishing, Div. of EMC Corp., *(EMC; 0-88436; 0-912022; 0-8219),* 300 York Ave., St. Paul, MN 55101 (SAN 201-3800) Tel 612-771-1555; Toll free: 800-328-1452.

Wholesalers & Distributors

EPM Pubns., 3085 W. Hwy. 89, Sedona, AZ 86336 (SAN 200-8025).

Early Single Parenting Project, 1005 Market St., No. 313, San Francisco, CA 94103 (SAN 200-433X).

East Coast Christian Distributor, 35 Readington Rd., P.O. Box 4200, Somerville, NJ 08876 (SAN 169-491X); Toll free: 800-526-3896 (Nationwide); Toll free: 800-942-7707 (NJ).

East Kentucky News, Inc., 229 Broadway, P.O. Box 510, Paintsville, KY 41240 (SAN 169-2879).

East Rock Pr., Inc., (*E Rock Pr; 0-910825*), HCR 68, Box 42, Cushing, ME 04563 (SAN 650-0242) Tel 207-354-2467; Orders to: 251 Dwight St., New Haven, CT 06511 (SAN 688-3907) Tel 203-624-8619.

East Texas Periodicals, 7171 Grand Blvd., Houston, TX 77054 (SAN 169-8265) Tel 713-748-8120; Toll free: 800-231-6648; Tel 800-392-4437 (in TX).

East-West Export Bks., C.O. Univ. Press Hawaii, 2840 Kolowalu St., Honolulu, HI 96822 (SAN 200-738X) Tel 808-948-8255.

Eastern Book Co., P.O. Box 4540, Portland, ME 04112-4540 (SAN 169-3050).

Eastern News Distributors, 250 W. 55th St., New York, NY 10011 (SAN 200-7711).

Eastern Subscription Agency, 5413 Winfield Ave., Philadelphia, PA 19131 (SAN 285-9467).

Easton News Co., 2601 Dearborn St., Easton, PA 18042 (SAN 169-7315).

Eastview Editions, Inc., (*Eastview; 0-89860*), P.O. Box 783, Westfield, NJ 07091 (SAN 169-4952) Tel 201-964-9485.

Eastwind Books & Arts, 1435-A Stockton St., San Francisco, CA 94133 (SAN 157-8650).

Eau Claire News Co., Inc., 2231 Heimstead, Eau Claire, WI 54701 (SAN 169-9059).

Eble Music Co., P.O. Box 2570, Iowa City, IA 52244 (SAN 282-6275).

Echo Books *See* Doubleday & Co., Inc.

Ecology Action of the Midpeninsula, (*0-9600772*), 2225 El Camino Real, Palo Alto, CA 94306 (SAN 221-5721).

Economical Wholesale Co., 6 King Philip Rd., Worcester, MA 01606 (SAN 169-3646).

Eden Hill Publishing *See* Signature Bks., Inc.

Ediciones Hispamerica, (*Edins Hispamerica; 0-935318*), 5 Pueblo Ct., Gaithersburg, MD 20878 (SAN 213-9200) Tel 301-948-3494.

Editorial Excelsior Corp., 15 N. Market St., San Jose, CA 95113 (SAN 157-8677).

Educ-Tech Corp., the, 65 Bailey Rd., Fairfield, CT 06430 (SAN 157-5392).

Educational Activities, Inc., (*Ed Activities; 0-914296; 0-89525*), 1937 Grand Ave., Baldwin, NY 11510 (SAN 207-4400) Tel 516-223-4666; Toll free: 800-645-3739; Orders to: P.O. Box 392, Freeport, NY 11520.

Educational Affiliates, 8 Newton Plaza, Plainview, NY 11803 (SAN 159-8511).

Educational Book Distributors, P.O. Box 551, San Mateo, CA 94401 (SAN 158-2259).

Educational Clearinghouse, Inc., P.O. Box 3951, Tallahassee, FL 32304 (SAN 282-6305).

Educational Data Center, 100 De Lasalle Dr., Romeoville, IL 60443 (SAN 672-8960).

Educational Exchange, 600 35th Ave., San Francisco, CA 94121 (SAN 287-2560) Tel 415-752-3302.

Educational Media Corp., (*Ed Media Corp; 0-932796*), P.O. Box 21311, Minneapolis, MN 55421 (SAN 212-4203) Tel 612-636-5098.

Educational Merchandising & Consulting, 8912 Mineral King Ct., Elk Grove, CA 95624 (SAN 200-6308).

Educational Subscription Agency, 3308 S. Cedar, Suite 1, Lansing, MI 48910 (SAN 285-9300).

Educational Technology Inc., 2224 Hewlett, Merrick, NY 11566 (SAN 282-6313) Tel 516-623-3200.

Educational Testing Service, (*Educ Testing Serv; 0-88685*), Rosedale Rd., Princeton, NJ 08541-6000 (SAN 238-034X) Tel 609-921-9000.

Educational Trade Publishing, 124 Central Ave., Crescent City, FL 32012 (SAN 200-7606).

Educators Software Discounts, P.O. Box 3046, Huntington Station, NY 11746 (SAN 653-4678) Tel 516-673-3535.

Edwards Brothers, Inc., (*Edwards Bros; 0-910546*), 2500 S. State St., P.O. Box 1007, Ann Arbor, MI 48106 (SAN 206-9814) Tel 313-769-1000.

Egret Pubns., (*Egret Pubns; 0-938425*), 594 Broadway, New York, NY 10012 (SAN 661-2393) Tel 212-226-1330.

Egypt News, P.O. Box E, Johnston City, IL 62951 (SAN 169-2046).

Eisenbrauns, (*Eisenbrauns; 0-931464*), P.O. Box 275, Winona Lake, IN 46590-0278 (SAN 200-7835) Tel 219-269-2011.

Elderly Instruments, 1100 N. Washington, Lansing, MI 48906 (SAN 293-4388).

Elder's Book Store, 2115 Elliston Pl., Nashville, TN 37203 (SAN 218-7205) Tel 615-327-1867.

Electronic Arts, (*Elect Arts; 0-914535; 1-55543*), 1820 Gateway Dr., San Mateo, CA 94404 (SAN 285-4880) Tel 415-571-7171; Toll free: 800-245-4525 (outside CA).

Elek-Tek, Inc., 6557 N. Lincoln Ave., Chicago, IL 60645-3986 (SAN 695-5215) Tel 312-677-7660; Toll free: 800-621-1269.

Elf Software Distributors, 1330 12th Ave., P.O. Box 1237, Longview, WA 98632 (SAN 655-024X) Tel 206-577-8989; Toll free: 800-422-2511.

Elisabeth Sifton Books *See* Viking-Penguin, Inc.

Elizabeth City News Agency, 504-508 E. Elizabeth St., Elizabeth City, NC 27909 (SAN 169-6386).

Elk Grove Books *See* Childrens Pr.

Elkhart City News & Bookstore, Inc., 519 S. Main St., Elkhart, IN 46514 (SAN 169-2321).

Elko, James, 3590 Bayside Ln., San Diego, CA 92109 (SAN 200-7185) Tel 619-488-8471.

Ellis News Co., 480 Ninth St., San Francisco, CA 94103 (SAN 169-0183).

Ellsworth Magazine Serv. Inc, 332 S. Michigan, Chicago, IL 60604 (SAN 285-936X).

Elsevier-Dutton, Inc., 2 Park Ave., New York, NY 10016 (SAN 282-6348) Tel 212-725-1818; Toll free: 800-526-0275 (Orders).

Elsevier-Phaidon *See* Dutton, E. P.

Emerald *See* Dell Publishing Co., Inc.

Empire Comics, 1176 Mt. Hope Ave., Rochester, NY 14620 (SAN 169-6181).

Empire News of Jamestown, Foot Ave. & Extension St., Box 2029, Sta. A, Jamestown, NY 14701 (SAN 169-5371).

Empire State Bks., 2989 Lodi Rd., Interlaken, NY 14847-0299 (SAN 697-2748) Tel 607-532-4997; P.O. Box 299, Interlaken, NY 14847-0299 (SAN 697-2756).

Empire State News Co., 125 McKesson Pkwy., Cheektowaga, NY 14225 (SAN 169-5177).

English Language Services, Div. of Washington Educational Research Associates, Inc., (*Eng Language; 0-87789; 0-89285; 0-89318*), 5761 Buckingham Pkwy., Culver City, CA 90230 (SAN 281-6326) Tel 213-642-09941 NW Science Park Dr., Portland, OR 97229 (SAN 281-6334).

Enrichment Reading Corp. of America, Iron Ridge, WI 53035 (SAN 159-8546).

Enslow, Ridley, Pubs *See* Enslow Pubs., Inc.

Enslow Pubs., Inc., (*Enslow Pubs; 0-89490*), Bloy St. & Ramsey Ave., Box 777, Hillside, NJ 07205 (SAN 213-7518) Tel 201-964-4116.

Entomological Reprint Specialists, (*Entomological Repr; 0-911836*), P.O. Box 77224, Dockweiler Sta., Los Angeles, CA 90007 (SAN 201-4602) Tel 213-227-1285.

Enyi, Donatus O., Div. of World Trend, USA, (*D Enyi; 0-937171*), 1514 First St., NW, Washington, DC 20001 (SAN 658-5264) Tel 202-387-2019; Dist. by: World Trend USA, P.O. Box 1886, Washington, DC 20013 (SAN 200-6820) Tel 202-387-2619.

Epply, Harry L, Book Co., 155 N. Gardner St., Scottsburg, IN 47170 (SAN 159-8554).

Equipment Environments, Inc., Security Systems Div., (*Equip Environ*), P.O. Box 3442, Nashua, NH 03061 (SAN 678-6782) Tel 603-883-9980; Toll free: 800-782-9788.

Erlbaum, Lawrence, Assocs., Inc., (*L Erlbaum Assocs; 0-89859; 0-8058*), 365 Broadway, Hillsdale, NJ 07642 (SAN 213-960X) Tel 201-666-4110.

Esquire, Inc., Div. of Follett Corp., (*Esquire; 0-695*), 1010 W. Washington Blvd., Chicago, IL 60607 (SAN 200-2035).

Esquire Subscription Agency, 1255 Portland Place, Boulder, CO 80302 (SAN 287-4741).

European Book, 925 Larkin St., San Francisco, CA 94109 (SAN 169-0191).

European Pubs. Representatives, 11-03 46th Ave., Long Island City, NY 11101 (SAN 169-5452).

Evans Distributing, 3128 W. Clarendon, Phoenix, AZ 85017 (SAN 200-6448).

Eveready Superior Products, Subs. of Stanislaus Imports, Inc., (*0-918182*), P.O. Box 77103, San Francisco, CA 94103 (SAN 210-1998) Tel 415-626-6535; Toll free: 800-848-1986 (CA Only); Toll free: 800-227-4376 (Outside CA); Dist. by: Stanislaus Imports, Inc., 75 Arkansas St., San Francisco, CA 94107 (SAN 210-1998) Tel 415-626-6535.

Evergreen Bks. *See* Grove Pr.

Evergreen-Black Cat Bks. *See* Grove Pr.

Evergreen Publishing Co., (*Evergreen Calif; 0-939083*), 136 S. Atlantic Blvd., Monterey Park, CA 91754 (SAN 662-9113) Tel 818-281-3622; Dist. by: East Wind Bks. & Art, 1435 Stockton St., San Francisco, CA 94133 (SAN 200-7584). Do not confuse with Evergreen Pub., North Andover, MA, or Evergreen Pub., Seattle, WA.

Excalibur Hobbies, 170 Massachusetts Ave, Arlington, MA 02174 (SAN 158-2755) Tel 617-643-0180.

Exchange & Gifts Dept., Univ. of Kansas Libraries, Lawrence, KS 66045 (SAN 282-6380).

Executive Bks., Div. of Life Management Services, Inc., (*Executive Bks; 0-937539*), P.O. Box 1044, Harrisburg, PA 17108 (SAN 156-5419) Tel 717-763-1950; 4280 Carlisle Pike, Camp Hill, PA 17011 (SAN 156-5400).

Expediters of the Printed Word, Ltd., P.O. Box 1305, Long Island City, NY 11101 (SAN 282-6399).

Explorer Bks. *See* Viking-Penguin, Inc.

Expotek, 2017 E. Cactus, Phoenix, AZ 85022 (SAN 654-0163) Tel 602-482-0400; Toll free: 800-528-8960.

Express Publishing Co., 305 Decatur St., New Orleans, LA 70130 (SAN 293-3713) Tel 504-524-6963.

EZ Cookin' Bk. Co., (*EZ Cookin; 0-937545*), 9925 Currant Ave., Fountain Valley, CA 92708 (SAN 240-9364).

F & SF Book Co., P.O. Box 415, Staten Island, NY 10302 (SAN 169-6262); 78 Ravenhurst Ave., Staten Island, NY 10310 (SAN 169-6270).

F & W Pubns., Inc., 9933 Aliance Rd., Cincinnati, OH 45242 (SAN 287-0274) Tel 513-984-0717; Toll free: 800-543-4644.

FEC News Distributing, 2601 Mercer Ave., West Palm Beach, FL 33401 (SAN 200-6677); 4010 Sivan Rd., Ft. Myers, FL 33901 (SAN 156-4420).

Facts on File, Inc., Subs. of Commerce Clearing Hse., (*Facts on File; 0-87196; 0-8160*), 460 Park Ave. S., New York, NY 10016 (SAN 201-4696) Tel 212-683-2244; Toll free: 800-322-8755. *Imprints:* Checkmark (Checkmark).

Fairbanks News Agency, 307 Ladd Ave., Fairbanks, AK 99701 (SAN 168-9282).

Fairchild Bks., Div. of Fairchild Pubns., (*Fairchild; 0-87005*), 7 E. 12th St., New York, NY 10003 (SAN 201-470X) Tel 212-741-4280.

Fairfield Book Service Co., 150 Margherita Lawn, Stratford, CT 06497 (SAN 169-0868).

Fairfield County News Co., Inc., Paperback Div., P.O. Box 1981, Bridgeport, CT 06601 (SAN 169-0663).

Falcon Books *See* Smith, Gibbs M., Inc.

Falk, W. E., P.O. Box 610937, 140 NE 123rd St, North Miami, FL 33161 (SAN 169-118X).

Fall River News Co., Inc., 144 Robeson St., P.O. Box 1070, Fall River, MA 02722 (SAN 169-3425).

Family Bookstore, 36 Briarbrook Dr., Seekonk, MA 02771 (SAN 159-8562).

Family History World, P.O. Box 22045, Salt Lake City, UT 84122 (SAN 282-6402) Tel 801-532-3327 (SAN 159-673X).

Family Life Ministries, Box 297, Hendersonville, TN 37075 (SAN 159-8570).

Family Reading Service, 1209 Toledo Dr., Albany, GA 31705 (SAN 169-1376).

Fanta Co., 21 Central Ave., Albany, NY 12210 (SAN 158-5134).

Far West Book Service, 3515 NE Hassalo, Portland, OR 97232 (SAN 107-6760) Tel 503-234-7664.

Farmer's Digest Inc., Box 363, Brookfield, WI 53005 (SAN 159-8597).

Farrar, Straus & Giroux, Inc., *(FS&G; 0-374),* 19 Union Sq., W., New York, NY 10003 (SAN 206-782X) Tel 212-741-6900; Toll free: 800-242-7737. *Imprints:* Bell Books (Bell); FS&G Paperbacks (FS&G Pap); L. C. Page Co. (Page); Sunburst Books (Sunburst); Vision Books (Vision).

Fascient Book Corp, 400 Riverside Dr., New York, NY 10025 (SAN 130-1101).

Fawcett Pubns., Inc., c/o Joe Costa, Greenwich, CT 06830 (SAN 281-7055).

Faxon Co., The, *(Faxon; 0-87305),* 15 SW Park, Westwood, MA 02090 (SAN 159-8619) Tel 617-329-3350; Toll free: 800-225-6055.

Fayette County News Agency, 343 E. Main St., Uniontown, PA 15401 (SAN 169-765X).

Feffer & Simon, Inc., 100 Park Ave., New York, NY 10017 (SAN 200-6804) Tel 212-686-0888.

Feffer & Simons *See* **Burgess International Group, Inc.**

Feldheim, Philipp, Inc., *(Feldheim; 0-87306),* 200 Airport Executive Pk., Spring Valley, NY 10977 (SAN 164-9671) Tel 914-356-2282.

Fell, Frederick, Pubs., Inc., *(Fell; 0-8119),* 2500 Hollywood Blvd., Suite 302, Hollywood, FL 33020 (SAN 208-2365) Tel 305-925-5242; Toll free: 800-526-7626; Dist. by: Pubs. Distribution Ctr., 25 Branca Rd., East Rutherford, NJ 07073 (SAN 200-5018) Tel 201-939-6064. *Imprints:* Pegasus Rex (Pegasus Rex).

Fennell, Reginald F., 1002 W. Michigan, Jackson, MI 49202 (SAN 159-6071).

Festival Books *See* **Abingdon Pr.**

Fiddlecase Bks., HC 63 Box 104, East Alstead, NH 03602 (SAN 200-7495).

Film Coat, 131-30th NE Unit, No. 6, Auburn, WA 98002 (SAN 200-5212).

Financial Freedom Pubs., *(Finan Freedom; 0-942360),* 9260 E. Colonville Rd., Clare, MI 48617 (SAN 281-7101) Tel 517-386-7729; Dist. by: Financial Freedom Consultants, P.O. Box 268, Clare, MI 48617 (SAN 281-711X) Tel 517-386-7720.

Findlay News Agency, P.O. Box 747, Findlay, OH 45840 (SAN 169-6750).

Fine Associates, 1 Farragut Square S., Washington, DC 20006 (SAN 169-0914).

Finn News Agency, 116 N. Cowen St., P.O. Box 300, Garrett, IN 46738 (SAN 169-2356).

Fireside Paperbacks *See* **Simon & Schuster, Inc.**

First Impressions Printing, Marketing & Design Services, 1601 Ware Bottom Spring Rd., Chester, VA 23831 (SAN 200-4712) Tel 804-748-4467.

First Presbyterian Church, 682 Mulberry St., Macon, GA 31201 (SAN 200-4550).

First United Methodist Church, 300 E. Washington St., Kirksville, MO 63501 (SAN 200-7460) Tel 816-665-7712.

Fischer Magazine Agency, 1166 Fairmount Ave., St. Paul, MN 55105 (SAN 285-9866).

Flavin Associates, Inc., 1740 W. Big Beaver Rd., Troy, MI 48084 (SAN 200-4941).

Fleet Books, P.O. Box 98074, Atlanta, GA 30329 (SAN 695-5657) Tel 404-325-9214.

Fleetbooks, S. A., 100 Park Ave., New York, NY 10017 (SAN 215-0530).

Flora & Fauna Pubns., Div. E. J. Brill Publishing Co., *(Flora & Fauna; 0-916846),* 4300 NW 23rd Ave., Suite 100, Gainesville, FL 32606 (SAN 220-2468) Tel 904-371-9858.

Florida Classics Library, *(Florida Classics; 0-912451),* P.O. Drawer 1657, Pt. Salerno, FL 33492-1657 (SAN 265-2404) Tel 305-546-9380.

Florida Library Service, 33 Harrison Ave., Panama City, FL 32401 (SAN 169-1244).

Florida School Book Depository, P.O. Box 6578, 5633 Doolittle Rd., Jacksonville, FL 32236 (SAN 161-8423).

Flower Films & Video, *(Flower Films Video; 0-933621),* 10341 San Pablo Ave., El Cerrito, CA 94530 (SAN 692-4646) Tel 415-525-0942.

Fogarty News Co., P.O. Box Y, Pittsburgh, KS 66762 (SAN 169-2747).

Follett Corp., *(0-401; 0-695),* 1000 W. Washington Blvd., Chicago, IL 60607 (SAN 169-1783).

Fondo Cultural Latinoamericano, Box 1784, San Diego, CA 92112 (SAN 159-8627).

Fontana Paperbacks *See* **Watts, Franklin, Inc.**

Forest Sales & Distributing, 2616 Spain St., New Orleans, LA 70117 (SAN 157-5511).

Forsyth Travel Library, *(Forsyth Travel; 0-9614539),* Box 2975, Shawnee Mission, KS 66201 (SAN 169-2755) Tel 913-384-3440.

Foul Play Press *See* **Countryman Pr., Inc.**

Franciscan Herald Pr., *(Franciscan Herald; 0-8199),* 1434 W. 51st St., Chicago, IL 60609 (SAN 201-6621) Tel 312-254-4462.

Frangipani Pr., P.O. Box 669, 1928 Arlington Rd., Bloomington, IN 47402 (SAN 169-2313) Tel 812-332-3307; Toll free: 800-367-4002.

Frank Mailing Services, P.O. Box 3038, La Mesa, CA 92041 (SAN 291-6312).

Franklin Book Co., 7804 Montgomery Ave., Elkins Park, PA 19117 (SAN 121-4160).

Franklin County News Agency, 99 Elm St., Greenfield, MA 01301 (SAN 169-345X).

Franklin Readers Service, 2001 O St. N.W., Washington, DC 20036 (SAN 285-9599).

Franklin Square Overseas, P.O. Box 1943, Birmingham, AL 35201 (SAN 285-9637).

Free Beaches Documentation Center, *(Naturists),* P.O. Box 132, Oshkosh, WI 54902 (SAN 223-8861) Tel 414-231-9950; Dist. by: Naturists, P.O. Box 132, Oshkosh, WI 54902 (SAN 223-887X) Tel 414-231-9950.

Free Life Editions *See* **Universe Bks., Inc.**

Freeman, Alver R., 8315 Dupont Ave., Minneapolis, MN 55420 (SAN 223-0690).

Freihofer, A. G., 175 Fifth Ave., New York, NY 10010 (SAN 285-9602).

French, Samuel, Inc., *(French; 0-573),* 45 W. 25th St., New York, NY 10010 (SAN 206-4170) Tel 212-206-8990; 7625 Sunset Blvd., Hollywood, CA 90046 (SAN 200-6855) Tel 213-876-0570.

French & Spanish Book Corporation, 115 5th Ave, New York, NY 10003 (SAN 169-5754).

Friedman, Herbert N., Associates, Box 637, Middletown, NY 10940 (SAN 169-5525).

Friends of the Univ. of Rochester Libraries *See* **Univ. Pr. of Virginia**

Friendship Pr., Subs. of National Council of the Churches of Christ USA, *(Friend Pr; 0-377),* 475 Riverside Dr., Rm. 772, New York, NY 10027 (SAN 201-5773) Tel 212-870-2495; Orders to: Friendship Pr. Distribution, P.O. Box 37844, Cincinnati, OH 45237 (SAN 201-5781) Tel 513-761-2100.

Fris News Co., 194 River Ave., Holland, MI 49423 (SAN 159-8643).

Front Row Experience, *(Front Row; 0-915256),* 540 Discovery Bay Blvd., Byron, CA 94514 (SAN 207-1274) Tel 415-634-5710.

FS&G Paperbacks *See* **Farrar, Straus & Giroux, Inc.**

Fulmont News Co., P.O. Box 389, Amsterdam, NY 12010 (SAN 169-5029); 182 Division St., Amsterdam, NY 12010 (SAN 200-7487).

Fultz News Agency, 114 N. Locust St., Denton, TX 76201 (SAN 169-8168).

GRF Ltd., Box 257, Fulton, CA 95439 (SAN 222-9757).

Galahad Bks., Div. of A & W Pubs. Inc., *(0-88365),* 166 Fifth Ave., New York, NY 10010 (SAN 169-5762) Tel 212-691-4688. *Imprints:* Lemon Tree Press (Lemon Tree Pr).

Gale Research Co., Subs. of International Thomson Information, Inc., *(Gale; 0-8103),* Book Tower, Detroit, MI 48226 (SAN 213-4373) Tel 313-961-2242; Toll free: 800-223-4253.

Galesburg News Agency Inc., 5 E. Simmons St., Galesburg, IL 61401 (SAN 169-1945).

Galilee *See* **Doubleday & Co., Inc.**

Gallen, Richard *See* **Pocket Bks., Inc.**

Gallopade: Carole Marsh Bks., *(Gallopade Carole Marsh Bks; 0-935326; 1-55609),* General Delivery, Bath, NC 27808 (SAN 213-8441) Tel 919-923-4291.

Gallup Distributing Co., 503 N. Third, Gallup, NM 87301 (SAN 169-4987).

Galveston News Agency, P.O. Box 750, Galveston, TX 77550 (SAN 169-8230).

Gam Printers & Grace Christian Bookstore, P.O. Box 25, Sterling, VA 22170 (SAN 158-7218).

Gamco Industries, Inc., Subs. of Siboney, *(Gamco Indus; 0-924157; 1-55506),* P.O. Box 1911, Big Spring, TX 79720-0211 (SAN 656-318X) Tel 915-267-6327; Toll free: 800-351-1404.

Gannon, William, *(Gannon; 0-88307),* 205 E. Palace Ave., Santa Fe, NM 87501 (SAN 201-5889) Tel 505-983-1579.

Gardiner, Howard, Inc., 1743 Dallas Trade Mart, Dallas, TX 75207 (SAN 200-6944) Tel 214-748-3387.

Garland Press, *(0-9606974),* 1611 Hilton AVE., Columbia, GA 31906 (SAN 223-1840).

Garrett Book Company, P.O. Box 1588, Ada, OK 74820 (SAN 652-1169); Toll free: 800-654-9366. 5.

Gasman News Agency, 511 First Ave. N., Escanaba, MI 49829 (SAN 169-3794).

Gateway Editions *See* **Contemporary Bks., Inc.**

Gateway Editions *See* **Regnery Bks.**

Gaunt, William W., & Sons, Inc., *(W W Gaunt; 0-912004),* 3011 Gulf Dr., Holmes Beach, FL 33510-2199 (SAN 202-9413) Tel 813-778-5211.

Gaus, Theo, Ltd., *(Gaus; 0-912444),* P.O. Box 1168, Brooklyn, NY 11202 (SAN 203-4174) Tel 718-625-4651.

Gaylenot Publishing, 740 Monroe Way, Placentia, CA 92670 (SAN 200-5972).

Gaynor News Co., Inc., 225 Fourth Ave., Mount Vernon, NY 10551 (SAN 169-555X).

Gedare Enterprises, Inc., 3450 Meadowbrook Dr., Napa, CA 94558 (SAN 200-5433) Tel 707-255-7042.

Gelber Marketing, Inc., 200 Fifth Ave., New York, NY 10010 (SAN 200-5727).

Gem Guides, 3677 San Gabriel, Pico Rivera, CA 90660 (SAN 200-4577) Tel 213-692-5492.

Gemini Enterprises, P.O. Box 22769, GMF, Agana, GU 96921 (SAN 128-1402).

Genealogical Institute, *(Genealog Inst; 0-940764),* P.O. Box 22045, Salt Lake City, UT 84122 (SAN 662-0175) Tel 801-532-3327; Dist. by: Family History World, P.O. Box 22045, Salt Lake City, UT 84122 (SAN 282-6402).

General Birch Services, 395 Concord Ave., Belmont, MA 02178 (SAN 169-3255).

General Electric Co., Technical Promotion & Training Services, *(GE Tech Prom & Train; 0-932078),* 1 River Rd., Bldg. 22, Rm. 232, Box MK, Schenectady, NY 12345 (SAN 206-9911).

Genesis I Builders, P.O. Box 2278, Salt Lake City, UT 84110 (SAN 200-4267) Tel 801-363-5109.

George Mc. CO. Inc., P.O. Box 15671, Salt Lake City, UT 84115 (SAN 220-2514).

Georgia/Florida News Co., Box 2067, Waycross, GA 31501 (SAN 159-8686).

German & International Bookstore, 1767 N. Vermont Ave., Los Angeles, CA 90027 (SAN 168-9762).

German News, 220 E. 86th St., New York, NY 10028 (SAN 164-985X).

Germans From Russia Heritage Society, P.O. Box 1671, Bismark, ND 58502 (SAN 293-3128) Tel 701-223-6167.

Gernshack Library *See* **TAB Bks., Inc.**

Gerold International, 35-23 Utopia Pkwy., Flushing, NY 11358 (SAN 129-959X).

Gibson, Dot, Pubns., *(D Gibson; 0-941162),* P.O. Box 117, Waycross, GA 31502 (SAN 200-4143); 161 Knight Ave. Cir., Waycross, GA 31501 (SAN 660-9287) Tel 912-285-2848.

Giletto, Sebastian Ben, 1127 Watkins St., Philadelphia, PA 19148 (SAN 240-8635).

Gingerbread Hse. *See* **Dutton, E. P.**

Gingery, David J., *(D J Gingery; 0-9604330),* 2045 Boonville, Springfield, MO 65803 (SAN 214-3771) Tel 417-866-7770.

Giniger, K. S., Bks. *See* **Stackpole Bks., Inc.**

Glad Day Bks., *(0-936686),* 43 Winter St., Boston, MA 02108 (SAN 221-282X) Tel 617-542-0144.

Glenwood Distributors, 124 Vandalia, Collinsville, IL 62234 (SAN 158-1740).

Global Library Marketing Services, 3712 Commercial St., NE, Contoocook, NH 03229 (SAN 159-1231).

Globe Pequot Pr., Subs. of Boston Globe, *(Globe Pequot; 0-87106),* Old Chester Rd., Chester, CT 06412 (SAN 201-9892) Tel 203-526-9572; Toll free: 800-243-0495 Orders only; P.O. Box Q, Chester, CT 06412 (SAN 658-0769) Tel 203-526-9572; Toll free: 800-962-0973 (CT only).

Gloucester Pr. *See* Watts, Franklin, Inc.

Glynn, James A., 2 Monte Vista Dr., Bakersfield, CA 93305 (SAN 200-7355).

Gnomon Pr., *(Gnomon Pr; 0-917788),* P.O. Box 106, Frankfort, KY 40602-0106 (SAN 209-0104) Tel 502-223-1858.

Goldberg, Herman, Subscription Agency, P.O. Box 426, Medford, MA 02155 (SAN 285-9858).

Goldberg, Louis, 139 Main St., Nazareth, PA 18064 (SAN 169-7536).

Golden Gate *See* Childrens Pr.

Golden Gate Magazine Co., Box 3681, San Francisco, CA 94119 (SAN 169-0205).

Golden Hind Publishing Co., 36 W. Del Rio Circle, Tempe, AZ 85282 (SAN 215-8434).

Golden Pr. *See* Western Pub. Co., Inc.

Golden Triangle Periodical Distributor, Box 6526, Beaumont, TX 77705 (SAN 169-8052).

Goldman, S., -Otzar Hasefarim Inc., 33 Canal St., New York, NY 10002 (SAN 169-5770).

Goldsmith, A. F., & Co., 89 Margin St., Salem, MA 01970 (SAN 169-3573).

Good Apple, Inc., *(Good Apple; 0-916456; 0-86653),* P.O. Box 299, Carthage, IL 62321 (SAN 208-6646) Tel 217-357-3981; Toll free: 800-435-7234.

Goodwin, Ruby L., 138 N. Third St., Douglas, WY 82633 (SAN 200-5239) Tel 307-358-2166.

Gopher News Co., 9000 Tenth Ave. N., Minneapolis, MN 55427 (SAN 169-4103).

Gospel Distributors, 1212 Main, Alexandria, LA 71301 (SAN 158-4758).

Gould Athletic Supply, 3156 N 96th St., Milwaukee, WI 53222-3499 (SAN 169-9148).

Goyescas Corp. of Florida, 2155 NW 26th Ave., Miami, FL 33142 (SAN 169-1120).

Granary Bks., 212 N. Second St., Minneapolis, MN 55401 (SAN 200-6227) Tel 612-338-4376.

Great Debate Series *See* Contemporary Bks., Inc.

Great Lakes Readers Service, P.O. Box 1114, Trolley Station, Detroit, MI 48231 (SAN 285-9912).

Great Northern Epson, Div. of Epson America, Inc., 3050 Ranchview Lane, Plymouth, MN 55447 (SAN 285-7898) Tel 612-559-0992.

Great Outdoors Publishing Co., *(Great Outdoors; 0-8200),* 4747 28th St., N., St. Petersburg, FL 33714 (SAN 201-6273) Tel 813-525-6609; Toll free: 800-433-5560 (Florida only).

Great Tradition, The, 750 Adrian Way, Suite 111, San Rafael, CA 94903 (SAN 200-5743) Tel 415-492-9382; Toll free: 800-634-2665.

Greater Spiral, The, *(Greater Spiral),* P.O. Box 12515, Portland, OR 97212 (SAN 200-6383).

Green, Wayne, Ent., Subs. of International Data Group, *(Green Pub Inc; 0-88006),* Rte. 202, N., Peterborough, NH 03458 (SAN 219-7855) Tel 603-525-4201.

Green Gate Books, 1162 Latham, P.O. Box 934, Lima, OH 45802 (SAN 169-6785).

Green River Forge Ltd., P.O. Box 257, Fulton, CA 95439 (SAN 200-8114).

Greenville News Co., Inc., P.O. Box 1313, Greenville, MS 38702 (SAN 169-4197).

Gregg International, *(Gregg Intl; 0-576),* Old Post Rd., Brookfield, VT 05036 (SAN 695-2046) Tel 802-276-3162.

Grenoble Bks., *(Granoble Bks; 0-931013),* 1931 Vernier Rd., Grosse Pointe Woods, MI 48236 (SAN 678-9722) Tel 313-884-5255 (SAN 200-8076).

Grimes, John F., Magazine Agency, 1737 Mclaran AVe., St. Louis, MO 63147 (SAN 285-967X).

Grossett & Dunlap, Inc. *See* Putnam Publishing Group, The

Grove Pr., *(Grove; 0-8021; 0-394),* 920 Broadway, New York, NY 10010 (SAN 201-4890) Tel 212-529-3600; Toll free: 800-638-6460. *Imprints:* Black Cat Books (BC); Evergreen Books (Ever); Evergreen-Black Cat Books (EverBC); Zebra Books (Zebra).

Growth Publishing, *(Growth Pub; 0-931225),* P.O. Box 661, Herndon, VA 22070 (SAN 682-9112) Tel 703-471-1160.

Gruter Institute for Law & Behavioral Research, *(Gruter Inst),* 158 Goya Rd., Portola Valley, CA 94025 (SAN 200-5859) Tel 415-854-2034.

Gryphon Hse., Inc., *(Gryphon Hse; 0-87659),* 3706 Otis St., P.O. Box 275, Mount Rainier, MD 20712 (SAN 169-3190) Tel 301-779-6200; Toll free: 800-638-0928.

Guardian Book Co., 1045 Northville Dr., Toledo, OH 43612 (SAN 169-6882); 8464 Brown St., Ottawa Lake, MI 49267 (SAN 163-7355).

Guidance Assocs., Inc., Communications Park, P.O. Box 3000, Mount Kisco, NY 10549 (SAN 679-7407) Tel 914-666-4100; Toll free: 800-431-1242.

Gulf Coast News Agency, 4002 Loop W. 175 P.O. Box 2057, Victoria, TX 77902 (SAN 169-846X); P.O. Box X, Gulfport, MS 39501 (SAN 169-4200).

Gulf States Book Fair, P.O. Box 7422, 2901 Mill St., Mobile, AL 36607 (SAN 158-7870).

Guscott Magazine Agency, 2903 Hunging Rd., Shaker Heights, OH 44120 (SAN 285-9920).

Gutcheon Patchworks, 611 Broadway, New York, NY 10012 (SAN 200-5352); P.O. Box 57, Prince St. Station, New York, NY 10012 (SAN 200-6146) Tel 212-505-0305.

H & R Educational Subscription Agency Inc., Box 207, Cunning, GA 30130 (SAN 285-970X).

HP Bks., Subs. of Knight-Ridder Newspapers, Inc., *(HP Bks; 0-912656; 0-89586),* P.O. Box 5367, Tucson, AZ 85703 (SAN 201-6087) Tel 602-888-2150; Toll free: 800-528-4923.

Habibur Rahman, 502 N. Elm St., Centralia, IL 62801 (SAN 209-5939).

Hackensack News Co., Inc., 600 Washington Ave., Carlstadt, NJ 07072 (SAN 169-4626).

Hadax Electronics, 79 Hazel St., Glen Cove, NY 11542 (SAN 169-6597) Tel 516-676-3386.

Haddon Craftsmen Distribution Ctr., 1205 O'Neil Hwy., Dunmore, PA 18512 (SAN 200-7746) Tel 717-342-1449.

Haessner Publishing, Inc., *(Haessner Pub; 0-87799),* P. O. Box 89, Newfoundland, NJ 07435 (SAN 201-6028).

Hagerstown News Distributors, 29 N. Prospect St., Hagerstown, MD 21740 (SAN 169-3166).

Hagstrom Map Co., Inc., Subs. of American Map Corp., *(Hagstrom Map; 0-910684),* 46-35 54th Rd., Maspeth, NY 11378 (SAN 203-543X) Tel 718-784-0055.

Halacha Publications, *(Halacha Pubns; 0-931585),* 418 Twelfth St., Lakewood, NJ 08701 (SAN 683-1958) Tel 914-434-3090.

Haldeman, R. W., & Assocs., 445 N. Pennsylvania, Indianapolis, IN 46202 (SAN 200-576X).

Hale, Robert, & Co., 1840 130th Ave., NE, Suite 10, Bellevue, WA 98005 (SAN 200-6995) Tel 206-881-5212.

Halgo, Inc., *(Halgo Inc; 0-9613805),* 2732 Maryland Ave., Baltimore, MD 21218 (SAN 679-4157) Tel 301-467-8186 (SAN 699-5861); Orders to: P.O. Box 4866, Hampden Sta., Baltimore, MD 21211 (SAN 202-7348).

Halley's Comet Watch '86, Inc., 158 W. Boston Post Rd., Box AB, Mamaroneck, NY 10543 (SAN 200-5840).

Halsted Pr., Div. of John Wiley & Sons, Inc., *(Halsted Pr; 0-470),* 605 Third Ave., New York, NY 10158 (SAN 202-2680) Tel 212-850-6465; Toll free: 800-526-5368.

Hamakor Judaica Inc., 6112 N. Lincoln Ave., Chicago, IL 60659 (SAN 169-1791).

Hamilton Advertising Agency, Blue Mountain Lake, NY 12812 (SAN 202-3202) Tel 518-352-7772.

Hamilton News Co., Ltd., Hannay Lane, Glenmont, NY 12077 (SAN 169-5312).

Hamon, Gerard, 7 S. Ridge Rd., Larchmont, NY 10538 (SAN 663-5571) Tel 914-833-0011.

Hampton Distributing, 11 2nd Ave. NW, Hampton, IA 50441 (SAN 129-0525).

Han Books, 3607 Baring St., Philadelphia, PA 19104 (SAN 214-2864) Tel 215-382-1410.

Hand Associates, 1238 Campus Dr., Berkeley, CA 04708 (SAN 281-5524) Tel 415-848-1064.

Hand Pr., *(Hand Pr; 0-9605620),* 12015 Coyne St., Los Angeles, CA 90049 (SAN 218-4788) Tel 213-472-9691; Dist. by: Aperture, Millerton, NY 12546 (SAN 201-1832).

Handler News Agency, Box 2145, Grand Island, NE 68801 (SAN 169-4405).

Handy Books *See* Harcourt Brace Jovanovich, Inc.

Hansen Hse., 860 West Ave., Miami Beach, FL 33139 (SAN 200-7908) Tel 305-532-5461; Toll free: 800-327-8202.

Hanson-Bennett Magazine Agency, 826 S. N.W. Highway, Barrington, IL 60010 (SAN 285-9734).

Harbinger Books *See* Harcourt Brace Jovanovich, Inc.

Harbor Hse. Pubs., Subs. of Seaway Review, Inc., *(Harbor Hse MI; 0-937360),* 221 Water St., Boyne City, MI 49712 (SAN 200-5751) Tel 616-582-2814.

Harbrace Paperback Library *See* Harcourt Brace Jovanovich, Inc.

HarBraceJ Juvenile Bks. *See* Harcourt Brace Jovanovich, Inc.

Harcourt Brace Jovanovich, Inc., *(HarBraceJ; 0-15),* 1250 Sixth Ave., San Diego, CA 92101 (SAN 200-2736) Tel 619-699-6335; Toll free: 800-543-1918; Harcourt Brace Jovanovich Bldg., Orlando, FL 32887 (SAN 200-2299). *Imprints:* B F P (Books for Professionals) (BFP); Handy Books (Handy); Harbinger Books (Hbgr); Harbrace Paperback Library (HPL); Harcourt Brace Jovanovich, Inc., College Dept. (HC); Harvest Books (Harv); HarBraceJ Juvenile Books (HJ); Law & Business, Inc. (Law & Business); Psychological Corporation (Psych Corp); Voyager Books (VoyB).

Harcourt Brace Jovanovich, Inc., College Dept. *See* Harcourt Brace Jovanovich, Inc.

Harmony Bks. *See* Crown Pubs., Inc.

Harmony Book Co., 1795 Third St., Beaver, PA 15009 (SAN 158-0213).

Harmony Books, *(0-517),* One Park Ave., New York, NY 10016 (SAN 213-4357) Tel 212-532-9200; Toll free: 800-526-4264.

Harness, Miller, 235 Murray Hill Pkwy., East Rutherford, NJ 07073 (SAN 169-5789).

Harper & Row Pubs., Inc., *(Har-Row; 0-06),* 10 E. 53rd St., New York, NY 10022 (SAN 200-2086) Tel 212-207-7099; Toll free: 800-242-7737; 1700 Montgomery St., San Francisco, CA 94111 (SAN 215-3734) Tel 415-989-9000; Dist. by: Harper & Row Pubs. Inc., Keystone Industrial Pk., Scranton, PA 18512 (SAN 215-3742). *Imprints:* Barnes & Noble Books (B&N Bks); Canfield Press (Canfield Pr); Colophon Books (CN); Cornelia & Michael Bessie Books (C&M Bessie Bks); Harper Crest (HarCrest); Harper Religious Books (HarpR); Harper Trade Books (HarpT); Harper's College Division (HarpC); Harrow Books Paperback Department (HW); Icon Editions (Icon Edns); International Department (IntlDept); Lippincott, J. B., /Harper & Row Medical Division (Harper Medical); Open University (Open U); Perennial Fiction Library (Perennial Fiction Lib); Perennial Library (PL); Perennial Mystery Library (Perennial Mystery Library); School Department (SchDept); Torchbooks (Torch); Torchbooks Library Binding (Torch Lib).

Harper Crest *See* Harper & Row Pubs., Inc.

Harper Religious Bks. *See* Harper & Row Pubs., Inc.

Harper Trade Bks. *See* Harper & Row Pubs., Inc.

Harper's College Division *See* Harper & Row Pubs., Inc.

Harpswell Pr., *(Harpswell Pr; 0-88448),* 132 Water St., Gardiner, ME 04345 (SAN 208-1199) Tel 207-582-1899.

Harris News Agency, P.O. Box 1224, North Platte, NE 69101 (SAN 169-4421).

Harrisburg News Co., 2244 N. 7th St., P.O. Box 1953, Harrisburg, PA 17105 (SAN 169-7374).

Harrow Bks. Paperback Dept. *See* Harper & Row Pubs., Inc.

Harrowood Books, *(Harrowood Bks; 0-915180),*
3943 N. Providence Rd., Newtown Square,
PA 19073 (SAN 207-1622)
Tel 215-353-5585.
Harsand Distributing, P.O. Box 515, Holmen,
WI 54636 (SAN 200-7223)
Tel 608-526-3848.
Harter, Edwin C. Jr., , 47 Hardy Rd., Levittown,
PA 19056 (SAN 282-633X).
Harvard Univ. Pr., *(Harvard U Pr; 0-674),* 79
Garden St., Cambridge, MA 02138
(SAN 200-2043) Tel 617-495-2600.
Harvest Books *See* Harcourt Brace Jovanovich,
Inc.
Harvest Distributors, Box 20248, Denver, CO
80220 (SAN 159-8694).
Harwal Publishing Company *See* Wiley, John, &
Sons, Inc.
Haventa Ltd., S. Harpswell, ME 04079
(SAN 285-9823).
Hawaiian Magazine Distributor, 746 Auahi St.,
Honolulu, HI 96813 (SAN 169-1619).
Hawkeye Book & Magazine Co., Box 231,
Redfield, SD 57469 (SAN 159-8708).
Haworth Pr., Inc., The, *(Haworth Pr; 0-917724;
0-86656),* 28 E. 22nd St., New York, NY
10010-6194 (SAN 211-0156)
Tel 212-228-2800.
Hawthorn Bks. *See* Dutton, E. P.
Haxby News Co., 427 College St., Box 3090,
Bowling Green, KY 42101
(SAN 169-2801).
Haynes, Ronald N., Pubs., Inc., *(0-88021),* P.O.
Box 2748, Palm Springs, CA 92263
(SAN 219-6603) Tel 714-320-8822.
Hazel Rice, 1206 Dartmouth Rd., Madison, WI
53705 (SAN 200-6928)
Tel 608-233-6543.
Healthcare Pr., *(Healthcare Pr; 0-9613775),*
P.O. Box 4488, Rollingbay, WA 98061
(SAN 678-9749)
Tel 206-842-5243.
Hearst Corp., International Circulation Div.,
250 W. 55th St., 12th Flr., New York, NY
10019 (SAN 169-5800); Toll free:
800-223-0288.
Heath, D. C., Co., *(Heath; 0-669; 0-278;
0-88408),* 125 Spring St., Lexington, MA
02173 (SAN 213-7526) Tel 617-862-6650;
Toll free: 800-428-8071; Orders to: D. C.
Heath & Co. Distribution Ctr., 2700 Richardt
Ave., Indianapolis, IN 46219
(SAN 202-2885) Tel 317-359-5585.
Imprints: Swift, Sterling
(Sterling Swift).
Hebrew Publishing Co., *(Hebrew Pub; 0-88482),*
100 Water St., Brooklyn, NY 11202-0875
(SAN 201-5404) Tel 718-858-6928.
Hebrew Union College Press *See* Ktav
Publishing Hse., Inc.
Hein, William S., & Co., Inc., *(W S Hein;
0-89941; 0-930342),* Hein Bldg., 1285 Main
St., Buffalo, NY 14209 (SAN 210-9212)
Tel 716-882-2600; Toll free:
800-828-7571.
Heinman, W. S., Imported Bks., *(Heinman;
0-88431),* 225 W. 57th St., Rm. 404, New
York, NY 10019 (SAN 121-6201)
Tel 212-757-7628; P.O. Box 926, New York,
NY 10023 (SAN 660-935X).
Heldref Pubns., Div. of The Helen Dwight Reid
Educational Foundation, *(Heldref Pubns;
0-916882),* 4000 Albemarle St., NW,
Washington, DC 20016 (SAN 208-0788)
Tel 202-362-6445.
Helena News Agency, Box 6017, Helena, MT
59601 (SAN 169-4375).
Helix, 310 S. Racine St., Chicago, IL 60607
(SAN 111-915X)
Tel 312-944-4400.
Hello Reader *See* Scholastic, Inc.
Hensley, Charles, 2207 Loftin Rd., Waco, TX
76703 (SAN 281-5532)
Tel 817-776-5687.
Herald Hse., *(Herald Hse; 0-8309),* P.O. Box
HH, Independence, MO 64055
(SAN 202-2907) Tel 816-252-5010; Toll
free: 800-821-7550.
Herbert Furse-Bookman, 1461 Baffin Rd.,
Glenview, IL 60025
(SAN 159-8724).
Hermitage, 2269 Shadowood, Ann Arbor, MI
48104 (SAN 239-4413).
Hermitage, *(Hermitage; 0-938920),* P.O. Box
410, Tenafly, NJ 07670 (SAN 239-4413)
Tel 201-894-8247.

Hi-Country Data Systems, P.O. Box 4258,
Woodland Park, CO 80863
(SAN 287-2625).
Hiawatha Bk. Co., *(Hiawatha Bondurant),* 7567
NE 102nd Ave., Bondurant, IA 50035
(SAN 162-8348)
Tel 515-967-4025.
Hicks News Agency Inc., 1426 N.E. Eighth
Ave., Ocala, FL 32670
(SAN 159-8732).
Hidden House *See* Music Sales Corp.
Highland Bks. *See* Berkley Publishing Group
Hilgard News Agency Inc., 2609 17th St. NE,
P.O. Box 338, Great Falls, MT 59414
(SAN 169-4367).
Hill, Ellen C., RR 1, Box 64, Montpelier, VT
05651 (SAN 200-7851)
Tel 802-223-2720.
Hill, Lawrence, & Co., Inc., *(Lawrence Hill;
0-88208),* 520 Riverside Ave., Westport, CT
06880 (SAN 214-1221) Tel 203-226-5980;
Dist. by: Independent Publishers Group, 1
Pleasant Ave., Port Washington, NY 11050
(SAN 287-2544) Tel 516-944-9325; Dist.
by: Lawrence Hill & Co., Inc., 520 Riverside
Ave., Westport, CT 06880 (SAN 214-1221)
Tel 203-226-5980.
Hill City News Agency Inc., 3228 Odd Fellow
Rd., Lynchburg, VA 24501
(SAN 169-8656).
Hillsboro News, P.O. Box 23846, Tampa, FL
33622 (SAN 169-1325).
Himber's Books, 1380 W. Second Ave., Eugene,
OR 97402 (SAN 169-7099).
Hippocrene Bks., Inc., *(Hippocrene Bks;
0-87052; 0-88254),* 171 Madison Ave., New
York, NY 10016 (SAN 213-2060)
Tel 718-454-2366.
Hispano-American Pubns., Inc., 45-57 Davis St.,
Long Island City, NY 11101
(SAN 169-5460).
Historical Films, P.O. Box 46505, Los Angeles,
CA 90046 (SAN 200-7274)
Tel 213-656-4420.
Historical Research Associates, Box 4275,
Bisbee, AZ 85603 (SAN 240-1355).
Hobby Bk. Distributors, 3150 State Line Rd.,
North Bend, OH 45052 (SAN 200-6669).
Hoey, Joanne Nobes, 33 E.Centennial Dr.,
Medford, NJ 08055 (SAN 238-7921).
Hogrefe International, Affil. of C. J. Hogrefe,
(Hogrefe Intl; 0-88937), P.O. Box 51,
Lewiston, NY 14092 (SAN 293-2792)
Tel 716-754-1455.
Holcomb, J.R., Co., 3000 Quigley Rd.,
Cleveland, OH 44113 (SAN 282-5856)
Tel 216-621-6580.
Holiday Enterprises Inc., Easley Hywy. 123,
Greenville, SC 29602 (SAN 169-779X);
Drawer 1208, Greenville, SC 29602
(SAN 159-7280).
Holistic Health, *(Holistic Health),* 1214 Tenth
Ave., Seattle, WA 98122 (SAN 200-6286).
Holley International Company, *(0-9609136),* 63
Kercheval Ave., Grosse Point Farms, MI
48236 (SAN 241-5178) Tel 313-882-0405.
Holman, A.J., Bible Pub., Div. of Baptist Sunday
Schl. Bd., *(Holman; 0-87981),* 127 Ninth
Ave., N., Nashville, TN 37234
(SAN 202-3016) Tel 615-251-2520; Toll
free: 800-251-3225.
Holos Gallery, 194 North St., Willimantic, CT
06226 (SAN 264-4363) Tel 203-423-7370.
Holt, Henry, & Co., *(H Holt & Co; 0-8050),*
521 Fifth Ave., New York, NY 10175
(SAN 200-6472) Tel 212-599-7600. Former
trade-book arm of Holt, Rinehart & Winston.
Acquired in 1985 by Verlagsgruppe Georg
von Holtzbrinck, from CBS. *Imprints:*
North-South Books (North South Bks).
Holt College Dept. *See* Holt, Rinehart &
Winston, Inc.
Holt Elementary Bks. *See* Holt, Rinehart &
Winston, Inc.
Holt Information Systems *See* Holt, Rinehart &
Winston, Inc.
Holt, Rinehart & Winston, Inc., Div. of CBS
College Publishing, *(HR&W; 0-03),* 383
Madison Ave., New York, NY 10017
(SAN 200-2108) Tel 212-750-1330.
Imprints: Holt College Department (HoltC);
Holt Elementary Books (HoltE); Holt
Information Systems (HIS); Owl Books (Owl
Bks).
Holyoke News Co., Inc., 720 Main St., P.O. Box
990, Holyoke, MA 01041 (SAN 169-3468);
Toll free: 800-628-8372.

Homestead Book, Inc., *(Homestead Bk;
0-930180),* 6101 22nd Ave., NW, Seattle,
WA 98107 (SAN 169-8796)
Tel 206-782-4532; Toll free: 800-426-6777;
Orders to: P.O. Box 31608, Seattle, WA
98103 (SAN 662-037X).
Homewood-Flossmor News Agency, 1930 Ridge
Rd., Homewood, IL 60430
(SAN 169-1988).
Homing Pigeon, The, Rte. 1, P.O. Box 813,
Elgin, TX 78621 (SAN 157-0617)
Tel 512-276-7962.
Honor Books, *(Honor Bks; 0-931446),* P.O. Box
641, Rapid City, SD 57709
(SAN 208-0877).
Hopkins, Tom, International, Inc., *(T Hopkins
Intl),* 7531 E. Second St., Scottsdale, AZ
85252 (SAN 200-5174) Tel 602-949-0786;
Toll free: 800-528-0446; P.O. Box 1969,
Scottsdale, AZ 85252 (SAN 658-2850).
Horizon Bk. Promotions, Inc., 95 Madison Ave.,
New York, NY 10016 (SAN 695-7021)
Tel 212-696-9171. Remainders.
Horizon Communications Pubs./Distributors,
(Horizon Comms; 0-913945), 2710 San
Diego, SE, Albuquerque, NM 87106
(SAN 286-7761) Tel 505-266-3431.
Horizon Pr., *(Horizon; 0-8180),* P.O. Box 402,
New York, NY 10108 (SAN 202-3040)
Tel 212-757-4420.
Hotchkiss House, Inc., *(Hotchkiss House;
0-912220),* 14 Shelter Creek Ln., Fairport,
NY 14450 (SAN 159-5415).
Hotho, Victor, & Co., Box 9738, Ft. Worth, TX
76107 (SAN 169-8192); 353 E. 72nd St.,
New York, NY 10021 (SAN 169-5797).
Houghton Mifflin Co., *(HM; 0-395; 0-87466),* 1
Beacon St., Boston, MA 02108
(SAN 200-2388) Tel 617-725-5000; Toll
free: 800-225-3362; Orders to: Wayside Rd.,
Burlington, MA 01803 (SAN 215-3793)
Tel 617-272-1500. *Imprints:* Houghton
Trade Books (HoughtonT); Piper Books
(Piper); Riverside Editions (RivEd); Riverside
Literature Series (RivLit); Riverside Reading
Series (RRS); Riverside Studies in Literature
(RivSL); Sandpiper Paperbacks (Sandpiper);
Sentry Editions (SenEd).
Houghton Trade Bks. *See* Houghton Mifflin Co.
Houston Paperback Distributor, 9215 Stella
Link Rd., Houston, TX 77025
(SAN 169-8273).
Howard-Moineau, Henrietta, P.O. Box 235,
West Boylston, MA 01505
(SAN 296-1288).
Howard's for Pet Supplies, 3244 S. Claiborn
Ave., P.O. Box 4144, New Orleans, LA
70178 (SAN 157-8731).
Howell Bk. Hse., Inc., *(Howell Bk; 0-87605),*
Helmsley Bldg., 230 Park Ave., New York,
NY 10169 (SAN 202-3075)
Tel 212-986-4488.
Hubbard, Drawer 100, Defiance, OH 43512
(SAN 169-6726).
Hubert News Agency, Inc., P.O.Box 31,
Wilmington, OH 45177
(SAN 169-6904).
Hudson County News Co., 1305 Paterson Plank
Rd., North Bergen, NJ 07047
(SAN 169-4782).
Hudson Valley News Distributors, P.O. Box
1236, Newburgh, NY 12550
(SAN 169-6084).
Human Dynamics, Inc., 3260 Southern Place,
Garland, TX 75043
(SAN 200-478X).
Human Sciences Pr., Inc., *(Human Sci Pr;
0-87705; 0-89885),* 72 Fifth Ave., New
York, NY 10011 (SAN 200-2159)
Tel 212-243-6000; Dist. by Independent
Pubs. Group, 1 Pleasant Ave., Port
Washington, NY 11050
(SAN 287-2544).
Humanics, Ltd., *(Humanics Ltd; 0-89334),* P.O.
Box 7447, Atlanta, GA 30309
(SAN 208-3833) Tel 404-874-2176; Toll
free: 800-874-8844; 1389 Peachtree St. NE,
Suite 370, Atlanta, GA 30309
(SAN 658-0882).
Humanities Pr., International, Inc., *(Humanities;
0-391),* 171 First Ave., Atlantic Highlands,
NJ 07716-1289 (SAN 201-9272)
Tel 201-872-1441; Toll free: 800-221-3845
(orders).

687

Hunt Manufacturing Co., 230 S. Broad St., Philadelphia, PA 19102 (SAN 678-7339) Tel 215-732-7700; Toll free: 800-524-0916 (Pennsylvania only).

Hunt News Co., 766 Broad, Weymouth, MA 02189 (SAN 169-3638).

Hunter Hse., Inc., *(Hunter Hse; 0-89793),* Box 1302, Claremont, CA 91711 (SAN 281-7969) Tel 714-624-2277; c/o Publisher's Services, Box 2510, Novato, CA 94948 (SAN 281-7977) Tel 415-883-3530; Dist. by: Bookpeople, 2929 Fifth St., Berkeley, CA 94710 (SAN 169-2488) Tel 415-549-3030; Dist. by: Publishers Group West, 5855 Beaudry St., Emeryville, CA 94608 (SAN 202-8522) Tel 415-658-3453; Dist. by: Distributors, The, 702 S. Michigan, South Bend, IN 46618 (SAN 212-0364) Tel 219-232-8500; Dist. by: New Leaf Distributors, The, 1020 White St., SW, Atlanta, GA 30310 (SAN 169-1449) Tel 404-658-3453; Dist. by: Quality Bks., Inc., 918 Sherwood Dr., Lake Bluff, IL 60044-2204 (SAN 169-2127) Tel 312-498-4000; Dist. by: Devorss & Co., P.O. Box 550, Marina del Rey, CA 90294 (SAN 168-9886) Tel 213-870-7478; Dist. by: Inland Bk. Co., P.O. Box 261, 22 Hemingway Ave., East Haven, CT 06512 (SAN 200-4151) Tel 203-467-4257; Dist. by: Great Tradition, The, 750 Adrian Way, Suite 111, San Rafael, CA 94903 (SAN 200-5743) Tel 415-492-9382.

Huntington News Agency, 121 Erskine Ln., Scott Depot, WV 25560 (SAN 169-8974).

Husker News Co., First & Locust Sts., Atlantic, IA 50022 (SAN 169-2577).

Huyler, Jean Wiley, Communications, 922 N. Pearl, A-27, Tacoma, WA 98406 (SAN 238-8022).

ILIR Pubns., University of Michigan, Victor Vaughan Bldg., 1111 E. Catherine St., Ann Arbor, MI 48109-2054 (SAN 287-2536).

IPS Information Processing Supplies, 251 Frontage Rd., Suite 20, Burr Ridge, IL 60521 (SAN 699-0800) Tel 312-654-0110; Toll free: 800-323-5569.

Iaconi Book Imports, 300 Pennsylvania Ave., San Francisco, CA 94107 (SAN 161-1364).

IBC *See* McGraw-Hill Bk. Co.

ICD Rehabilitation & Research Center, 340 E 24 St, New York, NY 10010 (SAN 270-885X).

Icea Bk. Ctr., P.O. Box 20048, Minneapolis, MN 55420 (SAN 285-9114) Tel 612-854-8660.

ICEL, University of San Francisco, San Francisco, CA 94117 (SAN 210-0991) Tel 415-666-6886.

Icon Editions *See* Harper & Row Pubs., Inc.

Idaho News Agency, 1825 N. 15th St., Coeur D'Alene, ID 83814 (SAN 169-1651).

Ideal Foreign Books, 132-10 Hillside Ave., Richmond Hill, NY 11418 (SAN 169-6173).

IFI, Plenum *See* Plenum Publishing Corp.

Illini Bks. *See* Univ. of Illinois Pr.

Illinois Institute of Technology, *(IL Inst Tech),* 10 W. 32nd St., Chicago, IL 60616 (SAN 230-8304); Dist. by: Univ. of Chicago Pr., 5801 Ellis Ave., 3rd Flr., S., Chicago, IL 60637 (SAN 202-5280) Tel 312-962-7693.

Illinois News Service, 1301 SW Washington St., Peoria, IL 61602 (SAN 169-216X).

Illinois State Historical Society, *(Ill St Hist Soc; 0-912226),* Old State Capitol, Springfield, IL 62701 (SAN 203-7971) Tel 217-782-4836.

Ilma Printing & Publishing, *(Ilma Print And Pub; 0-930317),* P.O. Box 251, Tarzana, CA 91356 (SAN 260-3381) Tel 818-344-3375; 5068 Mecca Ave., Tarzana, CA 91356 (SAN 680-098X).

Image Books *See* Doubleday & Co., Inc.

Image Processing Systems, *(Image Process; 0-924507),* 6409 Appalachian Way, Madison, WI 53705 (SAN 265-5977) Tel 608-233-5033.

Impact Bks., Inc., *(Impact Bks MO; 0-89228),* 137 W. Jefferson, Kirkwood, MO 63122 (SAN 214-0330) Tel 314-833-3309.

Imperial News Co., 255 Pinelawn Rd., Melville, NY 11747 (SAN 169-5509).

Imported Books, Box 4414, Dallas, TX 75208 (SAN 169-8095) Tel 214-941-6497.

Imported Pubns., Inc., *(Imported Pubns; 0-8285),* 320 W. Ohio St., Chicago, IL 60610 (SAN 169-1805) Tel 312-787-9017; Toll free: 800-345-2665.

Independent Magazine Co., 2340 Fairfax Ave., Los Angeles, CA 90016 (SAN 159-8783).

Independent News, 75 Rockefeller Plaza, New York, NY 10019 (SAN 208-6158).

Independent Publishers Group, 1 Pleasant Ave., Port Washington, NY 11050 (SAN 287-2544).

Indiana Univ. Pr., *(Ind U Pr; 0-253),* Tenth & Morton Sts., Bloomington, IN 47405 (SAN 202-5647) Tel 812-335-7681. Do not confuse with Indian U Pr OK. *Imprints:* Midland Books (MB).

Info Twenty-One Booksellers, *(Info Twenty One Bksellers),* P.O. Box 12 FMT, El Cerrito, CA 94530-0012 (SAN 290-6880).

Information Handling Services, *(IHS; 0-910972; 0-89847),* 15 Inverness Way E., P.O. Box 1154, Englewood, CO 80150 (SAN 203-7254); Toll free: 800-525-7052. Prepackaged & custom services on 8mm & 16mm roll microfilm & 24X & 48X microfiche with accompanyng hard copy. Products include federal & military specifications & standards, Industry standards, government procurement packages, product & vendor catalog data, and educational materials.

Information Translation Service, P.O. Box 1271, Canoga Park, CA 91304 (SAN 211-1691) Tel 818-883-9246.

Informedia, 103 Godwin Ave., Midland Park, NJ 07432 (SAN 268-8689).

Infotek, Inc., *(0-924311),* 56 Camille Lane, East Patchogue, NY 11772 (SAN 294-3786) Tel 516-289-9682.

Infotools, Subs. of Micro Dealer Support, Inc., 502 Tamal Plaza, Corta Madera, CA 94925 (SAN 697-8320) Tel 415-927-0600.

Ingham Publishing, Inc., *(Ingham Pub; 0-9611804),* P.O. Box 12642, St. Petersburg, FL 33733 (SAN 286-1127) Tel 813-343-4811.

Ingram Bk. Co., *(Ingrams TN),* 347 Reedwood Dr., Nashville, TN 37217 (SAN 169-7978); Toll free: 800-251-5902.

Inkworks Pr., *(Inkworks; 0-930712),* 4220 Telegraph Ave., Oakland, CA 94609 (SAN 281-8124) Tel 415-652-7111; Dist. by: Carrier Pigeon, 40 Plympton St., Boston, MA 02118 (SAN 169-3301) Tel 617-542-5679.

Inland Bk. Co., P.O. Box 261, 22 Hemingway Ave., East Haven, CT 06512 (SAN 200-4151) Tel 203-467-4257; Toll free: 800-243-0138.

Inland Empire Periodicals, 4800 N. Yellowstone, Idaho Falls, ID 83401 (SAN 169-166X).

Inland Empire Periodicals Inc., 2695 Church St., Baker, OR 97814 (SAN 169-703X).

Inmac, *(Inmac),* 2465 Augustine Dr., Santa Clara, CA 95054 (SAN 678-5298) Tel 408-727-1970; Toll free: 800-547-5444.

Inner Traditions International, Ltd., *(Inner Tradit; 0-89281),* Park St., Rochester, VT 05767 (SAN 208-6948); Orders to: Harper & Row Pubs., Inc., Keystone Industrial Pk., Scranton, PA 18512 (SAN 215-3742). *Imprints:* Astrologer's Library (Astrologers Lib); Destiny Books (Destiny Bks); Lindisfarne Press (Lindisfarne Pr).

Inspiration Books, 6035 S. Central Ave., P.O. Box 8249, Phoenix, AZ 85066 (SAN 168-9320).

Inspirational Marketing Inc., Box 301, Indianola, IA 50125 (SAN 208-6557).

Institute for Advanced Studies of World Religions, The, *(Inst Adv Stud Wld; 0-915078),* 2150 Center Ave., Fort Lee, NJ 07024 (SAN 265-3885).

Institute for Information Management, *(Inst Info Mgmt; 0-931900),* Pruneyard Towers, 1901 S. Boscom Ave., Suite 230, Campbell, CA 95008 (SAN 209-0686) Tel 408-559-6911.

Institute for Rational-Emotive Therapy, *(Inst Rational-Emotive; 0-917476),* 45 E. 65th St., New York, NY 10021 (SAN 210-3079) Tel 212-535-0822.

Institute of Electrical & Electronics Engineers, *(Inst Electrical; 0-87942),* 345 E. 47th St., New York, NY 10017 (SAN 203-8064) Tel 212-705-7900; Orders to: IEEE Service Ctr., 445 Hoes Ln., Piscataway, NJ 08854 (SAN 203-8072) Tel 201-981-1393.

Institute of Living Skills, P.O. Box 1461, Fallbrook, CA 92028 (SAN 239-1090) Tel 619-728-6437.

Instructo, McGraw-Hill *See* McGraw-Hill Bk. Co.

Instructor Sub Agency, Bank Street, Dansville, NY 14437 (SAN 285-9947).

Instrument Society of America, *(Instru Soc; 0-87664; 1-55617),* P.O. Box 12277, 67 Alexander Dr., Research Triangle Park, NC 27709 (SAN 202-7054) Tel 919-549-8411.

Intel Corp., *(Intel Corp; 0-917017; 1-55512),* 3065 Bowers Ave., SC6-60, Santa Clara, CA 95051 (SAN 277-1446) Tel 408-496-7973; Toll free: 800-548-4725.

Interbook, Inc., *(Interbk Inc; 0-913456; 0-89192),* 131 Varick St., 2nd Fl., New York, NY 10013 (SAN 202-7070) Tel 212-691-7248.

Interbook Inc., Subs. of Haynes Pubns., *(Interbook; 0-946609),* 861 Lawrence Dr., Newbury Park, CA 91320 (SAN 662-3034) Tel 805-498-6703; Orders to: 14895 E. 14th St., Suite 370, San Leandro, CA 94577 (SAN 662-3042) Tel 415-352-9221.

Interbusiness Corp., 345 N. Wolf Rd., Wheeling, IL 60090 (SAN 287-3532) Tel 312-459-8866; Toll free: 800-237-3762.

InterMountain Periodical Distributors, 812 W 17th St., Ogden, UT 84404 (SAN 169-8508).

International Assn. of Assessing Officers, *(Intl Assess; 0-88329),* 1313 E. 60th St., Chicago, IL 60637-9990 (SAN 205-0277) Tel 312-947-2069; Orders to: Prepaid, P.O. Box 88874, Chicago, IL 60680-1874 (SAN 691-9529) Tel 312-947-2044.

International Bk. Ctr., *(Intl Bk Ctr; 0-917062; 0-86685),* 2007 Laurel Dr., P.O. Box 295, Troy, MI 48099 (SAN 169-4014) Tel 313-879-8436.

International Business & Management Institute University Town Centre, P.O. Box 4082, Irvine, CA 92716 (SAN 282-647X) Tel 714-552-8494.

International Cassette Corp., P.O. Box 1928, Greenville, TX 75401 (SAN 696-8848).

International Commercial Service, Subs. of International ICS Group, *(Intl Comm Serv; 0-935402),* P.O. Box 4082, Irvine, CA 92716 (SAN 281-8183) Tel 714-552-8494; Dist. by: IBMI-International Commercial Services, Univ. Town Ctr., P.O. Box 4082, Irvine, CA 92716 (SAN 281-8183) Tel 714-552-8494.

International Communications *See* Watts, Franklin, Inc.

International Dept. *See* Harper & Row Pubs., Inc.

International Human Resources, Business & Legal Research Assn., 3843 Mass Ave. N.W., Washington, DC 20016 (SAN 200-495X).

International Luthier Supply, Inc., P.O. Box 15444, Tulsa, OK 74112 (SAN 287-2579).

International Magazine Service, 1 N. Superior St., Sandusky, OH 44870 (SAN 285-9955).

International Marine Publishing Co., Subs. of Diversified Communications Inc., *(Intl Marine; 0-87742; 0-8286),* 21 Elm St., Camden, ME 04843 (SAN 202-716X) Tel 207-236-4342; Toll free: 800-328-0059 (Trade Customers Only).

International Pubns. Service, Div. of Taylor & Francis, Inc., *(Intl Pubns Serv; 0-8002),* 242 Cherry St., Philadelphia, PA 19106-1906 (SAN 169-5819) Tel 215-238-0939; Toll free: 800-821-8312.

International Pubs. Service, Inc., *(IPS),* P.O. Box 230, Accord, MA 02018 (SAN 654-9357) Tel 617-749-2966.

International Readers league, One N. Superior St., Sandusky, OH 44870 (SAN 285-9971).

International Service Co., 333 Fourth Ave., Indialantic, FL 32903 (SAN 169-5134).

International Society for General Semantics, *(Intl Gen Semantics; 0-918970),* 834 Mission St., 2nd flr., San Francisco, CA 94103 (SAN 203-8161) Tel 415-543-1747; P.O. Box 2469, San Francisco, CA 94126 (SAN 669-1315).

International Specialized Bk. Services, *(Intl Spec Bk; 0-89955),* 5602 NE Hassalo St., Portland, OR 97213-3640 (SAN 169-7129) Tel 503-287-3093; Toll free: 800-547-7734.

International Univs. Pr., Inc., *(Intl Univs Pr; 0-8236),* 59 Boston Post Rd., P.O. Box 1524, Madison, CT 06443-1524 (SAN 202-7186) Tel 203-245-4000.

International University Booksellers, Inc., 30 Irving Place, New York, NY 10003 (SAN 169-5827).

International Violin Co., 4026 W. Belvedere Ave., Baltimore, MD 21215 (SAN 282-728X).

InterSoft, Inc., *(InterSoft Inc; 0-928429),* 14023 NE Eighth St., Bellevue, WA 98007 (SAN 658-0076) Tel 206-643-7787.

Interstate Distributor Co., Inc., 199 Commander Shea Blvd., Quincy, MA 02171 (SAN 159-8805).

Interstate Periodical Distributors, P.O. Box 2237, Madison, WI 53701 (SAN 169-9105); Box 2305, Rockford, IL 61131 (SAN 169-2194).

Iowa & Illinois News, P.O. Box 2470, 8645 Northwest Blvd., Davenport, IA 52809 (SAN 169-2607).

Iowa News Distributing Co., Box 1042, Waterloo, IA 51102 (SAN 169-2690).

Iowa Periodicals, P.O. Box 1309, Cedar Rapids, IA 52406 (SAN 169-2593); P.O. Box 1297, Des Moines, IA 50305 (SAN 169-2615); 2412 Falls Ave., Waterloo, IA 50701 (SAN 169-2690).

Iowa State Univ. Pr., *(Iowa St U Pr; 0-8138),* 2121 S. State Ave., Ames, IA 50010 (SAN 202-7194) Tel 515-292-0140.

Irish Bks. & Media, *(Irish Bks Media; 0-937702),* 683 Osceola Ave., St. Paul, MN 55105 (SAN 215-1987) Tel 612-647-5678.

Irvington Pubs., *(Irvington; 0-89197; 0-8290; 0-8422),* 740 Broadway, New York, NY 10003 (SAN 207-2408) Tel 212-777-4100.

Irwin, Richard D., Inc., Subs. of Dow Jones & Co., Inc., *(Irwin; 0-256),* 1818 Ridge Rd., Homewood, IL 60430 (SAN 206-8400) Tel 312-798-6000; Toll free: 800-323-4560.

Islamic Bk. Service, 10900 W. Washington, Indianapolis, IN 46231 (SAN 169-2453).

Island Heritage/Worldwide Distributors, *(Island Herit-Wrldwide Dist; 0-931548),* 1819 Kahai St., Honolulu, HI 96819-3136 (SAN 211-3392) Tel 808-531-0133.

JMI Software Consultants, Inc., Subs. of Landmark Technology Corp., *(JMI Soft; 0-924733),* 904 Sheble Ln., Spring House, PA 19477 (SAN 295-124X) Tel 215-628-0840.

JM Pubns., P.O. Box 837, Brentwood, TN 37027 (SAN 200-7975).

James & Law Co., The, P.O. Box 2468, Clarksburg, WV 26302 (SAN 169-894X); Middletown Mall I-79 & Us 250, Fairmont, WV 26554 (SAN 169-8604).

Jeanies Classics, *(Jeanies Classics; 0-9609672),* 2123 Oxford St., Rockford, IL 61103 (SAN 271-7395) Tel 815-968-4544; Dist. by: Jeanies Classics Publishing, P.O. Box 4303, Rockford, IL 61110 (SAN 271-7409).

Jefferson, Thomas, Research Center, *(T Jefferson Res Ctr; 0-938308),* 1143 N. Lake Ave., Pasadena, CA 91104 (SAN 239-670X) Tel 818-798-0791.

Jefferson News Co., Inc., 2316 First Ave. S., Birmingham, AL 35233 (SAN 168-9193).

Jei-Ai Publishing Company, Incorporated, *(Jei-Ai Pub Co),* 2101 1/2 Bush St., San Francisco, CA 94115 (SAN 293-7980) Tel 415-922-4780; Dist. by: Jei-Ai International Corp., P.O. Box 10115, Beverly Hills, CA 90213 (SAN 293-7999) Tel 213-986-4644.

Jende-Hagan, Inc., *(Jende-Hagan; 0-939650),* P.O. Box 177-A, Frederick, CO 80530 (SAN 169-0574) Tel 303-833-2030; 541 Oak St., Frederick, CO 80530 (SAN 658-1404). *Imprints:* Platte 'n Press (Platte n Pr); Renaissance House (Renaissance Hse).

Jenison News Agency, Box 186, Dowagiac, MI 49047 (SAN 159-8821).

Jewish Bookshelf, The, Box 434, Teaneck, NJ 07666 (SAN 169-4928).

Jitco, Specialized Book Distributors, 1601 Research Blvd., Rockville, MD 20850 (SAN 169-3220) Tel 301-984-2800.

JJV Associates, 107 S. Lowell Ave., Syracuse, NY 13204 (SAN 158-7234).

JMT Associates, P.O. Box 192, Normal, AL 35762 (SAN 214-0926).

Joe Goldfeder Music Enterprises, P.O. Box 660, Lynbrook, NY 11563 (SAN 203-6177).

John Jay Pr., *(John Jay Pr; 0-89444),* 444 W. 56th St., New York, NY 10019 (SAN 210-2196) Tel 212-489-3592.

Johns Hopkins Univ. Pr., *(Johns Hopkins; 0-8018),* 701 W. 40th St., Suite 275, Baltimore, MD 21211 (SAN 202-7348) Tel 301-338-6956.

Johnson Bks., Div. of Johnson Publishing Co., *(Johnson Bks; 0-933472; 1-55566),* P.O. Box 990, Boulder, CO 80301 (SAN 201-0313) Tel 303-443-1576; 1880 S. 57th Ct., Boulder, CO 80301 (SAN 658-1013).

Johnson News Agency, P.O. Box 9009, Moscow, ID 83843 (SAN 169-1678).

Jonathan David Pubs., Inc., *(Jonathan David; 0-8246),* 68-22 Eliot Ave., Middle Village, NY 11379 (SAN 169-5274) Tel 718-456-8611.

Jones & Bartlett Pubs., Inc., *(Jones & Bartlett; 0-86720),* 20 Park Plaza, Boston, MA 02116 (SAN 285-0893) Tel 617-482-5243; Toll free: 800-832-0034 (Orders only). *Imprints:* Marine Science International (Marine Sci Intl).

Joplin News Co., Inc., Drawer Y, Pittsburg, KS 66762 (SAN 159-8848).

Joyce Media Inc., *(Joyce Media; 0-917002),* P.O. Box 57, Action, CA 93510 (SAN 208-7197) Tel 805-269-1169.

Judaic Specialties, 45 Broad St., Carlstadt, NJ 07072 (SAN 129-640X).

Julian Press *See* Crown Pubs., Inc.

Junius Book Distributors, P.O. Box 85, Fairview, NJ 07022 (SAN 169-4944).

Justice, John, 107 W. Main St., Rte. 9, Hedgesville, WV 25427 (SAN 167-3386).

Juvenile Bks. *See* Simon & Schuster, Inc.

Kable News Co., Inc., 777 Third Ave., New York, NY 10017 (SAN 169-5835); Toll free: 800-223-6640.

Kahn, Joan, Bk., A *See* St. Martin's Pr., Inc.

Kalamazoo Nature Center, Inc., 7000 N. Westnedge Ave., Kalamazoo, MI 49007 (SAN 268-2478).

Kalimat Pr., *(Kalimat; 0-933770),* 1600 Sawtelle Blvd., Suite 34, Los Angeles, CA 90025 (SAN 213-7666) Tel 213-479-5668; Toll free: 800-323-1880.

Kalispell News Agency, 1500 Airport Rd., Kalispell, MT 59901 (SAN 169-4383).

Kalmbach Publishing Co., *(Kalmbach; 0-89024),* 1027 N. Seventh St., Milwaukee, WI 53233 (SAN 201-0399) Tel 414-272-2060; Toll free: 800-558-1544.

Kampmann & Co., Inc., *(Kampmann),* 9 E. 40th St., New York, NY 10016 (SAN 202-5191) Tel 212-685-2928; Toll free: 800-526-7626.

Kansas State Reading Circle, 715 W. Tenth St., C-170, Topeka, KS 66601 (SAN 169-2771).

Kapitan Szabo Publishers, *(Kapitan Szabo; 0-916845),* 2120 Pennsylvania Ave. NW, Washington, DC 20037 (SAN 200-4607).

Kaplan School Supply, 600 Jonestown Rd., Winston-Salem, NC 27103 (SAN 169-6521).

Karr, Jean, & Co., 5656 Third St., NE, Washington, DC 20011 (SAN 169-0922) Tel 202-529-6789. Specialize in juvenile titles.

Kaufmann, William, Inc., *(W Kaufmann; 0-913232; 0-86576),* 95 First St., Los Altos, CA 94022 (SAN 202-9383) Tel 415-948-5810; Dist. by: Publishers Group West, 5855 Beaudry St., Emeryville, CA 94608 (SAN 202-8522) Tel 415-658-3453.

Kazi Pubns., *(Kazi Pubns; 0-935782; 0-933511),* 1215 W. Belmont Ave., Chicago, IL 60657 (SAN 162-3397) Tel 312-327-7598.

Kelleher, William F., 544 Westview Ave., Cliffside Park, NJ 07010 (SAN 169-4650).

Kenan Pr. *See* Simon & Schuster, Inc.

Kent News Agency Inc., P.O. Box 661, Scottsbluff, NE 69361 (SAN 169-4448).

Keramos, P.O. Box 7500, Ann Arbor, MI 48107 (SAN 169-3670).

Kerhulas News Co., 1069 1/2 E. Main, P.O. Box 369, Union, SC 29379 (SAN 169-7838).

Kerr, Charles H., Publishing, Co., *(C H Kerr; 0-88286),* 1740 W. Greenleaf Ave., Chicago, IL 60626 (SAN 207-7043) Tel 312-465-7774.

Kewanee News Agency, Main St., Kewanee, IL 61443 (SAN 159-8856).

Key Book Service, Inc., *(Key Bk Serv; 0-934636),* 425 Asylum St., Bridgeport, CT 06610 (SAN 169-0671) Tel 203-334-2165; Toll free: 800-243-2790.

Key Bks. International, 24 Windham Dr., Huntington Station, NY 11746 (SAN 169-5347).

Key News Agency Inc., 351 107th St.-Gulfside, Marathon, FL 33050 (SAN 169-1066).

Keystone Bks. *See* Pennsylvania State Univ. Pr.

Keystone Readers Service, Inc., P.O. Box 1798, Philadelphia, PA 19105 (SAN 285-998X).

Kids Books, 237 Stamford Industrial Pk., 737 Canal St., Bldg 22, Stamford, CT 06902 (SAN 169-0795).

Kindred Pr., *(Kindred Pr),* Box L, Hillsboro, KS 67063 (SAN 205-8634) Tel 316-947-3151; Orders to: 616 Walnut Ave., Scottdale, PA 15683 (SAN 202-2915) Tel 412-887-8500.

King of the Road Maps, P.O. Box 55758, Seattle, WA 98155 (SAN 200-6553).

King's Crown Paperbacks *See* Columbia Univ. Pr.

Kings News,Inc., Box 160, Grand Forks, ND 58206-0160 (SAN 169-6564).

Kinokuniya Bookstores, 1581 Webster St., San Francisco, CA 94115 (SAN 121-8441).

Kinokuniya Pubns. Service of New York, 10 W. 49th St., New York, NY 10020 (SAN 157-5414).

Kinsella News Co., 1704 N. Leg Ct., Box 12248, Augusta, GA 30904 (SAN 159-8864) Tel 404-738-8826.

Kluwer Academic Pubs., Subs. of Kluwer NV, *(Kluwer Academic; 0-89838),* 101 Philip Dr., Assinippi Pk., Norwell, MA 02061 (SAN 211-481X) Tel 617-871-6600; Orders to: P.O. Box 358, Accord Sta., Hingham, MA 02018-0358 (SAN 662-0647).

Knapp Press *See* Crown Pubs., Inc.

Knowledge Industry Pubns., Inc., Subs. of Knowledge Industry Sciences, *(Knowledge Indus; 0-914236; 0-86729),* 701 Westchester Ave., White Plains, NY 10604 (SAN 214-2082) Tel 914-328-9157; Toll free: 800-248-5474. *Imprints:* American Society for Information Science (ASIS).

Koch News Co., 2120 S. Meridian St., Indianapolis, IN 46225 (SAN 169-2380).

Kodansha International USA, Ltd., Subs. of Kodansha, Ltd. (Japan), *(Kodansha; 0-87011),* c/o Harper & Row Pubs., 10 E. 53rd St., New York, NY 10022 (SAN 201-0526) Tel 212-207-7050; Toll free: 800-242-7737; Dist. by: Harper & Row Pubs., Inc., Keystone Industrial Pk., Scranton, PA 18512 (SAN 215-3742); Orders to: Mail Order Dept., P.O. Box 1531, Hagertown, MD 21741 (SAN 662-0671).

Koen Book Distributors, 514 N. Read Ave., Cinnaminson, NJ 08077 (SAN 169-4642).

Kokomo News Agency, 220 E. Sycamore St., Kokomo, IN 46901 (SAN 169-2399).

Kolb News Agency Inc., 7044 S. Elmer Ave., Whittier, CA 90602 (SAN 169-0469).

Kordak School & Library Book Shop, Box 18316, Oklahoma City, OK 73118 (SAN 159-8872).

Kraftbilt Products, 7659 E. 46th Pl., Tulsa, OK 74145 (SAN 200-7673) Tel 918-628-1260; Toll free: 800-331-7290.

Kraus Reprint & Periodicals (KRP), *(Kraus Repr; 0-527; 3-601; 3-262; 0-8115),* Rte. 100, Millwood, NY 10546 (SAN 201-0542) Tel 914-762-2200.

Kroger, Frank, P.O. Box 20037, Seattle, WA 98102 (SAN 200-6006) Tel 206-325-9077; Toll free: 800-325-9077.

Ktav Publishing Hse., Inc., *(Ktav; 0-87068; 0-88125),* Box 6249, Hoboken, NJ 07030 (SAN 201-0038); 900 Jefferson St., Hoboken, NJ 07030 (SAN 658-1056) Tel 201-963-9524. *Imprints:* Hebrew Union College Press (HUC Pr).

Kuykendalls Press, Bookstore Div., P.O. Box 627, Athens, AL 35611-0627 (SAN 168-9185).

L & B Enterprises, 1205 S. Ivy Way, Denver, CO 80224 (SAN 200-7681) Tel 303-756-4563.

L & M News Co., 1301 Hwy. 70 E., New Bern, NC 28560 (SAN 169-6459).

L. D. S. Books, P.O. Box 67, MCS, Dayton, OH 45402 (SAN 282-5864).

LMC, P.O. Box 355, Linthicum Heights, MD 21077 (SAN 200-7169) Tel 301-766-1211.

L M S Distribution Center, P.O. Box 2614, LaCrosse, WI 54601 (SAN 220-0678).

L-S Distributors, 480 Ninth St., San Francisco, CA 94103 (SAN 169-0213) Tel 415-861-6300.

LZB Publishing Co., (*LZB Pub; 0-9615899*), 102 SE 44th, Portland, OR 97215 (SAN 696-9828) Tel 503-232-0972.

L. C. Page Co. *See* Farrar, Straus & Giroux, Inc.

La Belle News Agency, 814 Univ. Blvd., Steubenville, OH 43952 (SAN 169-6858).

La Cite Des Livres, 2306-08 Westwood Blvd., Los Angeles, CA 90064 (SAN 168-9789).

La Crosse News Agency, 620 State St., P.O. Box 85, La Crosse, WI 54601 (SAN 169-9075).

La Moderna Poesia, 5246 SW Eighth St., Miami, FL 33134 (SAN 169-1139).

Labelmaster, 5724 N. Pulaski Rd., Chicago, IL 60646 (SAN 218-480X).

Lakeland News Co., Inc., P.O. Box 1506, Lakeland, FL 33802 (SAN 169-1031).

Lakeport Distributors, Inc., 139 W. 18th St., P.O. Box 6195, Erie, PA 16512 (SAN 169-734X).

Lamkin/Jordan Assocs., 20 Park Plaza, Rm. 480, Boston, MA 02116 (SAN 200-710X) Tel 617-542-8689.

Landau Book Co., Inc., (*Landau; 0-910864*), P.O. Box 570, Long Beach, NY 11561 (SAN 201-064X).

Landmark Book Co., (*Landmark NY*), 260 Fifth Ave, New York, NY 10000 (SAN 216-4051) Tel 212-696-5430.

Landmarks Commission Village of Oak Park *See* Chicago Review Pr., Inc.

Langdon, Larry, Pubns., (*Langdon Pubns; 0-943726*), 34735 Perkins Creek Rd., Cottage Grove, OR 97424-9450 (SAN 241-0427).

Langley Pr., The, (*Langley Pr; 0-911607*), 821 Georgia St., Key West, FL 33040 (SAN 264-164X) Tel 305-294-3156.

Lanson's Inc., 12566 S.W. Main St., Portland, OR 97223 (SAN 204-9511).

Lantern Bks. *See* Pocket Bks., Inc.

Lark Communications *See* Van Nostrand Reinhold Co., Inc.

Las Americas Anaya, 37 Union Square, New York, NY 10003 (SAN 169-5851).

Las Vegas News Agency, 333 W. St. Louis, Las Vegas, NV 89102 (SAN 110-4063).

Lash Distributors, 3636 Pennsy Dr., Landover, MD 20785 (SAN 169-3131).

Last Post, The, P.O. Box 630134, Bronx, NY 10463-9992 (SAN 200-755X).

Latcorp, Ltd., 10 Norden Ln., Huntington Station, NY 11746 (SAN 159-8910).

Latta, J.S., Inc., 1502 Fourth Ave., P.O. Box 2668, Huntington, WV 25726 (SAN 169-8982); Toll free: 800-642-3450 (WV Only); Toll free: 800-624-3501 (KY,OH,VA,MD,TN).

Latter Day Saints Bookstore, 44 E. South Temple, Salt Lake City, UT 84101 (SAN 205-5190).

Laurel Editions *See* Dell Publishing Co., Inc.

Laurel Leaf Library *See* Dell Publishing Co., Inc.

Law & Business, Inc. *See* Harcourt Brace Jovanovich, Inc.

Law Distributors, 14415 S. Main St., Gardena, CA 90248 (SAN 212-3681) Tel 213-321-3275; Toll free: 800-421-1893.

Le Jacq Publishing, Inc., (*Le Jacq Pub; 0-937716*), 53 Park Pl., New York, NY 10007 (SAN 658-4020) Tel 212-766-4300.

Learning Arts, P.O. Box 179, Wichita, KS 67201 (SAN 654-0376) Tel 316-682-6594.

Learning Research Project, P.O. Box 19312, Washington, DC 20036 (SAN 282-5961).

Lebanon Valley News Co., 37 S. 8th St., Lebanon, PA 17042 (SAN 169-7420).

Lectorum Pubns., (*Lectorum Pubns*), 137 W. 14th St., New York, NY 10011 (SAN 169-586X).

Leeward Pubns., Inc. *See* Presidio Pr.

Lemon Tree Press *See* Galahad Bks.

Lenox Hill Publishing and Distributing Corp., (*0-8337*), 235 E. 44th St., New York, NY 10017 (SAN 282-597X); Toll free: 800-223-0766.

Leonard, Hal, Publishing Corp., (*H Leonard Pub Corp; 0-9607350; 0-88188*), 8112 W. Bluemound Rd., P.O. Box 13819, Milwaukee, WI 53213 (SAN 239-250X) Tel 414-774-3630; Toll free: 800-558-4774.

Lescron Enterprises, P.O. Box B, Johnson City, NY 13790 (SAN 169-538X) Tel 607-729-4588; Toll free: 800-847-1669. All types of remainders & promotionals; cloth & paper, adult fiction & non-fiction, juvenile, mass market paper, quality trade paper, scholarly, art, educational, cookbooks & reference books.

Lesnick News, 2442 Mottman Rd. SW, Tumwater, WA 98502 (SAN 169-8877).

Levine, J., Religious Specials, 58 Eldridge St., New York, NY 10002 (SAN 169-5878).

Lewis, John W., Enterprises, 168 Perez St., P.O. Box 3375, Santurce, PR 00936 (SAN 169-9334).

Lexington Bks., Div. of D. C. Heath & Co., (*Lexington Bks; 0-669*), ; Toll free: 800-235-3565; Dist. by: D. C. Heath & Co., 125 Spring St., Lexington, MA 02173 (SAN 213-7526) Tel 617-862-6650; Orders to: Phyllis McGuinness, 125 Spring St., Lexington, MA 02173 (SAN 662-0701) Tel 617-860-1204.

Liberal Arts Pr. *See* Bobbs-Merrill Co.

Liberal Pr., The, (*Liberal Pr; 0-934659*), P.O. Box 160361, Las Colinas, TX 75016 (SAN 200-5360); Dist. by: Publishers Assocs., P.O. Box 160361, Las Colinas, TX 75106-9998 (SAN 200-6979) Tel 817-478-8564.

Liberation Distributors, P.O. Box 5341, Chicago, IL 60680 (SAN 169-880X).

Liberty Pr., Div. of Oldham & Associates, (*Liberty Pr; 0-936860*), 500 W. 1200 S., Orem, UT 84057 (SAN 264-1747).

Liberty Publishing Co., Inc., (*Liberty Pub; 0-89709*), P.O. Box 298, P.O. Box 298, Cockeysville, MD 21030 (SAN 211-030X) Tel 301-667-6680; 50 Scott Adam Rd., Cockeysville, MD 21030 (SAN 658-1145).

Libra-Bound TM Books, Box 19197, Greensboro, NC 27410 (SAN 159-8945).

Library Book Selection Service, P.O. Box 277, 2714 McGraw Dr., Bloomington, IL 61701 (SAN 169-1740).

Library of Psychological Anthropology *See* Psychohistory Pr.

Library Pr. *See* Open Court Publishing Co.

Library Professional Pubns. *See* Shoe String Pr., Inc.

Library Research Assocs., Inc., Subs. of Empire State Fiction, (*Lib Res; 0-912526*), Dunderberg Rd., RD 5, Box 41, Monroe, NY 10950 (SAN 201-0887) Tel 914-783-1144.

Library Systems & Services, Inc., A Gaylord Co., (*Lib Syst Serv*), 20251 Century Blvd., Germantown, MD 20874 (SAN 129-9611) Tel 301-428-3400; Toll free: 800-638-8725.

Libreria Bereana, 1825 San Alejandro, Urb San Ignacio, Rio Piedras, PR 00927 (SAN 169-9288).

Libreria Veiga, 151 Luna St., San Juan, PR 00901 (SAN 159-8961).

Libros Espanoles, 5455 SW Eighth St., Miami, FL 33134 (SAN 169-1147) Tel 305-442-0409.

LIDCO, 2849 Georgia Ave., NW, Washington, DC 20001 (SAN 282-6011).

Lifetime Learning Pubns. *See* Van Nostrand Reinhold Co., Inc.

Light Impressions Corp., (*Light Impressions; 0-87992*), 439 Monroe Ave. P.O. Box 940, Rochester, NY 14603 (SAN 169-619X) Tel 716-271-8960; Toll free: 800-828-6216.

Light of Egypt, Box 76862, Stanford Sta., Los Angeles, CA 90005 (SAN 159-8988).

Lighthouse Hill Publishing, (*Lighthouse Hill Pub; 0-9608690*), 279 Edinboro Rd., Lighthouse Hill, Staten Island, NY 10306 (SAN 238-0706) Tel 718-987-7586.

Lilly News Agency, P.O. Box 2218, Jonesboro, AR 72401 (SAN 168-9452).

Lincoln News Agency, P.O. Box 80267, Lincoln, NE 68501 (SAN 169-4413).

Linden Pr. *See* Simon & Schuster, Inc.

Lindisfarne Press *See* Inner Traditions International, Ltd.

Lindsay News & Photo Service Inc., 3025 Niagra St., MPO 948, Niagara Falls, NY 14303 (SAN 169-6092).

Lindsay Pubns., Inc., (*Lindsay Pubns; 0-917914*), P.O. Box 12, Bradley, IL 60915 (SAN 209-9462).

Ling's International Books, 7531 Convoy Ct., P.O Box 82684, San Diego, CA 92138 (SAN 169-0116).

Linnet *See* Shoe String Pr., Inc.

Lion Services Co., P.O. Box 667, Coronado, CA 92118 (SAN 168-9568).

Lippincott, J. B., , Harper & Row Medical Div. *See* Harper & Row Pubns., Inc.

Listen for Pleasure, Ltd., (*Listen Pleasure; 0-88646*), 1 Colomba Dr., Niagara Falls, NY 14305 (SAN 157-0668) Tel 716-298-5150; Toll free: 800-962-5200.

Listner's Pr., (*Listeners Pr; 0-9616943*), 75 Old Mill Rd., Rochester, NY 14618 (SAN 661-7840) Tel 716-244-8775; Dist. by: Adler Publishing Co., Panorama Plaza, Box 25333, Rochester, NY 14625 (SAN 285-6808) Tel 716-377-5804.

Little, Brown & Co., Div. of Time, Inc., (*Little; 0-316*), 34 Beacon St., Boston, MA 02108 (SAN 200-2205) Tel 617-227-0730; Toll free: 800-343-9204; Orders to: 200 West St., Waltham, MA 02254 (SAN 281-8892). *Imprints:* Little, Brown Medical Division (Little Med Div).

Little Dania's Juvenile Promotions, Div. of Booksmith Promotional Co., (*Little Danias*), 432 Park Ave. S., New York, NY 10016 (SAN 169-5681). Juvenile remainders & promotional assortments.

Little Simon *See* Simon & Schuster, Inc.

Little, Brown Medical Div. *See* Little, Brown & Co.

Living Bks., Inc., 12155 Magnolia Ave., Bldg. 11-B, Riverside, CA 92503 (SAN 169-006X) Tel 714-354-7330; Toll free: 800-854-4746; Toll free: 800-922-0047 (CA).

Living Language Seminars, (*Living Language*), 211 Greenoaks Dr., Atherton, CA 94025 (SAN 694-4035) Tel 415-324-3434; Dist. by: Ballard & Tighe, 480 Atlas St., Brea, CA 92621 (SAN 200-7991).

Llewellyn Pubns., Div. of Chester-Kent, Inc., (*Llewellyn Pubns; 0-87542*), P.O. Box 64383, St. Paul, MN 55164-0383 (SAN 201-100X) Tel 612-291-1970; Toll free: 800-843-6666; 213 E. Fourth St., St. Paul, MN 55101 (SAN 658-1161).

Loehr, Louise, 163 W. Main St., Kutztown, PA 19530 (SAN 200-8300).

Loge News Co., 1312 W. Florida St., Evansville, IN 47710 (SAN 169-233X).

Login Brothers Book Co., 1450 W. Randolph, Chicago, IL 60607 (SAN 169-183X).

Login Brothers East, 1550 Enterprise Rd., Twinsburg, OH 44087 (SAN 156-4439); Toll free: 800-321-8778.

Login Brothers New Jersey, 135 Dutch Lane, P.O. Box 2700, Fairfield, NJ 07006 (SAN 157-1427).

Logos Bks. *See* Contemporary Bks., Inc.

Lone Star College Bk., P.O. Box 19569, Austin, TX 78766 (SAN 200-6626).

Lone Star School Book Depository, 4640 Harry Haines Blvd., Dallas, TX 75235 (SAN 200-5697).

Long Play, Inc., 2611 E. Franklin Ave., Minneapolis, MN 55406 (SAN 206-6375).

Long Shadow Bks. *See* Pocket Bks., Inc.

Longman, Inc., Subs. of Longman Group USA, (*Longman; 0-582; 0-8013*), 95 Church St., White Plains, NY 10601 (SAN 202-6856) Tel 914-993-5000. *Imprints:* Drumbeat (Drumbeat).

Longwood Publishing Group, Inc., (*Longwood Pub Group; 0-89341*), 27 S. Main St, Wolfeboro, NH 03894-2069 (SAN 209-3170) Tel 603-569-4576; Toll free: 800-343-9444.

Loompanics Unlimited, (*Loompanics; 0-915179*), P.O. Box 1197, Port Townsend, WA 98368 (SAN 206-4421) Tel 206-385-5087.

Lord's Line, (*Lords Line; 0-915952*), 1734 Armour Lane, Redondo Beach, CA 90278 (SAN 207-7086) Tel 213-542-5575.

Lorrah & Hitchcock Pubs., Inc., *(Lorrah & Hitchcock; 0-89809),* 301 S. 15th St., Murray, KY 42071 (SAN 220-7915).

Los Angeles Mart, 1933 S Broadway, Suite 665, Los Angeles, CA 90007 (SAN 168-9797); Toll free: 800-556-2665 (Outside Ca); Toll free: 800-262-2665 (Inside CA).

Lotus Lignt Pubns., Affil. of Specialized Software, *(Lotus Light; 0-941524),* P.O. Box 2, Wilmot, WI 53192 (SAN 239-1120) Tel 414-862-2395.

Louisville News Co., P.O. Box 99008, Louisville, KY 40299 (SAN 169-2852).

Louisville News Co., 201 Oak St., Columbia, KY 42728 (SAN 169-281X).

Love Ministries, Inc., P.O. Box 69, Worthville, KY 41098 (SAN 662-2089).

Lovejoy Pr., The *See* **Paragon Bk. Gallery, Ltd.**

Lowell Pr., *(Lowell Pr; 0-913504; 0-932845),* 115 E. 31st St., Box 411877, Kansas City, MO 64141 (SAN 207-0774) Tel 816-753-4545.

Lubbock News Co., 118 E. 70th St., Lubbock, TX 79408 (SAN 169-8338).

Lubrecht & Cramer, Ltd., *(Lubrecht & Cramer; 0-934454),* RD 1, Box 244 Rte. 42 Forestburgh Rd., Forestburgh, NY 12777 (SAN 214-1256) Tel 914-794-8539.

Luce, Robert B., Inc., *(Luce; 0-88331),* 425 Asylum St., Bridgeport, CT 06610 (SAN 201-1069) Tel 203-334-2165; Toll free: 800-243-2790; Orders to: 540 Barnum Ave., Bridgeport, CT 06608 (SAN 201-1077) Tel 203-366-1900.

Lucky Star *See* **Scholastic, Inc.**

Ludington News Co., 901 Water St., Port Huron, MI 48060 (SAN 169-3972); 1600 E. Grand Blvd., Detroit, MI 48211 (SAN 169-3751); 2201 S. Dort Hwy., Flint, MI 48507 (SAN 169-3816).

Lueth, Shirley, 1409 Ninth St., Aurora, NE 68818 (SAN 282-5910).

Luthier's Mercantile, 412 Moore Ln., Healdsburg, CA 95448 (SAN 293-437X).

Luzerne County News Co., 152 N. Pennsylvania Ave., Wilkes Barre, PA 18701 (SAN 169-7676).

Lyons, Nick, Books *See* **Doubleday & Co., Inc.**

MAGIC, Inc., 1950 Craig Rd., St. Louis, MO 63146 (SAN 200-6022).

M & B Fulfillment Services, *(M & B Fulfillment),* 540 Barnum Ave., Bridgeport, CT 06610 (SAN 282-6062) Tel 203-366-1900.

M & J Book Fair Service, 2307 Sherwood Circle, Bloomington, MN 55431 (SAN 169-4030).

M & M News Agency, Civic Industrial Park, La Salle, IL 61301 (SAN 169-2062).

MBF Sports, Inc., 3940 Higuera St., Culver City, CA 90232-2505 (SAN 283-9717) Tel 213-204-1551.

MCA Pr., 575 Scarsdale Rd., Crestwood, NY 10707 (SAN 200-5514).

MCE, Inc., *(MCE Inc; 0-917999),* 157 S. Kalamazoo Mall, Suite 250, Kalamazoo, MI 49007 (SAN 285-5267) Tel 616-345-8681; Toll free: 800-421-4157.

MIT Pr., *(MIT Pr; 0-262),* 28 Carleton St., Cambridge, MA 02142 (SAN 202-6414) Tel 617-253-2884.

M R K Enterprizes, P.O. Box 416, Waterford, MI 48095 (SAN 239-4928).

M-S News Co., Inc., P.O. Box 11165, Wichita, KS 67202 (SAN 169-2798).

Macalester Park Bookstore, *(Macalester; 0-910924),* 1571 Grand Ave., St. Paul, MN 55105 (SAN 110-8077) Tel 612-698-8877.

McCalls, 230 Park Ave., New York, NY 10017 (SAN 286-0090).

McCuen, Gary E., Pubns., Inc., *(G E McCuen Pubns; 0-86596),* 411 Mallalieu Dr., Hudson, WI 54016 (SAN 691-909X) Tel 715-386-5662.

McElderry Bk. *See* **Atheneum Pubs.**

McGraw-Hill Bk. Co., *(McGraw; 0-07; 0-914410),* 1221 Ave. of the Americas, New York, NY 10020 (SAN 200-2248) Tel 212-512-2000; Toll free: 800-628-0004; Orders to: Princeton Rd., Hightstown, NJ 08520 (SAN 200-254X) Tel 609-426-5254; Orders to: 8171 Redwood Hwy., Novato, CA 94947 (SAN 200-2566) Tel 415-897-5201; Orders to: 13955 Manchester Rd., Manchester, MO 63011 (SAN 200-2558) Tel 314-227-1600. *Imprints:* Architectural Record Books (Architectural Rec Bks); BYTE Books (BYTE Bks); C T B/McGraw-Hill (CTB McGraw Hill); Chemical Engineering (Chem Eng); I B C (IBC); Instructo/McGraw-Hill (Instructo); Pre-Test (Pre-Test); Pre-Text Series (Pre-Text Series); Professional & Reference Book Division (Prof & Ref Bk Div).

MacGregor News Agency, 1733 Industrial Park Dr., Mount Pleasant, MI 48858 (SAN 169-3921).

McGregor Subscription Agency, Mt. Morris, IL 61054 (SAN 286-0147); Toll free: 800-852-7404.

McKnight Sales Co, P.O. Box 4138, Pittsburgh, PA 15202 (SAN 169-7587).

McMahon Vintage Radio, P.O. Box 1331, N. Highlands, N. Highlands, CA 95660 (SAN 282-6356) Tel 916-332-8262.

Macmillan Publishing Co., Inc., *(Macmillan; 0-02),* 866 Third Ave., New York, NY 10022 (SAN 202-5574) Tel 212-702-2000; Toll free: 800-257-5755; Orders to: Front & Brown Sts., Riverside, NJ 08370 (SAN 202-5582). Do not confuse with McMillan Pubns., Woodridge, IL. *Imprints:* Acorn Books (Acorn); Aladdin Books (Aladdin Bks); Berlitz (Berlitz); Collier Books (Collier); Crowell-Collier Press (CCPr); Dove Books (Dove).

Macoy Publishing & Masonic Supply Co., Inc., *(Macoy Pub; 0-910928; 0-88053),* P.O. Box 9759, Richmond, VA 23228 (SAN 202-2265) Tel 804-262-6551.

MacRae, Julia *See* **Watts, Franklin, Inc.**

MacRae's Indian Book Dist., 1605 Cole St., P.O. Box 652, Enumclaw, WA 98022 (SAN 157-5473) Tel 206-825-3737.

Made Simple Books *See* **Doubleday & Co., Inc.**

Madrona Pubs., Inc., *(Madrona Pubs; 0-914842; 0-88089),* P.O. Box 22667, Seattle, WA 98122 (SAN 212-0283); 113 Madrona Pl., E., Seattle, WA 98112 (SAN 281-9678) Tel 206-325-3973; Dist. by: Interbook, 14895 E. 14th St., Suite 370, San Leandro, CA 94577 (SAN 202-5191) Tel 415-352-9221.

Mafex Associates, Inc., *(Mafex; 0-87804),* 90 Cherry St., Johnstown, PA 15902 (SAN 202-2591) Tel 814-535-3597.

Mag-Cia Distributors, Cerra 722, Santurce, PR 00907 (SAN 156-4528).

Magazine Distributors, Inc., 15 Sparks St., Plainville, CT 06062 (SAN 169-0817).

Magazine Supply House Inc., 30 Washington Square, Worchester, MA 01604 (SAN 286-0066).

Magazines, Inc., 1135 Hammond St., Bangor, ME 04401 (SAN 169-3034); Toll free: 800-432-7993 (Maine Only).

Magee Bk. Store, 118 N. Montezuma St., Prescott, AZ 86301 (SAN 200-6588).

Magna Books (Nancy Olds), Buttonwood, Sannibel, FL 33957 (SAN 200-4267) Tel 813-472-6777.

Magnuson Marketing, Inc., 605 E. Fourth St., Willmar, MN 56201 (SAN 200-6561).

Magtek Media, 17 Church Ave., Brooklyn, NY 11218 (SAN 692-2511) Tel 718-851-8383; Toll free: 800-221-0869.

Maher, Richard, Sales, P.O. Box 531 N, Salt Lake City, UT 84054 (SAN 158-8141).

Mahoning Valley Distributing Agency, Inc., 2556 Rush Blvd., Youngstown, OH 44507 (SAN 169-6920).

Mailhouse, Inc., 8711 Glendale Ave., S., Minneapolis, MN 55420 (SAN 282-6194) Tel 612-881-8888.

Main Line Book Co., Inc., P.O. Box 914, Bryn Mawr, PA 19010 (SAN 169-7331); Toll free: 800-523-0458.

Main Street Press *See* **Universe Bks., Inc.**

Maine Writers & Publishers Alliance, *(Maine Writers),* 25 A Forest Ave., Portland, ME 04101 (SAN 224-2303) Tel 207-729-6333; P.O. Box 7542OTS, Portland, ME 04112 (SAN 693-9805).

Majors, J. A., P.O. Box 819074, Dallas, TX 75061-9074 (SAN 169-8117); 3770A Zip Industrial Blvd., Atlanta, GA 30354 (SAN 169-1406) Tel 404-768-4956; 3909 Bienville St., New Orleans, LA 70119 (SAN 169-2984); 1806 Southgate, Houston, TX 77030 (SAN 169-8281).

Management Associates, P.O. Box 230, Chestnut Hill, MA 02167 (SAN 212-050X).

Manchester News Co., Inc., 30 Rundlett Hill Rd., Bedford, NH 03102 (SAN 169-4480).

Manhattan Institute for Policy Research Book *See* **Universe Bks., Inc.**

Manitowoc News Agency, 907 S. Eighth St., Manitowoc, WI 54220 (SAN 159-9046).

Mankind Research Foundation, 1315 Apple Ave., Silver Spring, MD 20910 (SAN 208-4422).

ManRoot Press, *(0-914433),* Box 982, South San Francisco, CA 94080 (SAN 201-5811) Tel 707-996-9551.

Manson News Distributors, 634 South Ave., Box 1211, Rochester, NY 14620 (SAN 169-6203) Tel 716-244-3880.

Manufacturers Productivity Ctr., ITT Ctr., 10 W. 35th St., Chicago, IL 60616 (SAN 694-9606).

Many Feathers Southwest Books & Maps, 5738 N. Central, Phoenix, AZ 85012 (SAN 158-8877).

Marboro Bks., *(Marboro Bks; 0-88029),* 205 Moonachie Rd., Moonachie, NJ 07074 (SAN 150-8059). Publishers' remainders (primarily hardcover) & hardcover reprints to trade, institutional & foreign markets. Specialize in art, biography, history, literature & quality fiction.

Marco Book Distributors, *(0-88298),* P.O. Box 108, Rugby Sta., Brooklyn, NY 11203 (SAN 169-5142).

Mardelva News Co., Inc., 635 Homer St., Salisbury, MD 21801 (SAN 169-3247).

Marine Science International *See* **Jones & Bartlett Pubs., Inc.**

Marketing Systems Corp., 1100 State Hwy. 33, Ham. Square, NJ 08690 (SAN 286-004X).

Marlin Pubns. International, Inc., *(Marlin; 0-930624),* P.O. Box 649, Plandomen, NY 11030 (SAN 210-9824) Tel 516-365-3788.

Marquette County Historical Soc., Inc., *(Marquette Cnty; 0-938746),* 213 N. Front St., Marquette, MI 49855 (SAN 205-8871) Tel 906-226-3571.

Marshall, J. L., News, 5109 Winton Rd., P.O. Box 14249, Cincinnati, OH 45214 (SAN 169-6610).

Marshall-Mangold Distribution Co., 4805 Nelson Ave., Baltimore, MD 21215 (SAN 169-3115).

Marshall News Co., 19 Jackson St., Batavia, NY 14020 (SAN 169-5045).

Marshalltown News Agency, 24 N. First Ave., Marshalltown, IA 50158 (SAN 169-2674).

Marston's, P.O. Box 789, Presque Isle, ME 04769 (SAN 169-3069); Presque Isle Shopping Plaza, Presque Isle, ME 04769 (SAN 169-3077).

Martin, Jack, News Agency, P.O. Box 6427, Tyler, TX 75711 (SAN 169-8451).

Martin, Louis J., & Assocs., Inc., *(L J Martin; 0-916800),* Box 247, Rye, NY 10580 (SAN 209-0945) Tel 914-967-0978. Remainder sales.

Maruzen International Co., 1251 Ave. of the Americas, Suite 1780, New York, NY 10020 (SAN 286-0058).

Marwill Book Co., Cass and Warren Aves., Detroit, MI 48201 (SAN 225-2112).

Maryland Historical Pr., *(Maryland Hist Pr; 0-917882),* 9205 Tuckerman St., Lanham, MD 20706 (SAN 202-6147) Tel 301-577-5308.

Maryland News Distribution Co., 1621 Cole St., Baltimore, MD 21203 (SAN 169-3123); P.O. Box 1777, Baltimore, MD 21203 (SAN 281-9872).

Massachusetts Institute of Technology Pr. *See* **MIT Pr.**

Wholesalers & Distributors

Matagiri, Mount Tremper, NY 12457 (SAN 169-5541).
Matthews Medical Book Co., 11559 Rock Island, St. Louis, MO 63043 (SAN 169-4316); Toll free: 800-633-2665.
Maxwell Scientific International, Inc., *(Maxwell Sci Intl; 0-8277),* 395 Saw Hill River Rd., Elmsford, NY 10523 (SAN 203-9761) Tel 914-592-9141.
Maya Publishing Co. *See* Univ. Pr. of Virginia
Mayapple Pr., *(Mayapple Pr; 0-932412),* P.O. Box 3185, Kent, OH 44240 (SAN 212-1913) Tel 216-678-2775.
Mayday Software, *(0-925190),* P.O. Box 66, Rock Creek Rd., Phillips, WI 54555 (SAN 287-6167) Tel 715-339-3966.
Mayflower Bks. *See* Dell Publishing Co., Inc.
MC-P Applications, Inc., 1630 Oakland Rd., Suite A114, San Jose, CA 95131 (SAN 654-4959) Tel 408-293-3360; Toll free: 800-292-3360.
Meader Book Distributing, 1686 Gervais Ave., Saint Paul, MN 55109 (SAN 169-4162).
Meadville News Co., Inc., 105 Mead Ave., Meadville, PA 16335-3597 (SAN 169-7455).
Medallion Bks. *See* Berkley Publishing Group
Media Productions & Marketing, Inc., *(Media Prods & Mktg; 0-939644),* 2440 "O" St., Suite 202, Lincoln, NE 68510-1125 (SAN 216-6372) Tel 402-474-2676.
Media Products, *(Media Prod Chatsworth),* 21540 Prairie St., Unit C, Chatsworth, CA 91311 (SAN 200-6960) Tel 818-341-3156; Toll free: 800-262-7367.
Media Unlimited Inc., *(Media Unltd; 0-930394),* P.O. Box I, Alameda, CA 94501 (SAN 210-6124); Toll free: 800-428-0902.
Mediatech, 737 Bishop St., Suite 2790, Honolulu, HI 96813 (SAN 200-6456).
Medical & Professional Books, 45 Hudson, Ridgewood, NJ 07450 (SAN 158-927X).
Medical & Technical Books,Inc., 11511 Tennessee Ave., Los Angeles, CA 90064 (SAN 168-9800) Tel 213-879-1607; Toll free: 800-421-7149.
Medicine Bow Post, P.O. Box 56, Medicine Bow, WY 82329 (SAN 200-7053) Tel 307-379-2255.
Mehlman, Terry, Box E-94, Richmond, IN 47374 (SAN 200-6065).
Melton Book Co., Inc., 111 Leslie St., Dallas, TX 75207 (SAN 169-8133); Toll free: 800-527-7830.
Melville Memorial Library, State Univ. of New York at Stony Brook, Stony Brook, NY 11794 (SAN 200-4275).
Menasha Ridge Pr., Inc., *(Menasha Ridge; 0-940752; 0-89732),* P.O. Box 59257, Birmingham, AL 35259 (SAN 219-7294) Tel 205-991-0373; Dist. by: Simon & Schuster, 1230 Ave. of the Americas, New York, NY 10020 (SAN 200-2450) Tel 212-245-6400. *Imprints:* Book Arts (Book Arts).
Mendocino Software Co., Inc., *(Mendocino Soft; 0-925240),* P.O. Box 1564, Willits, CA 95490 (SAN 265-489X) Tel 707-459-9130.
Mentor Bks. *See* New American Library
Merced News Co., P.O. Box 857, Merced, CA 95341 (SAN 168-9894).
Mercedes Book Distributors Corp., 60 Imlay St., Brooklyn, NY 11231 (SAN 169-5150).
Mercer Univ. Pr., *(Mercer Univ Pr; 0-86554),* Macon, GA 31207 (SAN 220-0716) Tel 912-744-2880.
Mercury Distributors, P.O. Box 25616, Seattle, WA 98125 (SAN 169-8818).
Meridian Bks. *See* New American Library
Merle Distributing Co., 27222 Plymouth Rd., Detroit, MI 48239 (SAN 169-3778); Toll free: 800-233-9380 (Orders).
Metacom, Inc., *(Metacom Inc; 0-88676),* 1401 B. West River Rd., Minneapolis, MN 55411 (SAN 265-279X) Tel 612-588-2781; Toll free: 800-328-4818.
Metropolitan Museum of Art, *(Metro Mus Art; 0-87099),* Fifth Ave. & 82nd St., New York, NY 10028 (SAN 202-6279) Tel 212-879-5500; Dist. by: Univ. of Chicago Pr., 5801 Ellis Ave. S., 3rd Flr., Chicago, IL 60637 (SAN 202-5280) Tel 312-962-7693.
Metropolitan Music Co., Mountain Rd., Stowe, VT 05672 (SAN 282-6437).
Metropolitan News Co., 47-25 34th, Long Island City, NY 11101 (SAN 159-9089).
Miami Valley News Agency, 2127 Old Troy Pike, Dayton, OH 45404 (SAN 169-6718).

Michelman, Herbert, Bks. *See* Crown Pubs., Inc.
Michiana News Service, 2232 S. 11th St., Niles, MI 49120 (SAN 110-5051).
Michigan State Univ. Pr., *(Mich St U Pr; 0-87013),* 1405 S. Harrison Rd., 25 Manly Miles Bldg., East Lansing, MI 48824 (SAN 202-6295) Tel 517-355-9543; Dist. by: Wayne State Univ. Pr., Leonard N. Simons Bldg., 5959 Woodward Ave., Detroit, MI 48202 (SAN 202-5221) Tel 313-577-4601.
Micro-80, Inc., *(Micro-Eighty; 0-925350),* 2665 N. Busby Rd., Oak Harbor, WA 98277 (SAN 287-6388).
Micro Match, *(Micro Match),* 958 Foothill Blvd., La Canada, CA 91011 (SAN 692-1221) Tel 818-952-1185; Toll free: 800-345-4706.
Micro-Media, *(Micro Med),* 61 S. Lake Ave., P.O. Box 4509, Pasadena, CA 91106 (SAN 287-6752).
Micro Pace Computers, 1510 N. Neil St., Champaign, IL 61820 (SAN 200-7762) Tel 217-356-1883.
Micro Works, Inc., The, *(Micro Works),* 1942 S. El Camino Real, Encinitas, CA 92024 (SAN 277-6049) Tel 619-942-2400.
Microdistributors International, Inc., Subs. of Medcomp Technologies, Inc., *(Microdist Intl; 0-918025),* 34 Maple Ave., P.O. Box 8, Armonk, NY 10504 (SAN 296-158X) Tel 914-273-6480.
Mid-Cal Periodical Distributors, 6211 Power Inn Rd., Box 20486, Sacramento, CA 95820 (SAN 169-0078).
Mid Continent News Co., Box 25489, Oklahoma City, OK 73125 (SAN 169-7005).
Mid-Pacific Book Distributors Ltd., 150 Haili St., Hilo, HI 96720 (SAN 169-1597).
Mid Penn Magazine Agency, 100 Eck Cir., Williamsport, PA 17701 (SAN 169-7692).
Mid South Manufacturing Agency, Inc., Box 4585, Jackson, MS 39216 (SAN 286-0163).
Mid-State Distributors, 1203 W. Walnut St., Jacksonville, IL 62650 (SAN 169-2038).
Middle Tennessee News Co., Rte. 4, Shelbyville, TN 37160 (SAN 169-8001).
Middletown News Agency, 1223 Hook Dr., P.O. Box B, Middletown, OH 45042 (SAN 169-6815).
Midland Bks. *See* Indiana Univ. Pr.
Midtown Auto Books, 212 Burnet Ave., Syracuse, NY 13203 (SAN 169-6289).
Midtown Stationery & Supply Co., 2658 Pittman Dr., Silver Spring, MD 20910 (SAN 699-4105) Tel 301-588-6777.
Midway Reprint *See* Univ. of Chicago Pr.
Midwest Distributors, P.O. Box 4642, Kansas City, MO 64109 (SAN 219-5038).
Midwest European Pubns., 915 Foster St., Evanston, IL 60201 (SAN 169-1937).
Midwest Library Service, *(Midwest Lib Serv),* 11443 St. Charles Rock Rd., Bridgeton, MO 63044-9986 (SAN 169-4243) Tel 314-739-3100.
Midwest Natural Foods, 170 April Dr., Ann Arbor, MI 48103 (SAN 169-3689).
Midwest Publishing & Distributing Service, P.O. Box 239, Portage, WI 53901 (SAN 200-805X).
Mikofsky, Anton, Turtle Island Foundation & Barbary Coast, 57 W. 84th St., New York, NY 10024 (SAN 219-5747).
Milford House, Div. of Longwood Pub. Group, *(Milford Hse; 0-87821),* 51 Washington St., Dover, NH 03820 (SAN 202-6368); Toll free: 800-343-9444.
Milligan News Co., Inc., 150 N. Autumn St., San Jose, CA 95110 (SAN 169-0272).
Minerva Sci Bookseller Inc., 175 Fifth Ave., New York, NY 10010 (SAN 286-0171).
Minor-Dixon Magazine Service, P.O. Box 8211, Lexington, KY 40503 (SAN 286-018X).
Minstrel Books *See* Simon & Schuster, Inc.
Mission House, 1670 E 1300 South, Salt Lake City, UT 84105 (SAN 158-8052).
Mississippi Library Media & Supply Co., P.O. Box 108, Brandon, MS 39042-0108 (SAN 169-4189) Tel 601-939-7571; Toll free: 800-357-7566.
Missouri Archaeological Society, *(MO Arch Soc; 0-943414),* P.O. Box 958, Columbia, MO 65205 (SAN 238-8316).
Missouri Book Services, P.O. Box 637, Columbia, MO 65205 (SAN 140-7015); Toll free: 800-325-0577.

Mitchell, Anita V, *(A V Mitchell; 0-931155),* 171 W. 57 St., New York, NY 10019 (SAN 679-3800) Tel 212-246-3631; Dist. by: Peninsula, 156 Fifth Ave, New York, NY 10010 (SAN 200-5069).
Mitchell, Mary, 2810 R St., NW, Washington, DC 20007 (SAN 200-4100) Tel 202-333-2401.
Mix Publications, *(Mix Pubns; 0-918371),* 2608 Ninth St., Berkeley, CA 94710 (SAN 657-3657) Tel 415-843-7901.
Mobile News Co., 3001 Mill St., Box 7501, Mobile, AL 36607 (SAN 168-924X).
Modelsmart, 1017 E. 48th St., New York, NY 10017 (SAN 200-4305).
Modern Books/Crafts Inc., P.O. Box 38, Greens Farms, CT 06436 (SAN 161-5653).
Modern Curriculum Pr., Div. of Esquire, Inc., *(Modern Curr; 0-87895; 0-8136),* 13900 Prospect Rd., Cleveland, OH 44136 (SAN 206-6572); Toll free: 800-321-3106.
Modern Library College Edition *See* Random Hse., Inc.
Modern Liturgy *See* Resource Pubns., Inc.
Modesto News Co., P.O. Box 5038, Modesto, CA 95352 (SAN 168-9908).
Moffat Publishing Co., Inc., *(Moffat Pub; 0-86670),* Box 236, Nutley, NJ 07110 (SAN 217-2569) Tel 201-235-9444.
Montfort Pubns., Div. of Montfort Missionaries, *(Montfort Pubns; 0-910984),* 26 S. Saxon Ave., Bay Shore, NY 11706 (SAN 169-5053) Tel 516-665-0726.
Montgomery News Co., P.O. Box 1149, Montgomery, AL 36102 (SAN 168-9258).
Monthly Review Pr., Div. of Monthly Review Foundation, Inc., *(Monthly Rev; 0-85345),* 155 W. 23rd St., New York, NY 10011 (SAN 202-6481) Tel 212-691-2555.
Montrose Publishing Co., 10-20 S. Main St., Montrose, PA 18801 (SAN 200-6898) Tel 717-278-1141; Toll free: 800-782-5474.
Moody, J.S., 211 Fireside Rd., Falmouth, ME 04105 (SAN 282-5872) Tel 207-781-4571.
Mook & Blanchard, 546 S. Hofgaarden, P.O. Box 1295, La Puente, CA 91749-1295 (SAN 168-9703).
Moonlight Editions *See* Schocken Bks., Inc.
Moore-Cottrell Sub. Agencies, Seven N. Main St., North Cohocton, NY 14868 (SAN 285-9203).
More, Thomas, Assn., 223 W. Erie St., Chicago, IL 60610 (SAN 169-1880) Tel 312-951-2100.
Moretus Pr., Inc., The, *(Moretus Pr; 0-89679),* P.O. Box 867, Ossining, NY 10562-0867 (SAN 211-2523) Tel 914-941-0409.
Morgan & Morgan, Inc., Affil. of Morgan Pr., Inc., *(Morgan; 0-87100),* 145 Palisade St., Dobbs Ferry, NY 10522 (SAN 202-5620) Tel 914-693-0023.
Morgan Kaufmann Pubs., Inc., *(Morgan Kaufmann; 0-934613),* 95 First St., Suite 120, Los Altos, CA 94022 (SAN 693-918X) Tel 415-941-4960; Orders to: P.O. Box 50490, Palo Alto, CA 94303 (SAN 200-2272) Tel 415-965-4081.
Morlock News Co., Inc., 496 Duanesburg Rd., Schenectady, NY 12306 (SAN 169-6246).
Morningside Bookshop, *(Morningside Bkshop),* P.O. Box 1087, Dayton, OH 45401 (SAN 202-2206) Tel 513-461-6736.
Morrell, Charles, & Associates, 1569 Palifadef Dr., Pacific Palifadef, CA 90272 (SAN 200-4585).
Morris Aviation Ltd., P.O. Box 718, Statesborough, GA 30458 (SAN 200-4593) Tel 912-489-8161.
Morris County Historical Society, *(M C H S; 0-910301),* P.O. Box 170 M, Morristown, NJ 07960 (SAN 241-4104) Tel 201-267-3465.
Morrow, William, & Co., Inc., Subs. of Hearst Corp., *(Morrow; 0-688),* 105 Madison Ave., New York, NY 10016 (SAN 202-5760) Tel 212-889-3050; Toll free: 800-631-1199; Orders to: Wilmor Warehouse, 6 Henderson Dr., West Caldwell, NJ 07006 (SAN 202-5779). *Imprints:* Quill Paperbacks (Quill); Reynal (Reynal).
Mosby, C.V., Co., Subs. of The Times Mirror Co., *(Mosby; 0-8016),* 11830 Westline Industrial Dr., St. Louis, MO 63146 (SAN 200-2280) Tel 314-872-8370; Toll free: 800-325-4177.
Moshy Brothers Inc., 89 Chambers St., New York, NY 10007 (SAN 169-5886).

Mother Lode Distributing, 119 E. Theall St., Sonora, CA 95370-5798 (SAN 169-0361).

Motheroot Pubns., (Motheroot; 0-934238), P.O. Box 8306, Pittsburgh, PA 15218-0306 (SAN 216-4205) Tel 412-731-4453.

Motorbooks International, Pubs. & Wholesalers, Inc., Subs. of Motorbooks Zenith Aviation, (Motorbooks Intl; 0-87938), 729 Prospect Ave., Osceola, WI 54020 (SAN 169-9164) Tel 715-294-3345; Toll free: 800-826-6600; Orders to: Box 2, Osceola, WI 54020 (SAN 699-5462).

Mountain Plains Supply Co., 5175 W. Yale, Fort Logan, CO 80236 (SAN 159-9119).

Mountain States News Distributor, P.O. Drawer P, Fort Collins, CO 80522 (SAN 169-0566).

Moza Pubns., Ltd., 5010 Austin Rd., Chattanooga, TN 37443 (SAN 157-860X).

Mullare News Agency, Inc., P.O. Box 578, Brockton, MA 02401 (SAN 169-3379).

Multi-Media Education, P.O. Box 35396, Detroit, MI 48235 (SAN 200-7126) Tel 313-342-1261.

Multi Media Resource Ctr., (MMRC; 0-9603968; 0-914684), 1525 Franklin St., San Francisco, CA 94109 (SAN 206-6017) Tel 415-673-5100.

Multilingual Books, P.O. Box 440632-Tamiami Sta., Miami, FL 33144 (SAN 169-1155).

Multitech Electronics, Inc., (Multitech Elect), 1012 Stewart Dr., Sunnyvale, CA 94086 (SAN 692-1949) Tel 408-773-8400; Toll free: 800-538-1542.

Mumford Library Book Sales, 7847 Bayberry Dr., Jacksonville, FL 32216 (SAN 156-7721); Rte. 2, Box 135, Hwy 544, Plano, TX 75074 (SAN 169-8400).

Muscogee News Co., P.O. Box 13645, Atlanta, GA 30324 (SAN 169-1414); Box 2628, Columbus, GA 31902 (SAN 169-149X).

Museum Shop, 100 W. 14th Ave., Denver, CO 80204 (SAN 200-4704) Tel 303-575-2253.

Music Sales Corp., (Music Sales; 0-8256), 24 E. 22nd St., New York, NY 10010 (SAN 282-0277) Tel 212-254-2100; Toll free: 800-431-7187; Orders to: Music Sales Distribution Ctr., 5 Bellvale Rd., P.O. Box 572, Chester, NY 10918 (SAN 662-0876) Tel 914-469-2271. Imprints: Acorn Music Press (Acorn); Amsco Music (Amsco Music); Hidden House (Hidden Hse); Oak Pubns. (Oak).

Mustang Publishing, (Mustang Pub; 0-914457), P.O. Box 9327, New Haven, CT 06533 (SAN 289-6702) Tel 203-624-5485; Dist. by: Kampmann & Co., Inc., 9 E. 40th St., New York, NY 10016 (SAN 202-5191) Tel 212-685-2928.

NCCPA Headquarters, Department of Journalism, Memphis State Univ., Memphis, TN 38152 (SAN 282-0390).

NTC Distributing Co., Inc., 25 Berry St., Framingham, MA 01701 (SAN 159-9135).

Nancy Roberts' Collection, 3600 Chevington Rd., Charlotte, NC 28211 (SAN 696-723X).

Napa Book Co., 1134 Main St., Napa, CA 94558 (SAN 122-2732).

Napsac Reproductions, (Napsac Reprods; 0-934426), Rte. 1 Box 646, Marble Hill, MO 63764 (SAN 222-4607) Tel 314-238-2010.

Narada Distributors, 1804 E. North St., Milwaukee, WI 53202 (SAN 200-7649); Toll free: 800-862-7232.

Nascorp, Inc., 528 E. Lorain St., Oberlin, OH 44074 (SAN 169-6823) Tel 216-775-8048; Toll free: 800-321-3883 (Orders Only); Toll free: 800-362-5422 (Ohio).

National Art Education Assn., (Natl Art Ed; 0-937652), 1916 Association Dr., Reston, VA 22091 (SAN 203-7084) Tel 703-860-8000.

National Assn. for Search & Rescue, (Natl Assn Search & Rescue), P.O. Box 50178, Washington, DC 20004 (SAN 224-3164).

National Assn. of College Stores, (NACS), 528 E. Lorain St., Oberlin, OH 44074 (SAN 231-4088) Tel 216-775-7777; Toll free: 800-321-3883.

National Assn. of Home Builders, Div. of The National Assn. of Home Manufacturers, (Nat Assn H Build; 0-86718), 15th & M Sts., NW, Washington, DC 20005 (SAN 207-7035); Toll free: 800-368-5242.

National Assn. of Wholesale Distributors, (Natl Assn Wholesale Dists), 1725 K St., NW, Washington, DC 20006 (SAN 224-9820) Tel 202-872-0885.

National Bk. Distributors, 1578 Litton Dr., Stone Mountain, GA 30083 (SAN 169-1570); 6301 Forbing Rd., Little Rock, AR 72209 (SAN 169-3735); 625 Bev. Rd., Youngstown, OH 44512 (SAN 169-6939); 1125 King St., Alexandria, VA 22314-2993 (SAN 169-8613).

National Braille Pr., (Natl Braille Pr; 0-939173), 88 St. Stephen St., Boston, MA 02115 (SAN 273-0952).

National Business Journals Division Periodicals Buyers, 280 Madison Ave., New York, NY 10016 (SAN 285-9211).

National Catholic Reading Distributor, 545 Island Rd., Ramsey, NJ 07446 (SAN 169-4855).

National College of District Attorneys, (Natl Coll DA), Univ. of Houston, Bates College of Law, Houston, TX 77004 (SAN 225-0934) Tel 713-749-1571.

National Computer Communications Corp., 260 West Ave., Stamford, CT 06904 (SAN 678-3619) Tel 203-357-0004; Toll free: 800-243-9006.

National Concrete Burial Vault Assn., (Nat Conc Burial), Box 1031, Battle Creek, MI 49016 (SAN 273-2297).

National Criminal Reference Service, P.O. Box 6000, Rockville, MD 20850 (SAN 200-7320).

National Distribution Ctr., 2100 Ogden Ave., Lisle, IL 60532 (SAN 200-6251).

National Education Ctr., 1300 N. Bristoll, Newport Beach, CA 92660 (SAN 200-8041).

National Lawyers Guild Report, P.O. Box 14023, Washington, DC 20044 (SAN 212-5315) Tel 202-223-3111.

National Learning Corp., (Natl Learning; 0-8373; 0-8293), 212 Michael Dr., Syosset, NY 11791 (SAN 206-8869) Tel 516-921-8888; Toll free: 800-645-6337. Educational, commercial, industrial and government sales.

National Magazine Service, P.O. Box 4200, Pittsburgh, PA 15202 (SAN 169-7595).

National Organization Service, Inc., Div. of National Org. Ser. Inc., 401 Shops Bldg., Des Moines, IA 50309 (SAN 107-1548).

National Pr., Inc., (Natl Pr Inc; 0-915765), 7508 Wisconsin Ave., Bethesda, MD 20814 (SAN 293-8839) Tel 301-657-1616.

National Sales Inc., 1818 W. 2300 South, Salt Lake City, UT 84119 (SAN 159-9127).

National Software Marketing, (0-925776), 4701 McKinley St., Hollywood, FL 33021 (SAN 265-7252) Tel 305-625-6062.

National Technical Information Service, U. S. Dept. of Commerce, (Natl Tech Info; 0-934213), 5285 Port Royal Rd., Springfield, VA 22161 (SAN 205-7255) Tel 703-487-4838.

National Textbook Co., (Natl Textbk; 0-8442; 0-8325), 4255 W. Touhy Ave., Chicago, IL 60646 (SAN 169-2208) Tel 312-679-5500; Toll free: 800-854-4014. Imprints: Passport Books (Passport Bks).

National Writers Pr., The, Div. of National Writers Club, Subs. of Association Headquarters, Inc., (Natl Writ Pr; 0-88100), 1450 S. Havana, Suite 620, Aurora, CO 80012 (SAN 240-320X) Tel 303-751-7844.

Naturegraph Pubns., Inc., (Naturegraph; 0-911010; 0-87961), P.O. Box 1075, Happy Camp, CA 96039 (SAN 202-8999) Tel 916-493-5353.

Naturists, P.O. Box 132, Oshkosh, WI 54902 (SAN 223-887X) Tel 414-231-9950.

Nazarene Publishing Hse., (Nazarene; 0-8341), P.O. Box 527, Kansas City, MO 64141 (SAN 202-9022) Tel 816-931-1900.

Nebraska Book, P.O. Box 80529, Lincoln, NE 68501 (SAN 122-2902).

Neff-Kane See Presidio Pr.

Neighborhood Per. Club, Northland Towers, 650 Northland Blvd., Suite 21, Cincinnati, OH 45240 (SAN 285-9262).

Neilson Library, Office of the Director of Technical Services, Northhampton, MA 01063 (SAN 204-6040) Tel 413-584-2700.

Nelson News Agency, 728 First Ave., N., Fort Dodge, IA 50501 (SAN 169-2658).

Nelson News Inc., 4651 F St., Omaha, NE 68117 (SAN 169-443X).

Ner Tamid Book Distributors, P.O. Box 10401, West Palm Beach, FL 33404 (SAN 169-135X).

Net Productions, Box AA, Woodland Park, CO 80863 (SAN 159-9143).

Network, P.O. Box 2246, Berkeley, CA 94702 (SAN 159-0332).

Networx Data Products Co., Inc., 188 Main St., Northport, NY 11768 (SAN 695-5177) Tel 516-754-2798; Toll free: 800-531-0019.

New Age Bible & Philosophy Ctr., (New Age Bible; 0-933963), 1139 Lincoln Blvd., Santa Monica, CA 90403 (SAN 693-0697) Tel 213-395-4346; Dist. by DeVorss & Co., P.O. Box, 1046 Princeton Dr., Marina del Rey, CA 90294 (SAN 168-9886) Tel 213-870-7478.

New Alexandria Books, 122 S. Cayuga St., Ithaca, NY 14850 (SAN 159-4958).

New American Library, (NAL; 0-451; 0-452; 0-453), 1633 Broadway, New York, NY 10019 (SAN 206-8079) Tel 212-397-8000; Orders to: P.O. Box 999, Bergenfield, NJ 07621 (SAN 206-8087) Tel 201-387-0600. Imprints: Mentor Books (Ment); Meridian Books (Mer); Onyx (Onyx); Plume Books (Plume); Signet Books (Sig); Signet Classics (Sig Classics); Signette (Sgnt).

New American Library See Norton, W. W., & Co., Inc.

New England Mobile Book Fair, 82 Needham St., Newton Highlands, MA 02158 (SAN 169-3530); 84 Needham St., Newton Highlands, MA 02161 (SAN 282-0498).

New Era Pr., (0-9610380), P.O. Box 29, Farmingdale, NY 11735 (SAN 264-2441) Tel 516-277-9708; 161 Damarack St., Islip, NY 11751 (SAN 264-245X).

New Haven News Agency, P.O. Box 1624, New Haven, CT 06506 (SAN 169-0744).

New Jersey Books, Inc., 59 Market St., Newark, NJ 07102 (SAN 156-5443); 713 Cedar Lane, Teaneck, NJ 07666 (SAN 159-7310).

New Jersey State News Co., Canal Dr. & Deliha Rd., Pleasantville, NJ 08232 (SAN 169-457X).

New Leaf Distributing, The, 1020 White St., SW, Atlanta, GA 30310 (SAN 169-1449) Tel 404-755-2665; Toll free: 800-241-3829.

New Leaf Pr., (New Leaf; 0-89221), P.O. Box 311, Green Forest, AR 72638 (SAN 207-9518) Tel 501-438-5288; Toll free: 800-643-9535.

New London News Co., P.O. Box 711, New London, CT 06320 (SAN 169-0752).

New Mexico Periodicals, 401 Harper, P.O. Box 1806, Carlsbad, NM 88220 (SAN 169-4979).

New Mexico School Book Depository Inc., 2920 Rufina, Santa Fe, NM 87501 (SAN 169-5002).

New Pathways, 103 Goldencrest Ave., Waltham, MA 02154 (SAN 679-3703).

New Woman Pr., (New Woman), 2000 King Mountain Trail, Sunny Valley, OR 97497-9799 (SAN 209-8474).

New World Resource Center, 1476 W. Irving Park, Chicago, IL 60613 (SAN 169-1848).

New York Periodical Distributors, Industrial Plaza, Potsdam, NY 13676 (SAN 169-6149).

New York Poetry Forum, Inc., 3064 Albany Cresant, Apt. 54, Bronx, NY 10463 (SAN 200-8092).

New York Zoetrope, (NY Zoetrope; 0-918432), 80 E. 11th St., New York, NY 10003 (SAN 209-6293) Tel 212-420-0590; Toll free: 800-242-7546.

Newark Book Center, 162 Washington St., Newark, NJ 07102 (SAN 122-3011).

Newborn Enterprises, Inc., P.O. Box 1713, Altoona, PA 16603 (SAN 169-7242); Toll free: 800-227-0285 (PA Only).

Newell, M., Co. Builders, Pub., Subs. of M. Newell Company Builders, (M Newell Co; 0-9615901), 16731 74th NE, Bothell, WA 98011 (SAN 696-6640) Tel 206-488-2844.

News Supply Co., 1316 W. Mermod, Carlsbad, NM 88220 (SAN 159-9151).

Newsdealers Supply Co., Inc., 5800 W. Main, Dothan, AL 36301 (SAN 168-9215).

Newsstand Distributors, 155 W. 14th St., Ogden, UT 84404 (SAN 169-8494); Toll free: 800-453-2145; Toll free: 800-231-4834 (in UT).

Niagara County News, 70 Nicholls St., Lockport, NY 14094 (SAN 169-541X).

Nielsen, Elaine, P.O. Box 599, Ogallala, NE 69153 (SAN 200-7975).

Nienhuis Montessori, USA, Inc., 320 Pioneer Way, Mountain View, CA 94041 (SAN 200-2817).

Nightsun Books *See* **Adler Publishing Co.**

Niles News Agency, P.O. Box 495, Niles, MI 49120 (SAN 159-916X).

Nippon Shuppan Hanbai U.S.A., Inc., *(Nippon),* 1123 Dominguez St., Unit K, Carson, CA 90746 (SAN 670-6797).

Noel's Trophy Products, P.O. Box 1181, Sterling, IL 61081 (SAN 692-8447).

Noll's Educational Books & Toys, P.O. Box 55, 201 E. 2nd St., Arthur, IA 51431 (SAN 169-2569).

Nolo Pr., *(Nolo Pr; 0-917316; 0-87337),* 950 Parker St., Berkeley, CA 94710 (SAN 206-7935) Tel 415-549-1976.

Nor-Cal News Co., 2040 Petalua Blvd., P.O. Box 2508, Petaluma, CA 94953 (SAN 169-0035).

North Carolina News Co., P.O. Box 1007, Durham, NC 27701 (SAN 169-6378).

North Carolina School Book Depository, 811 W. Hargett St., Raleigh, NC 27602 (SAN 169-6467).

North Central Book Distributor, 12855 W. Silver Spring Dr., Butler, WI 53007 (SAN 169-9040); Toll free: 800-558-0580; 12855 W. Silver Spring Dr., Butler, WI 54409 (SAN 169-9032).

North Country Book Express, Inc./Solstice Press, *(NC Bk Express; 0-932722),* 112 W. Fourth St., P.O. Box 9223, Moscow, ID 83843 (SAN 169-1686) Tel 208-882-0888.

North Country Bks., Inc., *(North Country; 0-932052),* P.O. Box 506, Sylvan Beach, NY 13157 (SAN 287-0231) Tel 315-762-5140; 18 Irving Pl., Utica, NY 13501 (SAN 287-024X) Tel 315-735-4877.

North Plains Pr., Div. of Dakota North Plains Corp., *(North Plains; 0-87970),* P.O. Box 1830, Aberdeen, SD 57402-1830 (SAN 202-9243); 1216 S. Main St., Aberdeen, SD 57401 (SAN 660-9392) Tel 605-225-5360.

North Shore Distributors, 411 N. Wolf Rd., Wheeling, IL 60090 (SAN 169-2275).

North Shore News Co., Inc., 150 Blossom St., Lynn, MA 01902 (SAN 169-3492).

North-South Books *See* **Holt, Henry, & Co.**

Northeast News Co., Box 669, Kingston, NY 12401 (SAN 169-5398).

Northeastern Univ. Pr., *(NE U Pr; 0-930350; 1-55553),* 360 Huntington Ave., Huntington Plaza, Suite 272, Northeastern Univ., Boston, MA 02115 (SAN 205-3764) Tel 617-437-5480; Orders to: P.O. Box 250, Ithaca, NY 14851 (SAN 282-0668).

Northern Arizona News, P.O. Box 1947, 1709 N East St., Flagstaff, AZ 86002 (SAN 168-9290).

Northern Arizona Univ. Bookstore, P.O. Box 6044, Flagstaff, AZ 86011 (SAN 200-7541) Tel 602-523-4041.

Northern News Co., Harbor-Patoskey Rd., P.O., Box 543, Petoskey, MI 49770 (SAN 169-3964).

Northern School Supply Co., P.O. Box 2627, Fargo, ND 58108 (SAN 169-6548); Toll free: 800-342-4365 (ND Only); Toll free: 800-437-4012 (MN & SD).

Northland Pr., Div. of Justin Industries, *(Northland; 0-87358),* P.O. Box N, Flagstaff, AZ 86002 (SAN 202-9251) Tel 602-774-5251; Toll free: 800-FINE-BKS; Toll free: 800-46-BOOKS (AZ).

Northstar Commemoratives, Inc., P.O. Box 803, Lakeville, MN 55044-0803 (SAN 200-6545).

Northwest Jewish Book Service, 2084 Bayard Ave., St. Paul, MN 55116 (SAN 159-9178).

Northwest News Co., Inc., 101 S. California, Missoula, MT 59806 (SAN 169-4391) Tel 406-721-7801; P.O. Box 4965, Missoula, MT 59806 (SAN 660-9406).

Northwest Sub Service, P.O. Box 145, Twin Falls, ID 83301 (SAN 285-9270).

Norton, W. W., & Co., Inc., *(Norton; 0-393),* 500 Fifth Ave., New York, NY 10110 (SAN 202-5795) Tel 212-354-5500; Toll free: 800-223-2584. *Imprints:* New American Library (NAL); Norton College Division (NortonC); Norton Library (Norton Lib).

Norton College Div. *See* **Norton, W. W., & Co., Inc.**

Norton Library *See* **Norton, W. W., & Co., Inc.**

Norton News Agency, Box 696, Dubuque, IA 52004-0696 (SAN 169-2631); 1467 Service Dr., Winona, MN 55987 (SAN 156-4889).

Nothing New, P.O. Box 714, Silver Spring, MD 20901 (SAN 213-9812).

Nottonson, Mathew, & Co., Inc, 10945 Burbank Blvd., North Hollywood, CA 91601 (SAN 200-6812) Tel 818-985-0344.

Novation, Inc., *(Novation Inc),* 20409 Prairie St., Chatsworth, CA 91311 (SAN 276-9859) Tel 818-996-5060.

Nueces News Agency, 501 Hereford, Corpus Christi, TX 78408 (SAN 169-8079).

Nunciata Publishing, *(Nunciata),* P.O. Box 570122, Houston, TX 77257 (SAN 285-6883); Dist. by: Associated Advertisers Services, .

Nuth Bks., P.O. Box 5793, Denver, CO 80217 (SAN 200-6596).

Nutri-Books Corp., P.O. Box 5793, Denver, CO 80223 (SAN 169-054X); Toll free: 800-525-9030; 790 W. Tennessee Ave., Denver, CO 80223 (SAN 295-3404) Tel 303-778-8383.

NY New Papers, 611 Broadway, New York, NY 10012 (SAN 200-8130) Tel 212-777-6157.

Nystrom-Eye Gate, Div. of Herff Jones, *(Nystrom; 0-88463),* 3333 Elston Ave., Chicago, IL 60618 (SAN 203-5529) Tel 312-463-1144; Toll free: 800-621-8086.

Oak Pubns. *See* **Music Sales Corp.**

Oaktree Publishing Co., 9601 Aero Drive, Suite 202, San Diego, CA 92123 (SAN 200-4747).

Odyssey Distributing Co., 717 Grant St., Suite 200, Santa Monica, CA 90405 (SAN 157-0188).

Oelgeschlager, Gunn & Hain, Inc., *(Oelgeschlager; 0-89946),* 131 Clarendon St., Boston, MA 02116 (SAN 213-6937) Tel 617-437-9620.

Ogden News Co., P.O. Box 2000, Ogden, UT 84404 (SAN 274-2535).

Ohio Poetry Therapy Ctr. & Library, 2384 Hardestry Dr., S., Columbus, OH 43204 (SAN 200-5107).

Ohio State University Bookstores, 1315 Kinnear Rd., Columbus, OH 43212 (SAN 209-5637).

Ohio State Univ., ERIC Clearinghouse for Science, Mathematics, & Environmental Education Analysis Ctr., 1200 Chambers Rd., Rm. 310, Columbus, OH 43212 (SAN 274-256X) Tel 614-422-6717.

Oil City News Co., 208 E. 2nd St., Oil City, PA 16301 (SAN 169-7501).

Oklahoma City News Agency, P.O. Box 25489, Oklahoma City, OK 73125 (SAN 169-7005).

Oklahoma News Co., 909 W. 23rd St., Tulsa, OK 74107 (SAN 169-7013).

Oklahoma School & Office Supply, P.O. Box 1549, Muskogee, OK 74401 (SAN 169-6963).

Old Harbor Bks., 201 Lincoln St., Sitka, AK 99835 (SAN 200-5670).

Oliver, George L., Co., P.O. Box 1842, Fremont, CA 94538 (SAN 200-6111) Tel 415-651-6720; 44834 S. Grimmer Blvd., Fremont, CA 94538 (SAN 200-612X).

Ollis Bk. Corp., 28 E. 35th St., Steger, IL 60475 (SAN 169-2224) Tel 312-755-5151; Toll free: 800-323-0343; P.O. Box 258, Steger, IL 60475 (SAN 658-1323).

Olson News Co., P.O. Box 129, Ishpeming, MI 49849 (SAN 169-3832).

Omega Pr., Div. of Sufi Order in the West, *(Omega Pr NM; 0-930872),* P.O. Box 574, Lebanon Springs, NY 12114 (SAN 214-1493) Tel 518-794-8181; Dist. by: New Leaf Distributing, 1020 White St., SW, Atlanta, GA 30310 (SAN 169-1449) Tel 404-755-2665; Dist. by: Omega Pr., P.O. Box 574, Lebanon Springs, NY 12114 (SAN 214-1493) Tel 518-794-8181.

Omni Books, Subs. of Omco, Inc., (0-942518), 3040 Charlevoix Dr. SE, Grand Rapids, MI 49505 (SAN 238-1826) Tel 616-949-2250; Toll free: 800-243-8144.

Omnibook, Menomonee Falls, WI 53051 (SAN 282-6941) Tel 414-781-2866.

Omnibooks, 456 Vista Del Mar Drive, Aptos, CA 95003-4832 (SAN 168-9487) Tel 408-688-4098.

One Candle Pr., *(One Candle; 0-914032),* P.O. Box 888681, Atlanta, GA 30356 (SAN 658-1331) Tel 404-394-6870.

One World Products, Inc., Box L, Taos, NM 87571-0599 (SAN 200-7657) Tel 505-758-4144; Toll free: 800-541-1398, ext. 123-456; Toll free: 800-526-4500, ext. 123-456.

Online, Inc., 11 Tannery Ln., Weston, CT 06883 (SAN 200-822X) Tel 203-227-8466.

Online, Inc., *(Online; 0-910965),* 989 Ave. of the Americas, 15th flr., New York, NY 10018 (SAN 264-2735) Tel 212-279-8890.

Onondaga News Agency, 474 E. Brighton Ave., Syracuse, NY 13210 (SAN 169-6297).

Onyx *See* **New American Library**

Open Court Publishing Co., Div. of Carus Corp., *(Open Court; 9-12050; 0-89688; 0-8126; 0-87548),* 315 5th St., Peru, IL 61354 (SAN 202-5876) Tel 815-223-2520; Toll free: 800-435-6850; Toll free: 800-892-6831. *Imprints:* Library Press (Library Pr).

Open Univ. *See* **Harper & Row Pubs., Inc.**

Optimum Book Marketing Co., *(Optimum Bk),* 171 Madison Ave., New York, NY 10016 (SAN 209-2794).

Orange News Co., 3840 Vineland Rd., Orlando, FL 32811 (SAN 169-1201) Tel 305-841-8738.

Orbit Books, 43 Timberline Dr., Poughkeepsie, NY 12603 (SAN 169-6157).

Original Music *See* **Riverrun Pr.**

Orion *See* **Signature Bks., Inc.**

Oryx Pr., *(Oryx Pr; 0-912700; 0-89774),* 2214 N. Central Ave., Phoenix, AZ 85004-1483 (SAN 220-0201) Tel 602-254-6156; Toll free: 800-457-6799.

Oshkosh News Co., P.O. Box 46, Oshkosh, WI 54901 (SAN 159-9186).

Osiander Book Trade, 35 W. 38th St., Suite 3W, New York, NY 10016 (SAN 130-0970).

Otto News Agency, 265 N. Ash St., Twin Falls, ID 83301 (SAN 169-1708).

Outdoor Life Bks. *See* **Crown Pubs., Inc.**

Outdoorsman, The, P.O. Box 268, Allston Sta., Boston, MA 02215 (SAN 169-3352).

Overlook Pr., *(Overlook Pr; 0-87951),* 12 W. 21st St., 12th Flr., New York, NY 10010 (SAN 202-8360) Tel 212-337-5472; Toll free: 800-631-3577; Orders to: RR 1 Box 496, Woodstock, NY 12498; Dist. by: Viking-Penguin, Inc., 40 W. 23rd St., New York, NY 10010 (SAN 200-2442) Tel 212-337-5200.

Owl Bks. *See* **Holt, Rinehart & Winston, Inc.**

Ozark Magazine Distributing Inc., 1630 N. Eldon, Springfield, MO 65801 (SAN 169-4332).

Ozark News Agency Inc., P.O. Box 1150, Fayetteville, AR 72701 (SAN 168-9436); Box 6007, Springfield, MO 65806 (SAN 282-0951).

P & G Wholesale, P.O. Box 1548, Fargo, ND 58102 (SAN 156-4536).

PCB Industries, 11 Sugarbush, Coram, NY 11727 (SAN 200-7800) Tel 516-331-3884.

PC Network, 320 W. Ohio St., Chicago, IL 60610 (SAN 654-3219) Tel 312-280-0002; Toll free: 800-621-SAVE.

PDA Enterprises, *(0-936344),* P.O. Box 1762, Wayne, NJ 07470 (SAN 222-0989) Tel 201-628-1259.

PEP Distributors, 2070 Rosewood Ln., Lima, OH 45806 (SAN 200-4194).

P M G, International, 1343 Columbia, No. 405, Richardson, TX 75081 (SAN 200-4763).

PMS Industries, Div. of Proto Systems of Atlanta, *(PMS Indus; 0-931463),* 1790 Hembree Rd., Alpharetta, GA 30201 (SAN 683-1486) Tel 404-475-1818.

PW Communications, *(0-88722),* 400 Plaza Dr., Secaucus, NJ 07094 (SAN 286-8490).

Pabnassus Imprint, 21 Camal Rd., Box 335, Orleans, MA 02653 (SAN 200-5158).

Pacific Computer, 13240 Northup Way Suite 4, Bellevue, WA 98005 (SAN 679-9558) Tel 206-641-7233.

Pacific Literary Assocs., 4102 E. 27th St., Tucson, AZ 85711 (SAN 200-7770).

Pacific Magazine-Book Wholesaler, P.O. Box 5245, Tacoma, WA 98405 (SAN 274-3884).

Pacific Northwest Bks., P.O. Box 314, Medford, OR 97501 (SAN 200-5263) Tel 503-664-4442.

Pacific Pipeline, Inc., *(Pacific Pipeline),* 19215 66th Ave. S., Kent, WA 98032 (SAN 208-2128) Tel 206-872-5523; Toll free: 800-562-4647 (WA); P.O. Box 3711, Seattle, WA 98124 (SAN 169-8834); Toll free: 800-426-4727 (OR,ID,MT,NV, & Northern CA).

Pacific Search Pr., *(Pacific Search; 0-914718; 0-931397),* 222 Dexter Ave. N., Seattle, WA 98109 (SAN 202-8476) Tel 206-682-5044; Toll free: 800-858-0628.

Pacific Star & Stripes, A.P.O., San Francisco, CA 96503 (SAN 274-3973).

Pacific Subscription Service, P.O. Box 811, FDR Sta., New York, NY 10150 (SAN 157-5422).

Pacific Trade Group, P.O. Box 668, Pearl City, HI 96782-0668 (SAN 169-1635). Hardcover & quality Paperback Supplier of Hawaiian & Pacific Titles to Stores & Libraries.

Padre Productions, *(Padre Prods; 0-914598),* P.O. Box 1275, San Luis Obispo, CA 93406 (SAN 202-8484) Tel 805-543-5404.

Paige Book Service, P.O. Box 3, Mendham, NJ 07945 (SAN 127-533X).

Paladin Pr., *(Paladin Pr; 0-87364),* P.O. Box 1307, Boulder, CO 80306 (SAN 212-0305); Toll free: 800-824-7888; 2523 Broadway Ave., Boulder, CO 80302 (SAN 662-1066) Tel 303-443-7250. *Imprints:* Sycamore Island Books (Sycamore Island).

Palmer Distributing Co., 350 Wake Robin Ave., P.O. Box 830, Corvallis, OR 97339 (SAN 169-7072).

Palmer News Co. Inc., 1050 Republican, P.O. Box 1040, Topeka, KS 66601 (SAN 169-278X).

Palmer Pubns., *(0-9602060),* 25 W. 45th St., New York, NY 10036 (SAN 205-3381) Tel 212-586-4820.

Palmetto News Co., 307 Falls St., Greenville, SC 29601 (SAN 169-7803).

Palo Alto Book Service, 200 California Ave., Palo Alto, CA 94306 (SAN 128-5203).

Palomino Pr., *(Palomino Pr; 0-9610036),* 86-07 144th St., Briarwood, NY 11433 (SAN 241-5739) Tel 718-297-5053; Dist. by: Quality Bks., 918 Sherwood Dr., Lake Bluff, IL 60044-2204 (SAN 169-2127); Dist. by: Baker & Taylor Co., 50 Kirby Ave., Somerville, NJ 08876 (SAN 169-4901).

Palos Verdes Bk. Co., *(Palos Verdes; 0-936848),* P.O. Box 456, Lomita, CA 90717 (SAN 218-4532) Tel 904-383-8727.

Pan American Navigation Service, Inc., *(Pan Am Nav; 0-87219),* P.O. Box 9046, Van Nuys, CA 91409 (SAN 202-8506) Tel 818-345-2744; Toll free: 800-423-5932.

Panjandrum Bks., *(Panjandrum; 0-915572),* 11321 Iowa Ave., Suite 1, Los Angeles, CA 90025 (SAN 282-1257) Tel 213-477-8771; Dist. by: Baker & Taylor (Western Div.), 380 Edison Way, Reno, NV 89564 (SAN 169-4464) Tel 702-786-6700; Dist. by: Talman Co., Inc., 150 Fifth Ave., Rm. 514, New York, NY 10011 (SAN 200-5204) Tel 212-620-3182; Dist. by: Blackwell North America, 6024 SW. Jean Rd., Bldg. G, Lake Oswego, OR 97034 (SAN 656-4917) Tel 503-684-1140; Dist. by: Bookpeople, 2929 Fifth St., Berkeley, CA 94710 (SAN 168-9517); Dist. by: Shakti Distributors, 1020 White St, SW, Atlanta, GA 30310 (SAN 200-7258); Dist. by: Coutts Library Services, 736-738 Cayugo St., Lewiston, NY (SAN 169-5401).

Paper Vision Press *See* **Western Tanger Pr.**

Paperback Books Inc., 141-B E Little Creek Rd., Norfolk, VA 23505 (SAN 169-8672).

Paperback Supply Co., 4121 Forest Park, Saint Louis, MO 63108 (SAN 169-4324); Toll free: 800-325-8404; Toll free: 800-392-4756 (in MO).

Papermac Bks. *See* **St. Martin's Pr., Inc.**

Para Research, Inc., *(Para Res; 0-914918),* 85 Eastern Ave., P.O. Box 61, Gloucester, MA 01930 (SAN 213-4438) Tel 617-283-3438.

Paragon Bk. Gallery, Ltd., *(Paragon; 0-8188),* 2130 Broadway, New York, NY 10023 (SAN 213-1986) Tel 212-496-2378. *Imprints:* Center for East Asian Studies (Ctr E Asian Stud); Lovejoy Press, The (Lovejoy).

Pargh, B. A., Co., Inc., 1283 Murfreesboro Rd., Nashville, TN 37217 (SAN 285-712X) Tel 615-366-3000; Toll free: 800-227-1000.

Parker Publishing Co. *See* **Prentice-Hall, Inc.**

Parliament News Co., Inc., 12011 Sherman Rd., North Hollywood, CA 91605 (SAN 168-9924).

Passaic County News Co., 56-70 Beech St., Paterson, NJ 07501 (SAN 169-4812).

Passport Books *See* **National Textbook Co.**

Pathfinder Pr., *(Path Pr NY; 0-87348),* 410 West St., New York, NY 10014 (SAN 202-5906) Tel 212-741-0690.

Patry Edgar, 11 Charlemont Rd., Medford, MA 02155 (SAN 282-695X).

Paulist Pr., *(Paulist Pr; 0-8091),* 997 MacArthur Blvd., Mahwah, NJ 07430 (SAN 202-5159) Tel 201-825-7300; Toll free: 800-325-9521. *Imprints:* Deus Books (Deus).

Paulsen, G., Co., 27 Sheep Davis Rd., Concord, NH 03301-1596 (SAN 169-4499).

Peacock Bks. *See* **Penguin Bks., Inc.**

Peanut Brigade, P.O. Box 237, Plains, GA 31780 (SAN 210-976X) Tel 912-924-8287.

Peanut Butter Publishing, Subs. of McGraw Mountain, Inc., *(Peanut Butter; 0-89716),* 911 Western Ave., Suite 401, Maritime Bldg., Seattle, WA 98104 (SAN 213-0623); Dist. by: Pacific Pipeline, 19215 66th Ave., S., Kent, WA 98032 (SAN 662-1490) Tel 206-872-5523.

Peck, Walter, Magazine Agency, 331 Bank of Galesburg Bldg., Galesburg, IL 61401 (SAN 285-9319).

Pee Dee News Co., Inc., P.O. Box 4569, Florence, SC 29501 (SAN 169-7781).

Pegasus Rex *See* **Fell, Frederick, Pubs., Inc.**

Pekin News Agency, 522 Court St., Pekin, IL 61554 (SAN 169-2151).

Pelican Bks. *See* **Penguin Bks., Inc.**

Pelican Publishing Co., Inc., *(Pelican; 0-911116; 0-88289),* 1101 Monroe St., Gretna, LA 70053 (SAN 212-0623) Tel 504-368-1175; P.O. Box 189, Gretna, LA 70053 (SAN 658-1374) Tel 504-368-1175.

Pembridge Press (England) *See* **Shoe String Pr., Inc.**

Penco-Pacific Books Wholesale, 1958 Leslie St., San Mateo, CA 94403 (SAN 169-0302).

Pendragon Hse., *(Pendragon Hse; 0-916988),* 107 Delaware Ave., Suite 425, Buffalo, NY 14202-2872 (SAN 208-8037).

Penguin Bks., Inc., *(Penguin; 0-14),* 40 W. 23rd St., New York, NY 10010 (SAN 202-5914) Tel 212-807-7300; Toll free: 800-631-3577. *Imprints:* Peacock Books (Peacock); Pelican Books (Pelican); Peregrine Books (Peregrine); Puffin Books (Puffin).

Peninsula, *(Peninsula),* 156 Fifth Ave., New York, NY 10010 (SAN 200-5069).

Peninsula Computer Group, 35 V. Wainwright Dr., Poquoson, VA 23662 (SAN 200-5131).

Peninsula News, 1944 Leslie St., San Mateo, CA 94403 (SAN 169-0302).

Peninsula Publishing, Inc., *(Peninsula WA; 0-918146),* P.O. Box 412, Port Angeles, WA 98362 (SAN 210-1300) Tel 206-457-7550; Dist. by: Pacific Pipeline, 19215 66th Ave. S., Kent, WA 98032 (SAN 208-2128) Tel 206-872-5523.

Penn News Co., 944 Franklin St., Johnstown, PA 15905 (SAN 169-7390).

Pennsylvania State Univ. Pr., *(Pa St U Pr; 0-271),* 215 Wagner Bldg., University Park, PA 16802 (SAN 213-5760) Tel 814-865-1327. *Imprints:* Keystone Books (Keystone Bks).

Pennywheel Press, Rd 2, Loop Rd., Poultney, VT 05764 (SAN 150-7907).

Pentalic *See* **Taplinger Publishing Co., Inc.**

Pentecostal Publishing Hse., Subs. of United Pentecostal Church, (0-912315), 8855 Dunn Rd., Hazelwood, MO 63042 (SAN 219-3817) Tel 314-837-7300.

People Lovers Bks, 27 N. Gore, Webster Groves, MO 63117 (SAN 200-6243).

People's Place Booklets, Main St., Intercourse, PA 17534 (SAN 270-5389) Tel 717-768-7171; Toll free: 800-762-7171.

Peppercorn *See* **Putnam Publishing Group, The**

Peregrine Bks. *See* **Penguin Bks., Inc.**

Peregrine Smith Books *See* **Smith, Gibbs M., Inc.**

Perennial Fiction Library *See* **Harper & Row Pubs., Inc.**

Perennial Library *See* **Harper & Row Pubs., Inc.**

Perennial Mystery Library *See* **Harper & Row Pubs., Inc.**

Perennial Pubns., *(Perennial Pubns; 0-9612234),* P.O. Box 32, Gainesville, GA 30503 (SAN 289-2588) Tel 404-536-3611; Dist. by: Dot Gibson Distributors, 161 Knight Ave. Cir, Waycross, GA 31501 (SAN 200-4143); Dist. by: The Collection, Inc., 2101 Kansas City Rd., Olathe, KS 66061 (SAN 200-6359) Tel 913-764-1811.

Perfect School Organization, 21 Henderson Dr., West Caldwell, NJ 07006 (SAN 285-9327).

Perfect Subscription Co., 841 Chestnut St., Philadelphia, PA 19107 (SAN 285-9335).

Perfection Form Company, The, *(0-89598; 0-8124),* 1000 N. Second Ave., Logan, IA 51546 (SAN 221-0010); Orders to: Sterling Pub. Co., Inc., 2 Park Ave., New York, NY 10016 (SAN 669-2370).

Performance Software, 1009 Sycamore Sq., Midlothian, VA 23113 (SAN 287-0800) Tel 804-794-1012.

Performance Software, *(Perform Soft),* P.O. Box 82, Dearborn, MI 48120 (SAN 295-2327).

Pergamon Brassey's International Defence Pubs., Maxwell House, Fairview Pk., Elmsford, NY 10523 (SAN 200-741X) Tel 914-592-7700.

Pergamon Pr., Inc., *(Pergamon; 0-08),* Maxwell Hse., Fairview Pk., Elmsford, NY 10523 (SAN 213-9022) Tel 914-592-7700.

Perigree Bks. *See* **Putnam Publishing Group, The**

Periodical Management Group, 1101 N. Frio, P.O. Box 7609, San Antonio, TX 78207 (SAN 156-4978).

Periodical Merchandisers, E. Rte. 316, Mattoon, IL 61938 (SAN 169-2089).

Periodical Pubs. Ser Bureau, One North Superior St., Sandusky, OH 44870 (SAN 285-9351).

Periodical Services, Inc., P.O. Box 367, Stockton, NJ 08559 (SAN 200-6707).

Perma Bound Bks., Subs. of Hertzberg-New Method, *(Perma Bound; 0-916056; 0-8479),* 617 E. Vandalia Rd., Jacksonville, IL 62650 (SAN 169-2003) Tel 217-243-5451; Toll free: 800-637-6581.

Perrin, Thomas W., Inc., *(Perrin Inc; 0-933825),* P.O. Box 190, 5 Glen Rd., Rutherford, NJ 07070 (SAN 200-6510) Tel 201-460-7912; Toll free: 800-321-7912.

Perry Enterprises, *(Perry Enterprises; 0-941518),* 2666 N. 650 E, Provo, UT 84604 (SAN 239-0175) Tel 801-375-9529.

Perry's News Agency, 240 E. Grand Ave., Wisconsin Rapids, WI 54494 (SAN 169-9237).

Persea Bks., Inc., *(Persea Bks; 0-89255),* 225 Lafayette St., New York, NY 10012 (SAN 212-8233) Tel 212-431-5270.

Persona Pr., *(Persona LA; 0-940142),* 522 Dumaine, Apt. 3, New Orleans, LA 70116 (SAN 293-3136) Tel 504-561-0221.

Persona Press, *(Persona Pr; 0-931906),* P.O. Box 14022, San Francisco, CA 94114 (SAN 212-3002) Tel 415-775-6143.

Peton Corp., P.O. Box 11925, Salt Lake City, UT 84147 (SAN 169-8559).

Petras Press *See* **Riverrun Pr.**

Phaidon *See* **Dutton, E. P.**

Phanes Pr., *(Phanes Pr; 0-933999),* P.O. Box 6114, Grand Rapids, MI 49516 (SAN 692-879X) Tel 616-949-5678.

Phila Books Co., Inc., 201 W. 89th St., New York, NY 10024 (SAN 159-9224).

Phillips News Co., P.O. Box 160, Hutchinson, KS 67501 (SAN 169-2704).

Philomel Bks. *See* **Putnam Publishing Group, The**

Philosophical Publishing Co., *(Philos Pub; 0-932785),* R. D. 3, Clymeir Road, Quakertown, PA 18951 (SAN 295-8430) Tel 215-536-5168.

Philosophical Research Society, Inc., *(Philos Res; 0-89314),* 3910 Los Feliz Blvd., Los Angeles, CA 90027 (SAN 205-3829) Tel 213-663-2167.

Pica Press *See* **Universe Bks., Inc.**

Pica Special Studies *See* **Universe Bks., Inc.**

Pick Pubns., Inc., *(Pick Pub MI; 0-936526),* 28715 Greenfield Rd., Southfield, MI 48076 (SAN 282-1648) Tel 313-443-1799; Toll free: 800-247-1559.

Pickwick Int'l, Inc., 7500 Excelsion, Minneapolis, MN 55426 (SAN 285-9378).

Piedmont Magazine & Paperback Book Service, 814 E. Orr St., Anderson, SC 29621 (SAN 169-7730).

Pierson, A.M., Box 1236, Binghamton, NY 13902 (SAN 169-507X).

Pietro Deiro Music Headquarters, 123 Greenwich Ave., New York, NY 10014 (SAN 282-5880) Tel 212-675-5460.

Pikes News Agency, Drawer 1230, Wilson, NC 27893 (SAN 169-6505).

Pikes Peak News Agency, Box 15094, Colorado Springs, CO 80935 (SAN 169-0507).

Pineapple Pr., Inc., *(Pineapple Pr; 0-910923),* 202 Pineapple St., Englewood, FL 33533 (SAN 285-0850); Orders to: P.O. Box 314, Englewood, FL 33533 (SAN 285-0869) Tel 813-475-2238.

Pioneer Publishing Co., 1618 Eighth Ave., Kearney, NE 68847 (SAN 159-9240).

Piper Bks. *See* Houghton Mifflin Co.

Pittsfield News Co., Inc., 27 Reed St., Pittsfield, MA 01201 (SAN 124-2768).

Pivot *See* Taplinger Publishing Co., Inc.

Plains Distribution Service, P.O. Box 3112, 340 7th Ave, Fargo, ND 58103 (SAN 169-6556).

Planet Productions, P.O. Box 1641, Boulder, CO 80306 (SAN 282-5899) Tel 415-549-3030; Toll free: 800-227-1516.

Plant, W.E.C., Enterprises, *(W E C Plant Ent; 0-913611),* Box 030096, Ft. Lauderdale, FL 33303 (SAN 285-3612) Tel 305-467-3512

Platte 'n Press *See* Jende-Hagan, Inc.

Plenum Medical Bk. Co. *See* Plenum Publishing Corp.

Plenum Pr. *See* Plenum Publishing Corp.

Plenum Publishing Corp., *(Plenum Pub; 0-306),* 233 Spring St., New York, NY 10013 (SAN 201-9248) Tel 212-620-8000; Toll free: 800-221-9369; 170 Le Grand Ave., Northvale, NJ 07647 (SAN 658-1412). *Imprints:* Consultants Bureau (Consultants); I F I/Plenum (IFI-Plenum); Plenum Medical Book Company (Plenum Med Bk); Plenum Press (Plenum Pr); Plenum Rosetta (Rosetta).

Plenum Rosetta *See* Plenum Publishing Corp.

Plum Nelly Press, Inc., The, *(Plum Nelly),* 1201 Hixson Pike, Chattanooga, TN 37405 (SAN 216-1745) Tel 615-266-0585.

Plume Bks. *See* New American Library

PMG International, 1104 Summit Ave., Plano, TX 75074 (SAN 200-4739) Tel 214-423-0312.

Pocahontas Pr., Inc., *(Pocahontas Pr; 0-936015),* 2805 Wellesley Ct., Blacksburg, VA 24060 (SAN 696-6195) Tel 703-951-0467.

Pocket Bks., Inc., Div. of Simon & Schuster, Inc., *(PB; 0-671),* 1230 Ave. of the Americas, New York, NY 10020 (SAN 202-5922) Tel 212-246-2121; Toll free: 800-223-2336; Orders to: 200 Old Tappan, Old Tappan, NJ 07675 (SAN 662-1147) Tel 201-767-5000. *Imprints:* Gallen, Richard (Gallen); Lantern Books (Lantern); Long Shadow Books (Long Shadow Bks); Poseidon Press (Poseidon); Timescape (Timescape); Wallaby (Wallaby).

Point *See* Scholastic, Inc.

Polybook Distributors, 30 S. Sixth Ave., P.O. Box 109, Mt. Vernon, NY 10550 (SAN 169-5568).

Polycrystal Book Service, *(Polycrystal Bk Serv; 0-9601304),* P.O. Box 27, Western Springs, IL 60558 (SAN 212-6753) Tel 312-246-3818.

Pomona Valley News Agency, 10736 Fremont Ave., Ontario, CA 91762 (SAN 169-0019).

Popular Subscription Service, P.O. Box 1566, Terre Haute, IN 47808 (SAN 285-9386).

Portland News Co., 270 Western Ave., P.O. Box 1728, South Portland, ME 04104 (SAN 159-3093).

Portsmouth News Agency, 3051 Walnut St., Portsmouth, OH 45662 (SAN 169-6831).

Poseidon Press *See* Pocket Bks., Inc.

Potter, Clarkson N., Bks. *See* Crown Pubs., Inc.

Potter Library Services, 223 S 60th St., Milwaukee, WI 53214 (SAN 169-9229).

Pottstown News Co., 557 W. High St., Pottstown, PA 19464 (SAN 169-7609).

Pottsville Magazine Distributors, 1907 Elk Ave, Pottsville, PA 17901 (SAN 169-7617).

Poudre Valley News Co., Drawer P, Ft. Collins, CO 80521 (SAN 169-0566).

Poway Historical & Memorial Society, *(Poway Hist; 0-914137),* 17105 Tam O'Shanter Dr., Poway, CA 92064 (SAN 293-4736) Tel 619-487-7199; Orders to: Poway Historical & Memorial Society, 12916 Community Rd., Poway, CA 92064 (SAN 293-4744) Tel 619-748-5004; Dist. by: Poway Historical and Memorial Society, P.O. Box 19, Poway, CA 92064 (SAN 293-4752); Dist. by: Poway Chamber of Commerce, 13505 Midland Rd., Poway, CA 92064 (SAN 293-4779) Tel 619-748-0016; Dist. by: Iverson Book Center, 13446 Poway Rd., Poway, CA 92064 (SAN 293-4787) Tel 619-486-2665.

Prager, Max R., 205 Barlow Dr., Brooklyn, NY 11234 (SAN 285-9890).

Pratik Pubns., P.O. Box 11133, Merrillville, IN 46411 (SAN 200-7878).

Pratz News Agency, Box 892, Deming, NM 88030 (SAN 159-9275).

Pre-Test *See* McGraw-Hill Bk. Co.

Pre-Text Series *See* McGraw-Hill Bk. Co.

Precision Visuals, Inc., 6260 Lookout Rd., Boulder, CO 80301 (SAN 284-060X) Tel 303-530-9000.

Premart Incorporated, 1948 S. La Cienega Blvd., Los Angeles, CA 90034 (SAN 283-9717).

Prentice-Hall, Inc., *(P-H; 0-13),* Rte. 9W, Englewood Cliffs, NJ 07632 (SAN 200-2175) Tel 201-592-2000; Orders to: 200 Old Tappan Rd., Old Tappan, NJ 07675 (SAN 215-3939) Tel 201-767-5049. *Imprints:* Appleton-Century-Crofts (Appleton-Century-Crofts); Business & Professional Division (Busn); Parker Publishing Company (Parker); Prism Books (Prism); Reward Books (Reward); Spectrum Books (Spec).

Presidio Pr., *(Presidio Pr; 0-89141),* 31 Pamaron Way, Novato, CA 94947 (SAN 214-2759) Tel 415-883-1373. *Imprints:* Leeward Publications, Inc. (Leeward Pubns).(Neff-Kane).

Press Pacifica, *(Pr Pacifica; 0-916630),* 1230 Kainui Dr., Kailua, HI 96734 (SAN 169-1635) Tel 808-261-6594.

Presse Import, Academic Enterprises Ltd. 20 Simmons Dr., Milford, MA 01757 (SAN 156-661X).

Presser, Theodore, Co., *(Presser Co; 0-934009),* Presser Place, Bryn Mawr, PA 19010 (SAN 203-5553) Tel 215-525-3636.

Price, Stern, Sloan, Pubs., Inc., *(Price Stern; 0-8431),* 410 N. La Cienega Blvd., Los Angeles, CA 90048 (SAN 202-0246) Tel 213-657-6100; Toll free: 800-421-0892; 1900 Sacramento St., Los Angeles, CA 90021 (SAN 658-148X); Toll free: 800-227-8801 (In California).

Primarily Paper, Inc., Rm. 304-Orange UMAGA, Minnetonka, MN 55343 (SAN 663-4524) Tel 612-462-3229.

Primier Publishers, Incorporated, P.O. Box 16254, Fort Worth, TX 76133 (SAN 289-9418).

Prince, E. A., & Sons, Box 436, Anderson, SC 29622 (SAN 169-7749).

Prince Paperback *See* Crown Pubs., Inc.

Princeton Univ. Pr., *(Princeton U Pr; 0-691),* 41 William St., Princeton, NJ 08540 (SAN 202-0254) Tel 609-452-4900; Orders to: Marge Weiland, 3175 Princeton Pike, Lawrenceville, NJ 08648 (SAN 662-1171) Tel 609-896-1344.

Printed Editions, *(Printed Edns; 0-914162),* P.O. Box 27, Sta. Hill Rd., Barrytown, NY 12507 (SAN 206-5851) Tel 914-758-6488; Dist. by: Writers & Books, 740 University Ave., Rochester, NY 14607 (SAN 156-9678) Tel 716-473-2590; Dist. by: Small Pr. Distribution, 1814 San Pablo Ave., Berkeley, CA 94702 (SAN 204-5826) Tel 415-549-3336.

Printed Matter, Inc., *(Printed Matter; 0-89439),* 7 Lispenard St., New York, NY 10013 (SAN 169-5924) Tel 212-925-0325.

Printed Products Inc., *(Printed Prod),* 101 SW 25th, Oklahoma City, OK 73109 (SAN 227-0056) Tel 405-232-3009.

Printers Shop, The, 4047 Transport, Palo Alto, CA 94303 (SAN 293-3780) Tel 415-494-6802.

Printing Services, Inc., 3249 NW 38th St., Miami, FL 33142 (SAN 200-7096) Tel 305-633-2571.

Prism Bks. *See* Prentice-Hall, Inc.

Pro-Ed, *(Pro Ed; 0-936104),* 5341 Industrial Oaks Blvd., Austin, TX 78735 (SAN 222-1349) Tel 512-892-3142.

Professional & Reference Bk. Div. *See* McGraw-Hill Bk. Co.

Professional Book Distributor, 2727 Scioto Pkwy., Columbus, OH 43220 (SAN 126-6039).

Professional Bk. Service, 3 Neshaminy Interplex, Suite 301, Trevose, PA 19047 (SAN 697-2152) Tel 215-638-3111.

Professional Pubns., Inc., *(Prof Pub Inc; 0-912045; 0-932276),* P.O. Box 199, San Carlos, CA 94070 (SAN 264-6315) Tel 415-593-9119.

Progress News Co., 187 Cottage St., P.O. Box 627, Poughkeepsie, NY 12602 (SAN 169-6165).

Progressive News Co., 1105 W. College Ave., State College, PA 16801 (SAN 169-7641).

Progressive Pilot Seminars *See* Aviation Bk. Co.

Prosperity & Profits Unlimited, Distribution Services, *(Prosperity & Profits),* Box 570213, Houston, TX 77257-0213 (SAN 200-4682).

Protecto Enterprises, *(Protecto Ent),* P.O. Box 550, Barrington, IL 60010 (SAN 285-7448) Tel 312-382-5244.

Psychohistory Pr., Div. of Atcom, Inc., Pubs., *(Psychohistory Pr),* 2315 Broadway, New York, NY 10024 (SAN 201-8926) Tel 212-873-5900; Toll free: 800-521-7004.

Psychological Corp. *See* Harcourt Brace Jovanovich, Inc.

Pubns. Unlimited, P.O. Box 100, Boyton Beach, FL 33435 (SAN 285-9432).

Publishers Assocs., P.O. Box 160361, Las Colinas, TX 75106-9998 (SAN 200-6979) Tel 817-478-8564.

Pubs. Business Service, Inc., 173 W. Madison St., Chicago, IL 60602 (SAN 285-9459).

Pubs. Clearing House, 382 Channel Dr., Port Washington, NY 11050 (SAN 285-9440).

Pubs. Continental Sales Corp., 2601 E. Michigan St., Michigan City, IN 46360 (SAN 285-9475).

Publishers Distribution Center, 25 Branca Rd., Rutherford, NJ 07073 (SAN 200-5018) Tel 201-939-6064.

Pubs. Distribution Service, 7509 Cantrell Rd., Little Rock, AR 72207 (SAN 282-5937).

Publishers Group West, *(Publishers Group),* 5855 Beaudry St., Emeryville, CA 94608 (SAN 202-8522) Tel 415-658-3453; Toll free: 800-982-8319.

Publishers Mark, The, *(Pub Mark; 0-9614636),* 255 B Bluff Ct., Barrington, IL 60010 (SAN 691-9154) Tel 312-381-6451; Dist. by: Paperback Supply, 4121 Forest Park Ave., St. Louis, MO 63108 (SAN 169-4324); Dist. by: Richardson's Education, 2014 Low Ellen Ln., Houston, TX 77018 (SAN 691-9170); Dist. by: The Publishers Mark, P.O. Box 267, Cary, IL 60013 (SAN 694-0153); Dist. by: Baker & Taylor, Eastern Div., 50 Kirby Ave., Somerville, NJ 08876 (SAN 169-4901).

Publishers Marketing Group, 1104 Summit Ave., Plainview, TX 75074 (SAN 262-0995) Tel 214-423-0312.

Pubs. News Co.-Northern Indiana News Agency, P.O. Box 458, New Buffalo, MI 49117 (SAN 169-393X).

Publishers Services, *(Pub Service; 0-937602),* P.O. Box 2510, Novato, CA 94948 (SAN 201-3037) Tel 415-883-3530; 11A Commercial Blvd., Novato, CA 94947 (SAN 200-7223) Tel 415-883-3140.

Publishers West, *(Pubs West; 0-930863),* P.O. Box 27719, San Diego, CA 92128 (SAN 677-7821) Tel 619-296-1500; Toll free: 800-345-1995; 4535 30th St., No. 212, San Diego, CA 92116 (SAN 200-674X).

Publishing Ctr. for Cultural Resources, Inc., *(Pub Ctr Cult Res; 0-89062),* 625 Broadway, New York, NY 10012 (SAN 274-9025) Tel 212-260-2010.

Pueblo News Co., Inc., 4841 Warehouse Dr., Pueblo, CO 81008 (SAN 169-0620).

Puett Electronics, P.O. Box 28572, Dallas, TX 75228 (SAN 205-4035) Tel 214-321-0927.

Puffin Bks. *See* **Penguin Bks., Inc.**

Pullum Corp., The, G3500 Flushing Rd., Suite 450, Flint, MI 48504 (SAN 200-7797) Tel 313-733-2662.

Puski-Corvin, *(Puski-Corvin; 0-930888),* 251 E. 82nd St., New York, NY 10028 (SAN 682-8485).

Putnam Publishing Group, The, *(Putnam Pub Group; 0-399),* 200 Madison Ave., New York, NY 10016 (SAN 202-5531); Toll free: 800-631-8571. *Imprints:* Coward, McCann & Geoghegan (Coward); Grossett & Dunlap, Inc. (G&D); Peppercorn (Peppercorn); Perigee Books (Perigee); Philomel Books (Philomel); Putnam's, G. P., Sons (Putnam); Seaview (Seaview); Wideview (Wideview).

Putnam's, G. P., Sons *See* **Putnam Publishing Group, The**

Pyxidium Pr., *(Pyxidium Pr; 0-936568),* Box 462, Old Chelsea Sta., New York, NY 10011 (SAN 214-4514) Tel 212-242-5224.

Q Corporation, *(Q Corp; 0-9604108),* 49 Sheridan Ave., Albany, NY 12221 (SAN 221-6310).

QSP, P.O. Box 10203, Des Moines, IA 50381 (SAN 285-9882).

Quail Ridge Pr., Inc., *(Quail Ridge; 0-937552),* P.O. Box 123, Brandon, MS 39042 (SAN 214-2201); Dist. by: Dot Gibson Pubns., 161 Knight Ave. Cir., Waycross, GA 31501 (SAN 241-3760) Tel 912-285-2848; Dist. by: Southwest Cookbook Distributors, 1901 S. Shore Dr., Bonham, TX 75418 (SAN 200-4925) Tel 214-583-8898; Dist. by: Quail Ridge Pr., P.O. Box 123, Brandon, MS 39042 (SAN 214-2201).

Quality Books, Inc., *(Quality Bks IL; 0-89196),* 918 Sherwood Dr., Lake Bluff, IL 60044-2204 (SAN 169-2127); Toll free: 800-323-4241 (Libraries Only). Warehouse open for walk-through buyers. *Imprints:* Book Value International (Bk Value Intl); Domus Books (Domus Bks).

Quality School Plan, Inc., P.O. Box 301, Pleasantville, NY 10570 (SAN 285-953X).

Quantum Press *See* **Doubleday & Co., Inc.**

Quartus Bks., Div. of Quartus Foundation, *(Quartus Bks; 0-942082),* P.O. Box 26683, Austin, TX 78755 (SAN 238-0080) Tel 512-335-8346; Dist. by: Quartus Books, P.O. Box 26683, Austin, TX 78755 (SAN 238-0080) Tel 512-335-8346; Dist. by: New Leaf Distributing Co., 1020 White St., Sw, Atlanta, GA 30310 (SAN 169-1449) Tel 404-755-2665.

Queen City Brass Pubns., P.O. Box 75054, Cincinnati, OH 45275 (SAN 200-7436).

Queue, Inc., *(Queue Inc; 0-87200; 0-87492),* 798 North Ave., Bridgeport, CT 06606 (SAN 265-3397) Tel 203-335-0908; Toll free: 800-232-2224.

Quik Cook Inc., 439 Central Ave., Rochester, NY 14605 (SAN 200-5115) Tel 716-546-7663.

Quill Paperbacks *See* **Morrow, William, & Co., Inc.**

Quilt Digest Pr., The, *(Quilt Digest Pr; 0-913327),* 955 14th St., San Francisco, CA 94114 (SAN 293-4531) Tel 415-431-1222; Dist. by: Publishers Group West, 5855 Beaudry St., Emeryville, CA 94608 (SAN 202-8522) Tel 415-658-3453.

Qwilkins Printers, 4000 West Rd., Cortland, NY 13045 (SAN 200-7738).

R & K Distributors, P.O. Box 1044, St. George, UT 84770 (SAN 200-6154).

R & W Distribution Inc., 87 Bright St., Jersey City, NJ 07302 (SAN 169-4723).

R.C. Law & Co., Inc., *(R C Law & Co; 0-939925),* 579 S. State College Blvd., Fullerton, CA 92631 (SAN 200-609X) Tel 714-871-0940.

Racet Computes, Ltd., *(Racet Comp; 0-918105),* 1855 W. Katella, Suite 255, Orange, CA 92667 (SAN 277-5743) Tel 714-997-4950.

Rachles, Samuel, Inc., Box 266, Passaic, NJ 07055 (SAN 169-4804).

Raiko Corp., *(Raiko; 0-910263),* P.O. Box 597, New York, NY 10003 (SAN 240-9542) Tel 212-783-2597.

Railsback, Leigh M. Sub. Agency, 1276 N. Lake Ave., Pasadena, CA 91104 (SAN 285-9548).

Rainbow Bks., *(Rainbow Books; 0-935834),* Dept. 1-H, P.O. Box 1069, Moore Haven, FL 33471 (SAN 213-5515) Tel 813-946-0293; Dist. by: Quality Bks. (Library orders only), 918 Sherwood Dr., Lake Bluff, IL 60044-2204 (SAN 169-2127).

Rainier News Inc., 1122 80th St. SW, Everett, WA 98203 (SAN 169-8745).

Rajneesh Pubns., Inc., Div. of Rajneesh Foundation International, *(Rajneesh Pubns; 0-88050),* P.O. Box 1510, Boulder, CO 80306 (SAN 240-0987) Tel 303-665-6611.

Raleigh News Agency, 2420 Crabtree Blvd., P.O. Box 18706, Raleigh, NC 27619 (SAN 169-6475).

Rampart Institute, *(Rampart Inst),* Box 4, Fullerton, CA 90247 (SAN 282-6410).

Ramsey News Co., P.O. Box 1507, Warsaw, IN 46580 (SAN 169-2526).

Random House Audiobooks *See* **Random Hse., Inc.**

Random Hse., Inc., *(Random; 0-394; 0-676),* Random Hse. Publicity, (11-6), 201 E. 50th St., New York, NY 10022 (SAN 202-5507) Tel 212-572-8030; Toll free: 800-638-6460; Orders to: 400 Hahn Rd., Westminster, MD 21157 (SAN 202-5515). Do not confuse Random House's imprint 'Vintage' with any other company with a similar name, particularly Vintage Pr., East Hanover, NJ. *Imprints:* Books for Young Readers (BYR); Modern Library College Edition (MLCE); Random House Audiobooks (Random Audiobks); Random House Business Division (RanB); Random House College Division (RanC); Stanyan Books (Stanyan Bks); Vintage College Books (VinC); Vintage Trade Books (Vin).

Random Hse. Business Div. *See* **Random Hse., Inc.**

Random Hse. College Div. *See* **Random Hse., Inc.**

Ravengate Press, *(Ravengate Pr; 0-911218),* P.O. Box 103, Cambridge, MA 02238 (SAN 203-090X) Tel 617-456-8181.

Raylon Corp., 345 Morgantown Rd., P.O. Box 91, Reading, PA 19603 (SAN 200-6529).

Read 'n Play Inc., Box 788, 255 Royal Poinciana Way, Palm Beach, FL 33480 (SAN 169-1228); 7821 Brier St., Philadelphia, PA 19152 (SAN 169-7307).

Read News Agency, 1110 14th St., P.O. Box 1339, Tuscaloosa, AL 35403 (SAN 168-9266).

Readers Service Bureau, 2550 Golf Rd., Glenview, IL 60025 (SAN 285-9580).

Readex Book Exchange, Box 1125, Carefree, AZ 85331 (SAN 159-9291).

Reading At Home, P.O. Box 948, Lowell, MA 01853 (SAN 285-9572).

Reading Circle, The, P.O. Box 8458, Columbus, OH 43201 (SAN 169-670X).

Reading Matters, Inc., 64 Walnut St., Brookline, MA 02146 (SAN 200-5891).

Readmore Pubns. Inc., 140 Cedar St., New York, NY 10006 (SAN 159-9313).

Real Estate Information Network, Inc. (REINET), P.O. Box 257, 39 Jewett Pl., Nyack, NY 10960 (SAN 655-4628) Tel 914-358-2335.

Reca International Corp., 150 Haven, P.O. Box 951, Port Washington, NY 11050 (SAN 200-6332).

Red River News Co., 950 Frontage Rd., Box 2491, Monroe, LA 71202 (SAN 169-2925).

Redding Red Bluff News, P.O. Box 718, Redding, CA 96001 (SAN 159-933X).

Redwing Book Co., 44 Linden St., Brookline, MA 02146 (SAN 163-3597) Tel 617-738-4664.

Reference Book Center, 175 Fifth Ave., New York, NY 10010 (SAN 159-9356).

Reference Library Guild, Box 77, Homecrest Sta., Brooklyn, NY 11229 (SAN 169-5169).

Regent Book Co., Inc., 101A Rte 4b, Saddle Brook, NJ 07662 (SAN 169-4715).

Regional Sub Bureau, P.O. Box 416, Hightstown, NJ 08520 (SAN 285-9661).

Regnery Bks., Div. of Regnery Gateway, Inc., *(Regnery Bks; 0-89526),* 700 E St., SE, Washington, DC 20003 (SAN 210-5578); Dist. by: Independent Pubs. Group, 1 Pleasant Ave., Port Washington, NY 11050 (SAN 287-2544). *Imprints:* Gateway Editions (Gateway Editions).

Reid News Agency, 3065 Carriker Lane, Soquel, CA 95073 (SAN 169-037X).

Reid Publishing, *(Reid Pub; 0-942628),* P.O. Box 5, Albert Lea, MN 56007 (SAN 238-566X) Tel 507-377-0858.

Renaissance Greeting Cards Inc., P.O. Box 127, Springvale, ME 04083 (SAN 200-4836).

Renaissance House *See* **Jende-Hagan, Inc.**

Repass, Mary E., P.O. Box 68, Louisa, KY 41230 (SAN 223-1042).

Reprint Co., *(Reprint; 0-87152),* P.O. Box 5401, 601 Hillcrest Offices, Spartanburg, SC 29304 (SAN 203-3828) Tel 803-582-0732.

Reprint Distribution Service Inc., P.O. Box 249, Kent, CT 06757 (SAN 169-0728).

Research Bks., Inc., 38 Academy St., P.O. Box 1507, Madison, CT 06443 (SAN 169-0701) Tel 203-245-3279.

Research Service Corp., P.O. Box 16549, Ft. Worth, TX 76133 (SAN 169-8206); 801 Asbury Ave., Ocean City, NJ 08226 (SAN 282-2512).

Resource Pubns., Inc., *(Resource Pubns; 0-89390),* 160 E. Virginia St., No. 290, San Jose, CA 95112 (SAN 209-3081) Tel 408-286-8505; Toll free: 800-228-2028.

Reward Bks. *See* **Prentice-Hall, Inc.**

Rex News Agency, Inc., 34 Queen City Dr., Cumberland, MD 21502 (SAN 159-9364).

Reyen, Richard R., Associates, 436 Demarest Ave., Oradell, NJ 07649 (SAN 282-731X) Tel 201-261-7450.

Reynal *See* **Morrow, William, & Co., Inc.**

Rhinelander News Agency, Star Rte. 2, Crescent Lake, WI 54501 (SAN 159-9372).

Rhode Island Bicentennial Foundation *See* **Rhode Island Pubns. Society**

Rhode Island Pubns. Society, *(RI Pubns Soc; 0-917012),* 189 Wickenden St., Providence, RI 02903 (SAN 219-9696) Tel 401-272-1776. *Imprints:* Rhode Island Bicentennial Foundation (RI Bicent Found).

Rhodes News Agency, 917 Island, Boise, ID 83706 (SAN 159-9380).

Richardson's Educators, 2014 Lou Ellen Ln., Houston, TX 77018 (SAN 169-829X) Tel 713-688-2244; Toll free: 800-392-8562 (TX); Toll free: 800-231-0588.

Ridge Book Service, Ridge Rd., Hankins, NY 12741 (SAN 282-6453).

Rietman, Jaap, *(Jaap Rietman; 0-930034),* 167 Spring St., New York, NY 10012 (SAN 205-2105) Tel 212-966-7044.

Rio Grande Book Co., 1101 Upas Ave., McAllen, TX 78501 (SAN 169-8354).

Rishor News Co., Inc., P.O. Box 2036, Butler, PA 16001 (SAN 159-9402).

Rittenhouse Bk. Distributors, *(Rittenhouse; 0-87381),* 511 Feheley Dr., King of Prussia, PA 19406 (SAN 213-4454) Tel 215-277-1414; Toll free: 800-345-6425.

Ritter Book Co., 111 N. Wabash Ave., Chicago, IL 60602 (SAN 169-1856).

River Mist Distributors, 624 University Ave., Palo Alto, CA 94301 (SAN 200-7827).

Riverrun Pr., Affil. of John Calder Pubs. (London, UK), *(Riverrun NY; 0-7145; 0-86676),* 1170 Broadway, Rm. 807, New York, NY 10001 (SAN 240-9917) Tel 212-889-6850; Dist. by: Kampmann & Co., Inc., 9 E. 40th St., New York, NY 10016 (SAN 202-5191) Tel 212-685-2928. *Imprints:* Breachwood Publications (Breachwood Pubns); Original Music (Original Music); Petras Press (Petras Press).

Riverside Bk. & Bible Hse., Inc., 1500 Riverside Dr., P.O. Box 370, Iowa Falls, IA 50126 (SAN 169-2666) Tel 515-648-4269; Toll free: 800-247-5111.

Riverside Editions *See* **Houghton Mifflin Co.**

Riverside Literature Series *See* **Houghton Mifflin Co.**

Riverside Reading Series *See* **Houghton Mifflin Co.**

Riverside Studies in Literature *See* **Houghton Mifflin Co.**

Rizzoli International Pubns., Inc., *(Rizzoli Intl; 0-8478),* 597 Fifth Ave., New York, NY 10017 (SAN 207-7000) Tel 212-223-0100; Toll free: 800-433-1238.

Roadrunner Library Service, 1221 E. Washington St., Phoenix, AZ 85034 (SAN 168-9339).

Roanoke News Agency, 1714 Ninth St. SE, Roanoke, VA 24013 (SAN 169-8702) Tel 703-345-4977.

Robec Distributors, P.O. Box 1001, 675 Bethlehem Pike, Montgomeryville, PA 18936 (SAN 677-9484) Tel 215-368-9300.

Roberts, F. M., Enterprises, *(F M Roberts; 0-912746),* P.O. Box 608, Dana Point, CA 92629-0608 (SAN 201-4688) Tel 714-493-1977.

Robinson, Ruth E., Bks., *(Robinson Bks; 0-9603556),* Rte. 7, Box 162A, Morgantown, WV 26505 (SAN 213-4322) Tel 304-594-3140.

Rochester News Agency, 421 1st Ave., NW, Rochester, MN 55901 (SAN 169-4138) Tel 507-282-8641.

Rock, Leonard, Magazine Service, 43 Grove St., Rockville, CT 06066 (SAN 285-9688).

Rockbottom Bks., 1224 W. Van Buren St., Chicago, IL 60607 (SAN 200-769X).

Rockland Catskill Inc., 26 Church St., Spring Valley, NY 10977 (SAN 169-6254); Toll free: 800-950-1088.

Rocky Mount News Agency, 2 Great State Ln., Rocky Mount, NC 27801 (SAN 169-6483).

Rodale Pr., *(Rodale Pr Inc; 0-87857),* 33 E. Minor St., Emmaus, PA 18049 (SAN 200-2477) Tel 215-967-5171; Toll free: 800-527-8200.

Rodeo News Publishing, P.O. Box 587, Pauls Valley, OK 73075 (SAN 200-7940).

Rogers, Gay Ann, *(G A Rogers),* Box 181, Claremont, CA 91711 (SAN 287-301X).

Rogers, Will Memorial & Museum, P.O. Box 157, Claremore, OK 74017 (SAN 280-3003).

Rogue Valley News Agency, Inc., 3100 Merriman Rd., Medford, OR 97501 (SAN 169-7137).

Roland Corp., 7200 Dominion Cir., Los Angeles, CA 90040 (SAN 200-5956).

Rome News Co., Inc., 12 Redmond Ct., Rome, GA 30161 (SAN 169-1546).

Rose of Sharon Press, Inc., *(Rose Sharon Pr; 0-932502),* G.P.O. Box 2432, New York, NY 10116 (SAN 212-3207) Tel 914-736-2521.

Ross Bk. Service, 3718 Seminary Rd., Alexandria, VA 22304 (SAN 661-1079) (SAN 200-6634).

Rothman, Fred B., & Co., *(Rothman; 0-8377),* 10368 W. Centennial Rd., Littleton, CO 80127 (SAN 159-9437) Tel 303-979-5657; Toll free: 800-457-1986. Acquired Rothman Reprints.

Roundtable Pr., *(Roundtable Pr; 0-934512),* 4 Linden Sq., Wellesley, MA 02181-4709 (SAN 282-2628) Tel 617-235-5320. Do not confuse with Roundtable Pub. in Santa Monica, CA.

Running Pr. Bk. Pubs., *(Running Pr; 0-89471),* 125 S. 22nd St., Philadelphia, PA 19103 (SAN 204-5702) Tel 215-567-5080; Toll free: 800-428-1111.

Rushmore News Inc., 924 E. St. Andrew, Rapid City, SD 57701 (SAN 169-7846).

Russell News Agency Inc., Box 158, Sarasota, FL 33578 (SAN 169-1287).

Rutland News Co., Box 579, Rutland, VT 05701 (SAN 169-8591).

Ruzicka, Joseph, Inc., Box 21568, Greensboro, NC 27420 (SAN 159-9445); Toll free: 800-221-4552 (In GA,SC,TN,VA,NC,WV,MD,Only).

S & S News & Greeting, 277 North American Bank, Skyway Bldg., St.Paul, MN 55101 (SAN 159-9453).

S & W Distributors Inc., 1020 E. Wendover Ave., P.O. Box 6724, Greensboro, NC 27405 (SAN 169-6416).

SDP, INc., 13848 Ventura Blvd. Suite 7, Sherman Oaks, CA 91423 (SAN 292-823X) Tel 818-986-5461.

STBS, 50 W. 23rd St., New York, NY 10010 (SAN 200-6162) Tel 212-206-8795.

Safeguard Business Systems, Inc., *(Safeguard Bus; 0-923046),* P.O. Box 6000, Fort Washington, PA 19034 (SAN 200-4445) Tel 215-641-5000; Toll free: 800-523-6660; 455 Maryland Dr., Fort Washington, PA 19034 (SAN 697-306X).

Safeguard Security, Inc., P.O. Box 1051, Dept. SMP, Flint, MI 48501 (SAN 663-4532).

Sage Bks. *See* Swallow Pr.

Sage Computer Co., 35 N. Edison, Suite 4, Reno, NV 89502 (SAN 287-2676).

Sage Pubns., Inc., *(Sage; 0-8039),* 275 S. Beverly Dr., Beverly Hills, CA 90212 (SAN 204-7217) Tel 213-274-8003.

St. Luke's Pr., *(St Luke TN; 0-918518),* Mid-Memphis Tower, 1407 Union Ave., Suite 401, Memphis, TN 38104 (SAN 210-0029) Tel 901-357-5441; Toll free: 800-524-5554 (dial 4617, orders).

St. Marie's Gopher News, 308 S. Lake Ave., Meier Hoff Bldg., Duluth, MN 55805 (SAN 169-4065).

St. Martin's Pr., Inc., Subs. of Macmillan Pubs., *(St Martin; 0-312; 0-9603648),* 175 Fifth Ave., New York, NY 10010 (SAN 200-2132) Tel 212-674-5151; Toll free: 800-221-7945; 165 Marlborough St., Boston, MA 02116 (SAN 650-0560). *Imprints:* Kahn, Joann, Book, A (J Kahn); Papermac Books (Papermac).

Saint Mary Seminary Bookstore, 1227 Ansel Rd., Cleveland, OH 44108 (SAN 169-667X).

St. Mary's County Historical Society, P.O. Box 212, Leonardtown, MD 20650 (SAN 200-5468) Tel 301-475-2467.

St. Mary's Pr., Subs. of Christian Brothers of Minnesota, *(St Mary's; 0-88489),* Terrace Heights, Winona, MN 55987 (SAN 203-073X) Tel 507-452-9090; Toll free: 800-533-8095.

Saks News Inc., P.O. Box 1857, Bismarck, ND 58502 (SAN 169-653X).

Salem News Agency, 1745 23rd St. S.E., Salem, OR 97302 (SAN 169-720X).

Sams, Howard W., & Co., Div. of Macmillan, Inc., *(Sams; 0-672),* 4300 W. 62nd St., Indianapolis, IN 46268 (SAN 203-3577) Tel 317-298-5400; Toll free: 800-428-3602.

Samson International Book Distributors, 1004 grand Blvd., Deer Park, NY 11729 (SAN 159-2246); Toll free: 800-446-4480.

San Diego Periodical Distributors, P.O. Box 82108, San Diego, CA 92138 (SAN 169-0132).

San Val Inc., 10883 Metro Court, Maryland Heights, MO 63043 (SAN 159-947X); Toll free: 800-535-4465.

Sandoval Distributing Co., Box 5465, Tucson, AZ 85705 (SAN 159-9488).

Sandpiper Book Service, 39 Danbury Rd., Wilton, CT 06897 (SAN 169-0884).

Sandpiper Paperbacks *See* Houghton Mifflin Co.

Sands of California, Box 9871, San Jose, CA 95117 (SAN 275-2069).

Santa Barbara Botanic Garden, *(Santa Barb Botanic; 0-916436),* 1212 Mission Canyon Rd., Santa Barbara, CA 93105 (SAN 208-8398) Tel 805-682-4726.

Santa Barbara News Agency, 879 S. Kellogg Ave., Goleta, CA 93017 (SAN 168-9665).

Saranac Lake News Co., Box 711, Saranac Lake, NY 12983 (SAN 169-6238).

Saturday Evening Post Co. School Plan, P.O. Box 1463, Indianapolis, IN 46202 (SAN 285-9742).

Savoyard Bks. *See* Wayne State Univ. Pr.

Sayre Publishing, P.O. Box 1337, Scarsdale, NY 10583 (SAN 201-0925) Tel 914-725-2280.

Scanlon Clocks, P.O. Box 379, Modesto, CA 95353 (SAN 284-9690) Tel 204-524-9789.

Schad, Tennyson, 575 Madison Ave., New York, NY 10022 (SAN 208-242X).

Schaeffer News Agency, 23-25 Wall St., Auburn, NY 13021 (SAN 169-5037).

Schar Publishing Co., *(Schar Pub Co; 0-9611830),* 2541 W. Ainslie St., Chicago, IL 60625 (SAN 240-8279) Tel 312-784-2186; Dist. by: K. V. Schar, 2541 W. Ainslie St., Chicago, IL 60625 (SAN 240-8287).

Schiffer Publishing, Ltd., *(Schiffer; 0-916838; 0-88740),* 1469 Morstein Rd., West Chester, PA 19380 (SAN 208-8428) Tel 215-696-1001.

Schirmer, E. C., Music Co., Inc., *(E C Schirmer; 0-911318),* 138 Ipswich St., Boston, MA 02215 (SAN 201-3517) Tel 617-236-1935.

Schirmer Bks., Div. of Macmillan Publishing Co., Inc., *(Schirmer Bks; 0-911320),* 866 Third Ave., New York, NY 10022 (SAN 222-9544); Toll free: 800-257-5755.

Schnell's Book Service, 529 Maurice River Blvd., Vineland, NJ 08360-2698 (SAN 127-8339).

Schocken Bks., Inc., *(Schocken; 0-8052),* 62 Cooper Sq., New York, NY 10003 (SAN 213-7585) Tel 212-475-4900. *Imprints:* Moonlight Editions (Moonlight Edns).

Schoenhof's Foreign Books, Inc., Subs. of Editions Gallimard, *(Schoenhof; 0-87774),* 76A Mount Auburn St., Cambridge, MA 02138 (SAN 212-0062) Tel 617-547-8855. French, Italian, Portuguese, Russian, Polish, Ukranian and Spanish linguistics, classics, dictionaries & grammars in over one hundred languages.

Scholarly Book Center, 3828 Hawthorn Ct., Waukegan, IL 60087 (SAN 169-2259).

Scholarly Pubns., *(Scholarly Pubns; 0-88065; 1-55528),* 7310 El Cresta Dr., Houston, TX 77083 (SAN 650-0587) Tel 713-879-8319.

Scholarly Resources, Inc., *(Scholarly Res Inc; 0-8420),* 104 Greenhill Ave., Wilmington, DE 19805 (SAN 203-2619) Tel 302-654-7713; Toll free: 800-772-8937. Source materials on 35mm microfilm, monographs, reference books & microfiche. Subjects: ethnic studies, genealogy, history, law, military studies & political science. Government documents, journals, manuscript collections & newspapers.

Scholastic Hardcover *See* Scholastic, Inc.

Scholastic, Inc., *(Scholastic Inc; 0-590),* 730 Broadway, New York, NY 10003 (SAN 202-5442) Tel 212-505-3000; Toll free: 800-392-2179; Orders to: P.O. Box 7502, 2931 E. McCarty St., Jefferson City, MO 65102 (SAN 202-5450). *Imprints:* Apple Paperbacks (Apple Paperbacks); Blue Ribbon Books (Blue Ribbon Bks); Citation Press (Citation); Hello Reader (Hello Reader); Lucky Star (Lucky Star); Point (Point); Scholastic Hardcover (Scholastic Hardcover); Seesaw Books (Seesaw Bks); Starline (Starline); Sunfire (Sunfire); Vagabond (Vagabond); Wildfire Press (Wildfire); Windswept Books (Windswept Bks); Wishing Star Books (Wishing Star Bks).

Scholium International, Inc., *(Scholium Intl; 0-87936),* 265 Great Neck Rd., Great Neck, NY 11021 (SAN 169-5282) Tel 516-466-5181.

School Aid Co., *(Sch Aid; 0-87385),* 911 Colfax Dr., P.O. Box 123, Danville, IL 61832 (SAN 158-3719); Toll free: 800-447-2665.

School Aids, 6867 Van Gogh Dr., Baton Rouge, LA 70806 (SAN 169-2909) Tel 504-926-4498.

School Computer Systems, Inc., Jeanne Dr., Putnam Valley, NY 10579 (SAN 200-5905) Tel 914-528-2456.

School Dept. *See* Harper & Row Pubs., Inc.

School Products Co., Inc., 1201 Broadway, New York, NY 10001 (SAN 159-9496).

Schroeder News Co., P.O. Box 796, Merced, CA 95113 (SAN 159-950X).

Schroeder's Book Haven, Rte. 1, P.O. Box 2820, Dickinson, TX 75539 (SAN 122-7998).

Schulze News Co., 2907 Palma Dr., Ventura, CA 93003 (SAN 169-0434) Tel 805-642-9759.

Schuylkill News Service, 107 N. Railroad St., Pottsville, PA 17901 (SAN 159-9518).

Schwartz-Rosenblum, Inc., 2906 W. Devon Ave., Chicago, IL 60659 (SAN 169-1864).

Scientific & Medical Pubs., 16 E. 34th St., New York, NY 10016 (SAN 169-5940).

Scotch-Irish Foundation, 13 Thompson Dr., Havertown, PA 19083 (SAN 224-4993) Tel 215-446-0417.

Scott, Foresman & Co., Subs. of SFN Co., *(Scott F; 0-673),* 1900 E. Lake Ave., Glenview, IL 60025 (SAN 200-2140) Tel 312-729-3000.

Scott Krauss News Agency, P.O. Box 193, Columbus, OH 43216 (SAN 169-6696).

Scribble Shack Book Distributor, 2800 Spring Blvd., Eugene, OR 97403 (SAN 159-9526).

Scribner's, Charles, Sons, Div. of Macmillan Publishing Co., *(Scribner; 0-684),* 115 Fifth Ave., New York, NY 10003 (SAN 200-2191) Tel 212-614-1300; Toll free: 800-257-5755; Orders to: Order Dept., Front & Brown Sts., Riverside, NJ 08075 (SAN 282-6550).

Scripture Press Pubns., Inc., *(SP Pubns; 0-88207; 0-89693),* 1825 College Ave., Wheaton, IL 60187 (SAN 222-9471) Tel 312-668-6000; Toll free: 800-323-9409. *Imprints:* Sonflower Books (Sonflower Bks).

Sea Gate, 657 Fifth Ave., Brooklyn, NY 11215 (SAN 200-5336).

Seaboard Sub Agency, 44 S. Fulton St., P.O. Box 1482, Allentown, PA 18105 (SAN 285-9718).

Seaview *See* **Putnam Publishing Group, The**

Sebastian Publishing Co., *(Sebastian Pub Co; 0-913347),* 1109 Royal Ln., San Carlos, CA 94070 (SAN 287-4466) Tel 415-598-0310; Dist. by: Pacific Pipeline, Inc., 19215 66th Ave., S., Kent, WA 98032 (SAN 287-4466) Tel 206-872-5523; Dist. by: Sebastian Publishing Co., 1109 Royal Ln., San Carlos, CA 94070 (SAN 287-4466) Tel 415-598-0310; Dist. by: Baker & Taylor, Western Div., 380 Edison Way, Reno, NV 89564 (SAN 169-4464) Tel 702-786-6700.

Second Genesis, 1112 NE 21st St., Portland, OR 97232 (SAN 158-9490).

Seesaw Books *See* **Scholastic, Inc.**

Select Magazines, Inc., 8 E. 40th St., New York, NY 10016 (SAN 293-4531).

Selections Book Fairs, 4505 N. High St., Columbus, OH 43214 (SAN 128-3766) Tel 614-262-0189.

Selective Books, Box 1140, Clearwater, FL 33517 (SAN 159-9534).

Selzer Books, 705 Willow Ave., Ukiah, CA 95482 (SAN 211-6146) Tel 707-462-1630.

Semler News Agency, P.O. Box 350, New Castle, PA 16101 (SAN 169-7471); Box 526, Morgantown, WV 26505 (SAN 169-8990).

Seneca News Agency, Box 631, Geneva, NY 14456 (SAN 169-5304).

Senic Computer Systems, 14852 NE 31st Cir., Redmond, WA 98052 (SAN 287-2684).

Sentai Distributors, 8735 Shirley, Northridge, CA 91324 (SAN 168-9959).

Sentry Editions *See* **Houghton Mifflin Co.**

Sepher-Hermon Pr., Inc., *(Hermon; 0-87203),* 1265 46th St., Brooklyn, NY 11219 (SAN 169-5959) Tel 718-972-9010.

Serenade-Saga *See* **Zondervan Publishing Hse.**

Serendipity Couriers, 1945-Q Francisco Blvd., San Rafael, CA 94901 (SAN 169-0329).

Servatius News Agency, 601 Second St., Clarkston, WA 99403 (SAN 169-8737).

Service, 73 S. 3rd Ave., P.O. Box 1145, Mount Vernon, NY 10551 (SAN 159-0251).

Service News Co., 1306 N. 23rd St., P.O. Box 3788, Wilmington, NC 28406 (SAN 169-6491); P.O. Box 5027, Macon, GA 31208 (SAN 169-152X); Pope's Island, Box D-629, New Bedford, MA 02742 (SAN 169-3514).

Seven Hills Bks., Div. of Books for the Decorative Arts, Inc., *(Seven Hills Bks; 0-911403),* 49 Central Ave., Suite 300, Cincinnatti, OH 45202 (SAN 169-6629) Tel 513-381-3881.

Sextant *See* **Childrens Pr.**

Shapolsky Bks. *See* **Shapolsky, Steimatzky**

Shapolsky/Steimatzky, *(Shapolsky Steimatzky; 0-933503),* 56 E. 11th St., New York, NY 10003 (SAN 200-8068) Tel 212-505-2505. *Imprints:* Shapolsky Bks. (Shapolsky Bks).

Sharing Co., The, *(Sharing Co; 0-941500),* P.O. Box 2224, Austin, TX 78768-2224 (SAN 211-0563) Tel 512-452-4366.

Sharon News Agency Co., 527 Silver St., Sharon, PA 16146 (SAN 169-7633).

Shasta General Systems, P.O. Box 19661, Houston, TX 77224-9661 (SAN 285-9777) Tel 713-493-0300.

Shatswell, Bruce, *(Bruce Shatswell),* 10 Phillips Ave., Apt. 2, Lynn, MA 01902 (SAN 200-6103) Tel 617-595-8511.

Shearer Communications, *(Shearer Pub; 0-940672),* 406 Post Oak Rd., Fredericksburg, TX 78624 (SAN 218-5989) Tel 512-997-6529.

Sheboygan News Agency, Box 1145, Sheboygan, WI 53801 (SAN 169-9180).

Sher Distributing Co., P.O. Box 126, 767 Park Sta., Paterson, NJ 07503 (SAN 169-4820).

Sheriar Pr., Inc., *(Sheriar Pr; 0-913078),* 1414 Madison St., S., North Myrtle Beach, SC 29582 (SAN 203-2457) Tel 803-272-5333.

Shinder's Book Co., 600 Hennepin Ave., Minneapolis, MN 55403 (SAN 169-4111).

Shoe String Pr., Inc., *(Shoe String; 0-208),* P.O. Box 4327, Hamden, CT 06514 (SAN 213-2079) Tel 203-248-6307; 925 Sherman Ave., Hamden, CT 06514 (SAN 696-9410). *Imprints:* Archon Books (Archon Bks); Bingley, Clive, Limited (England) (Pub. by Bingley England); Cooper (Cooper); CT Academy (CT Academy); Library Professional Publications (Lib Prof Pubns); Linnet (Linnet); Pembridge Press (England) (Pub. by Pembridge Pr UK); Tompson & Rutter, Incorporated (Pub. by Thompson & Rutter, Inc.)

Shoppers Guide Press, Box 1021, Alpine, TX 79830 (SAN 159-9550).

Shreveport News Agency, P.O. Box 6108, 9211 Black Rd., Shreveport, LA 71106 (SAN 169-300X); 1303 Enterprise Rd., Alexandria, LA 71301 (SAN 169-2887); 501 Orange, Box 2491, Monroe, LA 71202 (SAN 169-2925).

SIE Pub., 31312 Via Colinas, Suite 10003, Westlake Village, CA 91362 (SAN 240-9054) Tel 818-991-3400.

Siebert's Inc., Box 9010, Little Rock, AR 72219 (SAN 159-9569).

Sierra News Co., 21 Locust St., Reno, NV 89520 (SAN 169-4472).

Sifria Distributors, 729 Ave. N, Brooklyn, NY 11230 (SAN 206-0019).

Signature Bks., Inc., *(Signature Bks; 0-941214),* 350 S. 400 E., Salt Lake City, UT 84111 (SAN 217-4391) Tel 801-531-1483. *Imprints:* Eden Hill Publishing (Eden Hill Pub); Orion (Orion).

Signet Bks. *See* **New American Library**

Signet Classics *See* **New American Library**

Signette *See* **New American Library**

Sigo Pr., *(Sigo Pr; 0-938434),* 77 N. Washington St., No. 201, Boston, MA 02114 (SAN 216-3020) Tel 617-523-2321.

Siler's Library Distributors, 2737 Bienville Ave., New Orleans, LA 70119 (SAN 169-2992).

Silky Way Inc., 1226 Hilltop Mall Rd., Richmond, CA 94804 (SAN 169-3328).

Silver, Robert, Assocs., *(R Silver; 0-937414),* 307 E. 37th St., New York, NY 10016 (SAN 241-5801) Tel 212-686-5630.

Silver Bow News Distributing Co., Inc., 219 E. Park St., Butte, MT 59701 (SAN 169-4359).

Silverstein, Max, & Son, Inc., 15 Clarkson St., Providence, RI 02904 (SAN 282-3152); Box 6527, Providence, RI 02940 (SAN 282-3160).

Simon & Schuster, Inc., Div. of Gulf & Western, *(S&S; 0-671),* 1230 Ave. of the Americas, New York, NY 10020 (SAN 200-2450) Tel 212-245-6400; Toll free: 800-223-2348. *Imprints:* Fireside Paperbacks (Fireside); Juvenile Books (Juveniles); Kenan Press (Kenan Pr); Linden Press (Linden Pr); Little Simon (Little Simon); Minstrel Books (Minstrel Bks); Touchstone Books (Touchstone Bks); Wallaby (Wallaby); Wyndham Books (Wyndham Bks).

Skills, 150 Searing St., Amherst, MA 01002 (SAN 215-8795) Tel 413-549-2686.

Skipworth Press, Inc., *(Skipworth Pr; 0-931804),* 5811 Windsor Dr., Mechanicsville, VA 23111 (SAN 211-6480); Dist. by: First Impressions Printing, Marketing & Design Services, 1601 Ware Bottom Spring Rd., Chester, VA 23831 (SAN 200-4712) Tel 804-748-4461.

Slack, Inc., *(Slack Inc; 0-913590; 0-943432; 1-55642),* 6900 Grove Rd., Thorofare, NJ 08086 (SAN 201-8632) Tel 609-848-1000; Toll free: 800-257-8290.

Slavica Pubs., Inc., *(Slavica; 0-89357),* P.O. Box 14388, Columbus, OH 43214 (SAN 208-8576) Tel 614-268-4002.

Slawenski, J. W., Computer Keyboard Co., 616 Ninth St., Union City, NJ 07087 (SAN 677-6523) Tel 201-863-0999.

Slawson Communications, Inc., *(Slawson Comm; 0-915391),* 3719 Sixth Ave., San Diego, CA 92103-4316 (SAN 200-6901) Tel 619-291-9126.

Sleepy Hollow Book Co., P.O. Box 374, Rockland, MA 02370 (SAN 169-3557).

Small Pr. Distribution, Inc., *(Small Pr Dist; 0-914068),* 1814 San Pablo Ave, Berkeley, CA 94702 (SAN 204-5826) Tel 415-549-3336.

Small Pr. Traffic, 3599 24th St., San Francisco, CA 94114 (SAN 200-7371) Tel 415-285-8394.

Smith, A. W., & Son, 69 Seneca St., Hornell, NY 14843 (SAN 108-8181).

Smith, Gibbs M., Inc., *(Gibbs M Smith; 0-87905),* P.O. Box 667, Layton, UT 84041 (SAN 201-9906) Tel 801-554-9800; Toll free: 800-421-8714. *Imprints:* Falcon Books (Falcon Bks); Peregrine Smith Books (Peregrine Smith).

Smith, Howard, Brokerage Inc., 2317 N. Marbury Rd., Pittsburgh, PA 15221 (SAN 286-0023).

Smith, L. E., Wholesale Distributors, Inc., 302 York St., Gettysburg, PA 17325-1996 (SAN 169-7366).

Smith, W. H., and Son, 112 Madison Ave., New York, NY 10016 (SAN 211-609X); Toll free: 800-645-9990 (Corporate Office); Toll free: 800-932-0070 (Orders Only).

Smith News Agency, 118 S. Mitchell St., Cadillac, MI 49601 (SAN 169-3727).

Smith Novelty Co., Inc., Div. of Smith News Co., Inc., *(Smith Novelty; 0-938765),* 460 Ninth St., San Francisco, CA 94103 (SAN 216-2326) Tel 415-861-4900.

Smith's Inc., 53 Main St., Plymouth, MA 02360 (SAN 169-3549).

Smithsonian Institution Pr., *(Smithsonian; 0-87474),* 955 L'Enfant Plaza, Suite 2100, Washington, DC 20560 (SAN 206-8044) Tel 202-287-3765; Orders to: Customer Services, P.O. Box 4866, Hampden Sta., Baltimore, MD 21211 (SAN 206-8052) Tel 301-338-6963.

Snake River Periodical Distributors Inc., 2695 Church St., Baker, OR 87914 (SAN 159-9585).

Snyder Magazine Agency, 4817 W. 62nd Terr., Shawnee Mission, KS 66205 (SAN 285-9750) Tel 913-722-6766.

Society for Visual Education, Inc., *(Soc for Visual; 0-89290),* 1345 Diversey Pkwy., Chicago, IL 60614 (SAN 208-3930) Tel 312-525-1500; Toll free: 800-621-1900.

Society of American Magicians, *(SAM),* 325 Maple St., Lynn, MA 01904 (SAN 260-3691) Tel 617-595-8325; Dist. by: Society of American Magicians, P.O. Box 268, Mango, FL 33550 (SAN 669-2672).

Soft-Kat, Inc., 16130 Stagg St., Van Nuys, CA 91406 (SAN 678-3635) Tel 818-781-5280; Toll free: 800-641-1057.

Softsell, *(Softsell),* 546 N. Oak St., Inglewood, CA 90302 (SAN 287-6760) Tel 213-412-1700; Toll free: 800-645-7777; Toll free: 800-645-7778 (orders only).

Software America, 5001-A Forbes Blvd., Lanham, MD 20706 (SAN 654-6714) Tel 301-459-2100; Toll free: 800-638-9579.

Software Distributors, 10023 Jefferson Blvd., Culver City, CA 90230 (SAN 684-4138) (SAN 285-7073).

Software Link, Inc., *(Soft Link; 0-927031),* 8601 Dunwoody Pl., Suite 632, Atlanta, GA 30338 (SAN 653-3817) Tel 404-998-0700.

Somba Bookstore, Capital Plaza, 3155 Main St., Hartford, CT 01614 (SAN 200-5441).

Sonflower Books *See* **Scripture Press Pubns., Inc.**

Sort Card Co., The, Box 901, Boulder, CO 80302 (SAN 159-9607).

Sounds of Zion, 5180 S. 300 W, Unit U, Murray, UT 84107 (SAN 200-7525).

South Atlantic News, 1426 NE Eighth Ave., Ocala, FL 32678 (SAN 169-1198).

South Carolina Educational Communications, Inc., *(SC Ed Comm Inc; 0-943274),* 19 Springdale Ln., Spartanburg, SC 29302 (SAN 293-2601); Dist. by: South Carolina ETV, P.O. Drawer L, Columbia, SC 29250 (SAN 293-261X) Tel 803-758-7284.

South Georgia News Agency, P.O. Box 197, Waycross, GA 31501 (SAN 169-1589).

South Louisiana News Co., Crowley Rayne Industrial Park, 102 Industrial Dr., Rayne, LA 70578 (SAN 169-2917).

South Sky Book Co., 5501 University Way NE, Seattle, WA 98105 (SAN 157-8618).

South Texas Distributing, 1011 N. Frio, P.O. Box 7608, San Antonio, TX 78207 (SAN 156-4994).

Southeast Periodicals, P.O. Box 340008, Coral Gables, FL 33134 (SAN 238-6909).

Southeastern Library Service, Box 44, Gainesville, FL 32602 (SAN 159-9615).

Southeastern Printing Co., 215 22nd Ave., Meridian, MS 39301 (SAN 200-5484).

Southern Book & Supply Co., Easley Hwy. 123, Greenville, SC 29602 (SAN 169-7811).

Southern Book Co., Fasley Hwy 123, Greenville, SC 29602 (SAN 169-7811).

Southern Book Service, 3625 E. Tenth Ct., Hialeah, FL 33013 (SAN 169-0981).

Southern California Book Co., Inc., 2219 S. Union Ave., Los Angeles, CA 90007 (SAN 168-9827).

Southern Library Bindery Co., 2952 Sidco Dr., Nashville, TN 37204 (SAN 169-7986).

Southern Michigan News Co., *(Southern MI News),* 5601 Enterprise Dr., Lansing, MI 48910 (SAN 169-3883); Toll free: 800-248-2213; Toll free: 800-828-2140 in Michigan.

Southern News Co., 202 14th St., NW, Atlanta, GA 30318 (SAN 169-1457).

Southern Star, Inc., P.O. Box 968, Harrison, AR 72601 (SAN 213-2435).

Southern Tier News Co., P.O. Box 2128, Elmira Heights, NY 14903 (SAN 169-5223).

Southern Wisconsin News, Rte. 3, 4838 S. John Paul Rd., Milton, WI 53563 (SAN 169-9121).

Southwest Book Services, Inc., *(Southwest Bk Servs),* 4951 Top Line Dr., Dallas, TX 75247 (SAN 211-8696).

Southwest Cookbook Distributors Inc., 1901 South Shore Dr., Bonham, TX 75418 (SAN 200-4925) Tel 214-583-8898.

Southwest Data Systems, *(SW Data Systs; 0-932721),* 3017 San Fernando Blvd., Burbank, CA 91504 (SAN 688-3192) Tel 818-841-1610; Toll free: 800-325-3488.

Southwest News Co., Box 5465, Tucson, AZ 85704 (SAN 159-9631).

Southwest Parks & Monuments Assn., *(SW Pks Mnmts; 0-911408),* 221 N. Court, Tucson, AZ 85701 (SAN 202-750X) Tel 602-622-1999.

Southwest Periodicals Distributing Co., P.O. Box 5465, Tucson, AZ 85705 (SAN 168-9398).

Southwestern Bk. Distributors, 1221 E. Washington, Phoenix, AZ 85034-1101 (SAN 160-2373).

Southwestern Stringed Instruments & Accessories, 1228 E. Prince Rd., Tucson, AZ 85719 (SAN 200-4003).

Sovereign News Co., 2075 E. 65th St., Cleveland, OH 44103 (SAN 169-6688).

Spama, 267 Fourth Ave., Brooklyn, NY 11215 (SAN 169-5967).

Spanish Bookstore-Wholesale, The, 2326 Westwood Blvd, Los Angeles, CA 90064 (SAN 168-9835).

Spanish House Distributors, 1360 NW 88th Ave., Miami, FL 33172 (SAN 169-1171).

Spanishtech, Inc., Div. of Editor's Bureau, Ltd., Box 68, Westport, CT 06881 (SAN 289-9620). Technical Spanish-English dictionaries to professional translators, libraries, egineering schools, etc. Technical/business titles & dictionaries in French, German, & other modern languages.

Sparks & Co., 979 Summer St., Stamford, CT 06905 (SAN 200-7444) Tel 203-967-3617.

Special Child Pubns., *(Spec Child; 0-87562),* P.O. Box 33548, Seattle, WA 98133 (SAN 203-2317) Tel 206-771-5711.

Specialized Bk. Service, 1418 Barnum Ave., Stratford, CT 06497 (SAN 166-9788).

Specialty Promotions, 640 E 79th, Chicago, IL 60619 (SAN 169-1872).

Spectrum Bks. *See* **Prentice-Hall, Inc.**

Speedimpex USA, Inc., 45-45 39th St., Long Island City, NY 11101 (SAN 169-5479).

Speer Books, *(Speer Bks; 0-917832),* 333 Ash St., Red Bluff, CA 96080 (SAN 208-3566).

Spielman Co., P. O. Box 15741, New Orleans, LA 70175 (SAN 276-9646) Tel 504-899-7670.

Spokane Periodicals Distributor Inc., P.O. Box 4067, Spokane, WA 99202 (SAN 169-8850).

Sporting Book Center, Inc., *(0-932748),* Canaan, NY 12029 (SAN 222-8734).

Sports Products, Inc., P.O. Box 1975, Grand Central Sta., New York, NY 10017 (SAN 282-3551) Tel 203-846-4897; Box 392, Ridgefield, CT 06877 (SAN 282-356X).

Sportsman's Market, Inc., *(0-912796),* Clermont County Airport, Batavia, OH 45103 (SAN 205-0803) Tel 513-732-2411; Toll free: 800-543-8663.

Spring Arbor Distributors, 10885 Textile Rd., Belleville, MI 48111 (SAN 158-9016) Tel 313-481-0900; Toll free: 800-521-3990.

Spring Arbor-West, 5600 NE Hassalo St., Portland, OR 97213 (SAN 169-7196).

Spring Church Book Co., P.O. Box 127, Spring Church, PA 15686 (SAN 212-7075).

Spring Pubs., P.O. Box 222069, Dallas, TX 75222 (SAN 282-6127).

Springer-Verlag New York, Inc., Subs. of Springer-Verlag GmbH & Co. KG, *(Springer-Verlag; 0-387),* 175 Fifth Ave., New York, NY 10010 (SAN 203-2228) Tel 212-460-1500; Toll free: 800-526-7254.

Springfield News Agency, P.O. Box 31, Springfield, IL 62705 (SAN 169-2216).

Stacey's Division of Bro-Dart, 1236 S. Hatcher, City of Industry, CA 91744 (SAN 159-9658).

Stackpole Bks., Inc., *(Stackpole; 0-8117),* P.O. Box 1831, Cameron & Kelker Sts., Harrisburg, PA 17105 (SAN 202-5396) Tel 717-234-5041; Toll free: 800-READ-NOW. *Imprints:* Giniger, K. S., Books (K S Giniger).

Standard News, Harvard & Selleck St., Stamford, CT 06902 (SAN 169-0841).

Standish *See* **Dell Publishing Co., Inc.**

Stanislaus Imports, Inc., 75 Arkansas St., San Francisco, CA 94107 (SAN 210-1998) Tel 415-431-7122.

Stanyan Bks. *See* **Random Hse., Inc.**

Star News Co., 307 E. Tucumcari Blvd., Tucumcari, NM 88401 (SAN 169-5010).

Starkmann Book Service, 43 Church St., Winchester, MA 01890 (SAN 126-6128).

Starline *See* **Scholastic, Inc.**

Starlite Distributors, *(Starlite; 0-931941),* P.O. Box 20729, Reno, NV 89515 (SAN 200-7789).

Starmont Hse., *(Starmont Hse; 0-916732; 0-930261),* P.O. Box 851, Mercer Island, WA 98040 (SAN 208-8703) Tel 206-232-8484.

State Mutual Bk. & Periodical Service, Ltd., *(State Mutual Bk; 0-89771),* 521 Fifth Ave., 17th Flr., New York, NY 10017 (SAN 658-3849) Tel 212-682-5844.

State News Agency, 610 Industrial Ave., Greensboro, NC 27406 (SAN 169-6424).

State News Co., State News Bldg., Rockland, ME 04841 (SAN 169-3085).

Station Hill Pr., *(Station Hill Pr; 0-930794),* Station Hill Rd., Barrytown, NY 12507 (SAN 214-1485); Dist. by: Small Press Dist., 1814 San Pablo Ave., Berkeley, CA 94702 (SAN 204-5826) Tel 415-549-3336; Dist. by: Inland Bk. Co., P.O. Box 261, 22 Hemingway St., East Haven, CT 06512 (SAN 200-4151) Tel 203-467-4257; Dist. by: Station Hill Pr., Sta. Hill Rd., Barrytown, NY 12507 (SAN 214-1485); Dist. by: Writers & Bks., 740 University Ave., Rochester, NY 14607 (SAN 662-152X) Tel 716-473-2590.

Statler News Agency, P.O. Box 992, Laredo, TX 78040 (SAN 169-8311).

Stein & Day, *(Stein & Day; 0-8128),* Scarborough Hse., Briarcliff Manor, NY 10510 (SAN 203-3461) Tel 914-762-2151.

Sterling Publishing Co., Inc., *(Sterling; 0-8069),* 2 Park Ave., New York, NY 10016 (SAN 211-6324) Tel 212-532-7160; 900 Magnolia Ave., Elizabeth, NJ 07201 (SAN 658-1773). *Imprints:* Davis Publications (Davis Pubns).

Sterling Rock Falls News Agency, 30 W. Third St., Sterling, IL 61081 (SAN 169-2232).

Stevenson, Robert Louis, Schl., The *See* **Univ. of Texas Pr.**

Stevenson's Genealogical Ctr., 230 W. 1230 N., Provo, UT 84604-2534 (SAN 200-8106).

Stewart-MacDonald Corp., 21 N. Shafer St., Athens, OH 45701 (SAN 293-4396).

Stiles, D. B., P.O. Box 812, Gautier, MS 39553 (SAN 262-4303).

Stinna Co., 4725 SE 49th St., Portland, OR 97206 (SAN 200-5778).

Stoelting Company, *(Stoelting Co),* 1350 S. Kostner Ave., Chicago, IL 60623 (SAN 275-8172) Tel 312-522-4500.

Stofflet News Co., 7240 Jackson Rd., Ann Arbor, MI 48108 (SAN 159-9666).

Storie/McOwen Pubs., Inc., *(Storie McOwen; 0-912367),* P.O. Box 308, Manteo, NC 27954 (SAN 265-0940) Tel 919-473-5881.

Story Hse. Corp., *(Story Hse Corp; 0-87157),* Bindery Ln., Charlotteville, NY 12036 (SAN 169-5193) Tel 607-397-8725; Toll free: 800-428-1008 (NY State); Toll free: 800-847-2105 (Outside NY).

Straight Talk Distributing, P.O. Box 750, Point Reyes Station, CA 94956 (SAN 282-311X).

Stratton Intercontinental Medical Book Corp., 381 Park Ave. S., New York, NY 10016 (SAN 159-9674).

Straw into Gold, 3006 San Pablo, Berkely, CA 94702 (SAN 239-4448).

Strawberry Hill Pr., *(Strawberry Hill; 0-89407),* 2594 15th Ave., San Francisco, CA 94127 (SAN 238-8103) Tel 415-664-8112.

Strong's News Agency, 4932 W. Pasadena Ave., Glendale, AZ 85301 (SAN 168-9312).

Stroup News Agency Inc., 491 Broadway, Saratoga Springs, NY 12866 (SAN 159-9682).

Studio Bks. *See* **Viking-Penguin, Inc.**

Stull & Co., Since 1870, Inc., *(Stull & Co),* 120 Wall St., New York, NY 10005 (SAN 211-3317).

Subscription Acct., 84 Needham, Newton Highlands , MA 02161 (SAN 285-9424).

Subscription House, Inc., 607 Boylston St., Boston, MA 02116 (SAN 285-9343).

Subscription Service Co., First Ave. N. at 13th St., Birmingham, AL 35223 (SAN 285-9394).

Subscription Service Inc., The, P.O. Box 2777, Des Moines, IA 50315 (SAN 285-922X).

Subterranean Co, 1327 W. 2nd, P.O. Box 10233, Eugene, OR 97440 (SAN 169-7102) Tel 503-343-6324.

Success Education Assn., Box 175, Roanoke, VA 24002 (SAN 159-9690).

Successful Living, Inc., 9905 Hamilton Rd., Eden Prairie, MN 55344 (SAN 213-0939).

Suck-Egg Mule, P.O. Box 4435, Albuquerque, NM 87196 (SAN 200-4615).

Summer Institute of Linguistics, Academic Pubns, *(Summer Inst Ling; 0-88312; 1-55671),* 7500 W. Camp Wisdom Rd., Dallas, TX 75236 (SAN 204-6466) Tel 214-298-3331 Tel 214-298-3331.

Summit City News Agency, 3926 Mobile Ave., Fort Wayne, IN 46805 (SAN 169-2348).

Sun & Moon Pr., *(Sun & Moon CA; 0-940650),* P.O. Box 481170, Los Angeles, CA 90048 (SAN 216-3063) Tel 213-653-6711; 6363 Wilshire Blvd., Suite 115, Los Angeles, CA 90048 (SAN 658-179X).

Sun Life, *(Sun Life; 0-937930),* Greystone, Thaxton, VA 24174 (SAN 240-8333) Tel 703-586-4898.

Sun News Co., 3600 75th Terrace N., P.O. Box 2050, Pinellas Park, FL 33565 (SAN 169-1260).

Sun Warrior, Inc., 660 Newport Ctr., Suite 750, Newport Beach, CA 92660 (SAN 200-7959).

Sunburst Bks. *See* **Farrar, Straus & Giroux, Inc.**

Sunburst Communications, Inc., *(Sunburst Comm; 0-911831; 1-55636),* 39 Washington Ave., Pleasantville, NY 10570 (SAN 213-5620) Tel 914-769-5030; Toll free: 800-431-1934.

Sundance Pubs., *(Sundance Pubs; 0-940146),* Newtown Rd., Littleton, MA 01460 (SAN 220-3073) Tel 617-486-9201; Toll free: 800-343-8204.

Sunfire *See* **Scholastic, Inc.**

Sunflower Books, Div. of W.H. Smith Publishers Inc., *(Sunflower Bks),* 112 Madison Ave., New York, NY 10016 (SAN 658-2435); Toll free: 800-932-0070. Remainders, reprints & promotional books.

Sunflower Univ. Pr., *(Sunflower U Pr; 0-89745),* 1531 Yuma, Manhattan, KS 66502-4228 (SAN 218-5075); 1531 Yuma, Manhattan, KS 66502-4228 (SAN 658-1811) Tel 913-532-6733.

Sunland School Plans, 2317 Seventh Ave. S., Birmingham, AL 35223 (SAN 285-9483).

Superior News Agency, Box 697, Rolla, MO 65401 (SAN 159-9712).

Support Services, 222 Milk St., Westboro, MA 01581 (SAN 200-5700).

Surf & Sand, P.O. Box 1312, Largo, FL 33540 (SAN 200-7886).

Surguine, Ray, & Co., Inc., Drawer J, Boulder, CO 80302 (SAN 169-0493).

Swallow Pr., *(Swallow; 0-8040),* Ohio Univ. Pr., Scott Quadrangle, Rm. 144, Athens, OH 45701 (SAN 202-5663) Tel 614-594-5852; Toll free: 800-638-3030; Orders to: Harper & Row Pubs., Inc., Order Service Dept., Keystone Industrial Pk., Scranton, PA 18512 (SAN 202-5671). *Imprints:* Sage Books (SB); Western Sage Paperbacks (WSage).

Swedenborg Foundation, Inc., *(Swedenborg; 0-87785),* 139 E. 23rd St., New York, NY 10010 (SAN 202-7526) Tel 212-673-7310.

Swedenborg Library, 79 Newbury St., Boston, MA 02116 (SAN 208-9440).

Swenson, Jim, 2610 Rvsd Lane NE, Rochester, MN 55901 (SAN 285-9505).

Swift, Sterling *See* **Heath, D. C., Co.**

Swift News Agency, 338 E. Hwy. 50, Poncha Springs, CO 81242 (SAN 169-0639); P.O. Box 160, Poncha Springs, CO 81242 (SAN 282-3810).

Sycamore Island Bks. *See* **Paladin Pr.**

Symmes Systems, *(Symmes Syst; 0-916352),* P.O. Box 8101, Atlanta, GA 30306 (SAN 169-1465) Tel 404-876-7260.

Synthesis Pubns., *(Synthesis Pubns; 0-89935),* P.O. Box 40099, San Francisco, CA 94140 (SAN 282-3888) Tel 415-824-1665.

Systems Planning Associates, Pubns. Div., *(Systems Planning),* 3 Aliber Place, Keene, NH 03431 (SAN 287-3028) Tel 603-357-4005.

TAB Bks., Inc., *(TAB Bks; 0-8306; 0-8168),* P.O. Box 40, Blue Ridge Summit, PA 17214 (SAN 202-568X) Tel 717-794-2191; Toll free: 800-233-1128. Acquired Windcrest Software. *Imprints:* Gernshack Library (Gernshack); T A B/T P R (TAB/TPR); TAB-Aero (TAB-Aero).

T A B, T P R *See* **TAB Bks., Inc.**

TA Bookstore, 1772 Vallejo, San Francisco, CA 94123 (SAN 159-9720).

TBN Enterprises, *(TBN Ent; 0-935554),* Box 55, Alexandria, VA 22313 (SAN 206-2380) Tel 703-684-6111.

TCB Enterprise, 20 E. Main St., Denville, NJ 07834 (SAN 200-7894).

TIC Publishing, *(T I C Pub; 0-88745; 0-87444),* Five S. Union St., Lawrence, MA 01843 (SAN 291-7963) Tel 617-685-9943; Dist. by: Technical Impex Corp., Five S. Union St., Lawrence, MA 01843 (SAN 291-7971).

T.I.S., Inc., Div. of T.I.S. Enterprises, *(TIS Inc; 0-89917),* P.O. Box 669, 1928 Arlington Rd., Bloomington, IN 47402 (SAN 169-2313) Tel 812-332-3307; Toll free: 800-367-4002.

TAB-Aero *See* **TAB Bks., Inc.**

Tallahassee News Co., Inc., 1818 S. Monroe, Tallahassee, FL 32301 (SAN 169-1309).

Talman Co., The, 150 Fifth Ave., Rm. 514, New York, NY 10011 (SAN 200-5204) Tel 212-620-3182.

Taniguchi, Fusao, Sub Agency, 62 Funchal, Honolulu, HI 96813 (SAN 285-9556).

Taplinger Publishing Co., Inc., *(Taplinger; 0-8008),* 132 W. 22nd St., New York, NY 10011 (SAN 213-6821) Tel 212-741-0801. *Imprints:* Crescendo (Crescendo); Pentalic (Pentalic); Pivot (Pivot).

Targeted Communications, *(Targeted Comm; 0-933117),* P.O. Box 1148, Cleveland, OH 44120-0868 (SAN 689-4674); 3644 Rolliston Rd., Cleveland, OH 44120-5137 (SAN 662-7730) Tel 216-921-8074.

Tatnuck BookSeller, The, 647 Chandler St., Worcester, MA 01602 (SAN 169-3654).

Taunton News Co., Eight Cohannet Court, Taunton, MA 02780 (SAN 169-3581).

Taylor-Carlisle, *(Taylor-Carlisle),* 451 Greenwich St., New York, NY 10013 (SAN 169-6017) Tel 212-226-0707.

Taylor Museum of the Colorado Springs Fine Arts Ctr. *See* **Colorado Springs Fine Arts Ctr.**

Taylor Publishing Co., Subs. of Insilco, *(Taylor Pub; 0-87833),* 1550 Mockingbird Ln., Dallas, TX 75235 (SAN 202-7631) Tel 214-637-2800.

Teachers Exchange, 6916A Sunrise Blvd., Citrus Heights, CA 95610 (SAN 200-8254) Tel 916-723-4711.

Teachers Exchange of San Francisco, 28 Dawnview, San Francisco, CA 94131 (SAN 169-0248).

Teamsters For A Democratic Union, P.O. Box 10128, Detroit, MI 48210 (SAN 200-4755).

Techmar, 23600 Mercantile Rd., Cleveland, OH 44122 (SAN 287-0819).

Technical Book Co., 2056 Westwood Blvd., Los Angeles, CA 90025 (SAN 168-9851).

Technical Books of America, 425 Asylum St., Bridgeport, CT 06610 (SAN 159-9739).

Teitan Pr., Inc., The, *(Teitan Pr; 0-933429),* 339 W. Barry, Suite 16B, Chicago, IL 60657 (SAN 200-8211) Tel 312-929-7892.

Telebooks Company, *(0-88096),* One Lincoln Plaza, Suite 39A, New York, NY 10023 (SAN 240-2866).

Temple News Agency, P.O. Box 1090, Temple, TX 76501 (SAN 169-8435).

Temple of Kriya Yoga, The, *(Temple Kriya Yoga; 0-9613099),* 2414 N. Kedzie Ave., Chicago, IL 60647 (SAN 240-9348) Tel 312-795-0031.

Ten Speed Pr., *(Ten Speed Pr; 0-913668; 0-89815),* P.O. Box 7123, Berkeley, CA 94707 (SAN 202-7674) Tel 415-845-8414; Toll free: 800-841-BOOK.

Terrell's Bindery, 3620 Buena Vista, Nashville, TN 37218 (SAN 200-6324) Tel 615-242-1051.

Terschluse, M., 727 Westbourne Dr., Suite 112, West Hollywood, CA 90069 (SAN 212-0364) Tel 213-659-9083.

Texas A & M Univ. Pr., *(Tex A&M Univ Pr; 0-89096),* Drawer "C", College Station, TX 77843 (SAN 207-5237) Tel 409-845-1436; Lewis St., Univ. Campus, College Station, TX 77843 (SAN 658-1919).

Texas Art Supply, 2001 Montrose Blvd., Houston, TX 77006 (SAN 169-8303).

Texas Library Book Sales, 1002 Springdale Rd., P.O. Box 6110, Austin, TX 78762 (SAN 169-8044).

Texas Monthly Pr., Subs. of Mediatex Communication Corp., *(Texas Month Pr; 0-932012; 0-87719),* P.O. Box 1569, Austin, TX 78767 (SAN 200-2531); Toll free: 800-252-4437 (TX only); 3900-D Drossett Dr., Austin, TX 78744 (SAN 658-1927) Tel 512-476-7085.

Texas Periodical Distributors, 4602 Warehouse Lane, P.O. Box 2609, Laredo, TX 78041 (SAN 169-832X).

Texas Publisher Services, P.O. Box 160472, San Antonio, TX 78280 (SAN 200-5697).

Texas School Book Depository, 8301 Ambassador Row, Dallas, TX 75247 (SAN 169-815X); Toll free: 800-527-5267.

Textile Artists Supplies, 3006 San Pablo Ave., Berkeley, CA 94702 (SAN 282-6461).

Textile Museum, *(Textile Mus; 0-87405),* 2320 S St., NW, Washington, DC 20008 (SAN 205-4264) Tel 202-667-0441.

Thames Book Co., 34 Truman St., P.O. Box 97, New London, CT 06320 (SAN 169-0760).

The Collection Inc., Box 11465, Memphis, TN 38111 (SAN 289-9574). Organizations: Symphonies, Junior Leagues, Museum Etc.

Theosophy Co., *(Theosophy; 0-938998),* 245 W. 33rd St., Los Angeles, CA 90007 (SAN 295-3560) Tel 213-748-7244; 347 E. 72nd St., New York, NY 10021 (SAN 295-3579).

Thieme, Inc., Subs. of Georg Thieme Verlag, *(Thieme Inc; 0-913258; 0-86577),* 381 Park Ave., S., New York, NY 10016 (SAN 169-5983) Tel 212-683-5088.

Thieme-Stratton, Inc. *See* **Thieme, Inc.**

Thinking Caps, Inc., *(Thinking Caps; 0-9610876),* P.O. Box 7239, Phoenix, AZ 85011 (SAN 239-4960) Tel 602-956-1515.

Third Pyramid, Inc., *(Third Pyramid; 0-916479),* P.O. Box 260, Watertown, WI 53094-0260 (SAN 296-0052) Tel 414-699-2441.

Thomas Brothers Maps, *(Thomas Bros Maps; 0-88130),* 17731 Cowan, Irvine, CA 92714 (SAN 158-8192) Tel 714-863-1984; Toll free: 800-432-8430 (CA Only).

Thomas Computer Corp., 5633 W. Howard St., Chicago, IL 60648 (SAN 695-5223) Tel 312-647-0880; Toll free: 800-621-3906.

Thompson School Book Depository, 39 N.E. 24th St., Oklahoma City, OK 73105 (SAN 159-9747).

Thorsons Pubs., Inc., Subs. of Thorsons Publishing Group (Great Britain), *(Thorsons Pubs; 0-7225),* 1 Park St., Rochester, VT 05767 (SAN 277-7398) Tel 802-767-3174; Dist. by: Inner Traditions, Park St., Rochester, VT 05767 (SAN 208-6948); Orders to: Harper & Row Pubs., Inc., Keystone Industrial Pk., Scranton, PA 18512 (SAN 215-3742).

Three Continents Pr., *(Three Continents; 0-89410; 0-914478),* 1636 Connecticut Ave., NW, Suite 501, Washington, DC 20009 (SAN 212-0070) Tel 202-332-3885.

Three Presses Agency, 39 Tompkins St., Staten Island, NY 10304 (SAN 200-6391).

Thresholds Publishing Co. - Book, 2009 N. Douglas, Springfield, MO 65803 (SAN 159-5423).

Ticom Systems, Inc., *(0-927544),* 13470 Washington Blvd., Marina del Rey, CA 90291 (SAN 287-2692) Tel 415-829-7550.

Tide-Mark Pr., Ltd, *(Tide-Mark; 0-936846),* P.O. Box 813, Hartford, CT 06142 (SAN 222-1802) Tel 203-289-0363.

Tiffin News Agency, 49 N. Washington St., Tiffin, OH 44883 (SAN 169-6866).

Time Bomb Productions, *(Time Bomb Prod; 0-931161),* 905 Olympic Way W., Suite 6, Seattle, WA 98119 (SAN 679-3916) Tel 206-284-5996; Toll free: 800-521-0714 (ext 260); Dist. by: Pacific Pipeline Inc., 19215 66th Ave. S., Kent, WA 98032 (SAN 208-2128) Tel 206-872-5523; Dist. by: Menasha Ridge Press, Rte. 3, Box 450, Hillsboro, NC 27278 (SAN 219-7294).

Time-Life Bks., Div. of Time, Inc., *(Time-Life; 0-8094),* 777 Duke St., Alexandria, VA 22314 (SAN 202-7836) Tel 703-838-7198; Toll free: 800-621-7026; 4200 N Industrial Blvd., Indianapolis, IN 46254 (SAN 658-1951); Toll free: 800-631-8081; Toll free: 800-343-9204; Dist. by: Little, Brown & Co., 34 Beacon St., Boston, MA 02106 (SAN 281-8892) Tel 617-227-0730; Dist. by: Morgan & Morgan Co., 145 Palisades St., Dobbs Ferry, NY 10522 (SAN 202-5620); Orders to: Silver Burdett Co., 250 James St., Morristown, NJ 07960 (SAN 204-5982). Lib. & School Orders to: Silver Burdett Co.

Timescape *See* **Pocket Bks., Inc.**

Title Bks., Inc., *(Title Books),* P.O. Box 31170, Birmingham, AL 35233 (SAN 168-9207) Tel 205-324-2596.

Toastmaster International, *(Toastmaster),* 2200 N. Grand Ave., P.O. Box 10400, Santa Ana, CA 92711 (SAN 206-1112) Tel 714-542-6793.

Tokyo Sales Corp., 521 Fifth Ave., New York, NY 10019 (SAN 128-8555).

Tompson & Rutter, Inc. *See* **Shoe String Pr., Inc.**

Torah Umesorah Pubns., *(Torah Umesorah; 0-914131),* 160 Broadway, New York, NY 10003 (SAN 218-9992) Tel 212-227-1000.

Torchbooks *See* **Harper & Row Pubs., Inc.**

Torchbooks Library Binding *See* **Harper & Row Pubs., Inc.**

Toronto Univ. Press, 33 E. Tupper St., Buffalo, NY 14203 (SAN 200-4224).

Toth News Co., 152 N. Pennsylvania Ave., Wilkes Barre, PA 18701 (SAN 159-9755).

Touchstone Bks. *See* **Simon & Schuster, Inc.**

Tova Press, Incorporated, *(Tova Pr Inc; 0-915227),* 575 8th Ave., New York, NY 10018 (SAN 289-8535) Tel 212-695-5735.

Tower Books, 2538 Watt Ave., Sacramento, CA 95821 (SAN 169-0086).

Town & Country News Co., Rte. 1, Hwy. 29, Box 396, Ailey, GA 30410 (SAN 108-6723); Box 471, Vidalia, GA 30474 (SAN 276-0703).

Tracheon Enterprises, P.O. Box 747, Clayton, GA 30525 (SAN 169-1481).

Trailtree Bookshop, 44 Main St P.O. Box 233, Oldwick, NJ 08858 (SAN 130-223X).

Trans-Educom, P.O. Box 996, Bellevue, WA 98009 (SAN 169-8753) Tel 206-392-1965.

Transaction Bks., *(Transaction Bks; 0-87855; 0-88738),* Rutgers Univ., New Brunswick, NJ 08903 (SAN 202-7941) Tel 201-932-2280.

Transamerican & Export News Co., 591 Camino de la Reina St., San Diego, CA 92108-3192 (SAN 169-0140).

Transworld Distribution Services, Inc., 80 Northfield Ave., Raritan Center, Edison, NJ 08817 (SAN 213-1978).

Tree Frog Trucking Co., 318 SW Taylor St., Portland, OR 97204 (SAN 169-7188).

Tri-County Distributors, 112 E. Van Buren St., Joliet, IL 60432 (SAN 169-2054).

Tri County News Agency, 202 W. Point Ave., P.O. Box 1, Dunkirk, NY 14048 (SAN 108-8106).

Tri-County News Co., Inc., 1376 W. Main St., Santa Maria, CA 93454 (SAN 169-0345).

Tri-County Periodicals Distributors, 112-114 E. Van Buren St., Joliet, IL 60432 (SAN 169-2054).

Tri-State News Agency, Box 778, Johnson City, TN 37601 (SAN 169-7897); 434 Thompson Ave., East Liverpool, OH 43920 (SAN 282-4744).

Tri-State Railway Historical Society Inc., *(Tri-State Rail; 0-9607444),* P.O. Box 2243, Clifton, NJ 07015-2243 (SAN 239-3301) Tel 201-488-5429.

Triangle News Co., Inc., 301 Munson Ave., McKees Rocks, PA 15136 (SAN 169-7447).

Trinidad News Service, 216 W. Main, Trinidad, CO 81082 (SAN 169-0647).

Trinity News Co., Box 1806, Ft. Worth, TX 76101 (SAN 169-8214).

Troll Assocs., Subs. of Educational Reading Services, *(Troll Assocs; 0-89375; 0-8167),* 320 State Hwy. 17, Mahwah, NJ 07430 (SAN 169-4758) Tel 201-529-4000; Toll free: 800-526-5289.

Trow, F.P., News Agency, Inc., 90 W. Pearl St., Nashua, NH 03060 (SAN 169-4553).

Troy News Co., Inc., Educational Div., 176 Third, Troy, NY 12181 (SAN 169-6300).

Troyka, 5600 NE Hassalo St., Portland, OR 97213 (SAN 169-7196).

Truck Press, *(Truck Pr; 0-916562),* P.O. Box 2204, Short Beach, CT 06405 (SAN 208-3531) Tel 203-467-4257; Orders to: Inland Book Co., 22 Hemingway Ave., E. Haven, CT 06512 (SAN 204-1871).

Tucson Museum of Art, *(Tucson Mus Art; 0-911611),* 140 N. Main, Tucson, AZ 85705 (SAN 280-798X) Tel 602-624-2333.

Tucson News Agency, Box 5465, Tucson, AZ 85705 (SAN 168-9401).

Tulane Univ., *(Tulane Univ; 0-87409),* Dist. by: Tulane University, Howard-Tilton Memorial Library, Special Collections Division, New Orleans, LA 70118 (SAN 207-5458).

Tulare County News, Box 831, Visalia, CA 93279 (SAN 169-0442).

Turnbull & Willoughby Pubs., Inc., *(Turnbull & Willoughby; 0-943084),* 1151 W. Webster, Chicago, IL 60614 (SAN 240-4311) Tel 312-348-3181; Orders to: Contemporary Bk., Inc., 180 N. Michigan Ave., Chicago, IL 60601 (SAN 669-2478) Tel 312-782-9181.

Turner Subscription Agency, The, 116 E. 16th St., New York, NY 10003 (SAN 107-7112).

Tuttle, Charles E., Co., Inc., *(C E Tuttle; 0-8048),* P.O. Box 410, 28 S. Main St., Rutland, VT 05701-0410 (SAN 213-2621) Tel 802-773-8930.

Twin City News Agency, 316 N. Third St., P.O. Box 466, Layfayette, IN 47902 (SAN 169-2402).

Two Trees Micro Software, Div. of ELMS, 708 S. Fourth, Terre Haute, IN 47807 (SAN 200-5484) Tel 812-235-9828.

UBC Book Co., Inc., 2517 San Pablo Ave., Oakland, CA 94612 (SAN 168-9991).

UNM Bookstore, Univ. of New Mexico, Albuquerque, NM 87131 (SAN 207-3218) Tel 505-277-4241.

UOI Co., *(UOI Co; 0-913929),* 15445 Ventura Blvd., Sherman Oaks, CA 91403 (SAN 286-9047) Tel 818-785-5050.

Ubiquity Distributors, 1050 E. Fourth St., Brooklyn, NY 11230 (SAN 200-7428) Tel 718-789-3137.

Ulverscroft Large Print Books Limited, *(Ulverscroft),* 279 Boston St., Guilford, CT 06437 (SAN 208-3035) Tel 203-453-2080.

Unarius Pubns., *(Unarius Pubns; 0-932642; 0-935097),* 145 S. Magnolia Ave., El Cajon, CA 92020 (SAN 168-9614) Tel 619-447-4170.

Unicorn Music Co, Inc., The, 170 NE 33rd St., Ft. Lauderdale, FL 33334 (SAN 200-8297) Tel 305-563-1844.

Unicorn Publishing Hse., Inc., The, *(Unicorn Pub; 0-88101),* 1148 Parsippany Blvd., Parsippany, NJ 07054 (SAN 240-4567) Tel 201-334-0353; 300 Raritan Ctr. Pkwy., Edison, NJ 08818 (SAN 658-2087).

Unilit, 5600 N.E Hassalo St., Portland, OR 97213 (SAN 211-7851); Toll free: 800-547-8020.

Uniontown News Agency, Rte. 119 N., Uniontown, PA 15401 (SAN 159-9798).

Unique Pubns., Subs. of CFW Enterprises,INC., *(Unique Pubns; 0-86568),* 4201 W. Vanowen Pl., Burbank, CA 91505 (SAN 214-3313) Tel 818-845-2656; Toll free: 800-332-3330.

United Book Service, 1310 San Fernando Rd., Los Angeles, CA 90065 (SAN 168-986X).

United Magazine Distributor of Connecticut Inc., Harvard & Selleck, Stamford, CT 06902 (SAN 169-085X).

United News Co., Inc., 850 E. Luzerne St., Philadelphia, PA 19124 (SAN 168-9495); 111 Lake St., P.O. Box 3426, Bakersfield, CA 93305 (SAN 169-7579) Tel 805-323-7864.

U. S. Games Systems, Inc., *(US Games Syst; 0-913866; 0-88079),* 38 E. 32nd St., New York, NY 10016 (SAN 158-6483) Tel 212-685-4300.

U. S. Government Printing Office, *(Gov Printing Office),* USGPO Stop SSMR, Washington, DC 20401 (SAN 206-152X) Tel 202-783-3238; Orders to: Superintendent of Documents, Washington, DC 20402-9325 (SAN 658-0785) Tel 202-783-3238.

United Subscription Service, 142 Mineola Ave., Roslyn Heights, NY 11577 (SAN 286-0104).

United Synagogue Book Service, Subs. of United Synagogue of America, *(United Syn Bk; 0-8381),* 155 Fifth Ave., New York, NY 10010 (SAN 203-0551) Tel 212-533-7800.

Univelt, Inc., *(Univelt Inc; 0-912183; 0-87703; 0-914548),* P.O. Box 28130, San Diego, CA 92128 (SAN 204-8868) Tel 619-746-4005; 740 Metcalf St., Suite 13, Escondido, CA 92025 (SAN 658-2095).

Universal Distributors, Monroe, NH 03771 (SAN 159-9801).

Universal Subscription Service, P.O. Box 35445, Houston, TX 77035 (SAN 287-4768).

Universe Bks., Inc., Div. of South Park Pr., *(Universe; 0-87663; 1-55550),* 381 Park Ave. S., New York, NY 10016 (SAN 202-537X) Tel 212-685-7400. *Imprints:* Free Life Editions (Free Life); Main Street Press (Main St); Manhattan Institute for Policy Research Book (Man Inst Pol Res); Pica Press (Pica Pr); Pica Special Studies (Pica Spec Stud).

University Assocs., *(Univ Assocs; 0-88390),* 8517 Production Ave., San Diego, CA 92121 (SAN 203-333X) Tel 619-578-5900; 8535 Production Ave., San Diego, CA 92121 (SAN 658-2109).

University Book Service, 2424 W. Granville Rd., Worthington, OH 43085 (SAN 282-4841); P.O. Box 637, Columbia, MO 65201 (SAN 282-485X).

University Bookstore, 4326 University Way, NE, Seattle, WA 98105 (SAN 216-9754) Tel 206-634-3400.

University Microfilms, Inc., Div. of Bell & Howell, *(Univ Microfilms; 0-8357),* 300 N. Zeeb Rd., Ann Arbor, MI 48106 (SAN 212-2464) Tel 313-761-4700; Toll free: 800-521-0600; Toll free: 800-343-5299 (Canada). Serials and newspapers in microform, reprints of articles and issues, dissertations published and available on demand. Imprints: Books on Demand, reprinting of out-of-print books, and UMI Research Press, scholarly and professional book publishing.

Univ. of Alabama Pr., *(U of Ala Pr; 0-8173),* P.O. Box 2877, University, AL 35486 (SAN 202-5272) Tel 205-348-5180.

Univ. of Alaska Pr., *(U of Alaska Pr; 0-912006),* Univ. of Alaska, Vice Chancellor of Research & Advanced Study, Signer's Hall, Fairbanks, AK 99775-1580 (SAN 203-3011) Tel 907-474-6389.

Univ. of Arizona Pr., *(U of Ariz Pr; 0-8165),* 1615 E. Speedway, Tucson, AZ 85719 (SAN 205-468X) Tel 602-795-0583; 250 E Valencia, Tucson, AZ 85706 (SAN 658-2125).

University of California, UCD Bookstore, UCD Bookstore, Davis, CA 95616 (SAN 200-4267).

Univ. of Chicago Pr., Div. of Univ. of Chicago, *(U of Chicago Pr; 0-226),* 5801 Ellis Ave., 3rd Flr., S., Chicago, IL 60637 (SAN 202-5280) Tel 312-962-7693; Toll free: 800-621-2736; Orders to: 11030 S. Langley Ave., Chicago, IL 60628 (SAN 202-5299) Tel 312-568-1550. *Imprints:* Chicago Original Paperback (Chicago Original Paperback); Chicago Visual Library (Chicago Visual Lib); Midway Reprint (Midway Reprint).

Univ. of Hawaii Bookstore, 2465 Campus Rd., Honolulu, HI 96822 (SAN 295-1827).

Univ. of Illinois Pr., *(U of Ill Pr; 0-252),* 54 E. Gregory Dr., Champaign, IL 61820 (SAN 202-5310) Tel 217-333-0950; Toll free: 800-242-7737; Orders to: Harper & Row, Inc., Keystone Industrial Pk., Scranton, PA 18512 (SAN 215-3742); Orders to: Univ. of Illinois Pr., P.O. Box 1650, Hagerstown, MD 21741. *Imprints:* Illini Books (IB).

Univ. of Massachusetts, Dept. of Geology & Geography, Amherst, MA 01003 (SAN 282-6143).

Univ. of Massachusetts Pr., *(U of Mass Pr; 0-87023),* P.O. Box 429, Amherst, MA 01004 (SAN 203-3089) Tel 413-545-2217.

Univ. of Minnesota Pr., *(U of Minn Pr; 0-8166),* 2037 University Ave., SE, Minneapolis, MN 55414 (SAN 213-2648) Tel 612-624-6055.

Univ. of Nebraska Pr., *(U of Nebr Pr; 0-8032),* 901 N. 17th St., Lincoln, NE 68588-0520 (SAN 202-5337) Tel 402-472-3581. *Imprints:* Bison Books (Bison).

Univ. of New Mexico Pr., *(U of NM Pr; 0-8263),* Journalism Bldg., Rm. 220, Albuquerque, NM 87131 (SAN 213-9588) Tel 505-277-2346.

Univ. of North Carolina Pr., *(U of NC Pr; 0-8078),* P.O. Box 2288, Chapel Hill, NC 27514 (SAN 203-3151) Tel 919-966-3561.

Univ. of Notre Dame Pr., *(U of Notre Dame Pr; 0-268),* P.O. Box L, Notre Dame, IN 46556 (SAN 203-3178) Tel 219-239-6346; Toll free: 800-242-7737; Dist. by: Harper & Row Pubs., Keystone Industrial Pk., Scranton, PA 18512 (SAN 215-3742).

Univ. of Pittsburgh Pr., *(U of Pittsburgh Pr; 0-8229),* 127 N. Bellefield Ave., Pittsburgh, PA 15260 (SAN 203-3216) Tel 412-624-4110; Toll free: 800-242-7737; Dist. by: Harper & Row Pubs., Inc., Keystone Industrial Pk., Scranton, PA 18512 (SAN 215-3742).

Univ. of Texas Pr., *(U of Tex Pr; 0-292),* P.O. Box 7819, Austin, TX 78713-7819 (SAN 212-9876) Tel 512-471-7233; Toll free: 800-252-3206 (Orders Only). *Imprints:* Stevenson, Robert Louis, School, The (Stevenson Sch).

Univ. of Toronto Pr., *(U of Toronto Pr; 0-8020),* 33 E. Tupper St., Buffalo, NY 14203 (SAN 214-2651) Tel 716-852-0342.

University of Utah, Bureau of Economic & Business Research, *(Univ Utah; 0-942486),* 401 Kendall D. Garff Bldg., Salt Lake City, UT 84112 (SAN 238-5899) Tel 801-581-7274.

Univ. of Washington Pr., *(U of Wash Pr; 0-295),* P.O. Box 50096, Seattle, WA 98145-5096 (SAN 212-2502) Tel 206-543-4050; Toll free: 800-441-4115.

Univ. of West Florida, John C. Pace Library, Pensacola, FL 32504 (SAN 204-0581) Tel 904-474-2492.

Univ. Pr. of New England, *(U Pr of New Eng; 0-87451),* 3 Lebanon St., Hanover, NH 03755 (SAN 203-3283) Tel 603-646-3349.

Univ. Pr. of Virginia, *(U Pr of Va; 0-8139),* P.O. Box 3608, Univ. Sta., Charlottesville, VA 22903 (SAN 202-5361) Tel 804-924-3468. *Imprints:* Bird & Bull Press, The (Bird & Bull Pr); Colonial Society of Massachusetts (Colonial Soc MA); Friends of the University of Rochester Libraries (Friends U Rochester); Maya Publishing Company (Maya Pub Co).

Urban Land Institute, *(Urban Land; 0-87420),* 1090 Vermont Ave. NW, Washington, DC 20005 (SAN 203-3399) Tel 202-289-8500.

US Distribution Ctr., 13119 Glenfield, Detroit, MI 48213 (SAN 289-145X).

US Judo Assn., 19 N. Union Blvd., Colorado Springs, CO 80909 (SAN 276-3257).

Vagabond *See* **Scholastic, Inc.**

Valladares, L., & Son, 1200 Duval St., Key West, FL 33040 (SAN 159-981X).

Valley Distributors Inc., 2947 Felton Rd., Norristown, PA 19401 (SAN 169-7498).

Valley Lights Pubns., *(Valley Lights; 0-9606482),* P.O. Box 1537, Ojai, CA 93023 (SAN 219-8320) Tel 805-646-9888.

Valley News Co., 1305 Stadium Rd., Mankato, MN 56001 (SAN 169-4073).

Valley News Service, 1919 Garfield Ave., Parkersburg, WV 26101 (SAN 169-9008).

Valley Periodical Distributors, P.O. Box 3167, Burbank, CA 91504 (SAN 168-9525).

Valley Pubs. *See* **Western Tanger Pr.**

Van Dyke News Agency, 5671 E. Fountain Way, Fresno, CA 93727 (SAN 168-9630).

Van Horn Office Supply, P.O. Box 1060, Van Horn, TX 79855 (SAN 287-6485) Tel 915-283-2920.

Van Nostrand Reinhold Co., Inc., Div. of International Thomson Organisation, Inc., *(Van Nos Reinhold; 0-442; 0-8436),* 115 Fifth Ave., New York, NY 10003 (SAN 202-5183) Tel 212-254-3232; Orders to: VNR Order Processing, 7625 Empire Dr., Florence, KY 41042 (SAN 202-5191) Tel 606-525-6600. *Imprints:* Lark Communications (Lark Comms); Lifetime Learning Pubns. (Lifetime Pubns.).

Vanguard Books, *(Vanguard Bks; 0-917702),* P.O. Box 3566, Chicago, IL 60654 (SAN 213-8212) Tel 312-342-3425.

Vanguard Pr., Inc., *(Vanguard; 0-8149),* 424 Madison Ave., New York, NY 10017 (SAN 202-9316) Tel 212-753-3906.

Vanous, Arthur, Co., *(Vanous; 0-89918),* P.O. Box 650279, Vero Beach, FL 32965 (SAN 169-4871) Tel 305-562-9186.

Vantage Sales & Marketing Inc., 27 Bucknell Dr., Hazlet, NJ 07730 (SAN 200-5719).

Variety Arts, Inc., 305 Riverside Dr., Suite 4A, New York, NY 10025 (SAN 200-691X); Toll free: 800-221-2154.

Ventura Corp., 415 Bayview Ave., P.O. Box 811, Amityville, NY 11701 (SAN 685-8023) Tel 516-842-1000.

VerDugo Pr., *(VerDugo Pr; 0-941140),* 6715 Sunset Blvd., Hollywood, CA 90028 (SAN 239-572X); Dist. by: Hollywood Reporter, 6715 Sunset Blvd., Hollywood, CA 90028 (SAN 217-3824) Tel 213-464-7411.

Verham News Corp., 75 Main St., West Lebanon, NH 03784 (SAN 169-4561).

Verry, Lawrence, Inc., *(Verry; 0-8426),* P.O. Box 215, Mystic, CT 06355 (SAN 202-5205) Tel 203-536-3104.

Vestal Pr., Ltd., *(Vestal; 0-911572),* P.O. Box 97, 320 N. Jensen Rd., Vestal, NY 13850 (SAN 205-4825) Tel 607-797-4872.

Vet Text, Colorado State Univ., Veterinary Teaching Hospital, Ft. Collins, CO 80523 (SAN 200-7150) Tel 303-491-7101.

Viders, Arthur J., Co., Inc., P.O. Box 151896, Tampa, FL 33684 (SAN 169-1333).

Viking Kestrel *See* **Viking-Penguin, Inc.**

Viking-Penguin, Inc., *(Viking; 0-670),* 40 W. 23rd St., New York, NY 10010 (SAN 200-2442) Tel 212-337-5200; Toll free: 800-631-3577; Orders to: 299 Murray Hill Pkwy., East Rutherford, NJ 07073 (SAN 282-5074). *Imprints:* Compass Books (Comp); Elisabeth Sifton Books (E Sifton Bks); Explorer Books (Exp); Studio Books (Studio); Viking Kestrel (Viking Kestrel).

Vinabind, Box 340, Steelville, MO 65565 (SAN 159-9828).

Vincennes News Agency, P.O. Box 245, Vincennes, IN 47591 (SAN 169-2518).

Vintage College Bks. *See* **Random Hse., Inc.**

Vintage Trade Bks. *See* **Random Hse., Inc.**

Virago *See* **Doubleday & Co., Inc.**

Virginia Periodical Distributors, Box 2240, Norfolk, VA 23501 (SAN 169-8680).

Virginia Polytechnic Inst. & State Univ. Manufacturing Processes Laboratory, 302 Whittemore Hall, Blacksburg, VA 24061 (SAN 291-6134) Tel 703-961-5565.

Vision Bks. *See* **Farrar, Straus & Giroux, Inc.**

Vision Books, *(Vision Bks; 0-942024),* 790 Commercial Ave., Coos Bay, OR 97420 (SAN 293-4256) Tel 503-267-4232 Dist. by: Vision Books, 790 Commercial Ave., Coos Bay, OR 97420 (SAN 293-4264) Tel 503-267-4232; Dist. by: DeVorss & Co.,Inc., P.O. Box 550, 1046 Princeton Dr., Marina del Rey, CA 90294 (SAN 168-9886); Dist. by: Bookpeople, 2929 Fifth St., Berkeley, CA 94710 (SAN 168-9517); Dist. by: Publishers Group West, 5855 Beaudry St., Emeryville, CA 94608 (SAN 202-8522); Dist. by: New Leaf Distributing, 1020 White St. SW, Atlanta, GA 30310 (SAN 169-1449) Tel 404-755-2665; Dist. by: Ingram Book Co., 347 Reedwood Dr., Nashville, TN 37217 (SAN 169-7978).

Vitali Import Co., P.O. Box 249, Maywood, CA 90270 (SAN 282-535X).

Vitality Distributors, 1010 NW. 51st Place, Fort Lauderdale, FL 33309 (SAN 169-0973).

VOELZ Educational Services, 1528 Vista Ave., Janesville, WI 53545 (SAN 200-4291) Tel 608-752-0211.

Voyager Bks. *See* **Harcourt Brace Jovanovich, Inc.**

Voyles News Agency, P.O. Box 399, Richmond, IN 47374 (SAN 169-247X).

Vroman's, 2085 E. Foothill Blvd., Pasadena, CA 91109 (SAN 169-0027).

Wabash Valley News Agency, 569 N. 13th St., Terre Haute, IN 47808 (SAN 169-250X).

Wadsworth Publishing Co., Subs. of International Thomson Organization, Ltd., *(Wadsworth Pub; 0-534; 0-927794; 0-7150),* 10 Davis Dr., Belmont, CA 94002 (SAN 200-2213) Tel 415-595-2350; Toll free: 800-831-6996. *Imprints:* Continuing Education Division (Continuing Ed).

Walck, Henry Z., Inc., Div. of David McKay Co. Inc., *(Walck; 0-8098),* 2 Park Ave., New York, NY 10016 (SAN 285-1121) Tel 212-340-9800; Toll free: 800-327-4801 (Orders).

Waldenbooks Co., Inc., 201 Highridge Rd., Stamford, CT 06904 (SAN 656-4593).

Walker & Co., Div. of Walker Publishing Co., Inc., *(Walker & Co; 0-8027),* 720 Fifth Ave., New York, NY 10019 (SAN 202-5213) Tel 212-265-3632.

Walker Art Center, Vineland Pl., Minneapolis, MN 55403 (SAN 206-1880) Tel 612-375-7600.

Walker, Evans & Cogswell Co., *(Walker Evans & Cogswell),* 5300 Rivers Ave., North Charleston, SC 29405 (SAN 265-4121) Tel 803-747-8761.

Wallaby *See* **Pocket Bks., Inc.**

Wallaby *See* **Simon & Schuster, Inc.**

Wallace's College Book Co., 928 Nandino Blvd., P.O. Box 11518, Lexington, KY 40576-1518 (SAN 169-2844).

Walnut Pr., *(Walnut AZ; 0-931318),* 12010 Hillcrest Dr., Sun City, AZ 85351 (SAN 285-113X) Tel 602-972-5814; Orders to: LTO Enterprises, 6036 N. 10th Way, Phoenix, AZ 85014 (SAN 662-1805) Tel 602-265-7765.

Walsh Assocs., 1 Greentree Ctr., Suite 201, Marlton, NJ 08053 (SAN 200-5999).

Walsh-Jamaica Church Goods, 89-52 165th St., Jamaica, NY 11432 (SAN 159-5363).

Warner Brothers Pubns., Inc., *(0-89724),* 265 Secaucus Rd., Secaucus, NJ 07094 (SAN 203-0586) Tel 201-348-0700; Toll free: 800-638-0005 (Orders).

Warner Pr. Pubs., *(Warner Pr; 0-87162),* 1200 E. Fifth St., Anderson, IN 46012 (SAN 202-9472) Tel 317-644-7721; Toll free: 800-428-6409; Orders to: P.O. Box 2499, Anderson, IN 46018 (SAN 691-4241).

Warwick Pr. *See* **Watts, Franklin, Inc.**

Washington News Co., 16 S. Main St., Washington, PA 15301 (SAN 159-9836).

Washington State Trial Lawyers Assn., 225 S. Washington, Seattle, WA 98125 (SAN 290-0114) Tel 206-464-1011.

Waterfront Pr., *(Waterfront NJ; 0-943862),* 52 Maple Ave., Maplewood, NJ 07040 (SAN 241-5941) Tel 201-762-1565.

Waterways Project, 799 Greenwich St., New York, NY 10014 (SAN 219-5402).

Watson, W. R., & Staff, 1181 Euclid Ave., Berkeley, CA 94708 (SAN 286-0155).

Watson-Guptill Pubns., Inc., Div. of Billboard Pubns., Inc., *(Watson-Guptill; 0-8230; 0-8174; 0-87165),* 1 Astor Plaza, 1515 Broadway, New York, NY 10036 (SAN 282-5384) Tel 212-764-7518; Toll free: 800-526-3641 (Orders & Customer Service); Orders to: 1695 Oak St., Lakewood, NJ 08701 (SAN 282-5392). *Imprints:* Art & Antique Books (Art & Antique); Billboard Books (Billboard Bks); Whitney Library (Whitney Lib).

Watts, Franklin, Inc., Subs. of Grolier, Inc., *(Watts; 0-531),* Shermann Tpke., Danbury, CT 06816 (SAN 285-1156) Tel 212-686-7070; Toll free: 800-672-6672. *Imprints:* Business Travelers, Incorporated (Busn Travel); College Division (College Div); Fontana Paperbacks (Fontana Pap); Gloucester Press (Gloucester Pr); International Communications (Intl Communications); MacRae, Julia (MacRae); Warwick Press (Warwick).

Wausau News Agency, 601 Third St., Wausau, WI 54401 (SAN 169-9210).

Waverly News Co., 17 State St., Newburyport, MA 01950 (SAN 169-3522).

Waverly Pr., 428 E. Preston St., Baltimore, MD 21202 (SAN 206-2968).

Waymark Bks. *See* **Doubleday & Co., Inc.**

Wayne State Univ. Pr., *(Wayne St U Pr; 0-8143),* Leonard N. Simons Bldg., 5959 Woodward Ave., Detroit, MI 48202 (SAN 202-5221) Tel 313-577-4601. *Imprints:* Savoyard Books (Savoyard).

Wedgestone Pr., *(Wedgestone Pr; 0-911459),* P.O. Box 175, Winfield, KS 67156 (SAN 276-5888) Tel 316-221-2779.

Weedy Rail Bks. *See* **David & Charles, Inc.**

Weekends Inc., Box 337, Salem, IL 62881 (SAN 159-9852).

Weiner News Co., 1011 N. Frio, P.O. Box 7608, San Antonio, TX 78207 (SAN 169-8427).

Weiser, Samuel, Inc., *(Weiser; 0-87728),* P.O. Box 612, York Beach, ME 03910 (SAN 202-9588) Tel 207-363-4393; Toll free: 800-843-6666; Toll free: 800-423-7087 orders.

Well News Service, 2400 N. High St., Columbus, OH 43202 (SAN 159-9860).

Wellman Publishing, Subs. of Wellman Writing Service, *(Wellman Pub; 0-931703),* P.O. Box 484, Folsom, CA 95630 (SAN 683-7441) Tel 916-988-9671.

Wellsboro Historical Society, P.O. Box 724, Wellsboro, PA 16901 (SAN 216-3969).

Welsh News Agency, Inc., 40 W. Fourth St., Mansfield, OH 44902 (SAN 122-6401).

Wenatchee News Agency, 814 S. Wenatchee Ave., Wenatchee, WA 98801 (SAN 169-8885).

West Publishing Co., *(West Pub; 0-8299; 0-314),* P.O. Box 64526, 50 W. Kellogg Blvd., St. Paul, MN 55102-1611 (SAN 202-9618) Tel 612-228-2500; Toll free: 800-328-9352.

Wholesalers & Distributors

West Tennessee News Co., 54 Lawrence Switch Rd., Jackson, TN 38301 (SAN 169-7870).
West Texas News Co., 1214 Barranca, P.O. Box 26488, El Paso, TX 79926 (SAN 169-8184).
West Virginia Periodical Distributor, P.O. Box 487, Scott Depot, WV 25560 (SAN 169-8923) Tel 304-757-8831; Toll free: 800-344-5680 (In West Virginia).
Westchester Book Service, Box 13, Riverdale Sta., Bronx, NY 10471 (SAN 159-9879).
Western Book Distributors, 2970 San Pablo Ave., Berkeley, CA 94702 (SAN 158-4332) Tel 415-849-0100. Remainders by title & promotional assortments; half-price paperback promotions.
Western Illinois News Co., Rte. 4, Box 376, Macomb, IL 61455 (SAN 169-2070).
Western Merchandisers, 520 W. 38th St., Houston, TX 77018 (SAN 156-4633); P.O. Box 32270, Amarillo, TX 79120 (SAN 169-8028); 4105 Holly St., Denver, CO 80216 (SAN 156-4641); Memphis, TN 38118 (SAN 156-8086); 2800 W. Story Rd., Suite 200, Irving, TX 75038 (SAN 156-8094); 1562 Hayes Dr., Manhattan, KS 66502 (SAN 156-8108).
Western Michigan News, (Western Michigan), P.O. Box 7264, Seymour Sq. Sta., Grand Rapids, MI 49508 (SAN 169-3875); P.O. Box 10, 301 S. Rath Ave., Ludington, MI 49431 (SAN 169-3905).
Western Periodical Distribution, 3850 W. First Ave., P.O. Box 15003, Eugene, OR 97440 (SAN 169-7110).
Western Psychological Services, Div. of Manson Western Corp., (Western Psych; 0-87424), 12031 Wilshire Blvd., Los Angeles, CA 90025 (SAN 202-9634) Tel 213-478-2061.
Western Pub. Co., Inc., (Western Pub; 0-307), 850 Third Ave., New York, NY 10022 (SAN 202-523X) Tel 212-753-8500; 1220 Mound Ave., Racine, WI 53401 (SAN 669-2982) Tel 414-633-2431; Orders to: Dept. M, P.O. Box 700, Racine, WI 53401; Dist. by: Childrens Pr., 1224 W. Van Buren St., Chicago, IL 60607 (SAN 201-9264) Tel 312-666-4200. Do not confuse with Western Publisher, Lake Worth, FL. Imprints: Golden Press (Golden Pr).
Western Sage Paperbacks See Swallow Pr.
Western States Book Service, P.O. Box 855, Clackamas, OR 97015 (SAN 200-5662) Tel 503-657-9838; Toll free: 800-547-9755 (Ext. 15 for orders).
Western Tanager Pr., (Western Tanager; 0-934136), 1111 Pacific Ave., Santa Cruz, CA 95060 (SAN 220-0155) Tel 408-425-1111. Imprints: Paper Vision Press (Paper Vision); Valley Publishers (Valley Calif).
Weston, Edward, Graphic Inc., 19355 Business Ctr. Dr., Northridge, CA 91324 (SAN 168-9967); Toll free: 800-222-3941 (Orders Only).
Westview Pr., (Westview; 0-89158; 0-86531; 0-8133), 5500 Central Ave., Boulder, CO 80301 (SAN 219-970X) Tel 303-444-3541.
Whitaker Hse., (Whitaker Hse; 0-88368), Pittsburgh & Colfax Sts., Springdale, PA 15144 (SAN 203-2104) Tel 412-274-4440; Toll free: 800-245-2422.
White, A., Publishing Co., (A White Pub; 0-9613812), c/o Linn 19 Essex St., New York, NY 10002 (SAN 679-3878) Tel 212-673-5080; Dist. by: Printed Matter Inc, 7 Lispenard St., New York, NY 10013 (SAN 169-5924) Tel 212-925-0325.
White-Hatch Group, 6625 Springbark, Suite 14, Los Angeles, CA 90056 (SAN 200-6405).
Whitehouse Publishing of Oklahoma, (Whitehouse Pubs OK; 0-934193), 208 E. Owen K. Garriot, Enid, OK 73701 (SAN 693-4412) Tel 405-242-6775; Dist. by: White Manufacturing & Distribution, 208 E. Owen K. Garriot, Enid, OK 73701 (SAN 693-4420).
Whiting News Co., 1417 119th St., Whiting, IN 46394 (SAN 169-2542).
Whitlock & Company, 10001 Roosevelt Rd., Westchester, IL 60153 (SAN 285-9645).
Whitney, Bill, P.O. Box 20 Mott Academic Ctr., Olivet, MI 49076 (SAN 282-6801).
Whitney Library See Watson-Guptill Pubns., Inc.
Whole Health Bk. Co., The, 4735 Wunder Ave., Trevose, PA 19047 (SAN 200-6073) Tel 215-322-2880.

Wholesale Distributors, RR 3, P.O. Box 126, Burlington, IA 52601 (SAN 145-8051).
Wholesome Life Distributing, P.O. Box 26204, Encino, CA 91426-2204 (SAN 200-7533) Tel 818-986-7629.
Wideview See Putnam Publishing Group, The
Wilcox & Follet Co., 1000 W. Washington Blvd., Chicago, IL 60607 (SAN 169-1899).
Wilderness Pr., (Wilderness Pr; 0-89997; 0-911824), 2440 Bancroft Way, Berkeley, CA 94704-1676 (SAN 203-2139) Tel 415-843-8080.
Wildfire Press See Scholastic, Inc.
Wildlife Pubns., Inc., 1014 NW 14th Ave., Gainesville, FL 32601 (SAN 130-4313) Tel 904-378-7944.
Wiley, John, & Sons, Inc., (Wiley; 0-471; 0-8260), 605 Third Ave., New York, NY 10158 (SAN 200-2272) Tel 212-850-6418. Imprints: Harwal Publishing Company (Harwal Pub Co).
Will Judy Publishing Co., P.O. Box 5270, Chicago, IL 60680 (SAN 159-9909).
Williams & Wilkins Co., Div. of Waverly Pr., Inc., (Williams & Wilkins; 0-683), 428 E. Preston St., Baltimore, MD 21202 (SAN 202-5175) Tel 301-528-8521; Toll free: 800-638-0672.
Williamson Publishing Co., (Williamson Pub Co; 0-913589), Church Hill Rd., P.O. Box 185, Charlotte, VT 05445 (SAN 285-3884) Tel 802-425-2102.
Willow Creek Pr., Div. of Wisconsin Sportsman, (Willow Creek Pr; 0-932558), P.O. Box 2266, Oshkosh, WI 54903 (SAN 211-2825) Tel 414-233-4143; Toll free: 800-341-7770; Orders to: 2663 Oregon St., Oshkosh, WI 54901 (SAN 662-1880) Tel 414-233-4143.
Wills Educational Sales (Libra Bound), P.O. Box 209, Greensboro, NC 27419 (SAN 169-6432).
Wilshire Bk. Co., (Wilshire; 0-87980), 12015 Sherman Rd., North Hollywood, CA 91605-3781 (SAN 205-5368) Tel 213-875-1711.
Wilson & Sons, P.O. Box 996, Bellevue, WA 98009 (SAN 129-0010).
Wimmer Brothers Bks., (Wimmer Bks), 4210 BF Goodrich Blvd., Memphis, TN 38181 (SAN 209-6544) Tel 901-362-8900.
Wind, Sun & Stars, Pheasant Ridge Rd., West Redding, CT 06896 (SAN 212-6540) Tel 203-938-9476.
Windfall See Doubleday & Co., Inc.
Windham County News Co., 85-91 Main St., Brattleboro, VT 05301 (SAN 159-9917).
Windhover See Berkley Publishing Group
Windmill Bks. See Dutton, E. P.
Windswept Books See Scholastic, Inc.
Wine Appreciation Guild, The, (Wine Appreciation; 0-932664), 155 Connecticut St., San Francisco, CA 94107 (SAN 201-9515) Tel 415-864-1202; Toll free: 800-242-9462 (Orders only).
Winebaum News Inc., 145 Heritage Ave., Portsmouth, NH 03801 (SAN 169-4529).
Winston-Derek Pubs.,Inc., (Winston-Derek; 0-938232; 1-55523), P.O. Box 90883, Nashville, TN 37209 (SAN 216-4760) Tel 615-321-0535; Toll free: 800-826-1888; Dist. by: Baker & Taylor Co., Midwest Div., 5 Gladiola Ave., Momence, IL 60954 (SAN 169-2100).
Wisconsin Authors & Pubs. Alliance, The, 34 S. Pontiac Dr., Janesville, WI 53545 (SAN 200-6057).
Wisconsin Folklife Ctr., Folklore Village Farm, Rte. 3, Dodgeville, WI 53533 (SAN 200-7843).
Wisconsin Periodical Distributors, 16150 W. Lincoln Ave., New Berlin, WI 53151 (SAN 169-9156).
Wishing Star Books See Scholastic, Inc.
Wit 'n Wisdom, 870 N. Lake St., Aurora, IL 60506 (SAN 145-5702); 18 S. River St., Aurora, IL 60504 (SAN 145-5710); 32 Meadowdale S/Ctr., Carpentersville, IL 60110 (SAN 145-5729).
Wolfcreek Wilderness Supply, P.O. Box 596, Blairsville, GA 30512 (SAN 169-1473).
Wolfe News Service Inc., 1125 Stark St., Utica, NY 13502 (SAN 169-6319).
Wolper Sales Agency, 250 W. 57th St., Rm. 2429, New York, NY 10019 (SAN 285-9785) Tel 212-265-3660.
Womrath's Bookshops & Libraries Inc., 180 Varick St, New York, NY 10014 (SAN 169-6068).

Wongco Merchandising, 303 5th Ave., New York, NY 10016 (SAN 129-5462).
Woods Hole Pr., Subs. of Job Shop, (Woods Hole Pr; 0-915176), 3 Water St. P.O. Box 305, Woods Hole, MA 02543 (SAN 210-332X) Tel 617-548-9600.
Woodstock News Agency, 530 Judd St., Woodstock, IL 60098 (SAN 169-2283).
Woonsocket News Co., Inc., 200 Cato St., Woonsocket, RI 02895 (SAN 169-7722).
Word Works, Inc., (Word Works; 0-915380), P.O. Box 42164, Washington, DC 20015 (SAN 293-4426) Tel 202-554-3014.
Workman Publishing Co., Inc., (Workman Pub; 0-911104; 0-89480), 1 W. 39th St., New York, NY 10018 (SAN 203-2821) Tel 212-398-9160; Toll free: 800-722-7202.
World Bible Pubs., Inc., Subs. of Riverside Bk. & Bible, (World Bible; 0-529; 0-8326), 795 Sharon Dr., Westlake, OH 44145 (SAN 215-2789) Tel 216-241-4370; Toll free: 800-247-5195; Orders to: P.O. Box 370, Iowa Falls, IA 50126 (SAN 215-2797) Tel 800-247-5111.
World Readers Service, Inc., 248 Sisson Ave., Hartford, CT 06153 (SAN 285-9653).
World Wide Furbearer Conference, Inc. Book Distribution Center, 1111 E. Cold Spring Lane, Baltimore, MD 21239 (SAN 263-2217).
World Wide Media Service Inc., 386 Park Ave. S., New York, NY 10016 (SAN 165-1684).
World Wide Pubns., Box 1240, Minneapolis, MN 55440 (SAN 159-9941).
World Wide Pubns., 230 Park Ave., New York, NY 10017 (SAN 285-9793).
World Wisdom Books, (Wrld Wisdom Bks; 0-941532), P.O. Box 2682, Bloomington, IN 47402-2682 (SAN 239-1406) Tel 812-332-1663; Dist. by: Bookpeople, 2929 Fifth St., Berkeley, CA 94710 (SAN 168-9517) Tel 415-549-3030; Dist. by: New Leaf, 1020 White St., SW, Atlanta, GA 30310 (SAN 169-1449) Tel 404-755-2665; Dist. by: Great Tradition, The, 750 Adrian Way, Suite 111, San Rafael, CA 94903 (SAN 200-5743) Tel 415-492-9382.
Worlds of Wonder, (Worlds Wonder; 1-55578), 4209 Technology Dr., Fremont, CA 94538 (SAN 699-993X) Tel 415-659-4300.
Worldvision Enterprises, Inc., (Worldvision), 660 Madison Ave., New York, NY 10021 (SAN 200-6235) Tel 212-832-3838.
Worldwide Books, Div. of Kraus-Thompson Organization, Ltd., (World Wide Bks), 37-39 Antwerp St., Boston, MA 02135 (SAN 287-7805) Tel 617-787-9100.
Worldwide Distributors, 550 N. Nimitz Hwy., Honolulu, HI 96814 (SAN 169-1627).
Worldwide Evangelization Crusade, 709 Pennsylvania Ave, Fort Washington, PA 19034 (SAN 276-8577).
Worzalla Publishing Co., 3535 Jefferson St., Stevens Point, WI 54481 (SAN 200-4771).
Wright Book/Educational, 2195 Owendale Dr., Dayton, OH 45439 (SAN 159-9968).
Writers & Books, 740 University Ave., Rochester, NY 14607 (SAN 156-9678) Tel 716-473-2590.
Writers Digest Bks., Div. of F&W Publications, Inc., (Writers Digest; 0-89879; 0-911654), 9933 Alliance Rd., Cincinnati, OH 45242 (SAN 212-064X) Tel 513-984-0717; Toll free: 800-543-4644.
Wybel Distribution Co., 101 S. Hough St., Barrington, IL 60010 (SAN 159-3668).
Wyndham Bks. See Simon & Schuster, Inc.
Wyoming Book Co., Inc., Box 505, Cheyenne, WY 82001 (SAN 159-9976).
Wyoming News Co., Box 528, Worland, WY 82401 (SAN 169-9261).
Wyoming Periodical Distributor, P.O. Box 2340, Casper, WY 82601 (SAN 169-9245).
X-S Books, Inc., 725 Dell Rd., Carlstadt, NJ 07072 (SAN 169-4634) Tel 201-935-4493. Remainders & promotional books to trade & institutional markets; specialize in art & general trade titles, juveniles, songbooks, texts, clothbound & paperback; title-by-title & promotional assortments.
Xenvirons, (0-9609202), 1630 Salford St., Postal Drawer 222, Salford, PA 18957 (SAN 241-4805) Tel 215-287-8622.
Yakima News Agency Inc., P.O. Box 2399, Yakima, WA 98902 (SAN 169-8893).

Yale Univ. Pr., *(Yale U Pr; 0-300),* 302 Temple St., New Haven, CT 06520 (SAN 203-2740) Tel 203-436-7584; Orders to: 92A Yale Sta., New Haven, CT 06520 (SAN 203-2759) Tel 203-436-7582.

Yankee Book Peddler, Inc., Maple St., Contoocook, NH 03229 (SAN 169-4510).

Yankee Bks., Div. of Yankee Publishing, Inc., *(Yankee Bks; 0-911658; 0-89909),* Main St., Dublin, NH 03444 (SAN 293-4434) Tel 603-563-8111; Toll free: 800-258-5327; Orders to: Yankee Bks., Trade Sales Div., Depot Sq., Peterborough, NH 03458 (SAN 293-4442) Tel 603-924-3807.

Yankee News Co., Box 2689, Waterbury, CT 06705-2689 (SAN 169-0876).

Yardbird Publishing Co., Inc., *(Yardbird Pub; 0-918410),* P.O. Box 2370, Station A, Berkeley, CA 94702 (SAN 208-9343) Tel 415-841-6500.

Ye Olde Genealogie Shoppe, P.O. Box 39128, Indianapolis, IN 46239 (SAN 200-7010).

Year Bk. Medical Pubs., Inc., Subs. of Times Mirror, *(Year Bk Med; 0-8151),* 35 E. Wacker Dr., Chicago, IL 60601 (SAN 205-5600) Tel 312-726-9733; Toll free: 800-621-9262.

Yingling, George, 399 Cheltenham Dr., Dayton, OH 45459 (SAN 200-772X).

York News Agency, 1141 S. Edgar St., P.O. Box 1187, York, PA 17405 (SAN 169-7706).

York News Co., Inc., Affil. of Anderson News Ctr. Reader's World, P.O. Box 1030, Anderson, IN 46015 (SAN 169-2291) Tel 317-642-9911; Toll free: 800-382-5292.

Young, R. J., *(R J Young),* P.O. Box 816, Ithaca, NY 14850 Tel 607-387-9560.

Young News Inc., 205 S. Second St., Saginaw, MI 48607 (SAN 169-3999).

Young's News Agency, 124 W. Cherry, Paris, TX 75460 (SAN 169-8370).

Yuma News Inc., P.O. Box 5780, Yuma, AZ 85364 (SAN 168-941X).

Z-80 Data Systems, *(0-928549),* P.O. Box 28355, Columbus, OH 43228

Zebra Bks. *See* **Grove Pr.**

Zenith Books *See* **Doubleday & Co., Inc.**

Zephyr *See* **Doubleday & Co., Inc.**

Zephyr-BFYR *See* **Doubleday & Co., Inc.**

Zephyr Pr. AZ, *(Zephyr Pr AZ; 0-913705),* 430 S. Essex Ln., Tucson, AZ 85711 (SAN 270-6830) Tel 602-623-2022.

Zion's Book Store, 254 S. Main St., Salt Lake City, UT 84101 (SAN 239-1457).

Zondervan Publishing Hse., Div. of Zondervan Corp., *(Zondervan; 0-310),* 1415 Lake Dr. SE, Grand Rapids, MI 49506 (SAN 203-2694) Tel 616-698-6900; Toll free: 800-253-1309 (wholesale orders, bookstores); Toll free: 800-253-4475 (retail orders). *Imprints:* Clarion Classics (Clarion Class); Serenade-Saga (Serenade-Saga).

Zook News Agency, P.O. Box 111 U, Eureka, CA 95501 (SAN 168-9622).

Zubal, John T., Inc., *(Zubal Inc; 0-939738),* 2969 W. 25th St., Cleveland, OH 44113 (SAN 165-5841) Tel 216-241-7640.

GEOGRAPHIC INDEX TO WHOLESALERS AND DISTRIBUTORS

The *Geographic Index to Wholesalers and Distributors* lists the companies found in the *Wholesalers and Distributors Index* alphabetically within each state. Puerto Rico, Guam, and the U.S. Virgin Islands are also included. City name appears in parentheses following company name.

ALABAMA
ANCO Management Services (Florence)
Alabama Bk. Store (Tuscaloosa)
Allenson, Alec R., Inc. (Geneva)
Anderson News Co. (Florence)
Browser, The (Mobile)
Core, Howard, & Co. (Munford)
EBSCO Industries, Inc. (Birmingham)
Franklin Square Overseas (Birmingham)
Gulf States Book Fair (Mobile)
Jefferson News Co., Inc. (Birmingham)
JMT Associates (Normal)
Kuykendalls Press, Bookstore Div. (Athens)
Menasha Ridge Pr., Inc. (Birmingham)
Mobile News Co. (Mobile)
Montgomery News Co. (Montgomery)
Newsdealers Supply Co., Inc. (Dothan)
Read News Agency (Tuscaloosa)
Subscription Service Co. (Birmingham)
Sunland School Plans (Birmingham)
Title Bks., Inc. (Birmingham)
Univ. of Alabama Pr. (University)

ALASKA
Alaska News Agency Inc. (Anchorage)
Alaska Pacific Univ. Pr. (Anchorage)
Aleutian Pribilof Islands Assn., Inc. (AANG ANGAGIN) (Anchorage)
Applecart Programs for Education (Juneau)
Fairbanks News Agency (Fairbanks)
Old Harbor Bks. (Sitka)
Univ. of Alaska Pr. (Fairbanks)

ARIZONA
B.G. Enterprises, Inc. (Scottsdale)
Bobbie Holladay (Phoenix)
Bradshaw, Bob (Sudona)
Central Arizona Distributing (Glendale)
Club Products (Jacksonville)
Computer Mat (Lake Haven City)
Custom Computer Technology (West Sedona)
EPM Pubns. (Sedona)
Evans Distributing (Phoenix)
Expotek (Phoenix)
Golden Hind Publishing Co. (Tempe)
HP Bks. (Tucson)
Historical Research Associates (Bisbee)
Hopkins, Tom, International, Inc. (Scottsdale)
Inspiration Books (Phoenix)
Magee Bk. Store (Prescott)
Many Feathers Southwest Books & Maps (Phoenix)
North Arizona News Agency (Flagstaff)
Northern Arizona News (Flagstaff)
Northern Arizona Univ. Bookstore (Flagstaff)
Northland Pr. (Flagstaff)
Oryx Pr. (Phoenix)

Pacific Literary Assocs. (Tucson)
Readex Book Exchange (Carefree)
Roadrunner Library Service (Phoenix)
Sandoval Distributing Co. (Tucson)
Southwest News Co. (Tucson)
Southwest Parks & Monuments Assn. (Tucson)
Southwest Periodicals Distributing Co. (Tucson)
Southwestern Bk. Distributors (Phoenix)
Southwestern Stringed Instruments & Accessories (Tucson)
Strong's News Agency (Glendale)
Thinking Caps, Inc. (Phoenix)
Tucson Museum of Art (Tucson)
Tucson News Agency (Tucson)
Univ. of Arizona Pr. (Tucson)
Walnut Pr. (Sun City)
Yuma News Inc. (Yuma)
Zephyr Pr. AZ (Tucson)

ARKANSAS
Arkansas News Co. (Fort Smith)
Cicero Bible Pr. (Harrison)
Lilly News Agency (Jonesboro)
New Leaf Pr. (Green Forest)
Ozark News Agency Inc. (Fayetteville)
Pubs. Distribution Service (Little Rock)
Siebert's Inc. (Little Rock)
Southern Star, Inc. (Harrison)

CALIFORNIA
ABC Book Distributors (San Francisco)
ACS Pubns., Inc. (San Diego)
AHA, Inc. (Santa Cruz)
AIMS Media (Van Nuys)
ANSCO (Gardena)
ARA Services, Magazine & Bk. Div. (Los Angeles)
ARA Services, Magazine & Bk. Div. (San Diego)
Action Distributing (Huntington Beach)
Activity Resources Co., Inc. (Hayward)
Adams Periodical Service (Vallejo)
Advanced Professional Development, Inc. (North Hollywood)
Akiba Pr. (Oakland)
Alchemy Bks. (San Francisco)
Alfred Publishing Co., Inc. (Sherman Oaks)
All America Distributors (Los Angeles)
Altarinda Books (Orinda)
Amatix, Inc. (Inglewood)
Amber West Corp. (Placentia)
America Ado, Inc. (Torrance)
American Casting Association (San Rafael)
Anacapa Bks. (Berkeley)
Ancient Future (Kentfield)
Angel Book Distribution Center (Monterey)
Apothecary Shop, The (Walnut Creek)
Apple Country Ltd. (Julian)

Aqua-Craft II (San Diego)
Arrowhead Magazine Co., Inc. (San Bernardino)
Ashton-Tate Publishing Group (Torrance)
Asian Humanities Pr. (Berkeley)
Astro Analytics Pubns. (Van Nuys)
Aurobindo Books (Pomona)
Auromere, Inc. (Pomona)
Aviation Bk. Co. (Glendale)
Aviation Bk. Co. (Glendale)
Axlon, Inc. (Sunnyvale)
B & H Books (San Rafael)
Baja Trail Pubns., Inc. (Huntington Beach)
Ballard & Tighe, Inc. (Brea)
Barbary Coast Bks. (Oakland)
Baver, Dorothy (El Cajon)
Beagle Brothers (San Diego)
Before Columbus Foundation (Berkeley)
Bell Controls (San Rafael)
Bell Magazine (Seaside)
Berkeley Educational Paperbacks (Berkeley)
Bertel Distributing Co. (Beverly Hills)
Beyda & Associates Inc. (Van Nuys)
Bickel Agency (Santa Barbara)
Bilingual Educ. Servs., Inc. (Los Angeles)
Blue Cat (Walnut)
Blue Wind Press (Berkeley)
Bonanza Industries (Los Angeles)
Book Mart, The (Inglewood)
Booklegger, The (Grass Valley)
Booklink Distributors (San Luis Obispo)
Bookpeople (Berkeley)
Borden Publishing Co. (Alhambra)
Borgo Pr. (San Bernardino)
Boswell, S.R., Co. (Los Angeles)
Brewmaster (San Leandro)
Bridge Pubns. Inc. (Los Angeles)
Bud Plant, Inc. (Grass Valley)
Bud Plant Number Two (Hayward)
Business Media Resources (Mill Valley)
Business/Technology Information Service (Orinda)
C.J. Jung Institute (Los Angeles)
Cal-West Periodicals (Oakland)
Calendars Unlimited (Santa Rosa)
Calico Subscription Co. (Milpitas)
Capra Pr. (Santa Barbara)
Celestial Arts Pub. Co. (Berkeley)
ChartGuide Ltd. (Anaheim)
Chico News Agency (Chico)
Christian Book Distributors (Compton)
Church of Scientology Pubns. Organization (Los Angeles)
Clark, Arthur H., Co. (Glendale)
Classroom Reading Service (Montebello)
Cogan Books (Fullerton)
Cole, David M./Outreach Books (Corona)
College Book Co. of California Inc. (Garden Grove)
Communication Line (Union City)

Geographic Index

Beal's News Agency (Olney)
Beck's Book Store (Chicago)
Block & Company, Inc. (Wheeling)
Bloomington News Agency (Bloomington)
Bound to Stay Bound Book (Jacksonville)
Buckley Pubns., Inc. (Chicago)
Business Computer Systems (Oak Brook)
Caroline Hse., Inc. (Naperville)
Casa Escobar (Chicago)
Catholic Bookrack Service (Riverside)
Centralia News Co. (Centralia)
Champaign-Urbana News Agency (Champaign)
Chas Levy Circulating (Chicago)
Chicago Review Pr., Inc. (Chicago)
Childrens Pr. (Chicago)
Church Richards Co. (Westchester)
Com-Pute Services (Oak Park)
Common Sense Ltd. (Norwood Park)
Computer Book Service (Hillside)
Contemparary Books Inc (Chicago)
Contemporary Bks., Inc. (Chicago)
Cook, David C., Publishing Co. (Elgin)
Cuban Boy's Spanish Books (Chicago)
DELTAK, Inc. (Naperville)
Dianco (Chicago)
Doctor of Northbrook Court, The (Northbrook)
Dow Jones-Irwin, Inc. (Homewood)
E & R Development Co. (Jacksonville)
Educational Data Center (Romeoville)
Egypt News (Johnston City)
Elek-Tek, Inc. (Chicago)
Ellsworth Magazine Serv. Inc (Chicago)
Esquire, Inc. (Chicago)
Follett Corp. (Chicago)
Franciscan Herald Pr. (Chicago)
Galesburg News Agency Inc. (Galesburg)
Glenwood Distributors (Collinsville)
Good Apple, Inc. (Carthage)
Habibur Rahman (Centralia)
Hamakor Judaica Inc. (Chicago)
Hanson-Bennett Magazine Agency (Barrington)
Helix (Chicago)
Herbert Furse-Bookman (Glenview)
Homewood-Flossmor News Agency (Homewood)
IPS Information Processing Supplies (Burr Ridge)
Illinois Institute of Technology (Chicago)
Illinois News Service (Peoria)
Illinois State Historical Society (Springfield)
Imported Pubns., Inc. (Chicago)
Interbusiness Corp. (Wheeling)
International Assn. of Assessing Officers
   (Chicago)
Irwin, Richard D., Inc. (Homewood)
Jeanies Classics (Rockford)
Kazi Pubns. (Chicago)
Kerr, Charles H., Publishing, Co. (Chicago)
Kewanee News Agency (Kewanee)
Labelmaster (Chicago)
Liberation Distributors (Chicago)
Library Book Selection Service (Bloomington)
Lindsay Pubns., Inc. (Bradley)
Login Brothers Book Co. (Chicago)
M & M News Agency (La Salle)
McGregor Subscription Agency (Mt. Morris)
Manufacturers Productivity Ctr. (Chicago)
Micro Pace Computers (Champaign)
Mid-State Distributors (Jacksonville)
Midwest European Pubns. (Evanston)
More, Thomas, Assn. (Chicago)
National Distribution Ctr. (Lisle)
National Textbook Co. (Chicago)
New World Resource Center (Chicago)
Noel's Trophy Products (Sterling)
North Shore Distributors (Wheeling)
Nystrom-Eye Gate (Chicago)
Ollis Bk. Corp. (Steger)
Open Court Publishing Co. (Peru)
PC Network (Chicago)
Peck, Walter, Magazine Agency (Galesburg)
Pekin News Agency (Pekin)
Periodical Merchandisers (Mattoon)
Perma Bound Bks. (Jacksonville)
Polycrystal Book Service (Western Springs)
Protecto Enterprises (Barrington)
Pubs. Business Service, Inc. (Chicago)
Publishers Mark, The (Barrington)
Quality Books, Inc. (Lake Bluff)
Readers Service Bureau (Glenview)
Ritter Book Co. (Chicago)
Rockbottom Bks. (Chicago)
Schar Publishing Co. (Chicago)
Scholarly Book Center (Waukegan)
School Aid Co. (Danville)
Schwartz-Rosenblum, Inc. (Chicago)
Scott, Foresman & Co. (Glenview)
Scripture Press Pubns., Inc. (Wheaton)
Society for Visual Education, Inc. (Chicago)
Specialty Promotions (Chicago)

Springfield News Agency (Springfield)
Sterling Rock Falls News Agency (Sterling)
Stoelting Company (Chicago)
Teitan Pr., Inc., The (Chicago)
Temple of Kriya Yoga, The (Chicago)
Thomas Computer Corp. (Chicago)
Tri-County Distributors (Joliet)
Tri-County Periodicals Distributors (Joliet)
Turnbull & Willoughby Pubs., Inc. (Chicago)
Univ. of Chicago Pr. (Chicago)
Univ. of Illinois Pr. (Champaign)
Vanguard Books (Chicago)
Weekends Inc. (Salem)
Western Illinois News Co. (Macomb)
Whitlock & Company (Westchester)
Wilcox & Follet Co. (Chicago)
Will Judy Publishing Co. (Chicago)
Wit 'n Wisdom (Aurora)
Woodstock News Agency (Woodstock)
Wybel Distribution Co. (Barrington)
Year Bk. Medical Pubs., Inc. (Chicago)

INDIANA

Alexandria House (Alexandria)
Beaver News Co., Inc. (Rensselaer)
Biofeedback & Stress Management Services
   (Schererville)
Black Magazine Agency (Logansport)
Bloomington Distribution Group (Bloomington)
CRS/Communication Ctr. (South Bend)
Cards Books N Things (La Porte)
Cummins News Co. (Bloomington)
DeLong Subscription Agency (Lafayette)
Distributors, The (South Bend)
Diversified Marketing Serv. Co. (Indianapolis)
Eisenbrauns (Winona Lake)
Elkhart City News & Bookstore, Inc. (Elkhart)
Epply, Harry L., Book Co. (Scottsburg)
Finn News Agency (Garrett)
Frangipani Pr. (Bloomington)
Haldeman, R. W., & Assocs. (Indianapolis)
Indiana Univ. Pr. (Bloomington)
Islamic Bk. Service (Indianapolis)
Koch News Co. (Indianapolis)
Kokomo News Agency (Kokomo)
Loge News Co. (Evansville)
Mehlman, Terry (Richmond)
Popular Subscription Service (Terre Haute)
Pratik Pubns. (Merrillville)
Pubs. Continental Sales Corp. (Michigan City)
Ramsey News Co. (Warsaw)
Sams, Howard W., & Co. (Indianapolis)
Saturday Evening Post Co. School Plan
   (Indianapolis)
Summit City News Agency (Fort Wayne)
T.I.S., Inc. (Bloomington)
Twin City News Agency (Layfayette)
Two Trees Micro Software (Terre Haute)
Univ. of Notre Dame Pr. (Notre Dame)
Vincennes News Agency (Vincennes)
Voyles News Agency (Richmond)
Wabash Valley News Agency (Terre Haute)
Warner Pr. Pubs. (Anderson)
Whiting News Co. (Whiting)
World Wisdom Books (Bloomington)
Ye Olde Genealogie Shoppe (Indianapolis)
York News Co., Inc. (Anderson)

IOWA

Ames News Agency Inc. (Ames)
Armstrong Systems & Consulting (Davenport)
Budget Marketing Service (Des Moines)
Cohn News Agency (Muscatine)
Des Moines News Agency (Des Moines)
Eble Music Co. (Iowa City)
Hampton Distributing (Hampton)
Hiawatha Bk. Co. (Bondurant)
Husker News Co. (Atlantic)
Inspirational Marketing Inc. (Indianola)
Iowa & Illinois News (Davenport)
Iowa News Distributing Co. (Waterloo)
Iowa Periodicals (Cedar Rapids)
Iowa State Univ. Pr. (Ames)
Marshalltown News Agency (Marshalltown)
National Organization Service, Inc. (Des Moines)
Nelson News Agency (Fort Dodge)
Noll's Educational Books & Toys (Arthur)
Norton News Agency (Dubuque)
Perfection Form Company, The (Logan)
QSP (Des Moines)
Riverside Bk. & Bible Hse., Inc. (Iowa Falls)
Subscription Service Inc., The (Des Moines)
Wholesale Distributors (Burlington)

KANSAS

Allen Pr., Inc. (Lawrence)

American Econo-Clad Service
   (Topeka)
American Magazine Service (Topeka)
Bookbinders Store, The (Topeka)
Bookmark, Inc., The (Kansas City)
Capper, F., Publications (Topeka)
Collection Inc. The (Olathe)
Darr Subscription Agency (Centralia)
Exchange & Gifts Dept. (Lawrence)
Fogarty News Co. (Pittsburgh)
Forsyth Travel Library (Shawnee Mission)
Joplin News Co., Inc. (Pittsburg)
Kansas State Reading Circle (Topeka)
Kindred Pr. (Hillsboro)
Learning Arts (Wichita)
M-S News Co., Inc. (Wichita)
Palmer News Co. Inc. (Topeka)
Phillips News Co. (Hutchinson)
Snyder Magazine Agency (Shawnee Mission)
Sunflower Univ. Pr. (Manhattan)
Wedgestone Pr. (Winfield)

KENTUCKY

American Printing House for the Blind
   (Louisville)
Basin News Co. (Paducah)
Berry, P. D., (Louisa)
Central Kentucky Books (Mayking)
Central Kentucky News Co. (Lexington)
Collector Bks. (Paducah)
East Kentucky News, Inc. (Paintsville)
Gnomon Pr. (Frankfort)
Haxby News Co. (Bowling Green)
Lorrah & Hitchcock Pubs., Inc. (Murray)
Louisville News Co. (Louisville)
Louisville News Co. (Columbia)
Love Ministries, Inc. (Worthville)
Minor-Dixon Magazine Service (Lexington)
Repass, Mary E. (Louisa)
Wallace's College Book Co. (Lexington)

LOUISIANA

ARA Periodical Services (Kenner)
Bayou Bks. (Gretna)
Bayou News Agency (Baton Rouge)
Computer Library (New Orleans)
Express Publishing Co. (New Orleans)
Forest Sales & Distributing (New Orleans)
Gospel Distributors (Alexandria)
Howard's for Pet Supplies (New Orleans)
Pelican Publishing Co., Inc. (Gretna)
Persona Pr. (New Orleans)
Red River News Co. (Monroe)
School Aids (Baton Rouge)
Shreveport News Agency (Shreveport)
Siler's Library Distributors (New Orleans)
South Louisiana News Co. (Rayne)
Spielman Co. (New Orleans)

MAINE

Arcane Books (York Harbor)
Augusta News Co. (Augusta)
Clark, Stephen (Waterville)
Coyote Love Pr. (Portland)
East Rock Pr., Inc. (Cushing)
Eastern Book Co. (Portland)
Harpswell Pr. (Gardiner)
Haventa Ltd. (S. Harpswell)
International Marine Publishing Co. (Camden)
Magazines, Inc. (Bangor)
Maine Writers & Publishers Alliance (Portland)
Marston's (Presque Isle)
Moody, J.S. (Falmouth)
Portland News Co. (South Portland)
Renaissance Greeting Cards Inc. (Springvale)
State News Co. (Rockland)
Weiser, Samuel, Inc. (York Beach)

MARYLAND

ARA Services (Cottage City)
Bernan Assocs., Inc. (Lanham)
Blue Ridge News Inc. (Frederick)
Bon-Jay Sales (Baltimore)
Bookfare (Rockville)
Bookman Publishing (Baltimore)
Camden Hse., Inc. (Baltimore)
Ciener Enterprises (Baltimore)
Computerized Management Systems, Incorporated
   (Baltimore)
Cox, Betty, Assocs. (Baltimore)
Cucumber Information Systems (Rockville)
Cultural Hispana (Silver Spring)
Ediciones Hispamerica (Gaithersburg)
Gryphon Hse., Inc. (Mount Rainier)

Geographic Index

Geographic Index

Story Hse. Corp. (Charlotteville)
Stratton Intercontinental Medical Book Corp.
  (New York)
Stroup News Agency Inc. (Saratoga Springs)
Stull & Co., Since 1870, Inc. (New York)
Sunburst Communications, Inc. (Pleasantville)
Sunflower Books (New York)
Swedenborg Foundation, Inc. (New York)
Talman Co., The (New York)
Taplinger Publishing Co., Inc. (New York)
Taylor, Carlisle (New York)
Taylor-Carlisle (New York)
Telebooks Company (New York)
Thieme, Inc. (New York)
Three Presses Agency (Staten Island)
Tokyo Sales Corp. (New York)
Torah Umesorah Pubns. (New York)
Toronto Univ. Press (Buffalo)
Tova Press, Incorporated (New York)
Tri County News Agency (Dunkirk)
Troy News Co., Inc., Educational Div. (Troy)
Turner Subscription Agency, The (New York)
Ubiquity Distributors (Brooklyn)
U. S. Games Systems, Inc. (New York)
United Subscription Service (Roslyn Heights)
United Synagogue Book Service (New York)
Universe Bks., Inc. (New York)
Univ. of Toronto Pr. (Buffalo)
Van Nostrand Reinhold Co., Inc. (New York)
Vanguard Pr., Inc. (New York)
Variety Arts, Inc. (New York)
Ventura Corp. (Amityville)
Vestal Pr., Ltd. (Vestal)
Viking-Penguin, Inc. (New York)
Walck, Henry Z., Inc. (New York)
Walker & Co. (New York)
Wallaby Bks. (New York)
Walsh-Jamaica Church Goods (Jamaica)
Warner Pubs Services (New York)
Waterways Project (New York)
Watson-Guptill Pubns., Inc. (New York)
Watts, Franklin, Incorporated (New York)
Westchester Book Service (Bronx)
Western Pub. Co., Inc. (New York)
White, A., Publishing Co. (New York)
Wiley, John, & Sons, Inc. (New York)
Wolfe News Service Inc. (Utica)
Wolper Sales Agency (New York)
Womrath's Bookshops & Libraries Inc. (New
  York)
Wongco Merchandising (New York)
Workman Publishing Co., Inc. (New York)
World Wide Media Service Inc. (New York)
World Wide Pubns. (New York)
Worldvision Enterprises, Inc. (New York)
Writers & Books (Rochester)
Young, R. J. (Ithaca)

NORTH CAROLINA

Alexander News Co. (Asheville)
Armstrong, J.B., News Agency
  (Winston-Salem)
Back-to-Basics Books (Hendersonville)
Book Fare (Greensboro)
Book Mark (Greensboro)
Bright Horizons (Ashville)
Carolina News Co. (Fayetteville)
Celo Pr. (Burnsville)
Connemara Trading Co. (Chapel Hill)
Cop, W. T. (Goldsboro)
Dixie News Co. (Charlotte)
Duke Univ. Pr. (Durham)
Elizabeth City News Agency
  (Elizabeth City)
Gallopade: Carole Marsh Bks. (Bath)
Instrument Society of America (Research
  Triangle Park)
Kaplan School Supply (Winston-Salem)
L & M News Co. (New Bern)
Libra-Bound TM Books (Greensboro)
Nancy Roberts' Collection (Charlotte)
North Carolina News Co. (Durham)
North Carolina School Book Depository
  (Raleigh)
Pikes News Agency (Wilson)
Raleigh News Agency (Raleigh)
Rocky Mount News Agency
  (Rocky Mount)
Ruzicka, Joseph, Inc. (Greensboro)
S & W Distributors Inc. (Greensboro)
Service News Co. (Wilmington)
State News Agency (Greensboro)
Storie/McOwen Pubs., Inc. (Manteo)
Univ. of North Carolina Pr. (Chapel Hill)
Wills Educational Sales (Libra Bound)
  (Greensboro)

NORTH DAKOTA

Germans From Russia Heritage Society
  (Bismark)
Kings News,Inc. (Grand Forks)
Northern School Supply Co. (Fargo)
P & G Wholesale (Fargo)
Plains Distribution Service (Fargo)
Saks News Inc. (Bismarck)

OHIO

Ability Development, Inc. (Athens)
Amateur Computer Society of Central Ohio
  (Columbus)
Awareness & Health, Unlimited (Columbus)
BNR Pr. (Port Clinton)
Barnhart's Computer Ctr. (Urbana)
Bartley Subscription Agency (Cleveland)
Blue Bird Publishing (Columbus)
Book Caboose (Centerville)
Brunner News Agency (Lima)
Buckeye News Co. (Toledo)
Budget Reading Service (Sandusky)
Budgit Reader Service (Sandusky)
CBS Computers, Inc. (North Canton)
C-Spec Corp. (Dayton)
Central News of Sandusky (Sandusky)
Circular Ltd. (Cleveland)
Datacom Computer Sales & Supplies (Medina)
De Sales Literature (Cincinnati)
Defiance Wholesale News (Defiance)
EAL Enterprises, Inc. (Cleveland)
F & W Pubns., Inc. (Cincinnati)
Field (Poetry Serial only) (Oberlin)
Findlay News Agency (Findlay)
Green Gate Books (Lima)
Guardian Book Co. (Toledo)
Guscott Magazine Agency (Shaker Heights)
Hobby Bk. Distributors (North Bend)
Holcomb, J.R., Co. (Cleveland)
Hubbard (Defiance)
Hubert News Agency, Inc. (Wilmington)
International Magazine Service (Sandusky)
International Readers league (Sandusky)
L. D. S. Books (Dayton)
La Belle News Agency (Steubenville)
Login Brothers East (Twinsburg)
Mahoning Valley Distributing Agency, Inc.
  (Youngstown)
Marshall, J. L., News (Cincinnati)
Mayapple Pr. (Kent)
Miami Valley News Agency (Dayton)
Middletown News Agency (Middletown)
Modern Curriculum Pr. (Cleveland)
Morningside Bookshop (Dayton)
Nascorp, Inc. (Oberlin)
National Assn. of College Stores (Oberlin)
Neighborhood Per. Club (Cincinnati)
Ohio Poetry Therapy Ctr. & Library (Columbus)
Ohio State University Bookstores (Columbus)
Ohio State Univ., ERIC Clearinghouse for
  Science, Mathematics, & Environmental
  Education Analysis Ctr. (Columbus)
PEP Distributors (Lima)
Periodical Pubs. Ser Bureau (Sandusky)
Portsmouth News Agency (Portsmouth)
Professional Book Distributor (Columbus)
Queen City Brass Pubns. (Cincinnati)
Reading Circle, The (Columbus)
Saint Mary Seminary Bookstore (Cleveland)
Scott Krauss News Agency (Columbus)
Selections Book Fairs (Columbus)
Seven Hills Bks. (Cincinnati)
Slavica Pubs., Inc. (Columbus)
Sovereign News Co. (Cleveland)
Sportsman's Market, Inc. (Batavia)
Stewart-MacDonald Corp. (Athens)
Swallow Pr. (Athens)
Targeted Communications (Cleveland)
Techmar (Cleveland)
Tiffin News Agency (Tiffin)
University Book Service (Worthington)
Well News Service (Columbus)
Welsh News Agency, Inc. (Mansfield)
World Bible Pubs., Inc. (Westlake)
Wright Book/Educational (Dayton)
Writers Digest Bks. (Cincinnati)
Yingling, George (Dayton)
Z-80 Data Systems (Columbus)
Zubal, John T., Inc. (Cleveland)

OKLAHOMA

A-K News Co. (Oklahoma City)
ARA Services (Oklahoma City)
American Assn. of Petroleum Geologists (Tulsa)
American Chiropractic Academic Press
  (Oklahoma City)

American Small Business Computers, Inc. (Pryor)
Blackwells (Tulsa)
Garrett Book Company (Ada)
International Luthier Supply, Inc. (Tulsa)
Kordak School & Library Book Shop (Oklahoma
  City)
Kraftbilt Products (Tulsa)
Mid Continent News Co. (Oklahoma City)
Oklahoma City News Agency (Oklahoma City)
Oklahoma News Co. (Tulsa)
Oklahoma School & Office Supply (Muskogee)
Printed Products Inc. (Oklahoma City)
Rodeo News Publishing (Pauls Valley)
Will Rogers Memorial & Museum (Claremore)
Thompson School Book Depository (Oklahoma
  City)
Whitehouse Publishing of Oklahoma (Enid)

OREGON

Adler, Leo (Baker)
Bay News Co. (Portland)
Bible Gift Shop (Portland)
Child Study Clinic (Portland)
Controlled-C Software, Inc. (Portland)
Coos Bay Distributors (Coos Bay)
Delcon Corp. (Eddyville)
Don & Linda's Suitcase of Books
  (Oregon City)
Douglas County Museum (Roseburg)
Far West Book Service (Portland)
Greater Spiral, The (Portland)
Himber's Books (Eugene)
Inland Empire Periodicals Inc. (Baker)
International Specialized Bk. Services
  (Portland)
LZB Publishing Co. (Portland)
Langdon, Larry, Pubns. (Cottage Grove)
Lanson's Inc. (Portland)
New Woman Pr. (Sunny Valley)
Pacific Northwest Bks. (Medford)
Palmer Distributing Co. (Corvallis)
Rogue Valley News Agency, Inc.
  (Medford)
Salem News Agency (Salem)
Scribble Shack Book Distributor (Eugene)
Second Genesis (Portland)
Snake River Periodical Distributors Inc.
  (Baker)
Spring Arbor-West (Portland)
Stinna Co. (Portland)
Subterranean Co (Eugene)
Tree Frog Trucking Co. (Portland)
Troyka (Portland)
Unilit (Portland)
Vision Books (Coos Bay)
Western Periodical Distribution (Eugene)
Western States Book Service (Clackamas)

PENNSYLVANIA

A C L D (Pittsburgh)
A D F D Pubns. (Philadephia)
Abramovic Associates (Kittanning)
Alico International, Inc. (Pittsburgh)
Allentown News Agency, Inc. (Allentown)
Anthracite News Co. (Scranton)
Apollo Library Book Supplier (Philadelphia)
Associated Libraries Inc. (Philadelphia)
Atlantic Books (Montgomery)
BMC International, Inc. (Upper Darby)
Banner of Truth, The (Carlisle)
Berkshire News, Inc. (West Reading)
Bethlehem News Agency (Bethlehem)
Black Box Corp. (Pittsburgh)
Booksellers of Bethlehem (Bethlehem)
Brodart Co. (Williamsport)
Buck Musical Instruments Products (New
  Britain)
Candence Subscription Agency (Philadelphia)
Caucasian Rugs (Pittsburgh)
Central Wholesale (Pittsburgh)
Chapter & Cask (Glenshaw)
Christian Literature Crusade, Inc. (Fort
  Washington)
County News Agency, Inc. (Lancaster)
Crown & Covenant Pubns. (Pittsburgh)
Dinosaur Discounts (Edgemont)
Eastern Subscription Agency (Philadelphia)
Easton News Co. (Easton)
Executive Bks. (Harrisburg)
Fayette County News Agency (Uniontown)
Franklin Book Co. (Elkins Park)
Giletto, Sebastian Ben (Philadelphia)
Goldberg, Louis (Nazareth)
Haddon Craftsmen Distribution Ctr. (Dunmore)
Han Books (Philadelphia)
Harmony Book Co. (Beaver)

By Hand & Foot, Ltd. (Brattleboro)
Country News Distributor (Brattleboro)
Countryman Pr., Inc. (Woodstock)
Creative Expressions (Colchester)
Daily Bread (Richford)
David & Charles, Inc. (North Pomfret)
Gregg International (Brookfield)
Hill, Ellen C. (Montpelier)
Inner Traditions International, Ltd. (Rochester)
Metropolitan Music Co. (Stowe)
Pennywheel Press (Poultney)
Rutland News Co. (Rutland)
Thorsons Pubs., Inc. (Rochester)
Tuttle, Charles E., Co., Inc. (Rutland)
Williamson Publishing Co. (Charlotte)
Windham County News Co. (Brattleboro)

VIRGINIA

A B & C Sales (Alexandria)
ACEF pubns. (Great Falls)
Agribookstore/Winrock (Arlington)
Almanac of Seapower, The (Arlington)
Alpic Library Co. (Virginia Beach)
American Alliance for Health, Physical Education, Recreation & Dance (Reston)
American Chiropractic Assn. (Arlington)
Andrik Associates (Alexandria)
Arlington Bk. Co. (Arlington)
Byrrd Enterprises, Inc. (Alexandria)
Capitol News Agency (Richmond)
Career Management Concepts, Inc. (Chesapeake)
Center for Assn. Pubns. (Falls Church)
Choice Books (Harrisonburg)
Computer Generated Data (Virgina Beach)
Danville News Agency (Danville)
Dominion News Co. (Newport News)
ECA Assocs. (Chesapeake)
First Impressions Printing, Marketing & Design Services (Chester)
Gam Printers & Grace Christian Bookstore (Sterling)
Growth Publishing (Herndon)
Hill City News Agency Inc. (Lynchburg)
Macoy Publishing & Masonic Supply Co., Inc. (Richmond)
National Art Education Assn. (Reston)
National Technical Information Service, U. S. Dept. of Commerce (Springfield)
Paperback Books Inc. (Norfolk)
Peninsula Computer Group (Poquoson)
Performance Software (Midlothian)
Pocahontas Pr., Inc. (Blacksburg)
Roanoke News Agency (Roanoke)
Ross Bk. Service (Alexandria)
Skipworth Press, Inc. (Mechanicsville)
Success Education Assn. (Roanoke)
Sun Life (Thaxton)
TBN Enterprises (Alexandria)
Time-Life Bks. (Alexandria)
Univ. Pr. of Virginia (Charlottesville)
Virginia Periodical Distributors (Norfolk)
Virginia Polytechnic Inst. & State Univ. Manufacturing Processes Laboratory (Blacksburg)

WASHINGTON

Adams News (Seattle)
Apple Puget Sound Program Library Exchange Co-op (Renton)
Baggins Books (Bellingham)
Big Country Bks., Inc. (Blaine)
Book Service Unlimited (Lynnwood)
CDI Information Systems, Inc. (Bellevue)
CP Pubns. (Port Angeles)
Cascade News Co. (Longview)
Creative Communications (Edmonds)
Elf Software Distributors (Longview)
Film Coat (Auburn)
Hale, Robert, & Co. (Bellevue)
Healthcare Pr. (Rollingbay)
Holistic Health (Seattle)
Homestead Book, Inc. (Seattle)
Huyler, Jean Wiley, Communications (Tacoma)
InterSoft, Inc. (Bellevue)
King of the Road Maps (Seattle)
Kroger, Frank (Seattle)
Lesnick News (Tumwater)
Loompanics Unlimited (Port Townsend)
MacRae's Indian Book Dist. (Enumclaw)
Madrona Pubs., Inc. (Seattle)
Mercury Distributors (Seattle)
Micro-80, Inc. (Oak Harbor)
Newell, M., Co. Builders, Pub. (Bothell)
Pacific Computer (Bellevue)
Pacific Magazine-Book Wholesaler (Tacoma)
Pacific Pipeline, Inc. (Kent)
Pacific Search Pr. (Seattle)
Peanut Butter Publishing (Seattle)
Peninsula Publishing, Inc. (Port Angeles)
Rainier News Inc. (Everett)
Senic Computer Systems (Redmond)
Servatius News Agency (Clarkston)
South Sky Book Co. (Seattle)
Special Child Pubns. (Seattle)
Spokane Periodicals Distributor Inc. (Spokane)
Starmont Hse. (Mercer Island)
Time Bomb Productions (Seattle)
Trans-Educom (Bellevue)
University Bookstore (Seattle)
Univ. of Washington Pr. (Seattle)
Washington State Trial Lawyers Assn. (Seattle)
Wenatchee News Agency (Wenatchee)
Wilson & Sons (Bellevue)
Yakima News Agency Inc. (Yakima)

WEST VIRGINIA

Bluefield News Agency Inc. (Bluefield)
Huntington News Agency (Scott Depot)
James & Law Co., The (Clarksburg)
Justice, John (Hedgesville)
Latta, J.S., Inc. (Huntington)
Robinson, Ruth E., Bks. (Morgantown)
Valley News Service (Parkersburg)
West Virginia Periodical Distributor (Scott Depot)

WISCONSIN

ARA Services (New Berlin)
American Media Corp. (Milwaukee)
Appleton News Agency (Appleton)
Arbit Bks., Inc. (Milwaukee)
Arrowhead News Co. (Antigo)
Badger Periodicals Distributors (Appleton)
Capital City (Madison)
Catholic Book & Supply Co. (South Milwaukee)
Clergy Book Service (Butler)
Coleman School Supply Inc. (Green Bay)
Conkey's Bookstore (Appleton)
DEMCO Period Bound Books, Inc.. (Madison)
Eau Claire News Co., Inc. (Eau Claire)
Enrichment Reading Corp. of America (Iron Ridge)
Farmer's Digest Inc. (Brookfield)
Free Beaches Documentation Center (Oshkosh)
Gould Athletic Supply (Milwaukee)
Harsand Distributing (Holmen)
Hazel Rice (Madison)
Image Processing Systems (Madison)
Interstate Periodical Distributors (Madison)
Kalmbach Publishing Co. (Milwaukee)
L M S Distribution Center (LaCrosse)
La Crosse News Agency (La Crosse)
Leonard, Hal, Publishing Corp. (Milwaukee)
Lotus Light Pubns. (Wilmot)
McCuen, Gary E., Pubns., Inc. (Hudson)
Manitowoc News Agency (Manitowoc)
Mayday Software (Phillips)
Midwest Publishing & Distributing Service (Portage)
Motorbooks International, Pubs. & Wholesalers, Inc. (Osceola)
Narada Distributors (Milwaukee)
Naturists (Oshkosh)
North Central Book Distributor (Butler)
Omnibook (Menomonee Falls)
Oshkosh News Co. (Oshkosh)
Perry's News Agency (Wisconsin Rapids)
Potter Library Services (Milwaukee)
Rhinelander News Agency (Crescent Lake)
Sheboygan News Agency (Sheboygan)
Southern Wisconsin News (Milton)
Third Pyramid, Inc. (Watertown)
VOELZ Educational Services (Janesville)
Wausau News Agency (Wausau)
Willow Creek Pr. (Oshkosh)
Wisconsin Authors & Pubs. Alliance, The (Janesville)
Wisconsin Folklife Ctr. (Dodgeville)
Wisconsin Periodical Distributors (New Berlin)
Worzalla Publishing Co. (Stevens Point)

WYOMING

Books A Go Go (Laramie)
Casper Magazine Agency (Casper)
Goodwin, Ruby L. (Douglas)
Medicine Bow Post (Medicine Bow)
Wyoming Book Co., Inc. (Cheyenne)
Wyoming News Co. (Worland)
Wyoming Periodical Distributor (Casper)

Geographic Index

NEW PUBLISHERS

The *New Publishers Index* is arranged alphabetically by the abbreviation used in the bibliographic entries in *Books in Print*. This index lists publishers added to the R.R. BOWKER Co.'s Publisher Authority Database since the last edition of *Books in Print*. Following the abbreviation, the full company name is given. Some of these new publishers have not yet provided title information to the R.R. Bowker Co. These companies' books are not listed in the Title or Author Indexes to *Books in Print*.

AFTAC Ent
A F T A C Enterprises (0-938029)
Aftermath
Aftermath (0-936579)
Agapao
Agapao Unlimited, Incorporated (0-937305)
Agee Pub
Agee Publishers, Incorporated (0-935265)
Agnes Press
Agnes Press, The (0-936033)
Agribookstore
Agribookstore/Winrock
Agronomy Pubns
Agronomy Publications (0-9616847)
AIA San Antonio
American Institute of Architects, San Antonio Chapter (0-9616842)
Airth Pubns
Airth Publications (0-9616720)
AJFP
American Journal of Forensic Psychiatry (0-935645)
AL Cattlemen
Alabama Cattlemen's Association (0-9616023)
Alan I Press
Alan I Press (0-938827)
Alcom Inc
Alcom, Incorporated (0-936129)
Alcott Pr WA
Alcott Press, The (0-9616180)
Alcove Pub Co OR
Alcove Publishing Company (0-937473)
Alef Bet Comns
Alef Bet Communications (0-9616488)
Alembic Mktg
Alembic Marketing Partners (0-9616368)
Alert Pubs
Alert Publishers (0-938033)
Alexander & Alexander
Alexander & Alexander Publishers (0-939353)
Alexander Pub
Alexander Publishing (0-939067)
Alexandria Assn
Alexandria Association, The (0-9616541)
Alfred Bay
Bay, Alfred (0-9615634)
Alfred Pub
Alfred Publishing Company, Incorporated (0-88284)
Alger Cnty Hist Soc
Alger County Historical Society (0-9617008)
Alimar Pub
Alimar Publishing Company (0-9616034)
Alistair Pr
Alistair Press (0-9616489)
Alive Films
Alive Films, Incorporated (0-937113)
Alivening Pubns
Alivening Publications (0-9616707)
Allan-Michaels
Allan-Michaels Corporation, The (1-55621)
Allbooks
Allbooks (0-9616527)
Allegheny Pubns
Allegheny Publications (0-938037)
Allenby Pr
Allenby Press (0-9615419)
Allergan Humphrey
Allergan Humphrey, Incorporated (0-939425)
Allgau Bks
Allgau Books (0-936887)
Alliance Plus
Alliance Plus (0-9617034)
Alliance Schl Health
Alliance for School Health (0-9616270)
Allin Ent
Allin Enterprises (0-936181)
Almaas Pubns
Almaas Publications (0-936713)
Almin
Almin Press (0-9615631)
Alms Hse Pr
Alms House Press (0-939689)
Alpenglow Pr
Alpenglow Press (0-935997)
Alpha Beto Music
Alpha-Beto Music (0-9616528)
Alpha Omega Pub
Alpha Omega Publisher (0-937059)
Alpha Pub MN
Alpha Publishers (0-9615632)
Alpha Pubns OH
Alpha Publications (0-939427)
Alpine WY
Alpine Press (0-9615114)

Alt Currents
Alternating Currents (0-937435)
Alta House
Alta House (0-9616970)
Alta Vista Bks
Alta Vista Books (0-936761)
Altair Pub UT
Altair Publishing Company (0-938117)
Alter Abortion
Alternatives to Abortion, Inc. (0-9615457)
Alter Currents
Alternating Currents Press (0-9617221)
Alter Parent
Alternative Parenting Publications (0-935893)
Altern Eighties
Alternatives for the Eighties (0-9617089)
Altern World
Alternative World Foundation, Incorporated (0-938035)
Altro Health Rehab
Altro Health & Rehabilitation Service (0-937607)
Am Archives Pubs
American Archives Publishers (0-938039)
Am Assoc Med
American Association for Medical Transcription (0-935229)
Am Canal & Transport
American Canal & Transportation Center (0-933788)
Am Cancer Westchester
American Cancer Society, Westchester Division, Incorporated (0-9616598)
Am Cooking
American Cooking Guild, The (0-942320)
Am Dent Health
American Dental Association Health Foundation (0-934510)
Am Eagle Pub
American Eagle Publishing (0-935431)
Am Fish FL
American Fisheries Society, Florida Chapter (0-9616676)
Am Hasbourgh
American Hasbourgh Dynasty Company (0-936037)
Am Inst Arch Res
American Institute for Archaeological Research, Incorporated (0-937923)
Am Inst Taxidermy
American Institute of Taxidermy, Incorpoarted (0-9616088)
Am Intl Dev
American International Development Studies, Incorporated (0-9616279)
Am Nonsmokers Rights
American Nonsmokers' Rights Foundation (0-9616473)
Am Passage Mktg
American Passage Marketing Corporation (0-937649)
Am Pro Educ
American Professional Education, Incorporated (0-938401)
Am Studies Ctr
American Studies Center, The (0-931727)
Am Travel Pubns
American Travel Publications, Incorporated (0-936929)
Amchan Pubns
Amchan Publications (0-9617132)
AMCUMC Ministries
Alaska Missionary Conference of the United Methodist Church, Conference Council on Ministries (0-9616802)
Amadeus Oregon
Amadeus Press, Incorporated (0-931340)
Amador Pubs
Amador Publishers (0-938513)
Amana Found
Amana Preservation Foundation (0-9616200)
Amateur Radio
A R O Y, Incorporated (0-9615633)
Amazing Even
Amazing Events Unlimited (0-936237)
Amdulaine Pubns
Amdulaine Publications, Incorporated (0-9615780)
Amelia
Amelia (0-936545)
Amer Cancer Soc OR
American Cancer Society, Oregon Division (0-9617128)
Amer Christian Hist Inst
American Christian History Institute (0-9616201)

Amer Due Process
Americans For Due Process, Incorporated (0-9617222)
Amer Econ Dev Council
American Economic Development Council (0-9616567)
Amer Immigration
American Immigration Control Foundation (0-9636247)
Amer Inst Bank
American Institute of Banking (0-935183)
Amer Inst Mgnt
American Institute of Management (0-935517)
Amer Inst Small Bus
American Institute of Small Business (0-939069)
Amer Motor
American Motor Logs (0-936207)
Amer Oral Health Inst Pr
American Oral Health Institute Press (0-936837)
Amer Pictures
American Pictures Foundation
Amer Practice Build
American Practice Builders (0-939111)
Amer Scientific
American Scientic Corporation (0-9617163)
Amer Sec Bill
Americans for Second Bill of Rights (0-936527)
American Ad Pr
American Advisory Press, Incorporated (0-937387)
American Ap Tech
American Applied Technologies (0-937425)
American Demo
American Demographics (0-936889)
American Hist
American Historic Homes (0-9615481)
American Imagery
American Imagery Institute (0-9616350)
American Mueller
American V. Mueller (0-937433)
American Res
American Research Council (0-8282)
Americana Pr
Americana Press (0-9616144)
Americana Pubns
Americana Publications (0-935407)
Americas Watch
Americas Watch. *Imprint of* Fund Free Expression
Amerimark Inc
Amerimark, Incorporated (1-55537)
Amish Men Pub
Amish Mennonite Publications (0-935409)
AMJ Graffica
A M J Graffica, Incorporated (0-935575)
AMP Educ Servs
A M P Educational Services (0-937429)
AMR Educ Sys
A M R Educational Systems (1-55536)
AMS Kansas
A M S Publishing (0-936869)
AMTF
Ascended Master Teaching Foundation (0-939051)
Analytichem
Analytichem International, Incorporated (0-9616096)
Anapauo Farm
Anapauo Farm, Incorporated (0-9616899)
Anchor & Acorn
Anchor & Acorn Press (0-936931)
Anchor & Dolphin
Anchor & Dolphin Publishing Company, The (0-9615944)
Anchor Comm
Anchor Communications (0-935633)
Anderson Negotiations
Anderson Negotiations/Communications (0-938515)
Andesign
Andesign (0-9615556)
Andujar Comn Tech
Andujar Communication Technologies, Incorporated (0-938086)
Anechron Three Pr
Anechron Three Press. *Imprint of* First Intl Pub
Angelica Pr
Angelica Press, The (0-9617261)
Another Way
Another Way Publishing (0-937251)
Ansayre Pr
Ansayre Press (0-937369)

Ansley Pubns
Ansley Publications (0-939113)
Answering the Call
Answering the Call (0-9616490)
Answers Pr
Answers Press (0-937651)
Anthoensen Pr
Anthoensen Press (0-937703)
Anthony Pr NV
Anthony Press (0-9615557)
Antique Acres
Antique Acres Press (0-9615861)
Anundsen Pub
Anundsen Publishing Company
ANZ Religious Pubns
A N Z Religious Publications
Appalach Bkground
Appalachian Background, Incorporated
(0-939115)
Applause Theater Bk Pubs
Applause Theater Book Publishers
(0-936839)
Apple Pr Pub
Apple Press Publishing (0-9615833)
Apple Pub Wisc
Apple Publishing Company (0-937891)
Applied Innovations
Applied Innovations (0-938831)
Applied Pub MN
Applied Publishing (0-935679)
Applied Sys Inst
Applied Systems Institute, Incorporated
(0-935731)
Aptos Pub
Aptos Publishing Company (0-938187)
Aqua Explorers
Aqua Explorers, Incorporated (0-9616167)
Aquarelle Pr
Aquarelle Press (0-9616679)
Aquatic Adv Pubns
Aquatic Adventure Publications (0-9616150)
Aquilevie
Aquilevie (0-9616035)
AR Legis Digest
Arkansas Legislative Digest, Inc. (0-935765)
AR Symphony Orch
Arkansas Symphony Orchestra Society
Guild (0-9615625)
Arana Press
Arana Press, Incorporated (0-9617108)
Arbogast Pub
Arbogast Publishing Company (1-55598)
Arbolyn Pubns
Arbolyn Publications (0-937909)
Arc Pr AR
Arc Press (0-938041)
Arcadia Pubns
Arcadia Publications (0-938829)
Arcas Pr
Arcas Press (0-9615753)
Arch Lic Seminar
Architectural License Seminars,
Incorporated (0-937705)
Archibald Pub
Archibald Publishing (0-937819)
Archon Inst Leader Dev
Archon Institute for Leadership
Development, Incorporated, The
(0-9616203)
Ardsley Pr
Ardsley Press (0-937253)
AREPO
Astrosophical Research & Esoteric
Publishing Oddities Corporation (0-938359)
ARI Pub Co
A R I Publishing Company (0-9616419)
Arkbridge Assn
Arkbridge Association (0-9616312)
ARL Pub
A R L Publishing (0-936419)
Armagh Press
Armagh Press, The (0-9617109)
Armen Review
Armenian Review, Incorporated (0-935353)
Armenian Her
Armenian Heritage Press (0-935411)
Armstrong Chapel
Armstrong Chapel (0-9616073)
Arnold Assocs
Arnold, William, Associates, Incorporated
(0-9615458)
Arriflex
Arriflex Corporation (0-936763)
Arrigo CA
Arrigo, Hargreaves, Nishimura
Arrowood Pr
Arrowood Press (0-88486)

Art Alliance
Art Alliance Press (0-87982)
Art Bks Intl
Art Books International, Limited (0-88168;
0-933516)
ART Prod
A R T Productions (0-938671)
Art/Tech
Art/Tech, Incorporated (0-939181)
Artech Assocs
Artech Associates (0-936539)
Artra Pub
Artra Publishing, Incorporated (0-936725)
Artronix
Artronix Data Corporation (0-935479)
Arts & Learning
Arts & Learning Services Foundation
(0-938541)
Arts Factory
Arts Factory, The (0-9615873)
Aruba Pub
Aruba Publishing Company (0-936251)
Arvada Hist
Arvada Historical Society (0-9615540)
Arwyn Map
Arwyn Map Company (0-936039)
As-Siddiquyah
As-Siddiquyah Publishers (0-935631)
Ascend Motivational
Ascend Motivational Publishers (0-936891)
Ascot Pub
Ascot Publishing Company (0-936621)
Asia Fellows
Asia Fellows (0-9617287)
Asia Watch
Asia Watch. *Imprint of* Fund Free
Expression
ASME Gear Res
ASME Gear Research Institute (0-9617215)
Aspect Found
Aspect Foundation (0-939073)
Assessment Res
Assessment Research (0-937987)
Assistance League
Assistance League of Corvallis (0-9616597)
Assn Schl Librnship
International Association of School
Librarianship (0-9617248)
Assoc Integ
Association for Integrative Studies, The
(0-9615764)
Assoc Media Cos
Associated Media Companies Limited
(0-938731)
Assoc Parents
Associated Parents Group of Hillsborough,
Incorporated (0-9616566)
Astonisher Pr
Astonisher Press (0-937255)
Astrologize Am
Astrologize America (0-939585)
Astropoint Res
Astropoint Research Associates (0-9615454)
AT&T Comns
American Telephone &
Telegraph-Communications (0-938963)
ATG Co Parma
A T G Company (0-9616072)
Atkins Video
Atkins Video Society (0-9616437)
Atlanta Pro
Atlanta Professional Women's Directory,
Inc. (0-935197)
Atlantic Coast
Atlantic Coastal Equity Corporation
(0-935635)
Atlantic Lakeland
Atlantic Publishing (0-938677)
Atlas Powder
Atlas Powder Company (0-9616284)
Atonement Ent
Atonement Enterprises (0-9616739)
Atre Soft
Atre Software, Incorporated (0-937989)
Attic Discoveries
Attic Discoveries (0-936253)
Attic Salt
Attic Salt Press, The (0-9615512)
Auburn Pr
Auburn Press, Incorporated (0-938205)
Audio Pr
Audio Press, The (0-939643)
Audubon MD
Audubon Naturalist Society of the Central
Atlantic States, Incorporated (0-939587)
Audubon Pk Pr
Audubon Park Press (0-9616452)

Aug Col Pr
Augustana College Press, The (0-9615558)
Augusta Jr Womans
Augusta Junior Woman's Club, Incorporated
(0-9615980)
Augustine Fellow
Augustine Fellowship, Sex & Love Addicts
Anonymous, Fellowship-wide Services, Inc.,
The (0-9615701)
Aunt Louise Pub
Aunt Louise Publishing Company
(0-9616652)
Aura Pub Co
Aura Publishing Company (0-9615513)
Austin Univ Forestry
Austin, Stephen F., State University, School
of Forestry (0-938361)
Authors Note
Author's Note (0-938927)
Authors Unltd
Authors Unlimited (1-55666)
Auto Pub
Auto Publishing (0-938517)
AV Enter Pr
A V Enterprises Press (0-9615715)
Avantage Pub
Avantage Publishing (0-938733)
Avanyu Pub
Avanyu Publishing, Incorporated (0-936755)
Avenue B
Avenue B (0-939691)
Avery Pr Inc
Avery Press, Incorporated (0-937321)
Avva
Avva, Incorporated (0-938013)
Awakening Heart Pubns
Awakening Heart Publications (0-9616529)
Axcess Soft
Axcess Software, Incoporated (0-938929)
Axelrod Pub
Axelrod Publishing of Tampa Bay
(0-936417)
Ayt Ventures Pubs
Ayt Ventures Publishers (0-937895)
AZ Antique Direct
Arizona Antique Directory, The
(0-9615549)
AZ Archaeol
Arizona Archaeological Society (0-939071)
AZ Univ ARP
Arizona State University Anthropological
Research Papers (0-936249)
AZSU Theatre
Arizona State University, Department of
Theatre (0-938675)
B A H Publishing
B A H Publishing Co. (0-9617236)
B A Trice
Trice, Bernie A. (0-9616006)
B & C Pub
B & C Publishing (0-937239)
B & E Pub Co
Butterfly & The Eagle Publishing Company,
The (0-9615560)
B & K Fisher
Fisher, Bill & Kay (0-9603004)
B B Choate
Choate, Betty Burton (0-9616352)
B-B Leather
B-B Leather (0-9616569)
B C Decker
Decker, B. C., Incorporated (0-941158;
1-55664)
B Cogill
Cogill, Burgess (0-9617227)
B Collins
Collins, B. (0-9615515)
B Corona
Corona, Belva (0-9616840)
B Drewry
Drewry, Betty (0-9615928)
B Fuller Pub
Fuller, Ben, Publishing Company (0-938807)
B G Heyman
Heyman, Barbara G. (0-9616831)
B Gill
Gill, Bernard
B Hubbard
Hubbard, Bill (0-9616674)
B J Gill
Gill, Bernard Jamil (0-9616510)
B J Raheb
Raheb, Barbara J. (0-938759)
B Johnson Pub
Johnson, Blake, Publisher (0-9615685)
B Martin Pubs
Martin, Ben, Publishers (0-936449)

B Minkow
Minkow, Barry (0-9615900)
B Montgomery
Montgomery, Barbara (0-9615738)
B Rabin
Rabin, Barry (0-9603968)
B S Prods
B. S. Productions (0-939565)
B Segal
Segal, Berty, Incorporated (0-938395)
B Sheldon
Sheldon, Bill, Publisher (0-9616668)
B Twitchell
Twitchell, Bob (0-9616798)
B Wilson KY
Wilson, Billy (0-9617160)
B Wood Assocs
Wood, Bob, Associates (0-937863)
B Woodley Pr
Woodley, Bob, Memorial Press, The (0-939391)
Bacadaa
Bacadaa, Limited (0-9616763)
Backspace Ink
Backspace Ink (0-9616675)
Backwoods Bks
Backwoods Books (0-938833)
Baen Bks
Baen Books (1-55594)
Baffico Breger
Baffico/Breger Video, Incorporated (0-939243)
Baikar Assn
Baikar Association, Incorporated (0-936893)
Bakar Press
Bakar Press (0-939295)
Baker-Berwick
Baker-Berwick Publications, Incorporated (0-938403)
Baker Bk
Baker Book House (0-8010)
Baker Voorhis
Baker, Voorhis & Company, Incorporated (0-8320)
Balaban Pub
Balaban Publishing Company (0-9617121)
Balch I E S
Balch Institute (0-937437)
Balcones Co
Balcones Company (0-9615782)
Baldwin Manor Pr
Baldwin Manor Press (0-9617094)
Ballantrae Tech
Ballantrae Technical Books (0-936333)
Ballyhoo Bks
Ballyhoo Books (0-936335)
Bambook Pubns
Bambook Publications (0-939567)
BAN Pub Boston
B A N Publishing Company (0-938357)
Bandar Log
Bandar Log, Incorporated (0-9617036)
Banjar Pubns
Banjar Publications (0-9617181)
Bank St Pr
Bank Street Press, The (0-935505)
Banner Bks
Banner Books, Incorporated (0-9615938)
Banner Books CA
Banner Books (0-939693)
Bar Co
Bar Company (0-9615482)
Bararossa Pr
Barbarossa Press (0-9617086)
Barbara Schwartz
Schwartz, Barbara (0-936627)
Barbary Coast Bks
Barbary Coast Books (0-936041)
Barbed Wire Pr
Barbed Wire Press (0-935269)
Barber Co
Barber Company (0-937125)
Barking Dog
Barking Dog Press (0-937131)
Barlina Bks
Barlina Books, Incorporated (0-937525)
Baron Pub Co
Baron Publishing Company, Incorporated (0-935843)
Barrie Rd Bks
Barrie Road Books (0-937293)
Barrington Hse
Barrington House Publishing Company (0-935323)
Barrington MA
Barrington Press (0-9616920)

Bartleby
Bartleby, The, a Cape Elizabeth Journal (0-937981)
Barton Pub
Barton Publishing Company (0-9616702)
Base Eight
Base Eight Publishing (0-938207)
Basin Plateau Pr
Basin/Plateau Press (0-9617133)
Baxter Group
Baxter Group, The (0-938949)
Bay Area CA
Bay Area Explorers (0-9615635)
Bay Area Pilipino
Bay Area Pilipino Writers (0-9616181)
Bay Inst SF
Bay Institute of San Francisco (0-937995)
Bay Vil Womens
Bay Village Women's Club & Foundation (0-9616678)
Bayberry NY
Bayberry Press (0-936403)
Baylin Gale
Baylin/Gale Productions (0-917893)
Bayway Bks
Bayway Books (0-938363)
BE Pubs
B E Publishers (0-9617074)
Beagle Bks NY
Beagle Books, Incorporated (0-8441)
Bean Pub Co
Bean Publishing Company (0-935905)
Beanstalk Prod
Beanstalk Productions, Incorporated (0-937629)
Bear Crk Pubns
Bear Creek Publications (0-936005)
Bear Hollow Pr
Bear Hollow Press (0-938209)
Beardsley Pr
Beardsley Press, The (0-9616445)
Beatitude SF
Beatitude (0-9617010)
Beau Bayou
Beau Bayou Publishing Company (0-935619)
Beaumont Bks
Beaumont Books (0-9616108)
Beaver Tails
Beaver Tails & Dorsal Fins (0-9615949)
Becoming Pr
Becoming Press (0-9616204)
Bed & Breakfast
Bed & Breakfast Registry (0-9616205)
Bedford Bks
Bedford Books (0-935199)
Bedford Hills Pub
Bedford Hills Publishing Company, Incorporated (0-936153)
Bedford Pr
Bedford Press Publishers (0-938491)
Bee Tree
Bee Tree Productions (0-937083)
Beginning Pr
Beginning Press (0-9615514)
Behav Sci Ctr Pubs
Behavioral Science Center, Incorporated, Publishers (0-938837)
Behavior Sci Systs
Behavior Science Systems, Incorporated (0-936787)
Behavioral Sci
Behavioral Science Research Press, Incorporated (0-935907)
Behavioronics
Behavioronics (0-938679)
Bel-Del Ent
Bel-Del Enterprises, Limited, The (0-9616893)
Belle Grove
Belle Grove, Incorporated (0-9616530)
Belle Trac
Belle Trac Corporation (0-9615835)
Bench Pr NY
Bench Press (0-9616160)
Benchmark Ltd
Benchmark Publications, Limited (0-9615467)
Benchmark Pr
Benchmark Press, Incorporated (0-936157)
Benjamin Pr
Benjamin Press (0-936317)
Bennett-Edwards
Bennett-Edwards (0-9617271)
Benton Cutter Pr
Benton-Cutter Press, The (0-9615702)
Bentwood Pr
Bentwood Press (0-938839)

Berea College Pr
Berea College Press (0-938211)
Berg Am
Berg America Company, Limited (0-9616074)
Bergano Bk Co
Bergano Book Company (0-917408)
Bergee Corp
Bergee Corporation, A (0-935413)
Berger Pub
Berger Publishing Company, The (0-9616397)
Bergquist Pub
Bergquist Publishing (0-9615483)
Bergwall Ed Soft
Bergwall Educational Software, Incorporated (0-8064; 0-943008)
Berkshire Hse
Berkshire House Publishers (0-936399)
Berkshire Soft
Berkshire Software Company (0-938213)
Berle Bks
Berle Books (0-9617296)
Berry Good Child Bks
Berry Good Children's Books (0-9616555)
Best Bks CA
Best Books Publishing (0-936255)
Best Cookbks
Best Cookbooks, Incorporated (0-935687)
Best Friends
Best of Friends (0-9615950)
Bestsell Pubns
Bestsell Publications (0-9616807)
Beverly Found
Beverly Foundation, The (0-938485)
Bey-Len Cat Bks
Bey-Len Cat Books (0-9615398)
Bhaktive Inst
Bhaktivedanta Institute of Religion & Culture, The (0-936405)
Biblia Candida
Biblia Candida (0-9617134)
Bibliotec Systems & Pub
Bibliotechnology Systems & Publishing Company (0-936857)
Big Hse Pub
Big House Publishing Company (0-937529)
Big Nickel
Big Nickel Publications (0-936433)
Big Red Cartoon
Big Red Cartoon Company (0-9616098)
Big Santa Hist
Big Santa Anita Historical Society (0-9615421)
Big Valley Pub
Big Valley Publishing Company (0-9616795)
Bigelow Soc
Bigelow Society, Incorporated, The (0-9616682)
Biggs Pubs
Biggs Publishers (0-9616590)
Bijon
Bijon (0-938391)
BILR Corp
B I L R Corporation, The (0-937177)
Bio Graphics
Bio-Graphics Publishing (0-935649)
Bio Marine
Bio-Marine Images (0-9617106)
Biocomm
Biocomm (0-938841)
Biograph Bks
Biograph Books (0-938311)
Bird Prof Pubns
Bird Professional Publications (0-9616174)
Bird Shoal Bks
Bird Shoal Books (0-9617135)
Birth & Parenting
Birth & Parenting Publications (0-9615484)
Bixter Bks
Bixter Books (0-936933)
BIZ Pub
B. I. Z. Publishing (0-9615544)
Bk Paper Group
Book & Paper Group, The (0-937685)
Bks By Brooks
Books by Brooks (0-9616207)
Bks of Truth
Books of Truth (0-939399)
Bkworld Pub
Bookworld Publishing Company, Incorporated (1-55633)
Black Current
Black Current Press, The (0-938975)
Black Flag Pr
Black Flag Press (0-937259)
Black Graphics
Black Graphics (0-939569)

Black Pursuit
Black Pursuit, Incorporated (0-935979)
Blackpot Enterprises
Blackpot Enterprises (0-937823)
Blackstone Pub
Blackstone Publishing Company (0-9615836)
Blackwells Pr
Blackwells Press (0-930513)
Blarney Co
Blarney Company, The (0-9616083)
Blip Prods
Blip Productions (0-936917)
Blk Fam Inst Pub
Black Family Institute Publishers (0-939205)
Blk Pumpkin Pr
Black Pumpkin Press (0-9616206)
BLOC Devel
B L O C Development Corporation
(0-938843)
Blondo-Campbell
Blondo/Campbell (0-9616654)
Blue Boar Pr
Blue Boar Press, The (0-9617182)
Blue Heron WA
Blue Heron Press (0-935317)
Blue J
Blue J, Incorporated (0-936531)
Blue Poppy
Blue Poppy Enterprises Press (0-936185)
Blue Rooster Pr
Blue Rooster Press (0-9617075)
Blue Scarab
Blue Scarab Press (0-937179)
Blue Tulip Pr
Blue Tulip Press (0-9616163)
Blumarts Inc
Blumarts, Incorporated (0-935875)
Bnos Zion
Bnos Zion of Bobov, Incorporated
(0-937143)
Bobbeh Meisehs
Bobbeh Meisehs Press (0-9616933)
Boca Raton Museum
Boca Raton Museum of Art (0-936859)
Body Blueprints
Body Blueprints (0-9617110)
Bodymind Bks
Bodymind Books (0-938405)
Boggaston
Boggaston Book Company, The (0-937085)
Bold Age Pr
Bold Age Press (0-936841)
Bold Prodns
Bold Productions (0-938267)
Bollenbaugh Hill
Bollenbaugh Hill Books (0-937653)
Bolton Pr
Bolton Press (0-9616326)
Bomb Shelter Prop
Bomb Shelter Propaganda (0-938309)
Bond Res
Bond Research (0-939511)
Boofish Bks
Boofish Books (0-9616709)
Bookaset Edns
Bookaset Editions (0-936043)
Bookmaker WA
Bookmaker, The (0-939075)
Bookman Waianae
Bookman Publishing Company (0-942070)
Bookmarks-USA
Bookmarks/USA (0-935867)
Bookscraft
Bookscraft, Incorporated (0-937137)
Bored Feet Pubns
Bored Feet Publications (0-939431)
Boring Soft
Boring Software Company (0-936793)
BOS Pubns
B O S Publications (0-9616119)
Boston Bk & Art
Boston Book & Art Publishers (0-8435)
Boston Bks
Boston Books (0-9616683)
Boston Map
Boston Map Company, The (0-938543)
Bottom Line Soft
Bottom Line Software (0-937973)
Bowden Pub
Bowden Publishing (0-9616177)
Boxes & Arrows
Boxes & Arrows (0-939479)
Boyd Co
Boyd Company, The (0-9616796)
Boyertown Hist
Boyertown Area Historical Society
(0-9616068)

Boyne Bks
Boyne Books (0-9615889)
Brad Pub Co
Bradford Publishing Co. (0-935355)
Bradford Pr MA
Bradford Press (0-9615783)
Bradford Pubs
Bradford Publishers (0-936935)
Bradford Soft
Bradford Software (0-935507)
Bradley Bks
Bradley Books (0-936765)
Bradley Comm
Bradley Communications (0-936045)
Bradley Pubns
Bradley Publications (0-89748)
Brady St Pr
Brady Street Press (0-9616168)
Braemar Pr
Braemar Press (0-9616791)
Braidwood Pub
Braidwood Publishing Company (0-9616790)
Branch Redd
Branch Redd (0-9615784)
Brandt Bks
Brandt Books (0-9616327)
Breck School
Breck School (0-9617136)
Breed Manual Pubns
Breed Manual Publications (0-938681)
Breland & Farmer
Breland & Farmer, Designers, Incorporated
(0-938007)
Bremer Bks
Bremer Books (0-9615766)
Brendon Hill Pub
Brendon Hill Publishing Company
(0-937751)
Bret Scot Pr
Scot, Bret, Press (0-936443)
Brevis Corp
Brevis Corporation (0-9617125)
Brewers Pubns
Brewers Publications (0-937381)
Bright Morning
Bright Morning Publications (0-937101)
Bright Ring
Bright Ring Publishing (0-935607)
Bristen Pr
Bristen Press (0-936337)
Brob Hse Bks
Brob House Books (0-938407)
Bronx Bks
Bronx Books (0-9616765)
Brookman Stamp
Brookman Stamp Company (0-936937)
Brost Heus
Brost-Heus (0-9616109)
Brouhaha Pub
Brouhaha Publishing Company (0-9616036)
Brown Cnty Hist Soc
Brown County Historical Society,
Incorporated (0-9616808)
Brown House
Brown House Communications (0-936895)
Brown Unlimited
Brown Unlimited (0-9615755)
Brynmorgen
Brynmorgen Press, Incorporated
(0-9615984)
Brynwood Pub
Brynwood Publishing Company (0-937615)
Bubbling-Well
Bubbling-Well Press (0-938045)
Buck Mntn Pr
Buck Mountain Press (0-9616710)
Buckeye Pr
Buckeye Press (0-9615559)
Buckle Pr
Buckle Press (0-9616809)
Bucknell U Pr
Bucknell University Press (0-8387)
Bulldog Club Amer
Bulldog Club of America, Division III
(0-9616531)
Bunneys Guides
Bunney's Guides (0-9616711)
Burlage Corp
Burlage Corporation (0-9616208)
Buros Inst Mental
Buros Institute of Mental Measurements
(0-910674)
Burtt Co
Burtt & Company (0-937087)
Business Plan
Business Plan Publishing (0-936257)
Busn Legal Reports
Business & Legal Reports (1-55645)

Busn Media Res
Business Media Resources (0-938545)
Busn Pub TX
Business Publishing Company
Busy Bees
Busy Bees (0-9617073)
Butterfield
Butterfield Press (0-935767)
Butterfly Bks
Butterfly Books (0-939077)
Butternut & Blue
Butternut & Blue (0-935523)
BW Enterprises
B W Enterprises Publishing Company
(0-9616280)
BYU CSCVL
Center for the Study of Christian Values in
Literature (0-939555)
BYU Family Commun Hist
Brigham Young University, Family &
Community History Center (0-938605)
Byzantium Pr
Byzantium Press (0-937439)
C A Wilson
Wilson, Charles A. (0-9616261)
C & S Michaud
Michaud, Carole & Susan (0-9617264)
C B Enterprises
C B Enterprises (0-9616997)
C B Pratt
Pratt, Collin B. (0-9617049)
C Bergbower
Bergbower, Cornelius (0-9616653)
C Bernard Gallery Ltd
Bernard, Claude, Gallery, Limited
(0-936827)
C Boast & C Nyberg
Boast, Carol, & Cheryl Rae Nyberg
(0-9616293)
C Carr
Carr, Claudia
C Drumm Bks
Drumm, Chris, Books (0-936055)
C E NY NJ
Coalition for Equity of New York & New
Jersey (0-9617090)
C Gersna
Gersna, Charles (0-9615747)
C Kinsinger
Kinsinger, Chris (0-9615612)
C L Bishop
Bishop, Charles Lawrence (0-9616120)
C L Simmons
Simmons, Carol Lynn (0-9615885)
C L Vidano Pub
Vidano, Carl L., Publishing Company
(0-9616606)
C Latin Schls
Charlotte Latin Schools, Incorporated
(0-9615616)
C Logan
Logan, Carolyn (0-9602804)
C M Ltd
Cox-Miller Limited (0-9617244)
C P Pubns TN
C & P Publications (0-9617092)
C R LaDow
LaDow, Charles R. (0-9617232)
C R Winkler Ltd
Winkler, Charles R., Limited (0-9615613)
C T Collopy
Collopy, C. T. (0-9617234)
C T Olivo
Olivo, C. Thomas, Associates (0-938561)
C Tuszynski
Tuszynski, Carole (0-9617170)
C Two F Inc
C Two F, Incorporated (0-9616328)
CA Clock
California Clock Company (0-939513)
CA Dreamers
California Dreamers, Incorporated
(0-939471)
CA Ed Plan
California Education Plan (0-936047)
CA Farmer Pub
California Farmer Publishing Company
(0-936815)
CA Guitar Archv
California Guitar Archives (0-939297)
CA Inst Arts
California Institute of the Arts
CA Med Pubns
California Medical Publications (0-9615638)

CA Supreme Ct
California Supreme Court (0-936629)
Cabashon Pub
Cabashon Publishing (0-937825)
Cabell Cty Med Soc
Cabell County Medical Society (0-9616839)
CAD Ventures Unltd
Computer Aided Design Ventures Unlimited
(0-937687)
Cain Lockhart
Cain-Lockhart Press (0-937133)
Caissa Edit
Caissa Editions (0-939433)
Calem Pub Co
Calem Publishing Company (0-9616444)
Caliban
Caliban Press (0-936897)
Calico Barn
Calico Barn (0-9616848)
Califia Prod
Califia Productions (0-938521)
Call Pub Co
Call Publishing Company (0-939589)
Callahan CA
Callahan, John D. (0-9615767)
Calli Callul
Calli Callul (0-9617223)
Calliopes Corner
Calliopes Corner, Three A.M. Press
(0-938219)
Callwyn
Callwyn Books U. S. A. (0-9615639)
Camas Pr
Camas Press, The (0-9616066)
Cambia WA
Cambia (0-938221)
Cambria Records
Cambria Records & Publishing (0-936939)
Cambrian Pr
Cambrian Press (0-936669)
Cambridge Arch Pr
Cambridge Architectural Press (0-937999)
Cambridge Strat
Cambridge Stratford, Limited (0-935637)
Camden Harbor Pr
Camden Harbor Press (0-935853)
Camelot Consult
Camelot Consultants (0-938481)
Cancer Res
Cancer Research, Incorporated (0-938547)
Candy Apple Pub
Candy Apple Publishing Company
(0-9616464)
Cane Patch
Cane Patch, The (0-9615765)
Cannon-S & K
Cannon/S & K, Incorporated (0-9616991)
Canon Pr
Canon Press (0-939651)
Canon Pubs
Canon Publishers, Limited (0-9616591)
Cantor Art Gallery
College of the Holy Cross, Cantor Art
Gallery (0-9616183)
Canyon Pr
Canyon Press (0-936899)
Canyonlands
Canyonlands Natural History Association
(0-937407)
Cap K Pubns
Cap K Publications (0-9616532)
Capaco
Capaco (0-9615837)
Cape Ann Antiques
Cape Ann Antiques (0-9616832)
Cape Cod Hist Pubns
Cape Cod Historical Publications
(0-9616740)
Capital Futures Assocs
Capital Futures Associates, Limited
(0-939397)
Capital Pub Co
Capital Publishing Company (0-9615703)
Capitalist Pr OH
Capitalist Press (0-938770)
Capitol VA
Capitol Publications, Limited, Education
Research Group (0-937925)
Caravelle NY
Caravelle Books, Incorporated (0-501)
Carderock Pr
Carderock Press (0-938813)
Cardi-Bel
Cardi-Bel, Incorporated (0-938119)
Cardinal Prod
Cardinal Productions (0-939245)
Career Mgmt
Career Management Associates (0-937595)

Career Mgmt Consult
Career Management Consultants
(0-9616157)
Career Resources
Career Resources Company (0-9616617)
Carefree Living
Carefree Living Company (0-938411)
Caregiving Resc
Caregiving Resources (0-939273)
Carikean Pub
Carikean Publishing (0-9616741)
Carith Hse
Carith House (0-9616697)
Carleton Pr
Carleton Press (0-9615890)
Carlette Pub
Carlette Publishing (0-9615423)
Carlino Co
Carlino & Company (0-937827)
Carlyle Sports
Carlyle Sports, Incorporated (0-9616136)
Carnegie Forum Ed Eco
Carnegie Forum on Education & the
Economy (0-9616685)
Carol Dunne
Dunne, Carol (0-9616138)
Carolina Banks Pub
Carolina Banks Publishing (0-9617003)
Carolina Pr
Carolina Press (0-9616475)
Carpe Librum
Carpe Librum (0-9617242)
Carri Pub
Carri Publishing (0-935771)
Carriage House
Carriage House Press (NY; 0-939713)
Carrington Hse Ltd
Carrington House, Limited (0-936695)
Carrousels D
Carrousels & Dreams Publishing
(0-9615874)
CARS
Council of American Revolutionary Sites
(0-9616323)
CartoGraphics
CartoGraphics, Incorporated (0-937441)
Carvin Pub
Carvin Publishing, Incorporated (0-9616390)
Casa Unidad
Casa de Unidad (0-9615977)
CASE Third Wave
C A S E/Third Wave Publishing (0-937951)
Cassandra Pr
Cassandra Press (0-9615875)
Cassette Concepts
Cassette Concepts, Incorporated (0-935525)
Castleton Pub
Castleton Publishing (0-935885)
Catering
Catering to You, Incorporated (0-935271)
Catholic Bulletin Pub
Catholic Bulletin Publishing Co. (0-935587)
Catnip Pr
Catnip Press (0-9615475)
Catskill Ctr Conserv
Catskill Center for Conservation &
Development, Incorporated (0-9616712)
CAVU Pr
C A V U Press (0-9616265)
CBN Univ
C B N University (1-55574)
CC Studios
C C Studios, Incorporated (1-55592)
CCFL Bahamian
C C F L Bahamian Field Station (0-935909)
CCVI Pub
C C V I Publishing (0-935579)
CCW Pubns
C C W Publications (0-9615561)
CDC Pr
C D C Press (0-935769)
CDI Inc
C D I , Incorporated (0-939021)
CDT Pub
C D T Publishing Company (0-9616998)
Cedar Elm Pub
Cedar Elm Publishing Company
(0-9617161)
Cedar River Pub
Cedar River Publishing Company
(0-938047)
CEL Educ Resc
C E L Educational Resources (0-938815)
Celebrate One
Celebrate One (0-937893)
Cenotto Pubns
Cenotto Publications (0-938121)

Center City
Center City Financial Group (0-937341)
Centerpoint Pr
Centerpoint Press (0-937897)
Centra Pubns
Centra Publications (0-9617288)
Central Am Res
Central America Resource Center
(0-938049)
Centurion Pr AZ
Centurion Press (0-935527)
CEO Pubns
C E O Publications (0-937415)
Cerberus Assocs
Cerberus Associates, Incorporated
(0-936397)
CERF Inc
Coastal Education & Research Foundation,
Incorporated (0-938415)
Certain Ethnic
Certain Ethnic Publishing (0-9615918)
Certified Feelings
Certified Feelings, Incorporated (0-936903)
Chaco Pr
Chaco Press (0-9616019)
Chal Public
Challenge Publications, Inc. (0-935415)
Champ Pr Inglewood
Champion Press (0-936691)
Champaign Pub Lib
Champaign Public Library & Information
Center (0-9617184)
Champaign Syst
Champaign Systems, Incorporated
(0-937547)
Channels Children
Channels to Children (0-9616396)
Chanticleer CA
Chanticleer (0-9615876)
Chapman Assocs
Chapman Associates (0-937243)
Charlemarie
Charlemarie Press (0-937181)
Charleston Pr
Charleston Press (0-935773)
Charm City Assocs
Charm City Associates (0-9617229)
Chase Comns
Chase Communications, Incorporated
(0-9615565)
Chatsworth
Chatsworth Press (0-917181)
Chatterbox Voice Lrn Syst
Chatterbox Voice Learning Systems
(0-939557)
CHB Goodyear Comm
Childrens Hospital of Buffalo, Josephine
Goodyear Committee (0-9616699)
CHC Pub
Colon Health Center Publishing Company
(0-9616184)
Cheetah Pub
Cheetah Publishing Company (0-936241)
Chelonia Pr
Chelonia Press (0-938947)
Cheltenham Pr
Cheltenham Press (0-9615838)
Chenonta
Chenonta, Incorporated (0-938845)
Cherokee Pubns
Cherokee Publications (0-935741)
Chesapeake Bay Pr
Chesapeake Bay Press (0-938225)
Chess Info Res Ctr
Chess Information & Research Center
(0-9617207)
Chess Pub
Chess Publications (0-935273)
Chester Hse Pubs
Chester House Publishers (0-935763)
Cheswick Pr
Cheswick Press (0-9616686)
Chi Ofc Fine Arts
Chicago Office of Fine Arts, Department of
Cultural Affairs (0-938903)
Chicago Rep
Chicago Reporter, The (0-9615553)
Chicago Zoo
Chicago Zoological Society (0-913934)
Chiefton Pub
Chiefton Publishing, Incorporated
(0-9615945)
Child Care Admin
Child Care Administrative Services
(0-937261)
Child Council SF
Children's Council of San Francisco
(0-937711)

Child Savers
Child-Savers, Incorporated (0-936049)
Child Ventures
Children's Ventures, Incorporated (0-9615985)
Chilton Corp
Chilton Corporation (0-9616037)
Chinese Acad Prof Soc
Chinese Academic & Professional Society of Mid-America (0-9616137)
Chisum Pub
Chisum Publishing, Incorporated (0-937689)
Chiuzac Ltd
Chiuzac, Limited
Choice Pub CA
Choice Publishing Company (0-9615891)
Choral Resource
Choral Resource Seminars (0-9616618)
Chris Pub UT
Christopher Publishing (0-936863)
Christ Serv Ctrs
Christian Service Centers, Incorporated (0-936801)
Christ United Meth Ch
Christ United Methodist Church (0-9616507)
Christlife Pubs
Christlife Publishers (0-939079)
Chrstn Pub Palm Springs
Christian Publishing Company (0-939501)
Chrysopylon
Chrysopylon Publishers (0-9615640)
CHSSC Phila
Chestnut Hill Senior Services Center (0-9616330)
Church God
Church of God, Department of General Education (0-937443)
Church Man Pub
Church of Man Publishing Company (0-936435)
Cincinnati Schl
Cincinnati School of Hypnosis, The (0-936139)
Cinco Puntos
Cinco Puntos Press (0-938317)
Circa Pr Portland
Circa Press (0-936339)
CIS Inc
C I S, Incorporated (0-9615562)
CITA NY
Court Interpreters & Translators Association, Incorporated (0-939733)
Citizen Pub
Citizen Publishing (0-9615867)
City of Cleveland
City of Cleveland (0-9615479)
City of Cocoa Beach
City of Cocoa Beach, Florida (0-9616571)
Cityhill Pub
Cityhill Publishing (0-939159)
CL Pubns Inc
C L Publications, Incorporated (0-9615697)
Clar Call Bks
Clarion Call Books (0-935993)
Clarions Call Pub
Clarion's Call Publishing (0-9617176)
Clark Pub KY
Clark Publishing (0-939053)
Clarksburg-Harrison
Clarksburg-Harrison Bicentennial Committee (0-9615566)
Classic Cons
Classic Consultants Press (0-935499)
Classic Fire
Classic Fire Pictures (0-938229)
Classic Theatre Child
Classic Theatre for Children (0-938735)
Classics Comp
Classics on Computer (0-938523)
Clear Fork Pub
Clear Fork Publishing
Clear Fork Ranch
Clear Fork Ranch, Incorporated (0-9616868)
Clearwater
Clearwater Junior Woman's Club (0-9615642)
Cleydale Engineering
Cleydale Engineering (0-937303)
Click Inc
Click!, Incorporated (0-937187)
Cloak Dagger
Cloak & Dagger Publications (0-937617)
Clothespin Fever Pr
Clothespin Fever Press (0-9616572)
Cloud Pr
Cloud Marauder Press (0-935713)

Cloud Ridge Pr
Cloud Ridge Press (0-9615617)
Cloudcap
Cloudcap (0-938567)
Clvlnd Clinic Found
Cleveland Clinic Foundation (0-9615424)
Cmnty Arts
Community Arts, Incorporated (0-9617165)
Cntnt Pubs SF
Continent Publishers (0-9616169)
CO Legal Pub
Colorado Legal Publishing Company, Incorporated (0-936381)
CO Mtn Club Found
Colorado Mountain Club Foundation, The (0-9617023)
Coastline Assoc
Coastline Associate (0-9615425)
COB Assocs
C O B Associates, Incorporated (0-938409)
Cobb Group
Cobb Group, Incorporated, The (0-936767)
Cobble Mickle Bks
Cobble & Mickle Books
Cochran Pub
Cochran Publishing Company (0-936259)
Cockpit Mgmt Trng
Cockpit Management Training, Incorporated (0-938051)
Cocoa Beach W
Cocoa Beach Woman's Club (0-9615567)
Cogan Prod
Cogan Productions (0-939025)
Coit & Assocs
Coit & Associates (0-936475)
Colbben Pub
Colbben Publishing Company (0-938123)
Cold Dreams Ent
Cold Dreams Enterprises (0-937549)
Colden Method
Colden United Methodist Women (0-9615568)
Cole Hse Inc
Cole House, Incorporated (0-936297)
Colleagues Pr Inc
Colleagues Press, Incorporated (0-937191)
Colleen Ent
Colleen Enterprises, Incorporated (0-9616698)
College Choice
College Choice Publications (0-935275)
Colonial Pr AL
Colonial Press (0-938991)
Colonial Pub
Colonial Publishing, Incorporated (0-939435)
Colophone Pub
Colophone Publishing (0-937873)
Color Center
Color Center U. S. A., Inc. (0-9615447)
Colum Pr MD
Columbia Press (0-936051)
Columba Pub
Columba Publishing Company (0-938655)
Columbia Enter
Columbia Enterprise (0-937343)
Columbus Single
Columbus Single Scene (0-935913)
Columbus Youth Hostels
Columbus Council of American Youth Hostels (0-9616175)
Coman Assocs
Coman Associates
Comet Pr
Comet Press (0-939517)
Comet Pub
Comet Publishing Company, The (0-9616742)
Comico Comic Co
Comico The Comic Company (0-938965)
Comm Architects
Communication Architects (0-935597)
Comm Natl Security
Committee for National Security, The (0-937115)
Comm Networks
Communication Networks, Incorporated (0-935419)
Comm Research Assocs
Communication Research Associates, Incorporated (0-9615952)
Comm Support Solidarity
Committee in Support of Solidarity, Inc. (0-935417)
Commodity Ctr
Commodity Center Corporation (0-9615644)
Common Hap
Common-Sense Happiness (0-9615786)

Commun Design-MLM
Communications by Design/MLM (0-9615477)
Commun Service
Community Service Publications (0-9615812)
Comns Monitor Pr
Communications Monitor Press. *Imprint of* First Intl Pub
Comp Info Sci
Comprehensive Information Sciences, Incorporated (0-936477)
Comp Res
Computer Research Corporation (0-939559)
Comparable Worth
Comparable Worth Project (0-9615953)
Compass Bk Pub
Compass Book Publishers (0-937507)
Comprehen Health Educ
Comprehensive Health Education Foundation (0-935529)
CompTech
CompTech Publishers, Incorporated (0-935397)
Computech Inc
Computech, Incorporated (0-936165)
Computer Times
Computer Times (0-935743)
Computers & ME
Computers & ME, Limited (0-935349)
Comtech Pub Div
Comtech, Publishing Division (0-9616370)
Conagree Pubns
Conagree Publications (0-938599)
Concept Develop
Concept Development Associates, Inc. (0-935745)
Concept Synergy
Concept: Synergy (1-55638)
Concepts Pub MA
Concepts Publishing (0-9611712)
Concerned Comms
Concerned Communications (0-936785)
Concord Friends
Concord Friends Meeting (0-9617060)
Concordia Theo Sem
Concordia Theological Seminary (0-9615927)
Conde Cent Bk Comm
Conde Centennial Book Committee
Conn Hospice
Connecticut Hospice, Incorporated, The (0-936479)
Connell & Connell
Connell & Connell, Incorporated (0-9616573)
Conscience & Military Tax
Conscience & Military Tax Campaign-U. S. (0-9616313)
Consortium Soft
Consortium Soft (0-939519)
Constellation Pr
Constellation Press, Incorporated (0-9616620)
Construct Bkstore
Construction Bookstore, Inc. (0-935715)
Construct Trade
Construction Trade Publications (0-9616849)
Consult Serv NW
Consultant Services Northwest, Incorpor (0-9617216)
Contact Edit
Contact Editions (0-937645)
Contemp Image
Contemporary Image Advertising, Limited (0-9616743)
Contemplative Bks
Contemplative Books (0-939419)
Continental Servs
Continental Services, Limited (0-9616277)
Conway Twitty
Twitty, Conway, Enterprises (0-9616438)
Cooling Spring
Cooling Spring Press, The (0-935883)
Cooper-Hewitt Museum
Cooper-Hewitt Museum (0-910503)
Cooper Hse Pub
Cooper House Publishing Company (0-939121)
Copouts Ink
Copouts Ink (0-938417)
Copprfld NYC
Copperfield Press, The (0-9617037)
Copy Concepts
Copy & Concepts, Limited (0-937983)

Coral Gables Pub
Coral Gables Publishing Company,
Incorporated (0-938993)
Corey & Co
Corey & Company Designers (0-9615538)
Corinth Pub
Corinthian Publications (0-935915)
Cormorant Bks
Cormorant Books (0-936261)
Cornell Manu
Cornell University Libraries, Department of
Manuscripts & University Archives
(0-935995)
Cornell Ornithology
Cornell Laboratory of Ornithology
(0-938027)
Cornick
Cornick Concepts, Incorporated (0-9615516)
Cornrows & Co
Cornrows & Company (0-939183)
Cornucop Pub
Carolina Cornucopia Educational Publishing
Company (0-935911)
Corp Cmnt Col TV
Corporation for Community College
Television (0-9617111)
Corporate Support Systs
Corporate Support Systems (0-936879)
CorpTech
Corporate Technology Information Services,
Incorporated (0-936507)
Corpus Christi Area
Corpus Christi Area Garden Council,
Incorporated
Corridor Pub
Corridor Publishing Company (0-936053)
Corsi
Corsi, Petro (0-9615871)
Corwin Pubs
Corwin Publishers, Incorporated (0-938569)
Cos Sci Orange
Cosmic Science Publisher (0-9615973)
Cott Ind Phoenix
Cottage Industry, Incorporated (0-9615721)
Cottage
Cottage Craft (0-935203)
Cottonwood Bks
Cottonwood Books (0-935775)
Coun Tall Bldg
Council on Tall Buildings & Urban Habitat
(0-939493)
Council Public TV
Council for Public Television, Channel Six,
Incorporated (0-9616209)
Country Pr Mohawk
Country Press (0-9616225)
Country Pub
Country Publisher (0-935777)
Coyote Bks MN
Coyote Books (0-9616901)
Coyote Press
Coyote Press (1-55567)
Coyote Prod
Coyote Productions (0-936147)
CR Pub
C R Publishing, Incorporated (0-938467)
CRA Readers Serv
C R A Readers Service (0-9616505)
Craftree
Craftree (1-55564)
Cram Cassettes
Cram Cassettes (1-55651)
Cranberry Pr
Cranberry Press, The (0-9615645)
Creat Conc Children
Creative Concepts for Children (0-938231)
Creation Sci Fellowship
Creation Science Fellowship, Incorporated
(0-9617068)
Creative AV
Creative AV Things, Incorporated
(0-937927)
Creative Catalyst
Creative Catalyst (1-55663)
Creative Develop Pr
Creative Developmental Press (0-9615723)
Creative Foods
Creative Foods, Limited (0-9615708)
Creative Forum
Creative Forum Publishing (0-936411)
Creative Intl
Creative Ventures International (0-9615787)
Creative Part
Creative Partners (0-9615930)
Creative Walking
Creative Walking, Incorporated (0-939041)

Creative Words Pubns
Creative with Words Publications
(0-936945)
Creatv Pubns UT
Creative Publications (0-9616992)
Creighton Pub
Creighton Publishing (0-9617139)
Cremona Found
Cremona Foundation, Incorporated, The
(0-936325)
CRI NH
Computer Resources, Incorporated
(0-938193)
CRI Pubns
C R I Publications (0-935689)
CRIC Prod
CRIC Productions, Incorporated (0-935357)
Cricket Software
Cricket Software (0-936727)
Criterion Pubns
Criterion Publications (0-937969)
Critical Book
Critical Thinking Book Company (0-935475)
Crop Dust Pr
Crop Dust Press (0-9616621)
Crosscurrents
Crosscurrents
Crown Min
Crown Ministries International (0-935779)
CRPS
Center for Research on Population &
Security (0-937307)
Crystal Butterfly
Crystal Butterfly Prints & Press (0-938233)
Crystal Cove
Crystal Cove Press (0-9616787)
Crystal Intl Pub
Crystal International Publishing Company
(0-9616622)
Crystal Rainbow
Crystal Rainbow Publishing Company
(0-938125)
CST Jewish-Christian
College of St. Thomas, Center for
Jewish-Christian Learning (0-9616619)
CSU Sacto Lib
California State University, Sacramento
Library (0-938847)
CSUN Disabled
California State University at Northridge,
Office of Disabled Student Services
(0-937475)
CT Farm Bureau Assn
Connecticut Farm Bureau Association, Inc.
(0-9615485)
CT River Water
Connecticut River Watershed Council,
Incorporated (0-9616371)
Ctr Agri & Rural Dev
Center for Agricultural & Rural
Development (0-936911)
Ctr Bio-Gerontology
Center for Bio-Gerontology, The (0-937777)
Ctr Black Success
Center for Black Success, The (0-9616936)
Ctr Comp Assisted
Center for Computer Assisted Research in
the Humanities (0-936943)
Ctr Law Related
Center for Law-Related Education
(0-937709)
Ctr Mex Studies
Center for U. S.-Mexican Studies (0-935391)
Ctr Polish
Center for Polish Studies & Culture
(0-9615564)
Ctr Politics
Center for Responsive Politics (0-939715)
Ctr Sacred Healing
Center for Sacred Healing Arts Publishing
Company (0-936901)
Ctr Self Suff
Center for Self-Sufficiency Publishing
(0-910811)
Ctr Study Aging
Center for the Study of Aging, Incorporated
(0-937829)
Ctr Study Language
Center for the Study of Language &
Information (0-937073)
Curriers Fine Art
Currier's Fine Art Appraisals & Publishing
(0-935277)
Custom Graphics
Custom Graphics Press (0-9616766)
CWRU Dept Surgery
Case Western Reserve University,
Department of Surgery (0-9616613)

Cypress CA
Cypress (0-938995)
Cypress Creek Pubns
Cypress Creek Publications (0-937755)
D A Ruud
Ruud, David A., Publishing (0-939145)
D & B Corp
D & B Corporation (0-936905)
D & D Harling
Harling, Donn & Deborah (0-9617013)
D & J Pr
D & J Press (0-937757)
D & M Lena
Lena, Dan & Marie (0-9617032)
D & M Pub
D & M Publishing Company (0-9616713)
D & P Pub
D & P Publishing Company (0-938319)
D B Enterprises
D & B Enterprises (0-937349)
D B Wright
Wright, Deonne Beasley
D C Gordon
Gordon, David C. (0-9616919)
D C Martin
Martin, Dan C. (0-9616747)
D C Mauldin
Mauldin, Douglas C.
D C Rau
Rau, Diantha Christine (0-935557)
D Crank Pubns
Crank, David, Publications (0-936437)
D D Novick
Novick, Dorothy Dina (0-9617274)
D Eichner
Eichner, Debbie (0-9615887)
D Enyi
Enyi, Donatus O. (0-937171)
D F Abrell
Abrell, Diana F. (0-9616706)
D F Davio
Davio, Dorothy F. (0-9615718)
D G Prather
Prather, DeWitt G. (0-9616836)
D G S Skelton
Skelton, Dorothy Geneva Simmons
(0-9616290)
D H Shubin
Shubin, Daniel H.
D Hyk Pub Co
Hyk, Doyle, Publishing Company
(0-9615817)
D Ives
Ives, Dorthea S. (0-9616225)
D J Content
Content, Derek J., Rare Books, Inc.
(0-935681)
D K Blenderman
Blenderman, Doretta K. (0-9615637)
D Kushner Ltd
Kushner, Daniel, , Limited (0-9615694)
D L Barber Ventures
Barber, D. L., Ventures (0-938895)
D L Jensen
Jensen, Deana L. (0-9615793)
D M Wagner
Wagner, D. M., Enterprises (0-937053)
D M Whiteside
Whiteside, Dora M., Publisher (0-938353)
D March
March, David (0-9615493)
D Maurer
Maurer, Diane, Hand-Marbled Papers
(0-9616863)
D Mysiewicz
Mysiewicz, Deborah, Publishers,
Incorporated (0-936451)
D Powell
Powell, Dan
D-Q Univ Pr
D-Q University Press (0-935279)
D R Kronour
Kronour, David R., Publishing Company
(0-9616118)
D R Pub
D & R Publishing (0-937445)
Daedalus Act
Daedalus Acting Lab (0-9615815)
Dah A Dee
Dah-A-Dee, Incorporated (0-9616561)
Daheshist
Daheshist Publishing Company, The
(0-935359)
Dajan Ent
Dajan Enterprises (0-9615542)
Dakota Kids
Dakota Kids Company (0-938165)

Dakota Special
Dakota Specialties (0-935337)
Dale Bks CA
Dale Books, Incorporated (0-935917)
Dallas Jr Forum
Dallas Junior Forum (0-9617187)
Dallas Sandt
Dallas Sandt Company (0-936263)
Dallas South Memorial
Dallas Southern Memorial Association, The (0-9615569)
Damar Pub
Damar Publishing (0-938421)
DaNa Pubns
DaNa Publications (0-937103)
D&S Publishing
D & S Publishing (0-9615954)
Danly Prods
Danly Productions, Incorporated (0-9617278)
Danmark Enterprises
Danmark Enterprises, Limited (0-9616596)
Dare Co
Dare-Co. (0-936729)
Data Analysis
Data Analysis Group (0-936677)
Data Description
Data Description Incorporated (0-935321)
Data Res MN
Data Research, Incorporated (0-939675)
DataCompatable
DataCompatable (0-938793)
Datafax Corp
Datafax Corporation (0-935169)
Datalan Inc
Datalan, Incorporated (0-9617245)
Daughter Cult
Daughter Culture Publications (0-935281)
Daughters of HI
Daughters of Hawaii (0-938851)
Davar Pub
Davar Publishing Company, Incorporated (0-937831)
Davenport Pub
Davenport Publishing (0-9616110)
Davicone Inc
Davicone, Incorporated (0-937089)
David Pub MN
David Publishing (0-9616767)
Davis Pub
Davis Publishing Company (0-9615877)
Daymaker Pub
Daymaker Publishing Company (0-938601)
Dazet Creations
Dazet Creations, Incorporated (0-936209)
DBJ Pub
D B J Publishing (0-9616870)
Dead Reckoning
Dead Reckoning Press (0-935733)
Dearen Pub
Dearen, Leah, Publishing (0-938575)
Decision-Making
Decision-Making Center (0-9616604)
Deep Sea Pr
Deep Sea Press (0-939591)
Deer Xing Camp
Deer Crossing Camp Press (0-938525)
Deercreek Pubs
Deercreek Publishers (0-9616768)
Dees Delights
Dee's Delights, Incorporated (0-938685)
Dekalb
Dekalb Historical Society (0-9615459)
Del Sol Editores
Del Sol Editores (0-9616267)
Delmar Pub
Del Mar Publishing (0-935361)
Delta Queen
Delta Queen Steamboat Company, The (0-937331)
Den Rey Pubns
Den Rey Publications (0-9617113)
Denali Press
Denali Press, The (0-938737)
Dendrobium Bks
Dendrobium Books (0-936831)
Denver Ctr Performing Arts
Denver Center for the Performing Arts, The (0-936947)
DePauw Univ
DePauw University (0-936631)
Designer Bks
Designer Books (0-9616966)
Dev Markets
Developing Markets, Incorporated (0-936949)

Devel Self Rel
Development through Self-Reliance, Incorporated (0-936731)
DeVore & Sons
DeVore & Sons, Incorporated (1-55665)
Dia Press
Dia Press (0-9615517)
Diabetes Ctr MN
Diabetes Center, Incorporated (0-937721)
Dialectics Workshop
Dialectics Workshop (0-939275)
Diamond Bks
Diamond Books. *Imprint of* Almaas Pubns
Diamond Pr PA
Diamond Press (0-9615843)
Dickenson Pr
Dickenson Press (0-9615487)
Dickerson Pr
Dickerson Press (0-9615621)
Digit Concept
Digital Concept Systems, Incorporated (0-936327)
Dilettante
Dilettante Press, Incorporated (0-935421)
Dillingham Pr
Dillingham Press (0-9616071)
Dimedinha Inc
Dimedinha, Incorporated (0-9616453)
Dimension Four Unltd
Dimension Four Unlimited (0-937805)
Dionex Corp
Dionex Corporation (0-9617173)
Dioscorides Pr
Dioscorides Press, Incorporated (0-931146)
Direct Intl
Direct International, Incorporated (0-9616409)
Directory Creat Servs DC
Directory of Washington Creative Services (0-938053)
Discovery Calif
Discovery Press (0-9617131)
DITO Pub
D I T O Publishing (0-937929)
Divers Pubns
Diversified Publications (0-939593)
Diversity Okla
Diversity Press (0-936715)
Divine Love Pub
Divine Love Publishing Company (0-9617038)
DJs Guides
D J's Guides (0-9615919)
DL Inc
D L, Incorporated (0-937075)
DM Pub
D. M. Publishing Company (0-938419)
DMC Pubns
D M C Publications (0-9616810)
Do-It Pub Group
Do-It Publishing Group (0-936265)
Doc Bk Pubs
Documentary Book Publishers Corporation (0-935503)
Doc Reprocessors
Document Reprocessors Publications (0-9616850)
Doctors Pr
Doctors' Ophthalmic Press (0-9617262)
Dolice Graphics
Dolice Graphics (0-935901)
Dolores SF
Mission Dolores (0-912748)
Dominica Inst
Dominica Institute, The (0-935959)
Dominus Vobiscum Pub
Dominus Vobiscum Publishing, Incorporated (0-9617076)
Dormition Pubns
Dormition Skete Publications (0-935889)
Dorward Photo
Dorward, D. M., Photography (0-9615729)
Dos Pasos Ed
Dos Pasos Editores, Incorporated (0-9615403)
Double A
Double A Publications (0-9615550)
Double E Pubs
Double E Publishers (0-936195)
Double Eagle
Double Eagle Book Company (0-935781)
Double H Pubns
Double H Publications (0-9615469)
Double Page
Double Page, Incorporated (0-935711)
Double Talk
Double Talk (0-9615839)

Double Trouble Day
Double Trouble Day. *Imprint of* White Hse
Douglas Cty Planning
Douglas County Planning Department (0-9616574)
Down Home Pr
Down Home Press (0-937697)
Down the Shore Pub
Down the Shore Publishing (0-9615208)
Down to Earth Pubns
Down to Earth Publications (0-939301)
DP Books
D P Books (0-939299)
DRACO
D R A C O (0-9617189)
Draco Prod Pubns
Draco Productions & Publications (0-936121)
Drakes View Publishing
Drakes View Publishing (0-939123)
Drame Pr
Drame Press (0-9617190)
Drift Group
Drift Group, The (0-938365)
Dry Eye Inst
Dry Eye Institute (0-9616938)
DT Pubs
D T Publishers (0-9616069)
DTM Intl
D T M International (0-9616210)
Duck Dist
Duck Distributing (0-9616420)
Dujarie Pr
Dujarie Press (0-8275)
Duncan & Gladstone
Duncan & Gladstone Publishing Company (0-9616212)
Dunwoody Pubs
Dunwoody Publishers (0-9616895)
Duval Bibb Pub
Duval-Bibb Publishing Company (0-937713)
Dvorak Intl
Dvorak International Federation (0-9615788)
Dynamic Graph
Dynamic Graphics, Incorporated (0-939437)
Dynamic Reflections
Dynamic Reflections (0-9616971)
Dynamic Teaching
Dynamic Teaching Company (0-937899)
Dynamis Corp
Dynamis Corporation (0-936173)
Dynasty Pub
Dynasty Publishing (0-936541)
D'Zign Land Survey Dev
D'Zign Land Survey & Development (0-9616846)
E A Burtt
Burtt, E. A. (0-9616132)
E A Zimmer
Zimmer, Elizabeth A. (0-9615968)
E B Enterprise
E & B Enterprise (0-9616364)
E Bailey
Bailey, Emma (0-9615823)
E Birkby
Birkby, Evelyn (0-9615636)
E Bond Pubs
Bond, E., Publishers, Incorporated (0-935521)
E D Seaborn
Seaborn, Evan D. (0-9616393)
E D Swiger
Swiger, Elizabeth D. (0-9616245)
E E Newman
Newman, Evelyn E., Group (0-9616356)
E F Briggs
Briggs, Everett F. (0-9615976)
E H Warner
Warner, Elizabeth Hall (0-9615972)
E Hitzel
Hitzel, Ed (0-9612852)
E Houston
Houston, Estelle (0-9615652)
E J Lefkowicz
Lefkowicz, Edward J., Incorporated (0-9617194)
E J Mahoney
Mahoney, Eugene J. (0-9615994)
E Kurtzman
Kurtzman, Elene (0-9615907)
E M Bentz
Bentz, Edna M. (0-9615420)
E M Kelley
Kelley, Etna M.
E M Schmutz
Schmutz, Ervin M. (0-9617156)

E Mace
Mace, Evelyn (0-9616632)
E Pataki
Pataki, Eva (0-9615932)
E R Peterson
Peterson, E. R. (0-9616442)
E Schultz
Schultz, Elva (0-9616431)
E Wegeleben
Wegeleben, Eilene, Enterprises (0-9616861)
EA Enas
Enas, Enas A. (0-9616232)
Eades Pub
Eades Publishing Company (0-9615892)
Eagle Bank Pr
Eagle Bank Press (0-937501)
Eaglenest Pub
Eaglenest Publishing Company (0-9616392)
Eagles Five
Eagles Five, The (0-9616745)
Ear-Lit
Ear-Literature. *Imprint of* Pierce Ellis Ent
Earhart Pr
Earhart Press (0-937061)
Earnest Pubns
Earnest Publications (0-9616789)
Earth Sci Assocs
Earth Science Associates (0-9616753)
East Rock Ltd
East Rock Press, Limited (0-9615543)
Eastwood Orem
Eastwood Publishing Company (0-9617053)
Easy Read Pub
Easy Read Publishing Corporation
(0-937199)
Eccles Pr
Eccles Press (0-9616812)
Eco Images
Eco Images (0-938423)
Ecofunding
Ecofunding Press (0-936529)
Ed Data Res
Educational Data Resources (0-9616851)
Ed Tamm
Tamm, Edward (0-9616793)
Ed Venture CA
Ed-Venture Films/Books (0-935873)
Eden Games
Eden Games, Incorporated (0-937655)
Eden Project Pubs
Eden Project, Publishers (0-939385)
Edgewood Pubs
Edgewood Publishers (0-9616151)
Edgeworth Pub
Edgeworth Publishing Company, Limited
(0-939191)
Edging Ahead Pr
Edging Ahead Press (0-9615488)
Edicion Kerigma
Ediciones Kerigma (0-938127)
Ediciones Arauco
Ediciones Arauco
Edis Anderson
Anderson, Edis J. (0-9616097)
Edit Arcos
Editorial Arcos, Incorporated (0-937509)
Edit Concepts
Editorial Concepts, Incorporated (0-939193)
Edit Roche
Editorial Roche (0-939081)
Edu Strategies
Educational Strategies (0-9615789)
Educ Comp Syst
Educational Computer Systems,
Incorporated (0-935919)
Educ Lrn Syst
Educational Learning Systems, Incorporated
(0-939303)
Educ Materials
Educational Materials Company (0-937117)
Educ Pr FL
Educational Press (0-9616075)
Educ Pubns
Educators' Publications, Inc. (0-935423)
Educ Strategies
Educational Strategies, Incorporated
(0-938809)
Educ Tech IL
Educational Technology (1-55639)
Educated Eye
Educated Eye Press, The (0-9615607)
Eduplay
Eduplay (0-935609)
EduTech Courseware
EduTech Courseware (0-938581)
Edutrends
Edutrends, Incorporated (0-935987)

Edwards & Manley
Edwards, Carol L., & Kathleen E. B.
Manley, Publishers (0-9615687)
EE Ford
Ford, Edward E., Publishing (0-9616716)
EEPC Pub
E E P C Publishing Company (0-937699)
EFQ Pubns
E F Q Publications (0-937265)
EG Bkslr Pubs
E G Booksellers & Publishers (0-938979)
Egret Pub Co
Egret Publishing Company, The (0-9615730)
Egret Pubns
Egret Publications (0-938425)
EK Pub Co
E K Publishing Company (0-937833)
EKB Bks
E K B Books (0-9616714)
Elect Bkshelf
Electronic Bookshelf, Incorporated, The
(0-935325)
Electro Horiz
Electro-Horizons Publications (0-939527)
ELEMENT Pubs
ELEMENT Publishers, Incorporated
(0-939393)
Elenchus Ent
Elenchus Enterprises, Incorporated
(0-936953)
Elite Pub Co
Elite Publishing Company, Incorporated
(0-935589)
Elliott & Hammett
Elliott, Carroll, & Ellen Gale Hammett
(0-9615630)
Elsa II Pub
Elsa Two Publications (0-939595)
Emerald CA
Emerald Publishing Company (0-935675)
Emerald NV
Emerald Publishing (0-9615757)
Emerald People
Emerald People Productions (0-938055)
Emerald Pub MI
Emerald Publishing (0-9617095)
Emerg Med Tech Pr
Emergency Medical Technology Press.
Imprint of First Intl Pub
Eminent Pubns
Eminent Publications Enterprises (0-936955)
Emmanuel Christian
Emmanuel Christian Ministries (0-9615955)
Empak Enter
Empak Enterprises, Incorporated
(0-9616156)
Empire Pub Co
Empire Publishing Company, The
(0-9616213)
Emprise Pubns
Emprise Publications (0-938129)
Empyrean Pubns
Empyrean Publications (0-935283)
Enabling Tech Inc
Enabling Technologies, Incorporated
(0-936299)
Encode Comp Serv
Encode Computer Services (0-939439)
End Age Ministries
End of the Age Ministries (0-936131)
End is Here Pubns
End is Here Publications, The (0-9607640)
Endless Rhymes
Endless Rhymes & Lines (0-9615717)
Endowment Res Human Bio
Endowment for Research in Human
Biology, The (0-938321)
Enetai Pr
Enetai Press (0-9615811)
Engdahl Typo
Engdahl Typography (0-939489)
Ent Emmanuel
Enterprises for Emmanuel (0-9616332)
Enteracom Inc
Enteracom, Incorporated (0-936509)
Enterpress
Enterpress Partners (0-939355)
Enterprise Bks UT
Enterprise Books (0-936957)
Entre Group
Entrepreneur Group (0-936133)
Envoy Press
Envoy Press, Incorporated (0-938719)
Epic Pub Inc
Epic Publishing, Incorporated (0-9616122)
Equality Pr
Equality Press (0-938795)

Erie Art Mus
Erie Art Museum (0-9616623)
Esmond Julie Pub
Esmond Julie Publishing (0-9616333)
Esperanto Soc
Esperanto Society of Chicago (0-9615986)
Etheridge Minist
Etheridge, G. & M., Ministries,
Incorporated (0-937417)
Ethiopian Ent
Ethiopian Cookbook Enterprise (0-9616345)
Eubanks Intl Pubns
Eubanks International Publications,
Incorporated (0-9616214)
Euclid Pr
Euclid Press (0-936583)
Eurofit Pub
Eurofit Publishing Company (0-938821)
Europa AZ
Europa Company (0-937215)
Euterpe Pr
Euterpe Press (0-9616315)
Evangel Pr & Drama Serv
Evangeline Press & Dramatists Service, Inc.
(0-935425)
Evangel Pubns
Evangel Publications (0-935515)
Evangelical Lit
Evangelical Literature League, The
(0-939125)
Evergreen Calif
Evergreen Publishing Company (0-939083)
Evergreen Ed
Evergreen Educational Services (0-9616769)
Evergreen Pub WA
Evergreen Publishing Company (0-937627)
EVKAR Pub
E V K A R Publishing (0-9616965)
Excogitations
Excogitations (0-939597)
Exec Chauffeuring
Executive Chauffeuring School (0-9616215)
Exec Grapevine
Executive Grapevine, Incorporated
Exec Systems
Executive Systems, Incorporated (0-937867)
Exeter Pub
Exeter Publishing Company (0-937193)
Expansion Pr
Expansion Press (0-9616099)
Experiment Pr
Experiment Press, The (0-936141)
Expro Pr
Expro Press (0-936391)
Exxon Human Resources
Exxon Corporation. Human Resources
(0-938933)
F & F Pub
F & F Publishing Company (0-9616875)
F Babineaux
Babineaux, Floyd (0-9616648)
F Evans-Kimbrell
Evans-Kimbrell, Frances (0-9616264)
F H Balenseifer
Balensiefer, F. H. (0-9617228)
F J Adams
Adams, Florence J. (0-9617276)
F L Beddow
Beddow, F. Lorlene (0-9615982)
F L Colon
Colon, Fernando L., Jr. (0-9615643)
F M Bruington
Bruington, F. M. (0-9616838)
F Magazine
F Magazine, Incorporated (0-936959)
F Morrow
Morrow, Felix, Publisher (0-9615659)
F O Copley
Copley, Frank O. (0-9615724)
F R Dougherty
Dougherty, F. Robert (0-936267)
F W Readel
Readel, Fred W. (0-9616822)
Fabrication Pr
Fabrication Press (0-9616233)
Facets Multimed
Facets Multimedia, Incorporated
(0-9615518)
Facing Hist
Facing History & Ourselves National
Foundation, Incorporated (0-9615841)
Factor Pub
Factor Publishing Company (0-935629)
Fads Fashions
Fads & Fashions Company (0-9616534)
Fahnestock
Fahnestock Studios (0-936057)

G E Moir
Moir, George E. (0-9616974)
G Gessert
Gessert, George (0-9615895)
G Graham
Graham, Gordon, & Company (0-9616353)
G H Alsterda
Alsterda, Grayce Harper (0-9617035)
G H Irwin & Co
Irwin, G. H., & Company (0-936243)
G J Abraham
Abraham, George J. (0-9617177)
G J Mauer
Mauer, George J. (0-9616803)
G LedBetter
LedBetter, Gwenda (0-9617007)
G Markim
Markim, Greg, Publishers (0-938251)
G Oberling
Oberling, Grace (0-9616924)
G Van Wariebey
Van Wariebey, Glean (0-916829)
G Wolf
Wolf, George (0-9616503)
GAIA Services
G A I A Services (0-9616496)
Gallant Pub CA
Gallant Publishing Company (0-9616219)
Gallery Fine
Gallery for Fine Photography (0-9615647)
Gallery Schlesinger Boisante
Gallery Schlesinger-Boisante (0-9614661)
Gallup NJ
Gallup Organization, The
GAMA Comns
G A M A Communications (0-938853)
Gamliels Pub
Gamliel's Pub (0-9616579)
Gamma Infinity
Gamma Infinity, Incorporated (0-935869)
Gannon U Pr
Gannon University Press (0-936063)
Gap Mountain
Gap Mountain Books (0-9615520)
Gardner-O'Brien
Gardner-O'Brien Fine Arts Reasearch,
Incorporated (0-9616580)
Gardner Pub
Gardner Publishing, Incorporated
(0-9617183)
Garnet Pr
Garnet Press (0-938133)
Garnet Pub CA
Garnet Publishing Company (0-935793)
Garrett & String
Garrett & Stringer, Incorporated
(0-9615791)
Garrett Corp
Garrett Corporation, The (0-9617029)
Garrett Pub
Garrett Publishing Company (0-939085)
Gasogene Pr
Gasogene Press (0-938501)
Gateway Arts
Gateway Arts (0-935327)
Gateway MO
Gateway Publishing, Incorporated
(0-9616128)
Gateway Pr
Gateway Press (0-936533)
Gateway Prod
Gateway Productions, Incorporated
(0-936769)
Gateway Pubns
Gateway Publications (0-937661)
Gavelston Arts
Galveston Arts (0-9616139)
Gaylord's Guides
Gaylord's Guides, Limited (0-936907)
GCT Pub
G C T Publishing Company, Incorporated
(0-937659)
Geary L Baese
Baese, Geary L. (0-9615510)
GEC Research
G E C Research Press (0-939525)
Gekko Press
Gekko Press (0-9616903)
Gemini Pubns TX
Gemini Publications (0-938427)
Gen Hall
General Hall, Incorporated (0-930390)
Gen Syst Sci
General Systems Science Corporation
(0-938235)
Gene Press
Gene Press (0-939087)

Genealogic Ent
Genealogical Enterprises (0-9616020)
General Comns
General Communications, Incorporated
(0-939185)
Genesis Inc
Genesis, Incorporated (0-9615457)
Genesis Pr
Genesis Press (0-9615923)
Genesis Two
Genesis Two (0-9615649)
Genius Pub
Genius Publishing (0-935925)
Genl Edu Media
General Edu-Media, Incorporated
(0-939531)
Genova Inc
Genova, Incorporated (0-9616509)
Gentle Wind
A Gentle Wind (0-939065)
Gentrace Assocs
Gentrace Associates, Incorporated
(0-936065)
Geo Space
Geo-Space Research Foundation (0-936961)
GeoApp Pub Co
GeoApp Publishing Company (0-9615842)
Geoprint
Geoprint, Incorporated (0-9616454)
Georgetown Herit
Georgetown Heritage Society (0-936149)
Gerecor
Gerecor, Limited (0-935613)
Geriatric Educ
Geriatric Educational Consultants
(0-937663)
Getwell Church
Getwell Church of Christ (0-9615751)
Giant Poplar Pr
Giant Poplar Press (0-9616536)
Giffard Pubns
Giffard Publications (0-937411)
Gilbert Res
Gilbert Research (0-937975)
Gillespie Co
Gillespie & Company (0-9616404)
Gimbaling Gourmet
Gimbaling Gourmet Press (0-9617263)
Ginger Jolley
Jolley, Ginger (0-9616228)
Giordano-Webb
Giordano-Webb Publications (0-935795)
Girtman Pr
Girtman Press (0-9616220)
Glenn Educ Med
Glenn Educational Medical Services,
Incorporated (0-937449)
Glenn-Ryan Pub
Glenn-Ryan Publishing (0-936963)
Global Acad Pubs
Global Academic Publishers (1-55633)
Global Bks
Global Books (0-9617235)
Global Games
Global Games, Incorporated (0-9616154)
Global Man
Global Management, Incorporated
(0-935871)
Global Studies Ctr
Global Studies Center, The (0-937585)
Globe Pr Bks
Globe Press Books (0-936385)
Glorycliff Pub
Glorycliff Publishing Company (0-938571)
Gloy Enter
Gloy Enterprises (0-9616051)
Glyndwr Resc
Glyndwr Resources (0-937505)
Glynn Pubns
Glynn Publications (0-9616342)
Gnsis Pubns Tucson
Genesis Publications, Incorporated
(0-936633)
Gold Robes Pr
Golden Robes Press (0-9616140)
Gold Run Pubs
Gold Run Publishers (0-9615975)
Gold Stein Pr
Gold Stein Press (0-938237)
Golden Adler
Golden Adler Books (0-9616094)
Golden Argosy
Golden Argosy Publishing Company
(0-9615618)
Golden Bear Pub
Golden Bear Publishing, Incorporated
(0-938295)

Golden Gate SF
Golden Gate Press (0-9616288)
Golden Hands Pr
Golden Hands Press (0-9616422)
Golden Hinde Pub
Golden Hinde Publishing (0-936717)
Golden Horseshoe
Golden Horseshoe (0-9617096)
Golden Palm Pr
Golden Palm Press (0-937319)
Goldfield San Diego
Goldfield Publications, Incorporated
(0-936341)
Goldstein MN
Goldstein Gallery, University of Minnesota
(0-939719)
Goldstein Soft
Goldstein Software, Incorporated (0-939933)
Good Old Spot Pr
Good Old Spot Press (0-9616718)
Good Soldier Pubns
Good Soldier Publications (0-9616499)
Goodlife Pubs
Goodlife Publishers (0-938593)
Goodmaster Bks
Goodmaster Books (0-937235)
Gopher
Gopher Graphics (0-936511)
Gospel Themes Pr
Gospel Themes Press (0-938855)
Graduate Group
Graduate Group, The (0-938609)
Graeme Pub
Graeme Publishing Corporation (0-937587)
Graffeo's Hostess
Graffeo's Hostess Helper, Incorporated
(0-9616869)
Graham Pubns
Graham Publications, Incorporated
(0-936167)
Grammar
Grammar Simplified (0-9616040)
Grand River
Grand River Press (0-936343)
Grand Strand
Grand Strand Humane Society (0-9616053)
Granite Pubs
Granite Publishers (0-935669)
Grant Corner Inn
Grant Corner Inn (0-9616719)
Grapevine Inc
Grapevine, Incorporated (0-937931)
Graphic Enter NC
Graphic Enterprises of the Carolinas
(0-936135)
Graphic Pr LA
Graphic Press, Incorporated (0-936183)
Graphic World
Graphic World
Graphitti Designs
Graphitti Designs (0-936211)
Grass Roots Montana
Grass Roots Publishing (0-9616221)
Grasshopper Pubns
Grasshopper Publications (0-937139)
Gravity Pub
Gravity Publishing (0-936067)
Gray Falcon Pr
Gray Falcon Press (0-935335)
Gray Pubns CA
Gray Publications
Great Advent Pub
Great Adventure Publishing, Inc. (0-936069)
Great Am Gift
Great American Gift Company, The
(1-55569)
Great Bear Pr
Great Bear Press, The (0-938559)
Great Game Pro
Great Game Products (0-935307)
Great Wash Re
Greater Washington Research Center
(0-935535)
Greater Alton Jr League
Junior League of Greater Alton (0-9615898)
Greater Works
Greater Works Outreach (0-9616324)
Greatland Graphics
Greatland Graphics/Puffin Press (0-936425)
Green Fields Bks
Green Fields Books (0-937715)
Green Pubns
Green, Bill, Publications (0-9616095)
Green Val World
Green Valley World, Incorporated
(0-913444)
Greenfield Bks
Greenfield Books (0-9615576)

Greenhigh
  Greenhigh Publishers (0-9615770)
Greenhouse Pub
  Greenhouse Publishing Company
    (0-9616844)
Greenhse Pr
  Greenhouse Press (0-9615912)
Greenlawn Pr
  Greenlawn Press (0-937779)
Greensboro Symphony
  Greensboro Symphony Guild (0-9617247)
GreenTower Pr
  GreenTower Press (0-9616467)
Greeting Card Assn
  Greeting Card Association (0-938369)
Grenadier Bks
  Grenadier Books, Incorporated (0-935691)
Grendhal Poetry Review
  Grendhal Poetry Review Press, The
    (0-938781)
Grey Towers Pr
  Grey Towers Press (0-938549)
Greycliff Pub
  Greycliff Publishing Company
Grgtwn U Law Ctr
  Georgetown University Law Center
Griesinger Films
  Griesinger Films (0-9616762)
Grindle Pr
  Grindle Press (0-937065)
Gritz La Ritz
  Gritz La Ritz (0-939679)
Grooming
  Grooming Made E-Z (0-9615460)
Gross Johnson
  Gross & Johnson Publishing Company
    (0-935351)
Grosvenor Soc
  Grosvenor Society, The (Friends of the
    Buffalo & Erie County Public Library;
    0-9615896)
Grosvenor USA
  Grosvenor U. S. A. (0-901269)
Grove Educ Tech
  Grove Educational Technologies (0-936735)
Grove Farm Home
  Grove Farm Homestead & Waioli Mission
    House (0-9617174)
Growth Resources
  Growth Resources, Incorporated (0-936965)
GRQ Inc
  G R Q, Incorporated
Grt Plains Emporium
  Great Plains Emporium (0-9616365)
Gruter Inst
  Gruter Institute for Law & Behavioral
    Research
Grynberg Pub
  Grynberg Publishing Corporation (0-935537)
Gryphon Bks
  Gryphon Books (0-936071)
GSMNH
  Great Smoky Mountains Natural History
    Association (0-937207)
Guggenrobin Pubs
  Guggenrobin Publishers (0-936967)
Guide Pr WI
  Guide Press (0-9615699)
Guide-Pro Assocs
  Guide-Pro Associates (0-9615947)
Guidepost Pubs & Dists
  Guidepost Publishers & Distributors, Inc.
    (0-936217)
Guitar Editions
  Guitar Editions, Incorporated (0-939721)
Guitar Found Amer
  Guitar Foundation of America (0-9616877)
Gulf Coast Pub
  Gulf Coast Publishing Company (0-939127)
Gulfport Hist
  Gulfport Historical Society (0-9615746)
Gumbs & Thomas
  Gumbs & Thomas Publishers (0-936073)
Gurze Bks
  Gurze Books (0-936077)
Gut Level Pub
  Gut-Level Publishing (0-9616814)
Gwendolyn Pr
  Gwendolyn Press (0-937503)
H & E Van Pelt
  Van Pelt, Harold & Erica (0-9616785)
H C Molinoff
  Molinoff, Henry C. (0-9616983)
H D Saunders
  Saunders, H. Duane (0-9616461)
H E Wheeler
  Wheeler, Harris E., Publisher (0-9616830)

H Hayashi
  Hayashi, Hiroshi (0-9616815)
H Holt & Co
  Holt, Henry, & Company (0-8050)
H J Dhillon
  Dhillon, Harinder J. (0-9617188)
H J WIlliams
  Williams, H. J. (0-9616843)
H M Ward Lab
  Ward, H. M., Memorial Laboratory,
    Incorporated (0-9615506)
H Ouimette
  Ouimette, Helen (0-9617116)
H Peck Bks
  Peck, Herbert Books (0-9617153)
H R O'Donnell Guild
  O'Donnell, Hugh Roe, Guild, The
    (0-9617208)
H R Schwab
  Schwab, Henry R., /Doberman Books
    (0-939681)
H S S W I
  Huron Shores Summer Writing Institute
    (0-939345)
H W H Meyer
  Meyer, Herbert W. H. (0-9616723)
H Webb
  Webb, Helen (0-9615859)
H Williams
  Williams, Howard D. (0-9615684)
Haberman Pr
  Haberman Press (0-9617000)
Hague Pr
  Hague Press, The (0-936851)
Hailstone
  Hailstone (0-9616979)
Halevy Finan Pubns
  Halevy Financial Publications (0-935651)
Half Court Pr
  Half Court Press (0-937619)
Half Halt Pr
  Half Halt Press (0-939481)
Hall Reunion
  Hall Reunion, The (0-9617071)
Halleys Comet
  Halley's Comet (0-937451)
Hallwalls Inc
  Hallwalls, Incorporated (0-936739)
Hamiltons Pub
  Hamilton's Publishing (0-939129)
Hammer Mntn Bk
  Hammer Mountain Book Halls (0-9616659)
Hammond Pubns
  Hammond Publications (0-937979)
Hampton Mae
  Hampton Mae Institute (0-9616511)
Hanna-Barbera Prod
  Hanna-Barbera Productions, Incorporated
    (0-936817)
Hanover Pub KY
  Hanover Publishing Company (0-936021)
Hansen Reshanov
  Hansen-Reshanov Consultants, Incorporated
    (0-937553)
Hanuman Bks
  Hanuman Books (0-937815)
Happibook Pr
  Happibook Press (0-937395)
Happy Val Whittier
  Happy Valley Publishers (0-936805)
Harbinger FL
  Harbinger Publishing (0-939441)
Harbinger Group
  Harbinger Group, Incorporated (0-935963)
Harbor Hse MI
  Harbor House Publishers (0-937360)
Harbor Pr
  Harbor Press (0-936197)
Hard Soft Pr
  Hard/Soft Press (0-938611)
Harmony Inst Pr
  Harmony Institute Press (0-938687)
Harmony Mark
  Harmony Mark, Incorporated (0-9616761)
Harp & Lion
  Harp & Lion Press (0-936345)
Harp N Harmonica
  Harp 'N Harmonica Music Publishing
    Company (0-936601)
Harper Coloron
  Harper Coloron (0-9616278)
Harpers Ferry Pr
  Harpers Ferry Press (0-9616354)
Hart Eden Pr
  Hart-Eden Press (0-937497)
Harvard U GSD
  Harvard University Graduate School of
    Design (0-935617)

Harvest Age
  Harvest Age Ministries (0-9616405)
Harvest IL
  Harvest Publications (0-935797)
Hascom Pubs
  Hascom Publishers (0-935927)
Hastings Pr
  Hastings Press (0-935799)
Hat Tree Studio
  Hat Tree Studio
Hatch's Dist
  Hatch's Distributors (0-939723)
Hatfield Hse Pub
  Hatfield House Publishing Company
    (0-9617030)
Hattori Corp
  Hattori Corporation of America (0-936971)
Hausladen Pub
  Hausladen Publishing (0-9617130)
Havin Fun Inc
  Havin' Fun, Incorporated (0-937513)
Hawaii CTE
  Hawaii Council of Teachers of English
    (0-9616581)
Hawk Hands Pr
  Hawk Hands Press (0-9615827)
Hawk Migration Assn
  Hawk Migration Association of North
    America (0-938239)
Hawthorne Co
  Hawthorne Publishing Company
    (0-9617238)
Hay House
  Hay House (0-937611)
Hayes Pub
  Hayes Publishing, Limited (0-88625)
Hays Humane Soc
  Hays Humane Society (0-9616537)
Hayward Area Hist
  Hayward Area Historical Society (0-936427)
Hazard Mgmt
  Hazard Management Co., Inc. (0-935623)
HDL Pubs
  H D L Publishing Company (0-937359)
Heal Tao Bks
  Healing Tao Books (0-935621)
Health Alert Pr
  Health Alert Press (0-936571)
Health Med Amer
  Health Media of America (0-937325)
Healthtalk
  Healthtalk (0-936439)
Hearn Assocs
  Hearn Associates (0-9615450)
HearSay Pr
  HearSay Press (0-938613)
Heart Ctry TN Pubns
  Heart Country Tennessee Publications
    (0-9616334)
Heartfire Mktg
  Heartfire Marketing (0-935211)
Hearthstone CO
  Hearthstone, Incorporated (0-9616308)
HeartLight Pubns
  HeartLight Publications (0-9615911)
Hearts & Crafts
  Hearts & Crafts (0-9617072)
Heartspring Unltd
  Heartspring Unlimited (0-9615606)
Heavenow Prod
  Heavenow Productions (0-9616770)
Heene Enter
  Heene Enterprises (0-9616054)
Heirloom Pub
  Heirloom Publishing (0-938015)
Helen Pub
  Helen Publishing Company (0-9617192)
Heli World Pr
  Heli-World Press (0-939177)
Helix Pr VA
  Helix Press (0-935653)
Helmers Howard Pub
  Helmers & Howard, Publishers,
    Incorporated (0-939443)
Helpful Beginnings
  Helpful Beginnings (0-938783)
Helsinki Watch
  Helsinki Watch. Imprint of Fund Free
    Expression
HEMA Pub
  H E M A Publishing (0-938805)
Heming W Studies
  Hemingway Western Studies Research
    Center (0-932129)

Henart Bks
Henart Books (0-938059)
Henchanted Bks
Henchanted Books (0-9615756)
Hendricks-Ferguson
Hendricks-Ferguson (0-9615468)
Herbal Res Pub
Herbal Research Publishing (0-937643)
Herit Pub CA
Heritage Publishing Company (0-936011)
Herit Pub NC
Heritage Publishing Company (0-936013)
Herit Pubs Servs
Heritage Publishers Services (0-939379)
Heritage Computer
Heritage Computer Corporation (0-935433)
Heritage Margaretville
Heritage Publications (0-937213)
Heritage PA
Heritage Trails (0-936441)
Hermetician Pr
Hermetician Press (0-935895)
Hermit Pr FL
Hermit Press (0-939017)
Heroic Pub Inc
Heroic Publishing, Incorporated (0-936079)
Heroica Bks
Heroica Books (0-935539)
Heron Pr CA
Heron Press (0-935999)
Herring Pr
Herring Press
HI Pr Cold Spring
H I Press of Cold Spring, Incorporated (0-9615988)
Hi-Time Pub
Hi-Time Publishing Corporation (0-937997)
High Energy Res
High-Energy Electrostatics Research (0-936199)
High Falls Pubns
High Falls Publications (0-9617217)
High Impact
High Impact Press (0-935435)
High South Pubns
High South Publications (0-9616492)
Higher Self Pub
Higher Self Publishing (0-938241)
Highlands Dev
Highlands Development Company (0-9616816)
Highlight Bks
Highlight Books (0-9616715)
Highlights NJ
Highlights (0-9616366)
Hightech Pubns
Hightech Publications (0-936551)
Hillary Pr
Hillary Press (0-935367)
Hillman CT
Hillman Company (0-938307)
Hilton Head PTA
Hilton Head Elementary PTA (0-9615726)
HIMACHAL
H I M A C H A L (0-9617065)
Hippogriff Pubns
Hippogriff Publications (0-936973)
Hispanic Bk Dist
Hispanic Book Distributors & Publishers, Incorporated (0-938243)
Hist Assn FL
Historical Association of Southern Florida (0-935761)
Hist Natchez
Historic Natchez Foundation, The (0-936549)
Hist Res Reposit
Historical Research Repository, Inc. (0-935319)
Historic Frankfort
Historic Frankfort, Inc. (0-9615489)
Historic Seattle
Historic Seattle Preservation & Development Authority (0-9616090)
Historical Pubns
Historical Publications (0-9616470)
Hlth Challenge
Health Challenge Press (0-935929)
Hlth Homeopathy
Health & Homeopathy Publishing, Incorporated (0-9616800)
Hlth Psy Pubns
Health Psychology Publications (0-9617145)
HMJ Ltd
Holtvluwer, Meyers, & John, Limited (0-938431)
Holistic Growth
Holistic Growth Publications (0-9606544)

Holland Pub Hse
Holland Publishing House (0-9616660)
Hollow Hills Pr
Hollow Hills Press (0-9616455)
Hollywood Bowl
Hollywood Bowl Cookbook, The (0-9615792)
Hollywood Pub
Hollywood Publishing Company (0-9617040)
Home Schl Headquarters
Home School Headquarters Press (0-9615578)
Home Sweet Home
Home Sweet Home Publications (0-9616817)
Home Vision
Home Vision (0-938957)
Homeland Pubns
Homeland Publications (0-939445)
Hoofnagle Graph
Hoofnagle Graphics (0-9616468)
Hope Pr
Hope Press (0-9615878)
Horizon Trust
Horizon Trust Company (0-9616335)
Horvath Sculpture
Horvath Sculpture & Graphics, Incorporated (0-9616359)
Hosp Council S Cal
Hospital Council of Southern California (0-939089)
Hot House Pr
Hot House Press (0-9616939)
Hothem Hse
Hothem House (0-9617041)
Hour Press
Hour Press (0-939131)
Houston Pub
Houston Publishing (0-9616818)
Howard & Assocs
Howard & Associates (0-935801)
Howarth Pr
Howarth Press, Incorporated, The (0-939533)
Howell Pr
Howell Press (0-936975)
Howell Pr VA
Howell Press, Incorporated (0-9616878)
Hoyle Bks
Hoyle Books (0-937351)
HPS Durham
Historic Preservation Society of Durham (0-9615577)
HR Assocs
H R Associates (0-9616423)
HRH Systems
H R H Systems, Incorporated (0-936737)
Hse Better Sales
House of Better Sales (0-9617290)
Hse of Peace
House of Peace (0-936269)
Hse of Starr
House of Starr, Incorporated (0-938857)
Hse UKE Pubns
House Of U K E Publications, Incorporated (0-937749)
Hughes Pub Co
Hughes Publishing Company (0-9616112)
Hugworks
Hugworks (0-936835)
Hulogos'i Inc
Hulogos'i Communications, Incorporated (0-938493)
Human Dev Educ Lab
Human Development & Educational Laboratories, Incorporated (0-939309)
Human Growth Dev
Human Growth & Development Associates (0-9616626)
Humanities Arts Pr
Humanities & Arts Press (0-9616835)
Hundred Pound Pr
Hundred Pound Press, The (0-939483)
Hunter Pub NC
Hunter Publishing Company (0-9615429)
Husky Bks AK
Husky Books of Alaska (0-938061)

HWH Creative Prod
H W H Creative Productions, Incorporated (0-936969)
Hybrid Pub
Hybrid Publishing (0-9616539)
I Stephanus Pub
Stephanus, Isidore, Sons Publishing (0-9615964)
IA Conf Com Arch
Iowa Conference Commission on Archives & History (0-9616298)
Iberian Pub
Iberian Publishing Company (0-935931)
Ibersoft
Ibersoft, Incorporated (0-935287)
Ibis Pr TX
Ibis Press of College Station, Texas (0-935215)
Ibis Pub VA
Ibis Publishing (0-935005)
IBS Press
I B S Press (0-9616605)
ICBS Inc
International Consortium of Businesses & Services, Incorporated (0-938197)
ICER
Institute for Computer Engineering Research (0-937227)
ICJ Corp
I. C. J. Corporation (0-9615943)
Icon Pr
Icon Press (0-9615471)
ICU Group
I C U Group, The (0-936395)
Idaho Press Club
Idaho Press Club, The (0-9616307)
Ideas Inc OR
Ideas!, Incorporated (0-939447)
If & Win Pub
If & Win Publishing (0-9617025)
IFBL Press
I F B L Press (0-938327)
IGJ Pubns
I G J Publications (0-9617042)
Illiterati Pr
Illiterati Press (0-937837)
Imagefax Pub
Imagefax Publishing (0-939255)
Imagery Enter
Imagery Enterprises (0-9615579)
IMG Inc
I M G, Incorporated (0-936271)
Impact II
Impact II (0-939229)
ImPress IL
ImPress (0-939535)
Impressions TX
Impressions (0-9616121)
In Pursuit Entertainment
In Pursuit of Entertainment (0-938489)
In Tradition Pub
In the Tradition Publishing Company (0-935369)
IN Univ IAS
Indiana University, Institute for Advanced Study (0-936679)
Inagrams
Inagrams (0-9615653)
Index-Citator
Index/Citator System, Incorporated (0-936603)
Index Hse
Index House (0-936697)
Indian Crossing Bks
Indian Crossing Books (0-9616222)
Indian Peaks Pub
Indian Peaks Publishing Company (0-9616582)
Indiv Educ Syst
Individualized Education Systems (0-938911)
Indiv Potentials
Individual Potentials Unlimited (0-9616223)
Infection Control
Infection Control Publications (0-936751)
Info All Bk
Info-All Book Company (0-9617218)
Info Arts
Information Arts (0-937665)
Info Dynamics
Information Dynamics, Inc. (0-935437)
Info Guides
Information Guides (0-938329)
Info Referral Fed
Information & Referral Federation of Los Angeles County, Incorporated (0-938371)
Info to Go
Info to Go (0-936201)

J R Berry
  Berry, John R., Evangelistic Association
  (0-9616900)
J R Taylor
  Taylor, James R., Publisher (0-9616670)
J Stafford
  Stafford, Joseph, Publisher (0-9617123)
J T Maltsberger
  Maltsberger, John T. (0-9616355)
J T Pub Co
  J. T. Publishing Company (0-9615455)
J Terrell
  Terrell, Judy (0-9616780)
J Thompson Pub
  Thompson, Joseph M., Publisher
  (0-9616281)
J V Bush
  Bush, Joseph V., Incorporated (0-9616684)
J Van Impe
  Van Impe, Jack, Ministries (0-934803)
J W Brown Pub
  Brown, J. W., Publishing, Incorporated
  (0-938215)
J W Warner
  Warner, John W., Incorporated, Publishers
  (0-938097)
J Y Cho
  Cho, Jun Young (0-9617185)
J Y Sundstrom
  Sundstrom, Jessie Y. (0-936281)
JAARS Inc
  J A A R S, Incorporated (0-9615959)
JABA
  J A B A (0-938583)
Jacar Pr
  Jacar Press (0-936481)
Jack Scott
  Scott, Jack (0-9616029)
Jack Shank
  Shank, Jack (0-9616123)
Jackson Games
  Jackson, Steve, Games, Incorporated
  (1-55634)
Jackson Pubns
  Jackson Publications (0-937457)
Jadd Pub Hse
  Jadd Publishing House (0-9616772)
Jade Pubns
  Jade Publications (0-937399)
Jaguar Bks
  Jaguar Books (0-937723)
Jahan Bk Co
  Jahan Book Company (0-936665)
Jamenair Ltd
  Jamenair, Limited (0-938667)
James Manning
  Manning, James, Publisher (0-9616234)
James Pr Inc
  James Press, Incorporated (0-9617280)
James Pub Santa Ana
  James Publishing, Incorporated (0-938065)
Janes Pub Eugene
  Janes Publishing (0-938333)
JanJe Pr
  JanJe Press (0-9617148)
Jantrex & Co
  Jantrex & Company (0-9615490)
Janus Pr FL
  Janus Press (0-9616341)
Jasmine Pub
  Jasmine Publishing Company (0-938861)
Jason Pub OH
  Jason Publishing, Incorporated (0-938067)
JB & Me
  J B & Me (0-9616226)
JCMC Louisiana
  Jewish Council Millenium Covenant
JD Pub & Seminars
  J D Publishing & Seminars (0-937841)
JD Pubs
  J. D. Publishers (0-9616688)
JEF Pr
  J E F Press (0-9616022)
Jeff Burkett
  Burkett, Jeff (0-9616303)
Jehara Pr
  Jehara Press (0-9616227)
Jesse Bks
  Jesse Books (0-9616027)
Jest Four You Pub
  Jest Four You Publishing (0-9615794)
Jewel Pr
  Jewel Press (0-937093)
Jewish Ed Soc Res
  Jewish Educators for Social Responsibility
  (0-9615897)
JFJ Assocs
  J F J Associates (0-935707)

JFJ Pub
  J F J Publishing (0-9616148)
JHAFRP
  Jackson Hole Alliance for Responsible
  Planning (0-9617014)
Jim Cook
  Cook, Jim, Publisher (0-936941)
Jim Lyons
  Lyons, Jim (0-9616231)
JKL Pubs
  J K L Publishers (0-935757)
JL Press
  J L Press (0-939279)
JM Pubns
  J M Publications, Incorporated (0-9615844)
Joe Miller Pub
  Miller, Joe, Publishing (0-9616542)
Johnny Alfalfa Sprout
  Johnny Alfalfa Sprout (0-9616229)
Johns Johns & Johns
  Johns, Johns, & Johns (0-939091)
Johnston AR
  Johnston Publishing Company (0-936853)
Joi Prod Enter
  Joi Production Enterprises (0-9616294)
Jomilt Pubns
  Jomilt Publications (0-9616076)
Joshua I Minist
  Joshua I Ministries, Incorporated (0-939313)
Journey Co
  Journey Company (0-9616469)
JOV Pubns
  J. O. V. Publications (0-936321)
Joy Money Pub
  Joy of Money Publishing (0-9616661)
JP Designs
  J P Designs (0-9616904)
Jr Guild Rocky Mt NC
  Junior Guild of Rocky Mount, North
  Carolina, The (0-9616940)
Jr League Durham & Orange
  Junior League of Durham & Orange
  Counties, Inc. (0-9615845)
Jr League Fresno
  Junior League of Fresno (0-9615379)
Jr League Salt Lake City
  Junior League Salt Lake City, Incorporated,
  The (0-9616972)
Jr League Tucson
  Junior League of Tucson, Incorporated
  (0-9616403)
Jr League Winston-Salem
  Junior League of Winston-Salem, Inc.
  (0-9615429)
Jr Serv DeLand
  Junior Service League of DeLand Florida
  (0-9616689)
Jr Serv Rome
  Junior Service League of Rome, Inc.
  (0-9615581)
Jr Welfare SC
  Junior Welfare League of Florence, South
  Carolina, Incorporated (0-9615863)
JSL Editions
  J S L Editions (0-938615)
Jt Border Research
  Joint Border Research Institute (0-937795)
JTG Nashville
  J T G of Nashville (0-938971)
Judson St Pr
  Judson Street Press (0-9617149)
Jugglebug
  Jugglebug (0-9615521)
Jules' Bks
  Jules' Books (0-939537)
Junction Pr
  Junction Press, The (0-935935)
JuneRose Prod
  JuneRose Productions (0-9617043)
Justice Syst Pr
  Justice Systems Press (0-937935)
Justim Pub
  Justim Publishing Company (0-938691)
K Alstad
  Alstad, Ken, Company (0-9616985)
K & A Pubns
  K & A Publications (0-9616230)
K & R Pub
  K & R Publishing (0-9616178)
K C Terry
  Terry, Keith C., Associates (0-937043)
K E Dunlay
  Dunlay, Kate E. (0-9617024)
K E Nemouneh
  Ketab-E-Nemouneh (0-9616820)
K-Four Ent
  K Four Enterprises, Incorporated (0-939473)

K G Jewell
  Jewell, Kenneth G. (0-9615908)
K G Wilks
  Wilks, Karl Glyn (0-9616912)
K Hansen
  Hansen, Kathryn
K J Callahan
  Callahan, Kathleen J. (0-9615563)
K L Maddalena
  Maddalena, Kris Louis (0-9616189)
K L Vilips
  Vilips, Kathryn L., Studios, Incorporated
  (0-938473)
K Singh Pub
  Singh, Kirpal, Publishing (0-9615501)
K W Canipe
  Canipe, Kenneth W. (0-9616329)
K W Huskey
  Huskey, K. W., Associates (0-9604840)
Kaleidoscope Pubns
  Kaleidoscope Publications (0-938001)
Kaptur Pr
  Kaptur Press (0-936987)
Karan Mktg
  Karan Marketing (0-9616852)
Karlins Kitchen
  Karlin's Kitchen (0-9615941)
Kay Assocs
  Kay Associates (0-9616188)
KCI Comns
  K C I Communications, Incorporated
  (0-937583)
Kedcograph
  Kedcograph Company (0-936605)
Keeling Inc
  Keeling, Incorporated (0-9616525)
Keilco Inc
  Keilco, Incorporated (0-9615732)
Kelby Pub
  Kelby Publishing (0-937555)
Keller Intl Pub
  Keller International Publishing Corporation
  (0-937843)
Kelly Ent
  Kelly Enterprises (0-9615582)
Kemetic Inst
  Kemetic Institute (0-939539)
Kennedy King Col
  Kennedy-King College (0-938299)
Kensington Hist
  Kensington Historical Press
Kent & Co
  Kent, Edward, & Company (0-935625)
Kentucky Mining
  Kentucky Mining Institute (0-9615443)
Kentucky Rifle
  Kentucky Rifle Association (0-9615925)
Key Pubns
  Key Publications (0-937141)
Keymate Syst
  Keymate Systems (0-936379)
KGI Pr
  K G I Press (0-936349)
KGI Pub
  K G I Publishing (0-939231)
Khorassan Pr
  Khorassan Press (0-9617114)
Kid Power Ent
  Kid Power Enterprises (0-935441)
Kids In Distress
  Kids In Distress, Incorporated (0-9615864)
Kidsmart
  Kidsmart (0-936985)
Kilgore Assocs
  Kilgore, Jack, & Associates (0-935809)
Kilthau West Pubns
  Kilthau-West Publications (0-939347)
Kimberly Pr
  Kimberly Press (0-9615913)
Kimdar Bks
  Kimdar Books (0-939541)
Kincaid Pubs
  Kincaid Publishers (0-9616989)
Kingman Pub
  Kingman-Block Publishing, Incorporated
  (0-937353)
Kinko's Pub
  Kinko's Publishing Group (1-55577)
Kinser Pub
  Kinser Publishing, Incorporated (0-9615659)
Kinucan & Brons
  Kinucan & Brons, Publishers (0-9615444)
Kiplinger Wash Eds
  Kiplinger Washington Editors, Incorporated,
  The (0-938721)
Kitchen Classics
  Kitchen Classics (0-9615522)

Kitchen Wisdom
Kitchen Wisdom Publishing Company (0-937383)
Kiyler Creations
Kiyler Creations (0-936025)
Klassic Advert & Pub
Klassic Advertising & Publishing Company (0-9615523)
Kneeling Santa
Kneeling Santa (0-9616286)
Knowing Pr
Knowing Press, The (0-936927)
Knowledge Unltd
Knowledge Unlimited (0-9616043)
Knoxville News-Sentinel
Knoxville News-Sentinel Company, Incorporated (0-9615656)
Koolewong
Koolewong, Limited (0-935221)
Kraken Pr
Kraken Press (0-936623)
Kraus Sikes
Kraus Sikes, Incorporated (0-9616012)
KS Historical Soc
Logan County Kansas Historical Society (0-9617260)
Kutenai Pr
Kutenai Press, The (0-937459)
KY Derby Mus
Kentucky Derby Museum, The (0-9617103)
L A Dillon
Dillon, Lacy A. (0-9616811)
L A Wells
Wells, L. A., Company (0-9616256)
L B Dallum
Dallum, Linda Brinkman (0-9616937)
L Benton Geneal
Benton, Linn, Genealogical Services (0-939509)
L C Moore
Moore, Louis C. (0-9616361)
L Cope Pub
Cope, L, Publishing (0-9617214)
L D Butler
Butler, Larry D. (0-9616497)
L Davis Inst
Davis, Leonard, Institute of Health Economics (0-937695)
L Garcia
Garcia, Lois
L Giblin
Giblin, Les (0-9616416)
L Hansen Enter
Hansen, Ludela, Enterprises (0-935685)
L Howard Pubns
Howard, Leslie, Publications (0-937717)
L J McCann
McCann, Lester J. (0-9616935)
L Joseph
Joseph, Lillian (0-9616829)
L M Haines
Haines, Leland M.
L Paquin Pub
Paquin, Larue, Publishing (0-9615547)
L R Balick
Balick, Lillian R. (0-9615834)
L Roth
Roth, Lora (0-9616242)
L S Reeks
Reeks, Lindsay S. (0-9616950)
L Tatum
Tatum, Larry (0-9616249)
L W Laframboise
Laframboise, Leon W. (0-9613855)
La Bonne Vie
La Bonne Vie, Incorporated (0-9615991)
La Cassette Intl
La Cassette Gourmet International, Limited (0-935443)
LA Contemp Exhib
Los Angeles Contemporary Exhibitions (0-937335)
La Jolla Pub CA
La Jolla Publishing Company (0-935365)
La La Ltd
La-La Limited (0-937991)
LA Municipal Art
Los Angeles Municipal Art Gallery Associates (0-936429)
LAD Pub
L A D Publishing (0-938723)
Ladies Home
Ladies Home Journal Books (0-935639)
Ladybug Pr
Ladybug Press (0-9616662)
Lager Pub Co
Lager Publishing Company (0-9615524)

Lahontan Images
Lahontan Images (0-938373)
Laid Back Pubns
Laid-Back Publications (0-9615714)
Lake Aire
Lake Aire, Incorporated (0-936989)
Lake Champlain
Lake Champlain Publishing Company, The (0-9616412)
Lake Placid Climb
Lake Placid Climbing School, Incorporated (0-9615992)
Lakeside Hist
Lakeside Historical Society, The (0-9615935)
Lakewood Ctr Assocs
Lakewood Center Associates (0-9617239)
Lalo Pubns
Lalo Publications (0-9616941)
Lambda Christian
Lambda Christian Fellowship (0-9616853)
Lambert Gann Pub
Lambert-Gann Publishing Company (0-939093)
Land & Land
Land & Land Publishing Division (0-935545)
Land O' Sky Aero
Land O' Sky Aeronautics, Incorporated (0-9616608)
Landmarke Lancer
Landmarke Lancer Publishing Company (0-937639)
Landon Pubns
Landon Publications (0-937355)
Landsberry Pr
Landsberry Press (0-9616788)
Landy Assocs
Landy & Associates (0-9617077)
Langdon & Langdon
Langdon & Langdon (0-938741)
Langley Pubns
Langley Publications, Incorporated (0-936991)
Language Intl
Language International (0-935655)
Lapierre Bks
Lapierre Books (0-9615846)
Larsen's Outdoor
Larsen's Outdoor Publishing (0-936513)
Larson Pub
Larson Publishing Company
LaserSet Press
LaserSet Press (0-939315)
Last Things
Last Things Press (0-9616435)
Lattice Pr
Lattice Press (0-9616721)
Laughing Loon
Laughing Loon Publications (0-9616337)
Lauri Inc
Lauri, Incorporated (0-937763)
Law Anthology
Law Anthology Annuals (0-936607)
Lawyers Pr
Lawyers Press (0-937337)
Lay Counsel Inst
Lay Counseling Institute (0-936709)
LB Pubns
L B Publications (0-9616746)
Ldrshp Pubns Miami
Leadership Publications, Incorporated (0-938389)
Le Jacq Pub
Le Jacq Publishing, Incorporated (0-937716)
Leader Learn Ctr
Leader Learning Center, Incorporated (0-936919)
Learn Deve
Learning Development Systems Publications (0-936585)
Learn N Laugh
Learn-N-Laugh Books (0-9616408)
Learn to Flirt
Learn to Flirt (0-9616376)
Learning Systs Grp
Learning Systems, Limited Group (0-924893)
Ledena Pub
Ledena Publishing (0-9615795)
Lee Pub CA
Lee Publishing (0-939171)
Lee Pub Co NH
Lee Publishing Company (0-9616394)
LeeRosa Pubs
LeeRosa Publishers (0-935547)
Lefever
Lefever, Barbara Susan (0-9614690)

Legacy Pr VA
Legacy Press (0-9617028)
Legislative Track
Legislative Tracking Service, The (0-938585)
Lehigh Univ Pr
Lehigh University Press (0-934223)
Leland Hist
Leland Historical Foundation (0-9615430)
Les Femmes Gourmets
Les Femmes Gourmets (0-9616100)
LeTourneau Pr
LeTourneau Press (0-935899)
Level Four Comm
Level Four Communications (0-936995)
Lewis Pub Hse
Lewis Publishing House (0-937225)
Lewis-Roth
Lewis & Roth Publishers (0-936083)
Lexicon Bks
Lexicon Books (0-937069)
LFive Soc
LFive Society (0-935291)
LGO Pub
L G O Publishing (0-936483)
LI Lib Resources
Long Island Library Resources Council (0-938435)
Liberty Hse Pr
Liberty House Press, Incorporated (0-937765)
Liberty Press TX
Liberty Press, Incorporated (0-938743)
Liberty Pubns FL
Liberty Publications (0-938487)
Libra Press Chi
Libra Press (0-938863)
Libra Pub IL
Libra Publishing Company (0-938335)
Life Awareness
Life Awareness Publications (0-936351)
Life Energy Media
Life Energy Media (0-937725)
Life Enrichment
Life Enrichment Publications (0-936275)
Life in Hell
Life in Hell (0-9615657)
Life Press
Life Press (0-939317)
Life-Renewal
Life-Renewal, Incorporated (0-936221)
Life Survival Digest
Life Survival Digest, Incorporated (0-938811)
Lifeboat Pr
Lifeboat Press (0-939563)
Lifecircle
Lifecircle Publications (0-935815)
LifeCom
LifeCom (0-9615722)
Lifestyle Pubns
Lifestyle Publications (0-937877)
Lifetouch Inc
Lifetouch Incorporated (0-9617259)
Light & Sound
Light & Sound Communications, Incorporated (1-55626)
Light Ventures
Light Ventures (0-939453)
Light Work
Light Work Visual Studies, Inc. (0-935445)
Lighthouse Trg Inst
Lighthouse Training Institute (0-938475)
Lightway Pubns
Lightway Publications, International (0-938617)
Ligonier Comm
Ligonier Sesquicentennial Commission (0-9615431)
Lilmat Pr
Lilmat Press (0-935401)
Lindberg Pub
Lindberg Publishing Company (0-9615993)
Linden Tree
Linden Tree, The (0-937463)
Line Drive
Line Drive Publishing
Lingo Pubs
Lingo Publishers (0-937145)
Linwood Oregon
Linwood Press (0-9616942)
Linworth Pub
Linworth Publishing, Incorporated (0-938865)
Lion Lamb Pr
Lion/Lamb Press (0-9616424)
Lion Pubs
Lion Publishers (0-936635)

Lion USA
Lion Publishing (0-7459)
Lionhart Inc Pub
Lionhart, Incorporated, Publisher (0-9617033)
LISP Co
L I S P Company, The (0-924856)
LISP Machine
LISP Machine (1-55530)
Listen & Learn
Listen & Learn (0-938137)
Listeners Pr
Listener's Press (0-9616943)
Litaruan Lit
Litaruan Literature (0-937557)
Litlaw Found
Litlaw Foundation, The (0-9615761)
Little Book
Little Book Publishing Company, The (0-9616080)
Little Gnome
Little Gnome Delights (0-9615584)
Littlegreen
Littlegreen. *Imprint of* Chris Pub UT
Living Stone Pubs
Living Stone Publishers (0-936637)
Livingston County
Livingston County Genealogical Society (0-9616142)
LJC Bks Pr
L J C Books Press (0-937461)
Lkng Glass Pubns
Looking Glass Publications (0-936485)
Lloyd Simone Pub
Lloyd-Simone Publishing Company (0-938249)
LMI Books
L M I Books (0-9616921)
Lokman Pub Co
Lokman Publishing Company (0-937105)
Lollipop LA
Lollipop Books Company (0-9615509)
Loma Linda U
Loma Linda University Medical Center-Medical Library (0-9615491)
Lomatewama
Lomatewama, Ramson (0-935825)
London Bkshop
London Bookshop Limited (0-939281)
Lonely Planet
Lonely Planet Publications (0-908086)
Longwood Cottage
Longwood Cottage Publishing (0-9616338)
Loras Coll Pr
Loras College Press (0-936875)
Lord Byron Stamps
Lord Byron Stamps (0-938139)
Loren Bks
Loren Books (0-939605)
Lotus Publishing
Lotus Publishing (0-9617249)
Louis & Corsell
Louis & Corsell, Incorporated (0-935339)
Loup Valley
Loup Valley Queen (0-9615586)
Love in Bloom Pub
Love in Bloom Publishing (0-9616630)
Love Pub LA
Love Publishing (0-939359)
Loyalty Mktg
Loyalty Marketing Company, The (0-9617002)
Lrn Technology
Learning Technology, Incorporated (1-55641)
Lrn Unltd Pr
Learning Unlimited Press (0-9617078)
LSU Geosci Pubns
Louisiana State University, Geoscience Publications (0-938909)
Lucas Comns
Lucas Communications Group, Incorporated (0-9616276)
Lucas/Evans Bks
Lucas/Evans Books (0-937291)
Lucia Gallery
Lucia Gallery (0-9616961)
Lucian Pr
Lucian Press (0-9937297)
Lucifer Inc
Lucifer, Incorporated (0-935375)
Lueth Hse Pub
Lueth House Publishing Company (0-937911)

Lux Natura
Lux Natura (0-937727)
LYFE Foundation
L Y F E Foundation (0-9616418)
Lymelite Group
Lymelite Group, Incorporated (0-9615796)
Lyn-Bar Pub
Lyn-Bar Publishing Group (0-938069)
Lyn-Von Enter
Lyn-Von Enterprises (0-937151)
Lynch Bros Ent
Lynch Brothers Enterprises, Incorporated (0-9617150)
Lyons Busn & Pro
Lyons Business & Professional Association (0-9615472)
Lyrica
Lyrica (0-937129)
LZB Pub
L Z B Publishing Company (0-9615899)
M A Fenton
Fenton, Mark A. (0-9616217)
M A Greer
Greer/Martha A. (0-9617179)
M A Lawrence
Lawrence, Mark A. (0-9616610)
M A Lynes
Lynes, Martha A. (0-9616631)
M A Seguin
Seguin, Mary A. (0-9616951)
M & H Enter
M & H Enterprises (0-936997)
M Anthony Pubns
Michael Anthony Publications (0-9615979)
M Berman
Berman, Morris, Studio, Incorporated (0-939197)
M C Michaels
Michaels, M. C., Enterprises (0-9616182)
M C Ullrich
Ullrich, Marion Chambers, Publisher (0-9617091)
M C Winchester
Winchester, M. C., Publishing (0-9616703)
M Corrieri
Corrieri, Michael, Jr. (0-9615686)
M E Becraft
Becraft, Melvin E. (0-9615981)
M E Nilles
Nilles, Mary E. (0-9616845)
M Elks
Elks, Mary (0-9616039)
M F Sohn Pubns
Sohn, Mark F., Publications (0-9616911)
M F Turner Pub
Turner, M. F., Publishing (0-9616007)
M G Chambers
Chambers, Melvett G. (0-9616522)
M J Light
Light, Melvin J.
M J P Barry
Barry, M. J. P. (0-9617009)
M K Look
Look, Margaret K. (0-9616922)
M L Henderson
Henderson, Mahlon Lucas (0-9616434)
M L Higgins
Higgins, Mae L. (0-9616410)
M L King Pr
King, Martin Luther, Press (0-937644)
M M Enter
McAlister, Marcia, Enterprises
M M Hofmann
Hofmann, Margaret M. (0-937761)
M M Muhammad
Muhammad, Mustafa M., Publications (0-9616801)
M M Strauss
Strauss, Mary Miller (0-9616837)
M M Wrede
Wrede, Mary M. (0-9615969)
M Morishima
Morishima, Michael (0-9616866)
M Murdock
Murdock, Maureen (0-9616379)
M Nesbit
Nesbit, Martha (0-9617126)
M Newell Co
Newell, M., Company Builders, Publisher (0-9615901)
M Press
M Press, The (0-9617067)
M R Wimer
Wimer, Margaret R. (0-9617069)
M Renino
Renino, Marjorie C. H. (0-9615866)

M Scheid
Scheid, Margaret M., Author Publisher (0-9616115)
M Serrett Howard
Howard, Marilyn Serrett (0-9616125)
M Sillars
Sillars, Mal, Weather Consultants, Incorporated (0-9616885)
M Sloane
Sloane, Mark, & Company (0-938347)
M Springer
Springer, Miloslay (0-9616955)
M Stensrud
Stensrud, Mary (0-9616956)
M T Smith
Smith, Michael T. (0-9616494)
M V Micka
Micka, Mary Virginia, & Associates (0-9617046)
M W Hardwick
Hardwick, M. Warren (0-9616067)
M Weaver
Weaver, Marilyn (0-9615682)
M Wyatt
Wyatt, Margert (0-9616117)
M-Z Info
M-Z Information (0-937559)
Ma Cherie Chienne
Ma Cherie Chienne (0-9616477)
Mabern & Hart
Mabern & Hart (0-9616773)
MC Corp Stillwater
M C Corporation of Stillwater, The (0-9617195)
McDougal Pub TX
McDougal Publishing (0-9616143)
McElyer Pubns
McElyer Publications (0-9615622)
McHenry Mansion
McHenry Mansion Foundation Press (0-9615926)
MacIlo Pub
MacIlo Publishing Company (0-9616512)
McKechnie
McKechnie (0-939577)
McMallec Pub
McMallec Publishing Company (0-938745)
McMurry Pub
McMurry, Cathryn (0-9615936)
McNichols Pub
McNichols Publishing Company (0-935227)
Macrobiotics Aids Rsch
Macrobiotics & Aids Research Project (0-9617097)
Macrobit Corp
Macrobit Corporation (0-939573)
MacVeigh
MacVeigh, Poppy E. (0-9615594)
Madison Pr TX
Madison Press (0-938867)
Madison Pub
Madison Publishing, Incorporated (0-938141)
Madrigal Pub
Madrigal Publishing Company (0-9617098)
Mage In Nation
Mage-In-Nation Company, Incorporated (0-9615749)
Magee Ent
Magee Enterprises (0-938167)
Magee Pubns
Magee Publications (0-937267)
Magic By Gosh
Magic By Gosh (0-9615492)
Magnaform
Magnaform Corporation (0-937845)
Magnetic Way
Magnetic Way, The (0-938997)
Magnolia Homes
Magnolia Homes Tour, Incorporated (0-9616756)
Magnum Pub
Magnum Publishing (0-937917)
Magpie Pr
Magpie Press (0-935469)
Main St Media
Main Street Media (0-938143)
Main St Pub
Main Street Publishing, Inc. (0-935399)
Main Stage Pubns
Main Stage Publications, Incorporated (0-936447)
Maitland Enter
Maitland Enterprises (0-936759)
Makana
Makana Ka Koloe Publishing (0-935223)
MAKO Pub
M A K O Publishing Company (0-9616963)

Mandyn Co
Mandyn Company, The (0-9617251)

Manivelle Pr
Manivelle Press (0-9616106)

Manor of Grace
Manor of Grace (0-9616513)

Marathon Pr CA
Marathon Press (0-937309)

Marcroft Prods
Marcroft Productions (0-935849)

Marell Ent
Marell Enterprise (0-9617088)

Marilyn Dorf
Dorf, Marilyn (0-9616211)

Marine Environ
Marine Environmental Sciences Consortium (0-938917)

Mariposa Arts
Mariposa Arts (0-9617172)

Mariposa Pub
Mariposa Publishing Company (0-9615709)

Maris & Assocs
Maris & Associates (0-937517)

Marist Inst
Marist Institute for Public Opinion (0-939319)

Maritime Assn
Martime Association of the Port of New York/New Jersey, The (0-9616995)

Markay Enter
Markay Enterprises (0-9616055)

Market Intell
Marketing Intelligence (0-9615978)

Markins Enter
Markins Enterprises (0-937729)

Marlor Prod
Marlor Productions (0-9616973)

Marna Pr
Marna Press (0-9617151)

Martha J Stone
Stone, Martha Jane (0-9617084)

Martin Press
Martin Press (0-9617044)

Marvett Pub
Marvett, Michael E., Publishing Company (0-9615734)

Marwolf Pub
Marwolf Publishing (0-9615847)

Maryland Locale
Maryland Locale, Limited (0-9616584)

Mason Cty Hist
Mason County Historical Society (0-935693)

Masonic Lodge Soft
Masonic Lodge Software (0-939321)

Mass Hist Work
Massachusetts History Workshop (0-9615588)

Massenet Soc
Massenet Society American Branch (0-9615735)

Massey Law
Massey, Alyne Queener, Law Library (0-935449)

MassMkt Bks
MassMarket Books (0-939211)

Masterpiece Pub
Masterpiece Publishing Co. (0-935699)

Mastery Dev
Mastery Development (0-937153)

Mathesis Pubns
Mathesis Publications, Incorporated (0-935225)

Mathhart Pubs
Mathhart Publishers (0-9615589)

Mathis Pubs
Mathis Publishers, Incorporated (0-935491)

Matvest Media
Matvest Media, Incorporated (0-9616155)

Maurice Collection
Mister Maurice Collection (0-935721)

Maurice Monet
Monet, Maurice, Publishing Company (0-9616235)

Maxivation Mktg
Maxivation Marketing (0-937731)

Maya Pubns
Maya Publications (0-938693)

Maynard-Thomas
Maynard-Thomas Publishing (0-935253)

Mazzei
Center for Mazzei Studies (0-916322)

MB Books
M B Books (0-935811)

MD Pub Co
Maryland Publishing Company (0-9615995)

MD Token Medal Soc
Maryland Token & Medal Society, Incorporated (0-9616945)

MD Vet Med Assn
Maryland Veterinary Medical Association (0-9615658)

Mdwsweet Pr
Meadowsweet Press (0-9617297)

Me & My Inner Self
Me & My Inner Self, Incorporated (0-9617045)

ME Appalach Trail
Maine Appalachian Trail Club, Incorporated (0-9616457)

ME Geneal Soc
Maine Genealogical Society (0-9615551)

ME Hist Preserv
Maine Historic Preservation Commission (0-935447)

Meadowlark Pubns
Meadowlark Publications (0-9615590)

Med Aesthetics
Medical Aesthetics (0-937465)

Med Alt Press
Medical Alternatives Press (0-935813)

Med/Av Pub
Med/Av Publishing Company (0-939135)

Med Consumers
Medical Consumers Publishing Company (0-936401)

Med Hist Pub
Medical History Publishing Associates (0-9616748)

Med River Pub
Medicine River Publishing Company (0-9616479)

Medallion Bks CA
Medallion Books, Incorporated (1-55627)

Medea Pub Co
Medea Publishing Company (0-9615432)

Medi-Ed Pr
Medi-Ed Press (0-936741)

Media & Travel Pubns
Media & Travel Publications (0-937367)

Media Loc
Medical Locations & Permits (0-935657)

Media Servs
Media Services (0-9616262)

Media Weavers
Media Weavers (0-936085)

Mediac Pr
Mediac Press (0-9616446)

MediaHlth Pubns
MediaHealth Publications (0-938669)

Medicaldisc
Medicaldisc Reporter (0-936999)

Medicina Bio
Medicina Biologica

MediSci Pubs
MediScience Publishers (0-938869)

Mega Corp
Mega Corporation (0-9616170)

Megan Pubns
Megan Publications (0-9616663)

MegaSoft
MegaSoft (0-939095)

Melcher Software
Melcher Software (0-935977)

Melior Pubns
Melior Publications (0-9616441)

Melissa Data
Melissa Data Company (0-937467)

Melrose Hist
Melrose Historical Society (0-9615451)

Memory Bks
Memory Books

Memory Impact Pub
Memory Impact Publishing (0-9616664)

Men North
Men of the North (0-939703)

Menlo Pr
Menlo Press (0-939607)

Menus Pacific NW
Menus from the Pacific North West (0-9615525)

Mercedes-Benz
Mercedes-Benz of North America, Incorporated (0-936573)

Mercer Isl Preschl
Mercer Island Preschool Association (0-936353)

Mercury Pub
Mercury Publishing (0-935717)

Mercy Ambulance
Mercy Ambulance & Saint Mary's Hospital (0-9615819)

Mercy & Truth
Mercy & Truth Publishers (0-9615494)

Mercy Oceans
Mercy Oceans Publications (0-937847)

Meridian Educ
Meridian Education Corporation (0-936007)

Meridian Oklahoma
Meridian Press (0-9615776)

Mermaid Bks
Mermaid Books (0-9617196)

Merril Pr
Merril Press (0-936783)

Merz Prod
Merz Productions (0-937001)

Messing Pub
Messing, Simon D., Publisher (0-9615946)

Metal Bldg
Metal Building Manufacturers Association, Incorporated (0-9615996)

Metamorphic Pr
Metamorphic Press (0-9615848)

Metier
Metier (0-936087)

Metro Ctr Educ
Metropolitan Center for Educational Research, Development & Training (0-935405)

Metro WI
Metro Publications (0-936537)

MGM Assocs
M G M & Associates (0-9616923)

Mgmt Tele Pub
Management Telecommunications Publishing (0-938303)

MHM Pub
M H M Publishing (0-936833)

MI Adventure Pubns
M. I. Adventure Publications (0-9616395)

MI City Hist
Michigan City Historical Society Inc. (0-935549)

MI Dept Hist
Michigan Department of State (0-935719)

MI Instructor
M I Instructor Series (0-937371)

Miami Dade Environ
Miami-Dade Community College Environmental Center (0-936487)

Micamar Pub
Micamar Publishing (0-937373)

MICATA
American Translators Association, Mid-America Chapter (0-9616557)

Mich St Univ
Michigan State University, African Studies Center (0-939323)

Michael Paul
Paul, Michael (0-9616367)

Micro Analysis
Micro Analysis & Design, Incorporated (0-937197)

Micro Data Mgmt
Micro Data Management, Incorporated (0-938623)

Micro Demo
Micro Demographics, Incorporated (0-935965)

Micro Pro Litera Pr
Micro Pro Litera Press (0-939477)

Micro Tech
Micro-Tech Index, The (0-9617152)

MicroDesigns
MicroDesigns (0-938799)

Mid-Amer Pub Hse KS
Mid-America Publishing House (0-939543)

Mid Atl Reg Pr
Middle Atlantic Regional Press of the Apostolic Faith Churches of God (0-9616056)

Mid East Assess
Middle East Assessments Group (0-937783)

Mid-Hudson Lib
Mid-Hudson Library System (0-936213)

Middlewood Pr
Middlewood Press (0-935961)

Midgard Pr
Midgard Press (0-9615948)

Midnight Oil Pr
Midnight Oil Press (0-937269)

Midnight Pr
Midnight Press (0-9616400)

Midwest Inst Design
Midwest Institute for Design Research, Incorporated (0-937169)

Midwest Media
Midwest Media Associates (0-9616013)

Midwest Motor Mart
Midwest Motor Mart (0-9617015)

Midwest Villages
Midwest Villages & Voices Publications (0-935697)

Mike Murdock
Murdock, Mike, Evangelistic Association (0-937427)
Milbeck Pr
Milbeck Press (0-9615752)
Mile Sq Pub
Mile Square Publisher, Incorporated (0-9616759)
Milestone MN
Milestone Press (0-936091)
Milestone Pr
Milestone Press (0-9615736)
Milestones Unltd
Milestones, Unlimited (0-9616833)
Mills Sanderson
Mills & Sanderson, Publishers (0-938179)
Milw Acad Med
Milwaukee Academy of Medicine Press (0-9617070)
Mind Comn
Mind Communication, Incorporated (0-938871; 1-55667)
Minds Eye Illinois
Mind's Eye Publishing Company, The (0-939249)
Mind's Eye Inc
In the Mind's Eye, Incorporated (0-9616164)
Ministering Angel
Ministering Angel (0-9617005)
Minor Heron
Minor Heron Press (0-9615914)
MIP Pub
M I P (Multi Image Presentations) Publishing (0-9617204)
Miracle Months
Miracle Months, The (0-936515)
Mirage Bks
Mirage Books (0-939137)
Miriam Press
Miriam Press, The (0-939409)
Miskar Pub
Miskar Publishing Company (0-936681)
Missing Diag
Missing Diagnosis, Inc. (0-9615758)
MIT Comm Visual Arts
Massachusetts Institute of Technology, Committee on the Visual Arts (0-938437)
MIU Neurosci Pr
Mahanshi International University Neuroscience Press (0-9616944)
MJH Info Servs
M J H Information Services (0-939289)
Mkt Bk Pubns
Market Book Publications (0-9616994)
Mktg Consult Intl
Marketing Consultants International, Incorporated (0-937195)
Mktg Mgnt Inst
Marketing & Management Institute, Incorporated (0-9616722)
MMI Press
M M I Press (0-936445)
MMO Music
M M O Music Group Inc. (0-935647)
MN Coun Found
Minnesota Council of Foundations (0-9616378)
Mntn Brook Pubns
Mountain Brook Publications (0-938747)
Mntn Grizzly Pubns
Mountain Grizzly Publications (0-9616480)
Mntn Memories Bks
Mountain Memories Books (0-938985)
Mockingbooks
Mockingbooks (0-9615626)
Modal Logic
Modal Logic Corporation (0-937003)
Modern Studies Group
Modern Studies Group. *Imprint of* Heroica Bks
Modular Info Syst
Modular Information Systems (0-939325)
Moe-Tavation
Moe-Tavation (0-9615797)
Mohsena Memorial
Mohsena Memorial Trust (0-9617273)
Mom & Pop Pub
Mom & Pop Publishing Company (0-937469)
Mona Pubns
Mona Publications (0-937849)
Monarch Trails Pubns
Monarch Trails Publications (0-9616665)
Money Pub
Money Publishing (0-9616077)
Money Success Prog
Money & Success Program (0-9616879)

Monkfish Pub
Monkfish Publishing Corporation (0-9615623)
Monogram Pr
Monogram Press, Incorporated (0-938107)
Monroe Pr
Monroe Press (0-936781)
Monson Trading
Monson Trading, Limited (0-937667)
Mont Sci Pubns
Montgomery Scientific Publications (0-935643)
Montecito Pr
Montecito Press (0-935377)
Monterey Audubon
Monterey Peninsula Audubon Society (0-9615798)
Moonlight Pr IL
Moonlight Press (0-9616493)
Moorefields Pr
Moorefields Press (0-9615920)
Morav Music Found
Moravian Music Foundation Press (0-941642)
More Info
More Information (0-936355)
Morgan Pr TX
Morgan Press
Morning Star Gal
Morning Star Gallery (0-9617085)
Morris Pub CA
Morris Publishing Company of San Francisco (0-9616472)
Morrissette
Morrissette (0-9615627)
Mortensen Educ Prods
Mortensen Educational Products, Incorporated (0-937005)
Mortgage Tech
Mortgage Techniques (0-9615886)
Morton Ln Pr
Morton Lane Press (0-938695)
Mountain Movers
Mountain Movers Ministry (0-9616309)
Mountain Pr CA
Mountain Press (0-9616070)
Moving Picture Co
Moving Picture Company, Incorporated, The (1-55565)
MPI Home Video
M P I Home Video (1-55607)
Mrng Star SF
Morning Star Press (0-937937)
MSA Inc
M S A, Incorporated (0-9616897)
Mt Eden Hist
Mount Eden Historical Publishers (0-936193)
Mt Hood Pub
Mount Hood Publishing Company (0-938071)
Mt Shasta Pubns
Mount Shasta Publications (0-9616478)
Mtn Lamp Pubns
Mountain Lamp Publications (0-9615526)
Multi Strategy Pubs
Multi-Strategy Publishers, Incorporated (0-9616896)
Multilingual
Multilingual Typesetting (0-9616413)
Multiple Breath Music
Multiple Breath Music Company (0-939407)
Muncy Manuscripts
Muncy Manuscripts, Incorporated (0-9617231)
Museums Council
Museums Council of New Jersey, The (0-9616363)
Music Child Pr
Music for Children Press (0-9616737)
Music In Action
Music In Action (0-939139)
Music Study
Music Study Services (0-936245)
Music Works
Music Works (0-9617272)
Musical Alternatives
Musical Alternatives (0-9616599)
Musicbiz Pub
Musicbiz Publishing Company (0-937965)
N Am Man-Boy
North American Man/Boy Love Association (0-9615497)
N Amer Hunt Club
North American Hunting Club, Incorporated (0-914697)

N Amer Pubs
North American Publishers, Incorporated (0-9617079)
N & D Pub Co
N & D Publishing Company (0-9616044)
N C Hinds Pub
Hinds, Norman C., Jr., Publishing Co. (0-935541)
N Fonville
Fonville, Naomi (0-9616421)
N H Gershman
Gershman, Norman H., Gallery, Incorporated (0-9617237)
N Hall
Hall, Norman, Ministries (0-938429)
N Koch
Koch, Nora (0-9615583)
N L Endeavors
N. L. Endeavors (0-936803)
N Mathis
Mathis, Nathaniel (0-9616389)
N Melkonian
Melkonian, Norman (0-9616320)
NAES Alexandria
National Association of Elementary School Principals (0-939327)
Naftaolh Pubns
Naftaolh Publications (0-9616130)
Nags Head Art
Nags Head Art (0-9616344)
Naire Ent
Naire, Bill O., Enterprises (0-9615799)
Namaste Pubns
Namaste Publications (0-938147)
Napoleonic Heritage
Napoleonic Heritage Books (0-937811)
Nat Assn Pro Upholsterers
National Association of Professional Upholsterers
Nat Coun Handicapped
National Council on the Handicapped (0-936825)
Nat Data Service
National Data Service for Higher Education (0-937767)
Nat Kidney GA
National Kidney Foundation of Georgia, Inc. (0-9615527)
Nat Legal Ctr Pub Interest
National Legal Center for the Public Interest (0-937299)
Nat Minority
National Minority Campus Chronicle (0-935483)
Nat Pubs CA
National Publishers (0-935551)
Nat Seafood Educ
National Seafood Educators (0-9616426)
Nataraj Bks
Nataraj Books
National Addiction
National Addiction Research Foundation (0-937119)
National Railway Hist Soc
National Railway Historical Society, Incorporated, Atlanta Chapter (0-939037)
Natl Adoption
National Committee for Adoption (0-9615820)
Natl Attorneys Pubns
National Attorney's Publications, Incorporated (0-936855)
Natl Coll Chiro
National College of Chiropractic (0-9615849)
Natl Color Graphics
National Color Graphics, Incorporated (0-9616045)
Natl Dissem Ctr
National Dissemination Center (0-89857)
Natl Encyclopedia
National Encyclopedia Corporation (0-938171)
Natl Graves Assn
National Graves Association of Ireland (0-9616291)
Natl Mus Amer Art
National Museum of American Art, Smithsonian Institute (0-937311)
Natl Womens Hist
National Women's History Project (0-938625)
Natter Pub
Natter Publishing Company (0-936143)
Natural Designs
Natural Designs (0-9616179)
Naturally Beaut You
Naturally Beautiful You (0-9616880)

Naturetrek Comn
Naturetrek Communications (0-9616236)
NB Mktg
N B Marketing (0-939417)
NBECI
National Business & Education Collaborative, Incorporated (0-938697)
NCRCRD
North Central Regional Center for Rural Development (0-936913)
NDCF
National Defense Council Foundation (0-936277)
NE Agri Engineer
Northeast Regional Agricultural Engineering Service (0-935817)
NE Marine Advisory
Northeast Marine Advisory Council (0-9616907)
Neely Pub
Neely Publishing Company (0-9616947)
Neiman
Neiman, Michele (0-9615461)
Nel Mar Enter
Nel-Mar Enterprises (0-9615760)
Nelson Graphics
Nelson Graphics (0-936881)
Neri & Assocs
Neri & Associates (0-9615528)
Ness Press
Ness Press (0-938749)
Network Ani-Males & Females
Network for Ani-Males & Females, Incorporated (0-938073)
Network Media
Network Media, Incorporated (0-939455)
Neubauer Pr
Neubauer Press (0-9617265)
New Atlantis
New Atlantis Press (0-9615480)
New Breed Pr
New Breed Press (0-9617166)
New Collectors
New Collectors Group (0-9616634)
New Dir Salem
New Directions Publishing (0-938393)
New Eng & Reg All
New England & Regional Allergy Proceedings (0-936587)
New Fortress Pub
New Fortress Publications (0-937799)
New Hope AL
New Hope (0-936625)
New Idea Pr
New Idea Press, Incorporated (0-9617099)
New Issues
New Issues, Incorporated (0-9616275)
New Life Pubns
New Life Publications (0-935379)
New Life Pubs
New Life Publishers (0-9616016)
New Mississippi
New Mississippi, Incorporated (0-9616362)
New Past Pr
New Past Press, Incorporated, The (0-938627)
New Place Pr
New Place Press (0-9617167)
New Ray Pr
New Ray Press (0-936303)
New Sci Pr
New Science Press (0-9616114)
New Vistas Pub
New Vistas Publishing (0-9616881)
New Ways Min
New Ways Ministry (0-935877)
New Ways Work
New Ways to Work
New World OH
New World Books (0-9615748)
New Year Pubns
New Year Publications (0-935341)
Newbold Ent
Newbold Enterprises (0-9616906)
Newlight Bks
Newlight Books (0-9615740)
Newmark Pub
Newmark Publishing Company (0-938539)
NewSage Press
NewSage Press (0-939165)
Newspaper Syn
Newspaper Syndication Specialists (0-9615800)
Newtowne Pub
Newtowne Publishing (0-9615705)
Next Question
Next Question Please (0-938527)

NHI Press
N H I Press (0-9617115)
NIA Techniques
N I A Techniques, Incorporated (0-939529)
Nierenberg-Zeif
Nierenberg & Zeif Publishers (0-936305)
Night Owl Pub
Night Owl Publishing (0-9616237)
Night Tree Pr
Night Tree Press (0-935939)
Nightjar Pr
Nightjar Press (0-938751)
Nightphlyte
Nightphlyte Creations (0-9616514)
Nina & Zelik
Nina & Zelik, Incorporated (0-9616558)
Ninth St Ctr
Ninth Street Center, Incorported (0-932961)
NMSU CLAS
New Mexico State University, Center for Latin American Studies (0-937793)
No Secrets Pr
No Secrets Press (0-936779)
Nook Pubs
Nook Publishers, The (0-938339)
Nordbook
Nordbook (0-9616967)
North Bks
North Books (0-939495)
North Gull Pub
North Gull Publishing (0-936753)
North Ridge Bks
North Ridge Books (0-937813)
North South Bks
North-South Books. *Imprint of* H Holt & Co
North West Bk
North West Book Arts (0-937631)
Northcross Hse
Northcross House (0-9617256)
Northstar Pub
Northstar Publishing Company (0-938255)
Northwest Denver
Northwest Denver Books (0-9616057)
Northwest Home
Northwest Home Designing, Incorporated (0-936909)
Northwoods IL
Northwoods Country Collection (0-936847)
Nova Pub IL
Nova Publishing Company (0-935755)
NSIEE
National Society for Internships & Experiential Education (0-937883)
Nurseline Assocs
Nurseline Associates, Incorporated (0-9616339)
NV Families Proj
Nevada Families Project (0-9616633)
NW Perfection Pub
Northwest Perfection Publishers (0-9616757)
NY Circus Pubns
New York Circus Publications, Incorporated
NY Ind Labor
New York State School of Industrial & Labor Relations, Cornell Extension (0-9615917)
NYC Pub Co
New York City Publishing Company (0-9614772)
NYCCWMH
New York City Coalition for Women's Mental Health (0-9616028)
NYS Dept Environ Conserv
New York State Department of Environmental Conservation (0-9615433)
O Ichazo
Ichazo, Oscar, Company (0-937201)
O L Hope
Hope, Orville L.
O M Allred
Allred, O. M., Publications (0-936035)
O Millien
Millien, Oneal, Publishing Company (0-9617055)
O Parker Pub
Parker, Oliver, Publisher (0-937155)
Oak Hill Bks
Oak Hill Books (0-9616701)
Oak Lodge Pub
Oak Lodge Publishing (0-9615661)
Oakton Hills Pubns
Oakton Hills Publications (0-939047)
Oasis Bks
Oasis Books (0-939213)

Oasis Intl
Oasis International Communications, Incorporated (0-938341)
Oberlin Pr Times
Oberlin Press of the Times
Oblong Pr
Oblong Press (0-9616635)
Oboe Bks
Oboe Books (0-935659)
OBriens Auto Racing Pubns
O'Brien's Auto Racing Publications (0-9616916)
Ocean Pub
Ocean Publishing (0-936867)
Ocean View Pr
Ocean View Press (0-938075)
Oceanic Inst
Oceanic Institute, The (0-9617016)
O'Connor Pub.
O'Connor Publishing Company (0-9615466)
Octopus Bks
Octopus Books (1-55580)
ODOT
Oregon Department of Transportation (0-9616754)
Official Shit Co
Official Shit Company (0-9616172)
Offset Hse
Offset House
Ogden Shepard Pub
Ogden Shepard Publishing Company (0-937313)
OK Pub
O K Publishing (0-9616615)
OK Wildlife Fed
Oklahoma Wildlife Federation (0-937733)
Old Betsy Bks
Old Betsy Books (0-9616636)
Old Bk Shop Pubn
Old Book Shop Publication (0-938673)
Old Golf Shop
Old Golf Shop, Incorporated (0-936557)
Old Harbor Pr
Old Harbor Press (0-9615529)
Olimpo Pub Hse
Olimpo Publishing House (0-938873)
Olive Pierce
Pierce, Olive (0-9617101)
Olympian King Co
Olympian King Company (0-9615662)
Omega Three Project
Omega-Three Project, Incorporated (0-9616775)
Omni Lrn Syst
Omni Learning Systems, Incorporated (0-938257)
Omni Worldwide
Omni Worldwide Corporation (0-938259)
Omnibus Pr
Omnibus Press (0-939383)
Omnicom
Omnicom, Incorporated (0-937375)
OMT Assn
Ovulation Method Teachers Association (0-9616481)
On the Road Pub
On the Road Publishing (0-9616316)
Onager Pub
Onager Publishing (0-936491)
Once Upon Stories
Once Upon Some Stories Publishing Company (0-9617219)
One-Horse Pr
One-Horse Press (0-935941)
One-Shot Antelope Hunt
One-Shot Antelope Hunt Foundation, The (0-9617178)
One World Enter
One World Enterprises (0-937939)
Optical Data
Optical Data Corporation (0-939187)
Optimus Prod
Optimus Productions
OR Students Writing
Oregon Students Writing & Art Foundation (0-9616058)
Orbital Pr
Orbital Press, Limited (0-936453)
Ordinal Bks
Ordinal Books (0-939381)
Ordinary Man
Ordinary Man Publishing Company (0-936407)
Oregon Pr
Oregon Press (0-936667)
O'Reilly & Assocs
O'Reilly & Associates, Incorporated (0-937175)

Org Equal Educ Sexes
Organization for Equal Education of the Sexes (0-9616645)
Organica Pr
Organica Press (0-939157)
Orion Pr GA
Orion Press (0-936639)
Orion Press FL
Orion Press (0-938629)
Ortalda & Assocs
Ortalda & Associates (0-9616101)
Ortho Info
Ortho Information Services (0-89721; 0-917102)
Osage Pub
Osage Publishing (0-9616666)
Otter Nonsense
Otter Nonsense (0-9616238)
Otto Pubs
Otto Publishers (0-9615548)
Out Mouths Pr
Out of Mouths Press (0-9616776)
Out of Harm's
Out of Harm's Way, Incorporated (0-9616239)
Outer Ring Pub
Outer Ring Publishing (0-936235)
Overseas Net
Overseas Development Network (0-935747)
Owen Cty Hist Soc
Owen County Historical Society (0-9617100)
Owen Pub
Owen Publishing Company (0-939349)
Oxxi Inc
Oxxi, Incorporated (0-938385)
Oyster Bay Hist
Oyster Bay Historical Society (0-9615929)
P & E Moschetta
Moschetta, Paul & Evelyn, Doctors
P & H Ent
P & H Enterprises (0-9615690)
P B Glahn
Glahn, Peggy Blanchard (0-9615821)
P C Prods
Chase, Peter, Productions (0-9617243)
P D Smith
Smith, Philip D. (0-9616643)
P Donchian Pubns
Donchian, Peter, Publications (0-9615881)
P Duvivier
Duvivier, Paul (0-9616873)
P F Chanteloup
Chanteloup, Paul Francis (0-9616655)
P Fare Bks
Fare, Pam, Books (0-9615998)
P Harper
Harper, Phyllis (0-9615704)
P J Martinez
Pepper Jones Martinez, Inc. (0-935759)
P Kowalkowski
Kowalkowski, Pat (0-9616583)
P L Gilbert
Gilbert, Pedro L. (0-9616124)
P M Satterfield
Satterfield, Phillip Michael (0-9616014)
P Maravelas
Maravelas, Paul
P N Nielsen
Nielsen, Peter N., Enterprises, Limited (0-9616855)
P R Sullivan
Sullivan, Phyllis R. (0-9615470)
P Regan
Regan, Pat (0-9615826)
P Wilson Pub
Wilson, Pierre, Publishing Company (0-9616033)
PA Acad Fine Arts
Pennsylvania Academy of Fine Arts, The. *Imprint of* Art Bks Intl
Pac Horizons Pubns
Pacific Horizons Publications (0-938375)
Pac Whale Found Pr
Pacific Whale Foundation Press (0-938725)
Pace Educ Systems
Pace Educational Systems, Incorporated (0-935385)
Pace Pub Co
Pace Publishing Company (0-936683)
Pacific Pubs
Pacific Publishers (0-936521)
Pacifica Pr
Pacifica Press (0-935553)
Packard Pr Fin
Packard Press, Financial Publications Division (0-936093)

Padre Pio Pubs
Padre Pio Publishers (0-9615916)
Page Wand
Page/Wand Press (0-9615663)
Paige Pubns
Paige Publications (0-938699)
Palm Pub Co
Palm Publishing Company (0-936187)
Palm Tree Pub
Palm Tree Publishing, Incorporated (0-935627)
Palmen Inst
Palmen Institute, The (0-9617213)
Palmer Memorial
Palmer Memorial Episcopal Church (0-9617291)
Palmetto Pr
Palmetto Press, Incorporated (0-9615619)
Pamela Pubns
Pamela Publications (0-938003)
Panda Bks Pubs
Panda Books, Publishers (0-937541)
Panda Press VA
Panda Press (0-9616700)
P&D Pub
P & D Publishing Company (0-9616614)
Panorama Van Nuys
Panorama Publishing Company (0-937671)
Panoramic Pr CA
Panoramic Press (0-937879)
Paper Cloud Pr
Paper Cloud Press, The (0-9615850)
Paper Corp Am
Paper Corporation of America (0-936239)
Paper Dreams
Paper Dreams (0-937149)
Paperback Video
Paperback Video, Incorporated (0-937621)
Papp Hist Pubns
Papp Historical Publications (0-937735)
Parachute Pr
Parachute Press, Incorporated (0-938753)
Paradesa Edit
Paradesa Editions (0-937943)
Paradigm Corp
Paradigm Corporation
Paradise
Paradise Plus (0-9616059)
Paradise Pl
Paradise Place (0-9616821)
Paragon Group
Paragon Group, Incorporated, The (0-9615902)
Paragraphics
Paragraphics (0-9616637)
Paragraphics Pr
Paragraphics Press (0-939175)
Parallax Pr
Parallax Press (0-938077)
Parallel Integ
Parallel Integration (0-9617281)
Parallel Lines
Parallel Lines, Incorporated (0-9616882)
Paramount Bks
Paramount Books (0-9616024)
Parents as Tchrs
Parents as Teachers (0-9616691)
Park Ave Pubns
Park Avenue Publications (0-938149)
Park Pubns Ltd
Parkside Publications Limited (0-9617266)
Park Row Pr
Park Row Press (0-935749)
Parkhurst Br
Parkhurst Brook Publishers (0-9615664)
Parkrail
Parkrail (0-9616240)
Parkway
Parkway Press (0-9610176)
Parrott Pr
Parrott Press (0-9616749)
Parsonage Pr
Parsonage Press, The (0-9615872)
Partyline Enter
Partyline Enterprises (0-9616680)
Pasadena Public Lib
South Pasadena Public Library (0-9617293)
Pasha Pubns
Pasha Publications, Inc. (0-935453)
Passepartout
Passepartout Travel Publisher (0-935981)
Passport NY Rest
Passport to New York Restaurants (0-937413)
Patch & Frazzle
Patch & Frazzle Press. *Imprint of* Boyd Co
Pateo Pub
Pateo Publishing Company (0-936797)

Pathfinder HI
Pathfinder Publications
Pazmany Aircraft
Pazmany Aircraft Corporation (0-9616777)
PC Ctr NC
P C Center, Incorporated, The (0-939215)
PDC French Comm
Prairie du Chien Year of the French Committee (0-9615831)
Peaceable Kingdom
Peaceable Kingdom Press (0-936001)
Peach Pub Co
Peach Publishing Company (0-9615999)
Peachpit Pr
Peachpit Press (0-938151)
Peacock Glenview
Peacock Enterprises (0-937673)
Pearce Evetts
Pearce-Evetts Publishing (0-936823)
Pearson Consul
Pearson Consulting (0-938265)
Pecan Tree Pr
Pecan Tree Press (0-938169)
Pediatric Therapies
Pediatric Therapies, Incorporated (0-937977)
Peel Prod
Peel Productions, Incorporated (0-939217)
Pegasus Prose
Pegasus Prose (0-9617240)
Pelican Pr
Pelican Press (0-938937)
Pember Lib Mus
Pember Library & Museum (0-9616427)
Pembroke CT
Pembroke Press (0-938563)
Pencil Pr
Pencil Press (0-9615665)
Pencraft C Jennings
Pencraft of Chris Jennings, The (0-9616295)
Pencraft Pr
Pencraft Press, Incorporated (0-936771)
Pendelton Lane
Pendelton Lane Publishing (0-937851)
Pendleton Pubns
Pendleton Publications (0-9616609)
Penguin Comns
Penguin Communications Group (0-938269)
Peninsular Pub Co
Peninsular Publishing Company (0-9616000)
Penn Pubs
Pennsylvania Publishers Grunwald, Incorporated
Penn State Food
Pennsylvania State University, Department of Food Science (0-9616407)
Pennant Pr
Pennant Press (0-913458)
Pennington Pub
Pennington Publishing (0-936599)
Pennon Pr
Pennon Press (0-937941)
PennyByte Pubs
PennyByte Publishers (0-9616594)
Pennywhistle Pr
Pennywhistle Press, The (0-938631)
Penton Overseas
Penton Overseas, Incorporated (0-939001)
People for Life
People for Life, Incorporated (0-938755)
People Media
People-Media, Incorporated (0-9615591)
People Patch
People Patch, Incorporated (0-936535)
Peopleism Pubns
Peopleism Publications (0-937009)
Peoria Med Soc
Peoria Medical Society Auxilary, Inc. (0-9615434)
Peregrine CA
Peregrine Falcon Company (0-939649)
Perf Syst Pr
Performance Systems Press (0-938757)
Performing Arts
Performing Arts Referral Service (0-9616927)
Pergot Pr
Pergot Press (0-936865)
Periwinkle
Periwinkle Press (0-9615666)
Persepolis Pr
Persepolis Press (0-9615741)
Persimmon NY
Persimmon Press (0-9615462)
Person Person Network
Person to Person Network (0-937993)
Personal Growth
Personal Growth Resources (0-937477)

Personal Selling
Personal Selling Power (0-939613)
Personal Touch
Personal Touch, A (0-9616317)
Personnel Decisions
Personnel Decisions, Incorporated
(0-938529)
Persun & Berlin
Persun & Berlin, Publishers (0-936111)
PES Inc WI
Professional Education Systems,
Incorporated
Peter Brooks
Brooks, Peter (0-9617203)
Peters Corp NM
Peters Corporation (0-935037)
Petit Appetit
Petit Appetit (0-9616883)
Petruska-Petruska
Petruska-Petruska Publication (0-936189)
Pettway Kipp Pub
Pettway & Kipp Publishing Company
(0-937561)
Peyton Hse Pr
Peyton House Press (0-939097)
Phaedrus WI
Phaedrus (0-9616380)
Phillips Pub
Phillips Publishing, Incorporated (0-938657)
Philomod Corp
Philomod Corporation (0-938545)
Philosopher Pr
Philosopher Press (0-9617048)
Philosophia Pr
Philosophia Press (3-88405)
Phobia Soc Am
Phobia Society of America (0-935943)
Phoenix Children
Phoenix with Children (0-9616482)
Phoenix Med Comn
Phoenix Medical Communication
(0-938633)
Phoenix Pr FL
Phoenix Press (0-9616898)
Phoenix Pr NJ
Phoenix Press Services, Incorporated
(0-936671)
Phoenix Syst GA
Phoenix Systems, Incorporated (0-936019)
Photo Res Ctr
Photographic Resource Center (0-9615801)
Photog West Graphics
Photography West Graphics, Incorporated
(0-9616515)
Photoglass Pr
Photoglass Press (0-9616724)
PI Pubns
P. I. Publications (0-935383)
Pic Gramics Pubns
Pic-Gramics Publications (0-937914)
Pickens County Pub
Pickens County Publishing (0-937229)
Pickle Pr
Pickle Press (0-9615499)
Pictorial Legends
Pictorial Legends (0-939031)
Picture Bk Studio USA
Picture Book Studio, USA (0-88708;
0-907234)
Pidcock Pr
Pidcock Press (0-9616111)
Pie Light Pub
Pie Light Publishing (0-9616725)
Piedmont Pr OH
Piedmont Press (0-9616908)
Pierce Ellis Ent
Pierce-Ellis Enterprises (0-938701)
Pigeon River
Pigeon River Country Association, Inc.
(0-9615851)
Pike Fischer
Pike & Fischer, Incorporated (0-937275)
Pilgrimage Pub
Pilgrimage Publishing, Incorporated
(0-935819)
Pill Enter
Pill Enterprises (0-9616021)
Pin High Pubns
Pin High Publications, Incorporated
(0-937479)
Pinal Cnty Schl Ofc
Pinal County School Office (0-9616993)
Pinerolo Pub
Pinerolo Publishing Company (0-9616692)
Pinnaroo
Pinnaroo Publishing (0-939705)
Pinus
Pinus Strobus Press (0-9615771)

Pinyon Pr
Pinyon Press (0-936323)
Pioneer Balloon
Pioneer Balloon Company (0-9616600)
Pioneer Englewood
Pioneer Publishing & Distributing
(0-937881)
Pioneer Graph
Pioneer Graphics (0-936711)
Pip Prods
Pip Productions (0-936151)
Pipeline Pubns
Pipeline Publications (0-938189)
Piping Indust Prog & Ed
Piping Industry Progress & Education Trust
Fund (0-936387)
Pisces Pr AZ
Pisces Press (0-9616565)
Pittenbruach Pr
Pittenbruach Press (0-938875)
Planet Watch Pubns
Planet Watch Publications (0-9617168)
Planners Pr
Planners Press (0-918286)
Platonic Acad Pr
Platonic Academy Press, The (0-937011)
Playwrights Pr
Playwrights Press (0-9617282)
Pleasant Co
Pleasant Company (0-937295)
Pleiades Pr
Pleiades Press/Studio Graphics Workshop
(0-9616152)
Plum Apple Pub
Plum Apple Publishing (0-9616794)
Plum Grove Bks
Plum Grove Books (0-9616856)
PMnet
PMnet (0-935293)
Pocahontas Pr
Pocahontas Press, Incorporated (0-936015)
Pocket Pal Pub
Pocket Pal Publishing Company (0-938079)
Pocket Pro
Pocket Pro (0-9615593)
Poe Soc Baltimore
Poe, Edgar Allan, Society of Baltimore, The
(0-9616449)
Poets Alive Pr
Poets Alive Press (0-936641)
Pogment Pr
Pogment Press, The (0-938823)
Poiletman Pub
Poiletman Publishing Company (0-937519)
Pointe Pubs
Pointe Publishers, Incorporated (0-935897)
Poko Press
Poko Press (0-9616929)
Polaroid Corp
Polaroid Corporation (0-9616459)
Police Bkshelf
Police Bookshelf (0-936279)
Polonia Bkstore & Pubs
Polonia Bookstore & Publishers, Company
(0-935455)
Polyconomics
Polyconomics, Incorporated (0-938081)
Pomegranate Pr
Pomegranate Press, Limited (0-938817)
Pomona Val Writers
Pomona Valley Writers Association
(0-939503)
Pony Pr
Pony Press (0-9616501)
Poopsies
Poopsie's Incorporated (0-9616060)
Poppy Pr
Poppy Press (0-9616145)
Popular Med Pr
Popular Medicine Press (0-936575)
Porcella Studios
Porcella Studios (0-936589)
Portack Pr
Portack Press (0-938163)
Porter Co PA
Porter Company, The (0-936095)
Portland Litho
Portland Litho (0-9615157)
Portola CA
Portola Press (0-936559)
Positive Attitude
Positive Attitude Press (0-936383)
Posy Pubns
Posy Publications (0-9616061)
Potboiler Pr
Potboiler Press (0-939329)

Potes Poets
Potes & Poets Press, Incorporated
(0-937013)
Potomac Val Pr
Potomac Valley Press
Power Dynamics Inc
Power Dynamics, Incorporated (0-936643)
Pr Peachtree
Press of Peachtree Presbyterian Church,
Incorporated, The (0-9616001)
Practical Allergy
Practical Allergy Research Foundation
(0-9616318)
Practical Arch
Practical Archivists, Incorporated
(0-938019)
Practical Tech
Practical Technology, Incorporated
(0-938877)
Practice Mgmt
Practice Management Associates, Limited
(1-55538)
Prairie Bk Ctr
Prairie Book Arts Center (0-935983)
Prairie Wind Bks
Prairie Wind Books (0-9616585)
Pratt Pub Co
Pratt Publishing Company (0-9615750)
Premier Pubns
Premier Publications (0-9617080)
Pres Soc Asheville
Preservation Society of Asheville &
Buncombe County, Incorporated (0-937481)
Presbyterian Homes
Presbyterian Homes, Incorporated
(0-9616428)
Preser Trust
Preservation Trust of Vermont (0-9615706)
Press N Amer
Press North America (0-938271)
Press on SF
Press on Press (0-9616792)
Presser Le Pas
Presser Le Pas (0-9616726)
Prestige Video
Prestige Video (1-55533)
Pretty Good TX
Pretty Good Publishing (0-9130020)
Pretty Penny Pr
Pretty Penny Press, Incorporated (0-938509)
Primary Pub
Primary Publishing Company (0-9616563)
Primo Prod
Primo Productions (0-936357)
Princet Res Pr
Princeton Research Press (0-936231)
Princeton Dept Hist
Princeton University, Department of History
(0-938495)
Princeton Pub
Princeton Publishing (0-915038)
Principals Lib
Principal's Library, The (0-9617117)
Priority GA
Priority Press (0-9615772)
Priory Pr IL
Priory Press, The (0-8296)
Priory Prods
Priory Productions (0-936161)
Prism Enter Corp
Prism Entertainment Corporation (1-55668)
Pro Canto
Pro Canto Press (0-935751)
Pro-Motion Music
Pro-Motion Music (0-939141)
Pro Pacific
Pro Pacific, Incorporated (0-9616429)
Pro-Se Law
Pro-Se Law Project, Incorporated
(0-937945)
Pro Se Pubns
Pro Se Publications (0-9617267)
Pro Serve Corp
Pro Serve Corporation of Sarasota, Inc.
(0-936177)
Procter Gamble Educ
Procter & Gamble Educational Services
(0-938973)
ProDesign
ProDesign, Incorporated (0-931141)
Prodigal Publishing
Prodigal Publishing Company (0-9617285)
Productivity Rsch
Productivity Research International,
Incorporated (0-9616778)
Prof Comn Inc
Professional Communications, Incorporated
(0-937211)

Prof Desk Ref
Professional Dest References, Incorporated
(0-939735)
Prof Driver Prods
Professional Driver Products Corporation
(0-935879)
Prof Jones
Professor Jones Professional Handicapping
Systems (1-55604)
Prof Pub Radford
Professional Publishing Company (0-937419)
Progenitor Soc
Progenitor Genealogical Society,
Incorporated (0-9616381)
Program Assocs
Program Information Associates (0-935555)
Programs Educ
Programs for Education, Incorporated
(0-935493)
Progressive Pubns
Progressive Publications (0-937157)
ProLogo
ProLogo (0-9616884)
Prometheus Bound
Prometheus Bound (0-9616867)
Prometheus Ent
Prometheus Enterprises (0-9617155)
Promise Pub CA
Promise Publishing, Incorporated (0-939497)
Promontory Pub
Promontory Publishing, Incorporated
(0-938703)
Promotions Unlimit
Promotions Unlimited (0-914749)
Prospectors Ad Serv
Prospector's Advertising Service
(0-9616047)
Proton Pub Hse
Proton Publishing House, Incorporated
(0-939019)
Proven Perf
Proven Performances (0-9615869)
Prsnl Power Pr
Personal Power Press (0-9616046)
PRWCT
Platte River Whooping Crane Trust,
Incorporated (0-938441)
PS Media Inc
Palm Springs Media, Incorporated
(0-939271)
PSI Assocs MD
P S I & Associates (0-938261)
Psych Bks
Psychiatric Books (0-9615865)
Psycho Dynamics Pr
Psycho Dynamics Press (0-937605)
Pt Orchard Spec
Port Orchard Specialties (0-9616198)
Public Safety
Public Safety Automation (0-939257)
Publitex Intl
Publitex International Corporation
(0-938083)
Publius Pub
Publius Publishing (0-937947)
Pubs Mktg Corp
Publishers Marketing Corporation
(0-937593)
Puddin Head Pr
Puddin' Head Press (0-9615879)
Pugh Killeen
Pugh-Killeen Associates (0-937853)
Pumpkin Guides
Pumpkin Guides (0-938011)
Pumpkin Hse Pr
Pumpkin House Press (0-937499)
Pumpkin Ltd
Pumpkin Limited (0-9617017)
Purdue U Fiction
Purdue University, Modern Fiction Studies
(0-9615802)
Pussy Willow
Pussy Willow Press (0-9615763)
Pyramid Designs Pr
Pyramid Designs Press (0-937071)
QED Press
Q. E. D. Press (0-9615997)
Quality Bks OH
Quality Books (0-9616274)
Quality Comn
Quality Communication (0-939143)
Quality Pr MI
Quality Press (0-9616002)
Quality Time
Quality Time Video (0-937095)
Quantum Comns
Quantum Communications (0-938939)

Quark Pub
Quark Publishing Company (0-937949)
Quay Assocs
Quay Associates (0-9616062)
Quest NW Pub
Quest Northwest Publishing Company
(1-55585)
Queue Pubns
Queue Publications, Incorporated
(0-9615691)
Quietude Prod
Quietude Productions (0-936775)
Quinn Pubns
Quinn Publications
Quintilone Ent
Quintilone Enterprises (0-9616980)
Quixsilver Pr
Quixsilver Press (0-9615768)
Quonochontaug
Quonochontaug Press, The (0-937245)
R & M Pub NV
R & M Publishing, Incorporated
(0-9616779)
R B Boies
Boies, Robert Brice (0-9616981)
R B Cross Co
Cross, Richard B., Company
R C Law & Co
R. C. Law & Company, Incorporated
(0-939925)
R C Thomas
Thomas, Robert C. (0-9616250)
R D Pub
R & D Publishing, Incorporated (0-937483)
R D Wuraftic
Wuraftic, Robert D. (0-9616959)
R deLatour
deLatour, Ruggles, Incorporated (0-938291)
R Dodson
Dodson, Rita (0-9615511)
R Dominguez
Dominguez, Richard (0-9616928)
R E Troisi
Troisi, Ralph E. (0-9615474)
R Eshelman
Eshelman, Ruth (0-9617140)
R F Brand
Brand, Robert F. (0-9615727)
R F S Cecrle
Cecrle, Ruth Fay Straub (0-9616159)
R Franklin
Franklin, Rasilon (0-9616052)
R Hoppin
Hoppin, Ruth (0-9615957)
R J Dundas Pubns
Dundas, Richard J., Publications
(0-9617093)
R J Fisher
Fisher, Raymond John (0-9616984)
R K Ettema
Ettema, Ross K.
R L Reeder
Reeder, Robert L., Publisher (0-9616667)
R Lynch
Lynch, Ruth (0-9617250)
R M D Bruce
Bruce, Russell, M. D. (0-9617241)
R N Adlen
Adlen, R. N., Publishing Company
(0-938113)
R Paul Pub
Paul, Reginald F., Publisher (0-9616241)
R Q Putney
Putney, R. Q. (0-9616443)
R S Brodkey
Brodkey, Robert S. (0-9616374)
R S Francis
Francis, Reynold S. (0-9616349)
R S Kelley
Kelley, Rosemary Sue (0-9616905)
R S Oatman
Oatman, Russell Swinton (0-9616593)
R S Wood
Wood, R. S., & Company (0-937635)
R Severino
Severino, Roberto (0-937389)
R Stockman & Coyote
Record Stockman & Coyote Cowboy
Company (0-939343)
R Sutherland
Sutherland, Ruth (0-9616133)
R Talsorian
Talsorian, R., Incorporated (0-937279)
R V Greeves
Greeves, R. V., Art Gallery (0-9616999)
R Van Trees
Van Trees, Robert V. (0-9616282)

R W Elliott
Elliott, R. W. (0-9616575)
R W Enterprises
R & W Enterprises (0-9616382)
R W Strain
Strain, Robert W., Publishing, Incorporated
(0-939727)
R Walter
Walter, Russ, Publisher (0-939151)
R Wettenstein
Wettenstein, Raphael (0-9617252)
R Wismer
Wismer, Romaine (0-9617021)
Raccoon Memphis
Raccoon Books, Incorporated (0-938507)
Radiol Mgmt Comm
Radiological Management Communications,
Limited (0-938705)
Railway Loco Hist
Railway & Locomotive Historical Society,
Incorporated (0-9616102)
Rainbow Assocs
Rainbow Associates (0-9615830)
Rainbow Disc
Rainbow Disc (0-9616048)
Rainbow Heaven
Rainbow Heaven, Incorporated (0-938881)
Rainbow Nursery
Rainbow Publishing Company, First United
Nursery School (0-9616693)
Rainforest Pub
Rainforest Publishing (0-937017)
RAK Pub
R A K Publishing Company (0-9616948)
Raleigh Little
Raleigh Little Theatre, Incorporated
(0-9615689)
Raleigh Pub
Raleigh Publishing Company (0-9615775)
RAM Assocs WI
RAM Associates (0-9617209)
Ramadan Pr
Ramadan Press (0-935387)
Ramif Julian
Ramifications, Unlimited (0-936789)
Ramshorn Pub
Ramshorn Publishing Company (0-9615478)
Randale Resources
Randale Resources (0-9616728)
Randy Fox
Fox, Randy (0-9616578)
Rapport Unltd Pubns
Rapport Unlimited Publications (0-9616729)
Raven Rocks Pr
Raven Rocks Press (0-9615779)
Raving Fest
Raving Festival Association Women's Board
(0-9615803)
Ray Hinkle
Hinkle, Ray, Publishers (0-9616373)
Rayburn Pr
Rayburn Press, The (0-9615942)
Raymark Pub
RayMark Publishing, Incorporated
(0-9617275)
Rays Energy
Rays Energy Consultants (0-936561)
RB Pubns CA
R B Publications (0-9616727)
RCS Co
R C S Company (0-938153)
Read A Bol
Read A Bol Group, The (0-938155)
Read Bks Pubs
Read Books Publishers (0-937869)
Reading Fun
Reading Fun (0-9616296)
Real Estate Invest
Real Estate Investment Associates
(0-9616730)
Reality Bks
Reality Books Limited (0-9616930)
RealSoft NC
RealSoft, Incorporated (0-939259)
Reavco Pub
Reavco Publishing (0-935695)
Recess Press
Recess Press (0-9616784)
Reconstructionist Pr
Reconstructionist Press (0-935457)
Red Mountain Mus
Red Mountain Museum (0-936359)
Redbud
Redbud (0-938763)
Redpath Pr
Redpath Press (1-55628)
Redrock Ent
Redrock Enterprises (0-936821)

Redwood Press
Redwood Press (0-939061)
Ref Presby Theo
Reformed Presbyterian Theological
Seminary (0-9616417)
Ref Rsch Serv
Reference & Research Services (0-937855)
Referral Serv
Referral Service, The (0-9616300)
Reflection CA
Reflection Publishing (CA; 0-939725)
Reflection Pub
Reflection Publishing (0-9616564)
Reflex Bks
Reflex Books (0-9616430)
Reflex Mgmt Pub
Reflex Management Publishing (0-935459)
Regal Rebel Rouser
Regal Rebel Rouser Creations (0-9616909)
Regency Bks
Regency Books (0-910019)
Rehi Bks
Rehi Books (0-938273)
Reinecke Assocs
Reinecke Associates (0-9617064)
Reinforcement Lrn
Reinforcement Learning, Incorporated
(0-937901)
Reis Network
Reis Network (0-9616384)
Relation Family Comns
Relationship & Family Communications
(0-937905)
Reliance Health
Reliance Health Systems (0-9615436)
Relocation Realty
Relocation/Realty Consultants, Incorporated
(0-939361)
Remcon Pub
Remcon Publishing, Incorporated
(0-937183)
Rember Pub
Rember Publishing (0-939101)
Rembrandt Pr
Rembrandt Press (0-9617169)
Rememberbooks
Rememberbooks (0-935231)
Remembrance Pr
Remembrance Press, The (0-9617210)
Renaissance OH
Renaissance Publications (0-936645)
Rendezvous Pubns
Rendezvous Publications (0-938447)
Renfrew Group
Renfrew Group, The (0-935601)
Renn Pr NOLA
Renaissance Press, Incorporated (0-9616289)
Republican Co
Republican Company (0-9615852)
Rescan Assocs Inc
Rescan Associates, Incorporated (0-937737)
Resource Direct
Resource Directories (0-937521)
Resurge Pr
Resurge Press
Reunion Pub Hse
Reunion Publishing House (0-938173)
Revival Teach
Revival Teaching (0-9616360)
Reward Systs Servs
Reward Systems Services, Incorporated
(0-938115)
Reynolds Pub
Reynolds Publishing Company (0-938343)
RF Prod
R F Productions (0-936523)
RFTS Prod
R F T S Productions (0-939401)
RGK Pubns
R G K Publications (0-9616383)
Rhema Inc Pub
Rhema, Incorporated Publishers (0-935945)
Rheumatoid
Rheumatoid Disease Foundation, The
(0-9615437)
RHM & Assocs
R H M & Associates (0-9616949)
Rhombus Pub
Rhombus Publishing Company (0-936455)
RHOPAR Corp
R. H. O. P. A. R. Corporation, The
(0-937015)
RI Coll Alumni
Rhode Island College Alumni Association
(0-9616171)
RI Hist Preserv
Rhode Island Historical Preservation
Commission (0-939261)

RI Spec Olym
Rhode Island Special Olympics (0-9615853)
Ribe
Ribe (0-9616049)
Richards Pub OK
Richards Publishing (0-9616017)
Richmond Hse
Richmond House (0-939505)
RICO Law
R I C O Law Reporter
Right Brain Pub
Right Brain Publishing (0-935295)
Riverdale Systs
Riverdale Systems Design, Incorporated
(0-939545)
Riverrun Piermont
Riverrun Press (0-936415)
Riverside Bks
Riverside Books (0-938777)
Riverstone Pr
Riverstone Press (0-9617206)
RKO Homevideo
R K O Homevideo (1-55545)
RMK Pub
R M K Publishing (0-938879)
Road Runner Pr
Road-Runner Press (0-9615668)
Robbies Creations
Robbie's Creations, Incorporated
(0-9616639)
Roberta Pr
Roberta Press (0-9615742)
Roberts CA
Roberts Publishing (0-9616192)
Robinson Assocs
Robinson & Associates (0-9615804)
Rock Found
Rock Foundation (0-937691)
Rockabilia Pr
Rockabilia Press (0-9616805)
Rockin Enter
Rockin Enterprises, Inc. (0-9616081)
Rockport Art Assn
Rockport Art Association, Incorporated
(0-9616560)
Rockport Pubs
Rockport Publishers (0-935603)
Rocky Top Pubns
Rocky Top Publications (0-937317)
RoCoCo
RoCoCo (0-938275)
Rod L Evans
Evans, Rod L. (0-9616533)
Rodale Inst
Rodale Institute (0-935641)
Rogers Hist Mus
Rogers Historical Museum (0-9616640)
Rogue Wave Pub
Rogue Wave Publishing Company
(0-938005)
Roman Inc
Roman, Incorporated (0-937739)
Romanian Hist
Romanian Historical Studies (0-937019)
Romantic Tidings
Romantic Tidings Books (0-935235)
Ron Denzer
Denzer, Ron, Publishing (0-9616331)
Roncorp
Roncorp, Incorporated (0-939103)
Rondy Pubns
Rondy Publications (0-9616638)
Room to Write
Room to Write (0-938449)
Rose Pr NJ
Rose Press (0-9616603)
Rose Star
Rose Star Creations (0-936719)
Rose Strandtmann
Rose-Strandtmann Joint Venture
(0-9617102)
Rosecott Pub
Rosecott Publishing (0-9615940)
Rosenthal Assocs
Rosenthal, Daniel, & Associates,
Incorporated (0-9615814)
Ross St
Ross Street Press (0-9615463)
Roswell Hist
Roswell Historical Society, Incorporated
(0-9615854)
Rosycross Pr
Rosycross Press (0-9070196)
Round Oak
Round Oak Company (0-9616910)
Rovan Prod Co
Rovan Productions Company (0-9615500)

Rowillan Pub
Rowillan Publishing Company (0-935237)
Royal Pr
Royal Press (0-9616641)
RPI Schl Arch
Rensselaer Polytechnic Institute, School of
Architecture (0-937919)
RRCP
Reconstructionist Rabbinical College Press
(0-938945)
RTI
Relationship Training Institute (0-935559)
RtwouSk Inc
RTwouSK, Incorporated (0-9616894)
Rucker & Rylander
Rucker, Ellie, & Carole Rylander
(0-9615692)
Rudolph Johnson
Johnson, Rudolph, Training & Development,
Incorporated (0-937221)
Runyon Pub
Runyon Publishing Company (0-936699)
Russian Orthodox Ch
Russian Orthodox Church of The Nativity
of Christ (0-9617062)
Rutgers PR Studies
Rutgers University, Puerto Rican Studies
(0-9615805)
Ryder Pub Co
Ryder Publishing Company (0-935973)
Rynd Comm
Rynd Communications (0-932500)
S A Ward
Ward, S. Alexander (0-939189)
S Akhtar
Akhtar, Salman (0-9615818)
S Betzina
Betzina, Sandra (0-9615614)
S Breeland
Breeland, Samuel (0-9615422)
S C Blaffer Found
Blaffer, Sarah Campbell, Foundation
(0-9615615)
S Eller
Eller, Sylvia (0-9617012)
S F Kelley
Kelley, Sarah F., Publisher (0-9615960)
S F Temmer
Temmer, Stephen F., Publishing Company
(0-9617200)
S Ganek
Ganek, Selene (0-9616186)
S H Nelson
Nelson, Scott H. (0-9616436)
S H Stone
Stone, Sarah Howard, Incorporated
(0-937773)
S Heisler
Heisler, Suzanne (0-9617054)
S J Shrubsole
Shrubsole, S. J., Corporation (0-9616646)
S Locke
Locke, Sue Hennigan (0-9615585)
S P Sill Pub
Sill, Stephen P., Publishing Company
(0-9615806)
S Ramsey
Ramsey, Sylvia
S Roberts & Assocs
Roberts, Sam, & Associates (0-9615473)
S Rusch
Rusch, Shari (0-9615922)
S S Howe
Howe, Shirley Swift (0-9616538)
S Shanelle
Shanelle, Sally (0-9616642)
S Sobredo Tech Serv
Sobredo, Sergio, Technical Services
(0-9616888)
S Van Vliet
Van Vliet, Sherrie
S Yonay
Yonay, Shahar (0-9616783)
Sabayt Pubns
Sabayt Publications (0-9616649)
Sabio Pub
Sabio Publishing Company (0-9617050)
Sacred Heart Convent
Sacred Heart Convent of Houston, Texas
(0-9617026)
Sacrum Pr
Sacrum Press (0-937543)
Saddlebag Bks
Saddlebag Books (0-936457)
SAG Pubns
S A G Publications (0-9616105)
Sagamore Bks MI
Sagamore Books, Incorporated

Sage Oregon
Sage Publishing Company, Incorporated (0-937485)
Sage Pr
Sage Press (0-9615725)
Saguaro Pr
Saguaro Press (0-935561)
Sakura Press
Sakura Press (0-936845)
Salem Pub
Salem Publishing Company (0-939475)
Sallyforth
Sallyforth, Incorporated (0-939413)
Salt Resc
Salt Resources, Incorporated (0-9616562)
Samara Pubns
Samara Publications (0-935513)
San Antonio Jr Forum
San Antonio Junior Forum Publications (0-9616917)
San Die Cooking
San Diego's Cooking (0-9617211)
San Diego Art Ctr
San Diego Art center (0-939003)
Sanctuary Pr
Sanctuary Press (0-935971)
Sandbar
Sandbar Willow Press (0-9615711)
S&K Assocs
Stein & Kolber Associates (0-936565)
Sandscape Pr
Sandscape Press (0-936721)
Sangamon Pub Aff
Sangamon State University, Office of Public Affairs Communication (0-938943)
Sangwyne
Sangwyne (0-938387)
Santa Fe Botanical
Santa Fe Botanical Research & Education Project (0-9616460)
Santos Santos Pubns
Santos-Santos Publications (0-9616484)
Satori Pr
Satori Press (0-9617268)
Satori Resources
Satori Resources (0-937277)
Saugus Hist
Saugus Historical Society (0-936363)
Savadove Prod
Savadove Productions, Incorporated (0-938707)
SBA Coven
Coven, Susan B. Anthony (0-937081)
Scand Philatelic
Scandinavian Philatelic Foundation (0-936493)
Sceptre Pub
Sceptre Publishing Company (0-9615855)
Scharff Assocs
Scharff Associates (0-937558)
Schildge Pub
Schildge Publishing Company (0-9615595)
Schl St Pr
School Street Press (0-939105)
Scholars Bks
Scholars Books (0-938659)
Schoolhouse Pr
Schoolhouse Press (0-9615669)
Schrello Market
Schrello Direct Marketing (0-935823)
Sci Comm Intl
Scientific Communication International (0-936097)
Sci Med Pr
Science-Med Press (0-9617051)
Sci Therapeutics Info
Scientific Therapeutics Information (0-936871)
Scion Info Servs
Scion Information Services (0-936495)
Scop & Gleeman
Scop & Gleeman (0-9616986)
Scorpio Pr
Scorpio Press, The (0-938727)
Scorpio Pubns
Scorpio Publications (0-936099)
Scott-Wesley
Scott-Wesley Publishing (0-936137)
Screaming Suicide
Screaming Suicide Press (0-936365)
Scribe Write
Scribe Write (0-939909)
Sea Lion Pub
Sea Lion Publishing Company (0-9616266)
Sea Sports Pubns
Sea Sports Publications (0-9616399)
Sea Studios
Sea Studios (0-9616824)

Seabird Pub
Seabird Publishing (0-938105)
Seacoast Poets
Seacoast Poets (0-936367)
Seahorse Pr
Seahorse Press, The (0-938787)
Seajay Pr
Seajay Press, The (0-935239)
Search-One
Search-One Productions (0-9616694)
Seas Pubns
Seas Publications (0-937677)
Seawinds Pr
Seawinds Press (0-9616375)
Sebastian LI
Sebastian Publishing Company (0-9616731)
Second City Soft
Second City Software (0-937023)
Secret Garden
Secret Garden (0-939263)
Security Seminars
Security Seminars Press (0-936101)
SEE Pub Co
S. E. E. Publishing Co. (0-937147)
Seesaw Music
Seesaw Music Corporation (0-937205)
Segue NYC
Segue (0-937804)
Seibert Assocs
Seibert Associates (0-939461)
Selena Pr
Selena Press (0-938451)
Self Help Dist
Self-Help Distributors, Incorporated (0-937487)
Self-Sufficiency
Self-Sufficiency Association (0-9616968)
Seneca Pk Pub
Seneca Park Publishing (0-9616447)
Sensible Sol
Sensible Solutions, Incorporated
September Pr
September Press, Incorporated (0-937159)
Sequoia NYC
Sequoia Press, Incorporated (0-939033)
SERA Presents
S E R A Presents (0-938883)
SERC NAHRO
Southeastern Regional Council of the National Association of Housing & Redevelopment Officials (0-939647)
Serendip Illinois
Serendipity (0-9616864)
Sergio Pub
Sergio Publishing, Incorporated (0-936003)
Service Press NE
Service Press (0-9617063)
SES Johnson Div
Signal Environmental Systems, Incorporated, Johnson Division (0-9616456)
Seton Med Ctr
Seton Medical Center (0-9616516)
Seven Worlds Pr
Seven Worlds Press (0-936497)
Sewing Sampler
Sewing Sampler Productions (0-937679)
SF Dance Coalition
San Francisco Bay Area Dance Coalition (0-9616244)
SFO Pr
S F O Press (0-937741)
SFP Designs
S F P Designs, Incorporated (0-936361)
SH Press
S H Press (0-938157)
Shadduck-Sullivan
Shadduck & Sullivan (0-935975)
Shades Blue Pubns
Shades of Blue Publications (0-9616669)
Shadowood Pubns
Shadowood Publications (0-937025)
Shadyside Presby
Shadyside Presbyterian Church, The (0-9615554)
Shamro Creative Prod
Shamro Creative Productions (0-939711)
Shasta FL
Shasta Publications (0-9615596)
Shaw Pub
Shaw Publishers, Incorporated (0-9615773)
Shawnee Print
Shawnee Printing Company (0-939371; 0-9604662)
Shaynew Pr
Shaynew Press (0-936705)

Sheehan Indust
Sheehan Industries (0-9617018)
Sheffield Wisc
Sheffield Publishing Company (0-88133; 0-917974)
Shelcor Pub
Shelcor Publishing, Incorporated (0-937107)
Shell House
Shell House, Incorporated (0-9615700)
Shemco
Shemco (0-937057)
Sheorue Pr
Shoerue Press (0-9616292)
Sherlock
Sherlock (0-9616268)
SHHH
Self Help for Hard of Hearing People, Incorporated (0-935473)
Shikar Pub
Shikar Publishing Company (0-938199)
Shoe Tree Pr
Shoe Tree Press (0-936915)
Shofar Pubns
Shofar Publications, Incorporated (0-936685)
Shopware Educ
Shopware Educational Systems (1-55669)
Shore-Campbell
Shore/Campbell Publishing (0-938297)
Showcase
Showcase Charbo-Miles (0-938201)
Shrewd Pubns
Shrewd Publications (0-936103)
Shu Pub
Shu Publishing Company (0-938885)
Shumway Family Hist
Shumway Family History Services (0-938717)
Sierra Press
Sierra Press, The (0-939365)
Sierra Santa Fe
Sierra Club, Santa Fe Group (0-9616458)
Siftsoft
Siftsoft (0-936687)
Sigma Pub
Sigma Publishing Company, Incorporated (0-937027)
Signal Media
Signal Media Corporation (0-9616677)
Signals Pub
Signals Publishing Company (0-9615962)
Signature Pub
Signature Publishing Corporation (0-939147)
Signpost
Signpost Press, Incorporated, The (0-936563)
Silk Butterfly Pr
Silk Butterfly Press. *Imprint of* Panda Bks Pubs
Silo Pubs
Silo Publishers, The (0-937109)
Silver Skates
Silver Skates Publishing Company (0-936105)
Silverbell Pr
Silverbell Press (0-937489)
Simons Meredith
Simons & Meredith (0-938277)
Simp Soft Computer
Simple Soft Computer Services (0-939463)
Simple Prod
Simple Productions (0-938497)
Sinclaire Pr
Sinclaire Press (0-9616886)
Singing Stars Pr
Singing Stars Press (0-936319)
Single Action Prod
Single Action Productions (0-938887)
Singular Hse Pr
Singular House Press (0-9616388)
SIR Inc
S I R Incorporated (1-55534)
Sisters Christ Charity
Sisters of Christian Charity (0-9616887)
Sisters Divine
Sisters of the Divine Savior (0-9616092)
Sisters St Mary OR
Sisters of Saint Mary of Oregon (0-9616750)
Six Lights
Six Lights (0-938919)
SKD Publishing
Sharon Kimberly Damon Publishing Company (0-937875)
Sko Studios
S K O Studios (0-9615546)
Sky Road Pr
Sky Road Press (0-9616544)
Skylight Prod
Skylight Productions (0-938111)

Skyward Bound Pub
Skyward Bound Publishing (0-9617212)
Slash Burn Pr
Slash & Burn Press (0-938345)
Slate Pr
Slate Press (0-9616193)
Sliabhair
Sliabhair (0-937785)
SLPOTCI
Sacred Lands Project of the Christic
Institute (0-9616823)
SMC Corp
S M C Corporation (0-939547)
Small Busn Success Pr
Small Business Success Press. *Imprint of*
First Intl Pub
Small Helm Pr
Small Helm Press (0-938453)
Small-Small Pr
Small-Small Press (0-9616143)
Smile Pubns
Smile Publications (0-9616018)
Smith Prod
Smith Productions (0-9616545)
Smith Slogans
Smith's Slogans & Sayings (0-939403)
Smyres Pubns
Smyres Publications (0-9616952)
Snipe Pub
Snipe Publishing Company, The (0-9617027)
Snow Lion Graphics
Snow Lion Graphics (0-9617066)
SO Metro
S O Metro (0-9616398)
Sobell Assocs
Sobell Associates (0-937613)
Soc Alu Wm
Society of the Alumni of the College of
William & Mary in Virginia, Inc.
(0-9615670)
Soc Inter Celtic
Society of Inter-Celtic Arts & Culture
(0-936651)
Soc Nursing Prof
Society of Nursing Professionals, The
Soccer Ed
Soccer Education (0-9616953)
Social Sys Pr
Social Systems Press (0-935563)
Soda-Licious
Soda-Licious (0-9616340)
Soft Direct
Software Directions, Inc. (0-936517)
Soft Shop Pr
Software Shop Press, The (0-937405)
Soft Tech MI
Soft Tech, Incorporated (0-938087)
SoftCorp FL
SoftCorp, Incorporated (0-937701)
Softlaw Pub
Softlaw Publishing Company (0-9616248)
Software Dev
Software Development Corporation
(0-937333)
Softwriters Dev
Softwriters Development Corporation
(0-939673; 0-9616781)
Soho Press
Soho Press, Incorporated, The (0-939149)
Solar Pr
Solar Press (0-9616785)
Solarium Analy
Solarium Analytika (0-935861)
Solomon Assocs
Solomon Associates (0-9617198)
Solson Pubns
Solson Publications (0-9615671)
Somerset Hse
Somerset House Corporation (0-938941)
Somm
Somm (0-9615807)
Son-Rise Pubns
Son-Rise Publications (0-936369)
Son Rise Williston
Son Rise Publications (0-938355)
Son West Pubs
Son/West Publishers (0-9616546)
Songa Pubns
Songa Publications (0-936017)
Sonoma Lea Hist
Sonoma League for Historic Preservation
(0-9616547)
SOS Minist Pr
S O S Ministries Press (0-938573)
SOSREF
Save Our Schools Research & Education
Foundation (0-938159)

Soul Pubns
Soul Publications (0-937327)
Sound Approach
Sound Approach, Incorporated (0-939265)
Sound Ent
Sound Enterprises Publishing Company
(0-935565)
Sound Feelings
Sound Feelings Publishing (0-9615963)
Sound Food Co
Sound Food Company (0-9615672)
Sounds Kansas
Sounds of Kansas (0-9615597)
Source Pub
Source Publishing (0-9615719)
Source Pubns
Source Publications (0-937589)
South Moulton Pr
New South Moulton Press (0-939731)
South Mtn Pr
South Mountain Press, Incorporated
(0-937339)
South Pub Assn
Southern Publishing Association (0-8127)
South Star Pub
South Star Publishing Company (0-938637)
South Utah St
Southern Utah State College Library
(0-935615)
Southern Inst Pr
Southern Institute Press (0-9615502)
Southern Pines
Southern Pines Centennial Committee
(0-9617019)
Southern Pub
Southern Publishing Company (0-9616517)
Southern Pubns
Southern Publications (0-9617083)
Southwest Pub
Southwest Publishing Company (0-9615438)
SP Press Intl
S P Press International, Incorporated
(0-9617129)
Space News Pub
Space News Publishing Company
(0-936591)
Space Travel & Astron Res
Space Travel & Astronautic Research
Society (0-935313)
Spadra Pr
Spadra Press (0-937161)
Span Inc
Span, Incorporated (0-938281)
Sparkiestuff
Sparkiestuff (0-9616616)
Spec Child Friends
Special Children's Friends, Incorporated
(0-939331)
Spec Hse NY
Specialties of the House (0-9615769)
Special Bks
Special Books (0-939641)
Special Info Prod
Specialized Information Products (0-937563)
Special Places
Special Places, Incorporated (0-936777)
Special Resc Pubns
Special Resource Publications (0-938639)
Spectrum Bus Syst
Spectrum Business Systems, Incorporated
(0-936499)
Spectrum Music
Spectrum Music Press (0-938555)
Spectrum Pubns
Spcetrum Publications, Limited (0-9616287)
Spedco Assocs
Spedco Associates, Incorporated
(0-9615856)
Speech Bin
Speech Bin, The (0-937857)
Spell Assoc
Spell, Leonard, & Associates (0-9615439)
Spencers Intl
Spencer's International Enterprises
(0-937771)
Spiral Galaxy
Spiral Galaxy Publishing (0-9617056)
Spiricult Pub
Spiricult Publishing (0-938803)
Spirit Christ
Spirit of Christ Ministries (0-9615536)
Spirit Faith
Spirit of Faith Ministries (0-936371)
Spirit Speaks
Spirit Speaks (0-938283)

Spiritual Warfare
Spiritual Warfare Ministries (0-9615445)
Sportnet
Sportnet, Incorporated (0-9616011)
Sports Hall Oblivion
Sports Hall of Oblivion (0-938455)
Sports Info Serv
Sports Information Service (0-936301)
Sports Market
Sports Marketing, Incorporated (0-936169)
Sports Psych Pubns
Sports Psychology Publications (0-9616954)
SportSoft
SportSoft, Incorporated (0-939267)
SportsWare
SportsWare (0-938709)
Spraysaver Pubns
Spraysaver Publications (0-9616523)
Spring Harbor
Spring Harbor Press (0-935891)
Spur Pubs
Spur Publishers (0-9615503)
Sq One Pubs
Square One Publishers, Incorporated
(0-938961)
St Alban Pr CA
St. Alban Press, San Diego (0-935461)
St Andrew Pr
St. Andrew Press (0-939485)
St Anthony Northport
Saint Anthony of Padua School (0-9616243)
St Anthony Orthodox
Saint Anthony Orthodox Publications
(0-936649)
St Clair Pub
Saint Clair Publishing (0-9616319)
ST David's Soc of WY Val
St. David's Society of Wyoming Valley
St Herman AK
Saint Herman of Alaska Brotherhood
(0-938635)
St John Evang
Saint John the Evangelist Church
(0-9616134)
St Johns Pub
Saint John's Publishing (0-938577)
St Joseph Hosp
Saint Joseph Hospital (0-9616857)
St Louis Human
Saint Louis Humanities Forum (0-9616369)
St Maurice Church
Saint Maurice Church (0-9615563)
St Thomas Aca
St. Thomas Academy (0-9615710)
Staging & Stuff
Staging & Stuff (0-935723)
Stained Glass
Stained Glass Images, Incorporated
(0-936459)
Stamp Out Sheep Pr
Stamp Out Sheep Press. *Imprint of* Sq One
Pubs
Standards Eng
Standards Engineering Society (0-9616825)
Star Athlete
Star Athlete (0-937565)
Star City Pubns
Star City Publications (0-9615937)
Star Power Prod
Star Power Productions (0-938641)
Starfield Pr
Starfield Press (0-9616826)
Starhaven
Starhaven (0-936315)
Starlight Houston
Starlight Publishing Company (0-9616401)
Starlight Pubns
Starlight Publications (0-9615667)
Starports Pub
Starports Publishing (0-9616977)
Stat Med Pub
Stat Medical Publishing Company
(0-935463)
State AK Nat Res
State of Alaska, Department of Natura l
Resources (0-9616003)
State House Pr
State House Press (0-938349)

Statistikon Corp
　　Statistikon Corporation, The
Stenotype Educ
　　Stenotype Educational Products,
　　Incorporated (0-938643)
Step By Step Pubns
　　Step By Step Publications (0-9615611)
Step Stones Pr
　　Stepping Stones Press (0-9616502)
Sterling Hgts Geneal
　　Sterling Heights Genealogical & Historical
　　Society (0-9616495)
Sterling Life Ins
　　Sterling Life Insurance Company
　　(0-9617162)
Stevens Pub
　　Stevens, Gareth, Publishing (0-918831;
　　1-55532)
Stindt Bks
　　Stindt Books (0-9615465)
STL Intl
　　S T L International, Incorporated
　　(0-936215)
Stock-Breznau
　　Stock & Breznau Publishing Co. (0-936525)
Stockton Pr
　　Stockton Press (0-935859; 0-943818)
Stone Age Pr
　　Stone Age Press of Alaska (0-9615808)
Stone Canyon Pr
　　Stone Canyon Press (0-937641)
Stone Hse NY
　　Stone House Press (0-937035)
Stonecrest Pr
　　Stonecrest Press (0-9616004)
Stonehaven Pubs
　　Stonehaven Publishers (0-937775)
Stonehill Pr
　　Stonehill Press (0-937167)
Stoneridge Pub
　　Stoneridge Publishing (0-938767)
Storm Mtn Pubs
　　Storm Mountain Publishers (0-939167)
Storyviews Pub
　　Storyviews Publishing Company (0-9617057)
Stpngstns Pr NY
　　Steppingstones Press (0-935821)
Str Software
　　Strider Software (0-936921)
Strafford Pubns
　　Strafford Publications, Incorporated
　　(0-9616858)
Straight St Pub
　　Straight Street Publishing, Incorporated
　　(0-936309)
Strategic Systs
　　Strategic Learning Systems (0-937037)
Stratmar Ed Sys
　　Stratmar Educational Systems, Incorporated
　　(0-935465)
Streamline Pub
　　Streamline Publishing Company (0-938457)
Streamline Soft
　　Streamline Software Systems, Incorporated
　　(0-939333)
Street Sense Pubns
　　Street Sense Publications (0-9616732)
STTU Spc Unit
　　S T T U, Specialized Training Unit
　　(0-939235)
Student Success
　　Student Success (0-9615809)
Studio Pr
　　Studio Press, Limited (0-9615598)
Studio Workshop Pr
　　Studio Workshop Press (0-9616269)
Sturges Pub
　　Sturges Publishing Co. (0-936373)
Style Pubns
　　Style Publications (0-9616246)
StyleWare
　　StyleWare, Incorporated (0-939677)
Subar Pubns
　　Subar Publications (0-939411)
Substance Faith
　　Substance of Faith Ministries (0-937357)
Successful Living
　　Successful Living Press (0-937743)
Sudden Jungle Pr
　　Sudden Jungle Press (0-937567)
Sue Robinson
　　Robinson, Sue (0-9617332)
Suffolk Cnty Hist Soc
　　Suffolk County Historical Society
　　(0-938769)
Sullen Art Pr
　　Sullen Art Press (0-9616752)

Sulveri
　　Sulveri (0-9615545)
Summit Pr CO
　　Summit Press CO (0-936163)
Sun Pr FL
　　Sun Press of Florida (0-937039)
Sun Star Pubns
　　Sun Star Publications (0-937787)
Sunbank Pub Co
　　Sunbank Publishing Company (0-9616190)
Sunbelt Pub Co
　　Sunbelt Publishing Company (0-9616247)
Sunbow Pubns
　　Sunbow Publications (0-9615610)
Sunburst Pr CA
　　Sunburst Press (0-9615673)
Suncoast Prof Pub
　　Suncoast Professional Publishing
　　Corporation (0-937569)
Sundance Vent
　　Sundance/Venture Resources (0-935389)
Sunlakes Pub
　　Sunlakes Publishing Company (0-9615884)
Sunnyvale Psy
　　Sunnyvale Psychotherapy (0-9615762)
Sunrise Artistries
　　Sunrise Artistries, Incorporated (0-936519)
Sunrise Texas
　　Sunrise Publications (0-937789)
Sunrise Vent
　　Sunrise Ventures (0-9615674)
Sunset Video
　　Sunset Video, Incorporated (0-936155)
Sunshine Pr
　　Sunshine Press (0-936223)
Sunshine TX
　　Sunshine Press (0-9615743)
SUNY Compar Educ Ctr
　　State University of New York at Buffalo,
　　Comparative Education Center (0-937033)
Sure Found
　　Sure Foundation (0-936595)
Surfer Pubns
　　Surfer Publications, Incorporated (0-939337)
Susquehanna U Pr
　　Susquehanna University Press (0-941664)
Sustaining Syst
　　Sustaining Systems (0-939335)
Sutton Pubns
　　Sutton Publications (0-9617199)
Suwannee Poetry
　　Suwannee Poetry (0-938285)
SW Educ Ent
　　Southwest Educational Enterprises
　　(0-937029)
SW Univ Press
　　Southwest University Press (0-937681)
SWAC Pr
　　S W A C Press
Swan Pr
　　Swan Press (0-9615530)
Sweetwater Pr
　　Sweetwater Press (0-9615504)
Swenson Pub
　　Swenson Publishing (0-9615688)
Swim Safe
　　Swim Safe (0-939627)
Swiss Village
　　Swiss Village Book Store (0-9615744)
Sword Shield Release
　　Sword & Shield Release (0-938471)
Symbiosis Bks
　　Symbiosis Books (0-9615903)
Synaptic Pr
　　Synaptic Press (0-9616988)
Syncretic Prod
　　Syncretic Productions, Incorporated
　　(0-935863)
Synergetics
　　Synergetics (0-936501)
Synergy Pr
　　Synergy Press (0-9616548)
Systems Co
　　Systems Company (0-937041)
Systemsware
　　Systemsware Corporation, The (0-938801)
T & G Harburn
　　Harburn, Todd & Gerald E., Publishers
　　(0-9617171)
T & J Sports Cards
　　T & J Sports Cards (0-937903)
T & R Pubs
　　T & R Publishers (0-936809)
T B J Pubns
　　T B J Publications (0-935855)
T B Swain & Son
　　Swain, Thomas B., & Son (0-938915)

T J Designs
　　T. J. Designs (0-939287)
T J Shillea
　　Shillea, Thomas John (0-9616925)
T Leagjeld
　　Leagjeld, Ted (0-9616127)
T R & C Pubs
　　Thompson, Roberts & Clare, Publishers
T Redding
　　Redding, Thomas, & Associates (0-939099)
T Sawyer Bks
　　Tom Sawyer Books (0-937573)
TA Assocs
　　T A Associates (0-9617020)
Tabard Pr
　　Tabard Press (0-914427)
Tabb Thetford Pubs
　　Tabb, Jeanne J., & Margaret Ann Thetfor,
　　Publishers (0-9616931)
Table Talk Bridge
　　Table Talk Bridge Club (0-9616705)
Tahoma Pubns
　　Tahoma Publications (0-9616969)
Tai Chi Ctr NY
　　Tai Chi Chuan Center of New York
　　(0-9616586)
Talking Tree Pr
　　Talking Tree Press (0-9616957)
Tallstone Pub
　　Tallstone Publishing (0-936191)
Tambra Pub
　　Tambra Publishing (0-9615698)
Tan Pr
　　Tan Press (0-9615754)
Tangelwuld
　　Tangelwuld Press (0-934667)
Tanro Co
　　Tanro Company (0-9617220)
Taosedon Pr
　　Taosedon Press (0-9615915)
Tarantula Pr
　　Tarantula Press (0-935737)
Tartan Tiger
　　Tartan Tiger (0-935827)
Tatnic Pr
　　Tatnic Press, The (0-9615599)
Taverly-Churchill
　　Taverly-Churchill (0-9616595)
Taylor Cty Hist Soc
　　Taylor County & Historical Society
　　(0-9617105)
Taylor Pubns
　　Taylor Publications (0-935881)
Taylor Pubs
　　Taylor Publishers (0-935947)
Taylor Taylor
　　Taylor, Taylor & Taylor (0-9616149)
TCNFPC
　　Twin Cities Natural Family Planning
　　Center, Incorporated (0-9616827)
Teak Wood Pr
　　Teak Wood Press (0-937281)
TEC Pubns
　　T E C Publications (0-937533)
Tech Analysis
　　Technical Analysis, Incorporated (0-938773)
Tech Educ Conslt
　　Technical Educational Consultants
　　(0-939247)
Technics Pubns
　　Technics Publications, Inc. (0-935159)
Technipubs
　　Technipubs, Incorporated (0-936743)
Techsonic Ind
　　Techsonic Industries, Incorporated
　　(0-9616859)
Tecohio Pub Co
　　Tecohio Publishing Company (0-9616116)
Tecolote Pubns
　　Tecolote Publications (0-938711)
Tekakwitha Ins
　　Tekakwitha Institute of Ancient Man
　　(0-935569)
TEL Pubs
　　T E L Publishers, Limited (1-55588)
Telex Russian Educ Bks
　　Telex-Russian Educational Books,
　　Incorporated (0-938181)
Telford Pr
　　Telford Press, The (0-936923)
Tembo Prod
　　Tembo Productions, Incorporated
　　(0-938177)
Templar Pr OH
　　Templar Press (0-939039)
Temple Geneal
　　Temple Genealogical Society (0-9616195)

U KS Dept Art Music
University of Kansas, Department of Art & Music Education & Music Therapy (0-936117)

U M H & C
University of Minnesota Hospital & Clinic, Consultation/Education Division (0-937423)

U Miami N-S Ctr
University of Miami North/South Center, Graduate School of International Studies (0-935501)

U MO Plant Bio
University of Missouri-Columbia, Interdisciplinary Plant Biochemistry & Physiology Group (0-936463)

U Nebr IANR
University of Nebraska, Institute of Agriculture & Natural Resources (0-9616828)

U New Haven Pr
University of New Haven Press (0-936285)

U of FL African Studies
University of Florida Center for African Studies (0-935833)

U Penn South Asia
University of Pennsylvania, Department of South Asia Regional Studies (0-936115)

U-Read Pubns
U-Read Publications (0-938925)

U Temecula Pr
University of Temecula Press (0-936283)

U WI Sea Grant
University of Wisconsin Sea Grant Institute (0-936287)

UCal Berk CLRE
University of California, Berkeley, Center for Labor Research & Education (0-937817)

UCP NYC
United Cerebral Palsy of New York City, Incorporated (0-9616554)

UCPANB
United Cerebral Palsy Association of the North Bay (0-9616891)

UH CRDG
University of Hawaii at Manoa, Curriculum Research & Development Group (0-937049)

Ukrainian Her Co
Ukrainian Heritage Company (0-936113)

Ultima Thule Pub
Ultima Thule Publishing Company (0-938203)

UMHB Pr
University of Mary Hardin-Baylor Press (0-9616297)

Underhill Enter
Underhill Enterprises (0-9616734)

Underwater Spec Ltd
Underwater Specialists, Limited (0-936655)

Uneeda Pr
Uneeda Press (0-9617283)

Unique Pubs
Unique Publishers (0-936811)

United Comns
United Communications of America, Incorporated (0-937047)

United Galactic Pub
United Galactic Publishing Foundation Press. *Imprint of* First Intl Pub

United Pub Co
United Publishing Company (0-937323)

United Pubs Intl
United Publishers International, Limited (0-939499)

United Seminars Amer
United Seminars of America, Incorporated (0-938093)

United Spirit
United Spiritual Temple (0-935611)

Univ AZ Mex Amer Studies
University of Arizona, Mexican American Studies & Research Center (0-939363)

Univ Book Hse
University Book House (0-936461)

Univ CA Dutch Studies
University of California, Dutch Studies Program (0-9616744)

Univ Chi Ctr Hlth
University of Chicago, Center for Health Administration Studies (0-9616519)

Univ CO Dept Hist
University of Colorado-Denver, Department of History (0-937859)

Univ GA Nat Res
University of Georgia Institute of Natural Resources (0-935835)

Univ Health Ctr
University of Oklahoma Health/Science Center, Department of Family Medicine (0-9617230)

Univ Houston Mex Amer
University of Houston, Mexican American Studies Program (0-939709)

Univ Lions Club
University Lions Club Foundation of Seattle, The (0-9617052)

Univ MI Dental
University of Michigan Program in Dental Public Health (0-935837)

Univ MN Art Mus
University of Minnesota, University Art Museum (0-938713)

Univ MS Schl Engin
University of Mississippi School of Engineering, The (0-937099)

Univ Pr San Francisco
University Press (0-9616978)

Univ Pub Assocs
University Publishing Associates, Incorporated (0-8026)

Univ Pub CA
Universal Publishing (0-9617022)

Univ Pub Group
University Publishing Group (1-55572)

Univ Pub Inc
University Publishing, Incorporated (0-938381)

Univ RI Ocean Mgt
University of Rhode Island, Center for Ocean Management Studies (0-938095)

Univ South ME
University of Southern Maine, College of Education (0-939561)

Univ TN Alumni
University of Tennessee National Alumni Association, The (0-9616311)

Upper Rm Pub
Upper Room Publishing Company (0-938645)

Upper Strata
Upper Strata Ink, Incorporated (0-9616589)

Ursus Pr NY
Ursus Press (0-9615441)

US Court Tennis
U. S. Court Tennis Association (0-9615695)

US HHS
U. S. Department of Health and Human Services (1-55672)

US Holocaust Mem
United States Holocaust Memorial Council (0-9616518)

US LST Assn
United States L S T Association (0-9616588)

US Space Found
United States Space Foundation (0-9616962)

USA Pub CA
U S A Publishing Company (0-938446)

USA Pubs
U S A Publishers (0-936577)

USAF Aux
U. S. Air Force Auxiliary, Oklahoma Wing (0-938893)

USR Group
U S R Group (0-936593)

UT Arts Festival
Utah Arts Festival Foundation, Incorporated (0-939011)

Utah Geo Series
Utah Geographic Series, Incorporated (0-936331)

UTX SLIS
University of Texas at Austin, Graduate School of Library & Information Science (0-938729)

V A Bradford
Bradford, Vance A. (0-9615983)

V A Ostendorf
Ostendorf, Virginia A., Incorporated (0-937007)

V J P Enter
V J P Enterprises (0-9615924)

V Lockman
Lockman, Vic (0-936175)

V Lopez
Lopez, Violet (0-9615909)

V Luker
Luker, Vera G. (0-9615733)

V Parrish Pub
Parrish, Vernon, Publishing (0-9615774)

V S FitzPatrick
FitzPatrick, V. S. (0-937173)

V Sharp Pub
Sharp, Vera, Publishing Company (0-9616987)

VA Army Natl Guard
Virginia Army National Guard Foundation (0-9616860)

VA Cardinal Pubns
Virginia Cardinal Publications, Incorporated (0-938951)

VA Ctr Creative Arts
Virginia Center for Creative Arts

Vaishnava
Vaishnava Research Institute (0-935485)

Val Geol Pubns
Valley Geological Publications (0-9616520)

Valaske Pub
Valaske Publishing (0-9616601)

Valee Studios
Valee Studios (0-9615939)

Valley Bk
Valley Book Company (0-9616255)

Van Arsdale Video
Van Arsdales Video Travel Guides (0-939005)

Vance Pubns
Vance Publications (0-938595)

Vanderbilt Pubns
Vanderbilt University Publications in Anthropology (0-935462)

Vanderkolk
Vanderkolk Publishing (0-9617269)

Vanessapress
Vanessapress

Variena Publishing
Variena Publishing (0-939225)

Variety Artists Bks
Variety Artists Books (0-939639)

Vashon Pt Prod
Vashon Point Productions (0-9616103)

VC Pub
V C Publishing (0-935333)

Vector Inter
Vector Intercontinental (0-937907)

Vel-or Co
Vel-or Company (0-9615906)

Venture Assocs
Venture Associates, Incorporated (0-9616346)

Venture Indus
Venture Industries, Incorporated (0-937051)

Venture Pr AZ
Venture Press (0-936465)

Vergin Pr
Vergin Press (0-935839)

Verve Pr
Verve Press (0-937363)

Vervir
Vervir, Incorporated (0-935247)

Very Healthy Ent
Very Healthy Enterprises (0-9615452)

Very Vera
Very Vera (0-937747)

Vestron Video
Vestron Video, Incorporated (0-8051)

Vetco Printing
Vetco Printing & Publishing (0-9616448)

Vets Prof Mgmt
Veternarians Professional Management Company (0-936233)

Vibrante Pr
Vibrante Press (0-935301)

Vicious Cir Pr
Vicious Circle Press (0-936393)

Vicris Pubn
Vicris Publication (0-9616644)

Victorian Video
Victorian Video Productions (0-936225)

Victory Pub
Victory Publishing (0-935303)

VICY
Virgin Islands Commission on Youth (0-937421)

Video Assocs
Video Associates, Incorporated (1-55593)

Video Award
Video Award Motion Pictures, Incorporated (0-936311)

Video Pubns Ltd
Video Publications Limited (0-935667)

Video Travel
Video Travel, Incorporated (1-55629)

Video Treas
Video Treasures (1-55529)

VIEW Inc
V I E W, Incorporated (0-8030)

Vigilantero Pr
Vigilantero Press (0-9616829)
Vil Oak Pk
Village of Oak Park (0-9616915)
Village Hse Pubs
Village House Publishers (0-9617255)
Villanova U Ath
Villanova University, Athletic Department
(0-9615910)
VIP Directory
V I P Directory, The (0-937955)
VIP Int
V I P International, Incorporated
(0-9615601)
Vision Ventures
Vision Ventures, Incorporated (0-9616958)
Visionary Pub
Visionary Publishing, Incorporated
(0-937223)
Visions Success
Visions for Success, Incorporated
(0-9616406)
Visual Attraction
Visual Attraction (0-9617201)
Visual Comm
Visual Communications, Inc. (0-9615759)
Visual Educ Assn
Visual Education Association (1-55637)
Vita Sign
Vita-Sign (0-939389)
Volunteer Council
Volunteer Council of the Tulsa Philharmonic
Society, Incorporated (0-9617004)
Voyager Pub FL
Voyager Publishing, Incorporated
(0-938161)
Voyager Pub Hse
Voyager Publishing House (0-9616751)
Vydex Mgmt
Vydex Management Group, Incorporated
(0-935663)
W A Hutchinson
Hutchinson, William A. (0-9615427)
W Bittinger
Bittinger, Wayne (0-9616990)
W C Cullar
Cullar, W. Clytes (0-9616504)
W C Hays
Hays, William C. (0-9616625)
W D Staples
Staples, Walter D. (0-9616385)
W Dean Editions
Dean, Wayne, Editions (0-9616161)
W E May
May, William E. (0-9616086)
W G Weger
Weger, William G. (0-9617058)
W Griffin Assocs
Griffin, Wesley, Associates (0-9617144)
W J Stewart
Stewart, William J. (0-9615440)
W James Pr
James, William, Press (0-938537)
W L Bates
Bates, William L., Publisher (0-9615781)
W L Morford
Morford, Wanda L. (0-9616543)
W N Becht
Becht, W. Nicholas (0-9617254)
W Nehmer
Nehmer, Wilford (0-9616386)
W P S Pub Co
W P S Publishing Company (0-935841)
W P Smedley
Smedley, W. P., Company (0-938279)
W Schocken
Schocken, Wolfgang A. (0-9615883)
W Stery
Stery, William, Company (0-937913)
W T Doyle
Doyle, William T. (0-9615486)
WA State U Vet
Washington State University, Department of
Veterinary Microbiology & Pathology
(0-936375)
Waggoner Cent
Waggoner Centennial Eighty-Six Committee
(0-9616552)
Walt Whitman
Whitman, Walt Center for the Arts &
Humanities (0-9615683)
Walter Griffin
Griffin, Walter (0-9616153)
Wandering You Pr
Wandering You Press (0-9617104)
War Eagle Cooks
War Eagle Cooks (0-9616521)

Ward's Natl Sci
Ward's Natural Science Establishment,
Incorporated (0-89873)
Warehouse Pub
Warehouse Publishing Company
(0-9616841)
Warrbek Video
Warrbek Video Productions (0-937403)
Warren Bk Pub
Warren Book Publishing Company
(0-938287)
Warrior Pub
Warrior Publishing, Incorporated
(0-9615507)
Warrior Pub WI
Warrior Publishing (0-9616735)
Wary Canary
Wary Canary Press (0-9616126)
Wasatch Educ Syst
Wasatch Education Systems (0-938897)
Wash Intl Assocs
Washington International Associates
Wash Proj Arts
Washington Project for the Arts (0-937237)
Wash Res Assocs
Washington Research Associates (0-937801)
Wash Trail Assn
Washington Trails Association (0-936289)
Water St Missouri
Water Street Publishers (0-9616799)
Waterfall LA
Waterfall Press, The (0-930684)
Waterfront DC
Waterfront Press, The (0-935957)
Waters Edge
Water's Edge Publishing Company
(0-9615609)
Waterway Pr
Waterway Press (0-936689)
Watson Pub Hse
Watson Publishing House (0-939035)
Waverly Comm Hse
Waverly Community House, Incorporated
(0-9616433)
Waverly Pub
Waverly Publishers (0-9615681)
Wayne Omari Ed Game
Wayne-Omari Educational Game Company
(0-9616325)
WCF Pubns
W C F Publications (0-9615904)
WCP Pubns
W C P Publications (0-937365)
Weatherly Pr
Weatherly Press (0-935727)
Webb Country
Webb Country Kennel
Weber Oil
Weber Oil Company (0-9616358)
Weeks Ent
Weeks Enterprises (0-9615604)
Wegferd Pubns
Wegferd Publications (0-937861)
Weidenfeld
Weidenfeld & Nicolson (1-55584)
Wellingham-Jones
Wellingham-Jones, Patricia (0-939221)
Wellness Inst
Wellness Institute, Incorporated (0-9617202)
Wellspring Ent
Wellspring Enterprises (0-937575)
Wellspring Ukiah
Wellspring Books (0-9616568)
Welstar Pubns
Welstar Publications (0-938503)
West Wind Prod
West Winds Productions, Incorporated
(0-935969)
Westcoast Pub
Westcoast Publishing Company (0-937957)
Westerfield
Westerfield, Scott (0-9615537)
Western Bks
Western Books (0-938463)
Western Fish Pr
Western Fisherman's Press (0-9617059)
Western MA Pubs
Western Massachusetts Publishers
(0-9616486)
Western Prof
Western Profiles Publishing Company
(0-937231)
Western Son Acad
Western Son Academy (0-938647)
Westfield Ctr Early Keyboard
Westfield Center for Early Keyboard
Studies, Incorporated (0-9616755)

Westlake Pub
Westlake Publishing Company (0-935709)
Westloch Pubns
Westloch Publications (0-9616964)
Westminster Trading
Westminster Trading Corporation, The
(0-938953)
Westpark Bks
Westpark Books (0-936205)
WestView Pub
WestView Publishing Company (0-937535)
Westwood Ent
Westwood Enterprises (0-9617118)
Westwood Pr
Westwood Press, Incorporated (0-936159)
WFHAAVSC
World Federation of Health Agencies for
the Advancement of Voluntary Surgical
Contraception (0-935955)
Whale Pub
Whale Publishing (0-9616487)
Whale Pubns
Whale Publications (0-9615448)
Wheaton Resource
Wheaton Resource Corporation (0-936657)
Wheedle Inc
Wheedle, Incorporated (0-936873)
Wheel Pr
Wheel Press, Incorprated (0-936747)
Wheelgun Pr
Wheelgun Press (0-937289)
Where to Find OR in OR
Where to Find The Oregon in Oregon
(0-9616696)
Whirling Vortices
Whirling Vortices (0-9616147)
White Hse
White House Theater, The (0-9615860)
White Lion Pr
White Lion Press (0-9615707)
White Rhino Pr
White Rhinoceros Press, The (0-9616760)
Whitehall Co
Whitehall Company (0-87655)
Whitehaven Pub
Whitehaven Publishing (0-936291)
Whitehorse
Whitehorse (0-937591)
Whites Creek Pr
Whites Creek Press (0-9616918)
Whitfield Pub
Whitfield Publishing Company (0-938649)
Whitt
Whitt, Jane Chapman (0-9615446)
Whitts Three Ent
Whitt's Three Enterprises (0-9617082)
Who's Who Electro
Who's Who in Consumer Electronics,
Incorporated (0-935305)
WI Conf United Meth Ch
Wisconsin Annual Conference of the United
Methodist Church, The (0-938779)
Wide Horiz Pr
Wide Horizons Press (0-938109)
Widening Horizons
Widening Horizons, Incorporated
(0-9616310)
Wild Clover Bks
Wild Clover Books (0-9616008)
Willamette Kayak Canoe Club
Willamette Kayak & Canoe Club
(0-9616257)
Willco Pub
Willco Publishing (0-937579)
William Dana
William & Dana Company (0-9616258)
Williams-Wright Pub
Williams/Wright Publishers (0-937961)
Willow Pr
Willow Press (0-9617159)
Willowdale Pr
Willowdale Press (0-9613955)
Wilmer Graph
Wilmer Graphics, Incorporated (0-9615967)
Wilson Crewe
Wilson & Crewe (0-9616673)
Wilson Pub Inc
Wilson Publishing, Incorporated (0-9616299)
Wind & Sea Pr
Wind & Sea Press (0-9616009)
Wind River Bks
Wind River Books (0-938023)
Windrose Pub
Windrose Publications (0-9615508)
Windsor Pr
Windsor Press, Inc., The. *Imprint of*
Gamliels Pub

Windstar Bks
Windstar Books (0-9616306)
Windwalker Pr
Windwalker Press (0-938025)
Wings Pub Prod
Wings Publishing & Production Company
(0-9616010)
Winners Pub
Winners Publishing Company (0-938099)
Winnetka Pr
Winnetka Press (0-938901)
Winning St Paul
Winning Publications (0-9617124)
Winston & Beck
Winston & Beck (0-9615921)
WinterSpring Pr
WinterSpring Press (0-938651)
Wires Ltd
Wires, Limited (0-9616173)
Wiscott Ent
Wiscott Enterprises (0-938533)
WLCJ
Women's League for Conservative Judaism
(0-936293)
Wms & Assocs IA
Williams & Associates (0-938185)
Wndsr Locks Hist Soc
Windsor Locks Historical Society
Wolfdog Pubns
Wolfdog Publications (0-9616191)
Woman's Pr
Woman's Press, The (0-9614878)
Womens Referral Serv
Women's Referral Service, Incorporated
(0-937121)
Wood Moor Ent
Wood Moor Enterprises (0-936307)
Woodley Pubns
Woodley Publications (0-937623)
Woodruff Pub
Woodruff Publishing Company (0-9616165)
Woods Colt Pr
Woods Colt Press
Woodside Pr
Woodside Press (0-9615870)
Woodside Pr ID
Woodside Press (0-938191)
Woodworkers Index
Woodworker's Index (0-9616050)
Word Dynamics
Word Dynamics Concept (0-939023)
Word In Rhyme
Word In Rhyme Publishing Company, The
Word Picture Prod
Word Picture Productions (0-937865)
Word Play DC
Word Play (0-938761)
Wordpix Serv
Wordpix Services (0-9615971)
WordSmith Inc
WordSmith, Incorporated (0-936295)
Wordspinner Pr
Wordspinner Press (0-939043)
Workshop Pubns
Workshop Publications (0-939223)
Workshops Unltd
Workshops Unlimited (0-9616926)
World Class Ski
World Class Ski Tuning (0-9615712)

World Guide
World Guide Corporation
(0-939491)
World Mission
World Missionary Assistance Plan
(0-9615442)
World Music Pr
World Music Press (0-937203)
World Peace Univ
World Peace University (0-939169)
World Univ Amer
World University of America (0-939375)
World Yesterday
World of Yesterday, The (0-936505)
Worlds Wonder
Worlds of Wonder (1-55578)
Worldwide Travel
Worldwide Travel & Tourism Center
(0-9690625)
Wormwood Pr
Wormwood Press (0-937523)
Wounded Coot
Wounded Coot Greetings (0-935583)
WPL Assocs
W P L Associates, Incorporated (0-9605442)
Wrdsmith Pubns
Wordsmith Publications (0-9615608)
Wright Hand
Wright Hand Book Keeping (0-9616960)
Wright Pub
Wright, Curtis, Publishing (0-935249)
Wright Pub VA
Wright Publishing Company (0-9617119)
Wrinkles
Wrinkles (0-9616463)
Write Protect
Write Protect Publishing Company
(0-935393)
Write Words
Write Words, Incorporated, The (0-938597)
Write Your Life
Write for Your Life (0-9616259)
Writers W Alameda
Writers West of Alameda, Incorporated
(0-9616107)
Writing Soft Intl
Writing Software International (0-939227)
WRK Prods
W R K Productions (0-939579)
Wrld Mission Crusade
World Mission Crusade (0-938351)
Wrldwide Trav SB
Worldwide Travel Series (0-938653)
Wrobleski
Wrobleski (0-935585)
WV Business Pub
West Virginia Business Publishing
Corporation (0-937683)
WV Highlands
West Virginia Highlands Conservancy
(0-9616553)
WV Univ Coop Ext
West Virginia University Cooperative
Extension Service (0-9616194)
WV Womens Found
West Virginia Women's Foundation
(0-9617031)
WWAI
Who's Who in Artificial Intelligence

WWF Bks
W W F Books (0-9616263)
wY'east Consulting
wY'east Consulting (0-9616865)
Wyndham Pub
Wyndham Publishing Company
(0-938775)
XPrime
XPrime Corporation (0-937185)
XyloPub Ltd
XyloPub, Limited (0-9616862)
Y C B A C
You Can Be a Classic, Incorporated
(0-939285)
Yacht Imp
Yacht Import Services (0-935471)
Yaker Enviro
Yaker Environmental Systems, Incorporated
(0-937055)
Yellow Stone Pr
Yellowstone Press (0-9617253)
Yes Intl
Yes International (0-936663)
You Are Winner
You Are a Winner (0-9615778)
Young Ideas
Young Ideas (0-9616786)
Young Pr Idaho
Young Press (0-9616273)
Your New Beginning
Your New Beginning (0-9616892)
Youth Mission
Youth with a Mission International
(0-9615534)
Yuganta Pr
Yuganta Press (0-938999)
Yummy Designs
Yummy Designs (0-936467)
YWCA WA
Young Womens Christian Association of
Seattle (0-9615533)
Z P Wesolowski
Wesolowski, Zdzislaw P. (0-937527)
Zaram Promo
Zaram Promotional Concepts (0-935395)
Zarathustrotemo Pr
Zarathustrotemo Press, The (0-937581)
Zarcon Pr
Zarcon Press (0-9604916)
Zero Pub
Zero Publishing Company (0-9615716)
Zieleks Co
Zieleks Company (0-936675)
Zilzal Pr
Zilzal Press (0-938397)
Zincs Career Guide
Zincs Career Guidance (0-939469)
Zo Pub
Zo Publishing (0-938465)
Zon Intl Pub
Z O N International Publishing Company
(0-939549)
Zone Pr
Zone Press (0-936469)
Zytech Western Pub
Zytech Western Publishing (0-936749)
ZZYZX Pub
Z Z Y Z X Publishing Company,
Incorporated (0-938103)

INACTIVE & OUT-OF-BUSINESS PUBLISHERS

The *Inactive & Out of Business* index is arranged alphabetically by company name, and lists companies that have either gone out of business, or have moved without leaving a forwarding address. The R. R. Bowker Co. has used its best efforts to collect and prepare this index. If the users of this publication know the current addresses for any of these companies, please write to the R. R. Bowker Co., 245 W. 17th St., New York, N.Y. 10011, Attention: Names & Numbers Dept.

A & P Bks, *(A & P Books; 0-86550),* 4592 E. Second St., Benicia, CA 94510 (SAN 237-997X)

A B Hansen, *(Hansen, Arne B.; 0-9600842),* P.O. Box 10638, Glendale, CA 91209 (SAN 207-3811)

A C Gardner, *(Gardner, Arthur C.; 0-9602152),* 601 Eastview Ave., Somerset, MA 02726 (SAN 212-3525)

A-Corn Bks, *(A-Corn Books; 0-933083),* 273AHV, Southbury, CT 06488 (SAN 689-5255)

A D F Myers, *(Myers, Anna Dell Fillingim),* Box 4055, Mountain View, CA 94040 (SAN 212-954X)

A F Matthews, *(Matthews, Allan F.),* 963 Saigon Rd., McLean, VA 22101 (SAN 201-114X) Tel 703-356-7561

A G Harter, *(Harter, A. G.),* 663 Fifth Ave., New York, NY 10022 (SAN 207-6780) Tel 212-355-5633

A Petersen, *(Petersen, Arona S.),* Orders to: St. Thomas Graphics, St. Thomas, VI 00801 (SAN 209-1100)

A R Koester Bks, *(Koester, Arthur R., Books; 0-9602558),* P.O. Box 344, Burbank, CA 91503-0344 (SAN 213-0971)

A S Campbell, *(Campbell, Alice S.; 0-9600664),* 7806 S. 250 E., Lafayette, IN 47905 (SAN 202-3571) Tel 317-538-3479

AAR-Tantalus, *(AAR/Tantalus, Inc.; 0-931052),* 711 W. 14th St., Suite C, Austin, TX 78701 (SAN 281-2371) Tel 512-476-3225; Orders to: P.O. Box 893, Austin, TX 78767 (SAN 281-238X)

Aardvark Pubs, *(Aardvark Pubs. Inc.; 0-917384),* Div. of Bookthrift, Inc., One West 39th St., New York, NY 10018 (SAN 208-9424) Tel 212-221-4610

Aaron Pubs, *(Aaron Pubs., Inc.; 0-936076),* P.O. Box 2572, Sarasota, FL 33578 (SAN 214-0896)

Aasen, *(Aasen, Andreas; 0-9603056),* 1210 Dolores St., San Francisco, CA 94110 (SAN 213-2311) Tel 415-285-9417

ABC *Imprint of* **Sportshelf**

Academy, *(Academy Court),* 176 Academy Lane, Sonoma, CA 95476 (SAN 209-0252)

Accent Edns, *(Accent Editions; 0-942842),* 446 E. 78th St., New York, NY 10021 (SAN 240-1827) Tel 212-737-0072

Ackerman-Rorex, *(Ackerman-Rorex Corp.; 0-942112),* 930 W. Oak St., Ft. Collins, CO 80521 (SAN 239-5266); Dist. by: Jean Ford Assocs., Quail Park F4, 801 S. Rancho Dr., Las Vegas, NV 89106 (SAN 239-5274)

Acme Law, *(Acme Law Book Co., Inc.; 0-910012),* Post Office Bldg., Amityville, NY 11701 (SAN 201-2219) Tel 516-799-8686

Acre Pr, *(Acre Press),* 1515 Mason, Apt. 706, Dearborn, MI 48124 (SAN 213-2737)

Action Child Transport Safety, *(Action for Child Transportation Safety),* P O Box 266, Bothell, WA 98011 (SAN 225-9737)

Action Comp, *(Action Computers),* 79 Prichard St., Fitchburg, MA 01420 (SAN 287-5268) Tel 617-343-9280

Acton Hse, *(Acton House, Inc.; 0-89202),* Div. of CRW Corp., 5005 Newport Dr., Rolling Meadows, IL 60008 (SAN 208-5119) Tel 213-553-7012

Admiralty Pub Hse, *(Admiralty Publishing House, Ltd.; 0-913544),* P.O. Box 191, Annapolis, MD 21404 (SAN 201-1905) Tel 301-268-5291

Adobe Hse Pubns, *(Adobe House Pubns; 0-938062),* 1080 Kaibab No. 75B, Flagstaff, AZ 86001 (SAN 265-3737)

Adobe Pr, *(Adobe Press; 0-933004),* 515 Isleta Blvd. S.W., Box 12334, Albuquerque, NM 87105 (SAN 213-022X) Tel 505-873-1155

Adolph Green, *(Green, Adolph, Publishing Co.; 0-9602198),* P.O. Box 337, Arlington, TX 76010 (SAN 212-7164)

Adoption Pr, *(Adoption Pr.),* P.O. Box 584, Minneapolis, MN 55440 (SAN 219-7510)

Adrian, *(Adrian Press; 0-910024),* 157 W. 57th St., New York, NY 10019 (SAN 201-226X) Tel 212-265-6637

Adriatic Stamp, *(Adriatic Stamp Co.; 0-9603474),* P.O. Box 1651, Maitland, FL 32751 (SAN 213-4497)

Aeolian
See Woolf Quarterly

Aesthetic Accidents, *(Aesthetic Accidents Unltd.; 0-9603458),* 434 Greenwich St., New York, NY 10013 (SAN 213-4527)

African Am Trading, *(African American Trading Co.),* P.O. Box 43585, Los Angeles, CA 90043 (SAN 216-2156) Tel 213-294-2314

African Policy, *(African Policy Institute),* 120 Wall St., Suite 1044, New York, NY 10005 (SAN 215-1235)

Afterimage, *(Afterimage Book Pubs.; 0-934862),* P.O. Box 31064, El Paso, TX 79931 (SAN 213-232X) Tel 915-562-4578

Afterthought Bks, *(Afterthought Books; 0-915290),* 147 Woodmont Blvd., Nashville, TN 37205 (SAN 207-4125) Tel 615-292-4919

Agate Pr, *(Agate Press, Inc.; 0-937266),* 51 E. 42nd St., New York, NY 10017 (SAN 220-1348)

Agora Pr, *(Agora Press; 0-934622),* P.O. Box 1085, La Jolla, CA 92038 (SAN 213-2745)

Agriware Co
See Agriware Pubns

Agriware Pubns, *(Agriware Pubns.; 0-912859),* P.O. Box 1927, Mankato, MN 56002-1927 (SAN 282-9614)

Ahday Pubs, *(Ahday Pubs.; 0-910031),* Div. of the Neighbor-Link Inc., 5530 E. 79th St., Indianapolis, IN 46250 (SAN 241-1954) Tel 317-849-0404

Air Taxi Comm Pilots, *(Air Taxi & Commercial Pilots Assn.),* 14030 Connecticut Ave., No. 6720, Silver Spring, MD 20906 (SAN 688-7147)

Airbrush, *(Airbrush Digest Bk. Pr.; 0-918511),* 521 SW 11th Ave., Portland, OR 97205 (SAN 657-5668)

AJK Pubns Co, *(AJK Pubns. Co.),* 3207 Villa Highland, Pasadena, CA 91107 (SAN 669-6325)

AL Coun Comp Ed, *(Alabama Council for Computer Education),* P.O. Box 6105, Dothan, AL 36302 (SAN 676-7567)

Al Kitab Sudan, *(Al Kitab Sudan & Rene Productions; 0-914388),* 9846 A St., Oakland, CA 94603 (SAN 206-7196)

Alameda, *(Alameda Poets; 0-916734),* P.O. Box 1751, Alameda, CA 94501 (SAN 208-2667)

Alamo Comp, *(Alamo Computer Co.),* 1234 Avant, San Antonio, TX 78210 (SAN 287-5284) Tel 512-534-7782

Albion, *(Albion Corp., Co.; 0-87843),* 174 Redwood Highway, San Rafael, CA 94903 (SAN 201-2421) Tel 415-479-1000

Alcott Pr, *(Alcott Press, Inc.; 0-936998),* P.O. Box 335, Edwardsville, IL 62025 (SAN 215-2916) Tel 618-656-7445

Aldebaran Rev, *(Aldebaran Review; 0-917744),* 2209 California St., Berkeley, CA 94703 (SAN 209-6978) Tel 415-549-2456

Alder Pr, *(Alder Press Inc.; 0-9601940),* P.O. Box 25361, Houston, TX 77005 (SAN 212-0100)

Aldine, *(Aldine Publishing Co.; 0-202),* 529 S. Wabash Ave., Chicago, IL 60605 (SAN 212-6338)

Aldine
See Beresford Bk Serv

Alexandria Hse, *(Alexandria Hse. Bks.; 0-932496),* Div. of Kephart Communications, Inc., 901 N. Washington St., Suite 605, Alexandria, VA 22314 (SAN 218-8104) Tel 703-836-3313

All in All, *(All in All Alliance, Ltd.; 0-912819),* P.O. Box 910, New York, NY 10003 (SAN 262-0006) Tel 212-475-2048

All This, *(All This & Less Pubs.; 0-915682),* Regents 509, NMSU, Las Cruces, NM 88003 (SAN 207-7795)

Allwyn Pr, *(Allwyn Press; 0-911768),* P.O. Box 240, Washington Bridge Sta., New York, NY 10033 (SAN 201-2502) Tel 212-796-0498

Alpha Centurion, *(Alpha Centurion Publishing Co.),* P.O. Box 6117, St Petersburg, FL 33706 (SAN 207-2017)

Alpha IN, *(Alpha Pubns.; 0-937400),* P.O. Box 655, Winona Lake, IN 46590 (SAN 216-2180)

Alpha Omega, *(Alpha Omega Publishing Co.; 0-931608),* P.O. Box 4130, Medford, OR 97501 (SAN 211-5042) Tel 503-826-7302

Alpha-Omega Bk, *(Alpha/Omega Book Publishers, Inc.; 0-938764),* 605 W. 113th St. Suite 82, New York, NY 10025 (SAN 237-9279) Tel 212-864-4638

Alpha-Omega Bks
See Alpha-Omega Bk

Alpha Pr Wis, *(Alpha Press; 0-914416),* 10721 W. Capitol Dr., Suite 201, Milwaukee, WI 53222 (SAN 201-1220)

Alpha Printing, *(Alpha Printing Ltd.; 0-937268),* 6301-B Central Ave., N.W., Albuquerque, NM 87105 (SAN 215-6172)

Altamira Lascaux, *(Altamira/Lascaux Pubs.),* P.O. Box 564, Housatonic, MA 01236 (SAN 210-606X)

Altar Bks, *(Altar Books, Altar Records, Altar Film Productions; 0-941148),* P.O. Box 404, Luray, VA 22835 (SAN 239-5126)

Alto Pr, *(Alto Press),* P.O. Box 973, Nogales, AZ 85621 (SAN 206-2208) Tel 602-281-1568

Alva Johnson, *(Johnson, Alva J.; 0-9602608),* 211 Fireside Rd., Falmouth, ME 04105 (SAN 281-2800) (SAN 282-5872)

Am Assn Soc Direct, *(American Assn. of Social Directories; 0-89077),* 10889 Wilshire Blvd., Los Angeles, CA 90024 (SAN 207-1223)

Am Ethnic, *(American Ethnic Press; 0-9605766),* P.O. Box 1994, Grand Central Sta., New York, NY 10163 (SAN 216-2199)

Am Guide Pubns, *(American Guide Pubns.; 0-932948),* P.O. Box 1000, Glendale, CA 91209 (SAN 215-126X) Tel 213-956-3716

Am Inst Bio Sci, *(American Institute of Biological Sciences; 0-936829),* Eastern Illinois Univ., Charleston, IL 61920 (SAN 225-1469)

Am Love Letters, *(American Love Letters Inc.; 0-916083),* 8306 Wilshire Blvd., Suite 194, Beverly Hills, CA 90211 (SAN 294-894X) Tel 213-471-1752

Am Mizrachi Women, *(American Mizrachi Women's Publishing Co.),* 615 Nye Ave., Irvington, NJ 07111 (SAN 213-9065)

Am Natl Pub, *(American National Publishing Co.; 0-913514),* 237 Plymouth Bldg., 12 S. Sixth Street, Minneapolis, MN 55402 (SAN 200-0119) Tel 612-338-3362 *Imprints:* Shannon (Shannon); Yellow Bird (Yellow Bird).

Am Pub House, *(American Publishing House),* P.O. Box 256, Union City, NJ 07087 (SAN 240-1320)

Am Register, *(American Register of Exporters & Importers),* 1 Penn Plaza, New York, NY 10001 (SAN 203-5227) Tel 212-695-0500

Am Res Pr, *(American Research Press; 0-937616),* 5153 Elkmont, Rancho Palos Verdes, CA 90274 (SAN 215-2924)

Am Samizdat, *(American Samizdat; 0-935500),* 724 Tenth Ave., Apt. 4A, New York, NY 10019 (SAN 213-4578) Tel 212-586-5780

Am Spaniel, *(American Spaniel Club),* 12 Wood Ln. S., Woodmere, NY 11598-2298 (SAN 225-5553) Tel 516-295-1693

Ambassador Pubns, *(Ambassador Pubns.),* P.O. Box 4206, Clearwater, FL 33518 (SAN 202-4780)

Amber Beetle, *(Amber Beetle Press; 0-937432),* 6315 Camac St., Philadelphia, PA 19141 (SAN 240-818X)

Amber Crest
See Bk Pools

Ambiente Environ, *(Ambiente Environmental Concerns; 0-937302),* P.O. Box 13622, San Antonio, TX 78213 (SAN 210-881X) Tel 512-344-0730

Amigo Pr, *(Amigo Pr.; 0-935098),* 620 Lombardi Ln., Laguna Beach, CA 92652 (SAN 213-2796) Tel 714-494-2302

Ampersand, *(Ampersand Pr.; 0-910128),* P.O. Box 241, Princeton, NJ 08540 (SAN 206-9644)

Ampersand Editions, *(Ampersand Editions),* Suite 218, 109 Minna St., San Francisco, CA 94105 (SAN 240-0804); Dist. by: O, P.O. Box 1768, Novato, CA 94948 (SAN 240-0804)

AMTEC, *(AMTEC; 0-941450),* 1028 N. Lake Ave., Suite 103, Pasadena, CA 91104 (SAN 239-3557) *Imprints:* Mgmt Tech (Management Technologies).

AMW, *(Aabbott McDonnell Winchester; 0-89519),* 450 Seventh Ave., New York, NY 10001 (SAN 212-2685)

Anacapa Pr, *(Anacapa Pr.; 0-9613276),* 3382 Rexford, Ventura, CA 93033 (SAN 653-7448) Tel 805-488-1085

Ancient Age, *(Ancient Age Press; 0-9605224),* P.O. Box 84431, Veterans Administration Branch, Los Angeles, CA 90073 (SAN 215-837X)

Andor Pub, *(Andor Publishing Co., Inc.; 0-89319),* P.O. Box 19, Wilton, CT 06897-0019 (SAN 208-5267)

Anemone Pr, *(Anemone Press),* 1612 19th St., N.W., Washington, DC 20009 (SAN 211-3066)

Anim Welfare, *(Animal Welfare Encyclopedia),* 701 S. Federal Ave., Butler, IN 46721 (SAN 227-3780)

ANKH, *(ANKH Publishing Co., Inc.; 0-933528),* 105 Mechanic St., Fayetteville, NY 13066 (SAN 212-3991) Tel 315-637-5239

ANKHCO FL, *(ANKHCO; 0-9604318),* 909 Breakers Ave. Suite 507, Ft. Lauderdale, FL 33304 (SAN 215-2932) Tel 305-566-8800

Ann Arbor Pr, *(Ann Arbor Press; 0-914644),* 1540 Northwood St., Box 1863, Ann Arbor, MI 48103 (SAN 201-1794) Tel 313-663-1416

Anthelion Pr, *(Anthelion Press, Inc.; 0-89185),* P.O. Box 614, Corte Madera, CA 94925 (SAN 208-0575) Tel 415-924-5311

Anthropology Res, *(Anthropology Resource Center, Inc.; 0-932978),* P.O. Box 15266, Washington, DC 20003-0266 (SAN 212-2642); Dist. by: Cultural Survival, 11 Divinity Ave., Cambridge, MA 02138 (SAN 200-5034)

ANU Pr, *(Australian National Univ. Pr.; 0-7081),* P.O. Box 1365, New York, NY 10023 (SAN 650-0072) Tel 212-799-3854; Dist. by: Publishers Distribution Ctr., Box C831, Rutherford, NJ 07070 (SAN 650-0080) Tel 201-440-8311

Anvil Pr, *(Anvil Pr.; 0-918552),* P.O. Box 37, Millville, MN 55957 (SAN 203-4794) Tel 507-798-2366

ApaGuides, *(ApaGuides),* Dist. by: Bookpeople, 2929 Fifth St., Berkeley, CA 94710 (SAN 168-9517)

Apeiron Pr, *(Apeiron Press; 0-931958),* P.O. Box 5930, Chicago, IL 60680 (SAN 216-6162)

Apocrypha, *(Apocrypha Press),* P.O. Box 12519, Tucson, AZ 85711 (SAN 207-0421)

Apotheca, *(Apotheca Press, Ltd.; 0-930002),* 175 W. Wieuca Rd., N.E., Suite 122, Atlanta, GA 30342 (SAN 210-3400)

Appellate Pub, *(Appellate Publishing; 0-9603848),* P. O. Box 10687, Edgemont Branch, Golden, CO 80401 (SAN 213-828X)

Apple-One, *(Apple One Pub.; 0-915612),* 3923 W. 6th St. Suite 416, Los Angeles, CA 90020 (SAN 204-4927) Tel 213-381-6003

Apple Pie Pr, *(Apple Pie Press; 0-914152),* Dist. by: Ten Speed Press, P.O. Box 7123, Berkeley, CA 94707 (SAN 202-7674) Tel 415-845-8414

Applied Sci Pubs
See ASP Englewood

Aqua-Sol Ent, *(Aqua-Sol Enterprises; 0-9604874),* P.O. Box 18646, Fort Worth, TX 76118 (SAN 220-0317) Tel 817-284-8003

Aquarius Pub Co, *(Aquarius Publishing),* Dist. by: Bookpeople, 2929 Fifth St., Berkeley, CA 94710 (SAN 168-9517) Tel 415-549-9033

Ar-Ce-Em, *(Ar-Ce-Em Conglomerate; 0-9614823),* P.O. Box 3114, Princeton, NJ 08540 (SAN 693-0115) Tel 609-448-5360

Arbor Claremont, *(Arbor Press, The; 0-9607108),* Box 846, Claremont, CA 91711 (SAN 238-9061) Tel 714-624-2698

Arca & Co, *(Arca & Co. Pubs.; 0-918198),* Box 7037, Houston, TX 78712 (SAN 210-1653) Tel 512-264-1059

Archives Ink, *(Archives Ink, Ltd.; 0-915528),* P.O. Box 1776, 16 Prospect Ave., Haworth, NJ 07641 (SAN 207-7132) Tel 201-384-4777

Arete Pubns, *(Arete Pubns.; 0-9602148),* 8655 E. Vista Dr., Scottsdale, AZ 85253 (SAN 212-2065)

Argonaut Bks, *(Argonaut Books, Inc.; 0-914270),* C/O Ebel, 2160 Center Ave., Fort Lee, NJ 07024 (SAN 211-2140)

Arica Pr, *(Arica Press; 0-915086),* P.O. Box 4405, Grand Central Sta., New York, NY 10017 (SAN 207-1584)

Ariel Bks
See Ariel Pr

Ariel Pr, *(Ariel Press),* P.O. Box 9183, Berkeley, CA 94709 (SAN 207-7841) Tel 415-548-8204

Aries Pr, *(Aries Pr.; 0-933646),* P.O. Box 30081, Chicago, IL 60630 (SAN 212-7210) Tel 312-725-8300

Ariz Maps & Bks, *(Arizona Maps & Books),* Box 1133, Sedona, AZ 86336 (SAN 206-4618)

Ark Hse NY, *(Ark House Ltd.; 0-935764),* 100 E. 42nd St., New York, NY 10017 (SAN 213-8298) Tel 212-697-0205; Dist. by: Irvington Pubs., Inc., 551 Fifth Ave., New York, NY 10017 (SAN 207-2408)

Ark Val Pubns, *(Arkansas Valley Publications; 0-910625),* 2628 Mt. Vernon, Springfield, MO 65802 (SAN 267-6443) Tel 417-865-1184

Arlington Ent, *(Arlington Enterprises),* P.O. Box 4381, Arlington, VA 22204 (SAN 207-6721)

Armchair Pr, *(Armchair Press),* 123 Dorchester, Scarsdale, NY 10583 (SAN 209-7028)

Armadillo Pr, *(Armadillo Pr.; 0-912556),* 905 W. 29th St., Austin, TX 78705 (SAN 203-4905) Tel 512-472-7757

Arnold & Assocs, *(Arnold, Jack, & Associates),* 7426 Caminito Carlotta, San Diego, CA 92120 (SAN 211-2124) Tel 714-287-7742

ARS Pubns, *(Anderson Ritchie & Simon, (ARS Pubns.),* 3044 Riverside Dr., Los Angeles, CA 90039 (SAN 208-2233)

Art Glass Exchange, *(Art Glass Exchange, The; 0-932988),* 2960 Arroyo Drive N., San Diego, CA 92103 (SAN 212-8284) Tel 714-295-4079

Art Ideas, *(Art Ideas),* P.O. Box 54A, Yorkville, IL 60560 (SAN 207-592X) Tel 312-554-3850

Artemis Pr, *(Artemis Press; 0-9604664),* P.O. Box 58572, Los Angeles, CA 90058 (SAN 220-0333) Tel 213-692-6556

Artisan Pr, *(Artisan Pr.),* Dist. by: Bookpeople, 2929 Fifth St., Berkeley, CA 94710 (SAN 168-9517) Tel 415-549-3033

Artists USA
See Foun Adv Artists

Arum Pr, *(Arum Press, The; 0-931338),* 3180 University Ave., Suite 230, San Diego, CA 92104 (SAN 211-2841) Tel 714-281-0980

Asia Lib Ser, *(Asia Library Services),* P.O. Box C, Auburn, NY 13021 (SAN 207-0790)

Asis So&So, *(As Is/So & So Press),* 2864 Folsom, San Francisco, CA 94110 (SAN 219-1148)

ASP Englewood, *(Applied Science Pubs.; 0-85334),* 44 Edge St., Englewood, NJ 07631 (SAN 238-0072)

Aspen Pubns, *(Aspen Pubns.; 0-9603756),* 839 S. 250 West, Orem, UT 84057 (SAN 214-2309) Tel 801-225-2403

Aspen Ski Masters, *(Aspen Ski Masters; 0-9600570),* P.O. Box 3071, Aspen, CO 81611 (SAN 203-4980) Tel 303-925-7159

Assert Train Inst, *(Assertive Training Institute; 0-9603958),* P.O. Box 3201, Flagstaff, AZ 86003 (SAN 221-590X)

Assn Busn Prof, *(Association of Business & Professional Women in Construction),* 331 Madison Ave., 3rd Flr., New York, NY 10017 (SAN 689-514X)

Assn Enviro Sci, *(Association of Environmental Scientists & Engineers),* 1001 SW Fifth Ave., Suite 1000, Portland, OR 97204 (SAN 689-6111)

Assn Libertarian Fem, *(Association of Libertarian Feminists),* 7821 Sayonara Dr., Apt. D, Citrus Heights, CA 59610 (SAN 225-6762)

Assn Mgmt Excel, *(Association for Management Excellence),* 25000 Euclid Ave., Cleveland, OH 44117 (SAN 689-4429)

Assn Travel Mkt Exec, *(Assn. of Travel Marketing Executives),* 53 Church St., Stonington, CT 06378 (SAN 689-7592)

Assoc Indus, *(Associated Industries of New York State Inc.),* 150 State St., Albany, NY 12207 (SAN 226-4463)

Assoc Pubs NY, *(Associated Pubs.; 0-940902),* 40 Fairview Ave., White Plains, NY 10603 (SAN 223-1611) Tel 914-997-0671

Astarte, *(Astarte, Inc.; 0-917506),* P.O. Box 404, Sausalito, CA 94965 (SAN 207-6152)

Aston Hall, *(Aston Hall Pubns, Inc.; 0-89936),* 1835 Hicks Rd., Rolling Meadows, IL 60008 (SAN 213-0068)

ASTPHND, *(Association of State & Territorial Public Health Nutrition Directors),* 1015 18th St., Washington, DC 20036 (SAN 224-3881)

Asylum Hill, *(Asylum Hill, Inc.; 0-9602952),* 243 Sigaurney St., Hartford, CT 06105 (SAN 213-0114)

Atavistic Pr, *(Atavistic Press; 0-915718),* 4605 Campus Ave., No. 8, San Diego, CA 92116 (SAN 208-0540)

Athenian Hse, *(Athenian House Pubs.; 0-936038),* P.O. Box 90968, Nashville, TN 37209 (SAN 213-9103)

Atlantis-by-the-Sea, *(Atlantis-by-the-Sea, Ltd.; 0-89200),* 745 Seventh Ave., New York, NY 10019 (SAN 211-7193)

Atlantis Rising, *(Atlantis Rising; 0-932932),* 308 Eureka St., San Francisco, CA 94114 (SAN 212-2669)

Audubon Pub Co, *(Audubon Publishing Co.; 0-910629),* P.O. Box 581, Owensboro, KY 42302-0581 (SAN 263-2462)

Augustan Lib, *(Augustan Library; 0-916948),* 250 Touchstone Place, Suite 20, West Sacramento, CA 95691 (SAN 207-0413)

Augustus Pub, *(Augustus, Michael, Publishing Co.; 0-9604618),* 802 W. Main, Madisonville, TX 77864 (SAN 238-9118)

Aura Pub, *(Aura Publishing Co.; 0-911643),* 1747 47th St., Brooklyn, NY 11204 (SAN 237-9317)

Aurelian Pr, *(Aurelian Pr.; 0-918844),* P.O. Box 366, Wilmette, IL 60091 (SAN 210-3907) Tel 312-251-6718

Auricle Pr, *(Auricle Press; 0-939904),* 499 Humboldt St., Santa Rosa, CA 95404 (SAN 216-7875)

Auriga, *(Auriga; 0-9602738),* Box F, 8 Candlelight Ct., Clifton Park, NY 12065 (SAN 212-8780)

Automation Print, *(Automation Printing; 0-9603984),* P.O. Box 12201, El Cajon, CA 92022 (SAN 223-4483)

Autumn Pr, *(Autumn Press; 0-914398),* 1318 Beacon St., Brookline, MA 02146 (SAN 207-043X) Tel 617-738-5680

Auxano Pr, *(Auxano Press; 0-933364),* P.O. Box 281, Greenlawn, NY 11740 (SAN 212-4807)

Avery Pr, *(Avery Pr.),* P.O. Box 7396, Atlanta, GA 30357 (SAN 210-9131)

Avion Aviation Bks, *(Avion Aviation Books; 0-913241),* P.O. Box 4596, Oak Brook, IL 60521 (SAN 285-8916) Tel 312-986-5682

Avocation Pubs, *(Avocation Pubs.; 0-934200),* 50 King St., Suite 3D, New York, NY 10014 (SAN 213-2826)

AWAIC, *(Abused Womens Aid in Crisis),* GPO Box 1699, New York, NY 10001 (SAN 237-2975) Tel 212-686-3628

Awareness, *(Awareness Press; 0-917868),* 3649 Elliot S., Apt. 1, Minneapolis, MN 55407 (SAN 209-5262)

AWM Co, *(A. W. M. Company; 0-89105),* P.O. Box 7643, Ann Arbor, MI 48107 (SAN 207-2025) Tel 313-482-7623

AZ Hse Pub, *(Arizona Hse., Publishing; 0-918747),* 611 Miller Valley Rd., Suite 53, Prescott, AZ 86301 (SAN 657-5692) Tel 602-778-9164

B & E Ent, *(B & E Enterprises, Pubs.; 0-915454),* P.O. Box 984, Everett, WA 98206 (SAN 207-7140)

B Ferguson, *(Ferguson, Brenda),* 9854 Fairfax Square, No. 216, New Orleans, VA 22030 (SAN 210-9921)

B Haskewitch, *(Haskewitch, B.),* 701 Empire Blvd., Apt. 1A, Brooklyn, NY 11213 (SAN 207-2033) Tel 212-756-8786

B Hilltop Pr, *(Byram Hilltop Press; 0-9605876),* P.O. Box Z, Andover, NJ 07821 (SAN 216-3934) Tel 201-786-6264

B K Bugge, *(Bugge, Brian K.; 0-9601708),* P.O. Box 598, Staten Island, NY 10314 (SAN 211-5980) Tel 212-442-1405

B M Osowitz, *(Osowitz, B. M.),* 1118 S. Broad St., Trenton, NJ 08611 (SAN 211-6766); Orders to: 1111 N.W. 40th Ave., Pompano, FL 33066 (SAN 211-6774)

B Owens
See Working Pr CA

B Potter, *(Potter, Bill, Golf Professional),* P.O. Box 12-606, Albany, NY 12212 (SAN 265-3796)

B Rust, *(Ventura Press (B Rust)),* 781 Ventura St., Richmond, CA 94805 (SAN 202-4322)

B Rynders Pubns, *(Rynders, B., Pubns.; 0-9601872),* 1514-21 Ave., N.W., New Brighton, MN 55112 (SAN 212-4475)

B Seitz, *(Seitz, Beatrice West),* 214 W. Van Buren St., Janesville, WI 53545 (SAN 203-9435) Tel 608-754-6175

Backpacker Inc
See Foot Trails

Backwards & Backwards, *(Backwards & Backwards; 0-910253),* 101 S. Rocky River Dr., Suite 407, Berea, OH 44017 (SAN 241-4724)

Baier Pubns, *(Baier, Paul M.; 0-9602276),* 114 Canton St., Troy, PA 16947 (SAN 223-4947)

Bainbridge, *(Bainbridge, Inc.; 0-915234),* 1012 St. Louis St., Edwardsville, IL 62025 (SAN 207-1231) Tel 618-656-4817

Bala Pub Div, *(Bala Publishing Division),* 1500 W. 3rd Ave., Suite 329, Columbus, OH 43212 (SAN 215-0573)

Bald Eagle, *(Bald Eagle Press; 0-910196),* 273 Woodland Dr., State College, PA 16801 (SAN 202-3733) Tel 814-238-6167

Bale of Turtle, *(Bale of Turtle Press; 0-912802),* 35 High St., Armonk, NY 10504 (SAN 202-3741)

Baleen Pr, *(Baleen Press; 0-912074),* P.O. Box 13448, Phoenix, AZ 85002 (SAN 201-4068) Tel 212-751-2600

Baltica Pr, *(Baltica Press, Pubs.; 0-910198),* Dist. by: Old Lithuanian Press, 423 Mayfair Lane, Louisville, KY 40207 (SAN 207-5296) Tel 502-897-1241

Bananas, *(Bananas Inc.),* 3025 1/2 Shattuck, Berkeley, CA 94705 (SAN 217-6521)

Banner Bks Intl, *(Banner Books International; 0-89491),* 13415 Ventura Blvd., Sherman Oaks, CA 91423 (SAN 210-0401) Tel 213-990-0024

Bannister Assoc, *(Bannister Associates; 0-89578),* P.O. Box 52, Still River, MA 01467 (SAN 211-0016)

Banta, *(Banta, George, Co.),* Banta's Greek Exchange, Menasha, WI 54952 (SAN 202-375X) Tel 414-722-7771

Bar-None, *(Bar-None Press; 0-9605672),* 6520 Selma Ave., No. 538, Los Angeles, CA 90028 (SAN 216-1079)

Barclay Hse, *(Barclay House; 0-87682),* Div. of American Art Enterprises, Inc., 21322 Lassen St., Chatsworth, CA 91311 (SAN 201-7342) Tel 213-882-5900

Barnard Pr, *(Barnard Press Pubs.),* P.O. Box 622, La Jolla, CA 92038 (SAN 211-6561) Tel 714-488-8151

Barnett, *(Barnett, P.),* 25 Sagamore Rd., Bronxville, NY 10708 (SAN 202-4381)

Baronet, *(Baronet Pub. Co.; 0-89437),* 509 Madison Ave., New York, NY 10022 (SAN 210-1734) Tel 212-752-7331

Baroque, *(Baroque Press, Inc.),* P.O. Box 553, Maplewood, NJ 07040 (SAN 202-3776)

Barrington, *(Barrington Pr., Inc.; 0-938814),* 200 James St., Barrington, IL 60010 (SAN 216-1095) Tel 312-381-9200; Dist. by: Berkshire Traveller Pr., Pine St., Stockbridge, MA 01262 (SAN 201-4424) Tel 413-298-3636

Bartco, *(Bartco Ltd.; 0-936374),* P.O. Box 26634, St. Louis, MO 63122 (SAN 215-059X)

Baseball Facts, *(Baseball Facts; 0-939906),* P.O. Box 3529, Trenton, NJ 08629 (SAN 216-7883)

Basic Medicine, *(Basic Medicine Books; 0-913736),* P.O. Box 40129, San Francisco, CA 94140 (SAN 201-4513) Tel 415-845-5656

Basic Science Prep Ctr, *(Basic Science Preparation Ctr.; 0-9604722),* 55 Willow Tree Lane, Irvine, CA 92715 (SAN 215-7276); Orders to: 1601 Vivian Ln., Louisville, KY 40205 (SAN 215-7284)

Baskin Pubs, *(Baskin Pubs.; 0-935854),* P.O. Box 3127, San Diego, CA 92103 (SAN 214-1043)

Batchelor Dean, *(Batchelor, Dean, Pubns.; 0-914792),* 1155 Katella, Laguna Beach, CA 92651 (SAN 206-331X); Dist. by: Haessner Publishing, Inc., Drawer B, Newfoundland, NJ 07435 (SAN 201-6028)

Baukol Pub, *(Baukol, Philip J., Publishing; 0-9601110),* 5838 Black Olive Dr., No. 20, Paradise, CA 95969 (SAN 209-6579) Tel 916-872-0248

Bay Area Gallery, *(Bay Area Gallery Guidebook; 0-9607460),* 4141 Fruitvale Ave., Oakland, CA 94602 (SAN 238-6321) Tel 415-530-6821

Bay Bks, *(Bay Books; 0-89171),* 909 N. Beverly Glen Blvd., Bel Air, CA 90024 (SAN 207-3161)

Bayard Gallery, *(Bayard Gallery Pubns.; 0-933290),* 233 Broadway E., Seattle, WA 98102 (SAN 212-7229)

BCI Investments, *(B C I Investments; 0-9613024),* 330 S. State Suite 101-103, Ann Arbor, MI 48104 (SAN 293-9045) Tel 313-665-5273

BCP NY, *(Best Cellar Press; 0-932874),* 51 Marilyn Pkwy., Rochester, NY 14624 (SAN 212-4041)

Beach Assocs, *(Beach Associates; 0-910339),* P.O. Box 2010, Orlando, FL 32802 (SAN 241-2721) Tel 305-843-4919

Beacon Hill Pr Seattle, *(Beacon Hill Pr. of Seattle; 0-9613176),* 3419 Lincoln Way, Lynwood, WA 98036 (SAN 295-639X)

Beaconsfield, *(Beaconsfield, C.; 0-910202),* 1360 N. Rowell Ave., Fresno, CA 93703 (SAN 202-3849)

Bearmoth Pr, *(Bearmoth Press, The),* P.O. Box 399, Lomita, CA 90717 (SAN 210-9972)

Bearstone-Shepherd Pub, *(Bearstone/Shepherd Publishing; 0-941152),* 661 Fischer Bldg., Dubuque, IA 52001 (SAN 670-722X)

Beauty & Health, *(Beauty & Health Publishing Corp.; 0-914014),* 1010 3rd Ave., New York, NY 10021 (SAN 202-3881) Tel 212-752-8506

Bede, *(Bede Pr. & Bede Records, Inc.; 0-911970),* Box 36m32, 5350 Wilshire Blvd., Los Angeles, CA 90036 (SAN 206-7358)

Bedminster, *(Bedminster Press; 0-87087),* Vreeland Ave., Totowa, NJ 07512 (SAN 206-7102) Tel 201-256-0700

Bee Bks, *(Bee Books, Inc.; 0-930898),* Div. of Barton Educational Enterprises & Distributors, Inc., 7532 Nohopa Cove, Germantown, TN 38138 (SAN 211-5905)

Beers, *(Beers, J., & Co.),* Orders to: Freshwater Press, Inc., 258 The Arcade, Cleveland, OH 44114 (SAN 201-6699) Tel 216-241-0373

Behavior Mod Tech, *(Behavior Modification Technology, Inc.; 0-89025),* 6214 Presidential Court SW, Ft. Myers, FL 33907 (SAN 205-6054) Tel 813-489-1478

Behaviordelia, *(Behaviordelia, Inc.; 0-914474),* P.O. Box 1044, Kalamazoo, MI 49005 (SAN 201-7539) Tel 616-382-5611

Beinfeld Pub, *(Beinfeld Publishing, Inc.; 0-917714),* 12767 Saticoy St., North Hollywood, CA 91605 (SAN 215-6261)

Being Inc, *(Being Inc.; 0-915412),* P.O. Box 742, Ojai, CA 93023 (SAN 207-2041)

Bell Bks, *(Bell Books),* 4649 Yarmouth Lane, Youngstown, OH 44512 (SAN 217-2283)

Bell-Dell, *(Bell-Dell Co.),* P.O. Box 20624, Chicago, IL 60620 (SAN 205-6062)

Belmont-Tower
See Tower Bks

Bench Pr, *(Bench Pr.; 0-916534),* P.O. Box 24635, Oakland, CA 94623 (SAN 208-2217)

Bentley Pr, *(Bentley Press, The; 0-9608572),* 2542 Camino Alfredo, Santa Fe, NM 87501 (SAN 238-2400) Tel 505-471-5668

Berceau Pubns., *(Berceau Pubns.; 0-934859),* 101 Broadway E., P.O. Box 20217, Seattle, WA 98102 (SAN 694-5597)

Beresford Bk Serv, *(Beresford Book Service; 0-89953),* 1525 E. 53rd St., Suite 431, Chicago, IL 60615 (SAN 212-9957)

Berkshire Writ, *(Berkshire Writers, Inc.; 0-9609540),* c/o Post Office & David Emblidge, Lenox, MA 01240 (SAN 260-1664)

Beta Alpha Psi, *(Beta Alpha Psi),* Univ. of Nebraska, Dept. of Accounting, Lincoln, NE 68588 (SAN 689-8130)

Beta Bk, *(Beta Book Co.; 0-89293),* 10857 Valiente Court, San Diego, CA 92124 (SAN 208-0397) Tel 714-293-3832

Bethlehem Bks, *(Bethlehem Bks.; 0-914869),* P.O. Box 773, Hillsboro, OR 97123 (SAN 289-0607)

Bethlen Pr, *(Bethlen Press, Inc.; 0-917718),* P.O. Box 637, Ligonier, PA 15658 (SAN 209-2190) Tel 412-238-9244

Beyond Barogue
See Beyond Baroque

Beyond Baroque, *(Beyond Baroque Foundation Pubns.),* 681 Venice Blvd., Venice, CA 90291 (SAN 208-4708) Tel 213-822-3006

Bezalel Art, *(Bezalel Art; 0-914734),* 11 Essex St., New York, NY 10002 (SAN 204-0719) Tel 212-228-5982

Bibl Based Develop, *(Biblically Based Developmental Training Books, Inc.; 0-937442),* P.O. Box 15124, Atlanta, GA 30333 (SAN 216-0188)

Bible Lit, *(Bible Literature Pubns.; 0-910236),* 937 Lassen View Dr., Lake Almanor Peninsula, CA 96137 (SAN 201-7318) Tel 916-259-3906

Bible Voice, *(Bible Voice, Inc.; 0-89728),* P.O. Box 7491, Van Nuys, CA 91409 (SAN 211-7843) Tel 213-781-2900; Dist. by: Unilit, 5600 N.E. Hassalo St., Portland, OR 97213 (SAN 211-7851) Tel 800-547-8020

Biblio Pr, *(Bibliography Press),* 111 N. Wabash, Rm. 1310, Chicago, IL 60602 (SAN 207-5016)

Big Sky Bks, *(Big Sky Books),* 151 Hampton Rd., Southampton, NY 11968 (SAN 207-7892)

Bighorn Bks., *(Bighorn Books),* 853 Ogden St., No. 5, Denver, CO 80218 (SAN 202-3326)

Billfel Creative, *(Billfel Creative Press; 0-917544),* 1586 Lawrence Rd., Lawrenceville, NJ 08648 (SAN 208-4309) Tel 609-882-1924

Bingham Pub, *(Bingham Publishing Co.; 0-9601796),* 1318 Harrison St., Wichita Falls, TX 76309 (SAN 211-3511)

Bio Res Inst
See World Natural Hist

Biobooks
See Sullivan Bks Intl

Biological Sci, *(Biological Sciences Curriculum Study),* P.O. Box 930, Boulder, CO 80306 (SAN 201-372X) Tel 303-666-6558

Birch Tree Pr, *(Birch Tree Press; 0-9603124),* 315 S. San Gabriel Blvd., Pasadena, CA 91107 (SAN 213-9111)

Bk Pools, *(Book Pools Ltd.),* 77 W. 55th St., Suite 3-H, New York, NY 10019 (SAN 284-9607); Orders to: P.O. Box 249, Corona, CA 91720 (SAN 284-9615)

Bks Australia, *(Books Australia),* 15601 SW 83rd Ave., Miami, FL 33157 (SAN 212-0658) Tel 305-251-3934

Bks Canada, *(Books Canada),* 33 E. Tupper St., Buffalo, NY 14203 (SAN 201-4378)

Bks for Bet Living, *(Books for Better Living; 0-88491; 0-87056),* Div. of American Art Enterprises, Inc., 21322 Lassen St., Chatsworth, CA 91311 (SAN 201-7334) Tel 213-882-5900

Bks for Libs, *(Books for Libraries, Inc.; 0-8369; 0-518),* 1 Dupont St., Plainview, NY 11803 (SAN 202-4098) Tel 516-938-8100

Bks in Focus, *(Bks., in Focus, Inc.; 0-916728),* P.O. Box 3481, New York, NY 10163 (SAN 208-5607) Tel 212-490-0334

Bks of Wall St, *(Books of Wall Street; 0-918632),* 2524 Cedar Springs, Dallas, TX 75201 (SAN 210-2943) Tel 214-748-7831

Black Am Pubns, *(Black American Pubns.; 0-917885),* P.O. Box 6085, No. 619, Big Spring, TX 79720 (SAN 656-965X) Tel 915-332-3247

Black Foxx Pubs, *(Black Foxx Pubs.; 0-9601142),* P.O. Box 686, Soledad Prison Facility, Soledad, CA 93960 (SAN 209-3456); c/o Harlo Pr., 50 Victor Ave., Detroit, MI 48203 (SAN 202-2745)

Black Hope Found, *(Black Hope Foundation, Inc.; 0-911734),* 1925 Vermont, No. 9, Toledo, OH 43624 (SAN 209-1631)

Black River, *(Black River Writers; 0-916692),* P.O. Box 15853, Sacramento, CA 95813 (SAN 206-4782); Orders to: P.O. Box 2491, East St. Louis, IL 62201 (SAN 206-4790) Tel 916-482-0799

Blackburn Coll, *(Blackburn College Press),* Lumpkin Library, Carlinville, IL 62626 (SAN 201-4335)

Blacksun Pubns, *(Blacksun Pubns.; 0-9611964),* 882 Oakland Dr., Atlanta, GA 30310 (SAN 286-7478)

Blair Pub, *(Blair Publishing Co.; 0-9607782),* P.O. Box 329-B, Bandon, OR 97411 (SAN 237-9392)

Blenheim Pub, *(Blenheim Publishing House; 0-918288),* 4128 Bon Hill Rd., Arlington Heights, IL 60004 (SAN 209-3677)

Blessing Bks, *(Blessing Bks.; 0-934861),* P.O. Box 15998, Salt Lake City, UT 84115 (SAN 694-5600) Tel 801-278-7708

Blind Beggar, *(Blind Beggar Press; 0-940738),* 2059 McGraw Ave., Suite 12G, Bronx, NY 10462 (SAN 219-7154)

Blis Pr, *(Blis Press),* 138 Concourse East, Brightwaters, NY 11718 (SAN 237-9384)

Blue & Gray, *(Blue & Gray Press, Inc; 0-914926),* 605 Merrit St., Nashville, TN 37203 (SAN 209-6382) Tel 615-244-1478

Blue Dolphin, *(Blue Dolphin Enterprises, Inc.; 0-943128),* c/o Pacific Comics, 8423 Production Ave., San Diego, CA 92121 (SAN 239-3573)

Blue Max Pr, *(Blue Max Press, Inc.; 0-916674),* 630 N. College Ave., Suite 312, Indianapolis, IN 46204 (SAN 208-2209) Tel 317-632-2502

Blue Wolf, *(Blue Wolf Press; 0-936714),* 1240 Pine St., Boulder, CO 80302 (SAN 214-2872)

Bluestocking, *(Bluestocking Books; 0-931458),* 1732 32nd Ave., Seattle, WA 98122 (SAN 212-4823)

BO Imprint of **Inscape Corp**

Boardwell-Kloner, *(Boardwell-Kloner),* 323 S. Franklin, Rm. 804, Chicago, IL 60606 (SAN 219-127X)

Boating Writers, *(Boating Writers International),* Box 19900, Milwaukee, WI 53219 (SAN 689-822X)

Bodine, *(Bodine & Assocs., Inc., Pubs.; 0-910254),* The Quadrangle, Suite 132, Village of Cross Keys, Baltimore, MD 21210 (SAN 201-4246) Tel 301-433-7491

Bogden & Quigley, *(Bogden & Quigley, Inc.; 0-8005),* Subs. of Wadsworth Publishing Co., 10 Davis Dr., Belmont, CA 94002 (SAN 206-8478)

Boggle, *(Boggle Pubns.; 0-930532),* 425 E. Sixth St., New York, NY 10009 (SAN 210-5721) Tel 212-260-3064

Bolder Bks, *(Bolder Books, Inc.; 0-918282),* 10 E. 40th St., Suite 2109, New York, NY 10016 (SAN 210-1785) Tel 212-689-5980

Bolder Landry, *(Bolder Landry),* 8925 San Salvador Circle, Buena Park, CA 90620 (SAN 210-9344)

Bond-Parkhurst, *(Bond, Parkhurst Books; 0-87880),* Dist. by: W. W. Norton & Co., Inc., 500 Fifth Ave., New York, NY 10036 (SAN 202-5795) Tel 212-354-5500

Boojum Pr, *(Boojum Pr.; 0-9610186),* 18758 Bryant St., Northridge, CA 91324 (SAN 268-3989)

Book Texas, *(Book Publishers of Texas; 0-910779),* P.O. Box 8262, Tyler, TX 75711-8262 (SAN 260-1672)

Bookhaus, *(Bookhaus),* 545 La Salle, Monroe, MI 48161 (SAN 209-0244)

Booklore Pub
See Booklore Pubs

Booklore Pubs, *(Booklore Pubs., Inc.; 0-931110),* P.O. Drawer 3679, Sarasota, FL 33578 (SAN 212-6427) Tel 813-758-1533

Books AK, *(Books Alaska),* Box 4020-A, Anchorage, AK 99507 (SAN 212-8802)

Bookstax, *(Bookstax of Britain, Ltd.; 0-915356),* 200 Park Ave., Pan Am Bldg., Suite 303E, New York, NY 10017 (SAN 205-6070) Tel 212-268-2421

Bookworld Comm, *(Bookworld Communications Corp.; 0-914242),* P.O. Box 4081, Louisville, KY 40204 (SAN 201-4203)

Border-Mtn Pr, *(Border-Mountain Press; 0-916428),* P.O. Box 1296, Benson, AZ 85602 (SAN 208-0052)

Bormerl, *(Bormerl Oaks Press; 0-911948),* 1210 D. Alhambra Circle, Coral Gables, FL 33146 (SAN 201-4181)

Boston Womens
See Public Works

Bowers & Ruddy, *(Bowers & Ruddy Galleries, Research Facility; 0-914490),* 5525 Willshire Blvd., Los Angeles, CA 90036 (SAN 168-9746)

Bowery Pub, *(Bowery Publishing; 0-9602038),* P.O. Box 12784, Reno, NV 89510 (SAN 212-484X)

Bozo Pr, *(Bozo Press; 0-936774),* P.O. Box 6207, Hilton Head Island, SC 29938 (SAN 216-3411)

Bradford Pr, *(Bradford Press, Inc.; 0-915064),* P.O. Box A3935, Chicago, IL 60690 (SAN 207-0669)

Bradley CPA, *(Bradley CPA Study Aids, Inc.; 0-932788),* 23875 Ventura Blvd., Suite 202B, Calabasas, CA 91302 (SAN 212-338X) Tel 818-340-3779

Bradley David Assocs, *(Bradley David Associates, Ltd.; 0-9601694),* Box 5279, 909 Third Ave., New York, NY 10150 (SAN 211-7282) Tel 212-246-1114

Brady Pr, *(Brady Press; 0-934620),* Div. of KDI Productions, P.O. Box 10012, Jacksonville, FL 32207 (SAN 213-2117) Tel 904-733-8445

Braemar Bks
See Pembroke Pr

BrainStorm Bks, *(BrainStorm Books),* P.O. Box 1407, Tustin, CA 92681 (SAN 216-342X)

Braintree, *(Braintree Pubns.),* P.O. Box 194, Rheem Valley, CA 94570 (SAN 212-1824)

Branch Pr, *(Branch Press; 0-912690),* P.O. Box 229, Bayside, NY 11561 (SAN 202-4195) Tel 516-775-6402; Orders to: P.O. Box 297, New Hyde Park, NY 11040 (SAN 202-4209)

Brandywine Bks, *(Brandywine Books; 0-9604986),* 5020 73rd St., Suite B, San Diego, CA 92115 (SAN 216-020X)

Brasch & Brasch, *(Brasch & Brasch, Pubs., Inc.; 0-89554),* 104 W. C St., Ontario, CA 91762 (SAN 203-3443) Tel 714-986-3631

Brasch & M
See Brasch & Brasch

Braun, *(Braun, C. F., & Co.; 0-910292),* 1000 S. Fremont, Alhambra, CA 91802 (SAN 202-4217)

Bread-N-Butter, *(Besche's Bread 'n' Butter Productions, Inc.; 0-9602282),* Rte. 4, Box 187, Georgetown, DE 19947 (SAN 212-7296) Tel 302-856-6073

Brewers, *(Brewer Bulletin),* P.O. Box 190, Crystal Lake, IL 60014 (SAN 224-0874) Tel 815-459-2231

Briar Co, *(Briar Co., The),* 109 Minna St., San Francisco, CA 94105 (SAN 218-4702)

Bridgeport Pub, *(Bridgeport Publishing Co.; 0-89668),* P.O. Box 148, Oakland, CA 94604 (SAN 211-2205) Tel 415-834-5183

Brigham St Hse, *(Brigham Street Hse.; 0-912482),* 7050 Chris Ln., Salt Lake City, UT 84121 (SAN 202-4225)

Brighton Pub Co, *(Brighton Publishing Co.; 0-89832),* 131 NW Fourth St., Corvallis, OR 97330 (SAN 213-0475)

Brite Offset, *(Brite Offset),* 418 W. 25th St., 7th Floor, New York, NY 10001 (SAN 210-9948)

British Am Bks, *(British American, Bks.; 0-89979),* P.O. Box 302, Willits, CA 95490 (SAN 201-9353)

Bro-Dart Found, *(Bro-Dart Foundation; 0-912654),* 1807 Pembroke Rd., Greensboro, NC 27408 (SAN 204-3890) Tel 919-275-7336; c/o Brodart Publishing Co., 500 Arch St., Williamsport, PA 17701 (SAN 204-3904) Tel 717-326-2461

Bro William Pr, *(Brother William Press),* Dist. by: Bookpeople, 2929 Fifth St., Berkeley, CA 94710 (SAN 168-9517)

Brombacher, *(Brombacher Books; 0-89085),* 691 S. 31st St., Richmond, CA 94804 (SAN 208-3779) Tel 415-232-5380

Brookdale Pr, *(Brookdale Pr.; 0-912650),* 184 Brookdale Rd., Stamford, CT 06903 (SAN 208-3744) Tel 203-322-2474

Brooke Hse, *(Brooke House Pubs., Inc.; 0-912588),* 9010 Reseda Blvd., Suite 226, Northridge, CA 91324 (SAN 203-6746) Tel 213-349-1700

Brooks-Sterling, *(Brooks-Sterling Co.; 0-914418),* 1490 Laurenita Way,, Alamo, CA 94507 (SAN 206-4820) Tel 415-934-3510

Brown Burro, *(Brown Burro Press; 0-918054),* P.O. Box 2863D, Pasadena, CA 91105 (SAN 210-1815) Tel 213-449-2669

Brown Penny, *(Brown Penny Press),* 2555 Agate, Eugene, OR 97403 (SAN 209-5335) Tel 503-687-0361

Brown U Pr, *(Brown Univ. Press; 0-87057),* University Pr. of New England, 3 Lebanon St., Hanover, NH 03755 (SAN 201-9256) Tel 603-646-3348

BRTP Prods, *(BRTP Productions, Inc.; 0-9602280),* 60 Hawthorne Place, Manhasset, NY 11030 (SAN 212-4815)

Bryden, *(Bryden Press; 0-9603510),* P.O. Box 364, Muncie, IN 47305 (SAN 213-7283)

Bryn Mawr, *(Bryn Mawr Press, Inc.; 0-89299),* P.O. Box 690, Bryn Mawr, PA 19010 (SAN 208-5011) Tel 215-665-1965

Buckminster Pr, *(Buckminster Pr.; 0-9610094),* 159A Heritage Hills, Somers, NY 10589 (SAN 268-506X)

Burkett, *(Burkett, Ray De Vere, Pub. Co.; 0-912742),* 1431 Emmett St., Evansville, IN 47713 (SAN 203-8579) Tel 312-464-3102

Burkhard, *(Burkhard, Arthur),* 10 Farewell Place, Cambridge, MA 02138 (SAN 202-490X) Tel 617-547-2716

Burnett Family Gen, *(Burnett Family Genealogical Association, Inc.; 0-9608266),* 3891 Commander Dr., Atlanta, GA 30341 (SAN 240-3471) Tel 404-455-6445

Burning Bush, *(Burning Bush Pubns.; 0-937528),* 103 Middleton Pl., Jeffersonville, PA 19403 (SAN 215-1340) Tel 215-630-8839

Burntcoat Corp, *(Burntcoat Corp.),* Box 350, Hampden, ME 04444 (SAN 216-3454)

Business Brokers, *(Business Brokers Association),* P.O. Box 23934, Fort Lauderdale, FL 33307 (SAN 214-2333) Tel 305-561-1392

Busn Info, *(Business Information Display, Incorporated; 0-938596),* 4202 Sorrento Valley Blvd. Suite J, San Diego, CA 92121 (SAN 238-6879)

Busn Mgmt Res, *(Business Management Research; 0-936602),* 1668 Lombard, San Francisco, CA 94123 (SAN 215-3173) Tel 415-775-4740; Dist. by: Kampmann and Co., 9 E. 40th St., New York, NY 10016 (SAN 201-3800)

Busn Pr, *(Business Pr.),* Dist. by: Taplinger Publishing Co., 132 W. 22nd St., New York, NY 10011 (SAN 213-6821)

Busn Systems Res
See Computer Strat

Busn Writer Pubns, *(Business Writer Pubns.; 0-943022),* Div. of Wash. Advertising Public Relations, 910 17th St NW, Washington, DC 20006 (SAN 240-348X)

Byline Books, *(Byline Books; 0-943996),* 5805C N. Grand Blvd., Oklahoma City, OK 73118 (SAN 240-9690)

C A Jones, *(Jones, Charles A., Publishing Co.; 0-8396),* Div. of Wadsworth Publishing Co., ; c/o Wadsworth Publishing Co., 10 Davis Dr., Belmont, CA 94002 (SAN 200-2213)

C A Krause, *(Krause, Corinne Azen; 0-9604104),* P.O. Box 81096, Pittsburgh, PA 15217 (SAN 214-0462); Dist. by: Caroline House, 2 Ellis Place, Ossining, NY 10562 (SAN 211-2299)

C & B Functional, *(C & B Functional Resumes),* 1414 Miravalle Ave., Los Altos, CA 94022 (SAN 210-8917)

C Banks, *(Banks, Carl),* 1533 W. 85th St., Los Angeles, CA 90047 (SAN 208-2748)

C C Burgess, *(Burgess, Carl C.),* 12816 14th, Yucaipa, CA 92399 (SAN 212-405X)

C Cannon, *(Cannon, C.),* P.O. Box 4671, San Francisco, CA 94101 (SAN 207-0944)

C Catton, *(Catton, Cliff; 0-9602398),* 3 Forest St., Newton Highlands, MA 02161 (SAN 212-2715)

C Clements, *(Clements, Christine),* 1257 E. 81st St., Los Angeles, CA 90001 (SAN 215-7381)

C F Martin, *(Martin, Charles Fontaine; 0-9609984),* P.O. Box 57, Wayland, MA 01778 (SAN 272-2631) Tel 617-369-2226

C Fredericks, *(Fredericks, Carl)* Orders to: Circle Publications, P.O. Box 34, Lyndhurst, NJ 07071 (SAN 209-2093)

C Gallo, *(Gallo, Cristino; 0-9604174),* 1107 E. Ocean View Ave. No. 9, Norfolk, VA 23503 (SAN 214-3062) Tel 804-587-7744; Dist. by: Book Service of Puerto Rico, 102 Avenida De Diego, Santurce, PR 00907 (SAN 214-3070)

C Horn, *(Horn, Calvin, Pubs., Inc.; 0-910750),* P.O. Box 4204, Albuquerque, NM 87106 (SAN 201-9493) Tel 505-268-9226

C Kerr Ent, *(Kerr, Charles, Enterprises, Inc.; 0-936002),* 129 N. Main St., New Hope, PA 18938 (SAN 213-7674) Tel 215-862-3353

C L Neal, *(Neal, Clarke L.),* 456 Skeel, Mountain Lakes, NJ 07046 (SAN 239-4634)

C-Life Inst, *(C-Life Institute),* Box 261, Boulder Creek, CA 95006 (SAN 212-6087)

C M I Pubns, *(C.M.I. Pubns.),* P.O. Box 47075, Dallas, TX 75247 (SAN 209-5440)

C N Vogel
See Vogel Bk

C P Graham
See GramWel Pr

C Stark, *(Stark, Claude, & Co., Pubs.; 0-89007),* P.O. Box 843, Brookline Village, 21 Station St., Boston, MA 02147 (SAN 206-9857) Tel 617-734-2045

C Taylor Pub, *(Taylor, C., Publishing; 0-916811),* 2081 Fairweather Rd., Santa Ana, CA 92705 (SAN 670-6851) Tel 714-544-9113; Dist. by: Publishers Group West, 5855 Beaudry St., Emeryville, CA 94608 (SAN 202-8522)

C V Holland
See Hol-Land Bks

C W Bell
See Bell Bks

C Young, *(Young, Chesley),* P.O. Box 112, Cathedral Sta., New York, NY 10025 (SAN 206-958X)

Cactus Vick, *(Cactus Vick Enterprises; 0-918958),* P.O. Box 2498, Little Rock, AR 72203 (SAN 210-3974) Tel 501-778-3514

Cadleon Pr, *(Cadleon Press; 0-9600310),* P.O. Box 24, San Francisco, CA 94101 (SAN 201-9507)

Cal Living Bks, *(California Living Books; 0-89395),* The Hearst Bldg., Suite 501, Third & Market Sts., San Francisco, CA 94103 (SAN 211-4208)

Calabrese Pubns, *(Calabrese Pubns.; 0-911699),* P.O. Box 7138, Hicksville, NY 11801 (SAN 263-9580)

Calao Pubs, *(Calao Publishers),* 302 W. 5400 S., Suite 104, Salt Lake City, UT 84107 (SAN 240-8724)

Calico Mse Pubns, *(Calico Mouse; 0-943134),* 924 Sespe Ave. W., Fillmore, CA 93015 (SAN 240-5210) Tel 805-524-0172

Calico Papers, *(Calico Papers, The),* Rte. 1, Cochecton, NY 12726 (SAN 210-8925) Tel 914-932-8309

Calm Harbor, *(Calm Harbor),* P.O. Box 548, Vero Beach, FL 32960 (SAN 209-2808) Tel 305-569-2125

Calvary Baptist, *(Calvary Baptist Church),* Calvary Bookstore, 139 W. 57th St., New York, NY 10019 (SAN 202-5000) Tel 212-247-3233

Camberleigh & Hall, *(Camberleigh & Hall, Pubs.; 0-935880),* P.O. Box 18914, N. Hills Sta., Raleigh, NC 27619 (SAN 214-1116)

Camblos-Winger, *(Camblos-Winger; 0-9602706),* P.O. Box 15424, Asheville, NC 28813 (SAN 212-8896) Tel 704-274-2794

Cambridge Corp, *(Cambridge Corp.; 0-939008),* P.O. Box 64, Cambridge, MA 01938 (SAN 216-1117)

Cambridge Intl, *(Cambridge International, Pr.; 0-9600900),* 6 Saxony Dr., Warwick, RI 02886 (SAN 223-6559)

Cameo Pr, *(Cameo Press; 0-937868),* 373 Fifth Ave., Suite 1102, New York, NY 10016 (SAN 216-1125)

Cameo Pub, *(Cameo Publishing Co.; 0-9610814),* P.O. Box 1576, Belgrade, MT 59714 (SAN 265-2048)

Camera Graphic, *(Camera/Graphic Press Ltd.; 0-918696),* P.O. Box 1702, F.D.R. Sta., New York, NY 10022 (SAN 210-1424) Tel 212-832-0760

Campaign Political, *(Campaign for Political Rights),* 201 Massachusetts Ave. NE, Suite 316, Washington, DC 20002 (SAN 237-627X)

Campaigner, *(Campaigner Pubns., Inc.; 0-918388),* 304 W. 58th St, New York, NY 10019 (SAN 210-0479) Tel 212-247-8820

Campgrounds, *(Campgrounds Unlimited; 0-913788),* c/o Europa Camping & Caravaning, 2306 Sixth, Clay Center, KS 67432 (SAN 207-4249)

Campione, *(Campione, Michael J.; 0-9600186),* 2202 New Albany Rd., Cinnaminson, NJ 08077 (SAN 202-506X) Tel 609-829-6098

Camward Hse, *(Camward House; 0-936460),* P.O. Box 268, E. Patrick St. Sta., Frederick, MD 21701 (SAN 214-1833)

Can-Do Bks, *(Can-Do-Books; 0-9604192),* 2119 Lone Oak Ave., Napa, CA 94558 (SAN 214-1841)

Canadian-Hungarian, *(Canadian-Hungarian Pubs.),* c/o Martin K. Kiss, 20916 Fairpark Dr., Fairview Park, OH 44176 (SAN 206-4642)

Canopy Creations, *(Canopy Creations),* Box 113, Bloomfield, IA 52537 (SAN 211-6340)

Capital Pub DC, *(Capital Pubs., Inc.; 0-87277),* P.O. Box 6235, Washington, DC 20015 (SAN 202-5108)

Capital Wash
See Capital Pub DC

Capitalist Reporter, *(Capitalist Reporter Pr.; 0-933722),* 1501 Broadway, Suite 810, New York, NY 10036 (SAN 213-0319)

Capitol Pubns, *(Capitol Pubns., Inc.; 0-917870),* 2430 Pennsylvania Ave., NW Suite G-12, Washington, DC 20037 (SAN 210-0487) Tel 202-452-1600

Capstone, *(Capstone Book Press; 0-912068),* 6126 W. 64th Ave., Arvada, CO 80003 (SAN 202-5116)

Caribou Pr, *(Caribou Press; 0-9608496),* 106 Liberty Ave., New Rochelle, NY 10805 (SAN 240-6136) Tel 914-636-3863

Carley Pubns, *(Carley Pubns.),* P.O. Box 551, Farmingdale, NY 11735 (SAN 207-2106)

Carmel Pubns, *(Carmel Pubns.),* P.O. Box 4324 Grand Central Sta., New York, NY 10017 (SAN 201-8713)

Carnegie Coun Policy, *(Carnegie Council on Policy Studies in Higher Education; 0-931050),* 2150 Shattuck Ave., Berkeley, CA 94704 (SAN 211-5506)

Carolingian, *(Carolingian Press),* 46 Centre St., Haddonfield, NJ 08033 (SAN 207-799X) Tel 609-795-7887

Carrier Pigeon, *(Carrier Pigeon; 0-932870),* P.O. Box 2783, Boston, MA 02208 (SAN 169-3301) Tel 617-542-5679

Carroll Bk Serv, *(Carroll Book Service, Inc.),* P.O. Box 1776, North Tarrytown, NY 10591 (SAN 206-9520) Tel 914-631-1776

Carrollton Pr, *(Carrollton Press, Inc., U.S. Historical Documents Institute; 0-8408),* 1911 Fort Meyer Dr., Arlington, VA 22209 (SAN 201-7946) Tel 703-525-5942

CaseCo, *(CaseCo),* 101 Lafayette, Spartanburg, SC 29302 (SAN 240-1371)

Casha Pubns, *(Casha Pubns; 0-917660),* 227 W. 149th St., New York, NY 10039 (SAN 209-2026) Tel 212-926-8577

Cashman Pr, *(Cashman Press; 0-913224),* c/o Cashman, Picard & Lederman, 25 W. 43rd St., New York, NY 10036 (SAN 206-7064)

Casino Gaming, *(Casino Gaming Specialists; 0-9605112),* 1 Britton Place, Suite 16, Voorhees, NJ 08043 (SAN 215-8507)

Cassandra Pubns, *(Cassandra Pubns., Noe Valley Poets Workshop),* 143 Moffitt St., San Francisco, CA 94131 (SAN 207-7590) Tel 415-239-1253

Castle Designs, *(Castle Designs; 0-942844),* 2120 Mistletoe Ct., Plano, TX 75023 (SAN 240-0863) Tel 214-867-0067

Catalist Golf, *(Catalist Golf; 0-9614680),* 2521 1/2 S. Vista Way, No. 168, Oceanside, CA 92054 (SAN 692-509X)

Cataract Pr, *(Cataract Press; 0-914764),* P.O. Box 4875, Chicago, IL 60680-4875 (SAN 201-8748) Tel 416-638-0659

Cather Bk, *(Cather Book),* P.O. Box 893, Merrimack College, North Andover, MA 01845 (SAN 207-2114) Tel 617-683-7111

Cauce Pubs, *(Cauce, Cesar, Pubs. & Distributors; 0-86686),* 44 Fifth Ave. Box 120, Brooklyn, NY 11217 (SAN 216-5287)

Cauldron, *(Cauldron Pr.),* 8347 Delmar, No. 1-S, St. Louis, MO 63124 (SAN 210-914X)

Cave Canem Bks, *(Cave Canem Books; 0-9607244),* 120 E. 46th St. No. 98, New York, NY 10003 (SAN 239-1732)

CE Crime Pubns, *(Council of Europe, European Committee on Crime Problems, Pubns., Section),* Dist. by: Manhattan Publishing Co., 225 Lafayette St., New York, NY 10012 (SAN 237-6962)

Cedar Creek OK, *(Cedar Creek Press; 0-935286),* P.O. Box 1051, Stillwater, OK 74074 (SAN 213-2966)

Cedar Rock, *(Cedar Rock Press; 0-930024),* 1121 Madeline, New Braunfels, TX 78130 (SAN 213-2699) Tel 512-625-6002

Cedars Co, *(Cedars Co.),* 30516 S.E. 392nd St., Enumclaw, WA 98022 (SAN 207-3994)

CEI Pub Co, *(C.E.I. Publishing Co.; 0-88407),*
100 S. Jefferson, Athens, AL 35611
(SAN 201-7881) Tel 205-232-0565

Celebration Pr, *(Celebration Press; 0-933010),*
P.O. Box 76, Nobleboro, ME 04555
(SAN 211-8440) Tel 207-563-8269

Celebrity Pub, *(Celebrity Publishing, Inc.;
0-943406),* 185 Rte. 17, Mahwah, NJ 07430
(SAN 240-6152) Tel 201-529-4339

Celeste Bks, *(Celeste Books; 0-912437),* 9624
S.E. Pardee, Portland, OR 97266
(SAN 265-2102) Tel 503-774-4446

Celeste Pub
See Celeste Bks

Celtic Cross, *(Celtic Cross Books),* P.O. Box
728, Windsor, VT 05089 (SAN 211-660X)
Tel 802-674-6617

Centaur Dumfries, *(Centaur Pubns.; 0-9602404),*
P.O. Box 188, Dumfries, VA 22026
(SAN 213-9154) Tel 703-670-3527

Centaur Pubn VA, *(Centaur Pubn. Co.;
0-932700),* 7807 Stovall Ct., Lorton, VA
22079 (SAN 212-0771)

Center Hill, *(Center Hill Communications;
0-917459),* Box 23414, Nashville, TN 37202
(SAN 657-081X) Tel 615-834-4795

Central Pub, *(Central Publishing Co.; 0-931622),*
P.O. Box 24021, Cincinnati, OH 45224
(SAN 211-5514)

Century Three, *(Century Three Press; 0-933400),*
304 S. 13th St., Lincoln, NE 68508
(SAN 213-2125)

CERA, *(CERA; 0-936706),* P.O. Box 18103,
San Francisco, CA 94118 (SAN 215-8515)

Cerred Bks Co
See E R Brown Pub

Chadwick Hse, *(Chadwick House Pubs., Ltd.;
0-938102),* 25 W. Portola, Los Altos, CA
94022 (SAN 214-1167)

Chameleon, *(Chameleon Pubns.; 0-939988),* P.O.
Box 151 Tidwater Trial, Fredericksburg, VA
22402 (SAN 216-7972) Tel 703-373-2010

Chancellor Pr, *(Chancellor Press, Inc.;
0-913798),* 186 E. 64th St., New York, NY
10021 (SAN 201-8756) Tel 212-752-3043

Chandler Davis, *(Chandler-Davis Publishing Co.;
0-910346),* P.O. Box 736, West Trenton, NJ
08628 (SAN 203-6355) Tel 609-882-0800

Change Mag, *(Change Magazine Press;
0-915390),* P.O. Box 2023, New Rochelle,
NY 10802 (SAN 207-1347)
Tel 914-235-8700

Chanticleer FL, *(Chanticleer Pr.; 0-9612442),*
1428 State St., Suite 107, Sarasota, FL 33577
(SAN 289-176X) Tel 813-371-8544

Chapman Morris & Williams, *(Chapman, Morris,
Williams, Ltd.),* Dist. by: Tennyson Schad,
575 Madison Ave., New York, NY 10022
(SAN 208-242X)

Character Bks, *(Character Bks.; 0-942056),* P.O.
Box 22073, San Diego, CA 92122
(SAN 238-6305)

Charismatic, *(Charismatic Bookshelf; 0-943878),*
10205 NW 25th Pl., Gainesville, FL 32606
(SAN 241-1016)

CharLee Pr, *(CharLee Press; 0-910815),* P.O.
Box 5015, Richmond, CA 94805
(SAN 262-4583) Tel 415-237-1194

Charles Barrett Inc, *(Barrett, Charles, Inc.,
Pubs.; 0-941606),* 1303 Avocado Place, Suite
235, Newport Beach, CA 92660
(SAN 239-0663) Tel 714-640-1328

Charlotte Pubs, *(Charlotte Pubs.; 0-914878),*
P.O. Box 57126, Los Angeles, CA 90057
(SAN 203-4107)

Charter Hse, *(Charter House Pubs., Inc.;
0-8202),* P.O. Box 12037, Nashville, TN
37212 (SAN 204-5907) Tel 615-254-5842

Chem Econ, *(Chemical Economic Services;
0-912060),* P.O. Box 468, Palmer Square,
Princeton, NJ 08540 (SAN 201-9833)
Tel 609-921-8468

Chem Elements Pub, *(Chemical Elements
Publishing Co.),* 529 Mission Dr., Camarillo,
CA 93010 (SAN 201-9841)
Tel 805-482-6067

Cherry Hill, *(Cherry Hill Books; 0-910366),* 202
Highland Ave., Cheshire, CT 06410
(SAN 201-985X) Tel 203-272-8065

Chesford Inc, *(Chesford Inc.),* 373 Fifth Ave.
Suite 1016, New York, NY 10016
(SAN 211-2256) Tel 212-889-3023

Chess Visions, *(Chess Visions, Inc.; 0-939786),*
P.O. Box 430372, South Miami, FL 33143
(SAN 216-8847)

Chestnut, *(Chestnut Pubns.; 0-917454),* Box
124, Old Sudbury Rd., Lincoln, MA 01773
(SAN 209-0635) Tel 617-259-9437

Chicago Theology & Culture, *(Chicago Institute
of Theology & Culture, The; 0-936978),*
5401 S. Cornell Ave., Chicago, IL 60645
(SAN 213-9928)

Chicken Walk, *(Chicken Walk Books),* 1301A
East Chestnut, Santa Ana, CA 92701
(SAN 211-352X)

Child Study, *(Child Study Association of
America/Wel-Met, Inc.; 0-87183),* 853
Broadway, New York, NY 10003
(SAN 203-6487)

Chilmark, *(Chilmark Press, Inc.; 0-87285),* 147
E. 81st St., 1E, New York, NY 10028
(SAN 203-6495) Tel 212-663-2640

Chinmoy, *(Sri Chinmoy Lighthouse; 0-87847),*
86-14 Parsons Blvd., Jamaica, NY 11432
(SAN 203-6509) Tel 212-657-4827

Chiro Educational Serv, *(Chiropractic
Educational Services),* 534 Union Arcade
Bldg., Davenport, IA 52801
(SAN 213-0378)

Chong-Donnie, *(Chong-Donnie; 0-938918),* 246
E. 62nd St., New York, NY 10021
(SAN 216-1087)

Choose Cherish, *(Choose & Cherish; 0-918008),*
212 E. 48th St., New York, NY 10017
(SAN 210-1882) Tel 212-355-0560

Chowder Chapbks, *(Chowder Chapbooks),* 2858
Kingston Dr., Madison, WI 53713
(SAN 211-2272)

Chr Evidence, *(Christian Evidence League;
0-910374),* P.O. Box 173, Malverne, NY
11565 (SAN 203-6533)

Christian Herald, *(Christian Herald Bks.;
0-915684; 0-86693),* 40 Overlook Dr.,
Chappaqua, NY 10514 (SAN 208-1474)
Tel 914-769-9000

Christian Success, *(Christian Success Publishing
House; 0-934178),* P.O. Box 10871,
Yakiman, WA 98909 (SAN 213-0386)

Church Bks, *(Church Books; 0-916778),* Rte. 4,
Box 27A, Greenville, SC 29605
(SAN 208-595X) Tel 803-277-5714

Church of Divine
See Evang Authors

Cider Pr, *(Cider Press; 0-914994),* P.O. Box
10115, Columbus, OH 43201
(SAN 207-1088)

Cimino Pubns, *(Cimino Pubns., Inc.; 0-9600588),*
1646 New Hwy, Farmingdale, NY 11735
(SAN 209-0996)

Cine-Grafic, *(Cine/Grafic Pubns.; 0-9600240),*
P.O. Box 430, Hollywood, CA 90028
(SAN 203-6592) Tel 213-462-8670

Cine-Graphic
See Cine-Grafic

Cinnamon Pr, *(Cinnamon Press Ltd.; 0-930612),*
Box 426, Denver, CO 80201
(SAN 211-9404)

Circle Pr, *(Circle Press; 0-89248),* Subs. of the
Christ Circle Inc., P.O. Box N, Boulder
Creek, CA 95006 (SAN 208-5984)
Tel 408-338-2141

Citizens Law, *(Citizens Law Library; 0-89648),*
6 W. Loudoun St., P.O. Box 1745, Leesburg,
VA 22075 (SAN 211-1543)

Citrus Hse, *(Citrus Hse., Inc.; 0-915238),* P.O.
Box 2061, Beverly Hills, CA 90213
(SAN 207-1134) Tel 213-388-3954

Clancy Pubns, *(Clancy Pubns., Inc.; 0-940058),*
2505 N. Alvernon Way, Tucson, AZ 85712
(SAN 220-2107)

Clarion
See Paradox Pub Co

Clarion Call, *(Clarion Call Literature;
0-9604294),* 1634 Pittman St., Missoula, MT
59801 (SAN 213-8387)

Clarion Pubns, *(Clarion Pubns.),* P. O. Box
1600, San Luis Obispo, CA 93406
(SAN 210-8895)

Cleaning Equip Mfgs, *(Cleaning Equipment
Manufacturers Assn.),* 6043 Hudson Rd.,
Suite 110, St. Paul, MN 55125
(SAN 689-9226)

Clearstream Pr, *(Clearstream Pr.; 0-911225),*
601 W. 14th St., Austin, TX 78701
(SAN 283-989X) Tel 512-476-2525

Clearwater OR, *(Clearwater Press; 0-9605512),*
1115 V Ave., La Grande, OR 97855
(SAN 216-1176)

Clemco, *(Clemco),* Box 1362, Manhattan Beach,
CA 90266 (SAN 207-1096)
Tel 213-372-6448

Clover Press, *(Clover Press),* P.O. Box 227,
Cardiff-by-the-Sea, CA 92007
(SAN 293-1192) Tel 619-942-3841; 1242
Evergreen, Cardiff-by-the-Sea, CA 92007
(SAN 651-9768)

Cobb Ent, *(Cobb Enterprizes; 0-9602968),* P.O.
Box 7156-A, St. Louis, MO 63177
(SAN 215-630X) Tel 314-436-3127

Cobbers, *(Cobbers; 0-934680),* Div. of
Martensen Co., Inc., P.O. Box 261,
Williamsburg, VA 23187 (SAN 213-4802)
Tel 804-220-2828

Cobden Pr, *(Cobden Pr.; 0-930439),* P.O. Box
119, Meriden, CT 06450 (SAN 682-9589)

Coda Pubns, *(Coda Pubns.; 0-934118),* 1 Dallas
Ctr., Suite 1750, Dallas, TX 75251
(SAN 223-7415)

CoDoC, *(Cooperation in Documentation &
Communication; 0-914958),* 361 Athol Ave.,
Oakland, CA 94606 (SAN 207-0685)

Col-Bob Assocs, *(Col-Bob Associates, Inc.),* 250
E. 52nd St., New York, NY 10022
(SAN 208-1458) Tel 212-281-2193

Cold Mtn Pr, *(Cold Mountain Press; 0-915496),*
4406 Duval, Austin, TX 78751
(SAN 207-379X)

Coleraine Pr, *(Coleraine Press, Inc.; 0-913016),*
Hook Rd., Bedford, NY 10506
(SAN 206-7307) Tel 914-234-7980

Collage Pr, *(Collage Press; 0-917516),* P.O. Box
5552, Baltimore, MD 21204
(SAN 207-4613)

Collector Circle, *(Collector Circle),* P.O. Box
12600, 1313 S. Killian Dr., Lake Park, FL
33403 (SAN 225-5359)

Collectors Edns, *(Collectors Editions, Ltd.;
0-87681),* Dist. by: Van Nostrand Reinhold
Co., 300 Pike St., Cincinnati, OH 45202
(SAN 202-5191)

Collectors' Info, *(Collectors' Information
Bureau; 0-930785),* 1860 Lake Dr., East
Grand Rapids, MI 49506 (SAN 677-6116)
Tel 616-456-6673

Collins Pubs, *(Collins, William, Pubs., Inc.),*
2080 W. 117th St., Cleveland, OH 44111
(SAN 205-4930); 200 Madison Ave., Suite
1405, New York, NY 10016
(SAN 205-4949)

Collins-World
See Collins Pubs

Colo Fiber, *(Colorado Fiber Ctr., Inc.; 0-937452),*
P.O. Box 2049, Boulder, CO 80306
(SAN 215-1383)

Colo St U Comm, *(Colorado State Univ.,
Institute in Technical & Industrial
Communications; 0-910414),* Colorado State
Univ., Social Science Bldg., Rm. C225, Fort
Collins, CO 80523 (SAN 206-7056)

Colonial Pr, *(Colonial Press),* 1 Saddle Rd.,
Cedar Knolls, NJ 07927 (SAN 207-463X)

Colorist Pr, *(Colorist Press, The; 0-9609086),* 25
Colborne Rd., Brighton, MA 02135
(SAN 241-4848) Tel 617-254-2458

Columbia Graphs, *(Columbia Graphs),* P.O. Box
445, Danielson, CT 06239 (SAN 203-5731)

Comm Bio Pest, *(Committee for Biological Pest
Control),* P.O. Box 2810, San Ysidro, CA
92173 (SAN 203-574X) Tel 714-234-1492

Comm Found, *(Communication Foundation),* P.
O. Box 11689, Santa Rosa, CA 95406
(SAN 208-144X) Tel 707-525-1350

Comm People, *(Community People Pr.;
0-914391),* P.O. Box 30361, Los Angeles,
CA 90030 (SAN 289-6176)

Comm Serv Corp, *(Communication Service
Corp.; 0-87659),* 1333 Connecticut Ave.,
N.W., Washington, DC 20015
(SAN 206-9040)

Comm Serv Found, *(Community Service
Foundation; 0-9608066),* P.O. Box 70,
Sellersville, PA 18960 (SAN 240-2092)
Tel 215-257-4131

Comm Urban Justice, *(Committee for Urban
Justice),* 136 Warren St., Boston, MA 02119
(SAN 209-2352)

Common Table, *(Common Table, The;
0-933228),* 216 Crown St., Rm 506, New
Haven, CT 06510 (SAN 212-7350)
Tel 203-776-7073

Commonsense, *(Commonsense Pubns.;
0-911734),* 1925 Vermont Ave., Toledo, OH
43624 (SAN 206-9059)

Commonweal Bks, *(Commonwealth Books, Inc.;
0-918596),* P.O. Box 4433, Lexington, KY
40504 (SAN 210-5330)

Community Psychol, *(Community Psychological
Consultants, Inc.),* 1740 Gulf Dr., St. Louis,
MO 63130 (SAN 209-1313)

Comox, *(Comox Bks.; 0-912276),* Div. of Eric
Duncan Literary Properties, 1756 Garnet
Ave., San Diego, CA 92109
(SAN 202-1773) Tel 619-272-7744

Comp Media
See Compumedia

Comp Stations, *(Computer Stations, Inc.; 0-913249),* 11610 Page Service Dr., St. Louis, MO 63141 (SAN 284-1835) Tel 314-432-7019

Comp Tech Consult, *(Computer Technology Consultants),* 1552 Summit Ave., Cardiff-by-the Sea, CA 92007 (SAN 674-6721)

Comp Users Ed, *(Computers Users In Education),* 2148 Sanos Dr., Tempe, AZ 85281 (SAN 673-4545)

Comp Using Educs
See Comp Using KY

Comp Using KY, *(Computer-Using Educators of Kentucky),* Univ. of Louisville, Louisville, KY 40292 (SAN 674-799X)

Compton & Rowe, *(Compton & Rowe, Pubs.; 0-931372),* P.O. Box 786, Sausalito, CA 94965 (SAN 211-4852) Tel 415-435-0951

Compumedia, *(Compumedia),* 2211 Norfolk, Suite 700, Houston, TX 77098-4044 (SAN 677-895X) Tel 713-524-6565

Computer Strat, *(Computer Strategies; 0-9603584; 0-913505),* 10218 Chimney Hill, Dallas, TX 75243 (SAN 213-6589) Tel 214-644-0222

Computex, *(Computex),* 17321 El Camino Real, Houston, TX 77058 (SAN 675-841X)

Computing Pubns, *(Computing Pubns., Inc.),* Princeton Forrestal Ctr., 101 College Rd. E, Princeton, NJ 08540 (SAN 681-9842)

Condor Pub Co, *(Condor Publishing Co., Inc.; 0-89516),* 29 E. Main St., Westport, CT 06880 (SAN 210-3494) Tel 203-226-9591

Confed Arms, *(Confederate Arms Pubs.; 0-87833),* P.O. Box 220802, Charlotte, NC 28222 (SAN 281-5230)

Congreve Pub, *(Congreve Publishing Co., Inc.; 0-930186),* P.O. Box 5241, FDR Sta., New York, NY 10150 (SAN 281-5486)

Conn Coll Bkshp, *(Connecticut College Bookshop),* New London, CT 06320 (SAN 206-4863) Tel 203-443-0025

Connect Pr, *(Connections Pr.; 0-930474),* P.O. Box 502, Davis, CA 95616 (SAN 212-8969)

Connections, *(Connections, Inc.),* 4950 Miller Rd., No. 133, Scottsdale, AZ 85251 (SAN 201-9019)

Connexions, *(Connexions; 0-940546),* P.O. Box 30580, Seattle, WA 98103 (SAN 218-5369) Tel 206-782-7838

Consol Cap, *(Consolidated Capital; 0-930032),* 333 Hegenberger Rd., Oakland, CA 94621 (SAN 210-5349) Tel 415-638-3000

Consortium
See McGrath

Consortium Imprint of McGrath

Consumer Age Pr, *(Consumer Age Press; 0-914448),* P.O. Box 279, Syracuse, NY 13214 (SAN 203-5847) Tel 315-446-6262

Consumer Assoc, *(Consumer Associates; 0-9602442),* P.O. Box 13257, Pittsburgh, PA 15243 (SAN 222-9722) Tel 412-344-5560

Consumer Credit Project, *(Consumer Credit Project Inc.),* 261 Kimberly, Dept. T, Barrington, IL 60010 (SAN 225-6428) Tel 312-381-2113

Consumer News, *(Consumer News Inc.; 0-89696),* 813 National Press Bldg., Washington, DC 20045 (SAN 208-6077) Tel 202-737-1190

Contemp Crafts, *(Contemporary Crafts, Inc.),* c/o Hancraft Studios, 248 Pomona Mall W., Pomona, CA 91766 (SAN 219-9556) Tel 714-626-9658

Contemp Poetry, *(Contemporary Poetry Press; 0-939610),* P.O. Box 88, Lansing, NY 14882 (SAN 216-3535)

Contemp Pub
See Nursing Res

Continent Pub, *(Continental Publishing Hse.; 0-915002),* 2116 NE 18th Ave., Portland, OR 97212 (SAN 211-3112) Tel 503-282-1383

Contraband, *(Contraband Press),* P.O. Box 4073, Sta. A, Portland, ME 04101 (SAN 209-7206)

Cook-McDowell, *(Cook-McDowell Pubns.),* 1233 Sweeney St., Owensboro, KY 42301 (SAN 217-2321)

Cope Allied Pub, *(Cope Allied Publishing; 0-935658),* P.O. Box 458, Cypress, TX 77429 (SAN 213-8417)

Cordova, *(Cordova Printing),* 10777 Coloma Rd., Rancho Cordova, CA 95670 (SAN 207-5954)

Corner, *(Corner Book Shop; 0-910442),* 102 Fourth Ave., New York, NY 10003 (SAN 203-5928) Tel 212-254-7714

Corwin, *(Corwin Books; 0-89474),* One Century Plaza, 2029 Century Park, E., Los Angeles, CA 90067 (SAN 208-614X) Tel 213-552-9111; Dist. by: Independent News, 75 Rockefeller Plaza, New York, NY 10019 (SAN 208-6158)

Cosmic Consciousness, *(Cosmic Consciousness Creations, Inc.; 0-916274),* P. O. Box 307 S., Miami, FL 33143 (SAN 208-1466)

Cosmos Bks, *(Cosmos Books),* Dist. by: Books New China, 52 E. Broadway, New York, NY 10002 (SAN 169-5673)

Cosmos Store, *(Cosmos Store, The; 0-939540),* 2409 Honolulu Ave., Suite 3, Montrose, CA 91020 (SAN 216-6666) Tel 818-790-8569

Country Bks, *(Country Books),* P.O. Box 278, Boonville, NY 13309 (SAN 206-4898)

Country Print, *(Country Printing, Inc.),* P.O. Box 240, Pequot Lakes, MN 56472 (SAN 208-189X) Tel 218-568-8521

Country Prods, *(Country Productions; 0-9606224),* 14237 Detroit Ave., Lakewood, OH 44107 (SAN 217-5118)

Courier-Gazette
See Courier of Maine

Courier of Maine, *(Courier of Maine Books; 0-913954),* 1 Park Dr., Rockland, ME 04841 (SAN 203-6002) Tel 207-594-4401

Courthouse Pr, *(Courthouse Press; 0-911736),* P.O. Box 205, Floral Park, NY 11002 (SAN 203-6010) Tel 516-437-9463

Cove Pr, *(Cove Press),* Whistlestop Mall 240, Rockport, MA 01966 (SAN 209-1011)

Cozzolino Assocs, *(Cozzolino Associates; 0-9601408),* One Conifer Dr., Mendham, NJ 07945 (SAN 211-2264)

CPA Study
See Bradley CPA

Crabapple Pr, *(Crabapple Press; 0-89548),* Div. of Communication Design, Inc., 300 North St., Meadville, PA 16335 (SAN 210-4083) Tel 814-724-1117

Cranberry, *(Cranberry Press, Inc.; 0-918130),* 30 Hotaling Place, San Francisco, CA 94111 (SAN 210-1149) Tel 415-421-5672

Cranium Pr, *(Cranium Press),* 243 Collins St., San Francisco, CA 94118 (SAN 202-1986)

Creat Image Assocs, *(Creative Image Assocs.; 0-912077),* 101 E. Fowling St., Playa del Rey, CA 90291 (SAN 264-7281) Tel 213-821-6788

Creat Learning, *(Creative Learning Co., Inc.; 0-941802),* 402 Clydebank Ct., Louisville, KY 40243 (SAN 239-1929) Tel 502-245-0408

Creation Sci, *(Creation Science Research Center; 0-88213),* P.O. Box 23195, San Diego, CA 92123 (SAN 203-6096) Tel 714-569-8673

Creative Assoc, *(Creative Associates; 0-941588),* 1911 N. Higley Rd., Mesa, AZ 85205 (SAN 239-0817) Tel 602-985-3724

Creative Bk Co, *(Creative Bk. Co.; 0-88409),* P.O. Box 2244, Hollywood, CA 90028 (SAN 695-6742)

Creative Eye, *(Creative Eye Press; 0-916480),* P.O. Box 4191, Modesto, CA 95352 (SAN 208-6182) Tel 209-524-8603

Creative Gen, *(Creative Genius; 0-911657),* P.O. Box 20,000, Dept. 203, Houston, TX 77021 (SAN 263-9882)

Creative Pr, *(Creative Press; 0-912512),* P.O. Box 1058, Claremont, CA 91711 (SAN 203-6118) Tel 714-593-5060

Creative Pubns, *(Creative Pubns.; 0-88488),* Affil. of Westinghouse Learning Corp., 5005 W. 110th St., Oak Lawn, IL 60453 (SAN 206-7617)

Crehore, *(Crehore, John Davenport; 0-910466),* 1523 E. 28th Ave., No. 2, Oakland, CA 94601 (SAN 203-6134) Tel 415-533-2251

Crescent Pubns, *(Crescent Pubns., Inc.; 0-914184),* 5410 Wilshire Blvd., Suite 400, Los Angeles, CA 90036 (SAN 202-2036)

CRF, *(Citizens' Research Foundation),* 245 Nassau St., Princeton, NJ 08540 (SAN 203-1175) Tel 609-924-0246

Croft MD, *(Croft, Inc.; 0-86673),* 4601 York Rd., Baltimore, MD 21212 (SAN 216-2334)

Crone-Atwood, *(Crone-Atwood Pubns., Co.),* 1037 E. Parkway, Suite 205, Memphis, TN 38104 (SAN 208-3116) Tel 901-274-6143

Cross Roads, *(Cross Roads Pubns.),* 2751 Buford Hwy. N.E., Suite 720, Atlanta, GA 30324 (SAN 211-7908) Tel 404-325-7857

Crossroads MA, *(Crossroads Pr.; 0-918456),* Epstein Bldg., Brandeis Univ., Waltham, MA 02154 (SAN 216-2342)

Crossroads Pr, *(Crossroads Press, Inc.),* P.O. Box 833, Honolulu, HI 96808 (SAN 218-6950) Tel 808-521-0021

Crow, *(Crow),* 5430 Del Rio Rd., Sacramento, CA 95822 (SAN 209-7257) Tel 916-441-5358

Croydon, *(Croydon House; 0-910472),* P.O. Box 1302, Miami, FL 33161 (SAN 203-8714)

CRR Pub Co, *(CRR Publishing Co.),* 1156 15th St. NW, Rm. 724, Washington, DC 20025 (SAN 237-6016)

Crystal Bananas, *(Crystal Bananas; 0-931885),* P.O. Box 975, Manhattanville Sta., New York, NY 10027 (SAN 686-046X)

Crystal Prism, *(Crystal Prism Corp.; 0-940236),* P. O. Box 7387, Menlo Park, CA 94025 (SAN 223-2154) Tel 415-851-1633

Ctr Cont Celeb, *(Center for Contemporary Celebration),* 1400 E. 53rd St., Chicago, IL 60615 (SAN 201-9051)

Ctr Human Servs, *(Center for Human Services; 0-915852),* 39 Church St., New Haven, CT 06510 (SAN 209-2107) Tel 203-624-6911; Orders to: P.O. Box 1268, New Haven, CT 06505 (SAN 209-2115)

Ctr Info Am, *(Center for Information on America),* Washington Depot, CT 06793 (SAN 695-5622) Tel 203-868-2602

Ctr Intl Educ
See Lat Am Stud

Ctr Minorities, *(Center on Minorities & Criminal Justice; 0-940826),* State Univ. of New York at Albany, Schl. of Criminal Justice, Albany, NY 12222 (SAN 239-4170)

Ctr Womans Own, *(Center for A Woman's Own Name; 0-914332),* 261 Kimberley Rd., Barrington, IL 60010 (SAN 206-3417) Tel 312-381-2113

Cucamonga, *(Cucamonga Press; 0-918190),* P.O. Box 632, Cucamonga, CA 91730 (SAN 209-5483) Tel 714-985-1921

Culinary, *(Culinary World, Inc.; 0-917872),* 111 E. 65th St., New York, NY 10021 (SAN 210-0614) Tel 212-628-0066

Cultivators Res Serv, *(Cultivator's Research Service),* P.O. Box 447, Tesuque, NM 87574 (SAN 237-9473)

Cultural Pr, *(Cultural Press; 0-910476),* 517 Madison St., Waukesha, WI 53186 (SAN 203-8757)

Culver City, *(Culver City Cannon Co.; 0-910517),* 4220 Irving Place, Culver City, CA 90230 (SAN 260-1796) Tel 213-839-6498

Cumberland, *(Cumberland Journal),* P.O. Box 2648, Harrisburg, PA 17105 (SAN 219-161X)

Cummington Pub, *(Cummington Publishing, Inc.; 0-938350),* 17 Old Orchard Rd., New Rochelle, NY 10804 (SAN 215-7497)

Cumorah Pub, *(Cumorah Publishing Co.; 0-940720),* 572 W. 440 S., Orem, UT 84057 (SAN 238-9282)

Curlew Music, *(Curlew Music Publishers, Inc.),* 1311 North Highland Ave., Hollywood, CA 90028 (SAN 207-0294)

Current Documents, *(Current Documents & Info.),* P.O. Box 1134, Langley Park, MD 20787 (SAN 241-3744)

Cusack, *(Cusack, Betty B.; 0-911448),* 35 West Rd., West Yarmouth, MA 02673 (SAN 203-879X)

Custom Hse Pubns, *(Custom House Pubns.; 0-942086),* 5450 Kleberg, Houston, TX 77056 (SAN 238-454X) Tel 713-622-5150

Cycle-Gram, *(Cycle-Gram Associates; 0-913020),* P.O. Box 4462, North Hollywood, CA 91607 (SAN 203-8803)

Cycle Pr, *(Cycle Press; 0-914320),* 18 Warner Place, Brooklyn, NY 11201 (SAN 206-6319)

Cyrco Pr, *(Cyrco Press, Inc.; 0-915326),* 342 Madison Ave., New York, NY 10017 (SAN 200-2027) Tel 212-682-8410

D Anderson Assoc, *(Anderson, Douglas, & Associates),* 100 W. Ann St., Ann Arbor, MI 48104 (SAN 295-9593)

D B Lovett, *(Lovett, Donald B.; 0-9603328),* Rt. 1, Magalia, CA 95954 (SAN 213-3369)

D Bishop, *(Bishop, David),* 319 Boonslick, St. Charles, MO 63301 (SAN 218-4699)

D C Parker, *(Parker, D. Coffey),* 28 Abbot Rd., Springfield, IL 62704 (SAN 216-003X) Tel 217-787-7620

D D Davis, *(Davis, Duane D.; 0-9605658),* 123 E. Idaho, Sandpoint, ID 83864 (SAN 238-1273) Tel 208-263-3014

D D Murphy, *(Murphy, Dennis D.; 0-918788),* 3404 N. Romero Rd., Box 9, Tucson, AZ 85705 (SAN 210-3125)

D H Ent, *(D. H. Enterprises; 0-934628),* P.O. Box 201, Grawn, MI 49637 (SAN 212-3444) Tel 616-943-8260

D H Sanderson, *(Sanderson, Dorothy H.),* 15 Maple Ave., Ellenville, NY 12428 (SAN 202-0793) Tel 914-647-5305

D H Tolzmann, *(Tolzmann, Don Heinrich),* 2545 Harrison Ave, Cincinnati, OH 45211 (SAN 206-6335)

D Kermode, *(Kermode, Doug; 0-9602202),* P.O. Box 8087, Long Beach, CA 90808 (SAN 212-3665)

D L Hennessey, *(Hennessey, D. L, Co.; 0-9602958),* P.O. Box 281, Berkeley, CA 94701 (SAN 223-1069) Tel 415-526-1614

D Lewis Pub, *(Lewis, David, Pubns; 0-912012),* 216 W. 89th St., New York, NY 10024 (SAN 201-2898) Tel 212-799-1144

D Lyons, *(Lyons, David),* Forest Ridge Apts.-16C Hampshire Dr.,, Nashua, NH 03063 (SAN 212-9515); Orders to: 16 Hampshire Dr., Room C, Nashua, NH 03063 (SAN 212-9523)

D M Battle Pubns, *(Battle, Dennis M., Pubns.; 0-933464),* P.O. Box 67, Elyria, OH 44036 (SAN 212-8748) Tel 216-323-1729

D M Gaev, *(Gaev, Dorothy M.; 0-9600968),* Upminister H164, Deerfield Beach, FL 33441 (SAN 208-2071)

D Polk, *(Polk, Donice; 0-9605430),* 1973 Reedy, Highland, CA 92346 (SAN 215-9767)

D W Harmon, *(Harmon, Donald W.; 0-916314),* P.O. Box 1645, Downey, CA 90241 (SAN 208-3639)

Dacryone Pr, *(Dacryone Pr.; 0-918893),* 141 Cricket Ave., Ardmore, PA 19003 (SAN 669-9693)

Dafran Hse, *(Dafran House Pubs., Inc.),* 185 Bethpage Sweet Hollow Rd., Old Bethpage, NY 11804 (SAN 206-4928)

Daisy, *(Daisy Press; 0-935424),* P.O. Box 884, La Mesa, CA 92041 (SAN 213-7089)

Dale Bks, *(Dale Books),* 51 Springdale Ave., Waterbury, CT 06708 (SAN 208-3124) Tel 203-753-0255

Dale Books Inc, *(Dale Books, Inc.; 0-89559),* Subs. of Davis Pubns. Inc., 380 Lexington Ave., New York, NY 10017 (SAN 211-1918) Tel 212-949-9190

Dallas Pub, *(Dallas Publishing, Inc.; 0-941282),* 4560 Belt Line Rd., Suite 200, Dallas, TX 75234 (SAN 238-9304)

Dame Inc, *(Dame, Robert F., Inc.; 0-936328),* 511 Research Rd., Richmond, VA 23236 (SAN 223-5757)

Damerell Pub, *(Damerell Publishing; 0-911343),* 7 W. 14th St., Apt. 6R, New York, NY 10011 (SAN 269-5758) Tel 212-242-8945

Danbury Pr, *(Danbury Pr.),* P.O. Box 613, Suffern, NY 10901 (SAN 213-8905) Tel 914-357-0420

Dancing Fox Pr *Imprint of Pegasus Pr WA*

Dancing Rock, *(Dancing Rock Press; 0-931022),* 67 Albion St., San Francisco, CA 94103 (SAN 211-1926)

Dandrea, *(Dandrea, Robert A.; 0-9600662),* P.O. Box 6536, Colorado Springs, CO 80934 (SAN 201-2960)

Dante Univ Bkshlf, *(Dante Univ. Bookshelf),* Dist. by: Branden Press, Inc., P.O. Box 843, 21 Station St., Brookline Village, MA 02147 (SAN 201-4106) Tel 617-734-2045

Danube Inc, *(Danube, Inc.; 0-9607208),* 428-7 Silver Oaks Dr., Kent, OH 44240 (SAN 238-9312)

D'arc Pr, *(D'arc Press),* 340 W. 72nd St., New York, NY 10023 (SAN 207-9895)

Dark Horse, *(Dark Horse, Inc.; 0-937762),* 17705 S. Western Ave., Suite 1, Gardena, CA 90248 (SAN 216-2350)

Darvill Outdoor, *(Darvill Outdoor Pubns.; 0-915740),* 1819 Hickox Rd., Mt. Vernon, WA 98273 (SAN 207-5423) Tel 206-424-1298

Datafax, *(Datafax Marketing Services; 0-9612342),* 32 S. 14th St., Richmond, IN 47374 (SAN 289-1867) Tel 317-962-1301

Daughterayne, *(Daughterayne; 0-942762),* 2829 1/2 Carleton St., San Diego, CA 92106 (SAN 238-8456) Tel 619-222-5052

Davlin Pubns, *(Davlin Pubns., Inc.; 0-914670),* 13521 Alondra Blvd., Santa Fe Springs, CA 90670 (SAN 203-8838) Tel 213-649-2620

Dawson County, *(Dawson County Bicentennial Committee),* 1500 River Ave., Glendive, MT 59330 (SAN 207-3129) Tel 406-365-2760

Day Care & Child Dev *See* Day Care Coun

Day Care Coun, *(Day Care Council of America, Inc.; 0-936746),* 1602 17th St., NW, Washington, DC 20009 (SAN 203-4581)

DB Music, *(D.B. Music Company; 0-942760),* P.O. Box 953, Ojai, CA 93023 (SAN 240-2130) Tel 805-646-0086

DCT Ent, *(DCT Enterprises; 0-9604998),* 2888 Bluff St., Suite 218, Boulder, CO 80301 (SAN 216-0285)

De La Ree, *(De La Ree, Gerry, Publisher; 0-938192),* 7 Cedarwood Lane, Saddle River, NJ 07458 (SAN 207-8309) Tel 201-327-6621

Dean & Assoc, *(Dean & Associates; 0-933370),* P.O. Box 2943, Eugene, OR 97402 (SAN 212-6524)

Dean Co WA, *(Dean Co. of Washington; 0-934256),* P.O. Box 339, Selinsgrove, PA 17870-0339 (SAN 216-2385) Tel 717-743-5588

Deccom, *(DECCOM; 0-9608350),* P.O. Box 22085-B, Phoenix, AZ 85028 (SAN 240-6241) Tel 602-996-0036

Decibel, *(Decibel Books; 0-914672),* P.O. Box 358, Norman, OK 73070 (SAN 205-616X)

Dedicated Systems Corp, *(Dedicated Systems Corp.; 0-914153),* Subs. of Feature Group, Inc., 2440 E. Commercial Blvd., Suite 4, Fort Lauderdale, FL 33308 (SAN 287-6442)

Defense Res, *(Defense Research Institute, Inc.),* 733 N. Van Buren St., Milwaukee, WI 53202 (SAN 223-9892)

Del Mus Nat Hist, *(Delaware Museum of Natural History; 0-913176),* P.O.Box 3937, Greenville, DE 19807 (SAN 201-3126) Tel 302-658-9111

Delancey Pr, *(Delancey Press; 0-9601128),* 441 W. 22nd St., Gdn, New York, NY 10011 (SAN 209-2344)

Delaney, *(Delaney Pubns.; 0-915856),* Dist. by: Buckley Publications, Inc, 233 E. Erie St., Suite 402, Chicago, IL 60611 (SAN 208-1954) Tel 312-943-2066

Delanie Way, *(Delanie Way Pub.; 0-9602290),* 685 Delanie Way, Stone Mountain, GA 30083 (SAN 212-8993) Tel 404-292-9121

Delphian Pr, *(Delphian Press; 0-89739),* Sheridan, OR 97378 (SAN 211-7029)

Deluxe Co, *(Deluxe Co., The; 0-938012),* P.O. Box 4246, Shreveport, LA 71104 (SAN 215-7527)

Denlingers, *(Denlingers Pubs., Ltd.; 0-87714),* P.O. Box 76, Fairfax, VA 22030 (SAN 203-3150) Tel 703-631-1500

Dental Control, *(Dental Control Products, Inc.),* 590 Valley Rd., Upper Montclair, NJ 07043 (SAN 208-3132)

DeOro Bks, *(DeOro Bks.; 0-930482),* 1090 Bay Oaks Dr., Los Osos, CA 93403 (SAN 210-718X) Tel 805-528-4353

Derby Assoc, *(Derby Assocs.; 0-9604692),* 601 Capitol Ctr., 344 W. Dayton St., Madison, WI 53703 (SAN 215-2010)

Derring-Do, *(Derring-Do Pr.; 0-9606638),* P.O. Box 1233, Mountainside, NJ 07092 (SAN 223-7652)

Desert Pub CA, *(Desert Publishing),* 255 N. El Cielo Rd., Suite 164, Palm Springs, CA 92262 (SAN 216-1265)

Deuce, *(Deuce of Clubs Press; 0-9600200),* 927 Mad River Rd., Arcata, CA 95521 (SAN 203-8897) Tel 707-822-2000

Develop Unltd, *(Development Unltd Inc.; 0-914029),* P.O. Box 95415, Seattle, WA 98145 (SAN 286-746X) Tel 206-774-8660

Devlin Hse, *(Devlin House Pubs.; 0-916874),* Box 114, Medfield, MA 02052 (SAN 208-3159) Tel 617-359-6839

Diana Pr, *(Diana Press, Inc.; 0-88447),* 4400 Market St., Oakland, CA 94608 (SAN 206-3549) Tel 415-658-5558

Dianic Pubns, *(Dianic Pubns.; 0-9610450),* P.O. Box 2528, Berkeley, CA 94703 (SAN 240-4710)

Dickenson, *(Dickenson Publishing Co.; 0-8221),* c/o Wadsworth, Inc., 10 Davis Dr., Belmont, CA 94002 (SAN 200-2213) Tel 415-595-2350

Dill Pub, *(Dill Publishing; 0-9604332),* 2627 O St., Sun Valley, CA 91352 (SAN 281-6016); 2940 S. 74th, Lincoln, NE 68506 (SAN 281-6024)

Directories Intl, *(Directories International, Inc.; 0-912794),* 1718 Sherman Ave., Evanston, IL 60201 (SAN 201-3312) Tel 312-491-0019

Directory of Art, *(Directory of Art & Antique Restoration; 0-916116),* 465 California St., Suite 815, San Francisco, CA 94104 (SAN 207-2130)

Discovery Pub, *(Discovery Publishing Co.; 0-932422),* 404 W. Chestnut, Yakima, WA 98902 (SAN 212-1581)

Diversified Ent, *(Diversified Enterprises, Inc.; 0-9601790),* Box 15, Posen, MI 49776 (SAN 211-6367) Tel 517-379-4678

Dixie Pub, *(Dixie Publishing Co.; 0-89817),* P.O. Box 1021, Port Heuneme, CA 93041 (SAN 212-4181)(Triangle Publishing).

DJD Prods, *(DJD Productions; 0-9603964),* 1712 S. Highland, Arlington Heights, IL 60005 (SAN 214-0012) Tel 312-640-7778

Doctor Jazz, *(Dr. Jazz Pr.; 0-934002),* 2208 Chapel Hill Rd., Birmingham, AL 35216 (SAN 215-6369)

Doggeral Pr, *(Doggeral Press; 0-933726),* 417 Seaview, Santa Barbara, CA 93108 (SAN 216-3683)

Dolphin Aquatics, *(Dolphin Aquatics; 0-9602982),* 97 Parry Rd., Stamford, CT 06907 (SAN 201-3355) Tel 203-322-7944

Don Quixote, *(Don Quixote Publishing Hse.; 0-914333),* P.O. Box 643, Pt. Orange, FL 32029 (SAN 289-6990)

Donato Music, *(Donato Music Publishing Co.; 0-935058),* P.O. Box 415, New York, NY 10013 (SAN 207-4753) Tel 212-877-2741

Doneve Designs, *(Doneve Designs, Inc.; 0-89715),* P.O. Box 1072, Saratoga, CA 95070 (SAN 211-4895) Tel 408-867-7556

Dorn Bks, *(Dorn Books; 0-934070),* 7101 York Ave. S., Minneapolis, MN 55435 (SAN 223-3584)

Dos Reals Pub, *(Dos Reals Publishing; 0-915004),* 2490 Channing Way, Berkeley, CA 94704 (SAN 207-2157) Tel 415-548-6810

Dothard, *(Dothard, R. L., Associates; 0-912668),* R.D. 2, Brattleboro, VT 05301 (SAN 201-3371) Tel 802-254-9009

Douglas-West, *(Douglas-West Pubs., Inc.; 0-913264),* Dist. by: Book Pool International, P.O. Box 249, Corona, CA 91270 (SAN 269-7513)

Downhome, *(Downhome Publishing Co.; 0-935124),* P.O. Box 813, Forest Grove, OR 97116 (SAN 213-6198)

Dragon Co, *(Dragon Co.; 0-937456),* P.O. Box 14682, Houston, TX 77021 (SAN 215-7543)

Dragonfly Pr, *(Dragonfly Press; 0-940072),* P.O. Box 8771, Toledo, OH 43623 (SAN 220-2158) Tel 419-475-4037

Dragtooth Pr, *(Dragtooth Press),* 3930 N. W. Witham Hill Dr., No. 140, Corvallis, OR 97330 (SAN 206-9482)

Dream Place, *(Dream Place Pubns.; 0-930486),* 484 Lake Park Ave.,Suite 130, Oakland, CA 94610 (SAN 211-7053) Tel 415-832-4427

Dreambooks, *(Dreambooks),* P.O. Box 1836, Kingsville, TX 78363 (SAN 240-141X)

Dreams Unltd, *(Dreams Unlimited; 0-939874),* P.O. Box 247, Middleton, WI 53562 (SAN 215-7551) Tel 608-836-6575

Dreier Educ, *(Dreier Educational Systems, Inc.; 0-87673),* 25 S. Fifth Ave., Box 1291, Highland Park, NJ 08904 (SAN 201-3401) Tel 201-572-2112

Drinkwatchers, *(Drinkwatchers),* 14 Riverside Ave., Haverstraw, NY 10927 (SAN 210-1165)

Droke-Hallux, *(Droke House/Hallux; 0-8375),* 116 W. Orr St., Box 2027, Anderson, SC 29621 (SAN 203-8951) Tel 803-226-7231

Drug Abuse, *(Drug Abuse Council),* 1828 "L" St., N.W., Washington, DC 20036 (SAN 203-8609) Tel 202-785-5200

Drum & Spear, *(Drum & Spear Press, Inc.; 0-87782),* 1371 Fairmont St., N. W., Washington, DC 20009 (SAN 206-6998)

DSA *See* Educ Info Group

DTS Pub, *(DTS Publishing; 0-9610940),* 114 Natal Way, Vista, CA 92083 (SAN 265-2307)

Dublin Pr, *(Dublin Press; 0-9604238),* Sunnyvale, CA 94087 (SAN 214-3658); c/o Debby Of Dublin, 214 El Paso S/C, San Jose, CA 95130 (SAN 669-067X)

DuBois Zone Pr, *(DuBois Zone Press, The; 0-931498),* 516 11th Ave., Grafton, WI 53024 (SAN 212-8071)

Duck Pr, *(Duck Press; 0-9604364),* Box 1024, New York, NY 10009 (SAN 214-3666); Orders to: Energy Earth Communications Inc., Box 1141, Galveston, TX 77553 (SAN 214-3674)

Ducks Bks, *(Ducks Books; 0-913858),* P.O. Box 307, Ben Lomond, CA 95005 (SAN 203-896X) Tel 408-336-8887

Ducky Ent, *(Ducky, B. K., Enterprises),* 8836 S. Vermont Ave., No. 2, Los Angeles, CA 90044 (SAN 215-1413) Tel 213-377-0216

Duke Pr IL, *(Duke Press; 0-931234),* 8917 W. Cermak Rd., N. Riverside, IL 60546 (SAN 211-9455)

Dumbarton Pr, *(Dumbarton Press; 0-9600822),* P.O. Box 639, Newark, CA 94560 (SAN 209-1410)

Dunhere, *(Dunhere Pub. Co.; 0-89452),* Div. of Dunhere Composition House, Ltd., 115 Christopher St., 6th Fl., New York, NY 10014 (SAN 210-1939) Tel 212-989-0746

Dunn & Webster, *(Dunn & Webster Inc., Pubs.; 0-89761),* 10 Bull St., Newport, RI 02840 (SAN 211-9463) Tel 401-846-8361

Dwelling Sculpt, *(Dwelling Sculpture Institute),* 431 Crestvale Dr, Sierra Madre, CA 91024 (SAN 225-2655)

Dymax, *(Dymax; 0-918138),* P. O. Box 310, Menlo Park, CA 94025 (SAN 209-6617) Tel 415-323-6117

Dynamic Learn Corp, *(Dynamic Learning Corp.; 0-915890),* 59 Commercial Wharf, Boston, MA 02110 (SAN 209-049X) Tel 617-742-9493 Imprints: Telegraph (Telegraph Books).

Dynamics Pr, *(Dynamics Press; 0-917490),* 2633 E. 28th St., No. 602, Signal Hill, CA 90806 (SAN 209-0619) Tel 213-776-7030

E & E Pub, *(E & E Publishing Co.),* 27 Franklin Ave., Souderton, PA 18964 (SAN 211-3546) Tel 215-723-6689

E & L Instru, *(E & L Instruments; 0-89704),* 61 First St., Derby, CT 06418 (SAN 211-4151)

E C Stanton Pub, *(Stanton, Elizabeth Cady, Pub., Co.),* 5857 Marbury Rd., Bethesda, MD 20034 (SAN 207-2173) Tel 301-229-7067

E Dickinson Bks, *(Emily Dickinson Books),* 4508 38th St., Brentwood, MD 20722 (SAN 209-200X)

E E Jennings, *(Jennings, E. E., Publishing; 0-9613044),* 103 Pierce, Box 65, Whiteface, TX 79379 (SAN 294-0396) Tel 806-287-1182

E M Underwood, *(Underwood, E. M., Pub; 0-932410),* P.O. Box 4295, San Leandro, CA 94579 (SAN 212-5749); Orders to: P.O. Box 1107, Livermore, CA 94550 (SAN 212-5757)

E Menzie Imports, *(Menzie, Eleanor, Imports),* 3240 Pico Blvd., Santa Monica, CA 90405 (SAN 209-214X) Tel 213-392-7398

E R Brown Pub, *(Edward, R. Brown Publishing Co.; 0-912231),* P.O. Box 796, Laurel, MD 20707 (SAN 265-105X) Tel 301-490-5949

E S John, *(John, Edna S.),* 1481 "D" St., Springfield, OR 97477 (SAN 209-2050)

E Whittle & F A Dockery, *(Whittle, E., & F. A. Dockery; 0-9604046),* 795-B Beech Cir. NW, Cleveland, TN 37311 (SAN 214-168X)

Eagle Pr, *(Eagle Pr., Inc.),* P.O. Box 64935, Baton Rouge, LA 70806 (SAN 208-158X) Tel 504-344-7443

Eagle Pubs, *(Eagle Pubs.; 0-9600634),* P.O. Box 1267, Chicago, IL 60690 (SAN 201-3533)

Earth Magic, *(Earth Magic Productions; 0-9604128),* P.O. Box 1202, FDR Sta., New York, NY 10022 (SAN 214-1892)

Earth Pub Ents, *(Earth Publishing Enterprises, Inc.),* P. O. Box 430273, South Miami, FL 33143 (SAN 201-2855)

East & West Pubns, *(East & West Pubns., New York; 0-935886),* P.O. Box 17421, West Hartford, CT 06117 (SAN 206-099X)

East River Anthol, *(East River Anthology; 0-917238),* 75 Gates Ave., Montclair, NJ 07042 (SAN 208-6344) Tel 201-746-5941

East-West Pubns
See East & West Pubns

Easter Pub, *(Easter Publishing Co.; 0-930642),* P.O. Box 1244, Mobile, AL 36601 (SAN 211-1241)

ECA Pub, *(ECA Publishing Co.),* P.O. Box 1057, Menlo Park, CA 94025 (SAN 206-9431) Tel 415-325-7569

Echenian Church, *(Echenian Church, The; 0-9603134),* P.O. Box 11893, Reno, NV 89510 (SAN 212-4998)

Echo Hse, *(Echo House; 0-910528),* 150 Broadway, New York, NY 10038 (SAN 204-1782)

Eckman Ctr, *(Eckman Center; 0-934752),* P.O. Box 621, Woodland Hills, CA 91365 (SAN 207-219X) Tel 213-347-4445

Ecology Pr, *(Ecology Press; 0-9603002),* P.O. Box 694, Alamo, CA 94507 (SAN 213-0505)

Econ Behavior, *(Economic Behavior Institute),* P. O. Box 879, Huntington Beach, CA 92648 (SAN 208-1415)

Ed Bk Crafters, *(Educational Book Crafters, Inc.; 0-912826),* 71 Boulevard, Westwood, NJ 07675 (SAN 203-8323)

Ed Consortium
See ECA Pub

Ed Inst Pr, *(Educational Institute Press),* P.O. Box 2537, Laguna Beach, CA 92653 (SAN 203-8331) Tel 714-830-0972

Ed Med & Info Sys, *(Educational Media & Information Systems; 0-913470),* P.O. Box 2411, Fort Collins, CO 80522 (SAN 203-834X)

Ed Res Inst, *(Educational Research Institute; 0-9600426),* 5328-A Bahia Blanca, Laguna Hills, CA 92653 (SAN 203-8366) Tel 714-586-8162

Ed Resources, *(Educational Resources Unlimited, Inc.; 0-915912),* P.O. Box 43, Baker, NV 89311 (SAN 208-6352) Tel 702-234-7213

Ed Sci, *(Educational Science Consultants; 0-912990),* P.O. Box 1674, San Leandro, CA 94577 (SAN 201-3657)

Eden, *(Eden Publishing House; 0-910532),* 1724 Chouteau Ave., St. Louis, MO 63103 (SAN 201-3673) Tel 314-421-1544

Eden Hall Pr, *(Eden Hall Press; 0-933090),* P.O. Box 67534, Los Angeles, CA 90067 (SAN 212-8519)

EdMart Intl, *(EdMart International; 0-89485),* 177 White Plains Rd., Tarrytown, NY 10591 (SAN 210-0770) Tel 914-332-0931

Edmond Pub Co., *(Edmond Publishing Co.; 0-912954),* P.O. Box 364, Branchport, NY 14418 (SAN 201-3711)

Edns Vilo, *(Editions Vilo, Inc.; 0-86710),* 500 Fifth Ave., Suite 1423, New York, NY 10110 (SAN 216-7271)

Educ Bk Pubs, *(Educational Book Pubs., Inc.),* 1175 N.E. 125th St., Suite 303, North Miami, FL 33161 (SAN 204-1650) Tel 305-891-7471

Educ Ent, *(Educational Enterprises),* Dist. by: Potter Library Services, Inc., 223 S. 60 St., Milwaukee, WI 53214 (SAN 169-9229)

Educ Impact, *(Educational Impact; 0-89076),* P.O. Box 355, Blackwood, NJ 08012 (SAN 207-0175) Tel 609-228-3555

Educ Indus, *(Education Industries, Inc.; 0-86652),* P.O. Box 52, Madison, WI 53701 (SAN 216-1273)

Educ Info Group, *(Educational Information Group),* 45 Miles Standish Dr., Marlborough, MA 01752 (SAN 210-8933) Tel 617-481-5335

Educ Interest, *(Educators Interest Group of the San Diego Computer Society),* P.O. Box 81537, San Diego, CA 92138 (SAN 655-086X)

Effies Bks, *(Effie's Books),* 1420 45th St., Emeryville, CA 94608 (SAN 209-5548)

Egar Pr, *(Egar Press, Inc.; 0-916484),* Brashears Ctr., 1400 N. Harbor Blvd., P.O. Box 5409, Suite 240, Fullerton, CA 92635 (SAN 208-3647) Tel 714-879-7423

Eilean Ban Pub, *(Eilean Ban Publishing Co.; 0-918702),* P.O. Box 116, Stafford, VA 22554 (SAN 211-416X) Tel 703-695-3506

EKNE, *(American Assn. of Elementary-Kindergarten-Nursery Educators),* 1201 Sixteenth St., Washington, DC 20036 (SAN 207-3285)

El Fuego Aztlan, *(El Fuego de Aztlan Pubns.; 0-936470),* 3408 Dwinelle Hall, Univ. of Calif., Berkeley, CA 94720 (SAN 213-4888) Tel 415-642-3859

Electrical, *(Electrical Electronics Materials Distributors),* 16 W. 56th St., New York, NY 10019 (SAN 690-1425)

Elephant Pub, *(Elephant Publishing Corp.; 0-914654),* 176 Clinton Ave., Brooklyn, NY 11205 (SAN 206-7528) Tel 212-875-3666; Dist. by: Morgan & Morgan, Inc., 145 Palisade St., Dobbs Ferry, NY 10522 (SAN 202-5620)

Elgen Pub Co, *(Elgen Publishing Co.; 0-935774),* 1004 Taurus Dr., Colorado Springs, CO 80906 (SAN 214-2392)

Elijah Pr, *(Elijah Press; 0-9608472),* 24 1/2 Center St., Rutland, VT 05701 (SAN 240-6381) Tel 802-773-7215

Eller, *(Eller Books),* La Verne College, 1950 Third St., La Verne, CA 91750 (SAN 201-3797) Tel 714-593-3511

Ellman Studio, *(Ellman, Sylvia Stone, Studio),* P.O. Box 1416, Berkley, MI 48072 (SAN 215-8604) Tel 313-559-0479

Elm Tree Pr, *(Elm Tree Press; 0-918856),* P.O. Box 185, La Crosse, WI 54601 (SAN 209-1801) Tel 608-637-3205

Elysian Fields, *(Elysian Fields Publishing),* 1603 Burton St., Rockford, IL 61103 (SAN 212-0879)

Emet Bks, *(Emet Books Inc.; 0-89476),* Box 501, Millwood, NY 10546 (SAN 209-4320) Tel 914-941-0043; Dist. by: Whirlwind Book Co., 80 Fifth Ave., Suite 1106, New York, NY 10011 (SAN 208-6239) Tel 212-691-7280

Emmanuel Pr, *(Emmanuel Press; 0-917028),* P.O. Box 158, Saratoga, CA 95070 (SAN 209-3324)

Emporium Pubns, *(Emporium Pubns.; 0-88278),* 28 Sackville St., Charlestown, MA 02129 (SAN 201-3835) Tel 617-241-9549

EMR Pubns, *(EMR Pubns.; 0-930308),* P.O. Box 4007, Bryan, TX 77805 (SAN 209-5556) Tel 409-779-5060

Enchanted Knolls, *(Enchanted Knolls Pr.; 0-915055),* 50 Kipling Dr., No. 3, Mill Valley, CA 94941 (SAN 289-9205)

Endeco Pub, *(Endeco Publishing Co.),* P. O. Box 930, Lemon Grove, CA 92045 (SAN 208-161X)

Energy Earth, *(Energy Earth Communications, Inc.; 0-934004),* P.O. Box 1141, Galveston, TX 77553 (SAN 223-2448)

Engwd Cliffs Coll, *(Englewood Cliffs College),* Hudson Terr., Englewood Cliffs, NJ 07632 (SAN 201-3894)

Ensign Prods, *(Ensign Production; 0-912085),* 460 N. University, No. 5, Provo, UT 84601 (SAN 287-7465)

Entrepreneurs, *(Entrepreneurs' Library, Inc.),* P.O. Box 17729, Fountain Hills, AZ 85268 (SAN 262-0219)

Environ Sci Serv, *(Environmental Science Services),* Div. of Park Publishing Co., 333 Hudson St., New York, NY 10013 (SAN 206-9407)

Eon Bks, *(Eon Books; 0-916306),* 6356 Van Nuys Blvd., Suite 215, Van Nuys, CA 91401 (SAN 207-995X)

Equity Pub CA, *(Equity Publishing Co.; 0-939206),* P.O. Box 10443, Santa Ana, CA 92711 (SAN 216-2431)

Ermine Pubs, *(Ermine Pubs., Inc.; 0-89343),* 6253 Hollywood Blvd., No. 312, Hollywood, CA 90028 (SAN 208-6220) Tel 213-461-3256; Dist. by: Whirlwind Book Co., 80 Fifth Ave., Suite 1106, New York, NY 10011 (SAN 208-6239) Tel 212-691-7280

Ernst, *(Ernst, Rick, Publishing Co.; 0-9603110),* P.O. Box 22940, Denver, CO 80222 (SAN 213-4896)

Essaye Pub, *(Essaye Publishing Co.; 0-939756),* 22713 Ventura Blvd., Suite F, Woodland Hills, CA 91364 (SAN 216-3780)

Estate Bk, *(Estate Book Sales),* 2824 Pennsylvania Ave, NW, Washington, DC 20007 (SAN 207-6373) Tel 202-965-4274

Estimators Handbk, *(Estimators Handbook),* 750 Whitmore, Detroit, MI 48203 (SAN 205-6194) Tel 313-345-5047

Etcetera Pr, *(Etcetera Press),* P. O. Drawer 27100, Columbus, OH 43227 (SAN 203-8455) Tel 614-436-7428

Eureka Pr, *(Eureka Press, Inc.; 0-89803),* 140 Main St., Gloucester, MA 01930 (SAN 238-4299) Tel 617-283-3459

Europa Camping, (Europa Camping & Caravaning), 2306 Sixth St., Clay Center, KS 67432 (SAN 207-4249) Tel 913-632-5280

Evang Authors, (Evangelist Authors Society), P.O. Box 6523, Anaheim, CA 92806 (SAN 207-6748)

Evans Pub Co, (Evans Publishing Co.), 5344 Shalley Circle, Ft. Myers, FL 33907 (SAN 214-2414)

Everest Pub, (Everest Publishing Co.; 0-931034), Box 2686 Century Sta., Raleigh, NC 27602 (SAN 211-4658) Tel 919-787-8009

Evolutionary, (Evolutionary Press; 0-943408), 2418 Clement St., San Francisco, CA 94121 (SAN 240-642X) Tel 415-221-9222; Orders to: Mindbody Press, 1749 Vine St., Berkeley, CA 94703 (SAN 680-0319) Tel 415-644-8242

Examiner Spec Proj
See Cal Living Bks

Excelsior Bks, (Excelsior Books, Inc.; 0-918283), Box 911, Orange, CA 92666-0911 (SAN 670-7408) Tel 714-978-0121; Dist. by: Baker & Taylor Southeast Div., Mount Olive Rd., Commerce, GA 30599 (SAN 169-1503) Tel 404-335-5000; Dist. by: Baker & Taylor Western Div., 380 Edison Way, Reno, NV 89564 (SAN 169-4464) Tel 702-786-6700; Dist. by: Baker & Taylor Eastern Div., 50 Kirby Ave., Somerville, NJ 08876 (SAN 169-4901) Tel 201-722-8000; Dist. by: Baker & Taylor Midwest Div., 501 S. Gladioulus Ave., Momence, IL 60954 (SAN 169-2100) Tel 815-472-2444; Dist. by: Ingram Book Co., 347 Reedwood Dr., Nashville, TN 37217 (SAN 169-7978) Tel 800-251-5900; Dist. by: Ingram Book Co., 16175 Stevens St., City of Industry, CA 91744 (SAN 168-9541); Dist. by: Ingram Book Co., 8301 Sherwick Ct., Jessup, MD 20794 (SAN 169-3174); Dist. by: Publishers Group West, 5855 Beaudry St., Emeryville, CA 94608 (SAN 202-8522) Tel 800-982-8319; Dist. by: Distributors The, 702 S. Michigan, South Bend, IN 46618 (SAN 200-4631) Tel 219-232-8500; Dist. by: Book Dynamics, 836 Broadway, New York, NY 10003 (SAN 169-5649) Tel 212-254-7798

Exceptional, (Exceptional Books, Inc.; 0-910570), P.O. Box 592, Ansonia Sta., New York, NY 10023 (SAN 203-848X)

Exordium Pr, (Exordium Press; 0-912784), P.O. Box 635, Akron, OH 44309 (SAN 203-8501)

Exotic Beauties, (Exotic Beauties Press, Inc.; 0-918378), 403 W. 21st St., New York, NY 10011 (SAN 210-0800) Tel 212-929-4183

Expedition Pr, (Expedition Press; 0-939924), P.O. Box 1198, Kalamazoo, MI 49006 (SAN 218-8111)

Expertise, (Expertise, The; 0-9605184), 14426 Kingsdale, Lawndale, CA 90260 (SAN 239-3891)

Explore Kansas, (Explore Kansas), Dist. by: Campgrounds Unlimited, P.O. Box 248, Wakefield, KS 67487 (SAN 203-8528)

Explorer Pub Co, (Explorer Publishing Co.), P.O. Box 385, Boston, MA 02117 (SAN 212-9027) Tel 617-536-3583

Extension Texts, (Extension Texts; 0-9600624), P.O. Box 357, Cambridge, MA 02138 (SAN 203-8544)

F A Fleet, (Fleet, Fred A., II; 0-933542), P.O. Box 235, Washington, PA 15301 (SAN 212-5048)

F A I R, (FAIR-Federation for American Immigration Reform; 0-935776), 2028 P St., NW, Washington, DC 20036 (SAN 213-7372)

F & J Pub Corp, (F&J Publishing Corporation; 0-89311), 30941 Agoura Rd., Suite 232, Westlake Village, CA 91361 (SAN 208-368X)

F & L Assocs, (F & L Assocs.), P.O. Box 8034, Long Beach, CA 90808 (SAN 238-8359)

F Apple, (Apple, Faye), P.O. Box 3036, W. Durham Sta., Durham, NC 27705 (SAN 219-953X) Tel 919-286-2250

F D Smith, (Smith, Frank D. (Tony) , Jr.; 0-9600944), P.O. Box 1032, Catersville, GA 30120 (SAN 208-8592) Tel 404-382-0622

F F Farmer, (Ford Fergie Farmer Publishing Co,), 40 Park Hill Ave., Millbury, MA 01527 (SAN 213-4950) Tel 617-754-4612

F H Smith, (Smith, Florence H.; 0-89279), P.O. Box 551, Chesterton, IN 46304 (SAN 295-1061)

F Widutis, (Widutis, Florence), 3318 Gumwood Dr., Hyattsville, MD 20783 (SAN 208-2284) Tel 301-422-3609

Fabmath, (Fabmath; 0-937138), P.O. Box 568, Warrington, PA 18976 (SAN 214-3690)

Fairbanks Bks, (Fairbanks Books; 0-914830), 815 17th St., Bellingham, WA 98225 (SAN 206-4030) Tel 206-733-3852

Fandom Unltd, (Fandom Unlimited Enterprises; 0-9607178), P.O. Box 70868, Sunnyvale, CA 94086 (SAN 239-0906)

Far Eastern Cult, (Far Eastern Cultural Studies Institute; 0-918972), 7 Forrest Court, East Grand Forks, MN 56721 (SAN 210-4237) Tel 218-773-9483

Farrar Bks, (Farrar Books), 73 Poplar St., Garden City, NY 11530 (SAN 207-2246) Tel 516-747-2936

Farrar Pub, (Farrar Publishing; 0-9605588), 25 Library Ave., Warrensburg, NY 12885 (SAN 216-1311) Tel 518-623-4551

Fed Statistics, (Federal Statistics Users' Conference), 4620 Lee Hwy., Suite 201, Arlington, VA 22207 (SAN 691-2117)

Fedora Bks, (Fedora Books), P.O. Box 265, Hopedale, MA 01747 (SAN 207-5628)

Feldco Ent, (Feldco Enterprises; 0-9603550), Woodward Bldg., Suite 100, Birmingham, AL 35203 (SAN 213-0564)

Feldspar, (Feldspar; 0-9607396), P.O. Box 2375, Stanford, CA 94305 (SAN 239-5312)

Felis Hadiken, (Felis-Hadiken Publications; 0-9609262), 16C Division St., Glens Falls, NY 12801 (SAN 260-0552)

Fellowship TX, (Fellowship Pr.; 0-9610420), 1116 W. Felix Ave., Fort Worth, TX 76115 (SAN 264-0341)

Felten, (Felten, Charles J.; 0-9600312), 1532 Essex Dr., N., St. Petersburg, FL 33710 (SAN 205-5775)

Fibonacci Corp, (Fibonacci Corp.; 0-915494), 2231 Rucker Ave., Everett, WA 98201 (SAN 208-2373)

FID, (Food Industries Directories; 0-933194), 25 Broad St., New York, NY 10004 (SAN 211-3155) Tel 212-344-1450

Fidelis Pubs, (Fidelis Pubs., Inc.), P.O. Box 1334, Palm Desert, CA 92261 (SAN 212-0895) Tel 714-345-5346

Fides
See Fides Claretian

Fides Claretian, (Fides/Claretian; 0-8190), 221 W. Madison St., Chicago, IL 60606 (SAN 201-4807) Tel 312-236-7783

Fieldstead Inst, (Fieldstead Institute; 0-940240), Box CV, Irvine, CA 92716 (SAN 220-3324)

Fieldston, (Fieldston Pr.; 0-912166), P.O. Box 3413, New York, NY 10163 (SAN 205-5783)

Filipino Info, (Filipino Information Service; 0-941124), P.O. Box 12215, San Francisco, CA 94112 (SAN 217-362X) Tel 415-433-3024

Filmrow Pubns, (Filmrow Pubns.), 8272 Sunset Blvd., West Hollywood, CA 90046 (SAN 281-708X) Tel 213-654-8310; 12349 Milbank St., Studio City, CA 91604 (SAN 281-7098) Tel 213-761-2627

Financial Tech, (Financial Technology Ltd.; 0-915292), 4 Echo Lane, New Brunswick, NJ 08816 (SAN 207-169X) Tel 201-998-2700

Finch, (Finch/Story; 0-914411), 1029 Judy Ct., Dubuque, IA 52001 (SAN 289-6230) Tel 319-556-0659

Fintzenberg, (Fintzenberg Pubs; 0-914928), 3700 Gulf Dr. No. 216, Holmes Beach, FL 33510 (SAN 206-7951) Tel 813-778-1825

Fireplug Pr, (Fireplug Press; 0-932494), 2461 N. Clark, Chicago, IL 60657 (SAN 212-0909)

Fireside Pub, (Fireside Publishing; 0-9612846), 209 West Ave. N, Lovington, NM 88260 (SAN 289-9825) Tel 505-396-2094

First Circle Pr, (First Circle Pr.; 0-933693), 233 Acton Pl., Oakland, CA 94606 (SAN 692-5243)

FitCom Corp, (Fitcom Corp.; 0-930447), 737 W. Chester Pike, Havertown, PA 19083 (SAN 670-9524) Tel 215-789-3355

Five Star Pubs, (Five Star Pubs.), Box 1398, Tupelo, MS 38801 (SAN 211-7959)

Five Trees, (Five Trees Press), 1061 Folsom St., San Francisco, CA 94103 (SAN 209-7419) Tel 415-552-2122

Flaherty Pub, (Flaherty Publishing; 0-9615222), 1108 E. Fifth, No. 23, P.O. Box 481, Corona, CA 91718 (SAN 695-1546)

Flower Mound Writ, (Flower Mound Writing Company; 0-910655), Box 37, Mango, FL 34262-0037 (SAN 262-6632)

Flower Truth, (Flower of Truth Publishing Co.; 0-9608164), P.O. Box 763, Anchorage, AK 99587 (SAN 240-2203)

Flowerpot Mtn Pr, (Flowerpot Mountain Pr.; 0-9610768), P.O. Box 3711, Lawrence, KS 66044 (SAN 264-6153)

Flying Three Ent, (Flying 3 Enterprises), P.O. Box 690, Littleton, CO 80120 (SAN 207-1703) Tel 303-795-8402

Folksmedia Pub, (Folksmedia Publishing Co.; 0-9608526), P.O. Box 9206, Palm Springs, CA 92263 (SAN 240-6500)

Foot Trails, (Foot Trails Pubns., Inc.; 0-933710), The Pottingshed, Bedford Rd., Greenwich, CT 06830 (SAN 213-2389); Dist. by: Simon & Schuster, Inc., 1230 Ave. of the Americas, New York, NY 10020 (SAN 200-2450) Tel 212-245-6400

Football Ill, (Football Rules Illustrated Publishing Co.; 0-9600364), P.O. Box 3005, Austin, TX 78764 (SAN 206-4243)

Foothills Pr, (Foothills Pr.; 0-917284), P.O. Box 458, Pittsfield, MA 01202 (SAN 208-4171)

Forecasting Software, (Forecasting Software Corp.; 0-916756), 390 Plandome Rd., Suite 203, Manhasset, NY 11030 (SAN 208-1997)

Foreign Travel, (Foreign Travel Features), P.O. Box 5125, Lighthouse Point, FL 33064 (SAN 238-8138)

Foreworks, (Foreworks; Interval Books; Flaming Sparrow Press; 0-943292), Box 9747, North Hollywood, CA 91609 (SAN 240-6519) Tel 818-982-0467

Forkner Pub Inc, (Forkner Publishing Co., Inc.; 0-912036), P.O. Box 652, Ridgewood, NJ 07451 (SAN 658-845X)

Forrest Printing, (Forrest Printing; 0-89023), P.O. Box 105, Grand Haven, MI 49417 (SAN 239-8524)

Fort Concho, (Fort Concho Sketches Publishing Co.), P.O. Box 5262, San Angelo, TX 76902 (SAN 206-4731)

Fort Sullivan, (Fort Sullivan Chapter (Daughters of the American Revolution)), P.O. Box 33055, Charleston, SC 29407 (SAN 209-4371)

Forty Whacks, (40 Whacks Press; 0-939264), P.O. Box 591, Shelton, CT 06484 (SAN 220-1542) Tel 203-366-8060

FOSG
See FOSG Pubns

FOSG Pubns, (FOSG Pubns.; 0-913464), Box 239, Oradell, NJ 07649 (SAN 201-6559)

Foto Res
See F F Farmer

Fotoflip Bk, (Fotoflip Book Co.; 0-917602), Box 26337, San Jose, CA 95159 (SAN 209-2700) Tel 408-296-2570

Foun Adv Artists, (Foundation for the Advancement of Artists; 0-912916), 1315 Walnut St. Bldg., Philadelphia, PA 19107 (SAN 201-1425)

Foun Pub, (Foundation Pubs.; 0-910620), 4101 San Jacinto St., Houston, TX 77004 (SAN 205-5848)

Foundry TCP, (Foundry, the Third Coast Pr.), P.O. Box 05191, Detroit, MI 48225 (SAN 241-0192); 18920 Woodcrest, Harper Woods, MI 48225 (SAN 658-0734)

Four Corners, (Four Corners Explorer), P.O. Box 759, Cortez, CO 81321 (SAN 283-9539)

Four Star, (Four Star Press, The), 815 N. Labrea Ave., P.O. Box 301, Los Angeles, CA 90302 (SAN 217-1031)

Four Winds
See Four Winds Pr

Four Winds Pr, (Four Winds Press), Box 126, Bristol, FL 32321 (SAN 209-7435)

Foxcroft Pub, (Foxcroft Publishing; 0-9612414), 30 Lincoln Plaza, Suite 28E, New York, NY 10023 (SAN 289-2324)

Frank Bk Corp, (Frank Book Corp.; 0-89332), Dist. by: Enslow Publishers, Box 301, Short Hills, NJ 07078 (SAN 209-0651)

Franklin CT, (Franklin; 0-9604424), 203 Broad St., No. 2, New London, CT 06320 (SAN 214-3755)

Franklin Pr
See Franklin Pr OH

Franklin Pr OH, (Franklin Press, The; 0-933034), P.O. Box 437, 166 S. Franklin St., Chagrin, OH 44022 (SAN 211-7320)

Franklin Pub Locust, (Franklin Publishing Co.; 0-87133), 2047 Locust St., Philadelphia, PA 19103 (SAN 201-663X) Tel 215-563-3837

Frederick Ent, (Frederick Enterprises; 0-9607180), 845 Calderwood Ln., Pasadena, CA 91107 (SAN 239-0914)

Free-Camp, (Free-Camp Press; 0-9604004), c/o Gerry, 1326 Nautilus St., La Jolla, CA 92037 (SAN 270-3289)

Free Life, (Free Life Editions; 0-914156), 41 Union Sq., W., New York, NY 10003 (SAN 201-6648) Tel 212-989-3750

Freedom Unltd, (Freedom Unlimited; 0-938014), P.O. Box 599, Garden Grove, CA 92642 (SAN 215-644X)

Freeman Mutuels, (Freeman Mutuels Management; 0-9608022), 1734 E. 16th St., Loveland, CO 80537 (SAN 239-6432)

Freeman Pub Co, (Freeman Publishing Company; 0-911939), P.O. Box 703, Van Nuys, CA 91408 (SAN 264-049X); 5463 Newcastle Ave., Apt. 6, Encino, CA 91316 (SAN 264-0503)

Freshwater Log
See Waterfront OH

Friendly World, (Friendly World Enterprises; 0-914668), P.O. Box 361, Pepeekeo, HI 96783 (SAN 205-6224) Tel 808-963-6864

Friends Aberdeen, (Friends of the Aberdeen Public Library; 0-9605152), 121 E. Market St., Aberdeen, WA 98520 (SAN 215-7632)

Front St, (Front Street Pubs.; 0-931502), 129 Front St., Rm. 301, New York, NY 10005 (SAN 212-3517)

Frontier Bk, (Frontier Book Co.), P.O. Box 805, Fort Davis, TX 79734 (SAN 206-4197)

Fulcourte Pr, (Fulcourte Press; 0-933354), P.O. Box 1961, Decatur, GA 30031 (SAN 212-6109) Tel 404-378-5750

Fund Exchange, (Funding Exchange; 0-9601974), 4111 24th St., San Francisco, CA 94114 (SAN 211-9919) Tel 415-285-2005; Orders to: Bookpeople, 2929 Fifth St., Berkeley, CA 94710 (SAN 168-9517) Tel 800-227-1516

Fundaburk, (Fundaburk, Emma Lila, Pub.; 0-910642), P.O. Box 231, Luverne, AL 36049 (SAN 205-597X)

Funkshunal, (Funkshunal Features; 0-932442), P.O. Box 47728, Los Angeles, CA 90047 (SAN 212-212X) Tel 213-778-5422

Fut Stoch Dynamics, (Future Stokchastic Dynamics, Inc.), c/o Yale L. Meltzer, 141-10 82nd Dr., Jamaica, NY 11435 (SAN 240-060X)

Future Syst-TLH, (Future Systems/TLH Associates; 0-941506), Minnesota Bldg., Suite 900, St. Paul, MN 55101 (SAN 239-0922)

G & BJ's Serv, (G & BJ's Services; 0-9604838), 1350 Grandridge Blvd., Kennewick, WA 99336 (SAN 215-6474)

G & R Pubns, (G & R Publications; 0-931643), P.O. Box 4661, Ithaca, NY 14852 (SAN 683-7468)

G Collar, (Collar, Grant), 213 S. Fairchild St., Yreka, CA 96097 (SAN 203-2023)

G D Kieffer, (Kieffer, George David ,Pub.; 0-9609344), P.O. Box 67874, Los Angeles, CA 90067 (SAN 260-2156) Tel 213-556-5522

G D Krug, (Krug, Gerald Daniel; 0-9612890), 1680 N. Vine, Suite 102, Hollywood, CA 90028 (SAN 291-2449) Tel 213-465-8218

G D L Inc, (G.D.L., Inc.; 0-937358), P.O. Box 1248, Birmingham, MI 48011 (SAN 215-1464)

G E Gaylord, (Gabriel Emerson Gaylord), 242 E. 12th St., C-27, Indianapolis, IN 46204 (SAN 207-2262)

G G L Pub Co, (GGL Publishing Co., Inc.; 0-9610198), 322 Hancock Street, Henderson, KY 42420 (SAN 264-0538)

G H Crumpler, (Crumpler, Gus H.), 413 N. Center St., Harrison, AR 72601 (SAN 209-1658) Tel 501-741-4612

G I Read, (Read, George Isaac), 340 Ventura St., No. 17, Palo Alto, CA 94306 (SAN 207-6845)

Gains, (Gains Publishing Co.; 0-917432), P.O. Box 1157, Alhambra, CA 91802 (SAN 209-1887) Tel 213-282-1244

Gala Bks, (Gala Books & Gifts; 0-912448), 25221 Calle Sombre, Laguna Niguel, CA 92677 (SAN 203-4131) Tel 714-495-3759

Galilee Pr, (Galilee Pr.; 0-9612682), P.O. Box 11625, Oakland, CA 94611 (SAN 289-2073)

Galleon Pubns
See Galleon-Whitehurst

Galleon-Whitehurst, (Galleon Pubns.; 0-918602), 12 Tiffany Rd., No. 6, Salem, NH 03079 (SAN 210-9158)

Galliard Pr, (Galliard Press; 0-936616), P.O. Box 296, Claremont, CA 91711 (SAN 214-2422)

Galvin Pub, (Galvin Publishing Co.; 0-932976), 384 City National Bank Bldg., Detroit, MI 48226 (SAN 211-7347)

Gamblers, (Gambler's Book Club/GBC Press; 0-911996; 0-89650), 630 S. 11th St., P.O. Box 4115, Las Vegas, NV 89127 (SAN 203-414X) Tel 702-382-7555

Garcia River, (Garcia River Press; 0-932708), P.O. Box 527, Point Arena, CA 95468 (SAN 212-2790)

Garden Studio, (Garden Studio, The; 0-932934), R.D.2, Box 190, Richmond, VT 05477 (SAN 212-6591) Tel 802-434-3524

Garrett-Helix, (Garrett Pubns.-Helix Press; 0-912326), Orders to: Taplinger Publishing Co., 200 Park Ave., S., New York, NY 10003 (SAN 213-6821)

Garrick Bks, (Garrick Books), 407 N. Aurora, Ithaca, NY 14850 (SAN 207-2289)

GateFord Pubns, (Gateford Pubns.; 0-916126), P.O. Box 92, Collingswood, NJ 08108 (SAN 207-1711)

Gateway, (Gateway Bookshop; 0-9600172), Ferndale, Bucks County, PA 18921 (SAN 203-4166) Tel 215-346-7416

Gateway Book, (Gateway Book Publishing Co.), P.O. Box 171, Sewickley, PA 15143 (SAN 209-6633) Tel 412-264-9549

Gauche Media, (Gauche Media; 0-931506), 2356 N.W. Irving, Portland, OR 97210 (SAN 212-0968)

Gaylord Prof Pubns, (Gaylord Professional Pubns.; 0-915794), Div. of Gaylord Brothers, Inc., P.O. Box 4901, Syracuse, NY 13221 (SAN 208-421X) Tel 315-457-5070

Geis, (Geis, Bernard, Assocs., Inc.; 0-87035), 128 E. 56th St., New York, NY 10022 (SAN 203-4190) Tel 212-752-1975

Gemini Bks, (Gemini Books), P.O. Box 10313, Eugene, OR 97440 (SAN 215-1480)

Gemini Pr DC, (Gemini Press; 0-940246), Box 5154, Greensboro, NC 27435 (SAN 217-5215)

Gen Learn Pr, (General Learning Press; 0-382), Div. of Silver Burdett Co., 250 James St., Morristown, NJ 07960 (SAN 207-172X) Tel 201-285-7942

Genealogy Res, (Genealogy Research; 0-9603214), 4309 44th Ave., Sacramento, CA 95824 (SAN 211-9501)

Genie Ent, (Genie Enterprises; 0-9608594), Terwilliger Rd. Extension, Hyde Park, NY 12538 (SAN 238-289X)

Gentle Pr, (Gentle Pr., The), P.O. Box 47, Medina, OH 44258 (SAN 240-1460)

GeoBooks, (GeoBooks; 0-914462), 171 Second St., Rm. 401, San Francisco, CA 94105 (SAN 206-7471)

Geriatric Pr, (Geriatric Pr.; 0-9601874), 907 E. Second, McCook, NE 69001 (SAN 211-8548) Tel 308-345-2733

Gingko Hse, (Gingko House Pubs.; 0-917156), W. 20 Sumner No. 104, Spokane, WA 99204 (SAN 208-0850) Tel 509-747-8355

Giuseffi-Crum Ent, (Giuseffi-Crum Enterprises; 0-9613645), P.O. Box 1977, Evanston, IL 60201 (SAN 692-4999)

Glasgow Bks Ltd, (Glasgow Books, Ltd.), Imperial Bank Tower, 701 B St., Suite 1300, San Diego, CA 92101 (SAN 676-8431)

Glass Bell, (Glass Bell Press; 0-9603072), 5053 Commonwealth, Detroit, MI 48208 (SAN 207-8333) Tel 313-898-7972

Glendon Assoc, (Glendon Associate; 0-932124), 2220 S. Beverly Glen Blvd., Los Angeles, CA 90064 (SAN 212-3533); Orders to: Below, Tobex Associates, 5700 Buchingham Pkwy., Los Angeles, CA 90067 (SAN 212-3541)

Glendon Hse
See Glendon Assoc

Glenwood, (Glenwood Pubs.; 0-911760), P.O. Box 880, Felton, CA 95018 (SAN 203-431X) Tel 408-335-4406

Globe Agency, (Globe Agency), P.O. Box 72238, Los Angeles, CA 90002 (SAN 210-5357) Tel 213-632-0256

Globe Pubs Texas, (Globe Pubs. International), 2205 Maryland St., Baytown, TX 77520 (SAN 203-4328) Tel 713-427-7740

Gloucester, (Gloucester Computer Business Co., Inc.), 6 Brooks Rd., Gloucester, MA 01930-1503 (SAN 692-185X) Tel 617-283-7719

Gluxlit Pr, (Gluxlit Press; 0-930524), P.O. Box 11165, Dallas, TX 75223 (SAN 211-9528)

Gneiss Bks, (Gneiss Books), P.O. Box 92, 283 Jackson St., Spring Grove, PA 17362 (SAN 240-1479)

Gododdin Pub, (Gododdin Publishing; 0-9603274), P.O. Box 5242, Everett, WA 98206 (SAN 213-6686)

Golden Door, (Golden Door Pubns., Inc.; 0-912596), 310 Madison Ave., New York, NY 10017 (SAN 213-0661) Tel 212-697-3137

Golden Eagle Pubs, (Golden Eagle Pubs.; 0-912129), 2706 W. Alameda Ave., Denver, CO 80219 (SAN 265-3850)

Golden Mtn, (Golden Mountain Press; 0-935062), P.O. Box 2387, Ithaca, NY 14850 (SAN 209-1976)

Golden Touch Ent, (Golden Touch Enterprises), P.O. Box 2408, West Palm Beach, FL 33401 (SAN 209-0090)

Golden Tri Pubns, (Golden Triangle Pubns.; 0-9614349), 659 15th St., Manhattan Beach, CA 90266 (SAN 692-4921)

Golden Valley
See GV Lutheran Coll

Gonzales, (Gonzales, Andrew), 1984 73rd St., Brooklyn, NY 11204 (SAN 210-3052)

Good Bk Pr, (Good Book Press), 12860 Muscatine St., Arleta, CA 91371 (SAN 210-1467) Tel 213-767-7660

Good Times Pub, (Good Times Publishing Co., Inc.), P.O. Box 625, Indian Rocks Beach, FL 33535 (SAN 208-4465)

Good Vibes, (Good Vibes; 0-913435), P.O. Box 32413, Minneapolis, MN 55432 (SAN 285-8428) Tel 612-571-9274

Goodlion, (Goodlion Pub.; 0-912844), c/o School of Art, Institute of Chicago, Michigan & Adams, Chicago, IL 60603 (SAN 203-4395) Tel 312-326-7080

Gothic Pr, (Gothic Pr.; 0-913045), 4998 Perkins Rd., Baton Rouge, LA 70808 (SAN 283-0949) Tel 504-766-2906

Gourmet Bks, (Gourmet Books, Inc.; 0-933166), 560 Lexington Ave., New York, NY 10022 (SAN 205-2768) Tel 212-371-1330

Govt Requirement Kits, (Government Requirement Kit; 0-941058), 1801 N. Meridian, Suite A, Tallahassee, FL 32303 (SAN 295-3323) Tel 904-385-9467

Graham Educ, (Graham Educational Products), Div. of Fun Publishing Co., 6200 Allisonville Rd., Indianapolis, IN 46220 (SAN 209-3375) Tel 317-253-2557; Orders to: P.O. Box 40283, Indianapolis, IN 46240 (SAN 209-3383)

GramWel Pr, (GramWel Studies & Stills Pr.), P.O. Box 912, Charlottesville, VA 22902 (SAN 209-7230)

Grand Canyon, (Grand Canyon Pubns., Inc.; 0-9604276), 443 S. 600 East St., Salt Lake City, UT 84102 (SAN 214-381X) Tel 801-272-2824

Grand Trine, (Grand Trine Pubns., Inc.; 0-915532), P.O. Box 7225, Hollywood, FL 33021 (SAN 207-6225)

Grantsman Ent, (Grantsman Enterprises Together), 6222 Beach Dr., Panama City, FL 32407 (SAN 209-0147) Tel 904-234-9021

Grape Hill Pr, (Grape Hill Press; 0-9610320), P.O. Box 1402, Greensboro, NC 27402 (SAN 264-066X) Tel 919-373-7028

Grape Pr, (Grape Press, the; 0-9608228), 142 Citizens Bank Center, Richardson, TX 75080 (SAN 234-3110)

Graphic Story, (Graphic Story Press; 0-914406), P. O. Box 16168, Long Beach, CA 90806 (SAN 201-6303) Tel 213-436-8172

Grasshopper NY, (Grasshopper Press; 0-918218), P.O. Box 331, Dewitt, NY 13214 (SAN 210-2072) Tel 315-479-5998

Graves Ent, (Graves, Michael P., Enterprises; 0-9603814), 621 S. Third Ave., Wausau, WI 54401 (SAN 213-9251)

Gray Pubns, (Gray, Edgar, Pubns.), P.O. Box 181, Kalamazoo, MI 49005 (SAN 205-3306) Tel 616-344-7070

Inactive/Out-of-Business

Gray-Zone, *(Gray-Zone Press; 0-9600516)*, Felicity Lane, Torrington, CT 06790 (SAN 203-4441)

Graystone Pub Co, *(Graystone Publishing Co.; 0-933468)*, 450 E. 81st St., New York, NY 10028 (SAN 212-9434)

Great Am Edns, *(Great American Editions, Ltd.; 0-913826)*, 111 E. 80th St., New York, NY 10021 (SAN 201-629X) Tel 212-744-5369

Great Am Pub, *(Great American Publishing Co.; 0-934632)*, 5513 Hwy. 290 W., Austin, TX 78735 (SAN 213-5043)

Great Lakes Pub, *(Great Lakes Publishing Co., Inc.; 0-933300)*, Box 461, Hudson, OH 44236 (SAN 201-6281)

Great Nat Soc Poet, *(Greater National Society of Poets, Inc.; 0-940088)*, 3023 W. Hillsborough Ave., Tampa, FL 33614 (SAN 214-3828) Tel 813-626-0225

Great Wall Pr, *(Great Wall Press; 0-913466)*, P. O. Box 1352, Hazelwood, MO 63043 (SAN 201-6265)

Greatlakes Liv, *(Greatlakes Living Press; 0-89635; 0-915498)*, 180 N. Michigan Ave., Chicago, IL 60601 (SAN 207-3153) Tel 312-782-9181

Greeno Hadden, *(Greeno, Hadden & Co., Ltd.; 0-913550)*, 518 Central St., Winchendon, MA 01475 (SAN 201-6192) Tel 617-297-1006

Greenwich Pr, *(Greenwich Press; 0-911708)*, 82 Christopher St., New York, NY 10014 (SAN 203-4530) Tel 212-242-0114

Greylock Pubs, *(Greylock Pubs.; 0-89223)*, 13 Spring St., Stamford, CT 06901 (SAN 207-9755)

Grid Pub, *(Grid Publishing Co.; 0-88244)*, 2950 N. High St., P.O. Box 14466, Columbus, OH 43214 (SAN 201-8403) Tel 614-261-6565

Grilled Flowers Pr, *(Grilled Flowers Press; 0-931238)*, P.O. Box 3254, Durango, CO 81302 (SAN 213-0718)

Gro-Pub, *(Gro-Pub; 0-914990)*, 13193 E. Bethany Place, Denver, CO 80232 (SAN 207-740X) Tel 303-755-7537; Orders to: P.O. Box 22629, Denver, CO 80222 (SAN 207-7418)

Group Envirn Ed, *(Group for Environmental Education)*, 1541 Samson St., Philadephia, PA 19102 (SAN 670-7106) Tel 215-496-0268; Dist. by: Publishing Center for Cultural Resoucres, 625 Broadway, New York, NY 10012 (SAN 274-9025)

Group One, *(Group One, Inc.)*, 6248 121st St., S. E., Bellevue, WA 98006 (SAN 201-6141)

Grunwald & Radcliff, *(Grunwald & Radcliff Publishers)*, 5049 Adm. Wright Rd., No. 344, Virginia Beach, VA 23462 (SAN 289-9388)

Guadalupian, *(Guadalupian Enterprises; 0-931645)*, 722 Ward Parkway 606, Kansas City, MO 64112 (SAN 683-7417)

Guide Living, *(Guide to Living Publications, Inc.; 0-913567)*, 5627 Government St., Baton Rouge, LA 70806 (SAN 285-2632)

Guild of Tutors, *(Guild of Tutors, International College; 0-89615)*, 1019 Gavley Ave., Los Angeles, CA 90024 (SAN 211-9587)

Guild Prof Trans
See Translation Research

Gulf Coast Cattleman, *(Gulf Coast Cattleman)*, P.O. Box 29367, San Antonio, TX 78229 (SAN 223-7865)

Guynes Pub, *(Guynes Publishing Co.)*, 615 N. Stanton St., El Paso, TX 79901 (SAN 209-0112)

GV Lutheran Coll, *(Golden Valley Lutheran College Bookstore)*, 6125 Olson Hwy., Minneapolis, MN 55422 (SAN 203-4360)

Gygi, *(Gygi, Robert N.; 0-9607592)*, 1338 NE 28th St., Portland, OR 97232 (SAN 239-4316)

H & A Herman, *(Herman, H. & A., Publishing Co.; 0-910718)*, R.F.D. No. 1 Box 211-2, Cameron, SC 29030 (SAN 203-4670)

H & H Publish, *(H & H Publishing)*, P.O. Box 547, Springfield, IL 62705 (SAN 286-3499)

H & H Systems, *(H & H Systems, Inc.; 0-9607594)*, 838 Grant St. Suite 310, Denver, CO 80203 (SAN 238-4590) Tel 303-832-5753

H C McElroy, *(McElroy, Harry C.)*, Box 284, San Carlos, AZ 85550 (SAN 212-1115)

H C Wells, *(Wells, H. C.; 0-930666)*, P.O. Box 2480, Pasadena, CA 91105 (SAN 211-4682)

H C Wilson, *(Wilson, Harold C.; 0-9600760)*, 320 Central Park W., New York, NY 10025 (SAN 206-8230) Tel 212-580-0698

H D Baldridge, *(Baldridge, H. David, Captain USN (Ret.))*, P.O. Box 15216, Sarasota, FL 33579 (SAN 211-5212) Tel 813-922-4796

H D Seyer, *(Seyer, Herman D.; 0-9600784)*, 6534 No. Bungalow Lane, Fresno, CA 93704 (SAN 207-3749) Tel 209-734-7537

H P Intl Users, *(International Users Group Special Interest Group Education)*, 289 S. San Antonio Rd., Suite 205, Los Altos, CA 94022 (SAN 671-6814)

H R Nestler Inc, *(Nestler, Harold R., Inc.)*, 13 Pennington Ave., Waldwick, NJ 07463 (SAN 209-0341) Tel 201-444-7413

H S Pub Corp, *(Health Science Publishing Corp.; 0-88238)*, 451 Greenwich St., New York, NY 10013 (SAN 201-6060) Tel 212-966-6658

Hacanbar, *(Hacanbar Associates)*, Apt. 419, 2201 Pennsylvania Ave., Philadelphia, PA 19103 (SAN 209-4444)

Haddonfield Hse, *(Haddonfield House; 0-88366)*, Div. of Griffin Press Inc., 300 Kings Hwy., E., Haddonfield, NJ 08033 (SAN 201-6036) Tel 609-795-3552

Haddonfield Pubs, *(Haddonfield Pubs.; 0-915460)*, P.O. Box 216, Haddonfield, NJ 08033 (SAN 212-5080) Tel 609-428-1282

Hadley Group, *(Hadley Group, Inc.; 0-913624)*, 808 S. Fourth St., Philadelphia, PA 19147 (SAN 201-5471) Tel 215-336-6700

Haitian Soc, *(Haitian Society of Pubns.; 0-914280)*, 359 Nostrand Ave., Brooklyn, NY 11216 (SAN 201-9094)

Haldon Pubns, *(Haldon Pubns., Inc.)*, 1204 N. 20th Ave., Hollywood, FL 33020 (SAN 213-5051) Tel 305-929-1956; Orders to: P.O. Box 2226, Hollywood, FL 33022 (SAN 213-506X)

Hallen Pub, *(Hallen Publishing Co.; 0-912992)*, 1962 Kirby Way, San Jose, CA 95124 (SAN 204-0190) Tel 408-377-0835

Hallmark Bks, *(Hallmark Books; 0-942322)*, 12 Jennings Ct., Shelby, OH 44875 (SAN 239-5509)

Hall's Bks, *(Hall's Books)*, Rte. 2, Box 239, Honea Path, SC 29654 (SAN 208-0974)

Halsey Pub, *(Halsey Publishing Co.)*, Dist. by: Construction Publishing Co., Inc., Box 88, Darien, CT 06820 (SAN 201-9108)

Halter Pubs, *(Halter Pubs.; 0-918776)*, 1132 N. 34th St., Phoenix, AZ 85008 (SAN 210-4334) Tel 602-956-2859

Hamilton Pr, *(Hamilton Press; 0-89648)*, 4720 Hancock Dr., Boulder, CO 80303 (SAN 219-0869); Dist. by: Chapter & Cask, P.O. Box 113, Glenshaw, PA 15116 (SAN 219-0877)

Hamilton Pr
See Citizens Law

Hampton Inst Pr, *(Hampton Institute Press; 0-915108)*, Hampton Institute, Lawrenceville, VA 23868 (SAN 201-9116) Tel 804-848-3865; 102 Park Dr., Lawrenceville, VA 23868 (SAN 201-9124) Tel 804-848-3865; Orders to: Dictionary, P.O. Box 711, St Paul's College, Lawrenceville, VA 23868 (SAN 201-9132)

Handel & Sons, *(Handel & Sons Publishing, Inc.; 0-917080)*, c/o Ambit Pubns., Inc., 4227 Herschel, Suite 107, Dallas, TX 75219 (SAN 216-5260) Tel 214-522-0102

Hanover Press, *(Hanover Press, the; 0-942966)*, P.O. Box 27760, Los Angeles, CA 90027 (SAN 240-2289) Tel 213-660-9583

Hanover Pubns, *(Hanover Pubns., Inc.; 0-918710)*, 200 Park Ave., Suite 303E, New York, NY 10017 (SAN 211-3961)

Hansen & Miller, *(Hansen & Miller; 0-9601312)*, P.O. Box 1 Kenwood, Lower Lake, CA 95452 (SAN 211-0709)

Harbinger Lib *Imprint of* **Harbinger Pr**

Harbinger Pr, *(Harbinger Press; 0-936092)*, 347 Willow Ave., Corte Madera, CA 94925 (SAN 213-7437) Tel 415-924-6490
Imprints: Harbinger Lib (Harbinger Press Library).

Harbor Hse Bk, *(Harbor House Books Ltd.; 0-916800)*, Subs. of Louis J. Martin & Associates, Inc., 95 Madison Ave., New York, NY 10016 (SAN 208-6735) Tel 212-725-2157

Harbor Hse Pub, *(Harbor House Publishing Ltd.; 0-930430)*, Quarterman Harbor, Box 748, Vashon Island, WA 98070 (SAN 211-0199) Tel 206-567-4910

Harbor Pub CA
See Busn Mgmt Res

Harbour Hse, *(Harbour House; 0-917254)*, 9406 Dartridge, Dallas, TX 75238 (SAN 209-0678)

Harbour Pub, *(Harbour Publishing Co.)*, 7200 34th St. South, Sky Harbor Bldg. 2-D, St. Petersburg, FL 33711 (SAN 206-4987) Tel 813-867-3361

Harco Inc, *(Harco, D. W., Inc.; 0-9607570)*, 11719 Jones Rd. Suite 103, Houston, TX 77070 (SAN 239-4405)

Hardwood Bks, *(Hardwood Books; 0-935332)*, 75 Algonquin Park, Plattsburgh, NY 12901 (SAN 218-4370)

Hare Ed, *(Hare Editions; 0-916740)*, The Kensington Hse., Apt. 616, 200 W. 20th St., New York, NY 10011 (SAN 208-6751)

Harmonious Pubns, *(Harmonious Pubns.; 0-912687)*, 7725 E. Redfield Dr., No. 101, Scottsdale, AZ 85260 (SAN 282-7840) Tel 602-996-1289

Harmony Hse, *(Harmony House; 0-934330)*, 266 Waverly Dr., Elgin, IL 60120 (SAN 211-6065)

Harold Hse, *(Harold House, Pubs.; 0-930138)*, P.O. Box 59, 203 Walnut St., Marshall, AR 72650 (SAN 210-7392) Tel 501-448-5170

Harper Mag Pr, *(Harper's Magazine Press)*, 10 E. 53rd St., New York, NY 10022 (SAN 202-2753) Tel 212-593-7000

Harris Calif, *(Harris Publishing Co.; 0-917228)*, 248 S. Rexford Dr., Beverly Hills, CA 90212 (SAN 208-3965) Tel 213-274-2962

Hart, *(Hart Assocs.; 0-8055)*, 12 E. 12th St., New York, NY 10003 (SAN 202-2761) Tel 212-260-2430

Hartung, *(Hartung, Marion T.; 0-913910)*, 814 Constitution St., Emporia, KS 66801 (SAN 206-5355) Tel 316-342-6200

Hartwell Assocs, *(Hartwell Assocs.; 0-9604116)*, RO 7-Box 147, Middletown, NY 10940 (SAN 287-7503); Dist. by: Orange County Genealogical Society, 101 Main St., Goshen, NY 10924 (SAN 220-021X)

Harvard Group, *(Harvard Group, Inc., The; 0-942408)*, Harvard Sq., P.O. Box 223, Cambridge, MA 02138 (SAN 238-163X)

Harvest Pr Texas, *(Harvest Press, Inc.; 0-930718)*, P.O. Box 7971, Waco, TX 76701 (SAN 211-4038) Tel 817-752-5544

Harvey, *(Harvey House, Pubs.; 0-8178)*, 20 Waterside Plaza, New York, NY 10010 (SAN 202-2796) Tel 212-889-9520; Orders to: 128 W. River St., Chippewa Falls, WI 54729 (SAN 202-280X) Tel 715-723-2814

Hawley Cooke Orr, *(Hawley, Cooke, & Orr Pubs.; 0-937246)*, P.O. Box 6052, Louisville, KY 40207 (SAN 214-3844) Tel 502-893-0133

Haydarabad Hist Soc, *(Haydarabad Historical Society; 0-930811)*, 2462 Dalton, Wichita, KS 67210 (SAN 694-1311)

Head Imports, *(Head Imports)*, Aspen, CO 81611 (SAN 204-0344); Dist. by: Bookpeople, 2929 Fifth St., Berkeley, CA 94710 (SAN 168-9517)

Headstart Pr, *(Headstart Pr.; 0-935189)*, 9731 Sky View, Dallas, TX 75228 (SAN 695-5029)

Health Aids, *(Health Aids Pubns.)*, 612 N. Michigan Ave., Chicago, IL 60611 (SAN 207-2335) Tel 312-787-6505

Health Con NC, *(Health Science Consortium, Inc.; 0-938938)*, 103 Laurel Ave., Carrboro, NC 27510 (SAN 216-1397) Tel 919-942-8731

Health Pubns, *(Health Pubns.)*, 200 Park Ave., S., Suite 1101, New York, NY 10003 (SAN 204-0360) Tel 212-777-6400

HealthRight, *(HealthRight Publishing; 0-911433)*, 760 Market St., Suite 315, San Francisco, CA 94102 (SAN 270-7209) Tel 415-776-0969

Healthstyles Pubns, *(Healthstyles Pubns.; 0-941344)*, 3800 W. 80th St., Suite 660, Minneapolis, MN 55431 (SAN 238-9894)

Heart Am Bible, *(Heart of America Bible Society)*, 5528 Lydia St., Kansas City, MO 64110 (SAN 207-2343) Tel 816-333-3278

Hearthside, *(Hearthside Press, Inc.; 0-8208)*, Orders to: Ingram Book Co., 347 Redwood Dr., Nashville, TN 37217 (SAN 202-2869)

Heathcote, *(Heathcote Pubs.; 0-9602350)*, P.O. Box 135, Monmouth Jct., NJ 08852 (SAN 212-5358) Tel 201-297-4891

Heidelberg Pubs, (Heidelberg Pubs., Inc.; 0-913206), 1003 Brown Bldg., Austin, TX 78701 (SAN 201-5501)

Helicon House, (Helicon House), P.O. Box 1254, La Jolla, CA 92038 (SAN 221-0983)

Helios Vt, (Helios; 0-87931), Pawlet, VT 05761 (SAN 204-0425) Tel 802-325-3360

Hemlock Pr, (Hemlock Press), Rte. 1, Box 549, Alburtis, PA 18011 (SAN 208-0842) Tel 215-682-7332

Hendel, (Hendel & Reinke; 0-918656), 2800 Route St., Suite 247A, Dallas, TX 75201 (SAN 209-4479)

Henry Clay, (Clay, Henry, Press; 0-87642), P.O. Box 116, Lexington, KY 40501 (SAN 204-0468) Tel 606-266-4133

Hen's Pub, (Hen's Publishing Co.; 0-9607820), P.O. Box 13112, Portland, OR 97213 (SAN 239-5533)

Herbal Med, (Herbal Medicine Research Foundation; 0-930074), P.O. Box 29187, San Antonio, TX 78229 (SAN 210-6019) Tel 512-699-0783

Herbert Pubs, (Herbert Pubs.; 0-935780), P.O. Box 162, Mount Laurel, NJ 08054 (SAN 214-0268)

Heretic Bks, (Heretic Bks.), 175 Fifth Ave., Suite 814, New York, NY 10010 (SAN 204-8570)

Heritage Hse Pubs, (Heritage House Pubs.; 0-917172), P.O. Box 4228, Tallahassee, FL 32303 (SAN 208-3655) Tel 904-386-7924

Herman Pub, (Herman Publishing, Inc.; 0-89046; 0-89047), 45 Newbury St., Boston, MA 02116 (SAN 213-2044) Tel 617-536-5810
Imprints: Marine Educ (Marine Educational Services).

Hermes, (Hermes Pubns.; 0-910720), P.O. Box 397, Los Altos, CA 94022 (SAN 204-0492)

Herrick Hse, (Herrick House; 0-935670), P.O. Box 1051, Monrovia, CA 91016 (SAN 213-6716) Tel 213-358-0362

High Window Pr, (High Window Press; 0-934886), P.O. Box 2238, Santa Barbara, CA 93120 (SAN 213-3199) Tel 805-969-6645

Highland Hse, (Highland House Pubs., Inc.; 0-918712), 814 "H" St., N.W., Washington, DC 20001 (SAN 210-3583)

Hilarian Bks, (Hilarian Books; 0-937168), 535 Cordova Rd., Suite 422, Santa Fe, NM 87501 (SAN 238-8820)

Hill Hse Pr, (Hill House Press, Pubs.; 0-915602), Old Lane & Chester Rd., Chester, VA 23831 (SAN 201-5412) Tel 804-262-0228

Hillcrest Ent, (Hillcrest Enterprises; 0-912994), Country Club Drive, Long Beach, CA 90807 (SAN 204-0530)P.O. Box 14437, Long Beach, CA 90801 (SAN 204-0549)

Hilltop Pr, (Hilltop Press; 0-9603346), 333 W. Emerson St., Melrose, MA 02176 (SAN 203-4077) Tel 617-665-7569

Himalaya Hse, (Himalaya House; 0-89654), P.O. Box 792, Wheat Ridge, CO 80033 (SAN 211-1969) Tel 303-423-3170

HKR Pub Co, (H.K.R. Publishing CO., Inc.; 0-9609550), P.O. Box 286, Carolina Beach, NC 28428 (SAN 270-7888); Dist. by: Publishers Marketing Group International (Exclusive), 1343 Columbia Dr., Suite 405, Richardson, TX 75081 (SAN 262-0995) Tel 214-690-5050

HM Prof Med Div, (Houghton Mifflin Professional Pubs., Medical Div.; 0-89289), 2 Park St., Boston, MA 02107 (SAN 208-807X) Tel 617-725-5019

HM Prof Pubs
See HM Prof Med Div

Hoffman Pubns, (Hoffman Pubns., Inc.; 0-934890), P.O. Box 11299, Fort Lauderdale, FL 33339 (SAN 203-1264)

Hol-Land Bks, (Hol-Land Bks.; 0-932092), Holland Bks. & Posters, Bonita Springs, FL 33923 (SAN 206-8567)

Holbrook, (Holbrook Press, Inc.; 0-205), Subs. of Allyn & Bacon, Inc., Rockleigh, NJ 07647 (SAN 202-2974) Tel 617-482-9220

Holly Hill, (Holly Hill Pubs.; 0-9606508), Holly Hill-1639-D,Goshen Clubhouse Dr., Augusta, GA 30906 (SAN 219-3396) Tel 404-798-6180

HollyBrooke Hse Inc, (Hollybrooke Press; 0-933356), 1605 E. Charleston Blvd., Las Vegas, NV 89110 (SAN 221-0932)

Holsen Pubns, (Holsen Pubns.; 0-912897), 125 E. 32nd St., Box 216, Durango, CO 81301 (SAN 283-0434)

Home Index Pubns, (Home Index Pubns.; 0-912023), P.O. Box 93, Clovis, CA 93613 (SAN 281-7861) Tel 209-224-5674; 4672 N. Barton, Fresno, CA 93726 (SAN 281-787X)

Home Planet, (Home Planet Pubns.; 0-913802), 1771 1st Ave., New York, NY 10028 (SAN 201-5609) Tel 212-534-2372; Orders to: P.O. Box 415, Stuyvesant Sta., New York, NY 10009 (SAN 201-5617)

Honeycomb Lib, (Honeycomb Library; 0-936081), 109 North St., Danbury, CT 06810 (SAN 696-8309)

Hopewell, (Hopewell Bks., Inc.; 0-910839), 1670 Sturbridge Dr., RD 1, Sewickley, PA 15143 (SAN 270-8264) Tel 412-366-3287

Hopkinson, (Hopkinson & Blake, Pubs.; 0-911974), 50 W. 34th St., New York, NY 10001 (SAN 202-3032) Tel 212-947-8282

Horizon Pub
See Bezalel Art

Horowitz, (Horowitz, Stanley), P.O. Box 1077, Flushing, NY 11352 (SAN 206-4332)

Houlberg Dev, (Houlberg Development; 0-932287), P.O. Box 271075, Escondido, CA 92027 (SAN 687-8202) Tel 619-747-6379

Howard Pubs, (Deceased.; 0-9614288), c/o Taft 212 W. 22nd St., New York, NY 10011 (SAN 687-4495) Tel 212-242-5450

Hse of Gemini, (House of Gemini), P.O. Box 7803, Philadelphia, PA 19101 (SAN 204-076X) Tel 215-222-7555

Hse of One Pub, (House of One Publishing Co.), Box 3407, Portland, OR 97208 (SAN 211-3953)

Hse of Talos, (House of Talos Pubs., The; 0-935970), 125 Loree Dr., East Lansing, MI 48823 (SAN 213-9308) Tel 517-337-0723

Hse of Words, (House of Words; 0-917876), 207 E. Buffalo St., No. 518, Milwaukee, WI 53202 (SAN 211-0695) Tel 414-453-1945

Human Dev East, (Human Development East, Inc.; 0-932292), c/o East Asia Research Institute, 850 National Press Bldg., 14th & F Sts., NW, Washington, DC 20045 (SAN 211-1314)

Human Res Pr, (Human Resources Pr.; 0-930287), P.O. Box 24240, Los Angeles, CA 90024 (SAN 670-8420) Tel 213-474-5175

Human Rights Women, (Human Rights for Women Incorporated), 1128 National Press Bldg, Washington, DC 20045 (SAN 227-292X)

Human Serv Dev, (Human Services Development Center; 0-938850), P.O. Box 161809, Sacramento, CA 95816 (SAN 219-788X)

Humanics, (Humanics Associates; 0-89269), 1100 Spring St., Suite 340, Atlanta, GA 30309 (SAN 219-662X) Tel 404-875-0088

Humanitas Pr
See Wexford

Humanity Pubns, (Humanity Pubns.), 27 S. Maple St., Shelburne Falls, MA 01370 (SAN 209-0430) Tel 413-625-6823

Humbird Hopkins, (Humbird Hopkins Inc., Pubs.; 0-931854), P.O. Box 49813, Los Angeles, CA 90049 (SAN 211-4992) Tel 213-824-2008

Humbug Gulch Pr, (Humbug Gulch Press; 0-912996), P.O. Box 204, Amarillo, TX 79105 (SAN 204-0786) Tel 806-352-4935

HumLife
See Dill Pub

Humorhouse, (Humorhouse Pubs.), 4077 W. Third St., No. 106, Los Angeles, CA 90020 (SAN 223-1425)

Hutchinsons, (Hutchinsons; 0-943368), 26 Main St., Orleans, MA 02653 (SAN 240-6764) Tel 617-255-8458

Hydra Bk
See Warm Wind Bks

I-Seventy-Four, (I-74 Press; 0-940096), Estes Park 4F, Carrboro, NC 27510 (SAN 217-0752)

IAM Ent, (IAM Enterprises, Inc.; 0-910469), 8930 Foster Lane, Overland Park, KS 66212 (SAN 260-0730) Tel 913-649-3695

IAUS, (Institute for Architecture & Urban Studies, The; 0-932628), 8 W. 40th St., New York, NY 10018 (SAN 213-5167) Tel 212-398-9474

IBC *Imprint of* **Sportshelf**

IBR Pub, (IBR Publishing, Inc.; 0-911693), 2414 Forsyth Rd., Orlando, FL 32807 (SAN 264-1054)

ICRPP, (International Ctr. for Research & Public Policy; 0-937807), P.O. Box 1131, Washington, DC 20036 (SAN 659-2538); 1900 M St., NW, Washington, DC 20036 (SAN 659-2546)

Ideal Pubns *Imprint of* **Westinghouse Learn**

IDOC, (IDOC/North America, Inc.; 0-89021), 145 E. 49th St., Suite 6D, New York, NY 10017 (SAN 206-5371) Tel 212-752-5121

IEM-HOTEP, (IEM-HOTEP Assn.; 0-932806), 250 NW Ninth St., Boca Raton, FL 33432 (SAN 212-4270) Tel 305-392-8514

IHI Pr, (IHI Pr.), International Homophilics Institute, 165 Marlborough St., Boston, MA 02116 (SAN 209-5688)

IHPress, (IHPress, Inc.; 0-936870), P.O. Box 1437, Downtown Sta., Billings, MT 59101 (SAN 215-1537)

IHR Pr, (Institute of Human Relations Press; 0-914252), P.O. Box 62, Old Bethpage, NY 11804 (SAN 206-7420)

Ilkon Pr, (Ilkon Press; 0-916832), 210 Riverside Dr., Apt 6-G, New York, NY 10025 (SAN 208-6883) Tel 212-663-2579

Ill Regional Lib Coun, (Illinois Regional Library Council; 0-917060), 425 N. Michigan, Suite 1303, Chicago, IL 60611 (SAN 208-6905) Tel 312-828-0928

IMA Ed, (IMA Education & Research Foundation; 0-918486), P.O. Box 526, Newtonville, NY 12128 (SAN 210-105X) Tel 518-434-3859

Image Bldrs
See TIB Pubns

Immaculate Heart, (Immaculate Heart College Pr.), 2021 N. Western Ave., Los Angeles, CA 90027 (SAN 204-8507)

Immediate Pr, (Immediate Press), 13 Spring St., Stamford, CT 06901 (SAN 216-1494) Tel 203-327-5770

Impact Tenn, (Impact Books; 0-914850; 0-86608), Div. of the Benson Co., 365 Great Circle Rd., Nashville, TN 37228 (SAN 202-6872) Tel 615-259-9111; Dist. by: Zondervan Corp., 1415 Lake Dr. SE, Grand Rapids, MI 49506 (SAN 203-2694) Tel 616-698-6900

Imperial Pr, (Imperial Pr.; 0-913445), 2210 Wilshire Blvd., Suite 777, Santa Monica, CA 90403 (SAN 285-1709)

Imprimis, (Imprimis Press; 0-937600), 8809 Stonewall Rd., Manassas, VA 22110 (SAN 215-3203)

Incunabula, (Incunabula Collection; 0-930226), 277 Hillside Ave., Nutley, NJ 07110 (SAN 210-3591) Tel 201-667-8502

Ind American, (Independent American), P.O. Box 636, Littleton, CO 80120 (SAN 206-4359)

Ind Cam Ent, (Independent Cambridge Enterprises; 0-9609138), 12881 Western Ave., Suite A, Garden Grove, CA 92641 (SAN 241-5240)

Ind Pr, (Independence Press; 0-910122), Rte. One, Waupaca, WI 54981 (SAN 283-2690)

Indep Pubs, (Independent Pubs.; 0-9608134), 415 Medical Dr., Bountiful, UT 84010 (SAN 240-2327) Tel 801-298-2471

Independ Unltd, (Independence Unlimited; 0-931040), 27 Gardner St., Portsmouth, NH 03801 (SAN 213-8484)

Independence Unltd
See Independ Unltd

Independent Study, (Independent Study), Orders to: University of California Extension, Independent Study, Berkeley, CA 94720 (SAN 208-0087) Tel 415-642-7343

Index Co, (Index Co.; 0-914054), 319 Elm St., Kalamazoo, MI 49007 (SAN 202-6910)

Index Pubs, (Index Pubs.; 0-934692), 26 St. Mark's Pl., New York, NY 10003 (SAN 213-5140); c/o Russica Book & Art Store, 799 Broadway, New York, NY 10003 (SAN 212-310X) Tel 212-473-7480

Indian Pocahontas Club, (Indian Women's Pocahontas Club), 323 N. Choctaw, Claremore, OK 74017 (SAN 208-3272)

Indian Pr
See Indian Pubns

Indian Pubns, (Indian Pubns.; 0-934170), 1869 Second Ave., New York, NY 10029 (SAN 212-808X)

Indigena, (Indigena Pubns.; 0-9602972), 133 Brooks Ave., Venice, CA 90291 (SAN 213-0866)

Indus Rel Wkshp, *(Industrial Relations Workshop Seminars, Inc.; 0-930692),* 43-70 Kessina Blvd., New York, NY 11354 (SAN 204-8604) Tel 212-762-2000

Info Policy Design, *(Information for Policy Design; 0-916282),* Lafayette, NY 13084 (SAN 208-2896) Tel 315-677-9278

Info Research, *(Information Research Associates),* P. O. Box 623, Chapel Hill, NC 27514 (SAN 207-0367)

Info Services
See Virgin Islands Biol

Inner Circle, *(Inner Circle Publishing Co.; 0-938284),* P.O. Box 1617, Detroit, MI 48231 (SAN 215-7780)

Innovations, *(Innovations, Inc.; 0-918544),* P.O. Box 1862, Memphis, TN 38101 (SAN 219-7928)

Inscape Corp, *(Inscape Corp.; 0-87953),* 1629 "K" St., N.W., Suite 5107, Washington, DC 20006 (SAN 207-0731) Tel 301-469-7788; Orders to: Inscape Customer Service, P.O. Box 978, Edison, NJ 08817 (SAN 207-074X) *Imprints:* BO (Black Orpheus); NP (New Perspectives).

Insight Pubns, *(Insight Pubns.),* 5096 Village Dr., Las Vegas, NV 89122 (SAN 213-2206) Tel 702-452-7427; Orders to: Box 12752, Las Vegas, NV 89112 (SAN 213-2214)

Inspirational Bks, *(Inspirational Books),* 5104 Glenwood, Chicago, IL 60640 (SAN 213-3261) Tel 312-649-5316

Inst Energy, *(Institutes for Energy Development, Inc.; 0-89419),* 101 SW 25th St., Oklahoma City, OK 73107 (SAN 209-9322) Tel 405-232-2801

Inst Free Enterprise, *(Institute for Free Enterprise Education),* 2721 Leameadow Dr., Plano, TX 75075 (SAN 207-5555) Tel 214-424-5888

Inst Human NY, *(Institute for Human Studies; 0-932340),* Box 240, Gardiner, NY 12525 (SAN 211-710X); Orders to: 14 South Division St., Peekskill, NY 10566 (SAN 211-7118)

Inst Jewish Stud, *(Institute of Jewish Studies, Inc.),* P.O. Box 220394, Charlotte, NC 28222 (SAN 211-2450) Tel 704-366-4655

Inst Occup Res, *(Institute for Occupational Research; 0-9611530),* 1260 21st St. NW, No. 801, Washington, DC 20036 (SAN 285-3256)

Integrated Info, *(Integrated Information Analysis),* P.O. Box 1447, St. Louis, MO 63178 (SAN 208-4619)

InterAction, *(InterAction Books; 0-932808),* Rte. 1, Hwy. 5 South, Heber Springs, AR 72543 (SAN 212-2820)

InterCulture, *(InterCulture Associates; 0-88253; 0-89253),* Quaddick Rd., P.O. Box 277, Thompson, CT 06277 (SAN 202-7097) Tel 203-923-9494

Interface Calif, *(Interface California Corp.; 0-915580),* 106 T St., P.O. Box 3611, Eureka, CA 95501 (SAN 209-3774) Tel 707-442-8112; Dist. by: Stein & Day Pubs., Scarborough House, Briarcliff Manor, NY 10510 (SAN 203-3461) Tel 914-762-2151

Interface Calif
See Northtown Bks

Interface Unl, *(Interface Unlimited),* P.O. Box 8583, Toledo, OH 43623 (SAN 208-1008) Tel 419-531-4022

Interfacia Inc, *(Interfacia, Inc.; 0-917634),* Div. of Creative Informatics, P.O. Box 4422, Chicago, IL 60680 (SAN 213-6724) Tel 312-643-9050

Interperson Pr, *(Interperson Press; 0-940942),* 913 N. Shore Dr., Crystal Lake, IL 60014 (SAN 217-3832) Tel 815-459-1795

Interserv Pub, *(Interservice Publishing Co., Inc.; 0-86695),* P.O. Box 5437 Dept. X, San Francisco, CA 94101 (SAN 216-6003) Tel 415-465-0187

Interstate Guide, *(Interstate Guides; 0-916577),* P.O. Box 13359, Philadelphia, PA 19101 (SAN 297-1879) Tel 215-382-5016

Intl Banker, *(International Banker Association),* P O Box 7780, Washington, DC 20044 (SAN 224-6457) Tel 301-249-5005

Intl Beefalo, *(International Beefalo Breeders Assn.),* Box 670, Citrus Heights, CA 95611 (SAN 691-4535)

Intl Bks, *(International Books),* P.O. Box 6970, Washington, DC 20032 (SAN 207-2394)

Intl Bus Schls Comp Users Group, *(International Business Schls Computer Users Group, The; 0-934691),* Georgia Tech., College og Management, Atlanta, GA 30306 (SAN 694-3756)

Intl Chrono, *(International Chronologies),* P.O. Box 3235 GCPO, New York, NY 10017 (SAN 207-9798)

Intl Comm Natl Pks, *(International Commission on National Parks and Protected Areas),* Div. of International Union for Conservation of Nature and Natural Resources, P O Box 19027, Washington, DC 20036 (SAN 224-1641)

Intl Coun Future of the Univ, *(International Council on the Future of the Univ.; 0-930160),* 745 Fifth Ave., New York, NY 10022 (SAN 210-7465) Tel 212-421-0170

Intl Econ Pubns, *(International Economy Pubns; 0-942368),* P.O. Box 10897, Bakersfield, CA 93389 (SAN 239-7358)

Intl Inst Psych, *(International Institute of Preventive Psychiatry, The; 0-939210),* 13415 Ventura Blvd., Sherman Oaks, CA 91423 (SAN 216-504X)

Intl Lit Pub Inc, *(International Literary Publishing Inc.; 0-915885),* P.O. Box 659, Elyria, OH 44035 (SAN 294-0477) Tel 216-322-6149

Intl Program Labs, *(International Program of Laboratories for Population Statistics; 0-89383),* NCNB Plaza, 136 E. Rosemary St., Suite 400, Chapel Hill, NC 27514 (SAN 211-0229) Tel 919-966-1131

Intl Ref Bks, *(International Reference Books),* 111 N. Wabash, Rm. 1310, Chicago, IL 60602 (SAN 207-5377)

Intl Res Inst, *(International Research Institute for Political Science),* Box 199, College Park, MD 20740 (SAN 210-1203)

Intl Study Time, *(International Society for the Study of Time),* P.O. Box 815, Westport, CT 06881 (SAN 225-3852)

Intl Tree Crops, *(International Tree Crops Institute U.S.A., Inc.; 0-938240),* P.O. Box 888, Winters, CA 95694 (SAN 216-2598)

Intl Wine Soc, *(International Wine Society; 0-89219),* 304 E. 45th St., New York, NY 10017 (SAN 209-083X)

Inwood Pr, *(Inwood Press; 0-914772),* 128 Post Ave., New York, NY 10034 (SAN 206-5444) Tel 212-569-4941

Irfan, *(Irfan; 0-917220),* 160 W. 71 St., New York, NY 10023 (SAN 211-8076)

Iron Horse, *(Iron Horse Publishing Co., Inc.; 0-914380),* P.O. Box 1182, Southfield, MI 48075 (SAN 206-5452) Tel 313-354-5698

Iroquois Hse, *(Iroquois House, Pubs.; 0-931980),* Box 249, Mountain Park, NM 88325 (SAN 212-8101) Tel 505-682-2751

ITA, *(Initial Teaching Alphabet Pubns., Inc.; 0-273),* Subs. of Pitman Pub. Corp., 6 Davis Dr., Belmont, CA 94002 (SAN 203-8234) Tel 415-592-7810

Ivan Pub, *(Ivan Publishing, Inc.; 0-9602578),* P.O. Box 17947, San Antonio, TX 78217 (SAN 212-6702) Tel 512-828-7995

Ivy Pr, *(Ivy Press Inc., The; 0-933372),* 2121 N. Akard, Dallas, TX 75201 (SAN 212-9108) Tel 800-527-9250

J & J Pub, *(J & J Publishing),* 1088 Madison Ave., New York, NY 10028 (SAN 211-1950) Tel 212-535-7399

J Barker, *(Barker, Joseph),* 4000 N. 7th St., S-102, Dept. 133, Phoenix, AZ 85014 (SAN 240-8775) Tel 602-955-7326

J Fein, *(Fein, Jess; 0-9604366),* 118 Massachusetts Ave., Boston, MA 02115 (SAN 215-0735)

J H Schwartz, *(Schwartz, J. H., Rev.),* 1633 N. Missouri, Peoria, IL 61603 (SAN 208-1644)

J Halliburton, *(Halliburton, John),* 2217 Belmont Blvd., Apt. B, Nashville, TN 37212 (SAN 211-0253)

J Howell, *(Howell, John, Books; 0-910760),* 434 Post St., San Francisco, CA 94102 (SAN 203-8994) Tel 415-781-7795

J Hughes, *(Hughes, John, & Co.; 0-912743),* 7811 Via Sonrisa, Scottsdale, AZ 85258 (SAN 282-7778) Tel 602-991-9730

J J Connors, *(Connors, John J.),* 3811 Grantley Rd., Toledo, OH 43613 (SAN 208-2446) Tel 419-474-6836

J K Rice, *(Rice, James K.),* 715 Ratton La., Stockton, CA 95205 (SAN 287-1742)

J L Hauck, *(Hauck, Judith L., Mrs.),* 3470 N Alpine Rd., Rockford, IL 61111 (SAN 211-2442)

J L Smith, *(Smith, Jerry L.; 0-9602136),* P.O. Box 485, Melbourne, AR 72556 (SAN 212-3126) Tel 501-368-7239

J Lessmann, *(Lessmann, Judy; 0-9600994),* 6702 Fairfax, Lincoln, NE 68505 (SAN 208-7340) Tel 402-466-5311

J Lloyd Corp, *(Lloyd, Joseph, Corp.; 0-916490),* 2009 Thornwood, Wilmette, IL 60091 (SAN 281-9163)

J M Vles, *(Vles, Joseph, M.; 0-9608452),* 137 Washington Rd., Princeton, NJ 08540 (SAN 240-4982)

J N Casavis, *(Casavis, James N.),* 32 Twin Lakes Dr., Monsey, NY 10952 (SAN 206-4561)

J N Meredith, *(Meredith, Joseph N.; 0-9609300),* Lewisburg Manor, Apt. 127, 344 N. Court St., Lewisburg, WV 24901 (SAN 241-404X)

J N Summers, *(Summers, June Nay; 0-9605332),* P.O. Box 334, Tecate, CA 92080 (SAN 215-921X) Tel 619-478-5285

J Sherrill, *(Sherrill, John),* P.O. Box 8623, Austin, TX 78712 (SAN 213-165X)

J Strand, *(Strand, Janann; 0-9600780),* P.O. Box 50325, Pasadena, CA 91105-0325 (SAN 293-4027) Tel 818-799-3153; Orders to: P.O. Box 50325, Pasadena, CA 91105-0325 (SAN 293-4035) Tel 818-799-3153

J T White, *(White, James T., & Co.; 0-88371),* 1700 State Hwy. 3, Clifton, NJ 07013 (SAN 202-7291) Tel 201-773-9300

J W Powell, *(Powell, James Wooldridge; 0-9601518),* 1025 Arno Rd., Kansas City, MO 64113 (SAN 211-3988) Tel 816-361-9796

J W Van De Water
See Jonsalvania

J W Wills, *(Wills, J. W., Publishing Co.; 0-916716),* P.O. Box 457, Upper Marlboro, MD 20870 (SAN 208-9203) Tel 301-262-0941

Ja-Mar Pubs, *(Ja-Mar Pubs.; 0-941556),* P.O. Box 296, Huntsville, TX 77340 (SAN 239-2380)

Jaal Product, *(Jaal Productions; 0-9611908),* 9953 La Tuna Canyon Rd., Sun Valley, CA 91352 (SAN 286-1240) Tel 818-767-6164

Jacada Pubns, *(Jacada Pubns.; 0-915700),* Northway Square Bldg. 2150 N. 10th St., Suite 350, Seattle, WA 98133 (SAN 207-3897) Tel 206-362-3001

Jacaranda Pr, *(Jacaranda Press, Inc.; 0-89151),* 872 Massachusetts Ave., Cambridge, MA 02139 (SAN 207-6918)

Jack Delany, *(Delany, Jack; 0-9600340),* 1136 Fort View Place, Cincinnati, OH 45202 (SAN 203-9044)

Jada Assocs, *(Jada Associates),* P.O. Box 33348, Hillcrest Sta., San Diego, CA 92103 (SAN 207-1916)

Jalamap, *(Jalamap Pubns., Inc.; 0-934750),* 601 D St., South Charleston, WV 25303-0917 (SAN 216-1478) Tel 304-744-1353

Jalapeno Pr, *(Jalapeno Press; 0-935342),* Rte. 2, Box 600, Bandon, OR 97411 (SAN 213-8514)

Jam Jar, *(Jam Jar Press; 0-9606276),* 201 Chestnut St., P.O. Box 348, Towanda, PA 18848 (SAN 217-5304) Tel 717-265-9601

James Pub, *(James Publishing Co.),* Rte. 1, Box 114-K, Winchester, VA 22601 (SAN 211-0768)

James T A, *(James, Timothy A; 0-9608478),* 3818 W. Sahauro Dr. Apt. 30-203, Phoenix, AZ 85029 (SAN 285-0346) Tel 602-863-1280; 1319 Newport Gap Pike, Wilmington, DE 19804 (SAN 285-0354) Tel 800-441-7596

Jamestown Found, *(Jamestown Foundation, Inc.; 0-917394),* P.O. Box J. F., Williamsburg, VA 23185 (SAN 208-9580) Tel 804-229-1607

Janzen Assoc, *(Janzen, P., Associates; 0-9604458),* P.O. Box 231, Libertyville, IL 60048 (SAN 215-1588)

Jarrow, *(Jarrow Press, Inc; 0-912190),* Div. of Anchor Society, Inc., 2398 Pine St., San Francisco, CA 94115 (SAN 201-0216)

Java Bks, *(Java Books),* P.O. Box 81, Morro Bay, CA 93442 (SAN 240-0618)

JB Indexes, *(JB Indexes; 0-89358),* 2377 Virginia St., Berkeley, CA 94709 (SAN 208-7103) Tel 415-848-8376

Jeffers-Carr, *(Jeffers-Carr Assocs.; 0-9603954),* 307 E. 44th St., New York, NY 10017 (SAN 281-8418) Tel 212-599-2327

Jeffrey Leonard Pubs, *(Jeffrey-Leonard Publishing; 0-942100),* 2614 Jalmia Dr., Los Angeles, CA 90046 (SAN 237-9643)

Jem Pubs, *(Jem Pubs.; 0-931076),* 4923 60th St., Kenosha, WI 53142 (SAN 211-1578)

Jemco Ent, *(Jemco Enterprises; 0-9602760),* 820 N. Franklin St., Chicago, IL 60610 (SAN 213-7631); Dist. by: Chicago Review Press, 215 W. Ohio St., Chicago, IL 60610 (SAN 213-764X) Tel 312-644-5457

Jenrich Assoc, *(Jenrich Associates),* P.O. Box 805, Springfield, VA 22150 (SAN 203-9052)

Jewish Recon, *(Jewish Reconstructionist Foundation; 0-910808),* 15 W. 86th St, New York, NY 10024 (SAN 201-0259) Tel 212-787-1500

Jimora Assoc, *(Jimora Associated Publishing Co.; 0-918392),* MPO Box 7047, Chicago, IL 60680 (SAN 210-0355) Tel 312-994-4846

Johnsen, *(Johnsen Publishing Co.; 0-910814),* 1135 "R" St., Lincoln, NE 68508 (SAN 203-9095) Tel 402-432-0111

Johnson Higgins, *(Johnson & Higgins; 0-9601248),* 95 Wall St., New York, NY 10005 (SAN 210-4458) Tel 212-482-5303

Johnson VA, *(Johnson Publishing Co., Inc.; 0-934572),* P.O. Box 192, Forest, VA 24551 (SAN 215-0875) Tel 804-525-4129

Jokos Pub, *(Jokos Publishing; 0-9613926),* 601 Rio Grande, Austin, TX 78701 (SAN 686-1776)

Jon-Juan, *(Jon-Juan, Inc.),* P.O. Box 239, Guilderland, NY 12084 (SAN 237-966X)

Jonsalvania, *(Jonsalvania Publishing Co.),* Russell Rd., Canton, NY 13617 (SAN 214-1671) Tel 315-386-4007

Journal Pubns, *(Journal Pubns., Inc.; 0-935676),* 6416 S. Western Ave., Whittier, CA 90606 (SAN 213-6287)

Journey Bks, *(Journey Books, Inc.; 0-933156),* P.O. Box 100, Clarksville, MD 21029 (SAN 212-2839)

Joy Pr, *(Joy Press; 0-913662),* Big Sur, CA 93920 (SAN 206-9466) Tel 408-667-2200; Dist. by: Bookpeople, 2929 Fifth St., Berkeley, CA 94710 (SAN 168-9509)

Joy Pub CA, *(Joy Publishing Co.; 0-933376),* 450 Sutter St., Suite 930, San Francisco, CA 94108 (SAN 221-4733)

Joyce Pr, *(Joyce Press Inc.; 0-89325),* 7341 Clairemont Mesa Blvd., San Diego, CA 92111 (SAN 208-7219) Tel 714-565-6133

Jubilee Bks, *(Jubilee Books; 0-914300),* Box 1460, New York, NY 10001 (SAN 209-2549)

Jubilee Comm, *(Jubilee Communications; 0-942600),* Suite 230, Statler off. Bldg., Boston, MA 02116 (SAN 240-0758)

Judaic Heritage, *(Judaic Heritage Society),* 866 United Nations Plaza, New York, NY 10017 (SAN 207-1975)

Jurgensen Pub
See Skylight Health

Just in Time Pub, *(Just in Time Publishing; 0-943208),* 2031 36th Ave., Longview, WA 98632 (SAN 240-5423) Tel 206-425-4678

Justice Pr, *(Justice Press, Inc.; 0-936802),* P.O. Box 16204, Tampa, FL 33617 (SAN 214-3178)

Justice Pubs, *(Justice Pubs.; 0-941348),* P.O. Box 35360, Los Angeles, CA 90035 (SAN 238-9991) Tel 213-995-3329

Justice Sys, *(H. More; 0-914526),* P.O. Box 681, Santa Cruz, CA 95061 (SAN 202-7380) Tel 408-423-1650

Justice T Reason, *(Reason, Justice T., Pubns.; 0-9600322),* 616 N. 36th St., McAllen, TX 78501 (SAN 203-9125) Tel 516-686-8678

JWP Dev, *(JWP Development),* Box 2531, Culver City, CA 90230 (SAN 211-7355)

K B S Pr, *(K.B.S. Press; 0-942020),* P.O. Box 665, Kenmore, WA 98028 (SAN 237-9686) Tel 206-488-8065

K C Lyden, *(Lyden, Kathryn; 0-9609152),* 1085 Laurel Ave., Marysville, CA 95901 (SAN 241-3949) Tel 916-743-8059

K Key Pubns, *(K Key Pubns.),* P.O. Box 4805, Washington, DC 20008 (SAN 207-9682)

K M Gentile, *(K.M. Gentile Publishing/Singing Wind Press; 0-935896),* 4164 W. Pine, St. Louis, MO 63108 (SAN 214-3917) Tel 314-535-2118

K R C Dev, *(KRC Development Council; 0-917440),* 431 Valley Rd., New Canaan, CT 06840 (SAN 207-9690) Tel 203-972-0401

K Sefer, *(Kiryat Sefer, Ltd.; 965-17),* c/o Ridgefield Pub. Co., 6925 Canby Ave., Suite 104, Reseda, CA 91335 (SAN 215-8035)

K-Ten Pubns, *(K-10 Pubns.; 0-9607002),* P.O. Box 345, Spearfish, SD 57783 (SAN 238-8871)

KaChunk Pr, *(KaChunk Press; 0-9604292),* Box 1043, Iowa City, IA 52244 (SAN 214-3194)

Kaedmon, *(Kaedmon Publishing Co.; 0-913002),* 150 Broadway, Suite 915, New York, NY 10038 (SAN 201-0380) Tel 212-267-2913

Kagg Pr, *(Kagg Press; 0-912200),* 9910 Columbus Circle, Nw, Albuquerque, NM 87114 (SAN 203-9133) Tel 505-898-4541

Kanchenjunga Pr, *(Kanchenjunga Press; 0-913600),* 22 Rio Vista Lane, Red Bluff, CA 96080 (SAN 202-652X)

Kapa, *(Kapa Associates Ltd.; 0-915870),* Pacific International Bldg., 677 Ala Moana Blvd., Honolulu, HI 96813 (SAN 209-4037) Tel 808-521-6398

Karlyn, *(Karlyn Publishing & Consulting),* P.O. Box 38125, Urbana, OH 43078 (SAN 209-0333)

Karneke, *(Karneke Pubs),* P.O. Box 3371, Santa Monica, CA 90404 (SAN 209-455X) Tel 213-826-5098

Kells Ltd, *(Kells, Ltd.),* P.O. Box 871, Anderson, SC 29621 (SAN 207-2459) Tel 803-224-0029

Keltner, *(Keltner Statistical Service, Inc.),* 1004 Baltimore Ave., Kansas City, MO 64105 (SAN 203-9176) Tel 816-421-8488

Kemery-Yentz, *(Kemery, Phil/Jeff Yentz; 0-939940),* 8771 Southwestern Blvd., Apt. 1151, Dallas, TX 75206 (SAN 216-826X) Tel 214-748-8407

Kemsley Pub
See Foot Trails

Kenmore, *(Kenmore Press; 0-918298),* P.O. Box 773-C, Pasadena, CA 91104 (SAN 209-9411) Tel 213-798-8078

Kennard Carter, *(Carter, Kennard),* 160 H V Cove, Dover, DE 19901 (SAN 212-4076)

Kennington Pr, *(Kennington Press; 0-9608908),* 525 North Belt, Suite 600C, Houston, TX 77060 (SAN 289-520X)

Kensington, *(Kensington Pr., The; 0-915843),* 9607 Kingston Rd., Kensington, MD 20895 (SAN 213-8921) Tel 301-949-2530; Orders to: PBS Box 643, Cambridge, MA 02139 (SAN 694-955X) Tel 617-491-6562

Kensington Pr
See Kensington

Kephart Comm Inc
See Alexandria Hse

Kerr, *(Kerr Printing Co.),* 458 E. King St., Chambersburg, PA 17201 (SAN 201-0445) Tel 717-263-1015

Key Ray Pub, *(Key Ray Publishing; 0-930678),* Box 196, Osseo, MN 55369 (SAN 211-0776)

Key West Bk, *(Key West Book & Card Co.),* 534-6 Fleming St., Key West, FL 33040 (SAN 211-6197)

Keyline Pubs, *(Keyline Pubs.),* Div. of LTP, Inc., P.O. Box 31534, Billings, MT 59107 (SAN 215-2517)

Khalsa, *(Khalsa, Vikram K., & Dharm Darshan K. Khalsa; 0-940992),* P.O. Box 3041, San Diego, CA 92103 (SAN 219-6719) Tel 714-299-4196

Kindinger, *(Kindinger, Michael),* 931 W. 3rd Ave., Columbus, OH 43216 (SAN 215-3238) Tel 614-294-3227

King, *(King, Dale Stuart, Pub.; 0-912762),* 432 E. Mohave Dr., No. 5 Rear, Tucson, AZ 85705 (SAN 201-0453) Tel 602-888-2569

King & Cowen, *(King & Cowen),* 299 Park Ave, New York, NY 10017 (SAN 211-0261)

King Pubs, *(King Pubns.; 0-917676),* P.O. Box 19332, Washington, DC 20036 (SAN 209-2387) Tel 202-332-7079

Kingsfield, *(Kingsfield Publishing Co.; 0-938494),* 10405 Town & Country Way, Suite 100, Houston, TX 77024 (SAN 215-8825)

Kingston Pubns, *(Kingston Pubns.; 0-940256),* P.O. Box 2225, San Diego, CA 92112 (SAN 218-4877) Tel 714-435-8411

Kiplinger Pr, *(Kiplinger Press),* 2300 Seventh St., Los Angeles, CA 90057 (SAN 295-0138)

KLONH Bks, *(KLONH Books),* 1795 Chestnut, San Francisco, CA 94123 (SAN 206-7404)

KMB Pubns, *(KMB Pubns.; 0-9603522),* P.O. Box 2511, Lancaster, CA 93534 (SAN 213-8549)

Knowledge Network, *(Knowledge Network, Inc., The; 0-934707),* 95 W. 95th St., New York, NY 10025 (SAN 694-1486) Tel 212-666-4665

Koala Pr, *(Koala Press; 0-940610),* 1216 State St., Suite 504, Santa Barbara, CA 93101 (SAN 218-5172) Tel 805-962-4214

Koheleth Pub, *(Koheleth Publishing Co.; 0-913964),* 750 Gonzalez Dr., San Francisco, CA 94132 (SAN 203-9230)

Koinonia Prods, *(Koinonia Productions; 0-86635),* 5920 Dante, Stockton, CA 95207 (SAN 238-0633)

Kovanda, *(Kovanda, William James; 0-9606658),* Box 27, Albion, CA 95410 (SAN 223-1190) Tel 707-937-4919

Kraemer, *(Kraemer, Elsa; 0-9600526),* 93-41 222nd St., Queens Village, NY 11428 (SAN 203-9249) Tel 212-468-4117

Krag Pubns, *(Krag Pubns.),* 1217-8th St., S.E., Minneapolis, MN 55414 (SAN 213-098X)

Kruzas Assoc, *(Kruzas, Anthony T., Associates),* 1810 Longshore Dr., Ann Arbor, MI 48103 (SAN 215-2150) Tel 313-665-7189; Dist. by: Gale Research Co., Book Tower, Detroit, MI 48226 (SAN 213-4373) Tel 313-961-2242

Kummer, *(Kummer, Jerome M., M.D.; 0-9600054),* Drawer 769, Santa Monica, CA 90406 (SAN 203-9257)

Kylix Pr, *(Kylix Press; 0-914408),* 1485 Maywood, Ann Arbor, MI 48103 (SAN 206-5525) Tel 313-761-5399

L A Pop, *(L. A. Pop Books),* Box 24941, Los Angeles, CA 90024 (SAN 211-0814) Tel 213-466-7127

L Alcaro, *(Alcaro, Lucia),* 80 Rock Hill Rd., Clifton, NJ 07013 (SAN 212-6389)

L Gerlinger, *(Gerlinger/Lorena),* 4666 Pratt Rd., Hadley, MI 48440 (SAN 207-9291) Tel 313-797-4833

L Gray Pub, *(Gray, Lee, Publishing; 0-9603976),* 187 James Ave., Red Bluff, CA 96080 (SAN 213-7402)

L H Richardson
See D L Hennessey

L Mark Lib, *(Mark, Lynn, Library; 0-918322),* 279 E. 44th St., No. 9H, New York, NY 10017 (SAN 209-6242) Tel 212-697-4379

L Maynard, *(Maynard, Louis),* 5922 S. Sunnylane Rd., Oklahoma City, OK 73135 (SAN 207-2483) Tel 405-799-2148

L Olds, *(Olds, Lee),* P.O. Box 40731, San Francisco, CA 94110 (SAN 206-1597); Dist. by: Bookpeople, 2929 Fifth St., Berkeley, CA 94710 (SAN 168-9517)

L Silberman, *(Silberman, Leonard; 0-9605080),* P.O. Box 12519, Santa Ana, CA 92712 (SAN 238-0854)

L V Fay, *(Fay, Loren V.; 0-942238),* 87 Edgewood Ave., Albany, NY 12203 (SAN 215-2509)

L Ziman, *(Ziman, Larry; 0-933456),* P.O. Box 67485, Los Angeles, CA 90067 (SAN 212-8179)

La Belle, *(La Belle, Gary),* 19 Sterling Place, Glen Rock, NJ 07452 (SAN 209-6684)

La Monte Crape, *(La Monte Crape Publisher),* 412 N. Washington St., Butler, PA 16001 (SAN 207-2521)

LA Pub Co, *(Los Angeles Publishing Co.; 0-913924),* P. O. Box 5135, Sherman Oaks, CA 91413 (SAN 201-0593) Tel 805-259-4749

LaBarre F E, *(La Barre, Frederick E.; 0-9604086),* P. O. Box 156, North Troy, VT 05859 (SAN 221-6221)

LaFray Pub
See Lafray Young Pub

Lafray Young Pub, *(Lafray Young Pub. Co.; 0-942084),* P.O. Box 292227, Ft. Lauderdale, FL 33329 (SAN 281-8639) Tel 305-584-0303; 5901 SW 43rd St., Davie, FL 33314 (SAN 281-8647)

LaGrange Bks, *(LaGrange Books; 0-933115),* P.O. Box 60, La Grange, TN 38046 (SAN 690-0089)

Lake County, *(Lake County Press),* Box 669, Ronan, MT 59864 (SAN 215-6709); Dist. by: Montana Writers, Inc., Box 21133, Billings, MT 59104 (SAN 215-6717)

Lakes & Prairies Pr, *(Lakes & Prairies Press; 0-9607780),* 6334 N. Sheridan Rd, Chicago, IL 60660 (SAN 239-5614)

Lakeside Pub Co, *(Lakeside Publishing Co.; 0-913053),* P.O. Box 129, Pewaukee, WI 53072 (SAN 283-1317)

Lakshmi, (Lakshmi California Corp.; 0-941868), 9514 la Jolla Farms Rd., La Jolla, CA 92037 (SAN 239-2496) Tel 714-452-9221

Lamplight Pub, (Lamplight Publishing Inc.; 0-88308), 548 W. 26th St., New York, NY 10001 (SAN 287-0193) Tel 212-695-8222; c/o Scroll Press, 2858 Valerie Court, Merrick, NY 11566 (SAN 287-0207) Tel 516-379-4283

Lancaster Hse Pr, (Lancaster House Press; 0-914356), 36 Freshmeadow Dr., Lancaster, PA 17603 (SAN 202-6619)

Land Values, (Land Values), 2821 Frontier Dr., Midland, TX 79701 (SAN 206-6270) Tel 915-683-2922; Orders to: P.O. Box 1533, Midland, TX 79702 (SAN 206-6289)

Landmark Pub, (Landmark Publishing Corp.; 0-918200), Div. of Clearwater Corp., Box 3287, Burlington, VT 05402 (SAN 210-2242) Tel 802-372-4522

Lane & Assoc, (Lane & Associates; 0-89882), Box 3063, La Jolla, CA 92037 (SAN 220-7419)

Lansky & Assoc, (Lansky & Associates; 0-932672), 18318 Minnetonka Blvd, Deephaven, MN 55391 (SAN 212-7555) Tel 612-473-5400

Laranmark Pr, (Laranmark Pr.; 0-910937), Div. of Laranmark, Inc., 220 Main St., Neshkoro, WI 54960 (SAN 271-9606) Tel 414-293-4377 Imprints: Unicorn-Star (Unicorn-Star Inc.).

Larousse, (Larousse & Co., Inc.; 0-88332), Affil. of Librairie Larousse USA, Inc., 572 Fifth Ave., New York, NY 10036 (SAN 202-6643) Tel 212-575-9515; Dist. by: E. P. Dutton, 2 Park Ave., New York, NY 10016 (SAN 282-6267) Tel 212-725-1818

Larson, (Larson, David U.), P.O. Box 599, Boynton Beach, FL 33435 (SAN 211-4291)

Lascaux
See Altamira Lascaux

Lash Pubns, (Lash Pubns.; 0-9607150), P.O. Box 32873, Detroit, MI 48232 (SAN 239-0043) Tel 313-886-0555

Lat Am Stud, (Latin American Studies, Univ. of Houston), 401 Hoffman Hall, Univ. of Houston, Houston, TX 77004 (SAN 207-7191) Tel 713-749-4885

Latham, (Latham Publishing Corp.; 0-918674), 41 E. 42nd St., New York, NY 10017 (SAN 210-1505) Tel 212-687-0804

Latigo Pr, (Latigo Press; 0-935752), 8320 E. Monterosa Ave., Scottsdale, AZ 85251 (SAN 213-6317)

Laurel Inst, (Laurel Institute, The; 0-87012), RD 1, Box 10, Farmington, PA 15437 (SAN 215-6741)

Laurel Pub, (Laurel Publishing Corp.; 0-89170), Box 6194, 21 Churchill Rd., Hamden, CT 06517 (SAN 208-0354)

Lavender & Red, (Lavender & Red Union), P.O. Box 3503, Hollywood, CA 90028 (SAN 207-5636)

Law of One, (Law of One, The), 3412 Pacific Ave., Forest Grove, OR 97116 (SAN 210-9093)

Lawton Pr, (Lawton Press; 0-933044), 673 Pelham Rd., Suite 16E, New Rochelle, NY 10805 (SAN 212-2871)

Lazy Pr, (Lazy Pr., The), 2520 N. Lincoln Ave., Chicago, IL 60614 (SAN 285-1210) Tel 312-934-8451

Le Voyageur, (Le Voyageur Publishing), 1319 Wentwood Dr., Irving, TX 75061 (SAN 201-0739)

Leaf Pr, (Leaf Press; 0-940360), 4014 Santa Monica Blvd, Los Angeles, CA 90029 (SAN 222-9803)

League of MN, (League of Minnesota), 300 Hanover Bldg., St. Paul, MN 55101 (SAN 218-8201) Tel 612-222-2861

Learn, (Learn), 1535 S. Kipling Pkwy. C300, Lakewood, CO 80226 (SAN 692-7130)

Learn Mich, (Learn; 0-9604634), 827 CNB Bldg., Detroit, MI 48226 (SAN 215-2533)

Learning Inst NC, (Learning Institute of North Carolina), 1006 Lamond Ave., Durham, NC 27701 (SAN 203-865X)

Learning Res, (Learning Resources Corp.; 0-913406), 2817 N. Dorr Ave., Fairfax, VA 22030 (SAN 202-6686) Tel 703-573-3371

Lecouver, (Lecouver Press Co.; 0-910870), 749 N.E. 71st St., Boca Raton, FL 33432 (SAN 203-9311)

Lederer Street & Zeus, (Lederer, Street & Zeus Co), 2121 Allston Way, Berkeley, CA 94704 (SAN 208-2810) Tel 415-845-1342

Lee Pubns, (Lee Pubns.; 0-910872), 105 Suffolk Rd., Wellesley Hills, MA 02181 (SAN 203-932X)

Leeger Pr, (Leeger Press; 0-9609706), P.O. Box 371, Norwalk, CT 06851 (SAN 262-7914); 29 Lockwood Ln., Norwalk, CT 06851 (SAN 262-7922)

Leeward Pubns, (Leeward Pubns., Inc.; 0-915268), P.O. Box 149, Annapolis, MD 21404 (SAN 218-4885)

LeFax, (LeFax Publishing Co.; 0-87684), 2867 E. Allegheny Ave., Philadelphia, PA 19134 (SAN 201-0771)

Legacy Of Love, (Legacy Of Love, A), 1638 Daniels Dr., North Fort Meyers, FL 33903 (SAN 283-2992)

Legacy Pr, (Legacy Press; 0-914682), P.O. Box 783, Rhinelander, WI 54501 (SAN 201-078X) Tel 715-362-4296

Legacy Pub Co, (Legacy Publishing Co.; 0-918784), 2008 Perkins Rd., Baton Rouge, LA 70808 (SAN 210-4539) Tel 504-343-0366

Legal First Aid, (Legal First Aid), 899 Ellis St., San Francisco, CA 94109 (SAN 206-4391) Tel 415-441-4044

Legal Mgmt Serv, (Legal Management Services, Inc.; 0-937542), 250 W. 94th St., New York, NY 10025 (SAN 220-066X) Tel 212-864-6169; Dist. by: LMS Distribution Center, P.O. Box 2614, LaCrosse, WI 54601 (SAN 220-0678)

Legal Res, (Legal Researcher, The; 0-913055), 1377 K St., NW, Suite 164, Washington, DC 20005 (SAN 283-1376)

Leisure Bks CT, (Leisure Books), P.O. Box 270, Norwalk, CT 06852 (SAN 215-2258)

Leitz, (Leitz, E.), Dist. by: Morgan & Morgan, 145 Palisades St., Dobbs Ferry, NY 10522 (SAN 202-5620)

Lemma, (Lemma Publishing Corp.; 0-87696), 509 Fifth Ave., New York, NY 10017 (SAN 202-6694)

Lenox Hill, (Lenox Hill Press), Div. of Crown Publishing, Inc., 235 E. 44th St., New York, NY 10017 (SAN 201-0801) Tel 212-687-5250

Leopold, (Leopold-Littleberry Pr.; 0-941756), 2124 Kittredge, Box 52, Berkeley, CA 94704 (SAN 239-2518) Tel 415-845-2206

Leornian Educ & Res, (Leornian Educational & Resource Network; 0-917216), P.O. Box 181, Center Conway, NH 03813 (SAN 208-4317)

Les Femmes Pub, (Les Femmes Publishing; 0-89407), P.O. Box 7327, Berkeley, CA 94707 (SAN 207-7353)

Lets Save Children, (Let's Save the Children, Inc.; 0-89017), P.O. Box 20747, Chicago, IL 60620 (SAN 206-5541) Tel 312-548-0356

Levine Pr, (Levine Press), P.O. Box 517, Cascade, CO 80809 (SAN 209-0309)

Lez Pr, (Lez Pr.; 0-932005), P.O. Box 4387, Portland, OR 97208 (SAN 686-1008)

Lib Auto Res Con, (Library Automation Research Consulting Associates (Larc Press, Ltd.); 0-88257), P.O. Box 27235, Tempe, AZ 85282 (SAN 202-6732) Tel 602-968-2023

Lib News Serv, (Liberation News Service), 17 W. 17 St, New York, NY 10011 (SAN 225-7173)

Liberation Bk, (Liberation Bookstore), P.O. Box 17, Radio City Sta., New York, NY 10019 (SAN 206-4006)

Liberation Sup
See LSM Pr

Liberator Pr, (Liberator Press; 0-930720), Box 7128, Chicago, IL 60680 (SAN 213-1072) Tel 312-243-3791

Liberty Bk, (Liberty Book Co.), 374 Morris St., Albany, NY 12208 (SAN 204-3734) Tel 518-463-0483

Liberty LA, (Liberty Publishing (LA); 0-918229), 2252 W. Beverly Blvd., Suite 210, Los Angeles, CA 90057 (SAN 657-2804)

Libra Pub, (Libra Publishing Corp.; 0-915122), 1 Executive Dr., Burlington, VT 05401 (SAN 207-3455)

Libty Pr IA, (Liberty Press; 0-939272), 905 Leroy St., Muscatine, IA 52761 (SAN 216-4086)

Libty Pr MI, (Liberty Press; 0-9604958), 2115 Mark Ave., Lansing, MI 48912 (SAN 215-7845)

Life Pubns IL, (Life Pubns., Inc.), Box 72, Ina, IL 62846 (SAN 211-8610)

Lighted Way, (Lighted Way), 1515 Palisades Dr. Ste N., Pacific Palisades, CA 90272 (SAN 226-6733) Tel 213-459-5861

LightSong, (LightSong), 1325 Rimrock Dr., San Jose, CA 95120 (SAN 209-1607)

Lignum Pr, (Lignum Pr., Ltd.), P.O. Box 90027, Atlanta, GA 30329 (SAN 697-2624)

Lillian, (Lillian & M. E.; 0-918174), 11 Tudor Dr., Northport, NY 11788 (SAN 209-5742) Tel 516-757-5615

Lillibridge Bks, (Lillibridge Books), P. O. Box 1975, Albion, MI 49224 (SAN 207-7507) Tel 517-629-9210

LINC, (LINC Associates, Inc.), Morse Rd., Suite 215, Columbus, OH 43229 (SAN 670-7068)

Lincoln Hse
See OSV Fabric Shop

Linden Lane, (Linden Lane Press; 0-9913827), 134 Glen Ave., Milburn, NJ 07041 (SAN 286-1674) Tel 201-376-6932

Lingua Hse, (Lingua House; 0-916636), 915 W. Jackson, Pasadena, CA 91101 (SAN 281-8833) Tel 213-440-1261; Dist. by: Academic Pubns.-Summer Institute of Linguistics, 7500 W. Camp Wisdom Rd., Dallas, TX 75236 (SAN 282-6658)

Lion Serv Co, (Lion Services Co. - Publishing & Distribution; 0-9601018), 4535 W. Sahara, Suite 105-7a, Las Vegas, NV 89102 (SAN 208-7383) Tel 702-735-3814

Lionheart, (Lionheart Books, U.S.A.; 0-949894), Box 2820, Chula Vista, CA 92012 (SAN 277-6944)

Literary, (Literary Mart; 0-910896), P.O. Box 5425, Milwaukee, WI 53211 (SAN 203-9370)

Literary Herald, (Literary Herald Pr.; 0-9602124), 408 Oak St., Danville, IL 61832 (SAN 212-5242)

Literati Pr, (Literati Press, Pubs.; 0-933744), The Olive Bldg., 18 E. Sunrise Hwy., Freeport, NY 11520 (SAN 212-8586)

Litho Textbk, (Lithographic Textbook Publishing Co.; 0-9600060), 5719 S. Spaulding, Chicago, IL 60629 (SAN 201-095X) Tel 312-776-7234

Litoral Arts Pr, (Litoral Arts Press; 0-940612), 1063 31st St., San Pedro, CA 90731 (SAN 222-9854) Tel 213-547-4526

Little Bks, (Little Books; 0-915686), P.O. Box 9, Fort Lee, NJ 07024 (SAN 207-3668)

Littleman, (Littleman Press; 0-9608264), Box 7262, Seattle, WA 98133 (SAN 240-9534)

Littoral Bks, (Littoral Books), P.O. Box 7355, Downtown Sta., Portland, ME 04112 (SAN 209-0392)

Living Bks NY, (Living Books Ltd.), P.O. Box 604, New York, NY 10036 (SAN 206-4413) Tel 212-222-5464

Living Black Hist, (Living Black History; 0-8181), c/o Pay-O-Matic, Unit No. 186, 254 Kingston Ave., Brooklyn, NY 11213 (SAN 211-6081)

Living Hand, (Living Hand), Millis Rd., Box 252, Stanfordville, NY 12581 (SAN 207-2572)

Living Word, (Living Word Pubns.; 0-88467), 4964 W. Cullom Ave., Chicago, IL 60641 (SAN 202-6813) Tel 312-725-8660

Livingston Marine, (Livingston Marine Services, Inc.; 0-931938), 17 Battery Place, Room 1631, New York, NY 10004 (SAN 212-9124)

Logan County, (Logan County Heritage Foundation; 0-9611816), P.O. Box 396, Lincoln, IL 62656 (SAN 285-0435) Tel 217-732-8878; Lincoln Public Library, 725 Pekin St., Lincoln, IL 62656 (SAN 285-0443)

London Bk, (London Bk. Co.), 212 N. Orange, Glendale, CA 91203 (SAN 207-2580)

Lone Raven, (Lone Raven Publishing Co., Inc.; 0-933914), P.O. Box 1739, Anchorage, AK 99510 (SAN 213-5337)

Lone Star Pubs, (Lone Star Pubs., Inc.; 0-914872), P.O. Box 9774, Austin, TX 78766 (SAN 210-8283) Tel 512-452-5413

Longs College, (Long's College Book Co.; 0-910906), 1836 N. High St., Columbus, OH 43201 (SAN 205-244X) Tel 614-294-4674

Longship Pr, (Longship Press; 0-917712), Crooked Lane, Nantucket, MA 02554 (SAN 209-4576) Tel 207-722-3344; Orders to: RFD 1, Box 124, Brooks, ME 04921 (SAN 209-4584)

Los Angeles Pub, *(Los Angeles Pub., Co.; 0-913924)*, P.O. Box 54119, Terminal Annex, Los Angeles, CA 90054 (SAN 207-2599)

Lost Data, *(Lost Data Press; 0-937468)*, 4410C Burnett Rd., Austin, TX 78756 (SAN 281-935X); Orders to: Weare News Co., Baker Hill Rd., Sutton, NH 03221 (SAN 281-9368); Orders to: The Distributors, 702 S. Michigan, South Bend, IN 46618 (SAN 212-0364); Orders to: Whole Earth Bookstore, Fort Mason Center, Bldg. D, San Francisco, CA 94123 (SAN 281-9384); Orders to: Back to Basics Books, The Mother Earth News, 105 Stony Mountain Rd., Hendersonville, NC 28739 (SAN 281-9392); Orders to: Lindsay Publications, 152 W. Baker St., Mantieno, IL 60950 (SAN 281-9406)

Lotus Ashram, *(Lotus Ashram, Inc., The)*, 113 Francis St., Goose Creek, SC 29445 (SAN 211-8106) Tel 803-572-4564

LSM Pr, *(LSM Press; 0-919914)*, P.O. Box 2077, Oakland, CA 94604 (SAN 210-7651) Tel 415-635-4863

LTB *Imprint of* **Sportshelf**

Lucas, *(Lucas Brothers Pubs.; 0-87543)*, 909 Lowry Mall Missouri Bookstore, Columbia, MO 65201 (SAN 201-1050) Tel 314-442-6161

Lucky Pubns, *(Lucky Pubns.; 0-932342)*, P.O. Box 19307, Las Vegas, NV 89119 (SAN 211-741X) Tel 702-564-3895

Luna Pr, *(Luna Press; 0-914466)*, P.O. Box 1049, Brooklyn, NY 11202 (SAN 203-4034)

Luther Coll Pr, *(Luther College Press)*, Decorah, IA 52101 (SAN 202-2397) Tel 319-387-1166

Lyceum Bks, *(Lyceum Books; 0-915336)*, P.O. Box 113, Wilton, CT 06897 (SAN 208-113X)

Lyl Inc, *(Lyl Inc)*, P.O. Box 15439, Long Beach, CA 90815 (SAN 210-9115) Tel 213-433-1523

Lynell Mkting, *(Lynell Marketing, Inc.; 0-9607932)*, 1432 County Line Rd., Huntington Valley, PA 19006 (SAN 238-4353)

M & B, *(M & B Publishing Co.; 0-930496)*, 1 Emerald St., Norwalk, CT 06850 (SAN 212-1905) Tel 203-846-4294

M & M Grap, *(M&M Graphics; 0-912359)*, P.O. Box 373, Annadale, VA 22003-0373 (SAN 265-1629) Tel 703-978-6117

M & P Frierson, *(Frierson, Meade & Penny)*, 3705 Woodvale Rd., Birmingham, AL 35223 (SAN 206-2135)

M Bergerie, *(Bergerie, Maurine; 0-9604234)*, 201 Pollard Ave., New Iberia, LA 70560 (SAN 214-2848)

M D Falley, *(Falley, Margaret Dickson)*, 1500 Sheridan Rd., Wilmette, IL 60091 (SAN 208-1989) Tel 312-251-4588

M Farley, *(Farley, Mike; 0-933850)*, P.O. Box 24A08, Los Angeles, CA 90024 (SAN 213-053X)

M G Wolfe, *(Wolfe, Mary G.; 0-9603406)*, 23 Quartz Mill Rd., Newark, DE 19711 (SAN 210-9786) Tel 302-239-7571

M Golub, *(Golub, Millin)*, 1095 Second Ave., Apartment 2RN, New York, NY 10022 (SAN 207-5075) Tel 212-449-0990

M H Smith, *(Smith, Michael Holley; 0-931768)*, 600-B E. Bee Caves Rd., Austin, TX 78746 (SAN 212-5617) Tel 512-327-4443

M J Stone, *(Stone, M. J., Co.; 0-9601888)*, P.O. Box 12793, Seattle, WA 98101 (SAN 212-6974) Tel 206-682-0350

M K Heller, *(Heller, Marjorie K.; 0-915362)*, Box 78, Bayside, NY 11361 (SAN 209-066X) Tel 718-229-7715

M M Chamberlain, *(Chamberlain, Mildred Mosher; 0-9604142)*, 128 Potters Ave., Warwick, RI 02886 (SAN 215-0654)

M O Pub Co, *(M.O. Publishing Co.; 0-932044)*, 14322 Howard Rd., Dayton, MD 20836 (SAN 211-6707)

M Toma, *(Toma, Michael; 0-9612504)*, Box 444, Manteca, CA 95336 (SAN 292-3408)

M Waby, *(Waby, Marian; 0-9615680)*, 552-44 Bean Creek Rd., Scotts Valley, CA 95066 (SAN 208-0966) Tel 408-438-0567

MA Poverty Law, *(Massachusetts Poverty Law Ctr.; 0-910001)*, 2 Park Sq., Boston, MA 02116 (SAN 241-5577)

Maaroufa Pr, *(Maaroufa Press, Inc.; 0-88425)*, 610 N. Fairbanks Court, 3rd Floor, Chicago, IL 60611 (SAN 202-215X) Tel 312-337-2411

McGrath, *(McGrath Publishing Co.; 0-8434)*, P.O. Box 9001, Wilmington, NC 28402 (SAN 212-0275) *Imprints:* Consortium (Consortium Books).

McKinley Pub, *(McKinley Publishing Co.; 0-910942)*, P.O. Box 77, Ocean City, NJ 08226 (SAN 207-0472)

McMillion Pubns, *(McMillion Pubns.; 0-942792)*, 2333 Emery, Denton, TX 76201 (SAN 240-2521)

Macrae, *(Macrae Smith Co.; 0-8255)*, Rtes. 54 & Old 147, Turbotville, PA 17772 (SAN 202-6007)

Madison Co, *(Madison Co.; 0-913808)*, P.O. Box 206, Berea, KY 40403 (SAN 203-9524) Tel 606-986-9744

Madison Pub
See Madison Co

Mafdet, *(Mafdet Press; 0-918534)*, 1313 S. Jefferson Ave., Springfield, MO 65807 (SAN 209-9497) Tel 417-866-5141

Magic Circle Bk, *(Magic Circle Book Shop)*, 10 Grace Ave., Great Neck, NY 11021 (SAN 227-1273)

Maguey Pr, *(Maguey Pr., The; 0-930778)*, P.O. Box 3395, Tucson, AZ 85722 (SAN 213-3686)

Mahony, *(Mahony, Patrick; 0-913742)*, 5885 Locksley Place, Hollywood, CA 90068 (SAN 203-9559) Tel 213-467-9903

Malter Westerfield, *(Malter-Westerfield Publishing Co.; 0-911718)*, P.O. Box 343, San Clemente, CA 92672 (SAN 203-9583)

Maltese Bks, *(Maltese Books; 0-912664)*, P.O. Box 781, Redondo Beach, CA 90277 (SAN 212-7598)

Manch Lane, *(Manchester Lane Editions)*, 1409 Nicholson St., N.W., Washington, DC 20011 (SAN 203-9613) Tel 202-726-3121

Mandala Pr, *(Mandala Pr.; 0-933158)*, 5010 Randall Dr., Wilmington, NC 28403 (SAN 212-9159) Tel 919-791-5719

Manessier, *(Manessier Publishing Co.; 0-910950)*, Box C, Bryn Mawr, CA 92318 (SAN 203-9621)

Manhattan Pub Co, *(Manhattan Publishing Co.)*, Div. of U.S. & World Pubns., Inc., 225 Lafayette St., New York, NY 10012 (SAN 213-442X)

Manifest Destiny, *(Manifest Destiny Books; 0-914852)*, P.O. Box 57, Dorchester, MA 02124 (SAN 206-7889) Tel 617-288-8765 Tel 617-423-4340

Mann Pubs, *(Mann Pubs.; 0-936632)*, P.O. Box 7 AK, Jersey City, NJ 07307 (SAN 214-0543) Tel 201-659-8324

Manoa Pr, *(Manoa Pr., Inc.; 0-9605502)*, Box 25355, Honolulu, HI 96825 (SAN 215-9643)

Manville Pub, *(Manville Publishing)*, P.O. Box 10091, Phoenix, AZ 85064 (SAN 207-6306)

Mara, *(Mara Books, Inc.; 0-87787)*, 1318 Second St., Santa Monica, CA 90401 (SAN 202-6074)

Mara Pr MA, *(Mara Press; 0-940616)*, Box 790, Marblehead, MA 01945 (SAN 213-4144) Tel 617-631-0624

Maranatha Evangelical
See Maranatha Hse Pubs

Maranatha Hse Pubs, *(Maranatha House Pubs.; 0-89337)*, 705 S. Hwy. 101, Solana Beach, CA 92075 (SAN 208-4414) Tel 714-755-0962

Marand Pub Co, *(Marand Publishing Co.; 0-86567)*, 9237 West Third St., Beverly Hills, CA 90210 (SAN 215-0948)

Marando Pr, *(Marando Press, Inc.; 0-932518)*, 99 Park Ave., New York, NY 10016 (SAN 211-9161)

Margaritas Bks Brown, *(Margarita's Bks. for Brown Eyes; 0-918536)*, 1203 23rd Ave., San Diego, CA 92120 (SAN 209-9543) Tel 619-239-4621

Margin Bks, *(Margin Books)*, 2912 N. Hackett, Milwaukee, WI 53211 (SAN 207-3676)

Marina Mind, *(Marina Mind Science Center)*, 4018 Redwood, Los Angeles, CA 90066 (SAN 208-2756)

Marine Educ *Imprint of* **Herman Pub**

Mariner, *(Mariner Books; 0-910954)*, Route 2, Box A 45, Flat Rock, NC 28731 (SAN 203-9672) Tel 704-693-8045

Mariners Boston, *(Mariners Pr., Inc., The; 0-913352)*, P.O. Box 540, Boston, MA 02117-0540 (SAN 203-9680)

Market Comm, *(Market Communications, Inc.; 0-930820)*, 225 E. Michigan St., Milwaukee, WI 53202 (SAN 211-3694) Tel 414-276-6600

Market Pul, *(MarketPul Corporation; 0-9608940)*, 525 E. Monaco Pl., Tuscon, AZ 85704 (SAN 241-3345) Tel 602-746-8973

Marlborough Hse, *(Marlborough House, Inc.)*, 230 Marlborough St., Boston, MA 02116 (SAN 206-4448)

Marnel Pr, *(Marnel Press, The)*, Div. of AFM Enterprises, Inc., 6355 Topanga Canyon Blvd., Suite 219, Woodland Hills, CA 91367 (SAN 212-6303) Tel 213-888-2990

Martin Pr, *(Martin Press; 0-914976)*, P.O. Box 25464, Los Angeles, CA 90025 (SAN 207-4761)

Mason Parks, *(Mason Parks Press; 0-9601004)*, P.O. Box 46, Newton Lower Falls, MA 02162 (SAN 208-7588)

Master Key, *(Master Key Pubns.; 0-935434)*, P.O. Box 519, Bonita, CA 92002 (SAN 213-4152) Tel 619-475-5554

Masters, *(Masters Press, Inc.; 0-89251)*, Div. of Merchants Pub. Co., 20 Mills St., Kalamazoo, MI 49001 (SAN 208-7596) Tel 616-385-1842

Mastery Learning, *(Mastery Learning Systems; 0-935144)*, 450 E. Strawberry Dr., No. 39, Mill Valley, CA 94941 (SAN 213-3377)

Mathiesen Edns, *(Mathiesen Editions; 0-917412)*, 45 Lauriston St., Providence, RI 02906 (SAN 207-6217) Tel 401-351-1878

Mathplots, *(Mathplots; 0-913889)*, 2617 Lake Michigan Dr. NW, Grand Rapids, MI 49504 (SAN 286-8202) Tel 616-453-8652

Matrix Pubns, *(Matrix Pubns., Inc.; 0-936554)*, 222 Williams St., Providence, RI 02906 (SAN 215-1618) Tel 401-421-2068

Maxigraphics, *(Maxigraphics, Inc.)*, R.D. No. 2, Box 123, Phillipsburg, NJ 08885 (SAN 211-0369) Tel 201-454-1544

Maya, *(Maya)*, 1222 Solano Ave., Albany, CA 94706 (SAN 206-8761) Tel 415-548-8204

Mayflower Press NJ, *(Mayflower Press; 0-9602216)*, 26 Tulp Court, Clifton, NJ 07013 (SAN 212-372X)

Mazgeen Pr, *(Mazgeen Press; 0-915330)*, P.O. Box 70, Key West, FL 33040 (SAN 207-1797) Tel 305-294-0734

ME Crim Justice, *(Maine Criminal Justice Planning & Assistance Agency)*, 11 Parkwood Dr., Augusta, ME 04430 (SAN 226-9309)

Med Info Pubns, *(Medical Information Pubns., Inc.; 0-939308)*, 143 W. 29th St., 3rd Fl., New York, NY 10001 (SAN 216-5384) Tel 212-364-2154

Med Student Pubs, *(Medical Student Pubs.; 0-910015)*, P.O. Box 190291, Dallas, TX 75219 (SAN 241-340X)

Medal Print, *(Medal Printing Co.; 0-917692)*, 183 Benefit St., Pawtucket, RI 02861 (SAN 210-1238) Tel 401-724-3586

Media, *(Media Books)*, 400 E. 89th St., New York, NY 10028 (SAN 203-9818) Tel 212-534-0366

Media America, *(Media America, Inc.; 0-916474)*, 12 E. Market St., Bethlehem, PA 18018 (SAN 208-1040) Tel 215-866-2207

Media Pubns, *(Media Pubns.; 0-943214)*, 2706 W. Sahuaro Dr., Bldg. 8-201, P.O. Box 1504, Phoenix, AZ 85001 (SAN 240-5504)

Mediaworks, *(Mediaworks, The; 0-918072)*, Box 4494, Boulder, CO 80306 (SAN 209-4606) Tel 303-494-1439

MEDS Corp, *(M. E. D. S. Corp.; 0-916420)*, 97-99 Stuyvesant Ave, Newark, NJ 07106 (SAN 207-7094) Tel 201-899-7856

Melodious Pubns, *(Melodious Pubns.; 0-941086)*, 68 Smith Street, Brockport, NY 14420 (SAN 219-7979) Tel 716-637-4622

Melodyland, *(Melodyland Pubs.; 0-918818)*, Div. of Melodyland Christian Center, 10 Freedman Way, Anaheim, CA 92806 (SAN 210-4628) Tel 714-635-6391

Menaid, *(Menaid Press International; 0-918424)*, Div. of Fichter Enterprises, P.O. Box 25008, Colorado Springs, CO 80936 (SAN 209-9578)

Mercantine Pr, *(Mercantine Press; 0-933962)*, 4351 Washington St., Lincoln, NE 68506 (SAN 212-9175) Tel 402-489-2626

Mercury Comm, (*Mercury Communications Corp.; 0-917772*), 734 Chestnut St., Santa Cruz, CA 95060 (SAN 211-6227) Tel 408-425-8444

Merit Pubns, (*Merit Pubns., Inc.; 0-87803*), 610 NE 124th St., N. Miami, FL 33161 (SAN 211-4380)

Merton Pr, (*Merton Pr.; 0-933959*), Atlantic Bank Bldg., Suite 604, St Augustine, FL 32084 (SAN 686-9254)

Meta Pr, (*Meta Pr.; 0-940408*), P.O. Box 3077, Brooklyn, NY 11202 (SAN 683-292X)

Metaphysical, (*Metaphysical & Christian Science; 0-910964*), P.O. Box 6454, Metropolitan Sta., Los Angeles, CA 90055 (SAN 203-9877)

Methods Pr, (*Methods Press; 0-910968*), P.O. Box 14154, University Sta., Minneapolis, MN 55414 (SAN 203-9885) Tel 612-633-3697

Metro TN, (*Metropolitan Books; 0-914011*), Div. of Communications Group Inc., 1861 Poplar Ave., No. 2, Memphis, TN 38104 (SAN 289-0399) Tel 901-725-4047; P.O. Box 38112, Memphis, TN 38112 (SAN 289-0402)

Mgmt Tech *Imprint of* AMTEC

Mich Muse, (*Michigan Muse; 0-932996*), P.O. Box 8061, Ann Arbor, MI 48107 (SAN 212-6788)

Mich St U Busn, (*Michigan State Univ. Division of Research Grad School of Business Administration; 0-87744*), 5J Berkey Hall, East Lansing, MI 48824 (SAN 202-6287) Tel 517-355-7560

Mid-West, (*Mid-West Debate Bureau; 0-911930*), Pubns. Dept., Box 8, Normal, IL 61761 (SAN 207-0502)

Midwest Pub IN, (*Midwest Publishing Co.; 0-935728*), P.O. Box 33247, 2057 Sloan Ave., Indianapolis, IN 46203 (SAN 214-252X)

Midwest Pub NE, (*Midwest Publishing Co.; 0-918798*), P.O. Box 33, Ceresco, NE 68017 (SAN 205-843X) Tel 402-665-5351

Milkbottles Only, (*Milkbottles Only Organization*), P O Box 5456, Newport News, VA 23605 (SAN 225-5413)

Millennium Pub, (*Millennium Publishing House, Inc.; 0-917812*), 507 W. Holly Rd., Virginia Beach, VA 23451 (SAN 209-9608) Tel 804-422-3493; Main Office - 3333 Connecticut N.W., Washington, DC 20008 (SAN 209-9616)

Miller, (*Miller, Charlotte; 0-9606646*), 1008 Sansome Ct., Modesto, CA 95350 (SAN 219-6050) Tel 209-267-1357

Milwaukee Journal, (*Milwaukee Journal, Public Service Bureau*), 333 W. State St., Milwaukee, WI 53201 (SAN 240-0561) Tel 414-224-2120

Minerva Pr, (*Minerva Press; 0-8476*), Tel 201-256-8600; Orders to: Biblio Distribution Centre, 81 Adams Dr., Box 327, Totowa, NJ 07511 (SAN 211-724X)

Mini-Word, (*Mini-Word Editions; 0-935358*), P.O. Box 3314, Champaign, IL 61820 (SAN 213-5388)

MINMOR, (*MINMOR Publishing Co.; 0-918976*), 14 Germain St., Worcester, MA 01602 (SAN 210-4652) Tel 617-757-8463

Minn Assn Ed, (*Minnesota Assn. for Educational Data Systems*), 2221 University Ave., Minneapolis, MN 55414 (SAN 677-9689) Tel 612-631-2926

Minn Jaycees, (*Minnesota Jaycees*), 8800 W. Hwy. 7, Minneapolis, MN 55426 (SAN 203-9958)

Miracle Pub Co
See Miracle Pub Co TX

Miracle Pub Co TX, (*Miracle Publishing Co.; 0-911197*), 13515 Southwest Freeway, Sugar Land, TX 77478 (SAN 272-4618); Dist. by: Publishers Marketing Group, 1104 Summit Ave., Plainview, TX 75074 (SAN 262-0995)

MJG Co, (*MJG Co.; 0-932632*), P.O. Box 7743, Midland, TX 79708-0743 (SAN 212-2901) Tel 915-682-3184

MJT Intl Pubns, (*MJT International Pubns.; 0-86707*), P.O. Box 1879, 2824 S. 3000 W., Ogden, UT 84401 (SAN 216-633X) Tel 801-731-3486

Mod Pubs, (*Modern Pubs.; 0-9600812*), 1326 Davies Rd., Far Rockaway, NY 11691 (SAN 207-1452)

Model Tech, (*Model Technology, Inc.; 0-9601840*), 323 W. Cedar, Chillicothe, IL 61523 (SAN 212-1964)

Modern Day Topics, (*Modern Day Topics Publishing House, Inc.; 0-931648*), P.O. Box 9702, Savannah, GA 31412 (SAN 211-8645) Tel 912-234-0611

Modern Ed, (*Modern Education Pubs.*), P.O. Box 93, Saratoga, CA 95070 (SAN 206-6580)

Mona Pub, (*Mona Publishing Co., Ltd.; 0-938952*), 79 Wall St., Suite 501, New York, NY 10005 (SAN 215-9716)

Monegon Ltd, (*Monegon, Ltd.; 0-940520*), 4 Professional Dr., No. 130, Gaithersburg, MD 20879 (SAN 238-8049)

Mono Basin Res, (*Mono Basin Research Group, The; 0-939714*), Box 66, Lee Vining, CA 93541 (SAN 285-0664) Tel 714-647-6496; Forestry Sciences Lab, 3200 Jefferson Way, Corvalles, OR 97331 (SAN 285-0672) Tel 503-757-4633

Mono Bk, (*Mono Book Corp.; 0-87662*), 116 S. Main St. 4th Floor, Wilkes-Barre, PA 18701 (SAN 202-2465) Tel 717-824-8761

Monona, (*Monona-Driver Book Co.; 0-910982*), 110 Henuah Cir., Madison, WI 53716 (SAN 204-0026) Tel 608-222-1973

Montemora Found, (*Montemora Foundation, Inc., The; 0-935528*), 198 1/2 Main St., Nyack, NY 10960 (SAN 213-9383)

Monticello Pr, (*Monticello Press; 0-9607056*), 1330 Camp St., New Orleans, LA 70130 (SAN 239-0124) Tel 504-521-6744

Moore Pub Co
See F Apple

Mordecai, (*Plaut, Mordecai; 0-9612088*), 868 E. Seventh St., No. 2C, Brooklyn, NY 11230 (SAN 286-8512) Tel 718-434-8293

Morel Bks, (*Morel Books; 0-9607370*), 2918 Hillegass Ave., Suite C, Berkeley, CA 94705 (SAN 239-460X)

Moss Pubns, (*Moss Pubns.; 0-930870*), P.O. Box 644, Berkeley, CA 94701 (SAN 211-0822) Tel 415-653-6458

Mossy Rock WA, (*Mossy Rock Publishing Co.; 0-936938*), 808 106th NE, Bellevue, WA 98004 (SAN 215-2134)

Mothers Hen, (*Mother's Hen; 0-914370*), P.O. Box 99592, San Francisco, CA 94109 (SAN 206-1635)

Motiv Pub, (*Motivational Publishing Co.; 0-9614232*), 16 Island Ave., Miami Beach, FL 33139 (SAN 686-791X)

Motor Bus Soc, (*Motor Bus Society, Inc.*), Railroad Sta., Depot Plaza, White Plains, NY 10606 (SAN 208-4740)767 Valley Rd., Upper Montclair, NJ 07043 (SAN 208-4759)

Mountain Life Pr, (*Mountain Life Pr.; 0-9615071*), P.O. Box 560, Canandaigua, NY 14424 (SAN 693-9171)

Mountain Pub Servs, (*Mountain Publishing Services; 0-931158*), Box 507, Hollister, MO 65672 (SAN 211-7452) Tel 417-334-1523

Mountain View, (*Mountain View Publishing Co.*), Tin Cup Rd., Darby, MT 59829 (SAN 212-8381)

Movie Idea
See World Faith Ex

Mr Mileage, (*Mr. Mileage*), P.O. Box 4800H, Tucson, AZ 85717 (SAN 211-2981)

Mss Info, (*Mss Information Corp.; 0-8422*), P.O. Box 985, Edison, NJ 08817 (SAN 202-8840) Tel 201-225-1900

Muns, (*Muns, George F.; 0-9604924*), 721 E. Blanco Blvd., P.O. Box 878, Bloomfield, NM 87413 (SAN 220-0740) Tel 505-632-3987

Murray, (*Murray, Samuel; 0-910996*), 477 Main St., Box 398, Wilbraham, MA 01095 (SAN 206-6599)

Murrison Co, (*Murrison Co., The; 0-9602110*), 3879 Northstrand Dr., Decatur, GA 30035 (SAN 216-1656) Tel 404-289-5012

Murzin Pub, (*Murzin Publishing; 0-911199*), Box 8527, Deerfield Beach, FL 33441 (SAN 272-5584) Tel 305-427-3060

Mus Bus Bks *Imprint of* **Tree by River**

Muscle Games, (*Muscle Games; 0-9603864*), P.O. Box 51, Fairview Village, PA 19409 (SAN 213-9391)

Muse Pr Oreg, (*Muse Press, Oregon Ltd.; 0-912906*), Trail, OR 97541 (SAN 202-8859) Tel 503-878-2377

Museum Restoration, (*Museum Restoration Service*), Bridge Authority Bldg., Ogdensburg, NY 13669 (SAN 203-1558)

Mutual, (*Mutual Publishing Co.; 0-9600244*), 3315 Wisconsin Ave., N.W., Suite 106, Washington, DC 20016 (SAN 204-0166)

Mycroft, (*Mycroft Business Press; 0-910998*), P.O. Box 702, Columbia, MO 65205 (SAN 204-0174) Tel 314-445-6872

MYM Pub Co, (*M Y M Publishing Co.; 0-932601*), P.O. Box 23257, Santa Barbara, CA 93121 (SAN 687-7540)

Mystery Hill, (*Mystery Hill Press*), Four Paige Rd., Litchfield, NH 03051 (SAN 210-3133)

Mystic Cult, (*Mystic Cult Pub. Co.*), Box 31462, San Francisco, CA 94131 (SAN 209-4045)

Mythos Pr, (*Mythos Press; 0-9609682*), P.O. Box 589, Kalamazoo, MI 49005 (SAN 264-2301)

N & Out, (*N & Out Publishing Co., Inc.; 0-914967*), 9533 Wickersham, Suite 2061, Dallas, TX 75238 (SAN 289-3363)

N Country Pr, (*North Country Press; 0-916196*), P.O. Box 12, 223, Seattle, WA 98112 (SAN 207-7523) Tel 206-329-8372

N Jersey Cons Foun
See NJ Cons Foun

N M Searles, (*Searles, Nancy M.; 0-9613894*), 4104 Bloomingdale Ave., Valparaiso, IN 46383 (SAN 682-3033) Tel 219-462-7405

N S Davies, (*Davies, Nina S.; 0-9600020*), 213 State St., New Orleans, LA 70116 (SAN 206-9687)

Naamikika Pub Co, (*Naamikika Publishing; 0-943146*), c/o Daimyo, Schribner & Hart Co., 1008 Bonnie Doon, Juneau, AK 99801-9440 (SAN 240-7280)

NACA, (*National Assn. for Court Administration, National Ctr. for State Courts*), 1660 Lincoln St., Rm. 200, Denver, CO 80203 (SAN 226-6369)

NACAC, (*NACAC*), 1346 Connecticut Ave., NW, Suite 229, Washington, DC 20036 (SAN 219-8002)

Nadller Concepts, (*Nadller Concepts; 0-9606038*), 192-17 Union Turn, Flushing, NY 11366 (SAN 216-9142) Tel 212-591-4167

Nameless, (*Nameless Press; 0-9603608*), P.O. Box 538, Jonestown, TX 78641 (SAN 213-4195) Tel 512-267-1961

Narconon, (*Narconon; 0-917958*), 6425 Hollywood Blvd., Suite 206, Hollywood, CA 90028 (SAN 209-9683) Tel 213-469-8347

Nash Pub, (*Nash Publishing Co.; 0-8402*), 1290 Ave. of Americas, Suite 4150, New York, NY 10019 (SAN 202-8883) Tel 212-977-9500

Nat Assn Black, (*National Assn. of Black Reading/Language Education*), Milton Bennion Hall 142, The Univ. of Utah, Salt Lake City, UT 84112 (SAN 696-0685)

Nat Inform Ctr, (*National Information Ctr.; 0-911912*), P.O. Box 370, Somerville, NJ 08876 (SAN 203-8315)

Nat Learn Res, (*Natural Learning Resources; 0-936214*), 5151 Monroe, P.O. Box 8443, Toledo, OH 43623 (SAN 214-0640)

Nationwide Pr, (*Nationwide Press, Ltd.; 0-917188*), 2860 S. Circle Drive/S. Bldg., Suite 108, Clorado Springs, CO 80906 (SAN 208-7812) Tel 303-576-6777

Natl Alli Cardio, (*National Alliance of Cardiovascular Technologists*), 5901 Encina, Suite B-1, Santa Barbara, CA 93117 (SAN 688-6787)

Natl Assoc Businessmen, (*National Associated Businessmen, Inc.*), 1000 Connecticut Ave. Bldg., Washington, DC 20036 (SAN 224-1935) Tel 202-296-5773

Natl Capital, (*National Capital Speakers Assn.*), 1725 K St., N.W., Suite 607, Washington, DC 20006 (SAN 241-5690) Tel 202-296-8970

Natl Charities Info Bureau
See Natl Info Bur

Natl Consumer, (*National Consumer Research*), 6 E. 45th St., New York, NY 10017 (SAN 208-1377)

Natl Coun Alt, (*National Council for Alternative Work Patterns; 0-911583*), 1925 K St. NW, Suite 308, Washington, DC 20006 (SAN 264-231X)

Natl Educ Pr, (*National Educational Press*), 5604 Rhode Island Ave., Hyattsville, MD 20781 (SAN 203-7122) Tel 301-699-9300

Natl Elim Death Tax
See Tax Info Ctr

Natl Info Bur, (*National Information Bureau; 0-914259*), 419 Park Ave. S., New York, NY 10016 (SAN 260-3950) Tel 212-532-8595

Inactive/Out-of-Business

Natl Info Ctr
See Nat Inform Ctr
Natl Light Represent, *(National Assn. of Lighting Representatives),* 16 W. 56th St., New York, NY 10019 (SAN 688-8291)
Natl Minor CPA, *(National Assn. of Minority CPA Firms),* 1424 K St. NW, Box 661, Washington, DC 20044 (SAN 688-8607)
Natl Noise Control, *(National Assn. of Noise Control Oficials),* Box 2618, Ft. Walton Beach, FL 32549 (SAN 688-8747)
Natl Obesity, *(National Council of Obesity),* 650 N. Bronson Ave., Los Angeles, CA 90004 (SAN 224-4527)
Natl Optional Parent, *(National Alliance for Optional Parenthood),* 2010 Massachusetts Ave Nw, Washington, DC 20036 (SAN 225-9613)
Natl PIRG DC, *(National Public Interest Research Group),* 1129 21st St. NW, Washington, DC 20036 (SAN 273-7221)
Natl Recipro Assn, *(National Reciprocal Assn.),* 777 14th St. NW, Suite 236, Washington, DC 20005 (SAN 689-4615)
Natl Safety Mgmt, *(National Safety Management Society),* 6060 Duke St., Alexandria, VA 22304 (SAN 689-4755)
Natl Tumor Regist, *(National Tumor Registrar's Assn.),* Box 4454, Grand Central Sta., New York, NY 10163 (SAN 689-576X)
Naturalists Dir, *(Naturalists' Directory),* P.O. Box 583, South Orange, NJ 07079 (SAN 203-1590)
Nautical Bks, *(Nautical Bks.; 0-931284),* P.O. Box 331, Stoughton, WI 53589 (SAN 209-1216)
Naylor, *(Naylor Co.; 0-8111),* P.O. Box 1838, San Antonio, TX 78206 (SAN 202-9014)
NCUEA, *(National Ctr. for Urban Ethnic Affairs; 0-940798),* P.O. Box 33279, Washington, DC 20033 (SAN 219-8010)
NE Board Higher Ed, *(New England Board of Higher Education; 0-916220),* 40 Grove St., Wellesley, MA 02181 (SAN 220-9365)
NE Law Inst, *(New England Law Institute),* 89 Beach St., Boston, MA 02111 (SAN 227-1079)
Nebraska Assn, *(Nebraska Assn. for Educational Data Systems),* P.O. Box 37267, Omaha, NE 68137 (SAN 674-7787)
Nefertiti, *(Nefertiti Head Pr.; 0-918722),* Drawer J. Univ. Sta., Austin, TX 78712 (SAN 209-6749)
Negative Pr, *(Negative Press; 0-9601624),* 848 E. 28th St., Apt. C-7, Brooklyn, NY 11210 (SAN 211-5360)
Nellen Pub, *(Nellen Publishing Co. Inc.; 0-8424),* Box 18, Newton, NJ 07860 (SAN 211-2590) Tel 201-383-0114
NELP, *(National Educational Laboratory Pubs. Inc.; 0-89965),* P.O. Box 1003, Austin, TX 78767 (SAN 208-7782) Tel 512-385-7084; Orders to: 813 Airport Blvd., Austin, TX 78702 (SAN 208-7790)
Nevada Hist Soc, *(Nevada Historical Society),* Southern Nevada Office, 1555 E. Flamingo, Suite 238, Las Vegas, NV 89109 (SAN 211-2582) Tel 702-734-9716
New Age Pr NM, *(New Age Press Inc.),* 320 Artist Rd., Santa Fe, NM 87501 (SAN 215-7942) Tel 505-982-1500
New Age Pub Ctr, *(New Age Publishing Center),* 405 N. Frances, Apt. A, Chicago, IL 60606 (SAN 217-1198) Tel 608-251-4828
New Albion, *(New Albion Books),* 3002 W. Camelback Rd., No. 10, Phoenix, AZ 85017 (SAN 211-6243)
New Am Res Inst, *(New American Research Institute, Inc.),* 1300 W. Belmont Ave., Chicago, IL 60657 (SAN 225-705X)
New Benjamin, *(New Benjamin Franklin Hse., The; 0-933488),* 304 W. 58th St., 5th Flr., New York, NY 10019 (SAN 212-6168) *Imprints:* Univ Edns (University Editions).
New Community, *(New Community Projects, Inc.; 0-9603468),* 449 Cambridge St., Union Square, Allston, MA 02134 (SAN 207-2645) Tel 617-783-3060
New Day Pub Co, *(New Day Publishing Co.; 0-916853),* 457 Beckham Dr., San Jose, CA 95123 (SAN 654-4401) Tel 408-226-1383
New Division, *(New Division Pubns.; 0-918724),* 34 Chelmsford St, Chelmsford, MA 01824 (SAN 210-3168) Tel 617-251-8685
New Earth, *(New Earth Books; 0-918258),* 58 St. Marks Place, New York, NY 10003 (SAN 209-6277) Tel 212-673-1682

New Eng Pub, *(New England Pub. Co.; 0-932268),* 200 Glendale Rd., Stratford, CT 06497 (SAN 212-2499) Tel 203-375-3252
New England Marine
See URI MAS
New Hope, *(New Hope Publishing Co.; 0-915460),* Dist. by: Midway Copy Services, P.O. Box 378, Lahaska, PA 18931 (SAN 202-9103) Tel 212-794-5757
New House, *(New House Pubs.; 0-913516),* 413 Guilford Ave., Queensboro, NC 27401 (SAN 212-2936)
New Issues Pr, *(New Issues Press, Inc.; 0-913944),* 1024 Alachua St., Tallahassee, FL 32302 (SAN 203-7351) Tel 904-222-4972
New Jersey Assn, *(New Jersey Assn. for Educational Data Systems),* W. Park Ave., Oakhurst, NJ 07755 (SAN 677-9743) Tel 201-531-6600
New Renaissance, *(New Renaissance Workshop; 0-9600464),* P.O. Box 421, Ojai, CA 93023 (SAN 202-912X)
New Republic, *(New Republic Books; 0-915220),* 1220 19th St. N.W., Washington, DC 20036 (SAN 207-2653) Tel 202-331-7494
New Viewpoints, *(New Viewpoints),* Affil. of Franklin Watts, Inc., 730 Fifth Ave., New York, NY 10019 (SAN 213-7798) Tel 212-757-4050
Newark News, *(Newark News Radio Club),* P.O. Box 539, Newark, NJ 07101 (SAN 223-9329)
Newedi Pr, *(Newedi Press; 0-89342),* Bowling Green Univ., Dept. of English, Bowling Green, OH 43403 (SAN 208-4457)
Newport Pub, *(Newport Publishing Co.; 0-940008),* 3990 Westerly Place, No. 100, Newport Beach, CA 92660 (SAN 216-8448) Tel 714-673-3096
News Circle, *(News Circle),* P.O. Box 74637, Los Angeles, CA 90057 (SAN 206-510X) Tel 213-483-5111; 2007 Wilshire Blvd., Suite 900, Los Angeles, CA 90057 (SAN 206-5118)
Newsweek, *(Newsweek; 0-88225),* 444 Madison Ave., New York, NY 10022 (SAN 202-9170) Tel 212-350-2528
Nikko Enter, *(Nikko Enterprises; 0-9613221),* 1516 E. Tropicana, Las Vegas, NV 89109 (SAN 295-7329) Tel 702-796-1114
NIRH, *(National Institute of Reboundology & Health Inc.; 0-938302),* 7416 212th SW, Edmonds, WA 98020 (SAN 215-0964)
NJ Cons Foun, *(New Jersey Conservation Foundation; 0-913234),* 300 Mendham Rd., Morristown, NJ 07960 (SAN 206-9725)
Noble Craft, *(Noble Craft; 0-915733),* Subs. of Texas West Scenes, Inc., 925 N. Judge Ely Blvd., Abeline, TX 79601 (SAN 293-8901) Tel 915-676-9141
Noble Prentiss, *(Noble Prentiss Publishing Co.; 0-914892),* P.O. Box 3101, Simi Valley, CA 93063 (SAN 206-1694)
Nopoly Pr, *(Nopoly Press, Inc.; 0-930950),* Box 1930, Dept. M-10, Wilmington, DE 19899 (SAN 212-1220) Tel 302-764-2126
North Am Consumer, *(North American Consumer's Group Press),* 3747 S.E. Washington, Portland, OR 97124 (SAN 214-0683)
Northampton County, *(Northampton County Bicentennial Center),* 61 N. Third St., Easton, PA 18042 (SAN 209-2972)
Northernaire, *(Northernaire Pubns.; 0-9603380),* 717 Arlington Way, Martinez, CA 94553 (SAN 212-7806)
Northtown Bks, *(Northtown Books),* 957 "H" St., Arcata, CA 95521 (SAN 213-943X) Tel 707-822-2834
Northwest Illust, *(Northwest Illustrated; 0-86519),* 745 Fifth Ave., New York, NY 10151 (SAN 239-5371)
Northwoods Pr, *(Northwoods Press; 0-89002),* Div. of Romar, Inc., R.D. 1, Meadows of Dan, VA 24120 (SAN 208-449X) Tel 703-659-7441
Nostalgia Pr, *(Nostalgia Press, Inc.; 0-87897),* 72 Franklin Ave., Franklin Square, NY 11010 (SAN 205-3721) Tel 516-488-4748; Orders to: P.O. Box 293, Franklin Square, NY 11010 (SAN 205-373X)
Nova Pr, *(Nova Press; 0-914220),* Orders to: Phoenix Inc., 4518 Burnet Rd., Austin, TX 78756 (SAN 200-4062) Tel 512-459-0252

Nowadays Co, *(Nowadays Co.; 0-932405),* 32 W. Anapamu, Suite 400, Santa Barbara, CA 93101 (SAN 686-7197) Tel 805-962-0998
NP *Imprint of Inscape Corp*
Numismata Orient, *(Numismata Orientalia),* P.O. Box 212, Tenafly, NJ 07676 (SAN 211-674X)
Nursing Res, *(Nursing Resources; 0-913654),* 12 Lakeside Office Park, Wakefield, MA 01880 (SAN 203-5863) Tel 617-246-3130
NYC Ctr Learn, *(New York City Regional Center for Life-Long Learning; 0-914436),* City Univ. of New York, 101 W. 31st St., 7th Fl., New York, NY 10001 (SAN 206-605X) Tel 212-564-9385
O T Benfey, *(Benfey, Otto Theodor; 0-9602020),* 801 Woodbrook Dr., Greensboro, NC 27410 (SAN 212-209X) Tel 919-292-1062
Oak Cottage, *(Oak Cottage Press; 0-940840),* 2 Forest St., Brattleboro, VT 05301 (SAN 219-8045)
Oak Hill, *(Oak Hill Press; 0-915184),* 230 Payson Rd., Belmont, MA 02178 (SAN 207-1770) Tel 617-484-3145
Oak Leaf, *(Oak Leaf Press; 0-935370),* 33 Union Square W., New York, NY 10003 (SAN 213-4233)
Oakwood Pr, *(Oakwood Pr., The; 0-915418),* P.O. Box 541, McMinnville, OR 97128 (SAN 207-6837) Tel 503-835-5855
Oasis Pr CA, *(Oasis Press (Ca); 0-9603712),* P. O. Box 99041, San Diego, CA 92109 (SAN 221-7295)
Ocean Inc, *(Ocean, Inc.; 0-912043),* P.O. Box 2331, Springfield, VA 22152-0331 (SAN 264-6838) Tel 703-323-1928
Ocean Living, *(Ocean Living Institute; 0-915338),* Box 470, Kearny, NJ 07032 (SAN 207-1886)
Odakai *Imprint of Okpaku Communications*
Odd John, *(Odd John Co.; 0-9601412),* 2318 33rd St., Santa Monica, CA 90405 (SAN 211-0407) Tel 213-450-4216
Odyssey Pub Co, *(Odyssey Publishing Co.; 0-934494),* 1161-21st Ave. E., Seattle, WA 98112 (SAN 213-6929)
Off off Broadway, *(Off Off Broadway Alliance; 0-933750),* 162 W. 56th St., Room 206, New York, NY 10019 (SAN 213-134X) Tel 212-757-4473
Okpaku Communications, *(Okpaku Communications Corp.; 0-89388),* Div. of Third Pr. Review of Bks. Co., 330 Seventh Ave., New York, NY 10001 (SAN 202-5701) *Imprints:* Odakai (Odakai Books).
Old Mill, *(Old Mill Press; 0-934700),* 13 Walter Ave., Norwalk, CT 06851 (SAN 214-0705)
Oligodynamics, *(Oligodynamics Press),* P.O. Box 29102, San Antonio, TX 78229 (SAN 208-0222)
Olivant, *(Olivant Press; 0-87956),* P.O. Box 1409, Homestead, FL 33030 (SAN 205-3578)
Oliver Pr, *(Oliver Press; 0-914400),* Dist. by: Charles Scribner's Sons, Shipping & Billing Depts., Vreeland Ave., Totowa, NJ 70512 (SAN 282-6550)
Olympia, *(Olympia Press),* 220 Park Ave., S., New York, NY 10003 (SAN 204-5591) *Imprints:* Ophelia (Ophelia Books); Travellers Comp (Travellers Companion Ser.).
Olympic Pr, *(Olympic Press; 0-930784),* P.O. Box 999, Montclair, NJ 07043 (SAN 210-6175) Tel 201-678-4453
Omega Comms, *(Omega Communications; 0-88678),* 110 Hillside Ave., Springfield, NJ 07081 (SAN 277-6987)
Omega Pub Co, *(Omega Publishing Co., Inc.),* P.O. Box 323, Snohomish, WA 98290 (SAN 213-781X)
Online Invest, *(Online Investing, Inc.; 0-931853),* P.O. Box 178, Pennington, NJ 08534 (SAN 686-001X)
Open Door Pubns, *(Open Door Pubns.; 0-939310),* 850 Seventh Ave., Suite 705, New York, NY 10019 (SAN 220-1798) Tel 212-581-6470
Open Sesame, *(Open Sesame Publishing Co.; 0-933578),* 2000 Center St., Suite 1323, Berkeley, CA 94704 (SAN 212-7822) Tel 415-526-6204
Open U, *(Open Univ. Educational Media, Inc.),* 110 E. 59th St., New York, NY 10022 (SAN 209-4649) Tel 212-935-8965

Ophelia *Imprint of* **Olympia**

Orbiting Bk, *(Orbiting Book Service; 0-914326),* P.O. Box 13, New York, NY 10038 (SAN 202-8298) Tel 212-853-3071

Orenda-Unity, *(Orenda Publishing/Unity Pr.; 0-913300),* 61 Camino Alto, Suite 100, Mill Valley, CA 94941 (SAN 282-0811); Orders to: Network, Inc., P.O. Box 2246, Berkeley, CA 94702 (SAN 282-082X)

Organ Hist Soc, *(Organ Historical Society, Inc., The; 0-913499),* P.O. Box 26811, Richmond, VA 23261 (SAN 285-8282) Tel 804-264-2126

Oriental Art, *(Oriental Art Prices Current),* 17070 Collins Ave., North Miami Beach, FL 33160 (SAN 211-626X)

Original Pr, *(Original Press; 0-935812),* Div. of Throckmorton Publishing Co., 561 Milltown Rd., North Brunswick, NJ 08902 (SAN 213-9618)

Oriole Edns
See S A Russell

Orion Pr, *(Orion Pr.; 0-912971),* Box 20-184, Columbus, OH 43220 (SAN 283-3387)

ORourke, *(O'Rourke Pubns.; 0-911196),* P.O. Box 1118, Lake Alfred, FL 33850 (SAN 203-7785) Tel 813-956-1686

Orphic Pr, *(Orphic Press; 0-9606894),* Box 2072, Glenview, IL 60025 (SAN 217-4111) Tel 312-827-1715

OSV Fabric Shop, *(Old Sturbridge Village Fabric Shop at Lincoln House; 0-910940),* Rte. 20, Sturbridge, MA 01566 (SAN 203-9362) Tel 617-347-3952

Our Land-Toren, *(Our Land/Toren Development Inc.; 0-939474),* 44 Montgomery St., San Francisco, CA 94104 (SAN 216-4299)

Ourobourus, *(Ourobourus Institute/Unlimited Publishing; 0-918538),* 324 E. 35th St., Suite 6-A, New York, NY 10016 (SAN 209-9772) Tel 212-344-2222

Out Sky Pr, *(Out of the Sky Press; 0-9603292),* P.O. Box 998, Saratoga, CA 95070 (SAN 218-446X)

Output, *(Output Systems Corp.; 0-912234),* 2300 S. Ninth St., Arlington, VA 22204 (SAN 203-784X) Tel 703-521-2300

Overbeck Pr, *(Overbeck Publishing Co.),* 1216 S. University, Ann Arbor, MI 48104 (SAN 203-6894) Tel 313-663-9333

Owen & Jenkins, *(Owen-Jenkins, Inc.; 0-918144),* 1112 Richview Rd., Tallahassee, FL 32301 (SAN 209-326X) Tel 904-877-3330

Owen Pr, *(Owen Press; 0-9607988),* 212 Grand Ave., Ojai, CA 93023 (SAN 238-5511)

Owl Pr, *(Owl Press; 0-911084),* P.O. Box 709, Annapolis, MD 21404 (SAN 203-7858) Tel 301-267-6456

P A Abbott, *(Abbott, P.A., Pubns.; 0-938564),* P.O. Box 2085, Kalamazoo, MI 49003 (SAN 220-1410)

P A Janzen
See Janzen Assoc

P & P Moses Yanes, *(Poet & Printer Moses Yanes; 0-913726),* 13850 Big Basin Way, Boulder Creek, CA 95006 (SAN 240-0588)

P J Baukol
See Baukol Pub

P Odegard, *(Odegard, Peter; 0-9600524),* Rt. 1, St. Croix Cove, Hudson, WI 54016 (SAN 205-6372)

P Richmond, *(Richmond, Paul, & Co.; 0-912640),* 1100 Glendon Ave., Suite 1517, West Los Angeles, CA 90021 (SAN 213-9626)

P S Allen, *(Allen, Philip S.),* 815 Yucca St., Port Hueneme, CA 93041 (SAN 207-4168) Tel 805-486-0707

P S Brown, *(Brown, P .S.; 0-9604148),* 2306 Union St., San Francisco, CA 94123 (SAN 215-2983)

P Sawyer, *(Sawyer, Philip L.; 0-911308),* 108 South St., Auburn, NY 13021 (SAN 206-8311)

P Townsend-Beddoes, *(Townsend-Beddoes, Peggy; 0-9606478),* 365 S. 18th St., Harrisburg, PA 17104 (SAN 218-5997) Tel 717-233-1511

Paananen & Paulsen, *(Paananen & Paulsen Corp.),* P.O. Box 365, Waite-Park, MN 56387 (SAN 209-1690) Tel 612-743-2697

Pace Pub, *(Pace Publishing, Inc.; 0-940138),* 6009 Wayzata Blvd., Suite 105, Minneapolis, MN 55416 (SAN 220-3014) Tel 612-546-3111

Pachyderm Pr, *(Pachyderm Press; 0-910403),* Suite 2806, 15 Charles Plaza, Baltimore, MD 21201 (SAN 260-1133) Tel 301-547-0184

Pacific Ed Pubns, *(Pacific Educational Pubns.),* 2121 McKinley St., Honolulu, HI 96822 (SAN 204-9147)

Pacific Lang, *(Pacific Language Institute; 0-910669),* 32 W. Anapamu St., Suite 246, Santa Barbara, CA 93101 (SAN 262-1274)

Pacific Perceptions, *(Pacific Perceptions, Inc.),* 3718 Vinton Ave., Suite 5, Los Angeles, CA 90034 (SAN 206-3743)

Pacific Perceptions
See Pacific Perceptions

Pacific Transport, *(Pacific Transportation Archives; 0-934430),* 547 Pine Ave., Sunnyvale, CA 94086 (SAN 213-2281)

Pacul Pubns, *(Pacul Pubns.),* 4011 Bryant Ave. S., Minneapolis, MN 55409 (SAN 206-1724)

Paddington, *(Paddington Press, Ltd.),* 95 Madison Ave, New York, NY 10016 (SAN 209-4673) Tel 212-689-4801; Orders to: Grosset & Dunlap, 51 Madison Ave., New York, NY 10010 (SAN 201-4912)

Pageant-Poseidon, *(Pageant-Poseidon),* 155 W. 15th St., New York, NY 10011 (SAN 202-8492) Tel 212-929-5956

Pagurian, *(Pagurian Press; 0-88932; 0-919364),* Dist. by: Baker & Taylor, 1515 Broadway, New York, NY 10036 (SAN 169-5606) Tel 212-673-6600

Paideia Pr, *(Paideia Press; 0-912490),* 4997 Robindale Lane, Memphis, TN 38117 (SAN 204-9163)

Paisano, *(Paisano Press, Inc.; 0-911102),* P.O. Box 85, Balboa Island, CA 92662 (SAN 204-9171) Tel 714-673-5393

Palmetto FL, *(Palmetto Publishing Co.; 0-915096),* 4747 28th St., N., St. Petersburg, FL 33714 (SAN 207-5229)

Palmetto Pub
See Palmetto FL

Palo Duro Pr, *(Palo Duro Pr.),* 2613 Third Ave., Canyon, TX 79015 (SAN 205-3373) Tel 806-655-3974

PAM Pubs, *(PAM Pubs.; 0-932724),* 51 Carmel Ave., Salinas, CA 93901 (SAN 212-534X)

Pana Creation, *(Pana Creation; 0-915300),* P. O. Box 2133, La Mesa, CA 92041 (SAN 207-1800) Tel 714-464-3727

Panache, *(Panache),* P.O. Box 89, Princeton, NJ 08540 (SAN 206-3026)

P&A Quill, *(P & A Quill Press, Inc.),* 3022 N. Bartlett Ave., Milwaukee, WI 53211 (SAN 212-4327)

Panther Hse, *(Panther House, Ltd.; 0-87676),* Box 3552, GCPO, New York, NY 10017 (SAN 202-8646)

Pao-Chung, *(Pao-Chung Hsu; 0-9601328),* P.O. Box 567, Carrollton, TX 75006 (SAN 209-5920) Tel 214-436-6262

Papenguth, *(Papenguth, Goldeen; 0-9600540),* 2201 Carson St., Lafayette, IN 47904 (SAN 204-9236)

Paraclete Bks, *(Paraclete Books; 0-936100),* GPO 2058, New York, NY 10001 (SAN 214-4352) Tel 212-849-5849

Paradise Pub Co, *(Paradise Publishing Co.; 0-916519),* c/o Entrepreneurs American Enterprises, 23760 Fenkell, Suite 301A, P.O. Box 5127, Dearborn, MI 48128-0127 (SAN 295-4753) Tel 313-537-1951

Paradox, *(Paradox Pr.; 0-930872),* 1570 Pacheco St., Santa Fe, NM 87501 (SAN 215-3300)

Paradox Pub Co, *(Paradox Publishing Co.; 0-89422),* 2476 Buttonwood Court, Florissant, MO 63031 (SAN 209-5416) Tel 314-838-0241

Parameter Pr, *(Parameter Press; 0-88203),* 705 Main St., Wakefield, MA 01880 (SAN 202-8662) Tel 617-245-9290

Paranoid Pr, *(Paranoid Press),* P.O. Box 2421, San Francisco, CA 94126 (SAN 204-9244)

Paris Pubns, *(Paris Pubns., Inc.; 0-912248),* 2 Haven Ave., Port Washington, NY 11050 (SAN 202-8700) Tel 516-883-4650

Park Ave Bks, *(Park Avenue Books, Inc.; 0-942418),* GPO Box 1886, New York, NY 10116 (SAN 238-1850) Tel 212-689-0269

Parrot Mtn, *(Parrot Mountain, Inc.),* P.O. Box 246, Ranchita, CA 92066 (SAN 215-2215) Tel 714-782-3335

Parsindo Pubs, *(Parsindo Pubs., Inc.; 0-913084),* P.O. Box 342, St. Louis, MO 63166 (SAN 204-9287)

Parsley Pr, *(Parsley Press; 0-9608222),* 5 Granger Rd., Westboro, MA 01581 (SAN 240-4214) Tel 617-366-2511

Parthenon Bks, *(Parthenon Books),* 9808 Amanita Dr., Tujunga, CA 91042 (SAN 209-3111) Tel 213-249-4017

Parthenon Pr, *(Parthenon Press; 0-942276),* 51 E. 42nd St., Suite 517, New York, NY 10017 (SAN 239-5835) Tel 212-361-7400

Partisan Pr, *(Partisan Pr., Inc.; 0-935150),* P.O. Box 31387, Seattle, WA 98103 (SAN 215-6946)

Partridge, *(Partridge Pubns. of California; 0-913306),* 1833 Franklin Canyon Dr., Beverly Hills, CA 90210 (SAN 204-9295) Tel 213-276-9096

Partridge Pr
See Partridge

Passage Pub, *(Passage Publishing; 0-933240),* 708 Warren N., Seattle, WA 98109 (SAN 212-4335)

Pattecky Music, *(Pattecky Music Pubs.; 0-9602178),* Box T, College Park, MD 20740 (SAN 213-7844)

Pavilion Pub, *(Pavilion Publishing Co.),* Box 668, Riverhead, NY 11901 (SAN 202-8743)

PC Abstracts, *(PC Abstracts),* P.O. Box 1058, Jenks, OK 74037 (SAN 677-8984) Tel 918-299-5323

Peace & Gladness, *(Peace & Gladness Press; 0-940460),* P.O. Box 11478, San Francisco, CA 94101 (SAN 219-8088) Tel 415-586-1782

Peace on Earth, *(Peace on Earth Press; 0-942992),* P.O. Box 3947, Stanford, CA 94305 (SAN 240-4222); P.O. Box 128, Bedford, MA 01730 (SAN 240-4230)

Peace Pr
See Citrus Hse

Peachtree Park, *(Peachtree Park Pr.; 0-933690),* 67 Peachtree Park Dr., Atlanta, GA 30309 (SAN 213-1374) Tel 404-351-4523

Pear Tree, *(Pear Tree Pubns.; 0-918578),* P.O. Box 517, Ashland, OR 97520 (SAN 209-9802) Tel 503-482-3717

Pedicenter Pr, *(Pedicenter Press),* P.O. Box 3494, Jackson, TN 38301 (SAN 207-6209)

Peebles Pr, *(Peebles Pr., International, Inc.; 0-85690),* 1865 Broadway, New York, NY 10023 (SAN 207-0529)

Peerless Pub CO, *(Peerless Publishing Co.),* 1989 Broadway, Denver, CO 80202 (SAN 212-0437)

Pegasus Pr CA, *(Pegasus Press),* 735 Dolores, Stanford, CA 94305 (SAN 215-2606); Dist. by: Aviation Book Co., 1640 Victory Blvd., Glendale, CA 91201 (SAN 212-0259) Tel 213-240-1771

Pegasus Pr WA, *(Pegasus Press; 0-943268),* P.O. Box 1350, Vashon Island, WA 98070 (SAN 130-4283) *Imprints:* Dancing Fox Pr (Dancing Fox Press).

Pehrson Pub Inc, *(Pehrson Publisher Inc; 0-931467),* 20 Clinton St., New York, NY 10002 (SAN 683-1524)

Peloquin Pubns, *(Peloquin Pubns.; 0-936448),* P.O. Box 121, Richland, WA 99352 (SAN 214-0845)

Peloria Pubns, *(Peloria Publishing Co.; 0-913465),* 100 N. Blount St., Raleigh, NC 27604 (SAN 285-1822) Tel 919-828-7576

Pemberley Pr, *(Pemberley Pr.; 0-9607830),* 180 W. 58th St., New York, NY 10019 (SAN 238-1052) Tel 212-757-9631

Pembroke Pr, *(Pembroke Press; 0-911159),* c/o Braemar Books-Pembroke Press, 127 E. 59th St., No. 201, New York, NY 10022 (SAN 268-4373) Tel 212-421-1950

Pencader Pubs, *(Pencader Pubs.; 0-916712),* P.O. Box 299, Newark, DE 19711 (SAN 207-9844)

Penelope Pr, *(Penelope Press; 0-9607018),* P.O. Box 31882, Seattle, WA 98103 (SAN 239-4723)

Penna Crime, *(Pennsylvania Crime Commission),* 259 Radnor-Chester Rd. P.O. Box 45, St. Davids, PA 19087 (SAN 226-7101)

Penny, *(Penny Press),* P.O. Box 534, Camino, CA 95709 (SAN 204-9422)

Pennyfarthing, *(Pennyfarthing Press; 0-930800),* 2000 Center St., No. 1226, Berkeley, CA 94704 (SAN 211-920X) Tel 415-845-1990

Pentelic Pr, *(Pentelic Press; 0-913110),* 1032 Cambridge Crescent, Norfolk, VA 23508 (SAN 204-9414)

Peoples Pr, *(People's Press; 0-914750),* 2680 21st St., San Francisco, CA 94110 (SAN 204-9406) Tel 415-282-0856

Peradam Pub Hse, *(Peradam Pub. Hse.; 0-930434),* P.O. Box 992, Port Oxford, OR 97465 (SAN 274-5089)

Perception, *(Perception Press; 0-930176),* P.O. Box 265, Port Bolivar, TX 77650 (SAN 209-4738) Tel 713-684-3880

Percom Data, *(Percom Data Corp.),* 2703 National Place, Garland, TX 75041-2346 (SAN 277-514X) Tel 214-840-3032

Perennial Pr, *(Perennial Press, Inc.),* Dist. by: McAvoy Publications International, Inc., 650 Palisades Ave., Box, 1271, Englewood Cliffs, NJ 07632 (SAN 207-3137)

Perfect Horizons Pubns, *(Perfect Horizons Pubns.; 0-9606742),* P.O. Box 7000-300, Palos Verdes Peninsula, CA 90274 (SAN 219-6239) Tel 213-541-3487

Performance List, *(Performance Listing; 0-9613813),* 613 Notabene Dr., Alexandria, VA 22305 (SAN 656-0539) Tel 703-548-4536

Perkins Pubns, *(Perkins Pubns.; 0-934974),* 1442 A Walnut St., Suite 165, Berkeley, CA 94709 (SAN 213-5442) Tel 415-644-2190

Permo Pr, *(Permo Press),* Box 16249, Seattle, WA 98116 (SAN 213-3482) Tel 206-937-5114

Perriday Inc, *(Perriday, Inc.; 0-9615435),* P.O. Box 41666, Chicago, IL 60641 (SAN 695-9377) Tel 312-777-5236

Persephone, *(Persephone Pr.; 0-930436),* P.O. Box 7222, Watertown, MA 02172 (SAN 211-9218) Tel 617-924-0336

Persimmon, *(Persimmon Press; 0-9605424),* P.O. Box 30721, 3128 Calle Noguera, Santa Barbara, CA 93105 (SAN 216-0528)

Personnel Dev, *(Personnel Development Associates; 0-911128),* P.O. Box 3005 Roosevelt Field Sta., Garden City, NY 11530 (SAN 206-6629) Tel 516-746-7868

Perspective, *(Perspective Pubns., Inc.; 0-911130),* 509 Madison Ave., New York, NY 10022 (SAN 201-8799) Tel 212-752-2212

Peterson Comp, *(Peterson Computing Services; 0-926181),* 6 S. Main St., Pittsford, NY 14534 (SAN 656-2256) Tel 716-385-2997

Petterle Pubns, *(Petterle Publications; 0-9613574),* 3 Greenside Way, San Rafael, CA 94901 (SAN 670-154X) Tel 415-456-2291

Phantasy Pr, *(Phantasy Press),* 358 State St., Brooklyn, NY 11217 (SAN 204-9473)

Pharaoh Prods, *(Pharaoh Productions; 0-937598),* P.O. Box 1102, Spring Valley, CA 92077 (SAN 215-2657)

Pharr, *(Pharr, Emory C.),* 5704 8th Rd., North Arlington, VA 22205 (SAN 211-0482) Tel 703-243-6989

Phila Bk Co, *(Philadelphia Bk. Co., Inc.; 0-916074),* 1 Brown St., Philadelphia, PA 19123 (SAN 206-5126)

Phileas Deigh, *(Phileas Deigh Corp.; 0-9604200),* 600 Old Country Rd., Suite 321, Garden City, NY 11530 (SAN 214-2171)

Philo Pr, *(Philo Press; 0-941650),* Box 277, Youngstown, NY 14174 (SAN 239-2801) Tel 716-285-2355

Philos Pr, *(Philosophy Press, The; 0-940284),* P.O. Box 1600, Uniontown, PA 15401 (SAN 218-4311) Tel 412-329-8727

Philosophic Res, *(Philosophic Resources; 0-915422),* P.O. Box 4722, Poughkeepsie, NY 12603 (SAN 209-3588) Tel 914-471-0568

Phinmarc Bks, *(Phinmarc Books),* P.O. Box 1075, Crockett, TX 75835 (SAN 274-600X) Tel 713-544-5137

PHIP Inc, *(PHIP, Inc.; 0-931994),* P.O. Box 707, Fort Lee, NJ 07024 (SAN 211-6278)

Phoenix Laguna, *(Phoenix),* P.O. Box 2225, Laguna Hills, CA 92653 (SAN 215-9031)

Phoenix Pubns, *(Phoenix Publications, Inc.; 0-933924),* 1133 Marian Way, Sacramento, CA 95818 (SAN 212-5439) Tel 916-446-1702; 712 Montgomery St., San Francisco, CA 94111 (SAN 212-5447) Tel 415-421-0960; P.O. Box 6262, Lake Tahoe, CA 95730 (SAN 212-5455) Tel 916-583-5614

PhoeniXongs, *(PhoeniXongs; 0-918360),* P.O. Box 608036, Chicago, IL 60626 (SAN 209-1453) Tel 312-274-0054

Photos Compendium, *(Photographer's Compendium; 0-89613),* P.O. Box 730, Sunnymead, CA 92388 (SAN 211-0431) Tel 714-676-5034

Pikes Peak, *(Pikes Peak Poets, Inc.),* P.O. Box 6411, Colorado Springs, CO 80934 (SAN 215-904X)

Pikeville Coll, *(Pikeville College Press; 0-933302),* Pikeville, KY 41501-1194 (SAN 212-1298) Tel 606-432-9227

Pilatus Pr, *(Pilatus Press; 0-9614915),* P.O. Box 32148, Minneapolis, MN 55432 (SAN 693-417X)

Pilgrim PA, *(Pilgrim Press),* 1505 Race St., Philadelphia, PA 19102 (SAN 237-7969)

Pilgrim Pub, *(Pilgrim Publishing Co.; 0-916034),* 3109 14th Ave., P.O. Box 2181, Chattanooga, TN 37409-0181 (SAN 207-4893) Tel 615-698-5545

Pillar Bks, *(Pillar Books; 0-89129),* c/o Harcourt Brace Jovanovich, Inc., 757 Third Ave., New York, NY 10017 (SAN 200-2299) Tel 212-754-3100

Pilot Pr, *(Pilot Press Books; 0-88324),* P.O. Box 2662, Grand Rapids, MI 49501 (SAN 202-0025) Tel 616-532-6471

Pilot Rev, *(Pilot Review Service),* 548 Pintura Dr., Santa Barbara, CA 93111 (SAN 206-3050) Tel 805-967-3264

Pilot Rock, *(Pilot Rock, Inc.; 0-89374),* 934 H St., P.O. Box ZZ, Arcata, CA 95521 (SAN 208-9637) Tel 707-822-4851

Pin Oak Pub Co, *(Pin Oak Publishing Co.; 0-910157),* P.O. Box 10471 G. S., Springfield, MO 65804 (SAN 241-242X) Tel 417-883-9957

Pine St Pr, *(Pine Street Press; 0-915224),* 872 Pine St., Winnetka, IL 60093 (SAN 212-1301)

Pinecliff
   See HM Prof Med Div

Piney Branch, *(Piney Branch Press; 0-902054),* 5000 Piney Branch Rd., Fairfax, VA 22030 (SAN 220-2689)

Pinnacle Bks, *(Pinnacle Bks.; 0-523),* Subs. of First Tarent, Inc., 1430 Broadway, New York, NY 10018 (SAN 662-3395) Tel 212-719-5900

Pioneer Ga, *(Pioneer Press, Inc.; 0-915006),* 2100 Parklane Dr., Atlanta, GA 30345 (SAN 238-8154) Tel 404-939-3512

Pisces Eye, *(Pisces' Eye, The; 0-9604470),* P.O. Box 12642, Seattle, WA 98111 (SAN 219-9815)

Pisces Print, *(Pisces Printer, The; 0-9604206),* Box 4625, Irvine, CA 92716 (SAN 214-4409)

Pisces Pub, *(Pisces Publishing Corp., Inc.; 0-914858),* P.O. Box 805, Belden Sta., Norwalk, CT 06852 (SAN 208-2500)

Pitkin, *(Pitkin Pr.; 0-9606332),* 353 W. 56th St., Apt.4-I, New York, NY 10019 (SAN 222-9811) Tel 212-582-5125; Dist. by: Caroline House, 920 W. Industrial Dr., Aurora, IL 60506 (SAN 211-2280) Tel 312-897-2050

Pitman Pub MA, *(Pitman Publishing, Inc.; 0-273),* Subs. of Pitman plc, 1020 Plain St., Marshfield, MA 02050 (SAN 220-2697) Tel 617-837-1331

Pitt Pr, *(Pitt Press; 0-931996),* Box 105, Yellow Springs, OH 45387 (SAN 211-7584)

Pixie Pr, *(Pixie Press; 0-914978),* 8515 Fieldway Dr., Randallstown, MD 21133 (SAN 207-0901)

Pizzuto Ltd Pub, *(Pizzuto, Ltd., Pubs.; 0-910441),* 6979 Ferncroft Ave., San Gabriel, CA 91775 (SAN 241-4325) Tel 818-285-5131

Plain Talk, *(Plain Talk Pr.),* Box 16023, Irvine, CA 92714 (SAN 219-9464)

Planet Pr, *(Planet Press),* 1500 E. Walnut St., Columbia, MO 65201 (SAN 208-4341) Tel 314-443-1144

Planetary Pr, *(Planetary Pr.; 0-938330),* P.O. Box 4641, Baltimore, MD 21212 (SAN 216-0536)

Plantagenet Pr, *(Plantagenet Press; 0-917462),* Box 271, Dobbs Ferry, NY 10522 (SAN 208-4236)

Playmore & Prestige, *(Playmore & Prestige Pubs.),* 200 Fifth Ave, New York, NY 10159 (SAN 219-340X) Tel 212-924-7447

PMS King, *(PMS/King Publishing Co.; 0-918504),* P.O. Box 692, Jackson, CA 95642 (SAN 209-9861) Tel 209-223-3805

Pocketbook Pr, *(Pocketbook Press; 0-930087),* 71 Mercer St., New York, NY 10012 (SAN 670-1620) Tel 212-925-9497

Poet Gal Pr, *(Poet Gallery Pr.; 0-913054),* P.O. Box 1206, New York, NY 10021 (SAN 204-9015)

Poetry, *(Poetry; 0-9607750),* P.O. Box 1117, New York, NY 10028 (SAN 239-5886)

Polacsek, *(Polacsel, John F.),* 321 Ninth St., Elyria, OH 44035 (SAN 240-0626)

Polaris Pubns, *(Polaris Pubns.; 0-9607342),* 4273 Polaris Pkwy., Janesville, WI 53545 (SAN 239-5894)

Polaski Co, *(Polaski Co., Inc.; 0-914288),* P.O. Box 7466, Philadelphia, PA 19101 (SAN 205-1478) Tel 215-665-1990

Polis Pr, *(Polis Press, Inc.; 0-932756),* 150 Claremont Ave., No. 1E, New York, NY 10027 (SAN 212-5471)

Polyanthos, *(Polyanthos, Inc.),* Drawer 51359, New Orleans, LA 70151 (SAN 205-180X) Tel 504-566-7406 Orders to: P.O. Box 20180 Birmingham, AL 35216 (SAN 688-4032)

Pomegranate, *(Pomegranate Pr.; 0-915192),* P.O. Box 181, Cambridge, MA 02140 (SAN 207-883X)

Pomerica Pr, *(Pomerica Press, Ltd.; 0-918732),* 386 Pararso, New York, NY 10016 (SAN 211-0504) Tel 212-685-0808; Dist. by: Franklin Watts Inc., 730 Fifth Ave., New York, NY 10019 (SAN 200-223X) Tel 212-757-4050

Pomona Bks, *(Pomona Books; 0-915839),* Div. of Athena Pubns, Ltd., 505 Court St., Brooklyn, NY 11231 (SAN 294-085X) Tel 212-237-0277

Popejoy, *(Popejoy, Charles L. "Jack"),* 620 Seatter St., Juneau, AK 99801 (SAN 211-7592) Tel 907-586-1203

Porch Pubns, *(Porch Pubns.; 0-932968),* 5310 E. Taylor, Phoenix, AZ 85008 (SAN 282-1753)

Porthole Pr, *(Porthole Press),* P. O. Box 417, Belmont, MA 02178 (SAN 208-1768) Tel 617-484-0988

Portola Inst, *(Portola Institute; 0-914774),* 485 Hamilton Ave., Palo Alto, CA 94301 (SAN 206-6130) Tel 415-323-7769

Postgrad Intl, *(Postgraduate International, Inc.; 0-918924),* Provincial Executive Bldg., Suite 145, 2201 Route 38, Cherry Hill, NJ 08002 (SAN 210-3664) Tel 609-482-0410

Postscript, *(Postscript Productions; 0-9604850),* P.O. Box 307, Suisun City, CA 94585 (SAN 215-7004)

Potomac Assoc, *(Potomac Associates; 0-913998),* 1707 "L" St., N.W., Washington, DC 20036 (SAN 202-0165) Tel 202-883-1640; Dist. by: Basic Books, Inc., 10 E. 53rd St., New York, NY 10022 (SAN 201-4521)

Power Mad, *(Power Mad Press; 0-935444),* 156 W. 27th St., No. 5W, New York, NY 10001 (SAN 213-4292)

Power Pub Inc, *(Power Publishers, Inc.; 0-9600086),* 60 Vose Ave., South Orange, NJ 07079 (SAN 203-1965)

Pr Circumstances, *(Press of Circumstances; 0-942422),* Box 2357, Central Valley, CA 96019 (SAN 219-8126) Tel 916-246-1092

Pr of Case WR, *(Press of Case Western Reserve Univ.; 0-8295),* Frank Adgate Quail Bldg., Cleveland, OH 44106 (SAN 202-0203) Tel 216-368-3770

Pragma Applications, *(Pragma Applications; 0-9608426),* P.O. Box 1497, Broken Arrow, OK 74012 (SAN 240-7493) Tel 918-258-4168

Pragmatix Mgmt, *(Pragmatix Management Resources),* 408 SW Second, No. 425, Portland, OR 97204 (SAN 217-2623)

Prairie Bk, *(Prairie Book Co.; 0-915518),* P.O. Box 1244, Plainview, TX 79072 (SAN 206-8575)

Prairie Poet, *(Prairie Poet Books; 0-913996; 0-915284),* P.O. Box 35, Charleston, IL 61920 (SAN 205-6399)

Pranayama Pubns, *(Pranayama Pubns.),* 1836 Rock Court, Cleveland, OH 44118 (SAN 208-1857)

Pre-Mer, *(Pre-Mer Publishing Co.; 0-918458),* 175 Fifth Ave., New York, NY 10010 (SAN 202-0238)

Prensa Pubns, *(Prensa Pubns., Inc.; 0-935828),* 900 S. Quince St., B-909, Denver, CO 80231 (SAN 213-8689)

Preserv Pr CA, *(Preservation Press; 0-9611016),* 109 Miramonte Rd., Walnut Creek, CA 94596 (SAN 277-7002)

Presse World, *(Presse World International Inc.; 0-938508),* 3595 St. Gaudens Rd., Miami, FL 33133 (SAN 220-2719)

Pretty Good Pubns, (Pretty Good Pubns.; 0-914063), Div. of MinneSNOWta Co., 230 Nicollet Mall, Minneapolis, MN 55440 (SAN 287-5055)

Pretzel Pr, (Pretzel Press, The; 0-936980), 1220 N. Gayoso St., New Orleans, LA 70119 (SAN 214-4441)

Prince Comm, (Prince Communications, Inc.; 0-914302), 99 Madison Ave., New York, NY 10016 (SAN 201-887X) Tel 212-683-7840

Prince Pubs, (Prince Pubs.; 0-915618), 349 E. Northfield Rd., Livingston, NJ 07039 (SAN 207-3323) Tel 201-994-1523

Prince Scientific, (Prince Scientific Press; 0-933340), P.O. Box 2355, Univ. of GA Sta., Athens, GA 30602 (SAN 212-548X)

Prince W Sound, (Prince William Sound Bks.; 0-9613146), P.O. Box 1313, Valdez, AK 99686 (SAN 294-9628)

Printers Ink, (Printers In Assoc.), P.O. Box 8872, St. Louis, MO 63102 (SAN 207-1045)

Printery, (Printery), 349 E. Bodley, Kirkwood, MO 63122 (SAN 207-8848) Tel 314-822-4142

Products Corp, (Products Corp., Unlimited; 0-914518), 205 Farnsworth Rd., Waterville, OH 43566 (SAN 201-8896) Tel 419-878-7621

Prof Assn Secty, (Professional Assn. of Secretarial Services), 2200 E. 104th Ave., 103, Northglenn, CO 80233 (SAN 689-9536)

Prof Busn Serv, (Professional Business Services, Co.; 0-935154), 5 Grandview Ave., Pittsburgh, PA 15211 (SAN 213-3520) Tel 412-381-8010

Prof Impressions, (Professional Impressions, Inc.; 0-934098), 203A-180 Allen Rd., Atlanta, GA 30328 (SAN 217-1252)

Prof Pubns FL, (Professional Pubns., Inc.; 0-918262), P.O. Box 12848, Univ. Sta., Gainesville, FL 32604 (SAN 210-3230) Tel 904-375-0772

Profile Pr, (Profile Press), 245 Seventh Ave., New York, NY 10001 (SAN 214-1272)

Progress Pr WA, (Progress Press; 0-935792), P.O. Box 5019, Seattle, WA 98105 (SAN 214-1280)

Progress Pubs, (Progress Pubs.), Dist. by: Four Continent Book Corp., 156 Fifth Ave., New York, NY 10010 (SAN 226-6962)

Proj Pub & Des, (Project Publishing & Design; 0-915082), 1119 Colorado Ave., Suite 104, Santa Monica, CA 90404 (SAN 207-1150) Tel 213-393-9631

Promontory Pr UT, (Promontory Press; 0-935242), 2640 Washington Blvd., Suite 301, Ogden, UT 84401 (SAN 213-3563) Tel 801-392-7655

Prospect, (Prospect Books; 0-913710), P.O. Box 57, Prospect, NY 13435 (SAN 205-4000) Tel 315-896-2249

Prosperity Pr, (Prosperity Pr.; 0-935686), Drawer 210, Queens Village, NY 11429 (SAN 214-1299)

Providence AL, (Providence Press, The; 0-9604378), P.O. Box 253, Florence, AL 35631 (SAN 216-289X)

Provident, (Provident Press, The; 0-9603298), P.O. Box 1112, Covina, CA 91722 (SAN 213-6767) Tel 213-339-9407

Provision, (Provision House; 0-935446), P.O. Box 5487, Austin, TX 78763 (SAN 213-5485) Tel 512-452-1417

Psychenutrition, (Psychenutrition, Inc.; 0-939466), P.O. Box 3184, Manhattan Beach, CA 90266 (SAN 216-440X) Tel 213-545-7012

Psychiatry & Behavioral, (Psychiatry & Behavioral Science Associates), P.O. Box 197, Haverford, PA 19041 (SAN 209-2328)

Psychic Forum, (Psychic Forum, The; 0-941762), P.O. Box 2464, Modesto, CA 95351 (SAN 239-2852)

Psyon Pubns, (Psyon Pubns.), P.O. Box 2403, San Anselmo, CA 94960 (SAN 241-578X)

PT Marketing, (P. T. Marketing; 0-9605106), 13836 Bora Bora Way, Marina del Rey, CA 90291 (SAN 220-0805)

Pub Unlimited, (Pubs Unlimited; 0-942232), 6155 Westerville Rd. Box 239, Westerville, OH 43081 (SAN 239-8648)

Pub Wks Hist, (Public Works Historical Society), 1776 Massachusetts Ave. NW, Washington, DC 20036 (SAN 237-823X)

Public Works, (Public Works, Inc., The; 0-918556), Rfd 1, P.O. Box 896, Putney, VT 05346 (SAN 206-8524) Tel 802-387-6682

Pubns Living, (Pubns. for Living; 0-912128), 888 California Trail, St. Charles, MO 63303 (SAN 205-1044) Tel 314-928-7234

Pubs Agency, (Publishers Agency, Inc.; 0-87781), Subs. of Pubco Corp., McLean, VA, 1411 Ford Rd., Bensalem, PA 19020 (SAN 209-0953) Tel 215-638-7000

Pubs Print Hse, (Publisher's Printing House), 117 E. Main St., Berne, IN 46711 (SAN 206-6793)

Pundarika, (Pundarika Pubns.), P.O. Box 444, Mountain Home, NC 28758 (SAN 215-9082)

Purdy Prods Inc, (Purdy, David W., Productions, Inc.; 0-9613225), 2125 Jackson Bluff Rd., Cond. S-201, Tallahassee, FL 32304 (SAN 295-1223) Tel 904-575-3233

Purple Prose Pr, (Purple Prose Pr., The; 0-931801), 400 Napoleon Rd., Bowling Green, OH 43402 (SAN 684-779X) Tel 419-354-2051

PW Pubns, (PW Pubns.), 37 Ramparts Ct., P.O. Box 35311, Colorado Springs, CO 80936 (SAN 239-5959)

Pyle, (Pyle, Donna; 0-9606944), 2858 Leeward Ave., No. 203, Los Angeles, CA 90005 (SAN 239-4782)

Pylon, (Pylon Pr., Inc.; 0-918524), 108-19 67th Rd., Forest Hills, NY 11375 (SAN 209-9888)

Pynyon, (Pynyon Press, The; 0-930544), 820 Piedmont Ave., N.E. Apt. 2, Atlanta, GA 30308 (SAN 211-3732) Tel 404-875-5412

Quail Pub, (Quail Street Publishing Co., Inc.; 0-89307), 1200 Quail St., Suite 110, Newport Beach, CA 92666 (SAN 209-2271)

Quantum Pubs, (Quantum Pubs.; 0-934644), 94 Rugby Rd., Brooklyn, NY 11226 (SAN 202-2777) Tel 212-856-3116

Quatro-L Pr, (Quatro-L Press; 0-931677), P.O. Box 970696, Miami, FL 33197 (SAN 683-7654)

Queen City Pubs, (Queen City Pubs.; 0-9600880), 420 Canberra, Box 95, Knoxville, TN 37919 (SAN 208-0869)

Quill Pubns, (Quill Pubns.; 0-916608), 1260 Coast Village Circle, Santa Barbara, CA 93108 (SAN 208-3442) Tel 805-969-2542

R A Traina, (Traina, Robert A.; 0-9601396), 505 Bellvue Ave., Wilmore, KY 40390 (SAN 207-2785) Tel 606-858-3405

R D Pace, (Pace, R. D., Co.), P.O. Box 174, Huntington Beach, CA 92648 (SAN 210-9506) Tel 714-536-8558

R E Martin, (Martin, R. E., Pub.), P.O. Box 165, Ryder Sta., Brooklyn, NY 11234 (SAN 204-658X)

R E Stauffer, (Stauffer, Richard E.; 0-9606604), P.O. Box 54, Old Zionsville, PA 18068 (SAN 212-6966) Tel 215-398-3015

R Feathers, (Feathers, Richard, Jr.; 0-9600730), 211-24th St, Cocoa Beach, FL 32931 (SAN 202-9847)

R Fox, (Fox, Rachel, Publisher; 0-943582), P.O. Box 89, Brookline, MA 02146 (SAN 240-6527) Tel 617-734-9552

R H Godfrey, (Godfrey, Robert H.), P.O. Box 873, Garden Grove, CA 92642 (SAN 207-5830)

R H Sang & Son, (Sang, R. H., & Son Pubs. Inc.; 0-932844), 345 Royal Poinciana Plaza, Palm Beach, FL 33480 (SAN 212-968X)

R Haupt, (Haupt, Rudy, & Co., Inc.; 0-935274), 231 Hay Ave., Johnstown, PA 15902 (SAN 213-3164) Tel 814-536-7536

R L Thomas, (Thomas, Ralph L.), 5023 Frew Ave., Pittsburgh, PA 15213 (SAN 207-3315) Tel 412-683-4420

R Milford, (Milford, Richard; 0-936292), 22 Gerdes Ave., Verona, NJ 07044 (SAN 214-056X)

R Mitchell, (Mitchell, Ralph; 0-9604106), P.O. Box 0971, Kenosha, WI 53141 (SAN 214-4190) Tel 414-657-7642

R Moore & B Watson, (Moore, R. Aloysia, & Bernice Bozeman Watson), Box 459, Duarte, CA 91010 (SAN 209-5866)

R Pagliotti, (Pagliotti, Rick; 0-9602694), 342 Pebble Hill Place, Santa Barbara, CA 93111 (SAN 212-9582) Tel 805-967-4630

R T Matthews, (Matthews, Robert T.; 0-9601150), 2400 Pfefferkorn Rd., West Friendship, MD 21794 (SAN 210-2358)

R W Baron, (Baron, Richard W., Publishing Co.; 0-87777), Orders to: E. P. Dutton & Co., Inc., 210 Park Ave., S., New York, NY 10003 (SAN 201-0070)

RA Corp, (RA Corp.; 0-934434), P.O. Box 483, Stanhope, NJ 07874 (SAN 213-3601) Tel 201-347-2715

Ragnar Pr, (Ragnar Press, Inc.; 0-912735), P.O. Box 92, West Carrollton, OH 45449 (SAN 283-216X) Tel 513-859-8661

Rahamah Pubns, (Rahamah Pubns.; 0-9603634), P.O. Box 135, Lowell, MA 01853 (SAN 216-292X)

Railsearch, (Railsearch Publishing, Inc.; 0-937060), P.O. Box 84, Chalfont, PA 18914 (SAN 214-4549)

Rainbow Bridge, (Rainbow Bridge; 0-914198), 3548 22nd St., San Francisco, CA 94140 (SAN 202-9839) Tel 212-734-3178

Rainbow Pr, (Rainbow Press), 425 Riverside Dr., New York, NY 10025 (SAN 207-2807) Tel 212-663-2398

Rainbow Pr CA, (Rainbow Press, The), 5901 Warner Ave., Huntington Beach, CA 92649 (SAN 217-1260)

Rainbow Spirit, (Rainbow Spirit Pr.; 0-9611054), Box 421528, Rm.425, San Francisco, CA 94142-1528 (SAN 283-3077)

Rainbows End, (Rainbow's End Co.; 0-9608780), P.O. Box 173, Baden, PA 15005 (SAN 238-3489)

Raindance, (Raindance Pr.; 0-9605952), 1118-15th Ave. E., Seattle, WA 98112 (SAN 216-6437); Dist. by: University Bkstore, 4326 University Way, N.E., Seattle, WA 98105 (SAN 216-9754)

Rainville Rose, (Rainville Rose Pubns.; 0-938066), 2505 E. Thousand Oaks Blvd., Suite 266, Thousand Oaks, CA 91360 (SAN 216-2938)

Raja Pr CA, (Raja Press; 0-9605926), 5534 Fremont St., Oakland, CA 94608 (SAN 217-1287)

Ralling Hall, (Ralling Hall; 0-9602518), 1200 Washington St., San Francisco, CA 94108 (SAN 218-4591)

RaMar, (RaMar Press; 0-935798), Seven Lakes Box 548, West End, NC 27376 (SAN 213-7879) Tel 919-673-0571

Rampart Hse, (Rampart House, Ltd.; 0-89773), 1900 Bank of America Tower, One City Dr., West Orange, CA 92668 (SAN 212-1344)

Rampart Pub, (Rampart Publishing; 0-9606446), 26 Cape Cod, Irvine, CA 92714 (SAN 218-5830) Tel 714-552-8418

Rams Head, (Rams Head, Inc.; 0-915014), 353 Sacramento St., San Francisco, CA 94111 (SAN 206-5177) Tel 415-986-3294

Randen, (Randen Publishing Co.; 0-918330), P.O. Box 3157, Culver City, CA 90230 (SAN 209-5084) Tel 213-464-0876

Randolph-Harris, (Randolph-Harris, Inc.; 0-931666), 1518 6th St., Berkeley, CA 94710 (SAN 212-0453) Tel 415-524-9710

Rapier Pr, (Rapier Press, The; 0-939066), P.O. Box 44911, Tacoma, WA 98444 (SAN 218-5024)

Rare Repr, (Rare Reprints, Inc.; 0-89592), 610 NE 124th St., Miami, FL 33161 (SAN 211-2027)

Raspberry, (Raspberry Hill), P.O. Box 193, Oshtemo, MI 49077 (SAN 207-1533)

Rating Pubns, (Rating Pubns., Inc.; 0-914472), P.O. Box 342, Murray Hill Sta., New York, NY 10016 (SAN 202-9804)

Raven Print, (Raven Printing Co., Inc.; 0-89023), 317 S. Beechtree, Grand Haven, MI 49417 (SAN 206-6173) Tel 616-525-8005

Raven Pubs AKA, (Raven Pubs. AKA, Inc.), 425 Stocking, N.W., Grand Rapids, MI 49504 (SAN 215-3378) Tel 616-459-3377

RD Comm, (R D Communications; 0-914138), P.O. Box 683, Ridgefield, CT 06877 (SAN 202-9790) Tel 203-438-3335

Read-Moore Pubns, (Read-Moore Pubns.), 340 Ventura St., No. 17, Palo Alto, CA 94306 (SAN 209-1208)

Readers Pr CA, (Reader's Press; 0-930166), P.O. Box 3136, Newport Beach, CA 92663 (SAN 210-6574)

Rearick, (Rearick, Ron & Marg, Pubs.; 0-9609206), 14601 NE 50th Pl., E-Z, Bellevue, WA 98006 (SAN 241-4430)

Recipe Pr, (Recipe Press; 0-939796), 2307 W. 28th Ave., Eugene, OR 97405 (SAN 216-9290) Tel 503-687-0294

Recorded Sound, *(Recorded Sound Research; 0-916262),* 1627 Moody Court, Peoria, IL 61604 (SAN 207-6535) Tel 309-674-2008

Red Clay, *(Red Clay Books; 0-911692),* 6366 Sharon Hills Rd., Charlotte, NC 28210 (SAN 202-9774) Tel 704-366-9624

Red Haw Pr, *(Red Haw Press; 0-918904),* P.O. Box 436, La Jolla, CA 92038 (SAN 210-3257)

Red River, *(Red River Press; 0-938898),* 4806 Danberry, Wichita Falls, TX 76308 (SAN 216-1788)

Red Studio, *(Red Studio Press; 0-916320),* 200 22nd Ave. S., Minneapolis, MN 55454 (SAN 208-3434) Tel 612-339-2042

Redgold, *(Redgold, Inc.; 0-932234),* 10398 Rockingham Dr., Suite 1, Sacramento, CA 95827 (SAN 211-6839) Tel 916-366-1356

Redgrave Info, *(Redgrave Information Resources Corp.; 0-88276),* P.O. Box 408, 3 Sylvan Rd. S., Westport, CT 06880 (SAN 202-9766) Tel 203-226-9523

Reed Bks, *(Reed Books; 0-89169),* Subs. of Addison House, ; c/o Addison House, Morgan's Run, Danbury, NH 03220 (SAN 210-5543) Tel 603-768-3903

Reel Trophy, *(Reel Trophy Pubns.),* P.O. Box 19085, Portland, OR 97219 (SAN 206-104X) Tel 503-245-2424

Ref Guides, *(Reference Guides; 0-939228),* Rte. 2, Box 162, Detroit, TX 75436 (SAN 220-1402) Tel 214-674-5403

Regal Pub Co, *(Regal Publishing Co.; 0-9604598),* P.O. Box 76846, Atlanta, GA 30328 (SAN 215-1782)

Regency Pubs CA, *(Regency Pubs., Inc.; 0-937554),* 2213 Liadero Canyon Rd., Suite 101, Westlake Village, CA 91361 (SAN 215-3386)

Regina Pub Hse
See Fintzenberg

Regional Ctr Educ, *(Regional Ctr. for Educational Training; 0-915892),* 45 Lyme Rd., Hanover, NH 03755 (SAN 208-8282)

Reidmore Bks, *(Reidmore Bks. Oregon; 0-939284),* P.O. Box 2598, Eugene, OR 97402 (SAN 216-2946)

Release, *(Release Press; 0-913722),* 478 Seventh St., Brooklyn, NY 11215 (SAN 215-1049)

Relex, *(Relex, Inc.; 0-89149),* Dist. by: J. Philip O'hara Inc., 20 E. Huron, Chicago, IL 60611 (SAN 207-4664)

Religious Pub, *(Religious Publishing Co.; 0-916138),* 198 Allendale Rd., King of Prussia, PA 19406 (SAN 205-9436) Tel 215-265-9400

Renner Pub, *(Renner Pub.; 0-942922),* 17811 Davenport Rd. No. 42, Dallas, TX 75252 (SAN 240-1134)

Res Comm Korean, *(Blue River Pubns.; 0-930433),* 101 Tamalpais Rd., Berkeley, CA 94708 (SAN 670-9907)

Res Pr KS, *(Research Press, Inc.),* 4500 W. 72nd Terrace, Prairie Village, KS 66208 (SAN 240-1207) Tel 913-362-9667

Research, *(Research; 0-930442),* 2444 Charlemagne Ave., Long Beach, CA 90815 (SAN 210-6590) Tel 213-597-3718

Reward Pub, *(Reward Publishing; 0-9610280),* P.O. Box 124, Eugene, OR 97440 (SAN 264-343X)

Reyn Pub Co, *(Reyn Publishing Co.; 0-936366),* 14240 E. 14th St., San Leandro, CA 94578 (SAN 214-1345)

Rhineburgh Pr, *(Rhineburgh Pr., Inc.; 0-9604746),* 595 Madison Ave., New York, NY 10022 (SAN 215-3394) Tel 212-355-0162

Rich-Errington, *(Rich-Errington; 0-915898),* P.O. Box 546, Bay City, MI 48706 (SAN 207-6691) Tel 517-893-6730

Ridge Hse, *(Ridge Hse. Pr.),* Box 600, Hayden Lake, ID 83835 (SAN 210-623X)

Ridgefield Pub, *(Ridgefield Publishing Co.; 0-86628),* 6925 Canby Ave., Suite 104, Reseda, CA 91335 (SAN 215-8035)

Rigel, *(Rigel, Inc.; 0-937234),* 131 Asl Lane, Elkton, MD 21921 (SAN 214-4581)

Right White Line, *(Right White Line; 0-918926),* 531 N. Inlet, Lincoln City, OR 97367 (SAN 209-6536) Tel 503-994-9840

Rijes Corp, *(Rijes Corp.; 0-916741),* 3 E. Huron, Chicago, IL 60610-0616 (SAN 654-4614); P.O. Box 14843, Chicago, IL 60614 (SAN 669-3903)

Rio Grande Pub, *(Rio Grande Publishing Co.),* 3315 Stanford Dr., N.E, Albuquerque, NM 87107 (SAN 208-0796)

Rising Tide, *(Rising Tide),* P.O. Box 7795, Ben Franklin Sta., Washington, DC 20044 (SAN 226-8094)

Rising Wolf, *(Rising Wolf, Inc.; 0-936710),* 1304 Jackson, Missoula, MT 59802 (SAN 214-459X)

Ritchie, *(Ritchie, Ward, Press; 0-378),* 474 S. Arroyo Pkwy., Pasadena, CA 91105 (SAN 202-5485) Tel 213-793-1163

Riverhouse Pubns, *(Riverhouse Pubns.; 0-933258),* 20 Waterside Plaza, New York, NY 10010 (SAN 212-6850) Tel 212-685-2376

Riverrun Pr, *(Riverrun Press),* 111 Hasell St., Hillsborough, NC 27278 (SAN 208-4112) Tel 919-732-4875

Riverside Pr, *(Riverside Pr., The; 0-912285),* P.O. Box 133, Riverside, CT 06878 (SAN 265-0932) Tel 203-637-3084

Riverwood Pubs, *(Riverwood Pubs., Ltd.; 0-914762),* 500 E. 77th St., Suite 1204, New York, NY 10162 (SAN 206-5185) Tel 212-737-9304

RMP Inc, *(RMP Inc. Pubs.),* P.O. Box 36679, Los Angeles, CA 90036 (SAN 213-361X)

Robinson & Wat
See Robinsons Bks

Robinsons Bks, *(Robinson's Books; 0-7224),* c/o Jenks, 1462 N. Stanley Ave., Rm. 206, Los Angeles, CA 90046 (SAN 262-0693) Tel 213-876-3250

Rock Pub, *(Rock Publishing Co.; 0-9601804),* 3667 San Pascual Ave., Las Vegas, NV 89110 (SAN 212-6869)

Rock Spring, *(Rock Spring Pubns.),* 610 South View Terr., Alexandria, VA 22314 (SAN 206-846X)

Rocketlab, *(Rocketlab; 0-9600198),* P.O. Box 1139, Florence, OR 97439 (SAN 204-6911) Tel 503-997-8940

ROCOM, *(ROCOM Press; 0-89119),* Nutley, NJ 07110 (SAN 206-3689); Orders to: 1 Sunset Ave., Montclair, NJ 07042 (SAN 206-3697)

Rojan Mus, *(Rojan Music Pubns.; 0-912151),* 951 N. 45th, P.O. Box 31475, Seattle, WA 98103 (SAN 264-7869) Tel 206-634-1320

Roller Coaster Pubns, *(Roller Coaster Pubns.),* P.O. Box 18058, Denver, CO 80218 (SAN 212-6877)

Rook Pr, *(Rook Press; 0-916684),* 805 W. First Ave., Jerry, PA 15627 (SAN 208-3353)

Rose Garden, *(Rose Garden Press, The; 0-9611684),* P.O. Box 749, Pittsburg, CA 94565 (SAN 284-933X) Tel 415-427-5994

Rosetta Pub Co, *(Rosetta Publishing Co., The; 0-935850),* P.O. Box 17942, Raleigh, NC 27619 (SAN 213-7909) Tel 919-787-8517

Rota Pr, *(Rota Press; 0-87908),* P.O. Box 332, Waverly, IA 50677 (SAN 206-8648)

RPM Pub, *(RPM Publishing Co.; 0-932918),* 355 Lexington Ave., New York, NY 10017 (SAN 212-307X)

RSV Pub, *(R.S.V. Publishing, Inc.; 0-933514),* Box 182, Times Plaza, Brooklyn, NY 11217 (SAN 212-6184)

RSVP Pub & Dist, *(RSVP Pub. & Distributor; 0-913752),* P.O. Box 252, Brookfield, IL 60513 (SAN 204-7063)

Rubenstein, *(Rubenstein, Steve; 0-941228),* 1445 Union St., No. 1, San Francisco, CA 94109 (SAN 239-3816)

Rucker Ent, *(Rucker Enterprises),* 3511 Henderson Rd., Greensboro, NC 27410 (SAN 208-094X) Tel 919-294-4918; Orders to: P.O. Box 19107, Greensboro, NC 27410 (SAN 208-0958)

Ruddy Duck Pr, *(Ruddy Duck Pr.; 0-910697),* Div. of Glazier Pubs., P.O. Box 7324, Fremont, CA 94536 (SAN 260-258X)

Runeskald Pr, *(Runeskald Press; 0-915446),* P.O. Box 612, Annapolis, MD 21404 (SAN 207-1908) Tel 301-268-1069

Running Wild, *(Running Wild; 0-939350),* P.O. Box 1211, Lafayette, CA 94549 (SAN 216-4930) Tel 415-283-7363

Rusoff Bks, *(Rusoff Books; 0-917932),* 1302 S.E. 4th St., Minneapolis, MN 55414 (SAN 209-3057) Tel 612-331-3335

Rusthoi, *(Rusthoi Soul Winning Pubns.; 0-911288),* P.O. Box 595, Montrose, CA 91020 (SAN 204-708X) Tel 818-241-7244

Rutan Pub, *(Rutan Publishing; 0-936222),* 2717 Lyndale Ave. S., Minneapolis, MN 55408 (SAN 215-9147)

Ryerse, *(Ryerse Publishing Co.; 0-9603388),* 40 Bernice Dr., Freehold, NJ 07728 (SAN 206-3719) Tel 201-462-5068

S A Russell, *(Russell, S.A.; 0-88211),* 120 E. 81st St., New York, NY 10028 (SAN 202-8336) Tel 212-861-3102

S Ambaras, *(Ambaras, Samuel, Inc.; 0-913268),* P.O. Box 138, New York, NY 10031 (SAN 202-9693)

S Appalachian Res, *(Southern Appalachian Resource Catalog),* 15 Rosewood Ave., Asheville, NC 28801 (SAN 215-109X)

S Green, *(Green, Sherwood),* 219 S. D St., P.O. Box 101, Madera, CA 93637 (SAN 226-3947)

S Higgins, *(Higgins, Shaun, Pub.; 0-918928),* E2621 27th Ave., Spokane, WA 99203 (SAN 210-4369) Tel 509-535-7350

S K Chapman, *(Chapman, Sarah K.),* P.O. Box 3684, Sarasota, FL 33578 (SAN 263-9696)

S M Hartman, *(Hartman, S. M.),* P.O. Box 7162, Baltimore, MD 21218 (SAN 206-3727) Tel 301-243-0616

S P Howell, *(Howell, Susan P., Enterprises; 0-9603076),* Box 116 B, Hebron, CT 06248 (SAN 212-7458)

S R Ohler, *(Ohler, Samuel R.; 0-9609934),* Box 4611, Pittsburgh, PA 15206 (SAN 274-2594) Tel 412-687-5943

S T Black, *(Black, Sidney T.),* Box 522, Simsbury, CT 06070 (SAN 213-8344)

S W S, *(SWS Pubns.),* 1634 Red Cedar Trail, Dallas, TX 75248 (SAN 655-2617)

S Z Press, *(SZ Pr.; 0-930125),* P.O. 383, Cathedral Sta., New York, NY 10025 (SAN 218-3374)

Saalfield, *(Saalfield Publishing Co.; 0-509),* Saalfield Square, Akron, OH 44301 (SAN 206-8494)

Sabin, *(Sabin Publishing Co.),* 6361 Celia Vista Dr., San Diego, CA 92115 (SAN 204-7187)

Sable Pub, *(Sable Publishing Corp.; 0-914832),* P.O. Box 788, Arlington, TX 76010 (SAN 207-754X) Tel 817-265-5001

Safety Consul, *(Safety Consultants, Inc.),* 3140 Kingsley Dr., Florissant, MO 63033 (SAN 206-3735) Tel 314-921-6776

Sag Scriptory, *(Sagittarian Scriptory Enterprises; 0-931908),* 2674 Laurel Dr., Fairfield, CA 94533 (SAN 212-4483) Tel 707-427-3446

Sagamore Pr, *(Sagamore Press; 0-936640),* 227 Madison Blvd., Terre Haute, IN 47803 (SAN 215-1804)

Sagarin Pr, *(Sagarin Press; 0-915298),* Box 251, Sand Lake, NY 12153 (SAN 207-396X) Tel 518-674-2998

Salem Pr OR, *(Salem Press of Oregon),* 1021 Oregon National Bldg., 610 SW Alder, Portland, OR 97205 (SAN 262-0332)

Salem Pub Lib, *(Salem Public Library; 0-9603390),* 821 E. State St., Salem, OH 44460 (SAN 209-6781) Tel 216-332-0042

Salt City Print, *(Salt City Printing Co.; 0-9612588),* P.O. Box 429, 21 E. 4th, Hutchinson, KS 67501 (SAN 289-4084); 204 Curtis St., Hutchinson, KS 67501 (SAN 289-4092) Tel 316-662-2131

Salt Lick, *(Salt Lick Pr.; 0-913918),* 5107 Martin Ave., Austin, TX 78751 (SAN 202-0823)

Samsara Group Corp, *(Samsara Group Corp.; 0-932021),* P.O. Box 1693, South Bend, IN 46634-1693 (SAN 686-0850) Tel 219-288-0693

San Bernardino Bar, *(San Bernardino County Bar Association),* 364 N. Arrowhead Ave., San Bernardino, CA 92401 (SAN 226-3734)

Sanchiz Pr, *(Sanchiz Press; 0-9607384),* 1500 Massachusetts Ave. NW, No. 409, Washington, DC 20005 (SAN 239-6076)

S&S Co CA
See S&S Co OR

S&S Co OR, *(S&S Co., The),* 11047 Antiock Rd, Central Point, OR 97502 (SAN 212-2588) Tel 503-826-7870

Santa Fe Assocs, *(Santa Fe Assocs.; 0-932138),* P.O. Box 1649, Rancho Santa Fe, CA 92067 (SAN 222-9552)

Santam, *(Santam Two, Ltd.),* Box 11642, Phoenix, AZ 85017 (SAN 215-1812)

Santemara, *(Santemara Pubns.; 0-9603304),* P.O. Box 1217, Minnetonka, MN 55343 (SAN 210-9530) Tel 612-474-5313

Sar Sholem, *(Sar Sholem of Jerusalem),* P.O. Box 577, Fern Park, FL 32730 (SAN 212-3118)

Savings Am, *(OK Street Inc.; 0-917278),* 12800 Hillcrest Rd., Suite 215, Dallas, TX 75230 (SAN 209-2131) Tel 214-387-0953

Saxon, *(Saxon House),* Dist. by: Atheneum Pubs., 597 Fifth Ave., New York, NY 10017 (SAN 209-3162)

SC Prodns, *(Southern California Productions; 0-9601956),* P.O. Box 1128M, Carlsbad, CA 92008 (SAN 212-386X) Tel 714-434-1626

Schab Gallery, *(Schab, William H., Gallery, Inc.),* 37 W. 57th St., New York, NY 10019 (SAN 205-1451) Tel 212-758-0327

Schick Sunn, *(Schick Sunn Classic Books; 0-917214),* Div. of Sun Classic Pictures, Inc., P.O. Box 268, Hever City, UT 84032 (SAN 208-8401) Tel 801-654-28481554 Sepulveda Blvd., Los Angeles, CA 90025 (SAN 208-841X)

Schlegel Pubns, *(Schlegel Pubns.; 0-9603358),* 172 Conneaut Dr., Pittsburgh, PA 15239 (SAN 213-1609) Tel 412-325-1226

Schleiger, *(Schleiger, Arlene; 0-9600098),* 4416 Valli Vista Rd, Colorado Springs, CO 80915 (SAN 204-7330) Tel 303-591-8642

School Liv Ca, *(School of Living),* P.O. Box 425, San Diego, CA 92103 (SAN 204-5737)

Schulte, *(Schulte, Terry T.),* Box 1672, St. Cloud, MN 56301 (SAN 216-0102)

Sci Fiction, *(Science Fiction Resources; 0-918364),* 101 Newtown Rd., Port Washington, NY 11050 (SAN 210-0037) Tel 516-883-9142; 148 E. 74th St., New York, NY 10021 (SAN 210-0045) Tel 212-988-7526

Sci Sports, *(Scientific Sports, Inc.; 0-912637),* 618 N. 104th St., Milwaukee, WI 53226 (SAN 282-8103) Tel 414-453-8159

Sci-Tech, *(Science-Tech Publishing Co.),* P.O. Box 2277, Sta. A, Champaign, IL 61820 (SAN 207-0847)

Scientific Meet, *(Scientific Meetings Pubns.),* Poway, CA 92064 (SAN 211-2051)

Scientific Res, *(Scientific Research Services; 0-914314),* 389 N Highland Ave., Hollywood, CA 90038 (SAN 202-9936) Tel 213-874-4101

Scribe Pub Corp, *(Scribe Publishing Corp.; 0-915748),* 1219 Westlake Ave. N., Suite 108, Seattle, WA 98109 (SAN 209-5130) Tel 206-284-9747

Scribe's Cham, *(Scribe's Chamber Pubns.; 0-912293),* P.O. Box 2123, E. Peoria, IL 61611 (SAN 265-2005) Tel 309-699-6034

Scrimshaw Calif, *(Scrimshaw Press (California); 0-912020),* 6040 Claremont Ave, Oakland, CA 94618 (SAN 202-5434) Tel 415-658-2323

Sea Jay Pub, *(Sea Jay Publishing),* 3778 S. 6670 West, Salt Lake City, UT 84120 (SAN 214-4700)

Sea Lion, *(Sea Lion Pubns.; 0-939880),* 1716 India St., San Diego, CA 92101 (SAN 216-9320) Tel 619-232-2626

Sea of Storms, *(Sea of Storms; 0-931910),* P.O. Box 22613, San Francisco, CA 94122 (SAN 211-4518) Tel 707-795-2098

Seaboard Pr, *(Seaboard Press; 0-9600532),* 153 Blanchard Rd., Drexel Hill, PA 19026 (SAN 204-7403)

Seacoast Prods, *(Seacoast Productions, Inc.; 0-911817),* 728 E. Sunset Blvd., Fort Walton Beach, FL 32548 (SAN 289-5579) Tel 904-862-2550

Seaforth Pubns, *(Seaforth Pubns.; 0-933496),* 12211 Coit Rd., Bratenahl, OH 44108 (SAN 212-5552) Tel 216-681-4561; Orders to: 117 Pine Acres Dr., Spartanburg, SC 29302 (SAN 212-5560) Tel 803-579-1666

Seagull Pubns., *(Seagull Pubns., Inc.; 0-930290),* 1736 E. 53rd St., Brooklyn, NY 11234 (SAN 210-1378) Tel 212-338-6622

Seagulls Artistic, *(Seagulls Artistic Pubns.; 0-941110),* 1608 Nogales St. No. 177, Rowland Heights, CA 91748 (SAN 217-4359)

Seaholm, *(Seaholm Interstate Directories Inc.),* P.O. Box 205, New Paltz, NY 12561 (SAN 211-5409) Tel 914-255-0907

Seashell
See Seashell Pr

Seashell Pr, *(Seashell Pr.; 0-935378),* P.O. Box 747, El Cajon, CA 92022 (SAN 213-9642); Dist. by: Communication Creativity, 5644 La Jolla Blvd., La Jolla, CA 92037 (SAN 210-3478)

Second Storey Pr, *(Second Storey Press; 0-915634),* P.O. Box 63, St. Genevieve, MO 63670 (SAN 208-0451)

Secure Futures, *(Secure Futures Pubns.; 0-938064),* P.O. Box 3362, San Diego, CA 92103 (SAN 215-708X) Tel 619-692-0588

Secureware, *(Secureware; 0-912639),* P.O. Box 1074, Wheeling, IL 60090 (SAN 283-3123)

Select Pub, *(Select Publishing; 0-9606458),* P.O. Box 85707, Los Angeles, CA 90072 (SAN 218-5970)

Self, *(Self),* Box 1498, Quincy, CA 95917 (SAN 209-5157)

Self Defense, *(Self Defense Kaleidoscope Pubns.; 0-910193),* 3607 Maple Ave., Oakland, CA 94602 (SAN 241-452X)

Senna & Shih, *(Senna & Shih, Inc.; 0-89460),* P.O. Box 1091, 21 Beacon St., Boston, MA 02103 (SAN 210-2692) Tel 617-491-0858

Senseis DoJo, *(Sensei's DoJo Supply),* P.O. Box 1164, Hollywood, CA 90028 (SAN 208-3213)

Sentinel Star, *(Sentinel Star Co.; 0-9605772),* P.O. Box 2833, Orlando, FL 32802 (SAN 206-3786) Tel 305-420-5535

Septima, *(Septima, Inc.),* P.O. Box 2096, Sarasota, FL 33578 (SAN 213-5884) Tel 813-349-4634

Sequoia Pr, *(Sequoia Press),* P.O. Box 9889, Berkeley, CA 94703 (SAN 286-3456)

Serendipity, *(Serendipity Systems, Inc.; 0-926782),* 419 W. Seneca St., Ithaca, NY 14850 (SAN 264-8784) Tel 607-277-4889

Serv League IL, *(Service League of Lutheran General Hospital; 0-9609292),* 1775 Dempster St., Park Ridge, IL 60068 (SAN 260-1338) Tel 312-696-6105

Servicios Intles, *(Servicios Internacionales; 0-943236),* P.O. Box 51, La Marque, TX 77568 (SAN 214-137X)

Seven Buffaloes, *(Seven Buffaloes Press; 0-916380),* P.O. Box 214, Big Timber, MT 59011 (SAN 208-8452)

Seventy-Six, *(Seventy-Six Press; 0-89245),* P.O. Box 725, Seal Beach, CA 90740 (SAN 208-2004) Tel 213-596-3491

Sextant Sys, *(Sextant Publishing Company),* 716 E St., SE, Washington, DC 20003 (SAN 695-0434) Tel 202-544-0900

Seymour-Smith, *(Seymour-Smith Pubs.),* P.O. Box 53025, San Jose, CA 95123 (SAN 213-6953)

SF Bk Co, *(San Francisco Book Co., Inc.; 0-913374),* Box 3760, San Francisco, CA 94119 (SAN 202-0815) Tel 415-681-1166

Shannon Imprint of Am Natl Pub

Shannon Pubns, *(Shannon Pubns),* P.O. Box 21918, Denver, CO 80221 (SAN 226-7985)

Sharain Bks, *(Sharain Bks.; 0-9609740),* 3712 Ortega Ct., Palo Alto, CA 94303 (SAN 262-0782) Tel 415-493-3596

Shattuck Pr, *(Shattuck Press; 0-911405),* 3025 Shattuck Ave., Berkeley, CA 94705 (SAN 275-3065) Tel 415-843-3211

Shaw Inc, *(Shaw, Mara Lynn, Inc.; 0-9605602),* 165 E. 72nd St., Suite 12N, New York, NY 10021 (SAN 216-1664)

Sheffield Pr, *(Sheffield Press; 0-917044),* P.O. Box 723, Manhattan Beach, CA 90266 (SAN 208-4953) Tel 213-545-7974

Sheptow, *(Sheptow Pubns.; 0-932886),* 3161 Fillmore St., San Francisco, CA 94123 (SAN 212-2316) Tel 415-563-4630

Sherbourne
See Charter Hse

Sherry Daniel, *(Daniel, Sherry; 0-9611244),* P.O. Box 567, Fredericksburg, TX 78624 (SAN 283-4251)

Shiloh, *(Shiloh, Ailon; 0-918580),* P. O. Box 16851, Tampa, FL 33687 (SAN 210-0126)

Shondo-Shando, *(Shondo-Shando Press; 0-9601754),* P.O. Box 887, Quincy, IL 62301 (SAN 212-2596) Tel 217-214-4192

Shoreland Pr, *(Shoreland Press; 0-913479),* P.O. Box 1158, Mountainside, NJ 07092 (SAN 285-8509) Tel 201-276-1967

Shoreline Pub, *(Shoreline Publishing; 0-938306),* 212-08 75th Ave., Bayside, NY 11364 (SAN 215-8108)

Short Course, *(Short Course Pubns.; 0-932734),* 1333 So. Fifth Av., Arcadia, CA 91006 (SAN 212-5609)

Shrewd Info, *(Shrewd Information Press; 0-930660),* Box 39641, Los Angeles, CA 90039 (SAN 211-1683)

Sibyl-Child, *(Sibyl-Child Press),* Box 1773, Hyattsville, MD 20788 (SAN 211-1675)

Sight&Sound, *(Sight&Sound Press; 0-9601098),* P.O. Box 1333, Pacifica, CA 94044 (SAN 209-5998)

Silma Inc, *(Silma Delta Research; 0-913223),* 4804 NW 79th Ave., No. 302, Miami, FL 33166 (SAN 283-4081) Tel 305-594-4696

Silver Dog, *(Silver Dog Press; 0-915244),* P.O. Box 23324, Oakland, CA 94623 (SAN 207-3099)

Silver Pennies, *(Silver Pennies Press; 0-9607040),* 1365 E. 30th Ave., Eugene, OR 97405 (SAN 239-0353) Tel 503-345-6286

Simon-Day, *(Simon-Day Publishing Co.),* 255 Flores St., Suite 175, San Mateo, CA 94403 (SAN 204-871X) Tel 415-349-1908

Simply Superb, *(Simply Superb Pubns.; 0-9612530),* 110 Walnut Ave., Cranford, NJ 07016 (SAN 297-181X)

Simpson-Hirshman, *(Simpson-Hirshman Publishing; 0-938406),* 1008 Western Ave., Seattle, WA 98104 (SAN 215-8124)

Simul Pubns, *(Simulations Pubns, Inc.; 0-917852),* 257 Park Ave. S., New York, NY 10010 (SAN 210-0150) Tel 212-673-4103

Sincere Pr, *(Sincere Press; 0-912534),* Box 17599, Tucson, AZ 85731 (SAN 204-6016)

Singer Island, *(Singer Island Press; 0-935860),* 2649 Lake Dr., Singer Island, FL 33404 (SAN 213-800X)

Sixth House Pr Inc, *(Sixth Hse. Pr., Inc., The; 0-913911),* P.O. Box 10458, St. Petersburg, FL 33733 (SAN 286-8741)

SJS Pub Inc, *(S J S Publishing, Inc.),* 2314 S. Vineyard Ave. "E", Ontario, CA 91761 (SAN 265-363X) Tel 714-947-8035

Ski Touring Coun, *(Ski Touring Council, Inc.),* W. Hill Road, Troy, VT 05868 (SAN 224-5884) Tel 802-744-2472

Skyfire
See Expertise

Skyflight Intl, *(Skyflight International),* 1505 11th St., Manhattan Beach, CA 90266 (SAN 264-3928)

Skylight Health, *(Skylight Health; 0-9610112),* 14713 E. Caspian Pl., Aurora, CO 80014 (SAN 271-8421) Tel 303-337-0650

Skylite Bks
See Skylite Comm

Skylite Comm, *(Skylite Communications Inc.; 0-9607770),* 625 N. Michigan Ave., Suite 500, Chicago, IL 60611 (SAN 226-8000)

Sloan-Kettering, *(Sloan-Kettering Institute for Cancer Research; 0-88485),* 1275 York Ave., New York, NY 10021 (SAN 206-7986) Tel 212-879-3000

Slugsweat Pub, *(Slugsweat Publishing; 0-915437),* P.O. Box 4832, Washington, DC 20008 (SAN 291-4360) Tel 202-775-8340

Small Busn Pubs, *(Small Business Pubns., Inc.; 0-9605436),* Box 5SC 800 Bearses Way, Hyannis, MA 02601 (SAN 215-9163)

Small Pleasures, *(Small Pleasures Press; 0-913481),* 88 Virginia St., No. 29, Seattle, WA 98101 (SAN 285-1881) Tel 206-624-1985

Small Wonder, *(Small Wonder Enterprises),* Orders to: RPM Distributors, 5862 Wicomico Ave., Rockville, MD 20852 (SAN 206-9962)

Smilepower, *(Smilepower Institute; 0-918802),* 1225 Nadina St., San Mateo, CA 94402 (SAN 210-5071) Tel 415-341-6042

Smoke Shop, *(Smoke Shop Press, The; 0-939572),* 108 Waterman St., No. 2A, Providence, RI 02906 (SAN 216-4515)

Snail Bks, *(Snail Books; 0-931264),* 3940 Algonquin Dr., Suite 164, Las Vegas, NV 89109 (SAN 212-1409)

Soaring Symposia, *(Soaring Symposia; 0-914600),* Route 1, Box 157-F, Keyser, WV 26726 (SAN 202-991X) Tel 301-786-4697

Soc Philatel Am, *(Society of Philatelic Americans),* Box 30286, Cleveland, OH 44130 (SAN 691-2303)

Soc Prot Unborn, *(Society for the Protection of the Unborn Through Nutrition),* 17 N Wabash, Chicago, IL 60602 (SAN 224-3938) Tel 312-332-2334

Soc Radio Person, *(Society of Radio Personalities and Programmers),* 1719 W. 91st Pl., Kansas City, MO 64114 (SAN 223-9744) Tel 816-444-3500

Soc Res Assoc
See Social Res

Soc Span Stud, *(Society of Spanish Studies; 0-913784),* 9944 Harriet Ave., S., Bloomington, MN 55420 (SAN 210-5454)

Soccer
See Sportshelf

Social Interest, *(Social Interest Pr., Inc., The; 0-939654),* 670 Northwestern Ave., Wooster, OH 44691 (SAN 216-6453)

Social Res, (Social Research Associates), 335 N.E. 53rd St., Seattle, WA 98105 (SAN 209-1755) Tel 206-632-0578

Software Supply, (Software Supply; 0-9603792), 731 Henrietta Ave., Sunnyvale, CA 94086 (SAN 214-1434)

Software TX, (Software Concepts), 105-106 Preston Valley S.C., Dallas, TX 75230 (SAN 287-6027) Tel 214-458-0330

Soggy Cracker Pr, (Soggy Cracker Pr.; 0-9607934), 1136 SE 32nd Terr., Cape Coral, FL 33904 (SAN 239-863X)

Solo Inc, (Solo Publishing, Inc.; 0-9610216), 14450 NE 29th Pl., Suite 115, Bellevue, WA 98007 (SAN 275-6595) Tel 206-882-3303

Solobooks, (Solobooks; 0-939004), P.O. Box 2292, Modesto, CA 95351 (SAN 216-4523)

Something Else, (Something Else Press, Inc.), P.O. Box H, Baiton, VT 05822 (SAN 203-2341)

Sonica Pr, (Sonica Pr.), P.O. Box 42720, Los Angeles, CA 90042 (SAN 216-1966)

Sono Pubs, (Sono Pubs.; 0-916898), 554 N. Arden Blvd., Los Angeles, CA 90004 (SAN 208-8649) Tel 213-467-3597

Sonoran Desert, (Sonoran Desert Press), P.O. Box 729, Phoenix, AZ 85001 (SAN 203-2031)

Sonrise Prods, (SONrise Productions), 746 E. 79th St., Box 186, Chicago, IL 60619 (SAN 215-8159)

Sound Advice, (Sound Advice Enterprises; 0-943668), 40 Holly Ln., Roslyn Heights, NY 11577 (SAN 238-3799) Tel 516-621-2445

Soundview Bks, (Soundview Bks.; 0-934924), 100 Heights Rd., Darien, CT 06820 (SAN 214-1477) Tel 203-655-1436

Source Bks NM, (Source Books; 0-942234), 1608 Caminito Monica, Santa Fe, NM 87501 (SAN 226-8027)

Source Pubs, (Source Pubs., Inc.; 0-87915), 261 Madison Ave.,Rm. No. 1102, New York, NY 10017 (SAN 204-6113) Tel 212-687-9615

Sourcebooks CA, (Sourcebooks; 0-933422), 18758 Bryant Rd., Northridge, CA 91324 (SAN 213-1692)

South Pass Pr, (South Pass Press; 0-932068), 8338 E. Gilbert, Wichita, KS 67207 (SAN 204-6121)

Southern-Lite, (Southern-Lite Publishing Co.; 0-942050), P.O. Box 12187, Atlanta, GA 30355 (SAN 239-4871) Tel 404-351-9365

Southern Pr, (Southern Press, Inc.; 0-915536), 301 Terry Hutchens Bldg., 102 Clinton Ave. W., Huntsville, AL 35801 (SAN 207-334X)

Southern Typeset, (Southern Typesetting Co.), P.O. Box 43701, Atlanta, GA 30336 (SAN 207-2882) Tel 404-832-8269

Sovereign Bks, (Sovereign Bks.), Div. of Simon & Schuster, ; c/o Cornerstone Library, 1230 Ave. of the Americas, New York, NY 10020 (SAN 200-2450) Tel 212-245-6400

Soycrafters Assoc, (Soycrafters Assn. of North America), Sunrise Farm, Health Rd., Colrain, MA 01340 (SAN 691-2540)

Spaceman Pr, (Spaceman Press; 0-9603546), 139 Carmel Ave., Pacific Grove, CA 93950 (SAN 213-5949) Tel 408-372-5915

SP&M, (Serran Pagan/Muntadas; 0-9604114), 301 E. 22nd St., New York, NY 10010 (SAN 215-1073)

Spanish Pub, (Spanish Publicity; 0-9607386), 200 Prairie Dell, Austin, TX 78752 (SAN 239-488X)

Spartacus, (Spartacus; 0-917372), 234 Fifth Ave., Third Fl., New York, NY 10001 (SAN 208-6042)

Spartacus Pr, (Spartacus Press; 0-89432), P.O. Box 71, South Dartmouth, MA 02748 (SAN 208-9963)

Spec Features Wkshp, (Special Features Workshop; 0-917466), 32 Warnock Dr., Westport, CT 06880 (SAN 209-0767) Tel 203-226-9370

Spec Learn Corp, (Special Learning Corp.; 0-89568), P.O. Box 306, Guilford, CT 06437 (SAN 211-4542); 42 Boston Post Rd., Guilford, CT 06437 (SAN 658-1668)

Spencer Pubs, (Spencer, Daniel, Pubs.; 0-936496), 31970 Pacific Coast Hwy, Malibu, CA 90265 (SAN 215-1839)

Sperr & Douth, (Sperr & Douth, Inc.; 0-912902), 663 Fifth Ave., New York, NY 10022 (SAN 204-6210) Tel 212-757-6454

Spex Intl, (Spex International, Ltd.; 0-943816), 51 E. 42nd St., Suite 517, New York, NY 10017 (SAN 238-3802) Tel 212-490-0077

Sportshelf, (Sportshelf & Soccer Assocs.; 0-392), P.O. Box 634, New Rochelle, NY 10802 (SAN 202-5388) Imprints: ABC (Australian Book Center); IBC (Irish Book Center); LTB (Leisure Time Books); SpS (Sport Shelf Books).

SpS Imprint of Sportshelf

Spurr Design, (Spurr, John, Design; 0-931312), P.O. Box 11249, Palo Alto, CA 94306 (SAN 211-2043)

Spyglass, (Spyglass Co.; 0-914922), 2415 Mariner Square Dr., Alameda, CA 94501 (SAN 207-3587) Tel 415-769-8410

Spyglass Catalog
See Spyglass

St Albans Church, (St. Alban's Episcopal Church; 0-9606174), P.O. Box 1104, Hixson, TN 37343 (SAN 217-1309) Tel 615-842-1342

St Albans Episcopal
See St Albans Church

St Charles Hse, (St. Charles House, Pubs.; 0-88263), Empire Rd., Box 505, St. Charles, IL 60174 (SAN 206-8656)

St Heironymous, (St. Heironymous Press, Inc.; 0-913718), P.O. Box 9431, Berkeley, CA 94709 (SAN 203-3550) Tel 415-549-1405

St Johns, (St. Johns Univ. Press; 0-87075), Grand Central & Utopia Pkwy., Jamaica, NY 11439 (SAN 204-6245) Tel 212-969-8000

St Le Macs Pr, (St. Le Macs, Pierre, Press; 0-913030), 450 Park Plaza Professional Bldg., Houston, TX 77004 (SAN 204-6253) Tel 713-523-8181; Orders to: 2615 Marilee, No. 1, Houston, TX 77057 (SAN 204-6261) Tel 713-783-2721

St Peters Coll, (St. Peters College Press; 0-930568), Jersey City, NJ 07306 (SAN 222-4240)

St Petersburg Times, (St. Petersburg Times Publishing Co.; 0-9605382), P.O. Box 1121, St. Petersburg, FL 33731 (SAN 216-0617)

St Willibrord, (St. Willibrord's Press; 0-912134), P.O. Box 528, Zuni, NM 87329 (SAN 204-630X)

Stadia Sports Pub, (Stadia Sports Publishing), 370 E. 76th St., New York, NY 10021 (SAN 203-3534) Tel 212-532-0450

ST&A, (S. T. & A.; 0-936702), P.O. Box 480530, Los Angeles, CA 90048 (SAN 214-4646)

Standard Edns, (Standard Editions; 0-918746), P.O. Box 1297, Stuyvesant Sta., New York, NY 10009 (SAN 212-1646)

Standing Orders, (Standing Orders, Inc.; 0-8491), 156 5th Ave., Suite 1122, New York, NY 10010 (SAN 214-2066); Orders to: P.O. Box 183, Patterson, NY 12563 (SAN 214-2074)

Starform, (Starform, Inc.; 0-9604946), 1775 Old County Rd., No, 9, Belmont, CA 94002 (SAN 216-1818)

Stash, (Stash, Inc.; 0-932204), 118 S. Bedford St., Madison, WI 53703 (SAN 211-6499) Tel 608-251-4200

State Art Pubs, (State of the Art Pubs.; 0-9614183), P.O. Box 408627, Chicago, IL 60640 (SAN 686-6654) Tel 312-649-7010

State Indus Dir, (State Industrial Directories Corp.; 0-916112), 2 Penn Plaza, New York, NY 10001 (SAN 208-8711) Tel 212-564-0340

State Ptg, (State Printing Co.; 0-911432), P.O. Box 1388, 1305 Sumter St., Columbia, SC 29202 (SAN 204-6334)

State St Pubns, (State Street Pubns.; 0-936150), 2357 State St., Suite C, San Diego, CA 92101 (SAN 213-9677)

Statistics, (Statistics, Inc.; 0-911434), c/o Edwards Brothers, Inc., 2500 S. State St., Ann Arbor, MI 48104 (SAN 223-0348) Tel 313-769-1000

Steam Pr, (Steam Press), 38 45th St. D, Oakland, CA 94609 (SAN 210-9611)

Steam Trains Soo, (Steam Trains of the Soo), 1012 Holly Lane, Fortuna, CA 95540 (SAN 211-2736)

Stechert, (Stechert Macmillan, Inc.; 0-8355), 7250 Westfield Ave., Pennsauken, NJ 08110 (SAN 202-2648) Tel 609-662-7730; Dist. by: Macmillan Pub. Co., Inc., Riverside, NJ 08075 (SAN 202-5582)

Steel Rails, (Steel Rails West Publishing; 0-935250), 1930 Marlette Ave., Reno, NV 89503 (SAN 213-5965) Tel 702-331-0129

Stein Pub, (Stein Publishing House; 0-911440), 526 S. State St., Chicago, IL 60605 (SAN 204-6377)

Steinbach, (Steinbach, Marie De Bruyn; 0-9600298), 6624 Seaboard Ave., Jacksonville, FL 32244 (SAN 206-9865)

Stern Pub Group, (Stern Publishing Group; 0-912679), 414 N. Sycamore Ave., Los Angeles, CA 90036 (SAN 282-759X) Tel 213-934-1435

Stewart, (Stewart, Henry; 0-911444), 253 Main St., East Aurora, NY 14052 (SAN 204-6407)

Still Point Pr, (Still Point Press; 0-941660), P.O. Box 1606, 223 W. First St., Mansfield, OH 44901 (SAN 239-3190) Tel 419-526-2227

Stillhouse Hollow, (Stillhouse Hollow Publishing Co.; 0-9602272), Orders to: First Ladies of Texas, P.O. Box 3015, Temple, TX 76502 (SAN 212-4599)

Stillwater Canyon Pr, (Stillwater Canyon Press; 0-933762), P.O. Box 1557, Sedona, AZ 86002 (SAN 282-3691) Tel 602-774-3778; Dist. by: Bob Bradshaw, P.O. Box 195, Sudona, AZ 86336 (SAN 282-6836) Tel 602-282-7385

Stock Poetry, (Stock Poetry; 0-918874), 630 E. 14, No. 3, New York, NY 10009 (SAN 209-6021) Tel 212-673-0781

Stone-Crock-Buzzard Pr, (Stone-Crock-Buzzard Press; 0-931354), 10 West Canal St., Monsey, NY 10952 (SAN 211-5204)

Stone Hse Pr, (Stone Hse. Pr.; 0-933622), Fairfax, VT 05454 (SAN 213-1714) Tel 802-849-6557

Stone Pr MI, (Stone Pr.), 1790 Grand River, Okemos, MI 48864 (SAN 207-902X)

Stone Wall Pubns
See Stone-Crock-Buzzard Pr

Stonehenge, (Stonehenge Bks.; 0-937050), 12375 E. Cornell Ave., Unit No. 7, Arora, CO 80014 (SAN 216-454X)

Stonehill Pub Co, (Stonehill Publishing Co., Inc.; 0-88373), 1140 Ave. of Americas, 19th Fl., New York, NY 10036 (SAN 203-3437) Tel 212-658-5980; Dist. by: Farrar, Straus & Giroux, Inc., 19 Union Square, New York, NY 10003 (SAN 206-782X) Tel 212-741-6900

Stormy Karma, (Stormy Karma Books), 912 Broadway E., No. 1, Seattle, WA 98102 (SAN 209-2905)

Storyfold, (Storyfold, Inc.; 0-89008), 48 Pleasant St., Newburyport, MA 01950 (SAN 203-2066) Tel 617-462-9511

Strait, (Strait & Co.; 0-917854), P.O. Box 331, Princeton, NJ 08540 (SAN 209-889X) Tel 609-924-4098

Stratford Pr, (Stratford Press Inc.), 11340 W. Olympic Blvd. Suite 140, Los Angeles, CA 90064 (SAN 282-3713) Tel 213-477-1955; Dist. by: Harper & Row, Publishers Inc., 10 E. 53rd St., New York, NY 10022 (SAN 282-3721) Tel 212-593-7000

Strathmore Pr, (Strathmore Press; 0-942858), P.O. Box 2289, Athens, OH 45701 (SAN 240-1614)

Strawn, (Strawn Studios, Inc.; 0-943548), 761 Knolls Ctr., West Des Moines, IA 50265 (SAN 238-3853)

Street Fiction, (Street Fiction Pr., Inc.; 0-914908), 130 Touro St., P.O. Box 625, Newport, RI 02840 (SAN 207-0863) Tel 401-847-1067

Strong-Church, (Strong-Church Enterprises Press), 2238 Morello Blvd., Pleasant Hill, CA 94523 (SAN 216-4566)

Strongforce, (Strongforce, Inc.; 0-9601626), 2121 Decatur Place N.W., Washington, DC 20008 (SAN 211-5417)

Strug Comm Pr, (Strugglers' Community Pr.; 0-913491), 2003 W. 67th Pl., Chicago, IL 60636 (SAN 285-1970)

Studio Four, (Studio 4 Products; 0-9603612), 4439 Village Rd., Long Beach, CA 90808 (SAN 213-7003)

Studio NY, (Studio Press; 0-9610514), 122 Glen Rd. S., Rome, NY 13440 (SAN 264-4177) Tel 315-337-9322

Studio Pr
See Studio Pr PA

Studio Pr CA, (Studio Press, The), P.O. Box 3479, Hollywood, CA 90078 (SAN 286-3553); 8033 Sunset, Los Angeles, CA 90078 (SAN 286-3561)

Studio Pr PA, *(Studio Press; 0-918368),* P.O. Box 361, Upper Darby, PA 19082 (SAN 209-8903)

Studio Three Thousand, *(Studio 3000; 0-915100),* P.O. Box 122, Ansonia Sta., New York, NY 10023 (SAN 207-0871) Tel 212-787-3687

Studium Corp, *(Studium Corp.),* 40 Cooper Square, New York, NY 10003 (SAN 215-2754)

Successful, *(Successful Farming; 0-927270),* 1716 Locust, Des Moines, IA 50336 (SAN 653-9157) Tel 515-284-2385

Successful Achiev, *(Successful Achievement, Inc.; 0-910008),* P.O. Box 7297, Lexington, KY 40502 (SAN 204-644X) Tel 606-255-9603

Sufism Reoriented, *(Sufism Reoriented, Inc.; 0-915828),* 1300 Boulevard Way, Walnut Creek, CA 94595 (SAN 207-4869) Tel 415-938-4822

Sullivan Bks Intl, *(Sullivan Books International; 0-913620),* 153 MacAlvey, Martinez, CA 94553 (SAN 206-4774)

Sumac, *(Sumac Press; 0-911462),* 613 N. 22nd St., La Crosse, WI 54601 (SAN 206-8699) Tel 608-782-1290

Summer House, *(Summer House Pubns.; 0-935736),* Box 16257, Baltimore, MD 21210 (SAN 213-8026)

Sun Pr NY, *(Sun Pr.; 0-9601260),* 308 E. 94th St., New York, NY 10028 (SAN 698-1445)

Sunbury Pr, *(Sunbury Press; 0-915548),* P.O. Box 1778, Raleigh, NC 27602 (SAN 207-3943) Tel 919-832-6417

Sunflowers KS, *(Sunflowers; 0-939726),* RR 1, Box 262, Clearwater, KS 67026 (SAN 216-7638) Tel 316-545-7587

Sunn Classic Bks
See Schick Sunn

Sunrise MO, *(Sunrise Publishing Co.; 0-86629),* LL652 Fairgrove Ind. Blvd., Maryland Heights, MO 63043 (SAN 216-1907)

Sunrise PA, *(Sunrise Publishing Co.),* P.O. Box 215, Hatfield, PA 19440 (SAN 216-0641)

Sunshine Bks, *(Sunshine Books Ltd.; 0-934606),* 1089 W. Park St., Long Beach, NY 11561 (SAN 213-1749) Tel 516-889-4370

Sunshine Entr, *(Sunshine Enterprises; 0-943326),* P.O. Box 403, 210 E. Main, Collinsville, IL 62234 (SAN 240-5717) Tel 618-345-7022

Sunspark Pr, *(Sunspark Press),* Box 91, Greenleaf, OR 97445 (SAN 211-2728)

Supreme Ct Hist, *(Supreme Court Historical Society),* 1629 K St, Washington, DC 20006 (SAN 226-3874)

Surry County, *(Surry County School of Badminton, Ltd.),* Dist. by: Surry County School of Badminton, Ltd., 12819 S.E. 45th Place, Bellevue, WA 98006 (SAN 207-088X)

Survey Pub Co, *(Survey Publishing Co.; 0-916510),* 600 E. Eighth St., Kansas City, MO 64106 (SAN 202-7488)

Sweetwater Edns, *(Sweetwater Editions; 0-941438),* 131 E. 66th St., New York, NY 10021 (SAN 239-393X)

Swenk-Tuttle, *(Swenk-Tuttle Press, Inc.; 0-911472),* 15 E. Kirby, Apt. 1231, Detroit, MI 48202 (SAN 209-5181)

Sylvan Pr VA, *(Sylvan Press Pubs., Ltd.; 0-935254),* P.O. Box 15125, Richmond, VA 23227 (SAN 213-8034)

Symposia Special, *(Symposia Specialists; 0-88372),* 1480 N.E. 129th St., Miami, FL 33161 (SAN 202-0564) Tel 305-891-0658

Synapse Pubns, *(Synapse Pubns.; 0-935170),* Washington Plaza, 1420 Centre Ave., Suite 1806, Pittsburgh, PA 15219 (SAN 214-1507) Tel 412-765-3140

Synecology, *(Synecology Press, Inc.; 0-931774),* 309 E. 15th St., Tempe, AZ 85281 (SAN 212-2359) Tel 602-967-4173

Synergistic Soft, *(Synergistic Software; 0-927323),* 830 N. Riverside Dr., Suite 201, Renton, WA 98055 (SAN 264-9357) Tel 206-226-3216

Synergy Enter, *(Synergy Enterprises; 0-9614049),* 2174 Union St., San Franciso, CA 94123 (SAN 684-9075) Tel 415-928-0591

Syntonic Res, *(Syntonic Research, Inc.),* 663 Fifth Ave., New York, NY 10022 (SAN 202-7569)

Syntronic Pr, *(Syntronic Press; 0-914665),* 6255 Sunset Blvd., Suite 110-24, Hollywood, CA 90028 (SAN 289-6125) Tel 818-353-2171

T A Murphy, *(Murphy, Thomas A., Pub.),* 414 B Suite Buck Ave., Vacaville, CA 95688 (SAN 218-4958)

T B Sword, *(Sword, Thula Bieri; 0-9600746),* 85 N. Madison Ave., Pasadena, CA 91101 (SAN 207-2939) Tel 213-449-5382

T Hill, *(Hill, Thompson, Publishing; 0-914739),* 5443 S. Woodlawn - 2S, Chicago, IL 60615 (SAN 656-9056)

T Kassel, *(Kassel, Tichi Wilkerson),* 6517 Sunset Blvd., Hollywood, CA 90028 (SAN 699-8410)

T L Jaynes, *(Jaynes, Thomas L.; 0-935514),* P.O. Box 144055, Coral Gables, FL 33114-4055 (SAN 213-8522)

T Redd
See DTS Pub

T Sawchenko, *(Sawchenko, Terry, D. D. S.),* 2101 E. Camelback Rd., Phoenix, AZ 85016 (SAN 209-1321)

Taconic Pubs, *(Taconic Pubs.; 0-9603308),* P.O. Box 296, South Egremont, MA 01258 (SAN 212-7032) Tel 413-528-0683

Talespinner, *(Talespinner Pubns., Inc.; 0-934926),* 4543 Pleasant Ave., S., Minneapolis, MN 55409 (SAN 213-3814) Tel 612-823-7216; Orders to: P.O. Box 19087, Minneapolis, MN 55419 (SAN 213-3822)

Tantric Pr, *(Tantric Press; 0-9609746),* P.O. Box 126306, San Diego, CA 92112 (SAN 275-9225)

Tasa Pub Co, *(Tasa Publishing Co.; 0-935698),* P.O. Box 35053, Edina, MN 55435 (SAN 216-0668)

Tate Gallery, *(Tate Gallery Pubns.),* P.O. Box 428, Truchas, NM 87578 (SAN 205-4159)

Tats, *(Tat's, Inc.; 0-911478),* 927 Bellis St., Newport Beach, CA 92660 (SAN 205-4167)

Taugus Hse, *(Taugus House Pubs., Inc.; 0-938556),* 1890 San Pablo Dr., San Marcos, CA 92069 (SAN 215-9236)

Taurean Horn, *(Taurean Horn Press; 0-931552),* 601 Leavenworth No.45, San Francisco, CA 94109 (SAN 210-8658)

Tax Facts, *(Tax Facts),* Box 9009, Amarillo, TX 79105 (SAN 206-2690) Tel 806-372-2228

Tax Info Ctr, *(Tax Information Center),* Rte. 1, New Concord, OH 43762 (SAN 203-1582)

Tchr Tested Materials, *(Teacher Tested Materials),* 105 Elm St., Paoli, IN 47454 (SAN 216-4604)

Tea Hse Pubns, *(Tea House Pubns.; 0-935256),* P.O. Box 7000-163, Palos Verdes Peninsula, CA 90274 (SAN 212-9744) Tel 213-377-5974

Tea Rose Pr, *(Tea Rose Pr.; 0-940302),* P.O. Box 591, East Lansing, MI 48823 (SAN 217-5800) Tel 517-882-6083

Teapot Pubs, *(Teapot Pubs.; 0-917068),* P.O. Box 19, Dearborn, MI 48124 (SAN 208-3248)

Tech Educ Co, *(Technical Education Co., Inc.; 0-939402),* P.O. Box 18738, Irvine, CA 92713 (SAN 216-4612)

Tech Handbk, *(Technical Handbook Pubns., Inc.; 0-941114),* P.O. Box 2841, Woburn, MA 01888 (SAN 282-4000) Tel 617-657-7360; Orders to: Intercom Corporation, P.O. Box 2841, Woburn, MA 01888 (SAN 282-4019)

Tech Mgmt, *(Technology Management, Inc.),* 57 Kilvert St., Warwick, RI 02886 (SAN 212-0496); Dist. by Management Assocs., Box 230, Chestnut Hill, MA 02167 (SAN 212-050X)

Tech Recog Corp, *(Technology Recognition Corporation; 0-933980),* 1382 Old Freeport Rd., Pittsburgh, PA 15238 (SAN 213-3857)

Technico Bks, *(Technico Books; 0-9607678),* Box 20hc-Orangehurst, Fullerton, CA 92633 (SAN 239-5622)

Tecolote Pr, *(Tecolote Press, Inc.; 0-915030),* P.O. Box 188, Glenwood, NM 88039 (SAN 207-1851) Tel 505-539-2183

Telamon, *(Telamon; 0-9610974),* P.O. Box 26648, San Francisco, CA 94126-6648 (SAN 265-2277) Tel 415-752-2143

Telegraph Imprint of **Dynamic Learn Corp**

Temple Bar, *(Temple Bar Bookshop),* 9 Boylston St., Cambridge, MA 02138 (SAN 211-0997)

Temple Pub Co, *(Temple Publishing Co. Inc.; 0-917090),* P.O. Box 28722, Dallas, TX 75218 (SAN 208-4031)

Tennis, *(Tennis for Travelers; 0-911490),* 407 Blade St., Cincinnati, OH 45216 (SAN 205-4213) Tel 513-242-3100

Ter Bear, *(Ter Bear Publishing; 0-910927),* P.O. Box 287B, Santa Rosa, CA 95402 (SAN 264-4290)

Ter-Lyn, *(Ter-Lyn Co.; 0-939664),* 4090 Jason St., Denver, CO 80211 (SAN 220-1011) Tel 303-455-2132

Terra Pub, *(Terra Publishing; 0-9603238),* P.O. Box 99103, Jeffersontown, KY 40299 (SAN 212-7997) Tel 502-895-0557

TerraComms, *(TerraComms; 0-935865),* 8033 Sunset Blvd., Suite 3533, Hollywood, CA 90046 (SAN 696-1525)

Terrell Pub, *(Terrell Publishing Co.; 0-933148),* 1687 Richland Rd. S.W., Atlanta, GA 30311 (SAN 212-3134)

Tespressco, *(Tespressco),* P.O. Box 128, Willingboro, NJ 08046 (SAN 209-1348)

Tex Portfolio
See Cedar Rock

Texan-Am Pub, *(Texan-American Publisher's Co.; 0-935622),* 3008 West Ohio, Midland, TX 79701 (SAN 213-3865) Tel 915-699-1934

Texan Hse, *(Texan House, Inc.; 0-915702),* P.O. Box 9812, Austin, TX 78766 (SAN 207-9372)

Textile Bk, *(Textile Bk. Service, Inc.; 0-87245),* P.O. Box 25, 86 Flower Ave, Washington, NJ 08808 (SAN 206-7714)

TGI Pub, *(TGI Publishing Co.; 0-933465),* 363 El Cajon Blvd., El Cajon, CA 92020 (SAN 691-6899)

Thadian Pubns, *(Thadian Pubns.; 0-930516),* P.O. Box 129, North Haven, CT 06473 (SAN 210-9379)

Thai-Am Pubs, *(Thai-American Pubs.; 0-915806),* 101 Park Ave., Suite 1436N, New York, NY 10017 (SAN 208-2535) Tel 212-683-0501

Thailand Bks
See Asia Lib Ser

The Inspiration, *(Inspiration Press, The),* P.O. Box 245, Iowa City, IA 52240 (SAN 209-4517)

The Little Brown House, *(The Little Brown House Publishing Co.; 0-915782),* P.O. Box 46, Harpers Ferry, WV 25425 (SAN 207-4230) Tel 304-535-2493

Theare Corp, *(Theare Corp.; 0-9602164),* P.O. Box 13693, Sacramento, CA 95813 (SAN 212-3142)

Thelema Pub TN
See Troll Pub

Theta Bks, *(Theta Books, Inc.; 0-917972),* P.O. Box 600, Clearwater, FL 33517 (SAN 209-8946) Tel 813-446-3556

Theta Pr, *(Theta Press International; 0-918244),* 1518 E. Del Rio Dr., Tempe, AZ 85282 (SAN 208-1725)

Thinkers Pr, *(Thinker's Pr.; 0-938650),* 1026 Arlington Ct., Davenport, IA 52803 (SAN 239-4952) Tel 319-323-7117

Thinking Lizard, *(Thinking Lizard; 0-936498),* 1500 Royal Crest Dr., Apt. 122, Austin, TX 78741 (SAN 222-013X)

Third Century, *(Third Century Fund; 0-9603360),* 1370-C Cabrillo Park Dr., Santa Ana, CA 92701 (SAN 212-8004) Tel 714-547-1700

Third Pr
See Okpaku Communications

This Pr, *(This Press; 0-935074),* 1004 Hampshire St., San Francisco, CA 94110 (SAN 209-7869) Tel 415-821-3452

Thomas Hse
See Thomas Pub Co

Thomas Pub Co, *(Thomas Publishing Company; 0-9607680),* P.O. Box 661, Caldwell, TX 77836 (SAN 239-5630)

Thomson Pub Ent CO, *(Thomson Publishing Enterprises; 0-9603642),* 2343 Vaughn Way, Suite 204-Heatheridge, Aurora, CO 80014 (SAN 213-8751)

Three D Pub, *(Three-D D D Publishing; 0-9611764),* 6521 Racquet Club Dr., Lauderhill, FL 33319 (SAN 285-3833) Tel 305-733-9900

Three Herons, *(Three Herons Press),* P.O. Box 340-A, Rte. 3, Three Rivers, MI 49093 (SAN 207-9089) Tel 616-442-2725

Three in One Concepts, *(Three in One Concepts, Inc.),* P.O. Box 4492, Glendale, CA 91202 (SAN 211-2760)

Three PB, *(Three PB Publishing Co.; 0-89152),* 219-221 Parkade, Cedar Fall, IA 50613 (SAN 207-6659) Tel 319-277-3381

Three Pound Pr, *(Three Pound Press; 0-941666),* P.O. Box 4308, Albuquerque, NM 87196 (SAN 239-328X)

Three Tree Pr, *(Three Tree Press; 0-9604198),* P.O. Box 261, Kalamazoo, MI 49005 (SAN 221-5942)

Thresh Pubns, *(Thresh Pubns.; 0-9600572; 0-913664),* 3027 Gateway Rd., P.O. Box 580, Bethel Island, CA 94511 (SAN 202-7828)

Threshold Bks, *(Threshold Books; 0-914186),* 365 Martha St., Susanville, CA 96130 (SAN 205-437X) Tel 916-257-3979

Thunderbird Pr, *(Thunderbird Press),* 2747 W. Windrose Dr., Phoenix, AZ 85029 (SAN 206-7722)

TIB Pubns, *(TIB Pubns.; 0-931882),* Div. of The Image Builders, 6600 NW 21st Ave., Fort Lauderdale, FL 33309 (SAN 211-500X) Tel 305-975-0113

Ticket Bk, *(Ticket Book, The; 0-9601950),* P.O. Box 1087, La Jolla, CA 92038 (SAN 211-9870) Tel 714-292-5999

Time-Lee Pubns, *(Time-Lee Pubns.; 0-937210),* 9804 Edgewater Dr., Orlando, FL 32803 (SAN 214-3275) Tel 305-299-1020

Timely Pubns, *(Timely Pubns.; 0-916548),* P.O. Box 81563, San Diego, CA 92138 (SAN 208-4279)

Timothy Bks, *(Timothy Books; 0-914964),* Div. of Hearthstone Pubns., Inc., 915 Fifth Ave., Box 567, Williamsport, PA 17701 (SAN 207-0898)

Tip Cloud Prods, *(Tip of the Cloud Productions; 0-910611),* P.O. Box 83, Orange, CA 92666 (SAN 260-146X)

Titan Pr, *(Titan Press; 0-930054),* P.O. Box 5139, Santa Monica, CA 90405 (SAN 210-6736) Tel 213-837-8041

Today Pubs, *(Today Pubs., Inc.; 0-933629),* 2100 N. Collins Blvd., Richardson, TX 75080 (SAN 692-476X) Tel 214-783-7008

Tomato Pubns, *(Tomato Pubns.; 0-934166),* Preston Hollow, NY 12469 (SAN 213-6007)

Tools for Schools, *(Tools for Schools, Inc.; 0-933242),* 164 27th St., San Francisco, CA 94110 (SAN 212-9787) Tel 415-282-2526

Topic, *(Topic, Inc.),* 6736 Washburn Ave., Minneapolis, MN 55423 (SAN 207-5784)

Torskript Pubs, *(Torskript Pubs.; 0-913048),* P.O. Box 297, San Francisco, CA 94101 (SAN 205-4434)

Tortilla, *(Tortilla Press; 0-932738),* 1291 E. Howard, Pasadena, CA 91104 (SAN 212-7067)

Tortoise Pr, *(Tortoise Press, The; 0-939518),* 4870 Hart Dr., San Diego, CA 92116-2339 (SAN 220-1909) Tel 213-378-7061

Total Univ Bk, *(Total Universe Book Co.),* P.O. Box 143, Dearborn, MI 48121 (SAN 209-6870)

Touchstone Pub KY, *(Touchstone Publishing Co.; 0-87963),* 1941 Bishop Lane, Suite 901, Louisville, KY 40218 (SAN 202-7895)

Touraine, *(Touraine Pub. Corp.; 0-920542),* 350 5th Ave., Suite 3308, New York, NY 10001 (SAN 211-5441) Tel 212-564-8658

Toward the Light, *(Toward the Light Publishing Hse.; 0-937054),* 16645 Bosque Dr., Encino, CA 91436 (SAN 214-4956)

Tower
See Tower Bks

Tower Bks, *(Tower Pubns., Inc.; 0-505),* Two Park Ave., Suite 910, New York, NY 10016 (SAN 212-016X) Tel 212-679-7707; Dist. by: Capital Distributor Co., Two Park Ave. Suite 910, New York, NY 10016 (SAN 212-016X) Tel 212-679-7707

Town Forum, *(Town Forum, Inc.),* P.O. Box 569, Cerro Gordo Ranch, Cottage Grove, OR 97424 (SAN 209-7915) Tel 503-942-7720

Townsend Pr, *(Townsend Press; 0-935990),* 767 East Oakwood Blvd., Chicago, IL 60653 (SAN 206-8249)

Townsend Pub Co., *(Townsend Pub. Co.; 0-930212),* P.O. Box 15102, Winston-Salem, NC 27103 (SAN 210-1521) Tel 919-766-5481

Toyon Pub, *(Toyon Publishing, Inc.; 0-89048),* Railroad Sq. Box S., San Luis Obispo, CA 93405 (SAN 207-1215)

TPA Publishing, *(TPA Publishing; 0-912651),* 2022 Taravel St., Box 5357, San Francisco, CA 94116 (SAN 283-3549) Tel 415-564-2055

TPS, *(T.P.S. Pubns.; 0-911476),* P.O. Box 142, College Park, MD 20740 (SAN 205-4450); Orders to: Daughters of Saint Paul.

Track & Field US, *(Track & Field Association, United States of America),* 10920 Ambassador Dr., Suite 322, Kansas City, MO 64153 (SAN 224-5981)

Trafalgar Hse, *(Trafalgar House Publishing, Inc.; 0-913880),* 360 E. 65th St., New York, NY 10021 (SAN 205-4485) Tel 212-772-7010

Trail-R, *(Trail-R Club of America; 0-87593),* 610 W. Ninth Ave., Suite 14, Escondido, CA 92025 (SAN 205-4493) Tel 714-743-8648; Orders to: P.O. Box 1376, Beverly Hills, CA 90213 (SAN 205-4507)

Trans World Pub, *(Trans World Pubs., Inc.; 0-933399),* P.O. Box 2353, Salt Lake City, UT 84110 (SAN 691-5264)

Transcult Comm, *(Transcultural Communications Center; 0-916796),* 909 Stonehill Ln., Los Angeles, CA 90049 (SAN 208-8932) Tel 213-476-1064

Transcultural Pr, *(Transcultural Press of the East & West; 0-916842),* 204 Makee Rd., Honolulu, HI 96815 (SAN 208-3558)

Transitour, *(Transitour Inc.; 0-939108),* 111 St. Charles Ave., New Orleans, LA 70130 (SAN 216-2008)

Translation Research, *(Translation Research Institute; 0-917564),* 5914 Pulaski Ave., Philadelphia, PA 19144 (SAN 207-2319) Tel 215-848-7084

Travel Advisor, *(Travel Advisor, Inc.; 0-932074),* 4710 Auth Pl., S.E., Suite 765, Washington, DC 20023 (SAN 212-5730) Tel 301-423-3416

Travel Mark Cons, *(Travel Marketing Consultant Service; 0-914776),* 37 Haverford Rd., Hicksville, NY 11801 (SAN 202-800X) Tel 516-581-2225

Travel News, *(Travel News; 0-915080),* 2500 Wilshire Blvd., Suite 720, Los Angeles, CA 90057 (SAN 207-0812)

Travelers Digest Edns, *(Traveler's Digest Editions; 0-936578),* 106 Perry St., New York, NY 10014 (SAN 214-1531); Dist. by: Small Press Assn., P.O. Box 1264, Radio City Sta., New York, NY 10019 (SAN 214-154X)

Travellers Comp Imprint of **Olympia**

Treacor Pubns, *(Treacor Pubns.; 0-934187),* 1776 Ygnacio Valley Rd., Suite 21, Walnut Creek, CA 94598 (SAN 693-3882)

Trebor Pr, *(Trebor Press, Ltd.; 0-88030),* P.O. Box 32725, Oklahoma City, OK 73123 (SAN 217-4464) Tel 405-789-1714

Tree by River, *(Tree by the River Publishing; 0-935174),* P.O. Box 413, Riverside, CA 92502 (SAN 213-389X) Imprints: Mus Bus Bks (Music Business Books).

Tree Line, *(Tree Line Books; 0-931476),* P.O. Box 1062, Radio City Sta., New York, NY 10019 (SAN 212-3896)

Treehouse Prods, *(Treehouse Productions; 0-926530),* W. 905 Riverside, Suite 305, Spokane, WA 99201 (SAN 283-4286) Tel 509-484-6856

Tri-Sci New Thought, *(Tri-Science Pubs.; 0-935040),* 4009 S. Layman Ave., Pico Rivera, CA 90660 (SAN 209-2581)

Tri-Science Pubs
See Tri-Sci New Thought

Trice Bks, *(Trice Bks., Inc.; 0-916249),* 4709 Keema Ave., Sacramento, CA 95842 (SAN 294-9806)

Trident, *(Trident Press; 0-671),* Div. of Simon & Schuster, Inc., 630 Fifth Ave., New York, NY 10020 (SAN 202-8026) Tel 212-245-6400

Trinity Bks, *(Trinity Books; 0-934310),* P.O. Box 8882, East Hartford, CT 06108 (SAN 202-8042) Tel 203-528-0408; Dist. by: Selene Books, P.O. Box 136, Kew Gardens, NY 11415 (SAN 689-2442)

Trinity Pr, *(Trinity Press; 0-912046),* Trinity Episcopal Church, 708 Bethlehem Pike, Ambler, PA 19002 (SAN 202-8050) Tel 215-646-0416

Triple T Pub, *(Triple "T" Publishing Co.; 0-9606122),* 175 Fifth Ave., New York, NY 10010 (SAN 216-8642) Tel 212-677-2200

Troisieme-Canadian, *(Troisieme-Canadian Pubs.; 0-932938),* P.O. Box 4281, Grand Central Sta., New York, NY 10017 (SAN 212-3177)

Troll Pub, *(Troll Publishing Co.; 0-933454),* Box 90213, Nashville, TN 37209 (SAN 212-7059) Tel 615-297-4436

Troubadour Texas, *(Troubadour Press; 0-916462),* 39 S. La Salle St., Suite 825, Chicago, IL 60603 (SAN 208-2632)

Truth Pubs, *(Truth Pubs.; 0-9602182),* P.O. Box 304, La Jolla, CA 92038 (SAN 212-3185) Tel 714-459-1470

Tunbridge, *(Tunbridge Pr.; 0-911538),* P.O. Box 345, New York, NY 10021 (SAN 205-4620)

Tupelo Pr, *(Tupelo Press; 0-9607276),* P.O. Box 1515, Yosemite Lodge, CA 95389 (SAN 239-3336) Tel 209-379-2473

Turnip Pr, *(Turnip Press; 0-914118),* 53 Vassar St., Rochester, NY 14607 (SAN 202-8107); Dist. by: Light Impressions, P.O. Box 3012, Rochester, NY 14614 (SAN 169-619X)

Turnstone, *(Turnstone Press; 0-932658),* P.O. Box 1500, Santa Cruz, CA 95061 (SAN 212-3894) Tel 408-425-8081

Turnstyle, *(Turnstyle),* 4975 Andever Ave., San Diego, CA 92120 (SAN 208-1741) Tel 805-685-1190

Turtle Island, *(Turtle Island Press; 0-932284),* 218 N. Thirteenth St., Philadelphia, PA 19107 (SAN 212-8705) Tel 215-568-2542

Twentieth Century, *(Twentieth Century Books; 0-86649),* Div. of Automated Reproductions, 745 Seventh Ave., New York, NY 10019 (SAN 216-3128)

Twenty-First Cent, *(Twenty-First Century Publishing),* One Park Ave., New York, NY 10016 (SAN 206-6726)

Two Continents, *(Two Continents Publishing Group, Inc.; 0-8467),* 171 Madison Ave., New York, NY 10016 (SAN 203-2996) Tel 212-685-4371

Two Horses, *(Two Horses Pr.),* 1950 W. Ruthrauff Rd., Tucson, AZ 85705 (SAN 276-1351)

Two Step Bks, *(Two Step Books; 0-931018),* P.O. Box 2942, Oakland, CA 94618 (SAN 211-7657)

Twos Co Music, *(Two's Co. Music; 0-9604626),* P.O Box 1199, Lawrence, KS 66044 (SAN 239-4995)

U Ctr Intl St, *(University Center for International Studies; 0-916002),* G-6 Mervis Hall, Univ. of Pittsburgh, Pittsburgh, PA 15260 (SAN 210-5799) Tel 412-624-6024

U Houston Intl Affairs
See Lat Am Stud

U Iowa Lab Poli Sci, *(University of Iowa, Department of Political Science, Laboratory for Political Research),* Main Campus, Iowa City, IA 52240 (SAN 262-1215) Tel 319-353-2121

U KY Busn, *(Univ. of Kentucky, College of Business & Economics Ctr. for Public Affairs),* 409 Commerce Bldg., Lexington, KY 40506 (SAN 226-9198)

U of Louisville, *(Univ. of Louisville; 0-89291),* Louisville, KY 40208 (SAN 215-2266)

U of Minn Morris, *(Univ. of Minnesota, Morris; 0-9601118),* Morris, MN 56267 (SAN 209-6889) Tel 612-589-2211

UC Ctr S&SE Asian, *(Univ., of California, Berkeley, Ctr. for SE Asian Studies),* Orders to: Cellar Book Shop, 18090 Wyoming, Detroit, MI 48221 (SAN 213-4330) Tel 415-642-6000

Uintah Pr, *(Uintah Press; 0-936234),* P.O. Box 420, Port Townsend, WA 98368 (SAN 214-1574)

Ujamaa Dev Educ, *(Ujamaa Developmental Education),* 2218 Oakwood Dr., E. Palo Alto, CA 94303 (SAN 211-2795)

Ulrich Corp NY, *(Ulrich, H., Corp.; 0-936500),* R.D. 3, Peekskill, NY 10566 (SAN 214-2031)

Ultima Corp, *(Ultima Corp. of West Palm Beach; 0-940656),* P.O. Box 15974, 4341 Southern Blvd., West Palm Beach, FL 33406 (SAN 219-8282)

Ultimate Bk, *(Ultimate Book Source),* Needmore, PA 17238 (SAN 209-1399) Tel 717-294-3739

Ultray Co, *(Ultray Co.),* 10306 Otis St., South Gate, CA 90280 (SAN 210-962X) Tel 213-567-4132

Umbrella Studios, *(Umbrella Studios; 0-9607582),* 1631 19th, Boulder, CO 80302 (SAN 239-9881) Tel 303-449-9338

Unica Inc, *(Unica, Inc.; 0-941852),* 16401 S. Mayleon Dr., Plainfield, IL 60544 (SAN 219-1016) Tel 815-436-9195

Unicorn-Star Imprint of **Laranmark**

Unique Ent, *(Unique Enterprises),* 1225 N. Edgemont, No. 34, Los Angeles, CA 90029 (SAN 215-9821)

United Pub NY, *(United Publishing Co., The; 0-938584),* P.O. Box 719, East Worcester, NY 12064 (SAN 215-9260)

United Seabears, *(United Seabears Corp.;
0-89532),* 1888 Century Park E., Suite 1209,
Los Angeles, CA 90067 (SAN 210-5209)
Tel 213-556-3756

Unity Pr
See Orenda-Unity

Univ Edns *Imprint of* **New Benjamin**

Univ Ga Lib, *(University of Georgia, Libraries;
0-915246),* Athens, GA 30602
(SAN 207-1606) Tel 404-542-2716

Univ Graphics, *(Univ. Graphics; 0-934932),*
Southern Illinois University, Carbonda, IL
62901 Tel 618-536-3325

Univ Hardcovers, *(University Hardcovers),* 3049
Sugarloaf Dr., Riverside, CA 92507
(SAN 212-3908)

Univ Life, *(Universal Life Bookshelf),* 10770
Katella Ave. 25, Anaheim, CA 92804
(SAN 219-3418)

Univ Park, *(Univ. Park Pr.; 0-8391),* 300 N.
Charles St., Baltimore, MD 21201
(SAN 204-8833) Tel 301-547-0700; P.O.
Box 434, Grand Central Sta., New York, NY
10163 (SAN 658-2184)

Univ Philatelic, *(Universal Philatelic Cover
Society),* 1909 Nut Tree Dr. Nw, Salem, OR
97304 (SAN 224-0270) Tel 503-371-3831

Univ Pr Inc, *(Univ. Pr., Inc., The; 0-9603614),*
Div. Of University Services Institute, P.O
Box 24268, Cleveland, OH 44124
Tel 216-442-0800

Univ Pub & Dist, *(Universal Publishing &
Distributing Corp.; 0-426),* 235 E. 45th St.,
New York, NY 10023 (SAN 212-0186)
Tel 212-683-3000

Universal Marketing Service, Inc.
See Ter-Lyn

Unlimited Pubns, *(Unlimited Pubns),* 4755 1/2
Elmwood Ave., Los Angeles, CA 90004
(SAN 209-6463)

Update Pub Intl, *(Update Publishing
International, Inc.),* 44 Engle St.,
Englewood, NJ 07631 (SAN 211-8734); c/o
Jack Burgess, 2175 Lemoine Ave., Ft. Lee,
NJ 07024 (SAN 220-1356)
Tel 201-592-0739

Upland Pr, *(Upland Pr.; 0-932554),* P.O. Box
7390, Chicago, IL 60680 (SAN 211-8742)
Tel 312-489-4667

URI MAS, *(University of Rhode Island, Marine
Advisory Serv.; 0-938412),* Univ. of Rhode
Island, URI Marine Advisory Service,
Narragansett, RI 02882-1197
(SAN 209-0708) Tel 401-792-6211

Uriel Pubns, *(Uriel Pubns.; 0-9603956),* Box
287, Taylor, ND 58656 (SAN 213-5655)
Tel 701-974-3566

Urizen Bks, *(Urizen Bks., Inc.; 0-89396;
0-916354),* 66 W. Broadway, New York, NY
10007 (SAN 208-9408)

Ursa Major, *(Ursa Major Press; 0-9605888),*
521 Fifth Ave., New York, NY 10017
(SAN 216-468X)

Ursus Pr, *(Ursus Press; 0-9615441),* P.O. Box
14220, Chicago, IL 60614 (SAN 262-1045)

US Hist Doc, *(U.S. Historical Documents
Institute Inc.; 0-88222),* 4600 Lee Hwy.,
Suite 212, Arlington, VA 22207
(SAN 201-7938)

US Parachute Assn, *(United States Parachute
Association),* 1440 Duke St., Alexandria,
VA 22314 (SAN 224-5779)
Tel 703-836-3495

US Tennis, *(U.S. Tennis Survey, Inc.; 0-918682),*
1013 Cornwell Pl., Ann Arbor, MI 48104
(SAN 210-5489)

USA Intl Pub, *(U.S.A.-International Pubs.;
0-9608114),* US/P.O. Box 6349,
Washington, DC 20015 (SAN 240-2920)

USA Pub Co, *(USA Publishing Co., Inc.),* 530
E. 72nd St., New York, NY 10021
(SAN 227-1222)

V A Lorenzen, *(Lorenzen, Violet; 0-9602174),*
606 S. Mentor Ave., Pasadena, CA 91106
(SAN 221-7961)

V-R Information, *(V-R Information Systems,
Inc.; 0-937508),* 5818 Balcones Dr., Austin,
TX 78731 (SAN 209-4959)

Vacation Pub, *(Vacation Publishing Co.),* 2412
PV Dr. W., Palos Verdes Estates, CA 90274
(SAN 204-4680); Orders to: P.O. Box 1191,
Palos Verdes Estates, CA 90274
(SAN 207-4699)

Valeur Pub Ltd, *(Valeur Publishing Ltd.;
0-9615602),* 75-6008 Alii Dr., No. 3109,
Kailua-Kona, HI 96745-4482
(SAN 695-0949); P.O. Box 4482,
Kailua-Kona, HI 96745-4482
(SAN 699-6051)

Valley Pubns, *(Valley Pubns.; 0-911562),* 348
Seventh St., Huntington, WV 25701
(SAN 207-320X) Tel 304-523-7181

Van Lee Guides, *(Van Lee Guides),* P.O. Box
367, Duluth, GA 30136 (SAN 240-8953)

Vanguard Public Foun
See Fund Exchange

Vanilla, *(Vanilla Pr.; 0-917266),* 2400 Colfax
Ave. S., Minneapolis, MN 55405
(SAN 208-9084) Tel 612-374-4726

Vanity, *(Vanity Press; 0-917938),* P.O. Box
15064, Atlanta, GA 30333
(SAN 209-519X) Tel 404-874-5462

Variety Pr, *(Variety Press),* 5214 Starkridge,
Houston, TX 77035 (SAN 213-5671)
Tel 713-721-5919

Venture Calif, *(Venture Press; 0-915894),* 2204
Plaza De Flores Rancho La Costa, Carlsbad,
CA 92008 (SAN 207-4672)
Tel 714-438-5166

Venture Pub Co, *(Venture Publishing Co.;
0-931478),* 155 W. 72nd St., New York, NY
10023 (SAN 211-3813) Tel 212-873-7580

Venture Pubns, *(Venture Pubns. Inc.),* 11157
1/2 W. Washington Blvd., Culver City, CA
90230 (SAN 208-371X) Tel 213-838-5333

Verbeke, *(Verbeke, Christian F., Rare Books,
Inc.; 0-911850),* 7 Pond St., Newburyport,
MA 01950 (SAN 205-4795)
Tel 617-462-8740

Veritas Pubns, *(Veritas Pubns.; 0-938264),* P.O.
Box 4418, Arlington, VA 22204
(SAN 215-9279) Tel 703-979-1159

Verity Pr, *(Verity Press; 0-913120),* 25045
Muerland, Southfield, MI 48075
(SAN 205-4809)

Vermeer Arts, *(Vermeer Arts, Ltd.; 0-934744),*
709 Tomahawk Trail, Kerrville, TX 78028
(SAN 212-9809)

Vernon-Nesgan, *(Vernon-Nesgan; 0-933223),*
Joint venture of Vernon Pubns., Inc. &
Nesgan, Inc., 109 W. Mercer St., Seattle,
WA 98119 (SAN 691-7267)
Tel 206-285-2050

Veronica Pr, *(Veronica Press; 0-9607094),* P.O.
Box 42075, Cincinnati, OH 45242
(SAN 239-0531) Tel 513-677-0319

Verta Pr, *(Verta Pr.; 0-930876),* 15 Randolph
Pl., NW, Washington, DC 20001
(SAN 203-168X) Tel 202-387-0414

VI-OP, *(VI-OP Inc.),* 2836 W. Main St., KLM
Bldg., Kalamazoo, MI 49007
(SAN 211-5824)

VIA Pr, *(VIA Press; 0-9600946),* 1726 Lincoln,
No. 4, Berkeley, CA 94703
(SAN 208-3736) Tel 415-848-4801

Vic, *(Vic Press, The; 0-933333),* 1001 Ruppel,
Suite 503, Pueblo, CO 81001
(SAN 205-4841) Tel 303-549-2714

Victory Day, *(Victory Day Co.; 0-930554),* P.
O. Box 1332, Saratoga Springs, NY 12866
(SAN 282-504X)

Victory Pr, *(Victory Press; 0-9609908),* Carlton,
OR 97111 (SAN 276-5063)

Village CA, *(Village Pr., The; 0-910497),* P.O.
Box 310, Fallbrook, CA 92028
(SAN 282-5082) Tel 619-728-4305; Dist.
by: Aviation Book Co., 1640 Victory Blvd.,
Glendale, CA 91201 (SAN 212-0259)
Tel 213-240-1771

Village Psych
See Backwards & Backwards

Vintage Bk Co, *(Vintage Book Co.; 0-938164),*
Box 16182, Elway Sta., St. Paul, MN 55116
(SAN 220-1062)

Virdon Assoc, *(Virdon Associates, Inc.),* P.O.
Box 221, Mount Holly Springs, PA 17065
(SAN 211-5468)

Virgin Islands Biol, *(Virgin Islands Biological
Offices; 0-9601490),* Box 305, Frederiksted,
St. Croix, VI 00840 (SAN 211-4267)

Visible Lang, *(Visible Language Workshop;
0-938334),* E15-443 MIT, 20 Ames St.,
Cambridge, MA 02139 (SAN 220-2808)

Vista CA, *(Vista Pubns.; 0-932740),* 830 26th
St., Santa Monica, CA 90403
(SAN 213-7046) Tel 213-828-3258

Vistula Pr, *(Vistula Pr., The),* 328 Anthony Cir.,
Charlotte, NC 28211 (SAN 282-5171)
Tel 704-364-0035

Visual Art, *(Visual Arts Productions; 0-9610164),*
175 Prospect St., East Orange, NJ 07017
(SAN 276-525X)

Visual Materials, *(Visual Materials, Inc.;
0-88337),* 4170 Grove Ave., Gurnee, IL
60031 (SAN 206-0396)

VKM, *(VKM Publishing Co.; 0-916440),* P.O.
Box 11102, Fort Worth, TX 76109
(SAN 208-0281) Tel 817-923-6959

Vogel Bk, *(Vogel Book Co.; 0-9600656),* P.O.
Box 103, Bellevue, WA 98009
(SAN 207-4966) Tel 206-455-0973

Volga Pr, *(Volga Pr.; 0-9615278),* 2123 Ave. G,
Scottsbluff, NE 69361 (SAN 694-3829)
Tel 308-635-3263

Volta Press, *(Volta Press Inc., The; 0-910437),*
20 W. Mosholu Pkwy, Suite 26F, Bronx, NY
10468 (SAN 241-4732) Tel 212-928-2970

Volume Dist, *(Volume Distributing Co.;
0-912982),* P.O. Box 178, Seaford, VA
23696 (SAN 205-4884)

Vortex Pub, *(Vortex Publishing Co., Inc.),* P.O.
Box 489, Cornwall, NY 12518
(SAN 207-6055)

Voyager Pr, *(Voyager Press),* Box 337, Grand
Marais, MI 49839 (SAN 212-3223)

VPC Pr, *(VPC Pr; 0-912664),* c/o Maltese
Books, P.O. Box 781, Redondo Beach, CA
90277 (SAN 212-7598)

VT Ed Comp, *(Vermont Educational Computer
Technology Organization),* Box 1271,
Montpelier, VT 05602 (SAN 674-656X)
Tel 802-828-3111

W Fraser Pubs, *(Fraser, Worden, Pubs.;
0-936582),* Box 2032, Stanford, CA 94305
(SAN 214-3763)

W H Easton, *(Easton, William H.; 0-9601160),*
3818 Bowsprit Circle, Westlake Village, CA
93161 (SAN 210-072X) Tel 213-889-2667

W J Harris, *(Harris, Walter J.; 0-9608156),*
(SAN 205-5366)

W Jacob Johnson, *(Johnson, William Jacob;
0-9601008),* 1604 E. Fremont Dr., Tempe,
AZ 85282 (SAN 208-7170)
Tel 602-838-1297

W R Palmer
See Heathcote

W Shaughnessy, *(Shaughnessy, William;
0-9613665),* P.O. Box 2375, Glens Falls, NY
12801 (SAN 682-0565)

W W Blaney, *(Blaney, Warren W.; 0-9607156),*
26412 Jacinto Dr., Mission Viejo, CA 92692
(SAN 237-9805)

W W Kirby, *(Kirby, Walter, W.),* 1351 N.
Austin Ave., Chicago, IL 60657
(SAN 237-7411)

W W Pro Inter, *(Williams-Wallace Productions
Intl. Inc.),* 826 Pine St., Second Flr.,
Niagara Falls, NY 14301 (SAN 287-265X)

Wagoner, *(Wagoner, George; 0-9600178),* 4318
Glenridge Dr., Carmichael, CA 95608
(SAN 205-5007) Tel 916-967-6988

Waldeck Pubns, *(Waldeck Pubns.),* 258
Montecito Ave., Prismo Beach, CA 93449
(SAN 211-9242)

Walden Bk Co, *(Walden Book Co.; 0-681),* 179
Ludlow, Stamford, CT 06904
(SAN 203-1752)

Waldorf Pr, *(Waldorf Press; 0-914614),* Dept. of
Education, Linen Hall Basement, Adelphi
Univ., Cambridge Ave., Garden City, NY
11530 (SAN 203-1760) Tel 516-294-8700

Waldrop Pubns, *(Waldrop Pubns.; 0-9603364),*
Box 396, Mt. Baldy, CA 91759
(SAN 208-4007) Tel 714-985-6128

Walker Pr KY, *(Walker Press, The),* P.O. Box
22144, Louisville, KY 40222
(SAN 210-9662)

Wallflower, *(Wallflower Press; 0-9606260),* P.O.
Box 1275, Bridgehampton, NY 11932
(SAN 217-1392)

Walliker Pubs, *(Walliker Pubs. Inc.; 0-89400),*
Box 760, Williamsburg, VA 07920
(SAN 209-6137)

Wallingford, *(Wallingford Press),* P.O. Box 153,
Wallingford, PA 19086 (SAN 210-5500)

Wallis Pubns, *(Wallis Pubns.; 0-930148),* 3485
Sylvan Lane, Melbourne, FL 32935
(SAN 210-5675) Tel 305-727-1270

Warm Wind Bks, *(Warm Wind Books),* Box 57,
Clinton, WA 98236 (SAN 218-429X)

Warrington, *(Warrington & Company;
0-911735),* P.O. Box 907, Orinda, CA 94563
(SAN 264-4827)

Warwick, *(Warwick Pubs.; 0-930156),* 2616 N.
W. 33rd St., Oklahoma City, OK 73112
(SAN 210-3303) Tel 405-943-9095

Wash Gasohol, *(Washington Gasohol Commission; 0-939864),* 1299 A. St. SE, Ephrata, WA 98823 (SAN 216-7735) Tel 509-754-2447

Wash Media, *(Washington Media Services, Ltd.; 0-914286),* 414 Hungerford Dr., Suite 300, Rockville, MD 20850 (SAN 203-1779) Tel 301-340-2098

Wash Sq East, *(Washington Square East, Pubs.; 0-913086),* 109 Logan Lane, Wallingford, PA 19086 (SAN 206-8982)

Wash Wkshops Pr, *(Washington Workshops Press; 0-913528),* 1329 "E" St., N.W., Suite 1111, Washington, DC 20004 (SAN 202-9499) Tel 202-638-4357

Washburn, *(Washburn, Ives, Inc.),* Subs. of David McKay Co., Inc., 750 Third Ave., New York, NY 10017 (SAN 202-9502) Tel 212-661-1700

Washburn Pr MN, *(Washburn Pr.; 0-939862),* 2753 Upland Ct., Plymouth, MN 55447 (SAN 216-941X)

Washingtonian, *(Washingtonian Books; 0-915168),* 1828 L St., N.W. Suite 200, Washington, DC 20036 (SAN 207-4206) Tel 202-296-3600

Water Foun, *(Water Foundation; 0-9603252),* 1119 Chapala St., Santa Barbara, CA 93101 (SAN 213-3997) Tel 805-963-8739

Water Res Congr, *(Water Resources Congress),* 955 L'Enfant Plaza N., NW, Suite 1101, Washington, DC 20024 (SAN 690-1565)

Waterfall Pr, *(Waterfall Pr.; 0-932278),* 2122 Junction Ave., El Cerritto, CA 94530 (SAN 211-7665)

Waterford Pub, *(Waterford Publishing Co.; 0-942052),* 221 Waterford Pkwy. N., Waterford, CT 06385 (SAN 239-5797)

Waterfront OH, *(Waterfront Bks. (OH); 0-9603006),* 108 W. Perry St., Port Clinton, OH 43452 (SAN 213-0610) Tel 419-734-1430

Wavary Pr, *(Wavary Press),* P.O. Box 5113, Kent, WA 98031 (SAN 211-7673)

Wayside, *(Wayside Press),* P.O. Box 475, Cottonwood, AZ 86326 (SAN 209-8024)

Wazum Pubns, *(Wazum Pubns.),* Box 600, New York, NY 10019 (SAN 210-9395) Tel 212-260-0762

Weatherleaf Pr, *(Weatherleaf Press, The; 0-938912),* 233 S. Second St., DeKalb, IL 60115 (SAN 238-7646) Tel 815-758-4841

Webb & Bower, *(Webb & Bower),* 521 Fifth Ave., New York, NY 10017 (SAN 239-3999)

Weber, *(Weber, S. A, D'Editions),* Dist. by: Biblio Distribution Center, 81 Adams Dr., Totowa, NJ 07512 (SAN 211-724X) Tel 201-256-8600

Wedgewood Pr, *(Wedgwood Press; 0-911602),* 178 West St., Needham Hts., MA 02194 (SAN 206-2976)

Weight Control, *(Weight Control Institute; 0-9608232),* 4225 Wade Way, Salt Lake City, UT 84119 (SAN 240-3285) Tel 801-968-4099

Welch, *(Welch, Wendell R., Publishing House; 0-918494),* 136 Eighth Ave. No., Nashville, TN 37203 (SAN 209-9152); Dist. by: Brass Pr., 136 Eighth Ave. N., Nashville, TN 37203 (SAN 201-8608) Tel 615-254-8969

Wesselhoeft Assoc, *(Wesselhoeft Associates, Inc.; 0-941954),* 3885 Lawrence Dr., Oscoda, MI 48750 (SAN 238-4884) Tel 517-739-3886

West-Lewis, *(West-Lewis Publishing Co.; 0-913984),* P.O. Box 1750, San Francisco, CA 94101 (SAN 202-960X)

Western Ed Soc, *(Western Educational Society For Telecommunications),* Arizona State Univ., Tempe, AZ 85287 (SAN 673-4588) Tel 602-965-3506

Western Search, *(Western Search Inc.),* P.O. Box 334, Seahurst, WA 98062 (SAN 213-8808) Tel 206-453-9041

Western Soc Res, *(Western Social Research Pubs.),* Box 306, Del Mar, CA 92014 (SAN 216-4744)

Westinghouse Learn, *(Westinghouse Learning Corp.; 0-88250; 0-8496; 0-89099),* 5005 W. 110th St., Oak Lawn, IL 60453 (SAN 209-4967) Tel 312-425-0800 Imprints: Ideal Pubns (Ideal Publications).

Westlake, *(Westlake, Kevin L.; 0-9604862),* RR 2, Montpelier, ID 83254 (SAN 215-7136)

Westland Pub Co, *(Westland Publishing Co.; 0-89121),* P.O. Box 2061, Scottsdale, AZ 85252 (SAN 207-6969)

Wexford, *(Wexford Press; 0-911628),* 3 Wexford St., Needham Heights, MA 02194 (SAN 206-0388) Tel 617-449-1500

Weyand-Shaw, *(Weyand/Shaw Pubns.; 0-9601922),* 5460 Whiteoak, Suite B-203, Encino, CA 91316 (SAN 211-9269) Tel 213-783-1820

Wheelchair Bowlers, *(Wheelchair Bowlers of Southern California; 0-9605306),* 6512 Cadiz Cir., Huntington Beach, CA 92647 (SAN 215-9848)

White House Bk Co, *(White House Book Co.; 0-9611884),* 729 Curtis St., Albany, CA 94706 (SAN 286-0821) Tel 415-526-2083

White Mtn Pub, *(White Mountain Pub. Co.; 0-917978),* 13801 N. Cave Creek Rd., Phoenix, AZ 85022 (SAN 209-9195) Tel 602-971-2720

White Oak, *(White Oak Publishing House; 0-932556),* P.O. Box 3089, Redwood City, CA 94064 (SAN 210-9646) Tel 415-367-7320

Whitehead Pub
See Clearstream Pr

Whitehouse, *(Whitehouse Pubns.),* 1134 Valerio St., Van Nuys, CA 91406 (SAN 209-6161)

Whitmer Pub Co, *(Whitmer Publishing Co.; 0-935176),* 1353 S.E. 32nd Ave., Portland, OR 97214 (SAN 212-9833) Tel 503-233-2684

Wholelife Pubns, *(Wholelife Pubns.; 0-932470),* P.O. Box 810, Yonkers, NY 10702 (SAN 212-7105)

Why Not, *(Why Not Creations),* P.O. Box 1467, Monterey, CA 93940 (SAN 211-383X)

Wild West Pub, *(Wild West Publishing Hse.; 0-914006),* P.O. Box 1199, San Francisco, CA 94101 (SAN 203-2201)

Wildcat Canyon, *(Wildcat Canyon Books; 0-936034),* P.O. Box 5115, Richmond, CA 94805 (SAN 285-1172) Tel 415-285-6319; 1332 Shotwell St., San Francisco, CA 94110 (SAN 285-1180)

Wildman Pr, *(Wildman Pr.),* 70 Greenwich Ave., Suite 377, New York, NY 10011 (SAN 265-3842)

Wilkerson Assocs, *(Wilkerson Associates),* P.O. Box 711, Gig Harbor, WA 98335 (SAN 210-9689) Tel 206-858-9076

William-F, *(William-Frederick Press; 0-87164),* 308 E. 79th St., New York, NY 10021 (SAN 205-5309) Tel 212-628-1995

Williams Ent, *(Williams, Bill, Enterprises; 0-934488),* 188 Merchant St., Honolulu, HI 96809 (SAN 220-1089)

Willing Pub, *(Willing Publishing Co.),* 251 S. San Gabriel Blvd., San Gabriel, CA 91778 (SAN 205-5325); Dist. by: Devorss & Co., 1641 Lincoln Blvd., Santa Monica, CA 90404 (SAN 168-9886)

Willow Hse, *(Willow Hse. Pubs.; 0-912450),* 143 Hahn Rd., Aptos, CA 95003 (SAN 205-535X) Tel 408-688-4128

Wiluk Pr, *(Wiluk Press),* P.O. Box 2548, Silver Spring, MD 20910 (SAN 209-3685) Tel 301-585-1274

Win Bks, *(Win Books, Inc.; 0-916140),* P. O. Box 547, Rifton, NY 12471 (SAN 207-9534) Tel 914-339-4585

Wind Pub, *(Wind Publishing; 0-933312),* P.O. Box 253, Corona Del Mar, CA 92625 (SAN 212-4645)

Windmill Pr, *(Windmill Press),* 1369 Linwood, Holland, MI 49423 (SAN 208-2853)

Wine Adv, *(Wine Advisory Board; 0-911914),* 717 Market St., San Francisco, CA 94103 (SAN 203-2910) Tel 415-392-0252

Wine Pr, *(Wine Press; 0-911634),* P.O. Box 82, Concord, MA 01742 (SAN 205-5384)

Wings Man Inc, *(Wings of Man, Inc.; 0-9607322),* 11 Monroe St., Garfield, NJ 07026 (SAN 239-3484) Tel 201-340-0895

Winona Catawba, *(Winona Catawba Press Publishing; 0-9603974),* P.O. Box 40742, San Francisco, CA 94140 (SAN 214-1736)

Winthrop, *(Winthrop Pubs., Inc.; 0-87626),* Subs. of Prentice-Hall, Inc., 17 Dunster St., Cambridge, MA 02138 (SAN 200-2345)

Wisconsin Audubon, *(Wisconsin Audubon Council, Inc.),* Dist. by: Potter School & Library Services, Inc., 6927 W. North Ave., Wauwatosa, WI 53213 (SAN 169-9229)

Wisconsin Hse, *(Wisconsin House Book Pubs.; 0-88361),* P.O. Box 2118, Madison, WI 53701 (SAN 203-2899) Tel 608-251-3222

Wisdom, *(Wisdom Pubns.; 0-911636),* P.O. Box 81, San Diego, CA 92112 (SAN 205-5422)

WMD Pub, *(WMD Pubns.; 0-912754),* P.O. Box 198, Islip, NY 11751 (SAN 206-6661)

Wollaston, *(Wollaston Inc.),* 18 Peachtree Ave., F-1, Atlanta, GA 30305 (SAN 209-634X)

Wollstonecraft, *(Wollstonecraft, Inc.; 0-88381),* 6399 Wilshire Blvd., Los Angeles, CA 90048 (SAN 203-2848) Tel 213-653-1745

Women & Lit, *(Women & Literature Collective; 0-915052),* P.O. Box 441, Cambridge, MA 02138 (SAN 208-9815) Tel 617-628-0216

Women Writing, *(Women Writing Press; 0-917648),* P.O. Box 1035, Cathedral Sta., New York, NY 10025 (SAN 208-9874) Tel 212-222-3563

Women's Club Farmingdale, *(Women's Club of Farmingdale),* Farmingdale, NY 11735 (SAN 217-2917)

Women's Guide, *(Women's Guide to Books Press),* c/o Mss Information Corp., 655 Madison Ave., New York, NY 10021 (SAN 207-6519) Tel 212-688-0020

Woodstock Edns, *(Woodstock Editions/Public Relations; 0-933632),* P.O. Box 9096, Marina del Rey, CA 90295 (SAN 212-629X)

Woodward Bks, *(Woodward Books; 0-916028),* P.O. Box 773, Corte Madera, CA 94925 (SAN 208-0737) Tel 415-388-5095

Woolf Quarterly, *(Virginia Woolf Quarterly Pr.; 0-89363),* P.O. Box 4904, San Ysidro, CA 92073 (SAN 209-2484)

Woolley Pub, *(Woolley Publishing, Inc.; 0-918513),* P.O. Box 4152, Cherry Hill, NJ 08034 (SAN 657-7369)

Wordpress, *(Wordpress; 0-915104),* 1191 Santa Fe, Albany, CA 94706 (SAN 207-091X)

Working Pr, *(Working Press of the Nation),* Orders to: National Research Bureau, Inc., 424 N. Third St., Burlington, IA 52601 (SAN 205-7344) Tel 319-752-5415

Working Pr CA, *(Working Press; 0-9602462),* P.O. Box 687, Livermore, CA 94550 (SAN 212-7717) Tel 415-886-9823

World Authors, *(World Authors, Ltd.; 0-89975),* 191/2 E. 62nd St., New York, NY 10021 (SAN 213-974X) Tel 212-759-7305; Dist. by: Hippocrene Books, Inc., 171 Madison Ave., New York, NY 10016 (SAN 213-2060) Tel 212-685-4371

World Bio Pr, *(World Biography Press),* 25 E. Washington St., Rm. 823, Chicago, IL 60602 (SAN 207-5024)

World Citizens, *(World Citizens Assembly),* P.O. Box 2063, San Francisco, CA 94126 (SAN 209-2719)

World Digest
See World Natural Hist

World Faith Ex, *(World Faith Exchange; 0-930909),* 74 York St., York, ME 03909 (SAN 679-6796)

World Intl, *(World International Enterprises, Inc.),* P.O. Box 1611, North Miami, FL 33161 (SAN 209-2123) Tel 305-538-2869

World Issues, *(World Issues Information Bureau; 0-9605110),* 1234 W. Loyola Ave., Chicago, IL 60626 (SAN 215-7179)

World Natural Hist, *(World Natural History Pubns.; 0-916846),* P.O. Box 550, Marlton, NJ 08053 (SAN 208-9297) Tel 609-654-6500

World Union Natl Soc, *(World Union National Society),* Box 5505, Arlington, VA 22205 (SAN 225-7092)

World View IL, *(World View Pubns.; 0-933774),* P.O. Box 6057, Chicago, IL 60680 (SAN 212-9841)

World View Pubns
See World View IL

World-Wide Bk, *(World-Wide Book Service),* Box 544, New York, NY 10010 (SAN 159-7183) Tel 212-673-6160; 251 Third Ave., New York, NY 10010 (SAN 695-6297)

Worldwide Ref, *(Worldwide Reference Sources),* 200 Park Ave., Suite 303 E., New York, NY 10017 (SAN 207-4982)

Worthy Labor Pr, *(Worthy Labor Press),* 1315 Monterey St., Richmond, CA 94804 (SAN 203-1833)

Wright-Allen, *(Wright-Allen Press, Inc.; 0-9600294; 0-914700),* 238 Main St., Cambridge, MA 02142 (SAN 205-5554) Tel 617-491-6826

Wrightwill Pub, *(Wrightwill Publishing Co.),* 256 S. Robertson Blvd., Beverly Hills, CA 90211 (SAN 220-1135) Tel 213-926-6994

Write-A-Book, *(Write-A-Book; 0-943682),* 3297 Las Vegas Blvd. N., No. L-F, Las Vegas, NV 89030 (SAN 238-4205) Tel 702-644-4622

Writers Group, *(Writers Group, Dearborn MI. Branch of the American Assn. of Univ. Women; 0-9609430),* 1515 Mason, Apt.706, Dearborn, MI 48124 (SAN 260-2814) Tel 313-278-6934

Writers' Group
See Writers Group

Writers Pub Serv, *(Writers Publishing Service Co.; 0-910303),* 3422 S. 84th St. 9, Tacoma, WA 98409 (SAN 276-8666)

Writers West, *(Writers West Books),* Dept. of English, Univ. of Colorado, Colorado Springs, CO 80907 (SAN 212-3266) Tel 303-593-3155; Dist. by: Swallow Press, Inc., 811 W. Junior Terrace, Chicago, IL 60613 (SAN 202-5671) Tel 312-871-2760

Wrongtree Pr, *(Wrongtree Pr.),* Box 930, Bolinas, CA 94924 (SAN 207-5822)

Wyman-Hammond, *(Wyman, Richard, /Peter Hammond; 0-9600468),* RFD 1, Chester Depot, VT 05144 (SAN 203-2775)

Wynaud Pr, *(Wynaud Press; 0-9603312),* 3005 Ronna, Las Cruces, NM 88001 (SAN 212-3282) Tel 505-524-3132

Xerox College, *(Xerox College Publishing; 0-536),* A Xerox Education Co., 191 Spring St., Lexington, MA 02173 (SAN 203-2767) Tel 617-861-1670

XYLO Pubns, *(XYLO Pubns.),* 405 W. Washington Dept. 84, San Diego, CA 92103-1994 (SAN 295-0286)

Yama Trans, *(Yama Trans Co.; 0-942512),* 24228 Hawthorne Blvd., Torrance, CA 90505 (SAN 238-2105) Tel 213-378-8700

Yellow Bird *Imprint of* **Am Natl Pub**

Yeshiva U Pr, *(Yeshiva University Press; 0-89362),* 186th St. & Amsterdam Ave., New York, NY 10033 (SAN 206-0000) Tel 212-568-8400; Dist. by: Sifria Distributors, 729 Ave. N, Brooklyn, NY 11230 (SAN 206-0019)

York-Mail Print, *(York-Mail Print, Inc.; 0-913126),* P.O. Box 489, Unadilla, NY 13849 (SAN 203-2716) Tel 607-369-9108

Yorkshire Pub, *(Yorkshire Publishing Co.; 0-9604732),* P.O. Box 309, Princeton Junction, NJ 08550 (SAN 215-7195)

Yossarian Pub, *(Yossarian Publications; 0-9609824),* P.O. Box 18713, Denver, CO 80218 (SAN 262-110X)

Young Davis Pr, *(Young Davis Press; 0-931914),* 30473 Mulholland Hwy., H 14, Agoura, CA 91301 (SAN 211-4593) Tel 818-706-1862

Youngjohn Pubns, *(Youngjohn Publications; 0-912321),* 1275 Fourth St., Santa Rosa, CA 95404 (SAN 276-9514)

Your Heritage, *(Your Heritage Books, Inc.; 0-911668),* 928 Public Ledger Bldg., Philadelphia, PA 19106 (SAN 205-5627)

Youth Lib, *(Youth Liberation Press, Inc.; 0-918946),* P.O. Box 524, Brooklyn, NY 11215 (SAN 207-9240) Tel 212-242-3270

Youth Sports, *(Youth Sports Press; 0-936446),* 6801 S. LaGrange Rd., LaGrange, IL 60525 (SAN 214-4948)

YTT Pub, *(Yesterday/Today/Tomorrow Publishing; 0-911685),* No., 619, 1626 N. Wilcox Ave., Hollywood, CA 90028 (SAN 264-5157) Tel 213-786-1202

Z Prods, *(Z Productions; 0-9605032),* Rt. Three, Box 12, Pavo, GA 31778 (SAN 214-1787) Tel 912-859-2861

Zanon Pubns, *(Zanon Pubns.),* 9600 Armley Ave., Whittier, CA 90604 (SAN 216-4825)

Zapoleon, *(Zapoleon, M. W.; 0-9614542),* 816 SE Riviera Isle, Fort Lauderdale, FL 33301 (SAN 691-7437) Tel 305-467-1631

ZED Bks, *(Z.E.D Books; 0-940874),* P.O. Box 1668, Burbank, CA 91507 (SAN 219-6573) Tel 213-353-4389

Zeitgeist, *(Zeitgeist; 0-87649),* P.O. Box 595, Saugatuck, MI 49453 (SAN 205-566X) Tel 616-857-4183

Zephyrus Pr, *(Zephyrus Press, Inc.; 0-914264),* 417 Maitland Ave., Teaneck, NJ 07666 (SAN 203-1817) Tel 201-833-0717

Zook, *(Zook Consulting & Publishing; 0-933222),* P.O. Box 3643, Lawrence, KS 66044 (SAN 212-3959)